2

Stanley Gibbons
SIMPLIFIED
CATALOGUE

# Stamps of the World

## 1998 Edition

An illustrated and priced three-volume guide to the postage stamps of the whole world, excluding changes of paper, perforation, shade and watermark

VOLUME 1

**FOREIGN COUNTRIES A–J**

STANLEY GIBBONS LTD
London and Ringwood

**By Appointment to**
**Her Majesty the Queen**
**Stanley Gibbons Limited**
**London**
**Philatelists**

**63rd Edition**

**Published in Great Britain by**
**Stanley Gibbons Ltd**
**Publications Editorial, Sales Offices and Distribution Centre**
**5, Parkside, Christchurch Road,**
**Ringwood, Hampshire BH24 3SH**
**Telephone 01425 472363**

**ISBN: 085259-429-1**

**Published as Stanley Gibbons Simplified Stamp Catalogue from 1934 to 1970, renamed Stamps of the World in 1971, and produced in two (1982–88) or three (from 1989) volumes as Stanley Gibbons Simplified Catalogue of Stamps of the World.**
**This volume published September 1997**



S.G. Item No. 2881 (98)

Origination by BPC Whitefriars Ltd, Tunbridge Wells, Kent
Printed in Great Britain by Bemrose Security Printing, London & Derby

Stanley Gibbons
SIMPLIFIED CATALOGUE

# Stamps of the World

**This popular catalogue is a straightforward three-volume listing of the stamps that have been issued everywhere in the world since the very first–Great Britain's famous Penny Black in 1840.**

This edition continues the three-volume format. Volume 1 (Foreign countries A–J) appears in September, Volume 2 (Foreign countries K–Z) in October, and Volume 3 covering Commonwealth countries in November.

Readers are reminded that the Catalogue Supplements, published in each issue of **Gibbons Stamp Monthly,** can be used to update the listings in **Stamps of the World** as well as our twenty-two part standard catalogue. To make the supplement even more useful the Type numbers given to the illustrations are the same in the Stamps of the World as in the standard catalogues. The first Catalogue Supplement to this Volume appeared in the August 1997 issue of **Gibbons Stamp Monthly.**

**Gibbons Stamp Monthly** can be obtained through newsagents or on postal subscription from Stanley Gibbons Publications, 5, Parkside, Christchurch Road, Ringwood, Hants BH24 3SH.

**The catalogue has many important features:**

- As an indication of current values virtually every stamp is priced. Thousands of alterations have been made since the last edition.
- By being set out on a simplified basis that excludes changes of paper, perforation, shade, watermark, gum or printer's and date imprints it is particularly easy to use. (For its exact scope see "Information for users" pages following.)
- The thousands of illustrations and helpful descriptions of stamp designs make it of maximum appeal to collectors with thematic interests.
- Its catalogue numbers are the world-recognised Stanley Gibbons numbers throughout.
- Helpful introductory notes for the collector are included, backed by much historical, geographical and currency information.
- A very detailed index gives instant location of countries in this volume, and a cross-reference to those included in the other volumes.

Over 2,473 stamps and 860 new illustrations have been added to the listings in this volume. Last year's three-volume edition contained over 330,490 stamps and 79,375 illustrations.

The listings in this edition are based on the standard catalogues: Part 1 (British Commonwealth) (1998 edition), Part 2 (Austria & Hungary) (5th edition), Part 3 (Balkans) (3rd edition), Part 4 (Benelux) (4th edition), Part 5 (Czechoslovakia & Poland) (5th edition), Part 6 (France) (4th edition), Part 7 (Germany) (5th edition), Part 8 (Italy & Switzerland) (5th edition), Part 9 (Portugal & Spain) (4th edition), Part 10 (Russia) (4th edition), Part 11 (Scandinavia) (4th edition), Part 12 (Africa since Independence A-E) (2nd edition), Part 13 (Africa since Independence F-M) (1st edition), Part 14 (Africa since Independence N-Z) (1st edition), Part 15 (Central America) (2nd edition), Part 16 (Central Asia) (3rd edition), Part 17 (China) (5th edition), Part 18 (Japan & Korea) (4th edition), Part 19 (Middle East) (5th edition), Part 20 (South America) (3rd edition), Part 21 (South-East Asia) (3rd edition) and Part 22 (United States) (4th edition).

Important price revisions made specially for this edition include Belgium, Belgian Colonies, Cameroun, Colombia, Denmark, Danish West Indies, Faroe Islands, Finland, France, Greenland and Iceland.

# Stanley Gibbons Stamp Catalogue
# Complete List of Parts

**1 British Commonwealth**
(Annual in two volumes)

## Foreign Countries

**2 Austria & Hungary** (5th edition, 1994)
Austria · Bosnia & Herzegovina · U.N. (Vienna) · Hungary

**3 Balkans** (3rd edition, 1987)
Albania · Bulgaria · Greece & Islands · Rumania · Yugoslavia

**4 Benelux** (4th edition, 1993)
Belgium & Colonies · Netherlands & Colonies · Luxembourg

**5 Czechoslovakia & Poland** (5th edition, 1995)
Czechoslovakia · Bohemia & Moravia · Slovakia · Poland

**6 France** (4th edition, 1993)
France · Colonies · Post Offices · Andorra · Monaco

**7 Germany** (5th edition, 1996)
Germany · States · Colonies · Post Offices

**8 Italy & Switzerland** (5th edition, 1997)
Italy & Colonies · Fiume · San Marino · Vatican City · Trieste · Liechtenstein · Switzerland · U.N. (Geneva)

**9 Portugal & Spain** (4th edition, 1996)
Andorra · Portugal & Colonies · Spain & Colonies

**10 Russia** (4th edition, 1991)
Russia · Baltic States · Mongolia · Tuva

**11 Scandinavia** (4th edition, 1994)
Aland Islands · Denmark · Faroe Islands · Finland · Greenland · Iceland · Norway · Sweden

**12 Africa since Independence A-E** (2nd edition, 1983)
Algeria · Angola · Benin · Bophuthatswana · Burundi · Cameroun · Cape Verde · Central African Republic · Chad · Comoro Islands · Congo · Djibouti · Equatorial Guinea · Ethiopia

**13 Africa since Independence F-M** (1st edition, 1981)
Gabon · Guinea · Guinea-Bissau · Ivory Coast · Liberia · Libya · Malagasy Republic · Mali · Mauritania · Morocco · Mozambique

**14 Africa since Independence N-Z** (1st edition, 1981)
Niger Republic · Rwanda · St. Thomas & Prince · Senegal · Somalia · Sudan · Togo · Transkei · Tunisia · Upper Volta · Venda · Zaire

**15 Central America** (2nd edition, 1984)
Costa Rica · Cuba · Dominican Republic · El Salvador · Guatemala · Haiti · Honduras · Mexico · Nicaragua · Panama

**16 Central Asia** (3rd edition, 1992)
Afghanistan · Iran · Turkey

**17 China** (5th edition, 1995)
China · Taiwan · Tibet · Foreign P.O.s

**18 Japan & Korea** (4th edition, 1997)
Japan · Ryukyus · Korean Empire · South Korea · North Korea

**19 Middle East** (5th edition, 1996)
Bahrain · Egypt · Iraq · Israel · Jordan · Kuwait · Lebanon · Oman · Qatar · Saudi Arabia · Syria · U.A.E. · Yemen

**20 South America** (3rd edition, 1989)
Argentina · Bolivia · Brazil · Chile · Colombia · Ecuador · Paraguay · Peru · Surinam · Uruguay · Venezuela

**21 South-East Asia** (3rd edition, 1995)
Bhutan · Indonesia · Kampuchea · Laos · Myanmar · Nepal · Philippines · Thailand · Vietnam

**22 United States** (4th edition, 1994)
U.S. & Possessions · Canal Zone · Marshall Islands · Micronesia · Palau · U.N. (New York, Geneva, Vienna)

## Thematic Catalogues

Stanley Gibbons Catalogues for use with **Stamps of the World.**
**Collect Aircraft on Stamps** (1st edition, 1994)
**Collect Birds on Stamps** (4th edition, 1996)
**Collect Butterflies and Other Insects on Stamps** (1st edition, 1991)
**Collect Chess on Stamps** (out of print)
**Collect Fungi on Stamps** (2nd edition, 1997)
**Collect Mammals on Stamps** (out of print)
**Collect Railways on Stamps** (new edition in preparation)
**Collect Shells on Stamps** (1st edition, 1995)
**Collect Ships on Stamps** (2nd edition, 1993)

# Information for users

## Aim

The aim of this catalogue is to provide a straightforward illustrated and priced guide to the postage stamps of the whole world to help you to enjoy the greatest hobby of the present day.

## Arrangement

The catalogue lists countries in alphabetical order and there is a complete index at the end of each volume. For ease of reference country names are also printed at the head of each page.

Within each country, postage stamps are listed first. They are followed by separate sections for such other categories as postage due stamps, parcel post stamps, express stamps, official stamps, etc.

All catalogue lists are set out according to dates of issue of the stamps, starting from the earliest and working through to the most recent. New issues received too late for inclusion in the main lists will be found as "Addenda" at the end of each volume.

## Scope of the Catalogue

The *Simplified Catalogue of Stamps of the World* contains listings of postage stamps only. Apart from the ordinary definitive, commemorative and air-mail stamps of each country – which appear first in each list – there are sections for the following where appropriate:

- postage due stamps
- parcel post stamps
- official stamps
- express and special delivery stamps
- charity and compulsory tax stamps
- newspaper and journal stamps
- printed matter stamps
- registration stamps
- acknowledgement of receipt stamps
- late fee and too late stamps
- military post stamps
- recorded message stamps
- personal delivery stamps

We receive numerous enquiries from collectors about other items which do not fall within the categories set out above and which consequently do not appear in the catalogue lists. It may be helpful, therefore, to summarise the other kinds of stamp that exist but which we deliberately exclude from this postage stamp catalogue.

## We do *not* list the following:

**Fiscal or revenue stamps:** stamps used solely in collecting taxes or fees for non-postal purposes. Examples would be stamps which pay a tax on a receipt, represent the stamp duty on a contract or frank a customs document. Common inscriptions found include: Documentary, Proprietary, Inter. Revenue, Contract Note.

**Local stamps:** postage stamps whose validity and use are limited in area, say to a single town or city, though in some cases they provided, with official sanction, services in parts of countries not covered by the respective government.

**Local carriage labels and Private local issues:** many labels exist ostensibly to cover the cost of ferrying mail from one of Great Britain's offshore islands to the nearest mainland post office. They are not recognised as valid for national or international mail. Examples: Calf of Man, Davaar, Herm, Lundy, Pabay, Stroma. Items from some other places have only the status of tourist souvenir labels.

**Telegraph stamps:** stamps intended solely for the prepayment of telegraphic communication.

**Bogus or "phantom" stamps:** labels from mythical places or non-existent administrations. Examples in the classical period were Sedang, Counani, Clipperton Island and in modern times Thomond and Monte Bello Islands. Numerous labels have also appeared since the War from dissident groups as propaganda for their claims and without authority from the home governments. Common examples are labels for "Free Albania", "Free Rumania" and "Free Croatia" and numerous issues for Nagaland, Indonesia and the South Moluccas ("Republik Maluku Selatan").

**Railway letter fee stamps:** special stamps issued by railway companies for the conveyance of letters by rail. Example: Talyllyn Railway. Similar services are now offered by some bus companies and the labels they issue likewise do not qualify for inclusion in the catalogue.

**Perfins** ("perforated initials"): numerous postage stamps may be found with initial letters or designs punctured through them by tiny holes. These are applied by private and public concerns as a precaution against theft and do not qualify for separate mention.

# Information for users

**Labels:** innumerable items exist resembling stamps but – as they do not prepay postage – they are classified as labels. The commonest categories are:

— propaganda and publicity labels: designed to further a cause or campaign;

— exhibition labels: particularly souvenirs from philatelic events;

— testing labels: stamp-size labels used in testing stamp-vending machines;

— Post Office training school stamps: British stamps overprinted with two thick vertical bars or SCHOOL SPECIMEN are produced by the Post Office for training purposes;

— seals and stickers: numerous charities produce stamp-like labels, particularly at Christmas and Easter, as a means of raising funds and these have no postal validity.

**Cut-outs:** items of postal stationery, such as envelopes, cards and wrappers, often have stamps impressed or imprinted on them. They may usually be cut out and affixed to envelopes, etc., for postal use if desired, but such items are not listed in this catalogue.

Collectors wanting further information about exact definitions are referred to *Philatelic Terms Illustrated,* published by Stanley Gibbons and containing many illustrations in colour (third edition price £7.50 plus £3 postage and packing).

There is also a priced listing of the postal fiscals of Great Britain in our Part 1 *(British Commonwealth)* Catalogue and in Volume 1 of the *Great Britain Specialised* Catalogue (5th and later editions).

Although, as stated, none of the above qualify for inclusion in this postage stamp catalogue, this does not imply that they are of no interest to certain collectors. Indeed, in the 1950s, a group was formed in Great Britain called the "Cinderella Stamp Club", whose object is the study of all those stamps which Stanley Gibbons do *not* list in their catalogues.

## Catalogue Numbers

Stanley Gibbons catalogue numbers are recognised universally and any individual stamp can be identified by quoting the catalogue number (the one at the left of the column) prefixed by the name of the country and the letters "S.G.". Do not confuse the catalogue number with the type numbers which refer to illustrations.

## Prices

Prices in the left-hand column are for unused stamps and those in the right-hand column for used. Prices are given in pence and pounds:

100 pence (p) = 1 pound (£1).

Prices are shown as follows:

10 means 10p (10 pence);
1.75 means £1.75 (1 pound and 75 pence);
For £100 and above, prices are in whole pounds.

Our prices are for stamps in fine average condition, and in issues where condition varies we may ask more for the superb and less for the sub-standard.

The minimum catalogue price quoted is 10p. For individual stamps prices between 10p and 30p are provided as a guide for catalogue users. The lowest price charged for individual stamps purchased from Stanley Gibbons is 30p.

The prices quoted are generally for the cheapest variety of stamps but it is worth noting that differences of watermark, perforation, or other details, outside the scope of this catalogue, may often increase the value of the stamp.

Prices quoted for mint issues are for single examples. Those in se-tenant pairs, strips, blocks or sheets may be worth more.

Where prices are not given in either column it is either because the stamps are not known to exist in that particular condition, or, more usually, because there is no reliable information as to value.

All prices are subject to change without prior notice and we give no guarantee to supply all stamps priced. Prices quoted for albums, publications, etc. advertised in this catalogue are also subject to change without prior notice.

Due to different production methods it is sometimes possible for new editions of Parts 2 to 22 to appear showing revised prices which are not included in that year's *Stamps of the World.*

## Unused Stamps

In the case of stamps from *Great Britain* and the *Commonwealth,* prices for unused stamps of Queen Victoria to King George V are for lightly hinged examples; unused prices of King Edward VIII to Queen Elizabeth II issues are for unmounted mint. The prices of unused *Foreign* stamps are for lightly hinged examples for those issued before 1946, thereafter for examples unmounted mint.

## Used Stamps

Prices for used stamps generally refer to postally used examples, though for certain issues they are for cancelled-to-order.

# Information for users

## Guarantee

All stamps supplied by us are guaranteed originals in the following terms:

If not as described, and returned by the purchaser, we undertake to refund the price paid to us in the original transaction. If any stamp is certified as genuine by the Expert Committee of the Royal Philatelic Society, London, or by B.P.A. Expertising Ltd., the purchaser shall not be entitled to make any claim against us for any error, omission or mistake in such certificate.

Consumers' statutory rights are not affected by the above guarantee.

## Currency

At the beginning of each country brief details give the currencies in which the values of the stamps are expressed. The dates, where given, are those of the earliest stamp issues in the particular currency. Where the currency is obvious, e.g. where the colony has the same currency as the mother country, no details are given.

## Illustrations

Illustrations of any surcharges and overprints which are shown and not described are actual size; stamp illustrations are reduced to $\frac{3}{4}$ linear, *unless otherwise stated.*

## "Key-Types"

A number of standard designs occur so frequently in the stamps of the French, German, Portuguese and Spanish colonies that it would be a waste of space to repeat them. Instead these are all illustrated on page xii together with the descriptive names and letters by which they are referred to in the lists.

## Type Numbers

These are the bold figures found below each illustration. References to "Type **6**", for example, in the lists of a country should therefore be understood to refer to the illustration below which the number **"6"** appears. These type numbers are also given in the second column of figures alongside each list of stamps, thus indicating clearly the design of each stamp. In the case of Key-Types – see above – letters take the place of the type numbers.

Where an issue comprises stamps of similar design, represented in this catalogue by one illustration, the corresponding type numbers should be taken as indicating this general design.

Where there are blanks in the type number column it means that the type of the corresponding stamps is that shown by the last number above in the type column of the same issue.

A dash (–) in the type column means that no illustration of the stamp is shown.

Where type numbers refer to stamps of another country, e.g. where stamps of one country are overprinted for use in another, this is always made clear in the text.

## Stamp Designs

Brief descriptions of the subjects of the stamp designs are given either below or beside the illustrations, at the foot of the list of the issue concerned, or in the actual lists. Where a particular subject, e.g. the portrait of a well-known monarch, recurs frequently the description is not repeated, nor are obvious designs described.

Generally, the unillustrated designs are in the same shape and size as the one illustrated, except where otherwise indicated.

## Surcharges and Overprints

Surcharges and overprints are usually described in the headings to the issues concerned. Where the actual wording of a surcharge or overprint is given it is shown in bold type.

Some stamps are described as being "Surcharged in words", e.g. **TWO CENTS,** and others "Surcharged in figures and words", e.g. **20 CENTS,** although of course many surcharges are in foreign languages and combinations of words and figures are numerous. There are often bars, etc., obliterating old values or inscriptions but in general these are only mentioned where it is necessary to avoid confusion.

No attention is paid in this catalogue to colours of overprints and surcharges so that stamps with the same overprints in different colours are not listed separately.

Numbers in brackets after the descriptions of overprinted or surcharged stamps are the catalogue numbers of the unoverprinted stamps.

Note – the words "inscribed" or "inscription" always refer to wording incorporated in the design of a stamp and not surcharges or overprints.

## Coloured Papers

Where stamps are printed on coloured paper the description is given as e.g. "4c. black on blue" – a stamp printed in black on blue paper. No attention is paid in this catalogue to differences in the texture of paper, e.g. laid, wove.

# Information for users

## Watermarks

Stamps having different watermarks, but otherwise the same, are not listed separately. No reference is therefore made to watermarks in this volume.

## Stamp Colours

Colour names are only required for the identification of stamps, therefore they have been made as simple as possible. Thus "scarlet", "vermilion", "carmine" are all usually called red. Qualifying colour names have been introduced only where necessary for the sake of clearness.

Where stamps are printed in two or more colours the central portion of the design is in the first colour given, unless otherwise stated.

## Perforations

All stamps are perforated unless otherwise stated. No distinction is made between the various gauges of perforation but early stamp issues which exist both imperforate and perforated are usually listed separately.

Where a heading states "Imperf. or perf." or "Perf. or rouletted" this does not necessarily mean that all values of the issue are found in both conditions.

## Dates of Issue

The date given at the head of each issue is that of the appearance of the earliest stamp in the series. As stamps of the same design or issue are usually grouped together a list of King George VI stamps, for example, headed "1938" may include stamps issued from 1938 to the end of the reign.

## Se-tenant Pairs

Many modern issues are printed in sheets containing different designs or face values. Such pairs, blocks, strips or sheets are described as being "se-tenant" and they are outside the scope of this catalogue, although reference to them may occur in instances where they form a composite design.

## Miniature Sheets

These are outside the scope of this catalogue but are listed in all other Stanley Gibbons catalogues.

## "Appendix" Countries

We regret that, since 1968, it has been necessary to establish an Appendix (at the end of each country as appropriate) to which numerous stamps have had to be consigned. Several countries imagine that by issuing huge quantities of unnecessary stamps they will have a ready source of income from stamp collectors – and particularly from the less-experienced ones. Stanley Gibbons refuse to encourage this exploitation of the hobby and we do not stock the stamps concerned.

Two kinds of stamp are therefore given the briefest of mentions in the Appendix, purely for the sake of record. Administrations issuing stamps greatly in excess of true postal needs have the offending issues placed there. Likewise it contains stamps which have not fulfilled all the normal conditions for full catalogue listing.

These conditions are that the stamps must be issued by a legitimate postal authority, recognised by the government concerned, and are adhesives, valid for proper postal use in the class of service for which they are inscribed. Stamps, with the exception of such categories as postage dues and officials, must be available to the general public at face value with no artificial restrictions being imposed on their distribution.

The publishers of this catalogue have observed, with concern, the proliferation of 'artificial' stamp-issuing territories. On several occasions this has resulted in separately inscribed issues for various component parts of otherwise united states or territories.

Stanley Gibbons Publications have decided that where such circumstances occur, they will not, in the future, list these items in the SG catalogue without first satisfying themselves that the stamps represent a genuine political, historical or postal division within the country concerned. Any such issues which do not fulfil this stipulation will be recorded in the Catalogue Appendix only.

Stamps in the Appendix are kept under review in the light of any newly acquired information about them. If we are satisfied that a stamp qualifies for proper listing in the body of the catalogue it is moved there.

## "Undesirable Issues"

The rules governing many competitive exhibitions – including the Melville Competition – are set by the Fédération Internationale de Philatelie and stipulate a downgrading of marks for stamps classed as "undesirable issues".

This catalogue can be taken as a guide to status. All stamps in the main listings and Addenda are acceptable. Stamps in the Appendix should not be entered for competition as these are the "undesirable issues".

# Information for users

Particular care is advised with Aden Protectorate States, Ajman, Bhutan, Chad, Fujeira, Khor Fakkan, Manama, Ras al Khaima, Sharjah, Umm al Qiwain and Yemen. Totally bogus stamps exist (as explained in Appendix notes) and these are to be avoided also for competition. As distinct from "undesirable stamps" certain categories are not covered in this catalogue purely by reason of its scope (see page v). Consult the particular competition rules to see if such are admissible even though not listed by us.

## Where to Look for More Detailed Listings

The present work deliberately omits details of paper, perforation, shade and watermark. But as you become more absorbed in stamp collecting and wish to get greater enjoyment from the hobby you may well want to study these matters.

All the information you require about any particular postage stamp will be found in the main Stanley Gibbons Catalogues.

Commonwealth countries in Volume 3 are covered by the Part 1 (British Commonwealth) Catalogue published annually in two volumes.

For foreign countries you can easily find which catalogue to consult by looking at the country headings in the present book.

To the right of each country name are code letters specifying which volume of our main catalogues contains that country's listing.

The code letters are as follows:

Pt. 2 Part 2
Pt. 3 Part 3 etc.

(See page iv for complete list of Parts.)

So, for example, if you want to know more about Chinese stamps than is contained in the *Simplified Catalogue of Stamps of the World* the reference to

**CHINA** Pt. 17

guides you to the Gibbons Part 17 *(China)* Catalogue listing for the details you require.

New editions of Parts 2 to 22 appear at irregular intervals.

## Correspondence

Whilst we welcome information and suggestions we must ask correspondents to include the cost of postage for the return of any stamps submitted plus registration where appropriate. Letters should be addressed to The Catalogue Editor at Ringwood.

Where information is solicited purely for the benefit of the enquirer we regret we cannot undertake to reply unless stamps or reply coupons are sent to cover the postage.

## Identification of Stamps

**We regret we do not give opinions as to the genuineness of stamps, nor do we identify stamps or number them by our Catalogue.**

Users of this catalogue are referred to our companion booklet entitled *Stamp Collecting — How to Identify Stamps.* It explains how to look up stamps in this catalogue, contains a full checklist of stamp inscriptions and gives help in dealing with unfamiliar scripts. It is available from Stanley Gibbons at £2.95, postage extra.

## Stanley Gibbons would like to complement your collection

**At Stanley Gibbons we offer a range of services which are designed to complement your collection.**

Our modern stamp shop, the largest in Europe, together with our rare stamp department has one of the most comprehensive stocks of Great Britain in the world, so whether you are a beginner or an experienced philatelist you are certain to find something to suit your special requirements.

Alternatively through our Mail Order services you can control the growth of your collection from the comfort of your own home. Our Postal Sales Department regularly sends out mailings of Special Offers. We can also help with your wants list—so why not ask us for those elusive items?

And don't forget Stanley Gibbons Auctions which holds regular sales each year. Come along in person or send in a written bid for the items you require. For details of current subscription rates for Auction catalogues write to Stanley Gibbons Auctions, 399 Strand, London WC2R 0LX.

Why not take advantage of the many services we have to offer? Visit our premises in the Strand or, for more information, write to the appropriate address on page x.

# Stanley Gibbons Holdings Plc Addresses

**Stanley Gibbons Limited, Stanley Gibbons Auctions** 399 Strand, London WC2R 0LX

Telephone 0171 836 8444 Fax 0171 836 7342 for all departments.

**Auction Room and Specialist Stamp Departments.** Open Monday–Friday 9.30 a.m. to 5 p.m.

**Shop.** Open Monday–Friday 8.30 a.m. to 6 p.m. and Saturday 10 a.m. to 4 p.m.

**Fraser's**

Autographs, photographs, letters and documents
399 Strand, London WC2 0LX
Telephone 0171 836 8444 Fax 0171 836 7342

Monday–Friday 9 a.m. to 5.30 p.m. and Saturday 10 a.m. to 4 p.m.

**Stanley Gibbons Publications**

5 Parkside, Christchurch Road, Ringwood, Hants BH24 3SH.
Telephone 01425 472363 (24 hour answerphone service) Fax 01425 470247.
E-mail: info@stangib.demon.co.uk

**Publication Showroom** (at above address). Open Monday–Friday 9 a.m. to 3 p.m.

**Publications Mail Order.** FREEPHONE 0800 611622. Monday–Friday 8.30 a.m. to 5 p.m.
**Trade Desk:** 01425 478776
Monday–Friday 8.30 a.m. to 5 p.m.

**Urch Harris & Co.**

1 Denmark Avenue, Bristol BS1 5HD.
Telephone 0117 9349333 Fax 0117 9273037.

Monday–Friday 8.30 a.m. to 5 p.m.

## Stanley Gibbons Publications Overseas Representation

Stanley Gibbons Publications are represented overseas by the following sole distributors (*), distributors (**) or licensees (***).

**Australia***
Lighthouse Philatelic (Aust.) Pty. Ltd., P.O. Box 763, Strawberry Hills, New South Wales, 2012 Australia.

Stanley Gibbons (Australia) Pty. Ltd.***
P.O. Box 863J, Melbourne 3001, Australia.

**Belgium and Luxembourg****
Davo c/o Philac, Rue du Midi 48, Bruxelles, 1000 Belgium.

**Canada***
Lighthouse Publications (Canada) Ltd., 255 Duke Street, Montreal, Quebec, Canada H3C 2M2

**Denmark****
Davo c/o Lindner Falzlos, Gl Randersvej 28, 8450 Hammel, Denmark

**Finland****
Davo c/o Suomen Postimerkkeily Ludvingkatu 5 SF-00130 Helsinki, Finland.

**France***
Davo France (Casteilla), 10, Rue Leon Foucault, 78184 St. Quentin Yvelines Cesex, France.

**Germany** and Austria*
Leuchtturm Albenverlag, Paul Koch KG Am Spakenberg 45, Postfach 1340, D-2054 Geesthacht, Germany.

**Hong Kong****
Po-on Stamp Service, G.P.O. Box 2498, Hong Kong.

**Israel****
Capital Stamps, P.O. Box 3769, Jerusalem 91036, Israel.

**Italy***
Secrian Srl, Via Pantelleria 2, I-20156, Milan, Italy.

**Japan****
Japan Philatelic Co. Ltd., P.O. Box 2, Suginami-Minami, Tokyo, Japan.

**Netherlands***
Davo Publications, P.O. Box 411, 7400 AK Deventer, Netherlands.

**New Zealand*****
Stanley Gibbons (New Zealand) Ltd., P.O. Box 80, Wellington, New Zealand.

**Norway****
Davo Norge A/S, P.O. Box 738 Sentrum, N-0105, Oslo, Norway.

**Singapore*****
Stanley Gibbons (Singapore) Pte Ltd., Raffles City P.O. Box 1689, Singapore 9117.

**South Africa****
Republic Coin and Stamp Accessories (Pty) Ltd., P.O. Box 11199, Johannesburg, RSA 2000.

**Sweden***
Chr Winther Soerensen AB, Box 43, S-310 Knaered, Sweden.

**Switzerland****
Phila Service, Burgstrasse 160, CH 4125, Riehen, Switzerland.

**West Indies/Caribbean****
Hugh Dunphy, P.O. Box 413, Kingston 10, Jamaica, West Indies.

# Abbreviations

| | | |
|---|---|---|
| Anniv. | denotes | Anniversary |
| Assn. | ,, | Association |
| Bis. | ,, | Bistre |
| Bl. | ,, | Blue |
| Bldg. | ,, | Building |
| Blk. | ,, | Black |
| Br. | ,, | British *or* Bridge |
| Brn. | ,, | Brown |
| B.W.I. | ,, | British West Indies |
| C.A.R.I.F.T.A. | ,, | Caribbean Free Trade Area |
| Cent. | ,, | Centenary |
| Chest. | ,, | Chestnut |
| Choc. | ,, | Chocolate |
| Clar. | ,, | Claret |
| Coll. | ,, | College |
| Commem. | ,, | Commemoration |
| Conf. | ,, | Conference |
| Diag. | ,, | Diagonally |
| E.C.A.F.E. | ,, | Economic Commission for Asia and Far East |
| Emer. | ,, | Emerald |
| E.P.T. Conference | ,, | European Postal and Telecommunications Conference |
| Exn. | ,, | Exhibition |
| F.A.O. | ,, | Food and Agriculture Organization |
| Fig. | ,, | Figure |
| G.A.T.T. | ,, | General Agreement on Tariffs and Trade |
| G.B. | ,, | Great Britain |
| Gen. | ,, | General |
| Govt. | ,, | Government |
| Grn. | ,, | Green |
| Horiz. | ,, | Horizontal |
| H.Q. | ,, | Headquarters |
| Imperf. | ,, | Imperforate |
| Inaug. | ,, | Inauguration |
| Ind. | ,, | Indigo |
| Inscr. | ,, | Inscribed or inscription |
| Int. | ,, | International |
| I.A.T.A. | ,, | International Air Transport Association |
| I.C.A.O. | ,, | International Civil Aviation Organization |
| I.C.Y. | ,, | International Co-operation Year |
| I.G.Y. | ,, | International Geophysical Year |
| I.L.O. | ,, | International Labour Office (or later, Organization) |
| I.M.C.O. | ,, | Inter-Governmental Maritime Consultative Organization |
| I.T.U. | ,, | International Telecommunication Union |
| Is. | ,, | Islands |
| Lav. | ,, | Lavender |
| Mar. | ,, | Maroon |
| mm. | ,, | Millimetres |
| Mult. | ,, | Multicoloured |
| Mve. | denotes | Mauve |
| Nat. | ,, | National |
| N.A.T.O. | ,, | North Atlantic Treaty Organization |
| O.D.E.C.A. | ,, | Organization of Central American States |
| Ol. | ,, | Olive |
| Optd. | ,, | Overprinted |
| Orge. *or* oran. | ,, | Orange |
| P.A.T.A. | ,, | Pacific Area Travel Association |
| Perf. | ,, | Perforated |
| Post. | ,, | Postage |
| Pres. | ,, | President |
| P.U. | ,, | Postal Union |
| Pur. | ,, | Purple |
| R. | ,, | River |
| R.S.A. | ,, | Republic of South Africa |
| Roul. | ,, | Rouletted |
| Sep. | ,, | Sepia |
| S.E.A.T.O. | ,, | South East Asia Treaty Organization |
| Surch. | ,, | Surcharged |
| T. | ,, | Type |
| T.U.C. | ,, | Trades Union Congress |
| Turq. | ,, | Turquoise |
| Ultram. | ,, | Ultramarine |
| U.N.E.S.C.O. | ,, | United Nations Educational, Scientific & Cultural Organization |
| U.N.I.C.E.F. | ,, | United Nations Children's Fund |
| U.N.O. | ,, | United Nations Organization |
| U.N.R.W.A. | ,, | United Nations Relief and Works Agency for Palestine Refugees in the Near East |
| U.N.T.E.A. | ,, | United Nations Temporary Executive Authority |
| U.N.R.R.A. | ,, | United Nations Relief and Rehabilitation Administration |
| U.P.U. | ,, | Universal Postal Union |
| Verm. | ,, | Vermilion |
| Vert. | ,, | Vertical |
| Vio. | ,, | Violet |
| W.F.T.U. | ,, | World Federation of Trade Unions |
| W.H.O. | ,, | World Health Organization |
| Yell. | ,, | Yellow |

**Arabic Numerals**

As in the case of European figures, the details of the Arabic numerals vary in different stamp designs, but they should be readily recognised with the aid of this illustration:

| ٠ | ١ | ٢ | ٣ | ٤ |
|---|---|---|---|---|
| 0 | 1 | 2 | 3 | 4 |
| ٥ | ٦ | ٧ | ٨ | ٩ |
| 5 | 6 | 7 | 8 | 9 |

# Key-Types

(see note on page vii)

## French Group

A. "Blanc."

B. "Mouchon."

C. "Merson."

D. "Tablet."

E.

F.

G.

H.

"International Colonial Exhibition."

I. "Faidherbe."

J. "Palms."

K. "Balay."

L. "Natives."

M. "Figure."

## German Group

N. "Yacht."

O. "Yacht."

## Spanish Group

X. "Alfonso XII."

Y. "Baby."

Z. "Curly Head"

## Portuguese Group

P. "Crown."

Q. "Embossed."

R. "Figures."

S. "Carlos."

T. "Manoel."

U. "Ceres."

V. "Newspaper."

W. "Due."

# STANLEY GIBBONS SIMPLIFIED CATALOGUE OF STAMPS OF THE WORLD—VOLUME 1 FOREIGN COUNTRIES A-J

## ABU DHABI — Pt. 19

The largest of the Trucial States in the Persian Gulf. Treaty relations with Great Britain expired on 31 December 1966, when Abu Dhabi Post Office took over the postal services (issues before this date are listed in Vol 3). On 18 July 1971, seven of the Gulf shaikhdoms, including Abu Dhabi, agreed to form the State of the United Arab Emirates. The federation came into being on 1 Aug., 1972.

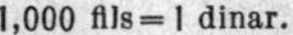

1,000 fils = 1 dinar.

**9.** Shaikh Zaid bin Sultan al Nahayyan. **10.**

**1967.**

| No. | Type | Description | Unused | Used |
|---|---|---|---|---|
| 26. | – | 5 f. red and green .. | 20 | 15 |
| 27. | – | 15 f. red and brown .. | 30 | 10 |
| 28. | – | 20 f. red and blue .. | 50 | 15 |
| 29. | – | 35 f. red and violet .. | 60 | 20 |
| 30. | **9.** | 40 f. green .. .. | 80 | 20 |
| 38. | **10.** | 40 f. green .. .. | 1·10 | 85 |
| 31. | **9.** | 50 f. brown .. .. | 1·00 | 25 |
| 39. | **10.** | 50 f. brown .. .. | 1·40 | 60 |
| 32. | **9.** | 60 f. blue .. .. .. | 1·10 | 30 |
| 40. | **10.** | 60 f. blue .. .. .. | 2·40 | 85 |
| 33. | **9.** | 100 f. red .. .. .. | 1·75 | 40 |
| 41. | **10.** | 100 f. red .. .. .. | 6·50 | 1·60 |
| 34. | – | 125 f. brown and green .. | 3·50 | 1·40 |
| 35. | – | 200 f. brown and blue .. | 15·00 | 3·00 |
| 36. | – | 500 f. violet and orange | 11·00 | 5·50 |
| 37. | – | 1 d. blue and green .. | 20·00 | 10·00 |

DESIGNS—As Types **9/10**.—VERT. 5 f. to 35 f. National flag. HORIZ. (47 × 27 mm.) 125 f. Mountain gazelle. 200 f. Lanner falcon. 500 f. 1 d. Palace. Each with portrait of Ruler.

**11.** Human Rights Emblem and Shaikh Zaid.

**1968.** Human Rights Year.

| No. | Type | Description | Unused | Used |
|---|---|---|---|---|
| 42. | **11.** | 35 f. multicoloured .. | 1·25 | 50 |
| 43. | | 60 f. multicoloured .. | 2·00 | 60 |
| 44. | | 150 f. multicoloured .. | 3·70 | 1·40 |

**12.** Arms and Shaikh Zaid.

**1968.** Anniv. of Shaikh Zaid's Accession.

| No. | Type | Description | Unused | Used |
|---|---|---|---|---|
| 45. | **12.** | 5 f. multicoloured .. | 1·25 | 20 |
| 46. | | 10 f multicoloured .. | 1·25 | 20 |
| 47. | | 100 f. multicoloured .. | 3·50 | 1·25 |
| 48. | | 125 f. multicoloured .. | 5·00 | 1·90 |

**13.** New Construction.

**1968.** 2nd Anniv. of Shaikh's Accession. "Progress in Abu Dhabi". Multicoloured.

| No. | Description | Unused | Used |
|---|---|---|---|
| 49. | 5 f. Type **13** .. .. .. | 55 | 20 |
| 50. | 10 f. Airport buildings (46½ × 34 mm.) .. .. | 1·25 | 50 |
| 51. | 35 f. Shaikh Zaid, bridge and Northern Goshawk (59 × 34 mm.) .. .. | 9·50 | 2·75 |

**14.** Petroleum Installations.

**15.** Shaikh Zaid.

**1969.** 3rd Anniv. of Shaikh's Accession. Petroleum Industry. Multicoloured.

| No. | Description | Unused | Used |
|---|---|---|---|
| 52. | 35 f. Type **14** .. .. | 75 | 30 |
| 53. | 60 f. Marine drilling platform .. .. .. | 2·75 | 95 |
| 54. | 125 f. Separator platform, Zakum field .. .. | 4·00 | 1·50 |
| 55. | 200 f. Tank farm .. .. | 5·00 | 2·25 |

**1970.**

| No. | Type | Description | Unused | Used |
|---|---|---|---|---|
| 56. | – | 5 f. multicoloured .. | 30 | 15 |
| 57. | **15.** | 10 f. multicoloured .. | 40 | 15 |
| 58. | – | 25 f. multicoloured .. | 75 | 15 |
| 59. | **15.** | 35 f. multicoloured .. | 1·00 | 15 |
| 60. | | 50 f. multicoloured .. | 1·50 | 25 |
| 61. | – | 60 f. multicoloured .. | 1·60 | 30 |
| 62. | **15.** | 70 f. multicoloured .. | 2·50 | 45 |
| 63. | – | 90 f. multicoloured .. | 3·25 | 75 |
| 64. | – | 125 f. multicoloured .. | 4·50 | 1·25 |
| 65. | – | 150 f. multicoloured .. | 5·50 | 1·50 |
| 66. | – | 500 f. multicoloured .. | 20·00 | 8·00 |
| 67. | – | 1 d. multicoloured .. | 35·00 | 13·00 |

DESIGNS: Nos. 56, 58, 61 and 63 as Type **15,** but frames changed, and smaller country name. 125 f. Arab stallion. 150 f. Mountain gazelle. 500 f. Fort Jahili. 1 d. Great Mosque.

No. 67 has face value in Arabic only.

**17.** Shaikh Zaid and "Mt. Fuji" (T. Hayashi).

**1970.** "Expo 70" World Fair, Osaka, Japan.

| No. | Type | Description | Unused | Used |
|---|---|---|---|---|
| 68 | **17** | 25 f. multicoloured .. | 1·00 | 30 |
| 69 | | 35 f. multicoloured .. | 1·25 | 30 |
| 70 | | 60 f. multicoloured .. | 2·00 | 1·25 |

**18.** Abu Dhabi Airport.

**19.** Pres. G. A. Nasser.

**1970.** 3rd Anniv. of Shaikh's Accession. Multicoloured.

| No. | Description | Unused | Used |
|---|---|---|---|
| 71. | 25 f. Type **18** .. .. | 1·75 | 40 |
| 72. | 60 f. Airport entrance .. | 3·00 | 95 |
| 73. | 150 f. Aerial view of Abu Dhabi (vert.) .. | 7·00 | 3·25 |

**1971.** Gamal Nasser (President of Egypt) Commemoration.

| No. | Type | Description | Unused | Used |
|---|---|---|---|---|
| 74 | **19** | 25 f. black on pink .. | 1·60 | 60 |
| 75 | | 35 f. black on lilac .. | 2·25 | 80 |

**20.** Motorised Patrol.

**1971.** 5th Anniv of Shaikh's Accession. Defence Force. Multicoloured.

| No. | Description | Unused | Used |
|---|---|---|---|
| 76 | 35 f. Type **20** .. | 2·50 | 80 |
| 77 | 60 f. Patrol-boat "Baniyas" | 3·50 | 1·25 |
| 78 | 125 f. Armoured car .. | 7·00 | 1·75 |
| 79 | 150 f. Hawker Hunter FGA.76 jet fighters | 9·00 | 2·75 |

**1971.** No. 60 surch.

| No. | Type | Description | Unused | Used |
|---|---|---|---|---|
| 80. | **15.** | 5 f. on 50 f. multicoloured | 48·00 | 40·00 |

**22.** Dome of the Rock.

**1972.** Dome of the Rock, Jerusalem. Multicoloured.

| No. | Description | Unused | Used |
|---|---|---|---|
| 81. | 35 f. Type **22** .. .. | 6·25 | 2·25 |
| 82. | 60 f. Mosque entrance .. | 9·50 | 3·00 |
| 83. | 125 f. Mosque dome .. | 17·00 | 6·75 |

**1972.** Provisional Issue. Nos. 56/67 optd. **UAE** and arabic inscription.

| No. | Type | Description | Unused | Used |
|---|---|---|---|---|
| 84. | – | 5 f. multicoloured .. | 1·00 | 1·00 |
| 85. | **15.** | 10 f. multicoloured .. | 1·00 | 60 |
| 86. | – | 25 f. multicoloured .. | 1·50 | 1·50 |
| 87. | **15.** | 35 f. multicoloured .. | 2·25 | 1·75 |
| 88. | | 50 f. multicoloured .. | 3·50 | 3·50 |
| 89. | – | 60 f. multicoloured .. | 4·00 | 4·00 |
| 90. | **15.** | 70 f. multicoloured .. | 5·00 | 5·00 |
| 91. | – | 90 f. multicoloured .. | 7·00 | 7·00 |
| 92. | – | 125 f. multicoloured .. | 22·00 | 22·00 |
| 93. | – | 150 f. multicoloured .. | 30·00 | 30·00 |
| 94. | – | 500 f. multicoloured .. | 70·00 | 70·00 |
| 95. | – | 1 d. multicoloured .. | £130 | £130 |

For later issues see **UNITED ARAB EMIRATES.**

## AFGHANISTAN — Pt. 16

An independent Country in Asia, to N.W. of Pakistan. Now a republic, the country was formerly ruled by monarchs from 1747 to 1973.

1871. 60 paisa = 12 shahi = 6 sanar = 3 abasi = 2 kran = 1 rupee.
1920. 60 paisa = 2 kran = 1 rupee.
1926. 100 poul (pul) = 1 afghani (rupee).

> The issues from 1860 to 1892 (Types **1 to 16**) are difficult to classify because the values of each set are expressed in native script and are generally all printed in the same colour. As it is not possible to list these in an intelligible simplified form we would refer users to the detailed list in the Stanley Gibbons Part 16 (Central Asia) Catalogue.

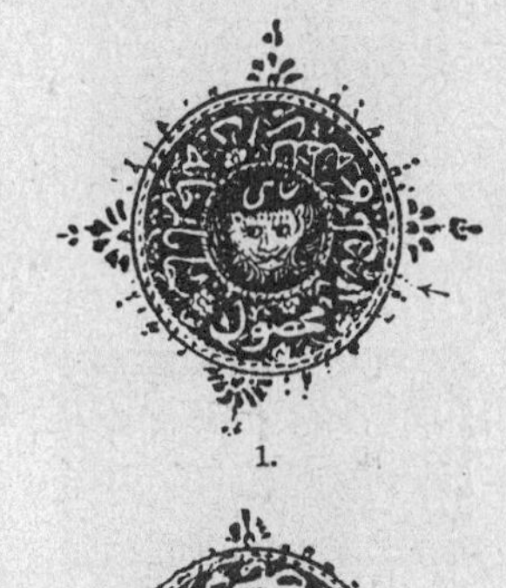

1.

4.

5. 6.

8.

10.

12.

16.

**17.** National Coat of Arms.

**1893.** Dated "1310".

| No. | Type | Description | Unused | Used |
|---|---|---|---|---|
| 147 | **17** | 1 a. black on green .. | 2·75 | 2·75 |
| 148 | | 1 a. black on red .. | 3·00 | 2·75 |
| 149a | | 1 a. black on purple .. | 3·25 | 3·00 |
| 150 | | 1 a. black on yellow .. | 3·00 | 2·75 |
| 151 | | 1 a. black on orange .. | 3·75 | 2·50 |
| 152 | | 1 a. black on blue .. | 5·00 | 4·25 |

**18.** (1 Rupee).

**1894.** Undated.

| No. | Type | Description | Unused | Used |
|---|---|---|---|---|
| 153. | **18.** | 2 a. black on green .. | 10·00 | 6·00 |
| 154. | | 1 r. black on green .. | 12·00 | 7·50 |

**20.** 1 Abasi.

**23.** National Coat of Arms.

**24.**

**1907.** Imperf., roul. or perf.

| No. | Type | Description | Unused | Used |
|---|---|---|---|---|
| 156a. | **20.** | 1 a. green .. .. | 10·00 | 8·50 |
| 157. | – | 2 a. blue .. .. | 5·50 | 5·50 |
| 158. | – | 1 r. green .. .. | 7·50 | 9·00 |

The 2 a. and 1 r. are in similar designs.

**1909.** Perf.

| No. | Type | Description | Unused | Used |
|---|---|---|---|---|
| 165 | **23** | 2 paisa brown .. .. | 2·50 | 3·50 |
| 166 | **24** | 1 a. blue .. .. | 4·50 | 1·50 |
| 168 | | 1 a. red .. .. .. | 90 | 80 |
| 169 | – | 2 a. green .. .. | 2·25 | 2·00 |
| 170a | – | 2 a. bistre .. .. | 1·50 | 2·25 |
| 171 | – | 1 r. brown .. .. | 4·00 | 4·25 |
| 172 | – | 1 r. olive .. .. | 5·50 | 5·50 |

The frames of the 2 a. and 1 r. differ from Type **24.**

**27.** Royal Star of Order of Independence.

**29.** Crest of King Amanullah.

28.

**1920.** 1st Anniv of End of War of Independence. Size 39 × 47 mm.

173 **27** 10 p. red .. .. 22·00 22·00
174 20 p. purple .. .. 40·00 42·00
175 30 p. green .. .. 80·00 85·00

**1921.** Size 23 × 29 mm.

177 **27** 10 p. red .. .. 75 75
178 20 p. purple .. .. 1·50 1·50
180b 30 p. green .. .. 2·50 2·25

**1923.** 5th Independence Day. Optd with T **28.**

181 **27** · 10 p. red .. .. 35·00 35·00
181a 20 p. brown .. .. 40·00 40·00
182 30 p. green .. .. 45·00 45·00

**1924.** 6th Independence Day.

183 **29** 10 p. brown (24 × 32 mm) 30·00 30·00

**29a.** **30.** Crest of King Amanullah.

**1924.**

183b **29a** 5 kr. blue .. .. 30·00 35·00
183c 5 r. mauve .. .. 14·00 20·00

**1925.** 7th Independence Day.

184 **29** 10 p. brown (29 × 37 mm) 30·00 28·00

**1926.** 7th Anniv of Independence.

185 **29** 10 p. blue (26 × 33 mm) 5·50 7·50

**1927.** 8th Anniv of Independence.

186 **30** 10 p. mauve .. .. 10·00 9·00

**31.** **32.**

**33.**

Types **31/3**, **36/37** and **41**, National Seal.

**1927.** Perf or imperf.

188 **31** 15 p. red .. .. 85 75
189 **32** 30 p. green .. .. 1·40 85
190 **33** 60 p. blue .. .. 2·25 2·00

See also Nos. 207/13.

**34.** Crest of King Amanullah.

**1928.** 9th Anniv of Independence.

191 **34** 15 p. red .. .. 3·50 3·25

**36.** **37.**

**1928.**

193 **36** 10 p. green .. .. 85 65
194 **37** 25 p. red .. .. 1·00 75
195 – 40 p. blue .. .. 1·25 95
196 – 50 p. red .. .. 1·75 95

The frames of the 40 and 50 p. differ from Type **37.**

See also Nos. 207/13.

**41.** **42.** Independence Memorial.

**1929.**

207 **36** 10 p. brown .. .. 1·75 1·25
208 **31** 15 p. blue .. .. 1·75 1·10
209 **37** 25 p. blue .. .. 1·75 1·10
210 **41** 30 p. green .. .. 2·25 1·25
211 – 40 p. red .. .. 2·50 1·50
212 – 50 p. blue .. .. 2·50 2·00
213 **33** 60 p. black .. .. 2·75 2·00

**1931.** 13th Independence Day.

214 **42** 20 p. red .. .. 3·25 2·25

**46.** National Assembly Building. **50.** Mosque at Balkh.

**1932.** Inaug. of National Council.

215. – 40 p. brown (31 × 24 mm.) 65 65
216. – 60 p. violet (29 × 26 mm.) 95 85
217. **46.** 80 p. red .. .. 1·25 1·00
218. – 1 a. black (24 × 27 mm.) 10·00 9·00
219. – 2 a. blue (36 × 25 mm.) 4·50 4·25
220. – 3 a. green (36 × 24 mm.) 5·00 4·00

Designs: Nos. 215/16, 218/19, Council Chamber. 3 a. National Assembly Building (different).

**1932.**

221. **50.** 10 p. brown .. .. 50 30
222. – 15 p. brown .. .. 40 35
223. – 20 p. red .. .. 60 25
224. – 25 p. green .. .. 75 25
225. – 30 p. red .. .. 75 25
226. – 40 p. orange .. .. 90 45
227. – 50 p. blue .. .. 1·40 1·40
228. – 60 p. blue .. .. 1·25 1·00
229. – 80 p. violet .. .. 2·25 2·00
230. – 1 a. blue .. .. 4·25 80
231. – 2 a. purple .. .. 4·50 2·50
232. – 3 a. red .. .. 5·50 3·25

Designs—32 × 23 mm: 15 p. Kabul Fortress. 20, 25 p. Parliament House, Darul Funun, Kabul. 40 p. Memorial Pillar of Knowledge and Ignorance, Kabul. 1 a. Ruins at Balkh. 2 a. Minarets at Herat. 32 × 16 mm: 30 p. Arch of Paghman. 23 × 32 mm: 60 p. Minaret at Herat. 23 × 25 mm: 30 p. Arch at Qalai Bust, near Kandahar. 50 p. Independence Memorial, Kabul. 16 × 32 mm: 3 a. Great Buddha at Bamian.

See also Nos. 237/51.

**62.** Independence Memorial. **63.** National Liberation Monument, Kabul.

**1932.** 14th Independence Day.

233. **62.** 1 a. red .. .. 5·50 3·75

**1932.** Commemorative Issue.

234 **63** 80 p. red .. .. 2·75 2·00

**64.** Arch of Paghman.

**1933.** 15th Independence Day.

235. **64.** 50 p. blue .. .. 2·75 2·00

**65.** Independence Memorial.

**1934.** 16th Independence Day.

236. **65.** 50 p. green .. .. 3·25 2·75

**1934.** As Nos. 219/20 and 221/30 but colours changed, and new values.

237. **50.** 10 p. violet .. .. 25 15
238. – 15 p. green .. .. 40 15
239. – 20 p. mauve .. .. 45 15
240 – 25 p. red .. .. 50 25
241. – 30 p. orange .. .. 60 30
242. – 40 p. black .. .. 65 35
243. – 45 p. blue .. .. 2·00 1·50
244. – 45 p. red .. .. 45 25
245. – 50 p. red .. .. 75 25
246. – 60 p. violet .. .. 80 45
247. – 75 p. red .. .. 3·00 2·25
248. – 75 p. blue .. .. 1·00 80
248b. – 80 p. brown .. .. 1·50 85
249. – 1 a. mauve .. .. 2·25 2·00
250. – 2 a. grey .. .. 4·25 3·00
251. – 3 a. blue .. .. 4·50 3·50

Designs (new values)—34 × 23 mm: 45 p. Royal Palace, Kabul. 20 × 34 mm: 75 p. Hunters Canyon Pass, Hindu Kush.

**68.** Independence Memorial. **69.** Firework Display.

**1935.** 17th Independence Day.

252. **68.** 50 p. blue .. .. 3·25 2·75

**1936.** 18th Independence Day.

253 **69** 50 p. mauve .. .. 3·50 2·75

**70.** Independence Memorial and Mohamed Nadir Shah. **71.** Mohamed Nadir Shah.

**1937.** 19th Independence Day. Perf. or imperf.

254. **70.** 50 p. brown and violet 2·50 2·25

**1938.** 20th Independence Day. Perf. or imperf.

255. **71.** 50 p. brown and blue 2·25 2·25

**72.** Aliabad Hospital. **74.** Mohamed Nadir Shah.

**1938.** Obligatory Tax. Int. Anti-Cancer Fund.

256. **72.** 10 p. green .. .. 3·25 5·00
257. – 15 p. blue .. .. 3·25 5·00

Design—44 × 28 mm. 15 p. Pierre and Marie Curie.

**1939.** 21st Independence Day.

258. **74.** 50 p. red .. .. 2·25 1·50

**76.** Darul Funun Parliament House, Kabul. **79.** Independence Memorial.

**82.** Mohamed Zahir Shah.

**83.** Sugar Mill, Baghlan.

**1939.**

259 **76** 10 p. purple (36½ × 24 mm) .. .. 25 20
260 15 p. green (34 × 21 mm) 35 20
261 20 p. purple (34 × 22½ mm) .. .. 40 25
262 – 25 p. red .. .. 45 30
263 – 25 p. green .. .. 30 25
264 – 30 p. orange .. .. 40 25
265 – 35 p. orange .. .. 1·00 65
266 – 40 p. grey .. .. 80 45
267 **79** 45 p. red .. .. 80 40
268 50 p. orange .. .. 60 25
269 60 p. violet .. .. 75 25
270 – 70 p. violet .. .. 1·50 65
271 – 70 p. purple .. .. 1·50 65
272 – 75 p. blue .. .. 2·25 75
273 – 75 p. purple .. .. 1·75 1·90
274 – 75 p. red .. .. 2·50 2·50
275 – 80 p. brown .. .. 1·50 80
276 **82** 1 a. purple .. .. 1·50 75
277 – 1 a. purple .. .. 1·50 80
278d **83** 1 a. 25 blue .. .. 1·60 70
279a – 2 a. red .. .. 2·25 1·00
280 – 3 a. blue .. .. 3·50 1·60

Designs—31 × 19 mm: 25, 30 p. Royal Palace, Kabul. 30 × 18 mm: 40 p. Royal Palace, Kabul. 30 × 21 mm: 70 p. Ruins at Qalai Bust, near Kandahar. 35½ × 21½ mm: 75 p. Independence Memorial and Mohamed Nadir Shah. 34½ × 21 mm: 80 p. As 75 p. 35 × 20 mm: 1 a. (No. 277), 2 a. Mohamed Zahir Shah. 3 a. As Type **82** but head turned more to left. 19 × 31 mm: 35 p. Minarets at Herat.

**85.** Potez 25A2 over Kabul.

**1939.** Air.

280a. **85.** 5 a. orange .. .. 3·50 4·50
280b. 10 a. blue .. .. 3·75 4·50
280c. 20 a. green .. .. 6·50 7·50

See also Nos. 300/2.

**86.** Mohamed Nadir Shah. **87.** Arch of Paghman.

**1940.** 22nd Independence Day.

281. **86.** 50 p. green .. .. 2·25 1·50

**1941.** 23rd Independence Day.

282. – 15 p. green .. .. 6·00 3·75
283. **87.** 50 p. brown .. .. 1·75 1·50

Design: (19 × 29½ mm.) 15 p. Independence Memorial.

**87b.** Mohamed Nadir Shah and Arch of Paghman. **88.** Independence Memorial and Mohamed Nadir Shah.

**1942.** 24th Independence Day.

284. – 35 p. green .. .. 4·25 3·75
285. **87b.** 125 p. blue .. .. 2·75 2·25

Design—vert. 35 p. Independence Memorial in medallion.

**1943.** 25th Independence Day.

286. – 35 p. red .. .. 12·00 9·50
287. **88.** 1 a. 25 blue .. .. 2·50 2·25

Design—horiz. 35 p. Independence Memorial seen through archway and Mohamed Nadir Shah in oval frame.

**89.** Arch of Paghman. **90.** Independence Memorial and Mohamed Nadir Shah.

**1944.** 26th Independence Day.

288. **89.** 35 p. red .. .. 1·25 75
289. **90.** 1 a. 25 blue .. .. 2·25 2·00

**91.** Mohamed Nadir Shah and Independence Memorial. **92.** Arch of Paghman and Mohamed Nadir Shah.

**1945.** 27th Independence Day.

290. **91.** 35 p. red .. .. 2·25 75
291. **92.** 1 a. 25 blue .. .. 3·75 2·00

**93.** Independence Memorial. **94.** Mohamed Nadir Shah and Independence Memorial.

**1946.** 28th Independence Day. Dated "1946".
292. – 15 p. green .. .. 1·25 75
293. **93.** 20 p. mauve .. .. 2·00 85
294. – 125 p. blue .. .. 3·25 2·00
DESIGNS—HORIZ. 15 p. Mohamed Zahir Shah. VERT. 125 p. Mohamed Nadir Shah.

**1947.** 29th Independence Day. Dated "1947".
295 – 15 p. green .. .. 1·00 60
296 – 35 p. mauve .. .. 1·25 75
297 **94** 125 p. blue .. .. 3·25 2·00
DESIGNS—HORIZ. 15 p. Mohamed Zahir Shah and ruins of Kandahar Fort. 35 p. Mohamed Zahir Shah and Arch of Paghman.

95. Hungry Boy. 96. Independence Memorial.

**1948.** Child Welfare Fund.
298 **95** 35 p. green .. .. 5·00 4·25
299 – 125 p. blue .. .. 5·00 4·25
DESIGN—26 × 33½ mm. 125 p. Hungry boy in vertical frame.
See also No. 307.

**1948.** Air. As T **85** but colours changed.
300 **85** 5 a. green .. .. 25·00 25·00
301 10 a. orange .. .. 25·00 25·00
302 20 a. blue .. .. 25·00 25·00

**1948.** 30th Independence Day. Dated "1948".
303 – 15 p. green .. .. 75 35
304 **96** 20 p. mauve .. .. 1·00 40
305 – 125 p. blue .. .. 2·00 1·00
DESIGNS—VERT. 15 p. Arch of Paghman. HORIZ 125 p. Mohamed Nadir Shah.

97. U.N. Symbol.

**1948.** 3rd Anniv of U.N.O.
306 **97** 1 a. 25 blue .. .. 11·00 9·00

98. Hungry Boy. 99. Victory Monument.

**1949.** Obligatory Tax. Child Welfare Fund.
307. – 35 p. orange .. .. 3·25 1·75
308. **98.** 125 p. blue .. .. 3·25 1·75
DESIGN—HORIZ. 35 p. as Type **98** but 29 × 22½ mm.

**1949.** 31st Independence Day. Dated "1949" (Nos. 310/11).
309. **99.** 25 p. green .. .. 80 40
310. – 35 p. mauve .. .. 1·00 45
311. – 1 a. 25 blue .. .. 2·25 1·25
DESIGNS—HORIZ. 35 p. Mohamed Zahir Shah and Ruins of Kandahar Fort. 1 a. 25, Independence Memorial and Mohamed Nadir Shah.

100. Arch of Paghman.

**1949.** Obligatory Tax. 4th Anniv of U.N.O.
312 **100** 125 p. green .. .. 16·00 10·00

101. King Mohamed Zahir Shah and Map of Afghanistan.

**1950.** Obligatory Tax. Return of King Mohamed Zahir Shah from Visit to Europe.
313 **101** 125 p. green .. .. 3·75 1·50

102. Hungry Boy. 103. Mohamed Nadir Shah.

**1950.** Obligatory Tax. Child Welfare Fund.
314. **102.** 125 p. green .. .. 4·50 2·50

**1950.** 32nd Independence Day
315. **103.** 35 p. brown .. .. 70 45
316. 125 p. blue .. .. 2·25 75

104.

**1950.** Obligatory Tax. 5th Anniv of U.N.O.
317 **104** 1 a. 25 blue .. .. 7·50 4·50

106.

**1950.** 19th Anniv of Faculty of Medicine, Kabul.
318. **106.** 35 p. green (postage) .. 1·25 75
319. – 1 a. 25 blue .. .. 4·25 2·25

320. **106.** 35 p. red (obligatory tax) 1·25 60
321. – 1 a. 25 black .. .. 8·50 2·75
DESIGN: Nos. 319 and 321, Sanatorium. Nos. 318 and 320 measure 38½ × 25½ mm. and Nos. 319 and 321, 45 × 30 mm.

107. Minaret at Herat. 110. Mosque at Balkh.

109. Mohamed Zahir Shah. 118.

**1951.**
322 **107** 10 p. brown and yellow 25 20
323 15 p. brown and blue 40 20
324 – 20 p. black .. .. 8·00 4·25
325 **109** 25 p. green .. .. 40 15
326 **110** 30 p. red .. .. 45 20
327 **109** 35 p. violet .. .. 50 20
328 – 40 p. brown .. .. 55 20
329 – 45 p. blue .. .. 55 20
330 – 50 p. black .. .. 1·50 25
331 – 60 p. black .. .. 1·25 25
332 – 70 p. black, red & grn 60 25
333 – 75 p. red .. .. 1·00 40
334 – 80 p. black and red .. 1·75 75
335 – 1 a. violet and green 1·25 60
336 **118** 125 p. black and purple 1·40 75
337 2 a. blue .. .. 2·25 70
338 3 a. blue and black .. 4·25 1·00
DESIGNS—19 × 29 mm: 20 p. Buddha of Bamian. 45 p. Maiwand Victory Monument. 60 p. Victory Towers, Ghazni. 22 × 28 mm: 75, 80 p., 1 a. Mohamed Zahir Shah. 28 × 19 mm: 40 p. Ruins at Qalai Bust. 70 p. Flag. 30 × 19 mm: 50 p. View of Kandahar.
See also Nos. 425/425k.

119. Douglas DC-3 over Kabul.

121. Arch of Paghman.

120. Shepherdess.

**1951.** Air.
339 **119** 5 a. red .. .. 3·50 75
339a 5 a. green .. .. 1·60 55
340 10 a. grey .. .. 8·00 1·60
341 20 a. blue .. .. 12·00 2·75
See also Nos. 415a/b.

**1951.** Obligatory Tax. Child Welfare Fund.
342 **120** 35 p. green .. .. 1·50 95
343 – 125 p. blue .. .. 1·50 95
DESIGN—34½ × 44 mm. 125 p. Young shepherd.

(122.) (123.)

**1951.** 33rd Independence Day. Optd. with T **122**.
344. **121.** 35 p. black and green 1·10 60
345. – 125 p. blue .. 2·75 1·25
DESIGN (34 × 18½ mm): 125 p. Mohamed Nadir Shah and Independence Memorial.
See also Nos. 360/1b and 418/19.

**IMPERF. STAMPS.** From 1951 many issues were made available imperf. from limited printings.

124. Flag of Pashtunistan.

**1951.** Obligatory Tax. Pashtunistan Day.
346 **124** 35 p. brown .. .. 1·75 1·00
347 – 125 p. blue .. .. 3·25 2·25
DESIGN—42½ × 21½ mm. 125 p. Afridi tribesman.

125. Dove and Globe. 126. Avicenna (physician).

**1951.** Obligatory Tax. United Nations Day.
348 **125** 35 p. mauve .. .. 1·00 50
349 – 125 p. blue .. .. 2·50 2·00
DESIGN—VERT. 125 p. Dove and globe.

**1951.** Obligatory Tax. 20th Anniv. of Faculty of Medicine.
350 **126** 35 p. mauve .. .. 3·00 1·25
351 125 p. blue .. .. 1·00 3·25

127. Amir Sher Ali and First Stamp. 128. Children and Postman.

**1951.** Obligatory Tax. 76th Anniv. of U.P.U.
352. **127.** 35 p. brown .. .. 75 50
353. – 35 p. mauve .. .. 75 50
354. **127.** 125 p. blue .. .. 1·25 75
355. – 125 p. blue .. .. 1·25 75
DESIGN: Nos. 353 and 355, Mohamed Zahir Shah and first stamp.

**1952.** Obligatory Tax. Child Welfare Fund.
356. **128.** 35 p. brown .. .. 75 60
357. – 125 p. violet .. .. 1·50 85
DESIGN—HORIZ. 125 p. Girl dancing (33 × 23 mm.)

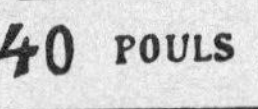



(129.) 131. Soldier and Flag of Pashtunistan.

**1952.** Obligatory Tax. Birth Millenary of Avicenna (physician and philosopher).
(a) Surch with T **129**.
358 **110** 40 p. on 30 p. red .. 3·50 2·50

(b) Surch. **MILLIEME ANNIVERSAIRE DE BOALI SINAI BALKI 125 POULS** in frame.
359. **110.** 125 p. on 30 p. red .. 4·50 2·75

**1952.** 34th Independence Day. As Nos. 344/5 but (a) optd. with T **123**.
360. 35 p. black and green .. 3·25 2·25
361. 125 p. blue .. .. 3·25 2·25
(b) Without opt.
361a. 35 p. black and green .. 1·50 65
361b. 125 p. blue .. .. 3·25 1·25

**1952.** Obligatory Tax. Pashtunistan Day.
362. **131.** 35 p. red .. .. 65 55
363. 125 p. blue .. .. 1·10 1·10

132. Orderly and Wounded Soldier. 134. Staff of Aesculapius.

133.

**1952.** Obligatory Tax. Red Crescent Day.
364. **132.** 10 p. green .. .. 50 40

**1952.** Obligatory Tax. United Nations Day.
365. **133.** 35 p. red .. .. 75 50
366. 125 p. turquoise .. 1·75 1·25

**1952.** Obligatory Tax. 21st Anniv. of Faculty of Medicine.
367. **134.** 35 p. brown .. .. 80 50
368. 125 p. blue .. .. 2·25 1·50

135. Stretcher Bearers and Wounded.

**1953.** Obligatory Tax. Red Crescent Day.
369. **135.** 10 p. green and brown .. 70 70
370. – 10 p. brown and orange 70 70
DESIGN: No. 370, Wounded soldier, orderly and eagle.

136. Prince Mohamed Nadir. 138. Flags of Afghanistan and Pashtunistan.

137. Mohamed Nadir Shah and Flag-bearer.

**1953.** Obligatory Tax. Children's Day.
371. **136.** 35 p. orange .. .. 40 25
372. 125 p. blue .. .. 85 60

**1953.** 35th Year of Independence. Inscr. "1953".
373. **137.** 35 p. green .. .. 40 35
374. – 125 p. violet .. .. 1·10 65
DESIGN—VERT. 125 p. Independence Memorial and Mohamed Nadir Shah.

**1953.** Obligatory Tax. Pashtunistan Day. Inscr. "1953".
375. **138.** 35 p. red .. .. 40 20
376. – 125 p. blue .. .. 85 55
DESIGN—HORIZ. 125 p. Badge of Pashtunistan. (26 × 20 mm.)

139. U.N. Emblem. 140. Mohamed Nadir Shah.

**1953.** Obligatory Tax. United Nations Day.
377. **139.** 35 p. mauve .. .. 85 75
378. 125 p. blue .. .. 2·00 1·25

**1953.** Obligatory Tax. 22nd Anniv. of Faculty of Medicine.

| | | | | |
|---|---|---|---|---|
| 379 | 140 | 35 p. orange .. .. | 1·25 | 1·25 |
| 380 | – | 125 p. blue .. .. | 2·50 | 2·75 |

DESIGN: 125 p. As Type 140 but inscribed "1953" and with French inscription.

No. 379 was wrongly inscribed "23rd" in Arabic (the extreme right-hand figure in the second row of the inscription) and No. 380 was wrongly inscribed "XXIII" and had the words "ANNIVERSAIRE" and "MEDECINE" wrongly spelt "ANNIVERAIRE" and "MADECINE". These mistakes were subsequently corrected but the corrected stamps are much rarer than the original issue.

141. Children's Band and Map of Afghanistan. 142. Mohamed Nadir Shah and Cannon.

**1954.** Obligatory Tax. Child Welfare Fund.

| | | | | |
|---|---|---|---|---|
| 381. | 141. | 35 p. violet .. .. | 50 | 25 |
| 382. | | 125 p. blue .. .. | 1·50 | 1·00 |

**1954.** 36th Independence Day.

| | | | | |
|---|---|---|---|---|
| 383. | 142. | 35 p. red .. .. | 75 | 50 |
| 384. | | 125 p. blue .. .. | 2·25 | 1·00 |

143. Hoisting the Flag. 144.

**1954.** Obligatory Tax. Pashtunistan Day.

| | | | | |
|---|---|---|---|---|
| 385. | 143. | 35 p. orange .. .. | 75 | 50 |
| 386. | | 125 p. blue .. .. | 2·00 | 1·10 |

**1954.** Red Crescent Day.

| | | | | |
|---|---|---|---|---|
| 387. | 144. | 20 p. red and blue .. | 75 | 30 |

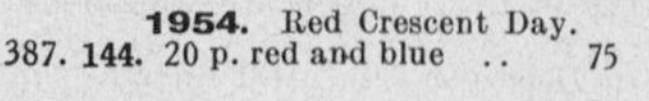

145. U.N. Flag and Map. 146. Globe and Clasped Hands.

**1954.** United Nations Day and 9th Anniv. of U.N.O.

| | | | | |
|---|---|---|---|---|
| 388. | 145. | 35 p. red .. .. | 1·25 | 1·25 |
| 389. | | 125 p. blue .. .. | 3·25 | 3·25 |

**1955.** 10th Anniv of Signing of U.N. Charter.

| | | | | |
|---|---|---|---|---|
| 390 | 146 | 35 p. green .. .. | 75 | 50 |
| 391 | – | 125 p. blue .. .. | 1·75 | 1·00 |

DESIGN—28½ × 36 mm. 125 p. U.N. emblem and flags.

See also Nos. 403/4.

147. Amir Sher Ali and Mohamed Zahir Shah.

**1955.** 85th Anniv of Postal Service.

| | | | | |
|---|---|---|---|---|
| 392 | 147 | 35 p. + 15 p. red .. | 1·25 | 55 |
| 393 | | 125 p. + 25 p. grey .. | 2·00 | 1·00 |

148. Children on Swing. 149. Mohamed Nadir Shah (centre) and brothers.

**1955.** Child Welfare Fund.

| | | | | |
|---|---|---|---|---|
| 394. | 148. | 35 p. + 15 p. green .. | 1·00 | 60 |
| 395. | | 125 p. + 25 p. violet .. | 2·00 | 1·10 |

**1955.** 37th Year of Independence.

| | | | | |
|---|---|---|---|---|
| 396 | 149 | 35 p. blue .. .. | 70 | 45 |
| 397 | | 35 p. mauve .. .. | 70 | 45 |
| 398 | – | 125 p. violet .. .. | 1·50 | 1·00 |
| 399 | – | 125 p. purple .. .. | 1·50 | 1·00 |

DESIGN: 125 p. Mohamed Zahir Shah and battle scene.

150. 151. Red Crescent.

**1955.** Obligatory Tax. Pashtunistan Day.

| | | | | |
|---|---|---|---|---|
| 400. | 150. | 35 p. brown .. .. | 60 | 30 |
| 401. | | 125 p. green .. .. | 1·75 | 50 |

**1955.** Obligatory Tax. Red Crescent Day

| | | | | |
|---|---|---|---|---|
| 402. | 151. | 20 p. red and grey .. | 40 | 40 |

152. U.N. Flag. 153. Child on Slide.

**1955.** Obligatory Tax. 10th Anniv. of United Nations.

| | | | | |
|---|---|---|---|---|
| 403. | 152. | 35 p. brown .. .. | 90 | 60 |
| 404. | | 125 p. blue .. .. | 1·75 | 1·10 |

**1956.** Children's Day.

| | | | | |
|---|---|---|---|---|
| 405. | 153. | 35 p. + 15 p. blue .. | 60 | 40 |
| 406. | | 140 p. + 15 p. brown .. | 1·90 | 85 |

154. Independence Memorial and Mohamed Nadir Shah. 155. Exhibition Building.

**1956.** 38th Year of Independence.

| | | | | |
|---|---|---|---|---|
| 407. | 154. | 35 p. green .. .. | 60 | 35 |
| 408. | | 140 p. blue .. .. | 2·40 | 95 |

**1956.** International Exhibition, Kabul.

| | | | | |
|---|---|---|---|---|
| 409. | 155. | 50 p. brown .. .. | 75 | 35 |
| 410. | | 50 p. blue .. .. | 75 | 35 |

156. Pashtun Square, Kabul. 157. Mohamed Zahir Shah and Crescent.

**1956.** Pashtunistan Day.

| | | | | |
|---|---|---|---|---|
| 411. | 156. | 35 p. + 15 p. violet .. | 40 | 25 |
| 412. | | 140 p. + 15 p. brown .. | 1·00 | 70 |

**1956.** Obligatory Tax. Red Crescent Day.

| | | | | |
|---|---|---|---|---|
| 413. | 157. | 20 p. green and red .. | 55 | 25 |

158. Globe and Sun. 159. Children on See-saw.

**1956.** U.N. Day and 10th Anniv. of Admission of Afghanistan into U.N.O.

| | | | | |
|---|---|---|---|---|
| 414. | 158. | 35 p. + 15 p. blue .. | 1·00 | 95 |
| 415. | | 140 p. + 15 p. brown .. | 2·00 | 1·75 |

**1957.** Air. As Nos. 339/40 but colours changed.

| | | | | |
|---|---|---|---|---|
| 415a | 119 | 5 a. blue .. .. | 2·50 | 60 |
| 415b | | 10 a. violet .. .. | 3·50 | 1·25 |

**1957.** Child Welfare Fund.

| | | | | |
|---|---|---|---|---|
| 416. | 159. | 35 p. + 15 p. red .. | 75 | 55 |
| 417. | | 140 p. + 15 p. blue .. | 1·50 | 1·25 |

**1957.** 39th Independence Day. As Nos. 344/5 but 35 p. has longer Arabic opt. (19 mm.) and 125 p. optd. **39 em Anv.**

| | | | | |
|---|---|---|---|---|
| 418. | 121. | 35 p. black and green | 85 | 45 |
| 419. | | 125 p. blue .. .. | 1·10 | 85 |

162. Pashtu Flag. 163. Red Crescent Headquarters, Kabul.

**1957.** Pashtunistan Day.

| | | | | |
|---|---|---|---|---|
| 420. | 162. | 50 p. red .. .. | 1·00 | 60 |
| 421. | | 155 p. violet .. .. | 1·50 | 1·10 |

No. 421 is inscr. "JOURNEE DU PASHTUNISTAN" beneath flag instead of Pushtu characters.

**1957.** Obligatory Tax. Red Crescent Day.

| | | | | |
|---|---|---|---|---|
| 422. | 163. | 20 p. blue and red .. | 50 | 25 |

164. U.N. Headquarters, New York. 166. Children Bathing.

165. Buzkashi Game.

**1957.** U.N. Day.

| | | | | |
|---|---|---|---|---|
| 423. | 164. | 35 p. + 15 p. brown .. | 50 | 40 |
| 424. | | 140 p. + 15 p. blue .. | 1·00 | 1·00 |

**1957.** As stamps of 1951 but colours changed, and new value.

| | | | | |
|---|---|---|---|---|
| 425 | 110 | 30 p. brown .. .. | 40 | 20 |
| 425a | – | 40 p. red .. .. | 55 | 20 |
| 425b | – | 50 p. yellow .. .. | 75 | 15 |
| 425c | – | 60 p. blue .. .. | 85 | 15 |
| 425d | – | 75 p. violet .. .. | 95 | 15 |
| 425e | – | 80 p. brown & violet | 1·10 | 15 |
| 425f | – | 1 a. blue and red .. | 75 | 20 |
| 425g | 165 | 140 p. purple & green | 2·25 | 60 |
| 425k | 118 | 2 a. blue .. .. | 5·75 | 50 |
| 425h | | 3 a. black and orange | 2·75 | 1·10 |

**1958.** Child Welfare Fund.

| | | | | |
|---|---|---|---|---|
| 426. | 166. | 35 p. + 15 p. red .. | 65 | 40 |
| 427. | | 140 p. + 15 p. brown | 75 | 65 |

167. Mohamed Nadir Shah and Old Soldier. 168. Exhibition Buildings.

**1958.** 40th Independence Day.

| | | | | |
|---|---|---|---|---|
| 428. | 167. | 35 p. green .. .. | 45 | 25 |
| 429. | | 140 p. brown .. .. | 1·10 | 85 |

**1958.** Int. Exn., Kabul.

| | | | | |
|---|---|---|---|---|
| 430. | 168. | 35 p. green .. .. | 40 | 25 |
| 431. | | 140 p. red .. .. | 1·10 | 65 |

169. 170. President Bayar.

**1958.** Pashtunistan Day.

| | | | | |
|---|---|---|---|---|
| 432. | 169. | 35 p. + 15 p. turquoise | 40 | 25 |
| 433. | | 140 p. + 15 p. brown .. | 1·10 | 65 |

**1958.** Visit of Turkish President.

| | | | | |
|---|---|---|---|---|
| 434. | 170. | 50 p. blue .. .. | 45 | 25 |
| 435. | | 100 p. brown .. .. | 75 | 35 |

171. Red Crescent and Map of Afghanistan. 172.

**1958.** Obligatory Tax. Red Crescent Day.

| | | | | |
|---|---|---|---|---|
| 436 | 171 | 25 p. red and green .. | 35 | 15 |

**1958.** "Atoms for Peace".

| | | | | |
|---|---|---|---|---|
| 437. | 172. | 50 p. blue .. .. | 50 | 40 |
| 438. | | 100 p. purple .. .. | 85 | 65 |

173. Flags of U.N. and Afghanistan. 174. U.N.E.S.C.O. Headquarters, Paris.

**1958.** U.N. Day.

| | | | | |
|---|---|---|---|---|
| 439. | 173. | 50 p. multicoloured .. | 75 | 75 |
| 440. | | 100 p. multicoloured .. | 1·50 | 1·25 |

**1958.** Inauguration of U.N.E.S.C.O. Headquarters Building, Paris.

| | | | | |
|---|---|---|---|---|
| 441. | 174. | 50p. green .. .. | 75 | 65 |
| 442. | | 100 p. brown .. .. | 75 | 75 |

175. Globe and Torch. 176. Tug-of-War.

**1958.** 10th Anniv of Declaration of Human Rights.

| | | | | |
|---|---|---|---|---|
| 443 | 175 | 50 p. mauve .. .. | 40 | 40 |
| 444 | | 100 p. purple .. .. | 60 | 70 |

**1959.** Child Welfare Fund.

| | | | | |
|---|---|---|---|---|
| 445 | 176 | 35 p. + 15 p. purple .. | 45 | 40 |
| 446 | | 165 p. + 15 p. mauve .. | 1·25 | 60 |

177. Mohamed Nadir Shah and Flags. 178. Tribal Dance.

**1959.** 41st Independence Day.

| | | | | |
|---|---|---|---|---|
| 447. | 177. | 35 p. red .. .. | 50 | 40 |
| 448. | | 165 p. violet .. .. | 1·25 | 60 |

**1959.** Pashtunistan Day.

| | | | | |
|---|---|---|---|---|
| 449 | 178 | 35 p. + 15 p. green .. | 40 | 25 |
| 450 | | 165 p. + 15 p. orange .. | 1·00 | 65 |

179. Badge-sellers. 180. Horseman.

**1959.** Obligatory Tax. Red Crescent Day.

| | | | | |
|---|---|---|---|---|
| 451. | 179. | 25 p. red and violet .. | 35 | 15 |

**1959.** United Nations Day.

| | | | | |
|---|---|---|---|---|
| 452 | 180 | 35 p. + 15 p. orange .. | 30 | 25 |
| 453 | | 165 p. + 15 p. green .. | 65 | 45 |

181. "Uprooted Tree". 182. Buzkashi Game.

183. Buzkashi Game.

**1960.** World Refugee Year.

| | | | | |
|---|---|---|---|---|
| 454. | 181. | 50 p. orange .. .. | 15 | 10 |
| 455. | | 165 p. blue .. .. | 35 | 25 |

**1960.**

| | | | | |
|---|---|---|---|---|
| 456. | 182. | 25 p. pink .. .. | 50 | 20 |
| 457. | | 25 p. violet .. .. | 50 | 20 |
| 458. | | 25 p. olive .. .. | 60 | 15 |
| 459. | | 50 p. turquoise .. | 1·25 | 50 |
| 460. | | 50 p. blue .. .. | 1·25 | 15 |
| 460a. | | 50 p. orange .. .. | 40 | 15 |
| 461. | 183. | 100 p. olive .. .. | 65 | 25 |
| 462. | | 150 p. orange .. .. | 55 | 25 |
| 463. | | 175 p. brown .. .. | 2·50 | 50 |
| 464. | | 2 a. green .. .. | 1·25 | 85 |

184. Children receiving Ball.

**1960.** Child Welfare Fund.
465. **184.** 75 p.+25 p. blue .. 50 30
466. 175 p.+25 p. green .. 80 40

185. Douglas DC-6 over Mountains.

**1960.** Air.
467. **185.** 75 p. violet .. .. 65 25
468. 125 p. blue .. .. 75 35
469. 5 a. olive .. .. 1·75 60

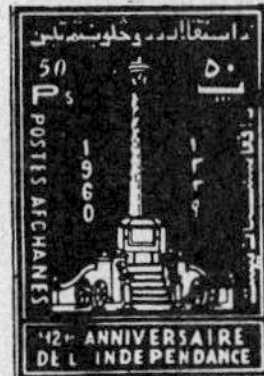

186. Independence Monument, Kabul. 188. Insecticide Sprayer.

187.

**1960.** 42nd Independence Day.
470. **186.** 50 p. blue .. .. 40 25
471. 175 p. mauve .. .. 1·10 35

**1960.** Pashtunistan Day.
472. **187.** 50 p.+50 p. red .. 50 25
473. 175 p.+50 p. blue .. 1·25 95

**1960.** Anti-Malaria Campaign Day.
474. **188.** 50 p.+50 p. orange .. 1·25 1·25
475. 175 p.+50 p. brown .. 2·75 1·60

189. Mohamed Zahir Shah.

**1960.** King's 46th Birthday.
476. **189.** 50 p. brown .. .. 60 50
477. 150 p. red .. .. 1·60 45

190. Ambulance.

**1960.** Red Crescent Day
478. **190.** 50 p.+50 p. violet & red 75 55
479. 175 p.+50 p. blue & red 1·90 1·10

191. Teacher with Globe and Children.

**1960.** Literacy Campaign.
480. **191.** 50 p. mauve .. .. 45 35
481. 100 p. green .. .. 1·10 45

192. Globe and Flags. 195. Mir Wais Nika (patriot).

**1960.** U.N. Day.
482. **192.** 50 p. purple .. .. 30 30
483. 175 p. blue .. .. 1·00 65

**1960.** Olympic Games, Rome. Optd. **1960** in figures and in Arabic and Olympic Rings.
484. **183.** 175 p. brown .. .. 1·50 1·75

**1960.** World Refugee Year. Nos. 454/5 surch + **25 Ps.**
485 **181** 50 p.+25 p. orange .. 1·25 1·75
486 165 p.+25 p. blue .. 1·25 1·75

**1960.** Mir Wais Nika Commem.
487 **195** 50 p. mauve .. .. 65 40
488 175 p. blue .. .. 1·10 55

The very numerous issues of Afghanistan which we do not list appeared between 21 April 1961 and 15 March 1964 (both dates inclusive), and were made available to the philatelic trade by an agency acting under the authority of a contract granted by the Afghanistan Government.

It later became evident that token supplies were only placed on sale in Kabul for a few hours and some of these sets contained stamps of very low denominations for which there was no possible postal use.

When the contract for the production of these stamps expired in 1963 it was not renewed and the Afghanistan Government set up a Philatelic Advisory Board to formulate stamp policy. The issues from No. 489 onwards were made in usable denominations and placed on sale without restriction in Afghanistan and distributed to the trade by the Philatelic Department of the G.P.O. in Kabul.

Issues not listed here will be found recorded in the Appendix at the end of this country. It is believed that some of the higher values from the agency sets were utilised for postage in late 1979.

196. Band Amir Lake.

**1961.**
489. **196.** 3 a. blue .. .. 45 25
490. 10 a. purple .. .. 1·25 1·00

197. Independence Memorial. 198. Tribesmen.

**1963.** 45th Independence Day.
491. **197.** 25 p. green .. .. 25 20
492. 50 p. orange .. .. 25 20
493. 150 p. mauve .. .. 45 25

**1963.** Pashtunistan Day.
494. **198.** 25 p. violet .. .. 20 20
495. 50 p. blue .. .. 25 20
496. 150 p. brown .. .. 55 35

199. Assembly Building.

**1963.** National Assembly.
497. **199.** 25 p. brown .. .. 15 15
498. 50 p. red .. .. 20 20
499. 75 p. brown .. .. 25 20
500. 100 p. olive .. .. 25 15
501. 125 p. lilac .. .. 30 20

200. Balkh Gate. 201. Kemal Ataturk.

**1963.**
502. **200.** 3 a. brown .. .. 95 25

**1963.** 25th Death Anniv of Kemal Ataturk.
503 **201** 1 a. blue .. .. 15 20
504 3 a. violet .. .. 60 40

202. Mohamed Zahir Shah. 203. Afghan Stamp of 1878.

**1963.** King's 49th Birthday.
505 **202** 25 p. green .. .. 20 20
506 50 p. grey .. .. 25 20
507 75 p. red .. .. 25 25
508 100 p. brown .. .. 35 20

**1964.** "Philately". Stamp Day.
509. **203.** 1 a. 25 blk., grn. & gold 25 20
510. 5 a. black, red and gold 45 35

204. Kabul International Airport.

**1964.** Air. Inaug. of Kabul Int. Airport.
511 **204** 10 a. green and purple 75 25
512 20 a. purple and green 1·10 40
513 50 a. turquoise & blue 2·50 1·00

205. Kandahar International Airport.

**1964.** Air. Inaug. of Kandahar Int. Airport.
514. **205.** 7 a. 75 brown .. .. 65 40
515. 9 a. 25 blue .. .. 85 75
516. 10 a. 50 green .. .. 1·10 90
517. 13 a. 75 red .. .. 1·25 90

206. Unisphere and Flags. 207. "Flame of Freedom".

**1964.** New York World's Fair.
518. **206.** 6 a. black, red & green 25 20

**1964.** 1st U.N. "Human Rights" Seminar, Kabul.
519. **207.** 3 a. 75 multicoloured 25 15

208. Snow Leopard.

**1964.** Afghan Wildlife.
520 **208** 25 p. blue and yellow 55 15
521 – 50 p. green and red .. 60 15
522 – 75 p. purple and blue 60 15
523 – 5 a. brown and green 75 20
ANIMALS—VERT. 50 p. Ibex. HORIZ. 75 p. Argali. 5 a. Yak.

209. Herat. 210. Hurdling.

**1964.** Tourist Publicity. Inscr. "1964".
524. **209.** 25 p. brown and blue 20 15
525. – 75 p. blue and ochre .. 25 15
526. – 3 a. black, red & green 40 25
DESIGNS—VERT. 75 p. Tomb of Gowhar Shad, Herat. HORIZ. 3 a. Map and flag.

**1964.** Olympic Games, Tokyo.
527. **210.** 25 p. sepia, red & bistre 15 10
528. – 1 a. sepia, red & blue .. 15 10
529. – 3 a. 75 sepia, red & grn. 40 25
530. – 5 a. sepia, red & brown 50 25
DESIGNS—VERT. 1 a. Diving. HORIZ. 3 a. 75. Wrestling. 5 a. Football.

211. Afghan Flag. 212. Pashtu Flag.

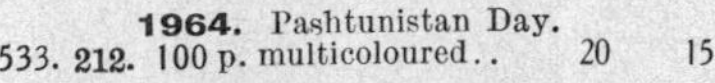

**1964.** 46th Independence Day.
531. **211.** 25 p. multicoloured .. 20 15
532. 75 p. multicoloured .. 25 15
On the above the Pushtu inscription "33rd Anniversary" is blocked out in gold.

**1964.** Pashtunistan Day.
533. **212.** 100 p. multicoloured .. 20 15

213. Mohamed Zahir Shah. 214. "Blood Transfusion".

**1964.** King's 50th Birthday.
534. **213.** 1 a. 25 green and gold 25 20
535. 3 a. 75 red and gold .. 40 35
536. 50 a. black and gold .. 2·75 2·00

**1964.** Red Crescent Day.
537. **214.** 1 a.+50 p. red & black 20 15

215. Badges of Afghanistan and U.N.

**1964.** U.N. Day.
538. **215.** 5 a. blue, black & gold 20 15

216. Doves with Necklace. 217. M. Jami.

**1964.** Women's Day.
539. **216.** 25 p. blue, green & pink 15 15
540. 75 p. blue, grn. & lt. bl. 15 15
541. 1 a. blue, green & silver 25 10

**1964.** 550th Birth Anniv. of Mowlana Jami (poet).
542. **217.** 1 a. 50 cream, grn. & blk. 1·00 85

218. Scaly-bellied Green Woodpecker. 220. "The Red City".

219. I.T.U. Emblem and Symbols.

**1965.** Birds. Multicoloured.
543 1 a. 25 Type **218** .. .. 2·25 50
544 3 a. 75 Lanceolated jay (vert) .. .. 4·50 1·25
545 5 a. Himalayan monal pheasant (vert) .. 5·25 2·40

**1965.** Centenary of I.T.U.
546. **219.** 5 a. black, red and blue .. .. 50 25

**1965.** Tourist Publicity. Inscr. "1965" Multicoloured.
547. 1 a. Type **220** .. .. 25 10
548. 3 a. 75 Bami Yan (valley and mountains) .. 35 20
549. 5 a. Band-E-Amir (lake and mountains) .. .. 55 25

221. I.C.Y. Emblem.

**1965.** Int. Co-operation Year.
550. **221.** 5 a. multicoloured .. 40 35

222. Douglas DC-3 and Emblem.

**1965.** 10th Anniv. of Afghan Airlines (ARIANA).
551 **222** 1 a. 25 multicoloured 30 10
552 – 5 a. black, blue & pur 85 20
553 – 10 a. multicoloured .. 1·50 50
DESIGNS: 5 a. Convair CV 240. 10 a. Douglas DC-6A.

**223.** Mohamed Nadir Shah. **224.** Pashtu Flag.

**1965.** 47th Independence Day.
554. **223.** 1 a. brown, blk. & green 40 10

**1965.** Pashtunistan Day.
555. **224.** 1 a. multicoloured .. 35 10

**225.** Promulgation of New Constitution.

**1965.** New Constitution.
556. **225.** 1 a. 50 black and green 30 15

**226.** Mohamed Zahir Shah. **227.** First-Aid Post.

**1965.** King's 51st Birthday.
557 **226** 1 a. 25 brn, bl & pink 25 10
558 6 a. indigo, purple & bl 35 30
See also Nos. 579/80, 606/7 and 637/8.

**1965.** Red Crescent Day.
559. **227.** 1 a. 50+50 brown, green and red .. 20 15

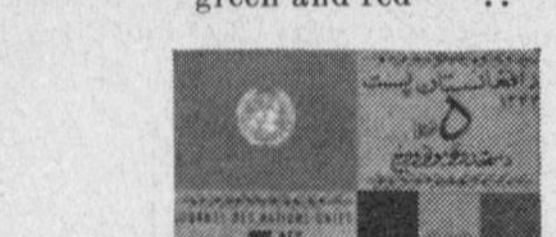

228. U.N. and Afghan Flags.

**1965.** U.N. Day.
560. **228.** 5 a. multicoloured .. 20 20

229. Fat-tailed Gecko.

**1966.** Reptiles. Multicoloured.
561 3 a. Type **229** .. .. 40 20
562 4 a. "Agama caucasica" (lizard) .. .. 55 20
563 8 a. "Testudo horsfieldi" (tortoise) .. .. 70 35

**230.** Cotton. **231.** Footballer.

**1966.** Agriculture Day. Multicoloured.
564 1 a. Type **230** .. .. 20 10
565 5 a. Silkworm moth (caterpillar) .. .. 40 20
566 7 a. Oxen .. .. .. 45 30

**1966.** World Cup Football Championship, England.
567. **231.** 2 a. black and red .. 25 15
568. 6 a. black and blue .. 50 25
569. 12 a. black and brown 1·00 50

**232.** Independence Memorial.

**1966.** Independence Day.
570. **232.** 1 a. multicoloured .. 15 10
571. 3 a. multicoloured .. 30 15

**233.** Pashtu Flag.

**1966.** Pashtunistan Day.
572. **233.** 1 a. blue .. .. 25 10

**234.** Founding Members.

**1966.** Red Crescent Day.
573 **234** 2 a.+1 a. green & red 25 10
574 5 a.+1 a. brn & mve 45 15

**235.** Map of Afghanistan.

**1966.** Tourist Publicity. Multicoloured.
575 2 a. Type **235** .. .. 20 10
576 4 a. Bagh-i-Bala, former Palace of Abdur Rahman .. .. 40 20
577 8 a. Tomb of Abdur Rahman, Kabul .. .. 55 40

**1966.** King's 52nd Birthday. Portrait similar to T **226** but with position of inscr. changed. Dated "1966".
579. 1 a. green .. .. .. 25 10
580. 5 a. brown .. .. 35 15

**236.** Mohamed Zahir Shah and U.N. Emblem.

**1966.** U.N. Day. Inscr. "20TH ANNIVERSAIRE DES REFUGIES".
581. **236.** 5 a. green, brn. & emer. 35 15
582. 10 a. red, grn. & lemon 70 25

237. Children Dancing.

**1966.** Child Welfare Day.
583 **237** 1 a.+1 a. red & green 20 10
584 3 a.+2 a. brown & yell 40 20
585 7 a.+3 a. green & pur 65 40

**238.** Construction of Power Station. **239.** U.N.E.S.C.O. Emblem.

**1967.** Afghan Industrial Development. Multicoloured.
586. 2 a. Type **238** .. .. 20 10
587. 5 a. Handwoven carpet (vert.) .. .. 25 15
588. 8 a. Cement works .. 35 25

**1967.** 20th Anniv. (1966) of U.N.E.S.C.O.
589. **239.** 2 a. multicoloured .. 25 15
590. 6 a. multicoloured .. 40 15
591. 12 a. multicoloured .. 85 20

**240.** I.T.Y. Emblem. **241.** Inoculation.

**1967.** Int. Tourist Year.
592. **240.** 2 a. black, blue & yellow 10 10
593. – 6 a. black, blue & brn. 35 20
DESIGN: 6 a. I.T.Y. emblem on map of Afghanistan.

**1967.** Anti-tuberculosis Campaign.
595. **241.** 2 a.+1 a. black & yell. 15 10
596. 5 a.+2 a. brown & pink 35 25

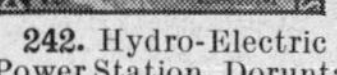

**242.** Hydro-Electric Power Station, Dorunta. **243.** Rhesus Macaque.

**1967.** Development of Electricity for Agriculture.
597. **242.** 1 a. lilac and green .. 10 10
598. – 6 a. turquoise & brown 30 20
599. – 8 a. blue and purple .. 35 25
DESIGNS—VERT. 6 a. Dam. HORIZ. 8 a. Reservoir, Jalalabad.

**1967.** Wildlife.
600. **243.** 2 a. blue and buff .. 30 10
601. – 6 a. sepia and green .. 55 25
602. – 12 a. brown and blue 85 50
ANIMALS—HORIZ. 6 a. Striped hyena. 12 a. Goitred gazelles.

**244.** " Saving the Guns at Maiwand " (after R. Caton Woodville). **245.** Pashtu Dancers.

**1967.** Independence Day.
603. **244.** 1 a. brown and red .. 20 10
604. 2 a. brown and mauve 30 15

**1967.** Pashtunistan Day.
605. **245.** 2 a. violet and purple 25 10

**1967.** King's 53rd Birthday. Portrait similar to T **226** but with position of inscr. changed. Dated " 1967 ".
606. 2 a. brown .. .. 15 10
607. 8 a. blue .. .. .. 50 25

**246.** Red Crescent. **247.** U.N. Emblem and Fireworks.

**1967.** Red Crescent Day.
608. **246.** 3 a. + 1 a. red, black and olive .. .. 15 10
609. 5 a. + 1 a. red, black and blue .. .. 25 15

**1967.** U.N. Day.
610. **247.** 10 a. multicoloured .. 45 25

**248.** Wrestling. **249.** Said Jamal-ud-Din Afghan.

**1967.** Olympic Games, Mexico City.
611. **248.** 4 a. purple and green .. 25 10
612. – 6 a. brown and red .. 40 15
DESIGN: 6 a. Wrestling—a " throw ".

**1967.** 70th Death Anniv of Said Afghan.
614. **249.** 1 a. purple .. .. 10 10
615. 5 a. brown .. .. 35 15

**250.** Bronze Vase. **251.** W.H.O. Emblem.

**1967.** Archaeological Treasures (11th–12th century Ghasnavide era).
616 **250** 3 a. brown and green 25 10
617 – 7 a. green and yellow 45 20
DESIGN: 7 a. Bronze jar.

**1968.** 20th Anniv. of W.H.O.
619. **251.** 2 a. blue and bistre .. 15 10
620. 7 a. blue and red .. 25 15

**252.** Karakul Sheep. **253.** Map of Afghanistan.

**1968.** Agricultural Day.
621. **252.** 1 a. black and yellow .. 10 10
622. 6 a. brown, blk. & blue 40 15
623. 12 a. brn., sepia & blue 55 25

**1968.** Tourist Publicity. Multicoloured.
624 2 a. Type **253** .. .. 20 10
625 3 a. Victory Tower, Ghazni (21×31 mm) .. .. 25 10
626 16 a. Mausoleum, Ghazni (21×31 mm) .. .. 65 35

**254.** Queen Humaira. **255.** European Black Vulture.

**1968.** Mothers' Day.
627. **254.** 2 a.+2 a. brown .. 15 15
628. 7 a.+2 a. green .. 50 35

**1968.** Wild Birds. Multicoloured.
629. 1 a. Type **255** .. .. 1·00 40
630. 6 a. Eagle owl .. .. 2·25 1·10
631. 7 a. Greater flamingoes .. 3·25 1·25

**256.** " Pig-sticking ". **257.** Flowers on Gun-carriage.

**1968.** Olympic Games, Mexico. Mult.
632. 2 a. Olympic flame and rings (vert.) .. .. 15 10
633. 8 a. Type **256** .. .. 35 20
634. 12 a. Buzkashi game .. 50 30
No. 632 is 21×31 mm.

**1968.** Independence Day.
635. **257.** 6 a. multicoloured .. 25 15

**HAVE YOU READ THE NOTES AT THE BEGINNING OF THIS CATALOGUE?**
These often provide answers to the enquiries we receive.

258. Pashtu Flag.

259. Red Crescent.

**1968.** Pashtunistan Day.
636. 258. 3 a. multicoloured .. 20 10

**1968.** King's 54th Birthday. Portrait similar to T 226 but differently arranged and in smaller size. (21 × 31 mm.)
637. 2 a. blue .. .. .. 20 10
638. 8 a. brown .. .. 30 25

**1968.** Red Crescent Day.
639 259 4 a.+1 a. multicoloured 30 20

260. Human Rights Emblem.

261. Maolala Djalalodine Balkhi.

**1968.** U.N. Day and Human Rights Year.
640 260 1 a. brown, bis & grn 10 10
641 2 a. black, bistre & vio 15 10
642 6 a. violet, bis & pur 35 15

**1968.** 695th Death Anniv of Maolala Djalalodine Balkhi (historian).
644 261 4 a. mauve and green 20 10

262. Temple Painting.

263. I.L.O. Emblem.

**1969.** Archaeological Treasures (Bagram era).
645 262 1 a. red, yellow & grn 25 10
646 – 3 a. purple and violet 45 20
DESIGN: 3 a. Carved vessel.

**1969.** 50th Anniv. of I.L.O.
648. 263. 5 a. black and yellow 25 15
649. 8 a. black and blue .. 45 20

264. Red Cross Emblems.

266. Mother & Child.

**1969.** 50th Anniv. of League of Red Cross Societies.
650. 264. 3 a. + 1 a. multicoloured 45 20
651. 5 a. + 1 a. multicoloured 65 20
On Nos. 650/1 the commemorative inscription in English and Pushtu for the 50th anniversary of the League of Red Cross Societies has been obliterated by gold bars.

**1969.** Mother's Day.
654. 266. 1 a.+1 a. brown & yell. 20 20
655 4 a.+1 a. violet & mve. 40 40

267. Road Map of Afghanistan.

268. Bust (Hadda era).

**1969.** Tourist Publicity. Badakshan and Pamir Region. Multicoloured.
657. 2 a. Type **267** .. .. 25 10
658. 4 a. Pamir landscape .. 25 15
659. 7 a. Mountain mule transport .. .. .. 45 25

**1969.** Archaeological Discoveries. Mult.
661 1 a. Type **268** .. .. 10 10
662 5 a. Vase and jug (Bagram period) .. .. 40 15
663 10 a. Statuette (Bagram period) .. .. .. 65 20

269. Mohamed Zahir Shah & Queen Humaira.

270. Map and Rising Sun.

**1969.** Independence Day.
664. 269. 5 a. red, blue and gold 40 15
665. 10 a. green, pur. & gold 55 25

**1969.** Pashtunistan Day.
666. 270. 2 a. red and blue .. 25 10

271. Mohamed Zahir Shah.

272. Red Crescent.

**1969.** King's 55th Birthday.
667. 271. 2 a. multicoloured .. 20 10
668. 6 a. multicoloured .. 45 15

**1969.** Red Crescent Day.
669. 272. 6 a.+1 a. multicoloured 60 20

273. U.N. Emblem, Afghan Arms and Flag.

**1969.** United Nations Day.
670. 273. 5a. multicoloured .. 25 15

274. I.T.U. Emblem.

275. Indian Crested Porcupine.

**1969.** World Telecommunications Day.
671. 274. 6 a. multicoloured .. 20 15
672. 12 a. multicoloured .. 40 25

**1969.** Wild Animals. Multicoloured.
673 1 a. Type **275** .. .. 20 10
674 3 a. Wild boar .. .. 45 10
675 8 a. Bactrian red deer .. 65 15

276. Footprint on the Moon.

277. "Cancer the Crab".

**1969.** 1st Man on the Moon.
676. 276. 1 a. multicoloured .. 10 10
677. 3 a. multicoloured .. 15 10
678. 6 a. multicoloured .. 20 15
679. 10 a. multicoloured .. 35 30

**1970.** W.H.O. "Fight Cancer" Day.
680 277 2 a. red, dp grn & grn 15 10
681 6 a. red, dp blue & bl 25 20

278. Mirza Bedel.

279. I.E.Y. Emblem.

**1970.** 250th Death Anniv of Mirza Abdul Quader Bedel (poet).
682 278 5 a. multicoloured .. 30 10

**1970.** Int. Education Year.
683. 279. 1 a. black .. .. 10 10
684. 6 a. red .. .. 25 10
685. 12 a. green .. .. 50 25

280. Mother and Child.

281. U.N. Emblem, Scales and Satellite.

**1970.** Mother's Day.
686. 280. 6 a. multicoloured .. 25 20

**1970.** 25th Anniv of United Nations.
687 281 4 a. blue, dp bl & yell 15 15
688 6 a. blue, dp bl & red 25 15

282. Map of Afghanistan with Location of Sights.

283. Common Quail.

**1970.** Tourist Publicity. Inscr. "1970". Multicoloured.
689. 282. 2 a. black, green & blue 20 10
690. – 3 a. multicoloured .. 25 10
691. – 7 a. multicoloured .. 55 15
DESIGNS (36×26 mm.) 3 a. Lakeside Mosque, Kabul. 7 a. Arch of Paghman.

**1970.** Wild Birds. Multicoloured.
692. 2 a. Type **283** .. .. 1·40 50
693. 4 a. Golden eagle .. .. 2·75 80
694. 6 a. Ring-necked pheasant 3·25 1·25

284. Shah Reviewing Troops.

285. Group of Pashtus.

**1970.** Independence Day.
695. 284. 8 a. multicoloured .. 35 35

**1970.** Pashtunistan Day.
696. 285. 2 a. blue and red .. 35 10

286. Mohamed Zahir Shah.

287. Red Crescent Emblems.

**1970.** King's 56th Birthday.
697. 286. 3 a. violet and green .. 15 10
698. 7 a. purple and blue 55 15

**1970.** Red Crescent Day.
699 287 2 a. black, red and gold 15 10

288. U.N. Emblem and Plaque.

**1970.** United Nations Day.
700. 288. 1 a. multicoloured .. 10 10
701. 5 a. multicoloured .. 15 25



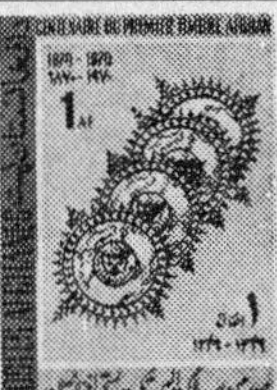
289. Afghan Stamps of 1871.

**1970.** Centenary of First Afghan Stamps.
702 289 1 a. black, blue & orge 20 10
703 4 a. black, yellow & bl 25 15
704 12 a. black, blue & lilac 45 25

290. Global Emblem.

**1971.** World Telecommunications Day.
705 290 12 a. multicoloured .. 50 25

291. "Callimorpha principalis".

292. Lower half of old Kushan Statue.

**1971.** Butterflies and Moths. Multicoloured.
706 1 a. Type **291** .. .. 30 10
707 3 a. "Epizygaenella afghana" .. .. 45 10
708 5 a. "Parnassius autocrator" .. .. 75 15

**1971.** U.N.E.S.C.O. Kushan Seminar.
709. 292. 6 a. violet and yellow 35 15
710. 10 a. purple and blue 55 20

293. Independence Memorial.

**1971.** Independence Day.
711. 293. 7 a. multicoloured .. 40 15
712. 9 a. multicoloured .. 55 20

294. Pashtunistan Square, Kabul.

**1971.** Pashtunistan Day.
713. 294. 5 a. purple .. .. 35 15

295. Mohamed Zahir Shah and Kabul Airport.

**1971.** Air. Multicoloured.
714 50 a. Type **295** .. .. 3·25 3·00
715 100 a. King, airline emblem and Boeing 727 airplane 3·50 2·50

296. Mohamed Zahir Shah.

297. Map, Nurse and Patients.

**1971.** King's 57th Birthday.

716. 296. 9 a. multicoloured .. 40 25
717. 17 a. multicoloured .. 75 35

**1971.** Red Crescent Day.

718. 297. 8 a. multicoloured .. 40 15

298. Emblem of Racial Equality Year. 299. Human Heart.

**1971.** United Nations Day.

719. 298. 24 a. blue .. .. 1·25 50

**1972.** World Health Day and World Heart Month.

720. 299. 9 a. multicoloured .. 35 20
721. 12 a. multicoloured .. 45 25

300. "Tulipa lanata". 301. Buddha of Hadda.

**1972.** Afghan Flora and Fauna. Mult.

722. 7 a. Type 300 .. .. 60 60
723. 10 a. Chukar partridge (horiz.) .. .. .. 3·75 1·40
724. 12 a. Lynx (horiz.) .. 1·25 1·00
725. 18 a. "Allium stipitatum" 1·25 1·10

**1972.** Tourist Publicity.

726. 301. 3 a. blue and brown .. 25 15
727. – 7 a. green and red .. 40 20
728. – 9 a. purple and green .. 50 25

DESIGNS: 7 a. Greco-Bactrian seal, 250 B.C. 9 a. Greek temple, Ai-Khanum, 3rd-2nd cent. B.C.

302. King with Queen Humaira at Independence Parade.

**1972.** Independence Day.

729. 302. 25 a. multicoloured .. 1·50 1·25

303. Wrestling. 304. Pathan and Mountain View.

**1972.** Olympic Games, Munich. Various Wrestling Holds as T 303.

730. 4 a. multicoloured .. 25 10
731. 8 a. multicoloured .. 40 20
732. 10 a. multicoloured .. 55 25
733. 19 a. multicoloured .. 75 30
734. 21 a. multicoloured .. 95 30

**1972.** Pashtunistan Day.

736. 304. 5 a. multicoloured .. 40 10

305. Mohamed Zahir Shah.

**1972.** King's 58th Birthday.

737. 305. 7 a. blue, black & gold 50 15
738. 14 a. brown, blk & gold. 90 35

306. Ruined Town and Refugees.

**1972.** Red Crescent Day.

739. 306. 7 a. black, red & blue .. 50 15

307. E.C.A.F.E. Emblem.

**1972.** U.N. Day. 25th Anniv of U.N. Economic Commission for Asia and the Far East.

740 307 12 a. black and blue .. 45 25

308. Ceramics.

**1973.** Afghan Handicrafts. Multicoloured.

741. 7 a. Type 308 .. .. 40 25
742. 9 a. Embroidered coat (vert.) 55 25
743. 12 a. Coffee set (vert.) .. 65 35
744. 16 a. Decorated boxes .. 90 35

309. W.M.O. and Afghan Emblems.

**1973.** Centenary of World Meteorological Organization.

746. 309. 7 a. green and mauve 50 15
747. 14 a. red and blue .. 1·00 30

310. Emblems and Harvester.

**1973.** 10th Anniv. of World Food Programme.

748 310 14 a.+7 a. purple & bl 1·00 1·00

311. Al-Biruni. 312. Association Emblem.

**1973.** Birth Millenary of Abu-al Rayhan al-Biruni (mathematician and philosopher).

749 311 10 a. multicoloured .. 60 30

**1973.** Family Planning Week.

750 312 9 a. purple and orange 60 20

313. Himalayan Monal Pheasant.

**1973.** Birds. Multicoloured.

751. 8 a. Type 313 .. .. 2·25 2·00
752. 9 a. Great crested grebe .. 2·75 2·25
753. 12 a. Himalayan snowcock 3·25 3·00

314. Buzkashi Game.

**1973.** Tourism.

754. 314. 8 a. black .. .. 40 15

315. Firework Display.

**1973.** Independence Day.

755. 315. 12 a. multicoloured .. 55 25

316. Landscape and Flag. 317. Red Crescent.

**1973.** Pashtunistan Day.

756. 316. 9 a. multicoloured .. 60 20

**1973.** Red Crescent.

757 317 10 a. multicoloured .. 85 25

318. Kemal Ataturk.

**1973.** 50th Anniv. of Turkish Republic.

758. 318. 1 a. blue .. .. 25 10
759. 7 a. brown .. .. 80 15

319. Human Rights Flame.

**1973.** 25th Anniv. of Declaration of Human Rights.

760. 319. 12 a. blue, blk. & silver 40 25

320. Asiatic Black Bears.

**1974.** Wild Animals. Multicoloured.

761. 5 a. Type 320 .. .. 35 10
762. 7 a. Afghan hound .. 55 20
763. 10 a. Goitred gazelle .. 70 25
764. 12 a. Leopard .. .. 90 30

321. "Workers".

**1974.** Labour Day.

766. 321. 9 a. multicoloured .. 35 15

322. Arch of Paghman and Independence Memorial.

**1974.** Independence Day.

767. 322. 4 a. multicoloured .. 40 10
768. 11 a. multicoloured .. 50 20

323. Arms of Afghanistan and Hands clasping Seedling.

**1974.** 1st Anniv of Republic. Multicoloured.

769 4 a. Type 323 .. .. 40 10
770 5 a. Republican flag (36×26 mm) .. .. 50 15
771 7 a. Gen. Mohammed Daoud (26×36 mm) .. 65 15
772 15 a. Soldiers and arms .. 1·00 25

324. Lesser Spotted Eagle.

**1974.** Afghan Birds. Multicoloured.

774. 1 a. Type 324 .. .. 1·25 40
775. 6 a. White-fronted goose, ruddy shelduck and greylag goose .. .. 2·75 70
776. 11 a. Common crane and common coots .. .. 4·25 1·10

325. Flags of Pashtunistan and Afghanistan.

**1974.** Pashtunistan Day.

777. 325. 5 a. multicoloured .. 20 15

326. Republic's Coat of Arms.

**1974.**

778 326 100 p. green .. .. 65 25

327. Pres. Daoud. 328. Arms and Centenary Years.

**1974.**

779 327 10 a. multicoloured .. 35 20
780 16 a. multicoloured .. 1·00 40
781 19 a. multicoloured .. 65 40
782 21 a. multicoloured .. 75 35
783 22 a. multicoloured .. 1·25 50
784 30 a. multicoloured .. 1·50 50

**1974.** Centenary of U.P.U.

785 328 7 a. green, blk & gold 20 10

329. "UN" and U.N. Emblem. 330. Pres. Daoud.

**1974.** United Nations Day.

786. 329. 5 a. blue and ultram... 35 10

**1975.**
787. **330.** 50 a. multicoloured .. 1·50 85
788. 100 a. multicoloured .. 3·00 1·60

**331.** Minaret, Jam. **332.** Afghan Flag.

**1975.** South Asia Tourist Year. Multicoloured.
789 **331** 7 a. Type **331** .. 30 15
790 14 a. "Griffon and Lady" (2nd century) 55 30
791 15 a. Head of Buddha (4th–5th century) .. 65 30

**1975.** Independence Day.
793. **332.** 16 a. multicoloured .. 70 25

**333.** Rejoicing Crowd.

**1975.** 2nd Anniv of Revolution.
794 **333** 9 a. multicoloured .. 45 15
795 12 a. multicoloured .. 65 20

**334.** I.W.Y. Emblem. **335.** Rising Sun and Flag.

**1975.** International Women's Year.
796. **334.** 9 a. black, blue & purple 50 15

**1975.** Pashtunistan Day.
797. **335.** 10 a. multicoloured .. 40 15

**336.** Wazir M. Akbar Khan. **337.** Independence Monument and Arms.

**1976.** 130th Death Anniv of Akbar Khan (resistance leader).
798 **336** 15 a. multicoloured .. 50 25

**1976.** Independence Day.
799. **337.** 22 a. multicoloured .. 60 30

**338.** Pres. Daoud raising Flag. **339.** Mountain.

**1976.** 3rd Anniv. of Republic.
800. **338.** 30 a. multicoloured .. 85 50

**1976.** Pashtunistan Day.
801. **339.** 16 a. multicoloured .. 50 30

**340.** Arms.

**1976.**
802. – 25 p. salmon .. .. 40 25
803. **340.** 50 p. green .. .. 50 15
804. 1 a. blue .. .. 50 10
DESIGN: 25 p. As Type **340** but with Arms on left and inscription differently arranged.

**341.** Flag and Monuments on Open Book.

**1977.** Independence Day.
805. **341.** 20 a. multicoloured .. 45 30

**342.** Presidential Address.

**1977.** Election of First President and New Constitution. Multicoloured.
806. 7 a. President Daoud and Election .. .. 40 10
807. 8 a. Type **342** .. .. 45 10
808. 10 a. Inaugural ceremony 65 15
809. 18 a. Promulgation of new constitution .. 85 30
Nos. 806 and 809 are larger, 45 × 27 mm.

**343.** Medal. **344.** Crowd with Afghan Flag.

**1977.** 80th Death Anniv. of Sayed Jamaluddin Afghan (reformer).
811. **343.** 12 a. blk., blue & gold 40 20

**1977.** Republic Day.
812. **344.** 22 a. multicoloured .. 65 35

**345.** Dancers around Fountain. **346.** Dome of the Rock.

**1977.** Pashtunistan Day.
813. **345.** 30 a. multicoloured .. 90 50

**1977.** Palestinian Welfare.
814 **346** 12 a. + 3 a. black, gold and pink .. .. 2·00 60

**347.** Arms and Carrier Pigeon.

**1977.**
815. **347.** 1 a. blue and black .. 50 15

**348.** President Daoud acknowledging Crowd.

**1978.** 1st Anniv. of Presidential Election.
816. **348.** 20 a. multicoloured .. 75 40

**349.** U.P.U. Emblem on Map of Afghanistan.

**1978.** 50th Anniv. of Admission to U.P.U.
817. **349.** 10 a. gold, green & blk. 40 15

**350.** Transmitting Aerial and Early Telephone.

**1978.** 50th Anniv. of Admission to I.T.U.
818. **350.** 8 a. multicoloured .. 35 10

**351.** Red Crescent, Red Cross and Red Lion Emblems.

**1978.** Red Crescent.
819. **351.** 3 a. black .. .. 40 15

**352.** Arms.

**1978.**
820. **352.** 1 a. red and gold .. 45 15
821. 4 a. red and gold .. 75 10

**353.** Ruin, Qalai Bust. **354.** Afghans with Flag.

**1978.** Independence Day. Multicoloured.
822 16 a. Buddha, Bamian .. 75 25
823 22 a. Type **353** .. .. 85 40
824 30 a. Women in national costume .. .. 1·50 75

**1978.** Pashtunistan Day.
825. **354.** 7 a. red and blue .. 50 15

**355.** Crest and Symbols of the Five Senses. **356.** Flag.

**1978.** International Literacy Day.
826. **355.** 20 a. red .. .. 85 35

**1978.** "The Mail is in the Service of the People".
827. **356.** 8 a. red, gold & brown 60 15
828. 9 a. red, gold & brown 90 15

**357.** Martyr. **358.** President Mohammed Taraki.

**1978.** "The People's Democratic Party Honours its Martyrs".
829. **357.** 18 a. green .. .. 95 30

**1978.** 14th Anniv. of People's Democratic Party.
830. **358.** 12 a. multicoloured .. 85 10

**359.** Emancipated Woman. **360.** Farmers planting Tree.

**1979.** Women's Day.
831. **359.** 14 a. blue and red .. 85 40

**1979.** Farmer's Day.
832. **360.** 1 a. multicoloured .. 45 15

**361.** Map and Census Taking.

**1979.** First Complete Population Census.
833. **361.** 3 a. black, blue and red 50 15

**362.** Pres. Taraki reading "Khalq".

**1979.** First Publication of "Khalq" (party newspaper).
834 **362** 2 a. multicoloured .. 55 15

**363.** Pres. Taraki and Tank. **364.** Pres. Taraki.

**1979.** 1st Anniv of Sawr Revolution (1st issue).
835 **363** 50 p. multicoloured .. 60 15

**1979.** 1st Anniv of Sawr Revolution (2nd issue). Multicoloured.
836 4 a. Type **364** .. .. 40 10
837 5 a. Revolutionary H.Q. and Tank Monument, Kabul (47 × 32 mm) .. 55 10
838 6 a. Command room, Revolutionary H.Q. (vert) .. .. 65 15
839 12 a. House where first Khalq Party Congress was held (vert) .. 90 25

**365.** Carpenter and Blacksmith.

**1979.** Workers' Solidarity.
840. **365.** 10 a. multicoloured .. 85 15

**366.** Children on Map of Afghanistan.

**1979.** International Year of the Child.
841. **366.** 16 a. multicoloured .. 1·50 65

**367.** Revolutionaries and Kabul Monuments.
**368.** Afghans and Flag.

**1979.** Independence Day.
842. **367.** 30 a. multicoloured .. 1·25 65

**1979.** Pashtunistan Day.
843. **368.** 9 a. multicoloured .. 75 15

**369.** U.P.U. Emblem and Arms on Map.

**1979.** Stamp Day.
844. **369.** 15 a. multicoloured .. 60 20

**370.** Headstone and Tomb.

**1979.** Martyrs' Day.
845. **370.** 22 a. multicoloured .. 1·60 45

**371.** Doves around Globe.

**1979.**
845a. **371.** 2 a. blue and red .. 85 15

**372.** Woman with Baby, Dove and Rifle.
**374.** Healthy Non-smoker and Prematurely Aged Smoker.

**373.** Farmers receiving Land Grants.

**1980.** International Women's Day.
846. **372.** 8 a. multicoloured .. 1·10 25

**1980.** Farmers' Day.
847. **373.** 2 a. multicoloured .. 1·75 65

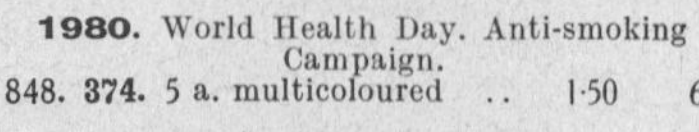

**1980.** World Health Day. Anti-smoking Campaign.
848. **374.** 5 a. multicoloured .. 1·50 60

**375.** " Lenin speaking from Tribune ".

**1980.** 110th Birth Anniv. of Lenin.
849. **375.** 12 a. multicoloured .. 2·50 75

**376.** Crowd and Clenched Fist.

**1980.** 2nd Anniv. of Sawr Revolution.
850. **376.** 1 a. multicoloured .. 65 15

**377.** Quarry Worker and Blacksmith.

**1980.** Workers' Solidarity.
851. **377.** 9 a. multicoloured .. 45 15

**378.** Football.
**379.** Soldiers attacking Fortress.

**1980.** Olympic Games, Moscow. Mult.
852 3 a. Type **378** .. .. 60 15
853 6 a. Wrestling .. .. 65 15
854 9 a. Pigsticking .. .. 75 15
855 10 a. Buzkashi .. .. 85 20

**1980.** Independence Day.
856 **379** 3 a. multicoloured .. 60 15

**380.** Pashtus with Flag.

**1980.** Pashtunistan Day.
857. **380.** 25 a. multicoloured .. 1·00 35

**381.** Post Office.

**1980.** World U.P.U. Day.
858. **381.** 20 a. multicoloured .. 85 35

**382.** Buzhashi.

**1980.**
859. **382.** 50 a. multicoloured .. 1·60 1·10
860. 100 a. multicoloured .. 3·00 1·25

**383.** Arabic " H ", Medina Mosque and Kaaba.

**1981.** 1400th Anniv. of Hegira.
861. **383.** 13 a.+2 a. multicoloured 1·50 25

**384.** Mother and Child with Dove and Globe.

**1981.** International Women's Day.
862. **384.** 15 a. multicoloured .. 95 25

**385.** Ox Plough, Tractor and Planting of Trees.

**1981.** Farmers' Day.
863. **385.** 1 a. multicoloured .. 80 20

**386.** Urial.
**387.** Crowd and Afghan Arms.

**1981.** Protected Wildlife.
864 **386** 12 a. multicoloured .. 75 50

**1981.** 3rd Anniv. of Sawr Revolution.
865. **387.** 50 p. brown .. .. 55 10

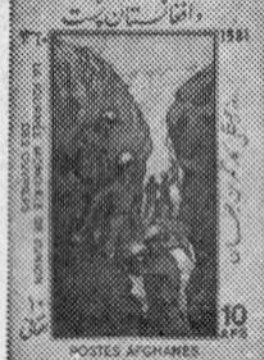

**388.** Road Workers in Ravine.
**389.** Red Crescent enclosing Scenes of Disaster and Medical Aid.

**1981.** Workers' Day.
866. **388.** 10 a. multicoloured .. 65 20

**1981.** Red Crescent Day.
867. **389.** 1 a.+4 a. multicoloured 50 60

**390.** Satellite Receiving Station.
**391.** Map enclosing playing Children.

**1981.** World Telecommunications Day.
868. **390.** 9 a. multicoloured .. 50 15

**1981.** International Children's Day.
869. **391.** 15 a. multicoloured .. 65 30

**392.** Afghans and Monument.

**1981.** Independence Day.
870 **392** 4 a. multicoloured .. 65 15

**393.** Pashtus around Flag.
**394.** Terracotta Horseman.

**1981.** Pashtunistan Day.
871. **393.** 2 a. multicoloured .. 55 15

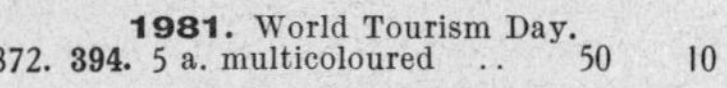

**1981.** World Tourism Day.
872. **394.** 5 a. multicoloured .. 50 10

**395.** Siamese Twins and I.Y.D.P. Emblem.

**1981.** International Year of Disabled Persons.
873 **395** 6 a.+1 a. multicoloured 65 40

**396.** Harvesting.

**1981.** World Food Day.
874. **396.** 7 a. multicoloured .. 60 15

**397.** Peace, Solidarity and Friendship Organization Emblem.
**398.** Heads and Clenched Fist on Globe and Emblem.

**1981.** Afro-Asian Peoples' Solidarity Meeting.
875 **397** 8 a. blue .. .. 65 15

**1981.** International Anti-apartheid Year.
876 **398** 4 a. multicoloured .. 40 10

**399.** Lion (bas-relief at Stara Zagora).

**1981.** 1300th Anniv. of Bulgarian State.
877. **399.** 20 a. stone, pur. & red 1·10 40

**400.** Mother rocking Cradle.

**1982.** Women's Day.
878. **400.** 6 a. multicoloured .. 45 10

**401.** Farmers.
**402.** Judas-tree.

**1982.** Farmers' Day.
879. **401.** 4 a. multicoloured .. 50 10

**1982.** Plants. Multicoloured.

| | | | |
|---|---|---|---|
| **880.** | 3 a. Type **402** .. .. | 25 | 10 |
| **881.** | 4 a. Hollyhock .. .. | 50 | 10 |
| **882.** | 16 a. Rhubarb .. .. | 95 | 30 |

**403.** Hands holding Flags and Tulip.

**404.** Dimitrov.

**1982.** 4th Anniv. of Sawr Revolution.
883. **403.** 1 a. multicoloured .. 85 15

**1982.** Birth Centenary of Georgi Dimitrov (Bulgarian statesman).
884. **404.** 30 a. multicoloured .. 1·50 60

**405.** Blacksmith, Factory Workers Weaver and Labourer.

**1982.** Workers' Day.
885. **405.** 10 a. multicoloured .. 60 20

**406.** White Storks.

**407.** Brandt's Hedgehog.

**1982.** Birds. Multicoloured.

| | | | |
|---|---|---|---|
| 886 | 6 a. Type **406** .. .. | 2·00 | 65 |
| 887 | 11 a. Goldfinches .. .. | 2·75 | 85 |

**1982.** Animals. Multicoloured.

| | | | |
|---|---|---|---|
| **888.** | 3 a. Type **407** .. .. | 35 | 15 |
| **889.** | 14 a. Cobra .. .. | 45 | 25 |

**408.** National Monuments.

**409.** Pashtus and Flag.

**1982.** Independence Day.
890. **408.** 20 a. multicoloured .. 85 40

**1982.** Pashtunistan Day.
891. **409.** 32 a. multicoloured .. 1·60 55

**410.** Tourists.

**1982.** World Tourism Day.
892. **410.** 9 a. multicoloured .. 55 20

**411.** Postman delivering Letter, Post Office and U.P.U. Emblem.

**1982.** World U.P U. Day
893. **411.** 4 a. multicoloured .. 60 20

**412.** Family eating Meal.

**413.** U.N. Emblem illuminating Globe.

**1982.** World Food Day.
894 **412.** 9 a. multicoloured .. 85 20

**1982.** 37th Anniv. of United Nations.
895. **413.** 15 a. multicoloured .. 80 30

**414.** Earth Satellite Station.

**1982.** I.T.U. Delegates' Conference, Nairobi.
896. **414.** 8 a. multicoloured .. 55 15

**415.** Dr. Robert Koch.

**416.** Hand holding Torch, Globe and Scales.

**1982.** Cent. of Discovery of Tubercle Bacillus.
897. **415.** 7 a. blk., brn. & pink 40 25

**1982.** 34th Anniv. of Declaration of Human Rights.
898. **416.** 5 a. multicoloured .. 30 15

**417.** Lions.

**1982.** Wild Animals. Multicoloured.

| | | | |
|---|---|---|---|
| 899 | 2 a. Type **417** .. .. | 20 | 10 |
| 900 | 7 a. Asiatic wild asses .. | 40 | 25 |
| 901 | 12 a. Sable (vert) .. | 85 | 35 |

**418.** Woman releasing Dove.

**419.** Mir Alicher-e-Nawai (poet).

**1983.** International Women's Day.
902 **418** 3 a. multicoloured .. 20 10

**1983.** Mir Alicher-e-Nawai and his Times Study Decade.
903 **419** 22 a. multicoloured .. 65 25

**420.** Distributing Land Ownership Documents.

**1983.** Farmers' Day.
904. **420.** 10 a. multicoloured .. 50 20

**421.** Revolution Monument.

**1983.** 5th Anniv. of Sawr Revolution.
905. **421.** 15 a. multicoloured .. 45 20

**422.** World Map and Hands holding Cogwheel.

**1983.** Labour Day.
906 **422** 20 a. multicoloured .. 55 20

**423.** Broadcasting Studio, Dish Aerial, Satellites and Television.

**1983.** World Communications Year. Mult.

| | | | |
|---|---|---|---|
| **907.** | 4 a. Type **423** .. .. | 25 | 10 |
| **908.** | 11 a. Telecommunications headquarters .. .. | 45 | 15 |

**424.** Hands holding Child.

**425.** Arms and Map of Afghanistan.

**1983.** International Children's Day.
909 **424** 25 a. multicoloured .. 60 25

**1983.** 2nd Anniv. of National Fatherland Front.
910. **425.** 1 a. multicoloured .. 25 10

**426.** Apollo.

**427.** Racial Segregation.

**1983.** Butterflies.

| | | | |
|---|---|---|---|
| 911 | 9 a. Type **426** .. .. | 35 | 25 |
| 912 | 13 a. Swallowtail .. .. | 85 | 45 |
| 913 | 21 a. Small tortoiseshell (horiz) .. .. | 1·00 | 55 |

**1983.** Anti-apartheid Campaign.
914 **427** 10 a. multicoloured .. 35 15

**428.** National Monuments.

**429.** Pashtus with Flag.

**1983.** Independence Day.
915 **428** 6 a. multicoloured .. 30 10

**1983.** Pashtunistan Day.
916. **429.** 3 a. multicoloured .. 30 10

**430.** Afghan riding Camel.

**1983.** World Tourism Day.

| | | | |
|---|---|---|---|
| 917 | **430** 5 a. multicoloured .. | 25 | 10 |
| 918 | – 7 a. brown and black | 35 | 15 |
| 919 | – 12 a. multicoloured .. | 45 | 15 |
| 920 | – 16 a. multicoloured .. | 65 | 15 |

DESIGNS—VERT. 7 a. Stone carving. 16 a. Carved stele. HORIZ. 12 a. Three statuettes.

**431.** Winter Landscape.

**1983.** Multicoloured.

| | | | |
|---|---|---|---|
| **921.** | 50 a. Type **431** .. .. | 1·40 | 25 |
| **922.** | 100 a. Woman with camel | 2·75 | 30 |

**432.** " Communications ".

**1983.** World Communications Year. Mult.

| | | | |
|---|---|---|---|
| **923.** | 14 a. Type **432** .. .. | 55 | 15 |
| **924.** | 15 a. Ministry of Communications, Kabul .. | 55 | 15 |

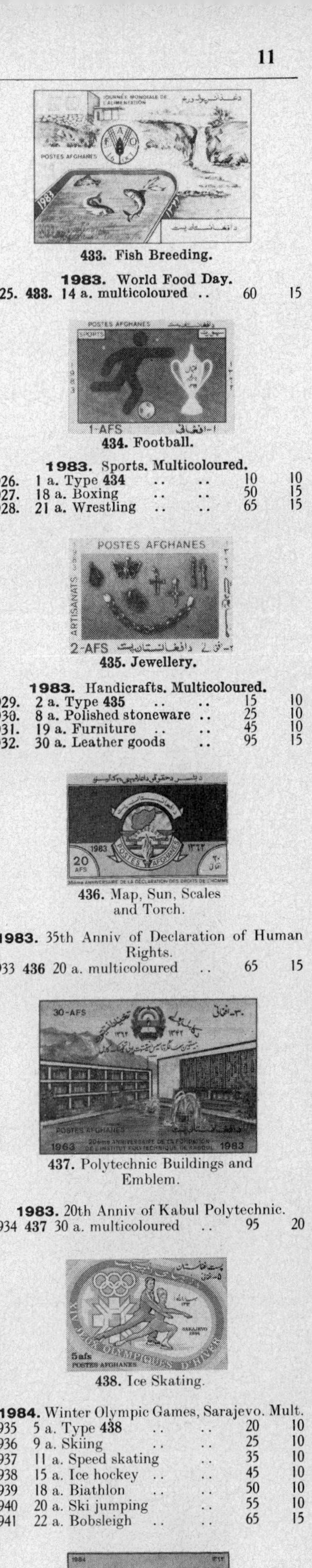

**433.** Fish Breeding.

**1983.** World Food Day.
925. **433.** 14 a. multicoloured .. 60 15

**434.** Football.

**1983.** Sports. Multicoloured.

| | | | |
|---|---|---|---|
| **926.** | 1 a. Type **434** .. .. | 10 | 10 |
| **927.** | 18 a. Boxing .. .. | 50 | 15 |
| **928.** | 21 a. Wrestling .. .. | 65 | 15 |

**435.** Jewellery.

**1983.** Handicrafts. Multicoloured.

| | | | |
|---|---|---|---|
| **929.** | 2 a. Type **435** .. .. | 15 | 10 |
| **930.** | 8 a. Polished stoneware .. | 25 | 10 |
| **931.** | 19 a. Furniture .. .. | 45 | 10 |
| **932.** | 30 a. Leather goods .. | 95 | 15 |

**436.** Map, Sun, Scales and Torch.

**1983.** 35th Anniv of Declaration of Human Rights.
933 **436** 20 a. multicoloured .. 65 15

**437.** Polytechnic Buildings and Emblem.

**1983.** 20th Anniv of Kabul Polytechnic.
934 **437** 30 a. multicoloured .. 95 20

**438.** Ice Skating.

**1984.** Winter Olympic Games, Sarajevo. Mult.

| | | | |
|---|---|---|---|
| 935 | 5 a. Type **438** .. .. | 20 | 10 |
| 936 | 9 a. Skiing .. .. | 25 | 10 |
| 937 | 11 a. Speed skating .. | 35 | 10 |
| 938 | 15 a. Ice hockey .. .. | 45 | 10 |
| 939 | 18 a. Biathlon .. .. | 50 | 10 |
| 940 | 20 a. Ski jumping .. | 55 | 10 |
| 941 | 22 a. Bobsleigh .. .. | 65 | 15 |

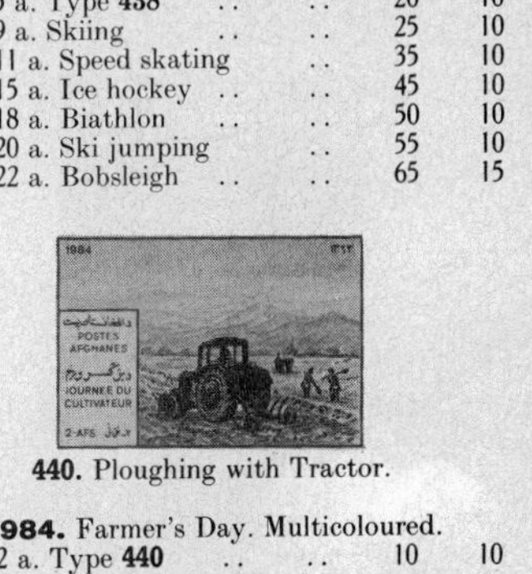

**440.** Ploughing with Tractor.

**1984.** Farmer's Day. Multicoloured.

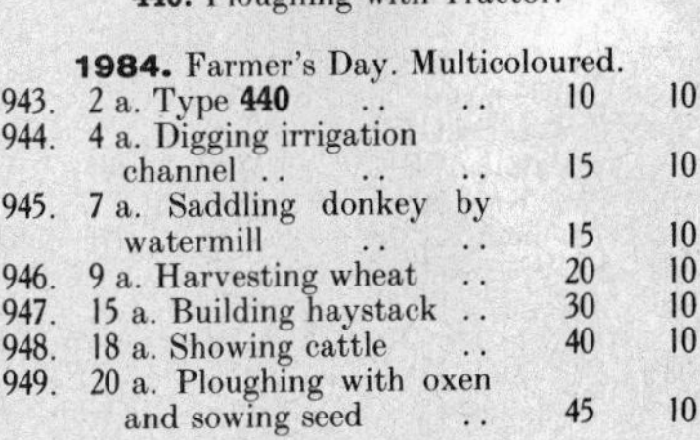

| | | | |
|---|---|---|---|
| **943.** | 2 a. Type **440** .. .. | 10 | 10 |
| **944.** | 4 a. Digging irrigation channel .. .. | 15 | 10 |
| **945.** | 7 a. Saddling donkey by watermill .. .. | 15 | 10 |
| **946.** | 9 a. Harvesting wheat .. | 20 | 10 |
| **947.** | 15 a. Building haystack .. | 30 | 10 |
| **948.** | 18 a. Showing cattle .. | 40 | 10 |
| **949.** | 20 a. Ploughing with oxen and sowing seed .. | 45 | 10 |

**441.** "Luna I".

**1984.** World Aviation and Space Navigation Day. Multicoloured.

950. 5 a. Type **441** .. .. 15 10
951. 8 a. "Luna II" .. .. 25 10
952. 11 a. "Luna III" .. .. 35 10
953. 17 a. "Apollo XI" .. .. 40 10
954. 22 a. "Soyuz VI" .. .. 55 15
955. 28 a. "Soyuz VII" .. .. 55 15
956. 34 a. "Soyuz VI", "VII" and "VIII" .. .. 75 15

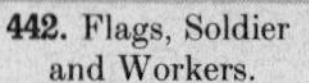

**442.** Flags, Soldier and Workers. **443.** Hunting Dog.

**1984.** 6th Anniv. of Sawr Revolution.

958. **442.** 3 a. multicoloured .. 30 10

**1984.** Animals. Multicoloured.

959 1 a. Type **443** .. .. 10 10
960 2 a. Argali .. .. 20 10
961 6 a. Przewalski's horse (horiz) .. .. 45 10
962 8 a. Wild boar .. .. 60 10
963 17 a. Snow leopard (horiz) 1·25 15
964 19 a. Tiger (horiz) .. 1·75 20
965 22 a. Indian elephant .. 2·25 25

**444.** Postal Messenger.

**1984.** 19th U.P.U. Congress, Hamburg. Mult.

966 25 a. Type **444** .. .. 75 15
967 35 a Post rider .. .. 1·10 20
968 40 a. Bird with letter .. 1·40 20

**445.** Antonov AN-2.

**1984.** 40th Anniv of Ariana Airline. Mult.

970 1 a. Type **445** .. .. 10 10
971 4 a. Ilyushin Il-12 .. 15 10
972 9 a. Tupolev Tu-104A .. 45 10
973 10 a. Ilyushin Il-18 .. 70 10
974 13 a. Yakovlev Yak-42 .. 85 10
975 17 a. Tupolev Tu-154 .. 1·10 15
976 21 a. Ilyushin Il-86 .. 1·25 15

**446.** Ettore Bugatti and Bugatti "43".

**1984.** Motor Cars. Multicoloured.

977 2 a. Type **446** .. .. 10 10
978 5 a. Henry Ford and Ford "A", 1903 .. .. 15 10
979 8 a. Rene Panhard and 1899 model .. .. 25 10
980 11 a. Gottlieb Daimler and Daimler "DB 18", 1935 30 10
981 12 a. Karl Benz and Benz "Victoris", 1893 .. 40 10
982 15 a. Armand Peugeot and Peugeot "Vis-a-vis", 1892 .. .. 45 10
983 22 a. Louis Chevrolet and Chevrolet sedan, 1925 .. 55 10

**447.** Open Book showing Monuments and Fortress.

**1984.** Independence Day.

984. **447.** 6 a. multicoloured .. 30 10

**448.** Truck on Mountain Road and Pashtunistan Badge.

**1984.** Pashtunistan Day.

985. **448.** 3 a. multicoloured .. 25 10

**449.** Arch at Qalai Bust. **450.** Pine Cone.

**1984.** World Tourism Day. Multicoloured.

986 1 a. Type **449** .. .. 10 10
987 2 a. Ornamented belt .. 15 10
988 5 a. Kabul monuments .. 15 10
989 9 a. Statuette (vert) .. 25 10
990 15 a. Buffalo riders in snow 45 10
991 19 a. Camel in ornate caparison .. .. 60 10
992 21 a. Buzkashi players .. 65 10

**1984.** World Food Day. Multicoloured.

993. 2 a. Type **450** .. .. 10 10
994. 4 a. Walnuts .. .. 20 10
995. 6 a. Pomegranate .. .. 25 10
996. 9 a. Apples .. .. .. 35 10
997. 13 a. Cherries .. .. 45 10
998. 15 a. Grapes .. .. 55 10
999. 26 a. Pears .. .. .. 85 10

**451.** Globe and Emblem.

**1985.** 20th Anniv (1984) of Peoples' Democratic Party.

1000 **451** 25 a. multicoloured .. 85 10

**452.** Cattle. **453.** Map and Geologist.

**1985.** Farmers' Day. Multicoloured.

1001 1 a. Type **452** .. .. 10 10
1002 3 a. Mare and foal .. 15 10
1003 7 a. Galloping horse .. 25 10
1004 8 a. Grey horse (vert) .. 30 10
1005 15 a. Karakul sheep and sheepskins .. .. 45 10
1006 16 a. Herder watching over cattle and sheep .. 65 10
1007 25 a. Family with pack camels .. .. 85 10

**1985.** Geologists' Day.

1008 **453** 4 a. multicoloured .. 25 10

**454.** Satellite.

**1985.** 20th Anniv of "Intelsat" Communications Satellite. Multicoloured.

1009 6 a. Type **454** .. .. 45 10
1010 9 a. "Intelsat III" .. 55 10
1011 10 a. Rocket launch (vert) 75 10

**455** "Visitors for Lenin" (V. Serov). **456** Revolutionaries with Flags.

**1985.** 115th Birth Anniv of Lenin. Mult.

1012 10 a. Type **455** .. .. 50 10
1013 15 a. "With Lenin" (detail, V. Serov) .. 65 10
1014 25 a. Lenin and Red Army fighters .. 85 10

**1985.** 7th Anniv of Sawr Revolution.

1016 **456** 21 a. multicoloured .. 85 10

**457.** Olympic Stadium and Moscow Skyline.

**1985.** 12th World Youth and Students' Festival, Moscow. Multicoloured.

1017 7 a. Type **457** .. .. 20 10
1018 12 a. Festival emblem .. 40 10
1019 13 a. Moscow Kremlin .. 45 10
1020 18 a. Doll .. .. 60 10

**458.** Soviet Memorial, Berlin-Treptow, and Tank before Reichstag.

**1985.** 40th Anniv of End of World War II. Multicoloured.

1021 6 a. Type **458** .. .. 45 10
1022 9 a. "Mother Homeland" war memorial, Volgograd, and fireworks over Moscow Kremlin 60 10
1023 10 a. Cecilienhof Castle, Potsdam, and flags of United Kingdom, U.S.S.R. and U.S.A. .. 75 10

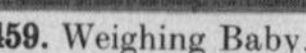

**459.** Weighing Baby. **460.** Purple Blewit.

**1985.** U.N.I.C.E.F. Child Survival Campaign. Multicoloured.

1024. 1 a. Type **459** .. .. 10 10
1025. 2 a. Vaccinating child .. 15 10
1026. 4 a. Breastfeeding baby 25 10
1027. 5 a. Mother and child .. 25 10

**1985.** Fungi. Multicoloured.

1028 3 a. Type **460** .. .. 15 10
1029 4 a. Flaky-stemmed witches' mushroom .. 25 15
1030 7 a. The blusher .. .. 35 20
1031 11 a. Brown birch bolete 50 35
1032 12 a. Common ink cap .. 60 35
1033 18 a. "Hypholoma sp." .. 85 40
1034 20 a. "Boletus aurantiacus" .. .. 90 40

**461.** Emblems.

**1985.** United Nations Decade for Women.

1035. **461.** 10 a. multicoloured 50 10

**462.** Evening Primrose.

**1985.** "Argentina '85" International Stamp Exhibition, Buenos Aires. Flowers. Mult.

1036 2 a. Type **462** .. .. 10 10
1037 4 a. Cockspur coral tree .. 15 10
1038 8 a. "Tillandsia aeranthos" .. .. 25 10
1039 13 a. Periwinkle .. .. 40 10
1040 18 a. Marvel-of-Peru .. 60 10
1041 25 a. "Cypella herbertii" 85 10
1042 30 a. "Clytostoma callistegioides" .. 1·00 10

**463.** Building.

**1985.** Independence Day.

1044. **463.** 33 a. multicoloured 1·40 15

**464.** Dancers in Pashtunistan Square, Kabul.

**1985.** Pashtunistan Day.

1045. **464.** 25 a. multicoloured 1·10 10

**465.** Guldara Stupa.

**1985.** 10th Anniv of World Tourism Organization. Multicoloured.

1046 1 a. Type **465** .. .. 10 10
1047 2 a. Mirwais tomb (vert) 10 10
1048 10 a. Buddha of Bamian (vert) .. .. .. 35 10
1049 13 a. No Gumbad mosque (vert) .. .. .. 50 10
1050 14 a. Pule Kheshti mosque .. .. .. 55 10
1051 15 a. Arch at Qalai Bust 60 10
1052 20 a. Ghazni minaret (vert) .. .. .. 85 10

**466.** Boxing.

**1985.** Sport. Multicoloured.

| | | | |
|---|---|---|---|
| 1053 | 1 a. Type **466** .. .. | 10 | 10 |
| 1054 | 2 a. Volleyball .. .. | 15 | 10 |
| 1055 | 3 a. Football (vert) .. | 40 | 10 |
| 1056 | 12 a. Buzkashi .. .. | 45 | 10 |
| 1057 | 14 a. Weightlifting .. | 55 | 10 |
| 1058 | 18 a. Wrestling .. .. | 55 | 10 |
| 1059 | 25 a. Pigsticking .. | 75 | 10 |

**467.** Fruit Stall.

**1985.** World Food Day.

| | | | | |
|---|---|---|---|---|
| 1060. | **467.** | 25 a. multicoloured | 75 | 10 |

**468.** Flags and U.N. Building, New York. **469.** Magpie.

**1985.** 40th Anniv. of United Nations Organization.

| | | | | |
|---|---|---|---|---|
| 1061. | **468.** | 22 a. multicoloured | 75 | 10 |

**1985.** Birds Multicoloured.

| | | | |
|---|---|---|---|
| 1062. | 2 a. Type **469** .. .. | 15 | 10 |
| 1063. | 4 a. Green woodpecker .. | 75 | 35 |
| 1064. | 8 a. Ring-necked pheasants .. .. | 80 | 35 |
| 1065. | 13 a. Bluethroat, goldfinch and hoopoe .. | 1·25 | 65 |
| 1066. | 18 a. Peregrine falcons .. | 1·50 | 75 |
| 1067. | 25 a. Chukar partridge .. | 2·10 | 1·10 |
| 1068. | 30 a. Eastern white pelicans (horiz.) .. | 2·75 | 1·25 |

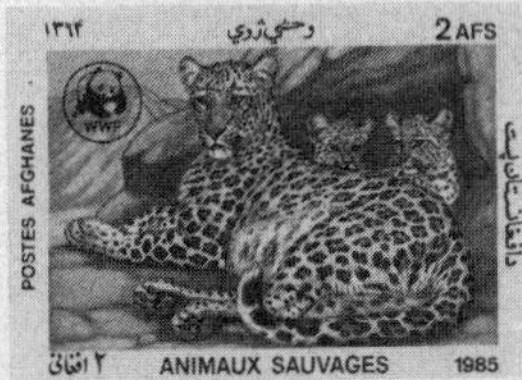


**470.** Leopard and Cubs.

**1985.** World Wildlife Fund. The Leopard. Multicoloured.

| | | | |
|---|---|---|---|
| 1070. | 2 a. Type **470** .. .. | 10 | 10 |
| 1071. | 9 a. Head of leopard .. | 35 | 10 |
| 1072. | 11 a. Leopard .. .. | 55 | 10 |
| 1073. | 15 a. Leopard cub .. | 85 | 10 |

**471.** Triumph "650" and Big Ben Tower.

**1985.** Motor Cycles. Multicoloured.

| | | | |
|---|---|---|---|
| 1074 | 2 a. Type **471** .. .. | 10 | 10 |
| 1075 | 4 a. Motobecane and Eiffel Tower, Paris .. | 15 | 10 |
| 1076 | 8 a. Motor cycle and Don Quixote monument, Madrid .. .. | 25 | 10 |
| 1077 | 13 a. Honda and Mt. Fuji, Japan .. .. .. | 40 | 10 |
| 1078 | 18 a. Jawa and Old Town Hall clock, Prague .. | 50 | 10 |
| 1079 | 25 a. Motor cycle and T.V. Tower, Berlin .. | 70 | 10 |
| 1080 | 30 a. Motor cycle and Colosseum, Rome .. | 85 | 10 |

**472.** Crowd with Flags.

**1986.** 21st Anniv. of Peoples' Democratic Party.

| | | | | |
|---|---|---|---|---|
| 1082. | **472.** | 2 a. multicoloured .. | 25 | 10 |

**473.** Lenin writing.

**1986.** 27th Soviet Communist Party Congress, Moscow.

| | | | | |
|---|---|---|---|---|
| 1083. | **473.** | 25 a. multicoloured | 70 | 10 |

**474.** "Vostok 1".

**1986.** 25th Anniv of First Manned Space Flight. Multicoloured.

| | | | |
|---|---|---|---|
| 1084 | 3 a. Type **474** .. .. | 10 | 10 |
| 1085 | 7 a. Russian Cosmonaut Medal (vert) .. .. | 25 | 10 |
| 1086 | 9 a. Launch of "Vostok 1" (vert) .. .. | 30 | 10 |
| 1087 | 11 a. Yuri Gagarin (first man in space) (vert) .. | 45 | 10 |
| 1088 | 13 a. Cosmonauts reading newspaper .. .. | 45 | 10 |
| 1089 | 15 a. Yuri Gagarin and Sergei Pavlovich Korolev (rocket designer) .. .. | 55 | 10 |
| 1090 | 17 a. Valentina Tereshkova (first woman in space) (vert) | 65 | 10 |

**475.** Footballers. **476.** Lenin.

**1986.** World Cup Football Championship, Mexico. Designs showing various footballing scenes.

| | | | | |
|---|---|---|---|---|
| 1091. | **475.** | 3 a. multicoloured .. | 10 | 10 |
| 1092. | – | 4 a. multicoloured (horiz.) .. .. | 15 | 10 |
| 1093. | – | 7 a. multicoloured (horiz.) .. .. | 25 | 10 |
| 1094. | – | 11 a. multicoloured | 45 | 10 |
| 1095. | – | 12 a. multicoloured (horiz.) .. .. | 45 | 10 |
| 1096. | – | 18 a. multicoloured | 65 | 10 |
| 1097. | – | 20 a. multicoloured | 75 | 10 |

**1986.** 116th Birth Anniv of Lenin.

| | | | | |
|---|---|---|---|---|
| 1099 | **476** | 16 a. multicoloured .. | 60 | 10 |

**477.** Delegates voting.

**1986.** 1st Anniv. of Supreme Council Meeting of Tribal Leaders.

| | | | | |
|---|---|---|---|---|
| 1100. | **477.** | 3 a. brown, red and blue .. .. | 25 | 10 |

**478.** Flags and Crowd **479** Worker with Cogwheel and Globe

**1986.** 8th Anniv. of Sawr Revolution.

| | | | | |
|---|---|---|---|---|
| 1101. | **478.** | 8 a. multicoloured .. | 30 | 10 |

**1986.** Labour Day.

| | | | | |
|---|---|---|---|---|
| 1102 | **479** | 5 a. multicoloured .. | 25 | 10 |

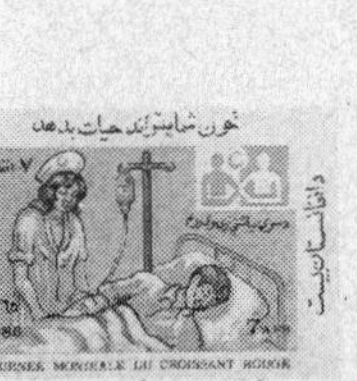
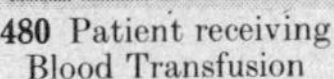

**480** Patient receiving Blood Transfusion **481** St. Bernard

**1986.** International Red Cross/Crescent Day.

| | | | | |
|---|---|---|---|---|
| 1103 | **480** | 7 a. multicoloured .. | 45 | 10 |

**1986.** Pedigree Dogs. Multicoloured.

| | | | |
|---|---|---|---|
| 1104 | 5 a. Type **481** .. .. | 20 | 10 |
| 1105 | 7 a. Rough collie .. | 25 | 10 |
| 1106 | 8 a. Spaniel .. .. | 35 | 10 |
| 1107 | 9 a. Long-haired dachshund .. .. | 35 | 10 |
| 1108 | 11 a. German shepherd .. | 45 | 10 |
| 1109 | 15 a. Bulldog .. .. | 60 | 10 |
| 1110 | 20 a. Afghan hound .. | 85 | 10 |

**482** Fish **483** Mother and Children

**1986.** Fishes. Multicoloured.

| | | | |
|---|---|---|---|
| 1111 | 5 a. Type **482** .. .. | 15 | 10 |
| 1112 | 7 a. Blue striped fish .. | 25 | 10 |
| 1113 | 8 a. Black and red striped fish .. .. | 30 | 10 |
| 1114 | 9 a. Black and yellow horizontally-striped fish | 35 | 10 |
| 1115 | 11 a. Fish with black and yellow patterned back | 45 | 10 |
| 1116 | 15 a. Green and red striped fish .. .. | 60 | 10 |
| 1117 | 20 a. Fish with large dorsal fin .. .. | 75 | 10 |

**1986.** World Children's Day Multicoloured.

| | | | |
|---|---|---|---|
| 1118 | 1 a. Type **483** .. .. | 10 | 10 |
| 1119 | 3 a. Woman holding boy and emblem .. .. | 15 | 10 |
| 1120 | 9 a. Circle of children on map (horiz) .. .. | 30 | 10 |

**484** Locomotive

**1986.** 19th-century Railway Locomotives. Designs showing various locomotives.

| | | | | |
|---|---|---|---|---|
| 1121 | **484** | 4 a. multicoloured .. | 20 | 10 |
| 1122 | – | 5 a. multicoloured .. | 30 | 10 |
| 1123 | – | 6 a. multicoloured .. | 35 | 10 |
| 1124 | – | 7 a. multicoloured .. | 45 | 10 |
| 1125 | – | 8 a. multicoloured .. | 55 | 10 |
| 1126 | – | 9 a. multicoloured .. | 65 | 10 |
| 1127 | – | 11 a. multicoloured .. | 85 | 10 |

**485** Cobra

**1986.** Animals. Multicoloured.

| | | | |
|---|---|---|---|
| 1128 | 3 a. Type **485** .. .. | 10 | 10 |
| 1129 | 4 a. Lizards (vert) .. | 10 | 10 |
| 1130 | 5 a. Praying mantis .. | 15 | 10 |
| 1131 | 8 a. Beetle (vert) .. | 20 | 15 |
| 1132 | 9 a. Spider .. .. | 25 | 20 |
| 1133 | 10 a. Snake .. .. | 25 | 20 |
| 1134 | 11 a. Scorpions .. .. | 25 | 20 |

Nos. 1130/2 and 1134 are wrongly inscribed "Les Reptiles".

**487** National Monuments **488** 11th-century Ship

**1986.** Independence Day.

| | | | | |
|---|---|---|---|---|
| 1136 | **487** | 10 a. multicoloured .. | 40 | 10 |

**1986.** "Stockholmia 86" International Stamp Exhibition. Sailing Ships. Multicoloured.

| | | | |
|---|---|---|---|
| 1137 | 4 a. Type **488** .. .. | 30 | 15 |
| 1138 | 5 a. Roman galley .. | 40 | 15 |
| 1139 | 6 a. English royal kogge | 55 | 15 |
| 1140 | 7 a. Early dhow .. .. | 60 | 15 |
| 1141 | 8 a. Nao .. .. .. | 70 | 15 |
| 1142 | 9 a. Ancient Egyptian ship .. .. .. | 75 | 15 |
| 1143 | 11 a. Medieval galeasse .. | 85 | 15 |

**489** Tribesmen **490** State Arms

**1986.** Pashtunistan Day.

| | | | | |
|---|---|---|---|---|
| 1145 | **489** | 4 a. multicoloured .. | 25 | 10 |

**1986.** Supreme Council Meeting of Tribal Leaders.

| | | | | |
|---|---|---|---|---|
| 1146 | **490** | 3 a. gold, blue & black | 25 | 10 |

**491** Labourer reading **492** Dove and U.N. Emblem

**1986.** World Literacy Day.

| | | | | |
|---|---|---|---|---|
| 1147 | **491** | 2 a. multicoloured .. | 20 | 10 |

**1986.** International Peace Year.

| | | | | |
|---|---|---|---|---|
| 1148 | **492** | 12 a. black and blue .. | 40 | 10 |

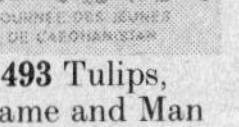

**493** Tulips, Flame and Man with Rifle **494** Crowd and Flags

**1986.** Afghanistan Youth Day.

| | | | | |
|---|---|---|---|---|
| 1149 | **493** | 3 a. red and black .. | 25 | 10 |

**1987.** 9th Anniv of Sawr Revolution.

| | | | | |
|---|---|---|---|---|
| 1150 | **494** | 3 a. multicoloured .. | 25 | 10 |

**495** Map and Dove **496** Oral Rehydration

**1987.** National Reconciliation.
1151 495 3 a. multicoloured .. 25 10

**1987.** International Children's Day. Mult.
1152 1 a. Type **496** .. .. 10 10
1153 5 a. Weighing babies .. 15 10
1154 9 a. Vaccinating babies .. 25 10

497 Conference Delegates

498 "Pieris sp."

**1987.** 1st Anniv of Tribal Conference.
1155 497 5 a. multicoloured .. 25 10

**1987.** Butterflies and Moths. Multicoloured.
1156 7 a. Type **498** .. .. 30 20
1157 9 a. Brimstone and unidentified butterfly 35 20
1158 10 a. Garden tiger moth (horiz) .. .. 40 25
1159 12 a. "Parnassius sp." .. 45 25
1160 15 a. Butterfly (unidentified) (horiz) .. 60 40
1161 22 a. Butterfly (unidentified) (horiz) .. 65 40
1162 25 a. Butterfly (unidentified) .. .. 75 45

499 People on Hand

**1987.** 1st Local Government Elections.
1163 499 1 a. multicoloured .. 20 10

501 "Sputnik 1"

502 Old and Modern Post Offices

**1987.** 30th Anniv of Launch of "Sputnik 1" (first artificial satellite). Multicoloured.
1165 10 a. Type **501** .. .. 35 10
1166 15 a. Rocket launch .. 45 10
1167 25 a. "Soyuz"–"Salyut" space complex .. 65 10

**1987.** World U.P.U. Day.
1168 502 22 a. multicoloured .. 75 10

503 Monument and Arch of Paghman

**1987.** Independence Day.
1169 503 3 a. multicoloured .. 20 10

504 "Communications"

**1987.** United Nations Day.
1170 504 42 a. multicoloured .. 1·25 15

505 Lenin

506 Castor Oil Plant

**1987.** 70th Anniv of Russian Revolution.
1171 505 25 a. multicoloured .. 95 10

**1987.** Plants. Multicoloured.
1172 3 a. Type **506** .. .. 15 10
1173 6 a. Liquorice .. .. 30 10
1174 9 a. Camomile .. .. 40 10
1175 14 a. Thorn apple .. 60 10
1176 18 a. Chicory .. .. 80 10

507 Field Mice

508 Four-stringed Instrument

**1987.** Mice. Multicoloured.
1177 2 a. Type **507** .. .. 15 10
1178 4 a. Brown and white mice (horiz) .. .. 20 10
1179 8 a. Ginger mice (horiz) .. 25 10
1180 16 a. Black mice (horiz) .. 45 10
1181 20 a. Spotted and ginger mice (horiz) .. .. 55 10

**1988.** Musical Instruments. Multicoloured.
1182 1 a. Type **508** .. .. 10 10
1183 3 a. Drums .. .. 15 10
1184 5 a. Two-stringed instruments with two pegs .. 20 10
1185 15 a. Two-stringed instrument with ten pegs .. 45 10
1186 18 a. Two-stringed instruments with fourteen or ten pegs .. .. 60 10
1187 25 a. Four-stringed bowed instruments .. .. 85 10
1188 33 a. Two-stringed bowed instruments .. .. 1·25 10

509 Mixed Arrangement

510 Emblems and Means of Communication

**1988.** Flowers. Multicoloured.
1189 3 a. Type **509** .. .. 15 10
1190 5 a. Tulips (horiz) .. 20 10
1191 7 a. Mallows .. .. 25 10
1192 9 a. Small mauve flowers 35 10
1193 12 a. Marguerites .. 50 10
1194 15 a. White flowers .. 65 10
1195 24 a. Red and blue flowers (horiz) .. .. 1·00 10

**1988.** 60th Anniv of Membership of U.P.U. and I.T.U.
1196 510 20 a. multicoloured .. 65 10

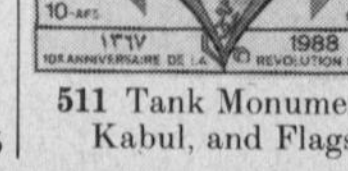

511 Tank Monument, Kabul, and Flags

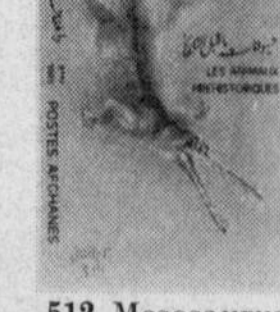

512 Mesosaurus

**1988.** 10th Anniv of Sawr Revolution.
1197 511 10 a. multicoloured .. 40 10

**1988.** Prehistoric Animals. Multicoloured.
1198 3 a. Type **512** .. .. 15 10
1199 5 a. Styracosaurus (horiz) 25 10
1200 10 a. Uintatherium (horiz) 45 10
1201 15 a. Protoceratops (horiz) 65 10
1202 20 a. Stegosaurus (horiz) 85 10
1203 25 a. Ceratosaurus .. 1·10 10
1204 30 a. Moa .. .. 1·50 45

513 Baskets and Bowl of Fruit

**1988.** Fruit. Multicoloured
1205 2 a. Type **513** .. .. 10 10
1206 4 a. Baskets of fruit .. 15 10
1207 7 a. Large basket of fruit 25 10
1208 8 a. Bunch of grapes on branch (vert) .. .. 25 10
1209 16 a. Buying fruit from market stall .. .. 45 10
1210 22 a. Arranging fruit on market stall .. .. 65 10
1211 25 a. Stallholder weighing fruit (vert) .. .. 80 10

514 Memorial Pillar of Knowledge and Ignorance, Kabul

515 Heads encircled with Rope

**1988.** Independence Day.
1212 514 24 a. multicoloured .. 90 10

**1988.** Pashtunistan Day.
1213 515 23 a. multicoloured .. 80 10

516 Flags and Globe

517 Anniversary Emblem

**1988.** Afghan–Soviet Space Flight.
1214 516 32 a. multicoloured .. 90 10

**1988.** 125th Anniv of International Red Cross.
1215 517 10 a. multicoloured .. 50 10

518 Rocket and V. Tereshkova

**1988.** 25th Anniv of First Woman Cosmonaut Valentina Tereshkova's Space Flight. Mult.
1216 10 a. Type **518** .. .. 40 10
1217 15 a. Bird, globe and rocket (vert) .. .. 65 10
1218 25 a. "Vostok 6" and globe .. .. .. 90 10

519 Decorated Metal Vessels

520 Indian Flag and Nehru

**1988.** Traditional Crafts. Multicoloured.
1219 2 a. Type **519** .. .. 10 10
1220 4 a. Pottery .. .. 15 10
1221 5 a. Clothing (vert) .. 20 10
1222 9 a. Carpets .. .. 25 10
1223 15 a. Bags .. .. 45 10
1224 23 a. Jewellery .. .. 65 10
1225 50 a. Furniture .. 1·25 10

**1988.** Birth Cent of Jawaharlal Nehru (Indian statesman).
1226 520 40 a. multicoloured .. 1·50 25

521 Emeralds

522 Ice Skating

**1988.** Gemstones. Multicoloured.
1227 13 a. Type **521** .. 60 15
1228 37 a. Lapis lazuli .. 1·40 25
1229 40 a. Rubies .. .. 1·75 25

**1988.** Winter Olympic Games, Calgary. Mult.
1230 2 a. Type **522** .. .. 10 10
1231 5 a. Slalom .. .. 20 10
1232 9 a. Two-man bobsleigh .. 35 10
1233 22 a. Biathlon .. .. 65 10
1234 37 a. Speed skating .. 1·40 20

523 Old City

**1988.** International Campaign for Preservation of Old Sana'a, Yemen.
1236 523 32 a. multicoloured .. 90 10

524 Emblem

**1989.** 2nd Anniv of Move for National Reconciliation.
1237 524 4 a. multicoloured .. 20 10

525 Bishop and Game from "The Three Ages of Man" (attr. Estienne Porchier)

**1989.** Chess. Multicoloured.
1238 2 a. Type **525** .. .. 10 10
1239 3 a. Faience queen and 14th-century drawing of Margrave Otto IV of Brandenburg and his wife playing chess .. 20 10
1240 4 a. French king and game .. .. 25 10
1241 7 a. King and game .. 35 10
1242 16 a. Knight and game .. 55 10
1243 24 a. Arabian pawn and "Great Chess" .. 85 10
1244 45 a. Bishop and teaching of game .. .. 1·40 15

Nos. 1240/4 show illustrations from King Alfonso X's "Book of Chess, Dice and Tablings".

526 "The Old Jew"

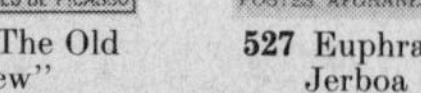

527 Euphrates Jerboa

**1989.** Picasso Paintings. Multicoloured.
1245 4 a. Type **526** .. .. 25 10
1246 6 a. "The Two Harlequins" .. .. 25 10
1247 8 a. "Portrait of Ambrouse Vollar" .. 25 10
1248 22 a. "Majorcan Woman" 65 10
1249 35 a. "Acrobat on Ball" 1·25 15

**1989.** Animals. Multicoloured.
1251 3 a. Type **527** .. .. 20 10
1252 4 a. Asiatic wild ass .. 25 10
1253 14 a. Lynx .. .. 60 10
1254 35 a. Lammergeier .. 2·25 70
1255 44 a. Markhor .. .. 1·50 20

**528** Bomb breaking, Dove and Woman holding Wheat

**529** Cattle

**1989.** International Women's Day (1988).
1257 **528** 8 a. multicoloured .. 25 10

**1989.** Farmers' Day. Multicoloured.
1258 1 a. Type **529** .. .. 10 10
1259 2 a. Ploughing with oxen and tractors .. .. 10 10
1260 3 a. Picking cotton .. 10 10

**530** Dish Aerial

**1989.** World Meteorology Day. Multicoloured.
1261 27 a. Type **530** .. .. 1·00 15
1262 32 a. World Meteorological Organization emblem and state arms 1·25 15
1263 40 a. Data-collecting equipment (vert) .. 1·50 15

**531** Rejoicing Crowd

**1989.** 11th Anniv of Sawr Revolution.
1264 **531** 20 a. multicoloured .. 75 10

**532** Outdoor Class

**533** Eiffel Tower and Arc de Triomphe

**1989.** Teacher's Day.
1265 **532** 42 a. multicoloured .. 1·50 15

**1989.** Bicentenary of French Revolution.
1266 **533** 25 a. multicoloured .. 90 15

**534** Transmission Mast

**1989.** 10th Anniv of Asia–Pacific Telecommunity.
1267 3 a. Type **534** .. .. 10 10
1268 27 a. Dish aerial .. .. 1·00 15

**535** National Monuments

**536** Pashtu

**1989.** Independence Day.
1269 **535** 25 a. multicoloured .. 90 15

**1989.** Pashtunistan Day.
1270 **536** 3 a. multicoloured .. 10 10

**537** White Spoonbill

**1989.** Birds. Multicoloured.
1271 3 a. Type **537** .. .. 15 15
1272 5 a. Purple swamphen .. 35 15
1273 10 a. Eurasian bittern (horiz) .. .. 60 25
1274 15 a. Eastern white pelican .. .. 80 35
1275 20 a. Red-crested pochard 1·10 40
1276 25 a. Mute swan .. .. 1·40 50
1277 30 a. Common cormorant (horiz) .. .. 1·60 60

**538** Duchs, 1910

**1989.** Vintage Cars. Multicoloured.
1278 5 a. Type **538** .. .. 20 10
1279 10 a. Ford, 1911 .. .. 35 10
1280 20 a. Renault, 1911 .. 75 10
1281 25 a. Russo-Balte, 1911 .. 90 15
1282 30 a. Fiat, 1926 .. .. 1·00 15

NEWSPAPER STAMPS

N 35.

**1928.**
N 192. N 35. 2 p. blue .. .. 3·50 4·50

**1929.**
N 205. N 35. 2 p. red .. .. 25 45

N 43.

**1932.**
N 215 N 43 2 p. red .. .. 40 60
N 216 2 p. black .. 25 65
N 217 2 p. green .. 25 75
N 219 2 p. red .. .. 45 75

N 75. Coat of Arms.

**1939.**
N 259 N 75 2 p. green .. 15 55
N 260 2 p. mve (no gum) 15 75

**1969.** As Type N 75, but larger and with different Pushtu inscr.
N 652 100 p. green .. .. 15 20
N 653 150 p. brown .. .. 15 20

OFFICIAL STAMPS

O 27. O 86.

**1909.**
O 173. O 27. red .. .. .. 1·10 1·10

**1939.** Design 22½ × 28 mm.
O 281. O 86. 15 p. green .. .. 85 75
O 282. 30 p. brown .. 1·25 1·25
O 283. 45 p. red .. .. 1·00 1·00
O 284. 1 a. mauve .. .. 1·60 1·50

**1954.** Design 24½ × 31 mm.
O 285b. O 86. 50 p. red .. .. 1·00 60

**1965.** Design 24 × 30½ mm.
O 287 O 86 50 p. pink .. .. 1·25 60

PARCEL POST STAMPS

P 27.

**1909.**
P 173 P 27 3 s. brown .. 1·00 1·50
P 174 3 s. green .. .. 1·50 2·50
P 175 1 k. green .. .. 1·50 2·50
P 176 1 k. red .. .. 1·50 2·25
P 177 1 r. orange .. 2·75 2·75
P 178 1 r. grey .. .. 20·00
P 179 1 r. brown .. 1·50 1·50
P 180 2 r. red .. .. 2·75 2·75
P 181 2 r. blue .. .. 5·00 5·50

## INDEX

Countries can be quickly located by referring to the index at the end of this volume.

P 28. Old Habibia College, Kabul.

**1921.**
P 182. P 28. 10 p. brown .. 3·50 4·50
P 183. 15 p. brown .. 4·50 5·50
P 184. 30 p. purple .. 8·50 5·50
P 185. 1 r. blue .. .. 10·00 10·00

**1923.** 5th Independence Day. Optd with T 28.
P 186 P 28 10 p. brown .. 60·00
P 187 15 p. brown .. 65·00
P 188 30 p. purple .. £110

P 35. P 36.

**1928.**
P 192. P 35. 2 a. orange .. 5·50 4·25
P 193. P 36. 3 a. green .. 10·00 10·00

**1930.**
P 214. P 35. 2 a. green .. 6·50 6·50
P 215. P 36. 3 a. brown .. 8·50 10·00

REGISTRATION STAMP

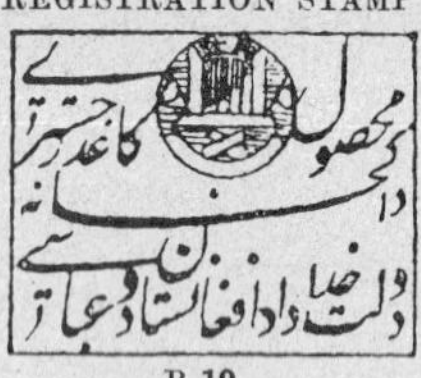
R 19.

**1894.** Undated.
R 155. R 19. 2 a. black on green. 8·00 7·00

### APPENDIX

The following stamps have either been issued in excess of postal needs or have not been available to the public in reasonable quantities at face value. Such stamps may later be given full listing if there is evidence of regular postal use.

**1961.**

Agriculture Day. Fauna and Flora. 2, 2, 5, 10, 15, 25, 50, 100, 150, 175 p.

Child Welfare. Sports and Games. 2, 2, 5, 10, 15, 25, 50, 100, 150, 175 p.

U.N.I.C.E.F. Surch. on 1961 Child Welfare issue. 2+25, 2+25, 5+25, 10+25, 15 p.+25 p.

Women's Day. 50, 175 p.

Independence Day. Mohamed Nadir Shah. 50, 175 p.

Int. Exhib., Kabul. 50, 175 p.

Pashtunistan Day. 50, 175 p.

Nat. Assembly. 50, 175 p.

Anti-Malaria Campaign. 50, 175 p.

King's 47th Birthday. 50, 175 p.

Red Crescent Day. Fruits. 2, 2, 5, 10, 15, 25, 50, 100, 150, 175 p.

Afghan Red Crescent Fund. 1961 Red Crescent Day issue surch. 2+25, 2+25, 5+25, 10+25, 15 p. + 25 p.

United Nations Day. 1, 2, 3, 4, 50, 75, 175 p.

Teachers' Day. Flowers and Educational Scenes. 2, 2, 5, 10, 15, 25, 50, 100, 150, 175 p.

U.N.E.S.C.O. 1961 Teachers' Day issue surch. 2+25, 2+25, 5+25, 10+25, 15 p.+25 p.

**1962.**

15th Anniv (1961) of U.N.E.S.C.O. 2, 2, 5, 10, 15, 25, 50, 75, 100 p.

Ahmed Shah Baba. 50, 75, 100 p.

Agriculture Day. Animals and Products. 2, 2, 5, 10, 15, 25, 50, 75, 100, 125 p.

Independence Day. Marching Athletes. 25, 50, 150 p.

Women's Day. Postage 25, 50 p.; Air 100, 175 p.

Pashtunistan Day. 25, 50, 150 p.

Malaria Eradication. 2, 2, 5, 10, 15, 25, 50, 75, 100, 150, 175 p.

National Assembly. 25, 50, 75, 100, 125 p.

Fourth Asian Games, Jakarta, Indonesia. Postage 1, 2, 3, 4, 5 p.; Air 25, 50, 75, 100 150, 175 p.

Children's Day. Sports and Produce. Postage 1, 2, 3, 4, 5 p.; Air 75, 150, 200 p.

King's 48th Birthday. 25, 50, 75, 100 p.

Red Crescent Day. Fruits and Flowers. Postage 1, 2, 3, 4, 5 p.; Air 25, 50, 100 p.

Boy Scouts' Day. Postage 1, 2, 3, 4 p.; Air 25, 50, 75, 100 p.

1st Anniv. of Hammarskjold's Death. Surch on 1961 U.N.E.S.C.O. issue. 2+20, 2+20, 5+20, 10+20, 15+20, 25+20, 50+20, 75+20, 100 p.+20 p.

United Nations Day. Postage 1, 2, 3, 4, 5 p.; Air 75, 100, 125 p.

Teachers' Day. Sport and Flowers. Postage 1, 2, 3, 4, 5 p.; Air 100, 150 p.

World Meteorological Day. 50, 100 p.

**1963.**

Famous Afghans Pantheon, Kabul. 50, 75, 100 p.

Agriculture Day. Sheep and Silkworms. Postage 1, 2, 3, 4, 5 p.; Air 100, 150, 200 p.

Freedom from Hunger. Postage 2, 3, 300 p.; Air 500 p.

Malaria Eradication Fund. 1962 Malaria Eradication issue surch. 2+15, 2+15, 5+15, 10+15, 15+15, 25+15, 50+15, 75+15, 100+15. 150+15, 175 p.+15 p.

World Meteorological Day. Postage 1, 2, 3, 4, 5 p.; Air 200, 300, 400, 500 p.

"GANEFO" Athletic Games, Djakarta, Indonesia. Postage 2, 3, 4, 5, 10 p., 9 a.; Air 300, 500 p.

Red Cross Cent. Postage 2, 3, 4, 5, 10 p.; Air 100 200 p., 4, 6 a.

Nubian Monuments Preservation. Postage 100, 200, 500 p.; Air 5 a., 7 a. 50.

**1964.**

Women's Day (1963). 2, 3, 4, 5, 10 p.

Afghan Boy Scouts and Girl Guides. Postage 2, 3, 4, 5, 10 p.; Air 2, 2, 2 a. 50, 3, 4, 5, 12 a.

Child Welfare Day (1963). Sports and Games. Postage 2, 3, 4, 5, 10 p.; Air 200, 300 p.

Afghan Red Crescent Society. Postage 100, 200 p.; Air 5 a., 7 a. 50.

Teachers' Day (1963). Flowers. Postage 2, 3, 4, 5, 10 p.; Air 3 a., 3 a. 50.

United Nations Day (1963). Postage 2, 3, 4, 5, 10 p.; Air 100 p., 2, 3 a.

15th Anniv. of Human Rights Declaration. Surch. on 1964 United Nations Day issue. Postage 2+50, 3+50, 4+50, 5+50, 10 p.+50 p.; Air 100 p.+50 p., 2a+50 p., 3a.+50 p.

U.N.I.C.E.F. (dated 1963). Postage 100, 200 p.; Air 5 a, 7 a. 50.

Malaria Eradication (dated 1963). Postage 2, 3, 4, 5 p., 10 p. on 4 p.; Air 2, 10 a.

## AJMAN — Pt. 19

One of the Trucial States in the Persian Gulf. On 18 July 1971, seven Gulf shaikhdoms, including Ajman, formed the State of the United Arab Emirates. The federation became effective on 1 August 1972.

1964. 100 naye paise = 1 rupee.
1967. 100 dirhams = 1 riyal.

1. Shaikh Rashid bin Humaid al Naimi and Arab Stallion. 2. Kennedy in Football Kit.

**1964.** Multicoloured.
(a) Size 34½ × 23 mm.
1. 1 n.p. Type 1 .. .. 15 15
2. 2 n.p. Striped fish .. 15 15
3. 3 n.p. Dromedary .. 15 15
4. 4 n.p. Blue fish .. 15 15
5. 5 n.p. Tortoise .. 15 15
6. 10 n.p. Spotted fish .. 20 15
7. 15 n.p. White stork .. 40 15
8. 20 n.p. Black-headed gulls 40 15
9. 30 n.p. Lanner falcon .. 50 15
(b) Size 42½ × 27 mm.
10. 40 n.p. Type 1 .. .. 20 20
11. 50 n.p. Striped fish .. 20 20
12. 70 n.p. Dromedary .. 25 25
13. 1 r. Blue fish .. .. 40 30
14. 1 r. 50 Tortoise .. 50 50
15. 2 r. Spotted fish .. 90 75
(c) Size 53 × 34 mm.
16. 3 r. White stork .. 1·40 1·10
17. 3 r. Black-headed gulls .. 3·50 2·25
18. 10 r. Lanner falcon .. .. 6·25 4·75

**1964.** Pres. Kennedy Commem. Perf. or imperf.
19. 2. 10 n.p. purple and green .. 15 15
20. – 15 n.p. violet & turquoise 15 15
21. – 50 n.p. blue and brown .. 20 20
22. – 1 r. turquoise and sepia .. 35 35
23. – 2 r. olive and purple 75 65
24. – 3 r. brown and green .. 1·25 95
25. – 5 r. brown and violet .. 2·25 2·10
26. – 10 r. brown and blue .. 5·00 3·75
DESIGNS—Various pictures of Kennedy: 15 n.p. Diving. 50 n.p. As naval officer. 1 r. Sailing with Mrs. Kennedy. 2 r. With Mrs. Eleanor Roosevelt. 3 r. With wife and child. 5 r. With colleagues. 10 r. Full-face portrait.

3. Start of Race.

**1965.** Olympic Games. Tokyo. Perf. or imperf.
27. 3. 5 n.p. slate, brn. & mauve 15 15
28. – 10 n.p. red, bronze & blue 15 15
29. 3. 15 n.p. brn., violet & green 15 15
30. – 25 n.p. black, blue and red 15 15
31. – 50 n.p. slate, purple & blue 20 20
32. – 1 r. blue, green & purple .. 55 35
33. – 1 r. 50 purple, violet & grn. 75 50
34. – 2 r. blue, purple & ochre .. 1·25 90
35. – 3 r. violet, brown & blue .. 1·90 1·25
36. – 5 r. purple, green & yellow 2·50 2·10
DESIGNS: 10 n.p., 1 r. 50. Boxing. 25 n.p. 2 r. Judo. 50 n.p., 5 r. Gymnastics. 1 r., 3 r. Sailing.

4. First Gibbons Catalogue and Alexandria (U.S.) 5 c. Postmaster's Stamp.

**1965.** Stanley Gibbons Catalogue Centenary Exhibition, London. Multicoloured.
37. 5 n.p. Type 4 .. .. 15 15
38. 10 n.p. Austria (6 k.) scarlet "Mercury" newspaper-tamp 15 15
39. 15 n.p. British Guiana "One Cent", 1856 .. .. 15 15
40. 25 n.p. Canada "Twelvepence Black", 1851 .. .. 15 15
41. 50 n.p. Hawaii "Missionary" 2 c., 1851 .. 25 25
42. 1 r. Mauritius "Post Office" 2d. blue, 1847 .. .. 40 40
43. 3 r. Switzerland "Double Geneva" 5 c.+5 c., 1843 .. 1·40 1·25
44. 5 r. Tuscany 3 lire, 1860 .. 2·75 2·10
The 5, 15 and 50 n.p. and 3 r. also include the First Gibbons Catalogue and the others, the Gibbons "Elizabethan" Catalogue.

**1965.** Pan Arab Games, Cairo. Perf. or imperf. Nos. 29, 31 and 33/5 optd. (a) Optd. **PAN ARAB GAMES CAIRO 1965.**
45. 3. 15 n.p. brown, violet & grn. 15 15
46. – 50 n.p. slate, purple & blue 25 25
47. – 1 r. 50 purple, violet & grn. 90 90
48. – 2 r. blue, red and ochre .. 1·25 1·25
49. – 3 r. violet, brown and blue 2·00 2·00
(b) Optd. as Nos. 45/9 but equivalent in Arabic.
50. 3. 15 n.p. brown, violet & grn. 15 15
51. – 50 n.p. slate, purple & blue 25 25
52. – 1 r. 50 purple, violet & grn. 90 90
53. – 2 r. blue, red & ochre .. 1·25 1·25
54. – 3 r. violet, brown & blue .. 2·00 2·00

**1965.** Air. Designs similar to Nos. 1/9, but inscr. "AIR MAIL". Multicoloured.
(a) Size 42½ × 25½ mm.
55. 15 n.p. Type 1 .. .. 15 15
56. 25 n.p. Striped fish .. 15 15
57. 35 n.p. Dromedary .. 20 15
58. 50 n.p. Blue fish .. 25 15
59. 75 n.p. Tortoise .. 40 20
60. 1 r. Spotted fish .. 60 25
(b) Size 53 × 34 mm.
61. 2 r. White stork .. 1·75 60
62. 3 r. Black-headed gull .. 3·75 1·25
63. 5 r. Lanner falcon .. 6·00 2·00

**1966.** Stamp Cent. Exn., Cairo. Nos. 38/9 and 41/3 optd. **STAMP CENTENARY EXHIBITION CAIRO, JANUARY 1966,** and pyramid motif.
73. 10 n.p. multicoloured .. 15 15
74. 15 n.p. multicoloured .. 15 15
75. 50 n.p. multicoloured .. 25 25
76. 1 r. multicoloured .. 65 65
77. 3 r. multicoloured .. 1·75 1·75

8. Sir Winston Churchill and Tower Bridge.

**1966.** Churchill Commem. Each design includes portrait of Churchill. Multicoloured.

| | | | |
|---|---|---|---|
| 79. | 25 n.p. Type **8** .. .. | 15 | 15 |
| 80. | 50 n.p. Buckingham Palace | 25 | 15 |
| 81. | 75 n.p. Blenheim Palace .. | 40 | 20 |
| 82. | 1 r. British Museum | 50 | 25 |
| 83. | 2 r. St. Paul's Cathedral in wartime .. .. .. | 1·00 | 40 |
| 84. | 3 r. National Gallery and St. Martin in the Fields Church .. .. .. | 1·50 | 60 |
| 85. | 5 r. Westminster Abbey .. | 2·50 | 90 |
| 86. | 7 r. 50 Houses of Parliament at night .. .. .. | 3·75 | 1·60 |

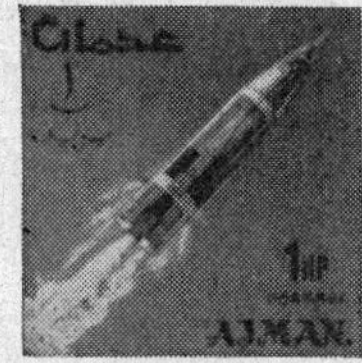


9. Rocket.

**1966.** Space Achievements. Multicoloured.

(a) Postage. Size As T **9**.

| | | | |
|---|---|---|---|
| 88. | 1 n.p. Type **9** .. .. | 15 | 15 |
| 89. | 3 n.p. Capsule .. .. | 15 | 15 |
| 90. | 5 n.p. Astronaut entering capsule in space .. .. | 15 | 15 |
| 91. | 10 n.p. Astronaut outside capsule in space .. .. | 15 | 15 |
| 92. | 15 n.p. Astronauts & globe | 15 | 15 |
| 93. | 25 n.p. Astronaut in space.. | 25 | 15 |

(b) Air. Size 38 × 38 mm.

| | | | |
|---|---|---|---|
| 95. | 50 n.p. As Type **9** .. .. | 25 | 15 |
| 96. | 1 r. Astronauts and globe .. | 40 | 20 |
| 97. | 3 r. Astronaut outside capsule in space .. .. .. | 1·25 | 40 |
| 98. | 5 r. Capsule .. .. .. | 3·25 | 90 |

**1967.** Various issues with currency names changed by overprinting in **Dh.** or **Riyals.**

(a) Postage. Nos. 1/18 (1964 Definitives).

| | | | |
|---|---|---|---|
| 99. | 1 d. on 1 n.p. .. .. | 15 | 15 |
| 100. | 2 d. on 2 n.p. .. .. | 15 | 15 |
| 101. | 3 d. on 3 n.p. .. .. | 15 | 15 |
| 102 | 4 d. on 4 n.p. .. .. | 15 | 15 |
| 103. | 5 d. on 5 n.p. .. .. | 15 | 15 |
| 104. | 10 d. on 10 n.p. .. .. | 15 | 15 |
| 105. | 15 d. on 15 n.p. .. .. | 1·25 | 15 |
| 106. | 20 d. on 20 n.p. .. .. | 1·25 | 15 |
| 107. | 30 d. on 30 n.p. .. .. | 1·25 | 15 |
| 108. | 40 d. on 40 n.p. .. .. | 20 | 15 |
| 109. | 50 d. on 50 n.p. .. .. | 20 | 15 |
| 110. | 70 d. on 70 n.p. .. .. | 40 | 25 |
| 111. | 1 r. on 1 r. .. .. | 50 | 25 |
| 112. | 1 r. 50 on 1 r. 50 .. | 65 | 30 |
| 113. | 2 r. on 2 r. .. .. | 1·00 | 65 |
| 114. | 3 r. on 3 r. .. .. | 1·50 | 70 |
| 115. | 5 r. on 5 r. .. .. | 2·50 | 1·25 |
| 116. | 10 r. on 10 r. .. .. | 7·50 | 2·75 |

(b) Air. Nos. 55/63 (Airmails).

| | | | |
|---|---|---|---|
| 117. | 15 d. on 15 n.p. .. .. | 15 | 15 |
| 118. | 25 d. on 25 n.p. .. .. | 15 | 15 |
| 119. | 35 d. on 35 n.p. .. .. | 25 | 15 |
| 120. | 50 d. on 50 n.p. .. .. | 20 | 15 |
| 121. | 75 d. on 75 n.p. .. .. | 45 | 25 |
| 122. | 1 r. on 1 r. .. .. | 50 | 50 |
| 123. | 2 r. on 2 r. .. .. | 1·25 | 70 |
| 124. | 3 r. on 3 r. .. .. | 2·50 | 1·25 |
| 125. | 5 r. on 5 r. .. .. | 3·50 | 2·40 |

**NEW CURRENCY SURCHARGES.** Nos. 19/44 and 79/98 are known surch. in new currency (dirhams and riyals), in limited quantities, but there is some doubt as to whether they were in use locally.

11. Motor-car.

**1967.** Transport.

| | | | | |
|---|---|---|---|---|
| 135 | **11** | 1 d. brn. & black (post.) | 15 | 15 |
| 136 | – | 2 d. blue and brown .. | 15 | 15 |
| 137 | – | 3 d. mauve and black | 15 | 15 |
| 138 | – | 4 d. blue and brown .. | 15 | 15 |
| 139 | – | 5 d. green and black .. | 15 | 15 |
| 140 | – | 15 d. blue and brown .. | 25 | 15 |
| 141 | – | 30 d. brown and black | 25 | 15 |
| 142 | – | 50 d. black and brown | 50 | 15 |
| 143 | – | 70 d. violet and black | 65 | 15 |
| 144 | **11** | 1 r. green & brown (air) | 40 | 15 |
| 145 | – | 2 r. mauve and black .. | 1·00 | 25 |
| 146 | – | 3 r. black and brown .. | 1·60 | 40 |
| 147 | – | 5 r. brown and black .. | 2·25 | 1·00 |
| 148 | – | 10 r. blue and brown .. | 5·75 | 1·25 |

DESIGNS: 2 d., 2 r. Motor coach; 3 d., 3 r. Motor cyclist; 4 d., 5 r. Boeing 707 airliner; 5 d., 10 r. "Brasil" (liner); 15 d. "Yankee" (sail training and cruise ship); 30 d. Cameleer; 50 d. Arab horse; 70 d. Sikorsky S-58 helicopter.

**HAVE YOU READ THE NOTES AT THE BEGINNING OF THIS CATALOGUE?**

These often provide answers to the enquiries we receive.

OFFICIAL STAMPS

**1965.** Designs similar to Nos. 1/9, additionally inscr. "ON STATE'S SERVICE". Multicoloured.

(1) Postage. Size 43 × 26 mm.

| | | | |
|---|---|---|---|
| O 64. | 25 n.p. Type **1** .. .. | 15 | 15 |
| O 65. | 40 n.p. Striped fish .. | 15 | 15 |
| O 66. | 50 n.p. Dromedary .. | 20 | 15 |
| O 67. | 75 n.p. Blue fish .. .. | 45 | 25 |
| O 68. | 1 r. Tortoise .. .. | 85 | 40 |

(ii) Air. (a) Size 43 × 26 mm.

| | | | |
|---|---|---|---|
| O 69. | 75 n.p. Spotted fish .. | 40 | 15 |

(b) Size 53 × 34 mm.

| | | | |
|---|---|---|---|
| O 70. | 2 r. White stork .. .. | 1·25 | 35 |
| O 71. | 3 f. Black-headed gulls .. | 1·75 | 50 |
| O 72. | 5 f. Lanner falcon .. | 5·50 | 1·25 |

**1967.** Nos. O 64/72 with currency names changed by overprinting in **Dh.** or **Riyals.**

| | | | |
|---|---|---|---|
| O 126. | 25 d. on 25 n.p. .. | 15 | 15 |
| O 127. | 40 d. on 40 n.p. .. | 15 | 15 |
| O 128. | 50 d. on 50 n.p. .. | 20 | 15 |
| O 129. | 75 d. on 75 n.p. (No. O 67) .. .. | 45 | 45 |
| O 130. | 75 d. on 75 n.p. (No. O 69) .. .. | 45 | 45 |
| O 131. | 1 r. on 1 r. .. .. | 60 | 60 |
| O 132. | 2 r on 2 r. .. .. | 6·00 | 3·00 |
| O 133. | 3 r. on 3 r. .. .. | 11·00 | 4·50 |
| O 134. | 5 r on 5 r. .. .. | 17·00 | 8·50 |

For later issues see **UNITED ARAB EMIRATES.**

## APPENDIX

From June 1967 very many stamp issues were made by a succession of agencies which had been awarded contracts by the Ruler, sometimes two agencies operating at the same time. Several contradictory statements were made as to the validity of some of these issues which appeared 1967–72 and for this reason they are only listed in abbreviated form.

**1967.**

50th Birth Anniv. of President J. F. Kennedy. Air 10, 20, 40, 70 d., 1 r. 50, 2, 3, 5 r.

Paintings. Postage. Arab Paintings 1, 2, 3, 4, 5, 30, 70 d.; Air. Asian Paintings 1, 2, 3, 5 r.; Indian Painting 10 r.

Tales from "The Arabian Nights". Postage 1, 2, 3, 10, 30, 50, 70 d.; Air 90 d., 1, 2, 3 r.

World Scout Jamboree, Idaho. Postage 30, 70 d., 1 r.; Air 2, 3, 4 r.

Olympic Games, Mexico (1968). Postage 35, 65, 75 d., 1 r.; Air 1 r. 25, 2, 3, 4 r.

Winter Olympic Games, Grenoble (1968). Postage 5, 35, 60, 75 d.; Air 1, 1 r. 25, 2, 3 r.

Pres. J. Kennedy Memorial. Die-stamped on gold foil. Air 10 r.

Paintings by Renoir and Terbrughghen. Air 35, 65 d., 1, 2 r. × 3.

**1968.**

Paintings by Velasquez. Air 1 r × 2, 2 r. × 2.

Winter Olympic Games, Grenoble. Die-stamped on gold foil. Air 7 r.

Paintings from Famous Galleries. Air. 1 r × 4, 2 r. × 6.

Costumes. Air 30 d. × 2, 70 d. × 2, 1 r. × 2, 2 r. × 2.

Olympic Games, Mexico, Postage 1 r. × 4.; Air 2 r. × 4.

Satellites and Spacecraft. Air 30 d. × 2, 70 d. × 2, 1 r. × 2, 2 r. × 2, 3 r. × 2.

Paintings. Hunting Dogs. Air 2 r. × 6.

Paintings. Adam and Eve. Air 2 r. × 4.

Human Rights Year. Kennedy Brothers and Martin Luther King. Air 1 r. × 3, 2 r. × 3.

Kennedy Brothers Memorial. Postage 2 r.; Air 5 r.

Sports Champions. Inter-Milano Football Club. Postage 5, 10, 15, 20, 25 d.; Air 10 r.

Sports Champions. Famous Footballers. Postage 15, 20, 50, 75 d., 1 r.; Air 10 r.

Cats. Postage 1, 2, 3 d.; Air 2, 3 r.

Olympic Games, Mexico. Die-stamped on gold foil. Air 5 r.

5th Death Anniv. of Pres. J. Kennedy. On gold foil. Air 10 r.

Paintings of the Madonna. Air 30, 70 d., 1, 2, 3 r.

Space Exploration. Postage 5, 10, 15, 20, 25 d.; Air 15 r.

Olympic Games, Mexico. Gold Medals. Postage 2 r × 4: Air 5 r. × 4.

Christmas. Air 5 r.

**1969.**

Sports Champions. Cyclists. Postage 1, 2, 5, 10, 15, 20 d.; Air 12 r.

Sports Champions. German Footballers. Postage 5, 10, 15, 20, 25 d.; Air 10 r.

Sports Champions. Motor-racing Drivers. Postage 1, 5, 10, 15, 25 d.; Air 10 r.

Motor-racing Cars. Postage 1, 5, 10, 15, 25 d.; Air 10 r.

Sports Champions. Boxers. Postage 5, 10, 15, 20 d.; Air 10 r.

Sports Champions. Baseball Players. Postage 1, 2, 5, 10, 15 d.; Air 10 r.

Birds. Air 1 r. × 11.

Roses. 1 r. × 6.

Wild Animals. Air 1 r. × 6.

Paintings. Italian Old Masters. 5, 10, 15, 20 d. 10 r.

Paintings. Famous Composers. Air 5, 10, 25 d., 10 r.

Paintings. French Artists. 1 r × 4.

Paintings. Nudes. Air 2 r × 4.

Three Kings Mosaic. Air 1 r. × 2, 3 r. × 2.

Kennedy Brothers. Air 2, 3, 10 r.

Olympic Games, Mexico. Gold Medal Winners. Postage 1, 2 d., 10 r.; Air 10 d., 5, 10 r.

Paintings of the Madonna. Postage 10 d.; Air 10 r.

Space Flight of "Apollo 9". Optd. on 1968 Space Exploration issue. Air 15 r.

Space Flight of "Apollo 10". Optd. on 1968 Space Exploration issue. Air 15 r.

1st Death Anniv. of Gagarin. Optd. on 1968 Space Exploration issue. 5 d.

2nd Death Anniv. of Edward White. Optd. on 1968 Space Exploration issue. 10 d.

1st Death Anniv. of Robert Kennedy. Optd. on 1969 Kennedy Brothers issue. Air 2 r.

European Football Championship. Optd. on 1968 Famous Footballers issue. Air 10 r.

Olympic Games, Munich (1972). Optd. on 1969 Mexico Gold Medal Winners issue. Air 10 d., 5, 10 r.

Moon Landing of "Apollo 11". Air 1, 2, 5 r.

Moon Landing of "Apollo 11". Circular designs on gold or silver foil. Air 3 r. × 3, 5 r. × 3, 10 r. × 14.

Paintings. Christmas. Postage 1, 2, 3, 4, 5, 15 d.; Air 2, 3 r.

**1970.**

"Apollo" Space Flights. Postage 1, 2, 4, 5, 10 d.; Air 3, 5 r.

Birth Bicent. of Napoleon Bonaparte. Die-stamped on gold foil. Air 20 r.

Paintings. Easter. Postage 5, 10, 12, 30, 50, 70 d.; Air 1, 2 r.

Moon Landing. Die-stamped on gold foil. Air 20 r.

Paintings by Michelangelo. Postage 1, 2, 4, 5, 8, 10 d.; Air 3, 5 r.

World Cup Football Championships, Mexico. Air 25, 50, 75 d., 1, 2, 3 r.

"Expo 70" World Fair, Osaka, Japan. Japanese Paintings. Postage 1, 2, 3, 4, 5, 10, 15 d.; Air 1, 5 r.

Birth Bicent. Napoleon Bonaparte. Postage 1, 2, 4, 5, 10 d.; Air 3, 5 r.

Paintings. Old Masters. Postage 1, 2, 5, 6, 10 d.; Air 1, 2, 3r.

Space Flight of "Apollo 13". Air 50, 75, 80 d., 1, 2, 3 r.

World Cup Football Championships, Mexico. Die-stamped on gold foil. Air 20 r.

Olympic Games, 1960-1972. Postage 15, 30, 50, 70 d.; Air 2, 5 r.

"Expo 70" World Fair, Osaka, Japan. Pavilions. 1, 2, 3, 4, 10, 15 d.; Air 1, 3 r.

Brazil's Victory in World Cup Football Championship. Optd. on 1970 World Football Cup issue. Air 25, 50, 75 d. 1, 2, 3 r.

"Gemini" and "Apollo" Space Flights. Postage 1, 2, 3, 4, 5, 6, 8, 10, 12, 15, 20, 25, 30, 35, 40, 50 d.; Air 1, 1 r. 50, 2, 3 r.

Vintage and Veteran Cars. Postage 1, 2, 4, 5, 8, 10 d.; Air 2, 3 r.

Pres. D. Eisenhower Commem. Postage 30, 50, 70 d.; Air 1, 2, 3 r.

Paintings by Ingres. Air 25, 30, 35, 50, 70, 85 d., 1, 2 r.

500th Birth Anniv. (1971) of Albrecht Durer. Air 25, 30, 35, 50, 70, 85 d., 1, 2 r.

Christmas Paintings. Air 25, 30, 35, 50, 70. 85 d., 1, 2 r.

Winter Olympic Games, Sapporo, Japan (1972). Die-stamped on gold foil. Air 20 r.

Meeting of Eisenhower and De Gaulle, 1942. Die-stamped on gold foil Air 20 r.

General De Gaulle Commem. Air 25, 50, 75 d., 1, 2, 3 r.

Winter Olympic Games, Sapporo, Japan (1972). Sports. Postage 1, 2, 5, 10 d.; Air 3, 5 r.

J. Rindt, World Formula 1 Motor-racing Champion. Die-stamped on gold foil. Air 20 r.

**1971.**

"Philatokyo" Stamp Exhibition Tokyo. Japanese Paintings. Air 25, 30, 35, 50, 70, 85 d. 1, 2 r.

Mars Space Project. Air 50, 75, 80 d., 1, 2, 3 r.,

Napoleonic Military Uniforms. Postage 5, 10, 15, 20, 25, 30 d.; Air 2, 3 r.

Olympic Games, Munich (1972). Sports. Postage 10, 15, 25, 30, 40 d.; Air 1, 2, 3 r.

Paintings by Modern Artists. Air 25, 30, 35, 50, 70, 85 d.; 1, 2 r.

Paintings by Famous Artists. Air 25, 30, 35, 50, 70, 85 d., 1, 2 r.

25th Anniv. of United Nations. Optd. on 1971 Modern Artists issue. Air 25, 30, 35, 50, 70, 85 d., 1, 2 r.

Olympic Games, Munich (1972). Sports. Postage 1, 2, 3, 4, 5, 6, 8, 10, 12, 15, 20, 25, 30, 35, 40, 50 d.; Air 1, 1 r. 50, 2, 3 r.

Butterflies. Air 25, 30, 35, 50, 70, 85 d., 1, 2 r.

Space Flight of "Apollo 14". Postage 15, 25, 50, 60, 70 d.; Air 5 r.

Winter Olympic Games, 1924-1968. Postage 30, 40, 50, 75 d., 1 r.; Air 2 r.

Signs of the Zodiac. 1, 2, 5, 10, 12, 15, 25, 30, 35, 45, 50, 60 d.

Famous Men. Air 65, 70, 75, 80, 85, 90 d., 1, 1 r. 25, 1 r. 50, 2, 2 r. 50, 3 r.

Death Bicent. of Beethoven. 20, 30, 40, 60 d., 1 r. 50, 2 r.

Dr. Albert Schweitzer Commem. 20, 30, 40, 60 d. 1 r. 50, 2 r.

Tropical Birds. Postage 1, 2, 3, 4, 5, 10 d.; Air 2, 3 r.

Paintings by French Artists. Postage 1, 2, 3, 4, 5, 10 d.; Air 2, 3 r.

Paintings by Modern Artists. Postage 1, 2, 3, 4, 5, 10 d.; Air 2, 3 r.

Paintings by Degas. Postage 1, 2, 3, 4, 5, 10 d.; Air 2, 3 r.

Paintings by Titian. Postage 1, 2, 3, 4, 5, 10 d.; Air 2, 3 r.

Paintings by Renoir. Postage 1, 2, 3, 4, 5, 10 d.; Air 2, 3 r.

Space Flight of "Apollo 15" Postage 25, 40, 50, 60 d., 1 r.; Air 6 r.

"Philatokyo" Stamp Exhibition, Tokyo. Stamps. Postage 10, 15, 20, 30, 35, 50, 60, 80 d.; Air 1, 2 r.

Tropical Birds. Postage 1, 2, 3, 5, 7, 10, 12, 15, 20, 25, 30, 40 d.; Air 50, 80 d., 1, 3 r.

Paintings depicting Venus. Postage 1, 2, 3, 4, 5, 10 d.; Air 2, 3 r.

13th World Scout Jamboree, Asagiri, Japan. Scouts. Postage 1, 2, 3, 5, 7, 10, 12, 15, 20, 25, 30, 35, 40, 50, 65, 80 d.; Air 1, 1 r. 25, 1 r. 50, 2 r.

Lions International Clubs. Optd. on 1971 Famous Paintings issue. Air 25, 30, 35, 50, 70, 85 d., 1, 2 r.

13th World Scout Jamboree, Asagiri, Japan. Japanese Paintings. Postage 20, 30, 40, 60, 75 d.; Air 3 r.

25th Anniv. of U.N.I.C.E.F. Optd. on 1971 Scout Jamboree (paintings) issue. Postage 20, 30, 40, 60, 75 d.; Air 3 r.

Christmas 1971. (1st series. Plain frames.) Portraits of Popes. Postage 1, 2, 3, 4, 5, 10 d.; Air 2, 3 r.

Modern Cars. Postage 10, 15, 25, 40, 50 d.; Air 3 r.

Olympic Games, Munich (1972). Show-jumping. Embossed on gold foil. Air 20 r.

Exploration of Outer Space. Postage 15, 25, 50, 60, 70 d.; Air 5 r.

Royal Visit of Queen Elizabeth II to Japan. Postage 1, 2, 3, 4, 5, 10 d.; Air 2, 3 r.

Meeting of Pres. Nixon and Emperor Hirohito of Japan in Alaska. Design as 3 r. value of 1970 Eisenhower issue but value changed and optd. with commemorative inscr. Air 5 r. (silver opt.), 5r. (gold opt.).

"Apollo" Astronauts. Postage 5, 20, 35, 40, 50 d.; Air 1, 2, 3 r.

Discoverers of the Universe. Astronomers and Space-scientists. Postage 5, 10, 15, 20, 25, 30 d.; Air 2, 5 r.

"ANPHILEX 71" Stamp Exhibition, New York. Air 2 r. 50.

Christmas 1971. Portraits of Popes (2nd series. Ornamental frames). Postage 1, 2, 3, 4, 5, 10 d.; Air 2, 3 r.

Royal Silver Wedding of Queen Elizabeth II and Prince Philip (1972). Air 1, 2, 3 r.

Space Flight of "Apollo 16". Postage 20, 30, 40, 50, 60 d.; Air 3, 4 r.

Fairy Tales. "Baron Munchhausen" stories. Postage 1, 2, 4, 5, 10 d.; Air 3 r.

World Fair, Philadelphia (1976). Paintings. Postage 25, 50, 75 d.; Air 5 r.

Fairy Tales. Stories of the Brothers Grimm. Postage 1, 2, 4, 5, 10 d.; Air 3 r.

European Tour of Emperor Hirohito of Japan. Postage 1, 2, 4, 5, 10 d.; Air 6 r.

13th World Scout Jamboree, Asagiri, Japan. Postage 5, 10, 15, 20, 25 d.; Air 5 r.

Winter Olympic Games, Sapporo, Japan (1972). Postage 5, 10, 15, 20, 25 d.; Air 5 r.

Olympic Games, Munich (1972). Postage 5, 10, 15, 20, 25 d.; Air 5 r.

"Japanese Life". Postage 10 d. × 4, 20 d. × 4. 30 d. × 4, 40 d. × 4, 50 d. × 4; Air 3 r. × 4.

Space Flight of "Apollo 15". Postage 5, 10, 15, 20, 25, 50 d.; Air 1, 2, 3, 5 r.

"Soyuz 11" Disaster. Air 50 d., 1 r., 1 r. 50.

"The Future in Space". Postage 5, 10, 15, 20, 25, 50 d.

2500th Anniv. of Persian Empire. Postage 10, 20, 30, 40, 50 d., Air 3 r.

Cats. Postage 10, 15, 20, 25 d.; Air 50 d., 1 r.

50th Anniv. of Tutankhamun Tomb Discovery. Postage 1, 2, 3, 4, 5, 6, 7, 8, 9, 10, 11, 12, 13, 14, 15, 16 d.; Air 1 r × 4.

400th Birth Anniv. of Johannes Kepler (astronomer). Postage 50 d.; Air 5 r. Famous Men. Air. 1 r × 5.

**1972.**

150th Death Anniv. of Napoleon (1971). Postage 10, 20, 30, 40 d.; Air 1, 2, 3, 4 r.

1st Death Anniv. of General De Gaule. Postage 10, 20, 30, 40 d.; Air 1, 2, 3, 4 r.

Wild Animals (1st series). Postage 5, 10, 15, 20, 25, 30, 35, 40 d.

Tropical Fish. Postage 5, 10, 15, 20, 25 d.; Air 50, 75 d., 1 r.

Famous Musicians. Postage 5 d. × 3, 10 d. × 3, 15 d. × 3, 20 d. × 3, 25 d. × 3, 30 d. × 3, 35 d. × 3, 40 d. × 3.

Easter. Postage 5, 10, 15, 20, 25 d.; Air 5 r.

Wild Animals (2nd series). Postage 5, 10, 15, 20, 25 d.; Air 5 r.

"Tour de France" Cycle Race. Postage 5, 10, 15, 20, 25, 30, 35, 40, 45, 50, 55 d.; Air 60, 65, 70, 75, 80, 85, 90, 95 d., 1 r.

Many other issues were released between 1 September 1971, and 1 August 1972, but their authenticity has been denied by the Ajman Postmaster-General. Certain issues of 1967-69, exist overprinted to commemorate other events but the Postmaster-General states that these are unofficial.

Ajman joined the United Arab Emirates on 1 August 1972 and Ministry of Communications assumed responsibility for the postal services. Further stamps inscribed "Ajman" issued after that date were released without authority and had no validity.

## ALAND ISLANDS Pt. 11

Aland is an autonomous province of Finland. From 1984 separate stamps were issued for the area although stamps of Finland could also still be used there.

On 1 January 1993 Aland assumed control of its own postal service and Finnish stamps ceased to be valid there.

100 pennia = 1 markka.

1. Fishing Boat.

2. "Pommern" (barque) and Car Ferries, Mariehamn West Harbour.

**1984.**

1 1 10 p. mauve .. .. 10 10
2 20 p. green .. .. 10 10
3 50 p. green .. .. 10 10
4 – 1 m. green .. .. 25 20
5 1 1 m. 10 blue .. .. 35 20
6 1 m. 20 black .. 35 20
7 1 m. 30 green .. 50 20
8 – 1 m. 40 multicoloured 35 30
9a – 1 m. 50 multicoloured 35 30
10 – 1 m. 90 multicoloured 45 40
12 – 3 m. blue, green & blk 70 70
14 – 10 m. black, chestnut and brown .. 2·25 2·25
15 – 13 m. multicoloured .. 3·00 3·00

DESIGNS—20×29 mm: 1 m. 50, Midsummer pole, Storby village. 21×31 mm: 13 m. Rug, 1793. 26×32 mm: 3 m. Map of Aland Islands. 30×20 mm: 1 m. Farjsund Bridge. 31×21 mm: 1 m. 40, Aland flag; 1 m. 90, Mariehamn Town Hall. 32×26 mm: 10 m. Seal of Aland showing St. Olaf (patron saint).

**1984.** Seafaring and Shipping.

16. 2. 2 m. multicoloured .. 2·75 2·75

3. Grove of Ashes and Hazels.

4. Map, Compass and Measuring Instrument.

**1985.** Aland Scenes. Multicoloured.

17. 2 m. Type 3 .. .. .. 60 60
18. 5 m. Kokar Church and shore .. .. .. 1·25 1·25
19. 8 m. Windmill and farm .. 1·75 1·75

**1986.** Nordic Orienteering Championships, Aland.

20. 4. 1 m. 60 multicoloured .. 1·25 1·25

5. Clay Hands and Burial Mounds, Skamkulla.

6. "Onnigeby" (drawing, Victor Westerholm).

**1986.** Archaeology. Multicoloured.

21 1 m. 60 Type 5 .. .. 40 40
22 2 m. 20 Bronze staff from Finby and Apostles .. 60 60
23 20 m. Monument at ancient court site, Saltvik, and court in session (horiz) .. 4·25 4·25

**1986.** Centenary of Onnigeby Artists' Colony.

24. 6. 3 m. 70 multicoloured .. 1·40 1·40

7. Eiders.

8. Firemen in Horse-drawn Cart.

**1987.** Birds. Multicoloured.

25. 1 m. 70 Type 7 .. .. 4·00 2·00
26. 2 m. 30 Tufted ducks .. 70 70
27. 12 m. Velvet scoters .. 3·00 3·00

**1987.** Centenary of Mariehamn Fire Brigade.

28. 8. 7 m. multicoloured .. 2·75 2·75

9. Meeting and Item 3 of Report.

10. Loading Mail Barrels at Eckero.

**1987.** 70th Anniv. of Aland Municipalities Meeting, Finstrom.

29. 9. 1 m. 70 multicoloured .. 1·25 1·25

**1988.** 350th Anniv. of Postal Service.

30. 10. 1 m. 80 multicoloured .. 1·40 1·40

11. Ploughing with Horses.

12. Baltic Galeass "Albanus".

**1988.** Centenary of Agricultural Education in Aland.

31. 11. 2 m. 20 multicoloured .. 1·40 1·40

**1988.** Sailing Ships. Multicoloured.

32 1 m. 80 Type 12 .. .. 1·40 1·40
33 2 m. 40 Schooner "Ingrid" (horiz) .. .. .. 2·40 2·40
34 11 m. Barque "Pamir" (horiz) .. .. .. 3·75 3·75

13 St. Olaf's Church, Jomala

14 Elder-flowered Orchid

**1988.**

35 13 1 m. 40 multicoloured .. 1·25 1·25

**1989.** Orchids. Multicoloured.

36 1 m. 50 Type 14 .. .. 1·25 1·25
37 2 m. 50 Narrow-leaved helleborine .. .. 1·25 1·25
38 14 m. Lady's slipper .. 3·75 3·75

15 Teacher and Pupils

16 St. Michael's Church, Finstrom

**1989.** 350th Anniv of First Aland School, Saltvik.

39 15 1 m. 90 multicoloured .. 1·25 1·25

**1989.**

40 16 1 m. 50 multicoloured .. 1·25 1·25

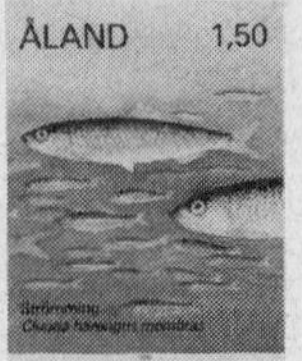
17 Baltic Herring

18 St. Andrew's Church, Lumparland

**1990.** Fishes. Multicoloured.

41 1 m. 50 Type 17 .. .. 60 60
42 2 m. Northern pike .. 75 75
43 2 m. 70 European flounder 1·00 1·00

**1990.**

44 18 1 m. 70 multicoloured .. 60 60

19 "St. Catherine" (fresco, St. Anna's Church, Kumlinge)

20 West European Hedgehog

**1990.**

45 19 2 m. multicoloured .. 75 75

**1991.** Mammals. Multicoloured.

46 1 m. 60 Type 20 .. .. 50 50
47 2 m. 10 Eurasian red squirrel .. .. .. 75 75
48 2 m. 90 Roe deer .. .. 1·00 1·00

22 Canoeing

23 "League of Nations Meeting, Geneva, 1921" (print by F. Rackwitz)

**1991.** Nordic Countries' Postal Co-operation. Tourism. Multicoloured.

50 2 m. 10 Type 22 .. .. 75 75
51 2 m. 90 Cycling .. .. 1·00 1·00

**1991.** 70th Anniv of Aland Autonomy.

52 23 16 m. multicoloured .. 5·25 5·25

24 St. Mathias's Church, Vardo

25 Von Knorring (after Karl Jansson)

**1991.**

53 24 1 m. 80 multicoloured .. 60 60

**1992.** Birth Bicentenary of Rev. Frans Peter von Knorring (social reformer).

54 25 2 klass (1 m. 60) mult .. 50 50

26 Barque "Herzogen Cecilie" and Wheat Transport Route Map

27 Ranno Lighthouse

**1992.** 48th International Association of Cape Horners Congress, Mariehamn.

55 26 1 klass (2 m. 10) mult .. 65 65

**1992.** Lighthouses. Multicoloured.

56 2 m. 10 Type 27 .. .. 65 65
57 2 m. 10 Salskar .. .. 65 65
58 2 m. 10 Lagskar .. .. 65 65
59 2 m. 10 Market .. .. 65 65

28 "Lemland Landscape"

**1992.** Birth Centenary of Joel Pettersson (painter). Multicoloured.

60 2 m. 90 Type 28 .. .. 75 75
61 16 m. "Self-portrait" .. 4·00 4·00

29 Delegates processing to Church Service

30 St. Catherine's Church, Hammarland

**1992.** 70th Anniv of First Aland Provincial Parliament.

62 29 3 m. 40 multicoloured .. 85 85

**1992.**

63 30 1 m. 80 multicoloured .. 45 45

31 Arms

32 Fiddler

**1993.** Postal Autonomy.

64 31 1 m. 60 multicoloured .. 40 40

**1993.** Nordic Countries' Postal Co-operation. Tourism. Exhibits from Jan Karlsgarden Open-air Museum.

66 32 2 m. red, pink & black .. 50 50
67 – 2 m. 30 blue, blk & azure 55 55

DESIGN—HORIZ: 2 m. 30, Boathouse.

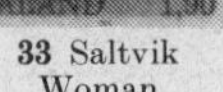
33 Saltvik Woman

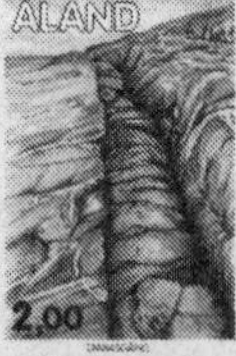
34 Diabase Dyke, Sottunga

**1993.** Costumes. Multicoloured.

68 1 m. 90 Type 33 .. .. 45 45
69 3 m. 50 Eckero and Brando women and Mariehamn couple .. .. .. 85 85
70 17 m. Finstrom couple .. 4·00 4·00

**1993.** Aland Bedrock (1st series). Mult.

71 2 m. Type **34** .. .. 50 50
72 2 m. 70 Pillow lava, Kumlinge .. .. 65 65
73 6 m. Folded gneiss .. 1·50 1·50
See also Nos. 75/7.

**35** Mary Magdalene Church, Sottunga

**36** Boulder Field, Dano Gamlan

**1993.**

74 **35** 1 m. 80 multicoloured .. 45 45

**1994.** Aland Bedrock (2nd series). Mult.

75 10 p. Type **36** .. .. 10 10
76 1 m. 60 Drumlin (hillock), Markusbole .. .. 40 40
77 2 m. 90 The Red Cow (islet), Lumparn .. .. 70 70

**37** Glanville's Fritillary ("Melitaea cinxia")

**38** Genetic Diagram

**1994.** Butterflies. Multicoloured.

78 2 m. 30 Type **37** .. .. 60 60
79 2 m. 30 "Quercusia querqus" .. .. 60 60
80 2 m. 30 Clouded apollo ("Parnassius mnemosyne") .. .. 60 60
81 2 m. 30 "Hesperia comma" 60 60

**1994.** Europa. Medical Discoveries. Mult.

82 2 m. 30 Type **38** (discovery of Von Willebrand's disease (hereditary blood disorder)) .. .. 60 60
83 2 m. 90 Molecular diagram (purification of heparin by Erik Jorpes) .. 75 75

**39** Comb Ceramic and Pitted Ware Pottery

**40** St. John the Baptist's Church, Sund

**1994.** The Stone Age.

84 **39** 2 m. 40 brown .. .. 65 65
85 – 2 m. 80 blue .. .. 75 75
86 – 18 m. green .. .. 4·75 4·75
DESIGNS—VERT. 2 m. 80, Stone tools. HORIZ. 18 m. Canoe and tent by river (reconstruction of Stone-age village, Langbergsoda).

**1994.**

87 **40** 2 m. multicoloured .. 50 50

**41** Pitcher of Kallskar

**42** Skuta

**1995.** Traces of Ice Age. Multicoloured.

88 2 m. 30 Type **41** .. .. 60 60
89 3 m. 40 Erratic boulder, Torsskar, Kokar Osterbygge (horiz) .. 90 90
90 7 m. Pothole, Bano, Foglo (horiz) .. .. .. 1·90 1·90

**1995.** Cargo Sailing Ships. Multicoloured.

91 2 m. 30 Type **42** .. .. 70 70
92 2 m. 30 Well-boat (Sump) 70 70
93 2 m. 30 Farm boat (Storbat) .. .. 70 70
94 2 m. 30 Jakt .. .. 70 70

**43** National Colours and E.U. Emblem

**44** Doves and Cliffs

**1995.** Admission of Aland Islands to European Union.

95 **43** 2 m. 90 multicoloured .. 90 90

**1995.** Europa. Peace and Freedom. Mult.

96 2 m. 80 Type **44** .. .. 85 85
97 2 m. 80 Dove, night sky and island .. .. .. 85 85

**45** Golf

**46** Race

**1995.** Nordic Countries' Postal Co-operation. Tourism. With service indicator. Mult.

98 2 klass (2 m.) Type **45** .. 60 60
99 1 klass (2 m. 30) Sport fishing .. .. .. 70 70

**1995.** Optimist World Dinghy Championships, Mariehamn.

100 **46** 3 m. 40 multicoloured 1·00 1·00

**47** St. George's Church, Geta

**48** St. Olaf

**1995.**

101 **47** 2 m. multicoloured .. 60 60

**1995.**

102 **48** 4 m. 30 multicoloured .. 1·25 1·25

**49** Fish holding Flag in Mouth ("Greetings from Aland")

**50** Landing on Branch

**1996.** Greetings Stamps. With service indicator. Multicoloured.

103 1 klass Type **49** .. 70 70
104 1 klass Bird holding flower in beak ("Congratulations") .. .. 70 70

**1996.** The Eagle Owl. Multicoloured.

105 2 m. 40 Type **50** .. .. 75 75
106 2 m. 40 Perched on branch 75 75
107 2 m. 40 Adult owl .. 75 75
108 2 m. 40 Juvenile owl .. 75 75
Nos. 105/6 form a composite design.

**51** Sally Salminen (novelist)

**1996.** Europa. Famous Women. Mult.

109 2 m. 80 Type **51** .. .. 75 75
110 2 m. 90 Fanny Sundstrom (politician) .. .. 80 80

**52** Choir

**53** "Haircut"

**1996.** "Aland 96" Song and Music Festival, Mariehamn.

111 **52** 2 m. 40 multicoloured .. 65 65

**1996.** 150th Birth Anniv of Karl Jansson (painter).

112 **53** 18 m. multicoloured .. 5·00 5·00

**54** "Trilobita asaphus"

**55** Brando Church

**1996.** Fossils. Multicoloured.

113 40 p. Type **54** .. .. 10 10
114 9 m. "Gastropoda euomophalus" .. .. 2·50 2·50

**1996.**

115 **55** 2 m. multicoloured .. 55 55

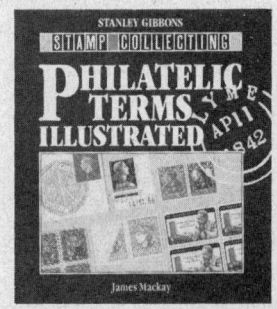

## ALAOUITES Pt. 19

A coastal district of Syria, placed under French mandate in 1920. Became the Republic of Latakia in 1930. Incorporated with Syria in 1937

100 centimes = 1 piastre.

**1925.** Stamps of France surch **ALAOUITES** and value in French and Arabic.

1 **11** 0 p. 10 on 2 c. purple .. 1·50 2·25
2 **18** 0 p. 25 on 5 c. orange .. 1·75 2·00
3 **15** 0 p. 75 on 15 c. green .. 2·50 2·50
4 **18** 1 p. on 20 c. brown .. 1·60 2·25
5 1 p. 25 on 25 c. blue .. 2·25 2·50
6 1 p. 50 on 30 c. red .. 6·25 6·75
7 2 p. on 35 c. violet .. 1·40 2·25
8 **13** 2 p. on 40 c. red and blue 2·75 3·00
9 2 p. on 45 c. green & blue 6·25 6·75
10 3 p. on 60 c. violet & blue 3·00 3·75
11 **15** 3 p. on 60 c. violet .. 6·50 6·75
12 4 p. on 85 c. red .. 1·40 1·75
13 **13** 5 p. on 1 f. red & yellow 4·25 4·75
14 10 p. on 2 f. orange & grn 5·00 5·75
15 25 p. on 5 f. blue and buff 7·25 8·00

**1925.** "Pasteur" issue of France surch **ALAOUITES** and value in French and Arabic.

16 **30** 0 p. 50 on 10 c. green .. 1·50 1·75
17 0 p. 75 on 15 c. green .. 1·60 1·75
18 1 p. 50 on 30 c. red .. 1·50 2·25
19 2 p. on 45 c. red .. 2·25 2·25
20 2 p. 50 on 50 c. blue .. 2·25 2·50
21 4 p. on 75 c. blue .. 2·75 3·25

**1925.** Air. Stamps of France optd **ALAOUITES Avion** and value in French and Arabic.

22 **13** 2 p. on 40 c. red and blue 6·00 6·75
23 3 p. on 60 c. violet & blue 8·50 10·50
24 5 p. on 1 f. red & yellow 6·25 6·50
25 10 p. on 2 f. orange & grn 6·00 6·75

**1925.** Pictorial stamps of Syria (1925) optd **ALAOUITES** in French and Arabic.

26 0 p. 10 violet .. .. 45 1·25
27 0 p. 25 black .. .. 70 1·40
28 0 p. 50 green .. .. 75 65
29 0 p. 75 red .. .. 80 1·50
30 1 p. purple .. .. 1·40 1·25
31 1 p. 25 green .. .. 1·25 1·50
32 1 p. 50 pink .. .. 1·25 1·10
33 2 p. brown .. .. 1·25 65
34 2 p. 50 blue .. .. 1·75 1·90
35 3 p. brown .. .. 1·10 95
36 5 p. violet .. .. 1·10 1·25
37 10 p. purple .. .. 1·90 1·40
38 25 p. blue .. .. 2·75 3·75

**1925.** Air. Nos. 33 and 35/37 optd **AVION** in French and Arabic.

40 2 p. brown .. .. 1·25 2·25
41 3 p. brown .. .. 1·00 2·25
42 5 p. violet .. .. 1·25 2·25
43 10 p. purple .. .. 1·10 2·25

**1926.** Air. Air stamps of Syria with airplane overprint optd **ALAOUITES** in French and Arabic.

44 2 p. brown .. .. 2·00 3·00
45 3 p. brown .. .. 2·00 3·00
46 5 p. violet .. .. 2·50 3·00
47 10 p. purple .. .. 2·00 2·75

See also Nos. 59/60 and 63.

**1926.** Pictorial stamps of 1925 surcharged.

53 05 on 0 p. 10 violet .. 45 1·25
54 2 p. on 1 p. 25 green .. 9·50 5·00
48 3 p. 50 on 0 p. 75 red .. 1·25 75
49 4 p. on 0 p. 25 black .. 1·25 80
56 4 p. 50 on 0 p. 75 red .. 3·25 2·00
50 6 p. on 2 p. 50 blue .. 1·60 70
57 7 p. 50 on 2 p. 50 blue .. 2·50 1·10
51 12 p. on 1 p. 25 green .. 1·60 1·40
58 15 p. on 25 p. blue .. 5·00 3·50
52 20 p. on 1 p. 25 green .. 1·50 2·25

**1929.** Air. (a) Pictorial stamps of Syria optd with airplane and **ALAOUITES** in French and Arabic.

59 0 p. 50 green .. .. 1·50 2·25
60 1 p. purple .. .. 4·50 5·00
61 25 p. blue .. .. 20·00 25·00

(b) Nos. 54 and 58 of Alaouites optd with airplane

62 2 p. on 1 p. 25 green .. 2·25 2·50
63 15 p. on 25 p. blue .. 22·00 26·00

### POSTAGE DUE STAMPS

**1925.** Postage Due stamps of France surch **ALAOUITES** and value in French and Arabic.

D26 **D 11** 0 p. 50 on 10 c. brn 2·25 3·00
D27 1 p. on 20 c. green .. 2·00 3·00
D28 2 p. on 30 c. red .. 2·00 3·00
D29 3 p. on 50 c. purple 2·00 3·00
D30 5 p. on 1 f. purple on yellow .. 2·00 3·00

**1925.** Postage Due stamps of Syria (Nos. D192/6) optd **ALAOUITES** in French and Arabic.

D44 0 p. 50 brown on yellow .. 45 1·60
D45 1 p. red on red .. .. 65 1·75
D46 2 p. black on blue .. 95 2·25
D47 3 p. brown on red .. 1·25 2·75
D48 5 p. black on green .. 1·90 3·50

For later issues see **LATAKIA**.

## ALBANIA Pt. 3

Albania, formerly part of the Turkish Empire, was declared independent on 28 November 1912, and this was recognised by Turkey in treaty of 30 May 1913. After chaotic conditions during and after the First World War a republic was established in 1925. Three years later the country became a kingdom. From 7 April 1939 until December 1944, Albania was occupied, firstly by the Italians and then by the Germans. Following liberation a republic was set up in 1946.

1913. 40 paras = 1 piastre or grosch.
1913. 100 qint = 1 franc.
1947. 100 qint = 1 lek.

**1913.** Various types of Turkey optd. with double-headed eagle and **SHQIPENIA.**

3 **28** 2 pa. green (No. 271) .. £325 £300
4 5 pa. brown (No. 261) .. £325 £325
2 **25** 10 pa. green (No. 252) .. £550 £500
5 **28** 10 pa. green (No. 262) .. £275 £180
12 10 pa. green (No. 289) .. £550 £500
11 10 pa. on 20 pa. red .. £900 £900
6 20 pa. red (No. 263) .. £160 £140
13 20 pa. red (No. 290) .. £550 £500
7 1 pi. blue (No. 264) .. £180 £180
14a 1 pi. blue (No. 291) .. £1300 £1200
15 1 pi. black on red (No. D 288) .. .. £2250 £1900
8 2 pi. black (No. 265) .. £350 £325
14b 2 pi. black (No. 292) ..
1 **25** 2½ pi. brown (No. 239) £650 £500
9 **28** 5 pi. purple (No. 267) .. £1000 £850
10 10 pi. red (No. 268) .. £3250 £3000

Postat e Qeverries së Përkohëshme — të Shqipënies — 10 para

2.

**1913.**

16. **2.** 10 pa. violet .. .. 14·50 11·00
17. 20 pa. red and grey .. 16·00 14·00
18. 1 g. grey .. .. 16·00 16·00
19. 2 g. blue and violet .. 18·00 15·00
20. 5 g. violet and blue .. 25·00 22·00
21. 10 g. blue and violet .. 25·00 22·00

20 PARA 20 — 3.

SHQIPENIA E LIRE — GJERGJ KASTRIOTI — 1 FR. 1 — 4. Castriota Skanderbeg.

**1913.** Independence Anniversary.

22. **3.** 10 pa. black and green .. 4·75 3·25
23. 20 pa. black and red .. 6·00 4·75
24. 30 pa. black and violet .. 6·00 4·75
25. 1 g. black and blue .. 8·75 6·00
26. 2 g. black .. .. 12·50 8·25

**1913.**

27. **4.** 2 q. brown and yellow .. 1·60 1·60
28. 5 q. green and yellow .. 1·60 1·60
29. 10 q. red .. .. 1·60 1·60
30. 25 q. blue .. .. 1·60 1·60
31. 50 q. mauve and red .. 3·75 3·75
32. 1 f. brown .. .. 12·50 10·50

**1914.** Arrival of Prince William of Wied. Optd. **7 Mars 1461 RROFTE MBRETI 1914.**

33. **4.** 2 q. brown and yellow .. 35·00 27·00
34. 5 q. green and yellow .. 35·00 27·00
35. 10 q. red .. .. 35·00 27·00
36. 25 q. blue .. .. 35·00 27·00
37. 50 q. mauve and red .. 35·00 27·00
38. 1 f. brown.. .. 35·00 27·00

**1914.** Surch.

40. **4.** 5 pa. on 2 q. brown & yell. 2·25 2·25
41. 10 pa. on 5 q. green & yell. 2·25 2·25
42. 20 pa. on 10 q. red .. 3·75 3·00
43. 1 g. on 25 q. blue .. 4·00 3·75
44. 2 g. on 50 q. mauve & red 4·75 4·75
45. 5 g. on 1 f. brown .. 16·00 11·50

**1914.** Valona Provisional Issue. Optd. **POSTE D'ALBANIE** and Turkish inscr. in circle with star in centre.

45a. **4.** 2 q. brown and yellow .. £225 £225
45b. 5 q. green and yellow ..
45c. 10q. red and rose .. 10·50 10·50
45d. 25 q. blue .. .. 10·50 10·50
45e. 50 q. mauve and red .. 10·50 10·50
45f. 1 f. brown .. .. £550
45g. 5 pa. on 2 q. br. & yell.. 45·00 45·00
45h. 10 pa. on 5 q. grn. & yell. 75·00 75·00
45i. 20 pa. on 10 q. red & rose 22·00 22·00
45j. 1 gr. on 25 q. blue .. 10·50 10·50
45k. 2 gr. on 50 q. mve. & red 22·00 22·00
45l. 5 gr. on 1 f. brown .. 25·00 25·00

KORÇE — SHQIPERIE — VETQEVERITARE — 25 CTS — 11.

POSTA — Shkodra — SHQIPNIS — 12.

**1917.** Inscribed "SHQIPERIE KORCE VETQEVERITARE" or "REPUBLIKA KORCE SHQIPETARE" or "QARKU-POSTES-I-KORCES".

75. **11.** 1 c. brown and green .. 16·00 10·50
76. 2 c. red and green .. 16·00 10·50
77. 3 c. grey and green .. 16·00 10·50
78. 5 c. green and black .. 12·50 7·25
79. 10 c. red and black .. 12·50 7·25
72. 25 c. blue and black .. 12·50 7·25
80. 50 c. violet and black .. 12·50 9·00
81. 1 f. brown and black .. 12·50 9·00

**1919.** Fiscal stamps used by the Austrians in Albania. Handstamped with control.

96. **12.** (2) q. on 2 h. brown .. 7·25 7·25
97. 5 q. on 16 h. green .. 7·25 7·25
98. 10 q. on 8 h. red .. 7·25 7·25
86. 25 q. on 64 h. blue .. 7·25 7·25
93. 50 q. on 32 h. violet .. 7·25 7·25
101. 1 f. on 1.28 k. brn. on blue 9·75 9·75

Three sets may be made of this issue according to whether the handstamped control is a date, a curved comet or a comet with straight tail.

**1919.** No. 43 optd. **SHKODER 1919.**

103. **4.** 1 g. on 25 q. blue .. 5·50 5·50

**1919.** Fiscal stamps surch. **POSTAT SHQIPTARE** and new value.

104. **12.** 10 q. on 2 h. brown .. 5·50 5·50
111. 10 q. on 8 h. red .. 5·50 5·50
112. 15 q. on 8 h. red .. 5·50 5·50
113. 20 q. on 16 h. green .. 5·50 5·50
113a. 25 q. on 32 h. violet .. 5·50 5·50
107. 25 q. on 64 h. blue .. 5·50 5·50
108. 50 q. on 32 h. violet .. 5·50 5·50
113b. 50 q. on 64 h. blue .. 14·50 14·50
113c. 1 f. on 96 h. orange .. 5·50 5·50
113d. 2 f. on 160 h. violet .. 10·50 10·50

SHQIPENIE — 5 QINTAR 5 — 17. Prince William I.

POSTE SHQIPTARE — 10 — 19. Skanderbeg.

**1920.** Optd. with double-headed eagle and **SHKODRA** or surch. also.

114. **17.** 1 q. grey .. .. 35·00 45·00
115. 2 q. on 10 q. red .. 7·25 9·00
116. 5 q. on 10 q. red .. 7·25 9·00
117. 10 q. red .. .. 7·25 9·00
118. 20 q. brown .. .. 25·00 32·00
119. 25 q. blue .. .. £225 £375
120. 25 q. on 10 q. red .. 7·25 9·00
121. 50 q. violet .. .. 29·00 35·00
122. 50 q. on 10 q. red .. 7·25 9·00

**1920.** Optd. with posthorn.

123. **19.** 2 q. orange .. .. 10·50 9·00
124. 5 q. green .. .. 14·50 16·00
125. 10 q. red .. .. 29·00 30·00
126. 25 q. blue .. .. 60·00 30·00
127. 50 q. green .. .. 10·50 10·50
128. 1 f. mauve .. .. 10·50 10·50

Stamps as Type **19** also exist optd. **BESA** meaning "Loyalty".

**1922.** No. 123 surch. with value in frame.

143. **19.** 1 q. on 2 q. orange .. 7·25 3·00

5 QIND — POSTA SHQYPTARE — 5 QIND — 24.

**1922.** Views.

144. **24.** 2 q. orange (Gjinokaster) 1·75 1·75
145. 5 q. green (Kanina) .. 1·25 1·25
146. 10 q. red (Berat) .. 1·25 1·25
147. 25 q. blue (Veziri Bridge) 1·25 1·25
148. 50 q. turquoise (Rozafat) 1·25 1·25
149. 1 f. violet (Korce) .. 1·60 1·60
150. 2 f. olive (Durres) .. 5·50 5·50

**1924.** Opening of National Assembly. Optd. **TIRANE KALLNUER 1924** in frame with **Mbledhje Kushtetuese** above.

151. **24.** 2 q. orange .. .. 10·50 7·25
152. 5 q. green .. .. 10·50 7·25
153. 10 q. red .. .. 10·50 7·25
154. 25 q. blue .. .. 10·50 7·25
155. 50 q. turquoise .. 10·50 7·25

**1924.** No. 144 surch. with value and bars.

156. **24.** 1 on 2 q. orange .. 5·50 5·50

**1924.** Red Cross. (a) Surch. with small red cross and premium.

157. **24.** 5 q. + 5 q. green .. 14·50 10·50
158. 10 q. + 5 q. red .. 14·50 10·50
159. 25 q. + 5 q. blue .. 14·50 10·50
160. 50 q. + 5 q. turquoise 14·50 10·50

(b) Nos. 157/60 with further surch. of large red cross and premium.

161 **24** 5 q.+5 q.+5 q. green 16·00 10·50
162 10 q.+5 q.+5 q. red .. 16·00 10·50
163 25 q.+5 q.+5 q. blue 16·00 10·50
164 50 q.+5 q.+5 q. green 16·00 10·50

**1925.** Return of Government to Capital. Optd. **Triumf' i. legalitetit 24 Dhetuer 1924.**

164a. **24.** 1 on 2 q. orange (No. 156) 5·50 4·75
165. 2 q. orange .. .. 5·50 4·75
166. 5 q. green .. .. 5·50 4·75
167. 10 q. red .. .. 5·50 4·75
168. 25 q. blue .. .. 5·50 4·75
169. 50 q. turquoise .. 7·25 5·50
170. 1 f. violet .. .. 7·25 7·25

**1925.** Proclamation of Republic. Optd. **Republika Shqiptare 21 Kallnduer 1925.**

171. **24.** 1 on 2 q. orange (No. 156) 5·50 4·00
172. 2 q. orange .. .. 5·50 4·00
173. 5 q. green .. .. 5·50 4·00
174. 10 q. red .. .. 5·50 4·00
175. 25 q. blue .. .. 5·50 4·00
176. 50 q. turquoise .. 5·50 4·00
177. 1 f. violet .. .. 7·25 5·50

**1925.** Optd. **Republika Shqiptare.**

178. **24.** 1 on 2 q. orange (No. 156) 1·50 1·40
179. 2 q. orange .. .. 1·50 1·40
180. 5 q. green .. .. 1·50 1·40
181. 10 q. red .. .. 1·50 1·40
182. 25 q. blue .. .. 1·50 1·40
183. 50 q. turquoise .. 1·50 1·40
184. 1 f. violet .. .. 4·25 3·75
185. 2 f. olive .. .. 5·00 3·75

POSTA AERORE — SHQYPTARE — 32.

**1925.** Air.

186. **32.** 5 q. green .. .. 3·00 3·00
187. 10 q. red .. .. 3·00 3·00
188. 25 q. blue .. .. 3·00 3·00
189. 50 q. green .. .. 5·50 5·50
190. 1 f. black and violet .. 9·00 9·00
191. 2 f. violet and olive .. 12·50 12·50
192. 3 f. green and brown .. 16·00 16·00

REP. SHQIPTARE — 1 QINDAR 1 — 33.

REPUBLIKA SHQIPTARE — 2 FR. AR. 2 — 34.

Pres. Ahmed Zogu, later King Zog I.

**1925.**

193. **33.** 1 q. orange .. .. 10 15
194. 2 q. brown .. .. 10 15
195. 5 q. green .. .. 10 15
196. 10 q. red .. .. 10 15
197. 15 q. brown .. .. 1·50 1·25
198. 25 q. blue .. .. 35 15
199. 50 q. turquoise.. .. 1·50 1·25
200. **34.** 1 f. blue and red .. 2·25 1·60
201. 2 f. orange and green .. 2·25 1·60
202. 3 f. purple and brown.. 5·50 4·25
203. 5 f. black and violet .. 7·25 6·00

**1927.** Air. Optd. **Rep. Shqiptare.**

204. **32.** 5 q. green .. .. 10·50 10·50
205. 10 q. red .. .. 10·50 10·50
206. 25 q. blue .. .. 9·50 9·50
207. 50 q. green .. .. 6·50 6·50
208. 1 f. black and violet .. 7·25 6·50
209. 2 f. violet and olive .. 11·50 10·50
210. 3 f. green and brown.. 16·00 14·50

**1927.** Optd. **A.Z.** and wreath.

211. **33.** 1 q. orange .. .. 1·10 90
212. 2 q. brown .. .. 45 25
213. 5 q. green .. .. 2·40 55
214. 10 q. red .. .. 45 35
215 15 q. brown .. .. 12·50 9·75
216. 25 q. blue .. .. 75 15
217. 50 q. turquoise.. .. 75 15
218. **34.** 1 f. blue and red .. 1·10 55
219. 2 f. orange and green .. 1·10 75
220. 3 f. purple and brown.. 1·75 1·50
221. 5 f. black and violet .. 3·25 2·50

**1928.** Air. Valona-Brindisi First Flight. Optd. **REP. SHQYPTARE Fluturim' i 1-ar Vlone-Brindisi 21.IV.1928.**

222. **32.** 5 q. green .. .. 9·00 10·50
223. 10 q. red .. .. 9·00 10·50
224. 25 q. blue .. .. 9·00 10·50
225. 50 q. green .. .. 14·50 17·00
226. 1 f. black and violet .. £100 £110
227. 2 f. violet and olive .. £100 £110
228. 3 f. green and brown .. £100 £110

**1928.** Surch. in figures and bars.

229. **33.** 1 on 10 q. red (No. 214) 1·10 35
230. 5 on 25 q. blue (No. 216) 1·10 35

Pres. Ahmed Zogu, later King Zog I.
39. 40.

**1928.** National Assembly. Optd. **Kujtim Mbledhjes Kushtetuese 25.8.28.**

231. 39. 1 q. brown 6·50 4·25
232. 2 q. grey 6·50 4·25
233. 5 q. green 6·50 4·25
234. 10 q. red 6·50 4·25
235. 15 q. brown 18·00 18·00
236. 25 q. blue 6·50 4·25
237. 50 q. lilac 8·00 6·50
238. 40. 1 f. black and blue 6·50 4·25

**1928.** Accession of King Zog I. Optd. **Mbretnia Shqiptare Zog I 1.IX.1928.**

239. 39. 1 q. brown 18·00 18·00
240. 2 q. grey 18·00 18·00
241. 5 q. green 14·50 14·50
242. 10 q. red 10·50 9·00
243. 15 q. brown 14·50 10·50
244. 25 q. blue 14·50 10·50
245. 50 q. lilac 14·50 12·50
246. 40. 1 f. black and blue 16·00 14·50
247. 2 f. black and green 16·00 14·50

**1928.** Optd. **Mbretnia-Shqiptare** only.

248. 39. 1 q. brown 1·10 75
249. 2 q. grey 1·10 55
250. 5 q. green 5·50 75
251. 10 q. red 1·10 55
252. 15 q. brown 22·00 14·50
253. 25 q. blue 1·10 55
254. 50 q. lilac 1·50 55
255. 40. 1 f. black and blue 2·50 2·25
256. 2 f. black and green 2·50 2·40
257. 3 f. olive and red 7·25 3·75
258. 5 f. black and violet 9·00 7·25

**1929.** Surch. **Mbr. Shqiptare** and new value.

259. 33. 1 on 50 q. turquoise 55 55
260. 5 on 25 q. blue 60 55
261. 15 on 10 q. red 1·00 85

**1929.** King Zog's 35th birthday. Optd. **RROFT-MBRETI 8.X.1929.**

262. 33. 1 q. orange 9·75 9·75
263. 2 q. brown 9·75 9·75
264. 5 q. green 9·75 9·75
265. 10 q. red 9·75 9·75
266. 25 q. blue 9·75 9·75
267. 50 q. green 10·50 10·50
268. 34. 1 f. blue and red 17·00 17·00
269. 2 f. orange and green 17·00 17·00

**1929.** Air. Optd. **Mbr. Shqiptare.**

270. 32. 5 q. green 9·00 10·50
271. 10 q. red 9·00 10·50
272. 25 q. blue 18·00 21·00
273. 50 q. green 50·00 60·00
274. 1 f. black and violet £225 £250
275. 2 f. violet and olive £275 £325
276. 3 f. green and brown £550 £650

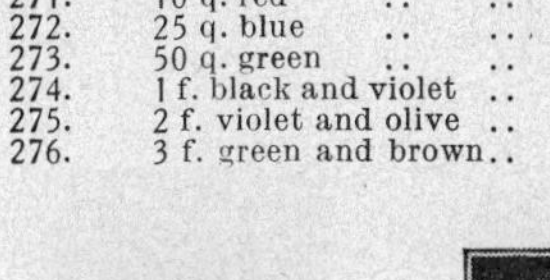

49. Lake of Butrinto.

50. King Zog I.

**1930.** 2nd Anniv. of Accession of King Zog I. Various designs.

277. 49. 1 q. grey 15 15
278. 2 q. orange 15 15
279. 50. 5 q. green 15 10
280. 10 q. red 45 45
281. 15 q. brown 55 45
282. 25 q. blue 55 45
283. 49. 50 q. turquoise 75 60
284. – 1 f. violet 1·60 80
285. – 2 f. blue 1·90 80
286. – 3 f. green 5·50 1·40
287. – 5 f. brown 7·25 3·50

DESIGNS—VERT. 1 f., 2 f. Zog Bridge. HORIZ. 3 f., 5 f. Old Wall.

53. Junkers F-13.

**1930.** Air. T **53** and similar view.

288. 53. 5 q. green 2·25 2·25
289. 15 q. red 2·25 2·25
290. 20 q. blue 2·25 2·25
291. 50 q. olive 3·75 3·25
292. – 1 f. blue 6·00 5·75
293. – 2 f. brown 22·00 22·00
294. – 3 f. violet 25·00 24·00

**1931.** Air. Optd. **TIRANE-ROME 6 KORRIK 1931.**

295. 53. 5 q. green 9·00 9·00
296. 15 q. red 9·00 9·00
297. 20 q. blue 9·00 9·00
298. 50 q. olive 9·00 9·00
299. – 1 f. blue 50·00 50·00
300. – 2 f. brown 50·00 50·00
301. – 3 f. violet 50·00 50·00

**1934.** 10th Anniv. of Revolution. Optd. **1924-24 Dhetuer-1934.**

302. 49. 1 q. grey 4·25 4·25
303. 2 q. orange 4·25 4·25
304. 50. 5 q. green 4·25 4·25
305. 10 q. red 4·25 4·25
306. 15 q. brown 4·25 4·25
307. 25 q. blue 4·25 4·25
308. 49. 50 q. turquoise 6·50 5·50
309. – 1 f. violet (No. 284) 9·00 8·00
310. – 2 f. blue (No. 285) 16·00 16·00
311. – 3 f. green (No. 286) 22·00 22·00

56. Horse and Flag of Skanderbeg.

57. Albania in chains.

**1937.** 25th Anniv. of Independence.

312. 56. 1 q. violet 15 15
313. 57. 2 q. brown 25 20
314. – 5 q. green 75 55
315. 56. 10 q. olive 75 75
316. 57. 15 q. red 1·10 90
317. – 25 q. blue 2·25 1·60
318. 56. 50 q. green 4·25 2·75
319. 57. 1 f. violet 10·00 5·00
320. – 2 f. brown 12·50 8·00

DESIGNS: 5 q., 25 q., 2 f. As Type **57**, but eagle with opened wings.

58. King Zog and Bride.

**1938.** Royal Wedding.

321. 58. 1 q. purple 15 15
322. 2 q. brown 15 20
323. 5 q. green 15 25
324. 10 q. olive 1·10 65
325. 15 q. red 1·10 1·00
326. 25 q. blue 3·75 1·40
327. 50 q. green 5·75 3·75
328. 1 f. violet 12·50 6·50

59. National Emblems.

60. King Zog.

**1938.** 10th Anniv. of Accession.

329. – 1 q. violet 15 50
330. 59. 2 q. red 25 35
331. – 5 q. green 75 40
332. 60. 10 q. brown 60 1·00
333. – 15 q. red 1·50 1·00
334. 60. 25 q. blue 1·75 1·10
335. 59. 50 q. black 7·25 2·40
336. 60. 1 f. green 12·50 5·50

DESIGN: 1 q., 5 q., 15 q. As Type **60**, but Queen's portrait.

## ITALIAN OCCUPATION

**1939.** Optd. **Mbledhja Kushtetuese 12—IV—1939 XVII.** (a) Postage.

337. 49. 1 q. grey 75 75
338. 2 q. orange 75 75
339. 50. 5 q. green 55 55
340. 10 q. red 55 55
341. 15 q. brown 1·50 1·25
342. 25 q. blue 1·75 1·60
343. 49. 50 q. turquoise 2·50 1·75
344. – 1 f. violet (No. 284) 3·75 2·25
345. – 2 f. blue (No. 285) 4·25 4·25
346. – 3 f. green 9·00 9·00
347. – 5 f. brown 10·50 10·50

(b) Air. Optd. as Nos. 337/47 or surch. also.

348. 53. 5 q. green 4·25 3·75
349. 15 q. red 3·00 3·75
350. 20 q. on 50 q. olive 7·25 7·25

62. Gheg.

64. Broken Columns, Botrint.

63. King Victor Emmanuel.

65. King and Fiat G18V Airplane.

**1939.**

351. 62. 1 q. blue (postage) 75 20
352. – 2 q. olive 75 35
353. – 3 q. brown 75 35
354. – 5 q. green 75 10
355. 63. 10 q. brown 75 10
356. 15 q. red 75 15
357. 25 q. blue 75 15
358. 30 q. violet 1·75 1·10
359. – 50 q. violet 2·50 90
360. – 65 q. brown 5·50 3·00
361. – 1 f. green 5·50 2·25
362. – 2 f. red 12·50 7·25
363. 64. 3 f. black 16·00 16·00
364. – 5 f. purple 25·00 18·00

365. 65. 20 q. brown (air) 45·00 10·50

DESIGNS—SMALL VERT. 2 q. Tosk man. 3 q. Gheg woman. 5 q., 65 q. Profile of King Victor Emmanuel. 50 q. Tosk woman. LARGE HORIZ. 1 f. Hillside landscape. 2 f. Veziri Bridge. 5 f. Amphitheatre Ruins, Berat.

66. Sheep Farming.

67. King Victor Emmanuel.

**1940.** Air.

366. 66. 5 q. green 1·50 1·10
367. – 15 q. red 1·75 1·75
368. – 20 q. blue 4·25 2·50
369. – 50 q. brown 5·00 4·25
370. – 1 f. green 6·50 6·50
371. – 2 f. black 12·50 12·50
372. – 3 f. purple 24·00 24·00

DESIGNS: Savoia Marchetti S.M.75 airplane and—HORIZ. 20 q. King of Italy and harbour; 1 f. Bridge. VERT. 15 q. Areial map; 50 q. Girl and valley; 2 f. Archway and wall; 3 f. Women waving.

**1942.** 3rd Anniv of Italian Occupation.

373 67 5 q. green 1·10 1·10
374 10 q. brown 1·10 1·10
375 15 q. red 1·25 1·10
376 25 q. blue 1·25 1·10
377 65 q. brown 2·25 1·40
378 1 f. green 2·50 2·25
379 2 f. purple 2·50 2·25

**1942.** No. 352 surch. **1 QIND.**

380. 1 q. on 2 q. olive 1·75 2·25

69.

**1943.** Anti-Tuberculosis Fund.

381. 69. 5 q.+5 q. green 1·10 1·10
382. 10 q.+10 q. brown 1·10 1·10
383. 15 q.+10 q. red 1·10 1·10
384. 25 q.+15 q. blue 1·75 1·75
385. 30 q.+20 q. violet 1·75 1·75
386. 50 q.+25 q. orange 1·75 1·75
387. 65 q.+30 q. grey 2·50 2·50
388. 1 f.+40 q. brown 3·25 3·25

## GERMAN OCCUPATION

**1943.** Postage stamps of 1939 optd. **14 Shtator 1943** or surch. also.

389. – 1 q. on 3 q. brn. (No. 353) 1·60 3·00
390. – 2 q. olive (No. 352) 1·60 3·00
391. – 3 q. brown (No. 353) 1·60 3·00
392. – 5 q. green (No. 354) 1·60 3·00
393. 63. 10 q. brown 1·60 3·00
394. – 15 q. red (No. 356) 1·60 3·00
395. – 25 q. blue (No. 357) 1·60 3·00
396. – 30 q. violet (No. 358) 1·60 3·00
397. – 50 q. on 65 q. brown (No. 360) 2·50 5·50
398. – 65 q. brown (No. 360) 2·50 5·50
399. – 1 f. green (No. 361) 13·50 18·00
400. – 2 f. red (No. 362) 16·00 65·00
401. 64. 3 f. black 90·00 £225

71. War Refugees.

(73.)

**1944.** War Refugees' Relief Fund.

402. 71. 5 q. + 5 q. green 4·25 12·00
403. 10 q. + 5 q. brown 4·25 12·00
404. 15 q. + 5 q. lake 4·25 12·00
405. 25 q. + 10 q. blue 4·25 12·00
406. 1 f. + 50 q. olive 4·25 12·00
407. 2 f. + 1 f. violet 4·25 12·00
408. 3 f. + 1 f. 50 orange 4·25 12·00

## INDEPENDENT STATE

**1945.** Nos. 353/8 and 360/2 surch. **QEVERIJA/DEMOKRAT./E SHQIPERISE/22-X-1944** and value.

409. 30 q. on 3 q. brown 5·50 5·50
410. 40 q. on 5 q. green 5·50 5·50
411. 50 q. on 10 q. brown 5·50 5·50
412. 60 q. on 15 q. red 5·50 5·50
413. 80 q. on 25 q. blue 5·50 5·50
414. 1 f. on 30 q. violet 5·50 5·50
415. 2 f. on 65 q. brown 5·50 5·50
416. 3 f. on 1 f. green 5·50 5·50
417. 5 f. on 2 f. red 6·00 6·00

**1945.** 2nd Anniv of Formation of People's Army. Surch as T 73.

418. 49. 30 q. on 1 q. grey 3·75 3·75
419. 60 q. on 1 q. grey 3·75 3·75
420. 80 q. on 1 q. grey 3·75 3·75
421. 1 f. on 1 q. grey 7·25 7·25
422. 2 f. on 2 q. orange 9·00 9·00
423. 3 f. on 50 q. green 18·00 24·00
424. – 5 f. on 2 f. blue (No. 285) 27·00 35·00

**1945.** Red Cross Fund. Surch. with Red Cross **JAVA EK.K. SHQIPTAR 4-11 MAJ 1945** and value.

425. 69. 30 q.+15 q. on 5 q.+5 q. green 7·25 7·25
426. 50 q.+25 q. on 10 q.+10 q. brown 7·25 7·25
427. 1 f.+50 q. on 15 q.+10 q. red 18·00 18·00
428. 2 f.+1 f. on 25 q.+15 q. blue 27·00 27·00

75. Labinot.

77. Globe, Dove and Olive branch.

**1945.**

429. 75. 20 q. green 75 90
430. 30 q. orange 1·00 1·40
431. – 40 q. brown 1·00 1·40
432. – 60 q. red 1·40 2·00
433. – 1 f. red 3·00 4·00
434. – 3 f. blue 18·00 20·00

DESIGNS: 40 q., 60 q., Bridge at Berat. 1 f., 3 f. Permet landscape.

**1946.** Constitutional Assembly. Optd. **ASAMBLEJA KUSHTETUESE 10 KALLNUER 1946.**

435. 75. 20 q. green 1·10 1·10
436. 30 q. orange 1·50 1·50
437. – 40 q. brown (No. 431) 1·75 1·75
438. – 60 q. red (No. 432) 3·00 3·00
439. – 1 f. red (No. 433) 10·50 10·50
440. – 3 f. blue (No. 434) 18·00 18·00

## PEOPLE'S REPUBLIC

**1946.** Int. Women's Congress. Perf. or imperf.

441. 77. 20 q. mauve and red 75 75
442. 40 q. lilac and red 1·10 1·10
443. 50 q. violet and red 1·60 1·60
444. 1 f. blue and red 3·75 3·75
445. 2 f. blue and red 5·50 5·50

**1946.** Proclamation of Albanian People's Republic. Optd. **REPUBLIKA POPULLORE E SHQIPERISE.**

446. 75. 20 q. green 1·25 1·25
447. 30 q. orange 1·40 1·40
448. – 40 q. brown (No. 431) 2·50 2·50
449. – 60 q. red (No. 432) 5·00 5·00
450. – 1 f. red (No. 433) 10·50 10·50
451. – 3 f. blue (No. 434) 20·00 20·00

**1946.** Albanian Red Cross Congress. Surch. **KONGRESI K.K.SH 24. 25–11–46** and premium.

452. 75. 20 q. + 10 q. green 18·00 18·00
453. 30 q. + 15 q. orange 18·00 18·00
454. – 40 q. + 20 q. brown 18·00 18·00
455. – 60 q. + 30 q. red 18·00 18·00
456. – 1 f. + 50 q. red 18·00 18·00
457. – 3 f. + 1 f. 50 blue 18·00 18·00

79. Athletes.

80. Kemal Stafa.

**1946** Balkan Games.

458. 79. 1 q. black 12·50 10·50
459. 1 q. green 12·50 10·50
460. 5 q. brown 12·50 10·50
461. 10 q. red 12·50 10·50
462. 20 q. blue 12·50 10·50
463. 40 q. lilac 14·50 10·50
464. 1 f. orange 30·00 29·00

**1947.** 5th Death Anniv. of Kemal Stafa (National hero).

465. 80. 20 q. brown .. .. 9·00 9·00
466. 28 q. blue .. .. 9·00 9·00
467. 40 q. brown .. .. 9·00 9·00

81. Railway Construction.

**1947.** Construction of Durres-Elbasan Railway.

468. 81. 1 q. black .. .. 3·75 90
469. 4 q. green .. .. 3·75 90
470. 10 q. brown .. .. 3·75 1·10
471. 15 q. red .. .. 3·75 1·10
472. 20 q. black .. .. 9·00 1·25
473. 28 q. blue .. .. 12·50 1·60
474. 40 q. purple .. .. 24·00 9·00
475. 68 q. brown .. .. 30·00 16·00

82. Partisans. 83. Enver Hoxha and Vasil Shanto.

**1947.** 4th Anniv. of Formation of People's Army. Inscr. "1943–1947".

476. 82. 16 q. brown .. .. 7·25 4·50
477. 83. 20 q. brown .. .. 7·25 4·50
478. – 28 q. blue .. .. 7·25 4·50
479. – 40 q. brown and mauve 7·25 4·50

DESIGNS—HORIZ. 28 q. Infantry column. VERT. 40 q. Portrait of Vojo Kushi.

84. Ruined Conference Building.

**1947.** 3rd Anniv. of Peza Conf.

480. 84. 2 l. purple .. .. 5·50 3·75
481. 2 l. 50 blue .. .. 5·50 3·75

85. War Invalids. 86. Peasants.

**1947.** 1st Congress of War Invalids.

482. 85. 1 l. red .. .. 9·00 9·00

**1947.** Agrarian Reform. Inscr. "REFORMA AGRARE".

483. 86. 1 l. 50 purple .. .. 7·25 6·50
484. – 2 l. brown .. .. 7·25 6·50
485. – 2 l. 50 blue .. .. 7·25 6·50
486. – 3 l. red .. .. 7·25 6·50

DESIGN—HORIZ. 2 l. Banquet. 2 l. 50, Peasants rejoicing VERT. 3 l. Soldier being chaired.

87. Burning Village.

**1947.** 3rd Anniv. of Liberation. Inscr. "29–XI–1944–1947".

487. 87. 1 l. 50 red .. .. 3·75 3·75
488. – 2 l. 50 purple .. .. 3·75 3·75
489. – 5 l. blue .. .. 7·25 5·50
490. – 8 l. mauve .. .. 10·50 7·25
491. – 12 l. brown .. .. 18·00 12·50

DESIGNS: 2 l. 50, Riflemen. 5 l. Machine-gunners. 8 l. Mounted soldier. 12 l. Infantry column.

**1948.** Nos. 429/34 surch. in "lek".

492. 75. 0 l. 50 on 30 q. orange .. 35 35
493. 1 l. on 20 q. green .. 90 90
494. – 2 l. 50 on 60 q. red .. 2·50 2·25
495. – 3 l. on 1 f. red .. 3·00 3·00
496. – 5 l. on 3 f. blue .. 4·75 4·25
497. – 12 l. on 40 q. brown 12·00 10·50

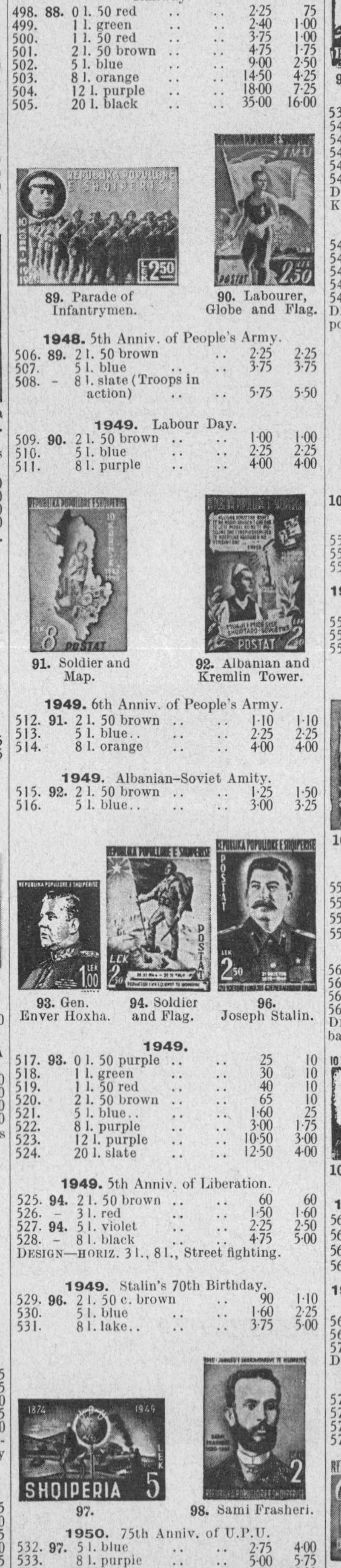

88. Railway Construction.

**1948.** Construction of Durres-Tirana Railway.

498. 88. 0 l. 50 red .. .. 2·25 75
499. 1 l. green .. .. 2·40 1·00
500. 1 l. 50 red .. .. 3·75 1·00
501. 2 l. 50 brown .. .. 4·75 1·75
502. 5 l. blue .. .. 9·00 2·50
503. 8 l. orange .. .. 14·50 4·25
504. 12 l. purple .. .. 18·00 7·25
505. 20 l. black .. .. 35·00 16·00

89. Parade of Infantrymen. 90. Labourer, Globe and Flag.

**1948.** 5th Anniv. of People's Army.

506. 89. 2 l. 50 brown .. 2·25 2·25
507. 5 l. blue .. .. 3·75 3·75
508. – 8 l. slate (Troops in action) .. .. 5·75 5·50

**1949.** Labour Day.

509. 90. 2 l. 50 brown .. .. 1·00 1·00
510. 5 l. blue .. .. 2·25 2·25
511. 8 l. purple .. .. 4·00 4·00

91. Soldier and Map. 92. Albanian and Kremlin Tower.

**1949.** 6th Anniv. of People's Army.

512. 91. 2 l. 50 brown .. .. 1·10 1·10
513. 5 l. blue .. .. 2·25 2·25
514. 8 l. orange .. .. 4·00 4·00

**1949.** Albanian–Soviet Amity.

515. 92. 2 l. 50 brown .. .. 1·25 1·50
516. 5 l. blue .. .. 3·00 3·25

93. Gen. Enver Hoxha. 94. Soldier and Flag. 96. Joseph Stalin.

**1949.**

517. 93. 0 l. 50 purple .. .. 25 10
518. 1 l. green .. .. 30 10
519. 1 l. 50 red .. .. 40 10
520. 2 l. 50 brown .. .. 65 10
521. 5 l. blue .. .. 1·60 25
522. 8 l. purple .. .. 3·00 1·75
523. 12 l. purple .. .. 10·50 3·00
524. 20 l. slate .. .. 12·50 4·00

**1949.** 5th Anniv. of Liberation.

525. 94. 2 l. 50 brown .. .. 60 60
526. – 3 l. red .. .. 1·50 1·60
527. 94. 5 l. violet .. .. 2·25 2·50
528. – 8 l. black .. .. 4·75 5·00

DESIGN—HORIZ. 3 l., 8 l., Street fighting.

**1949.** Stalin's 70th Birthday.

529. 96. 2 l. 50 c. brown .. .. 90 1·10
530. 5 l. blue .. .. 1·60 2·25
531. 8 l. lake .. .. 3·75 5·00

97. 98. Sami Frasheri.

**1950.** 75th Anniv. of U.P.U.

532. 97. 5 l. blue .. .. 2·75 4·00
533. 8 l. purple .. .. 5·00 5·75
534. 12 l. black .. .. 9·00 10·00

**1950.** Literary Jubilee. Inscr. "1950—JUBILEU I SHKRIMTAREVE TE RILINDJES".

535. 98. 2 l. green .. .. 1·10 85
536. – 2 l. 50 brown .. .. 1·50 1·40
537. – 3 l. red .. .. 1·75 2·00
538. – 5 l. blue .. .. 3·00 3·00

PORTRAITS: 2 l. 50, A. Zako (Cajupi). 3 l. Naim Frasheri. 5 l. K. Kristoforidhi.

99. Vuno-Himare. 100. Stafa and Shanto.

**1950.** Air.

539. 99. 0 l. 50 black .. .. 75 75
540. – 1 l. purple .. .. 75 75
541. – 2 l. blue .. .. 1·40 1·40
542. 99. 5 l. green .. .. 5·00 5·00
543. – 10 l. blue .. .. 10·50 10·50
544. – 20 l. violet .. .. 18·00 18·00

DESIGNS: 1 l., 10 l. Rozafat Shkodor. 2 l., 20 l. Keshtjelle-Butrinto.

**1950.** Albanian Patriots.

545. – 2 l. green .. .. 1·25 1·25
546. – 2 l. 50 violet .. .. 1·50 1·50
547. – 3 l. red .. .. 2·50 2·25
548. – 5 l. blue .. .. 3·00 2·50
549. 100. 8 l. brown .. .. 8·00 7·25

DESIGNS: Nos. 545/9 each show five different portraits.

101. Arms and Flags. 102. Skanderbeg.

**1951.** 5th Anniv. of Republic.

550. 101. 2 l. 50 red .. .. 1·50 1·60
551. 5 l. blue .. .. 3·75 3·75
552. 8 l. black .. .. 5·50 5·75

**1951.** 483rd Death Anniv. of Skanderbeg (patriot).

553. 102. 2 l. 50 brown .. .. 1·50 1·40
554. 5 l. violet .. .. 3·00 3·25
555. 8 l. bistre .. .. 4·75 4·75

103. Gen. Enver Hoxha and Assembly. 104. Child and Globe.

**1951.** 7th Anniv. of Permet Congress.

556. 103. 2 l. 50 brown .. .. 90 90
557. 3 l. red .. .. 1·10 1·10
558. 5 l. blue .. .. 2·00 2·00
559. 8 l. mauve .. .. 3·75 3·75

**1951.** Int. Children's Day.

560. 104. 2 l. green .. .. 1·40 1·00
561. – 2 l. 50 brown .. .. 1·60 1·40
562. – 3 l. red .. .. 2·40 1·60
563. 104. 5 l. blue .. .. 3·25 2·25

DESIGN—HORIZ. 2 l. 50, 3 l. Nurse weighing baby.

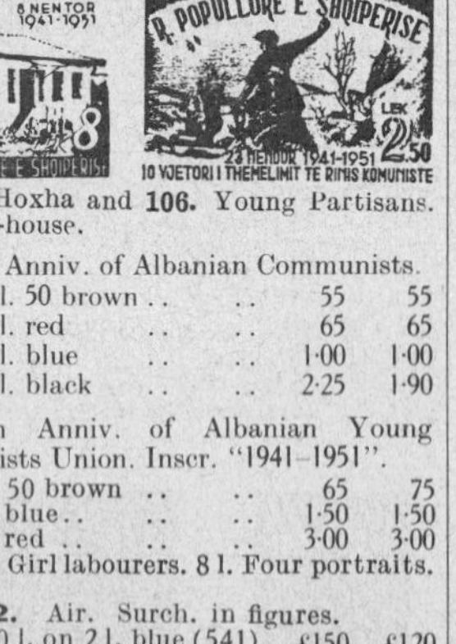

105. Enver Hoxha and Meeting-house. 106. Young Partisans.

**1951.** 10th Anniv. of Albanian Communists.

564. 105. 2 l. 50 brown .. .. 55 55
565. 3 l. red .. .. 65 65
566. 5 l. blue .. .. 1·00 1·00
567. 8 l. black .. .. 2·25 1·90

**1951.** 10th Anniv. of Albanian Young Communists Union. Inscr. "1941–1951".

568. 106. 2 l. 50 brown .. .. 65 75
569. – 5 l. blue .. .. 1·50 1·50
570. – 8 l. red .. .. 3·00 3·00

DESIGNS. 5 l. Girl labourers. 8 l. Four portraits.

**1952.** Air. Surch. in figures.

571. – 0.50 l. on 2 l. blue (541) £150 £120
572. 99. 0.50 l. on 5 l. green .. 32·00 22·00
573. – 2 l. 50 on 5 l. green .. £225 £130
574. – 2 l. 50 on 10 l. blue (543) 32·00 22·00

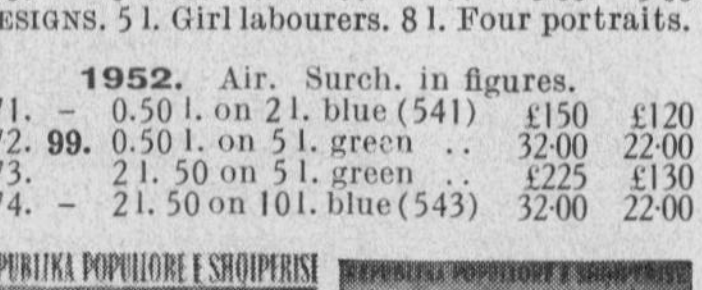

108. Factory. 109. Soldiers and Flags.

**1953.**

575. 108. 0 l. 50 brown .. .. 75 10
576. – 1 l. green .. .. 70 10
577. – 2 l. 50 sepia .. .. 1·60 20
578. – 3 l. red .. .. 2·00 35
579. – 5 l. blue .. .. 3·75 90
580. – 8 l. olive .. .. 4·00 1·10
581. – 12 l. purple .. .. 5·50 1·40
582. – 20 l. blue .. .. 12·50 3·25

DESIGNS—HORIZ. 1 l. Canal. 2 l. 50, Girl and cotton mill. 3 l. Girl and sugar factory. 5 l. Film studio. 8 l. Girl and textile machinery. 20 l. Dam. VERT. 12 l. Pylon and hydro-electric station.

**1954.** 10th Anniv. of Liberation.

583. 109. 0 l. 50 lilac .. .. 10 10
584. 1 l. green .. .. 55 10
585. 2 l. 50 brown .. .. 1·00 60
586. 3 l. red .. .. 1·75 75
587. 5 l. blue .. .. 2·50 1·10
588. 8 l. purple .. .. 4·75 3·00

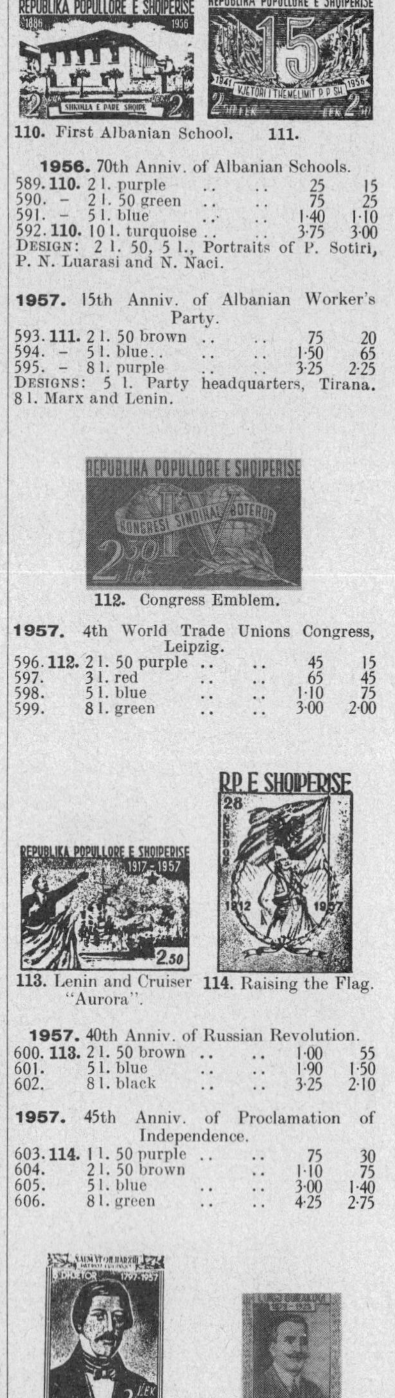

110. First Albanian School. 111.

**1956.** 70th Anniv. of Albanian Schools.

589. 110. 2 l. purple .. .. 25 15
590. – 2 l. 50 green .. .. 75 25
591. – 5 l. blue .. .. 1·40 1·10
592. 110. 10 l. turquoise .. .. 3·75 3·00

DESIGN: 2 l. 50, 5 l., Portraits of P. Sotiri, P. N. Luarasi and N. Naci.

**1957.** 15th Anniv. of Albanian Worker's Party.

593. 111. 2 l. 50 brown .. .. 75 20
594. – 5 l. blue .. .. 1·50 65
595. – 8 l. purple .. .. 3·25 2·25

DESIGNS: 5 l. Party headquarters, Tirana. 8 l. Marx and Lenin.

112. Congress Emblem.

**1957.** 4th World Trade Unions Congress, Leipzig.

596. 112. 2 l. 50 purple .. .. 45 15
597. 3 l. red .. .. 65 45
598. 5 l. blue .. .. 1·10 75
599. 8 l. green .. .. 3·00 2·00

113. Lenin and Cruiser "Aurora". 114. Raising the Flag.

**1957.** 40th Anniv. of Russian Revolution.

600. 113. 2 l. 50 brown .. .. 1·00 55
601. 5 l. blue .. .. 1·90 1·50
602. 8 l. black .. .. 3·25 2·10

**1957.** 45th Anniv. of Proclamation of Independence.

603. 114. 1 l. 50 purple .. .. 75 30
604. 2 l. 50 brown .. .. 1·10 75
605. 5 l. blue .. .. 3·00 1·40
606. 8 l. green .. .. 4·25 2·75

115. Naum Veqilharxhi. 116. Luigj Gurakuqi.

**1958.** 160th Birth Anniv. of Naum Veqilharxhi (patriot).

607. 115. 2 l. 50 brown .. .. 80 30
608. 5 l. blue .. .. 1·50 60
609. 8 l. purple .. .. 3·25 1·50

**1958.** Removal of Ashes of L. Gurakuqi (patriot).

610. 116. 1 l. 50 green .. .. 20 20
611. 2 l. 50 brown .. .. 75 60
612. 5 l. blue .. .. 1·10 75
613. 8 l. sepia .. .. 3·00 1·10

117. Freedom Fighters. 118. Soldiers in Action.

**1958.** 50th Anniv. of Battle of Mashkullore.

614. **117.** 2 l. 50 ochre .. .. 60 20
615. – 3 l. green .. .. 80 20
616. **117.** 5 l. blue.. .. .. 1·25 75
617. – 8 l. brown .. .. 2·50 1·50

DESIGN: 3 l., 8 l., Tree and buildings.

**1958.** 15th Anniv. of Albanian People's Army.

618. **118.** 1 l. 50 green .. .. 20 15
619. – 2 l. 50 brown .. .. 60 25
620. **118.** 8 l. red .. .. .. 1·60 1·40
621. – 11 l. blue .. .. 2·40 2·25

DESIGN: 2 l. 50, 11 l. Tank-driver, sailor, infantryman and tanks.

119. Bust of Apollo and Butrinto Amphitheatre. 120. F. Joliot-Curie and Council Emblem.

**1959.** Cultural Monuments Week.

622. **119.** 2 l. 50 brown .. .. 75 25
623. 6 l. 50 green .. .. 3·00 1·40
624. 11 l. blue .. .. 4·25 2·50

**1959.** 10th Anniv. of World Peace Council.

625. **120.** 1 l. 50 red .. .. 2·25 80
626. 2 l. 50 violet .. .. 5·00 2·00
627. 11 l. blue .. .. 10·50 6·00

121. Basketball. 122. Soldier.

**1959.** 1st National Spartacist Games.

628. **121.** 1 l. 50 violet .. .. 65 30
629. – 2 l. 50 green .. .. 1·00 25
630. – 5 l. red .. .. .. 1·60 1·25
631. – 11 l. blue .. .. 5·50 3·25

DESIGNS: 2 l. 50, Football. 5 l. Running. 11 l. Runners with torches.

**1959.** 15th Anniv. of Liberation.

632. **122.** 1 l. 50 red .. .. 45 20
633. – 2 l. 50 brown .. .. 1·25 35
634. – 3 l. green .. .. 1·40 40
635. – 6 l. 50 red .. .. 2·75 4·00

DESIGNS: 2 l. 50, Security guard. 3 l. Harvester. 6 l. 50, Laboratory workers.

123. Mother and Child. 124.

**1959.** 10th Anniv. of Human Rights.

636. **123.** 5 l. blue .. .. 7·25 1·40

**1960.** 50th Anniv. of Int. Women's Day.

637. **124.** 2 l. 50 brown .. .. 1·00 55
638. 11 l. red.. .. .. 4·00 1·40

125. Congress Building. 126. A. Moisiu. 127. Lenin.

**1960.** 40th Anniv. of Lushnje Congress.

639. **125.** 2 l. 50 brown .. .. 55 25
640. 7 l. 50 blue .. .. 1·50 80

**1960.** 80th Birth Anniv. of Alexandre Moisiu (actor).

641. **126.** 3 l. brown .. .. 65 45
642. 11 l. green .. .. 2·25 80

**1960.** 90th Birth Anniv. of Lenin.

643. **127.** 4 l. turquoise .. .. 1·60 30
644. 11 l. red.. .. .. 5·00 1·10

128. Vaso Pasha. 129. Frontier Guard. 130. Family with Policeman.

**1960.** 80th Anniv. of Albanian Alphabet Study Association.

645. **128.** 1 l. olive .. .. 25 15
646. – 1 l. 50 brown .. .. 75 20
647. – 6 l. 50 blue .. .. 1·60 75
648. – 11 l. red.. .. .. 3·75 1·40

DESIGNS: 1 l. 50, Jani Vreto. 6 l. 50, Sami Frasheri. 11 l. Association statutes.

**1960.** 15th Anniv. of Frontier Force.

649. **129.** 1 l. 50 red .. .. 50 30
650. 11 l. blue .. .. 3·00 1·40

**1960.** 15th Anniv. of People's Police.

651. **130.** 1 l. 50 green .. .. 55 25
652. 8 l. 50 brown .. .. 3·00 1·25

131. Normal School, Elbasan. 132. Soldier and Cannon.

**1960.** 50th Anniv. of Normal School, Elbasan.

653. **131.** 5 l. green .. .. 2·50 1·40
654. 6 l. 50 purple .. .. 2·50 1·40

**1960.** 40th Anniv. of Battle Vlore.

655. **132.** 1 l. 50 sepia .. .. 75 25
656. 2 l. 50 lake .. .. 1·10 40
657. 5 l. blue .. .. 2·50 90

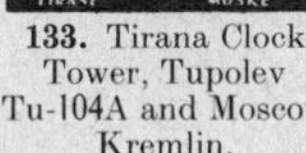


133. Tirana Clock Tower, Tupolev Tu-104A and Moscow Kremlin.

134. Federation Emblem.

**1960.** 2nd Anniv. of Tirana–Moscow Jet Air Service.

658. **133.** 1 l. brown .. .. 1·00 75
659. 7 l. 50 blue .. .. 3·75 1·40
660. 11 l. 50 grey .. .. 6·00 3·00

**1960.** 15th Anniv. of World Democratic Youth Federation.

661. **134.** 1 l. 50 blue .. .. 25 15
662. 8 l. 50 red .. .. 1·40 85

135. Ali Kelmendi. 136. Flags of Albania and Russia, and Clasped Hands. 137. Marx and Lenin.

**1960.** 60th Birth Anniv. of Kelmendi (Communist).

663. **135.** 1 l. 50 olive .. .. 55 20
664. 11 l. purple .. .. 1·40 85

**1961.** 15th Anniv. of Albanian-Soviet Friendship Society.

665. **136.** 2 l. violet .. .. 55 20
666. 8 l. red .. .. 1·75 75

**1961.** 4th Albanian Workers' Party Congress.

667. **137.** 2 l. red .. .. 55 20
668. 8 l. blue .. .. 1·60 80

138. Malsi e Madhe (Shkoder) Costume. 139. European Otter.

**1961.** Provincial Costumes.

669. **138.** 1 l. black .. .. 75 20
670. – 1 l. 50 purple .. .. 1·10 25
671. – 6 l. 50 blue .. .. 3·75 1·10
672. – 11 l. red.. .. .. 7·25 2·40

COSTUMES: 1 l. 50, Malsi e Madhe (Shkoder) (female). 6 l. 50, Lume. 11 l. Mirdite.

**1961.** Albanian Fauna.

673. **139.** 2 l. 50 blue .. .. 3·75 90
674. – 6 l. 50 green (Eurasian badger) .. .. 7·25 2·25
675. – 11 l. brown (Brown bear) .. .. 10·50 3·75

140. Dalmatian Pelicans. 141. Cyclamen.

**1961.** Albanian Birds.

676. **140.** 1 l. 50 red on pink .. 5·00 65
677. – 7 l. 50 violet on blue .. 6·75 2·00
678. – 11 l. brown on pink .. 9·50 2·25

BIRDS: 7 l. 50, Grey Heron. 11 l. Little Egret.

**1961.** Albanian Flowers.

679. **141.** 1 l. 50 purple and blue.. 1·75 25
680. – 8 l. orange and purple.. 3·25 1·40
681. – 11 l. red and green .. 5·75 2·25

FLOWERS: 8 l. Forsythia. 11 l. Lily.

142. M. G. Nikolla. 143. Lenin and Marx on Flag.

**1961.** 50th Birth Anniv. of Nikolla (poet).

682. **142.** 0 l. 50 brown .. .. 35 30
683. 8 l. 50 green .. .. 1·90 1·40

**1961.** 20th Anniv. of Albanian Workers' Party.

684. **143.** 2 l. 50 red .. .. 90 25
685. 7 l. 50 purple .. .. 2·00 90

144. 145. Yuri Gagarin and "Vostok I".

**1961.** 20th Anniv. of Albanian Young Communists Union.

686. **144.** 2 l. 50 blue .. .. 90 25
687. 7 l. 50 purple .. .. 1·60 1·00

**1962.** World's First Manned Space Flight.

(a) Postage.

688. **145** 0 l. 50 blue .. .. 90 15
689. 4 l. purple .. .. 3·75 90
690. 11 l. green .. .. 9·00 3·00

(b) Air. Optd. **POSTA AJRORE**.

691. **145.** 0 l. 50 blue on cream .. 35·00 35·00
692. 4 l. purple on cream .. 35·00 35·00
693. 11 l. green on cream .. 35·00 35·00

147. P. N. Luarasi. 148. Campaign Emblem.

**1962.** 50th Death Anniv. of Petro N. Luarasi (patriot).

694. **147.** 0 l. 50 blue .. .. 75 15
695. 8 l. 50 brown .. .. 3·00 75

**IMPERF. STAMPS.** Many Albanian stamps from No. 696 onwards exist imperf. and/or in different colours from limited printings.

**1962.** Malaria Eradication.

696. **148.** 1 l. 50 green .. .. 15 10
697. 2 l. 50 red .. .. 20 10
698. 10 l. purple .. .. 1·10 65
699. 11 l. blue .. .. 1·60 90

149. Camomile. 150. Throwing the Javelin.

**1962.** Medicinal Plants.

700. **149.** 0 l. 50 yell., grn. & blue 30 15
701. – 8 l. green, yell. & grey 1·40 85
702. – 11 l. 50 violet, green and ochre .. .. 2·25 1·10

PLANTS: 8 l. Silver linden. 11 l. 50, Sage.

**1962.** Olympic Games, Tokyo, 1964. (1st issue). Inscr. as in T **102**.

703. – 0 l. 50 black and blue.. 15 10
704. – 2 l. 50 sepia and brown 60 10
705. – 3 l. black and blue .. 75 15
706. **150.** 9 l. purple and red .. 2·25 65
707. – 10 l. black and olive .. 2·50 90

DESIGNS—VERT. 0 l. 50, Diving. 2 l. 50, Pole-vaulting. 10 l. Putting the shot. HORIZ. 3 l. Olympic flame.

See also Nos. 754/8, 818/21 and 842/51.

151. "Sputnik 1" in Orbit. 152. Footballer and Ball in Net.

**1962.** Cosmic Flights.

708. **151.** 0 l. 50 yellow and violet 55 15
709. – 1 l. sepia and green .. 75 20
710. – 1 l. 50 yellow and red.. 1·25 30
711. – 20 l. blue and purple.. 8·25 2·75

DESIGNS: 1 l. Dog "Laika" and "Sputnik II". 1 l. 50, Artificial satellite and Sun. 20 l. "Lunik III" photographing Moon.

**1962.** World Football Championships, Chile.

712. **152.** 1 l. orange and purple 15 10
713. – 2 l. 50 green and turq. 90 15
714. **152.** 6 l. 50 brown & mauve 1·75 20
715. – 15 l. turquoise & purple 2·50 60

DESIGN: 2 l. 50, 15 l. As Type **152** but Globe in place of ball in net.

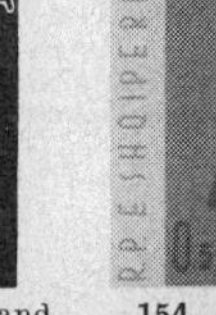


153. "Europa" and Albanian Maps. 154. Dardhe Woman.

**1962.** Tourist Publicity.

716. **153.** 0 l. 50 red, yell. & myrtle 25 25
717. – 1 l. red, violet and blue 1·25 1·25
718. – 2 l. 50 red and blue .. 7·25 7·25
719. **153.** 11 l. red, yellow & grey 14·50 14·50

DESIGN: 1 l., 2 l. 50, Statue and map.

**1962.** Costumes of Albania's Southern Region.

720. **154.** 0 l. 50 red and blue .. 20 10
721. – 1 l. brown and buff .. 25 10
722. – 2 l. 50 violet and green 1·25 35
723. – 14 l. brown and green 3·75 1·40

COSTUMES: 1 l. Devoll man. 2 l. 50, Lunxheri woman. 14 l. Gjirokaster man.

155. Chamois. 156. Golden Eagle.

**1962.** Albanian Animals.

724. **155.** 0 l. 50 purple and green 45 10
725. – 1 l. black and yellow.. 1·25 25
726. – 1 l. 50 black and brown 1·75 30
727. – 15 l. brown and green 18·00 3·25

ANIMALS—HORIZ. 1 l. Lynx. 1 l. 50, Wild boar. VERT. 15 l. Roe-deer.

**1962.** 50th Anniv. of Independence.

728. **156.** 1 l. brown and red .. 75 10
729. – 3 l. black and bistre.. 1·75 75
730. – 16 l. black and red .. 8·00 2·50

DESIGNS: 3 l. I. Qemali. 16 l. "RPSH" and Golden Eagle.

157. Revolutionaries.

158. Henri Dunant and Globe.

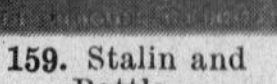

159. Stalin and Battle.

160. Nikolaev and "Vostok 3".

**1963.** 45th Anniv. of October Revolution.
731. 157. 5 l. violet & yellow .. 1·10 55
732. – 10 l. black and red .. 2·25 1·25
DESIGN: 10 l. Statue of Lenin.

**1963.** Red Cross Cent. Cross in red.
733. 158. 1 l. 50 black and red .. 55 15
734. 2 l. 50 blk., red & blue 75 25
735. 6 l. black, red & green 1·40 75
736. 10 l. black, red & yellow 2·75 1·40

**1963.** 20th Anniv. of Battle of Stalingrad.
737. 159. 8 l. black and green (postage) .. .. 8·25 2·25
738. – 7 l. red and green (air) 8·00 1·75
DESIGN: 7 l. "Lenin" flag, map, tanks, etc.

**1963.** 1st "Team" Manned Space Flights.
739. 160. 2 l. 50 sepia and blue .. 60 25
740. – 7 l. 50 black & turquoise 1·40 80
741. – 20 l. sepia and violet .. 5·00 2·40
DESIGNS—HORIZ. 7 l. 50, Globe, "Vostok 3" and "Vostok 4". VERT. 20 l. P. Popovic and "Vostok 4".

161. "Polyphylla fullo".

162. Policeman and Allegorical Figure.

**1963.** Albanian Insects.
742. 161. 0 l. 50 brown & green .. 55 20
743. – 1 l. 50 brown and blue 1·10 55
744. – 8 l. violet and red .. 5·75 1·50
745. – 10 l. black and yellow 7·25 2·75
INSECTS: 1 l. 50 "Lucanus cervus". 8 l. "Procerus gigas". 10 l. "Cicindela albanica".

**1963.** 20th Anniv. of Albanian Security Police.
746. 162. 2 l. 50 blk., pur. & red 75 35
747. 7 l. 50 blk., lake and red 2·75 70

163. Great Crested Grebe.

164. Official Insignia and Postmark of 1913.

**1963.** Birds. Multicoloured.
748. 0 l. 50 Type 163 .. .. 60 25
749. 3 l. Golden Eagle .. .. 2·50 1·50
750. 6 l. 50 Grey Partridge .. 6·25 3·00
751. 11 l. Capercaillie .. .. 10·50 4·75

**1963.** 50th Anniv. of First Albanian Stamps.
752. 164. 5 l. multicoloured .. 1·75 75
753. – 10 l. green, black & red 3·00 1·40
DESIGN: 10 l. Albanian stamps of 1913, 1937 and 1962.

165. Boxing.

166. Gen. Enver Hoxha and Labinoti Council Building.

**1963.** Olympic Games, Tokyo (1964) (2nd issue).
754. 165. 2 l. slate, red & yellow 55 55
755. – 3 l. brn., blue & orange 75 20
756. – 5 l. purple, brown and blue .. .. 1·10 30
757. – 6 l. black, grey & green 1·50 75
758. – 9 l. blue and brown .. 3·00 1·25
SPORTS: 3 l. Basketball. 5 l. Volleyball. 6 l. Cycling. 9 l. Gymnastics.

**1963.** 20th Anniv. of Albanian People's Army.
759. 166. 1 l. 50 yell., blk. & red 35 15
760. – 2 l. 50 bistre, brn. & bl. 90 25
761. – 5 l. blk., drab & turq. 1·60 80
762. – 6 l. blue, buff & brown 2·40 1·25
DESIGNS: 2 l. 50, Soldier with weapons. 5 l. Soldier attacking. 6 l. Peacetime soldier.

167. Gagarin.

168. Volleyball (Rumania).

**1963.** Soviet Cosmonauts. Portraits in yellow and brown.
763. 167. 3 l. violet .. .. 90 15
764. – 5 l. deep blue .. .. 1·25 30
765. – 7 l. violet and grey .. 2·00 55
766. – 11 l. blue and purple .. 3·25 90
767. – 14 l. blue and turquoise 4·25 1·25
768. – 20 l. blue .. .. 6·50 3·00
COSMONAUTS: 5 l. Titov. 7 l. Nikolaev. 11 l. Popovich. 14 l. Bykovsky. 20 l. Valentina Tereshkova.

**1963.** European Sports Events, 1963.
769. 168. 2 l. red, black & olive 75 15
770. – 3 l. bistre, black & red 75 25
771. – 5 l. orange, black & grn. 1·10 55
772. – 7 l. green, black & pink 1·75 75
773. – 8 l. red, black & blue 3·00 1·00
SPORTS: 3 l. Weightlifting (Sweden). 5 l. Football (European Cup). 7 l. Boxing (Russia). 8 l. Ladies' Rowing (Russia).

169. "Iphiclides podalirius".

**1963.** Butterflies and Moths. Multicoloured.
774 1 l. Type 169 .. .. 60 20
775 2 l. "Euplagia quadripunctaria" .. .. 70 25
776 4 l. "Gonepteryx rhamni" 1·75 75
777 5 l. "Acherontia atropos" 2·50 65
778 8 l. "Anthocharis cardamines" .. .. .. 3·75 1·40
779 10 l. "Inachis io" .. 5·50 2·00

170. Lunik I.

DESIGNS: 3 l. Lunik II. 5 l. Lunik III. 8 l. Venus I. 12 l. Mars I.

**1963.** Air. Cosmic Flights.
780. 170. 2 l. olive, yell. & orge. 35 20
781. – 3 l. multicoloured .. 90 20
782. – 5 l. olive, yell. & pur. 1·40 55
783. – 8 l. red, yell. & violet 2·25 1·00
784. – 12 l. red, orange & blue 4·00 3·25

171. Food Processing Works.

172. Shield and Banner.

**1963.** Industrial Buildings.
785. 171. 2 l. 50 red on pink .. 75 15
786. – 20 l. green on green .. 4·25 1·10
787. – 30 l. purple on blue .. 6·50 1·75
788. – 50 l. bistre on cream 8·25 3·00
DESIGNS—VERT. 20 l. Naphtha refinery. 30 l. Fruit-bottling plant. HORIZ. 50 l. Copper-processing works.

**1963.** First Army and Defence Aid Association, Congress.
789. 172. 2 l. multicoloured .. 35 25
790. 8 l. multicoloured .. 1·50 1·40

173. Young Men of Three Races.

**1963.** 15th Anniv. of Declaration of Human Rights.
791. 173. 3 l. black and ochre .. 65 55
792. 5 l. blue and ochre .. 1·40 85
793. 7 l. violet and ochre .. 2·25 1·40

174. Bobsleighing.

175. Lenin.

**1963.** Winter Olympic Games, Innsbruck. Inscr. "1964".
794. 174. 0 l. 50 black and blue .. 15 15
795. – 2 l. 50 blk., red & grey 75 20
796. – 6 l. 50 blk., yell. & grey 1·50 30
797. – 12 l. 50 red, blk. & grn. 3·00 1·40
DESIGNS—VERT. 2 l. 50, Skiing. 12 l. 50, Figure-skating. HORIZ. 6 l. 50, Ice-hockey.

**1964.** 40th Death Anniv. of Lenin.
798. 175. 5 l. olive and bistre .. 1·10 35
799. 10 l. olive and bistre .. 1·50 85

176. Hurdling.

177. Sturgeon.

**1964.** "GANEFO" Games. Jakarta (1963).
800. 176. 2 l. 50 blue and lilac 75 20
801. – 3 l. brown and green .. 1·10 25
802. – 6 l. 50 lake and blue .. 1·40 35
803. – 8 l. ochre and blue .. 2·25 75
SPORTS—HORIZ. 3 l. Running. 6 l. 50, Rifle-shooting. VERT. 8 l. Basketball.

**1964.** Fishes. Multicoloured.
804. 0 l. 50 Type 177 .. .. 15 10
805. 1 l. Gilthead .. .. 55 10
806. 1 l. 50 Striped mullet .. 75 15
807. 2 l. 50 Carp .. .. 1·00 25
808. 6 l. 50 Mackerel .. 2·50 90
809. 10 l. Salmon .. .. 4·00 1·50

178. Eurasian Red Squirrel.

**1964.** Forest Animals. Multicoloured.
810. 1 l. Type 178 .. .. 20 15
811. 1 l. 50 Beech marten .. 35 15
812. 2 l. Red fox .. .. 65 20
813. 2 l. 50 East European hedgehog .. .. 75 25
814. 3 l. Brown hare .. .. 85 65
815. 5 l. Golden jackal .. .. 1·40 50
816. 7 l. Wild cat .. .. 1·90 90
817. 8 l. Wolf .. .. 3·75 1·10

179. Lighting Olympic Torch.

DESIGNS: 5 l. Torch and globes. 7 l. Olympic Flag and Mt. Fuji. 10 l. Olympic Stadium, Tokyo.

**1964.** Olympic Games, Tokyo (3rd issue). Inscr. "DREJT TOKIOS".
818. 179. 3 l. yell., buff & green 25 10
819. – 5 l. blue, violet and red 55 20
820. – 7 l. lt. blue, blue & yell. 80 25
821. – 10 l. multicoloured .. 1·10 75

180. Soldiers and hand clutching rifle, and Inscription.

**1964.** 20th Anniv. of Permet Congress.
822. 180. 2 l. sepia, red & orange 15 10
823. – 5 l. multicoloured .. 75 45
824. – 8 l. sepia, red & brown 1·50 80
DESIGNS (each with different inscription at right): 5 l. Albanian Arms. 8 l. Gen. Enver Hoxha.

181. Revolutionaries with Flag.

182. Full Moon.

**1964.** 40th Anniv. of Revolution.
825. 181. 2 l. 50 black and red .. 20 15
826. 7 l. 50 black & mauve 90 40

**1964.** "Verso Tokyo" Stamp Exhibition, Rimini (Italy). Optd. **Rimini 25-VI-64.**
827. 10 l. blue, violet, orange and black (No. 821) .. 7·25 7·25

**1964.** Moon's Phases.
828. 182. 1 l. yellow and violet .. 25 10
829. – 5 l. yellow and blue .. 1·00 55
830. – 8 l. yellow and blue .. 1·60 75
831. – 11 l. yellow and green 3·75 1·10
PHASES: 5 l. Waxing Moon. 8 l. Half-Moon. 11 l. Waning Moon.

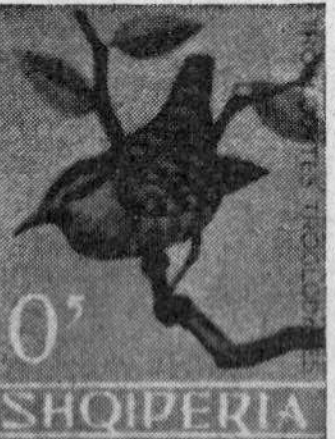


184. Winter Wren.

186. Running and Gymnastics.

**1964.** Albanian Birds. Multicoloured.
832. 0 l. 50 Type 184 .. .. 30 20
833. 1 l. Penduline tit .. .. 95 25
834. 2 l. 50 Green woodpecker .. 1·90 25
835. 3 l. Treecreeper .. .. 2·25 40
836. 4 l. European nuthatch .. 3·00 80
837. 5 l. Great tit .. .. 3·25 1·25
838. 6 l. Goldfinch .. .. 3·75 1·90
839. 18 l. Golden oriole .. .. 9·00 4·50

**1964.** Air. Riccione "Space" Exn. Optd **Riccione 23-8-1964.**
840. 170. 2 l. olive, yell. & orge. 10·50 10·50
841. – 8 l. red, yellow & violet (No. 783) .. 25·00 25·00

**1964.** Olympic Games, Tokyo.
842. 186. 1 l. red, blue and green 15 10
843. – 2 l. brown, blue & violet 20 15
844. – 3 l. brn., violet & olive 30 15
845. – 4 l. olive, turq. & blue 45 20
846. – 5 l. turq., purple & red 75 55
847. – 6 l. ult., lt. blue & orge. 90 65
848. – 7 l. green, orge. & blue 1·25 80
849. – 8 l. grey, green & yell. 1·25 95
850. – 9 l. lt. blue, yell. & pur. 1·25 1·10
851. – 10 l. brn., grn. & turq. 1·60 1·40
SPORTS: 2 l. Weightlifting and judo. 3 l. Horse-jumping and cycling. 4 l. Football and water-polo. 5 l. Wrestling and boxing. 6 l. Various sports and hockey. 7 l. Swimming and yachting. 8 l. Basketball and volleyball. 9 l. Rowing and canoeing. 10 l. Fencing and pistol-shooting.

187. Chinese Republican Emblem.

188. Karl Marx.

**1964.** 15th Anniv. of Chinese People's Republic. Insc. "I TETOR 1949 1964".
852. 187. 7 l. red, black & yellow 1·40 75
853. – 8 l. black, red & yellow 2·50 1·10
DESIGN—HORIZ. 8 l. Mao Tse-tung.

**1964.** Cent. of "First International".
854. 188. 2 l. black, red & lavender 90 20
855. – 5 l. slate .. .. 2·40 75
856. – 8 l. black, red and buff 4·00 1·25
DESIGNS: 5 l. St. Martin's Hall, London. 8 l. F. Engels.

189. J. de Rada.

190. Arms and Flag.

**1964.** 150th Birth Anniv. of Jeronim de Rada (poet).

857. **189.** 7 l. green .. .. 1·40 55
858. 8 l. violet .. .. 2·25 1·00

**1964.** 20th Anniv. of Liberation.

859. **190.** 1 l. multicoloured .. 15 15
860. – 2 l. blue, red & yellow 55 15
861. – 3 l. brown, red & yellow 90 55
862. – 4 l. green, red & yellow 1·25 75
863. – 10 l. black, red and blue 3·00 1·40

DESIGNS—HORIZ. 2 l. Industrial scene. 3 l. Agricultural scene. 4 l. Laboratory worker. VERT. 10 l. Hands holding Constitution hammer and sickle.

**191.** Mercury. 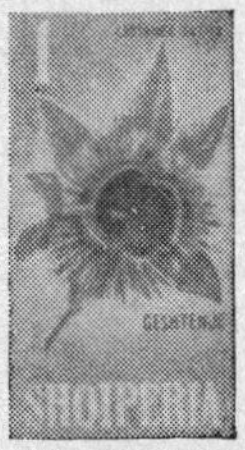 **192.** Chestnut.

**1964.** Solar System Planets. Multicoloured.

864. 1 l. Type **191** .. .. 20 15
865. 2 l. Venus .. .. .. 40 20
866. 3 l. Earth .. .. .. 60 25
867. 4 l. Mars .. .. .. 75 30
868. 5 l. Jupiter .. .. 95 35
869. 6 l. Saturn .. .. .. 1·40 45
870. 7 l. Uranus .. .. 1·60 55
871. 8 l. Neptune .. .. 1·75 1·10
872. 9 l. Pluto .. .. .. 1·90 1·40

**1965.** Winter Fruits. Multicoloured.

873. 1 l. Type **192** .. .. 20 10
874. 2 l. Medlars .. .. 30 15
875. 3 l. Persimmon .. .. 65 20
876. 4 l. Pomegranate .. .. 85 30
877. 5 l. Quince .. .. .. 1·40 35
878. 10 l. Orange .. .. 2·40 90

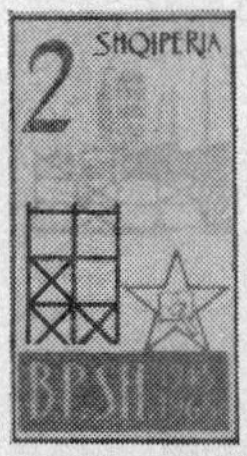

**193.** "Industry".  **194.** Buffalo Grazing.

**1965.** 20th Anniv. of Albanian Trade Unions. Inscr. "B.P.S.H. 1945–1965".

879. **193.** 2 l. red, pink & black 3·00 2·75
880. – 5 l. black, grey & ochre 6·00 4·75
881. – 8 l. blue, lt. blue & blk. 7·25 5·50

DESIGNS: 5 l. Set square, book and dividers ("Technocracy"). 8 l. Hotel, trees and sunshade ("Tourism").

**1965.** Water Buffaloes.

882. **194.** 1 l. multicoloured .. 45 10
883. – 2 l. multicoloured .. 95 15
884. – 3 l. multicoloured .. 1·60 25
885. – 7 l. multicoloured .. 4·00 90
886. – 12 l. multicoloured .. 7·25 2·25

DESIGNS: 2 l. to 12 l. As Type **194** showing different views of Buffalo.

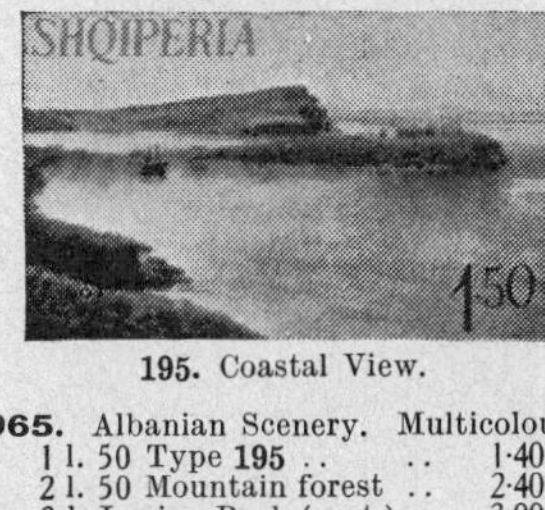

**195.** Coastal View.

**1965.** Albanian Scenery. Multicoloured.

887. 1 l. 50 Type **195** .. .. 1·40 70
888. 2 l. 50 Mountain forest .. 2·40 1·00
889. 3 l. Lugina Peak (vert.) .. 3·00 1·25
890. 4 l. White River, Thethi (vert.) .. .. .. 3·75 1·60
891. 5 l. Dry Mountain .. 4·75 2·25
892. 9 l. Lake of Flowers, Lure 10·50 4·00

**196.** Frontier Guard.  **197.** Rifleman.

**1965.** 20th Anniv. of Frontier Force.

893 **196** 2 l. 50 multicoloured .. 1·75 75
894 12 l. 50 multicoloured 7·25 3·00

**1965.** European Shooting Championships, Bucharest.

895. **197.** 1 l. purple, red & violet 15 10
896. – 2 l. pur., ultram. & blue 55 15
897. – 3 l. red and pink .. 75 25
898. – 4 l. multicoloured .. 1·10 25
899. – 15 l. multicoloured .. 4·50 1·75

DESIGNS: 2 l., 15 l. Rifle-shooting (different). 3 l. "Target" map. 4 l. Pistol-shooting.

**198.** I.T.U. Emblem and Symbols.  **199.** Beliajev.

**1965.** Cent. of I.T.U.

900. **198.** 2 l. 50 mve., blk. & grn. 1·60 20
901. 12 l. 50 blue, blk. & vio. 6·00 1·40

**1965.** Space Flight of "Voskhod 2".

902. **199.** 1 l. 50 brown and blue 15 10
903. – 2 l. blue, ultram. & lilac 25 10
904. – 6 l. 50 brown & mauve 1·10 30
905. – 20 l. yell., blk. & blue .. 4·00 1·10

DESIGNS: 2 l. "Voskhod 2". 6 l. 50, Leonov. 20 l. Leonov in space.

**200.** Marx and Lenin.  **201.** Mother and Child.

**1965.** Postal Ministers' Congress, Peking.

907. **200.** 2 l. 50 sepia, red & yell. 65 25
908. 7 l. 50 green, red & yell. 2·75 1·10

**1965.** Int. Children's Day. Multicoloured.

909. 1 l. Type **201** .. .. 20 10
910. 2 l. Children planting tree 40 15
911. 3 l. Children and construction toy (horiz.) .. 65 15
912. 4 l. Child on beach .. 80 25
913. 15 l. Child reading book .. 3·75 1·50

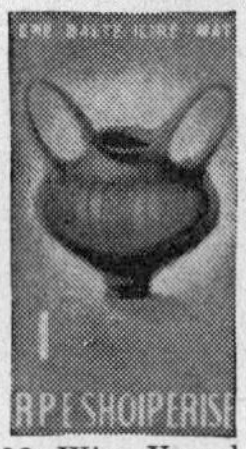

**202.** Wine Vessel.  **203.** Fuchsia.

**1965.** Albanian Antiquities. Multicoloured.

914. 1 l. Type **202** .. .. 15 10
915. 2 l. Helmet and shield .. 35 10
916. 3 l. Mosaic of animal (horiz.) 75 20
917. 4 l. Statuette of man .. 1·40 25
918. 15 l. Statuette of headless and limbless man .. 3·75 1·40

**1965.** Albanian Flowers. Multicoloured.

919. 1 l. Type **203** .. .. 20 10
920. 2 l. Cyclamen .. .. 65 15
921. 3 l. Lilies .. .. .. 1·00 20
922. 3 l. 50 Iris .. .. .. 1·25 20
923. 4 l. Dahlia .. .. .. 1·40 30
924. 4 l. 50 Hydrangea .. .. 1·50 30
925. 5 l. Rose .. .. .. 1·75 60
926. 7 l. Tulips .. .. .. 2·40 75

(Currency revaluation 10 (old) leks = 1 (new) lek).

**1965.** Surch.

927. 5 q. on 30 l. (No. 787) .. 15 15
928. 15 p. on 30 l. (No. 787) .. 40 15
929. 25 q. on 50 l. (No. 788) .. 55 20
930. 80 q. on 50 l. (No. 788) .. 1·90 75
931. 1 l. 10 on 20 l. (No. 786) .. 2·75 1·00
932. 2 l. on 20 l. (No. 786) .. 5·50 1·90

**205.** White Stork.  **206.** "War Veterans" (after painting by B. Sejdini).

**1965.** Migratory Birds. Multicoloured.

933. 10 q. Type **205** .. .. 40 10
934. 20 q. European cuckoo .. 1·00 30
935. 30 q. Hoopoe .. .. 1·50 55
936. 40 q. European bee-eater .. 2·00 75
937. 50 q. European night jar .. 2·25 1·10
938. 1 l. 50 Common quail .. 7·25 3·25

**1965.** War Veterans Conf.

939. **206.** 25 q. brown and black 2·75 75
940. 65 q. blue and black .. 6·50 1·50
941. 1 l. 10 black .. .. 9·00 2·25

**207.** Hunter stalking Capercaillie.  **208.** "Nerium oleander".

**1965.** Hunting.

942. **207.** 10 q. multicoloured .. 75 20
943. – 20 q. brown, sep. & grn. 75 15
944. – 30 q. multicoloured .. 1·60 70
945. – 40 q. purple and green 2·00 80
946. – 50 q. brn., blue & blk. 1·75 50
947. – 1 l. brown, bistre & grn. 3·75 90

DESIGNS: 20 q. Shooting roe deer, 30 q. Ring-necked pheasant. 40 q. Shooting mallard. 50 q. Dogs chasing wild boar. 1 l. Hunter and brown hare.

**1965.** Mountain Flowers. Multicoloured.

948. 10 q. Type **208** .. .. 25 15
949. 20 q. "Myosotis alpestris" 35 15
950. 30 q. "Dianthus glacialis" 55 25
951. 40 q. "Nymphaea alba" .. 1·10 35
952. 50 q. "Lotus corniculatus" 1·40 45
953. 1 l. "Papaver rhoeas" .. 3·25 1·40

**209.** Tourist Hotel, Fier.  **210.** Freighter "Teuta".

**1965.** Public Buildings.

954. **209.** 5 q. black and blue .. 10 10
955. – 10 q. black and buff .. 15 10
956. – 15 q. black and green 20 10
957. – 25 q. black and violet 75 15
958. – 65 q. black and brown 1·25 35
959. – 80 q. black and green 1·50 45
960. – 1 l. 10 black and purple 2·25 50
961. – 1 l. 60 black and blue 3·00 1·25
962. – 2 l. black and pink .. 4·25 1·40
963. – 3 l. black and grey .. 8·00 2·40

BUILDINGS: 10 q. Peshkopi Hotel. 15 q. Sanatorium, Tirana. 25 q. "House of Rest", Pogradec. 65 q. Partisans Sports Palace, Tirana. 80 q. "House of Rest", Dajti Mountain. 1 l. 10, Palace of Culture, Tirana. 1 l. 60, Adriatic Hotel, Durres. 2 l. Migjeni Theatre, Shkoder. 3 l. "A. Moisiu" Cultural Palace, Durres.

**1965.** Evolution of Albanian Ships.

964. **210.** 10 q. green .. .. 30 15
965. – 20 q. bistre and green 45 15
966. – 30 q. blue .. .. 60 25
967. – 40 q. violet .. .. 85 35
968. – 50 q. red and rose .. 1·75 45
969. – 1 l. brown and ochre .. 3·25 85

DESIGNS: 20 q. Punt. 30 q. 19th-century sailing ship. 40 q. 18th-century brig. 50 q. Freighter "Vlora". 1 l. Illyrian galliots.

**211.** Head of Brown Bear.  **212.** Championships Emblem.

**1965.** Brown Bears. Different Bear designs, as T **211**.

970. – 10 q. brown and buff .. 25 10
971. – 20 q. brown and buff .. 65 15
972. – 30 q. brown, red & buff 90 30
973. – 35 q. brown and buff .. 1·10 35
974. – 40 q. brown and buff .. 1·40 40
975. **211.** 50 q. brown and buff .. 2·25 45
976. – 55 q. brown and buff .. 3·00 75
977. – 60 q. brown, red and buff 4·50 2·40

The 10 q. to 40 q. are vert.

**1965.** 7th Balkan Basketball Championships, Tirana. Multicoloured.

978. 10 q. Type **212** .. .. 15 10
979. 20 q. Competing players .. 35 10
980. 30 q. Clearing ball .. .. 75 15
981. 50 q. Attempted goal .. 1·90 20
982. 1 l. 40 Medal and ribbon .. 3·75 90

**213.** Arms on Book.  **214.** Cow.

**1966.** 20th Anniv. of Albanian People's Republic.

983. **213.** 10 q. gold, red & brown 15 10
984. – 20 q. gold, bl. & ultram. 20 15
985. – 30 q. gold, yell. & brn. 75 20
986. – 60 q. gold, apple & green 1·40 65
987. – 80 q. gold, red & brown 2·25 75

DESIGNS (Arms and): 20 q. Chimney stacks. 30 q. Ear of corn. 60 q. Hammer, sickle and open book. 80 q. Industrial plant.

**1966.** Domestic Animals. Animals in natural colours; inscr. in black: frame colours given

988. **214.** 10 q. turquoise .. 25 15
989. – 20 q. green .. .. 75 20
990. – 30 q. blue .. .. 1·10 25
991. – 35 q. lavender .. 1·25 30
992. – 40 q. pink .. .. 1·50 30
993. – 50 q. yellow .. .. 1·75 35
994. – 55 q. blue .. .. 2·00 60
995. – 60 q. yellow .. .. 4·00 85

ANIMALS—HORIZ. 20 q. Pig. 30 q. Sheep. 35 q. Goat. 40 q. Dog. VERT. 50 q. Cat. 55 q. Horse. 60 q. Ass.

**215.** Football.  **216.** A. Z. Cajupi.

**1966.** World Cup Football Championships (1st series).

996. **215.** 5 q. orge., grey & buff 10 10
997. – 10 q. multicoloured .. 15 10
998. – 15 q. blue, yell. & buff 20 10
999. – 20 q. multicoloured .. 30 15
1000. – 25 q. sepia, red and buff 40 15
1001. – 30 q. brn., green & buff 45 25
1002. – 35 q. green, blue & buff 75 25
1003. – 40 q. brown red and buff 80 30
1004. – 50 q. multicoloured .. 90 55
1005. – 70 q. multicoloured .. 1·25 80

DESIGNS: Footballer and map showing 10 q. Montevideo (1930). 15 q. Rome (1934). 20 q. Paris (1938). 25 q. Rio de Janeiro (1950). 30 q. Berne (1954). 35 q. Stockholm (1958). 40 q. Santiago (1962). 50 q. London (1966). 70 q. World Cup and football.

See also Nos. 1035/42.

**1966.** Birth Cent. of Andon Cajupi (poet).

1006. **216.** 40 q. indigo and blue .. 1·10 55
1007. 1 l. 10 bronze and green 2·50 1·10

**217.** Painted Lady ("Vanessa cardui").  **218.** W.H.O. Building.

**1966.** Butterflies and Dragonflies. Mult.

1008. 10 q. Type **217** .. .. 25 10
1009. 20 q. Damsel-fly ("Calopteryx virgo") 35 10
1010. 30 q. Pale Clouded Yellow ("Colias hyale"). .. 45 15
1011. 35 q. Damsel-fly ("Calopteryx splendens") 55 20
1012. 40 q. Damsel-fly ("Calopteryx splendens") (different) .. 70 20
1013. 50 q. European Swallowtail ("Papilio machaon") 1·40 35
1014. 55 q. Yellow butterfly ("Colias myrmidone") 1·50 35
1015. 60 q. "Neptis lucilla" .. 3·50 90

The 20, 35 and 40 q. are dragonflies, remainder are butterflies.

**1966.** Inaug. of W.H.O. Headquarters, Geneva.

1016. **218.** 25 q. black and blue .. 40 10
1017. – 35 q. blue and orange 1·10 15
1018. – 60 q. red, blue & green 1·40 30
1019. – 80 q. blue, yell. & brn. 2·40 55

DESIGNS—VERT. 35 q. Ambulance and patient. 60 q. Nurse and mother weighing baby. HORIZ. 80 q. Medical equipment.

**219.** Leaf Star.  **220.** "Luna 10".

**1966.** "Starfish". Multicoloured.

1020. 15 q. Type **219** .. .. 25 10
1021. 25 q. Spiny Star .. .. 45 15
1022. 35 q. Brittle Star .. 1·00 20
1023. 45 q. Sea Star .. .. 1·40 25
1024. 50 q. Blood Star .. .. 1·50 35
1025. 60 q. Sea Cucumber .. 2·00 35
1026. 70 q. Sea Urchin .. 3·50 1·50

**1966.** "Luna 10". Launching.

1027. **220.** 20 q. multicoloured .. 60 15
1028. – 30 q. multicoloured .. 80 20
1029. **220.** 70 q. multicoloured .. 1·50 30
1030. – 80 q. multicoloured .. 3·00 90

DESIGN: 30 q., 80 q. Earth, Moon and trajectory of "Luna 10".

**221.** Water-Level Map of Albania. **222.** Footballers (Uruguay, 1930).

**1966.** Int. Hydrological Decade.

1031. **221.** 20 q. blk., orge. & red 45 15
1032. – 30 q. multicoloured .. 90 20
1033. – 70 q. black and violet 1·90 35
1034. – 80 q. multicoloured .. 2·40 1·10

DESIGNS: 30 q. Water scale and fields. 70 q. Turbine and electricity pylon. 80 q. Hydrological decade emblem.

**1966.** World Cup Football Championships (2nd series). Inscriptions and values in black.

1035. **222.** 10 q. purple and ochre 15 10
1036. – 20 q. olive and blue .. 25 10
1037. – 30 q. slate and red .. 65 15
1038. – 35 q. red and blue .. 75 15
1039. – 40 q. brown and green 90 15
1040. – 50 q. green and brown 1·10 45
1041. – 55 q. green and mauve 1·10 85
1042. – 60 q. ochre and red .. 2·25 1·25

DESIGNS: (Various footballers representing World Cup winners): 20 q. Italy, 1934. 30 q. Italy, 1938. 35 q. Uruguay, 1950. 40 q. West Germany, 1954. 50 q. Brazil, 1958. 55 q. Brazil, 1962. 60 q. Football and names of 16 finalists in 1966 Championships.

**223.** Tortoise.

**1966.** Reptiles. Multicoloured.

1043. 10 q. Type **223** .. .. 15 10
1044. 15 q. Grass snake .. 25 15
1045. 25 q. Swamp tortoise .. 40 20
1046. 30 q. Lizard .. .. 50 25
1047. 35 q. Salamander .. 60 30
1048. 45 q. Green lizard .. 1·10 35
1049. 50 q. Slow-worm .. 1·10 65
1050. 90 q. Sand viper .. 2·75 1·25

**224.** Siamese Cat. **225.** P. Budi (writer).

**1966.** Cats. Multicoloured.

1051. 10 q. Type **224** .. .. 20 15
1052. 15 q. Tabby .. .. 25 15
1053. 25 q. Kitten .. .. 80 25
1054. 45 q. Persian .. .. 1·50 35
1055. 60 q. Persian .. .. 2·00 80
1056. 65 q. Persian .. .. 2·25 90
1057. 80 q. Persian .. .. 2·75 1·10

Nos. 1053/7 are horiz.

**1966.** 400th Birth Anniv. of P. Budi.

1058. **225.** 25 q. bronze and flesh 35 20
1059. 1 l. 75 purple & green 2·75 1·60

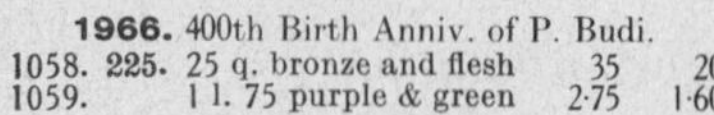

**226.** U.N.E.S.C.O. Emblem.

**1966.** 20th Anniv. of U.N.E.S.C.O. Mult.

1060. 5 q. Type **226** .. .. 15 10
1061. 15 q. Tulip and open book 30 15
1062. 25 q. Albanian dancers .. 85 20
1063. 1 l. 55 Jug & base of column 4·25 1·40

**227.** Borzoi.

**1966.** Dogs. Multicoloured.

1064. 10 q. Type **227** .. .. 35 10
1065. 15 q. Kuvasz .. .. 45 15
1066. 25 q. Setter .. .. 1·10 20
1067. 45 q. Cocker Spaniel .. 1·60 75
1068. 60 q. Bulldog .. .. 1·75 90
1069. 65 q. St. Bernard .. 2·40 1·00
1070. 80 q. Dachshund .. 3·00 1·40

**228.** Hand holding Book. **229.** Ndre Mjeda (poet).

**1966.** 5th Workers Party Congress, Tirana. Multicoloured.

1071. 15 q. Type **228** .. .. 35 10
1072. 25 q. Emblems of agriculture and industry .. 75 10
1073. 65 q. Hammer and sickle, wheat and industrial skyline .. .. .. 1·60 30
1074. 95 q. Hands holding banner on bayonet & implements 2·75 55

**1966.** Birth Cent. of Ndre Mjeda.

1075. **229.** 25 q. brown and blue 65 20
1076. 1 l. 75 brown & green 3·75 1·40

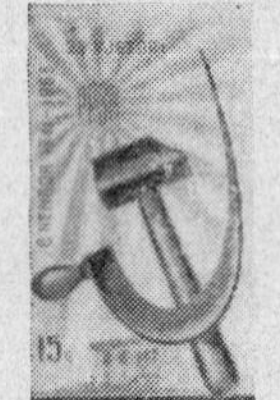

**230.** Hammer and Sickle. **231.** Young Communists and Banner.

**1966.** 25th Anniv. of Albanian Young Communists' Union. Multicoloured.

1077. 15 q. Type **230** .. .. 35 10
1078. 25 q. Soldier leading attack 75 10
1079. 65 q. Industrial worker .. 1·60 30
1080. 95 q. Agricultural and industrial vista .. 2·75 55

**1966.** 25th Anniv. of Young Communists Union. Multicoloured.

1081. 5 q. Manifesto (vert.) .. 10 10
1082. 10 q. Type **231** .. .. 20 10
1083. 1 l. 85 Partisans and banner (vert.) .. 3·25 1·10

**232.** Golden Eagle. **233.** Hake.

**1966.** Birds of Prey. Multicoloured.

1084. 10 q. Type **232** .. .. 65 20
1085. 15 q. White-tailed sea eagle .. .. .. 95 35
1086. 25 q. Griffon vulture .. 1·60 80
1087. 40 q. European sparrow hawk .. .. 2·40 1·00
1088. 50 q. Osprey .. .. 3·00 1·25
1089. 70 q. Egyptian vulture .. 4·25 1·75
1090. 90 q. Common kestrel .. 4·75 2·40

**1967.** Fishes. Multicoloured.

1091. 10 q. Type **233** .. .. 25 10
1092. 15 q. Red Mullet .. .. 40 10
1093. 25 q. Opah .. .. 90 15
1094. 40 q. Wolf fish .. .. 1·10 25
1095. 65 q. Lumpsucker .. 1·40 60
1096. 80 q. Swordfish .. .. 2·25 70
1097. 1 l. 15 Father Lasher .. 2·50 1·25

**234.** Dalmatian Pelicans.

**1967.** Dalmatian Pelicans. Mult.

1098. 10 q. Type **234** .. .. 30 20
1099. 15 q. Three pelicans .. 65 30
1100. 25 q. Pelican and chicks at nest .. .. .. 1·75 50
1101. 50 q. Pelicans "taking off" and airborne .. .. 3·75 60
1102. 2 l. Pelican "yawning" .. 10·00 3·00

**235.** "Camellia williamsi". **236.** Congress Emblem.

**1967.** Flowers. Multicoloured.

1103. 5 q. Type **235** .. .. 15 10
1104. 10 q. "Chrysanthemum indicum" .. .. 20 10
1105. 15 q. "Althaea rosea" .. 25 10
1106. 25 q. "Abutilon striatum" 80 15
1107. 35 q. "Paeonia chinensis" 1·10 15
1108. 65 q. "Gladiolus gandavensis" .. .. 1·75 35
1109. 80 q. "Freesis hybrida" .. 2·25 55
1110. 1 l. 15 "Dianthus caryophyllus" .. .. 2·50 1·50

**1967.** 6th. Trade Unions Congress, Tirana.

1111. **236.** 25 q. red, sepia & lilac 90 15
1112. 1 l. 75 red, grn. & grey 4·00 1·60

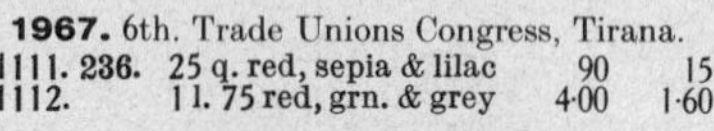

**237.** Rose.

**1967.** Roses. Designs as T **237**.

1113. **237.** 5 q. multicoloured .. 20 10
1114. – 10 q. multicoloured .. 50 10
1115. – 15 q. multicoloured .. 60 10
1116. – 25 q. multicoloured .. 75 10
1117. – 35 q. multicoloured .. 90 20
1118. – 65 q. multicoloured .. 70 35
1119. – 80 q. multicoloured .. 1·60 45
1120. – 1 l. 65 multicoloured 4·00 1·10

**238.** Borsh Coast.

**1967.** Albanian Riviera. Multicoloured.

1121 15 q. Butrinti (vert) .. 35 15
1122 20 q. Type **238** .. 45 15
1123 25 q. Piqeras village .. 80 25
1124 45 q. Coastal view .. 1·25 25
1125 50 q. Himara coast .. 1·40 35
1126 65 q. Fishing boat, Saranda .. .. 2·00 50
1127 80 q. Dhermi .. .. 2·25 90
1128 1 l. Sunset at sea (vert) .. 3·75 1·40

**239.** Fawn.

**1967.** Roe Deer. Multicoloured.

1129. 15 q. Type **239** .. .. 45 10
1130. 20 q. Head of buck (vert.) 45 15
1131. 25 q. Head of doe (vert.) 85 15
1132. 30 q. Doe and fawn .. 85 20
1133. 35 q. Doe and new-born fawn .. .. .. 1·25 25
1134. 40 q. Young buck (vert.) 1·25 30
1135. 65 q. Buck and doe (vert.) 2·50 90
1136. 70 q. Running deer .. 3·00 1·25

**240.** Costumes of Malesia e Madhe Region. **241.** Battle Scene and Newspaper.

**1967.** National Costumes. Multicoloured.

1137. 15 q. Type **240** .. .. 30 10
1138. 20 q. Zadrima .. .. 40 15
1139. 25 q. Kukesi .. .. 50 15
1140. 45 q. Dardhe .. .. 60 30
1141. 50 q. Myzeqe .. .. 65 60
1142. 65 q. Tirana .. .. 1·25 75
1143. 80 q. Dropulli .. .. 1·50 90
1144. 1 l. Laberise .. .. 2·00 1·10

**1967.** 25 Years of the Albanian Popular Press. Multicoloured.

1145. 25 q. Type **241** .. .. 60 15
1146. 75 q. Newspapers and printery .. .. 1·60 45
1147. 2 l. Workers with newspaper .. .. .. 3·75 1·40

**242.** University, Torch and Open Book. **243.** Soldiers and Flag.

**1967.** 10th Anniv. of Tirana University.

1148. **242.** 25 q. multicoloured .. 40 25
1149. 1 l. 75 multicoloured 2·50 1·00

**1967.** 25th Anniv. of Albanian Democratic Front. Multicoloured.

1150. 15 q. Type **243** .. .. 20 10
1151. 65 q. Pick, rifle and flag .. 90 20
1152. 1 l. 20 Torch and open book 1·60 65

**244.** Grey Rabbits.

**1967.** Rabbit-breeding. Multicoloured.

1153. 15 q. Type **244** .. .. 15 10
1154. 20 q. Black and white rabbit (vert.) .. .. 25 10
1155. 25 q. Brown hare .. 65 10
1156. 35 q. Brown rabbits .. 1·00 15
1157. 40 q. Common rabbits .. 1·25 15
1158. 50 q. Grey rabbit (vert.) 1·50 55
1159. 65 q. Head of white rabbit (vert.) .. .. 2·25 75
1160. 1 l. White rabbit .. 3·00 1·10

**245.** "The Marriage Ceremony" (detail, K. Idromeno).

**1967.** Albanian Paintings.

1161. **245.** 15 q. multicoloured .. 55 10
1162. – 20 q. multicoloured .. 80 10
1163. – 25 q. multicoloured .. 1·10 10
1164. – 45 q. multicoloured .. 2·25 10
1165. – 50 q. multicoloured .. 2·40 15
1166. – 65 q. multicoloured .. 3·25 55
1167. – 80 q. multicoloured .. 4·25 80
1168. – 1 l. multicoloured .. 7·25 1·10

DESIGNS—VERT. 20 q. "Head of the Prophet David" (detail, 16th-cent. fresco). 45 q. Ancient mosaic head (from Durres). 50 q. Detail, 16th-cent. icon (30 × 51 mm.) 1 l. "Our Sister" (K. Idromeno). HORIZ.—(51 × 30 mm.): 25 q. "Commandos of the Hakmarrja Battalion" (S. Shijaku). 65 q. "Co-operative" (farm women, Z. Shoshi). 80 q. "Street in Korce" (V. Mio).

**246.** Lenin and Stalin.

**1967.** 50th Anniv. of October Revolution. Multicoloured.
1169. 15 q. Type **246** .. .. 15 10
1170. 25 q. Lenin with soldiers 55 10
1171. 50 q. Lenin addressing meeting .. .. 1·00 20
1172. 1 l. 10 Revolutionaries .. 2·40 60
The 25 q. and 50 q. are vert.

**247.** Turkey. **248.** First Aid.

**1967.** Domestic Fowl. Multicoloured.
1173. 15 q. Type **247** .. 15 10
1174. 20 q. Goose .. .. 45 10
1175. 25 q. Hen .. .. 65 10
1176. 45 q. Cockerel .. .. 1·10 15
1177. 50 q. Guinea-fowl .. 1·25 45
1178. 65 q. Grey lag goose .. 1·60 55
1179. 80 q. Mallard .. .. 2·25 75
1180. 1 l. Chicks .. .. 3·00 1·10
Nos. 1178/80 are horiz.

**1967.** 6th Red Cross Congress, Tirana. Mult.
1181. 15 q.+5 q. Type **248** .. 90 55
1182. 25 q.+5 q. Stretcher case 1·60 90
1183. 65 q.+25 q. Heart patient 4·50 3·00
1184. 80 q.+40 q. Nurse holding child .. .. .. 7·75 4·75

**249.** Arms of Skanderbeg. **250.** Winter Olympic Emblem.

**1967.** 500th Death Anniv. of Castriota Skanderbeg (patriot). (1st issue.) Mult.
1185. 10 q. Type **249** .. 15 10
1186. 15 q. Skanderbeg .. 15 10
1187. 25 q. Helmet and sword 45 10
1188. 30 q. Kruja Castle .. 55 15
1189. 35 q. Petrela Castle .. 65 20
1190. 65 q. Berati Castle .. 1·25 25
1191. 80 q. Meeting of chiefs .. 1·50 55
1192. 90 q. Battle of Albulena 1·60 2·00
See also Nos. 1200/7.

**1967.** Winter Olympic Games, Grenoble. Multicoloured.
1193. 15 q. Type **250** .. 10 10
1194. 25 q. Ice-hockey .. 15 10
1195. 30 q. Figure-skating .. 20 10
1196. 50 q. Skiing (slalom) .. 35 15
1197. 80 q. Skiing (downhill) .. 60 25
1198. 1 l. Ski-jumping .. .. 1·40 35

**251.** Skanderbeg Memorial, Tirana. **252.** Alpine Dianthus.

**1968.** 500th Death Anniv. of Castriota Skanderbeg. (2nd issue.) Multicoloured.
1200. 10 q. Type **251** .. .. 20 10
1201. 15 q. Skanderbeg portrait 25 10
1202. 25 q. Skanderbeg portrait (diff.) .. .. .. 80 10
1203. 30 q. Equestrian statue, Kruja .. .. .. 1·00 15
1204. 35 q. Skanderbeg and mountains .. .. 1·25 15
1205. 65 q. Bust of Skanderbeg 2·25 15
1206. 80 q. Title page of biography .. .. 2·50 75
1207. 90 q. "Skanderbeg battling with the Turks" (painting) .. 3·00 1·10
The 35 q. and 90 q. are horiz.

**1968.** Flowers. Multicoloured.
1208. 15 q. Type **252** .. 15 10
1209. 20 q. Chinese dianthus .. 20 10
1210. 25 q. Pink carnation .. 25 10
1211. 50 q. Red carnation & bud 75 15
1212. 80 q. Two red carnations 1·25 45
1213. 1 l. 10 Yellow carnations 1·60 75

**253.** Ear of Wheat and Electricity Pylon. **254.** Long-horned Goat.

**1968.** 5th Agricultural Co-operative Congress. Multicoloured.
1214. 25 q. Type **253** .. .. 35 10
1215. 65 q. Tractor (horiz.) .. 1·10 40
1216. 1 l. 10 Cow .. .. 1·60 35

**1968.** Goats. Multicoloured.
1217. 15 q. Zane female .. 15 10
1218. 20 q. Kid.. .. .. 15 10
1219. 25 q. Long-haired capore 25 10
1220. 30 q. Black goat at rest 30 10
1221. 40 q. Kids dancing .. 65 10
1222. 50 q. Red and piebald goats .. .. .. 80 15
1223. 80 q. Long-haired ankara .. .. 1·40 25
1224. 1 l. 40 Type **254** .. .. 2·50 75
The 15 q., 20 q. and 25 q. are vert.

**255.** Zef Jubani. **256.** Doctor using Stethoscope.

**1968.** 150th Birth Anniv. of Zef Jubani (patriot).
1225. **255.** 25 q. brown, & yellow 20 15
1226. 1 l. 75 blue, blk. & vio. 2·00 80

**1968.** 20th Anniv. of W.H.O.
1227. **256.** 25 q. red and green .. 35 10
1228. – 65 q. blk., blue & yell. 1·00 20
1229. – 1 l. 10 brown & black 1·50 35
DESIGNS—HORIZ. 65 q. Hospital and microscope. VERT. 1 l. 10, Mother feeding child.

**257.** Servicewoman.

**1968.** 25th Anniv. of Albanian Women's Union.
1230. **257.** 15 q. brown, turq. & salmon .. .. 20 10
1231. – 25 q. turq. and green 30 15
1232. – 60 q. brn. & ochre .. 90 25
1233. – 1 l. vio. & light violet 1·50 50
DESIGNS: 25 q. Teacher. 60 q. Farm-girl. 1 l. Factory-worker.

**258.** Karl Marx. **259.** Heliopsis.

**1968.** 150th Birth Anniv. of Karl Marx. Multicoloured.
1234. 15 q. Type **258** .. 35 15
1235. 25 q. Marx addressing students .. .. 75 15
1236. 65 q. "Das Kapital", "Communist Manifesto" and marchers .. .. 1·40 55
1237. 95 q. Karl Marx .. .. 3·00 75

**1968.** Flowers. Multicoloured.
1238. 15 q. Type **259** .. 10 10
1239. 20 q. Red flax .. .. 10 10
1240. 25 q. Orchid .. .. 15 10
1241. 30 q. Gloxinia .. .. 25 10
1242. 40 q. Orange lily .. 45 10
1243. 80 q. Hippeastrum .. 1·25 20
1244. 1 l. 40 Purple magnolia 2·40 80

**260.** A. Frasheri and Torch. **261.** "Shepherd" (A. Kushi).

**1968.** 90th Anniv. of Prizren Defence League.
1245. **260.** 25 q. black & green 35 10
1246. – 40 q. multicoloured 85 15
1247. – 85 q. multicoloured 1·40 35
DESIGNS: 40 q. League headquarters. 85 q. Frasheri's manifesto and partisans.

**1968.** Paintings in Tirana Gallery. Mult.
1248. 15 q. Type **261** .. .. 10 10
1249. 20 q. "Tirana" (V. Mio) (horiz.) .. .. 15 10
1250. 25 q. "Highlander" (G. Madhi) .. .. 20 10
1251. 40 q. "Refugees" (A. Buza) .. .. 65 10
1252. 80 q. "Partisans at Shahin Matrakut" (S. Xega) 1·25 45
1253. 1 l. 50 "Old Man" (S. Papadhimitri) .. 2·40 90
1254. 1 l. 70 "Shkoder Gate" (S. Rrota) .. .. 3·00 1·10

**262.** Soldiers and Armoured Vehicles.

**1968.** 25th Anniv of People's Army. Mult.
1256 15 q. Type **262** .. .. 30 10
1257 25 q. Sailor & naval craft 75 15
1258 65 q. Pilot and Ilyushin Il-28 and Mikoyan Gurevich MiG-17 aircraft (vert) .. .. 2·25 75
1259 95 q. Soldier and patriots 3·25 1·10

**263.** Common Squid.

**1968.** Marine Fauna. Multicoloured.
1260 15 q. Type **263** .. 20 10
1261 20 q. Common lobster .. 15 10
1262 25 q. Common northern whelk .. .. 55 10
1263 50 q. Edible crab .. 90 35
1264 70 q. Spiny lobster .. 1·25 55
1265 80 q. Common green crab 1·50 75
1266 90 q. Norwegian lobster scampi .. .. 1·60 1·25

**264.** Relay-racing.

**1968.** Olympic Games, Mexico. Mult.
1267. 15 q. Type **264** .. .. 10 10
1268. 20 q. Running .. .. 15 10
1269. 25 q. Throwing the discus 20 10
1270. 30 q. Horse-jumping .. 25 10
1271. 40 q. High-jumping .. 30 10
1272. 50 q. Hurdling .. .. 35 15
1273. 80 q. Football .. .. 70 25
1274. 1 l. 40 High diving .. 1·50 75

**265.** Enver Hoxha (Party Secretary). **266.** Alphabet Book.

**1968.** Enver Hoxha's 60th Birthday.
1276. **265.** 25 q. blue .. .. 30 20
1277. 35 q. purple .. .. 75 25
1278. 80 q. violet .. .. 1·50 80
1279. 1 l. 10 brown .. 1·60 1·25

**1968.** 60th Anniv. of Monastir Language Congress.
1281. **266.** 15 q. lake and green 55 10
1282. 85 q. brown and green 2·75 50

**267.** Bohemian Waxwing.

**1968.** Birds. Diamond-shaped designs as **T 267**. Multicoloured.
1283. 15 q. Type **267** .. .. 50 15
1284. 20 q. Rose-coloured starling .. .. 65 15
1285. 25 q. Common kingfishers .. .. 1·00 25
1286. 50 q. Long-tailed tit .. 1·40 65
1287. 80 q. Wallcreeper .. 2·75 80
1288. 1 l. 10 Bearded reedling 3·50 1·25

**268.** Mao Tse-tung.

**1968.** Mao Tse-tung's 75th Birthday.
1289. **268.** 25 q. blk., red & gold 75 25
1290. 1 l. 75 blk., red & gold 3·75 1·50

**269.** Adem Reka (dock foreman). **270.** Meteorological Equipment.

**1969.** Contemporary Heroes. Multicoloured.
1291. 5 q. Type **269** .. .. 10 10
1292. 10 q. Pjeter Lleshi (telegraph linesman) .. 10 10
1293. 15 q. M. Shehu and M. Kepi (fire victims) .. 15 10
1294. 25 q. Shkurte Vata (railway worker) .. .. 35 20
1295. 65 q. Agron Elezi (earthquake victim) .. .. 85 20
1296. 80 q. Ismet Bruca (school teacher) .. .. 1·10 35
1297. 1 l. 30 Fuat Cela (blind Co-op leader) .. .. 1·60 45

**1969.** 20th Anniv. of Albanian Hydro-Meteorology. Multicoloured.
1298. 15 q. Type **270** .. .. 55 15
1299. 25 q. "Arrow" indicator 90 20
1300. 1 l. 60 Met. balloon and isobar map .. .. 4·25 1·25

**271.** "Student Revolutionaries" (P. Mele).

**1969.** Albanian Paintings since 1944. Mult.
1301. 5 q. Type **271** .. .. 10 10
1302. 25 q. "Partisans 1914" (F. Haxhiu) .. .. 15 10
1303. 65 q. "Steel Mill" (C. Ceka) 65 10
1304. 80 q. "Reconstruction" (V. Kilica) .. .. 75 25
1305. 1 l. 10 "Harvest" (N. Jonuzi) .. .. 1·25 30
1306. 1 l. 15 "Seaside Terraces" (S. Kaceli) .. .. 1·50 90
SIZES: The 25 q., 80 q., 1 l. 10, and 1 l. 15 are 50 × 30 mm.
Nos. 1302/6 are horiz.

272. "Self-portrait".

273. Congress Building.

**1969.** 450th Death Anniv. of Leonardo da Vinci.

1308. 272. 25 q. agate, brn. & gold 25 10
1309. – 35 q. agate, brn. & gold 55 15
1310. – 40 q. agate, brn. & gold 75 15
1311. – 1 l. multicoloured .. 1·60 75
1312. – 2 l. agate, brn. & gold 3·25 1·60

DESIGNS–VERT. 35 q. "Lilies". 1 l. "Portrait of Beatrice". 2 l. "Portrait of a Lady". HORIZ: 40 q. Design for "Helicopter".

**1969.** 25th Anniv. of Permet Congress. Mult.

1314. 25 q. Type **273** .. .. 30 20
1315. 2 l. 25 Two partisans .. 3·75 2·40

274. "Viola albanica".

275. Plum.

**1969.** Flowers. Viola Family. Multicoloured.

1317. 5 q. Type **274** .. .. 10 10
1318. 10 q. "Viola hortensis" 10 10
1319. 15 q. "Viola heterophylla" 15 10
1320. 20 q. "Viola hortensis" (diff.) 20 15
1321. 25 q. "Viola odorata" .. 30 15
1322. 80 q. "Viola hortensis" (diff.) 1·10 75
1323. 1 l. 95 "Viola hortensis" (diff.) .. .. .. 1·90 1·50

**1969.** Fruit Trees (Blossom and Fruit). Multicoloured.

1324. 10 q. Type **275** .. .. 10 15
1325. 15 q. Lemon .. .. 10 10
1326. 25 q. Pomegranate .. 45 10
1327. 50 q. Cherry .. .. 90 15
1328. 80 q. Apricot .. .. 1·50 75
1329. 1 l. 20 Apple .. .. 2·50 1·25

276. Throwing the Ball.

277. Gymnastics.

**1969.** 16th European Basketball Championships, Naples. Multicoloured.

1330. 10 q. Type **276** .. .. 15 10
1331. 15 q. Trying for goal .. 15 10
1332. 25 q. Ball and net (horiz.) 30 10
1333. 80 q. Scoring a goal .. 1·00 20
1334. 2 l. 20 Intercepting a pass 2·40 90

**1969.** National Spartakiad. Multicoloured.

1335. 5 q. Pickaxe, rifle, flag and stadium .. .. 10 10
1336. 10 q. Type **277** .. .. 10 10
1337. 15 q. Running .. .. 15 10
1338. 20 q. Pistol-shooting .. 20 10
1339. 25 q. Swimmer on starting block .. .. .. 25 10
1340. 80 q. Cycling .. .. 90 20
1341. 95 q. Football .. .. 1·10 40

278. Mao Tse-tung.

279. Enver Hoxha.

**1969.** 20th Anniv. of Chinese People's Republic. Multicoloured.

1342. 25 q. Type **278** .. .. 55 15
1343. 85 q. Steel ladle and control room (horiz.) 1·75 55
1344. 1 l. 40 Rejoicing crowd .. 3·50 1·10

**1969.** 25th Anniv. of 2nd National Liberation Council Meeting, Berat. Multicoloured.

1345. 25 q. Type **279** .. 20 10
1346. 80 q. Star and Constitution 75 15
1347. 1 l. 45 Freedom-fighters 1·40 35

280. Entry of Provisional Government, Tirana.

**1969.** 25th Anniv. of Liberation. Mult.

1348. 25 q. Type **280** .. .. 15 10
1349. 30 q. Oil Refinery .. 30 10
1350. 35 q. Combine Harvester 65 10
1351. 45 q. Hydro-electric power station .. .. 1·00 10
1352. 55 q. Soldier & partisans 1·40 55
1353. 1 l. 10 People rejoicing .. 2·50 1·10

281. Stalin.

282. Head of Woman.

**1969.** 90th Birth Anniv. of Joseph Stalin.

1354. 281. 15 q. lilac .. .. 10 10
1355. 25 q. blue .. .. 15 10
1356. 1 l. brown .. .. 90 25
1357. 1 l. 10 blue .. .. 1·10 30

**1969.** Mosaics. (1st series). Multicoloured.

1358. 15 q. Type **282** .. .. 10 10
1359. 25 q. Floor pattern .. 15 10
1360. 80 q. Bird and Tree .. 75 15
1361. 1 l. 10 Diamond floor pattern .. .. .. 1·00 25
1362. 1 l. 20 Corn in oval pattern 1·40 30

Nos. 1359/61 are horiz.

See also Nos. 1391/6, 1564/70 and 1657/62.

283. Manifesto and Congress Building.

285. "Lilium cernum".

284. "25" and Workers.

**1970.** 50th Anniv. of Lushnje Congress.

1363. 283. 25 q. black, red & grey 25 15
1364. – 1 l. 25 blk., yell. & grn. 1·60 75

DESIGN: 1 l. 25, Lushnje postmark of 1920.

**1970.** 25th Anniv. of Albanian Trade Unions.

1365. 284. 25 q. multicoloured .. 25 10
1366. 1 l. 75 multicoloured 1·60 80

**1970.** Lilies. Multicoloured.

1367. 5 q. Type **285** .. .. 10 10
1368. 15 q. "Lilium candidum" 15 10
1369. 25 q. "Lilium regale" .. 15 10
1370. 80 q. "Lilium martagon" 1·10 15
1371. 1 l. 10 "Lilium tigrinum" 1·50 55
1372. 1 l. 15 "Lilium albanicum" 1·60 75

Nos. 1370/2 are horiz.

286. Lenin.

**1970.** Birth Cent. of Lenin. All values black, silver and red.

1373. 5 q. Type **286** .. .. 10 10
1374. 15 q. Lenin making speech 10 10
1375. 25 q. As worker .. 15 10
1376. 95 q. As revolutionary .. 85 30
1377. 1 l. 10 Saluting .. .. 1·25 35

Nos. 1374/6 are all horiz.

287. Frontier Guard.

**1970.** 25th Anniv. of Frontier Force.

1378. 287. 25 q. multicoloured .. 35 10
1379. 1 l. 25 multicoloured 1·40 40

288. Jules Rimet Cup.

**1970.** World Cup Football Championships, Mexico. Multicoloured.

1380. 5 q. Type **288** .. .. 10 10
1381. 10 q. Aztec Stadium .. 10 10
1382. 15 q. Three footballers 15 10
1383. 25 q. Heading goal .. 20 10
1384. 65 q. Two footballers .. 35 15
1385. 80 q. Two footballers .. 90 20
1386. 2 l. Two footballers .. 2·25 40

289. New U.P.U. Headquarters Building.

**1970.** New U.P.U. Headquarters Building, Berne.

1388. 289. 25 q. blue, blk. & new bl. 15 10
1389. 1 l. 10 pink, blk. & orge. 1·10 30
1390. 1 l. 15 turq., blk. & grn. 1·25 40

290. Birds and Grapes.

**1970.** Mosaics (2nd series). Multicoloured.

1391. 5 q. Type **290** .. .. 10 10
1392. 10 q. Waterfowl .. .. 15 10
1393. 20 q. Pheasant and tree-stump .. .. .. 15 10
1394. 25 q. Bird and leaves .. 25 10
1395. 65 q. Fish .. .. 80 20
1396. 2 l. 25 Peacock (vert.) .. 2·00 75

291. Harvesters and Dancers.

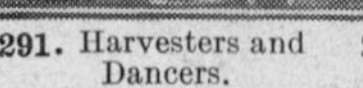

292. Partisans going into Battle.

**1970.** 25th Anniv. of Agrarian Reform.

1397. 291. 15 q. lilac and black .. 15 10
1398. – 25 q. blue and black .. 20 10
1399. – 80 q. brown and black 75 15
1400. – 1 l. 30 brown & black 1·10 30

DESIGNS: 25 q. Ploughed fields and open-air conference. 80 q. Cattle and newspapers. 1 l. 30, Combine-harvester and official visit.

**1970.** 50th Anniv. of Battle of Vlore.

1401. 292. 15 q. brn., orge. & blk. 15 10
1402. – 25 q. brn., yell. & blk. 25 10
1403. – 1 l. 60 myrtle, green and black .. .. 1·25 75

DESIGNS: 25 q. Victory parade. 1 l. 60, Partisans.

293. "The Harvesters" (I. Sulovari).

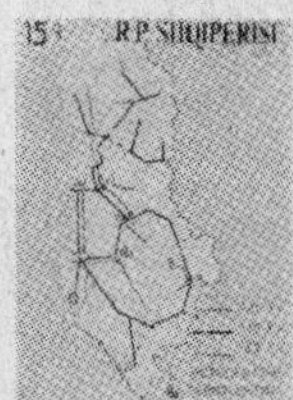

294. Electrification Map.

**1970.** 25th Anniv. of Liberation. Prize winning Paintings. Multicoloured.

1404. 5 q. Type **293** .. .. 10 10
1405. 15 q. "Return of the Partisan" (D. Trebicka) 10 10
1406. 25 q. "The Miners" (N. Zajmi) .. .. 15 10
1407. 65 q. "Instructing the Partisans" (H. Nallbani) 30 15
1408. 95 q. "Making Plans" (V. Kilica) .. .. 75 45
1409. 2 l. "The Machinist" (Z. Shoshi) .. .. 2·25 80

The 15 q. and 2 l. are vert.

**1970.** Rural Electrification Completion. Multicoloured.

1411. 15 q. Type **294** .. 15 10
1412. 25 q. Lamp and graph 20 10
1413. 80 q. Erecting power lines 75 15
1414. 1 l. 10 Uses of electricity 1·25 45

295. Engels.

L.V BEETHOVEN
SHQIPERIA 5

296. Beethoven's Birthplace.

**1970.** 150th Birth Anniv. of Friedrich Engels.

1415. 295. 25 q. blue and bistre 20 10
1416. – 1 l. 10 purple & bistre 1·10 50
1417. – 1 l. 15 olive and bistre 1·10 60

DESIGNS: 1 l. 10, Engels as a young man. 1 l. 15, Engels making speech.

**1970.** Birth Bicent. of Beethoven.

1418. 296. 5 q. violet and gold 10 10
1419. – 15 q. purple and silver 10 10
1420. – 25 q. green and gold 20 10
1421. – 65 q. purple and silver 45 15
1422. – 1 l. 10 blue and gold .. 90 25
1423. – 1 l. 80 black and silver 1·75 40

DESIGNS-VERT. Beethoven: 15 q. In silhouette. 25 q. As young man. 65 q. Full-face. 1 l. 10, Profile. HORIZ. 1 l. 80, Stage performance of "Fidelio".

297. Republican Emblem.

**1971.** 25th Anniv. of Republic.

1424. 297. 15 q. multicoloured .. 10 10
1425. – 25 q. multicoloured .. 15 10
1426. – 80 q. blk., gold & grn. 90 15
1427. – 1 l. 30 blk., gold & brn. 1·25 65

DESIGNS: 25 q. Proclamation. 80 q. Enver Hoxha. 1 l. 30, Patriots.

297a. Tractor Factory, Tirana.

**1971.** Industry. Multicoloured.

1427a. 10 q. Type **297a** .. .. £130 75·00
1427b. 15 q. Fertiliser factory, Fier .. .. .. £130 75·00
1427c. 20 q. Superphosphate factory, Lac (vert.) .. £130 75·00
1427d. 25 q. Cement factory, Elbasan .. .. £130 75·00

**298.** 'Storming the Barricades''.

**1971.** Cent. of Paris Commune.

1428. – 25 q. blue & deep bl. 15 10
1429. – 50 q. green & grey .. 30 10
1430. **298.** 65 q. chest & brown 40 15
1431. – 1 l. 10 lilac & violet 65 25

DESIGNS—VERT. 25 q. "La Marseillaise". 50 q. Women Communards. HORIZ. 1 l. 10, Firing squad.

**299.** "Conflict of Race''. **300.** Tulip.

**1971.** Racial Equality Year.

1432. **299.** 25 q. black & brown 15 10
1433. 1 l. 10 black & red .. 75 20
1434. 1 l. 15 black and red 85 25

**1971.** Hybrid Tulips. Designs as T **300.**

1435. **300.** 5 q. multicoloured .. 10 10
1436. – 10 q. multicoloured .. 10 10
1437. – 15 q. multicoloured .. 15 10
1438. – 20 q. multicoloured .. 15 10
1439. – 25 q. multicoloured .. 45 10
1440. – 80 q. multicoloured .. 1·25 15
1441. – 1 l. multicoloured .. 1·60 55
1442. – 1 l. 45 multicoloured 3·00 1·25

**301.** "Postrider". **302.** Globe and Satellite (1970).

**1971.** 500th Birth Anniv. of Albrecht Durer (painter and engraver).

1443. **301.** 10 q. black and green 10 10
1444. – 15 q. black and blue 30 10
1445. – 25 q. black and blue 45 10
1446. – 45 q. black and purple 75 10
1447. – 65 q. multicoloured .. 1·10 20
1448. – 2 l. 40 multicoloured 2·75 90

DESIGNS.—VERT. 15 q. "Three Peasants". 25 q. "Peasant Dancers". 45 q. "The Bagpiper". HORIZ. 65 q. "View of Kalchreut". 2 l. 40, "View of Trient".

**1971.** Chinese Space Achievements. Mult.

1450. 60 q. Type **302** .. 75 20
1451. 1 l. 20 Public Building, Tirana .. .. 1·25 30
1452. 2 l. 20 Globe and satellite (1971). 2·50 60

The date on No. 1451 refers to the passage of Chinese satellite over Tirana.

**304.** Crested Tit.

**1971.** Birds. Multicoloured.

1457. 5 q. Type **304** .. .. 15 10
1458. 10 q. Serin .. .. 15 10
1459. 15 q. Linnet .. .. 20 10
1460. 25 q. Firecrest .. .. 80 15
1461. 45 q. Rock Thrush .. 1·25 40
1462. 60 q. Blue Tit .. .. 2·25 75
1463. 2 l. 40 Chaffinch .. .. 8·50 6·75

**305.** Running.

**1971.** Olympic Games (1972). (1st issue). Multicoloured.

1464. 5 q. Type **305** .. .. 10 10
1465. 10 q. Hurdling .. .. 10 10
1466. 15 q. Canoeing .. .. 10 10
1467. 25 q. Gymnastics .. 20 10
1468. 80 q. Fencing .. .. 50 20
1469. 1 l. 05 Football .. .. 95 20
1470. 3 l. 60 Diving .. .. 3·50 1·00

See also Nos. 1522/29.

**306.** Workers with Banner. **307.** "XXX" and Red Flag.

**1971.** 6th Workers' Party Congress. Mult.

1472. 25 q. Type **306** .. .. 20 10
1473. 1 l. 05 Congress hall .. 1·25 85
1474. 1 l. 20 "VI", flag, Congress Hall, star and rifle (vert.) 1·50 1·10

**1971.** 30th Anniv. of Albanian Workers' Party. Multicoloured.

1475. 15 q. Workers and industry (horiz.) .. .. .. 25 10
1476. 80 q. Type **307** .. .. 90 65
1477. 1 l. 55 Enver, Hoxha and flags (horiz.) .. .. 1·75 1·50

**308.** "Young Man" (R. Kuci)

**1971.** Albanian Paintings. Multicoloured.

1478. 5 q. Type **308** .. .. 10 10
1479. 15 q. "Building Construction" (M. Fushekati) .. 10 10
1480. 25 q. "Partisan" (D. Jukniu) .. .. 15 10
1481. 80 q. "Fighter Pilots" (S. Kristo) (horiz.) .. 90 15
1482. 1 l. 20 "Girl Messenger" (A. Sadikaj) (horiz.) .. 1·25 55
1483. 1 l. 55 "Medieval Warriors" (S. Kamberi) (horiz.) .. 1·75 1·10

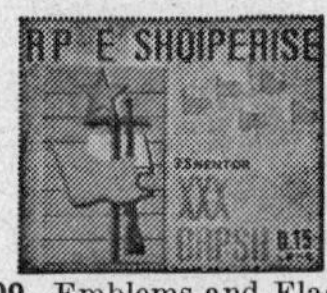


**309.** Emblems and Flags.

**1971.** 30th Anniv. of Albanian Young Communists' Union.

1485. **309.** 15 q. multicoloured .. 15 10
1486. 1 l. 35 multicoloured 1·60 80

**310.** Village Girls.

**1971.** Albanian Ballet "Halili and Hajria". Multicoloured.

1487. 5 q. Type **310** .. 10 10
1488. 10 q. Parting of Halili and Hajria .. .. 15 10
1489. 15 q. Hajria before Sultan Suleiman .. .. 15 10
1490. 50 q. Hajria's marriage .. 75 15
1491. 80 q. Execution of Halili 1·10 55
1492. 1 l. 40 Hajria killing her husband 2·00 1·10

**311.** Rifle-shooting (Biathlon).

**1972.** Winter Olympic Games, Sapporo, Japan. Multicoloured.

1493. 5 q. Type **311** .. .. 10 10
1494. 10 q. Tobogganing .. 10 10
1495. 15 q. Ice-hockey .. .. 10 10
1496. 20 q. Bobsleighing .. 15 10
1497. 50 q. Speed-skating .. 25 15
1498. 1 l. Slalom skiing .. 95 25
1499. 2 l. Ski-jumping .. .. 1·75 85

**312.** Wild Strawberries.

**1972.** Wild Fruits. Multicoloured.

1501. 5 q. Type **312** .. .. 10 10
1502. 10 q. Blackberries .. 10 10
1503. 15 q. Hazelnuts .. .. 15 10
1504. 20 q. Walnuts .. .. 20 10
1505. 25 q. Strawberry-tree fruit 25 15
1506. 30 q. Dogwood berries 40 15
1507. 2 l. 40 Rowanberries .. 2·25 1·00

**313.** Human Heart. **314.** Congress Delegates.

**1972.** World Health Day. Multicoloured.

1508. 1 l. 10 Type **313** .. .. 1·10 25
1509. 1 l. 20 Treatment of cardiac patient .. .. 90 35

**1972.** 7th Albanian Trade Unions Congress. Multicoloured.

1510. 25 q. Type **314** .. .. 25 15
1511. 2 l. 05 Congress Hall .. 1·60 90

**315.** Memorial Flame.

**1972.** 30th Anniv. of Martyrs' Day, and Death of Kemal Stafa.

1512. **315.** 15 q. multicoloured .. 15 10
1513. – 25 q. blk., orge. & grey 20 10
1514. – 1 l. 90 blk. & ochre .. 1·60 30

DESIGNS—VERT. 25 q. "Spirit of Defiance" (statue). HORIZ. 1 l. 90, Kemal Stafa (martyr).

**316.** "Camellia japonica Kamelie".

**1972.** Camellias.

1515. **316.** 5 q. multicoloured .. 10 10
1516. – 10 q. multicoloured .. 15 10
1517. – 15 q. multicoloured .. 15 10
1518. – 25 q. multicoloured .. 20 10
1519. – 45 q. multicoloured .. 35 10
1520. – 50 q. multicoloured .. 45 15
1521. – 2 l. 50 multicoloured 3·00 2·00

DESIGNS: Nos. 1516/21, Various Camellias as Type **316**.

**317.** High-jumping.

**1972.** Olympic Games, Munich (2nd issue). Multicoloured.

1522. 5 q. Type **317** .. .. 10 10
1523. 10 q. Running .. .. 10 10
1524. 15 q. Putting the shot .. 10 10
1525. 20 q. Cycling .. .. 10 10
1526. 25 q. Pole-vaulting .. 15 10
1527. 50 q. Hurdling .. .. 30 15
1528. 75 q. Hockey .. .. 55 20
1529. 2 l. Swimming .. .. 1·60 65

**318.** Articulated bus.

**1972.** Modern Transport. Multicoloured.

1531. 15 q. Type **318** .. .. 10 10
1532. 25 q. Diesel locomotive 50 10
1533. 80 q. Freighter "Tirana" 80 15
1534. 1 l. 05 Motor-car .. 70 20
1535. 1 l. 20 Container lorry .. 1·10 45

**319.** "Trial of Strength".

**1972.** 1st Nat. Festival of Traditional Games. Multicoloured.

1536. 5 q. Type **319** .. .. 10 10
1537. 10 q. Pick-a-back ball game 10 10
1538. 15 q. Leaping game .. 10 10
1539. 25 q. Rope game .. 15 10
1540. 90 q. Leap-frog .. .. 55 15
1541. 2 l. Women's throwing game 1·40 65

**320.** Newspaper "Mastheads".

**1972.** 30th Anniv. of Press Day.

1542. **320.** 15 q. black and blue 15 10
1543. – 25 q. grn., red & blk. 20 10
1544. – 1 l. 90 blk. & mauve 1·60 85

DESIGNS: 25 q. Printing-press and partisan. 1 l. 90, Workers with newspaper.

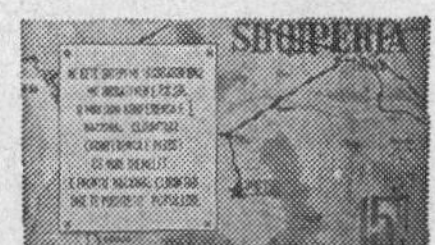


**321.** Location Map and Commemorative Plaque.

**1972.** 30th Anniv. of Peza Conf. Mult.
1545. 15 q. Type **321** .. 15 10
1546. 25 q. Partisans with flag .. 25 10
1547. 1 l. 90 Conference Memorial 1·60 85

**322.** " Partisans Conference " (S. Capo).

**1972.** Albanian Paintings. Multicoloured.
1548. 5 q. Type **322** .. .. 10 10
1549. 10 q. " Head of Woman " (I. Lulani) (vert.) .. 10 10
1550. 15 q. " Communists " (L. Shkreli) (vert.) .. 10 10
1551. 20 q. " Nendorit, 1941 " (S. Shijaku) (vert.) .. 15 10
1552. 50 q. " Farm Woman " (Z. Shoshi) (vert.) .. 55 15
1553. 1 l. " Landscape " (D. Trebicka) .. .. 1·10 45
1554. 2 l. " Girls with Bicycles " (V. Kilica) .. .. 2·25 1·10

**323.** Congress Emblem. **324.** Lenin.

**1972.** 6th Congress of Young Communists' Union.
1556. **323.** 25 q. gold, red & silver 25 10
1557. – 2 l. 05 multicoloured 1·75 90
DESIGN: 2 l. 05, Young worker and banner.

**1972.** 55th Anniv. of Russian October Revolution. Multicoloured.
1558. **324.** 1 l. 10 multicoloured 1·10 55
1559. – 1 l. 20 red, blk. & pink 1·10 65
DESIGN: 1 l. 10, Hammer and Sickle.

**325.** Albanian Soldiers.

**1972.** 60th Anniv. of Independence.
1560. **325.** 15 q. blue, red & blk. 10 10
1561. – 25 q. multicoloured .. 20 15
1562. – 65 q. multicoloured .. 40 15
1563. – 1 l. 25 black and red 90 65
DESIGNS—VERT. 25 q. Ismail Qemali. 1 l. 25, Albanian double-eagle emblem. HORIZ. 65 q. "Proclamation of Independence".

**326.** Cockerel (mosaic).

**1972.** Ancient Mosaics from Apolloni and Butrint (3rd series). Multicoloured.
1564. 5 q. Type **326** .. .. 10 10
1565. 10 q. Bird (vert.) .. .. 10 10
1566. 15 q. Partridges (vert.) .. 15 10
1567. 25 q. Warrior's leg .. 20 10
1568. 45 q. Nude on dolphin (vert.) .. .. .. 30 15
1569. 50 q. Fish (vert.) .. 35 15
1570. 2 l. 50 Warrior's head .. 2·75 1·50

**327.** Nicolas Copernicus.

**1973.** 500th Birth Anniv. of Copernicus. Multicoloured.
1571. 5 q. Type **327** .. .. 10 10
1572. 10 q. Copernicus and signatures .. 10 10
1573. 25 q. Engraved portrait .. 15 10
1574. 80 q. Copernicus at desk .. 90 20
1575. 1 l. 20 Copernicus and planets .. .. .. 1·40 55
1576. 1 l. 60 Planetary diagram 1·60 75

**328.** Policeman and Industrial Scene.

**1973.** 30th Anniv. of State Security Police.
1577. **328.** 25 q. blk., bl. & light bl. 25 15
1578. – 1 l. 80 multicoloured 1·60 1·25
DESIGN: 1 l. 80, Prisoner under escort.

**329/330.** Cactus Flowers.

**1973.** Cacti. As T **329/30.**
1579. **329.** 10 q. multicoloured .. 10 10
1580. **330.** 15 q. multicoloured .. 10 10
1581. – 20 q. multicoloured .. 15 10
1582. – 25 q. multicoloured .. 15 10
1583. – 30 q. multicoloured .. 4·00 1·50
1584. – 65 q. multicoloured .. 75 15
1585. – 80 q. multicoloured .. 90 20
1586. – 2 l. multicoloured .. 10 75
Nos. 1579/86 are arranged together se-tenant within the sheet and in alternate formats as Types **329/30**.

**331.** Common Tern.

**1973.** Sea Birds. Multicoloured.
1587. 5 q. Type **331** .. .. 20 10
1588. 15 q. White-winged black tern .. .. .. 20 10
1589. 25 q. Black-headed gull 65 15
1590. 45 q. Great black-headed gull .. .. .. 1·00 30
1591. 80 q. Slender-billed gull 1·60 65
1592. 2 l. 40 Sandwich tern .. 5·25 2·00

**332.** Postmark of 1913, and Letters.

**1973.** 600th Anniv. of First Albanian Stamps. Multicoloured.
1593. 25 q. Type **332** .. .. 55 15
1594. 1 l. 80 Postman and postmarks .. .. .. 3·00 1·25

**333.** Albanian Woman.

**1973.** 7th Albanian Women's Congress.
1595 **333** 25 q. red and pink .. 20 10
1596 1 l. 80 blk, orge & yell 1·50 1·25
DESIGN: 1 l. 80, Albanian female workers.

**334.** " Creation of the General Staff " (G. Madhi).

**1973.** 30th Anniv. of Albanian People's Army. Multicoloured.
1597. 25 q. Type **334** .. .. 10·50 4·50
1598. 40 q. " August 1949 " (sculpture by Sh. Haderi) (vert.) .. .. 10·50 4·50
1599. 60 q. "Generation after Generation" (Statue by H. Dule) (vert.) .. 10·50 4·50
1600. 80 q. " Defend Revolutionary Victories " (M. Fushekati) .. 10·50 4·50

**335.** " Electrification " (S. Hysa).

**1973.** Albanian Paintings. Multicoloured.
1601. 5 q. Type **335** .. .. 10 10
1602. 10 q. " Textile Worker " (E. Nallbani) (vert.) .. 10 10
1603. 15 q. " Gymnastics Class " (M. Fushekati) .. .. 10 10
1604. 50 q. " Aviator " (F. Stamo) (vert.) .. 55 10
1605. 80 q. " Downfall of Fascism " (A. Lakuriqi) .. .. 80 15
1606. 1 l. 20 " Koci Bako " (demonstrators—P. Mele) (vert.) .. .. 1·25 20
1607. 1 l. 30 " Peasant Girl " (Z. Shoshi) (vert.) .. 1·50 25

**336.** " Mary Magdalene ". **338.** Weightlifting.

**337.** Goalkeeper with Ball.

**1973.** 400th Birth Anniv. of Caravaggio. Paintings. Multicoloured.
1609. 5 q. Type **336** .. .. 10 10
1610. 10 q. " The Guitar Player " (horiz.) .. 10 10
1611. 15 q. Self-portrait .. 15 10
1612. 50 q. " Boy carrying Fruit " .. .. 55 15
1613. 80 q. " Basket of Fruit " (horiz.) .. .. .. 80 20
1614. 1 l. 20 " Narcissus " .. 1·25 55
1615. 1 l. 30 " Boy peeling Apple " .. .. 2·00 80

**1973.** World Cup Football Championships, Munich (1974) (1st issue). Multicoloured.
1617. **337.** 5 q. multicoloured .. 10 10
1618. – 10 q. multicoloured .. 10 10
1619. – 15 q. multicoloured .. 10 10
1620. – 20 q. multicoloured .. 15 10
1621. – 25 q. multicoloured .. 20 10
1622. – 90 q. multicoloured .. 1·25 15
1623. – 1 l. 20 multicoloured 1·60 25
1624. – 1 l. 25 multicoloured 1·75 75
DESIGNS: Nos. 1618/24 are similar to Type **337**, showing goalkeepers saving goals.
See also Nos. 1663/70.

**1973.** World Weightlifting Championships, Havana, Cuba.
1626. **338.** 5 q. multicoloured .. 10 10
1627. – 10 q. multicoloured 10 10
1628. – 25 q. multicoloured .. 15 10
1629. – 90 q. multicoloured .. 80 20
1630. – 1 l. 20 mult. (horiz.) 1·00 30
1631. – 1 l. 60 mult. (horiz.) .. 1·40 35
DESIGNS: Nos. 1627/31 are similar to Type **338**, showing various lifts.

**339.** Ballet Scene. **340.** Mao Tse-tung.

**1973.** "Albanian Life and Work". Multicoloured.
1632 5 q. Cement Works, Kavaje .. .. 10 10
1633 10 q. "Ali Kelmendi" lorry factory (horiz) .. 10 10
1634 15 q. Type **339** .. .. 15 10
1635 20 q. Combine-harvester (horiz) .. .. 20 10
1636 25 q. "Telecommunications" .. .. 20 10
1637 35 q. Skier and hotel, Dajt (horiz) .. .. 30 10
1638 60 q. Llogora holiday village (horiz) .. 45 15
1639 80 q. Lake scene .. 55 20
1640 1 l. Textile mill (horiz) .. 40 15
1641 1 l. 20 Furnacemen (horiz) 70 20
1642 2 l. 40 Welder and pipeline (horiz) .. .. 1·75 45
1643 3 l. Skanderbeg Statue, Tirana .. .. 2·40 55
1644 5 l. Roman arches, Durres 3·75 1·50

**1973.** 80th Birth Anniv. of Mao Tse-tung. Multicoloured.
1645. 85 q. Type **340** .. 90 15
1646. 1 l. 20 Mao saluting .. 1·50 75

**341.** " Horse's Head " (Gericault)

**1974.** 150th Death Anniv. of Jean-Louis Gericault (French painter).
1647. **341.** 10 q. multicoloured .. 10 10
1648. – 15 q. multicoloured .. 10 10
1649. – 20 q. black and gold .. 15 10
1650. – 25 q. blk., lilac & gold 20 10
1651. – 1 l. 20 multicoloured 1·40 25
1652. – 2 l. 20 multicoloured 3·00 1·10
DESIGNS—VERT. 15 q. " Male Model " (Gericault). 20 q. " Man and Dog ". 25 q. " Head of a Negro ". 1 l. 20, Self-portrait. HORIZ. 2 l. 20, " Battle of the Giants ".

**342.** "Lenin with Crew of the 'Aurora' " (D. Trebicka).

**1974.** 50th Death Anniv. of Lenin. Mult.
1654. 25 q. Type **342** .. .. 20 10
1655. 60 q. " Lenin " (P. Mele) (vert.) .. .. 90 15
1656. 1 l. 20 " Lenin " (seated) (V. Kilica) (vert.) .. 1·75 1·10

**343.** Duck.

**1974.** Ancient Mosaics from Butrint Pogradec and Apolloni (4th series). Mult.
1657. 5 q. Duck (different) .. 10 10
1658. 10 q. Bird and flower .. 10 10
1659. 15 q. Ornamental basket and grapes .. .. 10 10
1660. 25 q. Type **343** .. .. 15 10
1661. 40 q. Donkey and cockerel 30 15
1662. 2 l. 50 Dragon .. .. 2·50 1·00

**344.** Shooting at Goal.

**1974.** World Cup Football Championships, Munich (2nd issue).
1663. **344.** 10 q. multicoloured .. 10 10
1664. – 15 q. multicoloured .. 10 10
1665. – 20 q. multicoloured .. 15 10
1666. – 25 q. multicoloured .. 20 10
1667. – 40 q. multicoloured .. 30 10
1668. – 80 q. multicoloured .. 90 20
1669. – 1 l. multicoloured .. 1·10 20
1670. – 1 l. 20 multicoloured 1·40 40
DESIGNS: Nos. 1664/70, Players in action similar to Type **344**.

**345.** Memorial and Arms. **346.** " Solanum dulcamara ".

**1974.** 30th Anniv. of Permet Congress. Mult.
1672. 25 q. Type **345** .. .. 15 10
1673. 1 l. 80 Enver Hoxha and text .. .. .. 1·25 35

**1974.** " Useful Plants ". Multicoloured.
1674. 10 q. Type **346** .. .. 10 10
1675. 15 q. " Arbutus uva-ursi " (vert.) .. .. .. 10 10
1676. 20 q. " Convallaria majalis " (vert.) .. 10 10
1677. 25 q. "Colchicum autumnale " (vert.) .. 15 10
1678. 40 q. " Borago officinalis " 65 10
1679. 80 q. "Saponaria officinalis" 1·25 15
1680. 2 l. 20 " Gentiane lutea " 3·00 1·10

**347.** Revolutionaries.

**1974.** 50th Anniv. of 1924 Revolution.
1681. **347.** 25 q. mve., blk. & red 15 10
1682. – 1 l. 80 multicoloured 1·10 35
DESIGN—VERT. 1 l. 80, Prominent revolutionaries.

**348.** Redwing.

**1974.** Song Birds. Multicoloured.
1683. 10 q. Type **348** .. .. 15 10
1684. 15 q. European Robin .. 25 10
1685. 20 q. Greenfinch .. .. 30 10
1686. 25 q. Bullfinch (vert.) .. 40 20
1687. 40 q. Hawfinch (vert.) .. 1·00 25
1688. 80 q. Blackcap (vert.) .. 2·75 65
1689. 2 l. 20 Nightingale (vert.) 5·25 1·90

**349.** Globe and Post Office Emblem.

**1974.** Cent. of Universal Postal Union. Multicoloured.
1690. **349.** 85 q. multicoloured .. 75 20
1691. – 1 l. 20 green, lilac and violet .. .. 1·00 30
DESIGN: 1 l. 20, U.P.U. emblem.

**350.** "Widows" (Sali Shijaku).

**1974.** National Paintings. Multicoloured.
1693. 10 q. Type **350** .. .. 10 10
1694. 15 q. "Road Construction" (Danish Jukniu) .. 10 10
1695. 20 q. "Fulfilling the Plans" (Clirim Ceka) .. .. 10 10
1696. 25 q. "The Call to Action" (Spiro Kristo) .. .. 15 10
1697. 40 q. "The Winter Battle" (Sabaudin Xhaferi) .. 20 10
1698. 80 q. "Three Comrades" (Clirim Ceka) .. .. 35 15
1699. 1 l. "Step by Step, Aid the Partisans" (Guri Madhi) 75 15
1700. 1 l. 20 "At the War Memorial" (Kleo Nini) .. .. 85 25
Nos. 1694, 1696, and 1698 are vert. designs.

**351.** Chinese Festivities.

**1974.** 25th Anniv. of Chinese People's Rebublic. Multicoloured.
1702. **351.** 85 q. multicoloured .. 75 20
1703. – 1 l. 20 blk., red & gold 1·10 25
DESIGN—VERT. 1 l. 20, Mao Tse-tung.

**352.** Volleyball.

**353.** Berat.

**1974.** National Spartakiade. Multicoloured.
1704. 10 q. Type **352** .. .. 10 10
1705. 15 q. Hurdling .. .. 10 10
1706. 20 q. Hoop exercises .. 10 10
1707. 25 q. Stadium parade .. 10 10
1708. 40 q. Weightlifting .. 15 10
1709. 80 q. Wrestling .. .. 35 15
1710. 1 l. Rifle shooting .. 65 20
1711. 1 l. 20 Football .. .. 75 20

**1974.** 30th Anniv. of 2nd Berat Liberal Council Meeting.
1712. **353.** 25 q. red and black .. 15 10
1713. – 80 q. brn., yell. & blk. 65 15
1714. – 1 l. purple & black .. 1·00 45
DESIGNS—HORIZ. 80 q. "Liberation" frieze. VERT. 1 l. Council members walking to meeting.

**354.** Security Guards patrolling Industrial Plant.

**1974.** 30th Anniv. of Liberation. Mult.
1715. 25 q. Type **354** .. .. 10 10
1716. 35 q. Chemical industry 15 10
1717. 50 q. Agricultural produce .. .. 25 10
1718. 80 q. Cultural activities 35 15
1719. 1 l. Scientific technology 70 20
1720. 1 l. 20 Railway construction .. .. .. 75 45

**355.** Head of Artemis.

**356.** Clasped hands.

**1974.** Archaeological Discoveries. Mult.
1722. **355.** 10 q. blk., mve. & silver 10 10
1723. – 15 q. blk., grn. & silver 10 10
1724. – 20 q. blk., buff & silver 10 10
1725. – 25 q. blk., mve. & silver 15 10
1726. – 40 q. multicoloured .. 15 10
1727. – 80 q. blk., blue & silver 60 15
1728. – 1 l. blk., grn. & silver 80 15
1729. – 1 l. 20 blk., sep. & silver 1·50 65
DESIGNS: 15 q. Statue of Zeus. 20 q. Statue of Poseidon. 25 q. Illyrian helmet. 40 q. Greek amphora. 80 q. Bust of Agrippa. 1 l. Bust of Demosthenes. 1 l. 20, Bust of Bilia.

**1975.** 30th Anniv. of Albanian Trade Unions. Multicoloured.
1731. 25 q. Type **356** .. .. 15 10
1732. 1 l. 80 Workers with arms raised .. .. .. 1·10 45

**357.** "Cichorium intybus".

**358.** Head of Jesus. (detail, Doni Tondo).

**1975.** Albanian Flowers. Multicoloured.
1733. 5 q. Type **357** .. .. 10 10
1734. 10 q. "Sempervivum montanum" .. .. 10 10
1735. 15 q. "Aquilegia alpina" 10 10
1736. 20 q. "Anemone hortensis" 10 10
1737. 25 q. "Hibiscus trionum" 10 10
1738. 30 q. "Gentiana kochiana" 15 10
1739. 35 q. "Lavatera arborea" 15 10
1740. 2 l. 70 "Iris graminea" .. 1·60 60

**1975.** 500th Birth Anniv. of Michelangelo. Multicoloured.
1741. **358.** 5 q. multicoloured .. 10 10
1742. – 10 q. brn., grey & gold 10 10
1743. – 15 q. brn., grey & gold 10 10
1744. – 20 q. sepia, grey & gold 15 10
1745. – 25 q. multicoloured .. 15 10
1746. – 30 q. brn., grey & gold 15 10
1747. – 1 l. 20 brn., grey & gold 75 25
1748. – 3 l. 90 multicoloured 2·25 90
DESIGNS: 10 q. " The Slave ". 15 q. " Head of Dawn ". 20 q. " Awakening giant ". 25 q. " Cumaenian Sybil ". 30 q. " Lorenzo di Medici ". 1 l. 20, "David". 3 l. 90, " Delphic Sybil ".

**359.** Horseman.

**1975.** "Albanian Transport of the Past". Multicoloured.
1750 5 q. Type **359** .. .. 10 10
1751 10 q. Horse and cart .. 10 10
1752 15 q. Ferry .. .. 20 10
1753 20 q. Barque .. .. 20 10
1754 25 q. Horse-drawn cab .. 15 10
1755 3 l. 35 Early motor car .. 2·40 75

**360.** Frontier Guard.

**1975.** 30th Anniv. of Frontier Force. Mult.
1756. 25 q. Type **360** .. .. 15 10
1757. 1 l. 80 Guards patrolling industrial plant .. 1·50 80

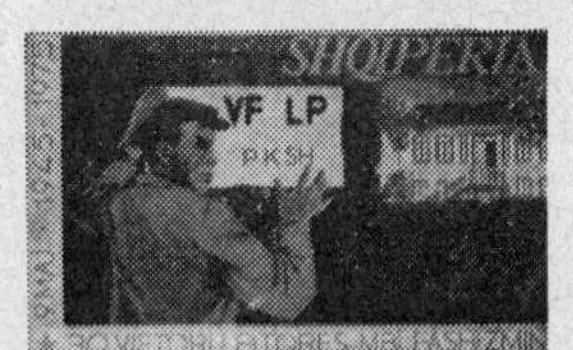

**361.** Patriot affixing anti-fascist Placard.

**1975.** 30th Anniv. of Victory over Fascism. Multicoloured.
1758. 25 q. Type **361** .. .. 10 10
1759. 60 q. Partisans in battle .. 25 10
1760. 1 l. 20 Patriot defeating Nazi soldier .. .. 1·25 55

**362.** European Wigeon.

**1975.** Albanian Wildfowl. Multicoloured.
1761. 5 q. Type **362** .. .. 10 10
1762. 10 q. Red-crested pochard .. .. 15 10
1763. 15 q. White-fronted goose .. .. .. 20 15
1764. 20 q. Pintail .. .. 20 15
1765. 25 q. Red-breasted merganser .. .. 35 15
1766. 30 q. Eider .. .. 70 20
1767. 35 q. Whooper swans .. 85 20
1768. 2 l. 70 Common shoveler 5·25 1·75

**363.** " Shyqyri Kanapari " (Musa Qarri).

**1975.** Albanian Paintings. People's Art Exhibition, Tirana. Multicoloured.
1769. 5 q. Type **363** .. .. 10 10
1770. 10 q. " Sea Rescue " (Agim Faja) .. .. .. 10 10
1771. 15 q. " 28 November 1912" (Petri Ceno) (horiz.) .. 10 10
1772. 20 q. " Workers' Meeting " (Sali Shijaka) .. .. 10 10
1773. 25 q. " Shota Galica " (Ismail Lulani) .. .. 10 10
1774. 30 q. " Victorious Fighters " (Nestor Jonuzi) .. 15 10
1775. 80 q. " Partisan Comrades " (Vilson Halimi) .. 55 15
1776. 2 l. 25 " Republic Day Celebration " (Fatmir Haxhiu) (horiz.) .. 1·40 1·10

**364.** Farmer with Declaration of Reform.

**1975.** 30th Anniv. of Agrarian Reform. Mult.
1778. 15 q. Type **364** .. .. 10 10
1779. 2 l. Agricultural scene .. 1·25 65

**365.** Dead Man's Fingers.

**366.** Cycling.

**1975.** Marine Corals. Multicoloured.
1780. 5 q. Type **365** .. .. 10 10
1781. 10 q. " Paramuricea chamaeleon " .. .. 10 10
1782. 20 q. Red Coral .. 10 10
1783. 25 q. Tube Coral or Sea Fan .. .. .. .. 25 10
1784. 3 l. 70 " Cladocora cespitosa " .. .. 3·75 1·50

**1975.** Olympic Games, Montreal (1976). Multicoloured.
1785. 5 q. Type **366**. .. .. 10 10
1786. 10 q. Canoeing .. .. 10 10
1787. 15 q. Handball .. .. 10 10
1788. 20 q. Basketball .. .. 10 10
1789. 25 q. Water-polo .. .. 15 10
1790. 30 q. Hockey .. .. 15 10
1791. 1 l. 20 Pole-vaulting .. 75 20
1792. 2 l. 05 Fencing .. .. 1·25 30

**367.** Power Lines leading to Village.

**1975.** 5th Anniv. of Electrification of Albanian Countryside. Multicoloured.
1794. **367.** 15 q. multicoloured .. 10 10
1795. – 25 q. vio., red & lilac 15 10
1796. – 80 q. blk., turq. & grn. 75 15
1797. – 85 q. buff, brn. & ochre 1·10 75
DESIGNS: 25 q. High power insulators. 80 q. Dam and power station. 85 q. T.V. pylons and emblems of agriculture and industry.

**368.** Berat.

**1975.** Air. Tourist Resorts. Mult.
1798. 20 q. Type **368** .. .. 10 10
1799. 40 q. Gjirokaster .. .. 15 10
1800. 60 q. Sarande .. .. 25 10
1801. 90 q. Durres .. .. 35 20
1802. 1 l. 20 Krujae .. .. 75 25
1803. 2 l. 40 Boga .. .. 1·40 80
1804. 4 l. 05 Tirana .. .. 2·50 1·40

**369.** Child, Rabbit and Bear planting Saplings.

**1975.** Children's Tales. Multicoloured.
1805. 5 q. Type **369** .. .. 10 10
1806. 10 q. Mrs. Fox and cub .. 10 10
1807. 15 q. Ducks in school .. 10 10
1808. 20 q. Bears building .. 10 10
1809. 25 q. Animals watching television .. .. 15 10
1810. 30 q. Animals with log and electric light bulbs 15 10
1811. 35 q. Ants with spade and guitar .. .. .. 30 10
1812. 2 l. 70 Boy and girl with sheep and dog .. 1·60 75

**370.** Arms and Rejoicing Crowd.

**1976.** 30th Anniv. of Albanian People's Republic. Multicoloured.
1813. 25 q. Type **370** .. .. 15 10
1814. 1 l. 90 Folk-dancers .. 1·25 35

**371.** Ice-hockey.

**1976.** Winter Olympic Games, Innsbruck. Multicoloured.
1815. 5 q. Type **371** .. .. 10 10
1816. 10 q. Speed-skating .. 10 10
1817. 15 q. Rifle-shooting (biathlon) 10 10
1818. 50 q. Ski-jumping .. 25 10
1819. 1 l. 20 Skiing (slalom) .. 80 20
1820. 2 l. 30 Bobsleighing .. 1·60 40

**372.** " Colchicum autumnale ".

**1976.** Medicinal Plants. Multicoloured.
1822. 5 q. Type **372** .. .. 10 10
1823. 10 q. " Atropa belladonna " 10 10
1824. 15 q. " Gentiana lutea " 10 10
1825. 20 q. " Aesculus hippocastanum " .. 10 10
1826. 70 q. " Polystichum filix " 30 15
1827. 80 q. " Althaea officinalis " 50 15
1828. 2 l. 30 " Datura stamonium " .. .. 2·00 90

**373.** Wooden Bowl and Spoon.

**1976.** Ethnographical Studies Conference, Tirana. Albanian Artifacts. Multicoloured.
1829. 10 q. Type **373** .. .. 10 10
1830. 15 q. Flask (vert.) .. 10 10
1831. 20 q. Ornamental handles (vert.) .. .. .. 10 10
1832. 25 q. Pistol and dagger .. 15 10
1833. 80 q. Hand-woven rug (vert.) .. .. .. 60 15
1834. 1 l. 20 Filigree buckle and earrings .. .. 90 20
1835. 1 l. 40 Jugs with handles (vert.) .. .. .. 1·10 75

**374.** " Founding the Co-operatives " (Zef Shoshi).

**1976.** Albanian Paintings. Multicoloured.
1836. 5 q. Type **374** .. .. 10 10
1837. 10 q. " Going to Work " (Agim Zajmi) (vert.) .. 10 10
1838. 25 q. " Listening to Broadcast " (Vilson Kilica) .. 15 10
1839. 40 q. " Female Welder " (Sabaudin Xhaferi) (vert.) .. .. 15 10
1840. 50 q. " Steel Workers " (Isuf Sulovari) (vert.) 20 10
1841. 1 l. 20 " 1942 Revolt " (Lec Shkreli) (vert.) .. 80 20
1842. 1 l. 60 " Returning from Work " (Agron Dine) 1·10 30

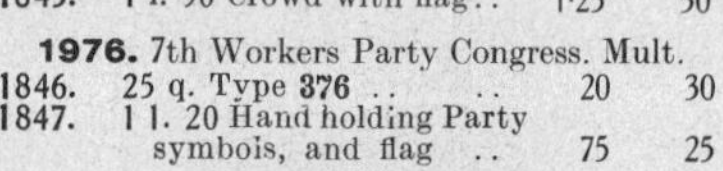
**375.** Demonstrators attacking Police.
**376.** Party Flag, Industry and Agriculture.

**1976.** 35th Anniv. of Hoxha's Anti-Fascist Demonstration. Multicoloured.
1844. 25 q. Type **375** .. .. 15 10
1845. 1 l. 90 Crowd with flag .. 1·25 50

**1976.** 7th Workers Party Congress. Mult.
1846. 25 q. Type **376** .. .. 20 30
1847. 1 l. 20 Hand holding Party symbols, and flag .. 75 25

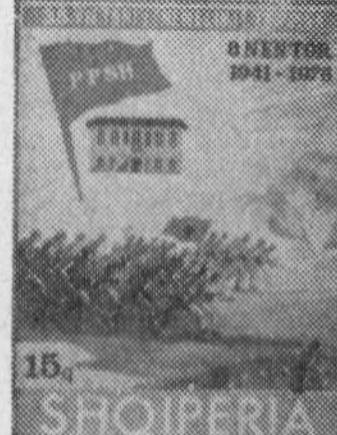

**377.** Communist Advance.

**1976.** 35th Anniv. of Workers' Party. Mult.
1848. 15 q. Type **377** .. .. 15 10
1849. 25 q. Hands holding emblems and revolutionary army 15 10
1850. 80 q. " Reconstruction " 35 15
1851. 1 l. 20 " Heavy Industry and Agriculture " .. 85 20
1852. 1 l. 70 " The Arts "-ballet 1·25 25

**378.** Young Communist.

**1976.** 35th Anniv. of Young Communists' Union. Multicoloured.
1853. 80 q. Type **378** .. .. 60 30
1854. 1 l. 25 Young Communists in action .. .. 80 35

**379.** Ballet Dancers.

**1976.** Albanian Ballet.
1855. **379.** 10 q. multicoloured .. 10 10
1856. – 15 q. multicoloured .. 10 10
1857. – 20 q. multicoloured .. 10 10
1858. – 25 q. multicoloured .. 15 10
1859. – 80 q. multicoloured .. 40 15
1860. – 1 l. 20 multicoloured 60 20
1861 – 1 l. 40 multicoloured 75 25
DESIGNS: 15 q. to 1 l. 40, Various ballet scenes.

**380.** Bashtoves Castle.
**381.** Skanderbeg's Shield and Spear.

**1976.** Albanian Castles.
1863. **380.** 10 q. black and blue .. 10 10
1864. – 15 q. black and green 10 10
1865. – 20 q. black and grey 15 10
1866. – 25 q. black and ochre 20 10
1867. – 80 q. black and red .. 50 15
1868. – 1 l. 20 black and blue 60 20
1869. – 1 l. 40 black and red .. 75 25
DESIGNS: 15 q. Gjirokaster. 20 q. Ali Pash Tepelenes. 25 q. Petreles. 80 q. Berat. 1 l. 20, Durresi. 1 l. 40, Krujes.

**1977.** Skanderbeg's Army Commemoration. Multicoloured.
1870. 15 q. Type **381** .. .. 75 15
1871. 80 q. Helmet, sword and scabbard .. .. 2·50 70
1872. 1 l. Halberd, spear, bow and arrows .. .. 4·00 90

**382.** Ilya Oiqi.
**383.** Polyvinyl-chloride Plant, Vlore.

**1977.** Albanian Heroes. Multicoloured.
1873. 5 q. Type **382** .. .. 10 10
1874. 10 q. Ilia Dashi .. .. 10 10
1875. 25 q. Fran Ndue Ivanaj 30 10
1876. 80 q. Zeliha Allmetaj .. 75 15
1877. 1 l. Ylli Zaimi .. .. 80 25
1878. 1 l. 90 Isuf Plloci .. 1·50 45

**1977.** 6th Five-Year Plan. Multicoloured.
1879. 15 q. Type **383** .. .. 10 10
1880. 25 q. Naphtha plant, Ballsh 15 10
1881. 65 q. Hydro-electric station, Fjerzes .. .. 75 15
1882. 1 l. Metallurgical combinate, Elbasan .. 1·10 30

**384.** Shote Galica.
**385.** Crowd and Martyrs' Monument, Tirana.

**1977.** 50th Death Anniv. of Shote Galica (Communist partisan).
1883. **384.** 80 q. red and pink .. 45 25
1884. – 1 l. 25 grey and blue .. 80 40
DESIGN: 1 l. 25, Shote Galica and father.

**1977.** 35th Anniv. of Martyrs' Day. Mult.
1885. 25 q. Type **385** .. .. 15 10
1886. 80 q. Clenched fist and Albanian flag .. .. 40 20
1887. 1 l. 20 Bust of Qemal Stafa 75 40

**386.** Doctor calling at Village House.
**387.** Workers outside Factory.

**1977.** " Socialist Transformation of the Villages ". Multicoloured.
1888. 5 q. Type **386** .. .. 10 10
1889. 10 q. Cowherd with cattle 10 10
1890. 20 q. Harvesting .. 10 10
1891. 80 q. Modern village .. 75 30
1892. 2 l. 95 Tractor and greenhouse .. .. .. 2·50 90

**1977.** 8th Trade Unions Congress. Mult.
1893. 25 q. Type **387** .. .. 15 15
1894. 1 l. 80 Three workers with flags .. .. .. 1·25 55

**388.** Advancing Soldiers.
**389.** Two Girls with Handkerchiefs.

**1977.** " All the People are Soldiers ". Mult.
1895. 15 q. Type **388** .. .. 10 10
1896. 25 q. Enver Hoxha and marching soldiers .. 15 10
1897. 80 q. Soldiers and workers 50 20
1898. 1 l. The Armed Forces .. 65 25
1899. 1 l. 90 Marching soldiers and workers .. .. 1·50 55

**1977.** National Costume Dances (1st series). Multicoloured.
1900. 5 q. Type **389** .. .. 10 10
1901. 10 q. Two male dancers .. 10 10
1902. 15 q. Man and woman in kerchief dance .. 10 10
1903. 25 q. Two male dancers .. 15 10
1904. 80 q. Two women dancers 50 20
1905. 1 l. 20 " Elbow dance " .. 75 25
1906. 1 l. 55 Two women with kerchiefs .. .. 1·00 45
See also Nos. 1932/6 and 1991/5.

**390.** Armed Worker with Book.
**391.** " Beni Ecen Vet ".

**1977.** New Constitution.
1908. **390.** 25 q. gold, red and black .. .. 20 10
1909. – 1 l. 20 gold, red and black .. .. 1·00 30
DESIGN: 1 l. 20, Industrial and agricultural symbols and hand with book.

**1977.** Albanian Films.
1910. **391.** 10 q. green and grey 10 10
1911. – 15 q. multicoloured .. 10 10
1912. – 25 q. green, blk. & grey 15 10
1913. – 80 q. multicoloured .. 50 20
1914. – 1 l. 20 brown and grey 60 25
1915. – 1 l. 60 multicoloured 1·10 35
DESIGNS: 15 q. " Rruge te Bardha ". 25 q. " Rrugicat qe Kerkonin Diell ". 80 q. " Ne Fillim te Veres ". 1 l. 20, " Lulekuqet Mbi Mure ". 1 l. 60, " Zonja nga Qyteti ".

**392.** Rejoicing Crowd and Independence Memorial, Tirana.
**393.** " Farm Workers ".

**1977.** 65th Anniv of Independence. Mult.
1916 15 q. Type **392** .. .. 10 10
1917 25 q. Independence leaders marching in Tirana .. .. 20 10
1918 1 l. 65 Albanians dancing under national flag .. 1·10 40

**1977.** Paintings by V. Mio. Multicoloured.
1919. 5 q. Type **393** .. .. 10 10
1920. 10 q. " Landscape in the Snow " .. .. .. 10 10
1921. 15 q. " Sheep under a Walnut Tree, Springtime " .. .. 10 10
1922. 25 q. " Street in Korce " 10 10
1923. 80 q. " Riders in the Mountains " .. .. 55 15
1924. 1 l. " Boats by the Seashore " .. .. 75 20
1925. 1 l. 75 " Tractors Ploughing " .. .. .. 1·00 25

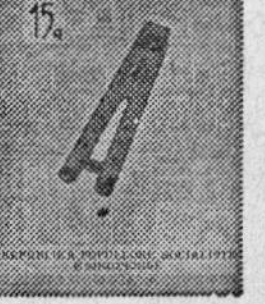

**394.** Pan Flute.
**395.** " Tractor Drivers " (D. Trebicka).

**1978.** Folk Music Instruments.
1927. **394.** 15 q. red, blk. & grn. 10 10
1928. – 25 q. yell., blk. & violet 35 10
1929. – 80 q. red, blk. & blue 1·25 15
1930. – 1 l. 20 yell., blk. & blue 2·00 20
1931. – 1 l. 70 lilac, blk. & grn. 3·50 1·10
DESIGNS: 25 q. Single-string goat's head fiddle. 80 q. Trumpet. 1 l. 20, Drum. 1 l. 70, Bagpipes.

**1978.** National Costume Dances (2nd series). As T **389**. Multicoloured.

| | | | |
|---|---|---|---|
| 1932. | 5 q. Girl dancers with scarves | 10 | 10 |
| 1933. | 25 q. Male dancers | 10 | 10 |
| 1934. | 80 q. Kneeling dancers | 35 | 15 |
| 1935. | 1 l. Female dancers | 60 | 20 |
| 1936. | 2 l. 30 Male dancers with linked arms | 1·50 | 45 |

**1978.** Paintings of the Working Class. Multicoloured.

| | | | |
|---|---|---|---|
| 1937. | 25 q. Type **395** | 10 | 10 |
| 1938. | 80 q. "Steeplejack" (S. Kristo) | 25 | 15 |
| 1939. | 85 q. "A Point in the Discussion" (S. Milori) | 30 | 15 |
| 1940. | 90 q. "Oil Rig Crew" (A. Cini) (vert.) | 40 | 15 |
| 1941. | 1 l. 60 "Metal Workers" (R. Karanxha) | 70 | 25 |

**396.** Boy and Girl.

**1978.** International Children's Day. Mult.

| | | | |
|---|---|---|---|
| 1943. | 5 q. Type **396** | 10 | 10 |
| 1944. | 10 q. Boy and girl with pickaxe and rifle | 10 | 10 |
| 1945. | 25 q. Children dancing | 10 | 10 |
| 1946. | 1 l. 80 Classroom scene | 1·75 | 40 |

**397.** Woman with Pickaxe and Rifle.

**1978.** Eighth Women's Union Congress.

| | | | |
|---|---|---|---|
| 1947. **397.** | 25 q. red and gold | 15 | 10 |
| 1948. – | 1 l. 95 red and gold | 1·60 | 45 |

DESIGN: 1 l. 95, Peasant, Militia Guard and industrial installation.

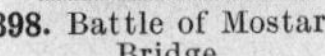

**398.** Battle of Mostar Bridge. **399.** Guerillas and Flag.

**1978.** Centenary of the League of Prizren.

| | | | |
|---|---|---|---|
| 1949. **398.** | 10 q. multicoloured | 10 | 10 |
| 1950. – | 25 q. multicoloured | 15 | 10 |
| 1951. – | 80 q. multicoloured | 40 | 15 |
| 1952. – | 1 l. 20 light blue, black and deep blue | 65 | 25 |
| 1953. – | 1 l. 65 buff, black and brown | 90 | 35 |
| 1954. – | 2 l. 60 light green, black and deep green | 1·40 | 55 |

DESIGNS: 25 q. Spirit of Skanderbeg. 80 q. Albanians marching under national flag. 1 l. 20, Riflemen. 1 l. 65, Abdyl Frasheri (founder). 2 l. 60, League Headquarters, Prizren.

**1978.** 35th Anniv. of People's army.

| | | | |
|---|---|---|---|
| 1956. | 5 q. Type **399** | 10 | 10 |
| 1957. | 25 q. Men of armed forces (horiz.) | 15 | 10 |
| 1958. | 1 l. 90 Men of armed forces, civil guards and Young Pioneers | 1·75 | 45 |

**1978.** International Fair, Riccione. No. 1832 surch. **3.30**l. **RICCIONE 78 26.8.78.**

| | | | |
|---|---|---|---|
| 1959. | 3 l. 30 on 25 q. mult. | 9·00 | 2·75 |

**401.** Man with Target Rifle. **402.** Kerchief Dance.

**1978.** National Shooting Championships.

| | | | |
|---|---|---|---|
| 1960. **401.** | 25 q. black & yellow | 15 | 10 |
| 1961. – | 80 q. black & orange | 35 | 15 |
| 1962. – | 95 q. black and red | 45 | 20 |
| 1963. – | 2 l. 40 black and red | 1·50 | 45 |

DESIGNS—VERT. 80 q. Woman with machine carbine. 2 l. 40, Pistol shooting. HORIZ. 95 q. Shooting from prone position.

**1978.** National Folklore Festival, Gjirokaster. Multicoloured.

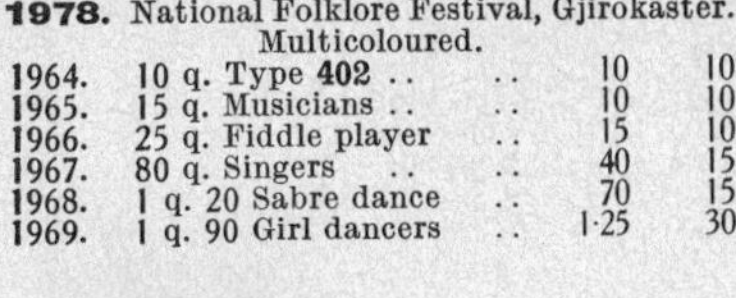

| | | | |
|---|---|---|---|
| 1964. | 10 q. Type **402** | 10 | 10 |
| 1965. | 15 q. Musicians | 10 | 10 |
| 1966. | 25 q. Fiddle player | 15 | 10 |
| 1967. | 80 q. Singers | 40 | 15 |
| 1968. | 1 q. 20 Sabre dance | 70 | 15 |
| 1969. | 1 q. 90 Girl dancers | 1·25 | 30 |

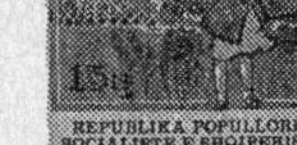

**403.** Enver Hoxha. (after V. Kilica). **404.** Woman with Wheatsheaf.

**1978.** Enver Hoxha's 70th Birthday.

| | | | |
|---|---|---|---|
| 1970. **403.** | 80 q. multicoloured | 55 | 15 |
| 1971. | 1 l. 20 multicoloured | 80 | 20 |
| 1972. | 2 l. 40 multicoloured | 1·25 | 55 |

**1978.** Agriculture and Stock Raising. Multicoloured.

| | | | |
|---|---|---|---|
| 1974. | 15 q. Type **404** | 15 | 10 |
| 1975. | 25 q. Woman with boxes of fruit | 20 | 10 |
| 1976. | 80 q. Shepherd and flock | 80 | 45 |
| 1977. | 2 l. 60 Dairymaid and cattle | 3·00 | 1·60 |

**405.** Pupils entering School. **406.** Dora D'Istria.

**1978.**

| | | | |
|---|---|---|---|
| 1978. **405.** | 5 q. brown, light brn., and gold | 10 | 10 |
| 1979. – | 10 q. blue, light blue and gold | 10 | 10 |
| 1980. – | 15 q. violet, lilac and gold | 10 | 10 |
| 1981. – | 20 q. brown, light brn., and gold | 10 | 10 |
| 1982. – | 25 q. red, pink and gold | 15 | 10 |
| 1983. – | 60 q. green, light green and gold | 75 | 35 |
| 1984. – | 80 q. blue, light blue and gold | 95 | 45 |
| 1985. – | 1 l. 20 mauve, light mauve and gold | 1·40 | 75 |
| 1986. – | 1 l. 60 blue, light blue and gold | 1·75 | 1·10 |
| 1987. – | 2 l. 40 green, light green and gold | 2·50 | 1·75 |
| 1988. – | 3 l. blue, light blue and gold | 3·00 | 3·00 |

DESIGNS: 10 q. Telephone, letters, telegraph wires and switchboard operators. 15 q. Pouring molten iron. 20 q. Dancers, musical instruments book and artist's materials. 25 q. Newspapers, radio, television and broadcasting tower. 60 q. Assistant in clothes shop. 80 q. Militia-men and women, tanks, ships, aircraft and radar equipment. 1 l. 20, Industrial complex and symbols of industry. 1 l. 60, Train and lorry. 2 l. 40, Workers hoeing fields, cattle and girl holding wheat sheaf. 3 l. Microscope and nurse holding up baby.

**1979.** 150th Birth Anniv. of Dora D'Istria (pioneer of women's rights).

| | | | |
|---|---|---|---|
| 1989. **406.** | 80 q. green and black | 75 | 15 |
| 1990. – | 1 l. 10 grey and black | 1·10 | 90 |

DESIGN: 1 l. 10, Full-face portrait.

**1979.** National Costume Dances (3rd series). As Type **389**. Multicoloured.

| | | | |
|---|---|---|---|
| 1991. | 15 q. Girl dancers with scarves | 10 | 10 |
| 1992. | 25 q. Male dancers | 15 | 10 |
| 1993. | 80 q. Girl dancers with scarves (different) | 45 | 15 |
| 1994. | 1 l. 20 Male dancers with pistols | 70 | 25 |
| 1995. | 1 l. 40 Female dancers with linked arms | 1·10 | 30 |

**407.** Stone-built Galleried House. **408.** Aleksander Moissi.

**1979.** Traditional Albanian Houses. (1st series). Multicoloured.

| | | | |
|---|---|---|---|
| 1996. | 15 q. Type **407** | 10 | 10 |
| 1997. | 25 q. Tower house (vert.) | 15 | 10 |
| 1998. | 80 q. House with wooden galleries | 75 | 15 |
| 1999. | 1 l. 20 Galleried tower house (vert.) | 1·10 | 25 |
| 2000. | 1 l. 40 Three-storied fortified house (vert.) | 1·50 | 55 |

See also Nos. 2116/19.

**1979.** Birth Cent. of Aleksander Moissi (actor).

| | | | |
|---|---|---|---|
| 2002 **408** | 80 q. grn, blk & gold | 55 | 15 |
| 2003 – | 1 l. 10 brn, blk & gold | 90 | 20 |

DESIGN: 1 l. 10, Aleksander Moissi (different).

**409.** Vasil Shanto.

**1979.** Anti-fascist Heroes (1st series). Multicoloured.

| | | | |
|---|---|---|---|
| 2004. | 15 q. Type **409** | 10 | 10 |
| 2005. | 25 q. Qemal Stafa | 20 | 10 |
| 2006. | 60 q. Type **409** | 35 | 10 |
| 2007. | 90 q. As 25 q. | 40 | 25 |

See also Nos. 2052/5, 2090/3, 2126/9, 2167/70, 2221/4, 2274/7 and 2313/5.

**410.** Soldier, Crowd and Coat of Arms.

**1979.** 35th Anniv. of Permet Congress. Multicoloured.

| | | | |
|---|---|---|---|
| 2008. | 25 q. Soldier, factories and wheat | 20 | 10 |
| 2009. | 1 l. 65 Type **410** | 80 | 35 |

**411.** Albanian Flag.

**1979.** 5th Albanian Democratic Front Congress.

| | | | |
|---|---|---|---|
| 2010. **411.** | 25 q. multicoloured | 20 | 10 |
| 2011. | 1 l. 65 multicoloured | 1·00 | 35 |

**412.** "Ne Stervitje" (Arben Basha).

**1979.** Paintings. Multicoloured.

| | | | |
|---|---|---|---|
| 2012. | 15 q. Type **412** | 10 | 10 |
| 2013. | 25 q. "Shtigje Lufte" (Ismail Lulani) | 10 | 10 |
| 2014. | 80 q. "Agim me Fitore" (Myrteza Fushekati) | 65 | 15 |
| 2015. | 1 l. 20 "Gjithe Populli ushtare" (Muhamet Deliu) | 1·00 | 20 |
| 2016. | 1 l. 40 "Zjarret Ndezur Mbajme" (Jorgji Gjikopulli) | 1·25 | 75 |

**413.** Athletes round Party Flag. **414.** Founder-president

**1979.** 35th Anniv. of Liberation Spartakiad. Multicoloured.

| | | | |
|---|---|---|---|
| 2018. | 15 q. Type **413** | 10 | 10 |
| 2019. | 25 q. Shooting | 10 | 10 |
| 2020. | 80 q. Girl gymnast | 55 | 15 |
| 2021. | 1 l. 10 Football | 80 | 20 |
| 2022. | 1 l. 40 High jump | 1·00 | 30 |

**1979.** Cent. of Albanian Literary Society.

| | | | |
|---|---|---|---|
| 2023. – | 25 q. blk., brn. & gold | 15 | 10 |
| 2024. **414.** | 80 q. blk., brn. & gold | 40 | 15 |
| 2025. – | 1 l. 20 black, blue and gold | 60 | 25 |
| 2026. – | 1 l. 55 black, violet & gold | 85 | 35 |

DESIGNS: 25 q. Seal and Charter. 1 l. 20, Headquarters Building. 1 l. 55, 1879 Headquarters Building.

**415.** Congress Building.

**1979.** 35th Anniv. of Berat Congress. Mult.

| | | | |
|---|---|---|---|
| 2028. | 25 q. Arms and Congress Document | 20 | 10 |
| 2029. | 1 l. 65 Type **415** | 1·25 | 45 |

**416.** Workers and Industrial Complex. **417.** Joseph Stalin.

**1979.** 35th Anniv. of Liberation. Mult.

| | | | |
|---|---|---|---|
| 2030. | 25 q. Type **416** | 15 | 10 |
| 2031. | 80 q. Wheat and hand grasping hammer and pickaxe | 35 | 10 |
| 2032. | 1 l. 20 Open book, star and musical instrument | 50 | 25 |
| 2033. | 1 l. 55 Open book, compasses and gear wheel | 80 | 35 |

**1979.** Birth Centenary of Joseph Stalin.

| | | | |
|---|---|---|---|
| 2034. **417.** | 80 q. blue and red | 35 | 20 |
| 2035. – | 1 l. blue and red | 75 | 35 |

DESIGN: 1 l. 10, Stalin and Enver Hoxha.

**418.** Fireplace and Pottery, Korce.

**1980.** Interiors (1st series). Multicoloured.

| | | | |
|---|---|---|---|
| 2036. | 25 q. Type **418** | 15 | 15 |
| 3037. | 80 q. Carved bed above and weapons, Shkoder | 45 | 35 |
| 2038. | 1 l. 20 Cooking hearth and carved chair, Mirdite | 1·00 | 75 |
| 2039. | 1 l. 35 Turkish-style chimney, dagger and embroidered jacket, Gjirokaster | 1·25 | 70 |

See also Nos. 2075/8.

**419.** Lacework. **420.** Aleksander Xhuvani.

**1980.** Handicrafts. Multicoloured.

| | | | |
|---|---|---|---|
| 2040. | 25 q. Pipe and Flask | 15 | 15 |
| 2041. | 80 q. Leather handbags | 50 | 30 |
| 2042. | 1 l. 20 Carved Eagle and embroidered rug | 65 | 55 |
| 2043. | 1 l. 35 Type **419** | 85 | 60 |

**1980.** Birth Cent. of Dr. Aleksander Xhuvani.

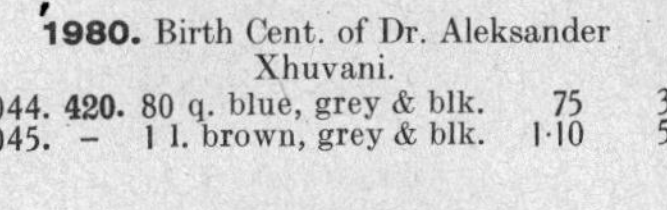

| | | | |
|---|---|---|---|
| 2044. **420.** | 80 q. blue, grey & blk. | 75 | 30 |
| 2045. – | 1 l. brown, grey & blk. | 1·10 | 55 |

**421** Insurrectionists.

**1980.** 70th Anniv. of Kosovo Insurrection.

| | | | |
|---|---|---|---|
| 2046. **421.** | 80 q. black and red | 75 | 30 |
| 2047. – | 1 l. black and red | 1·10 | 75 |

DESIGN: 1 l. Battle scene.

422. " Soldiers and Workers helping Stricken Population " (D. Jukniu and L. Lulani). 423. Lenin.

**1980.** 1979 Earthquake Relief.
2048. 422. 80 q. multicoloured .. 75 35
2049. 1 l. multicoloured .. 1·10 75

**1980.** 110th Birth Anniv. of Lenin.
2050. 423. 80 q. grey, red & pink 75 40
2051. 1 l. multicoloured .. 1·10 55

424. Misto Mame and Ali Demi.

**1980.** Anti-fascist Heroes (2nd series). Mult.
2052. 25 q. Type 424 .. .. 15 10
2053. 80 q. Sadik Staveleci, Vojo Kushi and Xhoxhi Martini .. .. 35 30
2054. 1 l. 20 Bule Naipi and Persefoni Kokedhima 60 55
2055. 1 l. 35 Ndoc Deda, Hydajet Lezha, Naim Gjylbegu, Ndoc Mazi and Ahmet Haxhia .. .. 75 60

425. " Mirela ".

**1980.** Children's Tales. Multicoloured.
2056. 15 q. Type 425 .. .. 10 10
2057. 25 q. " Shkarravina " .. 10 10
2058. 80 q. " Ariu Artist " .. 40 30
2059. 2 l. 40 " Pika e Ujit " .. 1·75 1·25

426. " The Enver Hoxha Tractor Combine " (S. Shijaku and M. Fushekati). 427. Decorated Door (Pergamen miniature).

**1980.** Paintings from Gallery of Figurative Arts, Tirana. Multicoloured.
2060. 25 q. Type 426 .. .. 15 10
2061. 80 q. " The Welder " (Harilla Dhima) .. 40 30
2062. 1 l. 20 " Steel Erector " (Petro Kokushta) .. 60 65
2063. 1 l. 35 " Harvest Festival " (Pandeli Lena) 70 55

**1980.** Art of the Middle Ages. Each black and gold.
2065. 25 q. Type 427 .. .. 10 10
2066. 80 q. Bird (relief) .. 40 20
2067. 1 l. 20 Crowned Lion (relief) 65 65
2068. 1 l. 35 Pheasant (relief) .. 70 55

428. Divjaka.

**1980.** National Parks. Multicoloured.
2069. 80 q. Type 428 .. .. 40 25
2070. 1 l. 20 Lura .. .. 90 65
2071. 1 l. 60 Thethi .. 1·50 90

429 Flag, Arms and rejoicing Albanians

**1981.** 35th Anniv. of Albanian People's Republic. Multicoloured.
2073. 80 q. Type 429 .. .. 65 25
2074. 1 l. Crowd and flags outside People's Party Headquarters .. 60 40

**1981.** Interiors (2nd series). Multicoloured.
2075. 25 q. As T 418 .. .. 15 10
2076. 80 q. Sleeping mats and spirit keg, Labara .. 40 25
2077. 1 l. 20 Fireplace, and covered dish mat .. 90 45
2078. 1 l. 35 Interior and embroidered jacket, Dibres 1·10 55

430. Wooden Cot.

**1981.** Folk Art. Multicoloured.
2079. 25 q. Type 430 .. .. 15 10
2080. 80 q. Bucket and flask .. 40 25
2081. 1 l. 20 Embroidered slippers .. .. 60 35
2082. 1 l. 35 Jugs .. .. 70 75

431. Footballers.

**1981.** World Cup Football Championship. Eliminating Rounds. Multicoloured.
2083. 25 q. Type 431 .. .. 1·10 55
2084. 80 q. Tackle .. .. 3·25 1·50
2085. 1 l. 20 Player kicking ball 4·75 2·00
2086. 1 l. 35 Goalkeeper saving goal .. .. .. 5·50 2·50

432. Rifleman. 433. Acrobats.

**1981.** Centenary of Battle of Shtimje.
2087. 80 q. Type 432 .. .. 55 30
2088. 1 l. Albanian with sabre 70 45

**1981.** Anti-fascist Heroes (3rd series). As T 424. Multicoloured.
2090. 25 q. Perlat Rexhepi and Branko Kadia .. 15 15
2091. 80 q. Xheladin Beqiri and Hajdah Dushi .. 45 30
2092. 1 l. 20 Koci Bako, Vasil Laci and Mujo Ulqinaku 75 50
2093. 1 l. 35 Mine Peza and Zoja Cure .. .. .. 85 60

**1981.** Children's Circus.
2094. – 15 q. blk., grn. & stone 10 10
2095. – 25 q. blk., blue & grey 15 10
2096. 433. 80 q. blk., mve. & pink 40 30
2097. – 2 l. 40 blk., orge. & yell. 1·40 1·25

DESIGNS: 15 q. Monocyclists. 25 q. Human pyramid. 2 l. 40, Acrobats spinning from marquee pole.

434. " Rallying to the Flag, December 1911 " (A. Zajmi).

**1981.** Paintings. Multicoloured.
2098. 25 q. "Allies" (Sh. Hysa) (horiz.) .. .. 15 10
2099. 80 q. "Azem Galica breaking the Ring of Turks" (A. Buza) (horiz.) .. .. 45 25
2100. 1 l. 20 Type 434 .. .. 60 40
2101. 1 l. 35 "My Flag is my Heart" (L. Cefa) .. 1·00 80

435. Weightlifting.

**1981.** Albanian Participation in International Sports. Multicoloured.
2103. 25 q. Rifle shooting .. 15 10
2104. 80 q. Type 435 .. .. 45 30
2105. 1 l. 20 Volleyball .. .. 65 45
2106. 1 l. 35 Football .. .. 1·00 70

436. Flag and Hands holding Pickaxe and Rifle. 437. Industrial and Agricultural Symbols.

**1981.** 8th Workers' Party Congress.
2107. 436. 80 q. red, brown and black .. .. 50 30
2108. – 1 l. red and black .. 60 45

DESIGN: 1 l. Party flag, hammer and sickle.

**1981.** 40th Anniv. of Workers' Party. Mult.
2109. 80 q. Type 437 .. .. 50 30
2110. 2 l. 80 Albanian flag and hand holding pickaxe and rifle .. .. 1·75 1·10

438. Pickaxe, Rifle and Young Communists Flag. 439. F. S. Noli.

**1981.** 40th Anniv. of Young Communists' Union. Multicoloured.
2112. 80 q. Type 438 .. .. 55 30
2113. 1 l. Workers' Party flag and Young Communists emblem .. .. 85 50

**1981.** Birth Cent. of F. S. Noli (author).
2114. 439. 80 q. green and gold 45 30
2115. 1 l. 10 brown and gold 65 45

**1982.** Traditional Albanian Houses (2nd series). As T 407, but vert. Multicoloured.
2116. 25 q. House in Bulqize .. 15 10
2117. 80 q. House in Kosovo .. 45 30
2118. 1 l. 20 House in Bicaj .. 75 55
2119. 1 l. 55 House in Mat .. 90 70

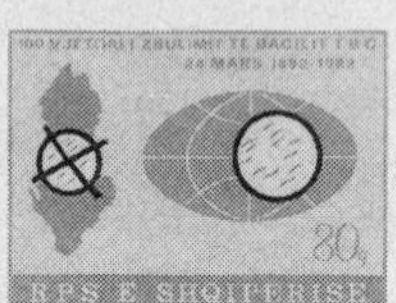


440. Map, Globe and Bacillus.

**1982.** Centenary of Discovery of Tubercle Bacillus.
2120. 440. 80 q. multicoloured 65 35
2121. – 1 l. 10 brown and deep brown .. .. 85 55

DESIGN: 1 l. 10, Robert Koch (discoverer), microscope and bacillus.

441. "Prizren Castle" (G. Madhi).

**1982.** Paintings of Kosova. Mult.
2122. 25 q. Type 441 .. .. 20 10
2123. 80 q. " House of the Albanian League, Prizren " (K. Buza) (horiz.) .. .. 55 25
2124. 1 l. 20 " Mountain Gorge, Rogove " (K. Buza) .. 70 60
2125. 1 l. 55 " Street of the Hadhji, Zekes " (G. Madhi) .. .. 90 65

**1982.** Anti-fascist Heroes (4th series). As T 424. Multicoloured
2126. 25 q. Hibe Palikuqi and Liri Gero .. .. 15 10
2127. 80 q. Mihal Duri and Kojo Karafili .. .. 50 30
2128. 1 l. 20 Fato Dudumi, Margarita Tutulani and Shejnaze Juka .. 65 40
2129. 1 l. 55 Memo Meto and Gjok Doci .. .. 85 60

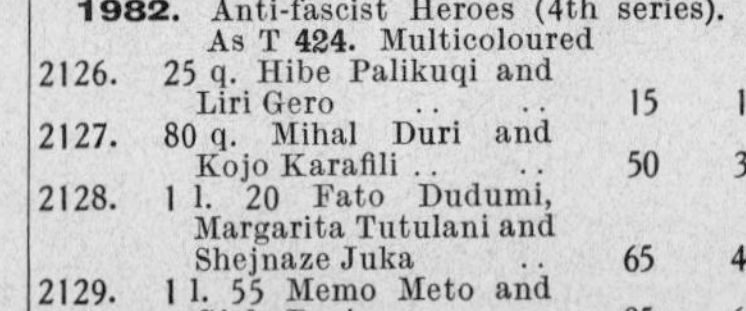

442. Factories and Workers.

**1982.** Ninth Trade Unions' Congress. Mult.
2130. 80 q. Type 442 .. .. 55 30
2131. 1 l. 10 Congress emblem 70 45

443. Ship in Harbour.

**1982.** Children's Paintings. Multicoloured.
2132. 15 q. Type 443 .. .. 15 10
2133. 80 q. Forest camp .. 60 30
2134. 1 l. 20 House .. .. 80 40
2135. 1 l. 65 House and garden 1·10 60

444. "Village Festival" (Danish Jukniu).

**1982.** Paintings from Gallery of Figurative Arts, Tirana. Multicoloured.
2136. 25 q. Type 444 .. .. 20 10
2137. 80 q. " The Hydro-electric Station Builders " (Ali Miruku) .. .. 45 30
2138. 1 l. 20 " Steel Workers " (Clirim Ceka) .. .. 75 50
2139. 1 l. 55 " Oil Drillers " (Pandeli Lena) .. 95 70

445. "Voice of the People" (party newspaper). 446. Heroes of Peza Monument.

**1982.** 40th Anniv. of Popular Press. Mult.
2141. 80 q. Type 445 .. ..
2142. 1 l. 10 Hand duplicator producing first edition of "Voice of the People" .. ..

**1982.** 40th Anniv. of Democratic Front. Mult.
2143. 80 q. Type 446 .. .. 75 30
2144. 1 l. 10 Peza Conference building and marchers with flag .. .. 70 65

447. Congress Emblem.

**1982.** Eighth Youth Communists' Union Congress.
2145. 447. 80 q. multicoloured .. 75 30
2146. 1 l. 10 multicoloured 70 65

448. Tapestry.

**1982.** Handicrafts. Multicoloured.

| | | | |
|---|---|---|---|
| 2147 | 25 q. Type **448** .. .. | 20 | 10 |
| 2148 | 80 q. Bags (vert.).. .. | 50 | 30 |
| 2149 | 1 l. 20 Butter churns .. | 70 | 45 |
| 2150 | 1 l. 55 Jug (vert.).. .. | 1·00 | 90 |

**449.** Freedom Fighters.

**1982.** 70th Anniv. of Independence.

| | | | |
|---|---|---|---|
| 2151. | **449.** 20 q. deep red, red and black.. .. | 15 | 10 |
| 2152. | – 1 l. 20 black, green & red .. .. | 70 | 50 |
| 2153. | – 2 l. 40 brown, buff & red .. .. | 1·50 | 1·25 |

DESIGNS: 20 q. Ismail Qemali (patriot) and crowd around Building. 2 l. 40, Six Freedom fighters. (58 × 55 mm).

**450.** Dhermi.

**1982.** Coastal Views. Multicoloured.

| | | | |
|---|---|---|---|
| 2155. | 25 q. Type **450** .. .. | 15 | 10 |
| 2156. | 80 q. Sarande .. .. | 50 | 30 |
| 2157. | 1 l. 20 Ksamil .. .. | 75 | 50 |
| 2158. | 1 l. 55 Lukove .. .. | 1·00 | 90 |

**451.** Male Dancers. **452.** Karl Marx.

**1983.** Folk Dance Assemblies Abroad. Mult.

| | | | |
|---|---|---|---|
| 2159. | 25 q. Type **451** .. .. | 15 | 10 |
| 2160. | 80 q. Male dancers and drummer .. .. | 50 | 30 |
| 2161. | 1 l. 20 Musicians.. .. | 70 | 40 |
| 2162. | 1 l. 55 Group of female dancers.. .. | 1·00 | 90 |

**1983.** Death Centenary of Karl Marx.

| | | | |
|---|---|---|---|
| 2163. | **452.** 80 q. multicoloured.. | 50 | 30 |
| 2164. | 1 l. 10 multicoloured | 80 | 50 |

**453.** Electricity Generation.

**1983.** Energy Development.

| | | | |
|---|---|---|---|
| 2165. | **453.** 80 q. blue and orange | 50 | 30 |
| 2166. | – 1 l. 10 mauve & green | 80 | 50 |

DESIGN: 1 l. 10, Gas and oil production.

**1983.** Anti-fascist Heroes (5th series). As T **424**. Multicoloured.

| | | | |
|---|---|---|---|
| 2167. | 25 q. Asim Zeneli and Nazmi Rushiti .. | 15 | 10 |
| 2168. | 80 q. Shyqyri Ishmi, Shyqyri Alimerko and Myzafer Asqeriu .. .. | 45 | 30 |
| 2169. | 1 l. 20 Qybra Sokoli, Qeriba Derri & Ylbere Bilibashi | 75 | 45 |
| 2170. | 1 l. 55 Themo Vasi and Abaz Shehu .. .. | 95 | 65 |

**454.** Congress Emblem. **455.** Cycling.

**1983.** Ninth Women's Union Congress.

| | | | |
|---|---|---|---|
| 2171. | **454.** 80 q. multicoloured.. | 50 | 40 |
| 2172. | 1 l. 10 multicoloured | 60 | 50 |

**1983.** Sport and Leisure. Multicoloured.

| | | | |
|---|---|---|---|
| 2173. | 25 q. Type **455** .. .. | 20 | 10 |
| 2174. | 80 q. Chess .. .. | 90 | 45 |
| 2175. | 1 l. 20 Gymnastics .. | 1·10 | 60 |
| 2176. | 1 l. 55 Wrestling.. .. | 1·25 | 70 |

**456.** Soldier & Militia.

**1983.** 40th Anniv. of People's Army.

| | | | |
|---|---|---|---|
| 2177. | **456.** 20 q. gold and red .. | 15 | 10 |
| 2178. | – 1 l. 20 gold and red.. | 75 | 45 |
| 2179. | – 2 l. 40 gold and brown | 1·50 | 1·25 |

DESIGNS: 1 l. 20 Soldier. 2 l. 40 Factory guard.

**457.** "Sunny Day" (Myrteza Fushekati).

**1983.** Paintings from Gallery of Figurative Arts, Tirana. Multicoloured.

| | | | |
|---|---|---|---|
| 2180. | 25 q. Type **457** .. .. | 15 | 10 |
| 2181. | 80 q. "Morning Gossip" (Niko Progri) .. .. | 50 | 35 |
| 2182. | 1 l. 20 "29th November, 1944" (Harilla Dhimo) | 75 | 45 |
| 2183. | 1 l. 55 "Demolition" (Pandi Mele) .. .. | 1·00 | 60 |

**1983.** National Folklore Festival, Gjirokaster. As T **402**. Multicoloured.

| | | | |
|---|---|---|---|
| 2185. | 25 q. Sword dance .. | 20 | 10 |
| 2186. | 80 q. Kerchief dance .. | 60 | 35 |
| 2187. | 1 l. 20 Musicians.. .. | 90 | 55 |
| 2188. | 1 l. 55 Women dancers with garlands .. .. | 1·00 | 70 |

**458.** Enver Hoxha. **459.** W.C.Y. Emblem and Globe.

**1983.** 75th Birthday of Enver Hoxha.

| | | | |
|---|---|---|---|
| 2189. | **458.** 80 q. multicoloured.. | 40 | 30 |
| 2190. | 1 l. 20 multicoloured | 65 | 45 |
| 2191. | 1 l. 80 multicoloured | 1·25 | 75 |

**1983.** World Communications Year.

| | | | |
|---|---|---|---|
| 2193. | **459.** 60 q. multicoloured.. | 35 | 20 |
| 2194. | 1 l. 20 bl., orge. & blk. | 55 | 40 |

**460.** "Combine to Triumph" (J. Keraj).

**1983.** Skanderbeg Epoch in Art. Mult.

| | | | |
|---|---|---|---|
| 2195. | 25 q. Type **460** .. .. | 20 | 10 |
| 2196. | 80 q. "The Heroic resistance at Krujes" (N. Bakalli) .. .. | 50 | 30 |
| 2197. | 1 l. 20 "United we are Unconquerable by our Enemies" (N. Progri) | 75 | 45 |
| 2198. | 1 l. 55 "Assembly at Lezhe" (B. Ahmeti) .. | 1·00 | 60 |

**461.** Amphitheatre, Butrint (Buthrotum).

**1983.** Graeco-Roman Remains in Illyria. Multicoloured.

| | | | |
|---|---|---|---|
| 2200. | 80 q. Type **461** .. .. | 50 | 35 |
| 2201. | 1 l. 20 Colonnade, Apoloni Cesma (Apollonium) .. .. | 80 | 55 |
| 2202. | 1 l. 80 Vaulted gallery, of amphitheatre, Dyrrah (Epidamnus) .. .. | 1·10 | 75 |

**462.** Man's Head from Apoloni. **463.** Clock Tower, Gjirokaster.

**1984.** Archaeological Discoveries (1st series). Multicoloured.

| | | | |
|---|---|---|---|
| 2203. | 15 q. Type **462** .. .. | 15 | 10 |
| 2204. | 25 q. Tombstone from Korce .. .. .. | 20 | 10 |
| 2205. | 80 q. Woman's head from Apoloni .. .. | 50 | 30 |
| 2206. | 1 l. 10 Child's head from Tren .. .. .. | 75 | 55 |
| 2207. | 1 l. 20 Man's head from Dyrrah .. .. | 80 | 60 |
| 2208. | 2 l. 20 Bronze statuette of Eros from Dyrrah | 1·50 | 1·10 |

See also Nos. 2258/61.

**1984.** Clock Towers.

| | | | |
|---|---|---|---|
| 2209. | **463.** 15 q. purple .. .. | 15 | 10 |
| 2210. | – 25 q. brown .. .. | 20 | 10 |
| 2211. | – 80 q. violet .. .. | 50 | 30 |
| 2212. | – 1 l. 10 red .. .. | 75 | 55 |
| 2213. | – 1 l. 20 green .. .. | 80 | 60 |
| 2214. | – 2 l. 20 brown .. | 1·50 | 1·10 |

DESIGNS: 25 q. Kavaje. 80 q. Elbasan. 1 l. 10 Tirane. 1 l. 20 Peqin. 2 l. 20 Kruje.

**464.** Student with Microscope. **465.** Enver Hoxha.

**1984.** 40th Anniv. of Liberation (1st issue). Multicoloured.

| | | | |
|---|---|---|---|
| 2215. | 15 q. Type **464** .. .. | 15 | 10 |
| 2216. | 25 q. Soldier with flag .. | 20 | 10 |
| 2217. | 80 q. Schoolchildren .. | 55 | 30 |
| 2218. | 1 l. 10 Soldier, ships, airplanes and weapons | 85 | 55 |
| 2219. | 1 l. 20 Workers with flag | 95 | 65 |
| 2220. | 2 l. 20 Armed guards on patrol .. .. .. | 1·50 | 1·25 |

See also Nos. 2255/6.

**1984.** Anti-fascist Heroes (6th series). As T **424**. Multicoloured.

| | | | |
|---|---|---|---|
| 2221. | 15 q. Manush Alimani, Mustafa Matohiti and Kastriot Muco .. | 10 | 10 |
| 2222. | 25 q. Zaho Koka, Reshit Collaku and Maliq Muco .. .. .. | 15 | 10 |
| 2223. | 1 l. 20 Lefter Talo, Tom Kola and Fuat Babani | 75 | 50 |
| 2224. | 2 l. 20 Myslysm Shyri, Dervish Hekali and Skender Caci .. .. | 1·50 | 1·10 |

**1984.** 40th Aniv. of Permet Congress.

| | | | |
|---|---|---|---|
| 2225. | **465.** 80 q. brown, orange and red .. .. | 50 | 40 |
| 2226. | – 1 l. 10 black, yellow and lilac .. .. | 80 | 60 |

DESIGN: 1 l. 10, Resistance fighter (detail of monument).

**466.** Children reading Comic. **467.** Football in Goal.

**1984.** Children. Multicoloured.

| | | | |
|---|---|---|---|
| 2227. | 15 q. Type **466** .. .. | 15 | 10 |
| 2228. | 25 q. Children with toys . | 20 | 15 |
| 2229. | 60 q. Children gardening and rainbow .. .. | 50 | 30 |
| 2230. | 2 l. 80 Children flying kite bearing Albanian arms .. .. .. | 2·00 | 1·50 |

**1984.** European Football Championship Finals. Multicoloured.

| | | | |
|---|---|---|---|
| 2231. | 15 q. Type **467** .. .. | 15 | 10 |
| 2232. | 25 q. Referee and football | 20 | 10 |
| 2233. | 1 l. 20 Football and map of Europe .. .. | 85 | 50 |
| 2234. | 2 l. 20 Football and pitch | 1·50 | 1·10 |

**468.** "Freedom is Here". Myrteza Fushekati).

**1984.** Paintings from Gallery of Figurative Arts, Tirana. Multicoloured.

| | | | |
|---|---|---|---|
| 2235. | 15 q. Type **468** .. .. | 15 | 10 |
| 2236. | 25 q. "Morning" (Zamir Mati) (vert.) .. .. | 20 | 10 |
| 2237. | 80 q. "My Darling" (Agim Zajmi) (vert.).. | 60 | 35 |
| 2238. | 2 l. 60 "For the Partisans" (Arben Basha).. .. .. | 1·75 | 1·50 |

**469.** Mulberry. **471.** Truck driving through Forest.

**1984.** Flowers. Multicoloured.

| | | | |
|---|---|---|---|
| 2240. | 15 q. Type **469** .. .. | 20 | 10 |
| 2241. | 25 q. Plantain .. .. | 55 | 10 |
| 2242. | 1 l. 20 Hypericum .. | 2·75 | 1·00 |
| 2243. | 2 l. 20 Edelweiss.. .. | 5·50 | 2·25 |

**1984.** Forestry. Multicoloured.

| | | | |
|---|---|---|---|
| 2245. | 15 q. Type **471** .. .. | 15 | 10 |
| 2246. | 25 q. Transporting logs on overhead cable .. | 25 | 10 |
| 2247. | 1 l. 20 Sawmill in forest | 80 | 45 |
| 2248. | 2 l. 20 Lumberjack sawing down trees .. | 1·50 | 1·25 |

**472.** Gjirokaster. **473.** Football.

**1984.** "Eurphila '84" International Stamp Exhibition, Rome.

| | | | |
|---|---|---|---|
| 2249. | **472.** 1 l. 20 multicoloured | 90 | 70 |

**1984.** 5th National Spartakiad. Mult.

| | | | |
|---|---|---|---|
| 2250. | 15 q. Type **473** .. .. | 15 | 10 |
| 2251. | 25 q. Running .. .. | 20 | 10 |
| 2252. | 80 q. Weightlifting .. | 55 | 30 |
| 2253. | 2 l. 20 Pistol shooting .. | 1·50 | 1·25 |

**474.** Agriculture and Industry.

**1984.** 40th Anniv. of Liberation (2nd issue). Multicoloured.

| | | | |
|---|---|---|---|
| 2255. | 80 q. Type **474** .. .. | 50 | 35 |
| 2256. | 1 l. 10 Soldiers and flag | 75 | 55 |

**1985.** Archaeological Discoveries (2nd series). As T **462** showing Illyrian finds. Mult.

| | | | |
|---|---|---|---|
| 2258. | 15 q. Pot.. .. .. | 15 | 10 |
| 2259. | 80 q. Terracotta head of woman .. .. | 55 | 30 |
| 2260. | 1 l. 20 Terracotta bust of Aphrodite .. .. | 90 | 55 |
| 2261. | 1 l. 70 Bronze statuette of Nike .. .. | 1·50 | 1·10 |

476. Kapo (bust). 477. Running.

**1985.** 70th Birthday of Hysni Kapo (politician).
2262. **476.** 90 q. black and red .. 60 60
2263. 1 l. 10 black and blue 1·00 50

**1985.** "Olymphilex '85" Olympic Stamps Exhibition, Lausanne. Multicoloured.
2264. 25 q. Type **477** .. .. 20 10
2265. 60 q. Weightlifting .. 45 20
2266. 1 l. 20 Football .. .. 90 55
2267. 1 l. 50 Pistol shooting .. 1·40 95

478. Bach. 479. Hoxha.

**1985.** 300th Birth Anniv. of Johann Sebastian Bach (composer).
2268. **478.** 80 q. orge. brn. & blk. 2·25 75
2269. – 1 l. 20 blue, deep blue & black .. .. 3·25 1·10
Design:—1 l. 20, Bach's birthplace, Eisenach.

**1985.** Enver Hoxha Commemoration.
2270. **479.** 80 q. multicoloured 80 55

480. Frontier Guards. 481. Scarf on Rifle Barrel.

**1985.** 40th Anniv. of Frontier Force. Mult.
2272. 25 q. Type **480** .. .. 20 10
2273. 80 q. Frontier guard .. 55 30

**1985.** Anti-fascist Heroes (7th series). As T **424**. Multicoloured.
2274. 25 q. Mitro Xhani, Nimete Progonati and Kozma Nushi .. .. 20 10
2275. 40 q. Ajet Xhindoli, Mustafa Kacaci and Estref Caka .. .. 35 15
2276. 60 q. Celo Sinani, Llambro Andoni and Meleo Gosnishti .. 45 20
2277. 1 l. 20 Thodhori Mastora, Fejzi Micoli and Hysen Cino .. .. .. 90 85

**1985.** 40th Anniv. of V.E. (Victory in Europe) Day. Multicoloured.
2278 25 q. Type **481** .. .. 20 10
2279 80 q. Crumpled swastika and hand holding rifle butt .. .. .. 55 30

482. "Primary School" (Thoma Malo).

**1985.** Paintings from Gallery of Figurative Arts, Tirana. Multicoloured.
2280. 25 q. Type **482**. .. .. 20 10
2281. 80 q. "Heroes and Mother" (Hysen Devolli) (vert.) .. 80 30
2282. 90 q. "Mother writing" (Angjelin Dodmasej) (vert.) .. .. 90 60
2283. 1 l. 20 "Women off to Work" (Ksenofen Dilo) .. .. .. 1·25 55

483. Scoring a Goal. 484. Oranges.

**1985.** 10th World Basketball Championship, Spain.
2285. **483.** 25 q. blue and black 20 10
2286. – 80 q. green and black 55 30
2287. – 1 l. 20 violet & blk. 90 55
2288. – 1 l. 60 red and black 1·40 1·00
Designs: 80 q. Player running with ball. 1 l. 20, Defending goal. 1 l. 60, Defender capturing ball.

**1985.** Fruit Trees. Multicoloured.
2289. 25 q. Type **484** .. .. 20 10
2290. 80 q. Plums .. .. 1·50 55
2291. 1 l. 20 Apples .. .. 2·25 80
2292. 1 l. 60 Cherries .. .. 3·25 1·50

485. Kruja. 486. War Horse Dance.

**1985.** Architecture.
2293. **485.** 25 q. black and red .. 20 10
2294. – 80 q. black, grey and brown .. .. 1·10 30
2295. – 1 l. 20 black, brown and blue .. 1·50 55
2296. – 1 l. 60 black, brown and red .. .. 2·25 1·00
Designs: 80 q. Gjirokastra. 1 l. 20 Berat. 1 l. 60 Shkoder.

**1985.** National Folklore Festival. Dances.
2297. **486.** 25 q. brown, red & black .. .. 20 10
2298. – 80 q. brown, red & black .. .. 55 30
2299. – 1 l. 20 brn., red & blk. 90 55
2300. – 1 l. 60 brn, red & blk 1·40 1·00
Designs: 80 q. Pillow dance. 1 l. 20 Ladies' kerchief dance. 1 l. 60 Men's one-legged pair dance.

487. State Arms. 488. Dam across River Drin.

**1986.** 40th Anniv. of Albanian People's Republic.
2302. **487.** 25 q. gold, red and black .. .. 20 10
2303. – 80 q. multicoloured 1·10 65
Design: 80 q. "Comrade Hoxha announcing the News to the People" (Vilson Kilica) and arms.

**1986.** Enver Hoxha Hydro-electric Power Station. Multicoloured.
2304. 25 q. Type **488** .. .. 75 35
2305. 80 q. Control building .. 3·00 1·50

489. "Gymnospermium shqipetarum". 490. Maksim Gorky (writer).

**1986.** Flowers. Multicoloured.
2306. 25 q. Type **489** .. .. 20 10
2307. 1 l. 20 "Leucojum valentinum" .. .. 2·00 90

**1986.** Anniversaries.
2308. **490.** 25 q. brown .. .. 20 10
2309. – 80 q. violet .. .. 1·10 55
2310. – 1 l. 20 green .. .. 1·60 1·10
2311. – 2 l. 40 purple .. 3·75 2·50
Designs: 25 q. Type **490** (50th death anniv.). 80 q. Andre Ampere (physicist and mathematician. 150th death anniv.). 1 l. 20. James Watt (inventor, 250th birth anniv.). 2 l. 40, Franz Liszt (composer, death cent.).

**1986.** Anti-fascist Heroes (8th series). As T **424**. Multicoloured.
2313. 25 q. Ramiz Aranitasi, Inajete Dumi and Laze Nuro Ferraj .. 20 10
2314. 80 q. Dine Kalenja, Kozma Naska, Met Hasa and Fahri Ramadani .. .. 90 55
2315. 1 l. 20 Hiqmet Buzi, Bajram Tusha, Mumin Selami and Hajredin Bylyshi .. .. 1·25 90

491. Trophy on Globe.

**1986.** World Cup Football Championship, Mexico. Multicoloured.
2316. 25 q. Type **491** .. .. 20 10
2317. 1 l. 20 Goalkeeper's hands and ball .. 90 80

492. Tyre within Ship's Wheel, Train and Traffic Lights.

**1986.** 40th Anniv. of Transport Workers' Day.
2319. **492.** 1 l. 20 multicoloured 1·75 1·25

493. Naim Frasheri (poet).

**1986.** Celebrities. Multicoloured.
2320. 30 q. Type **493** .. .. 35 10
2321. 60 q. Ndre Mjeda (poet) 75 45
2322. 90 q. Petro Nini Luarasi (journalist) .. .. 1·25 65
2323. 1 l. Andon Zako Cajupi (poet) .. .. .. 1·25 75
2324. 1 l. 20 Millosh Gjergj Nikolla Migjeni (revolutionary writer) 1·50 80
2325. 2 l. 60 Urani Rumbo (women's education pioneer) .. .. 4·00 2·50

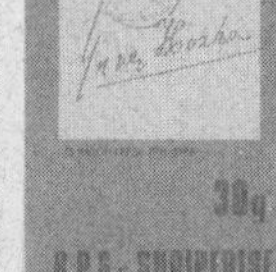


494. Flag. 495. Party Stamp and Enver Hoxha's Signature.

**1986.** 9th Workers' Party Congress, Tirana.
2326. **494.** 30 q. multicoloured 1·10 55

**1986.** 45th Anniv. of Worker's Party.
2327. **495.** 30 q. red, grey and gold .. .. 55 10
2328. – 1 l. 20 multicoloured 1·60 1·00
Design: 1 l. 20, Profiles of Marx, Engels, Lenin and Stalin and Tirana house where Party was founded.

496. Martyrs' Monument. 497. Marble Head of Aesculapius.

**1986.**
2329. **496.** 10 q. blue .. .. 10 10
2330. 20 q. red .. .. 10 10
2331. 30 q. red .. .. 10 10
2332. 50 q. brown .. .. 10 10
2333. 60 q. green .. .. 15 10
2334. 80 q. red .. .. 40 10
2335. 90 q. blue .. .. 45 35
2336. 1 l. 20 green .. .. 55 45
2337. 1 l. 60 purple .. 80 55
2338. 2 l. 20 green .. .. 1·10 75
2339. 3 l. brown .. .. 1·40 1·00
2340. 6 l. yellow .. .. 3·25 2·25

**1987.** Archeological Discoveries. Mult.
2341. 30 q. Type **497** .. .. 10 10
2342. 80 q. Terracotta figure of Aphrodite .. .. 65 10
2343. 1 l. Bronze figure of Pan 80 45
2344. 1 l. 20 Limestone head of Jupiter .. .. 1·25 90

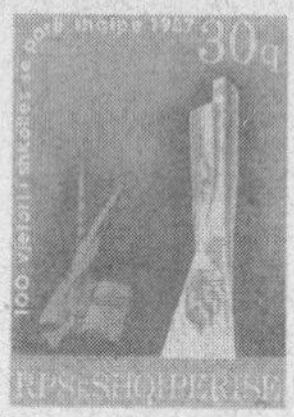

498. Monument and Centenary Emblem. 499. Victor Hugo (writer) (185th birth anniv.)

**1987.** Centenary of First Albanian School. Multicoloured.
2345. 30 q. Type **498** .. .. 10 10
2346. 80 q. First school building, Kora .. 65 10
2347. 1 l. 20 Soldier running, girl reading and boy doing woodwork .. .90 65

**1987.** Anniversaries.
2348. **499.** 30 q. violet, lavender and black .. .. 10 10
2349. – 80 q. brown, light brown and black .. 65 10
2350. – 90 q. deep blue, blue and black .. .. 75 45
2351. – 1 l. 30 deep green, green and brown .. 1·25 90
Designs: 80 q. Galileo Galilei (astronomer) (345th death anniv.). 90 q. Charles Darwin (naturalist) (105th death anniv.) 1 l. 30, Miguel de Cervantes Saavedra (writer) (440th birth anniv.).

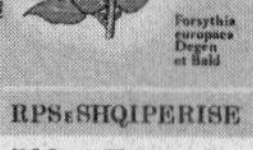

500. "Forsythia europaea". 501. Congress Emblem.

**1987.** Flowers. Multicoloured.
2352. 30 q. Type **500** .. .. 10 10
2353. 90 q. "Moltkia doerfleri" 75 35
2354. 2 l. 10 "Wulfenia baldacii" .. .. 1·90 1·25

**1987.** 10th Trade Unions Congress, Tirana.
2355. **501.** 1 l. 20 deep red, red and gold .. .. 1·10 65

**502.** "The Bread of Industry" (Myrteza Fushekati).

**1987.** Paintings from Gallery of Figurative Arts, Tirana. Multicoloured.
2356. 30 q. Type **502** .. .. 10 10
2357. 80 q. "Partisan Gift" (Skender Kokobobo) .. 55 10
2358. 1 l. "Sowers" (Bujar Asllani) (horiz.) .. 75 35
2359. 1 l. 20 "At the Foundry" (Clirim Ceka) (horiz.) 1·10 75

**503.** Throwing the Hammer.

**1987.** World Light Athletics Championships, Rome. Multicoloured.
2360. 30 q. Type **503** .. .. 10 10
2361. 90 q. Running .. .. 65 35
2362. 1 l. 10 Putting the shot 90 65

**504.** Themistokli Germenji (revolutionary, 60th death).

**1987.** Celebrities' Anniversaries. Mult.
2364. 30 q. Type **504** .. .. 10 10
2365. 80 q. Bajram Curri (organizer of Albanian League, 125th birth) .. 55 10
2366. 90 q. Aleks Stavre Drenova (poet, 40th death) .. .. .. 65 35
2367. 1 l. 30 Gjerasim D. Qiriazi (educational pioneer, 126th birth) .. 80 55

**505.** Emblem. **506.** National Flag.

**1987.** 9th Young Communists' Union Congress, Tirana.
2368. **505.** 1 l. 20 multicoloured 75 55

**1987.** 75th Anniv. of Independence.
2369. **506.** 1 l. 20 multicoloured 75 55

**507.** Post Office Emblem. **508.** Lord Byron (writer, bicentenary).

**1987.** 75th Anniv. of Albanian Postal Administration. Multicoloured.
2370. 90 q. Type **507** .. .. 7·25 4·75
2371. 1 l. 20 National emblem on bronze medallion .. 9·50 9·50

**1988.** Birth Anniversaries.
2372. **508.** 30 q. black & orge... 3·00 1·25
2373. – 1 l. 20 black & mve. 11·50 9·50
DESIGN: 1 l. 20, Eugene Delacroix (painter, 190th anniv.).

**509.** Oil Derrick, Tap, Houses and Wheat Ears. **510.** "Sideritis raeseri".

**1988.** 40th Anniv. of W.H.O.
2374. **509.** 90 q. multicoloured 7·25 3·75
2375. 1 l. 20 multicoloured 9·50 8·75

**1988.** Flowers. Multicoloured.
2376. 30 q. Type **510** .. .. 2·40 1·25
2377. 90 q. "Lunaria telekiana" .. .. 7·25 3·75
2378. 2 l. 10 "Sanguisorba albanica" .. .. 12·00 12·00

**511.** Flag and Woman with Book.

**1988.** 10th Women's Union Congress, Tirana.
2379. **511.** 90 q. black, red and orange .. .. 7·25 4·75

**512** Footballers **513** Clasped Hands

**1988.** 8th European Football Championship, West Germany. Multicoloured.
2380 30 q. Type **512** .. .. 35 10
2381 80 q. Players jumping for ball .. .. .. 90 55
2382 1 l. 20 Player being tackled .. 1·25 90

**1988.** 110th Anniv of League of Prizren. Mult.
2384 30 q. Type **513** .. .. 4·00 2·40
2385 1 l. 20 League Head-quarters, Prizren .. 15·00 14·50

**514** Flag, Woman with Rifle and Soldier **515** Mihal Grameno (writer and composer)

**1988.** 45th Anniv of People's Army. Mult.
2386 60 q. Type **514** .. .. 7·75 5·75
2387 90 q. Army monument, partisans and Labinot house .. .. .. 11·50 10·50

**1988.** Multicoloured.
2388 30 q. Type **515** .. 1·75 1·25
2389 90 q. Bajo Topulli (revolutionary) .. .. 5·50 1·50
2390 1 l. Murat Toptani (sculptor and poet) .. 7·25 4·75
2391 1 l. 20 Jul Variboba (poet) 9·50 9·50

**516** Migjeni

**1988.** 50th Death Anniv of Millosh Gjergj Nikolla (Migjeni) (writer).
2392 **516** 90 q. silver and brown 5·75 4·00

**517** "Dede Skurra" **518** Bride wearing Fezzes, Mirdita

**1988.** Ballads. Each black and grey.
2393 30 q. Type **517** .. .. 3·75 2·40
2394 90 q. "Young Omer" .. 10·50 9·50
2395 1 l. 20 "Gjergj Elez Alia" 14·50 12·00

**1988.** National Folklore Festival, Gjirokaster. Wedding Customs. Multicoloured.
2396 30 q. Type **518** .. .. 7·25 4·75
2397 1 l. 20 Pan Dance, Gjirokaster .. .. 24·00 24·00

**519** Hoxha

**1988.** 80th Birth Anniv of Enver Hoxha. Mult.
2398 90 q. Type **519** .. .. 4·00 3·00
2399 1 l. 20 Enver Hoxha Museum (horiz) .. 5·50 5·50

**520** Detail of Congress Document

**1988.** 80th Anniv of Monastir Language Congress. Multicoloured.
2400 60 q. Type **520** .. .. 9·50 7·25
2401 90 q. Alphabet book and Congress building ... 14·50 14·50

**521** Steam Locomotive and Map showing 1947 Railway line

**1989.** Railway Locomotives. Multicoloured.
2402 30 q. Type **521** .. .. 10 10
2403 90 q. Steam locomotive and map of 1949 network .. .. 55 15
2404 1 l. 20 Diesel locomotive and 1978 network .. 75 55
2405 1 l. 80 Diesel locomotive and 1985 network .. 1·10 75
2406 2 l. 40 Diesel locomotive and 1988 network .. 3·00 1·50

**522** Entrance to Two-storey Tomb

**1989.** Illyrian Archaeology.
2407 **522** 30 q. blk, brn & grey 10 10
2408 – 90 q. black and green 55 15
2409 – 2 l. 10 multicoloured 1·10 1·00
DESIGNS: 90 q. Buckle showing battle scene; 2 l. 10, Earring depicting head.

**523** Mother mourning Son **524** "Aster albanicus"

**1989.** "Kostandini and Doruntina" (folk tale). Multicoloured.
2410 30 q. Type **523** .. .. 10 10
2411 80 q. Mother weeping over tomb and son rising from dead .. .. 45 10
2412 1 l. Son and his sister on horseback .. .. 55 15
2413 1 l. 20 Mother and daughter reunited .. 65 15

**1989.** Flowers. Multicoloured.
2414 30 q. Type **524** .. .. 10 10
2415 90 q. "Orchis paparisti" 55 15
2416 2 l. 10 "Orchis albanica" 1·10 75

**525** Johann Strauss (composer, 90th death anniv) **526** State Arms, Workers' Party Flag and Crowd

**1989.** Anniversaries. Each brown and gold.
2417 30 q. Type **525** .. .. 10 10
2418 80 q. Marie Curie (physicist, 55th death anniv) .. .. 45 10
2419 1 l. Federico Garcia Lorca (writer, 53rd death anniv) .. .. 55 15
2420 1 k. 20 Albert Einstein (physicist, 110th birth anniv) .. .. 65 15

**1989.** 6th Albanian Democratic Front Congress, Tirana.
2421 **526** 1 l. 20 multicoloured .. 75 55

**527** Storming of the Bastille

**1989.** Bicentenary of French Revolution.
2422 **527** 90 q. multicoloured .. 45 15
2423 – 1 l. 20 blue, red & blk 65 40
DESIGN: 1 l. 20, Monument.

528 Galley

529 Pjeter Bogdani (writer, 300th anniv)

**1989.** Ships.

2424 528 30 q. green and black .. 10 10
2425 – 80 q. blue and black .. 25 10
2426 – 90 q. blue and black .. 30 15
2427 – 1 l. 30 lilac and black .. 95 55

DESIGNS: 80 q. Kogge; 90 q. Schooner; 1 l. 30, Container ship.

**1989.** Death Anniversaries. Multicoloured.

2428 30 q. Type **529** .. .. 10 10
2429 80 q. Gavril Dara (writer, centenary) .. .. 40 10
2430 90 q. Thimi Mitko (writer, centenary (1990)) .. 45 15
2431 1 l. 30 Kole Idromeno (painter, 50th anniv) .. 70 45

530 Engels, Marx and Marchers

531 Gymnastics

**1989.** 125th Anniv of "First International". Multicoloured.

2432 90 q. Type **530** .. .. 45 15
2433 1 l. 20 Factories, marchers and worker with pick-axe and rifle .. .. 65 45

**1989** 6th National Spartakiad. Multicoloured.

2434 30 q. Type **531** .. .. 10 10
2435 80 q. Football .. .. 40 10
2436 1 l. Cycling .. .. 50 15
2437 1 l. 20 Running .. .. 60 45

532 Revolutionary

533 Chamois

**1989.** 45th Anniv of Liberation. Mult.

2438 30 q. Type **532** .. .. 10 10
2439 80 q. Date .. .. 40 10
2440 1 l. State arms .. .. 50 15
2441 1 l. 20 Young couple .. 60 45

**1990.** Endangered Animals. Chamois. Mult.

2442 10 q. Type **533** .. .. 10 10
2443 30 q. Mother and young .. 10 10
2444 80 q. Chamois keeping lookout .. .. 40 10
2445 90 q. Head of chamois .. 45 15

534 Eagle

**1990.** Masks. Multicoloured.

2446 30 q. Type **534** .. .. 10 10
2447 90 q. Sheep .. .. 45 15
2448 1 l. 20 Goat .. .. 60 45
2449 1 l. 80 Stork .. .. 95 75

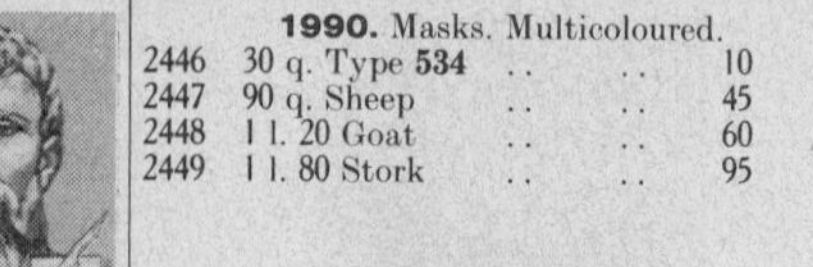

535 Caesar's Mushroom

**1990.** Fungi. Multicoloured.

2450 30 q. Type **535** .. .. 20 10
2451 90 q. Parasol mushroom .. 80 20
2452 1 l. 20 Cep .. .. 1·10 55
2453 1 l. 80 "Clathrus cancelatus" .. .. 1·75 90

536 Engraving Die

**1990.** 150th Anniv of the Penny Black. Mult.

2454 90 q. Type **536** .. .. 45 15
2455 1 l. 20 Mounted postal messenger .. .. 60 45
2456 1 l. 80 Mail coach passengers reading letters .. .. .. 95 75

537 Mascot and Flags

**1990.** World Cup Football Championship, Italy. Multicoloured.

2457 30 q. Type **537** .. .. 10 10
2458 90 q. Mascot running .. 45 15
2459 1 l. 20 Mascot preparing to kick ball .. .. 60 45

538 Young Van Gogh and Paintings

**1990.** Death Centenary of Vincent van Gogh (painter). Multicoloured.

2461 30 q. Type **538** .. .. 10 10
2462 90 q. Van Gogh and woman in field .. 45 15
2463 2 l. 10 Van Gogh in asylum .. .. 1·10 75

539 Gjergj Elez Alia lying wounded

**1990.** Gjergj Elez Alia (folk hero). Mult.

2465 30 q. Type **539** .. .. 10 10
2466 90 q. Alia being helped onto horse .. .. 45 15
2467 1 l. 20 Alia fighting Bajloz 60 45
2468 1 l. 80 Alia on horseback and severed head of Bajloz .. .. 95 65

540 Mosque

541 Pirroja

**1990.** 2400th Anniv of Berat. Multicoloured.

2469 30 q. Type **540** .. .. 10 10
2470 90 q. Square building and bridges .. .. 20 15
2471 1 l. 20 River .. .. 45 15
2472 1 l. 80 Onufri .. .. 65 45
2473 2 l. 40 Nikolla .. .. 85 60

**1990.** Illyrian Heroes. Each black.

2474 30 q. Type **541** .. .. 10 10
2475 90 q. Teuta .. .. 20 15
2476 1 l. 20 Bato .. .. 25 15
2477 1 l. 80 Bardhyli .. .. 65 45

542 School and "Globe" of Books

543 "Albanian Horsemen" (Eugene Delacroix)

**1990.** International Literacy Year.

2478 542 90 q. multicoloured .. 20 15
2479 1 l. 20 multicoloured 25 15

**1990.** Albanians in Art. Multicoloured.

2480 30 q. Type **543** .. .. 10 10
2481 1 l. 20 "Albanian Woman" (Camille Corot) .. .. .. 25 15
2482 1 l. 80 "Skanderbeg" (anon) .. .. 65 45

544 Boletini

545 Armorial Eagle

**1991.** 75th Death Anniv of Isa Boletini (revolutionary). Multicoloured.

2483 90 q. Type **544** .. .. 20 10
2484 1 l. 20 Boletini and flag .. 25 15

**1991.** 800th Anniv (1990) of Founding of Arberi State.

2485 545 90 q. multicoloured .. 20 10
2486 1 l. 20 multicoloured 25 15

546 "Woman reading"

547 "Cistus albanicus" E. F. Warburg

**1991.** 150th Birth Anniv of Pierre Auguste Renoir (artist). Multicoloured.

2487 30 q. Type **546** .. .. 10 10
2488 90 q. "The Swing" .. 20 10
2489 1 l. 20 "The Boat Club" (horiz) .. .. 25 15
2490 1 l. 80 Still life (detail) (horiz) .. .. 60 20

**1991.** Flowers. Multicoloured.

2492 30 q. Type **547** .. .. 10 10
2493 90 q. "Trifolium pilczii" 20 10
2494 1 l. 80 "Lilium albanicum" .. .. 60 20

548 Rozafa breastfeeding Child

549 Mozart conducting

**1991.** Imprisonment of Rozafa (folk tale). Multicoloured.

2495 30 q. Type **548** .. .. 10 10
2496 90 q. The three brothers talking to old man .. 20 10
2497 1 l. 20 Building of walls around Rozafa .. 25 15
2498 1 l. 80 Figures symbolizing water flowing between stones .. .. .. 60 20

**1991.** Death Bicentenary of Wolfgang Amadeus Mozart (composer). Multicoloured.

2499 90 q. Type **549** .. .. 20 10
2500 1 l. 20 Mozart and score 25 15
2501 1 l. 80 Mozart composing 60 20

550 Vitus Bering

**1992.** Explorers. Multicoloured.

2503 30 q. Type **550** .. .. 10 10
2504 90 q. Christopher Columbus .. .. 15 10
2505 1 l. 80 Ferdinand Magellan 35 20

551 Otto Lilienthal's Biplane Glider, 1896

**1992.** Aircraft. Multicoloured.

2506 30 q. Type **551** .. .. 10 10
2507 80 q. Clement Ader's "Avion III", 1897 .. 15 10
2508 90 q. Wright Brothers' Type A, 1903 .. .. 15 10
2509 1 l. 20 Concorde .. .. 25 15
2510 1 l. 80 Tupolev Tu-114 .. 35 20
2511 2 l. 40 Dornier Do-31E .. 45 30

Nos. 2510/11 are wrongly inscribed "Tu-114" and "Dernier" respectively.

552 Ski Jumping

**1992.** Winter Olympic Games, Albertville. Multicoloured.

2512 30 q. Type **552** .. .. 10 10
2513 90 q. Skiing .. .. 15 10
2514 1 l. 20 Ice skating (pairs) 25 15
2515 1 l. 80 Luge .. .. 35 20

553 "Europe" and Doves

**1992.** Admission of Albania to European Security and Co-operation Conference at Foreign Ministers' Meeting, Berlin. Mult.

2516 90 q. Type **553** .. .. 10 10
2517 1 l. 20 Members' flags and map .. .. .. 10 10

554 Envelopes and Emblem

**1992.** Admission of Albania to E.P.T. Conference. Multicoloured.

2518 90 q. Type **554** .. .. .. 10 10
2519 1 l. 20 Emblem and tape reels .. .. .. 10 10

555 Everlasting Flame

**1992.** National Martyrs' Day. Multicoloured.

2520 90 q. Type **555** .. .. 10 10
2521 4 l. 10 Poppies (horiz) .. 10 10

556 Pictograms

**1992.** European Football Championship, Sweden.

2522 **556** 30 q. lt green & green 10 10
2523 – 90 q. red and blue .. 10 10
2524 – 10 l. 80 ochre & brown 10 15
DESIGNS: 90 q., 10 l. 80, Different pictograms.

557 Lawn Tennis

**1992.** Olympic Games, Barcelona. Mult.

2526 30 q. Type **557** .. .. 10 10
2527 90 q. Baseball .. .. 10 10
2528 1 l. 80 Table tennis .. 10 10

558 Map and Doves

**1992.** European Unity.

2530 **558** 1 l. 20 multicoloured 10 10

559 Native Pony

**1992.** Horses. Multicoloured.

2531 30 q. Type **559** .. .. 10 10
2532 90 q. Hungarian nonius .. 10 10
2533 1 l. 20 Arab (vert) .. 10 10
2534 10 l. 60 Haflinger (vert) .. 15 10

560 Map of Americas, Columbus and Ships

**1992.** Europa. 500th Anniv of Discovery of America by Columbus. Multicoloured.

2535 60 q. Type **560** .. .. 10 10
2536 3 l. 20 Map of Americas and Columbus meeting Amerindians .. .. 10 10

561 Mother Teresa

562 Pope John Paul II

**1992.** Mother Teresa (Agnes Gonxhe Bojaxhi) (founder of Missionaries of Charity).

2538 **561** 40 q. red .. .. 10 10
2539 60 q. brown .. .. 10 10
2540 1 l. violet .. .. 10 10
2541 1 l. 80 grey .. .. 10 10
2542 2 l. red .. .. 10 10
2543 2 l. 40 green .. .. 10 10
2544 3 l. 20 blue .. .. 10 10
2545 5 l. violet .. .. 10 10
2546 5 l. 60 purple .. .. 10 10
2547 7 l. 20 green .. .. 10 10
2548 10 l. orange .. .. 10 10
2549 18 l. orange .. .. 25 15
2550 20 l. purple .. .. 30 15
2551 25 l. green .. .. 35 20
2552 60 l. green .. .. 85 50

**1993.** Papal Visit.

2555 **562** 16 l. multicoloured .. 20 10

**1993.** Nos. 2329/32 and 2335 surch **POSTA SHQIPTARE** and new value.

2556 **496** 3 l. on 10 q. blue .. 10 10
2557 6 l. 50 on 20 q. red .. 10 10
2558 13 l. on 30 q. red .. 15 10
2559 20 l. on 90 q. blue .. 25 15
2560 30 l. on 50 q. brown .. 35 20

564 Lef Nosi (first Postal Minister)

565 "Life Weighs Heavily on Man" (A. Zajmi)

**1993.** 80th Anniv of First Albanian Stamps.

2561 **564** 6 l. 50 bistre and olive 10 10

**1993.** Europa. Contemporary Art. Mult.

2562 3 l. Type **565** .. .. 10 10
2563 7 l. "The Green Star" (E. Hila) (horiz) .. 10 10

566 Running

**1993.** Mediterranean Games, Agde and Roussillon (Languedoc), France. Mult.

2565 3 l. Type **566** .. .. 10 10
2566 16 l. Canoeing .. .. 20 10
2567 21 l. Cycling .. .. 25 15

567 Bardhi

568 Mascot and Flags around Stadium

**1993.** 350th Death Anniv of Frang Bardhi (scholar).

2569 **567** 6 l. 50 brown and stone 10 10

**1994.** World Cup Football Championship, U.S.A. Multicoloured.

2571 42 l. Type **568** .. .. 60 40
2572 68 l. Mascot kicking ball 95 60

569 Gjovalin Gjadri (construction engineer)

571 Richard Wagner

570 Emblem and Benz

**1994.** Europa. Discoveries and Inventions.

2573 **569** 50 l. deep brown, chestnut and brown 70 45
2574 – 100 l. deep brown, chestnut and brown 1·40 90
DESIGN: 100 l. Karl Ritter von Ghega (railway engineer).

**1995.** 150th Birth Anniv (1994) of Karl Benz (engineer). Multicoloured.

2576 5 l. Type **570** .. .. 10 10
2577 10 l. Modern Mercedes motor car .. .. 15 10
2578 60 l. First four-wheel Benz motor car, 1886 .. 85 55
2579 125 l. Pre-war Mercedes touring car .. .. 1·75 1·10

**1995.** Composers. Each brown and gold.

2580 3 l. Type **571** .. .. 10 10
2581 6 l. 50 Edvard Grieg .. 10 10
2582 11 l. Charles Gounod .. 15 10
2583 20 l. Pyotr Tchaikovsky 30 20

572 Intersections

**1995.** 50th Anniv (1994) of Liberation.

2584 **572** 50 l. black and red .. 70 45

573 Ali Pasha

**1995.** 250th Birth Anniv (1994) of Ali Pasha of Tepelene (Pasha of Janina, 1788–1820).

2585 **573** 60 l. black, yell & brn 85 55

574 Veskopoja, 1744 (left half)

577 Hands holding Olive Branch

576 Palace of Europe, Strasbourg

**1995.** 250th Anniv (1994) of Veskopoja Academy. Multicoloured.

2587 42 l. Type **574** .. .. 60 40
2588 68 l. Veskopoja, 1744 (right half) .. .. 95 60
Nos. 1587/8 were issued together, se-tenant, forming a composite design.

**1995** Admission of Albania to Council of Europe.

2590 **576** 25 l. black and blue .. 30 20
2591 – 85 l. multicoloured .. 1·00 65
DESIGN: 85 l. State arms and map.

**1995.** Europa. Peace and Freedom. Mult.

2592 50 l. Type **577** .. .. 60 40
2593 100 l. Dove flying over hands .. .. .. 1·10 70

578 Mice sitting around Table and Stork with Fox

**1995.** 300th Death Anniv of Jean de La Fontaine (writer). Multicoloured.

2595 2 l. Type **578** .. .. 10 10
2596 3 l. Stork with foxes around table .. .. 10 10
2597 25 l. Frogs under tree .. 30 20

579 Bee on Flower

580 Fridtjof Nansen

**1995.** The Honey Bee. Multicoloured.

2599 5 l. Type **579** .. .. 10 10
2600 10 l. Bee and honeycomb .. 10 10
2601 25 l. Bee on comb .. 30 20

**1995.** Explorers. Multicoloured.

2602 25 l. Type **580** .. 30 20
2603 25 l. James Cook .. 30 20
2604 25 l. Roald Amundsen .. 30 20
2605 25 l. Robert Scott .. 30 20
Nos. 2602/5 were issued together, se-tenant, forming a composite design.

581 Flags outside U.N. Building, New York

**1995.** 50th Anniv of U.N.O. Multicoloured.

2606 2 l. Type **581** .. .. 10 10
2607 100 l. Flags flying to right outside U.N. building, New York .. .. 1·10 70

582 Male Chorus

583 "Poet"

**1995.** National Folklore Festival, Berat. Multicoloured.

| | | | |
|---|---|---|---|
| 2608 | 5 l. Type **582** .. .. | 10 | 10 |
| 2609 | 50 l. Female participant | 60 | 40 |

**1995.** Jan Kukuzeli (11th-century poet, musician and teacher). Abstract representations of Kukuzeli. Multicoloured.

| | | | |
|---|---|---|---|
| 2610 | 18 l. Type **583** .. .. | 20 | 10 |
| 2611 | 20 l. "Musician" .. | 25 | 15 |

584 Church and Preacher, Berat Kruje

585 Paul Eluard

**1995.** 20th Anniv of World Tourism Organization. Multicoloured.

| | | | |
|---|---|---|---|
| 2613 | 18 l. Type **584** .. .. | 20 | 10 |
| 2614 | 20 l. Street, Shkoder .. | 25 | 15 |
| 2615 | 42 l. Buildings, Gjirokaster .. .. | 50 | 30 |

**1995.** Poets' Birth Centenaries. Multicoloured.

| | | | |
|---|---|---|---|
| 2616 | 25 l. Type **585** .. .. | 30 | 20 |
| 2617 | 50 l. Sergei Yessenin .. | 60 | 40 |

586 Louis, Film Reel and Projector

**1995.** Centenary of Motion Pictures. Lumiere Brothers (developers of cine camera). Mult.

| | | | |
|---|---|---|---|
| 2618 | 10 l. Type **586** .. .. | 10 | 10 |
| 2619 | 85 l. Auguste, film reel and cinema audience .. | 1·00 | 65 |

587 Presley

**1995.** 60th Birth Anniv of Elvis Presley (entertainer). Multicoloured.

| | | | |
|---|---|---|---|
| 2620 | 3 l. Type **587** .. .. | 10 | 10 |
| 2621 | 60 l. Presley (different) .. | 70 | 45 |

588 Banknotes of 1925

589 "5", crumbling Star, Open Book and Peace Dove

**1995.** 70th Anniv of Albanian National Bank. Multicoloured.

| | | | |
|---|---|---|---|
| 2622 | 10 l. Type **588** .. .. | 10 | 10 |
| 2623 | 25 l. Modern banknotes .. | 30 | 20 |

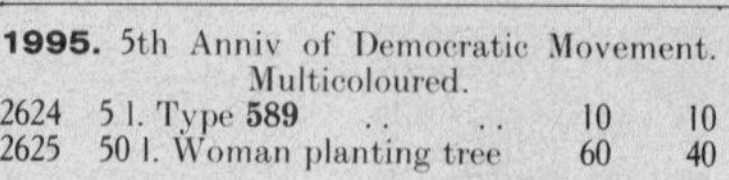

**1995.** 5th Anniv of Democratic Movement. Multicoloured.

| | | | |
|---|---|---|---|
| 2624 | 5 l. Type **589** .. .. | 10 | 10 |
| 2625 | 50 l. Woman planting tree | 60 | 40 |

590 Mother Teresa

591 Football, Union Jack, Map of Europe and Stadium

**1996.** Europa. Famous Women.

| | | | | |
|---|---|---|---|---|
| 2626 | **590** | 25 l. multicoloured .. | 30 | 20 |
| 2627 | | 100 l. multicoloured .. | 1·10 | 70 |

**1996.** European Football Championship, England. Multicoloured.

| | | | |
|---|---|---|---|
| 2629 | 25 l. Type **591** .. .. | 30 | 20 |
| 2630 | 100 l. Map of Europe, ball and player .. .. | 1·10 | 70 |

## EXPRESS LETTER STAMPS

### ITALIAN OCCUPATION

**E 67.** King Victor Emmanuel.

**1940.**

| | | | | |
|---|---|---|---|---|
| E 373. | E 67. | 25 q. violet .. .. | 4·25 | 3·75 |
| E 374. | | 50 q. red .. .. | 9·00 | 9·00 |

No. E 374 is inscr. "POSTAT EXPRES".

**1943.** Optd. **14 Shtator 1943.**

| | | | | |
|---|---|---|---|---|
| E 402. | E 67. | 25 q. violet .. .. | 7·00 | 18·00 |

## POSTAGE DUE STAMPS

**1914.** Optd. **TAKSE** through large letter **T.**

| | | | | |
|---|---|---|---|---|
| D 33. | 4. | 2 q. brown and yellow .. | 10·50 | 3·00 |
| D 34. | | 5 q. green and yellow .. | 10·50 | 4·25 |
| D 35. | | 10 q. red .. .. | 14·50 | 3·00 |
| D 36. | | 25 q. blue .. .. | 18·00 | 3·00 |
| D 37. | | 50 q. mauve and red .. | 22·00 | 7·50 |

**1914.** Nos. 40/45 optd. **TAKSE.**

| | | | | |
|---|---|---|---|---|
| D 46. | 4. | 10 pa. on 5 q. grn. & yell. | 3·75 | 3·00 |
| D 47. | | 20 pa. on 10 q. red .. | 3·75 | 3·00 |
| D 48. | | 1 g. on 25 q. blue .. | 3·75 | 3·00 |
| D 49. | | 2 g. on 50 q. mve. & red | 3·75 | 3·00 |

**1919.** Fiscal stamps optd. **TAXE.**

| | | | | |
|---|---|---|---|---|
| D 89. | 12. | (4) q. on 4 h. pink .. | 8·00 | 8·00 |
| D 90. | | (10) q. on 10 k. red on grn. | 8·00 | 8·00 |
| D 91. | | 20 q. on 2 k. orange .. | 8·00 | 8·00 |
| D 92. | | 50 q. on 5 k. brown on yellow .. .. | 8·00 | 8·00 |

D 20. Fortress of Shkoder.

D 22.

D 35.

**1920.** Optd. with posthorn.

| | | | | |
|---|---|---|---|---|
| D 129. | D 20. | 4 q. olive .. .. | 1·10 | 1·25 |
| D 130. | | 10 q. red .. .. | 1·25 | 1·50 |
| D 131. | | 20 q. brown .. | 1·25 | 1·50 |
| D 132. | | 50 q. black .. .. | 1·75 | 2·00 |

**1922.**

| | | | | |
|---|---|---|---|---|
| D 141. | D 22. | 4 q. black on red .. | 1·75 | 1·90 |
| D 142. | | 10 q. black on red .. | 1·75 | 1·90 |
| D 143. | | 20 q. black on red .. | 1·75 | 1·90 |
| D 144. | | 50 q. black on red .. | 1·75 | 1·90 |

**1922.** Optd. **Republika Shiqiptare.**

| | | | | |
|---|---|---|---|---|
| D 186. | D 22. | 4 q. black on red .. | 2·25 | 2·40 |
| D 187. | | 10 q. black on red .. | 2·25 | 2·40 |
| D 188. | | 20 q. black on red .. | 2·25 | 2·40 |
| D 189. | | 50 q. black on red .. | 2·25 | 2·40 |

**1925.**

| | | | | |
|---|---|---|---|---|
| D 204. | D 35. | 10 q. blue .. .. | 75 | 90 |
| D 205. | | 20 q. green .. | 1·10 | 1·10 |
| D 206. | | 30 q. brown .. | 1·50 | 1·50 |
| D 207. | | 50 q. dark brown .. | 2·25 | 2·25 |

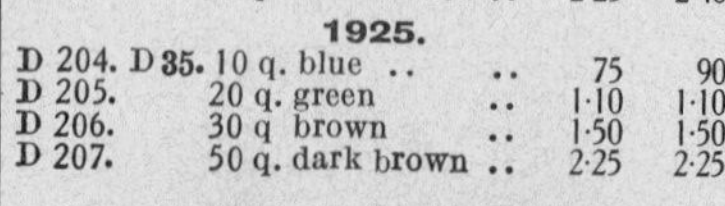

**D 53.** Arms of Albania. **D 67.**

**1930.**

| | | | | |
|---|---|---|---|---|
| D 288. | D 53. | 10 q. blue .. .. | 5·50 | 5·50 |
| D 289. | | 20 q. red .. .. | 1·75 | 1·75 |
| D 290. | | 30 q. violet .. .. | 1·75 | 1·75 |
| D 291. | | 50 q. green .. | 1·75 | 1·75 |

**1936.** Optd. **Takse.**

| | | | | |
|---|---|---|---|---|
| D 312. | 50. | 10 q. red .. .. | 18·00 | 16·00 |

**1940.**

| | | | | |
|---|---|---|---|---|
| D 373. | D 67. | 4 q. red .. .. | 35·00 | 35·00 |
| D 374. | | 10 q. violet .. .. | 18·00 | 18·00 |
| D 375. | | 20 q. brown .. | 18·00 | 18·00 |
| D 376. | | 30 q. blue .. .. | 22·00 | 22·00 |
| D 377. | | 50 q. red .. .. | 22·00 | 22·00 |

# ALEXANDRIA Pt. 6

**Issues of the French P.O. in this Egyptian port. The French Post Offices in Egypt closed on 31 March 1931.**

1899. 100 centimes = 1 franc.
1921. 10 milliemes = 1 piastre.

**1899.** Stamps of France optd. **ALEXANDRIE.**

| | | | | |
|---|---|---|---|---|
| 1. | 10. | 1 c. black on blue .. | 65 | 60 |
| 2. | | 2 c. brown on yellow | 95 | 1·25 |
| 3. | | 3 c. grey .. .. | 1·10 | 1·40 |
| 4. | | 4 c. brown on grey .. | 90 | 1·40 |
| 5. | | 5 c. green .. .. | 1·75 | 1·25 |
| 7. | | 10 c. black on lilac .. | 4·00 | 4·50 |
| 9. | | 15 c. blue .. .. | 4·00 | 2·50 |
| 10. | | 20 c. red on green .. | 5·50 | 6·25 |
| 11. | | 25 c. black on red .. | 3·75 | 45 |
| 12. | | 30 c. brown .. .. | 3·75 | 7·50 |
| 13. | | 40 c. red on yellow .. | 7·25 | 8·50 |
| 15. | | 50 c. red .. .. | 17·00 | 9·50 |
| 16. | | 1 f. olive .. .. | 11·00 | 9·75 |
| 17. | | 2 f. brown on blue .. | 75·00 | 60·00 |
| 18. | | 5 f. mauve on lilac .. | £110 | 95·00 |

**1902.** "Blanc," "Mouchon" and "Merson" key-types, inscr "ALEXANDRIE".

| | | | | |
|---|---|---|---|---|
| 19 | A | 1 c. grey .. .. | 30 | 15 |
| 20 | | 2 c. purple .. .. | 30 | 65 |
| 21 | | 3 c. red .. .. | 30 | 55 |
| 22 | | 4 c. brown .. .. | 40 | 85 |
| 24 | | 5 c. green .. .. | 95 | 40 |
| 25 | B | 10 c. red .. .. | 1·00 | 20 |
| 26 | | 15 c. red .. .. | 1·60 | 40 |
| 27 | | 15 c. orange .. .. | 1·10 | 90 |
| 28 | | 20 c. brown .. .. | 1·75 | 45 |
| 29 | | 25 c. blue .. .. | 95 | 10 |
| 30 | | 30 c. mauve .. .. | 2·75 | 1·75 |
| 31 | C | 40 c. red and blue .. | 1·90 | 1·25 |
| 32 | | 50 c. brown and lilac .. | 3·75 | 45 |
| 33 | | 1 f. red and green .. | 5·50 | 45 |
| 34 | | 2 f. lilac and buff .. | 11·00 | 2·75 |
| 35 | | 5 f. blue and buff .. | 13·00 | 13·50 |

**1915.** Red Cross. Surch **5c** and Red Cross.

| | | | | |
|---|---|---|---|---|
| 36 | B | 10 c. + 5 c. red .. .. | 35 | 1·10 |

**1921.** Surch thus, **15 Mill.**, in one line (without bars).

| | | | | |
|---|---|---|---|---|
| 37 | A | 2 m. on 5 c. green .. | 2·25 | 3·50 |
| 38 | | 3 m on 3 c. red .. .. | 4·00 | 4·25 |
| 39 | B | 4 m. on 10 c. red .. | 2·50 | 2·75 |
| 40a | A | 5 m. on 1 c. grey .. | 4·50 | 4·25 |
| 41 | | 5 m. on 4 c. brown .. | 4·50 | 4·25 |
| 42 | B | 6 m. on 15 c. orange .. | 1·60 | 2·50 |
| 43 | | 8 m. on 20 c. brown .. | 3·00 | 3·25 |
| 44 | | 10 m. on 25 c. blue .. | 1·10 | 2·25 |
| 45 | | 12 m. on 30 c. mauve .. | 10·00 | 10·50 |
| 46 | A | 15 m. on 2 c purple .. | 4·00 | 4·25 |
| 47 | C | 15 m. on 40 c. red & blue | 10·00 | 11·00 |
| 48 | | 15 m. on 50 c. brn & lilac | 4·25 | 5·50 |
| 49 | | 30 m. on 1 f. red & green | £140 | £130 |
| 50 | | 60 m. on 2 f. lilac & buff | £200 | £200 |
| 51 | | 150 m. on 5 f. bl & buff | £275 | £275 |

**1921.** Surch thus, **15 MILLIEMES**, in two lines (without bars).

| | | | | |
|---|---|---|---|---|
| 53 | A | 1 m. on 1 c. grey .. | 80 | 1·75 |
| 54 | | 2 m. on 5 c. green .. | 75 | 1·60 |
| 55 | B | 4 m. on 10 c. red .. | 2·25 | 2·25 |
| 65 | | 4 m. on 10 c. green .. | 1·00 | 1·60 |
| 56 | A | 5 m. on 3 c. orange .. | 3·25 | 3·75 |
| 57 | B | 6 m. on 15 c. orange .. | 75 | 1·75 |
| 58 | | 8 m. on 20 c. brown .. | 60 | 1·25 |
| 59 | | 10 m. on 25 c. blue .. | 45 | 70 |
| 60 | | 10 m. on 30 c. mauve .. | 2·50 | 2·50 |
| 61 | C | 15 m. on 50 c. brn & lilac | 2·50 | 2·50 |
| 66 | B | 15 m. on 50 c. blue .. | 1·75 | 1·00 |
| 62 | C | 30 m. on 1 f. red and grn | 2·00 | 1·60 |
| 63 | | 60 m. on 2 f. lilac & buff | £1500 | £1700 |
| 67 | | 60 m. on 2 f. red & green | 7·25 | 5·50 |
| 64 | | 150 m. on 5 f. blue & buff | 9·25 | 5·75 |

**1925.** Surch in milliemes with bars over old value.

| | | | | |
|---|---|---|---|---|
| 68 | A | 1 m. on 1 c. grey .. | 25 | 1·40 |
| 69 | | 2 m. on 5 c. orange .. | 40 | 1·25 |
| 70 | | 2 m. on 5 c. green .. | 1·40 | 1·75 |
| 71 | B | 4 m. on 10 c. green .. | 30 | 1·60 |
| 72 | A | 5 m. on 3 c. red .. .. | 70 | 1·25 |
| 73 | B | 6 m. on 15 c. orange .. | 35 | 1·60 |
| 74 | | 8 m. on 20 c. brown .. | 40 | 1·60 |
| 75 | | 10 m. on 25 c. blue .. | 40 | 50 |
| 76 | | 15 m. on 50 c. blue .. | 1·40 | 65 |
| 77 | C | 30 m. on 1 f. red & green | 1·75 | 65 |
| 78 | | 60 m. on 2 f. red & green | 2·25 | 2·75 |
| 79 | | 150 m. on 5 f. blue & buff | 3·00 | 3·25 |

**1927.** Altered key-types, inscr. "Mm" below value.

| | | | | |
|---|---|---|---|---|
| 80. | A. | 3 m. orange .. .. | 70 | 1·60 |
| 81. | B. | 15 m. blue .. .. | 80 | 35 |
| 82. | | 20 m. mauve .. .. | 2·50 | 2·75 |
| 83. | C. | 50 m. red and green .. | 7·25 | 7·25 |
| 84. | | 100 m. bl. and yellow | 9·25 | 8·50 |
| 85. | | 250 m. green and red .. | 17·00 | 12·00 |

**1927.** Sinking Fund. As No. 81, colour changed, surch **+5 Mm Caisse d'Amortissement.**

| | | | | |
|---|---|---|---|---|
| 86. | B. | 15 m. + 5 m. orange .. | 2·00 | 2·75 |
| 87. | | 15 m. + 5 m. red .. | 2·75 | 2·75 |
| 88. | | 15 m. + 5 m. brown .. | 5·00 | 5·50 |
| 89. | | 15 m. + 5 m. lilac .. | 7·75 | 8·75 |

POSTAGE DUE STAMPS

**1922.** Postage Due Stamps of France surch. in milliemes.

D65 D 11 2 m. on 5 c. blue .. 1·00 2·25
D66 4 m. on 10 c. brown .. 1·25 2·25
D67 10 m. on 30 c. red .. 1·50 2·50
D68 15 m. on 50 c. purple 1·40 2·50
D69 30 m. on 1 f. purple on yellow .. 1·25 3·50

D 10.

**1928.**

D 90. D 10. 1 m. grey .. .. 1·40 1·75
D 91. 2 m. blue .. 1·40 1·60
D 92. 4 m. pink .. .. 1·75 1·90
D 93. 5 m. olive .. 1·50 1·60
D 94. 10 m. red .. .. 1·75 1·90
D 95. 20 m. purple .. 1·60 1·75
D 96. 30 m. green .. 3·50 3·50
D 97. 40 m. lilac.. .. 3·25 3·50

This set was issued for use in both Alexandria and Port Said.

## ALGERIA Pt. 6; Pt. 12

French territory in N. Africa. Stamps of France were used in Algeria from July 1958, until 3 July 1962, when the country achieved independence following a referendum.

1924. 100 centimes = 1 franc.
1964. 100 centimes = 1 dinar.

**1924.** Stamps of France optd. **ALGERIE.**

1. 11. ½ c. on 1 c. grey .. .. 10 25
2. 1 c. grey .. .. .. 10 25
3. 2 c. red .. .. .. 10 30
4. 3 c. red .. .. .. 10 30
5. 4 c. brown .. .. 10 30
6. 18. 5 c. orange .. .. 10 15
7. 11. 5 c. green .. .. 15 20
8. 30. 10 c. green .. .. 20 20
9. 18. 10 c. green .. .. 15 20
10. 15. 15 c. green .. .. 15 20
11. 30. 15 c. green .. .. 20 25
12. 18. 15 c. brown .. .. 10 15
13. 20 c. brown .. .. 20 10
14. 25 c. blue .. .. 10 10
15. 30. 30 c. red .. .. 15 30
16. 18. 30 c. blue .. .. 15 15
17. 30 c. red* .. .. 25 30
18. 35 c. violet .. .. 15 25
19. 13. 40 c. red and blue .. 20 25
20. 18. 40 c. olive .. .. 30 60
21. 13. 45 c. green and blue .. 25 45
22. 30. 45 c. red .. .. 30 40
23. 50 c. blue .. .. 20 25
24. 15. 60 c. violet .. .. 30 35
25. 65 c. red .. .. 20 25
26. 30. 75 c. blue .. .. 25 35
27. 15. 80 c. red .. .. 50 65
28. 85 c. red .. .. 35 40
29. 13. 1 f. red and green .. 55 80
30. 18. 1 f. 05 red .. .. 55 90
31. 13. 2 f. red and green .. 60 1·00
32. 3 f. violet and blue .. 1·50 2·00
33. 5 f. blue and yellow .. 5·00 8·00

*No. 17 was only issued pre-cancelled and the price in the unused columns is for stamps with full gum.

3. Street in the Casbah.  4. Mosque of Sidi Abderahman.  5. Grand Mosque.

6. Bay of Algiers.

**1926.**

34 3 1 c. green .. .. 10 10
35 2 c. purple .. .. 10 10
36 3 c. orange .. .. 10 10
37 5 c. green .. .. 10 10
38 10 c. mauve .. .. 10 10
39 4 15 c. brown .. .. 10 10
40 20 c. green .. .. 10 10
41 20 c. red .. .. 15 15
43 25 c. green .. .. 10 10
44 25 c. blue .. .. 30 30
46 30 c. blue .. .. 15 25
47 30 c. green .. .. 50 70
48 35 c. violet .. .. 60 90
49 40 c. green .. .. 10 10
50 5 45 c. purple .. .. 20 20
51 50 c. blue .. .. 25 15
53 50 c. red .. .. 35 10
54 60 c. green .. .. 10 10
55 65 c. brown .. .. 75 65
56 3 65 c. blue .. .. 75 10
57 5 75 c. red .. .. 25 30
58 75 c. blue .. .. 1·50 20
59 80 c. orange .. .. 30 45
60 90 c. red .. .. 2·75 3·00
61 6 1 f. purple and green .. 40 20
62 5 1 f. 05 brown .. .. 35 30
63 1 f. 10 mauve .. .. 3·00 3·00
64 6 1 f. 25 ultramarine & blue 55 80
65 1 f. 50 ultramarine & blue 1·00 25
66 2 f. brown and green .. 1·00 15
67 3 f. red and mauve .. 2·75 80
68 5 f. mauve and red .. 4·50 2·50
69 10 f. red and brown .. 35·00 22·00
70 20 f. green and violet .. 4·25 4·25

**1926.** Surch. ½ centime.

71. 3 ½ c. on 1 c. olive .. .. 15 60

**1927.** Wounded Soldiers of Moroccan War Charity Issue. Surch. with star and crescent and premium.

72. 3. 5 c.+5 c. green .. .. 50 85
73. 10 c.+10 c. mauve .. 50 85
74. 4. 15 c.+15c. brown .. 50 85
75. 20 c.+20 c. red .. 50 85
76. 25 c.+25 c. green .. 50 85
77. 30 c. +30 c. blue .. 50 85
78. 35 c.+35 c. violet .. 50 85
79. 40 c.+40 c. olive .. 50 85
80. 5. 50 c.+50 c. blue .. 60 90
81. 80 c.+80 c. orange .. 60 90
82. 6. 1 f.+1 f. purple & green 60 90
83. 2 f. +2 f. brown & green 15·00 22·00
84. 5 f.+5 f. mauve and red 24·00 35·00

**1927.** Surch in figures.

85 4 10 on 35 c. violet .. 10 20
86 25 on 30 c. blue .. .. 10 10
87 30 on 25 c. green .. .. 15 10
88 5 65 on 60 c. green .. .. 40 45
89 90 on 80 c. orange .. .. 40 25
90 1 f. 10 on 1 f. 05 brown .. 20 25
91 6 1 f. 50 on 1 f. 25 ultramarine and blue .. 85 50

**1927.** Surch. **5 c.**

92. 11. 5 c. on 4 c. brown (No. 5) 15 25

11. Railway Terminus, Oran.

**1930.** Cent. of French Occupation.

93. 11. 5 c. + 5 c. orange .. 6·00 6·25
94. – 10 c. + 10 c. olive .. 5·75 6·25
95. – 15 c. + 15 c. brown .. 4·75 6·25
96. – 25 c. + 25 c. grey .. 4·75 6·25
97. – 30 c. + 30 c. red .. 4·75 6·25
98. – 40 c. + 40 c. green .. 4·75 6·25
99. – 50 c. + 50 c. blue .. 4·75 6·25
100. – 75 c. + 75 c. purple .. 4·50 6·25
101. – 1 f. + 1 f. orange .. 4·75 6·25
102. – 1 f. 50 + 1 f. 50 blue .. 4·50 6·25
103. – 2 f. + 2 f. red .. .. 4·50 6·25
104. – 3 f. + 3 f. green .. 4·50 6·25
105. – 5 f. + 5 f. red and green 9·00 15·00

DESIGNS—HORIZ. 10 c. Constantine. 15 c. Admiralty, Algiers. 25 c. Algiers. 30 c. Ruins of Timgad. 40 c. Ruins of Djemila. VERT. 50 c. Ruins of Djemila. 75 c. Tlemcen. 1 f. Ghardaia. 1 f. 50, Tolga. 2 f. Touaregs. 3 f. Native Quarter, Algiers. 5 f. Mosque, Algiers.

12. Bay of Algiers, after painting by Verecque.

**1930.** N. African Int. Philatelic Exn.

106 12 10 f.+10 f. brown .. 12·00 13·00

15. Admiralty and Penon Lighthouse. Algiers.

DESIGNS—HORIZ. A, In the Sahara. B, Arc de Triomphe, Lambese. C, Ghardaia, Mzab. D, Marabouts, Touggourt. E, El Kebir Mosque, Algiers. VERT. F, Colomb Bechar-Oued. G, Cemetery, Tlemcen.

**1936.**

107. A. 1 c. blue .. .. 10 10
108. F. 2 c. purple .. .. 10 10
109. B. 3 c. green .. .. 10 10
110. C. 5 c. mauve .. .. 15 10
111. 15. 10 c. green .. .. 10 10
112. D. 15 c. red .. .. 25 10
113. G. 20 c. green .. .. 10 10
114. E. 25 c. purple .. .. 45 10
115. C. 30 c. green .. .. 45 10
116. D. 40 c. purple .. .. 10 10
117. G. 45 c. blue .. .. 75 1·50
118. 15. 50 c. red .. .. 55 20
119. A. 65 c. brown .. .. 3·00 3·50
120. 65 c. red .. .. 85 10
121. 70 c. brown .. .. 20 15
122. F. 75 c. slate .. .. 35 10
124. B. 90 c. red .. .. 85 25
125. E. 1 f. brown .. .. 35 10
126. 15. 1 f. 25 violet .. .. 50 40
127. 1 f. 25 red .. .. 25 25
128. F. 1 f. 50 blue .. .. 1·00 30
129. 1 f. 50 red .. .. 1·50 1·50
130. C. 1 f. 75 orange .. .. 20 10
131. B. 2 f. purple .. .. 20 10
132. A. 2 f. 25 green .. .. 8·50 11·00
133. E. 2 f. 25 blue .. .. 75 25
134. C. 2 f. 50 blue .. .. 1·50 1·00
135. G. 3 f. mauve .. .. 25 10
136. E. 3 f. 50 blue .. .. 1·50 1·50
137. 15. 5 f. slate .. .. 35 15
138. F. 10 f. orange .. .. 40 30
139. D. 20 f. blue .. .. 75 90

17. Exhibition Pavilion.  18. Constantine in 1837.

**1937.** Paris Int. Exn.

140. 17. 40 c. green .. .. 25 30
141. 50 c. red .. .. 25 20
142. 1 f. 50 blue .. .. 30 35
143. 1 f. 75 black .. .. 40 65

**1937.** Cent. of Capture of Constantine.

144. 18. 65 c. red .. .. 30 20
145. 1 f. brown .. .. 2·25 65
146. 1 f. 75 blue .. .. 35 20
147. 2 f. 15 purple .. .. 25 15

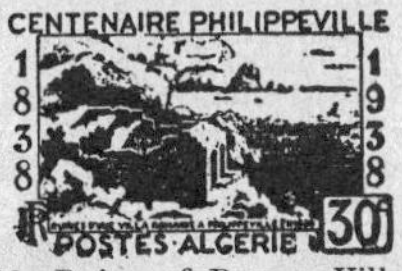

19. Ruins of Roman Villa.

**1938.** Centenary of Philippeville.

148. 19. 30 c. green .. .. 55 60
149. 65 c. blue .. .. 40 20
150. 75 c. purple .. .. 75 90
151. 3 f. red .. .. .. 1·75 1·90
152. 5 f. brown .. .. 2·75 2·75

**1938.** 20th Anniv of Armistice Day. No. 132 surch **1918-11 Nov.-1938 0.65+0.35.**

153 65 c.+35 c. on 2 f. 25 green 40 1·25

**1938.** Surch **0.25**.

154 15 25 c. on 50 c. red .. 40 15

22. Caillie, Lavigerie and Duveyrier.

**1939.** Sahara Pioneers' Monument Fund.

155. 22. 30 c.+20 c. green .. 1·00 1·00
156. 90 c.+60 c. red .. 75 85
157. 2 f. 25+75 c. blue .. 5·50 7·75
158. 5 f.+5 f. black .. 12·00 18·00

23. "Extavia" (freighter) in Algiers Harbour.

**1939.** New York World's Fair.

159. 23. 20 c. green .. .. 80 1·00
160. 40 c. purple .. .. 80 1·00
161. 90 c. brown .. .. 65 25
162. 1 f. 25 red .. .. 3·25 3·00
163. 2 f. 25 blue .. .. 95 70

**1939.** Surch. with new values and bars or cross.

173. 3. 50 c. on 65 c. blue .. 35 10
173c. B. 90 c.+ 60 c. red (No. 124) 40 10
164. 3. 1 f. on 90 c. red .. 40 10

25. Algerian Soldiers.  26. Algiers.

**1940.** Soldiers' Dependants' Relief Fund. Surch. + and premium.

166. 25. 1 f.+1 f. blue .. .. 65 75
167. 1 f.+2 f. red .. .. 50 70
168. 1 f.+4 f. green .. .. 70 90
169. 1 f.+9 f. brown .. 1·00 1·25

**1941.**

170 26 30 c. blue .. .. 15 15
171 70 c. brown .. .. 15 10
172 1 f. red .. .. 15 10

**1941.** Marshal Petain. As T 155 of France but inscr. "ALGERIE".

174. 1 f. blue .. .. 25 15

**1941.** National Relief Fund. As No. 174, but surch +4 f and colour changed.

175 1 f.+4 f. black .. .. 20 35

**1942.** National Relief Fund. Surch. **SECOURS NATIONAL+4 f.**

176. 1 f.+4 f. blue (No. 174) 35 55

**1942.** Various altered types.

(a) As T 26, but without "RF".

177. 26. 30 c. blue .. .. 40 40

(b) As T 5, but without "REPUBLIQUE FRANCAISE".

178. 5. 40 c. grey .. .. 35 40
179. 50 c. red .. .. 20 25

(c) As No. 129 but without "RF".

180. F. 1 f. 50 red .. .. 35 35

32. Arms of Oran.  35. "La Marseillaise".  36. Allegory of Victory.

**1942.** Coats of Arms.

190 A 10 c. lilac .. .. 20 25
191 32 30 c. green .. .. 30 35
181 B 40 c. violet .. .. 20 25
192 40 c. lilac .. .. 45 55
182 32 60 c. red .. .. 15 15
194 B 70 c. blue .. .. 15 25
195 A 80 c. green .. .. 30 40
183 B 1 f. 20 green .. .. 15 25
184 A 1 f. 50 red .. .. 15 15
198 32 2 f. blue .. .. 20 25
186 B 2 f. 40 red .. .. 15 25
187 A 3 f. blue .. .. 20 25
188 B 4 f. blue .. .. 25 25
201 32 4 f. 50 purple .. .. 10 10
189 5 f. green .. .. 20 20

ARMS: A, Algiers. B, Constantine.

**1943.** As T 172 of France (Petain), but inscr. "POSTES ALGERIE".

202. 1 f. 50 red .. .. 15 30

**1943.**

203. 35. 1 f. 50 red .. .. 20 30
204. 36. 1 f. 50 blue .. .. 20 20

**1943.** Surch **2f**.

205 32 2 f. on 5 f. orange .. 15 20

38. Summer Palace, Algiers.  39. Mother and Children.

**1943.**

206. 38. 15 f. grey .. .. 90 95
207. 20 f. green .. .. 65 60
208. 50 f. red .. .. 50 50
209. 100 f. blue .. .. 1·40 1·40
210. 200 f. brown .. .. 2·50 1·40

**1943.** Prisoners of War Relief Fund.

211. 39. 50 c.+4 f. 50 pink .. 45 80
212. 1 f. 50+8 f. 50 green .. 45 80
213. 3 f.+12 f. blue.. .. 45 80
214. 5 f.+15 f. brown .. 45 80

**1944.** As T 209 ("Marianne") of France, but inscr. "POSTES ALGERIE".

215. 10 c. grey .. .. 15 15
216. 30 c. lilac .. .. 15 25
217. 50 c. red .. .. 10 15
218. 80 c. green .. .. 10 15
219. 1 f. 20 lilac .. .. 10 25
220. 1 f. 50 blue .. .. 10 10
221. 2 f. 40 red .. .. 10 25
222. 3 f. violet .. .. 15 25
223. 4 f. 50 black .. .. 25 25

**1944.** As T 208 (Gallic cock) of France, but inscr. "POSTES ALGERIE".

224. 40 c. red .. .. 30 35
225. 1 f. green .. .. 15 10
226. 2 f. red .. .. 15 15
227. 2 f. brown .. .. 30 10
228. 4 f. blue .. .. 30 10
229. 10 f. black .. .. 60 50

**1944.** Surch **0f.30.**

230 4 0 f. 30 on 15 c. brown .. 15 35

No. 230 was only issued pre-cancelled and the price in the unused column is for stamp with full gum.

**1945.** Types of France optd. **ALGERIE.**

247. 239. 10 c. black and blue .. 10 25
231. 217. 40 c. mauve .. .. 20 30
232. 50 c. blue .. .. 15 10
248. – 50 c. brown, yellow and red (No. 973) .. 25 50
233. 218. 60 c. blue .. .. 25 35
236. 136. 80 c. green .. .. 25 25
237. 1 f. blue .. .. 10 10
234. 218. 1 f. red .. .. 10 10
238. 136. 1 f. 20 violet .. .. 15 30
235. 218. 1 f. 50 lilac .. .. 15 20
239. 136. 2 f. brown .. .. 35 20
242. 219. 2 f. green .. .. 10 10
240. 136. 2 f. 40 red .. .. 35 40
241. 3 f. orange .. .. 35 30
243. 219. 3 f. red .. .. 10 10
244. 4 f. 50 blue .. .. 80 10
245. 5 f. green .. .. 10 10
246. 10 f. blue .. .. 40 40

**1945.** Airmen and Dependants Fund. Type of France (bombers) optd **RF ALGERIE**.
249 169 1 f. 50+3 f. 50 blue .. 35 45

**1945.** Postal Employees War Victims' Fund. Type of France overprinted **ALGERIE**.
250. 223. 4 f.+6 f. brown .. 30 40

**1945.** Stamp Day. Type of France (Louis XI) optd **ALGERIE**.
251 228 2 f.+3 f. purple .. 45 60

**1946.** No. 184 surch **0f50 RF**.
252 50 c. on 1 f. 50 red .. 15 20

**1946.** Type of France overprinted **ALGERIE** and surcharged **2 F**.
253. 136 2 f. on 1 f. 50 c. brown 15 10

46. Potez 56 over Algiers.

**1946.** Air.
254. 46. 5 f. red .. .. .. 20 10
255. 10 f. blue .. .. 20 10
256. 15 f. green .. .. 45 10
257a. 20 f. brown .. .. 35 10
258. 25 f. violet .. .. 60 10
259. 40 f. black .. .. 65 20

**1946.** Stamp Day. Type of France (de la Varane), optd. **ALGERIE**.
260. 241. 3 f.+2 f. red .. .. 75 85

47. Children at a Spring. 49. Arms of Constantine.

**1946.** Charity. Inscr. as in T 47.
261. 47. 3 f. + 17 f. green .. 70 1·00
262. – 4 f. + 21 f. red .. 70 1·00
263. – 8 f. + 27 f. purple .. 2·50 4·00
264. – 10 f. + 35 f. blue .. 70 1·00
DESIGNS—VERT. 4 f. Boy gazing skywards. 8 f. Laurel-crowned head. HORIZ. 10 f. Soldier looking at Algerian coast.

**1947.** Air. Surch — 10%.
265. 46. "—10%" on 5 f. red .. 20 10

**1947.** Stamp Day. Type of France (Louvois), optd. **ALGERIE**.
266. 253. 4 f. 50+5 f. 50 blue .. 60 70

**1947.** Various Arms.
267 49 10 c. green and red .. 10 15
268 A 50 c. black and orange 10 10
269 B 1 f. blue and yellow .. 10 10
270 49 1 f. 30 black and blue .. 50 80
271 A 1 f. 50 violet and yellow 10 10
272 B 2 f. black and green .. 20 10
273 49 2 f. 50 black and red .. 55 75
274 A 3 f. red and green .. 15 20
275 B 3 f. 50 green and purple 10 25
276 49 4 f. brown and green .. 10 10
277 A 4 f. 50 blue and red .. 20 10
278 5 f. black and blue .. 25 10
279 B 6 f. brown and red .. 35 10
280 8 f. brown and blue .. 30 10
281 49 10 f. pink and brown .. 40 10
282 A 15 f. black and red .. 50 10
ARMS: A, Algiers. B, Oran.
See also Nos. 364/8 and 381/3.

**1947.** Air. 7th Anniv. of Gen. de Gaulle's Call to Arms. Surch with Lorraine Cross and **18 Juin 1940 + 10 Fr.**
283. 46. 10 f. + 10 f. blue .. 70 75

**1947.** Resistance Movement Type of France surch **ALGERIE +10f.**
284 261 5 f.+10 f. grey .. 50 55

**1948.** Stamp Day. Type of France (Arago) optd. **ALGERIE.**
285. 267. 6 f. + 4 f. green .. 70 90

**1948.** Air. 8th Anniv. of Gen. de Gaulle's Call to Arms. Surch. with Lorraine Cross and **18 JUIN 1940 + 10 Fr.**
286. 46. 5 f. + 10 f. red .. 70 80

**1948.** General Leclerc Memorial. Type of France surch **ALGERIE +4f.**
287 270 6 f.+4 f. red .. .. 60 75

57. Battleship "Richelieu". 58. White Storks over Minaret.

**1949.** Naval Welfare Fund.
288. 57. 10 f.+15 f. blue .. 4·50 5·00
289. – 18 f.+22 f. red .. 4·75 5·00
DESIGN: 18 f. Aircraft-carrier "Arromanches".

**1949.** Air.
290. 58. 50 f. green .. .. 4·00 30
291. – 100 f. brown .. .. 1·75 30
292. 58. 200 f. red .. .. 11·00 3·25
293. – 500 f. blue .. .. 17·00 12·00
DESIGN—HORIZ. 100, 500 f. Dewoitine D-338 trimotor airplane over valley dwellings.

**1949.** Stamp Day. Type of France (Choiseul), optd. **ALGERIE.**
294. 278. 15 f.+5 f. mauve .. 85 1·50

60. French Colonials. 61. Statue of Duke of Orleans.

**1949.** 75th Anniv. of U.P.U.
295. 60. 5 f. green .. .. 1·25 1·40
296. 15 f. red .. .. 1·25 1·40
297. 25 f. blue .. .. 3·00 4·00

**1949.** Air. 25th Anniv. of First Algerian Postage Stamp.
298. 61. 15 f.+20 f. brown .. 3·75 4·00

62. Grapes. 63. Foreign Legionary.

**1950.**
299 62 20 f. pur, grn & dp pur 1·25 80
300 – 25 f. brown, green & blk 1·40 1·00
301 – 40 f. orange, green & brn 3·00 1·50
DESIGNS: 25 f. Dates. 40 f. Oranges and lemons.

**1950.** Stamp Day. Type of France (Postman), optd. **ALGERIE.**
302. 292. 12 f.+3 f. brown .. 1·40 1·50

**1950.** Foreign Legion Welfare Fund.
303. 63. 15 f.+5 f. green .. 1·40 1·50

64. R. P. de Foucauld and Gen. Laperrine.

**1950.** 50th Anniv of French in the Sahara (25 f.) and Unveiling of Monument to Abd-el-Kader (40 f.).
304 64 25 f.+5 f. black & green 3·25 3·50
305 – 40 f.+10 f. dp brn & brn 3·25 3·50
DESIGN: 40 f. Emir Abd-el-Kader and Marshal Bugeaud.

65. Col. C. d'Ornano.

**1951.** Col. d'Ornano Monument Fund.
306 65. 15 f.+5 f. purple, brown and black .. 80 90

**1951.** Stamp Day. Type of France (Travelling Post Office sorting van), optd. **ALGERIE.**
307. 300. 12 f.+3 f. brown .. 3·00 4·00

66. Apollo of Cherchel. 67. Algerian War Memorial. 68. Medaille Militaire

**1952.**
308. 66. 10 f. sepia .. .. 25 35
309. – 12 f. brown .. .. 40 10
310. – 15 f. blue .. .. 20 10
311. – 18 f. red .. .. 45 35
312. – 20 f. green .. .. 45 15
313. 66. 30 f. blue .. .. 70 60
STATUES: 12 f., 18 f. Isis of Cherchel. 15 f., 20 f. Boy and eagle.

**1952.** Stamp Day. Type of France (Mail Coach), optd. **ALGERIE.**
314. 319. 12 f.+3 f. blue .. 1·60 1·75

**1952.** African Army Commem.
315. 67. 12 f. green .. .. 60 60

**1952.** Military Medal Cent.
316. 68. 15 f. + 5 f. brown, yellow and green .. 1·90 1·90

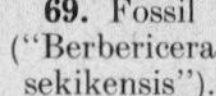

69. Fossil ("Berbericeras sekikensis"). 73. Members of Corps and Camel.

72. Bou-Nara.

**1952.** 19th Int Geological Convention, Algiers.
317 69 15 f. red .. .. 2·00 2·00
318 – 30 f. blue .. .. 1·40 1·40
DESIGN: 30 f. Phonolite Dyke, Hoggar.

**1952.** 10th Anniv. of Battle of Bir-Hakeim. Type of France surch. **ALGERIE+5 F.**
319. 325. 30 f.+5 f. blue .. 1·60 1·75

**1952.** Red Cross Fund.
320. – 8 f.+2 f. red and blue.. 1·60 1·60
321. 72. 12 f.+3 f. red .. .. 2·50 2·75
DESIGN: 8 f. El-Oued and map of Algeria.

**1952.** 500th Anniv. of Sahara Corps.
322. 73. 12 f. brown .. .. 1·10 1·25

**1953.** Stamp Day. Type of France (Count D'Argenson), optd. **ALGERIE.**
323. 334. 12 f.+3 f. violet .. 1·25 1·25

74. "Victory" of Cirta. 75. E. Millon.

**1954.** Army Welfare Fund.
324. 74. 15 f.+5 f. brn. & sepia 70 80

**1954.** Military Health Service.
325. 75. 25 f. sepia and green .. 1·25 40
326. – 40 f. lake and brown .. 1·25 55
327. – 50 f. indigo and blue .. 1·75 35
DOCTORS—VERT. 40 f. F. Maillot. HORIZ. 50 f. A. Laveran.

**1954.** Stamp Day. Type of France (Lavalette), optd. **ALGERIE.**
328. 346. 12 f.+3 f. red .. 85 95

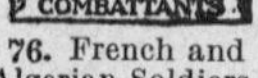

76. French and Algerian Soldiers. 77. Foreign Legionary.

**1954.** Old Soldiers' Welfare Fund.
329. 76. 15 f.+5 f. sepia .. 50 55

**1954.** Foreign Legion Welfare Fund.
330. 77. 15 f.+5 f. green .. 1·50 1·75

**HAVE YOU READ THE NOTES AT THE BEGINNING OF THIS CATALOGUE?**
These often provide answers to the enquiries we receive.

78. 79. Darguinah Hydro-electric Station. 80. Court-yard of Bardo Museum.

**1954.** 3rd International Congress of Mediterranean Citrus Fruit Culture.
331 78 15 f. blue and indigo .. 90 1·00

**1954.** 10th Anniv. of Liberation. Type of France ("D-Day") optd. **ALGERIE.**
332. 348. 15 f. red .. .. 75 70

**1954.** Inaug. of River Agrioun Hydro-electric installations.
333. 79. 15 f. purple .. .. 85 90

**1954.**
334 80 10 f. brown & lt brown 30 10
335 12 f. orange and brn (I) 30 10
336 12 f. orange & brn (II) 30 25
337 15 f. blue and light blue 35 30
338 18 f. carmine and red .. 55 50
339 20 f. green & light green 50 50
340 25 f. lilac and mauve .. 50 10
12 f. "POSTES" and "ALGERIE" in orange (I) or in white (II).

**1954.** 150th Anniv of Presentation of First Legion of Honour. As No. 1223 of France optd **ALGERIE.**
341 356 12 f. green .. .. 70 75

81. Red Cross Nurses. 82. St. Augustine.

**1954.** Red Cross Fund. Cross in red.
342. 81. 12 f.+3 f. blue.. .. 2·50 2·75
343. – 15 f.+5 f. violet .. 3·25 3·25
DESIGN: 15 f. J.H. Dunant and Djemila ruins.

**1954.** 1600th Birth Anniv. of St. Augustine.
344. 82. 15 f. brown .. .. 60 70

83. Earthquake Victims and Ruins 84. Statue of Aesculapius and El Kettar Hospital.

**1954.** Orleansville Earthquake Relief Fund. Inscr. as in T 83.
345. 83. 12 f.+4 f. brown .. 1·50 1·75
346. 15 f.+5 f. blue.. .. 1·50 1·60
347. – 18 f.+6 f. mauve .. 1·75 1·90
348 – 20 f.+7 f. violet .. 1·90 1·90
349. – 25 f.+8 f. lake.. .. 2·25 2·50
350. – 30 f.+10 f. turquoise .. 2·25 2·50
DESIGNS—HORIZ. 18 f., 20 f. Red Cross workers. 25 f., 30 f. Stretcher-bearers.

**1955.** Stamp Day. Type of France (Balloon Post), optd. **ALGERIE.**
351. 364. 12 f.+3 f. blue .. 1·10 1·10

**1955.** 30th French Medical Congress.
352. 84. 15 f. red.. .. .. 70 60

85. Ruins of Tipasa. 86. Widows and Children.

**1955.** Bimillenary of Tipasa.
353. 85. 50 f. brown .. .. 50 20

**1955.** 50th Anniv. of Rotary Int. Type of France, optd. **ALGERIE.**
354. 361. 30 f. blue .. .. 90 80

**1955.** Type of France ("France") inscr. "ALGERIE".
355. 362. 15 f. red .. .. 30 10
356. 20 f. blue .. .. 45 40

**1955.** War Victims Welfare Fund.
357. **86.** 15 f.+5 f. indigo & blue 65 70

**87.** Grand Kabylie. **88.**

**1955.**
358 87 100 f. indigo and blue .. 2·25 30

**1956.** Anti-Cancer Fund.
359. **88.** 15 f.+5 f. brown .. 75 80

**1956.** Stamp Day. Type of France ("Francis of Taxis"), optd. **ALGERIE.**
360. **383.** 12 f.+3 f. red .. 75 80

**89.** Foreign Legion Retirement Home, Sidi Bel Abbes.

**1956.** Foreign Legion Welfare Fund.
361. **89.** 15 f.+5 f. green .. 1·40 1·40

**90.** Marshal Franchet d'Esperey (after J. Ebstein).

**1956.** Birth Centenary of Marshal Franchet d'Esperey.
362. **90.** 15 f. indigo and blue .. 80 80

**91.** Marshal Leclerc and Memorial.

**1956.** Marshal Leclerc Commem.
363. **91.** 15 f. brown and sepia .. 70 80

**1956.** Various arms as T 49.
364 1 f. green and red .. 25 25
365 3 f. blue and green .. 50 50
366 5 f. blue and yellow .. 40 15
367 6 f. green and red .. 30 30
368 12 f. blue and red .. 60 60
DESIGNS: 1 f. Bone. 3 f. Mostaganem. 5 f. Tlemcen. 6 f. Algiers. 12 f. Orleansville.

**92.** Oran.

**1956.**
369 92 30 f. purple .. .. 55 15
370 35 f. red .. .. 1·00 90

**1957.** Stamp Day. Type of France. ("Felucca") optd. **ALGERIE.**
371. **403.** 12 f.+3 f. purple .. 1·00 1·00

**93.** Electric Train Crossing Viaduct.

**1957.** Electrification of Bone-Tebessa Railway Line.
372. **93.** 40 f. turquoise & green 1·00 20

**94.** Fennec Fox.

**1957.** Red Cross Fund. Cross in red.
373. **94.** 12 f.+3 f. brown .. 4·50 5·00
374. – 15 f.+5 f. sepia (White Storks) .. .. 6·00 6·00

**1957.** 17th Anniv of Gen. de Gaulle's Call to Arms. Surch **18 JUIN 1940 +5f.**
375 91 15 f.+5 f. red & carmine 1·10 1·10

**96.** Beni Bahdel Barrage, Tlemcen. **97.** "Horseman Crossing Ford" (after Delacroix).

**1957.** Air.
376 96 200 f. red .. .. 4·25 3·50

**1957.** Army Welfare Fund. Inscr. "Oeuvres Sociales De L'Armee".
377. **97.** 15 f.+5 f. red .. .. 5·00 5·00
378. – 20 f.+5 f. green .. 4·50 5·00
379. – 35 f.+10 f. blue .. 4·50 5·00
DESIGNS—HORIZ. 20 f. "Lakeside View" (after Fromentin). VERT. 35 f. "Arab Dancer" (after Chasseriau).

**1958.** Stamp Day. Type of France (rural service), optd. **ALGERIE.**
380. **421.** 15 f.+5 f. brown .. 85 95

**1958.** Arms. As T 49 but inscr. "REPUBLIQUE FRANCAISE" instead "RF" at foot.
381. 2 f. red and blue .. .. 55 65
382. 6 f. green and red .. 16·00 16·00
383. 10 f. purple and green .. 55 45
ARMS: 2 f. Tizi-Ouzou. 6 f. Algiers. 10 f. Setif.

**99.** "Strelitzia Reginae". **100.**

**1958.** Algerian Child Welfare Fund.
384. **99.** 20 f. + 5 f. orange, violet and green .. .. 2·25 2·50

**1958.** Marshal de Lattre Foundation.
385. **100.** 20 f.+5 f. red, grn. & bl. 1·25 1·25

**INDEPENDENT STATE**

**1962.** Stamps of France optd. **EA** (with serifs) and with bars obliterating "REPUBLIQUE FRANCAISE".
386. **344.** 10 c. green .. .. 70 35
387. **463.** 25 c. grey and red .. 45 20
393. – 45 c. violet, purple and sepia (No. 1463) .. 5·00 4·00
394. – 50 c. purple and green (No. 1464) .. .. 5·00 4·00
395. – 1 f. brown, blue and myrtle (No. 1549) .. 2·25 1·10

**103a.** Maps of Africa and Algeria.

**1962.** War Orphans' Fund.
395a. **103a.** 1 f. + 9 f. green, blk. and red .. .. £325

**1962.** As pictorial types of France but inscr. "REPUBLIQUE ALGERIENNE".
396. – 5 c. turq., grn. and brn. 15 10
397. **438.** 10 c. blue and sepia .. 20 10
398. – 25 c. red, slate & brn. 45 10
399. – 95 c. blue, buff & sepia 2·75 80
400. – 1 f. sepia and green .. 1·90 1·40
DESIGNS—VERT. 5 c. Kerrata Gorges. 25 c. Tlemcen Mosque. 95 c. Oil derrick and pipe-line at Hassi-Massaoud, Sahara. HORIZ. 1 f. Medea.

**104.** Flag, Rifle and Olive Branch. **105.** Campaign Emblem and Globe.

**1963.** "Return of Peace". Flag in green and red. Inscription and background colours given.
401. **104.** 5 c. bistre .. .. 15 10
402. 10 c. blue .. .. 20 10
403. 25 c. red .. .. 1·90 10
404. 95 c. violet .. .. 1·40 65
405. – 1 f. green .. .. 1·25 30
406. – 2 f. brown .. .. 3·00 65
407. – 5 f. purple .. .. 5·50 2·50
408. – 10 f. black .. .. 20·00 12·00
DESIGN: 1 f. to 10 f. As Type **104** but with dove and broken chain added.

**1963.** Freedom from Hunger.
409. **105.** 25 c. yell., green and red 40 20

**106.** Clasped Hands. **107.** Map and Emblems.

**1963.** National Solidarity Fund.
410. **106.** 50 c.+20 c. red, green and black .. .. 1·10 55

**1963.** 1st Anniv. of Independence.
411. **107.** 25 c. multicoloured .. 50 20

**108.** "Arab Physicians" (13th cent. MS.). **109.** Branch of Orange-tree.

**1963.** 2nd Arab Physicians Union Congress.
412. **108.** 25 c. brown, grn. & bistre 1·60 45

**1963.**
413. **109.** 8 c. orange and bronze* 10 10
414. 20 c. orange and green* 15 10
415. 40 c. orange and turq.* 45 20
416. 55 c. orange and green* 80 45
*These stamps were only issued precancelled, the unused prices being for stamps with full gum.

**110.** "Constitution". **111.** "Freedom Fighters".

**1963.** Promulgation of Constitution.
417. **110.** 25 c. red, green & sepia 55 25

**1963.** 9th Anniv. of Revolution.
418. **111.** 25 c. red, grn. & brn. 55 20

**112.** Centenary Emblem. **113.** Globe and Scales of Justice.

**1963.** Red Cross Centenary.
419. **112.** 25 c. blue, red and yellow 80 55

**1963.** 15th Anniv. of Declaration of Human Rights.
420. **113.** 25 c. black and blue .. 60 20

**114.** Labourers. **115.** Map of Africa and Flags.

**1964.** Labour Day.
421. **114.** 50 c. multicoloured .. 1·10 35

**1964.** 1st Anniv. of Africa Day, and African Unity Charter.
422. **115.** 45 c. red, orange & bl. 80 30

**116.** Tractors. **117.** Rameses II in War Chariot, Abu Simbel.

**1964.**
423. **116.** 5 c. purple .. .. 10 10
424. – 10 c. brown .. .. 10 10
425. – 12 c. green .. .. 45 15
426. – 15 c. blue .. .. 35 15
427. – 20 c. yellow .. .. 35 10
428. **116.** 25 c. red .. .. 45 10
429. – 30 c. violet .. .. 40 10
430. – 45 c. lake .. .. 55 20
431. – 50 c. blue .. .. 55 10
432. – 65 c. orange .. .. 65 15
433. **116.** 85 c. green .. .. 1·10 20
434. – 95 c. red .. .. 1·40 20
DESIGNS: 10 c., 30 c., 65 c. Apprentices. 12 c. 15 c., 45 c. Research scientist. 20 c., 50 c. 95 c. Draughtsman and bricklayer.

**1964.** Nubian Monuments Preservation.
435. **117.** 20 c. purple, red & blue 80 35
436. – 30 c. ochre, turq. & red 90 45
DESIGN: 30 c. Heads of Rameses II.

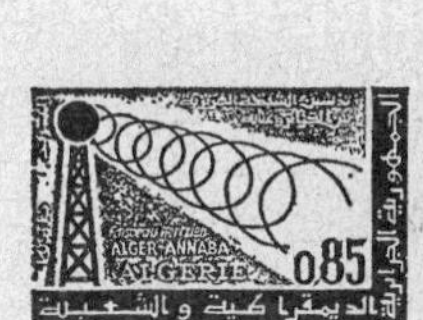

**118.** Hertzian-wave Radio Transmitting Pylon. **119.** Fair Emblems.

**1964.** Inauguration of Algiers–Annaba Radio–Telephone Service.
437. **118.** 85 c. black, blue & brn. 1·60 55

**1964.** Algiers Fair.
438. **119.** 30 c. blue, yell. & red .. 40 15

**120.** Gas Plant. **121.** Planting Trees. **122.** Children.

**1964.** Inaug. of Natural Gas Plant at Arzew.
439. **120.** 25 c. bl., yell. & vio. 65 45

**1964.** Reafforestation Campaign.
440. **121.** 25 c. green, red & yellow 40 20

**1964.** Children's Charter.
441. **122.** 15 c. blue, green & red 40 20

**123.** Mehariste Saddle. **124.** Books Aflame.

**1965.** Saharan Handicrafts.
442. **123.** 20 c. multicoloured .. 45 20

**1965.** Reconstitution of Algiers University Library.
443. **124.** 20 c.+5 c. red, black and green .. .. 45 30

**125.** I.C.Y. Emblem.

**1965.** Int. Co-operation Year.
444. **125.** 30 c. black, green & red 80 35
445. 60 c. black, green & blue 1·10 40

126. I.T.U. Emblem and Symbols.

**1965.** Centenary of I.T.U.

446. 126. 60 c. violet, ochre & grn. 80 40
447. 95 c. brn., ochre & lake 1·10 45

127. Musicians playing Rebbah and Lute.

**1965.** Mohamed Racim's Miniatures (1st series). Multicoloured.

448. 30 c. Type 127 .. .. 1·40 55
449. 60 c. Musicians playing derbouka and tarr .. 1·90 85
450. 5 d. Algerian princess and sand gazelle .. .. 11·00 6·75

See also Nos. 471/3.

128. Cattle.

**1966.** Rock-paintings of Tassili-N-Ajjer (1st series).

451. 128. 1 d. brn., ochre & pur. 4·00 2·25
452. – 1 d. multicoloured .. 4·00 2·25
453. – 2 d. brn., buff & brown 8·25 4·00
454. – 3 d. multicoloured .. 9·00 5·00

DESIGNS—VERT. No. 452, Peuhl shepherd. No. 454, Peuhl girls. HORIZ. No. 453, Ostriches. See also Nos. 474/7.

129. Pottery. 130. Meteorological Instruments

**1966.** Grand Kabylie Handicrafts.

455. 129. 40 c. brown, sepia & blue 40 20
456. – 50 c. orge., green & red 55 30
457. – 70 c. black, red & blue.. 1·10 45

DESIGNS—HORIZ. 50 c. Weaving. VERT. 70 c. Jewellery.

**1966.** World Meteorological Day.

458. 130. 1 d. purple, green & blue 1·10 40

131. Open Book, Cogwheel and ear of Corn. 132. W.H.O. Building.

**1966.** Literacy Campaign.

459. 131. 30 c. black and ochre.. 35 20
460. – 60 c. red, black & grey 55 30

DESIGN: 60 c. Open primer, cogwheel and ear of corn.

**1966.** Inaug. of W.H.O. Headquarters, Geneva.

461. 132. 30 c. turq., green & brn. 40 30
462. 60 c. slate, blue & brown 70 35

133. Mohammedan Scout Emblem and Banner. 134. Soldiers and Battle Casualty.

**1966.** 30th Anniv. of Algerian Mohammedan Scouts, and 7th Arab Scout Jamboree, Jedaid (Tripoli). Multicoloured.

463. 30 c. Type 133 .. .. 45 30
464. 1 d. Jamboree emblem .. 1·40 55

**1966.** Freedom Fighters' Day.

465. 134. 30 c.+10 c. multicoloured 80 55
466. 95 c.+10 c. multicoloured 1·40 1·10

135. Massacre Victims. 136. Emir Abd-el-Kader.

**1966.** Deir Yassin Massacre (1948).

467 135 30 c. black and red .. 45 20

**1966.** Return of Emir Abd-el-Kader's Remains.

468. 136. 30 c. multicoloured .. 20 10
469. 95 c. multicoloured .. 90 35

See also Nos. 498/502.

137. U.N.E.S.C.O. Emblems. 138. Bardo Museum.

**1966.** 20th Anniv. of U.N.E.S.C.O.

470. 137. 1 d. multicoloured .. 90 35

**1966.** Mohamed Racim's Miniatures (2nd series). As T 127. Multicoloured.

471. 1 d. Horseman .. .. 3·25 1·10
472. 1 d. 50 Algerian bride .. 5·00 1·60
473. 2 d. Barbarossa .. .. 7·75 2·75

**1967.** Rock-paintings of Tassili-N-Ajjer (2nd series). As T 128.

474. 1 d. violet, buff and purple 3·25 1·60
475. 2 d. brown, buff & purple 5·50 3·25
476. 2 d. brown, purple & buff 5·00 2·75
477. 3 d. brown, buff & black.. 8·25 4·50

DESIGNS: No. 474, Cow. No. 475, Antelope. No. 476, Archers. No. 477, Warrior.

**1967.** "Musulman Art". Multicoloured.

478. 35 c. Type 138 .. .. 35 15
479. 95 c. La Kalaa minaret (vert.) .. .. 80 40
480. 1 d. 30 Sedrata ruins .. 1·40 55

139. Ghardaia.

**1967.** Air.

481. 139. 1 d. brn., green & purple 1·10 45
482. – 2 d. brown, green & blue 2·50 1·25
483. – 5 d. brown, green & blue 6·75 2·75

DESIGNS: 2 d. Sud Aviation SE210 Caravelle over El Oued (Souf). 5 d. Tipasa.

140. View of Moretti.

**1967.** Int. Tourist Year. Multicoloured.

484. 40 c. Type 140 .. .. 55 35
485. 70 c. Tuareg, Tassili (vert.) 1·10 45

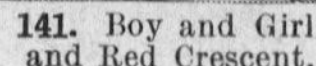

141. Boy and Girl, and Red Crescent. 142. Ostrich.

**1967.** Algerian Red Crescent Organization.

486. 141. 30 c.+10 c. brown, red and green .. .. 65 40

**1967.** Sahara Fauna. Multicoloured.

487. 5 c. Shiny-tailed Lizard (horiz.) .. .. .. 35 30
488. 20 c. Type 142 .. .. 2·25 75
489. 40 c. Sand gazelle .. .. 90 45
490. 70 c. Fennec foxes (horiz.) 1·40 80

143. Dancers with Tambourines. 144. "Athletics".

**1967.** National Youth Festival.

491. 143. 50 c. black, yell. & blue 80 35

**1967.** 5th Mediterranean Games, Tunis.

492. 144. 30 c. black, blue & red 50 30

145. Skiing. 146. Scouts supporting Jamboree Emblem.

**1967.** Winter Olympic Games, Grenoble (1968).

493. 145. 30 c. blue, grn. & ult. 80 35
494. – 95 c. grn., violet & brn. 1·40 65

DESIGN—(36 × 26 mm.)—HORIZ. 95 c. Olympic rings and competitors.

**1967.**

498. 136. 5 c. purple .. .. 15 10
499. 10 c. green .. .. 10 10
500. 25 c. orange .. .. 20 10
501. 30 c. black .. .. 30 10
502. 30 c. violet .. .. 35 10
496. 50 c. red .. .. 50 15
497. 70 c. blue .. .. 50 20

The 10 c. value exists in two versions, differing in the figures of value and inscription at bottom right.

**1967.** World Scout Jamboree, Idaho.

503. 146. 1 d. multicoloured .. 1·60 65

**1967.** No. 428 surch.

504. 116. 30 c. on 25 c. red .. 50 15

148. Kouitra. 149. Nememcha Carpet.

**1968.** Musical Instruments. Multicoloured.

505. 30 c. Type 148 .. .. 45 20
506. 40 c. Lute .. .. 65 30
507. 1 d. 30 Rebbah .. .. 2·25 90

**1968.** Algerian Carpets. Multicoloured.

509. 30 c. Type 149 .. .. 80 45
510. 70 c. Guergour .. .. 1·40 80
511. 95 c. Djebel-Amour .. 2·25 1·00
512. 1 d. 30 Kalaa .. .. 2·75 1·10

150. Human Rights Emblem and Globe.

**1968.** Human Rights Year.

513. 150. 40 c. red, yell. & bl. 60 30

151. W.H.O. Emblem. 152. Emigrant.

**1968.** 20th Anniv. of W.H.O.

514. 151. 70 c. yellow, blk. & blue 60 30

**1968.** Emigration of Algerians to Europe.

515. 152. 30 c. brn., slate & blue 45 15

153. Scouts holding Jamboree Emblem. 154. Torch and Athletes.

**1968.** 8th Arab Scouts Jamboree, Algiers.

516. 153. 30 c. multicoloured .. 55 20

**1968.** Olympic Games, Mexico. Mult.

517. 30 c. Type 154 .. .. 50 35
518. 50 c. Football .. .. 85 40
519. 1 d. Allegory of Games (horiz.) .. .. 1·40 80

155. Barbary Sheep. 156. "Neptune's Chariot," Timgad.

**1968** Protected Animals. Multicoloured.

520. 40 c. Type 155 .. .. 65 30
521. 1 d. Red deer .. .. 1·60 55

**1968.** Roman Mosaics. Multicoloured.

522. 40 c. "Hunting Scene" (Djemila) (vert.) .. 50 20
523. 95 c. Type 156 .. 1·10 45

157. Miner. 158. Opuntia.

**1968.** "Industry, Energy and Mines".

524. 157. 30 c. multicoloured .. 40 15
525. – 30 c. silver and red .. 40 15
526. – 95 c. red, blk. & silver 1·10 35

DESIGNS: No. 525, Coiled spring ("Industry"). No. 526, Symbol of radiation ("Energy").

**1969.** Algerian Flowers. Multicoloured.

527. 25 c. Type 158 .. .. 55 45
528. 40 c. Dianthus .. .. 85 55
529. 70 c. Rose .. .. .. 1·40 65
530. 95 c. Strelitzia .. .. 2·25 1·10

See also Nos. 621/4.

159. Djorf Torba Dam, Oued Guir.

**1969.** Saharan Public Works. Multicoloured.

531. 30 c. Type **159** .. .. 45 20

532. 1 d. 50 Route Nationale No. 51 .. .. .. 1·60 65

**160.** Desert Mail-coach of 1870. **161.** The Capitol, Timgad.

**1969.** Stamp Day.

533. **160.** 1 d. sepia, brn. & blue 1·40 55

**1969.** Roman Ruins in Algeria. Multicoloured.

534. 30 c. Type **161** .. .. 45 15

535. 1 d. Septimius Temple, Djemila (horiz.) .. 1·10 40

**162.** I.L.O. Emblem. **164.** Carved Bookcase.

**1969.** 50th Anniv. of I.L.O.

536. **162.** 95 c. red, yellow and black .. .. 1·00 40

**1969.** No. 425 surch.

537. 20 c. on 12 c. green .. 35 10

**1969.** Handicrafts. Multicoloured.

538. 30 c. Type **164** .. .. 40 20

539. 60 c. Copper tray .. .. 60 30

540. 1 d. Arab saddle .. .. 1·25 50

**165.** "Africa" Head. **166.** Astronauts on Moon.

**1969.** 1st Pan-African Cultural Festival, Algiers.

541. **165.** 30 c. multicoloured .. 35 20

**1969.** 1st Man on the Moon.

542. **166.** 50 c. multicoloured .. 85 35

**167.** Bank Emblem. **168.** Flood Victims.

**1969.** 5th Anniv. of African Development Bank.

543. **167.** 30 c. black, yellow & bl. 45 20

**1969.** Aid for 1969 Flood Victims.

544. **168.** 30 c.+10 c. black, flesh and blue .. .. 60 40

545. – 95 c.+25 c. brown, blue and purple .. .. 1·25 70

DESIGN: 95 c. Helping hand for flood victims.

**169.** "Algerian Women" (Dinet).

**1969.** Dinet's Paintings. Multicoloured.

546. 1 d. Type **169** .. 1·60 65

547. 1 d. 50 "The Look-outs" (Dinet) .. .. 2·25 1·00

**170.** "Mother and Child".

**1969.** "Protection of Mother and Child".

548. **170.** 30 c. multicoloured .. 50 30

**171.** "Agriculture". **172.** Postal Deliveries by Donkey and Mail Van.

**1970.** Four Year Plan.

549. **171.** 25 c. multicoloured .. 20 15

550. – 30 c. multicoloured .. 40 15

551. – 50 c. black and purple 45 20

DESIGNS: (LARGER, 49 × 23 mm.): 30 c. "Industry and Transport". 50 c. "Industry" (abstract).

**1970.** Stamp Day.

552. **172.** 30 c. multicoloured .. 45 20

**173.** Royal Prawn. **174.** Oranges.

**1970.** Marine Life. Multicoloured.

553 30 c. Type **173** .. .. 45 20

554 40 c. Noble pen (mollusc) 75 35

555 75 c. Neptune's basket .. 1·10 45

556 1 d. Red coral .. 1·60 65

**1970.** "Expo 70". World Fair, Osaka, Japan. Multicoloured.

557. 30 c. Type **174** .. .. 55 20

558. 60 c. Algerian Pavilion .. 55 35

559. 70 c. Bunches of grapes .. 1·10 45

**175.** Olives and Bottle of Olive-oil.

**1970.** World Olive-oil Year.

560. **175.** 1 d. multicoloured .. 1·40 65

**176.** New U.P.U. H.Q. Building.

**1970.** Inauguration of New U.P.U. Headquarters Building.

561. **176.** 75 c. multicoloured .. 60 30

**177.** Crossed Muskets.

**1970.** Algerian 18th-century Weapons. Multicoloured.

562. 40 c. Type **177** .. .. 85 45

563. 75 c. Sabre (vert.) .. 1·10 65

564. 1 d. Pistol .. .. 1·60 90

**178.** Arab League Flag, Arms and Map. **179.** Lenin.

**1970.** 25th Anniv. of Arab League.

565. **178.** 30 c. multicoloured .. 45 15

**1970.** Birth Centenary of Lenin.

566. **179.** 30 c. bistre and ochre 1·10 30

**180.** Exhibition Palace.

**1970.** 7th International Algiers Fair.

567. **180.** 60 c. green .. .. 55 35

**181.** I.E.Y. and Education Emblems.

**1970.** Int. Education Year. Multicoloured.

568. 30 c. Type **181** .. .. 35 15

569. 3 d. Illuminated Koran (30 × 41 mm.) .. .. 2·40 1·40

**182.** Great Mosque, Tlemcen.

**1970.** Mosques.

570. **182.** 30 c. multicoloured .. 30 15

571. – 40 c. brown & bistre .. 45 15

572. – 1 d. multicoloured .. 85 30

DESIGNS—VERT. 40 c. Ketchaoua Mosque, Algiers. 1 d. Sidi-Okba Mosque.

**183.** "Fine Arts".

**1970.** Algerian Fine Arts.

573. **183.** 1 d. orange, green and light green .. .. 90 35

**184.** G.P.O., Algiers.

**185.** Hurdling. **186.** "Racial Equality".

**1971.** Stamp Day.

574. **184.** 30 c. multicoloured .. 65 30

**1971.** 6th Mediterranean Games, Izmir (Turkey).

575. **185.** 20 c. grey and blue .. 35 15

576. – 40 c. grey and green .. 50 30

577. – 75 c. grey and brown 85 40

DESIGNS—VERT. 40 c. Gymnastics. 75 c. Basket-ball.

**1971.** Racial Equality Year.

578. **186.** 60 c. multicoloured .. 60 30

**187.** Symbols of Learning, and Students.

**1971.** Inaug. of Technological Institutes.

579. **187.** 70 c. multicoloured .. 65 20

**188.** Red Crescent Banner.

**1971.** Red Crescent Day.

580. **188.** 30 c.+10 c. red & green 55 35

**189.** Casbah, Algiers.

**1971.** Air.

581. **189.** 2 d. multicoloured .. 1·90 85

582. – 3 d. violet and black .. 2·75 1·40

583. – 4 d. multicoloured .. 3·25 1·60

DESIGNS: 3 d. Port of Oran. 4 d. Rhumel Gorges.

**190.** Aures Costume. **191.** U.N.I.C.E.F. Emblem, Tree and Animals.

**1971.** Regional Costumes (1st series). Multicoloured.

584. 50 c. Type **190** .. .. 90 45

585. 70 c. Oran .. .. 1·00 65

586. 80 c. Algiers .. .. 1·25 80

587. 90 c. Djebel-Amour .. 1·60 90

See also Nos. 610/13, and 659/62.

**1971.** 25th Anniv. of U.N.I.C.E.F.

588. **191.** 60 c. multicoloured .. 60 35

**192.** Lion of St. Mark's.

**1971.** U.N.E.S.C.O. "Save Venice" Campaign. Multicoloured.

589. 80 c. Type **192** .. .. 90 45

590. 1 d. 15 Bridge of Sighs .. 1·60 80

**193.** Cycling. **194.** Book and Book-mark.

**1972.** Olympic Games, Munich. Mult.

591. 25 c. Type **193** .. .. 35 15

592. 40 c. Throwing the javelin (vert.) .. .. 40 20

593. 60 c. Wrestling (vert.) .. 65 40

594. 1 d. Gymnastics (vert.) .. 1·10 45

**1972.** Int. Book Year.

595. **194.** 1d. 15 red, black & brn. 70 40

**195.** Algerian Postmen. **196.** Jasmine.

**1972.** Stamp Day.
596. **195.** 40 c. multicoloured .. 45 15

**1972.** Flowers. Multicoloured.
597. 50 c. Type **196** .. .. 50 30
598. 60 c. Violets .. .. 55 35
599. 1 d. 15 Tuberose.. .. 1·40 50

**197.** Olympic Stadium. **198.** Festival Emblem.

**1972.** Inaug. of Cheraga Olympic Stadium.
600. **197.** 50 c. grn., brn. & vio. 55 30

**1972.** 1st Festival of Arab Youth.
601. **198.** 40 c. brn., yellow & grn. 45 15

**199.** Rejoicing Algerians. **201.** Child posting Letter.

**1972.** 10th Anniv. of Independence.
602. **199.** 1 d. multicoloured .. 95 50

**1972.** Regional Costumes (2nd series). As T **190.** Multicoloured.
610. 50 c. Hoggar .. .. 1·10 55
611. 60 c. Kabylie .. .. 1·10 55
612. 70 c. Mzab .. .. 1·40 80
613. 90 c. Tlemcen .. .. 1·60 90

**1973.** Stamp Day.
614. **201.** 40 c. multicoloured .. 35 15

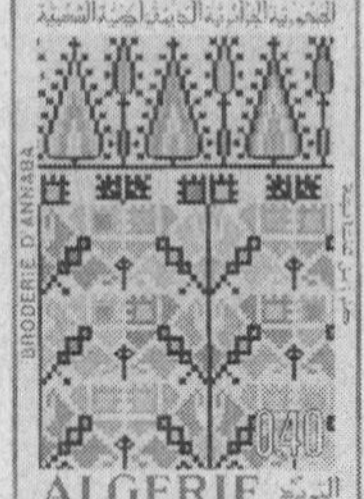


**202.** Ho-Chi-Minh and Map. **203.** Annaba Embroidery.

**1973.** "Homage to the Vietnamese People".
615. **202.** 40 c. multicoloured .. 60 30

**1973.** Algerian Embroidery. Multicoloured.
616. 40 c. Type **203** .. .. 50 30
617. 60 c. Algiers embroidery .. 70 40
618. 80 c. Constantine embroidery .. .. 1·00 50

**204.** "Food Cultivation". **206.** O.A.U. Emblem.

**205.** Serviceman and Flag.

**1973.** 10th Anniv. of World Food Programme.
619. **204.** 1 d. 15 multicoloured 65 30

**1973.** National Service.
620. **205.** 40 c. multicoloured .. 45 15

**1973.** Algerian Flowers. As T **158.** Mult.
621. 30 c. Type **158** .. .. 45 20
622. 40 c. As No. 529 .. .. 55 35
623. 1 d. As No. 528 .. .. 1·25 55
624. 1 d. 15 As No. 530 .. 1·60 65

**1973.** 10th Anniv. of Organization of African Unity.
625. **206.** 40 c. multicoloured .. 45 20

**207.** Peasant Family.

**1973.** Agrarian Revolution.
626. **207.** 40 c. multicoloured .. 50 20

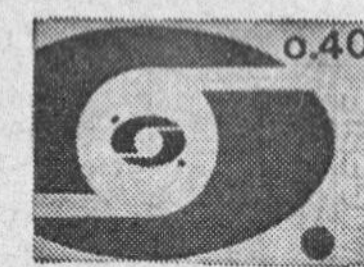


**208.** Scout Badge on Map. **209.** P.T.T. Symbol.

**1973.** 24th World Scouting Congress, Nairobi, Kenya.
627. **208.** 80 c. mauve .. .. 60 30

**1973.** Inaug. of New P.T.T. Symbol.
628. **209.** 40 c. orange and blue 45 15

**210.** Conference Emblem. **211.** "Skikda Harbour".

**1973.** 4th Summit Conference of Non-Aligned Countries, Algiers.
629. **210.** 40 c. multicoloured .. 35 15
630. 80 c. multicoloured .. 60 20

**1973.** Opening of Skikda Port.
631. **211.** 80 c. multicoloured .. 60 30

**212.** Young Workers. **213.** Arms of Algiers.

**1973.** Volontariat Students' Volunteer Service.
632. **212.** 40 c. multicoloured .. 45 20

**1973.** Millenary of Algiers.
633. **213.** 2 d. multicoloured .. 2·25 1·10

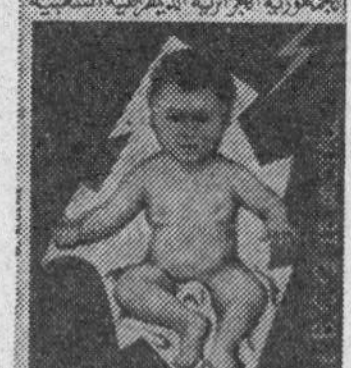


**214.** "Protected Infant".

**1974.** Anti-TB Campaign.
634. **214.** 80 c. multicoloured .. 60 35

**215.** Industrial Scene.

**1974.** Four Year Plan.
635. **215.** 80 c. multicoloured 65 30

**216.** Arabesque Motif.

**1974.** Birth Millenary of Abu-al Rayhan al-Biruni (mathematician and philosopher).
636. **216.** 1 d. 50 multicoloured 1·60 1·10

**217.** Map and Arrows. **218.** Upraised Weapon and Fist.

**1974.** Meeting of Maghreb Committee for Co-ordination of Posts and Telecommunications, Tunis.
637. **217.** 40 c. multicoloured .. 45 20

**1974.** Solidarity with South African People's Campaign.
638. **218.** 80 c. black and red .. 55 20

**219.** Algerian Family.

**1974.** Homage to Algerian Mothers.
639. **219.** 85 c. multicoloured .. 55 20

**220.** Urban Scene.

**1974.** Children's Drawings. Multicoloured.
640. 70 c. Type **220** .. .. 60 15
641. 80 c. Agricultural scene .. 70 30
642. 90 c. Tractor and sunrise 90 45
Nos. 641/2 are size, 49 × 33 mm.

**1974.** "Floralies 1974" Flower Show Algiers. Nos. 623/4 optd. **FLORALIES 1974.**
643. 1 d. multicoloured .. 1·25 65
644. 1 d. 15 multicoloured .. 1·60 1·00

**222.** Automatic Stamp-vending Machine. **223.** U.P.U. Emblem on Globe.

**1974.** Stamp Day.
645. **222.** 80 c. multicoloured .. 55 20

**1974.** Centenary of U.P.U.
646. **223.** 80 c. multicoloured .. 60 30

**224.** Revolutionaries.

**1974.** 20th Anniv. of Revolution. Mult.
647. 40 c. Type **224** .. .. 35 15
648. 70 c. Armed soldiers (vert.) 45 20
649. 95 c. Raising the flag (vert.) 70 20
650. 1 d. Algerians looking to Independence .. .. 95 30

**225.** "Towards the Horizon". **226.** Ewer.

**1974.** "Horizon 1980".
651. **225.** 95 c. red, brn. & blk.. 60 30

**1974.** Algerian 17th-century Brassware. Mult.
652. 50 c. Type **226** .. .. 40 20
653. 60 c. Coffee pot .. .. 45 30
654. 95 c. Sugar basin .. .. 65 40
655. 1 d. Bath vessel .. .. 95 50

**1975.** No. 622 surch.
656. 50 c. on 40 c. multicoloured 1·10 45

**228.** Games Emblem.

**1975.** 7th Mediterranean Games (1st issue).
657. **228.** 50 c. vio., grn. & yell.. 40 15
658. 1 d. orge., vio. & blue .. 70 20

**1975.** Regional Costumes (3rd series). As T **190.** Multicoloured.
659. 1 d. Algiers .. .. 1·10 60
660. 1 d. The Hogger .. .. 1·10 60
661. 1 d. Oran .. .. 1·10 60
662. 1 d. Tlemcen .. .. 1·10 60

**229.** Labour Emblems.

**1975.** 10th Anniv. of Arab Labour Organizations.
663. **229.** 50 c. brown .. .. 45 10

**230.** Transfusion.

**1975.** Blood Collection and Transfusion Service.

664. **230.** 50 c. multicoloured .. 55 30

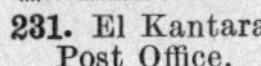

**231.** El Kantara Post Office.

**232.** Policeman and Oil Rig on Map of Algeria.

**1975.** Stamp Day.

665. **231.** 50 c. multicoloured .. 45 15

**1975.** Police Day.

666. **232.** 50 c. multicoloured .. 45 20

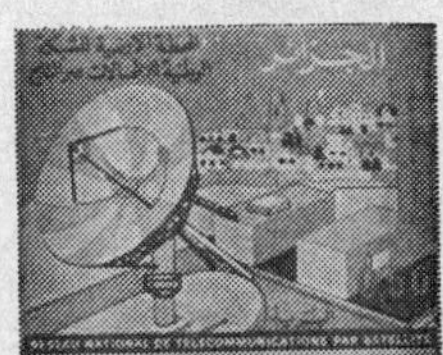

**233.** Ground Receiving Aerial.

**1975.** Satellite Telecommunications. Mult.

667. 50 c. Type **233** .. .. 40 15
668. 1 d. Map of receiving sites 65 20
669. 1 d. 20 Main and subsidiary ground stations .. .. 85 30

**234.** Revolutionary with Flag.

**235.** Swimming.

**1975.** 20th Anniv. of "Skikda" Revolution.

670. **234.** 1 d. multicoloured .. 60 30

**1975.** 7th Mediterranean Games, Algiers (2nd issue). Multicoloured.

671. 25 c. Type **235** .. .. 15 10
672. 50 c. Wrestling .. .. 30 15
673. 70 c. Football (vert.) .. 50 20
674. 1 d. Athletics (vert.) .. 65 30
675. 1 d. 20 Handball (vert.) .. 85 45

**236.** "Setif-Guelma-Kherrata".

**237.** Map of the Maghreb and A.P.U. Emblem.

**1975.** 30th Anniv. of Setif, Guelma and Kherrata Massacres (1st issue).

677. **236.** 5 c. black and orange 10 10
678. 10 c. black and green 10 10
679. 25 c. black and blue .. 15 10
680. 30 c. black and brown 20 10
681. 50 c. black and green 30 10
682. 70 c. black and red .. 40 15
683. 1 d. black and red .. 60 30

See also No. 698.

**1975.** 10th Arab Postal Union Congress, Algiers.

684. **237.** 1 d. multicoloured .. 60 30

**HAVE YOU READ THE NOTES AT THE BEGINNING OF THIS CATALOGUE?**

These often provide answers to the enquiries we receive.

**238.** Mosaic, Palace of the Bey, Constantine.

**1975.** Historic Buildings.

685. **238.** 1 d. multicoloured .. 85 35
686. – 2 d. multicoloured .. 1·60 80
687. – 2 d. 50 black and brown 2·25 1·10

DESIGNS—VERT. 2 d. Medersa Sidi-Boumediene Oratory, Tlemcen. HORIZ. 2 d. 50, Palace of the Dey, Algiers.

**239.** University Building.

**240.** Red-billed Fire Finch.

**1975.** Millenary of Al-Azhar University, Cairo.

688. **239.** 2 d. multicoloured .. 1·60 65

**1976.** Algerian Birds (1st series). Mult.

689. 50 c. Type **240** .. .. 1·25 60
690. 1 d. 40 Black-headed bush shrike (horiz.) .. .. 2·00 1·00
691. 2 d. Blue-tit .. .. 2·40 1·10
692. 2 d. 50 Black-bellied sand-grouse (horiz.) .. .. 2·75 1·50

See also Nos. 722/5.

**241.** Early and Modern Telephones.

**242.** Map and Angolan Flag.

**1976.** Telephone Cent.

693. **241.** 1 d. 40 multicoloured 85 40

**1976.** "Solidarity with Republic of Angola".

694. **242.** 50 c. multicoloured .. 45 15

**243.** Child on Map.

**244.** Postman.

**1976.** Solidarity with People of Western Sahara.

695. **243.** 50 c. multicoloured .. 45 20

**1976.** Stamp Day.

696. **244.** 1 d. 40 multicoloured 85 35

**245.** People, Microscope and Slide.

**246.** "Setif-Guelma-Kherrata".

**1976.** Campaign Against Tuberculosis.

697. **245** 50 c. multicoloured .. 45 15

**1976.** 30th Anniv. of Setif, Guelma and Kherrata Massacres (2nd issue).

698. **246.** 50 c. yellow and blue 45 10

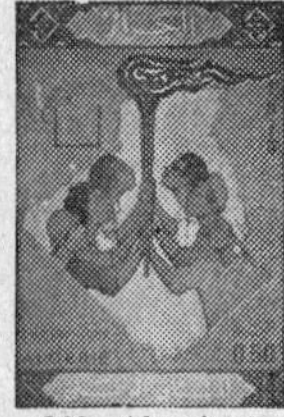

**247.** Ram's Head and Landscape.

**248.** Algerians holding Torch.

**1976.** Sheep Raising.

699. **247.** 50 c. multicoloured .. 45 20

**1976.** National Charter.

700. **248.** 50 c. multicoloured .. 50 15

**249.** Flag and Map.

**250.** Map of Africa.

**1976.** Solidarity with the Palestinian People.

701. **249.** 50 c. multicoloured .. 50 15

**1976.** 2nd Pan-African Commercial Fair, Algiers.

702. **250.** 2 d. multicoloured .. 1·40 50

**251.** Blind Man making Brushes.

**253.** Soldiers planting Seedlings.

**252.** Open Book.

**1976.** Rehabilitation of the Blind. Mult.

703. 1 d. 20 Type **251** .. 80 35
704. 1 d. 40 "The Blind Man" (E. Dinet) (horiz.) .. 1·10 50

**1976.** The Constitution.

705. **252.** 2 d. multicoloured .. 1·40 55

**1976.** Protection against Sahara Encroachment.

706. **253.** 1 d. 40 multicoloured 1·10 45

**254.** Arabic Inscription.

**1976.** Election of President Boumedienne.

707. **254.** 2 d. multicoloured .. 1·40 55

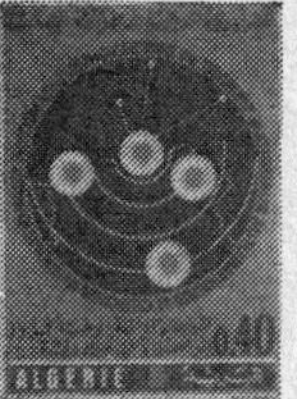

**255.** Map of Telephone Centres.

**256.** "Pyramid" of Heads.

**1977.** Inauguration of Automatic Telephone Dialling System.

708. **255.** 40 c. multicoloured .. 35 15

**1977.** 2nd General Population and Housing Census.

709. **256.** 60 c. on 50 c. mult. .. 45 15

**257.** Museum Building.

**258.** El Kantara Gorges.

**1977.** Sahara Museum, Ouargla.

710. **257.** 60 c. multicoloured .. 55 35

**1977.** Booklet stamps.

711. **258.** 20 c. green and cream 10 10
712. 60 c. mauve and cream 15 10
713. 1 d. brown and cream 45 15

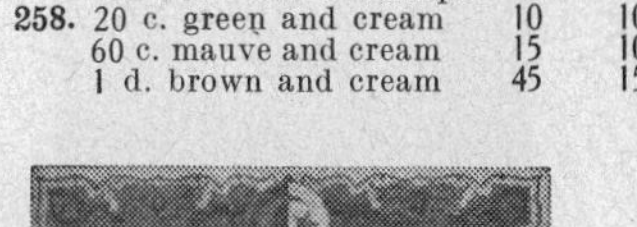

**259.** Assembly in Session.

**1977.** National Assembly.

714. **259.** 2 d. multicoloured .. 1·10 45

**260.** Soldiers with Flag.

**261.** Soldier with Flag.

**1977.** Solidarity with People of Zimbabwe.

715. **260.** 2 d. multicoloured .. 1·10 45

**1977.** Solidarity with People of Namibia.

716. **261.** 3 d. multicoloured .. 1·75 65

**262.** "Winter".

**1977.** Roman Mosaics. "The Seasons". Multicoloured.

717. 1 d. 20 Type **262** .. .. 1·25 65
718. 1 d. 40 "Autumn" .. 1·35 65
719. 2 d. "Summer" .. .. 1·75 1·10
720. 3 d. "Spring" .. .. 2·40 1·40

**1977.** Algerian Birds (2nd series). As T **240**. Multicoloured.

722. 60 c. Tristram's Warbler 1·10 60
723. 1 d. 40 Moussier's Redstart (horiz.) .. .. .. 1·50 75
724. 2 d. Temminck's Horned Lark (horiz.) .. .. 2·25 1·10
725. 3 d. Hoopoe .. .. 3·50 1·60

263. Horseman.

264. Ribbon and Games Emblem.

**1977.** "The Cavaliers" (performing horsemen). Multicoloured.
726. 2 d. Type **263** .. .. 1·60 65
727. 5 d. Three horsemen (horiz.) .. .. .. 3·75 1·60

**1977.** Third African Games, Algiers (1978) (1st issue). Multicoloured.
728. 60 c. Type **264** .. .. 45 20
729. 1 d. 40 Symbolic design and emblem .. .. 1·10 45
See also Nos. 740/4.

265. Tessala el Merdja.

**1977.** Socialist Agricultural Villages.
730. **265.** 1 d. 40 multicoloured .. 85 35

266. Almohad. Dirhem 12th-Century.

**1977.** Ancient Coins. Multicoloured.
731. 60 c. Type **266** .. .. 45 30
732. 1 d. 40 12th-century Alomhad dinar .. .. .. 1·00 40
733. 2 d. 11th-century Almorarid dinar .. .. .. 1·40 70

267. Cherry ("Cerasus avium").

269. Children with Traffic Signs opposing Car.

**1978.** Fruit Tree Blossom. Multicoloured.
734. 60 c. Type **267** .. .. 45 20
735. 1 d. 20 "Persica vulgaris" (peach) .. .. .. 80 55
736. 1 d. 30 "Amygdalus communis" (almond) .. 80 55
737. 1 d. 40 "Malus communis" (crab apple) .. .. 1·10 65

**1978.** Surch.
738. **236.** 60 c. on 50 c. black and green .. .. 55 15

**1978.** Road Safety for Children.
739. **269.** 60 c. multicoloured .. 50 20

270. Boxing and Map of Africa.

**1978.** Third African Games, Algiers (2nd issue). Multicoloured.
740. 40 c. Sports emblems and volleyball (horiz.) .. 20 10
741. 60 c. Olympic rings and table tennis symbol .. .. 35 15
742. 1 d. 20 Basket-ball symbol (horiz.) .. .. .. 70 30
743. 1 l. 30 Hammer throwing symbol .. .. .. 70 40
744. 1 d. 40 As Type **270** .. 90 40

271. Patient returning to Family.

**1978.** Anti-Tuberculosis Campaign.
745. **271.** 60 c. multicoloured .. 50 20

272. Ka'aba, Mecca.

**1978.** Pilgrimage to Mecca.
746. **272.** 60 c. multicoloured .. 50 10

273. Road Building. 274. Triangular Brooch

**1978.** African Unity Road.
747. **273.** 60 c. multicoloured .. 50 15

**1978.** Jewellery (1st series). Multicoloured.
748. 1 d. 20 Type **274** .. .. 90 45
749. 1 d. 35 Circular brooch .. 1·10 55
750. 1 d. 40 Anklet .. .. 1·40 65
See also Nos. 780/2 and 833/5.

275. President Houari Boumedienne.

276. Books and Hands holding Torch.

**1979.** President Boumedienne Commemoration (1st issue).
751. **275.** 60 c. brown, red and turquoise .. .. 45 20
See also No. 753.

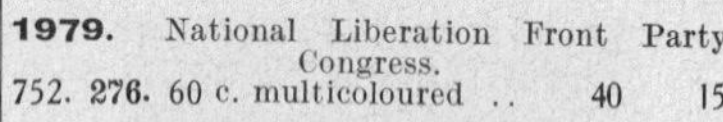
**1979.** National Liberation Front Party Congress.
752. **276.** 60 c. multicoloured .. 40 15

277. President Houari Boumedienne.

**1979.** President Boumedienne Commemoration (2nd issue).
753. **277.** 1 d. 40 multicoloured .. 95 40

278. Arabic Inscription

279. White Storks

**1979.** Election of President Chadli Bendjedid.
754. **278.** 2 d. multicoloured .. 1·25 35

**1979.** Air.

755. **279.** 10 d. blue, black & red 6·00 2·00

280. Ben Badis.

281. Globe within Telephone Dial.

**1979.** 90th Birth Anniv. of Sheikh Abdelhamid Ben Badis (journalist and education pioneer).
756. **280.** 60 c. multicoloured .. 40 15

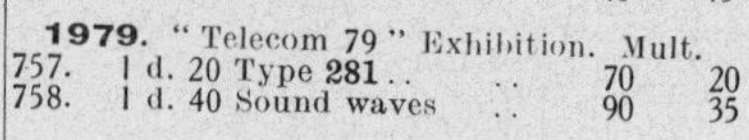
**1979.** "Telecom 79" Exhibition. Mult.
757. 1 d. 20 Type **281** .. .. 70 20
758. 1 d. 40 Sound waves .. 90 35

282. Children dancing on Globe.

**1979.** International Year of the Child. Multicoloured.
759. 60 c. Picking Dates .. 40 10
760. 1 d. 40 Type **282** (vert.) .. 85 35

283. Kabylie Nuthatch

284. Fighting for the Revolution and Construction work.

**1979.**
761. **283.** 1 d. 40 multicoloured 3·00 1·25

**1979.** 25th Anniv. of Revolution. Mult.
762. 1 d. 40 Type **284** .. .. 80 20
763. 3 d. Algerians with flag .. 1·75 65

285. Arabic Inscription.

**1979.** 1400th Anniv. of Hegira.
764. **285.** 3 d. gold, turq. & blue 1·60 65

286. Return of Dionysus (right detail).

287. Books.

**1980.** Dionysus Mosaic, Setif. Multicoloured.
765. 1 d. 20 Type **286** .. .. 80 35
766. 1 d. 35 Centre detail .. 90 45
767. 1 d. 40 Left detail .. 1·00 65
Nos. 765/7 were issued together, se-tenant, forming a composite design.

**1980.** Day of Knowledge.
768 287 60 c. brown, yell & grn 40 10

288. Five Year Plan.

289. Olympic Flame.

**1980.** Extraordinary Congress of National Liberation Front Party.
769. **288.** 60 c. multicoloured .. 40 15

**1980.** Olympic Games, Mosocw. Mult.
770. 50 c. Type **289** .. .. 35 10
771. 1 d. 40 Oylmpic sports (horiz.) .. .. .. 80 30

290. Figures supporting O.P.E.C. Emblem.

**1980.** 20th Anniv. of Organization of Petroleum Exporting Countries.
772. **290.** 60 c. grn., bl. and red 40 10
773. – 1 d. 40 green and blue 95 35
DESIGN: 1 d. 40, O.P.E.C. emblem on world map.

291. Aures.

**1980.** World Tourism Conference, Manila. Multicoloured.
774. 50 c. Type **291** .. .. 35 15
775. 1 d. El Oued .. .. 65 20
776. 1 d. 40 Tassili .. .. 90 35
777. 2 d. Algiers .. .. 1·40 50

292. Ibn Sina.

**1980.** Birth Millenary of Ibn Sina Avicenna (philosopher).
778. **292.** 3 d. multicoloured .. 1·60 65

293. Earthquake Devastation.

**1980.** El Asnam Earthquake Relief.
779. **293.** 3 d. multicoloured .. 1·60 45

**1980.** Jewellery (2nd series). As T **274**. Multicoloured.
780. 60 c. Necklace .. .. 45 20
781. 1 d. 40 Earrings and bracelet .. .. .. 80 45
782. 2 d. Diadem (horiz.) .. 1·25 55

294. Emblem.

**1981.** Five Year Plan.
783. **294.** 60 c. multicoloured .. 35 10

295. Basket-worker.

**1981.** Traditional Arts. Multicoloured.

784. 40 c. Type **295** .. .. 20 10

785. 60 c. Spinning .. .. 35 15

786. 1 d. Copper-smith .. 55 20

787. 1 d. 40 Jeweller .. .. 80 35

296. Cedar " Cedrus atlantica ".

**1981.** World Tree Day. Multicoloured.

788. 60 c. Type **296** .. .. 35 10

789. 1 d. 40 Cypress "Cupressus dupreziana .. .. 80 35

297. Mohamed Bachir el Ibrahimi. 298. Children and Blackboard (Basic Schooling).

**1981.** Day of Knowledge.

790. **297.** 60 c. multicoloured .. 35 10

791. **298.** 60 c. multicoloured .. 35 10

299. Archer, Dog and Internal Organs.

**1981.** 12th International Hydatidological Congress, Algiers.

792. **299.** 2 d. multicoloured .. 1·40 45

300. Dish Aerial and Caduceus. 301. " Disabled ".

**1981.** World Telecommunications Day.

793. **300.** 1 d. 40 multicoloured 80 20

**1981.** International Year of Disabled People.

794. **301.** 1 d. 20 blue, red and orange .. .. 65 15

795. – 1 d. 40 multicoloured 80 15

DESIGN: 1d. 40. Disabled people and hand holding flower.

302. " Papilio machaon ".

**1981.** Butterflies. Multicoloured.

796. 60 c. Type **302** .. .. 45 15

797. 1 d. 20 " Rhodocera rhamni gonepteryx rhamni " .. 80 35

798. 1 d. 40 " Charaxes jasius " 1·00 50

799. 2 d. " Papilio podalirius " 1·40 65

303. Mediterranean Monk Seal. 304. Man holding Ear of Wheat.

**1981.** Nature Protection. Multicoloured.

800. 60 c. Type **303** .. .. 55 35

801. 1 d. 40 Barbary ape .. 1·10 80

**1981.** World Food Day.

802. **304.** 2 d. multicoloured .. 1·00 40

305. Cattle, Jabbaren.

**1981.** Cave Paintings. Multicoloured.

803. 60 c. Mouflon, Tan Zoumaitek 35 15

804. 1 d. Type **305** .. .. 55 20

805. 1 d. 60 Cattle, Iherir (horiz.) 80 35

806. 2 d. One-horned bull, Jabbaren (horiz.) .. 1·10 40

306. Galley.

**1981.** Algerian Ships of 17th and 18th Centuries. Multicoloured.

807 60 c. Type **306** .. .. 55 25

808 1 d. 60 Xebec .. .. 1·40 45

307. Footballers with Cup. 308. Microscope.

**1982.** World Cup Football Championship, Spain. Multicoloured.

809. 80 c. Type **307** .. .. 45 15

810. 2 d. 80 Footballers and ball (horiz.) .. .. .. 1·40 50

**1982.** Centenary of Discovery of Tubercle Bacillus.

811. **308.** 80 c. blue, light blue and orange .. .. 45 15

309. Mirror.

**1982.** Popular Traditional Arts. Mult.

812. 80 c. Type **309** .. .. 45 15

813. 2 d. Whatnot .. .. 1·00 40

814. 2 d. 40 Chest (48 × 32 mm.) 1·40 55

310. New Mosque, Algiers. 311. " Callitris articulata ".

**1982.** Algerian Sights before 1830 (1st series). Size 32 × 22 mm.

815. **310.** 80 c. brown .. .. 35 15

816. – 2 d. 40 violet .. .. 90 45

817. – 3 d. green .. .. 1·25 55

DESIGNS: 2 d. 40, Sidi Boumedienne Mosque, Tlemcen. 3 d. Garden of Dey, Algiers.

See also Nos. 859/62, 873/5, 880/2, 999/1001, 1054/6 and 1075/86.

**1982.** Medicinal Plants. Multicoloured.

818. 50 c. Type **311** .. .. 30 10

819. 80 c. " Artemisia herba-alba " .. .. .. 40 15

820. 1 d. " Ricinus communis " 55 20

821. 2 d. 40 "Thymus fontanesii 1·25 50

312. Independence Fighter. 313. Congress House.

**1982.** 20th Anniv. of Independence. Mult.

822. 50 c. Type **312** .. .. 30 10

823. 80 c. Modern soldiers .. 40 15

824. 2 d. Algerians and symbols of prosperity .. .. 1·00 45

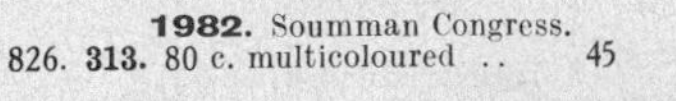

**1982.** Soumman Congress.

826. **313.** 80 c. multicoloured .. 45 10

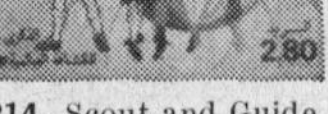

314. Scout and Guide releasing Dove. 315. Child.

**1982.** 75th Anniv. of Boy Scout Movement.

827. **314.** 2 d. 80 multicoloured .. 1·40 45

**1982.** Palestinian Children.

828. **315.** 1 d. 60 multicoloured 80 20

316. Waldrapp.

**1982.** Nature Protection. Multicoloured.

829. 50 c. Type **316** .. .. 60 50

830. 80 c. Houbara bustard (vert.) .. .. .. 75 75

831. 2 d. Tawny eagle .. .. 2·10 1·40

832. 2 d. Lammergeier (vert.) .. 2·75 1·50

317. Mirror. 318. " Abies numidica ".

**1983.** Silver Work.

833. **317.** 50 c. silver, black & red 20 10

834. – 1 d. multicoloured .. 45 30

835. – 2 d. silver, blk., & pur. 90 45

DESIGNS:—VERT. 1 d. Perfume flasks. HORIZ. 2 d. Belt buckle.

**1983.** World Tree Day. Multicoloured.

836. 80 c. Type **318** .. .. 40 15

837. 2 d. 80 " Acacia raddiana " 1·50 55

319. Mineral. 320. Customs Officer.

**1983.** Mineral Resources.

838. **319.** 70 c. multicoloured .. 55 20

839. 80 c. multicoloured .. 55 30

840. 1 d. 20 multicoloured (horiz.) .. .. 85 55

841. 2 d. 40 multicoloured (horiz.) .. .. 1·60 90

**1983.** 30th Anniv. of Customs Co-operation Council.

842. **320.** 80 c. multicoloured .. 55 20

321. Emir Abdelkader.

**1983.** Death Cent. of Emir Abdelkader.

843. **321.** 4 d. multicoloured .. 1·75 70

322. Fly Agaric. 323. Ibn Khaldoun.

**1983.** Mushrooms. Multicoloured.

844 50 c. Type **322** .. .. 65 25

845 80 c. Death cap .. .. 95 50

846 1 d. 40 "Pleurotus eryngii" 2·10 75

847 2 d. 80 "Terfezia leonis" 3·50 1·50

**1983.** Ibn Khaldoun Commemoration.

848. **323.** 80 c. multicoloured .. 55 20

324. W.C.Y. Emblem and Post Office. 325. Goat and Tassili Mountains.

**1983.** World Communications Year. Mult.

849. 80 c. Type **324** .. .. 45 15

850. 2 d. 40 W.C.Y. emblem and telephone switch box .. 1·10 40

**1983.** Tassili World Patrimony. Mult.

851. 50 c. Type **325** .. .. 30 10

852. 80 c. Touaregs .. .. 40 15

853. 2 d. 40 Rock paintings .. 1·10 40

854. 2 d. 80 Rock formation .. 1·40 55

326. Sloughi.

**1983.** Sloughi. Multicoloured.

855. 80 c. Type **326** .. .. 55 20

856. 2 d. 40 Sloughi .. .. 1·40 65

327. Symbols of Economic Progress.

**1983.** 5th National Liberation Front Party Congress.

857 **327** 80 c. multicoloured .. 55 30

**1984.** Views of Algeria before 1830 (2nd series). As T **310**.
859. 10 c. blue .. .. .. .. 10 10
860. 1 d. purple .. .. .. .. 40 15
861. 2 d. blue .. .. .. .. 80 35
862. 4 d. red .. .. .. .. 1·60 55
DESIGNS: 10 c. Oran. 1 d. Sidi Abderahmane Mosque, Et Taalibi. 2 d. Bejaia. 4 d. Constantine.

**328.** Jug.

**329.** Fountain.

**1984.** Pottery. Multicoloured.
863. 80 c. Type **328** .. .. 40 20
864. 1 d. Dish (horiz.) .. .. 50 20
865. 2 d. Lamp .. .. .. 1·00 45
866. 2 d. 40 Jug (horiz.) .. 1·25 55

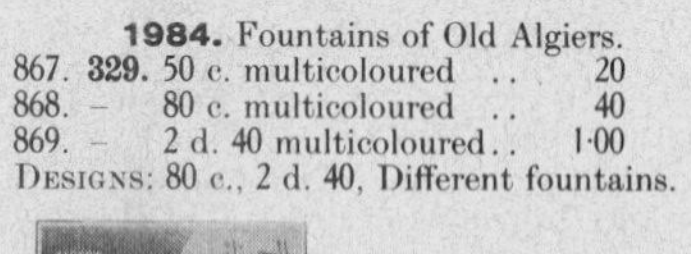

**1984.** Fountains of Old Algiers.
867. **329.** 50 c. multicoloured .. 20 15
868. – 80 c. multicoloured .. 40 20
869. – 2 d. 40 multicoloured .. 1·00 55
DESIGNS: 80 c., 2 d. 40, Different fountains.

**330.** Dove, Flames and Olympic Rings.

**331.** Stallion.

**1984.** Olympic Games, Los Angeles.
870. **330.** 1 d. multicoloured .. 60 30

**1984.** Horses. Multicoloured.
871. 80 c. Type **331** .. .. 45 35
872. 2 d. 40 Mare .. .. 1·40 80

**1984.** Views of Algeria before 1830 (3rd series). As T **310**.
873. 5 c. purple .. .. .. 10 10
874. 20 c. blue .. .. .. 10 10
875. 70 c. violet .. .. .. 30 15
DESIGNS: 5 c. Mustapha Pacha. 20 c. Bab Azzoun. 70 c. Mostaganem.

**332.** Lute.

**1984.** Musical Instruments. Multicoloured.
876. 80 c. Type **332** .. .. 45 20
877. 1 d. Drum .. .. .. 55 20
878. 2 d. 40 One-stringed instrument .. .. .. 1·25 55
879. 2 d. 80 Bagpipes .. .. 1·40 65

**1984.** Views of Algeria before 1830 (4th series). As T **310**.
880. 30 c. red and black .. 15 10
881. 40 c. black .. .. .. 20 10
882. 50 c. brown .. .. 30 10
DESIGNS: 30 c. Algiers from Admiralty. 40 c. Kolea. 50 c. Algiers from aqueduct.

**333.** Partisans in Mountains and Flag.

**1984.** 30th Anniv. of Revolution.
883. **333.** 80 c. multicoloured .. 55 20

**334.** Map of M'Zab Valley.

**1984.** M'Zab Valley. Multicoloured.
885. 80 c. Type **334** .. .. 45 10
886. 2 d. 40 M'Zab town .. 1·25 45

**335.** Coffee Pot.

**336.** Bluefin Tuna.

**1985.** Ornamental Tableware.
887. **335.** 80 c. black, silver and yellow .. .. 35 20
888. – 2 d. black, silver and green .. .. 90 45
889. – 2 d. 40 black, silver and pink .. .. .. 1·25 55
DESIGNS—HORIZ. 2 d. Bowl. VERT. 2 d. 40, Lidded jar.

**1985.** Fishes. Multicoloured.
890. 50 c. Type **336** .. .. 35 15
891. 80 c. "Sparus aurata" .. 55 20
892. 2 d. 40 Giant grouper .. 1·40 70
893. 2 d. 80 "Mustelus mustelus" .. .. 1·60 85

**337.** Birds in Flight and Emblem.

**1985.** National Games.
894. **337.** 80 c. multicoloured .. 50 15

**338.** Stylized Trees.

**339.** Algiers Casbah.

**1985.** Environmental Protection. Mult.
895. 80 c. Type **338** .. .. 40 15
896. 1 d. 40 Stylized waves .. 70 20

**1985.**
897. **339.** 20 c. blue and cream 10 10
898. 80 c. green & cream .. 45 10
899. 2 d. 40 brown and cream .. .. 1·25 10

**340.** Dove within "40".

**341.** Figures linking arms and Emblem.

**1985.** 40th Anniv. of U.N.O.
900. **340.** 1 d. multicoloured .. 60 20

**1985.** 1st National Youth Festival.
901. **341.** 80 c. multicoloured .. 50 15

**342.** Figures linking arms on Globe and Dove.

**343.** O.P.E.C. Emblem.

**1985.** International Youth Year. Mult.
902. 80 c. Type **342** .. .. 45 15
903. 1 d. 40 Doves making globe with laurels .. .. 65 20

**1985.** 25th Anniv. of Organization of Petroleum Exporting Countries.
904. **343.** 80 c. multicoloured .. 50 20

**344.** Mother and Children.

**345.** Chetaibi Bay.

**1985.** Family Planning. Multicoloured.
905. 80 c. Type **344** .. .. 40 15
906. 1 d. 40 Doctor weighing baby .. .. .. 65 20
907. 1 d. 70 Mother breast feeding baby .. .. .. 85 30

**1985.** Tourist Sites.
908. **345.** 80 c. bl., grn. & brn. 35 15
909. – 2 d. brn., grn. & blue 1·00 30
910. – 2 d. 40, brn., grn. & bl. 1·10 40
DESIGNS—VERT. 2 d. El Meniaa. HORIZ. 2 d. 40, Bou Noura.

**346.** "Palm Grove".

**347.** Line Pattern.

**1985.** Paintings by N. Dinet. Multicoloured.
911. 2 d. Type **346** .. .. 1·10 55
912. 3 d. "Palm Grove" (diff.) .. 1·60 85

**1985.** Weavings. Multicoloured.
913. 80 c. Type **347** .. .. 50 35
914. 1 d. 40 Diamond pattern .. 90 50
915. 2 d. 40 Patterned horizontal stripes .. 1·40 85
916. 2 d. 80 Vertical and horizontal stripes .. 1·90 1·40

**348.** "Felis margarita".

**349.** Oral Vaccination.

**1986.** Wild Cats. Multicoloured.
917. 80 c. Type **348** .. .. 45 35
918. 1 d. Caracal .. .. 55 45
919. 2 d. Wild cat .. .. 1·25 90
920. 2 d. 40 Serval (vert.) .. 1·60 1·10

**1986.** U.N.E.S.C.O. Child Survival Campaign. Multicoloured.
921. 80 c. Type **349** .. .. 45 20
922. 1 d. 40 Sun behind mother and baby .. .. 90 35
923. 1 d. 70 Children playing .. 1·10 55

**350.** Industrial Skyline, Clasped Hands and Emblem.

**351.** Books and Crowd.

**1986.** 30th Anniv. of Algerian General Worker's Union.
924. **350.** 2 d. multicoloured .. 1·10 45

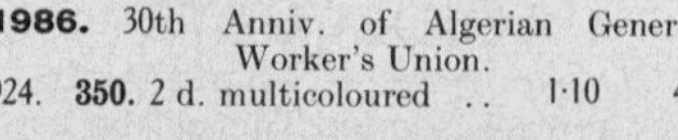

**1986.** National Charter.
925. **351.** 4 d. multicoloured .. 2·25 1·00

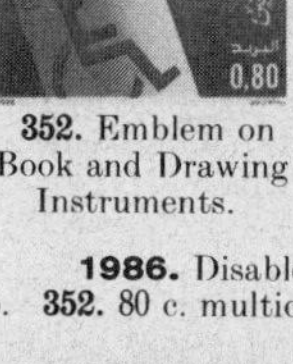

**352.** Emblem on Book and Drawing Instruments.

**353.** Children playing.

**1986.** Disabled Persons' Day.
926. **352.** 80 c. multicoloured .. 50 20

**1986.** Anti-tuberculosis Campaign.
927. **353.** 80 c. multicoloured .. 55 30

**354.** Sombrero on Football.

**355.** Courtyard with Fountain.

**1986.** World Cup Football Championship, Mexico. Multicoloured.
928. 2 d. Type **354** .. .. 1·00 40
929. 2 d. 40 Players and ball .. 1·25 45

**1986.** Traditional Dwellings. Multicoloured.
930. 80 c. Type **355** .. .. 45 20
931. 2 d. 40 Courtyard with two beds of shrubs .. .. 1·40 70
932. 3 d. Courtyard with plants in tall pot .. .. 1·75 1·00

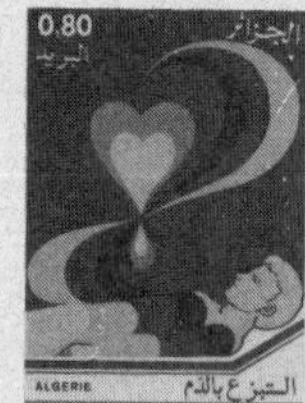

**356.** Heart forming Drop over Patient.

**357.** Transmission Mast as Palm Tree.

**1986.** Blood Donors.
933. **356.** 80 c. multicoloured .. 90 30

**1986.** Opening of Hertzian Wave Communications (Southern District).
934. **357.** 60 c. multicoloured .. 35 15

**358.** Studded Gate.

**1986.** Mosque Gateways. Multicoloured.
935. 2 d. Type **358** .. .. 1·00 45
936. 2 d. 40 Ornate gateway .. 1·25 65

**359.** Dove.

**1986.** International Peace Year.
937. **359.** 2 d. 40 multicoloured 1·25 45

**INDEX**
Countries can be quickly located by referring to the index at the end of this volume.

**360.** Girl dancing. **361.** "Narcissus tazetta"

**1986.** Folk Dances. Multicoloured.

938. 80 c. Type **360** .. .. 45 20
939. 2 d. 40 Woman with purple dress dancing .. .. 1·25 55
940. 2 d. 80 Veiled sword dancer 1·25 55

**1986.** Flowers. Multicoloured.

941. 80 c. Type **361** .. .. 45 20
942. 1 d. 40 "Iris unguicularis" 80 45
943. 2 d. 40 "Capparis spinosa" 1·10 65
944. 2 d. 80 "Gladiolus segetum" 1·40 90

**362.** "Algerian Family". **363.** Earrings.

**1987.** Paintings by Mohammed Issiakhem in National Museum. Multicoloured.

945. 2 d. Type **362** .. .. 1·10 55
946. 5 d. "Man and Books" .. 2·50 1·60

**1987.** Jewellery from Aures. Multicoloured.

947. 1 d. Type **363** .. .. 45 30
948. 1 d. 80 Bangles .. .. 80 45
949. 2 d. 90 Brooches .. .. 1·25 85
950. 3 d. 30 Necklace (horiz.) .. 1·40 95

**364.** Boy and Girl.

**1987.** Rock Carvings. Multicoloured.

951. 1 d. Type **364** .. .. 55 35
952. 2 d. 90 Goat .. .. 1·40 1·10
953. 3 d. 30 Animals .. .. 1·60 1·10

**365.** Baby holding Syringe "Umbrella". **366.** Workers and Circles.

**1987.** African Vaccination Year.

954. **365.** 1 d. multicoloured .. 45 20

**1987.** Voluntary Service.

955. **366.** 1 d. multicoloured .. 45 20

**367.** People and Buildings.

**1987.** 3rd General Population Census.

956. **367.** 1 d. multicoloured .. 45 20

**368.** 1962 War Orphans' Fund Stamps and Magnifying Glass.

**1987.** 25th Anniv. of Independent Algeria Stamps.

957. **368.** 1 d. 80 multicoloured 80 50

**369.** Hand holding Torch. **370.** Actors in Spotlight.

**1987.** 25th Anniv. of Independence.

958. **369.** 1 d. multicoloured .. 45 20

**1987.** Amateur Theatre Festival, Mostaganem. Multicoloured.

960. 1 d. Type **370** .. .. 40 15
961. 1 d. 80 Theatre .. .. 70 40

**371.** Discus Thrower. **372.** Greater Flamingo.

**1987.** Mediterranean Games, Lattaquie. Multicoloured.

962. 1 d. Type **371** .. .. 40 15
963. 2 d. 90 Tennis player (vert.) .. .. 1·10 50
964. 3 d. 30 Footballer .. .. 1·40 65

**1987.** Birds. Multicoloured.

965. 1 d. Type **372** .. .. 45 35
966. 1 d. 80 Purple swamphen 90 75
967. 2 d. 50 Black-shouldered kite .. .. 1·75 95
968. 2 d. 90 Red kite .. .. 1·90 1·25

**373.** Reservoir.  **374.** Map, Transmitter and Radio Waves.

**1987.** Agriculture. Multicoloured.

969. 1 d. Type **373** .. .. 45 15
970. 1 d. Forestry (36×28 mm.) 45 15
971. 1 d. Foodstuffs (25×37 mm.) .. .. 45 15
972. 1 d. Erecting hedge against desert (25×37 mm.) .. 45 15

**1987.** African Telecommunications Day.

973. **374.** 1 d. multicoloured .. 45 20

**375.** Motorway.

**1987.** Transport. Multicoloured.

974. 2 d. 90 Type **375** .. .. 1·10 45
975. 3 d. 30 Diesel locomotive and passenger train .. 1·40 55

**376.** Houari Boumedienne University, Algiers.

**1987.** Universities. Multicoloured.

976. 1 d. Type **376** .. .. 40 15
977. 2 d. 50 Oran University .. 90 35
978. 2 d. 90 Constantine University .. .. 1·10 45
979. 3 d. 30 Emir Abdelkader University, Constantine (vert.) .. .. .. 1·40 55

**377.** Wheat, Sun and Farmer ploughing with Oxen. **378.** Emblem as Sun above Factories.

**1988.** 10th Anniv. of International Agricultural Development Fund.

980. **377.** 1 d. multicoloured .. 40 20

**1988.** Autonomy of State-owned Utilities.

981. **378.** 1 d. multicoloured .. 40 20

**379.** Woman's Face and Emblem.  **380.** Globe, Flag, Dove and Scout Salute.

**1988.** International Women's Day.

982. **379.** 1 d. multicoloured .. 40 20

**1988.** 75th Anniv. of Arab Scouting.

983. **380.** 2 d. multicoloured .. 80 35

**381.** Bau-Hanifia.  **382.** Running.

**1988.** Spas. Multicoloured.

984. 1 d. Type **381** .. .. 40 15
985. 2 d. 90 Chellala .. .. 1·10 45
986. 3 d. 30 Righa-Ain Tolba .. 1·25 50

**1988.** Olympic Games, Seoul.

987. **382.** 2 d. 90 multicoloured 1·00 45

**383** Pencil and Globe  **384** Barbary Ape

**1988.** International Literacy Day.

988 **383** 2 d. 90 multicoloured .. 1·00 45

**1988.** Endangered Animals. Barbary Ape. Multicoloured.

989 50 c. Type **384** .. .. 20 10
990 90 c. Ape family .. .. 35 15
991 1 d. Ape's head and shoulders (vert) .. 40 20
992 1 d. 80 Ape in tree (vert) .. 70 35

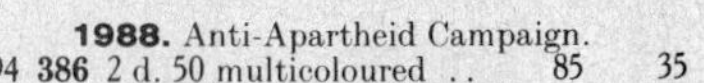

**385** Family Group  **386** Different Races raising Fists

**1988.** 40th Anniv of W.H.O.

993 **385** 2 d. 90 multicoloured .. 1·00 45

**1988.** Anti-Apartheid Campaign.

994 **386** 2 d. 50 multicoloured .. 85 35

**387** Emblem **388** Man irrigating Fields

**1988.** 6th National Liberation Front Party Congress.

995 **387** 1 d. multicoloured .. 40 15

**1988.** Agriculture. Multicoloured.

996 1 d. Type **388** .. .. 40 15
997 1 d. Fields, cattle and man picking fruit .. .. 40 15

**389** Constantine  **390** Courtyard

**1989.**

998 **389** 1 d. deep green & green 30 10

**1989.** Views of Algeria before 1830 (5th series). As T **310**.

999 2 d. 50 green .. .. 60 35
1000 2 d. 90 green .. .. 80 15
1001 5 d. brown and black .. 1·50 70

DESIGNS: 2 d. 50, Bay; 2 d. 90, Harbour; 5 d. View of harbour through archway.

**1989.** National Achievements. Multicoloured.

1002 1 d. Type **390** .. .. 35 20
1003 1 d. Flats (housing) .. 35 20
1004 1 d. Gateway, Timimoun (tourism) .. .. 35 20
1005 1 d. Dish aerial and telephones (communications) .. .. 35 20

**391** Oran Es Senia Airport

**1989.** Airports. Multicoloured.

1006 2 d. 90 Type **391** .. 85 35
1007 3 d. 30 Tebessa airport .. 95 45
1008 5 d. Tamanrasset airport (vert) ... .. .. 1·60 90

**392** Irrigation

**393** Soldiers at Various Tasks

**1989.** Development of South. Multicoloured
1009 1 d. Type **392** .. .. 30 15
1010 1 d. 80 Ouargla secondary school .. .. .. 50 30
1011 2 d. 50 Gas complex, Hassi R'mel (vert) .. 70 35

**1989.** 20th Anniv of National Service.
1012 **393** 2 d. multicoloured .. 55 20

**394** Locusts and Crop Spraying

**1989.** Anti-Locusts Campaign.
1013 **394** 1 d. multicoloured .. 30 15

**395** Mother and Baby

**1989.** International Children's Day.
1014 **395** 1 d.+30 c. mult .. 40 30

**396** Moon

**1989.** 20th Anniv of First Manned Landing on Moon. Multicoloured.
1015 2 d. 90 Type **396** .. 85 35
1016 4 d. Astronaut on moon 1·10 55

**397** Globe and Emblem

**1989.** Cent of Interparliamentary Union.
1017 **397** 2 d. 90 mauve, brown and gold .. .. 85 30

**398** Fruits and Vegetables

**1989.** National Production.
1018 **398** 2 d. multicoloured .. 55 35
1019 – 3 d. multicoloured .. 85 50
1020 – 5 d. multicoloured .. 1·40 85
DESIGNS: 3, 5 d. Various fruits and vegetables.

**399** Atlantic Bonito

**400** "35" and Soldier with Rifle

**1989.** Fishes. Multicoloured.
1021 1 d. Type **399** .. .. 30 15
1022 1 d. 80 Target dory .. 55 30
1023 2 d. 90 Gunner bream .. 85 45
1024 3 d. 30 Broadbill swordfish .. .. .. 95 55

**1989.** 35th Anniv of Revolution.
1025 **400** 1 d. multicoloured .. 30 10

**401** Bank Emblem, Cogwheel, Factory and Wheat

**402** Satan's Mushroom

**1989.** 25th Anniv of African Development Bank.
1026 **401** 1 d. multicoloured .. 30 15

**1989.** Fungi. Multicoloured.
1027 1 d. Type **402** .. .. 60 20
1028 1 d. 80 Yellow stainer .. 1·10 40
1029 2 d. 90 Parasol mushroom 1·75 60
1030 3 d. 30 Saffron milk cap 1·90 70

**403** Emblem

**404** Sun, Arm and Face

**1990.** 10th Anniv of Pan-African Postal Union.
1031 **403** 1 d. multicoloured .. 30 15

**1990.** Rational Use of Energy.
1032 **404** 1 d. multicoloured .. 30 15

**405** Emblem

**406** Ceramics

**1990.** African Nations Cup Football Championship.
1033 **405** 3 d. multicoloured .. 85 40

**1990.** Industries. Multicoloured.
1034 2 d. Type **406** .. .. 55 30
1035 2 d. 90 Car maintenance 85 35
1036 3 d. 30 Fishing .. .. 1·25 35

**407** Pictogram and Olympic Rings

**408** Pylons on Map

**1990.** World Cup Football Championship, Italy. Multicoloured.
1037 2 d. 90 Type **407** .. 85 35
1038 5 d. Trophy, ball and flag 1·40 65

**1990.** Rural Electrification.
1039 **408** 2 d. multicoloured .. 55 20

**409** Young Workers

**410** Members' Flags

**1990.** Youth.
1040 2 d. Type **409** .. .. 55 20
1041 3 d. Youth in crowd (vert) 85 30

**1990.** Arab Maghreb Union Summit Conf.
1042 **410** 1 d. multicoloured .. 30 15

**411** Anniversary Emblem

**1990.** 30th Anniv of O.P.E.C.
1043 **411** 2 d. multicoloured .. 50 20

**412** House and Hand holding Coin

**413** Flag, Rifle and Hands with Broken Manacles

**1990.** Savings Day.
1044 **412** 1 d. multicoloured .. 20 10

**1990.** Namibian Independence.
1045 **413** 3 d. multicoloured .. 60 15

**414** Duck

**415** Dome of the Rock and Palestinians

**1990.** Domestic Animals. Multicoloured.
1046 1 d. Type **414** .. .. 20 10
1047 2 d. Hare (horiz) .. 45 20
1048 2 d. 90 Turkey .. .. 65 35
1049 3 d. 30 Cock (horiz) .. 90 55

**1990.** Palestinian "Intifada" Movement.
1050 **415** 1 d.+30 c. mult .. 35 20

**416** Crowd with Banners

**417** Families in Countryside

**1990.** 30th Anniv of 11 December 1960 Demonstration.
1051 **416** 1 d. multicoloured .. 20 10

**1990.** Campaign against Respiratory Diseases.
1052 **417** 1 d. multicoloured .. 20 10

**418** Sunburst, Torch and Open Book

**419** Bejaia

**1991.** 2nd Anniv of Constitution.
1053 **418** 1 d. multicoloured .. 20 10

**1991.** Views of Algeria before 1830 (6th series). As T **310**.
1054 1 d. 50 red .. .. 35 10
1055 4 d. 20 green .. .. 90 35
DESIGNS: 1 d. 50, Kolea; 4 d. 20, Constantine.

**1991.** Air. Multicoloured.
1056 10 d. Type **419** .. .. 1·90 85
1057 20 d. Annaba .. .. 4·00 1·90

**420** "Jasminum fruticans"

**421** "Trip to the Country" (Mehdi Medrar)

**1991.** Flowers. Multicoloured.
1058 2 d. Type **420** .. .. 45 20
1059 4 d. "Dianthus crinitus" 90 35
1060 5 d. "Cyclamen africanum" .. .. 1·10 55

**1991.** Children's Drawings. Multicoloured.
1061 3 d. Type **421** .. .. 65 20
1062 4 d. "Children playing" (Ouidad Bounab) .. 90 35

**422** Emblem

**1991.** 3rd Anniv of Arab Maghreb Union Summit Conference, Zeralda.
1063 **422** 1 d. multicoloured .. 20 10

423 Figures and Emblem

**1991.** 40th Anniv of Geneva Convention on Status of Refugees.

1064 **423** 3 d. multicoloured .. 65 20

424 Coded Letter and Target

**1991.** World Post Day (1065) and "Telecom 91" International Telecommunications Exhibition, Geneva (1066). Multicoloured.

1065 1 d. 50 Type **424** .. 35 15
1066 4 d. 20 Exhibition and I.T.U. emblems (vert) 95 35

425 Spanish Festoon

**1991.** Butterflies. Multicoloured.

1067 2 d. Type **425** .. .. 20 15
1068 4 d. "Melitaea didyma" 45 30
1069 6 d. Red admiral .. 65 45
1070 7 d. Large tortoiseshell .. 90 65

426 Chest Ornament

427 Woman

**1991.** Silver Jewellery from South Algeria. Multicoloured.

1071 3 d. Necklaces .. .. 35 20
1072 4 d. Type **426** .. .. 45 30
1073 5 d. Enamelled ornament 55 45
1074 7 d. Bangles (horiz) .. 90 70

**1992.** Views of Algeria before 1830. As previous issues and new values. Size $30\frac{1}{2} \times 21$ mm.

1075 5 c. purple .. .. 10 10
1076 10 c. blue .. .. 10 10
1077 20 c. blue .. .. 10 10
1078 30 c. red and black .. 10 10
1079 50 c. brown .. .. 10 10
1080 70 c. lilac .. .. 10 10
1081 80 c. brown .. .. 10 10
1082 1 d. brown .. .. 10 10
1083 2 d. blue .. .. 10 10
1084 3 d. green .. .. 20 10
1085 4 d. red .. .. 25 10
1086 6 d. 20 blue .. .. 70 20
1087 7 d. 50 red .. .. 85 20

DESIGNS: 5 c., 6 d. 20, As No. 873; 10 c., 7 d. 50, As No. 859; 20 c. As No. 1000; 30 c. As No. 1001; 50 c. As No. 882; 70 c. As No. 875; 80 c. Type **310**; 1 d. As No. 860; 2 d. As No. 861; 3 d. As No. 817; 4 d. As No. 1055.

**1992.** International Women's Day.

1095 **427** 1 d. 50 multicoloured 20 10

428 Dorcas Gazelle

429 Algiers

**1992.** Gazelles. Multicoloured.

1096 1 d. 50 Type **428** .. 15 10
1097 6 d. 20 Edmi gazelle .. 70 45
1098 8 d. 60 Addra gazelle .. 95 55

**1992.**

1099 **429** 1 d. 50 brown & lt brn 15 10
1132 2 d. blue .. .. 10 10
1147 3 d. blue .. .. 10 10

430 Runners

431 Doves and Flags

**1992.** Olympic Games, Barcelona.

1100 **430** 6 d. 20 multicoloured 70 30

**1992.** 30th Anniv of Independence.

1101 **431** 5 d. green, red & black 55 20

432 "Ajuga iva"

433 Computerized Post Office Equipment

**1992.** Medicinal Plants. Multicoloured.

1102 1 d. 50 Type **432** .. 15 10
1103 5 d. 10 Buckthorn .. 55 30
1104 6 d. 20 Milk thistle .. 70 35
1105 8 d. 60 French lavender .. 1·00 50

**1992.** World Post Day. Modernization of Postal Service.

1106 **433** 1 d. 50 multicoloured 15 10

434 Boudiaf

**1992.** Mohammed Boudiaf (chairman of Committee of State) Commemoration.

1107 **434** 2 d. multicoloured .. 20 15
1108 8 d. 60 multicoloured 95 55

435 2nd-century B.C. Numidian Coin

**1992.** Coinage. Multicoloured.

1109 1 d. 50 Type **435** .. 15 10
1110 2 d. 14th-century Zianide dinar .. .. .. 20 15
1111 5 d. 10 11th-century Almoravid dinar .. 55 20
1112 6 d. 20 19th-century Emir Abd-el-Kader coin .. 70 35

436 Sea-horse

437 Algiers Door Knocker

**1992.** Marine Animals. Multicoloured.

1113 1 d. 50 Type **436** .. 15 10
1114 2 d. 70 Loggerhead turtle 35 15
1115 6 d. 20 Dragon moray eel 70 35
1116 7 d. 50 Lobster .. .. 85 50

**1993.** Door Knockers. Multicoloured.

1117 2 d. Type **437** .. .. 10 10
1118 5 d. 60 Constantine .. 30 15
1119 8 d. 60 Tlemcen .. .. 50 25

438 Medlar Blossom

**1993.** Fruit-tree Blossom. Multicoloured.

1120 4 d. 50 Type **438** .. 25 10
1121 8 d. 60 Quince (vert) .. 50 25
1122 11 d. Apricot (vert) .. 60 30

439 Patrol Boat, Emblem and Flag

440 Grain Storage Jar

**1993.** 20th Anniv of Coastguard Service.

1123 **439** 2 d. multicoloured .. 10 10

**1993.** Traditional Utensils. Multicoloured.

1124 2 d. Type **440** .. .. 10 10
1125 5 d. 60 Grindstone .. 30 15
1126 8 d. 60 Oil-press .. .. 50 25

441 Mauretanian Royal Mausoleum, Tipaza

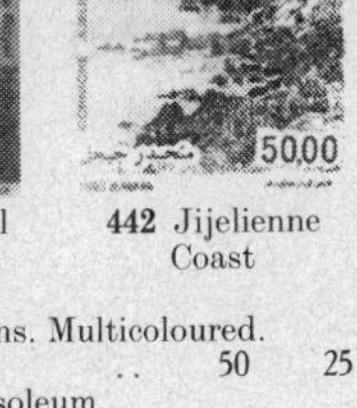

442 Jijelienne Coast

**1993.** Mausoleums. Multicoloured.

1127 8 d. 60 Type **441** .. 50 25
1128 12 d. Royal Mausoleum, El Khroub .. .. 65 30

**1993.** Air.

1129 **442** 50 d. green, brn & bl 2·75 1·25

443 Annaba

444 Chameleon

**1993.** Ports. Multicoloured.

1130 2 d. Type **443** .. .. 10 10
1131 8 d. 60 Arzew .. .. 50 25

**1993.** Reptiles. Multicoloured.

1133 2 d. Type **444** .. .. 10 10
1134 8 d. 60 Desert monitor (horiz) .. .. 50 25

445 Tipaza

446 Map, Processing Plant and Uses of Hydrocarbons

**1993.** Tourism. Multicoloured.

1135 2 d. Type **445** .. .. 10 10
1136 8 d. 60 Kerzaz .. .. 25 10

**1993.** 30th Anniv of Sonatrach (National Society for Transformation and Commercialisation of Hydrocarbons).

1137 **446** 2 d. multicoloured .. 10 10

447 Dove, Flag and "18"

448 Crown of Statue of Liberty, Football, U.S. Flag and Trophy

**1994.** National Chahid Day.

1138 **447** 2 d. multicoloured .. 10 10

**1994.** World Cup Football Championship, U.S.A.

1139 **448** 8 d. 60 multicoloured 25 10

449 Monkey Orchid

450 Hoggar Script on Stone

**1994.** Orchids. Multicoloured.

1140 5 d. 60 Type **449** .. 15 10
1141 8 d. 60 "Orphrys lutea" .. 25 10
1142 11 d. Bee orchid .. .. 35 15

**1994.** Ancient Communication. Mult.

1143 3 d. Type **450** .. .. 10 10
1144 10 d. Abizar stele .. 30 15

451 Flags and Olympic Rings

452 Figures and City on Globe

**1994.** Cent of Int Olympic Committee.

1145 **451** 12 d. multicoloured .. 35 15

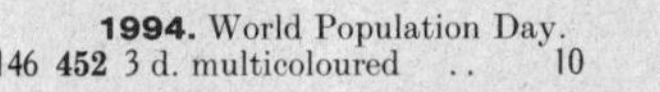

**1994.** World Population Day.

1146 **452** 3 d. multicoloured .. 10 10

453 Sandstone

454 Brooches

**1994.** Minerals. Multicoloured.

1148 3 d. Type **453** .. .. 10 10
1149 5 d. Cipolin .. .. 15 10
1150 10 d. Turitella shells in chalk .. .. .. 25 15

**1994.** Saharan Silver Jewellery. Mult.

1151 3 d. Type **454** .. .. 10 10
1152 5 d. Belt (horiz) .. .. 15 10
1153 12 d. Bracelets (horiz) .. 30 15

## MINIMUM PRICE

The minimum price quoted is 10p which represents a handling charge rather than a basis for valuing common stamps. For further notes about prices see introductory pages.

455 Soldiers

456 Ladybirds on Leaves

**1994.** 40th Anniv of Revolution.
1154 455 3 d. multicoloured .. 10 10

**1994.** Insects. Multicoloured.
1155 3 d. Type 456 .. .. 10 10
1156 12 d. Beetle ("Buprestidae") on plant .. .. .. 30 15

457 Virus and Family

**1994.** World Anti-AIDS Campaign Day.
1157 457 3 d. black, blue & mve 10 10

458 Algiers

459 Southern Algeria

**1994.** Regional Dances. Multicoloured.
1158 3 d. Type 458 .. .. 10 10
1159 10 d. Constantine .. 25 15
1160 12 d. Alaoui .. .. 30 15

**1995.** 20th Anniv of World Tourism Organization.
1161 459 3 d. multicoloured .. 10 10

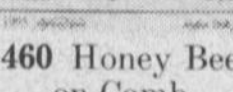
460 Honey Bee on Comb

461 Dahlia

**1995.** Bee-keeping. Multicoloured.
1162 3 d. Type 460 .. .. 10 10
1163 13 d. Bee on flower (horiz) 35 20

**1995.** Flowers. Multicoloured.
1164 3 d. Type 461 .. .. 10 10
1165 10 d. Zinnias .. .. 25 15
1166 13 d. Lilac .. .. 35 20

462 Circular Design

463 Doves, Graves, Victims and Soldiers

**1995.** Stucco Work from Sedrata (4th century after Hegira).
1167 462 3 d. brown .. .. 10 10
1168 – 4 d. green .. .. 10 10
1169 – 5 d. brown .. .. 15 10
DESIGNS—4 d. Circular design within square; 5 d. Stylized flowers.

**1995.** 50th Anniv of End of Second World War. Multicoloured.
1170 463 3 d. multicoloured .. 10 10

464 Water Pollution

465 Players and Anniversary Emblem

**1995.** Environmental Protection. Mult.
1172 3 d. Type 464 .. .. 10 10
1173 13 d. Air pollution .. 35 20

**1995.** Centenary of Volleyball.
1174 465 3 d. multicoloured .. 10 10

466 Map and Pylon

467 Children and Schoolbag Contents

**1995.** Electrification.
1175 466 3 d. multicoloured .. 10 10

**1995.** National Solidarity.
1176 467 3 d.+50 c. mult .. 10 10

468 Doves and Anniversary Emblem

469 Pitcher from Lakhdaria

**1995.** 50th Anniv of U.N.O.
1177 468 13 d. multicoloured .. 30 15

**1995.** Traditional Pottery.
1178 469 10 d. brown .. .. 20 10
1179 – 20 d. brown .. .. 45 25
1180 – 21 d. brown .. .. 45 25
1181 – 30 d. brown .. .. 65 35
DESIGNS: 20 d. Water jug (Aokas); 21 d. Jar (Larbaa nath Iraten); 30 d. Jar (Ouadhia).

470 Common Shelduck

**1995.** Water Birds. Multicoloured.
1182 3 d. Type 470 .. .. 10 10
1183 5 d. Common snipe .. 10 10

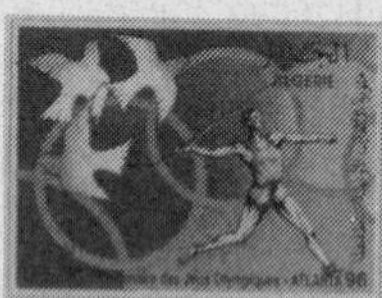
471 Doves flying over Javelin Thrower and Olympic Rings

**1996.** Centenary of Modern Olympic Games and Olympic Games, Atlanta.
1184 471 20 d. multicoloured .. 45 25

472 Fringed Bag

473 Pasteur Institute

**1996.** Handicrafts. Leather Bags. Mult.
1185 5 d. Type 472 .. .. 10 10
1186 16 d. Shoulder bag with handle (vert) .. .. 35 20

**1996.** Centenary (1994) of Algerian Pasteur Institute.
1187 473 5 d. multicoloured .. 10 10

474 Arabic Script and Computer

**1996.** Scientific and Technical Education Day. Multicoloured.
1188 5 d. Type 474 .. .. 10 10
1189 16 d. Dove, fountain pen and symbols (vert) .. 35 20
1190 23 d. Pencil, pen, dividers and satellite over Earth on pages of open book (vert) .. .. .. 50 25

475 Iron Ore, Djebel Quenza

**1996.** Minerals. Multicoloured.
1191 10 d. Type 475 .. .. 20 10
1192 20 d. Gold, Tirek-Amesmessa .. .. 45 25

476 "Pandoriana pandora"

**1996.** Butterflies. Multicoloured.
1193 5 d. Type 476 .. .. 10 10
1194 10 d. "Coenonympha pamphilus" .. .. 20 10
1195 20 d. Painted lady .. 45 25
1196 23 d. Marbled white .. 50 25

## POSTAGE DUE STAMPS

**1926.** As Postage Due stamps of France, but inscr. "ALGERIE".
D 34. D 11. 5 c. blue .. .. 10 25
D 35. 10 c. brown .. 10 25
D 36. 20 c. olive .. .. 15 25
D 37. 25 c. red .. .. 15 50
D 38. 30 c. red .. .. 15 15
D 39. 45 c. green .. .. 60 60
D 40. 50 c. purple .. 10 10
D 41. 60 c. green .. .. 1·50 1·75
D 42. 1 f. red on yellow .. 20 15
D 249. 1 f. 50 lilac .. .. 45 40
D 43. 2 f. mauve .. .. 30 35
D 250. 2 f. blue .. .. 45 40
D 44. 3 f. blue .. .. 25 40
D 251. 5 f. red .. .. 45 40
D 252. 5 f. green .. .. 90 55

**1926.** As Postage Due stamps of France but inscr. "ALGERIE".
D 45. D 19. 1 c. olive .. .. 10 25
D 46. 10 c. violet .. .. 10 35
D 47. 30 c. bistre .. .. 10 30
D 48. 60 c. red .. .. 25 25
D 49. 1 f. violet .. .. 5·00 4·00
D 50. 2 f. blue .. .. 6·50 2·00

**1927.** Nos. D36, D39 and D37 surch.
D 92. D 11. 60 on 20 c. olive .. 75 60
D 93. 2 f. on 45 c. green .. 85 1·25
D 94. 3 f. on 25 c. red .. 70 90

**1927.** Nos. D 45/8 surch.
D 95. D 19. 10 c. on 30 c. bistre 2·50 2·75
D 96. 1 f. on 1 c. olive .. 85 95
D 97. 1 f. on 60 c. red .. 15·00 30
D 98. 2 f. on 10 c. violet .. 5·25 9·00

**1942.** As 1926 issue, but without "RF".
D 181. D 11. 30 c. red .. .. 30 35
D 182. 2 f. mauve .. .. 35 35

**1944.** No. 208 surch **TAXE P. C. V. DOUANE 20 Fr.**
D230 38 20 f. on 50 f. red .. 35 40

**1944.** Surch. **T O.50.**
D 231. 4. 50 c. on 20 c. green .. 30 35

**1947.** Postage Due Stamps of France optd. **ALGERIE.**
D 283. – 10 c. brown (No. D 985) 15 30
D 284. – 30 c. purple (No. D 986) 20 30

D 53.

**1947.**
D 285. D 53. 20 c. red .. .. 15 30
D 286. 60 c. blue .. .. 25 30
D 287. 1 f. brown .. .. 10 25
D 288. 1 f. 50 olive .. 55 80
D 289. 2 f. red .. .. 20 30
D 290. 3 f. violet .. .. 20 25
D 291. 5 f. blue .. .. 20 30
D 292. 6 f. black .. .. 30 45
D 293. 10 f. purple .. 30 25
D 294. 15 f. myrtle .. 55 55
D 295. 20 f. green .. .. 30 25
D 296. 30 f. red .. .. 65 60
D 297. 50 f. black .. .. 1·25 1·10
D 298. 100 f. blue .. .. 6·25 4·00

## INDEPENDENT STATE

**1962.** Postage Due stamps of France optd. **EA** and with bar obliterating "**REPUBLIQUE FRANCAISE**".
D 391. D 457 5 c. mauve .. 11·00 11·00
D 392. 10 c. red .. 11·00 11·00
D 393. 20 c. brown .. 11·00 11·00
D 394. 50 c. green .. 22·00 22·00
D 395. 1 f. green .. 45·00 45·00
The above also exist with larger overprint applied with handstamps.

D 107. Scales of Justice.

D 200. Ears of Corn.

**1963.**
D 411. D107. 5 c. red and olive .. 10 10
D 412. 10 c. olive and red 10 10
D 413. 20 c. blue and black 35 20
D 414. 50 c. brown and green 80 55
D 415. 1 f. violet and orange 1·40 1·25

**1968.** No. D 415 surch.
D 508. D 107. 60 c. on 1 f. violet and orange .. 55 40

**1972.**
D603 D 200 10 c. brown .. 10 10
D604 20 c. brown .. 10 10
D605 40 c. orange .. 20 10
D606 50 c. blue .. 20 10
D607 80 c. brown .. 45 20
D608 1 d. green .. 55 35
D609 2 d. blue .. .. 1·10 65
D610 3 d. violet .. 15 10
D611 4 d. purple .. 20 10

## ALLENSTEIN Pt. 7

A district of E. Prussia retained by Germany as the result of a plebiscite in 1920. Stamps issued during the plebiscite period.

100 pfennig = 1 mark.

**1920.** Stamps of Germany inscr "DEUTSCHES REICH" optd **PLEBISCITE OLSZTYN ALLENSTEIN**.

1 **17** 5 pf. green .. .. 10 20
2 10 pf. red .. .. 10 20
3 **24** 15 pf. violet .. .. 10 20
4 15 pf. purple .. .. 7·00 10·00
5 **17** 20 pf. blue .. .. 15 20
6 30 pf. blk & orge on buff 30 30
7 40 pf. black and red .. 20 25
8 50 pf. blk & pur on buff 15 25
9 75 pf. black and green 25 25
10 **18** 1 m. red .. .. 60 70
11 1 m. 25 green .. .. 50 60
12 1 m. 50 brown .. .. 60 1·00
13b **20** 2 m. 50 red .. .. 1·25 5·00
14 **21** 3 m. black .. .. 1·25 1·60

**1920.** Stamps of Germany inscr. "DEUTSCHES REICH" optd. **TRAITE DE VERSAILLES** etc. in oval.

15. **17.** 5 pf. green .. .. 15 25
16. 10 pf. red .. .. 15 25
17. **24.** 15 pf. violet .. .. 15 40
18. 15 pf. purple .. .. 30·00 38·00
19. **17.** 20 pf. blue .. .. 15 40
20. 30 pf. blk. & orge. on buff 20 25
21. 40 pf black and red .. 20 25
22. 50 pf. blk. & pur. on buff 15 15
23. 75 pf. black and green .. 15 15
24. **18.** 1 m red .. .. 45 55
25. 1 m. 25 green .. .. 60 70
26. 1 m. 50 brown .. .. 60 70
27. **20.** 2 m. 50 red .. .. 80 2·00
28. **21.** 3 m. black .. .. 1·00 1·25

## ALSACE AND LORRAINE Pt. 7

Stamps used in parts of France occupied by the German army in the war of 1870–71, and afterwards temporarily in the annexed provinces of Alsace and Lorraine.

100 pfennig = 1 mark.

1.

**1870.**

1. **1.** 1 c. green .. .. .. 45·00 £100
3. 2 c. brown .. .. .. 48·00 £110
6. 4 c. grey .. .. .. 80·00 50·00
8. 5 c. green .. .. .. 50·00 8·00
10. 10 c. brown .. .. .. 35·00 3·75
14. 20 c. blue .. .. .. 60·00 9·00
16. 25 c. brown .. .. .. £110 70·00

For 1940 issues see separate lists for Alsace and Lorraine under German Occupations.

## ANDORRA Pts. 6 & 9

An independent state in the Pyrenees under the joint suzerainty of France and Spain.

### FRENCH POST OFFICES

100 centimes = 1 franc.

**1931.** Stamps of France, optd. **ANDORRE.**

F 1. **11.** ½ c. on 1 c. grey .. 50 60
F 2. 1 c. grey .. .. 50 60
F 3. 2 c. red .. .. 60 70
F 4. 3 c. orange .. .. 60 70
F 5. 5 c. green .. .. 1·25 1·40
F 6. 10 c. lilac .. .. 1·50 1·75
F 7. **18.** 15 c. brown .. .. 2·75 3·00
F 8. 20 c. mauve .. .. 4·00 4·50
F 9. 25 c. brown .. .. 4·00 4·50
F 10. 30 c. green .. .. 4·00 4·50
F 11. 40 c. blue .. .. 6·00 7·00
F 12. **15.** 45 c. lilac .. .. 8·00 9·00
F 13. 50 c. red .. .. 6·00 6·50
F 14. 65 c. green .. .. 11·00 13·00
F 15. 75 c. mauve .. .. 16·00 18·00
F 16. **18.** 90 c. red .. .. 19·00 21·00
F 17. **15.** 1 f. blue .. .. 20·00 22·00
F 18. **18.** 1 f. 50 blue .. .. 25·00 28·00
F 19. **13.** 2 f. red and green .. 18·00 20·00
F 20. 3 f. mauve and red .. 60·00 70·00
F 21. 5 f. blue and orange .. £100 £120
F 22. 10 f. green and red .. £225 £250
F 23. 20 f. mauve and green £275 £325

**F 3.** Our Lady's Chapel, Meritxell.

**F 5.** St. Michael's Church, Engolasters.

**1932.**

F 24. **F 3.** 1 c. slate .. .. 35 35
F 25. 2 c. violet .. .. 50 50
F 26. 3 c. brown .. .. 35 35
F 27. 5 c green .. .. 50 50
F 28. A. 10 c. lilac .. .. 80 80
F 29. **F 3.** 15 c. red .. .. 1·25 1·25
F 30. A. 20 c. mauve .. .. 7·00 6·00
F 31. **F 5.** 25 c. brown .. .. 3·00 3·00
F 32. A. 25 c. brown .. .. 8·50 9·50
F 33. 30 c. green .. .. 2·10 1·90
F 34. 40 c. blue .. .. 7·00 5·50
F 35. 40 c. brown .. .. 80 90
F 36. 45 c. red .. .. 7·50 7·50
F 37. 45 c. green .. .. 3·50 4·00
F 38. **F 5.** 50 c. mauve .. .. 8·50 7·00
F 39. A. 50 c. violet .. .. 3·75 4·00
F 40. 50 c. green .. .. 1·60 1·75
F 41. 55 c. violet .. .. 14·00 14·00
F 42. 60 c. brown .. .. 70 80
F 43. **F 5.** 65 c. green .. .. 35·00 32·00
F 44. A. 65 c. blue .. .. 10·00 10·00
F 45. 70 c. red .. .. 1·60 1·60
F 46. **F 5.** 75 c. violet .. .. 5·00 5·00
F 47. A. 75 c. blue .. .. 3·00 3·25
F 48. 80 c. green .. .. 17·00 18·00
F 49. B. 80 c. green .. .. 35 35
F 50. 90 c. red .. .. 4·00 4·00
F 51. 90 c. green .. .. 3·00 3·50
F 52. 1 f. green .. .. 12·00 9·00
F 53. 1 f. red .. .. 16·00 15·00
F 54. 1 f blue .. .. 30 35
F 55. 1 f. 20 violet .. .. 30 35
F 56. **F 3.** 1 f. 25 mauve .. .. 38·00 38·00
F 57. 1 f. 25 red .. .. 3·50 3·50
F 58. B. 1 f. 30 brown .. .. 30 35
F 59. C. 1 f. 50 blue .. .. 14·00 14·00
F 60. B. 1 f. 50 red .. .. 30 30
F 61. 1 f. 75 violet .. .. 85·00 75·00
F 62. B. 1 f. 75 blue .. .. 32·00 32·00
F 63. 2 f. mauve .. .. 7·00 7·00
F 64. **F 3.** 2 f. red .. .. 1·00 1·00
F 65. 2 f. green .. .. 35 35
F 66. 2 f. 15 violet .. .. 40·00 42·00
F 67. 2 f. 25 blue .. .. 5·00 5·00
F 68. 2 f. 40 red .. .. 30 30
F 69. 2 f. 50 black .. .. 6·00 6·00
F 70. 2 f. 50 blue .. .. 1·60 1·60
F 71. B. 3 f. brown .. .. 8·00 8·00
F 72. **F 3.** 3 f. brown .. .. 35 40
F 73. 4 f. blue .. .. 35 40
F 74. 4 f. 50 violet .. .. 1·00 1·25
F 75. C. 5 f. brown .. .. 50 50
F 76. 10 f. violet .. .. 50 50
F 78. 15 f. blue .. .. 60 60
F 79. 20 f. red .. .. 60 60
F 81. A. 50 f. blue .. .. 1·50 1·50

DESIGNS—HORIZ. A, St. Anthony's Bridge. C, Andorra la Vella. VERT. B, Valley of Sant Julia.

**1935.** No. F38 surch **20c**.

F82 **F 5** 20 c. on 50 c. purple 12·00 12·00

**F 9.**

**F 13.** Andorra la Vella.

**F 10.**

**F 14.** Councillor Jaume Bonell.

**1936.**

F 83. **F 9.** 1 c. black .. .. 10 10
F 84. 2 c. blue .. .. 10 10
F 85. 3 c. brown .. .. 10 10
F 86. 5 c. red .. .. 10 10
F 87. 10 c. blue .. .. 10 10
F 88. 15 c. mauve .. .. 1·75 1·75
F 89. 20 c. green .. .. 15 15
F 90. 30 c. red .. .. 45 45
F 91. 30 c. black .. .. 25 25
F 92. 35 c. green .. .. 45·00 45·00
F 93. 40 c. brown .. .. 40 40
F 94. 50 c. green .. .. 40 40
F 95. 60 c. blue .. .. 40 40
F 96. 70 c. violet .. .. 40 40

**1944.**

F 97. **F 10.** 10 c. violet .. .. 10 10
F 98. 30 c. red .. .. 10 10
F 99. 40 c. blue .. .. 10 10
F 100. 50 c. red .. .. 10 10
F 101. 60 c. black .. .. 10 10
F 102. 70 c. mauve .. .. 10 10
F 103. 80 c. green .. .. 10 10
F 104. 1 f. blue .. .. 45 45
F 105. D. 1 f. purple .. .. 15 15
F 106. 1 f. 20 blue .. .. 15 15
F 107. 1 f. 50 red .. .. 15 15
F 108. 2 f. green .. .. 15 10
F 109. E. 2 f. 40 red .. .. 20 20
F 110. 2 f. 50 red .. .. 3·00 2·50
F 111. 3 f. brown .. .. 15 15
F 112. D. 3 f. red .. .. 4·00 4·00
F 113. E. 4 f. blue .. .. 15 15
F 114. 4 f. green .. .. 80 80
F 115. D. 4 f. brown .. .. 1·50 1·50
F 116. E. 4 f. 50 brown .. .. 15 15
F 117. **F 13.** 4 f. 50 blue .. .. 6·00 6·00
F 118. 5 f. blue .. .. 15 15
F 119. 5 f. green .. .. 75 40
F 120. E. 5 f. green .. .. 2·50 2·50
F 121. 5 f. violet .. .. 5·00 5·00
F 122. **F 13.** 6 f. red .. .. 25 15
F 123. 6 f. purple .. .. 40 40
F 124. E. 6 f. green .. .. 4·00 4·00
F 125. **F 13.** 8 f. blue .. .. 75 75
F 126. E. 8 f. brown .. .. 50 35
F 127. **F 13.** 10 f. green .. .. 15 15
F 128. 10 f. blue .. .. 1·00 50
F 129. 12 f. red .. .. 80 80
F 130. 12 f. green .. .. 80 70
F 131. **F 14.** 15 f. purple .. .. 35 35
F 132. **F 13.** 15 f. red .. .. 40 40
F 133. 15 f. brown .. .. 5·50 4·00
F 134. **F 14.** 18 f. blue .. .. 2·50 2·50
F 135. **F 13.** 18 f. red .. .. 14·00 9·00
F 136. **F 14.** 20 f. blue .. .. 40 40
F 137. 20 f. violet .. .. 2·00 2·00
F 138. 25 f. red .. .. 3·00 3·00
F 139. 25 f. blue .. .. 1·25 1·25
F 140. 30 f. blue .. .. 20·00 10·00
F 141. 40 f. green .. .. 2·50 2·50
F 142. 50 f. brown .. .. 1·25 90

DESIGNS—HORIZ: D, Church of St. John of Caselles. E, House of the Valleys.

**F 15.** Chamois and Pyrenees.

**F 16.** Les Escaldes.

**1950.** Air.

F 143. **F 15.** 100 f. blue .. .. 60·00 40·00

**1955.**

F144 **F 16** 1 f. blue (postage) .. 15 15
F145 – 2 f. green .. .. 15 15
F146 – 3 f. red .. .. 15 15
F147 – 5 f. brown .. .. 15 15
F148 – 6 f. green .. .. 30 30
F149 – 8 f. red .. .. 45 45
F150 – 10 f. violet .. .. 65 65
F151 – 12 f. blue .. .. 75 75
F152 – 15 f. red .. .. 75 55
F153 – 18 f. blue .. .. 90 90
F154 – 20 f. violet .. .. 1·50 1·00
F155 – 25 f. brown .. .. 1·75 1·25
F156 – 30 f. blue .. .. 22·00 15·00
F157 – 35 f. blue .. .. 7·50 6·00
F158 – 40 f. green .. .. 28·00 28·00
F159 – 50 f. red .. .. 2·50 1·75
F160 – 65 f. violet .. .. 7·00 7·00
F161 – 70 f. brown .. .. 3·50 3·50
F162 – 75 f. blue .. .. 40·00 40·00
F163 – 100 f. green (air) .. 8·00 5·00
F164 – 200 f. red .. .. 18·00 9·00
F165 – 500 f. blue .. .. 80·00 45·00

DESIGNS—VERT. 15 f. to 25 f. Gothic cross, Andorra la Vella. 100 f. to 500 f. East Valira River. HORIZ. 6 f. to 12 f. Santa Coloma Church. 30 f. to 75 f. Les Bons village.

New currency. 100 (old) francs = 1 (new franc.)

**F 21.**

**F 22.** Gothic Cross, Meritxell.

**1961.**

F 166. **F 21.** 1 c. grey, blue and slate (postage) .. 10 10
F 167. 2 c. light orange, black and orange 10 10
F 168. 5 c. light green, black and green 10 10
F 169. 10 c. pink, black and red .. .. 10 10
F 170. 12 c. yellow, purple & green .. 90 90
F 171. 15 c. light blue, black and blue .. 10 10
F 172. 18 c. pink, black and mauve 90 90
F 173. 20 c. light yellow brown and yellow .. 15 15
F 174. **F 22.** 25 c. blue, violet and green .. 25 20
F 175. 30 c. purple, red and green .. 30 30
F 175a. 40 c. green & brown 35 35
F 176. 45 c. blue, indigo and green .. 12·00 12·00
F 176a. 45 c. brown, blue and violet .. 80 80
F 177. 50 c. multicoloured 1·00 1·00
F 177a. 60 c. brown & chestnut .. 50 50
F 178. 65 c. olive, blue and brown .. 18·00 18·00
F 179. 85 c. multicoloured 18·00 18·00
F 179a. 90 c. green, blue and brown .. 1·00 1·00
F 180. 1 f. blue, brown and turquoise .. 1·00 1·00
F 181. – 2 f. green, red and purple (air) .. 90 90
F 182. – 3 f. purple, blue and green .. 1·25 90
F 183. – 5 f. orange, purple and red .. 2·50 1·50
F 184. – 10 f. green & blue 4·00 2·00

DESIGNS—As Type **F 22:** 60 c. to 1 f. Engolasters Lake. 2 f. to 10 f. Incles Valley.

**F 23.** "Telstar" Satellite and part of Globe.

**1962.** 1st Trans-Atlantic TV Satellite Link.

F 185. **F 23.** 50 c. violet & blue 1·40 1·40

**F 24.** "La Sardane" (dance).

**1963.** Andorran History (1st issue).

F 186. **F 24.** 20 c. purple, mauve and green .. 3·50 3·50
F 187. – 50 c. red and green 5·00 5·00
F 188. – 1 f. green, blue and brown .. .. 8·00 8·00

DESIGNS—LARGER (48½ × 27 mm.): 50 c. Charlemagne crossing Andorra. (48 × 27 mm.): 1 f. Foundation of Andorra by Louis le Debonnaire.

See also Nos. F.190/1.

**F 25.** Santa Coloma Church and Grand Palais, Paris.

**1964.** "PHILATEC 1964" Int. Stamp Exhibition, Paris.

F 189. **F 25.** 25 c. green, purple and brown .. 1·50 1·50

**1964.** Andorran History (2nd issue). As Nos. F187/8 inscribed "1964".

F190 60 c. green, chest & brn 13·00 13·00
F191 1 f. blue, sepia and brown 13·00 13·00

**DESIGNS (48½ × 27 mm.): 60 c. "Napoleon re-establishes the Andorran Statute, 1806". 1 f. "Confirmation of the Co-Government, 1288".**

**F 26.** Virgin of Santa Coloma.

**F 27.** "Syncom", Morse Key and Pleumeur-Bodou Centre.

**1964.** Red Cross Fund.

F 192. **F 26.** 25 c.+10 c. red, green and blue 18·00 18·00

**1965.** Cent. of I.T.U.

F 193. **F 27.** 60 c. violet, blue and red .. .. 4·50 4·50

F 28. Andorra House, Paris.

F 29. Chair-lift.

**1965.** Opening of Andorra House, Paris.
F 194. F 28. 25 c. brown, olive and blue . . . . 1·00 1·00

**1966.** Winter Sports.
F 195. F 29. 25 c. grn., pur. & bl. 1·00 1·00
F 196. – 40 c. brown, blue & red . . . . 1·50 1·50
DESIGN—HORIZ. 40 c. Ski-lift.

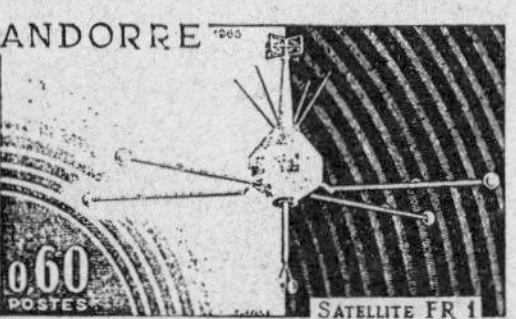
F 30. Satellite "FR 1".

**1966.** Launching of Satellite "FR 1".
F 197. F 30. 60 c. blue, emerald and green . . 1·75 1·75

F 31. Europa "Ship".

F 32. Cogwheels.

**1966.** Europa.
F 198. F 31. 60 c. brown . . 3·50 3·50

**1967.** Europa.
F 199. F 32. 30 c. indigo & blue 2·25 2·25
F 200. 60 c. red and purple 3·75 3·75

F 33. "Folk Dancers" (statue).

F 34. Telephone and Dial.

**1967.** Cent. (1966) of New Reform.
F 201. F 33. 30 c. grn., ol. & slate 1·00 1·00

**1967.** Inaug. of Automatic Telephone Service.
F 202. F 34. 60 c. blk., vio. & red 1·25 1·25

F 35. Andorran Family.

**1967.** Institution of Social Security.
F 203. F 35. 2 f. 30 brn. & purple 7·50 7·50

F 36. "The Temptation".

F 37. Downhill Skiing.

**1967.** 16th-Century Frescoes in House of the Valleys (1st series).
F 204. F 36. 25 c. red and black 50 50
F 205. – 30 c. purple & violet 70 70
F 206. – 60 c. blue & indigo 1·25 1·25
FRESCOES: 30 c. "The Kiss of Judas". 60 c. "The Descent from the Cross".
See also Nos. F 210/12.

**1968.** Winter Olympic Games, Grenoble.
F 207. F 37. 40 c. pur., orge. & red 1·25 1·25

F 38. Europa "Key".

**1968.** Europa.
F 208. F 38. 30 c. blue and slate 5·00 5·00
F 209. 60 c. violet & brown 7·00 7·00

**1968.** 16th-Century Frescoes in House of the Valleys (2nd series). Designs as Type F 36.
F 210. 25 c. deep green and green . . . . . . 55 55
F 211. 30 c. purple and brown 80 80
F 212. 60 c. brown and red . . 1·40 1·40
FRESCOES: 25 c. "The Beating of Christ". 30 c. "Christ Helped by the Cyrenians". 60 c. "The Death of Christ".

F 39. High Jumping.

**1968.** Olympic Games, Mexico.
F 213. F 39. 40 c. brown & blue 1·25 1·25

F 40. Colonnade.

F 41. Canoeing.

**1969.** Europa.
F 214. F 40. 40 c. grey, bl. & red 5·00 5·00
F 215. 70 c. red, grn. & bl. 8·00 8·00

**1969.** World Kayak-Canoeing Championships, Bourg-St. Maurice.
F 216. F 41. 70 c. deep blue, blue and green . . 2·00 2·00

**1969.** European Water Charter. Similar to T 639 of France.
F 217. 70 c. black, blue & ultram. 4·50 4·50

F 42. "The Apocalypse".

F 43. Handball Player.

**1969.** Altar-screen, Church of St. John of Caselles (1st series). "The Revelation of St. John".
F218 F 42 30 c. red, vio & brn 75 75
F219 – 40 c. bis, brn & grey 95 95
F220 – 70 c. pur, lake & red 1·50 1·50
DESIGNS: 40 c. Angel "clothed with cloud with face as the sun, and feet as pillars of fire" (Rev. 10). 70 c. Christ with sword and stars, and seven candlesticks.
See also Nos. F 225/7, F233/5 and F 240/2.

**1970.** 7th World Handball Championships, France.
F 221. F 43. 80 c. blue, brown & deep blue . . 2·00 2·00

F 44. "Flaming Sun".

F 45. Putting the Shot.

**1970.** Europa.
F 222. F 44. 40 c. orange . . 3·50 3·50
F 223. 80 c. violet . . 7·00 7·00

**1970.** 1st European Junior Athletic Championships, Paris.
F 224. F 45. 80 c. purple & blue 2·25 2·25

**1970.** Altar-screen, Church of St. John of Caselles (2nd series.) Designs as Type F 42.
F 225. 30 c. violet, brown & red 75 75
F 226. 40 c. green and violet . . 90 90
F 227. 80 c. red, blue and green 1·75 1·75
DESIGNS: 30 c. Angel with keys and padlock. 40 c. Angel with pillar. 80 c. St. John being boiled in cauldron of oil.

F 46. Ice Skaters.

F 47. Capercaillie.

**1971.** World Ice Skating Championships, Lyon.
F228 F 46 80 c. vio, pur & red 2·00 2·00

**1971.** Nature Protection.
F 229. F 47. 80 c. multicoloured 3·00 3·00
F 230. – 80 c. brn., grn. & blue 2·50 2·50
DESIGN: No. F 230 Brown bear.

F 48. Europa Chain.

**1971.** Europa.
F 231. F 48. 50 c. red . . 5·00 5·00
F 232. 80 c. green . . 7·50 7·50

**1971.** Altar-screen, Church of St. John of Caselles (3rd series). As Type F 42.
F 233. 30 c. grn., brn. & myrtle 75 75
F 234. 50 c. brn., orge. & lake 1·10 1·10
F 235. 90 c. blue, pur. & brn. 1·75 1·75
DESIGNS: 30 c. St. John in temple at Ephesus. 50 c. St. John with cup of poison. 90 c. St. John disputing with pagan philosophers.

**1972.** Europa. As T 691 of France.
F 236. 50 c. multicoloured . . 4·50 4·50
F 237. 90 c. multicoloured . . 7·00 7·00

F 50. Golden Eagle.

**1972.** Nature Protection.
F238 F 50 60 c. ol, grn & pur 3·00 3·00

F 51. Rifle-shooting.

F 52. General De Gaulle.

**1972.** Olympic Games, Munich.
F 239. F 51. 1 f. purple . . . . 2·50 2·50

**1972.** Altar-screen, Church of St. John of Caselles (4th series). As Type F 42.
F 240. 30 c. pur., grey & grn. 70 70
F 241. 50 c. grey and blue . . 1·10 1·10
F 242. 90 c. green and blue . . 1·75 1·75
DESIGNS: 30 c. St. John in discussion with bishop. 50 c. St. John healing a cripple. 90 c. Angel with spear.

**1972.** 5th Anniv. of Gen. De Gaulle's Visit to Andorra.
F243 F 52 50 c. blue . . . . 1·50 1·50
F244 – 90 c. red . . . . 2·00 2·00
DESIGN: 90 c. Gen. De Gaulle in Andorra la Vella, 1967.
See also Nos. F434/5.

F 53. Europa "Posthorn".

**1973.** Europa.
F 245. F 53. 50 c. multicoloured 5·00 5·00
F 246. 90 c. multicoloured 8·00 8·00

F 54. "Virgin of Canolich" (wood carving).

F 55. Lily.

**1973.** Andorran Art.
F 247. F 54. 1 f. lilac, blue & drab 2·50 2·50

**1973.** Pyrenean Flowers (1st series). Mult.
F 248. 30 c. Type F 55 . . 40 40
F 249. 50 c. Columbine . . . . 1·25 1·25
F 250. 90 c. Wild pinks . . 75 75
See also Nos. F 253/5 and F 264/6.

F 56. Blue Tit.

F 57. "The Virgin of Pal".

**1973.** Nature Protection. Birds. Mult.
F 251. 90 c. Type F 56 . . . . 1·90 1·90
F 252. 1 f. Lesser spotted woodpecker . . . . 1·90 1·90
See also Nos. F 259/60.

**1974.** Pyrenean Wild Flowers (2nd series). As Type F 55. Multicoloured.
F 253. 45 c. Iris . . . . 20 15
F 254. 65 c. Tobacco Plant . . 35 35
F 255. 90 c. Narcissus . . 70 70

**1974.** Europa. Church Sculptures. Mult.
F 256. 50 c. Type F 57 . . . . 5·00 5·00
F 257. 90 c. "The Virgin of Santa Coloma" . . 9·00 9·00

F 58. Arms of Andorra.

F 59. Letters crossing Globe.

**1974.** Meeting of Co-Princes, Cahors.
F 258. F 58. 1 f. blue, violet and orange . . . . 1·25 1·25

**1974.** Nature Protection. Birds. As Type F 56. Multicoloured.
F 259. 60 c. Citril finch . . 2·25 2·25
F 260. 80 c. Bullfinch . . . . 2·25 2·25

**1974.** Cent. of Universal Postal Union
F 261. F 59. 1 f. 20 red, grey & brn. 1·50 1·50

F 60. " Calvary ".

**1975.** Europa. Paintings from La Cortinada Church. Multicoloured.
F 262. 80 c. Type F 60 .. .. 5·00 5·00
F 263. 1 f. 20 "Coronation of St. Martin (horiz.) .. 8·00 8·00

**1975.** Pyrenean Flowers (3rd series). As Type F 55.
F 264. 60 c. multicoloured .. 25 25
F 265. 80 c. multicoloured .. 1·25 1·25
F 266. 1 f. 20 yellow, red and green .. .. .. 60 60
DESIGNS: 60 c. Gentian. 80 c. Anemone. 1 f. 20, Colchicum.

F 61. " Arphila " Motif.

**1975.** " Arphila 75 " International Stamp Exhibition, Paris.
F 267. F 61. 2 f. red, grn. & blue 1·75 1·75

F 62. Pres. Pompidou (Co-prince of Andorra).
F 63. " La Pubilla " and Emblem.

**1976.** President Pompidou of France Commem.
F 268. F 62. 80 c. blk. & vio. .. 80 80

**1976.** International Women's Year.
F269 F 63 1 f. 20 blk, pur & bl 1·25 1·25

F 64. Skier. F 65. Telephone and Satellite.

**1976.** Winter Olympic Games, Innsbruck.
F 270. F 64. 1 f. 20 black, green and blue .. .. 1·10 1·10

**1976.** Telephone Centenary.
F 271. F 65. 1 f. grn., blk. & red 1·00 1·00

F 66. Catalan Forge.

**1976.** Europa.
F 272. F 66. 80 c. brn., bl. & grn. 1·25 1·25
F 273. – 1 f. 20 red, green and black .. 2·00 2·00
DESIGN: 1 f. 20, Andorran folk-weaving.

**HAVE YOU READ THE NOTES AT THE BEGINNING OF THIS CATALOGUE?**
These often provide answers to the enquiries we receive.

F 67. Thomas Jefferson.

F 68. Ball-trap (clay pigeon) Shooting.

**1976.** Bicent. of American Revolution.
F 274. F 67. 1 f. 20 deep green, brown and green 1·10 1·10

**1976.** Olympic Games, Montreal.
F 275. F 68. 2 f. brn., vio. & grn. 1·50 1·50

F 69. New Chapel.

**1976.** New Chapel of Our Lady, Meritxell.
F 276. F 69. 1 f. grn., pur. & brn. 85 85

F 70. Apollo.

F 71. Stoat.

**1976.** Nature Protection. Butterflies. Mult.
F277 80 c. Type F 70 .. .. 2·00 2·00
F278 1 f. 40 Camberwell beauty 1·25 1·25

**1977.** Nature Protection.
F 279. F 71. 1 f. grey, blk. & blue 1·25 1·25

F 72. Church of St. John of Caselles.

F 73. Book and Flowers.

**1977.** Europa.
F 280. F 72. 1 f. pur., grn. & bl. 1·50 1·50
F 281. – 1 f. 40 indigo, green & blue .. .. 1·75 1·75
DESIGN: 1 f. 40, St. Vicens Chateau.

**1977.** 1st Anniv. of Institute of Andorran Studies.
F 282. F 73. 80 c. brn., grn. & bl. 90 90

F 74. St. Roma.

**1977.** Reredos St. Roma's Chapel, Les Bons.
F283 F 74 2 f. multicoloured .. 1·25 1·25

F 75. General Council Assembly Hall.

F 76. Eurasian Red Squirrel.

**1977.** Andorran Institutions.
F 284. F 75. 1 f. 10 red, bl. & brn. 1·50 1·50
F 285. – 2 f. brown and red 1·25 1·25
DESIGN—VERT. 2 f. Don Guillem d'Areny Plandolit.

**1978.** Nature Protection.
F 286. F 76. 1 f. brn., grn. & olive 65 65

F 77. Escalls Bridge.

F 78. Church at Pal.

**1978.** 700th Anniv. of Parity Treaties (1st issue).
F287 F 77 80 c. green, brn & bl 60 60
See also No. F292.

**1978.** Europa.
F 288. F 78. 1 f. brown, green and red .. .. 1·75 1·75
F 289. – 1 f. 40 brown, blue and red .. .. 2·00 2·00
DESIGN: 1 f. 40, Charlemagne's House.

F 79. " Virgin of Sispony ".

**1978.** Andorran Art.
F 290. F 79. 2 f. multicoloured 1·25 1·25

F 80. Tribunal Meeting.

**1978.** Tribunal of Visura.
F 291. F 80. 1 f. 20 multicoloured 75 75

F 81. Treaty Text.

**1978.** 700th Anniv. of Parity Treaties (2nd issue).
F 292. F 81. 1 f. 50 brown, green and red .. .. 90 90

F 82. Chamois.

F 83. Rock Ptarmigans.

**1978.** Nature Protection.
F 293. F 82. 1 f. brown, light brown and blue 30 30

**1979.** Nature Protection.
F 294. F 83. 1 f. 20 multicoloured 1·10 1·10

F 84. Early 20th Century Postman and Church of St. John of Caselles.
F 85. Wall painting, Church of St. Cerni. Nagol.

**1979.** Europa.
F 295. F 84. 1 f. 20 black, brown and green .. 1·00 1·00
F 296. – 1 f. 70 brown, green and maroon .. 1·50 1·50
DESIGN: 1 f. 70, Old French Post Office, Andorra.

**1979.** Pre-Romanesque Art.
F 297. F 85. 2 f. green, pink and brown .. .. 90 90
See also No. F 309.

F 86. Boy with Sheep.

F 87. Co-Princes Monument (Luigiteruggi).

**1979.** International Year of the Child.
F 298. F 86. 1 f. 70 multicoloured 70 70

**1979.** Co-Princes Monument.
F 299. F 87. 2 f. deep green, green and red .. 90 90

F 88. Judo.

F 89. Cal Pal, La Cortinada.

**1979.** World Judo Championships, Paris.
F 300. F 88. 1 f. 30 black, deep blue and blue .. 60 60

**1980.**
F 301. F 89. 1 f. 10 brown, blue and green .. 50 50

F 90. Cross-country Skiing.

F 91. Charlemagne.

**1980.** Winter Olympics, Lake Placid.
F 302. F 90. 1 f. 80 ultramarine, blue and red .. 1·25 1·25

**1980.** Europa.
F 303. F 91. 1 f. 30 brown, chestnut and red .. 45 45
F 304. – 1 f. 80 green and brown .. .. 70 70
DESIGN: 1 f. 80, Napoleon I.

F 93. Dog's-tooth Violet.

F 94. Cyclists.

**1980.** Nature Protection. Multicoloured.
F306 1 f. 10 Type F 93 .. 40 40
F305 1 f. 30 Pyrenean lily .. 40 40

**1980.** World Cycling Championships.
F307. F 94. 1 f. 20 violet, mauve and brown .. 40 40

F 95. House of the Valleys.

**1980.** 400th Anniv. of Restoration of House of the Valleys (meeting place of Andorran General Council).
F 308. F 95. 1 f. 40 brown, violet and green .. 40 40

**1980.** Pre-Romanesque Art. As Type F 85. Multicoloured.
F309 2 f. Angel (wall painting, Church of St. Cerni, Nagol) (horiz) .. 1·00 1·00

F 97. Shepherds' Huts, Mereig.

**1981.** Architecture.
F 310. F 97. 1 f.40 brown & bl. 50 50

F 98. Bear Dance (Emcamp Carnival).

F 99. Bonelli's Warbler.

**1981.** Europa.
F 311. F 98. 1 f. 40 black, green and blue .. 50 50
F 312. – 2 f. black, blue and red .. .. 75 75
DESIGN: 2 f. El Contrapas (dance).

**1981.** Nature Protection. Birds. Mult.
F313 1 f. 20 Type F 99 .. 60 60
F314 1 f. 40 Wallcreeper .. 65 65

F 100. Fencing.

**1981.** World Fencing Championships, Clermont-Ferrand.
F 315. F 100. 2 f. blue and black 65 65

F 101. Chasuble of St. Martin (miniature).

**1981.** Art.
F 316. F 101. 3 f. multicoloured 1·25 1·25

F 102. Fountain, Sant Julia de Loria.

F 103. Symbolic Disabled.

**1981.** International Decade of Drinking Water.
F 317. F 102. 1 f. 60 blue & brn. 50 50

**1981.** International Year of Disabled Persons.
F 318 F 103 2 f. 30 bl, red & grn. 75 75

F 104. Scroll and Badge (creation of Andorran Executive Council, 1981).

F 105. Footballer running to right.

**1982.** Europa.
F 319. F 104. 1 f. 60 blue, brown and orange .. 60 60
F 320. – 2 f. 30 blue, black and orange .. 80 80
DESIGN: 2 f. 30, Hat and cloak (creation of Land Council,1419).

**1982.** World Cup Football Championship, Spain.
F 321. F 105. 1 f. 60 brown and red .. .. 60 60
F 322. – 2 f. 60 brown and red .. .. 80 80
DESIGN: 2 f. 60, Footballer running to left.

F 107. Wall Painting, La Cortinada Church.

**1982.** Romanesque Art.
F 324. F 107. 3 f. multicoloured 1·25 1·25

F 108. Wild Cat.

F 109. Dr. Robert Koch.

**1982.** Nature Protection.
F 325. F 108. 1 f. 80 black, green and grey 90 90
F 326. – 2 f. 60 brn. & grn. 90 90
DESIGN: 2 f. 60, Scots Pine.

**1982.** Cent. of Discovery of Tubercle Bacillus.
F 327. F 109. 2 f. 10 lilac .. 65 65

F 110. St. Thomas Aquinas.

F 111. Montgolfier and Charles Balloons over Tuileries, Paris.

**1982.** St. Thomas Aquinas Commemoration.
F 328. F 110. 2 f. deep brown, brown & grey 65 65

**1983.** Bicentenary of Manned Flight.
F 329. F 111. 2 f. grn., red & brn. 65 65

F 112. Silver Birch.

**1983.** Nature Protection.
F 330. F 112. 1 f. red, brown & green .. .. 30 30
F 331. – 1 f. 50 green, blue and brown .. 50 50
DESIGN: 1 f. 50, Brown trout.

F 113. Mountain Cheesery.

**1983.** Europa.
F 332. F 113. 1 f. pur. & vio... 70 70
F 333. – 2 f. 60 red, mauve and purple .. 1·10 1·10
DESIGN: 2 f. 60, Catalan forge.

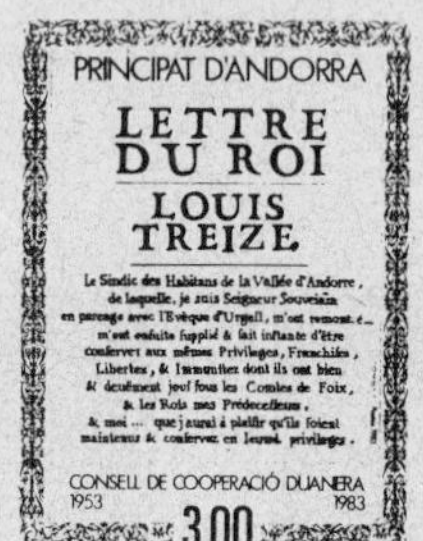


F 114. Royal Edict of Louis XIII.

**1983.** 30th Anniv. of Customs Co-operation Council.
F 334. F 114. 3 f. black & slate 90 90

**F 115. Early Coat of Arms.**

**1983.** Inscr "POSTES".
F335 F 115 5 c. green and red 10 10
F336 10 c. dp grn & grn 10 10
F337 20 c. violet & mve 10 10
F338 30 c. purple & vio 15 15
F339 40 c. blue & ultram 15 15
F340 50 c. black and red 15 10
F341 1 f. lake and red .. 20 15
F342 1 f. 90 green .. 1·50 1·50
F343 2 f. red and brown 75 50
F344 2 f. 10 green .. 70 50
F345 2 f. 20 red .. 50 50
F346 2 f. 30 red .. 75 50
F347 3 f. green & purple 1·00 1·00
F348 4 f. orange & brn 2·00 1·50
F349 5 f. brown and red 1·10 80
F350 10 f. red and brown 2·25 1·50
F351 15 f. grn & dp grn 3·50 2·75
F352 20 f. blue and brn 4·00 2·75

For design as Type F 115 but inscribed "LA POSTE" see Nos. F446/9.

F 116. Wall Painting, La Cortinada Church.

F 117. Plandolit House.

**1983.** Romanesque Art.
F 354. F 116. 4 f. multicoloured 1·50 1·50

**1983.**
F 355. F 117. 1 f. 60 brn. & grn. 45 45

F 118. Snowflakes and Olympic Torch.

**1984.** Winter Olympic Games, Sarajevo.
F 356. F 118. 2 f. 80 red, blue and green .. 90 90

F 119. Pyrenees and Council of Europe Emblem.

**1984.** Work Community of Pyrenees Region.
F 357. F 119. 3 f. bl. & brown 1·00 1·00

F 120. Bridge.

**1984.** Europa.
F 358. F 120. 2 f. green .. 75 75
F 359. 2 f. 80 red .. 1·00 1·00

F 121. Sweet Chestnut.

**1984.** Nature Protection.
F 360. F 121. 1 f. 70 grn., brn. and purple .. 55 55
F 361. – 2 f. 10 green and brown .. 70 70
DESIGN: 2 f. 10, Walnut.

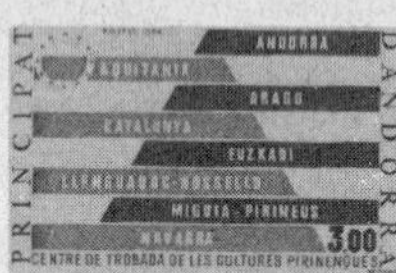


F 122. Centre Members.

**1984.** Pyrenean Cultures Centre, Andorra.
F 362. F 122. 3 f. blue, orange and red .. 90 90

F 123. "St. George" (detail of fresco, Church of St. Cerni, Nagol).

**1984.** Pre-Romanesque Art.
F 363. F 123. 5 f. multicoloured 1·50 1·50

F 124. Sant Julia Valley.

F 125. Title Page of "Le Val d'Andorre" (comic opera).

**1985.**
F 364. F 124. 2 f. green, olive and brown .. 75 75

**1985.** Europa.

F 365. F **125.** 2 f. 10 green .. 1·00 1·00
F 366. – 3 f. brown and deep brown .. 1·50 1·50

Design: 3 f. Musical instruments within frame.

F **126.** Teenagers holding up ball. F **127.** Mallard.

**1985.** International Youth Year.

F 367. F **126.** 3 f. red & brown 90 90

**1985.** Nature Protection. Multicoloured.

F 368. 1 f. 80 Type **127** .. .. 70 70
F 369. 2 f. 20 Goldfinch .. 90 90

F **128.** St. Cerni and Angel (fresco, Church of St. Cerni, Nagol).

**1985.** Pre-Romanesque Art.

F370 F **128** 5 f. multicoloured 1·50 1·50

F **130.** 1979 Europa Stamp.

**1986.** Inauguration of Postal Museum.

F 381. F **130.** 2 f. 20 brown and green .. .. 75 75

F **131.** Ansalonga. F **132.** Players

**1986.** Europa.

F 382. F **131.** 2 f. 20 black and blue .. .. 1·00 1·00
F 383. – 3 f. 20 black and green .. .. 1·75 1·75

Design: 3 f. 20, Pyrenean chamois.

**1986.** World Cup Football Championship, Mexico.

F 384. F **132.** 3 f. green, black and deep green 1·25 1·25

F **133.** Angonella Lakes.

**1986.**

F385 F **133** 2 f. 20 multicoloured 75 75

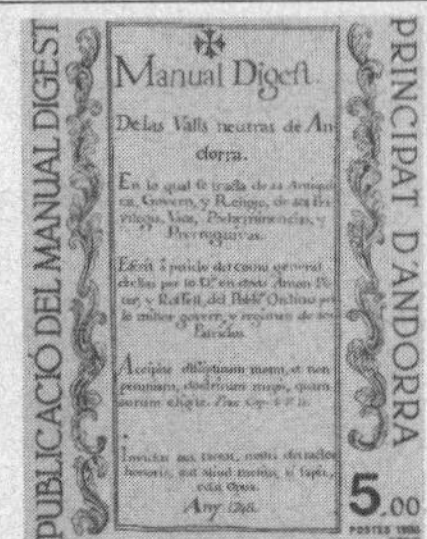


F **134.** Title Page of "Manual Digest", 1748.

**1986.** "Manual Digest".

F 386. F **134.** 5 f. black, olive and brown .. 1·50 1·50

F **135.** Dove with Twig. F **136.** St. Vincent's Chapel, Enclar.

**1986.** International Peace Year.

F387 F **135** 1 f. 90 blue & indigo 75 75

**1986.**

F 388. F **136.** 1 f. 90 brown, black & green 75 75

F **137.** Arms. F **138.** Meritxell Chapel.

**1987.** Visit of French Co-prince (French president).

F 389. F **137.** 2 f. 20 mult. .. 1·75 1·75

**1987.** Europa.

F 390. F **138.** 2 f. 20 purple and red .. .. 1·00 1·00
F 391. – 3 f. 40 violet and blue .. .. 1·50 1·50

Design: 3 f. 40, Ordino.

F **139.** Ransol. F **140.** Horse.

**1987.**

F 392. F **139.** 1 f. 90 mult. .. 90 90

**1987.** Nature Protection. Multicoloured.

F393 1 f. 90 Type F **140** .. 90 90
F394 2 f. 20 Isabel (moth) .. 1·25 1·25

F **141.** Arualsu (fresco, La Cortinada Church).

**1987.** Romanesque Art.

F395 F **141** 5 f. multicoloured 1·75 1·75

F **142.** Walker with Map by Signpost.

**1987.** Walking.

F 396. F **142.** 2 f. purple, green and deep green 75 75

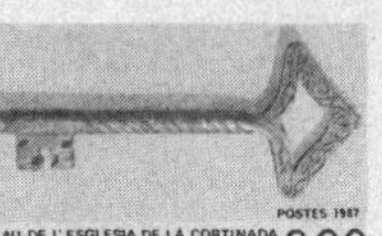

F **143.** Key. F **144.** Arms.

**1987.** La Cortinada Church Key.

F397 F **143** 3 f. multicoloured 1·25 1·25

**1988.**

F398 F **144** 2 f. 20 red .. 85 85
F399 2 f. 30 red .. 70 70
F400 2 f. 50 red .. 70 70
F401 2 f. 80 red .. 60 60

Nos. F400/1 are inscribed "LA POSTE".

F **145.** Bronze Boot and Mountains. F **146.** Players.

**1988.** Archaeology.

F407 F **145** 3 f. multicoloured 1·25 1·25

**1988.** Rugby.

F 408. F **146.** 2 f. 20 black, yell. and grn. 90 90

F **147.** Enclar Aerial. F **148.** Les Escaldes Hot Spring.

**1988.** Europa. Transport and Communications. Each green, brown and blue.

F 409. 2 f. 20 Type F **147** .. 1·00 1·00
F 410. 3 f. 60 Hand pointing to map on screen (tourist information) .. .. 1·50 1·50

**1988.**

F411 F **148** 2 f. 20 bl, brn & grn 90 90

F **149.** Ansalonga Pass. F **150.** Pyrenean Shepherd Dog.

**1988.**

F 412. F **149.** 2 f. blue, green and olive .. 75 75

**1988.** Nature Protection. Multicoloured.

F 413. 2 f. Type F **150** .. .. 85 85
F 414. 2 f. 20 Hare .. .. 95 95

F **151.** Fresco, Andorra La Vella Church.

**1988.** Romanesque Art.

F415. F **151.** 5 f. multicoloured 1·75 1·75

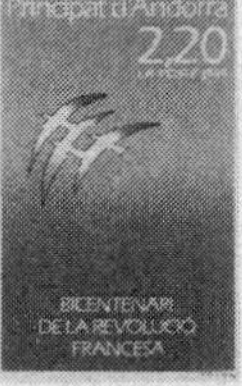

F **152** Birds F **153** Pal

**1989.** Bicentenary of French Revolution.

F416 F **152** 2 f. 20 violet, black and red .. .. 90 90

**1989.**

F417 F **153** 2 f. 20 violet & blue 90 90

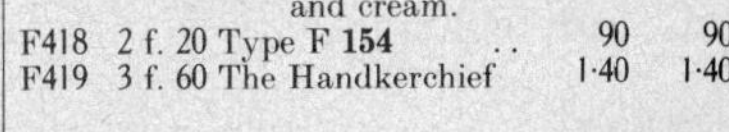

F **154** The Strong Horse

**1989.** Europa. Children's Games. Each brown and cream.

F418 2 f. 20 Type F **154** .. 90 90
F419 3 f. 60 The Handkerchief 1·40 1·40

F **155** Wounded Soldiers F **156** Archaeological Find and St. Vincent's Chapel, Enclar

**1989.** 125th Anniv of International Red Cross.

F420 F **155** 3 f. 60 brown, black and red .. 1·25 1·25

**1989.** Archaeology.

F421 F **156** 3 f. multicoloured 1·00 1·00

F **157** Wild Boar

**1989.** Nature Protection.

F422 F **157** 2 f. 20 black, green and brown .. 90 90
F423 – 3 f. 60 black, green and deep green 1·25 1·25

DESIGN: 3 f. 60, Palmate newt.

F **158** Retable of St. Michael de la Mosquera, Encamp

**1989.**

F424 F **158** 5 f. multicoloured 1·75 1·75

F 159 La Margineda Bridge

**1990.**

| | | | | |
|---|---|---|---|---|
| F425 | F 159 | 2 f. 30 blue, brown and turquoise .. | 75 | 75 |

F 160 Llorts Iron Ore Mines

**1990.**

| | | | | |
|---|---|---|---|---|
| F426 | F 160 | 3 f. 20 multicoloured | 1·00 | 1·00 |

F 161 Exterior of Old Post Office, Andorra La Vella

**1990.** Europa. Post Office Buildings.

| | | | | |
|---|---|---|---|---|
| F427 | F 161 | 2 f. 30 red & black | 75 | 75 |
| F428 | – | 3 f. 20 violet & red | 1·10 | 1·10 |

DESIGN: 3 f. 20, Interior of modern post office.

F 162 Censer, St. Roma's Chapel, Les Bons

F 163 Wild Roses

**1990.**

| | | | | |
|---|---|---|---|---|
| F429 | F 162 | 3 f. multicoloured | 1·00 | 1·00 |

**1990.** Nature Protection. Multicoloured.

| | | | |
|---|---|---|---|
| F430 | 2 f. 30 Type F 163 .. | 75 | 75 |
| F431 | 3 f. 20 Otter (horiz) .. | 1·10 | 1·10 |

F 164 Tobacco-drying Sheds, Les Bons

**1990.**

| | | | | |
|---|---|---|---|---|
| F432 | F 164 | 2 f. 30 yellow, black and red .. | 75 | 75 |

F 165 Part of Mural from Santa Coloma Church

**1990.**

| | | | | |
|---|---|---|---|---|
| F433 | F 165 | 5 f. multicoloured | 1·75 | 1·75 |

**1990.** Birth Centenary of Charles de Gaulle (French statesman). As Nos. F243/4 but values and inscriptions changed.

| | | | | |
|---|---|---|---|---|
| F434 | F 52 | 2 f. 30 blue .. | 80 | 80 |
| F435 | | 3 f. 20 red .. | 1·10 | 1·10 |

F 166 Coin from St. Eulalia's Church, Encamp

**1990.**

| | | | | |
|---|---|---|---|---|
| F436 | F 166 | 3 f. 20 multicoloured | 1·10 | 1·10 |

F 167 Chapel of Sant Roma Dels Vilars

F 168 Emblem and Track

**1991.**

| | | | | |
|---|---|---|---|---|
| F437 | F 167 | 2 f. 50 bl, blk & grn | 75 | 75 |

**1991.** 4th European Small States Games.

| | | | | |
|---|---|---|---|---|
| F438 | F 168 | 2 f. 50 multicoloured | 80 | 80 |

F 169 Television Satellite

F 170 Bottles

**1991.** Europa. Europe in Space. Mult.

| | | | |
|---|---|---|---|
| F439 | 2 f. 50 Type F 169 .. | 90 | 90 |
| F440 | 3 f. 50 Globe, telescope and eye (horiz) .. | 1·25 | 1·25 |

**1991.** Artefacts from Tomb of St. Vincent of Enclar.

| | | | | |
|---|---|---|---|---|
| F441 | F 170 | 3 f. 20 multicoloured | 1·10 | 1·10 |

F 171 Sheep

**1991.** Nature Protection.

| | | | | |
|---|---|---|---|---|
| F442 | F 171 | 2 f. 50 brn, bl & blk | 80 | 80 |
| F443 | – | 3 f. 50 brown, mauve and black | 1·10 | 1·10 |

DESIGN: 3 f. 50, Pyrenean cow.

F 172 Players

**1991.** World Petanque Championship, Engordany.

| | | | | |
|---|---|---|---|---|
| F444 | F 172 | 2 f. 50 black, bistre and red .. | 85 | 85 |

F 173 Mozart, Quartet and Organ Pipes

**1991.** Death Bicentenary of Wolfgang Amadeus Mozart (composer).

| | | | | |
|---|---|---|---|---|
| F445 | F 173 | 3 f. 40 bl, blk & turq | 1·25 | 1·25 |

**1991.** As Type F 115 but inscr "LA POSTE".

| | | | | |
|---|---|---|---|---|
| F446 | F 115 | 2 f. 20 green .. | 60 | 50 |
| F447 | | 2 f. 40 green .. | 60 | 50 |
| F448 | | 2 f. 50 red .. | 60 | 50 |
| F449 | | 2 f. 70 green .. | 70 | 70 |
| F450 | | 2 f. 80 red .. | 60 | 50 |
| F451 | | 3 f. red .. .. | 80 | 80 |

F 174 "Virgin of the Remedy of Sant Julia and Sant Germa"

F 175 Slalom

**1991.**

| | | | | |
|---|---|---|---|---|
| F455 | F 174 | 5 f. multicoloured | 1·25 | 1·25 |

**1992.** Winter Olympic Games, Albertville. Multicoloured.

| | | | |
|---|---|---|---|
| F456 | 2 f. 50 Type F 175 .. | 80 | 80 |
| F457 | 3 f. 40 Figure skating .. | 1·25 | 1·25 |

F 176 St. Andrew's Church, Arinsal

**1992.**

| | | | | |
|---|---|---|---|---|
| F458 | F 176 | 2 f. 50 black & buff | 75 | 75 |

F 177 Navigation Instrument and Columbus's Fleet

F 178 Canoeing

**1992.** Europa. 500th Anniv of Discovery of America by Columbus. Multicoloured.

| | | | |
|---|---|---|---|
| F459 | 2 f. 50 Type F 177 .. | 80 | 80 |
| F460 | 3 f. 40 Fleet, Columbus and Amerindians .. | 1·25 | 1·25 |

**1992.** Olympic Games, Barcelona. Mult.

| | | | |
|---|---|---|---|
| F461 | 2 f. 50 Type F 178 .. | 80 | 80 |
| F462 | 3 f. 40 Shooting .. | 1·25 | 1·25 |

F 179 Globe Flowers

F 180 "Martyrdom of St. Eulalia" (altarpiece, St. Eulalia's Church, Encamp)

**1992.** Nature Protection. Multicoloured.

| | | | |
|---|---|---|---|
| F463 | 2 f. 50 Type F 179 .. | 80 | 80 |
| F464 | 3 f. 40 Griffon vulture (horiz) .. .. | 1·25 | 1·25 |

**1992.**

| | | | | |
|---|---|---|---|---|
| F465 | F 180 | 4 f. multicoloured | 1·25 | 1·25 |

F 181 "Ordino Arcalis 91" (Mauro Staccioli)

**1992.** Modern Sculpture. Multicoloured.

| | | | |
|---|---|---|---|
| F466 | 5 f. Type F 181 .. .. | 1·50 | 1·50 |
| F467 | 5 f. "Storm in a Teacup" (Dennis Oppenheim) (horiz) .. .. | 1·50 | 1·50 |

F 182 Grau Roig

F 183 "Estructures Autogeneradores" (Jorge du Bon)

**1993.** Ski Resorts. Multicoloured.

| | | | |
|---|---|---|---|
| F468 | 2 f. 50 Type F 182 .. | 80 | 80 |
| F469 | 2 f. 50 Ordino .. .. | 80 | 80 |
| F470 | 2 f. 50 Soldeu el Tarter .. | 80 | 80 |
| F471 | 3 f. 40 Pal .. .. | 1·25 | 1·25 |
| F472 | 3 f. 40 Arinsal .. .. | 1·25 | 1·25 |

**1993.** Europa. Contemporary Art.

| | | | | |
|---|---|---|---|---|
| F473 | F 183 | 2 f. 50 deep blue, blue and violet | 85 | 85 |
| F474 | – | 3 f. 40 mult .. | 1·25 | 1·25 |

DESIGN—HORIZ. 3 f. 40, "Fisicromia per Andorra" (Carlos Cruz-Diez).

F 184 Common Blue

F 185 Cyclist

**1993.** Nature Protection. Butterflies. Mult.

| | | | |
|---|---|---|---|
| F475 | 2 f. 50 Type F 184 .. | 80 | 80 |
| F476 | 4 f. 20 "Nymphalidae" .. | 1·25 | 1·25 |

**1993.** Tour de France Cycling Road Race.

| | | | | |
|---|---|---|---|---|
| F477 | F 185 | 2 f. 50 multicoloured | 80 | 80 |

F 186 Smiling Hands

**1993.** 10th Anniv of Andorran School.

| | | | | |
|---|---|---|---|---|
| F478 | F 186 | 2 f. 80 multicoloured | 80 | 80 |

F 187 "A Pagan Place" (Michael Warren)

**1993.** Modern Sculpture.

| | | | | |
|---|---|---|---|---|
| F479 | F 187 | 5 f. black and blue | 1·25 | 1·25 |
| F480 | – | 5 f. multicoloured | 1·25 | 1·25 |

DESIGN: No. F480, "Pep, Lu, Canolic, Ton, Meritxell, Roma, Anna, Pau, Carles, Eugenia,....and Others" (Erik Dietman).

**MORE DETAILED LISTS**
are given in the Stanley Gibbons Catalogues referred to in the country headings.
For lists of current volumes see Introduction.

F 188 Cross-country Skiing

F 189 Constitution Monument

**1994.** Winter Olympic Games, Lillehammer, Norway.
F481 F **188** 3 f. 70 multicoloured 1·10 1·10

**1994.** 1st Anniv of New Constitution.
F482 F **189** 2 f. 80 mult .. 80 80
F483 – 3 f. 70 black, yellow and mauve .. 1·10 1·10
DESIGN: 3 f. 70, Stone tablet.

F **190** AIDS Virus

**1994.** Europa. Discoveries and Inventions. Multicoloured.
F484 2 f. 80 Type F **190** .. 80 80
F485 3 f. 70 Radio mast .. 1·10 1·10

F **191** Competitors' Flags and Football

F **192** Horse Riding

**1994.** World Cup Football Championship, U.S.A.
F486 F **191** 3 f. 70 multicoloured 1·10 1·10

**1994.** Tourist Activities. Multicoloured.
F487 2 f. 80 Type F **192** .. 80 80
F488 2 f. 80 Mountain biking 80 80
F489 2 f. 80 Climbing .. 80 80
F490 2 f. 80 Fishing .. 80 80

F **193** Scarce Swallowtail

F **194** "26 10 93"

**1994.** Nature Protection. Butterflies. Mult.
F491 2 f. 80 Type F **193** .. 80 80
F492 4 f. 40 Small tortoiseshell 1·25 1·25

**1994.** Meeting of Co-Princes.
F493 F **194** 2 f. 80 multicoloured 70 70

F **195** Emblem

F **196** Globe, Goal and Player

**1995.** European Nature Conservation Year.
F494 F **195** 2 f. 80 multicoloured 70 70

**1995.** 3rd World Cup Rugby Championship, South Africa.
F495 F **196** 2 f. 80 multicoloured 70 70

F **197** Dove and Olive Twig ("Peace")

**1995.** Europa. Peace and Freedom. Mult.
F496 2 f. 80 Type F **197** .. 70 70
F497 3 f. 70 Flock of doves ("Freedom") .. .. 90 90

F **198** Emblem

**1995.** 15th Anniv of Caritas Andorrana (welfare organization).
F498 F **198** 2 f. 80 multicoloured 70 70

F **199** Caldea Thermal Baths, Les Escaldes-Engordany

**1995.**
F499 F **199** 2 f. 80 multicoloured 70 70

F **200** National Auditorium, Ordino

**1995.**
F500 F **200** 3 f. 70 black & buff 90 90

F **201** "Virgin of Merixtell"

**1995.**
F501 F **201** 4 f. 40 multicoloured 1·25 1·25

F **202** Brimstone

F **203** National Flag over U.N. Emblem

**1995.** Nature Protection. Butterflies. Mult.
F502 2 f. 80 Type F **202** .. 70 70
F503 3 f. 70 Marbled white (horiz) .. .. 90 90

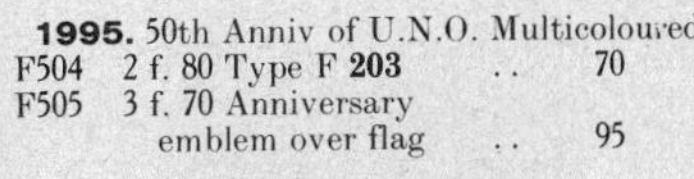

**1995.** 50th Anniv of U.N.O. Multicoloured.
F504 2 f. 80 Type F **203** .. 70 70
F505 3 f. 70 Anniversary emblem over flag .. 95 95

F **204** National Flag and Palace of Europe, Strasbourg

**1995.** Admission of Andorra to Council of Europe.
F506 F **204** 2 f. 80 mult .. 70 70

F **205** Emblem

F **206** Basketball

**1996.** 4th Borrufa Trophy Skiing Competition.
F507 F **205** 2 f. 80 mult .. 70 70

**1996.**
F508 F **206** 3 f. 70 red, black and yellow .. 95 95

F **207** Children

**1996.** 25th Anniv of Our Lady of Merixtell Special School.
F509 F **207** 2 f. 80 mult .. 70 70

F **208** European Robin

**1996.** Nature Protection. Multicoloured.
F510 3 f. Type F **208** .. .. 80 80
F511 3 f. 80 Great tit .. .. 1·00 1·00

F **209** Cross, St. James's Church, Engordany

F **210** Ermessenda de Castellbo

**1996.** Religious Objects. Multicoloured.
F512 3 f. Type F **209** .. .. 80 80
F513 3 f. 80 Censer St. Eulalia's Church, Encamp (horiz) .. 1·00 1·00

**1996.** Europa. Famous Women.
F514 F **210** 3 f. multicoloured 80 80

F **211** Chessman

F **212** Canillo

**1996.** Chess.
F515 F **211** 4 f. 50 red, blk & bl 1·10 1·10

**1996.** No value expressed. Self-adhesive.
F516 F **212** (3 f.) multicoloured 80 80

F **213** Cycling, Running and Throwing the Javelin

**1996.** Olympic Games, Atlanta.
F517 F **213** 3 f. multicoloured 80 80

POSTAGE DUE STAMPS

**1931.** Postage Due stamps of France optd. **ANDORRE.**
FD 24. D **11.** 5 c. blue.. .. 1·25 1·50
FD 25. 10 c. brown .. 1·25 1·50
FD 26. 30 c. red.. .. 50 75
FD 27. 50 c. purple .. 1·25 1·50
FD 28. 60 c. green .. 14·00 15·00
FD 29. 1 f. brown on yellow .. 1·00 1·25
FD 30. 2 f. mauve .. 8·50 9·00
FD 31. 3 f. mauve .. 1·50 1·75

**1931.** Postage Due Stamps of France optd. **ANDORRE.**
FD 32. D **43.** 1 c. green .. 1·25 1·50
FD 33. 10 c. red .. 2·75 4·00
FD 34. 60 c. red.. .. 15·00 22·00
FD 35. 1 f. green .. 75·00 £100
FD 36. 1 f. 20 on 2 f. blue 50·00 65·00
FD 37. 2 f. brown .. £120 £150
FD 38. 5 f. on 1 f. purple 60·00 75·00

FD **7.**

FD **10.**

FD **11.** Wheat Sheaves.

**1935.**
FD 82. FD **7.** 1 c. green .. 1·75 2·00

**1937.**
FD 97. FD **10.** 5 c. blue .. 5·00 6·00
FD 98. 10 c. brown .. 5·00 6·00
FD 99. 2 f. mauve .. 6·00 5·00
FD 100. 5 f. orange .. 11·00 12·50

**1943.**
FD 101a. FD **11.** 10 c. brown .. 35 40
FD 102. 30 c. mauve .. 60 70
FD 103. 50 c. green .. 70 85
FD 104. 1 f. blue .. 40 50
FD 105. 1 f. 50 red .. 4·00 4·75
FD 106. 2 f. blue .. 75 90
FD 107. 3 f. red .. 1·50 1·75
FD 108. 4 f. violet .. 3·50 4·00
FD 109. 5 f. mauve .. 2·50 2·75
FD 110. 10 f. orange .. 3·50 4·00
FD 111. 20 f. brown .. 4·50 5·00

**1946.** As Type FD **11,** but inscribed "TIMBRE-TAXE".
FD 143. 10 c. brown .. .. 50 60
FD 144. 1 f. blue .. .. 50 60
FD 145. 2 f. blue .. .. 60 70
FD 146. 3 f. brown .. .. 1·75 2·00
FD 147. 4 f. violet .. .. 2·75 3·00
FD 148. 5 f. red .. .. .. 1·75 2·00
FD 149. 10 f. orange .. .. 2·50 2·75
FD 150. 20 f. brown .. .. 6·00 7·00
FD 151. 50 f. green .. .. 23·00 24·00
FD 152. 100 f. green .. .. 80·00 85·00

**1961.** As Nos. FD143/52 but new values and colours.
FD 185. 5 c. red.. .. .. 3·00 3·50
FD 186. 10 c. orange .. .. 6·00 7·00
FD 187. 20 c. brown .. .. 9·00 10·00
FD 188. 50 c. green .. .. 15·00 17·00

**1964.** Designs as Nos. D 1650/6 of France, but inscr. "ANDORRE".
FD 192. 5 c. red, grn. & pur. .. 10 10
FD 193. 10 c. blue, grn. & pur. 10 10
FD 194. 15 c. red, green & brn. 10 10
FD 195. 20 c. pur., grn. & turq. 20 20
FD 196. 30 c. blue, grn. & brn. 25 25
FD 197. 40 c. yell., red & grn. 30 30
FD 198. 50 c. red, grn. & blue 40 40

FD **129.** Holly Berries.

**1985.** Fruits.
FD 371. FD **129.** 10 c. red and green .. 10 10
FD 372. – 20 c. brown and blue 10 10
FD 373. – 30 c. green and red 10 10
FD 374. – 40 c. brown and black 15 15
FD 375. – 50 c. olive and violet 20 20
FD 376. – 1 f. green and blue .. 40 40
FD 377. – 2 f. red and brown .. 80 80
FD 378. – 3 f. purple and green 1·25 1·25
FD 379. – 4 f. olive and blue .. 1·50 1·50
FD 380. – 5 f. olive and red .. 1·90 1·90

DESIGNS: 20 c. Wild plum. 30 c. Raspberry. 40 c. Dogberry. 50 c. Blackberry. 1 f. Juniper. 2 f. Rose hip. 3 f. Elder. 4 f. Bilberry. 5 f. Strawberry.

## SPANISH POST OFFICES

100 centimos = 1 peseta.

**1928.** Stamps of Spain optd. **CORREOS ANDORRA.**

| No. | Type | Description | Mint | Used |
|---|---|---|---|---|
| 1. | **68.** | 2 c. green .. .. | 50 | 50 |
| 2. | | 5 c. red .. .. .. | 75 | 75 |
| 3. | | 10 c. green .. .. | 1·00 | 1·00 |
| 5. | | 15 c. blue .. .. | 1·75 | 1·75 |
| 6. | | 20 c. violet .. .. | 1·75 | 1·75 |
| 7. | | 25 c. red .. .. | 2·50 | 2·50 |
| 8. | | 30 c. brown .. .. | 8·00 | 8·00 |
| 9. | | 40 c. blue .. .. | 8·50 | 8·50 |
| 10. | | 50 c. orange .. .. | 8·50 | 8·50 |
| 11. | **69.** | 1 p. grey .. .. | 12·50 | 12·50 |
| 12. | | 4 p. red .. .. | 70·00 | 70·00 |
| 13. | | 10 p. brown .. .. | 95·00 | 95·00 |

**2.** House of the Valleys. **3.** General Council of Andorra.

**1929.**

| No. | Type | Description | Mint | Used |
|---|---|---|---|---|
| 14 | **2** | 2 c. green .. .. | 1·00 | 1·00 |
| 26 | | 2 c. brown .. .. | 1·00 | 1·00 |
| 15 | – | 5 c. purple .. .. | 2·00 | 2·00 |
| 27 | – | 5 c. brown .. .. | 1·25 | 1·25 |
| 16 | – | 10 c. green .. .. | 2·00 | 2·00 |
| 17 | – | 15 c. blue .. .. | 2·50 | 2·50 |
| 30 | – | 15 c. green .. .. | 3·50 | 3·50 |
| 18 | – | 20 c. violet .. .. | 2·50 | 2·50 |
| 33 | – | 25 c. red .. .. | 1·50 | 1·50 |
| 20 | **2** | 30 c. brown .. .. | 70·00 | 35·00 |
| 34 | | 30 c. red .. .. | 1·50 | 1·25 |
| 21 | – | 40 c. blue .. .. | 3·00 | 3·00 |
| 36 | **2** | 45 c. red .. .. | 1·00 | 75 |
| 22 | – | 50 c. orange .. .. | 3·00 | 3·00 |
| 38 | **2** | 60 c. blue .. .. | 3·00 | 3·00 |
| 23 | **3** | 1 p. slate .. .. | 11·00 | 11·00 |
| 39 | | 4 p. purple .. .. | 38·00 | 38·00 |
| 40 | | 10 p. brown .. .. | 42·00 | 42·00 |

DESIGNS: 5, 40 c. Church of St. John of Caselles. 10, 20, 50 c. Sant Julia de Loria. 15, 25 c. Santa Coloma Church.

**7.** Councillor Manuel Areny Bons. **11.** Map.

**1948.**

| No. | Type | Description | Mint | Used |
|---|---|---|---|---|
| 41. | F. | 2 c. olive .. .. | 35 | 1·00 |
| 42. | | 5 c. orange .. .. | 35 | 1·00 |
| 43. | | 10 c. blue .. .. | 35 | 1·00 |
| 44. | **7.** | 20 c. purple .. .. | 4·00 | 1·00 |
| 45. | | 25 c. orange .. .. | 4·00 | 1·00 |
| 46. | G. | 30 c. green .. .. | 10·00 | 3·00 |
| 47. | H. | 50 c. green .. .. | 15·00 | 3·50 |
| 48. | I. | 75 c. blue .. .. | 14·00 | 4·00 |
| 49. | H. | 90 c. purple .. .. | 2·00 | 1·50 |
| 50. | I. | 1 p. red .. .. | 14·00 | 4·00 |
| 51. | G. | 1 p. 35 violet .. .. | 6·00 | 6·00 |
| 52. | **11.** | 4 p. blue .. .. | 11·00 | 7·00 |
| 53. | | 10 p. brown .. .. | 20·00 | 8·00 |

DESIGNS—VERT. F, Edelweiss. G, Arms. H, Market Place, Ordino. I, Shrine near Meritxell Chapel.

**12.** Andorra La Vella. **13.** St. Anthony's Bridge.

**1951.** Air.

| No. | Type | Description | Mint | Used |
|---|---|---|---|---|
| 54. | **12.** | 1 p. brown .. .. | 17·00 | 7·00 |

**1963.**

| No. | Type | Description | Mint | Used |
|---|---|---|---|---|
| 55. | **13.** | 25 c. brown and black .. | 20 | 10 |
| 56. | – | 70 c. black and green .. | 20 | 20 |
| 57. | – | 1 p. lilac and grey .. | 30 | 15 |
| 58. | – | 2 p. violet and lilac .. | 30 | 20 |
| 59. | – | 2 p. 50 deep red and purple .. .. | 70 | 70 |
| 60. | – | 3 p. slate and black .. | 60 | 40 |
| 61. | – | 5 p. purple and brown .. | 2·00 | 2·00 |
| 62. | – | 6 p. red and brown .. | 2·50 | 2·00 |

DESIGNS—VERT. 70 c. Anyos meadows (wrongly inscr. AYNOS). 1 p. Canillo. 2 p. Santa Coloma Church. 2 p. 50, Arms. 6 p. Virgin of Meritxell. HORIZ. 3 p. Andorra la Vella. 5 p. Ordino.

**14.** Daffodills. **15.** "Communications".

**1966.** Pyrenean Flowers.

| No. | Type | Description | Mint | Used |
|---|---|---|---|---|
| 63. | **14.** | 50 c. blue and slate .. | 10 | 10 |
| 64. | – | 1 p. purple and brown .. | 20 | 20 |
| 65. | – | 5 p. blue and green .. | 2·00 | 1·75 |
| 66. | – | 10 p. slate and violet .. | 1·00 | 1·00 |

DESIGNS: 1 p. Carnation. 5 p. Narcissus. 10 p. Anemone (wrongly inscr. "HELEBORUS CONI").

**1972.** Europa.

| No. | Type | Description | Mint | Used |
|---|---|---|---|---|
| 67. | **15.** | 8 p. multicoloured .. | 80·00 | 70·00 |

**16.** Encamp Valley. **17.** Volleyball.

**1972.** Tourist Views. Multicoloured.

| No. | Description | Mint | Used |
|---|---|---|---|
| 68. | 1 p. Type **16** .. .. | 50 | 30 |
| 69. | 1 p. 50 La Massana .. | 60 | 60 |
| 70. | 2 p. Skis and snowscape, Pas de la Casa .. | 1·25 | 1·00 |
| 71. | 5 p. Lake Pessons (horiz.) | 1·50 | 90 |

**1972.** Olympic Games, Munich. Mult.

| No. | Description | Mint | Used |
|---|---|---|---|
| 72. | 2 p. Type **17** .. .. | 30 | 30 |
| 73. | 5 p. Swimming (horiz.) .. | 40 | 40 |

**18.** St. Anthony's Auction.

**1972.** Andorran Customs. Multicoloured.

| No. | Description | Mint | Used |
|---|---|---|---|
| 74. | 1 p. Type **18** .. .. | 15 | 10 |
| 75. | 1 p. 50 "Les Caramelles" (choir) .. .. | 20 | 20 |
| 76. | 2 p. Nativity play (Christmas) .. | 20 | 15 |
| 77. | 5 p. Giant Cigar (vert.) .. | 60 | 45 |
| 78. | 8 p. Carved shrine, Meritxell (vert.) .. .. | 75 | 75 |
| 79. | 15 p. "La Marratxa" (dance) .. .. | 1·25 | 75 |

**19.** "Peoples of Europe." **20.** "The Nativity".

**1973.** Europa.

| No. | Type | Description | Mint | Used |
|---|---|---|---|---|
| 80. | **19.** | 2 p. black, red & blue .. | 20 | 15 |
| 81. | – | 8 p. red, brown and black .. .. | 70 | 40 |

DESIGN: 8 p. Europa "Posthorn".

**1973.** Christmas. Frescoes from Meritxell Chapel. Multicoloured.

| No. | Description | Mint | Used |
|---|---|---|---|
| 82. | 2 p. Type **20** .. .. | 20 | 15 |
| 83. | 5 p. "Adoration of the Kings" .. .. | 60 | 40 |

**21.** "Virgin of Ordino". **22.** Oak Cupboard and Shelves.

**1974.** Europa. Sculptures. Multicoloured.

| No. | Description | Mint | Used |
|---|---|---|---|
| 84. | 2 p. Type **21** .. .. | 1·00 | 75 |
| 85. | 8 p. Cross .. .. | 2·00 | 2·00 |

**1974.** Arts and Crafts. Multicoloured.

| No. | Description | Mint | Used |
|---|---|---|---|
| 86. | 10 p. Type **22** .. .. | 1·75 | 1·00 |
| 87. | 25 p. Crown of the Virgin of the Roses .. .. | 2·75 | 1·50 |

**23.** U.P.U. Monument, Berne.

**1974.** Cent. of Universal Postal Union.

| No. | Type | Description | Mint | Used |
|---|---|---|---|---|
| 88. | **23.** | 15 p. multicoloured .. | 1·25 | 1·00 |

**24.** "The Nativity".

**1974.** Christmas. Carvings from Meritxell Chapel. Multicoloured.

| No. | Description | Mint | Used |
|---|---|---|---|
| 89. | 2 p. Type **24** .. .. | 50 | 35 |
| 90. | 5 p. "Adoration of the Kings" .. .. | 1·60 | 1·25 |

**25.** 19th-century Postman and Church of St. John of Caselles. **26.** "Peasant with Knife".

**1975.** "Espana 75" International Stamp Exhibition, Madrid.

| No. | Type | Description | Mint | Used |
|---|---|---|---|---|
| 91. | **25.** | 3 p. multicoloured | 20 | 20 |

**1975.** Europa. 12th-century Romanesque Paintings from La Cortinada Church. Mult.

| No. | Description | Mint | Used |
|---|---|---|---|
| 92. | 3 p. Type **26** .. .. | 1·00 | 75 |
| 93. | 12 p. "Christ" .. .. | 1·75 | 1·50 |

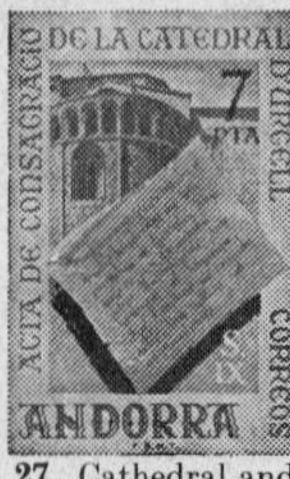


**27.** Cathedral and Consecration Text.

**1975.** 1100th Anniv. of Consecration of Urgel Cathedral.

| No. | Type | Description | Mint | Used |
|---|---|---|---|---|
| 94. | **27.** | 7 p. multicoloured .. | 1·25 | 1·25 |

**28.** "The Nativity".

**1975.** Christmas Paintings from La Cortinada Church. Multicoloured.

| No. | Description | Mint | Used |
|---|---|---|---|
| 95. | 3 p. Type **28** .. .. | 35 | 35 |
| 96. | 7 p. "Adoration of The Kings" .. .. .. | 50 | 50 |

**29.** Copper Cauldron. **30.** Slalom Skiing.

**1976.** Europa. Multicoloured.

| No. | Description | Mint | Used |
|---|---|---|---|
| 97 | 3 p. Type **29** .. .. | 25 | 25 |
| 98 | 12 p. Wooden marriage chest (horiz) .. .. | 85 | 85 |

**1976.** Olympic Games, Montreal. Mult.

| No. | Description | Mint | Used |
|---|---|---|---|
| 99. | 7 p. Type **30** .. .. | 25 | 25 |
| 100. | 15 p. Canoeing (horiz.) .. | 60 | 60 |

**31.** "The Nativity".

**1976.** Christmas. Carvings from La Massana Church. Multicoloured.

| No. | Description | Mint | Used |
|---|---|---|---|
| 101. | 3 p. Type **31** .. .. | 15 | 15 |
| 102. | 25 p. "Adoration of the Kings" .. .. .. | 55 | 55 |

**32.** Ansalonga.

**1977.** Europa. Multicoloured.

| No. | Description | Mint | Used |
|---|---|---|---|
| 103. | 3 p. Type **32** .. .. | 20 | 20 |
| 104. | 12 p. Xuclar .. .. | 55 | 55 |

**33.** Boundary Cross.

**1977.** Christmas. Multicoloured.

| No. | Description | Mint | Used |
|---|---|---|---|
| 105. | 5 p. Type **33** .. .. | 25 | 25 |
| 106. | 12 p. St. Michael's Church, Engolasters .. .. | 60 | 60 |

**35.** House of the Valleys.

**1978.** Europa. Multicoloured.

| No. | Description | Mint | Used |
|---|---|---|---|
| 108 | 5 p. Type **35** .. .. | 20 | 20 |
| 109 | 12 p. Church of St. John of Caselles .. .. | 50 | 50 |

**36.** Crown, Mitre and Crook. **37.** "Holy Family".

**1978.** 700th Anniv. of Parity Treaties.

| No. | Type | Description | Mint | Used |
|---|---|---|---|---|
| 110. | **36.** | 5 p. multicoloured .. | 35 | 35 |

**1978.** Christmas. Frescoes in St. Mary's Church, Encamp. Multicoloured.
111. 5 p. Type **37** .. .. 10 10
112. 25 p. "Adoration of the Kings" .. .. .. 45 45

**38.** Young Woman's Costume. **39.** Old Post Bus.

**1979.** Local Costumes. Multicoloured.
113. 3 p. Type **38** .. .. 10 10
114. 5 p. Young man's costume 10 10
115. 12 p. Newly-weds .. .. 25 25

**1979.** Europa.
116 **39** 5 p. green & blue on yell 20 20
117 – 12 p. lilac & red on yell 50 50
DESIGN: 12 p. Pre-stamp letters.

**40.** Drawing of Boy and Girl. **41.** Agnus Dei, Santa Coloma Church.

**1979.** International Year of the Child.
118. **40.** 19 p. blue, red and black .. .. 30 30

**1979.** Christmas. Multicoloured.
119. **41.** 8 p. Sant Coloma Church .. .. 15 15
120. 25 p. Type **41** .. .. 35 35

**42.** Pere d'Urg. **43.** Antoni Fiter i Rosell.

**1979.** Bishops of Urgel, Co-princes of Andorra (1st series).
121 **42** 1 p. blue and brown .. 10 10
122 – 5 p. red and violet .. 10 10
123 – 13 p. brown and green 20 20
DESIGNS: 5 p. Joseph Caixal. 13 p. Joan Benlloch.
See also Nos. 137/8, 171, 182 and 189.

**1980.** Europa.
124. **43.** 8 p. brown, ochre and green .. .. 15 15
125. – 19 p. black, green and deep green .. .. 30 30
DESIGN: 19 p. Francesc Cairat i Freixes.

**44.** Skiing.

**1980.** Olympic Games, Moscow.
126. **44.** 5 p. turq., red and blk. 10 10
127. – 8 p. multicoloured .. 10 10
128. – 50 p. multicoloured .. 45 45
DESIGNS: 8 p. Boxing. 50 p. Shooting.



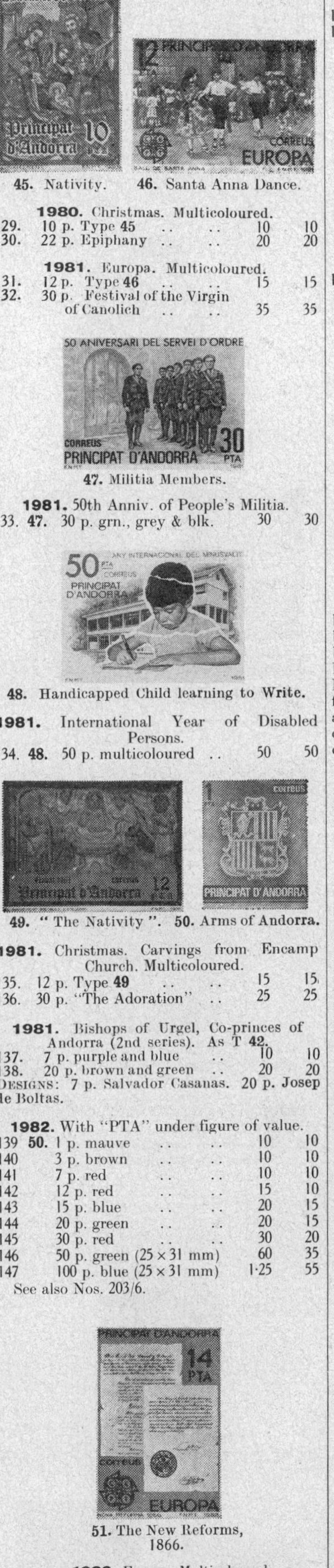

**45.** Nativity. **46.** Santa Anna Dance.

**1980.** Christmas. Multicoloured.
129. 10 p. Type **45** .. .. 10 10
130. 22 p. Epiphany .. .. 20 20

**1981.** Europa. Multicoloured.
131. 12 p. Type **46** .. .. 15 15
132. 30 p. Festival of the Virgin of Canolich .. .. 35 35

**47.** Militia Members.

**1981.** 50th Anniv. of People's Militia.
133. **47.** 30 p. grn., grey & blk. 30 30

**48.** Handicapped Child learning to Write.

**1981.** International Year of Disabled Persons.
134. **48.** 50 p. multicoloured .. 50 50

**49.** "The Nativity". **50.** Arms of Andorra.

**1981.** Christmas. Carvings from Encamp Church. Multicoloured.
135. 12 p. Type **49** .. .. 15 15
136. 30 p. "The Adoration" .. 25 25

**1981.** Bishops of Urgel, Co-princes of Andorra (2nd series). As T **42**.
137. 7 p. purple and blue .. 10 10
138. 20 p. brown and green .. 20 20
DESIGNS: 7 p. Salvador Casanas. 20 p. Josep de Boltas.

**1982.** With "PTA" under figure of value.
139 **50.** 1 p. mauve .. .. 10 10
140 3 p. brown .. .. 10 10
141 7 p. red .. .. 10 10
142 12 p. red .. .. 15 10
143 15 p. blue .. .. 20 15
144 20 p. green .. .. 20 15
145 30 p. red .. .. 30 20
146 50 p. green (25×31 mm) 60 35
147 100 p. blue (25×31 mm) 1·25 55
See also Nos. 203/6.

**51.** The New Reforms, 1866.

**1982.** Europa. Multicoloured.
154. 14 p. Type **51** .. .. 25 25
155. 33 p. Reform of the Institutions, 1981 .. 35 55

**52.** Footballers.

**1982.** World Cup Football Championship, Spain. Multicoloured.
156. 14 p. Type **52** .. .. 65 65
157. 33 p. Tackle .. .. 1·10 1·10

**53.** Arms and 1929 1 p. stamp.

**1982.** National Stamp Exhibition.
158. **53.** 14 p. black and green 30 30

**54.** Spanish and French Permanent Delegations Buildings. **55.** "Virgin and Child" (statue from Andorra la Vella Parish Church).

**1982.** Anniversaries.
159. **54.** 9 p. brown and blue .. 10 10
160. – 23 p. blue and brown 20 20
161. – 33 p. black and green 35 35
DESIGNS—VERT. 9 p. Type **54** (centenary of Permanent Delegations). 23 p. "St. Francis feeding the Birds" (after Ciambue) (800th birth anniv. of St. Francis of Assisi). 33 p. Title page of "Relacio sobre la Vall de Andorra" (birth centenary of Tomas Junoy (writer)).

**1982.** Christmas. Multicoloured.
162. 14 p. Type **55** .. .. 15 15
163. 33 p. Children beating log with sticks .. .. 35 35

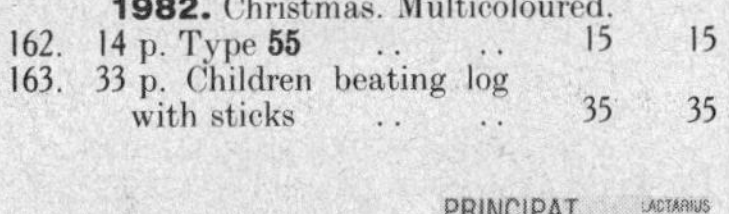

**56.** Building Romanesque Church. **57.** "Lactarius sanguifluus".

**1983.** Europa.
164. **56.** 16 p. grn., pur. & blk. 20 20
165. – 38 p. brown, bl. & blk. 45 45
DESIGN: 38 p. 16th-century water mill.

**1983.** Nature Protection.
166. **57.** 16 p. multicoloured .. 70 50

**58.** Ballot Box on Map and Government Building.

**1983.** 50th Anniv. of Universal Suffrage in Andorra.
167. **58.** 10 p. multicoloured .. 15 15

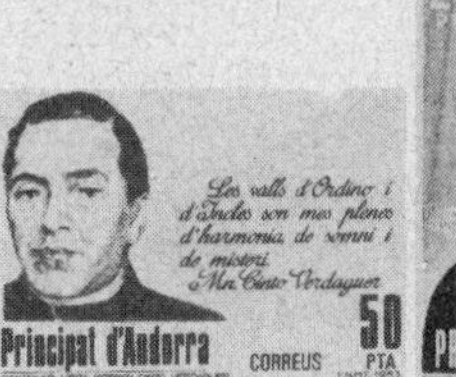

**59.** Mgr. Cinto Verdaguer. **60.** Jaume Sansa Nequi.

**1983.** Centenary of Mgr. Cinto Verdaguer's Visit.
168. **59.** 50 p. multicoloured .. 50 50

**1983.** Air. Jaume Sansa Nequi (Verger-Episcopal) Commemoration.
169. **60.** 20 p. deep brn. & brn. 20 20

**61.** Wall Painting, Church of San Cerni, Nagol.

**1983.** Christmas.
170. **61.** 16 p. multicoloured .. 20 20

**1983.** Bishops of Urgel, Co-princes of Andorra (3rd series). As T **42**.
171 26 p. brown and red .. 25 25
DESIGN: 26 p. Joan Laguarda.

**62.** Ski Jumping.

**1984.** Winter Olympic Games, Sarajevo.
172. **62.** 16 p. multicoloured .. 20 20

**63.** Exhibition and F.I.P. Emblems.

**1984.** "Espana 84" International Stamp Exhibition, Madrid.
173. **63.** 26 p. multicoloured .. 30 30

**64.** Bridge.

**1984.** Europa.
174. **64.** 16 p. brown .. .. 25 25
175. 38 p. blue .. .. 45 45

**65.** Hurdling.

**1984.** Olympic Games, Los Angeles.
176. **65.** 40 p. multicoloured .. 50 50

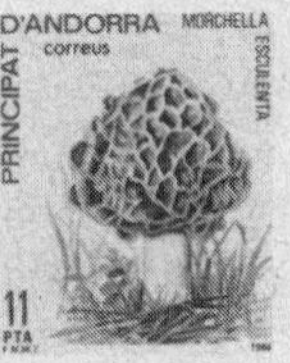

**66.** Common Morel.

**1984.** Nature Protection.
177. **66.** 11 p. multicoloured .. 2·50 2·50

**67.** Pencil, Brush and Pen. **68.** The Holy Family (wood carvings).

**1984.** Pyrenean Cultures Centre, Andorra.

178. **67.** 20 p. multicoloured .. 25 25

**1984.** Christmas.

179. **68.** 17 p. multicoloured .. 20 20

**69.** Mossen Enric Marfany and Score.

**1985.** Europa.

180. **69.** 18 p. green, purple and brown .. .. 25 25

181. – 45 p. brown and green 60 60

DESIGN: 45 p. Musician with viola (fresco detail, La Cortinada Church).

**1985.** Air. Bishops of Urgel, Co-princes of Andorra (4th series). As T **42**.

182 20 p. brown and ochre .. 25 25

DESIGN: 20 p. Ramon Iglesias.

**70.** Beefsteak Morel.

**71.** Pal.

**1985.** Nature Protection.

183. **70.** 30 p. multicoloured .. 70 70

**1985.**

184. **71.** 17 p. deep blue & blue 20 20

**72.** Angels. (St. Bartholomew's Chapel).

**1985.** Christmas.

185. **72.** 17 p. multicoloured .. 20 20

**73.** Scotch Bonnet.

**74.** Sun, Rainbow, Lighthouse and Fish.

**1986.** Nature Protection.

186. **73.** 30 p. multicoloured .. 70 70

**1986.** Europa. Each blue, red and green.

187. 17 p. Type **74** .. .. 20 20

188. 45 p. Sun and trees on rocks .. .. .. 55 55

**1986.** Bishops of Urgel, Co-princes of Andorra (5th series). As T **42**.

189. 35 p. blue and brown .. 40 40

DESIGN: 35 p. Justi Guitart.

**75.** Bell of St. Roma's Chapel, Les Bons.

**76.** Arms.

**1986.** Christmas.

190. **75.** 19 p. multicoloured .. 20 20

**1987.** Meeting of Co-princes.

191. **76.** 48 p. multicoloured .. 60 60

**77.** Interior of Chapel.

**79.** Cep.

**1987.** Europa. Meritxell Chapel.

192 **77** 19 p. brown and blue .. 25 25

193 – 48 p. blue and brown .. 65 65

DESIGN: 48 p. Exterior of Chapel.

**1987.** Nature Protection.

195. **79.** 100 p. multicoloured .. 1·75 1·75

**80.** Extract from "Doctrina Pueril" by Ramon Llull.

**1987.** Christmas.

196. **80.** 20 p. multicoloured .. 20 20

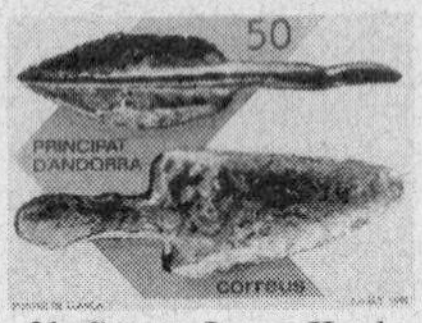

**81.** Copper Lance Heads.

**1988.** Archaeology.

197 **81** 50 p. multicoloured .. 50 50

**82.** Early 20th-century Trader and Pack Mules.

**83.** Pyrenean Mountain Dog.

**1988.** Europa. Communications. Each blue and red.

198. 20 p. Ancient road, Les Bons .. .. 25 25

199. 45 p. Type **82** .. .. 55 55

**1988.** Nature Protection.

200. **83.** 20 p. multicoloured .. 40 40

**84** Commemorative Coin

**86** Leap-frog

**85** Church of St. John of Caselles

**1988.** 700th Anniv of Second Parity Treaty.

201 **84** 20 p. black, grey & brn 20 20

**1988.** Christmas.

202 **85** 20 p. multicoloured .. 20 20

**1988.** As T **50** but without "PTA" under figure of value.

203 20 p. green .. .. 20 15

204 50 p. green (25 × 31 mm) .. 55 40

205 100 p. blue (25 × 31 mm) .. 1·10 75

206 500 p. brown (25 × 31 mm) 5·50 3·75

**1989.** Europa. Children's Games. Mult.

210 20 p. Type **86** .. .. 40 40

211 45 p. Girl trying to pull child from grip of other children (horiz) .. 90 90

**87** St. Roma's Chapel, Les Bons

**1989.**

212 **87** 50 p. black, green & blue 55 55

**88** Anniversary Emblem

**89** "Virgin Mary" (detail of altarpiece, Les Escaldes Church)

**1989.** 125th Anniv of International Red Cross.

213 **88** 20 p. multicoloured .. 25 25

**1989.** Christmas.

214 **89** 20 p. multicoloured .. 20 20

**90** Old French and Spanish Post Offices, Andorra La Vella

**1990.** Europa. Post Office Buildings. Mult.

215 20 p. Type **90** .. .. 25 25

216 50 p. Modern Spanish post office, Andorra La Vella (vert) .. .. .. 65 65

**91** "Gomphidius rutilus"

**1990.** Nature Protection.

217 **91** 45 p. multicoloured .. 75 75

**92** Plandolit House

**93** Angel, La Massana Church

**1990.**

218 **92** 20 p. brown and yellow 20 20

**1990.** Christmas.

219 **93** 25 p. brown, stone & red 25 25

**94** Throwing the Discus

**1991.** European Small States' Games. Mult.

220 25 p. Type **94** .. .. 25 25

221 45 p. High jumping and running .. .. 45 45

**95** "Olympus 1" Satellite

**96** Parasol Mushroom

**1991.** Europa. Europe in Space. Mult.

222 25 p. Type **95** .. .. 30 30

223 55 p. Close-up of "Olympus 1" telecommunications satellite (horiz) .. 60 60

**1991.** Nature Protection.

224 **96** 45 p. multicoloured .. 65 65

**97** "Virgin of the Three Hands" (detail of triptych in Meritxell Chapel by Maria Assumpta Ortado i Maimo)

**98** Woman fetching Water from Public Tap

**1991.** Christmas.

225 **97** 25 p. multicoloured .. 25 25

**1992.**

226 **98** 25 p. multicoloured .. 25 25

**99** "Santa Maria"

**100** White-water Canoeing

**1992.** Europa. 500th Anniv of Discovery of America by Columbus.

227 **99** 27 p. multicoloured .. 30 30

228 – 45 p. brown, red & orge 50 50

DESIGN—HORIZ. 45 p. Engraving of King Ferdinand from map sent by Columbus to Ferdinand and Queen Isabella the Catholic.

**1992.** Olympic Games, Barcelona.

229 **100** 27 p. multicoloured .. 30 30

**101** Benz "Velo", 1894

**102** "Nativity" (Fra Angelico)

**1992.** National Motor Car Museum, Encamp.

230 **101** 27 p. multicoloured .. 30 30

**1992.** Christmas.

231 **102** 27 p. multicoloured .. 30 30

103 Chanterelle

**1993.** Nature Protection.

| No. | Type | Description | | |
|---|---|---|---|---|
| 232 | 103 | 28 p. multicoloured .. | 40 | 40 |

104 "Upstream" (J. A. Morrison)

**1993.** Europa. Contemporary Art. Mult.

| No. | Description | | |
|---|---|---|---|
| 233 | 28 p. Type 104 .. .. | 30 | 30 |
| 234 | 45 p. "Ritme" (Angel Calvente) (vert) .. | 45 | 45 |

105 Society Emblem on National Colours

106 Illuminated "P" (Galceran de Vilanova Missal)

**1993.** 25th Anniv of Andorran Arts and Letters Circle.

| No. | Type | Description | | |
|---|---|---|---|---|
| 235 | 105 | 28 p. multicoloured .. | 30 | 30 |

**1993.** Christmas.

| No. | Type | Description | | |
|---|---|---|---|---|
| 236 | 106 | 28 p. multicoloured .. | 30 | 30 |

108 Sir Alexander Fleming and Penicillin

**1994.** Europa. Discoveries.

| No. | Type | Description | | |
|---|---|---|---|---|
| 238 | 108 | 29 p. multicoloured .. | 40 | 40 |
| 239 | – | 55 p. blue and black .. | 55 | 55 |

DESIGN: 55 p. Test tube and AIDS virus.

109 "Hygrophorus gliocyclus"

110 "Madonna and Child" (anon)

**1994.** Nature Protection.

| No. | Type | Description | | |
|---|---|---|---|---|
| 240 | 109 | 29 p. multicoloured .. | 40 | 40 |

**1994.** Christmas.

| No. | Type | Description | | |
|---|---|---|---|---|
| 241 | 110 | 29 p. multicoloured .. | 30 | 30 |

111 Madriu Valley (south)

**1995.** European Nature Conservation Year. Multicoloured.

| No. | Description | | |
|---|---|---|---|
| 242 | 30 p. Type 111 .. .. | 30 | 30 |
| 243 | 60 p. Madriu Valley (north) | 60 | 60 |

112 Sun, Dove and Barbed Wire

113 "Flight into Egypt" (altarpiece, St. Mark and St. Mary Church, Encamp)

**1995.** Europa. Peace and Freedom.

| No. | Type | Description | | |
|---|---|---|---|---|
| 244 | 112 | 60 p. green, orge & blk | 60 | 60 |

**1995.** Christmas.

| No. | Type | Description | | |
|---|---|---|---|---|
| 245 | 113 | 30 p. multicoloured .. | 30 | 30 |

114 Palace of Europe, Strasbourg

**1995.** Admission of Andorra to Council of Europe.

| No. | Type | Description | | |
|---|---|---|---|---|
| 246 | 114 | 30 p. multicoloured .. | 30 | 30 |

115 "Ramaria aurea"

**1996.** Nature Protection. Multicoloured.

| No. | Description | | |
|---|---|---|---|
| 247 | 30 p. Type 115 .. .. | 30 | 30 |
| 248 | 60 p. Black truffles | 60 | 60 |

116 Isabelle Sandy (writer)

**1996.** Europa. Famous Women.

| No. | Type | Description | | |
|---|---|---|---|---|
| 249 | 116 | 60 p. multicoloured .. | 60 | 60 |

## EXPRESS LETTER STAMPS

**1928.** Express Letter stamp of Spain optd. **CORREOS ANDORRA.**

| No. | Type | Description | | |
|---|---|---|---|---|
| E 15. | E 53. | 20 c. red .. .. | 22·00 | 22·00 |

E 4. Lammergeier over Pyrenees.

E 12. Eurasian Red Squirrel (after Durer) and Arms.

**1929.**

| No. | Type | Description | | |
|---|---|---|---|---|
| E 41. | E 4. | 20 c. red .. .. | 6·00 | 6·00 |

**1949.**

| No. | Type | Description | | |
|---|---|---|---|---|
| E 54. | E 12. | 25 c. red .. .. | 4·00 | 4·00 |

# ANGOLA Pt. 9; Pt. 12

Republic of Southern Africa. Independent of Portugal since 11th November, 1975.

1870. 1000 reis = 1 milreis.
1913. 100 centavos = 1 escudo.
1932. 100 centavos = 1 angolar.
1954. 100 centavos = 1 escudo.
1977. 100 lweis = 1 kwanza.

**1870.** "Crown" key-type inscribed "ANGOLA".

| No. | Type | Description | | |
|---|---|---|---|---|
| 7 | P | 5 r. black .. .. | 1·00 | 95 |
| 17 | | 10 r. yellow .. .. | 8·75 | 4·25 |
| 31 | | 10 r. green .. .. | 2·75 | 1·25 |
| 9 | | 20 r. bistre .. .. | 1·50 | 95 |
| 26 | | 20 r. red .. .. | 4·75 | 3·50 |
| 10 | | 25 r. red .. .. | 5·25 | 2·40 |
| 27 | | 25 r. purple .. .. | 3·75 | 1·25 |
| 19b | | 40 r. blue .. .. | 80·00 | 48·00 |
| 33 | | 40 r. yellow .. .. | 2·75 | 2·00 |
| 12 | | 50 r. green .. .. | 20·00 | 7·50 |
| 30 | | 50 r. blue .. .. | 12·00 | 1·25 |
| 21a | | 100 r. lilac .. .. | 1·40 | 95 |
| 22 | | 200 r. orange .. .. | 1·75 | 1·10 |
| 23a | | 300 r. brown .. .. | 1·90 | 1·50 |

**1886.** "Embossed" key-type inscribed "PROVINCIA DE ANGOLA".

| No. | Type | Description | | |
|---|---|---|---|---|
| 35 | Q | 5 r. black .. .. | 4·25 | 2·40 |
| 36 | | 10 r. green .. .. | 4·25 | 2·40 |
| 37 | | 20 r. red .. .. .. | 6·50 | 4·50 |
| 39 | | 25 r. mauve .. .. | 4·50 | 1·00 |
| 40 | | 40 r. brown .. .. | 5·00 | 2·50 |
| 41 | | 50 r. blue .. .. | 5·75 | 1·40 |
| 42 | | 100 r. brown .. .. | 7·50 | 3·50 |
| 43 | | 200 r. violet .. .. | 10·50 | 4·75 |
| 44 | | 300 r. orange .. .. | 10·50 | 4·75 |

**1894.** "Figures" key-type inscribed "ANGOLA".

| No. | Type | Description | | |
|---|---|---|---|---|
| 49 | R | 5 r. orange .. .. | 85 | 40 |
| 62 | | 10 r. mauve .. .. | 1·60 | 55 |
| 63 | | 15 r. brown .. .. | 1·60 | 95 |
| 54 | | 20 r. lavender .. .. | 1·90 | 1·10 |
| 74 | | 25 r. green .. .. | 1·00 | 75 |
| 66 | | 50 r. blue .. .. | 2·00 | 95 |
| 67 | | 75 r. red .. .. .. | 4·25 | 2·25 |
| 68 | | 80 r. green .. .. | 4·00 | 3·00 |
| 69 | | 100 r. brown on buff .. | 4·25 | 3·00 |
| 70 | | 150 r. red on rose .. | 7·50 | 5·00 |
| 77 | | 200 r. blue on blue .. | 7·50 | 5·75 |
| 78 | | 300 r. blue on brown .. | 7·50 | 5·75 |

**1894.** No. N 51 with circular surch. **CORREIOS DE ANGOLA 25 REIS.**

| No. | Type | Description | | |
|---|---|---|---|---|
| 79b. | V. | 25 r. on $2\frac{1}{2}$ r. brown .. | 27·00 | 25·00 |

**1898.** "King Carlos" key-type inscribed "ANGOLA".

| No. | Type | Description | | |
|---|---|---|---|---|
| 80. | S. | $2\frac{1}{2}$ r. grey .. .. | 20 | 20 |
| 81. | | 5 r. orange .. .. | 20 | 20 |
| 82. | | 10 r. green .. .. | 20 | 20 |
| 83. | | 15 r. brown .. .. | 1·10 | 55 |
| 142. | | 15 r. green .. .. | 45 | 40 |
| 84. | | 20 r. lilac .. .. | 25 | 20 |
| 85. | | 25 r. green .. .. | 65 | 25 |
| 143. | | 25 r. red .. .. .. | 30 | 10 |
| 86. | | 50 r. blue .. .. | 95 | 35 |
| 144. | | 50 r. brown .. .. | 2·25 | 1·10 |
| 145. | | 65 r. blue .. .. | 3·00 | 2·75 |
| 87. | | 75 r. red .. .. | 3·00 | 1·40 |
| 146. | | 75 r. purple .. .. | 1·00 | 70 |
| 88. | | 80 r. mauve .. .. | 3·00 | 1·40 |
| 89. | | 100 r. blue on blue .. | 60 | 40 |
| 147. | | 115 r. brown on pink .. | 3·00 | 2·75 |
| 148. | | 130 r. brown on yellow .. | 3·00 | 2·75 |
| 90. | | 150 r. brown on buff .. | 3·00 | 2·25 |
| 91. | | 200 r. purple on pink .. | 1·75 | 60 |
| 92. | | 300 r. blue on pink .. | 2·00 | 1·75 |
| 149. | | 400 r. blue on yellow .. | 2·00 | 1·60 |
| 93. | | 500 r. black on blue .. | 2·25 | 1·75 |
| 94. | | 700 r. mauve on yellow .. | 9·50 | 6·75 |

**1902.** "Embossed," "Figures" and "Newspaper" key-types of Angola surch.

| No. | Type | Description | | |
|---|---|---|---|---|
| 98 | R | 65 r. on 5 r. orange .. | 3·00 | 2·25 |
| 100 | | 65 r. on 10 r. mauve .. | 2·25 | 1·60 |
| 102 | | 65 r. on 20 r. violet .. | 4·00 | 2·25 |
| 104 | | 65 r. on 25 r. green .. | 2·25 | 1·75 |
| 95 | Q | 65 r. on 40 r. brown .. | 3·50 | 2·10 |
| 96 | | 65 r. on 300 r. orange .. | 3·50 | 2·10 |
| 106 | | 115 r. on 10 r. green .. | 4·00 | 2·00 |
| 109 | R | 115 r. on 80 r. green .. | 4·50 | 3·50 |
| 111 | | 115 r. on 100 r. brn. on buff | 3·75 | 2·10 |
| 113 | | 115 r. on 150 r. red on rose | 5·50 | 4·25 |
| 108 | Q | 115 r. on 200 r. violet .. | 4·00 | 1·90 |
| 120 | R | 130 r. on 15 r. brown .. | 2·25 | 1·50 |
| 116 | Q | 130 r. on 50 r. blue .. | 4·25 | 3·00 |
| 124 | R | 130 r. on 75 r. red .. | 3·25 | 1·75 |
| 118 | Q | 130 r. on 100 r. brown .. | 2·75 | 1·90 |
| 126 | R | 130 r. on 300 r. bl. on brn. | 7·50 | 4·75 |
| 136 | V | 400 r. on $2\frac{1}{2}$ r. brown .. | 55 | 50 |
| 127 | Q | 400 r. on 5 r. black .. | 6·25 | 5·25 |
| 128 | | 400 r. on 20 r. red .. | 25·00 | 16·00 |
| 130 | | 400 r. on 25 r. mauve .. | 6·25 | 3·25 |
| 131 | R | 400 r. on 50 r. pale blue .. | 2·75 | 2·00 |
| 133 | | 400 r. on 200 r. blue on blue | 3·50 | 2·40 |

**1902.** "King Carlos" key-type of Angola optd. **PROVISORIO.**

| No. | Type | Description | | |
|---|---|---|---|---|
| 138. | S. | 15 r. brown .. .. | 80 | 45 |
| 139. | | 25 r. green .. .. | 65 | 30 |
| 140. | | 50 r. blue .. .. | 1·40 | 70 |
| 141. | | 75 r. red .. .. | 2·00 | 1·50 |

**1905.** No. 145 surch. **50 REIS** and bar.

| No. | Type | Description | | |
|---|---|---|---|---|
| 150 | S. | 50 r. on 65 r. blue .. | 1·25 | 75 |

**1911.** "King Carlos" key-type optd. **REPUBLICA.**

| No. | Type | Description | | |
|---|---|---|---|---|
| 151 | S | $2\frac{1}{2}$ r. grey .. .. | 20 | 15 |
| 152 | | 5 r. orange .. .. | 20 | 15 |
| 153 | | 10 r. green .. .. | 20 | 15 |
| 154 | | 15 r. green .. .. | 20 | 15 |
| 155 | | 20 r. lilac .. .. | 20 | 15 |
| 156 | | 25 r. red .. .. | 20 | 15 |
| 157 | | 50 r. brown .. .. | 75 | 55 |
| 232 | | 50 r. blue (No. 140) .. | 75 | 45 |
| 224 | | 75 r. purple .. .. | 45 | 30 |
| 234 | | 75 r. red (No. 141) .. | 1·50 | 1·10 |
| 225 | | 100 r. blue on blue .. | 95 | 95 |
| 160 | | 115 r. brown on pink .. | 75 | 45 |
| 161 | | 130 r. brown on yellow | 75 | 45 |
| 226 | | 200 r. purple on pink .. | 85 | 45 |
| 163 | | 400 r. blue on yellow .. | 1·00 | 50 |
| 164 | | 500 r. black on blue .. | 1·10 | 50 |
| 165 | | 700 r. mauve on yellow | 1·40 | 65 |

**1912.** "King Manoel" key type inscr. "ANGOLA" optd. **REPUBLICA.**

| No. | Type | Description | | |
|---|---|---|---|---|
| 166. | T. | $2\frac{1}{2}$ r. lilac .. .. | 20 | 20 |
| 167. | | 5 r. black .. .. | 20 | 20 |
| 168. | | 10 r. green .. .. | 20 | 20 |
| 169. | | 20 r. red .. .. .. | 20 | 20 |
| 170. | | 25 r. brown .. .. | 20 | 20 |
| 171. | | 50 r. blue .. .. | 45 | 35 |
| 172. | | 75 r. brown .. .. | 50 | 45 |
| 173. | | 100 r. brown on green .. | 1·00 | 65 |
| 174. | | 200 r. green on pink .. | 1·00 | 70 |
| 175. | | 300 r. black on blue .. | 1·00 | 70 |

**1912.** "King Carlos" key-type of Angola optd. **REPUBLICA** and surch.

| No. | Type | Description | | |
|---|---|---|---|---|
| 176 | S | $2\frac{1}{2}$ on 15 r. green .. | 1·50 | 1·00 |
| 177 | | 5 on 15 r. green .. .. | 1·25 | 90 |
| 178 | | 10 on 15 r. green .. | 1·25 | 80 |
| 179 | | 25 on 75 r. red (No. 141) | 22·00 | 15·00 |
| 180 | | 25 on 75 r. purple .. | 1·60 | 1·25 |

**1913.** Surch. **REPUBLICA ANGOLA** and value in figures on "Vasco da Gama" issues of

(a) **Portuguese Colonies.**

| No. | Description | | |
|---|---|---|---|
| 181. | $\frac{1}{4}$ c. on $2\frac{1}{2}$ r. green .. | 45 | 35 |
| 182. | $\frac{1}{2}$ c. on 5 r. red .. .. | 45 | 35 |
| 183. | 1 c. on 10 r. purple .. | 45 | 35 |
| 184. | $2\frac{1}{2}$ c. on 25 r. green .. | 45 | 35 |
| 185. | 5 c. on 50 r. blue .. | 45 | 35 |
| 186. | $7\frac{1}{2}$ c. on 75 r. brown .. | 1·90 | 1·60 |
| 187. | 10 c. on 100 r. brown .. | 80 | 55 |
| 188. | 15 c. on 150 r. bistre .. | 65 | 55 |

(b) **Macao.**

| No. | Description | | |
|---|---|---|---|
| 189. | $\frac{1}{4}$ c. on $\frac{1}{2}$ a. green .. | 75 | 65 |
| 190. | $\frac{1}{2}$ c. on 1 a. red .. | 75 | 65 |
| 191. | 1 c. on 2 a. purple .. | 65 | 50 |
| 192. | $2\frac{1}{2}$ c. on 4 a. green .. | 55 | 45 |
| 193. | 5 c. on 8 a. blue .. | 55 | 45 |
| 194. | $7\frac{1}{2}$ c. on 12 a. brown .. | 1·90 | 1·10 |
| 195. | 10 c. on 16 a. brown .. | 1·10 | 65 |
| 196. | 15 c. on 24 a. bistre .. | 85 | 65 |

(c) **Timor.**

| No. | Description | | |
|---|---|---|---|
| 197. | $\frac{1}{4}$ c. on $\frac{1}{2}$ a. green .. | 75 | 65 |
| 198. | $\frac{1}{2}$ c. on 1 a. red .. | 75 | 65 |
| 199. | 1 c. on 2 a. purple .. | 65 | 50 |
| 200. | $2\frac{1}{2}$ c. on 4 a. green .. | 55 | 40 |
| 201. | 5 c. on 8 a. blue .. | 55 | 50 |
| 202. | $7\frac{1}{2}$ c. on 12 a. brown .. | 1·90 | 1·10 |
| 203. | 10 c. on 16 a. brown .. | 1·00 | 65 |
| 204. | 15 c. on 24 a. bistre .. | 90 | 65 |

**1914.** "Ceres" key-type inscr. "ANGOLA".

| No. | Type | Description | | |
|---|---|---|---|---|
| 296 | U. | $\frac{1}{4}$ c. olive .. .. | 10 | 10 |
| 297 | | $\frac{1}{2}$ c. black .. .. | 10 | 10 |
| 298 | | 1 c. green .. .. | 10 | 10 |
| 299 | | $1\frac{1}{2}$ c. brown .. .. | 10 | 10 |
| 300 | | 2 c. red .. .. | 10 | 10 |
| 301 | | 2 c. grey .. .. | 15 | 15 |
| 281 | | $2\frac{1}{2}$ c. violet .. .. | 10 | 10 |
| 303 | | 3 c. orange .. .. | 10 | 10 |
| 304 | | 4 c. red .. .. | 10 | 10 |
| 305 | | $4\frac{1}{2}$ c. grey .. .. | 10 | 10 |
| 284a | | 5 c. blue .. .. | 10 | 10 |
| 307 | | 6 c. mauve .. .. | 10 | 10 |
| 308 | | 7 c. blue .. .. | 10 | 10 |
| 309 | | $7\frac{1}{2}$ c. brown .. .. | 10 | 10 |
| 288 | | 8 c. grey .. .. | 10 | 10 |
| 311 | | 10 c. brown .. .. | 10 | 10 |
| 312 | | 12 c. brown .. .. | 15 | 15 |
| 313 | | 12 c. green .. .. | 15 | 15 |
| 291 | | 15 c. purple .. .. | 15 | 10 |
| 314 | | 15 c. pink .. .. | 10 | 10 |
| 315 | | 20 c. green .. .. | 35 | 25 |
| 316 | | 24 c. blue .. .. | 40 | 35 |
| 317 | | 25 c. brown .. .. | 40 | 35 |
| 217 | | 30 c. brown on green .. | 1·10 | 75 |
| 318 | | 30 c. green .. .. | 15 | 10 |
| 218 | | 40 c. brown on pink .. | 1·10 | 75 |
| 319 | | 40 c. blue .. .. | 40 | 15 |
| 219 | | 50 c. orange on pink .. | 3·50 | 2·50 |
| 320 | | 50 c. purple .. .. | 35 | 15 |
| 321 | | 60 c. blue .. .. | 40 | 25 |
| 322 | | 60 c. red .. .. | 25·00 | 20·00 |
| 322a | | 80 c. pink .. .. | 55 | 25 |
| 220 | | 1 e. green on blue .. | 2·10 | 1·50 |
| 323 | | 1 e. red .. .. | 50 | 25 |
| 325 | | 1 e. blue .. .. | 1·00 | 55 |
| 326 | | 2 e. purple .. .. | 1·10 | 65 |
| 327 | | 5 e. brown .. .. | 4·00 | 3·25 |
| 328 | | 10 e. pink .. .. | 11·00 | 8·00 |
| 329 | | 20 e. green .. .. | 32·00 | 25·00 |

**1914.** Provisional stamps of 1902 optd. **REPUBLICA.**

| No. | Type | Description | | |
|---|---|---|---|---|
| 233 | S. | 50 r. on 65 r. blue .. | 1·50 | 1·40 |
| 256 | Q. | 115 r. on 10 r. green .. | 80 | 60 |
| 258 | R. | 115 r. on 80 r. green .. | 65 | 60 |
| 261 | | 115 r. on 100 r. brown on buff .. .. .. | 55 | 45 |
| 263 | | 115 r. on 150 r. red on rose | 85 | 60 |
| 266 | Q. | 115 r. on 200 r. violet .. | 60 | 40 |
| 267 | R. | 130 r. on 15 r. brown .. | 55 | 40 |
| 246 | Q. | 130 r. on 50 r. blue .. | 6·50 | 6·50 |
| 269 | R. | 130 r. on 75 r. red .. | 1·10 | 55 |
| 273 | Q. | 130 r. on 100 r. brown .. | 45 | 40 |
| 274 | R. | 130 r. on 300 r. bl. on brn. | 45 | 40 |
| 254 | V. | 400 r. on $2\frac{1}{2}$ r. brown .. | 25 | 20 |

## INDEX

Countries can be quickly located by referring to the index at the end of this volume.

**1919.** Stamps of 1911, 1912 or 1914 surch.

| No. | Description | Unused | Used |
|---|---|---|---|
| 332 S | ½ c. on 75 r. purple | 55 | 45 |
| 331 T | ½ c. on 75 r. brown | 35 | 30 |
| 336 | 1 c. on 50 r. blue | 65 | 60 |
| 335 S | 2½ c. on 100 r. blue on bl | 65 | 30 |
| 334 | 2½ c. on 100 r. brn on grn | 65 | 55 |
| 337 | 4 c. on 130 r. brn on yell | 65 | 55 |
| 339 U | $04 on 15 c. purple | 45 | 45 |
| 340 | $04 on 15 c. pink | 7·50 | |
| 341 T | $00.5 on 75 r. brown | 50 | 45 |
| 342 U | $00.5 on 7½ c. brown | 65 | 55 |

**1925.** Nos. 136 and 133 surch **Republica 40 C.**

| No. | Description | Unused | Used |
|---|---|---|---|
| 345. V. | 40 c. on 400 r. on 2½ r. brown | 25 | 25 |
| 343. R. | 40 c. on 400 r. on 200 r. blue on blue | 25 | 25 |

**1931.** "Ceres" key-type of Angola surch.

| No. | Description | Unused | Used |
|---|---|---|---|
| 347. U. | 50 c. on 60 c. red | 55 | 55 |
| 348. | 70 c. on 80 c. pink | 1·40 | 85 |
| 349. | 70 c. on 1 e. blue | 1·10 | 85 |
| 350. | 1 e. 40 on 2 e. purple | 90 | 55 |

17. Ceres.

**1932.**

| No. | Description | Unused | Used |
|---|---|---|---|
| 351. 17. | 1 c. brown | 10 | 10 |
| 352. | 5 c. sepia | 10 | 10 |
| 353. | 10 c. mauve | 10 | 10 |
| 354. | 15 c. black | 10 | 10 |
| 355. | 20 c. grey | 10 | 10 |
| 356. | 30 c. green | 10 | 10 |
| 357. | 35 c. green | 3·00 | 1·25 |
| 358. | 40 c. red | 15 | 10 |
| 359. | 45 c. blue | 45 | 40 |
| 360. | 50 c. brown | 15 | 10 |
| 361. | 60 c. olive | 30 | 15 |
| 362. | 70 c. brown | 30 | 15 |
| 363. | 80 c. green | 20 | 10 |
| 364. | 85 c. red | 1·50 | 85 |
| 365. | 1 a. red | 35 | 10 |
| 366. | 1 a. 40 blue | 3·00 | 1·50 |
| 367. | 1 a. 75 blue | 5·75 | 1·60 |
| 368. | 2 a. mauve | 1·25 | 15 |
| 369. | 5 a. green | 2·40 | 50 |
| 370. | 10 a. brown | 5·75 | 95 |
| 371. | 20 a. orange | 14·00 | 1·90 |

**1934.** Surch.

| No. | Description | Unused | Used |
|---|---|---|---|
| 380 17 | 5 c. on 80 c. green (A) | 25 | 10 |
| 419 | 5 c. on 80 c. green (B) | 30 | 25 |
| 413 | 10 c. on 45 c. blue | 65 | 55 |
| 381 | 10 c. on 80 c. green | 45 | 20 |
| 414 | 15 c. on 45 c. blue | 65 | 55 |
| 382 | 15 c. on 80 c. green | 65 | 25 |
| 415 | 20 c. on 85 c. red | 65 | 55 |
| 374 | 30 c. on 1 a. 40 blue | 1·00 | 85 |
| 416 | 35 c. on 85 c. red | 65 | 55 |
| 417 | 50 c. on 1 a. 40 blue | 65 | 55 |
| 418 | 60 c. on 1 a. red | 3·25 | 3·00 |
| 375 | 70 c. on 2 a. mauve | 1·25 | 95 |
| 376 | 80 c. on 5 a. green | 2·10 | 1·00 |

(A) surch. **0.05 Cent.** in one line; (B) surch. **5 CENTAVOS** on two lines.

**1935.** "Due" key-type surch **CORREIOS** and new value.

| No. | Description | Unused | Used |
|---|---|---|---|
| 377. W. | 5 c. on 6 c. brown | 85 | 65 |
| 378. | 30 c. on 50 c. grey | 85 | 65 |
| 379. | 40 c. on 50 c. grey | 85 | 65 |

22. Vasco da Gama.

27. Airplane over Globe.

**1938.** Name and value in black.

| No. | Description | Unused | Used |
|---|---|---|---|
| 383. 22. | 1 c. olive (postage) | 10 | 10 |
| 384. | 5 c. brown | 10 | 10 |
| 385. | 10 c. red | 10 | 10 |
| 386. | 15 c. purple | 10 | 10 |
| 387. | 20 c. grey | 10 | 10 |
| 388. – | 30 c. purple | 15 | 10 |
| 389. – | 35 c. green | 20 | 15 |
| 390. – | 40 c. brown | 10 | 10 |
| 391. – | 50 c. mauve | 10 | 10 |
| 392. – | 60 c. black | 25 | 15 |
| 393. – | 70 c. violet | 25 | 15 |
| 394. – | 80 c. orange | 25 | 15 |
| 395. – | 1 a. red | 25 | 15 |
| 396. – | 1 a. 75 blue | 70 | 30 |
| 397. – | 2 a. red | 1·00 | 30 |
| 398. – | 5 a. olive | 3·50 | 30 |
| 399. – | 10 a. blue | 8·00 | 45 |
| 400. – | 20 a. brown | 14·00 | 90 |
| 401. 27. | 10 c. red (air) | 20 | 15 |
| 402. | 20 c. violet | 20 | 15 |
| 403. | 50 c. orange | 20 | 15 |
| 404. | 1 a. blue | 20 | 15 |
| 405. | 2 a. red | 30 | 15 |
| 406. | 3 a. green | 65 | 20 |
| 407. | 5 a. brown | 1·75 | 25 |
| 408. | 9 a. red | 2·40 | 70 |
| 409. | 10 a. mauve | 3·25 | 80 |

Designs: 30 c. to 50 c. Mousinho de Albuquerque. 60 c. to 1 a. "Fomento" (symbolising Progress). 1 a. 75, 2, 5 a. Prince Henry the Navigator. 10, 20 a. Afonso de Albuquerque.

28. Portuguese Colonial Column.

31. Arms of Angola.

**1938.** President's Colonial Tour.

| No. | Description | Unused | Used |
|---|---|---|---|
| 410. 28. | 80 c. green | 1·10 | 85 |
| 411. | 1 a. 75 blue | 8·00 | 1·90 |
| 412. | 20 a. brown | 19·00 | 10·50 |

**1945.** Nos. 394/6 surch.

| No. | Description | Unused | Used |
|---|---|---|---|
| 420 | 5 c. on 80 c. orange | 50 | 30 |
| 421 | 50 c. on 1 a. red | 50 | 30 |
| 422 | 50 c. on 1 a. 75 blue | 50 | 30 |

**1947.** Air.

| No. | Description | Unused | Used |
|---|---|---|---|
| 423a 31 | 1 a. brown | 4·00 | 1·50 |
| 423b | 2 a. green | 4·00 | 1·50 |
| 423c | 3 a. orange | 4·25 | 1·50 |
| 423d | 3 a. 50 orange | 8·25 | 1·75 |
| 423e | 5 a. green | 45·00 | 4·50 |
| 423f | 6 a. pink | 45·00 | 7·50 |
| 423g | 9 a. red | £130 | 80·00 |
| 423h | 10 a. green | £120 | 30·00 |
| 423i | 20 a. blue | £120 | 30·00 |
| 423j | 50 a. black | £190 | 90·00 |
| 423k | 100 a. yellow | £350 | £250 |

32. S. Miguel Fortress Luanda.

33. Our Lady of Fatima.

**1948.** Tercentenary of Restoration of Angola. Inscr "Tricentenario da Restauracao de Angola 1648–1948".

| No. | Description | Unused | Used |
|---|---|---|---|
| 424. 32. | 5 c. violet | 10 | 10 |
| 425. – | 10 c. brown | 30 | 15 |
| 426. – | 30 c. green | 10 | 10 |
| 427. – | 50 c. purple | 10 | 10 |
| 428. – | 1 a. red | 25 | 10 |
| 429. – | 1 a. 75 blue | 50 | 10 |
| 430. – | 2 a. green | 50 | 10 |
| 431. – | 5 a. black | 1·75 | 30 |
| 432. – | 10 a. mauve | 3·75 | 55 |
| 433. – | 20 a. blue | 8·00 | 1·10 |

Designs—horiz. 10 c. Our Lady of Nazareth Hermitage, Luanda. 1 a. Surrender of Luanda. 5 a. Inscribed Rocks of Yelala. 20 a. Massangano Fortress. vert. (portraits): 30 c. Don John IV. 50 c. Salvador Correia de Sa Benevides. 1 a. 75, Dioga Cao. 7 a. Manuel Cerveira Pereira. 10 a. Paulo Dias de Novais.

**1948.** Honouring Our Lady of Fatima.

| No. | Description | Unused | Used |
|---|---|---|---|
| 434. 33. | 50 c. red | 1·25 | 1·00 |
| 435. | 3 a. blue | 3·25 | 2·00 |
| 436. | 6 a. orange | 13·50 | 5·00 |
| 437. | 9 a. red | 27·00 | 6·50 |

35. River Chiumbe.

36. Pedras Negras.

**1949.**

| No. | Description | Unused | Used |
|---|---|---|---|
| 438 35 | 20 c. blue | 30 | 15 |
| 439 36 | 40 c. brown | 30 | 10 |
| 440 – | 50 c. red | 30 | 10 |
| 441 – | 2 a. 50 blue | 1·60 | 30 |
| 442 – | 3 a. 50 grey | 1·60 | 1·40 |
| 443 – | 15 a. green | 13·50 | 1·40 |
| 444 – | 50 a. green | 75·00 | 4·75 |

Designs—As T 35: 50 c. Luanda; 2 a. 50, Bandeira; 3 a. 50, Mocamedes; 50 a. Braganza Falls. 31 × 26 mm: 15 a. River Cubal.

37. Aircraft and Globe.

38. "Tentativa Feliz".

**1949.** Air.

| No. | Description | Unused | Used |
|---|---|---|---|
| 445. 37. | 1 a. orange | 30 | 10 |
| 446. | 2 a. brown | 65 | 10 |
| 447. | 3 a. mauve | 90 | 10 |
| 448. | 6 a. green | 2·00 | 50 |
| 449. | 9 a. purple | 2·75 | 1·10 |

**1949.** Cent. of Founding of Mocamedes.

| No. | Description | Unused | Used |
|---|---|---|---|
| 450. 38. | 1 a. purple | 5·25 | 60 |
| 451. | 4 a. green | 13·50 | 1·60 |

39. Letter and Globe.

40. Reproduction of "Crown" key-type.

**1949.** 75th Anniv. of U.P.U.

| No. | Description | Unused | Used |
|---|---|---|---|
| 452. 39. | 4 a. green | 6·00 | 2·40 |

**1950.** Philatelic Exhibition and 80th Anniv of First Angolan Stamp.

| No. | Description | Unused | Used |
|---|---|---|---|
| 453. 40. | 50 a. green | 95 | 30 |
| 454. | 1 a. red | 95 | 45 |
| 455. | 4 a. black | 3·25 | 1·25 |

41. Bells and Dove.

42. Angels holding Candelabra.

**1950.** Holy Year.

| No. | Description | Unused | Used |
|---|---|---|---|
| 456. 41. | 1 a. violet | 65 | 10 |
| 457. 42. | 4 a. black | 3·00 | 55 |

43. Dark Chanting Goshawk.

44. Our Lady of Fatima.

**1951.** Birds. Multicoloured.

| No. | Description | Unused | Used |
|---|---|---|---|
| 458 | 5 c. Type **43** | 30 | 30 |
| 459 | 10 c. Racquet-tailed roller | 30 | 30 |
| 460 | 15 c. Bateleur | 55 | 55 |
| 461 | 20 c. European bee eater | 75 | 75 |
| 462 | 50 c. Giant kingfisher | 55 | 40 |
| 463 | 1 a. Yellow-headed barbet | 55 | 40 |
| 464 | 1 a. 50 African open-bill stork | 75 | 60 |
| 465 | 2 a. Southern ground hornbill | 75 | 60 |
| 466 | 2 a. 50 African skimmer | 75 | 60 |
| 467 | 3 a. Shrika | 65 | 60 |
| 468 | 3 a. 50 Barrow's bustard | 65 | 60 |
| 469 | 4 a. African golden oriole | 1·10 | 60 |
| 470 | 4 a. 50 Eastern long-tailed shrike | 1·10 | 1·00 |
| 471 | 5 a. Red-shouldered glossy starling | 6·50 | 1·00 |
| 472 | 6 a. Sharp-tailed glossy starling | 5·75 | 2·75 |
| 473 | 7 a. Fan-tailed whydah | 5·75 | 2·75 |
| 474 | 10 a. Half-collared kingfisher | 45·00 | 3·00 |
| 475 | 12 a. 50 White-crowned shrike | 6·00 | 6·00 |
| 476 | 15 a. White-winged starling | 6·00 | 6·00 |
| 477 | 20 a. Yellow-billed hornbill | 85·00 | 18·00 |
| 478 | 25 a. Violet starling | 27·00 | 10·00 |
| 479 | 30 a. Sulphur-breasted bush shrike | 27·00 | 11·50 |
| 480 | 40 a. Secretary bird | 45·00 | 15·00 |
| 481 | 50 a. Peach-faced lovebird | £110 | 48·00 |

The 10, 15 and 20 c., 2 a. 50, 3 a., 4 a. 50, 12 a. 50 and 30 a. are horiz, the remainder vert.

**1951.** Termination of Holy Year.

| No. | Description | Unused | Used |
|---|---|---|---|
| 482. 44. | 4 a. orange | 1·90 | 1·00 |

45. Laboratory.

46. The Sacred Face.

**1952.** 1st Tropical Medicine Congress, Lisbon.

| No. | Description | Unused | Used |
|---|---|---|---|
| 483. 45. | 1 a. grey and blue | 60 | 25 |

**1952.** Missionary Art Exhibition.

| No. | Description | Unused | Used |
|---|---|---|---|
| 484 46 | 10 c. blue and flesh | 15 | 15 |
| 485 | 50 c. green and stone | 40 | 15 |
| 486 | 2 a. purple and flesh | 2·00 | 30 |

47. Leopard.

48. Stamp of 1853 and Colonial Arms.

**1953.** Angolan Fauna. Multicoloured.

| No. | Description | Unused | Used |
|---|---|---|---|
| 487 | 5 c. Type **47** | 15 | 15 |
| 488 | 10 c. Sable antelope (vert) | 15 | 15 |
| 489 | 20 c. African elephant (vert) | 15 | 15 |
| 490 | 30 c. Eland (vert) | 15 | 15 |
| 491 | 40 c. Crocodile | 15 | 15 |
| 492 | 50 c. Impala (vert) | 15 | 15 |
| 493 | 1 a. Mountain zebra (vert) | 30 | 15 |
| 494 | 1 a. 50 Sitatunga (vert) | 15 | 15 |
| 495 | 2 a. Black rhinoceros | 45 | 15 |
| 496 | 2 a. 30 Gemsbok (vert) | 30 | 15 |
| 497 | 2 a. 50 Lion (vert) | 45 | 15 |
| 498 | 3 a. African buffalo | 40 | 15 |
| 499 | 3 a. 50 Springbok (vert) | 40 | 15 |
| 500 | 4 a. Blue wildebeest (vert) | 9·25 | 20 |
| 501 | 5 a. Hartebeest (vert) | 75 | 15 |
| 502 | 7 a. Warthog (vert) | 95 | 20 |
| 503 | 10 a. Waterbuck (vert) | 1·25 | 20 |
| 504 | 12 a. 50 Hippopotamus (vert) | 4·25 | 1·25 |
| 505 | 15 a. Greater kudu (vert) | 4·25 | 1·25 |
| 506 | 20 a. Giraffe (vert) | 5·75 | 80 |

**1953.** Portuguese Stamp Centenary.

| No. | Description | Unused | Used |
|---|---|---|---|
| 507 48 | 50 c. multicoloured | 65 | 45 |

49. Father M. da Nobrega and Sao Paulo.

50. Route of President's Tour.

**1954.** 4th Cent. of Sao Paulo.

| No. | Description | Unused | Used |
|---|---|---|---|
| 508. 49. | 1 e. black and buff | 40 | 20 |

**1954.** Presidential Visit.

| No. | Description | Unused | Used |
|---|---|---|---|
| 509 50 | 35 c. multicoloured | 15 | 10 |
| 510 | 4 e. 50 multicoloured | 1·00 | 45 |

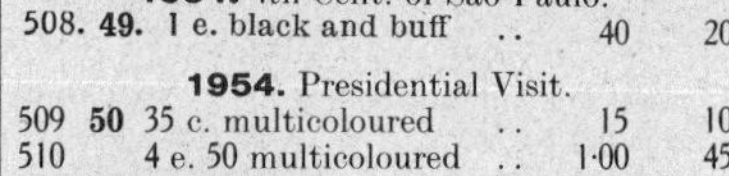

51. Map of Angola

52. Col. A. de Paiva.

**1955.** Map multicoloured. Angola territory in colour given.

| No. | Description | Unused | Used |
|---|---|---|---|
| 511. 51. | 5 c. white | 15 | 15 |
| 512. | 20 c. salmon | 15 | 15 |
| 513. | 50 c. blue | 15 | 15 |
| 514. | 1 e. orange | 15 | 15 |
| 515. | 2 e. 30 yellow | 75 | 30 |
| 516. | 4 e. blue | 1·50 | 15 |
| 517. | 10 e. green | 1·75 | 15 |
| 518. | 20 e. white | 2·50 | 1·10 |

**1956.** Birth Centenary of De Paiva.

| No. | Description | Unused | Used |
|---|---|---|---|
| 519 52 | 1 e. black, blue & orange | 25 | 20 |

53. Quela Chief.

54. Father J. M. Antunes.

**1957.** Natives. Multicoloured.

| No. | Description | Unused | Used |
|---|---|---|---|
| 520 | 5 c. Type **53** | 15 | 15 |
| 521 | 10 c. Andulo flute player | 15 | 15 |
| 522 | 15 c. Dembos man and woman | 15 | 15 |
| 523 | 20 c. Quissama dancer (male) | 15 | 15 |
| 524 | 30 c. Quibala family | 15 | 15 |
| 525 | 40 c. Bocolo dancer (female) | 15 | 15 |
| 526 | 50 c. Quissama woman | 15 | 15 |
| 527 | 80 c. Cuanhama woman | 20 | 15 |
| 528 | 1 e. 50 Luanda widow | 1·60 | 15 |
| 529 | 2 e. 50 Bocolo dancer (male) | 1·60 | 15 |
| 530 | 4 e. Muquixe man | 80 | 15 |
| 531 | 10 e. Cabinda chief | 1·40 | 30 |

**1957.** Birth Centenary of Father Antunes.

| No. | Description | Unused | Used |
|---|---|---|---|
| 532 54 | 1 e. multicoloured | 55 | 30 |

**55.** Exhibition Emblem, Globe and Arms.

**1958.** Brussels Int. Exn.
533. **55.** 1 e. 50 multicoloured .. 45 40

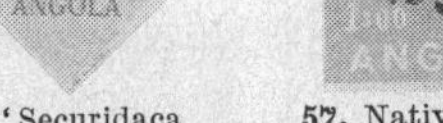

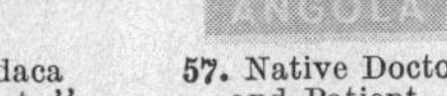

**56.** "Securidaca longipedunculata". **57.** Native Doctor and Patient.

**1958.** 6th Int. Tropical Medicine Congress.
534. **56.** 2 e. 50 multicoloured .. 1·50 90

**1958.** 75th Anniv of Maria Pia Hospital, Luanda.
535. **57.** 1 e. brown, black & blue 30 20
536. – 1 e. 50 multicoloured .. 80 40
537. – 2 e. 50 multicoloured .. 1·50 75
DESIGNS: 1 e. 50, 17th-century doctor and patient. 2 e. 50, Present-day doctor, orderly and patients.

**58.** Welwitschia (plant). **59.** Old Map of West Africa.

**1959.** Cent. of Discovery of Welwitschia.
538. **58.** 1 e. 50 multicoloured .. 70 30
539. – 2 e. 50 multicoloured .. 1·00 40
540. – 5 e. multicoloured .. 1·60 40
541. – 10 e. multicoloured .. 5·00 1·25
DESIGNS: 2 e. 50, 5 e., 10 e. Various types of Welwitschia ("Welwitschia mirabilis").

**1960.** 500th Death Anniv. of Prince Henry the Navigator.
542. **59.** 2 e. 50 multicoloured .. 40 20

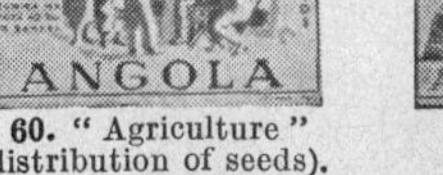

**60.** "Agriculture" (distribution of seeds). **61.**

**1960.** 10th Anniv. of African Technical Co-operation Commission.
543. **60.** 2 e. 50 multicoloured .. 50 20

**1961.** Angolan Women. As T **61**. Portraits multicoloured; background colours given.
544. 10 c. green .. .. 10 10
545. 15 c. blue .. .. 10 10
546. 30 c. yellow .. .. 10 10
547. 40 c. grey .. .. 10 10
548. 60 c. brown .. .. 10 10
549. 1 e. 50 turquoise .. .. 10 10
550. 2 e. lilac .. .. 75 10
551. 2 e. 50 lemon .. .. 75 10
552. 3 e. pink .. .. 2·75 20
553. 4 e. olive .. .. 1·40 20
554. 5 e. blue .. .. 90 20
555. 7 e. 50 yellow .. .. 1·25 60
556. 10 e. buff .. .. 90 45
557. 15 e. brown .. .. 1·40 60
558. 25 e. red .. .. 1·90 90
559. 50 e. grey .. .. 4·25 1·90

**62.** Weightlifting.

**1962.** Sports. Multicoloured.
560 50 c. Flying .. .. 15 15
561 1 e. Rowing .. .. 80 15
562 1 e. 50 Water polo .. 55 20
563 2 e. 50 Putting the shot .. 70 20
564 4 e. 50 High jumping .. 55 40
565 15 e. Type **62** .. .. 1·40 1·00

**63.** "Anopheles funestus" (mosquito). **64.** Gen. Norton de Matos (statue).

**1962.** Malaria Eradication.
566. **63.** 2 e. 50 multicoloured .. 1·00 55

**1962.** 50th Anniv. of Nova Lisboa.
567 **64.** 2 e. 50 multicoloured .. 40 20

**65.** Red Locusts.

**1963.** 15th Anniv. of Int. Locust Eradication Service.
568. **65.** 2 e. 50 multicoloured .. 65 30

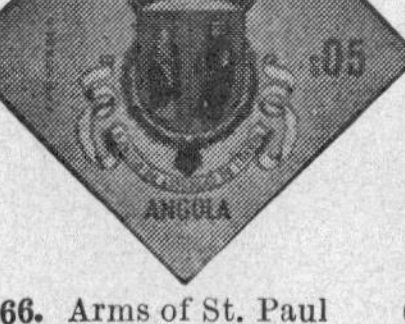

**66.** Arms of St. Paul of the Assumption, Luanda. **67.** Rear-Admiral A. Tomas.

**1963.** Angolan Civic Arms (1st series). Mult.
569. 5 c. Type **66** .. .. 15 15
570. 10 c. Massangano .. .. 15 15
571. 30 c. Muxima .. .. 15 15
572. 50 c. Carmona .. .. 15 15
573. 1 e. Salazar .. .. 45 15
574. 1 e. 50 Malanje .. .. 90 15
575. 2 e. Henry of Carvalho .. 45 15
576. 2 e. 50 Mocamedes .. 2·50 40
577. 3 e. Novo Redondo .. 65 15
578. 3 e. 50 St. Salvador (Congo) 75 15
579. 5 e. Luso .. .. 65 25
580. 7 e. 50 St. Philip (Benguela) 90 75
581. 10 e. Lobito .. .. 1·00 65
582. 12 e. 50 Gabela .. .. 1·25 1·00
583. 15 e. Sa da Bandeira .. 1·25 1·00
584. 17 e. 50 Silva Porto .. 2·00 1·75
585. 20 e. Nova Lisboa .. 2·00 1·60
586. 22 e. 50 Cabinda .. .. 2·00 1·75
587. 30 e. Serpa Pinto .. .. 2·50 2·25
See also Nos. 589/610.

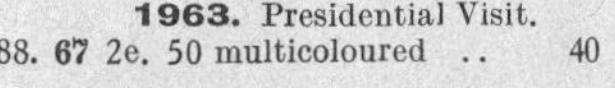

**1963.** Presidential Visit.
588. **67** 2e. 50 multicoloured .. 40 15

**68.** Arms of Sanza-Pombo. **69.** Map of Africa, Boeing 707 and Lockheed Super Constellation Airliners.

**1963.** Angolan Civic Arms (2nd series). Mult.
589. 15 c. Type **68** .. .. 10 10
590. 20 c. St. Antonio do Zaire .. 10 10
591. 25 c. Ambriz .. .. 10 10
592. 40 c. Ambrizete .. .. 10 10
593. 50 c. Catete .. .. 10 10
594. 70 c. Quibaxe .. .. 10 10
595. 1 e. Maquela do Zombo .. 15 10
596. 1 e. 20 Bembe .. .. 10 10
597. 1 e. 50 Caxito .. .. 50 10
598. 1 e. 80 Dondo .. .. 25 20
599. 2 e. 50 Damba .. .. 1·75 10
600. 4 e. Cuimba .. .. 35 15
601. 6 e. 50 Negage .. .. 35 30
602. 7 e. Quitexe .. .. 60 40
603. 8 e. Mucaba .. .. 60 50
604. 9 e. 31 de Janeiro .. .. 85 75
605. 11 e. Novo Caipemba .. 1·00 85
606. 14 e. Songo .. .. 1·10 1·00
607. 17 e. Quimbele .. .. 1·25 1·10
608. 25 e. Noqui .. .. 1·50 1·10
609. 35 e. Santa Cruz .. .. 2·10 1·75
610. 50 e. General Freire .. 2·75 1·50

**1963.** 10th Anniv. of T.A.P. Airline.
611. **69.** 1 e. multicoloured .. 40 20

**70.** Bandeira Cathedral. **71.** Dr. A. T. de Sousa

**1963.** Angolan Churches. Mult.
612. 10 c. Type **70** .. .. 10 10
613. 20 c. Landana .. .. 10 10
614. 30 c. Luanda (Cathedral) 10 10
615. 40 c. Gabela .. .. 10 10
616. 50 c. St. Martin, Bay of Tigers (Chapel) .. .. 10 10
617. 1 e. Melange (Cathedral) .. 15 10
618. 1 e. 50 St. Peter, Chibia .. 15 10
619. 2 e. Benguela .. .. 20 10
620. 2 e. 50 Jesus, Luanda .. 25 10
621. 3 e. Camabatela .. .. 30 15
622. 3 e. 50 Cabinda Mission .. 40 15
623. 4 e. Vila Folgares .. 40 25
624. 4 e. 50 Arrabida, Lobito .. 50 25
625. 5 e. Cabinda .. .. 55 30
626. 7 e. 50 Cacuso, Malange .. 85 50
627. 10 e. Lubanga Mission .. 1·10 50
628. 12 e. 50 Huila Mission .. 1·25 70
629. 15 e. Island Cape, Luanda 1·50 80
The 1 e., 2 e., 3 e., 4 e., 4e. 50, 7 e. 50, 12 e. 50 and 15 e. are horiz., the rest vert.

**1964.** Cent. of National Overseas Bank.
630. **71.** 2 e. 50 multicoloured .. 55 25

**72.** Arms and Palace of Commerce, Luanda. **73.** I.T.U. Emblem and St. Gabriel.

**1964.** Cent. of Luanda Commercial Assn.
631. **72.** 1 e. multicoloured .. 20 15

**1965.** Cent. of I.T.U.
632. **73.** 2 e. 50 multicoloured .. 80 40

**74.** Boeing 707 over Petroleum Refinery. **75.** Fokker F.27 Friendship over Luanda Airport.

**1965.** Air. Multicoloured.
633 1 e. 50 Type **74** .. .. 80 10
634 2 e. 50 Cambabe Dam .. 80 10
635 3 e. Salazar Dam .. 1·10 10
636 4 e. Captain Trofilo Duarte Dam .. .. .. 1·10 15
637 4 e. 50 Creveiro Lopes Dam 80 15
638 5 e. Cuango Dam .. 80 20
639 6 e. Quanza Bridge .. 1·25 30
640 7 e. Captain Trofilo Duarte Railway Bridge .. 1·90 40
641 8 e. 50 Dr. Oliveira Salazar Bridge .. .. 2·25 70
642 12 e. 50 Captain Silva Carvalho Railway Bridge 2·50 1·00
Nos. 634/42 are horiz and each design includes a Boeing 707 airliner overhead.

**1965.** 25th Anniv. of Direccao dos Transportes Aereos (Angolan airline).
643. **75.** 2 e. 50 multicoloured .. 25 15

**76.** Arquebusier, 1539. **77.** St. Paul's Hospital, Luanda, and Sarmento Rodrigues Commercial and Industrial School.

**1966.** Portuguese Military Uniforms. Mult.
644. 50 c. Type **76** .. .. 10 10
645. 1 e. Arquebusier, 1640 .. 10 10
646. 1 e. 50 Infantry officer, 1777 .. .. 15 10
647. 2 e. Infantry standard-bearer, 1777 .. .. 20 10
648. 2 e. 50 Infantryman, 1777 20 10
649. 3 e. Cavalry officer, 1783 .. 25 10
650. 4 e. Trooper, 1783 .. 30 15
651. 4 e. 50 Infantry officer, 1807 .. .. 40 20
652. 5 e. Infantryman, 1807 .. 50 20
653. 6 e. Cavalry officer, 1807 70 20
654. 8 e. Trooper, 1807 .. 1·00 30
655. 9 e. Infantryman, 1873 .. 1·00 45

**1966.** 40th Anniv. of National Revolution.
656. **77.** 1 e. multicoloured .. 20 15

**78.** Emblem of Brotherhood. **79.** Mendes Barata and Cruiser "Don Carlos I".

**1966.** Cent. of Brotherhood of the Holy Spirit.
657. **78.** 1 e. multicoloured .. 15 15

**1967.** Cent of Military Naval Assn. Mult.
658 1 e. Type **79** .. .. 55 25
659 2 e. 50 Augusto de Castilho and sail/steam corvette "Mindelo" .. .. 65 30

**80.** Basilica of Fatima. **81.** 17th-cent Map and M. C. Pereira (founder).

**1967.** 50th Anniv. of Fatima Apparitions.
660. **80.** 50 c. multicoloured .. 15 10

**1967.** 350th Anniv. of Benguela.
661. **81.** 50 c. multicoloured .. 15 10

**82.** Town Hall, Uige-Carmona. **83.** "The Three Orders".

**1967.** 50th Anniv. of Uige-Carmona.
662. **82.** 1 e. multicoloured .. 15 10

**1967.** Portuguese Civil and Military Orders. Multicoloured.
663. 50 c. Type **83** .. .. 10 10
664. 1 e. "Tower and Sword" 10 10
665. 1 e. 50 "Avis" .. .. 10 10
666. 2 e. "Christ" .. .. 10 10
667. 2 e. 50 "St. James of the Sword" 10 10
668. 3 e. "Empire" .. .. 20 10
669. 4 e. "Prince Henry" .. 25 15
670. 5 e. "Benemerencia" .. 30 25
671. 10 e. "Public Instruction" 60 25
672. 20 e. "Agricultural and Industrial Merit" .. 1·25 70

**84.** Belmonte Castle. **85.** Francisco Inocencio de Souza Countinho.

**1968.** 500th Birth Anniv. of Pedro Cabral (explorer). Multicoloured.
673. 50 c. Our Lady of Hope .. 15 15
674. 1 e. Type **84** .. .. 20 15
675. 1 e. 50 St. Jeronimo's hermitage .. .. 25 15
676. 2 e. 50 Cabral's fleet .. 70 15
The 50 c., 1 e. 50, and 2 e. 50 are vert.

**1969.** Bicent of Novo Redondo (Angolan city).
677 **85** 2 e. multicoloured .. 25 15

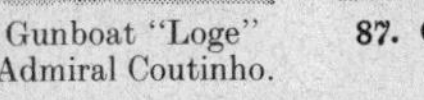

**86.** Gunboat "Loge" and Admiral Coutinho. **87.** Compass.

**1969.** Birth Cent. of Admiral Gago Coutinho.
678. **86.** 2 e. 50 multicoloured .. 60 20

**1969.** 500th Birth Anniv. of Vasco da Gama (explorer).
679. **87.** 1 e. multicoloured .. 15 10

**88.** L. A. Rebello de Silva. **89.** Gate of Jeronimos.

**1969.** Cent. of Overseas Administrative Reforms.
680. **88.** 1 e. 50 multicoloured .. 15 10

**1969.** 500th Birth Anniv of King Manoel I.
681 **89** 3 e. multicoloured .. 20 15

**90.** "Angolasaurus bocagei". **91.** Marshal Carmona.

**1970.** Fossils and Minerals. Multicoloured.
682 50 c. Type **90** .. .. 35 15
683 1 e. Ferro-meteorite .. 35 15
684 1 e. 50 Dioptase .. .. 55 35
685 2 e. "Gondwanidium validium" .. .. 55 35
686 2 e. 50 Diamonds .. .. 55 35
687 3 e. Estromatolitos .. 55 35
688 3 e. 50 Shark ("Procarcharodon megalodon") 90 55
689 4 e. Lungfish ("Microceratodus angolensis") .. 90 55
690 4 e. 50 Muscovite (mica) .. 90 55
691 5 e. Barytes .. .. 90 55
692 6 e. "Nostoceras helicinum" 1·60 75
693 10 e. "Rotula orbiculus angolensis" .. .. 1·75 1·00

**1970.** Birth Cent. of Marshal Carmona.
694. **91.** 2 e. 50 multicoloured .. 25 15

**92.** Cotton-picking.

**1970.** Cent. of Malanje Municipality.
695. **92.** 2 e. 50 multicoloured .. 30 20

**93.** Mail Steamers "Infante Dom Henrique" and "Principe Perfeito" and 1870 5 r. Stamp. **94.** Map and Emblems.

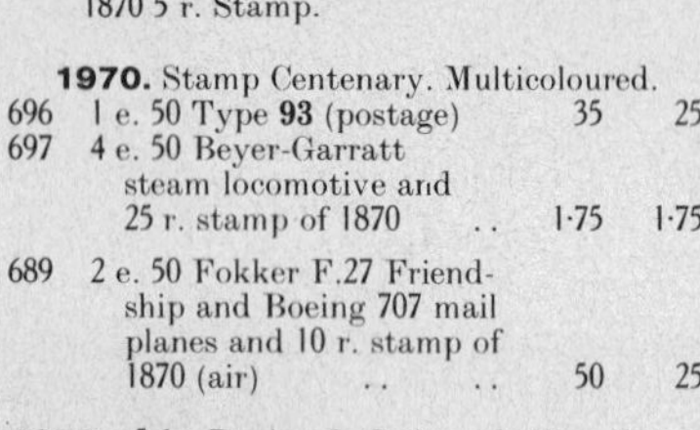

**1970.** Stamp Centenary. Multicoloured.
696 1 e. 50 Type **93** (postage) 35 25
697 4 e. 50 Beyer-Garratt steam locomotive and 25 r. stamp of 1870 .. 1·75 1·75
689 2 e. 50 Fokker F.27 Friendship and Boeing 707 mail planes and 10 r. stamp of 1870 (air) .. .. 50 25

**1971.** 5th Regional Soil and Foundation Engineering Conference, Luanda.
700 **94** 2 e. 50 multicoloured .. 20 15

**96.** 16th-century Galleon at Mouth of Congo. **97.** Sailing Yachts.

**1972.** 400th Anniv of Camoens' "The Lusiads" (epic poem).
704 **96** 1 e. multicoloured .. 30 15

**1972.** Olympic Games, Munich.
705. **97.** 50 c. multicoloured .. 30 15

**98.** Fairey IIID Seaplane "Santa Cruz" near Fernando de Noronha.

**1972.** 50th Anniv. of 1st Flight Lisbon-Rio de Janeiro.
706. **98.** 1 e. multicoloured .. 20 15

**99.** W. M. O. Emblem.

**1974.** Centenary of W.M.O.
707. **99.** 1 e. multicoloured .. 20 15

**100.** Dish Aerials.

**1974.** Inauguration of Satellite Communications Station Network.
708 **100** 2 e. multicoloured .. 25 20

**101.** Doris Harp.

**1974.** Sea Shells. Multicoloured.
709 25 c. Type **101** .. .. 10 10
710 30 c. West African murex 10 10
711 50 c. Scaly-ridged venus .. 10 10
712 70 c. Filose latirus 10 10
713 1 e. "Cymbium cisium" .. 10 10
714 1 e. 50 West African helmet 15 10
715 2 e. Rat cowrie .. 15 10
716 2 e. 50 Butterfly cone .. 25 10
717 3 e. Bubonian conch .. 25 15
718 3 e. 50 "Tympanotonus fuscatus" .. .. 30 15
719 4 e. Great ribbed cockle .. 30 15
720 5 e. Lightning moon .. 40 15
721 6 e. Lion's-paw scallop .. 45 20
722 7 e. Giant tun .. 60 25
723 10 e. Rugose donax .. 80 30
724 25 e. Smith's distorsio .. 2·25 90
725 30 e. "Olivancilaria acuminata" .. .. 2·25 1·00
726 35 e. Giant hairy melongena .. .. 2·75 1·25
727 40 e. Wavy-leaved turrid 3·50 1·40
728 50 e. American sundial .. 4·50 1·75

**1974.** Youth Philately. No. 511 optd **1974 FILATELIA JUVENIL**.
729 **51** 5 c. multicoloured .. 35 50

**103.** Arm with Rifle and Star. **104.** Diquiche-ua-Puheue Mask.

**1975.** Independence.
730. **103.** 1 e. 50 multicoloured 10 10

**1975.** Angolan Masks. Multicoloured.
731. 50 c. Type **104** .. .. 10 10
732. 3 e. Bui ou Congolo mask 15 10

**105.** Workers. **107.** President Agostinho Neto.

**1976.** Workers' Day.
733. **105.** 1 e. multicoloured .. 10 10

**1976.** Stamp Day. Optd. **DIA DO SELO 15 Junho 1976 REP, POPULAR DE.**
734. **51.** 10 e. multicoloured .. 1·25 75

**1976.** Independence. 1st Anniv.
735. **107.** 50 c. black and grey .. 10 10
736. 2 e. purple and grey .. 10 10
737. 3 e. blue and grey .. 10 10
738. 5 e. brown and buff .. 15 10
739. 10 e. brown and drab .. 25 10

**1976.** St. Silvestre Games. Optd. **S. Silvestre Rep. Popular de.**
741. **62.** 15 e. multicoloured .. 55 35

**1977.** Nos. 518, 724/5 and 728 optd. **REPUBLICA POPULAR DE.**
742. 20 e. Type **51** .. .. 1·40 40
743. 25 e. "Cymatium trigonum" .. .. 60 15
744. 30 e. "Olivancilaria acuminata" .. .. 75 25
745. 50 e. "Solarium granulatum" .. .. .. 1·25 40

**111.** Child receiving Vaccine. **112.** Map of Africa and Flag.

**1977.** Polio Vaccination Campaign.
746. **111.** 2 k. 50 blue & black .. 10 10

**1977.** MPLA Congress.
747. **112.** 6 k. multicoloured .. 20 15

**113.** Human Rights Flame. **114.** Emblem.

**1979.** 30th Anniv. of Declaration of Human Rights.
748. **113.** 2 k. 50 yell., red & blk. 15 10

**1979.** International Anti-apartheid Year.
749. **114.** 1 k. multicoloured .. 10 10

**115.** Child raising Arms to Light. **117.** President Agostinho Neto.

**1980.** International Year of the Child (1979).
750. **115.** 3 k. 50 multicoloured 15 10

**1980.** Nos. 697/8 optd. **REPUBLICA POPULAR DE.**
751 4 e. 50 mult (postage) .. 1·00 1·00
752 2 e. 50 multicoloured (air) 15 10

**1980.** National Heroes Day. Multicoloured.
753. 4 k. 50 Type **117** .. 15 10
754. 50 k. Pres. Neto with machine-gun .. .. 1·25 70

**118.** Arms and Workers. **119.** "The Liberated Angolan" (A. Vaz de Carvalho).

**1980.** "Popular Power"
755. **118.** 40 k. blue and black .. 1·00 55

**1980.** 5th Anniv. of Independence.
756. **119.** 5 k. 50 multicoloured 15 10

**120.** Running. **121.** Millet.

**1980.** Olympic Games, Moscow.
757. **120.** 9 k. pink and red .. 20 10
758. – 12 k. light blue and blue 30 10
DESIGN: 12 k. Swimming.

**1980.** Angolan Produce. Multicoloured.
759. 50 l. Type **121** .. .. 10 10
760. 5 k. Coffee .. .. 15 10
761. 7 k. 50 Sunflower .. 20 10
762. 13 k. 50 Cotton .. .. 30 15
763. 14 k. Petroleum .. .. 30 15
764. 16 k. Diamonds .. .. 35 20

**1981.** Nos. 708, 713/16 and 718/27 with "REPUBLICA PORTUGUESA" inscr obliterated. (a) Dish aerials.
765 **100** 2 e. multicoloured .. 10 10

(b) Sea Shells. Multicoloured.
766 1 e. "Cymbium cisium" .. 10 10
767 1 e. 50 West African helmet 15 10
768 2 e. Rat cowrie .. .. 20 10
769 2 e. 50 Butterfly cone .. 25 10
770 3 e. 50 "Tympanotonus fuscatus" .. .. 30 10
771 4 e. Great ribbed cockle .. 35 15
772 5 e. Lighting moon .. 40 15
773 6 e. Lion's-paw scallop .. 45 20
774 7 e. Giant tun .. .. 50 20
775 10 e. Rugose donax .. 70 25
776 25 e. Smith's distorsio .. 1·75 30
777 30 e. "Olivancilaria acuminata" .. .. 1·90 65
778 35 e. Giant hairy melongena .. .. 2·40 90
779 40 e. Wavy-leaved turrid 3·00 1·00

**122.** Prisoner and Protesting Crowd.

**1981.** 5th Anniv. of Soweto Riots in South Africa.
780. **122.** 4 k. 50 black, red and silver .. .. 20 15

**123.** Basketball and Volleyball.

**1981.** Second Central African Games. Multicoloured.
781. 50 l. Cycling and Tennis .. 10 10
782. 5k. Judo and Boxing .. 20 15
783. 6 k. Type **123** .. .. 25 15
784. 10 k. Handball and football .. .. .. 40 20

**124.** Statuette.

**125.** " Charaxes kahldeni f. homeyri ".

**1981.** " Turipex 81 ".

785 **124.** 9 k. multicoloured .. 40 20

**1982.** Butterflies. Multicoloured.

787. 50 l. Type **125** .. .. 10 10
788. 1 k. " Abantis gambesiaca " 10 10
789. 5 k. " Catacroptera cloanthe " .. .. 25 30
790. 9 k. " Myrina ficedula " (vert.) .. .. .. 60 25
791. 10 k. " Colotis danae " .. 60 25
792. 15 k. " Acraea acrita bella " 80 30
793. 100 k. " Precis hierta cebrese " .. .. 5·25 2·40

**126.** " Silence of Night ".

**127.** Worker and Building.

**1982.** 5th Anniv. of Admission to United Nations. Multicoloured.

794. 5 k. 50 Type **126** .. .. 25 15
795. 7 k. 50 " Cotton Fields " 35 15

**1982.** 20th Anniv. of Angola Laboratory of Engineering. Multicoloured.

797. 9 k. Laboratory Building (horiz.) .. .. .. 40 20
798. 13 k. Type **127** (Research in construction materials) 45 25
799. 100 k. Geotechnical equipment .. .. .. 4·00 2·25

**128.** " Albizzia versicolor ".

**1983.** Flowers (1st series). Multicoloured.

800. 5 k. " Dichrostachys glomerata " .. .. 25 10
801. 12 k. " Amblygonocarpus obtusangulus " .. 45 20
802. 50 k. Type **128** .. .. 2·00 1·10

**129.** Angolan Woman and Emblem.

**1983.** 1st Angolan Women's Organization Congress.

803. **129.** 20 k. multicoloured .. 80 25

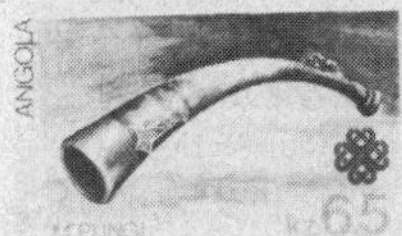


**130.** M'pungi (horn).

**1983.** World Communications Year. Mult.

804. 6 k. 50 Type **130** .. .. 25 20
805. 12 k. Mondu (drum) .. 50 45

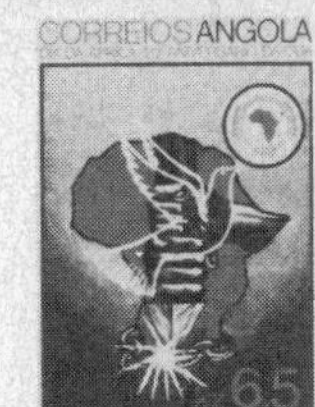


**131.** Spear breaking Chain around South Africa.

**1983.** 30th Anniv. of Organization of African Unity.

806. **131.** 6 k. 50 multicoloured .. 30 25

**132.** " Antestiopsis lineaticollis intricata ".

**1983.** " Brasiliana 83 " International Stamp Exhibition, Rio de Janeiro. Harmful Insects. Multicoloured.

807. 4 k. 50 Type **132** .. .. 25 15
808. 6 k. 50 " Stephanoderes hampei " .. .. 35 25
809. 10 k. " Zonocerus variegatus " 60 45

**133.** Map of Africa and E.C.A. Emblem.

**1983.** 25th Anniv. of Economic Commission for Africa.

810. **133.** 10 k. multicoloured .. 45 40

**134.** Collecting Mail.

**136.** Dove.

**135.** "Parasa karschi".

**1983.** 185th Anniv. of Postal Service. Multicoloured.

811. 50 l. Type **134** .. .. 10 10
812. 3 k. 50 Unloading mail from aircraft (horiz.) .. 20 15
813. 5 k. Sorting mail (horiz.) .. 35 25
814. 15 k. Posting letter .. 85 80
815. 30 k. Collecting mail from private box (horiz.) .. 1·75 1·50

**1984.** Moths. Multicoloured.

817. 50 l. Type **135** .. .. 10 10
818. 1 k. "Diaphone angolensis" 10 10
819. 3 k. 50 "Choeropais jucunda" .. .. .. 30 15
820. 6 k. 50 "Hespagarista rendalli" .. .. .. 50 35
821. 15 k. "Euchromia guineensis" .. .. .. 95 80
822. 17 k. 50 "Mazuca roseistriga" .. .. .. 1·10 95
823. 20 k. "Utetheisa callima" 1·40 1·25

**1984.** First National Union of Angolan Workers Congress.

824. **136.** 30 k. multicoloured .. 1·75 1·50

**137.** Flag and Agostinho Neto.

**1984.** 5th National Heroes Day. Mult.

825. 10 k. 50 Type **137** .. .. 50 45
826. 36 k. 50 Flag and Agostinho Neto (different) .. .. 1·60 1·50

**138.** Southern Ground Hornbill.

**1984.** Birds. Multicoloured.

827. 10 k. 50 Type **138** .. .. 90 90
828. 14 k. Palm-nut vulture .. 1·25 1·25
829. 16 k. Goliath heron .. 1·50 1·50
830. 19 k. 50 Eastern white pelican .. .. .. 1·75 1·75
831. 22 k. African spoonbill .. 2·00 2·00
832. 26 k. South African crowned crane .. .. 2·40 2·40

**139.** Greater Kudu.

**1984.** Mammals. Multicoloured.

833. 1 k. Type **139** .. .. 10 10
834. 4 k. Springbok .. .. 25 15
835. 5 k. Chimpanzee .. .. 30 25
836. 10 k. African buffalo .. 55 50
837. 15 k. Sable antelope .. 80 65
838. 20 k. Aardvark .. .. 1·25 1·10
839. 25 k. Spotted hyena .. 1·50 1·25

**140.** San Pedro da Barra Fortress.

**1985.** Monuments. Multicoloured.

840. 5 k. Type **140** .. .. 25 20
841. 12 k. 50 Nova Oerias ruins 60 55
842. 18 k. Antiga cathedral ruins, M'Banza Kongo .. 80 75
843. 26 k. Massangano fortress 1·25 1·10
844. 39 k. Escravatura museum 1·75 1·60

**141.** Flags on World Map.

**142.** Flags and "XXV".

**1985.** 5th Anniv. of Southern Africa Development Co-ordination Conference. Mult.

845. 1 k. Type **141** .. .. 10 10
846. 11 k. Off-shore drilling .. 80 50
847. 57 k. Conference session .. 2·50 2·40

**1985.** 25th Anniv. of National Union of Angolan Workers.

848. **142.** 77 k. multicoloured .. 3·50 3·25

**143.** "Lonchocarpas sericeus".

**1985.** Medicinal Plants. Multicoloured.

849. 1 k. Type **143** .. .. 10 10
850. 4 k. "Gossypium sp." .. 20 15
851. 11 k. Senna .. .. 50 45
852. 25 k. 50 "Gloriosa superba" 1·10 1·00
853. 55 k. "Cochlospermum angolensis" .. .. 2·50 2·40

**144.** Map of Angola as Dove and Conference Emblem.

**1984.** Ministerial Conference of Non-aligned Countries, Luanda.

854. **144.** 35 k. multicoloured .. 1·60 1·50

**145.** Dove and U.N. Emblem.

**1985.** 40th Anniv. of U.N.O.

855. **145.** 12 k. 50 multicoloured 60 55

**146.** Cement Works.

**1985.** 10th Anniv. of Independence. Mult.

856. 50 l. Type **146** .. .. 10 10
857. 5 k. Timber yard .. .. 20 15
858. 7 k. Quartz .. .. .. 30 25
859. 10 k. Iron works .. .. 50 45

**147.** Emblem, Open Book, Soldier, Farmer and Factory.

**1985.** 2nd MPLA Congress.

861. **147.** 20 k. multicoloured .. 90 85

**148.** Runner on Track.

**1985.** 30th Anniv. of Demostenes de Almeida Clington Races. Multicoloured.

862. 50 l. Type **148** .. .. 10 10
863. 5 k. Two runners on road 20 15
864. 6 k. 50 Three runners on road .. .. .. 30 25
865. 10 k. Two runners on track 50 45

**149.** Map, Stadium and Players.

**150.** Crowd.

**1986.** World Cup Football Championship, Mexico.
866. **149.** 50 l. multicoloured .. 10 10
867. – 3 k. 50 multicoloured 15 15
868. – 5 k. multicoloured .. 30 25
869. – 7 k. multicoloured .. 35 30
870. – 10 k. multicoloured .. 50 45
871. – 18 k. multicoloured .. 85 70
DESIGNS: 3 k. 50 to 18 k. Different footballers.

**1986.** 25th Anniv. of Armed Independence Movement.
872. **150.** 15 k. multicoloured .. 75 70

**151.** Soviet Space Project.

**1985.** 25th Anniv. of First Man in Space. Multicoloured.
873. 50 l. Type **151** .. .. 10 10
874. 1 k. "Voskhod I" .. .. 10 10
875. 5 k. Cosmonaut on space walk .. .. .. 20 15
876. 10 k. Moon vehicle .. 50 45
877. 13 k. "Soyuz"–Apollo" link-up .. .. .. 60 55

**152.** National Flag and U.N. Emblem.
**153.** People at Work.

**1986.** 10th Anniv. of Angolan Membership of U.N.O.
878. **152.** 22 k. multicoloured .. 1·00 90

**1986.** 30th Anniv. of MPLA (Popular Movement for the Liberation of Angola). Multicoloured.
879. 5 k. Type **153** .. .. 20 15
880. 5 k. Emblem and people (29 × 36 mm.) .. .. 20 15
881. 5 k. Soldiers fighting .. 20 15
Nos. 879/81 were printed together, se-tenant, forming a composite design.

**154.** Lecturer and Students (Faculty of Engineering).
**155.** Ouioca.

**1986.** 10th Anniv. of Agostinho Neto University. Multicoloured.
882. 50 l. Type **154** .. .. 10 10
883. 7 k. Students and Judges (Faculty of Law) .. 30 25
884. 10 k. Students using microscopes and surgeons operating (Faculty of Medicine) .. .. 50 45

**1987.** Traditional Hairstyles. Multicoloured.
885. 1 k. Type **155** .. .. 10 10
886. 1 k. 50 Luanda .. .. 10 10
887. 5 k. Humbe .. .. 20 15
888. 7 k. Muila .. .. .. 35 25
889. 20 k. Muila (different) .. 80 70
890. 30 k. Lunda, Dilolo .. 1·25 1·00

**156.** "Lenin in the Smolny Institute" (detail, Serov).
**157.** Pambala Beach.

**1987.** 70th Anniv. of Russian Revolution.
891. **156.** 15 k. multicoloured .. 60 25

**1987.** Scenic Spots. Multicoloured.
892. 50 l. Type **157** .. .. 10 10
893. 1 k. 50 Quedas do Dala (waterfalls) .. .. 10 10
894. 3 k. 50 Black Feet Rocks, Pungo Adongo (vert.) .. 15 10
895. 5 k. Cuango River valley 20 15
896. 10 k. Luanda shore (vert.) 40 35
897. 20 k. Serra da Leba road .. 80 75

**158.** Emblem.
**159.** Dancers.

**1988.** 2nd Angolan Women's Organization Congress. Multicoloured.
898. 2 k. Type **158** .. .. 10 10
899. 10 k. Women engaged in various pursuits .. 40 35

**1988.** 10th Anniv. of Vitoria Carnival. Multicoloured.
900. 5 k. Type **159** .. .. 15 10
901. 10 k. Revellers .. .. 40 35

**160** Augusto N'Gangula (child revolutionary)

**1989.** Pioneers. Multicoloured.
902 12 k. Type **160** (20th death anniv) .. .. .. 50 45
903 15 k. Pioneers (25th anniv (1988) of Agostinho Neto Pioneers Organization) 60 55

**161** Luanda 1st August Sports Club (1979–81)

**1989.** 10th National Football League Championship. Championship Winners. Multicoloured.
904 5 k. Type **161** .. .. 15 15
905 5 k. Luanda Petro Atletico (1982, 1984, 1986–88) .. 15 15
906 5 k. Benguela 1st May Sports Club (1983, 1985) 15 15

**162** Watering Cabbages

**1990.** 10th Anniv (1987) of International Fund for Agricultural Development.
907 **162** 10 k. multicoloured .. 35 30

**163** 19th-century Middle-class Houses, Luanda

**1990.** Historical Buildings. Multicoloured.
908 1 k. Type **163** .. .. 10 10
909 2 k. Cidade Alta railway station .. .. .. 10 10
910 5 k. National Anthropology Museum .. 20 15
911 15 k. Palace of Ana Joaquina dos Santos .. 55 50
912 23 k. Iron Palace .. .. 80 75
913 36 k. Meteorological Observatory (vert) .. 1·25 1·10
914 50 k. Governor's Palace 1·75 1·60

**164** "General Machado" and Route Map

**1990.** Benguela (915) and Luanda Railways. Multicoloured.
915 5 k. Type **164** .. .. 20 15
916 12 k. Garratt locomotive (facing left) .. .. 40 35
917 12 k. Garratt locomotive (facing right) .. .. 40 35
918 14 k. Mikado steam locomotive .. .. .. 50 45

**165** Hydro-electric Production

**1990.** 10th Anniv of Southern Africa Development Co-ordinating Conference. Mult.
920 5 k. Type **165** .. .. 20 15
921 9 k. Oil industry .. .. 50 30

**166** Map in Envelope

**1990.** 10th Anniv of Pan-African Postal Union. Multicoloured.
922 4 k. Type **166** .. .. 15 10
923 10 k. Map consisting of stamps and envelopes .. 35 30

**167** "Muxima"

**1990.** "Stamp World London 90" International Stamp Exhibition. Paintings by Raul Indipwo. Multicoloured.
924 6 k. "Three Graces" (horiz) 20 15
925 9 k. Type **167** .. .. 30 25

**168** Antelope

**1990.** Protected Animals. Sable Antelope Multicoloured.
926 5 k. Type **168** .. .. 20 15
927 5 k. Male and female .. 20 15
928 5 k. Female .. .. 20 15
929 5 k. Female and young .. 20 15

**169** Porcelain Rose
**170** Zebra Drinking

**1990.** "Belgica 90" International Stamp Exhibition, Brussels. Flowers. Multicoloured.
930 5 k. Type **169** .. .. 20 15
931 8 k. Indian carnation .. 30 25
932 10 k. Allamanda .. .. 35 30

**1990.** International Literacy Year. Mult.
934 5 k. Type **170** .. .. 20 15
935 5 k. Butterfly .. .. 20 15
936 5 k. Horse's head .. 20 15

**171** Flag and People

**1990.** 10th Anniv of People's Assembly.
938 **171** 10 k. multicoloured .. 35 30

**172** Dove, Flag and Workers
**174** Marimba

**173** Uniform, 1961

**1990.** 3rd Popular Movement for the Liberation of Angola-Labour Party Congress.
939 **172** 14 k. multicoloured .. 50 45

**1991.** 30th Anniv of Armed Independence Movement. Freedom Fighters' Uniforms. Multicoloured.
940 6 k. Type **173** .. .. 20 15
941 6 k. Pau N'Dulo, 1962–63 20 15
942 6 k. Military uniform, 1968 20 15
943 6 k. Military uniform from 1972 .. .. .. 20 15

**1991.** Musical Instruments. Multicoloured.
944 6 k. Type **174** .. .. 10 10
945 6 k. Ngoma ya Mucupela (double-ended drum) .. 10 10
946 6 k. Ngoma la Txina (floor-standing drum) .. 10 10
947 6 k. Kissange .. .. 10 10

**175** Iona National Park

**1991.** African Tourism Year. Multicoloured.
948 3 k. Type **175** .. .. 10 10
949 7 k. Kalandula Falls .. 10 10
950 35 k. Lobito Bay .. .. 55 30
951 60 k. "Welwitchia mirabilis" .. .. .. 65 55

**176** Kabir of the Dembos

**1991.** "Espamer '91" Spain-Latin America Stamp Exhibition, Buenos Aires. Dogs. Mult.

| | | | |
|---|---|---|---|
| 953 | 5 k. Type **176** .. .. | 10 | 10 |
| 954 | 7 k. Ombua .. .. | 10 | 10 |
| 955 | 11 k. Kabir massongo .. | 15 | 10 |
| 956 | 12 k. Kawa tchowe .. | 15 | 10 |

**177** Judo **178** Mother and Child

**1991.** Olympic Games, Barcelona (1992) (1st issue). Multicoloured.

| | | | |
|---|---|---|---|
| 957 | 4 k. Type **177** .. .. | 10 | 10 |
| 958 | 6 k. Yachting .. .. | 10 | 10 |
| 959 | 10 k. Marathon .. | 15 | 10 |
| 960 | 100 k. Swimming .. .. | 1·10 | 95 |

**1991.** 13th Anniv of Angolan Red Cross. Mult.

| | | | |
|---|---|---|---|
| 961 | 20 k.+5 k. Type **178** .. | 30 | 20 |
| 962 | 40 k.+5 k. Zebra and foal | 50 | 40 |

**179** Quadrant and Galleon

**1991.** "Iberex '91" Stamp Exhibition. Navigational Instruments. Multicoloured.

| | | | |
|---|---|---|---|
| 963 | 5 k. Type **179** .. .. | 10 | 10 |
| 964 | 15 k. Astrolabe and caravel | 20 | 10 |
| 965 | 20 k. Cross-staff and caravel .. .. | 30 | 15 |
| 966 | 50 k. Navigation chart by Francisco Rodrigues and galleon .. .. .. | 80 | 50 |

**180** Common Eagle Ray **181** Mukixi wa Mbwesu Mask

**1992.** Rays. Multicoloured.

| | | | |
|---|---|---|---|
| 967 | 40 k. Type **180** .. .. | 25 | 20 |
| 968 | 50 k. Spotted duck-billed ray .. .. .. | 30 | 25 |
| 969 | 66 k. Atlantic mantas .. | 40 | 30 |
| 970 | 80 k. Brown ray .. .. | 50 | 40 |

**1992.** Quioca Painted Masks (1st series).

| | | | | |
|---|---|---|---|---|
| 972 | – | 60 k. orange & brown | 15 | 10 |
| 973 | – | 100 k. blk, verm & red | 25 | 20 |
| 974 | **181** | 150 k. pink and orange | 35 | 30 |
| 975 | – | 250 k. red and brown | 60 | 50 |

DESIGNS: 60 k. Kalelwa mask; 100 k. Mikixe wa Kino mask; 250 k. Cikunza mask.

See also Nos. 1006/7 and 1021/4.

**182** "Ptaeroxylon obliquum" **183** King and Missionaries

**1992.** "Lubrapex 92" Brazilian–Portuguese Stamp Exhibition, Lisbon. Medicinal Plants. Each brown, stone and deep brown.

| | | | |
|---|---|---|---|
| 976 | 200 k. Type **182** .. .. | 45 | 35 |
| 977 | 300 k. "Spondias mombin" | 70 | 55 |
| 978 | 500 k. "Parinari curatellifolia" .. .. | 1·25 | 1·00 |
| 979 | 600 k. "Cochlospermum angolense" .. .. | 1·40 | 1·10 |

**1992.** 500th Anniv (1991) of Baptism of First Angolans. Multicoloured.

| | | | |
|---|---|---|---|
| 980 | 150 k. Type **183** .. .. | 35 | 30 |
| 981 | 420 k. Ruins of M'Banza Congo Church .. | 1·00 | 80 |
| 982 | 470 k. Muxima Church .. | 1·10 | 90 |
| 983 | 500 k. Cross superimposed on children's faces .. | 1·25 | 1·00 |

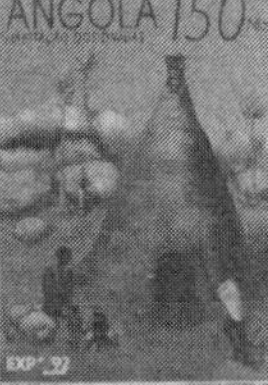

**184** Dimba House **185** Lovebirds

**1992.** "Expo '92" World's Fair, Seville. Traditional Houses. Multicoloured.

| | | | |
|---|---|---|---|
| 984 | 150 k. Type **184** .. .. | 35 | 30 |
| 985 | 330 k. Cokwe house .. | 80 | 65 |
| 986 | 360 k. Mbali house .. | 85 | 70 |
| 987 | 420 k. Ambwela house .. | 1·00 | 80 |
| 988 | 500 k. House of the Upper Zambezi .. | 1·25 | 1·00 |

**1992.** Nature Protection. Peach-faced Lovebirds. Multicoloured.

| | | | |
|---|---|---|---|
| 989 | 150 k. Type **185** .. .. | 35 | 30 |
| 990 | 200 k. Birds feeding .. | 45 | 35 |
| 991 | 250 k. Bird in hand .. | 60 | 50 |
| 992 | 300 k. Bird on perch .. | 70 | 55 |

**187** Hurdling **188** Women with Nets

**1992.** Olympic Games, Barcelona (2nd issue). Multicoloured.

| | | | |
|---|---|---|---|
| 994 | 120 k. Type **187** .. .. | 30 | 25 |
| 995 | 180 k. Cycling .. .. | 45 | 35 |
| 996 | 240 k. Roller hockey .. | 55 | 45 |
| 997 | 360 k. Basketball .. .. | 85 | 70 |

**1992.** Fishing. Multicoloured.

| | | | |
|---|---|---|---|
| 998 | 65 k. Type **188** .. .. | 15 | 10 |
| 999 | 90 k. Fishermen pulling in nets .. .. | 20 | 15 |
| 1000 | 100 k. Fishermen checking traps .. .. .. | 25 | 20 |
| 1001 | 120 k. Fishing canoes .. | 30 | 25 |

**190** Crowd with Ballot Papers around Ballot Box **191** Post Van

**1992.** 1st Free Elections. Multicoloured.

| | | | |
|---|---|---|---|
| 1003 | 120 k. Type **190** .. .. | 30 | 25 |
| 1004 | 150 k. Doves, map, people and ballot box .. | 35 | 30 |
| 1005 | 200 k. Dove, crowd and ballot box .. | 45 | 35 |

**1992.** Quioca Painted Masks (2nd series). As T **181**.

| | | | |
|---|---|---|---|
| 1006 | 72 k. brown, black & yell | 15 | 10 |
| 1007 | 80 k. red, black & brown | 20 | 15 |
| 1008 | 120 k. pink, black and red | 30 | 25 |
| 1009 | 210 k. black and yellow .. | 50 | 40 |

DESIGNS: 72 k. Cihongo mask; 80 k. Mbwasu mask; 120 k. Cinhanga mask; 210 k. Kalewa mask.

**1992.** Introduction of Express Mail Service in Angola. Multicoloured.

| | | | |
|---|---|---|---|
| 1010 | 450 k. Type **191** .. .. | 55 | 45 |
| 1011 | 550 k. Boeing 707 airplane | 65 | 50 |

**192** Weather Balloon **193** Rayed Hat

**1993.** World Meteorology Day. Meteorological Instruments. Multicoloured.

| | | | |
|---|---|---|---|
| 1012 | 250 k. Type **192** .. .. | 10 | 10 |
| 1013 | 470 k. Actinometer .. | 10 | 10 |
| 1014 | 500 k. Rain-gauge .. | 10 | 10 |

**1993.** Molluscs. Multicoloured.

| | | | |
|---|---|---|---|
| 1015 | 210 k. Type **193** .. .. | 10 | 10 |
| 1016 | 330 k. Bubonian conch .. | 15 | 10 |
| 1017 | 400 k. African pelican's foot .. .. .. | 15 | 10 |
| 1018 | 500 k. White spindle .. | 20 | 15 |

**1993.** Quioca Art (1st series). As T **181**.

| | | | |
|---|---|---|---|
| 1021 | 72 k. grey, red and brown | 10 | 10 |
| 1022 | 210 k. pink and brown .. | 10 | 10 |
| 1023 | 420 k. black, brn & orge | 10 | 10 |
| 1024 | 600 k. black, red & brown | 10 | 10 |

DESIGNS: 72 k. Men with vehicles; 210 k. Rider on antelope; 420 k. Bird-plane; 600 k. Carrying "soba".

See also Nos. 1038/41 and 1050/3.

**195** "Sansevieria cylindrica" **196** Atlantic Hawksbill Turtle laying Eggs and Green Turtle

**1993.** Cacti and Succulents. Multicoloured.

| | | | |
|---|---|---|---|
| 1025 | 360 k. Type **195** .. .. | 10 | 10 |
| 1026 | 400 k. Milk-bush .. | 10 | 10 |
| 1027 | 500 k. Indian fig .. | 10 | 10 |
| 1028 | 600 k. "Dracaena aubryana" .. .. | 10 | 10 |

**1993.** Sea Turtles. Multicoloured.

| | | | |
|---|---|---|---|
| 1029 | 180 k. Type **196** .. .. | 10 | 10 |
| 1030 | 450 k. Head of Atlantic hawksbill turtle and newly-hatched turtles | 10 | 10 |
| 1031 | 550 k. Leather-back turtle | 10 | 10 |
| 1032 | 630 k. Loggerhead turtles | 15 | 10 |

Nos. 1029/32 were issued together, se-tenant, forming a composite design.

**198** Vimbundi Pipe **199** St. George's Mushroom

**1993.** Tobacco Pipes. Multicoloured.

| | | | |
|---|---|---|---|
| 1034 | 72 k. Type **198** .. .. | 10 | 10 |
| 1035 | 200 k. Vimbundi pipe (different) .. .. | 10 | 10 |
| 1036 | 420 k. Mutopa calabash water pipe .. .. | 10 | 10 |
| 1037 | 600 k. Pexi carved-head pipe .. .. .. | 10 | 10 |

**1993.** Quioca Art (2nd series). As T **181**.

| | | | |
|---|---|---|---|
| 1038 | 300 k. brown and orange | 10 | 10 |
| 1039 | 600 k. red and brown .. | 10 | 10 |
| 1040 | 800 k. blk, orge & dp orge | 15 | 10 |
| 1041 | 1000 k. orange and brown | 20 | 15 |

DESIGNS: 300 k. Leopard and dog; 600 k. Rabbits; 800 k. Birds; 1000 k. Birds and cockerel.

**1993.** Fungi. Multicoloured.

| | | | |
|---|---|---|---|
| 1042 | 300 k. Type **199** .. .. | 55 | 15 |
| 1043 | 500 k. Death cap .. | 90 | 30 |
| 1044 | 600 k. "Amanita vaginata" .. .. | 1·10 | 35 |
| 1045 | 1000 k. Parasol mushroom | 1·90 | 60 |

**200** "Cinganji" (figurine of dancer, Bie province) **201** Orgy

**1994.** National Culture Day. "Hong Kong'94" International Stamp Exhibition. Mult.

| | | | |
|---|---|---|---|
| 1046 | 500 k. Type **200** .. .. | 10 | 10 |
| 1047 | 1000 k. Chief's staff with carved woman's head (Bie province) .. | 20 | 15 |
| 1048 | 1200 k. Statuette of traveller riding ox (Huambo province) .. | 25 | 20 |
| 1049 | 2200 k. Corn pestle (Ovimbundu) .. .. | 45 | 35 |

**1994.** Quioca Art (3rd series). As T **181**.

| | | | |
|---|---|---|---|
| 1050 | 500 k. multicoloured .. | 10 | 10 |
| 1051 | 2000 k. red and brown .. | 40 | 30 |
| 1051 | 2500 k. red and brown .. | 50 | 40 |
| 1053 | 3000 k. carmine and red | 60 | 50 |

DESIGNS: 500 k. Bird on plant; 2000 k. Plant with roots; 2500 k. Plant; 3000 k. Fern.

**1994.** AIDS Awareness Campaign. Mult.

| | | | |
|---|---|---|---|
| 1054 | 500 k. Type **201** .. .. | 10 | 10 |
| 1055 | 1000 k. Masked figure using infected syringe passing box of condoms to young couple .. | 10 | 10 |
| 1056 | 3000 k. Victims .. .. | 20 | 15 |

**202** Flag, Arrows and Small Ball

**1994.** World Cup Football Championship, U.S.A. Multicoloured.

| | | | |
|---|---|---|---|
| 1057 | 500 k. Type **202** .. .. | 10 | 10 |
| 1058 | 700 k. Flag, four arrows and large ball .. .. | 10 | 10 |
| 1059 | 2200 k. Flag, goal net and ball .. .. .. | 10 | 10 |
| 1060 | 2500 k. Flag, ball and boot | 10 | 10 |

**203** Brachiosaurus

**1994.** "Philakorea 1994" International and "Singpex '94" Stamp Exns. Dinosaurs. Mult.

| | | | |
|---|---|---|---|
| 1061 | 1000 k. Type **203** .. | 10 | 10 |
| 1062 | 3000 k. Spinosaurus .. | 10 | 10 |
| 1063 | 5000 k. Ouranosaurus .. | 10 | 10 |
| 1064 | 10000 k. Lesothosaurus .. | 15 | 10 |

**204** Birds

**1994.** Tourism. Multicoloured.

| | | | |
|---|---|---|---|
| 1066 | 2000 k. Type **204** .. | 10 | 10 |
| 1067 | 4000 k. Animals .. | 10 | 10 |
| 1068 | 8000 k. Women .. | 10 | 10 |
| 1069 | 10000 k. Men .. .. | 10 | 10 |

205 Dual-service Wall-mounted Post Box

**1994.** Post Boxes. Multicoloured.

| | | | |
|---|---|---|---|
| 1070 | 5000 k. Type **205** .. | 10 | 10 |
| 1071 | 7500 k. Wall-mounted philatelic post box .. | 10 | 10 |
| 1072 | 10000 k. Free-standing post box .. .. | 10 | 10 |
| 1073 | 21000 k. Multiple service wall-mounted post box | 25 | 15 |

206 "Heliothis armigera" (moth)

**1994.** Insects. Multicoloured.

| | | | |
|---|---|---|---|
| 1074 | 5000 k. Type **206** .. | 10 | 10 |
| 1075 | 6000 k. "Bemisia tabasi" | 10 | 10 |
| 1076 | 10000 k. "Dysdercus sp." (bug) .. .. .. | 10 | 10 |
| 1077 | 27000 k. "Spodoptera exigua" (moth) .. | 25 | 15 |

207 "100"

**1994.** Cent of Int Olympic Committee.

| | | | |
|---|---|---|---|
| 1078 | **207** 27000 k. red, yell & blk | 25 | 20 |

208 Pot

**1995.** Traditional Ceramics. With service indicator. Multicoloured. (a) INLAND POSTAGE. Inscr "PORTE NACIONAL".

| | | | |
|---|---|---|---|
| 1079 | (1°) Type **208** .. .. | 10 | 10 |
| 1080 | (2°) Pot with figure of woman on lid .. .. | 10 | 10 |

(b) INTERNATIONAL POSTAGE. Inscr "PORTE INTERNACIONAL".

| | | | |
|---|---|---|---|
| 1081 | (1°) Pot with man's head on lid .. .. .. | 20 | 15 |
| 1082 | (2°) Duck-shaped pot .. | 25 | 20 |

209 Making Fire

**1995.** The !Kung (Khoisan tribe). Mult.

| | | | |
|---|---|---|---|
| 1083 | 10000 k. Type **209** .. | 10 | 10 |
| 1084 | 15000 k. Tipping darts with poison .. .. | 15 | 10 |
| 1085 | 20000 k. Smoking .. | 20 | 15 |
| 1086 | 25000 k. Hunting .. | 20 | 15 |
| 1087 | 28000 k. Women and children .. .. | 25 | 20 |
| 1088 | 30000 k. Painting animals on walls .. .. | 25 | 20 |

## INDEX

Countries can be quickly located by referring to the index at the end of this volume.

210 Vaccinating Child against Polio

**1995.** 90th Anniv of Rotary International. Multicoloured. (a) Inscr in Portuguese.

| | | | |
|---|---|---|---|
| 1089 | 27000 k. Type **210** .. | 15 | 10 |
| 1090 | 27000 k. Examining baby | 15 | 10 |
| 1091 | 27000 k. Giving child vaccination .. .. | 15 | 10 |

(b) Inscr in English.

| | | | |
|---|---|---|---|
| 1092 | 27000 k. Type **210** .. | 15 | 10 |
| 1093 | 27000 k. As No. 1090 .. | 15 | 10 |
| 1094 | 27000 k. As No. 1091 .. | 15 | 10 |

Nos. 1089/91 and 1092/4 respectively were issued together, se-tenant, forming composite designs.

211 "Sputnik I" (satellite)

**1995.** World Telecommunications Day. Mult.

| | | | |
|---|---|---|---|
| 1096 | 27000 k. Type **211** .. | 15 | 10 |
| 1097 | 27000 k. "Intelsat" satellite and space shuttle .. .. | 15 | 10 |

### CHARITY TAX STAMPS

Used on certain days of the year as an additional tax on internal letters. If one was not used in addition to normal postage, postage due stamps were used to collect the deficiency and the fine.

**1925.** Marquis de Pombal Commem. stamps of Portugal but inscr. "ANGOLA".

| | | | |
|---|---|---|---|
| C 343. C **73.** | 15 c. violet .. .. | 30 | 25 |
| C 344. – | 15 c. violet .. .. | 30 | 25 |
| C 345. C **75.** | 15 c. violet .. .. | 30 | 25 |

C 15.

C 29.

C 52. Old Man.

**1929.**

| | | | |
|---|---|---|---|
| C 347. C **15.** | 50 c. blue .. .. | 1·60 | 60 |

**1939.** No gum.

| | | | |
|---|---|---|---|
| C 413. C **29.** | 50 c. green .. .. | 1·25 | 10 |
| C 414. | 1 a. red .. .. | 1·60 | 70 |

**1955.** Heads in brown.

| | | | |
|---|---|---|---|
| C646 C **52** | 50 c. orange .. | 15 | 10 |
| C647 – | 1 e. red (Boy) | 15 | 10 |
| C648 – | 1 e. 50 green (Girl) .. | 15 | 10 |
| C522 – | 2 e. 50 blue (Old woman) .. .. | 50 | 30 |

**1957.** Surch.

| | | | |
|---|---|---|---|
| C535 C **52** | 10 c. on 50 c. orange | 20 | 15 |
| C534 | 30 c. on 50 c. orange | 20 | 15 |

C 58. Mother and Child.

C 75. "Full Employment".

C 65. Yellow, White and Black Men.

**1959.**

| | | | |
|---|---|---|---|
| C 538. C **58.** | 10 c. black & orange .. | 15 | 15 |
| C 539. – | 30 c. black and slate .. | 15 | 15 |

DESIGN: 30 c. Boy and girl.

**1962.** Provincial Settlement Committee.

| | | | |
|---|---|---|---|
| C 568. C **65.** | 50 c. multicoloured | 20 | 10 |
| C 569. | 1 e. multicoloured .. | 40 | 20 |

**1965.** Provincial Settlement Committee.

| | | | |
|---|---|---|---|
| C 643. C **75.** | 50e. multicoloured | 15 | 10 |
| C 644. | 1 e. multicoloured .. | 15 | 10 |
| C 645. | 2 e. multicoloured .. | 20 | 15 |

C 95. Planting Tree.

**1972.** Provincial Settlement Committee.

| | | | |
|---|---|---|---|
| C 701. C **95.** | 50 c. red and brown | 15 | 15 |
| C 702. – | 1 e. black and green | 15 | 15 |
| C 703. – | 2 e. black and brown | 15 | 15 |

DESIGNS: 1 e. Agricultural workers. 2 e. Corncobs and flowers.

### NEWSPAPER STAMP

**1893.** "Newspaper" key-type inscribed "ANGOLA".

| | | | |
|---|---|---|---|
| N 51. V. | 2½ r. brown .. .. | 95 | 55 |

### POSTAGE DUE STAMPS

**1904.** "Due" key-type inscr. "ANGOLA".

| | | | |
|---|---|---|---|
| D 150. W. | 5 r. green .. .. | 15 | 15 |
| D 151. | 10 r. grey .. .. | 15 | 15 |
| D 152. | 20 r. brown .. .. | 25 | 20 |
| D 153. | 30 r. orange .. .. | 25 | 20 |
| D 154. | 50 r. brown .. .. | 30 | 20 |
| D 155. | 60 r. brown .. .. | 2·75 | 1·50 |
| D 156. | 100 r. mauve .. | 95 | 75 |
| D 157. | 130 r. blue .. .. | 95 | 85 |
| D 158. | 200 r. red .. .. | 3·25 | 1·50 |
| D 159. | 500 r. lilac .. .. | 3·00 | 1·50 |

See also Nos. D343/52.

**1911.** Nos. D150/9 optd. **REPUBLICA.**

| | | | |
|---|---|---|---|
| D 166. W. | 5 r. green .. .. | 15 | 10 |
| D 167. | 10 r. grey .. .. | 15 | 10 |
| D 168. | 20 r. brown .. .. | 15 | 10 |
| D 169. | 30 r. orange .. .. | 20 | 10 |
| D 170. | 50 r. brown .. .. | 20 | 15 |
| D 171. | 60 r. brown .. .. | 50 | 30 |
| D 172. | 100 r. mauve .. | 50 | 30 |
| D 173. | 130 r. blue .. .. | 50 | 35 |
| D 174. | 200 r. red .. .. | 50 | 35 |
| D 175. | 500 r. lilac .. .. | 65 | 40 |

**1921.** Values in new currency.

| | | | |
|---|---|---|---|
| D 343. W. | ½ c. green .. .. | 10 | 10 |
| D 344. | 1 c. grey .. .. | 10 | 10 |
| D 345. | 2 c. brown .. .. | 10 | 10 |
| D 346. | 3 c. orange .. .. | 10 | 10 |
| D 347. | 5 c. brown .. .. | 10 | 10 |
| D 348. | 6 c. brown .. .. | 10 | 10 |
| D 349. | 10 c. mauve .. .. | 10 | 10 |
| D 350. | 13 c. blue .. .. | 20 | 20 |
| D 351. | 20 c. red .. .. | 20 | 20 |
| D 352. | 50 c. grey .. .. | 20 | 20 |

**1925.** Marquis de Pombal stamps of Angola, as Nos. C343/5 optd. **MULTA.**

| | | | |
|---|---|---|---|
| D 353. C **73.** | 30 c. violet .. .. | 25 | 25 |
| D 354. – | 30 c. violet .. .. | 25 | 25 |
| D 355. C **75.** | 30 c. violet .. .. | 25 | 25 |

**1949.** Surch. **PORTEADO** and value.

| | | | |
|---|---|---|---|
| D 438. **17.** | 10 c. on 20 c. grey .. | 25 | 25 |
| D 439. | 20 c. on 30 c. green .. | 25 | 25 |
| D 440. | 30 c. on 50 c. brown .. | 25 | 25 |
| D 441. | 40 c. on 1 a. red .. | 50 | 50 |
| D 442. | 50 c. on 2 a. mauve .. | 75 | 75 |
| D 443. | 1 a. on 5 a. green .. | 85 | 85 |

D 45

**1952.** Numerals in red, name in black.

| | | | |
|---|---|---|---|
| D483 D **45** | 10 c. brown & olive | 15 | 15 |
| D484 | 30 c. green and blue | 15 | 15 |
| D485 | 50 c. brown & lt brn | 15 | 15 |
| D486 | 1 a. blue, grn & orge | 15 | 15 |
| D487 | 2 a. brown and red | 20 | 20 |
| D488 | 5 a. brown and blue | 30 | 30 |

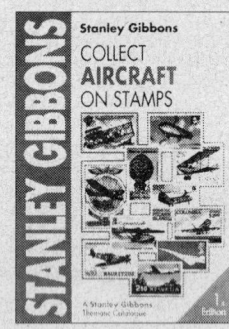

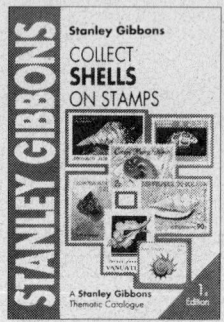

## ANGRA Pt. 9

A district of the Azores which used the stamps of the Azores except from 1892 to 1905.

1000 reis = 1 milreis.

**1892.** As T **4** of Funchal, inscr. "ANGRA".

16 5 r. yellow .. .. 2·25 1·40
5 10 r. mauve .. .. 2·50 1·40
6 15 r. brown .. .. 2·75 2·10
7 20 r. violet .. .. 2·75 2·10
8 25 r. green .. .. 3·50 55
9 50 r. blue .. .. 5·75 3·25
10 75 r. red .. .. 6·75 4·00
11 80 r. green .. .. 8·00 7·75
24 100 r. brown on yellow .. 29·00 11·00
13 150 r. red on rose .. 40·00 32·00
14 200 r. blue on blue .. 40·00 32·00
15 300 r. blue on brown .. 40·00 32·00

**1897.** "King Carlos" key-type inscr. "ANGRA".

28. S. 2½ r. grey .. .. .. 55 40
29. 5 r. red .. .. .. 55 40
30. 10 r. green .. .. .. 55 40
31. 15 r. brown .. .. 6·75 3·75
43. 15 r. green .. .. 60 45
32. 20 r. lilac .. .. 1·40 1·00
33. 25 r. green .. .. 2·10 1·00
44. 25 r. red .. .. 45 45
34. 50 r. blue .. .. 3·75 1·25
46. 65 r. blue .. .. 1·00 45
35. 75 r. red .. .. 2·50 1·25
47. 75 r. brown on yellow .. 9·75 8·50
36. 80 r. mauve .. .. 1·10 95
37. 100 r. blue on blue .. 2·00 1·25
48. 115 r. red on pink .. 2·00 1·60
49. 130 r. brown on cream .. 2·00 1·60
38. 150 r. brown on yellow .. 2·00 1·25
50. 180 r. grey on pink .. 2·25 2·10
39. 200 r. purple on pink .. 4·00 2·75
40. 300 r. blue on pink .. 5·75 4·50
41. 500 r. black on blue .. 13·00 10·50

## ANJOUAN Pt. 6

One of the Comoro Is. between Madagascar and the East coast of Africa. Used stamps of Madagscar from 1914 and became part of the Comoro Islands in 1950.

100 centimes = 1 franc.

**1892.** "Tablet" key-type inscr "SULTANAT D'ANJOUAN".

1 D 1 c. black on blue .. 80 85
2 2 c. brown on buff .. 1·00 1·00
3 4 c. brown on grey .. 1·50 1·50
4 5 c. green on green .. 3·00 2·25
5 10 c. black on lilac .. 3·25 2·75
14 10 c. red .. .. 9·50 8·75
6 15 c. blue .. .. 3·00 3·25
15 15 c. grey .. .. 6·00 6·00
7 20 c. red on green .. 3·25 3·75
8 25 c. black on pink .. 4·25 4·00
16 25 c. blue .. .. 7·50 7·50
9 30 c. brown on grey .. 12·50 8·50
17 35 c. black on yellow .. 4·75 3·25
10 40 c. red on yellow .. 18·00 14·00
18 45 c. black on green .. 85·00 50·00
11 50 c. red on pink .. 22·00 16·00
19 50 c. brown on blue .. 16·00 12·00
12 75 c. brown on orange .. 22·00 16·00
13 1 f. green .. .. 50·00 40·00

**1912.** Surch in figures.

20 D 05 on 2 c. brown on buff 60 60
21 05 on 4 c. brown on grey 50 60
22 05 on 15 c. blue .. .. 45 45
23 05 on 20 c. red on green 45 50
24 05 on 25 c. black on pink 45 45
25 05 on 30 c. brown on grey 60 70
26 10 on 40 c. red on yellow 60 65
27 10 on 45 c. black on green 65 85
28 10 on 50 c. red on pink .. 1·25 1·60
29 10 on 75 c. brown on orge 1·00 1·10
30 10 on 1 f. green .. .. 1·25 1·25

## ANNAM AND TONGKING Pt. 6

Later part of Indo-China and now included in Vietnam.

100 centimes = 1 franc.

**1888.** Stamps of French Colonies, "Commerce" type, surch. **A & T** and value in figures.

1. J. 1 on 2 c. brown on yellow .. 20·00 18·00
2. 1 on 4 c. lilac on grey .. 15·00 13·00
3. 5 on 10 c. black on lilac .. 16·00 15·00

## ANTIOQUIA Pt. 20

One of the states of the Granadine Confederation.

A department of Colombia from 1886, now uses Colombian stamps.

100 centavos = 1 peso.

1.  5.  6.

**1868.** Various arms designs. Imperf.

1. 1. 2½ c. blue .. .. .. £450 £225
2. – 5 c. green .. .. .. £350 £200
3. – 10 c. lilac .. .. .. £850 £385
4. – 1 p. red .. .. .. £300 £185

**1869.** Various frames. Imperf.

5. 5. 2½ c. blue .. .. .. 2·50 2·00
6. 5 c. green .. .. .. 3·25 3·00
8. 10 c. mauve .. .. .. 4·00 2·00
9. 20 c. brown .. .. .. 4·50 3·00
10. 6. 1 p. red .. .. .. 7·50 7·50

7.  15.

**1873.** Arms designs inscr. "E.S." (or "Eo. So." or "Estado Soberono") "de Antioquia". Imperf.

11. 7. 1 c. green .. .. .. 2·00 1·50
12. – 5 c. green .. .. .. 2·50 1·60
13. – 10 c. mauve .. .. 16·00 12·00
14. – 20 c. brown .. .. 4·00 2·50
15. – 50 c. blue .. .. .. 1·00 80
16. – 1 p. red .. .. .. 2·50 2·50
17. – 2 p. black on yellow .. 5·00 5·00
18. – 5 p. black on red .. 25·00 20·00

The 5 p. is larger (25½ × 31½ mm).

**1875.** Imperf.

20. 15. 1 c. black on green .. 60 60
43. 1 c. mauve .. .. 1·00 1·00
21. 1 c. black .. .. 60 60
52. 1 c. green .. .. 1·00 1·00
22. – 2½ c. blue (Arms) .. 80 80
23. – 5 c. green ("Liberty") 6·00 5·00
25. – 10 c. mauve (J. Berrio) 8·00 7·00

20. Condor.  21. Liberty.

23.  Liberty. 25.

**1879.** Imperf.

30. 20. 2½ c. blue .. .. .. 3·00 3·00
38. 2½ c. green .. .. .. 80 1·00
45. 2½ c. black on buff .. 3·00 3·00
39. 21. 5 c. green .. .. .. 85 1·00
40. 5 c. violet .. .. .. 1·75 1·00
32. – 10 c. violet (Arms) .. £250 £200
36. 23. 10 c. violet .. .. 50·00 16·00
41. 10 c. red .. .. .. 1·00 1·00
42. 21. 20 c. brown .. .. 1·25 1·25

**1883.** Various frames. Head of Liberty to left. Imperf.

53. 25. 5 c. brown .. .. 4·00 2·00
47. 5 c. yellow .. .. 3·00 2·50
48. 5 c. green .. .. 55·00 40·00
49. 10 c. green .. .. 2·00 2·00
50. 10 c. mauve .. .. 3·50 3·50
55. 10 c. blue .. .. 4·00 3·50
51. 20 c. blue .. .. 2·50 2·50

28.  31.

**1886.** Imperf.

57. 28. 1 c. green on pink .. 50 50
65. 1 c. red on lilac .. .. 30 30
58. 2½ c. black on orange .. 35 40
66. 2½ c. mauve on pink .. 50 40
59. 5 c. blue on buff .. 2·00 75
67. 5 c. red on green .. 2·25 2·25
68. 5 c. lake on buff .. 1·00 80
60. 10 c. red on buff .. 1·00 60
69. 10 c. brown on green .. 1·00 80
61. 20 c. purple on buff .. 1·00 60
62. 50 c. yellow on buff .. 2·00 2·00
63. 1 p. yellow on green .. 4·00 4·00
64. 2 p. green on lilac .. 4·00 4·00

**1888.** Various sizes and frames. Inscr. "MEDELLIN". Imperf.

70. 31. 2½ c. black on yellow .. 15·00 12·00
71 2½ c. red on white .. 2·50 2·50
72. 5 c. black on yellow .. 2·00 2·00
73. 5 c. red on orange .. 1·75 1·75

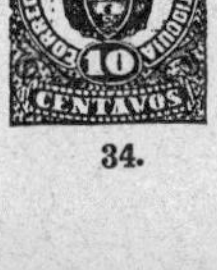

34. 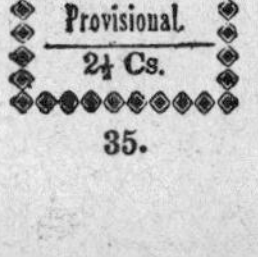 35.

**1889.** Arms in various frames.

74. 34. 1 c. black on red .. 10 10
75. 2½ c. black on blue .. 20 15
76. 5 c. black on yellow .. 45 25
77. 10 c. black on green .. 50 40
95. 10 c. brown .. .. 25 25
78. 20 c. blue .. .. 1·00 1·00
79. 50 c. brown .. .. 2·00 2·00
80. 50 c. green .. .. 1·75 1·75
81. 1 p. red .. .. 1·00 1·00
82. 2 p. black on mauve .. 7·50 6·00
83. 5 p. black on red .. 10·00 7·50

**1890.** Perf.

84. 35. 2½ c. black on buff .. 1·00 1·00
85. 5 c. black on yellow .. 1·00 1·00
86. 10 c. black on buff .. 4·75 4·75
87. 10 c. black on red .. 5·00 5·00
88. 20 c. black on yellow .. 5·00 5·00

36.  37.

**1892.**

89. 36. 1 c. brown on buff .. 50 40
90. 1 c. blue .. .. 20 20
91. 2½ c. violet on lilac .. 30 30
92. 2½ c. green .. .. 30 30
93. 5 c. black .. .. 80 60
94. 5 c. red .. .. 20 20

**1896.**

96. 37. 2 c. grey .. .. 40 40
107. 2 c. red .. .. 25 40
97. 2½ c. brown .. .. 40 40
108. 2½ c. blue .. .. 25 40
98. 3 c. red .. .. 50 50
109. 3 c. olive .. .. 25 40
99. 5 c. green .. .. 25 20
110. 5 c. yellow .. .. 20 30
100. 10 c. lilac .. .. 45 45
111. 10 c. brown .. .. 50 60
101. 20 c. brown .. .. 70 70
112. 20 c. blue .. .. 75 1·00
102. 50 c. sepia .. .. 90 90
113. 50 c. red .. .. 1·00 1·40
103. 1 p. black and blue .. 10·00 10·00
114. 1 p. black and red .. 10·00 10·00
104. 2 p. black and orange .. 40·00 40·00
115. 2 p. black and green .. 35·00 35·00
105. 5 p. black and mauve .. 50·00 50·00

39. Gen. Cordova.  43.

**1899.**

118. 39. ½ c. blue .. .. 10 10
119. 1 c. blue .. .. 10 10
120. 2 c. black .. .. 10 10
121. 3 c. red .. .. 10 10
122. 4 c. brown .. .. 10 10
123. 5 c. green .. .. 10 10
124. 10 c. red .. .. 10 10
125. 20 c. violet .. .. 10 10
126. 50 c. yellow .. .. 10 10
127. 1 p. green .. .. 10 15
128. 2 p. green .. .. 10 20

**1901.** Various frames.

132. 43. 1 c. red .. .. 10 15
133. 1 c. brown .. .. 25 25
134. 1 c. blue .. .. 25 25

Nos. 132 and 134 also exist with "CENTAVO" inside the rectangle below figure "1".

46.  47.  48. Girardot.

**1902.**

138. 46. 1 c. red .. .. 10 10
139. 1 c. blue .. .. 10 10
140. 2 c. blue .. .. 10 10
141. 2 c. violet .. .. 10 10
142. 3 c. green .. .. 10 10
143. 4 c. purple .. .. 10 10
144. 47. 5 c. red .. .. 10 10
145. 10 c. mauve .. .. 10 10
147. 20 c. green .. .. 15 10
148. 30 c. red .. .. 15 10
149. 48. 40 c. blue .. .. 15 10
150. 50 c. brown on yellow .. 20 20
152. – 1 p. black and violet .. 40 45
153. – 2 p. black and red .. 40 45
154. – 5 p. black and blue .. 50 55

DESIGN: 1 p. to 5 p. Dr. J. Felix de Restrepo.

No. 145 also exists with smaller head.

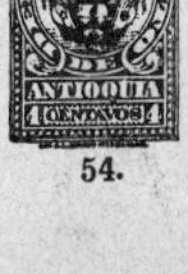

54.  55.  56. Zea.

**1903.**

159. 54. 4 c. brown .. .. 10 10
160. 5 c. blue .. .. 10 10
161. 55. 10 c. yellow .. .. 10 10
162. 20 c. lilac .. .. 10 10
163. 30 c. brown .. .. 30 30
164. 40 c. green .. .. 30 30
165. 50 c. red .. .. 10 15
166. 56. 1 p. green .. .. 25 20
167. 2 p. mauve (Rovira) .. 25 20
168. 3 p. blue (La Pola) .. 30 30
169. 4 p. red (Restrepo) .. 50 30
170. 5 p. brown (Madrid) .. 50 40
171. 10 p. red (Corral) .. 2·25 2·25

ACKNOWLEDGMENT OF RECEIPT STAMPS

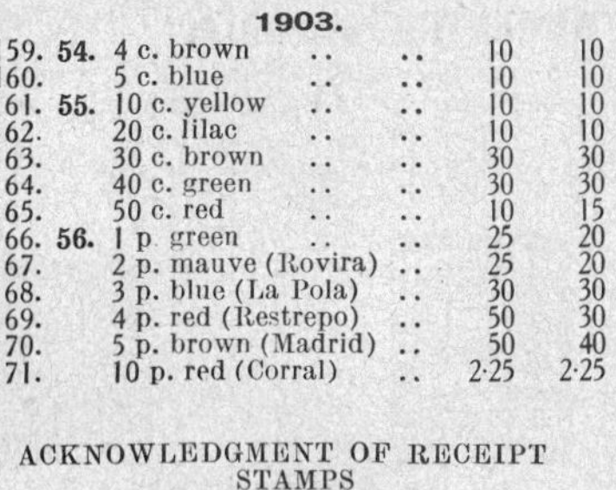

AR 53

**1902.**

AR157. AR 53 5 c. black on red 30 20
AR158. 5 c. green .. 10 10

REGISTRATION STAMPS

R 38.

**1896.**

R 106. R 38. 2½ c. pink .. .. 50 50
R 117. 2½ c. blue .. .. 60 60

R41. General Cordova.  R 42.

**1899.**

R 130. R 41. 2½ c. blue .. .. 10 10
R 131. R 42. 10 c. red .. .. 10 10

R 52.

**1902.**

R 156. R 52. 10 c. violet on green .. 10 10

TOO LATE STAMPS

L 40. Gen. Cordova.  L 51.

**1899.**

L 129. L40. 2½ c. green .. .. 10 10

**1901.** As T **43**, but inscr. "RETARDO" at sides.

L 137a. – 2½ c. purple .. 60 60

**1902.**

L 155. L51. 2½ c. lilac .. .. 10 10

## ARBE Pt. 8

During the period of D'Annunzio's Italian Regency of Carnaro (Fiume), separate issues were made for Arbe (now Rab).

100 centesimi = 1 lira.

**1920.** No. 148, etc. of Fiume optd. **ARBE.**

1. 5 c. green .. .. .. 2·50 2·50
2. 10 c. red .. .. .. 4·50 4·50
3. 20 c. brown .. .. .. 7·50 7·50
4. 25 c. blue .. .. .. 7·50 7·50
5. 50 on 20 c. brown .. .. 7·50 7·50
6. 55 on 5 c. green .. .. 7·50 7·50

EXPRESS LETTER STAMPS

**1920.** Nos. E163/4 of Fiume optd. **ARBE.**

E 7. 30 c. on 20 c. brown .. 42·00 35·00
E 8. 50 c. on 5 c. green .. 32·00 35·00

# ARGENTINE REPUBLIC Pt. 20

A republic in the S.E. of S. America formerly part of the Spanish Empire.

1858. 100 centavos = 1 peso.
1985. 100 centavos = 1 austral.
1992. 100 centavos = 1 peso.

1. Argentine Confederation. 3.

**1858.** Imperf.

| | | | | |
|---|---|---|---|---|
| 1. | 1. | 5 c. red | 1·60 | 9·50 |
| 2. | | 10 c. green | 2·25 | 55·00 |
| 3. | | 15 c. blue | 16·00 | £140 |

**1862.** Imperf.

| | | | | |
|---|---|---|---|---|
| 10. | 3. | 5 c. red | 20·00 | 24·00 |
| 8. | | 10 c. green | £160 | 75·00 |
| 9. | | 15 c. blue | £325 | £250 |

5. Rivadavia. 6.

**1864.** Imperf.

| | | | | |
|---|---|---|---|---|
| 24. | 5. | 5 c. red | £250 | 65·00 |
| 14. | 6. | 10 c. green | £1700 | £1000 |
| 15. | 5. | 15 c. blue | £8000 | £3500 |

**1864.** Perf.

| | | | | |
|---|---|---|---|---|
| 16. | 5. | 5 c. red | 35·00 | 14·00 |
| 17. | 6. | 10 c. green | 80·00 | 35·00 |
| 18. | 5. | 15 c. blue | £160 | 75·00 |

9. B. Rivadavia. 10. Gen. Belgrano. 11. Gen. San Martin.

**1867.** Perf.

| | | | | |
|---|---|---|---|---|
| 28. | 9. | 5 c. red | 12·00 | 75 |
| 29. | 10. | 10 c. green | 35·00 | 5·00 |
| 30a. | 11. | 15 c. blue | 50·00 | 15·00 |

12. Balcarce. 22. Sarsfield. 24. Lopez.

**1873.** Portraits. Perf.

| | | | | |
|---|---|---|---|---|
| 31. | 12. | 1 c. violet | 4·00 | 2·25 |
| 32. | – | 4 c. brown (Moreno) | 5·50 | 45 |
| 33. | – | 30 c. orange (Alvear) | £120 | 17·00 |
| 34. | – | 60 c. black (Posadas) | £120 | 5·50 |
| 35. | – | 90 c. blue (Saavedra) | 28·00 | 2·50 |

**1877.** Surch. with large figure of value.

| | | | | |
|---|---|---|---|---|
| 37. | 9. | 1 on 5 c. red | 55·00 | 17·00 |
| 38. | | 2 on 5 c. red | £110 | 70·00 |
| 39. | 10. | 8 on 10 c. green | £140 | 35·00 |

**1876.** Roul.

| | | | | |
|---|---|---|---|---|
| 36. | 9. | 5 c. red | £170 | 70·00 |
| 40. | | 8 c. lake | 28·00 | 30 |
| 41. | 10. | 16 c. green | 9·00 | 1·25 |
| 42. | 22. | 20 c. blue | 9·50 | 3·50 |
| 43. | 11. | 24 c. blue | 19·00 | 3·50 |

**1877.** Perf.

| | | | | |
|---|---|---|---|---|
| 46. | 24. | 2 c. green | 4·75 | 1·00 |
| 44. | 9. | 8 c. lake | 4·75 | 15 |
| 45. | 11. | 24 c. blue | 8·50 | 50 |
| 47. | – | 25 c. lake (Alvear) | 25·00 | 7·00 |

**1882.** Surch. **1/2** (**PROVISORIO**).

| | | | | |
|---|---|---|---|---|
| 51. | 9. | ½ on 5 c. red | 1·00 | 90 |

29. 33.

**1882.**

| | | | | |
|---|---|---|---|---|
| 52. | 29. | ½ c. brown | 1·60 | 90 |
| 55. | | 1 c. red | 4·00 | 1·25 |
| 54. | | 12 c. blue | 65·00 | 10·00 |

**1884.** Surch. **1884** and value in figs. or words.

| | | | | |
|---|---|---|---|---|
| 90. | 9. | ½ on 5 c. red | 3·00 | 2·25 |
| 92. | 11. | ½ c. on 15 c. blue | 2·25 | 1·75 |
| 94. | | 1 c. on 15 c. blue | 7·00 | 5·50 |
| 100. | 9. | 4 c. on 5 c. red | 10·00 | 6·00 |

**1884.**

| | | | | |
|---|---|---|---|---|
| 101 | 33 | ½ c. brown | 1·00 | 50 |
| 102 | | 1 c. red | 6·00 | 50 |
| 103 | | 12 c. blue | 28·00 | 1·40 |

34. Urquiza. 45. Mitre.

**1888.** Portrait types, inscr. "CORREOS ARGENTINOS".

| | | | | |
|---|---|---|---|---|
| 108 | 34 | ½ c. blue | 55 | 50 |
| 110 | – | 2 c. green (Lopez) | 10·00 | 7·00 |
| 111 | – | 3 c. green (Celman) | 1·90 | 70 |
| 113 | – | 5 c. red (Rivadavia) | 9·00 | 65 |
| 114 | – | 6 c. red (Sarmiento) | 24·00 | 16·00 |
| 115 | – | 10 c. brown (Avellaneda) | 16·00 | 1·25 |
| 116 | – | 15 c. orange (San Martin) | 16·00 | 1·75 |
| 117a | – | 20 c. green (Roca) | 13·00 | 1·40 |
| 118 | – | 25 c. violet (Belgrano) | 16·00 | 1·75 |
| 119 | – | 30 c. brown (Dorrego) | 24·00 | 2·75 |
| 120a | – | 40 c. grey (Moreno) | 24·00 | 3·25 |
| 121 | 45 | 50 c. blue | 85·00 | 9·00 |

60. Paz. 51. Rivadavia.

**1888.** Portrait types, inscr. "CORREOS Y TELEGRAFOS".

| | | | | |
|---|---|---|---|---|
| 137. | 60. | ½ c. green | 10 | 15 |
| 122. | – | ½ c. blue (Urquiza) | 30 | 15 |
| 123. | – | 1 c. brown (Sarsfield) | 95 | 20 |
| 125. | – | 2 c. violet (Derqui) | 95 | 15 |
| 126. | – | 3 c. green (Celman) | 2·25 | 45 |
| 127. | 51. | 5 c. red | 3·00 | 20 |
| 129. | – | 6 c. blue (Sarmiento) | 1·60 | 60 |
| 130. | – | 10 c. brown (Avellaneda) | 1·90 | 30 |
| 131. | – | 12 c. blue (Alberti) | 4·75 | 1·25 |
| 132. | – | 40 c. grey (Moreno) | 4·50 | 90 |
| 133. | – | 50 c. orange (Mitre) | 4·50 | 90 |
| 134. | – | 60 c. black (Posadas) | 17·00 | 3·00 |

**1890.** No. 131 surch. **1/4** and bars.

| | | | | |
|---|---|---|---|---|
| 135. | | ¼ on 12 c. blue | 40 | 35 |

52. Rivadavia. 63. La Madrid. 61. Rivadavia.

**1890.**

| | | | | |
|---|---|---|---|---|
| 128a. | 52. | 5 c. red | 2·25 | 15 |

**1891.** Portraits.

| | | | | |
|---|---|---|---|---|
| 139. | – | 1 p. blue (San Martin) | 45·00 | 6·50 |
| 140. | 63. | 5 p. blue | £225 | 24·00 |
| 141. | – | 20 p. green (G. Brown) | £325 | 70·00 |

**1891.**

| | | | | |
|---|---|---|---|---|
| 138. | 61. | 8 c. red | 1·40 | 25 |

65. Rivadavia. 66. Belgrano. 67. San Martin.

**1892.**

| | | | | |
|---|---|---|---|---|
| 142. | 65. | ½ c. blue | 20 | 15 |
| 143. | | 1 c. brown | 40 | 15 |
| 144. | | 2 c. green | 25 | 15 |
| 145. | | 3 c. orange | 70 | 15 |
| 146. | | 5 c. red | 70 | 15 |
| 147. | 66. | 10 c. red | 5·50 | 15 |
| 148. | | 12 c. blue | 2·75 | 15 |
| 149. | | 16 c. slate | 6·50 | 60 |
| 150. | | 24 c. sepia | 11·00 | 60 |
| 257. | | 30 c. orange | 8·00 | 50 |
| 151. | | 50 c. green | 10·00 | 50 |
| 188. | | 80 c. lilac | 12·00 | 50 |
| 152a. | 67. | 1 p. red | 10·00 | 80 |
| 190. | | 1 p. 20 black | 9·50 | 4·00 |
| 153. | | 2 p. green | 17·00 | 8·00 |
| 154. | | 5 p. blue | 42·00 | 3·00 |

70. Fleet of Columbus. 71. "Liberty" and Shield.

**1892.** 4th Cent. of Discovery of America by Columbus.

| | | | | |
|---|---|---|---|---|
| 219 | 70 | 2 c. blue | 12·00 | 4·50 |
| 220 | | 5 c. blue | 20·00 | 5·00 |

**1899.**

| | | | | |
|---|---|---|---|---|
| 221 | 71 | ½ c. brown | 15 | 15 |
| 222 | | 1 c. green | 10 | 10 |
| 223 | | 2 c. grey | 10 | 10 |
| 224 | | 3 c. orange | 95 | 15 |
| 225 | | 4 c. yellow | 1·75 | 15 |
| 226 | | 5 c. red | 10 | 10 |
| 227 | | 6 c. black | 1·10 | 20 |
| 228 | 71 | 10 c. green | 1·75 | 15 |
| 229a | | 12 c. blue | 1·10 | 30 |
| 230 | | 12 c. green | 1·10 | 30 |
| 231 | | 15 c. blue | 3·00 | 15 |
| 232 | | 16 c. orange | 8·50 | 4·25 |
| 233 | | 20 c. red | 2·25 | 15 |
| 234 | | 24 c. purple | 4·00 | 80 |
| 235 | | 30 c. red | 4·25 | 20 |
| 237 | | 50 c. blue | 5·50 | 15 |
| 238 | | 1 p. black and blue | 16·00 | 80 |
| 239 | | 5 p. black and orange | 65·00 | 11·00 |
| 240 | | 10 p. black and green | 60·00 | 11·00 |
| 241 | | 20 p. black and red | £225 | 32·00 |

The peso values are larger (19 × 32 mm).

73. Port Rosario. 74. Gen. San Martin.

**1902.** Completion of Port Rosario Dock.

| | | | | |
|---|---|---|---|---|
| 290. | 73. | 5 c. blue | 7·00 | 2·00 |

**1908.**

| | | | | |
|---|---|---|---|---|
| 291. | 74. | ½ c. violet | 15 | 10 |
| 292. | | 1 c. brown | 20 | 10 |
| 293. | | 2 c. brown | 60 | 10 |
| 294. | | 3 c. green | 75 | 35 |
| 295. | | 4 c. mauve | 1·50 | 35 |
| 296. | | 5 c. red | 35 | 10 |
| 297. | | 6 c. green | 85 | 25 |
| 298. | | 10 c. green | 1·75 | 10 |
| 299. | | 12 c. brown | 45 | 40 |
| 300. | | 12 c. blue | 1·40 | 10 |
| 301. | | 15 c. green | 1·90 | 90 |
| 302. | | 20 c. blue | 1·40 | 10 |
| 303. | | 24 c. red | 3·75 | 70 |
| 304. | | 30 c. red | 6·00 | 70 |
| 305. | | 50 c. black | 5·50 | 45 |
| 306. | – | 1 p. red and blue | 13·00 | 1·90 |

The 1 p. is larger (21½ × 27 mm.) with portrait at upper left.

76. Pyramid of May. 80. Saavedra.

78. Azcuenaga and Alberti.

**1910.** Centenary of Deposition of the Spanish Viceroy.

| | | | | |
|---|---|---|---|---|
| 366. | 76. | ½ c. blue and grey | 40 | 10 |
| 367. | – | 1 c. black and green | 40 | 10 |
| 368. | – | 2 c. black and green | 30 | 10 |
| 369. | 78. | 3 c. green | 85 | 10 |
| 370. | – | 4 c. green and blue | 85 | 15 |
| 371. | 80. | 5 c. red | 70 | 10 |
| 372. | – | 10 c. black and brown | 2·00 | 15 |
| 373. | – | 12 c. blue | 1·60 | 25 |
| 374. | – | 20 c. black and brown | 3·75 | 40 |
| 375. | – | 24 c. blue and brown | 2·00 | 1·00 |
| 376. | – | 30 c. black and lilac | 2·00 | 75 |
| 377. | – | 50 c. black and red | 5·00 | 1·00 |
| 378. | – | 1 p. blue | 12·00 | 3·50 |
| 379. | – | 5 p. purple and orange | 80·00 | 35·00 |
| 380. | – | 10 p. black and orange | £100 | 75·00 |
| 381. | – | 20 p. black and blue | £170 | £100 |

DESIGNS—VERT. 50 c. Crowds on 25 May 1810. 10 p. Centenary Monument. 20 p. San Martin. HORIZ. 1 c. Pena and Vieytes. 2 c. Meeting at Pena's house. 4 c. Fort of the Viceroys, Buenos Aires. 10 c. Distribution of cockades. 12 c. Congress Building. 20 c. Castelli and Matheu. 24 c. First National Council. 30 c. Belgrano and Larrea. 1 p. Moreno and Paso. 5 p. "Oath of the Junta".

90. Sarmiento. 91. Ploughman.

**1911.** Birth Cent. of President Sarmiento.

| | | | | |
|---|---|---|---|---|
| 382. | 90. | 5 c. black and brown | 70 | 40 |

**1911.**

| | | | | |
|---|---|---|---|---|
| 383. | 91. | 5 c. red | 40 | 15 |
| 384. | | 12 c. blue | 4·50 | 20 |

92. Ploughman.

94.

**1911.**

| | | | | |
|---|---|---|---|---|
| 395. | 92. | ½ c. violet | 20 | 20 |
| 396. | | 1 c. brown | 20 | 15 |
| 397. | | 2 c. brown | 40 | 15 |
| 398. | | 3 c. green | 50 | 20 |
| 399. | | 4 c. purple | 40 | 20 |
| 400. | | 5 c. red | 20 | 15 |
| 401. | | 10 c. green | 60 | 15 |
| 402. | | 12 c. blue | 1·60 | 15 |
| 403. | | 20 c. blue | 5·00 | 1·25 |
| 404. | | 24 c. brown | 3·75 | 20 |
| 405. | | 30 c. red | 2·00 | 70 |
| 406. | | 50 c. black | 6·00 | 70 |
| 408. | 94. | 1 p. red and blue | 7·00 | 1·10 |
| 409. | | 5 p. green and grey | 22·00 | 7·00 |
| 410. | | 10 p. blue and violet | 85·00 | 10·00 |
| 411. | | 20 p. red and blue | £200 | 70·00 |

95. Dr. F. N. Laprida.

97. San Martin.

96. Declaration of Independence.

**1916.** Centenary of Independence.

| | | | | |
|---|---|---|---|---|
| 417. | 95. | ½ c. violet | 20 | 15 |
| 418. | | 1 c. brown | 25 | 15 |
| 419. | | 2 c. brown | 20 | 15 |
| 420. | | 3 c. green | 50 | 15 |
| 421. | | 4 c. purple | 75 | 15 |
| 422. | 96. | 5 c. red | 35 | 15 |
| 423. | | 10 c. green | 1·60 | 15 |
| 424. | 97. | 12 c. blue | 75 | 15 |
| 425. | | 20 c. blue | 1·25 | 15 |
| 426. | | 24 c. red | 2·00 | 85 |
| 427. | | 30 c. red | 2·00 | 40 |
| 428. | | 50 c. black | 3·75 | 50 |
| 429. | | 1 p. red and blue | 11·00 | 4·50 |
| 430. | | 5 p. green and grey | £130 | 45·00 |
| 431. | | 10 p. blue and violet | £130 | 85·00 |
| 432. | | 20 p. red and grey | £190 | 75·00 |

98. San Martin.

100. Dr. Juan Pujol.

**1917.**

| | | | | |
|---|---|---|---|---|
| 433. | 98. | ½ c. violet | 20 | 15 |
| 434. | | 1 c. buff | 20 | 15 |
| 435. | | 2 c. brown | 20 | 15 |
| 436. | | 3 c. green | 70 | 15 |
| 454. | | 4 c. purple | 30 | 15 |
| 455. | | 5 c. red | 15 | 15 |
| 456. | | 10 c. green | 1·75 | 15 |
| 457. | – | 12 c. blue | 1·40 | 15 |
| 458. | – | 20 c. blue | 1·75 | 15 |
| 459. | – | 24 c. red | 5·00 | 2·25 |
| 460. | – | 30 c. red | 5·00 | 70 |
| 461. | – | 50 c. black | 4·50 | 70 |
| 445. | – | 1 p. red and blue | 4·50 | 20 |
| 446. | – | 5 p. green and grey | 19·00 | 3·50 |
| 447. | – | 10 p. blue and violet | 45·00 | 11·00 |
| 448. | – | 20 p. red and grey | 81·00 | 17·00 |

The 12 c. to 20 p. values are larger (21 × 27 mm.).

**1918.** Birth Centenary of Juan Pujol, 1st P.M.G. of Argentina.

| | | | | |
|---|---|---|---|---|
| 449. | 100. | 5 c. grey and bistre | 80 | 30 |

102. Mausoleum of Belgrano.

103. Creation of Argentine Flag.

**1920.** Death Cent. of Gen. Manuel Belgrano.

| | | | | |
|---|---|---|---|---|
| 478. | 102. | 2 c. red | 50 | 15 |
| 479. | 103. | 5 c. blue and red | 50 | 15 |
| 480. | – | 12 c. blue and green | 1·00 | 75 |

DESIGN—VERT. 12 c. Gen. Belgrano.

106. General Urquiza.

107. General Mitre.

108.

**1920.** Gen. Urquiza's Victory at Cepada.
488. 106. 5 c. blue .. .. 30 10

**1921.** Birth Centenary of Gen. Mitre.
490. 107. 2 c. brown .. .. 35 10
491. 5 c. blue .. .. 35 10

**1921.** 1st Pan-American Postal Congress.
492. 108. 3 c. lilac .. .. 75 25
493. 5 c. blue .. .. 1·00 15
494. 10 c. brown .. .. 1·25 35
495. 12 c. red .. .. 2·25 70

**1921.** As T 108, but smaller. Inscr "BUENOS AIRES AGOSTO DE 1921".
496. – 5 c. red .. .. 1·00 15

**1921.** As No. 496, but inscr. "REPUBLICA ARGENTINA" at foot.
511 – 5 c. red .. .. 35 25

112. 114. B. Rivadavia.

**1923.** With or without stop below "c".
513. 112. ½ c. purple .. .. 15 15
530. 1 c. brown .. .. 15 15
515. 2 c. brown .. .. 35 15
532. 3 c. green .. .. 15 15
533. 4 c. red .. .. 50 15
518. 5 c. red .. .. 15 15
535. 10 c. green .. .. 35 15
520. 12 c. blue .. .. 45 15
537. 20 c. blue .. .. 85 15
538. 24 c. brown .. .. 2·00 1·00
539. 25 c. violet .. .. 1·00 15
540. 30 c. red .. .. 2·00 15
541. 50 c. black .. .. 2·00 15
542. – 1 p. red and blue .. 2·25 15
543. – 5 p. green and lilac .. 17·00 70
544. – 10 p. blue and red .. 38·00 3·75
545. – 20 p. lake and slate .. 55·00 8·50
The peso values are larger (21 × 27 mm.).

**1926.** Rivadavia Centenary.
546. 114. 5 c. red .. .. 50 15

115. Rivadavia. 116. San Martin.

117. G.P.O. 1926. 118. G.P.O. 1826.

**1926.** Postal Centenary.
547. 115. 3c. green .. .. 15 15
548. 116. 5 c. red .. .. 10 15
549. 117. 12 c. blue .. .. 1·00 20
550. 118. 25 c. brown .. .. 1·75 15

120. Biplane and Globe. 122.

**1928.** Air.
558. 120. 5 c. red .. .. 1·75 50
559. 10 c. blue .. .. 2·75 85
560. – 15 c. brown .. .. 3·50 85
561. 120. 18 c. violet .. .. 4·25 3·25
562. – 20 c. blue .. .. 3·50 85
563. – 24 c. blue .. .. 6·00 2·75
564. 122. 25 c. violet .. .. 4·25 1·40
565. 30 c. red .. .. 5·50 1·00
566. – 35 c. red .. .. 6·00 1·00
567a. 120. 36 c. brown .. .. 3·25 1·40
568. – 50 c. black .. .. 6·00 50
569. – 54 c. brown .. .. 6·00 2·00
570. – 72 c. green .. .. 7·50 2·00
571. 122. 90 c. purple .. .. 10·00 1·00
572. 1 p. red and blue .. 12·00 70
573. 1 p. 08 blue and red .. 17·00 4·75
574. – 1 p. 26 green and violet 32·00 9·00
575. – 1 p. 80 red and blue .. 32·00 9·00
576. – 3 p. 60 blue and grey .. 65·00 22·00
DESIGNS—VERT. 15 c., 20 c., 24 c., 54 c., 72 c. Yellow-headed Caracara over sea. HORIZ. 35 c., 50 c., 1 p. 26, 1 p. 80, 3 p. 60. Andean Condor on mountain top.

124. Arms of Argentina and Brazil. 125. Torch illuminating New World.

**1928.** Cent. of Peace with Brazil.
577. 124. 5 c. red .. .. .. 1·00 35
578. 12 c. blue .. .. .. 1·60 70

**1929.** "Day of the Race" issue.
579. 125. 2 c. brown .. .. 85 20
580. – 5 c. red .. .. .. 95 15
581. – 12 c. blue .. .. 2·25 75
DESIGNS: 5 c. Symbolical figures, Spain and Argentina. 12 c. American offering laurels to Columbus.

'ZEPPELIN 1º VUELO 1930
(128.)

**1930.** Air. "Zeppelin". Europe-Pan-America Flight. Optd. with T 128.
587. – 20 c. blue (No. 562) .. 11·00 6·50
588. – 50 c. black (No. 568) .. 12·00 8·50
589. 122. 90 c. purple .. .. 9·00 6·50
584. 1 p. red and blue .. 20·00 13·00
585. – 1 p. 80 (No. 575) .. 65·00 38·00
586. – 3 p. 60 (No. 576) .. £190 £110

129. Soldier and Civilian Insurgents. 130. The Victorious March, 6 Sept., '30

**1930.** Revolution of 6 Sept., 1930.
592. 129. ½ c. violet .. .. 20 15
611. 130. ½ c. mauve .. .. 15 10
593 129. 1 c. green .. .. 25 15
612. 130. 1 c. black .. .. 1·00 40
594 2 c. lilac .. .. 35 15
595 129. 3 c. green .. .. 50 25
613. 130. 3 c. green .. .. 50 25
596. 129. 4 c. violet .. .. 40 25
614. 130. 4 c. lake .. .. 40 20
597. 129. 5 c. red .. .. 20 15
615. 130. 5 c. red .. .. 15 10
598. 129. 10 c. black .. .. 85 35
616 130. 10 c. green .. .. 1·00 25
599. 12 c. blue .. .. 85 25
600. 20 c. buff .. .. 85 20
601. 24 c. brown .. .. 3·25 1·50
602. 25 c. green .. .. 4·25 1·50
603. 30 c. violet .. .. 6·00 2·00
604. 50 c. black .. .. 9·00 2·75
605. 1 p. red and blue .. 17·00 10·00
606. 2 p. orange and black. 30·00 10·00
607. 5 p. black and green .. 90·00 40·00
608. 10 p. blue and lake .. £120 50·00
609. 20 p. blue and green .. £325 £120
610. 50 p. violet and green .. £900 £650

**1931.** 1st Anniv. of 1930 Revolution. Optd. **6 Septiembre 1930-1931.**
617. 112. 3 c. green (postage) .. 25 25
618. 10 c. green .. .. 70 70
619. 30 c. red .. .. 3·75 3·75
620. 50 c. black .. .. 3·75 3·75
621. 1 p. red and blue .. 4·25 3·75
623. 130. 2 p. orange and black .. 15·00 8·50
622. 112. 5 p. green and lilac .. 75·00 23·00
624. 129. 18 c. violet (air) .. 2·25 1·75
625. – 72 c. green (No. 570) .. 21·00 13·00
626. 122. 90 c. purple .. .. 16·00 12·00
627. – 1 p. 80 red and blue .. (No. 575) .. 40·00 30·00
628. – 3 p. 60 blue and grey (No. 576) .. 60·00 45·00

**1932.** Zeppelin Air stamps. Optd. **GRAF ZEPPELIN 1932.**
629. 120. 5 c. red .. .. 2·50 1·60
630. 18 c. violet .. .. 12·00 7·50
631. 122. 90 c. purple .. .. 35·00 20·00

134. Refrigerating Plant. 135. Port La Plata.

**1932.** 6th Int. Refrigerating Congress.
632. 134. 3 c. green .. .. 50 25
633. 10 c. red .. .. 1·25 15
634. 12 c. blue .. .. 3·50 1·40

**1933.** 50th Anniv. of La Plata City.
635. 135. 3 c. brown and green .. 75 25
636. – 10 c. purple and orange 60 20
637. – 15 c. blue .. .. 4·00 2·00
638. – 20 c. brown and lilac .. 2·00 1·00
639. – 30 c. red and green .. 16·00 6·00
DESIGNS: 10 c. President J. A. Roca. 15 c. Municipal buildings. 20 c. La Plata Cathedral. 30 c. Dr. D. Rocha.

139. Christ of the Andes. 141. "Liberty" with Arms of Brazil and Argentina.

**1934.** 32nd Int. Eucharistic Congress, Buenos Aires.
640. 139. 10 c. red .. .. 85 25
641. – 15 c. blue .. .. 1·60 55
DESIGN—HORIZ. 15 c. Buenos Aires Cathedral.

**1935.** Visit of President Vargas of Brazil. Inscr. "MAYO DE 1935".
642. 141. 10 c. red .. .. 85 25
643. – 15 c. blue .. .. 1·60 55
DESIGN: 15 c. Clasped hands and flags.

143. D. F. Sarmiento. 146. Prize Bull. 151. With Boundary Lines.

**1935.** Portraits.
644 ½ c. purple (Belgrano) .. 15 10
645 1 c. brown (Type 143) .. 15 10
646 2 c. brown (Urquiza) .. 15 10
647 3 c. green (San Martin) .. 15 10
648 4 c. grey (G. Brown) .. 10 10
653b 5 c. brown (Moreno) .. 15 10
650 6 c. green (Alberdi) .. 15 10
653d 10 c. red (Rivadavia) .. 25 10
651 12 c. purple (Mitre) .. 10 10
708 15 c. grey (Martin Guemes) 30 10
652 20 c. blue (Juan Martin Guemes) .. .. 25 10
653 20 c. blue (Martin Guemes) 15 10
See also Nos. 671 etc.

**1936.** Production and Industry.
676 146 15 c. blue .. .. 60 15
677a 20 c. blue (19½ × 26 mm) 15 15
755 20 c. blue (22 × 33 mm) 85 15
656 – 25 c. red and pink .. 15 15
757 – 30 c. brown and yellow 40 15
658 – 40 c. purple and mauve 35 15
659 – 50 c. red and salmon 25 15
660 151 1 p. blue and brown 17·00 75
760 – 1 p. blue and brown 1·90 15
661 – 2 p. blue and purple .. 85 15
662 – 5 p. green and blue .. 6·50 30
763 – 10 p. black and purple 6·00 1·00
764 – 20 p. brown and blue 6·50 1·00
DESIGNS—VERT. 25c. Ploughman; 50 c. Oilwell; 1 p. (No. 760) as Type 151 but without country boundaries; 5 p. Iguazu Falls; 10 p. Grapes; 20 p. Cotton-plant; HORIZ. 30 c. Patagonian ram; 40 c. Sugar-cane and factory; 2 p. Fruit products.

157. 158. President Sarmiento.

**1936.** Pan-American Peace Conference.
665. 157. 10 c. red .. .. 50 15

**1938.** President's 50th Death Anniv.
666. 158. 3 c. green .. .. 15 10
667. 5 c. red .. .. 15 10
668. 15 c. blue .. .. 15 10
669. 50 c. orange .. .. 1·90 1·10

159. "Pres. Sarmiento". 160. Allegory of the Post.

**1939.** Last Voyage of Cadet Ship "Presidente Sarmiento".
670. 159. 5 c. green .. .. 35 10

**1939.** Portraits as T 143.
671 – 2½ c. black .. .. 15 10
672 – 3 c. grey (San Martin) 15 10
672a – 3 c. grey (Moreno) 15 10
673 – 4 c. green .. .. 10 10
894 – 5 c. brown (16½ × 22½ mm) 10 10
674 – 8 c. orange .. .. 15 10
678 – 10 c. purple .. .. 15 10
675 – 12 c. red .. .. 15 10
895 – 20 c. lilac (21 × 27 mm) 20 10
895b – 20 c. lilac (19½ × 25½ mm) 15 10
PORTRAITS: 2½ c. L. Braille; 4 c. G. Brown; 5 c. Jose Hernandez; 8 c. N. Avellaneda; 10 c. B. Rivadavia. 12 c. B. Mitre; 20 c. G. Brown.

**1939.** 11th U.P.U. Congress, Buenos Aires.
679. 160. 5 c. red .. .. 15 10
680. – 15 c. grey .. .. 40 25
681. – 20 c. blue .. .. 40 10
682. – 25 c. green .. .. 85 35
683. – 50 c. brown .. .. 1·90 55
684. – 1 p. purple .. .. 2·00 80
685. – 2 p. mauve .. .. 9·50 6·00
686. – 5 p. violet .. .. 38·00 18·00
DESIGNS—VERT. 20 c. Seal of Argentina. 1 p. Symbols of postal communications. 2 p. Argentina, "Land of Promise" from a pioneer painting. HORIZ. 15 c. G.P.O. 25 c. Iguazu Falls. 50 c. Mt. Bonete. 5 p. Lake Frias.

165. Working-class Family and New Home. 167. North and South America.

**1939.** 1st Pan-American Housing Congress.
687. 165. 5 c. green .. .. 20 10

**1940.** 50th Anniv. of Pan-American Union.
688. 167. 15 c. blue .. .. 35 10

169. Airplane and Envelope. 172. Gen. French, Col. Beruti and Rosette of the "Legion de Patricios".

**1940.** Air.
689. 169. 30 c. orange .. .. 7·50 10
690. – 50 c. brown .. .. 8·50 15
691. 169. 1 p. red .. .. 2·50 10
692. – 1 p. 25 green .. .. 50 10
693. 169. 2 p. 50 blue .. .. 2·00 15
DESIGNS—VERT. 50 c. "Mercury"; 1 p. 25, Douglas DC-2 in clouds.

**1941.** 131st Anniv. of Rising against Spain.
694. 172. 5 c. blue .. .. 15 10

173. Marco M. de Avellaneda. 174. Statue of Gen. J.A. Roca.

**1941.** Death Cent of Avellaneda (patriot).
695 173 5 c. blue .. .. 15 10

**1941.** Dedication of Statue of Gen. Roca.
696. 174. 5 c. green .. .. 15 10

175. Pellegrini (founder) and National Bank. 176. Gen. Juan Lavalle.

178. Jose Manuel Estrada. 177. New P.O. Savings Bank.

**1941.** 50th Anniv. of National Bank.
697. 175. 5 c. lake .. .. 15 10

**1941.** Death Cent. of Gen. Lavalle.
698. 176. 5 c. blue .. .. 15 10

**1942.** Inaug. of P.O. Savings Bank.
699. 177. 1 c. green .. .. 15 10

**1942.** Birth Cent. of Estrada (patriot).
700. 178. 5 c. purple .. .. 15 10

180. G.P.O., Buenos Aires. 181. Proposed Columbus Lighthouse.

**1942.** Postage and Express stamps.
717. 180. 35 c. blue .. .. 1·90 15
746. 35 c. blue .. .. 40 15
No. 717 is inscribed "PALACIO CENTRAL DE CORREOS Y TELEGRAFOS" and No. 746. "PALACIO CENTRAL DE CORREOS Y TELECOMUNICACIONES".

**1942.** 450th Anniv of Discovery of America by Columbus.
721. 181. 15 c. blue .. .. 3·25 15

**182.** Dr. Paz (founder of "La Prensa"). **183.** Flag of Argentina and Books. **184.** Arms of Argentina.

**1942.** Birth Cent. of Dr. Jose C. Paz.
722. **182.** 5 c. blue .. .. 40 15

**1943.** 1st National Book Fair.
723. **183.** 5 c. blue .. .. 20 15

**1943.** Revolution of 4th June, 1943.
724. **184.** 5 c. red .. .. 20 15
725. 15 c. green .. .. 60 15
726. 20 c. blue (larger) .. 1·10 15

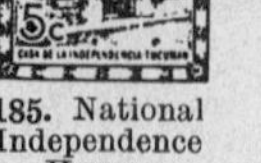

**185.** National Independence House. **186.** Head of Liberty, Money-box and Laurels.

**1943.** Restoration of Tucuman Museum.
727. **185.** 5 c. green .. .. 35 15

**1943.** 1st Savings Bank Conf.
728. **186.** 5 c. brown .. 15 10

**187.** Buenos Aires in 1800.

**1944.** Export Day.
729. **187.** 5 c. black .. .. 15 10

**188.** Postal Union of the Americas and Spain. **189.** G. Bell. **191.** Liner, Warship and Yacht.

**1944.** Postmen's Benefit Fund. Inscr. "PRO-CARTERO".
730. – 3 c.+2 c. black & violet 40 25
731. **188.** 5 c.+5 c. black & red 85 20
732. **189.** 10 c.+5 c. blk. & orge. 1·60 60
733. – 25 c.+15 c. blk. & brn. 1·90 1·00
734. – 1 p.+50 c. blk. & green 9·50 8·00

DESIGNS: 3 c. Samuel Morse. 25 c. Rowland Hill. 1 p. Columbus landing in America.

**1944.** Naval Week.
735. **191.** 5 c. blue .. .. 15 10

**192.** Argentina. **193.** Arms of Argentina.

**1944.** San Juan Earthquake Relief Fund.
736. **192.** 5 c.+10 c. blk. & olive 1·00 50
737. 5 c.+50 c. black & red 3·50 2·25
738. 5 c.+1 p. black & orge. 10·00 7·00
739. 5 c.+20 p. blk. & blue 25·00 17·00

**1944.** 1st Anniv of Revolution of 4 June 1943.
740. **193.** 5 c. blue .. .. 15 15

**194.** Archangel Gabriel. **195.** Cross of Palermo. **196.** Allegory of Savings.

**1944.** 4th National Eucharistic Congress.
741. **194.** 3 c. green .. .. 15 15
742. **195.** 5 c. red .. .. 15 15

**1944.** 20th Anniv. of Universal Savings Day.
743. **196.** 5 c. black .. .. 15 15

**197.** Reservists.

**1944.** Reservists' Day.
744. **197.** 5 c. blue .. .. 15 15

**198.** Bernardino Rivadavia. **199.** Rivadavia's Mausoleum.

**1945.** Rivadavia's Death Cent.
770. **198.** 3 c. green .. .. 15 15
771. – 5 c. red .. .. 15 15
772. **199.** 20 c. blue .. .. 15 15

DESIGN—As Type **198**: 5 c. Rivadavia and Scales of Justice.

**200.** San Martin. **201.** Monument to Andes Army, Mendoza.

**1945.**
773. **200.** 5 c. red .. .. 10 10

**1946.** "Homage to the Unknown Soldier of Independence".
776. **201.** 5 c. purple .. .. 15 15

**202.** Pres. Roosevelt. **203.** "Affirmation". **204.** Aeroplane over Iguazu falls.

**1946.** 1st Death Anniv. of Pres. Franklin Roosevelt.
777. **202.** 5 c. grey .. .. 10 10

**1946.** Installation of President Juan Peron.
778. **203.** 5 c. blue .. .. 15 15

**1946.** Air.
779. **204.** 15 c. red .. .. 15 10
780. – 25 c. green .. .. 20 10

DESIGN: 25 c. Airplane over Andes.

DESIGN: 60 c. Hand upholding globe.

**205.** "Flight".

**1946.** Aviation Week.
781. **205.** 15 c. green on green .. 55 10
782. – 60 c. purple on buff .. 55 15

**207.** "Argentina and Populace".

**1946.** 1st Anniv. of Peron's Defeat of Counter-Revolution.
783. **207.** 5 c. mauve .. .. 20 10
784. 10 c. green .. .. 30 10
785. 15 c. blue .. .. 60 25
786. 50 c. brown .. .. 85 70
787. 1 p. red .. .. 1·60 1·10

**208.** Money-box and Map. **209.** Industry.

**1946.** Annual Savings Day.
788. **208.** 30 c. red .. .. 35 10

**1946.** Industrial Exn.
789. **209.** 5 c. purple .. .. 10 10

**210.** Argentine–Brazil International Bridge. **211.** South Pole.

**1947.** Opening of Bridge between Argentina and Brazil.
790. **210.** 5 c. green .. .. 10 10

**1947.** 43rd Anniv. of 1st Argentine Antarctic Mail.
791. **211.** 5 c. violet .. .. 35 15
792. 20 c. red .. .. 90 15

**212.** "Justice". **213.** Icarus Falling.

**1947.** 1st Anniv of Col. Juan Peron's Presidency.
793 **212** 5 c. purple and buff .. 10 10

**1947.** "Week of the Wing".
794 **213** 15 c. purple .. .. 15 10

**214.** "Presidente Sarmiento". **215.** Cervantes and "Don Quixote".

**1947.** 50th Anniv. of Launching of Cadet Ship "Presidente Sarmiento".
795. **214.** 5 c. blue .. .. 30 10

**1947.** 400th Birth Anniv. of Cervantes.
796. **215.** 5 c. green .. .. 10 10

**216.** Gen. San Martin and Urn.

**1947.** Arrival from Spain of Ashes of Gen. San Martin's Parents.
797. **216.** 5 c. green .. .. 10 10

**217.** Young Crsadeurs. **218.** Statue of Araucarian Indian.

**1947.** Educational Crusade for Universal Peace.
798. **217.** 5 c. green .. .. 10 10
799. 20 c. brown .. .. 10 10

**1948.** American Indian Day.
801. **218.** 25 c. brown .. .. 25 10

**219.** Phrygian Cap and Sprig of Wheat. **220.** "Stop".

**1948.** 5th Anniv. of Anti-Isolationist Revolution of 4th June.
802. **219.** 5 c. blue .. .. 10 10

**1948.** Safety First Campaign.
803. **220.** 5 c. yellow and brown 15 10

**221.** Posthorn and Oak Leaves. **222.** Argentine Farmers.

**1948.** Bicentenary of Postal Service in Rio de la Plata.
804. **221.** 5 c. mauve .. .. 15 15

**1948.** Agriculture Day.
805. **222.** 10 c. brown .. .. 15 15

**223.** "Liberty and Plenty". **225.** Statue of Atlas.

**226.** Map, Globe and Compasses.

**1948.** Re-election of President Peron.
806. **223.** 25 c. red .. .. 15 15

**1948.** Air. 4th Meeting of Pan-American Cartographers.
807. **225.** 45 c. brown .. .. 35 10
808. **226.** 70 c. green .. .. 65 15

**227.** Winged Railway Wheel.

**1949.** 1st Anniv. of Nationalization of Argentine Railways.
809. **227.** 10 c. blue .. .. 15 15

**228.** Head of Liberty.

**1949.** Constitution Day.
810. **228.** 1 p. purple and red .. 35 15

**229.** Trophy and Target. **230.** "Intercommunication."

**1949.** Air. Int. Shooting Championship.
811. **229.** 75 c. brown .. .. 65 15

**1949.** 75th Anniv. of U.P.U.
812. **230.** 25 c. green and olive .. 20 15

## INDEX

Countries can be quickly located by referring to the index at the end of this volume.

231. San Martin.

233. Stamp Designer.

232. San Martin at Boulogne.

**1950.** San Martin's Death Cent. Dated "1850 1950".
813. – 10 c. purple and blue .. 15 10
814. 231. 20 c. brown and red .. 15 10
815. 232. 25 c. brown .. .. 15 10
816. – 50 c. blue and green .. 40 10
817. – 75 c. green and brown 40 10
818. – 1 p. green .. .. 1·00 20
819. – 2 p. purple .. .. 85 35
DESIGNS:—As Type **231**: 10, 50, 75 c. Portraits of San Martin. 2 p. San Martin Mausoleum. As Type **232**: 1 p. House where San Martin died.

**1950.** Int. Philatelic Exn., Buenos Aires.
820. 233. 10 c.+10 c. vio. (post.) 15 15

821. – 45 c.+45 c. blue (air) 40 25
822. – 70 c.+70 c. brown .. 60 40
823. – 1 p.+1 p. red .. 1·75 1·60
824. – 2 p. 50+2 p. 50 olive 9·50 7·00
825. – 5 p.+5 p. green .. 11·00 8·50
DESIGNS: 45 c. Engraver. 70 c. Proofing. 1 p. Printer. 2 p. 50, Woman reading letter. 5 p. San Martin.

234. S. America and Antarctic.

235. Douglas DC-3 and Andean Condor.

**1951.**
826. 234. 1 p. blue and brown .. 1·00 15

**1951.** Air. 10th Anniv. of State Airlines.
827. 235. 20 c. olive .. .. 40 15

236. Pegasus and Steam Locomotive.

**1951.** Five-Year Plan.
828. 236. 5 c. brown (postage) .. 15 15
829. – 25 c. green .. .. 45 10
830. – 40 c. purple .. .. 40 15

831. – 20 c. blue (air) .. 30 10
DESIGNS—HORIZ. 25 c. "President Peron" (liner) and common dolphin. VERT. 20 c. Douglas DC-4 and Andean condor. 40 c. Head of Mercury and telephone.

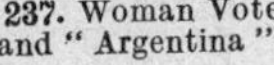
237. Woman Voter and "Argentina".

238. "Piety".

**1951.** Women's Suffrage in Argentina.
832. 237. 10 c. purple .. .. 10 10

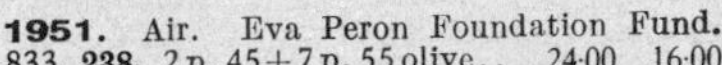
**1951.** Air. Eva Peron Foundation Fund.
833. 238. 2 p. 45+7 p. 55 olive .. 24·00 16·00

239. Eva Peron. 240.

**1952.** (a) Size 20×26 mm.
834. 239. 1 c. brown .. .. 10 10
835. 5 c. grey .. .. 10 10
836. 10 c. red .. .. 10 10
837. 20 c. red .. .. 10 10
838. 25 c. green .. .. 10 10
839. 40 c. purple .. .. 15 10
841. 45 c. blue .. .. 25 10
840. 50 c. bistre .. .. 25 10

(b) Size 22×33 mm. Without inscr. "EVA PERON".
842. 240. 1 p. brown .. .. 35 10
843. 1 p. 50 c. green .. 1·75 10
844. 2 p. red .. .. 50 10
845. 3 p. blue .. .. 85 15

(c) Size 22×33 mm. Inscr. "EVA PERON".
846. 240. 1 p. brown .. .. 60 10
847. 1 p. 50 c. green .. 80 10
848. 2 p. red .. .. 1·25 10
849. 3 p. blue .. .. 1·75 10

(d) Size 30½ × 40 mm. Inscr. "EVA PERON".
850. 240. 5 p. brown .. .. 1·75 40
851. 239. 10 p. red .. .. 4·75 1·40
852. 240. 20 p. green .. .. 13·00 4·50
853. 239. 50 p. blue .. .. 19·00 12·00

241. Indian Funeral Urn. 242. Rescue Ship "Uruguay".

**1953.** 4th Cent. of Santiago del Estero.
854. 241. 50 c. green .. .. 15 10

**1953.** 50th Anniv. of Rescue of the "Antarctic".
855. 242. 50 c. blue .. .. 60 10

243. Planting Flag in S. Orkneys.

244. "Telegraphs."

**1954.** 50th Anniv. of Argentine P.O. in South Orkneys.
856. 243. 1 p. 45 blue .. .. 1·40 10

**1954.** Int. Telecommunications Conference. Symbolical designs inscr. as in T **244**.
857. 244. 1 p. 50 purple .. 40 15
858. – 3 p. blue .. .. 1·40 25
859. – 5 p. red .. .. 1·60 60
DESIGNS—VERT. 3 p. "Radio". HORIZ. 5 p. "Television".

245. Pediment, Buenos Aires Stock Exchange.

246. Eva Peron.

**1954.** Cent. of Argentine Stock Exchange.
860. 245. 1 p. green .. .. 30 10

**1954.** 2nd Death Anniv. of Eva Peron.
861. 246. 3 p. red .. .. 1·60 20

247. San Martin.

249. Wheat.

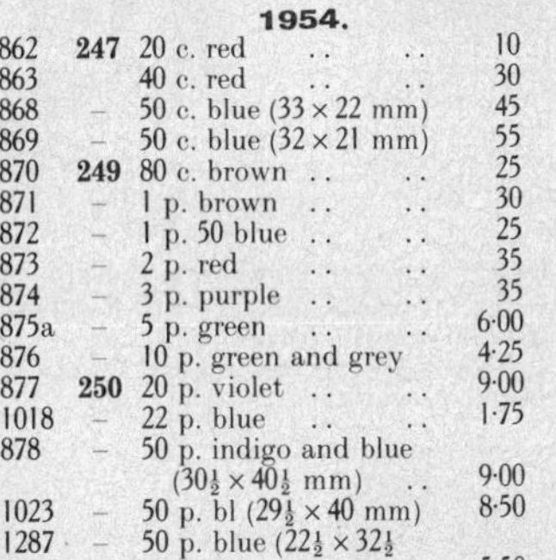
250. Mt. Fitz Roy.  248. "Prosperity".

**1954.**
862 247 20 c. red .. .. 10 10
863 40 c. red .. .. 30 10
868 – 50 c. blue (33×22 mm) 45 10
869 – 50 c. blue (32×21 mm) 55 10
870 249 80 c. brown .. .. 25 10
871 – 1 p. brown .. .. 30 10
872 – 1 p. 50 blue .. .. 25 10
873 – 2 p. red .. .. 35 10
874 – 3 p. purple .. .. 35 10
875a – 5 p. green .. .. 6·00 10
876 – 10 p. green and grey 4·25 10
877 250 20 p. violet .. .. 9·00 10
1018 – 22 p. blue .. .. 1·75 10
878 – 50 p. indigo and blue (30½×40½ mm) .. 9·00 15
1023 – 50 p. bl (29½×40 mm) 8·50 10
1287 – 50 p. blue (22½×32½ mm) .. .. 5·50 10
DESIGNS—As Type **249**: HORIZ. 50 c. Port of Buenos Aires. 1 p. Cattle. 2 p. Eva Peron Foundation. 3p. El Nihuil Dam. As Type **250**: VERT. 1 p. 50 c., 22 p. Industrial Plant. 5 p. Iguazu Falls. 50 p. San Martin. HORIZ. 10 p. Humahuaca Ravine.
For 43 p. in the design of the 1 p. 50, and 22 p. see No. 1021.
For 65 c. in same design see No. 1313.

**1954.** Cent. of Argentine Corn Exchange.
867. 248. 1 p. 50 c. grey .. 65 10

251. Clasped Hands and Congress Emblem.

252. Father and Son with Model Airplane.

**1955.** Productivity and Social Welfare Congress.
879. 251. 3 p. brown .. .. 90 10

**1955.** 25th Anniv. of Commercial Air Services.
880. 252. 1 p. 50 grey .. .. 40 10

253. "Liberation".

254. Forces Emblem.

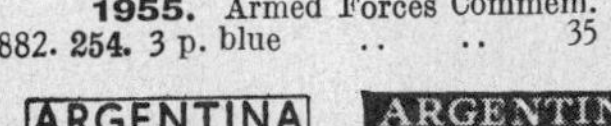
**1955.** Anti-Peronist Revolution of 16 Sept. 1955.
881. 253. 1 p. 50 olive .. .. 20 10

**1955.** Armed Forces Commem.
882. 254. 3 p. blue .. .. 35 10

255. Gen. Urquiza (after J. M. Blanes).

256. Detail from "Antiope" (Correggio).

**1956.** 104th Anniv. of Battle of Caseros.
883. 255. 1 p. 50 green .. .. 25 10

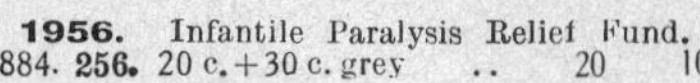
**1956.** Infantile Paralysis Relief Fund.
884. 256. 20 c.+30 c. grey .. 20 10

257. Coin and Die.

258. Corrientes Stamp of 1856.

259. Dr. J. G. Pujol.

260. Cotton, Chaco.

**1956.** 75th Anniv. of National Mint.
885. 257. 2 p. brown and sepia .. 20 10

**1956.** Cent. of 1st Argentine Stamps.
886. 258. 40 c. blue and green .. 15 10
887. 2 p. 40 mauve & brown 20 10
888. 259. 4 p. 40 blue .. .. 50 15
The 40 c. shows a 1 real stamp of 1856.

**1956.** New Provinces.
889. – 50 c. blue .. .. 10 10
890. 260. 1 p. lake .. .. 20 10
891. – 1 p. 50 green .. .. 30 10
DESIGNS—HORIZ. 50 c. Lumbering, La Pampa. VERT. 1 p. 50, Mate tea plant, Misiones.

261. "Liberty".

262. Detail from "Virgin of the Rocks" (Leonardo).

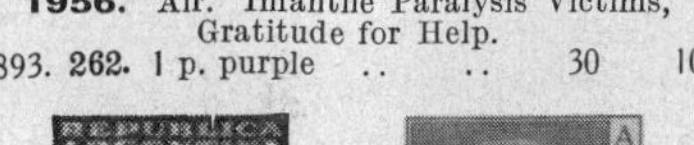
**1956.** 1st Anniv. of Revolution.
892. 261. 2 p. 40 mauve .. 25 10

**1956.** Air. Infantile Paralysis Victims, Gratitude for Help.
893. 262. 1 p. purple .. .. 30 10

264. Esteban Echeverria (writer).

265. F. Ameghino (anthropologist).

266. Roque Saenz Pena (statesman).

267. Franklin.

**1956.**
896. 264. 2 p. purple .. .. 20 10
897. 265. 2 p. 40 brown .. 30 10
898. 266. 4 p. 40 green .. .. 45 10

**1956.** 250th Birth Anniv. of Benjamin Franklin.
899. 267. 40 c. blue .. .. 25 10

268. Frigate "Hercules".

269. Admiral G. Brown.

**1957.** Death Centenary of Admiral Guillermo Brown.

900. **268.** 40 c. blue (postage) .. 30 10
901. – 2 p. 40 green .. .. 40 10
902. – 60 c. grey (air) .. 50 10
903. – 1 p. mauve .. .. 20 10
904. **269.** 2 p. brown .. .. 25 10

DESIGNS—HORIZ. 60 c. "Zefiro" and "Nancy" (sail warships) at Battle of Montevideo. 1 p. L. Rosales and T. Espora. VERT. 2 p. 40, Admiral Brown in later years.

**270.** Church of Santo Domingo.

**271.** Map of the Americas and Badge of Buenos Aires.

**1957.** 150th Anniv. of Defence of Buenos Aires.

905. **270.** 40 c green. .. .. 10 10

**1957.** Air. Inter-American Economic Conf.

906. **271.** 2 p. purple .. .. 35 10

**272.** "La Portena" (early locomotive).

**273.** Globe, Flag and Compass Rose.

**1957.** Cent. of Argentine Railways.

907. **272.** 40 c. sepia (postage) .. 25 10
908. – 60 c. grey (air) .. 25 10

DESIGN: 60 c. Diesel-electric locomotive.

**1957.** Air. Int. Tourist Congress Buenos Aires.

909. **273.** 1 p. brown .. .. 15 10
910. – 2 p. turquoise .. 20 10

DESIGN: 2 p. Symbolic key of tourism.

**274.** Head of Liberty.

**275.**

**276.** "Wealth in Oil".

**277.** La Plata Museum.

**1957.** Reform Convention.

911. **274.** 40 c. red .. .. 10 10

**1957.** Air. Int. Correspondence Week.

912. **275.** 1 p. blue .. .. 15 10

**1957.** 50th Anniv. of Argentine Oil Industry.

913. **276.** 40 c. blue .. .. 15 10

**1958.** 75th Anniv. of Founding of La Plata.

914. **277.** 40 c. black .. .. 15 10

**278.** Health Emblem and Flower.

**1958.** Air. Child Welfare.

915. **278.** 1 p.+50 c. red .. 20 20

**279.** Stamp of 1858 and River Ferry.

**280.** Stamp of 1858.

**1958.** Cent. of Argentine Confederation Stamps and Philatelic Exhibition, Buenos Aires.

916. **279.** 40 c.+20 c. purple and green (postage) .. 45 20
917. – 2 p. 40+1 p. 20 blue and black .. 40 25
918. – 4 p. 40+2 p. 20 purple and blue .. .. 60 40
919. **280.** 1 p.+50 c. blue and olive (air) .. .. 40 35
920. 2 p.+1 p. vio. & red 55 45
921. 3 p.+1 p. 50 brown and green .. .. 60 55
922. 5 p.+2 p. 50 red and olive.. .. .. 1·00 85
923. 10 p.+5 p. sep. & olive 2·25 1·90

DESIGNS—HORIZ. 2 p. 40, Magnifier, stamp album and stamp of 1858. 4 p. 40, P.O. building of 1858.

**281.** Locomotive and Arms of Argentina and Bolivia.

**282.** Douglas DC-6 over Map of Argentine–Bolivian Frontier.

**1958.** Argentine-Bolivian Friendship.

(a) Inaug. of Yacuiba-Santa Cruz Railway.

924. **281.** 40 c. red and slate .. 25 10

(b) Exchange of Presidential Visits.

925. **282.** 1 p. brown .. .. 15 10

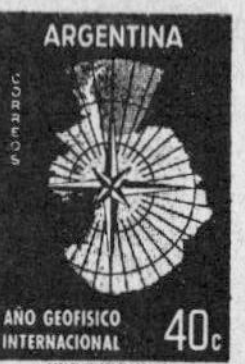

**283.** "Liberty and Flag".

**284.** Farman H.F.20 Biplane.

**1958.** Transfer of Presidential Mandate Head of "Liberty" in grey; inscr. black; flag yellow and blue; background colours given.

926. **283.** 40 c. buff .. .. 10 10
927. 1 p. salmon .. .. 15 10
928. 2 p. green .. .. 25 10

**1958.** 50th Anniv. of Argentine Aero Club.

929. **284.** 2 p. brown .. .. 20 10

**285.** National Flag Monument, Rosario.

**286.** Map of Antarctica.

**1958.** 1st Anniv. of Inauguration of National Flag Monument.

930. **285.** 40 c. grey and blue .. 10 10

**1958.** International Geophysical Year.

931. **286.** 40 c. black and red .. 50 10

**287.** Confederation stamp and "The Santa Fe Mail" (after J. L. Palliere).

**288.** Aerial view of Flooded Town.

**1958.** Cent. of Argentine Confederation Stamps.

932. – 40 c. grn. & blue (post.) 15 10
933. – 80 c. blue & yell. (air) 30 10
934. **287.** 1 p. blue and orange.. 20 10

DESIGNS: 40 c. First local Cordoba 5 c. stamp of 1858 and mailcoach; 80 c. Buenos Aires Type 1 of 1858 and "View of Buenos Aires" (after Deroy).

**1958.** Flood Disaster Relief Fund. Inscr. as in T 288.

935. **288.** 40 c.+20 c. brn. (post.) 15 10
936. – 1 p.+50 c. plum (air) 20 10
937. – 5 p.+2 p. 50 c. blue 80 85

DESIGNS—HORIZ. 1 p. Different aerial view of flooded town. 5 p. Motor-truck in flood-water and garage.

**289.** Child receiving Blood.

**290.** U.N. Emblem and "Dying Captive" (after Michelangelo).

**1958.** Leukaemia Relief Campaign.

938. **289.** 1 p.+50 c. red and black 15 10

**1959.** 10th Anniv. of Declaration of Human Rights.

939. **290.** 40 c. grey and brown 10 10

**291.** Hawker Siddeley Comet 4.

**1959.** Air. Inauguration of Comet Jet Airliners by Argentine National Airlines.

940 **291** 5 p. black and green .. 25 10

**292.** Orchids and Globe.

**293.** Pope Pius XII.

**1959.** 1st Int. Horticultural Exn., Buenos Aires.

941. **292.** 1 p. purple .. .. 15 10

**1959.** Pope Pius XII Commem.

942. **293.** 1 p. black and yellow 15 10

**294.** William Harvey.

PORTRAITS: 1 p. Claude Bernard. 1 p. 50, Ivan P. Pavlov.

**1959.** 21st Int. Physiological Science Congress. Medical Scientists.

943. **294.** 50 c. green .. .. 10 10
944. – 1 p. red .. .. 15 10
945. – 1 p. 50 brown .. 20 10

**295.** Creole Horse.

**296.** Tierra del Fuego.

**1959.**

946 – 10 c. green .. .. 10 10
947 – 20 c. purple .. .. 10 10
948 – 50 c. ochre .. .. 10 10
950 **295.** 1 p. red .. .. 10 10
1016 – 1 p. brown .. .. 10 10
1027 – 1 p. brown .. .. 10 10
1035 – 2 p. red .. .. 35 10
951 – 3 p. blue .. .. 10 10
1036 – 4 p. red .. .. 40 10
1283 **296.** 5 p. brown .. .. 60 10
1037 – 8 p. red .. .. 50 10
1286 – 10 p. brown .. .. 50 10
1038 – 10 p. red .. .. 70 10
1017 – 12 p. purple .. 90 10
954 – 20 p. green .. .. 3·25 10
1039 – 20 p. red .. .. 30 10
1019 – 23 p. green .. .. 4·50 10
1020 – 25 p. lilac .. .. 1·90 10
1021 – 43 p. lake .. .. 7·00 10
1022 – 45 p. brown .. .. 5·00 10
1025 – 100 p. blue .. .. 6·00 20
1026 – 300 p. violet.. .. 3·25 10
1032 – 500 p. green.. .. 1·60 30
1290 – 1,000 p. blue .. 3·75 90

DESIGNS: As Type **295**—HORIZ. 10 c. Spectacled Caiman. 20 c. Llama. 50 c. Puma. VERT 2 p.., 4 p., 8 p., 10 p. (No 1038). 20 p. (No. 1039), San Martin. As Type **296**—HORIZ. 3 p. Zapata Hill, Catamarca. 300 p. Mar del Plata (40 × 29½ mm.). VERT. 1 p. (No 1016) Sunflowers. 1 p. (No 1027) Sunflower (22 × 32 mm.). 10 p. (No. 1286) Inca Bridge, Mendoza. 12 p. Quebracho Colorado (tree). 20 p. (No. 954) Lake Nahuel Huapi. 23 p., 25 p. Red Quebrach tree. 43 p., 45 p. Industrial plant (30 × 39½ mm.). 100 p. Ski-jumper. 500 p. Red Deer (stag). 1,000 p. Leaping Salmon.

For those designs with face values in revalued currency, see Nos. 1300, etc.

**298.** Runner.

**299.**

**1959.** 3rd Pan-American Games, Chicago. Designs embody torch emblem. Centres and torch in black.

955. **298.** 20 c.+10 c. grn. (post.) 10 10
956. – 50 c.+20 c. yellow .. 15 15
957. – 1 p.+50 c. purple .. 15 15
958. – 2 p.+1 p. blue (air) .. 30 15
959. – 3 p.+1 p. 50 olive .. 45 30

DESIGNS—VERT. 50 c. Basketball. 1 p. Boxing. HORIZ. 2 p. Rowing. 3 p. High-diving.

**1959.** Red Cross Hygiene Campaign.

960. **299.** 1 p. red, blue & black 10 10

**300.** Child with Toys.

**301.** Buenos Aires 1 p. stamp of 1859.

**1959.** Mothers' Day.

961. **300.** 1 p. red and black .. 10 10

**1959.** Stamp Day.

962. **301.** 1 p. blue and grey .. 10 10

**302.** B. Mitre and J. J. de Urquiza.

**303.** Andean Condor.

**1959.** Cent. of Pact of San Jose de Flores.

963. **302.** 1 p. plum .. .. 10 10

**1960.** Child Welfare. Birds.

964. **303.** 20 c.+10 c. blue (post.) 25 15
965. – 50 c.+20 c. violet .. 30 15
966. – 1 p.+50 c. brown .. 45 25
967. – 2 p.+1 p. mauve (air) 50 30
968. – 3 p.+1 p. 50 green .. 70 50

BIRDS: 50 c. Fork-tailed Flycatcher. 1 p. Magellanic Woodpecker. 2 p. Red-winged Tinamou. 3 p. Greater Rhea.

**304.** "Uprooted Tree".

**305.** Abraham Lincoln.

**1960.** World Refugee Year.

969. **304.** 1 p. red and brown .. 10 10
970. 4 p. 20 purple & green 15 10

**1960.** 150th Birth Anniv. of Abraham Lincoln.

972. **305.** 5 p. blue .. .. 25 15

**306.** Saavedra and Chapter Hall, Buenos Aires.

**307.** Dr. L. Drago.

**1960.** 150th Anniv. of May Revolution.
973. **306.** 1 p. purple (postage).. 10 10
974. – 2 p. green .. .. 10 10
975. – 4 p. 20 grn. & grey .. 20 10
976. – 10 p. 70 blue and slate 40 15
977. – 1 p. 80 brown (air).. 10 10
978. – 5 p. purple & brown 30 10
DESIGNS—Chapter Hall and: 1 p. 80, Moreno, 2 p. Paso. 4 p. 20, Alberti and Azcuenaga. 5 p. Belgrano and Castelli. 10 p. 70, Larrea and Matheu.

**1960.** Birth Centenary of Drago.
980. **307.** 4 p. 20 brown .. 15 10

**308.** "Five Provinces". **309.** "Market Place 1810" (Buenos Aires).

**1960.** Air. New Argentine Provinces.
981. **308.** 1 p. 80 blue and red .. 10 10

**1960.** Air. Inter-American Philatelic Exn., Buenos Aires ("EFIMAYO") and 150th Anniv. of Revolution. Inscr. "EFIMAYO 1960".
982. **309.** 2 p.+1 p. lake .. 15 10
983. – 6 p.+3 p. grey .. 35 20
984 – 10 p. 70+5 p. 30 blue 60 35
985. – 20 p.+10 p. turquoise 1·00 85
DESIGNS: 6 p. "The Water Carrier". 10 p. 70, "The Landing Place", 20 p. "The Fort".

**310.** J. B. Alberdi. **311.** Seibo (Argentine National Flower).

**1960.** 150th Birth Anniv. of J. B. Alberdi (statesman).
986. **310.** 1 p. green .. .. 10 10

**1960.** Air. Chilean Earthquake Relief Fund. Inscr. "AYUDA CHILE".
987. **311.** 6 p.+3 p. red 30 25
988. – 10 p. 70+5 p. 30 red 40 35
DESIGN: 10 p. 70, Copihue (Chilean national flower).

**312.** Map of Argentina. **313.** Galleon.

**1960.** Census.
989 **312** 5 p. lilac .. .. 70 10

**1960.** 8th Spanish-American P.U. Congress.
990. **313.** 1 p. green (postage) .. 30 10
991. 5 p. brown .. .. 60 20
992. 1 p. 80 purple (air) .. 30 10
993. 10 p. 70 turquoise .. 75 30

**1960.** Air. U.N. Day. Nos. 982/5 optd **DIA DE LAS NACIONES UNIDAS 24 DE OCTUBRE.**
994. **309.** 2 p.+1 p. red .. 20 15
995. – 6 p.+3 p. black .. 25 25
996. – 10 p. 70+5 p. 30 blue 50 40
997. – 20 p.+10 p. turquoise 95 65

**315.** Blessed Virgin of Lujan. **316.** Jacaranda.

**1960.** 1st Inter-American Marian Congress.
998. **315.** 1 p. blue .. .. 10 10

**1960.** Int. Thematic Stamp Exn. ("TEMEX"). Inscr. "TEMEX-61".
999. **316.** 50 c.+50 c. blue .. 10 10
1000. – 1 p.+1 p. turquoise 10 10
1001. – 3 p.+3 p. brown .. 30 20
1002. – 5 p.+5 p. brown .. 50 30
FLOWERS: 1 p. Passion flowers. 3 p. Hibiscus. 5 p. Black lapacho.

**317.** Argentine Scout Badge. **318.** "Shipment of Cereals" (after B. Q. Martin).

**1961.** Int. Scout (Patrol) Camp.
1003. **317.** 1 p. red and black .. 15 10

**1961.** Export Campaign.
1004. **318.** 1 p. brown .. .. 15 10

**319.** Emperor Penguin and Chick. **320.** "America".

**1961.** Child Welfare. Inscr. "PRO-INFANCIA".
1005. – 4 p. 20+2 p. 10 brn. (postage) .. .. 1·25 65
1006. **319.** 1 p. 80+90 c. blk. (air) 55 45
DESIGN: 4 p. 20, Blue-eyed Cormorant.

**1961.** 150th Anniv. of Battle of San Nicolas.
1007. **320.** 2 p. black .. .. 30 10

**321.** Dr. M. Moreno. **322.** Emperor Trajan.

**1961.** 150th Death Anniv. of Dr. M. Moreno.
1008. **321.** 2 p. blue .. .. 15 10

**1961.** Visit of President of Italy.
1009. **322.** 2 p. green .. .. 15 10

**1961.** Americas Day. Nos. 999/1002 optd. **14 DE ABRIL DE LAS AMERICAS.**
1010. **316.** 50 c.+50 c. blue .. 10 10
1011. – 1 p.+1 p. turquoise 15 10
1012. – 3 p.+3 p. brown .. 20 20
1013. – 5 p.+5 p. brown .. 40 35

**324.** Tagore. **325.** San Martin Monument, Madrid.

**1961.** Birth Centenary of Rabindranath Tagore (Indian Poet).
1014. **324.** 2 p. violet on green.. 20 10

**1961.** Inaug. of Spanish San Martin Monument.
1015. **325.** 1 p. black .. .. 15 10

**331a.** Gen. Belgrano (after monument by Rocha, Buenos Aires). **333.** Antarctic Scene.

**1961.** Gen. Manuel Belgrano Commem.
1034. **331a.** 2 p. blue .. .. 15 10

**1961.** 10th Anniv. of San Martin Antarctic Base.
1044. **333.** 2 p. black .. .. 50 10

**334.** Conquistador and Sword. **335.** Sarmiento Statue (Rodin).

**1961.** 4th Cent. of Jujuy City.
1045. **334.** 2 p. red and black .. 15 10

**1961.** 150th Birth Anniv. of Sarmiento.
1046. **335.** 2 p. violet .. .. 15 10

**336.** Cordoba Cathedral. **343.** 15c. Stamp of 1862.

**1961.** "Argentina 62" Int. Philatelic Exn.
1047. **336.** 2 p.+2 p. purple (post.) 20 15
1048. – 3 p.+3 p. green .. 30 15
1049. – 10 p.+10 p. blue .. 85 50
1059. **343.** 6 p. 50+6 p. 50 blue and turquoise (air) 80 75
DESIGNS—HORIZ. 10 p. Buenos Aires Cathedral. VERT. 3 p. As Type **343** but showing 10 c. value and different inscr.

**337.** **338.** "The Flight into Egypt" (after Ana Maria Moncalvo).

**1961.** World Town-Planning Day.
1052. **337.** 2 p. blue and yellow 15 10

**1961.** Child Welfare.
1053. **338.** 2 p.+1 p. brown & lilac 15 10
1054. 10 p.+5 p. pur. & mve. 50 15

**339.** Belgrano Statue (C. Belleuse). **340.** Mounted Grenadier.

**1962.** 150th Anniv. of National Flag.
1055. **339.** 2 p. blue .. .. 15 10

**1962.** 150th Anniv. of Gen. San Martin's Mounted Grenadiers.
1056. **340.** 2 p. red .. .. 15 10

**341.** Mosquito and Emblem. **342.** Lujan Basilica.

**1962.** Malaria Eradication.
1057. **341.** 2 p. black and red .. 10 10

**1962.** 75th Anniv. of Coronation of the Holy Virgin of Lujan.
1058. **342.** 2 p. black and brown 10 10

**344.** Juan Jufre (founder). **345.** U.N.E.S.C.O. Emblem.

**1962.** 400th Anniv. of San Juan.
1060 **344** 2 p. blue .. .. 10 10

**1962.** Air. 15th Anniv. of U.N.E.S.C.O.
1061. **345.** 13 p. brown and ochre 30 15

**346.** "Flight". **347.** Juan Vucetich (fingerprints pioneer).

**1962.** 50th Anniv. of Argentine Air Force.
1062. **346.** 2 p. blue, blk. & pur. 15 10

**1962.** Vucetich Commem.
1063. **347.** 2 p. green .. .. 15 10

**348.** 19th-century Mail Coach. **350.** U.P.A.E. Emblem

**1962.** Air. Postman's Day.
1064. **348.** 5 p. 60 black and drab 15 10

**1962.** Air. Surch. **AEREO** and value.
1065. **296.** 5 p. 60 on 5 p. brown 30 15
1066. 18 p. on 5 p. brn. on grn. 1·25 20

**1962.** Air. 50th Anniv. of Postal Union of Latin America.
1067. **350.** 5 p. 60 blue .. .. 10 10

**351.** Pres. Sarmiento. **352.** Chalk-browed Mockingbird.

**1962.**
1073 **351** 2 p. green .. .. 70 10
1069 – 4 p. red .. .. 60 10
1075 – 6 p. red .. .. 1·40 10
1071 – 6 p. brown .. .. 10 10
1288 – 90 p. bistre .. .. 3·50 15
PORTRAITS: 4 p., 6 p. Jose Hernandez. 90 p. G. Brown.

**1962.** Child Welfare.
1076. **352.** 4 p.+2 p. sepia, turquoise and brown 90 50
1077. – 12 p.+6 p. brown, yellow and slate .. 1·90 1·40
DESIGN—VERT. 12 p. Rufous-collared Sparrow.
See also Nos. 1101/2, 1124/5, 1165/6, 1191/2, 1214/15, 1264/5, 1293/4, 1394/5, 1415/6 and 1441/2.

**353.** Skylark 3 Glider. **354.** "20 de Febrero" Monument, Salta.

**1963.** Air. 9th World Gliding Championships, Junin.
1078. **353.** 5 p. 60 black and blue 20 10
1079. – 11 p. black, red & blue 40 10
DESIGN: 11 p. Super Albatross glider.

**1963.** 150th Anniv. of Battle of Salta.
1080. **354.** 2 p. green .. .. 15 10

**355.** Cogwheels. **356.** National College.

**1963.** 75th Anniv. of Argentine Industrial Union.
1081. **355.** 4 p. red and grey .. 10 10

**1963.** Cent. of National College, Buenos Aires.
1082. **356.** 4 p. black and buff .. 10 10

**357.** Child drinking Milk. **358.** "Flight".

**1963.** Freedom from Hunger.
1083. **357.** 4 p. ochre, black & red 15 10

**1963.** Air. (a) As T **358.**

| | | | | |
|---|---|---|---|---|
| 1084. | **358.** | 5 p. 60 grn., mve. & pur. | 35 | 10 |
| 1085. | | 7 p. blk. & yellow (I) | 45 | 10 |
| 1086. | | 7 p. blk. & yellow (II) | 4·50 | 35 |
| 1087. | | 11 p. pur., grn. & blk. | 45 | 15 |
| 1088. | | 18 p. blue, red & mve. | 1·10 | 25 |
| 1089. | | 21 p. grey, red & brn. | 1·50 | 35 |

Two types of 7 p. I, "ARGENTINA" reads down, and II, "ARGENTINA" reads up as in Type **358.**

(b) As Type **358** but inscr. "REPUBLICA ARGENTINA" reading down.

| | | | |
|---|---|---|---|
| 1147. | 12 p. lake and brown | 1·75 | 15 |
| 1148. | 15 p. blue and red | 1·10 | 15 |
| 1149. | 26 p. ochre | 60 | 15 |
| 1150. | 27 p. 50 green and black | 1·75 | 30 |
| 1151. | 30 p. 50 brown and blue | 2·25 | 35 |
| 1292. | 40 p. lilac | 3·00 | 15 |
| 1153. | 68 p. green | 3·00 | 25 |
| 1154. | 78 p. blue | 1·25 | 35 |

See also Nos. 1374/80 in revalued currency.

**359.** Football.

**360.** Frigate "La Argentina" (after Bouchard).

**1963.** 4th Pan-American Games, Sao Paulo.

| | | | | |
|---|---|---|---|---|
| 1090. | **359.** | 4 p.+2 p. green, black and pink (postage) | 20 | 10 |
| 1091. | – | 12 p.+6 p. purple black and salmon | 30 | 25 |
| 1092. | – | 11 p.+5 p. red, black and green (air) | 35 | 25 |

DESIGNS: 11 p. Cycling. 12 p. Show-jumping.

**1963.** Navy Day.

| | | | | |
|---|---|---|---|---|
| 1093. | **360.** | 4 p. blue | 45 | 10 |

**361.** Assembly House and Seal. **363.** Queen Nefertari (bas-relief).

**362.** Battle Scene.

**1963.** 150th Anniv. of 1813 Assembly.

| | | | | |
|---|---|---|---|---|
| 1094. | **361.** | 4 p. black and blue | 15 | 10 |

**1963.** 150th Anniv. of Battle of San Lorenzo.

| | | | | |
|---|---|---|---|---|
| 1095. | **362.** | 4 p. blk. & grn. on grn. | 20 | 10 |

**1963.** U.N.E.S.C.O. Campaign for Preservation of Nubian Monuments.

| | | | | |
|---|---|---|---|---|
| 1096 | **363** | 4 p. black, grn & buff | 25 | 10 |

**364.** Government House. **365.** "Science".

**1963.** Presidential Installation.

| | | | | |
|---|---|---|---|---|
| 1097. | **364.** | 5 p. brown and pink | 15 | 10 |

**1963.** 10th Latin-American Neurosurgery Congress.

| | | | | |
|---|---|---|---|---|
| 1098. | **365.** | 4 p. blue, blk. & brown | 20 | 10 |

**366.** Blackboards. **367.** F. de las Carreras (President of Supreme Court).

**1963.** "Alliance for Progress".

| | | | | |
|---|---|---|---|---|
| 1099. | **366.** | 5 p. red, black & blue | 15 | 10 |

**1963.** Centenary of Judicial Power.

| | | | | |
|---|---|---|---|---|
| 1100. | **367.** | 5 p. green | 15 | 10 |

**1963.** Child Welfare. Vert. designs as T **352.** Multicoloured.

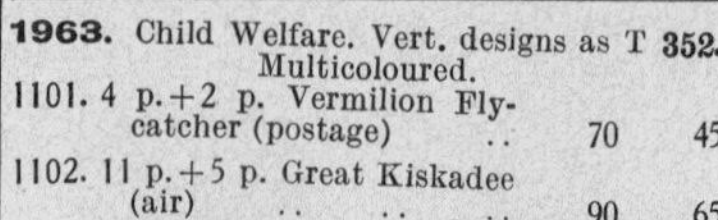

| | | | |
|---|---|---|---|
| 1101. | 4 p.+2 p. Vermilion Fly-catcher (postage) | 70 | 45 |
| 1102. | 11 p.+5 p. Great Kiskadee (air) | 90 | 65 |

**368.** Kemal Ataturk. **369.** "Payador" (after Castagnino).

**1963.** 25th Death Anniv. of Kemal Ataturk.

| | | | | |
|---|---|---|---|---|
| 1103. | **368.** | 12 p. grey | 30 | 10 |

**1964.** 4th Nat. Folklore Festival.

| | | | | |
|---|---|---|---|---|
| 1104. | **369.** | 4 p. blk., blue & ultram. | 15 | 10 |

**370.** Map of Antarctic Islands.

**371.** Jorge Newbery in 'Plane.

**1964.** Antarctic Claims Issue.

| | | | | |
|---|---|---|---|---|
| 1105. | **370.** | 2 p. bl. & ochre (post.) | 1·60 | 30 |
| 1106. | – | 4 p. bistre and blue | 2·40 | 35 |
| 1107. | – | 18 p. bl. & bistre (air) | 2·50 | 55 |

DESIGNS—VERT. (30×39½ mm.): 4 p. Map of Argentina and Antarctica. HORIZ. (as Type **291**): 18 p. Map of "Islas Malvinas" (Falkland Is.).

**1964.** 50th Death Anniv. of Jorge Newbery (aviator).

| | | | | |
|---|---|---|---|---|
| 1108. | **371.** | 4 p. green | 15 | 10 |

**372.** Pres. Kennedy.

**373.** Father Brochero

**1964.** President Kennedy Memorial Issue.

| | | | | |
|---|---|---|---|---|
| 1109. | **372.** | 4 p. blue and mauve | 15 | 10 |

**1964.** 50th Death Anniv. of Father J. G. Brochero.

| | | | | |
|---|---|---|---|---|
| 1110. | **373.** | 4 p. brown | 15 | 10 |

**374.** U.P.U. Monument, Berne.

**375.** Soldier of the Patricios Regiment.

**1964.** Air. 15th U.P.U. Congress, Vienna.

| | | | | |
|---|---|---|---|---|
| 1111. | **374.** | 18 p. purple and red | 50 | 20 |

**1964.** Army Day.

| | | | | |
|---|---|---|---|---|
| 1112. | **375.** | 4 p. multicoloured | 50 | 15 |

See also Nos. 1135, 1170, 1201, 1223, 1246, 1343, 1363, 1399, 1450, 1515, 1564, 1641 and 1678.

**376.** Pope John XXIII.

**377.** Olympic Stadium.

**1964.** Pope John Commem.

| | | | | |
|---|---|---|---|---|
| 1113. | **376.** | 4 p. black and orange | 20 | 10 |

**1964.** Olympic Games, Tokyo.

| | | | | |
|---|---|---|---|---|
| 1114. | **377.** | 4 p. + 2 p. brown, yellow and red (post.) | 15 | 15 |
| 1115. | – | 12 p.+6 p. blk. & grn. | 30 | 30 |
| 1116. | – | 11 p.+5 p. black and blue (air) | 65 | 65 |

DESIGNS—VERT. 11 p. Sailing. 12 p. Fencing.

**378.** University Arms.

**379.** Olympic Flame and Crutch.

**1964.** 350th Anniv. of Cordoba University.

| | | | | |
|---|---|---|---|---|
| 1117. | **378.** | 4 p. yellow, blue & blk. | 15 | 10 |

**1964.** Air. Invalids Olympic Games, Tokyo.

| | | | | |
|---|---|---|---|---|
| 1118. | **379.** | 18 p.+9 p. mult. | 35 | 45 |

**380.** "The Discovery of America" (Florentine woodcut).

**381.** Pigeons and U.N. Headquarters.

**1964.** Air. "Columbus Day" or ("Day of the Race").

| | | | | |
|---|---|---|---|---|
| 1119. | **380.** | 13 p. black and drab | 35 | 15 |

**1964.** United Nations Day.

| | | | | |
|---|---|---|---|---|
| 1120. | **381.** | 4 p. ultramarine & blue | 15 | 10 |

**382.** J. V. Gonzalez (medallion).

**383.** Gen. J. Roca.

**1964.** Birth Cent. of J. V. Gonzalez.

| | | | | |
|---|---|---|---|---|
| 1121. | **382.** | 4 p. red | 15 | 10 |

**1964.** 50th Death Anniv. of General Julio Roca.

| | | | | |
|---|---|---|---|---|
| 1122. | **383.** | 4 p. blue | 15 | 10 |

**384.** "Market-place, Montserrat Square" (after C. Morel).

**385.** Icebreaker "General San Martin" and Chinstrap Penguin.

**1964.** "Argentine Painters".

| | | | | |
|---|---|---|---|---|
| 1123. | **384.** | 4 p. sepia | 25 | 10 |

**1964.** Child Welfare. Vert. designs as T **352.** Multicoloured.

| | | | |
|---|---|---|---|
| 1124. | 4 p.+2 p. Red-crested Cardinal (post.) | 65 | 35 |
| 1125. | 18 p.+9 p. Chilean Swallow (air) | 1·25 | 80 |

**1965.** "National Territory of Tierra del Fuego, Antarctic and South Atlantic Isles".

| | | | | |
|---|---|---|---|---|
| 1126. | – | 2 p. purple (postage) | 50 | 10 |
| 1127. | **385.** | 4 p. blue | 1·75 | 30 |
| 1128. | – | 11 p. red (air) | 60 | 15 |

DESIGNS: 2 p. General Belgrano Base (inscr. "BASE DE EJERCITO" etc.). 11 p. Teniente Matienzo Joint Antarctic Base (inscr. "BASE CONJUNTA" etc.).

**1965.** Air. First Rio Plata Philatelists' Day. Optd. **PRIMERAS JORNADAS FILATELICAS RIOPLATENSES.**

| | | | | |
|---|---|---|---|---|
| 1129. | **358.** | 7 p. black & yellow (II) | 15 | 15 |

**387.** Young Saver.

**388.** I.T.U. Emblem.

**1965.** 50th Anniv. of National Postal Savings Bank.

| | | | | |
|---|---|---|---|---|
| 1130. | **387.** | 4 p. black and red | 10 | 10 |

**1965.** Air. Centenary of I.T.U.

| | | | | |
|---|---|---|---|---|
| 1131. | **388.** | 18 p. multicoloured | 40 | 15 |

**389.** I.Q.S.Y. Emblem. **390.** Soldier of the "Pueyrredon Hussars".

**1965.** Int. Quiet Sun Year and Space Research.

| | | | | |
|---|---|---|---|---|
| 1132. | **389.** | 4 p. black, orange and blue (postage) | 15 | 10 |
| 1133. | – | 18 p. red (air) | 30 | 20 |
| 1134. | – | 50 p. blue | 80 | 35 |

DESIGNS—VERT. 18 p. Rocket launching. HORIZ. 50 p. Earth, trajectories and space phenomena (both inscr. "INVESTIGACIONES ESPACIALES").

**1965.** Army Day (29th May).

| | | | | |
|---|---|---|---|---|
| 1135. | **390.** | 8 p. multicoloured | 70 | 15 |

See also Nos. 1170, 1201, 1223, 1246, 1343, 1363, 1399, 1450, 1515, 1564 and 1641.

**391.** Ricardo Guiraldes.

**392.** H. Yrigoyen (statesman).

**1965.** Argentine Writers (1st series). Each brown.

| | | | |
|---|---|---|---|
| 1136. | 8 p. Type **391** | 35 | 10 |
| 1137. | 8 p. E. Larreta | 35 | 10 |
| 1138. | 8 p. L. Lugones | 35 | 10 |
| 1139. | 8 p. R J. Payro | 35 | 10 |
| 1140. | 8 p. R. Rojas | 35 | 10 |

See also Nos. 1174/8.

**1965.** Hipolito Yrigoyen Commem.

| | | | | |
|---|---|---|---|---|
| 1141. | **392.** | 8 p. black and red | 15 | 10 |

**393.** "Children looking through a Window".

**1965.** Int. Mental Health Seminar.

| | | | | |
|---|---|---|---|---|
| 1142. | **393.** | 8 p. black and brown | 15 | 10 |

**394.** Ancient Map and Funeral Urn.

**395.** Mgr. Dr. J. Cagliero.

**1965.** 400th Anniv. of San Miguel de Tucuman.

| | | | | |
|---|---|---|---|---|
| 1143. | **394.** | 8 p. multicoloured | 15 | 10 |

**1965.** Cagliero Commem.

| | | | | |
|---|---|---|---|---|
| 1144. | **395.** | 8 p. violet | 15 | 10 |

**396.** Dante (statue in Church of the Holy Cross, Florence).

**397.** Sail Merchantman "Mimosa".

**1965.** 700th Birth Anniv. of Dante.

| | | | | |
|---|---|---|---|---|
| 1145. | **396.** | 8 p. blue | 15 | 10 |

**1965.** Cent. of Welsh Colonisation of Chubut and Foundation of Rawson.

| | | | | |
|---|---|---|---|---|
| 1146. | **397.** | 8 p. black and red | 35 | 10 |

**398.** Police Emblem on Map of Buenos Aires. **399.** Schoolchildren.

**1965.** Federal Police Day.
1155. **398.** 8 p. red .. .. 15 10

**1965.** 81st Anniv. of Law 1420 (Public Education).
1156. **399.** 8 p. black and green 15 10

**400.** St. Francis's Church, Catamarca. **401.** R. Dario (Nicaraguan poet).

**1965.** Brother Mamerto Esquiu Commem.
1157. **400.** 8 p. brown & yellow .. 15 10

**1965.** 50th Death Anniv. of Ruben Dario.
1158. **401.** 15 p. violet on grey 15 10

**402.** "The Orange-seller" (detail).

**1966.** Prilidiano Pueyrredon's Paintings. Designs show details from the original works, each printed in green.
1159. 8 p. Type **402** .. .. 80 45
1160. 8 p. "A Halt at the Village Grocer's Shop" 80 45
1161. 8 p. "San Fernando Landscape" .. .. 80 45
1162. 8 p. "Bathing Horses on the Banks of the River Plate" .. .. 80 45

**403.** Rocket "Centaur" and Antarctic Map. **404.** Dr. Sun Yat-sen.

**1966.** Air. Rocket Launches in Antarctica.
1163. **403.** 27 p. 50 red, blk. & blue 65 25

**1966.** Birth Cent. of Dr. Sun Yat-sen.
1164. **404.** 8 p. brown .. .. 80 25

**1966.** Child Welfare. Vert designs as T **352**, inscr. "R. ARGENTINA". Multicoloured.
1165. 8 p. + 4 p. Chilian Lapwing (postage) .. .. 1·00 55
1166. 27p. 50 + 12p. 50 Rufous Hornero (air) .. .. 1·25 85

**406.** "Human Races".

**1966.** Inaug. of W.H.O. Headquarters, Geneva.
1168. **406.** 8 p. black and brown 15 10

**407.** Magellan Gull.

**1966.** Air. 50th Anniv. of Naval Aviation School, Puerto Militar.
1169. **407.** 12 p. multicoloured .. 40 25

**1966.** Army Day (29th May). As T **390**.
1170. 8 p. multicoloured .. .. 65 15
DESIGN: 8 p. Militiaman of Guemes "Infernals".

**408.** Arms of Argentina.

**1966.** Air. "Argentina '66" Philatelic Exn. Buenos Aires.
1171. **408.** 10 p. + 10 p. mult. 2·00 1·60

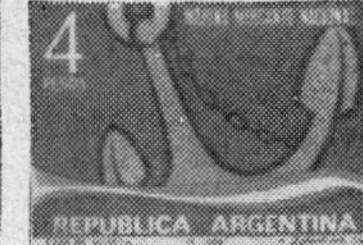


**410.** "Charity" Emblem. **411.** Anchor.

**1966.** Argentine Charities.
1173. **410.** 10 p. blue, black & grn. 25 15

**1966.** Argentine Writers (2nd series). Portraits as T **391**. Each green.
1174. 10 p. H. Ascasubi .. 40 10
1175. 10 p. Estanislao del Campo 40 10
1176. 10 p. M. Cane .. 40 10
1177. 10 p. Lucio V. Lopez .. 40 10
1178. 10 p. R. Obligado .. 40 10

**1966.** 25th Anniv. of Argentine Mercantile Marine.
1179. **411.** 4 p. multicoloured .. 25 15

**412.** L. Agote. **413.** Map and Flags of the American States.

**1966.** Argentine Scientists. Each violet.
1180. 10 p. Type **412** .. 40 10
1181. 10 p. J. B. Ambrosetti 40 10
1182. 10 p. M. I. Lillo .. .. 40 10
1183. 10 p. F. P. Moreno .. 40 10
1184. 10 p. F. J. Muniz .. 40 10

**1966.** 7th American Armies' Conf., Buenos Aires.
1185. **413.** 10 p. multicoloured 15 10

**414.** Bank Facade. **415.** La Salle Statue and College.

**1966.** 75th Anniv. of Argentine National Bank.
1186. **414.** 10 p. green .. .. 10 10

**1966.** 75th Anniv. of La Salle College, Buenos Aires.
1187. **415.** 10 p. black and brown 10 10

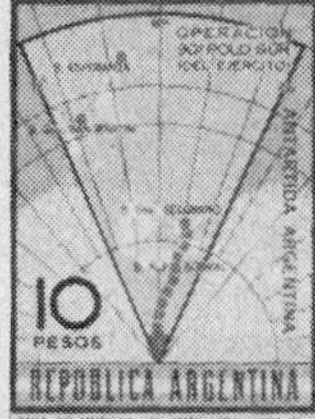

**416.** Antarctic Map with Expedition Route. **417.** Gen. J. M. de Pueyrredon.

**1966.** Argentine South Pole Expedition, 1965-66.
1188. **416.** 10 p. multicoloured .. 80 50

**1966.** Gen. J. M. de Pueyrredon Commem.
1189. **417.** 10 p. red .. .. 10 10

**418.** Gen. J. G. de Las Heras. **419.** Ancient Pot.

**1966.** Gen. Juan G. de Las Heras Commem.
1190. **418.** 10 p. black .. .. 10 10

**1967.** Child Welfare. Vert. designs as T **352**, inscr. "R. ARGENTINA". Multicoloured.
1191. 10 p. + 5 p. Scarlet-headed Blackbird (horiz.) (post.) 80 60
1192. 15 p. + 7 p. Blue and Yellow Tanager (air) .. 1·25 90

**1967.** 20th Anniv. of U.N.E.S.C.O.
1193. **419.** 10 p. multicoloured .. 15 10

**420.** "The Meal" (after F. Fader).

**1967.** Fernando Fader (painter).
1194. **420.** 10 p. brown .. .. 15 10

**421.** Juana Azurduy de Padilla. **422.** Schooner "Invencible".

**1967.** Famous Argentine Women. Each sepia.
1195. 6 p. Type **421** .. .. 30 10
1196. 6 p. J. M. Gorriti .. 30 10
1197. 6 p. C. Grierson .. 30 10
1198. 6 p. J. P. Manson .. 30 10
1199. 6 p. A. Storni .. .. 30 10

**1967.** Navy Day.
1200. **422.** 20p. multicoloured .. 95 15

**1967.** Army Day (29th May). As T **390**.
1201. 20 p. multicoloured .. 75 15
DESIGN: 20 p. Soldier of the Arribenos Regiment.

**424.** Suitcase and Dove. **425.** PADELAI Emblem and Sun.

**1967.** Int. Tourist Year.
1203. **424.** 20 p. multicoloured .. 15 10

**1967.** 75th Anniv. of PADELAI (Argentine Children's Welfare Assn.).
1204. **425.** 20 p. multicoloured .. 15 10

**426.** Teodoro Fels's Bleriot XI. **427.** Ferreyra's Oxwagon and Skyscrapers.

**1967.** Air. 50th Anniv. of 1st Argentine-Uruguay Airmail Flight.
1205. **426.** 26 p. brown, olive & bl. 30 10

**1967.** Cent. of Villa Maria.
1206. **427.** 20 p. multicoloured .. 15 10

**428.** "General San Martin" (from statue by M. P. Nunez de Ibarra). **429.** Interior of Museum.

**1967.** 150th Anniv. of Battle of Chacabuco.
1207. **428.** 20 p. brown & yellow 45 15
1208. – 40 p. blue .. .. 70 15
DESIGN—(48 × 31 mm.)—HORIZ. 40 p. "Battle of Chacabuco" (from painting by P. Subercaseaux).

**1967.** 10th Anniv. of Government House Museum.
1209. **429.** 20 p. blue .. .. 15 10

**430.** Pedro Zanni and "Provincia de Buenos Aires".

**1967.** Aeronautics Week.
1210. **430.** 20 p. multicoloured .. 15 10

**431.** Cadet Ship "General Brown" (from painting by E. Biggeri). **432.** Ovidio Lagos and Front Page of "La Capital" (newspaper).

**1967.** "Temex 67" Stamp Exhibition and 95th Anniversary of Naval Military School.
1211. **431.** 20 p. multicoloured .. 95 15

**1967.** Centenary of "La Capital".
1212. **432.** 20 p. brown .. .. 15 10

**433.** St. Barbara (from altar-painting, Segovia, Spain). **434.** "Sivori's Wife".

**1967.** Artillery Day (Dec. 4th).
1213. **433.** 20 p. red .. .. 15 10

**1967.** Child Welfare. Bird designs as T **352**. Multicoloured.
1214. 20 p. + 10 p. Amazon Kingfisher (postage) .. 75 40
1215. 26 p. + 13 p. Toco Toucan (air) .. .. 1·00 60

**1968.** 50th Death Anniv. of Eduardo Sivori (painter).
1216. **434.** 20 p. green .. .. 15 10

**435.** "Almirante Brown" Scientific Station. **436.** Man in Wheel-chair.

**1968.** "Antarctic Territories".
1217. – 6 p. multicoloured .. 60 15
1218. **435.** 20 p. multicoloured .. 85 20
1219. – 40 p. multicoloured .. 1·40 55
DESIGNS—VERT. ($22\frac{1}{2} \times 32$ mm.). 6 p. Map of Antarctic radio-postal stations. HORIZ. As Type **435**). 40 p. Aircraft over South Pole ("Trans-Polar Round Flight").

**1968.** Rehabilitation Day for the Handicapped.
1220. **436.** 20 p. black and green 20 10

437. "St. Gabriel" (detail from "The Annunciation" by Leonardo da Vinci).

438. Children and W.H.O. Emblem.

**1968.** St. Gabriel (patron saint of army communications).
1221. **437.** 20 p. mauve . . . . 15 10

**1968.** 20th Anniv. of W.H.O.
1222. **438.** 20 p. blue and red . . 15 10

**1968.** Army Day (29th May). As T **390.**
1223. 20 p. multicoloured . . 85 15
DESIGN: 20 p. Iriarte's artilleryman.

439. Full-rigged Cadet Ship "Libertad" (E. Biggeri).

**1968.** Navy Day.
1224. **439.** 20 p. multicoloured . . 95 15

440. G. Rawson and Hospital.

**1968.** Cent. of Guillermo Rawson Hospital.
1225. **440.** 6 p. bistre . . . . 15 10

441. Vito Dumas and "Legh II".

**1968.** Air. Vito Dumas' World Voyage in Yacht "Legh II".
1226. **441.** 68 p. multicoloured . . 60 20

442. Children crossing "Zebra".

**1968.** Road Safety.
1227. **442.** 20 p. multicoloured . . 20 10

443. "O'Higgins greeting San Martin" (P. Subercaseaux).

**1968.** 150th Anniv. of Battle of the Maipu.
1228 **443** 40 p. blue . . . . 70 20

444. Dr. O. Magnasco (Lawyer).

445. "The Sea" (E. Gomez).

446. "Grandmother's Birthday" (P. Lynch).

**1968.** Magnasco Commem.
1229. **444.** 20 p. brown . . . . 20 10

**1968.** Children's Stamp Design Competition.
1230. **445.** 20 p. multicoloured . . 20 15
1231. **446.** 20 p. multicoloured . . 20 15

447. Mar del Plata at Night.

448. Mounted Gendarme.

**1968.** 4th Plenary Assembly of Int. Telegraph and Telephone Consultative Committee, Mar del Plata.
1232. **447.** 20 p. black, yellow & blue (postage) . . 25 15
1233. – 40 p. black, mauve and blue (air) . . 35 15
1234. – 68 p. multicoloured . . 50 25
DESIGNS: (As Type **447**) 40 p. South America in Assembly hemisphere. (40×30 mm.). 68 p. Assembly emblem.

**1968.** National Gendarmerie.
1235. **448.** 20 p. multicoloured . . 30 10

449. Coastguard Cutter "Lynch".

450. A. de Anchorena and "Pampero".

**1968.** National Maritime Prefecture (Coastguard).
1236. **449.** 20 p. blk., grey & bl. 45 10

**1968.** Aeronautics Week.
1237. **450.** 20 p. multicoloured . . 30 10

451. St. Martin of Tours (A. Guido).

452. Bank Emblem.

**1968.** St. Martin of Tours (patron saint of Buenos Aires).
1238. **451.** 20 p. brown and lilac 15 10

**1968.** Municipal Bank of Buenos Aires.
1239. **452.** 20 p. blk., grn., yell. 15 10

453. Anniversary and A.L.P.I. Emblems.

**1968.** 25th Anniv. of "Flight Against Polio Assn." (A.L.P.I.).
1240. **453.** 20 p. green & red . . 20 10

454. "My Grandmother's Birthday" (Patricia Lynch).

**1968.** 1st "Solidarity" Philatelic Exn., Buenos Aires.
1241. **454.** 40 p.+20 p. mult. . . 30 30

455. "The Potter Woman" (Ramon Gomez Cornet).

456. Emblem of State Coalfields.

**1968.** Cent. of Whitcomb Gallery, Buenos Aires.
1242. **455.** 20 p. red . . . . 15 10

**1968.** Coal and Steel Industries. Mult.
1243 20 p. Type **456** . . . . 15 10
1244 20 p. Ladle and emblem of Military Steel-manufacturing Agency ("FM") . . . . 15 10

457. Illustration from Schmidl's book "Journey to the River Plate and Paraguay".

**1969.** Ulrich Schmidl Commem.
1245. **457.** 20 p. yellow, red & blk. 15 10

**1969.** Army Day (29 May). As T **390.**
1246 20 p. Sapper, Buenos Aires Army, 1856 . . 95 15

459. Sail Frigate "Hercules".

**1969.** Navy Day.
1247. **459.** 20 p. multicoloured . . 1·00 15

460. "Freedom and Equality" (from poster by S. Zagorski).

461. I.L.O. Emblem within Honeycomb.

**1969.** Human Rights Year.
1254. **460.** 20 p. black and yellow 15 10

**1969.** 50th Anniv. of I.L.O.
1255. **461.** 20 p. multicoloured . . 15 10

462. P. N. Arata (biologist).

463. Dish Aerial and Satellite.

**1969.** Argentine Scientists.
1256. **462.** 6 p. brown on yellow . . 35 15
1257. – 6 p. brown on yellow . . 35 15
1258. – 6 p. brown on yellow . . 35 15
1259. – 6 p. brown on yellow . . 35 15
1260. – 6 p. brown on yellow . . 35 15
PORTRAITS: No. 1257, M. Fernandez (zoologist). No. 1258, A. P. Gallardo (biologist). No. 1259, C. M. Hicken (botanist). No. 1260, E. L. Holmberg (botanist).

**1969.** Satellite Communications.
1261. **463.** 20 p. blk. & yell. (post.) 25 15
1262. – 40 p. blue (air) . . 55 20
DESIGN—HORIZ. 40 p. Earth station and dish aerial.

464. Nieuport 28 and Route Map.

**1969.** 50th Anniv of 1st Argentine Airmail Service.
1263 **464** 20 p. multicoloured . . 20 10

**1969.** Child Welfare. Vert. designs as T **352** inscr. "R. ARGENTINA". Multicoloured.
1264. 20 p.+10 p. White-faced Whistling Duck (post.) 1·00 45
1265. 26 p.+13 p. Lineated Woodpecker (air) . . 1·00 45

465. College Entrance.

466. General Pacheco, (from painting by R. Guidice).

**1969.** Cent. of Argentine Military College.
1266. **465.** 20 p. multicoloured . . 15 10

**1969.** Death Cent. of General Angel Pacheco.
1267. **466.** 20 p. green . . . . 15 10

467. Bartolome Mitre and Logotypes of "La Nacion".

468. J. Aguirre.

**1969.** Centenary of Newspapers "La Nacion" and "La Prensa".
1268. **467.** 20 p. blk., emer. & grn. 80 15
1269. – 20 p. blk. orge. & yell. 80 15
DESIGN: No. 1269 "The Lantern" (mast-head) and logotypes of "La Prensa".

**1969.** Argentine Musicians.
1270. **468.** 6 p. green and blue 65 15
1271. – 6 p. green and blue 65 15
1272. – 6 p. green and blue 65 15
1273. – 6 p. green and blue 65 15
1274. – 6 p. green and blue 65 15
MUSICIANS: No. 1271, F. Boero. No. 1272, C. Gaito. No. 1273, C. L. Buchardo. No. 1274, A. Williams.

469. Hydro-electric Project on Rivers Limay and Neuquen.

**1969.** National Development Projects. Multicoloured.
1275. 6 p. Type **469** (postage) . . 50 10
1276. 20 p. Parana-Santa Fe river tunnel . . . . 1·00 15
1277. 26 p. Atomic Power Plant, Atucha (air) . . 1·40 90

470. Lieut. B. Matienzo and Nieuport 28 Biplane.

**1969.** Aeronautics Week.
1278. **470.** 20 p. multicoloured . . 50 10

471. Capital "L" and Lions' Emblem.

472. "Madonna and Child" (after R. Soldi).

**1969.** 50th Anniv. of Lion's International.
1279. **471.** 20 p. olive, orge. & grn. 50 10

**1969.** Christmas.
1280. **472.** 20 p. multicoloured . . 80 35

**1970.** Child Welfare. As T **352**, but differently arranged and inscr. "REPUBLICA ARGENTINA". Multicoloured.
1293. 20 c.+10 c. Slender-tailed Woodstar (postage) . . 85 55
1294. 40 c.+20 c. Chilean Flamingo (air) . . 90 70
See also Nos. 1394/5, 1415/6 and 1441/2.

**474.** "General Belgrano" (from lithograph by Gericault). **475.** Early Fire Engine.

**1970.** Birth Bicentenary of General Manuel Belgrano.

1295. **474.** 20 c. brown .. .. 45 15
1296. – 50 c. blk., flesh & blue 80 25

DESIGN—HORIZ. (56 × 15 mm.): 50 c. "Monument to the Flag" (bas-relief by Jose Fioravanti).

**1970.** Air. Cent. of Buenos-Aires Fire Brigade.

1297. **475.** 40 c. multicoloured 60 10

**476.** Naval Schooner "Juliet", 1814.

**1970.** Navy Day.

1298. **476.** 20 c. multicoloured 1·25 15

**477.** San Jose Palace. **478.** General Belgrano.

**1970.** President Justo de Urquiza Commem.

1299. **477.** 20 c. multicoloured.. 15 10

**1970.** Revalued currency. Previous designs with values in centavos and pesos as T **478.** Inscr. "REPUBLICA ARGENTINA" or "ARGENTINA".

1300. 1 c. green (No. 1016) 15 10
1301. – 3 c. red (No. 951) .. 15 10
1302. **296.** 5 c. blue .. .. 15 10
1303. **478.** 6 c. blue .. .. 15 10
1304. 8 c. green .. .. 15 10
1305. – 10 c. brown (No. 1286)* 45 10
1306. – 10 c. red (No. 1286).. 65 10
1307. – 10 c. brown (No. 1286)* 55 10
1308. **478.** 10 c. brown .. .. 20 10
1309. – 25 c. brown .. .. 40 10
1310. **478.** 30 c. purple .. .. 10 10
1311. – 50 c. red .. .. 1·25 10
1312. **478.** 60 c. yellow .. .. 10 10
1313. – 65 c. brown (No. 878) 85 10
1314. – 70 c. blue .. .. 40 10
1315. – 90 c. green (No. 878) 3·75 10
1316. – 1 p. brown (as No. 1289, but 23 × 29mm.) 2·25 10
1317. – 1 p. 15 blue (No. 1288) 1·40 10
1318. – 1 p. 20 orange (No. 878) 1·40 10
1319. – 1 p. 20 red .. .. 35 10
1320. – 1 p.80 brn. (as No.1288) 1·50 10
1321. **478.** 1 p. 80 blue .. .. 20 10
1322. – 2 p. brown .. .. 20 10
1323. – 2 p. 70 bl. (as No. 878) 25 10
1323a.**478.** 3 p grey .. .. 15 10
1392. – 4 p. 50 green (as No. 1288) (G. Brown).. 80 10
1325. – 5 p. green (as No. 1032) 95 10
1326. – 6 p. red .. .. 25 10
1327. – 6 p. green .. .. 25 10
1328. – 7 p. 50 grn. (as No. 878) 85 10
1329. – 10 p. bl. (as No. 1033) 1·25 10
1329a. – 12 p. green .. .. 25 10
1329b. – 12 p. red .. .. 25 10
1330. – 13 p. 50 red (as No. 1288) 1·00 10
1331. – 13 p. 50 red (as No. 1288 but larger, 16 × 24 mm.) .. .. 1·00 10
1332. – 15 p. red .. .. 25 10
1333. – 15 p. blue .. .. 25 10
1334. – 20 p. red .. .. 40 10
1335. – 22 p. 50 bl. (as No. 878) (22 × 32½ mm.) .. 1·40 10
1393. – 22 p. 50 bl. (as No. 878) (26 × 39mm.) .. 1·40 10
1336. – 30 p. red .. .. 1·25 10
1337. **478.** 40 p. green .. .. 70 15
1338. – 40 p. red .. .. 40 10
1339. **478.** 60 p. blue .. .. 80 20
1340. – 70 p. blue .. .. 1·00 20
1340a.**478.** 90 p. green .. .. 1·25 30
1340b. – 100 p. red .. .. 85 25
1340c. – 110 p. red .. .. 60 15
1340d. – 120 p. red .. .. 70 20
1340e. – 130 p. red .. .. 90 25

DESIGNS—VERT. As Type **478.** 25 c., 50 c., 70 c., 1 p. 20, 2 p., 6 p., 12 p., 15 p. (No. 1332), 20 p., 30 p., 40 p. (No. 1338), 100 p., 110p., 120 p., 130 p. General Jose de San Martin. 15 p. (No. 1333), 70 p. Guillermo Brown.

* No. 1307 differs from Nos. 1305/6 in being without imprint. It also has "CORREOS" at top right.

**482.** Wireless Set of 1920 and Radio "Waves".

**1970.** 50th Anniv. of Argentine Radio Broadcasting.

1341. **482.** 20 c. multicoloured 15 10

**483.** Emblem of Education Year. **485.** "United Nations".

**484.** "Liberation Fleet leaving Valparaiso" (A. Abel).

**1970.** Air. Int. Education Year.

1342. **483.** 68 c. black and blue 30 15

**1970.** Military Uniforms. As T **390.** Mult.

1343 20 c. Military courier, 1879 1·00 50

**1970.** 150th Anniv. of Peruvian Liberation.

1344. **484.** 26 c. multicoloured .. 1·40 15

**1970.** 25th Anniv. of United Nations.

1345. **485.** 20 c. multicoloured 15 10

**486.** Cordoba Cathedral.

**1970.** 400th Anniv. of Tucuman Diocese.

1346. **486.** 50 c. blk. & grey (post.) 85 10
1347. – 40c. multicoloured (air) 85 20

DESIGN—HORIZ. 40 c. Chapel, Sumampa.

**487.** Planetarium.

**1970** Air. Buenos Aires Planetarium.

1348. **487.** 40 c. multicoloured.. 40 15

**488.** "Liberty" and Mint Building.

**1970.** 25th Anniv. of State Mint Building, Buenos Aires.

1349. **488.** 20 c. blk., grn. & gold 15 10

**489.** "The Manger" (H. G. Gutierrez). (Illustration reduced. Actual size 77 × 33 mm.)

**1970.** Christmas.

1350. **489.** 20 c. multicoloured .. 25 10

**490.** Jorge Newbery and Morane Saulnier Type L Airplane.

**1970.** Air. Aeronautics Week.

1351. **490.** 26 c. multicoloured .. 40 15

**491.** St. John Bosco and College Building.

**1970.** Salesian Mission in Patagonia.

1352. **491.** 20 c. black and green 15 10

**492.** "Planting the Flag".

**1971.** 5th Anniv. of Argentine Expedition to the South Pole.

1353. **492.** 20 c. multicoloured .. 1·50 60

**493.** Dorado. (Illustration reduced. Actual size 75 × 15 mm.)

**1971.** Child Welfare. Fishes. Multicoloured.

1354. 20 c. + 10 c. Type **493** (postage) .. .. 45 45
1355. 40 c. + 20 c. Mackerel (air) 40 35

**494.** Einstein and Scanners. **495.** E. I. Alippi.

**1971.** Electronics in Postal Development.

1356. **494.** 25 c. multicoloured.. 30 10

**1971.** Argentine Actors and Actresses. Each black and brown.

1357. 15 c. Type **495** .. .. 40 10
1358. 15 c. J. A. Casaberta .. 40 10
1359. 15 c. R. Casaux .. 40 10
1360. 15 c. Angelina Pagano 40 10
1361. 15 c. F. Parravicini .. 40 10

**496.** Federation Emblem.

**1971.** Inter-American Regional Meeting of Int. Roads Federation.

1362. **496.** 25 c. black and blue 15 10

**1971.** Army Day. Vert. designs as T **390.**

1363. 25 c. multicoloured .. 1·40 15

DESIGN: 25 c. Artilleryman of 1826.

**1971.** Navy Day. Horiz designs as T **476.**

1364. 25 c. multicoloured .. 1·75 15

DESIGN: Sloop "Carmen".

**498.** "General Guemes" (L. Gigli).

**1971.** 150th Death Anniv. of General M. de Guemes. Multicoloured.

1365. 25 c. Type **498** .. .. 55 20
1366. 25 c. "Death of Guemes" (A. Alice) .. .. 55 20

No. 1366 is larger, 84 × 29 mm.

**499.** Order of the Peruvian Sun.

**1971.** 150th Anniversary of Peruvian Independence.

1367. **499.** 31 c. yell., blk. & red 40 10

**500.** Stylised Tulip. **501.** Dr. A. Saenz (founder) (after Jose Gut).

**1971.** 3rd Int., and 8th National Horticultural Exhibition.

1368. **500.** 25 c. multicoloured.. 25 15

**1971.** 150th Anniv. of Buenos Aires University.

1369. **501.** 25 c. multicoloured.. 20 15

**502.** Arsenal Emblem.

**1971.** 30th Anniv. of Fabricaciones Militares (Arsenals).

1370. **502.** 25 c. multicoloured.. 20 15



**503.** Road Transport.

**1971.** Nationalised Industries.

1371 **503** 25 c. mult. (postage) 60 10
1372 – 65 c. multicoloured 1·50 35
1373 – 31 c. yellow, black and red (air) .. 70 25

DESIGNS: 31 c. Refinery and formula ("Petrochemicals"); 65 c. Tree and paper roll ("Paper and Cellulose").

**1971.** Air. Revalued currency. Face values in centavos.

1374 **358** 45 c. brown .. .. 3·75 15
1375 68 c. red .. .. 55 15
1376a 70 c. blue .. .. 1·00 15
1377 90 c. green .. .. 2·25 15
1378 1 p. 70 blue .. .. 55 10
1379 1 p. 95 green .. 55 15
1380 2 p. 65 purple .. 55 15

**504.** Constellation and Telescope.

**1971.** Cent. of Cordoba Observatory.

1381. **504.** 25 c. multicoloured 25 15

**505.** Capt. D. L. Candelaria and Morane Saulnier Type P Airplane.

**1971.** 25th Aeronautics and Space Week.

1382. **505.** 25 c. multicoloured 40 10

**506.** "Stamps". (Mariette Lydis). **507.** "Christ in Majesty" (tapestry by Butler).

**1971.** 2nd Charity Stamp Exhibition.

1383. **506.** 1 p.+50 c. mult. .. 35 35

**1971.** Christmas.

1384. **507.** 25 c. multicoloured.. 20 10

**1972.** Child Welfare. As T **352**, but differently arranged and inscribed "REPUBLICA ARGENTINA".

1394. 25 c.+10 c. Saffron Finch (vert.) .. .. .. 90 40

1395. 65 c.+30 c. Rufous-bellied Thrush (horiz.) 1·10 50

**508.** "Maternity" (J. Castagnino).

**1972.** 25th Anniv. of U.N.I.C.E.F.

1396. **508.** 25 c. black & brown 20 15

**509.** Treaty Emblem, "Libertad" (liner) and Almirante Brown Base.

**1972.** 10th Anniv. of Antarctic Treaty.

1397. **509.** 25 c. multicoloured 75 15

**510.** Postman's Mail Pouch.

**1972.** Bicent. of 1st Buenos Aires Postman.

1398. **510.** 25 c. multicoloured 15 10

**1972.** Army Day. As T **390.** Multicoloured.

1399. 25 c. Sergeant of Negro and Mulatto Battalion (1806-7) 1·00 15

**1972.** Navy Day. As T **476.** Multicoloured.

1400. 25 c. Brigantine "Santisima Trinidad" .. .. 1·40 15

**512.** Sonic Balloon. **513.** Oil Pump.

**1972.** National Meteorological Service.

1401. **512.** 25 c. multicoloured .. 25 15

**1972.** 50th Anniv. of State Oilfields (YPF).

1402. **513.** 45 c. blk., blue & gold 80 10

**514.** Forest Centre.

**1972.** 7th World Forestry Congress, Buenos Aires.

1403. **514.** 25 c. blk., bl. & light bl. 70 10

**515.** Arms and Cadet Ship "Presidente Sarmiento".

**1972.** Centenary of Naval School.

1404. **515.** 25 c. multicoloured.. 1·25 15

**516.** Baron A. de Marchi, Balloon and Voisin "Boxkite". **517.** Bartolome Mitre.

**1972.** Aeronautics Week.

1405. **516.** 25 c. multicoloured.. 40 10

**1972.** 150th Birth Anniv. of General Bartolome Mitre.

1406. **517.** 25 c. blue .. .. 10 10

**518.** Heart and Flower. **519.** "Martin Fierro" (J. C. Castignino).

**1972.** World Health Day.

1407. **518.** 90 c. blk., vio. & bl. .. 70 15

**1972.** Int. Book Year and Cent. of "Martin Fierro" (poem by Jose Hernandez). Multicoloured.

1408. 50 c. Type **519** .. .. 25 15

1409. 90 c. "Spirit of the Gaucho" (V. Forte) .. .. 75 20

**520.** Iguazu Falls.

**1972.** American Tourist Year.

1410. **520.** 45 c. multicoloured.. 30 10

**521.** "Wise Man on Horseback" (18th-century wood-carving). **522.** Cockerel Emblem.

**1972.** Christmas.

1411. **521.** 50 c. multicoloured.. 40 10

**1973.** 150th Anniv. of Federal Police Force.

1412. **522.** 50 c. multicoloured .. 20 10

**523.** Bank Emblem and First Coin. **525.** Presidential Chair.

**524.** Douglas DC-3 Aircraft and Polar Map.

**1973.** 150th Anniv. of Provincial Bank of Buenos Aires.

1413. **523.** 50 c. multicoloured.. 15 10

**1973.** 10th Anniv. of 1st Argentine Flight to South Pole.

1414. **524.** 50 c. multicoloured 90 20

**1973.** Child Welfare. As T **473**, but differently arranged and inscr. "R. ARGENTINA". Multicoloured.

1415. 50 c. + 25 c. Crested Screamer (vert.) .. 80 50

1416. 90 c. + 45 c. Saffron-cowled Blackbird (horiz.) 1·25 75

**1973.** Presidential Inaug.

1417. **525.** 50 c. multicoloured.. 20 10

**526.** San Martin and Bolivar.

**1973.** San Martin's Farewell to People of Peru. Multicoloured.

1418. 50 c. Type **526** .. .. 25 15

1419. 50 c. "San Martin" (after Gil de Castro) (vert.).. 25 15

**527.** "Eva Peron-Eternally with her People".

**1973.** Eva Peron Commemoration.

1420. **527.** 70 c. multicoloured.. 20 15

**528.** "House of Viceroy Sobremonte" (H. de Virgilio).

**1973.** 4th Centenary of Cordoba.

1421. **528.** 50 c. multicoloured.. 20 10

**529.** "Woman" (L. Spilimbergo).

**1973.** Philatelists' Day. Argentine Paintings. Multicoloured.

1422. 15 c.+15 c. "Nature Study" (A. Guttero) (horiz.).. .. .. 50 10

1423. 70 c. Type **529** .. .. 80 15

1424. 90 c.+90 c. "Nude" (M. C. Victorica) (horiz.) .. .. 85 70

See also Nos. 1434/6 and 1440.

**530.** "La Argentina" (sail frigate). **531.** Early and Modern Telephones.

**1973.** Navy Day.

1425. **530.** 70 c. multicoloured.. 1·00 15

**1973.** 25th Anniversary of National Telecommunications Enterprise (E.N.T.E.L.).

1426. **531.** 70 c. multicoloured.. 35 10

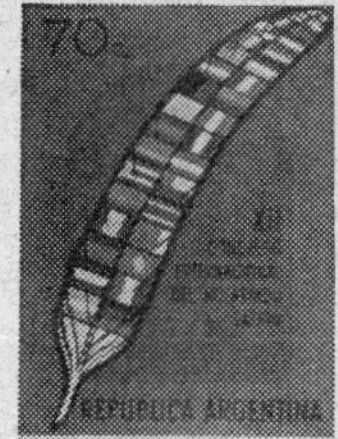

**532.** Quill Pen of Flags **533.** Lujan Basilica.

**1973.** 12th International Latin Notaries Congress.

1427. **532.** 70 c. multicoloured.. 25 15

**1973.**

1428. **533.** 18 c. brown and yell. 15 10

1429. 50 c. purple and black 15 10

1429a. 50 c. blue and brown 15 10

1430. 50 c. purple .. .. 15 10

**1973.** Transfer of Presidency to General Juan Peron. No. 1318 optd. **TRANSMISION DEL MANDO PRESIDENCIAL 12 OCTUBRE 1973.**

1431. 1 p. 20 orange .. 80 15

**535.** "Virgin and Child" (stained glass window).

**1973.** Christmas. Multicoloured

1432. 70 c. Type **535** .. .. 30 10

1433. 1 p. 20 "The Manger" (B. Venier) .. .. 60 15

**1974.** Argentine Paintings. As T **529.** Multicoloured.

1434. 50 c. "Houses" (E. Daneri) (horiz.) .. .. 30 10

1435. 70 c. "The Lama" (J. B. Planas) .. 35 15

1436. 90 c. "Homage to the Blue Grotto" (E. Pettoruti) (horiz.) .. .. 50 20

**536.** View of Mar del Plata.

**1974.** Centenary of Mar del Plata.

1437. **536.** 70 c. multicoloured.. 30 10

**537.** " Fray Justo Santa Maria de Oro " (anon.). **538.** Weather Contrasts.

**1974.** Birth Bicentenary of Fray Justo Santa Maria de Oro.
1438. **537.** 70 c. multicoloured 20 10

**1974.** Centenary of World Meteorological Organization.
1439. **538.** 1 p. 20 multicoloured 40 10

**1974.** " Prenfil 74 " Philatelic Press Exn., Buenos Aires. As No. 1435.
1440. 70 c. + 30 c. multicoloured 20 20

**1974.** Child Welfare. As T **352** but differently arranged and inscribed " REPUBLICA ARGENTINA ". Multicoloured.
1441. **70 c. + 30 c. Double-collared Seedeater** .. 65 45
1442. **1 p. 20 + 60 c. Hooded Siskin** .. .. .. 1·10 65

**539.** B. Roldan. **540.** O.E.A. Member Countries.

**1974.** Birth Cent. of Belisario Roldan (writer).
1443. **539.** 70 c. brown and blue 10 10

**1974.** 25th Anniv. of Organization of American States' Charter.
1444. **540.** 1 p. 38 multicoloured 15 10

**541.** Posthorn Emblem.

**1974.** Creation of State Posts & Telecommunications Enterprise (E.N.C.O.T.E.L.).
1445. **541.** 1 p. 20 bl., blk. & gold 40 10

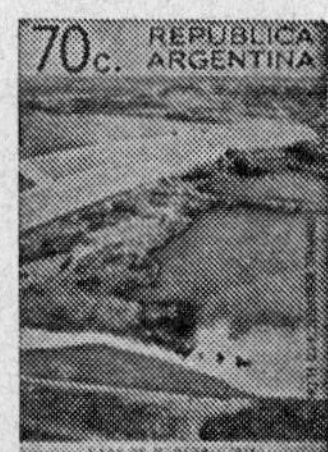


**542.** Flags of Member Countries. **543.** El Chocon Hydro-electric Complex.

**1974.** Sixth Meeting of River Plate Countries' Foreign Ministers.
1446. **542.** 1 p. 38 multicoloured 15 15

**1974.** Nationalised Industries. Multicoloured.
1447 70 c. Type **543** .. .. 35 10
1448 1 p. 20 Blast furnace, Somisa steel mills .. 55 25
1449 4 p. 50 General Belgrano Bridge (61 × 25 mm) .. 2·75 40

**1974.** Army Day. As T **390.** Multicoloured.
1450. 1 p. 20 Mounted Grenadier 70 15
See also Nos. 1515 and 1564.

**544.** A. Mascias and Bleriot XI.

**1974.** Air Force Day.
1451. **544.** 1 p. 20 multicoloured 75 15

**545.** Brigantine "Belgrano".

**1974.** 150th Anniv. of San Martin's Departure into Exile.
1452. **545.** 1 p. 20 multicoloured 1·25 15

**546.** San Francisco Convent, Santa Fe.

**1974.** 400th Anniv. of Santa Fe.
1453. **546.** 1 p. 20 multicoloured 45 10

**547.** Symbolic Posthorn.

**1974.** Cent. of U.P.U.
1454. **547.** 2 p. 65 multicoloured 70 10

**549.** Congress Building, Buenos Aires.

**1974.**
1456. **549.** 30 p. purple and yell. 1·25 10

**550.** Boy examining Stamp.

**1974.** International Year of Youth Philately.
1457. **550.** 1 p. 70 blk. & yell. .. 40 10

**551.** " Christmas in Peace " (V. Campanella).

**1974.** Christmas. Multicoloured.
1458. 1 p. 20 Type **551** .. 60 10
1459. 2 p. 65 " St. Anne and the Virgin Mary " .. .. 65 15

**552.** " Space Monsters " (R. Forner).

**1975.** Contemporary Argentine Paintings. Multicoloured.
1460. 2 p. 70 Type **552** .. .. 80 15
1461. 4 p. 50 " Sleep " (E. Centurion) .. .. 1·90 25

**553.** Cathedral and Weaver, Catamarca. (Illustration reduced. Actual size 83 × 29 mm.)

**1975.** Tourist Views (1st series). Mult.
1462. 1 p. 20 Type **553** .. 25 15
1463. 1 p. 20 Street scene and carved pulpit, Jujuy .. 25 15
1464. 1 p. 20 Monastery and tree-felling, Salta .. .. 25 15
1465. 1 p. 20 Dam and vase Santiago del Estero .. 25 15
1466. 1 p. 20 Colombres Museum and farm-cart, Tucuman 25 15
See also Nos. 1491/3.

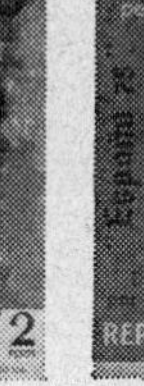


**554.** " We're Vaccinated Now ". (M. L. Alonso). **555.** " Don Quixote " (Zuloaga).

**1975.** Children's Vaccination Campaign.
1467. **554.** 2 p. multicoloured .. 50 15

**1975.** Air. " Espana 75 " International Stamp Exhibition, Madrid.
1468. **555.** 2 p. 75 black, yell. & red 60 15

**556.** Hugo S. Acuna and South Orkneys Base. (Illustration reduced. Actual size 83 × 29 mm.)

**1975.** Antarctic Pioneers. Multicoloured.
1469 2 p. Type **556** .. .. 45 10
1470 2 p. Francisco P. Moreno and Quetrihue Peninsula .. .. 45 10
1471 2 p. Capt. Carlos M. Moyano and Cerra Torre, Santa Cruz .. 45 10
1472 2 p. Lt. Col. Luis Piedra Buena and naval cutter "Luisito" in the Antarctic .. .. 95 15
1473 2 p. Ensign Jose M. Sobral and "Snow Hill" House .. .. .. 45 10

**557.** Valley of the Moon, San Juan Province. **559.** Eduardo Bradley and Balloon.

**1975.**
1474. **557.** 50 p. multicoloured .. 1·75 10
1474a. 300 p. multicoloured 4·00 1·75
1474b. – 500 p. multicoloured 9·50 1·60
1474c. – 1000 p. multicoloured 11·00 2·25
DESIGNS—HORIZ. 500 p. Admiral Brown Antarctic Station. 1000 p. San Francisco Church, Salta.

**1975.** Air. Surch.
1475. **358.** 9 p. 20 on 5 p. 60 gr., blue and purple .. 90 10
1476. 19 p. 70 on 5 p. 60 gr., blue and purple .. 1·40 20
1477. 100 p. on 5 p. 60 gr., blue and purple .. 5·00 90

**1975.** Air Force Day.
1478. **559.** 6 p. multicoloured .. 60 15

**560.** Sail Frigate "25 de Mayo".

**1975.** Navy Day.
1479. **560.** 6 p. multicoloured .. 80 15

**561.** " Oath of the 33 Orientales on the Beach of La Agraciada " (J. Blanes).

**1975.** 150th Anniv. of Uruguayan Independence.
1480. **561.** 6 p. multicoloured .. 30 15

**1975.** Air. Surch. **REVALORIZADO** and value.
1481. **358.** 9 p. 20 on 5 p. 60 gr., blue and purple .. 85 15
1482. 19 p. 70 on 5. 60 gr., blue and purple .. 1·40 30

**563.** Flame Emblem.

**1975.** 30th Anniv. of Pres. Peron's Seizure of Power.
1483. **563.** 6 p. multicoloured .. 35 15

**1975.** Surch. **REVALORIZADO** and value.
1484. **533.** 5 p. on 18 c. br. & yell. 45 10

**565.** Bridge and Flags of Argentina and Uruguay.

**1975.** " International Bridge " between Colon (Argentina) and Paysandu (Uruguay).
1485. **565.** 6 p. multicoloured .. 50 15

**566.** Posthorn Emblem. **568.** " The Nativity " (stained-glass window).

**1975.** Introduction of Postal Codes.
1486. **566.** 10 p. on 20 c. yellow, black and green .. 60 10

**1975.** Nos. 951 and 1288 surch. **REVALORIZADO** and value.
1487. 6 c. on 3 p. blue .. .. 15 10
1488. 30 c. on 90 p. bistre .. 15 10

**1975.** Christmas.
1489. **568.** 6 p. multicoloured .. 30 15

**569.** Stylised Nurse and Child. **570.** " Numeral ".

**1975.** Centenary of Children's Hospital.
1490. **569.** 6 p. multicoloured .. 60 10

**1975.** Tourist Views (2nd series). As T **553.** Multicoloured.
1491. 6 p. Mounted patrol and oil rig, Chubut .. 55 15
1492. 6 p. Glacier and sheep-shearing, Santa Cruz .. 55 15
1493. 6 p. Lake Lapataia, Tierra del Fuego, and Antarctic scene .. .. 55 15

**1976.**

1494. **570.** 12 c. grey and black 10 10
1495. 50 c. slate and green 10 10
1496. 1 p. red and black .. 10 10
1497. 4 p. blue and black .. 15 10
1498. 5 p. yellow and black 15 10
1499. 6 p. brown and black 15 10
1500. 10 p. grey and violet 20 10
1501. 27 p. green and black 55 10
1502. 30 p. blue and black .. 1·00 10
1503. 45 p. yellow and black 1·00 10
1504. 50 p. green and black 1·25 10
1505. 100 p. green and red 1·90 10

**571.** Airliner in Flight.

**1976.** 25th Anniv. of "Aerolineas Argentinas".
1513. **571.** 30 p. multicoloured .. 1·25 15

**572.** Sail Frigate "Heroina" and Map of Malvinas.

**1976.** Argentine Claims to Falkland Islands (Malvinas).
1514. **572.** 6 p. multicoloured .. 75 15

**1976.** Army Day. As T **390.** Multicoloured.
1515. 12 p. Infantryman of Condé's 7th Regiment .. 50 15

**573.** Louis Braille. **574.** Plush-crested Jay.

**1976.** Louis Braille (inventor of characters for the Blind). Commemoration.
1516. **573.** 19 p. 70 blue .. 30 15

**1976.** Argentine Philately. Multicoloured.
1517. 7 p. + 3 p. 50 Type **574** .. 60 35
1518. 13 p. + 6 p. 50 Yellow-collared Macaw .. 80 35
1519. 20 p. + 10 p. "Begonia micranthera" .. 65 40
1520. 40 p. + 20 p. "Echinopsis shaferi" (teasel) .. 90 55

**575.** Schooner "Rio de la Plata".

**1976.** Navy Day.
1521. **575.** 12 p. multicoloured .. 85 15

**576.** Dr. Bernardo Houssay (Medicine).

**1976.** Argentine Nobel Prize Winners.
1522 **576** 10 p. blk, orge & grey 30 10
1523 – 15 p. blk, yell & grey 35 15
1524 – 20 p. blk, brn & grey 50 25

Designs: 15 p. Dr. Luis Leloir (chemistry). 20 p. Dr. Carlos Lamas (peace).

**577.** Bridge and Ship.

**1976.** "International Bridge" between Unzue (Argentina) and Fray Bentos (Uruguay).
1525. **577.** 12 p. multicoloured .. 30 10

**578.** Cooling Tower and Pipelines.

**1976.** General Mosconi Petrochemical Project.
1526. **578.** 28 p. multicoloured .. 45 15

**579.** Teodoro Fels and Bleriot XI.

**1976.** Air Force Day.
1527. **579.** 15 p. multicoloured .. 40 10

**580.** "Nativity" (E. Chiapetto).

**1976.** Christmas.
1528. **580.** 20 p. multicoloured .. 50 10

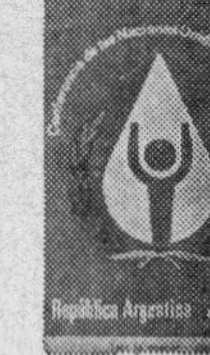


**581.** Dr. D. Velez Sarsfield (statesman). **582.** Conference Emblem.

**1977.** Death Cent. (1975) of Dr. D. V. Sarsfield.
1529 **581** 50 p. brown and red 60 15

**1977.** United Nations Water Conference.
1530. **582.** 70 p. multicoloured .. 70 25

**583.** "The Visit" (Horacio Butler).

**1977.** Plastic Arts. Multicoloured.
1531 50 p. Type **583** .. .. 50 15
1532 70 p. "Consecration" (M. P. Caride) (vert) .. 70 25

**584.** World Cup Emblem. **585.** City of La Plata Museum.

**1977.** World Cup Football Championship, Argentina. Multicoloured.
1533 30 p. Type **584** .. .. 50 15
1534 70 p. Stadium and flags (vert) .. .. 90 30

**1977.**

1535 **585** 5 p. black and brown 10 10
1536 – 10 p. black and blue 10 10
1538 – 20 p. black & yellow 10 10
1539 – 40 p. black and blue 20 10
1540 – 50 p. black & yellow 40 10
1541 – 50 p. black & brown 25 10
1542 – 100 p. black and pink 35 10
1543 – 100 p. black & orange 10 10
1544 – 100 p. black & green 10 10
1545 – 200 p. black and blue 50 20
1546 – 280 p. black and lilac 16·00 15
1547b – 300 p. black & yellow 85 10
1548 – 480 p. black & yellow 2·00 20
1549 – 500 p. black & green 2·00 15
1550 – 520 p. black & orange 2·00 20
1551 – 800 p. black & purple 2·50 25
1552a – 1000 p. black & gold 4·25 35
1553 – 1000 p. black & yell 3·00 35
1554 – 2000 p. multicoloured 2·25 35

Designs:—horiz. 10 p. House of Independence, Tucuman. 20 p. Type **585.** 50 p. (No. 1541), Cabildo, Buenos Aires. 100 p. Nos. 1542/3. Columbus Theatre, Buenos Aires. 280 p., 300 p. Rio Grande Museum Chapel, Tierra del Fuego. 480 p., 520 p., 800 p. San Ignacio Mission Church ruins. 500 p. Candonga Chapel. 1000 p. General Post Office, Buenos Aires (No. 1552 39×29 mm., No. 1553 32×21 mm.). 2000 p. Civic Centre, Bariloche. Vert. 40 p. Cabildo, Salta. 50 p. (No. 1540), Cabildo, Buenos Aires. 200 p. Monument to the Flag, Rosario.

**586.** Morse Key and Satellite.

**1977.** "Argentine Philately". Mult.
1560 10 p. + 5 p. Type **586** .. 25 15
1561 20 p. + 10 p. Old and modern mail vans .. 45 25
1562 60 p. + 30 p. Old and modern ships .. .. 1·25 1·00
1563 70 p. + 35 p. SPAD XIII and Boeing 707 aircraft 1·10 60

**1977.** Army Day. As T **390.** Multicoloured.
1564. 30 p. Trooper of 16th Lancers .. .. 50 15

**587.** Schooner "Sarandi".

**1977.** Navy Day.
1565. **587.** 30 p. multicoloured .. 75 15

**1977.** 150th Anniv. of Uruguay Post Office. As No. 1325 but colour changed. Surch. **100 PESOS 150 ANIV. DEL CORREO NACIONAL DEL URUGUAY.**
1566. 100 p. on 5 p. brown .. 1·25 40

**1977.** "Argentina '77" Exhibition. As No. 1474c, but inscribed "EXPOSICION ARGENTINA '77".
1567 160 p. + 80 p. multicoloured 3·00 2·25

**589.** Admiral Guillermo Brown.

**1977.** Birth Bicentenary of Admiral Guillermo Brown.
1568. **589.** 30 p. multicoloured .. 40 15

**590.** Civic Centre, Santa Rosa (La Pampa).

**1977.** Provinces of the Argentine. Mult.
1569. 30 p. Type **590** .. .. 40 20
1570. 30 p. Sierra de la Ventana (Buenos Aires) .. 40 20
1571. 30 p. Skiers at Chapelco, San Martin de los Andes, (Neuquen) .. 40 20
1572. 30 p. Lake Fonck (Rio Negro) .. .. 40 20

**591.** Savoia S.16 ter Flying Boat over Rio de la Plata.

**1977.** Air Force and 1926 Flight Buenos Aires–New York Commemoration.
1573 **591** 40 p. multicoloured .. 35 15

**592.** Jet Fighter Outline.

**1977.** 50th Anniv. of Military Aviation Factory.
1574. **592.** 30 p. bl., pale bl. & blk. 30 10

**593.** "The Adoration of the Kings" (stained glass window, Holy Sacrament Basilica, Buenos Aires). **595.** World Cup Emblem.

**1977.** Christmas.
1575. **593.** 100 p. multicoloured 1·25 20

**1978.** World Cup Football Championship, Argentina.
1577 **595** 200 p. green & blue .. 90 20

**596.** Rosario.

**1978.** World Cup Football Championship. (3rd issue). Match Sites. Multicoloured.
1578. 50 p. Type **596** .. .. 20 15
1579. 100 p. Cordoba .. .. 40 15
1580. 150 p. Mendoza .. .. 50 15
1581. 200 p. Mar del Plata .. 50 25
1582. 300 p. Buenos Aires .. 1·25 35

**597.** Children and Institute Emblem.

**1978.** 50th Anniv. of Inter-American Children's Institute.
1583. **597.** 100 p. multicoloured 40 15

**598.** "The Working Day" (B. Quinquela Martin).

**1978.** Argentine Art. Multicoloured.
1584. 100 p. Type **598** .. .. 55 15
1585. 100 p. "Bust of an Unknown Woman" (Orlando Pierri) .. .. .. 40 10

**599.** Players from Argentina, Hungary, France and Italy (Group One).

**1978.** World Cup Football Championship (4th issue).
1586. **599.** 100 p. multicoloured 35 10
1587. – 200 p. multicoloured 65 15
1588. – 300 p. multicoloured 95 20
1589. – 400 p. multicoloured 1·40 30

Designs: 200 p. Group Two players. 300 p. Group Three players. 400 p. Group Four players.

**600.** Hooded Siskin.

**1978.** Inter-American Philatelic Exhibition. Multicoloured.

1591. 50 p.+50 p. Type **600** .. 1·75 1·50
1592. 100 p.+100 p. Double-collared seedeater .. 2·00 2·00
1593. 150 p.+150 p. Saffron-cowled blackbird .. 2·50 2·10
1594. 200 p.+200 p. Vermilion flycatcher .. .. 2·75 2·40
1595. 500 p.+500 p. Great kiskadee .. .. 7·00 5·75

**601.** Young Tree with Support.

**1978.** Technical Co-operation among Developing Countries Conference, Buenos Aires.

1596 **601** 100 p. multicoloured .. 30 15

**603.** Bank Emblems of 1878 and 1978.

**1978.** Cent. of Bank of Buenos Aires.

1598. **603.** 100 p. multicoloured 30 15

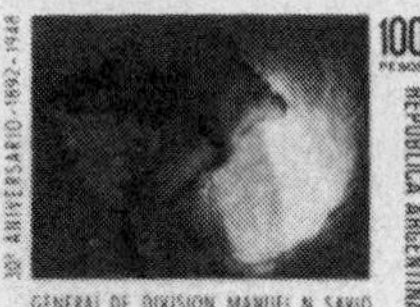


**604.** General Manuel Savio and Steel Production.

**1978.** 30th Death Anniv. of General Manuel Savio (director of military manufacturing).

1599. **604.** 100 p. multicoloured 30 15

**605.** San Martin. **606.** Numeral.

**1978.** Birth Bicent. of Gen. San Martin.

1600. **605.** 2000 p. green .. 5·50 30
1600a. 10000 p. blue .. 8·50 35

**1978.**

1601. **606.** 150 p. blue & light blue 40 20
1602. 180 p. blue & light blue 40 10
1603. 200 p. blue & light blue 30 15

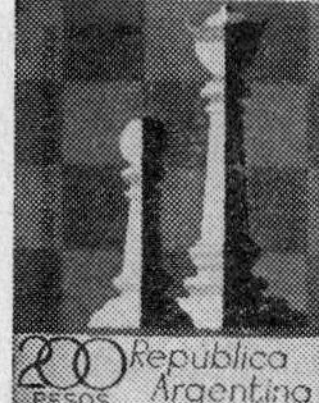

**607.** Chessboard, Pawn and Queen. **608.** Argentine Flag supporting Globe.

**1978.** 23rd Chess Olympiad, Buenos Aires.

1604 **607** 200 p. multicoloured .. 2·75 65

**1978.** 12th International Cancer Congress, Buenos Aires.

1605. **608.** 200 p. multicoloured 80 20

**609.** "Correct Franking."

**1978.** Postal Publicity.

1606. **609.** 20 p. blue .. .. 15 10
1607. – 30 p. green .. .. 15 10
1608. – 50 p. red .. .. 25 10

DESIGN—VERT. 30 p. "Collect postage stamps". HORIZ. 50 p. "Indicate the correct Post Code".

**610.** Push-pull Tug.

**1978.** 20th Anniv. of Argentine River Fleet. Multicoloured.

1609. 100 p. Type **610** .. .. 40 15
1610. 200 p. Tug "Legador" .. 75 25
1611. 300 p. Tug "Rio Parana Mini" .. .. .. 1·10 30
1612. 400 p. River passenger ship "Ciudad de Parana" .. .. 1·40 25

**611.** Bahia Blanca and Arms.

**1978.** 150th Anniv. of Bahia Blanca.

1613. **611.** 200 p. multicoloured 45 15

**612.** "To Spain" (Arturo Dresco).

**1978.** Visit of King and Queen of Spain.

1614. **612.** 300 p. multicoloured 3·25 25

**613.** Stained Glass window, San Isidro Cathedral, Buenos Aires.

**1978.** Christmas.

1615. **613.** 200 p. multicoloured 60 15

**614.** "Chacabuco Slope" (Pedro Subercaseaux).

**1978.** Birth Bicent. of General Jose de San Martin.

1616. 500 p. Type **614** .. .. 1·25 35
1617. 1000 p. "The Embrace of Maipo" (Pedro Subercaseaux) (vert.) .. 2·25 50

**615.** San Martin Stamp of 1877 and U.P.U. Emblem.

**1979.** Centenary of Argentine Membership of U.P.U.

1618 **615** 200 p. blue, blk & brn 35 15

**616.** Mariano Moreno (revolutionary).

**1979.** Celebrities.

1619 **616** 200 p. yell, blk & red 45 15
1620 – 200 p. bl, blk & dp bl 45 15

DESIGNS No. 1620, Adolfo Alsina (statesman).

**617.** "Still-Life" (Ernesto de la Carcova). **618.** Balcarce Antenna and Radio Waves.

**1979.** Argentine Paintings. Multicoloured.

1621. 200 p. Type **617** .. 60 15
1622. 300 p. "The Washer-woman" (F. Brughetti) 80 20

**1979.** Third Inter-American Telecommunications Conference.

1623. **618.** 200 p. multicoloured 60 15

**619.** Rosette. **620.** Olives.

**1979.**

1624 **619** 240 p. blue & brown 35 10
1625 260 p. blue and black 35 10
1626 290 p. blue & brown 40 10
1627 310 p. blue & purple 45 10
1628 350 p. blue and red 60 15
1629 450 p. blue & ultram 55 15
1630 600 p. blue and green 75 20
1631 700 p. blue and black 75 20
1632 800 p. blue & orange 75 10
1632a 1100 p. blue and grey 1·00 10
1632b 1500 p. blue & black 40 10
1632c 1700 p. blue & green 50 10

**1979.** Agricultural Products. Multicoloured.

1633. 100 p. Type **620** .. .. 25 10
1634. 200 p. Tea .. .. 50 25
1635. 300 p. Sorghum .. .. 65 40
1636. 400 p. Flax .. .. 1·00 55

**621.** "75" and Symbol.

**1979.** 75th Anniv. of Argentine Automobile Club.

1637. **621.** 200 p. multicoloured 35 15

**622.** Laurel Leaves and Army Emblem.

**1979.** Naming of Village Subteniente Berdina, Tucuman.

1638. **622.** 200 p. multicoloured 30 15

**623.** Wheat Exchange and Emblem.

**1979.** 125th Anniv. of Wheat Exchange, Buenos Aires.

1639. **623.** 200 p. blue, gold and black .. .. 30 15

**624.** "Uruguay" (sail/steam gunboat).

**1979.** Navy Day.

1640. **624.** 250 p. multicoloured 65 20

**1979.** Army Day. As T **390**. Multicoloured.

1641. 200 p. Trooper of Mounted Chasseurs, 1817 1·25 20

**625.** "Comodoro Rivadavia" (hydrographic survey ship).

**1979.** Naval Hydrographic Service.

1642. **625.** 250 p. multicoloured 65 20

**626.** Tree and Man Symbol.

**1979.** Ecology Day.

1643. **626.** 250 p. multicoloured 55 15

**627.** SPAD XIII and Vicente Almandos.

**1979.** Air Force Day.

1644. **627.** 250 p. multicoloured 80 20

**628.** "Military Occupation of Rio Negro by Gen. Julio A. Roca's Expedition" (detail, J. M. Blanes).

**1979.** Cent. of Conquest of the Desert.

1645. **628.** 250 p. multicoloured 70 20

**629.** Caravel "Magdalena".

**1979.** "Buenos Aires '80" International Stamp Exhibition. Multicoloured.

1646. 400 p.+400 p. Type **629** 4·50 3·25
1647. 500 p.+500 p. 3-masted sailing ship .. .. 5·50 4·00
1648. 600 p.+600 p. Corvette "Descubierta" .. 6·50 4·75
1649. 1500 p.+1500 p. Yacht "Fortuna" .. .. 13·50 12·00

**630.** Rowland Hill.

**631.** Francisco de Viedma y Narvaez Monument. (A. Funes and J. Agosta).

**1979.** Death Cent. of Sir Rowland Hill.
1650. **630.** 300 p. blk., grey & red 45 20

**1979.** Bicentenary of Founding of Viedma and Carmen de Patagone Towns.
1651. **631.** 300 p. multicoloured 70 20

**632.** Pope Paul VI. **633.** Molinas Church.

**1979.** Election of Pope John Paul I.
1652. **632.** 500 p. black .. 1·25 35
1653. – 500 p. black .. 1·25 35
DESIGN: No. 1653, Pope John Paul I.

**1979.** Churches. Multicoloured.
1654. 100 p. + 50 p. Purmamarca Church .. .. 30 15
1655. 200 p. + 100 p. Type **633** 45 20
1656. 300 p. + 150 p. Animana Church .. .. 75 35
1657. 400 p. + 200 p. San Jose de Lules Church .. 1·00 50

**1979.** 75th Anniv. of Rosario Philatelic Society. No. 1543 Optd.. **75 ANIV. SOCIEDAD FILATELICA DE ROSARIO.**
1658. 200 p. blue and black .. 70 20

**635.** Children's Faces, and Sun on Map of Argentina.

**1979.** Resettlement Policy.
1659. **635.** 300 p. yell., blk. & bl. 80 20

**636.** Stained Glass Window, Salta Cathedral.

**1979.** Christmas.
1660. **636.** 300 p. multicoloured 55 20

**637.** Institute Emblem.

**1979.** Centenary of Military Geographical Institute.
1661. **637.** 300 p. multicoloured 70 20

**638.** General Mosconi and Oil Rig.

**1979.** Birth Centenary of General Enrique Mosconi.
1662. **638.** 1000 p. blue and black 3·00 65

**640.** Rotary Emblem and Globe.

**1979.** 75th Anniv. of Rotary International.
1664. **640.** 300 p. multicoloured 2·00 25

**641.** Girl with Ruddy Ground Doves. **642.** Guillermo Brown.

**1979.** International Year of the Child.
1665. **641.** 500 p. brn., bl. & blk. 90 40
1666. – 1000 p. multicoloured 1·75 30
DESIGN: 1000 p. "Family"

**1980.**
1667. **642.** 5000 p. black .. 6·00 20
1668. 30000 p. black & blue 3·75 75

**643.** I.T.U. Emblem and Microphone.

**1980.** Regional Administrative Conference on Broadcasting, Buenos Aires.
1669. **643.** 500 p. bl., gold & ultram. 1·10 30

**644.** Organization of American States Emblem.

**1980.** Day of the Americas.
1670. **644.** 500 p. multicoloured 50 20

**645.** Angel.

**1980.** Cent. of Argentinian Red Cross.
1671. **645.** 500 p. multicoloured 60 20

**646.** Salto Grande Hydro-electric Complex.

**1980.** National Development Projects. Multicoloured.
1672. 300 p. Type **646** .. .. 50 20
1673. 300 p. Zarate-Brazo Largo bridge .. .. 50 20
1674. 300 p. Dish aerials, Balcarce .. .. 50 20

**647.** Hipolito Bouchard and Sail Frigate "La Argentina".

**1980.** Navy Day.
1675 **647** 500 p. multicoloured .. 90 30

**648.** "Villarino" and Woodcut of San Martin Theodore by Gericault.

**1980.** Cent. of Return of General Jose de San Martin's Remains.
1676. **648.** 500 p. multicoloured 90 30

**649.** "Gazeta de Buenos-Ayres" and Signature of Dr. Mariano Moreno (first editor).

**1980.** Journalists' Day.
1677. **649.** 500 p. multicoloured 60 20

**651.** Soldier feeding Dove.

**1980.** Army Day.
1679. **651.** 500 p. grn., blk. & gld. 90 30

**652.** Lt. Gen. Aramburu.

**1980.** 10th Death Anniv. of Lt. Gen. Pedro Eugenio Aramburu.
1680. **652.** 500 p. yellow and blk. 50 20

**653.** Gen. Juan Gregorio de Las Heras.

**1980.** National Heroes.
1681. **653.** 500 p. stone & black 60 20
1682. – 500 p. yell., blk. & pur. 60 20
1683. – 500 p. mauve & black 60 20
DESIGNS: No. 1682, Bernardino Rivadavia. No. 1683, Brigadier-General Jose Matias Zapiola.

**654.** University of La Plata.

**1980.** 75th Anniv. of La Plata University.
1684. **654.** 500 p. multicoloured 60 20

**655.** Major Francisco de Arteaga and Avro 504K.

**1980.** Air Force Day.
1685. **655.** 500 p. multicoloured 75 20

**656.** Flag and "Pencil" Figure. **658.** Congress Emblem.

**1980.** National Census.
1686. **656.** 500 p. black and blue 1·25 20

**1980.** National Marian Congress, Mendoza.
1688. **658.** 700 p. multicoloured 80 15

**659.** Heart pierced by Cigarette. **661.** Radio Antenna and Call Sign.

**1980.** Anti-smoking Campaign.
1689. **659.** 700 p. multicoloured 1·00 20

**1980.** Radio Amateurs.
1691. **661.** 700 p. blue, black and green .. .. 80 15

**662.** Academy Emblem. **663** Commemorative Medallion.

**1980.** 50th Anniv. of Technical Military Academy.
1692. **662.** 700 p. multicoloured 80 15

**1980.** Christmas. 150th Anniv. of Appearance of Holy Virgin to St. Catherine Laboure.
1693. **663.** 700 p. multicoloured 75 15

**664.** Plan of Lujan Cathedral and Outline of Virgin. **665.** Simon Bolivar.

**1980.** Christmas. 350th Anniv. of Appearance of Holy Virgin at Lujan.
1694. **664.** 700 p. green & brown 75 15

**1980.** 150th Death Anniv. of Simon Bolivar.
1695. **665.** 700 p. multicoloured 80 15

**666.** Football and Flags of Competing Nations.

**1981.** Gold Cup Football Competition, Montevideo.
1696. **666.** 1000 p. multicoloured 1·10 20

**667.** " Lujan Landscape " (Marcos Tiglio).

**1981.** Paintings. Multicoloured.
1697. 1000 p. Type **667** .. 95 20
1698. 1000 p. " Effect of Light on Lines" (Miguel Angel Vidal) .. .. .. 95 20

**668.** Congress Emblem.

**1981.** International Congress on Medicine and Sciences applied to Sport.
1699. **668.** 1000 p. bl., brn. & blk. 70 15

**669.** Esperanza Army Base, Antarctica.

**1981.** 20th Anniv of Antarctic Treaty. Mult.
1700 1000 p. Type **669** .. 1·50 50
1701 2000 p. Map of Vicecomodoro Marambio Island and De Havilland Twin Otter airplane (59½x25 mm) .. .. 2·00 80
1702 2000 p. Icebreaker "Almirante Irizar" .. 2·75 95

**670.** Military Club.

**1981.** Centenary of Military Club. Mult.
1703. 1000 p. Type **670** .. 60 20
1704. 2000 p. Blunderbusses .. 80 25

**671.** " Minuet " (Carlos E. Pellegrini).

**1981.** " Espamer '81 " International Stamp Exhibition, Buenos Aires (1st issue).
1705. **671.** 500 p. + 250 p. purple, gold and brown .. 60 45
1706. – 700 p. + 350 p. green, gold and brown .. 1·25 70
1707. – 800 p. + 400 p. brown, gold and deep brn. 1·25 80
1708. – 1000 p. + 500 p. mult. 1·60 1·40
DESIGNS: 700 p. " La Media Cana " (Carlos Morel). 800 p. " Cielito " (Carlos E. Pellegrini). 1000 p. " El Gato " (Juan Leon Palliere).
See also Nos. 1719 and 1720/1.

**672.** Juan A. Alvarez de Arenales.

**1981.** Celebrities Anniversaries.
1709. **672.** 1000 p. black, yellow and brown .. 70 20
1710. – 1000 p. black, pink and lilac .. .. 70 20
1711. – 1000 p. black, pale green and green .. 70 20
DESIGNS: No. 1709, Type **672** (patriot, 150th death anniv); No. 1710, Felix G. Frias (writer and politician, death centenary); No. 1711, Jose E. Uriburu (statesman, 150th birth centenary).

**1981.** 50th Anniv. of Bahia Blanca Philatelic and Numismatic Society. No. 1553 Optd. **50 ANIV DE LA ASOCIACION FILATELICA Y NUMISMATICA DE BAHIA BLANCA.**
1712 1000 p. black and yellow 2·25 40

**674.** World Map divided into Time Zones and Sun.

**1981.** Cent. of Naval Observatory.
1713. **674.** 1000 p. multicoloured 90 30

**675.** " St. Cayetano " (detail, stained glass window, San Cayetano Basilica).

**1981.** 500th Death Anniv. of St. Cayetano (founder of Teatino Order).
1714. **675.** 1000 p. multicoloured 70 20

**676.** Pablo Castaibert and Bleriot XI.

**1981.** Air Force Day.
1715. **676.** 1000 p. multicoloured 1·00 20

**677.** First Argentine Blast Furnace, Sierra de Palpala.

**1981.** 22nd Latin American Steel-makers Congress, Buenos Aires.
1716. **677.** 1000 p. multicoloured 70 20

**678.** Emblem of National Directorate for Special Education.
**679.** Sperm Whale and Map of Argentina and Antarctica.

**1981.** International Year of Disabled People.
1717. **678.** 1000 p. multicoloured 80 20

**1981.** Campaign against Indiscriminate Whaling.
1718. **679.** 1000p. multicoloured 3·00 25

**680.** "Espamer 81" Emblem and 15th-century Caravel.

**1981.** " Espamer 81 " International Stamp Exhibition, Buenos Aires. (2nd issue).
1719. **680.** 1300 p. pink, brown and black .. .. 55 20

**681.** " San Martin at the Battle of Bailen " (equestrian statuette).
**682.** Argentine Army Emblem.

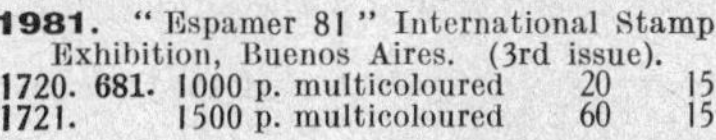

**1981.** " Espamer 81 " International Stamp Exhibition, Buenos Aires. (3rd issue).
1720. **681.** 1000 p. multicoloured 20 15
1721. 1500 p. multicoloured 60 15

**1981.** Argentine Army. 175th Anniv. of Infantry Regiment No. 1 "Patricios". Mult.
1722. 1500 p. Type **682** .. .. 55 20
1723. 1500 p. " Patricios " badge 55 20

**1981.** Philatelic Services Course, Postal Union of the Americas and Spain Technical Training School, Buenos Aires, Optd. **CURSO SUPERIOR DE ORGANIZACION DE SERVICIOS FILATELICOS-UPAE-BUENOS AIRES-1981.**
1724. **680.** 1300 p. pink, brown and black .. .. 1·40 20

**685.** " Patacon " (one peso piece).

**1981.** Cent. of First Argentine Coins.
1726. **685.** 2000 p. silver, black and purple .. 55 15
1727. – 3000 p. gold, black and blue .. .. 70 20
DESIGN: 3000 p. Argentino oro (five pesos piece).

**686.** Stained Glass Window, Church of Our Lady of Mercy, Tucuman.

**1981.** Christmas.
1728. **686.** 1500 p. multicoloured 1·00 20

**687.** " Drive Carefully ".
**688.** Francisco Luis Bernardez.

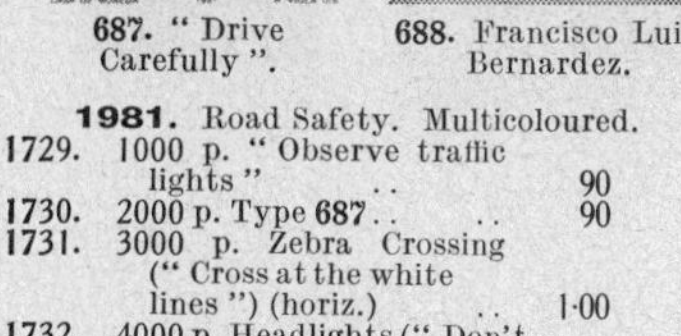

**1981.** Road Safety. Multicoloured.
1729. 1000 p. " Observe traffic lights " .. 90 20
1730. 2000 p. Type **687** .. .. 90 25
1731. 3000 p. Zebra Crossing (" Cross at the white lines ") (horiz.) .. 1·00 35
1732. 4000 p. Headlights (" Don't dazzle ") (horiz.) .. 1·75 45

**1982.** Authors. Multicoloured.
1733. 1000 p. Type **688** .. .. 75 20
1734. 2000 p. Lucio V. Mansilla 85 25
1735. 3000 p. Conrado Nale Roxlo 1·40 35
1736. 4000 p. Victoria Ocampo 2·00 45

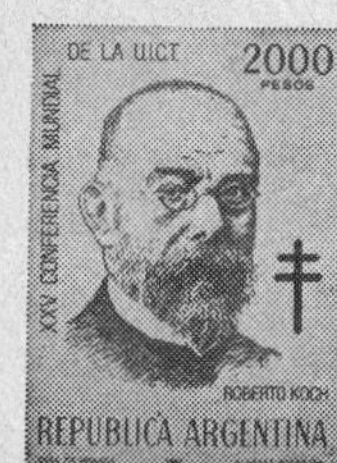

**689.** Emblem.
**690.** Dr. Robert Koch.

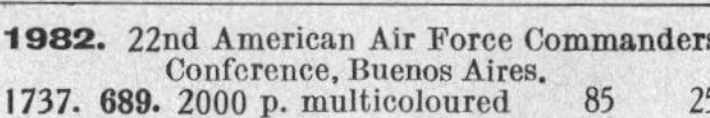

**1982.** 22nd American Air Force Commanders Conference, Buenos Aires.
1737. **689.** 2000 p. multicoloured 85 25

**1982.** 25th World Tuberculosis Conference, Buenos Aires.
1738. **690.** 2000 p. brown, red and black .. .. 60 25

**691.** Pre-Columbian Artwork and Signature of Hernando de Lerma (founder).

**1982.** 400th Anniv. of Salta City.
1739. **691.** 2000 p. green, black and gold .. .. 80 25

**1982.** Argentine Invasion of the Falkland Islands. Optd. **LAS MALVINAS SON ARGENTINAS.**
1741 **619** 1700 p. blue and green 60 20

**693.** " Poseidon with Trophies of War " (sculpture) and Naval Centre Arms.

**1982.** Centenary of Naval Centre.
1742. **693.** 2000 p. multicoloured 90 25

**694.** " Chorisia speciosa ".
**695.** Juan C. Sanchez.

**1982.** Flowers. Multicoloured.
1743. 200 p. " Zinnia peruviana " 10 10
1744. 300 p. "Ipomoea purpurea" 10 10
1745. 400 p. " Tillandsia aeranthos " .. .. .. 10 10
1746. 500 p. Type **694** .. .. 10 10
1747. 800 p. " Oncidium bifolium 10 10
1748. 1000 p. " Erythrina crista " .. .. .. 10 10
1749. 2000 p. " Jacaranda mimosifolia " .. .. 15 10
1750. 3000 p. " Bauhinia candicans " .. .. 25 10
1751. 5000 p. " Tecoma stans " 60 10
1752. 10000 p. " Tabebuia ipe " 1·25 15
1753. 20000 p. " Passiflora coerulea " .. .. 2·50 20
1754. 30000 p. " Aristolochia littoralis " .. 3·75 60
1755. 50000 p. " Oxalis enneaphylla" .. .. 6·00 80

**1982.** 10th Death Anniv. of Lt. Gen. Juan C. Sanchez.
1761. **695.** 5000 p. multicoloured 80 25

**696.** Don Luis Verne (first Commander).

**1982.** 153rd Anniv. of Political and Military Command for the Malvines.
1762. **696.** 5000 p. black & brown 1·25 50
1763. – 5000 p. light blue, blk. and blue .. .. 90 35
DESIGN: (82 × 28 mm.) No. 1763, Map of the South Atlantic Islands.

**697.** Pope John Paul II.
**698.** San Martin.

**1982.** Papal Visit.
1764. **697.** 5000 p. multicoloured 2·00 55

**1982.**
1765. **698.** 50000 p. brown & red 7·50 95

**699.** " The Organ Player " (detail Aldo Severi).

**700.** " Gen. de Sombras " (Sylvia Sieburger).

**1982.** Paintings. Multicoloured.

1766. 2000 p. Type **699** .. 40 20
1767. 3000 p. " Flowers " (Santiago Cogorno) .. 45 25

**1982.** " Argentine Philately ". Tapestries Multicoloured.

1768. 1000 p. + 500 p. Type **700** 20 15
1769. 2000 p. + 1000 p. " Interpretation of a Rectangle " (Silke Haupt) .. .. 30 20
1770. 3000 p. + 1500 p. " Canal " (detail, Beatriz Bongliani) (horiz.) .. .. 75 30
1771. 4000 p. + 2000 p. " Pueblito de Tilcara " (Tana Sachs) (horiz.) .. .. 75 55

**701.** Petrol Pump and Sugar Cane.

**704.** Map of Africa showing Namibia.

**703.** Belt Buckle with Argentine Scout Emblem.

**1982.** Alconafta (petrol-alcohol mixture) Campaign.

1772. **701.** 2000 p. multicoloured 40 10

**1982.** 50th Anniv. of Tucuman Philatelic Society. No. 1751 optd. **50o ANIVERSARIO SOCIEDAD FILATELICA DE TUCUMAN.**

1773. 5000 p. multicoloured .. 1·60 90

**1982.** 75th Anniv. of Boy Scout Movement.

1774. **703.** 5000 p. multicoloured 1·25 25

**1982.** Namibia Day.

1775. **704.** 5000 p. multicoloured 80 15

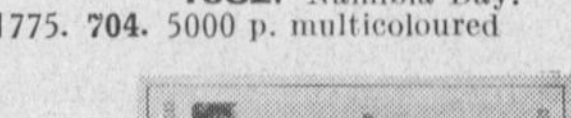

**705.** Rio Tercero Nuclear Power Station.

**1982.** Atomic Energy. Multicoloured.

1776. 2000 p. Type **705** .. 40 10
1777. 2000 p. Control room of Rio Tercero power station 40 10

**706.** Our Lady of Itati, Corrientes.

**707.** "Sidereal Tension" (M. A. Agatiello).

**1982.** Churches and Cathedrals of the North-east Provinces.

1778. **706.** 2000 p. green & black 25 15
1779. – 3000 p. grey & purple 35 15
1780. – 5000 p. blue & purple 55 20
1781. – 10000 p. brown & black 1·25 40

DESIGNS—VERT. 3000 p. Resistencia Cathedral, Chaco. HORIZ. 5000 p. Formosa Cathedral. 10000 p. Ruins of San Ignacio, Misiones.

**1982.** Art. Multicoloured.

1782. 2000 p. Type **707** .. 30 20
1783. 3000 p. " Sugerencia II " (E. MacEntyre) .. 45 20
1784. 5000 p. " Storm " (Carlos Silva) .. .. .. 75 25

**708.** Games Emblem and Santa Fe Bridge.

**1982.** Second " Southern Cross " Games, Rosario and Santa Fe.

1785. **708.** 2000 p. blue and black 45 10

**709.** Volleyball.

**1982.** Tenth Men's Volleyball World Championship.

1786. **709.** 2000 p. multicoloured 30 10
1787. 5000 p. multicoloured 60 20

**710.** Road Signs.

**1982.** 50th Anniv. of National Roads Administration.

1788. **710.** 5000 p. multicoloured 60 20

**711.** Monument to the Army of the Andes.

**1982.** Cent. of Los Andes Newspaper.

1789. **711.** 5000 p. multicoloured 50 20

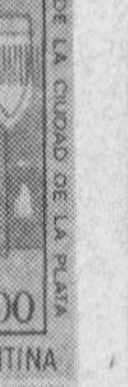

**712.** La Plata Cathedral.

**714.** Dr. Carlos Pellegriini (founder) (after J. Sorolla y Bastida).

**713.** First Oil Rig.

**1982.** Cent. of La Plata. Multicoloured.

1790. 5000 p Type **712** .. .. 85 20
1791. 5000 p. Municipal Palace 85 20

**1982.** 75th Anniv. of Discovery of Oil in Comodoro Rivadavia.

1793. **713.** 5000 p. multicoloured 80 25

**1982.** Centenary of Buenos Aires Jockey Club. Multicoloured.

1794. 5000 p. Jockey Club emblem 55 20
1795. 5000 p. Type **714** .. .. 55 20

**715.** Cross of St. Damian, Assisi.

**716.** " St. Vincent de Paul " (stained glass window, Our Lady of the Miraculous Medal, Buenos Aires).

**1982.** 800th Birth Anniv. of St. Francis of Assisi.

1796. **715.** 5000 p. multicoloured 1·25 20

**1982.** Christmas.

1797. **716.** 3000 p. multicoloured 1·75 15

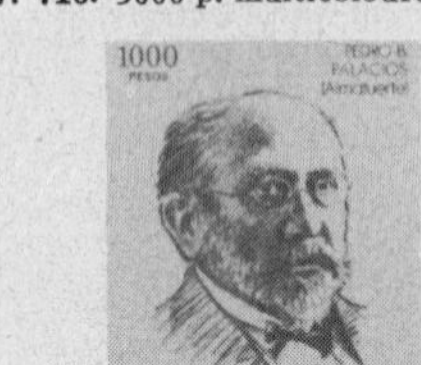


**717.** Pedro B. Palacios.

**1982.** Authors. Each red and green.

1798 1000 p. Type **717** .. 15 10
1799 2000 p. Leopoldo Marechal 20 10
1800 3000 p. Delfina Bunge de Galvez .. .. 25 10
1801 4000 p. Manuel Galvez .. 50 15
1802 5000 p. Evaristo Carriego 65 15

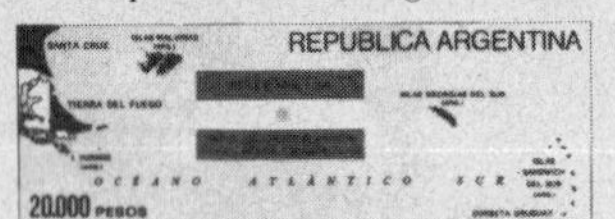


**718.** Argentine Flag and Map of South Atlantic Islands. (illustration reduced to half-size).

**1983.** 1st Anniv. of Argentine Invasion of Falkland Islands.

1803 **718** 20000 p. multicoloured 70 35

**719.** Sitram (automatic message transmission service) Emblem.

**1983.** Information Technology. Multicoloured

1804. 5000 p. Type **719** .. .. 1·00 20
1805. 5000 p. Red Arpac (data communications system) emblem .. .. 1·00 20

**720.** Naval League Emblem.

**1983.** Navy Day. 50th Anniv. of Naval League.

1806. **720.** 5000 p. multicoloured 50 15

**721.** Allegorical Figure (Victor Rebuffo).

**1983.** 25th Anniv. of National Arts Fund.

1807. **721.** 5000 p. multicoloured 45 15

**722.** Golden Saloon.

**1983.** 75th Anniv. of Columbus Theatre, Buenos Aires. Multicoloured.

1808. 5000 p. Type **722** .. .. 70 15
1809. 10000 p. Stage curtain .. 1·25 20

**(Currency reform. 10000 (old) pesos = 1 (new) peso.)**

**723.** Marbles.

**1983.** Argentine Philately. Children's Games (1st series). Multicoloured.

**1810.** 20 c. + 10 c. Type **723** .. 15 10
**1811.** 30 c. + 15 c. Skipping .. 30 15
**1812.** 50 c. + 25 c. Hopscotch .. 40 25
**1813.** 1 p. + 50 c. Boy with kite 60 40
**1814.** 2 p. + 1 p. Boy with Spinning top .. .. 70 55

See also Nos. 1870/4.

**724.** Maned Wolf.

**1983.** Protected Animals (1st series). Multicoloured.

1815. 1 p. Type **724** .. .. 35 10
1816. 1 p. 50 Pampas deer .. 55 15
1817. 2 p. Giant anteater .. 60 15
1818. 2 p. 50 Jaguar .. .. 75 25

See also Nos 1883/87

**1983.** Flowers. As T **694** but inscr in new currency. Multicoloured.

1819 5 c. Type **694** .. .. 10 10
1820 10 c. "Erythrina crista-galli" .. .. 10 10
1821 20 c. "Jacaranda mimosifolia" .. .. 10 10
1822 30 c. "Bauhinia candicans" .. .. 10 10
1823 40 c. "Eichhornia crassipes" .. .. 10 10
1824 50 c. "Tecoma stans" .. 10 10
1825 1 p. "Tabebuia ipe" .. 10 10
1826 1 p. 80 "Mutisia retusa" 15 10
1827 2 p. "Passiflora coerulea" 20 10
1828 3 p. "Aristolochia littoralis" .. .. 30 10
1829 5 p. "Oxalis enneaphylla" 50 10
1830 10 p. "Alstroemeria aurantiaca" .. .. 1·25 50
1831 20 p. "Ipomoea purpurea" 40 10
1832 30 p. "Embothrium coccineum" .. .. 4·00 3·00
1833 50 p. "Tillandsia aeranthos" .. .. 1·25 45
1834 100 p. "Oncidium bifolium" .. .. 1·90 55
1835 300 p. "Cassia carnaval" 80 20

**725.** " Founding of City of Catamarca " (detail, Luis Varela Lezana).

**1983.** 300th Anniv. of San Fernando del Valle de Catamarca.

1836. **725.** 1 p. multicoloured .. 30 10

**726.** Brother Mamerto Esquiu.

**727.** Bolivar (painting by Herrera Toro after engraving by C. Turner).

**1983.** Death Centenary of Brother Mamerto Esquiu, Bishop of Cordoba.
1837. **726.** 1 p. black, red & grey 30 10

**1983.** Birth Bicent. of Simon Bolivar.
1838 **727** 1 p. multicoloured .. 30 10
1839 – 2 p. red and black .. 60 15
DESIGN: 2 p. Bolivar (engraving by Kepper).

**728.** San Martin.

**729.** Gen. Toribio de Luzuriaga.

**1983.**
1840. **728.** 10 p. green & black 3·50 1·75
1841. – 20 p. blue & black .. 3·25 1·75
1842. **728.** 50 p. brown and blue 1·25 20
1843. – 200 p. black and blue 3·50 1·10
1844. – 500 p. blue & brown 1·75 25
DESIGNS: 20 p., 500 p. Guillermo Brown. 200 p. Manuel Belgrano.

**1983.** Birth Bicent. (1982) of Gen. Toribio de Luzuriaga.
1845. **729.** 1 p. multicoloured .. 30 10

**730.** Grand Bourg House, Buenos Aires.

**1983.** 50th Anniv. of Sanmartinian National Institute.
1846. **730.** 2 p. brown & black 55 15

**731.** Dove and Rotary Emblem.

**1983.** Rotary International South American Regional Conference, Buenos Aires.
1847. **731.** 1 p. multicoloured .. 55 20

**732.** Running Track and Games Emblem.

**1983.** Ninth Pan-American Games, Venezuela.
1848. **732.** 1 p. red, grn. & blk.. 35 15
1849. – 2 p. multicoloured .. 60 25
DESIGN: 2 p. Games emblem.

**733.** W.C.Y. Emblem.

**734.** "The Squash Peddler" (Antonio Berni).

**1983.** World Communications Year (1st Issue).
1850 **733** 2 p. multicoloured .. 55 20
See also Nos. 1853/6 and 1857.

**1983.** Argentine Paintings. Multicoloured.
1851. 1 p. Type **734** .. .. 35 10
1852. 2 p. "Figure in Yellow" (Luis Seoane) .. .. 55 20

**735.** Ox-drawn Wagon.

**736.** "Central Post Office, Buenos Aires" (Lola Frexas).

**1983.** World Communications Year. (2nd issue). Mail Transport. Multicoloured.
1853. 1 p. Type **735** .. .. 15 10
1854. 2 p. Horse-drawn mail cart .. .. 25 15
1855. 4 p. Locomotive "La Portena" .. .. 90 50
1856. 5 p. Tram .. .. 1·25 50

**1983.** World Communications Year (3rd issue).
1857 **736** 2 p. multicoloured .. 35 15

**737.** Rockhopper Penguin.

**738.** Coin of 1813.

**1983.** Fauna and Pioneers of Southern Argentina. Multicoloured.
1858a. 2 p. Type **737** .. 40 15
1858b 2 p. Wandering albatross .. .. 40 15
1858c 2 p. Black-browed albatross .. .. 40 15
1858d 2 p. Macaroni penguin 40 15
1858e 2 p. Luis Piedra Buena (after Juan R. Mezzadra) .. .. 40 15
1858f 2 p. Carlos Maria Moyano (after Mezzadra) .. .. 40 15
1858g 2 p. Luis Py (after Mezzadra) .. .. 40 15
1858h 2 p. Augusto Lasserre (after Horacio Alvarez Boero) .. 40 15
1858i 2 p. Light-mantled sooty albatross .. 40 15
1858j 2 p. Leopard seal .. 40 15
1858k 2 p. Crabeater seal .. 40 15
1858l 2 p. Weddell seal .. 40 15

**1983.** Transfer of Presidency.
1859. **738.** 2 p. silver, blk. & blue 35 15

**739.** "Christmas Manger" (tapestry by Silke).

**1983.** Christmas. Multicoloured.
1860. 2 p. Type **739** .. .. 35 15
1861. 3 p. Stained-glass window, San Carlos de Bariloche Church .. .. 55 20

**740.** Printing Cylinder and Newspaper.

**1984.** Centenary of "El Dia" Newspaper.
1862. **740.** 4 p. multicoloured .. 40 15

**741.** Compass Rose.

**1984.** "Espana 84" (Madrid) and "Argentina 85" (Buenos Aires) International Stamp Exhibitions (1st issue). Multicoloured.
1863. 5 p.+2 p. 50 Type **741** .. 50 15
1864. 5 p.+2 p. 50 Arms of Spain and Argentine Republic .. .. 50 15
1865. 5 p.+2 p. 50 Arms of Christopher Columbus 50 15
1866. 5 p.+2 p. 50 "Nina" .. 1·00 30
1867. 5 p.+2 p. 50 "Pinta" .. 1·00 30
1868. 5 p.+2 p. 50 "Santa Maria" .. .. .. 1·00 30
See also Nos. 1906/10, 1917/8 and 1920/4.

**742.** College.

**1984.** Centenary of Alejandro Carbo Teacher Training College, Cordoba.
1869 **742** 10 p. multicoloured .. 40 15

**1984.** Argentine Philately. Children's Games (2nd series). As T **723**. Multicoloured.
1870 2 p.+1 p. Blind man's buff .. .. .. 20 15
1871 3 p.+1 p. 50 Girls throwing hoop .. 30 25
1872 4 p.+2 p. Leap frog .. 40 35
1873 5 p.+2 p. 50 Boy rolling hoop .. .. .. 55 45
1874 6 p.+3 p. Ball and stick 60 55

**743.** Rowing and Basketball.

**1984.** Olympic Games, Los Angeles. Multicoloured.
1875. 5 p. Type **743** .. .. 25 15
1876. 5 p. Weightlifting and discus .. .. .. 25 15
1877. 10 p. Cycling and swimming .. .. 45 20
1878. 10 p. Pole vault and fencing .. .. .. 45 20

**744.** Wheat.

**1984.** Food Supplies. Multicoloured.
1879. 10 p. Type **744** (18th F.A.O. Latin American Regional Conference, Buenos Aires) .. .. .. 40 20
1880. 10 p. Sunflowers (World Food Day) .. .. 40 20
1881. 10 p. Maize (3rd National Maize Congress, Pergamino) .. .. .. 40 20

**745.** Stock Exchange.

**1984.** Cent. of Rosario Stock Exchange.
1882. **745.** 10 p. multicoloured 40 20

**1984.** Protected Animals (2nd series). As T **724**. Multicoloured.
1883. 20 p. Brazilian merganser 65 20
1884. 20 p. Black-fronted piping guan .. .. 65 20
1885. 20 p. Hooded grebes .. 65 20
1886. 20 p. Vicunas .. .. 65 20
1887. 20 p. Chilean guemal .. 65 20

**746.** Festival Emblem.

**1984.** First Latin American Theatre Festival, Cordoba.
1888. **746.** 20 p. multicoloured 25 15

**747.** "Apostles' Communion" (detail, Fra Angelico).

**1984.** 50th Anniv. of Buenos Aires International Eucharist Congress.
1889. **747.** 20 p. multicoloured 25 15

**748.** Antonio Oneto and Railway Station (Puerto Deseado).

**1984.** City Centenaries. Multicoloured.
1890 20 p. Type **748** .. .. 45 25
1891 20 p. 19th-century view and sail/steam corvette "Parana" (Ushuaia) .. 90 30

**749.** Glacier.

**1984.** World Heritage Site. Los Glaciares National Park. Multicoloured.
1892 20 p. Glacier (different) .. 30 10
1893 30 p. Type **749** .. .. 40 15

**1984.** 50th Anniv. of Buenos Aires Philatelic Centre. No. 1830 optd. **1934–50° ANIVERSARIO–1984 CENTRO FILATELICO BUENOS-AIRES.**
1894 10 p. multicoloured .. 20 15

**751.** "Jesus and the Star" (Diego Aguero).

**1984.** Christmas. Multicoloured.
1895. 20 p. Type **751** .. .. 30 15
1896. 30 p. "The Three Kings" (Leandro Ruiz) .. 40 15
1897. 50 p. "The Holy Family" (Maria Castillo) (vert.) 60 20

**752.** "Sheds (La Boca)" (Marcos Borio).

**753.** Angel J. Carranza (historian, 150th).

**1984.** Argentinian Paintings. Multicoloured.
1898. 20 p. Type **752** .. .. 30 20
1899. 20 p. "View of the Zoo" (Fermin Eguia) (horiz.) 80 20
1900. 20 p. "Floodlit Congress Building" (Francisco Travieso) .. .. 30 20

**1985.** Birth Anniversaries.
1901 **753** 10 p. dp blue & blue 15 10
1902 – 20 p. dp brown & brn 15 10
1903 – 30 p. dp blue & blue 20 15
1904 – 40 p. black & green .. 30 15
DESIGNS: 20 p. Estanislao del Campo (poet, 150th); 30 p. Jose Hernandez (journalist, 150th); 40 p. Vicente Lopez y Planes (President of Argentine Confederation 1827-28, birth bicent).

**754.** Guemes and "Infernal" (soldier).

**1985.** Birth Bicentenary of General Martin Miguel de Guemes (Independence hero).
1905 **754** 30 p. multicoloured .. 30 15

**755.** Teodoro Fels's Bleriot XI Gnome.

**1985.** "Argentina '85" International Stamp Exhibition, Buenos Aires (2nd issue). First Airmail Flights. Multicoloured.
1906 20 p. Type **755** (Buenos Aires–Montevideo, 1917) 30 10
1907 40 p. Junkers F-13L (Cordoba–Villa Dolores, 1925) .. .. .. 50 15
1908 60 p. Saint-Exupery's Latecoere 25 (first Bahia Blanca–Comodoro Rivadavia, 1929) .. .. .. .. 75 25
1909 80 p. "Graf Zeppelin" airship (Argentina–Germany, 1934) .. 1·10 45
1910 100 p. Consolidated PBY-5A Catalina amphibian (to Argentine Antarctic, 1952) .. .. .. 1·25 60

**756.** Central Bank.

**1985.** 50th Anniv. of Central Bank, Buenos Aires.
1911 **756** 80 p. multicoloured .. 65 20

**757.** Jose A. Ferreyra and "Munequitas Portenas".

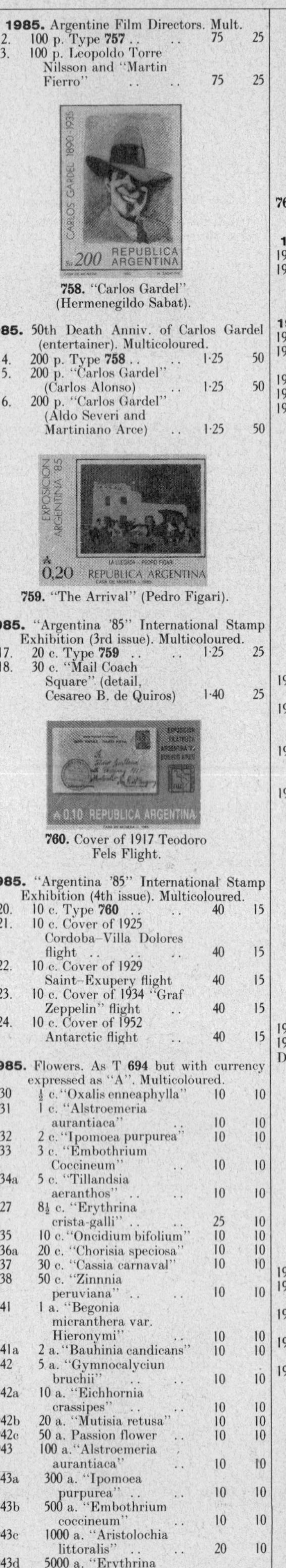

**1985.** Argentine Film Directors. Mult.
1912. 100 p. Type **757** .. .. 75 25
1913. 100 p. Leopoldo Torre Nilsson and "Martin Fierro" .. .. 75 25

**758.** "Carlos Gardel" (Hermenegildo Sabat).

**1985.** 50th Death Anniv. of Carlos Gardel (entertainer). Multicoloured.
1914. 200 p. Type **758** .. .. 1·25 50
1915. 200 p. "Carlos Gardel" (Carlos Alonso) .. 1·25 50
1916. 200 p. "Carlos Gardel" (Aldo Severi and Martiniano Arce) .. 1·25 50

**759.** "The Arrival" (Pedro Figari).

**1985.** "Argentina '85" International Stamp Exhibition (3rd issue). Multicoloured.
1917. 20 c. Type **759** .. .. 1·25 25
1918. 30 c. "Mail Coach Square" (detail, Cesareo B. de Quiros) 1·40 25

**760.** Cover of 1917 Teodoro Fels Flight.

**1985.** "Argentina '85" International Stamp Exhibition (4th issue). Multicoloured.
1920. 10 c. Type **760** .. .. 40 15
1921. 10 c. Cover of 1925 Cordoba–Villa Dolores flight .. .. .. 40 15
1922. 10 c. Cover of 1929 Saint–Exupery flight 40 15
1923. 10 c. Cover of 1934 "Graf Zeppelin" flight .. 40 15
1924. 10 c. Cover of 1952 Antarctic flight .. 40 15

**1985.** Flowers. As T **694** but with currency expressed as "A". Multicoloured.
1930 $\frac{1}{2}$ c. "Oxalis enneaphylla" 10 10
1931 1 c. "Alstroemeria aurantiaca" .. 10 10
1932 2 c. "Ipomoea purpurea" 10 10
1933 3 c. "Embothrium Coccineum" .. 10 10
1934a 5 c. "Tillandsia aeranthos" .. .. 10 10
1927 8$\frac{1}{2}$ c. "Erythrina crista-galli" .. .. 25 10
1935 10 c. "Oncidium bifolium" 10 10
1936a 20 c. "Chorisia speciosa" 10 10
1937 30 c. "Cassia carnaval" 10 10
1938 50 c. "Zinnia peruviana" .. .. 10 10
1941 1 a. "Begonia micranthera var. Hieronymi" .. 10 10
1941a 2 a. "Bauhinia candicans" 10 10
1942 5 a. "Gymnocalyciun bruchii" .. .. 10 10
1942a 10 a. "Eichhornia crassipes" .. .. 10 10
1942b 20 a. "Mutisia retusa" 10 10
1942c 50 a. Passion flower .. 10 10
1943 100 a. "Alstroemeria aurantiaca" .. 10 10
1943a 300 a. "Ipomoea purpurea" .. .. 10 10
1943b 500 a. "Embothrium coccineum" .. 10 10
1943c 1000 a. "Aristolochia littoralis" .. .. 20 10
1943d 5000 a. "Erythrina crista-galli" .. 95 75
1943e 10000 a. "Jacaranda mimosifolia" .. 1·90 1·75
No. 1297 is 15 × 23 mm in size, the remainder 22 × 32 mm.

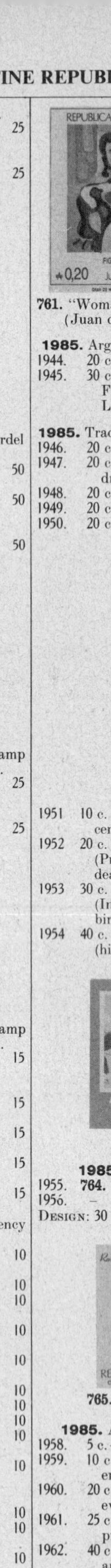

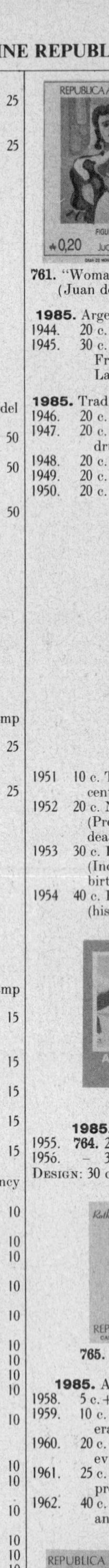

**761.** "Woman with Bird" (Juan del Prete).

**762.** Musical Bow.

**1985.** Argentinian Paintings. Multicoloured.
1944. 20 c. Type **761** .. .. 75 30
1945. 30 c. "Illuminated Fruits" (Fortunato Lacamera) .. .. 1·00 30

**1985.** Traditional Musical Instruments. Mult.
1946. 20 c. Type **762** .. .. 60 20
1947. 20 c. Long flute with drum accompaniment 60 20
1948. 20 c. Frame drum .. 60 20
1949. 20 c. Pan's flute .. .. 60 20
1950. 20 c. Jew's harp .. .. 60 20

**763.** Juan Bautista Alberdi (writer).

**1985.** Anniversaries.
1951 10 c. Type **763** (death centenary (1984)) .. 25 15
1952 20 c. Nicolas Avellaneda (President 1874–80, death centenary .. 50 25
1953 30 c. Brother Luis Beltran (Independence hero, birth bicent (1984)) .. 75 40
1954 40 c. Ricardo Levene (historian) (birth cent) 1·40 50

**764.** Roller Skaters.

**1985.** International Youth Year.
1955. **764.** 20 c. black and blue 25 20
1956. – 30 c. multicoloured .. 35 30
DESIGN: 30 c. "Disappointment".

**765.** "Rothschildia jacobaeae".

**1985.** Argentine Philately. Butterflies.
1958. 5 c. + 2 c. Type **765** .. 10 10
1959. 10 c. + 5 c. "Heliconius erato phyllis" .. .. 30 20
1960. 20 c. + 10 c. "Precis evarete hilaris" .. 60 40
1961. 25 c. + 13 c. "Cyanopepla pretiosa" .. 75 55
1962. 40 c. + 20 c. "Papilio androgeus" .. .. 1·25 90

**766.** Forclaz Windmill (Entre Rios).

**768.** "Birth of Our Lord" (Carlos Cortes).

**767.** Hand holding White Stick.

**1985.** Tourism. Argentine Provinces. Mult.
1963. 10 c. Type **766** .. .. 15 10
1964. 10 c. Sierra de la Ventana (Buenos Aires) .. 15 10
1965. 10 c. Potrero de los Funes artificial lake (San Luis) .. .. .. 15 10
1966. 10 c. Church belfry (North-west Argentina) 15 10
1967. 10 c. Magellanic penguins, Punta Tombo (Chubut) .. 1·25 20
1968. 10 c. Sea of Mirrors (Cordoba) .. .. 15 10

**1985.** National Campaign for the Prevention of Blindness.
1969. **767.** 10 c. multicoloured .. 15 10

**1985.** Christmas. Multicoloured.
1970. 10 c. Type **768** .. .. 30 15
1971. 20 c. "Christmas" (Hector Viola) .. 55 50

**769.** Rio Gallegos Cathedral.

**1985.** Centenary of Rio Gallegos.
1972. **769.** 10 c. multicoloured .. 15 10

**770.** Grape Harvesting.

**1986.** 50th Anniv. of Grape Harvest National Festival.
1973. **770.** 10 c. multicoloured .. 15 10

**771.** House of Valentin Alsina (Italian Period).

**1986.** Buenos Aires Architecture, 1880–1930. Multicoloured.
1974. 20 c. Type **771** .. .. 30 20
1975. 20 c. 1441 Calle Cerrito (French period) .. 30 20
1976. 20 c. Customs House (Academic period) (horiz.) .. .. 30 20
1977. 20 c. House, Avenido de Mayo (Art Nouveau) 30 20
1978. 20 c. Isaac Fernandez Blanco Museum (National Restoration period) (horiz.) .. 30 20

**772.** Jubany Base.

**773.** "Fountain of Nereid" (detail, Lola Mora).

**1986.** Argentine Antarctic Research. Mult.

1979. 10 c. Type **772** .. .. 20 20
1980. 10 c. Kerguelen fur seal 20 20
1981. 10 c. Southern sealion .. 20 20
1982. 10 c. General Belgrano Base .. .. .. 20 20
1983. 10 c. Pintado petrel .. 1·00 40
1984. 10 c. Black-browed albatross .. .. 1·00 40
1985. 10 c. King penguin .. 1·00 40
1986. 10 c. Giant petrel .. 1·00 40
1987. 10 c. Hugo Alberto Acuna (explorer) .. 40 20
1988. 10 c. Magellanic penguin 1·00 40
1989. 10 c. Paraguayan snipe 1·00 40
1990. 10 c. Captain Augustin Servando del Castillo (explorer) .. .. 20 20

**1986.** Sculpture. Multicoloured.

1991. 20 c. Type **773** .. .. 60 50
1992. 30 c. "Work Song" (detail, Rogelio Yrurtia) .. .. 90 75

**774.** Dr. Alicia Moreau de Justo (suffragist, d. 1986). **775.** Dr. Francisco Narciso Laprida.

**1986.** Anniversaries.

1993 **774** 10 c. black, yell & brn 30 10
1994 – 10 c. blk, turq & blue 30 10
1995 – 30 c. black, red & mve 90 75

DESIGNS: 1994, Dr. Emilio Ravignani (historian, birth centenary); 1995, Indira Gandhi (Prime Minister, of India 1st death anniversary).

**1986.** Birth Bicentenaries of Independence Heroes. Each brown, yellow and black.

1996. 20 c. Type **775** .. .. 50 45
1997. 20 c. Brigadier General Estanislao Lopez .. 50 45
1998. 20 c. General Francisco Ramirez .. .. 50 45

**776.** Namuncura. **777.** Drawing by Nazarena Pastor.

**1986.** Birth Centenary of Ceferino Namuncura (first Indian seminary student).

1999. **776.** 20 c. multicoloured .. 25 15

**1986.** Argentine Philately. Children's Drawings. Multicoloured.

2000. 5 c.+2 c. Type **777** .. 15 15
2001. 10 c.+5 c. Girl and boy holding flowers and balloon (Tatiana Valleistein) (horiz.) .. 20 20
2002. 20 c.+10 c. Boy and girl (Juan Manel Flores) .. 70 70
2003. 25 c.+13 c. Town and waterfront (Marcelo E. Pezzuto) (horiz.) .. 85 85
2004. 40 c.+20 c. Village (Esteban Diehl) (horiz.) .. .. 1·25 1·25

**1986.** No. 1825 surch **A0, 10**.

2005. 10 c. on 1 p. "Tabebuia ipe" .. .. .. 15 10

**779.** Argentine Team (value top left).

**1986.** Argentina, World Cup Football Championship (Mexico) Winners. Mult.

2006. 75 c. Type **779** .. .. 1·40 1·40
2007. 75 c. Argentina team (value top right) .. 1·40 1·40
2008. 75 c. Argentina team (value bottom left) .. 1·40 1·40
2009. 75 c. Argentina team (value bottom right) .. 1·40 1·40
2010. 75 c. Player shooting for goal .. .. .. 1·40 1·40
2011. 75 c. Player tackling and goalkeeper on ground 1·40 1·40
2012. 75 c. Player number 11 .. 1·40 1·40
2013. 75 c. Player number 7 .. 1·40 1·40
2014. 75 c. Crowd and Argentina player .. 1·40 1·40
2015. 75 c. West Germany player .. .. .. 1·40 1·40
2016. 75 c. Goalkeeper on ground .. .. .. 1·40 1·40
2017. 75 c. Footballers' legs .. 1·40 1·40
2018. 75 c. Hand holding World Cup trophy .. 1·40 1·40
2019. 75 c. Raised arm and crowded stadium .. 1·40 1·40
2020. 75 c. People with flags and cameras .. .. 1·40 1·40
2021. 75 c. Player's body and crowd .. .. .. 1·40 1·40

Nos. 2006/13 were printed together se-tenant in a sheetlet of eight stamps arranged in two blocks, each block forming a composite design. Nos. 2014/21 were similarly arranged in a second sheetlet.

**780.** Municipal Building.

2022. **780.** 20 c. multicoloured .. 50 45

**781.** Old Railway Station.

**1986.** Centenary of Trelew City.

2023. **781.** 20 c. multicoloured .. 30 15

**782.** Emblem and Colours.

**1986.** Mutualism Day.

2024. **782.** 20 c. multicoloured .. 25 15

**783.** "Primitive Retable" (Aniko Szabo).

**1986.** Christmas. Multicoloured.

2025. 20 c. Type **783** .. .. 20 10
2026. 30 c. "Everybody's Tree" (Franca Delacqua) .. .. 30 15

**784.** St. Rosa of Lima. **785.** Municipal Building.

**1986.** 400th Birth Anniv. of St. Rosa de Lima.

2027. **784.** 50 c. multicoloured .. 50 20

**1986.** Anniversaries. Multicoloured.

2028. 20 c. Type **785** (bicent. of Rio Cuarto city) .. 10 10
2029. 20 c. Palace of Justice, Cordoba (50th anniv.) 10 10

**786.** Marine Biology.

**1987.** 25th Anniv. of Antarctic Treaty. Multicoloured.

2030. 20 c. Type **786** .. .. 30 20
2031. 30 c. Study of native birds .. .. .. 1·25 30

**787.** Emblem.

**1987.** Centenary of National Mortgage Bank.

2033 **787** 20 c. yellow, brn & blk 20 15

**788.** Stylized Pine Trees.

**1987.** Argentine Co-operative Movement.

2034. **788.** 20 c. multicoloured .. 20 15

**789.** Pope.

**1987.** 2nd Visit of Pope John Paul II.

2035. **789.** 20 c. blue and red .. 40 10
2036. – 80 c. brown & green 1·60 55

DESIGN: 80 c. Pope in robes with Crucifix.

**790.** Flag forming "PAZ" (peace).

**1987.** International Peace Year.

2038. **790.** 20 c. blue, deep blue and black .. .. 20 15
2039. – 30 c. multicoloured .. 30 20

DESIGN: 30 c. "Pigeon" (sculpture, Victor Kaniuka).

**791.** "Polo Players" (Alejandro Moy). **792.** "Supplicant" (Museum of Natural Sciences, La Plata).

**1987.** World Polo Championships, Palermo.

2040. **791.** 20 c. multicoloured .. 25 15

**1987.** 14th International Museums Council General Conference, Buenos Aires. Mult.

2041 25 c. Conference emblem 45 15
2042 25 c. Shield of Potosi, (National History Museum, Buenos Aires) 45 15
2043 25 c. Statue of St. Bartholome, (Enrique Larreta Spanish Art Museum, Buenos Aires) 45 15
2044 25 c. Cudgel with animal design (Patagonia Museum, San Carlos de Bariloche) .. .. 45 15
2045 25 c. Type **792** .. .. 45 15
2046 25 c. Grate from Argentine Confederation House, (Entre Rios Historical Museum, Parana) .. .. 45 15
2047 25 c. Statue of St. Joseph, (Northern Historical Museum, Salta) .. 45 15
2048 25 c. Funeral urn, (Provincial Archaeological Museum, Santiago del Estero) .. .. 45 15

**793.** Pillar Box. **794.** "Metynnis maculatus".

**1987.** No. Value expressed.

(a) Inscr. "C" and "TARIFA INTERNA/HASTA 10 GRAMOS".

2049. **793.** (18 c.) red, black and yellow .. .. 45 15

(b) Inscr. "C" and "TARIFA INTERNA/DE 11 A 20 GRAMOS".

2050. **793.** (33 c.) black, yellow and green .. .. 45 15

**1987.** Argentine Philately. River Fishes. Multicoloured.

2051. 10 c.+5 c. Type **794** .. 30 10
2052. 10 c.+5 c. "Cynolebias nigripinnis" .. .. 30 10
2053. 10 c.+5 c. "Leporinus solarii" .. .. 30 10
2054. 10 c.+5 c. "Aphyocharax rathbuni" .. 30 10
2055. 10 c.+5 c. "Corydoras aeneus" .. .. 30 10
2056. 10 c.+5 c. "Thoracocharax securis" .. 30 10
2057. 10 c.+5 c. "Cynolebias melanotaenia" .. 30 10
2058. 10 c+5 c. "Cichlasoma facetum" .. .. 30 10
2059. 20 c.+10 c. "Tetragonopterus argente" .. 60 20
2060. 20 c.+10 c. "Hemigrammus caudovittatus" .. .. 60 20
2061. 20 c.+10 c. "Astyanax bimaculatus" .. .. 60 20
2062. 20 c.+10 c. "Gymnocorymbus ternetzi" .. 60 20
2063. 20 c.+10 c. "Hoplias malabaricus" .. .. 60 20
2064. 20 c.+10 c. "Aphyocharax rubripinnis" .. 60 20
2065. 20 c.+10 c. "Apistogramma agassizi" .. .. 60 20
2066. 20 c.+10 c. "Pyrrhulina rachoviana" .. .. 60 20

**INDEX**

Countries can be quickly located by referring to the index at the end of this volume.

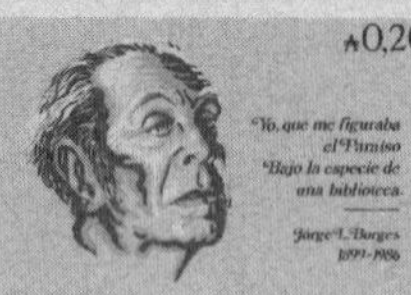


**796.** Jorge Luis Borges (writer).

**1987.** Anniversaries. Multicoloured.

2068 20 c. Type **796** (1st death anniversary) .. .. 25 10
2069 30 c. Armando Discepolo, (dramatist and theatre director, birth cent) .. 40 15
2070 50 c. Dr Carlos Alberto Pueyrredon (historian, birth centenary) .. 65 20

**797.** Drawing by Leonardo da Vinci.

**1987.** "The Post, a Medium for Communication and Prevention of Addictions".

2071. **797.** 30 c. multicoloured .. 40 15

**798.** "The Sower" (Julio Vanzo).

**1987.** 75th Anniv. of Argentine Farmers' Union.

2072. **798.** 30 c. multicoloured .. 40 15

**799.** Basketball.

**800.** Col. Maj. Ignacio Alvarez Thomas.

**1987.** 10th Pan-American Games, Indianapolis. Multicoloured.

2073. 20 c. Type **799** .. .. 15 10
2074. 30 c. Rowing .. .. 20 15
2075. 50 c. Yachting .. .. 65 15

**1987.** Anniversaries. Multicoloured.

2076 25 c. Type **800** (birth bicentenary) .. .. 35 10
2077 25 c. Col. Manuel Dorrego (birth bicentenary) .. 35 10
2078 50 c. 18th-century Spanish map of Falkland Islands (death bicent of Jacinto de Altolaguirre, governor of Islands) (horiz) .. .. 60 20
2079 50 c. "Signing the Accord" (Rafael del Villar) (50th anniv of House of Accord Museum, San Nicolas) (horiz) .. .. 60 20

**801.** Children as Nurse and Mother.

**1987.** U.N.I.C.E.F. Child Vaccination Campaign.

2080 **801** 30 c. multicoloured .. 40 15

**802.** Balloon.

**803.** "Nativity" (tapestry, Alisia Frega).

**1987.** Anniversaries. Multicoloured.

2081. 50 c. Type **802** (50th anniv. of LRA National Radio) .. 65 20
2082. 50 c. Celendonio Galvan Moreno (first editor) (50th anniv. of "Postas Argentinas" magazine) 65 20
2083. 1 a. Dr. Jose Marco del Pont (founder) (centenary of Argentina Philatelic Society) .. .. 1·25 45

**1987.** Christmas. Multicoloured.

2084. 50 c. Type **803** .. .. 10 10
2085. 1 a. Doves and flowers (tapestry, Silvina Trigos).. .. .. 10 10

**804.** Crested Oropendola, Baritu National Park.

**1987.** National Parks (1st series). Mult.

2086 50 c. Type **804** .. .. 1·00 30
2087 50 c. Otter, Nahuel Huapi National Park .. 1·00 30
2088 50 c. Night monkey, Rio Pilcomayo National Park .. .. .. 1·00 30
2089 50 c. Kelp goose, Tierra del Fuego National Park .. .. .. 1·00 30
2090 50 c. Alligator, Iguazu National Park .. 1·00 30

See also Nos. 2150/4, 2222/6 and 2295/9.

**805.** "Caminito" (Jose Canella).

**1988.** Historical and Tourist Sites. Mult.

2091 5 a. Type **805** .. 2·25 75
2090a 3 a. "Purmamarca" (Nestor Martin)(33 × 22 mm) .. .. .. .. 60 20
2092 10 a. "Old Almacen" (Jose Canella) (A) .. .. 4·50 1·50
2092a 10 a. "Old Almacen" (Jose Canella) (B) .. .. 1·25 45
2095 20 a. "Ushuaia" (Nestor Martin) (vert) .. 3·75 1·10
2099 50 a. Type **805** .. 1·25 45

10 a. A. Insr "Viejo Almacen". B. Inscr "El Viejo Almacen"

**806.** "Minstrel singing in a Grocer's Shop" (Carlos Morel).

**1988.** Argentine Paintings. Multicoloured.

2105. 1 a. Type **806** .. .. 50 15
2106. 1 a. "Curuzu" (detail, Candido Lopez) .. 50 15

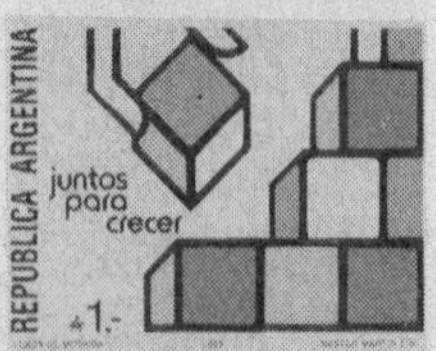


**807.** Hand arranging Coloured Cubes.

**1988.** Argentine–Brazil Economic Co-operation.

2107. **807.** 1 a. multicoloured .. 45 15

**808.** St. Anne's Chapel, Corrientes.

**1988.** 400th Annivs. of Corrientes and Alta Gracia. Multicoloured.

2108. 1 a. Type **808** .. .. 45 15
2109. 1 a. Alta Gracia church 45 15

**809.** Men Stacking Sacks.

**1988.** Labour Day. Details of mural "Cereals" (Nueve de Julio station, Buenos Aires underground railway). Multicoloured.

2110. 50 c. Type **809** .. .. 25 10
2111. 50 c. Sacks .. .. 25 10
2112. 50 c. Men unloading lorry 25 10
2113. 50 c. Horse and cart .. 25 10

Nos. 2110/13 were printed together, se-tenant, forming a composite design.

**810.** Steam Locomotive "Yatay" and Tender, 1888 (illustration ½ size).

**1988.** "Prenfil '88" Philatelic Literature Exhibition, Buenos Aires (1st issue). Railways. Multicoloured.

2114. 1 a. + 50 c. Type **810** .. 15 15
2115. 1 a. + 50 c. Electric passenger coach, 1914 15 15
2116. 1 a. + 50 c. Locomotive "B 15" and tender, 1942 .. .. .. 15 15
2117. 1 a. + 50 c. Electric locomotive "GT-22", 1988 .. .. .. 15 15

See also Nos. 2134/7.

**811.** Running.

**1988.** Olympic Games, Seoul. Multicoloured.

2118. 1 a. Type **811** .. .. 10 10
2119. 2 a. Football .. .. 20 15
2120. 3 a. Hockey .. .. 30 20
2121. 4 a. Tennis .. .. 40 35

**812.** Bank Facade.

**1988.** Centenary of Bank of Mendoza.

2122. **812.** 2 a. multicoloured .. 20 15

**813.** Arms of Guemes and National Guard Emblem.

**814.** "St. Cayetano (patron saint of workers)" (C. Quaglia).

**1988.** 50th Anniv. of National Guard.

2123. **813.** 2 a. multicoloured .. 20 15

**1988.** Philatelic Anniversaries and Events. Multicoloured.

2124. 2 a. Type **814** (50th anniv. of Liniers (Buenos Aires) Philatelic Circle) .. 45 15
2125. 3 a. "Our Lady of Carmen (patron saint of Cuyo)" (window, Carlos Quaglia) (50th anniv. of West Argentina Philatelic Society) .. .. 60 20

**815.** Sarmiento (after Mario Chierico) and Cathedral of the North School.

**1988.** Death Centenary of Domingo Faustino Sarmiento (President, 1868–74).

2127. **815.** 3 a. multicoloured .. 60 20

**816** "San Isidro" (Enrique Castro)

**1988.** Horse Paintings. Multicoloured.

2128 2 a. + 1 a. Type **816** .. 60 60
2129 2 a. + 1 a. "Waiting" (Gustavo Solari) .. 60 60
2130 2 a. + 1 a. "Beside the Pond" (F. Romero Carranza) .. 60 60
2131 2 a. + 1 a. "Mare and Colt" (Enrique Castro) 60 60
2132 2 a. + 1 a. "Under the Tail" (Enrique Castro) 60 60

**1988.** 21st International Urological Society Congress. No. 2091 optd **XXI CONGRESO DE LA SOCIEDAD INTERNACIONAL DE UROLOGIA SIU 88.**

2133 **805** 5 a. multicoloured .. 95 80

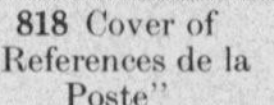

**818** Cover of "References de la Poste"

**821** "Virgin of Tenderness"

**820** Underground Train

**1988.** "Prenfil '88" Philatelic Literature Exhibition, Buenos Aires (2nd issue). Designs showing magazine covers. Multicoloured.

2134 1 a.+1 a. Type **818** .. 35 30
2135 1 a.+1 a. "Cronaca Filatelica" .. .. 20 20
2136 1 a.+1 a. "Co Fi" .. 75 35
2137 2 a.+2 a. "Postas Argentinas" .. .. 20 20

**1988.** 75th Anniv of Buenos Aires Underground Railway.

2139 **820** 5 a. multicoloured .. 95 80

**1988.** Christmas. Virgins in Ucrania Cathedral, Buenos Aires. Multicoloured.

2140 5 a. Type **821** .. 95 80
2141 5 a. "Virgin of Protection" .. .. 95 80

**822** Ushuaia and St. John

**1989.** Death Centenary (1988) of St. John Bosco (founder of Salesian Brothers).

2142 **822** 5 a. multicoloured .. 35 10

**823** "Rincon de los Areneros" (Justo Lynch)

**1989.** Paintings. Multicoloured.

2143 5 a. Type **823** .. .. 35 10
2144 5 a. "Blancos" (Fernando Fader) .. .. 35 10

**824** "Crowning with Thorns" and Church of Our Lady of Carmen, Tandil

**1989.** Holy Week. Multicoloured.

2145 2 a. Type **824** .. .. 15 10
2146 2 a. "Jesus of Nazareth" and Buenos Aires Cathedral .. .. 15 10
2147 3 a. "Our Lady of Sorrows" and Humahuaca Church, Jujuy .. .. .. 15 10
2148 3 a. "Jesus Meets His Mother" (statue) and La Quebrada Church, San Luis .. .. 15 10

**825** Shattering Drinking Glass

**1989.** Anti-alcoholism Campaign.

2149 **825** 5 a. multicoloured .. 25 10

**1989.** National Parks (2nd series). As T **804**. Multicoloured.

2150 5 a. Grey gallito, Lihue Calel National Park .. 65 20
2151 5 a. Lizard, El Palmar National Park .. 50 20
2152 5 a. Tapirs, Calilegua National Park .. 60 20
2153 5 a. Howler monkey, Chaco National Park .. 65 20
2154 5 a. Magellanic woodpecker, Los Glaciares National Park 65 20

**826** Emblem

**1989.** Centenary of Argentinian Membership of International Telecommunications Union.

2155 **826** 10 a. multicoloured .. 40 10

**827** Class 1A Glider Entries

**1989.** World Model Airplane Championships, La Cruz–Embals–Cordoba. Multicoloured.

2156 5 a. Type **827** .. .. 10 10
2157 5 a. Class 1B rubber-powered entries .. 10 10
2158 10 a. Class 1C petrol-engined entries .. 10 10

**828** "Diplomystes viedmensis"

**1989.** Argentine Philately. Fishes. Mult.

2159 10 a.+5 a. Type **828** .. 15 15
2160 10 a.+5 a. "Haplochiton taeniatus" .. .. 15 15
2161 10 a.+5 a. Perch .. 15 15
2162 10 a.+5 a. "Galaxias platei" .. .. 15 15
2163 10 a.+5 a. Brown trout .. 15 15

**829** "All Men are Born Free and Equal"

**1989.** Bicentenary of French Revolution.

2164 **829** 10 a. red, blue & blk 10 10
2165 – 15 a. black, red & bl 10 10

DESIGN: 15 a. "Marianne" (Gandon) and French flag.

**830** "Weser" (steamer)

**1989.** Immigration. Multicoloured.

2167 150 a. Type **830** .. .. 65 35
2168 200 a. Immigrants' hostel 40 35

**831** "Republic" (bronze bust)

**1989.** Transference of Presidency. Unissued stamp surcharged as in T **831**.

2170 **831** 300 a. on 50 a. mult 60 55

**832** Arms of Columbus and Title Page of "Book of Privileges"

**1989.** "Espamer '90" Spain–Latin America Stamp Exhibition. Chronicles of Discovery. Each yellow, black and red.

2171 100 a.+50 a. Type **832** .. 30 30
2172 150 a.+50 a. Illustration from "New Chronicle and Good Government" (Guaman Poma de Ayala) .. .. 40 40
2173 200 a.+100 a. Illustration from "Discovery and Conquest of Peru" (Pedro de Cieza de Leon) .. .. .. 60 60
2174 250 a.+100 a. Illustration from "A Journey to the River Plate" (Ulrico Schmidl) .. .. 70 70

**833** Fr. Guillermo Furlong and Title Page of "Los Jesuitas"

**1989.** Birth Anniversaries.

2175 **833** 150 a. black, lt green & green (centenary) 30 25
2176 – 150 a. black, buff and brown (centenary) 30 25
2177 – 200 a. black, light blue & blue (bicent) 40 35

DESIGNS: No. 2176, Dr. Gregorio Alvarez (physician) and title page of "Canto A Chos Mala"; 2177, Brigadier Gen. Enrique Martinez and "Battle of Maipu" (detail of lithograph, Theodore Gericault).

**834** Wooden Mask from Atajo

**835** "Policewoman with Children" (Diego Molinari)

**1989.** America. Pre-Columbian Artefacts. Multicoloured.

2178 200 a. Type **834** .. .. 40 35
2179 300 a. Urn from Punta de Balastro .. .. 60 55

**1989.** Federal Police Week. Winning entries in a schools' painting competition.

2180 100 a. Type **835** .. .. 20 15
2181 100 a. "Traffic policeman" (Carlos Alberto Sarago) 20 15
2182 150 a. "Adults and child by traffic lights" (Roxana Andrea Osuna) 30 25
2183 150 a. "Policeman and child stopping traffic at crossing" (Pablo Javier Quaglia) .. .. 30 25

**836** "Dream of Christmas" (Maria Carballido)

**1989.** Christmas. Multicoloured.

2184 200 a. Type **836** .. .. 40 35
2185 200 a. "Cradle Song for Baby Jesus" (Gato Frias) .. .. .. 40 35
2186 300 a. "Christ of the Hills" (statue, Chipo Cespedes) (vert) .. 60 55

**837** "Battle of Vuelta de Obligado" (Ulde Todo)

**1989.**

2187 **837** 300 a. multicoloured .. 1·10 65

**838** Port Building

**839** Aconcagua Peak and Los Horcones Lagoon

**1990.** Cent of Buenos Aires Port. Mult.

2188 200 a. Type **838** .. .. 10 10
2189 200 a. Crane and bows of container and sailing ships .. .. 10 10
2190 200 a. Lorry on quay and ships in dock .. .. 10 10
2191 200 a. Van and building 10 10

Nos. 2188/91 were printed together, se-tenant, forming a composite design.

**1990.** Aconcagua International Fair. Mult.

2192 500 a. Type **839** .. .. 10 10
2193 500 a. Aconcagua Peak and Los Horcones Lagoon (right-hand detail) .. .. 10 10

Nos. 2192/3 were printed together, se-tenant, forming a composite design.

**840** "75" and Girl with Savings Box

**1990.** 75th Anniv of National Savings and Insurance Fund.

2194 **840** 1000 a. multicoloured 20 15

**841** Footballer in Striped Shirt

**1990.** World Cup Football Championship, Italy. Multicoloured.

2195 2500 a. Type **841** .. 50 40
2196 2500 a. Upper body of footballer in blue shirt 50 40
2197 2500 a. Ball and foot-ballers' legs .. 50 40
2198 2500 a. Lower body of footballer .. 50 40

Nos. 2195/8 were printed together, se-tenant, forming a composite design.

842 Flowers

**1990.** Anti-drugs Campaign.
2199 **842** 2000 a. multicoloured 40 30

843 School Emblem and Pellegrini

**1990.** Centenary of Carlos Pellegrini Commercial High School.
2200 **843** 2000 a. multicoloured 40 30

844 "Calleida suturalis"

847 Players

845 Letters and Globe

**1990.** Argentine Philately. Insects. Mult.
2201 1000 a.+500 a. Type **844** 35 35
2202 1000 a.+500 a. "Adalia bipunctata" .. .. 35 35
2203 1000 a.+500 a. "Hippodamia convergens" .. 35 35
2204 1000 a.+500 a. "Nabis punctipennis" .. 35 35
2205 1000 a.+500 a. "Podisus nigrispinus" .. .. 35 35

**1990.** International Literacy Year.
2206 **845** 2000 a. multicoloured 40 30

**1990.** World Basketball Championship. Mult.
2208 **847** 2000 a. multicoloured 40 30

848 Junkers Ju 52/3m

**1990.** Air. 50th Anniv of LADE (airline). Mult.
2210 2500 a. Type **848** .. 60 45
2211 2500 a. Grumman SA-16 Albatross flying boat .. 60 45
2212 2500 a. Fokker Friendship 60 45
2213 2500 a. Fokker Fellowship 60 45

849 Arms of West Indies Maritime Post

**1990.** 14th Postal Union of the Americas and Spain Congress, Buenos Aires.
2214 **849** 3000 a. brown & black 60 50
2215 – 3000 a. multicoloured 90 60
2216 – 3000 a. multicoloured 90 60
2217 – 3000 a. multicoloured 60 50
DESIGNS: No. 2215, Sailing packet and despatch boat; 2216, "Rio Carcarana" (cargo liner); 2217, Boeing 707 airplane.

851 "Hamelia erecta" and Iguazu Falls

**1990.** America. Natural World. Multicoloured.
2219 3000 a. Type **851** .. 1·75 1·40
2220 3000 a. Sea cow, Puerto Deseado .. .. 1·75 1·40

852 U.P.U. Emblem on "Stamp"

**1990.** World Post Day.
2221 **852** 3000 a. multicoloured 1·75 1·40

**1990.** National Parks (3rd series). As T **804**. Multicoloured.
2222 3000 a. Anteater, El Rey National Park .. 2·00 1·40
2223 3000 a. Black-necked swans, Laguna Blanca National Park .. 2·00 1·40
2224 3000 a. Grey eagle-buzzard, Lanin National Park .. 2·00 1·40
2225 3000 a. Armadillo, Perito Moreno National Park 2·00 1·40
2226 3000 a. Pudu, Puelo National Park .. 2·00 1·40

853 Hands (after Michelangelo) and Army Emblem

**1990.** Centenaries of Salvation Army in Argentina (2227) and National University of the Littoral (2228). Multicoloured.
2227 3000 a. Type **853** .. 60 50
2228 3000 a. University building and emblem .. 60 50

854 Archangel Gabriel

856 "Landscape" (Pio Collivadino)

**1990.** Christmas. Stained glass windows by Carlos Quaglia from Church of Immaculate Conception, Villaguay. Mult.
2229 3000 a. Dove's wing and hand .. .. 60 50
2230 3000 a. Dove and Mary .. 60 50
2231 3000 a. Type **854** .. 60 50
2232 3000 a. Lower half of Mary and open book .. 60 50
2233 3000 a. Joseph .. .. 60 50
2234 3000 a. Star, shepherds and head of Mary .. 60 50
2235 3000 a. Manger .. 60 50
2236 3000 a. Baby Jesus in Mary's arms .. 60 50
2237 3000 a. Joseph with two doves and Mary .. 60 50
2238 3000 a. Simeon .. .. 60 50
2239 3000 a. Lower halves of Joseph and Mary .. 60 50
2240 3000 a. Lower half of Simeon and altar .. 60 50
Nos. 2229/32, 2233/6 and 2237/40 were printed together in se-tenant sheetlets of four stamps, each sheetlet forming a composite design of stained glass windows entitled "Incarnation of Son of God", "The Birth of Christ" and "Presentation of Jesus in the Temple".

**1991.** Paintings. Multicoloured.
2242 4000 a. Type **856** .. 1·25 95
2243 4000 a. "Weeping Willows" (Atilio Malinverno) (horiz) .. 1·25 95

858 Rosas

860 "Hernan, the Pirate" (Jose Salinas)

**1991.** Return of Remains of Brig. Gen. Juan Manuel de Rosas.
2245 **858** 4000 a. multicoloured 1·25 95

**1991.** Comic Strips. Each black and blue.
2247 4000 a. Type **860** .. 45 35
2248 4000 a. "Don Fulgencio" (Lino Palacio) .. 45 35
2249 4000 a. "Tablas Medicas de Salerno" (Oscar Conti) .. .. .. 45 35
2250 4000 a. "Buenos Aires en Camiseta" (Alejandro del Prado) .. .. 45 35
2251 4000 a. "Girls!" (Jose Divito) .. 45 35
2252 4000 a. "Langostino" (Eduardo Ferro) .. 45 35
2253 4000 a. "Mafalda" (Joaquin Lavado) .. 45 35
2254 4000 a. "Mort Cinder" (Alberto Breccia) .. 45 35

861 "Flags" (Maria Augustina Ferreyra)

**1991.** 700th Anniv of Swiss Confederation.
2255 **861** 4000 a. multicoloured 1·25 95

862 Divine Child Mayor

**1991.** 400th Anniv of La Rioja City.
2256 **862** 4000 a. multicoloured 1·25 95

863 Eduardo Bradley, Angel Zuloaga and Balloon "Eduardo Newbery"

**1991.** 75th Anniv of Crossing of Andes by Balloon.
2257 **863** 4000 a. multicoloured 45 35

864 "Vitoria" (Magellan's galleon)

**1991.** America. Voyages of Discovery. Mult.
2258 4000 a. Type **864** .. 70 40
2259 4000 a. Juan Diaz de Solis's fleet .. .. 70 40

865 "Virgin of the Valley, Catamarca" (top half))

**1991.** Christmas. Stained Glass Windows from Church of Our Lady of Lourdes, Santos Lugares, Buenos Aires. Multicoloured.
2260 4000 a. Type **865** .. 1·10 90
2261 4000 a. "Virgin of the Valley" (bottom half) 1·10 90
2262 4000 a. Church and "Virgin of the Rosary of the Miracle, Cordoba" (top half) .. 1·10 90
2263 4000 a. "Virgin of the Rosary of the Miracle" (bottom half) .. .. 1·10 90
Nos. 2260/3 were issued together, se-tenant, Nos. 2260/1 and 2262/3 forming composite designs.

866 Enrique Pestalozzi (editor) and Masthead

**1991.** Centenaries. Multicoloured.
2264 4000 a. Type **866** ("Argentinisches Tageblatt" (1989)) .. 1·10 90
2265 4000 a. Leandro Alem (founder) and flags (Radical Civic Union) 1·10 90
2266 4000 a. Marksman (Argentine Shooting Federation) .. .. 1·10 90
2267 4000 a. Dr. Nicasio Etchepareborda (first professor) and emblem (Buenos Aires Faculty of Odontology) .. 1·10 90
2268 4000 a. Dalmiro Huergo and emblem (Graduate School of Economics) 1·10 90

867 Gen. Juan Lavalle and Medal

**1991.** Anniversaries. Multicoloured.
2269 4000 a. Type **867** (150th death anniv) .. 1·25 95
2270 4000 a. Gen. Jose Maria Paz and Battle of Ituzaingo medal (birth bicentenary) .. .. 1·25 95

2271 4000 a. Dr. Marco Avellaneda and opening words of "Ode to the 25th May" (politician and writer, 150th death anniv) . . . . 1·25 95
2272 4000 a. William Henry Hudson and title page of "Far Away and Long Ago" (writer, 150th birth anniv) . . . . 1·25 95

868 "Castor" (rocket)

**1991.** "Iberoprenfil '92" Iberia–Latin America Philatelic Literature Exhibition, Buenos Aires (1st issue). Multicoloured.
2273 4000 a.+4000 a. Type **868** 1·00 1·00
2274 4000 a.+4000 a. "Lusat-1" satellite . . 1·00 1·00
See also Nos. 2313/14 and 2325/8.

869 Guiana Crested Eagle ("Morphnu guianensis")

871 Golden Tops

**1991.** Birds. Multicoloured.
2275 4000 a. Type **869** . . 1·50 1·00
2276 4000 a. Green-winged macaw ("Ara chloroptera") . . . . 1·50 1·00
2277 4000 a. Lesser rhea ("Pterocnemia pennata") . . . . 1·50 1·00

**1992.** Fungi.
2279 10 c. Type **871** . . . . 15 10
2280 25 c. Common ink cap . . 70 60
2281 38 c. Type **871** . . . . 1·00 85
2282 48 c. As 25 c. . . . . 1·00 85
2283 50 c. Granulated boletus . . 1·40 95
2284 51 c. Common morel . . 1·50 1·10
2285 61 c. Fly agaric . . . . 1·60 1·25
2286 68 c. Lawyer's wig . . 1·75 1·40
2289 1 p. As 61 c. . . . . 2·25 1·75
2290 1 p. 25 As 50 c. . . . . 2·40 1·90
2293 2 p. As 51 c. . . . . 4·50 3·50
For redrawn, smaller, designs see Nos. 2365/77.

**1992.** National Parks (4th series). Designs as T **804**. Multicoloured.
2295 38 c. Chucao tapaculo, Los Alerces National Park . . . . 1·25 85
2296 38 c. Opossum, Los Arrayanes National Park . . . . 1·25 85
2297 38 c. Giant armadillo, Formosa Nature Reserve . . . . 1·25 85
2298 38 c. Cavy, Petrified Forests Natural Monument . . . . 1·25 85
2299 38 c. Flamingo, Laguna de los Pozuelos Natural Monument . . . . 1·25 85

872 Soldier and Truck

**1992.** National Heroes Commemoration. Mult.
2300 38 c. Type **872** . . . . 50 40
2301 38 c. "General Belgrano" (cruiser) . . . . 65 40
2302 38 c. FMA Pucara fighter 50 40

873 "Carnotaurus sastrei"

874 "Tileforo Areco"

**1992.** Dinosaurs. Multicoloured.
2303 38 c.+38 c. Type **873** . . 2·25 2·25
2304 38 c.+38 c. "Amarga-saurus cazaui" 2·25 2·25

**1992.** Birth Centenary (1991) of Florencio Molina Campios (painter). Multicoloured.
2305 38 c. Type **874** . . . . 1·10 90
2306 38 c. "In the Shade" (horiz) . . . . 1·10 90

876 General Lucio N. Mansilla and Warships

**1992.** Birth Anniversaries. Multicoloured.
2308 38 c. Type **876** (bicent) . . 1·10 90
2309 38 c. Jose Manuel Estrada (historian, 150th) . . 1·10 90
2310 38 c. General Jose I. Garmendia (150th) . . 1·10 90

877 Hearts as Flowers

**1992.** Anti-drugs Campaign.
2311 **877** 38 c. multicoloured . . 1·10 90

878 Steam Pump Fire Engine and Calaza

**1992.** 140th Birth Anniv of Col. Jose Calaza (founder of fire service).
2312 **878** 38 c. multicoloured . . 1·10 90

879 "The Party"

**1992.** "Iberoprenfil '92" Iberia–Latin America Philatelic Literature Exhibition, Buenos Aires (2nd issue). Paintings by Raul Soldi. Multicoloured.
2313 76 c.+76 c. Type **879** . . 4·25 4·25
2314 76 c.+76 c. "Church of St. Anne of Glew" . . 4·25 4·25

880 Columbus, European Symbols and "Santa Maria"

**1992.** America. 500th Anniv of Discovery of America by Columbus. Multicoloured.
2315 38 c. Type **880** . . . . 65 40
2316 38 c. American symbols and Columbus . . 50 40

**1992.** 50th Anniv of Neuquen and Rio Negro Philatelic Centre. Unissued stamp as T **871** optd **50° ANIVERSARIO CENTRO FILATELICO DE NEUQUEN Y RIO NEGRO**. Multicoloured.
2317 1 p. 77 Verdigris agaric . . 2·75 2·00

882 "God Pays You"

883 Flags of Paraguay and Argentina as Stamps

**1992.** Argentine Films. Advertising posters. Multicoloured.
2318 38 c. Type **882** . . . . 1·00 80
2319 38 c. "The Turbid Waters" . . . . 1·00 80
2320 38 c. "Un Guapo del 900" 1·00 80
2321 38 c. "The Truce" . . 1·00 80
2322 38 c. "The Official Version" . . . . 1·00 80

**1992.** "Parafil '92" Paraguay–Argentina Stamp Exhibition, Buenos Aires.
2323 **883** 76 c.+76 c. mult . . 4·00 4·00

884 Angel and Baby Jesus

885 Punta Mogotes Lighthouse

**1992.** Christmas.
2324 **884** 38 c. multicoloured . . 1·00 80

**1992.** "Iberoprenfil '92" Iberia–Latin America Philatelic Literature Exhibition, Buenos Aires (3rd issue). Lighthouses. Multicoloured.
2325 38 c. Type **885** . . . . 1·00 80
2326 38 c. Rio Negro . . . . 1·00 80
2327 38 c. San Antonio . . 1·00 80
2328 38 c. Cabo Blanco . . 1·00 80

886 Campaign Emblem

887 "Sac-B" Research Satellite

**1992.** Anti-AIDS Campaign.
2329 **886** 10 c. black, red & blue 40 15
2330 – 26 c. multicoloured . . 75 65
DESIGN: 26 c. AIDS cloud over house of life.

**1992.** International Space Year.
2331 **887** 38 c. multicoloured . . 50 40

889 Footballers and Emblem

**1993.** Cent of Argentine Football Assn.
2333 **889** 38 c. multicoloured . . 1·25 95

890 Arquebusier and Arms of Francisco de Arganaras (founder)

892 Order of San Martin

**1993.** 400th Anniv of Jujuy.
2334 **890** 38 c. multicoloured . . 1·00 85

**1993.** Anniversaries. Multicoloured.
2336 38 c. Type **892** (50th anniv) . . . . 1·10 90
2337 38 c. Entrance to and emblem of National History Academy (centenary) . . . . 1·10 90

893 Flag-bearer and Arms of Gendarmerie

895 Snowy Egret ("Egretta thula")

894 Luis Candelaria and Morane Saulnier Type P Monoplane

**1993.** National Heroes Commemoration. Multicoloured.
2338 38 c. Type **893** . . . . 1·00 85
2339 38 c. Coastguard corvette 1·00 85

**1993.** 75th Anniv of First Flight over the Andes.
2340 **894** 38 c. multicoloured . . 50 40

**1993.** Paintings of Birds by Axel Amuchastegui. Multicoloured.
2341 38 c.+38 c. Type **895** . . 1·00 1·00
2342 38 c.+38 c. Scarlet-headed blackbird ("Amblyramphus holosericeus") . . 1·00 1·00
2343 38 c.+38 c. Red-crested cardinal ("Paroaria coronata") . . . . 1·00 1·00
2344 38 c.+38 c. Amazon king-fisher ("Chloroceryle amazona") . . . . 1·00 1·00

896 "Coming Home" (Adriana Zaefferer)

**1993.** Paintings. Multicoloured.
2345 38 c. Type **896** . . . . 50 40
2346 38 c. "The Old House" (Norberto Russo) . . 50 40

897 Pato

**1993.** 40th Anniv of Declaration of Pato as National Sport.

2347 **897** 1 p. multicoloured .. 1·40 1·10

898 Segurola's Pacara ("Enterolobium contortisiliquum")

**1993.** Old Trees in Buenos Aires. Mult.

2348 75 c. Type **898** (Puan and Baldomero Fernandez Moreno Streets) .. 1·00 80
2349 75 c. Pueyrredon's carob tree ("Prosopis alba") (Pueyrredon Square) .. 1·00 80
2350 1 p. 50 Alvear's coral tree ("Erythrina falcata") (Lavalle Square) .. 2·00 1·60
2351 1 p. 50 Avellaneda's magnolia ("Magnolia grandiflora") (Adolfo Berro Avenue) .. 2·00 1·60

899 Southern Right Whale

**1993.** America. Endangered Animals. Mult.

2352 50 c. Type **899** .. .. 70 55
2353 75 c. Commerson's dolphin 1·00 80

900 Star, Leaf and Bell (Christmas)

**1993.** Christmas and New Year. Festive Symbols. Multicoloured.

2354 75 c. Type **900** .. .. 1·00 80
2355 75 c. Leaf, sun and moon (New Year) .. .. 1·00 80
2356 75 c. Leaf and fir tree (Christmas) .. .. 1·00 80
2357 75 c. Fish and moon (New Year) .. .. .. 1·00 80

Nos. 2354/7 were issued together, se-tenant, forming a composite design.

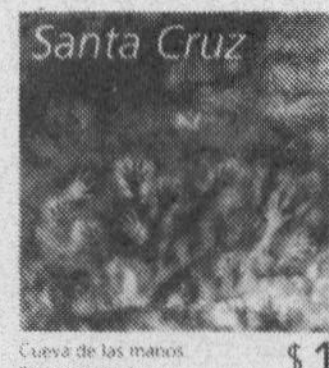

901 Cave Painting

**1993.** Cave of Hands, Santa Cruz.

2358 **901** 1 p. multicoloured .. 1·40 1·10

902 Emblem

**1994.** New Argentine Post Emblem.

2359 **902** 75 c. multicoloured .. 95 75

903 Brazil Player

904 Golden Tops

**1994.** World Cup Football Championship, U.S.A. (1st issue). Multicoloured.

2360 25 c. Germany player .. 30 20
2361 50 c. Type **903** .. .. 60 45
2362 75 c. Argentina player .. 95 75
2363 1 p. Italy player .. 1·25 1·00

See also Nos. 2380/3.

**1994.** Fungi. Multicoloured.

2365 10 c. Type **904** .. .. 20 10
2366 25 c. Common ink cap .. 55 20
2369 50 c. Granulated boletus 1·25 50
2374 1 p. Fly agaric .. .. 2·75 1·10
2377 2 p. Common morel .. 5·25 2·25

905 Argentine Player with Ball (Matias Taylor)

**1994.** World Cup Football Championship, U.S.A. (2nd issue). Winning entries in children's competition. Multicoloured.

2380 75 c. Type **905** .. .. 95 75
2381 75 c. Tackle (Torcuato Santiago Gonzalez Agote) .. .. 95 75
2382 75 c. Players (Julian Lisenberg) (horiz) .. 95 75
2383 75 c. Match scene (Maria Paula Palma) (horiz) .. 95 75

906 Black-throated Finch

**1994.** Animals of the Falkland Islands (Islas Malvinas). Multicoloured.

2384 25 c. Type **906** .. .. 30 20
2385 50 c. Gentoo penguins .. 60 45
2386 75 c. Falkland Islands flightless steamer ducks 95 75
2387 1 p. Southern elephant-seal .. .. .. 1·25 1·00

907 Town Arms

**1994.** Anniversaries. Multicoloured.

2388 75 c. Type **907** (400th anniv of San Luis) .. 95 75
2389 75 c. Arms (3rd anniv of provincial status of Tierra del Fuego, Antarctica and South Atlantic Islands) .. 95 75

908 Ladislao Jose Biro

**1994.** Inventors. Multicoloured.

2390 75 c. Type **908** (ball-point pen) .. .. .. 95 75
2391 75 c. Raul Pateras de Pescara (helicopter) .. 95 75
2392 75 c. Quirino Cristiani (animated films) .. 95 75
2393 75 c. Enrique Finochietto (surgical instruments) 95 75

909 Star, Purple Bauble and Bell

**1994.** United Nations Children's Fund in Argentina. Multicoloured.

2394 50 c. Type **909** .. .. 60 45
2395 75 c. Bell, red bauble and star .. .. .. 95 75

910 Children holding Globe (Ivana Mirna de Caro)

**1994.** "Care of the Planet". Children's Painting Competition. Multicoloured.

2396 25 c. Type **910** .. .. 30 20
2397 25 c. Girl polishing sunbeam and boy tending tree (Elena Tsouprik) .. 30 20
2398 50 c. Children of all races around globe (Estefania Navarro) (horiz) .. 60 45
2399 50 c. Globe as house (Maria Belen Gidoni) (horiz) .. .. 60 45

911 Star and Angel (The Annunciation)

**1994.** Christmas. Multicoloured.

2400 50 c. Type **911** .. .. 60 45
2401 75 c. Madonna and Child (Nativity) .. .. 95 75

912 Running

**1995.** 12th Pan-American Games, Mar del Plata. Multicoloured.

2402 75 c. Type **912** .. .. 95 75
2403 75 c. Cycling .. .. 95 75
2404 75 c. Diving .. .. 95 75
2405 1 p. 25 Football (vert) .. 1·60 1·25
2406 1 p. 25 Gymnastics (vert) 1·60 1·25

913 Postal Emblem

**1995.** Self-adhesive.

2407 **913** 25 c. yellow, bl & blk 30 20
2408 75 c. yellow, bl & blk 95 75

914 National Congress Building and "The Republic Triumphant" (statue, detail)

**1995.** New Constitution, August 1994.

2409 **914** 75 c. multicoloured .. 95 75

915 Letters and Disk

**1995.** 21st International Book Fair.

2410 **915** 75 c. multicoloured .. 95 75

916 Bay-winged Cowbird

**1995.** Birds. Multicoloured.

2412 5 p. Hooded siskin .. 6·50 5·00
2413 9 p. 40 Type **916** .. 12·00 9·50
2414 10 p. Rufous-collared sparrow .. .. 13·00 10·00

917 Clouds seen through Atrium

**1995.** Centenary of Argentine Engineers' Centre, Buenos Aires.

2420 **917** 75 c. multicoloured .. 95 75

920 Jose Marti

**1995.** Revolutionaries' Anniversaries. Mult.

| | | | |
|---|---|---|---|
| 2423 | 1 p. Type **920** (death centenary) .. .. | 1·25 | 1·00 |
| 2424 | 1 p. Antonio de Sucre (birth bicentenary) .. | 1·25 | 1·00 |

**921** Greater Rhea

**922** Cave Painting (Patagonia)

**1995.** Birds. Multicoloured.

| | | | |
|---|---|---|---|
| 2425 | 5 c. Type **921** .. .. | 10 | 10 |
| 2426 | 25 c. Penguin .. .. | 30 | 20 |
| 2427 | 50 c. Toco toucan .. | 60 | 45 |
| 2428 | 75 c. Andean condor .. | 95 | 75 |
| 2429 | 1 p. Barn owl .. .. | 1·25 | 1·00 |
| 2430 | 2 p. Olivaceous cormorant | 2·50 | 2·00 |
| 2431 | 2 p. 75 Cayenne plover .. | 3·50 | 2·75 |

**1995.** Animals. As T **921**. Multicoloured.

| | | | |
|---|---|---|---|
| 2436 | 25 c. Alligator .. .. | 30 | 20 |
| 2437 | 50 c. Red fox .. .. | 60 | 45 |
| 2438 | 75 c. Anteater .. .. | 95 | 75 |
| 2439 | 75 c. Vicuna .. .. | 95 | 75 |
| 2440 | 75 c. Sperm whale .. | 95 | 75 |

**1995.** Archaeology. Multicoloured.

| | | | |
|---|---|---|---|
| 2441 | 75 c. Type **922** .. .. | 95 | 75 |
| 2442 | 75 c. Stone mask (Tafi culture, Tucuman) .. | 95 | 75 |
| 2443 | 75 c. Anthropomorphic vase (Catamarca) .. | 95 | 75 |
| 2444 | 75 c. Woven cloth (North Patagonia) .. .. | 95 | 75 |

**923** Peron

**1995.** Birth Centenary of Juan Peron (President, 1946–55 and 1973–74).

| | | | | |
|---|---|---|---|---|
| 2445 | **923** | 75 c. blue and bistre .. | 95 | 75 |

**924** Postal Emblem on Sunflower

**1995.**

| | | | | |
|---|---|---|---|---|
| 2446 | **924** | 75 c. multicoloured .. | 95 | 75 |

**926** Christmas Tree

**1995.** Christmas. Multicoloured.

| | | | |
|---|---|---|---|
| 2448 | 75 c. Type **926** .. .. | 95 | 75 |
| 2449 | 75 c. "1996" .. .. | 95 | 75 |
| 2450 | 75 c. Glasses of champagne .. .. | 95 | 75 |
| 2451 | 75 c. Present .. .. | 95 | 75 |
| 2452 | 75 c. Type **926** .. .. | 95 | 75 |

**927** "Les 400 Coups" (dir. Franois Truffaut)

**1995.** Centenary of Motion Pictures. Each black, grey and orange.

| | | | |
|---|---|---|---|
| 2453 | 75 c. "Battleship Potemkin" (dir. Sergei Eisenstein) .. .. | 95 | 75 |
| 2454 | 75 c. "Casablanca" (dir. Michael Curtiz) .. | 95 | 75 |
| 2455 | 75 c. "Bicycle Theives" (dir. Vittorio de Sica) | 95 | 75 |
| 2456 | 75 c. Charlie Chaplin in "Limelight" .. .. | 95 | 75 |
| 2457 | 75 c. Type **927** .. .. | 95 | 75 |
| 2458 | 75 c. "Chronicle of an Only Child" (dir. Leonardo Favio) .. | 95 | 75 |

**928** Horse-drawn Mail Coach

**1995.** America (1994). Postal Transport. Multicoloured.

| | | | |
|---|---|---|---|
| 2459 | 75 c. Type **928** .. .. | 95 | 75 |
| 2460 | 75 c. Early postal van .. | 95 | 75 |

**929** Dirigible Airship

**1995.** The Sky. Multicoloured.

| | | | |
|---|---|---|---|
| 2461 | 25 c. Type **929** .. .. | 30 | 20 |
| 2462 | 25 c. Kite .. .. | 30 | 20 |
| 2463 | 25 c. Hot-air balloon .. | 30 | 20 |
| 2464 | 50 c. Balloons .. .. | 60 | 45 |
| 2465 | 50 c. Paper airplane .. | 60 | 45 |
| 2466 | 75 c. Airplane .. .. | 95 | 75 |
| 2467 | 75 c. Helicopter .. .. | 95 | 75 |
| 2468 | 75 c. Parachute .. .. | 95 | 75 |

## OFFICIAL STAMPS

**1884.** Optd. **OFICIAL.**

| | | | | |
|---|---|---|---|---|
| O 66. | **33.** | ½ c. brown .. .. | 8·00 | 6·00 |
| O 69. | | 1 c. red .. .. | 45 | 15 |
| O 70. | **24.** | 2 c. green .. .. | 45 | 15 |
| O 71. | – | 4 c. brown (No. 32) .. | 45 | 15 |
| O 72. | **9.** | 8 c. red .. .. | 45 | 15 |
| O 73. | **10.** | 10 c. green .. .. | 42·00 | 22·00 |
| O 76. | **33.** | 12 c. blue .. .. | 70 | 60 |
| O 77. | **10.** | 16 c. green .. .. | 1·90 | 75 |
| O 78. | **22.** | 20 c. blue .. .. | 8·00 | 6·00 |
| O 79. | **11.** | 24 c. blue (roul.) .. | 1·40 | 85 |
| O 80. | | 24 c. blue (perf.) .. | 1·25 | 70 |
| O 81. | – | 25 c. red (No. 47) .. | 9·50 | 6·50 |
| O 82. | – | 30 c. orange (No. 33) | 17·00 | 12·00 |
| O 83. | – | 60 c. black (No. 34) .. | 12·00 | 7·50 |
| O 84. | – | 90 c. blue (No. 35) .. | 8·50 | 6·50 |

**O 73.**

**1901.**

| | | | | |
|---|---|---|---|---|
| O 275. | **O 73.** | 1 c. grey .. .. | 25 | 10 |
| O 276. | | 2 c. brown .. .. | 35 | 15 |
| O 277. | | 5 c. red .. .. | 45 | 15 |
| O 278. | | 10 c. green .. .. | 50 | 15 |
| O 279. | | 30 c. blue .. .. | 3·50 | 85 |
| O 280. | | 50 c. orange .. | 1·90 | 65 |

**1938.** Optd. **SERVICIO OFICIAL** in two lines.

| | | | | |
|---|---|---|---|---|
| O 668 | **143** | 1 c. brown (No. 645) | 10 | 10 |
| O 669 | – | 2 c. brown (No. 646) | 10 | 10 |
| O 670 | – | 3 c. green (No. 647) | 10 | 10 |
| O 679 | – | 3 c. grey (No. 672) | 10 | 10 |
| O 771 | – | 3 c. grey (No. 751) | 1·40 | 35 |
| O 671 | – | 5 c. brown (No. 653b) | 10 | 10 |
| O 782 | **200** | 5 c. red (No. 773) | 10 | 10 |
| O 667 | – | 10 c. red (No. 653d) | 10 | 10 |
| O 773 | – | 10 c. purple (No. 678) | 10 | 10 |
| O 681 | **146** | 15 c. blue (No. 676) | 10 | 10 |
| O 774 | – | 15 c. grey (No. 708) | 10 | 10 |
| O 683 | **146** | 20 c. blue (19½ × 26 mm) .. .. | 50 | 10 |
| O 872 | **247** | 20 c. red .. .. | 10 | 10 |
| O 813 | – | 25 c. (No. 673) .. | 10 | 10 |
| O 674 | – | 40 c. (No. 658) .. | 10 | 10 |
| O 675 | – | 50 c. (No. 659) .. | 10 | 10 |
| O 676 | **152** | 1 p. (No. 760) .. | 10 | 10 |
| O 827 | **234** | 1 p. (No. 826) .. | 35 | 10 |
| O 778 | – | 2 p. (No. 661) .. | 10 | 10 |
| O 779 | – | 5 p. (No. 662) .. | 15 | 10 |
| O 780 | – | 10 p. (No. 763) .. | 25 | 10 |
| O 781 | – | 20 p. (No. 764) .. | 80 | 20 |

(b) Optd. SERVICIO OFICIAL in one line.

| | | | | |
|---|---|---|---|---|
| O 897 | – | 20 c. lilac (No. 895) | 15 | 10 |

**1953.** Eva Peron stamps optd. **SERVICIO OFICIAL.**

| | | | | |
|---|---|---|---|---|
| O 854. | **239.** | 5 c. grey .. .. | 10 | 10 |
| O 855. | | 10 c. red .. .. | 10 | 10 |
| O 856. | | 20 c. red .. .. | 10 | 10 |
| O 857. | | 25 c. green .. .. | 10 | 10 |
| O 858. | | 40 c. purple .. .. | 10 | 10 |
| O 859. | | 45 c. blue .. .. | 15 | 10 |
| O 860. | | 50 c. bistre .. .. | 10 | 10 |
| O 862. | **240.** | 1 p. brown (No. 846) | 10 | 10 |
| O 863. | | 1 p. 50 green (No. 847) | 25 | 10 |
| O 864. | | 2 p. red (No. 848) .. | 20 | 10 |
| O 865. | | 3 p. blue (No. 849) .. | 45 | 15 |
| O 866. | | 5 p. brown .. .. | 45 | 15 |
| O 867. | **239.** | 10 p. red .. .. | 3·25 | 2·00 |
| O 868. | **240.** | 20 p. green .. .. | 40·00 | 27·00 |

**1955.** Stamps of 1954 optd. **SERVICIO OFICIAL** in one line.

| | | | | |
|---|---|---|---|---|
| O 869. | **247.** | 20 c. red .. .. | 10 | 10 |
| O 870. | | 40 c. red .. .. | 10 | 10 |
| O 880. | – | 1 p. brown (No. 871) | 10 | 10 |
| O 882. | – | 3 p. purple (No. 874) | 10 | 10 |
| O 883. | – | 5 p. green (No. 875) .. | 30 | 10 |
| O 884. | – | 10 p. green & grey (No. 876) .. .. | 40 | 10 |
| O 886. | | 20 p. violet .. .. | 75 | 15 |

**1955.** Various stamps overprinted.

(a) Optd. **S. OFICIAL.**

| | | | | |
|---|---|---|---|---|
| O 896. | – | 5 c. brown (No. 894) | 10 | 10 |
| O 955. | – | 10 c. green (No. 946) | 10 | 10 |
| O 956. | – | 20 c. purple (No. 947) | 10 | 10 |
| O 879. | – | 50 c. blue (No. 868) .. | 20 | 10 |
| O 957. | – | 50 c. ochre (No. 948) | 10 | 10 |
| O 1034. | – | 1 p. brn. (No. 1016) .. | 10 | 10 |
| O 899. | **264.** | 2 p. purple .. .. | 10 | 10 |
| O 1050. | – | 2 p. red (No. 1035) .. | 10 | 10 |
| O 959. | – | 3 p. blue (No. 951) .. | 15 | 10 |
| O 1051. | – | 4 p. red (No. 1036) .. | 15 | 10 |
| O 961. | **296.** | 5p. brown .. .. | 20 | 10 |
| O 1052. | – | 8 p. red (No. 1037) .. | 15 | 10 |
| O 962. | – | 10 p. brown (No. 1286) | 15 | 10 |
| O 1053. | – | 10 p. red (No. 1038) .. | 15 | 10 |
| O 1036. | – | 12 p. dull purple (No. 1028) .. .. | 40 | 10 |
| O 964. | – | 20 p. green (No. 954) | 50 | 10 |
| O 1055. | – | 20 p. red (No. 1039) .. | 20 | 10 |
| O 1037. | – | 22 p. blue (No. 1018) | 50 | 10 |
| O 1038. | – | 23 p. green (No. 1019) | 50 | 10 |
| O 1039. | – | 25 p. lilac (No. 1020) | 50 | 10 |
| O 1040. | – | 43 p. lake (No. 1021) | 70 | 10 |
| O 1041. | – | 45 p. brn. (No. 1022) | 1·00 | 10 |
| O 1042. | – | 50 p. blue (No. 1023) | 1·25 | 10 |
| O 1043. | – | 50 p. blue (No. 1287) | 2·40 | 10 |
| O 1045. | – | 100 p. blue (No. 1289) | 1·25 | 40 |
| O 1046. | – | 300 p. violet (No. 1026) | 2·50 | 70 |

(b) Optd. **SERVICIO OFICIAL.**

| | | | | |
|---|---|---|---|---|
| O 900. | **265.** | 2 p. 40 brown .. | 20 | 10 |
| O 958. | – | 3 p. blue (No. 951) | 15 | 10 |
| O 901. | **266.** | 4 p. 40 green .. | 25 | 10 |
| O 960. | **296.** | 5 p. brown .. .. | 20 | 10 |
| O 887. | – | 50 p. indigo and blue (No. 878) .. | 1·25 | 10 |
| O 1049. | – | 500 p. grn. (No. 1032) | 4·00 | 90 |

For lists of stamps optd. **M.A., M.G., M.H., M.I., M.J.I., M.M., M.O.P.** or **M.R.C.** for use in ministerial offices see the Stanley Gibbons' Catalogue Part 20 (South America)

**1963.** Nos. 1068, etc., optd. **S. OFICIAL.**

| | | | | |
|---|---|---|---|---|
| O 1076. | **351.** | 2 p. green .. | 20 | 10 |
| O 1080. | – | 4 p. red (No. 1069) .. | 15 | 10 |
| O 1081. | – | 6 p. red (No. 1079) .. | 25 | 10 |
| O 1078. | – | 90 p. bistre (No. 1288) | 3·25 | 10 |

## RECORDED MESSAGE STAMPS.

RM **166.** Winged Messenger.

**1939.** Various symbolic designs inscribed "CORREOS FONOPOSTAL".

| | | | | |
|---|---|---|---|---|
| RM 688. | **RM 166.** | 1 p. 18 blue | 17·00 | 8·00 |
| RM 689. | – | 1 p. 32 blue | 17·00 | 8·00 |
| RM 690. | – | 1 p. 50 brown | 60·00 | 30·00 |

DESIGNS—VERT. 1 p. 32, Head of Liberty and National Arms. HORIZ. 1 p. 50, Record and winged letter.

# ARMENIA Pt. 10

Formerly part of Transcaucasian Russia. Temporarily independent after the Russian revolution of 1917. From 12 March 1922, Armenia, Azerbaijan and Georgia formed the Transcaucasian Federation. Issues for the federation were superseded by those of the Soviet Union in 1924.

With the dissolution of the Soviet Union in 1991 Armenia once again became independent.

NOTE. Only one price is given for Nos. 3/245 which applies to unused or cancelled to order. Postally used copies are worth more.

All the overprints and surcharges were handstamped and consequently were applied upright or inverted indiscriminately, some occurring only inverted.

1919. 100 kopeks = 1 rouble.
1994. 100 luma = 1 dram.

## NATIONAL REPUBLIC

28 May 1918 to 2 Dec 1920 and 18 Feb to 2 April 1921.

**1919.** Arms type of Russia and unissued Postal Savings Bank stamp (No. 6) surch. thus **k. 60. k** with or without stops. Imperf. or perf.

| | | | |
|---|---|---|---|
| 3. **22.** | 60 k. on 1 k. orange .. .. | 25 |
| 6. – | 60 k. on 1 k. red on buff .. | 6·00 |

Surch. in figures only.

| | | |
|---|---|---|
| 7. **22.** | 60 on 1 k. orange .. | **18·00** |
| 8. | 120 on 1 k. orange .. .. | **18·00** |

(**6.**) (**8.**)

**1919.** Stamps of Russia optd. as T **6** in various sizes, with or without frame. Imperf. or perf.

(a) Arms types.

| | | | |
|---|---|---|---|
| 53B | **22** | 1 k. orange .. .. .. | 9·00 |
| 54B | | 2 k. green .. .. .. | 30 |
| 55B | | 3 k. red .. .. .. | 30 |
| 11B | **23** | 4 k. red .. .. .. | 15 |
| 12B | **22** | 5 k. red .. .. .. | 15 |
| 13B | **23** | 10 k. blue .. .. .. | 25 |
| 14B | **22** | 10 on 7 k. blue .. .. | 20 |
| 15B | **10** | 15 k. blue and purple .. | 20 |
| 16B | **14** | 20 k. red and blue .. .. | 20 |
| 17 | **10** | 25 k. mauve and green .. | 35 |
| 45B | | 35 k. green and purple .. | 35 |
| 19B | **14** | 50 k. green and purple .. | 15 |
| 30B | **22** | 60 k. on 1 k. orange (No. 3) | 30 |
| 31B | **10** | 70 k. orange and brown .. | 20 |
| 32B | **15** | 1 r. orange and brown .. | 40 |
| 33B | **11** | 3 r. 50 green and brown .. | 75 |
| 23B | **20** | 5 r. green and blue .. .. | 85 |
| 62 | **11** | 7 r. yellow and black .. | 15·00 |
| 24B | | 7 r. pink and green .. .. | 1·75 |
| 52B | **20** | 10 r. grey, red and yellow .. | 1·75 |

(b) Romanov type.

| | | |
|---|---|---|
| 63B. | 4 k. red (No. 129) .. .. | 1·00 |

(c) Unissued Postal Savings Bank stamp.

| | | |
|---|---|---|
| 64A. | 1 k. red on buff .. .. | 2·00 |

**1920.** Stamps of Russia surch. as T **8** in various types and sizes. Imperf. or perf.

(a) Arms types.

| | | | |
|---|---|---|---|
| 94B | **22** | 1 r. on 60 k. on 1 k. orange (No. 3) .. .. .. | 60 |
| 65B | | 1 r. on 1 k. orange .. .. | 30 |
| 66B | | 3 r. on 3 k. red .. .. | 30 |
| 67B | | 3 r. on 4 k. red .. .. | 4·00 |
| 97B | | 5 r. on 2 k. green .. .. | 40 |
| 69B | **23** | 5 r. on 4 k. red .. .. | 75 |
| 70B | **22** | 5 r. on 5 k. red .. .. | 25 |
| 71B | | 5 r. on 7 k. blue .. .. | 70 |
| 72B | **23** | 5 r. on 10 k. blue .. .. | 25 |
| 73B | **22** | 5 r. on 10 on 7 k blue .. | 55 |
| 74B | **10** | 5 r. on 14 k. red and blue .. | 1·50 |
| 75B | | 5 r. on 15 k. blue and purple | 45 |
| 76B | **14** | 5 r. on 20 k. red and blue .. | 70 |
| 76aB | **10** | 5 r. on 20 on 14 k. red & bl. | 4·00 |
| 77B | | 5 r. on 25 k. mauve & grn... | 4·00 |
| 111B | **22** | 5 r. on 3 r. on 5 k. red .. | 5·50 |
| 78B | **10** | 10 r. on 25 k. mauve & grn. | 65 |
| 79B | | 10 r. on 35 k. green & pur. | 40 |
| 80B | **14** | 10 r. on 50 k. green & purple | 70 |
| 80aB | **9** | 25 r. on 1 k. orange .. | 22·00 |
| 80bB | | 25 r. on 3 k. red .. .. | 22·00 |
| 80cB | | 25 r. on 5 k. purple.. .. | 22·00 |
| 80dB | **22** | 25 r. on 10 on 7 k. blue .. | 22·00 |
| 80eB | **10** | 25 r. on 15 k. blue & purple | 22·00 |
| 81B | **14** | 25 r. on 20 k. red and blue | 2·75 |
| 82B | **10** | 25 r. on 25 k. mauve & green | 2·10 |
| 83B | | 25 r. on 35 k. green & purple | 1·50 |
| 84B | **14** | 25 r. on 50 k. green & purple | 1·50 |
| 85B | **10** | 25 r. on 70 k. orange & brn. | 2·25 |
| 104aB | **9** | 50 r. on 1 k. orange .. | 22·00 |
| 104bB | | 50 r. on 3 k. red .. .. | 22·00 |
| 85bB | **10** | 50 r. on 4 k. red .. .. | 22·00 |
| 104cB | **14** | 50 r. on 5 k. purple.. .. | 22·00 |
| 85cB | **10** | 50 r. on 15 k. blue & purple | 22·00 |
| 85dB | **14** | 50 r. on 20 k. red and blue | 22·00 |
| 85eB | **10** | 50 r. on 35 k. green & purple | 22·00 |
| 85fB | **14** | 50 r. on 50 k. green & purple | 13·00 |
| 105B | **10** | 50 r. on 70 k. orange & brn. | 3·00 |
| 106B | **15** | 50 r. on 1 r orange & brown | 85 |
| 107B | | 100 r. on 1 r. orange & brn. | 4·00 |
| 108B | **11** | 100 r. on 3 r. 50 grn. & brn. | 3·25 |
| 88B | **20** | 100 r. on 5 r. green and blue | 3·50 |
| 89B | **11** | 100 r. on 7 r. yellow & black | 13·00 |
| 90B | | 100 r. on 7 r. pink and green | 3·75 |
| 93B | **20** | 100 r. on 10 r. grey, red and yellow .. .. .. | 3·50 |

(b) Romanov issue of 1913.

112. 1 r. on 1 k. orange .. .. 4·00
113. 3 r. on 3 k. red .. .. 3·00
114. 5 r. on 4 k. red .. .. 2·25
115. 5 r. on 10 on 7 k. brown .. 2·25
116. 5 r. on 14 k. green .. .. 14·00
117. 5 r. on 20 on 14 k. green .. 3·50
118. 25 r. on 4 k. red .. .. 3·00
118a. 100 r. on 1 k. orange .. .. 35·00
119. 100 r. on 2 k. green .. .. 35·00
120. 100 r. on 3 r. violet .. .. 32·00

(c) War Charity issues of 1914 and 1915.

121. **15.** 25 r. on 1 k. grn. & red on yell. 22·00
122. 25 r. on 3 k. grn. & red on rose 20·00
123. 50 r. on 7 k. grn. & brn. on buff 16·00
124. 50 r. on 10 k. brown and blue 16·00
125. 100 r. on 1 k. grn. & red on yell. 16·00
126. 100 r. on 1 k. grey and brown 16·00
127. 100 r. on 3 k. grn. & red on rose 16·00
128. 100 r. on 7 k. grn. & brn. on buff 16·00
129. 100 r. on 10 k. brown & blue .. 16·00

**1920.** Arms types of Russia optd as T **6** in various sizes with or without frame, and surch as T **8** or with value only in various types and sizes. Imperf or perf.

155A **22** 1 r. on 60 k. on 1 k. orange (No. 3) .. .. .. 75
156A 3 r. on 3 k. red .. .. 1·10
157A 5 r. on 2 k. green .. .. 55
141A **23** 5 r. on 4 k. red .. .. 2·00
158A **22** 5 r. on 5 k. red .. .. 2·25
142A **23** 5 r. on 10 k. blue .. .. 2·00
143A **22** 5 r. on 10 on 7 k. blue .. 2·00
144A **10** 5 r. on 15 k. blue and purple 75
145A **14** 5 r. on 20 k. red and blue .. 75
132B **10** 10 r. on 15 k. blue & purple 5·50
145aB **14** 10 r. on 20 k. red and blue .. 7·00
146A **10** 10 r. on 25 k. mauve & grn. 75
147A 10 r. on 35 k. green and pur. 75
148A **14** 10 r. on 50 k. green & purple 1·25
159A **10** 10 r. on 70 k. orange & brn. 6·00
163A **22** 10 r. on 5 r. on 5 k. red .. 12·00
164A **10** 10 r. on 5 r. on 25 k. mauve and green .. .. .. 13·00
165A 10 r. on 5 r. on 35 k. green and purple .. .. 4·00
160 25 r. on 70 k. orge. & brown 3·00
161B **15** 50 r. on 1 r. orange & brown 1·00
135B **11** 100 r. on 3 r. 50 green & brown 1·25
151 **20** 100 r. on 5 r. green and blue 4·00
136A **11** 100 r. on 7 r. pink and green 4·00
154aA **20** 100 r. on 10 r. grey, red & yell. 6·00
166 100 r. on 25 r. on 5 r. green and blue .. .. .. 13·00

**1920.** Stamps of Russia optd. as T **6** in various sizes, with or without frame and surch. **10.** Perf.

(a) Arms types.

168. **14.** 10 on 20 k. red and blue .. 11·00
169. **10.** 10 on 25 k. mauve and green 11·00
170. 10 on 35 k. green and purple 8·00
171. **14.** 10 on 50 k. green and purple 9·00

(b) Romanov type.

172. 10 on 4 k. red (No. 129) .. 17·00

**1920.** Stamps of Russia optd. with monogram as in T **8** in various types and sizes and surch. **10.** Imperf. or perf.

(a) Arms types.

173. **23.** 10 on 4 k. red .. .. .. 18·00
174. **22.** 10 on 5 k. red .. .. 18·00
175. **10.** 10 on 15 k. blue and purple .. 18·00
176. **14.** 10 on 20 k. red and blue .. 12·00
176a. **10.** 10 on 20 on 14 k. red and blue 8·50
177. 10 on 25 k. mauve and green 8·00
178. 10 on 35 k. green and purple .. 8·00
179. **14.** 10 on 50 k. green and purple .. 8·00

(b) Romanov type.

181. 10 on 4 k. red (No. 129) .. 20·00

**11.**

**12.** Mt. Ararat.

Stamps in Types **11**, **12** and a similar horizontal type showing a woman spinning were printed in Paris to the order of the Armenian National Government, but were not issued in Armenia as the Bolshevists had assumed control. (Price 10 p. each).

## SOVIET REPUBLIC

2 Dec. 1920 to 18 Feb. 1921 and 2 April 1921 to 12 Mar. 1922.

**(13.)**

**1921.** Arms types of Russia surch. with T **13** Perf.

182. **15.** 5000 r. on 1 r. orange & brown 3·00
183. **11.** 5000 r. on 3 r. 50 grn. & brn. 3·00
184. **20.** 5000 r. on 5 r. green and blue 3·00
185. **11.** 5000 r. on 7 r. pink and green 3·00
186. **20.** 5000 r. on 10 r. grey, red & yell. 3·00

**14.** Common Crane.

**16.** Village Scene.

**1922.** Unissued stamps surch. in gold kopek Imperf.

187. **14.** 1 on 250 r. red .. .. 8·00
188. 1 on 250 r. slate .. .. 8·00
189. **16.** 2 on 500 r. red .. .. 3·25
190. 3 on 500 r. slate .. .. 1·25
191. – 4 on 1000 r. red .. .. 2·00
192. – 4 on 1000 r. slate .. .. 3·75
193. – 5 on 2000 r. slate .. .. 12·00
194. – 10 on 2000 r. red .. .. 12·00
195. – 15 on 5000 r. red .. .. 9·00
196. – 20 on 5000 r. slate .. .. 1·75

DESIGNS (sizes in mm.): 1000 r. Woman at well (17×26). 2000 r. Erivan railway station (35×24½). 5000 r. Horseman and Mt. Ararat (39½×24½).

**17.** Soviet Emblems.

**18.** Wall sculpture at Ani.

**19.** Mt. Aragatz.

**1922.** Unissued stamps as T **17/19** surch in gold kopeks in figures. Imperf or perf.

210 **17** 1 on 1 r. green .. .. 2·00
198 **18** 2 on 2 r. slate .. .. 4·50
212 – 3 on 3 r. red .. .. 8·00
213 – 4 on 25 r. green .. .. 1·75
201 – 5 on 50 r. red .. .. 2·25
215 – 10 on 100 r. orange .. .. 2·50
203 – 15 on 250 r. blue .. .. 1·50
204a **19** 20 on 500 r. purple .. .. 1·60
205 – 35 on 20,000 r. red .. .. 12·00
206a – 50 on 25,000 r. green .. 18·00
209 – 50 on 25,000 r. blue .. .. 2·50

DESIGNS (sizes in mm): 3 r. (29×22) and 250 r. (21×35) Soviet emblems. 25 r. (30×22½). 100 r. (34½×23) and 20,000 r. (43×27) Mythological sculptures, Ani. 50 r. (25½×37). Armenian soldier. 25,000 r. (45½×27½) Mt. Ararat.

The above and other values were not officially issued without the surcharges.

## TRANSCAUCASIAN FEDERATION ISSUES FOR ARMENIA

**1923.** As T **19**, etc., surch. in gold kopeks in figures. Imperf. or perf.

219 – 1 on 250 r. blue .. .. 2·40
217 **19** 2 on 500 r. purple .. .. 2·25
218 – 3 on 20,000 r. lake .. .. 6·50

**26.** Mt. Ararat and Soviet Emblems.

**28.** Ploughing.

**1923.** Unissued stamps in various designs as T **26/28** surch. in Transcaucasian roubles in figures. Perf.

227 **26** 10,000 r. on 50 r. green & red 80
228 – 15,000 r. on 300 r. blue & buff 80
229 – 25,000 r. on 400 r. blue & pink 80
240B – 30,000 r. on 500 r. violet & lilac 85
231 – 50,000 r. on 1000 r. blue .. 80
232 – 75,000 on 3000 r. blk. & grn... 1·00
233 – 100,000 r. on 2000 r. blk. & grey 1·40
243 – 200,000 r. on 4000 r. blk. & brn. 60
235 – 300,000 r. on 5000 r. blk. & red 2·00
245 **28** 500,000 r. on 10,000 r. blk. & red 75

DESIGNS (sizes in mm): 300 r. (26×35) Star over Mt. Ararat. 400 r. (26×34½) Soviet Emblems. 500 r. (26×34½) Crane (bird). 1000 r. (19×25) Peasant. 2000 r. (26×31) Human-headed bird from old bas-relief. 3000 r. (26½×36) Sower. 4000 r. (26×31½) Star and dragon. 5000 r. (26×32) Blacksmith.

## INDEPENDENT REPUBLIC

**31** Mount Ararat and National Colours

**1992.** 1st Anniv of Independence.

246 **31** 20 k. multicoloured .. 15 15
247 2 r. multicoloured .. 1·75 1·75
248 5 r. multicoloured .. 4·25 4·25

**32** Dish Aerial and World Map

**1992.** Inauguration of International Direct-dial Telephone System.

250 **32** 50 k. multicoloured .. 5·00 5·00

**33** Ancient Greek Wrestling

**34** National Flag

**1992.** Olympic Games, Barcelona. Mult.

251 40 k. Type **33** .. .. 10 10
252 3 r. 60 Boxing .. .. 95 95
253 5 r. Weightlifting .. 1·25 1·25
254 12 r. Gymnastic ring exercises .. .. 3·25 3·25

**1992.**

255 **34** 20 k. mult (postage) .. 10 10
256 – 1 r. black .. .. 25 25
257 – 3 r. brown .. .. 1·10 1·10
258 – 3 r. brown .. .. 20 20
259 – 5 r. black .. .. 2·00 2·00
260 – 20 r. grey .. .. 1·40 1·40
261 – 2 r. blue (air) .. .. 80 80

DESIGNS: 1 r. Goddess Waroubini statuette from 7th-century B.C. and Orgov radio-optical telescope; 2 r. Zvartnots Airport, Yerevan; 3 r. (No. 257) Goddess Anahit; 3 r. (No. 258) Runic tablet from 7th-century B.C.; 5 r. U.P.U. Monument, Berne; 20 r. Silver cup from third millenium B.C.

See also Nos. 275/82.

**36** Engraved 10th-century Tombstone, Makenis

**37** Garni Canyon

**1993.** Armenian Cultural History. Mult.

263 40 k. Type **36** .. .. 10 10
264 80 k. Illuminated page from Gospel of 1295 .. 20 20
265 3 r. 60 13th-century bas-relief, Gandzasar .. 80 80
266 5 r. "Glorious Mother of God" (18th-century painting, H. Hovnatanian) .. .. 1·40 1·40

**1993.** Landscapes. Multicoloured.

268 40 k. Type **37** .. .. 10 10
269 80 k. Shaki Falls, Zangezur 15 15
270 3 r. 60 River Arpa gorge, Vike .. .. .. 65 65
271 5 r. Lake Sevan (horiz) .. 90 90
272 12 r. Mount Ararat (horiz) 2·25 2·25

**38** Temple of Garni

**39** Reliquary for Arm of St. Thaddeus (17th century)

**1993.** "YEREVAN '93" International Stamp Exhibition.

273 **38** 10 r. red, black & brown 1·00 1·00

**1994.** As T **34** but new currency.

275 10 l. agate and brown .. 10 10
277 50 l. deep brown & brown 10 10
280 10 d. brown and grey .. 55 55
282 25 d. gold and red .. 1·25 1·25

DESIGNS: 10 l. Shivini, Sun God (Karmir-Blour); 50 l. Tayshaba, God of the Elements (Karmir-Blour); 10 d. Khaldi, Supreme God (Karmir-Blour); 25 d. National arms.

**1994.** Treasures of Etchmiadzin (seat of Armenian church). Multicoloured.

286 3 d. Descent from the Cross (9th-century wooden panel) .. .. 10 10
287 5 d. Gilded silver reliquary of Holy Cross of Khotakerats (1300) .. 10 10
288 12 d. Cross with St. Karapet's right hand (14th century) .. .. 65 65
289 30 d. Type **39** .. .. 1·40 1·40
290 50 d. Gilded silver chrism vessel (1815) .. .. 1·90 1·90

40 **(40)**

40 **(41)**

**1994.** Stamp Exns, Yerevan. (a) "Armenia '94" National Exn. No. 273 surch with T **40**.

291 **38** 40 d. on 10 r. red, black and brown .. .. 1·50 1·50

(b) "Armenia–Argentina" Exhibition. No. 273 surch with T **41**.

292 **38** 40 d. on 10 r. red, black and brown .. .. 1·50 1·50

**42** Cancelled Stamps of 1919

**43** Stadium and Arms of National Committee

**1994.** 75th Anniv of First Stamp Issue.

293 **42** 16 d. multicoloured .. 70 70

**1994.** Olympic Committees. Multicoloured.

294 30 d. Type **43** .. .. 55 55
295 40 d. Olympic rings (cent of Int Olympic Committee) .. .. 70 70

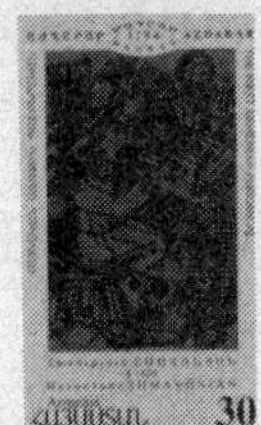
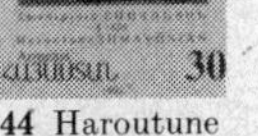

44 Haroutune Shmavonian    45 Ervand Otian

**1994.** Bicentenary of "Azdarar" (first Armenian periodical).
296 **44** 30 d. brown and green .. 70 70

**1994.** 125th Birth Anniversaries.
297 **45** 50 d. drab and brown .. 65 65
298 – 50 d. brown .. .. 65 65
DESIGN—HORIZ: 50 d. Levon Shant.

46 "Cross" (from Gospel)    47 Vazgen I

**1995.** 1700th Anniv (2001) of Christianity in Armenia. Works of art. Multicoloured.
299 60 d. Type **46** .. .. 90 90
300 70 d. "St. Bartholomew and St. Thaddeus the Apostles" (Hovnatan Hovnatanian) (45 × 39 mm) .. .. .. 1·00 1·00
301 70 d. "Kings Abhar and Trdat" (Mkrtoum Hovnatanian) (45 × 39 mm) .. .. .. 1·00 1·00
302 80 d. "St. Gregory the Illuminator" .. .. 1·25 1·25
303 90 d. "The Baptism of Armenian People" (H. Aivazovsky) .. .. 1·50 1·50

**1995.** 1st Death Anniv of Vazgen I (Patriarch of Armenian Orthodox Church).
305 **47** 150 d. black and grey .. 90 90

48 Black-polished Pottery    49 Red Kite and Oak

**1995.** Museum Artefacts (1st series). Mult.
306 30 d. Type **48** .. .. 45 45
307 60 d. Silver horn .. .. 90 90
308 130 d. Gohar carpet .. 1·75 1·75
See also Nos. 332/4.

**1995.** Birds and Trees. Multicoloured.
309 40 d. Type **49** .. .. 60 60
310 60 d. Golden eagle and juniper .. .. .. 80 80

50 Workers building "Honeycomb" Map

**1995.** Hyastan All-Armenian Fund.
311 **50** 90 d. multicoloured .. 1·40 1·40

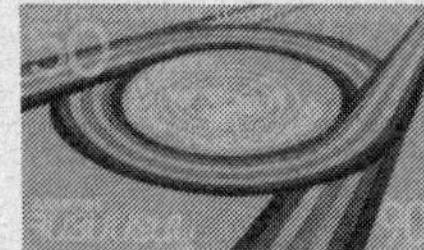

51 Rainbows around U.N. Emblem

**1995.** 50th Anniv of U.N.O.
312 **51** 90 d. multicoloured .. 1·40 1·40

52 Commander P. Kitsook (408th Rifle Division)

**1995.** 50th Anniv of End of Second World War. (a) Size 40 × 23 mm. Each black, orange and blue.
313 60 d. Type **52** .. .. 80 80
314 60 d. Commanders S. Chernikov, N. Tavartkeladze and V. Penkovsky (76th Alpine Rifle Red-banner (51st Guard) Division) .. 80 80
315 60 d. Commmanders S. Zakian, H. Babayan and I. Lyudnikov (390th Rifle Division) .. .. 80 80
316 60 d. Commanders A. Vasilian, M. Dobrovolsky, Y. Grechany and G. Sorokin (409th Rifle Division) .. .. 80 80
317 60 d. Commanders A. Sargissian and N. Safarian (89th Taman Triple Order Bearer Rifle Division) .. .. 80 80

(b) Size 23 × 35 mm. Each blue, orange and brown.
318 60 d. Marshal Hovhannes Baghramian .. .. 80 80
319 60 d. Admiral Hovhannes Issakov .. .. 80 80
320 60 d. General Marshal Hamazasp Babajanian 80 80
321 60 d. Marshal Sergey Khoudyakov .. .. 80 80

53 Ghevond Alishan (historian and geographer)

**1995.** Writers' Anniversaries.
323 **53** 90 d. multicoloured .. 70 70
324 – 90 d. multicoloured .. 70 70
325 – 90 d. blue and red .. 70 70
DESIGNS: No. 323, Type **53** (175th birth); 324, Grigor Artsruni (journalist, 150th birth); 325, Franz Werfel (50th death).

54 Sports and Concert Complex    55 Katsian and Spectators watching Flight

**1995.** Yerevan.
326 – 60 d. black and orange 15 15
327 – 80 d. black and pink .. 30 30
328 **54** 90 d. black and buff .. 45 45
329 – 100 d. black and buff .. 65 65
330 – 120 d. black and pink .. 95 95
DESIGNS—As T **54**: 60 d. Brandy distillery and wine cellars; 80 d. Abovian Street; 400 d. Panoramic view of Yerevan. 60 × 23 mm—100 d. Baghramian Avenue; 120 d. Republic Square.

**1995.** Museum Artefacts (2nd series). As T **48**. Multicoloured.
332 40 d. Four-wheeled carriages (horiz) .. 90 90
333 60 d. Bronze model of solar system .. .. 1·25 1·25
334 90 d. Tombstone .. .. 1·90 1·90

**1995.** Air. 86th Anniv of Artiom Katsian's 1909 World Record for Range and Altitude.
335 **55** 90 d. ochre, brown & bl 70 70

Հայփոստ 40

(56)

57 Griboedov

**1996.** No. 275 surch as T **56**.
336 40 d. on 10 l. agate & brn 15 15
337 100 d. on 10 l. agate & brn 50 50
338 150 d. on 10 l. agate & brn 75 75
339 200 d. on 10 l. agate & brn 1·00 1·00

**1996.** Birth Bicentenary of Aleksandr Griboedov (historian).
340 **57** 90 d. stone, brown & red 45 45

58 Hayrik Khrimian (patriarch of Armenian Orthodox Church, 175th birth anniv (1995))

**1996.** Anniversaries.
341 **58** 90 d. blue and brown (postage) .. .. 65 65
342 – 90 d. multicoloured .. 65 65
343 – 90 d. bl, grey & red (air) 65 65
DESIGNS—HORIZ: No. 342, Lazar Serebryakov (Admiral of the Fleet, birth bicentenary (1995)). VERT: No. 343, Nelson Stepanian (Second World War pilot, 50th death anniv (1994)).

59 Opening Frame from First Armenian Film

**1996.** Centenary of Motion Pictures.
344 **59** 60 d. black, grey & blue 50 50

60 Angel and Red Cross    61 Wild Goats

**1996.** 75th Anniv of Armenian Red Cross Society.
345 **60** 60 d. multicoloured .. 50 50

**1996.** Mammals. Multicoloured.
346 40 d. Type **61** .. .. 30 30
347 60 d. Leopards .. .. 35 35

62 Nansen and "Fram"

**1996.** Centenary of Return of Fridtjof Nansen's Arctic Expedition.
348 **62** 90 d. multicoloured .. 50 50

63 Cycling    64 Torch Bearer

**1996.** Olympic Games, Atlanta. Mult.
349 40 d. Type **63** .. .. 30 30
350 60 d. Triple jumping .. 35 35
351 90 d. Wrestling .. .. 55 55
Nos. 349/51 were issued together, se-tenant, the backgrounds forming a composite design showing ancient Greek athletes.

**1996.** Centenary of Modern Olympic Games.
352 **64** 60 d. multicoloured .. 45 45

65 G. Kasparian (first prize winner, "Chess in USSR" competition, 1939)    66 Tigran Petrosian (World chess champion, 1963–69) and Tigran Petrosian Chess House, Yerevan

**1996.** 32nd Chess Olympiad, Yerevan. Designs showing positions from previous games. Multicoloured.
353 40 d. Type **65** .. .. 50 50
354 40 d. Tigran Petrosian v. Mikhail Botvinnik (World Championship, Moscow, 1963) .. .. 50 50
355 40 d. Gary Kasparov v. Anatoly Karpov (World Championship, Leningrad, 1986) .. 50 50
356 40 d. Olympiad emblem .. 50 50

**1996.**
357 **66** 90 d. multicoloured .. 70 70

## ARUBA Pt. 4

An island in the Caribbean, formerly part of Netherlands Antilles. In 1986 became an autonomous country within the Kingdom of the Netherlands.

100 cents = 1 gulden.

**1.** Map.

**1986.** New Constitution.

1 **1** 25 c. yellow, blue & black .. 25 20
2 – 45 c. multicoloured .. 50 40
3 – 55 c. black, grey and red .. 70 70
4 – 100 c. multicoloured .. 1·10 1·10

DESIGNS:—VERT. 45 c. Aruban arms. 55 c. National anthem. HORIZ. 100 c. Aruban flag.

**2.** House.

**1986.**

5. **2.** 5 c. black and yellow .. 10 10
6. – 15 c. black and blue .. 15 10
7. – 20 c. black and grey .. 15 15
8. – 25 c. black and violet .. 25 15
9. – 30 c. black and red .. 90 35
10. – 35 c. black and bistre .. 40 30
12. – 45 c. black and blue .. 55 35
14. – 55 c. black and grey .. 50 45
15. – 60 c. black and blue .. 65 50
16. – 65 c. black and blue .. 70 55
18. – 75 c. black and brown .. 70 65
20. – 85 c. black and orange .. 75 70
21. – 90 c. black and green .. 80 75
22. – 100 c. black and brown 90 85
23. – 150 c. black and green .. 1·50 1·10
24. – 250 c. black and green .. 2·50 2·10

DESIGNS: 15 c. Clock tower; 20 c. Container crane; 25 c. Lighthouse; 30 c. Snake; 35 c. Burrowing owl; 45 c. Caribbean vase (shell); 55 c. Frog; 60 c. Water-skier; 65 c. Fisherman casting net; 75 c. Hurdy-gurdy; 85 c. Pot; 90, 250 c. Different cacti; 100 c. Maize; 150 c. Watapana Tree.

**3.** People and Two Ropes.

**1986.** "Solidarity". Multicoloured.

25. 30 c.+10 c. Type **3** .. .. 45 45
26. 35 c.+15 c. People and three ropes .. .. 55 55
27. 60 c.+25 c. People and one rope .. .. .. 90 90

**4.** Dove between Scenes of Peace and War.

**1986.** International Peace Year. Mult.

28. 60 c. Type **4** .. .. .. 60 60
29. 100 c. Doves flying over broken barbed wire .. 1·00 1·00

**5.** Boy and Caterpillar.

**6.** Engagement Picture.

**1986.** Child Welfare. Multicoloured.

30. 45 c.+20 c. Type **5** .. .. 65 65
31. 70 c.+25 c. Boy and shell .. 1·00 1·00
32. 100 c.+40 c. Girl and butterfly .. .. 1·40 1·40

**1987.** Golden Wedding of Princess Juliana and Prince Bernhard.

33 **6** 135 c. orange, black & gold 1·10 1·10

**7.** Queen Beatrix and Prince Claus.

**1987.** Royal Visit. Multicoloured.

34. 55 c. Type **7** .. .. .. 45 45
35. 60 c. Prince Willem-Alexander .. .. 50 50

**8.** Woman looking at Beach.

**1987.** Tourism. Multicoloured.

36. 60 c. Type **8** .. .. .. 50 40
37. 100 c. Woman looking at desert landscape .. .. 90 85

**9.** Child with Book on Beach.

**10.** Plantation.

**1987.** Child Welfare. Multicoloured

38. 25 c.+10 c. Type **9** .. .. 35 35
39. 45 c.+20 c. Children drawing christmas tree .. 60 60
40. 70 c.+30 c. Child gazing at Nativity crib .. .. 1·00 1·00

**1988.** "Aloe vera". Multicoloured.

41. 45 c. Type **10** .. .. 35 35
42. 60 c. Stem and leaves of plant .. .. .. 45 45
43. 100 c. Harvesting aloes .. 75 75

**11.** 25 c. Coin.

**12.** Bananaquits, Country Scene and "Love".

**1988.** Coins. Multicoloured.

44. 25 c. Type **11** .. .. 20 15
45. 55 c. Square 50 c. coin .. 45 45
46. 65 c. 5 c. and 10 c. coins .. 60 60
47. 150 c. 1 gulden coin .. 1·25 1·25

**1988.** Greetings Stamps. Multicoloured.

48 70 c. Type **12** .. .. 65 50
49 135 c. West Indian crown conch, West Indian chank (shells), seaside scene and "Love" .. 1·00 1·00

**13.** White Triangle on Shaded Background.

**14.** Torch.

**1988.** "Solidarity". 11th Young Men's Christian Association World Council. Mult.

50. 45 c.+20 c. Type **13** .. 60 60
51. 60 c.+25 c. Interlocking triangles .. .. 85 85
52. 100 c.+50 c. Shaded triangle on white background .. .. 1·25 1·25

**1988.** Olympic Games, Seoul. Multicoloured.

53. 35 c. Type **14** .. .. 30 30
54. 100 c. Games and Olympic emblems .. .. .. 80 80

**15** Jacks

**16** Children

**1988.** Child Welfare. Toys. Multicoloured.

55 45 c.+20 c. Type **15** .. 60 60
56 70 c.+30 c. Spinning top .. 85 85
57 100 c.+50 c. Kite .. .. 1·25 1·25

**1989.** Carnival. Multicoloured.

58 45 c. Type **16** .. .. 35 35
59 60 c. Girl in costume .. 50 50
60 100 c. Lights .. .. 85 85

**17** Maripampun

**18** Emblem

**1989.** Maripampun. Multicoloured.

61 35 c. Type **17** .. .. 40 40
62 55 c. Seed pods .. .. 60 60
63 200 c. Pod distributing seeds 1·75 1·75

**1989.** Universal Postal Union.

64 **18** 250 c. multicoloured .. 2·00 2·00

**19** Snake

**1989.** South American Rattlesnake.

65 **19** 45 c. multicoloured .. 40 35
66 – 55 c. multicoloured .. 55 45
67 – 60 c. multicoloured .. 65 50

DESIGNS: 55 c., 60 c. Snake (different).

**20** Spoon in Child's Hand

**21** Violin, Tambour and Cuatro Players

**1989.** Child Welfare. Multicoloured.

68 45 c.+20 c. Type **20** .. 50 50
69 60 c.+30 c. Child playing football .. .. .. 70 70
70 100 c.+50 c. Child's hand in adult's hand (vert) .. 1·25 1·25

**1989.** New Year. Dande Musicians. Mult.

71 25 c. Type **21** .. .. 20 15
72 70 c. Guitar and cuatro players and singer with hat .. .. .. 50 50
73 150 c. Cuatro, accordion and wiri players .. .. 1·10 1·10

**22** Tractor and Natural Vegetation

**1990.** Environmental Protection. Mult.

74 45 c. Type **22** .. .. 50 45
75 55 c. Face and wildlife (vert) 90 55
76 100 c. Marine life .. .. 1·25 1·10

**23** Giant Caribbean Anemone and Pederson's Cleaning Shrimp

**24** Ball

**1990.** Marine Life. Multicoloured.

77 60 c. Type **23** .. .. 70 60
78 70 c. Queen angelfish and red coral .. .. .. 80 70
79 100 c. Banded coral shrimp, fire sponge and yellow boring sponge .. 1·25 1·10

**1990.** World Cup Football Championship, Italy. Multicoloured.

80 35 c. Type **24** .. .. 40 35
81 200 c. Mascot .. .. 2·00 2·00

**25** Emblem of Committee of Tanki Leendert Association Youth Centre

**26** Clay Painting Stamps

**1990.** "Solidarity". Multicoloured.

82 55 c.+25 c. Type **25** 85 85
83 100 c.+50 c. Emblem of Foundation for Promotion of Responsible Parenthood .. .. 1·60 1·60

**1990.** Archaeology. Multicoloured.

84 45 c. Type **26** .. .. 50 45
85 60 c. Stone figure .. .. 70 60
86 100 c. Dabajuroid-style jar 1·25 1·10

**27** Sailboards and Fishes

**28** Mountain and Shoreline

**1990.** Child Welfare. Multicoloured.

87 45 c.+20 c. Type **27** .. 70 70
88 60 c.+30 c. Parakeets and coconut trees .. .. 95 95
89 100 c.+50 c. Kites and lizard 1·50 1·50

**1991.** Landscapes. Multicoloured.

90 55 c. Type **28** .. .. 60 55
91 65 c. Cacti and Haystack mountain .. .. 75 65
92 100 c. House, mountain and ocean, Jaburibari .. 1·25 1·10

**29** Woman holding Herbs ("Carer")

**30** "Ocimum sanctum"

**1991.** Women and Work. Multicoloured.

93 35 c. Type **29** .. .. 35 35
94 70 c. Women and kitchen ("Housewife") .. 70 70
95 100 c. Women and telephone ("Woman in the World") 1·00 1·00

**1991.** Medicinal Plants. Multicoloured.

96 65 c. Type **30** .. .. 75 70
97 75 c. "Jatropha gossypifolia" .. .. .. 85 75
98 95 c. "Croton flavens" .. 1·10 1·10

31 Fishing Net, Float and Needle

32 Child's Hand taking Book from Shelf

**1991.** Traditional Crafts.

99 **31** 35 c. black, ultram & bl 35 35
100 – 250 c. black, lilac & pur 2·50 2·50
DESIGNS: 250 c. Hat, straw and hat-block.

**1991.** Child Welfare. Multicoloured.

101 45 c.+25 c. Type **32** .. 70 70
102 60 c.+35 c. Child's finger pointing to letter "B" .. 1·10 1·10
103 100 c.+50 c. Child reading 1·60 1·60

33 Toucan saying "Welcome"

34 Government Decree of 1892 establishing first Aruban Post Office

**1991.** Tourism. Multicoloured.

104 35 c. Type **33** .. .. 55 35
105 70 c. Aruban youth welcoming tourist .. 70 70
106 100 c. Windmill and Bubali swamp .. .. .. 1·00 1·00

**1992.** Cent of Postal Service (1st issue). Mult.

107 60 c. Type **34** .. .. 50 50
108 75 c. Lieutenant-Governor's building (mail service office, 1892–1908) (horiz) .. 60 60
109 80 c. Present Oranjestad post office (horiz) .. 70 70
See also Nos. 117/19.

35 Equality of Sexes

**1992.** Equality. Multicoloured.

110 100 c. Type **35** .. .. 85 85
111 100 c. People of different races (equality of nations) 85 85

36 Aruban Flag, Guide Emblem and Girl Guides

37 Columbus, Map and Clouds

**1992.** "Solidarity". Multicoloured.

112 55 c.+30 c. Type **36** .. 75 75
113 100 c.+50 c. Open hand with Cancer Fund emblem .. .. 1·25 1·25

**1992.** 500th Anniv of Discovery of America by Columbus. Multicoloured.

114 30 c. Type **37** .. .. 25 25
115 40 c. Caravel (from navigation chart, 1525) 30 30
116 50 c. Indians, queen conch shell and 1540 map .. 50 40

38 "I Love Post" (Jelissa Boekhoudt)

**1992.** Child Welfare. Cent of Postal Service (2nd issue). Children's Drawings. Mult.

117 50 c.+30 c. Type **38** .. 60 60
118 70 c.+35 c. Airplane dropping letters (Marianne Fingal) .. 80 80
119 100 c.+50 c. Pigeon carrying letter in beak (Minorenti Jacobs) (vert) 1·10 1·10

39 Seroe Colorado Bridge

41 Rocks at Ayo

**1992.** Natural Bridges. Multicoloured.

120 70 c. Type **39** .. .. 55 55
121 80 c. Natural Bridge .. 60 60

**1993.** Rock Formations. Multicoloured.

123 50 c. Type **41** .. .. 40 40
124 60 c. Casibari .. .. 45 45
125 100 c. Ayo (different) .. 75 75

42 Traditional Instruments

43 Sailing

**1993.** Cock's Burial (part of St. John's Feast celebrations). Multicoloured.

126 40 c. Type **42** .. .. 30 30
127 70 c. "Cock's Burial" (painting, Leo Kuiperi) 50 50
128 80 c. Verses of song, yellow flag, and calabashes .. 60 60

**1993.** Sports. Multicoloured.

129 50 c. Type **43** .. .. 40 40
130 65 c. Land sailing .. 50 50
131 75 c. Windsurfing .. 55 55

44 Young Iguana

**1993.** The Iguana. Multicoloured.

132 35 c. Type **44** .. .. 25 25
133 60 c. Young adult .. 45 45
134 100 c. Adult (vert) .. 75 75

45 Aruban House, Landscape and Cacti

**1993.** Child Welfare. Multicoloured.

135 50 c.+30 c. Type **45** .. 60 60
136 75 c.+40 c. Face, bridge and sea (vert) .. .. 85 85
137 100 c.+50 c. Bridge, buildings and landscape 1·10 1·10

46 Owls

47 Athlete

**1994.** The Burrowing Owl Multicoloured.

138 5 c. Type **46** .. 10 10
139 10 c. Pair with young .. 10 10
140 35 c. Owl with locust in claw (vert) .. .. 25 25
141 40 c. Owl (vert) .. .. 30 30

**1994.** Centenary of International Olympic Committee. Multicoloured.

142 50 c. Type **47** .. .. 35 35
143 90 c. Baron Pierre de Coubertin (founder) .. 60 60

48 Family in House

49 Flags of U.S.A. and Aruba, Ball and Players

**1994.** "Solidarity". International Year of The Family. Multicoloured.

144 50 c.+35 c. Type **48** .. 60 60
145 100 c.+50 c. Family outside house .. .. 1·00 1·00

**1994.** World Cup Football Championship, U.S.A. Multicoloured.

146 65 c. Type **49** .. .. 45 45
147 150 c. Mascot .. .. 1·00 1·00

50 West Indian Cherry

51 Children with Umbrella sitting on Anchor (shelter and security)

**1994.** Wild Fruits. Multicoloured.

148 40 c. Type **50** .. .. 30 30
149 70 c. Geiger tree .. .. 50 50
150 85 c. "Pithecellobium unguis-cati" .. .. 60 60
151 150 c. Sea grape .. .. 1·00 1·00

**1994.** Child Welfare. Influence of the Family. Multicoloured.

152 50 c.+30 c. Type **51** .. 55 55
153 80 c.+35 c. Children in smiling sun (warmth of nurturing home) .. 80 80
154 100 c.+50 c. Child flying on owl (wisdom guiding the child) .. .. 1·00 1·00

52 Government Building, 1888

53 Dove, Emblem and Flags

**1995.** Historic Buildings. Multicoloured.

155 35 c. Type **52** .. .. 25 25
156 60 c. Ecury Residence, 1929 (vert) .. .. .. 40 40
157 100 c. Protestant Church, 1846 (vert) .. .. 70 70

**1995.** 50th Anniv of U.N.O. Multicoloured.

158 30 c. Type **53** .. .. 20 20
159 200 c. Emblem, flags, globe and doves .. .. 1·40 1·40

54 Casanova II and Rosettes

55 Cowpea

**1995.** Interpaso Horses. Multicoloured.

160 25 c. Type **54** .. .. 20 20
161 75 c. Horse performing Paso Fino .. .. 55 55
162 80 c. Horse performing Figure 8 (vert) .. .. 60 60
163 90 c. Girl on horseback (vert) .. .. .. 65 65

**1995.** Vegetables. Multicoloured.

164 25 c. Type **55** .. .. 20 20
165 50 c. Apple cucumber .. 35 35
166 70 c. Okra .. .. 50 50
167 85 c. Pumpkin .. .. 60 60

56 Hawksbill Turtle

57 Children holding Balloons outside House (Christina Trejo)

**1995.** Turtles. Multicoloured.

168 15 c. Type **56** .. .. 10 10
169 50 c. Green turtle .. 35 35
170 95 c. Loggerhead turtle .. 70 70
171 100 c. Leatherback turtle 70 70

**1995.** Child Welfare. Children's Drawings. Multicoloured.

172 50 c.+25 c. Type **57** .. 55 55
173 70 c.+35 c. Children at seaside (Julysses Tromp) 75 75
174 100 c.+50 c. Children and adults gardening (Ronald Tromp) .. 1·10 1·10

58 Henry Eman

59 Woman

**1996.** 10th Anniv of Internal Autonomy. Politicians. Multicoloured.

175 100 c. Type **58** .. .. 70 70
176 100 c. Juancho Irausquin 70 70
177 100 c. Shon Eman .. 70 70
178 100 c. Betico Croes .. 70 70

**1996.** America. Traditional Costumes. Mult.

179 65 c. Type **59** .. .. 45 45
180 70 c. Man .. .. .. 50 50
181 100 c. Couple dancing (horiz) .. .. .. 70 70

60 Running

61 Mathematical Instruments, "G" and Rising Sun

**1996.** Olympic Games, Atlanta. Mult.

182 85 c. Type **60** .. .. 60 60
183 130 c. Cycling .. .. 90 90

**1996.** "Solidarity". 75th Anniv of Freemasons' Lodge El Sol Naciente. Mult.

184 60 c.+30 c. Type **61** .. 65 65
185 100 c.+50 c. Globes on top of columns and doorway 1·00 1·00

EXPRESS MAIL SERVICE

E 40 Globe, Planets and Aruban Arms

**1993.**

E122 E **40** 200 c. multicoloured 1·50 1·50

# AUSTRIA Pt. 2

A state of Central Europe, part of the Austro-Hungarian Monarchy and Empire until 1918. At the end of the First World War the Empire was dismembered and German-speaking Austria became a Republic.

Austria was absorbed into the German Reich in 1938 and remained part of Germany until 1945. Following occupation by the four Allied Powers the Austrian Republic was re-established on 14 May 1945.

| | |
|---|---|
| 1850. | 60 kreuzer = 1 gulden. |
| 1858. | 100 kreuzer = 1 gulden. |
| 1899. | 100 heller = 1 krone. |
| 1925. | 100 groschen = 1 schilling. |
| 1938. | 100 pfennig = 1 German reichsmark. |
| 1945. | 100 groschen = 1 schilling. |

**1.** Arms of Austria. **4.** **5.**

### 1850. Imperf.

| | | | | |
|---|---|---|---|---|
| 6a. | 1. | 1 k. yellow | £1000 | 75·00 |
| 7. | | 2 k. black | £850 | 55·00 |
| 8a. | | 3 k. red | £325 | 2·00 |
| 9. | | 6 k. brown | £500 | 3·25 |
| 10. | | 9 k. blue | £700 | 1·75 |

**For stamps in Type 1 with values in "CENTES", see Lombardy and Venetia.**

### 1858.

| | | | | |
|---|---|---|---|---|
| 22. | 5. | 2 k. yellow | £650 | 32·00 |
| 23. | 4. | 3 k. black | £1000 | £225 |
| 24. | | 3 k. green | £800 | £140 |
| 25. | 5. | 5 k. red | £200 | 1·00 |
| 26. | | 10 k. brown | £500 | 2·50 |
| 27. | | 15 k. blue | £425 | 1·50 |

**For stamps in Types 4 and 5 with values in "SOLDI", see Lombardy and Venetia.**

The portraits on Austrian stamps to 1906 are of the Emperor Francis Joseph I.

**10.** **12.** Arms of Austria.

### 1860.

| | | | | |
|---|---|---|---|---|
| 33. | 10. | 2 k. yellow | £325 | 25·00 |
| 34. | | 3 k. green | £275 | 20·00 |
| 35. | | 5 k. red | £150 | 45 |
| 36. | | 10 k. brown | £225 | 1·40 |
| 37. | | 15 k. blue | £225 | 75 |

### 1863.

| | | | | |
|---|---|---|---|---|
| 45. | 12. | 2 k. yellow | £110 | 9·00 |
| 46. | | 3 k. green | £100 | 8·00 |
| 47. | | 5 k. red | 35·00 | 20 |
| 48. | | 10 k. blue | 80·00 | 1·40 |
| 49. | | 15 k. brown | £100 | 90 |

**AH 14.** **AH 16.** **20.**

### 1867.

| | | | | |
|---|---|---|---|---|
| 59. | AH 14. | 2 k. yellow | 8·00 | 70 |
| 60. | | 3 k. green | 30·00 | 45 |
| 62. | | 5 k. red | 2·00 | 10 |
| 63. | | 10 k. blue | 65·00 | 20 |
| 64. | | 15 k. brown | 4·25 | 3·00 |
| 65. | | 25 k. grey | 50 | £100 |
| 66. | AH 16. | 50 k. brown | 11·00 | 80·00 |

### 1883.

| | | | | |
|---|---|---|---|---|
| 70. | 20. | 2 k. brown | 5·00 | 4·00 |
| 71. | | 3 k. green | 4·50 | 25 |
| 72. | | 5 k. red | 10·00 | 10 |
| 73. | | 10 k. blue | 4·50 | 10 |
| 74. | | 20 k. grey | 55·00 | 4·00 |
| 75a. | | 50 k. mauve | £325 | 50·00 |

**23.** **24.** **25.**

### 1890.

| | | | | |
|---|---|---|---|---|
| 79 | 23 | 1 k. grey | 1·60 | 15 |
| 80 | | 2 k. brown | 25 | 10 |
| 81 | | 3 k. green | 40 | 10 |
| 82 | | 5 k. red | 40 | 10 |
| 83 | | 10 k. blue | 80 | 10 |
| 84 | | 12 k. purple | 3·25 | 20 |
| 85 | 23 | 15 k. purple | 1·25 | 20 |
| 86 | | 20 k. green | 32·00 | 1·40 |
| 87 | | 24 k. blue | 2·50 | 75 |
| 88 | | 30 k. brown | 2·00 | 35 |
| 89 | | 50 k. mauve | 8·50 | 6·00 |
| 90 | 24 | 1 g. blue | 1·25 | 1·75 |
| 105 | | 1 g. lilac | 42·00 | 3·00 |
| 91 | | 2 g. red | 3·25 | 9·00 |
| 106 | | 2 g. green | 18·00 | 25·00 |

### 1891. Figures in black.

| | | | | |
|---|---|---|---|---|
| 92. | 25. | 20 k. green | 1·10 | 10 |
| 93. | | 24 k. blue | 2·25 | 60 |
| 94. | | 30 k. brown | 1·10 | 15 |
| 95. | | 50 k. mauve | 1·25 | 20 |

**27.** **28.** **29.** **30.**

### 1899. Corner numerals in black on heller values.

| | | | | |
|---|---|---|---|---|
| 107 | 27. | 1 h. mauve | 70 | 10 |
| 139 | | 2 h. grey | 2·50 | 30 |
| 140 | | 3 h. brown | 30 | 10 |
| 141 | | 5 h. green | 20 | 10 |
| 142 | | 6 h. orange | 15 | 10 |
| 143 | 28. | 10 h. red | 15 | 10 |
| 144 | | 20 h. brown | 50 | 10 |
| 145 | | 25 h. blue | 50 | 10 |
| 146 | | 30 h. mauve | 1·60 | 65 |
| 147 | 29. | 35 h. green | 75 | 20 |
| 148 | | 40 h. green | 1·50 | 2·75 |
| 149 | | 50 h. blue | 4·00 | 6·50 |
| 150 | | 60 h. brown | 1·60 | 50 |
| 119a | 30. | 1 k. red | 1·75 | 10 |
| 120 | | 2 k. lilac | 45·00 | 25 |
| 121 | | 4 k. green | 3·75 | 6·50 |

**33.** **35.**

### 1904. Types as before, but with corners containing figures altered as T 33 and 35. Figures in black on white on 10 h. to 30 h. only.

| | | | | |
|---|---|---|---|---|
| 169 | 33. | 1 h. purple | 10 | 30 |
| 170 | | 2 h. black | 15 | 15 |
| 171 | | 3 h. brown | 20 | 10 |
| 183 | | 5 h. green | 30 | 10 |
| 173 | | 6 h. orange | 30 | 10 |
| 160 | 28. | 10 h. red | 1·75 | 10 |
| 161 | | 20 h. brown | 26·00 | 60 |
| 162 | | 25 h. blue | 30·00 | 60 |
| 177 | | 30 h. mauve | 38·00 | 3·25 |
| 178 | 35. | 35 h. green | 1·75 | 20 |
| 179 | | 40 h. purple | 1·75 | 70 |
| 180 | | 50 h. blue | 1·90 | 3·00 |
| 181 | | 60 h. brown | 1·75 | 45 |
| 168 | | 72 h. red | 80 | 80 |

### 1906. Figures on plain white ground and stamps printed in one colour.

| | | | | |
|---|---|---|---|---|
| 184. | 28. | 10 h. red | 40 | 10 |
| 185. | | 12 h. violet | 1·00 | 55 |
| 186. | | 20 h. brown | 2·50 | 10 |
| 187. | | 25 h. blue | 3·25 | 25 |
| 188. | | 30 h. red | 6·50 | 15 |

**37.** Francis Joseph I. **38.** Francis Joseph I.

**41.** Schonbrunn. **42.** Francis Joseph I.

### 1908. 60th Anniv of Emperor's Accession.

| | | | | |
|---|---|---|---|---|
| 189 | – | 1 h. black | 20 | 10 |
| 190 | – | 2 h. violet | 20 | 10 |
| 191 | – | 3 h. purple | 15 | 10 |
| 192 | 37 | 5 h. green | 15 | 10 |
| 193 | – | 6 h. brown | 55 | 60 |
| 194 | 37 | 10 h. red | 15 | 10 |
| 195 | – | 12 h. red | 1·25 | 80 |
| 196 | – | 20 h. brown | 2·75 | 15 |
| 197 | 37 | 25 h. blue | 1·75 | 10 |
| 198 | – | 30 h. green | 5·50 | 15 |
| 199 | – | 35 h. grey | 2·50 | 15 |
| 200 | 38 | 50 h. green | 50 | 15 |
| 201 | – | 60 h. red | 30 | 10 |
| 202 | 38 | 72 h. brown | 1·75 | 20 |
| 203 | – | 1 k. violet | 12·00 | 15 |
| 204 | 41 | 2 k. green and red | 20·00 | 40 |
| 205 | – | 5 k. purple and brown | 32·00 | 4·25 |
| 206 | 42 | 10 k. brown, bl & ochre | £170 | 65·00 |

DESIGNS—As Type **37**: 1 h. Charles VI. 2 h. Maria Theresa. 3 h. Joseph II. 6 h. Leopold II. 12 h. Francis I. 20 h. Ferdinand. 30 h. Francis Joseph I in 1848. 35 h. Same in 1878. As Type **38**: 60 h. Francis Joseph I on horseback. 1 k. Same in ceremonial robes. As Type **41**: 5 k. Hofburg.

**45.** **47.**

### 1910. 80th Birthday of Francis Joseph I. As issue of 1908 but with dates added as T 45.

| | | | |
|---|---|---|---|
| 223 | 1 h. black | 3·75 | 7·00 |
| 224 | 2 h. violet | 5·00 | 10·00 |
| 225 | 3 h. purple | 4·50 | 7·50 |
| 226 | 5 h. green | 15 | 15 |
| 227 | 6 h. brown | 2·50 | 6·00 |
| 228 | 10 h. red | 15 | 15 |
| 229 | 12 h. red | 3·25 | 7·00 |
| 230 | 20 h. brown | 6·00 | 7·00 |
| 231 | 25 h. blue | 75 | 90 |
| 232 | 30 h. green | 3·50 | 5·50 |
| 233 | 35 h. grey | 3·50 | 5·50 |
| 234 | 50 h. green | 4·25 | 10·00 |
| 235 | 60 h. red | 4·25 | 10·00 |
| 236 | 1 k. violet | 6·00 | 11·00 |
| 237 | 2 k. green and red | £130 | £225 |
| 238 | 5 k. purple and brown | 95·00 | £160 |
| 239 | 10 k. brown, blue & ochre | £190 | £325 |

### 1914. War Charity Funds.

| | | | | |
|---|---|---|---|---|
| 240 | 47 | 5 h.+(2 h.) green | 10 | 15 |
| 241 | | 10 h.+(2 h.) red | 15 | 20 |

**48.** Cavalry.

### 1915. War Charity Funds.

| | | | | |
|---|---|---|---|---|
| 242 | – | 3 h.+1 h. brown | 10 | 30 |
| 243 | 48 | 5 h.+2 h. green | 10 | 10 |
| 244 | – | 10 h. +2 h. red | 10 | 10 |
| 245 | – | 20 h.+3 h. green | 35 | 1·40 |
| 246 | – | 35 h.+3 h. blue | 2·00 | 3·00 |

DESIGNS: 3 h. Infantry. 10 h. Artillery. 20 h. Battleship "Viribus Unitas" (Navy). 35 h. Lohner Pfeilflieger B-1 biplane (Air Force).

**49.** Imperial Austrian Crown. **50.** Francis Joseph I.

**51.** Arms of Austria. **52.**

### 1916.

| | | | | |
|---|---|---|---|---|
| 247. | 49. | 3 h. violet | 10 | 10 |
| 248. | | 5 h. green | 10 | 10 |
| 249. | | 6 h. orange | 20 | 55 |
| 250. | | 10 h. red | 10 | 10 |
| 251. | | 12 h. blue | 25 | 1·10 |
| 252. | 50. | 15 h. red | 35 | 10 |
| 253. | | 20 h. brown | 3·00 | 10 |
| 254. | | 25 h. blue | 5·50 | 30 |
| 255. | | 30 h. slate | 4·75 | 55 |
| 256. | 51. | 40 h. olive | 15 | 10 |
| 257. | | 50 h. green | 15 | 10 |
| 258. | | 60 h. blue | 15 | 10 |
| 259. | | 80 h. brown | 15 | 10 |
| 260. | | 90 h. purple | 15 | 10 |
| 261. | | 1 k. red on yellow | 25 | 10 |
| 262aa. | 52. | 2 k. blue | 10 | 15 |
| 263aa. | | 3 k. red | 20 | 65 |
| 264a. | | 4 k. green | 1·00 | 1·25 |
| 265aa. | | 10 k. violet | 5·00 | 15·00 |

On Nos. 254/5 the portrait is full face. The 1 k. has floral sprays each side of the coat-of-arms.

**60.** Charles I.

### 1917.

| | | | | |
|---|---|---|---|---|
| 290. | 60. | 15 h. red | 10 | 10 |
| 291a. | | 20 h. green | 10 | 10 |
| 292. | | 25 h. blue | 30 | 10 |
| 293. | | 30 h. violet | 20 | 10 |

### 1918. Air. Optd FLUGPOST or surch also.

| | | | | |
|---|---|---|---|---|
| 296 | 52 | 1 k. 50 on 2 k. mauve | 2·00 | 3·25 |
| 297 | | 2 k. 50 on 3 k. brown | 8·50 | 17·00 |
| 298 | | 4 k. grey | 6·00 | 13·00 |

### 1918. Optd. Deutschosterreich.

| | | | | |
|---|---|---|---|---|
| 299. | 49. | 3 h. violet | 10 | 10 |
| 300. | | 5 h. green | 10 | 10 |
| 301. | | 6 h. orange | 20 | 1·00 |
| 302. | | 10 h. red | 10 | 10 |
| 303. | | 12 h. blue | 20 | 1·25 |
| 304. | 60. | 15 h. red | 15 | 90 |
| 305. | | 20 h. green | 10 | 10 |
| 306 | | 25 h. blue | 10 | 10 |
| 307. | | 30 h. violet | 10 | 10 |
| 308. | 51. | 40 h. olive | 10 | 10 |
| 309. | | 50 h. green | 50 | 1·00 |
| 310. | | 60 h. blue | 45 | 70 |
| 311. | | 80 h. brown | 10 | 10 |
| 312. | | 90 h. red | 15 | 30 |
| 313. | | 1 k. red on yellow | 15 | 15 |
| 314. | 52. | 2 k. blue | 10 | 10 |
| 315. | | 3 k. red | 20 | 80 |
| 316. | | 4 k. green | 1·00 | 2·00 |
| 317. | | 10 k. violet | 8·00 | 20·00 |

**64.** Posthorn. **65.** Republican Arms. **66.** "New Republic".

### 1919. Imperf. or perf.

| | | | | |
|---|---|---|---|---|
| 336. | 64. | 3 h. grey | 10 | 10 |
| 337. | 65. | 5 h. green | 10 | 10 |
| 338. | | 5 h. grey | 10 | 10 |
| 339. | 64. | 6 h. orange | 10 | 50 |
| 340. | 65. | 10 h. red | 10 | 10 |
| 342. | 64. | 12 h. blue | 10 | 60 |
| 343a. | | 15 h. brown | 10 | 10 |
| 344. | 66. | 20 h. green | 10 | 10 |
| 346. | 65. | 25 h. blue | 10 | 10 |
| 347. | 64. | 25 h. violet | 10 | 10 |
| 348. | 66. | 30 h. brown | 10 | 10 |
| 349. | | 40 h. violet | 10 | 10 |
| 350. | | 40 h. red | 10 | 10 |
| 351. | 65. | 45 h. green | 15 | 60 |
| 352. | 66. | 50 h. blue | 10 | 10 |
| 353. | 64. | 60 h. green | 10 | 10 |
| 354. | 65. | 1 k. red on yellow | 10 | 10 |
| 355. | | 1 k. blue | 10 | 10 |

**67.** Parliament Building. **71.** Republican Arms.

### 1919.

| | | | | |
|---|---|---|---|---|
| 356 | 67 | 2 k. black and red | 15 | 40 |
| 357 | | 2½ k. bistre | 10 | 20 |
| 358 | | 3 k. brown and blue | 10 | 15 |
| 359 | | 4 k. black and red | 10 | 15 |
| 360 | | 5 k. black | 10 | 15 |
| 361 | | 7½ k. purple | 10 | 35 |
| 362 | | 10 k. brown and green | 15 | 30 |
| 363 | | 20 k. brown and violet | 10 | 45 |
| 364 | | 50 k. violet on yellow | 25 | 90 |

### 1920.

| | | | | |
|---|---|---|---|---|
| 402. | 71. | 80 h. red | 10 | 10 |
| 403. | | 1 k. brown | 10 | 10 |
| 404. | | 1½ k. green | 10 | 10 |
| 405. | | 2 k. blue | 10 | 10 |
| 406. | | 3 k. black and green | 10 | 10 |
| 407. | | 4 k. claret and red | 10 | 10 |
| 408. | | 5 k. red and lilac | 10 | 10 |
| 409. | | 7½ k. brown and orange | 10 | 20 |
| 410. | | 10 k. blue and violet | 10 | 10 |

The frames of the 3 to 10 k. differ.

### 1920. Issues for Carinthian Plebiscite. Optd Karnten Abstimmung (Types 65/7 in new colours). (a) Perf.

| | | | | |
|---|---|---|---|---|
| 411 | 65 | 5 h. (+10 h.) grey on yellow | 45 | 1·00 |
| 412 | | 10 h. (+20 h.) red on pink | 50 | 1·00 |
| 413 | 64 | 15 h. (+30 h.) brown on yellow | 30 | 80 |
| 414 | 66 | 20 h. (+40 h.) green on blue | 35 | 70 |
| 415 | 64 | 25 h. (+50 h) purple on pink | 35 | 70 |
| 416 | 66 | 30 h. (+60 h.) brown on buff | 1·25 | 3·25 |
| 417 | | 40 h. (+80 h.) red on yellow | 40 | 90 |
| 418 | | 50 h. (+100 h.) indigo on blue | 35 | 55 |

419 **64** 60 h. (+120 h.) green on blue .. .. .. 1·25 3·25
420 **71** 80 h. (+160 h.) red .. 35 20
421 1 k. (+2 k.) brown .. 35 80
422 2 k. (+4 k.) blue .. 35 85

(b) Imperf

423 **67** 2½ k. (+5 k.) brown .. 40 1·00
424 3 k. (+6 k.) grn & bl .. 40 1·10
425 4 k. (+8 k.) vio & red 60 1·50
426 5 k. (+10 k.) blue .. 60 1·25
427 7½ k. (+15 k.) green .. 60 1·25
428 10 k. (+20 k.) red & grn 60 1·25
429 20 k. (+40 k.) brown and lilac .. .. 60 1·75

**The plebiscite was to decide whether Carinthia should be part of Austria or Yugoslavia, and the premium was for a fund to promote a vote in favour of remaining in Austria. The result was a vote for Austria.**

**1921.** Flood Relief Fund. Optd **Hochwasser 1920** (colours changed).

430. **65.** 5 h. (+10 h.) grey on yellow .. .. 20 50
431. 10 h. (+20 h.) brown .. 20 50
432. **64.** 15 h. (+30 h.) grey .. 20 50
433. **66.** 20 h. (+40 h.) green on yellow .. .. 20 50
434. **64.** 25 h. (+50 h.) blue on yellow .. .. 20 50
435. **66.** 30 h. (+60 h.) purple on blue .. .. 50 1·25
436. 40 h. (+80 h.) brown on red .. .. 55 1·40
437. 50 h. (+100 h.) green on blue .. .. 1·25 2·00
438. **64.** 60 h. (+120 h.) purple on yellow .. .. 30 1·25
439. **71.** 80 h. (+160 h.) blue .. 30 1·25
440. 1 k. (+2 k.) orge. on bl. 40 90
441. 1½ k. (+3 k.) green on yellow .. .. 20 45
442. 2 k. (+4 k.) brown .. 20 45
443. **67.** 2½ k. (+5 k.) blue .. 25 30
444. 3 k. (+6 k.) red & grn. 25 30
445. 4 k. (+8 k.) brn. & lilac 80 2·00
446. 5 k. (+10 k.) green .. 30 75
447. 7½ k. (+15 k.) red .. 30 90
448. 10 k. (+20 k.) grn. & bl. 30 1·00
449. 20 k. (+40 k.) purple and red .. .. 50 1·40

**80.** Pincers and Hammer. **81.** Ear of Corn.

**1922.**

461. **81.** ½ k. brown .. .. 10 70
462. **80.** 1 k. brown .. .. 10 10
463. 2 k. blue .. .. 10 10
464. **81.** 2½ k. brown .. .. 10 10
465. **80.** 4 k. purple .. .. 10 90
466. 5 k. green .. .. 10 10
467. **81.** 7½ k. violet .. .. 10 10
468. **80.** 10 k. red .. .. 10 10
469. **81.** 12½ k. green .. .. 10 10
470. 15 k. turquoise .. 10 10
471. 20 k. blue .. .. 10 10
472. 25 k. red .. .. 10 10
473. **80.** 30 k. grey .. .. 10 10
474. 45 k. red .. .. 10 10
475. 50 k. brown .. .. 10 10
476. 60 k. green .. .. 10 10
477. 75 k. blue .. .. 10 10
478. 80 k. yellow .. .. 10 10
479. **81.** 100 k. grey .. .. 10 10
480. 120 k. brown .. .. 10 10
481. 150 k. orange .. .. 10 10
482. 160 k. green .. .. 10 10
483. 180 k. red .. .. 10 10
484. 200 k. pink .. .. 10 10
485. 240 k. violet .. .. 10 10
486. 300 k. blue .. .. 10 10
487. 400 k. green .. .. 75 10
488. 500 k. yellow .. .. 10 10
489. 600 k. slate .. .. 10 10
490. 700 k. brown .. .. 75 10
491. 800 k. violet .. .. 65 1·50
492. **80.** 1000 k. mauve .. .. 50 10
493. 1200 k. red .. .. 30 40
494. 1500 k. orange .. .. 40 10
495. 1600 k. slate .. .. 2·25 2·25
496. 2000 k. blue .. .. 3·25 45
497. 3000 k. blue .. .. 8·00 80
498. 4000 k. blue on blue .. 5·00 3·00

**82.**

**85.** Mozart.

**1922.**

499. **82.** 20 k. sepia .. .. 10 10
500. 25 k. blue .. .. 10 10
501. 50 k. red .. .. 10 10
502. 100 k. green .. .. 10 10
503. 200 k. purple .. .. 10 10
504. 500 k. orange .. .. 15 70
505. 1000 k. violet on yellow 10 10
506. 2000 k. green on yellow 10 10
507. 3000 k. red .. .. 8·00 60
508. 5000 k. black .. .. 1·75 1·75
509. 10,000 k. brown .. .. 3·00 5·00

**1922.** Musicians' Fund.

519. – 2½ k. brown .. .. 7·00 10·00
520. **85.** 5 k. blue .. .. 1·25 1·75
521. – 7½ k. black .. .. 2·50 2·50
522. – 10 k. purple .. .. 2·50 2·75
523. – 25 k. green .. .. 4·50 6·50
524. – 50 k. red .. .. 2·50 3·25
525. – 100 k. green .. .. 8·00 10·00

Composers: 2½ k. Haydn. 7½ k. Beethoven. 10 k. Schubert. 25 k. Bruckner. 50 k. J. Strauss. 100 k. Wolf.

**87.** Hawk. **88.** W. Kress.

**1922.** Air.

546. **87.** 300 k. red .. .. 30 1·25
547. 400 k. green .. .. 4·00 12·00
548. 600 k. olive .. .. 15 80
549. 900 k. red .. .. 15 80
550. **88.** 1200 k. purple .. .. 15 80
551. 2400 k. slate .. .. 15 80
552. 3000 k. brown .. .. 3·00 7·00
553. 4800 k. blue .. .. 3·00 7·50

**89.** Bregenz. **90.** "Art the Comforter".

**1923.** Artists' Charity Fund.

554 **89** 100 k. green .. .. 2·50 4·50
555 – 120 k. blue .. .. 2·50 4·50
556 – 160 k. purple .. .. 2·50 4·50
557 – 180 k. purple .. .. 2·50 4·75
558 – 200 k. red .. .. 2·50 4·50
559 – 240 k. brown .. .. 3·50 4·50
560 – 400 k. brown .. .. 2·50 4·50
561 – 600 k. green .. .. 2·50 6·50
562 – 1000 k. black .. .. 2·50 7·00

Designs: 120 k. Salzburg. 160 k. Eisenstadt. 180 k. Klagenfurt. 200 k. Innsbruck. 240 k. Linz. 400 k. Graz. 600 k. Melk. 1000 k. Vienna.

**1924.** Artists' Charity Fund.

563. **90.** 100+300 k. green .. 3·50 6·50
564. – 300+900 k. brown .. 5·00 6·50
565. – 500+1500 k. purple .. 5·00 7·50
566. – 600+1800 k. turquoise 5·00 13·00
567. – 1000+3000 k. brown .. 8·50 15·00

Designs: 300 k. "Agriculture and Handicraft". 500 k. "Mother Love". 600 k. "Charity". 1000 k. "Fruitfulness".

**91.** **92.** Plains. **93.** Minorite Church, Vienna.

**1925.**

568. **91.** 1 g. grey .. .. 15 10
569. 2 g. red .. .. 40 10
570. 3 g. red .. .. 40 10
571. 4 g. blue .. .. 1·50 10
572. 5 g. brown .. .. 1·50 10
573. 6 g. blue .. .. 85 10
574. 7 g. brown .. .. 1·25 10
575. 8 g. green .. .. 4·00 10
576. **92.** 10 g. brown .. .. 40 10
577. 15 g. red .. .. 40 10
578. 16 g. blue .. .. 40 10
579. 18 g. green .. .. 80 55
580. – 20 g. violet .. .. 60 10
581. – 24 g. red .. .. 80 35
582. – 30 g. brown .. .. 60 10
583. – 40 g. blue .. .. 1·25 10
584. – 45 g. brown .. .. 1·50 10
585. – 50 g. grey .. .. 1·75 15
586. – 80 g. blue .. .. 4·25 4·50
587. **93.** 1 s. green .. .. 18·00 70
588. 2 s. red .. .. 6·00 11·00

Design: As T **92**.—20 g. to 80 g. Golden eagle on mountains.

**96.** Airman and Hansa Brandenburg C-1.

**97.** De Havilland D.H.34 and Common Crane.

**1925.** Air.

616 **96** 2 g. brown .. .. 25 80
617 5 g. red .. .. 15 15
618 6 g. blue .. .. 65 1·25
619 8 g. green .. .. 75 1·50
620 **97** 10 g. red .. .. 85 1·75
621 **96** 10 g. orange .. .. 85 1·25
622 **97** 15 g. red .. .. 70 1·00
623 **96** 15 g. mauve .. .. 30 50
624 20 g. brown .. .. 10·00 3·50
625 25 g. violet .. .. 2·50 5·50
626 **97** 30 g. purple .. .. 1·00 1·75
627 **96** 30 g. bistre .. .. 6·50 5·00
628 **97** 50 g. grey .. .. 1·00 1·90
629 **96** 50 g. blue .. .. 12·00 8·50
630 80 g. green .. .. 1·25 3·00
631 **97** 1 s. blue .. .. 2·25 3·00
632 2 s. green .. .. 1·75 3·25
633 3 s. brown .. .. 38·00 35·00
634 5 s. blue .. .. 11·00 18·00
635 10 s. brown on grey (25 × 32 mm) .. 7·00 16·00

**98.** Siegfried and Dragon.

**99.** Dr. Michael Hainisch.

**1926.** Child Welfare. Scenes from the Nibelung Legend.

636. **98.** 3+2 g. brown .. .. 65 65
637. – 8+2 g. blue .. .. 15 25
638. – 15+5 g. red .. .. 15 25
639. – 20+5 g. green .. .. 25 45
640. – 24+6 g. violet .. .. 25 45
641. – 40+10 g. brown .. 3·50 4·25

Designs: 8 g. Gunther's voyage. 15 g. Kriemhild and Brunhild. 20 g. Hagen and the Rhine maidens. 24 g. Rudiger and the Nibelungs. 40 g. Dietrich's fight with Hagen.

**1928.** 10th Anniv. of Republic and War Orphans and Invalid Children's Fund.

642. **99.** 10 g. (+10 g.) brown .. 5·50 8·50
643. 15 g. (+15 g.) red .. 5·50 8·50
644. 30 g. (+30 g.) black .. 5·50 8·50
645. 40 g. (+40 g.) blue .. 5·50 8·50

**100.** Gussing.

**101.** National Library, Vienna.

**1929.** Views. Size 25½ × 21½ mm.

646 **100** 10 g. orange .. .. 75 10
647 10 g. brown .. .. 75 10
648 – 15 g. purple .. .. 75 1·50
649 – 16 g. black .. .. 15 10
650 – 18 g. green .. .. 30 50
651 – 20 g. black .. .. 30 10
652 – 24 g. purple .. .. 4·50 5·50
654 – 30 g. violet .. .. 5·00 10
655 – 40 g. blue .. .. 7·00 10
656 – 50 g. violet .. .. 32·00 10
657 – 60 g. green .. .. 26·00 20
658 **101** 1 s. brown .. .. 5·00 15
659 – 2 s. green .. .. 8·50 7·00

Views—As T **100**: 15 g. Hochosterwitz. 16, 20 g. Durnstein. 18 g. Traunsee. 24 g. Salzburg. 30 g. Seewiesen. 40 g. Innsbruck. 50 g. Worthersee. 60 g. Hohenems. As T **101**: 2 s. St. Stephen's Cathedral, Vienna.

See also Nos. 678/91.

**102.** Pres. Wilhelm Miklas.

**104.** Johann Nestroy.

**1930.** Anti-tuberculosis Fund.

660 **102** 10 g. (+10 g.) brown 7·50 12·00
661 20 g. (+20 g.) red .. 7·50 12·00
662 30 g. (+30 g.) purple .. 7·50 12·00
663 40 g. (+40 g.) blue .. 7·50 12·00
664 50 g. (+50 g.) green .. 7·50 12·00
665 1 s. (+1 s.) brown .. 7·50 12·00

**1930.** Rotarian Congress. Optd with Rotary International emblem and **CONVENTION WIEN 1931**.

666. **100.** 10 g. (+10 g.) brown 32·00 42·00
667. – 20 g. (+20 g.) grey (No. 651) .. .. 32·00 42·00
668. – 30 g. (+30 g.) violet (No. 654) .. .. 32·00 42·00
669. – 40 g. (+40 g.) blue (No. 655) .. .. 32·00 42·00
670. – 50 g. (+50 g.) violet (No. 656) .. .. 32·00 42·00
671. **101.** 1 s. (+1 s.) brown .. 32·00 42·00

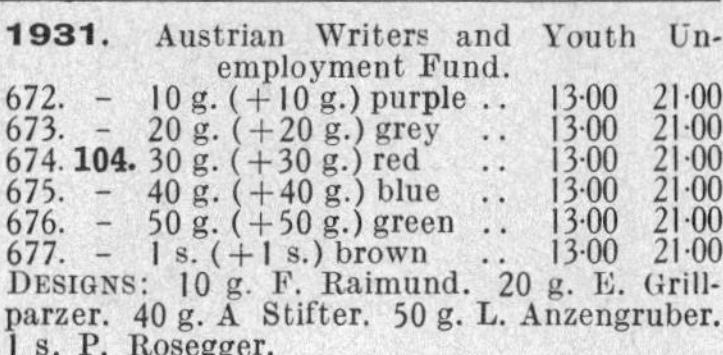

**1931.** Austrian Writers and Youth Unemployment Fund.

672. – 10 g. (+10 g.) purple .. 13·00 21·00
673. – 20 g. (+20 g.) grey .. 13·00 21·00
674. **104.** 30 g. (+30 g.) red .. 13·00 21·00
675. – 40 g. (+40 g.) blue .. 13·00 21·00
676. – 50 g. (+50 g.) green .. 13·00 21·00
677. – 1 s. (+1 s.) brown .. 13·00 21·00

Designs: 10 g. F. Raimund. 20 g. E. Grillparzer. 40 g. A Stifter. 50 g. L. Anzengruber. 1 s. P. Rosegger.

**105.**

**106.** Dr. Ignaz Seipel.

**1932.** Designs as No. 646 etc. but size reduced to 20½ × 16 mm as T **105**.

678 **105** 10 g. brown .. .. 65 10
679 – 12 g. green .. .. 1·50 10
680 – 18 g. green .. .. 1·40 2·00
681 – 20 g. black .. .. 65 10
682 – 24 g. red .. .. 5·50 10
683 – 24 g. violet .. .. 4·25 10
684 – 30 g. violet .. .. 17·00 10
685 – 30 g. red .. .. 4·00 10
686 – 40 g. blue .. .. 20·00 50
687 – 40 g. violet .. .. 6·50 15
688 – 50 g. violet .. .. 25·00 20
689 – 50 g. blue .. .. 7·00 20
690 – 60 g. green .. .. 50·00 1·50
691 – 64 g. green .. .. 13·00 15

Designs (new values): 12 g. Traunsee. 64 g. Hohenems.

**1932.** Death of Dr. Seipel (Chancellor), and Ex-Servicemen's Fund.

692. **106.** 50 g. (+50 g.) blue .. 11·00 14·00

**107.** Hans Makart.

**108.** The Climb.

**1932.** Austrian Painters.

693. – 12 g. (+12 g.) green .. 18·00 30·00
694. – 24 g. (+24 g.) purple 18·00 30·00
695. – 30 g. (+30 g.) red .. 18·00 30·00
696. **107.** 40 g. (+40 g.) grey .. 18·00 30·00
697. – 64 g. (+64 g.) brown 18·00 30·00
698. – 1 s. (+1 s.) red .. 18·00 30·00

Designs: 12 g. F. G. Waldmuller. 24 g. Von Schwind. 30 g. Alt. 64 g. Klimt. 1 s. A. Egger-Lienz.

**1933.** Int. Ski Championship Fund

699. **108.** 12 g. (+12 g.) green .. 8·50 11·00
700. – 24 g. (+24 g.) violet .. 90·00 £120
701. – 30 g. (+30 g.) red .. 14·00 20·00
702. – 50 g. (+50 g.) blue .. 90·00 £120

Designs: 24 g. Start. 30 g. Race. 50 g. Ski-jump.

**109.** "The Honeymoon" (M. von Schwind)

**111.** John Sobieski.

**1933.** Int Philatelic Exn, Vienna (WIPA).

703 **109** 50 g. (+50 g.) blue .. £120 £225

**1933.** 250th Anniv of Relief of Vienna and Pan-German Catholic Congress.

706. – 12 g. (+12 g.) green .. 24·00 30·00
707. – 24 g. (+24 g.) violet .. 20·00 24·00
708. – 30 g. (+30 g.) red .. 20·00 24·00
709. **111.** 40 g. (+40 g.) grey .. 35·00 45·00
710. – 50 g. (+50 g.) blue .. 20·00 24·00
711. – 64 g. (+64 g.) brown .. 28·00 40·00

Designs—Vert. 12 g. Vienna in 1683. 24 g. Marco d'Aviano. 30 g. Count von Starhemberg. 50 g. Charles of Lorraine. 64 g. Burgomaster Liebenberg.

**1933.** Winter Relief Fund. Surch with premium and **Winterhilfe** (5 g.) or **WINTERHILFE** (others).

712 **91** 5 g.+2 g. green .. 15 50
713 – 12 g.+3 g. blue (as 679) 15 50
714 – 24 g.+6 g. brn (as 682) 15 50
715 **101** 1 s.+50 g. red .. 32·00 42·00

114. 115.

**1934.**

716. **114.** 1 g. violet .. .. 10 10
717. 3 g. red .. .. .. 10 10
718. – 4 g. green .. .. 10 10
719. – 5 g. purple .. .. 10 10
721. – 6 g. blue .. .. 15 10
722. – 8 g. green .. .. 10 10
723. – 12 g. brown .. .. 10 10
724. – 20 g. brown .. .. 15 10
725. – 24 g. turquoise .. .. 10 10
726. – 25 g. violet .. .. 15 10
727. – 30 g. red .. .. 15 10
728. – 35 g. red .. .. 25 30
729 **115.** 40 g. grey .. .. 45 10
730. – 45 g. brown .. .. 40 10
731. – 60 g. blue .. .. 65 15
732. – 64 g. brown .. .. 80 10
733. – 1 s. purple .. .. 90 25
735. – 2 s. green .. .. 3·75 4·50
736. – 3 s orange .. .. 12·00 18·00
737 – 5 s. black .. .. 30·00 48·00

Designs (Austrian costumes of the districts named)—As Type **114**: 1, 3 g. Burgenland. 4, 5 g. Carinthia. 6, 8 g. Lower Austria. 12, 20 g. Upper Austria. 24, 25 g. Salzburg. 30, 35 g. Styria (Steiermark). As Type **115**: 40, 45 g. Tyrol. 60, 64 g. Vorarlberg. 1 s. Vienna. 2 s. Army officer and soldiers. 30 × 31 mm: 3 s. Harvesters. 5 s. Builders.

**117.** Chancellor Dollfuss. 118. Anton Pilgram.

**1934.** Dollfuss Mourning Stamp.

738 117 24 g. black .. .. 45 20

See also No. 762.

**1934.** Welfare Funds. Austrian Architects.

739. **118.** 12 g. (+12 g.) black .. 10·00 15·00
740. – 24 g. (+24 g.) violet 10·00 15·00
741. – 30 g. (+30 g.) red .. 10·00 15·00
742. – 40 g. (+40 g.) brown 10·00 15·00
743. – 60 g. (+60 g.) blue .. 10·00 15·00
744. – 64 g. (+64 g.) green 10·00 15·00

Designs: 24 g. Fischer von Erlach. 30 g. J. Prandtauer. 40 g. A. von Siccardsburg and E. van der Null. 60 g. H. von Ferstel. 64 g. Otto Wagner.

119. "Mother and Child" (J. Danhauser).

**1935.** Mothers Day.

745. **119.** 24 g. blue .. .. 45 15

**1935.** 1st Anniv of Assassination of Dr. Dollfuss.

762 117 24 g. blue .. .. 1·00 70

121. Maria Worth Castle, Carinthia. 122. Zugspitze Aerial Railway.

**1935.** Air. Designs showing Junkers airplane (except 10 s.) and landscape.

763. – 5 g. purple .. .. 10 25
764. **121.** 10 g. orange .. .. 10 15
765. – 15 g. green .. .. 50 80
766. – 20 g. blue .. .. 15 25
767. – 25 g. purple .. .. 15 25
768. – 30 g. red .. .. 15 25
769. – 40 g. green .. .. 15 30
770. – 50 g. blue .. .. 15 30
771. – 60 g. sepia .. .. 20 50
772. – 80 g. brown .. .. 20 60
773. – 1 s. red .. .. 20 70
774. – 2 s. green .. .. 5·00 5·50
775. – 3 s. brown .. .. 9·00 12·00
776. **122.** 5 s. green .. .. 3·50 9·50
777. – 10 s. blue .. .. 38·00 60·00

Designs—As T **121**: 5 g. Gussing Castle. 15 g. Durnstein. 20 g. Hallstatt. 25 g. Salzburg. 30 g. Dachstein Mts. 40 g. Wettersee. 50 g. Stuben am Arlberg. 60 g. St. Stephen's Cathedral, Vienna. 80 g. Minorite Church, Vienna. As T **122**: 1 s. River Danube. 2 s. Tauern railway viaduct. 3 s. Grossglockner mountain roadway. 10 s. Glider and yachts on the Attersee.

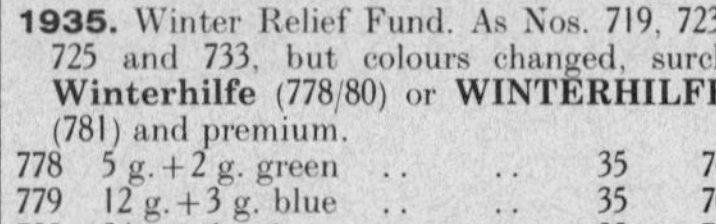

**1935.** Winter Relief Fund. As Nos. 719, 723, 725 and 733, but colours changed, surch **Winterhilfe** (778/80) or **WINTERHILFE** (781) and premium.

778 5 g. + 2 g. green .. .. 35 70
779 12 g. + 3 g. blue .. .. 35 70
780 24 g. + 6 g. brown .. .. 35 70
781 1 s. + 50 g. red .. .. 27·00 42·00

123. Prince Eugene of Savoy (born 1663, not 1667 as given). 124. Slalom Course Skier.

**1935.** Welfare Funds. Austrian Heroes.

782. **123.** 12 g. (+12 g.) brown .. 10·00 15·00
783. – 24 g. (+24 g.) green .. 10·00 15·00
784. – 30 g. (+30 g.) purple 10·00 15·00
785. – 40 g. (+40 g.) blue .. 10·00 15·00
786. – 60 g. (+ 60 g.) blue .. 10·00 15·00
787. – 64 g. (+64 g.) violet .. 10·00 15·00

Portraits: 24 g. Baron von Laudon. 30 g. Archduke Charles. 40 g. Field-Marshal Radetzky. 60 g. Vice-Admiral von Tegetthoff. 64 g. Field-Marshal Conrad von Hotzendorff.

**1936.** Int. Ski Championship Fund. Inscr. "WETTKAMPFE 1936".

788. **124.** 12 g. (+12 g.) green .. 3·00 3·25
789. – 24 g. (+24 g.) violet .. 5·50 4·50
790. – 35 g. (+35 g.) red .. 28·00 40·00
791. – 60 g. (+60 g.) blue .. 28·00 40·00

Designs: 24 g. Skier on mountain slope. 35 g. Woman slalom course skier. 60 g. View of Maria Theresienstrasse, Innsbruck.

125. Madonna and Child.

**1936.** Mothers' Day.

792. **125.** 24 g. blue .. .. 15 20

126. Chancellor Dollfuss. 127. " St. Martin sharing cloak ".

**1936.** 2nd Anniv. of Assassination of Dr. Dollfuss.

793. **126.** 10 s. blue .. .. £550 £700

**1936.** Winter Relief Fund. Inscr. " WINTERHILFE 1936/37 ".

794. **127.** 5 g. + 2 g. green .. 25 45
795. – 12 g. + 3 g. violet .. 25 45
796. – 24 g. + 6 g. blue .. 25 45
797. – 1 s. + 1 s. red .. 5·50 12·00

Designs: 12 g. " Healing the sick ". 24 g. " St. Elizabeth feeding the hungry ". 1 s. " Warming the poor ".

128. J Ressel. 129. Mother and Child.

**1936.** Welfare Funds. Austrian Inventors.

798. **128.** 12 g. (+12 g.) brown .. 2·25 4·00
799. – 24 g. (+24 g.) violet .. 2·50 4·00
800. – 30 g. (+ 30 g.) red .. 2·25 4·00
801. – 40 g. (+40 g.) black .. 2·25 4·00
802. – 60 g. (+60 g.) blue .. 2·25 4·00
803. – 64 g. (+64 g.) green .. 2·25 4·00

Portraits: 24 g. Karl Ritter von Ghega. 30 g. J. Werndl. 40 g. Carl Freih. Auer von Welsbach. 60 g. R. von Lieben. 64 g. V. Kaplan.

**1937.** Mothers' Day.

804. **129.** 24 g. red .. .. 20 20

130. "Maria Anna". 131. " Child Welfare".

**1937.** Centenary of Regular Danube Services of Danube Steam Navigation Co. Paddle-steamers.

805. **130.** 12 g. red .. .. 60 30
806. – 24 g. blue .. .. 60 30
807. – 64 g. green .. .. 60 75

Designs: 24 g. "Helios". 64 g. "Oesterreich".

**1937.** Winter Relief Fund. Inscr. " WINTERHILFE 1937 1938 "

808. **131.** 5 g. + 2 g. green .. 15 40
809. – 12 g. + 3 g. brown .. 15 40
810. – 24 g. + 6 g. blue .. 15 40
811. – 1 s. + 1 s. red .. 3·25 6·50

Designs: 12 g. " Feeding the Children ". 24 g. " Protecting the Aged ". 1 s. " Nursing the Sick."

132. Steam Locomotive "Austria". 133. Dr. G. Van Swieten.

**1937.** Railway Centenary.

812. **132.** 12 g. brown .. .. 10 10
813. – 25 g. violet .. .. 75 75
814. – 35 g. red .. .. 1·50 1·75

Designs: 25 g. Modern steam locomotive. 35 g. Electric locomotive.

**1937.** Welfare Funds. Austrian Doctors.

815. **133.** 5 g. (+5 g.) brown .. 2·00 4·00
816. – 8 g. (+8 g.) red .. 2·00 4·00
817. – 12 g. (+12 g.) brown .. 2·00 4·00
818. – 20 g. (+20 g.) green .. 2·00 4·00
819. – 24 g. (+24 g.) violet .. 2·00 4·00
820. – 30 g. (+30 g.) red .. 2·00 4·00
821. – 40 g. (+40 g.) olive .. 2·00 4·00
822. – 60 g. (+60 g.) blue .. 2·00 4·00
823. – 64 g. (+64 g.) purple 2·00 4·00

Designs: 8 g. L. A. von Auenbrugg. 12 g. K. von Rokitansky. 20 g. J. Skoda. 25 g. F. von Hebra. 30 g. F. von Arlt. 40 g. J. Hyrtl. 60 g. T. Billroth. 64 g. T. Meynert.

134. Nosegay and Signs of the Zodiac.

**1937.** Christmas Greetings.

824. **134.** 12 g. green .. .. 10 15
825. 24 g. red .. .. 10 15

**ALLIED OCCUPATION.** Nos. 826/905 were issued in the Russian Zone of occupation and Nos. 906/22 were a joint issue for use in the British, French and American zones.

**1945.** Hitler portrait stamps of Germany optd.
(a) Optd. **Osterreich** only.

826. **173.** 5 pf. green .. .. 10 25
827. 8 pf. red .. .. 10 25

(b) Optd. **Osterreich** and bar.

828. **173.** 6 pf. violet .. .. 15 35
829. 12 pf. red .. .. 15 35

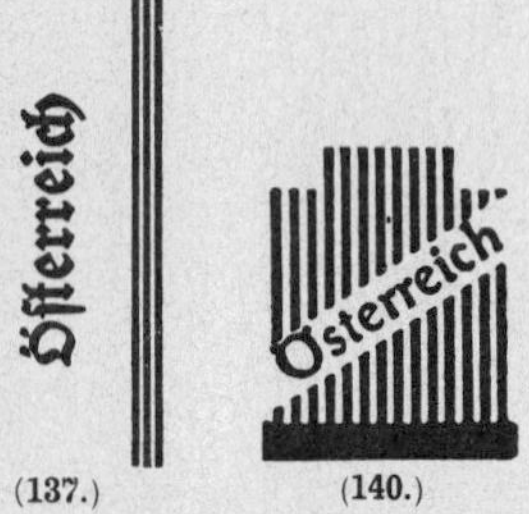


(137.) (140.)

**1945.** 1941 and 1944 Hitler stamps of Germany optd as Type **137**.

830 **173** 1 pf. grey .. .. 3·00 5·50
831 3 pf. brown .. .. 2·50 5·00
832 4 pf. grey .. .. 14·00 23·00
833 5 pf. green .. .. 2·50 4·00
834 6 pf. violet .. .. 30 55
835 8 pf. red .. .. 1·75 1·40
836 10 pf. brown .. .. 3·50 4·50
837 12 pf. red .. .. 30 55
838 15 pf. red .. .. 1·75 2·25
839 16 pf. green .. .. 30·00 60·00
840 20 pf. blue .. .. 5·00 7·50
841 24 pf. brown .. .. 30·00 60·00
842 25 pf. blue .. .. 2·25 4·00
843 30 pf. green .. .. 2·25 4·00
844 40 pf. mauve .. .. 3·00 5·50
845 **225** 42 pf. green .. .. 6·00 11·00
846 **173** 50 pf. green .. .. 4·50 7·50
847 60 pf. brown .. .. 5·50 10·00
848 80 pf. blue .. .. 4·50 9·00

853 **182** 1 rm. green .. .. 22·00 32·00
850 2 rm. violet .. .. 20·00 32·00
855 3 rm. red .. .. 38·00 70·00
856 5 rm. blue .. .. £325 £450

**1945.** Stamps of Germany surch **OSTERREICH** and new value.

857 **186** 5 pf. on 12+88 pf. grn 60 1·40
858 – 6 pf. on 6+14 pf brown and blue (No. 811) .. 6·50 11·00
859 **220** 8 pf. on 42+108 pf. brn 1·00 2·50
860 – 12 pf. on 3+7 pf. blue (No. 810) .. .. 60 1·40

**1948.** 1941 and 1944 Hitler stamps of Germany optd. as T **140**.

862 **173** 5 pf. green .. .. 40 2·25
863 6 pf. violet .. .. 30 1·75
864 8 pf. red .. .. 25 1·40
865 12 pf. red .. .. 35 2·25
866 30 pf. green .. .. 10·00 12·00
867a **225** 42 pf. green .. .. 35·00 40·00

141. New National Arms 142.

**1945.**

868 **141** 3 pf. brown .. .. 10 10
869 4 pf. blue .. .. 10 15
870 5 pf. green .. .. 10 10
871 6 pf. purple .. .. 10 10
872 8 pf. orange .. .. 10 10
873 10 pf. brown .. .. 10 10
874 12 pf. red .. .. 10 10
875 15 pf. orange .. .. 10 10
876 16 pf. green .. .. 10 20
877 20 pf. blue .. .. 10 10
878 24 pf. orange .. .. 10 10
879 25 pf. blue .. .. 10 10
880 30 pf. green .. .. 10 10
881 38 pf. blue .. .. 10 10
882 40 pf. purple .. .. 10 10
883 42 pf. grey .. .. 10 10
884 50 pf. green .. .. 10 15
885 60 pf. red .. .. 10 15
886 80 pf. violet .. .. 10 15
887 **142** 1 rm. green .. .. 10 30
888 2 rm. violet .. .. 15 40
889 3 rm. purple .. .. 20 60
890 5 rm. brown .. .. 30 70

Nos. 877/90 are larger, 24 × 28 mm.

144. Allegorical of the Home Land. 145. Posthorn.

**1945.** Austrian Welfare Charities.

905. **144.** 1 s. + 10 s. green .. 60 1·10

**1945.**

906. **145.** 1 g. blue .. .. 10 50
907. 3 g. orange .. .. 10 20
908. 4 g. brown .. .. 10 20
909. 5 g. green .. .. 10 10
910. 6 g. purple .. .. 10 10
911. 8 g. red .. .. 10 10
912. 10 g. grey .. .. 10 10
913. 12 g. brown .. .. 10 10
914. 15 g. red .. .. 10 20
915. 20 g. brown .. .. 10 20
916. 25 g. blue .. .. 10 20
917. 30 g. mauve .. .. 10 20
918. 40 g. blue .. .. 10 20
919. 60 g. olive .. .. 10 35
920. 1 s. violet .. .. 10 50
921. 2 s. yellow .. .. 25 1·00
922. 5 s. blue .. .. 30 1·25

146. Salzburg. 148. Durnstein.

**1945.** Views as T **146/8**.

923 – 3 g. blue .. .. 10 10
924 – 4 g. red .. .. 10 10
925 – 5 g. red .. .. 10 10
926 **146** 6 g. green .. .. 10 10
927 – 8 g. brown .. .. 10 10
928 – 8 g. purple .. .. 10 10
929 – 8 g. green .. .. 10 10
930 – 10 g. green .. .. 10 10

931 – 10 g. purple 10 10
932 – 12 g. brown 10 10
933 – 15 g. blue 10 10
934 – 16 g. brown 10 10
935 – 20 g. blue 10 10
936 – 24 g. green 10 10
937 – 25 g. grey 10 10
938 – 30 g. red 10 10
939 – 30 g. blue 30 30
940 – 35 g. red 10 10
941 – 38 g. green 10 10
942 – 40 g. grey 10 10
943 – 42 g. red 10 10
944 – 45 g. blue 30 55
945 – 50 g. blue 10 10
946 – 50 g. purple 30 40
947 – 60 g. blue 10 10
948 – 60 g. violet 2·00 2·00
949 – 70 g. blue 20 40
950 – 80 g. brown 20 55
951 – 90 g. green 1·00 1·40
952 148 1 s. brown 70 70
953 – 2 s. grey 2·50 3·50
954 – 3 s. green 90 1·00
955 – 5 s. red 1·25 1·25

DESIGNS—As Type 146. 3 g. Lermoos. 4 g. Iron-ore mine, Erzberg. 5 g. Leopoldsberg, Vienna. 8 g. (927), Prater Woods, Vienna. 8 g. (928/9), Town Hall Park, Vienna. 10 g. (930/1), Hochosterwitz. 12 g. Schafberg. 15 g. Forchtenstein. 16 g. Gesauseeingang. 23½ × 29 mm. 20 g. Gebhartsberg. 24 g. Holdrichsmuhle, near Modling. 25 g. Vent im Otztal. 30 g. (938/9), Neusiedler Lake. 35 g. Belvedere Palace, Vienna. 38 g. Langbath Lake. 40 g. Mariazell. 42 g. Traunstein. 45 g. Burg Hartenstein. 50 g. (945/6), Silvretta peaks, Vorarlberg. 60 g. (947/8), Semmering. 70 g. Badgastein. 80 g. Kaisergebirge. 90 g. Wayside shrine near Tragoss. As T 148. 2 s. St. Christof. 3 s. Heiligenblut. 5 s. Schonbrunn Palace, Vienna.

See also Nos. 1072/86a.

**1946.** 1st Anniv of U.N.O. No. 938 surch **26. JUNI 1945 +20 g 26. JUNI 1946** and globe.
971 30 g.+20 g. red 2·50 3·50

**151.** Dr. Karl Renner.

**1946.** 1st Anniv of Establishment of Renner Government.
972. 151. 1 s.+1 s. green 1·40 3·00
973. 2 s.+2 s. violet 1·40 3·00
974. 3 s.+3 s. purple 1·40 3·00
975. 5 s.+5 s. brown 1·40 3·00

**152.** Dagger and Map.

**(153.)**

**1946.** "Anti-Fascist" Exhibition.
977. 152. 5 g.+3 g. sepia 45 85
978. – 6 g.+4 g. green 30 55
979. – 8 g.+6 g. orange 30 55
980. – 12 g.+12 g. blue 30 55
981 – 30 g.+30 g. violet 30 65
982. – 42 g.+42 g. brown 30 65
983. – 1 s.+1 s. red 45 1·00
984. – 2 s.+2 s. red 50 1·60

DESIGNS: 6 g. Broom sweeping Nazi and Fascist emblems. 8 g. St. Stephen's Cathedral in flames. 12 g. Hand and barbed wire. 30 g. Hand strangling snake. 42 g. Hammer and broken column. 1 s. Hand and Austrian flag. 2 s. Eagle and smoking Nazi emblem.

**1946.** Congress of Society for Promotion of Cultural and Economic Relations with the Soviet Union. No. 932 optd with T 153.
985 12 g. brown 10 30

**154.** Mare and foal.

**155.** Ruprecht's Church, Vienna.

**1946.** Austria Prize Race Fund.
986. 154. 16+16 g. red 2·50 3·50
987. – 24+24 g. violet 2·50 3·00
988. – 60+60 g. green 2·50 3·00
989. – 1+1 s. blue 2·50 3·00
990. – 2+2 s. brown 2·50 4·00

DESIGNS: 24 g. Two horses' heads. 60 g. Racehorse clearing hurdle. 1 s. Three racehorses. 2 s. Three horses' heads.

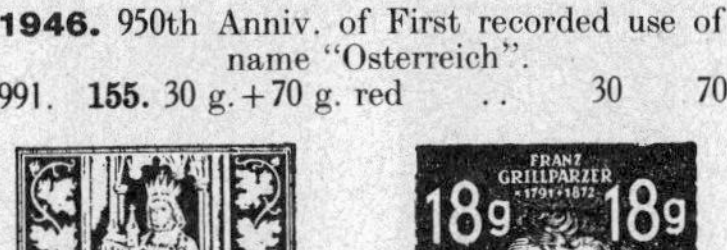

**1946.** 950th Anniv. of First recorded use of name "Osterreich".
991. 155. 30 g.+70 g. red 30 70

**156.** Statue of Duke Rudolf.

**157.** Franz Grillparzer (dramatic poet).

**1946.** St. Stephen's Cathedral Reconstruction Fund. Architectural and Sculptural designs.
992. 156. 3 g.+12 g. brown 15 40
993. – 5 g.+20 g. purple 15 40
994. – 6 g.+24 g. blue 15 40
995. – 8 g.+32 g. green 15 40
996. – 10 g.+40 g. blue 20 65
997. – 12 g.+48 g. violet 30 1·00
998. – 30 g.+1 s. 20 red 60 2·25
999. – 50 g.+1 s. 80 blue 85 2·50
1000. – 1 s.+5 s. purple 1·00 3·50
1001. – 2 s.+10 s. brown 1·75 9·00

DESIGNS: 5 g. Tomb of Frederick III. 6 g. Pulpit. 8 g. Statue of St. Stephen. 10 g. Statue of Madonna and Child. 12 g. Altar. 30 g. Organ. 50 g. Anton Pilgram. 1 s. North-east Tower. 2 s. South-west Spire.

**1947.** Famous Austrians.
1002. – 12 g. green 10 15
1003. 157. 18 g. purple 10 15
1004. – 20 g. green 40 15
1005. – 40 g. brown 9·00 5·00
1006. – 40 g. green 8·50 7·00
1007. – 60 g. lake 40 30

PORTRAITS: 12 g. Franz Schubert (composer). 20 g. Carl Michael Ziehrer (composer). 40 g. (No. 1005), Adalbert Stifter (poet). 40 g. (No. 1006), Anton Bruckner (composer). 60 g. Friedrich Amerling (painter).

**158.** Harvesting.

**159.** Airplane over Hinterstoder.

**1947.** Vienna Fair Fund.
1009. 158. 3 g.+2 g. brown 40 70
1010. – 8 g.+2 g. green 40 70
1011. – 10 g.+5 g. slate 40 70
1012. – 12 g.+8 g. violet 40 70
1013. – 18 g.+12 g. olive 40 70
1014. – 30 g.+10 g. purple 40 70
1015. – 35 g.+15 g. red 40 70
1016. – 60 g.+20 g. blue 40 70

DESIGNS: 8 g. Logging. 10 g. Factory. 12 g. Pithead. 18 g. Oil wells. 30 g. Textile machinery. 35 g. Foundry. 60 g. Electric cables.

**1947.** Air.
1017 – 50 g. brown 15 20
1018 – 1 s. purple 20 25
1019 – 2 s. green 35 40
1020 159 3 s. brown 1·75 2·50
1021 – 4 s. green 1·25 1·75
1022 – 5 s. blue 1·25 1·75
1023 – 10 s. blue 60 1·25

DESIGNS—Airplane over: 50 g. Windmill at St. Andra. 1 s. Heidentor. 2 s. Gmund. 4 s. Pragraten. 5 s. Torsaule. 10 s. St. Charles's Church, Vienna.

**160.** Beaker (15th cent.).

**161.** Racehorse.

**1947.** National Art Exn. Fund.
1024. 160. 3 g.+2 g. brown 20 50
1025. – 8 g.+2 g. green 20 50
1026. – 10 g.+5 g. red 20 50
1027. – 12 g.+8 g. violet 20 50
1028. – 18 g.+12 g. brown 20 50
1029. – 20 g.+10 g. violet 20 50
1030. – 30 g.+10 g. green 20 50
1031. – 35 g.+15 g. red 20 50
1032. – 48 g.+12 g. purple 20 50
1033. – 60 g.+20 g. blue 20 50

DESIGNS: 8 g. Statue of "Providence" (Donner). 10 g. Benedictine Monastery, Melk. 12 g. "Wife of Dr. Brante of Vienna". 18 g. "Children in a Window" (Waldmuller). 20 g. Belvedere Palace Gateway. 30 g. Figure of "Egeria" on fountain at Schonbrunn. 35 g. National Library, Vienna. 48 g. "Copper Printer's (Ernst Rohm) Workshop" (Ferdinand Schmutzer). 60 g. "Girl in Straw Hat" (Amerling).

**1947.** Vienna Prize Race Fund.
1034 161 60+20 g. blue on pink 15 30

**163.** Prisoner-of-War. **165.** Globe and Tape Machine.

**1947.** Prisoners-of-War Relief Fund.
1063. 163. 8 g.+2 g. green 15 30
1064. – 12 g.+8 g. brown 15 40
1065. – 18 g.+12 g. black 15 30
1066. – 35 g.+15 g. purple 15 30
1067. – 60 g.+20 g. blue 15 30
1068. – 1 s.+40 g. brown 15 50

DESIGNS: 12 g. Letter from home. 18 g. Gruesome camp visitor. 35 g. Soldier and family reunited. 60 g. Industry beckons returned soldier. 1 s. Soldier sowing.

**1947.** Nos. 934 and 941 surch.
1069 75 g. on 38 g. green 10 15
1070 1 s. 40 on 16 g. brown 40 15

**1947.** Telegraph Centenary.
1071 165 40 g. violet 10 20

**1947.** Currency Revaluation. As T **146.**
1072. 3 g. red (Lermoos) 10 10
1073. 5 g. red (Leopoldsberg) 10 10
1074. 10 g. red (Hochosterwitz) 10 10
1075. 15 g. red (Forchtenstein) 1·60 1·60

As T **146.** but larger (23½ × 29 mm.)
1076. 20 g. red (Gebhartsberg) 35 10
1077. 30 g. red (Neusiedler Lake) 60 15
1078. 40 g. red (Mariazell) 60 10
1079. 50 g. red (Silvretta Peaks) 70 10
1080. 60 g. red (Semmering) 8·00 1·25
1081. 70 g. red (Badgastein) 3·25 10
1082. 80 g. red (Kaisergebirge) 3·50 10
1083. 90 g. red (Wayside Shrine, Tragoss) 3·50 55

As T **148.**
1084. 1 s. violet (Durnstein) 55 10
1085. 2 s. violet (St. Christof) 70 15
1086. 3 s. violet (Heiligenblut) 10·00 85
1086a. 5 s. violet (Schonbrunn) 11·00 1·25

Nos. 1072/86a in new currency replaced previous issue at rate of 3 s. (old) = 1 s. (new).

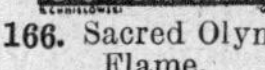
**166.** Sacred Olympic Flame.

**167.** Laabenbach Viaduct, Neulenbach.

**1948.** Fund for Entries to 5th Winter Olympic Games, St. Moritz.
1087 166 1 s.+50 g. blue 15 30

**1948.** Reconstruction Fund.
1088. 167. 10 g.+5 g. grey 20 20
1089. – 20 g.+10 g. violet 20 20
1090. – 30 g.+10 g. green 30 30
1091. – 40 g.+20 g. green 15 15
1092. – 45 g.+20 g. blue 10 15
1093. – 60 g.+30 g. red 10 15
1094. – 75 g.+35 g. purple 10 15
1095. – 80 g.+40 g. purple 10 15
1096. – 1 s.+50 g. blue 10 15
1097. – 1 s. 40+70 g. lake 25 35

DESIGNS (showing reconstruction): 20 g. Vermunt Lake Dam. 30 g. Danube Port, Vienna. 40 g. Erzberg open-cast mine. 45 g. Southern Railway Station, Vienna. 60 g. Flats. 75 g. Vienna Gas Works. 80 g. Oil refinery. 1 s. Mountain roadway. 1 s. 40, Parliament Building.

**169.** Violets.

**170.** Vorarlberg Montafon.

**1948.** Anti-tuberculosis Fund.
1098 169 10 g.+5 g. violet, mauve and green 25 10
1099 – 20 g.+10 g. green, lt green & yellow 15 10
1100 – 30 g.+10 g. brown, yellow and green 3·50 2·50
1101 – 40 g.+20 g. green, yellow and orange 50 20
1102 – 45 g.+20 g. purple, mauve and yellow 15 10
1103 – 60 g.+30 g. red, mauve and green 15 10
1104 – 75 g.+35 g. green, pink and yellow 15 10
1105 – 80 g.+40 g. blue, pink and green 25 15
1106 – 1 s.+50 g. blue, ultramarine & green 30 20
1107 – 1 s. 40+70 g. green, blue and yellow 75 50

FLOWERS: 20 g. Anemone. 30 g. Crocus. 40 g. Primrose. 45 g. Pasque flower. 60 g. Rhododendron. 75 g. Wild rose. 80 g. Cyclamen. 1 s. Gentian. 1 s. 40, Edelweiss.

**1948.** Provincial Costumes.
1108. – 3 g. grey 45 70
1109. – 5 g. green 10 10
1110. – 10 g. blue 10 10
1111. – 15 g. brown 50 10
1112. 170. 20 g. green 15 10
1113. – 25 g. brown 15 10
1114. – 30 g. red 2·25 10
1115. – 30 g. violet 15 10
1116. – 40 g. violet 2·25 10
1117. – 40 g. green 15 10
1118. – 45 g. blue 2·25 45
1119. – 50 g. brown 15 10
1120. – 60 g. red 20 10
1121. – 70 g. green 15 10
1122. – 75 g. blue 4·50 45
1123. – 80 g. rose 30 10
1124. – 90 g. purple 30·00 35
1125. – 1 s. blue 6·00 10
1126. – 1 s. red 60·00 10
1127. – 1 s. green 30 10
1128. – 1 s. 20 violet 35 10
1129. – 1 s. 40 brown 2·00 20
1130. – 1 s. 45 red 1·00 10
1131. – 1 s. 50 blue 90 10
1132. – 1 s. 60 red 30 10
1133. – 1 s. 70 blue 2·25 60
1134. – 2 s. green 30 10
1135. – 2 s. 20 slate 2·00 10
1136. – 2 s. 40 blue 80 10
1137. – 2 s. 50 brown 2·25 1·25
1138. – 2 s. 70 brown 55 60
1139. – 3 s. lake 1·50 10
1140. – 3 s. 50 green 13·00 10
1141. – 4 s. 50 purple 75 75
1142. – 5 s. purple 75 10
1143. – 7 s. olive 1·00 15
1144. – 10 s. grey 22·00 3·50

DESIGNS—As T 170: 3 g. "Tirol Inntal". 5 g. "Salzburg Pinzgau". 10, 75 g. "Steiermark Salzkammergut" (different designs). 15 g. "Burgenland Lutzmannsburg". 25 g., 1 s. 60 "Wien 1850" (two different designs). 30 g. (2) "Salzburg Pongau". 40 g. (2) "Wien 1840". 45 g. "Karnten Lesachtal". 50 g. "Vorarlberg Bregenzerwald". 60 g. "Karnten Lavanttal". 70 g. "Niederosterreich Wachau". 80 g. "Steiermark Ennstal". 90 g. "Steiermark Mittelsteier". 1 s. (3) "Tirol Pustertal". 1 s. 20 "Niederosterreich Wienerwald". 1 s. 40 "Oberosterreich Innviertel". 1 s. 45, "Wilten bei Innsbruck". 1 s. 50, "Wien 1853". 1 s. 70 "Ost Tirol Kals". 2 s. "Oberosterreich". 2 s. 20 "Ischl 1820". 2 s. 40, "Kitzbuhel". 2 s. 50 "Obersteiermark 1850". 2 s. 70, "Kleines Walsertal". 3 s. "Burgenland". 3 s. 50 "Niederosterreich 1850". 4 s. 50, "Gailtal". 5 s. "Zillertal". 7 s. "Steiermark Sulmtal". 25 × 35 mm: 10 s. "Wien 1850".

**172.** Kunstlerhaus.

**173.** Hans Makart.

**1948.** 80th Anniv. of Creative Artists' Assn.
1145. 172. 20 g.+10 g. green 6·00 6·00
1146. 173. 30 g.+15 g. brown 2·50 2·50
1147. – 40 g.+20 g. blue 2·50 2·50
1148. – 50 g.+25 g. violet 3·75 3·75
1149. – 60 g.+30 g. red 3·75 3·75
1150. – 1 s.+50 g. blue 5·50 5·50
1151. – 1 s. 40 g.+70 g. brown 9·00 9·00

PORTRAITS: 40 g. K. Kundmann. 50 g. A. von Siccardsburg. 60 g. H. Canon. 1 s. W. Unger. 1 s. 40 g. Friedr. Schmidt.

**174.** St. Rupert. **175.** Pres. Renner.

**1948.** Salzburg Cathedral Reconstruction Fund.

1152. **174.** 20 g.+10 g. green .. 3·75 6·00
1153. – 30 g.+15 g. brown .. 1·75 3·25
1154. – 40 g.+20 g. green .. 1·25 2·00
1155. – 50 g.+25 g. brown .. 25 50
1156. – 60 g.+30 g. red .. 25 50
1157. – 80 g.+40 g. purple .. 25 50
1158. – 1 s.+50 g. blue .. 35 70
1159. – 1 s. 40+70 g. green .. 75 1·25

DESIGNS: 30, 40, 50, 80 g. Views of Salzburg Cathedral. 60 g. St. Peter's. 1 s. Cathedral and Fortress. 1 s. 40, Madonna.

**1948.** 30th Anniv. of Republic.

1160. **175.** 1 s. blue .. .. 1·25 1·25

See also Nos. 1224 and 1333.

**176.** F. Gruber and J. Mohr. **177.** Boy and Hare.

**1948.** 130th Anniv. of Composition of Carol "Silent Night, Holy Night".

1161. **176.** 60 g. brown .. .. 4·50 4·50

**1949.** Child Welfare Fund.

1162. **177.** 40 g.+10 g. purple .. 12·00 12·00
1163. – 60 g.+20 g. red .. 12·00 12·00
1164. – 1 s.+25 g. blue .. 12·00 12·00
1165. – 1 s. 40+35 g. green .. 12·00 12·00

DESIGNS: 60 g. Two girls and apples in boot. 1 s. Boy and birthday cake. 1 s. 40, Girl praying before candle.

**178.** Boy and Dove. **179.** Johann Strauss.

**1949.** U.N. Int. Children's Emergency Fund.

1166. **178.** 1 s. blue .. .. 7·50 85

**1949.** 50th Death Anniv. of Johann Strauss, the younger (composer).

1167. **179.** 1 s. blue .. .. 2·50 1·50

See also Nos. 1174, 1207 and 1229.

**180.** Esperanto Star. **181.** St. Gebhard.

**1949.** Esperanto Congress, Vienna.

1168. **180.** 20 g. green .. .. 65 45

**1949.** Birth Millenary of St. Gebhard (Bishop of Vorarlberg).

1169. **181.** 30 g. violet .. .. 1·50 1·40

**182.** Seal of Duke Friedrich II, 1230. **183.** Allegory of U.P.U.

**1949.** Prisoners-of-War Relief Fund. Arms.

1170 **182** 40 g.+10 g. yell & brn 5·00 5·50
1171 – 60 g.+15 g. pink and purple .. .. 5·00 5·50
1172 – 1 s.+25 g. red & blue 5·00 5·50
1173 – 1 s. 60+40 g. pink and green .. .. 5·00 5·50

ARMS: 60 g. Princes of Austria, 1450. 1 s. Austria, 1600. 1 s. 60, Austria, 1945.

**1949.** Death Centenary of Johann Strauss, the elder (composer). Portrait as T **179** inscr "1804–1849".

1174 30 g. purple .. .. 2·75 2·00

**1949.** 75th Anniv of U.P.U.

1175 **183** 40 g. green .. .. 2·25 2·00
1176 – 60 g. red .. .. 2·25 2·00
1177 – 1 s. blue .. .. 4·00 5·50

DESIGNS: 60 g. Children holding "75". 1 s. Womens head.

**185.** Magnifying Glass and Covers. **186.** M. M. Daffinger.

**1949.** Stamp Day.

1206. **185.** 60 g.+15 g. brown .. 1·60 1·90

**1949.** 50th Death Anniv. of Karl Millocker (composer). Portrait as T **179** inscr. "1842–1899 KARL MILLOCKER".

1207. 1 s. blue .. .. .. 12·00 9·00

**1950.** 160th Birth Anniv of Moritz Michael Daffinger (painter).

1208 **186** 60 g. brown .. .. 3·50 4·00

**187.** A. Hofer.

**1950.** 140th Death Anniv. of Andreas Hofer (patriot).

1209. **187.** 60 g. violet .. .. 10·00 8·00

See also Nos. 1211, 1223, 1232, 1234, 1243, 1253, 1288 and 1386.

**188.** Stamp of 1850. **189.** Arms of Austria and Carinthia.

**1950.** Austrian Stamp Centenary.

1210. **188.** 1 s. black on yellow .. 1·10 75

**1950.** Death Centenary of Josef Madersperger (sewing machine inventor). Portrait as T **187**.

1211 60 g. violet .. .. 3·50 3·25

**1950.** 30th Anniv of Carinthian Plebiscite.

1212 **189** 60 g.+15 g. grn & brn 20·00 17·00
1213 – 1 s.+25 g. red & orge 23·00 19·00
1214 – 1 s. 70+40 g. blue and turquoise .. .. 23·00 20·00

DESIGNS: 1 s. Carinthian waving Austrian flag. 1 s. 70, Hand and ballot box.

**190.** Rooks. **191.** Philatelist.

**1950.** Air.

1215. **190.** 60 g. violet .. .. 5·00 2·00
1216. – 1 s. violet (Barn swallows) .. .. 27·00 18·00
1217. – 2 s. blue (Black-headed gulls) .. 15·00 6·00
1218. – 3 s. turquoise (Common cormorants) £120 75·00
1219. – 5 s. brown (Common buzzard) .. .. £120 75·00
1220. – 10 s. purple (Grey heron) .. .. 60·00 35·00
1221. – 20 s. sepia (Golden eagle) .. .. 9·00 4·25

**1950.** Stamp Day.

1222. **191.** 60 g.+15 g. green .. 4·50 5·50

**1950.** Birth Centenary of Alexander Girardi (actor). Portrait as T **187**.

1223 30 g. blue .. .. 1·10 90

**192.** Dr. Renner. **193.** Miner.

**1951.** Death of President Karl Renner.

1224. **192.** 1 s. black on lemon 80 15

**1951.** Reconstruction Fund.

1225. **193.** 40 g.+10 g. purple .. 9·50 9·50
1226. – 60 g.+15 g. green .. 9·50 9·50
1227. – 1 s.+25 g. brown .. 9·50 9·50
1228. – 1 s. 70+40 g. blue .. 9·50 9·50

DESIGNS: 60 g. Bricklayer. 1 s. Bridge-builder. 1 s. 70, Telegraph engineer.

**1951.** 150th Birth Anniv. of Joseph Lanner (composer). As T **179** but portrait of Lanner inscr. "1801 1843".

1229. 60 g. green .. 2·50 1·60

**194.** M. J. Schmidt. **195.** Scout Badge.

**1951.** 150th Death Anniv. of Schmidt (painter).

1230. **194.** 1 s. red .. .. 3·25 2·25

**1951.** Boy Scout Jamboree.

1231. **195.** 1 s. red, yellow & green 4·00 3·50

**1951.** 10th Death Anniv of Wilhelm Kienzl (composer). Portrait as T **187**.

1232 1 s. 50 blue .. .. 2·50 1·00

**196.** Laurel Branch and Olympic Emblem. **197.** Schrammel.

**1952.** 6th Winter Olympic Games, Oslo.

1233. **196.** 2 s. 40+60 g. green .. 13·00 15·00

**1952.** 150th Birth Anniv. of Karl Ritter von Ghega (railway engineer). As T **187** but portrait of Von Ghega inscr. "1802–1860".

1234. 1 s. green .. .. 4·75 90

**1952.** Birth Centenary of Josef Schrammel (composer).

1235 **197** 1 s. 50 g. blue .. .. 4·50 1·25

See also No. 1239.

**198.** Cupid and Letter. **199.** Breakfast Pavilion.

**1952.** Stamp Day.

1236. **198.** 1 s. 50 g.+35 g. purple 15·00 17·00

**1952.** Bicent. of Schonbrunn Menagerie.

1237. **199.** 1 s. 50 green .. .. 3·75 1·50

**200.** **202.**

**1952.** Int. Union of Socialist Youth Camp, Vienna.

1238. **200.** 1 s. 50 blue .. .. 3·00 75

**1952.** 150th Birth Anniv of Nikolaus Lenau (writer). Portrait as T **197**.

1239 1 s. green .. .. 3·00 1·40

**1952.** Int Children's Correspondence.

1240 **202** 2 s. 40 blue .. .. 6·00 1·75

**203.** "Christus Pantocrator" (sculpture). **204.** Hugo Wolf.

**1952.** Austrian Catholics' Day.

1241. **203.** 1 s.+25 g. olive .. 9·00 12·00

**1953.** 50th Death Anniv. of Wolf (composer).

1242. **204.** 1 s. 50 blue .. .. 8·00 1·00

**1953.** President Korner's 80th Birthday. As T **187** but portrait of Korner.

1243. 1 s. 50 blue .. .. 3·75 90

For 1 s. 50 black, see No. 1288.

**1953.** 60th Anniv of Austrian Trade Union Movement. As No. 955 (colour changed) surch **GEWERKSCHAFTS BEWEGUNG 60 JAHRE 1s+25g.**

1244 1 s.+25 on 5 s. blue .. 3·00 3·25

**206.** Linz National Theatre. **207.** Meeting house, Steyr.

**1953.** 150th Anniv of Linz National Theatre.

1245 **206** 1 s. 50 turquoise .. 13·00 2·00

**1953.** Vienna Evangelical School Rebuilding Fund.

1246. **207.** 70 g.+15 g. purple .. 20 30
1247. – 1 s.+25 g. blue .. 40 40
1248. – 1 s. 50+40 g. brown 70 75
1249. – 2 s. 40+60 g. green 2·75 3·50
1250. – 3 s.+75 g. lilac .. 7·50 9·00

DESIGNS: 1 s. J. Kepler (astronomer). 1 s. 50, Lutheran Bible, 1534. 2 s. 40, T. von Hansen (architect). 3 s. School after reconstruction.

**208.** Child and Christmas Tree. **209.**

**1953.** Christmas

1251. **208.** 1 s. green .. .. 80 15

See also No. 1266.

**1953.** Stamp Day.

1252. **209.** 1 s.+25 g. brown .. 3·00 4·00

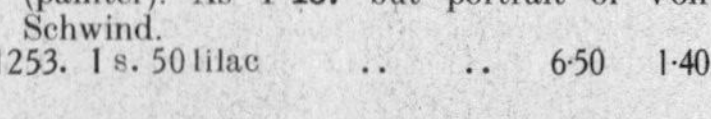

**1954.** 150th Birth Anniv. of M. Von Schwind (painter). As T **187** but portrait of Von Schwind.

1253. 1 s. 50 lilac .. .. 6·50 1·40

**210.** Baron K. von Rokitansky. **212.** Surgeon with Microscope.

**1954.** 150th Birth Anniv. of Von Rokitansky (anatomist).

1254 **210** 1 s. 50 violet .. 16·00 2·00

See also No. 1264.

**1954.** Avalanche Fund. As No. 953 (colour changed) surch **LAWINENOPFER 1954 1 s + 20 g.**

1255 1 s.+20 g. blue .. 15 15

**1954.** Health Service Fund.
1256. – 30 g.+10 g. violet.. 1·25 1·40
1257. **212.** 70 g.+15 g. brown.. 25 15
1258. – 1 s.+25 g. blue .. 30 20
1259. – 1 s. 45+35 g. green 40 30
1260. – 1 s. 50+35 g. red .. 5·50 5·50
1261. – 2 s. 40+60 g. purple 6·00 13·50
DESIGNS: 30 g. Boy patient and sun-ray lamp. 1 s. Mother and children. 1 s. 45, Operating theatre. 1 s. 50, Baby on scales. 2 s. 40, Red Cross nurse and ambulance.

**213.** Esperanto Star.

**214.** J. M. Rottmayr von Rosenbrunn.

**1954.** 50th Anniv of Esperanto in Austria.
1262 **213** 1 s. green & brown .. 2·75 25

**1954.** Birth Tercentenary of Rottmayr von Rosenbrunn (painter).
1263 **214** 1 s. green .. 6·00 2·25

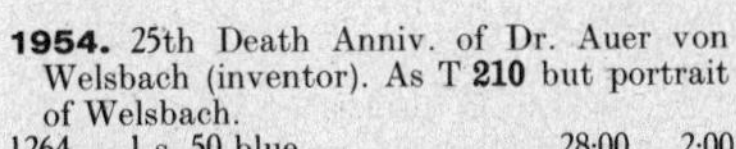

**1954.** 25th Death Anniv. of Dr. Auer von Welsbach (inventor). As T **210** but portrait of Welsbach.
1264. 1 s. 50 blue .. .. 28·00 2·00

**216.** Great Organ, Church of St. Florian.

**217.** 18th-century River Boat.

**1954.** 2nd Int. Congress of Catholic Church Music, Vienna.
1265. **216.** 1 s. brown .. .. 2·00 25

**1954.** Christmas. As No. 1251, but colour changed.
1266 **208** 1 s. blue .. .. 1·75 25

**1954.** Stamp Day.
1267. **217.** 1 s.+25 g. green .. 4·75 4·75

**218.** Arms of Austria and Newspapers.

**1954.** 150th Anniv of State Printing Works and 250th Anniv of "Wiener-Zeitung" (newspaper).
1268 **218** 1 s. black and red .. 1·50 15

**219.** " Freedom ".

**1955.** 10th Anniv. of Re-establishment of Austrian Republic.
1269. – 70 g. purple .. .. 1·40 15
1270. – 1 s. blue .. .. 6·50 15
1271. **219.** 1 s. 45 red .. .. 8·00 4·00
1272. – 1 s. 50 brown .. 21·00 15
1273. – 2 s. 40 green.. .. 8·50 4·50
DESIGNS: 70 g. Parliament Buildings. 1 s. Western Railway Terminus. 1 s. 50, Modern houses. 2 s. 40, Limberg Dam.

**1955.** Austrian State Treaty. As No. 888 but colour changed optd **STAATSVERTRAG 1955.**
1274 **142** 2 s. grey .. .. 75 25

**221.** " Strength through Unity ".

**1955.** 4th World Trades' Union Congress, Vienna.
1275. **221.** 1 s. blue .. .. 80 1·25

**222.** " Return to Work ".

**1955.** Returned Prisoners-of-War Relief Fund.
1276. **222.** 1 s.+25 g. brown .. 1·25 1·50

**223.** Burgtheater, Vienna.

**1955.** Re-opening of Burgtheater and State Opera House, Vienna.
1277. **223.** 1 s. 50 brown .. 4·00 20
1278. – 2 s. 40 blue (Opera House) .. .. 4·50 2·25

**224.** Globe and Flags.

**225.** Stamp Collector.

**1955.** 10th Anniversary of U.N.O.
1279. **224.** 2 s. 40 green.. .. 5·50 1·40

**1955.** Stamp Day.
1280. **225.** 1 s.+25 g. brown .. 3·50 3·75

**226.** Mozart.

**227.**

**1956.** Birth Bicent. of Mozart (composer).
1281. **226.** 2 s. 40 blue .. .. 2·25 70

**1956.** Admission of Austria into U.N.
1282. **227.** 2 s. 40 brown .. 11·00 1·00

**228.**

**229.** Vienna and Five New Towns.

**1956.** 5th World Power Conference, Vienna.
1283. **228.** 2 s. 40 blue .. .. 7·00 1·40

**1956.** 23rd Int. Town Planning Congress.
1284. **229.** 1 s. 45 red, blk. & grn. 1·75 55

**230.** J. B. Fischer von Erlach.

**231.** " Stamp Day ".

**1956.** Birth Tercentenary of Fischer von Erlach (architect).
1285. **230.** 1 s. 50 brown .. 75 1·25

**1956.** Stamp Day.
1286. **231.** 1 s.+25 g. red .. 1·60 2·50

**1956.** Hungarian Relief Fund. As No. 1173, but colours changed, surch **1956 1·50 +50 UNGARNHILFE.**
1287 1 s. 50+50 g. on 1 s. 60 +40 g. red and grey .. 20 30

**1957.** Death of President Korner. As No. 1243 but colour changed.
1288. 1 s. 50 black .. .. 1·50 1·50

**233.** J. Wagner von Jauregg.

**234.** Anton Wildgans.

**1957.** Birth Centenary of Wagner von Jauregg (psychiatrist).
1289. **233.** 2 s. 40 brown .. 2·25 90

**1957.** 25th Death Anniv. of Anton Wildgans (poet).
1290. **234.** 1 s. blue .. .. 25 20

**235.** Early and Modern Postal Coaches.

**1957.** 50th Anniv. of Postal Coach Service.
1291. **235.** 1 s. black on yellow.. 30 20

**237.** Mt. Gasherbrum II.

**236.** Mariazell Basilica.

**1957.** Austrian Himalaya-Karakorum Expedition, 1956.
1293. **237.** 1 s. 50 blue .. .. 45 20

**1957.** Buildings. (a) Size $20\frac{1}{2} \times 24\frac{1}{2}$ mm.
1295 – 20 g. purple .. .. 10 10
1296 – 30 g. green .. .. 15 10
1297 – 40 g. red .. .. 10 10
1298 – 50 g. grey .. .. 15 10
1299 – 60 g. brown .. .. 20 10
1300 – 70 g. blue .. .. 15 10
1301 – 80 g. brown .. .. 20 10
1302 **236** 1 s. brown .. .. 1·25 10
1303 – 1 s. brown .. .. 25 10
1304 – 1 s. 20 purple .. .. 30 10
1305 – 1 s. 30 green .. .. 20 10
1306 – 1 s. 40 blue .. .. 30 10
1307 – 1 s. 50 red .. .. 30 10
1308 – 1 s. 80 blue .. .. 30 10
1309 – 2 s. blue .. .. 3·50 10
1310 – 2 s. blue .. .. 30 10
1311 – 2 s. 20 green .. .. 60 10
1312 – 2 s. 50 violet .. .. 45 10
1313 – 3 s. blue .. .. 50 10
1314 – 3 s. 40 green .. .. 70 60
1315 – 3 s. 50 mauve .. .. 55 10
1316 – 4 s. violet .. .. 60 10
1317 – 4 s. 50 green .. .. 80 15
1318 – 5 s. 50 green .. .. 55 10
1319 – 6 s. violet .. .. 80 10
1320 – 6 s. 40 blue .. .. 1·00 80
1321 – 8 s. purple .. .. 1·25 15

(b) Larger
1322 – 10 s. green .. .. 2·50 15
1323 – 20 s. purple .. .. 2·00 45

(c) Smaller, size $17\frac{1}{2} \times 21$ mm
1324 – 50 g. grey .. .. 20 10
1325 **236** 1 s. brown .. .. 20 10
1326 – 1 s. 50 purple .. .. 20 10
DESIGNS: 20 g. Old Courtyard, Morbisch. 30 g. Vienna Town Hall. 40 g. Porcia Castle, Spittal. 50 g. Heiligenstadt flats. 60 g. Lederer Tower, Wels. 70 g. Archbishop's Palace, Salzburg. 80 g. Old farmhouse, Pinzgau. 1 s. (1303) Millstatt. 1 s. 20, Corn Measurer's House, Bruck-on-the-Mur. 1 s. 30, Schattenburg Castle. 1 s. 40, Klagenfurt Town Hall. 1 s. 50, "Rabenhof" Flats, Erdberg, Vienna. 1 s. 80, Mint Tower, Hall-in-Tyrol. 2 s. (1309) Christkindl Church. 2 s. (1310) Dragon Fountain, Klagenfurt. 2 s. 20, Beethoven's House, Heiligenstadt, Vienna. 2 s. 50, Danube Bridge, Linz. 3 s. "Swiss Portal", Imperial Palace, Vienna. 3 s. 40, Stein Gate, Krems-on-the-Danube. 3 s. 50, Esterhazy Palace, Eisenstadt. 4 s. Vienna Gate, Hainburg. 4 s. 50, Schwechat Airport. 5 s. 50, Chur Gate, Feldkirch. 6 s. Graz Town Hall. 6 s. 40, "Golden Roof", Innsbruck. 8 s. Steyr Town Hall. $22 \times 28\frac{1}{2}$ mm: 10 s. Heidenreichstein Castle. $28\frac{1}{2} \times 37\frac{1}{2}$ mm: 20 s. Melk Abbey.

**238.** Post Office, Linz.

**239.** Badgastein.

**1957.** Stamp Day.
1327. **238.** 1 s.+25 g. green .. 3·00 3·25

**1958.** International Alpine Ski Championships, Badgastein.
1328 **239** 1 s. 50 blue .. .. 20 15

**240.** Vickers Viscount 800.

**241.** Mother and Child.

**1958.** Austrian Airlines Inaugural Flight, Vienna–London.
1329. **240.** 4 s. red .. .. 45 20

**1958.** Mothers' Day.
1330. **241.** 1 s. 50 blue .. .. 15 15

**242.** Walther von der Vogelweide (after 12th-century manuscript).

**243.** Dr. O. Redlich.

**1958.** 3rd Austrian Choir Festival, Vienna.
1331. **242.** 1 s. 50 multicoloured 25 15

**1958.** Birth Cent of Dr. Oswald Redlich (historian).
1332. **243.** 2 s. 40 blue .. .. 30 20

**1958.** 40th Anniv. of Republic. As T **175** but inscr. "40 JAHRE".
1333. **175.** 1 s. 50 green.. .. 20 25

**244.** Post Office, Kitzbuhel.

**1958** Stamp Day.
1334 **244** 2 s. 40+60 g. blue .. 70 85

**245.** " E " building on Map of Europe.

**246.** Monopoly Emblem and Cigars.

**1959.** Europa.
1335. **245.** 2 s. 40 green.. .. 20 25

**1959.** 175th Anniv. of Austrian Tobacco Monopoly.
1336. **246.** 2 s. 40 brown .. 20 15

**247.** Archduke Johann.

**248.** Capercailie.

**1959.** Death Centenary of Archduke Johann of Austria.
1337 **247** 1 s. 50 green .. .. 20 15

**1959.** Int Hunting Congress, Vienna.
1338 **248** 1 s. purple .. .. 65 25
1339 – 1 s. 50 blue (Roebuck) 80 10
1340 – 2 s. 40 grn (Wild boar) 80 80
1341 – 3 s. 50 brown (Red deer family) .. 60 60

**249.** Haydn.  **250.** Tyrolean Eagle.

**1959.** 150th Death Anniv of Haydn.
1342 **249** 1 s. 50 purple .. 80 15

**1959.** 150th Anniv. of Tyrolese Rising.
1343. **250.** 1 s. 50 red .. .. 20 15

**251.** Microwave Transmitting Aerial Zugspitze.  **252.** Handball Player.

**1959.** Inaug of Austrian Microwave Network.
1344 **251** 2 s. 40 blue .. .. 20 20

**1959.** Sports.
1345 – 1 s. violet .. .. 25 20
1346 **252** 1 s. 50 green .. .. 70 35
1347 – 1 s. 80 red .. .. 45 45
1348 – 2 s. purple .. .. 30 20
1349 – 2 s. 20 blue .. .. 25 20
DESIGNS: 1 s. Runner. 1 s. 80, Gymnast. 2 s. Hurdling. 2 s. 20, Hammer thrower.

**253.** Orchestral Instruments.  **254.** Roman Coach.

**1959.** Vienna Philharmonic Orchestra's World Tour.
1350. **253.** 2 s. 40 black and blue 30 20

**1959.** Stamp Day.
1351. **254.** 2 s. 40+60 g. black and mauve .. 55 65

**255.** Refugees.  **256.** Pres. Adolf Scharf.

**1960.** World Refugee Year.
1352. **255.** 3 s. turquoise .. 30 30

**1960.** President's 70th Birthday.
1353. **256.** 1 s. 50 green .. .. 35 15

**257.** Youth Hostellers.  **258.** Dr. Anton Eiselsberg.

**1960.** Youth Hostels Movement.
1354. **257.** 1 s. red .. .. 15 15

**1960.** Birth Centenary of Dr. Anton Eiselsberg (surgeon).
1355. **258.** 1 s. 50 sepia and cream .. 65 20

**259.** Gustav Mahler.  **260.** Jakob Prandtauer.

**1960.** Birth Centenary of Gustav Mahler (composer).
1356. **259.** 1 s. 50 brown .. 65 20

**1960.** 300th Birth Anniv. of Jakob Prandtauer (architect).
1357. **260.** 1 s. 50 brown .. 35 15

**261.** Grossglockner Highway.  **262.** Ionic Capital.

**1960.** 25th Anniv. of Grossglockner Alpine Highway.
1358. **261.** 1 s. 80 blue .. .. 35 35

**1960.** Europa.
1359. **262.** 3 s. black .. .. 1·25 55

**263.** Griffen, Carinthia.

**1960.** 40th Anniv. of Carinthian Plebiscite.
1360. **263.** 1 s. 50 green .. .. 30 15

**264.** Examining Proof of Engraved Stamp.  **265.** "Freedom".

**1960.** Stamp Day.
1361. **264.** 3 s.+70 g. brown .. 40 70

**1961.** Austrian Freedom Martyrs' Commem.
1362 **265** 1 s. 50 red .. .. 20 15

**266.** Hansa Brandenburg C-1.  **267.** Transport and Multi-unit Electric Train.

**1961.** "LUPOSTA" Exn., Vienna, and 1st Austrian Airmail Service Commem.
1363. **266.** 5 s. blue .. .. 50 35

**1961.** European Transport Ministers' Meeting.
1364. **267.** 3 s. olive and red .. 1·10 40

**268.** "Mower in the Alps" (Detail, A. Egger-Lienz).  **269.** Observatory on Sonnblick Mountain.

**1961.** Cent. of Kunstlerhaus, Vienna. Inscr. as in T **268.**
1365. **268.** 1 s. purple and brown 20 15
1366. – 1 s. 50 lilac & brown .. 25 25
1367. – 3 s. green & brown .. 90 90
1368. – 5 s. violet & brown .. 60 60
PAINTINGS: 1 s. 50, "The Kiss" (after A. von Pettenkofen). 3 s. "Portrait of a Girl" (after A. Romako). 5 s. "The Triumph of Ariadne" (detail of Ariadne, after Hans Makart).

**1961.** 75th Anniv. of Sonnblick Meteorological Observatory.
1369. **269.** 1 s. 80 blue .. .. 40 35

**270.** Lavanttaler Colliery.  **271.** Mercury.

**1961.** 15th Anniv. of Nationalised Industries. Inscr. "JAHRE VERSTAATLICHTE UNTERNEHMUNGEN".
1370. **270.** 1 s. black .. .. 15 15
1371. – 1 s. 50 green .. .. 25 20
1372. – 1 s. 80 red .. .. 55 60
1373. – 3 s. mauve .. .. 70 75
1374. – 5 s. blue .. .. 1·25 1·25
DESIGNS: 1 s. 50, Turbine. 1 s. 80, Industrial plant. 3 s. Steelworks, Linz. 5 s. Oil refinery, Schwechat.

**1961.** World Bank Congress, Vienna.
1375. **271.** 3 s. black .. .. 40 25

**272.** Arms of Burgenland.  **273.** Liszt.

**1961.** 40th Anniv. of Burgenland.
1376. **272.** 1 s. 50 red, yell. & sep. 30 15

**1961.** 150th Birth Anniv. of Franz Liszt (composer).
1377. **273.** 3 s. brown .. .. 50 30

**274.** Rust Post Office.

**1961.** Stamp Day.
1378 **274** 3 s.+70 g. green .. 75 90

**275.** Court of Accounts.

**1961.** Bicentenary of Court of Accounts.
1379. **275.** 1 s. sepia .. .. 15 15

**276.** Glockner-Kaprun Power Station.

**1962.** 15th Anniv. of Electric Power Nationalization. Inscr. as in T **276.**
1380. **276.** 1 s. blue .. .. 20 15
1381. – 1 s. 50 purple .. 40 20
1382. – 1 s. 80 green .. .. 75 75
1383. – 3 s. brown .. .. 40 40
1384. – 4 s. red .. .. 40 30
1385. – 6 s. 40 black .. .. 1·50 1·75
DESIGNS: 1 s. 50, Ybbs-Persenbeug (Danube). 1 s. 80, Luner See. 3 s. Grossraming (Enns River). 4 s. Bisamberg Transformer Station. 6 s. 40, St. Andra Power Stations.

**1962.** Death Cent. of Johann Nestroy (playwright). As T **187** but portrait of Nestroy and theatrical masks.
1386. 1 s. violet .. .. 15 10

**277.** F. Gauermann.  **278.** Scout Badge and Handclasp.

**1962.** Death Centenary of Friedrich Gauermann (painter).
1387. **277.** 1 s. 50 blue .. .. 15 10

**1962.** 50th Anniv. of Austrian Scout Movement.
1388. **278.** 1 s. 50 green .. .. 30 20

**279.** Forest and Lake.

**1962.** "The Austrian Forest".
1389. **279.** 1 s. grey .. .. 25 15
1390. – 1 s. 50 brown .. 35 25
1391. – 3 s. myrtle .. .. 1·25 90
DESIGNS: 1 s. 50, Deciduous forest. 3 s. Fir and larch forest.

**280.** Electric Locomotive and First Steam Locomotive "Austria".

**1962.** 125th Anniv. of Austrian Railways.
1392. **280.** 3 s. black and buff .. 1·50 55

**281.** Engraving Die.  **282.** Postal Officials of 1863.

**1962.** Stamp Day.
1393. **281.** 3 s.+70 g. violet .. 1·00 1·40

**1963.** Cent. of Paris Postal Conference.
1394. **282.** 3 s. sepia and yellow 35 35

**283.** Hermann Bahr.  **284.** St. Florian (statue).

**1963.** Birth Cent. of Hermann Bahr (writer).
1395. **283.** 1 s. 50 sepia and blue .. 15 15

**1963.** Cent. of Austrian Voluntary Fire Brigade.
1396. **284.** 1 s. 50 black and pink 60 15

**285.** Flag and Emblem.

**1963.** 5th Austrian Trade Unions Federation Congress.
1397. **285.** 1 s. 50 red, sep. & grey 15 15

**286.** Crests of Tyrol and Austria.

**1963.** 600th Anniv. of Tyrol as an Austrian province.
1398. **286.** 1 s. 50 multicoloured 15 15

**287.** Prince Eugene of Savoy. **288.** Centenary Emblem.

**1963.** Birth Tercent. of Prince Eugene of Savoy.

1399. **287.** 1 s. 50 violet .. 30 15

**1963.** Centenary of Red Cross.

1400. **288.** 3 s. silver, red & blk. 35 25

**289.** Skiing (slalom).

**1963.** **Winter Olympic Games, Innsbruck, 1964. Centres black; inscr. gold; background colours given.**

1401. **289.** 1 s. grey .. .. 15 10
1402. – 1 s. 20 blue .. .. 15 15
1403. – 1 s. 50 grey .. .. 20 15
1404. – 1 s. 80 purple .. 25 25
1405. – 2 s. 20 green .. .. 75 65
1406. – 3 s. slate .. .. 35 20
1407. – 4 s. blue .. .. 1·00 1·00

Designs: 1 s. 20, Skiing (biathlon). 1 s. 50, Ski jumping. 1 s. 80, Figure skating. 2 s. 20, Ice hockey. 3 s. Tobogganing. 4 s. Bobsleighing.

**290.** Vienna "101" Post Office and Railway Shed. **291.** "The Holy Family" (Josef Stammel).

**1963.** Stamp Day.

1408. **290.** 3 s.+70 g. black and drab .. .. 80 90

**1963.** Christmas.

1409. **291.** 2 s. green .. .. 15 10

**292.** Nasturtium. **293.** Gothic Statue and Stained-glass Window.

**1964.** Int. Horticultural Exn., Vienna. Multicoloured.

1410. 1 s. Type **292** .. .. 15 10
1411. 1 s. 50 Peony .. .. 15 15
1412. 1 s. 80 Clematis .. 30 30
1413. 2 s. 20 Dahlia .. .. 45 60
1414. 3 s. Convolvulus .. 60 30
1415. 4 s. Mallow .. .. 70 75

**1964.** Romanesque Art Exhibition, Vienna.

1416 **293** 1 s. 50 blue and black 15 15

**294.** Pallas Athene and Interior of Assembly Hall, Parliament Building. **295.** "The Kiss" (Gustav Klimt).

**1964.** 2nd Parliamentary and Scientific Conference, Vienna.

1417. **294.** 1 s. 80 black & green 25 25

**1964.** Reopening of "Viennese Secession" Exhibition Hall.

1418. **295.** 3 s. multicoloured .. 40 25

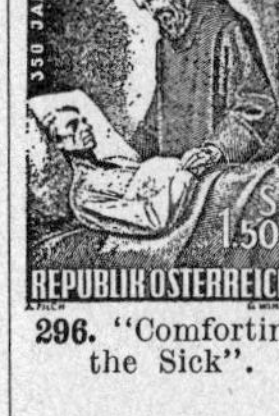

**296.** "Comforting the Sick". **297.** "Bringing News of the Victory at Kunersdorf" (Bellotto).

**1964.** 350th Anniv. of Order of Brothers of Mercy in Austria.

1419. **296.** 1 s. 50 blue .. .. 15 15

**1964.** 15th Universal Postal Union Congress, Vienna. Paintings.

1420 **297** 1 s. purple .. .. 10 10
1421 – 1 s. 20 brown .. 25 20
1422 – 1 s. 50 blue .. .. 15 10
1423 – 1 s. 80 violet .. 30 25
1424 – 2 s. 20 black .. .. 25 40
1425 – 3 s. purple .. .. 40 20
1426 – 4 s. green .. .. 40 60
1427 – 6 s. 40 purple .. 1·25 1·75

Paintings: 1 s. 20, "Changing Horses" (Hormann). 1 s. 50, "The Wedding Trip" (Schwind). 1 s. 80, "Postboys returning Home" (Raffalt). 2 s. 20, "The Vienna Mail Coach" (Klein); 3 s. "Changing Horses" (Gauermann). 4 s. "Postal Tracked-vehicle in Mountain Village" (Pilch). 6 s. 40, "Saalbach Post Office and Post-bus" (Pilch).

**298.** Vienna, from the Hochhaus (North). **299.** "Workers"

**1964.** "WIPA" Stamp Exn., Vienna (1965) (1st issue). Multicoloured.

1428. 1 s. 50+30 g. Type **298** 20 20
1429. 1 s. 50+30 g. North-east 20 20
1430. 1 s. 50+30 g. East .. 20 20
1431. 1 s. 50+30 g. South-east 20 20
1432. 1 s. 50+30 g. South .. 20 20
1433. 1 s. 50+30 g. South-west 20 20
1434. 1 s. 50+30 g. West .. 20 20
1435. 1 s. 50+30 g. North-west 20 20

The designs show a panoramic view of Vienna, looking to different points of compass (indicated on stamps). The inscription reads "Vienna welcomes you to WIPA 1965".

See also Nos. 1447/52.

**1964.** Cent. of Austrian Workers' Movement.

1436. **299.** 1 s. black .. .. 15 10

**300.** Europa "Flower". **301.** Radio Receiver Dial.

**1964.** Europa.

1437. **300.** 3 s. blue .. .. 30 15

**1964.** 40th Anniv. of Austrian Broadcasting Service.

1438. **301.** 1 s. sepia and red .. 15 10

**302.** Old Printing Press. **303.** Post-bus Station, St. Gilgen.

**1964.** 6th Int. Graphical Federation Congress, Vienna.

1439. **302.** 1 s. 50 black and drab 20 10

**1964.** Stamp Day.

1440. **303.** 3 s.+70 g. mult. .. 30 40

**304.** Dr. Adolf Scharf. **305.** "Reconstruction".

**1965.** President Scharf Commem.

1441. **304.** 1 s. 50 blue and black 20 15

**1965.** "20 Years of Reconstruction".

1442. **305.** 1 s. 80 lake .. .. 20 10

**306.** University Seal, 1365. **307.** "St. George" (after engraving by Altdorfer).

**1965.** 600th Anniv. of Vienna University.

1443. **306.** 3 s. red and gold .. 20 15

**1965.** Danubian Art.

1444. **307.** 1 s. 80 blue .. .. 20 20

**308.** I.T.U. Emblem, Morse Key and T.V. Aerial. **309.** F. Raimund.

**1965.** Centenary of I.T.U.

1445. **308.** 3 s. violet .. .. 20 15

**1965.** 175th Birth Anniv. of Ferdinand Raimund (actor and playwright).

1446. **309.** 3 s. purple .. .. 20 15

**310.** Egyptian Hieroglyphs on Papyrus. **311.** Gymnasts with Wands.

**1965.** "WIPA" Stamp Exhibition, Vienna (2nd issue). "Development of the Letter".

1447 **310** 1 s. 50+40 g. black and pink .. .. 10 10
1448 – 1 s. 80+50 g. black and yellow .. 15 15
1449 – 2 s. 20+60 g. black and lilac .. .. 50 50
1450 – 3 s.+80 g. blk & yell 25 25
1451 – 4 s.+1 s. black & blue 65 65
1452 – 5 s.+1 s. 20 blk & grn 75 75

Designs: 1 s. 80, Cuneiform writing. 2 s. 20, Latin. 3 c. Ancient letter and seal. 4 s. 19th-century letter. 5 s. Typewriter.

**1965.** 4th Gymnaestrada, Vienna.

1453 **311** 1 s. 50 black and blue 15 15
1454 – 3 s. black and brown 25 30

Designs: 3 s. Girls exercising with tambourines.

**312.** Dr. I. Semmelweis. **313.** F. G. Waldmuller (self-portrait).

**1965.** Death Centenary of Ignaz Semmelweis (physician).

1455 **312** 1 s. 50 lilac .. .. 20 10

**1965.** Death Centenary of F. G. Waldmuller (painter).

1456. **313.** 3 s. black .. .. 20 15

**314.** Red Cross and Gauze. **315.** Flag and Crowned Eagle.

**1965.** Red Cross Conf., Vienna.

1457. **314.** 3 s. red and black .. 30 15

**1965.** 50th Anniv. of Austrian Towns Union.

1458. **315.** 1 s. 50 multicoloured 15 10

**316.** Austrian Flag, U.N. Emblem and Headquarters.

**1965.** 10th Anniv. of Austria's Membership of U.N.O.

1459. **316.** 3 s. sep., red & bl. .. 20 20

**317.** University Building. **318.** Bertha von Suttner.

**1965.** 150th Anniv. of University of Technology, Vienna.

1460. **317.** 1 s. 50 violet .. 15 10

**1965.** 60th Anniv. of Nobel Peace Prize Award to Bertha von Suttner (writer).

1461. **318.** 1 s. 50 black .. .. 15 10

**319.** Postman delivering Mail.

**1965.** Stamp Day.

1462. **319.** 3 s.+70 g. green .. 20 30

**320.** Postal Code Map.

**1966.** Introduction of Postal Code System.

1463. **320.** 1 s. 50 blk., red & yell. 20 10

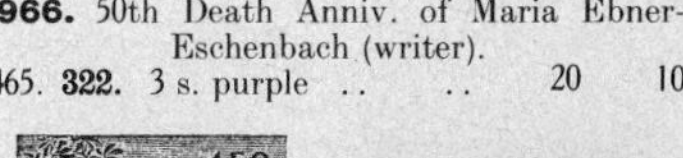


**321.** P.T.T. Headquarters. **322.** M. Ebner-Eschenbach.

**1966.** Centenary of Austrian Posts and Telegraphs Administration.

1464. **321.** 1 s. 50 black on cream .. .. 15 10

**1966.** 50th Death Anniv. of Maria Ebner-Eschenbach (writer).

1465. **322.** 3 s. purple .. .. 20 10

**323.** Big Wheel. **324.** Josef Hoffmann.

**1966.** Bicent. of Vienna Prater.

1466. **323.** 1 s. 50 green .. .. 15 10

**1966.** 10th Death Anniv. of Josef Hoffmann (architect).

1467. **324.** 3 s. brown .. .. 20 10

**325.** Bank Emblem. **326.** Arms of Wiener Neustadt.

**1966.** 150th Anniv. of Austrian Nat. Bank.
1468. **325.** 3 s. brn., grn. & drab 20 10

**1966.** "Wiener Neustadt 1440-93" Art Exn.
1469. **326.** 1 s. 50 multicoloured 15 10

**327.** Puppy. **328.** Columbine.

**1966.** 120th Anniv. of Vienna Animal Protection Society.
1470. **327.** 1 s. 80 black & yell. 30 10

**1966.** Alpine Flora. Multicoloured.

| | | | |
|---|---|---|---|
| 1471. | 1 s. 50, Type **328** .. | 20 | 15 |
| 1472. | 1 s. 80 Turk's Cap .. | 25 | 15 |
| 1473. | 2 s. 20 Wulfenia .. | 45 | 40 |
| 1474. | 3 s. Globe Flower .. | 45 | 35 |
| 1475. | 4 s. Orange Lily.. .. | 65 | 50 |
| 1476. | 5 s. Alpine Anemone .. | 75 | 50 |

**329.** Fair Building. **330.** Peter Anich.

**1966.** Wels International Fair.
1477 **329** 3 s. blue .. .. 20 10

**1966.** Death Bicentenary of Peter Anich (cartographer).
1478. **330.** 1 s. 80 black.. .. 15 10

**331.** "Suffering". **332.** "Eunuchus" by Terence (engraving, Johann Gruninger).

**1966.** 15th Int. Occupational Health Congress, Vienna.
1479. **331.** 3 s. black and red .. 20 10

**1966.** Austrian Nat. Library, Vienna. Mult.

| | | | |
|---|---|---|---|
| 1480. | 1 s. 50 Type **332** (Theatre collection) .. | 15 | 10 |
| 1481. | 1 s. 80 Detail of title page of Willem Blaeu's atlas (Cartography collection) .. .. | 15 | 15 |
| 1482. | 2 s. 20 "Herrengasse, Vienna" (Anton Stutzinger (Pictures and portraits collection) .. .. | 30 | 30 |
| 1483. | 3 s. Illustration from Rene of Anjou's "Livre du Cuer d'Amours Espris" (Manuscripts collection) .. .. .. | 35 | 25 |

**333.** Young Girl. **334.** Strawberries. **335.** 16th-cent. Postman.

**1966.** Austrian "Save the Children" Fund.
1484. **333** 3 s. black and blue .. 15 10

**1966.** Fruits. Multicoloured.

| | | | |
|---|---|---|---|
| 1485. | 50 g. Type **334** .. .. | 20 | 25 |
| 1486. | 1 s. Grapes .. .. | 20 | 15 |
| 1487. | 1 s. 50 Apple .. .. | 20 | 15 |
| 1488. | 1 s. 80 Blackberries .. | 20 | 25 |
| 1489. | 2 s. 20 Apricots .. .. | 25 | 25 |
| 1490. | 3 s. Cherries .. .. | 30 | 20 |

**1966.** Stamp Day.
1491. **335.** 3 s.+70 g. mult. .. 20 25

**336.** Arms of Linz University. **337.** Skater of 1867.

**1966.** Inaug. of Linz University.
1492. **336.** 3 s. multicoloured .. 20 10

**1967.** Cent. of Vienna Skating Assn.
1493. **337.** 3 s. indigo and blue 20 10

**338.** Dancer with Violin. **339.** Dr. Schonherr.

**1967.** Cent. of "Blue Danube" Waltz.
1494. **338.** 3 s. purple .. .. 70 30

**1967.** Birth Cent. of Dr. Karl Schonherr (poet).
1495. **339.** 3 s. brown .. .. 20 10

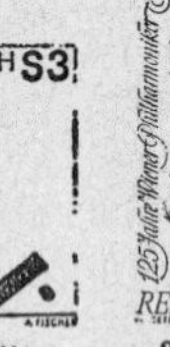

**340.** Ice Hockey Goalkeeper. **341.** Violin and Organ.

**1967.** World Ice Hockey Championships, Vienna.
1496. **340.** 3 s. blue and green .. 30 15

**1967.** 125th Anniv. of Vienna Philharmonic Orchestra.
1497. **341.** 3 s. 50 blue .. .. 40 20

**342.** "Mother and Children", (aquarelle, Peter Fendi). **343.** "Madonna" (Gothic wood-carving).

**1967.** Mother's Day.
1498. **342.** 2 s. multicoloured .. 15 15

**1967.** "Gothic Art in Austria" Exn., Krems.
1499. **343.** 3 s. green .. .. 20 15

**344.** Jewelled Cross. **345.** "The White Swan" (from Kokoschka's tapestry "Cupid and Psyche").

**1967.** "Salzburg Treasures" Exhibition, Salzburg Cathedral.
1500. **344.** 3 s. 50 multicoloured 20 20

**1967.** "Art of the Nibelungen District" Exn., Pochlarn.
1501. **345.** 2 s. multicoloured .. 20 15

## INDEX

Countries can be quickly located by referring to the index at the end of this volume.

**346.** Vienna.

**1967.** 10th European Talks, Vienna.
1502. **346.** 3 s. black and red .. 20 10

**347.** Champion Bull.

**1967.** Centenary of Ried Fair.
1503. **347.** 2 s. purple .. .. 20 10

**348.** Colorado Potato Beetle.

**1967.** 6th Int. Plant Protection Congress, Vienna.
1504. **348.** 3 s. multicoloured .. 20 15

**349.** Locomotive of 1867. **350.** "Christ" (fresco detail).

**1967.** Centenary of Brenner Railway.
1505. **349.** 3 s. 50 green & brn. 60 25

**1967.** Lambach Frescoes.
1506. **350.** 2 s. multicoloured .. 15 10

**351.** Prater Hall, Vienna. **352.** Rector's Medallion and Chain.

**1967.** Int. Trade Fairs Congress, Vienna.
1507. **351.** 2 s. purple and cream 15 10

**1967.** 275th Anniv. of Fine Arts Academy, Vienna.
1508. **352.** 2 s. brn., yell. & bl. 15 10

**353.** Bible on Rock (from commemorative coin of 1717). **355.** Memorial, Vienna.

**354.** Forest Trees.

**1967.** 450th Anniv of the Reformation.
1509 **353** 3 s. 50 blue .. .. 20 15

**1967.** 100 Years of Austrian University Forestry Studies.
1510. **354.** 3 s. 50 green.. .. 20 20

**1967.** 150th Anniv. of Land Registry.
1511. **355.** 2 s. green .. .. 15 10

**356.** "St. Leopold" (stained-glass window, Heiligenkreuz Monastery). **357.** "Music and Art".

**1967.** Margrave Leopold the Holy.
1512. **356.** 1 s. 80 multicoloured 15 10

**1967.** 150th Anniv. of Academy of Music and Dramatic Art, Vienna.
1513. **357.** 3 s. 50 black & vio... 30 15

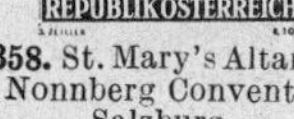

**358.** St. Mary's Altar, Nonnberg Convent, Salzburg. **359.** "The Letter-carrier" (from playing card).

**1967.** Christmas.
1514. **358.** 2 s. green .. .. 15 10

**1967.** Stamp Day.
1515. **359.** 3 s. 50+80 g. mult. 20 35

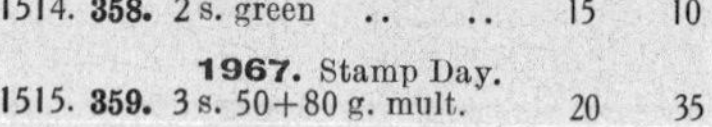

**360.** Ski Jump, Stadium and Mountains.

**1968.** Winter University Games, Innsbruck.
1516. **360.** 2 s. blue .. .. 30 10

**361.** C. Sitte. **362.** Mother and Child.

**1968.** 125th Birth Anniv. of Camillo Sitte (architect).
1517. **361.** 2 s. brown .. .. 15 10

**1968.** Mothers' Day.
1518. **362.** 2 s. olive .. .. 15 10

**363.** "Veterinary Medicine". **364.** Bride with Lace Veil.

**1968.** Bicent. of Vienna Veterinary College.
1519. **363.** 3 s. 50 gold, pur. & drab 20 15

**1968.** Centenary of Vorarlberg Lace.
1520. **364.** 3 s. 50 blue .. .. 45 20

**365.** Etrich Limousine.

**1968.** "IFA Wien 1968" Airmail Stamp Exn., Vienna.

1521. **365.** 2 s. brown .. .. 40 35
1522. – 3 s. 50 green .. .. 55 55
1523. – 5 s. blue .. .. 75 85

DESIGNS: 3 s. 50, Sud Aviation Caravelle. 5 s. Douglas DC-8.

**366.** Horse-racing.

**1968.** Cent. of Freudenau Gallop Races.

1524. **366.** 3 s. 50 brown .. 40 25

**367.** Landsteiner. **368.** P. Rosegger.

**1968.** Birth Cent. of Dr. Karl Landsteiner (physician and pathologist).

1525. **367.** 3 s. 50 blue .. .. 45 20

**1968.** 50th Death Anniv. of Peter Rosegger (writer).

1526. **368.** 2 s. green .. .. 15 15

**369.** A. Kauffmann (self-portrait). **370.** Statue of Young Man (Helenenberg site).

**1968.** Exn. of Angelica Kauffmann's Paintings, Bregenz.

1527. **369.** 2 s. violet .. .. 15 15

**1968.** Magdalensberg Excavations, Carinthia.

1528. **370.** 2 s. black and green .. 15 15

**371.** "The Bishop" (Romanesque carving). **372.** K. Moser.

**1968.** 750th Anniv. of Graz-Seckau Diocese.

1529. **371.** 2 s. grey .. .. 15 15

**1968.** 50th Death Anniv of Koloman Moser (graphic artist).

1530 **372** 2 s. brown and red .. 15 15

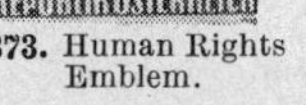

**373.** Human Rights Emblem. **374.** Arms and Provincial Shields.

**1968.** Human Rights Year.

1531. **373.** 1 s. 50 red, grn. & grey 15 15

**1968.** 50th Anniv. of Republic. Mult.

1532. 2 s. Type **374** .. .. 25 35
1533. 2 s. Karl Renner (first President of Second Republic) .. .. 25 35
1534. 2 s. First Article of Constitution .. .. 25 35

**375.** Crib, Oberndorf, Salzburg. **376.** Mercury.

**1968.** 150th Anniv. of "Silent Night, Holy Night" (carol).

1535. **375.** 2 s. green .. .. 25 10

**1968.** Stamp Day.

1536. **376.** 3 s. 50+80 g. green 20 30

**377.** Fresco (Troger), Melk Monastery. **378.** "Madonna and Child".

**1968.** Baroque Frescoes. Designs showing frescoes in locations given. Multicoloured.

1537 2 s. Type **377** .. .. 30 30
1538 2 s. Altenburg Monastery 30 30
1539 2 s. Rohrenbach-Greillenstein .. .. 30 30
1540 2 s. Ebenfurth Castle .. 30 30
1541 2 s. Halbthurn Castle .. 30 30
1542 2 s. Maria Treu Church, Vienna .. .. 30 30

Nos. 1537/9 are the work of Anton Troger and Nos. 1540/2 that of Franz Maulbertsch.

**1969.** 500th Anniv. of Vienna Diocese. Statues in St. Stephen's Cathedral, Vienna.

1543. **378.** 2 s. blue .. .. 30 30
1544. – 2 s. grey .. .. 30 30
1545. – 2 s. green .. .. 30 30
1546. – 2 s. purple .. .. 30 30
1547. – 2 s. black .. .. 30 30
1548. – 2 s. brown .. .. 30 30

DESIGNS: No. 1544, "St. Christopher". No. 1545, "St. George". No. 1546, "St. Paul". No. 1547, "St. Sebastian". No. 1548, "St. Stephen".

**379.** Parliament Building, Vienna.

**1969.** Interparliamentary Union Meeting, Vienna.

1549 **379** 2 s. green .. .. 15 15

**380.** Colonnade.

**1969.** Europa.

1550. **380.** 2 s. multicoloured .. 20 15

**381.** "Council Members". **382.** Soldiers.

**1969.** 20th Anniv. of Council of Europe.

1551. **381.** 3 s. 50 multicoloured 25 25

**1969.** Austrian Armed Forces.

1552. **382.** 2 s. brown and red .. 30 15

**384.** Maximilian's Armour. **385.** Viennese "Privilege" Seal.

**1969.** "Maximilian I" Exn., Innsbruck.

1554. **384.** 2 s. black .. .. 20 15

**1969.** 19th Int. Union of Local Authorities Congress, Vienna.

1555. **385.** 2 s. red, brown & ochre 15 10

**386.** Young Girl. **387.** Hands clasping Spanner.

**1969.** 20th Anniv. of "SOS" Children's Villages Movement.

1556. **386.** 2 s. brown and green 15 15

**1969.** 50th Anniv. of Int. Labour Organization.

1557. **387.** 2 s. green .. .. 15 10

**388.** Austrian "Flag" encircling Globe. **389.** "El Cid killing a Bull" (Goya).

**1969.** "Austrians Living Abroad" Year.

1558. **388.** 3 s. 50 red and green 20 15

**1969.** Bicentenary of Albertina Art Collection, Vienna. Multicoloured.

1559 2 s. Type **389** .. .. 30 30
1560 2 s. "Young Hare" (Durer) .. .. 30 30
1561 2 s. "Madonna with Pomegranate" (Raphael) 30 30
1562 2 s. "The Painter and the Amateur" (Bruegel) .. 30 30
1563 2 s. "Rubens's Son, Nicholas" (Rubens) 30 30
1564 2 s. "Self-portrait" (Rembrandt) .. .. 30 30
1565 2 s. "Madame de Pompadour" (detail, Guerin) .. .. 30 30
1566 2 s. "The Artist's Wife" (Schiele) .. .. 30 30

**390.** President Jonas. **391.** Posthorn and Lightning over Globe.

**1969.** President Franz Jonas's 70th Birthday.

1567. **390.** 2 s. blue and grey .. 15 10

**1969.** 50th Anniv. of Post and Telegraph Employees Union.

1568. **391.** 2 s. multicoloured .. 20 10

**392.** Savings Bank (c. 1450). **393.** "The Madonna" (Egger-Lienz).

**1969.** 150th Anniv. of Austrian Savings Bank.

1569. **392.** 2 s. green and silver 15 10

**1969.** Christmas.

1570. **393.** 2 s. purple and yellow 15 10

**394.** Unken, Salzburg, Post-house Sign (after F. Zeller). **395.** J. Schoffel.

**1969.** Stamp Day.

1571 **394** 3 s. 50+80 g. black, red and stone .. 20 30

**1970.** 60th Death Anniv. of Josef Schoffel ("Saviour of the Vienna Woods").

1572. **395.** 2 s. purple .. .. 15 10

**396.** St. Clement Hofbauer. **398.** Krimml Waterfalls.

**397.** Chancellor Leopold Figl.

**1970.** 150th Death Anniv. of St. Clement Hofbauer (theologian).

1573. **396.** 2 s. brown and green 15 10

**1970.** 25th Anniv. of Austrian Republic.

1574. **397.** 2 s. olive .. .. 25 15
1575. – 2 s. brown .. .. 25 15

DESIGN: No. 1575, Belvedere Castle.

**1970.** Nature Conservation Year.

1576 **398** 2 s. green .. .. 40 15

**399.** Oldest University Seal. **401.** Tower Clock, 1450–1550.

**400.** "Musikverein" Organ.

**1970.** 300th Anniv. of Leopold Franz University, Innsbruck.

1577. **399.** 2 s. black and red .. 15 10

**1970.** Cent. of "Musikverein" Building.

1578. **400.** 2 s. purple and gold 30 15

**1970.** Antique Clocks.

1579 **401** 1 s. 50 brown & cream 35 25
1580 – 1 s. 50 green & lt grn 35 25
1581 – 2 s. blue and pale blue 40 25
1582 – 2 s. red and purple .. 40 25
1583 – 3 s. 50 brown & buff 60 50
1584 – 3 s. 50 purple & lilac 60 50

DESIGNS: No. 1580, Empire "lyre" clock, 1790–1815. No. 1581, Pendant ball clock, 1600–50. No. 1582, Pocket-watch and signet, 1800–30. No. 1583, Bracket clock, 1720–60. No. 1584, "Biedermeier" pendulum clock and musical-box, 1820–50.

**402.** "The Beggar Student" (Millocker). **403.** Scene from "The Gipsy Baron" (J. Strauss).

**1970.** Famous Operettas.

1585 402 1 s. 50 turquoise & grn 45 25
1586 – 1 s. 50 blue and yellow 45 25
1587 – 2 s. purple and pink 50 25
1588 – 2 s. brown and green 50 25
1589 – 3 s. 50 blue and lt blue 70 60
1590 – 3 s. 50 blue and buff 70 60

OPERETTAS: No. 1586, "Die Fledermaus" (Johann Strauss the younger). 1587, "A Waltz Dream" (O. Straus). 1588, "The Birdseller" (C. Zeller). 1589, "The Merry Widow" (F. Lehar). 1590, "Two Hearts in Waltz-time" (R. Stoiz).

**1970.** 25th Anniv. of Bregenz Festival.
1591. **403.** 3 s. 50 bl., buff & ult. 30 20

**404.** Festival Emblem. **405.** T. Koschat.

**1970.** 50th Anniv. of Salzburg Festival.
1592. **404.** 3 s. 50 multicoloured 30 20

**1970.** 125th Birth Anniv. of Thomas Koschat (composer and poet).
1593. **405.** 2 s. brown .. 30 15

**406.** "Head of St. John", from sculpture "Mount of Olives", Ried Church (attributed to T. Schwanthaler).

**1970.** 13th World Veterans Federation General Assembly.
1594. **406.** 3 s. 50 sepia .. .. 20 20

**407.** Climbers and Mountains. **408.** A. Cossmann.

**1970.** "Walking and Mountaineering".
1595. **407.** 2 s. blue and mauve 30 15

**1970.** Birth Centenary of Alfred Cossmann (engraver).
1596. **408.** 2 s. brown .. .. 15 10

**409.** Arms of Carinthia. **410.** U.N. Emblem.

**1970.** 50th Anniv. of Carinthian Plebiscite.
1597. **409.** 2 s. multicoloured .. 20 15

**1970.** 25th Anniv. of United Nations.
1598. **410.** 3 s. 50 blue and black 20 20

**411.** "Adoration of the Shepherds". (carving, Garsten Monastery).

**1970.** Christmas.
1599. **411.** 2 s. blue .. .. 15 10

**412.** Saddle, Harness and Posthorn. **413.** Pres. K. Renner.

**1970.** Stamp Day.
1600. **412.** 3 s. 50+80 g. black, yellow and grey .. 20 35

**1970.** Birth Cent. of Pres. Renner.
1601. **413.** 2 s. purple .. .. 15 10

**414.** Beethoven (after painting by Waldmuller). **415.** E. Handel-Mazzetti.

**1970.** Birth Bicentenary of Beethoven.
1602 **414** 3 s. 50 black and stone 75 30

**1971.** Birth Centenary of Enrica Handel-Mazzetti (novelist).
1603. **415.** 2 s. brown .. .. 15 10

**416.** "Safety for Children".

**1971.** Road Safety.
1604. **416.** 2 s. multicoloured .. 50 15

**417.** Florentine Bowl, circa 1580.

**1971.** Austrian Art Treasures (1st series). Sculpture and Applied Art.
1605 417 1 s. 50 green and grey 30 30
1606 – 2 s. purple and grey 30 30
1607 – 3 s. 50 yell, brn & grey 55 55

DESIGNS: 2 s. Ivory equestrian statuette of Joseph I, 1693 (Matthias Steinle). 3 s. 50, Salt-cellar, circa 1570 (Cellini).

See also Nos. 1609/11, 1632/4 and 1651/3.

**418.** Shield of Trade Association. **419.** "Jacopo de Strada" (Titian).

**1971.** 23rd Int. Chamber of Commerce Congress, Vienna.
1608. **418.** 3 s. 50 multicoloured 20 20

**1971.** Austrian Art Treasures (2nd series).
1609. **419.** 1 s. 50 purple .. 30 30
1610. – 2 s. black .. .. 30 30
1611. – 3 s. 50 brown .. 55 55

PAINTINGS: 2 s. "The Village Feast" (Brueghel). 3 s. 50, "Young Venetian Woman" (Durer).

**420.** Notary's Seal. **421.** "St. Matthew" (altar sculpture).

**1971.** Austrian Notarial Statute Cent. Congress.
1612. **420.** 3 s. 50 purple & brown 20 20

**1971.** "Krems Millennium of Art" Exhib.
1613. **421.** 2 s. brown & purple 10 10

**422.** Dr. A. Neilreich. **423.** Singer with Lyre.

**1971.** Death Centenary of Dr. August Neilreich (botanist).
1614. **422.** 2 s. brown .. .. 15 10

**1971.** Int. Choir Festival, Vienna.
1615. **423.** 4 s. bl., gold & pale bl. 70 40

**424.** Arms of Kitzbuhel.

**1971.** 700th Anniv. of Kitzbuhel.
1616. **424.** 2 s. 50 multicoloured 20 15

**425.** Stock Exchange Building.

**1971.** Bicent. of Vienna Stock Exchange.
1617. **425.** 4 s. brown .. .. 20 20

**426.** Old and New Fair Halls. **427.** O.G.B. Emblem.

**1971.** "50 Years of Vienna Int. Fairs".
1618. **426.** 2 s. 50 purple .. 20 15

**1971.** 25th Anniv of Austrian Trade Unions Federation.
1619 **427** 2 s. multicoloured .. 15 15

**428.** Arms and Insignia. **429.** "Marcus" Veteran Car.

**1971.** 50th Anniv. of Burgenland Province.
1620. **428.** 4 s. multicoloured .. 30 15

**1971.** 75th Anniv of Austrian Automobile, Motor Cycle and Touring Club.
1621 **429** 4 s. black and green .. 55 30

**430.** Europa Bridge, Brenner Highway. **431.** Iron-ore Workings, Erzberg.

**1971.** Inaug. of Brenner Highway.
1622. **430.** 4 s. blue .. .. 70 30

**1971.** 25 Years of Nationalized Industries.
1623. **431.** 1 s. 50 brown .. 20 20
1624. – 2 s. blue .. .. 30 20
1625. – 4 s. green .. .. 75 55

DESIGNS: 2 s. Nitrogen Works, Linz. 4 s. Iron and Steel works, Linz.

**432.** Electric Train on the Semmering Line. **433.** E. Tschermak-Seysenegg.

**1971.** Railway Anniversaries.
1626 **432** 2 s. purple .. .. 60 30

**1971.** Birth Centenary of Dr. E. Tshermak-Seysenegg (biologist).
1627. **433.** 2 s. purple and grey 20 15

**434.** Angling. **435.** "The Infant Jesus as Saviour" (from miniature by Durer).

**1971.** Sports.
1628. **434.** 2 s. brown .. .. 30 15

**1971.** Christmas.
1629. **435.** 2 s. multicoloured .. 30 10

**436.** "50 Years".

**1971.** 50th Anniv of Austrian Philatelic Clubs Association.
1630 **436** 4 s.+1 s. 50 pur & gold 45 55

**437.** Franz Grillparzer (from miniature by Daffinger). **438.** Roman Fountain, Friesach.

**1972.** Death Cent of Grillparzer (dramatist).
1631 **437** 2 s. black, brn & stone 20 15

**1972.** Austrian Art Treasures (3rd series). Fountains.
1632. **438.** 1 s. 50 purple .. 30 30
1633. – 2 s. brown .. .. 40 40
1634. – 2 s. 50 green .. .. 55 65

DESIGNS: 2 s. Lead Fountain, Heiligenkreuz Abbey. 2 s. 50, Leopold Fountain, Innsbruck.

439. Hofburg Palace.

440. Heart Patient.

**1972.** 4th European Postal Ministers' Conference, Vienna.
1635. **439.** 4 s. violet .. .. 55 30

**1972.** World Heart Month.
1636. **440.** 4 s. brown .. .. 60 30

441. "Woman's Head" (sculpture, Gurk Cathedral).
442. Vienna Town Hall and Congress Emblem.

**1972.** 900th Anniv. of Gurk Diocese.
1637. **441.** 2 s. purple and gold 30 15

**1972.** 9th International Public and Co-operative Economy Congress, Vienna.
1638 **442** 4 s. black, red & yell 45 30

443. Lienz-Pelos Pylon Line.

**1972.** 25th Anniv. of Electric Power Nationalization.
1639. **443.** 70 g. violet and grey 10 10
1640. – 2 s. 50 brown and grey 25 25
1641. – 4 s. blue and grey .. 30 40
DESIGNS: 2 s. 50, Vienna-Semmering power station. 4 s. Zemm Dam and lake.

444. Runner with Torch.
445. "Hermes" (C. Laib).

**1972.** Passage of the Olympic Torch through Austria.
1642. **444.** 2 s. brown and red .. 20 15

**1972.** "Late Gothic Art" Exhib., Salzburg.
1643. **445.** 2 s. purple .. .. 30 15

446. Pears.
448. University Arms.

**1972.** Amateur Gardeners' Congress, Vienna.
1644. **446.** 2 s. 50 multicoloured 30 15

**1972.** Centenary of University of Agriculture, Vienna.
1646. **448.** 2 s. multicoloured .. 20 15

449. Old University Buildings (after F. Danreiter).
450. C. M. Ziehrer.

**1972.** 350th Anniv. of Paris Lodron University, Salzburg.
1647. **449.** 4 s. brown .. .. 55 35

**1972.** 50th Death Anniv. of Carl M. Ziehrer (composer and conductor).
1648. **450.** 2 s. red .. .. 40 15

451. "Virgin and Child", Inzersdorf Church.

**1972.** Christmas.
1649. **451.** 2 s. purple and green 30 10

452. 18th-century Viennese Postman.
453. State Sledge of Maria Theresa.

**1972.** Stamp Day.
1650. **452.** 4 s. + 1 s. green .. 65 70

**1972.** Austrian Art Treasures (4th series). Carriages from the Imperial Coach House.
1651. **453.** 1 s. 50 brown and bistre 25 15
1652. – 2 s. green and bistre .. 40 40
1653. – 2 s. 50 purple & bistre 60 65
DESIGNS: 2 s. Coronation landau. 2 s. 50, Hapsburg State Coach.

454. Telephone Network.
456. A. Petzold.

455. "Drug Addict".

**1972.** Completion of Austrian Telephone System Automation.
1654. **454.** 2 s. black and yellow 30 15

**1973.** Campaign against Drug Abuse.
1655. **455.** 2 s. multicoloured .. 1·00 30

**1973.** 50th Death Anniv of Alfons Petzold (writer).
1656 **456** 2 s. purple .. .. 20 15

457. Korner.
458. Douglas DC-9-80 Super Eighty.

**1973.** Birth Cent. of Pres. Theodor Korner (President, 1951–57).
1657. **457.** 2 s. purple and grey 30 15

**1973.** Austian Aviation Annivs.
1658. **458.** 2 s. blue and red .. 45 15

459. Otto Loewi.
460. "Succour"

**1973.** Birth Centenary of Otto Loewi (pharmacologist).
1659. **459.** 4 s. violet .. .. 50 30

**1973.** 25th Anniv. of Nat. Federation of Austrian Social Insurance Institutes.
1660. **460.** 2 s. blue .. .. 20 15

461. Telephone Dial within Posthorn.
463. Military Pentathlon.

462. Fair Emblem.

**1973.** Europa.
1661 **461** 2 s. 50 blk, yell & orge 40 15

**1973.** 25th Dornbirn Fair.
1662. **462.** 2 s. multicoloured .. 20 15

**1973.** 25th Anniv. of International Military Sports Council and 23rd Military Pentathlon Championships, Wiener Neustadt.
1663. **463.** 4 s. green .. .. 55 30

464. Leo Slezak.
465. Main Entrance, Hofburg Palace.

**1973.** Birth Centenary of Leo Slezak (operatic tenor).
1664. **464.** 4 s. brown .. .. 70 35

**1973.** 39th Int. Statistical Institute's Congress, Vienna.
1665. **465.** 2 s. brown, red & grey 20 15

466. "Admiral Tegetthof Icebound" (J. Payer).
467. I.U.L.C.S. Arms.

**1973.** Cent. of Discovery of Franz Josef Land.
1666. **466.** 2 s. 50 green .. .. 80 20

**1973.** 13th International Union of Leather Chemists' Societies Congress, Vienna.
1667 **467** 4 s. multicoloured .. 35 30

468. "Academy of Sciences, Vienna" (B. Bellotto).
469. Max Reinhardt.

**1973.** Centenary of Int. Meteorological Organization.
1668. **468.** 2 s. 50 violet .. 30 15

**1973.** Birth Centenary of Max Reinhardt (theatrical director).
1669 **469** 2 s. purple .. .. 30 15

470. F. Hanusch.
471. Light Harness Racing.

**1973.** 50th Death Anniv of Ferdinand Hanusch (politician).
1670 **470** 2 s. purple .. .. 20 15

**1973.** Cent. of Vienna Trotting Assn.
1671. **471.** 2 s. green .. .. 40 20

472. Radio Operator.

**1973.** 50th Anniv. of International Criminal Police Organization (Interpol).
1672. **472.** 4 s. violet .. .. 60 35

473. Petzval Camera Lens.
474. Aqueduct, Hollen Valley.

**1973.** "Europhot" (professional photographers) Congress, Vienna.
1673. **473.** 2 s. 50 multicoloured 40 20

**1973.** Centenary of Vienna's First Mountain-spring Aqueduct.
1674. **474.** 2 s. brn., red & bl. .. 30 15

475. Almsee.
476. "The Nativity" (stained-glass window, St. Erhard Church, Bretenau).

**1973.** Views. (a) Size 23 × 29 mm
1674a – 20 g. blue and lt blue 20 10
1675 – 50 g. green & lt green 15 10
1676 – 1 s. sepia and brown 15 10
1677 – 1 s. 50 purple & pink 30 10
1678 – 2 s. indigo and blue 30 10
1679 – 2 s. 50 dp lilac & lilac 30 10
1680 – 3 s. ultramarine & bl 55 10
1680a – 3 s. 50 brown & orge 65 10
1681 **475** 4 s. violet and lilac 60 10
1681a – 4 s. 20 black & grey 55 40
1682 – 4 s. 50 dp grn & grn 70 10
1683 – 5 s. violet and lilac 85 10
1683a – 5 s. 50 blue & violet 60 35
1683b – 5 s. 60 olive & green 65 80
1684 – 6 s. lilac and pink .. 1·25 10
1684a – 6 s. 50 blue & turq .. 85 20
1685 – 7 s. dp green & green 1·00 25
1685a – 7 s. 50 purple & mve 1·25 30
1686 – 8 s. brown and pink 1·00 10
1686a – 9 s. red and pink .. 1·25 60
1687 – 10 s. myrtle & green 1·00 10
1688 – 11 s. red and orange 10 15
1688a – 12 s. sepia and brown 1·25 25
1688b – 14 s. myrtle & green 1·50 25
1688c – 16 s. brown & orange 1·25 35
1688d – 20 s. green and bistre 1·75 40

(b) Size 28 × 37 mm
1689 – 50 s. violet and grey 4·50 1·50

(c) Size 17 × 20 mm
1690 – 3 s. ultramarine & bl 40 10
DESIGNS: 20 g. Friedstadt Keep, Muhlviertel. 50 g. Zillertal. 1 s. Kahlenbergerdorf, Vienna. 1 s. 50, Bludenz. 2 s. Old bridge, Finstermunz. 2 s. 50, Murau, Styria. 3 s. Bischofsmutze and Alpine farm. 3 s. 50, Osterkirche, Oberwart. 4 s. 20, Hirschegg, Kleinwalsertal. 4 s. 50, Windmill, Retz. 5 s. Ruins of Aggstein Castle. 5 s. 50, Peace Chapel, Stoderzinken. 5 s. 60, Riezlern, Kleinwalsertal. 6 s. Lindauer Hut, Ratikon Massif. 6 s. 50, Villach, Carinthia. 7 s. Falkenstein Castle. 7 s. 50, Hohensalzburg Fortress. 8 s. Votive column, Reiteregg, Styria. 9 s. Asten valley. 10 s. Neusiedlersee. 11 s. Enns. 12 s. Kufstein Fortress. 14 s. Weiszsee, Salzburg. 16 s. Bad Tatzmannsdorf open-air museum. 20 s. Myra Falls, Muggendorf. 50 s. Hofburg, Vienna.

**1973.** Christmas.
1691. **476.** 2 s. multicoloured .. 30 10

477. "Archangel Gabriel" (carving by Lorenz Luchsperger).
478. Dr. Fritz Pregl.

**1973.** Stamp Day.
1692 477 4 s.+1 s. purple .. 50 60

**1973.** 50th Anniv. of Award of Nobel Prize for Chemistry to Fritz Pregl.
1693. **478.** 4 s. blue .. .. 50 30

**479.** Telex Machine and Globe.

**480.** Hugo Hofmannsthal.

**1974.** 50th Anniv. of Radio Austria.
1694. **479.** 2 s. 50 blue & ultram. 20 15

**1974.** Birth Centenary of Hugo Hofmannsthal (writer).
1695 **480** 4 s. blue .. .. 35 30

**481.** Anton Bruckner (composer).

**1974.** Inauguration of Bruckner Memorial Centre, Linz.
1696. **481.** 4 s. brown .. .. 70 40

**482.** Vegetables.

**1974.** 2nd International Horticultural Show, Vienna. Multicoloured.
1697. 2 s. Type **482.** .. .. 40 25
1698. 2 s. 50 Fruit .. .. 45 40
1699. 4 s. Flowers .. .. 70 65

**483.** Head from Ancient Seal.

**484.** Karl Kraus.

**1974.** 750th Anniv. of Judenburg.
1700. **483.** 2 s. multicoloured .. 30 20

**1974.** Birth Cent. of Karl Kraus (poet).
1701. **484.** 4 s. red .. .. 35 30

**485.** "St. Michael" (wood-carving, Thomas Schwanthaler).

**486.** "King Arthur" (statue, Innsbruck).

**1974.** "Sculptures by the Schwanthaler Family" Exhibition, Reichersberg.
1702. **485.** 2 s. 50 green.. .. 40 20

**1974.** Europa.
1703. **486.** 2 s. 50 blue & brown 30 20

**487.** Early Dion Bouton Motor-tricycle.

**489.** I.R.U. Emblem.

**488.** Mask of Satyr's Head.

**1974.** 75th Anniv of Austrian Association of Motoring, Motor Cycling and Cycling.
1704 **487** 2 s. brown and grey .. 45 15

**1974.** "Renaissance in Austria" Exhibition, Schallaburg Castle.
1705. **488.** 2 s. blk., brn. & gold 30 15

**1974.** 14th International Road Haulage Union Congress, Innsbruck.
1706. **489.** 4 s. black and orange 40 25

**490.** F. A. Maulbertsch.

**491.** Gendarmes of 1849 and 1974.

**1974.** 205th Birth Anniv. of Franz Maulbertsch (painter).
1707. **490.** 2 s. brown .. .. 30 15

**1974.** 125th Anniv. of Austrian Gendarmerie.
1708. **491.** 2 s. multicoloured .. 45 15

**492.** Fencing.

**493.** Transport Emblems.

**1974.** Sports.
1709. **492.** 2 s. 50 blk. & orange 40 15

**1974.** European Transport Ministers' Conference, Vienna.
1710. **493.** 4 s. multicoloured .. 50 30

**494.** "St. Virgilius" (wood-carving).

**495.** Pres. F. Jonas.

**1974.** 1200 Years of Christianity in Salzburg.
1711. **494.** 2 s. blue .. .. 20 15

**1974.** President Franz Jonas. Commem.
1712. **495.** 2 s. black .. .. 20 15

**496.** F. Stelzhamer.

**497.** Diving.

**1974.** Death Cent. of Franz Stelzhamer (poet).
1713. **496.** 2 s. blue .. .. 20 15

**1974.** 13th European Swimming, Diving and Water-polo Championships.
1714. **497.** 4 s. brown and blue 55 30

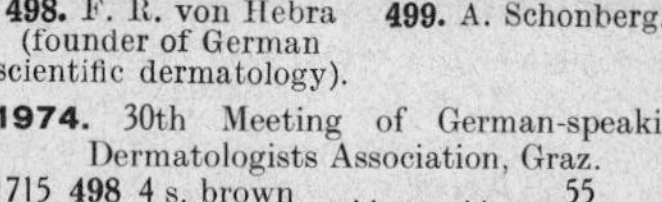

**498.** F. R. von Hebra (founder of German scientific dermatology).

**499.** A. Schonberg.

**1974.** 30th Meeting of German-speaking Dermatologists Association, Graz.
1715 **498** 4 s. brown .. .. 55 30

**1974.** Birth Centenary of Arnold Schonberg (composer).
1716. **499.** 2 s. 50 purple .. 50 20

**500.** Broadcasting Studios, Salzburg.

**501.** E. Eysler.

**1974.** 50th Anniv. of Austrian Broadcasting.
1717. **500.** 2 s. multicoloured .. 30 20

**1974.** 25th Death Anniv. of Edmund Eysler (composer).
1718. **501.** 2 s. green .. .. 30 15

**502.** 19th-century Postman and Mail Transpsort.

**1974.** Cent. of Universal Postal Union.
1719. **502.** 2 s. brown & mauve 35 15
1720. – 4 s. blue and grey .. 35 35
DESIGN: 4 s. Modern postman and mail transport.

**503.** Sports Emblem.

**1974.** 25th Anniv. of Football Pools in Austria.
1721. **503.** 70 g. red, black and green .. .. 15 10

**504.** Steel Gauntlet grasping Rose.

**1974.** Nature Protection.
1722. **504.** 2 s. multicoloured .. 30 20

**505.** C. D. von Dittersdorf.

**506.** Mail Coach and Post Office, of 1905.

**1974.** 175th Death Anniv. of Carl Ditters von Dittersdorf (composer).
1723. **505.** 2 s. green .. .. 30 15

**1974.** Stamp Day.
1724. **506.** 4 s.+2 s. blue .. 65 65

**507.** "Virgin Mary and Child" (wood-carving).

**508.** F. Schmidt.

**1974.** Christmas.
1725. **507.** 2 s. brown and gold 30 10

**1974.** Birth Centenary of Franz Schmidt (composer).
1726 **508** 4 s. black and stone .. 60 30

**509.** "St. Christopher and Child" (altarpiece).

**511.** Seat-belt around Skeletal Limbs.

**510.** Slalom.

**1975.** European Architectural Heritage Year and 125th Anniv. of Austrian Commission for Preservation of Monuments.
1727. **509.** 2 s. 50 brn. & grey .. 35 20

**1975.** Winter Olympics, Innsbruck (1976) (1st issue). Multicoloured.
1728. 1 s.+50 g. Type **510** 20 20
1729. 1 s. 50+70 g. Ice hockey 30 30
1730. 2 s.+90 g. Ski jumping 50 50
1731. 4 s.+1 s. 90 Bobsleighing 80 80
See also Nos. 1747/50.

**1975.** Car Safety-belts Campaign.
1732. **511.** 70 g. multicoloured.. 20 10

**512.** Stained Glass Window, Vienna Town Hall.

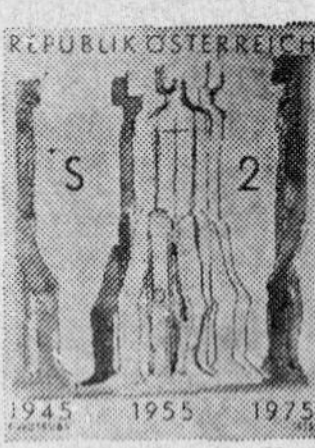

**513.** "The Buffer State".

**1975.** 11th European Communities' Day.
1733. **512.** 2 s. 50 multicoloured 40 20

**1975.** 30th Anniv of Foundation of the Austrian Second Republic.
1734 **513** 2 s. black and brown 30 15

**514.** Forest Scene.

**1975.** 50th Anniv. of Foundation of Austrian Forests Administration.
1735. **514.** 2 s. green .. .. 40 20

**515.** "The High Priest" (M. Pacher).

**516.** Gosaukamm Cable-way.

**1975.** Europa.
1736. **515.** 2 s. 50 multicoloured 30 20

**1975.** 4th International Ropeways Congress, Vienna.
1737 **516** 2 s. blue and red .. 30 15

**517.** J.Misson.

**1975.** Death Cent. of Josef Misson (poet).
1738. **517.** 2 s. brown and red .. 30 15

**518.** "Setting Sun".

**520.** L. Fall.

**519.** F. Porsche.

**1975.** National Pensioners' Association Meeting, Vienna.
1739. **518.** 1 s. 50 multicoloured 30 15

**1975.** Birth Centenary of Professor Ferdinand Porsche (motor engineer).
1740 **519** 1 s. 50 purple & green 30 15

**1975.** 50th Death Anniv. of Leo Fall (composer).
1741. **520.** 2 s. violet .. .. 35 15

**521.** Judo "Shoulder Throw".

**522.** Heinrich Angeli.

**1975.** World Judo Championships, Vienna.
1742 **521** 2 s. 50 multicoloured 30 20

**1975.** 50th Death Anniv. of Heinrich Angeli (court painter).
1743. **522.** 2 s. purple .. .. 30 15

**523.** J. Strauss.

**1975.** 150th Birth Anniv. of Johann Strauss the Younger (composer).
1744. **523.** 4 s. brown and ochre 75 35

**524.** "The Cellist".

**525.** "One's Own House".

**1975.** 75th Anniv of Vienna Symphony Orchestra.
1745 **524** 2 s. 50 blue and silver 40 20

**1975.** 50th Anniv. of Austrian Building Societies.
1746. **525.** 2 s. multicoloured .. 30 20

**1975.** Winter Olympic Games, Innsbruck (1976) (2nd issue). As T **510**. Mult.
1747. 70 g.+30 g. Figure-skating (pairs) .. 25 25
1748. 2 s.+1 s. Cross-country skiing .. .. .. 35 35
1749. 2 s. 50+1 s. Tobogganing 40 40
1750. 4 s.+2 s. Rifle-shooting (biathlon) .. .. 85 85

**526.** Scene on Folding Fan.

**1975.** Bicent of Salzburg State Theatre.
1751 **526** 1 s. 50 multicoloured 30 15

**527.** Austrian Stamps of 1850, 1922 and 1945.

**528.** "Virgin and Child" (Schottenaltar, Vienna).

**1975.** Stamp Day. 125th Anniv of Austrian Postage Stamps.
1752 **527** 4 s.+2 s. multicoloured 55 70

**1975.** Christmas.
1753. **528.** 2 s. lilac and gold .. 30 10

**529.** "Spiralbaum" (F. Hundertwasser).

**531.** Dr. R. Barany.

**1975.** Modern Austrian Art.
1754. **529.** 4 s. multicoloured .. 90 45

**1976.** Birth Centenary of Dr. Robert Barany (Nobel prizewinner for Medicine, 1915).
1756. **531.** 3 s. brown and blue 45 20

**532.** Ammonite Fossil.

**533.** 9th Century Coronation Throne.

**1976.** Centenary Exhibition, Vienna Natural History Museum.
1757. **532.** 3 s. multicoloured .. 50 20

**1976.** Millenary of Carinthia.
1758. **533.** 3 s. black and yellow 40 20

**534.** Stained Glass Window, Klosterneuburg.

**535.** "The Siege of Linz" (contemporary engraving).

**1976.** Babenberg Exhibition, Lilienfeld.
1759. **534.** 3 s. multicoloured .. 40 20

**1976.** 350th Anniv of the Peasants' War in Upper Austria.
1760 **535** 4 s. black and green .. 65 35

**536.** Bowler delivering Ball.

**1976.** 11th World Skittles Championships, Vienna.
1761. **536.** 4 s. black & orange .. 60 35

**537.** "St. Wolfgang" (altar painting by Michael Pacher).

**538.** Tassilo Cup, Kremsmunster.

**1976.** International Art Exhibition, St. Wolfgang.
1762. **537.** 6 s. purple .. .. 80 60

**1976.** Europa.
1763. **538.** 4 s. multicoloured .. 50 30

**539.** Fair Emblem.

**540.** Constantin Economo.

**1976.** 25th Austrian Timber Fair, Klagenfurt.
1764. **539.** 3 s. multicoloured .. 30 20

**1976.** Birth Centenary of Constantin Economo (brain specialist).
1765. **540.** 3 s. brown .. .. 45 25

**541.** Bohemian Court Chancellery, Vienna.

**1976.** Cent. of Administrative Court.
1766. **541.** 6 s. brown .. .. 70 60

**543.** Cancer the Crab.

**544.** U.N. Emblem and Bridge.

**1976.** Fight against Cancer.
1768. **543.** 2 s. 50 multicoloured 45 20

**1976.** 10th Anniv of U.N. Industrial Development Organization.
1769 **544** 3 s. blue and gold .. 40 20

**545.** Punched Tapes and Map of Europe.

**1976.** 30th Anniv. of Austrian Press Agency.
1770. **545.** 1 s. 50 multicoloured 15 15

**546.** V. Kaplan.

**1976.** Birth Centenary of Viktor Kaplan (inventor of turbine).
1771. **546.** 2 s. 50 multicoloured 25 15

**547.** "The Birth of Christ" (Konrad von Friesach).

**1976.** Christmas.
1772. **547.** 3 s. multicoloured .. 20 10

**548.** Postilion's Hat and Posthorn.

**1976.** Stamp Day.
1773 **548** 6 s.+2 s. black & lilac 60 80

**549.** R. M. Rilke.

**550.** "Augustin the Piper" (Arik Brauer).

**1976.** 50th Death Anniv of Rainer Maria Rilke (poet).
1774 **549** 3 s. violet .. .. 45 20

**1976.** Austrian Modern Art.
1775 **550** 6 s. multicoloured .. 40 50



**551.** City Synagogue.

**552.** N. J. von Jacquin.

**1976.** 150th Anniv. of Vienna City Synagogue.
1776. **551.** 1 s. 50 multicoloured 40 15

**1977.** 250th Birth Anniv. of Nikolaus Joseph Freiherrn von Jacquin (botanist).
1777 **552** 4 s. brown .. .. 30 30

**553.** Oswald von Wolkenstein.

**555.** A. Kubin.

**554.** Handball.

**1977.** 600th Birth Anniv. of Oswald von Wolkenstein (poet).
1778. **553.** 3 s. multicoloured .. 30 20

**1977.** World Indoor Handball Championships, Group B, Austria.
1779. **554.** 1 s. 50 multicoloured 20 15

**1977.** Birth Centenary of Alfred Kubin (writer and illustrator).
1780. **555.** 6 s. blue .. .. 80 55

**556.** Cathedral Spire.

**558.** I.A.E.A. Emblem.

**557.** F. Herzmanovsky-Orlando.

**1977.** 25th Anniv. of Reopening of St. Stephen's Cathedral, Vienna.
1781 **556** 2 s. 50 brown .. 35 15
1782 – 3 s. blue .. .. 45 35
1783 – 4 s. purple .. .. 55 55
DESIGNS: 3 s. West Front. 4 s. Interior.

**1977.** Birth Cent of Fritz Herzmanovsky-Orlando (writer).
1784 **557** 6 s. green and gold .. 80 55

**1977.** 20th Anniv of International Atomic Energy Agency.
1785 **558** 3 s. lt blue, gold & blue 30 20

**559.** Arms of Schwanenstadt.

**561.** Globe (Vincenzo Coronelli).

**560.** Attersee.

**1977.** 350th Anniv. of Schwanenstadt.
1786. **559.** 3 s. multicoloured .. 40 20

**1977.** Europa.
1787. **560.** 6 s. green .. .. 75 55

**1977.** 5th International Symposium and 25th Anniv. of Coronelli World Federation of Globe Friends.
1788 **561** 3 s. black and stone .. 40 20

562. Canoeist.

**1977.** World "White Water" Canoe Championships.
1789. **562.** 4 s. multicoloured .. 55 30

563. "The Samaritan" (Francesco Bassano).

**1977.** 50th Anniv. of Austrian Workers' Samaritan Federation.
1790. **563.** 1 s. 50 multicoloured 20 15

564. Papermakers' Arms. 565. " Freedom ".

**1977.** 17th Conference of European Committee of Pulp and Paper Technology.
1791 **564** 3 s. multicoloured .. 30 20

**1977.** Martyrs for Austrian Freedom.
1792. **565.** 2 s. 50 blue and red 30 20

566. Steam Locomotive, " Austria ", 1837. 567. " Madonna & Child " (wood carving Mariastein Pilgrimage, Church).

**1977.** 140th Anniv of Austrian Railways.
1793 1 s. 50 Type **566** .. .. 30 15
1794 2 s. 50 Type "214" steam locomotive (1928) .. 55 30
1795 3 s. Type "1044" electric locomotive (1974) .. 65 40

**1977.** Christmas.
1796. **567.** 3 s. multicoloured .. 30 10

568. " Danube Maiden " (Wolfgang Hutter). 569. Emanuel Herrmann (inventor of postcard).

**1977.** Austrian Modern Art.
1797. **568.** 6 s. multicoloured .. 80 55

**1977.** Stamp Day.
1798 **569** 6 s. + 2 s. brown and cinnamon .. 75 90

570. Egon Friedell.

**1978.** Birth Cent. of Egon Friedell (writer).
1799. **570.** 3 s. black and blue .. 30 20

571. Underground Train.

**1978.** Opening of Vienna Underground Railway.
1800 **571** 3 s. multicoloured .. 85 30

572. Rifleman and Skier.

**1978.** Biathlon World Championships, Hochfilzen.
1801. **572.** 4 s. multicoloured .. 55 35

573. Aztec Feather Shield.

**1978.** 30th Anniv. of Museum of Ethnology, Vienna.
1802. **573.** 3 s. multicoloured .. 30 20

574. Leopold Kunschak. 575 " Mountain Peasants ".

**1978.** 25th Death Anniv. of Leopold Kunschak (politician).
1803. **574.** 3 s. blue .. .. 30 20

**1978.** Birth Centenary of Suitbert Lobisser (wood engraver).
1804 **575** 3 s. brown and stone 30 20

576. Black Grouse, Hunting Satchel and Fowling Piece. 577. Map of Europe and Austrian Parliament Building.

**1978.** International Hunting Exn, Marchegg.
1805 **576** 6 s. blue, brown and turquoise .. .. 80 50

**1978.** 3rd Interparliamentary European Security Conference, Vienna.
1806 **577** 4 s. multicoloured .. 50 30

578. Riegersburg Castle, Styria.

**1978.** Europa.
1807. **578.** 6 s. purple .. .. 70 65

579. " Admont Pieta " (Salzburg Circle Master). 580. Ort Castle.

**1978.** "Gothic Art in Styria" Exhibition.
1808. **579.** 2 s. 50 black & ochre 30 15

**1978.** 700th Anniv of Gmunden Town Charter.
1809 **580** 3 s. multicoloured .. 30 20

581. Face surrounded by Fruit and Flowers. 582. Franz Lehar and Villa at Bad Ischl.

**1978.** 25th Anniv. of Austrian Association for Social Tourism.
1810. **581.** 6 s. multicoloured .. 75 55

**1978.** International Lehar Congress.
1811. **582.** 6 s. blue .. .. 70 45

583. Tools and Globe.

**1978.** 15th Congress of International Federation of Building and Wood Workers.
1812 **583** 1 s. 50 blk, yell & red 20 15

584. Knights Jousting.

**1978.** 700th Anniv. of Battle of Durnkrut and Jedenspeigen.
1813. **584.** 3 s. multicoloured .. 35 25

585. Bridge over River Drau. 586. City Seal, 1440.

**1978.** 1100th Anniv. of Villach.
1814. **585.** 3 s. multicoloured .. 30 20

**1978.** 850th Anniv. of Graz.
1815. **586.** 4 s. brn., grn. & grey 40 30

587. Angler. 588. Distorted Pattern.

**1978.** 25th Sport Fishing Championships, Vienna.
1816 **587** 4 s. multicoloured .. 50 30

**1978.** Handicapped People.
1817. **588.** 6 s. black and brown 70 55

589. Concrete Chain. 590. " Grace " (Albin Egger-Lienz).

**1978.** 9th International Concrete and Prefabrication Industry Congress, Vienna.
1818 **589** 2 s. 50 multicoloured 30 20

**1978.** European Family Congress.
1819. **590.** 6 s. multicoloured .. 60 50

591. Lise Meitner. 592. Victor Adler. (bust, Anton Hamek).

**1978.** Birth Cent. of Lise Meitner (physicist).
1820. **591.** 6 s. violet .. .. 65 50

**1978.** 60th Death Anniv. of Victor Adler (statesman).
1821. **592.** 3 s. black and red .. 30 20

593. Franz Schubert (after Josef Kriehuber). 594. "Madonna and Child" (Martino Altomonte, Wilhering Collegiate Church).

**1978.** 150th Death Anniv. of Franz Schubert (composer).
1822. **593.** 6 s. brown .. .. 1·10 55

**1978.** Christmas.
1823. **594.** 3 s. multicoloured .. 30 10

595. Post Bus, 1913.

**1978.** Stamp Day.
1824. **595.** 10 s. + 5 s. mult. .. 90 1·40

596. " Archduke Johann Hut, Grossglockner " (E. T. Compton).

**1978.** Cent. of Austrian Alpine Club.
1825. **596.** 1 s. 50 violet and gold 30 10

597. " Adam " (Rudolf Hausner). 598. Bound Hands.

**1978.** Austrian Modern Art.
1826 **597** 6 s. multicoloured .. 50 45

**1978.** 30th Anniv. of Declaration of Human Rights.
1827. **598.** 6 s. purple .. .. 55 45

599. "CCIR".

**1979.** 50th Anniv. of International Radio Consultative Committee.
1828. **599.** 6 s. multicoloured .. 70 45

600. Adult protecting Child.

**1979.** International Year of the Child.
1829. **600.** 2 s. 50 multicoloured 30 20

**601.** Air Rifle, Pistol and Target.

**1979.** Centenary of Austrian Shooting Club, and European Air Rifle and Air Pistol Shooting Championships.
1830. **601.** 6 s. multicoloured .. 75 45

**602.** "Franz I" (paddle-steamer).

**603.** Skater.

**1979.** 150th Anniv. of Danube Steam Navigation Company.
1831. **602.** 1 s. 50 blue .. .. 30 10
1832. – 2 s. 50 brown .. 50 25
1833. – 3 s. red .. .. 50 35
DESIGNS: 2 s. 50, Pusher tug "Linz". 3 s. "Theodor Korner" (passenger vessel).

**1979.** World Ice Skating and Dancing Championships. Vienna.
1834. **603.** 4 s. multicoloured .. 40 35

**604.** Fashion Drawing by Theo Zache, 1900.

**605.** Wiener Neustadt Cathedral.

**1979.** 50th Viennese International Ladies' Fashion Week.
1835. **604.** 2 s. 50 multicoloured 30 20

**1979.** 700th Anniv. of Wiener Neustadt Cathedral.
1836. **605.** 4 s. blue and grey .. 55 35

**606.** Relief from Emperor Joseph II Monument, Vienna.

**607.** Population Graph.

**1979.** Bicentenary of Education for the Deaf.
1837 **606** 2 s. 50 grn, blk & gold 30 20

**1979.** 150th Anniv. of Austrian Central Statistical Office.
1838. **607.** 2 s. 50 multicoloured 30 20

**608.** Laurenz Koschier (postal reformer).

**609.** Section through Diesel Engine.

**1979.** Europa.
1839 **608** 6 s. brown and ochre 55 45

**1979.** 13th Congress of International Combustion Engine Council.
1840. **609.** 4 s. multicoloured .. 35 30

**610.** Town Arms of Ried, Braunau and Scharding.

**1979.** Bicent. of Innviertel District.
1841. **610.** 3 s. multicoloured .. 30 20

**611.** Water Pollution.

**1979.** Prevention of Water Pollution.
1842. **611.** 2 s. 50 green and grey 30 20

**612.** Arms of Rottenmann.

**613.** Jodok Fink.

**1979.** 700th Anniv. of Rottenmann.
1843. **612.** 3 s. multicoloured .. 30 20

**1979.** 50th Death Anniv. of Jodok Fink (politician).
1844. **613.** 3 s. brown .. .. 30 20

**614.** Arms of Wels and Returned Soldiers League Badge.

**615.** Flower.

**1979.** Fifth European Meeting of Returned Soldiers.
1845. **614.** 4 s. green and black .. 45 30

**1979.** U.N. Conference on Science and Technology for Development, Vienna.
1846. **615.** 4 s. blue .. .. 40 30

**616.** Vienna International Centre.

**1979.** Opening of U.N.O. Vienna International Centre.
1847. **616.** 6 s. slate .. .. 65 55

**617.** Eye and Blood Vessels of Diabetic.

**1979.** 10th World Congress of International Diabetes Federation, Vienna.
1848 **617** 2 s. 50 multicoloured 35 20

**618.** Stanzer Valley seen from Arlberg Road Tunnel.

**1979.** 16th World Road Congress, Vienna.
1849. **618.** 4 s. multicoloured .. 60 30

**619.** Steam-driven Printing Press.

**1979.** 175th Anniv. of State Printing Works.
1850. **619.** 3 s. black and stone 40 20

**620.** Richard Zsigmondy.

**1979.** 50th Death Anniv. of Dr. Richard Zsigmondy (Nobel Prize winner for chemistry).
1851. **620.** 6 s. brown .. .. 60 45

**621.** Bregenz Festival and Congress Hall.

**1979.** Bregenz Festival and Congress Hall.
1852. **621.** 2 s. 50 lilac .. .. 30 20

**622.** Burning Match.

**1979.** "Save Energy".
1853. **622.** 2 s. 50 multicoloured 30 20

**623.** Lions Emblem.

**1979.** 25th European Lions Forum, Vienna.
1854. **623.** 4 s. yell., gold & lilac 45 20

**624.** Wilhelm Exner (founder).

**625.** "The Suffering Christ" (Hans Fronius).

**1979.** Centenary of Industrial Museum and Technical School, Vienna.
1855 **624** 2 s. 50 dp purple & pur 30 20

**1979.** Austrian Modern Art.
1856 **625** 4 s. black and stone .. 40 40

**626.** Series "52" Goods Locomotive.

**627.** August Musger.

**1979.** Centenary of Raab (Gyor)–Odenburg (Sopron)–Ebenfurt Railway.
1857 **626** 2 s. 50 multicoloured 60 40

**1979.** 50th Death Anniv. of August Musger (pioneer of slow-motion photography).
1858. **627.** 2 s. 50 black and grey 30 20

**628.** "Nativity" (detail of icon by Moses Subotic, St Barbara Church, Vienna).

**1979.** Christmas.
1859. **628.** 4 s. multicoloured .. 30 15

**629.** Neue Hofburg, Vienna.

**1979.** "WIPA 1981" International Stamp Exn, Vienna (1st issue). Inscr "1 Phase".
1860 **629** 16 s. + 8 s. mult .. 2·25 2·50
See also No. 1890.

**630.** Arms of Baden.

**631.** Loading Exports.

**1980.** 500th Anniv. of Baden.
1861. **630.** 4 s. multicoloured .. 50 30

**1980.** Austrian Exports.
1862. **631.** 4 s. blue, red & black 50 30

**632.** Rheumatic Hand holding Stick.

**633.** Emblems of 1880 and 1980.

**1980.** Fight against Rheumatism.
1863. **632.** 2 s. 50 red and blue .. 40 20

**1980.** Centenary of Austrian Red Cross.
1864. **633.** 2 s. 50 multicoloured 40 20

**634.** Kirchschlager.

**635.** Robert Hamerling.

**1980.** President Rudolf Kirchschlager's 65th Birthday.
1865. **634.** 4 s. brown and red .. 50 30

**1980.** 150th Birth Anniv. of Robert Hamerling (writer).
1866. **635.** 2 s. 50 green .. .. 30 25

**636.** Town Seal.

**637.** "Maria Theresa as a Young Woman" (Andreas Moller).

**1980.** 750th Anniv. of Hallein.
1867. **636.** 4 s. black and red .. 45 30

**1980.** Death Bicentenary of Empress Maria Theresa.
1868. **637.** 2 s. 50 purple .. 30 20
1869. – 4 s. blue .. .. 40 40
1870. – 6 s. brown .. .. 60 80
DESIGNS: 4 s. "Maria Theresa with St. Stephen's Crown" (Martin van Meytens). 6 s. "Maria Theresa as Widow" (Joseph Ducreux).

**638.** Flags of Treaty Signatories.

**639.** St. Benedict (statue, Meinrad Guggenbichler).

**1980.** 25th Anniv. of Austrian State Treaty.
1871. **638.** 4 s. multicoloured .. 45 30

**1980.** Congress of Austrian Benedictine Orders, Mariazell.
1872. **639.** 2 s. 50 green .. .. 30 20

**640.** " Hygieia " (Gustav Klimt). **641.** Dish Aerial, Aflenz.

**1980.** 175th Anniv. of Hygiene Education.
1873. **640.** 4 s. multicoloured .. 55 40

**1980.** Inauguration of Aflenz Satellite Communications Earth Station.
1874. **641.** 6 s. multicoloured .. 65 60

**642.** Steyr (copperplate engraving, 1693).

**1980.** Millenary of Steyr.
1875. **642.** 4 s. brn., blk. & gold 50 30

**643.** Oil Driller. **644.** Town Seal of 1267.

**1980.** 50th Anniv. of Oil Production in Austria.
1876. **643.** 2 s. 50 multicoloured 30 20

**1980.** 800th Anniv. of Innsbruck.
1877. **644.** 2 s. 50 yellow, black & red .. .. 30 20

**645.** Ducal Crown.

**1980.** 800th Anniv of Elevation of Styria to Dukedom.
1878 **645** 4 s. multicoloured .. 30 30

**646.** Leo Ascher. **647.** " Abraham " (illustration from " Viennese Genesis ").

**1980.** Birth Cent. of Leo Ascher (composer).
1879. **646.** 3 s. violet .. .. 50 30

**1980.** 10th Congress of International Organization for Study of the Old Testament.
1880. **647.** 4 s. multicoloured .. 30 30

**648.** Robert Stolz. **649.** Falkenstein Railway Bridge.

**1980.** Europa and Birth Centenary of Robert Stolz (composer).
1881. **648.** 6 s. red .. .. 60 55

**1980.** 11th International Association of Bridge and Structural Engineering Congress, Vienna.
1882. **649.** 4 s. multicoloured .. 55 35

**650.** " Moon Figure " (Karl Brandstatter). **651.** Customs Officer.

**1980.** Austrian Modern Art.
1883. **650.** 4 s. multicoloured .. 40 25

**1980.** 150th Anniv. of Customs Service.
1884. **651.** 2 s. 50 brown and red 30 20

**652.** Mast-head of 1810.

**1980.** 350th Anniv. of "Linzer Zeitung" (Linz newspaper).
1885. **652.** 2 s. 50 black, red & gold .. .. 30 20

**653.** Frontispiece of Waidhofen Municipal Book. **654.** Heads.

**1980.** 750th Anniv of Waidhofen.
1886 **653** 2 s. 50 multicoloured 30 20

**1980.** 25th Anniv. of Federal Army.
1887. **654.** 2 s. 50 green and red 30 20

**655.** Alfred Wegener. **656.** Robert Musil.

**1980.** Birth Centenary of Alfred Wegener (explorer and geophysicist).
1888. **655.** 4 s. blue .. .. 45 30

**1980.** Birth Cent. of Robert Musil (writer).
1889. **656.** 4 s. brown .. .. 30 30

**1980.** "WIPA 1981" International Stamp Exhibition, Vienna (2nd issue). Inscr "2. Phase".
1890 **629** 16 s. + 8 s. mult .. 1·75 2·25

**657.** " Adoration of the Kings " (stained glass window, Viktring Collegiate Church). **658.** Ribbon in National Colours.

**1980.** Christmas.
1891. **657.** 4 s. multicoloured .. 30 20

**1981.** 25th Anniv. of General Social Insurance Act.
1892. **658.** 2 s. 50 red, green & black .. .. 30 20

**659.** Unissued design for 1926 Child Welfare Stamps. **660.** Disabled Person operating Machine Tool.

**1981.** Birth Centenary of Wilhelm Dachauer (artist).
1894. **659.** 3 s. brown .. .. 30 20

**1981.** 3rd European Regional Conference of Rehabilitation International.
1895. **660.** 6 s. brn., bl. & red .. 45 40

**661.** Sigmund Freud. **662.** Long-distance Heating System.

**1981.** 125th Birth Anniv. of Sigmund Freud (psycho-analyst).
1896. **661.** 3 s. purple .. .. 45 25

**1981.** 20th International Union of Long-distance Heat Distributors Congress, Vienna.
1897. **662.** 4 s. multicoloured .. 30 30

**663.** " Azzo and his Vassals " (cover of Monastery's " bearskin " Manuscript). **664.** Maypole.

**1981.** Kuenring Exhibition, Zwettl Monastery.
1898. **663.** 3 s. multicoloured .. 30 25

**1981.** Europa.
1899. **664.** 6 s. multicoloured .. 60 55

**665.** Early Telephone.

**1981.** Cent. of Austrian Telephone System.
1900. **665.** 4 s. multicoloured .. 30 30

**666.** " The Frog King "

**1981.** Art Education in Schools.
1901. **666.** 3 s. multicoloured .. 50 25

**667.** Research Centre.

**1981.** 25th Anniv of Seibersdorf Research Centre.
1902 **667** 4 s. blue, dp bl & orge 30 30

**668.** Town Hall and Seal. **669.** Johann Florian Heller (chemist).

**1981.** 850th Anniv. of St. Veit-on-Glan.
1903. **668.** 4 s. yell., brn. & red 30 30

**1981.** 11th International Clinical Chemistry Congress, Vienna.
1904. **669.** 6 s. brown .. .. 50 50

**670.** Boltzmann. **671.** Otto Bauer.

**1981.** 75th Death Anniv. of Ludwig Boltzmann (physicist).
1905. **670.** 3 s. green .. .. 30 25

**1981.** Birth Centenary of Otto Bauer (writer and politician).
1906. **671.** 4 s. multicoloured .. 30 30

**672.** Chemical Balance. **673.** Impossible Construction (M. C. Escher).

**1981.** International Pharmaceutical Federation Congress, Vienna.
1907. **672.** 6 s. blk,. brn. and red 60 55

**1981.** 10th International Austrian Mathematicians' Congress, Innsbruck.
1908. **673.** 4 s. light blue, blue and deep blue .. 40 30

**674.** " Coronation of Virgin Mary " (detail). **675.** Compass Rose.

**1981.** 500th Anniv of Michael Pacher's Altarpiece at St. Wolfgang, Abersee.
1909 **674** 3 s. blue .. .. 30 20

**1981.** 75th Anniv. of Graz South-East Exhibition.
1910. **675.** 4 s. multicoloured .. 30 30

**676.** "Holy Trinity" (illuminated MS, 12th century).

**1981.** 16th International Congress of Byzantine Scholars, Vienna.
1911. **676.** 6s. multicoloured .. 55 55

**677.** Josef II. **678.** Hans Kelsen.

**1981.** Bicentenary of Toleration Act (giving freedom of worship to Protestants).
1912 **677** 4 s. black, blue & bis 30 30

**1981.** Bicentenary of Hans Kelsen (law lecturer and contributor to shaping of Austrian Constitution).
1913. **678.** 3 s. red .. .. 30 25

**679.** Full and Empty Bowls and F.A.O. Emblem.

**1981.** World Food Day.
1914. **679.** 6 s. multicoloured .. 50 50

680. "Between the Times" (Oscar Asboth).
681. Workers and Emblem.

**1981.** Austrian Modern Art.
1915. **680.** 4 s. multicoloured .. 30 30

**1981.** 7th International Catholic Employees' Meeting, Vienna-Lainz.
1916. **681.** 3 s. multicoloured .. 30 25

682. Hammer-Purgstall.

**1981.** 125th Death Anniv of Josef Hammer-Purgstall (orientalist).
1917 **682** 3 s. multicoloured .. 30 25

683. Julius Raab. 684. Stefan Zweig.

**1981.** 90th Birth Anniv. of Julius Raab (politician).
1918. **683.** 6 s. purple .. .. 55 55

**1981.** Birth Cent of Stefan Zweig (writer).
1919 **684** 4 s. lilac .. .. 50 35

685. Christmas Crib, Burgenland.

**1981.** Christmas.
1920. **685.** 4 s. multicoloured .. 45 20

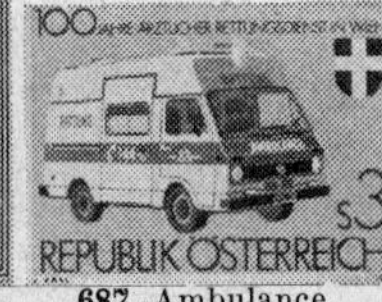


686. Arms of St. Nikola
687. Ambulance.

**1981.** 800th Anniv of St. Nikola-on-Danube.
1921 **686** 4 s. multicoloured .. 30 30

**1981.** Centenary of Vienna's Emergency Medical Service.
1922 **687** 3 s. multicoloured .. 30 25

688. Skier.
689. Dorotheum Building.

**1982.** Alpine Skiing World Championship, Schladming-Haus.
1923 **688** 4 s. multicoloured .. 45 30

**1982.** 275th Anniv. of Dorotheum Auction, Pawn and Banking Society.
1924. **689.** 4 s. multicoloured .. 30 30

690. Lifesaving. 691. St. Severin.

**1982.** 25th Anniv. of Austrian Water Life-saving Service.
1925. **690.** 5 s. bl., red & lt. bl. 60 50

**1982.** "St. Severin and the End of the Roman Period" Exhibition, Enns.
1926. **691.** 3 s. multicoloured .. 30 25

692. Sebastian Kneipp (pioneer of holistic medicine).
693. Printers' Coat of Arms.

**1982.** International Kneipp Congress, Vienna.
1927. **692.** 4 s. multicoloured .. 40 40

**1982.** 500th Anniv. of Printing in Austria.
1928. **693.** 4 s. multicoloured .. 30 30

694. Urine Analysis from "Canon medicinae" by Avicenna.
695. St. Francis preaching to Animals (miniature).

**1982.** Fifth European Union for Urology Congress, Vienna.
1929. **694.** 6 s. multicoloured .. 70 65

**1982.** "Franciscan Art and Culture in the Middle Ages" Exhibition, Krems-Stein.
1930. **695.** 3 s. multicoloured .. 40 25

696. Haydn and Birthplace, Rohrau.
697. Globe within Milk Churn.

**1982.** "Joseph Haydn and His Time". Exhibition, Eisenstadt.
1931. **696.** 3 s. green .. .. 50 25

**1982.** World Dairying Day.
1932. **697.** 7 s. multicoloured .. 60 60

698. Town Arms (1804 flag).
699. Tennis Player.

**1982.** 800th Anniv. of Gfohl.
1933. **698.** 4 s. multicoloured .. 30 30

**1982.** 80th Anniv. of Austrian Lawn Tennis Association.
1934. **699.** 3 s. multicoloured .. 35 25

700. Main Square, Langenlois.
701. Town Arms.

**1982.** 900th Anniv. of Langenlois.
1935. **700.** 4 s. multicoloured .. 30 30

**1982.** 800th Anniv. of Weiz.
1936. **701.** 4 s. multicoloured .. 30 30

702. Linz–Freistadt–Budweis Horse-drawn Railway.

**1982.** Europa.
1937. **702.** 6 s. brown .. .. 85 65

703. Ignaz Seipel. 704. Postbus.

**1982.** 50th Death Anniv. of Ignaz Seipel (Federal Chancellor).
1938. **703.** 3 s. purple .. .. 30 25

**1982.** 75th Anniv. of Postbus Service.
1939. **704.** 4 s. multicoloured .. 60 35

705. Rocket Launch.
706. Globe (Federal Office for Standardization and Surveying, Vienna).

**1982.** Second U.N. Conference on the Exploration and Peaceful Uses of Outer Space, Vienna.
1940. **705.** 4 s. multicoloured .. 55 40

**1982.** Geodesists' Day.
1941. **706.** 3 s. multicoloured .. 40 25

707. Great Bustard.

**1982.** Endangered Animals. Multicoloured.

| | | | |
|---|---|---|---|
| 1942. | 3 s. Type **707** .. .. | 65 | 40 |
| 1943. | 4 s. Eurasian beaver .. | 60 | 55 |
| 1944. | 6 s. Capercaillie .. .. | 1·10 | 85 |

708. Institute Building, Laxenburg.

**1982.** 10th Anniv. of International Institute for Applied Systems Analysis.
1945. **708.** 3 s. black and brown 30 20

709. St. Apollonia (patron saint of dentists).

**1982.** 70th International Dentists Federation Congress, Vienna.
1946 **709** 4 s. multicoloured .. 60 40

710. Emmerich Kalman. 711. Max Mell.

**1982.** Birth Centenary of Emmerich Kalman (composer).
1947. **710.** 3 s. blue .. .. 35 25

**1982.** Birth Cent. of Max Mell (writer).
1948. **711.** 3 s. multicoloured .. 30 25

712. Christmas Crib, Damuls Church.
713. Aerial View of Bosphorus.

**1982.** Christmas.
1949. **712.** 4 s. multicoloured .. 30 15

**1982.** Centenary of St. George's Austrian College, Istanbul.
1950. **713.** 4 s. multicoloured .. 35 35

714. "Mainz-Weber" Mailbox, 1870.

**1982.** Stamp Day.
1951. **714.** 6 s. + 3 s. multicoloured 60 1·00

715. "Muse of the Republic" (Ernst Fuchs).
716. Bank, Vienna.

**1982.** Austrian Modern Art.
1952 **715** 4 s. red and violet .. 30 30

**1983.** Cent. of Postal Savings Bank.
1953. **716.** 4 s. yell., blk. & bl. 30 30

717. Hildegard Burjan. 718. Linked Arms.

**1983.** Birth Centenary of Hildegard Burjan (founder of Caritas Socialis (religious sisterhood)).
1954 **717** 4 s. red .. .. 30 30

**1983.** World Communications Year.
1955. **718.** 7 s. multicoloured .. 60 65

**719.** Young Girl. **720.** Josef Matthias Hauer.

**1983.** 75th Anniv. of Children's Friends Organization.
1956. **719.** 4 s. blk., bl. & red .. 30 30

**1983.** Birth Centenary of Josef Matthias Hauer. (composer).
1957. **720.** 3 s. purple .. .. 35 25

**721.** Douglas DC-9-80 Super Eighty. **722.** Hands protecting Workers.

**1983.** 25th Anniv. of Austrian Airlines.
1958. **721.** 6 s. multicoloured .. 75 35

**1983.** Centenary of Government Work Inspection Law.
1959 **722** 4 s. grn, dp grn & brn 30 30

**723.** Wels (engraving, Matthaeus Merian).

**1983.** "Millenary of Upper Austria" Exhibition, Wels.
1960. **723.** 3 s. multicoloured .. 40 25

**724.** Human Figure, Heart and Electrocardiogram. **725.** Monastery Arms.

**1983.** Seventh World Symposium on Pacemakers.
1961. **724.** 4 s. red, mauve & blue 55 40

**1983.** 900th Anniv. of Gottweig Monastery.
1962. **725.** 3 s. multicoloured .. 30 25

**726.** Weitra.

**1983.** 800th Anniv of Weitra.
1963 **726** 4 s. black, red & gold 50 40

**727.** Cap, Stick, Ribbon and Emblems.

**1983.** 50th Anniv. of MKV and CCV Catholic Students' Organizations.
1964. **727.** 4 s. multicoloured .. 50 35

**728.** Glopper Castle and Town Arms. **729.** Hess.

**1983.** 650th Anniv. of Hohenems Town Charter.
1965. **728.** 4 s. multicoloured .. 30 30

**1983.** Europa. Birth Cent of Viktor Franz Hess (physicist and Nobel Prize winner).
1966 **729** 6 s. green .. .. 75 60

**730.** Vienna City Hall. **731.** Kiwanis Emblem and View of Vienna.

**1983.** 25th Anniv. of Vienna City Hall.
1967. **730.** 4 s. multicoloured .. 45 40

**1983.** Kiwanis International World and European Conference, Vienna.
1968. **731.** 5 s. multicoloured .. 50 45

**732.** Congress Emblem. **733.** Hasenauer and Natural History Museum, Vienna.

**1983.** Seventh World Psychiatry Congress, Vienna.
1969. **732.** 4 s. multicoloured .. 55 30

**1983.** 150th Birth Anniv. of Carl Freiherr von Hasenauer (architect).
1970. **733.** 3 s. brown .. .. 30 30

**734.** Institute for Promotion of Trade and Industry, Linz.

**1983.** 27th International Professional Competition for Young Skilled Workers, Linz.
1971. **734.** 4 s. multicoloured .. 30 30

**735.** Symbols of Penicillin V Efficacy and Cancer. **736.** Pope John Paul II.

**1983.** 13th International Chemotherapy Congress, Vienna.
1972. **735.** 5 s. red and green .. 75 45

**1983.** Papal Visit.
1973. **736.** 6 s. black, red & gold 75 55

**738.** Spectrum around Cross. **739.** Vienna Town Hall.

**1983.** Austrian Catholics' Day.
1975. **738.** 3 s. multicoloured .. 30 25

**1983.** Centenary of Vienna Town Hall.
1976. **739.** 4 s. multicoloured .. 40 30

**740.** Karl von Terzaghi.

**1983.** Birth Cent. of Karl von Terzaghi (soil mechanics and foundations engineer).
1977. **740.** 3 s. blue .. .. 30 25

**741.** Initials of Federation.

**1983.** Tenth Austrian Trade Unions Federation Congress.
1978. **741.** 3 s. red and black .. 30 25

**742.** "Evening Sun in Burgenland" (Gottfried Kumpf). **743.** Tram No. 5, 1883.

**1983.** Austrian Modern Art.
1979 **742** 4 s. multicoloured .. 55 40

**1983.** Centenary of Modling–Hinterbruhl Electric Railway.
1980 **743** 3 s. multicoloured .. 50 25

**744.** Boy looking at Stamped Envelope.

**1983.** Stamp Day.
1981 **744** 6 s. + 3 s. multicoloured 90 1·25

**745.** Francisco Carolinum Museum, Linz.

**1983.** 150th Anniv. of Upper Austrian Provincial Museum.
1982. **745.** 4 s. multicoloured .. 40 30

**746.** Crib by Johann Giner the Elder, Kitzbuhel Church.

**1983.** Christmas.
1983 **746** 4 s. multicoloured .. 45 20

**747.** Parliament Building. **748.** "St. Nicholas" (Maria Freund).

**1983.** Centenary of Parliament Building, Vienna.
1984. **747.** 4 s. blue .. .. 40 35

**1983.** Youth Stamp.
1985. **748.** 3 s. multicoloured .. 30 25

**749.** Wolfgang Pauli.

**1983.** 25th Death Anniv. of Wolfgang Pauli (Nobel physics prize winner).
1986. **749.** 6 s. brown .. .. 70 65

**750.** Gregor Mendel.

**1984.** Death Centenary of Gregor Mendel (geneticist).
1987 **750** 4 s. ochre and brown 60 40

**751.** Hanak at Work.

**1984.** 50th Death Anniv. of Anton Hanak (sculptor).
1988. **751.** 3 s. brown & black .. 30 25

**752.** Disabled Skier.

**1984.** Third World Winter Games for the Disabled, Innsbruck.
1989. **752.** 4 s. + 2 s. multicoloured 65 80

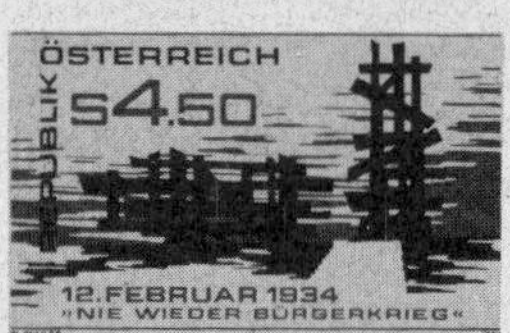


**753.** Memorial, Wollersdorf.

**1984.** 50th Anniv. of 1934 Insurrections.
1990. **753.** 4 s. 50 red and black 45 40

**754.** Founders' Stone. **755.** Geras Monastery.

**1984.** 900th Anniv. of Reichersberg Monastery.
1991. **754.** 3 s. 50 stone, brown and blue .. .. 30 30

**1984.** Monasteries and Abbeys.

| | | | | |
|---|---|---|---|---|
| 1992 | – | 50 g. yell, blk & grey | 10 | 10 |
| 1993 | – | 1 s. yellow, blk & mve | 10 | 10 |
| 1994 | – | 1 s. 50 yellow, red & bl | 15 | 10 |
| 1995 | – | 2 s. yellow, grn & blk | 20 | 10 |
| 1996 | 755 | 3 s. 50 yell, sep & brn | 35 | 10 |
| 1997 | – | 4 s. yell, purple & red | 40 | 10 |
| 1998 | – | 4 s. 50 yell, lilac & bl | 45 | 10 |
| 1999 | – | 5 s. yellow, pur & orge | 45 | 10 |
| 2000 | – | 5 s. 50 yellow, deep violet and violet .. | 50 | 10 |
| 2001 | – | 6 s. yell, grn & emer | 50 | 10 |
| 2002 | – | 7 s. yellow, green & bl | 60 | 15 |
| 2003 | – | 7 s. 50 yellow, deep brown and brown | 70 | 15 |
| 2004 | – | 8 s. yellow, blue & red | 75 | 20 |
| 2005 | – | 10 s. yell, red & grey | 85 | 30 |
| 2006 | – | 11 s. yellow, blk & brn | 95 | 55 |
| 2007 | – | 12 s. yell, brn & orge | 1·10 | 75 |
| 2008 | – | 17 s. yell, ultram & bl | 1·60 | 85 |
| 2009 | – | 20 s. yellow, brn & red | 1·75 | 1·10 |

DESIGNS: 50 g. Vorau Monastery. 1 s. Wettingen Abbey, Mehrerau. 1 s. 50, Monastery of Teutonic Order, Vienna. 2 s. Michaelbeuern Benedictine Monastery, Salzburg. 4 s. Stams Monastery. 4 s. 50, Schlagl Monastery. 5 s. St. Paul's Monastery, Lavanttal. 5 s. 50, St. Gerold's Priory, Vorarlberg. 6 s. Rein Monastery. 7 s. Loretto Monastery. 7 s. 50, Dominican Monastery, Vienna. 8 s. Cistercian Monastery, Zwettl. 10 s. Premonstratensian Monastery, Wilten. 11 s. Trappist Monastery, Engelszell. 12 s. Monastery of the Hospitallers, Eisenstadt. 17 s. St. Peter's Abbey, Salzburg. 20 s. Wernberg Convent, Carinthia.

756. Cigar Band showing Tobacco Plant.

757. Kostendorf.

**1984.** Bicent. of Tobacco Monopoly.
2012. **756.** 4 s. 50 multicoloured 45 35

**1984.** 1200th Anniv. of Kostendorf.
2013. **757.** 4 s. 50 multicoloured 45 35

758. Wheel Bearing.

**1984.** 20th International Federation of Automobile Engineers' Associations World Congress, Vienna.
2014. **758.** 5 s. multicoloured .. 50 45

759. Bridge.

760. Archduke Johann (after Schnorr von Carolsfeld).

**1984.** Europa. 25th Anniv of E.P.T. Conf.
2015 **759** 6 s. blue & ultramarine 70 65

**1984.** 125th Death Anniv. of Archduke Johann.
2016. **760.** 4 s. 50 multicoloured 50 35

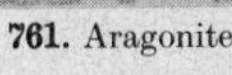


761. Aragonite.

762. Binding of "Das Buch vom Kaiser", by Max Herzig.

**1984.** "Ore and Iron in the Green Mark". Exhibition, Eisenerz.
2017. **761.** 3 s. 50 multicoloured 35 30

**1984.** Lower Austrian "Era of Emperor Franz Joseph: From Revolution to Grunderzeit" Exhibition, Grafenegg Castle.
2018. **762.** 3 s. 50 red and gold 40 30

763. Upper City Tower and Arms.

764. Dionysus (Virunum mosaic).

**1984.** 850th Anniv. of Vocklabruch.
2019. **763.** 4 s. 50 multicoloured 40 35

**1984.** Centenary of Carinthia Provincial Museum, Klagenfurt.
2020. **764.** 3 s. 50 stone, brown and grey .. .. 35 30

765. "Meeting of Austrian Army with South Tyrolean Reserves" (detail, Schnorr von Carolsfeld).

766. Ralph Benatzky.

**1984.** "Jubilee of Tyrol Province". Exhibition.
2021. **765.** 3 s. 50 multicoloured 40 30

**1984.** Birth Centenary of Ralph Benatzky (composer).
2022. **766.** 4 s. brown .. .. 55 40

767. Flood Control Barriers.

768. Christian von Ehrenfels.

**1984.** Cent. of Flood Control Systems.
2023. **767.** 4 s. 50 green .. .. 45 40

**1984.** 125th Death Anniv. of Christian von Ehrenfels (philosopher).
2024. **768.** 3 s. 50 multicoloured 30 30

769. Models of European Monuments.

**1984.** 25th Anniv of Minimundus (model world), Worthersee.
2025 **769** 4 s. yellow and black 40 40

770. Blockheide Eibenstein National Park.

**1984.** Natural Beauty Spots.
2026. **770.** 4 s. pink and olive .. 40 40

771. Electric Train on Schanatobel Bridge (Arlberg Railway Centenary).

**1984.** Railway Anniversaries.
2027. **771.** 3 s. 50 brown, gold and red .. .. 60 35
2028. – 4 s. 50 blue, silver and red .. .. 70 50

DESIGN: 4 s. 50, Electric train on Falkenstein Bridge (75th anniv of Tauern Railway).

772. Johann Georg Stuwer's Ascent in Montgolfier Balloon.

**1984.** Bicentenary of First Manned Balloon Flight in Austria.
2029. **772.** 6 s. multicoloured .. 65 40

773. Lake Neusiedl.

**1984.** Natural Beauty Spots.
2030 **773** 4 s. purple and blue .. 80 35

774. Palace of Justice, Vienna.

775. "Joseph Hyrtl" (window, Innsbruck Anatomy Institute).

**1984.** 20th International Bar Association Congress, Vienna.
2031. **774.** 7 s. multicoloured .. 50 55

**1984.** 7th European Anatomists' Congress, Innsbruck.
2032. **775.** 6 s. multicoloured .. 65 55

776. "Window". (Karl Korab).

777. Clock of Imms (astrolabe).

**1984.** Austrian Modern Art.
2033. **776.** 4 s. multicoloured .. 45 35

**1984.** 600th Birth Anniv. of Johannes von Gmunden (astronomer and mathematician).
2034. **777.** 3 s. 50 multicoloured 35 30

778. Quill.

779. Fanny Elssler.

**1984.** 125th Anniv. of Concordia Press Club.
2035. **778.** 4 s. 50 black, gold & red .. .. 40 35

**1984.** Death Centenary of Fanny Elssler (dancer).
2036. **779.** 4 s. multicoloured .. 60 40

780. "Holy Family" (detail, Aggsbach Old High Altar).

**1984.** Christmas.
2037. **780.** 4 s. 50 multicoloured 50 35

781. Detail from Burial Chamber Wall of Seschemnofer III.

782. Coat of Arms.

**1984.** Stamp Day.
2038. **781.** 6 s. + 3 s. multicoloured 80 1·10

**1985.** 400th Anniv. of Graz University.
2039. **782.** 3 s. 50 multicoloured 40 30

783. Dr. Lorenz Bohler.

**1985.** Birth Centenary of Prof. Dr. Lorenz Bohler (surgeon).
2040 **783** 4 s. 50 purple .. 55 35

784. Ski Jumping, Skiing and Emblem.

**1985.** World Nordic Skiing Championship, Seefeld.
2041. **784.** 4 s. multicoloured .. 60 35

785. Linz Cathedral.

786. Alban Berg.

**1985.** Bicentenary of Linz Diocese.
2042. **785.** 4 s. 50 multicoloured 55 35

**1985.** Birth Centenary of Alban Berg (composer).
2043. **786.** 6 s. blue .. .. 90 65

**787.** Institute Emblem. **788.** Stylized "B" and Clouds.

**1985.** 25th Anniv. of Institute for Vocational Advancement.
2044. **787.** 4 s. 50 multicoloured 45 40

**1985.** 2000th Anniv of Bregenz.
2045 788 4 s. black, ultram & bl 35 35

**789.** 1885 Registration Label. **790.** Josef Stefan.

**1985.** Centenary of Registration Labels in Austria.
2046. **789.** 4 s. 50 black, yellow and grey .. .. 45 40

**1985.** 150th Birth Anniversary of Josef Stefan (physicist).
2047. **790.** 6 s. brown, stone and red .. .. 80 65

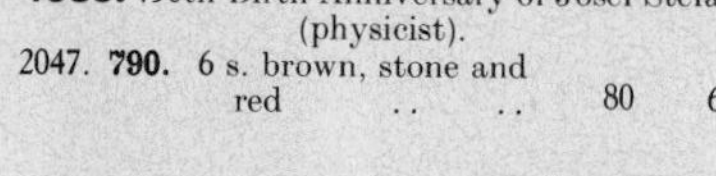

**791.** St. Leopold (Margrave and patron saint). **792.** "The Story-teller".

**1985.** Lower Austrian Provincial Exhibition, Klosterneuburg Monastery.
2048. **791.** 3 s. 50 multicoloured 45 35

**1985.** 150th Birth Anniv. of Franz Defregger (artist).
2049. **792.** 3 s. 50 multicoloured 45 40

**793.** Barbed Wire, Broken Tree and New Shoot. **794.** Johann Joseph Fux (composer).

**1985.** 40th Anniv. of Liberation.
2050. **793.** 4 s. 50 multicoloured 55 50

**1985.** Europa. Music Year.
2051. **794.** 6 s. brown and grey 90 65

**795.** Flags and Caduceus. **797.** Bishop's Gate, St. Polten.

**796.** Town and Arms.

**1985.** 25th Anniv. of European Free Trade Association.
2052. **795.** 4 s. multicoloured .. 65 45

**1985.** Millenary of Boheimkirchen.
2053. **796.** 4 s. 50 multicoloured 60 60

**1985.** Bicent. of St. Polten Diocese.
2054. **797.** 4 s. 50 multicoloured 55 40

**798.** Johannes von Nepomuk Church, Innsbruck. **799.** Garsten (copper-plate, George Matthaus Fischer).

**1985.** Gumpp Family (architects) Exhibition, Innsbruck.
2055. **798.** 3 s. 50 multicoloured 40 35

**1985.** Millenary of Garsten.
2056. **799.** 4 s. 50 multicoloured 65 55

**800.** U.N. Emblem and Austrian Arms.

**1985.** 40th Anniv. of United Nations Organization and 30th Anniv. of Austrian Membership.
2057. **800.** 4 s. multicoloured .. 60 40

**801.** Association Head-quarters, Vienna.

**1985.** 13th International Suicide Prevention Association Congress, Vienna.
2058. **801.** 5 s. brown, light yellow and yellow 70 55

**803.** Operetta Emblem and Spa Building. **804.** Fireman and Emblem.

**1985.** 25th Bad Ischl Operetta Week.
2060. **803.** 3 s. 50 multicoloured 60 40

**1985.** 8th International Fire Brigades Competition, Vocklabruck.
2061 804 4 s. 50 black, grn & red 75 45

**805.** Grossglockner Mountain Road.

**1985.** 50th Anniv. of Grossglockner Mountain Road.
2062. **805.** 4 s. multicoloured .. 60 40

**806.** Chessboard as Globe. **807.** "Founding of Konigstetten" (August Stephan).

**1985.** World Chess Association Congress, Graz.
2063. **806.** 4 s. multicoloured .. 60 40

**1985.** Konigstetten Millenary.
2064. **807.** 4 s. 50 multicoloured 65 40

**808.** Webern Church and Arms of Hofkirchen and Taufkircher. **809.** Dr. Adam Politzer.

**1985.** 1200th Anniversaries of Hofkirchen, Weibern and Taufkirchen.
2065. **808.** 4 s. 50 multicoloured 65 40

**1985.** 150th Birth Anniv. of Dr. Adam Politzer (otologist).
2066. **809.** 3 s. 50 violet .. 50 40

**810.** Emblem and View of Vienna.

**1985.** International Association of Forwarding Agents World Congress, Vienna.
2067. **810.** 6 s. multicoloured .. 65 60

**811.** "Clowns Riding High Bicycles" (Paul Flora).

**1985.** Austrian Modern Art.
2068. **811.** 4 s. multicoloured .. 65 40

**812.** St. Martin, Patron Saint of Burgenland. **813.** Roman Mounted Courier.

**1985.** 25th Anniv of Eisenstadt Diocese.
2069 812 4 s. 50 blk, bistre & red 65 40

**1985.** 50th Anniv. of Stamp Day.
2070. **813.** 6 s. + 3 s. mult. .. 1·00 1·10

**814.** Hanns Horbiger. **815.** "Adoration of the Christ Child" (marble relief).

**1985.** 125th Birth Anniv. of Hanns Horbiger (design engineer).
2071. **814.** 3 s. 50 purple and gold .. .. 40 30

**1985.** Christmas.
2072. **815.** 4 s. 50 multicoloured 50 15

**816.** Aqueduct.

**1985.** 75th Anniv. of Second Vienna Waterline.
2073. **816.** 3 s. 50 black, red and blue .. .. 40 30

**818.** Chateau de la Muette (headquarters).

**1985.** 25th Anniv. of Organization of Economic Co-operation and Development.
2080. **818.** 4 s. black, gold and mauve .. .. 45 40

**819.** Johann Bohm.

**1986.** Birth Cent. of Johann Bohm (founder of Austrian Trade Unions Federation).
2081. **819.** 4 s. 50 black and red 55 40

**820.** Dove and Globe.

**1986.** International Peace Year.
2082. **820.** 6 s. multicoloured .. 65 55

**821.** Push-button Dialling.

**1986.** Introduction of Digital Preselection Telephone System.
2083. **821.** 5 s. multicoloured .. 60 40

**822.** Albrechtsberger and Organ.

**1986.** 250th Birth Anniv. of Johann Georg Albrechtsberger (composer).
2084. **822.** 3 s. 50 multicoloured 50 35

823. Main Square and Arms.

1986. 850th Anniv. of Korneuburg.
2085. 823. 5 s. multicoloured .. 60 40

824. Kokoschka (self-portrait).

825. Council Flag.

1986. Birth Centenary of Oskar Kokoschka (artist).
2086. 824. 4 s. black and pink .. 50 35

1986. 30th Anniv. of Membership of Council of Europe.
2087. 825. 6 s. black, red & bl. 85 65

826. Holzmeister and Salzburg Festival Hall.

1986. Birth Centenary of Professor Clemens Holzmeister (architect).
2088. 826. 4 s. grey, brown and light brown .. 50 35

827. Road, Fabric Roll, and Congress Emblem.

1986. 3rd International Geotextile Congress, Vienna.
2089. 827. 5 s. multicoloured .. 60 40

828. Schlosshof Palace (after Bernardo Bellotto) and Prince Eugene.

1986. "Prince Eugene and the Baroque Era" Exhibition, Schlosshof and Niederweiden.
2090. 828. 4 s. multicoloured .. 55 40

829. St. Florian Monastery.

1986. Upper Austrian "World of Baroque" Exhibition, St. Florian Monastery.
2091. 829. 4 s. multicoloured .. 55 40

830. Herberstein Castle and Styrian Arms.

1986. "Styria—Bridge and Bulwark" Exhibition, Herberstein Castle, near Stubenberg.
2092. 830. 4 s. multicoloured .. 55 40

831. Large Pasque Flower.

1986. Europa.
2093. 831. 6 s. multicoloured .. 80 60

832. Wagner and Scene from Opera "Lohengrin".

1986. International Richard Wagner (composer) Congress, Vienna.
2094. 832. 4 s. multicoloured .. 60 40

833. Antimonite Crystal.

1986. Burgenland "Mineral and Fossils" Exhibition, Oberpullendorf.
2095. 833. 4 s. multicoloured .. 60 40

834. Martinswall, Zirl.

1986. Natural Beauty Spots.
2096. 834. 5 s. brown and blue 75 55

835. Waidhofen.

1986. 800th Anniv. of Waidhofen on Ybbs.
2097. 835. 4 s. multicoloured .. 50 40

836. Tschauko Falls, Ferlach.

1986. Natural Beauty Spots.
2098. 836. 5 s. green and brown 65 50

837. 19th-century Steam and Modern Articulated Trams.

1986. Centenary of Salzburg Local Transport System.
2099. 837. 4 s. multicoloured .. 60 40

838. Enns and Seals of Signatories.

1986. 800th Anniv. of Georgenberg Treaty (between Duke Leopold V of Austria and Duke Otakar IV of Styria).
2100. 838. 5 s. multicoloured .. 65 50

839. Tandler.

840. "Observatory, 1886" (A. Heilmann).

1986. 50th Death Anniv. of Julius Tandler (social reformer).
2101. 839. 4 s. multicoloured .. 60 40

1986. Centenary of Sonnblick Observatory.
2102. 840. 4 s. blk., bl. & gold 60 40

841. Man collecting Mandragora (from "Codex Tacuinum Sanitatis").

842. Fire Assistant.

1986. Seventh European Anaesthesia Congress, Vienna.
2103. 841. 5 s. multicoloured .. 75 45

1986. 300th Anniv. of Vienna Fire Brigade.
2104. 842. 4 s. multicoloured .. 70 40

843. Stoessl.

844. Viennese Hunting Tapestry (detail).

1986. 50th Death Anniv. of Otto Stoessl (writer).
2105. 843. 4 s. multicoloured .. 55 40

1986. Fifth International Oriental Carpets and Tapestry Conference, Vienna and Budapest.
2106. 844. 5 s. multicoloured .. 65 50

## MINIMUM PRICE

The minimum price quoted is 10p which represents a handling charge rather than a basis for valuing common stamps. For further notes about prices see introductory pages.

845. Minister in Pulpit.

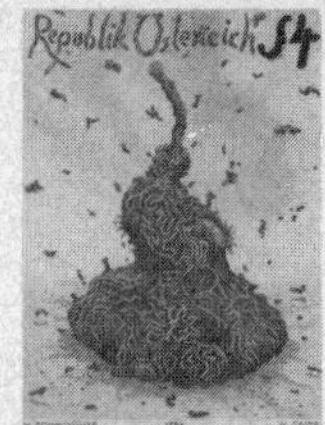
846. "Decomposition" (Walter Schmogner).

1986. 125th Anniv. of Protestants Act and 25th Anniv. of Protestants Law.
2107. 845. 5 s. black and violet 65 50

1986. Austrian Modern Art.
2108. 846. 4 s. multicoloured .. 55 40

847. Liszt, Birthplace and Score.

1986. 175th Birth Anniv. of Franz Liszt (composer).
2109. 847. 5 s. green and brown 70 50

849. Strettweg Religious Carriage.

1986. 175th Anniv. of Styrian Joanneum Museum.
2111. 849. 4 s. multicoloured .. 60 40

850. Nuremberg Letter Messenger" (16th-century woodcut).

852. Headquarters.

851. "Adoration of the Shepherds" (woodcut, Johann Georg Schwanthaler).

1986. Stamp Day.
2112. 850. 6 s. + 3 s. mult. .. 1·25 1·40

1986. Christmas.
2113. 851. 5 s. brown and gold 65 30

1986. 40th Anniv. of Federal Chamber of Trade and Industry.
2114. 852. 5 s. multicoloured .. 65 50

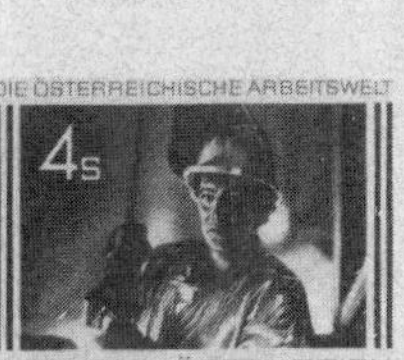
853. Foundry Worker.

854. "The Educated Eye".

**1986.** Austrian World of Work (1st series).
2115. **853.** 4 s. multicoloured .. 55 35
See also Nos. 2144, 2178, 2211, 2277, 2386, 2414 and 2428.

**1987.** Centenary of Adult Education in Vienna.
2116. **854.** 5 s. multicoloured .. 65 50

**855.** "Large Blue Madonna" (Anton Faistauer).

**1987.** Painters' Birth Centenaries. Mult.
2117. 4 s. Type **855** .. .. 50 35
2118. 6 s. "Self-portrait" (Albert Paris Gutersloh) .. .. 75 60

**856.** Hundertwasser House, Vienna. **857.** Ice Hockey Players.

**1987.** Europa and "Europalia 1987 Austria" Festival, Belgium.
2119. **856.** 6 s. multicoloured .. 75 60

**1987.** World Ice Hockey Championships, Vienna, and 75th Anniv. of Austrian Ice Hockey Association.
2120. **857.** 5 s. multicoloured .. 70 50

**858.** Austria Centre.

**1987.** Inauguration of Austria Conference Centre, Vienna.
2121. **858.** 5 s. multicoloured .. 65 45

**859.** Salzburg. **860.** Machine Shop, 1920.

**1987.** 700th Anniv. of Salzburg Town Charter.
2122. **859.** 5 s. multicoloured .. 70 50

**1987.** Upper Austrian "Work Men Machines, the Route to Industrialized Society" Exhibition, Steyr.
2123. **860.** 4 s. black and red .. 60 45

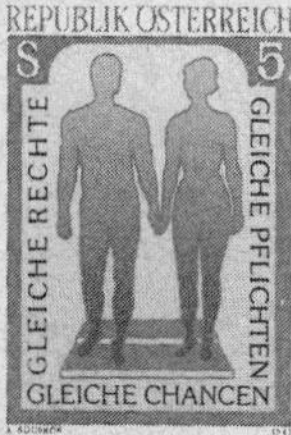

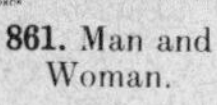

**861.** Man and Woman. **862.** "Adele Bloch-Bauer I" (detail, Gustav Klimt).

**1987.** Equal Rights for Men and Women.
2124. **861.** 5 s. multicoloured .. 65 45

**1987.** Lower Austrian "Era of Emperor Franz Joseph: Splendour and Misery" Exhibition, Grafenegg Castle.
2125. **862.** 4 s. multicoloured .. 65 45

**863.** Archbishop and Salzburg.

**1987.** 400th Anniv. of Election of Prince Wolf Dietrich von Raitenau as Archbishop of Salzburg.
2126. **863.** 4 s. multicoloured .. 50 40

**864.** Schnitzler. **865.** Lace and Arms.

**1987.** 125th Birth Anniv. of Arthur Schnitzler (dramatist).
2127. **864.** 6 s. multicoloured .. 75 60

**1987.** 1100th Anniv. of Lustenau.
2128. **865.** 5 s. multicoloured .. 65 50

**867.** Dachstein Giant Ice Cave.

**1987.** Natural Beauty Spots.
2130. **867.** 5 s. green and black 65 50

**868.** Engraver at Work. **869.** Dr. Karl Josef Bayer (chemist).

**1987.** 8th European Association of Engravers and Flexographers International Congress, Vienna.
2131 868 5 s. brn, pink & grey 60 50

**1987.** 8th International Light Metal Meeting, Leoben and Vienna.
2132. **869.** 5 s. multicoloured .. 65 50

**870.** Passenger Ferry. **871.** Office Building, Vienna.

**1987.** Centenary of First Achensee Steam Service.
2133. **870.** 4 s. multicoloured .. 65 35

**1987.** 10th Anniv. of Office of Ombudsmen.
2134. **871.** 5 s. black, yellow and red .. .. 65 45

**872.** Schrodinger. **873.** Freistadt Town Square.

**1987.** Birth Centenary of Erwin Schrodinger (physicist).
2135. **872.** 5 s. brown, cream and bistre .. 65 50

**1987.** 125th Anniv. of Freistadt Exhibitions.
2136. **873.** 5 s. multicoloured .. 65 50

**874.** Arbing Church.

**1987.** 850th Anniv. of Arbing.
2137. **874.** 5 s. multicoloured .. 65 45

**875.** Gauertal and Montafon Valleys, Voralberg.

**1987.** Natural Beauty Spots.
2138. **875.** 5 s. brown and yellow 70 50

**876.** Cyclist. **877.** Emblem.

**1987.** World Cycling Championship, Vienna and Villach.
2139. **876.** 5 s. multicoloured .. 70 45

**1987.** World Congress of International Institute of Savings Banks, Vienna.
2140. **877.** 5 s. multicoloured .. 65 50

**878.** Hofhaymer at Organ. **880.** Lammergeier.

**879.** Haydn and Salzburg.

**1987.** 450th Death Anniv. of Paul Hofhaymer (composer and organist).
2141. **878.** 4 s. blue, black and gold .. .. 75 45

**1987.** 250th Birth Anniv. of Michael Haydn (composer).
2142. **879.** 4 s. lilac .. .. 75 45

**1987.** 25th Anniv. of Alpine Zoo, Innsbruck.
2143. **880.** 4 s. multicoloured .. 90 35

**881.** Woman using Word Processor.

**1987.** Austrian World of Work (2nd series).
2144. **881.** 4 s. multicoloured .. 40 35

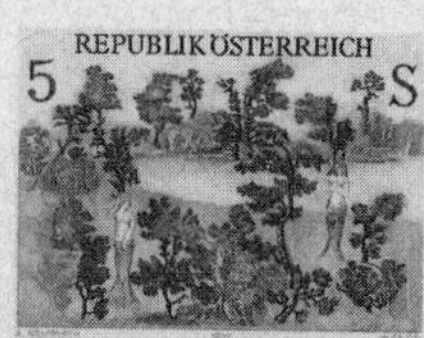

**882.** "Tree Goddesses" (Arnulf Neuwirth).

**1987.** Austrian Modern Art.
2145. **882.** 5 s. multicoloured .. 60 50

**883.** Lottery Wheel. **884.** Helmer.

**1987.** Bicentenary of Gambling Monopoly.
2146. **883.** 5 s. multicoloured .. 45 45

**1987.** Birth Centenary of Oskar Helmer (politician).
2147. **884.** 4 s. multicoloured .. 35 35

**885.** Gluck. **886.** Stagecoach and Passengers (lithograph, Carl Schuster).

**1987.** Death Bicentenary of Christoph Willibald Gluck (composer).
2148 885 5 s. brown and ochre 70 50

**1987.** Stamp Day.
2149. **886.** 6 s. + 3 s. multi. .. 90 1·25

**887.** Josef Mohr and Franz Xaver Gruber (composers of "Silent Night").

**1987.** Christmas.
2150. **887.** 5 s. multicoloured .. 80 35

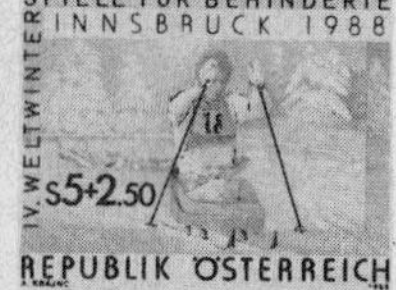

**888.** Bosco and Boys. **889.** Cross-country Sledging.

**1988.** International Educational Congress of St. John Bosco's Salesian Brothers, Vienna.
2151. **888.** 5 s. purple & orange  60  45

**1988.** 4th World Winter Games for the Disabled, Innsbruck.
2152. **889.** 5 s.+2 s. 50 mult. . .  65  75

**890.** Mach.

**891.** "Village with Bridge".

**1988.** 150th Birth Anniv. of Ernst Mach (physicist and philosopher).
2153. **890.** 6 s. multicoloured . .  70  50

**1988.** 25th Death Anniv. of Franz von Zulow (artist).
2154. **891.** 4 s. multicoloured . .  60  40

**892.** "The Confiscation" (Ferdinand Georg Waldmuller).

**1988.** "Patriotism and Protest: Viennese Biedermeier and Revolution" Exhibition, Vienna.
2155. **892.** 4 s. multicoloured . .  50  40

**893.** Barbed Wire, Flag and Crosses.

**1988.** 50th Anniv. of Annexation of Austria by Germany.
2156. **893.** 5 s. green, brown and red . . . .  45  40

**894.** Steam Locomotive "Aigen", Muhlkreis Railway, 1887.

**895.** European Bee Eater.

**1988.** Railway Centenaries. Multicoloured.
2157. 4 s. Type **894** . . . .  50  40
2158. 5 s. Modern electric tram and Josefsplatz stop (Viennese Local Railways Stock Corporation) . . . .  60  50

**1988.** 25th Anniv. of World Wildlife Fund Austria.
2159. **895.** 5 s. multicoloured . .  85  50

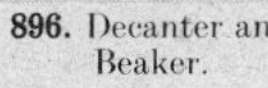

**896.** Decanter and Beaker.

**897.** Late Gothic Silver Censer.

**1988.** Styrian "Glass and Coal" Exhibition, Barnbach.
2160. **896.** 4 s. multicoloured . .  50  40

**1988.** Lower Austrian "Art and Monastic Life at the Birth of Austria" Exhibition, Seitenstetten Benedictine Monastery.
2161. **897.** 4 s. multicoloured . .  35  35

**898.** Taking Casualty to Ambulance and Red Cross.

**900.** Mattsee Monastery.

**899.** Dish Aerials, Aflenz.

**1988.** 125th Anniv. of Red Cross.
2162. **898.** 12 s. black, red and green . . . .  1·25  1·10

**1988.** Europa. Telecommunications.
2163. **899.** 6 s. multicoloured . .  70  50

**1988.** Salzburg "Bajuvars from Severin to Tassilo" Exhibition, Mattsee Monastery.
2164. **900.** 4 s. multicoloured . .  50  40

**901.** Weinberg Castle.

**902.** Horvath.

**1988.** Upper Austrian "Muhlviertel: Nature, Culture, Life" Exhibition, Weinberg Castle, near Kefermarkt.
2165. **901.** 4 s. multicoloured . .  45  40

**1988.** 50th Death Anniv of Odon von Horvath (writer).
2166 **902** 6 s. black and bistre . .  50  45

**903.** Stockerau Town Hall.

**1988.** 25th Anniv. of Stockerau Festival.
2167. **903.** 5 s. multicoloured . .  45  45

**904.** Motorway.

**905.** Brixlegg.

**1988.** Completion of Tauern Motorway.
2168. **904.** 4 s. multicoloured . .  50  40

**1988.** 1200th Anniv. of Brixlegg.
2169. **905.** 5 s. multicoloured . .  65  45

**906.** Klagenfurt (after Matthaus Merian).

**1988.** 400th Anniv. of Regular Postal Services in Carinthia.
2170. **906.** 5 s. multicoloured . .  50  40

**907.** Parish Church and Dean's House.

**1988.** 1200th Anniv of Brixen im Thale, Tyrol.
2171. **907.** 5 s. multicoloured . .  45  40

**908.** Krimml Waterfalls, Upper Tauern National Park.

**1988.** Natural Beauty Spots.
2172. **908.** 5 s. black and blue . .  50  40

**909.** Town Arms.

**1988.** 1100th Anniv. of Feldkirchen, Carinthia.
2173. **909.** 5 s. multicoloured . .  50  40

**910.** Feldbach.

**1988.** 800th Anniv of Feldbach.
2174 **910** 5 s. multicoloured . .  50  40

**911.** Ansfelden.

**912.** Hologram of Export Emblem.

**1988.** 1200th Anniv of Ansfelden.
2175 **911** 5 s. multicoloured . .  45  40

**1988.** Federal Economic Chamber Export Congress.
2176 **912** 8 s. multicoloured . .  1·25  1·25

**913.** Concert Hall.

**1988.** 75th Anniv. of Vienna Concert Hall.
2177. **913.** 5 s. multicoloured . .  50  40

**914.** Laboratory Assistant.

**1988.** Austrian World of Work (3rd series).
2178. **914.** 4 s. multicoloured . .  40  30

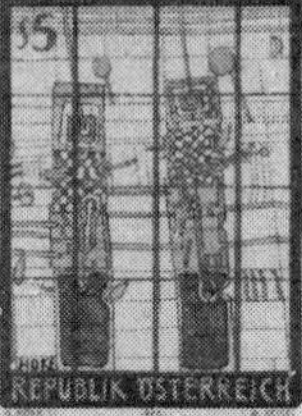


**915.** "Guards" (Giselbert Hoke).

**916** Schonbauer

**1988.** Austrian Modern Art.
2179. **915.** 5 s. multicoloured . .  50  40

**1988.** Birth Centenary of Dr. Leopold Schonbauer (neurosurgeon and politician).
2180 **916** 4 s. multicoloured . .  45  35

**917** Carnation

**918** Loading Railway Mail Van at Pardubitz Station, 1914

**1988.** Centenary of Austrian Social Democratic Party.
2181 **917** 4 s. multicoloured . .  40  35

**1988.** Stamp Day.
2182 **918** 6 s.+3 s. muticoloured  85  85

**919** "Nativity" (St. Barbara's Church, Vienna)

**920** "Madonna" (Lucas Cranach)

**1988.** Christmas.
2183 **919** 5 s. multicoloured . .  50  40

**1989.** 25th Anniv of Diocese of Innsbruck.
2184 **920** 4 s. multicoloured . .  40  35

**921** Margrave Leopold II leading Abbot Sigibold and Monks to Melk (detail of fresco, Paul Troger)

**1989.** 900th Anniv of Melk Benedictine Monastery.
2185 **921** 5 s. multicoloured .. 45 40

**922** Marianne Hainisch

**923** Glider and Paraskier

**1989.** 150th Birth Anniv of Marianne Hainisch (women's rights activist).
2186 **922** 6 s. multicoloured .. 60 50

**1989.** World Gliding Championships, Wiener Neustadt, and World Paraskiing Championships, Damuls.
2187 **923** 6 s. multicoloured .. 75 50

**924** "The Painting"

**926** Wittgenstein

**925** "Bruck an der Leitha" (17th-century engraving, Georg Vischer)

**1989.** 50th Death Anniv of Rudolf Jettmar (painter).
2188 **924** 5 s. multicoloured .. 45 40

**1989.** 750th Anniv of Bruck an der Leitha.
2189 **925** 5 s. multicoloured .. 45 40

**1989.** Birth Centenary of Ludwig Wittgenstein (philosopher).
2190 **926** 5 s. multicoloured .. 45 40

**927** Holy Trinity Church, Stadl–Paura

**928** Suess (after Josef Kriehuber) and Map

**1989.** 250th Death Anniv of Johann Michael Prunner (architect).
2191 **927** 5 s. multicoloured .. 45 40

**1989.** 75th Death Anniv of Eduard Suess (geologist and politician).
2192 **928** 6 s. multicoloured .. 65 55

**929** "Judenburg" (17th-century engraving, Georg Vischer)

**930** Steam Engine (Vinzenz Prick)

**1989.** Upper Styrian "People, Coins, Markets" Exhibition, Judenburg.
2193 **929** 4 s. multicoloured .. 40 35

**1989.** Lower Austrian "Magic of Industry" Exhibition, Pottenstein.
2194 **930** 4 s. blue and gold .. 45 35

**931** Radstadt

**1989.** 700th Anniv of Radstadt.
2195 **931** 5 s. multicoloured .. 45 40

**932** Wooden Salt Barge from Viechtau

**1989.** Europa. Children's Toys.
2196 **932** 6 s. multicoloured .. 75 45

**933** "St. Adalbero and Family before Madonna and Child" (Monastery Itinerary Book)

**935** Hansa Brandenburg C-1 Mail Biplane at Vienna, 1918

**934** "Gisela" (paddle-steamer)

**1989.** Upper Austrian "Graphic Art" Exhibition and 900th Anniv of Lambach Monastery Church.
2197 **933** 4 s. multicoloured .. 40 35

**1989.** 150th Anniv of Passenger Shipping on Traunsee.
2198 **934** 5 s. multicoloured .. 70 40

**1989.** Stamp Day.
2199 **935** 6 s.+3 s. mult .. 85 85

**936** St. Andra (after Matthaus Merian)

**1989.** 650th Anniv of St. Andra.
2200 **936** 5 s. multicoloured .. 50 40

**937** Strauss

**938** Locomotive

**1989.** 125th Birth Anniv of Richard Strauss (composer).
2201 **937** 6 s. red, brown & gold 60 50

**1989.** Centenary of Achensee Steam Rack-railway.
2202 **938** 5 s. multicoloured .. 45 40

**939** Parliament Building, Vienna

**1989.** Cent of Interparliamentary Union.
2203 **939** 6 s. multicoloured .. 60 45

**940** Anniversary Emblem

**1989.** Cent of National Insurance in Austria.
2204 **940** 5 s. multicoloured .. 45 40

**941** U.N.Building, Vienna

**1989.** 10th Anniv of United Nations Vienna Centre.
2205 **941** 8 s. multicoloured .. 75 65

**942** Lusthaus Water, Prater Woods, Vienna

**1989.** Natural Beauty Spots.
2206 **942** 5 s. black and buff .. 45 40

**943** Wildalpen and Hammerworks

**1989.** 850th Anniv of Wildalpen.
2207 **943** 5 s. multicoloured .. 50 40

**944** Emblem

**946** "Tree of Life" (Ernst Steiner)

**945** Palace of Justice, Vienna

**1989.** 33rd Congress of European Organization for Quality Control, Vienna.
2208 **944** 6 s. multicoloured .. 65 45

**1989.** 14th Congress of International Association of Criminal Law.
2209 **945** 6 s. multicoloured .. 65 45

**1989.** Austrian Modern Art.
2210 **946** 5 s. multicoloured .. 50 45

**947** Bricklayer

**948** Ludwig Anzengruber (150th birth anniv)

**1989.** Austrian World of Work (4th series).
2211 **947** 5 s. multicoloured .. 50 40

**1989.** Writers' Anniversaries. Multicoloured.
2212 4 s. Type **948** .. .. 40 30
2213 4 s. Georg Trakl (75th death anniv) .. .. 40 30

**949** Fried

**950** "Adoration of the Shepherds" (detail, Johann Carl von Reslfeld)

**1989.** 125th Birth Anniv of Alfred Fried (Peace Movement worker).
2214 **949** 6 s. multicoloured .. 65 45

**1989.** Christmas.
2215 **950** 5 s. multicoloured .. 50 40

**951** "Courier" (Albrecht Durer)

**952** Streif Downhill and Ganslern Slalom Runs

**1990.** 500th Anniv of Regular European Postal Services.
2216 **951** 5 s. chocolate, cinnamon and brown .. 50 40

**1990.** 50th Hahnenkamm Ski Championships, Kitzbuhel.
2217 **952** 5 s. multicoloured .. 50 40

**953** Sulzer

**954** Emich

**1990.** Death Centenary of Salomon Sulzer (creator of modern Synagogue songs).
2218 **953** 4 s. 50 multicoloured 45 35

**1990.** 50th Death Anniv of Friedrich Emich (microchemist).
2219 **954** 6 s. purple and green 65 45

**955** Emperor Friedrich III (miniature by Ulrich Schreier)

**1990.** 500th Anniv of Linz as Capital of Upper Austria.
2220 **955** 5 s. multicoloured .. 50 40

**956** University Seals

**1990.** 625th Anniv of Vienna University and 175th Anniv of Vienna University of Technology.
2221 **956** 5 s. red, gold and lilac 50 40

**957** South Styrian Vineyards

**1990.** Natural Beauty Spots.
2222 **957** 5 s. black and yellow 50 40

**958** Parish Church
**959** 1897 May Day Emblem

**1990.** 1200th Anniv of Anthering.
2223 **958** 7 s. multicoloured .. 65 60

**1990.** Centenary of Labour Day.
2224 **959** 4 s. 50 multicoloured 45 40

**960** "Our Dear Housewife of Seckau" (relief)
**961** Ebene Reichenau Post Office

**1990.** 850th Anniv of Seckau Abbey.
2225 **960** 4 s. 50 blue .. .. 45 35

**1990.** Europa. Post Office Buildings.
2226 **961** 7 s. multicoloured .. 65 60

**962** Thematic Stamp Motifs
**963** Makart (self-portrait)

**1990.** Stamp Day.
2227 **962** 7 s.+3 s. multicoloured 95 95

**1990.** 150th Birth Anniv of Hans Makart (painter).
2228 **963** 4 s. 50 multicoloured 45 35

**964** Schiele (self-portrait)
**965** Raimund

**1990.** Birth Cent of Egon Schiele (painter).
2229 **964** 5 s. multicoloured .. 50 40

**1990.** Birth Bicentenary of Ferdinand Raimund (actor and playwright).
2230 **965** 4 s. 50 multicoloured 45 40

**966** "The Hundred Guilden Note" (Rembrandt)

**1990.** 2nd International Christus Medicus Congress, Bad Ischl.
2231 **966** 7 s. multicoloured .. 65 60

**967** Hardegg

**1990.** 700th Anniv of Hardegg's Elevation to Status of Town.
2232 **967** 4 s. 50 multicoloured 45 40

**968** Oberdrauburg (copperplate engraving, Freiherr von Valvasor)
**970** Zdarsky skiing

**969** Church and Town Hall

**1990.** 750th Anniv of Oberdrauburg.
2233 **968** 5 s. multicoloured .. 50 40

**1990.** 850th Anniv of Gumpoldskirchen.
2234 **969** 5 s. multicoloured .. 50 40

**1990.** 50th Death Anniv of Mathias Zdarsky (developer of alpine skiing).
2235 **970** 5 s. multicoloured .. 50 40

**971** "Telegraph", 1880, and "Anton Chekhov", 1978

**1990.** 150th Anniv of Modern (metal) Shipbuilding in Austria.
2236 **971** 9 s. multicoloured .. 1·40 75

**972** Perkonig
**973** "Man of Rainbows" (Robert Zeppel-Sperl)

**1990.** Birth Centenary of Josef Friedrich Perkonig (writer).
2237 **972** 5 s. sepia, brn & gold 50 40

**1990.** Austrian Modern Art.
2238 **973** 5 s. multicoloured .. 50 40

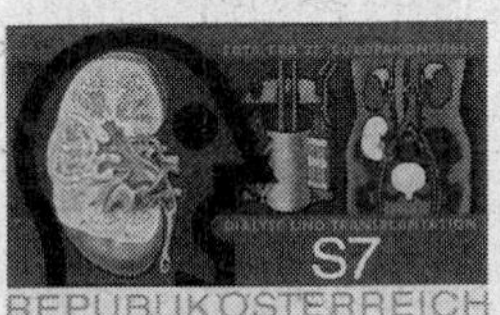

**974** Kidney, Dialysis Machine and Anatomical Diagram

**1990.** 27th European Dialysis and Transplantation Federation Congress, Vienna.
2239 **974** 7 s. multicoloured .. 65 60

**975** Werfel

**1990.** Birth Cent of Franz Werfel (writer).
2240 **975** 5 s. multicoloured .. 50 45

**976** U.N. and Austrian Flags

**1990.** 30th Anniv of Austrian Participation in United Nations Peace-keeping Forces.
2241 **976** 7 s. multicoloured .. 65 60

**977** Arms of Provinces

**1990.** 45th Anniv of First Provinces Conference (established Second Republic as Federal State).
2242 **977** 5 s. multicoloured .. 50 45

**978** University Seal
**979** Vogelsang

**1990.** 150th Anniv of Mining University, Leoben.
2243 **978** 4 s. 50 black, red & grn 45 35

**1990.** Death Cent of Karl von Vogelsang (Christian social reformer).
2244 **979** 4 s. 50 multicoloured 45 35

**980** Metal Workers

**1990.** Cent of Metal, Mining and Energy Trade Union.
2245 **980** 5 s. multicoloured .. 50 45

**981** Player
**982** Greenhouse

**1990.** 3rd World Ice Curling Championships, Vienna.
2246 **981** 7 s. multicoloured .. 65 60

**1990.** Reopening of Schonbrunn Greenhouse.
2247 **982** 5 s. multicoloured .. 50 45

**983** "Birth of Christ"
**984** Grillparzer

**1990.** Christmas. Detail of Altarpiece by Master Nikolaus of Verdun, Klosterneuburg Monastery.
2248 **983** 5 s. multicoloured .. 50 45

**1991.** Birth Bicentenary of Franz Grillparzer (dramatist).
2249 **984** 4 s. 50 multicoloured 50 40

**985** Skier
**986** Kreisky

**1991.** World Alpine Skiing Championships, Saalbach-Hinterglemm.
2250 **985** 5 s. multicoloured .. 55 45

**1991.** 80th Birth Anniv of Bruno Kreisky (Chancellor, 1970–82).
2251 **986** 5 s. multicoloured .. 55 45

987 Schmidt and Vienna Town Hall

**1991.** Death Centenary of Friedrich von Schmidt (architect).
2252 987 7 s. multicoloured .. 80 65

988 Fountain, Vienna

**1991.** Anniversaries. Multicoloured.
2253 4 s. 50 Type 988 (250th death anniv of Georg Raphael Donner (sculptor)) .. .. 50 40
2254 5 s. "Kitzbuhel in Winter" (birth cent of Alfons Walde (artist and architect)) .. 55 45
2255 7 s. Vienna Stock Exchange (death centenary of Theophil von Hansen (architect)) 80 65
See also No. 2269.

989 M. von Ebner-Eschenbach

**1991.** 75th Death Anniv of Marie von Ebner-Eschenbach (writer).
2256 989 4 s. 50 purple .. 50 40

991 Obir Stalactite Caverns, Eisenkappel

**1991.** Natural Beauty Spots.
2258 991 5 s. multicoloured .. 55 45

992 Spittal an der Drau (after Matthaus Merian)

**1991.** 800th Anniv of Spittal an der Drau.
2259 992 4 s. 50 multicoloured 50 40

993 "ERS-1" European Remote Sensing Satellite

**1991.** Europa. Europe in Space.
2260 993 7 s. multicoloured .. 80 65

994 "Garden Party" (Anthoni Bays)

**1991.** Vorarlberg "Clothing and People" Exhibition, Hohenems.
2261 994 5 s. multicoloured .. 55 45

995 Grein

**1991.** 500th Anniv of Grein Town Charter.
2262 995 4 s. 50 multicoloured 50 40

996 Bedding Plants forming Arms

**1991.** 1200th Anniv of Tulln.
2263 996 5 s. multicoloured .. 55 45

997 Military History Museum

**1991.** Vienna Museum Centenaries. Mult.
2264 5 s. Type 997 .. .. 55 45
2265 7 s. Museum of Art History .. .. 80 65

998 "B" and "P"

1000 Town Hall

999 Tunnel Entrance

**1991.** Stamp Day.
2266 998 7 s.+3 s. brown, sepia and black .. .. 1·10 1·10
This is the first of a series of ten annual stamps each of which will illustrate two letters. The complete series will spell out the words "Briefmarke" and "Philatelie".

**1991.** Opening of Karawanken Road Tunnel between Carinthia and Slovenia.
2267 999 7 s. multicoloured .. 80 65

**1991.** 5th Anniv of St. Polten as Capital of Lower Austria.
2268 1000 5 s. multicoloured .. 55 45

**1991.** 150th Birth Anniv of Otto Wagner (architect). As T 988. Multicoloured.
2269 4 s. 50 Karlsplatz Station, Vienna city railway .. 50 40

1001 Rowing

**1991.** Junior World Canoeing Championships and World Rowing Championships, Vienna.
2270 1001 5 s. multicoloured .. 55 45

1002 X-ray Tube 1003 Paracelsus

**1991.** European Radiology Congress, Vienna.
2271 1002 7 s. multicoloured .. 80 65

**1991.** 450th Death Anniv of Theophrastus Bombastus von Hohenheim (Paracelsus) (physician and scientist).
2272 1003 4 s. black, red & brn 45 35

1004 "Mir" Space Station

1005 Almabtrieb (driving cattle from mountain pastures) (Zell, Tyrol)

**1991.** "Austro Mir 91" Soviet–Austrian Space Flight.
2273 1004 9 s. multicoloured .. 1·00 80

**1991.** Folk Customs and Art (1st series). Mult.
2274 4 s. 50 Type 1005 .. 50 40
2275 5 s. Vintage Crown (Neustift, Vienna) .. 55 45
2276 7 s. Harvest monstrance (Nestelbach, Styria) .. 80 65
See also Nos. 2305/7, 2349/51, 2363/5, 2393/5, 2418 and 2432/3.

1006 Weaver

**1991.** Austrian World of Work (5th series).
2277 1006 4 s. 50 multicoloured 45 35

1007 "The General" (Rudolf Pointner)

1008 Raab

**1991.** Austrian Modern Art.
2278 1007 5 s. multicoloured .. 55 45

**1991.** Birth Centenary of Julius Raab (Chancellor, 1953–61).
2279 1008 4 s. 50 brn & chestnut 50 40

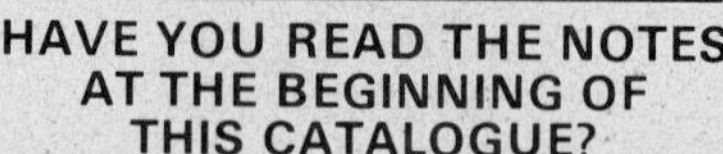

HAVE YOU READ THE NOTES AT THE BEGINNING OF THIS CATALOGUE?
These often provide answers to the enquiries we receive.

1009 "Birth of Christ" (detail of fresco, Baumgartenberg Church)

**1991.** Christmas.
2280 1009 5 s. multicoloured .. 55 45

1010 Clerks

**1992.** Centenary of Trade Union of Clerks in Private Enterprise.
2281 1010 5 s. 50 multicoloured 60 50

1011 Emblems of Games and Olympic Rings

**1992.** Winter Olympic Games, Albertville, and Summer Games, Barcelona.
2282 1011 7 s. multicoloured .. 80 65

1012 Competitor 1013 Hollow Stone, Klostertal

**1992.** 8th World Toboggan Championships on Natural Runs, Bad Goisern.
2283 1012 5 s. multicoloured .. 55 45

**1992.** Natural Beauty Spots.
2284 1013 5 s. multicoloured .. 55 45

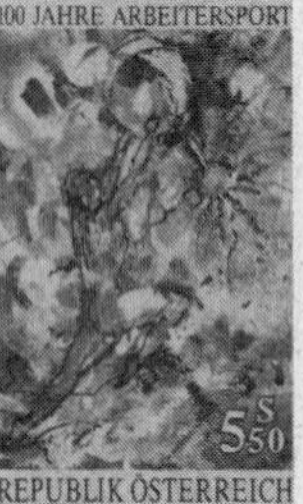


1014 Saiko

1015 "Athlete with Ball" (Christian Attersee)

**1992.** Birth Cent of George Saiko (writer).
2285 1014 5 s. 50 brown .. 60 50

**1992.** Cent of Workers' Sport Movement.
2286 1015 5 s. 50 multicoloured 60 50

1016 Franz Joseph Muller (chemist and mineralogist)

**1992.** Scientific Anniversaries. Multicoloured.

2287 5 s. Type **1016** (250th birth anniv) .. .. 55 45
2288 5 s. 50 Paul Kitaibel (botanist, 175th death anniv) .. .. 60 50
2289 6 s. Christian Doppler (physicist) (150th anniv of observation of Doppler Effect) .. 70 60
2290 7 s. Richard Kuhn (chemist, 25th death anniv) .. .. 80 65

**1018** First and Present Emblems

**1992.** Cent of Railway Workers' Trade Union.
2292 **1018** 5 s. 50 red and black 60 50

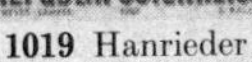

**1019** Hanrieder **1020** Scenes from "The Birdseller" (Zeller) and "The Beggar Student" (Millocker)

**1992.** 150th Birth Anniv of Norbert Hanrieder (writer).
2293 **1019** 5 s. 50 lilac & brown 60 50

**1992.** 150th Birth Anniversaries of Carl Zeller and Karl Millocker (composers).
2294 **1020** 6 s. multicoloured .. 70 60

**1021** Foundry and Process

**1992.** Ironworks Day. 40th Anniv of First LD-Process Steel Works, Linz.
2295 **1021** 5 s. multicoloured .. 55 45

**1022** Woodcut of the Americas by Sebastian Munster (from "Geographia Universalis" by Claudius Ptolomaus)

**1992.** Europa. 500th Anniv of Discovery of America by Columbus.
2296 **1022** 7 s. multicoloured .. 1·00 65

**1023** Dredger **1024** Rieger

**1992.** Centenary of Treaty for International Regulation of the Rhine.
2297 **1023** 7 s. multicoloured .. 1·00 65

**1992.** Centenary of Adoption of Pseudonym Reimmichl by Sebastian Rieger (writer).
2298 **1024** 5 s. brown .. .. 55 45

**1025** Flags and Alps **1026** Dr. Anna Dengel

**1992.** Alpine Protection Convention.
2299 **1025** 5 s. 50 multicoloured 60 50

**1992.** Birth Centenary of Dr. Anna Dengel (founder of Medical Missionary Sisters).
2300 **1026** 5 s. 50 multicoloured 60 50

**1027** "R" and "H"

**1992.** Stamp Day.
2301 **1027** 7 s.+3 s. mult .. 1·10 1·10
See note below No. 2266.

**1028** Town Hall

**1992.** 750th Anniv of First Documentation of Lienz as a Town.
2302 **1028** 5 s. multicoloured .. 55 45

**1029** "Billroth in Lecture Room" (A. F. Seligmann) **1030** Waldheim

**1992.** Austrian Surgery Society International Congress, Eisenstadt.
2303 **1029** 6 s. multicoloured .. 70 60

**1992.** Presidency of Dr. Kurt Waldheim.
2304 **1030** 5 s. 50 blk, red & grey 60 50

**1992.** Folk Customs and Art (2nd series). As T **1005**. Multicoloured.
2305 5 s. Target with figure of Zieler, Lower Austria, 1732 .. .. .. 55 45
2306 5 s. 50 Chest, Carinthia .. 60 50
2307 7 s. Votive tablet from Venser Chapel, Vorarlberg .. .. 80 65

**1031** Bridge over Canal

**1992.** Completion of Marchfeld Canal System.
2308 **1031** 5 s. multicoloured .. 55 45

**1032** "The Purification of Sea Water" (Peter Pongratz)

**1992.** Austrian Modern Art.
2309 **1032** 5 s. 50 multicoloured 60 50

**1033** Gateway, Hofburg Palace (venue)

**1992.** 5th International Ombudsmen's Conference, Vienna.
2310 **1033** 5 s. 50 multicoloured 60 50

**1034** Academy Seal **1035** "The Annunciation"

**1992.** 300th Anniv of Academy of Fine Arts, Vienna.
2311 **1034** 5 s. blue and red .. 55 45

**1992.** Death Bicentenary of Veit Koniger (sculptor).
2312 **1035** 5 s. multicoloured .. 55 45

**1036** "Birth of Christ" (Johann Georg Schmidt)

**1992.** Christmas.
2313 **1036** 5 s. 50 multicoloured 60 50

**1037** Earth and Satellite

**1992.** Birth Centenary of Hermann Potocnik (alias Noordung) (space travel pioneer).
2314 **1037** 10 s. multicoloured 1·10 90

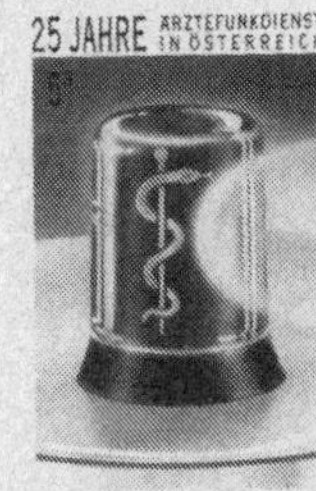

**1038** Dome of Michael Wing, Hofburg Palace, Vienna **1039** Emergency Vehicle's Flashing Lantern

**1993.** Architects' Anniversaries. Mult.
2315 5 s. Type **1038** (Joseph Emanuel Fischer von Erlach, 300th birth) .. 55 45
2316 5 s. 50 Kinsky Palace, Vienna (Johann Lukas von Hildebrandt, 325th birth) .. .. .. 60 50
2317 7 s. State Opera House, Vienna (Eduard van der Null and August Siccard von Siccardsburg, 125th death annivs) .. .. 80 65

**1993.** 25th Anniv of Radio-controlled Emergency Medical Service.
2318 **1039** 5 s. multicoloured .. 55 45

**1040** Wilder Kaiser Massif, Tyrol

**1993.** Natural Beauty Spots.
2319 **1040** 6 s. multicoloured .. 70 60

**1041** Mitterhofer Typewriter

**1993.** Death Centenary of Peter Mitterhofer (typewriter pioneer).
2320 **1041** 17 s. multicoloured .. 1·90 1·40

**1042** "Strada del Sole" (record sleeve)

**1993.** "Austro Pop" (1st series). Rainhard Fendrich (singer).
2321 **1042** 5 s. 50 multicoloured 60 50
See also Nos. 2356 and 2368.

**1043** Games Emblem

**1993.** Winter Special Olympics, Salzburg and Schladming.
2322 **1043** 6 s.+3 s. mult .. 1·00 1·00

**1044** Sealsfield **1045** Girl realising her Rights

**1993.** Birth Bicentenary of Charles Sealsfield (novelist).
2323 **1044** 10 s. red, blue & gold 1·10 90

**1993.** Ratification of United Nations Convention on Children's Rights.
2324 **1045** 7 s. multicoloured .. 80 65

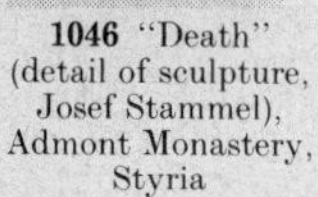

1046 "Death" (detail of sculpture, Josef Stammel), Admont Monastery, Styria

1047 "Flying Harlequin" (Paul Flora)

**1993.** Monasteries and Abbeys.

| | | | | |
|---|---|---|---|---|
| 2325 | – | 1 s. brown, blk & grn | 15 | 10 |
| 2328 | **1046** | 5 s. 50 blk, yell & grn | 60 | 50 |
| 2329 | – | 6 s. blk, mve & yell | 70 | 60 |
| 2330 | – | 7 s. brn, blk & grey | 80 | 65 |
| 2331 | – | 7 s. 50 brn, bl & blk | 85 | 70 |
| 2332 | – | 8 s. orange, blk & bl | 1·00 | 80 |
| 2334 | – | 10 s. black, bl & orge | 1·10 | 90 |
| 2339 | – | 20 s. black, bl & yell | 2·25 | 1·90 |
| 2340 | – | 26 s. orge, blk & bis | 3·50 | 3·00 |
| 2341 | – | 30 s. red, yell & blk | 3·50 | 3·00 |

DESIGNS: 1 s. The Annuncation (detail of crosier of Abbess), St. Gabriel Benedictine Abbey, Bertholdstein; 6 s. St. Benedict of Nursia (glass painting), Mariastern Abbey, Gwiggen; 7 s. Marble lion, Franciscan Monastery, Salzburg; 7 s. 50, Virgin Mary (detail of cupola painting by Paul Troger), Altenburg Monastery; 8 s. Early Gothic doorway, Wilhering Monastery; 10 s. "The Healing of St. Peregrinus" (altarpiece), Maria Luggau Monastery; 20 s. Hartmann Crosier, St. Georgenberg Abbey, Fiecht; 26 s. "Master Dolorosa" (sculpture), Franciscan Monastery, Schwaz; 30 s. Madonna and Child, Monastery of the Scottish Order, Vienna.

**1993.** Europa. Contemporary Art.
2345 **1047** 7 s. multicoloured .. 80 65

1048 Silhouette, Script and Signature

1049 "Hohentwiel" (lake steamer) and Flags

**1993.** 150th Birth Anniv of Peter Rosegger (writer and newspaper publisher).
2346 **1048** 5 s. 50 black & green 60 50

**1993.** Lake Constance European Region.
2347 **1049** 6 s. multicoloured .. 70 60

1050 Knights in Battle and "I"s

1051 Human Rights Emblem melting Bars

**1993.** Stamp Day.
2348 **1050** 7 s. + 3 s. gold, black and blue .. .. 1·10 1·10
See note below No. 2266.

**1993.** Folk Customs and Art (3rd series). As T **1005**. Multicoloured.
2349 5 s. Corpus Christi Day procession, Hallstatt, Upper Austria .. 55 45
2350 5 s. 50 Drawing the block (log), Burgenland .. 60 50
2351 7 s. Aperschnalzen (whipping the snow away), Salzburg .. 80 65

**1993.** United Nations World Conference on Human Rights, Vienna.
2352 **1051** 10 s. multicoloured .. 1·10 90

1052 Jagerstatter

1053 Train approaching Wolfgangsee

**1993.** 50th Death Anniv of Franz Jagerstatter (conscientious objector).
2353 **1052** 5 s. 50 multicoloured 60 50

**1993.** Centenary of Schafberg Cog Railway.
2354 **1053** 6 s. multicoloured .. 70 60

1054 "Self-portrait with Doll"

**1993.** Birth Cent of Rudolf Wacker (artist).
2355 **1054** 6 s. multicoloured .. 70 60

**1993.** "Austro Pop" (2nd series). Ludwig Hirsch (singer and actor). As T **1042**. Mult.
2356 5 s. 50 "Die Omama" (record sleeve) .. 60 50

1055 "Concert in Dornbacher Park" (Balthasar Wigand)

**1993.** 150th Anniv of Vienna Male Choral Society.
2357 **1055** 5 s. multicoloured .. 55 45

1056 "Easter" (Max Weiler)

1057 "99 Heads" (detail, Friedensreich Hundertwasser)

**1993.** Austrian Modern Art.
2358 **1056** 5 s. 50 multicoloured 60 50

**1993.** Council of Europe Heads of State Conference, Vienna.
2359 **1057** 7 s. multicoloured .. 80 65

1058 Statue of Athene, Parliament Building

1060 "Birth of Christ" (Krainburg Altar, Styria)

1059 Workers

**1993.** 75th Anniv of Austrian Republic.
2360 **1058** 5 s. multicoloured .. 55 45

**1993.** Centenary of 1st Austrian Trade Unions Congress.
2361 **1059** 5 s. 50 multicoloured 60 50

**1993.** Christmas.
2362 **1060** 5 s. 50 multicoloured 60 50

**1994.** Folk Customs and Art (4th series). As T **1005**. Multicoloured.
2363 5 s. 50 Rocking cradle, Vorarlberg .. .. 60 50
2364 6 s. Carved sleigh, Styria 70 60
2365 7 s. Godparent's bowl and lid, Upper Austria .. 80 65

1061 Winter Sports

**1994.** Winter Olympic Games, Lillehammer, Norway.
2366 **1061** 7 s. multicoloured .. 80 65

1062 Early Production of Coins

**1994.** 800th Anniv of Vienna Mint.
2367 **1062** 6 s. multicoloured .. 70 60

**1994.** "Austro Pop" (3rd series). Falco (Johann Holzel) (singer). As T **1042**. Mult.
2368 6 s. "Rock Me Amadeus" (record sleeve) .. 70 60

1063 "Reclining Lady" (detail, Herbert Boeckl)

**1994.** Birth Cent of Herbert Boeckl (painter).
2369 **1063** 5 s. 50 multicoloured 65 55

1064 North-west Tower of City Wall

**1994.** 800th Anniv of Wiener Neustadt.
2370 **1064** 6 s. multicoloured .. 70 60

1065 Lurgrotte (caves), Styria

**1994.** Natural Beauty Spots.
2371 **1065** 6 s. multicoloured .. 70 60

1066 Lake Rudolf (Teleki–Hohnel expedition to Africa, 1887)

**1994.** Europa. Discoveries.
2372 **1066** 7 s. multicoloured .. 80 65

1067 "E" and "L" as Ruins in Landscape

**1994.** Stamp Day.
2373 **1067** 7 s. + 3 s. mult .. 1·10 1·10
See note below No. 2266.

1068 "Allegory of Theology, Justice, Philosophy and Medicine" (detail of fresco, National Library)

**1994.** 300th Birth Anniv of Daniel Gran (artist).
2374 **1068** 20 s. multicoloured .. 2·25 1·90

1069 Scene from "The Prodigal Son" (opera, Benjamin Britten)

**1994.** 25th Anniv of Carinthian Summer Festival, Ossiach and Villach.
2375 **1069** 5 s. 50 gold and red 65 55

1070 Steam and Diesel Locomotives (Gailtal)

**1994.** Railway Centenaries. Multicoloured.
2376 5 s. 50 Type **1070** .. 65 55
2377 6 s. Steam and diesel locomotives (Murtal) .. 70 60

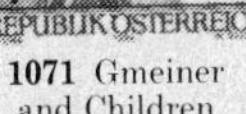

**1071** Gmeiner and Children  **1072** Seitz (bust, G. Ambrosi)

**1994.** 75th Birth Anniv of Hermann Gmeiner (founder of S.O.S. children's villages).
2378 **1071** 7 s. multicoloured .. 80 65

**1994.** 125th Birth Anniv of Karl Seitz (acting President, 1920).
2379 **1072** 5 s. 50 multicoloured 65 55

**1073** Bohm  **1075** Franz Theodor Csokor (dramatist and poet)

**1074** Ethnic Minorities on Map

**1994.** Birth Cent of Karl Bohm (conductor).
2380 **1073** 7 s. blue and gold .. 80 65

**1994.** Legal and Cultural Protection of Ethnic Minorities.
2381 **1074** 5 s. 50 multicoloured 65 55

**1994.** Writers' Anniversaries. Multicoloured.
2382 6 s. Type **1075** (25th death anniv) .. .. 70 60
2383 7 s. Joseph Roth (novelist, birth cent) .. 80 65

**1076** "Head" (Franz Ringel)  **1077** Money Box

**1994.** Austrian Modern Art.
2384 **1076** 6 s. multicoloured .. 70 60

**1994.** 175th Anniv of Savings Banks in Austria.
2385 **1077** 7 s. multicoloured .. 80 65

**1078** Air Hostess and Child

**1994.** Austrian World of Work (6th series).
2386 **1078** 6 s. multicoloured .. 70 60

**1079** Coudenhove-Kalergi and Map of Europe

**1994.** Birth Cent of Richard Coudenhove-Kalergi (founder of Paneuropa Union).
2387 **1079** 10 s. multicoloured 1·10 90

**1080** "Birth of Christ" (Anton Wollenek)  **1081** Map and Austrian and E.U. Flags

**1994.** Christmas.
2388 **1080** 6 s. multicoloured .. 70 60

**1995.** Austria's Entry into European Union.
2389 **1081** 7 s. multicoloured .. 80 65

**1082** Loos House, Michaelerplatz, Vienna

**1995.** 125th Birth Anniv of Adolf Loos (architect).
2390 **1082** 10 s. multicoloured .. 1·10 90

**1083** Sporting Activities

**1995.** 50th Anniv of Austrian Gymnastics and Sports Association.
2391 **1083** 6 s. multicoloured .. 70 60

**1084** Workers

**1995.** 75th Anniv of Workers' and Employees' Chambers (advisory body).
2392 **1084** 6 s. multicoloured .. 70 60

**1995.** Folk Costumes and Art (5th series). As T **1005**. Multicoloured.
2393 5 s. 50 Belt, Carinthia .. 70 60
2394 6 s. Costume of Hiata (vineyard guard), Vienna .. .. 80 65
2395 7 s. Gold bonnet, Wachau 90 75

**1085** State Seal  **1086** Heft Ironworks

**1995.** 50th Anniv of Second Republic.
2396 **1085** 6 s. multicoloured .. 80 65

**1995.** Carinthian "History of Mining and Industry" Exhibition, Heft, Huttenberg.
2397 **1086** 5 s. 50 multicoloured 70 60

**1087** Hiker in Mountains

**1995.** Centenary of Friends of Nature.
2398 **1087** 5 s. 50 multicoloured 70 60

**1088** Heidenreichstein National Park

**1995.** Natural Beauty Spots.
2399 **1088** 6 s. multicoloured .. 80 65

**1089** Woman and Barbed Wire around Skull  **1090** Map, Woman and Child and Transport

**1995.** Europa. Peace and Freedom.
2400 **1089** 7 s. multicoloured .. 90 75

**1995.** Meeting of European Ministers of Transport Conference, Vienna.
2401 **1090** 7 s. multicoloured .. 90 75

**1091** "F" and "A" on Vase of Flowers  **1093** St. Gebhard (stained glass window, Martin Hausle)

**1092** Set for "The Flying Dutchman"

**1995.** Stamp Day.
2402 **1091** 10 s. 50 multicoloured 1·40 1·25
See note below No. 2266.

**1995.** 50th Bregenz Festival.
2403 **1092** 6 s. multicoloured .. 80 65

**1995.** Death Millenary of St. Gebhard, Bishop of Konstanz (patron saint of Vorarlberg chuches).
2404 **1093** 7 s. 50 multicoloured 1·00 80

**1094** Members' Flags  **1095** Loschmidt

**1995.** 50th Anniv of U.N.O.
2405 **1094** 10 s. multicoloured .. 1·25 1·00

**1995.** Death Centenary of Josef Loschmidt (physical chemist).
2406 **1095** 20 s. blk, stone & brn 2·50 2·00

**1096** K. Leichter  **1097** Scene from "Jedermann" (Hugo von Hofmannsthal)

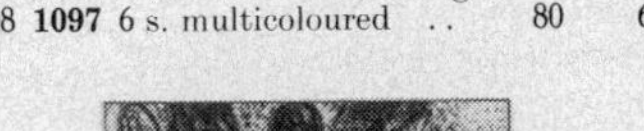

**1995.** Birth Centenary of Kathe Leichter (sociologist).
2407 **1096** 6 s. cream, blk & red 80 65

**1995.** 75th Anniv of Salzburg Festival.
2408 **1097** 6 s. multicoloured .. 80 65

**1098** "European Scene" (Adolf Frohner)

**1995.** Austrian Modern Art.
2409 **1098** 6 s. multicoloured .. 80 65

**1099** Franz von Suppe and "The Beautiful Galatea"

**1995.** Composers' Anniversaries. Scenes from operettas. Multicoloured.
2410 6 s. Type **1099** (death centenary) .. .. 80 65
2411 7 s. Nico Dostal and "The Hungarian Wedding" (birth centenary) .. 90 75

**1100** University Building

**1995.** 25th Anniv of Klagenfurt University.
2412 **1100** 5 s. 50 multicoloured 70 60

**1101** Hollenburg Castle

**1995.** 75th Anniv of Carinthian Referendum.
2413 **1101** 6 s. multicoloured .. 80 65

**1102** Postman

**1995.** Austrian World of Work (7th series).
2414 **1102** 6 s. multicoloured .. 80 65

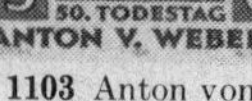

**1103** Anton von Webern (50th death)

**1104** Christ Child

**1995.** Composers' Anniversaries.
2415 **1103** 6 s. blue and orange 80 65
2416 – 7 s. red and orange .. 90 75
DESIGN: 7 s. Ludwig van Beethoven (225th birth).

**1995.** Christmas. 300th Anniv of Christkindl Church.
2417 **1104** 6 s. multicoloured .. 80 65

**1996.** Folk Customs and Art (6th series). As T **1005**.
2418 6 s. multicoloured .. 80 65
DESIGN: 6 s. Masked figures Roller and Scheller (Imst masquerades, Tyrol).

**1105** Empress Maria Theresia and Academy Building

**1996.** 250th Anniv of Theresian Academy, Vienna.
2419 **1105** 6 s. multicoloured .. 80 65

**1106** Ski Jumping

**1996.** World Ski Jumping Championships, Tauplitz and Bad Mitterndorf.
2420 **1106** 7 s. multicoloured .. 90 75

**1107** Terminal

**1996.** Completion of West Terminal, Vienna International Airport.
2421 **1107** 7 s. multicoloured .. 80 65

**1108** Hohe Tauern National Park

**1996.** Natural Beauty Spots.
2422 **1108** 6 s. multicoloured .. 70 60

## MINIMUM PRICE

The minimum price quoted is 10p which represents a handling charge rather than a basis for valuing common stamps. For further notes about prices see introductory pages.

**1109** "Mother and Child" (Peter Fendi)

**1110** Organ and Music

**1996.** Artists' Birth Bicentenaries. Mult.
2423 6 s. Type **1109** .. .. 70 60
2424 7 s. "Self-portrait" (Leopold Kupelwieser) 80 65

**1996.** Death Centenary of Anton Bruckner (composer).
2425 **1110** 5 s. 50 multicoloured 65 55

**1111** Kollmitz Castle (from copper engraving)

**1996.** 300th Death Anniv of Georg Vischer (cartographer and engraver).
2426 **1111** 10 s. black and stone 1·10 90

**1112** Old Market Square

**1996.** 800th Anniv of Klagenfurt.
2427 **1112** 6 s. multicoloured .. 70 60

**1113** Hotel Chef and Waitress

**1996.** Austrian World of Work (8th series).
2428 **1113** 6 s. multicoloured .. 70 60

**1114** Paula von Preradovic (writer)

**1115** "M" and "T" and Bluebirds (mosaic)

**1996.** Europa. Famous Women.
2429 **1114** 7 s. stone, brn & grey 70 60

**1996.** Stamp Day.
2430 **1115** 10 s.+5 s. mult .. 1·75 1·75
See note below No. 2266.

**1116** Mascot with Olympic Flag

**1996.** Olympic Games, Atlanta.
2431 **1116** 10 s. multicoloured .. 1·10 90

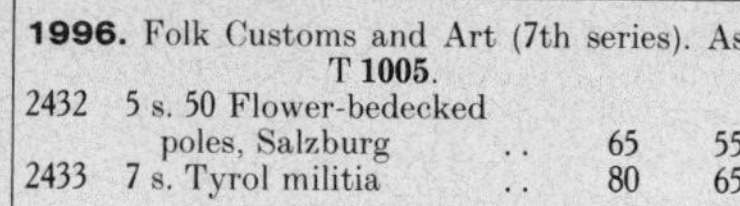

**1996.** Folk Customs and Art (7th series). As T **1005**.
2432 5 s. 50 Flower-bedecked poles, Salzburg .. 65 55
2433 7 s. Tyrol militia .. 80 65

**1117** Landscape

**1996.** 75th Anniv of Burgenland.
2434 **1117** 6 s. multicoloured .. 70 60

**1118** Mountaineers

**1119** Deed of Otto III, 996

**1996.** Centenary of Austrian Mountain Rescue Service.
2435 **1118** 6 s. multicoloured .. 70 60

**1996.** Millenary of Austria. Multicoloured.
2436 6 s. Type **1119** .. .. 70 60
2437 6 s. Archduke Joseph II (after Georg Weikert) and Archduchess Maria Theresia (after Martin van Meytens) .. .. 70 60
2438 7 s. "Duke Heinrich II" (stained glass window, Monastery of the Holy Cross) .. .. .. 80 65
2439 7 s. Arms in flames (1848 Revolution) .. .. 80 65
2440 7 s. Rudolf IV, the Founder .. .. 80 65
2441 7 s. Karl Renner (first Federal Republic president) .. .. 80 65
2442 10 s. Archduke Maximilian I (Holy Roman Emperor) (miniature from Statute Book of Order of the Golden Fleece) .. 1·10 90
2443 10 s. Seal and signature of Leopold Figl (State Treaty of 1955) .. 1·10 90
2444 20 s. Imperial crown of Rudolf II .. 2·40 2·00
2445 20 s. State arms, stars of Europe and "The Horsebreaker" (bronze by Josef Lax) (Austria and Europe) .. .. 2·40 2·00

**1120** "Power Station" (Reinhard Artberg)

**1996.** Austrian Modern Art.
2446 **1120** 7 s. multicoloured .. 80 65

**1121** Children of Different Nations

**1996.** 50th Anniv of U.N.I.C.E.F.
2447 **1121** 10 s. multicoloured .. 1·10 90

### IMPERIAL JOURNAL STAMPS

J **18**. J **21**. Arms of Austria. J **22**.

**1853.** Imperf.
J 67. J **18.** 1 k. blue .. .. 12·00 1·00
J 15. 2 k. green .. .. £2250 55·00
J 68. 2 k. brown .. .. 11·00 1·00
J 32. 4 k. brown .. .. £375 £1100

The 2 k. green has different corner ornaments.

For similar values in black or red, see Lombardy and Venetia Imperial Journal stamps, Nos. J22/4.

**1890.** Imperf.
J 76. J **21.** 1 k. brown .. .. 10·00 90
J 77. 2 k. green .. .. 11·00 1·25

**1890.** Perf.
J 78 J **22.** 25 k. red .. .. £100 £225

### NEWSPAPER STAMPS

N **2**. Mercury. N **8**. Francis Joseph I. N **11**. Francis Joseph I.

**1851.** Imperf.
N 11b. N **2.** (0.6 k.) blue £160 90·00
N 12. (6 k.) yellow .. £13000 £7500
N 13. (6 k.) red .. £35000 £50000
N 14. (30 k.) red .. £17000 £10000

**1858.** Imperf.
N 28. N **8.** (1 k. 05) blue .. £500 £600
N 29. (1 k. 05) lilac .. £700 £325

**1861.** Imperf.
N 38. N **11.** (1 k. 05) grey .. £140 £140

N **13**. Arms of Austria. AHN **17**. Mercury. N **19**.

**1863.** Imperf.
N 44. N **13.** (1 k. 05) lilac .. 32·00 12·00

**1867.** Imperf.
AHN 58b. AHN **17.** (1 k.) lilac 30 15

**1880.** Imperf.
N 69. N **19.** ½ k. green .. 5·50 60

N **31**. Mercury. N **43**.

**1899.** Imperf.
N 122. N **31.** 2 h. blue .. .. 15 10
N 123. 6 h. orange .. .. 1·75 1·25
N 124. 10 h. brown .. 70 70
N 125. 20 h. pink .. .. 1·25 1·25

**1908.** Imperf.
N 207. N **43.** 2 h. blue .. .. 40 10
N 208. 6 h. orange .. .. 4·00 30
N 209. 10 h. red .. .. 4·00 30
N 210. 20 h. brown .. 4·00 20

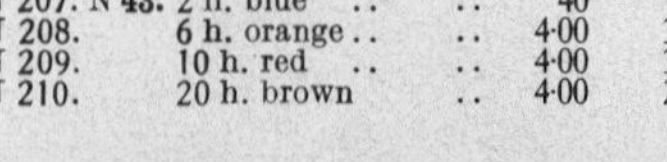

N **53**. Mercury. N **54**.

**1916.** Imperf.
N 266. N **53.** 2 h. brown .. .. 10 10
N 267. 4 h. green .. .. 15 55
N 268. 6 h. blue .. .. 15 80
N 269. 10 h. orange .. 20 55
N 270. 30 h. red .. .. 20 50

**1916.** For Express. Perf.
N 271. N **54.** 2 h. red on yellow 30 90
N 272. 5 h. green on yell. 30 90

N 61. Mercury. N 68.

**1917.** For Express. Perf.

N 294. N 61. 2 h. red on yellow.. 10 15
N 295. 5 h. green on yellow 10 15

**1919.** Optd. **Deutschosterreich.** Imperf.

N 318. N 53. 2 h. brown .. .. 10 10
N 319. 4 h. green .. .. 15 80
N 320. 6 h. blue .. .. 10 85
N 321. 10 h. orange .. 20 70
N 322. 30 h. red .. .. 10 50

**1919.** For Express. Optd. **Deutschosterreich.** Perf.

N 334. N 61. 2 h. red on yellow 10 15
N 335. 5 h. green on yell. 10 20

**1920.** Imperf.

N 365. N 68. 2 h. violet.. .. 10 10
N 366. 4 h. brown .. 10 15
N 367. 5 h. slate .. .. 10 10
N 368. 6 h. blue .. .. 10 10
N 369. 8 h. green .. .. 10 30
N 370. 9 h. bistre.. .. 10 10
N 371. 10 h. red .. .. 10 10
N 372. 12 h. blue .. .. 10 30
N 373. 15 h. mauve .. 10 10
N 374. 18 h. turquoise .. 10 10
N 375. 20 h. orange .. 10 15
N 376. 30 h. brown .. 10 10
N 377. 45 h. green .. 10 40
N 378. 60 h. red .. .. 10 15
N 379. 72 h. brown .. 10 50
N 380. 90 h. violet .. 10 60
N 381. 1 k. 20 red .. 10 90
N 382. 2 k. 40 green .. 10 65
N 383. 3 k. grey .. .. 10 35

**1921.** For Express. No. N334 surch **50 50.**

N450 N 61 50 on 2 h. red on yell 10 10

N 78. Mercury. N 79. Posthorn and Arrow.

**1921.** Imperf.

N452 N 78 45 h. grey .. .. 10 20
N453 75 h. red .. .. 10 40
N454 1 k. 50 green .. 10 60
N455 1 k. 80 blue .. 10 60
N456 2 k. 25 brown .. 10 90
N457 3 k. green .. .. 10 60
N458 6 k. purple .. 10 80
N459 7 k. 50 brown .. 20 1·00

**1921.** For Express. Perf.

N 460. N 79. 50 h. lilac on yellow 10 10

## POSTAGE DUE STAMPS

D 26. D 44.

**1894.** Perf.

D 96. D 26. 1 k. brown .. .. 2·25 1·25
D 97. 2 k. brown .. .. 3·50 2·25
D 98. 3 k. brown .. .. 3·00 80
D 99. 5 k. brown .. .. 2·75 40
D 100. 6 k. brown .. .. 3·25 5·50
D 101. 7 k. brown .. .. 1·25 4·00
D 102. 10 k. brown .. 5·00 40
D 103. 20 k. brown .. 80 5·00
D 104. 50 k. brown .. 40·00 50·00

**1899.** As Type **D 26.** but value in heller. Perf. or imperf.

D 126. D 26. 1 h. brown .. .. 15 30
D 127. 2 h. brown .. .. 30 10
D 128. 3 h. brown .. .. 15 15
D 129. 4 h. brown .. .. 30 10
D 130. 5 h. brown .. .. 20 10
D 131. 6 h. brown .. .. 20 10
D 132. 10 h. brown .. 30 10
D 133. 12 h. brown .. 50 40
D 134. 15 h. brown .. 60 60
D 135. 20 h. brown .. 35 20
D 136. 40 h. brown .. 80 60
D 137. 100 h. brown .. 3·25 1·75

**1908.** Perf.

D210. D44. 1 h. red .. .. 90 1·25
D211. 2 h. red .. .. 30 30
D212. 4 h. red .. .. 20 10
D213. 6 h. red .. .. 20 10
D214. 10 h. red .. .. 20 10
D215. 14 h. red .. .. 3·25 1·50
D216. 20 h. red .. .. 4·50 10
D217. 25 h. red .. .. 6·50 4·00
D218. 30 h. red .. .. 5·50 15
D219. 50 h. red .. .. 11·00 25
D220. 100 h. red .. .. 17·00 35
D221. 5 k. violet .. 42·00 11·00
D222. 10 k. violet .. £225 3·75

D 55. D 56.

**1916.**

D 273. D 55. 5 h. red .. .. 10 10
D 274. 10 h. red .. .. 10 10
D 275. 15 h. red .. .. 10 10
D 276. 20 h. red .. .. 10 10
D 277. 25 h. red .. .. 20 50
D 278. 30 h. red .. .. 10 15
D 279. 40 h. red .. .. 10 15
D 280. 50 h. red .. .. 1·00 1·25
D 281. D 56. 1 k. blue .. .. 15 10
D 282. 5 k. blue .. .. 1·75 2·00
D 283. 10 k. blue .. .. 2·25 1·00

**1916.** Nos. 189/90 optd **PORTO** or surch **15 15** also.

D284 1 h. black .. .. 10 10
D285 15 on 2 h. violet .. 20 25

**1917.** Unissued stamps as T **50** surch. **PORTO** and value.

D 286. 50. 10 on 24 h. blue .. 80 25
D 287. 15 on 36 h. violet .. 20 15
D 288. 20 on 54 h. orange .. 20 25
D 289. 50 on 42 h. brown .. 20 15

The above differ from Type **50** by showing a full-face portrait.

**1919.** Optd. **Deutschosterreich.**

D 323. D 55. 5 h. red .. .. 10 15
D 324. 10 h. red .. .. 10 15
D 325. 15 h. red .. .. 15 30
D 326. 20 h. red .. .. 25 30
D 327. 25 h. red .. .. 9·00 17·00
D 328. 30 h. red .. .. 15 25
D 329. 40 h. red .. .. 15 45
D 330. 50 h. red .. .. 30 1·10
D 331. D 56. 1 k. blue .. .. 5·00 10·00
D 332. 5 k. blue .. .. 8·00 11·00
D 333. 10 k. blue .. .. 8·00 3·75

D 69. D 70.

**1920.** Imperf or perf (**D 69**), perf (**D 70**).

D384 D 69 5 h. pink .. .. 10 25
D385 10 h. pink .. .. 10 15
D386 15 h. pink .. .. 10 1·25
D387 20 h. pink .. .. 10 15
D388 25 h. pink .. .. 10 1·00
D389 30 h. pink .. .. 10 25
D390 40 h. pink .. .. 10 15
D391 50 h. pink .. .. 10 15
D392 80 h. pink .. .. 10 20
D393 D 70 1 k. blue .. .. 10 15
D394 1½ k. blue .. .. 10 15
D395 2 k. blue .. .. 10 15
D396 3 k. blue .. .. 10 25
D397 4 k. blue .. .. 10 30
D398 5 k. blue .. .. 10 15
D399 8 k. blue .. .. 10 70
D400 10 k. blue .. .. 10 20
D401 20 k. blue .. .. 30 1·25

**1921.** No. 343a surch **Nachmarke 7½ K.** Perf.

D451 64 7½ k. on 15 h. bistre on grey .. .. 10 15

D 83. D 86.

**1921.**

D 510. D 83. 1 k. brown .. .. 10 20
D 511. 2 k. brown .. .. 10 30
D 512. 4 k. brown .. .. 10 65
D 513. 5 k. brown .. .. 10 20
D 514. 7½ k. brown .. 10 75
D 515. – 10 k. blue .. .. 10 25
D 516. – 15 k. blue .. .. 10 45
D 517. – 20 k. blue .. .. 10 50
D 518. – 50 k. blue .. .. 10 45

The 10 k. to 50 k. are larger (22 × 30 mm.).

**1922.**

D 526. D 83. 10 k. turquoise .. 10 25
D 527. 15 k. turquoise .. 10 50
D 528. 20 k. turquoise .. 10 30
D 529. 25 k. turquoise .. 10 90
D 530. 40 k. turquoise .. 10 30
D 531. 50 k. turquoise .. 10 1·00
D 532. D 86. 100 k. purple .. 10 10
D 533. 150 k. purple .. 10 10
D 534. 200 k. purple .. 10 10
D 535. 400 k. purple .. 10 10
D 536. 600 k. purple .. 10 45
D 537. 800 k. purple .. 10 10
D 538. D 86. 1000 k. purple .. 10 10
D 539. 1200 k. purple .. 1·10 2·25
D 540. 1500 k. purple .. 15 20
D 541. 1800 k. purple .. 2·00 7·00
D 542. 2000 k. purple .. 30 55
D 543. 3000 k. purple .. 7·00 14·00
D 544. 4000 k. purple .. 5·00 11·00
D 545. 6000 k. purple .. 7·50 18·00

D 94. D 120.

**1925.**

D589 D 94 1 g. red .. .. 10 10
D590 2 g. red .. .. 10 10
D591 3 g. red .. .. 10 10
D592 4 g. red .. .. 10 10
D593 5 g. red .. .. 10 10
D594 6 g. red .. .. 25 40
D595 8 g. red .. .. 15 20
D596 10 g. blue .. .. 10 10
D597 12 g. blue .. .. 10 10
D598 14 g. blue .. .. 15 10
D599 15 g. blue .. .. 10 10
D600 16 g. blue .. .. 25 15
D601 18 g. blue .. .. 1·40 3·25
D602 20 g. blue .. .. 10 10
D603 23 g. blue .. .. 60 10
D604 24 g. blue .. .. 1·25 10
D605 28 g. blue .. .. 1·00 20
D606 30 g. blue .. .. 20 10
D607 31 g. blue .. .. 1·25 15
D608 35 g. blue .. .. 1·25 10
D609 39 g. blue .. .. 1·50 10
D610 40 g. blue .. .. 1·00 1·25
D611 60 g. blue .. .. 1·00 1·25
D612 – 1 s. green .. .. 3·50 60
D613 – 2 s. green .. .. 32·00 2·75
D614 – 5 s. green .. .. £100 40·00
D615 – 10 s. green .. .. 42·00 3·50

DESIGN: 1 to 10 s. Horiziontal bands of colour.

**1935.**

D 746. D 120. 1 g. red .. .. 10 15
D 747. 2 g. red .. .. 10 20
D 748. 3 g. red .. .. 10 15
D 749. 5 g. red .. .. 10 10
D 750. – 10 g. blue .. .. 10 10
D 751. – 12 g. blue .. .. 10 10
D 752. – 15 g. blue .. .. 15 45
D 753. – 20 g. blue .. .. 15 10
D 754. – 24 g. blue .. .. 15 10
D 755. – 30 g. blue .. .. 15 15
D 756. – 39 g. blue .. .. 25 10
D 757. – 60 g. blue .. .. 60 1·25
D 758. – 1 s. green .. .. 70 30
D 759. – 2 s. green .. .. 1·40 85
D 760. – 5 s. green .. .. 3·00 2·75
D 761. – 10 s. green .. .. 4·50 60

DESIGNS: 10 to 60 g. As Type **D 120** but with background of horizontal lines. 1 to 10 s. As last, but with positions of figures, arms and inscriptions reversed.

D 143. D 162.

**1945.**

D 891. D 143. 1 pf. red .. .. 10 15
D 892. 2 pf. red .. .. 10 15
D 893. 3 pf. red .. .. 10 15
D 894. 5 pf. red .. .. 10 15
D 895. 10 pf. red .. .. 10 15
D 896. 12 pf. red .. .. 10 20
D 897. 20 pf. red .. .. 10 20
D 898. 24 pf. red .. .. 10 30
D 899. 30 pf. red .. .. 10 40
D 900. 60 pf. red .. .. 10 45
D 901. 1 rm. violet .. 10 45
D 902. 2 rm. violet .. 10 60
D 903. 5 rm. violet .. 10 65
D 904. 10 rm. violet .. 10 80

**1946.** Optd. **PORTO.**

D956. 145. 3 g. orange .. .. 10 10
D957. 5 g. green .. .. 10 10
D958. 6 g. purple .. .. 10 10
D959. 8 g. red .. .. 10 10
D960. 10 g. grey .. .. 10 15
D961. 12 g. brown .. .. 10 10
D962. 15 g. red .. .. 10 15
D963. 20 g. brown .. .. 10 10
D964. 25 g. blue .. .. 10 15
D965. 30 g. mauve .. .. 10 10
D966. 40 g. blue .. .. 10 10
D967. 60 g. green .. .. 10 10
D968. 1 s. violet .. .. 10 15
D969. 2 s. yellow .. .. 60 1·00
D970. 5 s. blue .. .. 50 70

**1947.**

D 1035. D 162. 1 g. brown .. .. 10 10
D 1036. 2 g. brown .. .. 10 10
D 1037. 3 g. brown .. .. 10 10
D 1038. 5 g. brown .. .. 10 10
D 1039. 8 g. brown .. .. 10 10
D 1040. 10 g. brown .. .. 10 10
D 1041. 12 g. brown .. .. 10 10
D 1042. 15 g. brown .. .. 10 10
D 1043. 16 g. brown .. .. 25 70
D 1044. 17 g. brown .. .. 20 70
D 1045. 18 g. brown .. .. 20 70
D 1046. 20 g. brown .. .. 35 10
D 1047. 24 g. brown .. .. 20 75
D 1048. 30 g. brown .. .. 15 20
D 1049. D 162. 36 g. brown .. .. 40 1·00
D 1050. 40 g. brown .. .. 10 10
D 1051. 42 g. brown .. .. 50 1·00
D 1052. 48 g. brown .. .. 50 1·00
D 1053. 50 g. brown .. .. 60 15
D 1054. 60 g. brown .. .. 15 20
D 1055. 70 g. brown .. .. 10 15
D 1056. 80 g. brown .. .. 3·75 2·50
D 1057. 1 s. blue .. .. 10 10
D 1058. 1 s. 15 blue .. .. 2·75 25
D 1059. 1 s. 20 blue .. .. 3·25 1·25
D 1060. 2 s. blue .. .. 30 25
D 1061. 5 s. blue .. .. 30 30
D 1062. 10 s. blue .. .. 35 30

D 184. D 817.

**1949.**

D 1178. D 184. 1 g. red .. .. 15 10
D 1179. 2 g. red .. .. 20 10
D 1180. 4 g. red .. .. 60 20
D 1181. 5 g. red .. .. 1·75 25
D 1182. 8 g. red .. .. 2·00 2·00
D 1183. 10 g. red .. .. 10 10
D 1184. 20 g. red .. .. 10 10
D 1185. 30 g. red .. .. 10 10
D 1186. 40 g. red .. .. 20 10
D 1187. 50 g. red .. .. 10 10
D 1188. 60 g. red .. .. 10·00 30
D 1189. 63 g. red .. .. 4·00 6·50
D 1190. 70 g. red .. .. 15 10
D 1191. 80 g. red .. .. 30 15
D 1192. 90 g. red .. .. 15 10
D 1193. 1 s. violet .. .. 15 10
D 1194. 1 s. 20 violet .. 20 15
D 1195. 1 s. 35 violet .. 50 10
D 1196. 1 s. 40 violet .. 25 25
D 1197. 1 s. 50 violet .. 25 10
D 1198. 1 s. 65 violet .. 50 30
D 1199. 1 s. 70 violet .. 50 30
D 1200. 2 s. violet .. .. 35 10
D 1201. 2 s. 50 violet .. 40 10
D 1202. 3 s. violet .. .. 45 10
D 1203. 4 s. violet .. .. 1·00 60
D 1204. 5 s. violet .. .. 75 45
D 1205. 10 s. violet .. .. 1·50 45

**1985.**

D2074 D 817 10 g. yellow & blk 10 10
D2075 20 g. red & black 10 10
D2076 50 g. orge & blk 10 10
D2077 1 s. blue & black 10 10
D2078 2 s. brown & blk 25 15
D2079 3 s. violet & black 35 20
D2080 5 s. yellow & blk 60 30
D2081 10 s. green & blk 1·10 1·10

## AUSTRIAN TERRITORIES ACQUIRED BY ITALY Pt. 2

Italian territory acquired from Austria at the close of the war of 1914-18, including Trentino and Trieste.

1918. 100 heller = 1 krone.
1918. 100 centesimi = 1 lira.
1919. 100 centesimi = 1 corona

### TRENTINO

**1918.** Stamps of Austria overprinted **Regno d'Italia Trentino 3 nov 1918.**

1 49 3 h. purple .. .. 2·00 2·50
2 5 h. green .. .. 1·50 1·60
3 6 h. orange .. .. 32·00 30·00
4 10 h. red .. .. 1·25 1·60
5 12 h. green .. .. £100 £100
6 60 15 h. brown .. .. 2·50 2·75
7 20 h. green .. .. 1·00 1·10
8 25 h. blue .. .. 21·00 24·00
9 30 h. violet .. .. 7·00 8·00
10 51 40 h. green .. .. 32·00 30·00
11 50 h. green .. .. 14·00 18·00
12 60 h. blue .. .. 28·00 26·00
13 80 h. brown .. .. 32·00 75·00
14 90 h. red .. .. £600 £550
15 1 k. red on yellow .. 32·00 35·00
16 52 2 k. blue .. .. £160 £180
17 4 k. green .. .. £900 £950
18 10 k. violet .. .. £16000

**1918.** Stamps of Italy optd. **Venezia Tridentina.**

19. 30. 1 c. brown .. .. 80 1·40
20. 31. 2 c. brown .. .. 80 1·40
21. 37. 5 c. green .. .. 80 1·40
22. 10 c. red .. .. .. 80 1·40
23. 41. 20 c. orange .. .. 80 1·40
24. 39. 40 c. brown .. .. 18·00 18·00
25. 33. 45 c. olive .. .. 11·00 18·00
26. 39. 50 c. mauve .. .. 12·00 22·00
27. 34. 1 l. brown and green .. 12·00 22·00

**1919.** Stamps of Italy surch. **Venezia Tridentina** and value.

28. 37. 5 h. on 5 c. green .. 40 85
29. 10 h. on 10 c. red .. 40 85
30. 41. 20 h. on 20 c. orange .. 40 85

### VENEZIA GIULIA

For use in Trieste and territory, Gorizia and province, and in Istria.

**1918.** Stamps of Austria optd **Regno d'Italia Venezia Giulia 3. XI. 18.**

31 49 3 h. purple .. .. 50 70
32 5 h. green .. .. 50 70
33 6 h. orange .. .. 75 1·10
34 10 h. red .. .. 2·75 85
35 12 h. green .. .. 1·40 1·90
36 60 15 h. brown .. .. 50 70
37 20 h. green .. .. 50 70
38 25 h. blue .. .. 3·50 4·25
39 30 h. purple .. .. 1·60 1·90
40 51 40 h. green .. .. 26·00 32·00
41 50 h. green .. .. 3·50 4·00
42 60 h. blue .. .. 5·50 7·00
43 80 h. brown .. .. 5·50 7·00
44 1 k. red on yellow .. 5·50 7·00
45 52 2 k. blue .. .. 70·00 80·00
46 3 k. red .. .. £120 £140
47 4 k. green .. .. £180 £180
48 10 k. violet .. .. £12000 £14000

**1918.** Stamps of Italy optd. **Venezia Giulia.**

49. 30. 1 c. brown .. .. 75 1·25
50. 31. 2 c. brown .. .. 75 1·25
51. 37. 5 c. green .. .. 20 40
52. 10 c. red .. .. .. 15 40
53. 41. 20 c. orange .. .. 25 50
54. 39. 25 c. blue .. .. 35 70
55. 40 c. brown .. .. 4·00 6·00
56. 33. 45 c. green .. .. 1·25 2·00
57. 39. 50 c. mauve .. .. 1·60 2·75
58. 60 c. red .. .. 18·00 30·00
59. 34. 1 l. brown and green .. 8·00 12·00

**1919.** Stamps of Italy surch. **Venezia Giulia** and value.

60. 37. 5 h. on 5 c. green .. 35 75
61. 41. 20 h. on 20 c. orange .. 35 75

#### EXPRESS LETTER STAMPS

**1919.** Express Letter stamp of Italy optd. **Venezia Giulia.**

E 60. E 35. 25 c. red .. .. 10·00 18·00

#### POSTAGE DUE STAMPS

**1918.** Postage Due Stamps of Italy optd. **Venezia Giulia.**

D60 D 12 5 c. mauve & orange 15 40
D61 10 c. mauve & orange 25 50
D62 20 c. mauve & orange 60 1·10
D63 30 c. mauve & orange 2·00 3·25
D64 40 c. mauve & orange 12·00 20·00
D65 50 c. mauve & orange 24·00 34·00
D66 1 l. mauve and blue 85·00 £100

#### GENERAL ISSUE

For use throughout the liberated area of Trentino, Venezia Giulia and Dalmatia.

**1919.** Stamps of Italy surch in new currency.

62 30 1 ce. di cor. on 1 c. brown 30 45
64 31 2 ce. di cor. on 2 c. brown 30 35
77 37 5 ce. di cor. on 5 c. green 20 50
78 10 ce. di cor. on 10 c. red 20 50
68 41 20 ce. di cor. on 20 c. orge 30 35
70 39 25 ce. di cor. on 25 c. blue 30 45
71 40 ce. di cor. on 40 c. brn 30 70
72 33 45 ce. di cor. on 45 c. grn 30 70
73 39 50 ce. di cor. on 50 c. mve 30 70
74 60 ce. di cor. on 60 c. red 30 85
75 34 1 cor. on 1 l. brown & grn 30 85
76 una corona on 1 l. brown and green .. .. 1·00 3·75
82 5 cor. on 5 l. blue and red 12·00 30·00
83 10 cor. on 10 l. grn & red 12·00 30·00

#### EXPRESS LETTER STAMPS

**1919.** Express Letter stamps of Italy surch. in new currency.

E 76. E 35. 25 ce. di cor. on 25 c. red .. .. 30 55
E 77. E 41. 30 ce. di cor. on 30 c. red and blue .. 50 1·10

#### POSTAGE DUE STAMPS

**1919.** Postage Due stamps of Italy surch in new currency.

D76 D 12 5 ce. di cor. on 5 c. mauve and orange 20 75
D77 10 ce. di cor. on 10 c. mauve and orange 20 75
D78 20 ce. di cor. on 20 c. mauve and orange 30 75
D79 30 ce. di cor. on 30 c. mauve and orange 40 75
D80 40 ce. di cor. on 40 c. mauve and orange 40 75
D81 50 ce. di cor. on 50 c. mauve and orange 40 75
D82 una corona on 1 l. mauve and blue .. 40 75
D86 1 cor. on 1 l. mauve and blue .. 2·50 7·00
D83 due corona on 2 l. mauve and blue .. 19·00 38·00
D87 2 cor. on 2 l. mve & bl 8·00 17·00
D84 cinque corona on 5 l. mauve and blue .. 19·00 38·00
D88 5 cor. on 5 l. mve & bl 8·00 17·00

## AUSTRO-HUNGARIAN MILITARY POST Pt. 2

### A. GENERAL ISSUES

100 heller = 1 krone.

**1915.** Stamps of Bosnia and Herzegovina optd **K.U.K. FELDPOST.**

1. 25. 1 h. olive .. .. .. 15 30
2. 2 h. blue .. .. .. 15 30
3. 3 h. lake .. .. .. 15 30
4. 5 h. green .. .. .. 10 15
5. 6 h. black .. .. .. 15 30
6. 10 h. red .. .. .. 10 15
7. 12 h. olive .. .. .. 20 40
8. 20 h. brown .. .. .. 30 50
9. 25 h. blue .. .. .. 30 40
10. 30 h. red .. .. .. 3·00 5·50
11. 26. 35 h. green .. .. 2·25 4·00
12. 40 h. violet .. .. 2·25 4·00
13. 45 h. brown .. .. 2·25 4·00
14. 50 h. blue .. .. 2·25 4·00
15. 60 h. purple .. .. 30 85
16. 72 h. blue .. .. 2·25 3·75
17. 25. 1 k. brown on cream .. 2·50 4·25
18. 2 k. indigo on blue .. 2·25 4·00
19. 26. 3 k. red on green .. 20·00 35·00
20. 5 k. lilac on grey .. 19·00 32·00
21. 10 k. blue on grey .. £140 £225

2. Francis Joseph.

**1915.**

22 2 1 h. green .. .. 10 15
23 2 h. blue .. .. 15 15
24 3 h. red .. .. 10 15
25 5 h. green .. .. 10 15
26 6 h. black .. .. 10 15
27 10 h. red .. .. 10 15
28 10 h. blue .. .. 10 15
29 12 h. green .. .. 10 20
30 15 h. red .. .. 10 10
31 20 h. brown .. .. 20 20
32 20 h. green .. .. 20 30
33 25 h. blue .. .. 15 15
34 30 h. red .. .. 15 30
35 35 h. green .. .. 30 35
36 40 h. violet .. .. 30 35
37 45 h. brown .. .. 30 35
38 50 h. deep green .. .. 30 30
39 60 h. purple .. .. 30 35
40 72 h. blue .. .. 30 35
41 80 h. brown .. .. 20 25
42 90 h. red .. .. 70 1·00
43 – 1 k. purple on cream .. 1·25 1·50
44 – 2 k. green on blue .. 1·00 70
45 – 3 k. red on green .. 75 1·40
46 – 4 k. violet on grey .. 75 2·00
47 – 5 k. violet on grey .. 20·00 30·00
48 – 10 k. blue on grey .. 2·75 6·00

The kronen values are larger, with profile portrait.

**1917.** As 1917 issue of Bosnia, but inscr. "K. u. K. FELDPOST".

49. 1 h. blue .. .. .. 10 10
50. 2 h. orange .. .. .. 10 10
51. 3 h. grey .. .. .. 10 10
52. 5 h. green .. .. .. 10 10
53. 6 h. violet .. .. .. 10 10
54. 10 h. brown .. .. .. 10 10
55. 12 h. blue .. .. .. 10 15
56. 15 h. red .. .. .. 10 10
57. 20 h. brown .. .. .. 10 10
58. 25 h. blue .. .. .. 30 30
59. 30 h. grey .. .. .. 10 15
60. 40 h. bistre .. .. .. 10 10
61. 50 h. green .. .. .. 10 10
62. 60 h. red .. .. .. 10 15
63. 80 h. blue .. .. .. 10 10
64. 90 h. purple .. .. .. 30 55
65. 2 k. red on buff .. .. 10 10
66. 3 k. green on blue .. .. 80 1·40
67. 4 k. red on green .. .. 14·00 15·00
68. 10 k. violet on grey .. 2·00 4·25

The kronen values are larger and the border is different.

**1918.** Imperial and Royal Welfare Fund. As 1918 issue of Bosnia, but inscr "K. UND K. FELDPOST".

69. 40. 10 h. (+10 h.) green .. 20 40
70. – 20 h. (+10 h.) red .. 20 40
71. 40. 45 h. (+10 h.) blue .. 20 40

#### NEWSPAPER STAMPS

N 4. Mercury.

**1916.**

N 49. N 4. 2 h. blue .. .. 15 20
N 50. 6 h. orange .. .. 45 90
N 51. 10 h. red .. .. 55 90
N 52. 20 h. brown .. .. 40 90

### B. ISSUES FOR ITALY

100 centesimi = 1 lira.

**1918.** General Issue stamps of 1917 surch. in figs. and words.

1. 2 c. on 1 h. blue .. .. 10 15
2. 3 c. on 2 h. orange .. .. 10 15
3. 4 c. on 3 h. grey .. .. 10 15
4. 6 c. on 5 h. green .. .. 10 20
5. 7 c. on 6 h. violet .. .. 10 20
6. 11 c. on 10 h. brown .. 10 20
7. 13 c. on 12 h. blue .. .. 10 20
8. 16 c. on 15 h. red .. .. 10 20
9. 22 c. on 20 h. brown .. 10 20
10. 27 c. on 25 h. blue .. 30 55
11. 32 c. on 30 h. grey .. 15 35
12. 43 c. on 40 h. bistre .. 15 40
13. 53 c. on 50 h. green .. 10 20
14. 64 c. on 60 h. red .. .. 20 65
15. 85 c. on 80 h. blue .. 10 30
16. 95 c. on 90 h. purple .. 10 30
17. 2 l. 11 on 2 k. red on buff .. 20 40
18. 3 l. 16 on 3 k. green on blue 60 1·10
19. 4 l. 22 on 4 k. red on green .. 70 1·40

#### NEWSPAPER STAMPS

**1918.** Newspaper stamps of General Issue surch. in figs. and words.

N 20. N 4. 3 c. on 2 h. blue .. 10 30
N 21. 7 c. on 6 h. orange .. 25 60
N 22. 11 c. on 10 h. red .. 25 60
N 23. 22 c. on 20 h. brown 25 60

**1918.** For Express. Newspaper stamps of Bosnia surch. in figs. and words.

N24 N 35 3 c. on 2 h. red on yellow .. .. 4·25 5·50
N25 6 c. on 5 h. green on yellow .. .. 4·25 5·50

#### POSTAGE DUE STAMPS

**1918.** Postage Due stamps of Bosnia surch. in figs. and words.

D 20. D 35. 6 c. on 5 h. red .. 2·25 5·50
D 21. 11 c. on 10 h. red .. 2·00 4·50
D 22. 16 c. on 15 h. red .. 70 1·40
D 23. 27 c. on 25 h. red .. 70 1·40
D 24. 32 c. on 30 h. red .. 70 1·40
D 25. 43 c. on 40 h. red .. 70 1·40
D 26. 53 c. on 50 h. red .. 70 1·40

### C. ISSUES FOR MONTENEGRO

100 heller = 1 krone.

**1917.** Nos. 28 and 30 of General Issues optd **K U K. MILIT. VERWALTUNG MONTENEGRO.**

1. 2. 10 h. blue .. .. .. 5·50 7·00
2. 15 h. red .. .. .. 5·50 7·00

### D. ISSUES FOR RUMANIA

100 bani = 1 leu.

**1917.** General Issue stamps of 1917, optd. **BANI** or **LEI.**

1. 3 b. grey .. .. .. 1·25 1·50
2. 5 b. green .. .. .. 1·25 1·25
3. 6 b. violet .. .. .. 1·25 1·25
4. 10 b. brown .. .. .. 15 15
5. 12 b. blue .. .. .. 90 1·25
6. 15 b. red .. .. .. 80 1·00
7. 20 b. brown .. .. .. 15 15
8. 25 b. blue .. .. .. 20 20
9. 30 b. grey .. .. .. 30 45
10. 40 b. bistre .. .. .. 30 40
11. 50 b. green .. .. .. 30 40
12. 60 b. red .. .. .. 30 40
13. 80 b. blue .. .. .. 15 20
14. 90 b. purple .. .. .. 35 45
15. 2 l. red on buff .. .. 45 60
16. 3 l. green on blue .. .. 60 85
17. 4 l. red on green .. .. 60 85

3. Charles I.

**1918.**

18. 3. 3 b. grey .. .. .. 15 30
19. 5 b. green .. .. .. 15 40
20. 6 b. violet .. .. .. 25 50
21. 10 b. brown .. .. .. 25 60
22. 12 b. blue .. .. .. 20 50
23. 15 b. red .. .. .. 15 30
24. 20 b. brown .. .. .. 15 30
25. 25 b. blue .. .. .. 15 30
26. 30 b. grey .. .. .. 15 30
27. 40 b. bistre .. .. .. 15 30
28. 50 b. green .. .. .. 20 50
29. 60 b. red .. .. .. 20 50
30. 80 b. blue .. .. .. 15 30
31. 90 b. purple .. .. .. 30 75
32. 2 l. red on buff .. .. 20 60
33. 3 l. green on blue .. .. 30 80
34. 4 l. red on green .. .. 35 85

### E. ISSUES FOR SERBIA

100 heller = 1 krone.

**1916.** Stamps of Bosnia optd. **SERBIEN.**

22. 25. 1 h. olive .. .. 1·75 2·75
23. 2 h. blue .. .. 1·75 2·75
24. 3 h. lake .. .. 1·60 2·25
25. 5 h. green .. .. 40 50
26. 6 h. black .. .. 90 1·75
27. 10 h. red .. .. 40 50
28. 12 h. olive .. .. 90 1·75
29. 20 h. brown .. .. 50 80
30. 25 h. blue .. .. 45 80
31. 30 h. red .. .. 45 80
32. 26. 35 h. green .. .. 45 80
33. 40 h. violet .. .. 45 80
34. 45 h. brown .. .. 45 80
35. 50 h. blue .. .. 45 80
36. 60 h. brown .. .. 45 80
37. 72 h. blue .. .. 45 80
38. 25. 1 k. brown on cream .. 60 90
39. 2 k. indigo on blue .. 60 90
40. 26. 3 k. red on green .. 60 90
41. 5 k. lilac on grey .. 60 90
42. 10 k. blue on grey .. 10·00 19·00

## AUSTRO-HUNGARIAN POST OFFICES IN THE TURKISH EMPIRE Pt. 2

Various Austro-Hungarian P.O.s in the Turkish Empire. Such offices had closed by 15 December 1914 except for several in Albania which remained open until 1915.

### A. LOMBARDY AND VENETIA CURRENCY

100 soldi = 1 florin

1. 2. 3.

**1867.**

1. 1. 2 s. yellow .. .. 1·10 22·00
9. 3 s. green .. .. 85 22·00
10. 5 s. red .. .. 25 14·00
11. 10 s. blue .. .. 55·00 70
5. 15 s. brown .. .. 12·00 4·25
6. 25 s. purple .. .. 11·00 32·00
7a. 2. 50 s. brown .. .. 1·00 38·00

**1883.**

14 3 2 s. black and brown .. 15 £110
15 3 s. black and green .. 80 23·00
16 5 s. black and red .. 15 13·00
17 10 s. black and blue .. 60 35
18 20 s. black and grey .. 4·00 4·50
19 50 s. black and mauve .. 85 13·00

### B. TURKISH CURRENCY

40 paras = 1 piastre.

**1886.** Surch. **10 PARA 10.**

21a. 3. 10 p. on 3 s. green .. 25 5·00

**1888.** Nos. 71/75a of Austria surch.

22. 20. 10 pa. on 3 k. green .. 2·50 6·00
23. 20 pa. on 5 k. red .. 40 6·50
24. 1 pi. on 10 k. blue .. 35·00 75
25. 2 pi. on 20 k. grey .. 1·25 2·00
26. 5 pi. on 50 k. lilac .. 1·40 12·00

**1890.** Stamps of Austria of 1890, the kreuzer values with lower figures of value removed, surch. at foot.

27. 23. 8 pa. on 2 k. brown .. 15 40
28. 10 pa. on 3 k. green .. 45 30
29. 20 pa. on 5 k. red .. 15 20
30. 1 pi. on 10 k. blue .. 30 10
31. 2 pi. on 20 k. olive .. 7·50 18·00
32. 5 pi. on 50 k. mauve .. 11·00 45·00
33. 24. 10 pi. on 1 g. blue .. 8·00 18·00
37. 10 pi. on 1 g. lilac .. 11·00 17·00
34. 20 pi. on 2 g. red .. 11·00 30·00
38. 20 pi. on 2 g. green .. 32·00 55·00

**1890.** Stamps of Austria of 1891, with lower figures of value removed, surch at foot.
35 25 2 pi. on 20 k. green .. 4·00 75
36 5 pi. on 50 k. mauve .. 2·50 2·00

**1900.** Stamps of Austria of 1899, the heller values with lower figures of value removed, surch. at foot.
46. 27. 10 pa. on 5 h. green .. 2·00 2·50
40. 28. 20 pa. on 10 h. red .. 4·00 65
48. 1 pi. on 25 h. blue .. 1·25 30
49. 29. 2 pi. on 50 h. blue .. 3·25 3·25
43. 30. 5 pi. on 1 k. red.. .. 70 20
44. 10 pi. on 2 k. lavender.. 1·90 2·00
45. 20 pi. on 4 k. green .. 1·50 4·50

**1903.** Stamps of Austria of 1899, with all figures of value removed, surch. at top and at foot.
55. 27. 10 pa. green .. .. 40 1·25
56. 28. 20 pa. red .. .. 80 55
57. 30 pa. mauve .. .. 55 2·25
58. 1 pi. blue .. .. 35 15
59. 29. 2 pi. blue .. .. 85 45

11. Francis Joseph I. 12.

**1908.** 60th Anniv of Emperor's Accession.
60 11 10 pa. green on yellow .. 15 10
61 20 pa. red on pink .. 20 10
62 30 pa. brown on buff .. 30 45
63 60 pa. purple on blue .. 50 3·00
70 1 pi. ultramarine & blue 35 40
65 12 2 pi. red on yellow .. 30 15
66 5 pi. brown on grey .. 50 70
67 10 pi. green on yellow .. 75 1·40
68 20 pi. blue on grey .. 1·75 3·25

POSTAGE DUE STAMPS

**1902.** Postage Due stamps as Type D 32 of Austria, but with value in heller, surch. with new value.
D 50. D 32. 10 pa. on 5 h. green 1·00 2·50
D 51. 20 pa. on 10 h. green 1·10 2·25
D 52. 1 pi. on 20 h. green.. 1·50 3·50
D 53. 2 pi. on 40 h. green.. 1·50 3·25
D 54. 5 pi. on 100 h. green 1·50 3·25

D 13.

**1908.**
D 71. D 13. ¼ pi. green .. .. 3·25 6·50
D 72. ½ pi. green .. .. 1·50 4·75
D 73. 1 pi. green .. .. 1·50 5·50
D 74. 1½ pi. green .. .. 70 10·00
D 75. 2 pi. green .. .. 2·00 10·00
D 76. 5 pi. green .. .. 2·00 7·00
D 77. 10 pi. green .. .. 14·00 £110
D 78. 20 pi. green .. .. 12·00 £120
D 79. 30 pi. green .. .. 14·00 11·00

C. FRENCH CURRENCY

100 centimes = 1 franc.

**1903.** Stamps of Austria surch **CENTIMES** or **FRANC**.
F1 27 5 c. on 5 h. green & blk 1·10 3·00
F2 28 10 c. on 10 h. red and black (No. 143) .. 75 3·25
F3 25 c. on 25 h. blue and black (No. 145) .. 30·00 20·00
F4 29 50 c. on 50 h. blue & blk 6·00 £110
F5 30 1 f. on 1 k. red .. 1·25 90·00
F6 2 f. on 2 k. lilac .. 9·00 2·25
F7 4 f. on 4 k. green .. 10·00 £400

**1904.** Stamps of Austria surch **CENTIMES**.
F14 33 5 c. on 5 h. green .. 75 3·00
F13 28 10 c. on 10 h. red and black (No. 160) 60 9·00
F10 25 c. on 25 h. blue and black (No. 176) 50 £100
F11 35 50 c. on 50 h. blue .. 1·00 £375

**1906.** Type of Austria surch **CENTIMES**.
F15 28 10 c. on 10 h. red (No. 184) 85 25·00
F16 15 c. on 15 h. violet and black (as No. 185) 80 34·00
No. 16 was not issued without the surcharge.

**1908.** 60th Anniv of Emperor's Accession. As Types 11/12 but in centimes or franc.
F17 11. 5 c. green on yellow .. 25 40
F18 10 c. red on pink .. 35 55
F19 15 c. brown on buff .. 40 3·25
F20 25 c. blue on blue .. 11·00 4·00
F21 12 50 c. red on yellow .. 1·75 20·00
F22 1 f. brown on grey .. 2·50 30·00

# AZERBAIJAN Pt. 10

Formerly part of the Russian Empire. Became independent on 27 May 1918, following the Russian Revolution. Soviet troops invaded the country on 27 April 1920, and a Soviet Republic followed. From 1 Oct. 1923 stamps of the Transcaucasian Federation were used but these were superseded by those of the Soviet Union in 1924.

With the dissolution of the Soviet Union in 1991, Azerbaijan once again became an independent state.

1919. 100 kopeks = 1 rouble.
1992. 100 qopik = 1 manat.

1. Standard-bearer. 6. Famine Supplies.

3. "Labour". 4. Petroleum Well.

**1919.** Imperf. Various designs.
1. 1. 10 k. multicoloured .. 25 30
2. – 20 k. multicoloured .. 15 30
3. – 40 k. olive, black & yellow 10 20
4. – 60 k. orange, blk. & yellow 10 15
5. – 1 r. blue, black and yellow 10 20
6. – 2 r. red, black and yellow 10 15
7. – 5 r. blue, black and yellow 10 25
8. – 10 r. olive, black & yellow 30 50
9. – 25 r. blue, black and red.. 30 60
10. – 50 r. olive, black and red.. 45 1·00
DESIGNS—HORIZ. 40 k. to 1 r. Reaper. 2 r. to 10 r. Citadel, Baku. 25 r., 50 r. Temple of Eternal Fires.

**1921.** Imperf.
11 3 1 r. green .. .. 10 20
12 4 2 r. brown .. .. 10 20
13 – 5 r. brown .. .. 10 20
14 – 10 r. grey .. .. 25 25
15 – 25 r. orange .. .. 10 25
16 – 50 r. violet .. .. 10 50
17 – 100 r. orange .. .. 15 50
18 – 150 r. blue .. .. 15 25
19 – 250 r. violet and buff .. 15 30
20 – 400 r. blue .. .. 15 45
21 – 500 r. black and lilac .. 15 45
22 – 1000 r. red and blue .. 15 35
23 – 2000 r. black and blue .. 15 40
24 – 3000 r. brown and blue 15 40
25 – 5000 r. green on olive .. 15 30
DESIGNS—HORIZ. 5 r., 3000 r. Bibi Eibatt Oilfield. 100 r., 5000 r. Goukasoff House. 400 r., 1000 r. Hall of Judgment, Khan's Palace. VERT. 10 r., 2000 r. Khan's Palace, Baku. 25 r., 250 r. Globe and Workers. 50 r. Maiden's Tower, Baku. 150 r., 500 r. Blacksmiths.

**1921.** Famine Relief. Imperf.
26. 6. 500 r. blue .. .. 25 85
27. – 1000 r. brown .. .. 65 1·00
DESIGN—VERT. 1000 r. Starving family.

For stamps of the above issues surcharged with new values, see Stanley Gibbons Part 10 (Russia) Catalogue.

12 Azerbaijan Map and Flag 15 Maiden's Tower, Baku

**1992.** Independence.
83 12 35 q. multicoloured .. 2·00 2·00

**1992.** Unissued stamp showing Caspian Sea surch **AZARBAYCAN** and new value.
84 25 q. on 15 k. multicoloured 30 30
85 35 q. on 15 k. multicoloured 40 40
86 50 q. on 15 k. multicoloured 60 60
87 1 m. 50 on 15 k. mult .. 1·75 1·75
88 2 m. 50 on 15 k. mult .. 3·00 3·00

**1992.** Dated "1992".
89 15 10 q. green and black .. 10 10
90 20 q. red and black .. 15 15
91 50 q. yellow and black .. 35 35
92 1 m. 50 blue and black .. 1·10 1·10
See also Nos. 101/4.

16 Akhalteka Horse

**1993.** Horses. Multicoloured.
93 20 q. Type 16 .. .. 10 10
94 30 q. Kabarda horse .. 10 10
95 50 q. Qarabair horse .. 15 15
96 1 m. Don horse .. .. 30 30
97 2 m. 50 Yakut horse .. 70 70
98 5 m. Orlov horse .. .. 1·40 1·40
99 10 m. Diliboz horse .. 2·75 2·75

**1993.** Dated "1993".
101 15 50 q. blue and black .. 15 15
102 1 m. mauve and black 30 30
103 2 m. 50 yellow and black 75 75
104 5 m. green and black .. 1·50 1·50

18 "Tulipa eichleri" 20 Map of Nakhichevan

19 Russian Sturgeon

**1993.** Flowers. Multicoloured.
105 25 q. Type 18 .. .. 10 10
106 50 q. "Puschkinia scilloides" .. .. 20 20
107 1 m. "Iris elegantissima" 40 40
108 1 m. 50 "Iris acutiloba" .. 60 60
109 5 m. "Tulipa florenskyii" 1·40 1·40
110 10 m. "Iris reticulata" 2·75 2·75

**1993.** Fishes. Multicoloured.
112 25 q. Type 19 .. .. 10 10
113 50 q. Starred sturgeon .. 20 20
114 1 m. Black sea roach .. 40 40
115 1 m. 50 Roach .. .. 60 60
116 5 m. Caspian salmon .. 1·40 1·40
117 10 m. Black-backed shad 2·75 2·75

**1993.** 70th Birthday of President Heydar Aliev.
119 – 25 m. black and red .. 55 55
120 20 25 m. multicoloured .. 55 55
DESIGN: No. 119, President Aliev.

21 Government Building, Baku 22 Flags, and Dish Aerials on Maps

**1993.**
122 21 25 q. black and yellow 10 10
123 30 q. black and green .. 15 15
124 50 q. black and blue .. 25 25
125 1 m. black and red .. 50 50

**1993.** Azerbaijan–Iran Telecommunications Co-operation.
126 22 15 q. multicoloured .. 1·40 1·40

23 National Colours and Islamic Crescent 24 State Arms

**1994.** National Day.
127 23 5 m. multicoloured .. 1·50 1·50

**1994.**
128 24 8 m. multicoloured .. 2·10 2·10

25 Sirvan Palace 26 Fuzuli

**1994.** Baku Architecture.
129 25 2 m. red, silver & black 55 55
130 – 4 m. green, silver & blk 1·10 1·10
131 – 8 m. blue, silver & black 2·25 2·25
DESIGNS: 4 m. Temple doorway; 8 m. Diwan-Chawa.

**1994.** 500th Birth Anniv (1992) of Mohammed ibn Suleiman Fuzuli (poet).
132 26 10 m. multicoloured .. 2·75 2·75

**1994.** No. 126 surch **IRAN–AZERBAYGAN** and value.
133 22 2 m. on 15 q. mult .. 10 10
134 20 m. on 15 q. mult .. 85 85
135 25 m. on 15 q. mult .. 95 95
136 50 m. on 15 q. mult .. 1·90 1·90

**1994.** Nos. 122/5 surch.
137 21 5 m. on 1 m. black & red 10 10
138 10 m. on 30 q. blk & grn 15 15
139 15 m. on 30 q. blk & grn 20 20
140 20 m. on 50 q. black & bl 25 25
141 25 m. on 1 m. blk & red 30 30
142 40 m. on 50 q. black & bl 50 50
143 50 m. on 25 q. blk & yell 60 60
144 100 m. on 25 q. black and yellow .. .. 1·25 1·25

29 Rasulzade

**1994.** 110th Birth Anniv of Mammed Amin Rasulzade (politician).
145 29 15 m. brown, ochre & blk 2·00 2·00

30 Mamedquluzade 32 Laumontite

31 Flaring Naphtha

**1994.** 125th Birth Anniv of Jalil Mamedquluzade (writer).
146 **30** 20 m. black, gold & blue .. 2·40 2·40

**1994.** 115th Anniv of Nobel Partnership to Exploit Black Sea Oil. Multicoloured.
147 15 m. Type **31** .. .. 35 35
148 20 m. Oil wells .. .. 55 55
149 25 m. "Zoroastr" (first oil tanker in Caspian Sea) 65 65
150 50 m. Nobel brothers and Petr Bilderling (partners) .. .. 1·25 1·25

**1994.** Minerals. Multicoloured.
152 5 m. Type **32** .. .. 35 35
153 10 m. Epidot calcite .. 70 70
154 15 m. Andradite .. .. 1·40 1·40
155 20 m. Amethyst .. .. 3·00 3·00

**33** Players

**1994.** World Cup Football Championship, U.S.A.
157 **33** 5 m. multicoloured .. 15 15
158 – 10 m. multicoloured .. 25 25
159 – 20 m. multicoloured .. 45 45
160 – 25 m. multicoloured .. 55 55
161 – 30 m. multicoloured .. 65 65
162 – 50 m. multicoloured .. 1·10 1·10
163 – 80 m. multicoloured .. 1·90 1·90
DESIGNS: 10 m. to 80 m. Match scenes.

**34** Posthorn

**1994.**
165 **34** 5 m. red and black .. 25 25
166 10 m. green and black .. 55 55
167 20 m. blue and black .. 1·10 1·10
168 25 m. yellow and black 1·40 1·40
169 40 m. brown and black 2·25 2·25

**35** Coelophysis and Segisaurus

**1994.** Prehistoric Animals. Multicoloured.
170 5 m. Type **35** .. 15 15
171 10 m. Pentaceratops and tyrannosaurids .. 25 25
172 20 m. Segnosaurus and oviraptor .. .. 45 45
173 25 m. Albertosaurus and corythosaurus .. .. 55 55
174 30 m. Igaunodons .. 65 65
175 50 m. Stegosaurus and allosaurus .. .. 1·10 1·10
176 80 m. Tyrannosaurus and saurolophus .. .. 1·90 1·90

**36** Nesting Grouse

**1994.** The Georgian Black Grouse Mult.
178 50 m. Type **36** .. 25 25
179 80 m. Grouse on mountain 55 55
180 100 m. Pair of grouse .. 70 70
181 120 m. Grouse in spring meadow .. .. 1·00 1·00

**1994.** No. 84 further surch **400 M.**
182 400 m. on 25 q. on 15 k. mult 95 95

**38** "Kapitan Razhabov" (tug)

**1994.** Ships. Multicoloured.
183 50 m. Type **38** .. .. 1·25 1·25
184 50 m. "Azerbaijan" (ferry) 1·25 1·25
185 50 m. "Merkuri 1" (ferry) 1·25 1·25
186 50 m. "Tovuz" (container ship) .. .. 1·25 1·25
187 50 m. "Ganzha" (tanker) 1·25 1·25
Nos. 183/7 were issued together, se-tenant, the backgrounds of which form a composite design of a map.

**40** White-tailed Sea Eagle

**1994.** Birds of Prey. Multicoloured.
189 10 m. Type **40** .. .. 45 45
190 15 m. Imperial eagle .. 75 75
191 20 m. Tawny eagle .. 85 85
192 25 m. Lammergeier (vert) 1·10 1·10
193 50 m. Saker falcon (vert) 2·25 2·25
Nos. 190/1 are wrongly inscribed "Aguila".

**41** "Felis libica caudata"

**1994.** Wild Cats. Multicolured.
195 10 m. Type **41** .. .. 55 55
196 15 m. Manul cat .. .. 65 65
197 20 m. Lynx .. .. 75 75
198 25 m. Leopard (horiz) .. 95 95
199 50 m. Tiger (horiz) .. 2·10 2·10

**42** Ancient Greek and Modern Javelin Throwers

**1994.** Centenary of International Olympic Committee. Multicoloured.
201 100 m. Type **42** .. .. 85 85
202 100 m. Ancient Greek and modern discus throwers 85 85
203 100 m. Baron Pierre de Coubertin (founder of modern games) and flame .. .. .. 85 85

**1995.** Nos. 89/92 and 101/4 surch.
204 **15** 250 m. on 10 q. green and black .. .. 1·25 1·25
205 250 m. on 20 q. red and black .. .. 1·25 1·25
206 250 m. on 50 q. yellow and black .. 1·25 1·25
207 250 m. on 1 m. 50 blue and black .. .. 1·25 1·25
208 500 m. on 50 q. blue and black .. .. 2·50 2·50
209 500 m. on 1 m. mauve and black .. 2·50 2·50
210 500 m. on 2 m. 50 yellow and black .. 2·50 2·50
211 500 m. on 5 m. green and black .. .. 2·50 2·50

**44** Apollo

**1995.** Butterflies. Multicoloured.
212 10 m. Type **44** .. .. 55 55
213 25 m. "Zegris menestho" 65 65
214 50 m. "Manduca atropos" 1·25 1·25
215 60 m. "Pararge adrastoides" .. .. 1·40 1·40

**45** Aleksei Urmanov (Russia) (gold, men's figure skating)

**48** "Polyorchis karafutoensis"

**1995.** Winter Olympic Games, Lillehammer, Norway. Medal Winners. Multicoloured.
217 10 m. Type **45** .. .. 30 30
218 25 m. Nancy Kerrigan (U.S.A.) (silver, women's figure skating) .. .. 65 65
219 40 m. Bonnie Blair (U.S.A.) (gold, women's 500 m. speed skating) (horiz) .. .. .. 1·10 1·10
220 50 m. Takanori Kano (Japan) (gold, men's ski jumping) (horiz) .. 1·25 1·25
221 80 m. Philip Laros (Canada) (silver, men's freestyle skiing) .. 2·10 2·10
222 100 m. German team (gold, three-man bobsleigh) .. 2·40 2·40

**1995.** Nos. 165/7 surch.
225 **34** 100 m. on 5 m. red & blk 25 25
226 250 m. on 10 m. green and black .. .. 1·25 1·25
227 500 m. on 20 m. bl & blk 2·50 2·50

**1995.** Marine Animals. Multicoloured.
228 50 m. "Loligo vulgaris" (horiz) .. .. 35 35
229 100 m. "Orchistoma pileus" (horiz) .. .. 70 70
230 150 m. "Pegea confoederata" (horiz) .. 1·10 1·10
231 250 m. Type **48** .. .. 1·75 1·75
232 300 m. "Agalma okeni" .. 2·25 2·25

**49** Matamata Turtle

**1995.** Tortoises and Turtles. Multicoloured.
234 50 m. Type **49** .. .. 35 35
235 100 m. Loggerhead turtle 70 70
236 150 m. Leopard tortoise .. 1·10 1·10
237 250 m. Indian star tortoise 1·75 1·75
238 300 m. Hermann's tortoise 2·25 2·25

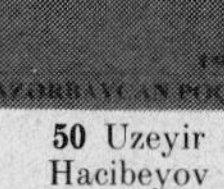

**50** Uzeyir Hacibeyov (composer, 110th)

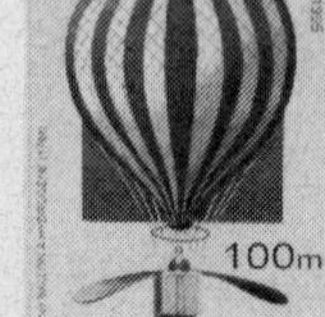

**53** Charles's Hydrogen Balloon, 1783

**1995.** Birth Anniversaries.
240 **50** 250 m. silver and black 70 70
241 – 400 m. gold and black .. 1·25 1·25
DESIGN: 400 m. Vakhid (poet, centenary).

**1995.** Nos. 84/88 surch.
242 200 m. on 2 m. 50 on 15 k. multicoloured .. .. 40 40
243 400 m. on 25 q. on 15 k. multicoloured .. .. 80 80
244 600 m. on 35 q. on 15 k. multicoloured .. .. 1·25 1·25
245 800 m. on 50 q. on 15 k. multicoloured .. .. 1·60 1·60
246 1000 m. on 1 m. 50 on 15 k. multicoloured .. .. 2·00 2·00

**1995.** Nos. 168/9 surch.
247 **34** 400 m. on 25 m. yellow and black .. .. 85 85
248 900 m. on 40 m. brown and black .. .. 1·75 1·75

**1995.** History of Airships. Multicoloured.
249 100 m. Type **53** .. .. 45 45
250 150 m. Tissandier Brothers' electrically-powered airship, 1883 .. .. 65 65
251 250 m. J.-B. Meusnier's elliptical balloon design, 1784 (horiz) .. .. 1·10 1·10
252 300 m. Baldwin's dirigible airship, 1904 (horiz) .. 1·25 1·25
253 400 m. U.S. Navy dirigible airship, 1917 (horiz) .. 1·75 1·75
254 500 m. Pedal-powered airship, 1909 (horiz) .. 2·25 2·25
No. 249 is wrongly dated.

**54** "Gymnopilus spectabilis"

**1995.** Fungi. Multicoloured.
256 100 m. Type **54** .. .. 45 45
257 250 m. Fly agaric .. 1·10 1·10
258 300 m. Parasol mushroom 1·25 1·25
259 400 m. "Hygrophorus spectosus" .. .. 1·75 1·75
The 250 m. is wrongly inscribed "agaris".

**55** "Paphiopedilum argus" and "Paphiopedilum barbatum"

**1995.** "Singapore'95" International Stamp Exhibition. Orchids. Multicoloured.
261 100 m. Type **55** .. .. 45 45
262 250 m. "Maxillaria picta" 1·10 1·10
263 300 m. "Laeliocattleya" .. 1·25 1·25
264 400 m. "Dendrobium nobile" .. .. .. 1·75 1·75

**56** Pres. Aliev and U.N. Secretary-General Boutros Boutros Ghali

**1995.** 50th Anniv of U.N.O.
266 **56** 250 m. multicoloured .. 3·00 3·00

**57** Players

**58** Eagle

**1995.** World Cup Football Championship, France (1998). Multicoloured.

267 100 m. Type **57** .. .. 30 30
268 150 m. Dribbling .. .. 45 45
269 250 m. Tackling .. .. 75 75
270 300 m. Preparing to kick ball .. .. .. 90 90
271 400 m. Contesting for ball 1·25 1·25

**1995.** Air.

273 **58** 2200 m. multicoloured .. 5·50 5·50

**59** Persian **60** Horse

**1995.** Cats. Multicoloured.

274 100 m. Type **59** .. .. 20 20
275 150 m. Chartreux .. 30 30
276 250 m. Somali .. .. 50 50
277 300 m. Longhair Scottish fold .. .. .. 60 60
278 400 m. Cymric .. .. 80 80
279 500 m. Turkish angora .. 1·00 1·00

**1995.** Flora and Fauna. Multicoloured.

281 100 m. Type **60** .. .. 15 15
282 200 m. Grape hyacinths (vert) .. .. .. 30 30
283 250 m. Beluga .. .. 45 45
284 300 m. Golden eagle .. 50 50
285 400 m. Tiger .. .. 65 65
286 500 m. Georgian black grouse nesting .. .. 85 85
287 1000 m. Georgian black grouse in meadow .. 1·75 1·75

**61** Lennon and Signature

**1995.** 15th Death Anniv of John Lennon (entertainer).

288 **61** 500 m. multicoloured .. 1·75 1·75

**62** American Steam Locomotive

**1996.** Railway Locomotives. Multicoloured.

289 100 m. Type **62** .. .. 45 45
290 100 m. Hudson steam locomotive .. .. 45 45
291 100 m. A-2-8-2 steam locomotive .. .. 45 45
292 100 m. German 23-2-6-2 steam locomotive .. 45 45
293 100 m. German 2-82 steam locomotive .. .. 45 45
294 100 m. Italian 2-0-2 steam locomotive .. .. 45 45
295 100 m. Japanese G-C5 steam locomotive .. 45 45
296 100 m. QJ steam locomotive No. 2710 .. 45 45
297 100 m. 0-10-0 steam locomotive .. .. 45 45

**63** Operating Theatre and Topcubasov

**1996.** Birth Centenary of M. Topcubasov (surgeon).

299 **63** 300 m. multicoloured .. 3·00 3·00

**64** Feast and Woman wearing Traditional Costume

**1996.** New Year.

300 **64** 250 m. multicoloured .. 2·00 2·00

**65** Carl Lewis (athletics, Los Angeles, 1984)

**1996.** Olympic Games, Atlanta. Previous Gold Medallists. Multicoloured.

301 50 m. Type **65** (wrongly inscr "1994") .. .. 25 25
302 100 m. Mohammed Ali (Cassius Clay) (boxing, Rome, 1960) .. .. 50 50
303 150 m. Li Ning (gymnastics, Los Angeles, 1984) .. .. 75 75
304 200 m. Said Aouita (5000 m., Los Angeles, 1984) .. 1·00 1·00
305 250 m. Olga Korbut (gymnastics, Munich, 1972) .. .. .. 1·25 1·25
306 300 m. Nadia Comeneci (gymnastics, Montreal, 1976) .. .. .. 1·50 1·50
307 400 m. Greg Louganis (diving, Los Angeles, 1984) .. .. .. 2·00 2·00

**66** "Maral-Gol"

**1996.** 5th Death Anniv of G. Aliev (painter). Multicoloured.

309 100 m. "Reka Cura" .. 1·40 1·40
310 200 m. Type **66** .. .. 2·75 2·75

**67** Behbudov and Globe

**1996.** 7th Death Anniv of Resid Behbudov.

311 **67** 100 m. multicoloured .. 1·10 1·10

**68** Mammadaliev and Flasks **69** National Flag and Government Building

**1996.** 1st Death Anniv of Yusif Mammadaliev (scientist).

312 **68** 100 m. multicoloured .. 1·10 1·10

**1996.** 5th Anniv of Republic.

313 **69** 250 m. multicoloured .. 2·00 2·00

**70** Dome of the Rock

**1996.** 3000th Anniv of Jerusalem. Mult.

314 100 m. Praying at the Wailing Wall .. .. 40 40
315 250 m. Interior of church 1·00 1·00
316 300 m. Type **70** .. .. 1·25 1·25

**71** German Shepherd

**1996.** Dogs. Multicoloured.

318 50 m. Type **71** .. .. 20 20
319 100 m. Basset hounds .. 40 40
320 150 m. Collies .. .. 60 60
321 200 m. Bull terriers .. 80 80
322 300 m. Boxers .. .. 1·25 1·25
323 400 m. Cocker spaniels .. 1·50 1·50

**72** "Tetraenura regia" **73** "Burgundy"

**1996.** Birds. Multicoloured.

325 50 m. Type **72** .. .. 20 20
326 100 m. Blue-naped mousebird .. .. 40 40
327 150 m. Asian black-headed oriole .. .. .. 60 60
328 200 m. Golden oriole .. 80 80
329 300 m. Common starling .. 1·25 1·25
330 400 m. Yellow-fronted canary .. .. .. 1·50 1·50

**1996.** Roses. Multicoloured.

332 50 m. Type **73** .. .. 20 20
333 100 m. "Virgo" .. .. 40 40
334 150 m. "Rose Gaujard" .. 60 60
335 200 m. "Luna" .. .. 80 80
336 300 m. "Lady Rose" .. 1·25 1·25
337 400 m. "Landora" .. 1·50 1·50

**74** Child **75** Spain v. Bulgaria

**1996.** 50th Anniv of U.N.I.C.E.F.

339 **74** 500 m. multicoloured .. 1·10 1·10

**1996.** European Football Championship, England. Multicoloured.

340 100 m. Type **75** .. .. 15 15
341 150 m. Rumania v. France 25 25
342 200 m. Czech Republic v. Germany .. .. 35 35
343 250 m. England v. Switzerland .. .. 45 45
344 300 m. Croatia v. Turkey 55 55
345 400 m. Italy v. Russia .. 75 75

**76** Chinese Junk

**1996.** Ships. Multicoloured.

347 100 m. Type **76** .. .. 25 25
348 150 m. "Danmark" (Danish full-rigged cadet ship) .. .. .. 35 35
349 200 m. "Nippon-Maru II" (Japanese cadet ship) .. 50 50
350 250 m. "Mircea" (Rumanian cadet ship) 55 55
351 300 m. "Kruzenshtern" (Russian cadet barque) 80 80
352 400 m. "Ariadne" (German cadet schooner) .. 1·10 1·10

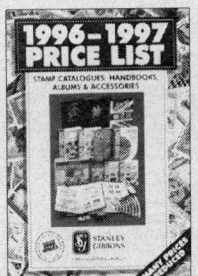

## AZORES Pt. 9

A group of islands in the Atlantic Ocean.

1868. 1000 reis = 1 milreis.
1912. 100 centavos = 1 escudo.

**NOTE.** Except where otherwise stated, Nos. 1/393 are all stamps of Portugal overprinted **ACORES**.

**1868.** Curved value labels. Imperf.

1 14 5 r. black .. .. £2250 £1500
2 10 r. yellow .. .. £1000 £7500
3 20 r. bistre .. .. £150 £130
4 50 r. green .. .. £150 £130
5 80 r. orange .. .. £170 £140
6 100 r. purple .. .. £170 £140

**1868.** Curved value labels. Perf.

7 14 5 r. black .. .. 55·00 55·00
9 10 r. yellow .. .. 70·00 55·00
10 20 r. bistre .. .. 55·00 50·00
11 25 r. pink .. .. 55·00 8·50
12 50 r. green .. .. £160 £150
13 80 r. orange .. .. £160 £150
14 100 r. lilac .. .. £160 £150
16 120 r. blue .. .. £130 95·00
17 240 r. lilac .. .. £475 £300

**1871.** Straight value labels.

38 15 5 r. black .. .. 10·00 6·75
39 10 r. yellow .. .. 22·00 13·00
73 10 r. green .. .. 60·00 50·00
29 15 r. brown .. .. 20·00 14·50
31 20 r. bistre .. .. 22·00 20·00
109 20 r. red .. .. £100 85·00
32 25 r. pink .. .. 12·50 3·25
33 50 r. green .. .. 65·00 32·00
54 50 r. blue .. .. £110 65·00
101b 80 r. orange .. .. 55·00 45·00
103 100 r. mauve .. .. 45·00 40·00
25 120 r. blue .. .. £120 £100
49 150 r. blue .. .. £130 £120
104 150 r. yellow .. .. 45·00 40·00
26 240 r. lilac .. .. £650 £550
50 300 r. lilac .. .. 65·00 45·00
94 1000 r. black .. .. 90·00 85·00

**1880.**

58 16 5 r. black .. .. 18·00 8·00
61 25 r. grey .. .. 40·00 6·50
61b 25 r. brown .. .. 40·00 6·50
60 17 25 r. grey .. .. £100 32·00
67 16 50 r. blue .. .. £120 29·00

**1882.**

136 19 5 r. grey .. .. .. 10·50 4·00
125 10 r. green .. .. 21·00 9·75
139 20 r. red .. .. .. 22·00 13·00
126 25 r. brown .. .. 14·50 3·00
141 25 r. mauve .. .. 22·00 2·10
142 50 r. blue .. .. 18·00 3·25
128 500 r. black .. .. £120 £110
129 500 r. mauve .. .. £100 70·00

**1894.** Prince Henry the Navigator.

143. **32.** 5 r. orange .. .. 2·25 2·25
144. 10 r. red .. .. 2·25 2·25
145. 15 r. brown .. .. 2·75 2·75
146. 20 r. lilac .. .. 3·00 3·00
147. 25 r. green .. .. 3·25 3·25
148. 50. r. blue .. .. 8·50 4·50
149. 75 r. red .. .. 15·00 6·50
150. 80 r. green .. .. 18·00 6·50
151. 100 r. brown on buff .. 18·00 5·50
152. 150 r. red .. .. 26·00 12·50
153. 300 r. blue on buff .. 28·00 20·00
154. 500 r. purple .. .. 50·00 30·00
155. 1000 r. black on buff .. £100 48·00

**1895.** St. Anthony of Padua.

156. **35.** $2\frac{1}{2}$ r. black .. .. 2·10 1·00
157. - 5 r. orange .. .. 6·50 2·00
158. - 10 r. mauve .. .. 6·50 3·00
159. - 15 r. brown .. .. 10·00 4·50
160. - 20 r. grey .. .. 10·00 6·50
161. - 25 r. purple and green .. 7·00 2·10
162. **37.** 50 r. brown and blue .. 22·00 10·00
163. 75 r. brown and red .. 32·00 28·00
164. 80 r. brown and green .. 35·00 32·00
165. 100 r. black and brown 35·00 28·00
166. - 150 r. red and brown .. 65·00 70·00
167. - 200 r. blue and brown .. 80·00 70·00
168. - 300 r. black and brown £100 75·00
169. - 500 r. brown & green £140 £100
170. - 1000 r. lilac and green .. £200 £150

**1898.** Vasco da Gama stamps as Nos. 378/385 of Portugal but inscr. "**ACORES**".

171. $2\frac{1}{2}$ r. green .. .. 2·25 95
172. 5 r. red .. .. 2·25 1·10
173. 10 r. purple .. .. 4·50 2·10
174. 25 r. green .. .. 4·50 2·10
175. 50 r. blue .. .. 6·75 6·50
176. 75 r. brown .. .. 14·00 10·00
177. 100 r. brown .. .. 18·00 10·00
178. 150 r. bistre .. .. 27·00 20·00

**1906.** "King Carlos" key-type inscr. "ACORES" and optd. with letters "A". "H" and "PD" in three of the corners.

179. **S.** $2\frac{1}{2}$ r. grey .. .. 30 30
180. 5 r. orange .. .. 30 30
181. 10 r. green .. .. 30 30
182. 20 r. lilac .. .. 45 40
183. 25 r. red .. .. 45 30
184. 50 r. blue .. .. 3·75 3·50
185. 75 r. brown on yellow 1·25 90
186. 100 r. blue on blue .. 1·25 1·00
187. 200 r. purple on pink 1·25 1·00
188. 300 r. blue on pink .. 4·25 3·50
189. 500 r. black on blue .. 10·50 9·00

7. King Manoel.

**1910.**

190. **7.** $2\frac{1}{2}$ r. lilac .. .. 35 30
191. 5 r. black .. .. 40 35
192. 10 r. green .. .. 40 35
193. 15 r. brown .. .. 60 50
194. 20 r. red .. .. .. 85 70
195. 25 r. brown .. .. 40 35
196. 50 r. blue .. .. 2·00 1·00
197. 75 r. brown .. .. 2·00 1·00
198. 80 r. grey .. .. 2·00 2·00
199. 100 r. brown on green .. 3·25 2·50
200. 200 r. green on pink .. 3·25 2·50
201. 300 r. black on blue .. 2·00 2·00
202. 500 r. brown and olive 6·00 5·25
203. 1000 r. black and blue .. 14·00 12·00

**1910.** Optd **REPUBLICA**.

204 7 $2\frac{1}{2}$ r. lilac .. .. 30 25
205 5 r. black .. .. 25 25
206 10 r. green .. .. 30 25
207 15 r. brown .. .. 1·25 1·00
208b 20 r. red .. .. 75 75
209 25 r. brown .. .. 25 25
210a 50 r. blue .. .. 1·00 75
211 75 r. brown .. .. 1·00 65
212 80 r. grey .. .. 1·00 65
213 100 r. brown on green .. 80 60
214 200 r. green on orange .. 80 60
215 300 r. black on blue .. 2·40 1·60
216 500 r. brown and green .. 2·75 2·25
217 1000 r. black and blue .. 5·75 3·75

**1911.** Vasco da Gama stamps of Azores optd **REPUBLICA**, some surch also.

218 $2\frac{1}{2}$ r. green .. .. 50 40
219 15 r. on 5 r. red .. .. 50 40
220 25 r. green .. .. 50 40
221 50 r. blue .. .. 1·50 1·00
222 75 r. brown .. .. 1·25 1·10
223 80 r. on 150 r. brown .. 1·25 1·25
224 100 r. brown .. .. 1·40 1·25
225 1000 r. on 10 r. purple .. 13·00 9·50

**1911.** Postage Due stamps optd or surch **REPUBLICA ACORES**.

226 D 48 5 r. black .. .. 95 85
227 10 r. mauve .. .. 2·00 85
228 20 r. orange .. .. 3·25 2·50
229 200 r. brown on buff 14·50 12·50
230 300 r. on 50 r. grey .. 14·50 12·50
231 500 r. on 100 r. red on pink .. 14·50 12·50

**1912.** "Ceres" type.

250 56 $\frac{1}{4}$ c. brown .. .. 35 30
273 $\frac{1}{2}$ c. black .. .. 40 20
252 1 c. green .. .. 80 60
274 1 c. brown .. .. 35 35
254 $1\frac{1}{2}$ c. brown .. .. 80 60
255 $1\frac{1}{2}$ c. green .. .. 40 40
256 2 c. red .. .. 60 45
257 2 c. orange .. .. 40 40
258 $2\frac{1}{2}$ c. lilac .. .. 60 45
259 3 c. red .. .. 40 40
278 3 c. blue .. .. 30 30
260 $3\frac{1}{2}$ c. green .. .. 40 40
261 4 c. green .. .. 40 40
401 4 c. orange .. .. 40 40
262 5 c. blue .. .. 60 45
280 5 c. brown .. .. 40 35
264 6 c. purple .. .. 40 40
282 6 c. brown .. .. 40 35
403 6 c. red .. .. 25 25
265 $7\frac{1}{2}$ c. brown .. .. 4·50 2·50
266 $7\frac{1}{2}$ c. blue .. .. 1·25 1·10
267 8 c. grey .. .. 60 45
283 8 c. green .. .. 55 40
284 8 c. orange .. .. 70 65
268 10 c. brown .. .. 4·50 2·00
285 10 c. red .. .. 80 40
286 12 c. blue .. .. 1·75 1·25
287 12 c. green .. .. 65 55
288 $13\frac{1}{2}$ c. blue .. .. 1·75 1·25
249 14 c. blue on yellow .. 1·60 1·25
269 15 c. purple .. .. 80 45
289 15 c. black .. .. 40 35
290 16 c. blue .. .. 65 60
243 20 c. brown on green .. 8·00 4·25
291 20 c. brown .. .. 65 55
292 20 c. green .. .. 80 65
293 20 c. drab .. .. 55 40
294 24 c. blue .. .. 60 35
295 56 25 c. pink .. .. 45 40
244 30 c. brown on pink .. 45·00 35·00
245 30 c. brown on yellow .. 1·60 1·25
296 30 c. brown .. .. 1·25 1·10
406 32 c. green .. .. 1·75 1·25
298 36 c. red .. .. 65 40
299 40 c. blue .. .. 65 45
300 40 c. brown .. .. 1·25 60
407 40 c. green .. .. 1·00 50
408 48 c. pink .. .. 2·50 2·00
246 50 c. orange on orange 4·00 2·00
247 50 c. orange on yellow 4·00 2·00
302 50 c. yellow .. .. 1·25 1·00
410 50 c. red .. .. 3·00 2·50
303 60 c. blue .. .. 1·25 1·00
304 64 c. blue .. .. 3·25 2·25
411 64 c. red .. .. 3·00 2·50
305 75 c. pink .. .. 3·25 2·50
412 75 c. red .. .. 2·25 2·00
306 80 c. purple .. .. 1·75 1·40
307 80 c. lilac .. .. 1·75 1·25
413 80 c. green .. .. 2·25 2·00
308 90 c. blue .. .. 1·75 1·40
309 96 c. red .. .. 4·75 2·25
248 1 e. green on blue .. 4·50 3·75
310 1 e. lilac .. .. 1·75 1·40
314 1 e. purple .. .. 2·40 2·10
414 1 e. red .. .. 28·00 20·00
311 1 e. 10 brown .. .. 1·90 1·40
312 1 e. 20 green .. .. 2·10 1·40
315 1 e. 20 buff .. .. 5·25 3·75
415 1 e. 25 blue .. .. 1·40 1·25
316 1 e. 50 purple .. .. 5·25 4·50
317 1 e. 50 lilac .. .. 5·25 4·50
400 1 e. 60 blue .. .. 2·50 1·10
313 2 e. green .. .. 5·75 3·25
319 2 e. 40 green .. .. 48·00 32·00
320 3 e. pink .. .. 55·00 32·00
321 3 e. 20 green .. .. 6·50 6·75
322 5 e. green .. .. 12·00 6·75
323 10 e. pink .. .. 32·00 19·00
324 20 e. blue .. .. 75·00 50·00

**1925.** C. C. Branco Centenary.

325. **65.** 2 c. orange .. .. 20 20
326. 3 c. green .. .. 20 20
327. 4 c. blue .. .. 20 20
328. 5 c. red .. .. 20 20
329. - 10 c. blue .. .. 20 20
330. - 16 c. orange .. .. 25 25
331. **67.** 25 c. red .. .. 25 25
332. - 32 c. green .. .. 40 40
333. **67.** 40 c. black and green 40 40
334. 48 c. purple .. .. 85 85
335. - 50 c. green .. .. 85 70
336. - 64 c. brown .. .. 85 70
337. - 75 c. grey .. .. 85 70
338. **67.** 80 c. brown .. .. 85 70
339. - 96 c. red .. .. 1·00 85
340. - 1 e. 50 blue on blue .. 1·00 85
341. **67.** 1 e. 60 blue .. .. 1·10 1·00
342. - 2 e. green on green .. 1·60 1·50
343. - 2 e. 40 red on orange .. 2·25 1·60
344. - 3 e. 20 black on green 3·00 3·00

**1926.** First Independence Issue.

345. **76.** 2 c. black and orange .. 30 30
346. - 3 c. black and blue .. 30 30
347. **76.** 4 c. black and green .. 30 30
348. - 5 c. black and brown .. 30 30
349. **76.** 6 c. black and orange .. 30 30
350. - 15 c. black and green .. 55 55
351. **77.** 20 c. black and violet .. 55 55
352. - 25 c. black and red .. 55 55
353. **77.** 32 c. black and green .. 55 55
354. - 40 c. black and brown .. 55 55
355. - 50 c. black and olive .. 1·10 1·10
356. - 75 c. black and red .. 1·10 1·10
357. - 1 e. black and violet .. 1·40 1·40
358. - 4 e. 50 black and green 4·75 4·75

**1927.** Second Independence Issue.

359. **80.** 2 c. black and brown .. 25 25
360. - 3 c. black and blue .. 25 25
361. **80.** 4 c. black and orange .. 25 25
362. - 5 c. black and brown .. 25 25
363. - 6 c. black and brown .. 25 25
364. - 15 c. black and brown 25 25
365. **80.** 25 c. black and grey .. 90 90
366. - 32 c. black and green .. 90 90
367. - 40 c. black and green .. 55 55
368. - 96 c. black and red .. 2·25 2·25
369. - 1 e. 60 black and blue .. 2·25 2·25
370. - 4 e. 50 black and yellow 5·00 5·00

**1928.** Third Independence Issue.

371. - 2 c. black and blue .. 25 25
372 **84.** 3 c. black and green .. 25 25
373. - 4 c. black and red .. 25 25
374. - 5 c. black and olive .. 25 25
375. - 6 c. black and brown .. 25 25
376. **84.** 15 c. black and grey .. 45 45
377. - 16 c. black and purple .. 55 55
378. - 25 c. black and blue .. 55 55
379. - 32 c. black and green .. 55 55
380. - 40 c. black and brown .. 55 55
381. - 50 c. black and red .. 1·10 1·10
382. **84.** 80 c. black and grey .. 1·10 1·10
383. - 96 c. black and red .. 2·10 2·10
384. - 1 e. black and mauve .. 2·10 2·10
385. - 1 e. 60 black and blue .. 2·10 2·10
386. - 4 e. 50 black and yellow 5·00 5·00

**1929** "Ceres" type surch. **ACORES** and new value.

387 56 4 c. on 25 c. pink .. 55 55
388 4 c. on 60 c. blue .. 1·00 1·00
389 10 c. on 25 c. pink .. 90 90
390 12 c. on 25 c. pink .. 90 90
391 15 c. on 25 c. pink .. 90 90
392 20 c. on 25 c. pink .. 1·60 1·60
393 40 c. on 1 e. 10 brown 3·00 3·00

14. 10 r. Stamp of 1868.

**1980.** 112th Anniv. of First Azores Stamps.

416. **14.** 6 e. 50 blk., yell. & red 20 10
417. - 19 e. 50 blk., pur. & blue 75 50

DESIGN: 19 e. 50, 100 r. stamp of 1868.

15. Map of the Azores.

**1980.** World Tourism Conference Manila, Philippines. Multicoloured.

419 50 c. Type **15** .. .. 10 10
420 1 e. Church .. .. 10 10
421 5 e. Windmill .. .. 40 10
422 6 e. 50 Traditional costume 40 10
423 8 e. Coastal scene .. 60 25
424 30 e. Coastal village .. 1·60 50

16. St. Peter's Cavalcade, Sao Miguel Island.

**1981.** Europa. Folklore.

425. **16.** 22 e. multicoloured .. 1·10 60

17. Bulls attacking Spanish Soldiers.

**1981.** 400th Anniv. of Battle of Salga. Mult.

427. 8 e. 50 Type **17** .. .. 35 10
428. 33 e. 50 Friar Don Pedro leading attack .. 1·60 70

18. "Myosotis azorica".

**1981.** Regional Flowers. Multicoloured.

429. 4 e. Type **18** .. .. 10 10
430. 7 e. "Tolpis azorica" .. 25 10
431. 8 e. 50 "Ranunculus azoricus" .. .. 25 10
432. 10 e. "Lactuca watsoniana" .. .. 45 10
433. 12 e. 50 "Hypericum foliosum" .. .. 15 10
434. 20 e. "Platanthera micranta" .. .. 50 35
435. 27 e. "Vicia dennesiana" .. 1·00 55
436. 30 e. "Rubus hochstetterorum" .. 60 25
437. 33 e. 50 "Azorina vidalii" 1·10 70
438. 37 e. 50 "Vaccinium cylindraceum" .. 85 50
439. 50 e. "Laurus azorica" .. 1·40 65
440. 100 e. "Juniperus brevifolia" .. .. 2·00 75

19. Embarkation of the Heroes of Mindelo.

20. Chapel of the Holy Ghost.

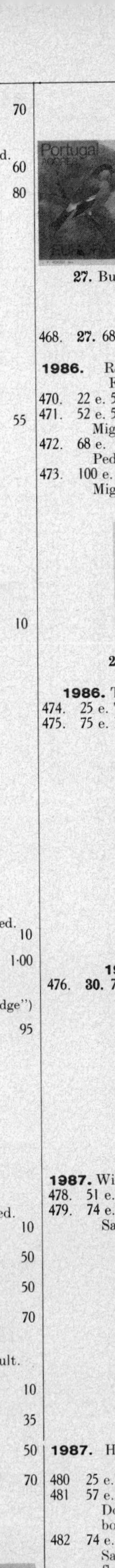

**1982.** Europa. Multicoloured.
445. **19.** 33 e. 50 multicoloured .. 1·75 70

**1982.** Regional Architecture. Multicoloured.
447. 27 e Type **20** .. .. .. 1·10 60
448. 33 e. 50 Chapel of the Holy Ghost (different) .. .. 1·40 80

**21.** Geothermal Power Station, Pico Vermeilho, Sao Miguel.

**1983.** Europa.
449. **21.** 37 e. 50 multicoloured .. 1·25 55

**22.** Flag of Azores.

**1983.** Flag.
451. **22.** 12 e. 50 multicoloured .. 60 10

**23.** Two "Holy Ghost" Jesters, Sao Miguel.

**1984.** Traditional Costumes. Multicoloured.
452. 16 e. Type **23** .. .. .. 45 10
453. 51 e. Two women wearing Terceira cloak .. .. 2·00 1·00

**1984.** Europa. As T **398** of Portugal ("Bridge") but additionally inscr "ACORES".
454. 51 e. multicoloured .. .. 1·60 95

**24.** "Megabombus ruderatus".

**1984.** Insects (1st series). Multiocloured.
456 16 e. Type **24** .. .. .. 25 10
457 35 e. Large white (butterfly) .. .. 90 50
458 40 e. "Chrysomela banksi" (leaf beetle) .. .. 1·10 50
459 51 e. "Phlogophora interrupta" (moth) .. 1·40 70

**1985.** Insects (2nd series). As T **24**. Mult.
460 20 e. "Polyspilla polyspilla" (leaf beetle) .. 30 10
461 40 e. "Sphaerophoria nigra" (hover fly) .. 85 35
462 46 e. Clouded yellow (butterfly) .. .. 1·10 50
463 60 e. Southern grayling (butterfly .. .. 1·25 70

**25.** Drummer. **26.** Jeque.

**1985.** Europa. Music Year.
464. **25.** 60 e. multicoloured .. 1·75 75

**1985.** Traditional Boats. Multicoloured.
466 40 e. Type **26** .. .. 1·00 70
467 60 e. Bote .. .. 1·60 70

**27.** Bullfinch. **28.** Alto das Covas Fountain, Terceira.

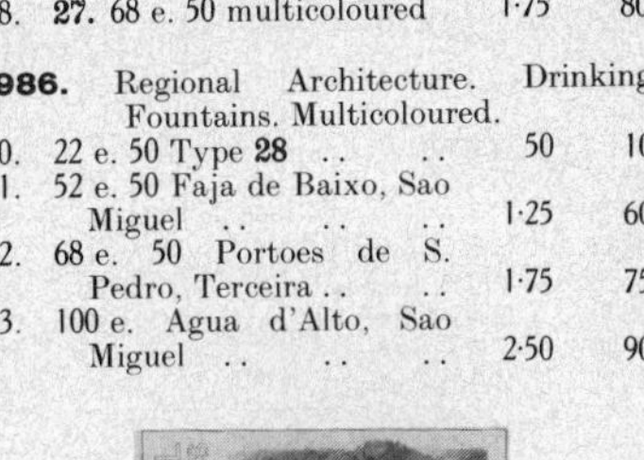

**1986.** Europa.
468. **27.** 68 e. 50 multicoloured 1·75 80

**1986.** Regional Architecture. Drinking Fountains. Multicoloured.
470. 22 e. 50 Type **28** .. .. 50 10
471. 52 e. 50 Faja de Baixo, Sao Miguel .. .. .. 1·25 60
472. 68 e. 50 Portoes de S. Pedro, Terceira .. .. 1·75 75
473. 100 e. Agua d'Alto, Sao Miguel .. .. .. 2·50 90

**29.** Ox Cart, Santa Maria.

**1986.** Traditional Carts. Multicoloured.
474. 25 e. Type **29** .. .. 55 10
475. 75 e. Ram cart, Sao Miguel 1·75 1·00

**30.** Regional Assembly Building (Correia Fernandes and Luis Miranda).

**1987.** Europa. Architecture.
476. **30.** 74 e. 50 multicoloured 1·60 85

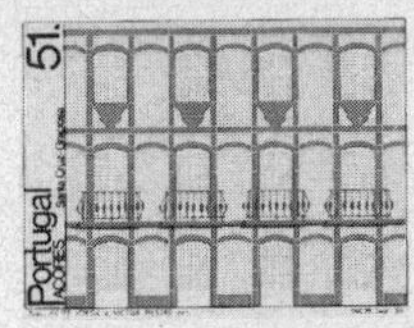

**31.** Santa Cruz, Graciosa.

**1987.** Windows and Balconies. Multicoloured.
478. 51 e. Type **31** .. .. 1·10 60
479. 74 e. 50 Ribeira Grande, Sao Miguel .. .. 1·50 65

**32.** A. C. Read's Curtiss NC-4 Flying Boat, 1919.

**1987.** Historic Airplane Landings in the Azores. Multicoloured.
480 25 e. Type **32** .. .. 45 10
481 57 e. E. F. Christiansen's Dornier Do-X flying boat, 1932 .. .. 1·25 85
482 74 e. 50 Italo Balbo's Savoia Marchetti S-55X flying boat, 1933 .. 1·40 70
483 125 e. Charles Lindbergh's Lockheed 8 Sirius seaplane "Tingmissartoq", 1933 .. .. .. 2·50 1·10

**33.** 19th-century Mule-drawn Omnibus.

**1988.** Europa. Transport and Communications.
484. **33.** 80 e. multicoloured .. 1·60 65

**34.** Wood Pigeon.

**1988.** Nature Protection. Birds (1st series). Multicoloured.
486 27 e. Type **34** .. .. 50 15
487 60 e. Woodcock .. .. 1·10 60
488 80 e. Roseate tern .. 1·25 70
489 100 e. Common buzzard .. 1·75 75
See also Nos. 492/5 and 500/3.

**35.** Azores Arms.

**1988.** Coats of Arms. Multicoloured.
490. 55 e. Type **35** .. .. 1·10 60
491. 80 e. Bettencourt family arms .. .. .. 1·40 70

**1989.** Nature Protection (2nd series). Goldcrest. As T **34**. Multicoloured.
492 30 e. Goldcrest perched on branch .. .. .. 55 20
493 30 e. Pair .. .. .. 55 20
494 30 e. Goldcrest on nest .. 55 20
495 30 e. Goldcrest with outspread wings .. 55 20

**36** Boy in Boat

**1989.** Europa. Children's Games and Toys.
496 **36** 80 e. multicoloured .. 1·40 70

**37** Pioneers

**1989.** 550th Anniv of Portuguese Settlement in Azores. Multicoloured.
498 29 e. Type **37** .. .. 50 10
499 87 e. Settler breaking land 1·50 85

**1990.** Nature Protection (3rd series). Bullfinch. As T **34**. Multicoloured.
500 32 e. Two bullfinches .. 75 20
501 32 e. Bullfinch on branch 75 20
502 32 e. Bullfinch landing on twig .. .. .. 75 20
503 32 e. Bullfinch on nest .. 75 20

**38** Vasco da Gama Post Office

**1990.** Europa. Post Office Buildings.
504 **38** 80 e. multicoloured .. 1·10 60

**39** Cart Maker

**1990.** Traditional Occupations. Multicoloured.
506 5 e. Type **39** .. .. 10 10
507 10 e. Viol maker .. .. 10 10
508 32 e. Potter .. .. 40 15
509 35 e. Making roof tiles .. 35 10
510 38 e. Carpenter .. .. 35 15
511 60 e. Tinsmith .. .. 95 45
512 65 e. Laying pavement mosaics .. .. 85 45
513 70 e. Quarrying .. .. 95 50
514 85 e. Basket maker .. 85 40
515 100 e. Cooper .. .. 1·50 80
516 110 e. Shaping stones .. 1·25 55
517 120 e. Boat builders .. 1·10 65

**40** "Hermes" Spaceplane

**1991.** Europa. Europe in Space.
520 **40** 80 e. multicoloured .. 1·00 60

**41** "Helena" (schooner)

**1991.** Inter-Island Transport. Multicoloured.
522 35 e. Type **41** .. .. 35 15
523 60 e. Beech Model 18 airplane, 1947 .. .. 65 35
524 80 e. "Cruzeiro do Canal" (ferry), 1987 .. .. 1·00 55
525 110 e. British Aerospace ATP airliner, 1991 .. 1·25 60

**42** "Santa Maria" off Azores

**1992.** Europa. 500th Anniv of Discovery of America by Columbus.
526 **42** 85 e. multicoloured .. 80 50

**43** "Insulano" (steamer, 1868)

**1992.** The Empresa Insulana de Navegacao Shipping Fleet. Multicoloured.
527 38 e. Type **43** .. .. 35 15
528 65 e. "Carvalho Araujo" (ferry, 1930) .. .. 60 35
529 85 e. "Funchal" (ferry, 1961) .. .. .. 80 45
530 120 e. "Terceirense" (freighter, 1948) .. 1·25 60

**44** Ox-mill

**1993.** Traditional Grinders. Multicoloured.

| | | | |
|---|---|---|---|
| 531 | 42 e. Type **44** .. .. | 40 | 20 |
| 532 | 130 e. Hand-mill .. .. | 1·25 | 65 |

**45** "Two Sirens at the Entrance of a Grotto" (Antonio Dacosta)

**46** Main Entrance, Praia da Vitoria Church, Terceira

**1993.** Europa. Contemporary Art.

| | | | |
|---|---|---|---|
| 533 **45** | 90 e. multicoloured .. | 1·00 | 50 |

**1993.** Doorways. Multicoloured.

| | | | |
|---|---|---|---|
| 535 | 42 e. Type **46** .. .. | 35 | 20 |
| 536 | 70 e. South door, Praia da Vitoria Church .. | 60 | 30 |
| 537 | 90 e. Main door, Ponta Delgada Church, Sao Miguel .. .. | 80 | 40 |
| 538 | 130 e. South door, Ponta Delgada Church .. | 1·10 | 60 |

**47** Floral Decoration, Our Lady of Sorrows, Caloura, Sao Miguel

**1994.** Tiles. Multicoloured.

| | | | |
|---|---|---|---|
| 539 | 40 e. Type **47** .. .. | 30 | 15 |
| 540 | 70 e. Decoration of crosses, Our Lady of Sorrows, Caloura, Sao Miguel .. | 60 | 30 |
| 541 | 100 e. "Adoration of the Wise Men", Our Lady of Hope Monastery, Ponta Delgada, Sao Miguel .. | 90 | 45 |
| 542 | 150 e. "St. Bras" (altar frontal), Our Lady of Anjos, Santa Maria .. | 1·40 | 70 |

**48** Monkey and Explorer with Model Caravel

**49** Doorway, St. Barbara's Church, Cedros, Faial

**1994.** Europa. Discoveries. Multicoloured.

| | | | |
|---|---|---|---|
| 543 **48** | 100 e. multicoloured .. | 90 | 50 |

**1994.** Manoeline Architecture. Multicoloured.

| | | | |
|---|---|---|---|
| 545 | 45 e. Type **49** .. .. | 35 | 20 |
| 546 | 140 e. Window, Ribeira Grande, Sao Miguel .. | 1·10 | 55 |

**50** Aristides Moreira da Motta

**1995.** Centenary of Decree decentralizing Government of the Azores and Madeira Islands. Pro-autonomy activists. Mult.

| | | | |
|---|---|---|---|
| 547 | 42 e. Type **50** .. .. | 35 | 20 |
| 548 | 130 e. Gil Mont'Alverne de Sequeira .. .. | 1·00 | 50 |

**HAVE YOU READ THE NOTES AT THE BEGINNING OF THIS CATALOGUE?**
These often provide answers to the enquiries we receive.

**51** Santana Palace, Ponta Delgada

**1995.** Architecture of Sao Miguel. Mult.

| | | | |
|---|---|---|---|
| 549 | 45 e. Type **51** .. .. | 35 | 20 |
| 550 | 80 e. Chapel of Our Lady of the Victories, Furnas | 65 | 35 |
| 551 | 95 e. Hospital, Ponta Delgada .. .. | 75 | 40 |
| 552 | 135 e. Ernesto do Canto's villa, Furnas .. .. | 1·10 | 55 |

**52** Contendas Lighthouse, Terceira (½-size illustration)

**1996.** Lighthouses. Multicoloured.

| | | | |
|---|---|---|---|
| 553 | 47 e. Type **52** .. .. | 40 | 20 |
| 554 | 78 e. Molhe Lighthouse, Sao Miguel .. .. | 60 | 30 |
| 555 | 98 e. Arnel Lighthouse, Sao Miguel .. .. .. | 80 | 40 |
| 556 | 140 e. Santa Clara Lighthouse, Sao Miguel | 1·10 | 55 |

**53** Natalia Correia (poet)

**1996.** Europa. Famous Women.

| | | | |
|---|---|---|---|
| 558 **53** | 98 e . multicoloured .. | 80 | 40 |

CHARITY TAX STAMPS

Used on certain days of the year as an additional postal tax on internal letters. The proceeds were devoted to public charities. If one was not affixed in addition to the ordinary postage, postage due stamps were used to collect the deficiency and the fine.

**1911.** No. 206 optd **ASSISTENCIA**.

| | | | |
|---|---|---|---|
| C218a **7** | 10 r. green .. .. | 1·10 | 75 |

**1913.** No. 252 optd. **ASSISTENCIA.**

| | | | |
|---|---|---|---|
| C 250. **56.** | 1 c. green .. .. | 3·50 | 2·50 |

**1915.** For the Poor. Charity stamp of Portugal optd **ACORES**.

| | | | |
|---|---|---|---|
| C251 C **58** | 1 c. red .. .. | 45 | 30 |

**1925.** No. C 251 surch. **15 ctvs.**

| | | | |
|---|---|---|---|
| C 325. C **58.** | 15 c. on 1 c. red .. | 80 | 55 |

**1925.** Portuguese Army in Flanders issue of Portugal optd **ACORES**.

| | | | |
|---|---|---|---|
| C 345. C **71.** | 10 c. red .. .. | 80 | 80 |
| C 346. | 10 c. green .. .. | 80 | 80 |
| C 347. | 10 c. blue .. .. | 80 | 80 |
| C 348. | 10 c. brown .. | 80 | 80 |

**1925.** As Marquis de Pombal issue of Portugal, inscr "ACORES".

| | | | |
|---|---|---|---|
| C 349. C **73.** | 20 c. green .. .. | 80 | 80 |
| C 350. – | 20 c. green .. .. | 80 | 80 |
| C 351. C **75.** | 20 c. green .. .. | 80 | 80 |

NEWSPAPER STAMPS

**1876.** Stamps of Portugal optd **ACORES**.

| | | | |
|---|---|---|---|
| N146 N **16** | 2 r. black .. | 4·00 | 2·10 |
| N150b N **17** | 2½ r. green .. | 4·00 | 1·25 |
| N150a | 2½ r. brown .. | 4·00 | 1·25 |

PARCEL POST STAMPS

**1921.** Stamps of Portugal optd **ACORES**.

| | | | |
|---|---|---|---|
| P 325. P **59.** | 1 c. brown .. | 40 | 40 |
| P 326. | 2 c. orange .. | 40 | 40 |
| P 327. | 5 c. brown .. | 40 | 40 |
| P 328. | 10 c. brown .. | 55 | 40 |
| P 329. | 20 c. blue .. .. | 55 | 40 |
| P 330. | 40 c. red .. .. | 55 | 40 |
| P 331. | 50 c. black .. .. | 70 | 65 |
| P 332. | 60 c. blue .. .. | 70 | 65 |
| P 333. | 70 c. brown .. | 1·75 | 1·60 |
| P 334. | 80 c. blue .. .. | 1·75 | 1·60 |
| P 335. | 90 c. violet .. | 1·75 | 1·60 |
| P 336. | 1 e. green .. .. | 1·75 | 1·60 |
| P 337. | 2 e. lilac .. .. | 2·75 | 2·50 |
| P 338. | 3 e. olive .. .. | 5·00 | 2·50 |
| P 339. | 4 e. blue .. .. | 5·75 | 2·50 |
| P 340. | 5 e. lilac .. .. | 5·75 | 5·00 |
| P 341. | 10 e. brown .. | 25·00 | 14·50 |

POSTAGE DUE STAMPS

Nos. D179/351 are stamps of Portugal overprinted **ACORES**.

**1904.**

| | | | |
|---|---|---|---|
| D 179. D **49.** | 5 r. brown .. | 90 | 80 |
| D 180. | 10 r. orange .. | 95 | 80 |
| D 181. | 20 r. mauve .. | 1·60 | 1·25 |
| D 182. | 30 r. green .. .. | 1·60 | 1·25 |
| D 183. | 40 r. lilac .. .. | 2·50 | 1·75 |
| D 184. | 50 r. red .. .. | 4·25 | 3·00 |
| D 185. | 100 r. blue .. .. | 5·50 | 4·50 |

**1911.** As last optd. **REPUBLICA.**

| | | | |
|---|---|---|---|
| D 218. D **49.** | 5 r. brown .. | 45 | 45 |
| D 219. | 10 r. orange .. | 45 | 45 |
| D 220. | 20 r. mauve .. | 65 | 55 |
| D 221. | 30 r. green .. .. | 65 | 55 |
| D 222. | 40 r. lilac .. .. | 1·00 | 75 |
| D 223. | 50 r. red .. .. | 5·00 | 5·00 |
| D 224. | 100 r. blue .. .. | 2·00 | 2·00 |

**1918.** Value in centavos.

| | | | |
|---|---|---|---|
| D325 D **49** | ½ c. brown .. | 50 | 50 |
| D326 | 1 c. orange .. | 50 | 50 |
| D327 | 2 c. purple .. | 50 | 50 |
| D328 | 3 c. green .. | 50 | 50 |
| D329 | 4 c. lilac .. .. | 50 | 50 |
| D330 | 5 c. red .. .. | 50 | 50 |
| D331 | 10 c. blue .. .. | 50 | 50 |

**1922.**

| | | | |
|---|---|---|---|
| D 332. D **49.** | ½ c. green .. .. | 30 | 30 |
| D 333. | 1 c. green .. .. | 35 | 35 |
| D 334. | 2 c. green .. .. | 35 | 35 |
| D 335. | 3 c. green .. .. | 60 | 35 |
| D 336. | 8 c. green .. .. | 60 | 35 |
| D 337. | 10 c. green .. .. | 60 | 35 |
| D 338. | 12 c. green .. .. | 60 | 35 |
| D 339. | 16 c. green .. .. | 60 | 35 |
| D 340. | 20 c. green .. .. | 60 | 35 |
| D 341. | 24 c. green .. .. | 60 | 35 |
| D 342. | 32 c. green .. .. | 60 | 35 |
| D 343. | 36 c. green .. .. | 60 | 35 |
| D 344. | 40 c. green .. .. | 60 | 35 |
| D 345. | 48 c. green .. .. | 60 | 35 |
| D 346. | 50 c. green .. .. | 60 | 35 |
| D 347. | 60 c. green .. .. | 60 | 35 |
| D 348. | 72 c. green .. .. | 60 | 35 |
| D 349. | 80 c. green .. .. | 3·50 | 2·75 |
| D 350. | 1 e. 20 green .. | 3·50 | 2·75 |

**1925.** Portuguese Army in Flanders.

| | | | |
|---|---|---|---|
| D 351. D **72.** | 20 c. brown .. | 80 | 65 |

**1925.** As Nos. C349/51, optd **MULTA**.

| | | | |
|---|---|---|---|
| D 352. C **73.** | 40 c. green .. .. | 80 | 80 |
| D 353. – | 40 c. green .. .. | 80 | 80 |
| D 354. C **75.** | 40 c. green .. .. | 80 | 80 |

## BADEN Pt. 7

In S.W. Germany. Formerly a Grand Duchy, now part of the German Federal Republic.

60 kreuzer = 1 gulden.

**1.**

**2.**

**1851.** Imperf.

| | | | |
|---|---|---|---|
| 1 **1** | 1 k. black on buff .. | £240 | £200 |
| 8 | 1 k. black on white .. | £160 | 20·00 |
| 3 | 3 k. black on yellow .. | £110 | 10·00 |
| 9 | 3 k. black on green .. | £140 | 3·75 |
| 10 | 3 k. black on blue .. | £250 | 20·00 |
| 5 | 6 k. black on green .. | £400 | 32·00 |
| 11 | 6 k. black on orange .. | £250 | 14·00 |
| 6 | 9 k. black on red .. | 70·00 | 12·00 |

**1860.** Shaded background behind Arms. Perf.

| | | | |
|---|---|---|---|
| 13 **2** | 1 k. black .. .. | 65·00 | 17·00 |
| 16 | 3 k. blue .. .. | 70·00 | 10·00 |
| 17 | 6 k. orange .. .. | £100 | 45·00 |
| 22 | 6 k. blue .. .. | £100 | 50·00 |
| 19 | 9 k. red .. .. | £225 | £120 |
| 25 | 9 k. brown .. .. | 80·00 | 60·00 |

**1862.** Uncoloured background behind Arms.

| | | | |
|---|---|---|---|
| 27 | 1 k. black .. .. .. | 40·00 | 11·00 |
| 28 | 3 k. red .. .. .. | 40·00 | 70 |
| 30 | 6 k. blue .. .. .. | 7·00 | 20·00 |
| 33 | 9 k. brown .. .. .. | 13·00 | 25·00 |
| 36 | 18 k. green .. .. .. | £300 | £550 |
| 38 | 30 k. orange .. .. | 22·00 | £1000 |

**1868** "K.R." instead of "KREUZER".

| | | | |
|---|---|---|---|
| 39 | 1 k. green .. .. .. | 3·00 | 4·00 |
| 41 | 3 k. red .. .. .. | 2·00 | 1·00 |
| 44 | 7 k. blue .. .. .. | 16·00 | 35·00 |

For issues of 1947 to 1964 see Germany: Allied Occupation (French Zone).

RURAL POSTAGE DUE STAMPS

**D 4.**

**1862.**

| | | | |
|---|---|---|---|
| D39 D **4** | 1 k. black on yellow .. | 5·00 | £250 |
| D40 | 3 k. black on yellow .. | 3·00 | £100 |
| D41 | 12 k. black on yellow | 32·00 | £10000 |

## BAGHDAD Pt. 19

A city in Iraq. Special stamps issued during Br. occupation in the War of 1914/18.

16 annas = 1 rupee.

**1917.** Various issues of Turkey surch. **BAGHDAD IN BRITISH OCCUPATION** and new value in annas.

A. Pictorial issues of 1913.

| | | | |
|---|---|---|---|
| 1. **32.** | ¼ a. on 2 pa. red .. | 80·00 | 90·00 |
| 2. **34.** | ¼ a. on 5 pa. purple .. | 55·00 | 60·00 |
| 3. – | ½ a. on 10 pa. grn. (516) | £550 | £600 |
| 4. **31.** | ½ a. on 10 pa. green .. | £850 | £1000 |
| 5. – | 1 a. on 20 pa. red (504).. | £300 | £300 |
| 6. – | 2 a. on 1 pi. blue (No. 518) | 90·00 | £110 |

B. As last but optd. with small star.

| | | | |
|---|---|---|---|
| 7. – | 1 a. on 20 pa. red .. | £170 | £180 |
| 8. – | 2 a. on 1 pi. blue .. | £2250 | £3000 |

C. Postal Jubilee issue.

| | | | |
|---|---|---|---|
| 9 **60** | ½ a. on 10 pa. red .. | £275 | £300 |
| 10b | 1 a. on 20 pa. blue .. | £650 | £750 |
| 11b | 2 a. on 1 pi. black & vio | 55·00 | 65·00 |

D. Optd. with Turkish letter "B"

| | | | |
|---|---|---|---|
| 12. **30.** | 2 a. on 1 pi. blue .. | £250 | £350 |

E. Optd. with star and Arabic date within crescent.

| | | | |
|---|---|---|---|
| 13. **30.** | ½ a. on 10 pa. green .. | 55·00 | 60·00 |
| 14. | 1 a. on 20 pa. red .. | £300 | £325 |
| 15. **23.** | 1 a. on 20 pa. red .. | £300 | £325 |
| 16. **21.** | 1 a. on 20 pa. red (No. N 185) .. .. | £2500 | £3250 |
| 17. **30.** | 2 a. on 1 pi. blue .. | 65·00 | 75·00 |
| 18. **21.** | 2 a. on 1 pi. blue .. | £110 | £120 |

F. Optd. as last but with date between star and crescent.

| | | | |
|---|---|---|---|
| 19. **23.** | ½ a. on 10 pa. green .. | 70·00 | 75·00 |
| 20. **60.** | ½ a. on 10 pa. red .. | £100 | £110 |
| 21. **30.** | 1 a. on 20 pa. red .. | 65·00 | 85·00 |
| 22. **28.** | 1 a. on 20 pa. red .. | £275 | £300 |
| 23. **15.** | 1 a. on 10 pa. on 20 pa. red | £140 | £140 |
| 24. **30.** | 2 a. on 1 pi. blue .. | £120 | £130 |
| 25. **28.** | 2 a. on 1 pi. blue .. | £1000 | £1200 |

## BAHRAIN Pt. 19

An independent shaikhdom on an archipelago in the Persian Gulf on the Arabian coast. For earlier Indian and British postal administrations, see Volume 3. The Bahrain Post Office took over on 1 January 1966.

1000 fils = 1 dinar.

21. Shaikh Isa bin Sulman al-Khalifa. 22. Ruler and Bahrain Airport.

**1966.**

139 21 5 f. green .. .. 10 10
140 10 f. red .. .. 15 15
141 15 f. blue .. .. 20 15
142 20 f. purple .. .. 20 15
143 22 30 f. black and green .. 25 15
144 40 f. black and blue .. 30 15
145 – 50 f. black and red .. 55 25
146 – 75 f. black and violet .. 70 35
147 – 100 f. blue and yellow .. 2·00 90
148 – 200 f. green and orange 8·00 1·90
149 – 500 f. brown and yellow 6·75 3·25
150 – 1 d. multicoloured .. 14·00 7·00

DESIGNS—As Type 22: 50 f., 75 f. Ruler and Mina Sulman deep-water harbour. VERT. (26½ × 42½ mm.): 100 f. Pearl-diving. 200 f. Lanner Falcon and horse-racing. 500 f. Serving coffee, and Ruler's Palace. LARGER (37 × 52½ mm.): 1 d. Ruler, crest, date-palm, horse, dhow, pearl necklace, mosque, coffee-pot and Bab-al-Bahrain (gateway).

23. Produce. 24. W.H.O. Emblem and Map of Bahrain.

**1966.** Trade Fair and Agricultural Show.

151. 23. 10 f. turquoise and red .. 25 15
152. 20 f. lilac and green .. 60 35
153. 40 f. blue and brown .. 1·25 50
154. 200 f. red and blue .. 6·00 3·75

**1968.** 20th Anniv. of World Health Organization.

155. 24. 20 f. black and grey .. 60 45
156. 40 f. black and turquoise 2·00 1·10
157. 150 f. black and red .. 8·00 4·25

25. View of Isa Town.

**1968.** Inaug. of Isa New Town. Mult.

158. 50 f. Type 25 .. .. 3·00 90
159. 80 f. Shopping centre .. 4·50 1·75
160. 120 f. Stadium .. .. 7·00 3·25
161. 150 f. Mosque .. .. 8·00 4·00

26. Symbol of Learning.

**1969.** 50th Anniv. of School Education in Bahrain.

162. 26. 40 f. multicoloured .. 1·25 75
163. 60 f. multicoloured .. 2·40 1·25
164. 150 f. multicoloured .. 6·50 3·25

27. Dish Aerial and Map of Arabian Gulf.

**1969.** Opening of Satellite Earth Station, Ras Abu Jarjour. Multicoloured.

165. 20 f. Type 27 .. .. 2·00 50
166. 40 f. Dish Aerial and palms (vert.) .. .. 4·00 80
167. 100 f. Type 27 .. .. 9·00 3·25
168. 150 f. As 40 f. .. .. 13·00 4·75

28. Arms, Map and Manama Municipality Building.

**1970.** 2nd Arab Cities Organization Conf., Manama.

169. 28. 30 f. multicoloured .. 1·25 1·25
170. 150 f. multicoloured .. 5·25 5·25

29. Copper Bull's Head, Barbar.

**1970.** 3rd Int. Asian Archaeology Conf. Bahrain. Multicoloured.

171. 60 f. Type 29 .. .. 2·50 1·60
172. 80 f. Palace of Dilmun excavations .. 3·25 2·00
173. 120 f. Desert gravemounds 4·75 2·75
174. 150 f. Dilmun seal .. 6·00 3·50

30. Vickers Super VC-10 Airliner, Big Ben, London, and Bahrain Minaret.

**1970.** 1st Gulf Aviation Vickers Super VC-10 Flight, Doha–London.

175 30 30 f. multicoloured .. 2·00 70
176 60 f. multicoloured .. 4·50 1·50
177 120 f. multicoloured .. 8·50 4·50

31. I.E.Y. Emblem and Open Book.

**1970.** Int. Education Year. Multicoloured.

178. 60 f. Type 31 .. .. 1·75 1·40
179. 120 f. Emblem and Bahraini children .. .. 4·25 3·75

32. Allegory of Independence. 34. Human Heart.

33. Arab Dhow with Arab League and U.N.O. Emblems.

**1971.** Independence Day and 10th Anniv. of Ruler's Accession. Multicoloured.

180. 30 f. Type 32 .. .. 1·75 90
181. 60 f. Government House 3·25 1·75
182. 120 f. Arms of Bahrain .. 8·00 4·00
183. 150 f. Arms of Bahrain (gold background) .. 11·00 5·50

**1972.** Bahrain's Membership of Arab League and United Nations. Multicoloured.

184. 30 f. Type 33 .. .. 2·50 95
185. 60 f. Type 33 .. .. 4·50 1·90
186. 120 f. Dhow Sails (vert.) .. 6·00 4·00
187. 150 f. As 120 f. .. .. 11·00 5·50

**1972.** World Health Day

188. 34. 30 f. multicoloured .. 2·00 2·00
189. 60 f. multicoloured .. 5·00 5·00

35. F.A.O. and U.N. Emblems.

**1973.** 10th Anniv of World Food Programme.

190 35 30 f. brown, red & green 2·75 2·75
191 60 f. brown, lt brn & grn 5·00 5·00

36. "Races of the World".

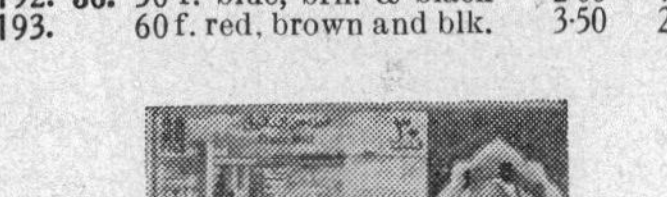

**1973.** 25th Anniv. of Declaration of Human Rights.

192. 36. 30 f. blue, brn. & black 2·00 1·00
193. 60 f. red, brown and blk. 3·50 2·50

38. Flour Mill.

**1973.** National Day. "Progress in Bahrain". Multicoloured.

195 30 f. Type 38 .. .. 1·00 75
196 60 f. Muharraq Airport .. 2·50 1·00
197 120 f. Sulmaniya Medical Centre .. .. 3·00 1·75
198 150 f. Aluminium Smelter 3·50 3·00

39. U.P.U. Emblem within Letters.

**1974.** Admission of Bahrain to U.P.U. Multicoloured.

199. 30 f. Type 39 .. .. 1·50 55
200. 60 f. U.P.U. emblem on letters 2·50 90
201. 120 f. Ruler and emblem on dove with letter in beak 2·25 1·90
202. 150 f. As 120 f. .. .. 3·25 2·75

Nos. 201/2 are larger, size 37 × 28 mm.

40. Traffic Lights and Directing Hands.

**1974.** International Traffic Day.

203. 40. 30 f. multicoloured .. 1·75 1·60
204. 60 f. multicoloured .. 4·00 3·50

41. U.P.U. "Stamp" and Mail Transport.

**1974.** Centenary of Universal Postal Union.

205. 41. 30 f. multicoloured .. 70 50
206. 60 f. multicoloured .. 1·25 90
207. 120 f. multicoloured .. 2·25 1·60
208. 150 f. multicoloured .. 2·75 1·90

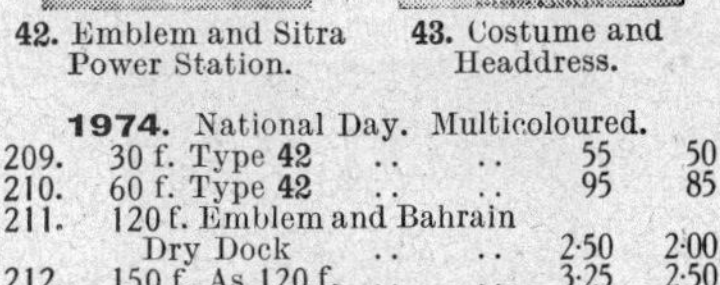

42. Emblem and Sitra Power Station. 43. Costume and Headdress.

**1974.** National Day. Multicoloured.

209. 30 f. Type 42 .. .. 55 50
210. 60 f. Type 42 .. .. 95 85
211. 120 f. Emblem and Bahrain Dry Dock .. .. 2·50 2·00
212. 150 f. As 120 f. .. .. 3·25 2·50

**1975.** Bahrain Women's Costumes.

213. 43. 30 f. multicoloured .. 60 50
214. – 60 f. multicoloured .. 1·25 1·10
215. – 120 f. multicoloured .. 2·00 1·90
216. – 150 f. multicoloured .. 2·50 2·40

DESIGNS: Nos. 214/16, Costumes similar to Type 43.

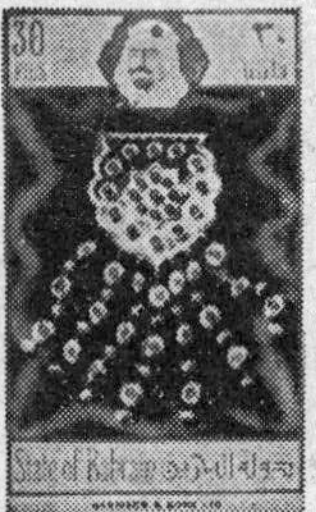

44. Jewelled Pendant. 45. Woman planting "Flower".

**1975.** Costume Jewellery. Multicoloured.

217. 30 f. Type 44 .. .. 60 50
218. 60 f. Gold crown .. 1·25 1·10
219. 120 f. Jewelled necklace .. 2·00 1·90
220. 150 f. Gold necklace .. 2·50 2·40

**1975.** International Women's Year. Mult.

221. 30 f. Type 45 .. .. 1·50 75
222. 60 f. Woman holding I.W.Y. emblem .. .. 3·00 1·75

46. Head of Horse.

**1975.** Horses. Multicoloured.

223a. 60 f. Type 46 .. .. 4·00 4·00
223b. 60 f. Grey .. .. 4·00 4·00
223c. 60 f. Grey with foal (horiz.) .. .. 4·00 4·00
223d. 60 f. Close-up of Arab with grey .. .. 4·00 4·00
223e. 60 f. Grey and herd of browns (horiz.) .. 4·00 4·00
223f. 60 f. Grey and brown (horiz.) .. .. 4·00 4·00
223g. 60 f. Arabs riding horses (horiz.) .. .. 4·00 4·00
223h. 60 f. Arab leading grey beside sea (horiz.) .. 4·00 4·00

47. National Flag. 48. Map of Bahrain within Cog and Laurel.

**1976.**

224 **47** 5 f. red, pink and blue 15 10
225 10 f. red, pink & green 15 10
226 15 f. red, pink & black 15 15
227 20 f. red pink & brown 15 15
227a **48** 25 f. black and grey .. 20 15
228 40 f. black and blue .. 20 15
228a 50 f. green, black & ol 25 15
228b 60 f. black and green 30 20
229 80 f. black and mauve 45 30
229b 100 f. black and red .. 55 45
230 150 f. black and yellow 90 85
231 200 f. black and yellow 1·10 1·00

**49.** Concorde Taking off.

**1976.** First Commercial Flight of Concorde (supersonic airliner). Multicoloured.

232 80 f. Type **49** .. .. 2·25 2·00
233 80 f. Concorde landing .. 2·25 2·00
234 80 f. Concorde en route .. 2·25 2·00
235 80 f. Concorde on runway 2·25 2·00

**50.** Soldier, Crest and Flag.

**52.** Shaikh Isa bin Sulman al-Khalifa.

**51.** King Khalid of Saudi Arabia and Shaikh of Bahrain with National Flags.

**1976.** Defence Force Cadets' Day.

237. **50.** 40 f. multicoloured .. 1·40 1·25
238. 80 f. multicoloured .. 2·50 2·25

**1976.** Visit to Bahrain of King Khalid of Saudi Arabia.

239. **51.** 40 f. multicoloured .. 1·50 1·25
240. 80 f. multicoloured .. 3·00 2·50

**1976.**

241. **52.** 300 f. green & pale green 2·25 1·60
242. 400 f. purple and pink .. 3·00 2·25
243. 500 f. blue and pale blue 3·75 3·00
244. 1 d. black and grey .. 7·50 4·75
244a. 2d. violet and lilac .. 15·00 11·00
244b. 3d. brown and pink .. 23·00 17·00

**53.** Ministry of Housing Emblem, Designs for Houses and Mosque.

**54.** A.P.U. Emblem

**1976.** National Day.

245. **53.** 40 f. multicoloured .. 1·25 1·00
246. 80 f. multicoloured .. 2·75 1·75

**1977.** 25th Anniv. of Arab Postal Union.

247. **54.** 40 f. multicoloured .. 1·25 1·00
248. 80 f. multicoloured .. 2·75 1·75

**55.** Dogs on Beach.

**1977.** Saluki Dogs. Multicoloured.

249a. 80 f. Type **55** .. .. 2·40 2·40
249b. 80 f. Dog and dromedaries .. .. 2·40 2·40
249c. 80 f. Dog and antelope .. 2·40 2·40
249d. 80 f. Dog on lawn of building .. .. 2·40 2·40
249e. 80 f. Head of dog .. 2·40 2·40
249f. 80 f. Heads of two dogs 2·40 2·40
249g. 80 f. Dog in scrubland .. 2·40 2·40
249h. 80 f. Dogs fighting .. 2·40 2·40

**56.** Arab Students and Candle.

**1977.** International Literacy Day.

250. **56.** 40 f. multicoloured .. 1·25 1·00
251. 80 f. multicoloured .. 2·75 1·75

**57.** Shipyard Installations and Arab Flags.

**1977.** Inauguration of Arab Shipbuilding and Repair Yard Co.

252. **57.** 40 f. multicoloured .. 1·25 1·00
253. 80 f. multicoloured .. 2·75 1·75

**58.** Microwave Antenna.

**1978.** 10th World Telecommunications Day.

254. **58.** 40 f. multicoloured .. 1·25 1·00
255. 80 f. silver, deep blue and blue .. .. 2·75 1·75

**59.** Child being helped to Walk.

**60.** Boom Dhow.

**1979.** International Year of the Child. Mult.

256. 50 f. Type **59** .. .. 1·00 80
257. 100 f. Hands protecting child .. .. .. 2·50 1·60

**1979.** Dhows. Multicoloured.

258. 100 f. Type **60** .. .. 2·40 2·40
259. 100 f. Baghla .. .. 2·40 2·40
260. 100 f. Shu'ai (horiz.) .. 2·40 2·40
261. 100 f. Ghanja (horiz.) .. 2·40 2·40
262. 100 f. Kotia .. .. 2·40 2·40
263. 100 f. Sambuk .. .. 2·40 2·40
264. 100 f. Jaliboot (horiz.) .. 2·40 2·40
265. 100 f. Zarook (horiz.) .. 2·40 2·40

**61.** Dome of Mosque, Mecca.

**1980.** 1400th Anniv. of Hejira.

266. **61.** 50 f. multicoloured .. 65 40
267. 100 f. multicoloured .. 1·60 1·25
268. 150 f. multicoloured .. 1·90 1·50
269. 200 f. multicoloured .. 2·50 2·00

**62.** Arab with Gyrfalcon.

**1980.** Falconry. Multicoloured.

271. 100 f. Type **62** .. .. 2·75 1·60
272. 100 f. Arab looking at Lanner Falcon on wrist .. 2·75 1·60
273. 100 f. Peregrine Falcon resting with outstretched wings .. .. .. 2·75 1·60
274. 100 f. Peregrine Falcon in Flight .. .. .. 2·75 1·60
275. 100 f. Gyrfalcon on pillar (with camels in background) (vert.) .. .. 2·75 1·60
276. 100 f. Gyrfalcon on pillar (closer view) (vert.) .. 2·75 1·60
277. 100 f. Close-up of Gyrfalcon facing right (vert.) .. 2·75 1·60
278. 100 f. Close-up of Lanner Falcon full-face (vert.) .. 2·75 1·60

**63.** Map and I.Y.D.P. Emblem.

**1981.** International Year for Disabled Persons.

279. **63.** 50 f. multicoloured .. 1·25 75
280. 100 f. multicoloured .. 2·25 1·75

**64.** Jubilee Emblem.

**1981.** 50th Anniv. of Electrical Power in Bahrain.

281. **64.** 50 f. multicoloured .. 1·25 75
282. 100 f. multicoloured .. 2·25 1·75

**65.** Carving.

**66.** Mosque.

**1981.** Handicrafts. Multicoloured.

283. 50 f. Type **65** .. .. 55 45
284. 100 f. Pottery .. .. 1·00 90
285. 150 f. Weaving .. .. 1·90 1·60
286. 200 f. Basket-making .. 2·25 2·10

**1981.** Mosques.

287. **66.** 50 f. multicoloured .. 70 55
288. – 100 f. multicoloured .. 1·40 1·10
289. – 150 f. multicoloured .. 2·00 1·75
290. – 200 f. multicoloured .. 2·75 2·50

DESIGNS: 100 f. to 200 f. As T **66** but showing different Mosques.

**67.** Shaikh Isa bin Sulman al-Khalifa.

**69.** Flags and Clasped Hands encircling Emblem.

**68.** Dorcas Gazelle.

**1981.** 20th Anniv of Coronation of Shaikh Isa bin Sulman al-Khalifa.

291 **67** 15 f. gold, grey & mauve 25 20
292 50 f. gold, grey and red 55 45
293 100 f. gold, grey & brn 1·10 95
294 150 f. gold, grey & blue 1·75 1·40
295 200 f. gold, grey & blue 2·10 2·10

**1982.** Al-Areen Wildlife Park. Multicoloured.

296. 100 f. Goitred gazelle .. 1·75 1·75
297. 100 f. Type **68** .. .. 1·75 1·75
298. 100 f. Dhub lizard .. .. 1·75 1·75
299. 100 f. Brown hares .. 1·75 1·75
300. 100 f. Arabian oryx .. 1·75 1·75
301. 100 f. Addax .. .. 1·75 1·75

**1982.** 3rd Supreme Council Session of Gulf Co-operation Council.

302. **69.** 50 f. multicoloured .. 65 50
303. – 100 f. multicoloured .. 1·40 1·10

**70.** Madinat Hamad.

**1983.** Opening of Madinat Hamad New Town. Multicoloured.

304. 50 f. Type **70** .. .. 65 50
305. 100 f. View of Madinat Hamad (different) .. 1·40 1·10

**71.** Shaikh Isa bin Sulman al-Khalifa.

**1983.** Bicentenary of Al-Khalifa Dynasty. Multicoloured.

306. 100 f. Type **71** .. .. 70 70
307. 100 f. Cartouche of Ali bin Khalifa al-Khalifa .. 70 70
308. 100 f. Isa bin Ali al-Khalifa 70 70
309. 100 f. Hamad bin Isa al-Khalifa .. .. .. 70 70
310. 100 f. Salman bin Hamad al-Khalifa .. .. 70 70
311. 100 f. Cartouche of Ahmed bin Mohammed al-Khalifa .. .. .. 70 70
312. 100 f. Cartouche of Salman bin Ahmed al-Khalifa .. 70 70
313. 100 f. Cartouche of Abdullah bin Ahmed al-Khalifa .. .. .. 70 70
314. 100 f. Cartouche of Mohammed bin Khalifa al-Khalifa .. .. 70 70

**72.** G.C.C. and Traffic and Licensing Directorate Emblems.

**1984.** Gulf Co-operation Council Traffic Week.

316. **72.** 15 f. multicoloured .. 25 20
317. 50 f. multicoloured .. 80 40
318. 100 f. multicoloured .. 1·25 75

**73.** Hurdling.

**1984.** Olympic Games, Los Angeles. Mult.
319. 15 f. Type **73** .. .. 20 20
320. 50 f. Show jumping .. .. 70 55
321. 100 f. Swimming .. .. 1·25 1·10
322. 150 f. Fencing .. .. 1·75 1·50
323. 200 f. Shooting .. .. 2·40 2·25

**74.** Manama and Emblem.

**1984.** Centenary of Postal Services.
324. **74.** 15 f. multicoloured .. 35 20
325. 50 f. multicoloured .. 1·00 50
326. 100 f. multicoloured .. 1·75 95

**75.** Spanish Mackerel.

**1985.** Fishes. Multicoloured.
327. 100 f. Type **75** .. .. 1·10 1·00
328. 100 f. Crocodile needlefish (three fishes) .. 1·10 1·00
329. 100 f. Grey grunt (fish swimming to left, blue and lilac background .. 1·10 1·00
330. 100 f. Pearlspotted rabbitfish (two fishes, blue and lilac background) .. 1·10 1·00
331. 100 f. Mullet (two fishes, green and pink background) .. .. .. 1·10 1·00
332. 100 f. Doublebar bream (green and grey background) .. .. .. 1·10 1·00
333. 100 f. Sobaity bream (blue background) .. .. 1·10 1·00
334. 100 f. Malabar grouper (green background) .. 1·10 1·00
335. 100 f. Longnosed emperor (pink anemone background) .. .. .. 1·10 1·00
336. 100 f. Golden trevally (fish swimming to right, blue and lilac background) .. 1·10 1·00

**76.** Hands cupping Emblem.

**1985.** Arabian Gulf States Social Work Week.
337. **76.** 15 f. multicoloured .. 20 15
338. 50 f. multicoloured .. 60 40
339. 100 f. multicoloured .. 1·00 70

**77.** I.Y.Y. Emblem.

**1986.** International Youth Year.
340. **77.** 15 f. multicoloured .. 20 15
341. 50 f. multicoloured .. 60 40
342. 100 f. multicoloured .. 1·00 70

**78.** Aerial View of Causeway.

**1986.** Opening of Saudi–Bahrain Causeway. Multicoloured.
343. 15 f. Type **78** .. .. 25 20
344. 50 f. Aerial view of island 60 40
345. 100 f. Aerial view of road bridge .. .. 1·00 70

**79.** Shaikh Isa bin Sulman al-Khalifa.

**1986.** 25th Anniv. of Accession of Shaikh Isa bin Sulman al-Khalifa.
346. **79.** 15 f. multicoloured .. 25 20
347. 50 f. multicoloured .. 60 40
348. 100 f. multicoloured .. 1·00 70

**80.** Emblem.

**1988.** 40th Anniv. of W.H.O.
350. **80.** 50 f. multicoloured .. 40 25
351. 150 f. multicoloured .. 1·25 90

**81.** Centre.

**1988.** Opening of Ahmed al-Fateh Islamic Centre.
352. **81.** 50 f. multicoloured .. 40 25
353. 150 f. multicoloured .. 1·25 90

**82** Running

**1988.** Olympic Games, Seoul. Multicoloured.
354 50 f. Type **82** .. .. 30 20
355 80 f. Dressage .. .. 60 40
356 150 f. Fencing .. .. 1·10 80
357 200 f. Football .. .. 1·90 1·40

**83** Emblem in "1988"

**1988.** 9th Supreme Council Meeting of Gulf Co-operation Council.
358 **83** 50 f. multicoloured .. 35 25
359 150 f. multicoloured .. 1·25 90

**84** Arab leading Camel

**85** Shaikh Isa bin Sulman al-Khalifa

**1989.** Camels. Multicoloured.
360 150 f. Type **84** .. .. 1·00 1·00
361 150 f. Arab leading camel (different) .. .. 1·00 1·00
362 150 f. Head of camel and pump-head .. .. 1·00 1·00
363 150 f. Close-up of Arab on camel .. .. .. 1·00 1·00
364 150 f. Arab riding camel .. 1·00 1·00
365 150 f. Two Arab camel-riders .. .. .. 1·00 1·00
366 150 f. Head of camel and camel-rider .. .. 1·00 1·00
367 150 f. Camel at rest in camp .. .. .. 1·00 1·00
368 150 f. Camels with calf .. 1·00 1·00
369 150 f. Heads of three camels .. .. .. 1·00 1·00
370 150 f. Camel in scrubland 1·00 1·00
371 150 f. Arab on camel .. 1·00 1·00
Nos. 366/71 are horiz.

**1989.** Multicoloured, colour of frame given.
372 **85** 25 f. green .. .. 20 10
373 40 f. grey .. .. 30 10
374 50 f. pink .. .. 30 10
375 60 f. brown .. .. 40 15
376 75 f. mauve .. .. 50 15
377 80 f. green .. .. 50 15
378 100 f. orange .. .. 70 25
379 120 f. violet .. .. 80 25
380 150 f. grey .. .. 1·00 35
381 200 f. blue .. .. 1·25 45

**86** Houbara Bustards

**1990.** The Houbara Bustards. Multicoloured.
383 150 f. Type **86** .. .. 1·00 1·00
384 150 f. Two bustards (facing each other) .. .. 1·00 1·00
385 150 f. Chicks and eggs .. 1·00 1·00
386 150 f. Adult and chick .. 1·00 1·00
387 150 f. Adult (vert) .. 1·00 1·00
388 150 f. In flight .. .. 1·00 1·00
389 150 f. Adult (facing right) 1·00 1·00
390 150 f. Young bird (vert) .. 1·00 1·00
391 150 f. Adult (facing left) .. 1·00 1·00
392 150 f. Bird in display plumage .. .. 1·00 1·00
393 150 f. Two bustards in display plumage .. 1·00 1·00
394 150 f. Two bustards with bridge in background .. 1·00 1·00

**87** Anniversary Emblem

**1990.** 40th Anniv of Gulf Air.
395 **87** 50 f. multicoloured .. 35 25
396 80 f. multicoloured .. 55 35
397 150 f. multicoloured .. 1·00 75
398 200 f. multicoloured .. 1·40 95

**88** Anniversary Emblem

**1990.** 50th Anniv of Bahrain Chamber of Commerce and Industry.
399 **88** 50 f. multicoloured .. 30 20
400 80 f. multicoloured .. 50 35
401 150 f. multicoloured .. 95 65
402 200 f. multicoloured .. 1·25 85

**89** I.L.Y. Emblem

**1990.** International Literacy Year.
403 **89** 50 f. multicoloured .. 30 20
404 80 f. multicoloured .. 50 35
405 150 f. multicoloured .. 95 65
406 200 f. multicoloured .. 1·25 85

**90** Crested Lark

**1991.** Birds. Multicoloured.
407 150 f. Type **90** .. .. 90 90
408 150 f. Hoopoe ("Upupa epops") .. .. 90 90
409 150 f. White-cheeked bulbul ("Pycnonotus leucogenys") .. .. 90 90
410 150 f. Turtle dove ("Streptopelia turtur") 90 90
411 150 f. Collared dove ("Streptopelia decaocto") .. .. 90 90
412 150 f. Common kestrel ("Falco tinnunculus") .. 90 90
413 150 f. House sparrow ("Passer domesticus") (horoz) .. .. 90 90
414 150 f. Great grey shrike ("Lanius excubitor") (horiz) .. .. .. 90 90
415 150 f. Rose-ringed parakeet ("Psittacula krameri") 90 90

**91** Shaikh Isa bin Sulman al-Khalifa

**1991.** 30th Anniv of Amir's Coronation.
416 **91** 50 f. multicoloured .. 30 20
417 A 50 f. multicoloured .. 30 20
418 **91** 80 f. multicoloured .. 45 30
419 A 80 f. multicoloured .. 45 30
420 **91** 150 f. multicoloured .. 90 60
421 A 150 f. multicoloured .. 90 60
422 **91** 200 f. multicoloured .. 1·10 75
423 A 200 f. multicoloured .. 1·10 75
DESIGN: A, The Amir and sunburst.

**92** White Stork ("Ciconia ciconia")

**1992.** Migratory Birds. Multicoloured.
425 150 f. Type **92** .. .. 80 80
426 150 f. European bee eater ("Merops apiaster") .. 80 80
427 150 f. Common starling ("Sturnus vulgaris") .. 80 80
428 150 f. Grey hypocolius ("Hypocolius ampelinus") .. .. .. 80 80
429 150 f. European cuckoo ("Cuculus canorus") .. 80 80
430 150 f. Mistle thrush ("Turdus viscivorus") .. 80 80
431 150 f. Common roller ("Coracias garrulus") .. 80 80
432 150 f. Goldfinch ("Carduelis carduelis") .. .. 80 80
433 150 f. Red-backed shrike ("Lanius collurio") .. 80 80
434 150 f. Redwing ("Turdus iliacus") (horiz) .. 80 80
435 150 f. Pied wagtail ("Motacilla alba") (horiz) .. 80 80
436 150 f. Golden oriole ("Oriolus oriolus") (horiz) .. 80 80
437 150 f. European robin ("Erithacus rubecula") 80 80
438 150 f. Nightingale ("Luscinia luscinia") .. 80 80
439 150 f. Spotted flycatcher ("Muscicapa striata") .. 80 80
440 150 f. Barn swallow ("Hirundo rustica") .. 80 80

**93** Start of Race

**1992.** Horse Racing. Multicoloured.

441 150 f. Type **93** .. .. 80 80
442 150 f. Parading in paddock 80 80
443 150 f. Galloping around bend .. .. .. 80 80
444 150 f. Galloping past national flags .. .. 80 80
445 150 f. Galloping past spectator stand .. 80 80
446 150 f. Head-on view of horses .. .. .. 80 80
447 150 f. Reaching winning post .. .. .. 80 80
448 150 f. A black and a grey galloping .. .. 80 80

**94** Show Jumping

**1992.** Olympic Games, Barcelona. Mult.

449 50 f. Type **94** .. .. 30 20
450 80 f. Running .. .. 45 30
451 150 f. Karate .. .. 85 55
452 200 f. Cycling .. .. 1·10 75

**95** Airport

**1992.** 60th Anniv of Bahrain International Airport.

453 **95** 50 f. multicoloured .. 30 20
454 80 f. multicoloured .. 45 30
455 150 f. multicoloured .. 85 55
456 200 f. multicoloured .. 1·10 75

**96** Girl skipping **98** Artillery Gun Crew

**97** Cable-cars and Pylons

**1992.** Children's Paintings. Multicoloured.

457 50 f. Type **96** .. .. 30 20
458 80 f. Women .. .. 45 30
459 150 f. Women preparing food (horiz) .. .. 85 55
460 200 f. Pearl divers (horiz) 1·10 75

**1992.** Expansion of Aluminium Industry. Multicoloured.

461 50 f. Type **97** .. .. 30 20
462 80 f. Worker in aluminium plant .. .. 45 30
463 150 f. Aerial view of aluminium plant .. 85 55
464 200 f. Processed aluminium 1·10 75

**1993.** 25th Anniv of Bahrain Defence Force. Multicoloured.

465 50 f. Type **98** .. .. 25 15
466 80 f. General Dynamics Fighting Falcon jet fighters, tanks and patrol boat .. 40 25
467 150 f. Missile corvette (horiz) .. .. .. 75 50
468 200 f. Fighting Falcon over Bahrain (horiz) .. 1·00 65

**99** Satellite View of Bahrain **100** Purple Heron

**1993.** World Meteorological Day. Mult.

469 50 f. Type **99** .. .. 30 20
470 150 f. Satellite picture of world (horiz) .. .. 75 60
471 200 f. Earth seen from space .. .. .. 1·25 85

**1993.** Water Birds. Multicoloured.

472 150 f. Type **100** .. .. 75 75
473 150 f. Moorhen ("Gallinula chloropus") .. .. 75 75
474 150 f. Socotra cormorant ("Phalacrocorax nigrogularis") .. 75 75
475 150 f. Crab plover ("Dromas ardeola") 75 75
476 150 f. Common kingfisher ("Alcedo atthis") .. 75 75
477 150 f. Lapwing ("Vanellus vanellus") .. .. 75 75
478 150 f. Oystercatcher ("Haematopus ostralegus") (horiz) .. 75 75
479 150 f. Black-crowned night heron ("Nycticorax nycticorax") .. .. 75 75
480 150 f. Caspian tern ("Sterna caspia") (horiz) 75 75
481 150 f. Turnstone ("Arenaria interpres") (horiz) 75 75
482 150 f. Water rail ("Rallus aquaticus") (horiz) .. 75 75
483 150 f. Mallard ("Anas platyrhyncos) (horiz) .. 75 75
484 150 f. Lesser black-backed gull ("Larus fuscus") (horiz) .. .. .. 75 75

**101** Fawn

**1993.** The Goitered Gazelle. Multicoloured.

485 25 f. Type **101** .. .. 15 10
486 50 f. Doe walking .. 25 15
487 50 f. Doe with ears pricked 25 15
488 150 f. Male gazelle .. 75 60

**102** "Lycium shawii" **103** Children and Silhouettes of Parents' Heads

**1993.** Wild Flowers. Multicoloured.

489 150 f. Type **102** .. .. 75 75
490 150 f. "Alhagi maurorum" 75 75
491 150 f. Caper-bush ("Caparis spinosa") .. .. 75 75
492 150 f. "Cistanche phelypae" .. .. 75 75
493 150 f. "Asphodelus tenuifolius" .. .. 75 75
494 150 f. "Limonium axillare" 75 75
495 150 f. "Cynomorium coccineum" .. .. 75 75
496 150 f. "Calligonum polygonoides" .. .. 75 75

**1994.** International Year of the Family.

497 **103** 50 f. multicoloured .. 20 15
498 80 f. multicoloured .. 30 20
499 150 f. multicoloured .. 65 45
500 200 f. multicoloured .. 80 55

**104** "Lepidochrysops arabicus" **105** Anniversary Emblem

**1994.** Butterflies. Mult. (a) Vert designs.

501 50 f. Type **104** .. .. 20 20
502 50 f. "Ypthima bolanica" 20 20
503 50 f. Desert grass yellow ("Eurema brigitta") .. 20 20
504 50 f. "Precis limnoria" .. 20 20
505 50 f. Small tortoiseshell ("Aglais urticae") .. 20 20
506 50 f. Protomedia ("Colotis protomedia") .. .. 20 20
507 50 f. Clouded mother-of-pearl (Salamis anacardii") .. .. 20 20
508 50 f. "Byblia ilithyia" .. 20 20

(b) Horiz designs.

509 150 f. Swallowtail ("Papilio machaon") .. .. 65 65
510 150 f. Blue ("Agrodiaetus loewii") .. .. 65 65
511 150 f. Painted lady ("Vanessa cardui") .. 65 65
512 150 f. Chequered swallow-tail ("Papilio demoleus") 65 65
513 150 f. Guineafowl ("Hama-numida daedalus") .. 65 65
514 150 f. "Funonia orithya" 65 65
515 150 f. "Funonia chorimine" 65 65
516 150 f. "Colias croceus" .. 65 65

**1994.** 75th Anniv of International Red Cross and Red Crescent.

517 **105** 50 f. multicoloured .. 20 15
518 80 f. multicoloured .. 30 20
519 150 f. multicoloured .. 65 45
520 200 f. multicoloured .. 80 55

**106** Goalkeeper

**1994.** World Cup Football Championship, U.S.A. Multicoloured.

521 50 f. Type **106** .. .. 20 15
522 80 f. Players .. .. 30 20
523 150 f. Players' legs .. 65 45
524 200 f. Player on ground .. 80 55

**107** Earth Station

**1994.** 25th Anniv of Ras Abu Jarjour Satellite Earth Station.

525 **107** 50 f. multicoloured .. 20 15
526 80 f. multicoloured .. 30 20
527 150 f. multicoloured .. 65 45
528 200 f. multicoloured .. 80 55

**108** Children on Open Book, Pen as Torch and School **109** Dove with "Olive Branch" of Members' Flags

**1994.** 75th Anniv of Education in Bahrain.

529 **108** 50 f. multicoloured .. 20 15
530 80 f. multicoloured .. 30 20
531 150 f. multicoloured .. 65 45
532 200 f. multicoloured .. 80 55

**1994.** 15th Gulf Co-operation Council Supreme Council Session, Bahrain.

533 **109** 50 f. multicoloured .. 20 15
534 80 f. multicoloured .. 30 20
535 150 f. multicoloured .. 65 45
536 200 f. multicoloured .. 80 55

**110** Date Palm in Bloom

**1995.** The Date Palm.

537 80 f. Type **110** .. .. 25 15
538 100 f Date palm with unripened dates .. 35 25
539 200 f. Dates ripening .. 65 45
540 250 f. Date palm trees with ripened dates .. .. 80 55

**111** Campaign Emblem

**1995.** World Health Day. Anti-poliomyelitis Campaign.

542 **111** 80 f. multicoloured .. 25 15
543 200 f. multicoloured .. 65 45
544 250 f. multicoloured .. 80 55

**112** Exhibition Emblem **114** Headquarters, Cairo

**113** Crops

**1995.** 1st National Industries Exhibition.

545 **112** 80 f. multicoloured .. 25 15
546 200 f. multicoloured .. 65 45
547 250 f. multicoloured .. 80 55

**1995.** 50th Anniv of F.A.O. Multicoloured.

548 80 f. Type **113** .. .. 25 15
549 200 f. Field of crops .. 65 45
550 250 f. Field of cabbages .. 80 55

**1995.** 50th Anniv of Arab League.

551 **114** 80 f. multicoloured .. 25 15
552 200 f. multicoloured .. 65 45
553 250 f. multicoloured .. 80 55

**115** U.N. Headquarters and Map of Bahrain

**1995.** 50th Anniv of U.N.O.

554 **115** 80 f. multicoloured .. 25 15
555 100 f. multicoloured .. 35 25
556 200 f. multicoloured .. 65 45
557 250 f. multicoloured .. 80 55

116 Tower

**1995.** Traditional Architecture. Mult.

| | | | | |
|---|---|---|---|---|
| 558 | | 200 f. Type **116** .. .. | 65 | 65 |
| 559 | | 200 f. Balcony .. .. | 65 | 65 |
| 560 | | 200 f. Doorway .. .. | 65 | 65 |
| 561 | | 200 f. Multi-storied facade | 65 | 65 |
| 562 | | 200 f. Entrance flanked by two windows .. .. | 65 | 65 |
| 563 | | 200 f. Three arched windows .. .. | 65 | 65 |

117 National Flag and Shaikh Isa Bin Sulman al-Khalifa

118 Bookcase and Open Book

**1995.** National Day. Multicoloured, colour of background given.

| | | | | |
|---|---|---|---|---|
| 564 | 117 | 80 f. blue | 25 | 15 |
| 565 | | 100 f. green .. .. | 35 | 25 |
| 566 | | 200 f. lilac .. .. | 65 | 45 |
| 567 | | 250 f. green .. .. | 85 | 55 |

**1996.** 50th Anniv of Public Library.

| | | | | |
|---|---|---|---|---|
| 568 | 118 | 80 f. multicoloured .. | 25 | 15 |
| 569 | | 200 f. multicoloured .. | 65 | 45 |
| 570 | | 250 f. multicoloured .. | 85 | 55 |

119 Divers on Ship

**1996.** Pearl Diving. Multicoloured.

| | | | | |
|---|---|---|---|---|
| 571 | | 80 f. Type **119** .. .. | 25 | 15 |
| 572 | | 100 f. Divers .. .. | 35 | 25 |
| 573 | | 200 f. Diver on sea-bed and ship .. .. .. | 65 | 45 |
| 574 | | 250 f. Diver with net .. | 85 | 55 |

120 Globe, Ship and Olympic Rings

**1996.** Olympic Games, Atlanta.

| | | | | |
|---|---|---|---|---|
| 576 | 120 | 80 f. multicoloured .. | 25 | 15 |
| 577 | | 100 f. multicoloured .. | 35 | 25 |
| 578 | | 200 f. multicoloured .. | 65 | 45 |
| 579 | | 250 f. multicoloured .. | 85 | 55 |

WAR TAX STAMPS

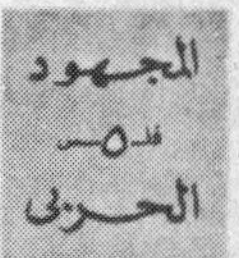

T 36. " War Effort ".

T 37. "War Effort".

**1973.**

T192 T **36** 5 f. blue and cobalt

**1973.**

| | | | | |
|---|---|---|---|---|
| T194a | T **37** | 5 f. blue .. .. | 1·00 | 10 |

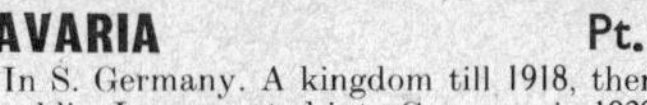

# BAVARIA Pt. 7

In S. Germany. A kingdom till 1918, then a republic. Incorporated into Germany in 1920.

1849. 60 kreuzer = 1 gulden.
1874. 100 pfennig = 1 mark.

1.

2. (Circle cut).

**1849.** Imperf.

| | | | | |
|---|---|---|---|---|
| 2. | 1. | 1 k. black .. .. .. | £550 | £1600 |

**1849.** Imperf. Circle cut by labels.

| | | | | |
|---|---|---|---|---|
| 3. | 2. | 3 k. blue .. .. .. | 40·00 | 1·75 |
| 24. | | 3 k. red .. .. .. | 38·00 | 3·50 |
| 7. | | 6 k. brown .. .. | £5000 | £140 |

**1850.** Imperf. As T 2, but circle not cut.

| | | | | |
|---|---|---|---|---|
| 8a. | 2. | 1 k. red .. .. .. | 80·00 | 80·00 |
| 21. | | 1 k. yellow .. .. | 60·00 | 17·00 |
| 11. | | 6 k. brown .. .. | 40·00 | 1·50 |
| 25. | | 6 k. blue .. .. .. | 55·00 | 7·50 |
| 16. | | 9 k. green .. .. .. | 55·00 | 9·00 |
| 28. | | 9 k. brown .. .. | 75·00 | 10·00 |
| 18. | | 12 k. red .. .. .. | £110 | £130 |
| 31. | | 12 k. green .. .. | 80·00 | 50·00 |
| 19. | | 18 k. yellow .. .. | £140 | £150 |
| 32. | | 18 k. red .. .. .. | £100 | £375 |

3.

6.

8.

**1867.** Imperf.

| | | | | |
|---|---|---|---|---|
| 34. | 3. | 1 k. green .. .. | 60·00 | 9·00 |
| 37. | | 3 k. red .. .. .. | 55·00 | 35 |
| 39. | | 6 k. blue .. .. .. | 30·00 | 14·00 |
| 41. | | 6 k. brown .. .. | 60·00 | 40·00 |
| 43. | | 7 k. blue .. .. .. | £350 | 8·50 |
| 46. | | 9 k. brown .. .. | 40·00 | 28·00 |
| 48. | | 12 k. mauve .. .. | £350 | 80·00 |
| 50. | | 18 k. red .. .. .. | 90·00 | £150 |
| 65. | 6. | 1 m. mauve .. .. | £475 | 60·00 |

**1870.** Perf.

| | | | | |
|---|---|---|---|---|
| 51. | 3. | 1 k. green .. .. | 1·25 | 1·00 |
| 69. | | 3 k. red .. .. .. | 35 | 3·50 |
| 55. | | 6 k. brown .. .. | 30·00 | 26·00 |
| 56. | | 7 k. blue .. .. .. | 1·40 | 2·40 |
| 59. | | 9 k. brown .. .. | 4·00 | 3·00 |
| 60. | | 10 k. yellow .. .. | 3·00 | 11·00 |
| 61. | | 12 k. mauve .. .. | £300 | £850 |
| 63. | | 18 k. red .. .. .. | 10·00 | 12·00 |

**1875.** Perf.

| | | | | |
|---|---|---|---|---|
| 120 | 8 | 2 pf. grey .. .. | 1·25 | 45 |
| 103 | | 3 pf. green .. .. | 5·50 | 2·00 |
| 121 | | 3 pf. brown .. .. | 10 | 10 |
| 122 | | 5 pf. green .. .. | 10 | 10 |
| 107 | | 5 pf. mauve .. .. | 14·00 | 2·50 |
| 123 | | 10 pf. red .. .. | 10 | 10 |
| 124 | | 20 pf. blue .. .. | 10 | 10 |
| 114 | | 25 pf. brown .. .. | 24·00 | 3·25 |
| 125 | | 25 pf. orange .. .. | 15 | 45 |
| 126 | | 30 pf. olive .. .. | 15 | 55 |
| 127 | | 40 pf. yellow .. .. | 15 | 75 |
| 86 | | 50 pf. red .. .. | 45·00 | 5·00 |
| 117 | | 50 pf. brown .. .. | 40·00 | 2·50 |
| 128 | | 50 pf. purple .. .. | 15 | 1·00 |
| 129 | | 80 pf. mauve .. .. | 1·75 | 3·00 |
| 100 | 6 | 1 m. mauve .. .. | 1·75 | 55 |
| 101a | | 2 m. orange .. .. | 3·00 | 4·50 |
| 136 | | 3 m. brown .. .. | 8·50 | 18·00 |
| 137 | | 5 m. green .. .. | 8·50 | 18·00 |

11. Prince Luitpold. 13.

**1911.** Prince Regent Luitpold's 90th Birthday.

| | | | | |
|---|---|---|---|---|
| 138. | 11. | 3 pf. brown on drab .. | 20 | 10 |
| 139. | | 5 pf. green on green .. | 20 | 10 |
| 140. | | 10 pf. red on buff .. | 20 | 10 |
| 141. | | 20 pf. blue on blue .. | 1·40 | 30 |
| 142. | | 25 pf. deep brown on buff | 2·00 | 1·25 |
| 143. | – | 30 pf. orange on buff .. | 1·00 | 75 |
| 144. | – | 40 pf. olive on buff .. | 1·75 | 75 |
| 145. | – | 50 pf. red on drab .. | 2·25 | 1·50 |
| 146. | – | 60 pf. green on buff .. | 2·50 | 1·50 |
| 147. | – | 80 pf. violet on drab .. | 6·00 | 3·25 |
| 148. | 13. | 1 m. brown on drab .. | 2·00 | 1·25 |
| 149. | | 2 m. green on green .. | 2·00 | 6·50 |
| 150. | | 3 m. red on buff .. | 14·00 | 25·00 |
| 151. | | 5 m. blue on buff .. | 20·00 | 24·00 |
| 152. | | 10 m. orange on yellow | 35·00 | 40·00 |
| 153. | | 20 m. brown on yellow.. | 20·00 | 20·00 |

The 30 pf. to 80 pf. values are similar to Type 11, but larger.

14.

**1911.** 25th Anniv. of Regency of Prince Luitpold.

| | | | | |
|---|---|---|---|---|
| 169. | 14. | 5 pf. yellow, green & black .. .. | 50 | 75 |
| 170. | | 10 pf. yellow, red & black .. .. | 60 | 1·50 |

15. King Ludwig III. 16.

**1914.** Imperf. or perf.

| | | | | |
|---|---|---|---|---|
| 171 | 15 | 2 pf. slate .. .. | 20 | 1·00 |
| 172 | | 2½ on 2 pf. slate .. | 20 | 1·00 |
| 173 | | 3 pf. brown .. .. | 20 | 1·00 |
| 175 | | 5 pf. green .. .. | 20 | 1·00 |
| 176 | | 7½ pf. green .. .. | 20 | 1·00 |
| 178 | | 10 pf. red .. .. | 20 | 1·00 |
| 179 | | 15 pf. red .. .. | 20 | 1·00 |
| 181 | | 20 pf. blue .. .. | 20 | 1·00 |
| 183 | | 25 pf. grey .. .. | 20 | 1·00 |
| 184 | | 30 pf. orange .. .. | 30 | 1·00 |
| 185 | | 40 pf. olive .. .. | 30 | 1·00 |
| 186 | | 50 pf. brown .. .. | 20 | 1·00 |
| 187 | | 60 pf. green .. .. | 30 | 1·00 |
| 188 | | 80 pf. violet .. .. | 20 | 1·25 |
| 189 | 16 | 1 m. brown .. .. | 20 | 1·25 |
| 190 | | 2 m. violet .. .. | 25 | 2·25 |
| 191 | | 3 m. red .. .. | 30 | 6·00 |
| 192 | – | 5 m. blue .. .. | 50 | 10·00 |
| 193 | – | 10 m. green .. .. | 1·25 | 50·00 |
| 194 | – | 20 m. brown .. .. | 3·25 | 65·00 |

The 5, 10 and 20 m. are larger.

**1919.** Peoples' State Issue. Overprinted **Volksstaat Bayern.** Imperf. or perf.

| | | | | |
|---|---|---|---|---|
| 195. | 15. | 3 pf. brown .. .. | 10 | 1·00 |
| 196. | | 5 pf. green .. .. | 10 | 1·00 |
| 197. | | 7½ pf. green .. .. | 10 | 1·00 |
| 198. | | 10 pf. lake .. .. | 10 | 1·00 |
| 199. | | 15 pf. red .. .. | 10 | 1·00 |
| 200. | | 20 pf. blue .. .. | 10 | 1·00 |
| 201. | | 25 pf. grey .. .. | 10 | 1·00 |
| 202. | | 30 pf. orange .. .. | 10 | 1·00 |
| 203. | | 35 pf. orange .. .. | 10 | 2·00 |
| 204. | | 40 pf. olive .. .. | 10 | 1·10 |
| 205. | | 50 pf. brown .. .. | 10 | 1·10 |
| 206. | | 60 pf. turquoise .. | 10 | 1·10 |
| 207. | | 75 pf. brown .. .. | 10 | 1·10 |
| 208. | | 80 pf. violet .. .. | 10 | 1·40 |
| 209. | 16. | 1 m. brown .. .. | 15 | 1·00 |
| 210. | | 2 m. violet .. .. | 30 | 1·40 |
| 211. | | 3 m. red .. .. | 45 | 4·00 |
| 212. | – | 5 m. blue (No. 192) .. | 70 | 14·00 |
| 213. | – | 10 m. green (No. 193).. | 1·10 | 32·00 |
| 214. | – | 20 m. brown (No. 194) | 2·25 | 40·00 |

**1919.** 1st Free State Issue. Stamps of Germany (inscr "DEUTSCHES REICH") optd **Freistaat Bayern**.

| | | | | |
|---|---|---|---|---|
| 215 | 24 | 2½ pf. grey .. .. | 15 | 70 |
| 216 | 10 | 3 pf. brown .. .. | 15 | 70 |
| 217 | | 5 pf. green .. .. | 15 | 70 |
| 218 | 24 | 7½ pf. orange .. .. | 15 | 1·00 |
| 219 | 10 | 10 pf. red .. .. | 15 | 1·25 |
| 220 | 24 | 15 pf. violet .. .. | 15 | 1·00 |
| 221 | 10 | 20 pf. blue .. .. | 15 | 65 |
| 222 | | 25 pf. blk. & red on yell. | 15 | 1·50 |
| 223 | 24 | 35 pf. brown .. .. | 15 | 1·75 |
| 224 | 10 | 40 pf. black and red .. | 30 | 1·60 |
| 225 | | 75 pf. black and green.. | 40 | 2·25 |
| 226 | | 80 pf. blk. & red on rose | 40 | 3·00 |
| 227 | 12 | 1 m. red .. .. | 85 | 6·00 |
| 228 | 13 | 2 m. blue .. .. | 1·10 | 10·00 |
| 229 | 14 | 3 m. black .. .. | 1·40 | 14·00 |
| 230 | 15 | 5 m. red and black .. | 1·60 | 14·00 |

**1919.** 2nd Free State Issue. Stamps of Bavaria overprinted **Freistaat Bayern.** Imperf. or perf.

| | | | | |
|---|---|---|---|---|
| 231. | 15. | 3 pf. brown .. .. | 10 | 1·40 |
| 232. | | 5 pf. green .. .. | 10 | 1·00 |
| 233. | | 7½ pf. green .. .. | 10 | 14·00 |
| 234. | | 10 pf. lake .. .. | 10 | 1·00 |
| 235. | | 15 pf. red .. .. | 10 | 1·00 |
| 236. | | 20 pf. blue .. .. | 10 | 1·00 |
| 237. | | 25 pf. grey .. .. | 10 | 1·25 |
| 238. | | 30 pf. orange .. .. | 10 | 1·25 |
| 239. | | 40 pf. olive .. .. | 10 | 6·00 |
| 240. | | 50 pf. brown .. .. | 10 | 1·25 |
| 241. | | 60 pf. turquoise .. | 20 | 9·00 |
| 242. | | 75 pf. brown .. .. | 55 | 12·00 |
| 243. | | 80 pf. violet .. .. | 20 | 3·50 |
| 244. | 16. | 1 m. brown .. .. | 30 | 2·25 |
| 245. | | 2 m. violet .. .. | 30 | 6·00 |
| 246. | | 3 m. red .. .. | 40 | 7·50 |
| 247. | – | 5 m. blue (No. 192) .. | 70 | 16·00 |
| 248. | – | 10 m. green (No. 193).. | 1·60 | 32·00 |
| 249. | – | 20 m. brown (No. 194) | 2·00 | 60·00 |

**1919.** War Wounded. Surch. **5 Pf. fur Kriegs-beschadigte Freistaat Bayern.** Perf.

| | | | | |
|---|---|---|---|---|
| 250. | 15. | 10 pf.+5 pf. lake .. | 30 | 1·75 |
| 251. | | 15 pf.+5 pf. red .. | 30 | 1·75 |
| 252. | | 20 pf.+5 pf. blue .. | 30 | 2·00 |

**1920.** Surch. **Freistaat Bayern** and value. Imperf. or perf.

| | | | | |
|---|---|---|---|---|
| 253. | 16. | 1 m. 25 pf. on 1 m. grn. | 20 | 1·10 |
| 254. | | 1 m. 50 pf. on 1 m. orge. | 20 | 3·25 |
| 255. | | 2 m. 50 pf. on 1 m. slate | 30 | 5·00 |

**1920.** No. 121 surch **20** in four corners.

| | | | | |
|---|---|---|---|---|
| 256 | 8 | 20 on 3 pf. brown .. | 20 | 1·10 |

26.

27.

28.

29.

30.

**1920.**

| | | | | |
|---|---|---|---|---|
| 257. | 26. | 5 pf. green .. .. | 20 | 1·00 |
| 258. | | 10 pf. orange .. .. | 20 | 1·00 |
| 259. | | 15 pf. red .. .. | 20 | 1·00 |
| 260. | 27. | 20 pf. violet .. .. | 20 | 1·00 |
| 261. | | 30 pf. blue .. .. | 15 | 1·25 |
| 262. | | 40 pf. brown .. .. | 15 | 1·25 |
| 263. | 28. | 50 pf. red .. .. | 15 | 1·40 |
| 264. | | 60 pf. turquoise .. | 15 | 2·00 |
| 265. | | 75 pf. red .. .. | 15 | 2·00 |
| 266. | 29. | 1 m. red and grey .. | 20 | 2·00 |
| 267. | | 1¼ m. blue and brown | 20 | 2·00 |
| 268. | | 1½ m. green and grey .. | 25 | 3·00 |
| 269. | | 2½ m. black and grey .. | 30 | 6·00 |
| 270. | 30. | 3 m. blue .. .. | 20 | 14·00 |
| 271. | | 5 m. orange .. .. | 40 | 14·00 |
| 272. | | 10 m. green .. .. | 80 | 20·00 |
| 273. | | 20 m. black .. .. | 1·00 | 30·00 |

OFFICIAL STAMPS

O 18.

**1916.**

| | | | | |
|---|---|---|---|---|
| O 195. | O 18. | 3 pf. brown.. .. | 20 | 75 |
| O 196. | | 5 pf. green .. .. | 20 | 75 |
| O 197. | | 7½ pf. green on green | 25 | 60 |
| O 198. | | 7½ pf. green .. | 25 | 60 |
| O 199. | | 10 pf. red .. .. | 25 | 60 |
| O 200. | | 15 pf. red on buff .. | 25 | 60 |
| O 201. | | 15 pf. red .. .. | 25 | 60 |
| O 202. | | 20 pf. blue on blue | 2·00 | 2·00 |
| O 203. | | 20 pf. blue .. .. | 20 | 60 |
| O 204. | | 25 pf. grey .. .. | 25 | 60 |
| O 205. | | 30 pf. orange .. | 25 | 60 |
| O 206. | | 60 pf. turquoise .. | 20 | 65 |
| O 207. | | 1 m. purple on buff.. | 60 | 3·50 |
| O 208. | | 1 m. purple.. .. | 2·50 | £350 |

**1919.** Optd. **Volksstaat Bayern.**

| | | | | |
|---|---|---|---|---|
| O 215. | O 18. | 3 pf. brown.. .. | 20 | 7·00 |
| O 216. | | 5 pf. green .. .. | 20 | 1·00 |
| O 217. | | 7½ pf. green .. | 20 | 9·00 |
| O 218. | | 10 pf. red .. .. | 20 | 1·00 |
| O 219. | | 15 pf. red .. .. | 20 | 60 |
| O 220. | | 20 pf. blue .. .. | 20 | 1·00 |
| O 221. | | 25 pf. grey .. .. | 20 | 1·00 |
| O 222. | | 30 pf. orange .. | 20 | 1·00 |
| O 223. | | 35 pf. orange .. | 20 | 1·00 |
| O 224. | | 50 pf. olive .. | 20 | 1·10 |
| O 225. | | 60 pf. turquoise .. | 25 | 3·25 |
| O 226. | | 75 pf. brown .. | 25 | 2·00 |
| O 227. | | 1 m. purple on buff | 90 | 3·00 |
| O 228. | | 1 m. purple .. | 3·50 | £400 |

O 31.

O 32.

O 33.

**1920.**

| | | | | |
|---|---|---|---|---|
| O 274. | O 31. | 5 pf. green .. .. | 10 | 6·00 |
| O 275. | | 10 pf. orange .. | 10 | 6·00 |
| O 276. | | 15 pf. red .. .. | 10 | 6·00 |
| O 277. | | 20 pf. violet .. | 10 | 6·00 |
| O 278. | | 30 pf. blue .. .. | 10 | 9·00 |
| O 279. | | 40 pf. brown .. | 10 | 9·00 |
| O 280. | O 32. | 50 pf. red .. .. | 10 | 22·00 |
| O 281. | | 60 pf. green .. | 10 | 8·00 |
| O 282. | | 70 pf. lilac .. | 10 | 24·00 |
| O 283. | | 75 pf. red .. .. | 10 | 27·00 |
| O 284. | | 80 pf. blue .. .. | 10 | 30·00 |
| O 285. | | 90 pf. olive .. | 10 | 45·00 |
| O 286. | O 33. | 1 m. brown.. .. | 10 | 32·00 |
| O 287. | | 1¼ m. green .. | 10 | 45·00 |
| O 288. | | 1½ m. red .. .. | 10 | 55·00 |
| O 289. | | 2½ m. blue .. .. | 10 | 60·00 |
| O 290. | | 3 m. lake .. .. | 30 | 75·00 |
| O 291. | | 5 m. deep olive .. | 1·50 | 90·00 |

POSTAGE DUE STAMPS

D 6.

**1862.** Inscr. "Bayer. Posttaxe" at top. Imperf.

| | | | | |
|---|---|---|---|---|
| D 34. | D 6. | 3 k. black | £120 | £350 |

**1870.** As Type D 6, but inscr. "Bayr. Posttaxe" at top. Perf.

| | | | | |
|---|---|---|---|---|
| D 65. | D 6. | 1 k. black | 9·00 | £650 |
| D 66. | | 3 k. black | 9·00 | £350 |

**1876.** Optd **Vom Empfanger zahlbar**.

| | | | | |
|---|---|---|---|---|
| D 130. | 8. | 2 pf. grey | 55 | 1·25 |
| D 131. | | 3 pf. grey | 35 | 1·50 |
| D 132. | | 5 pf. grey | 70 | 1·10 |
| D 133. | | 10 pf. grey | 50 | 35 |

**1895.** No. D131 surch **2** in each corner.

| | | | | |
|---|---|---|---|---|
| D134 | 8 | 2 on 3 pf. grey | † | £40000 |

RAILWAY OFFICIALS' STAMPS

**1908.** Stamps of 1876 optd. **E.**

| | | | | |
|---|---|---|---|---|
| R 133. | 8. | 3 pf. brown | 1·10 | 4·50 |
| R 134. | | 5 pf. green | 15 | 15 |
| R 135. | | 10 pf. red | 15 | 15 |
| R 136. | | 20 pf. blue | 35 | 60 |
| R 137. | | 50 pf. purple | 4·00 | 7·50 |

## BELARUS Pt. 10

Formerly a constituent republic of the Soviet Union, Belarus became independent in 1991.

100 kopeks = 1 rouble

1 12th-century Cross

**1992.**

| | | | | |
|---|---|---|---|---|
| 1 | 1 | 1 r. multicoloured | 1·50 | 1·50 |

2 Shyrma

3 Arms of Polotsk

**1992.** Birth Cent of R. R. Shyrma (composer).

| | | | | |
|---|---|---|---|---|
| 2 | 2 | 20 k. lt blue, blue & black | 75 | 75 |

**1992.**

| | | | | |
|---|---|---|---|---|
| 3 | 3 | 2 r. multicoloured | 1·90 | 1·90 |

See also Nos. 63 and 89/90.

4 Flag and Map

(5)

**1992.**

| | | | | |
|---|---|---|---|---|
| 4 | 4 | 5 r. multicoloured | 1·50 | 1·50 |
| 5 | – | 5 r. black, yellow and red | 1·50 | 1·50 |

DESIGN: No. 5, State arms.

**1992.** Millenary of Orthodox Church in Belarus. No. 1 optd with T **5**.

| | | | | |
|---|---|---|---|---|
| 6 | 1 | 1 r. multicoloured | 75 | 75 |

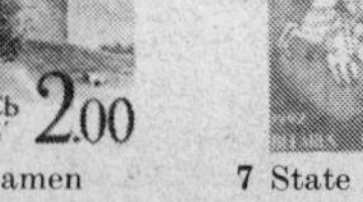

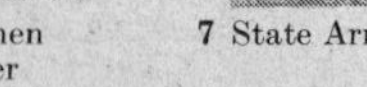

6 Kamen Tower

7 State Arms

**1992.** Ancient Buildings and Mounments. Multicoloured.

| | | | | |
|---|---|---|---|---|
| 8 | | 2 r. Type **6** | 40 | 40 |
| 9 | | 2 r. Calvinist church, Zaslavl | 40 | 40 |
| 10 | | 2 r. St. Euphrosyne's church, Polotsk | 40 | 40 |
| 11 | | 2 r. St. Boris Gleb church, Grodno (horiz) | 40 | 40 |
| 12 | | 2 r. Mir castle (horiz) | 40 | 40 |
| 13 | | 2 r. Nesvizh castle (horiz) | 40 | 40 |

**1992.**

| | | | | |
|---|---|---|---|---|
| 14 | 7 | 30 k. blue | 10 | 10 |
| 15 | | 45 k. green | 10 | 10 |
| 16 | | 50 k. green | 10 | 10 |
| 17 | | 1 r. brown | 15 | 15 |
| 18 | | 2 r. brown | 30 | 30 |
| 19 | | 3 r. yellow | 50 | 50 |
| 20 | | 5 r. blue | 80 | 80 |
| 21 | | 10 r. red | 1·60 | 1·60 |
| 22 | | 15 r. violet | 2·40 | 2·40 |
| 23 | | 25 r. green | 4·00 | 4·00 |
| 25 | | 50 r. mauve | 30 | 30 |
| 27 | | 100 r. red | 55 | 55 |
| 29 | | 150 r. purple | 85 | 85 |
| 30 | | 200 r. green | 20 | 20 |
| 31 | | 300 r. red | 30 | 30 |
| 32 | | 600 r. mauve | 65 | 65 |
| 33 | | 1000 r. red | 85 | 85 |
| 34 | | 3000 r. blue | 1·25 | 1·25 |

8 Jug and Bowl

**1992.** Pottery. Multicoloured.

| | | | | |
|---|---|---|---|---|
| 40 | | 1 r. Type **8** | 30 | 30 |
| 41 | | 1 r. Vases and jug on jug tree | 30 | 30 |
| 42 | | 1 r. Flagon | 30 | 30 |
| 43 | | 1 r. Jugs | 30 | 30 |

9 Chickens

**1993.** Corn Dollies. Multicoloured.

| | | | | |
|---|---|---|---|---|
| 44 | | 5 r. Type **9** | 15 | 15 |
| 45 | | 10 r. Woman and gunman (vert) | 30 | 30 |
| 46 | | 15 r. Woman (vert) | 45 | 45 |
| 47 | | 25 r. Man and woman (vert) | 75 | 75 |

10 Harezki

11 Emblem

**1993.** Birth Centenary of M. I. Harezki (author).

| | | | | |
|---|---|---|---|---|
| 48 | 10 | 50 r. purple | 75 | 75 |

**1993.** World Belarussian Congress, Minsk.

| | | | | |
|---|---|---|---|---|
| 49 | 11 | 50 r. red, gold and black | 75 | 75 |

12 "Man Over Vitebsk"

**1993.** Europa. Contemporary Art. Paintings by Marc Chagall. Multicoloured.

| | | | | |
|---|---|---|---|---|
| 50 | | 1500 r. Type **12** | 3·00 | 3·00 |
| 51 | | 1500 r. "Promenade" (vert) | 3·00 | 3·00 |

XVII ЗІМОВЫЯ
АЛІМПІЙСКІЯ
ГУЛЬНІ
ЛІЛЕХАМЕР,
НАРВЕГІЯ, 1994

1500

(13)

ЧЭМПІЯНАТ СВЕТУ
ПА ФУТБОЛУ.
ЗША, 1994

1500

(14)

**1993.** Sports Events. Nos. 4/5 variously surcharged. (a) Winter Olympic Games, Lillehammer, Norway (1994). Surch **Winter Pre-Olympic Games Lillehammer, Norway 1500** (in capitals on No. 44) or in Cyrillic as T **13**.

| | | | | |
|---|---|---|---|---|
| 53 | 4 | 1500 r. on 5 r. mult (in Cyrillic) | 2·40 | 2·40 |
| 54 | | 1500 r. on 5 r. mult (in English) | 2·40 | 2·40 |
| 55 | – | 1500 r. on 5 r. black, yellow and red (in Cyrillic) | 2·40 | 2·40 |
| 56 | – | 1500 r. on 5 r. black, yellow and red (in English) | 2·40 | 2·40 |

(b) World Cup Football Championship, U.S.A. (1994). Surch **WORLD CUP USA 94 1500** or in Cyrillic as T **14**.

| | | | | |
|---|---|---|---|---|
| 58 | 4 | 1500 r. on 5 r. mult (in Cyrillic) | 2·40 | 2·40 |
| 59 | | 1500 r. on 5 r. mult (in English) | 2·40 | 2·40 |
| 60 | – | 1500 r. on 5 r. black, yellow and red (in Cyrillic) | 2·40 | 2·40 |
| 61 | – | 1500 r. on 5 r. black, yellow and red (in English) | 2·40 | 2·40 |

**1993.** Town Arms. As T **3**. Multicoloured.

| | | | | |
|---|---|---|---|---|
| 63 | | 25 r. Minsk | 35 | 35 |

15 St. Stanislav's Church, Mogilev

**1993.**

| | | | | |
|---|---|---|---|---|
| 64 | 15 | 150 r. multicoloured | 75 | 75 |

16 Kastus Kalinowski (leader)

**1993.** 130th Anniv of Peasants' Uprising.

| | | | | |
|---|---|---|---|---|
| 65 | 16 | 50 r. multicoloured | 35 | 35 |

17 Princess Ragneda

18 Statue of Budny

**1993.** 10th-century Rulers of Polotsk. Mult.

| | | | | |
|---|---|---|---|---|
| 66 | | 75 r. Type **17** | 40 | 40 |
| 67 | | 75 r. Prince Ragvalod and map | 40 | 40 |

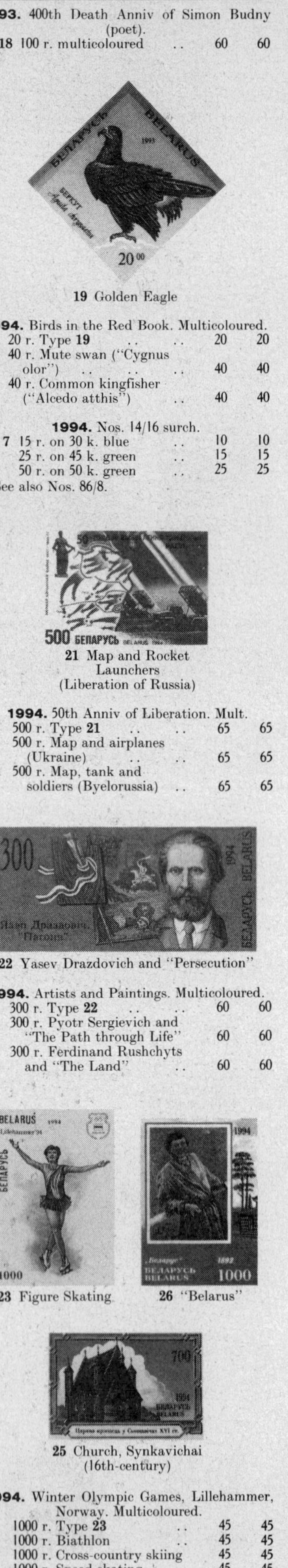

**1993.** 400th Death Anniv of Simon Budny (poet).

| | | | | |
|---|---|---|---|---|
| 68 | 18 | 100 r. multicoloured | 60 | 60 |

19 Golden Eagle

**1994.** Birds in the Red Book. Multicoloured.

| | | | | |
|---|---|---|---|---|
| 69 | | 20 r. Type **19** | 20 | 20 |
| 70 | | 40 r. Mute swan ("Cygnus olor") | 40 | 40 |
| 71 | | 40 r. Common kingfisher ("Alcedo atthis") | 40 | 40 |

**1994.** Nos. 14/16 surch.

| | | | | |
|---|---|---|---|---|
| 72 | 7 | 15 r. on 30 k. blue | 10 | 10 |
| 73 | | 25 r. on 45 k. green | 15 | 15 |
| 74 | | 50 r. on 50 k. green | 25 | 25 |

See also Nos. 86/8.

21 Map and Rocket Launchers (Liberation of Russia)

**1994.** 50th Anniv of Liberation. Mult.

| | | | | |
|---|---|---|---|---|
| 75 | | 500 r. Type **21** | 65 | 65 |
| 76 | | 500 r. Map and airplanes (Ukraine) | 65 | 65 |
| 77 | | 500 r. Map, tank and soldiers (Byelorussia) | 65 | 65 |

22 Yasev Drazdovich and "Persecution"

**1994.** Artists and Paintings. Multicoloured.

| | | | | |
|---|---|---|---|---|
| 78 | | 300 r. Type **22** | 60 | 60 |
| 79 | | 300 r. Pyotr Sergievich and "The Path through Life" | 60 | 60 |
| 80 | | 300 r. Ferdinand Rushchyts and "The Land" | 60 | 60 |

23 Figure Skating

26 "Belarus"

25 Church, Synkavichai (16th-century)

**1994.** Winter Olympic Games, Lillehammer, Norway. Multicoloured.

| | | | | |
|---|---|---|---|---|
| 81 | | 1000 r. Type **23** | 45 | 45 |
| 82 | | 1000 r. Biathlon | 45 | 45 |
| 83 | | 1000 r. Cross-country skiing | 45 | 45 |
| 84 | | 1000 r. Speed skating | 45 | 45 |
| 85 | | 1000 r. Ice hockey | 45 | 45 |

**1994.** Birds in the Red Book. As Nos. 69/71 but values changed. Multicoloured.

| | | | | |
|---|---|---|---|---|
| 86 | | 300 r. As Type **19** | 40 | 40 |
| 87 | | 400 r. As No. 70 | 55 | 55 |
| 88 | | 400 r. As No. 71 | 55 | 55 |

**1994.** Town Arms. As T **3**. Multicoloured.
89 700 r. Grodno . . . . 40 40
90 700 r. Vitebsk . . . . 40 40

**1994.** Religious Buildings. Multicoloured.
91 700 r. Type **25** . . . . 50 50
92 700 r. Sts. Peter and Paul's Cathedral, Gomel (19th-century) . . . . 50 50

**1994.** 150th Birth Anniv of Ilya Repin (painter). Multicoloured.
93 1000 r. Type **26** . . . . 60 60
94 1000 r. Repin Museum . . 60 60
Nos. 93/4 were issued together, se-tenant, forming a composite design.

**27** Tomasz Wojshezki and Battle Scene

**1995.** Bicentenary (1994) of Polish Insurrection. Multicoloured.
95 600 r. Type **27** . . . . 25 25
96 600 r. Jakub Jasinski . . 25 25
97 1000 r. Mikhail Aginski . . 40 40
98 1000 r. Tadeusz Kosciuszko 40 40

**28** Memorial

**29** Aleksandr Stepanovich Popov (radio pioneer)

**1995.** 50th Anniv of End of Second World War. Multicoloured.
99 180 r. Type **28** . . . . 20 20
100 600 r. Clouds and memorial 65 65

**1995.** Centenary of First Radio Transmission (by Guglielmo Marconi).
101 **29** 600 r. multicoloured . . 55 55

**30** Obelisk to the Fallen of the Red Army, Minsk

**31** Cherski

**1995.**
102 **30** 180 r. bistre and red . . 10 10
103 200 r. green and bistre 15 15
104 280 r. green and blue . . 25 25
107 600 r. purple and bistre 55 55

**1995.** 150th Birth Anniv of Ivan Cherski (explorer).
115 **31** 600 r. multicoloured . . 65 65

**32** Motal

**33** Head of Beaver

**1995.** Traditional Costumes. Multicoloured.
116 180 r. Type **32** . . . . 10 10
117 600 r. Vaukavysk-Kamyanets . . . . 55 55
118 1200 r. Pukhavits . . 1·10 1·10

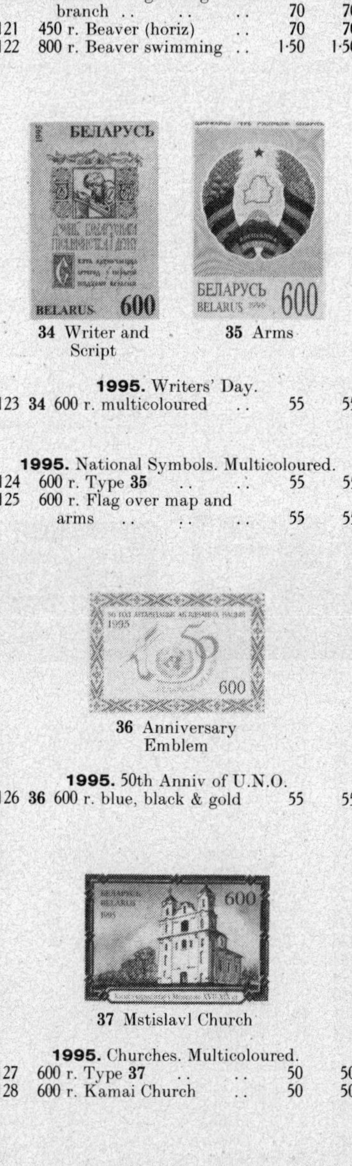

**1995.** The Eurasian Beaver. Multicoloured.
119 300 r. Type **33** . . . . 55 55
120 450 r. Beaver gnawing branch . . . . . . 70 70
121 450 r. Beaver (horiz) . . 70 70
122 800 r. Beaver swimming . . 1·50 1·50

**34** Writer and Script

**35** Arms

**1995.** Writers' Day.
123 **34** 600 r. multicoloured . . 55 55

**1995.** National Symbols. Multicoloured.
124 600 r. Type **35** . . . . 55 55
125 600 r. Flag over map and arms . . . . . . 55 55

**36** Anniversary Emblem

**1995.** 50th Anniv of U.N.O.
126 **36** 600 r. blue, black & gold 55 55

**37** Mstislavl Church

**1995.** Churches. Multicoloured.
127 600 r. Type **37** . . . . 50 50
128 600 r. Kamai Church . . 50 50

1995
125 год
з дня нараджэння
(38)

**1995.** 125th Birth Anniv of Ferdinand Rushchyts (artist). No. 80 optd with T **38**.
129 300 r. multicoloured . . 25 25

**39** Sukhoi and Aircraft

**1995.** Birth Centenary of P. V. Sukhoi (aircraft designer).
130 **39** 600 r. multicoloured . . 30 30

**41** Leu Sapega (statesman)

**1995.** 17th-century Belarussians. Mult.
132 600 r. Type **41** . . . . 15 15
133 1200 r. Kazimir Semyanovich (military scholar) . . . . . . 30 30
134 1800 r. Simyaon Polatski (writer) . . . . . . 60 60

**42** Lynx

**1996.** Mammals. Multicoloured.
135 1000 r. Type **42** . . . . 20 20
136 2000 r. Roe deer (vert) . . 40 40
137 2000 r. Brown bear . . 40 40
138 3000 r. Elk (vert) . . . . 60 60
139 5000 r. European bison . . 1·00 1·00

**1996.** Nos. 17 and 23 optd with capital letter.
140 **7** B (200 r.) on 1 r. brown 25 25
141 A (400 r.) on 25 r. green 15 15

**44** Krapiva

**1996.** Birth Centenary of Kandrat Krapiva (writer).
142 **44** 1000 r. multicoloured . . 35 35

**46** Purple Emperor ("Apatura iris")

**1996.** Butterflies and Moths. Multicoloured.
144 300 r. Type **46** . . . . 55 55
145 300 r. "Lopinga achine" . . 55 55
146 300 r. Scarlet tiger moth ("Callimorpha dominula") . . . . 55 55
147 300 r. Clifden's nonpareil ("Catocala fraxini") . . 55 55
148 300 r. Swallowtail ("Papilio machaon") . . . . 55 55
149 300 r. Apollo ("Parnassius apollo") . . . . 55 55
150 300 r. "Ammobiota hebe" 55 55
151 300 r. Palaeno sulphur yellow ("Colias palaeno") . . . . 55 55

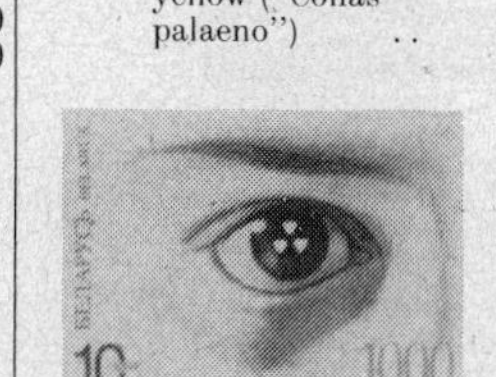

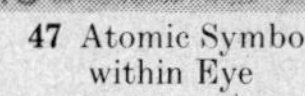

**47** Atomic Symbol within Eye

**48** State Arms

**1996.** 10th Anniv of Chernobyl Nuclear Disaster. Multicoloured.
153 1000 r. Type **47** . . . . 35 35
154 1000 r. Ruins of nuclear reactor . . . . . . 35 35
155 1000 r. Atomic symbol on diseased leaf . . . . 35 35
156 1000 r. Atomic symbol on boarded-up window . . 35 35

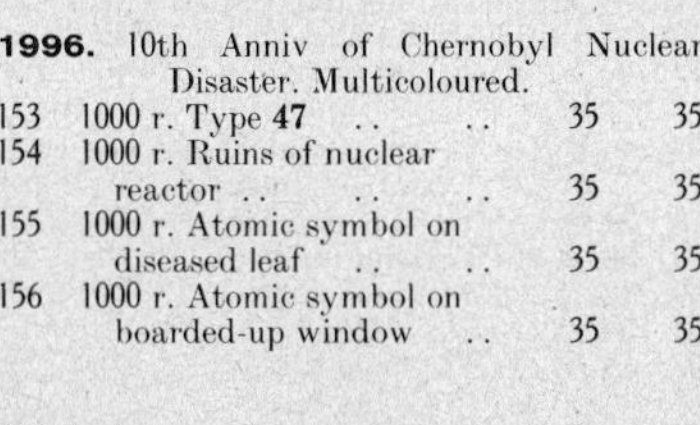

**1996.** Arms and value in black, background colours given.
160 **48** 100 r. blue . . . . 10 10
162 500 r. green . . . . 15 15
163 600 r. red . . . . 20 20
165 1000 r. orange . . . . 30 30
166 1500 r. mauve . . . . 45 45
167 1800 r. violet . . . . 55 55
169 2200 r. mauve . . . . 70 70
171 3300 r. yellow . . . . 85 85
173 5000 r. blue . . . . 1·00 1·00
176 10000 r. green . . . . 1·25 1·25
178 30000 r. brown . . . . 4·00 4·00
179 50000 r. red . . . . 6·25 6·25

**49** Russian and Belorussian Flags

**1996.** Russian–Belorussian Treaty.
182 **49** 1500 r. multicoloured . . 40 40

**50** Gymnastics

**51** Kapyl-Kletski

**1996.** Olympic Games, Atlanta. Mult.
183 3000 r. Type **50** . . . . 1·10 1·10
184 3000 r. Throwing the discus 1·10 1·10
185 3000 r. Weightlifting . . 1·10 1·10
186 3000 r. Wrestling . . 1·10 1·10

**1996.** Traditional Costumes. Multicoloured.
188 1800 r. Type **51** . . . . 35 35
189 2200 r. David-Garadots Turau . . . . . . 45 45
190 3300 r. Kobryn . . . . 1·10 1·10

## BELGIAN CONGO Pt. 4

A Belgian colony in Central Africa. Became independent in July, 1960. For later issues see Congo, Zaire, Katanga and South Kasai.

100 centimes = 1 franc.

### INDEPENDENT STATE OF THE CONGO

The Independent State of the Congo was established in 1885, with King Leopold II of the Belgians as ruler.

1. Leopold II. 5. Leopold II.

**1886.** Various frames.

| No. | Type | Description | Unused | Used |
|---|---|---|---|---|
| 1. | 1. | 5 c. green .. | 8·00 | 18·00 |
| 2. | | 10 c. red .. | 3·00 | 4·00 |
| 3. | | 25 c. blue .. | 35·00 | 32·00 |
| 4. | | 50 c. green | 6·00 | 6·00 |
| 5. | | 5 f. lilac .. | £275 | £225 |

**1887.** Surch. **COLIS-POSTAUX Fr. 3.50.**

| No. | Type | Description | Unused | Used |
|---|---|---|---|---|
| 6. | 1. | 3 f. 50 on 5 f. lilac | £850 | £600 |

**1887.**

| No. | Type | Description | Unused | Used |
|---|---|---|---|---|
| 7. | 5. | 5 c. green .. | 60 | 60 |
| 8. | | 10 c. red | 90 | 80 |
| 9. | | 25 c. blue .. | 85 | 70 |
| 10. | | 50 c. brown | 35·00 | 18·00 |
| 11. | | 50 c. grey | 2·00 | 13·00 |
| 12. | | 5 f. lilac .. | £750 | £300 |
| 13. | | 5 f. grey .. | 90·00 | 75·00 |
| 14. | | 10 f. orange | £350 | £250 |

**1887.** Surch. **COLIS-POSTAUX Fr. 3.50.**

| No. | Type | Description | Unused | Used |
|---|---|---|---|---|
| 15. | 5. | 3 f. 50 on 5 f. violet | £700 | £400 |

**1889.** Surch **COLIS-POSTAUX Fr. 3.50** in frame.

| No. | Type | Description | Unused | Used |
|---|---|---|---|---|
| 16. | 5. | 3 f. 50 on 5 f. violet | £550 | £300 |
| 17. | | 3 f. 50 on 5 f. grey | 95·00 | 65·00 |

7. Port of Matadi.

8. Stanley Falls. 13. Oil Palms.

14. Native Canoe.

**1894.** Inscr "ETAT INDEPENDANT DU CONGO".

| No. | Type | Description | Unused | Used |
|---|---|---|---|---|
| 18 | 7 | 5 c. black and blue | 11·00 | 11·00 |
| 24 | | 5 c. black and brown | 2·50 | 1·25 |
| 30 | | 5 c. black and green | 1·40 | 35 |
| 19 | 8 | 10 c. black and brown | 11·00 | 11·00 |
| 25 | | 10 c. black and blue | 1·10 | 90 |
| 31 | | 10 c. black and red | 2·75 | 35 |
| 26 | 13 | 15 c. black and brown | 3·00 | 40 |
| 20 | – | 25 c. black and orange | 3·00 | 2·00 |
| 32 | – | 25 c. black and blue | 2·50 | 90 |
| 27 | 14 | 40 c. black and green | 3·00 | 2·00 |
| 21 | – | 50 c. black and green | 2·50 | 90 |
| 33 | – | 50 c. black and brown | 5·25 | 60 |
| 22 | – | 1 f. black and violet | 16·00 | 10·00 |
| 35 | – | 1 f. black and red | £180 | 5·00 |
| 28 | – | 3 f. 50 black and red | £120 | 80·00 |
| 23 | – | 5 f. black and red | 35·00 | 24·00 |
| 29 | – | 10 f. black and green | 80·00 | 24·00 |

DESIGNS—HORIZ. 25 c. Inkissi Falls. 50 c. Railway Bridge over the M'pozo. 1 f. African elephant hunt. 3 f. 50 Congo village. 10 f. "Deliverance" (stern wheel paddle-steamer). VERT. 5 f. Bangala Chief Morangi and wife.

### BELGIAN CONGO

The Congo was annexed to Belgium in 1908 and was renamed the Belgian Congo.

**1909.** Nos. 23, 26/29 and 30/33 optd **CONGO BELGE.**

| No. | Type | Description | Unused | Used |
|---|---|---|---|---|
| 36 | 7 | 5 c. black and green | 2·00 | 1·50 |
| 37 | 8 | 10 c. black and red | 2·00 | 1·50 |
| 38 | 13 | 15 c. black and brown | 4·50 | 2·75 |
| 39 | – | 25 c. black and blue | 6·00 | 2·75 |
| 50 | 14 | 40 c. black and green | 2·00 | 2·00 |
| 51 | – | 50 c. black and brown | 3·75 | 1·75 |
| 52 | – | 1 f. black and red | 18·00 | 4·00 |
| 53 | – | 3 f. 50 black and red | 20·00 | 17·00 |
| 54 | – | 5 f. black and red | 38·00 | 22·00 |
| 55b | – | 10 f. black and green | 75·00 | 20·00 |

**1909.** As 1894 issue but inscr "CONGO BELGE".

| No. | Type | Description | Unused | Used |
|---|---|---|---|---|
| 56 | 7 | 5 c. black and green | 60 | 50 |
| 57 | 8 | 10 c. black and red | 55 | 35 |
| 58 | 13 | 15 c. black and brown | 23·00 | 12·00 |
| 59 | – | 50 c. black and bistre | 4·00 | 3·25 |

**1910.** As 1894 issue but inscr "CONGO BELGE BELGISCH-CONGO" with values in French and Flemish.

| No. | Type | Description | Unused | Used |
|---|---|---|---|---|
| 60 | 7 | 5 c. black and green | 50 | 20 |
| 61 | 8 | 10 c. black and red | 60 | 15 |
| 62 | 13 | 15 c. black and brown | 40 | 15 |
| 63 | – | 25 c. black and blue | 1·25 | 25 |
| 64 | 14 | 40 c. black and green | 2·00 | 1·75 |
| 65 | – | 50 c. black and bistre | 3·25 | 1·75 |
| 66 | – | 1 f. black and red | 3·25 | 2·40 |
| 68 | – | 3 f. black and red | 16·00 | 10·00 |
| 67 | – | 5 f. black and red | 23·00 | 22·00 |
| 69 | – | 10 f. black and green | 18·00 | 17·00 |

32. Port of Matadi.

33. Stanley Falls.

34. Inkissi Falls.

**1915.** New types as **32** to **34** (with value in words at top) and other types as 1910 all inscr. "CONGO BELGE" and "BELGISCH-CONGO".

| No. | Type | Description | Unused | Used |
|---|---|---|---|---|
| 70. | 32. | 5 c. black and green | 20 | 15 |
| 71. | 33. | 10 c. black and red | 20 | 15 |
| 72b. | 13. | 15 c. black and green | 25 | 20 |
| 73. | 34. | 25 c. black and blue | 95 | 25 |
| 74. | 14. | 40 c. black and red | 4·00 | 2·00 |
| 75. | – | 50 c. black and red | 6·50 | 2·00 |
| 76. | – | 1 f. black and olive | 2·25 | 60 |
| 77. | – | 5 f. black and orange | 1·40 | 60 |

**1918.** Types as before surch. with red cross and premium.

| No. | Type | Description | Unused | Used |
|---|---|---|---|---|
| 78. | 32. | 5 c.+10 c. blue & green | 20 | 25 |
| 79. | 33. | 10 c.+15 c. blue and red | 20 | 25 |
| 80. | 13. | 15 c.+20 c. blue & green | 20 | 25 |
| 81. | 34. | 25 c.+25 c. blue .. | 25 | 25 |
| 82. | 14. | 40 c.+40 c. blue & red .. | 35 | 45 |
| 83. | – | 50 c.+50 c. blue & red .. | 50 | 1·25 |
| 84. | – | 1 f.+1 f. blue and olive | 1·75 | 1·75 |
| 85. | – | 5 f.+5 f. blue & orange | 10·00 | 10·00 |
| 86. | – | 10 f.+10 f. blue & green | 95·00 | 95·00 |

38. Congo Wharf.

**1920.** Air.

| No. | Type | Description | Unused | Used |
|---|---|---|---|---|
| 87 | 38 | 50 c. black and orange | 20 | 10 |
| 88 | – | 1 f. black and violet | 20 | 10 |
| 89 | – | 2 f. black and blue | 55 | 20 |
| 90 | – | 5 f. black and green | 1·10 | 55 |

DESIGNS—HORIZ. 1 f. District stores. 2 f. Native canoes on beach. VERT. 5 f. Provincial prison.

**1921.** Stamps of 1910 surch.

| No. | Type | Description | Unused | Used |
|---|---|---|---|---|
| 91 | 14 | 5 c. on 40 c. black & green | 20 | 20 |
| 92 | – | 10 c. on 5 c. black & green | 20 | 20 |
| 93 | – | 15 c. on 50 c. blk. & olive | 25 | 50 |
| 94 | 13 | 25 c. on 15 c. blk. & yell. | 1·60 | 90 |
| 95 | 8 | 30 c. on 10 c. blk. & red | 25 | 25 |
| 96 | – | 50 c. on 25 c. blk. & blue | 1·75 | 90 |

**1921.** Stamps of 1910 optd. **1921.**

| No. | Type | Description | Unused | Used |
|---|---|---|---|---|
| 97. | | 1 f. black and red .. | 1·00 | 70 |
| 98. | | 3 f. black and red .. | 2·50 | 2·50 |
| 99. | | 5 f. black and lake .. | 8·00 | 8·00 |
| 100. | | 10 f. black and green .. | 5·50 | 4·00 |

**1922.** Stamps of previous issues variously surch. without bars.

| No. | Type | Description | Unused | Used |
|---|---|---|---|---|
| 101 | – | 5 c. on 50 c. black and lake (No. 75) | 60 | 50 |
| 102 | 32 | 10 c. on 5 c. black and green (No. 70) | 35 | 25 |
| 114 | 8 | 0.25 on 30 c. on 10 c. black & red (No. 95) | 9·00 | 9·00 |
| 115 | 33 | 0.25 on 30 c. on 10 c. blk. & red (No. 104) | 9·00 | 9·00 |
| 103 | 14 | 25 c. on 40 c. black and lake (No. 74) .. | 2·00 | 30 |
| 104 | 33 | 30 c. on 10 c. black and red (No. 71) .. | 20 | 20 |
| 105 | 34 | 50 c. on 25 c. black and blue (No. 73) | 40 | 25 |

**1922.** Stamps of 1915 surch. with new value and two bars **through** old values.

| No. | Type | Description | Unused | Used |
|---|---|---|---|---|
| 108 | 32 | 10 c. on 5 c. black & green | 40 | 35 |
| 110 | – | 10 c. on 1 f. black & olive | 50 | 50 |
| 112 | 14 | 25 c. on 40 c. black & lake | 70 | 30 |
| 113 | – | 25 c. on 5 f. blk. & orange | 1·40 | 1·40 |

46. Wood Carver. 56. Native Cattle.

**1923.**

| No. | Type | Description | Unused | Used |
|---|---|---|---|---|
| 117. | A. | 5 c. yellow | 15 | 10 |
| 118. | B. | 10 c. green | 15 | 10 |
| 119. | C. | 15 c. brown | 15 | 10 |
| 120. | D. | 20 c. olive | 15 | 10 |
| 121. | E. | 20 c. green | 15 | 10 |
| 122. | F. | 25 c. brown | 20 | 10 |
| 123. | 46. | 30 c. red | 30 | 40 |
| 124. | | 30 c. olive | 15 | 10 |
| 125. | | 35 c. green | 40 | 40 |
| 126. | D. | 40 c. purple | 15 | 10 |
| 142. | 56. | 45 c. purple | 30 | 25 |
| 127. | G. | 50 c. blue | 20 | 10 |
| 128. | | 50 c. orange | 30 | 10 |
| 143. | 56. | 60 c. red | 30 | 15 |
| 129. | E. | 75 c. orange | 30 | 20 |
| 130. | | 75 c. blue | 30 | 20 |
| 131. | 46. | 75 c. red | 20 | 10 |
| 132. | H. | 1 f. brown | 45 | 15 |
| 133. | | 1 f. blue | 35 | 10 |
| 134. | | 1 f. red .. | 60 | 10 |
| 135. | D. | 1 f. 25 blue | 30 | 20 |
| 136. | | 1 f. 50 blue | 30 | 15 |
| 137. | | 1 f. 75 blue | 3·50 | 3·00 |
| 138. | I. | 3 f. brown | 3·50 | 95 |
| 139. | J. | 5 f. grey | 9·50 | 4·50 |
| 140. | K. | 10 f. black | 20·00 | 6·00 |

DESIGNS: A, Ubangi woman. B, Baluba woman. C, Babuende woman. D, Ubangi man. E, Weaver. F, Basketmaker. G. Archer. H, Potter. I, Rubber worker. J, Palm oil. K, African elephant.

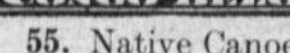

55. Native Canoe. 58. H. M. Stanley.

**1925.** Great War Colonial Memorial Fund. Inscr in French or in Flemish.

| No. | Type | Description | Unused | Used |
|---|---|---|---|---|
| 141 | 55 | 25 c.+25 c. black and red | 20 | 20 |

**1927.** No. 136 surch. **1.75.**

| No. | Type | Description | Unused | Used |
|---|---|---|---|---|
| 144. | | 1.75 on 1 f. 50 blue .. | 35 | 20 |

**1928.** 50th Anniv. of Stanley's Exploration of the Congo.

| No. | Type | Description | Unused | Used |
|---|---|---|---|---|
| 145. | 58. | 5 c. olive | 10 | 10 |
| 146. | | 10 c. violet | 10 | 10 |
| 147. | | 20 c. red | 20 | 15 |
| 148. | | 35 c. green | 65 | 60 |
| 149. | | 40 c. brown | 25 | 15 |
| 150. | | 60 c. sepia | 25 | 15 |
| 151. | | 1 f. red .. | 25 | 10 |
| 152. | | 1 f. 60 grey | 4·50 | 4·50 |
| 153. | | 1 f. 75 blue | 1·10 | 60 |
| 154. | | 2 f. brown | 75 | 25 |
| 155. | | 2 f. 75 purple | 4·50 | 30 |
| 156. | | 3 f. 50 red | 1·00 | 50 |
| 157. | | 5 f. turquoise | 80 | 20 |
| 158. | | 10 f. blue | 1·10 | 60 |
| 159. | | 20 f. red | 4·25 | 3·50 |

59. Nurse weighing Children. 60. Doctor and Tent Surgery.

**1930.** Congo Natives Protection Fund.

| No. | Type | Description | Unused | Used |
|---|---|---|---|---|
| 160 | 59 | 10 c.+5 c. red .. | 45 | 45 |
| 161 | – | 20 c.+10 c. brown | 60 | 60 |
| 162 | 60 | 35 c.+15 c. green | 95 | 95 |
| 163 | – | 60 c.+30 c. purple | 1·25 | 1·25 |
| 164 | – | 1 f.+50 c. red .. | 2·00 | 2·00 |
| 165 | – | 1 f. 75+75 c. blue | 3·00 | 3·00 |
| 166 | – | 3 f. 50+1 f. 50 red | 7·00 | 7·00 |
| 167 | – | 5 f.+2 f. 50 brown | 6·00 | 6·00 |
| 168 | – | 10 f.+5 f. black | 7·00 | 7·00 |

DESIGNS—VERT. 20 c. Missionary and child. 1 f. Dispenser attending patients. HORIZ. 60 c. Local hospital. 1 f. 75, Nurses and patients. 3 f. 50 Nurse bathing baby. 5 f. Operating theatre. 10 f. Children in school.

61. Native Kraal.

DESIGN: 30 f. Native porters.

**1930.** Air.

| No. | Type | Description | Unused | Used |
|---|---|---|---|---|
| 169. | 61. | 15 f. black and sepia .. | 2·00 | 85 |
| 170. | – | 30 f. black and purple .. | 2·25 | 90 |

**1931.** Surch.

| No. | Type | Description | Unused | Used |
|---|---|---|---|---|
| 171. | | 40 c. on 35 c. grn. (No. 148) | 60 | 50 |
| 177. | | 40 c. on 35 c. green (125) .. | 3·50 | 3·50 |
| 178. | | 50 c. on 45 c. purple (142) | 2·25 | 1·00 |
| 172. | | 1 f. 25 on 1 f. red (151) | 40 | 10 |
| 173. | | 2 f. on 1 f. 60 grey (152) | 80 | 30 |
| 174. | | 2 f. on 1 f. 75 blue (153) | 70 | 25 |
| 179. | | 2 f. on 1 f. 75 blue (137) .. | 10·00 | 8·50 |
| 175. | | 3 f. 25 on 2 f. 75 purple (155) | 2·75 | 1·75 |
| 180. | | 3 f. 25 on 3 f. brown (138) | 4·00 | 2·75 |
| 176. | | 3 f. 25 on 3 f. 50 red (156) | 4·00 | 4·00 |

67. Sankuru River. 68. Flute Players.

**1931.**

| No. | Type | Description | Unused | Used |
|---|---|---|---|---|
| 181. | 67. | 10 c. brown | 10 | 10 |
| 182. | – | 15 c. grey | 10 | 10 |
| 183. | – | 20 c. mauve | 10 | 10 |
| 184. | – | 25 c. blue | 10 | 10 |
| 185. | 68. | 40 c. green | 20 | 20 |
| 186. | – | 50 c. violet | 10 | 10 |
| 187. | – | 60 c. purple | 10 | 10 |
| 188. | – | 75 c. red | 10 | 10 |
| 189. | – | 1 f. red .. | 15 | 10 |
| 190. | – | 1 f. 25 brown .. | 15 | 10 |
| 190b. | – | 1 f. 50 black | 15 | 10 |
| 191. | – | 2 f. blue | 20 | 10 |
| 191a. | – | 2 f. 50 blue | 50 | 15 |
| 192. | – | 3 f. 25 grey | 75 | 30 |
| 193. | – | 4 f. lilac | 30 | 15 |
| 194. | – | 5 f. purple | 60 | 20 |
| 195. | – | 10 f. orange | 60 | 45 |
| 196. | – | 20 f. sepia | 1·75 | 1·60 |

DESIGNS—HORIZ. 15 c. Native kraal. 20 c. Waterfall. 25 c. Native kraal. 50 c. Native musicians. 1 f, 50, 2 f., 4 f. Riverside scenes (different views). 2 f. 50, 3 f. 25, Okapi. VERT. 60 c. Native flute-players and drummers. 75 c. Mangbethu woman. 1 f. Elephant transport. 1 f. 25, Native chief. 5 f. Pressing out tapioca. 10 f. Witch doctor. 20 f. Woman carrying latex.

**69.** Fokker F.VIIb/3m over Congo. **70.** King Albert I.

**1934.** Air.

| | | | | |
|---|---|---|---|---|
| 197 | 69 | 50 c. black .. .. | 15 | 15 |
| 198 | | 1 f. red .. .. | 20 | 15 |
| 199 | | 1 f. 50 green .. .. | 20 | 15 |
| 200 | | 3 f. brown .. .. | 25 | 10 |
| 201 | | 4 f. 50 blue .. .. | 30 | 15 |
| 202 | | 5 f. red .. .. | 30 | 10 |
| 203 | | 15 f. purple .. .. | 40 | 30 |
| 204 | | 30 f. red .. .. | 90 | 85 |
| 205 | | 50 f. violet .. .. | 3·00 | 2·00 |

**1934.** Death of King Albert.

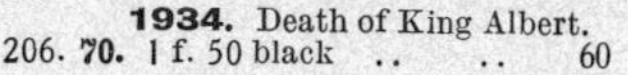

| | | | | |
|---|---|---|---|---|
| 206. | 70. | 1 f. 50 black .. .. | 60 | 30 |

**71.** The Kings of Belgium.

**1935.** 50th Anniv. of Independent State of the Congo.

| | | | | |
|---|---|---|---|---|
| 207. | 71. | 50 c. green .. .. | 1·00 | 50 |
| 208. | | 1 f. 25 red .. .. | 1·00 | 15 |
| 209. | | 1 f. 50 purple .. .. | 1·00 | 10 |
| 210. | | 2 f. 40 orange .. .. | 2·50 | 2·40 |
| 211. | | 2 f. 50 blue .. .. | 2·50 | 80 |
| 212. | | 4 f. violet .. .. | 2·50 | 1·60 |
| 213. | | 5 f. brown .. .. | 2·50 | 1·75 |

**1936.** Air. Surch **3.50F.**

| | | | | |
|---|---|---|---|---|
| 214 | 69 | 3 f. 50 on 3 f. brown .. | 20 | 10 |

**1936.** King Albert Memorial Fund. Surch. **+50 c.**

| | | | | |
|---|---|---|---|---|
| 215. | 71. | 1 f. 50+50 c. purple .. | 4·00 | 3·50 |
| 216. | | 2 f. 50+50 c. blue .. | 2·00 | 1·50 |

**74.** Queen Astrid and Congo Children. **76.** R. Molindi.

**1936.** Queen Astrid Fund for Congo Children.

| | | | | |
|---|---|---|---|---|
| 217. | 74. | 1 f. 25+5 c. brown .. | 50 | 45 |
| 218. | | 1 f. 50+10 c. red .. | 50 | 45 |
| 219. | | 2 f. 50+25 c. blue .. | 60 | 60 |

**1938.** Promotion of National Parks.

| | | | | |
|---|---|---|---|---|
| 220 | 76 | 5 c. black and violet .. | 10 | 10 |
| 221 | – | 90 c. brown and red .. | 35 | 30 |
| 222 | – | 1 f. 50 black and purple | 10 | 10 |
| 223 | – | 2 f. 40 brown and grey | 10 | 10 |
| 224 | – | 2 f. 50 black and blue .. | 25 | 15 |
| 225 | – | 4 f. 50 brown & green .. | 25 | 15 |

DESIGNS—VERT. 90 c. Bamboo-canes. 1 f. 50, R. Suza. 2 f. 40, R. Rutshuru. HORIZ. 2 f. 50, Mt. Karisimbi. 4 f. 50, Mitumba Forest.

**77.** Marabou stork and Ruppels Griffon.

DESIGNS: 1 f. 25, Kob. 1 f. 50 Young chimpanzees. 4 f. 50, Crocodiles. 5 f. Lioness.

**1939.** Leopoldville Zoological Gardens.

| | | | | |
|---|---|---|---|---|
| 226. | 77. | 1 f.+1 f. purple .. | 6·50 | 5·50 |
| 227. | – | 1 f. 25+1 f. 25 red .. | 5·50 | 5·50 |
| 228. | – | 1 f. 50+1 f. 50 violet .. | 6·00 | 6·00 |
| 229. | – | 4 f. 50+4 f. 50 green .. | 5·00 | 5·00 |
| 230. | – | 5 f.+5 f. brown .. | 5·00 | 5·00 |

**78.** King Albert Memorial, Leopoldville. **81.** "Belgium Shall Rise Again".

**1941.**

| | | | | |
|---|---|---|---|---|
| 231. | 78. | 10 c. grey .. .. | 20 | 20 |
| 232. | | 15 c. brown .. .. | 20 | 20 |
| 233. | | 25 c. blue .. .. | 30 | 25 |
| 234. | | 50 c. lilac .. .. | 20 | 20 |
| 235. | | 75 c. pink .. .. | 1·00 | 40 |
| 236. | | 1 f. 25 brown .. .. | 30 | 30 |
| 237. | | 1 f. 75 orange .. .. | 1·00 | 40 |
| 238. | | 2 f. 50 red .. .. | 60 | 15 |
| 239. | | 2 f. 75 blue .. .. | 90 | 75 |
| 240. | | 5 f. olive .. .. | 4·00 | 4·00 |
| 241. | | 10 f. red .. .. | 2·50 | 3·00 |

**1941.** Surch.

| | | | | |
|---|---|---|---|---|
| 242 | – | 5 c. on 1 f. 50 black and purple (No. 222) (postage) .. .. | 10 | 10 |
| 243 | 78 | 75 c. on 1 f. 75 orange | 20 | 20 |
| 244 | – | 2 f. 50 on 2 f. 40 brown and grey (No. 223) | 90 | 70 |
| 245 | 69 | 50 c. on 1 f. 50 grn (air) | 20 | 20 |

**1942.** War Relief Fund.

| | | | | |
|---|---|---|---|---|
| 246 | 81 | 10 f.+40 f. green .. | 95 | 95 |
| 247 | | 10 f.+40 f. blue .. | 95 | 95 |

**82.** Oil Palms. **84.** Leopard.

**1942.** Inscr. "BELGISCH CONGO BELGE".

| | | | | |
|---|---|---|---|---|
| 248. | 82. | 5 c. red .. .. | 10 | 10 |
| 249. | – | 50 f. black and blue .. | 4·50 | 1·00 |
| 250. | – | 100 f. black and red .. | 5·50 | 2·50 |

Inscr. "CONGO BELGE BELGISCH CONGO", or vice versa.

| | | | | |
|---|---|---|---|---|
| 251. | 82. | 10 c. olive .. .. | 10 | 10 |
| 252. | | 15 c. brown .. .. | 10 | 10 |
| 253. | | 20 c. blue .. .. | 10 | 10 |
| 254. | | 25 c. purple .. .. | 10 | 10 |
| 255. | | 30 c. blue .. .. | 10 | 10 |
| 256. | | 50 c. green .. .. | 10 | 10 |
| 257. | | 60 c. brown .. .. | 10 | 10 |
| 258. | – | 75 c. black and violet .. | 10 | 10 |
| 259. | – | 1 f. black and brown .. | 15 | 10 |
| 260. | – | 1 f. 25 black and red | 15 | 10 |
| 261. | 84. | 1 f. 75 brown .. .. | 75 | 45 |
| 262. | | 2 f. yellow .. .. | 75 | 15 |
| 263. | | 2 f. 50 red .. .. | 75 | 10 |
| 264. | – | 3 f. 50 olive .. .. | 20 | 10 |
| 265. | – | 5 f. orange .. .. | 45 | 15 |
| 266. | – | 6 f. blue .. .. | 40 | 10 |
| 267. | – | 7 f. black .. .. | 40 | 10 |
| 268. | – | 10 f. brown .. .. | 50 | 10 |
| 269. | – | 20 f. black and red .. | 4·00 | 1·00 |

DESIGNS—As Type **82**: 75 c. to 1 f. 25, Head of a native woman. 3 f. 50 to 10 f. Askari sentry. As Type **84**: 20 f. Okapi. 28x33 mm: 50 f. Head of woman. 100 f. Askari sentry.

**1944.** Red Cross Fund. Surch **Au profit de la Croix Rouge Ten voordeele van het Roode Kruis** (or with French and Flemish reversed) and additional value.

| | | | | |
|---|---|---|---|---|
| 269a | 82 | 50 c.+50 f. green .. | 2·40 | 2·40 |
| 269b | – | 1 f. 25+100 f. black and red (No. 260) | 2·40 | 2·40 |
| 269c | 84 | 1 f. 75+100 f. brown .. | 2·40 | 2·50 |
| 269d | – | 3 f. 50+100 f. green (No. 264) .. | 2·40 | 2·50 |

PORTRAITS — As Type **88**: 1 f. 50, Lavigerie. 3 f. Dhanis. 3 f. 50, Lambermont.

**87.** Driving Slaves to Market. **88.** Leopold II.

**1947.** 50th Anniv. of Abolition of Slavery in Belgian Congo.

| | | | | |
|---|---|---|---|---|
| 270. | 87. | 1 f. 25 brown .. .. | 20 | 10 |
| 270a. | – | 1 f. 50 violet .. .. | 1·50 | 25 |
| 270b. | – | 3 f. brown .. .. | 1·50 | 10 |
| 271. | – | 3 f. 50 blue .. .. | 25 | 10 |
| 272. | 88. | 10 f. orange .. .. | 50 | 15 |

**89.** Seated Figure. **90.** Railway Train and Map.

**1947.** Native masks and carvings as T **89.**

| | | | | |
|---|---|---|---|---|
| 273 | 89 | 10 c. orange .. .. | 10 | 10 |
| 274 | A | 15 c. blue .. .. | 10 | 10 |
| 275 | B | 20 c. blue .. .. | 10 | 10 |
| 276 | C | 25 c. red .. .. | 15 | 10 |
| 277 | D | 40 c. purple .. .. | 10 | 10 |
| 278 | 89 | 50 c. brown .. .. | 10 | 10 |
| 279 | A | 70 c. green .. .. | 10 | 10 |
| 280 | B | 75 c. purple .. .. | 10 | 10 |
| 281 | C | 1 f. purple and orange | 1·50 | 10 |
| 281a | A | 1 f. 20 brown and grey | 15 | 10 |
| 282 | D | 1 f. 25 purple and green | 25 | 15 |
| 282a | E | 1 f. 50 red and green .. | 15·00 | 3·50 |
| 282b | B | 1 f. 60 blue and grey .. | 20 | 15 |
| 283 | 89 | 2 f. red and orange .. | 20 | 10 |
| 283a | C | 2 f. 40 grn & turquoise | 30 | 15 |
| 284 | A | 2 f. 50 green and brown | 20 | 10 |
| 284a | E | 3 f. indigo and blue .. | 4·00 | 10 |
| 285 | B | 3 f. 50 green and blue | 3·50 | 20 |
| 286 | C | 5 f. purple and bistre .. | 1·00 | 10 |
| 287 | D | 6 f. green and orange | 1·25 | 10 |
| 287a | F | 6 f. 50 brown and red | 1·40 | 10 |
| 287b | D | 8 f. green and blue .. | 1·00 | 20 |
| 288 | E | 10 f. brown and violet | 3·25 | 10 |
| 289 | F | 20 f. brown and red .. | 1·60 | 10 |
| 290 | E | 50 f. black and brown | 3·00 | 25 |
| 291 | F | 100 f. black and red .. | 3·50 | 55 |

DESIGNS: A, Seated figure (different). B, Kneeling figure. C, Double mask. D, Mask. E, Mask with tassels. F, Mask with horns.

**1948.** 50th Anniv. of Matadi-Leopoldville Railway.

| | | | | |
|---|---|---|---|---|
| 292. | 90. | 2 f. 50 green and blue | 1·75 | 20 |

**91.** Globe and 19th-century Full-rigged Ship. **92.** Allegorical Figure and Map.

**1949.** 75th Anniv. of U.P.U.

| | | | | |
|---|---|---|---|---|
| 293. | 91. | 4 f. blue .. .. | 60 | 15 |

**1950.** 50th Anniv of "Comite Special du Katanga" (Chartered Company).

| | | | | |
|---|---|---|---|---|
| 294. | 92. | 3 f. slate and blue .. | 1·60 | 15 |
| 295. | | 6 f. 50 sepia and red .. | 1·60 | 25 |

**93.** "Littonia". **94.** St. Francis Xavier.

**1952.** Flowers. Multicoloured.

| | | | | |
|---|---|---|---|---|
| 296. | | 10 c. "Dissotis" .. .. | 10 | 10 |
| 297. | | 15 c. "Protea" .. .. | 10 | 10 |
| 298. | | 20 c. "Vellozia" .. .. | 10 | 10 |
| 299. | | 25 c. Type **93** .. .. | 10 | 10 |
| 300. | | 40 c. "Ipomoea" .. .. | 10 | 10 |
| 301. | | 50 c. "Angraecum" .. | 10 | 10 |
| 302. | | 60 c. "Euphorbia" .. | 10 | 10 |
| 303. | | 75 c. "Ochna" .. .. | 10 | 10 |
| 304. | | 1 f. "Hibiscus" .. .. | 10 | 10 |
| 305. | | 1 f. 25 "Protea" .. .. | 1·00 | 35 |
| 306. | | 1 f. 50 "Schizoglossum" .. | 30 | 10 |
| 307. | | 2 f. "Ansellia" .. .. | 30 | 10 |
| 308. | | 3 f. "Costus" .. .. | 30 | 10 |
| 309. | | 4 f. "Nymphaea" .. .. | 35 | 10 |
| 310. | | 5 f. "Thunbergia" .. .. | 40 | 10 |
| 311. | | 6 f. 50 "Thonningia" .. | 1·00 | 10 |
| 312. | | 7 f. "Gerbera" .. .. | 1·60 | 10 |
| 313. | | 8 f. "Gloriosa" .. .. | 2·00 | 15 |
| 314. | | 10 f. "Silene" .. .. | 2·75 | 10 |
| 315. | | 20 f. "Aristolochia" .. | 2·75 | 10 |
| 316. | | 50 f. "Eulophia" .. .. | 9·00 | 40 |
| 317. | | 100 f. "Cryptosepalum" .. | 13·00 | 1·25 |

SIZES: Nos. 296/315, 21 × 25½ mm. Nos. 316/7, 22½ × 32½ mm.

**1953.** 400th Death Anniv. of St. Francis Xavier.

| | | | | |
|---|---|---|---|---|
| 318. | 94. | 1 f. 50 c. black & blue | 60 | 30 |

**95.** Lake Kivu. **96.** Medallion.

**1953.** Kivu Festival.

| | | | | |
|---|---|---|---|---|
| 319. | 95. | 3 f. black and red .. | 1·25 | 20 |
| 320. | | 7 f. brown and blue .. | 1·25 | 25 |

**1954.** 25th Anniv. of Belgian Royal Colonial Institute. No. 322 has different frame.

| | | | | |
|---|---|---|---|---|
| 321. | 96. | 4 f. 50 grey and blue .. | 1·25 | 30 |
| 322. | | 6 f. 50 brown and green | 75 | 10 |

**97.** King Baudouin and Mountains. **98.** Badge and Map.

**1955.** Inscr "CONGO BELGE · BELGISCH CONGO" or vice versa.

| | | | | |
|---|---|---|---|---|
| 323 | 97 | 1 f. 50 black and red .. | 70 | 25 |
| 324 | – | 3 f. black and green .. | 75 | 15 |
| 325 | – | 4 f. 50 black and blue .. | 50 | 10 |
| 326 | – | 6 f. 50 black & purple .. | 70 | 10 |

DESIGNS: 3 f. Forest. 4 f. 50, River. 6 f. 50, Grassland.

**1955.** 5th Int. Congress of African Tourism. Inscr. in Flemish or French.

| | | | | |
|---|---|---|---|---|
| 327. | 98. | 6 f. 50 blue .. .. | 2·10 | 40 |

**1956.** Birth Bicentenary of Mozart. As T **316/17** of Belgium.

| | | | | |
|---|---|---|---|---|
| 328. | 316. | 4 f. 50+1 f. 50 violet | 3·00 | 1·40 |
| 329. | 317. | 6 f. 50+2 f. 50 blue .. | 4·00 | 2·00 |

**99.** Nurse with Children.

**1957.** Red Cross Fund. Cross in red.

| | | | | |
|---|---|---|---|---|
| 330 | 99 | 3 f.+50 c. blue .. | 85 | 40 |
| 331 | – | 4 f. 50+50 c. green .. | 85 | 40 |
| 332 | – | 6 f. 50+50 c. brown .. | 1·00 | 70 |

DESIGNS—HORIZ. 4 f. 50, Doctor inoculating patient. 6 f. 50, Nurse in tropical kit bandaging patient.

**100.** Belgian Monarchs. **101.** Roan Antelope.

**1958.** 50th Anniv. of Belgian Annexation of the Congo.

| | | | | |
|---|---|---|---|---|
| 333. | 100. | 1 f. red .. .. | 50 | 10 |
| 334. | | 1 f. 50 blue .. .. | 50 | 10 |
| 335. | | 3 f. red .. .. | 50 | 10 |
| 336. | | 5 f. green .. .. | 1·00 | 30 |
| 337. | | 6 f. 50 brown .. .. | 80 | 10 |
| 338. | | 10 f. violet .. .. | 1·00 | 10 |

**1959.** Wild Animals.

| | | | | |
|---|---|---|---|---|
| 339. | 101. | 10 c. brn., sepia & blue | 10 | 10 |
| 340. | – | 20 c. blue and red .. | 15 | 10 |
| 341. | – | 40 c. brown and blue .. | 15 | 10 |
| 342. | – | 50 c. multicoloured .. | 15 | 10 |
| 343. | – | 1 f. black, green & brn. | 25 | 10 |
| 344. | – | 1 f. 50 black and yellow | 30 | 10 |
| 345. | – | 2 f. black, brown & red | 30 | 10 |
| 346. | – | 3 f. black, purple & slate | 50 | 10 |
| 347. | – | 5 f. brown, green & sepia | 65 | 15 |
| 348. | – | 6 f. 50 brn., yell. & blue | 65 | 10 |
| 349. | – | 8 f. bistre, violet & brn. | 75 | 15 |
| 350. | – | 10 f. multicoloured .. | 85 | 10 |

DESIGNS—HORIZ. 20 c. White rhinoceros. 50 c. Demidoff's galago. 1 f. 50, African buffaloes. 3 f. African elephants. 6 f. 50, Impala. 10 f. Eland and common zebras. VERT. 40 c. Giraffe. 1 f. Gorilla. 2 f. Eastern Black and White Colobus monkey. 5 f. Okapis. 8 f. Giant ground pangolin.

**102.** Madonna and Child. **103.** "African Resources".

**1959.** Christmas.
351. **102.** 50c. brn., ochre & chest. 10 10
352. 1 f. brown, violet & blue 10 10
353. 2 f. brown, blue & grey 15 10

**1960.** 10th Anniv. of African Technical Co-operation Commission. Inscr. in French or Flemish.
354. **103.** 3 f. orange and grey 20 10

DESIGNS: 1 f. 50, Hurdling. 2 f. Football. 3 f. Throwing the javelin. 6 f. 60, Throwing the discus.

**104.** High Jumping.

**1960.** Child Welfare Fund.
355. **104.** 50 c.+25 c. blue & red 10 10
356. – 1 f. 50+50 c. red & grn. 15 10
357. – 2 f.+1 f. green & red 20 10
358. – 3 f.+1 f. 25 pur. & bl. 65 40
359. – 6 f. 50+3 f. 50 brn. & rec 80 1·00

POSTAGE DUE STAMPS

D 54. D 86.

**1923.**
D 141. D 54. 5 c. sepia 15 15
D 142a. 10 c. red 15 15
D 143. 15 c. violet 20 15
D 144. 30 c. green 30 25
D 145. 50 c. blue 40 35
D 146. 1 f. grey 45 30

**1943.**
D 270. D 86. 10 c. olive 10 10
D 271. 20 c. blue 10 10
D 272. 50 c. green 15 15
D 273. 1 f. brown 15 15
D 274. 2 f. orange 15 15

D 99.

**1957.**
D 330. D 99. 10 c. brown 10 10
D 331. 20 c. purple 10 10
D 332. 50 c. green 15 10
D 333. 1 f. blue 25 20
D 334. 2 f. red 35 30
D 335. 4 f. violet 50 50
D 336. 6 f. blue 60 50

For later issues see **CONGO (KINSHASA)** and **ZAIRE REPUBLIC.**

## BELGIAN OCCUPATION OF GERMANY Pt. 7

Stamps used in German territory occupied by Belgian Forces at the end of the War of 1914/18, and including the districts of Eupen and Malmedy, now incorporated in Belgium.

100 centimes = 1 Belgian franc.

**1919.** Stamps of Belgium optd. **ALLEMAGNE DUITSCHLAND.**
1. **51.** 1 c. orange 25 35
2. 2 c. brown 25 35
3. 3 c. grey 50 1·40
4. 5 c. green 65 65
5. 10 c. red 2·00 1·60
6. 15 c. violet 75 90
7. 20 c. purple 1·25 1·10
8. 25 c. blue 1·25 1·50
9. **63.** 25 c. blue 4·00 8·50
10. **52.** 35 c. black and brown 1·25 1·10
11. – 40 c. black and green 1·40 1·60
12. – 50 c. black and red 7·00 8·50
13. – 65 c. black and red 3·50 7·00
14. **55.** 1 f. violet 23·00 21·00
15. – 2 f. grey 45·00 48·00
16. – 5 f. bl. (FRANK, No. 194) 10·00 13·00
17. – 10 f. sepia 60·00 70·00

**1920.** Stamps of Belgium surch. **EUPEN & MALMEDY** and value.
18. **51.** 5 pf. on 5 c. green 40 50
19. 10 pf. on 10 c. red 45 65
20. 15 pf. on 15 c. violet 65 75
21. 20 pf. on 20 c. purple 70 1·25
22. 30 pf. on 25 c. blue 70 1·40
23. – 75 pf. on 50 c. blk. & red 17·00 24·00
24. **55.** 1 m. 25 on 1 f. violet 22·00 30·00

**1920.** Stamps of Belgium optd. **Eupen.**
25. **51.** 1 c. orange 25 35
26. 2 c. brown 25 35
27. 3 c. grey 45 1·40
28. 5 c. green 60 80
29. 10 c. red 75 1·10
30. 15 c. violet 1·25 1·40
31. 20 c. purple 1·25 1·50
32. 25 c. blue 1·25 1·60
33. **63.** 25 c. blue 5·00 9·00
34. **52.** 35 c. black and brown 1·50 2·75
35. – 40 c. black and green 1·75 2·75
36. – 50 c. black and red 6·50 7·50
37. – 65 c. black and red 3·75 8·50
38. **55.** 1 f. violet 22·00 22·00
39. – 2 f. grey 45·00 45·00
40. – 5 f. bl. (FRANK, No. 194) 10·00 15·00
41. – 10 f. sepia 55·00 75·00

**1920.** Stamps of Belgium optd. **Malmedy.**
42. **51.** 1 c. orange 25 35
43. 2 c. brown 25 35
44. 3 c. grey 45 1·40
45. 5 c. green 60 80
46. 10 c. red 75 1·10
47. 15 c. violet 1·25 1·40
48. 20 c. purple 1·25 1·50
49. 25 c. blue 1·25 1·60
50. **63.** 25 c. blue 5·00 9·00
51. **52.** 35 c. black and brown 1·50 2·75
52. – 40 c. black and green 1·75 2·75
53. – 50 c. black and red 6·50 7·00
54. – 65 c. black and red 3·75 8·50
55. **55.** 1 f. violet 22·00 22·00
56. – 2 f. grey 45·00 45·00
57. – 5 f. bl. (FRANK, No. 194) 10·00 15·00
58. – 10 f. sepia 55·00 70·00

POSTAGE DUE STAMPS

**1920.** Postage Due stamps of Belgium, 1919.
(a) Optd. **Eupen.**
D 1. 5 c. green 75 1·40
D 2. 10 c. red 1·50 2·00
D 3. 20 c. green 3·25 3·75
D 4. 30 c. blue 3·25 4·50
D 5. 50 c. grey 14·00 17·00

(b) Optd. **Malmedy.**
D 6. 5 c. green 1·25 1·40
D 7. 10 c. red 1·75 2·00
D 8. 20 c. green 8·50 12·00
D 9. 30 c. blue 5·00 9·00
D 10. 50 c. grey 8·50 12·00

## BELGIUM Pt. 4

An independent Kingdom of N.W. Europe.
100 centimes = 1 franc.

**1.** "Epaulettes". **3.** "Medallions".

**1849.** Imperf.
1. **1.** 10 c. brown £1700 70·00
2a. 20 c. blue £2000 45·00

**1861.** Imperf.
12 **3** 1 c. green £160 £110
13 10 c. brown £350 4·00
14 20 c. blue £375 6·00
5 40 c. red £1300 £375

**1863.** Perf.
24. **3.** 1 c. green 38·00 24·00
25. 10 c. brown 48·00 2·50
26. 20 c. blue 48·00 2·50
27. 40 c. red £300 22·00

**5.** **8.** **10.** "Small Lion".

**1865.** Various frames.
34. **5.** 10 c. grey 95·00 1·25
35. 20 c. blue £150 1·25
36. 30 c. brown £350 9·00
37. **8.** 40 c. red £400 15·00
38. **5.** 1 f. lilac £1100 70·00

**1866.**
43 **10** 1 c. grey 35·00 11·00
44 2 c. blue £110 65·00
45 5 c. brown £120 65·00

**11.** **13.** **14.**

**15.** **20.**

Types **13** to **20** and all later portraits to Type **38** are of Leopold II.

**1869.** Various frames.
46 **11** 1 c. green 6·00 10
59a 2 c. blue 13·00 2·00
60 5 c. buff 35·00 45
49 8 c. lilac 60·00 45·00
50 **13** 10 c. green 18·00 20
51b **14** 20 c. blue 70·00 80
62 **15** 25 c. bistre 55·00 1·75
53a **13** 30 c. buff 65·00 2·25
54b 40 c. red 60·00 5·00
55a **15** 50 c. grey £110 10·00
56 **13** 1 f. mauve £250 14·00
57a **20** 5 f. brown £1300 £1300

**21.** **25.**

**1883.** Various frames.
63. **21.** 10 c. red 18·00 2·00
64. – 20 c. grey £140 6·00
65. – 25 c. blue £225 30·00
66. – 50 c. violet £225 30·00

**1884.** Various frames.
67. **11.** 1 c. olive 10·00 50
68. 1 c. grey 4·00 10
69. 2 c. brown 11·00 1·25
70. 5 c. green 25·00 10
71. **25.** 10 c. red 7·00 10
72. – 20 c. olive £110 40
73. – 25 c. blue on red 9·00 15
74. – 35 c. brown 11·00 2·40
75. – 50 c. bistre 7·00 1·75
76. – 1 f. brown on green £600 14·00
77. – 2 f. lilac 42·00 30·00

**32.** **33.** **34.** Arms of Antwerp.

**1893.**
78a. **32.** 1 c. grey 40 10
79. 2 c. yellow 85 90
80. 2 c. brown 1·10 10
81. 5 c. green 4·50 10
82. **33.** 10 c. brown 1·40 10
83. 10 c. red 1·75 10
84. 20 c. olive 13·00 30
85. 25 c. blue 8·50 25
86a. 35 c. brown 18·00 1·00
87. 50 c. brown 42·00 16·00
88. 50 c. grey 42·00 2·00
89. 1 f. red on green 60·00 17·00
90. 1 f. orange 80·00 4·50
92. 2 f. mauve £120 10·00

The prices for the above and all following issues with the tablet are for stamps with the tablet attached. Without tablet, the prices will be about half those quoted.

See also Nos. 106/8.

**1894.** Antwerp Exhibition.
93. **34.** 5 c. green on red 3·25 2·25
94. 10 c. red on blue 2·50 2·00
95. 25 c. blue on red 80 90

**35.** St. Michael encountering Satan. **36.**

**1896.** Brussels Exhibition of 1897.
96. **35.** 5 c. violet 30 30
97. **36.** 10 c. red 4·50 2·75
98. 10 c. brown 15 20

**37.** **38.** **40.** St. Martin and the Beggar (from altarpiece by Van Dyck).

**1905.** Various frames.
99. **37.** 10 c. red 1·00 50
100. 20 c. olive 19·00 80
101. 25 c. blue 10·00 70
102. 35 c. purple 22·00 1·60
103. **38.** 50 c. grey 70·00 1·75
104. 1 f. orange 90·00 7·50
105. 2 f. mauve 65·00 19·00

**1907.** As T **32** but no scroll pattern between stamps and labels.
106. 1 c. grey 1·25 10
107. 2 c. red 12·00 4·25
108. 5 c. green 9·50 40

**1910.** Brussels Exhibition. A. Unshaded background. B. Shaded background.

A.
109. **40.** 1 c. (+1 c.) grey 1·00 1·00
110. 2 c. (+2 c.) purple 9·00 9·00
111. 5 c. (+5 c.) green 2·50 2·50
112. 10 c. (+5 c.) red 2·50 2·50

B.
113. **40.** 1 c. (+1 c.) green 2·50 2·50
114. 2 c. (+2 c.) purple 7·00 7·00
115. 5 c. (+5 c.) green 2·50 2·50
116. 10 c. (+5 c.) red 2·50 2·50

**1911.** Nos. 109/16 optd. **1911.**

A.
117. **40.** 1 c. (+1 c.) grey 28·00 18·00
118. 2 c. (+2 c.) purple 80·00 48·00
119. 5 c. (+5 c.) green 9·00 6·00
120. 10 c. (+5 c.) red 9·00 6·00

B.
121. **40.** 1 c. (+1 c.) green 42·00 26·00
122. 2 c. (+2 c.) purple 35·00 24·00
123. 5 c. (+5 c.) green 9·00 6·00
124. 10 c. (+5 c.) red 9·00 6·00

**1911.** Charleroi Exhibition. Nos. 109/16 optd. **CHARLEROI—1911.**

A.
125 **40** 1 c. (+1 c.) grey 5·00 3·00
126 2 c. (+2 c.) purple 15·00 12·00
127 5 c. (+5 c.) green 9·00 8·00
128 10 c. (+5 c.) red 9·00 8·00

B.
129 **40** 1 c. (+1 c.) green 5·00 3·00
130 2 c. (+2 c.) purple 15·00 10·00
131 5 c. (+5 c.) green 9·00 8·00
132 10 c. (+5 c.) red 9·00 8·00

**42.** **43.** **44.**

**45.** Albert I. **46.** (Larger head).

**1912.**
133. **42.** 1 c. orange 10 10
134. **43.** 2 c. brown 15 15
135. **44.** 5 c. green 10 10
136. **45.** 10 c. red 60 15
137. 20 c. olive 15·00 4·00
138. 35 c. brown 70 35
139. 40 c. green 17·00 14·00
140. 50 c. grey 60 45
141. 1 f. orange 3·50 2·50
142. 2f. violet 18·00 16·00
143. – 5 f. purple 80·00 24·00

The 5 f. is as Type **45** but larger (23 × 35 mm.).

**1912.** Large head.
148 **46** 10 c. red 10 10
145 20 c. green 20 20
150 25 c. blue 15 10
147 40 c. green 40 45

**47.** Merode Monument. **48.** Albert I.

**1914.** Red Cross.
151. **47.** 5 c. (+5 c.) red & green 3·00 3·00
152. 10 c. (+10 c.) red & pink 5·00 5·00
153. 20 c. (+20 c.) red & vio. 50·00 50·00

**1914.** Red Cross.
154. **48.** 5 c. (+5 c.) red & green 3·00 3·00
155. 10 c. (+10 c.) red 20 25
156. 20 c. (+20 c.) red & vio. 11·00 11·00

## INDEX

Countries can be quickly located by referring to the index at the end of this volume.

49. Albert I.

**1915.** Red Cross.
157. 49. 5 c. (+5 c.) red & green 6·00 2·10
158. 10 c. (+10 c.) red & pink 24·00 10·00
159. 20 c. (+20 c.) red & vio. 35·00 14·00

51. Albert I.

52. Cloth Hall, Ypres.

55. Freeing of the Scheldt.

**1915.**
170 51 1 c. orange .. .. 10 10
171 2 c. brown .. .. 15 10
179 3 c. grey .. .. 10 10
172 5 c. green .. .. 10 10
173 10 c. red .. .. 40 10
174 15 c. violet .. .. 1·40 10
175 20 c. purple .. .. 1·50 10
176 25 c. blue .. .. 35 15
188 52 35 c. black and brown .. 15 20
189 – 40 c. black and green .. 25 15
190 – 50 c. black and red .. 4·50 15
191 55 1 f. violet .. .. 26·00 25
192 – 2 f. grey .. .. 20·00 2·00
193 – 5 f. blue (FRANKEN) £275 £120
194 – 5 f. blue (FRANK) .. 1·40 1·00
195 – 10 f. brown .. .. 19·00 19·00
DESIGNS: As T 52. 40 c. Dinant. 50 c. Louvain. As T 55. 2 f. Annexation of the Congo. 5 f. King Albert at Furnes. 10 f. The Kings of Belgium.

**1918.** Red Cross. Surch with new value and cross. Some colours changed.
222 51 1 c.+1 c. orange .. 25 25
223 2 c.+2 c. brown .. 25 25
224 5 c.+5 c. green .. 60 60
225 10 c.+10 c. red .. 1·75 1·75
226 15 c.+15 c. purple .. 3·00 3·00
227 20 c.+20 c. brown .. 5·00 5·00
228 25 c.+25 c. blue .. 12·00 12·00
229 52 35 c.+35 c. black & vio 9·00 9·00
230 – 40 c.+40 c. black & brn 9·00 9·00
231 – 50 c.+50 c. black & blue 9·00 9·00
232 55 1 f.+1 f. grey .. .. 38·00 38·00
233 – 2 f.+2 f. green .. 70·00 80·00
234 – 5 f.+5 f. brown (FRANKEN) .. £190 £200
235 – 10 f.+10 f. blue .. £500 £500

63. "Perron" at Liege.

64. Albert I.

**1919.**
236a 63 25 c. blue .. .. 2·50 35

**1919.**
237. 64. 1 c. brown .. .. 10 10
238. 2 c. olive .. .. 10 10
239. 5 c. green .. .. 25 20
240. 10 c. red .. .. 20 10
241. 15 c. violet .. .. 20 10
242. 20 c. sepia .. .. 1·10 1·00
243. 25 c. blue .. .. 1·10 1·10
244. 35 c. brown .. .. 2·00 2·00
245. 40 c. red .. .. 4·50 4·50
246. 50 c. brown .. .. 8·50 8·50
247. 1 f. orange .. .. 38·00 38·00
248. 2 f. purple .. .. £325 £325
249. 5 f. red .. .. 80·00 80·00
250. 10 f. red .. .. 95·00 95·00
SIZES: 1 c., 2 c., 18½ × 21½ mm. 5 c. to 2 f., 22½ × 26½ mm. 5 f., 10 f., 27½ × 33 mm.

67. Discus thrower.

68. Charioteer.

**1920.** Olympic Games, Antwerp.
256. 67. 5 c. (+5 c.) green .. 1·50 1·75
257. 68. 10 c. (+5 c.) red .. 1·50 1·75
258. – 15 c. (+5 c.) brown .. 2·00 1·60
DESIGN—VERT. 15 c. Runner.

73. Hotel de Ville, Termonde.

76. Albert I.

**1920.**
308b 73 65 c. black and purple 40 15

**1921.** Nos. 256/8 surch **20 c. 20 c.**
309 67 20 c. on 5 c. green .. 40 20
310 68 20 c. on 10 c. red .. 20 15
311 – 20 c. on 15 c. brown .. 40 20

**1921.**
313. 76. 50 c. blue .. .. 25 10
314. 75 c. red .. .. 20 10
315. 75 c. blue .. .. 35 10
316. 1 f. sepia .. .. 50 10
317. 1 f. blue .. .. 35 10
318. 2 f. green .. .. 70 20
319. 5 f. purple .. .. 12·00 12·00
320. 5 f. brown .. .. 8·00 8·00
321. 10 f. red .. .. 8·50 7·00

**1921.** Surch **55 c. 55 c.**
322 73 55 c. on 65 c. black & pur 2·00 25

80.

81. Albert I.

**1922.** War Invalids Fund.
348 80 20 c.+20 c. brown .. 1·00 1·00

**1922.**
349. 81. 1 c. orange .. .. 10 10
350. 2 c. olive .. .. 10 10
351. 3 c. brown .. .. 10 10
352. 5 c. slate .. .. 10 10
353. 10 c. green .. .. 15 10
354. 15 c. plum .. .. 15 10
355. 20 c. brown .. .. 20 10
356. 25 c. purple .. .. 15 10
357. 25 c. violet .. .. 60 10
358. 30 c. red .. .. 35 10
359. 30 c. mauve .. .. 35 10
360. 35 c. brown .. .. 25 10
361. 35 c. green .. .. 50 15
362. 40 c. red .. .. 35 10
363. 50 c. bistre .. .. 45 10
364. 60 c. olive .. .. 2·00 10
365. 75 c. violet .. .. 55 55
366. 1 f. yellow .. .. 35 15
367. 1 f. red .. .. 50 10
368. 1 f. 25 blue .. .. 80 70
369. 1 f. 50 blue .. .. 1·50 15
370. 1 f. 75 blue .. .. 1·00 10
371. 2 f. blue .. .. 2·00 10
372. 5 f. green .. .. 18·00 1·50
373. 10 f. brown .. .. 48·00 8·00

83. Wounded Soldier.

**1923.** War Invalids Fund.
374. 83. 20 c.+20 c. slate .. 1·50 1·50

87. Leopold I and Albert I.

**1925.** 75th Anniv. of 1st Belgian Stamps.
410. 87. 10 c. green .. .. 8·00 8·00
411. 15 c. violet .. .. 3·00 3·00
412. 20 c. brown .. .. 3·00 3·00
413. 25 c. slate .. .. 3·00 3·00
414. 30 c. red .. .. 3·00 3·00
415. 35 c. blue .. .. 3·00 3·00
416. 40 c. sepia .. .. 3·00 3·00
417. 50 c. brown .. .. 3·00 3·00
418. 75 c. blue .. .. 3·00 3·00
419. 1 f. purple .. .. 6·50 6·50
420. 2 f. blue .. .. 4·00 4·00
421. 5 f. black .. .. 3·00 3·00
422. 10 f. red .. .. 7·00 7·00

88.

90.

**1925.** Anti-T.B. Fund.
423. 88. 15 c.+5 c. red & mauve 15 15
424. 30 c.+5 c. red and grey 15 10
425. 1 f.+10 c. red and blue 1·25 1·50

**1926.** Flood Relief. Type of 1922 surch **Inondations 30 c Watersnood.**
426 81 30 c.+30 c. green .. 30 40

**1926.** Flood Relief Fund. A. Shaded backgrounded. B. Solid background.
A.
427. 90. 1 f.+1 f. blue .. .. 5·50 5·50
B.
428. 90. 1 f.+1 f. blue .. .. 1·00 1·00

91.

92. Queen Elisabeth and King Albert.

**1926.** War Tuberculosis Fund.
429. 91. 5 c.+5 c. brown .. 15 15
430. 20 c.+5 c. brown .. 30 30
431. 50 c.+5 c. violet .. 20 10
432. 92. 1 f. 50+25 c. blue .. 50 40
433. 5 f.+1 f. red .. .. 5·00 5·00

**1927.** Stamps of 1922 surch.
434. 81. 3 c. on 2 c. olive .. 10 10
435. 10 c. on 15 c. plum .. 10 10
436. 35 c. on 40 c. red .. 15 10
437. 1 f. 75 on 1 f. 50 blue .. 95 40

94.

**1927.** Anti-T.B. Fund.
438. 94. 25 c.+10 c. brown .. 80 70
439. 35 c.+10 c. green .. 40 40
440. 60 c.+10 c. violet .. 20 20
441. 1 f. 75+25 c. blue .. 95 95
442. 5 f.+1 f. purple .. 4·00 4·25

96. Ogives.

97. Ruins of Orval Abbey.

**1928.** Orval Abbey Restoration Fund, Inscr. "ORVAL 1928" or "ORVAL".
461. 96. 5 c.+5 c. red and gold 20 20
462. – 25 c.+5 c. violet & gold 25 25
463. – 35 c.+10 c. green .. 75 75
464. – 60 c.+15 c. brown .. 75 20
465. – 1 f. 75+25 c. blue .. 2·50 1·60
466. – 2 f.+40 c. purple .. 18·00 16·00
467. – 3 f.+1 f. red .. .. 18·00 16·00
468. 97. 5 f.+5 f. lake .. .. 12·00 13·00
469. – 10 f.+10 f. sepia .. 12·00 13·00
DESIGNS—VERT. 35 c., 2 f. Cistercian monk stone-carving. 60 c., 1 f. 75, 3 f. Duchess Matilda retrieving her ring.

99. Mons Cathedral.

101. Malines Cathedral.

**1928.** Anti-T.B. Fund.
472. 99. 5 c.+5 c. red .. .. 15 15
473. – 25 c.+15 c. sepia .. 25 25
474. 101. 35 c.+10 c. green .. 1·10 1·10
475. – 60 c.+15 c. brown .. 20 20
476. – 1 f. 75+25 c. violet .. 7·50 7·50
477. – 5 f.+5 f. purple .. 15·00 15·00
DESIGNS—As Type 99: 25 c. Tournai Cathedral. As Type 101: 60 c. Ghent Cathedral. 1 f. 75, St. Gudule Cathedral, Brussels. 5 f. Louvain Library.

**1929.** Surch **BRUXELLES 1929 BRUSSEL 5 c** in frame.
478. 81. 5 c. on 30 c. mauve .. 10 10
479. 5 c. on 75 c. violet .. 15 15
480. 5 c. on 1 f. 25 c. blue .. 10 10
The above cancellation, whilst altering the original face value of the stamps, also constitutes a precancel, although stamps also come with additional ordinary postmark. The unused prices are for stamps with full gum and the used prices for stamps without gum, with or without postmarks. We do not list precancels where there is no change in face value.

104. The Belgian Lion.

105. Albert I.

**1929.**
487 104 1 c. orange .. .. 10 10
488 2 c. green .. .. 20 25
489 3 c. brown .. .. 10 10
490 5 c. green .. .. 10 10
491 10 c. bistre .. .. 10 10
492 20 c. mauve .. .. 1·00 10
493 25 c. red .. .. 20 10
494 35 c. green .. .. 25 10
495 40 c. purple .. .. 25 10
496 50 c. blue .. .. 25 10
497 60 c. mauve .. .. 1·40 10
498 70 c. brown .. .. 85 10
499 75 c. blue .. .. 1·40 10
500 75 c. brown .. .. 6·00 10
501 105 10 f. brown .. .. 14·00 3·00
502 20 f. green .. .. 75·00 20·00
503a 50 f. purple .. .. 14·00 14·00
504a 100 f. red .. .. 18·00 18·00

**1929.** Laying of first Stone towards Restoration of Orval Abbey. Nos. 461/9 optd. with crown over ornamental letter "L" and **19-8-29.**
543. 5 c.+5 c. red and gold .. 70·00 70·00
544. 25 c.+5 c. violet & gold .. 70·00 70·00
545. 35 c.+10 c. green .. .. 70·00 70·00
546. 60 c.+15 c. brown .. 70·00 70·00
547. 1 f. 75 c.+25 c. blue .. 70·00 70·00
548. 2 f.+40 c. purple .. .. 70·00 70·00
549. 3 f.+1 f. red .. .. 70·00 70·00
550. 5 f.+5 f. lake .. .. 70·00 70·00
551. 10 f.+10 f. sepia .. .. 70·00 70·00

109. Canal and Belfry, Bruges.

**1929.** Anti-T.B. Fund.
552. – 5 c.+5 c. brown .. 20 20
553. – 25 c.+15 c. grey .. 50 50
554. – 35 c.+10 c. green .. 50 50
555. – 60 c.+15 c. lake .. 25 20
556. – 1 f. 75+25 c. blue .. 7·50 7·50
557. 109. 5 f.+5 f. purple .. 21·00 21·00
DESIGNS—HORIZ. 5 c. Waterfall at Coo. 35 c. Menin Gate, Ypres. 60 c. Promenade d'Orleans, Spa. 1 f. 75, Antwerp Harbour. VERT. 25 c. Bayard Rock, Dinant.

110. Paul Rubens.

111. Zenobe Gramme.

**1930.** Antwerp and Liege Exns.
558. 110. 35 c. green .. .. 25 10
559. 111. 35 c. green .. .. 25 10

112. Ostend.

113. "Leopold II" by Jef Lempoels.

**1930.** Air.
560. 112. 50 c. blue .. .. 25 20
561. – 1 f. 50 brn. (St. Hubert) 2·40 2·40
562. – 2 f. green (Namur) .. 1·50 80
563. – 5 f. red (Brussels) .. 1·75 75
564. – 5 f. violet (Brussels) .. 25·00 30·00

**1930.** Centenary of Independence.
565. – 60 c. purple .. .. 20 10
566. 113. 1 f. red .. .. 65 40
567. – 1 f. 75 blue .. .. 2·00 1·25
PORTRAITS: 60 c. "Leopold I" by Lievin de Winne. 1 f. 75, King Albert I.

**1930.** I.L.O. Congress. Nos. 565/7 optd **B.I.T. OCT. 1930.**
569. 60 c. purple 2·00 2·00
570. 1 f. red 7·00 7·00
571. 1 f. 75 blue 15·00 15·00

116. Wynendaele.  117. Gaesbeek.

**1930.** Anti-T.B. Fund.
572. – 10 c.+5 c. mauve 15 15
573. 116. 25 c.+15 c. sepia 35 35
574. – 40 c.+10 c. purple 45 45
575. – 70 c.+15 c. slate 20 15
576. – 1 f.+25 c. red 5·00 5·00
577. – 1 f. 75+25 c. blue 4·00 4·00
578. 117. 5 f.+5 f. green 29·00 29·00
DESIGNS: 10 c. Bornhem. 40 c. Beloeil. 70 c. Oydonck. 1 f. Ghent. 1 f. 75, Bouillon.

**1931.** Surch **2 c.**
579 104 2 c. on 3 c. brown 10 10

**1931.** Surch. **BELGIQUE 1931 BELGIE 10c.**
580. 104. 10 c. on 60 c. mauve 40 10
See note below No. 480.

121.  Albert I. 123.

**1931.**
582. 121. 75 c. brn. (18×22 mm.) 1·00 10
583. 1 f. lake (21×23½ mm.) 20 10
584. 123. 1 f. 25 black 40 25
585. 1 f. 50 purple 1·25 25
586. 1 f. 75 blue 50 10
587. 2 f. brown 60 10
588. 2 f. 45 violet 2·00 25
589. 2 f. 50 sepia 8·00 50
590. 5 f. green 15·00 1·00
591. 10 f. red 42·00 11·00
See also No. 654.

125. Queen Elisabeth.  126. Reaper.  127. Mercury.

**1931.** Anti-Tuberculosis Fund.
593. 125. 10 c.+5 c. brown 25 20
594. 25 c.+15 c. violet 75 65
595. 50 c.+10 c. green 70 40
596. 75 c.+15 c. sepia 45 15
597. 1 f.+25 c. lake 7·00 6·00
598. 1 f. 75+25 c. blue 5·00 4·00
599. 5 f.+5 f. purple 45·00 45·00

**1932.** Surch. **BELGIQUE 1932. BELGIE 10 c.**
600. 104. 10 c. on 40 c. mauve 1·90 25
601. 10 c. on 70 c. brown 1·40 15
See Note below No. 480.

**1932.**
602. 126. 2 c. green 25 25
603. 127. 5 c. red 10 10
604. 126. 10 c. green 10 10
605. 127. 20 c. lilac 25 15
606. 126. 25 c. red 25 10
607. 127. 35 c. green 2·40 10

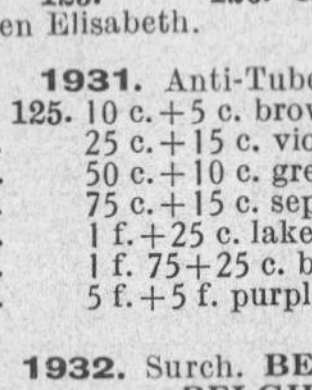

129. Cardinal Mercier. 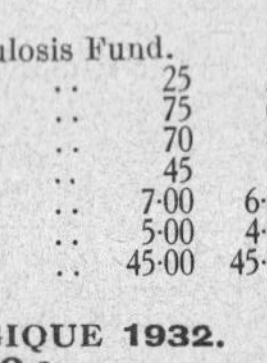 132.

**1932.** Cardinal Mercier Memorial Fund.
609. 129. 10 c.+10 c. purple 25 25
610. 50 c.+30 c. mauve 2·00 2·00
611. 75 c.+25 c. brown 2·00 2·00
612. 1 f.+2 f. red 5·50 5·50
613. – 1 f. 75+75 c. blue 55·00 55·00
614. – 2 f. 50+2 f. 50 brown 55·00 55·00
615. – 3 f.+4 f. 50 green 55·00 55·00
616. – 5 f.+20 f. purple 80·00 80·00
617. – 10 f.+40 f. red £140 £140
DESIGNS: 1 f. 75, 3 f. Mercier protecting refugees at Malines. 2 f. 50, 5 f. Mercier with busts of Aristotle and Thomas Aquinas. 10 f. Mercier when Professor at Louvain University.

**1932.** Infantry Memorial.
618 132 75 c.+3 f. 25 red 60·00 60·00
619 1 f. 75+4 f. 25 blue 60·00 60·00

133. Prof. Piccard's Stratosphere Balloon "F.N.R.S.", 1931. 134. Hulpe-Waterloo Sanatorium.

**1932.** Scientific Research Fund.
621. 133. 75 c. brown 2·40 10
622. 1 f. 75 blue 10·00 1·75
623. 2 f. 50 violet 18·00 10·00

**1932.** Anti-T.B. Fund.
624 134 10 c.+5 c. violet 20 20
625 25 c.+15 c. mauve 1·60 70
626 50 c.+10 c. red 1·50 50
627 75 c.+15 c. brown 1·00 20
628 1 f.+25 c. red 10·00 9·50
629 1 f. 75+25 c. blue 8·00 8·00
630 5 f.+5 f. green 75·00 75·00

**1933.** Lion type surch. **BELGIQUE 1933 BELGIE 10 c.**
631. 104. 10 c. on 40 c. mauve 12·00 2·00
632. 10 c. on 70 c. brown 12·00 85
See note below No. 480.

135. The Transept.  138. Anti-T.B. Symbol.

**1933.** Orval Abbey Restoration Fund. Inscr. "ORVAL".
633. – 5 c.+5 c. green 50·00 50·00
634. – 10 c.+15 c. dp. green 35·00 35·00
635. – 25 c.+15 c. brown 32·00 32·00
636. 135. 50 c.+25 c. lake 30·00 30·00
637. – 75 c.+50 c. dp. green 32·00 32·00
638. – 1 f.+1 f. 25 lake 35·00 38·00
639. – 1 f. 25+1 f. 75 sepia 35·00 38·00
640. – 1 f. 75+2 f. 75 blue 48·00 48·00
641. – 2 f.+3 f. mauve 45·00 45·00
642. – 2 f. 50+5 f. brown 45·00 45·00
643. – 5 f.+20 f. purple 55·00 55·00
644. – 10 f.+40 f. blue £225 £225
DESIGNS—VERT. 10 c. Abbey Ruins. 75 c. Belfry, new abbey. 1 f. Fountain, new abbey. HORIZ. 5 c. The old abbey. 25 c. Guests' Courtyard, new abbey. 1 f. 25, Cloister, new abbey. 1 f. 75, Foundation of Orval Abbey in 1131. 2 f. Restoration of the abbey, XVI and XVII centuries. 2 f. 50, Orval Abbey, XVIII century. 5 f. Prince Leopold laying foundation stone of new abbey. 10 f. The Virgin Mary (30×45 mm.).

**1933.** Anti-tuberculosis Fund.
646. 138. 10 c.+5 c. grey 50 35
647. 25 c.+15 c. mauve 2·00 2·00
648. 50 c.+10 c. brown 2·00 2·00
649. 75 c.+15 c. sepia 35·00 25
650. 1 f.+25 c. red 11·00 11·00
651. 1 f. 75+25 c. blue 24·00 24·00
652. 5 f.+5 f. purple £110 £110

**1934.** Lion type surch. **BELGIQUE 1934 BELGIE 10 c.**
653. 104. 10 c. on 40 c. mauve 12·00 85
See note below No. 480.

**1934.** King Albert's Mourning stamp.
654. 121. 75 c. black 15 10

140. Peter Benoit.  141. Brussels Palace.

**1934.** Benoit Centenary Memorial Fund.
658. 140. 75 c.+25 c. brown 5·00 5·00

**1934.** International Exhibition, Brussels.
659. – 35 c. green 50 10
660. 141. 1 f. red 90 10
661. – 1 f. 50 brown 4·00 70
662. – 1 f. 75 blue 4·25 80
DESIGNS: 35 c. Congo Palace. 1 f. 50, Old Brussels. 1 f. 75, Grand Palace of the Belgian section.

142. King Leopold III.  143. King Leopold III.

**1934.** War Invalids' Fund. (a) Size 18×22 mm. (b) Size 21 × 24 mm.
(i) Exhibition Issue.
663. 142. 75 c.+25 c. green (a) 13·00 13·00
664. 1 f.+25 c. purple (b) 11·00 11·00
(ii) Ordinary postage stamps.
665. 142. 75 c.+25 c. purple (a) 2·00 2·00
666. 1 f.+25 c. red (b) 5·00 5·00

**1934.**
667. 142. 70 c. green 20 10
668. 75 c. brown 50 10
669. 143. 1 f. red 2·00 20

144. Health Crusader.

**1934.** Anti-tuberculosis Fund. Cross in red.
670. 144. 10 c.+5 c. black 25 25
671. 25 c.+15 c. brown 2·00 2·00
672. 50 c.+10 c. green 80 80
673. 75 c.+15 c. dull purple 50 20
674. 1 f.+25 c. red 9·00 9·00
675. 1 f. 75+25 c. blue 9·00 9·00
676. 5 f.+5 f. purple 85·00 85·00

145. The Royal Children.

**1935.** Queen Astrid's Appeal.
680 145 35 c.+15 c green 80 80
681 70 c.+30 c. purple 80 80
682 1 f. 75+50 c. blue 2·00 2·00

146. "Mail-diligence".  151. Queen Astrid.

**1935.** Brussels Int. Exn.
683. 146. 10 c.+10 c. olive 30 20
684. 25 c.+25 c. brown 1·40 1·40
685. 35 c.+25 c. green 2·25 2·25

**1935.** Air. Surch with new value twice.
686 112 1 f. on 1 f. 50 brown 35 15
687 4 f. on 5 f. red 7·50 7·50

**1935.** Death of Queen Astrid. Mourning stamp.
713 151 70 c.+5 c. black 10 10

**1935.** Anti-Tuberculosis Fund. Black borders.
714. 151. 10 c.+5 c. olive 10 10
715. 25 c.+15 c. brown 15 15
716. 35 c.+5 c. green 15 15
717. 50 c.+10 c. mauve 20 20
718. 1 f.+25 c. red 60 60
719. 1 f. 75+25 c. blue 1·25 1·25
720. 2 f. 45+55 c. violet 2·25 2·25

152. State arms.  153.  155. King Leopold III.

**1936.**
727. 152. 2 c. green 10 10
728. 5 c. orange 10 10
729. 10 c. olive 10 10
730. 15 c. blue 10 10
731. 20 c. violet 10 10
732. 25 c. red 10 10
733. 25 c. yellow 10 10
734. 30 c. brown 35 10
735. 35 c. green 10 10
736. 40 c. lilac 35 10
737. 50 c. blue 20 10
738. 60 c. grey 20 10
739. 65 c. mauve 1·25 10
740. 70 c. green 20 10
741. 75 c. mauve 75 10
742. 80 c. green 8·50 15
743. 90 c. violet 70 10
744. 1 f. brown 60 10

**1936.** Various frames.
(a) Size 17½×22 mm.
745. 153. 70 c. brown 20 10
746. 75 c. olive 15 10
747. 1 f. red 10 10
(b) Size 21×24 mm.
748 153 1 f. red 25 10
749 1 f. 20 brown 1·50 10
750 1 f. 50 mauve 25 10
751 1 f. 75 blue 15 10
752 1 f. 75 red 30 10
753 2 f. violet 30 15
754 2 f. 25 black 25 10
755 2 f. 50 red 6·50 10
756 3 f. 25 brown 20 10
757 5 f. green 1·00 10
Nos. 746/7, 751/2, 754/5 and 757 are inscribed "BELGIE BELGIQUE".

**1936.**
760. 155. 1 f. 50 mauve 50 10
761. 1 f. 75 blue 20 10
762. 2 f. violet 50 10
763. 2 f. 25 violet 20 10
764. 2 f. 45 black 24·00 25
765. 2 f. 50 black 2·00 15
770. 3 f. brown 1·60 10
766. 3 f. 25 brown 20 10
771. 4 f. blue 3·50 10
767. 5 f. green 1·40 20
772. 6 f. red 10·00 10
768. 10 f. purple 50 10
769. 20 f. red 80 10
See also No. 2775.

158. Prince Baudouin.  159. Queen Astrid and Prince Baudouin.

**1936.** Anti-Tuberculosis Fund.
777. 158. 10 c.+5 c. brown 10 10
778. 25 c.+5 c. violet 10 10
779. 35 c.+5 c. green 10 10
780. 50 c.+5 c. brown 15 15
781. 70 c.+5 c. olive 10 10
782. 1 f.+25 c. red 1·00 1·00
783. 1 f. 75+25 c. blue 1·75 1·75
784. 2 f. 45+2 f. 55 purple 3·50 3·50

**1937.** Stamp of 1929 surcharged. **BELGIQUE 1937 BELGIE 10 c.**
785. 104. 10 c. on 40 c. purple 25 15
See note below No. 480.

**1937.** International Stamp Day.
786. 158. 2 f. 45 c.+2 f. 55 c. slate 1·60 1·60

**1937.** Queen Astrid Public Utility Fund.
787. 159. 10 c.+5 c. purple 10 10
788. 25 c.+5 c. olive 10 10
789. 35 c.+5 c. green 10 10
790. 50 c.+5 c. violet 15 15
791. 70 c.+5 c. black 10 10
792. 1 f.+25 c. red 1·00 1·00
793. 1 f. 75 c.+25 c. blue 2·10 2·10
794. 2 f. 45 c.+1 f. 55c. brown 5·00 5·00

160. Queen Elisabeth.  161. Princess Josephine Charlotte.

**1937.** Eugene Ysaye Memorial Fund.
795. 160. 70 c.+5 c. black 20 10
796. 1 f. 75+25 c. blue 45 40

**1937.** Anti-Tuberculosis Fund.
798. 161. 10 c.+5 c. green 10 10
799. 25 c.+5 c. brown 10 10
800. 35 c.+5 c. green 10 10
801. 50 c.+5 c. olive 15 15
802. 70 c.+5 c. purple 10 10
803. 1 f.+25 c. red 1·00 1·00
804. 1 f. 75+25 c. blue 1·10 1·10
805. 2 f. 45+2 f. 55 purple 3·50 3·50

164. King Leopold.

**1938.** Aeronautical Propaganda.
810. 164. 10 c.+5 c. purple 10 10
811. 35 c.+5 c. green 15 10
812. 70 c.+5 c. black 35 10
813. 1 f. 75+25 c. blue 2·10 2·10
814. 2 f. 45+2 f. 55 violet 3·00 3·50

165. Basilica of the Sacred Heart, Koekelberg.

**1938.** Building (Completion) Fund.
815. 165. 10 c.+5 c. brown 10 10
816. – 35 c.+5 c. green 10 10
817. 165. 70 c.+5 c. grey 10 10
818. – 1 f.+25 c. red 45 35
819. 165. 1 f. 75+25 c. blue 45 35
820. – 2 f. 45+2 f. 55 red 2·75 2·75
821. – 5 f.+5 f. green 8·00 8·00
DESIGNS—HORIZ. 35 c., 1 f., 2 f. 45, Front view of Basilica. VERT. 5 f. Interior view.

**1938.** Surch **2F50.**
823 155 2 f. 50 on 2 f. 45 black 8·00 10

**167.** Exhibition Pavilion.

**170.** Prince Albert of Liege.

**1938.** Int. Exhibition, Liege (1939). Inscr. "LIEGE 1939 LUIK".

824. – 35 c. green .. .. 10 10
825. **167.** 1 f. red .. .. 20 10
826. – 1 f. 50 brown .. .. 1·00 30
827. – 1 f. 75 blue .. .. 1·00 10

DESIGNS—VERT. 35 c. View of Liege. HORIZ. 1 f. 50, R. Meuse at Liege. 1 f. 75, Albert Canal and King Albert.

**1938.** Koekelberg Basilica Completion Fund. Surch.

828. – 40 c. on 35 c. + 5 c. grn. (No. 816) .. .. 25 25
829. **165.** 75 c. on 70 c. + 5 c. grey 25 25
830. – 2 f. 50 + 2 f. 50 on 2 f. 45 + 2 f. 55, red. (No. 820) .. .. 5·50 5·50

**1938.** Anti-Tuberculosis Fund.

831. **170.** 10 c. + 5 c. brown .. 10 10
832. 30 c. + 5 c. purple .. 10 10
833. 40 c. + 5 c. olive .. 10 10
834. 75 c. + 5 c. grey .. 10 10
835. 1 f. + 25 c. red .. 80 80
836. 1 f. 75 + 25 c. blue .. 1·00 1·00
837. 2 f. 50 + 2 f. 50 green 3·50 3·50
838. 5 f. + 5 f. purple .. 8·00 8·00

171. King Leopold and Royal Children.

**1939.** 75th Anniv. of Int. Red Cross Society.

839. – 10 c. + 5 c. brown .. 10 10
840. – 30 c. + 5 c. red .. 10 10
841. – 40 c. + 5 c. olive .. 10 10
842. **171.** 75 c. + 5 c. black .. 15 10
843. – 1 f. + 25 c. red .. 1·60 1·60
844. **171.** 1 f. 75 + 25 c. blue .. 1·00 1·00
845. – 2 f. 50 + 2 f. 50 violet 1·90 1·90
846. – 5 f. + 5 f. green .. 6·00 6·00

DESIGNS—VERT. 10 c. H. Dunant. 30 c. Florence Nightingale. 40 c. and 1 f. Queen Elisabeth and Royal children. 2 f. 50, Queen Astrid. HORIZ. 5 f. Queen Elisabeth and wounded soldier (larger).

173. Rubens's House (after engraving by Harrewijn).

175. Portrait by Memling.

**1939.** Rubens's House Restoration Fund.

847 **173** 10 c. + 5 c. brown .. 10 10
848 – 40 c. + 5 c. purple .. 10 10
849 – 75 c. + 5 c. green .. 20 20
850 – 1 f. + 25 c. red .. 1·60 1·60
851 – 1 f. 50 + 25 c. brown .. 2·00 2·00
852 – 1 f. 75 + 25 c. blue .. 3·00 3·00
853 – 2 f. 50 + 2 f. 50 purple 9·00 9·00
854 – 5 f. + 5 f. grey .. 12·00 12·00

DESIGNS—As Type **173**: VERT. 40 c. "Rubens's Sons, Albert and Nicholas". 1 f. "Helene Fourment (2nd wife) and Children". 1 f. 50, "Rubens and Isabella Brant" (1st wife). 1 f. 75, Rubens (after engraving by Pontius). 2 f. 50, "Straw Hat" (Suzanne Fourment). HORIZ. 75 c. Arcade of Rubens's house. 35 × 45 mm: 5 f. "The Descent from the Cross".

**1939.** Exn. of Memling's Paintings, Bruges.

855. **175.** 75 c. + 75 c. olive .. 1·50 1·50

**177.** Orval Abbey Cloisters and Belfry.

**180.** Thuin.

**1939.** Orval Abbey Restoration Fund. Inscr. "ORVAL".

861. – 75 c. + 75 c. olive .. 3·50 3·50
862. **177.** 1 f. + 1 f. red .. .. 1·75 1·75
863. – 1 f. 50 + 1 f. 50 brown 1·75 1·75
864. – 1 f. 75 + 1 f. 75 blue .. 2·40 2·40
865. – 2 f. 50 + 2 f. 50 mauve 6·00 6·00
866. – 5 f. + 5 f. purple .. 6·50 6·50

DESIGNS—As Type **177**: VERT. 75 c. Monks in laboratory. HORIZ. 1 f. 50, Monks harvesting. 1 f. 75, Aerial view of Orval Abbey. 52½ × 35½ mm: 2 f. 50, Cardinal Van Roey, Statue of the Madonna and Abbot of Orval. 5 f. Kings Albert and Leopold III and shrine.

**1939.** Anti-Tuberculosis Fund. Belfries.

868. – 10 c. + 5 c. olive .. 10 10
869. **180.** 30 c. + 5 c. brown .. 10 10
870. – 40 c. + 5 c. purple .. 10 10
871. – 75 c. + 5 c. grey .. 10 10
872. – 1 f. + 25 c. red .. 90 90
873. – 1 f. 75 + 25 c. blue .. 80 70
874. – 2 f. 50 + 2 f. 50 brown 7·50 7·50
875. – 5 f. + 5 f. violet .. 7·50 7·50

DESIGNS—As Type **180**: 10 c. Bruges. 40 c. Lier. 75 c. Mons. LARGER (21½ × 34 mm.); 1 f. Furnes. 1 f. 75, Namur 2 f. 50, Alost. 5 f. Tournai.

**182.** Arms of Mons.

**183.** Painting.

**184.** Monks studying Plans of Orval Abbey.

**1940.** Winter Relief Fund.

901. **182.** 10 c. + 5 c. black, red and green .. .. 10 10
902. – 30 c. + 5 c. mult. .. 10 10
903. – 40 c. + 10 c. mult. .. 10 10
904. – 50 c. + 10 c. mult. .. 10 10
905. – 75 c. + 15 c. mult. .. 10 10
906. – 1 f. + 25 c. mult. .. 20 15
907. – 1 f. 75 c. + 50 c. mult. 20 20
908. – 2 f. 50 c. + 2 f. 50 c. olive, red & black .. 1·00 90
909. – 5 f. + 5 f. purple, red, yellow and black .. 1·25 1·00

DESIGNS: 30 c. to 5 f. Arms of Ghent, Arlon, Bruges, Namur, Hasselt, Brussels, Antwerp and Liege, respectively.

**1941.** Orval Abbey Restoration Fund.

935 **183** 10 c. + 15 c. brown .. 25 25
936 – 30 c. + 30 c. grey .. 25 25
937 – 40 c. + 60 c. brown .. 25 25
938 – 50 c. + 65 c. violet .. 25 25
939 – 75 c. + 1 f. mauve .. 25 25
940 – 1 f. + 1 f. 50 red .. 25 25
941 **183** 1 f. 25 + 1 f. 75 green .. 25 25
942 – 1 f. 75 + 2 f. 50 blue .. 25 25
943 – 2 f. + 3 f. 50 mauve .. 25 25
944 – 2 f. 50 + 4 f. 50 brown 25 25
945 – 3 f. + 5 f. green .. 25 25
946 **184** 5 f. + 10 f. brown .. 90 90

DESIGNS—As Type **183**. 30 c., 1 f., 2 f. 50, Sculpture. 40 c., 2 f. Goldsmiths (Monks carrying candlesticks and cross). 50 c., 1 f. 75, Stained glass (Monk at prayer). 75 c., 3 f. Sacred music.

**1941.** Surch.

955. **152.** 10 c. on 30 c. brown .. 10 10
956. 10 c. on 40 c. lilac .. 10 10
957. **153.** 10 c. on 70 c. brown .. 10 10
958. 50 c. on 75 c. olive .. 20 15
959. **155.** 2 f. 25 on 2 f. 50 black 50 50

**189.** Maria Theresa.

**190.** St. Martin, Dinant.

**1941.** Soldiers' Families Relief Fund.

960. **189.** 10 c. + 5 c. black .. 10 10
961. – 35 c. + 5 c. green .. 10 10
962. – 50 c. + 10 c. brown .. 10 10
963. – 60 c. + 10 c. violet .. 10 10
964 – 1 f. + 15 c. red .. 10 10
965. – 1 f. 50 + 1 f. mauve .. 15 15
966. – 1 f. 75 + 1 f. 75 blue .. 15 15
967. – 2 f. 25 + 2 f. 25 brown 20 20
968. – 3 f. 25 + 3 f. 25 brown 30 30
969. – 5 f. + 5 f. green .. 50 50

PORTRAITS: 35 c. to 5 f. Charles of Lorraine, Margaret of Parma, Charles V, Johanna of Castile, Philip the Good, Margaret of Austria, Charles the Bold, Archduke Albert and Archduchess Isabella respectively.

**1941.** Winter Relief Fund. Statues.

970 **190** 10 c. + 5 c. brown .. 10 10
971 – 35 c. + 5 c. green .. 10 10
972 – 50 c. + 10 c. violet .. 10 10
973 – 60 c. + 10 c. brown .. 10 10
974 – 1 f. + 15 c. red .. 10 10
975 **190** 1 f. 50 + 25 c. green .. 20 20
976 – 1 f. 75 + 50 c. blue .. 20 20
977 – 2 f. 25 + 2 f. 25 mauve 25 25
978 – 3 f. 25 + 3 f. 25 brown 25 25
979 – 5 f. + 5 f. green .. 35 35

DESIGNS (Statues of St. Martin in churches)—As Type **190**: 35 c., 1 f. Lennick, St. Quentin. 50 c., 3 f. Beck, Limberg. 60 c., 2 f. 25, Dave on the Meuse. 1 f. 75, Hal, Brabant. 35 × 50 mm: 5 f. St. Trond.

**193.** Mercator.

**198.** Prisoner writing Letter.

**1942.** Anti-tuberculosis Fund. Portraits.

986 – 10 c. + 5 c. brown .. 10 10
987 – 35 c. + 5 c. green .. 10 10
988 – 50 c. + 10 c. brown .. 10 10
989 – 60 c. + 10 c. green .. 10 10
990 – 1 f. + 15 c. red .. 10 10
991 **193** 1 f. 75 + 50 c. blue .. 25 25
992 – 3 f. 25 + 3 f. 25 purple 20 20
993 – 5 f. + 5 f. violet .. 25 25
994 – 10 f. + 30 f. orange .. 1·25 1·25

SCIENTISTS—As T **193**: 10 c. Bolland. 35 c. Versale. 50 c. S. Stevin. 60 c. Van Helmont. 1 f. Dodoens. 3 f. 25, Oertell. 5 f. Juste Lipse. 25½ × 28½ mm: 10 f. Plantin.

**1942.** Prisoners of War Fund.

1000. **198.** 5 f. + 45 f. grey .. 5·50 5·50

**199.** St. Martin.

**200.** St. Martin sharing his cloak,

**1942.** Winter Relief Fund.

1001. **199.** 10 c. + 5 c. orange .. 10 10
1002. – 35 c. + 5 c. green .. 10 10
1003. – 50 c. + 10 c. brown .. 10 10
1004. – 60 c. + 10 c. black .. 10 10
1005. – 1 f. + 15 c. red .. 10 10
1006. – 1 f. 50 + 25 c. green .. 20 20
1007. – 1 f. 75 + 50 c. blue .. 20 20
1008. – 2 f. 25 + 2 f. 25 brn. 20 20
1009. – 3 f. 25 + 3 f. 25 purple 25 20
1010. **200.** 5 f. + 10 f. brown .. 90 90
1011. 10 f. + 20 f. brown and violet .. .. 90 80
1012. 10 f. + 20 f. red & vio. 90 80

DESIGNS: 60 c., 2 f. 25, 3 f. 25, horiz.; others vert.

**201.** Soldiers and Vision of Home.

**1943.** Prisoners of War Relief Fund.

1013. **201.** 1 f. + 30 f. red .. 2·00 2·00
1014. – 1 f. + 30 f. brown .. 2·00 2·00

DESIGN: No. 1014, Soldiers emptying parcel of books and vision of home.

**202.** Tiler.

DESIGNS: 35 c. Blacksmith. 50 c. Coppersmith. 60 c. Gunsmith. 1 f. Armourer. 1 f. 75 c. Goldsmith. 3 f. 25 c. Fishmonger. 5 f. Clockmaker.

**1943.** Anti-Tuberculosis Fund. Trades.

1015. **202.** 10 c. + 5 c. brown .. 10 10
1016. – 35 c. + 5 c. green .. 10 10
1017. – 50 c. + 10 c. brown .. 10 10
1018. – 60 c. + 10 c. green .. 10 10
1019. – 1 f. + 15 c. red .. 20 20
1020. – 1 f. 75 + 75 c. blue .. 20 20
1021. – 3 f. 25 + 3 f. 25 purple 35 35
1022. – 5 f. + 25 f. violet .. 50 50

**203.** Ornamental Letter.

**204.** Ornamental Letters.

**1943.** Orval Abbey Restoration Fund. Designs showing single letters forming "ORVAL".

1023. **203.** 50 c. + 1 f. black .. 20 20
1024. – 60 c. + 1 f. 90 violet 10 10
1025. – 1 f. + 3 f. red .. 10 10
1026. – 1 f. 75 + 5 f. 25 blue 10 10
1027. – 3 f. 25 + 16 f. 75 green 40 40
1028. **204.** 5 f. + 30 f. brown .. 70 50

**205.** St. Leonard's Church, Leon, and St. Martin.

**206.** Church of Notre Dame, Hal, and St. Martin.

**207.** St. Martin and River Scheldt.

DESIGNS: (Various churches and statues of St. Martin sharing his cloak). As Type **205**: HORIZ. 35 c. Dion-le-Val. 50 c. Alost. 60 c. Liege. 3 f. 25, Loppem. VERT. 1 f. Courtrai. 1 f. 75, Angre. As Type **207**: 10 f. brown Meuse landscape.

**1943.** Winter Relief Fund.

1029. **205.** 10 c. + 5 c. brown .. 10 10
1030. – 35 c. + 5 c. green .. 10 10
1031. – 50 c. + 15 c. green .. 10 10
1032. – 60 c. + 20 c. purple .. 10 10
1033. – 1 f. + 1 f. red .. 15 10
1034. – 1 f. 75 + 4 f. 25 blue 50 50
1035. – 3 f. 25 + 11 f. 75 mve. 75 60
1036. **206.** 5 f. + 25 f. blue .. 1·10 1·10
1037. **207.** 10 f. + 30 f. green .. 1·00 1·00
1038. – 10 f. + 30 f. brown .. 1·00 1·00

**208.** "Daedalus and Icarus".

**209.** Jan van Eyck.

**1944.** Red Cross.

1039. **208.** 35 c. + 1 f. 65 green .. 25 25
1040. – 50 c. + 2 f. 50 grey .. 25 25
1041. – 60 c. + 3 f. 40 brown 25 25
1042. – 1 f. + 5 f. red .. 50 50
1043. – 1 f. 75 + 8 f. 25 blue 30 25
1044. – 5 f. + 30 f. brown .. 30 25

DESIGNS: 50 c. "The Good Samaritan" (Jacob Jordsen). 60 c. "Christ healing the Paralytic" (detail). 1 f. "Madonna and Child". 1 f. 75, "Self-portrait". 5 f. "St. Sebastian".

Nos. 1039 and 1041/4 depict paintings by Anthony van Dyck.

**1944.** Prisoners of War Relief Fund.

1045. **209.** 10 c. + 15 c. violet .. 20 20
1046. – 35 c. + 15 c. green .. 20 20
1047. – 50 c. + 25 c. brown .. 20 20
1048. – 60 c. + 40 c. olive .. 20 20
1049. – 1 f. + 50 c. red .. 20 20
1050. – 1 f. 75 + 4 f. 25 blue 20 20
1051. – 2 f. 25 + 8 f. 25 slate 50 40
1052. – 3 f. 25 + 11 f. 25 brn. 20 20
1053. – 5 f. + 35 f. grey .. 50 45

PORTRAITS: 35 c. "Godefroid de Bouillon". 50 c. "Jacob van Maerlant". 60 c. "Jean Joses de Dinant". 1 f. "Jacob van Artevelde". 1 f. 75, "Charles Joseph de Ligne". 2 f. 25, "Andre Gretry". 3 f. 25, "Jan Moretus-Plantin". 5 f. "Ruusbroeck".

210. "Bayard and Four Sons of Aymon", Namur. 211. Lion Rampant.

**1944.** Anti-Tuberculosis Fund. Provincial legendary types.

1054. **210.** 10 c.+5 c. brown .. 10 10
1055. – 35 c.+5 c. green .. 10 10
1056. – 50 c.+10 c. violet .. 10 10
1057. – 60 c.+10 c. brown .. 10 10
1058. – 1 f.+15 c. red .. 10 10
1059. – 1 f. 75+5 f. 25 blue 20 20
1060. – 3 f. 25+11 f. 75 grn. 20 20
1061. – 5 f.+25 f. blue .. 30 25

Designs—vert. 35 c. "Brabo severing the giant's hand", Antwerp. 60 c. "Thyl Ulenspiegel" and "Nele", Flanders. 1 f. "St. George and the Dragon", Hainaut. 1 f. 75, "Genevieve of Brabant, with the Child and the Hind", Brabant. horiz. 50 c. "St. Hubert encounters the Hind with the Cross", Luxemburg. 3 f. 25, "Tchantches wrestling with the Saracen", Liege. 5 f. "St. Gertrude rescuing the Knight with the cards", Limburg.

**1944.** Inscr. "BELGIQUE-BELGIE" or "BELGIE-BELGIQUE".

1062. **211.** 5 c. brown .. .. 10 10
1063. 10 c. green .. .. 10 10
1064. 25 c. blue .. .. 10 10
1065. 35 c. brown .. .. 10 10
1066. 50 c. green .. .. 10 10
1067. 75 c. violet .. .. 10 10
1068. 1 f. red .. .. 10 10
1069. 1 f. 25 brown .. .. 10 10
1070. 1 f. 50 orange .. .. 20 20
1071. 1 f. 75 blue .. .. 10 10
1072. 2 f. blue .. .. 80 80
1073. 2 f. 75 mauve .. .. 10 10
1074. 3 f. red .. .. 20 20
1075. 3 f. 50 grey .. .. 20 20
1076. 5 f. olive .. .. 2·25 2·25
1077. 10 f. black .. .. 45 45

**1944.** Overprinted with large **V.**

1078. **152.** 2 c. green .. .. 10 10
1079. 15 c. blue .. .. 10 10
1080. 20 c. violet .. .. 10 10
1081. 60 c. grey .. .. 10 10

213. King Leopold III and "V". 214. War Victims.

215. Rebuilding Homes.

**1944.**

1082. **213.** 1 f. red .. .. 20 10
1083. 1 f. 50 mauve .. 25 10
1084. 1 f. 75 blue .. .. 25 25
1085. 2 f. violet .. .. 70 10
1086. 2 f. 25 green .. .. 35 25
1087. 3 f. 25 brown .. 25 10
1088. 5 f. green .. .. 75 10

**1945.** War Victims' Relief Fund.

1114. **214.** 1 f.+30 f. red .. 1·25 75
1115. **215.** 1¾ f.+30 f. blue .. 1·25 75
Nos. 1114/5 measure 50×35 mm.

**1945.** Post Office Employers' Relief Fund.

1119. **214.** 1 f.+9 f. red .. 25 15
1120. **215.** 1 f.+9 f. red .. 25 15

217. Resister.

218. Group of Resisters.

**1945.** Prisoners of War Relief Fund.

1121. **217.** 10 c.+15 c. orange .. 10 10
1122. – 20 c.+20 c. violet .. 10 10
1123. – 60 c.+25 c. brown .. 10 10
1124. – 70 c.+30 c. green .. 10 10
1125. **217.** 75 c.+50 c. brown .. 15 10
1126. – 1 f.+75 c. green .. 15 10
1127. – 1 f. 50+1 f. red .. 15 10
1128. – 3 f. 50+3 f. 50 blue 80 60
1129. **218.** 5 f.+40 f. brown .. 1·10 65

Designs—vert. 20 c., 1 f. Father and child. 60 c., 1 f. 50, Victim tied to stake. horiz. 70 c., 3 f. 50, Rifleman.

219. West Flanders. 222. Douglas DC-4.

**1945.** Anti-Tuberculosis Fund.

1130. **219.** 10 c.+15 c. green .. 10 10
1131. – 20 c.+20 c. red .. 10 10
1132. – 60 c.+25 c. brown .. 10 10
1133. – 70 c.+30 c. green .. 10 10
1134. – 75 c.+50 c. brown .. 10 10
1135. – 1 f.+75 c. violet .. 10 10
1136. – 1 f. 50+1 f. red .. 10 10
1137. – 3 f. 50+1 f. 50 blue 20 10
1138. – 5 f.+45 f. mauve .. 2·00 1·25

Arms designs—vert. 20 c. to 5 f. Arms of Luxemburg, East Flanders, Namur, Limburg, Hainaut, Antwerp, Liege and Brabant respectively.

**1946.** Air.

1165. **222.** 6 f. blue .. .. 35 10
1166. 8 f. 50 red .. .. 45 35
1167. 50 f. green .. .. 4·25 50
1168. 100 f. grey .. .. 7·50 50

**1946.** Surch. — 10% reducing the original value by 10%.

1171. **213.** "—10%" on 1 f. 50 mve. 35 10
1172. "—10%" on 2 f. violet 1·50 35
1173. "—10%" on 5 f. green 1·25 10

224. Paddle Steamer "Marie Henriette".

**1946.** Ostend-Dover Mail-boat Service Cent.

1174a. – 1 f. 35 blue .. .. 25 10
1175. **224.** 2 f. 25 green .. .. 55 10
1176. – 3 f. 15 grey .. .. 55 20

Designs—21½ × 18½ or 21 × 17 mm: 1 f. 35, Mail steamer "Prince Baudouin". As T **224**: 3 f. 15, Paddle-steamer "Diamant", formerly "Le Chemin de Fer".

225. Paratrooper.

**1946.** Air. Bastogne Monument Fund.

1177. **225.** 17 f. 50+62 f. 50 grn. 1·25 1·00
1178. 17 f. 50+62 f. 50 pur. 1·25 1·00

226. Father Damien. 227. E. Vandervelde.

228. Francois Bovesse.

**1946.** Belgian Patriots.

(a) Father Damien.

1179. **226.** 65 c.+75 c. blue .. 1·50 1·00
1180. – 1 f. 35+2 f. brown .. 1·50 80
1181. – 1 f. 75+18 f. lake .. 1·50 1·00

Designs—horiz. 1 f. 35, Molokai Leper Colony. vert. 1 f. 75, Damien's statue.

(b) Emile Vandervelde.

1182. **227.** 65 c.+75 c. green .. 1·40 70
1183. – 1 f. 35+2 f. blue .. 1·40 70
1184. – 1 f. 75+18 f. red .. 1·40 80

Designs—horiz. 1 f. 35, Vandervelde, miner, mother and child. vert. 1 f. 75, Sower.

(c) Francois Bovesse.

1185. – 65 c.+75 c. violet .. 1·40 80
1186. **228.** 1 f. 35+2 f. brown .. 1·40 80
1187. – 1 f. 75+18 f. red .. 1·40 80

Designs—vert. 65 c. Symbols of Patriotism and Learning. 1 f. 75, Draped memorial figures holding wreath and torch.

229. Pepin d'Herstal. 230. Allegory of "Flight".

**1946.** War Victims' Relief Fund.

1188. **229.** 75 c.+25 c. green .. 50 20
1189. – 1 f.+50 c. violet .. 40 40
1190. – 1 f. 50+1 f. purple .. 70 40
1191. – 3 f. 50+1 f. 50 blue 80 40
1192. – 5 f.+45 f. mauve .. 9·50 8·50
1194. – 5 f.+45 f. orange .. 9·50 8·50

Designs: 1 f. Charlemagne. 1 f. 50, Godfrey of Bouillon. 3 f. 50, Robert of Jerusalem. 5 f. Baudouin of Constantinople.

See also Nos. 1207/11, 1258/9 and 1302/6.

**1946.** Air.

1193. **230.** 2 f.+8 f. violet .. 40 30

231. Malines. 232. Joseph Plateau.

**1946.** Anti-Tuberculosis Fund. No date.

1195. **231.** 65 c.+35 c. red .. 60 25
1196. – 90 c.+60 c. olive .. 60 25
1197. – 1 f. 35+1 f. 15 green 60 35
1198. – 3 f. 15+1 f. 85 blue 70 40
1199. – 4 f. 50+45 f. 50 brn. 11·50 9·25

Designs—(Arms and Industries): 90 c. Dinant. 1 f. 35, Ostend. 3 f. 15, Verviers. 4 f. 50, Louvain.

See also Nos. 1212/16.

**1947.** Air. "Cipex" International Stamp Exhibition, New York. Nos. 1179/87 surch **LUCHTPOST POSTE AERIENNE** or **POSTE AERIENNE LUCHTPOST** and new value. (a) Father Damien.

1199a 1 f.+2 f. on 65 c.+75 c. blue .. .. 50 35
1199b 1 f. 50+2 f. 50 on 1 f. 35 +2 f. brown .. 50 35
1199c 2 f.+45 f. on 1 f. 75+ 18 f. red .. .. 50 35

(b) Emile Vandervelde.

1199d 1 f.+2 f. on 65 c.+75 c. green .. .. 50 35
1199e 1 f. 50+2 f. 50 on 1 f. 35 +2 f. blue .. 50 35
1199f 2 f.+45 f. on 1 f. 75 + 18 f. red .. 50 35

(c) Francois Bovesse.

1199g 1 f.+2 f. on 65 c.+75 c. violet .. .. 50 35
1199h 1 f. 50+2 f. 50 on 1 f. 35+2 f. brown .. 50 35
1199i 2 f.+45 f. on 1 f. 75+ 18 f. red .. .. 50 35

**1947.** Int. Film and Belgian Fine Arts Festival.

1200. **232.** 3 f. 15 blue .. .. 50 10

233. Adrien de Gerlache. 234. Explorers landing from "Belgica".

**1947.** 50th Anniv. of Belgian Antarctic Expedition.

1201. **233.** 1 f. 35 red .. .. 20 10
1202. **234.** 2 f. 25 grey .. .. 3·50 85

**1947.** War Victims' Relief Fund. Mediaeval Princes as T **229.**

1207. 65 c.+35 c. blue .. 1·00 35
1208. 90 c.+60 c. green .. 1·40 45
1209. 1 f. 35+1 f. 15 red .. 2·75 70
1210. 3 f. 15+1 f. 85 blue .. 3·00 85
1211. 20 f.+20 f. purple .. 40·00 32·00

Designs: 65 c. John II, Duke of Brabant. 90 c. Philippe of Alsace. 1 f. 35, William the Good. 3 f. 15, Notger, Bishop of Liege. 20 f. Philip the Noble.

**1947.** Anti-Tuberculosis Fund. Arms designs as T **231**, but dated "1947".

1212. 65 c.+35 c. orange .. 40 25
1213. 90 c.+60 c. purple .. 40 25
1214. 1 f. 35+1 f. 15 brown .. 40 25
1215. 3 f. 15+1 f. 85 blue .. 2·00 40
1216. 20 f.+20 f. green .. 18·00 12·50

Designs (Arms and Industries): 65 c. Nivelles. 90 c. St. Truiden. 1 f. 35, Charleroi. 3 f. 15, St. Nicholas. 20 f. Bouillon.

237. Chemical Industry. 240. Textile Machinery.

239. Antwerp Docks.

Designs—As Type **237**: 1 f. 35, 1 f. 75 green, Woman making lace. 1 f. 75 red, 2 f. 50, Agricultural produce. As Type **239**: 6 f., 6 f. 30, Steel works.

**1948.** National Industries.

1217 **237** 60 c. blue .. .. 25 10
1218 1 f. 20 brown .. 2·00 10
1219 – 1 f. 35 brown .. 25 10
1220 – 1 f. 75 green .. .. 40 10
1221 – 1 f. 75 red .. .. 30 10
1222 **239** 2 f. 25 grey .. .. 1·75 35
1223 – 2 f. 50 mauve .. 6·00 10
1224 **239** 3 f. purple .. .. 12·00 10
1225 **240** 3 f. 15 blue .. .. 1·50 10
1226 4 f. blue .. .. 7·00 10
1227 – 6 f. blue .. .. 15·00 10
1228 – 6 f. 30 purple .. 2·50 2·25

242. St. Benedict and King Totila. 243. St. Bega and Chevremont Castle.

**1948.** Achel Abbey Fund. Inscr. "ACHEL".

1232. **242.** 65 c.+65 c. brown .. 75 40
1233. – 1 f. 35+1 f. 35 green 80 60
1234. – 3 f. 15+2 f. 85 blue 2·75 1·25
1235. – 10 f.+10 f. purple .. 10·00 8·00

Designs—horiz. 1 f. 35, Achel Abbey. vert. 3 f. 15, St. Benedict as Law-Giver. 10 f. Death of St. Benedict.

**1948.** Chevremont Abbey Fund. Inscr. "CHEVREMONT".

1236. **243.** 65 c.+65 c. blue .. 60 40
1237. – 1 f. 35+1 f. 35 red .. 1·00 60
1238. – 3 f. 15+2 f. 85 blue 2·25 1·25
1239. – 10 f.+10 f. brown .. 9·50 7·25

Designs—horiz. 1 f. 35, Chevremont Basilica and Convent. vert. 3 f. 15, Madonna of Chevremont and Chapel. 10 f. Monk and Madonna of Mt. Carmel.

244. Statue of Anseele. 245. Ghent and E. Anseele.

**1948.** Inauguration of Edward Anseele (Socialist Leader) Statue.

1245. **244.** 65 c.+35 c. red .. 2·00 1·10
1246. **245.** 90 c.+60 c. grey .. 2·75 1·60
1247. – 1 f. 35+1 f. 15 brn. 1·60 1·10
1248. – 3 f. 15+1 f. 85 blue 6·00 3·25

Designs: 1 f. 35, Statue and Ed. Anseele. 3 f. 15, Reverse side of statue.

247. "Liberty". 248. "Resistance".

**1948.** Antwerp and Liege Monuments Funds.
1253. **247.** 10 f.+10 f. green 32·00 15·00
1254. **248.** 10 f.+10 f. brown 16·00 9·00

**249.** Cross of Lorraine.

**1948.** Anti-Tuberculosis Fund.
1255. **249.** 20 c.+5 c. green 20 10
1256. 1 f. 20+30 c. purple 70 35
1257. 1 f. 75+25 c. red 80 40
1258. – 4 f.+3 f. 25 blue 6·00 3·25
1259. – 20 f.+20 f. green 35·00 22·00
DESIGNS—As Type **229**: 4 f. Isabel of Austria. 20 f. Albert, Archduke of Austria.

**1949.** Surch. **1-1-49** at top, **31-XII-49** and value at bottom with posthorn in between. (a) Arms type.
1262. **152.** 5 c. on 15 c. blue 10 10
1263. 5 c. on 30 c. brown 10 10
1264. 5 c. on 40 c. lilac 10 10
1265. 20 c. on 70 c. green 10 10
1266. 20 c. on 75 c. mauve 10 10
(b) Anseele Statue.
1267. **244.** 10 c. on 65 c.+35 c. red 2·25 2·25
1268. **245.** 40 c. on 90 c.+60 c. grey 1·25 1·25
1269. – 80 c. on 1 f. 35+1 f. 15 brown 50 35
1270. – 1 f. 20 on 3 f. 15+1 f. 85 blue 1·25 1·25

**251.** King Leopold I. **252.** Forms of Postal Transport.

**1949.** Belgian Stamp Cent.
1271. **251.** 90 c. green (postage) 40 25
1272. 1 f. 75 brown 20 10
1273. 3 f. red 5·00 2·50
1274. 4 f. blue 3·50 55
1275. **252.** 50 f. brown (air) 38·00 14·00

**253.** St. Madeleine from "The Baptism of Christ". **255.** Hemispheres and Allegorical Figure.

**1949.** Exhibition of Paintings by Gerard David, Bruges.
1276. **253.** 1 f. 75 brown 55 15

**1949.** 75th Anniv. of U.P.U.
1296. **255.** 4 f. blue 3·50 1·60

**256.** Guido Gezelle. **257.** Arnica.

**1949.** 50th Death Anniv of Gezelle (poet).
1297 **256** 1 f. 75+75 c. green 1·50 1·10

**1949.** Anti-Tuberculosis and other Funds. (a) Flowers.
1298. **257.** 20 c. + 5 c. black, yellow and green 20 10
1299. – 65 c. + 10 c. black, green and buff 1·00 40
1300. – 90 c. + 10 c. black, blue and red 1·50 60
1301. – 1 f. 20 + 30 c. mult. 1·75 80
FLOWERS: 65 c. Thistle. 90 c. Periwinkle. 1 f. 20, Poppy.
(b) Portraits as T **229**.
1302. 1 f. 75+25 c. orange 65 20
1303. 3 f.+1 f. 50 red 8·00 5·00
1304. 4 f.+2 f. blue 8·50 5·00
1305. 6 f.+3 f. brown 14·00 9·00
1306. 8 f.+4 f. green 16·00 9·50
PORTRAITS: 1 f. 75, Philip the Good. 3 f. Charles V. 4 f. Maria Christina. 6 f. Charles of Lorraine. 8 f. Maria Theresa.

**260.** Anglo-Belgian Monument, Hertain. **261.** Allegory of Saving.

**1950.** Anglo-Belgian Union and other Funds.
1307. – 80 c.+20 c. green 90 60
1308. – 2 f. 50+50 c. red 4·50 2·75
1309 **260.** 4 f.+2 f. blue 6·50 4·75
DESIGNS—HORIZ. 80 c. Arms of Great Britain and Belgium. 2 f. 50, British tanks at Tournai.

**1950.** National Savings Bank Cent.
1310. **261.** 1 f. 75 sepia 50 10

**262.** Hurdling. **263.** Sikorski S-51 Helicopter and Douglas DC-4 leaving Melsbroeck.

**1950.** European Athletic Championships. Inscr. "HEYSEL 1950".
1311. **262.** 20 c.+5 c. green 25 10
1312. – 90 c.+10 c. purple 2·75 1·50
1313. – 1 f. 75+25 c. red 5·00 1·60
1314. – 4 f.+2 f. blue 28·00 16·00
1315. – 8 f.+4 f. green 30·00 18·00
DESIGNS—HORIZ. 1 f. 75, Relay racing. VERT. 90 c. Javelin throwing. 4 f. Pole vaulting. 8 f. Sprinting.

**1950.** Air. Inaug. of Helicopter Airmail Services and Aeronautical Committee's Fund.
1317. **263.** 7 f.+3 f. blue 7·50 4·00

**265.** Gentian. **266.** Sijsele Sanatorium.

**1950.** Anti-tuberculosis and other Funds. Cross in red.
1326 **265** 20 c.+5 c. blue, green and purple 20 10
1327 – 65 c.+10 c. green and brown 1·00 50
1328 – 90 c.+10 c. light green and green 1·40 75
1329 – 1 f. 20+30 c. blue, green & ultramarine 1·50 75
1330 **266** 1 f. 75+25 c. red 2·00 1·25
1331 – 4 f.+2 f. blue 13·00 7·50
1332 – 8 f.+4 f. green 21·00 14·00
DESIGNS—Flowers as Type **265**: 65 c. Rushes. 90 c. Foxglove. 1 f. 20, Sea lavender. Sanatoria as Type **266**: HORIZ. 4 f. Jauche. VERT. 8 f. Tombeek.

**267.** The Belgian Lion. **268.** "Science".

**1951.** (a) 17½ × 20½ mm.
1334 **267** 2 c. brown 10 10
1335 3 c. violet 10 10
1336 5 c. lilac 20 10
1336a 5 c pink 10 10
1337 10 c. orange 10 10
1338 15 c. mauve 10 10
1333 20 c. blue 10 10
1339 20 c. red 10 10
1340 25 c. green 1·25 10
1341 25 c. blue 10 10
1342 30 c. green 10 10
1343 40 c. brown 10 10
1344a 50 c. blue 25 10
1345 60 c. mauve 10 10
1346 65 c. purple 9·50 25
1347 75 c. lilac 10 10
1348 80 c. green 60 10
1349 90 c. blue 65 10
1350 1 f. red 10 10
1351 1 f. 50 grey 10 10
1353 2 f. green 15 10
1354 **267** 2 f. 50 brown 15 10
1355 3 f. mauve 15 10
1355a 4 f. purple 20 10
1355b 4 f. 50 blue 25 10
1355c 5 f. purple 20 10
(b) 20½ × 24½ mm.
1356 **267** 50 c. blue 30 10
1357 60 c. purple 60 50
1358a 1 f. red 10 10
(c) Size 17½ × 22 mm.
1359 **267** 50 c. blue 10 10
1360 1 f. pink 2·50 90
1361 2 f. green 35 15

**1951.** U.N.E.S.C.O. Fund. Inscr. "UNESCO".
1365. **268.** 80 c.+20 c. green 1·25 50
1366. – 2 f. 50+50 c. brown 8·00 5·00
1367. – 4 f.+2 f. blue 9·75 5·75
DESIGNS—HORIZ. 2 f. 50, "Education". VERT. 4 f. "Peace".

**269.** Fairey Tipsy Belfair Trainer I.

**1951.** Air. 50th Anniv of National Aero Club.
1368 – 6 f. blue 18·00 13·00
1369 **269** 7 f. red 18·00 13·00
Design: 6 f. Arsenal Air 100 glider.

**1951.** Air.
1370. – 6 f. brown (glider) 3·00 10
1371. **269.** 7 f. green 4·50 40

**270.** Monument. **272.** Queen Elisabeth.

**1951.** Political Prisoners' National Monument Fund.
1372. **270.** 1 f. 75+25 c. brown 2·00 60
1373. – 4 f.+2 f. blue 20·00 11·00
1374. – 8 f.+4 f. green 22·00 15·00
DESIGNS—HORIZ. 4 f. Breendonk Fort. VERT. 8 f. Side view of monument.

**1951.** Queen Elisabeth Medical Foundation Fund.
1376. **272.** 90 c.+10 c. grey 2·00 50
1377. 1 f. 75+25 c. red 4·00 75
1378. 3 f.+1 f. green 21·00 11·00
1379. 4 f.+2 f. blue 21·00 11·00
1380. 8 f.+4 f. sepia 40·00 12·50

**273.** Lorraine Cross and Dragon. **274.** Beersel Castle.

**1951.** Anti-Tuberculosis and other Funds.
1381. **273.** 20 c.+5 c. red 15 10
1382. 65 c.+10 c. blue 35 20
1383 90 c.+10 c. brown 40 30
1384. 1 f. 20+30 c. violet 80 50
1385. **274.** 1 f. 75+75 c. brown 1·60 90
1386. – 3 f.+1 f. green 9·50 6·25
1387. – 4 f.+2 f. blue 13·00 8·00
1388. – 8 f.+4 f. black 18·00 10·00
CASTLES—As Type **274**: VERT. 3 f. Horst Castle. 8 f. Veves Castle. HORIZ. 4 f. Lavaux St. Anne Castle.

For stamps as Type **273** but dated "1952" see Nos. 1416/19 and for those dated "1953" see Nos. 1507/10.

**276.** Consecration of the Basilica.

**1952.** 25th Anniv. of Cardinalate of Primate of Belgium and Koekelberg Basilica Fund.
1389. – 1 f. 75+25 c. brown 1·00 20
1390. – 4 f.+2 f. blue 11·00 5·50
1391. **276.** 8 f.+4 f. purple 14·00 9·00
DESIGNS—24×35 mm. 1 f. 75. Interior of Koekelberg Basilica. 4 f. Exterior of Koekelberg Basilica.

**277.** King Baudouin. **278.** King Baudouin.

**1952.**
1393. **277.** 1 f. 50 grey 90 10
1394. 2 f. red 35 10
1395. 4 f. blue 2·50 10
1396. **278.** 50 f. purple 18·00 15
1397 100 f. red 4·50 15

**279.** Francis of Taxis. **281.** A. Vermeylen.

**1952.** 13th U.P.U. Congress, Brussels. Portraits of Members of the House of Thurn and Taxis.
1398. **279.** 80 c. green 15 10
1399. – 1 f. 75 orange 15 10
1400. – 2 f. brown 50 10
1401. – 2 f. 50 red 1·00 40
1402. – 3 f. olive 1·00 10
1403. – 4 f. blue 1·00 10
1404. – 5 f. brown 2·50 35
1405. – 5 f. 75 violet 3·50 80
1406. – 8 f. black 16·00 3·00
1407. – 10 f. purple 20·00 7·50
1408. – 20 f. grey 85·00 30·00
1409. – 40 f.+10 f. turquoise £170 £110
DESIGNS—VERT. 1 f. 75, John Baptist. 2 f. Leonard. 2 f. 50, Lamoral. 3 f. Leonard Francis. 4 f. Lamoral Claud. 5 f. Eugene Alexander. 5 f. 75, Anselm Francis. 8 f. Alexander Ferdinand. 10 f. Charles Anselm. 20 f. Charles Alexander. 40 f. Beaulieu Chateau.

**1952.** Culture Fund. Writers.
1410. **281.** 65 c.+30 c. lilac 3·50 1·40
1411. – 80 c.+40 c. green 4·00 1·50
1412. – 90 c.+45 c. olive 4·00 1·60
1413. – 1 f. 75+75 c. lake 6·25 2·40
1414. – 4 f.+2 f. blue 26·00 14·00
1415. – 8 f.+4 f. sepia 28·00 14·00
PORTRAITS: 80 c. K. van de Woestijne. 90 c. C. de Coster. 1 f. 75, M. Maeterlinck. 4 f. E. Verhaeren. 8 f. H. Conscience.

A 4f. blue as No. 1414 and an 8f. lake as No. 1415 each se-tenant with a label showing a laurel wreath and bearing a premium "+9 fr." were put on sale by subscription only.

**282.** Arms, Malmedy. **284.** Dewe and Monument at Liege.

**1952.** Anti-tuberculosis and other Funds. As T **273** but dated "1952" and designs as T **282**.
1416. **273.** 20 c.+5 c. brown 10 10
1417. 80 c.+20 c. green 50 25
1418. 1 f. 20+30 c. purple 1·60 50
1419. 1 f. 50+50 c. olive 1·60 50
1420. **282.** 2 f.+75 c. red 2·00 80
1421. – 3 f.+1 f. 50 brown 16·00 10·50
1422. – 4 f.+2 f. blue 15·00 8·75
1423. – 8 f.+4 f. purple 16·00 10·50
DESIGNS—HORIZ. 3 f. Ruins, Burgreuland. VERT. 4 f. Dam, Eupen. 8 f. Saint and lion, St. Vith.

**1953.** Walthere Dewe Memorial Fund.
1435. **284.** 2 f.+1 f. lake 2·25 1·25

285. Princess Josephine Charlotte.

286. Fishing Boats. "Marcel", "De Meeuw" and "Jacqueline Denise".

**1953.** Red Cross National Disaster Fund. Cross in red.

1436. **285.** 80 c.+20 c. green .. 2·00 50
1437. 1 f. 20+30 c. brown 2·00 50
1438. 2 f.+50 c. lake .. 2·00 50
1439. 2 f. 50+50 c. red .. 12·00 7·50
1440. 4 f.+1 f. blue .. 11·00 6·00
1441. 5 f.+2 f. black .. 11·00 6·00

**1953.** Tourist Propaganda and Cultural Funds.

1442. **286.** 80 c.+20 c. green .. 1·40 60
1443. – 1 f. 20+30 c. brown 4·50 2·25
1444. – 2 f.+50 c. sepia .. 4·50 2·25
1445. – 2 f. 50+50 c. mauve 10·00 5·00
1446. – 4 f.+2 f. blue .. 17·00 8·50
1447. – 8 f.+4 f. green .. 23·00 10·50

DESIGNS—HORIZ. 1 f. 20, Bridge Bouillon. 2 f. Antwerp. VERT. 2 f. 50, Namur. 4 f. Ghent. 8 f. Freyr Rocks and River Meuse.

289. King Baudouin.

290.

**1953.**

(a) $21 \times 24\frac{1}{2}$ mm.

1453 **289** 1 f. 50 black .. .. 20 10
1454 2 f. red .. .. 6·50 10
1455 2 f. green .. .. 20 10
2188 2 f. 50 brown .. 15 10
1457 3 f. purple .. .. 20 10
1458 3 f. 50 green .. .. 20 10
1459 4 f. blue .. .. 60 10
1460 4 f. 50 brown .. 30 10
1462 5 f. violet .. .. 85 10
1463 6 f. mauve .. .. 40 10
1464 6 f. 50 grey .. .. 70·00 13·00
2189 7 f. blue .. .. 25 10
1466 7 f. 50 brown .. 60·00 14·00
1467 8 f. blue .. .. 40 10
1468 8 f. 50 purple .. 12·00 50
1469 9 f. olive .. .. 60·00 1·40
1470 12 f. turquoise .. 50 10
1471 30 f. orange .. .. 1·90 20

(b) $17\frac{1}{2} \times 22$ mm.

1472. **289.** 1 f. 50 black .. .. 35 25
1473. 2 f. 50 brown .. 4·75 6·50
1474. 3 f. mauve .. .. 45 10
1475. 3 f. 50 green .. .. 30 20
1476. 4 f. 50 brown .. 80 75

**1953.** European Child Welfare Fund.

1482. **290.** 80 c.+20 c. green .. 4·00 2·00
1483. 2 f. 50+1 f. red .. 25·00 18·00
1484. 4 f.+1 f. 50 blue .. 27·00 20·00

293. Ernest Malvoz.

296. King Albert Statue.

**1953.** Anti-Tuberculosis and other Funds. As T **273** but dated "1953" and portrait as T **293**.

1507. **273.** 20 c. +5 c. blue .. 10 10
1508. 80 c.+20 c. purple .. 75 35
1509. 1 f. 20+30 c. brown 1·25 1·00
1510. 1 f. 50+50 c. slate .. 1·50 1·25
1511. **293.** 2 f.+75 c. green .. 2·25 1·50
1512. – 3 f.+1 f. 50 red .. 11·00 7·25
1513. – 4 f.+2 f. blue .. 12·50 8·00
1514. – 8 f.+4 f. brown .. 13·50 9·50

PORTRAITS—VERT. 3 f. Carlo Forlanini. 4 f. Albert Calmette. HORIZ. 8 f. Robert Koch.

**1954.** Surch **20 c.** and **I-I-54** at top, **31-XII-54** at bottom and bars in between.

1515 **267** 20 c. on 65 c. purple 1·25 15
1516 20 c. on 90 c. blue .. 1·25 15

See note below No. 480.

**1954.** King Albert Memorial Fund.

1520. **296.** 2 f.+50 c. brown .. 4·00 2·00
1521. – 4 f.+2 f. blue .. 19·00 11·00
1522. – 9 f.+4 f. 50 black .. 17·00 11·00

DESIGNS—HORIZ. 4 f. King Albert Memorial. VERT. 9 f. Marche-les-Dames Rocks and medallion portrait.

298. Monument.

299. Breendonk Camp and Fort.

**1954.** Political Prisoners' National Monument Fund.

1531. **298.** 2 f.+1 f. red .. 12·00 6·00
1532. **299.** 4 f.+2 f. brown .. 28·00 14·00
1533. – 9 f.+4 f. 50 green .. 35·00 20·00

DESIGN—VERT. 9 f. As Type **298** but viewed from different angle.

300. Entrance to Beguinal House.

DESIGNS—HORIZ. 2 f. River scene. VERT. 4 f. Convent Buildings. 7 f. Cloisters. 8 f. Doorway. 9 f. Statue of our Lady of the Vineyard (larger 35×53 mm.).

**1954.** Beguinage of Bruges Restoration Fund.

1534. **300.** 80 c.+20 c. green .. 80 45
1535. – 2 f.+1 f. red .. 10·00 5·50
1536. – 4 f.+2 f. violet .. 13·00 8·00
1537. – 7 f.+3 f. 50 purple .. 26·00 16·00
1538. – 8 f.+4 f. brown .. 24·00 16·00
1539. – 9 f.+4 f. 50 blue .. 40·00 24·00

302. Map of Europe and Rotary Symbol.

**1954.** 50th Anniv of Rotary International and 5th Regional Conference, Ostend.

1540. **302.** 20 c. red .. .. 10 10
1541. – 80 c. green .. .. 25 15
1542. – 4 f. blue .. .. 1·50 25

DESIGNS: 80 c. Mermaid, "Mercury" and Rotary symbol. 4 f. Rotary symbol and hemispheres.

303. Child.

304. "The Blind Man and the Paralytic" (after Anto-Carte).

**1954.** Anti-T.B. and other Funds.

1543. **303.** 20 c.+5 c. green .. 15 10
1544. 80 c.+20 c. black .. 80 40
1545. 1 f. 20+30 c.brown 1·50 1·00
1546. 1 f. 50+50 c. violet 3·25 1·75
1547. **304.** 2 f.+75 c. red .. 6·25 3·00
1548. 4 f.+1 f. blue .. 15·00 10·00

305. Begonia and the Rabot.

DESIGNS—VERT. 2 f. 50, Azaleas and Chateau des Comtes. 4 f. Orchid and the "Three Towers".

**1955.** Ghent Flower Show.

1549. **305.** 80 c. red .. .. 30 15
1550. – 2 f. 50 sepia .. .. 6·25 2·00
1551. – 4 f. lake .. .. 4·75 40

## INDEX

Countries can be quickly located by referring to the index at the end of this volume.

306. "Homage to Charles V" (A. De Vriendt).

307. "Charles V" (Titian).

**1955.** Emperor Charles V Exhibition, Ghent.

1552. **306.** 20 c. red .. .. 10 10
1553 **307.** 2 f. green .. .. 60 10
1554. – 4 f. blue .. .. 4·50 1·00

DESIGN—As Type **306.** 4 f. "Abdication of Charles V" (L. Gallait).

308. Emile Verhaeren (after C. Montald).

309. "Textile Industry".

**1955.** Birth Cent. of Verhaeren (poet).

1555. **308.** 20 c. black .. .. 10 10

**1955.** 2nd Int. Textile Exhibition, Brussels.

1556. **309.** 2 f. purple .. .. 80 10

310. "The Foolish Virgin" (R. Wouters).

311. "The Departure of the Liege Volunteers in 1830" (Soubre).

**1955.** 3rd Biennial Sculpture Exn., Antwerp.

1557. **310.** 1 f. 20 green .. .. 1·25 25
1558. 2 f. violet .. .. 1·50 10

**1955.** Liege Exn. 125th Anniv. of 1830 Revolution.

1559. **311.** 20 c. green .. .. 10 10
1560. 2 f. brown .. .. 60 10

312. Ernest Solvay.

**1955.** Cultural Fund. Scientists.

1561. **312.** 20 c.+5 c. brown .. 10 10
1562. – 80 c.+20 c. violet .. 85 35
1563. – 1 f. 20+30 c. blue .. 4·00 2·00
1564. – 2 f.+50 c. red .. 4·00 2·00
1565. – 3 f.+1 f. green .. 10·50 6·75
1566. – 4 f.+2 f. brown .. 10·50 6·75

PORTRAITS—VERT. 80 c. Jean-Jacques Dony. 2 f. Leo H. Baekeland. 3 f. Jean-Etienne Lenoir. HORIZ. 1 f. 20, Egide Walschaerts. 4 f. Emile Fourcault and Emile Gobbe.

313. "The Joys of Spring" (E. Canneel).

314. E. Holboll (Danish postal official).

**1955.** Anti-T.B. and other Funds.

1567. **313.** 20 c.+5 c. mauve .. 10 10
1568. 80 c.+20 c. green .. 45 35
1569. 1 f. 20+30 c. brown 1·40 50
1570. 1 f. 50+50 c. violet 1·50 75
1571. **314.** 2 f.+50 c. red .. 6·50 3·75
1572. – 4 f.+2 f. blue .. 18·00 10·50
1573. – 8 f.+4 f. sepia .. 18·00 11·00

PORTRAITS—As Type **314:** 4 f. J. D. Rockefeller (philanthropist). 8 f. Sir R. W. Philip (physician).

315. Blood Donors Emblem.

316. Mozart when a Child.

317. Queen Elisabeth and Mozart Sonata.

**1956.** Blood Donors.

1574. **315.** 2 f. red .. .. 50 10

**1956.** Birth Bicentenary of Mozart. Inscr. as in T **316**.

1575. – 80 c.+20 c. green .. 50 15
1576. **316.** 2 f.+1 f. purple .. 3·00 2·00
1577. **317.** 4 f.+2 f. lilac .. 7·00 3·75

DESIGN—As Type **316.** 80 c. Palace of Charles de Lorraine, Brussels.

318.

319. Queen Elisabeth Medallion (Courtens).

**1956.** "Scaldis" Exn. in Tournai, Ghent and Antwerp.

1578. **318.** 2 f. blue .. .. 25 10

**1956.** 80th Birthday of Queen Elisabeth and Foundation Fund.

1579. **319.** 80 c.+20 c. green .. 45 20
1580. 2 f.+1 f. lake .. 3·00 1·60
1581. 4 f.+2 f. sepia .. 4·00 2·50

320.

321.

**1956.** Europa.

1582. **320.** 2 f. green .. .. 1·75 10
1583. 4 f. violet .. .. 9·00 30

**1956.** Electrification of Brussels-Luxembourg Railway Line.

1584. **321.** 2 f. blue .. .. 90 10

322. E. Anseele.

**1956.** Birth Cent. of Anseele (statesman).

1588. **322.** 20 c. purple .. .. 10 10

323. Medieval Ship.

324. Weighing a Baby.

**1956.** Anti-Tuberculosis and other Funds.

1589. **323.** 20 c.+5 c. brown .. 10 10
1590. 80 c.+20 c. green .. 60 30
1591. 1 f. 20+30 c. purple 60 35
1592. 1 f. 50+50 c. slate .. 1·00 60
1593. **324.** 2 f.+50 c. green .. 2·50 1·50
1594. – 4 f.+2 f. purple .. 10·00 6·75
1595. – 8 f.+4 f. red .. 11·00 7·25

DESIGNS—As Type **324:** HORIZ. 4 f. X-ray examination. VERT. 8 f. Convalescence and rehabilitation.

325. "Atomium" and Exhibition Emblem.
327. Emperor Maximilian I, with Messenger.

**1957.** Brussels Int. Exhibition, 1958.
1596. 325. 2 f. red .. .. 20 10
1597. 2 f. 50 green .. .. 25 10
1598. 4 f. violet .. .. 60 15
1599. 5 f. purple .. .. 1·00 30

**1957.** Stamp Day.
1603. 327. 2 f. red .. .. 25 10

328. Charles Plisnier and Albrecht Rodenbach (writers).

**1957.** Cultural Fund. Belgian Celebrities.
1604. 328. 20 c.+5 c. violet .. 10 10
1605. – 80 c.+20 c. brown .. 35 20
1606. – 1 f. 20+30 c. sepia .. 55 20
1607. – 2 f.+50 c. red .. 1·75 60
1608. – 3 f.+1 f. green .. 2·50 2·00
1609. – 4 f.+2 f. blue .. 3·25 2·50
DESIGNS: 80 c. Professors Emiel Vliebergh and Maurice Wilmotte. 1 f. 20, Paul Pastur and Julius Hoste. 2 f. Lodewijk de Raet and Jules Destree (politicians). 3 f. Constantin Meunier and Constant Permeke (artists). 4 f. Lieven Gevaert and Edouard Empain (industrialists).

329. Sikorsky S-58 Helicopter.

**1957.** Conveyance of 100,000th Passenger by Belgian Helicopter Service.
1610. 329. 4 f. bl., grn. & grey 1·40 45

330. Zeebrugge Harbour.

**1957.** 50th Anniv. of Completion of Zeebrugge Harbour.
1611. 330. 2 f. blue .. .. 70 10

331. King Leopold I entering Brussels (after Simonau).
332. Scout and Guide Badges.

**1957.** 126th Anniv. of Arrival of King Leopold I in Belgium.
1612. 331. 20 c. green .. .. 25 10
1613. – 2 f. mauve .. .. 85 10
DESIGN—HORIZ. 2 f. King Leopold I at frontier (after Wappers).

**1957.** 50th Anniv. of Boy Scout Movement and Birth Cent. of Lord Baden-Powell.
1614. 332. 80 c. brown .. .. 25 15
1615. – 4 f. green .. .. 1·25 30
DESIGN—VERT. 4 f. Lord Baden-Powell.

333. "Kneeling Woman" (after Lehmbruck).
334. "Agriculture and Industry".

**1957.** 4th Biennial Sculpture Exn.. Antwerp.
1616. 333. 2 f. 50 green .. .. 90 45

**1957.** Europa.
1617. 334. 2 f. purple .. .. 50 10
1618. 4 f. blue .. .. 1·50 30

335. Sledge-dog Team.

**1957.** Belgian Antarctic Expedition, 1957-58.
1619. 335. 5 f.+2 f. 50 orange, brown and grey .. 3·75 2·00

336. General Patton's grave at Hamm.
337. Adolphe Max.

**1957.** General Patton Memorial Issue.
1621. 336. 1 f.+50 c. black .. 90 45
1622. – 2 f. 50+50 c. green .. 1·40 50
1623. – 3 f.+1 f. brown .. 2·75 1·40
1624. – 5 f.+2 f. 50 slate .. 6·00 4·00
1625. – 6 f.+3 f. red .. 8·00 5·75
DESIGNS—HORIZ. 2 f. 50, Patton Memorial project at Bastogne. 3 f. Gen. Patton decorating Brig.-General A. MacAuliffe. 6 f. (51 × 35½ mm.) Tanks in action. VERT. 5 f. General Patton.

**1957.** 18th Death Anniv. of Burgomaster Adolphe Max (patriot).
1626. 337. 2 f. 50+1 f. blue .. 1·00 50

338. Queen Elisabeth with Doctors Depage and Debaisieux at a surgical operation.

**1957.** 50th Anniv. of "Edith Cavell-Marie Depage" and "St. Camille" Nursing Schools.
1627. 338. 30 c. red .. .. 15 10

339. "Carnival Kings of Fosses" (Namur).
340. "Infanta Isabella with Crossbow" (Brussels).

**1957.** Anti-Tuberculosis and other Funds. Provincial Legends.
1628. 339. 30 c.+20 c. pur. & yell. 10 10
1629. – 1 f.+50 c. sepia & blue 40 25
1630. – 1 f. 50+50 c. grey & red 50 35
1631. – 2 f.+1 f. black & grn. 55 35
1632. 340. 2 f. 50+1 f. green and mauve .. 1·50 75
1633. – 5 f.+2 f. black & blue 3·25 3·00
1634. – 6 f.+2 f. 50 lake & red 4·00 3·75
DESIGNS: As Type 339—HORIZ. 1 f. 50, "St. Remacle and the Wolf" (Liege). VERT. 1 f. "Op Signoorken" (Antwerp). 2 f. "The Long Man and the Pea Soup" (Limburg). As Type 340—HORIZ. 6 f. "Carnival Kings of Binche" (Hainaut). VERT. 5 f. "The Virgin with the Inkwell" (West Flanders).

341. Posthorn and Postilion's Badges.

**1958.** Postal Museum Day.
1635. 341. 2 f. 50 grey .. .. 20 10

342. Benelux Gate.

DESIGNS — HORIZ. 1 f. Civil Engineering Pavilion. 1 f. 50, Belgian Congo and Ruanda - Urundi Pavilion. 2 f. 50, "Belgium, 1900". 3 f. Atomium. 5 f. (49 × 33½ mm.) Telexpo Pavilion.

**1958.** Inaug. of Brussels Int. Exhibition. Inscr. as in T 342.
1636. 342. 30 c.+20 c. sepia, brown and violet .. 10 10
1637. – 1 f.+50 c. pur., slate and green .. .. 15 10
1638. – 1 f. 50+50 c. violet, turquoise and grn. 15 10
1639. – 2 f. 50+1 f. red, blue and vermilion .. 30 20
1640. – 3 f.+1 f. 50 blue, blk. and red .. .. 70 50
1641. – 5 f.+3 f. mve., black and blue .. .. 1·00 1·00

343. "Food and Agriculture Organization".

**1958.** United Nations Commem.
1642. – 50 c. grey (postage) .. 1·75 1·60
1643. 343. 1 f. red .. .. .. 10 10
1644. – 1 f. 50 blue .. .. 15 10
1645. – 2 f. purple .. .. 40 35
1646. – 2 f. 50 green .. .. 10 10
1647. – 3 f. turquoise .. .. 40 35
1648. – 5 f. mauve .. .. 15 15
1649. – 8 f. brown .. .. 60 60
1650. – 11 f. lilac .. .. 1·10 75
1651. – 20 f. red .. .. 3·00 3·00
1652. – 5 f. blue (air) .. .. 15 15
1653. – 6 f. green .. .. 20 20
1654. – 7 f. 50 violet .. .. 20 20
1655. – 8 f. sepia .. .. 20 20
1656. – 9 f. red .. .. 30 20
1657. – 10 f. brown .. .. 30 30
DESIGNS (Emblems and symbols)—HORIZ. 50 c. I.L.O. 2 f. 50, U.N.E.S.C.O. 3 f. U.N. Pavilion, Brussels Int. Exn. 6 f. World Meteorological Organization. 8 f. (No. 1649), Int. Monetary Fund. 8 f. (No. 1655), General Agreement on Tariffs and Trade. 10 f. Atomic Energy Agency. 11 f. W.H.O. 20 f. U.P.U. VERT. 1 f. 50, U.N.O. 2 f. World Bank. 5 f. (No. 1648), I.T.U. 5 f. (No. 1652), I.C.A.O. 7 f. 50, Protection of Refugees. 9 f. UNICEF.

344. Eugene Ysaye.
345. "Europa".

**1958.** Birth Cent. of Ysaye (violinist).
1658. 344. 30 c. blue and red .. 20 10

**1958.** Europa.
1659. 345. 2 f. 50, blue & red .. 20 10
1660. 5 f. red and blue .. 35 20

346. "Marguerite Van Eyck" (after Jan Van Eyck).

**1958.** Cultural Relief Funds. Paintings as T 346. Frames in brown and yellow.
1661. 346. 30 c.+20 c. myrtle 10 10
1662. – 1 f.+50 c. lake 50 35
1663. – 1 f. 50+50 c. blue .. 90 50
1664. – 2 f. 50+1 f. sepia .. 2·00 1·40
1665. – 3 f.+1 f. 50 red .. 3·25 1·90
1666. – 5 f.+3 f. blue .. 5·00 4·00
PAINTINGS—HORIZ. 1 f. "Carrying the Cross" (Hieronymus Bosch). 3 f. "The Rower" (James Ensor). VERT. 1 f. 50, "St. Donatien" (Jan Gossaert). 2 f. 50, Self-portrait (Lambert Lombard). 5 f. "Henriette with the Large Hat" (Henri Evenepoel).

347. "Hoogstraten".
348. Pax—"Creche vivante".

**1958.** Anti-Tuberculosis and other Funds. Provincial Legends.
1667. 347. 40 c.+10 c. bl. & grn. 10 10
1668. – 1 f.+50 c. sepia and yellow .. .. 30 20
1669. – 1 f. 50+50 c. purple and green .. .. 40 35
1670. – 2 f.+1 f. brown & red 50 35
1671. 348. 2 f. 50+1 f. red and green .. .. 1·40 80
1672. – 5 f.+2 f. purple & blue 3·25 3·00
1673. – 6 f.+2 f. 50 blue and red .. .. .. 4·00 3·50

DESIGNS: As Type 347—VERT. 1 f. "Jean de Nivelles". 1 f. 50, "Jeu de Saint Evermare a Russon". HORIZ. 2 f. "Les penitents de Furnes". As Type 348—HORIZ. "Marches de l'Entre Sambre et Meuse". VERT. 6 f. "Pax—Vierge".

349. "Human Rights".
350. "Europe of the Heart".

**1958.** 10th Anniv. of Human Rights Declaration.
1674. 349. 2 f. 50 slate .. .. 20 10

**1959.** "Heart of Europe". Fund for Displaced Persons.
1675. 350. 1 f.+50 c. purple .. 30 15
1676. 2 f. 50+1 f. green .. 80 45
1677. 5 f.+2 f. 50 brown .. 1·25 1·00

351. J. B. de Taxis taking the oath at the hands of Charles V (after J.-E. Van den Bussche).
352. N.A.T.O. Emblem.

**1959.** Stamp Day.
1680. 351. 2 f. 50 green .. .. 30 10

**1959.** 10th Anniv. of N.A.T.O.
1681. 352. 2 f. 50 blue and red 35 10
1682. 5 f. blue and green .. 90 55
On the 5 f. value the French and Flemish inscriptions are transposed.
For similar design but inscr. "1969", see No. 2112.

353. "Blood Transfusion".

DESIGN—As Type 353.—HORIZ. 2 f. 50, 3 f. Red Cross and broken sword ("Aid for the wounded").

354. J. H. Dunant and battle scene at Solferino, 1859.

**1959.** Red Cross Commem. Inscr. "1859 1959".
1683. 353. 40 c.+10 c. red & grey 10 10
1684. 1 f.+50 c. red & sepia 90 45
1685. 1 f. 50+50 c. red and lilac .. .. 2·00 90
1686. – 2 f. 50+1 f. red and myrtle .. .. 2·25 1·40
1687. – 3 f.+1 f. 50 red and blue .. .. 4·25 2·75
1688. 354. 5 f.+3 f. red & sepia 7·00 4·25

355. Philip the Good.
356. Arms of Philip the Good.

**1959.** Royal Library of Belgium Fund. Nos. 1689/94 have background in deep blue and bistre and bottom panel in deep olive.

1689. **355.** 40 c.+10 c. red .. 10 10
1690. – 1 f.+50 c. red .. 40 20
1691. – 1 f. 50+50 c. red .. 1·00 70
1692. – 2 f. 50+1 f. red .. 1·75 1·50
1693. – 3 f.+1 f. 50 red .. 2·75 2·25
1694. **356.** 5 f.+3 f. mult. .. 4·00 3·50

DESIGNS—As Type **355** (Holders of Order of the Golden Fleece): 1 f. Charles the Bold. 1 f. 50, Maximillian of Austria. 2 f. 50, Philip the Fair. 3 f. Charles V.

**358.** Town Hall, Oudenarde.

**359.** Pope Adrian VI.

**1959.** Oudenarde Town Hall Commem.
1699. **358.** 2 f. 50 purple .. 20 10

**1959.** 500th Birth Anniv. of Pope Adrian VI.
1700. **359.** 2 f. 50 red .. .. 20 10
1701. 5 f. blue .. .. 35 25

**360.** "Europa".

**361.** Boeing 707.

**1959.** Europa.
1702. **360.** 2 f. 50 red .. .. 20 10
1703. 5 f. turquoise .. 40 25

**1959.** Inauguration of Boeing 707 Airliners by SABENA.
1704 **361** 6 f. blue, grey & red .. 1·50 50

**362.** Antwerp fish (float).

**363.** Stavelot "Blancs Moussis" (carnival figures).

**1959.** Anti-Tuberculosis and other Funds. Carnival scenes.
1705. **362.** 40 c.+10 c. green, red and bistre .. .. 10 10
1706. – 1 f.+50 c. green, vio. and olive .. .. 35 25
1707. – 2 f.+50 c. yellow, purple & brown.. 40 35
1708. **363.** 2 f. 50+1 f. blue, vio. and grey .. .. 50 35
1709. – 3f.+1 f. purple, yell. and grey .. .. 1·50 1·00
1710. – 6 f.+2 f. blue, red and olive .. .. 3·25 3·00
1711. – 7 f.+3 f. black, yell., and blue .. .. 4·25 3·50

DESIGNS—As Type **362**—HORIZ. 1 f. Mons dragon (float). 2 f. Eupen and Malmedy clowns in chariot. As Type **363**—VERT. 3 f. Ypres jester. HORIZ. 6 f. Holy Family. 7 f. Madonna and child.

**364.** Countess Alexandrine of Taxis (tapestry)

**365.** Indian Azalea.

**1960.** Stamp Day.
1712. **364.** 3 f. blue .. .. 50 10

**1960.** Ghent Flower Show. Inscr. as in T **365**.
1713. **365.** 40 c. red and violet.. 15 10
1714. – 3 f. yell, red, & green 40 10
1715. – 6 f. red, green & blue 1·75 50

FLOWERS: 3 f. Begonia. 6 f. Anthurium and bromelia.

**366.** Refugee.

**367.** "Labour" (after Meunier).

**1960.** World Refugee Year. Inscr. as in T **366**.
1716. – 40 c.+10 c. purple .. 10 10
1717. **366.** 3 f.+1 f. 50 sepia .. 45 35
1718. – 6 f.+3 f. blue .. 1·40 90

DESIGNS: 40 c. Child refugee. 6 f. Woman refugee.

**1960.** 75th Anniv. of Belgian Socialist Party. Inscr. as in T **367**.
1720. **367.** 40 c. purple and red.. 15 10
1721. – 3 f. brown and red .. 50 15

DESIGN—HORIZ. 3 f. "Workers" (after Meunier).

**369.** Parachutist on ground.

**1960.** Parachuting. Designs bearing emblem of National Parachuting Club.
1726 – 40 c.+10 c black & bl 20 15
1727 – 1 f.+50 c. black & bl 1·25 50
1728 – 2 f.+50 c. black, blue and green .. .. 2·25 1·50
1729 – 2 f. 50+1 f. black, turquoise and green 4·00 2·40
1730 **369** 3 f.+1 f. black, blue and green .. .. 4·00 2·40
1731 6 f.+2 f. black, blue and green .. .. 4·50 2·75

DESIGNS—HORIZ. 40 c., 1 f., Parachutists dropping from Douglas DC-4 aircraft. VERT. 2 f., 2 f. 50, Parachutists descending.

**370.** Ship's Officer and Helmsman.

**1960.** Congo Independence.
1732 **370** 10 c. red .. .. 10 10
1733 – 40 c. red .. .. 10 10
1734 – 1 f. purple .. .. 50 15
1735 – 2 f. green .. .. 40 15
1736 – 2 f. 50 blue .. .. 50 15
1737 – 3 f. blue .. .. 50 10
1738 – 6 f. violet .. .. 1·75 70
1739 – 8 f. brown .. .. 6·00 4·50

DESIGNS—As Type **370**: 40 c. Doctor and nurses with patient. 1 f. Tree-planting. 2 f. Sculptors. 2 f. 50, Sport (putting the shot). 3 f. Broadcasting from studio. (52×35½ mm.). 6 f. Children with doll. 8 f. Child with globe.

**371.** Refugee Airlift.

**1960.** Congo Refugees Relief Fund.
1740. **371.** 40 c.+10 c. turquoise 10 10
1741. – 3 f.+1 f. 50 red .. 1·90 90
1742. – 6 f.+3 f. violet .. 3·50 3·00

DESIGNS—As Type **371**: 3 f. Mother and child. 35×51½ mm: 6 f. Boeing 707 airplane spanning map of aircraft route.

**1960.** Surch.
1743. **267.** 15 c. on 30 c. green.. 25 10
1744. 15 c. on 50 c. blue .. 10 10
1745. 20 c. on 30 c. green.. 25 10

**373.** Conference Emblem.

**374.** Young Stamp Collectors.

**1960.** 1st Anniv. of E.P.T. Conf.
1746. **373.** 3 f. lake .. .. 40 10
1747. 6 f. green .. .. 1·00 30

**1960.** "Philately for the Young" Propaganda.
1748. **374.** 40 c. black and bistre 10 10

**375.** Pouring Milk for Child.

**376.** Frere Orban (founder).

**1960.** United Nations Children's Fund.
1749. **375.** 40 c.+10 c. yellow, green and brown.. 10 10
1750. – 1 f.+50 c. red, blue and drab .. 90 50
1751. – 2 f.+50 c. bistre, green and violet .. 1·60 1·25
1752. – 2 f. 50+1 f. sepia, blue and red .. 1·75 1·25
1753. – 3 f.+1 f. violet, oran. and turquoise .. 1·90 1·50
1754. – 6 f.+2 f. brown, green and blue .. .. 3·50 2·00

DESIGNS: 1 f. Nurse embracing children. 2 f. Child carrying clothes, and ambulance. 2 f. 50, Nurse weighing baby. 3 f. Children with linked arms. 6 f. Refugee worker and child.

**1960.** Centenary of Credit Communal (Co-operative Bank).
1755. **376.** 10 c. brown and yellow 10 10
1756. 40 c. brown and green 10 10
1757. 1 f. 50 brown & violet 90 50
1758. 3 f. brown and red .. 90 10

**377.** Tapestry.

DESIGNS—VERT. 1 f. Crystalware. 2 f. Lace. HORIZ. 2 f. 50, Brassware. 3 f. Diamond-cutting. 6 f. Ceramics.

**1960.** Anti-T.B. and other Funds. Arts and Crafts.
1759. **377.** 40 c. + 10 c. ochre, brown and blue .. 10 10
1760. – 1 f.+50 c. blue, brn. and indigo .. 90 50
1761. – 2 f.+50 c. olive, blk. and brown .. 1·25 90
1762. – 2 f. 50+1 f. yellow and brown .. 2·00 1·50
1763. – 3 f.+1 f. black, brown and blue .. .. 2·50 1·90
1764. – 6 f.+2 f. lemon and black .. .. 3·50 2·50

**378.** King Baudouin and Queen Fabiola.

**379.** Nicolaus Rockox (after Van Dyck).

**1960.** Royal Wedding.
1765. **378.** 40 c. sepia and green 10 10
1766. 3 f. sepia and purple.. 30 10
1767 6 f. sepia and blue .. 85 30

**1961.** Surch. in figs. and **1961.** at top, **1962** at bottom and bars in between.
1768. **267.** 15 c. on 30 c. green.. 60 10
1769. 20 c. on 30 c. green.. 1·75 1·25
See note below No. 480.

**1961.** 400th Birth Anniv. of Nicolaus Rockox (Burgomaster of Antwerp).
1770. **379.** 3 f. black, bis. & brn. 25 10

**380.** Seal of Jan Bode.

**381.** K. Kats (playwright) and Father N. Pietkin (poet).

**1961.** Stamp Day.
1771. **380.** 3 f. sepia and brown.. 20 10

**1961.** Cultural Funds. Portrait in purple.
1772. 40 c.+10 c. lake and pink 10 10
1773. 1 f.+50 c. lake & brown 1·60 90
1774. 2 f.+50 c. red & yellow 2·75 1·75
1775. 2 f. 50+1 f. myrtle & sage 2·75 1·75
1776. 3 f.+1 f. blue & light blue 3·00 2·10
1777. 6 f.+2 f. blue & lavender 4·00 2·50

PORTRAITS: 40 c. Type **381**. 1 f. A. Mockel and J. F. Willems (writers). 2 f. J. van Rijswijck and X. Neujean (politicians). 2 f. 50, J. Demarteau (journalist) and A. van de Perre (politician). 3 f. J. David (litterateur) and A. du Bois (writer). 6 f. H. Vieuxtemps (violinist) and W. de Mol (composer).

**382.** White Rhinoceros.

**383.** Cardinal A.P. de Granville (first Archbishop).

**1961.** Philanthropic Funds. Animals of Antwerp Zoo.
1778. 40 c.+10 c. choc. & brn. 20 15
1779. 1 f.+50 c. brown & green 1·60 60
1780. 2 f.+50 c. sepia, red and black .. .. .. 1·75 90
1781. 2 f. 50+1 f. brown & red 1·60 90
1782. 3 f.+1 f. brown & orange 1·90 1·10
1783. 6 f.+2 f. ochre and blue 2·75 1·50

ANIMALS—VERT. 40 c. Type **382**. Przewalski horse and foal. 2 f. Okapi. HORIZ. 2 f. 50, Giraffe, 3 f. Lesser panda. 6 f. Elk.

**1961.** 400th Anniv. of Archbishopric of Malines.
1784. **383.** 40 c.+10 c. brown, red & purple .. 10 10
1785. – 3 f.+1 f. 50 mult. .. 70 40
1786. – 6 f.+3 f. bistre, violet and purple .. 90 80

DESIGNS: 3 f. Cardinal's Arms. 6 f. Symbols of Archbishopric and Malines.

**385.** "Interparliamentary Union".

**1961.** 50th Interparliamentary Union Conf., Brussels.
1791. **385.** 3 f. brown & turquoise 50 10
1792. 6 f. purple and red .. 70 50

**386.** Doves.

**1961.** Europa.
1793. **386.** 3 f. black and olive.. 20 10
1794. 6 f. black and brown 25 20

**387.** Reactor BR 2, Mol.

**388.** "The Mother and Child" (after Paulus).

**1961.** Euratom Commem.
1795. **387.** 40 c. green .. .. 10 10
1796. – 3 f. mauve .. .. 15 10
1797. – 6 f. blue .. .. 30 20

DESIGNS—VERT. 3 f. Heart of reactor BR 3, Mol. HORIZ. 6 f. View of reactor BR 3, Mol.

**1961.** Anti-T.B. and other Funds. Belgian paintings of mothers and children. Frames in gold.
1798. **388.** 40 c.+10 c. sepia .. 10 10
1799. – 1 f.+50 c. blue .. 35 35
1800. – 2 f.+50 c. red .. 90 50
1801. – 2 f. 50+1 f. lake .. 90 75
1802. – 3 f.+1 f. violet .. 90 75
1803. – 6 f.+2 f. myrtle .. 1·10 90

PAINTINGS: 1 f. "Maternal Love" (Navez). 2 f. "Maternity" (Permeke). 2 f. 50, "The Virgin and the Child" (Van der Weyden). 3 f. "The Virgin with the Apple" (Memling). 6 f. "The Myosotis Virgin" (Rubens).

**389.** Horta Museum.

**390.** Male Castle.

**1962.** Birth Cent. of Victor Horta (architect).
1804. **389.** 3 f. brown .. .. 15 10

**1962.** Cultural and Patriotic Funds. Buildings.
1805. **390.** 40 c.+10 c. green .. 10 10
1806. – 90 c.+10 c. mauve .. 20 20
1807. – 1 f.+50 c. lilac .. 45 40
1808. – 2 f.+50 c. violet .. 65 55
1809. – 2 f. 50+1 f. brown .. 85 90
1810. – 3 f.+1 f. turquoise .. 90 1·00
1811. – 6 f.+2 f. red .. 1·50 1·50
BUILDINGS—HORIZ. 90 c. Royal Library, Brussels. 2 f. Collegiate Church, Soignies. 6 f. Ypres Halls. VERT. 1 f. Notre-Dame Basilica, Tongres. 2 f. 50, Notre-Dame Church, Hanswijk, Malines. 3 f. St. Denis-en-Broqueroie Abbey.

**391.** 16th-Century Postilion. **392.** G. Mercator. (after F. Hogenberg)

**1962.** Stamp Day.
1812. **391.** 3 f. brown and green 20 10
See also No. 1997.

**1962.** 450th Birth Anniv. of Mercator (geographer).
1813. **392.** 3 f. sepia .. .. 15 10

**393.** Brother A. M. Gochet (scholar). **394.** Guianan Cock of the Rock.

**1962.** Gochet and Triest Commemoration.
1814 **393** 2 f. blue .. .. 15 10
1815 – 3 f. brown .. .. 20 10
PORTRAIT: 3 f. Canon P.-J. Triest (benefactor of the aged).

**1962.** Philanthropic Funds. Birds of Antwerp Zoo. Birds, etc., in natural colours; colours of name panel and inscription given.
1816. **394.** 40 c.+10 c. blue .. 15 15
1817. – 1 f.+50 c. blue & red 55 55
1818. – 2 f.+50 c. mve. & blk. 1·25 1·10
1819. – 2 f. 50+1 f. turq. & red 1·40 1·25
1820. – 3 f.+1 f. brn. & grn. 1·75 1·60
1821. – 6 f.+2 f. blue & red .. 3·25 3·00
BIRDS: 1 f. Red lory. 2 f. Knysna turaco. 2 f. 50, Keel-billed toucan. 3 f. Greater bird of paradise. 6 f. Congo peacock.

**395.** Europa "Tree". **396.** "Captive Hands" (after sculpture by Ianchelivici).

**1962.** Europa.
1822. **395.** 3 f. black, yell. & red 20 10
1823. 6 f. black, yell.& olive 30 20

**1962.** Concentration Camp Victims.
1824. **396.** 40 c. blue and black .. 10 10

**397.** Reading Braille. **398.** "Adam" (After Michelangelo).

**1962.** Handicapped Children Relief Funds.
1825. **397.** 40 c.+10 c. brown .. 10 10
1826. – 1 f.+50 c. red 30 25
1827. – 2 f.+50 c. mauve .. 1·00 80
1828. – 2 f. 50+1 f. green .. 90 60
1829. – 3 f.+1 f. blue 1·00 75
1830. – 6 f.+2 f. sepia 1·00 90
DESIGNS—VERT. 1 f. Girl solving puzzle. 2 f. 50, Crippled child with ball. 3 f. Girl walking with crutches. HORIZ. 2 f. Child with earphones. 6 f. Crippled boys with football.

**1962.** "The Rights of Man".
1831. **398.** 3 f. sepia and green .. 15 10
1832. 6 f. sepia and brown .. 30 20

**399.** Queen Louise-Marie. **400.** Menin Gate, Ypres.

**1962.** Anti-tuberculosis and other Funds. Belgian Queens in green and gold.
1833. 40 c.+10 c. Type **399** .. 10 10
1834. 40 c.+10 c. As T **399** but inscr. "ML" .. 10 10
1835. 1 f.+50 c. Marie-Henriette .. .. 55 35
1836. 2 f.+1 f. Elisabeth .. 70 50
1837. 3 f.+1 f. 50 Astrid .. 85 70
1838. 8 f.+2 f. 50 Fabiola 1·00 90

**1962.** Ypres Millenary.
1839. **400.** 1 f.+50 c. mult. .. 40 35

**401.** H. Pirenne. **402.** "Peace Bell".

**1963.** Birth Cent. of Henri Pirenne (historian).
1841. **401.** 3 f. blue .. .. 20 10

**1963.** Cultural Funds and Installation of "Peace Bell" in Koekelberg Basilica. Bell in yellow; "PAX" in black.
1842. **402.** 3 f.+1 f. 50 grn. & blue 1·25 1·00
1843. 6 f.+3 f. chestnut & brown .. .. 65 60

**403.** "The Sower" (after Brueghel). **404.** 17th-century Duel.

**1963.** Freedom from Hunger.
1845 **403** 2 f.+1 f. brown, black and green .. 25 20
1846 – 3 f.+1 f. brown, black and purple .. 30 20
1847 – 6 f.+2 f. yellow, black and brown .. 55 40
PAINTINGS—HORIZ. 3 f. "The Harvest" (Brueghel). VERT. 6 f. "The Loaf" (Anto Carte).

**1963.** 350th Anniv of Royal Guild and Knights of St. Michael.
1848 **404** 1 f. red and blue .. 10 10
1849 – 3 f. violet and green 20 10
1850 – 6 f. multicoloured .. 30 20
DESIGNS—HORIZ. 3 f. Modern fencing. VERT. 6 f. Arms of the Guild.

**405.** 19-century Mail-coach.

**1963.** Stamp Day.
1851. **405.** 3 f. black and ochre .. 30 10
See also No. 1998.

**406.** Hotel des Postes, Paris, and Belgian 1 c. Stamp of 1863. **407.** Child in Wheatfield.

**1963.** Cent. of Paris Postal Conference.
1852. **406.** 6 f. sep., mve. & grn. 35 25

**1963.** "8th May" Peace Movement.
1853. **407.** 3 f. multicoloured .. 15 10
1854. 6 f. multicoloured .. 25 20

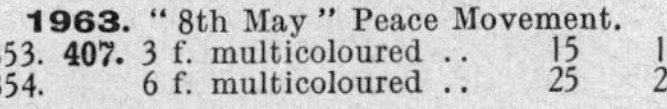

**408.** "Transport". **409.** Town Seal.

**1963.** European Transport Ministers' Conf., Brussels.
1855. **408.** 6 f. black and blue .. 45 25

**1963.** Int. Union of Towns Congress, Brussels.
1856. **409.** 6 f. multicoloured .. 25 20

**410.** Racing Cyclists. **411.** Sud Aviation SE 210 Caravelle.

**1963.** Belgian Cycling Team's Participation in Olympic Games, Tokyo (1964).
1857. **410.** 1 f.+50 c. mult. .. 15 20
1858. – 2 f.+1 f. multicoloured 20 30
1859. – 3 f.+1 f. 50 mult. .. 35 55
1860. – 6 f.+3 f. multicoloured 70 50
DESIGNS—HORIZ. 2 f. Group of cyclists. 3 f. Cyclists rounding bend. VERT. 6 f. Cyclists being paced by motor-cyclists.

**1963.** 40th Anniv. of SABENA Airline.
1861. **411.** 3 f. black & turquoise 25 10

**412.** "Co-operation". **413.** Princess Paola with Princess Astrid.

**1963.** Europa.
1862. **412.** 3 f. blk., brn. and red 70 10
1863. 6 f. blk., brn. & blue .. 90 25
No. 1863 is inscr. with "6 F" on the left, "BELGIE" at foot and "BELGIQUE" on right.

**1963.** Red Cross Cent. and Belgian Red Cross Fund. Cross in red.
1864. – 40 c.+10 c. red & yell. 10 10
1865. **413.** 1 f.+50 c. grey & yell. 30 15
1866. – 2 f.+50 c. mve. & yell. 40 20
1867. – 2 f. 50+1 f. bl. & yell. 55 20
1868. – 3 f.+1 f. sep. & yell. 55 30
1869. – 3 f.+1 f. bronze & yell. 1·75 1·90
1870. – 6 f.+2 f. grn. & yell. 80 1·00
DESIGNS—As T **413**: 40 c. Prince Philippe. 2 f. Princess Astrid. 2 f. 50, Princess Paola. 6 f. Prince Albert. 46×35 mm: 3 f. (2), Prince Albert and family.

**414.** J. Destree (writer).

**1963.** Jules Destree and H. Van de Velde Commems.
1871. **414.** 1 f. purple .. .. 10 10
1872. – 1 f. green .. .. 10 10
DESIGN: No. 1872, H. Van de Velde (architect).

**415.** Bas-reliefs from Facade of Postal Cheques Office (after O. Jespars). **416.** Balthasar Gerbier's Daughter.

**1963.** 50th Anniv. of Belgian Postal Cheques Office.
1873. **415.** 50 c. blk., blue & red 10 10

**1963.** T.B. Relief and Other Funds. Rubens's Drawings. Background buff; inscr. in black; designs colour given.
1874. **416.** 50 c.+10 c. blue .. 10 10
1875. – 1 f.+40 c. red .. 10 10
1876. – 2 f.+50 c. violet .. 20 15
1877. – 2 f. 50+1 f. green .. 45 30
1878. – 3 f.+1 f. brown .. 45 25
1879. – 6 f.+2 f. black .. 75 70
DRAWINGS—VERT. Rubens's children—1 f. Nicolas (aged 2). 2 f. Franz (aged 4). 2 f. 50, Nicolas (aged 6). 3 f. Albert (aged 3). HORIZ. (46½×35½ mm.). 6 f. Infant Jesus, St. John and two angels.

**417.** Dr. G. Hansen and Laboratory.

**1964.** Leprosy Relief Campaign.
1880. **417.** 1 f. black and brown 10 10
1881. – 2 f. brown and black 20 10
1882. – 5 f. black and brown 35 10
DESIGNS: 2 f. Leprosy hospital. 5 f. Father Damien.

**418.** A. Vesale (anatomist) with Model of Human Arm. **419.** Postilion.

**1964.** Belgian Celebrities.
1884. **418.** 50 c. black and green 10 10
1885. – 1 f. black and green .. 10 10
1886. – 2 f. black and green .. 15 10
DESIGNS—HORIZ. 1 f. J. Boulvin (engineer) and internal combustion engine. 2 f. H. Jaspar (statesman) and medallion.

**1964.** Stamp Day.
1887. **419.** 3 f. grey .. .. 20 10

**420.** Admiral Lord Gambier and U.S. Ambassador J. Q. Adams after signing treaty (from painting by Sir A. Forestier).

**1964.** 150th Anniv. of Signing of Treaty of Ghent.
1888. **420.** 6 f.+3 f. blue .. 40 40

**421.** Arms of Ostend. **422.** Ida of Bure (Calvin's wife).

**1964.** Millenary of Ostend.
1889. **421.** 3 f. multicoloured .. 15 10

**1964.** "Protestantism in Belgium".
1890. – 1 f.+50 c. blue .. 10 10
1891. **422.** 3 f.+1 f. 50 red .. 20 20
1892. – 6 f.+3 f. brown .. 35 35
PORTRAITS: 1 f. P. Marnix of St. Aldegonde (Burgomaster of Antwerp). 6 f. J. Jordaens (painter).

**423.** Globe, Hammer and Flame. **424.** Infantryman of 1918.

**1964.** Centenary of Socialist International.
1893. **423.** 50 c. red and deep blue 10 10
1894. – 1 f. red and deep blue 10 10
1895. – 2 f. red and deep blue 15 10
DESIGNS: 1 f. "SI" on Globe. 2 f. Flames.

**1964.** 50th Anniv. of German Invasion of Belgium. Multicoloured.
1896. 1 f.+50 c. Type **424** .. 15 10
1897. 2 f.+1 f. Colour sergeant of the Guides Regt., 1914 25 15
1898. 3 f.+1 f. 50 Trumpeter of the Grenadiers & Drummers of the Infantry and Carabiniers, 1914 .. 30 15

**425.** Soldier at Bastogne. **426.** Europa "Flower".

**1964.** "Liberation-Resistance". Mult.

| | | | | |
|---|---|---|---|---|
| 1899. | | 3 f.+1 f. Type **425** .. | 30 | 15 |
| 1900. | | 6 f.+3 f. Soldier at estuary of the Scheldt .. .. | 50 | 25 |

**1964.** Europa.

| | | | | |
|---|---|---|---|---|
| 1901. | **426.** | 3 f. grey, lake & green | 15 | 10 |
| 1902. | | 6 f. blue, green & lake | 30 | 20 |

DESIGN: 3 f. Waterside view of Abbey.

**429.** Pand Abbey, Ghent.

**1964.** Pand Abbey Restoration Fund.

| | | | | |
|---|---|---|---|---|
| 1905. | **429.** | 2 f.+1 f. blue, turq. and black .. .. | 15 | 15 |
| 1906. | – | 3 f.+1 f. brown, blue and purple .. | 15 | 15 |

**430.** King Baudouin, Queen Juliana and Grand Duchess Charlotte.

**1964.** 20th Anniv. of "BENELUX".

| | | | | |
|---|---|---|---|---|
| 1907. | **430.** | 3 f. purple, blue and olive .. .. | 20 | 10 |

**431.** "One of Charles I's Children" (Van Dyck). **432.** "Diamonds".

**1964.** T.B. Relief and Other Funds. Paintings of Royalty.

| | | | | |
|---|---|---|---|---|
| 1908. | **431.** | 50 c.+10 c. purple .. | 10 | 10 |
| 1909. | – | 1 f.+40 c. red .. | 15 | 10 |
| 1910. | – | 2 f.+1 f. purple .. | 20 | 20 |
| 1911. | – | 3 f.+1 f. grey .. | 30 | 20 |
| 1912. | – | 4 f.+2 f. violet .. | 35 | 25 |
| 1913. | – | 6 f.+3 f. violet .. | 40 | 25 |

DESIGNS—VERT. 1 f. "William of Orange and his fiancee, Marie" (Van Dyck). 2 f. "Portrait of a Little Boy" (E. Quellin and Jan Fyt). 3 f. "Alexander Farnese at the age of 12 Years" (A. Moro). 4 f. "William II, Prince of Orange" (Van Dyck). HORIZ—LARGER (46×35 mm.): 6 f. "Two Children of Cornelis De Vos" (C. de Vos).

**1965.** "Diamantexpo" (Diamonds Exn.). Antwerp.

| | | | | |
|---|---|---|---|---|
| 1914. | **432.** | 2 f. multicoloured .. | 15 | 10 |

**433.** "Textiles". **434.** Vriesia.

**1965.** "Textirama" (Textile Exn.), Ghent.

| | | | | |
|---|---|---|---|---|
| 1915. | **433.** | 1 f. black, red and blue | 10 | 10 |

**1965.** Ghent Flower Show. Inscr. "FLORALIES GANTOISES", etc. Multicoloured.

| | | | | |
|---|---|---|---|---|
| 1916. | | 1 f. Type **434** .. .. | 10 | 10 |
| 1917. | | 2 f. Echinocactus .. | 15 | 10 |
| 1918. | | 3 f. Stapelia .. | 20 | 10 |

**435.** Paul Hymans. **436.** Rubens.

**1965.** Birth Cent. of Paul Hymans (statesman).

| | | | | |
|---|---|---|---|---|
| 1919. | **435.** | 1 f. violet .. .. | 10 | 10 |

**1965.** Centenary of General Savings and Pensions Funds. Painters.

| | | | | |
|---|---|---|---|---|
| 1920. | **436.** | 1 f. sepia and mauve | 10 | 10 |
| 1921. | – | 2 f. sepia and turquoise | 10 | 10 |
| 1922. | – | 3 f. sepia and purple .. | 10 | 10 |
| 1923. | – | 6 f. sepia and red .. | 20 | 10 |
| 1924. | – | 8 f. sepia and blue .. | 30 | 25 |

PAINTERS: 2 f. Franz Snyders. 3 f. Adam van Noort. 6 f. Anthony van Dyck. 8 f. Jakob Jordaens.

**437.** "Sir Rowland Hill with Young Collectors" (detail from mural by J. Van den Bussche). **438.** 19th-century Postmaster.

**1965.** "Philately for the Young".

| | | | | |
|---|---|---|---|---|
| 1925. | **437.** | 50 c. green .. .. | 10 | 10 |

**1965.** Stamp Day.

| | | | | |
|---|---|---|---|---|
| 1926. | **438.** | 3 f. green .. .. | 20 | 10 |

**439.** Globe and Telephone.

**1965.** Centenary of I.T.U.

| | | | | |
|---|---|---|---|---|
| 1928. | **439.** | 2 f. black and purple | 10 | 10 |

**440.** Handclasp. **441.** Abbey Staircase.

**1965.** 20th Anniv of Liberation of Prison Camps.

| | | | | |
|---|---|---|---|---|
| 1929 | **440** | 50 c.+50 c. purple, black and bistre .. | 10 | 10 |
| 1930 | – | 1 f.+50 c. mult | 15 | 10 |
| 1931 | – | 3 f.+1 f. 50 black, purple and green | 25 | 20 |
| 1932 | – | 8 f.+5 f. mult .. | 75 | 65 |

DESIGNS—VERT. 1 f. Hand reaching for barbed wire. HORIZ. 3 f. Tank entering prison camp. 8 f. Rose within broken wall.

**1965.** Affligem Abbey.

| | | | | |
|---|---|---|---|---|
| 1933. | **441.** | 1 f. blue .. .. | 10 | 10 |

**442.** St. Jean Berchmans, Birthplace and Residence. **443.** Toc H Lamp and Arms of Poperinge.

**1965.** St. Jean Berchmans.

| | | | | |
|---|---|---|---|---|
| 1934. | **442.** | 2 f. brown & purple | 10 | 10 |

**1965.** 50th Anniv. of Founding of Toc H Movement at Talbot House, Poperinge.

| | | | | |
|---|---|---|---|---|
| 1935. | **443.** | 3 f. multicoloured .. | 10 | 10 |

**444.** Maison Stoclet, Brussels. **445.** Tractor ploughing.

**1965.** Josef Hoffman (architect) Commem.

| | | | | |
|---|---|---|---|---|
| 1936. | **444.** | 3 f.+1 f. grey & drab | 15 | 15 |
| 1937. | – | 6 f.+3 f. brown .. | 25 | 25 |
| 1938. | – | 8 f.+4 f. pur. & drab | 35 | 35 |

DESIGNS—Maison Stoclet: VERT. 6 f. Entrance hall. HORIZ. 8 f. Rear of building.

**1965.** 75th Anniv. of Boerenbond (Belgian Farmers' Assn.). Multicoloured.

| | | | | |
|---|---|---|---|---|
| 1939. | | 50 c. Type **445** .. .. | 10 | 10 |
| 1940. | | 3 f. Horse-drawn plough | 10 | 10 |

**446.** Europa "Sprig".

**1965.** Europa.

| | | | | |
|---|---|---|---|---|
| 1941. | **446.** | 1 f. black and pink .. | 10 | 10 |
| 1942. | | 3 f. black and green .. | 10 | 10 |

**447.** Jackson's Chameleon.

**1965.** Philanthropic Funds. Reptiles of Antwerp Zoo. Multicoloured.

| | | | | |
|---|---|---|---|---|
| 1943. | | 1 f.+50 c. Type **447** .. | 10 | 10 |
| 1944. | | 2 f.+1 f. Iguana .. | 20 | 15 |
| 1945. | | 3 f.+1 f. 50 Nile lizard .. | 20 | 20 |
| 1946. | | 6 f.+3 f. Komodo lizard | 45 | 35 |

**448.** J. Lebeau (after A. Schollaert). **449.** Leopold I (after 30 c. and 1 f. Stamps of 1865).

**1965.** Death Centenary of Joseph Lebeau (statesman).

| | | | | |
|---|---|---|---|---|
| 1948. | **448.** | 1 f. multicoloured .. | 10 | 10 |

**1965.** Death Cent. of King Leopold I.

| | | | | |
|---|---|---|---|---|
| 1949. | **449.** | 3 f. sepia .. .. | 10 | 10 |
| 1950. | – | 6 f. violet .. .. | 20 | 20 |

DESIGN: 6 f. As 3 f. but with different portrait frame.

**450.** Huy. **451.** Guildhouse.

**1965.** Tourist Publicity. Multicoloured.

| | | | | |
|---|---|---|---|---|
| 1951. | | 50 c. Type **450** .. .. | 10 | 10 |
| 1952. | | 50 c. Hoeilaart (vert.) .. | 10 | 10 |

See also Nos. 1995/6, 2025/6, 2083/4, 2102/3, 2123/4, 2159/60, 2240/1 and 2250/1.

**1965.** T.B. Relief and Other Funds. Public Buildings, Brussels.

| | | | | |
|---|---|---|---|---|
| 1953. | **451.** | 50 c.+10 c. blue .. | 10 | 10 |
| 1954. | - | 1 f.+40 c. turquoise | 10 | 10 |
| 1955. | - | 2 f.+1 f. purple .. | 15 | 15 |
| 1956. | - | 3 f.+1 f. 50 violet .. | 20 | 20 |
| 1957. | - | 10 f.+4 f. 50 sepia & grey .. .. | 50 | 50 |

BUILDINGS—HORIZ. 1 f. Brewers' House 2 f. Builders' House 3 f. House of the Dukes of Brabant. VERT. (24½×44½ mm.): 10 f. Tower of Town Hall.

**452.** Queen Elisabeth (from medallion by A. Courtens). **453.** "Peace on Earth".

**1965.** Queen Elisabeth Commem.

| | | | | |
|---|---|---|---|---|
| 1958. | **452.** | 3 f. black .. .. | 15 | 10 |

**1966.** 75th Anniv. of "Rerum Novarum" (papal encyclical). Multicoloured.

| | | | | |
|---|---|---|---|---|
| 1959. | | 50 c. Type **453** .. .. | 10 | 10 |
| 1960. | | 1 f. "Building for Tomorrow" (family and new building) .. .. | 10 | 10 |
| 1961. | | 3 f. Arms of Pope Paul VI (vert. 24½×45 mm.) .. | 10 | 10 |

**454.** Rural Postman. **455.** High Diving.

**1966.** Stamp Day.

| | | | | |
|---|---|---|---|---|
| 1964. | **454.** | 3 f. blk., lilac & buff .. | 10 | 10 |

**1966.** Swimming.

| | | | | |
|---|---|---|---|---|
| 1965. | **455.** | 60 c.+40 c. brown, green and blue .. | 10 | 10 |
| 1966. | – | 10 f.+4 f. brown, purple and green .. | 50 | 50 |

DESIGN: 10 f. Diving from block.

**456.** Iguanodon Fossil (Royal Institute of Natural Sciences). **457.** Eurochemic Symbol.

**1966.** National Scientific Institutions.

| | | | | |
|---|---|---|---|---|
| 1967. | **456.** | 1 f. black and green .. | 15 | 10 |
| 1968. | – | 2 f. blk., orge. & cream | 10 | 10 |
| 1969. | – | 2 f. multicoloured .. | 20 | 10 |
| 1970. | – | 3 f. multicoloured .. | 15 | 10 |
| 1971. | – | 3 f. gold, black and red | 15 | 10 |
| 1972. | – | 6 f. multicoloured .. | 65 | 15 |
| 1973. | – | 8 f. multicoloured .. | 75 | 30 |

DESIGNS—HORIZ. No. 1968, Kasai head (Royal Central African Museum). No. 1969, Snow crystals (Royal Meteorological Institute). VERT. No. 1970, "Scholar" (Royal Library). No. 1971, Seal (General Archives). No. 1972, Arend-Roland comet and telescope (Royal Observatory). No. 1973, Satellite and rocket (Space Aeronomy Inst.).

**1966.** European Chemical Plant, Mol.

| | | | | |
|---|---|---|---|---|
| 1974. | **457.** | 6 f. blk., red & drab | 20 | 15 |

**458.** A. Kekule. **460.** Rik Wouters (self-portrait).

**1966.** Centenary of Professor August Kekule's Benzene Formula.

| | | | | |
|---|---|---|---|---|
| 1975. | **458.** | 3 f. brn., blk. & blue | 15 | 10 |

**1966.** 19th World I.P.T.T. Congress, Brussels. Optd. **XIXe CONGRES IPTT** and emblem.

| | | | | |
|---|---|---|---|---|
| 1976. | **454.** | 3 f. black, lilac & buff | 10 | 10 |

**1966.** 50th Death Anniv. of Rik Wouters (painter).

| | | | | |
|---|---|---|---|---|
| 1977 | **460** | 60 c. multicoloured .. | 10 | 10 |

**461.** Minorites Convent, Liege.

**1966.** Cultural Series.

| | | | | |
|---|---|---|---|---|
| 1978. | **461.** | 60 c.+40 c. purple, blue and brown .. | 10 | 10 |
| 1979. | – | 1 f.+50 c. blue, purple and turquoise .. | 10 | 10 |
| 1980. | – | 2 f.+1 f. red, purple and brown .. | 10 | 10 |
| 1981. | – | 10 f.+4 f. 50 purple, turquoise and green | 60 | 60 |

DESIGNS: 1 f. Val-Dieu Abbey, Aubel. 2 f. Huy and town seal. 10 f. Statue of Ambiorix and castle, Tongres.

**463.** Europa "Ship". **464.** Surveying.

**1966.** Europa.
1989. **463.** 3 f. green .. .. 10 10
1990. 6 f. purple .. .. 30 20

**1966.** Antarctic Expeditions.
1991. **464.** 1 f.+50 c. green .. 20 10
1992. – 3 f.+1 f. 50 violet .. 40 20
1993. – 6 f.+3 f. lake .. 70 35
DESIGNS: 3 f. Commander A. de Gerlache and "Belgica" (polar barque). 6 f. "Magga Dan" (supply ship) and meteorological operations.

**1966.** Tourist Publicity. As T **450.** Multicoloured.
1995. 2 f. Bouillon .. .. 10 10
1996. 2 f. Lier (vert.) .. .. 10 10

**1966.** 75th Anniv of Royal Federation of Belgian Philatelic Circles. Stamps similar to Nos. 1812 and 1851 but incorporating "1890 1996" and F.I.P. emblem.
1997. **391.** 60 c. purple and green 10 10
1998. **405.** 3 f. purple and ochre 15 10

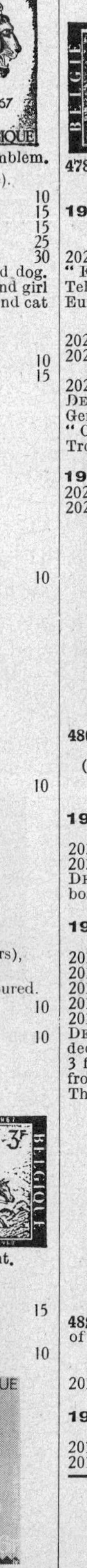

**466.** Children with Hoops. **467.** Lions Emblem.

**1966.** "Solidarity" (Child Welfare).
1999. – 1 f.+1 f. blk. & pink 10 10
2000. – 2 f.+1 f. blk. & green 20 15
2001. – 3 f.+1 f. 50 blk. & lav. 20 15
2002. **466.** 6 f.+3 f. brn. & flesh 30 25
2003. – 8 f.+3 f. 50 brn. & grn. 40 30
DESIGNS—VERT. 1 f. Boy with ball and dog. 2 f. Girl with skipping-rope. 3 f. Boy and girl blowing bubbles. HORIZ. 8 f. Children and cat playing "Follow My Leader".

**1967.** Lions Int.
2004. **467.** 3 f. sepia, blue & olive 20 10
2005. 6 f. sepia, violet & grn. 35 15

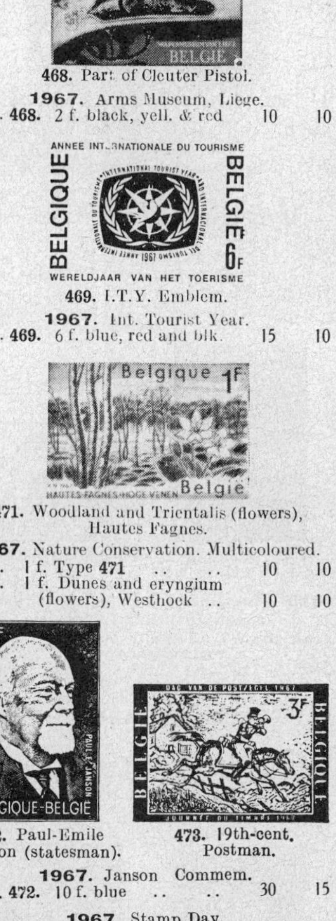

**468.** Part of Cleuter Pistol.

**1967.** Arms Museum, Liege.
2006. **468.** 2 f. black, yell. & red 10 10

**469.** I.T.Y. Emblem.

**1967.** Int. Tourist Year.
2007. **469.** 6 f. blue, red and blk. 15 10

**471.** Woodland and Trientalis (flowers), Hautes Fagnes.

**1967.** Nature Conservation. Multicoloured.
2009. 1 f. Type **471** .. .. 10 10
2010. 1 f. Dunes and eryngium (flowers), Westhoek .. 10 10

**472.** Paul-Emile Janson (statesman). **473.** 19th-cent. Postman.

**1967.** Janson Commem.
2011. **472.** 10 f. blue .. .. 30 15

**1967.** Stamp Day.
2012. **473.** 3 f. purple and red .. 15 10

**474.** Cogwheels. **475.** Flax Plant and Shuttle.

**1967.** Europa.
2013. **474.** 3 f. black, red & blue 15 10
2014. 6 f. black, yell. & grn. 30 20

**1967.** Belgian Linen Industry.
2015. **475.** 6 f. multicoloured .. 15 10

**476.** Kursaal in 19th Century.

**1967.** 700th Anniv. of Ostend's Rank as Town.
2016. **476.** 2 f. sepia, buff & bl. 10 10

**478.** With F.I.T.C.E. Emblem. **479.** Robert Schuman (statesman).

**1967.** European Telecommunications Day. "Stamp Day" design of 1967 incorporating F.I.T.C.E. emblem as T **478** in green.
2021. **478.** 10 f. sepia and blue .. 40 20
"F.I.T.C.E." "Federation des Ingenieurs des Tele-communications de la Communaute Europeenne."

**1967.** Charity.
2022. **479.** 2 f.+1 f. green .. 15 15
2023. – 5 f.+2 f. brown, yell. and black .. .. 25 25
2024. – 10 f.+5 f. mult. .. 70 70
DESIGNS—HORIZ. 5 f. Kongolo Memorial, Gentinnes (Congo Martyrs). VERT. 10 f. "Colonial Brotherhood" emblem (Colonial Troops Memorial).

**1967.** Tourist Publicity. As T **450.** Mult.
2025. 1 f. Ypres .. .. 10 10
2026. 1 f. Spontin .. .. 10 10

**480.** "Caesar Crossing the Rubicon" (Tournai Tapestry). **481.** "Jester in Pulpit" (from Erasmus's "Praise of Folly").

**1967.** Charles Plisnier and Lodewijk de Raet Foundations.
2028. **480.** 1 f. multicoloured .. 10 10
2029. – 1 f. multicoloured .. 10 10
DESIGN No. 2029, "Maximilian hunting boar" (Brussels tapestry).

**1967.** Cultural Series. "Erasmus and His Time".
2030. 1 f.+50 c. multicoloured 10 10
2031. 2 f.+1 f. multicoloured .. 15 15
2032. 3 f.+1 f. 50 multicoloured 15 15
2033. 5 f.+2 f. blk., red & crm. 20 20
2034. 6 f.+3 f. multicoloured .. 25 25
DESIGNS—VERT. 1 f. Type **481.** 2 f. "Jester declaiming" (from Erasmus' "Praise of Folly"). 3 f. Erasmus. 6 f. Pierre Gilles ("Aegidius"; from painting by Metzijs). HORIZ. 5 f. "Sir Thomas More's Family" (Holbein).

**482.** "Princess Margaret of York" (from miniature). **483.** Arms of Ghent University.

**1967.** "British Week".
2035. **482.** 6 f. multicoloured .. 20 15

**1967.** Universities of Ghent and Liege. Multicoloured.
2036. 3 f. Type **483** .. .. 10 10
2037. 3 f. Liege .. .. .. 10 10

**485.** Our Lady of Virga Jesse, Hasselt.

**1967.** Christmas.
2039 **485** 1 f. blue .. .. 10 10

**486.** "Children's Games" (section of Brueghel's painting).

**1967.** "Solidarity".
2040 **486** 1 f.+50 c. mult .. 15 15
2041 – 2 f.+50 c. mult .. 15 15
2042 – 3 f.+1 f. mult .. 15 15
2043 – 6 f.+3 f. mult .. 35 35
2044 – 10 f.+4 f. mult .. 50 50
2045 – 13 f.+6 f. mult .. 65 65
Nos. 2040/5 together form the complete painting.

**487.** Worker in Protective Hand. **489.** Army Postman (1916).

**1968.** Industrial Safety Campaign.
2046. **487.** 3 f. multicoloured .. 10 10

**1968.** Stamp Day.
2068. **489.** 3 f. pur., brn. & blue 10 10

**490.** Belgian 1 c. "Small Lion" Stamp of 1866. **491.** Grammont and Seal of Baudouin VI.

**1968.** Cent. of State Printing Works, Malines.
2069. **490.** 1 f. olive .. .. 10 10

**1968.** "Historical Series". Multicoloured.
2070. 2 f. Type **491** .. .. 10 10
2071. 3 f. Theux-Franchimont Castle & battle emblems 10 10
2072. 6 f. Archaeological discoveries, Spiennes .. 20 15
2073. 10 f. Roman oil lamp and town crest Wervik .. 30 25

**492.** Europa "Key". **493.** Queen Elisabeth and Dr. Depage.

**1968.** Europa.
2074. **492.** 3 f. gold, blk. & green 10 10
2075. 6 f. silver, black & red 30 20

**1968.** Belgian Red Cross Fund. Cross in red.
2076. **493.** 6 f.+3 f. sepia, black and green .. .. 45 25
2077. – 10 f.+5 f. sepia, black and green .. .. 65 45
DESIGN: 10 f. Queen Fabiola and baby.

**494.** Gymnastics. **495.** "Explosion".

**1968.** Olympic Games, Mexico. Multicoloured.
2078. 1 f.+50 c. Type **494** .. 10 10
2079. 2 f.+1 f. Weightlifting .. 10 10
2080. 3 f.+1 f. 50 Hurdling .. 15 15
2081. 6 f.+2 f. Cycling .. 20 20
2082. 13 f.+5 f. Yachting (vert. 24½×45 mm.) .. 45 55
Each design includes the Olympic "rings" and a Mexican cultural motif.

**1968.** Tourist Publicity. As Type **450.**
2083. 2 f. multicoloured .. 10 10
2084. 2 f. black, blue and green 10 10
DESIGNS: No. 2083, Farm-house and windmill, Bokrijk. No. 2084, Bath-house and fountain, Spa.

**1968.** Belgian Disasters. Victims Fund. Multicoloured.
2085. 10 f.+5 f. Type **495** .. 70 50
2086. 12 f.+5 f. "Fire" .. 70 50
2087. 13 f.+5 f. "Typhoon" .. 75 80

**496.** St. Laurent Abbey, Liege.

**1968.** "National Interest".
2088 **496** 2 f. black, bistre & bl 10 10
2089 – 3 f. brn, grey & lt brn 15 10
2090 – 6 f. black, bl & dp bl 25 15
2091 – 10 f. multicoloured .. 35 25
DESIGNS: 3 f. Church, Lissewege. 6 f. Canal-lock, Zandvliet. 10 f. Canal-lift, Ronquieres.

**497.** Undulate Triggerfish.

**1968.** "Solidarity" and 125th Anniv. of Antwerp Zoo. Designs showing fish. Multicoloured.
2092. 1 f.+50 c. Type **497** .. 15 15
2093. 3 f.+1 f. 50 Angel fish .. 20 20
2094. 6 f.+3 f. Scorpion fish .. 30 30
2095. 10 f.+5 f. Red striped butterfly fish .. .. 40 40

**498.** King Albert in Bruges (October, 1918). **499.** Lighted Candle.

**1968.** Patriotic Funds.
2096 **498** 1 f.+50 c. mult .. 10 10
2097 – 3 f.+1 f. 50 mult .. 15 15
2098 – 6 f.+3 f. mult .. 25 25
2099 – 10 f.+5 f. mult .. 70 50
DESIGNS—HORIZ. 3 f. King Albert entering Brussels (November, 1918). 6 f. King Albert in Liege (November, 1918). LARGER (46×35 mm.). 10 f. Tomb of the Unknown Soldier, Brussels.

**1968.** Christmas.
2100. **499.** 1 f. multicoloured .. 10 10

**500.** Cargo Ship in Ghent Canal.

**1968.** Ghent Maritime Canal.
2101. **500.** 6 f. black, brn., & blue 25 15

**1969.** Tourist Publicity. As Type **450.**
2102 1 f. black, bl & pur (vert) 10 10
2103 1 f. black, olive and blue 10 10
DESIGNS. No. 2102, Town Hall, Louvain. No. 2103, Valley of the Ourthe.

**501.** "Albert Magnis" (detail of wood carving by Quellin, Confessional, St. Paul's Church, Antwerp).

**1969.** St. Paul's Church, Antwerp, and Aulne Abbey Commem.
2104. **501.** 2 f. sepia .. .. 10 10
2105. – 3 f. black and mauve .. 10 10
DESIGN: 3 f. Aulne Abbey.

**502.** "The Travellers" (sculpture, Archaeological Museum, Arlon).

**503.** Broodjes Chapel, Antwerp.

**1969.** 2,000th Anniv. of Arlon.
2106. **502.** 2 f. purple .. .. 10 10

**1969.** "150 Years of Public Education in Antwerp".
2107. **503.** 3 f. black and grey .. 10 10

**504.** Mail Train.

**505.** Colonnade.

**1969.** Stamp Day.
2108. **504.** 3 f. multicoloured .. 30 10

**1969.** Europa.
2109. **505.** 3 f. multicoloured .. 15 10
2110. 6 f. multicoloured .. 25 20

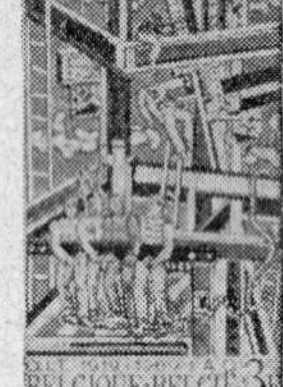

**507.** NATO Emblem.

**508.** "The Builders" (F. Leger).

**1969.** 20th Anniv. of NATO.
2112. **507.** 6 f. blue and brown 20 15

**1969.** 50th Anniv. of I.L.O.
2113. **508.** 3 f. multicoloured .. 10 10

**509.** "Houses" (I. Dimitrova).

**510.** Racing Cyclist.

**1969.** UNICEF "Philanthropy" Funds. Multicoloured.
2114. 1 f.+50 c. Type **509** .. 10 10
2115. 3 f.+1 f. 50 "My Art" (C. Patric) .. .. 15 15
2116. 6 f.+3 f. "In the Sun" (H. Rejchlova) .. 25 25
2117. 10 f.+5 f. "Out for a Walk" (P. Sporn) .. 45 45
No. 2117 is horiz.

**1969.** World Championship Cycle Races, Zolder.
2118. **510.** 6 f. multicoloured .. 20 15

**HAVE YOU READ THE NOTES AT THE BEGINNING OF THIS CATALOGUE?**
These often provide answers to the enquiries we receive.

**511.** Mgr. V. Scheppers.

**512.** National Colours.

**1969.** Monseigneur Victor Scheppers (founder of "Brothers of Mechlin") Commemoration.
2119. **511.** 6 f.+3 f. purple .. 30 35

**1969.** 25th Anniv. of BENELUX Customs Union.
2120. **512.** 3 f. multicoloured .. 15 10

**513.** Pascali Rose and Annevoie Gardens.

**1969.** Flowers and Gardens. Multicoloured.
2121. 2 f. Type **513** .. .. 10 10
2122. 2 f. Begonia and Lochristi Gardens .. .. 10 10

**1969.** Tourist Publicity. As Type **450**.
2123. 2 f. brown, red and blue.. 10 10
2124. 2 f. black, green and blue 10 10
DESIGNS: No. 2123, Veurne Furnes. No. 2124, Vielsalm.

**514.** "Feats of Arms" from "History of Alexander the Great" (Tournai, 15th century).

**516.** Wounded Soldier.

**515.** Astronauts and Location of Moon Landing.

**1969.** "Cultural Works" Tapestries. Mult.
2125. 1 f.+50 c. Type **514** .. 10 10
2126. 3 f.+1 f. 50 "The Violinist" from "Festival" (David Teniers II, Oudenarde, circa 1700) 15 15
2127. 10 f.+4 f. "The Paralytic", from "The Acts of the Apostles" (Brussels, circa 1517).. 70 70

**1969.** 1st Man on the Moon.
2128. **515.** 6 f. sepia .. .. 20 15

**1969.** 50th Anniv. of National War Invalids Works (O.N.I.G.).
2130. **516.** 1 f. green .. .. 10 10

**517.** "The Postman".

**519.** Count H. Carton de Wiart (from painting by G. Geleyn).

**518.** John F. Kennedy Motorway Tunnel, Antwerp.

**1969.** "Philately for the Young".
2131. **517.** 1 f. multicoloured .. 10 10

**1969.** Completion of Belgian Road-works. Multicoloured.
2132. 3 f. Type **518** .. .. 25 10
2133. 6 f. Loncin flyover, Wallonie motorway .. .. 25 20

**1969.** Birth Centenary of Count Henry Carton de Wiart (statesman).
2134. **519.** 6 f. sepia .. .. 20 15

**520.** "Barbu d' Anvers" (Cockerel).

**1969.** "The Poultry-yard" (poultry-breeding).
2135. **520.** 10 f.+5 f. mult. .. 80 80

**521.** "Le Denombrement de Bethleem" (detail, Brueghel).

**1969.** Christmas.
2136. **521.** 1 f. 50 multicoloured 10 10

**522.** Emblem, "Coin" and Machinery.

**523.** Window, St. Waudru Church, Mons.

**1969.** 50th Anniv. of National Credit Society (S.N.C.I.).
2137. **522.** 3 f. 50 brown and blue 10 10

**1969.** "Solidarity". Musicians in Stained-glass Windows. Multicoloured.
2138. 1 f. 50+50 c. Type **523** .. 15 15
2139. 3 f. 50+1 f. 50 's-Herenelderen Church 20 20
2140. 7 f.+3 f. St. Jacques Church, Liege.. .. 30 40
2141. 9 f.+4 f. Royal Museum of Art and history, Brussels .. .. 55 60
No. 2141 is larger, 36 × 52 mm.

**524.** Camellias.

**525.** Beech Tree in National Botanical Gardens.

**1970.** Ghent Flower Show. Multicoloured.
2142. 1 f. 50 Type **524**.. .. 10 10
2143. 2 f. 50 Water-lily .. 15 15
2144. 3 f. 50 Azaleas .. .. 15 10

**1970.** Nature Conservation Year. Mult.
2146. 3 f. 50 Type **525** .. 25 10
2147. 7 f. Birch .. .. 30 20

**526.** Young "Postman".

**1970.** "Philately for the Young".
2148. **526.** 1 f. 50 multicoloured 10 10

**527.** New U.P.U. Headquarters Building.

**1970.** New U.P.U. Headquarters Building.
2149. **527.** 3 f. 50 green.. .. 15 10

**528.** "Flaming Sun".

**1970.** Europa.
2150. **528.** 3 f. 50 cream, blk. & lake 20 10
2151. 7 f. flesh, black & blue 40 25

**529.** Open-air Museum, Bokrijk.

**530.** Clock-tower, Virton.

**1970.** Cultural Works. Multicoloured.
2152. 1 f. 50+50 c. Type **529**.. 20 20
2153. 3 f. 50+1 f. 50 Relay Post-house, Courcelles .. 25 25
2154. 7 f.+3 f. "The Reaper of Trevires" (bas-relief, Virton) .. .. 35 35
2155. 9 f.+4 f. Open-air Museum, Middelheim, (Antwerp) 40 40

**1970.** Historic Towns of Virton and Zelzate.
2156. **530.** 2 f. 50 violet & ochre 15 10
2157. – 2 f. 50 black and blue 30 10
DESIGN—HORIZ. No. 2157, Canal bridge, Zelzate.

**531.** Co-operative Alliance Emblem.

**1970.** 75th Anniv. of Int. Co-operative Alliance.
2158. **531.** 7 f. black and orange 20 10

**1970.** Tourist Publicity. As Type **450**.
2159 1 f. 50 green, blue & black 10 10
2160 1 f. 50, buff, blue & dp bl 10 10
DESIGNS—HORIZ. No. 2159, Kasterlee. VERT. No. 2160, Nivelles.

**532.** Allegory of Resistance Movements.

**533.** King Baudouin.

**1970.** 25th Anniv. of Prisoner of War and Concentration Camps Liberation.
2161. **532.** 3 f. 50+1 f. 50 black, red and green .. 20 20
2162. – 7 f.+3 f. black, red and mauve .. 30 35
DESIGN: 7 f. Similar to Type **532**, but inscr. "LIBERATION DES CAMPS", etc.

**1970.** King Baudouin's 40th Birthday.
2163. **533.** 3 f. 50 brown .. 15 10
See also Nos. 2207/23c. and 2335/9b.

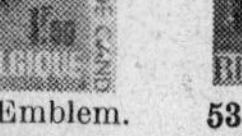

**534.** Fair Emblem.

**535.** U.N. Headquarters, New York.

**1970.** 25th Int. Ghent Fair.
2164. **534.** 1 f. 50 multicoloured 10 10

**1970** 25th Anniv. of United Nations.
2165. **535.** 7 f. blue and black.. 25 15

536. Queen Fabiola. 537. Angler's Rod and Reel.

**1970.** Queen Fabiola Foundation.
2166. **536.** 3 f. 50 black and blue 15 10

**1970.** Sports. Multicoloured.
2167. 3 f. 50+1 f. 50, Type **537** 30 30
2168. 9 f.+4 f. Hockey stick and ball .. .. .. 1·25 65

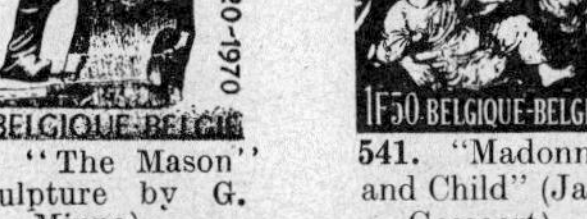


539. "The Mason" (sculpture by G. Minne). 541. "Madonna and Child" (Jan Gossaert).

540. Man, Woman and Hillside Town.

**1970.** 50th Anniv. of National Housing Society.
2170. **539.** 3 f. 50 brown & yell. 10 10

**1970.** 25th Anniv. of Belgian Social Security.
2171. **540.** 2 f. 50 multicoloured 10 10

**1970.** Christmas.
2172. **541.** 1 f. 50 brown .. 10 10

542. C. Huysmans (statesman). 543. Arms of Eupen, Malmedy and St. Vith.

**1970.** Cultural Works. Famous Belgians.
2173. **542.** 1 f. 50+50 c. brown and red .. .. 15 15
2174. – 3 f. 50+1 f. 50 brown and purple .. 15 15
2175. – 7 f.+3 f. brn. & green 30 30
2176. – 9 f.+4 f. brn. & blue 40 40
PORTRAITS: 3 f. 50, Cardinal J. Cardijn. 7 f. Maria Baers (Catholic social worker). 9 f. P. Pastur (social reformer).

**1970.** 50th Anniv. of Annexation of Eupen, Malmedy and St. Vith.
2177. **543.** 7 f. brown and sepia 25 10

544. "The Uneasy Town" (detail, Paul Delvaux). 545. Telephone.

**1970.** "Solidarity". Paintings. Mult.
2178. 3 f. 50+1 f. 50 Type **544** .. 20 20
2179. 7 f.+3 f. "The Memory" (Rene Magritte) .. 30 40

**1971.** Inaug. of Automatic Telephone Service.
2183. **545.** 1 f. 50 multicoloured 10 10

546. "Auto" Car. 547. Touring Club Badge.

**1971.** 50th Brussels Motor Show.
2184. **546.** 2 f. 50 black and red 30 10

**1971.** 75th Anniv. of Royal Touring Club of Belgium.
2185. **547.** 3 f. 50 gold, red & bl. 15 10

548. Tournai Cathedral. 549. "The Letter-box" (T. Lobrichon).

**1971.** 800th Anniv. of Tournai Cathedral.
2186. **548.** 7 f. blue .. .. 25 15

**1971.** "Philately for the Young".
2187. **549.** 1 f. 50 brown .. 10 10

550. Notre-Dame Abbey, Marche-les-Dames.

**1971.** Cultural Works.
2190. **550.** 3 f. 50+1 f. 50 blk., grn. & brn. .. 20 20
2191. – 7 f.+3 f. black, red and yellow .. 35 35
DESIGN: 7 f. Convent, Turnhout.

552. King Albert I, Jules Destree and Academy.

**1971.** 50th Anniv. of Royal Academy of French Language and Literature.
2201. **552.** 7 f. black and grey .. 25 20

553. Postman of 1855 (from lithograph, J. Thiriar). 554. Europa Chain.

**1971.** Stamp Day.
2202. **553.** 3 f. 50 multicoloured 10 10

**1971.** Europa.
2203. **554.** 3 f. 50 brown & black 15 10
2204. 7 f. green and black .. 25 25

555. Satellite Earth Station. 556. Red Cross.

**1971.** World Telecommunications Day.
2205. **555.** 7 f. multicoloured .. 30 15

**1971.** Belgian Red Cross.
2206. **556.** 10 f.+5 f. red & blk. 70 50

**1971.** As Type **533**, but without dates.

| | | | |
|---|---|---|---|
| 2207 | 1 f. 75 green .. .. | 30 | 10 |
| 2208 | 2 f. 25 green .. .. | 30 | 10 |
| 2208a | 2 f. 50 green .. .. | 20 | 10 |
| 2209 | 3 f. green .. .. | 30 | 10 |
| 2209a | 3 f. 25 plum .. .. | 20 | 10 |
| 2210 | 3 f. 50 brown .. .. | 30 | 10 |
| 2211 | 4 f. blue .. .. | 35 | 10 |
| 2212 | 4 f. 50 purple .. .. | 30 | 10 |
| 2212a | 4 f. 50 blue .. .. | 20 | 10 |
| 2213 | 5 f. violet .. .. | 30 | 10 |
| 2214 | 6 f. red .. .. | 30 | 10 |
| 2214b | 6 f. 50 violet .. .. | 30 | 10 |
| 2215 | 7 f. red .. .. | 30 | 10 |
| 2215b | 7 f. 50 mauve .. .. | 30 | 10 |
| 2216a | 8 f. black .. .. | 30 | 10 |
| 2217 | 9 f. sepia .. .. | 70 | 10 |
| 2217a | 9 f. brown .. .. | 35 | 10 |
| 2218a | 10 f. mauve .. .. | 40 | 10 |
| 2218b | 11 f. sepia .. .. | 55 | 10 |
| 2219 | 12 f. blue .. .. | 75 | 10 |
| 2219b | 13 f. blue .. .. | 60 | 10 |
| 2219c | 14 f. green .. .. | 60 | 10 |
| 2220 | 15 f. violet .. .. | 65 | 10 |
| 2220b | 16 f. green .. .. | 65 | 10 |
| 2220c | 17 f. purple .. .. | 65 | 10 |
| 2221 | 18 f. blue .. .. | 90 | 15 |
| 2221a | 18 f. turquoise .. .. | 70 | 10 |
| 2222a | 20 f. blue .. .. | 90 | 10 |
| 2222b | 22 f. black .. .. | 1·00 | 80 |
| 2222c | 22 f. turquoise .. .. | 90 | 10 |
| 2222d | 25 f. purple .. .. | 1·00 | 10 |
| 2223a | 30 f. orange .. .. | 1·25 | 10 |
| 2223b | 35 f. turquoise .. .. | 1·40 | 15 |
| 2223c | 40 f. blue .. .. | 1·75 | 10 |
| 2223d | 45 f. brown .. .. | 2·25 | 15 |

See also Nos. 2335/9.

557. Scientist, Adelie Penguins and "Erika Dan".

**1971.** 10th Anniv. of Antarctic Treaty.
2230. **557.** 10 f. multicoloured .. 1·25 80

558. "The Discus thrower" and Munich Cathedral. 559. G. Hubin (statesman).

**1971.** Olympic Games, Munich (1972) Publicity.
2231. **558.** 7 f.+3 f. blk. & blue 35 45

**1971.** Georges Hubin Commemoration.
2232. **559.** 1 f. 50 violet & black 10 10

560. Notre-Dame Abbey, Orval. 561. Processional Giants, Ath.

**1971.** 900th Anniv. of Notre-Dame Abbey, Orval.
2233. **560.** 2 f. 50 brown .. 10 10

**1971.** Historic Towns.
2234. **561.** 2 f. 50 multicoloured 10 10
2235. – 2 f. 50 brown .. 10 10
DESIGN—HORIZ. (46×35 mm.) No. 2235, View of Ghent.

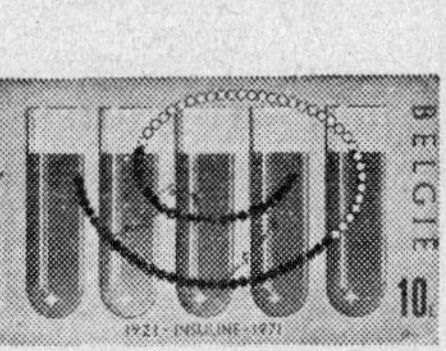


562. Test-tubes and Diagram. 563. Flemish Festival Emblem.

**1971.** 50th Anniv. of Discovery of Insulin.
2236. **562.** 10 f. multicoloured .. 70 25

**1971.** Cultural Works. Festivals. Mult.
2237. 3 f. 50+1 f. 50 Type **563** .. 15 20
2238. 7 f.+3 f. Walloon Festival emblem .. .. 50 35

564. Belgian Family and "50". 565. Dr. Jules Bordet (medical scientist).

**1971.** 50th Anniv. of "League of Large Families".
2239 **564** 1 f. 50 multicoloured 10 10

**1971.** Tourist Publicity. Designs similar to Type **450.**
2240. 2 f. 50 blk., brn. & blue 15 10
2241. 2 f. 50 blk., brn. & blue 15 10
DESIGNS: No. 2240, St. Martin's Church, Alost. No. 2241, Town Hall and belfry, Mons.

**1971.** Belgian Celebrities.
2242. **565.** 3 f. 50 green .. .. 20 10
2243. – 3 f. 50 brown .. 20 10
DESIGN: No. 2242, Type **565** (10th death anniv.) No. 2243, "Stijn Streuvels" (Frank Lateur, writer, birth cent.).

566. Achaemenid Tomb, Buzpar. 567. Elewijt Chateau.

**1971.** 2500th Anniv. of Persian Empire.
2244. **566.** 7 f. multicoloured .. 30 15

**1971.** "Belgica 72" Stamp Exhibition, Brussels (2nd issue).
2245. – 3 f. 50+1 f. 50 green 30 30
2246. **567.** 7 f.+3 f. brown .. 50 50
2247. – 10 f.+5 f. blue .. 80 80
DESIGNS—HORIZ. (52×35½ mm.). 3 f. Attre Chateau. 10 f. Royal Palace, Brussels.

568. F.I.B./V.B.N. Emblem. 569. "The Flight into Egypt" (15th-century Dutch School).

**1971.** 25th Anniv. of Federation of Belgian Industries.
2248. **568.** 3 f. 50 gold, blk. & bl. 10 10

**1971.** Christmas.
2249. **569.** 1 f. 50 multicoloured 10 10

**1971.** Tourist Publicity. Designs similar to Type **450.**
2250. 1 f. 50 blue and buff .. 15 10
2251. 2 f. 50 blue and buff .. 15 10
DESIGNS—HORIZ. 1 f. 50, Town Hall, Malines. VERT. 2 f. 50, Basilica, St. Hubert.

570. Luna Moth.

**1971.** "Solidarity". Insects in Antwerp Zoo. Multicoloured.
2252 1 f. 50+50 c. Type **570** .. 20 25
2253 3 f. 50+1 f. 50 "Tabanus bromius" (horse fly) (horiz) .. .. 25 30
2254 7 f.+3 f. "Polistes gallicus" (wasp) (horiz) 45 55
2255 9 f.+4 f. Green tiger beetle .. .. 55 65

572. Road Signs and Traffic Signals. 573. Book Year Emblem.

**1972.** 20th Anniv. of "Via Secura" Road Safety Organization.
2263. **572.** 3 f. 50 multicoloured 20 10

**1972** International Book Year.
2264. **573.** 7 f. blue, brn. & black 30 15

**574.** Coins of Belgium and Luxembourg

**576.** "Auguste Vermeylen" (I. Opsomer).

**1972.** 50th Anniv. of Belgo-Luxembourgeoise Economic Union.

2265 **574** 1 f. 50 silver, black and orange .. 15 10

**1972.** Birth Centenary of Auguste Vemeylen (writer).

2267. **576.** 2 f. 50 multicoloured 15 10

**577.** " Belgica 72 " Emblem.

**578.** Heart Emblem.

**1972.** "Belgica 72" Stamp Exn., Brussels (3rd Issue).

2268. **577.** 3 f. 50 purple, bl. & brn. 15 10

**1972.** World Heart Month.

2269. **578.** 7 f. multicoloured .. 35 15

**579.** Astronaut cancelling Letter on Moon.

**580.** "Communications".

**1972.** Stamp Day.

2270. **579.** 3 f. 50 multicoloured 15 10

**1972.** Europa.

2271. **580.** 3 f. 50 multicoloured 25 10
2272. 7 f. multicoloured .. 45 25

**581.** Quill Pen and Newspaper.

**582.** "UIC" on Coupled Wagons.

**1972.** "Liberty of the Press". 50th Anniv. of Belga News Agency and 25th Congress of International Federation of Newspaper Editors (F.I.E.J.).

2273. **581.** 2 f. 50 multicoloured 10 10

**1972.** 50th Anniv. of Int. Railways Union (U.I.C.).

2274. **582.** 7 f. multicoloured .. 35 20

See also No. P 2266.

**583.** Couvin.

**584.** Leopold I 10c. "Epaulettes" Stamp of 1849.

**1972.** Tourist Publicity.

2275 **583** 2 f. 50 purple, bl & grn 25 15
2276 – 2 f. 50 brown and blue 25 15

DESIGN—VERT. No. 2276, Aldeneik Church, Maaseik.

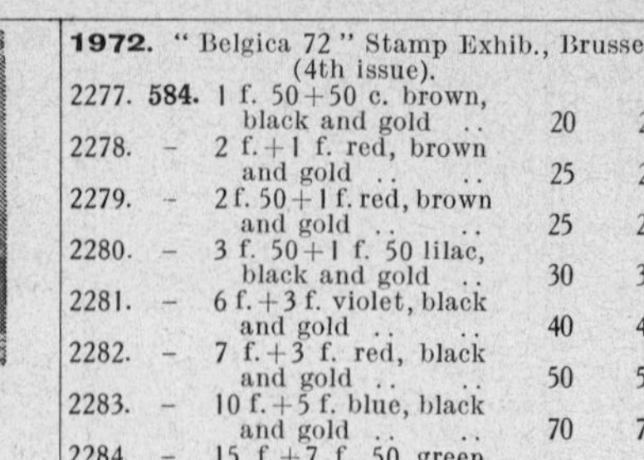

**1972.** " Belgica 72 " Stamp Exhib., Brussels (4th issue).

2277. **584.** 1 f. 50+50 c. brown, black and gold .. 20 20
2278. – 2 f.+1 f. red, brown and gold .. .. 25 25
2279. – 2 f. 50+1 f. red, brown and gold .. .. 25 25
2280. – 3 f. 50+1 f. 50 lilac, black and gold .. 30 30
2281. – 6 f.+3 f. violet, black and gold .. .. 40 40
2282. – 7 f.+3 f. red, black and gold .. .. 50 50
2283. – 10 f.+5 f. blue, black and gold .. .. 70 70
2284. – 15 f.+7 f. 50 green turquoise and gold 90 90
2285. – 20 f.+10 f. chestnut, brown and gold .. 1·50 1·50

DESIGNS: 2 f. Leopold I 40 c. " Medallion " of 1849. 2 f. 50, Leopold II 10 c. of 1883. 3 f. 50, Leopold II 50 c. of 1883. 6 f. Albert I 2 f. " Tin Hat " of 1919. 7 f. Albert I 50 f. of 1929. 10 f. Albert I 1 f. 75 of 1931. 15 f. Leopold III 5 f. of 1936. 20 f. Baudouin 3 f. 50 of 1970.

**585.** "Beatrice" (G. de Smet).

**586.** Emblem of Centre.

**1972.** "Philately for the Young".

2287. **585.** 3 f. multicoloured .. 15 10

**1972.** Inaug. of William Lennox Epileptic Centre, Ottignies.

2288. **586.** 10 f.+5 f. mult. .. 50 60

**587.** Dish Aerial and "Intelstat 4" Satellite.

**588.** Frans Masereel (wood-carver and painter).

**1972.** Inaug. of Satellite Earth Station, Lessive.

2289. **587.** 3 f. 50 blk., silver & bl. 20 10

**1972.** Masereel Commem.

2290. **588.** 4 f. 50 black and green 15 10

**589.** "Adoration of the Magi" (F. Timmermans).

**590.** "Empress Maria Theresa" (unknown artist).

**1972.** Christmas.

2291. **589.** 3 f. 50 multicoloured 15 10

**1972.** Bicentenary of Belgian Royal Academy of Sciences, Letters and Fine Arts.

2292. **590.** 2 f. multicoloured .. 15 10

**591.** Grey Lag Goose.

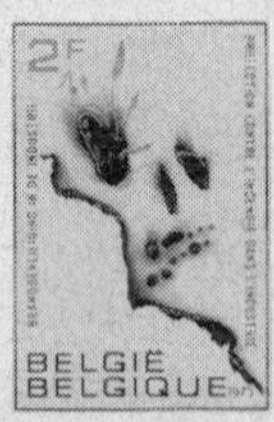

**592.** " Fire ".

**1972.** "Solidarity". Birds from Zwin Nature Reserve. Multicoloured.

2293. 2 f.+1 f. Type **591** 65 60
2294. 4 f. 50+2 f. Lapwing .. 95 85
2295. 8 f.+4 f. White stork .. 1·90 1·40
2296. 9 f.+4 f. 50 Common kestrel (horiz.) .. 2·00 1·60

**1973.** Industrial Buildings Fire Protection Campaign.

2297. **592.** 2 f. multicoloured .. 20 10

**593.** W.M.O. Emblem and Meteorological Equipment.

**595** W.H.O. Emblem as Man's "Heart".

**594.** Bijloke Abbey and Museum, Ghent.

**1973.** Centenary of World Meteorological Organization.

2298. **593.** 9 f. multicoloured .. 30 15

**1973.** Cultural Works. Religious Buildings.

2299. **594.** 2f.+1 f. green .. 20 30
2300. – 4 f. 50+2 f. brown .. 30 40
2301. – 8 f.+4 f. red .. 50 70
2302. – 9 f.+4 f. 50 blue .. 60 80

DESIGNS: 4 f. 50, Collegiate Church of St. Ursmer, Lobbes. 8 f. Park Abbey, Heverlee. 9 f. Floreffe Abbey.

**1973.** 25th Anniv of W.H.O.

2303 **595** 8 f. black, yellow & red 30 15

**596.** Ball in Hands.

**1973.** 1st World Basketball Championships for the Handicapped, Bruges.

2304. **596.** 10 f.+5 f. mult. .. 90 80

**597.** Europa "Posthorn".

**598.** Thurn and Taxis Courier (17th-cent.).

**1973.** Europa.

2305. **597.** 4 f. 50 bl., yell. & brn. 20 10
2306. – 8 f. bl., yell. and grn. 50 25

**1973.** Stamp Day.

2307. **598.** 4 f. 50 brown & red.. 15 10

**599.** Fair Emblem.

**600.** Arrows encircling Globe.

**1973.** 25th International Fair, Liege.

2308. **599.** 4 f. 50 multicoloured 15 10

**1973.** 5th World Telecommunications Day.

2309. **600.** 3 f. 50 multicoloured 15 10

**601.** "Sport" (poster for Ghent Exhibition, 1913).

**1973.** 60th Anniv. of Workers' Int. Sports Organization.

2310. **601.** 4 f. 50 multicoloured 20 10

**602.** Douglas DC-10-30CF and De Havilland D.H.9.

**1973.** 50th Anniv. of SABENA.

2311. **602.** 8 f. blk, blue & grey 35 15

**603.** Ernest Tips's Biplane, 1908.

**1973.** 35th Anniv. (1972) of "Les Vieilles Tiges de Belgique" (pioneer aviators' association).

2312. **603.** 10 f. blk., bl., & grn. 55 25

**604.** 15th-Century Printing-press.

**605.** "Woman Bathing" (fresco by Lemaire).

**1973.** Historical Events and Anniversaries.

2313. **604.** 2 f.+1 f. blk., brn. & red 15 20
2314. – 3 f. 50+1 f. 50 mult. 20 30
2315. – 4 f. 50+2 f. mult. .. 25 35
2316. – 8 f.+4 f. multicoloured 80 85
2317. – 9 f.+4 f. 50 mult. .. 80 90
2318. – 10 f.+5 f. mult. .. 2·25 2·50

DESIGNS—VERT. (As Type **604**.). 2 f. (500th anniv. of first Belgian printed book, produced by Dirk Martens). 3 f. 50, Head of Amon (Queen Elisabeth Egyptological Foundation. 50th anniv.). 4 f. 50, "Portrait of a Young Girl" (Petrus Christus, 500th death anniv.). HORIZ. (36×25 mm.). 8 f. Gold coins of Hadrian and Marcus Aurelius (Discovery of Roman treasure at Luttre-Liberchies). (52×35 mm.). 9 f. "Members of the Great Council" (Coessaert) (Great Council of Malines, 500th anniv.). 10 f. 18th-century sailing-ship (Ostend Merchant Company, 250th anniv.).

**1973.** Thermal Treatment Year.

2319. **605.** 4 f. 50 multicoloured 15 10

**606.** Adolphe Sax and Tenor Saxophone.

**607.** St. Nicholas Church, Eupen.

**1973.** Belgian Musical Instrument Industry.

2320. **606.** 9 f. multicoloured .. 45 15

**1973.** Tourist Publicity.

2321. **607.** 2 f. multicoloured .. 10 10

See also Nos. 2328/9, 2368/70, 2394/5, 2452/5, 2508/11, 2535/8, 2573/6, 2595/6 and 2614.

**608.** "Little Charles" (Evenepoel).

**609.** J. B. Moens (philatelist) and Perforations.

**1973.** "Philately for the Young".

2322. **608.** 3 f. multicoloured .. 15 10

**1973.** 50th Anniv. of Belgian Stamp Dealers Association.

2323. **609.** 10 f. multicoloured .. 30 20

**610.** "Adoration of the Shepherds" (H. van der Goes).

**611.** Motorway and Emblem.

**1973.** Christmas.
2324. **610.** 4 f. blue .. .. 15 10

**1973.** 50th Anniv. of Vlaamse Automobilistenbond" (VAB) (motoring organization).
2325. **611.** 5 f. multicoloured .. 25 10

**612.** L. Pierard (after sculpture by Ianchelevici).
**613.** Early Microphone.

**1973.** 21st Death Anniv. of Louis Pierard (politician and writer).
2326. **612.** 4 f. red and cream .. 15 10

**1973.** 50th Anniv. of Belgium Radio.
2327. **613.** 4 f. black and blue .. 15 10

**1973.** Tourist Publicity. As T **607**.
2328. 3 f. grey, brown and blue 15 10
2329. 4 f. grey and green .. 15 10
DESIGNS—HORIZ. 3 f. Town Hall, Leau. 4 f. Chimay Castle.

**614.** F. Rops (self-portrait).
**615.** Jack of Diamonds.

**1973.** 75th Death Anniv. of Felicien Rops (artist and engraver).
2330. **614.** 7 f. black and brown 30 10

**1973.** "Solidarity". Old Playing Cards. Mult.
2331. 5 f.+2 f. 50 Type **615** .. 60 60
2332. 5 f.+2 f. 50 Jack of Spades .. .. .. 60 60
2333. 5 f.+2 f. 50 Queen of Hearts .. .. .. 60 60
2334. 5 f.+2 f. 50 King of Clubs .. .. .. 60 60

**1973.** As Nos. 2207/23 but smaller; size 22×17 mm.
2335 **583** 3 f. green .. .. 1·00 80
2336 4 f. blue .. .. 30 15
2337 4 f. 50 blue .. .. 30 25
2338 5 f. mauve .. .. 20 10
2338c 6 f. red .. .. 20 15
2339 6 f. 50 violet .. 40 15
2339b 8 f. grey .. .. 30 10

**616.** King Albert (Baron Opsomer).
**617.** "Blood Donation".

**1974.** 40th Death Anniv. of King Albert I.
2340. **616.** 4 f. blue and black .. 15 10

**1974.** Belgian Red Cross. Multicoloured.
2341. 4 f.+2 f. Type **617** .. 30 30
2342. 10 f.+5 f. "Traffic Lights" (Road Safety) 70 70

**618.** "Protection of the Environment".
**619.** "Armand Jamar" (Self-portrait).

**1974.** Robert Schuman Association for the Protection of the Environment.
2343 **618** 3 f. multicoloured .. 20 10

**1974.** Belgian Cultural Celebrities. Mult.
2344 4 f.+2 f. Type **619** .. 25 30
2345 5 f.+2 f. 50 Tony Bergmann (author) and view of Lier .. .. 30 40
2346 7 f.+3 f. 50 Henri Vieuxtemps (violinist) and view of Verviers .. 65 75
2347 10 f.+5 f. "James Ensor" (self-portrait with masks) (35×52 mm) .. 75 90

**620.** N.A.T.O. Emblem.
**621.** Hubert Krains (Belgian postal administrator).

**1974.** 25th Anniv. of North Atlantic Treaty Organization.
2348. **620.** 10 f. blue and lt. blue 45 20

**1974.** Stamp Day.
2349 **621.** 5 f. black and grey .. 15 10

**622.** "Destroyed Town" (O. Zadkine).
**623.** Heads of Boy and Girl.

**1974.** Europa. Sculptures.
2350. **622.** 5 f. black and red .. 25 10
2351. – 10 f. black & blue .. 50 25
DESIGN: 10 f. "Solidarity" (G. Minne).

**1974.** 10th Lay Youth Festival.
2352 **623** 4 f. multicoloured .. 15 10

**625.** New Planetarium, Brussels.

**1974.** Historical Buildings.
2354. **625.** 3 f. brown and blue .. 15 10
2355. – 4 f. brown and red .. 20 15
2356. – 5 f. brown and green 25 10
2357. – 7 f. brown and yellow 30 20
2358. – 10 f. brn., orge. & blue 35 15
DESIGNS—As T **625**: HORIZ. 4 f. Pillory, Braine-le-Chateau. VERT. 10 f. Belfry, Bruges. 45×25 mm: 5 f. Ruins of Soleilmont Abbey. 7 f. "Procession" (fountain sculpture, Ghent).

**626.** "BENELUX".

**1974.** 30th Anniv of Benelux Customs Union.
2359 **626** 5 f. blue, grn & lt blue 20 10

**627.** "Jan Vekemans at the Age of Five" (Cornelis de Vos).
**628.** Self-portrait and Van Gogh House, Cuesmes.

**1974.** "Philately for the Young".
2360. **627.** 3 f. multicoloured .. 10 10

**1974.** Opening of Vincent Van Gogh House, Cuesmes.
2361. **628.** 10 f.+5 f. mult .. 50 65

**629.** Corporal Tresignies and Brule Bridge.

**1974.** 60th Death Anniv. of Corporal Leon Tresignies (war hero).
2362. **629.** 4 f. green & brown .. 20 10

**630.** Montgomery Blair and U.P.U. Emblem.
**631.** Graph within Head.

**1974.** Cent. of Universal Postal Union.
2363. **630.** 5 f. black & green .. 25 10
2364. – 10 f. black and red .. 45 30
DESIGN: 10 f. H. von Stephan and U.P.U. Monument.

**1974.** 25th Anniv. of Central Economic Council.
2365. **631.** 7 f. multicoloured .. 35 15

**632.** Rotary Emblem on Belgian Flag.
**633.** Wild Boar.

**1974.** 50th Anniv. of Rotary International in Belgium.
2366. **632.** 10 f. multicoloured .. 35 15

**1974.** 40th Anniv. of Granting of Colours to Ardennes Regiment of Chasseurs.
2367. **633.** 3 f. multicoloured .. 30 10

**1974.** Tourist Publicity. As Type **607**.
2368 3 f. brown and yellow .. 20 10
2369 4 f. green and blue .. 25 10
2370 4 f. green and blue .. 20 10
DESIGNS—VERT. No. 2368, Aarschot. HORIZ. No. 2369, Meeting of three frontiers, Gemmenich. 2370, Nassogne.

**634.** "Angel" (detail, "The Mystic Lamb" Brothers Van Eyck).
**635.** Gentian.

**1974.** Christmas.
2371. **634.** 4 f. purple .. .. 15 10

**1974.** "Solidarity". Flora and Fauna. Mult.
2372 4 f.+2 f. Type **635** .. 35 35
2373 5 f.+2 f. 50 Eurasian badger (horiz) .. 40 40
2374 7 f.+3 f. 50 Golden hunter (beetle) (horiz) .. 60 60
2375 10 f.+5 f. Spotted cat's-ear .. .. .. 80 80

**636.** Adolphe Quetelet. (after J. Odevaere).
**637.** Exhibition Emblem.

**1974.** Death Centenary of Adolphe Quetelet. (scientist).
2376. **636.** 10 f. black & brown 40 15

**1975.** "Themabelga" Stamp Exhibition, Brussels (1st issue).
2377. **637.** 6 f. 50 orange, black and green .. .. 15 10
See also Nos. 2411/6.

**MORE DETAILED LISTS**
are given in the Stanley Gibbons Catalogues referred to in the country headings.
For lists of current volumes see Introduction.

**638.** "Neoregelia carolinae".
**639.** Student and Young Boy.

**1975.** Ghent Flower Show. Multicoloured.
2378. 4 f. 50 Type **638** .. .. 20 10
2379. 5 f. "Tussilago petasites" 20 10
2380. 6 f. 50 "Azalea japonica" 25 10

**1975.** Cent of Charles Buls Normal School.
2381 **639** 4 f. 50 multicoloured 15 10

**640.** Foundation Emblem.
**641.** King Albert I.

**1975.** Centenary of Davids Foundation (Flemish cultural organisation).
2382. **640.** 5 f. multicoloured .. 20 10

**1975.** Birth Cent. of King Albert I.
2383. **641.** 10 f. black and pur. 30 15

**642.** Pesaro Palace, Venice.
**643.** "Postman of 1840" (J. Thiriar).

**1975.** Cultural Works.
2384. **642.** 6 f. 50+2 f. 50 brown 40 50
2385. – 10 f.+4 f. 50 purple 50 70
2386. – 15 f.+6 f. 50 blue .. 80 90
DESIGNS—HORIZ. 10 f. Sculpture Museum, St. Bavon Abbey, Ghent. VERT. 15 f. "Virgin and Child". (Michelangelo, 500th Birth Anniv.)

**1975.** Stamp Day.
2387. **643.** 6 f. 50 purple .. 30 10

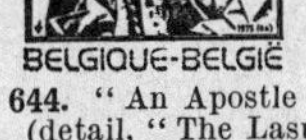

**644.** "An Apostle" (detail, "The Last Supper" Dirk Bouts).
**645.** Prisoners' Identification Emblems.

**1975.** Europa. Paintings.
2388. **644.** 6 f. 50 black, bl. & grn. 30 10
2389. – 10 f. blk., red & orge. 40 25
DESIGN: 10 f. "The Suppliant's Widow" (detail, "The Justice of Otho", Dirk Bouts).

**1975.** 30th Anniv. of Concentration Camps' Liberation.
2390. **645.** 4 f. 50 multicoloured 20 10

**646.** St. John's Hospice, Bruges.

**1975.** European Architectural Heritage Year.
2391. **646.** 4 f. 50 purple .. 25 10
2392. 5 f. green .. .. 25 10
2393. – 10 f. blue .. .. 40 15
DESIGNS—VERT. 5 f. St. Loup's Church, Namur. HORIZ. 10 f. Martyrs Square, Brussels.

**1975.** Tourist Publicity. As T **607**.
2394. 4 f. 50 brown, buff and red 20 10
2395. 5 f. multicoloured .. 20 10
DESIGN—VERT. 4 f. 50, Church, Dottignies. HORIZ. 5 f. Market Square, Saint Truiden.

**647.** G. Ryckmans and L. Cerfaux (founders), and Louvain University Library.

**648.** " Metamorphosis " (P. Mara).

**1975.** 25th Anniv. of Louvain Colloquium Biblicum (Biblical Scholarship Association).
2396. **647.** 10 f. sepia and blue 30 15

**1975.** Queen Fabiola Foundation for the Mentally Ill.
2397. **648.** 7 f. multicoloured .. 30 15

**649.** Marie Popelin (women's rights pioneer) and Palace of Justice.

**650.** " Assia " (Charles Despiau).

**1975.** International Women's Year.
2398. **649.** 6 f. 50 purple & green 30 10

**1975.** 25th Anniv. of Middelheim Open-air Museum. Antwerp.
2399. **650.** 5 f. black and green 20 10

**651.** Dr. Hemerijckx and Leprosy Hospital, Zaire.

**1975.** Dr. Frans Hemerijckx (treatment of leprosy pioneer) Commemoration.
2400 **651** 20 f.+10 f. mult .. 1·40 1·40

**652.** Canal Map.

**653.** "Cornelia Vekemans at the Age of Seven " (Cornelis de Vos).

**1975.** Opening of Rhine-Scheldt Canal.
2401. **652.** 10 f. multicoloured .. 35 15

**1975.** " Philately for the Young ".
2402. **653.** 4 f. 50 multicoloured 20 10

**654.** National Bank and F. Orban (founder).

**1975.** 125th Anniv. of Belgian National Bank.
2403. **654.** 25 f. multicoloured .. 1·10 25

**655.** Edmond Thieffry (pilot) and "Princess Marie-Jose".

**656.** University Seal.

**1975.** 50th Anniv. of First Flight, Brussels–Kinshasa.
2404. **655.** 7 f. purple and black 25 15

**1975.** 550th Anniv. of Louvain University.
2405. **656.** 6 f. 50 blk., grn. & bl. 20 10

**657.** " Angels " (detail, " The Nativity " R. de le Pasture).

**658.** Emile Moyson (Flemish Leader).

**1975.** Christmas.
2406. **657.** 5 f. multicoloured .. 15 10

**1975.** " Solidarity ".
2407. **658.** 4 f. 50+2 f. purple.. 25 30
2408. – 6 f. 50+3 f. green .. 35 40
2409. – 10 f.+5 f. vio., blk. & bl. 50 60
2410. – 13 f.+6 f. multicoloured 70 85

DESIGNS—VERT. 6 f. 50, Dr. Augustin Snellaert (Flemish literature scholar). 13 f. Detail of retable, St. Dymphne Church, Geel. HORIZ. 10 f. Eye within hand, and Braille characters (150th anniv. of introduction of Braille).

**659.** Cheese Seller.

**660.** "African" Collector.

**1975.** "Themabelga" International Thematic Stamp Exhibition, Brussels (2nd issue). Traditional Belgian Trades. Multicoloured.
2411. 4 f. 50+1 f. 50 Type **659** 30 20
2412. 6 f. 50+3 f. Potato seller 45 35
2413. 6 f. 50+3 f. Basket-carrier 45 35
2414. 10 f.+5 f. Prawn fisherman and pony (horiz.) 70 55
2415. 10 f.+5 f. Knife-grinder and cart (horiz.) .. 70 55
2416. 30 f.+15 f. Milk-woman with dog-cart (horiz.) 2·00 1·75

**1976.** Centenary of "Conservatoire Africain" (Charity Organization).
2417. **660.** 10 f.+5 f. mult. .. 70 50

**661.** Owl Emblem and Flemish Buildings.

**662.** Bicentennial Symbol.

**1976.** 125th Anniv. of Wilhems Foundation (Flemish cultural organization).
2418. **661.** 5 f. multicoloured .. 15 10

**1976.** Bicent. of American Revolution.
2419. **662.** 14 f. multicoloured .. 50 25

**663.** Cardinal Mercier.

**664.** " Vlaams Ekonomisch Verbond."

**1976.** 50th Death Anniv. of Cardinal Mercier.
2420. **663.** 4 f. 50 purple .. 20 10

**1976.** 50th Anniv. of Flemish Economic Federation.
2421. **664.** 6 f. 50 multicoloured 20 10

**665.** Swimming.

**666.** Money Centre Building, Brussels.

**1976.** Olympic Games, Montreal. Mult.
2422. 4 f. 50+1 f. 50 Type **665** 25 25
2423. 5 f.+2 f. Running (vert.) 35 35
2424. 6 f. 50+2 f. 50 Horse-jumping .. .. 50 50

**1976.** Stamp Day.
2425. **666.** 6 f. 50 brown .. 20 10

**667.** Queen Elisabeth playing Violin.

**668.** Basket-making.

**1976.** 25th Anniv. of Queen Elisabeth International Music Competitions.
2426. **667.** 14 f.+6 f. red & blk. 70 70

**1976.** Europa. Traditional Crafts. Mult.
2427. 6 f. 50 Type **668** .. 30 10
2428. 14 f. Pottery (horiz.) .. 50 30

**669.** Lorry on Motorway.

**670.** Queen Elisabeth.

**1976.** 14th Congress of International Road Haulage Union, Brussels.
2429. **669.** 14 f. blk., red & yell. 75 25

**1976.** Birth Cent. of Queen Elisabeth.
2430. **670.** 14 f. green .. .. 70 25

**673.** Ardennes Horses.

**1976.** 50th Anniv. of Ardennes Draught Horses Society.
2436. **673.** 5 f. multicoloured .. 30 10

**675.** "Madonna and Child" (detail).

**1976.** 400th Birth Anniv of Peter Paul Rubens (artist) (1st issue). Multicoloured.
2438 4 f. 50+1 f. 50 "Descent from the Cross" (detail) 25 25
2439 6 f. 50+3 f. "Adoration of the Shepherds" (detail) (24½ × 35 mm) .. .. 45 45
2440 6 f. 50+3 f. "Virgin of the Parrot" (detail) (24½ × 35 mm) .. .. 45 45
2441 10 f.+5 f. "Adoration of the Kings" (detail) (24½ × 35 mm) .. .. 75 75
2442 10 f.+5 f. "Last Communion of St. Francis" (detail) (24½ × 35 mm) 75 75
2443 30 f.+15 f. Type **675** .. 2·00 2·00

See also Nos. 2459 and 2497.

**676.** William the Silent, Prince of Orange.

**678.** Underground Train.

**677.** Modern Electric Train.

**1976.** 400th Anniv. of Pacification of Ghent.
2444. **676.** 10 f. green .. .. 35 15

**1976.** 50th Anniv. of National Belgian Railway Company.
2445. **677.** 6 f. 50 multicoloured 35 10

**1976.** Opening of Brussels Metro (Underground) Service.
2446 **678** 6 f. 50 multicoloured 40 10

**679.** " The Young Musician " (W. C. Duyster).

**680.** Charles Bernard (writer, birth cent.).

**1976.** " Philately for the Young " and Young Musicians' Movement.
2447. **679.** 4 f. 50 multicoloured 25 10

**1976.** Cultural Annivs.
2448. **680.** 5 f. purple .. .. 20 20
2449. – 5 f. red .. .. 20 20
2450. – 6 f. 50 brown .. 30 10
2451. – 6 f. 50 green .. .. 30 10

DESIGNS—VERT. No. 2449, Fernand Toussaint van Boelaere (writer) birth cent. 1975. No. 2450, "St. Jerome in Mountain Landscape" (J. le Patinier) (25th Anniv. of Charles Plisnier Foundation). HORIZ. No. 2451, "Story of the Blind" (P. Brueghel) (25th Anniv. of "Vereniging voor Beschaafde Omgangstaal" (Dutch language organisation)).

**1976.** Tourist Publicity. As T **607**.
2452. 4 f. 50 multicoloured .. 25 15
2453. 4 f. 50 multicoloured .. 25 15
2454. 5 f. brown and blue .. 30 15
2455. 5 f. brown and olive .. 30 15

DESIGNS—HORIZ. No. 2452, Hunnegem Priory, Grammont. No. 2454, River Lys, Sint-Martens-Latem. No. 2455, Chateau, Ham-sur-Heure. VERT. No. 2453, Remouchamps Caves.

**681.** " Child with Impediment " (Velasquez).

**682.** " The Nativity " (detail, Master of Flemalle).

**1976.** National Association for Aid to the Mentally Handicapped.
2456. **681.** 14 f.+6 f. mult. .. 85 85

**1976.** Christmas.
2457. **682.** 5 f. violet .. .. 15 10

**683.** Monogram.

**1977.** 400th Birth Anniv of Peter Paul Rubens (2nd issue).
2459 **683** 6 f. 50 black and lilac 25 10

**684.** Belgian Lion.

**1977.** (a) Size 17 × 20 mm.
2460. **684.** 50 c. brown .. .. 10 10
2461. 65 c. red .. .. 10 10
2462. 1 f. mauve .. .. 10 10
2463. 1 f. 50 grey .. .. 10 10
2464a. 2 f. orange .. .. 10 10
2465. 2 f. 50 green .. .. 15 10
2466. 2 f. 75 blue .. .. 20 20
2467a. 3 f. violet .. .. 15 10
2468. 4 f. brown .. .. 20 10
2469. 4 f. 50 blue .. .. 20 10
2470. 5 f. green .. .. 20 10
2471. 6 f. red .. .. 25 10
2472. 7 f. red .. .. 25 10
2473. 8 f. blue .. .. 40 10
2474. 9 f. orange .. .. 70 10

(b) 17 × 22 mm.

2475. 684. 1 f. mauve .. .. 10 10
2476. 2 f. orange .. .. 20 20
2477. 3 f. violet .. .. 25 25

685. Dr. Albert Hustin (pioneer of blood transfusion).

686. "50 Years of F.A.B.I.".

**1977.** Belgian Red Cross.

2478 685 6 f. 50 + 2 f. 50 red and black .. 35 35
2479 – 14 f. + 7 f. red, blue and black .. .. 75 75

Design: 14 f. + 7 f. Knee joint and red cross (World Rheumatism Year).

**1977.** 50th Anniv. of Federation of Belgian Engineers.

2480. 686. 6 f. 50 multicoloured 20 10

687. Jules Bordet School, Brussels (bicent).

688. Gulls in Flight.

**1977.** Cultural Annivs.

2481. 687. 4 f. 50 + 1 f. mult. .. 20 20
2482. – 4 f. 50 + 1 f. mult. .. 20 20
2483. – 5 f. + 2 f. multicoloured 30 30
2484. – 6 f. 50 + 2 f. mult. .. 40 40
2485. – 6 f. 50 + 2 f. red & blk. 40 40
2486. – 10 f. + 5 slate .. 50 50

Designs—vert. 24 × 37 mm: No. 2482, Marie-Therese College, Herve (bicentenary). 2483, Detail from "La Grande Pyramide Musicale" (E. Tytgat) (50th anniv of Brussels Philharmonic Society). 35 × 45 mm: No. 2486, Camille Lemonnier (75th anniv of Society of Belgian Authors writing in French). horiz. 35 × 24 mm: No. 2484, Lucien van Obbergh and stage scene (50th anniv of Union of Artists). 37 × 24 mm: No. 2485, Emblem of Humanist Society (25th anniv).

**1977.** 25th Anniv. of District 112 of Lions International.

2487. 688. 14 f. multicoloured .. 75 25

689. Footballers.

690. Pillar Box, 1852.

**1977.** 30th International Youth Tournament of European Football Association.

2488. 689. 10 f. + 5 f. mult. .. 75 60

**1977.** Stamp Day.

2489. 690. 6 f. 50 olive .. .. 25 10

691. Gileppe Dam, Jalhay.

692. "Mars and Mercury Association Emblem".

**1977.** Europa. Multicoloured.

2490 6 f. 50 Type 691 .. .. 30 10
2491 14 f. The Yser, Nieuport 55 25

**1977.** 50th Anniv. of Mars and Mercury Association of Reserve and Retired Officers.

2492. 692. 5 f. grn., blk. & brn. 15 10

693. De Hornes Coat of Arms.

694. "Self-Portrait".

**1977.** Historical Annivs.

2493. 693. 4 f. 50 lilac .. .. 20 10
2494. – 5 f. red .. .. 25 15
2495. – 6 f. 50 brown .. 30 10
2496. – 14 f. green .. .. 50 25

Designs and events—vert. 4 f. 50 Type 693 (300th anniv of creation of principality of Overijse under Eugene-Maximilien de Hornes). 6 f. 50 Miniature (600th anniv of Froissart's "Chronicles"). 14 f. "The Conversion of St. Hubert" (1250th death anniv). horiz. (45 × 24 mm). 5 f. Detail from "Oxford Chest" (675th anniv of Battle of Golden Spurs).

**1977.** 400th Birth Anniv of Peter Paul Rubens (3rd issue).

2497 694 5 f. multicoloured .. 15 10

695. "The Mystic Lamb" (detail, Brothers Van Eyck).

**1977.** 50th Anniv. of International Federation of Library Associations and Congress, Brussels.

2499. 695. 10 f. multicoloured .. 35 20

696. Gymnast and Footballer.

**1977.** Sports Events and Anniversaries.

2500. 696. 4 f. 50 red, blk. & grn. 20 10
2501. – 6 f. 50 blk., vio. & brn. (horiz.) .. .. 30 10
2502. – 10 f. turquoise, black and salmon .. 70 20
2503. – 14 f. grn., blk. & ochre 75 25

Designs—vert. 4 f. 50, Type 696 (50th anniv of Workers' Central Sports Association). 10 f. Basketball (20th European Championships). 14 f. Hockey (International Hockey Cup competition). horiz. 6 f. 50 Disabled fencers (Rehabilitation through sport).

697. Festival Emblem.

**1977.** "Europalia '77" Festival.

2504. 697. 5 f. multicoloured .. 20 10

699. "The Egg-seller" (Gustave de Smet).

700. "The Stamp Collectors" (detail, Constant Cap).

**1977.** Promoting Belgian Eggs.

2506. 699. 4 f. 50 blk. & ochre .. 20 10

**1977.** "Philately for the Young".

2507. 700. 4 f. 50 sepia .. .. 20 10

**1977.** Tourist Publicity. As Type 607.

2508. 4 f. 50 multicoloured .. 25 10
2509. 4 f. 50 blk., bl. & green 25 10
2510. 5 f. multicoloured .. 25 15
2511. 5 f. multicoloured .. 25 15

Designs—vert. No. 2508. Bailiff's House Gembloux. No. 2509, St. Aldegone's Church. horiz. No. 2510, View of Liege and statue of Mother and Child. No. 2511, View and statue of St. Nicholas.

701. "Nativity" (detail, R. de la Pasture).

702. Albert-Edouard Janssen (financier).

**1977.** Christmas.

2512. 701. 5 f. red .. .. 15 10

**1977.** "Solidarity".

2513. 702. 5 f. + 2 f. 50 black .. 35 35
2514. – 5 f. + 2 f. 50 red .. 35 35
2515. – 10 f. + 5 f. purple .. 70 70
2516. – 10 f. + 5 f. grey .. 70 70

Designs: No. 2514, Joseph Wauters (politician). No. 2516, Jean Capart (egyptologist). No. 2515, August de Boeck (composer).

703. Distressed Girl (Deserted Children).

704. Railway Signal as Arrows on Map of Europe.

**1978.** Philanthropic Works. Multicoloured.

2517. 4 f. 50 + 1 f. 50 Type 703 20 20
2518. 6 f. + 3 f. Blood pressure measurement (World Hypertension Month) 30 30
2519. 10 f. + 5 f. De Mick Sanatorium, Brasschaat (Anti-tuberculosis) (horiz.) .. .. 75 75

**1978.** "European Action" Multicoloured.

2520 10 f. Type 704 (25th anniv of European Conference of Transport Ministers) 60 15
2521 10 f. European Parliament Building, Strasbourg (first direct elections) 60 15
2522 14 f. Campidoglio Palace, Rome and map of EEC countries (20th anniv of Treaties of Rome) (horiz) .. 60 35
2523 14 f. Paul Henri Spaak (Belgian Prime Minister) (horiz) .. 50 35

705. Grimbergen Abbey.

**1978.** 850th Anniv. of Premonstratensian Abbey, Grimbergen.

2524. 705. 4 f. 50 brown .. 20 10

706. Emblem.

707. 5 f. Stamp of 1878.

**1978.** 175th Anniv. of Ostend Chamber of Commerce and Industry.

2525. 706. 8 f. multicoloured .. 35 10

**1978.** Stamp Day.

2526. 707. 8 f. brn., blk. & drab 35 10

708. Antwerp Cathedral.

709. Theatre and Characters from "The Brussels Street Singer".

**1978.** Europa. Multicoloured.

2527. 8 f. Type 708 .. .. 35 10
2528. 14 f. Pont des Trous, Tournai (horiz.) .. 50 20

**1978.** Cultural Annivs.

2529. 709. 6 f. + 3 f. multicoloured 45 45
2530. – 6 f. + 3 f. multicoloured 45 45
2531. – 8 f. + 4 f. brown .. 60 60
2532. – 10 f. + 5 f. brown .. 75 75

Designs and events: No. 2529, (Type 709) (Royal Flemish Theatre Cent.). No. 2530, Arquebusier with standard, arms and Company Gallery, Vise (Royal Company of Crossbowmen of Vise 400th anniv.). No. 2531, Karel van der Woestijne (poet) (birth cent.). No. 2532, Don John of Austria (signing of Perpetual Edict. 400th anniv.).

710. "Education".

711. "K. V. I.".

**1978.** Teaching. Multicoloured.

2533. 6 f. Type 710 (Municipal education in Ghent, 150th anniv.) .. .. 25 15
2534. 8 f. Paul Pastur Workers' University, Charleroi (75th anniv.) .. .. 30 10

**1978.** Tourist Publicity. As T 607.

2535. 4 f. 50 sepia, buff and blue .. .. 20 10
2536. 4 f. 50 multicoloured .. 20 10
2537. 6 f. multicoloured .. 25 10
2538. 6 f. multicoloured .. 25 10

Designs—vert. No. 2535, Jonathas House, Enghien. horiz. No. 2536, View of Wetteren and couple in local costume. 2537, Brussels tourist hostess. 2538, Carnival Prince and church tower.

**1978.** 50th Anniv. of Royal Flemish Association of Engineers.

2539. 711. 8 f. black and red .. 25 10

712. Young Stamp Collector.

713. Mountain Scenery.

**1978.** "Philately for the Young".

2540. 712. 4 f. 50 violet .. .. 15 10

**1978.** Olympic Games (1980) Preparation.

2541. 713. 6 f. + 2 f. 50 mult. .. 35 45
2542. – 8 f. + 3 f. 50 green, brown and black .. 50 60

Design: 8 f. Kremlin Towers.

714. "The Nativity" (detail, Bethlehem Door, Notre Dame, Huy).

715. Tabernacle, Brussels Synagogue (centenary).

**1978.** Christmas.

2544. 714. 6 f. black .. .. 20 10

**1978.** "Solidarity". Anniversaries.

2545. 715. 6 f. + 2 f. brown, grey and black .. .. 50 50
2546. – 8 f. + 3 f. multicoloured 35 35
2547. – 14 f. + 7 f. multicoloured 95 95

DESIGNS—HORIZ. (36×24 mm.). 8 f. Dancing figures (Catholic Students Action, 50th anniv.) 14 f. Father Dominique-Georges Pire and African Village (Award of Nobel Peace Prize, 20th anniv.).

**716.** Relief Workers giving First Aid.

**717.** " Till Eulenspiegel ". (legendary character).

**1978.** Belgian Red Cross. Multicoloured.
2548 8 f.+3 f. Type **716** .. 35 35
2549 16 f.+8 f. Skull smoking, bottle and syringe ("Excess kills") .. 95 95

**1979.** 10th Anniv. of Lay Action Centres.
2550. **717.** 4 f. 50 multicoloured 20 10

**718.** " European Dove ".

**719.** Millenary Emblem.

**1979.** First Direct Elections to European Assembly.
2551. **718.** 8 f. multicoloured .. 30 10

**1979.** Brussels Millenary (1st issue).
2552. **719.** 4 f. 50 brn., blk. & red 15 10
2553. 8 f. turq., blk. & grn. 25 10
See also Nos. 2559/62.

**720.** Sculpture at N.A.T.O. Headquarters and Emblem.

**721.** Drawing of Monument.

**1979.** 30th Anniv. of North Atlantic Treaty Organization.
2554. **720.** 30 f. blue, gold and light blue .. .. 1·25 25

**1979.** 25th Anniv. of Breendonk Monument.
2555. **721.** 6 f. orange and black 20 10

**722.** Railway Parcels Stamp, 1879.

**1979.** Stamp Day.
2556. **722.** 8 f. multicoloured .. 35 10

**723.** Mail Coach and Modern Post Van.

**1979.** Europa. Multicoloured.
2557. 8 f. Type **723** .. .. 30 10
2558. 14 f. Semaphore posts, satellite and dish aerial 50 25

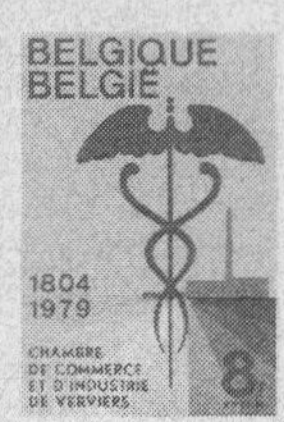


**724.** "Legend of Our Lady of Sablon" (detail of tapestry, Town Museum of Brussels).

**725.** Caduceus and Factory.

**1979.** Brussels Millenary (2nd issue). Multicoloured.
2559. 6 f.+2 f. Type **724** .. 30 30
2560. 8 f.+3 f. Different detail of tapestry .. .. 40 40
2561. 14 f.+7 f. " Legend of Our Lady of Sablon " (tapestry) .. .. 95 1·00
2562. 20 f.+10 f. Different detail of tapestry .. .. 1·40 1·40

**The tapestry shown on Nos. 2559/60 is from Brussels Town Museum and that on Nos. 2561/2 from the Royal Museum of Art and History.**

**1979.** 175th Anniv. of Verviers Chamber of Commerce.
2564. **725.** 8 f. multicoloured .. 25 10

**726.** " 50 " and Bank Emblem.

**1979.** 50th Anniv. of Professional Credit Bank.
2565. **726.** 4 f. 50 blue and gold 15 10

**727.** Bas-relief.

**1979.** 50th Anniv of Chambers of Trade and Commerce.
2566 **727** 10 f. crimson, orange and red .. .. 30 15

**728.** Cambre Abbey.

**1979.** Cultural Anniversaries.
2567 **728** 6 f.+2 f. mult .. 35 35
2568 – 8 f.+3 f. mult .. 40 40
2569 – 14 f.+7 f. black, orange and green .. 90 90
2570 – 20 f.+10 f. brown, red and grey .. .. 1·25 1·25

DESIGNS: 6 f. Type **728** (50th anniv of restoration). 8 f. Beauvoorde Chateau. 14 f. Barthelemy Dumortier (founder) and newspaper "Courrier de L'Escaut" (150th anniv). 20 f. Crypt, shrine and Collegiate Church of St. Hermes, Renaix (850th anniv of consecration).

**729.** " Tintin " with Dog, Stamps and Magnifier.

**1979.** " Philately for the Young ".
2571. **729.** 8 f. multicoloured .. 1·25 35

**730.** Le Grand-Hornu.

**1979.** Le Grand-Hornu Industrial Archaeological Site.
2572. **730.** 10 f.+5 f. blk. & grey 60 60

**1979.** Tourist Publicity. As T **607**.
2573. 5 f. multicoloured .. 25 10
2574. 5 f. multicoloured .. 25 10
2575. 6 f. black, turq. & green 25 10
2576. 6 f. multicoloured .. 25 10

DESIGNS—HORIZ. No. 2573, Royal African Museum, Tervuren, and hunters with hounds. 2575, St. John's Church, Poperinge, and statue of Virgin Mary. VERT. No. 2574, Belfry, Thuin, and men carrying religious image. 2576, St. Nicholas's Church and cattle market, Ciney.

**731.** Francois Auguste Gevaert.

**732.** Madonna and Child, Foy-Notre-Dame Church.

**1979.** Music. Each brown and ochre.
2577 5 f. Type **731** (150th birth anniv) .. .. 20 10
2578 6 f. Emmanuel Durlet .. 20 10
2579 14 f. Grand piano and string instruments (40th anniv of Queen Elisabeth Musical Chapel) .. .. 50 20

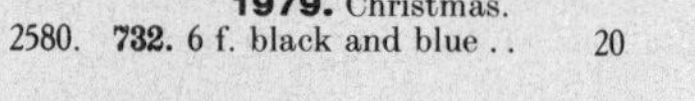

**1979.** Christmas.
2580. **732.** 6 f. black and blue .. 20 10

**733.** H. Heyman (politician, birth centenary).

**734.** "1830–1980".

**1979.** " Solidarity ".
2581. **733.** 8 f.+3 f. brown, green and black .. .. 40 40
2582. – 10 f.+5 f. mult .. 50 50
2583. – 16 f.+8 f. black, green and yellow .. 1·10 1·10

DESIGNS—VERT. As Type **733**. 10 f. War Invalids Organization medal (50th anniv.) HORIZ. (44×24 mm.). 16 f. Child's head and International Year of the Child emblem.

**1980.** 150th Anniv. of Independence (1st issue).
2584. **734.** 9 f. mauve and light mauve .. .. 30 10
See also Nos. 2597/2601.

**735.** Frans Van Cauwelaert.

**736.** Spring Flowers.

**1980.** Birth Centenary of Frans Van Cauwelaert (politician).
2585. **735.** 5 f. black .. .. 15 10

**1980.** Ghent Flower Show. Multicoloured.
2586. 5 f. Type **736** .. .. 25 10
2587. 6 f. 50 Summer flowers .. 30 15
2588. 9 f. Autumn flowers .. 35 10

**737.** Telephone and Diagram of Satellite Orbit.

**1980.** 50th Anniv. of Telegraph and Telephone Office.
2589. **737.** 10 f. multicoloured .. 35 15

**738.** 5 f. Airmail Stamp of 1930.

**1980.** Stamp Day.
2590. **738.** 9 f. multicoloured .. 30 10

**739.** St. Benedict of Nursia.

**1980.** Europa. Multicoloured.
2591. 9 f. Type **739** .. .. 30 10
2592. 14 f. Marguerite of Austria 50 30

**740.** Ivo van Damme.

**741.** Palais de la Nation.

**1980.** Ivo van Damme (athlete) Commemoration.
2593. **740.** 20 f.+10 f. mult .. 1·25 1·25

**1980.** 4th Interparliamentary Conference on European Co-operation and Security, Brussels.
2594 **741** 5 f. blue, lilac & black 20 10

**742.** Golden Carriage, Mons.

**1980.** Tourist Publicity. Multicoloured.
2595. 6 f. 50 Type **742** .. .. 25 15
2596. 6 f. 50 Damme .. .. 25 15

**743.** King Leopold I and Queen Louise-Marie.

**1980.** 150th Anniv. of Belgian Independence (2nd issue).
2597. **743.** 6 f. 50+1 f. 50 purple and black .. .. 25 25
2598. – 9 f.+3 f. blue & black 45 45
2599. – 14 f.+6 f. grn. & blk. 70 70
2600. – 17 f.+8 f. orge. & blk. 1·10 1·10
2601. – 25 f.+10 f. grn. & blk. 1·60 1·60

DESIGNS: 9 f. King Leopold II and Queen Marie-Henriette. 14 f. King Albert I and Queen Elisabeth. 17 f. King Leopold III and Queen Astrid. 25 f. King Baudouin and Queen Fabiola.

**744.** King Baudouin.

**745.** " Brewer " (detail, Reliquary of St. Lambert).

**1980.** King Baudouin's 50th Birthday.
2603. **744.** 9 f. red .. .. 30 10

**1980.** Millenary of Liege. Multicoloured.
2604. 9 f.+3 f. Type **745** .. 45 50
2605. 17 f.+6 f. "The Miner" (sculpture by Constantin Meunier) (horiz.) .. 1·10 1·10
2606. 25 f.+10 f. "Seat of Wisdom" (Madonna, Collegiate Church of St. John, Liege) .. 1·60 1·50

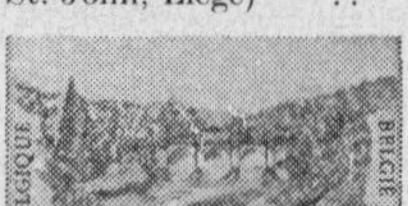

**746.** Chiny.

**1980.** Tourist Publicity.
2608. **746.** 5 f. multicoloured .. 20 10

**747.** Emblem of Cardiological League of Belgium.
**748.** Rodenbach (statue at Roulers).

**1980.** Heart Week.
2609. **747.** 14 f. light blue, red and blue .. .. 50 25

**1980.** Death Centenary of Albrecht Rodenbach (poet).
2610. **748.** 9 f. brown, blue and deep blue .. .. 30 10

**749.** "Royal Procession" (children of Thyl Uylenspiegel Primary School).

**1980.** "Philately for the Young".
2611. **749.** 5 f. multicoloured .. 30 10

**750.** Emblem.
**751.** "Garland of Flowers and Nativity" (attr. D. Seghers).

**1980.** 50th Anniv. of Belgian Broadcasting Corporation.
2612. **750.** 10 f. black and grey 30 10

**1980.** Christmas.
2613. **751.** 6 f. 50 multicoloured 30 10

**752.** Gateway, Diest.
**754.** Brain.

**1980.** Tourist Publicity.
2614. **752.** 5 f. multicoloured .. 20 10
See also Nos. 2648/51 and 2787/92.

**1981.** International Year of Disabled Persons. Multicoloured.
2637. 10 f.+5 f. Type **754** .. 50 60
2638. 25 f.+10 f. Eye .. .. 1·60 1·40

**755.** "Baron de Gerlache" (after F. J. Navez).
**756.** Emblem of 15th International Radiology Convention.

**1981.** Historical Anniversaries.
2639. **755.** 6 f. multicoloured .. 20 10
2640. – 9 f. multicoloured .. 30 10
2641. – 50 f. brown & yellow 2·25 50
DESIGNS—As T **755**: 6 f. Type **755** (1st President of Chamber of Deputies) (150th anniv of Chamber). 9 f. Baron de Stassart (1st President of Senate) (after F. J. Navez) (150th anniv of Senate). 35×51 mm: 50 f. Statue of King Leopold I by Geefs (150th anniv of royal dynasty).

**1981.** Belgian Red Cross.
2642. **756.** 10 f.+5 f. blue, black & red .. .. 50 60
2643. – 25 f.+10 f. blue, red & black .. .. 1·50 1·40
DESIGN: 25 f. Dove and globe symbolizing international emergency assistance.

**757.** Tchantches and Op-Signoorke (puppets).

**1981.** Europa. Multicoloured.
2644. 9 f. Type **757** .. .. 35 10
2645. 14 f. D'Artagnan and Woltje (puppets) .. 60 30

**758.** Stamp Transfer-roller depicting A. de Cock (founder of Postal Museum).
**759.** Ovide Decroly.

**1981.** Stamp Day.
2646. **758.** 9 f. multicoloured .. 30 10

**1981.** 110th Birth Anniv. of Dr. Ovide Decroly (educational psychologist).
2647. **759.** 35 f.+15 f. brn. & bl. 1·50 1·75

**1981.** Tourist Publicity. Designs as T **752**. Multicoloured.
2648. 6 f. Statue of our Lady of Tongre.. .. .. 25 15
2649. 6 f. Egmont Castle, Zottegem .. .. 25 15
2650. 6 f. 50 Dams on Eau d'Heure (horiz.) .. 25 15
2651. 6 f. 50 Tongerlo Abbey, Antwerp (horiz.) .. 25 15

**760.** Footballer.
**761.** Edouard Remouchamps (Walloon dramatist).

**1981.** Cent of Royal Antwerp Football Club.
2652 **760** 6 f. red, brown & black 10 30

**1981.** 125th Anniv of Society of Walloon Language and Literature.
2653 **761** 6 f. 50 brown and stone 30 10

**762.** French Horn.

**1981.** Centenary of De Vredekring Band, Antwerp.
2654. **762.** 6 f. 50 blue, mauve and black.. .. 30 10

**763.** Audit Office.

**1981.** 150th Anniv. of Audit Office.
2655. **763.** 10 f. purple .. .. 35 15

**765.** Tombs of Marie of Burgundy and Charles the Bold.

**1981.** Relocation of Tombs of Marie of Burgundy and Charles the Bold in Notre-Dame Church, Bruges.
2657. **765.** 50 f. multicoloured .. 2·25 50

**766.** Boy holding Globe in Tweezers.
**767.** King Baudouin.

**1981.** "Philately for Youth".
2658. **766.** 6 f. multicoloured .. 20 10

**1981.**
2659 **767** 50 f. light blue & blue 1·75 10
2660 65 f. mauve and black 2·75 60
2661 100 f. brown and blue 3·50 40

**768.** Max Waller (founder).
**769.** Nativity (miniature from "Missale ad usum d. Leodensis").

**1981.** Cultural Anniversaries.
2672. **768.** 6 f. multicoloured .. 20 10
2673. – 6 f. 50 multicoloured 25 15
2674. – 9 f. multicoloured .. 30 10
2675. – 10 f. multicoloured 50 15
2676. – 14 f. light brown and brown .. .. 50 25
DESIGNS: 6 f. Type **768** (centenary of literary review "La Jeune Belgique"). 6 f. 50, "Liqueur Drinkers" (detail, Gustave van de Woestyne) (birth centenary). 9 f. Fernand Severin (poet, 50th death anniv.). 10 f. Jan van Ruusbroec (mystic, 600th death anniv.). 14 f. Owl (La Pensee et les Hommes organization, 25th anniv.).

**1981.** Christmas.
2677. **769.** 6 f. 50 brown and black 25 10

**770.** Mounted Gendarme, 1832.
**771.** Cellist and Royal Conservatory of Music, Brussels.

**1981.** "Solidarity". Multicoloured.
2678 9 f.+4 f. Type **770** .. 55 55
2679 20 f.+7 f. Carabinier .. 1·25 1·25
2680 40 f.+20 f. Mounted Guide, 1843 .. .. 2·50 2·50

**1982.** 150th Anniversaries. Multicoloured.
2681. 6 f. 50 Type **771**.. .. 30 15
2682. 9 f. Front of former Law Court, Brussels (anniv. of judiciary) .. .. 35 10

**772.** Sectional View of Cyclotron.
**773.** Billiards.

**1982.** Science. Multicoloured.
2683. 6 f. Type **772** (Installation of cyclotron at National Radio-elements Institute, Fleurus) .. 25 10
2684. 14 f. Telescope and galaxy (Royal Observatory).. 65 25
2685. 50 f. Dr. Robert Koch and tubercle bacillus (centenary of discovery) 2·25 55

**1982.** Sports. Multicoloured.
2686. 6 f.+2 f. Type **773** .. 45 45
2687. 9 f.+4 f. Cycling .. 60 60
2688. 10 f.+5 f. Football .. 80 80
2689. 50 f.+14 f. Yacht "Treaty of Rome" .. 2·50 2·50

**774.** Joseph Lemaire (after Jean Maillard).
**775.** Voting (Universal Suffrage).

**1982.** Birth Centenary of Joseph Lemaire (Minister of State and social reformer).
2691. **774.** 6 f. 50 multicoloured 30 10

**1982.** Europa.
2692. **775.** 10 f. multicoloured .. 40 10
2693. – 17 f. green, blk. and grey .. .. 70 35
DESIGN: 17 f. Portrait and signature of Emperor Joseph II (Edict of Toleration).

**1982.** Surch. **1 F.**
2694. **684.** 1 f. on 5 f. green .. 10 10

**777.** 17th-century Postal Messenger.
**778.** "Tower of Babel" (Brueghel the Elder).

**1982.** Stamp Day.
2695. **777.** 10 f. multicoloured .. 40 10

**1982.** World Esperanto Congress, Antwerp.
2696. **778.** 12 f. multicoloured .. 75 20

**1982.** Tourist Publicity. As T **752.**
2697. 7 f. blue and light blue .. 30 15
2698. 7 f. black and green .. 30 15
2699. 7 f. 50 brown and light brown .. .. .. 30 15
2700. 7 f. 50 violet and lilac .. 30 15
2701. 7 f. 50 black and grey .. 30 15
2702. 7 f. 50 black and pink .. 30 15
DESIGNS—VERT. No. 2697, Gosselies Tower. No. 2698, Zwijveke Abbey, Termonde. No. 2701. Entrance gate, Grammont Abbey. No. 2702, Beveren pillory. HORIZ. No. 2699, Stavelot Abbey. No. 2700, Abbey ruins, Villers-la-Ville.

**780.** Louis Paul Boon (writer).
**781.** Abraham Hans.

**1982.** Cultural Anniversaries.
2707. **780.** 7 f. black, red and grey 25 15
2708. – 10 f. multicoloured .. 35 10
2709. – 12 f. milticoloured .. 45 25
2710. – 17 f. multicoloured .. 70 25
DESIGNS: 7 f. Type **780** (70th birth anniv.). 10 f. "Adoration of the Shepherds" (detail of Portinari retable) (Hugo van der Goes, 500th death anniv.). 12 f. Michel de Ghelderode (dramatist, 20th death anniv.). 17 f. "Motherhood" (Pierre Paulus, birth centenary (1981)).

**1982.** Birth Cent. of Abraham Hans (writer).
2711. **781.** 17 f. black, turquoise and blue .. .. 65 25

**782.** Children playing Football.

**1982.** "Philately for the Young". Scout Year.
2712. **782.** 7 f. multicoloured .. 60 10

## MINIMUM PRICE
The minimum price quoted is 10p which represents a handling charge rather than a basis for valuing common stamps. For further notes about prices see introductory pages.

**783.** Masonic Emblems. **784.** Star over Village.

**1982.** 150th Anniv. of Belgium Grand Orient (Freemasonry Lodge).
2713. **783.** 10 f. yellow & black 60 10

**1982.** Christmas.
2714 784 10 f. + 1 f. mult .. 55 45

**785.** Cardinal Cardijn.

**1982.** Birth Cent. of Cardinal Joseph Cardijn.
2715. **785.** 10 f. multicoloured .. 40 10

**786.** King Baudouin. **787.** King Baudouin.

**1982.**
2716 **786** 10 f. blue .. .. 40 10
2717 11 f. brown .. 45 10
2718 12 f. green .. .. 1·25 10
2719 13 f. red .. .. 55 10
2720 14 f. black .. .. 70 10
2721 15 f. red .. .. 1·50 15
2722 20 f. blue .. .. 80 10
2723 22 f. purple .. 2·25 75
2724 23 f. green .. .. 1·75 30
2725 24 f. grey .. .. 1·10 15
2726 25 f. blue .. .. 1·25 10
2727 30 f. brown .. 1·25 10
2728 40 f. red .. .. 1·75 10
2729 **787** 50 f. light brown, brown and black 2·40 15
2730 100 f. blue, deep blue and black .. 4·50 20
2731 200 f. light green, green & deep green 9·25 70

**788.** St. Francis preaching to the Birds. **789.** Messenger handing Letter to King in the Field.

**1982.** 800th Birth Anniv. of St. Francis of Assisi.
2736. **788.** 20 f. multicoloured .. 80 25

**1982.** "Belgica 82" Postal History Exhibition. Multicoloured.
2737. 7 f. + 2 f. Type **789** .. 50 50
2738. 7 f. 50 + 2 f. 50 Messenger, Basel (vert.) 50 50
2739. 10 f. + 3 f. Messenger, Nuremburg (vert.) .. 70 70
2740. 17 f. + 7 f. Imperial courier, 1750 (vert.) .. 1·10 1·10
2741. 20 f. + 9 f. Imperial courier, 1800 .. .. 1·25 1·25
2742. 20 f. + 10 f. Belgian postman, 1886 .. 1·50 1·50

**790.** Emblem. **791.** Horse Tram.

**1983.** 50th Anniv. of Caritas Catholica Belgica.
2744. **790.** 10 f. + 2 f. red & grey 55 55

**1983.** Trams. Multicoloured.
2745. 7 f. 50 Type **791** .. 35 20
2746. 10 f. Electric tram .. 45 10
2747. 50 f. Tram with trolley (invented by K. van de Poele) .. .. .. 2·40 80

**792.** Mountaineer. **793.** Brussels Buildings, Open Periodicals and Globe.

**1983.** Belgian Red Cross. Multicoloured.
2748. 12 f. + 3 f. Type **792** .. 80 80
2749. 20 f. + 5 f. Walker .. 1·10 1·10

**1983.** 24th International Periodical Press Federation World Congress, Brussels.
2750 **793** 20 f. multicoloured .. 85 20

**794.** Woman at Work.

**1983.** Women.
2751. **794.** 8 f. multicoloured .. 40 15
2752. – 11 f. multicoloured .. 50 10
2753. – 20 f. yell., brn & bl. 85 25

DESIGNS: 11 f. Woman at home. 20 f. Woman manager.

**795.** Graphic Representation of Midi Railway Station, Brussels.

**1983.** Stamp Day. World Communications Year.
2754. **795.** 11 f. black, red and blue .. .. 55 30

**796.** Procession of the Holy Blood.

**1983.** Procession of the Holy Blood, Bruges.
2755 **796** 8 f. multicoloured .. 40 15

**797.** "The Man in the Street". **798.** Hot-air Balloon over Town.

**1983.** Europa. Paintings by P. Delvaux. Multicoloured.
2756. 11 f. Type **797** .. .. 75 10
2757. 20 f. "Night Trains" (horiz.) .. .. 1·25 30

**1983.** Bicentenary of Manned Flight. Mult.
2758. 11 f. Type **798** .. .. 40 10
2759. 22 f. Hot-air balloon over countryside .. .. 85 25

**799.** Church of Our Lady, Hastiere. **800.** Milkmaid.

**1983.** Tourist Publicity. Multicoloured.
2760. 8 f. Type **799** .. .. 50 15
2761. 8 f. Tumulus, Landen .. 50 15
2762. 8 f. Park, Mouscron .. 50 15
2763. 8 f. Wijnendale Castle, Torhout .. .. 50 15

**1983.** Tineke Festival, Heule.
2764. **800.** 8 f. multicoloured .. 30 15

**801.** Plaque on Wall. **802.** Rainbow and Child.

**1983.** European Small and Medium-sized Industries and Crafts Year.
2765. **801.** 11 f. yell., blk. & red 60 10

**1983.** "Philately for the Young". 20th Anniv. of Queen Fabiola Village No. 1 (for handicapped people).
2766. **802.** 8 f. multicoloured .. 30 15

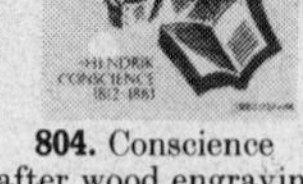


**803.** Textiles. **804.** Conscience (after wood engraving by Nelly Degouy).

**1983.** Belgian Exports (1st series). Multicoloured.
2767. 10 f. Type **803** .. .. 55 20
2768. 10 f. Steel beams (metallurgy) .. .. 55 20
2769. 10 f. Diamonds .. .. 55 20
See also Nos. 2777/80.

**1983.** Death Centenary of Hendrik Conscience (writer).
2770. **804.** 20 f. black & green .. 85 20

**805.** "Madonna" (Jef Wauters) **806.** 2nd Foot Regiment.

**1983.** Christmas.
2771. **805.** 11 f. + 1 f. mult. .. 50 40

**1983.** "Solidarity". Military Uniforms. Mult.
2772. 8 f. + 2 f. Type **806** .. 65 65
2773. 11 f. + 2 f. Lancer .. 85 85
2774. 50 f. + 12 f. Grenadier .. 3·00 3·00

**1983.** King Leopold III Commemoration.
2775. **155.** 11 f. black .. .. 55 10

**807.** Free University of Brussels. **808.** Albert I.

**1984.** 150th Anniv. of Free University of Brussels.
2776. **807.** 11 f. multicoloured .. 40 10

**1984.** Belgian Exports (2nd series). As T **803**. Multicoloured.
2777. 11 f. Retort and test tubes (chemicals) .. 50 25
2778. 11 f. Combine harvester (agricultural produce) 50 25
2779. 11 f. Ship, coach and train (transport) .. 50 25
2780. 11 f. Atomic emblem and computer terminal (new-technology) .. 50 25

**1984.** 50th Death Anniv. of King Albert I.
2781. **808.** 8 f. black and stone 30 15

**809.** Judo. **810.** Releasing Doves.

**1984.** Olympic Games. Los Angeles. Multicoloured.
2782 8 f. + 2 f. Type **809** .. 60 60
2783 12 f. + 3 f. Windsurfing (vert) .. .. .. 80 80

**1984.** 25th Anniv. of Movement without a Name.
2785 **810.** 12 f. multicoloured .. 50 10

**811.** Clasped Hands.

**1984.** 50th Anniv. of National Lottery.
2786. **811.** 12 f. + 3 f. mult. .. 65 65

**812.** St. John Bosco with Children. **813.** Bridge.

**1984.** 50th Anniv. of Canonization of St. John Bosco (founder of Salesians).
2787. **812.** 8 f. multicoloured .. 30 15

**1984.** Europa, 25th Anniv. of European Posts and Telecommunications Conference.
2788. **813.** 12 f. red and black .. 60 10
2789. 22 f. blue and black 1·00 25

**814.** Leopold II 1884 10 c. Stamp.

**1984.** Stamp Day.
2790. **814.** 12 f. multicoloured .. 45 10

**815.** Dove and Pencils.

**1984.** 2nd European Parliament Elections.
2791. **815.** 12 f. multicoloured .. 55 10

**816.** Shako. **817.** Church of Our Lady of the Chapel, Brussels.

**1984.** 150th Anniv. of Royal Military School.
2792. **816.** 22 f. multicoloured .. 95 20

**1984.** Tourist Publicity. Multicoloured.
2793. 10 f. Type **817** .. .. 45 15
2794. 10 f. St. Martin's Church and lime tree, Montigny-le-Tilleul .. 45 15
2795. 10 f. Belfry and Town Hall, Tielt (vert.) .. 45 15

**818.** "Curious Masks" (detail, James Ensor).

**1984.** Inauguration of Brussels Modern Art Museum.

2796 818 8 f. + 2 f. mult .. 60 60
2797 – 12 f. + 3 f. mult .. 75 75
2798 – 22 f. + 5 f. mult .. 1·25 1·25
2799 – 50 f. + 13 f. green, blue and black .. 2·75 2·75

DESIGNS: 12 f. "The Empire of Lights" (detail, Rene Magritte). 22 f. "The End" (detail, Jan Cox). 50 f. "Rhythm No. 6" (Jo Delahaut).

819. Symbolic Design.

820. Averbode Abbey.

**1984.** 50th Anniv. of Chirojeugd (Christian youth movement).

2800. 819. 10 f. yellow, violet and blue .. .. 45 15

**1984.** Abbeys.

2801. 820. 8 f. green and brown 30 15
2802. – 22 f. brown and deep brown .. .. 90 25
2803. – 24 f. green and pale green .. .. 95 25
2804. – 50 f. lilac and brown 2·25 45

DESIGNS—VERT. 22 f. Chimay. 24 f. Rochefort. HORIZ. 50 f. Affligem.

821. Smurf as Postman.

822. Child collecting Flowers.

**1984.** "Philately for the Young".

2805. 821. 8 f. multicoloured .. 80 15

**1984.** Children.

2806. 10 f. + 2 f. Type **822** .. 50 50
2807. 12 f. + 3 f. Children with globe .. .. .. 65 65
2808. 15 f. + 3 f. Child on merry-go-round .. 80 80

823. Meulemans.

824. Three Kings.

**1984.** Birth Centenary of Arthur Meulemans (composer).

2809 823 12 f. black & orange .. 60 10

**1984.** Christmas.

2810. 824. 12 f. + 1 f. mult. .. 55 55

825. St. Norbert.

826. "Virgin of Louvain" (attr. Jan Gossaert).

**1985.** 850th Death Anniv. of St. Norbert.

2811. 825. 22 f. brn. & light brn. 95 40

**1985.** "Europalia 85 Espana" Festival.

2812. 826. 12 f. multicoloured .. 45 10

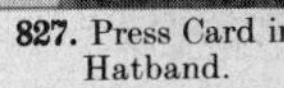

827. Press Card in Hatband.

828. Blood System as Tree.

**1985.** Centenary of Professional Journalists Association.

2814. 827. 9 f. multicoloured .. 40 15

**1985.** Belgian Red Cross. Blood Donations.

2815. 828. 9 f. + 2 f. mult. .. 50 50
2816. – 23 f. + 5 f. red, blue and black .. .. 1·10 1·10

DESIGN: 23 f. Two hearts.

829. "Sophrolaelio cattleya" "Burlingama".

830. Pope John Paul II.

**1985.** Ghent Flower Festival. Orchids. Multicoloured.

2817 12 f. Type **829** .. .. 60 15
2818 12 f. Phalaenopsis "Malibu" .. .. 60 15
2819 12 f. Tapeu orchid ("Vanda coerulea") .. 60 15

**1985.** Visit of Pope John Paul II.

2820. 830. 12 f. multicoloured .. 60 10

831. Rising Sun behind Chained Gates.

**1985.** Cent. of Belgian Workers' Party.

2821. 9 f. Type **831**. .. .. 45 15
2822. 12 f. Broken wall, flag and rising sun .. 45 10

832. Jean de Bast (engraver).

**1985.** Stamp Day.

2823. 832. 12 f. blue .. .. 45 10

834. Class "18" Steam Tram, 1896.

**1985.** Public Transport Year. Multicoloured.

2826. 9 f. Type **834** .. .. 60 15
2827. 12 f. "Elephant" (1835 locomotive) .. .. 70 10
2828. 23 f. Class "23" tank engine, 1904 .. .. 1·25 55
2829. 24 f. Class "1" Pacific locomotive, 1935 .. 1·25 35

835. Cesar Franck and Score.

**1985.** Europa. Music Year. Multicoloured.

2831 12 f. Type **835** .. .. 75 10
2832 23 f. Queen and king with viola dressed in music score (Queen Elisabeth International Music Competition) .. .. 1·25 30

836. Planned Canal Lock, Strepy-Thieu.

837. Church of Our Lady's Assumption, Avernas-le-Bauduin.

**1985.** Permanent International Navigation Congress Association Centenary Congress, Brussels. Multicoloured.

2833. 23 f. Type **836** .. .. 1·25 25
2834. 23 f. Aerial view of Zeebrugge harbour .. 1·25 25

**1985.** Tourist Publicity. Multicoloured.

2835. 12 f. Type **837** .. .. 50 15
2836. 12 f. Saint Martin's Church, Marcinelle (horiz.) .. .. 50 15
2837. 12 f. Roman tower and Church of old beguinage, Tongres .. 50 15
2838. 12 f. House, Wachtebeke (horiz.) .. .. 50 15

838. Queen Astrid.

839. Baking Matton Tart, Grammont.

**1985.** 50th Death Anniv. of Queen Astrid.

2839. 838. 12 f. light brown and brown .. .. 70 10

**1985.** Traditional Customs. Multicoloured.

2840. 12 f. Type **839** .. .. 50 15
2841. 24 f. Young people dancing on trumpet filled with flowers (cent of Red Youths, St. Lambert Cultural Circle, Hermalle-sous-Argenteau) .. .. 1·25 30

840. Dove and Concentration Camp.

**1985.** 40th Anniv. of Liberation. Mult.

2842. 9 f. Type **840** .. .. 45 15
2843. 23 f. Battle of the Ardennes .. .. 1·10 40
2844. 24 f. Troops landing at Scheldt estuary .. 1·40 30

841. Hawfinch.

842. Claes and Fictional Character.

**1985.** Birds (1st series). Multicoloured.

2845 1 f. Lesser spotted woodpecker ("Pic epeichette") .. .. 10 10
2846 2 f. Tree sparrow ("Moineau friquet") .. 10 10
2847 3 f. Type **841** .. .. 40 10
2847a 3 f. 50 European robin ("Rouge-gorge") .. 30 10
2848 4 f. Bluethroat ("Gorge-bleue") .. 15 10
2848a 4 f. 50 Stonechat ("Traquet patre") .. 20 10
2849 5 f. European nuthatch ("Sittelle torchepot") 50 10
2850 6 f. Bullfinch ("Bouvreuil") .. 50 10
2851 7 f. Blue tit ("Mesange bleue") .. .. 45 10
2852 8 f. Common kingfisher ("Martin-pecheur") .. 30 10
2853 9 f. Goldfinch ("Chardonneret") .. 1·10 10
2854 10 f. Chaffinch ("Pinson") .. .. 35 10

See also Nos. 3073/86 and 3307/12.

**1985.** Birth Cent. of Ernest Claes (writer).

2855. 842. 9 f. multicoloured .. 35 10

843. Youth.

844. Trazegnies Castle.

**1985.** "Philately for the Young". International Youth Year.

2856. 843. 9 f. multicoloured .. 35 10

**1985.** "Solidarity". Castles. Multicoloured.

2857. 9 f. + 2 f. Type **844** .. 60 60
2858. 12 f. + 3 f. Laarne .. 70 70
2859. 23 f. + 5 f. Turnhout .. 1·10 1·10
2860. 50 f. + 12 f. Colonster .. 2·40 2·40

845. Miniature from "Book of Hours of Duc de Berry".

**1985.** Christmas.

2861. 845. 12 f. + 1 f. mult .. 70 70

846. King Baudouin and Queen Fabiola.

**1985.** Royal Silver Wedding.

2862. 846. 12 f. grey, blue and deep blue .. .. 65 15

847. Map and 1886 25 c. Stamp.

848. Giants and Belfry, Alost.

**1986.** Centenary of First Independent State of Congo Stamp.

2863. 847. 10 f. blue, grey and deep blue .. .. 55 20

**1986.** Carnivals. Multicoloured.

2864. 9 f. Type **848** .. .. 40 20
2865. 12 f. Clown, Binche .. 60 10

849. Dove as Hand holding Olive Twig.

850. Emblem.

**1986.** International Peace Year.

2866. 849. 23 f. multicoloured .. 1·00 35

**1986.** 10th Anniv. of King Baudouin Foundation.

2867. 850. 12 f. + 3 f. blue, light blue and grey .. 1·00 1·00

851. Virgin Mary.

**1986.** "The Mystic Lamb" (altarpiece, Brothers Van Eyck). Multicoloured.

| | | | |
|---|---|---|---|
| 2868. | 9 f.+2 f. Type **851** .. | 70 | 70 |
| 2869. | 13 f.+3 f. Christ in Majesty .. .. | 90 | 90 |
| 2870. | 24 f.+6 f. St. John the Baptist .. .. | 1·75 | 1·75 |

852. Exhibits.

**1986.** Stamp Day. 50th Anniv. of Postal Museum, Brussels.

| | | | |
|---|---|---|---|
| 2872. | **852.** 13 f. multicoloured .. | 70 | 10 |

853. Living and Dead Fish and Graph.

854. Malinois Shepherd Dog.

**1986.** Europa. Multicoloured.

| | | | |
|---|---|---|---|
| 2873 | 13 f. Type **853** .. .. | 75 | 10 |
| 2874 | 24 f. Living and dead trees and graph .. | 1·50 | 30 |

**1986.** Belgian Dogs. Multicoloured.

| | | | |
|---|---|---|---|
| 2875. | 9 f. Type **854** .. .. | 60 | 15 |
| 2876. | 13 f. Tervuren shepherd dog .. .. .. | 80 | 10 |
| 2877. | 24 f. Groenendael cattle dog .. .. .. | 1·50 | 50 |
| 2878. | 26 f. Flanders cattle dog | 2·00 | 50 |

855. St. Ludger Church, Zele. 856. Boy, Broken Skateboard and Red Triangle.

**1986.** Tourist Publicity.

| | | | | |
|---|---|---|---|---|
| 2879 | 855 | 9 f. brown and flesh | 40 | 25 |
| 2880 | – | 9 f. red and pink .. | 40 | 25 |
| 2881 | – | 13 f. green & lt green | 60 | 15 |
| 2882 | – | 13 f. black and green | 60 | 15 |
| 2883 | – | 13 f. blue and azure | 60 | 15 |
| 2884 | – | 13 f. brn & pale brn | 60 | 15 |

DESIGNS—VERT. No. 2880, Town Hall, Wavre. 2882, Chapel of Our Lady of the Dunes, Bredene. HORIZ. 2881, Water-mills, Zwalm. 2883, Chateau Licot, Viroinval. 2884, Chateau d'Eynebourg, La Calamine.

**1986.** "Philately for the Young". 25th International Festival of Humour, Knokke.

| | | | |
|---|---|---|---|
| 2885. | **856.** 9 f. blk., grn. & red | 45 | 15 |

857. Constant Permeke (artist).

**1986.** Celebrities. Multicoloured.

| | | | |
|---|---|---|---|
| 2886 | 9 f. Type **857** (birth centenary) .. .. | 45 | 15 |
| 2887 | 13 f. Michael Edmond de Selys-Longchamps (naturalist) .. .. | 60 | 10 |
| 2888 | 24 f. Felix Timmermans (writer) (birth cent) .. | 1·25 | 40 |
| 2889 | 26 f. Maurice Careme (poet) .. .. .. | 1·40 | 40 |

858. Academy Building, Ghent.

**1986.** Centenary of Royal Academy for Dutch Language and Literature.

| | | | |
|---|---|---|---|
| 2890. | **858.** 9 f. blue .. .. | 45 | 15 |

859. Hops, Glass of Beer and Barley

**1986.** Belgian Beer.

| | | | |
|---|---|---|---|
| 2891. | **859.** 13 f. multicoloured .. | 80 | 15 |

860. Symbols of Provinces and National Colours.

**1986.** 150th Anniv. of Provincial Councils.

| | | | |
|---|---|---|---|
| 2892. | **860.** 13 f. multicoloured .. | 65 | 15 |

861. Lenoir, 1863.

**1986.** "Solidarity". Cars. Multicoloured.

| | | | |
|---|---|---|---|
| 2893. | 9 f.+2 f. Type **861** .. | 50 | 50 |
| 2894. | 13 f.+3 f. Pipe de Tourisme, 1911 .. | 1·00 | 1·00 |
| 2895. | 24 f.+6 f. Minerva 22 h.p., 1930 .. .. | 1·60 | 1·60 |
| 2896. | 26 f.+6 f. FN 8 cyl., 1931 | 1·40 | 1·40 |

862. Snow Scene.

**1986.** Christmas.

| | | | |
|---|---|---|---|
| 2897. | **862.** 13 f.+1 f. mult .. | 65 | 50 |

863. Tree and "100".

**1986.** Centenaries. Multicoloured.

| | | | |
|---|---|---|---|
| 2898. | 9 f. Type **863** (Textile Workers Christian Union) .. .. .. | 40 | 15 |
| 2899. | 13 f. Tree and "100" (Christian Unions) | 60 | 10 |

864. Corneel Heymans.

865. Emblem.

**1987.** Belgian Red Cross. Nobel Physiology and Medicine Prize Winners. Each black, red and stone.

| | | | |
|---|---|---|---|
| 2900. | 13 f.+3 f. Type **864** .. | 75 | 75 |
| 2901. | 24 f.+6 f. Albert Claude | 1·50 | 1·50 |

**1987.** "Flanders Technology International" Fair.

| | | | |
|---|---|---|---|
| 2902. | **865.** 13 f. multicoloured .. | 75 | 10 |

866. Bee Orchid. 868. Jakob Wiener (engraver).

867. "Waiting" (detail of mural, Gustav Klimt).

**1987.** European Environment Year. Mult.

| | | | |
|---|---|---|---|
| 2903. | 9 f.+2 f. Type **866** .. | 80 | 80 |
| 2904. | 24 f.+6 f. Small horse-shoe bat .. .. | 1·50 | 1·50 |
| 2905. | 26 f.+6 f. Peregrine falcon .. .. .. | 1·75 | 1·60 |

**1987.** "Europalia 87 Austria" Festival.

| | | | |
|---|---|---|---|
| 2906. | **867.** 13 f. multicoloured .. | 75 | 10 |

**1987.** Stamp Day.

| | | | |
|---|---|---|---|
| 2907. | **868.** 13 f. deep green and green .. .. | 75 | 10 |

869. Penitents' Procession, Furnes.

870. Louvain-la-Neuve Church (Jean Cosse).

**1987.** Folklore Festivals. Multicoloured.

| | | | |
|---|---|---|---|
| 2908. | 9 f. Type **869** .. .. | 40 | 15 |
| 2909. | 13 f. "John and Alice" (play), Wavre .. .. | 60 | 10 |

**1987.** Europa. Architecture. Multicoloured.

| | | | |
|---|---|---|---|
| 2910 | 13 f. Type **870** .. .. | 75 | 10 |
| 2911 | 24 f. St.-Maartensdal (Regional Housing Association tower block), Louvain (Braem, de Mol and Moerkerke) .. .. | 1·25 | 30 |

871. Statue of Gretry and Stage Set.

872. Virelles Lake.

**1987.** 20th Anniv. of Wallonia Royal Opera.

| | | | |
|---|---|---|---|
| 2912. | **871.** 24 f. multicoloured .. | 1·40 | 30 |

**1987.** Tourist Publicity. Multicoloured.

| | | | |
|---|---|---|---|
| 2913. | 13 f. St. Christopher's Church, Racour .. | 65 | 20 |
| 2914. | 13 f. Type **872** .. | 65 | 20 |
| 2915. | 13 f. Heimolen windmill, Keerbergen .. .. | 65 | 20 |
| 2916. | 13 f. Boondael Chapel .. | 65 | 20 |
| 2917. | 13 f. Statue of Jan Breydel and Pieter de Coninck, Bruges .. | 65 | 20 |

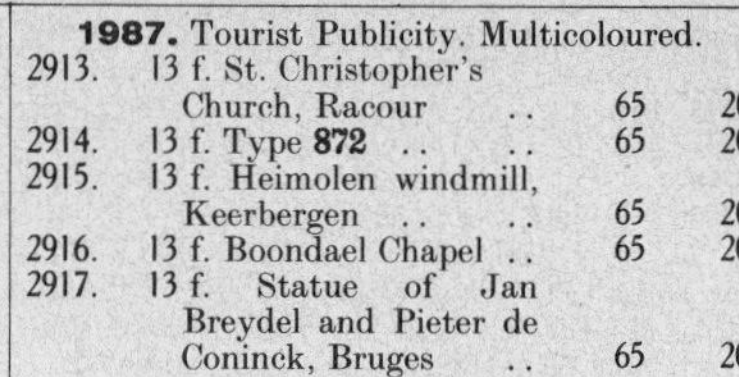

873. Rowing.

**1987.** Centenary of Royal Belgian Rowing Association (2918) and European Volleyball Championships (2919). Multicoloured.

| | | | |
|---|---|---|---|
| 2918. | 9 f Type **873** .. .. | 30 | 15 |
| 2919. | 13 f. Volleyball (27 × 37 mm.) .. .. | 60 | 10 |

874. Emblem.

**1987.** Foreign Trade Year.

| | | | |
|---|---|---|---|
| 2920. | **874.** 13 f. multicoloured .. | 65 | 10 |

875. "Leisure Time" (P. Paulus).

**1987.** Centenary of Belgian Social Law.

| | | | |
|---|---|---|---|
| 2921. | **875.** 26 f. multicoloured .. | 1·25 | 30 |

876, Willy and Wanda (comic strip characters).

**1987.** "Philately for the Young".

| | | | |
|---|---|---|---|
| 2922. | **876.** 9 f. multicoloured .. | 1·00 | 15 |

878. Rixensart Castle.

**1987.** "Solidarity". Castles. Multicoloured.

| | | | |
|---|---|---|---|
| 2928 | 9 f.+2 f. Type **878** .. | 40 | 50 |
| 2929 | 13 f.+3 f. Westerlo .. | 90 | 70 |
| 2930 | 26 f.+5 f. Fallais .. | 1·60 | 1·50 |
| 2931 | 50 f.+12 f. Gaasbeek .. | 3·25 | 3·25 |

879. "Madonna and Child" (Remi Lens).

880. Cross and Road.

**1987.** Christmas.
2932. **879.** 13 f.+1 f. mult .. 70 60

**1987.** 50th Anniv. of Yellow and White Cross (home nursing organization).
2933 **880** 9 f.+2 f. multicoloured 80 80

**881.** Newsprint ("Le Soir").

**1987.** Newspaper Centenaries.
2934. **881.** 9 f. multicoloured .. 30 15
2935. – 9 f. black and brown 30 15
DESIGN:—VERT. No. 2935, Type characters ("Het Laatste Nieuws" (1988)).

**882.** Lighthouse, "Snipe" (trawler) and Horse Rider in Sea.
**883.** "Flanders Alive" (cultural activities campaign).

**1988.** The Sea. Multicoloured.
2936 10 f. Type **882** .. .. 60 50
2937 10 f. "Asannot" (trawler) and people playing on beach .. .. 60 50
2938 10 f. Cross-channel ferry, yacht and bathing huts 60 50
2939 10 f. Container ship and sea birds .. .. 60 50
Nos. 2936/9 were issued together, se-tenant, forming a composite design.

**1988.** Regional Innovations.
2940 **883** 13 f. multicoloured .. 50 15
2941 – 13 f. black, yell & red 50 15
DESIGN: No. 2941, "Operation Athena" emblem (technological advancement in Wallonia).

**884.** 19th-century Postman (after James Thiriar).
**885.** "Bengale Triomphant".

**1988.** Stamp Day.
2942. **884.** 13 f. brown & cream 70 10

**1988.** Philatelic Promotion Fund. Illustrations from "60 Roses for a Queen" by Pierre-Joseph Redoute (1st series). Mult.
2943 13 f.+3 f. Type **885** .. 1·00 1·00
2944 24 f.+6 f. "Centfeuille cristata" .. .. 1·60 1·60
See also Nos. 2979/80 and 3009/10.

**886.** Non-polluting Motor.

**1988.** Europa. Transport and Communications. Multicoloured.
2946. 13 f. Dish aerial .. .. 80 10
2947. 24 f. Type **886** .. .. 1·25 30

**887.** Table Tennis.

**1988.** Olympic Games, Seoul. Multicoloured.
2948. 9 f.+2 f. Type **887** .. 80 80
2949. 13 f.+3 f. Cycling .. 1·00 1·00

**888.** Amay Tower.
**889.** Monnet.

**1988.** Tourist Publicity.
2951. **888.** 9 f. black and brown 35 25
2952. – 9 f. black and blue .. 35 25
2953. – 9 f. black, green and pink .. .. 35 25
2954. – 13 f. black and pink 70 15
2955. – 13 f. black and grey 70 15
DESIGNS—VERT. No. 2952 Lady of Hanswijk Basilica, Malines. 2954, Old Town Hall and village pump, Peer. HORIZ. No. 2953, St. Sernin's Church, Waimes. 2955, Basilica of Our Lady of Bon Secours, Peruwelz.

**1988.** Birth Centenary of Jean Monnet (statesman).
2956. **889.** 13 f. black and cream 75 10

**890.** Tapestry (detail) and Academy Building.
**891.** Antwerp Ethnographical Museum Exhibits.

**1988.** 50th Annivs. of Royal Belgian Academy of Medicine (2957) and Royal Belgian Academy of Sciences, Literature and Fine Arts (2958). Multicoloured.
2957. 9 f. Type **890** .. .. 30 20
2958. 9 f. Symbols of Academy and building .. .. 30 20

**1988.** Cultural Heritage. Multicoloured.
2959 9 f. Type **891** .. .. 35 15
2960 13 f. Tomb of Lord Gilles Othon and Jacqueline de Lalaing, St. Martin's Church, Trazegnies .. 45 10
2961 24 f. Organ, St. Bartholomew's Church, Geraardsbergen .. 1·25 30
2962 26 f. St. Hadelin's reliquary, St. Martin's Church, Vise .. .. 1·10 30

**892.** Spirou (comic strip character) and Stamp.

**1988.** "Philately for the Young". 50th Anniv. of "Spirou" (comic).
2963. **892.** 9 f. multicoloured .. 1·00 15

**893.** Jacques Brel (songwriter).

**1988.** "Solidarity". Death Anniversaries. Multicoloured.
2964 9 f.+2 f. Type **893** (10th) 70 75
2965 13 f.+3 f. Jef Denyn (carilloner) (47th) .. 1·00 85
2966 26 f.+6 f. Fr. Ferdinand Verbiest (astronomer) (300th) .. .. 1·60 1·60

**894** "75"

**1988.** 75th Anniv of Belgian Giro Bank.
2967 **894** 13 f. multicoloured .. 65 10

**895** Winter Scene

**1988.** Christmas.
2968 **895** 9 f. multicoloured .. 40 15

**896** Standard Bearer and Guards of Royal Mounted Escort
**897** Wooden Press, 1600

**1988.** 50th Anniv of Royal Mounted Escort.
2969 **896** 13 f. multicoloured .. 85 15

**1988.** Printing Presses.
2970 **897** 9 f. black, pink & blue 35 15
2971 – 24 f. brown, pink and deep brown .. 90 35
2972 – 26 f. green, pink and light green .. 1·25 35
DESIGNS: VERT—24 f. 18th cent Stanhope metal letterpress. HORIZ—26 f. 19th-century Krause lithographic press.

**898** "Crucifixion of Christ" (detail, Rogier van der Weyden)

**1989.** Belgian Red Cross. Paintings. Mult.
2973 9 f.+2 f. Type **898** .. 80 80
2974 13 f.+3 f. "Virgin and Child" (Gerard David) 1·10 1·10
2975 24 f.+6 f. "The Good Samaritan" (detail, Denis van Alsloot) .. 1·60 1·60

**899** Marche en Famenne

**1989.** Lace-making Towns.
2976 **899** 9 f. green, blk & brn 50 20
2977 – 13 f. blue, blk & grey 65 15
2978 – 13 f. red, black & grey 65 15
DESIGNS: No. 2977, Bruges; 2978, Brussels.

**1989.** Philatelic Promotion Fund. "60 Roses for a Queen" by Pierre-Joseph Redoute (2nd series). As T **885**. Multicoloured.
2979 13 f.+5 f. "Centfeuille unique melee de rouge" 90 1·00
2980 24 f.+6 f. "Bengale a grandes feuilles" .. 1·60 1·40

**900** Post-chaise and Mail Coach

**1989.** Stamp Day.
2982 **900** 13 f. yellow, blk & brn 65 10

**901** Marbles
**902** Palette on Column

**1989.** Europa. Children's Games and Toys. Multicoloured.
2983 13 f. Type **901** .. .. 65 10
2984 24 f. Jumping-jack .. 1·10 30

**1989.** 325th Anniv of Royal Academy of Fine Arts, Antwerp.
2985 **902** 13 f. multicoloured .. 60 10

**903** Brussels (Illustration reduced. Actual size 77×25 mm)

**1989.** 3rd Direct Elections to European Parliament.
2986 **903** 13 f. multicoloured .. 75 20

**904** Hand (detail, "Creation of Adam", Michelangelo)
**905** St. Tillo's Church, Izegem

**1989.** Bicentenary of French Declaration of Rights of Man.
2987 **904** 13 f. black, red & blue 60 15

**1989.** Tourist Publicity. Multicoloured.
2988 9 f. Type **905** .. 45 20
2989 9 f. Logne Castle, Ferrieres (vert) .. 45 20
2990 13 f. Antoing Castle (vert) 65 15
2991 13 f. St. Laurentius's Church, Lokeren (vert) 65 15

**906** Mallard

**1989.** Ducks. Multicoloured.
2992 13 f. Type **906** .. .. 75 75
2993 13 f. Green-winged teal ("Sarcelle d'Hiver") .. 75 75
2994 13 f. Common shoveler ("Canard Souchet") .. 75 75
2995 13 f. Pintail ("Canard Pilet") .. .. 75 75

907 "Shogun Uesugi Shigefusa" (Kamakura period wood figure)

**1989.** "Europalia 89 Japan" Festival.
2996 907 24 f. multicoloured .. 1·25 30

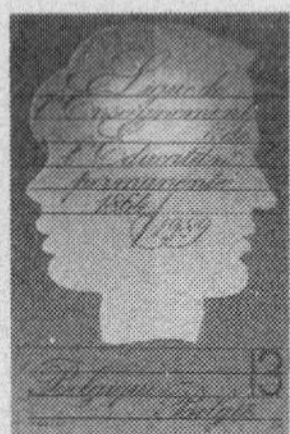

908 Profiles

909 Map

**1989.** 125th Anniv of League of Teaching and Permanent Education.
2997 908 13 f. multicoloured .. 60 10

**1989.** 150th Anniv of Division of Limburg between Netherlands and Belgium.
2998 909 13 f. multicoloured .. 75 10

910 Nibbs (comic strip character)

911 Flower Beds in Greenhouse

**1989.** "Philately for the Young".
2999 910 9 f. multicoloured .. 90 15

**1989.** "Solidarity". Royal Greenhouses, Laeken. Multicoloured.
3000 9 f. +3 f. Statue and greenhouses (horiz) .. 65 65
3001 13 f. +4 f. Type 911 .. 85 85
3002 24 f. +5 f. External view of greenhouse .. .. 1·40 1·40
3003 26 f. +6 f. Trees in greenhouse .. .. .. 1·75 1·75

912 Treble Clef

**1989.** 50th Anniv of Queen Elisabeth Musical Chapel, Waterloo.
3004 912 24 f. +6 f. mult .. 1·50 1·60

913 Army Musicians

**1989.** Christmas. Centenary of Salvation Army in Belgium.
3005 913 9 f. multicoloured .. 85 10

914 Fr. Damien and Church

915 Fr. Daens

**1989.** Death Cent of Fr. Damien (missionary).
3006 914 24 f. multicoloured .. 1·40 30

**1989.** 150th Birth Anniv of Fr. Adolf Daens (social reformer).
3007 915 9 f. turquoise & green 40 10

916 "Courier" (Albrecht Durer)

917 "Iris florentina"

**1990.** 500th Anniv of Regular European Postal Services.
3008 916 14 f. chocolate, buff and brown .. 85 10

**1990.** Philatelic Promotion Fund. "60 Roses for a Queen" by Pierre-Joseph Redoute (3rd series). As T 885. Multicoloured.
3009 14 f. +7 f. "Bengale Desprez" .. .. 1·25 1·40
3010 25 f. +12 f. "Bengale Philippe" .. .. 2·00 2·00

**1990.** Ghent Flower Show. Multicoloured.
3012 10 f. Type 917 .. .. 60 20
3013 14 f. "Cattleya harrisoniana" .. .. 85 15
3014 14 f. "Lilium bulbiferum" 85 15

918 Emilienne Brunfaut (women's rights activist)

**1990.** International Women's Day.
3015 918 25 f. red and black .. 1·40 30

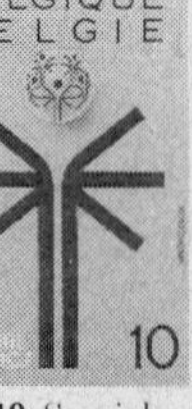

919 Special Olympics

921 "Postman Roulin" (Vincent van Gogh)

920 Water, Tap and Heart

**1990.** Sporting Events. Multicoloured.
3016 10 f. Type 919 .. .. 50 20
3017 14 f. Football (World Cup football championship, Italy) .. .. .. 85 15
3018 25 f. Disabled pictogram and ball (Gold Cup wheelchair basketball championship, Bruges) 1·50 40

**1990.** 75th Anniv of Foundation of National Water Supply Society (predecessor of present water-supply companies).
3019 920 14 f. multicoloured .. 70 10

**1990.** Stamp Day.
3020 921 14 f. multicoloured .. 85 10

922 Worker and Crowd

923 Liege 1 Post Office

**1990.** Centenary of Labour Day.
3021 922 25 f. brown, pink & blk 1·25 30

**1990.** Europa. Post Office Buildings.
3022 – 14 f. black and blue .. 90 10
3023 923 25 f. black and red .. 1·40 35
DESIGN—HORIZ. 14 f. Ostend 1 Post Office.

924 Monument of the Lys, Courtrai

**1990.** 50th Anniv of the 18 Days Campaign (resistance to German invasion).
3024 924 14 f. black, yell & red 85 15

925 Battle Scene
(2/3 size illustration, actual size 81 × 37 mm)

**1990.** 175th Anniv of Battle of Waterloo.
3026 925 25 f. multicoloured .. 1·40 90

926 Berendrecht Lock, Antwerp

927 King Baudouin

**1990.** Tourist Publicity. Multicoloured.
3027 10 f. Type 926 .. .. 40 20
3028 10 f. Procession of Bayard Steed, Termonde .. 40 20
3029 14 f. St. Rolende's March, Gerpinnes (vert) .. 60 15
3030 14 f. Lommel (1000th anniv) .. .. 60 15
3031 14 f. St. Clement's Church, Watermael .. 60 15

**1990.**
3032 927 14 f. multicoloured .. 80 10

928 Perch

**1990.** Fishes. Multicoloured.
3033 14 f. Type 928 .. .. 1·25 75
3034 14 f. Minnow ("Vairon") 1·25 75
3035 14 f. Bitterling ("Bouviere") .. .. 1·25 75
3036 14 f. Stickleback ("Epinoche") .. .. 1·25 75

929 Orchestra and Children
(½ size illustration, actual size 76 × 25 mm)

**1990.** "Solidarity". Multicoloured.
3037 10 f. +2 f. Type 929 (50th anniv of Jeunesses Musicales) .. .. 1·25 1·25
3038 14 f. +3 f. Count of Egmont (16th-century campaigner for religious tolerance) and Beethoven (composer of "Egmont" overture) .. 1·60 1·60
3039 25 f. +6 f. Jozef Cantre (sculptor) and sculptures (birth centenary) 2·50 2·50

930 Lucky Luke (comic strip character)

**1990.** "Philately for the Young".
3040 930 10 f. multicoloured .. 70 15

931 St. Bernard

**1990.** 900th Birth Anniv of St. Bernard (Abbot of Clairvaux and Church mediator).
3041 931 25 f. black and flesh .. 1·25 30

932 "Pepingen, Winter 1977" (Jozef Lucas)

**1990.** Christmas.
3042 932 10 f. multicoloured .. 55 10

933 "Self-portrait"

**1990.** 300th Death Anniv of David Teniers, the Younger (painter). Multicoloured.
3043 10 f. Type 933 .. .. 55 20
3044 14 f. "Dancers" .. .. 75 15
3045 25 f. "Peasants playing Bowls outside Village Inn" .. .. .. 1·25 40

934 King Baudouin and Queen Fabiola (photograph by Valeer Vanbeckbergen)

**1990.** Royal 30th Wedding Anniversary.
3046 934 50 f. +15 f. mult .. 6·50 6·50

**935** "Temptation of St. Anthony" (detail, Hieronymus Bosch)

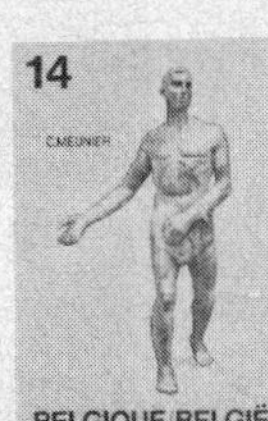

**936** "The Sower" (detail of "Monument to Labour", Brussels) (Constantin Meunier)

**1991.** Belgian Red Cross. Paintings. Mult.

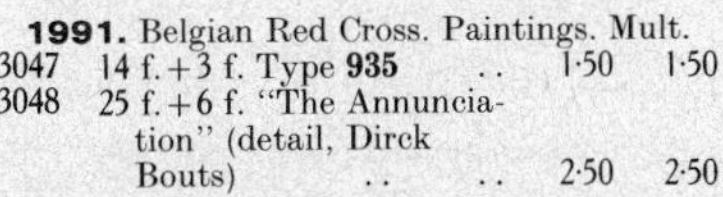

3047 14 f. + 3 f. Type **935** . . 1·50 1·50
3048 25 f. + 6 f. "The Annunciation" (detail, Dirck Bouts) . . . . 2·50 2·50

**1991.** 19th-Century Sculpture.

3049 **936** 14 f. blk & cinnamon 70 15
3050 – 25 f. black and blue . . 1·25 40

DESIGN: 25 f. Detail of Brabo Fountain, Antwerp (Jef Lambeaux).

**937** Rhythmic Gymnastics (European Youth Olympic Days, Brussels)

**1991.** Sports Meetings.

3051 **937** 10 f. grey, mve & blk 50 15
3052 – 10 f. grey, green & blk 50 15

DESIGN: No. 3052, Korfball (Third World Championship, Belgium).

**938** New Stamp Printing Office, Malines (Hugo van Hoecke)

**1991.** Stamp Day.

3053 **938** 14 f. multicoloured . . 70 15

**939** Cogwheels

**1991.** Centenary of Liberal Trade Union.

3054 **939** 25 f. new blue, light blue and blue . . 1·25 40

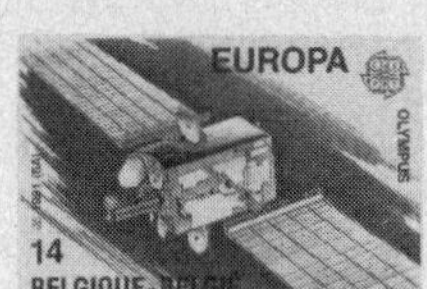

**940** "Olympus 1" Communications Satellite

**1991.** Europa. Europe in Space. Mult.

3055 14 f. Type **940** . . . . 70 15
3056 25 f. "Ariane 5" rocket carrying space shuttle "Hermes" . . . . 1·25 40

**941** Leo XIII's Arms and Standard, and Christian Labour Movement Banners

**1991.** Centenary of "Rerum Novarum" (encyclical letter from Pope Leo XIII on workers' rights).

3057 **941** 14 f. multicoloured . . 70 15

**942** "Isabella of Portugal and Philip the Good" (anon)

**1991.** "Europalia 91 Portugal" Festival.

3058 **942** 14 f. multicoloured . . 70 15

**943** Neptune Grottoes, Couvin

**1991.** Tourist Publicity. Multicoloured.

3059 14 f. Type **943** . . . . 70 15
3060 14 f. Dieleghem Abbey, Jette . . . . 70 15
3061 14 f. Niel Town Hall (vert) . . . . . . 70 15
3062 14 f. Hautes Fagnes nature reserve . . 70 15
3063 14 f. Giant Rolarius, Roeselare (vert) . . 70 15

**944** King Baudouin (photograph by Dimitri Ardelean)

**1991.** 60th Birthday (1990) and 40th Anniv of Accession to Throne of King Baudouin.

3064 **944** 14 f. multicoloured . . 1·10 15

**945** Academy Building, Caduceus and Leopold I

**1991.** 150th Anniv of Royal Academy of Medicine.

3065 **945** 10 f. multicoloured . . 50 15

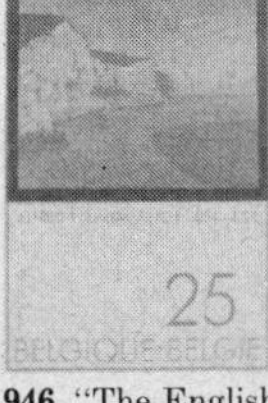

**946** "The English Coast at Dover"

**948** Hands reaching through Bars

**947** Death Cap

**1991.** 61st Death Anniv of Alfred Finch (painter and ceramic artist).

3066 **946** 25 f. multicoloured . . 1·25 40

**1991.** Fungi. Multicoloured.

3067 14 f. Type **947** . . . . 90 20
3068 14 f. The Blusher (inscr "Golmotte") . . . . 90 20
3069 14 f. Flaky-stemmed witches' mushroom (inscr "Bolet a pied rouge") . . . . 90 20
3070 14 f. "Hygrocybe persistens" (inscr "Hygrophore jaune conique") 90 20

**1991.** 30th Anniv of Amnesty International (3071) and 11th Anniv of Belgian Branch of Medecins sans Frontieres (3072). Mult.

3071 25 f. Type **948** . . . . 1·25 40
3072 25 f. Doctor examining baby . . . . . . 1·25 40

**1991.** Birds (2nd series). As T **841**. Mult.

3073 50 c. Goldcrest ("Roitelet Huppe") . . 10 10
3074 1 f. Mealy redpoll ("Sizerin Flamme") . . 10 10
3075 2 f. Blackbird ("Merle Noir") . . . . 10 10
3076 3 f. Reed bunting ("Bruant des Roseaux") 10 10
3077 4 f. Wagtail ("Bergeronette Grise") 15 10
3078 5 f. Barn swallow ("Hirondelle de Cheminee") . . . . 20 10
3078b 5 f. 50 Jay ("Geai des Chenes") . . 20 10
3079 6 f. Dipper ("Cincle Plongeur") . . 25 10
3079a 6 f. 50 Sedge-warbler ("Phragmite des Jones") 25 10
3080 7 f. Oriole ("Loriot") . . 30 10
3081 8 f. Great tit ("Mesange Charbonniere") . . 30 10
3082 9 f. Song thrush ("Grive Musicienne") . . 35 10
3083 10 f. Greenfinch ("Verdier") . . . . 40 15
3084 11 f. Winter wren ("Troglodyte Mignon") 45 15
3085 13 f. House sparrow ("Moineau Domestique") . . 50 15
3085a 14 f. Willow warbler ("Pouillot Fitis") . . 60 10
3086 16 f. Waxwing ("Jaseur Boreal") . . . . 60 15

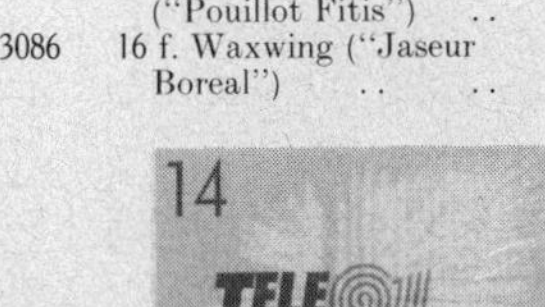

**949** Exhibition Emblem

**1991.** "Telecom 91" International Telecommunications Exhibition, Geneva.

3089 **949** 14 f. multicoloured . . 65 15

**950** Blake and Mortimer in "The Yellow Mark" (Edgar P. Jacobs)

**1991.** "Philately for the Young". Comic Strips. Multicoloured.

3090 14 f. Type **950** . . . . 1·25 60
3091 14 f. Cori the ship boy in "The Ill-fated Voyage" (Bob de Moor) . . 1·25 60
3092 14 f. "Cities of the Fantastic" (Francois Schuiten) . . 1·25 60
3093 14 f. "Boule and Bill" (Jean Roba) . . . . 1·25 60

**951** Charles Dekeukeleire

**1991.** "Solidarity". Film Makers.

3094 **951** 10 f. + 2 f. black, brown and green . . 80 50
3095 – 14 f. + 3 f. black, orange and brown 1·25 1·10
3096 – 25 f. + 6 f. black, ochre and brown . . 2·00 1·90

DESIGNS: 14 f. Jacques Ledoux; 25 f. Jacques Feyder.

**952** Printing Press forming "100" ("Gazet van Antwerpen")

**1991.** Newspaper Centenaries. Multicoloured.

3097 **952** 10 f. blk, lt grn & grn 45 15
3098 – 10 f. yellow, bl & blk 45 15

DESIGN: No. 3098, Cancellation on "stamp" ("Het Volk").

**953** "Our Lady rejoicing in the Child" (icon, Chevetogne Abbey)

**955** Speed Skating

**954** Mozart and Score

**1991.** Christmas.

3099 **953** 10 f. multicoloured . . 45 15

**1991.** Death Bicentenary of Wolfgang Amadeus Mozart (composer).

3100 **954** 25 f. pur, bl & ultram 1·10 35

**1992.** Olympic Games, Albertville and Barcelona. Multicoloured.

3101 10 f. + 2 f. Type **955** . . 80 80
3102 10 f. + 2 f. Baseball . . 80 80
3103 14 f. + 3 f. Tennis (horiz) 1·10 1·10
3104 25 f. + 6 f. Clay-pigeon shooting . . . . 1·75 1·75

**956** Fire Hose and Service Emblem

**957** Flames and Silhouette of Man

**1992.** Fire Service.

3105 **956** 14 f. multicoloured . . 65 15

**1992.** The Resistance.

3106 **957** 14 f. yellow, blk & red 65 15

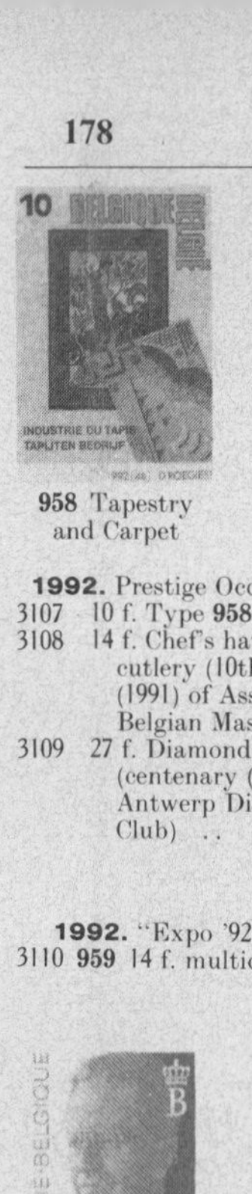

958 Tapestry and Carpet — 959 Belgian Pavilion and Exhibition Emblem

**1992.** Prestige Occupations. Multicoloured.

3107 10 f. Type **958** .. .. 45 15
3108 14 f. Chef's hat and cutlery (10th anniv (1991) of Association of Belgian Master Chefs) 65 15
3109 27 f. Diamond and "100" (centenary (1993) of Antwerp Diamond Club) .. .. .. 1·40 35

**1992.** "Expo '92" World's Fair, Seville.

3110 **959** 14 f. multicoloured .. 65 15

960 King Baudouin **961**

**1992.**

3111 **960** 15 f. red .. .. 60 20
3115 28 f. green .. .. 1·50 35
3120 **961** 100 f. green .. 4·75 40

962 Van Noten at Work — 963 "White Magic No. VI"

**1992.** Stamp Day. 10th Death Anniv of Jean van Noten (stamp designer).

3124 **962** 15 f. black and red .. 65 15

**1992.** Original Art Designs for Stamps. Mult.

3125 15 f. Type **963** .. .. 65 15
3126 15 f. "Colours" (horiz) .. 65 15

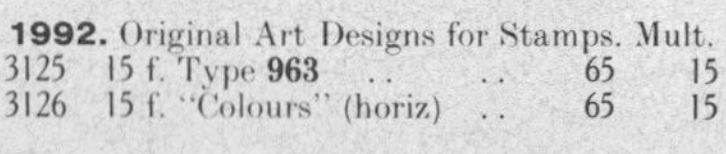

964 Compass Rose, Setting Sun and Harbour

**1992.** Europa. 500th Anniv of Discovery of America. Multicoloured.

3127 15 f. Type **964** .. .. 65 15
3128 28 f. Globe and astrolabe forming "500" .. 1·40 35

965 Faces of Different Colours

**1992.** Anti-racism.

3129 **965** 15 f. grey, blk & pink 65 15

966 "The Hamlet" (Jacob Smits)

**1992.** Belgian Paintings in Orsay Museum, Paris. Multicoloured.

3130 11 f. Type **966** .. .. 45 15
3131 15 f. "The Bath" (Alfred Stevens) .. .. 65 15
3132 30 f. "Man at the Helm" (Theo van Rysselberghe) .. .. 1·25 40

967 Proud Margaret — 968 Mannekin-Pis, Brussels

**1992.** Folk Tales. Multicoloured.

3133 11 f.+2 f. Type **967** .. 1·00 1·00
3134 15 f.+3 f. Witches ("Les Macrales") .. 1·40 1·40
3135 28 f.+6 f. Reynard the fox .. .. .. 2·40 2·40

**1992.** Tourist Publicity. Multicoloured.

3136 15 f. Type **968** .. .. 60 15
3137 15 f. Former Landcommandery of Teutonic Order, Alden Biesen (now Flemish cultural centre) (horiz) 60 15
3138 15 f. Andenne (1300th anniv) .. .. 60 15
3139 15 f. Carnival revellers on Fools' Monday, Renaix (horiz) .. .. 60 15
3140 15 f. Great Procession (religious festival), Tournai (horiz) .. 60 15

969 European Polecat

**1992.** Mammals. Multicoloured.

3141 15 f. Type **969** .. .. 1·00 40
3142 15 f. Eurasian red squirrel 1·00 40
3143 15 f. Eurasian hedgehog 1·00 40
3144 15 f. Common dormouse 1·00 40

970 Henri van der Noot, Jean van der Meersch and Jean Vonck

**1992.** 203rd Anniv of Brabant Revolution.

3145 **970** 15 f. multicoloured .. 60 15

**MORE DETAILED LISTS**
are given in the Stanley Gibbons Catalogues referred to in the country headings.
For lists of current volumes see Introduction.

971 Arms of Thurn and Taxis — 972 Gaston Lagaffe (cartoon character)

**1992.** 500th Anniv of Mention of Thurn and Taxis Postal Services in Lille Account Books.

3146 **971** 15 f. multicoloured .. 60 15

**1992.** "Philately for the Young".

3147 **972** 15 f. multicoloured .. 60 15

973 Star, "B" and Map

**1992.** European Single Market.

3148 **973** 15 f. multicoloured .. 60 15

974 Okapi — 975 "Place Royale in Winter" (Luc de Decker)

**1992.** 150th Anniv of Antwerp Zoo. Mult.

3149 15 f. Type **974** .. .. 60 15
3150 30 f. Golden-headed tamarin .. .. 1·25 40

**1992.** Christmas.

3151 **975** 11 f. multicoloured .. 45 15

976 "Man with Pointed Hat" (Adriaen Brouwer)

**1993.** Belgian Red Cross. Paintings. Mult.

3152 15 f.+3 f. Type **976** .. 1·50 1·50
3153 28 f.+7 f. "Nereid and Triton" (Peter Paul Rubens) (horiz) .. 3·00 3·00

977 Council of Leptines, 743

**1993.** Historical Events. Multicoloured.

3154 11 f. Type **977** .. .. 45 15
3155 15 f. Queen Beatrix and King Matthias I Corvinus of Hungary (detail of "Missale Romanum") (77×24 mm) .. .. .. 60 15
3156 30 f. Battle scene (Battles of Neerwinden, 1673 and 1773) .. .. 1·25 40

978 Town Hall

**1993.** Antwerp, European City of Culture. Multicoloured.

3158 15 f. Panorama of Antwerp (76×24 mm) 60 15
3159 15 f. Type **978** .. .. 60 15
3160 15 f. "Study of Women's Heads and Male Torso" (Jacob Jordaens) .. 60 15
3161 15 f. St. Job's altarpiece, Schoonbroek .. .. 60 15
3162 15 f. "Angels" (stained glass window by Eugeen Yoors, Mother of God Chapel, Marie-Josee Institute, Elisabethville) (vert) .. 60 15

979 1893 2 f. Stamp — 980 "Florence 1960" (Gaston Bertrand)

**1993.** Stamp Day.

3163 **979** 15 f. multicoloured .. 60 15

**1993.** Europa. Contemporary Art. Mult.

3164 15 f. Type **980** .. .. 60 15
3165 28 f. "The Gig" (Constant Permeke) .. .. 1·10 35

981 Red Admiral ("Vanessa atalanta")

**1993.** Butterflies. Multicoloured.

3166 15 f. Type **981** .. .. 60 15
3167 15 f. Purple emperor ("Apatura iris") .. 60 15
3168 15 f. Peacock ("Inachis io") .. .. 60 15
3169 15 f. Small tortoiseshell ("Aglais urticae") .. 60 15

982 Knot — 983 Mayan Warrior (statuette)

**1993.** 150th Anniv of Alumni of Free University of Brussels Association.

3170 **982** 15 f. blue and black .. 60 15

**1993.** "Europalia 93 Mexico" Festival.

3171 **983** 15 f. multicoloured .. 55 15

984 Ommegang, Brussels

**1993.** Folklore Festivals. Multicoloured.
3172 11 f. Type **984** .. .. 40 10
3173 15 f. Royale Moncrabeau, Namur .. .. 55 15
3174 28 f. Stilt-walkers, Merchtem (vert) .. 1·25 35

**985** La Hulpe Castle

**1993.** Tourist Publicity.
3175 **985** 15 f. black and blue .. 55 15
3176 – 15 f. black and lilac .. 55 15
3177 – 15 f. black and grey .. 55 15
3178 – 15 f. black and pink 55 15
3179 – 15 f. black and green 55 15
DESIGNS—HORIZ. No. 3176, Cortewalle Castle, Beveren; 3177, Jehay Castle; 3179, Raeren Castle. VERT—No. 3178, Arenberg Castle, Heverlee.

**986** Emblem

**1993.** 2nd International Triennial Textile Exhibition, Tournai.
3180 **986** 15 f. blue, red & black 55 15

**987** Presidency Emblem

**1993.** Belgian Presidency of European Community Council.
3181 **987** 15 f. multicoloured .. 55 15

**988** Magritte **989** King Baudouin

**1993.** 25th Death Anniv (1992) of Rene Magritte (artist).
3182 **988** 30 f. multicoloured .. 1·10 35

**1993.** King Baudouin Commemoration.
3183 **989** 15 f. black and blue .. 55 15

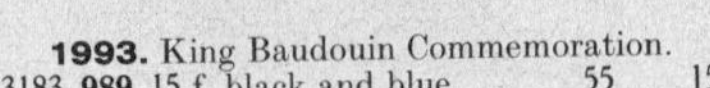

**990** Red and White Cat

**1993.** Cats. Multicoloured.
3184 15 f. Type **990** .. .. 80 40
3185 15 f. Tabby and white cat standing on rock .. 80 40
3186 15 f. Silver tabby lying on wall .. .. .. 80 40
3187 15 f. Tortoiseshell and white cat sitting by gardening tools .. 80 40

**991** Highlighted Cancer Cell **992** Frontispiece

**1993.** Anti-cancer Campaign.
3188 **991** 15 f. +3 f. mult .. 1·25 1·25

**1993.** 450th Anniv of "De Humani Corporis Fabrica" (treatise on human anatomy) by Andreas Vesalius.
3189 **992** 15 f. black, brn & red 55 15

**993** Natacha (cartoon character)

**1993.** "Philately for the Young".
3190 **993** 15 f. multicoloured .. 55 15

**994** Sun's Rays **995** "Madonna and Child" (statue, Our Lady of the Chapel, Brussels)

**1993.** 50th Anniv of Publication of "Le Faux Soir" (resistance newspaper).
3191 **994** 11 f. multicoloured .. 40 15

**1993.** Christmas.
3192 **995** 11 f. multicoloured .. 40 15

**996** Child looking at Globe

**1993.** Children's Town Councils.
3193 **996** 15 f. multicoloured .. 55 15



**997** King Albert II **998** King Albert II

**1993.**
3194 **997** 16 f. multicoloured .. 60 10
3196 16 f. turquoise & blue 1·00 10
3198 20 f. brown and stone 80 15
3203 30 f. purple & mauve 1·10 15
3204 32 f. orange & yellow 1·25 15
3205 40 f. red and mauve 1·60 15
3207 50 f. myrtle and green 2·00 15
3208 **998** 100 f. multicoloured 3·50 30
3209 200 f. multicoloured 7·25 50

**999** "Ma Toute Belle" (Serge Vandercam) **1000** Olympic Flames and Rings

**1994.** Painters' Designs. Multicoloured.
3210 16 f. Type **999** .. .. 60 15
3211 16 f. "The Malleable Darkness" (Octave Landuyt) (horiz) .. 60 15

**1994.** Sports. Multicoloured.
3212 16 f. +3 f. Type **1000** (cent of International Olympic Committee) .. 1·25 1·25
3213 16 f. +3 f. Footballers (World Cup Football Championship, U.S.A.) 1·25 1·25
3214 16 f. +3 f. Skater (Winter Olympic Games, Lillehammer, Norway 1·25 1·25

**1001** Hanriot HD-1 **1002** Masthead of "Le Jour-Le Courrier" (centenary)

**1994.** Biplanes. Multicoloured.
3215 13 f. Type **1001** .. .. 50 15
3216 15 f. Spad XIII .. .. 60 15
3217 30 f. Schreck FBA.H. flying boat .. .. 1·25 40
3218 32 f. Stamps and SV-4B 1·25 40

**1994.** Newspaper Anniversaries. Mult.
3219 16 f. Type **1002** .. .. 65 15
3220 16 f. Masthead of "La Wallonie" (75th anniv) (horiz) .. .. 65 15


**1003** "Fall of the Golden Calf" (detail, Fernand Allard l'Olivier)

**1994.** Centenary of Charter of Quaregnon (social charter).
3221 **1003** 16 f. multicoloured .. 65 15

**1004** 1912 5 f. Stamp **1005** Reconciliation of Duke John I and Arnold, Squire of Wezemaal

**1994.** Stamp Day. 60th Death Anniv of King Albert I.
3222 **1004** 16 f. purple, mve & bl 65 15

**1994.** 700th Death Anniv of John I, Duke of Brabant. Illustrations from 15th-century "Brabantse Yeesten". Multicoloured.
3223 13 f. Type **1005** .. .. 50 15
3224 16 f. Tournament at wedding of his son John to Margaret of York, 1290 .. .. .. 65 15
3225 30 f. Battle of Woeringen (77 × 25 mm) .. .. 1·25 40

**1006** Georges Lemaitre (formulator of expanding Universe and of "big bang" theory) **1008** St. Peter's Church, Bertem

**1007** Father Damien (missionary and leprosy worker)

**1994.** Europa. Discoveries and Inventions. Multicoloured.
3226 16 f. Type **1006** .. .. 65 15
3227 30 f. Gerardus Mercator (inventor of Mercator projection in cartography) 1·25 40

**1994.** Visit of Pope John Paul II. Mult.
3228 16 f. Type **1007** (beatification) .. 65 15
3229 16 f. St. Mutien-Marie (5th anniv of canonization) 65 15

**1994.** Tourist Publicity. Multicoloured.
3230 16 f. Type **1008** .. .. 65 15
3231 16 f. St. Bavo's Church, Kanegem (vert) .. 65 15
3232 16 f. Royal St. Mary's Church, Schaarbeek .. 65 15
3233 16 f. St. Gery's Church, Aubechies .. .. 65 15
3234 16 f. Sts. Peter and Paul's Church, St.-Severin en Condroz (vert) .. 65 20

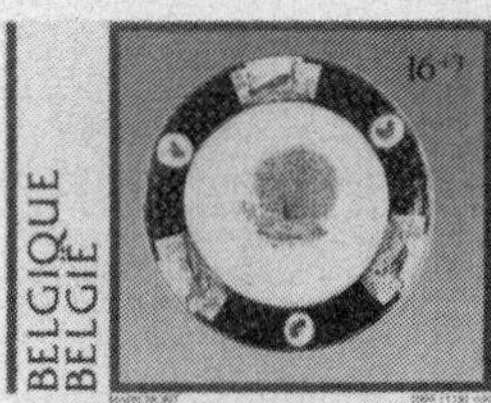

**1009** Tournai Porcelain Plate from Duke of Orleans Service (Mariemont Museum)

**1994.** Museum Exhibits. Multicoloured.
3235 16 f. +3 f. Type **1009** .. 1·25 1·25
3236 16 f. +3 f. Etterbeek porcelain coffee cup and saucer (Louvain Municipal Museum) .. 1·25 1·25

**1010** Guillame Lekeu (composer)

**1994.** Anniversaries. Multicoloured.
3238 16 f. Type **1010** (death centenary) .. .. 65 15
3239 16 f. Detail of painting by Hans Memling (500th death anniv) .. .. 65 15

**1011** Generals Crerar, Montgomery and Bradley and Allied Troops (½-size illustration)

**1994.** 50th Anniv of Liberation.
3240 **1011** 16 f. multicoloured .. 65 15

1012 Marsh Marigold ("Caltha palustris")

**1994.** Flowers. Multicoloured.

| | | | |
|---|---|---|---|
| 3241 | 16 f. Type **1012** .. .. | 65 | 15 |
| 3242 | 16 f. White helleborine ("Cephalanthera damasonium") .. | 65 | 15 |
| 3243 | 16 f. Sea bindweed ("Calystegia soldanella") .. .. | 65 | 15 |
| 3244 | 16 f. Broad-leaved helleborine ("Epipactis helleborine") .. .. | 65 | 15 |

1013 Cubitus (cartoon character)

1014 Simenon and Bridge of Arches, Liege

**1994.** "Philately for the Young".

3245 **1013** 16 f. multicoloured .. 65 15

**1994.** 5th Death Anniv of Georges Simenon (novelist).

3246 **1014** 16 f. multicoloured .. 65 15

The depiction of the bridge alludes to Simenon's first novel "Au Pont des Arches".

1015 Deaf Man and Butterfly

**1994.** "Solidarity".

3247 **1015** 16 f.+3 f. mult .. 75 75

1016 Santa Claus on Rooftop

**1994.** Christmas.

3248 **1016** 13 f. multicoloured .. 50 15

1017 Field and Flax Knife (Flax Museum, Courtrai)

**1995.** Museums. Multicoloured.

| | | | |
|---|---|---|---|
| 3249 | 16 f.+3 f. Type **1017** .. | 75 | 75 |
| 3250 | 16 f.+3 f. River and pump (Water and Fountain Museum, Genval) .. .. | 75 | 75 |

The premium was for the promotion of philately.

1018 Emblem

**1995.** Anniversaries. Anniversary emblems.

| | | | | |
|---|---|---|---|---|
| 3252 | **1018** | 16 f. red, blue & blk | 65 | 15 |
| 3253 | – | 16 f. multicoloured .. | 65 | 15 |
| 3254 | – | 16 f. red, grey & blk | 65 | 15 |
| 3255 | – | 16 f. red, blk & brn | 65 | 15 |

ANNIVERSARIES: No. 3252, 50th anniv of August Vermeylen Fund; 3253, Centenary of Touring Club of Belgium; 3254, Centenary of Federation of Belgian Enterprises; 3255, 50th anniv of Social Security in Belgium.

1019 "Hibiscus rosa-sinensis"

**1995.** Ghent Flower Show. Multicoloured.

| | | | |
|---|---|---|---|
| 3256 | 13 f. Type **1019** .. .. | 60 | 20 |
| 3257 | 16 f. Azalea .. .. | 70 | 20 |
| 3258 | 30 f. Fuchsia .. .. | 1·40 | 45 |

1020 Crossword Puzzle

1021 Frans de Troyer (promoter of thematic philately)

**1994.** Games and Pastimes. Multicoloured.

| | | | |
|---|---|---|---|
| 3259 | 13 f. Type **1020** .. .. | 60 | 20 |
| 3260 | 16 f. Chessman .. .. | 70 | 20 |
| 3261 | 30 f. Scrabble .. .. | 1·40 | 45 |
| 3262 | 34 f. Queen (playing cards) .. .. .. | 1·50 | 50 |

**1995.** Post Day.

3263 **1021** 16 f. blk, stone & orge 70 20

1022 Watch Tower and Barbed Wire Fence

**1995.** Europa. Peace and Freedom. Mult.

| | | | |
|---|---|---|---|
| 3264 | 16 f. Type **1022** (50th anniv of liberation of concentration camps) | 70 | 20 |
| 3265 | 30 f. Nuclear cloud (25th anniv of Non-Proliferation Treaty) .. | 1·40 | 45 |

1023 Soldiers of the Irish Brigade and Memorial Cross

**1995.** 250th Anniv of Battle of Fontenoy.

3266 **1023** 16 f. multicoloured .. 70 20

1024 U.N. Emblem

**1995.** 50th Anniv of U.N.O.

3267 **1024** 16 f. multicoloured .. 70 20

1025 "Sauvagemont, Maransart" (Pierre Alechinsky)

**1995.** Artists' Philatelic Creations.

| | | | | |
|---|---|---|---|---|
| 3268 | **1025** | 16 f. red, blk & yell | 70 | 20 |
| 3269 | – | 16 f. multicoloured .. | 70 | 20 |

DESIGN: No. 3269, "Telegram-style" (Pol Mara).

1026 Paul Cauchie (Brussels)

**1995.** Tourist Publicity. Art Nouveau house facades by named architects. Multicoloured.

| | | | |
|---|---|---|---|
| 3270 | 16 f. Type **1026** .. .. | 70 | 20 |
| 3271 | 16 f. Frans Smet-Verhas (Antwerp) .. .. | 70 | 20 |
| 3272 | 16 f. Paul Jaspar (Liege) | 70 | 20 |

1027 Anniversary Emblem

**1995.** Cent of Royal Belgian Football Assn.

3273 **1027** 16 f.+4 f. mult .. 90 90

1028 "Mercator" (Belgian cadet barque)

**1995.** Sailing Ships. Multicoloured.

| | | | |
|---|---|---|---|
| 3274 | 16 f. Type **1028** .. .. | 70 | 20 |
| 3275 | 16 f. "Kruzenshern" (Russian cadet barque) | 70 | 20 |
| 3276 | 16 f. "Sagres II" (Portuguese cadet barque) .. .. | 70 | 20 |
| 3277 | 16 f. "Amerigo Vespucci" (Italian cadet ship) .. | 70 | 20 |

1029 Princess Astrid and Globe

**1995.** Red Cross. Multicoloured.

| | | | |
|---|---|---|---|
| 3278 | 16 f.+3 f. Type **1029** (Chairwoman) .. | 85 | 85 |
| 3279 | 16 f.+3 f. Wilhelm Rontgen (discoverer of X-rays) and X-ray of hand .. .. .. | 85 | 85 |
| 3280 | 16 f.+3 f. Louis Pasteur (chemist) and microscope .. .. | 85 | 85 |

1030 1908 Minerva

**1995.** Motor Cycles. Multicoloured.

| | | | |
|---|---|---|---|
| 3281 | 13 f. Type **1030** .. .. | 60 | 20 |
| 3282 | 16 f. 1913 FN (vert) .. | 70 | 20 |
| 3283 | 30 f. 1929 La Mondiale .. | 1·40 | 45 |
| 3284 | 32 f. 1937 Gillet (vert) .. | 1·40 | 45 |

1031 Sammy (cartoon character)

**1995.** "Philately for the Young".

3285 **1031** 16 f. multicoloured .. 70 20

1032 Couple and Condom in Wrapper

1034 "Nativity" (from 15th-century breviary)

1033 King Albert II and Queen Paola (photograph by Christian Louis)

**1995.** "Solidarity". AIDS Awareness.

3286 **1032** 16 f.+4 f. mult .. 90 90

**1995.** King's Day.

3287 **1033** 16 f. multicoloured .. 70 20

**1995.** Christmas.

3288 **1034** 13 f. multicoloured .. 60 20

1035 Puppets, Walloon Museum, Liege

**1996.** Museums. Multicoloured.

| | | | |
|---|---|---|---|
| 3289 | 16 f.+4 f. Type **1035** .. | 80 | 80 |
| 3290 | 16 f.+4 f. National Gin Museum, Hasselt .. | 80 | 80 |

The premium was used for the promotion of philately.

1036 "Emile Mayrisch"

1037 "LIBERALISME"

**1996.** 70th Death Anniv of Theo van Rysselberghe (painter). No value expressed.
3292 **1036** A (16 f.) mult .. 65 15

**1996.** 150th Anniv of Liberal Party.
3293 **1037** 16 f. dp blue, vio & bl 65 15

**1038** Oscar Bonnevalle (stamp designer) and "Gelatenheid"

**1996.** Stamp Day.
3294 **1038** 16 f. multicoloured .. 65 15

**1039** Dragonfly ("Sympetrum sanguineum")

**1996.** 150th Anniv of Royal Institute of Natural Sciences of Belgium. Insects. Mult.
3295 16 f. Type **1039** .. .. 65 15
3296 16 f. Buff-tailed bumble bee ("Bombus terrestris") .. .. 65 15
3297 16 f. Stag beetle ("Lucanus cervus") .. 65 15
3298 16 f. May beetle ("Melolontha melolontha") .. .. 65 15
3299 16 f. European field cricket ("Gryllus campestris") .. .. 65 15
3300 16 f. Seven-spotted ladybird ("Coccinella septempunctata") .. 65 15

**1040** Yvonne Nevejean (rescuer of Jewish children) **1042** King Albert II

**1996.** Europa. Famous Women. Mult.
3301 16 f. Type **1040** .. .. 65 15
3302 30 f. Marie Gevers (poet) 1·25 40

**1996.** Birds (3rd series). As T **841**. Multicoloured.
3307 2 f. Redwing ("Grive mauvis") .. .. 10 10
3309 4 f. Pied flycatcher ("Gore-mouche noir") 15 10
3310 5 f. Starling ("Etourneau sansonnet") .. .. 20 10
3312 6 f. Siskin ("Tarin des aulnes") .. .. 25 10

**1996.** 62nd Birthday of King Albert II.
3327 **1042** 16 f. multicoloured .. 65 15
See also Nos. 3341/8.

**1043** Han sur Lesse Grottoes

**1996.** Tourist Publicity. Multicoloured.
3328 16 f. Type **1043** .. .. 65 15
3329 16 f. Statue of beguine, Begijnendijk .. .. 65 15

**1044** Royal Palace

**1996.** Brussels, Heart of Europe. Mult.
3330 16 f. Type **1044** .. .. 65 15
3331 16 f. St. Hubert Royal Galleries .. .. 65 15
3332 16 f. Le Petit Sablon, Egmont Palace (horiz) 65 15
3333 16 f. Jubilee Park (horiz) 65 15

**1045** 1900 Germain 6CV

**1996.** Cent of Motor Racing at Spa. Mult.
3334 16 f. Type **1045** .. .. 65 15
3335 16 f. 1925 Alfa Romeo P2 65 15
3336 16 f. 1939 Mercedes Benz W154 .. .. .. 65 15
3337 16 f. 1967 Ferrari 330P .. 65 15

**1046** Table Tennis

**1996.** Olympic Games, Atlanta. Mult.
3338 16 f. + 4 f. Type **1046** .. 80 80
3339 16 f. + 4 f. Swimming .. 80 80

**1996.**
3341 **1042** 16 f. blue .. .. 65 15
3345 28 f. brown .. .. 1·10 35
3348 50 f. green .. .. 2·00 65

**1047** "The Straw Hat" (Peter Paul Rubens) **1048** Philip the Fair

**1996.** Paintings by Belgian Artists in the National Gallery, London. Multicoloured.
3351 14 f. "St. Ivo" (Rogier van der Weyden) .. 55 20
3352 16 f. Type **1047** .. .. 65 15
3353 30 f. "Man in a Turban" (Jan van Eyck) .. 1·25 40

**1996.** 500th Anniv of Marriage of Philip the Fair and Joanna of Castile and Procession into Brussels. Details of triptych by the Master of Affligem Abbey at Zierikzee Town Hall. Multicoloured.
3354 16 f. Type **1048** .. .. 65 15
3355 16 f. Joanna of Castile .. 65 15



EXPRESS LETTER STAMPS

**E 107.** Ghent.

DESIGNS: 1 f. 75, Town Hall, Brussels. 2 f. 45, Eupen. 3 f. 50, Bishop's Palace, Liege. 5f. 25, Antwerp Cathedral.

**1929.**
E 530. – 1 f. 75 blue .. 50 20
E 531. E 107. 2 f. 35 red .. 1·50 20
E 581. – 2 f. 45 green .. 14·00 1·50
E 532. – 3 f. 50 purple .. 9·00 9·00
E 533. – 5 f. 25 olive .. 7·00 7·00

**1932.** No. E 581 surch. **2 Fr 50** and cross.
E 608. 2 f. 50 on 2 f. 45 grn. 11·00 1·25

MILITARY STAMPS

**1967.** As T **289.** (Baudouin) but with letter "M" within oval at foot.
M 2027. 1 f. 50 green .. .. 20 10

**1971.** As No. 2207/8a and 2209a but with letter "M" within oval at foot.
M 2224. 1 f. 75 green .. .. 50 30
M 2225. 2 f. 25 green .. .. 40 30
M 2226. 2 f. 50 green .. .. 35 30
M 2227. 3 f. 25 plum .. .. 40 20

NEWSPAPER STAMPS

**1928.** Railway Parcels stamps of 1923 optd. **JOURNAUX DAGBLADEN 1928.**
N 443. P 84. 10 c. red .. .. 25 20
N 444. 20 c. green .. .. 25 20
N 445. 40 c. olive .. .. 20 15
N 446. 60 c. orange .. .. 45 20
N 447. 70 c. brown .. .. 20 15
N 448. 80 c. violet .. .. 45 15
N 449. 90 c. slate .. .. 5·00 2·00
N 450. 1 f. blue .. .. 80 15
N 451. 2 f. olive .. .. 2·40 25
N 452. 3 f. red .. .. 2·40 40
N 453. 4 f. red .. .. 2·40 40
N 454. 5 f. violet .. .. 2·40 50
N 455. 6 f. brown .. .. 3·50 1·50
N 456. 7 f. orange .. .. 11·00 1·50
N 457. 8 f. brown .. .. 5·50 1·00
N 458. 9 f. purple .. .. 16·00 5·00
N 459. 10 f. green .. .. 6·00 1·50
N 460. 20 f. pink .. .. 24·00 6·00

**1929.** Railway Parcels stamps of 1923 optd. **JOURNAUX DAGBLADEN** only.
N 505. P 84. 10 c. red .. .. 20 20
N 506. 20 c. green .. .. 20 20
N 507. 40 c. olive .. .. 25 20
N 508. 60 c. orange .. .. 45 20
N 509. 70 c. brown .. .. 20 15
N 510. 80 c. violet .. .. 80 20
N 511. 90 c. slate .. .. 5·50 4·00
N 512. 1 f. blue .. .. 1·10 15
N 513. 1 f. 10 brown .. 4·00 1·00
N 514. 1 f. 50 blue .. 4·00 1·00
N 515. 2 f. olive .. .. 2·40 60
N 516. 2 f. 10 slate .. 12·00 9·00
N 517. 3 f. red .. .. 2·40 60
N 518. 4 f. red .. .. 2·40 60
N 519. 5 f. violet .. .. 2·40 60
N 520. 6 f. brown .. .. 3·75 1·10
N 521. 7 f. orange .. .. 11·00 1·10
N 522. 8 f. brown .. .. 5·50 1·10
N 523. 9 f. purple .. .. 14·00 8·00
N 524. 10 f. green .. .. 7·00 2·00
N 525. 20 f. pink .. .. 18·00 8·00

PARCEL POST STAMPS

Stamps issued at Belgian Post Offices only.

**1928.** Optd. **COLIS POSTAL POSTCOLLO.**
B 470. 81. 4 f. brown .. .. 5·50 1·40
B 471. 5 f. bistre .. .. 5·50 1·40

**B 106.** G.P.O., Brussels.

**1929.**
B 526. B 106. 3 f. sepia .. 1·00 10
B 527. 4 f. slate .. 1·00 10
B 528. 5 f. red .. 1·00 10
B 529. 6 f. purple .. 26·00 27·00

**1933.** Surch. **X4 4X.**
B 645. B 106. 4 f. on 6 f. purple 24·00 15

POSTAGE DUE STAMPS

**D 21.** **D 35.**

**1870.**
D 63. D 21. 10 c. green .. 3·00 1·50
D 64. 20 c. blue .. .. 25·00 3·00

**1895.**
D 96a. D 35. 5 c. green .. .. 15 10
D 97. 10 c. brown .. 14·00 1·40
D 101. 10 c. red .. .. 10 10
D 98a. 20 c. green .. 15 10
D 102. 30 c. blue .. .. 60 10
D 99. 50 c. brown .. 16·00 4·00
D 103. 50 c. grey .. .. 60 20
D 100. 1 f. red .. .. 14·00 9·00
D 104. 1 f. yellow .. .. 4·00 4·00

**1919.** As Type **D 35,** but value in colour on white background.
D 251 D 35 5 c. green .. .. 25 25
D 323 5 c. grey .. .. 10 10
D 252 10 c. red .. .. 50 25
D 324 10 c. green .. .. 10 10
D 253 20 c. green .. .. 4·00 80
D 325 20 c. brown .. .. 15 10
D 254 30 c. blue .. .. 1·40 20
D 326 30 c. red .. .. 50 35
D 327 35 c. green .. .. 20 20
D 328 40 c. brown .. .. 20 10
D 330 50 c. grey .. .. 30 10
D 329 50 c. blue .. .. 1·00 10
D 331 60 c. red .. .. 35 20
D 1146 65 c. green .. .. 5·00 2·40
D 332 70 c. brown .. .. 35 15
D 333 80 c. grey .. .. 35 15
D 334 1 f. violet .. .. 40 10
D 335 1 f. purple .. .. 45 10
D 336 1 f. 20 olive .. .. 60 10
D 337 1 f. 40 green .. .. 65 25
D 338 1 f. 50 olive .. .. 65 25
D 1147 1 f. 60 mauve .. .. 10·00 4·00
D 1148 1 f. 80 red .. .. 11·00 4·50
D 339 2 f. mauve .. .. 70 15
D 1149 2 f. 40 lavender .. 5·00 2·40
D 1150 3 f. red .. .. 1·75 40
D 340 3 f. 50 blue .. .. 70 15
D 1151 4 f. blue .. .. 8·00 40
D 1152 5 f. brown .. .. 2·75 20
D 1153 7 f. violet .. .. 2·75 1·40
D 1154 8 f. purple .. .. 7·50 6·00
D 1155 10 f. violet .. .. 5·50 2·40

**D 220.** **D 462.**

**1945.** Inscr. "A PAYER" at top and "TE BETALEN" at bottom, or vice versa.
D 1139. D 220. 10 c. olive .. .. 10 10
D 1140. 20 c. blue .. .. 10 10
D 1141. 30 c. red .. .. 10 10
D 1142. 40 c. blue .. .. 10 10
D 1143. 50 c. green .. .. 10 15
D 1144. 1 f. brown .. .. 10 10
D 1145. 2 f. orange .. .. 10 10

**1966.**
D 2812 D 462 1 f. mauve .. 10 10
D 2813 2 f. green .. 10 10
D 2814 3 f. blue .. 10 10
D 2815 4 f. green .. 15 15
D 1985ab 5 f. purple .. 25 15
D 2816 5 f. lilac .. 20 20
D 1986 6 f. brown .. 30 10
D 1987 7 f. red .. 35 20
D 2818 7 f. orange .. 25 25
D 2819 8 f. grey .. 30 30
D 2820 9 f. red .. 30 30
D 2821 10 f. brown .. 40 40
D 1988 20 f. green .. 70 50
D 2822 20 f. green .. 75 75

On No. D1988 the "F" is outside the shield; on No. D2822 it is inside.

RAILWAY PARCELS STAMPS

In Belgium the parcels service is largely operated by the Belgian Railways for which the following stamps were issued.

Certain stamps under this heading were also on sale at post offices in connection with a "small parcels" service. These show a posthorn in the design except for Nos. P 1116/18.

**P 21.**

**1879.**
P 63. P 21. 10 c. brown .. .. 40·00 4·50
P 64. 20 c. blue .. .. £120 15·00
P 65. 25 c. green .. .. £160 8·00
P 66. 50 c. red .. .. £1100 8·00
P 67. 80 c. yellow .. .. £1200 30·00
P 68. 1 f. grey .. .. £120 9·00

P 22.

**1882.**

| No. | Type | Description | Unused | Used |
|---|---|---|---|---|
| P 69 | P 22 | 10 c. brown | 16·00 | 1·25 |
| P 73 | | 15 c. grey | 7·00 | 7·00 |
| P 75 | | 20 c. blue | 60·00 | 2·50 |
| P 77 | | 25 c. green | 60·00 | 3·75 |
| P 78 | | 50 c. red | 60·00 | 80 |
| P 81 | | 80 c. yellow | 60·00 | 80 |
| P 84 | | 80 c. brown | 60·00 | 90 |
| P 86 | | 1 f. grey | £325 | 3·00 |
| P 87 | | 1 f. purple | £300 | 2·40 |
| P 88 | | 2 f. buff | £180 | 55·00 |

P 35.

**1895.** (Numerals in black except 1 f. and 2 f.).

| No. | Type | Description | Unused | Used |
|---|---|---|---|---|
| P 96. | P 35. | 10 c. brown | 9·00 | 60 |
| P 97. | | 15 c. slate | 9·00 | 7·00 |
| P 98. | | 20 c. blue | 15·00 | 1·00 |
| P 99. | | 25 c. green | 15·00 | 1·25 |
| P 100. | | 30 c. orange | 17·00 | 1·75 |
| P 101. | | 40 c. green | 23·00 | 1·60 |
| P 102. | | 50 c. red | 23·00 | 60 |
| P 103. | | 60 c. lilac | 45·00 | 60 |
| P 104. | | 70 c. blue | 45·00 | 1·00 |
| P 105. | | 80 c. yellow | 45·00 | 1·00 |
| P 106. | | 90 c. red | 55·00 | 1·60 |
| P 107. | | 1 f. purple | £150 | 2·25 |
| P 108. | | 2 f. buff | £180 | 13·00 |

P 37.

**1902.**

| No. | Type | Description | Unused | Used |
|---|---|---|---|---|
| P 109a. | P 35. | 10 c. slate & brown | 20 | 10 |
| P 110. | | 15 c. pur. & slate | 35 | 20 |
| P 111. | | 20 c. brn. & blue | 35 | 20 |
| P 112. | | 25 c. red & green | 50 | 25 |
| P 113. | | 30 c. green & orgc. | 35 | 20 |
| P 114. | | 35 c. green & brn. | 35 | 20 |
| P 115. | | 40 c. mauve & grn. | 50 | 25 |
| P 116. | | 50 c. mauve & pink | 20 | 10 |
| P 117. | | 55 c. blue & purple | 50 | 25 |
| P 118. | | 60 c. red and lilac | 20 | 10 |
| P 119. | | 70 c. red and blue | 20 | 10 |
| P 120. | | 80 c. purple & yell. | 20 | 10 |
| P 121. | | 90 c. green and red | 20 | 10 |
| P 122. | P 37. | 1 f. orange & purple | 20 | 10 |
| P 123. | | 1 f. 10 black & red | 20 | 10 |
| P 124. | | 2 f. green & bistre | 35 | 20 |
| P 125. | | 3 f. blue and black | 35 | 20 |
| P 126. | | 4 f. red & green | 1·90 | 80 |
| P 127. | | 5 f. green & orange | 1·50 | 65 |
| P 128. | | 10 f. purple & yell. | 1·10 | 50 |

**1915.** Stamps of 1912–14 optd. **CHEMINS DE FER SPOORWEGEN** and Winged Railway Wheel.

| No. | Type | Description | Unused | Used |
|---|---|---|---|---|
| P 160. | 44. | 5 c. green | £140 | |
| P 161. | 46. | 10 c. red | £160 | |
| P 162. | | 20 c. green | £200 | |
| P 163. | | 25 c. blue | £200 | |
| P 164. | 45. | 35 c. brown | £250 | |
| P 165. | 46. | 40 c. green | £225 | |
| P 166. | 45. | 50 c. grey | £225 | |
| P 167. | | 1 f. orange | £200 | |
| P 168. | | 2 f. violet | £1300 | |
| P 169. | – | 5 f. purple (No. 143) | £2750 | |

P 59. P 60.

**1916.**

| No. | Type | Description | Unused | Used |
|---|---|---|---|---|
| P 201. | P 59. | 10 c. blue | 70 | 30 |
| P 202. | | 15 c. olive | 1·40 | 1·40 |
| P 203. | | 20 c. red | 1·25 | 90 |
| P 204. | | 25 c. brown | 1·25 | 90 |
| P 205. | | 30 c. mauve | 1·00 | 70 |
| P 206. | | 35 c. grey | 1·00 | 70 |
| P 207 | | 40 c. orange | 2·00 | 2·00 |
| P 208. | | 50 c. bistre | 1·50 | 90 |
| P 209. | | 55 c. brown | 2·25 | 2·25 |
| P 210. | | 60 c. lilac | 1·50 | 80 |
| P 211. | | 70 c. green | 1·40 | 70 |
| P 212. | | 80 c. brown | 1·50 | 70 |
| P 213. | | 90 c. blue | 1·75 | 1·00 |
| P 214. | P 60. | 1 f. grey | 1·40 | 70 |
| P 215. | | 1 f. 10 bl. (FRANKEN) | 23·00 | 23·00 |
| P 216. | | 1 f. 10 bl. (FRANK). | 1·60 | 70 |
| P 217. | | 2 f. red | 30·00 | 1·25 |
| P 218. | | 3 f. violet | 30·00 | 1·25 |
| P 219. | | 4 f. green | 35·00 | 2·50 |
| P 220. | | 5 f. brown | 50·00 | 2·50 |
| P 221. | | 10 f. orange | 50·00 | 2·50 |

P 69. P 70.

**1920.**

| No. | Type | Description | Unused | Used |
|---|---|---|---|---|
| P259 | P 69 | 10 c. green | 1·25 | 35 |
| P280 | | 10 c. red | 35 | 25 |
| P281 | | 15 c. green | 25 | 25 |
| P261 | | 20 c. red | 1·50 | 35 |
| P282 | | 20 c. green | 60 | 25 |
| P262 | | 25 c. brown | 2·00 | 80 |
| P283 | | 25 c. blue | 60 | 25 |
| P263 | | 30 c. mauve | 24·00 | 22·00 |
| P284 | | 30 c. brown | 60 | 25 |
| P285 | | 35 c. brown | 75 | 50 |
| P286 | | 40 c. orange | 75 | 25 |
| P265 | | 50 c. bistre | 7·00 | 1·10 |
| P287 | | 50 c. red | 75 | 25 |
| P266 | | 55 c. brown | 7·50 | 6·00 |
| P288 | | 55 c. yellow | 4·00 | 3·50 |
| P267 | | 60 c. purple | 9·00 | 1·00 |
| P289 | | 60 c. red | 75 | 25 |
| P290 | | 70 c. green | 2·75 | 45 |
| P269 | | 80 c. brown | 38·00 | 1·25 |
| P291 | | 80 c. violet | 2·40 | 25 |
| P270 | | 90 c. blue | 10·00 | 1·00 |
| P292 | | 90 c. yellow | 28·00 | 28·00 |
| P293 | | 90 c. purple | 5·00 | 40 |
| P271 | P 70 | 1 f. grey | 75·00 | 1·25 |
| P272 | | 1 f. 10 blue | 24·00 | 1·25 |
| P273 | | 1 f. 20 green | 14·00 | 80 |
| P274 | | 1 f. 40 brown | 14·00 | 80 |
| P275 | | 2 f. red | 90·00 | 80 |
| P276 | | 3 f. mauve | £100 | 80 |
| P277 | | 4 f. green | £100 | 1·00 |
| P278 | | 5 f. brown | £100 | 60 |
| P279 | | 10 f. orange | £100 | 1·00 |

On Nos. P271/9 the engine has one head lamp.

**1920.** Three head lamps on engine.

| No. | Type | Description | Unused | Used |
|---|---|---|---|---|
| P 294. | P70. | 1 f. brown | 5·00 | 25 |
| P 296. | | 1 f. 10 blue | 1·75 | 25 |
| P 297. | | 1 f. 20 orange | 2·00 | 25 |
| P 298. | | 1 f. 40 yellow | 12·00 | 2·50 |
| P 299. | | 1 f. 60 green | 22·00 | 50 |
| P 300. | | 2 f. red | 24·00 | 35 |
| P 301. | | 3 f. red | 24·00 | 35 |
| P 302. | | 4 f. green | 24·00 | 35 |
| P 303. | | 5 f. violet | 20·00 | 35 |
| P 304. | | 10 f. yellow | £110 | 14·00 |
| P 305. | | 10 f. brown | 22·00 | 35 |
| P 306. | | 15 f. red | 22·00 | 35 |
| P 307. | | 20 f. blue | £300 | 2·50 |

P 79. P 84.

**1922.**

| No. | Type | Description | Unused | Used |
|---|---|---|---|---|
| P 341. | P 79. | 2 f. black | 6·00 | 50 |
| P 342. | | 3 f. brown | 60·00 | 50 |
| P 343. | | 4 f. green | 15·00 | 50 |
| P 344. | | 5 f. red | 15·00 | 50 |
| P 345. | | 10 f. brown | 15·00 | 50 |
| P 346. | | 15 f. red | 15·00 | 1·00 |
| P 347. | | 20 f. blue | £110 | 2·00 |

**1923.**

| No. | Type | Description | Unused | Used |
|---|---|---|---|---|
| P 375. | P 84. | 5 c. brown | 20 | 20 |
| P 376. | | 10 c. red | 10 | 10 |
| P 377. | | 15 c. blue | 20 | 20 |
| P 378. | | 20 c. green | 10 | 10 |
| P 379. | | 30 c. purple | 10 | 10 |
| P 380. | | 40 c. olive | 10 | 10 |
| P 381. | | 50 c. red | 10 | 10 |
| P 382. | | 60 c. orange | 10 | 10 |
| P 383. | | 70 c. brown | 10 | 10 |
| P 384. | | 80 c. violet | 15 | 10 |
| P 385. | | 90 c. slate | 1·40 | 10 |

Similar type, but horiz.

| No. | Type | Description | Unused | Used |
|---|---|---|---|---|
| P 386. | | 1 f. blue | 30 | 10 |
| P 388. | | 1 f. 10 orange | 2·75 | 25 |
| P 389. | | 1 f. 50 green | 2·75 | 25 |
| P 390. | | 1 f. 70 brown | 65 | 40 |
| P 391. | | 1 f. 80 red | 3·50 | 55 |
| P 392. | | 2 f. olive | 30 | 10 |
| P 393. | | 2 f. 10 green | 9·00 | 60 |
| P 394. | | 2 f. 40 violet | 3·75 | 70 |
| P 395. | | 2 f. 70 grey | 29·00 | 1·25 |
| P 396. | | 3 f. red | 35 | 10 |
| P 397. | | 3 f. 30 brown | 38·00 | 1·25 |
| P 398. | | 4 f. red | 35 | 10 |
| P 399. | | 5 f. violet | 60 | 10 |
| P 400. | | 6 f. brown | 35 | 10 |
| P 401. | | 7 f. orange | 80 | 10 |
| P 402. | | 8 f. brown | 60 | 10 |
| P 403. | | 9 f. purple | 2·50 | 10 |
| P 404. | | 10 f. green | 90 | 10 |
| P 405. | | 20 f. pink | 1·25 | 10 |
| P 406. | | 30 f. green | 5·00 | 15 |
| P 407. | | 40 f. slate | 35·00 | 1·25 |
| P 408. | | 50 f. bistre | 7·50 | 40 |

See Nos. P876/7 and P911/34.

**1924.** No. P 394 surch. **2 F 30** and bars.

| No. | Type | Description | Unused | Used |
|---|---|---|---|---|
| P 409. | | 2 f. 30 on 2 f. 40 violet | 2·75 | 40 |

P139. Steam locomotive "Goliath". P149. Diesel Locomotive.

**1934.**

| No. | Type | Description | Unused | Used |
|---|---|---|---|---|
| P 655. | P 139. | 3 f. green | 9·00 | 3·50 |
| P 656. | | 4 f. mauve | 2·00 | 10 |
| P 657. | | 5 f. red | 38·00 | 10 |

**1935.** Centenary of Belgian Railway.

| No. | Type | Description | Unused | Used |
|---|---|---|---|---|
| P 689. | P 149. | 10 c. red | 35 | 10 |
| P 690. | | 20 c. violet | 35 | 15 |
| P 691. | | 30 c. brown | 45 | 20 |
| P 692. | | 40 c. blue | 55 | 15 |
| P 693. | | 50 c. orange | 55 | 10 |
| P 694. | | 60 c. green | 80 | 15 |
| P 695. | | 70 c. blue | 90 | 15 |
| P 696. | | 80 c. black | 90 | 15 |
| P 697. | | 90 c. red | 90 | 45 |

Horiz. type. Early engine, "Le Belge".

| No. | Type | Description | Unused | Used |
|---|---|---|---|---|
| P 698. | | 1 f. purple | 90 | 10 |
| P 699. | | 2 f. black | 2·25 | 10 |
| P 700. | | 3 f. orange | 2·50 | 10 |
| P 701. | | 4 f. purple | 2·50 | 10 |
| P 702. | | 5 f. purple | 3·25 | 10 |
| P 703. | | 6 f. green | 4·50 | 10 |
| P 704. | | 7 f. violet | 18·00 | 10 |
| P 705. | | 8 f. black | 18·00 | 10 |
| P 706. | | 9 f. blue | 20·00 | 10 |
| P 707. | | 10 f. red | 20·00 | 10 |
| P 708. | | 20 f. green | 35·00 | 10 |
| P 709. | | 30 f. violet | 90·00 | 2·40 |
| P 710. | | 40 f. brown | 90·00 | 2·75 |
| P 711. | | 50 f. red | £100 | 2·40 |
| P 712. | | 100 f. blue | £225 | 48·00 |

P162. Winged Railway Wheel and Posthorn.

**1938.**

| No. | Type | Description | Unused | Used |
|---|---|---|---|---|
| P 806. | P 162. | 5 f. on 3 f. 50 green | 11·00 | 35 |
| P 807. | | 5 f. on 4 f. 50 pur. | 10 | 10 |
| P 808. | | 6 f. on 5 f. 50 red | 25 | 10 |
| P 1162. | | 8 f. on 5 f. 50 brn. | 70 | 10 |
| P 1163. | | 10 f. on 5 f. 50 blue | 75 | 10 |
| P 1164. | | 12 f. on 5 f. 50 vio. | 1·00 | 15 |

**1939.** Surch **M. 3Fr.**

| No. | Type | Description | Unused | Used |
|---|---|---|---|---|
| P867 | P 162 | 3 f. on 5 f. 50 red | 35 | 10 |

P176. Seal of the International Railway Congress.

**1939.** Int. Railway Congress, Brussels.

| No. | Type | Description | Unused | Used |
|---|---|---|---|---|
| P 856. | P 176. | 20 c. brown | 3·25 | 3·50 |
| P 857. | | 50 c. blue | 3·25 | 3·50 |
| P 858. | | 2 f. red | 3·25 | 3·50 |
| P 859. | | 9 f. green | 3·50 | 3·75 |
| P 860. | | 10 f. purple | 3·50 | 3·75 |

**1940.** As Nos. P 399 and P 404 but colours changed.

| No. | Type | Description | Unused | Used |
|---|---|---|---|---|
| P 876. | P 84. | 5 f. brown | 30 | 25 |
| P 877. | | 10 f. black | 4·50 | 4·00 |

**1940.** Optd. B in oval and two vert. bars.

| No. | Type | Description | Unused | Used |
|---|---|---|---|---|
| P 878. | P 84. | 10 c. red | 10 | 10 |
| P 879. | | 20 c. green | 10 | 10 |
| P 880. | | 30 c. purple | 10 | 10 |
| P 881. | | 40 c. olive | 10 | 10 |
| P 882. | | 50 c. red | 10 | 10 |
| P 883. | | 60 c. orange | 50 | 40 |
| P 884. | | 70 c. brown | 10 | 10 |
| P 885. | | 80 c. violet | 10 | 10 |
| P 886. | | 90 c. slate | 20 | 20 |
| P 887. | | 1 f. blue | 10 | 10 |
| P 888. | | 2 f. olive | 20 | 10 |
| P 889. | | 3 f. red | 20 | 10 |
| P 890. | | 4 f. red | 20 | 10 |
| P 891. | | 5 f. violet | 20 | 10 |
| P 892. | | 6 f. brown | 45 | 10 |
| P 893. | | 7 f. orange | 45 | 10 |
| P 894. | | 8 f. brown | 45 | 10 |
| P 895. | | 9 f. purple | 45 | 10 |
| P 896. | | 10 f. green | 45 | 10 |
| P 897. | | 20 f. pink | 1·00 | 10 |
| P 898. | | 30 f. green | 1·90 | 1·90 |
| P 899. | | 40 f. slate | 4·00 | 4·00 |
| P 900. | | 50 f. bistre | 2·00 | 1·25 |

**1940.** As Type P 84 but colours changed.

| No. | Type | Description | Unused | Used |
|---|---|---|---|---|
| P 911. | P 84. | 10 c. olive | 15 | 10 |
| P 912. | | 20 c. violet | 15 | 10 |
| P 913. | | 30 c. red | 15 | 10 |
| P 914. | | 40 c. blue | 15 | 10 |
| P 915. | | 50 c. green | 15 | 10 |
| P 916. | | 60 c. grey | 15 | 10 |
| P 917. | | 70 c. green | 15 | 10 |
| P 918. | | 80 c. orange | 20 | 10 |
| P 919. | | 90 c. lilac | 20 | 10 |

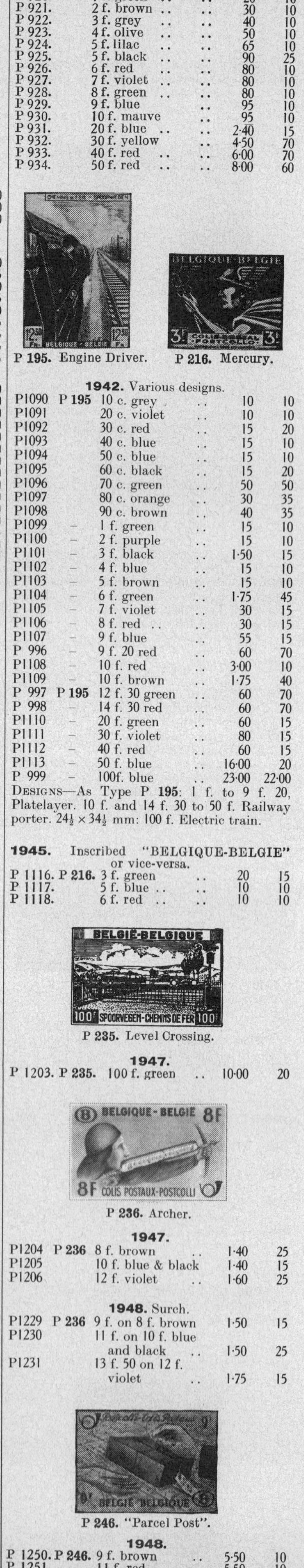

Similar design, but horizontal.

| No. | Type | Description | Unused | Used |
|---|---|---|---|---|
| P 920. | | 1 f. green | 20 | 10 |
| P 921. | | 2 f. brown | 30 | 10 |
| P 922. | | 3 f. grey | 40 | 10 |
| P 923. | | 4 f. olive | 50 | 10 |
| P 924. | | 5 f. lilac | 65 | 10 |
| P 925. | | 5 f. black | 90 | 25 |
| P 926. | | 6 f. red | 80 | 10 |
| P 927. | | 7 f. violet | 80 | 10 |
| P 928. | | 8 f. green | 80 | 10 |
| P 929. | | 9 f. blue | 95 | 10 |
| P 930. | | 10 f. mauve | 95 | 10 |
| P 931. | | 20 f. blue | 2·40 | 15 |
| P 932. | | 30 f. yellow | 4·50 | 70 |
| P 933. | | 40 f. red | 6·00 | 70 |
| P 934. | | 50 f. red | 8·00 | 60 |

P 195. Engine Driver. P 216. Mercury.

**1942.** Various designs.

| No. | Type | Description | Unused | Used |
|---|---|---|---|---|
| P1090 | P 195 | 10 c. grey | 10 | 10 |
| P1091 | | 20 c. violet | 10 | 10 |
| P1092 | | 30 c. red | 15 | 20 |
| P1093 | | 40 c. blue | 15 | 10 |
| P1094 | | 50 c. blue | 15 | 10 |
| P1095 | | 60 c. black | 15 | 20 |
| P1096 | | 70 c. green | 50 | 50 |
| P1097 | | 80 c. orange | 30 | 35 |
| P1098 | | 90 c. brown | 40 | 35 |
| P1099 | – | 1 f. green | 15 | 10 |
| P1100 | – | 2 f. purple | 15 | 10 |
| P1101 | – | 3 f. black | 1·50 | 15 |
| P1102 | – | 4 f. blue | 15 | 10 |
| P1103 | – | 5 f. brown | 15 | 10 |
| P1104 | – | 6 f. green | 1·75 | 45 |
| P1105 | – | 7 f. violet | 30 | 15 |
| P1106 | – | 8 f. red | 30 | 15 |
| P1107 | – | 9 f. blue | 55 | 15 |
| P 996 | – | 9 f. 20 red | 60 | 70 |
| P1108 | – | 10 f. red | 3·00 | 10 |
| P1109 | – | 10 f. brown | 1·75 | 40 |
| P 997 | P 195 | 12 f. 30 green | 60 | 70 |
| P 998 | – | 14 f. 30 red | 60 | 70 |
| P1110 | – | 20 f. green | 60 | 15 |
| P1111 | – | 30 f. violet | 80 | 15 |
| P1112 | – | 40 f. red | 60 | 15 |
| P1113 | – | 50 f. blue | 16·00 | 20 |
| P 999 | – | 100f. blue | 23·00 | 22·00 |

DESIGNS—As Type P 195: 1 f. to 9 f. 20, Platelayer. 10 f. and 14 f. 30 to 50 f. Railway porter. 24½ × 34½ mm: 100 f. Electric train.

**1945.** Inscribed "BELGIQUE-BELGIE" or vice-versa.

| No. | Type | Description | Unused | Used |
|---|---|---|---|---|
| P 1116. | P 216. | 3 f. green | 20 | 15 |
| P 1117. | | 5 f. blue | 10 | 10 |
| P 1118. | | 6 f. red | 10 | 10 |

P 235. Level Crossing.

**1947.**

| No. | Type | Description | Unused | Used |
|---|---|---|---|---|
| P 1203. | P 235. | 100 f. green | 10·00 | 20 |

P 236. Archer.

**1947.**

| No. | Type | Description | Unused | Used |
|---|---|---|---|---|
| P1204 | P 236 | 8 f. brown | 1·40 | 25 |
| P1205 | | 10 f. blue & black | 1·40 | 15 |
| P1206 | | 12 f. violet | 1·60 | 25 |

**1948.** Surch.

| No. | Type | Description | Unused | Used |
|---|---|---|---|---|
| P1229 | P 236 | 9 f. on 8 f. brown | 1·50 | 15 |
| P1230 | | 11 f. on 10 f. blue and black | 1·50 | 25 |
| P1231 | | 13 f. 50 on 12 f. violet | 1·75 | 15 |

P 246. "Parcel Post".

**1948.**

| No. | Type | Description | Unused | Used |
|---|---|---|---|---|
| P 1250. | P 246. | 9 f. brown | 5·50 | 10 |
| P 1251. | | 11 f. red | 5·50 | 10 |
| P 1252. | | 13 f. 50 black | 8·50 | 15 |

P 254. Locomotive, 1862.

**1949.** Locomotives from 1835 to 1951. Year given in brackets.

P 1277. ½ f. brown (1835) .. 30 10
P 1278. 1 f. red (Type P **254**) .. 40 10
P 1279. 2 f. blue (1875) .. 60 10
P 1280. 3 f. red (1884) .. 1·50 10
P 1281. 4 f. green (1901) .. 1·75 20
P 1282. 5 f. red (1902) .. 1·75 20
P 1283. 6 f. purple (1904) .. 2·00 20
P 1284. 7 f. green (1905) .. 2·50 20
P 1285. 8 f. blue (1906) .. 2·75 20
P 1286. 9 f. brown (1909) .. 3·75 20
P 1287. 10 f. olive (1910) .. 4·00 30
P 1295. 10 f. black & red (1905) 7·00 1·25
P 1288. 20 f. orange (1920) .. 7·00 20
P 1289. 30 f. blue (1928) .. 13·00 20
P 1290. 40 f. red (1930) .. 18·00 20
P 1291. 50 f. mauve (1935) .. 30·00 20
P 1292. 60 f. brown (1949) .. 17·00 20
P 1293. 100 f. red (1939) .. 55·00 80
P 1294. 300 f. violet (1951) .. £100 1·75

The 300 f. is larger (37½ × 25 mm.).

P 264. Loading Parcels.

DESIGNS—HORIZ. 11 f., 12 f., 17 f. Dispatch counter. 13 f., 15 f. Sorting compartment.

**1950.**

P 1318. – 11 f. orange .. 5·50 15
P 1319. – 12 f. purple .. 15·00 1·25
P 1320. – 13 f. green .. 5·50 10
P 1321. – 15 f. blue .. 12·00 25
P 1322. P **264.** 16 f. grey .. 5·50 10
P 1323. – 17 f. brown .. 6·00 15
P 1324. P **264.** 18 f. red .. .. 11·00 45
P 1325. 20 f. orange .. 6·00 15

P 271. Mercury.

**1951.** 25th Anniv. of National Belgian Railway Society.

P 1375. P **271.** 25 f. blue .. 9·00 8·00

**1953.** Nos. P 1318, P 1321 and P 1324 surch.

P 1448. – 13 f. on 15 f. blue 55·00 3·00
P 1449. – 17 f. on 11 f. orge. 24·00 1·00
P 1450. P **264.** 20 f. on 18 f. red 14·00 2·25

P 288. Electric Train and Brussels Skyline.

**1953.** Inaug. of Nord-Midi Junction.

P 1451. P **288.** 200 f. green .. £180 2·25
P 1452. 200 f. green and brown .. .. £190 5·50

P 291. "Nord" Station.

P 292. Central Station.

**1953.** Brussels Railway Stations.

P 1485. P **291.** 1 f. ochre .. .. 20 10
P 1486. 2 f. black .. .. 35 10
P 1487. 3 f. green .. .. 45 10
P 1488. 4 f. orange .. 80 10
P 1489. 5 f. brown .. 80 10
P 1490. – 5 f. brown .. 8·00 40
P 1491. P **291.** 6 f. purple .. 1·00 10
P 1492. 7 f. green .. .. 1·00 10
P 1493. 8 f. red .. .. 1·25 10
P 1494. 9 f. blue .. .. 1·75 10
P 1495. – 10 f. green .. 2·00 10
P 1496. – 10 f. black .. 1·00 30
P 1497. – 15 f. red .. .. 11·00 35
P 1498. – 20 f. blue .. .. 3·50 10
P 1498a. – 20 f. green .. 1·75 30
P 1499. – 30 f. purple .. 5·50 10
P 1500. – 40 f. mauve .. 7·00 10
P 1501. – 50 f. mauve .. 8·00 10
P 1501a. – 50 f. blue .. .. 3·25 40
P 1502. – 60 f. violet .. 16·00 10
P 1503. – 80 f. purple .. 22·00 10
P 1504. P **292.** 100 f. green .. 15·00 10
P 1505. 200 f. blue .. 75·00 50
P 1506. 300 f. mauve .. £140 1·00

DESIGNS—VERT. 5 f. (P 1490), 10 f. (P 1496), 15 f., 20 f. (P 1498a), 50 f. (P 1501a), "Congress" Station. 10 f. (P 1495), 20 f. (P 1498) to 50 f. (P 1501) "Midi" Station. HORIZ. 60 f., 80 f. "Chapelle" Station.

P 295. Electric Train and "Nord" Station, Brussels.

P 326. Mercury and Railway Winged Wheel.

**1953.**

P 1517. P **295.** 13 f. brown .. 16·00 35
P 1518. 18 f. blue .. 16·00 15
P 1519. 21 f. mauve .. 16·00 50

**1956.** Surch. in figures.

P 1585. P **295.** 14 f. on 13 f. brown 10·00 10
P 1586. 19 f. on 18 f. blue 10·00 10
P 1587. 22 f. on 21 f. mauve 10·00 15

**1957.**

P 1600. P **326.** 14 f. green .. 9·00 20
P 1601. 19 f. sepia .. 9·00 20
P 1602. 22 f. red .. .. 9·00 45

**1959.** Surch. **20 F.**

P 1678. P **326.** 20 f. on 19 f. sepia 25·00 15
P 1679. 20 f. on 22 f. red .. 25·00 45

P 357. Brussels "Nord" Station, 1861–1954.

DESIGNS—VERT. 24 f. Brussels "Midi" station, 1869-1949. HORIZ. 26 f. Antwerp Central station, 1905. 28 f. Ghent St. Pieter's station.

**1959.**

P 1695. P **357.** 20 f. olive .. 16·00 15
P 1696. – 24 f. red .. .. 7·00 15
P 1697. – 26 f. blue .. 7·50 1·25
P 1698. – 28 f. purple .. 7·00 1·00

P 368. Congress Seal, Diesel and Electric Locomotives.

**1960.** 75th Anniv. of Int. Railway Congress Assn.

P 1722. P **368.** 20 f. red .. .. 45·00 38·00
P 1723. 50 f. blue .. 45·00 35·00
P 1724. 60 f. purple .. 45·00 35·00
P 1725. 70 f. green .. 45·00 35·00

**1961.** Nos. P 1695/8 surch.

P 1787. P **357.** 24 f. on 20 f. olive 48·00 25
P 1788. – 26 f. on 24 f. red 6·50 25
P 1789. – 28 f. on 26 f. blue 6·50 30
P 1790. – 35 f. on 28 f. purple 6·00 30

P 477. Arlon Station.

**1967.**

P 2017. P **477.** 25 f. ochre .. 11·00 35
P 2018. 30 f. green .. 3·00 35
P 2019. 35 f. blue .. 4·50 85
P 2020. 40 f. red .. .. 23·00 40

P 488. Electric Train "Type 122"

**1968.**

P 2047. P **488.** 1 f. bistre .. .. 15 15
P 2048. 2 f. green .. .. 20 15
P 2049. 3 f. green .. .. 40 15
P 2050. 4 f. orange .. 40 15
P 2051. 5 f. brown .. .. 50 15
P 2052. 6 f. plum .. .. 40 15
P 2053. 7 f. green .. .. 50 15
P 2054. 8 f. red .. .. 60 15
P 2055. 9 f. blue .. .. 1·10 15
P 2056. – 10 f. green .. .. 2·00 15
P 2057. – 20 f. blue .. .. 1·50 15
P 2058. – 30 f. lilac .. .. 3·25 15
P 2059. – 40 f. violet .. 4·25 15
P 2060. – 50 f. purple .. 5·50 15
P 2061. – 60 f. violet .. 5·50 15
P 2062. – 70 f. brown .. 5·50 20
P 2063. – 80 f. purple .. 5·50 15
P 2063a. – 90 f. green .. .. 5·00 25
P 2064. – 100 f. green .. 8·50 15
P 2065. – 200 f. violet .. 12·00 35
P 2066. – 300 f. mauve .. 18·00 1·00
P 2067. – 500 f. yellow .. 28·00 1·25

DESIGNS: 10 f. to 40 f. Electric train ("Type 126"). 50 f., 60 f., 70 f., 80 f., 90 f. Electric train ("Type 160"). 100 f., 200 f., 300 f. Diesel-electric train ("Type 205"). 500 f. Diesel-electric train ("Type 210").

**1970.** Surch.

P 2180. P **477.** 37 f. on 25 f. ochre 55·00 5·00
P 2181. 48 f. on 35 f. blue 6·00 4·00
P 2182. 53 f. on 40 f. red 6·00 4·00

P 551. Ostend Station.

**1971.** Figures of value in black.

P 2192. P **551.** 32 f. ochre .. 1·50 50
P 2193. 37 f. grey .. 10·00 10·00
P 2194. 42 f. blue .. 2·00 50
P 2195. 44 f. mauve .. 2·00 50
P 2196. 46 f. violet .. 2·25 50
P 2197. 50 f. red .. .. 2·50 50
P 2198. 52 f. brown .. 11·00 11·00
P 2199. 54 f. green .. 4·50 1·00
P 2200. 61 f. blue .. 3·25 1·25

**1972.** Nos. P 2192/5 and P 2198/200. Surch. in figures.

P 2256. P **551.** 34 f. on 32 f. ochre 2·00 90
P 2257. 40 f. on 37 f. grey 2·25 90
P 2258. 47 f. on 44 f. mauve 2·25 90
P 2259. 53 f. on 42 f. blue 2·75 40
P 2260. 56 f. on 52 f. brown 2·75 1·00
P 2261. 59 f. on 54 f. green 3·50 1·00
P 2262. 66 f. on 61 f. blue 3·75 40

P 575. Emblems within Bogie Wheels.

**1972.** 50th Anniv. of Int. Railways Union (U.I.C.).

P 2266. P **575.** 100 f. black, red and green .. 13·00 2·50

See also No. 2274.

P 624. Global Emblem.

**1974.** 4th International Symposium of Railway Cybernetics, Washington.

P 2353. P **624.** 100 f. black, red and yellow .. 12·00 2·00

P 671. Railway Junction.

P 698. Railway Station at Night.

**1976.**

P 2431. P **671.** 20 f. blk., bl. & lilac 5·00 1·75
P 2432. 50 f. blk., grn. and turquoise .. 2·25 1·50
P 2433. 100 f. blk. & orge. 4·50 1·75
P 2434. 150 f. blk., mauve and deep mauve 6·50 1·75

**1977.**

P 2505. P **698.** 1000 f. mult. .. 40·00 7·50

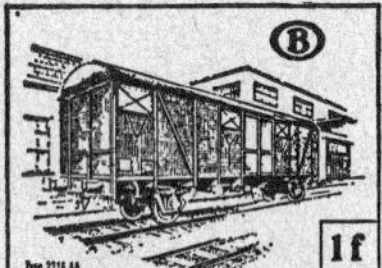

P 753. Goods Wagon, Type "2216 A8".

**1980.** Values in black.

P 2615. P **753.** 1 f. ochre .. .. 15 15
P 2616. 2 f. red .. .. 15 15
P 2617. 3 f. blue .. .. 15 15
P 2618. 4 f. blue .. .. 15 15
P 2619. 5 f. brown .. 20 15
P 2620. 6 f. orange .. 25 20
P 2621. 7 f. violet .. 25 20
P 2622. 8 f. black .. .. 30 20
P 2623. 9 f. green .. .. 40 40
P 2624. – 10 f. brown .. 40 30
P 2625. – 20 f. blue .. .. 1·00 30
P 2626. – 30 f. ochre .. 1·60 30
P 2627. – 40 f. mauve .. 2·00 30
P 2628. – 50 f. purple .. 2·50 30
P 2629. – 60 f. olive .. 3·00 30
P 2630. – 70 f. blue .. .. 3·75 2·00
P 2631. – 80 f. purple .. 4·00 60
P 2632. – 90 f. mauve .. 5·00 2·40
P 2633. – 100 f. red .. .. 5·50 1·00
P 2634. – 200 f. brown .. 10·00 1·25
P 2635. – 300 f. olive .. 16·00 1·60
P 2636. – 500 f. purple .. 27·00 2·40

DESIGNS: 10 f. to 40 f. Goods wagon, Type "3614 A5". 50 f. to 90 f. Self-discharging wagon, Type "1000 D". 100 f. to 500 f. Pneumatic discharging wagon Type "2000 G".

P 833. Train entering Station.

P 877. Buildings and Railway Locomotive.

**1985.** 150th Anniv of Belgian Railways. Paintings by P. Delvaux. Multicoloured.

P 2824. 250 f. Type P **833** .. 13·00 4·75
P 2825. 500 f. Trains in station 24·00 11·00

**1987.**

P 2923. P **877.** 10 f. red .. 40 25
P 2924. 20 f. green .. 80 50
P 2925. 50 f. brown .. 2·50 1·25
P 2926. 100 f. purple .. 5·00 2·40
P 2927. 150 f. brown .. 7·00 3·00

## RAILWAY PARCEL POSTAGE DUE STAMPS

PD 779. Train at Station.

**1982.**

PD 2703. PD **779.** 10 f. red & blk. 1·40 25
PD 2704. 20 f. grn & blk. 1·75 1·25
PD 2705. 50 f. brn. & blk. 3·50 65
PD 2706. 100 f. bl. & blk. 6·00 1·50

## RAILWAY OFFICIAL STAMPS

**For use on the official mail of the Railway Company.**

**1929.** Stamps of 1922 optd with winged wheel.

O 481. **81.** 5 c. slate .. .. 20 10
O 482. 10 c. green .. .. 40 15
O 483. 35 c. green .. .. 55 10
O 484. 60 c. olive .. .. 40 10
O 485. 1 f. 50 blue .. .. 20·00 15·00
O 486. 1 f. 75 blue .. .. 2·75 90

**1929.** Stamps of 1929 optd with winged wheel.

| | | | | |
|---|---|---|---|---|
| O534 | 104 | 5 c. green | 10 | 10 |
| O535 | | 10 c. bistre | 20 | 15 |
| O536 | | 25 c. red | 1·50 | 35 |
| O537 | | 35 c. green | 80 | 35 |
| O538 | | 40 c. purple | 80 | 15 |
| O539 | | 50 c. blue | 40 | 10 |
| O540 | | 60 c. mauve | 9·00 | 7·00 |
| O541 | | 70 c. brown | 3·50 | 1·00 |
| O542 | | 75 c. blue | 4·00 | 80 |

**1932.** Stamps of 1931–34 optd with winged wheel.

| | | | | |
|---|---|---|---|---|
| O620 | 126 | 10 c. green | 60 | 50 |
| O677 | 127 | 35 c. green | 7·50 | 30 |
| O678 | 142 | 70 c. green | 3·00 | 10 |
| O679 | 121 | 75 c. brown | 1·60 | 20 |

**1936.** Stamps of 1936 optd with winged wheel.

| | | | | |
|---|---|---|---|---|
| **O 721.** | **152.** | **10 c. olive** | 25 | 10 |
| **O 722.** | | **35 c. green** | 30 | 10 |
| **O 723.** | | **40 c. lilac** | 45 | 10 |
| **O 724.** | | **50 c. blue** | 60 | 10 |
| **O 725.** | **153.** | **70 c. brown** | 3·00 | 3·00 |
| **O 726.** | | **75 c. olive** | 75 | 15 |

**1941.** Optd **B** in oval frame.

| | | | | |
|---|---|---|---|---|
| O948 | 152 | 10 c. green | 10 | 10 |
| O949 | | 40 c. lilac | 20 | 20 |
| O950 | | 50 c. blue | 10 | 10 |
| O951 | 153 | 1 f. red (No. 747) | 10 | 10 |
| O952a | | 1 f. red (No. 748) | 20 | 10 |
| O953 | | 2 f. 25 black | 30 | 25 |
| O954 | 155 | 2 f. 25 violet | 50 | 35 |

**1942.** Nos. O 722, O 725 and O 726 surch.

| | | | | |
|---|---|---|---|---|
| **O 983.** | **152.** | **10 c. on 35 c. green** | 15 | 15 |
| **O 984.** | **153.** | **50 c. on 70 c. brown** | 20 | 10 |
| **O 985.** | | **50 c. on 75 c. olive** | 15 | 10 |

O 221. O 283.

**1946.** Designs incorporating letter "B".

| | | | | |
|---|---|---|---|---|
| O1156 | O 221 | 10 c. green | 15 | 10 |
| O1157 | | 20 c. violet | 2·40 | 45 |
| O1158 | | 50 c. blue | 15 | 10 |
| O1159 | | 65 c. purple | 3·75 | 40 |
| O1160 | | 75 c. mauve | 15 | 10 |
| O1161 | | 90 c. violet | 5·00 | 25 |
| O1240 | – | 1 f. 35 brown (as 1219) | 2·00 | 35 |
| O1241 | – | 1 f. 75 green (as 1220) | 5·00 | 35 |
| O1242 | 239 | 3 f. purple | 23·00 | 8·25 |
| O1243 | 240 | 3 f. 15 blue | 12·00 | 5·75 |
| O1244 | | 4 f. blue | 20·00 | 13·00 |

**1952.**

| | | | | |
|---|---|---|---|---|
| O1424 | O 283 | 10 c. orange | 35 | 10 |
| O1425 | | 20 c. red | 2·50 | 10 |
| O1426 | | 30 c. green | 1·50 | 45 |
| O1427 | | 40 c. brown | 40 | 10 |
| O1428 | | 50 c. blue | 50 | 10 |
| O1429 | | 60 c. mauve | 80 | 25 |
| O1430 | | 65 c. purple | 25·00 | 22·00 |
| O1431 | | 80 c. green | 3·50 | 80 |
| O1432 | | 90 c. blue | 6·00 | 1·00 |
| O1433 | | 1 f. red | 60 | 10 |
| O1433a | | 1 f. 50 grey | 10 | 10 |
| O1434 | | 2 f. 50 brown | 10 | 10 |

**1954.** As T **289** (King Baudouin) but with letter "B" incorporated in design.

| | | | |
|---|---|---|---|
| O 1523. | 1 f. 50 black | 35 | 10 |
| O 1524. | 2 f. red | 40·00 | 10 |
| O 1525. | 2 f. green | 35 | 10 |
| O 1526. | 2 f. 50 brown | 30·00 | 30 |
| O 1527. | 3 f. mauve | 1·75 | 10 |
| O 1528. | 3 f. 50 green | 65 | 10 |
| O 1529. | 4 f. blue | 1·25 | 25 |
| O 1530. | 6 f. red | 2·00 | 50 |

**1971.** As Nos. 2209/20 but with letter "B" incorporated in design.

| | | | |
|---|---|---|---|
| O2224 | 3 f. green | 1·50 | 75 |
| O2225 | 3 f. 50 brown | 20 | 15 |
| O2226 | 4 f. blue | 1·00 | 35 |
| O2227 | 4 f. 50 purple | 30 | 20 |
| O2228 | 4 f. 50 blue | 40 | 10 |
| O2229 | 5 f. violet | 35 | 10 |
| O2230 | 6 f. red | 20 | 10 |
| O2231 | 6 f. 50 violet | 25 | 20 |
| O2232a | 7 f. red | 35 | 20 |
| O2233 | 8 f. black | 30 | 15 |
| O2233a | 9 f. brown | 30 | 10 |
| O2234 | 10 f. red | 35 | 20 |
| O2235 | 15 f. violet | 60 | 20 |
| O2236 | 25 f. purple | 1·25 | 30 |
| O2237 | 30 f. brown | 1·40 | 30 |

**1977.** As T **684** but with letter "B" incorporated in design.

| | | | |
|---|---|---|---|
| O 2455. | 50 c. brown | 10 | 10 |
| O 2456. | 1 f. mauve | 10 | 10 |
| O 2457. | 2 f. orange | 15 | 10 |
| O 2458. | 4 f. brown | 10 | 10 |
| O 2459. | 5 f. green | 30 | 10 |

# BENIN Pt. 6; Pt. 12

A French possession on the W. coast of Africa incorporated, in 1899, into the colony of Dahomey.

100 centimes = 1 franc.

## A. FRENCH COLONY

**1892.** Stamps of French Colonies. "Commerce" type, optd. **BENIN.**

| | | | | |
|---|---|---|---|---|
| 1. | J. | 1 c. black on blue | £130 | £110 |
| 2. | | 2 c. brown on yellow | £110 | 90·00 |
| 3. | | 4 c. brown on grey | 38·00 | 35·00 |
| 4. | | 5 c. green on pale green | 11·50 | 10·00 |
| 5. | | 10 c. black on lilac | 65·00 | 50·00 |
| 6. | | 15 c. blue on pale blue | 25·00 | 10·00 |
| 7. | | 20 c. red on green | £200 | £190 |
| 8. | | 25 c. black on red | 75·00 | 45·00 |
| 9. | | 30 c. brown on drab | £150 | £130 |
| 10. | | 35 c. black on orange | £150 | £130 |
| 11. | | 40 c. red on yellow | £130 | £110 |
| 12. | | 75 c. red on pink | £325 | £275 |
| 13. | | 1 f. olive | £350 | £300 |

**1892.** Nos. 4 and 6 surch.

| | | | | |
|---|---|---|---|---|
| 14 | J | 01 on 5 c. green on pale green | £225 | £190 |
| 15 | | 40 on 15 c. blue on pale bl | £160 | 70·00 |
| 16 | | 75 on 15 c. blue on pale bl | £750 | £500 |

**1893.** "Tablet" key-type inscr "GOLFE DE BENIN" in red (1, 5, 15, 25, 75 c., 1 f.) or blue (others).

| | | | | |
|---|---|---|---|---|
| 17 | D | 1 c. black on blue | 2·25 | 2·10 |
| 18 | | 2 c brown on buff | 3·00 | 2·50 |
| 19 | | 4 c. brown on grey | 3·00 | 2·50 |
| 20 | | 5 c. green on pale green | 4·25 | 3·50 |
| 21 | | 10 c. black on lilac | 4·25 | 3·50 |
| 22 | | 15 c. blue | 22·00 | 17·00 |
| 23 | | 20 c. red on green | 12·50 | 8·75 |
| 24 | | 25 c. black on pink | 32·00 | 20·00 |
| 25 | | 30 c. brown on drab | 15·00 | 12·50 |
| 26 | | 40 c. red on yellow | 4·25 | 2·75 |
| 27 | | 50 c. red on pink | 3·75 | 2·50 |
| 28 | | 75 c. brown on orange | 7·50 | 6·25 |
| 29 | | 1 f. olive | 48·00 | 42·00 |

**1894.** "Tablet" key-type inscr "BENIN" in red (1, 5, 15, 25, 75 c., 1 f.) or blue (others).

| | | | | |
|---|---|---|---|---|
| 33 | D | 1 c. black on blue | 2·00 | 1·50 |
| 34 | | 2 c. brown on buff | 2·00 | 1·50 |
| 35 | | 4 c. brown on grey | 2·00 | 1·50 |
| 36 | | 5 c. green on pale green | 2·50 | 1·50 |
| 37 | | 10 c. black on lilac | 4·25 | 2·75 |
| 38 | | 15 c. blue | 5·75 | 2·75 |
| 39 | | 20 c. red on green | 5·75 | 4·00 |
| 40 | | 25 c. black on pink | 7·50 | 3·50 |
| 41 | | 30 c. brown on drab | 4·75 | 3·50 |
| 42 | | 40 c. red on yellow | 14·00 | 8·25 |
| 43 | | 50 c. red on pink | 19·00 | 8·75 |
| 44 | | 75 c. brown on orange | 11·50 | 8·25 |
| 45 | | 1 f. olive | 3·25 | 2·50 |

### POSTAGE DUE STAMPS

**1894.** Postage Due stamps of French Colonies optd. **BENIN.** Imperf.

| | | | | |
|---|---|---|---|---|
| D46. | U. | 5 c. black | £110 | 50·00 |
| D47. | | 10 c. black | £110 | 50·00 |
| D48. | | 20 c. black | £110 | 50·00 |
| D49. | | 30 c. black | £110 | 50·00 |

## B. PEOPLE'S REPUBLIC

**The Republic of Dahomey was renamed the People's Republic of Benin on 30 November 1975.**

185. Celebrations.

**1976.** Republic of Benin Proclamation. Multicoloured.

| | | | |
|---|---|---|---|
| 603. | 50 f. Type **185** | 50 | 30 |
| 604. | 60 f. President Kerekou making Proclamation | 70 | 30 |
| 605. | 100 f. Benin arms and flag | 1·25 | 65 |

186. Skiing.

**1976.** Air. Winter Olympic Games, Innsbruck. Multicoloured.

| | | | |
|---|---|---|---|
| 606. | 60 f. Type **186** | 90 | 45 |
| 607. | 150 f. Bobsleighing (vert.) | 1·60 | 95 |
| 608. | 300 f. Figure-skating | 3·50 | 2·00 |

**1976.** Various Dahomey stamps surch **POPULAIRE DU BENIN** and new value (609/11) or surch only (617/18).

| | | | | |
|---|---|---|---|---|
| 617. | **108.** | 50 f. on 1 f. multicoloured (postage) | 50 | 25 |
| 618. | – | 60 f. on 2 f. multicoloured (No. 415) | 60 | 35 |
| 609. | – | 135 f. brown, purple and blue (No. 590) (air) | 1·40 | 75 |
| 610. | – | 210 f. on 300 f. brown, red and blue (No. 591) | 2·10 | 1·10 |
| 611. | – | 380 f. on 500 f. brown, red and grn. (No. 592) | 3·75 | 1·90 |

188. Alexander Graham Bell, Early Telephone and Satellite.

**1976.** Telephone Centenary.

| | | | | |
|---|---|---|---|---|
| 612. | **188.** | 200 f. red, violet & brn. | 2·25 | 1·50 |

189. Basketball.

**1976.** Air. Olympic Games, Montreal. Multicoloured.

| | | | |
|---|---|---|---|
| **613.** | **60 f. Long jump (horiz.)** | 75 | 40 |
| **614.** | **150 f. Type 189** | 1·50 | 90 |
| **615.** | **200 f. Hurdling (horiz.)** | 2·10 | 1·25 |

**191. Scouts and Camp-fire.**

**1976. African Scout Jamboree, Jos, Nigeria.**

| | | | | |
|---|---|---|---|---|
| **619.** | **191.** | **50 f. purple, brn. & blk.** | 65 | 40 |
| **620.** | **–** | **70 f. brn., olive & blk.** | 90 | 50 |

**Design: 70 f. "Comradeship".**

**192.** Konrad Adenauer. **193.** Benin 1 c. Stamp, 1893, and Lion Cub.

**1976.** Air. Birth Centenary of Konrad Adenauer (German statesman).

| | | | | |
|---|---|---|---|---|
| **621.** | **192.** | **90 f. slate, blue & red** | 1·25 | 50 |
| **622.** | **–** | **250 f. blue, red & lt. bl.** | 3·25 | 1·40 |

**Design—horiz. 250 f. Adenauer and Cologne Cathedral.**

**1976.** Air. "Juvarouen 76" Youth Stamp Exhibition, Rouen.

| | | | | |
|---|---|---|---|---|
| **623.** | **–** | **60 f. blue & turquoise** | 90 | 40 |
| **624.** | **193.** | **210 f. red, brn. & olive** | 2·25 | 1·25 |

**Design—horiz. 60 f. Dahomey 60 f. Stamp of 1965, and children's silhouettes.**

**194.** Blood Bank, Cotonou.

**1976.** National Days of Blood Transfusion Service. Multicoloured.

| | | | |
|---|---|---|---|
| 625. | 5 f. Type **194** | 20 | 10 |
| 626. | 50 f. Casualty and blood clinic | 50 | 40 |
| 627. | 60 f. Donor, patient and ambulance | 90 | 50 |

**195.** Manioc. **196.** "Apollo" Emblem and Rocket.

**1976.** National Products Campaign Year. Multicoloured.

| | | | |
|---|---|---|---|
| 628. | 20 f. Type **195** | 25 | 15 |
| 629. | 50 f. Maize cultivation | 60 | 25 |
| 630. | 60 f. Cocoa trees | 80 | 35 |
| 631. | 150 f. Cotton plantation | 1·75 | 75 |

**1976.** 5th Anniv. of "Apollo 14" Space Mission.

| | | | | |
|---|---|---|---|---|
| **632.** | **196.** | **130 f. lake, brn. & blue** | 1·25 | 65 |
| **633.** | **–** | **270 f. blue, turq. & red** | 2·50 | 1·25 |

**Design: 270 f. Landing on Moon.**

REPUBLIQUE POPULAIRE DU BENIN HIPPOTRAGUE 10F POSTES 1976

**197.** Classroom. **198.** Roan Antelope.

**1976.** 3rd Anniv. of Bariba Periodical "Kparo".

| | | | | |
|---|---|---|---|---|
| 634. | **197.** | 50 f. multicoloured | 75 | 40 |

**1976.** Mammals in Pendjari National Park. Multicoloured.

| | | | |
|---|---|---|---|
| 635. | 10 f. Type **198** | 30 | 20 |
| 636. | 30 f. African buffalo | 55 | 45 |
| 637. | 50 f. Hippopotamus (horiz.) | 1·10 | 65 |
| 638. | 70 f. Lion | 1·25 | 75 |

**199.** "Freedom". **200.** "The Annunciation" (Master of Jativa).

**1976.** 1st Anniv. of Proclamation of Republic. Multicoloured.

| | | | |
|---|---|---|---|
| 639. | 40 f. Type **199** | 45 | 25 |
| 640. | 150 f. Maize cultivation | 1·40 | 75 |

**1976.** Air. Christmas. Multicoloured.

| | | | |
|---|---|---|---|
| 641. | 50 f. Type **200** | 65 | 30 |
| 642. | 60 f. "The Nativity" (David) | 75 | 40 |
| 643. | 270 f. "Adoration of the Magi" (Dutch school) | 3·00 | 1·60 |
| 644. | 300 f. "The Flight into Egypt" (Fabriano) (horiz.) | 3·25 | 2·00 |

**201.** Table Tennis and Games Emblem.

**1976.** West African University Games, Cotonou. Multicoloured.

| | | | |
|---|---|---|---|
| 645. | 10 f. Type **201** | 20 | 15 |
| 646. | 50 f. Sports Hall, Cotonou | 55 | 25 |

## INDEX

Countries can be quickly located by referring to the index at the end of this volume.

**202.** Loser with Ticket and Winner with Money.

**1977.** Air. 10th Anniv. of National Lottery.
647. **202.** 50 f. multicoloured .. 65 30

**203.** Douglas DC-10 crossing Globe. **205.** Adder.

**204.** Chateau Sassenage, Grenoble.

**1977.** Europafrique.
648. **203.** 200 f. multicoloured .. 2·25 2·00

**1977.** Air. 10th Anniv. of Int. French Language Council.
649. **204.** 200 f. multicoloured .. 1·90 95

**1977.** Reptiles and Domestic Animals. Multicoloured.
650. 2 f. Type **205** .. .. 20 15
651. 3 f. Tortoise .. .. 20 15
652. 5 f. Zebus .. .. .. 30 20
653. 10 f. Cats .. .. .. 45 20

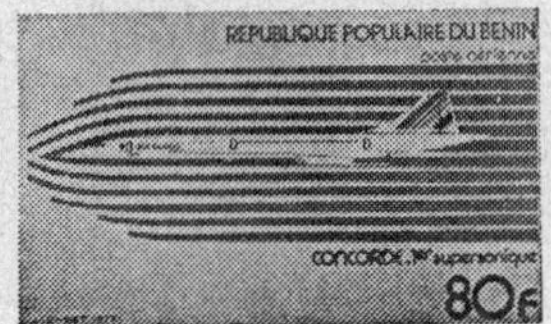

**206.** Concorde.

**1977.** Air. Aviation.
654. **206.** 80 f. red and blue .. 80 45
655. – 150 f. red, violet & grn. 1·75 80
656. – 300 f. vio., red & mve. 2·50 1·60
657. – 500 f. red, blue & grn. 5·00 2·75
DESIGNS: 150 f. "Graf Zeppelin". 300 f. Charles Lindbergh and "Spirit of St. Louis". 500 f. Charles Nungesser and Francois Coli with "L'Oiseau".

**207.** Footballer heading Ball. **208.** Rheumatic Patients.

**1977.** Air. World Football Cup Eliminators. Multicoloured.
658. 60 f. Type **207** .. .. 65 25
659. 200 f. Goalkeeper and players .. .. 1·90 90

**1977.** World Rheumatism Year.
660. **208.** 100 f. multicoloured .. 1·25 65

**209.** Karate. **210.** Mao Tse-tung.

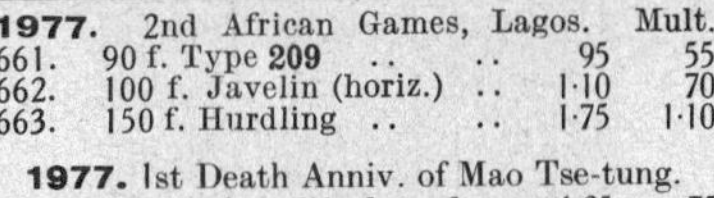

**1977.** 2nd African Games, Lagos. Mult.
661. 90 f. Type **209** .. .. 95 55
662. 100 f. Javelin (horiz.) .. 1·10 70
663. 150 f. Hurdling .. .. 1·75 1·10

**1977.** 1st Death Anniv. of Mao Tse-tung.
665. **210.** 100 f. multicoloured .. 1·25 75

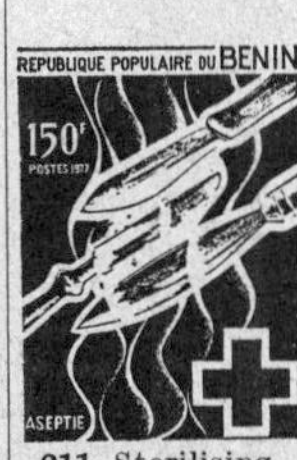

**211.** Sterilising Scalpels. **212.** " Miss Haverfield" (Gainsborough).

**1977.** 150th Birth Anniv. of Joseph Lister.
666. **211.** 150 f. grey, red & carm. 1·60 75
667. – 210 f. olive, grn. & red 2·25 1·10
DESIGN: 210 f. Lister and antiseptic spray.

**1977.** Air. Paintings.
668. **212.** 100 f. green & brown .. 1·25 40
669. – 150 f. brn., bistre & red 1·90 90
670. – 200 f. red and bistre .. 2·50 1·25
DESIGNS: 150 f. " Self-Portrait " (Rubens). 200 f. " Study of an Old Man " (da Vinci).

**213.** " Jarre Trouee " Emblem of King Ghezo (D'Abomey Museum). **214.** Atacora Waterfall.

**1977.** Historic Museums of Benin. Mult.
671. 50 f. Type **213** .. .. 55 35
672. 60 f. Mask (Porto-Novo Museum) (horiz.) .. .. 80 45
673. 210 f. D'Abomey Museum 2·10 1·10

**1977.** Tourism. Multicoloured.
674. 50 f. Type **214** .. .. 50 30
675. 60 f. Stilt houses, Ganvie (horiz.) .. .. 75 45
676. 150 f. Hut village, Savalou 1·90 95

**1977.** Air. 1st Commercial Concorde Flight. Paris–New York. No. 654 optd **1er Vol Commercial 22.11.77 Paris New-York**.
678 **206** 80 f. red and blue .. 1·25 75

**216.** " Viking " on Mars (" Operation Viking ", 1977).

**1977.** Air. Space Conquest Anniversaries.
679. **216.** 100 f. brn., olive & red 90 50
680. – 150 f. bl., turq. & mve. 1·40 75
681. – 200 f. brn., blue & red 2·25 95
682. – 500 f. bl., brn. & olive 5·50 2·75
DESIGNS AND EVENTS: 150 f. Sir Isaac Newton, apple and stars (250th death anniv.). 200 f. Komarov and " Soyuz 2 " over Moon (10th death anniv.). 500 f. Space dog " Laika " and rocket (20th anniv. of ascent into Space).

**217.** Monument, Red Flag Square, Cotonou. **218.** Mother and Child with Owl of Wisdom.

**1977.** Air. 1st Anniv. of Inauguration of Red Flag Square Monument.
683. **217.** 500 f. multicoloured .. 5·00 2·25

**1977.** Fight against Witchcraft. Mult.
684. 60 f. Type **218** .. .. 80 50
685. 150 f. Felling the tree of sorcery .. .. .. 2·00 1·00

**219.** " Suzanne Fourment ".

**1977.** Air. 400th Birth Anniv. of Rubens.
686. **219.** 200 f. brn., red & grn. 2·50 1·10
687. – 380 f. orange & brown 4·50 2·00
DESIGN: 380 f. " Albert Rubens ".

**220.** Battle Scene.

**1978.** " Victory over Imperialism ".
688. **220.** 50 f. multicoloured .. 80 40

**221.** Benin Houses and Map of Heads. **223.** Abdoulaye Issa.

**222.** Sir Alexander Fleming, Microscope and Drugs.

**1978.** General Population Census.
689. **221.** 50 f. multicoloured .. 65 25

**1978.** 50th Anniv. of Discovery of Antibiotics.
690. **222.** 300 f. multicoloured .. 3·75 1·90

**1978.** 1st Death Anniv. of Abdoulaye Issa.
691. **223.** 100 f. multicoloured .. 90 45

**224.** El Hadj Omar.

**1978.** Heroes of Anti-colonial Resistance.
692. – 90 f. multicoloured .. 80 40
693. **224.** 100 f. grn., grey & blue 95 55
DESIGN: 90 f. Samory Toure.

**225.** " Communications ".

**1978.** 10th World Telecommunications Day.
694. **225.** 100 f. multicoloured .. 1·25 65

**226.** Footballer and Stadium.

**1978.** World Cup Football Championship, Argentina. Multicoloured.
695. 200 f. Type **226** .. .. 1·60 85
696. 300 f. Tackling (vert.) .. 2·50 1·40
697. 500 f. Footballer and world map .. .. .. 4·50 2·10

**1978.** Argentina's Victory in World Cup Football Championship. Nos. 695/7 optd.
699. **226.** 200 f. multicoloured .. 1·75 1·10
700. – 300 f. multicoloured .. 2·50 1·75
701. – 500 f. multicoloured .. 4·50 3·00
OPTS: 200 f. **FINALE ARGENTINE: 3 HOLLANDE: 1.** 300 f. **CHAMPION 1978 ARGENTINE.** 500 f. **3e BRESIL, 4e ITALIE.**

**228.** Map, Olympic Flag and Basketball Players.

**1978.** Third African Games, Algiers. Multicoloured.
703. 50 f. Type **228** .. .. 50 25
704. 60 f. African map and Volleyball .. .. 70 40
705. 80 f. Cyclists and map of Algeria .. .. .. 85 45

**229.** Martin Luther King. **230.** Bicycle Taxi (Oueme).

**1978.** 10th Anniv. of Martin Luther King's Assassination.
707. **229.** 300 f. multicoloured .. 2·75 1·50

**1978.** Benin Provinces. Multicoloured.
708. 50 f. Type **230** .. .. 60 30
709. 60 f. Leather work (Borgou) 70 35
710. 70 f. Drums (Oueme) .. 90 45
711. 100 f. Calabash with burnt-work ornamentation (Zou) 1·25 50

**231.** " Stamps " and Magnifying Glass.

**1978.** Philatelic Exhibition, Riccione, Italy.
712. **231.** 200 f. multicoloured .. 1·90 95

**232.** Parthenon and Frieze showing Horsemen.

**1978.** Air. UNESCO Campaign for the Preservation of the Acropolis. Multicoloured.
713. 70 f. Acropolis and Frieze showing Procession .. 70 30
714. 250 f. Type **232** .. .. 2·10 1·00
715. 500 f. The Parthenon (horiz.) .. .. .. 4·25 1·90

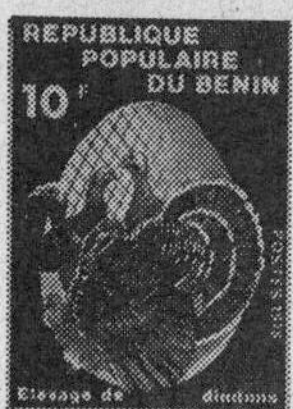

**235.** Turkeys. **236.** Post Runner and Boeing 747.

**1978.** Domestic Poultry. Multicoloured.
722. 10 f. Type **235** .. .. 15 15
723. 20 f. Ducks .. .. 30 15
724. 50 f. Chickens .. .. 80 35
725. 60 f. Guinea Fowl .. 95 45

**1978.** Centenary of U.P.U. Paris Congress. Multicoloured.
726. 50 f. Messenger of the Dahomey Kings (horiz.) 70 30
727. 60 f. Pirogue oarsman, boat and car .. .. 80 35
728. 90 f. Type **236** .. .. 1·00 50

**237.** Red-breasted Merganser and Baden 1851 1 k. Stamp.

**1978.** Air. "Philexafrique" Exhibition, Libreville (Gabon) (1st issue) and Int. Stamp Fair, Essen, West Germany. Mult.
729. 100 f. Type **237** .. .. 2·50 1·25
730. 100 f. African Buffalo and Dahomey 1966, 50 f. African Pygmy Goose stamp .. .. .. 2·50 1·25
See also Nos. 747/8.

**238.** Raoul Follereau.

**1978.** 1st Death Anniv. of Raoul Follereau (leprosy pioneer).
731. **238.** 200 f. multicoloured .. 1·50 75

**239.** Wilbur and Orville Wright and Wright Flyer I.

**1978.** Air. 75th Anniv. of First Powered Flight.
732. **239.** 500 f. blue, yell. & brn. 5·00 2·25

**240.** I.Y.C. Emblem. **241.** Hydrangea.

**1979.** International Year of the Child. Multicoloured.
733. 10 f. Type **240** .. .. 15 15
734. 20 f. Children in balloon .. 20 15
735. 50 f. Children dancing around globe .. .. 40 20

**1979.** Flowers. Multicoloured.
736. 20 f. Type **241** .. .. 20 20
737. 25 f. Assangokan .. .. 25 20
738. 30 f. Geranium .. .. 40 25
739. 40 f. Water Lily (horiz.) .. 45 25

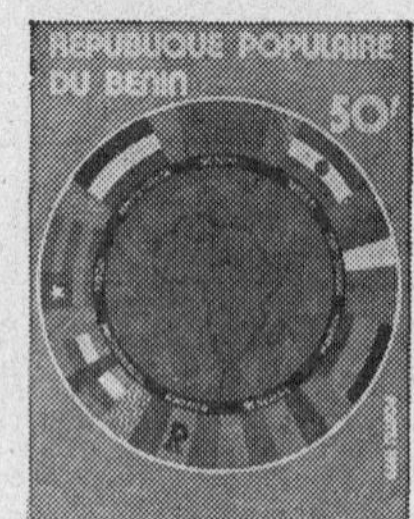

**242.** Flags around Map of Africa.

**1979.** O.C.A.M. Summit Meeting, Cotonou (1st series). Multicoloured.
740. 50 f. Type **242** .. .. 50 30
741. 60 f. Flags and map of Benin 65 40
742. 80 f. O.C.A.M. flag and map of member countries .. 90 45
See also Nos. 754/6.

**1979.** Various stamps surch.
743 **205** 50 f. on 2 f. mult (postage) .. ..
743a – 50 f. on 70 f. brown, green and black (No. 620)
744 **207** 50 f. on 60 f. mult (air) .. ..
745 **192** 50 f. on 90 f. blue, deep blue and red
746 – 50 f. on 150 f. mult (No. 607) .. ..
747 **189** 50 f. on 150 f. mult ..

**244.** Antenna, Satellite and Wave Pattern.

**1979.** World Telecommunications Day.
748. **244** 50 f. multicoloured .. 65 30

**245.** Headquarters Building.

**1979.** West African Savings Bank Building Opening.
749. **245.** 50 f. multicoloured .. 55 30

**246.** " Resolution " and " Discovery " in Karakakoa Bay, Hawaii.

**1979.** Air. Death Bicentenary of Capt. James Cook.
750. **246.** 20 f. blue, green & brown 60 30
751. – 50 f. brown, green & blue 70 40
DESIGN: 50 f. Cook's death at Kowrowa.

**247.** Guelede Mask, Abomey Tapestry and Fiery-breasted Bush Shrike.

**1979.** " Philexafrique " Stamp Exhibition, Gabon. (2nd issue).
752. **247.** 15 f. multicoloured .. 75 20
753. – 50 f. orge., yell. & turq. 95 55
DESIGN: 50 f. Lockheed Tristar 500, satellite, U.P.U. emblem and canoe post.

**1979.** Common African and Mauritian Organization Summit Conference, Cotonou. (2nd issue). Nos 740/2 optd. **26 AU 28 JUIN 1979.**
754. 50 f. Type **242** .. .. 55 30
755. 60 f. Map of Benin and flags of members .. 70 40
756. 80 f. OCAM flag and map showing member countries 90 45

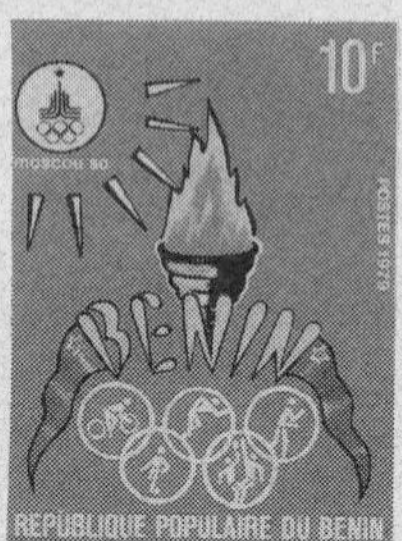

**249.** Olympic Flame, Benin Flags and Pictograms.

**1979.** Pre-Olympic Year. Multicoloured.
757. 10 f. Type **249** .. .. 20 15
758. 50 f. High jump .. .. 65 40

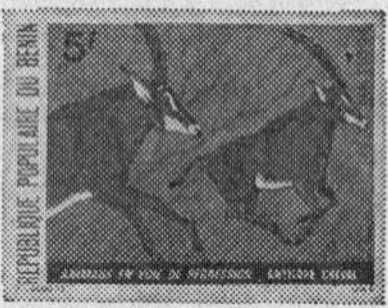

**250.** Roan Antelope.

**1979.** Endangered Animals. Multicoloured.
759. 5 f. Type **250** .. .. 20 15
760. 10 f. Giraffes (vert.) .. 25 20
761. 20 f. Chimpanzee .. .. 45 30
762. 50 f. African elephants (vert.) .. .. .. 1·00 75

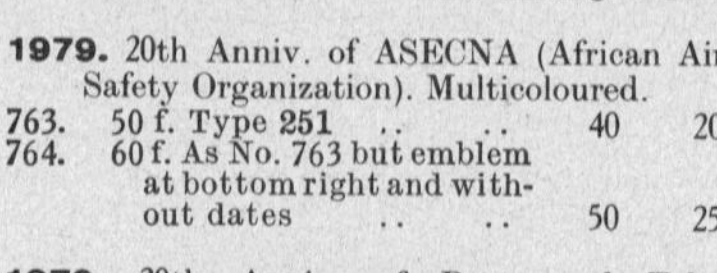

**251.** Emblem, Concorde and Map of Africa. **252.** Post Offices, Antenna, Telephone and Savings Book.

**1979.** 20th Anniv. of ASECNA (African Air Safety Organization). Multicoloured.
763. 50 f. Type **251** .. .. 40 20
764. 60 f. As No. 763 but emblem at bottom right and without dates .. .. 50 25

**1979.** 20th Anniv. of Posts and Telecommunications Office. Multicoloured.
765. 50 f. Type **252** .. .. 50 30
766. 60 f. Collecting, sorting and delivering mail .. 70 35

**253.** Rotary Emblem, Symbols of Services and Globe. **254.** Copernicus and Planetary System.

**1980.** 75th Anniv. of Rotary International. Multicoloured.
767. 90 f. Cotonou Rotary Club banner (vert.) .. .. 75 40
768. 200 f. Type **253** .. .. 1·50 75

**1980.** 50th Anniv. of Discovery of Planet Pluto. Multicoloured.
769. 70 f. Kepler and astrolabe 65 40
770. 100 f. Type **254** .. .. 90 50

**255.** Pharaonic Capital.

**1980.** 20th Anniv. of Nubian Monuments Preservation Campaign. Multicoloured.
771. 50 f. Type **255** .. .. 45 25
772. 60 f. Rameses II, Abu Simbel 55 40
773. 150 f. Temple, Abu Simbel (horiz.) .. .. .. 1·25 75

**256.** Lenin in Library.

**1980.** 110th Birth Anniv. of Lenin. Mult.
774. 50 f. Lenin and globe .. 50 25
775. 150 f. Type **256** .. .. 1·60 65

**257.** Monument.

**1980.** Martyrs. Square, Cotonou.
776. **257.** 50 f. multicoloured .. 40 15
777. – 60 f. multicoloured .. 50 20
778. – 70 f. multicoloured .. 55 25
779. – 100 f. multicoloured .. 80 30
DESIGNS—HORIZ. 60 f. to 100 f. Different views of the monument.

**258.** Farmer using Telephone. **259.** Assan.

**1980.** World Telecommunications Day. Multicoloured.
780. 50 f. Type **258** .. .. 40 25
781. 60 f. Telephone .. .. 50 25

**1980.** Traditional Musical Instruments. Multicoloured.
782. 5 f. Type **259** .. .. 10 10
783. 10 f. Tinbo (horiz.) .. 10 10
784. 15 f. Tam-tam sato .. 15 15
785. 20 f. Kora (horiz.) .. 15 15
786. 30 f. Gangan (horiz.) .. 45 25
787. 50 f. Sinhoun (horiz.) .. 65 40

## MINIMUM PRICE

The minimum price quoted is 10p which represents a handling charge rather than a basis for valuing common stamps. For further notes about prices see introductory pages.

260. Monument.

**1980.** King Gbehanzin Monument.

788. 260. 1000 f. multicoloured 9·50 6·25

261. Dieudonne Costes, Maurice Bellonte and "Point d'Interrogation".

**1980.** 50th Anniv. of First Paris–New York Non-stop Flight.

789. – 90 f. red, pale blue and blue .. .. 75 40
790. 261. 100 f. red, blue & flesh 90 50
DESIGN: 90 f. Airplane "Point d'Interrogation" and scenes of New York and Paris.

262. "Lunokhod I". 263. Show-jumping.

**1980.** 10th Anniv. of "Lunokhod I".

791. – 90 f. brn., bl. & vio. .. 75 50
792. 262. 210 f. pur., bl. & yell. 2·25 1·10
DESIGN: (48 × 36 mm.) 90 f. Rocket and "Lunokhod I".

**1980.** Olympic Games, Moscow. Multicoloured.

793. 50 f. Olympic Flame, running track, emblem and mascot Mischa the bear (horiz.) .. .. .. 45 20
794. 60 f. Type **263** .. .. 50 30
795. 70 f. Judo (horiz.) .. 70 40
796. 200 f. Olympic flag and globe surrounded by sports pictogram .. 1·50 75
797. 300 f. Weightlifting .. 2·50 1·25

264. O.C.A.M. Building.

**1980.** Common African and Mauritian Organization Village. Cotonou, Mult.

798. 50 f. Entrance to O.C.A.M. village .. .. .. 45 20
799. 60 f. View of village .. 50 20
800. 70 f. Type **264** .. .. 70 55

265. Dancers.

**1980.** Agbadja Dance. Multicoloured.

801. 30 f. Type **265** .. .. 40 25
802. 50 f. Singer and musicians 65 40
803. 60 f. Dancers & musicians 75 50

266. Casting a Net. 267. Philippines under Magnifying Glass.

**1980.** Fishing. Multicoloured.

804. 5 f. Type **266** .. .. 10 10
805. 10 f. Fisherman with catch (vert.) .. .. .. 15 15
806. 15 f. Line fishing .. .. 20 20
807. 20 f. Fisherman emptying eel-pot .. .. .. 25 20
808. 50 f. Hauling in a net .. 65 30
809. 60 f. Fish farm .. .. 75 30

**1980.** World Tourism Conference, Manila. Multicoloured.

810. 50 f. Type **267** .. .. 55 25
811. 60 f. Conference flag on globe .. .. .. 70 25

268. "Othreis materna". 269. Map of Africa and Posthorn.

**1980.** Insects. Multicoloured.

812. 40 f. Type **268** .. .. 55 25
813. 50 f. "Othreis fullonia" (butterfly) .. .. 70 25
814. 200 f. "Oryctes" sp. (beetle) .. .. .. 2·50 1·10

**1980.** 5th Anniv. of African Posts and Telecommunications.

815. 269. 75 f. multicoloured .. 65 25

270. Hands freed from Chains. 271. "Self-portrait".

**1980.** 30th Anniv. of Signing of Human Rights Convention. Multicoloured.

816. 30 f. Type **270** .. .. 25 15
817. 50 f. African pushing through bars .. .. .. 45 20
818. 60 f. Figure holding Human Rights flame .. .. 55 20

**1980.** 90th Death Anniv. of Van Gogh (artist). Multicoloured.

819. 100 f. Type **271** .. .. 1·60 65
820. 300 f. "The Postman Roulin" .. .. 4·00 1·90

272. Offenbach and Scene from "Orpheus in the Underworld".

**1980.** Death Centenary of Jacques Offenbach (composer).

821. 272. 50 f. black, red and green 50 25
822. – 60 f. blue, brn. & deep brn. 75 40
DESIGN: 60 f. Offenbach and scene from "La Vie Parisienne".

273. Kepler and Astronomical Diagram.

**1980.** 30th Death Anniv. of Johannes Kepler (astronomer).

823. 273. 50 f. red, blue and grey 55 25
824. – 60 f. blue, black and green 70 25
DESIGN: 60 f. Kepler, satellite and dish aerials.

274. Footballers. 275. Disabled Person holding Flower.

**1981.** Air. World Cup Football Championship. Multicoloured.

825. 200 f. Football and globe .. 1·50 55
826. 500 f. Type **274** .. .. 3·75 1·60

**1981.** International Year of Disabled People.

827. 275. 115 f. multicoloured .. 1·00 40

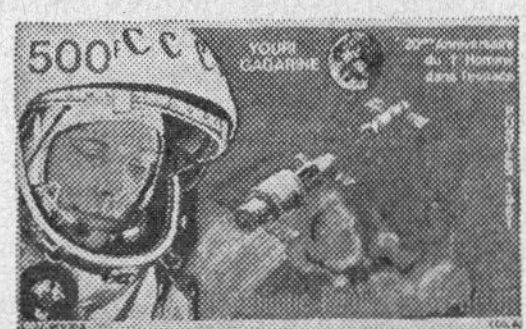

276. Yuri Gagarin.

**1981.** 20th Anniv. of First Man in Space.

828. 276. 500 f. multicoloured .. 4·50 2·50

277. I.T.U. and W.H.O. Emblems and Ribbons forming Caduceus. 278. Amaryllis.

**1981.** World Telecommunications Day.

829. 277. 115 f. multicoloured .. 90 40

**1981.** Flowers. Multicoloured.

830. 10 f. Type **278** .. .. 15 10
831. 20 f. "Eischornia crassipes" 25 20
832. 80 f. "Parkia biglobosa" 90 40

279. Hotel and Map.

**1981.** Opening of Benin Sheraton Hotel.

833. 279. 100 f. multicoloured .. 90 40

**1981.** Surch. **50 f.**

834. 216. 50 f. on 100 f. brown, green and red .. 45 20
835. 193. 50 f. on 210 f. red, brn. and green .. .. 45 20

HAVE YOU READ THE NOTES AT THE BEGINNING OF THIS CATALOGUE?
These often provide answers to the enquiries we receive.

281. Prince Charles, Lady Diana Spencer and Tower Bridge.

**1981.** Air. British Royal Wedding.

836. 281. 500 f. multicoloured .. 3·75 1·75

282. Guinea Pig.

**1981.** Domestic Animals. Multicoloured.

837. 5 f. Type **282** .. .. 15 10
838. 60 f. Cat .. .. .. 50 25
839. 80 f. Dogs .. .. .. 75 40

283. Heinrich von Stephan (founder of U.P.U.).

**1981.** World Universal Postal Union Day.

840. 283. 100 f. slate and red .. 75 40

284. Heads, Quill, Paper Darts and U.P.U. Emblem.

**1981.** International Letter Writing Week.

841. 284. 100 f. blue and purple 75 40

285. "The Dance".

**1981.** Air. Birth Centenary of Pablo Picasso. Multicoloured.

842. 300 f. Type **285** .. .. 2·50 95
843. 500 f. "The Three Musicians" .. .. .. 4·50 1·60

286. Globe, Map of Member Countries and Communication Symbols. 287. St. Theodore Stratilates (tile painting).

**1981.** 5th Anniv. of E.C.O.W.A.S. (Economic Community of West African States).
844. **286.** 60 f. multicoloured .. 65 25

**1981.** Air. Bulgarian State. 1300th Anniv.
845. **287.** 100 f. multicoloured .. 75 35

**288.** Tractor and Map.

**1981.** 10th Anniv. of West African Rice Development Association.
846. **288.** 60 f. multicoloured .. 65 25

**289.** Pope John Paul II.

**1982.** Air. Papal Visit.
847. **289.** 80 f. multicoloured .. 1·50 65

**290.** John Glenn.

**1982.** Air. 20th Anniv. of First United States Manned Space Flight.
848. **290.** 500 f. multicoloured .. 4·25 1·90

**291.** Dr. Robert Koch.

**1982.** Centenary of Discovery of Tubercle Bacillus.
849. **291.** 115 f. multicoloured .. 1·25 45

**292.** Washington, U.S. Flag and Map.

**1982.** 250th Birth Anniv. of George Washington.
850. **292.** 200 f. multicoloured .. 1·90 75

**1982.** Red Cross. Surch. **Croix Rouge 8 Mai 1982.**
851. **266.** 60 f. on 5 f. multicoloured 50 25

**294.** Map of Member Countries and Torch. **295.** Scouts round Campfire.

**1982.** Fifth Economic Community of West African States Summit, Cotonou.
852. **294.** 60 f. multicoloured .. 50 25

**1982.** Air. 75th Anniv. of Boy Scout Movement.
853. **295.** 105 f. multicoloured .. 95 50

**296.** Footballers.

**1982.** World Cup Football Championship, Spain. Multicoloured.
854. 90 f. Type **296** .. .. 75 40
855. 300 f. Leg with sock formed from flags of participating countries and globe/football .. .. .. 2·40 1·10

**1982.** African Posts and Telegraph Union. Surch. **" UAPT 1982 ".**
856. **282.** 60 f. on 5 f. mult. .. 65 30

**298.** Stamp of Map of France and Magnifying Glass.

**1982.** "Philexfrance 82" International Stamp Exhibition, Paris.
857 **298** 90 f. multicoloured .. 75 40

**1982.** World Cup Football Championship Results. Nos. 854/5. optd.
858. 90 f. Type **296** .. .. 75 40
859. 300 f. Leg with flags of participating countries and football "globe" .. 2·40 1·10

OVERPRINTS: 90 f. **"COUPE 82 ITALIE bat RFA 3-1"**. 300 f. **"COUPE 82/1 ITALIE/2 RFA/3 POLOGNE"**.

**1982.** Riccione Stamp Exhibition. Optd. **Riccione 1982.**
860. **231.** 200 f. multicoloured .. 1·50 65

**301.** Laughing Kookaburra. **302.** World Map and Satellite.

**1982.** Birds. Multicoloured.
861. 5 f. Type **301** .. .. 30 20
862. 10 f. Bluethroat (horiz.) .. 45 20
863. 15 f. Barn swallow .. 45 20
864. 20 f. Woodland kingfisher and Village weaver .. 70 25
865. 30 f. Reed warbler (horiz.) 1·10 35
866. 60 f. Warbler (horiz.) .. 1·40 50
867. 80 f. Eagle owl .. .. 2·50 95
868. 100 f. Sulphur-crested cockatoo .. .. .. 3·00 1·25

**1982.** I.T.U. Delegates' Conference, Nairobi.
869. **302.** 200 f. turq., blue & blk. 1·50 65

**303.** U.P.U. Emblem and Heads.

**1982.** U.P.U. Day.
870. **303.** 100 f. grn., blue & brn. 90 40

**305.** " Claude Monet in his Studio ".

**1982.** Air. 150th Birth Anniv. of Edouard Manet (artist).
876. **305.** 300 f. multicoloured .. 5·00 1·90

**306.** " Virgin and Child " (Grunewald).

**1982.** Air. Christmas. Multicoloured.
877. 200 f. Type **306** .. .. 1·90 95
878. 300 f. " Virgin and Child with Angels and Cherubins " (Correggio) .. 2·50 1·25

**307.** Pres. Mitterrand and Pres. Kerekou.

**1983.** Visit of President Mitterrand.
879. **307.** 90 f. multicoloured .. 1·10 45

**1983.** Various stamps surch.
880. – 60 f. on 50 f. multicoloured (No. 798) (postage) .. .. 45 20
881. – 60 f. on 70 f. multicoloured (No. 778) .. 45 20
882. **279.** 60 f. on 100 f. mult. .. 45 25
883. – 75 f. on 80 f. multicoloured (No. 832) .. 75 40
884. – 75 f. on 80 f. multicoloured (No. 839) .. 75 40
885. **262.** 75 f. on 210 f. red, blue and yellow (air) .. 65 35

**309.** Oil Rig and Support Vessels.

**1983.** Seme Oilfield.
886. **309.** 125 f. multicoloured .. 1·10 50

**1983.** Various stamps surch.
887. **267.** 5 f. on 50 f. mult. .. 10 10
888. **284.** 10 f. on 100 f. bl. & pur. 10 10
889. – 10 f. on 200 f. mult. (No. 659) .. .. 10 10
890. – 15 f. on 200 f. red and bistre (No. 670) .. 10 10
891. – 15 f. on 200 f. mult. (No. 796) .. .. 10 10
892. – 15 f. on 210 f. green, deep green and red (No. 667) .. .. 10 10
893. – 15 f. on 270 f. mult. (No. 643) .. .. 10 10
894. **219.** 20 f. on 200 f. brown, red and olive .. 20 10
895. – 25 f. on 70 f. mult. (No. 795) .. .. 25 10
896. – 25 f. on 210 f. mult. (No. 673) .. .. 20 10
897. – 25 f. on 270 f. blue, turq. & red (No. 633) 20 10
898. – 25 f. on 380 f. brown and red (No. 687) .. 25 10
899. – 30 f. on 200 f. brown, blue & red (No. 681) 30 20
900. **290.** 40 f. on 500 f. mult. .. 40 20
901. **282.** 75 f. on 5 f. mult. .. 55 40
902. – 75 f. on 100 f. red, blue and pink (No. 790) 55 40
903. – 75 f. on 150 f. mult. (No. 631) .. .. 55 40
904. – 75 f. on 150 f. violet, red & green (No. 655) 65 40
905. **211.** 75 f. on 150 f. grey, orge. and red .. 55 40
906. – 75 f. on 150 f. dp. brn., brn. & red (No. 669) 65 40

**311.** W.C.Y. Emblem.

**1983.** World Communications Year.
907. **311.** 185 f. multicoloured .. 1·50 65

**312.** Stamps of Benin and Thailand and World Map.

**1983.** Air. " Bangkok 1983 " International Stamp Exhibition.
908. **312.** 300 f. multicoloured .. 2·50 1·25

**313.** Hand with Tweezers and Stamp.

**1983.** " Riccione 83 " Stamp Fair, San Marino.
909. **313.** 500 f. multicoloured .. 3·75 1·60

**314.** First Aid. **315.** Carved Table and Chairs.

**1983.** 20th Anniv. of Benin Red Cross.
910. **314.** 105 f. multicoloured .. 95 50

**1983.** Benin Woodwork. Multicoloured.
911. 75 f. Type **315** .. .. 65 25
912. 90 f. Rustic table and chairs .. .. .. 90 40
913. 200 f. Monkeys holding box 1·60 65

**316.** Boeing 747, World Map and U.P.U. Emblem.

**1983.** U.P.U. Day.
914. **316.** 125 f. grn., bl. & brn. .. 1·00 50

**317.** Egoun. **318.** Rockcoco.

**1983.** Religious Cults. Multicoloured.
915. 75 f. Type **317** .. .. 65 30
916. 75 f. Zangbeto .. .. 65 30

**1983.** Hair-styles. Multicoloured.
917. 30 f. Type **318** .. .. 25 20
918. 75 f. Serpent .. .. 65 40
919. 90 f. Songas .. .. 90 45

**319.** Alfred Nobel.

**1983.** 150th Birth Anniv. of Alfred Nobel.
920. **319.** 300 f. multicoloured .. 2·50 1·25

**320.** " Madonna of Lorette " (Raphael).

**1983.** Air. Christmas.
921. **320.** 200 f. multicoloured .. 1·90 95

**1984.** Various stamps surch.
922. – 5 f. on 150 f. mult. (No. 685) (postage) 15 15
923. **316.** 5 f. on 125 f. green, blue and brown .. 1·50 1·25
924. **292.** 10 f. on 200 f. mult. .. 15 15
925. – 10 f. on 200 f. mult. (No. 913) .. .. 20 20
926. – 15 f. on 300 f. mult. (No. 820) .. .. 20 20
927. – 25 f. on 300 f. mult. (No. 644) .. .. 25 10
928. **276.** 40 f. on 500 f. mult. .. 1·00 90
929. **314.** 75 f. on 105 f. mult. .. 70 60
930. **275.** 75 f. on 115 f. mult. .. 70 45
931. **277.** 75 f. on 115 f. mult. .. 70 60
932. **291.** 75 f. on 115 f. mult. .. 70 60
933. **311.** 75 f. on 185 f. mult. .. 70 60
934. **302.** 75 f. on 200 f. turquise, blue and black .. 70 60
935. **320.** 15 f. on 200 f. mult. (air) 10 10
936. **285.** 15 f. on 300 f. mult. .. 10 10
937. **312.** 25 f. on 300 f. mult. .. 25 10
938. **281.** 40 f. on 500 f. mult. .. 30 25
939. **295.** 75 f. on 105 f. mult. .. 1·00 90
940. **306.** 90 f. on 200 f. mult. .. 70 45
941. **305.** 90 f. on 300 f. mult. .. 70 45

**322.** Flags, Agriculture and Symbols of Unity and Growth.

**323.** U.P.U. Emblem and Magnifying Glass.

**1984.** 25th Anniv. of Council of Unity.
942. **322.** 75 f. multicoloured .. 65 25
943. 90 f. multicoloured .. 75 30

**1984.** 19th Universal Postal Union Congress, Hamburg.
944. **323.** 90 f. multicoloured .. 75 30

**324.** Abomey-Calavi Ground Station.

**325.** Koumboro (Borgou).

**1984.** Inauguration of Abomy-Calavi Ground Station.
945. **324.** 75 f. multicoloured .. 65 40

**1984.** Traditional Costumes. Multicoloured.
946. 5 f. Type **325** .. .. 15 15
947. 10 f. Taka (Borgou) .. 20 20
948. 20 f. Toko (Atacora Province) .. .. 25 25

**326.** Olympic Mascot.

**327.** Plant and Starving Child.

**1984.** Air. Olympic Games, Los Angeles.
949. **326.** 300 f. multicoloured .. 2·50 1·25

**1984.** World Food Day.
950. **327.** 100 f. multicoloured .. 75 35

**328.** Anatosaurus.

**329.** "Virgin and Child" (detail, Murillo).

**1984.** Prehistoric Animals. Multicoloured.
951. 75 f. Type **328** .. .. 75 35
952. 90 f. Brontosaurus .. 1·00 40

**1984.** Air. Christmas.
953. **329.** 500 f. multicoloured .. 4·25 1·90

**1984.** Various stamps surch.
954 **203** 75 f. on 200 f mult. (postage) .. .. 1·50 1·25
955 **226** 75 f. on 200 f. mult. .. 1·25 1·00
956 – 75 f. on 300 f. mult. (No. 696) .. .. 1·25 1·00
957 **229** 75 f. on 300 f. mult. .. 70 45
958 – 90 f. on 300 f. mult. (No. 855) .. .. 1·25 1·00
959 – 90 f. on 500 f. mult. (No. 697) .. .. 1·25 1·00
960 – 90 f. on 500 f. mult. (No. 701) .. .. 1·25 1·00
961 **204** 75 f. on 200 f. mult. (air) .. .. 55 40
962 – 75 f. on 200 f. mult. (No. 825) .. .. 1·25 1·00
963 – 75 f. on 300 f. violet, red and mauve (No. 656) .. .. .. 1·50 1·25
964 – 75 f. on 300 f. mult. (No. 878) .. .. 55 40
965 **239** 90 f. on 500 f. blue, yellow and brown .. 1·50 1·25
966 – 90 f. on 500 f. mult. (No. 715) .. .. 70 40
967 – 90 f. on 500 f. mult. (No. 843) .. .. 70 40

**331.** Sidon Merchant Ship (2nd century).

**1984.** Air. Ships.
968 **331** 90 f. black, green & bl 90 50
969 – 125 f. multicoloured .. 1·40 75
DESIGN—VERT. 125 f. Sail merchantman "Wavertree", 1895.

**332.** Emblem on Globe and Hands reaching for Cultural Symbols.

**333.** Benin Arms.

**1985.** 15th Anniv. of Cultural and Technical Co-operation Agency.
970. **332.** 300 f. multicoloured .. 2·25 95

**1985.** Air. Postal Convention between Benin and Sovereign Military Order of Malta. Multicoloured.
971. 75 f. Type **333** .. .. 60 25
972. 75 f. Arms of Sovereign Military Order .. .. 60 25

**334.** Soviet Flag, Soldier and Tank.

**335.** Teke Dance, Borgou.

**1985.** 40th Anniv of End of Second World War.
973 **334** 100 f. multicoloured

**1985.** Traditional Dances. Multicoloured.
974 75 f. Type **335** .. .. 65 40
975 100 f. Tipen ti dance, Atacora .. .. 95 50

**1985.** Various Dahomey Stamps optd. **POPULAIRE DU BENIN** (985/6) or **REPUBLIQUE POPULAIRE DU BENIN** (others), Nos. 976/7 and 979/85 surch. also.
976 **174** 15 f. on 40 f. mult (postage) .. .. 20 10
977 **182** 25 f. on 40 f. brown, blue and violet (air) 20 10
978 **115** 40 f. black, pur & bl 25 10
978a – 75 f. on 85 f. brown, blue & grn (No. 468) 50 25
979 – 75 f. on 85 f. brown, blue & grn (No. 482) 50 25
980 **135** 75 f. on 100 f. purple, violet and green .. 50 25
981 – 75 f. on 125 f. green, blue & pur (No. 509) 50 25
982 **127** 90 f. on 20 f. brown, blue and green .. 65 40
983 – 90 f. on 150 f. purple blue & brn (No. 456) 65 40
984 – 90 f. on 200 f. green, red & blue (No. 438) 65 40
985 – 90 f. on 200 f. mult (No. 563) .. .. 65 40
986 – 150 f. mult (No. 562) 1·00 65

**338.** Oil Rig.

**1985.** Air. "Philexafrique" International Stamp Exhibition, Lome, Togo. (1st issue). Multicoloured.
987. 200 f. Type **338** .. .. 2·00 1·40
988. 200 f. Footballers .. .. 1·90 1·25
See also Nos. 999/1000.

**339.** Emblem.

**1985.** International Youth Year.
989. **339.** 150 f. multicoloured .. 1·10 55

**340.** Football between Globes.

**1985.** World Cup Football Championship, Mexico (1986) (1st issue).
990. **340.** 200 f. multicoloured .. 1·50 80
See also No. 1015.

**341.** Boeing 727, Map and Emblem.

**1985.** 25th Anniv. of Aerial Navigation Security Agency for Africa and Malagasy.
991. **341.** 150 f. multicoloured .. 1·25 90

**342.** "Boletus edulis."

**343.** Audubon and Arctic Skua.

**1985.** Fungi. Multicoloured.
992 35 f. Type **342** .. .. 1·40 45
993 40 f. "Amanita phalloides" 1·90 95
994 100 f. "Paxillus involutus" 4·50 1·90

**1985.** Birth Bicentenary of John J. Audubon (ornithologist). Multicoloured.
995. 150 f. Type **343** .. .. 2·00 1·10
996. 300 f. Audubon and oyster-catcher .. .. .. 4·50 2·40

**344.** Emblem, Hands and Dove.

**1985.** 40th Anniv. of United Nations Organization and 25th Anniv. of Benin's Membership.
997. **344.** 250 f. multicoloured .. 1·90 90

**345.** Stamps and Globe.

**1985.** "Italia '85" International Stamp Exhibition, Rome.
998. **345.** 200 f. multicoloured .. 1·50 80

**1985.** "Philexafrique" International Stamp Exhibition, Lome, Togo (2nd issue). As Type **338**. Multicoloured.
999 250 f. Forest and hand holding tools .. .. 2·50 1·60
1000 250 f. Magnifying glass over judo stamp .. 2·50 1·60

**1985.** Various Dahomey stamps optd. **Republique Populaire du Benin.** Nos 1001/9 and 1011 surch. also.
1001. – 75 f. on 35 f. mult. (No. 596) (postage) 50 25
1002. – 90 f. on 70 f. mult. (No. 419) .. .. 70 35
1003. – 90 f. on 140 f. mult. (No. 446) .. .. 70 35
1004. **113.** 100 f. on 40 f. red, brown and green .. 75 40
1005. – 150 f. on 45 f. mult. (No. 597) .. .. 1·10 65
1006. – 75 f. on 70 f. mult. (No. 342) (air) .. 1·40 1·75
1007. – 75 f. on 100 f. mult. (No. 251) .. .. 2·00 60
1008. **59.** 75 f. on 200 f. mult. 2·00 60
1009. – 90 f. on 250 f. mult. (No. 272) .. .. 2·00 60
1010. **110.** 100 f. multicoloured 45 40
1011. – 150 f. on 500 f. mult. (No. 252) .. .. 3·00 1·40
No. 1010 is surcharged on the unoverprinted unissued stamp subsequently issued as No. 422.

**349.** Church, Children playing and Nativity Scene.

**1985.** Air. Christmas.
1012. **349.** 500 f. multicoloured 4·00 1·60

**350.** Emblem.

**1986.** 10th Anniv. of African Parliamentary Union and Ninth Conference, Cotonou.
1013. **350.** 100 f. multicoloured 75 40

**351.** Halley, Comet and "Giotto" Space Probe.

**1986.** Appearance of Halley's Comet.
1014. **351.** 205 f. multicoloured 2·25 1·25

**352.** Footballers.

**1986.** World Cup Football Championship, Mexico (2nd issue). Multicoloured.
1015. **352.** 500 f. Footballers .. 3·75 1·75

**353.** Dead and Healthy Trees.

**354.** Amazone.

**1986.** Anti-desertification Campaign.
1016. **353.** 150 f. multicoloured 1·25 65

**1986.**
1017. **354.** 100 f. blue .. .. 65 20
1018. 150 f. purple .. 95 25

**355.** "Haemanthus".

**356.** "Inachis io", "Aglais urticae" and "Nymphalis antiopa".

**1986.** Flowers. Multicoloured.
1019 100 f. Type **355** .. .. 90 65
1020 205 f. "Hemerocallis" .. 1·90 1·00

**1986.** Butterflies. Multicoloured.
1021 150 f. Type **356** .. .. 1·50 95
1022 150 f. "Anthocharis cardamines", "Papilio machaon" and "Cynthia cardui" .. 1·50 95

**1986.** Various stamps of Dahomey surch **Republique Populaire du Benin** and new value.
1024 – 150 f. on 100 f. mult (444) (postage) ..
1025 – 15 f. on 85 f. mult (600) (air) .. ..
1026 – 25 f. on 200 f. mult (432)
1027 **150** 25 f. on 200 f. dp grn, vio & grn .. ..
1030 **175** 100 f. purple, ind & bl
1031 **128** 150 f. on 100 f. blue, violet and red ..

**358.** Statue and Buildings.

**359.** Bust of King Behanzin.

**1986.** Centenary of Statue of Liberty.
1032. **358.** 250 f. multicoloured 2·25 1·00

**1986.** King Behanzin.
1033. **359.** 440 f. multicoloured 3·75 1·90
For design in smaller size, see Nos. 1101/4.

**360.** Family with Crib, Church and Nativity Scene.

**1986.** Air. Christmas.
1034. **360.** 300 f. multicoloured 2·50 1·10

**361.** Rainbow and Douglas DC-10.

**362.** Emblem around Map in Cog.

**1986.** Air. 25th Anniv. of Air Afrique.
1035 **361** 100 f. multicoloured .. 70 45

**1987.** Brazil Culture Week, Cotonou.
1036. **362.** 150 f. multicoloured 1·10 50

**363.** Cotonou Centre for the Blind and Partially Sighted.

**1987.** Rotary International 910 District Conference, Cotonou.
1037. **363.** 300 f. multicoloured 2·50 1·10

**1987.** Various stamps of Dahomey optd **Republique Populaire du Benin**, Nos. 1038/9 and 1043/53 surch also.
1038 **129** 10 f. on 65 f. black, violet & red (post)
1039 – 15 f. on 100 f. red, blue & green (434)
1040 **98** 40 f. green, bl & brn
1043 **144** 10 f. on 65 f. black, yellow and purple (air) .. ..
1046 – 25 f. on 150 f. mult (487) .. ..
1047 – 30 f. on 300 f. mult (602) .. ..
1048 **140** 40 f. on 15 f. purple, green and blue ..
1049 – 40 f. on 100 f. mult (453) .. ..
1051 – 50 f. on 140 f. mult (601) .. ..
1052 – 50 f. on 500 f. mult (252) .. ..
1053 – 70 f. on 250 f. mult (462) .. ..
1054 – 80 f. mult (286) ..
1055 – 100 f. mult (429) ..
1055a – 100 f. mult (447) ..

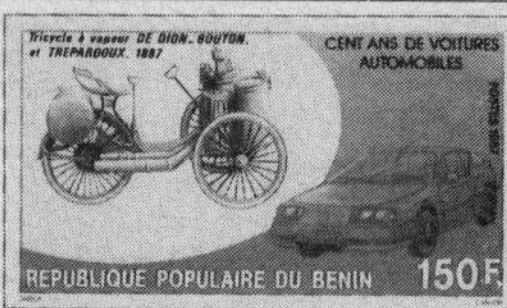

**365.** De Dion-Bouton and Trepardoux Steam Tricycle and Modern Ford Motor Car.

**1987.** Centenary of Motor Car. Multicoloured.
1058. 150 f. Type **365** .. .. 1·25 65
1059. 300 f. Daimler petrol motor car "Victoria" and modern Mercedes car .. .. .. 2·50 1·25

**366.** Baptism in the Python Temple.

**368.** G. Hansen and R. Follereau (leprosy pioneers) and Patients.

**367.** Shrimp.

**1987.** Ritual Ceremonies.
1060. **366.** 100 f. multicoloured 95 50

**1987.** Shellfish. Multicoloured.
1061. 100 f. Type **367** .. .. 95 50
1062. 150 f. Crab .. .. 1·25 75

**1987.** Anti-Leprosy Campaign.
1063. **368.** 200 f. multicoloured 1·90 95

**369.** Crop-spraying and Locusts.

**1987.** Anti-locust Campaign.
1064. **369.** 100 f. multicoloured 95 50

**370.** Fisherman and Farmer.

**1987.** Air. 10th Anniv. of International Agricultural Development Fund.
1065. **370.** 500 f. multicoloured 3·75 1·90

**371.** Nativity Scene in Moon and Father Christmas giving Sweets to Crowd.

**1987.** Christmas.
1066. **371.** 150 f. multicoloured 1·25 75

**372** Rally

**375** Hands holding Pot Aloft

**1988.** 15th Anniv (1987) of Start of Benin Revolution.
1067 **372** 100 f. multicoloured ..

**1988.** Various stamps surch.
(a) Stamps of Dahomey surch **Populaire du Benin** (1081c) or **Republique Populaire du Benin** (others).
1068 – 5 f. on 3 f. black & bl (173) (postage) ..
1069 – 20 f. on 100 f. mult (506) .. ..
1071 – 25 f. on 100 f. mult (576) .. ..
1073 – 50 f. on 45 f. mult (320) .. ..
1074 **178** 55 f. on 200 f. olive, brown and green
1076 **116** 10 f. on 50 f. black, orange & blue (air)
1077 **161** 15 f. on 150 f. red and black ..
1078 – 25 f. on 100 f. mult (526) .. ..
1079 **156** 25 f. on 100 f. blue, brown and violet
1079a **153** 40 f. on 35 f. mult ..
1080 – 40 f. on 100 f. mult (495) .. ..
1081 **162** 40 f. on 150 f. red, brown and blue ..
1081a **148** 100 f. brown & green
1081b **181** 125 f. on 75 f. lilac, red and green ..
1081c – 125 f. on 150 f. blue and purple (541) ..
1082 – 125 f. on 250 f. multicoloured (491)
1083 – 190 f. on 250 f. brown, green and red (594) .. ..

(b) No. 618 of Benin surch **Republique Populaire du Benin**
1085 – 10 f. on 60 f. on 2 f. multicoloured ..

(c) Stamps of Benin surch only
1086 **359** 125 f. on 440 f. mult (postage) ..
1087 **338** 125 f on 200 f. mult (air) .. ..
1088 – 190 f. on 250 f. mult (999) .. ..
1089 – 190 f. on 250 f. mult (1000) .. ..

**1988.** 25th Anniv of Organization of African Unity.
1094 **375** 125 f. multicoloured .. 95 40

**376** Resuscitation of Man pulled from River

**1988.** 125th Anniv of Red Cross Movement.
1095 **376** 200 f. multicoloured .. 1·50 1·00

**377** King

**378** Scout and Camp

**1988.** 20th Death Anniv of Martin Luther King (Civil Rights leader).
1096 **377** 200 f. multicoloured .. 1·50 75

**1988.** 1st Benin Scout Jamboree, Savalou.
1097 **378** 125 f. multicoloured .. 1·00 75

**379** Healthy Family and Health Care

**1988.** 40th Anniv of W.H.O. and 10th Anniv of "Health for All by 2000" Declaration.
1098 **379** 175 f. multicoloured .. 1·25 65

**380** Dugout Canoes and Houses

**1988.** Ganvie (lake village). Multicoloured.
1099 125 f. Type **380** .. .. 95 50
1100 190 f. Boatman and houses .. .. 1·60 75

**1988.** As T **359** but smaller (17 × 24 mm).
1101 **359** 40 f. black .. .. 25 15
1102 125 f. red .. .. 75 25
1103 190 f. blue .. .. 1·25 25
1104 220 f. green .. .. 1·50 40

**381** Adoration of the Magi

**1988.** Air. Christmas.
1105 **381** 500 f. multicoloured .. 3·75 1·90

**382** Offering to Hebiesso, God of Thunder

**1988.** Ritual Ceremony.
1106 **382** 125 f. multicoloured .. 95 50

**383** Roseate Tern

**1989.** Endangered Animals. Roseate Tern. Multicoloured.
1107 10 f. Type **383** .. .. 25 15
1108 15 f. Tern with fish .. 25 15
1109 50 f. Tern on rocks .. 1·00 40
1110 125 f. Tern flying .. 2·50 85

**HAVE YOU READ THE NOTES AT THE BEGINNING OF THIS CATALOGUE?**
These often provide answers to the enquiries we receive.

**384** Eiffel Tower

Republique Populaire du Benin
75f POSTES

**386** Tractor, Map and Pump

**1989.** Centenary of Eiffel Tower.
1111 **384** 190 f. multicoloured .. 1·60 1·00

**1989.** 30th Anniv of Agriculture Development Council.
1113 **386** 75 f. multicoloured ..

**387** Symbols of Revolution and France 1950 National Relief Fund Stamps

**1989.** Bicentenary of French Revolution and "Philexfrance 89" International Stamp Exhibition, Paris.
1114 **387** 190 f. multicoloured 1·90 1·25

**388** Burbot

**1989.** Fishes. Multicoloured.
1115 125 f. Type **388** .. .. 95 50
1116 190 f. Pike and salmon .. 1·40 75

**389** Circuit Breaker, Illuminated Road and Solar Energy Complex

**390** Lion within Wreath

**1989.** 20th Anniv of Benin Electricity Community.
1117 **389** 125 f. multicoloured .. 95 50

**1989.** Death Centenary of King Glele.
1118 **390** 190 f. multicoloured .. 1·40 75

**391** Nativity

**1989.** Christmas.
1119 **391** 200 f. multicoloured .. 1·50 90

**392** Anniversary Emblem and Means of Communications

**1990.** Centenary of Postal and Telecommunications Ministry (1st issue).
1120 **392** 125 f. multicoloured .. 95 50
See also No. 1127.

**393** Oranges

**1990.** Fruit and Flowers. Multicoloured.
1121 60 f. Type **393** .. .. 45 30
1122 190 f. Kaufmannia tulips (vert) .. .. .. 1·40 75
1123 250 f. Cashew nuts (vert) 1·90 1·10

**394** Launch of "Apollo 11" and Footprint on Moon

**1990.** 21st Anniv of First Manned Moon Landing.
1124 **394** 190 f. multicoloured .. 1·40 75

**395** Footballers

**1990.** World Cup Football Championship, Italy. Multicoloured.
1125 125f. Type **395** .. .. 95 50
1126 190 f. Mascot holding torch and pennant (vert) .. .. .. 1·40 65

LIQUE DU BE
190F

**396** Balloons, Emblem and Means of Communication

**398** De Gaulle

**1990.** Centenary of Postal and Telecommunications Ministry (2nd issue).
1127 **396** 150 f. multicoloured .. 1·10 55

**1990.** World Cup Finalists. No. 1125 optd **FINALE R.F.A.-ARGENTINE 1-0.**
1128 **395** 125 f. multicoloured .. 80 50

**1990.** Birth Centenary of Charles de Gaulle (French statesman) (1st issue).
1129 **398** 190 f. multicoloured .. 1·50 1·00
See also No. 1160.

**399** "Galileo" Space Probe orbiting Jupiter

**400** Nativity

**1990.** Space Exploration.
1130 **399** 100 f. multicoloured .. 75 50

**1990.** Christmas.
1131 **400** 200 f. multicoloured .. 1·50 1·00

**401** Hands pointing to Scales of Justice

**1990.** National Conference of Active Forces.
1132 **401** 125 f. multicoloured ..

**406** Different Cultures and Emblem

**1991.** African Tourism Year.
1150 **406** 190 f. multicoloured .. 1·50 1·00

**407** Tennis Player

**408** Flag and Arms

**1991.** Centenary of French Open Tennis Championships.
1151 **407** 125 f. multicoloured .. 95 50

**1991.** 31st Anniv of Independence.
1152 **408** 125 f. multicoloured .. 95 40

**1991.** "Riccione 91" Stamp Fair. No. 1130 optd **"Riccione 91"**.
1153 **399** 100 f. multicoloured .. 75 60

**410** Adoration of the Magi

**1991.** Christmas.
1154 **410** 125 f. multicoloured .. 95 40

411 Guelede Dancer

412 Mozart

**1991.**
1155 **411** 190 f. multicoloured .. 1·50 65

**1991.** Death Bicentenary of Wolfgang Amadeus Mozart (composer).
1156 **412** 1000 f. multicoloured 7·50 4·50

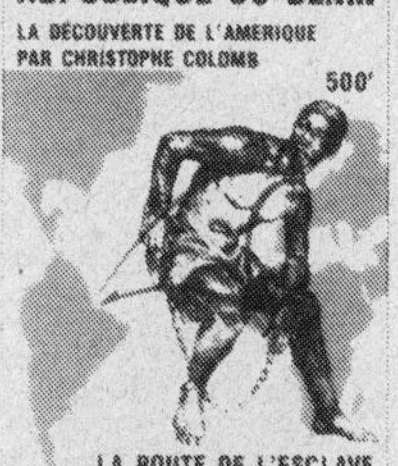


**413** Slave in Chains and Route Map

**1992.** 500th Anniv of Discovery of America by Columbus.
1157 **413** 500 f. black, brown and blue .. .. 3·75 2·50
1158 – 1000 f. multicoloured 7·00 5·00
DESIGN—HORIZ. 1000 f. Columbus landing at Guanahami, Bahamas.

**1992.** Birth Centenary (1990) of Charles de Gaulle (French statesman) (2nd issue). As No. 1129 but value changed.
1160 **398** 300 f. multicoloured .. 2·25 1·50

**414** Child, Produce and Emblems

**415** Pope John Paul II

**1992.** International Nutrition Conference, Rome.
1161 **414** 190 f. multicoloured .. 1·40 1·00

**1993.** Papal Visit.
1162 **415** 190 f. multicoloured .. 1·25 90

**416** Emblem and Voodoo Culture

**1993.** "Ouidah 92" Voodoo Culture Festival.
1163 **416** 125 f. multicoloured .. 75 50

**417** Well and Blue-throated Roller

**1993.** Possotome Artesian Well.
1164 **417** 125 f. multicoloured .. 75 50

**418** Map, Clasped Hands and Flags of Member Countries

**1993.** 30th Anniv of Organization of African Unity.
1165 **418** 125 f. multicoloured .. 70 40

**419** John F. Kennedy (President of United States, 1961–63)

**1993.** Death Anniversaries. Multicoloured.
1166 190 f. Type **419** (30th anniv) .. .. 85 45
1167 190 f. Dr. Martin Luther King (American civil rights campaigner, 25th anniv) (vert) .. .. 85 45

**1993.** Stamps of Dahomey variously optd or surch. (a) Optd **REPUBLIQUE DU BENIN**.
1190 **126** 100 f. mult (air) ..

(b) Optd **DU BENIN**.
1211 – 25 f. multicoloured (441) (postage) ..
1225 – 25 f. on 85 f. mult (600) (air) .. ..
1227 **140** 30 f. on 15 f. purple, green and blue ..
1231 – 125 f. on 70 f. multicoloured (383)

(c) Optd **BENIN**.
1266 – 300 f. brown, red and blue (591) (air) ..

**425** Water Polo

**1995.** Olympic Games, Atlanta (1996). Mult.
1278 45 f. Type **425** .. .. 10 10
1279 50 f. Throwing the javelin (vert) .. .. .. 15 10
1280 75 f. Weightlifting (vert) 20 10
1281 100 f. Tennis (vert) .. 25 15
1282 135 f. Baseball (vert) .. 35 20
1283 200 f. Synchronised swimming (vert) .. 50 25

**426** Paddle-steamer

**1995.** Ships. Multicoloured.
1285 40 f. Type **426** .. .. 10 10
1286 50 f. "Charlotte" .. 15 10
1287 75 f. "Citta di Catania" .. 20 10
1288 100 f. "Mountbatten" SR-N4 (hovercraft) .. 25 15
1289 135 f. "Queen Elizabeth 2" (liner) .. .. 35 20
1290 200 f. "Matsu-Nef" (atomic-powered freighter) .. .. 50 25

**427** Chimpanzee

**1995.** Primates. Multicoloured.
1292 50 f. Type **427** .. .. 15 10
1293 75 f. Mandrill .. .. 20 10
1294 100 f. Colobus .. .. 25 15
1295 135 f. Barbary ape .. 35 20
1296 200 f. Hamadryas baboon 50 25

**428** Tabby Shorthair

**1995.** Cats. Multicoloured.
1298 40 f. Type **428** .. .. 10 10
1299 50 f. Sorrel Abyssinian ("Ruddy red") .. 15 10
1300 75 f. White Persian long-hair .. .. .. 20 10
1301 100 f. Seal colourpoint .. 25 15
1302 135 f. Tabby point .. 35 20
1303 200 f. Black shorthair .. 50 25

**429** German Shepherd

**1995.** Dogs. Multicoloured.
1305 40 f. Type **429** .. .. 10 10
1306 50 f. Beagle .. .. 15 10
1307 75 f. Great dane .. .. 20 10
1308 100 f. Boxer .. .. 25 15
1309 135 f. Pointer .. .. 35 20
1310 200 f. Long-haired fox terrier .. .. .. 50 25

**430** Arms **431** Lion

**1995.**
1312 **430** 135 f. multicoloured .. 35 20
1313 150 f. multicoloured .. 35 20
1314 200 f. multicoloured .. 50 25

**1995.** Mammals. Multicoloured.
1315 50 f. Type **431** .. .. 15 10
1316 75 f. African buffalo .. 20 10
1317 100 f. Chimpanzee .. 25 15
1318 135 f. Impala .. .. 35 20
1319 200 f. Cape ground squirrel (horiz) .. 50 25

**432** Hawfinches

**433** "Dracunculus vulgaris"

**1995.** Birds and their Young. Multicoloured.
1321 40 f. Type **432** .. .. 10 10
1322 50 f. Spotted doves .. 15 10
1323 75 f. Peregrine falcons .. 20 10
1324 100 f. Blackburnian warblers .. .. 25 15
1325 135 f. Black-headed gulls 35 20
1326 200 f. Eastern white pelican .. .. 50 25

**1995.** Flowers. Multicoloured.
1327 40 f. Type **433** .. .. 10 10
1328 50 f. Daffodil .. .. 15 10
1329 75 f. Amaryllis .. .. 20 10
1330 100 f. Water-lily .. .. 25 15
1331 135 f. "Chrysanthemum carinatum" .. .. 35 20
1332 200 f. Iris .. .. 50 25

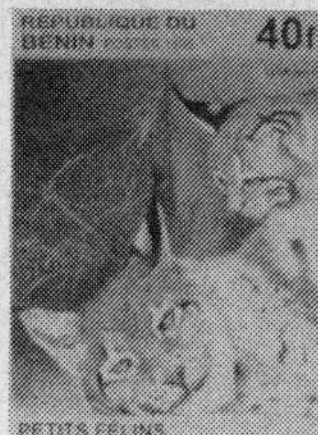


**434** Lynx

**435** "Angraecum sesquipedale"

**1995.** Big Cats and their Young. Mult.
1333 40 f. Type **434** .. .. 10 10
1334 50 f. Pumas .. .. 15 10
1335 75 f. Cheetahs .. .. 20 10
1336 100 f. Leopards .. .. 25 15
1337 135 f. Tigers .. .. 35 20
1338 200 f. Lions .. .. 50 25

**1995.** Orchids. Multicoloured.
1339 40 f. Type **435** .. .. 10 10
1340 50 f. "Polystachya virginea" .. .. 15 10
1341 75 f. "Disa uniflora" .. 20 10
1342 100 f. "Ansellia africana" 25 15
1343 135 f. "Angraecum eichlerianum" .. 35 20
1344 200 f. "Jumellea confusa" 50 25

**436** Emblem

**1995.** 6th Francophone Summit, Cotonou.
1345 **436** 150 f. multicoloured .. 35 20
1346 200 f. multicoloured .. 50 25

PARCEL POST STAMPS

**1982.** Optd. or surch. **Colis Postaux.**
**P 871.** – 100 f. multicoloured (No. 779) (postage) 75 40
**P 872. 256.** 100 f. on 150 f. multicoloured .. .. 75 40
**P 873.** – 300 f. multicoloured (No. 797) .. 2·25 1·10
**P 874. 260.** 1000 f. multicoloured 6·75 3·25
**P 875. 274.** 5000 f. on 500 f. multicoloured (air) .. 35·00 17·00

**1988.** No. 543 of Dahomey surch **Republique Populaire du Benin colis postaux 500 f.**
P1093 – 500 f. on 200 f. mult .. 3·00 1·90

POSTAGE DUE STAMPS

**D 233.** Pineapples.

**1978.** Fruits. Multicoloured.
**D 716.** 10 f. Type D **233** .. 25 20
**D 717.** 20 f. Cashew nuts (vert.) 40 30
**D 718.** 40 f. Oranges .. .. 70 50
**D 719.** 50 f. Breadfruit .. 90 65

**D 234.** Village Postman on Bicycle.

**1978.** Rural Post.
**D 720. D 234.** 60 f. brn., grn. & red 65 40
**D 721.** – 80 f. blue, brn. & red 75 45
**DESIGN:** 80 f. River village and postman in canoe.

## BERGEDORF Pt. 7

A German city on the Elbe, governed by Hamburg and Lubeck until 1867 when it was purchased by the former. In 1868 became part of North German Confederation.

16 schilling = 1 Hamburg mark.

1.

**1861.** Various sizes. Imperf.

| No. | Type | Description | Unused | Used |
|---|---|---|---|---|
| 1. | 1. | ½ s. black on lilac | £375 | |
| 2. | | ½ s. black on blue | 40·00 | £550 |
| 4. | | 1 s. black on white | 40·00 | £250 |
| 5. | | 1½ s. black on yellow | 20·00 | £1000 |
| 6. | | 3 s. black on red | £550 | |
| 7. | | 3 s. blue on red | 25·00 | £1300 |
| 8. | | 4 s. black on brown | 25·00 | £1800 |

## BHUTAN Pt. 21

**An independent territory in treaty relations with India and bounded by India, Sikkim and Tibet.**

100 chetrum = 1 ngultrum.

1. Postal Runner.

2. " Uprooted Tree " Emblem and Crest of Bhutan.

**1962.**

| No. | Type | Description | Unused | Used |
|---|---|---|---|---|
| 1 | 1 | 2 ch. red and grey | 10 | 10 |
| 2 | – | 3 ch. red and blue | 20 | 20 |
| 3 | – | 5 ch. brown and green | 1·00 | 1·00 |
| 4 | – | 15 ch. yellow, black and red | 10 | 10 |
| 5 | 1 | 33 ch. green and violet | 20 | 20 |
| 6 | – | 70 ch. ultramarine and blue | 60 | 60 |
| 7 | – | 1 n. 30 black and blue | 1·25 | 1·25 |

DESIGNS—HORIZ: 3, 70 ch. Archer. 5 ch., 1 n. 30, Yak. 15 ch. Map of Bhutan, Maharaja Druk Gyalpo and Paro Dzong (fortress and monastery).

**1962.** World Refugee Year.

| No. | Type | Description | Unused | Used |
|---|---|---|---|---|
| 8 | 2 | 1 n. red and blue | 45 | 45 |
| 9 | | 2 n. violet and green | 1·40 | 1·40 |

3. Accoutrements of Ancient Warrior.

4. " Boy filling box " (with grain).

**1962.** Membership of Colombo Plan.

| No. | Type | Description | Unused | Used |
|---|---|---|---|---|
| 10 | 3 | 33 ch. multicoloured | 20 | 20 |
| 11 | | 70 ch. multicoloured | 35 | 35 |
| 12 | | 1 n. 30 red, brown & yell | 80 | 80 |

**1963.** Freedom from Hunger.

| No. | Type | Description | Unused | Used |
|---|---|---|---|---|
| 13 | 4 | 20 ch. brown, blue & yell | 25 | 25 |
| 14 | | 1 n. 50 purple, brown & bl | 90 | 90 |

**1964.** Winter Olympic Games, Innsbruck, and Bhutanese Winter Sports Committee Fund. Nos. 10/12 surch **INNSBRUCK 1964 +50 ch**, Olympic rings and emblem.

| No. | Type | Description | Unused | Used |
|---|---|---|---|---|
| 15. | 3. | 33 ch. + 50 ch. mult. | 2·75 | 2·75 |
| 16. | | 70 ch. + 50 ch. mult. | 2·75 | 2·75 |
| 17. | | 1 n. 30 + 50 ch. mult. | 2·75 | 2·75 |

6. Dancer with upraised hands.

**1964.** Bhutanese Dancers. Multicoloured.

| No. | Type | Description | Unused | Used |
|---|---|---|---|---|
| 18 | | 2 ch. Standing on one leg (vert) | 10 | 10 |
| 19 | | 3 ch. Type 6 | 10 | 10 |
| 20 | | 5 ch. With tambourine (vert) | 10 | 10 |
| 21 | | 20 ch. As 2 ch. | 10 | 10 |
| 22 | | 33 ch. Type 6 | 15 | 15 |
| 23 | | 70 ch. With sword | 25 | 25 |
| 24 | | 1 n. With tasselled hat (vert) | 55 | 55 |
| 25 | | 1 n. 30 As 5 ch. | 70 | 70 |
| 26 | | 2 n. As 70 ch. | 1·25 | 1·25 |

7. Bhutanese Athlete.

9. Primula.

8. Flags at Half-mast.

**1964.** Olympic Games, Tokyo. Multicoloured.

| No. | Type | Description | Unused | Used |
|---|---|---|---|---|
| 27 | | 2 ch. Type 7 | 10 | 10 |
| 28 | | 5 ch. Boxing | 10 | 10 |
| 29 | | 15 ch. Type 7 | 10 | 10 |
| 30 | | 33 ch. As 5 ch. | 15 | 15 |
| 31 | | 1 n. Archery | 55 | 55 |
| 32 | | 2 n. Football | 90 | 90 |
| 33 | | 3 n. As 1 n. | 1·50 | 1·50 |

**1964.** Pres. Kennedy Commem.

| No. | Type | Description | Unused | Used |
|---|---|---|---|---|
| 34. | 8. | 33 ch. multicoloured | 20 | 20 |
| 35. | | 1 n. multicoloured | 55 | 55 |
| 36. | | 3 n. multicoloured | 1·25 | 1·25 |

**1965.** Flowers. Multicoloured.

| No. | Type | Description | Unused | Used |
|---|---|---|---|---|
| 37 | | 2 ch. Type 9 | 10 | 10 |
| 38 | | 5 ch. Gentian | 10 | 10 |
| 39 | | 15 ch. Type 9 | 10 | 10 |
| 40 | | 33 ch. As 5 ch. | 15 | 15 |
| 41 | | 50 ch. Rhododendron | 20 | 20 |
| 42 | | 75 ch. Peony | 30 | 30 |
| 43 | | 1 n. As 50 ch. | 30 | 30 |
| 44 | | 2 n. As 75 ch. | 70 | 70 |

**1965.** Churchill Commemoration. Optd **WINSTON CHURCHILL 1874 1965**.

| No. | Type | Description | Unused | Used |
|---|---|---|---|---|
| 45 | 1 | 33 ch. green and violet | 15 | 15 |
| 46 | 8 | 1 n. multicoloured | 45 | 45 |
| 47 | – | 1 n. multicoloured (No. 43) | 45 | 45 |
| 48 | – | 2 n. multicoloured (No. 44) | 75 | 75 |
| 49 | 8 | 3 n. multicoloured | 1·25 | 1·25 |

11. Pavilion and Skyscrapers.

**1965.** New York World's Fair. Mult.

| No. | Type | Description | Unused | Used |
|---|---|---|---|---|
| 50. | | 1 ch. Type 11 | 10 | 10 |
| 51. | | 10 ch. Buddha and Michelangelo's " Pieta " | 10 | 10 |
| 52. | | 20 ch. Bhutan houses and New York skyline | 10 | 10 |
| 53. | | 33 ch. Bhutan and New York bridges | 10 | 10 |
| 54. | | 1 n. 50 Type 11 | 55 | 55 |
| 55. | | 2 n. As 10 ch. | 90 | 90 |

**1965.** Surch.

| No. | Type | Description | Unused | Used |
|---|---|---|---|---|
| 56 | 2 | 5 ch. on 1 n. (No. 8) | 24·00 | 24·00 |
| 57 | | 5 ch. on 2 n. (No. 9) | 27·00 | 27·00 |
| 58 | – | 10 ch. on 70 ch. (No. 23) | 6·75 | 6·75 |
| 59 | – | 10 ch. on 2 n. (No. 26) | 6·75 | 6·75 |
| 60 | – | 15 ch. on 70 ch. (No. 6) | 5·00 | 5·00 |
| 61 | – | 15 ch. on 1 n. 30 (No. 7) | 5·00 | 5·00 |
| 62 | – | 20 ch. on 1 n. (No. 24) | 6·75 | 6·75 |
| 63 | – | 20 ch. on 1 n. 30 (No. 25) | 6·75 | 6·75 |

13. "Telstar" and Portable Transmitter.

**1966.** Cent of I.T.U. Multicoloured.

| No. | Type | Description | Unused | Used |
|---|---|---|---|---|
| 64 | | 35 ch. Type 13 | 20 | 20 |
| 65 | | 2 n. "Telstar" & morse key | 65 | 65 |
| 66 | | 3 n. "Relay" and headphones | 1·00 | 1·00 |

14. Asiatic Black Bear.

**1966.** Animals. Multicoloured.

| No. | Type | Description | Unused | Used |
|---|---|---|---|---|
| 68 | | 1 ch. Type 14 | 10 | 10 |
| 69 | | 2 ch. Snow leopard | 10 | 10 |
| 70 | | 4 ch. Pygmy hog | 10 | 10 |
| 71 | | 8 ch. Tiger | 10 | 10 |
| 72 | | 10 ch. Dhole | 10 | 10 |
| 73 | | 75 ch. As 8 ch. | 30 | 30 |
| 74 | | 1 n. Takin | 30 | 30 |
| 75 | | 1 n. 50 As 10 ch. | 45 | 45 |
| 76 | | 2 n. As 4 ch. | 80 | 80 |
| 77 | | 3 n. As 2 ch. | 1·00 | 1·00 |
| 78 | | 4 n. Type 14 | 1·25 | 1·25 |
| 79 | | 5 n. As 1 n. | 1·60 | 1·60 |

15. Simtoke Dzong (fortress).

**1966.**

| No. | Type | Description | Unused | Used |
|---|---|---|---|---|
| 80. | – | 5 c. brown | 15 | 15 |
| 81. | 15. | 15 ch. brown | 15 | 15 |
| 82. | | 20 ch. green | 20 | 20 |

DESIGN: 5 ch. Rinpung Dzong (fortress).

16. King Jigme Darji Wangchuk (obverse of 50 n.p. coin).

**1966.** 40th Anniv. of King Jigme Wangchuk's Accession (father of King Jigme Dorji Wangchuk). Circular designs, embossed on gold foil, backed with multicoloured patterned paper. Imperf.

Sizes: (a) Diameter 38 mm; (b) Diameter 50 mm; (c) Diameter 63 mm.

| No. | Type | Description | Unused | Used |
|---|---|---|---|---|
| | | (i) 50 n.p. Coin | | |
| 83 | 16 | 10 ch. green (a) | 20 | 20 |
| | | (ii) 1 r. Coin | | |
| 84 | 16 | 25 ch. green (b) | 25 | 25 |
| | | (iii) 3 r. Coin | | |
| 85 | 16 | 50 ch. green (c) | 50 | 50 |
| | | (iv) 1 sertum Coin | | |
| 86 | 16 | 1 n. red (a) | 90 | 90 |
| 87 | – | 1 n. 30 red (a) | 1·25 | 1·25 |
| | | (v) 2 sertum Coin | | |
| 88 | 16 | 2 n. red (b) | 1·75 | 1·75 |
| 89 | – | 3 n. red (b) | 2·75 | 2·75 |
| | | (vi) 5 sertum Coin | | |
| 90 | 16 | 4 n. red (c) | 3·75 | 3·75 |
| 91 | – | 5 n. red (c) | 4·50 | 4·50 |

Nos. 87, 89 and 91 show the reverse side of the coins (Symbol).

17. " Abominable Snowman ".

**1966.** " Abominable Snowman ". Various triangular designs.

| No. | Type | Description | Unused | Used |
|---|---|---|---|---|
| 92. | 17. | 1 ch. multicoloured | 10 | 10 |
| 93. | – | 2 ch. multicoloured | 10 | 10 |
| 94. | – | 3 ch. multicoloured | 10 | 10 |
| 95. | – | 4 ch. multicoloured | 10 | 10 |
| 96. | – | 5 ch. multicoloured | 10 | 10 |
| 97. | – | 15 ch. multicoloured | 10 | 10 |
| 98. | – | 30 ch. multicoloured | 10 | 10 |
| 99. | – | 40 ch. multicoloured | 20 | 20 |
| 100. | – | 50 ch. multicoloured | 20 | 20 |
| 101. | – | 1 n. 25 multicoloured | 35 | 35 |
| 102. | – | 2 n. 50 multicoloured | 70 | 70 |
| 103. | – | 3 n. multicoloured | 80 | 80 |
| 104. | – | 5 n. multicoloured | 1·40 | 1·40 |
| 105. | – | 6 n. multicoloured | 1·40 | 1·40 |
| 106. | – | 7 n. multicoloured | 1·75 | 1·75 |

**1967.** Air. Optd. **AIR MAIL** and helicopter motif.

| No. | Type | Description | Unused | Used |
|---|---|---|---|---|
| 107. | 6. | 33 ch. multicoloured | 10 | 10 |
| 108. | – | 50 ch. mult. (No. 41) | 15 | 15 |
| 109. | – | 70 ch. mult. (No. 23) | 20 | 20 |
| 110. | – | 75 ch. mult. (No. 42) | 25 | 25 |
| 111. | – | 1 n. mult. (No. 24) | 30 | 30 |
| 112. | – | 1 n. 50 mult. (No. 75) | 35 | 35 |
| 113. | – | 2 n. mult. (No. 76) | 35 | 35 |
| 114. | – | 3 n. mult. (No. 77) | 65 | 65 |
| 115. | 14. | 4 n. multicoloured | 90 | 90 |
| 116. | – | 5 n. mult. (No. 79) | 1·40 | 1·40 |

**INDEX**
Countries can be quickly located by referring to the index at the end of this volume.

20. "Lilium sherriffiae".

**1967.** Flowers. Multicoloured.

| No. | Type | Description | Unused | Used |
|---|---|---|---|---|
| 117 | | 3 ch. Type 20 | 10 | 10 |
| 118 | | 5 ch. "Meconopsis" | 10 | 10 |
| 119 | | 7 ch. "Rhododendron dhwoju" | 10 | 10 |
| 120 | | 10 ch. "Pleione hookeriana" | 10 | 10 |
| 121 | | 50 ch. Type 20 | 20 | 20 |
| 122 | | 1 n. As 5 ch. | 35 | 35 |
| 123 | | 2 n. 50 As 7 ch. | 90 | 90 |
| 124 | | 4 n. As 10 ch. | 1·40 | 1·40 |
| 125 | | 5 n. "Rhododendron giganteum" | 1·75 | 1·75 |

21. Scouts planting Sapling.

**1967.** Bhutanese Boy Scouts. Multicoloured.

| No. | Type | Description | Unused | Used |
|---|---|---|---|---|
| 126. | | 5 ch. Type 21 | 10 | 10 |
| 127. | | 10 ch. Scouts preparing meal | 10 | 10 |
| 128. | | 15 ch. Scout mountaineering | 20 | 20 |
| 129. | | 50 ch. Type 21 | 30 | 30 |
| 130. | | 1 n. 25. As 10 ch. | 45 | 45 |
| 131. | | 4 n. As 15 ch. | 1·25 | 1·25 |

**1967.** World Fair, Montreal. Nos. 53/5 optd **expo67** and emblem.

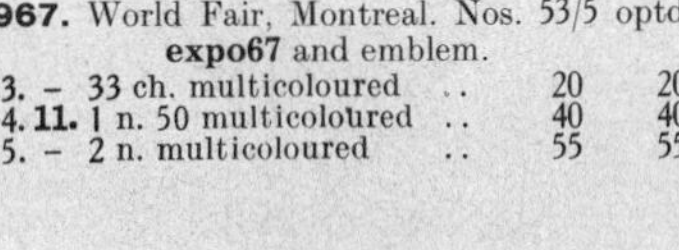

| No. | Type | Description | Unused | Used |
|---|---|---|---|---|
| 133. | – | 33 ch. multicoloured | 20 | 20 |
| 134. | 11. | 1 n. 50 multicoloured | 40 | 40 |
| 135. | – | 2 n. multicoloured | 55 | 55 |

23. Avro Lancaster Bomber.

**1967.** Churchill and Battle of Britain Commemoration. Multicoloured.

| No. | Type | Description | Unused | Used |
|---|---|---|---|---|
| 137 | | 45 ch. Type 23 | 25 | 25 |
| 138 | | 2 n. Supermarine Spitfire fighter | 50 | 50 |
| 139 | | 4 n. Hawker Hurricane Mk IIC fighter | 1·00 | 1·00 |

**1967.** World Scout Jamboree, Idaho. Nos. 126/31 optd. **WORLD JAMBOREE IDAHO, U.S.A. AUG. 1–9/67.**

| No. | Type | Description | Unused | Used |
|---|---|---|---|---|
| 141. | 21. | 5 ch. multicoloured | 10 | 10 |
| 142. | – | 10 ch. multicoloured | 10 | 10 |
| 143. | – | 15 ch. multicoloured | 10 | 10 |
| 144. | – | 50 ch. multicoloured | 30 | 30 |
| 145. | – | 1 n. 25 multicoloured | 55 | 55 |
| 146. | – | 4 n. multicoloured | 1·60 | 1·60 |

25. Painting.

**1967.** Bhutan Girl Scouts. Multicoloured.

| No. | Type | Description | Unused | Used |
|---|---|---|---|---|
| 148. | | 5 ch. Type 25 | 10 | 10 |
| 149. | | 10 ch. Playing musical instrument | 10 | 10 |
| 150. | | 15 ch. Picking fruit | 10 | 10 |
| 151. | | 1 n. 50 Type 25 | 30 | 30 |
| 152. | | 2 n. 50 As 10 ch. | 45 | 45 |
| 153. | | 5 n. As 15 ch. | 1·10 | 1·10 |

26. Astronaut in Space.

**1967.** Space Achievements. With laminated prismatic-ribbed plastic surface. Mult.

155. 3 ch. Type **26** (postage) .. 15 15
156. 5 ch. Space vehicle and astronaut .. .. 15 15
157. 7 ch. Astronaut and landing vehicle .. .. .. 20 20
158. 10 ch. Three astronauts in space .. .. .. 30 30
159. 15 ch. Type **26** .. .. 35 35
160. 30 ch. As 5 ch. .. .. 70 70
161. 50 ch. As 7 ch. .. .. 90 90
162. 1 n. 25 As 10 ch. .. 2·75 2·75
163. 2 n. 50 Type **26** (air) .. 90 90
164. 4 n. As 5 ch. .. .. 1·40 1·40
165. 5 n. As 7 ch. .. .. 2·25 2·25
166. 9 n. As 10 ch. .. .. 3·25 3·25

The laminated plastic surface gives the stamps a three-dimensional effect.

27. Tashichho Dzong.

**1968.**

168. **27.** 10 ch. purple and green 20 15

28. Elephant.

**1968.** Mythological Creatures.

169 **28** 2 ch. red, blue and brown (postage) .. 15 15
170 – 3 ch. pink, blue & grn 15 15
171 – 4 ch. orange, grn & bl 15 15
172 – 5 ch. blue, yell & pink 15 15
173 – 15 ch. green, pur & bl 15 15
174 **28** 20 ch. brn, blk & orge 15 15
175 – 30 ch. yellow, blk & bl 20 20
176 – 50 ch. bistre, grn & blk 25 25
177 – 1 n. 25 black, grn & red 25 25
178 – 2 n. yellow, vio & blk 35 35
179 **28** 1 n. 50 green, purple and yellow (air) .. 35 35
180 – 2 n. 50 red, black & bl 45 45
181 – 4 n. orange, grn & blk 65 65
182 – 5 n. brown, grey & orge 90 90
183 – 10 n. violet, grey & blk 1·75 1·75

DESIGNS: 3, 30 ch., 2 n. 50, Garuda. 4, 50 ch., 4 n. Tiger. 5 ch., 1 n. 25, 5 n. Wind horse. 15 ch., 2, 10 n. Snow lion.

29. Tongsa Dzong.

**1968.**

184. **29.** 50 ch. green .. .. 30 30
185. – 75 ch. brown and blue .. 35 35
186. – 1 n. blue and violet .. 40 40

DESIGNS: 75 ch. Daga Dzong. 1 n. Lhuntsi Dzong.

30. Ward's Trogon.

**1968.** Rare Birds.

187 2 ch. Red-faced liocichla (inscr "Crimson-winged laughing thrush") (horiz) (postage) .. .. 10 10
188 3 ch. Type **30** .. .. 15 15
189 4 ch. Burmese (inscr "Grey") peacock-pheasant (horiz) .. 20 20
190 5 ch. Rufous-necked hornbill .. .. 25 25
191 15 ch. Fire-tailed myzornis (horiz) .. .. .. 35 35
192 20 ch. As No. 187 .. .. 45 45
193 30 ch. Type **30** .. .. 50 50
194 50 ch. As No. 189 .. .. 55 55
195 1 n. 25 As No. 190 .. 75 75
196 2 n. As No. 191 .. .. 1·25 1·25
197 1 n. 50 As No. 187 (air) .. 85 85
198 2 n. 50 Type **30** .. .. 1·25 1·25
199 4 n. As No. 189 .. .. 1·90 1·90
200 5 n. As No. 190 .. .. 2·75 2·75
201 10 n. As No. 191 .. .. 5·25 5·25

31. Mahatma Gandhi.

**1969.** Birth Cent. of Mahatma Gandhi.

202. **31.** 20 ch. brown and blue 45 45
203. 2 n. brown and yellow 1·10 1·10

**1970.** Various stamps surch **5 CH** or **20 CH.**

(a) Fredom from Hunger (No. 14)

223 20 ch. on 1 n. 50 purple, brown and blue .. 2·25 2·25

(b) Animals (Nos. 75/9)

224 20 ch. on 1 n. 50 mult .. 2·25 2·25
225 20 ch. on 2 n. mult .. 2·25 2·25
204 20 ch. on 3 n. mult .. 90 90
205 20 ch. on 4 n. mult .. 90 90
206 20 ch. on 5 n. mult .. 90 90

(c) Abominable Snowmen (Nos. 101/6)

226 20 ch. on 1 n. 25 mult .. 2·25 2·25
227 20 ch. on 2 n. 50 mult .. 2·25 2·25
207 20 ch. on 3 n. mult .. 90 90
208 20 ch. on 5 n. mult .. 90 90
209 20 ch. on 6 n. mult .. 90 90
210 20 ch. on 7 n. mult .. 90 90

(d) Flowers (Nos. 124/5)

211 20 ch. on 4 n. mult .. 90 90
212 20 ch. on 5 n. mult .. 90 90

(e) Boy Scouts (Nos. 130/1)

228 20 ch. on 1 n. 25 mult .. 2·25 2·25
213 20 ch. on 4 n. mult .. 90 90

(f) Churchill (Nos. 138/9)

229 20 ch. on 2 n. mult .. 2·25 2·25
230 20 ch. on 4 n. mult .. 2·25 2·25

(g) 1968 Pheasants (Appendix)

231 20 ch. on 2 n. mult .. 3·50 3·50
214 20 ch. on 4 n. mult .. 2·00 2·00
232 20 ch. on 7 n. mult .. 3·50 3·50

(h) Mythological Creatures (Nos. 175/80 and 182/3)

233 5 ch. on 30 ch. yellow, black and blue (postage) 70 70
234 5 ch. on 50 ch. bistre, green and black .. 70 70
235 5 ch. on 1 n. 25 black, green and red .. 70 70
236 5 ch. on 2 n. yell, vio & blk 70 70
215 20 ch. on 2 n. yellow, violet and black .. .. 90 90
237 5 ch. on 1 n. 50 green, purple and brown (air) 70 70
238 5 ch. on 2 n. 50 red, black and blue .. .. 70 70
216 20 ch. on 5 n. brown, grey and orange .. .. 90 90
217 20 ch. on 10 n. violet, grey and black .. .. 90 90

(i) Rare Birds (Nos. 193/201)

239 20 ch. on 30 ch. mult (postage) .. .. 3·50 3·50
240 20 ch. on 50 ch. mult 3·50 3·50
241 20 ch. on 1 n. 25 mult 3·50 3·50
218 20 ch. on 2 n. mult 1·75 1·75
242 20 ch. on 1 n. 50 mult (air) 3·50 3·50
219 20 ch. on 2 n. 50 mult 2·00 2·00
220 20 ch. on 4 n. mult .. 2·00 2·00
221 20 ch. on 5 n. mult .. 2·00 2·00
222 20 ch. on 10 n. mult 2·00 2·00

(j) 1969 U.P.U. (Appendix)

243 20 ch. on 1 n. 05 mult .. 2·25 2·25
244 20 ch. on 1 n. 40 mult .. 2·25 2·25
245 20 ch. on 4 n. mult .. 2·25 2·25

For stamps surcharged with 55 or 90 ch. values, see Nos. 253/65 and for 25 ch. surcharges see Nos. 385/410.

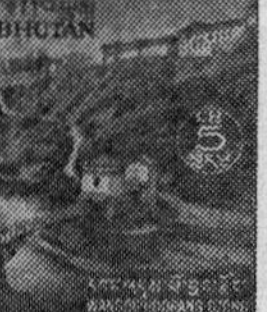

33. Wangdiphodrang Dzong and Bridge.

34. Book Year Emblem.

**1971.**

246. **33.** 2 ch. grey .. .. 10 10
247. 3 ch. mauve .. .. 10 10
248. 4 ch. violet .. .. 10 10
249. 5 ch. green .. .. 10 10
250. 10 ch. brown .. .. 10 10
251. 15 ch. blue .. .. 15 15
252. 20 ch. purple .. .. 20 20

**1971.** Various stamps surch **55CH** or **90CH.**

I. Dancers (Nos. 25/6)

253 55 ch. on 1 n. 30 mult .. 90 90
254 90 ch. on 2 n. mult .. 90 90

II. Animals (Nos. 77/8)

255 55 ch. on 3 n. mult .. 90 90
256 90 ch. on 4 n. mult .. 90 90

III. Boy Scouts (No. 131)

257 90 ch. on 4 n. mult .. 90 90

IV. 1968 Pheasants (Appendix)

258 55 ch. on 5 n. mult .. 3·00 3·00
259 90 ch. on 9 n. mult .. 3·00 3·00

V. Air. Mythological Creatures (No. 181)

260 55 ch. on 4 n. orange, green and black .. .. 55 55

VI. 1968 Mexico Olympics (Appendix)

261 90 ch. on 1 n. 05 mult .. 1·40 1·40

VII. Rare Birds (No. 196)

262 90 ch. on 2 n. mult .. 3·00 3·00

VIII. 1969 U.P.U. (Appendix)

263 55 ch. on 60 ch. mult .. 90 90

IX. 1970 New U.P.U. Headquarters (Appendix)

264 90 ch. on 2 n. 50 gold & red 6·00 6·00

X. 1971 Moon Vehicles (plastic-surfaced) (Appendix)

265 90 ch. on 1 n. 70 mult .. 90 90

**1972.** International Book Year.

266 **34** 2 ch. green and blue .. 15 15
267 3 ch. brown and yellow 15 15
268 5 ch. brown, orge & red 20 20
269 20 ch. brown and blue 15 15

35. Dochi.

**1972.** Dogs. Multicoloured.

270. 5 ch. Apsoo standing on hind legs (vert.) .. 10 10
271. 10 ch. Type **35** .. .. 10 10
272. 15 ch. Brown and white damci .. .. 15 15
273. 25 ch. Black and white damci .. .. 15 15
274. 55 ch. Apsoo lying down .. 20 20
275. 8 n. Two damci .. .. 1·60 1·60

36. King and Royal Crest.

**1974.** Coronation of King Jigme Singye Wangchuk. Multicoloured.

277 10 ch. Type **36** .. .. 10 10
278 25 ch. Bhutan Flag .. 10 10
279 1 n. 25 Good Luck signs .. 35 35
280 2 n. Punakha Dzong .. 55 55
281 3 n. Royal Crown .. 70 70

37. Mail Delivery by Horse.

**1974.** Centenary of U.P.U. Mult.

283 1 ch. Type **37** (postage) .. 10 10
284 2 ch. Early and modern locomotives .. 15 15
285 3 ch. "Hindoostan" (paddle-steamer) and "Iberia" (liner) .. 20 20
286 4 ch. Vickers Vimy and Concorde aircraft .. 30 30
287 25 ch. Mail runner and jeep 15 15
288 1 n. As 25 ch. (air) .. 30 30
289 1 n. 40 As 2 ch. .. 1·00 1·00
290 2 n. As 4 ch. .. .. 1·50 1·50

38. Family and W.P.Y. Emblem.

**1974.** World Population Year.

292. **38.** 25 ch. multicoloured .. 10 10
293. 50 ch. multicoloured .. 20 20
294. 90 ch. multicoloured .. 35 35
295. 2 n. 50 multicoloured .. 80 80

39. Eastern Courtier.

**1975.** Butterflies. Multicoloured.

297 1 ch. Type **39** .. .. 10 10
298 2 ch. Bamboo forester .. 10 10
299 3 ch. Tailed labyrinth .. 10 10
300 4 ch. Blue duchess .. 10 10
301 5 ch. Cruiser .. .. 15 15
302 10 ch. Bhutan glory .. 15 15
303 3 n. Bi-coloured commodore 65 65
304 5 n. Red-breasted jezebel 1·40 1·40

40. King Jigme Singye Wangchuk.

**1976.** King Jigme's 20th Birthday. Imperf.

(a) Diameter 39 mm.

306 **40** 15 ch. green on gold .. 10 10
307 1 n. red on gold .. 30 30
308 – 1 n. 30 red on gold .. 35 35

(b) Diameter 50 mm.

309 **40** 25 ch. green on gold .. 10 10
310 2 n. red on gold .. 45 45
311 – 3 n. red on gold .. 70 70

(c) Diameter 63 mm.

312 **40** 90 ch. green on gold .. 25 25
313 4 n. red on gold .. 1·10 1·10
314 – 5 n. red on gold .. 1·25 1·25

DESIGN: 1 n. 30, 3, 5 n. Decorative motif.

41. " Apollo ".

**1976.** "Apollo"–"Soyuz" Space Link. Mult.

315 10 n. Type **41** .. .. 2·40 2·40
316 10 n. "Soyuz" .. .. 2·40 2·40

42. Jewellery.

**1976.** Handicrafts and Craftsmen. Mult.

318 1 ch. Type **42** .. .. 10 10
319 2 ch. Coffee-pot, hand bell and sugar dish .. 10 10
320 3 ch. Powder horns .. 10 10
321 4 ch. Pendants and inlaid box .. .. .. 10 10
322 5 ch. Painter .. .. 10 10
323 15 ch. Silversmith .. 15 15
324 20 ch. Wood carver with tools .. .. .. 15 15
325 1 n. 50 Textile printer .. 35 35
326 10 n. Printer .. .. 2·75 2·75

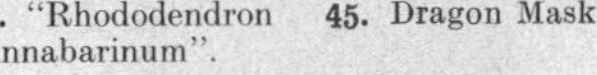

43. "Rhododendron cinnabarinum". 45. Dragon Mask.

44. Skiing.

**1976.** Rhododendrons. Multicoloured.

328. 1 ch. Type **43** .. .. 10 10
329. 2 ch. "R. campanulatum" 10 10
330. 3 ch. "R. fortunei" .. 10 10
331. 4 ch. "R. arboreum" .. 10 10
332. 5 ch. "R. arboreum" (different) .. .. 10 10
333. 1 n. "R. falconeri" .. 35 35
334. 3 n. "R. hodgsonii" .. 70 70
335. 5 n. "R. keysii" .. .. 1·40 1·40

**1976.** Winter Olympic Games, Innsbruck. Multicoloured.

337 1 ch. Type **44** .. .. 10 10
338 2 ch. Bobsleighing .. 10 10
339 3 ch. Ice hockey .. .. 10 10
340 4 ch. Cross-country skiing 10 10
341 5 ch. Women's figure skating .. .. 10 10
342 2 n. Downhill skiing .. 45 45
343 4 n. Speed skating .. 1·10 1·10
344 10 n. Pairs figure skating 2·40 2·40

**1976.** Ceremonial Masks. Laminated prismatic - ribbed plastic surface.

346. **45.** 5 ch. multicoloured (postage) .. .. 15 15
347. – 10 ch. multicoloured .. 15 15
348. – 15 ch. multicoloured .. 20 20
349. – 20 ch. multicoloured .. 20 20
350. – 25 ch. multicoloured .. 20 20
351. – 30 ch. multicoloured .. 20 20
352. – 35 ch. multicoloured .. 20 20
353. – 1 n. multicoloured (air) 35 35
354. – 2 n. multicoloured .. 65 65
355. – 2 n. 50 multicoloured .. 80 80
356. – 3 n. multicoloured .. 90 90

DESIGNS: 10 ch. to 3 n. Similar Bhutanese masks.

46. Orchid.

**1976.** Flowers. Multicoloured.

358. 1 ch. Type **46** .. .. 10 10
359. 2 ch. Orchid (different) .. 10 10
360. 3 ch. Orchid (different) .. 10 10
361. 4 ch. "Primula denticulata" .. .. .. 10 10
362. 5 ch. Arum .. .. .. 10 10
363. 2 n. Orchid (different) .. 40 40
364. 4 n. "Leguminosa" .. 70 70
365. 6 n. Rhododendron .. 1·40 1·40

47. Double Carp Emblem.

**1976.** 25th Anniv. of Colombo Plan.

367. 3 ch. Type **47** .. .. 10 10
368. 4 ch. Vase emblem .. 10 10
369. 5 ch. Geometric design .. 10 10
370. 25 ch. Design incorporating animal's face .. .. 30 30
371. 1 n. 25 Ornamental design 35 35
372. 2 n. Floral design .. .. 70 70
373. 2 n. 50 Carousel design .. 90 90
374. 3 n. Wheel design .. .. 1·10 1·10

48. Bandaranaike Conference Hall.

**1976.** 5th Non-aligned Countries Summit Conference, Colombo.

375. **48.** 1 n. 25 multicoloured .. 35 35
376. 2 n. 50 multicoloured .. 70 70

49. Liberty Bell.

**1978.** Anniversaries and Events. Mult.

377 20 n. Type **49** (bicentenary of U.S. independence) .. 4·50 4·50
378 20 n. Alexander Graham Bell early telephone (telephone centenary) 4·50 4·50
379 20 n. Archer (Olympic Games, Montreal) .. 4·50 4·50
380 20 n. Alfred Nobel (75th anniv of Nobel Prizes) 4·50 4·50
381 20 n. "Spirit of St. Louis" (50th anniv of Lindbergh's transatlantic flight) .. 4·50 4·50
382 20 n. Airship LZ3 (75th anniv of Zeppelin) .. 4·50 4·50
383 20 n. Queen Elizabeth II (25th anniv of Coronation) .. .. 4·50 4·50

**1978.** Provisionals. Various stamps surch **25 Ch** (385, 394) or **25 CH** (others).

I. Girl Scouts (No. 153)

385 25 ch. on 5 n. mult (postage) .. .. 1·40 1·40

II. Air. 1968 Mythological Creatures (Nos. 181 and 183)

386 25 ch. on 4 n. orange, green and black .. .. 1·40 1·40
387 25 ch. on 10 n. violet, grey and black .. .. 1·40 1·40

III. 1971 Admission to U.N. (Appendix)

388 25 ch. on 3 n. mult (postage) .. .. 1·40 1·40
389 25 ch. on 5 n. mult (air) .. 1·40 1·40
390 25 ch. on 6 n. mult .. 1·40 1·40

IV. Boy Scouts Anniv (Appendix)

391 25 ch. on 6 n. mult .. 1·40 1·40

V. 1972 Dogs (No. 275)

392 25 ch. on 8 n. mult .. 1·40 1·40

VI. 1973 Dogs (Appendix)

393 25 ch. on 4 n. mult .. 1·40 1·40

VII. 1973 "Indipex 73" (Appendix)

394 25 ch. on 3 n. mult (postage) .. .. 1·40 1·40
395 25 ch. on 5 n. mult (air) 1·40 1·40
396 25 ch. on 6 n. mult .. 1·40 1·40

VIII. U.P.U. (Nos. 289/90)

397 25 ch. on 1 n. 40 mult .. 3·00 3·00
398 25 ch. on 2 n. mult .. 1·50 1·50

IX. World Population Year (No. 295)

399 25 ch. on 2 n. 50 mult .. 1·40 1·40

X. Butterflies (Nos. 303/4)

400 25 ch. on 3 n. mult .. 1·40 1·40
401 25 ch. on 5 n. mult .. 1·40 1·40

XI. "Apollo"–"Soyuz" (Nos. 315/16)

402 25 ch. on 10 n. mult (315) 1·40 1·40
403 25 ch. on 10 n. mult (316) 1·40 1·40

XII. Handicrafts (No. 326)

404 25 ch. on 10 n. mult .. 1·40 1·40

XIII. Rhododendrons (No. 335)

405 25 ch. on 5 n. mult .. 1·40 1·40

XIV. Winter Olympics (Nos. 343/4)

406 25 ch. on 4 n. mult .. 1·40 1·40
407 25 ch. on 10 n. mult .. 1·40 1·40

XV. Flowers (Nos. 364/5)

408 25 ch. on 4 n. mult .. 1·40 1·40
409 25 ch. on 6 n. mult .. 1·40 1·40

XVI. Colombo Plan (No. 373)

410 25 ch. on 2 n. 50 mult .. 1·75 1·75

50. Mother and Child.

**1979.** International Year of the Child. Mult.

411. 2 n. Type **50** .. .. 55 55
412. 5 n. Mother carrying two children .. .. .. 1·25 1·25
413. 10 n. Children at school .. 2·25 2·25

51. Conference Emblem and Dove.

**1979.** 6th Non-Aligned Countries Summit Conference, Havana. Multicoloured.

415. 25 ch. Type **51** .. .. 20 20
416. 10 n. Emblem and Bhutanese symbols .. .. 2·75 2·75

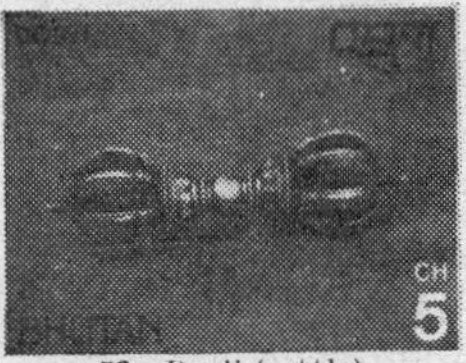

52. Dorji (rattle).

**1979.** Antiquities. Multicoloured.

417 5 ch. Type **52** .. .. 10 10
418 10 ch. Dilbu (hand bell) (vert) .. .. .. 10 10
419 15 ch. Jadum (cylindrical pot) (vert) .. .. 10 10
420 25 ch. Jamjee (teapot) .. 10 10
421 1 n. Kem (cylindrical container) (vert) .. 20 20
422 1 n. 25 Jamjee (different) 30 30
423 1 n. 70 Sangphor (ornamental vessel) (vert) .. 35 35
424 2 n. Jamjee (different) (vert) .. .. .. 45 45
425 3 n. Yangtho (pot with lid) (vert) .. .. .. 65 65
426 4 n. Battha (circular case) 90 90
427 5 n. Chhap (ornamental flask) (vert) .. .. 1·10 1·10

53. Rinpiang Dzong, Bhutan Stamp and Rowland Hill Statue.

**1980.** Death Cent of Sir Rowland Hill. Mult.

428 1 n. Type **53** .. .. 15 15
429 2 n. Dzong, Bhutan stamp and statue .. .. 35 35
430 5 n. Ounsti Dzong, Bhutan stamp and statue .. 1·10 1·10
431 10 n. Lingzi Dzong and British 1912 1d. stamp .. 2·25 2·25

54. Dungtse Lhakhang, Paro. 55. St. Paul's Cathedral.

**1981.** Monasteries. Multicoloured.

433. 1 n. Type **54** .. .. 30 30
434. 2 n. Kich Lhakhang, Paro (horiz.) .. .. 65 65
435. 2 n. 25 Kurjey Lhakhang (horiz.) .. .. 70 70
436. 3 n. Tangu, Thimphu (horiz. 90 90
437. 4 n. Cheri, Thimphu (horiz.) 1·10 1·10
438. 5 n. Chorten, Kora (horiz.) 1·40 1·40
439. 7 n. Tak-Tsang, Paro .. 1·75 1·75

**1981.** Wedding of Prince of Wales. Multicoloured.

440. 1 n. Type **55** .. .. 20 20
441. 5 n. Type **55** .. .. 90 90
442. 20 n. Prince Charles and Lady Diana Spencer .. 3·50 3·50
443. 25 n. As No. 442 .. .. 4·75 4·75

56. Orange-bellied Leafbird. 57. Footballers.

**1982.** Birds. Multicoloured.

445. 2 n. Type **56** .. .. 85 85
446. 3 n. Himalayan Monal Pheasant .. .. 1·40 1·40
447. 5 n. Ward's Trogon .. 2·40 2·40
448. 10 n. Mrs. Gould's Sunbird 4·25 4·25

**1982.** World Cup Football Championship. Spain.

450. **57.** 1 n. multicoloured .. 15 15
451. – 2 n. multicoloured .. 35 35
452. – 3 n. multicoloured .. 45 45
453. – 20 n. multicoloured .. 3·50 3·50

DESIGNS: 2 n. to 20 n. Various football scenes.

58. St. James's Palace. 59. Lord Baden-Powell (founder).

**1982.** 21st Birthday of Princess of Wales. Multicoloured.

455. 1 n. Type **58** .. .. 25 25
456. 10 n. Prince and Princess of Wales .. .. 1·75 1·75
457. 15 n. Windsor Castle .. 2·75 2·75
458. 25 n. Princess in wedding dress .. .. .. 4·50 4·50

**1982.** 75th Anniv of Boy Scout Movement. Multicoloured.

460 3 n. Type **59** .. .. 45 45
461 5 n. Scouts around campfire .. .. 90 90
462 15 n. Map reading .. 2·75 2·75
463 20 n. Pitching tents .. 3·50 3·50

60. Rama finds Mowgli.

**1982.** "The Jungle Book" (cartoon film). Multicoloured.

465 1 ch. Type **60** .. .. 10 10
466 2 ch. Bagheera leading Mowgli to Man-village .. 10 10
467 3 ch. Kaa planning attack on Bagheera and Mowgli 10 10
468 4 ch. Mowgli and elephants 10 10
469 5 ch. Mowgli and Baloo .. 10 10
470 10 ch. Mowgli and King Louie .. .. .. 10 10
471 30 ch. Kaa and Shere Khan .. .. .. 15 15
472 2 n. Mowgli, Baloo and Bagheera .. .. 45 45
473 20 n. Mowgli carrying jug for girl .. .. .. 4·75 4·75

**1982.** Birth of Prince William of Wales. Nos. 455/8 optd **ROYAL BABY 21.6.82.**

475 1 n. multicoloured .. 25 25
476 10 n. multicoloured .. 1·75 1·75
477 15 n. multicoloured .. 2·75 2·75
478 25 n. multicoloured .. 4·50 4·50

62. Washington surveying.

**1982.** 250th Birth Anniv. of George Washington and Birth Centenary of Franklin D. Roosevelt. Multicoloured.

480. 50 ch. Type 62 .. .. 10 10
481. 1 n. Roosevelt and Harvard University .. 15 15
482. 2 n. Washington at Valley Forge .. .. 35 35
483. 3 n. Roosevelt's mother and family .. .. 55 55
484. 4 n. Washington at Battle of Monmouth .. .. 70 70
485. 5 n. Roosevelt and the White House .. .. 90 90
486. 15 n. Washington and Mount Vernon .. .. 2·75 2·75
487. 20 n. Churchill, Roosevelt and Stalin at Yalta .. 3·50 3·50

**1983.** "Druk Air" Bhutan Air Service. Various stamps optd **DRUK AIR** (491) or **Druk Air** (others), No. 489 surch also.

489 42 30 ch. on 1 n. mult (postage) .. .. 2·25 2·25
490 – 5 n. multicoloured (Scouts, Appendix) .. 2·25 2·25
491 – 8 n. mult (No. 275) .. 2·25 2·25
492 – 5 n. mult ("Indipex 73", Appendix) (air) .. 2·75 2·75
493 – 7 n. mult (Munich Olympics, Appendix) 2·75 2·75

64. "Angelo Doni".

**1983.** 500th Birth Anniv of Raphael (artist). Multicoloured.

494 1 n. Type 64 .. .. 20 20
495 4 n. "Maddalena Doni" .. 70 70
496 5 n. "Baldassare Castiglione" .. .. 90 90
497 20 n. "Woman with Veil" 3·50 3·50

65. Ta-Gyad-Boom-Zu (the eight luck-bringing symbols).

**1983.** Religious Offerings. Multicoloured.

499. 25 ch. Type 65 .. .. 10 10
500. 50 ch. Doeyun Nga (the five sensory symbols) .. 15 15
501. 2 n. Norbu Chadun (the seven treasures) (47 × 41 mm) .. .. .. 55 55
502. 3 n. Wangpo Nga (the five sensory organs) .. .. 80 80
503. 8 n. Sha Nga (the five kinds of flesh) .. 1·75 1·75
504. 9 n. Men-Ra-Tor Sum (the sacrificial cake) (47 × 41 mm.) .. .. .. 2·00 2·00

66. Dornier Wal Flying Boat "Boreas".

**1983.** Bicent of Manned Flight. Mult.

506 50 ch. Type 66 .. .. 15 15
507 3 n. Savoia-Marchetti S.66 flying boat .. .. 65 65
508 10 n. Hawker Osprey biplane .. .. .. 2·50 2·50
509 20 n. Astra airship "Ville de Paris" .. .. 4·50 4·50

67. Mickey Mouse as Caveman.

68. Golden Langur.

**1984.** World Communications Year. Mult.

511. 4 ch. Type 67 .. .. 10 10
512. 5 ch. Goofy as printer .. 10 10
513. 10 ch. Chip 'n' Dale with morse key .. .. 10 10
514. 20 ch. Pluto talks to girl-friend on telephone .. 10 10
515. 25 ch. Minnie Mouse pulling record from bulldog .. .. 10 10
516. 50 ch. Morty and Ferdie with microphone and loudhailers .. .. 15 15
517. 1 n. Huey, Dewey, and Louie listening to radio 25 25
518. 5 n. Donald Duck watching television on buffalo 1·00 1·00
519. 20 n. Daisy Duck with computers and abacus .. 4·00 4·00

**1984.** Endangered Species. Multicoloured.

521. 50 ch. Type 68 .. .. 15 15
522. 1 n. Golden langur family in tree (horiz.) .. .. 25 25
523. 2 n. Male and female Golden langurs with young (horiz.) .. .. 45 45
524. 4 n. Group of langurs .. 1·00 1·00

69. Downhill Skiing.

70. "Sans Pareil", 1829.

**1984.** Winter Olympic Games, Sarajevo. Multicoloured.

526. 50 ch. Type 69 .. .. 10 10
527. 1 n. Cross-country skiing .. 20 20
528. 3 n. Speed skating .. .. 65 65
529. 20 n. Four-man bobsleigh .. 3·75 3·75

**1984.** Railway Locomotives. Multicoloured.

531. 50 ch. Type 70 .. .. 10 10
532. 1 n. "Planet", 1830 .. 30 30
533. 3 n. "Experiment" 1832 .. 75 75
534. 4 n. "Black Hawk", 1835 .. 1·00 1·00
535. 5 n. 50 "Jenny Lind", 1847 (horiz.) .. .. .. 1·25 1·25
536. 8 n. Semmering–Bavaria line engine, 1851 (horiz.) 1·90 1·90
537. 10 n. Great Northern No. 1, 1870 (horiz.) .. 2·25 2·25
538. 25 n. German National "tinder" engine, 1880 (horiz.) .. .. .. 5·75 5·75

71. Riley "Sprite", 1936.

**1984.** Cars. Multicoloured.

540. 50 ch. Type 71 .. .. 10 10
541. 1 n. Lanchester, 1919 .. 20 20
542. 3 n. Itala, 1907 .. .. 55 55
543. 4 n. Morris "Oxford (Bull-nose)", 1913 .. .. 70 70
544. 5 n. 50 Lagonda "LG6", 1939 .. .. .. 1·00 1·00
545. 6 n. Wolseley, 1903 .. 1·10 1·10
546. 8 n. Buick "Super", 1952 .. 1·60 1·60
547. 20 n. Maybach "Zeppelin", 1933 .. .. .. 3·75 3·75

72. Women's Archery.

73. Domkhar Dzong.

**1984.** Olympic Games, Los Angeles. Multicoloured.

549. 15 ch. Type 72 .. .. 10 10
550. 25 ch. Men's archery .. 10 10
551. 2 n. Table tennis .. .. 35 35
552. 2 n. 25 Basketball .. .. 40 40
553. 5 n. 50 Boxing .. .. 1·00 1·00
554. 6 n. Running .. .. 1·25 1·25
555. 8 n. Tennis .. .. .. 1·60 1·60

**1984.** Monasteries.

557 73 10 ch. blue .. .. 10 10
558 – 25 ch. red .. .. 10 10
559 – 50 ch. violet .. .. 10 10
560 – 1 n. brown .. .. 15 15
561 – 2 n. red .. .. 35 35
562 – 5 n. green .. .. 95 95

Designs: 25 ch. Shemgang Dzong. 50 ch. Chapcha Dzong. 1 n. Tashigang Dzong. 2 n. Pungthang Dzong. 5 n. Dechhenphoda Dzong.

74. "Magician Mickey".

**1984.** 50th Anniv of Donald Duck. Scenes from films. Multicoloured.

563 4 ch. Type 74 .. .. 10 10
564 5 ch. "Slide, Donald, Slide" .. .. .. 10 10
565 10 ch. "Donald's Golf Game" .. .. .. 10 10
566 20 ch. "Mr. Duck Steps Out" .. .. .. 10 10
567 25 ch. "Lion Around" .. 10 10
568 50 ch. "Alpine Climbers" 15 15
569 1 n. "Flying Jalopy" .. 25 25
570 5 n. "Frank Duck brings 'Em Back Alive" .. 1·10 1·10
571 20 n. "Good Scouts" .. 4·25 4·25

**1984.** Various stamps surch. (a) World Cup Football Championship, Spain (Nos. 450/3)

573 5 n. on 1 n. multicoloured 1·25 1·25
574 5 n. on 2 n. multicoloured 1·25 1·25
575 5 n. on 3 n. multicoloured 1·25 1·25
576 5 n. on 20 n. multicoloured 1·25 1·25

(b) 21st Birthday of Princess of Wales (Nos. 455/8)

578 5 n. on 1 n. multicoloured 85 85
579 5 n. on 10 n. multicoloured 85 85
580 5 n. on 15 n. multicoloured 85 85
581 40 n. on 25 n. mult .. 8·75 8·75

(c) Birth of Prince William of Wales (Nos. 475/8)

583 5 n. on 1 n. multicoloured 85 85
584 5 n. on 10 n. multicoloured 85 85
585 5 n. on 15 n. multicoloured 85 85
586 40 n. on 25 n. mult .. 7·75 7·75

(d) Wedding of Prince of Wales (Nos. 440/3)

588 10 n. on 1 n. multicoloured 2·10 2·10
589 10 n. on 5 n. multicoloured 2·10 2·10
590 10 n. on 20 n. mult .. 2·10 2·10
591 10 n. on 25 n. mult .. 2·10 2·10

(e) 75th Anniv of Boy Scout Movement (Nos. 460/3)

593 10 n. on 3 n. multicoloured 2·10 2·10
594 10 n. on 5 n. multicoloured 2·10 2·10
595 10 n. on 15 n. mult .. 2·10 2·10
596 10 n. on 20 n. mult .. 2·10 2·10

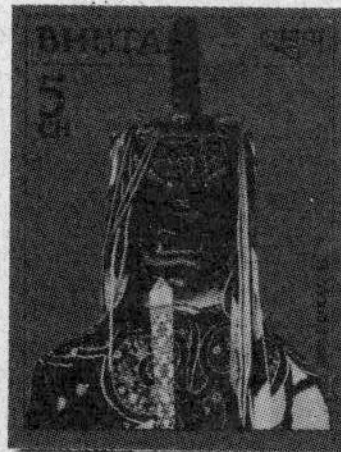
76. Shinje Choegyel.

77. Bhutan and U.N. Flags.

**1985.** The Judgement of Death Mask Dance. Multicoloured.

598 5 ch. Type 76 .. .. 10 10
599 35 ch. Raksh Lango .. 15 15
600 50 ch. Druelgo .. .. 15 15
601 2 n. 50 Pago .. .. 55 55
602 3 n. Telgo .. .. 60 60
603 4 n. Due Nakcung .. 70 70
604 5 n. Lha Karpo .. 1·00 1·00
605 5 n. 50 Nyalbum .. 1·10 1·10
606 6 n. Khimda Pelkyi .. 1·25 1·25

**1985.** 40th Anniv. of U.N.O.

608. 77. 50 ch. multicoloured .. 10 10
609. – 15 n. multicoloured .. 2·10 2·10
610. – 20 n. black and blue .. 3·00 3·00

Designs—vert. 15 n. U.N. building, New York. horiz. 20 n. Veterans' War Memorial Building, San Francisco (venue of signing of charter, 1945).

78. Mickey Mouse tramping through Black Forest.

**1985.** 150th Birth Anniv. of Mark Twain (writer) and International Youth Year. Multicoloured.

612. 50 ch. Type 78 .. .. 15 15
613. 2 n. Mickey Mouse, Donald Duck and Goofy on steamboat trip on Lake Lucerne .. .. .. 40 40
614. 5 n. Mickey Mouse, Donald Duck and Goofy climbing Rigi-Kulm .. 80 80
615 9 n. Mickey Mouse and Goofy rafting to Heidelberg on River Neckar .. .. .. 1·25 1·25
616 20 n. Mickey Mouse leading Donald Duck on horse back up the Riffelberg 3·50 3·50

Nos. 612/16 show scenes from "A Tramp Abroad" (cartoon film of Twain novel.)

79. Prince sees Rapunzel.

**1985.** Birth Bicentenaries (1985 and 1986) of Grimm Brothers (folklorists). Multicoloured.

618. 1 n. Type 79 .. .. 15 15
619. 4 n. Rapunzel (Minnie Mouse) in tower .. 55 55
620. 7 n. Mother Gothel calling to Rapunzel to let down her hair .. .. .. 85 85
621. 8 n. Prince climbing tower using Rapunzel's hair .. 1·25 1·25
622. 15 n. Prince proposing to Rapunzel .. .. 1·90 1·90

80. "Brewers Duck" (mallard).

**1985.** Birth Bicentenary of John J. Audubon (ornithologist). Audubon illustrations. Mult.

624 50 ch. Type 80 .. .. 10 10
625 1 n. "Willow Ptarmigan" (willow/red grouse) .. 15 15
626 2 n. "Mountain Plover" .. 45 45
627 3 n. "Red-throated Loon" (red-throated diver) .. 70 70
628 4 n. "Spruce Grouse" .. 85 85
629 5 n. "Hooded Merganser" 1·10 1·10
630 15 n. "Trumpeter Swan" (whooper swan) .. 3·00 3·00
631 20 n. "Common Goldeneye" .. .. 4·00 4·00

81. Members' Flags around Buddhist Design.

**1985.** South Asian Regional Co-operation Summit, Dhaka, Bangladesh.

634. 81. 50 ch. multicoloured .. 10 10
635. 5 n. multicoloured .. 80 80

82. Precious Wheel. 85. Mandala of Phurpa (Ritual Dagger).

**1986.** The Precious Symbols. Multicoloured.

636. 30 ch. Type **82** .. .. 10 10
637. 50 ch. Precious Gem .. 15 15
638. 1 n. 25 Precious Queen .. 15 15
639. 2 n. Precious Minister .. 30 30
640. 4 n. Precious Elephant .. 55 55
641. 6 n. Precious Horse .. 85 85
642. 8 n. Precious General .. 1·25 1·25

**1986.** Olympic Games Gold Medal Winners. Nos. 549/50 and 552/5 optd.

643 **72** 15 ch. **GOLD HYANG SOON SEO SOUTH KOREA** .. .. 15 15
644 – 25 ch. **GOLD DARRELL PACE USA** .. .. 15 15
645 – 2 n. 25 **GOLD MEDAL USA** .. .. 25 25
646 – 5 n. 50 **GOLD MARK BRELAND USA** .. 80 80
647 – 6 n. **GOLD DALEY THOMPSON ENGLAND** .. 85 85
648 – 8 n. **GOLD STEFAN EDBERG SWEDEN** 1·25 1·25

**1986.** "Ameripex 86" International Stamp Exhibition, Chicago. Various stamps optd **AMERIPEX 86**.

653. 8 n. mult. (No. 621) .. 1·10 1·10
650. 9 n. mult. (No. 615) .. 1·25 1·25
654. 15 n. mult. (No. 622) .. 2·00 2·00
651. 20 n. mult. (No. 616) .. 3·00 3·00

**1986.** Kilkhor Mandalas of Mahayana Buddhism. Multicoloured.

656. 10 ch. Type **85** .. .. 10 10
657. 25 ch. Mandala of Amitayus in Wrathful Form .. .. .. 10 10
658. 50 ch. Mandala of Overpowering Deities .. 15 15
659. 75 ch. Mandala of the Great Wrathful One .. 20 20
660. 1 n. Type **85** .. .. 20 20
661. 3 n. As 25 ch. .. .. 50 50
662. 5 n. As 50 ch. .. .. 75 75
663. 7 n. As 75 ch. .. .. 1·00 1·00

**1986.** 75th Anniv of Girl Guides. Nos. 460/3 optd **75th ANNIVERSARY GIRL GUIDES**.

664 3 n. multicoloured .. 45 45
665 5 n. multicoloured .. 65 65
666 15 n. multicoloured .. 2·00 2·00
667 20 n. multicoloured .. 3·00 3·00

87. Babylonian Tablet and Comet over Noah's Ark.

**1986.** Appearance of Halley's Comet. Mult.

669 50 ch. Type **87** .. .. 15 15
670 1 n. 17th-century print .. 15 15
671 2 n. 1835 French silhouette 35 35
672 3 n. Bayeux tapestry .. 50 50
673 4 n. Woodblock from "Nuremburg Chronicle" 70 70
674 5 n. Illustration of Revelation 6, 12–13 from 1650 Bible .. .. 85 85
675 15 n. Comet in constellation of Cancer .. 2·25 2·25
676 20 n. Decoration on Delft plate .. .. .. 3·25 3·25

88. Statue and "Libertad" (Argentine full-rigged cadet ship)

**1986.** Centenary of Statue of Liberty. Multicoloured.

678 50 ch. Type **88** .. .. 15 15
679 1 n. "Shalom" (Israeli liner) .. .. .. 15 15
680 2 n. "Leonardo da Vinci" (Italian liner) .. .. 35 35
681 3 n. "Mircea" (Rumanian cadet barque) .. .. 50 50
682 4 n. "France" (French liner) .. .. .. 70 70
683 5 n. S.S. "United States" (American liner) .. 85 85
684 15 n. "Queen Elizabeth 2" (British liner) .. .. 2·25 2·25
685 20 n. "Europa" (West German liner) .. .. 2·75 2·75

The descriptions of the ships on Nos. 678 and 681 were transposed in error.

89. "Santa Maria".

**1987.** 500th Anniv (1992) of Discovery of America by Columbus. Multicoloured.

687 20 ch. Type **89** .. .. 30 30
688 25 ch. Queen Isabella of Spain .. .. .. 15 15
689 50 ch. Flying fish .. 40 40
690 1 n. Columbus's coat of arms .. .. .. 25 25
691 2 n. Christopher Columbus 45 45
692 3 n. Columbus landing with Spanish soldiers .. 80 80

90. Canadian National Class "U1-f" Steam Locomotive.

**1987.** "Capex'87" International Stamp Exn, Toronto. Canadian Railways. Mult.

695 50 ch. Type **90** .. .. 15 15
696 1 n. Via Rail "L.R.C." electric locomotive .. 15 15
697 2 n. Canadian National GM "GF30t" diesel locomotive .. .. 35 35
698 3 n. Canadian National steam locomotive .. 50 50
699 8 n. Canadian Pacific steam locomotive .. 1·40 1·40
700 10 n. Via Express diesel locomotive .. .. 1·75 1·75
701 15 n. Canadian National "Turbotrain" .. .. 2·50 2·50
702 20 n. Canadian Pacific diesel-electric express locomotive .. .. 3·50 3·50

91. "Two Faces" (sculpture).

**1987.** Birth Centenary of Marc Chagall (artist). Multicoloured.

704. 50 ch. Type **91** .. .. 15 15
705. 1 n. "At the Barber's" .. 15 15
706. 2 n. "Old Jew with Torai" 35 35
707. 3 n. "Red Maternity" .. 50 50
708. 4 n. "Eve of Yom Kippur" 70 70
709. 5 n. "The Old Musician".. 85 85
710. 6 n. "The Rabbi of Vitebsk".. .. .. 85 85
711. 7 n. "Couple at Dusk" .. 1·25 1·25
712. 9 n. "The Artistes" .. 1·25 1·25
713. 10 n. "Moses breaking the Tablets".. .. .. 1·50 1·50
714. 12 n. "Bouquet with Flying Lovers" .. 1·75 1·75
715. 20 n. "In the Sky of the Opera" .. .. .. 3·00 3·00

92. Goofy (slalom).

**1988.** Winter Olympic Games, Calgary. Multicoloured.

717. 50 ch. Type **92** .. .. 15 15
718. 1 n. Donald Duck pushing Goofy at start (downhill skiing) .. .. .. 15 15
719. 2 n. Goofy in goal (ice hockey) .. .. .. 25 25
720. 4 n. Goofy (biathlon) .. 50 50
721. 7 n. Goofy and Donald Duck (speed skating) .. 85 85
722. 8 n. Minnie Mouse (figure skating) .. .. .. 1·00 1·00
723. 9 n. Minnie Mouse (free-style skating) .. .. 1·25 1·25
724. 20 n. Goofy and Mickey Mouse (two-man bobsleigh) .. .. 2·50 2·50

93. Stephenson's Railway Locomotive "Rocket", 1829

**1988.** Transport. Multicoloured.

726 50 ch. Pullman "Pioneer" sleeper, 1985 .. .. 15 15
727 1 n. Type **93** .. .. 15 15
728 2 n. Pierre Lallement's "Velocipede", 1866 .. 25 25
729 3 n. Benz "Patent Motor Wagon", 1866 .. .. 45 45
730 4 n. Volkswagen "Beetle" 60 60
731 5 n. Mississippi paddle-steamers "Natchez" and "Robert E. Lee", 1870 70 70
732 6 n. American "La France" motor fire engine, 1910 85 85
733 7 n. Frigate U.S.S. "Constitution", 1797 (vert) .. .. .. 85 85
734 9 n. Bell rocket belt, 1961 (vert) .. .. .. 1·25 1·25
735 10 n. Trevithick's railway locomotive, 1804 .. 1·40 1·40

No. 731 is wrongly inscribed "Natches" and No. 733 is wrongly dated "1787".

94 Dam and Pylon

**1988.** Chhukha Hydro-electric Project.

737 **94** 50 ch. multicoloured .. 15 15

**1988.** World Aids Day. Nos. 411/13 optd **WORLD AIDS DAY**.

738 **50** 2 n. multicoloured .. 35 35
739 – 5 n. multicoloured .. 95 95
740 – 10 n. multicoloured .. 1·75 1·75

96 "Diana and Actaeon" (detail)

**1989.** 500th Birth Anniv of Titian (painter). Multicoloured.

741 50 ch. "Gentleman with a Book" .. .. .. 15 15
742 1 n. "Venus and Cupid, with a Lute Player" (detail) .. .. .. 15 15
743 2 n. Type **96** .. .. 25 25
744 3 n. "Cardinal Ippolito dei Medici" .. .. 45 45
745 4 n. "Sleeping Venus" (detail) .. .. .. 50 50
746 5 n. "Venus risen from the Waves" (detail) .. 80 80
747 6 n. "Worship of Venus" (detail) .. .. .. 95 95
748 7 n. "Fete Champetre" (detail) .. .. .. 85 85
749 10 n. "Perseus and Andromeda" (detail) .. 1·75 1·75
750 15 n. "Danae" (detail) .. 2·10 2·10
751 20 n. "Venus at the Mirror" .. .. 2·50 2·50
752 25 n. "Venus and the Organ Player" (detail) 3·25 3·25

97 Volleyball

**1989.** Olympic Games, Seoul (1988). Mult.

754 50 ch. Gymnastics .. 15 15
755 1 n. Judo .. .. .. 15 15
756 2 n. Putting the shot .. 25 25
757 4 n. Type **97** .. .. 50 50
758 7 n. Basketball (vert) .. 1·00 1·00
759 8 n. Football (vert) .. 1·25 1·25
760 9 n. High jumping (vert) 1·50 1·50
761 20 n. Running (vert) .. 3·00 3·00

**1989.** "Fukuoka '89" Asia–Pacific Exhibition Nos. 598/606 optd **ASIA-PACIFIC EXPOSITION FUKUOKA '89**.

763 5 ch. multicoloured .. 10 10
764 35 ch. multicoloured .. 15 15
765 50 ch. multicoloured .. 15 15
766 2 n. 50 multicoloured .. 25 25
767 3 n. multicoloured .. 35 35
768 4 n. multicoloured .. 45 45
769 5 n. multicoloured .. 60 60
770 5 n. 50 multicoloured .. 75 75
771 6 n. multicoloured .. 95 95

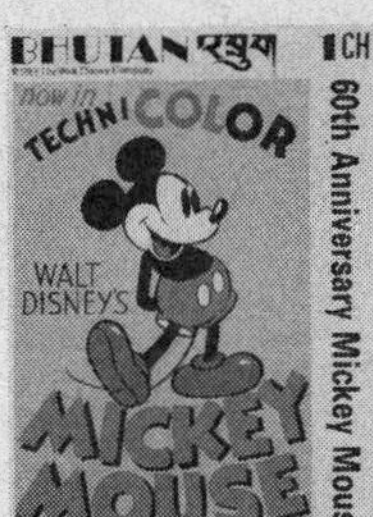


99 Mickey Mouse

**1989.** 60th Anniv of Mickey Mouse. Film Posters. Multicoloured.

| | | | |
|---|---|---|---|
| 772 | 1 ch. Type **99** .. .. | 10 | 10 |
| 773 | 2 ch. "Barnyard Olympics" | 15 | 15 |
| 774 | 3 ch. "Society Dog Show" | 15 | 15 |
| 775 | 4 ch. "Fantasia" .. .. | 15 | 15 |
| 776 | 5 ch. "The Mad Dog" .. | 15 | 15 |
| 777 | 10 ch. "A Gentleman's Gentleman" .. .. | 15 | 15 |
| 778 | 50 ch. "Symphony hour" | 15 | 15 |
| 779 | 10 n. "The Moose Hunt" | 1·25 | 1·25 |
| 780 | 15 n. "Wild Waves" .. | 2·00 | 2·00 |
| 781 | 20 n. "Mickey in Arabia" | 2·50 | 2·50 |
| 782 | 25 n. "Tugboat Mickey" .. | 3·25 | 3·25 |
| 783 | 30 n. "Building a Building" | 3·75 | 3·75 |

**100** "Tricholoma pardalotum"

**1989.** Fungi. Multicoloured.

| | | | |
|---|---|---|---|
| 785 | 50 ch. Type **100** .. .. | 15 | 15 |
| 786 | 1 n. "Suillus placidus" .. | 25 | 15 |
| 787 | 2 n. Royal boletus .. | 30 | 25 |
| 788 | 3 n. "Gomphidius glutinosus" .. .. | 45 | 40 |
| 789 | 4 n. Scarlet-stemmed boletus .. .. .. | 60 | 50 |
| 790 | 5 n. Elegant boletus .. | 70 | 60 |
| 791 | 6 n. "Boletus appendiculatus" .. .. | 95 | 80 |
| 792 | 7 n. Griping toadstool .. | 1·00 | 85 |
| 793 | 10 n. "Macrolepiota rhacodes" .. .. | 1·60 | 1·40 |
| 794 | 15 n. The blusher .. | 2·40 | 2·10 |
| 795 | 20 n. Death cap .. .. | 3·25 | 2·75 |
| 796 | 25 n. False death cap .. | 4·00 | 3·50 |

**101** "La Reale" (Spanish galley), 1680

**1989.** 30th Anniv of International Maritime Organization. Multicoloured.

| | | | |
|---|---|---|---|
| 798 | 50 ch. Type **101** .. .. | 15 | 15 |
| 799 | 1 n. "Turtle" (submarine), 1776 .. .. .. | 15 | 15 |
| 800 | 2 n. "Charlotte Dundas" (steamship), 1802 .. | 25 | 25 |
| 801 | 3 n. "Great Eastern" (paddle-steamer), 1858 .. | 40 | 40 |
| 802 | 4 n. H.M.S. "Warrior" (armoured ship), 1862 .. | 50 | 50 |
| 803 | 5 n. Mississippi river steamer, 1884 .. .. | 80 | 80 |
| 804 | 6 n. "Preussen" (full-rigged ship), 1902 .. .. | 1·00 | 1·00 |
| 805 | 7 n. U.S.S. "Arizona" (battleship), 1915 .. | 1·10 | 1·10 |
| 806 | 10 n. "Bluenose" (fishing schooner), 1921 .. | 1·75 | 1·75 |
| 807 | 15 n. Steam trawler, 1925 | 1·75 | 1·75 |
| 808 | 20 n. "Liberty" freighter, 1943 .. .. .. | 2·75 | 2·75 |
| 809 | 25 n. "United States" (liner), 1952 .. .. | 3·50 | 3·50 |

**102** Nehru

**103** Crimson-backed Woodpecker

**1989.** Birth Centenary of Jawaharlal Nehru (Indian statesman).

| | | | |
|---|---|---|---|
| 811 **102** | 1 n. brown .. .. | 15 | 15 |

No. 811 is erroneously inscribed "ch".

**1989.** Birds. Multicoloured.

| | | | |
|---|---|---|---|
| 812 | 50 ch. Type **103** .. .. | 10 | 10 |
| 813 | 1 n. Black-naped blue monarch .. .. | 15 | 15 |
| 814 | 2 n. White-crested laughing thrush .. .. .. | 35 | 35 |
| 815 | 3 n. Blood pheasant .. | 50 | 50 |
| 816 | 4 n. Plum-headed (inscr "Blossom-headed") parakeet .. .. | 70 | 70 |
| 817 | 5 n. Rosy minivet .. | 85 | 85 |
| 818 | 6 n. Chestnut-headed fulvetta (inscr "Tit-Babbler") (horiz) | 1·00 | 1·00 |
| 819 | 7 n. Blue pitta (horiz) .. | 1·00 | 1·00 |
| 820 | 10 n. Black-naped oriole (horiz) .. .. .. | 1·75 | 1·75 |
| 821 | 15 n. Green magpie (horiz) | 2·50 | 2·50 |
| 822 | 20 n. Three-toed kingfisher (horiz) .. .. .. | 3·50 | 3·50 |
| 823 | 25 n. Ibis bill (horiz) .. | 4·00 | 4·00 |

**104** "Best Friend of Charleston" (USA, 1830)

**105** "Charaxes harmodius"

**1990.** Steam Railway Locomotives. Mult.

| | | | |
|---|---|---|---|
| 825 | 50 ch. Type **104** .. .. | 10 | 10 |
| 826 | 1 n. Class "U" (France, 1949) .. .. .. | 15 | 15 |
| 827 | 2 n. "Consolidation" (USA, 1866) .. .. .. | 35 | 35 |
| 828 | 3 n. Locomotive luggage engine (Great Britain, 1843) .. .. .. | 50 | 50 |
| 829 | 4 n. Class "60-3" Shay (USA, 1913) .. .. | 70 | 70 |
| 830 | 5 n. "John Bull" (USA, 1831) .. .. .. | 75 | 75 |
| 831 | 6 n. "The Hercules" (USA, 1837) .. .. .. | 80 | 80 |
| 832 | 7 n. Eight-wheel tank engine (Great Britain, 1874) .. .. .. | 85 | 85 |
| 833 | 10 n. "The Illinois" (USA, 1852) .. .. .. | 1·25 | 1·25 |
| 834 | 15 n. German state locomotive (1935) .. | 2·50 | 2·50 |
| 835 | 20 n. American standard (1865) .. .. .. | 3·50 | 3·50 |
| 836 | 25 n. Class "Ps-4" (USA, 1926) .. .. .. | 4·00 | 4·00 |

**1990.** Butterflies. Multicoloured.

| | | | |
|---|---|---|---|
| 838 | 50 ch. Type **105** .. .. | 10 | 10 |
| 839 | 1 n. "Prioneris thestylis" | 15 | 15 |
| 840 | 2 n. Eastern courtier .. | 35 | 35 |
| 841 | 3 n. "Penthema lisarda" (horiz) .. .. .. | 50 | 50 |
| 842 | 4 n. Golden birdwing .. | 55 | 55 |
| 843 | 5 n. Great nawab .. | 65 | 65 |
| 844 | 6 n. "Polyura dolon" (horiz) .. .. .. | 1·00 | 1·00 |
| 845 | 7 n. Tailed labyrinth (horiz) .. .. .. | 1·10 | 1·10 |
| 846 | 10 n. "Delias descombesi" | 1·75 | 1·75 |
| 847 | 15 n. "Childreni childrena" (horiz) .. .. .. | 2·00 | 2·00 |
| 848 | 20 n. Leaf butterfly (horiz) | 3·50 | 3·50 |
| 849 | 25 n. "Elymnias malelas" (horiz) .. .. .. | 4·00 | 4·00 |

**106** "Renanthera monachica"

**107** "Plum Estate, Kameido"

**1990.** "Expo '90" Int. Garden and Greenery Exposition, Osaka. Orchids. Mult.

| | | | |
|---|---|---|---|
| 851 | 10 ch. Type **106** .. .. | 15 | 15 |
| 852 | 50 ch. "Vanda coerulea" .. | 15 | 15 |
| 853 | 1 n. "Phalaenopsis violacea" .. .. | 15 | 15 |
| 854 | 2 n. "Dendrobium nobile" | 35 | 35 |
| 855 | 5 n. "Vandopsis lissochiloides" .. .. | 85 | 85 |
| 856 | 6 n. "Paphiopedilum rothschildianum" .. | 95 | 95 |
| 857 | 7 n. "Phalaenopsis schilleriana" .. .. | 1·10 | 1·10 |
| 858 | 9 n. "Paphiopedilum insigne" .. .. | 1·40 | 1·40 |
| 859 | 10 n. "Paphiopedilum bellatulum" .. .. | 1·75 | 1·75 |
| 860 | 20 n. "Doritis pulcherrima" .. .. | 3·50 | 3·50 |
| 861 | 25 n. "Cymbidium giganteum" .. .. | 4·25 | 4·25 |
| 862 | 35 n. "Phalaenopsis mariae" .. .. | 5·75 | 5·75 |

**1990.** Death of Emperor Hirohito and Accession of Emperor Akihito of Japan. "100 Famous Views of Edo" by Ando Hiroshige. Multicoloured.

| | | | |
|---|---|---|---|
| 864 | 10 ch. Type **107** .. .. | 15 | 15 |
| 865 | 20 ch. "Yatsumi Bridge" | 15 | 15 |
| 866 | 50 ch. "Ayase River and Kanegafuchi" .. .. | 15 | 15 |
| 867 | 75 ch. "View of Shiba Coast" .. .. .. | 15 | 15 |
| 868 | 1 n. "Grandpa's Teahouse, Meguro" .. .. | 15 | 15 |
| 869 | 2 n. "Inside Kameido Tenjin Shrine" .. | 30 | 30 |
| 870 | 6 n. "Yoroi Ferry, Koami-cho" .. .. | 75 | 75 |
| 871 | 7 n. "Sakasai Ferry" .. | 80 | 80 |
| 872 | 10 n. "Fukagawa Lumberyards" .. .. | 1·25 | 1·25 |
| 873 | 15 n. "Suido Bridge and Surugadai" .. .. | 2·00 | 2·00 |
| 874 | 20 n. "Meguro Drum Bridge and Sunset Hill" | 3·50 | 3·50 |
| 875 | 25 n. "Atagoshita and Yabu Lane" .. .. | 4·25 | 4·25 |

**108** Thimphu Post Office

**1990.**

| | | | |
|---|---|---|---|
| 877 **108** | 1 n. multicoloured .. | 15 | 15 |

**109** Giant Panda

**1990.** Mammals. Multicoloured.

| | | | |
|---|---|---|---|
| 878 | 50 ch. Type **109** .. .. | 10 | 10 |
| 879 | 1 n. Giant panda in tree .. | 15 | 15 |
| 880 | 2 n. Giant panda with cub | 35 | 35 |
| 881 | 3 n. Giant panda (horiz) .. | 50 | 50 |
| 882 | 4 n. Giant panda eating (horiz) .. .. .. | 50 | 50 |
| 883 | 5 n. Tiger (horiz) .. .. | 60 | 60 |
| 884 | 6 n. Giant pandas pulling up bamboo (horiz) .. | 80 | 80 |
| 885 | 7 n. Giant panda and cub resting (horiz) .. .. | 85 | 85 |
| 886 | 10 n. Indian elephant (horiz) .. .. .. | 1·40 | 1·40 |
| 887 | 15 n. Giant panda beside fallen tree .. .. | 1·90 | 1·90 |
| 888 | 20 n. Indian muntjac (inscr "Barking deer") (horiz) | 3·50 | 3·50 |
| 889 | 25 n. Snow leopard (horiz) | 4·25 | 4·25 |

**110** Roim

**1990.** Religious Musical Instruments. Mult.

| | | | |
|---|---|---|---|
| 891 | 10 ch. Dungchen (large trumpets) .. .. | 10 | 10 |
| 892 | 20 ch. Dungkar (Indian chank shell) .. .. | 10 | 10 |
| 893 | 30 ch. Type **110** .. .. | 10 | 10 |
| 894 | 50 ch. Tinchag (cup cymbals) .. .. | 10 | 10 |
| 895 | 1 n. Dradu and drilbu (pellet drum and hand bell) .. .. .. | 15 | 15 |
| 896 | 2 n. Gya-ling (oboes) .. | 25 | 25 |
| 897 | 2 n. 50 Nga (drum) .. | 30 | 30 |
| 898 | 3 n. 50 Kang-dung (trumpets) .. .. | 50 | 50 |

**111** Penny Black and Bhutan 1962 2 ch. Stamp

**1990.** "Stamp World London 90" International Stamp Exhibition. 150th Anniv of the Penny Black. Multicoloured.

| | | | |
|---|---|---|---|
| 900 | 50 ch. Type **111** .. .. | 10 | 10 |
| 901 | 1 n. Oldenburg 1852 $1\frac{1}{30}$ th. stamp .. .. .. | 15 | 15 |
| 902 | 2 n. Bergedorf 1861 $1\frac{1}{2}$ s. stamp .. .. .. | 25 | 25 |
| 903 | 4 n. German Democratic Republic 1949 50 pf. stamp .. .. .. | 45 | 45 |
| 904 | 5 n. Brunswick 1852 1 sgr. stamp .. .. .. | 60 | 60 |
| 905 | 6 n. Basel 1845 $2\frac{1}{2}$ r. stamp | 65 | 65 |
| 906 | 8 n. Geneva 1843 5 c. + 5 c. stamp .. .. .. | 85 | 85 |
| 907 | 10 n. Zurich 1843 4 r. stamp | 1·10 | 1·10 |
| 908 | 15 n. France 1849 20 c. stamp .. .. .. | 2·00 | 2·00 |
| 909 | 20 n. Vatican City 1929 5 c. stamp .. .. .. | 2·40 | 2·40 |
| 910 | 25 n. Israel 1948 3 m. stamp .. .. .. | 2·75 | 2·75 |
| 911 | 30 n. Japan 1871 48 m. stamp .. .. .. | 3·50 | 3·50 |

Each value also depicts the Penny Black. No. 901 is wrongly inscribed "Oldenberg".

**112** Girls

**113** Temple of Artemis, Ephesus

**1990.** South Asian Association for Regional Co-operation Girl Child Year. Mult.

| | | | |
|---|---|---|---|
| 913 | 50 ch. Type **112** .. .. | 10 | 10 |
| 914 | 20 n. Girl .. .. .. | 2·50 | 2·50 |

**1991.** Wonders of the World. Designs featuring Walt Disney cartoon characters. Multicoloured.

| | | | |
|---|---|---|---|
| 915 | 1 ch. Type **113** .. .. | 10 | 10 |
| 916 | 2 ch. Statue of Zeus, Olympia .. .. | 10 | 10 |
| 917 | 3 ch. Pyramids of Egypt | 10 | 10 |
| 918 | 4 ch. Lighthouse of Alexandria, Egypt .. | 10 | 10 |
| 919 | 5 ch. Mausoleum, Halicarnassus .. .. | 10 | 10 |
| 920 | 10 ch. Colossus of Rhodes | 10 | 10 |
| 921 | 50 ch. Hanging Gardens of Babylon .. .. | 10 | 10 |
| 922 | 5 n. Mauna Loa Volcanoes, Hawaii (horiz) .. .. | 65 | 65 |
| 923 | 6 n. Carlsbad Caverns, New Mexico (horiz) .. | 80 | 80 |
| 924 | 10 n. Rainbow Bridge National Monument, Utah (horiz) .. .. | 1·40 | 1·40 |
| 925 | 15 n. Grand Canyon, Colorado (horiz) .. | 1·90 | 1·90 |
| 926 | 20 n. Old Faithful, Yellowstone National Park, Wyoming (horiz) | 2·50 | 2·50 |
| 927 | 25 n. Sequoia National Park, California (horiz) | 3·00 | 3·00 |
| 928 | 30 n. Crater Lake and Wizard Island, Oregon (horiz) .. .. .. | 3·50 | 3·50 |

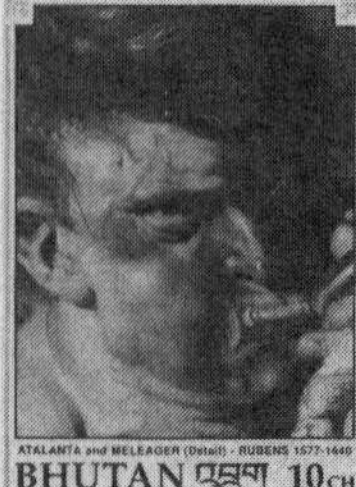


**114** "Atalanta and Meleager" (detail)

**1991.** 350th Death Anniv (1990) of Peter Paul Rubens (painter). Multicoloured.

| | | | |
|---|---|---|---|
| 930 | 10 ch. Type **114** .. .. | 10 | 10 |
| 931 | 50 ch. "The Fall of Phaeton" (detail) .. | 10 | 10 |
| 932 | 1 n. "Feast of Venus Verticordia" (detail) .. | 15 | 15 |
| 933 | 2 n. "Achilles slaying Hector" (detail) .. | 25 | 25 |
| 934 | 3 n. "Arachne punished by Minerva" (detail) .. | 35 | 35 |
| 935 | 4 n. "Jupiter receives Psyche on Olympus" (detail) .. .. | 45 | 45 |
| 936 | 5 n. "Atalanta and Meleager" (different detail) .. .. | 55 | 55 |
| 937 | 6 n. "Atalanta and Meleager" (different detail) .. .. | 70 | 70 |
| 938 | 7 n. "Venus in Vulcan's Furnace" (detail) .. | 1·00 | 1·00 |
| 939 | 10 n. "Atalanta and Meleager" (different detail) .. .. .. | 1·25 | 1·25 |
| 940 | 20 n. "Briseis returned to Achilles" (detail) .. | 2·50 | 2·50 |
| 941 | 30 n. "Mars and Rhea Sylvia" (detail) .. | 3·50 | 3·50 |

115 "Cottages, Reminiscence of the North"

**1991.** Death Centenary (1990) of Vincent van Gogh (painter). Multicoloured.

| | | | |
|---|---|---|---|
| 943 | 10 ch. Type **115** .. .. | 10 | 10 |
| 944 | 50 ch. "Head of a Peasant Woman with Dark Cap" | 10 | 10 |
| 945 | 1 n. "Portrait of a Woman in Blue" .. .. | 15 | 15 |
| 946 | 2 n. "Head of an Old Woman with White Cap (the Midwife)" .. | 35 | 35 |
| 947 | 8 n. "Vase with Hollyhocks" .. .. | 95 | 95 |
| 948 | 10 n. "Portrait of a Man with a Skull Cap" .. | 1·25 | 1·25 |
| 949 | 12 n. "Agostina Segatori sitting in the Cafe du Tambourin" .. .. | 1·40 | 1·40 |
| 950 | 15 n. "Vase with Daisies and Anemones" .. | 2·00 | 2·00 |
| 951 | 18 n. "Fritillaries in a Copper Vase" .. .. | 2·25 | 2·25 |
| 952 | 20 n. "Woman sitting in the Grass" .. .. | 2·50 | 2·50 |
| 953 | 25 n. "On the Outskirts of Paris" (horiz) .. .. | 3·25 | 3·25 |
| 954 | 30 n. "Chrysanthemums and Wild Flowers in a Vase" .. .. .. | 4·00 | 4·00 |

116 Winning Uruguay Team, 1930

**1991.** World Cup Football Championship. Multicoloured.

| | | | |
|---|---|---|---|
| 956 | 50 ch. Type **116** .. .. | 10 | 10 |
| 957 | 1 n. Italy, 1934 .. .. | 15 | 15 |
| 958 | 2 n. Italy, 1938 .. .. | 25 | 25 |
| 959 | 3 n. Uruguay, 1950 .. .. | 35 | 35 |
| 960 | 5 n. West Germany, 1954 | 60 | 60 |
| 961 | 10 n. Brazil, 1958 .. .. | 1·25 | 1·25 |
| 962 | 20 n. Brazil, 1962 .. .. | 2·50 | 2·50 |
| 963 | 25 n. England, 1966 .. | 3·00 | 3·00 |
| 964 | 29 n. Brazil, 1970 .. .. | 4·00 | 4·00 |
| 965 | 30 n. West Germany, 1974 | 4·00 | 4·00 |
| 966 | 31 n. Argentina, 1978 .. | 4·00 | 4·00 |
| 967 | 32 n. Italy, 1982 .. .. | 4·00 | 4·00 |
| 968 | 33 n. Argentina, 1986 .. | 4·25 | 4·25 |
| 969 | 34 n. West Germany, 1990 | 4·25 | 4·25 |
| 970 | 35 n. Stadium, Los Angeles (venue for 1994 World Cup) .. .. .. | 4·25 | 4·25 |

117 Bhutan and Japan State Flags

**1991.** "Phila Nippon '91" International Stamp Exhibition, Tokyo.

| | | | | |
|---|---|---|---|---|
| 972 | 117 | 15 n. multicoloured .. | 2·10 | 2·10 |

118 Teachers, Pupils and Hemisphere

**1992.** "Education for All by Year 2000".

| | | | | |
|---|---|---|---|---|
| 973 | 118 | 1 n. multicoloured .. | 15 | 15 |

119 Hurdler

120 "Santa Maria"

**1992.** Olympic Games, Barcelona. Mult.

| | | | |
|---|---|---|---|
| 974 | 25 n. Type **119** .. .. | 3·00 | 3·00 |
| 975 | 25 n. Body of hurdler .. | 3·00 | 3·00 |

Nos. 974/5 were issued together, se-tenant, forming a composite design.

**1992.** 500th Anniv of Discovery of America by Columbus. Multicoloured.

| | | | |
|---|---|---|---|
| 977 | 15 n. Type **120** .. .. | 1·10 | 1·10 |
| 978 | 20 n. Columbus .. .. | 1·50 | 1·50 |

121 Brandenburg Gate and rejoicing Couple

**1992.** 2nd Anniv of Reunification of Germany.

| | | | | |
|---|---|---|---|---|
| 980 | 121 | 25 n. multicoloured .. | 1·75 | 1·75 |

122 British Aerospace BAe 146 and Post Van

**1992.** 30th Anniv of Bhutan Postal Organization. Multicoloured.

| | | | |
|---|---|---|---|
| 982 | 1 n. Type **122** .. .. | 20 | 20 |
| 983 | 3 n. Rural letter courier .. | 25 | 25 |
| 984 | 5 n. Emptying post box .. | 45 | 45 |

123 Industry and Agriculture

124 Dragon

**1992.** 20th Anniv of Accession of King Jigme Singye Wangchuk. Multicoloured.

| | | | |
|---|---|---|---|
| 985 | 1 n. Type **123** .. .. | 10 | 10 |
| 986 | 5 n. British Aerospace RJ70 of National Airline | 35 | 35 |
| 987 | 10 n. House with water-pump .. .. .. | 70 | 70 |
| 988 | 15 n King Jigme Singye Wangchuk .. .. | 1·00 | 1·00 |

Nos. 985/8 were issued together, se-tenant, each horizontal pair within the block forming a composite design.

**1992.** International Volunteer Day.

| | | | | |
|---|---|---|---|---|
| 990 | 124 | 1 n. 50 multicoloured | 15 | 15 |
| 991 | | 9 n. multicoloured .. | 75 | 75 |
| 992 | | 15 n. multicoloured .. | 1·10 | 1·10 |

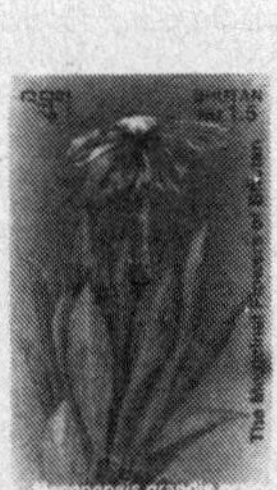
125 "Meconopsis grandis"

127 "The Love Letter" (Jean Honore Fragonard)

**1993.** Medicinal Flowers. Designs showing varieties of the Asiatic Poppy. Mult.

| | | | |
|---|---|---|---|
| 993 | 1 n. 50 Type **125** .. .. | 10 | 10 |
| 994 | 7 n. "Meconopsis" sp. .. | 50 | 50 |
| 995 | 10 n. "Meconopsis wallichii" .. .. | 70 | 70 |
| 996 | 12 n. "Meconopsis horridula" .. .. | 80 | 80 |
| 997 | 20 n. "Meconopsis discigera" .. .. | 1·40 | 1·40 |

**1993.** Paintings. Multicoloured.

| | | | |
|---|---|---|---|
| 1000 | 1 ch. Type **127** (postage) | 10 | 10 |
| 1001 | 2 ch. "The Writer" (Vittore Carpaccio) .. | 10 | 10 |
| 1002 | 3 ch. "Mademoiselle Lavergne" (Jean Etienne Liotard) .. | 10 | 10 |
| 1003 | 5 ch. "Portrait of Erasmus" (Hans Holbein) .. .. | 10 | 10 |
| 1004 | 10 ch. "Woman writing a Letter" (Gerard Terborch) .. .. | 10 | 10 |
| 1005 | 15 ch. Type **127** .. .. | 10 | 10 |
| 1006 | 25 ch. As No. 1001 .. | 10 | 10 |
| 1007 | 50 ch. As No. 1002 .. | 10 | 10 |
| 1008 | 60 ch. As No. 1003 .. | 10 | 10 |
| 1009 | 80 ch. As No. 1004 .. | 10 | 10 |
| 1010 | 1 n. Type **127** .. .. | 15 | 15 |
| 1011 | 1 n. 25 As No. 1001 .. | 20 | 20 |
| 1012 | 2 n. As No. 1002 (air) .. | 30 | 30 |
| 1013 | 3 n. As No. 1003 .. .. | 40 | 40 |
| 1014 | 6 n. As No. 1004 .. .. | 85 | 85 |

128 Lesser Panda

130 Namtheo-say

**1993.** Environmental Protection. Mult.

| | | | |
|---|---|---|---|
| 1016 | 7 n. Type **128** .. .. | 45 | 45 |
| 1017 | 10 n. One-horned rhinoceros .. .. | 70 | 70 |
| 1018 | 15 n. Black-necked crane and blue poppy .. | 1·00 | 1·00 |
| 1019 | 20 n. Takin .. .. | 1·25 | 1·25 |

Nos. 1016/19 were issued together, se-tenant, forming a composite design.

**1993.** Door Gods. Multicoloured.

| | | | |
|---|---|---|---|
| 1021 | 1 n. 50 Type **130** .. | 10 | 10 |
| 1022 | 5 n. Pha-ke-po .. .. | 40 | 40 |
| 1023 | 10 n. Chen-mi Jang .. | 80 | 80 |
| 1024 | 15 n. Yul-khor-sung .. | 1·25 | 1·25 |

131 "Rhododendron mucronatum"

132 Dog

**1994.** Flowers. Multicoloured.

| | | | |
|---|---|---|---|
| 1025 | 1 n. Type **131** .. .. | 10 | 10 |
| 1026 | 1 n. 50 "Anemone rupicola" .. .. | 10 | 10 |
| 1027 | 2 n. "Polemonium coeruleum" .. .. | 15 | 15 |
| 1028 | 2 n. 50 "Rosa marophylla" .. .. | 20 | 20 |
| 1029 | 4 n. "Paraquilegia microphylla" .. .. | 30 | 30 |
| 1030 | 5 n. "Aquilegia nivalis" | 40 | 40 |
| 1031 | 6 n. "Geranium wallichianum" .. | 45 | 45 |
| 1032 | 7 n. "Rhododendron campanulatum" (wrongly inscr "Rhodendron") .. | 55 | 55 |
| 1033 | 9 n. "Viola suavis" .. | 70 | 70 |
| 1034 | 10 n. "Cyananthus lobatus" .. .. | 80 | 80 |

**1994.** New Year. Year of the Dog. "Hong Kong '94" International Stamp Exhibition.

| | | | | |
|---|---|---|---|---|
| 1036 | 132 | 11 n. 50 multicoloured | 90 | 90 |

133 Trophy and Mascot

**1994.** World Cup Football Championship, U.S.A.

| | | | | |
|---|---|---|---|---|
| 1038 | 133 | 15 n. multicoloured .. | 55 | 55 |

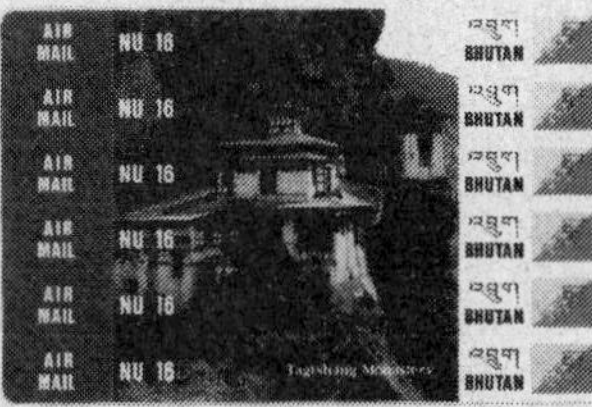

134 Tagtshang Monastery (½-size illustration)

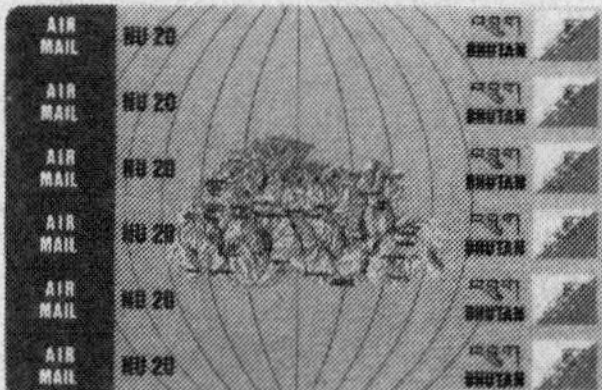

135 Relief Map of Bhutan (½-size illustration)

**1994.** Air. Self-adhesive.

| | | | | |
|---|---|---|---|---|
| 1039 | 134 | 16 n. multicoloured .. | 60 | 60 |
| 1040 | 135 | 20 n. multicoloured .. | 75 | 75 |

The individual stamps are peeled directly from the card backing. Each card contains six different designs with the same face value forming the composite designs illustrated. Each stamp is a horizontal strip with a label indicating the main class of mail covered by the rate at the left, separated by a vertical line of rouletting. The outer edges of the cards are imperforate.

138 Horseman with raised Sword

**1994.** 350th Anniv of Victory over Tibet–Mongol Army. Multicoloured.

| | | | |
|---|---|---|---|
| 1043 | 15 n. Type **138** .. .. | 55 | 55 |
| 1044 | 15 n. Archers and hand-to-hand sword fighting .. .. | 55 | 55 |
| 1045 | 15 n. Horseman with insignia on helmet amongst infantry .. | 55 | 55 |
| 1046 | 15 n. Drummer, piper and troops .. .. .. | 55 | 55 |

Nos. 1043/6 were issued together, se-tenant, forming a composite design of a battle scene and the Drugyel Dzong.

140 Lunar Rat

**1995.** New Year. Year of the Boar. Mult.

| | | | |
|---|---|---|---|
| 1048 | 10 ch. Type **140** .. .. | 10 | 10 |
| 1049 | 20 ch. Lunar ox .. .. | 10 | 10 |
| 1050 | 30 ch. Lunar tiger .. | 10 | 10 |
| 1051 | 40 ch. Lunar rabbit .. | 10 | 10 |
| 1052 | 1 n. Lunar dragon .. | 10 | 10 |
| 1053 | 2 n. Lunar snake .. | 10 | 10 |
| 1054 | 3 n. Lunar horse .. | 10 | 10 |
| 1055 | 4 n. Lunar sheep .. | 15 | 15 |
| 1056 | 5 n. Lunar monkey .. | 20 | 20 |
| 1057 | 7 n. Lunar rooster .. | 25 | 25 |
| 1058 | 8 n. Lunar dog .. .. | 30 | 30 |
| 1059 | 9 n. Lunar boar .. .. | 35 | 35 |

141 "Pleione praecox"

142 Human Resources Development

**1995.** Flowers. Multicoloured.

| | | | |
|---|---|---|---|
| 1061 | 9 n. Type **141** .. .. | 35 | 35 |
| 1062 | 10 n. "Primula calderina" | 35 | 35 |
| 1063 | 16 n. "Primula whitei" .. | 60 | 60 |
| 1064 | 18 n. "Notholirion macrophyllum" .. | 65 | 65 |

**1995.** 50th Anniv of U.N.O. Multicoloured.

| | | | |
|---|---|---|---|
| 1065 | 1 n. 50 Type **142** .. | 10 | 10 |
| 1066 | 5 n. Transport and Communications .. | 20 | 20 |
| 1067 | 9 n. Health and Population .. | 35 | 35 |
| 1068 | 10 n. Water and Sanitation .. | 35 | 35 |
| 1069 | 11 n. 50 U.N. in Bhutan | 45 | 45 |
| 1070 | 16 n. Forestry and Environment .. | 60 | 60 |
| 1071 | 18 n. Peace and Security | 65 | 65 |

## APPENDIX

The following stamps have either been issued in excess of postal needs or have not been available to the public in a reasonable quantities at face value. Such stamps may later be given full listing if there is evidence of regular postal use.

**1968.**

Bhutan Pheasants, 1, 2, 4, 8, 15 ch., 2, 4, 5, 7, 9 n.

Winter Olympic Games, Grenoble. Optd on 1966 Abominable Snowmen issue. 40 ch., 1 n. 25, 3, 6 n.

Butterflies (plastic-surfaced). Postage 15, 50 ch., 1 n. 25, 2 n., Air 3, 4, 5, 6 n.

Paintings (relief-printed). Postage 2, 4, 5, 10 45, 80 ch., 1 n. 05, 1 n. 40, 2, 3, 4, 5 n.; Air 1 n. 50, 2 n. 50, 6, 8 n.

Olympic Games, Mexico. 5, 45, 60, 80 ch., 1 n. 05, 2, 3, 5 n.

Human Rights Year. Die-stamped surch. on unissued "Coins". 15 ch. on 50 n.p., 33 ch. on 1 r., 9 n. on 3 r. 75.

Flood Relief. Surch. on 1968 Mexico Olympics issue. 5 ch. + 5 ch., 80 ch. + 25 ch., 2 n. + 50 ch.

**1969.**

Fish (plastic-surfaced). Postage 15, 20, 30 ch.; Air 5, 6, 7 n.

Insects (plastic-surfaced). Postage 10, 75 ch., 1 n. 25, 2 n.; Air 3, 4, 5, 6 n.

Admission of Bhutan to Universal Postal Union. 5, 10, 15, 45, 60 ch., 1 n. 05, 1 n. 40, 4 n.

5000 Years of Steel Industry. On steel foil. Postage 2, 5, 15, 45, 75 ch., 1 n 50, 1 n. 75, 2 n.; Air 3, 4, 5, 6 n.

Birds (plastic-surfaced). Postage 15, 50 ch., 1 n. 25, 2 n.; Air 3, 4, 5, 6 n.

Buddhist Prayer Banners. On silk rayon. 15, 75 ch., 2, 5, 6 n.

Moon Landing of "Apollo 11" (plastic-surfaced). Postage 3, 5, 15, 20, 25, 45, 50 ch. 1 n. 75; Air 3, 4, 5, 6 n.

**1970.**

Famous Paintings (plastic-surfaced). Postage 5, 10, 15 ch., 2 n. 75; Air 3, 4, 5, 6 n.

New U.P.U. Headquarters Building, Berne. 3, 10, 20 ch., 2 n. 50.

Flower Paintings (relief-printed). Postage 2, 3, 5, 10, 15, 75 ch., 1 n., 1 n. 40; Air 80, 90 ch., 1 n. 10, 1 n. 40, 1 n. 60, 1 n. 70, 3 n., 3 n. 50.

Animals (plastic-surfaced). Postage 5, 10, 20, 25, 30, 40, 65, 75, 85 ch.; Air 2, 3, 4, 5 n.

Conquest of Space (plastic-surfaced). Postage 2, 5, 15, 25, 30, 50, 75 ch., 1 n. 50; Air 2, 3, 6, 7 n.

**1971.**

History of Sculpture (plastic-moulded). Postage 10, 75 ch., 1 n. 25, 2 n.; Air 3, 4, 5, 6 n.

Moon Vehicles (plastic-surfaced). Postage 10 ch., 1 n. 70; Air 2 n. 50, 4 n.

History of the Motor Car (plastic-surfaced). Postage 2, 5, 10, 15, 20, 30, 60, 75, 85 ch., 1 n., 1 n. 20, 1 n. 55, 1 n. 80, 2 n., 2 n. 50; Air 4, 6, 7, 9, 10 n.

Bhutan's Admission to United Nations. Postage 5, 10, 20 ch., 3 n; Air 2 n. 50, 5, 6 n.

60th Anniv. of Boy Scout Movement. 10, 20, 50, 75 ch., 2, 6 n.

World Refugee Year. Optd. on 1971 United Nations issue. Postage 5, 10, 20 ch., 3 n.; Air 2 n. 50, 5, 6 n.

**1972.**

Famous Paintings (relief-printed). Postage 15, 20, 90 ch., 2 n. 50; Air 1 n. 70, 4 n. 60, 5 n. 40, 6 n.

Famous Men (plastic-moulded). Postage 10, 15, 55 ch.; Air 2, 6, 8 n.

Olympic Games, Munich. Postage 10, 15, 20, 30, 45 ch.; Air 35 ch., 1 n. 35, 7 n.

Space Flight of "Apollo 16" (plastic-surfaced). Postage 15, 20, 90 ch., 2 n. 50; Air 1 n. 70, 4 n. 60, 5 n. 40, 6 n.

**1973.**

Dogs. 2, 3, 15, 20, 30, 99 ch., 2 n. 50, 4 n.

Roses (on scent-impregnated paper). Postage 15, 25, 30 ch., 3 n.; Air 6, 7 n.

Moon Landing of "Apollo 17" (plastic-surfaced). Postage 10, 15, 55 ch. 2 n.; Air 7 n., 9 n.

"Talking Stamps" (miniature records). Postage 10, 25 ch., 1 n. 25, 7, 8 n.; Air 3, 9 n.

Death of King Jigme Dorji Wangchuk. Embossed on gold foil. Postage 10, 25 ch., 3 n.; Air 6, 8 n.

Mushrooms. 15, 25, 30 ch., 3, 6, 7 n.

"Indipex 73" Stamp Exhibition, New Delhi. Postage 5, 10, 15, 25 ch., 1 n. 25, 3 n.; Air 5, 6 n.



# BOHEMIA AND MORAVIA Pt. 5

Following the proclamation of Slovak Independence on 14 March, 1939, the Czech provinces of Bohemia and Moravia became a German Protectorate. The area was liberated in 1945 and returned to Czechoslovakia.

100 haleru = 1 koruna.

**1939.** Stamps of Czechoslovakia optd **BOHMEN u. MAHREN CECHY a MORAVA.**

| | | | | |
|---|---|---|---|---|
| 1 | **34** | 5 h. blue .. .. | 10 | 20 |
| 2 | | 10 h. brown .. .. | 10 | 20 |
| 3 | | 20 h. red .. .. | 15 | 20 |
| 4 | | 25 h. green .. .. | 10 | 20 |
| 5 | | 30 h. purple .. .. | 10 | 20 |
| 6 | **59** | 40 h. blue .. .. | 2·25 | 4·25 |
| 7 | **77** | 50 h. green .. .. | 10 | 20 |
| 8 | **60a** | 60 h. violet .. .. | 2·25 | 4·00 |
| 9 | **61** | 1 k. purple (No. 348) .. | 85 | 1·10 |
| 10 | | 1 k. purple (No. 395) .. | 35 | 55 |
| 11 | – | 1 k. 20 purple (No. 354) | 3·50 | 4·00 |
| 12 | **64** | 1 k. 50 red .. .. | 2·40 | 4·25 |
| 13 | – | 1 k. 60 green (No. 355a) | 2·40 | 4·25 |
| 14 | – | 2 k. green (No. 356) .. | 1·25 | 1·50 |
| 15 | – | 2 k. 50 blue (No. 357) .. | 3·00 | 3·75 |
| 16 | – | 3 k. brown (No. 358) .. | 3·00 | 3·75 |
| 17 | **65** | 4 k. violet .. .. | 3·25 | 5·50 |
| 18 | – | 5 k. green (No. 361) .. | 3·25 | 6·50 |
| 19 | – | 10 k. blue (No. 362) .. | 4·00 | 9·00 |

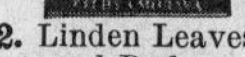

2. Linden Leaves and Buds.

5. Zlin.

3. Karluv Tyn Castle.

DESIGNS—As Type **3**: 40 h. Svikov Castle. 60 h. St. Barbara's Church, Kutna Hora. 1 k. St. Vitus's Cathedral, Prague. As Type **5**—VERT. 1 k. 20, 1 k. 50, Brno Cathedral. 2 k., 2 k. 50, Olomouc. HORIZ. 4 k. Ironworks, Moravska-Ostrava. 5 k., 10 k., 20 k. Karlsburg, Prague.

**1939.**

| | | | | |
|---|---|---|---|---|
| 20 | **2** | 5 h. blue .. .. .. | 10 | 10 |
| 21 | | 10 h. brown .. .. | 10 | 10 |
| 22 | | 20 h. red .. .. .. | 10 | 10 |
| 23 | | 25 h. green .. .. | 10 | 10 |
| 24 | | 30 h. purple .. .. | 10 | 10 |
| 25 | – | 40 h. blue .. .. | 10 | 10 |
| 26 | **3** | 50 h. green .. .. | 10 | 10 |
| 27 | – | 60 h. violet .. .. | 10 | 10 |
| 28 | – | 1 k. red .. .. .. | 10 | 10 |
| 29 | – | 1 k. 20 purple .. .. | 15 | 25 |
| 30 | – | 1 k. 50 red .. .. | 10 | 10 |
| 31 | – | 2 k. green .. .. | 10 | 10 |
| 32 | – | 2 k. 50 blue .. .. | 10 | 10 |
| 33 | **5** | 3 k. mauve .. .. | 10 | 10 |
| 34 | – | 4 k. grey .. .. .. | 10 | 10 |
| 35 | – | 5 k. green .. .. | 25 | 25 |
| 36 | – | 10 k. blue .. .. | 15 | 50 |
| 37 | – | 20 k. brown .. .. | 60 | 1·00 |

**1940.** As 1939 issue, but colours changed and new values.

| | | | | |
|---|---|---|---|---|
| 38 | **2** | 30 h. brown .. .. | 10 | 10 |
| 39 | | 40 h. orange .. .. | 10 | 10 |
| 40 | | 50 h. green .. .. | 10 | 10 |
| 44 | – | 50 h. green .. .. | 10 | 10 |
| 41 | **2** | 60 h. violet .. .. | 10 | 10 |
| 42 | | 80 h. orange .. .. | 10 | 10 |
| 45 | – | 80 h. blue .. .. | 10 | 20 |
| 43 | **2** | 1 k. brown .. .. | 10 | 10 |
| 46 | – | 1 k. 20 brown .. .. | 20 | 15 |
| 47 | – | 1 k. 20 red .. .. | 10 | 10 |
| 48 | – | 1 k. 50 pink .. .. | 10 | 10 |
| 49 | – | 2 k. green .. .. | 10 | 10 |
| 50 | – | 2 k. blue .. .. .. | 10 | 15 |
| 51 | – | 2 k. 50 blue .. .. | 10 | 10 |
| 52 | – | 3 k. green .. .. | 10 | 15 |
| 53 | – | 5 k. green .. .. | 15 | 10 |
| 54 | – | 6 k. brown .. .. | 15 | 20 |
| 55 | – | 8 k. green .. .. | 15 | 20 |
| 56 | – | 10 k. blue .. .. | 20 | 20 |
| 57 | – | 20 k. brown .. .. | 45 | 90 |

DESIGNS—As Type **3**: 50 h. (No. 44), Neuhaus Castle. 80 h. (No. 45), 3 k. Pernstyn Castle. 1 k. 20 (No. 46), 2 k. 50, Brno Cathedral. 1 k. 20 (No. 47), St. Vitus's Cathedral, Prague. 1 k. 50 St. Barbara's Church, Kutna Hora. 2 k. Pardubitz Castle. As Type **5**—HORIZ. 5 k. Bridge at Beching. 6 k. Samson Fountain, Budweis. 8 k. Kremsier. 10 k. Wallenstein Palace, Prague. 20 k. Karlsburg, Prague.

6. Red Cross Nurse and Wounded Soldier.

7. Patient in Hospital.

**1940.** Red Cross Relief Fund.

| | | | | |
|---|---|---|---|---|
| 58. | **6.** | 60 h.+40 h. blue.. .. | 40 | 50 |
| 59. | | 1 k. 20+80 h. plum .. | 45 | 55 |

**1941.** Red Cross Relief Fund.

| | | | | |
|---|---|---|---|---|
| 60. | **7.** | 60 h.+40 h. blue.. .. | 20 | 25 |
| 61. | | 1 k. 20+80 h. plum .. | 20 | 30 |

8. Anton Dvorak.

9. Harvesting.

10. Blast-furnace, Pilsen.

**1941.** Birth Cent. of Dvorak (composer).

| | | | | |
|---|---|---|---|---|
| 62. | **8.** | 60 h. violet .. .. | 15 | 15 |
| 63. | | 1 k. 20 brown .. .. | 20 | 30 |

**1941.** Prague Fair.

| | | | | |
|---|---|---|---|---|
| 64. | **9.** | 30 h. brown .. .. | 10 | 10 |
| 65. | | 60 h. green .. .. | 10 | 10 |
| 66. | **10.** | 1 k. 20 plum .. .. | 10 | 15 |
| 67. | | 2 k. 50 blue .. .. | 15 | 25 |

11. "Standetheater", Prague. 12. Mozart. (13.)

**1941.** 150th Death Anniv. of Mozart.

| | | | | |
|---|---|---|---|---|
| 68. | **11.** | 30 h.+30 h. brown .. | 10 | 10 |
| 69. | | 60 h.+60 h. green .. | 10 | 10 |
| 70. | **12.** | 1 k. 20+1 k. 20 red .. | 15 | 25 |
| 71. | | 2 k. 50+2 k. 50 blue .. | 15 | 30 |

**1942.** 3rd Anniv. of German Occupation. Optd. with T **13**.

| | | | |
|---|---|---|---|
| 72. | 1 k. 20 red (No. 47) .. | 20 | 40 |
| 73. | 2 k. 50 blue (No. 51) .. | 30 | 45 |

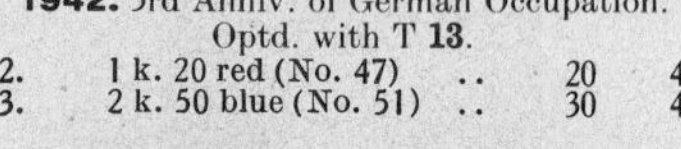

14. Adolf Hitler. 15.

**1942.** Hitler's 53rd Birthday.

| | | | | |
|---|---|---|---|---|
| 74. | **14.** | 30 h.+20 h. brown .. | 10 | 10 |
| 75. | | 60 h.+40 h. green .. | 10 | 10 |
| 76. | | 1 k. 20+80 h. purple | 10 | 10 |
| 77. | | 2 k. 50+1 k. 50 blue .. | 10 | 25 |

**1942.** Various sizes.

| | | | | |
|---|---|---|---|---|
| 78. | **15.** | 10 h. black .. .. | 10 | 10 |
| 79. | | 30 h. brown .. .. | 10 | 10 |
| 80. | | 40 h. blue .. .. | 10 | 10 |
| 81. | | 50 h. green .. .. | 10 | 10 |
| 82. | | 60 h. violet .. .. | 10 | 10 |
| 83. | | 80 h. orange .. .. | 10 | 10 |
| 84. | | 1 k. brown .. .. | 10 | 10 |
| 85. | | 1 k. 20 red .. .. | 10 | 10 |
| 86. | | 1 k. 50 red .. .. | 10 | 10 |
| 87. | | 1 k. 60 green .. .. | 10 | 15 |
| 88. | | 2 k. blue .. .. | 10 | 10 |
| 89. | | 2 k. 40 brown .. .. | 10 | 10 |
| 90. | | 2 k. 50 blue .. .. | 10 | 10 |
| 91. | | 3 k. olive .. .. | 10 | 10 |
| 92. | | 4 k. purple .. .. | 10 | 10 |
| 93. | | 5 k. green .. .. | 10 | 10 |
| 94. | | 6 k. brown .. .. | 10 | 10 |
| 95. | | 8 k. blue .. .. | 10 | 10 |
| 96. | | 10 k. green .. .. | 10 | 50 |
| 97. | | 20 k. violet .. .. | 15 | 75 |
| 98. | | 30 k. red .. .. | 20 | 80 |
| 99. | | 50 k. blue .. .. | 70 | 2·00 |

SIZES—$17\frac{1}{2} \times 21\frac{1}{2}$ mm. 10 h. to 80 h.; $18\frac{1}{2} \times 21$ mm. 1 k. to 2 k. 40 h.; $19 \times 24$ mm. 2 k. 50 h. to 8 k.; $24 \times 30$ mm. 10 k. to 50 k.

16. Nurse and Patient. 17. Mounted Postman.

**1942.** Red Cross Relief Fund.

| | | | | |
|---|---|---|---|---|
| 100. | **16.** | 60 h.+40 h. blue .. | 10 | 10 |
| 101. | | 1 k. 20+80 h. red .. | 10 | 10 |

**1943.** Stamp Day.

| | | | | |
|---|---|---|---|---|
| 102. | **17.** | 60 h. purple .. .. | 10 | 10 |

18. Peter Parler.

19. Adolf Hitler.

**1943.** Winter Relief Fund.

| | | | | |
|---|---|---|---|---|
| 103. | – | 60 h.+40 h. violet .. | 10 | 10 |
| 104. | **18.** | 1 k. 20+80 h. red .. | 10 | 10 |
| 105. | – | 2 k. 50+1 k. 50 blue .. | 10 | 15 |

DESIGNS: 60 h. Charles IV. 2 k. 50, King John of Luxembourg.

**1943.** Hitler's 54th Birthday.
106. 19. 60 h.+1 k. 40 violet .. 10 15
107. 1 k. 20+3 k. 80 red .. 15 20

20. Scene from "The Mastersingers of Nuremberg". 21. Richard Wagner.

**1943.** 130th Birth Anniv of Wagner.
108. 20. 60 h. violet .. .. 10 10
109. 21. 1 k. 20 red .. .. 10 10
110. – 2 k. 50 blue .. .. 10 15
DESIGN: 2 k. 50, Blacksmith scene from "Siegfried".

22. Reinhard Heydrich. 23. Arms of Bohemia and Moravia and Red Cross.

**1943.** 1st Death Anniv of Reinhard Heydrich (German Governor).
111 22 60 h.+4 k. 40 black .. 15 30

**1943.** Red Cross Relief Fund.
112. 23. 1 k. 20 + 8 k. 80 black and red .. .. 10 15

24. National Costumes. 25. Arms of Bohemia and Moravia.

**1944.** 5th Anniv. of German Occupation.
113. 24. 1 k. 20+3 k. 80 red .. 10 10
114. 25. 4 k. 20+18 k. 80 brown 10 10
115. 24. 10 k. + 20 k. blue .. 10 15

26. Adolf Hitler. 27. Smetana.

**1944.** Hitler's 55th Birthday.
116. 26. 60 h.+1 k. 40 brown .. 10 15
117. 1 k. 20 + 3 k. 80 green 10 15

**1944.** 600th Death Anniv of Bedrich Smetana (composer).
118. 27. 60 h.+1 k. 40 green .. 10 10
119. 1 k. 20+3 k. 80 red 10 15

28. St. Vitus's Cathedral, Prague. 29. Adolf Hitler.

**1944.**
120. 28. 1 k. 50 purple .. 10 15
121. 2 k. 50 violet .. .. 10 20

**1944.**
122. 29. 4 k. 20 green .. .. 10 30

NEWSPAPER STAMPS

N 6. Dove. N 19.

**1939.** Imperf.
N38 N 6 2 h. brown .. .. 10 15
N39 5 h. blue .. .. 10 15
N40 7 h. red .. .. 10 15
N41 9 h. green .. .. 10 15
N42 10 h. red .. .. 10 15
N43 12 h. blue .. .. 10 15
N44 20 h. green .. .. 10 15
N45 50 h. brown .. .. 10 20
N46 1 k. green .. .. 15 20

**1940.** For bulk postings. No. N42 optd GD-OT.
N60 N 6 10 h. red .. .. 50 1·00

**1943.** Imperf.
N106 N 19 2 h. brown .. .. 10 10
N107 5 h. blue .. .. 10 10
N108 7 h. red .. .. 10 10
N109 9 h. green .. .. 10 10
N110 10 h. red .. .. 10 10
N111 12 h. blue .. .. 10 10
N112 20 h. green .. .. 10 10
N113 50 h. brown .. .. 10 10
N114 1 k. green .. .. 10 20

OFFICIAL STAMPS

O 7. Numeral and Laurel Wreath. O 19. Eagle and Numeral.

**1941.**
O 60 O 7 30 h. brown .. .. 10 10
O 61 40 h. blue .. .. 10 10
O 62 50 h. green .. .. 10 10
O 63 60 h. green .. .. 10 10
O 64 80 h. red .. .. 40 15
O 65 1 k. brown .. .. 15 10
O 66 1 k. 20 red .. .. 15 10
O 67 1 k. 50 purple .. .. 30 15
O 68 2 k. blue .. .. 30 10
O 69 3 k. green .. .. 30 10
O 70 4 k. purple .. .. 40 45
O 71 5 k. yellow .. .. 1·00 70

**1943.**
O 106 O 19 30 h. brown .. .. 10 10
O 107 40 h. blue .. .. 10 10
O 108 50 h. green .. .. 10 10
O 109 60 h. violet .. .. 10 10
O 110 80 h. red .. .. 10 10
O 111 1 k. brown .. .. 10 10
O 112 1 k. 20 red .. .. 10 10
O 113 1 k. 50 brown .. .. 10 10
O 114 2 k. blue .. .. 10 15
O 115 3 k. green .. .. 10 15
O 116 4 k. purple .. .. 10 15
O 117 5 k. green .. .. 15 40

PERSONAL DELIVERY STAMPS

P 6.

**1939.**
P 38. P 6. 50 h. blue .. .. 40 80
P 39. 50 h. red .. .. 60 1·10

POSTAGE DUE STAMPS

D 6.

**1939.**
D 38. D 6. 5 h. red .. .. 10 10
D 39. 10 h. red .. .. 10 10
D 40. 20 h. red .. .. 10 10
D 41. 30 h. red .. .. 10 10
D 42. 40 h. red .. .. 10 10
D 43. 50 h. red .. .. 10 10
D 44. 60 h. red .. .. 10 10
D 45. 80 h. red .. .. 10 10
D 46. 1 k. blue .. .. 10 20
D 47. 1 k. 20 blue .. .. 15 20
D 48. 2 k. blue .. .. 35 60
D 49. 5 k. blue .. .. 40 70
D 50. 10 k. blue .. .. 65 1·10
D 51. 20 k. blue .. .. 1·75 2·75

## BOLIVAR Pt. 20

One of the states of the Granadine Confederation. A department of Colombia from 1886, now uses Colombian stamps.

1867. 100 centavos = 1 boliviano.

1. 2. 3.

**1863.** Imperf.
1. 1. 10 c. green .. .. £350 £275
2. 10 c. red .. .. 20·00 20·00
3. 1 p. red .. .. 10·00 10·00

**1872.** Various frames. Imperf.
4. 2. 5 c. blue .. .. 5·00 5·50
5. 3. 10 c. mauve .. .. 7·00 7·50
6. – 20 c. green .. .. 15·00 16·00
7. – 80 c. red .. .. 38·00 30·00

6. 7. 8.

**1874.** Imperf.
8. 6. 5 c. blue .. .. 12·00 7·50
9. 7. 5 c. blue .. .. 6·00 5·00
10. 8. 10 c. mauve .. .. 2·00 2·00

9. Simon Bolivar. 10. Simon Bolivar.

**1879.** Various frames. Dated "1879". White or blue paper. Perf.
14. 9. 5 c. blue .. .. 20 20
12. 10 c. mauve .. .. 20 20
13. 20 c. red .. .. 25 20

**1880.** Various frames. Dated "1880". White or blue paper.
19. 9. 5 c. blue .. .. 15 15
20. 10 c. mauve .. .. 25 25
21. 20 c. red .. .. 25 25
22. 80 c. green .. .. 2·00 2·00
23. 1 p. orange .. .. 2·75 2·75

**1882.**
30. 10. 5 p. red and blue .. 1·00 1·00
31. 10 p. blue and purple .. 1·00 1·00

11. Simon Bolivar. 12. Simon Bolivar.

**1882.** Various frames. Dated "1882".
32. 11. 5 c. blue .. .. 20 20
33. 10 c. mauve .. .. 20 20
34. 20 c. red .. .. 25 35
35. 80 c. green .. .. 55 55
36. 1 p. orange .. .. 65 60

**1883.** Various frames. Dated "1883".
37. 11. 5 c. blue .. .. 15 15
38. 10 c. mauve .. .. 20 20
39. 20 c. red .. .. 20 20
40. 80 c. green .. .. 45 55
41. 1 p. orange .. .. 55 80

**1884.** Various frames. Dated "1884".
42. 11. 5 c. blue .. .. 40 40
43. 10 c. mauve .. .. 15 15
44. 20 c. red .. .. 15 15
45. 80 c. green .. .. 20 25
46. 1 p. orange .. .. 45 55

**1885.** Various frames. Dated "1885".
47. 11. 5 c. blue .. .. 10 10
48. 10 c. mauve .. .. 10 10
49. 20 c. red .. .. 10 10
50. 80 c. green .. .. 20 25
51. 1 p. orange .. .. 55 35

**1891.**
56. 12. 1 c. black .. .. 15 20
57. 5 c. orange .. .. 35 25
58. 10 c. red .. .. 55 55
59. 20 c. blue .. .. 65 65
60. 50 c. green .. .. 95 95
61. 1 p. violet .. .. 95 95

13. Simon Bolivar. 20. J. M. del Castillo. 23.

**1903.** Various sizes and portraits. Imperf. or perf. On paper of various colours.
63. 13. 50 c. green .. .. 45 45
64. 50 c. blue .. .. 30 30
65. 50 c. violet .. .. 90 1·00
67. – 1 p. red .. .. 50 50
68. – 1 p. green .. .. 70 70
69. – 5 p. red .. .. 35 35
70b. – 10 p. blue .. .. 50 50
71. – 10 p. violet .. .. 2·50 2·50
PORTRAITS: 1 p. Fernandez Madrid. 5 p. Rodriguez Torices. 10 p. Garcia de Toledo.

**1904.** Various portraits. Imperf or perf.
77 20 5c. black .. .. 15 15
78 – 10c. brown (M. Anguiano) 15 15
80 – 20c. red (P.G. Ribon) 40 40

**1904.** Figures in various frames. Imperf.
81. 23. ½ c. black .. .. 30 25
82. 1 c. blue (horiz.) .. 50 50
83. 2 c. violet .. .. 75 70

ACKNOWLEDGMENT OF RECEIPT STAMPS

AR 19. AR 27.

**1903.** Imperf. On paper of various colours.
AR 75. AR 19. 20 c. orange .. 60 60
AR 76. 20 c. blue .. 50 50

**1904.** Imperf.
AR 85. AR 27. 2 c. red .. .. 1·00 1·00

LATE FEE STAMPS.

L 18.

**1903.** Imperf. On paper of various colours.
L 73. L 18. 20 c. red .. .. 30 30
L 74. 20 c. violet .. .. 30 30

REGISTRATION STAMPS

**1879.** As T 9 but additionally inscr. "CERTIFICADA".
R17. 9. 40 c. brown .. .. 60 60

**1880.** As previous issue dated "1880".
R 28. 9. 40 c. brown .. .. 30 35

**1882.** As T 11, but additionally inscr. "CERTIFICADA" Dated as shown.
R52. 11. 40 c. brown ("1882") 25 40
R53. 40 c. brown ("1883") 40 40
R54. 40 c. brown ("1884") 15 15
R55. 40 c. brown ("1885") 35 40

R 17.

**1903.** Imperf. On paper of various colours.
R 72. R 17. 20 c. orange .. 50 50

R 26.

**1904.** Imperf.
R 84. R 26. 5 c. black .. .. 2·00 2·00

## BOLIVIA Pt. 20

A republic of Central South America.

1867. 100 centavos = 1 boliviano.
1963. 100 centavos = 1 peso boliviano ($b).
1987. 100 centavos = 1 boliviano.

1. Condor. 4. (9 Stars).

**1867.** Imperf.
3a. 1. 5 c. green .. .. 2·40 3·00
10. 5 c. mauve .. .. £130 95·00
7. 10 c. brown .. .. £150 95·00
8. 50 c. yellow .. .. 13·50 20·00
11. 50 c. blue .. .. £225 £170
9. 100 c. blue .. .. 40·00 50·00
12. 100 c. green .. .. 95·00 90·00

**1868.** Nine stars below Arms. Perf.
32. 4. 5 c green .. .. 11·00 5·50
33. 10 c. red .. .. 15·00 5·50
34 50 c. blue .. .. 27·00 15·00
35. 100 c. orange .. .. 27·00 17·00
36. 500 c. black .. .. £250 £200

**1871.** Eleven stars below Arms. Perf.
37. 4. 5 c. green .. .. 5·50 3·50
38. 10 c. red .. .. 7·50 5·50
39. 50 c. blue .. .. 20·00 9·50
40. 100 c. orange .. .. 19·00 9·50
41. 500 c. black .. .. £950 £950

7. 11.

**1878.** Perf.
42. 7. 5 c. blue .. .. 5·50 2·50
43. 10 c. orange .. .. 4·50 1·90
44. 20 c. green .. .. 13·50 2·40
45. 50 c. red .. .. 70·00 6·75

**1887.** Eleven stars below Arms. Roul.
46. 4. 1 c. red .. .. 2·00 1·40
47. 2 c. violet .. .. 2·00 1·40
48. 5 c. blue .. .. 3·50 1·40
49. 10 c. orange .. .. 9·50 2·00

**1890.** Nine stars below Arms. Perf.
50. 4. 1 c. red .. .. 90 50
58. 2 c. violet .. .. 2·75 1·40
52. 5 c. blue .. .. 1·90 50
53. 10 c. orange .. .. 4·00 60
54. 20 c. green .. .. 8·00 1·00
55. 50 c. red .. .. 4·00 1·00
56. 100 c. yellow .. .. 8·00 2·00

**1893.** Eleven stars below Arms. Perf.
59. 4. 5 c. blue .. .. 3·50 1·40

**1894.**
63. 11. 1 c. bistre .. .. 60 60
64. 2 c. red .. .. 60 60
65. 5 c. green .. .. 60 60
66. 10 c. brown .. .. 60 40
67. 20 c. blue .. .. 2·00 85
68. 50 c. red .. .. 5·00 1·25
69. 100 c. red .. .. 12·00 4·25

12. Frias. 13.

**1897.**

77. 12. 1 c. green .. .. .. 70 50
78. – 2 c. red (Linares) .. .. 1·00 90
79. – 5 c. green (Murillo) .. 1·40 40
80. – 10 c. purple (Monteagudo) 1·25 40
81. – 20 c. black and red (J. Ballivian) .. .. 2·75 70
82. – 50 c. orange (Sucre) .. 2·75 1·40
83. – 1 b. blue (Bolivar) .. 2·75 3·00
84. 13. 2 b. multicoloured .. 20·00 27·00

18. Sucre. 19. A. Ballivian. 24.

**1899.**

92. 18. 1 c. blue .. .. .. 1·40 40
93. 2 c. red .. .. .. 1·00 25
94. 5 c. green .. .. .. 3·50 85
95. 5 c. red .. .. .. 1·00 50
96. 10 c. orange .. .. 1·40 70
97. 20 c. red .. .. .. 1·75 30
98. 50 c. brown .. .. 3·50 1·40
99. 1 b. lilac .. .. .. 1·00 1·00

**1901.**

100. 19. 1 c. red .. .. 35 15
101. – 2 c. green (Camacho) .. 40 25
102. – 5 c. red (Campero) .. 40 25
103. – 10 c. blue (J. Ballivian) 1·00 15
104. – 20 c. black and purple (Santa Cruz) .. .. 45 15
105. 24. 2 b. brown .. .. 2·40 1·75

25. 26. Murillo.

**1909.** Issued in La Paz. Cent. of Revolution of July, 1809. Centres in black.

110. 25. 5 c. blue .. .. 5·00 2·75
111. 26. 10 c. green .. .. 5·00 2·75
112. – 20 c. orange (Lanza) .. 5·00 2·75
113. – 2 b. red (Montes) .. 5·00 2·75

37. P. D. Murillo. F 8. Figure of Justice.

**1909.** Centenary of Beginning of War of Independence, 1809–25.

115. – 1 c. black and brown .. 25 15
116. – 2 c. black and green .. 35 25
117. 37. 5 c. black and red .. 35 10
118. – 10 c. black and blue .. 35 10
119. – 20 c. black and violet .. 40 25
120. – 50 c. black and bistre .. 60 35
121. – 1 b. black and brown .. 60 50
122. – 2 b. black and brown .. 1·00 70

PORTRAITS: 1 c. M. Betanzos. 2 c. I. Warnes. 10 c. B. Monteagudo. 20 c. E. Arze. 50 c. A. J. Sucre. 1 b. S. Bolivar. 2 b. M. Belgrano.

**1910.** Centenary of Liberation of Santa Cruz, Potosi and Cochabamba. Portraits as T **37**.

123. 5 c. black and green .. 25 10
124. 10 c. black and red .. 25 10
125. 20 c. black and blue .. 55 35

PORTRAITS: 5 c. I. Warnes. 10 c. M. Betanzos. 20 c. E. Arze.

**1911.** Nos. 101 and 104 surch. **5 Centavos 1911.**

127. 5 c. on 2 c. green .. .. 40 20
128. 5 c. on 20 c. blk. & pur... 10·00 10·00

**1912.** Stamps similar to F 8 optd. **CORREOS 1912** or surch. also.

130. F 8. 2 c. green .. .. 40 25
131. 5 c. orange .. .. 35 35
132. 10 c. red .. .. 85 50
129. 10 c. on 1 c. blue .. 35 15

**1913.** Portraits as 1901 and new types.

133. 19. 1 c. pink .. .. 35 25
134. – 2 c. red .. .. 35 20
135. – 5 c. green .. .. 40 10
136. – 8 c. yellow (Frias) .. 70 30
137. – 10 c. grey .. .. 70 25
139. – 50 c. purple (Sucre) .. 95 35
140. – 1 b. blue (Bolivar) .. 1·40 85
141. 24. 2 b. black .. .. 2·75 1·75

46. Monolith. 47. Mt. Potosi.

**1916.** Various sizes.

142. 46. ½ c. brown .. .. 20 20
143. 47. 1 c. green .. .. 25 15
144. – 2 c. black and red .. 30 15
145. – 5 c. blue .. .. 50 10
147. – 10 c. blue and orange .. 85 10

DESIGNS—HORIZ. 2 c. Lake Titicaca. 5 c. Mt. Illimani. 10 c. Parliament Building, La Paz.

51. 54. Morane Saulnier Type P Airplane.

**1919.**

158a. 51. 1 c. lake .. .. 15 10
158b. 2 c. violet .. .. 25 15
151. 5 c. green .. .. 35 10
152. 10 c. red .. .. 35 10
179. 15 c. blue .. .. 50 15
180. 20 c. blue .. .. 35 15
154. 22 c. blue .. .. 50 45
155. 24 c. violet .. .. 35 25
156. 50 c. orange .. .. 1·50 35
163. 1 b. brown .. .. 40 15
164. 2 b. brown .. .. 25 15

See also Nos. 194/206.

**1923.** Surch. **Habilitada** and value.

165. 51. 5 c. on 1 c. lake .. 35 25
169. 15 c. on 10 c. red .. 40 35
168. 15 c. on 22 c. blue .. 40 35

**1924.** Air. Establishment of National Aviation School.

170. 54. 10 c. black and red .. 30 25
171. 15 c. black and lake .. 1·10 70
172. 25 c. black and blue .. 55 35
173. 50 c. black and orange 1·10 70
174. – 1 b. black and brown 1·10 1·00
175. – 2 b. black and brown 2·25 2·00
176. – 5 b. black and violet .. 3·50 3·25

Nos. 174/6 have a different view.

57. Andean Condor.

**1925.** Centenary of Independence.

184 – 5 c. red on green .. 50 25
185 – 10 c. red on yellow .. 85 45
186 – 15 c. red .. .. 35 10
187 57 25 c. blue .. .. 2·25 60
188 – 50 c. purple .. .. 35 10
189 – 1 b. red .. .. 85 85
190 – 2 b. yellow .. .. 1·25 1·25
191 – 5 b. brown .. .. 1·40 1·40

DESIGNS—VERT: 5 c. Torch of Freedom. 10 c. Kantuta (national flower). 15 c. Pres. B. Saavedra. 50 c. Head of Liberty. 1 b. Mounted archer. 5 b. Marshal Sucre. HORIZ: 2 b. Hermes.

**1927.** Surch. **1927** and value

192. 51. 5 c. on 1 c. lake .. 1·40 50
193. 10 c. on 24 c. violet .. 1·40 85

**1928.**

194. 51. 2 c. yellow .. .. 35 25
195. 3 c. pink .. .. 40 35
196. 4 c. red .. .. 40 35
197. 20 c. olive .. .. 60 25
198. 25 c. blue .. .. 60 35
199. 30 c. violet .. .. 60 50
200. 40 c. orange .. .. 1·00 85
201. 50 c. brown .. .. 1·00 50
202. 1 b. red .. .. 1·25 85
203. 2 b. purple .. .. 1·75 1·75
204. 3 b. green .. .. 1·75 1·60
205. 4 b. lake .. .. 2·75 2·40
206. 5 b. brown .. .. 3·25 2·75

**1928.** Optd. **Octubre 1927** and star.

207. 51. 5 c. green .. .. 25 15
208. 10 c. grey .. .. 35 15
209. 15 c. red .. .. 50 35

**1928.** Surch. **15 cts. 1928.**

211. 51. 15 c. on 20 c. blue .. 5·00 5·00
213. 15 c. on 24 c. violet .. 95 50
216. 15 c. on 50 c. orange .. 70 40

66. "L.A.B." (Lloyd Aéreo Boliviano). 68. Andean Condor.

**1928.** Air.

217. 66. 15 c. green .. .. 55 55
218. 20 c. blue .. .. 20 10
219. 35 c. red .. .. 35 35

**1928.**

221. 68. 5 c. green .. .. 2·75 30
222. – 10 c. blue .. .. 35 10
223. – 15 c. red .. .. 35 10

DESIGNS: 10 c. Pres. Siles. 15 c. Map of Bolivia.

**1930.** Stamps of 1913 and 1916 surch **R.S. 21-4 1930** and value.

224. – 0.01 c. on 2 c. (No. 134) 70 70
225. – 0.03 c. on 2 c. (No. 144) 85 70
226. 46. 25 c. on ½ c. brown .. 70 50
227. – 25 c. on 2 c. (No. 144) 70 50

**1930.** Air. Optd. **CORREO AEREO R.S. 6-V-1930** or surch. **5 Cts.** also

228. 54. 5 c. on 10 c. blk. & red .. 8·00 10·00
229. 10 c. black and red .. 8·00 10·00
231. 15 c. black and lake .. 8·00 10·00
232. 25 c. black and blue .. 8·00 10·00
233. 50 c. black and orange 8·00 10·00
235. 1 b. black and brown .. £100 £100

**1930.** "Graf Zeppelin" Air stamps. Stamps of 1928 surch. **Z 1930** and value.

241. 66. 1 b. 50 on 15 c. green .. 20·00 27·00
242. 3 b. on 20 c. blue .. 20·00 27·00
243. 6 b. on 35 c. red .. 35·00 45·00

75. Junkers F-13 over Bullock Cart. 77. Pres. Siles.

78. Map of Bolivia. 79. Marshal Sucre.

**1930.** Air.

244. 75. 5 c. violet .. .. 65 40
245. – 15 c. red .. .. 65 40
246. – 20 c. yellow .. .. 65 40
247. 75. 35 c. green .. .. 65 15
248. – 50 c. blue .. .. 65 15
249. 75. 1 b. brown .. .. 65 20
250. – 2 b. red .. .. 65 30
251. 75. 3 b. grey .. .. 3·75 1·60

DESIGN: 15, 20, 50 c., 2 b. Junkers F-13 seaplane over river boat.

**1930.**

252. 77. 1 c. brown .. .. 25 25
253. – 2 c. green (Potosi) .. 85 35
254. – 5 c. blue (Illimani) .. 85 15
255. – 10 c. red (E. Abaroa) .. 85 15
256. 78. 15 c. violet .. .. 70 15
257. 35 c. red .. .. 1·40 70
258. 45 c. orange .. .. 1·40 70
259. 79. 50 c. slate .. .. 70 50
260. – 1 b. brown (Bolivar) .. 35 35

80. Symbols of Revolution.

**1931.** 1st Anniv. of Revolution.

263. 80. 15 c. red .. .. 1·40 35
264. 50 c. lilac .. .. 45 50

81.

**1932.** Air.

265. 81. 5 c. blue .. .. 45 50
266. 10 c. grey .. .. 50 25
267. 15 c. red .. .. 45 35
268. 25 c. orange .. .. 45 35
269. 30 c. green .. .. 40 35
270. 50 c. purple .. .. 40 35
271. 1 b. brown .. .. 40 35

**1933.** Surch. **Habilitada D.S. 13-7-1933** and value.

273. 51. 5 c. on 1 b. red .. 40 20
274. 78. 15 c. on 35 c. red .. 20 20
275. 15 c. on 45 c. orange .. 20 20
276. 51. 15 c. on 50 c. brown .. 85 15
277. 25 c. on 40 c. orange .. 40 15

83. 84. M. Baptista.

**1933.**

278. 83. 2 c. green .. .. 25 15
279. 5 c. blue .. .. 15 10
280. 10 c. red .. .. 40 25
281. 15 c. violet .. .. 25 15
282. 25 c. blue .. .. 60 40

**1935.** Ex-President Baptista Commemoration.

283. 84. 15 c. violet .. .. 50 20

85. Map of Bolivia. 86. Fokker Super Universal.

**1935.**

284. 85. 2 c. blue .. .. 25 15
285. 3 c. yellow .. .. 25 15
286. 5 c. green .. .. 25 15
287. 5 c. red .. .. 25 15
288. 10 c. brown .. .. 25 15
289. 15 c. blue .. .. 25 15
290. 15 c. red .. .. 25 15
291. 20 c. green .. .. 25 15
292. 25 c. blue .. .. 35 15
293. 30 c. red .. .. 35 25
294. 40 c. orange .. .. 60 20
295. 50 c. violet .. .. 60 15
296. 1 b. yellow .. .. 60 40
297. 2 b. brown .. .. 60 40

**1935.** Air.

298. 86. 5 c. brown .. .. 15 15
299. 10 c. green .. .. 15 15
300. 20 c. violet .. .. 15 15
301. 30 c. blue .. .. 15 15
302. 50 c. orange .. .. 35 15
303. 1 b. brown .. .. 35 30
304. 1½ b. yellow .. .. 1·00 15
305. 2 b. red .. .. 1·00 45
306. 5 b. green .. .. 1·25 45
307. 10 b. brown .. .. 2·10 85

**1937.** Surch. **Comunicaciones D.S. 25-2-37** and value in figures.

308. 83. 5 c. on 2 c. green .. 20 20
310. 15 c. on 25 c. blue .. 25 25
311. 30 c. on 25 c. blue .. 40 40
312. 51. 45 c. on 1 b. brown .. 50 50
313. 1 b. on 2 b. purple .. 60 60
314. 83. 2 b. on 25 c. blue .. 60 60
315. 80. 3 b. on 50 c. lilac .. 85 85
316. 5 b. on 50 c lilac .. 70 70

**1937.** Air. Surch. **Correo Aereo D.S. 25-2-37** and value in figures.

321. 75. 5 c. on 35 c. green .. 35 35
322. 66. 20 c. on 35 c. red .. 40 25
323. 50 c. on 35 c. red .. 75 40
324. 1 b. on 35 c. red .. 90 50
325. 54. 2 b. on 50 c. blk. & orge. 1·75 70
317. – 3 b. on 50 c. purple (No. 188) .. .. 90 35
318. – 4 b. on 1 b. red (No. 189) 75 70
319. 57. 5 b. on 2 b. orange .. 95 85
320. – 10 b. on 5 b. sepia (No. 191) .. .. 2·40 1·75
326. 54. 12 b. on 10 c. blk. & red 6·00 3·50
327. 15 b. on 10 c. blk. & red 6·00 2·25

89. Native School. 92. Junkers Ju52/3m over Cornfield.

**1938.**

328. 89 2c. red (postage) .. 10 10
329. – 10 c. orange .. .. 15 10
330. – 15 c. green .. .. 25 25
331. – 30 c. yellow .. .. 40 35
332. – 45 c. red .. .. 1·75 70
333. – 60 c. violet .. .. 50 35
334. – 75 c. blue .. .. 70 35
335. – 1 b. brown .. .. 1·00 35
336. – 2 b. buff .. .. 95 35

DESIGNS—VERT. 10 c. Oil Wells. 15 c. Industrial buildings. 30 c. Pincers and torch. 75 c. Indian and condor. HORIZ. 45 c. Sucre-Camiri railway map. 60 c. Natives and book. 1 b. Machinery 2 b. Agriculture.

337. – 20 c. red (air) .. .. 25 20
338. – 30 c. grey .. .. 25 20
339. – 40 c. yellow .. .. 25 20
340. 92. 50 c. green .. .. 35 20
341. – 60 c. blue .. .. 35 20
342. – 1 b. red .. .. 50 50
343. – 2 b. buff .. .. 1·25 20
344. – 3 b. brown .. .. 90 20
345. – 5 b. violet .. .. 4·50 50

DESIGNS—VERT. 20 c. Mint, Potosi. 30 c. Miner. 40 c. Symbolical of women's suffrage. 1 b. Pincers, torch and slogan. 3 b. New Government emblem. 5 b. Junkers aircraft over map of Bolivia. HORIZ. 60 c. Airplane and monument. 2 b. Airplane over river.

102. Llamas. 103. Arms.

**1939.**

| | | | | |
|---|---|---|---|---|
| 346. | 102. | 2 c. green | 70 | 50 |
| 347. | | 4 c. brown | 70 | 50 |
| 348. | | 5 c. mauve | 70 | 35 |
| 349. | – | 10 c. black | 70 | 50 |
| 350. | – | 15 c. green | 70 | 55 |
| 351. | – | 20 c. green | 70 | 35 |
| 352. | 103. | 25 c. yellow | 60 | 25 |
| 353. | | 30 c. blue | 60 | 35 |
| 354. | – | 40 c. red | 2·75 | 60 |
| 355. | – | 45 c. black | 2·75 | 60 |
| 356. | – | 60 c. red | 1·40 | 70 |
| 357. | – | 75 c. slate | 1·40 | 70 |
| 358. | – | 90 c. orange | 6·50 | 90 |
| 359. | – | 1 b. blue | 6·50 | 90 |
| 360. | – | 2 b. red | 7·50 | 90 |
| 361. | – | 3 b. violet | 9·00 | 1·25 |
| 362. | – | 4 b. brown | 4·00 | 1·40 |
| 363. | – | 5 b. purple | 5·00 | 1·60 |

DESIGNS—HORIZ. 10 c., 15 c. 20 c. Vicuna. 60 c., 75 c., Mountain Viscacha. 90 c., 1 b. Toco Toucan. 2 b., 3 b. Andean Condor. 4 b., 5 b. Jaguar. VERT. 40 c., 45 c. Cocoi Herons.

**107.** Virgin of Copacabana. **111.** Workman.

**1939.** Air. 2nd National Eucharistic Congress. Inscr. "II° CONGRESO EUCARISTICO NACIONAL".

| | | | | |
|---|---|---|---|---|
| 364. | – | 5 c. violet | 25 | 35 |
| 365. | 107. | 30 c. green | 20 | 20 |
| 366. | – | 45 c. blue | 60 | 20 |
| 367. | – | 60 c. red | 60 | 40 |
| 368. | – | 75 c. red | 45 | 40 |
| 369. | – | 90 c. blue | 30 | 25 |
| 370. | – | 2 b. brown | 50 | 25 |
| 371. | – | 4 b. mauve | 70 | 40 |
| 372. | 107. | 5 b. blue | 1·75 | 25 |
| 373. | – | 10 b. yellow | 3·50 | 25 |

DESIGNS—TRIANGULAR: 5 c., 10 b. Allegory of the Light of Religion. VERT. 45 c., 4 b. The "Sacred Heart of Jesus". 75 c., 90 c. S. Anthony of Padua. HORIZ. 60 c., 2 b. Facade of St. Francis's Church, La Paz.

**1939.** Obligatory Tax. Workers' Home Building Fund.

| | | | | |
|---|---|---|---|---|
| 374. | 111. | 5 c. violet | 35 | 10 |

**112.** Flags of 21 American Republics.

**1940.** 50th Anniv. of Pan-American Union.

| | | | | |
|---|---|---|---|---|
| 375. | 112. | 9 b. red, bl. & yell. | 70 | 70 |

**114.** Urns of Murillo and Sagarnaga. **117.** Shadow of Aeroplane on Lake Titicaca.

**1941.** 130th Death Anniv. of P. D. Murillo (patriot).

| | | | | |
|---|---|---|---|---|
| 376. | – | 10 c. purple | 10 | 10 |
| 377. | 114. | 15 c. green | 15 | 10 |
| 378. | – | 45 c. red | 15 | 15 |
| 379. | – | 1 b. 05 blue | 35 | 15 |

DESIGNS—VERT. 10 c. Murillo statue. 1 b. 05 Murillo portrait. HORIZ. 45 c. "Murillo dreaming in Prison".

**1941.** Air.

| | | | | |
|---|---|---|---|---|
| 380. | 117. | 10 b. green | 4·00 | 50 |
| 381. | | 20 b. blue | 4·50 | 85 |
| 382. | – | 50 b. mauve | 16·00 | 1·50 |
| 383. | – | 100 b. brown | 35·00 | 5·00 |

DESIGN: 50, 100 b. Andean condor over Mt. Illimani.

**119.** 1867 and 1941 Issues. **120.** "Union is Strength".

**1942.** First Students' Philatelic Exn., La Paz.

| | | | | |
|---|---|---|---|---|
| 384. | 119. | 5 c. mauve | 65 | 55 |
| 385. | | 10 c. orange | 65 | 55 |
| 386. | | 20 c. green | 1·10 | 60 |
| 387. | | 40 c. red | 1·25 | 65 |
| 388. | | 90 c. blue | 2·50 | 80 |
| 389. | | 1 b. violet | 3·75 | 2·00 |
| 390. | | 10 b. brown | 12·00 | 7·50 |

**1942.** Air. Chancellors' Meeting, Rio de Janeiro.

| | | | | |
|---|---|---|---|---|
| 391. | 120. | 40 c. red | 35 | 25 |
| 392. | | 50 c. blue | 35 | 25 |
| 393. | | 1 b. brown | 40 | 35 |
| 394. | | 5 b. mauve | 1·40 | 25 |
| 395. | | 10 b. purple | 1·75 | 1·60 |

**121.** Mt. Potosi. **122.** Chaquiri Dam.

**1943.** Mining Industry.

| | | | | |
|---|---|---|---|---|
| 396. | 121. | 15 c. brown | 25 | 15 |
| 397. | – | 45 c. blue | 25 | 15 |
| 398. | – | 1 b. 25 purple | 1·25 | 70 |
| 399. | – | 1 b. 50 green | 35 | 25 |
| 400. | – | 2 b. brown | 1·50 | 1·10 |
| 401. | 122. | 2 b. 10 blue | 50 | 40 |
| 402. | – | 3 b. orange | 2·00 | 1·25 |

DESIGNS—VERT. 45 c. Quechisla (at foot of Mt. Choroloque). 1 b. 25, Miner Drilling. HORIZ. 1 b. 50, Dam. 2 b. Truck Convoy. 3 b. Entrance to Pulacayo Mine.

**125.** Gen. Ballivian leading Cavalry Charge.

**1943.** Centenary of Battle of Ingavi.

| | | | | |
|---|---|---|---|---|
| 403. | 125. | 2 c. green | 10 | 10 |
| 404. | | 3 c. orange | 10 | 10 |
| 405. | | 25 c. purple | 15 | 10 |
| 406. | | 45 c. blue | 25 | 15 |
| 407. | | 3 b. red | 25 | 15 |
| 408. | | 4 b. purple | 40 | 25 |
| 409. | | 5 b. sepia | 55 | 35 |

**126.** Gen. Ballivian and Trinidad Cathedral.

**1943.** Centenary of Founding of El Beni. Centres in brown.

| | | | | |
|---|---|---|---|---|
| 410. | 126. | 5 c. green (postage) | 10 | 10 |
| 411. | | 10 c. purple | 15 | 15 |
| 412. | | 30 c. red | 15 | 15 |
| 413. | | 45 c. blue | 25 | 25 |
| 414. | | 2 b. 10 orange | 35 | 35 |
| 415. | – | 10 c. violet (air) | 10 | 10 |
| 416. | – | 20 c. green | 15 | 10 |
| 417. | – | 30 c. red | 20 | 15 |
| 418. | – | 3 b. blue | 25 | 20 |
| 419. | – | 5 b. black | 60 | 35 |

DESIGN: Nos. 415/19, Gen. Ballivian and mule convoy crossing bridge below airplane.

**127.** Trans. "Honour-Work-Law/All for the Country". **129.** Allegory of "Flight".

**1944.** Revolution of 20th December, 1943.

| | | | | |
|---|---|---|---|---|
| 420. | 127. | 20 c. orange (postage) | 10 | 10 |
| 421. | | 20 c. green | 10 | 10 |
| 422. | | 90 c. blue | 10 | 10 |
| 423. | | 90 c. red | 10 | 10 |
| 424. | – | 1 b. purple | 15 | 10 |
| 425. | – | 2 b. 40 brown | 20 | 15 |

DESIGN—VERT. 1 b., 2 b. 40, Clasped hands and flag.

| | | | | |
|---|---|---|---|---|
| 426. | 129. | 40 c. mauve (air) | 10 | 10 |
| 427. | – | 1 b. violet | 15 | 10 |
| 428. | – | 1 b. 50 green | 15 | 10 |
| 429. | – | 2 b. 50 blue | 35 | 15 |

DESIGN—HORIZ: 1 b. 50, 2 b. 50, Lockheed 10 Electra airplane and sun.

**131.** Posthorn and Envelope. **132.** Douglas DC-2 and National Airways Route Map.

**1944.** Obligatory Tax.

| | | | | |
|---|---|---|---|---|
| 430. | 131. | 10 c. red | 75 | 15 |
| 432. | | 10 c. blue | 75 | 15 |

Smaller Posthorn and Envelope.

| | | | | |
|---|---|---|---|---|
| 469. | | 10 c. red | 80 | 20 |
| 470. | | 10 c. yellow | 65 | 20 |
| 471. | | 10 c. green | 65 | 20 |
| 472. | | 10 c. brown | 65 | 20 |

**1945.** Air. Panagra Airways. 10th Anniv. of First La Paz-Tacna Flight.

| | | | | |
|---|---|---|---|---|
| 433. | 132. | 10 c. red | 15 | 10 |
| 434. | | 50 c. orange | 20 | 10 |
| 435. | | 90 c. green | 30 | 10 |
| 436. | | 5 b. blue | 45 | 15 |
| 437. | | 20 b. brown | 1·40 | 45 |

**133.** Lloyd-Aereo Boliviano Air Routes. **134.** L. B. Vincenti and J. I. de Sanjines Composers of National Anthem.

**1945.** Air. 20th Anniv of First National Air Service.

| | | | | |
|---|---|---|---|---|
| 438 | 133 | 20 c. blue, orge & vio | 10 | 10 |
| 439 | | 30 c. blue, orge & brn | 10 | 10 |
| 440 | | 50 c. blue, orge & grn | 10 | 10 |
| 441 | | 90 c. blue, orge & pur | 10 | 10 |
| 442 | | 2 b. blue and orange | 15 | 10 |
| 443 | | 3 b. blue, orange & red | 20 | 15 |
| 444 | | 4 b. blue, orge & bis | 40 | 15 |

**1946.** Cent. of National Anthem.

| | | | | |
|---|---|---|---|---|
| 445. | 134. | 5 c. black and mauve | 10 | 10 |
| 446. | | 10 c. black and blue | 10 | 10 |
| 447. | | 15 c. black and green | 10 | 10 |
| 448. | | 30 c. brown and red | 15 | 15 |
| 449. | | 90 c. brown and blue | 15 | 15 |
| 450. | | 2 b. brown and black | 40 | 15 |

**1947.** Surch. **1947 Habilitada Bs. 1.40.**

| | | | | |
|---|---|---|---|---|
| 451. | | 1 b. 40 on 75 c. blue (No. 334) (postage) | 15 | 10 |
| 452. | | 1 b. 40 on 75 c. slate (No. 357) | 15 | 10 |
| 455. | | 1 b. 40 on 75 c. red (No. 368) (air) | 15 | 10 |

**136.** Seizure of Government Palace. **137.** Mt. Illimani.

**1947.** Popular Revolution of 21 July, 1946.

| | | | | |
|---|---|---|---|---|
| 456. | 136. | 20 c. green (postage) | 10 | 10 |
| 457. | | 50 c. purple | 10 | 10 |
| 458. | | 1 b. 40 blue | 10 | 10 |
| 459. | | 3 b. 70 orange | 15 | 10 |
| 460. | | 4 b. violet | 25 | 15 |
| 461. | | 10 b. olive | 30 | 30 |
| 462. | 137. | 1 b. red (air) | 10 | 10 |
| 463. | | 1 b. 40 green | 10 | 10 |
| 464. | | 2 b. 50 blue | 15 | 15 |
| 465. | | 3 b. orange | 25 | 20 |
| 466. | | 4 b. mauve | 35 | 20 |

**138.** Arms of Bolivia and Argentina. **140.** Cross and Child.

**1947.** Meeting of Presidents of Bolivia and Argentina.

| | | | | |
|---|---|---|---|---|
| 467. | 138. | 1 b. 40 orange (postage) | 10 | 10 |
| 468. | | 2 b. 90 blue (air) | 25 | 25 |

**1948.** 3rd Inter-American Catholic Education Congress.

| | | | | |
|---|---|---|---|---|
| 473. | – | 1 b. 40 bl. & yell. (post.) | 35 | 10 |
| 474. | 140. | 2 b. green and orange | 50 | 15 |
| 475. | – | 3 b. green and blue | 55 | 20 |
| 476. | – | 5 b. violet and orange | 60 | 25 |
| 477. | – | 5 b. brown and green | 75 | 25 |
| 478. | – | 2 b. 50 orge. & yell. (air) | 30 | 35 |
| 479. | 140. | 3 b. 70 red and buff | 40 | 35 |
| 480. | – | 4 b. mauve and blue | 40 | 25 |
| 481. | – | 4 b. blue and orange | 40 | 15 |
| 482. | – | 13 b. 60 blue and green | 50 | 25 |

DESIGNS: 1 b. 40, 2 b. 50, Christ the Redeemer, Monument. 3 b., 4 b. (No. 480), Don Bosco. 5 b. (No. 476), 4 b. (No. 481), Virgin of Copacabana. 5 b. (No. 477), 13 b. 60, Pope Pius XII.



**141.** Map of S. America and Bolivian Auto Club Badge. **142.** Posthorn, Globe and Pres. G. Pacheco.

**1948.** Pan-American Motor Race.

| | | | | |
|---|---|---|---|---|
| 483. | 141. | 5 b. blue & pink (post.) | 1·00 | 20 |
| 484. | | 10 b. grn. & cream (air) | 1·10 | 25 |

**1950.** 75th Anniv. of U.P.U.

| | | | | |
|---|---|---|---|---|
| 485. | 142. | 1 b. 40 blue (postage) | 10 | 10 |
| 486. | | 4 b. 20 red | 10 | 10 |
| 487. | | 1 b. 40 brown (air) | 10 | 10 |
| 488. | | 2 b. 50 orange | 10 | 10 |
| 489. | | 3 b. 30 purple | 10 | 10 |

**1950.** Air. Surch. **XV ANIVERSARIO PANAGRA 1935-1950** and value.

| | | | | |
|---|---|---|---|---|
| 490. | 132. | 4 b. on 10 c. red | 10 | 10 |
| 491. | | 10 b. on 20 b. brown | 25 | 20 |

**1950.** No. 379 surch. **Bs 2.—Habilitada D.S. 6.VII.50.**

| | | | | |
|---|---|---|---|---|
| 492. | | 2 b. on 1 b. 05 blue | 15 | 10 |

**145.** Apparition at Potosi. **146.** Douglas DC-2.

**1950.** 400th Anniv. of Apparition at El Potosi.

| | | | | |
|---|---|---|---|---|
| 493. | 145. | 20 c. violet | 10 | 10 |
| 494. | | 30 c. orange | 10 | 10 |
| 495. | | 50 c. purple | 10 | 10 |
| 496. | | 1 b. red | 10 | 10 |
| 497. | | 2 b. blue | 15 | 10 |
| 498. | | 6 b. brown | 25 | 10 |

**1950.** Air. 25th Anniv. of Lloyd Aero Boliviano.

| | | | | |
|---|---|---|---|---|
| 499. | 146. | 20 c. orange | 15 | 10 |
| 500. | | 30 c. violet | 15 | 10 |
| 501. | | 50 c. green | 15 | 10 |
| 502. | | 1 b. yellow | 15 | 10 |
| 503. | | 3 b. blue | 15 | 10 |
| 504. | | 15 b. red | 50 | 15 |
| 505. | | 50 b. brown | 1·40 | 40 |

**1950.** Air. Surch. **Triunfo de la Democracia 24 de Sept. 49 Bs. 1.40.**

| | | | | |
|---|---|---|---|---|
| 506. | 137. | 1 b. 40 on 3 b. orange | 15 | 15 |

**148.** U.N. Emblem and Globe. **150.** St. Francis Gate.

**149.** Gate of the Sun, Tiahuanacu.

**1950.** 5th Anniv. of U.N.O.

| | | | | |
|---|---|---|---|---|
| 507. | 148. | 60 c. blue (postage) | 70 | 10 |
| 508. | | 2 b. green | 95 | 25 |
| 509. | | 3 b. 60 red (air) | 35 | 15 |
| 510. | | 4 b. 70 brown | 45 | 15 |

**1951.** 4th Centenary of Founding of La Paz. Centres in black.

| | | | | |
|---|---|---|---|---|
| 511. | 149. | 20 c. green (postage) | 10 | 10 |
| 512. | 150. | 30 c. orange | 10 | 10 |
| 513. | A. | 40 c. brown | 10 | 10 |
| 514. | B. | 50 c. red | 10 | 10 |
| 515. | C. | 1 b. purple | 10 | 10 |
| 516. | D. | 1 b. 40 violet | 15 | 15 |
| 517. | E. | 2 b. purple | 15 | 15 |
| 518. | F. | 3 b. mauve | 20 | 15 |
| 519. | G. | 5 b. red | 25 | 15 |
| 520. | H. | 10 b. sepia | 50 | 25 |
| 521. | 149. | 20 c. red (air) | 15 | 15 |
| 522. | 150. | 30 c. violet | 15 | 15 |
| 523. | A. | 40 c. slate | 15 | 15 |
| 524. | B. | 50 c. green | 15 | 15 |
| 525. | C. | 1 b. red | 20 | 20 |
| 526. | D. | 2 b. orange | 35 | 35 |
| 527. | E. | 3 b. blue | 35 | 35 |
| 528. | F. | 4 b. red | 40 | 40 |
| 529. | G. | 5 b. green | 40 | 40 |
| 530. | H. | 10 b. brown | 45 | 45 |

DESIGNS—HORIZ. As Type **149**: A, Camacho Avenue. B, Consistorial Palace. C, Legislative Palace. D, G.P.O. E, Arms. F, Pedro de la Casca authorizes plans of City. G, Founding the City. H, City Arms and Captain A. de Mendoza.

**151.** Tennis. **152.** Condor and Flag.

**1951.** Sports. Centres in black.

| | | | | |
|---|---|---|---|---|
| 531. | – | 20 c. blue (postage) | 15 | 10 |
| 532. | 151. | 50 c. red | 15 | 10 |
| 533. | – | 1 b. purple | 20 | 10 |
| 534. | – | 1 b. 40 yellow | 20 | 15 |
| 535. | – | 2 b. red | 25 | 15 |
| 536. | – | 3 b. brown | 55 | 50 |
| 537. | – | 4 b. blue | 70 | 50 |
| 538. | – | 20 c. violet (air) | 25 | 10 |
| 539. | – | 30 c. purple | 35 | 10 |
| 540. | – | 50 c. orange | 50 | 10 |
| 541. | – | 1 b. brown | 50 | 10 |
| 542. | – | 2 b. 50 orange | 70 | 40 |
| 543. | – | 3 b. sepia | 70 | 50 |
| 544. | – | 5 b. red | 1·40 | 1·00 |

DESIGNS—Postage: 20 c. Boxing. 1 b. Diving. 1 b. 40, Football. 2 b. Skiing. 3 b. Pelota. 4 b. Cycling. Air: 20 c. Horse-jumping. 30 c. Basket-ball. 50 c. Fencing. 1 b. Hurdling. 2 b. 50, Javelin. 3 b. Relay race. 5 b. La Paz Stadium.

**1951.** 100th National Flag Anniv. Flag in red, yellow and green.

| | | | | |
|---|---|---|---|---|
| 545. | 152. | 2 b. green | 10 | 10 |
| 546. | | 3 b. 50 c. blue | 10 | 10 |
| 547. | | 5 b. violet | 15 | 15 |
| 548. | | 7 b. 50 c. grey | 35 | 15 |
| 549. | | 15 b. red | 40 | 25 |
| 550. | | 30 b. brown | 85 | 50 |

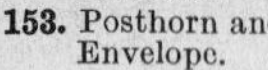

**153.** Posthorn and Envelope. **154.** E. Abaroa.

**1951.** Obligatory Tax.

| | | | | |
|---|---|---|---|---|
| 551 | – | 20 c. orange | 30 | 15 |
| 551b | – | 20 c. green | 30 | 15 |
| 552 | – | 20 c. bule | 30 | 15 |
| 553 | 153 | 50 c. green | 40 | 15 |
| 553d | | 50 c. red | 40 | 15 |
| 553e | | 3 b. green | 40 | 15 |
| 553f | | 3 b. bistre | 60 | 45 |
| 553g | | 5 b. violet | 65 | 15 |

DESIGN: 20c. Condor over posthorn and envelope.

**1952.** 73rd Death Anniv. of Abaroa (patriot).

| | | | | |
|---|---|---|---|---|
| 554. | 154. | 80 c. red (postage) | 10 | 10 |
| 555. | | 1 b. orange | 10 | 10 |
| 556. | | 2 b. green | 15 | 10 |
| 557. | | 5 b. blue | 20 | 15 |
| 558. | | 10 b. mauve | 35 | 15 |
| 559. | | 20 b. brown | 70 | 40 |
| 560. | | 70 c. red (air) | 10 | 10 |
| 561. | | 2 b. yellow | 15 | 15 |
| 562. | | 3 b. green | 15 | 15 |
| 563. | | 5 b. blue | 15 | 15 |
| 564. | | 50 b. purple | 70 | 50 |
| 565. | | 100 b. black | 75 | 70 |

**155.** Isabella the Catholic. **156.** Columbus Lighthouse.

**1952.** 500th Birth Anniv. of Isabella the Catholic.

| | | | | |
|---|---|---|---|---|
| 566. | 155. | 2 b. blue (postage) | 10 | 10 |
| 567. | | 6 b. 30 red | 25 | 15 |
| 568. | | 50 b. green (air) | 40 | 25 |
| 569. | | 100 b. brown | 45 | 35 |

**1952.** Columbus Memorial Lighthouse. On tinted papers.

| | | | | |
|---|---|---|---|---|
| 570. | 156. | 2 b. blue (postage) | 20 | 15 |
| 571. | | 5 b. red | 40 | 20 |
| 572. | | 9 b. green | 65 | 35 |
| 573. | | 2 b. purple (air) | 15 | 10 |
| 574. | | 3 b. 70 turquoise | 15 | 10 |
| 575. | | 4 b. 40 orange | 20 | 10 |
| 576. | | 20 b. brown | 45 | 10 |

**157.** Miner. **159.** Revolutionaries.

**158.** Villarroel, Paz Estenssoro and Siles Zuazo.

**1953.** Nationalization of Mining Industry.

| | | | | |
|---|---|---|---|---|
| 577. | 157. | 2 b. 50 c. red | 10 | 10 |
| 578. | | 8 b. violet | 15 | 10 |

**1953.** 1st Anniv. of Revolution of April 9th, 1952.

| | | | | |
|---|---|---|---|---|
| 579. | 158. | 50 c. mauve (postage) | 10 | 10 |
| 580. | | 1 b. red | 10 | 10 |
| 581. | | 2 b. blue | 10 | 10 |
| 582. | | 3 b. green | 10 | 10 |
| 583. | | 4 b. yellow | 10 | 10 |
| 584. | | 5 b. violet | 15 | 10 |
| 585. | | 3 b. 70 brown (air) | 15 | 15 |
| 590. | 159. | 6 b. mauve | 15 | 15 |
| 586. | 158. | 9 b. red | 15 | 15 |
| 587. | | 10 b. turquoise | 15 | 15 |
| 588. | | 16 b. orange | 15 | 15 |
| 591. | 159. | 22 b. 50 brown | 25 | 20 |
| 589. | 158. | 40 b. grey | 40 | 15 |

**1953.** Obligatory Tax. No. 551b and similar stamp surch **50 cts**.

| | | | | |
|---|---|---|---|---|
| 592 | | 50 c. on 20 c. mauve | 30 | 30 |
| 593 | | 50 c. on 20 c. green | 15 | 15 |

**161.** **162.** Ear of Wheat and Map.

**1954.** Obligatory Tax.

| | | | | |
|---|---|---|---|---|
| 594. | 161. | 1 b. lake | 25 | 10 |
| 595. | | 1 b. brown | 25 | 10 |

**1954.** 1st National Agronomical Congress.

| | | | | |
|---|---|---|---|---|
| 596. | 162. | 25 b. blue | 15 | 10 |
| 597. | | 85 b. brown | 35 | 15 |

**163.** Pres. Paz Estenssoro embracing Indian. **167.** Derricks.

**166.** Refinery.

**1954.** Air. 3rd Inter-American Indigenous Congress.

| | | | | |
|---|---|---|---|---|
| 598. | 163. | 20 b. brown | 10 | 10 |
| 599. | | 100 b. turquoise | 25 | 10 |

**1954.** 1st Anniv. of Agrarian Reform. As T **162**, but designs inscr. "REFORMA AGRARIA".

| | | | | |
|---|---|---|---|---|
| 600. | | 5 b. red (postage) | 10 | 10 |
| 601. | | 17 b. turquoise | 10 | 10 |
| 602. | | 27 b. mauve (air) | 10 | 15 |
| 603. | | 30 b. orange | 15 | 10 |
| 604. | | 45 b. purple | 25 | 10 |
| 605. | | 300 b. green | 70 | 25 |

DESIGNS—5 b., 17 b. Cow's head and map. 27 b. to 300 b. Indian peasant woman.

**1955.** Obligatory Tax. Nos. 553e and 553f surch **5.—D.S. 21-IV-55**.

| | | | | |
|---|---|---|---|---|
| 606 | 153 | 5 b. on 3 b. green | 25 | 10 |
| 607 | | 5 b. on 3 b. bistre | 25 | 10 |

**1955.** Development of Petroleum Industry.

| | | | | |
|---|---|---|---|---|
| 608. | 166. | 10 b. blue (postage) | 10 | 10 |
| 609. | | 35 b. red | 10 | 10 |
| 610. | | 40 b. green | 10 | 10 |
| 611. | | 50 b. purple | 15 | 10 |
| 612. | | 80 b. brown | 25 | 10 |
| 613. | 167. | 55 b. blue (air) | 10 | 10 |
| 614. | | 70 b. black | 20 | 10 |
| 615. | | 90 b. green | 30 | 10 |
| 616. | | 500 b. mauve | 45 | 40 |
| 617. | | 1000 b. brown | 85 | 75 |

**168.** Control Tower. **169.** Douglas DC-6B Aircraft.

**1957.** Obligatory Tax. Airport Building Fund.

| | | | | |
|---|---|---|---|---|
| 618 | 168 | 5 b. blue | 50 | 10 |
| 620 | – | 5 b. red | 50 | 10 |
| 619 | 169 | 10 b. green | 40 | 10 |
| 620b | – | 20 b. brown | 55 | 25 |

DESIGNS: 5 b. (No. 620), Douglas DC-6B over runway. 20 b. Lockheed Constellation in flight.

**1957** Currency revaluation. Founding of La Paz stamps of 1951 surch. Centres in black.

| | | | | |
|---|---|---|---|---|
| 621. | F. | 50 b. on 3 b. mauve (post.) | 10 | 10 |
| 622. | E. | 100 b. on 2 b. purple | 10 | 10 |
| 623. | C. | 200 b. on 1 b. purple | 15 | 10 |
| 624. | D. | 300 b. on 1 b. 40 violet | 20 | 10 |
| 625. | 149. | 350 b. on 20 c. green | 30 | 10 |
| 626. | A. | 400 b. on 40 c. brown | 30 | 10 |
| 627. | 150. | 600 b. on 30 c. orange | 40 | 10 |
| 628. | B. | 800 b. on 50 c. red | 45 | 10 |
| 629. | H. | 1000 b. on 10 b. sepia | 45 | 15 |
| 630. | G. | 2000 b. on 5 b. red | 50 | 25 |
| 631. | E. | 100 b. on 3 b. blue (air) | 10 | 10 |
| 632. | D. | 200 b. on 2 b. orange | 10 | 10 |
| 633. | F. | 500 b. on 4 b. red | 15 | 10 |
| 634. | C. | 600 b. on 1 b. red | 15 | 10 |
| 635. | 149. | 700 b. on 20 c. red | 30 | 15 |
| 636. | A. | 800 b. on 40 c. slate | 40 | 20 |
| 637. | 150. | 900 b. on 30 c. violet | 45 | 10 |
| 638. | B. | 1800 b. on 50 c. green | 45 | 35 |
| 639. | G. | 3000 b. on 5 b. green | 70 | 30 |
| 640. | H. | 5000 b. on 10 b. brown | 1·10 | 50 |

**172.** Congress Buildings (Santiago de Chile and Le Paz.) **173.** "Latin America" on Globe.

**1957.** 7th Latin-America Economic Congress, La Paz.

| | | | | |
|---|---|---|---|---|
| 641. | 172. | 150 b. bl. & grey (post.) | 10 | 10 |
| 642. | | 350 b. grey and brown | 20 | 10 |
| 643. | | 550 b. sepia and blue | 25 | 10 |
| 644. | | 750 b. green and red | 35 | 10 |
| 645. | | 900 b. brown and green | 50 | 15 |
| 646. | 173. | 700 b. vio. & lilac (air) | 15 | 10 |
| 647. | | 1200 b. brown | 25 | 15 |
| 648. | | 1350 b. red and mauve | 40 | 25 |
| 649. | | 2700 b. olive and turq. | 75 | 45 |
| 650. | | 4000 b. violet and blue | 95 | 50 |

**174.** Railway Train and Presidents of Bolivia and Argentina.

**1957.** Yacuiba-Santa Cruz Railway Inaug.

| | | | | |
|---|---|---|---|---|
| 651. | 174. | 50 b. orange (postage) | 30 | 15 |
| 652. | | 350 b. blue and light blue | 90 | 25 |
| 653. | | 1000 b. brown & cinna. | 2·10 | 50 |
| 654. | | 600 b. pur. & pink (air) | 80 | 25 |
| 655. | | 700 b. violet and blue | 1·50 | 50 |
| 656. | | 900 b. green | 2·10 | 30 |

**175.** Presidents and Flags of Bolivia and Mexico.

**1960.** Visit of Mexican President to Bolivia.

| | | | | |
|---|---|---|---|---|
| 657. | 175. | 350 b. olive (postage) | 15 | 10 |
| 658. | | 600 b. brown | 25 | 10 |
| 659. | | 1,500 b. sepia | 50 | 15 |
| 660. | | 400 b. red (air) | 25 | 10 |
| 661. | | 800 b. blue | 45 | 20 |
| 662. | | 2,000 b. green | 70 | 40 |

The President's visit to Bolivia did not take place.

**176.** Indians and Mt. Illimani. **177.** " Gate of the Sun", Tiahuanacu.

**1960.** Tourist Publicity.

| | | | | |
|---|---|---|---|---|
| 663. | 176. | 500 b. bistre (postage) | 30 | 10 |
| 664. | | 1000 b. blue | 50 | 15 |
| 665. | | 2000 b. sepia | 1·40 | 35 |
| 666. | | 4000 b. green | 2·50 | 1·75 |
| 667. | 177. | 3000 b. grey (air) | 1·25 | 75 |
| 668. | | 5000 b. orange | 1·90 | 75 |
| 669. | | 10,000 b. purple | 3·00 | 1·75 |
| 670. | | 15,000 b. violet | 4·25 | 3·00 |

**178.** Refugees. **179.** "Uprooted Tree".

**1960.** World Refuge Year.

| | | | | |
|---|---|---|---|---|
| 671. | 178. | 50 b. brown (postage) | 10 | 10 |
| 672. | | 350 b. purple | 15 | 10 |
| 673. | | 400 b. blue | 15 | 10 |
| 674. | | 1000 b. sepia | 50 | 15 |
| 675. | | 3000 b. green | 70 | 70 |
| 676. | 179. | 600 b. blue (air) | 35 | 35 |
| 677. | | 700 b. brown | 35 | 35 |
| 678. | | 900 b. turquoise | 40 | 35 |
| 679. | | 1800 b. violet | 40 | 40 |
| 680. | | 2000 b. black | 45 | 40 |

**180.** Jaime Laredo (violinist). **181.**

**1960.** Jaime Laredo Commem.

| | | | | |
|---|---|---|---|---|
| 681. | 180. | 100 b. green (postage) | 10 | 10 |
| 682. | | 350 b. lake | 20 | 10 |
| 683. | | 500 b. blue | 25 | 10 |
| 684. | | 1000 b. brown | 35 | 15 |
| 685. | | 1500 b. violet | 60 | 60 |
| 686. | | 5000 b. black | 2·00 | 2·00 |
| 687. | 181. | 600 b. plum (air) | 50 | 25 |
| 688. | | 700 b. olive | 50 | 35 |
| 689. | | 800 b. brown | 50 | 35 |
| 690. | | 900 b. blue | 70 | 35 |
| 691. | | 1800 b. turquoise | 1·00 | 1·00 |
| 692. | | 4000 b. grey | 2·00 | 70 |

**182.** Rotary Emblem and Nurse with Children. **183.**

**1960.** Founding of Children's Hospital by La Paz Rotary Club. Wheel in blue and yellow, foreground in yellow; background given.

| | | | | |
|---|---|---|---|---|
| 693. | 182. | 350 b. green (postage) | 15 | 10 |
| 694. | | 500 b. sepia | 25 | 10 |
| 695. | | 600 b. violet | 35 | 10 |
| 696. | | 1000 b. grey | 45 | 15 |
| 697. | | 600 b. brown (air) | 45 | 25 |
| 698. | | 1000 b. olive | 40 | 25 |
| 699. | | 1800 b. purple | 70 | 70 |
| 700. | | 5000 b. black | 2·00 | 80 |

**1960.** Air. Unissued stamp, surch. as in T **183**.

| | | | | |
|---|---|---|---|---|
| 701. | 183. | 1200 b. on 10 b. orange | 50 | 50 |

**184.** Design from Gate of the Sun. **185.** Flags of Argentina and Bolivia.

**1960.** Unissued Tiahuanacu Excavation stamps surch. as in T **184**. Gold back grounds.

| | | | | |
|---|---|---|---|---|
| 702. | | 50 b. on ½ c. red | 30 | 20 |
| 703. | | 100 b. on 1 c. red | 35 | 15 |
| 704. | | 200 b. on 2 c. black | 50 | 15 |
| 705. | | 300 b. on 5 c. green | 25 | 15 |
| 706. | | 350 b. on 10 c. green | 25 | 50 |
| 707. | | 400 b. on 15 c. blue | 35 | 15 |
| 708. | | 500 b. on 20 c. red | 35 | 15 |
| 709. | | 500 b. on 50 c. red | 40 | 15 |
| 710. | | 600 b. on 22½ c. green | 30 | 25 |
| 711. | | 600 b. on 60 c. violet | 45 | 30 |
| 712. | | 700 b. on 25 c. violet | 50 | 20 |
| 713. | | 700 b. on 1 b. green | 85 | 80 |
| 714. | | 800 b. on 30 c. red | 40 | 20 |
| 715. | | 900 b. on 40 c. green | 30 | 25 |
| 716. | | 1000 b. on 2 b. blue | 40 | 35 |
| 717. | | 1800 b. on 3 b. grey | 3·25 | 2·40 |
| 718. | | 4000 b. on 4 b. grey | 20·00 | 17·00 |
| 719. | | 5000 b. on 5 b. grey | 5·00 | 4·75 |

DESIGNS: Various gods, motifs and ornaments. SIZES: Nos. 702/6, As Type **184**. Nos. 707/17, As Type **184** but horiz. No. 718, 49 × 23 mm. No. 719, 50 × 52½ mm.

**1961.** Air. Visit of Pres. Frondizi of Argentina.
720. 185. 4000 b. multicoloured 70 60
721. – 6000 b. sepia and green 1·00 85
DESIGN: 6000 b. Presidents of Argentina and Bolivia.

186. Miguel de Cervantes (First Mayor of La Paz).

187. " United in Christ".

**1961.** M. de Cervantes Commem. and 4th Cent. of Santa Cruz de la Sierra (1500 b.).
722. 186. 600 b. violet and ochre (postage) .. .. 40 10
723. – 1500 b. blue & salmon 60 20
724. – 1400 b. brown & green (air) .. .. .. 60 25
DESIGNS: 1400 b. Portrait as Type 186 (diamond shape, 30½×30½ mm.). 1500 b. Nuflo de Chaves (vert. as Type 186).
See also Nos. 755/6.

**1962.** 4th National Eucharistic Congress, Santa Cruz.
725 187 1000 b. yellow, red and green (postage) .. 45 35
726 – 1400 b. yellow, pink and brown (air) .. 45 35
DESIGN: 1400 b. Virgin of Cotoca.

**1962.** Nos. 671/80 surch.
727 178 600 b. on 50 b. brown (postage) .. .. 25 15
728 900 b. on 350 b. purple 30 15
729 1000 b. on 400 b. blue 25 15
730 2000 b. on 1000 b. brn 25 30
731 3500 b. on 3000 b. green 45 45
732 179 1200 b. on 600 b. blue (air) .. .. 40 35
733 1300 b. on 700 b. brown 35 35
734 1400 b. on 900 b. green 40 35
735 2800 b. on 1800 b. vio 60 50
736 3000 b. on 2000 b. blk 60 50

189. Hibiscus.

190. Infantry.

**1962.** Flowers in actual colours; background colours given.
737. 189. 200 b. green (postage) 25 10
738. – 400 b. brown .. .. 25 10
739. – 600 b. deep blue .. 50 10
740. – 1000 b. violet .. .. 85 20
741. – 100 b. blue (air) .. 10 10
742. – 800 b. green .. .. 40 15
743. – 1800 b. violet .. .. 90 35
744. – 10,000 b. deep blue .. 4·50 2·25
FLOWERS: Nos. 738, 740 Orchids. No. 739, St. James' lily. Nos. 741/4, Types of Kantuta (national flowers).

**1962.** Armed Forces Commem.
745. 190. 400 b. mult. (postage) 10 10
746. – 500 b. multicoloured .. 15 10
747. – 600 b. multicoloured .. 20 15
748. – 2000 b. multicoloured 60 40
749. – 600 b. mult. (air) .. 35 15
750. – 1200 b. multicoloured 45 20
751. – 2000 b. multicoloured 65 35
752. – 5000 b. multicoloured 1·75 85
DESIGNS: No. 746, Cavalry. 747, Artillery. 748, Engineers. 749, Parachutists and aircraft. 750, 752, "Overseas Flights" (Lockheed Super Electra airplane over oxen-cart). 751, "Aerial Survey" (Douglas DC-3 airplane photographing ground).

191. Campaign Emblem.

192. Goal-keeper diving to save Goal.

**1962.** Malaria Eradication.
753. 191. 600 b. yellow, violet and lilac (postage) .. 25 15
754. – 2000 b. yellow, green and blue (air) .. 55 50
DESIGN: 2000 b. As No. 753 but with laurel wreath and inscription encircling emblem.

**1962.** Spanish Discoverers. As T 186 but inscribed " 1548–1962 ".
755. 600 b. mauve on blue (post.) 35 15
756. 1200 b. brown on yellow (air) 45 20
PORTRAITS: 600 b. A. de Mendoza. 1200 b. P. de la Gasca.
(Currency reform. 1000 (old) pesos=1 (new) pesos.)

**1963.** 21st South American Football Championships, La Paz. Multicoloured.
757 60 c. Type 192 (postage) .. 40 10
758 1 p. Goalkeeper saving ball 60 15
759 1 p. 40 Andean condor on football (air) .. .. 1·00 70
760 1 p. 80 Ball in corner of net 70 70
Nos. 758/60 are vertical.

193. Globe and Emblem.

194. Alliance Emblem.

**1963.** Freedom from Hunger.
761. 193. 60 c. yellow, blue and indigo (postage) .. 25 10
762. – 1 p. 20 yellow, blue and myrtle (air) .. .. 50 50
DESIGN: 1 p. 20, Ear of wheat across Globe.

**1963.** Air. " Alliance for Progress ".
763. 194. 1 p. 20 grn., bl. & bistre 55 35

195. Oil Derrick.

**1963.** 10th Anniv. of Revolution (1962).
764. 195. 10 c. grn. & brn. (post.) 10 10
765. – 60 c. sepia & orange .. 30 10
766. – 1 p. yellow, violet & grn. 35 15
767. – 1 p. 20 pink, brown and grey (air) .. .. 45 20
768. – 1 p. 40 green & ochre 55 25
769. – 2 p. 80 buff and slate 70 50
DESIGNS: 60 c. Map of Bolivia. 1 p. Students. 1 p. 20, Ballot box and voters. 1 p. 40, Peasant breaking chain. 2 p. 80, Miners.

196. Flags of Argentina and Bolivia.

197. Marshal Santa Cruz.

**1966.** Death Cent. of Marshal Santa Cruz.
770 196 10 c. mult. (postage) 10 10
771 60 c. multicoloured .. 20 10
772 1 p. multicoloured .. 35 15
773 2 p. multicoloured .. 50 20
774 197 20 c. blue (air) .. 10 10
775 60 c. green .. .. 20 10
776 1 p. 20 brown .. 50 35
777 2 p. 80 black .. .. 65 40

198. Generals Barrientos and Ovando, Bolivian Map and Flag.

199. Needy Children.

**1966.** Co-Presidents Commem.
778. 198. 60 c. mult. (postage) 20 10
779. 1 p. multicoloured .. 30 10
780. 2 p. 80 mult. (air) .. 95 70
781. 10 p. multicoloured .. 1·10 35

**1966.** Aid for Poor Children.
783. 199. 30 c. brown, sepia and ochre (postage) .. 15 10
784. – 1 p. 40 blk. & blue (air) 70 45
DESIGN: 1 p. 40, Mother and needy children.

**1966.** Commem Issues. Various stamps surch with inscr (as given below) and value.

(i) Red Cross Cent. Surch **Centenario de la Cruz Roja Internacional**
785 20 c. on 150 b. (No. 641) (postage) .. .. 10 10
786 4 p. on 4000 b. (No. 650) (air) .. .. .. 95 70

(ii) General Azurduy de Padilla. Surch. **Homenaje a la Generala J. Azurduy de Padilla.**
787. 30 c. on 550 b. (No. 643) .. 10 10
788. 2 p. 80 on 750 b. (No. 644) 70 35

(iii) Air. Tupiza Cent. Surch. **Centenario de Tupiza.**
789. 60 c. on 1350 b. (No. 648) .. 20 20

(iv) Air. 25th Anniv. of Bolivian Motor Club. Surch. **XXV Aniversario Automovil Club Boliviana.**
790. 2 p. 80 on 2700 b. (No. 649) 1·40 1·10

(v) Air. Cochabamba Philatelic Society Anniv. Surch **Aniversario Centro Filatelico Cochabamba.**
791. 1 p. 20 on 800 b. (No. 742) 35 25
792. 1 p. 20 on 1800 b. (No. 743) 35 25

(vi) Rotary Help for Children's Hospital. Surch. with value only. (a) Postage.
793. 1 p. 60 on 350 b. (No. 693) 45 15
794. 2 p. 40 on 500 b. (No. 694) 70 25
(b) Air.
795. 1 p. 40 on 1000 b. (No. 698) 45 45
796. 1 p. 40 on 1800 b. (No. 699) 45 45

(vii) 150th Anniv. of Coronilla Heroines. Surch. **CL. Aniversario Heroinas Coronilla.**
(a) Postage.
797. 60 c. on 350 b. (No. 682) .. 15 10
(b) Air.
798. 1 p. 20 on 800 b. (No. 689) 40 35

(viii) Air. Cent. of Hymn La Paz. Surch. **Centenario Himno Paceno.**
799. 1 p. 40 on 4000 b. (No. 692) 40 35

(ix) Air. 12th Anniv. of Agrarian Reform. Surch. **XII Aniversario Reforma Agraria.**
800. 10 c. on 27 b. (No. 602) .. 15 15

(x) Air. 25th Anniv. of Chaco Peace Settlement. Surch. **XXV Aniversario Paz del Chaco.**
801. 10 c. on 55 b. (No. 613) .. 15 15

All the following are surch. on Revenue stamps. The design shows a beach scene with palms, size 27×21½ mm.

(xi) Cent. of Rurrenabaque. Surch. **Centenario de Rurrenabaque.**
802. 1 p. on 10 b. brown .. 30 10

(xii) 25th Anniv. of Busch Government. Surch. **XXV Aniversario Gobierno Busch.**
803. 20 c. on 5 b. red .. .. 10 10

(xiii) 20th Anniv. of Villarroel Government. Surch. **XX Aniversario Gob. Villarroel.**
804. 60 c. on 2 b. green .. 15 10

(xiv) 25th Anniv. of Pando Department. Surch. **XXV Aniversario Dpto. Pando.**
(a) Postage.
805. 1 p. 60 on 50 c. violet .. 45 15
(b) Air. Surch. **Aereo** also.
806. 1 p. 20 on 1 b. blue .. 50 40

201. Sower.

202. " Macheteros ".

**1967.** 50th Anniv. of Lions Int. Mult.
807. 70 c. Type 210 (postage) .. 35 10
808. 2 p. Lions emblem and Inca obelisks (horiz.) (air) .. 55 45

**1968.** 9th Congress of the U.P.A.E (Postal Union of the Americas and Spain). Bolivian Folklore. Designs showing costumed figures. Multicoloured.
810. 30 c. Type 202 (postage) 10 10
811. 60 c. " Chunchos " .. 15 10
812. 1 p. " Wiphala " .. .. 25 15
813. 2 p. " Diablada " .. .. 50 20
814. 1 p. 20 " Pujllay " (air) .. 25 15
815. 1 p. 40 " Ujusiris " .. 35 20
816. 2 p. " Morenada " .. 50 25
817. 3 p. " Auki-aukis " .. 85 50

203. Arms of Tarija.

204. President G. Villarroel.

**1968.** 150th Anniv. of Battle of the Tablada (1817).
819. 203. 20 c. mult. (postage) .. 10 10
820. 30 c. multicoloured .. 10 10
821. 40 c. multicoloured .. 15 10
822. 60 c. multicoloured .. 20 10
823. – 1 p. multicoloured (air) 35 15
824. – 1 p. 20 multicoloured 40 15
825. – 2 p. multicoloured .. 70 35
826. – 4 p. multicoloured .. 70 50
DESIGNS: Nos. 823/6, Moto Mendez.

**1968.** 400th Anniv. of Cochabamba.
827. 204. 20 c. brn. & orge. (post.) 15 10
828. 30 c. brn. & turquoise 15 10
829. 40 c. brown & purple 15 10
830. 50 c. brown and green 15 10
831. 1 p. brown and bistre 35 10
832. – 1 p. 40 blk. & red (air) 35 25
833. – 3 p. black and blue .. 35 40
834. – 4 p. black and red .. 50 50
835. – 5 p. black and green .. 60 40
836. – 10 p. black and violet 1·10 75
DESIGN—HORIZ. 1 p. 40 to 10 p. Similar portrait of President.

205. Painted Clay Cup.

206. President J. F. Kennedy.

**1968.** 20th Anniv of U.N.E.S.C.O. (1966).
837 205 20 c. mult (postage) .. 15 10
838 60 c. multicoloured .. 40 25
839 – 1 p. 20 black & bl (air) 40 20
840 – 2 p. 80 black and green 45 45
DESIGNS: Nos. 839/40, U.N.E.S.C.O. emblem.

**1968.** 5th Death Anniv of John F. Kennedy (U.S. President).
841 206 10 c. black & grn (post) 15 10
842 4 p. black and violet 95 95
843 1 p. black & green (air) 35 20
844 10 p. black and red .. 1·90 1·90

207. I.T.U. Emblem.

208. Tennis Player.

**1968.** Cent. (1965) of I.T.U.
846. 207. 10 c. black grey and yellow (postage) .. 15 10
847. 60 c. black, orange and bistre .. .. 35 10
848. 1 p. 20 black, grey and yellow (air) .. 30 10
849. 1 p. 40 blk., blue & brn. 40 20

**1968.** South American Tennis Championships, La Paz.
850. 208. 10 c. black, brown and grey (postage) .. 20 10
851. 20 c. black, brn. & yell. 20 10
852. 30 c. black, brown & bl. 20 10
853. 1 p. 40 black, brown & orange (air) .. 45 25
854. 2 p. 80 blk., brn. & blue 50 50

209. Unofficial 1 r Stamp of 1863.

210. Rifle-shooting.

**1968.** Stamp Cent.
856. 209. 10 c. brown, black and green (postage) .. 15 10
857. 30 c. brn., blk. & blue 15 10
858. 2 p. brn., black & drab 25 10
859. – 1 p. 40 green, black and yellow (air) .. 50 25
860. – 2 p. 80 grn., blk. & pink 70 50
861. – 3 p. grn. blk. & lilac .. 70 50
DESIGNS: Nos. 859/61 First Bolivian stamp.

**1969.** Olympic Games, Mexico (1968).
863. 210. 40 c. black, red & orge. (postage) .. .. 15 10
864. – 50 c. black, red and green 15 10
865. – 60 c. black, blue & green 25 10
866. – 1 p. 20 black, green and ochre (air) .. 40 15
867. – 2 p. 80 blk., red & yell. 85 35
868. – 5 p. multicoloured .. 1·00 1·00
DESIGNS—HORIZ. 50 c. Horse-jumping. 60 c. Canoeing. 5 p. Hurdling. VERT. 1 p. 20, Running. 2 p. 80, Throwing the discus.

211. F. D. Roosevelt.

212. " Temensis laothoe violetta ".

**1969.** Air. Franklin D. Roosevelt Commem.
870 211 5 p. black, orange & brn 1·40 75

**1970.** Butterflies. Multicoloured.
871. 5 c. Type 212 (postage) .. 35 35
872. 10 c. "Papilio crassus" .. 70 70
873. 20 c. "Catagramma cynosura" .. .. .. 70 70
874. 30 c. "Eunica eurota flora" 70 70
875. 80 c. "Ituna phenarete" 70 70
876. 1 p. "Metamorpha dido wernichei" (air) .. 60 20
877. 1 p. 80 "Heliconius felix" 80 35
878. 2 p. 80 "Morpho casica" 1·75 1·75
879. 3 p. "Papilio yuracares" 1·90 1·75
880. 4 p. "Heliconsus melitus" 2·50 2·00

213. Scout mountaineering. 214. President A. Ovando and Revolutionaries.

**1970.** Bolivian Scout Movement. Mult.
882. 5 c. Type 213 (postage) .. 15 10
883. 10 c. Girl-scout planting shrub 15 10
884. 50 c. Scout laying bricks (air) 15 10
885. 1 p. 20 Bolivian scout badge 35 15

**1970.** Obligatory Tax. Revolution and National Day.
886. 214. 20 c. blk. & red (post.) 25 15
887. – 30 c. blk. & green (air) 25 15
DESIGN: 30 c. Pres. Ovando, oil derricks and laurel sprig.

**1970.** "Exfilca 70" Stamp Exhib., Caracas, Venezuela No. 706 further surch. **EXFILCA 70** and new value.
888 30 c. on 350 b. on 10 c. .. 15 10

**1970.** Provisionals. Various stamps surch.
889. 178. 60 c. on 900 b. on 350 b. (postage) .. .. 30 10
890. – 1 p. 20 on 1500 b. (No. 723) .. .. .. 50 15
891. 185. 1 p. 20 on 4000 b. (air) 35 15

217. Pres. G. Busch and Oil Derrick. 218. "Amaryllis escobar uriae".

**1971.** 32nd Death Anniv. of President G. Busch and 25th Death Anniv. of Pres. Villarroel.
892. 217. 20 c. blk. & lilac (post.) 35 10
893. – 30 c. black & blue (air) 30 10
DESIGN: 30 c. Pres. Villarroel and oil refinery.

**1971.** Bolivian Flora. Multicoloured.
894. 30 c. Type 218 (postage) 15 10
895. 40 c. "Amaryllis evansae 15 10
896. 50 c. "Amaryllis yungacensis" (vert.) .. .. 20 15
897. 2 p. "Gymnocalycium chiquitanum" (vert.) 55 35
898. 1 p. 20 "Amaryllis pseudopardina" (air) .. 45 15
899. 1 p. 40 "Rebutia kruegeri" (vert.) .. .. 60 15
900. 2 p. 80 "Lobivia pentlandii" .. .. 95 25
901. 4 p. "Rebutia tunariensis" (vert.) .. .. .. 1·60 50

219. Sica Sica Cathedral. 220. Pres. H. Banzer.

**1971.** "Exfilima" Stamp Exhibition, Lima, Peru.
903. 219. 20 c. multicoloured .. 15 10

**1972.** "Bolivia's Development".
904. 220. 1 p. 20 multicoloured .. 35 15

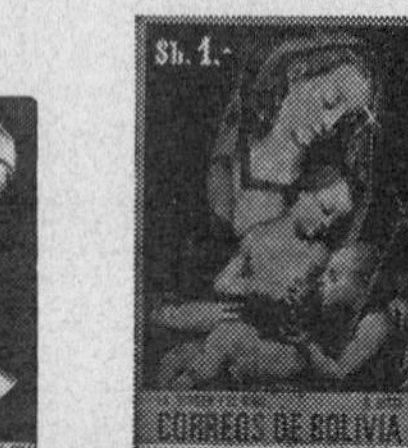

221. Chiriwano de Achocalla Dance. 222. "Virgin and Child" (B. Bitti).

**1972.** Folk Dances. Multicoloured.
905. 20 c. Type 221 (postage) .. 10 10
906. 40 c. Rueda Chapaca .. 20 15
907. 60 c. Kena-Kena .. .. 30 15
908. 1 p. Waca Thokori .. 40 25
909. 1 p. 20 Kusillo (air) .. 40 15
910. 1 p. 40 Taquirari .. .. 45 15

**1972.** Bolivian Paintings. Multicoloured.
911. 10 c. "The Washerwoman" (M. P. Holguin) (post.) 10 10
912. 50 c. "Coronation of the Virgin" (G. M. Berrio) 20 10
913. 70 c. "Arquebusier" (anon.) 25 10
914. 80 c. "St. Peter of Alcantara" (M. P. Holguin) 25 15
915. 1 p. Type 222 .. .. 35 15
916. 1 p. 40 "Chola Pacena" (G. de Rojas) (air) .. 40 10
917. 1 p. 50 "Adoration of the Kings" (G. Gamarra) .. 40 10
918. 1 p. 60 "Pachamama Vision" (A. Borda) .. 40 10
919. 2 p. "Idol's Kiss" (G. de Rojas) .. .. .. 40 25

223. Tarija Cathedral.

**1972.** "EXFILIBRA 72" Stamp Exhib., Rio de Janeiro.
920. 223. 30 c. multicoloured .. 15 10

224. National Arms.

**1972.** Air.
921. 224. 4 p. multicoloured .. 95 35

225. Santos Dumont and "14 bis".

**1973.** Air. Birth Centenary of Alberto Santos Dumont (aviation pioneer).
922. 225. 1 p. 40 black & yellow 1·25 45

226. "Echinocactus notocactus". 227. Power Station, Santa Isabel.

**1973.** Cacti. Multicoloured.
923. 20 c. Type 226 (postage) .. 10 10
924. 40 c. "Echinocactus lenninghaussii" .. 15 10
925. 50 c. "Mammillaria bocasana" .. .. 20 10
926. 70 c. "Echinocactus lenninghaussii" (different) 30 10
927. 1 p. 20 "Mammillaria bocasana" (different) (air) 40 15
928. 1 p. 90 "Opuntia cristata" 60 20
929. 2 p. "Echinocactus rebutia" 85 25

**1973.** Bolivian Development. Multicoloured.
930. 10 c. Type 227 (postage) .. 10 10
931. 20 c. Tin foundry .. .. 15 10
932. 90 c. Bismuth plant .. 40 10
933. 1 p. Gas plant .. .. 40 10
934. 1 p. 40 Bridge, Highways 1 and 4 (air) .. .. 50 15
935. 2 p. Railcar crossing bridge, Al Beni .. .. .. 1·50 50

228. "Cattleya nobilior". 229. Morane Saulnier Type P and Emblem.

**1974.** Orchids. Multicoloured.
936 20 c. Type 228 (postage) .. 10 10
937 50 c. "Zygopetalum bolivianum" .. .. 20 10
938 1 p. "Huntleya melagris" 35 10
939 2 p. 50 "Cattleya luteola" (horiz) (air) .. .. 90 25
940 3 p. 80 "Stanhopaea" .. 1·00 35
941 4 p. "Catasetum" (horiz) 1·00 45
942 5 p. "Maxillaria" .. .. 1·75 50

**1974.** Air. 50th Anniv of Bolivian Air Force. Multicoloured.
944 3 p. Type 229 .. .. 75 50
945 3 p. 80 Douglas DC-3 crossing Andes .. .. 1·25 70
946 4 p. 50 Triplane trainer and Morane Saulnier Paris I aircraft .. .. 1·25 70
947 8 p. Col. Rafael Pabon and biplane fighter .. .. 1·75 1·40
948 15 p. Jet airliner on "50" 3·75 2·00

230. General Sucre (after J. Wallpher).

**1974.** 150th Anniv. of Battle of Ayacucho.
949. 230. 5 p. multicoloured .. 75 55

231. U.P.U. and Exhibition Emblems.

**1974.** Centenary of U.P.U. and Expo U.P.U. (Montevideo) and Prenfil U.P.U. (Buenos Aires) Stamp Exhibitions.
950. 231. 3 p. 50 grn., blk. & blue 70 45

232. Lions Emblem and Steles.

**1975.** 50th Anniv. of Lions International in Bolivia.
951. 232. 30 c. multicoloured .. 35 10

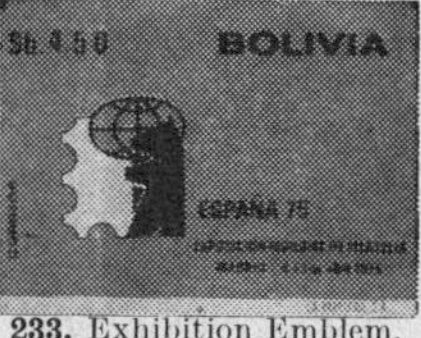

233. Exhibition Emblem.

**1975.** "Espana 75" International Stamp Exhibition, Madrid.
952. 233. 4 p. 50 multicoloured 55 35

234. Emblem of Meeting. 235. Arms of Pando.

**1975.** Cartagena Agreement. First Meeting of Postal Ministers, Quito, Ecuador.
953. 234. 2 p. 50 silver, vio. & blk. 45 30

**1975.** 150th Anniv. of Republic (1st issue). Provincial Arms. Multicoloured.
955. 20 c. Type 235 (postage) .. 10 10
956. 2 p. Chuzuisaca .. .. 50 35
957. 3 p. Cochabamba .. .. 70 50
958. 20 c. Beni (air) .. .. 10 10
959. 30 c. Tarija .. .. 10 10
960. 50 c. Potosi .. .. 10 10
961. 1 p. Oruro .. .. .. 40 20
962. 2 p. 50 Santa Cruz .. 50 50
963. 3 p. La Paz .. .. 70 50
See also Nos. 965/78.

236. Presidents Perez and Banzer. 237. Pres. Victor Paz Estenssoro.

**1975.** Air. Visit of Pres. Perez of Venezuela.
964. 236. 3 p. multicoloured .. 75 55

**1975.** 150th Anniv. of Republic. (2nd issue).
965. 30 c. Type 237 (postage) 10 10
966. 60 c. Pres. Thomas Frias 15 10
966a. 1 p. Ismael Montes .. 20 10
967. 2 p. 50 Aniceto Arce .. 50 25
968. 7 p. Bautista Saavedra .. 95 35
969. 10 p. Jose Manuel Pando 1·40 50
970. 15 p. Jose Maria Linares 1·75 1·75
971. 50 p. Simon Bolivar .. 6·75 6·75
972. 50 c. Rene Barrientos Ortuno (air) .. .. 15 10
973. 2 p. Francisco B. O'Connor .. .. 50 25
973a. 3 p. 80 Gualberto Villaroel .. .. 70 50
974. 4 p. 20 German Busch .. 70 70
975. 4 p. 50 Pres. Hugo Banzer Suarez .. 70 70
976. 20 p. Jose Ballivian .. 2·75 1·40
977. 30 p. Pres. Andres de Santa Cruz .. .. 3·50 3·50
978. 40 p. Pres. Antonio Jose de Sucre .. .. 4·50 4·50
Nos. 965/70, 972/4 and 976/78 are smaller, 24 × 33 mm.

238. Laurel Wreath and L.A.B. Emblem. 239. "EXFIVIA".

**1975.** Air. 50th Anniv of Lloyd-Aero Boliviano (national airline). Multicoloured.
979 1 p. Type 238 .. .. 15 10
980 1 p. 50 Douglas DC-9 and L.A.B. route map (horiz) 35 15
981 2 p. Guillermo Kyllmann (founder) and Junkers F-13 aircraft (horiz) .. 45 25

**1975.** Obligatory Tax. As No. 893 but inscr. "XXV ANIVERSARIO DE SU GOBIERNO".
982. 30 c. black and blue .. 30 10

**1975.** "Exfivia 75". Stamp Exhibition.
983. 239 3 p. multicoloured .. 70 35

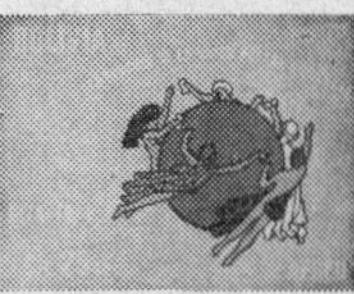

240. U.P.U. Emblem.

**1975.** Air. Centenary (1974) of U.P.U.
984 240 25 p. multicoloured .. 2·00 2·00

241. Chiang Kai-shek.

**1976.** 1st Death Anniv. of President Chiang Kai-shek.
985. 241. 2 p. 50 multicoloured 60 25

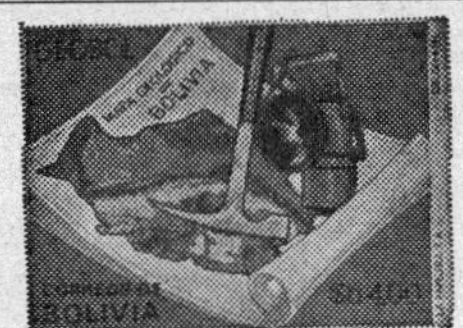

242. Geological Hammer, Lamp and Map.

**1976.** Bolivian Geological Institute.
986. **242.** 4 p. multicoloured .. 55 55

243. Naval Insignia.

**1976** . Navy Day.
987. **243.** 50 c. multicoloured .. 25 10

244. Douglas DC-10 and Divided Roundel.

**1976.** 50th Anniv. of Lufthansa Airline.
988. **244.** 3 p. multicoloured .. 90 35

245. Bolivian Boy Scout and Badge.

**1976.** 60th Anniv. of Bolivian Boy Scouts.
989. **245.** 1 p. multicoloured .. 50 20

246. Battle Scene. 247. Brother Vicente Bernedo (missionary).

**1976.** Bicent. of American Revolution.
990. **246.** 4 p. 50 multicoloured 95 45

**1976.** Brother Vicente Bernedo Commemoration.
992. **247.** 1 p. 50 multicoloured 35 15

248. Rainbow over La Paz, Police Handler with Dog. 249. Bolivian Family.

**1976.** 150th Anniv. of Police Service.
993. **248.** 2 p. 50 multicoloured 40 25

**1976.** National Census.
994. **249.** 2 p. 50 multicoloured 55 35

250. Pedro Poveda (educator).

**1976.** Poveda Commemoration.
995. **250.** 1 p. 50 multicoloured .. 35 15

251. Arms, Bolivar and Sucre. 252. "Numeral".

**1976.** International Bolivarian Societies Congress.
996 **251** 1 p. 50 multicoloured .. 55 25

**1976.**
997. **252.** 20 c. brown .. .. 10 10
998. 1 p. blue .. .. 25 10
999. 1 p. 50 green .. .. 40 10

253. Boy and Girl. 254. Caduceus.

**1977.** Christmas 1976 and 50th Anniv. of Inter-American Children's Institute.
1000. **253.** 50 c. multicoloured .. 15 10

**1977.** National Seminar on "Chagas Disease".
1001. **254.** 3 p. multicoloured .. 70 10

255. Court Buildings, La Paz. 256. Tower and Map.

**1977.** 150th Anniv. of Bolivian Supreme Court. Multicoloured.
1002. 2 p. 50 Type **255** .. 30 10
1003. 4 p. Dr. Manuel M. Urcullu, first President .. 45 10
1004. 4 p. 50 Dr. Pantaleon Dalence, President, 1883–89 .. .. 50 10

**1977.** 90th Anniv. of Oruro Club.
1005. **256.** 3 p. multicoloured .. 50 15

257. Newspaper Mastheads. 258. Games' Poster.

**1977.** Bolivian Newspapers. Multicoloured.
1006. 1 p. 50 Type **257** .. .. 25 10
1007. 2 p. 50 " Ultima Hora " and Alfredo Alexander (horiz.) .. .. 35 10
1008. 3 p. " El Diaro " and Jose Carrasco (horiz.) .. 45 15
1009. 4 p. " Los Tiempos " and Demetrio Canelas .. 50 15
1010. 5 p. 50 " Presencia " .. 70 20

**1977.** 8th Bolivarian Games, La Paz.
1011. **258.** 5 p. multicoloured .. 70 20

259. Tin Miner and Mining Corporation Emblem. 260. Miners, Globe and Chemical Symbol for Tin.

**1977.** 25th Anniv. of Bolivian Mining Corporation.
1012. **259.** 3 p. multicoloured .. 40 30

**1977.** International Tin Symposium, La Paz.
1013. **260.** 6 p. multicoloured.. 55 30

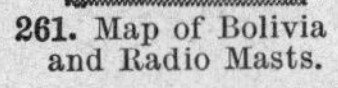

261. Map of Bolivia and Radio Masts. 263. " Eye ", Compass, Key and Law Book.

**1977.** 50th Anniv. of Bolivian Radio.
1014. **261.** 2 p. 50 multicoloured 35 10

**1977.** " Exfivia 77 " Philatelic Exhibition, Cochabamba. No. 719 surch. **EXFIVIA-77 $ b. 5.—**.
1015. 5 p. on 5,000 b. on $ b. 5 grey and gold .. .. 85 15

**1978.** 50th Anniv. of Audit Department.
1016. **263.** 5 p. multicoloured .. 45 15

264. Aesculapius Staff and Map of Andean Countries. 265. Map of the Americas. 266. Mt. Illimani.

**1978.** Fifth Meeting of Andean Countries' Health Ministers.
1017. **264.** 2 p. orange and black 40 10

**1978.** World Rheumatism Year (1977).
1018. **265.** 2 p. 50 blue and red 35 15

**1978.**
1019. **266.** 50 c. green and blue.. 10 10
1020. – 1 p. yellow and brown 15 10
1021. – 1 p. 50 grey and red.. 25 10
DESIGNS—HORIZ. 1 p. 50, Mt. Cerro de Potosi. VERT. 1 p. Pre-Columbian monolith.

267. Central Bank. 268. Jesus with Children.

**1978.** 50th Anniv. of Bank of Bolivia.
1022. **267.** 7 p. multicoloured .. 70 25

**1979.** International Year of the Child.
1023. **268.** 8 p. multicoloured .. 60 15

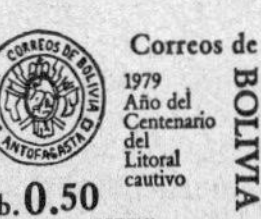


269. Antofagasta Cancellation.

270. Antofagasta.

**1979.** Centenary of Loss of Littoral Department to Chile.
1024. **269.** 50 c. brown and black 10 10
1025. – 1 p. mauve and black 15 10
1026. – 1 p. 50 green & black 25 10
1027. **270.** 5 p. 50 multicoloured 40 15
1028. – 6 p. 50 multicoloured 55 20
1029. – 7 p. multicoloured .. 55 20
1030. – 8 p. multicoloured .. 60 25
1031. – 10 p. multicoloured .. 75 35
DESIGNS—HORIZ. 1 p. La Chimba cancel. 1 p. 50, Mejillonos cancel. VERT. (As Type **270**). 6 p. 50, Woman in chains. 7 p. Eduardo Abaroa. 8 p. Map of Department, 1876. 10 p. Arms of Litoral.

271. Map and Radio Club Emblem. 272. Runner and Games Emblem.

**1979.** Radio Club of Bolivia.
1032. **271.** 3 p. multicoloured .. 40 10

**1979.** 1st "Southern Cross" Games. Mult.
1033 6 p. 50 Type **272** .. 55 20
1034 10 p. Gymnast .. 75 35

273. Bulgarian Stamp of 1879. 274. " Exfilmar " Emblem.

**1979.** " Philaserdica 79 ", (Philatelic Exhibition, Sofia, Bulgaria.
1035. **273.** 2 p. 50 black, yellow and light yellow .. 30 10

**1979.** " Exfilmar 79 " Maritime Philatelic, Exhibition, La Paz.
1036. **274.** 2 p. blue, black and light blue .. .. 20 20

275. O.A.S. Emblem and Map. 276. Franz Tamayo (lawyer).

**1979.** Ninth Congress of Organization of American States, La Paz.
1037. **275.** 6 p. multicoloured .. 50 20

**1979.** Anniversaries and Events.
1038. **276.** 2 p. 80 light grey, black and grey .. .. 35 10
1039. – 5 p. multicoloured .. 35 20
1040. – 5 p. multicoloured .. 35 20
1041. – 6 p. multicoloured .. 45 20
1042. – 9 p. 50 multicoloured 75 35
DESIGNS—VERT. 2 p. 80, Type **276** (birth centenary). 5 p. (No. 1039) U.N. emblem and delegates (18th CEPAL Sessions, La Paz). 5 p. (No. 1042), Gastroenterological laboratory (Japanese health co-operation). 6 p. Radio mast (50th anniv. of national radio). HORIZ. 9 p. 50, Puerto Suarez iron ore deposits.

277. 500c. Stamp of 1871, Exhibition Emblem and Flag. 278. Juana Azurduy de Padilla.

**1980.** "Exfilmar" Bolivian Maritime Stamp Exhibtion, La Paz.
1043 **277** 4 p. multicoloured .. 50 15

**1980.** Birth Bicentenary of Juana Azurduy de Padilla (Independence heroine).
1044. **278.** 4 p. multicoloured .. 55 15

279. Jean Baptiste de la Salle (founder).

**1980.** 300th Anniv. of Brothers of Christian Schools.
1045. **279.** 9 p. multicoloured .. 75 30

280. " Victory in a Chariot ", Emblem and Flags.

**1980.** " Espamer 80 " International Stamp Exhibition, Madrid.
1046. **280.** 14 p. multicoloured.. 1·10 45

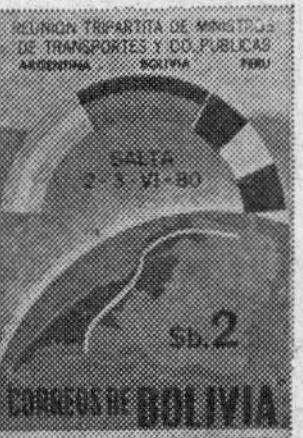

281. Flags over Map of South America. 282. Diesel Locomotive.

**1980.** Meeting of Public Works and Transport Ministers of Argentina, Bolivia and Peru.
1047. **281.** 2 p. multicoloured .. 25 10

**1980.** Inauguration of Santa Cruz-Trinidad Railway, Third Section.
1048. **282.** 3 p. multicoloured .. 65 40

**283.** Soldier and Citizen with Flag destroying Communism.

**284.** Scarlet Macaw.

**1981.** 1st Anniv. of 17 July Revolution. Multicoloured.

1049. 1 p. Type **283** .. .. 15 10
1050. 3 p. Flag shattering hammer and sickle on map .. 35 10
1051. 40 p. Flag on map of Bolivia showing provinces .. 3·50 85
1052. 50 p. Rejoicing crowd (horiz.) .. .. 4·00 85

**1981.** Macaws. Multicoloured.

1053. 4 p. Type **284** .. .. 75 40
1054. 7 p. Green-winged macaw .. .. .. 1·25 60
1055. 8 p. Blue and yellow macaw .. .. .. 1·60 65
1056. 9 p. Red-fronted macaw 1·60 75
1057. 10 p. Yellow-collared macaw .. .. .. 1·75 75
1058. 12 p. Hyacinth macaw .. 2·25 85
1059. 15 p. Military macaw .. 2·75 1·00
1060. 20 p. Chestnut-fronted macaw .. .. .. 3·50 1·10

**285.** Virgin and Child receiving Flower.

**286.** Emblem.

**1981.** Christmas.

1061. **285.** 1 p. pink and red .. 15 10
1062. – 2 p. light blue and blue 30 10
DESIGN: 2 p. Child and star. (horiz.)
See also No. 1080.)

**1982.** 22nd American Air Force Commanders' Conference, Buenos Aires.

1063. **286.** 14 p. multicoloured .. 1·10 35

**287.** Cobija.

**288.** Simon Bolivar.

**1982.** 75th Anniv. of Cobija City.

1064. **287.** 28 p. multicoloured 30 20

**1982.** Birth Bicent. of Simon Bolivar.

1065. **288.** 18 p. multicoloured 35 25

**289.** Dish Antenna.

**290.** Footballers.

**1982.** World Communication Year.

1066. **289.** 26 p. multicoloured .. 30 20

**1982.** World Cup Football Championship, Spain. Multicoloured.

1067. 4 p. Type **290** .. .. 20 10
1068. 100 p. "The Final Number" (Picasso) .. 1·25 65

**291.** Boy playing Football.

**1982.** Bolivian Youth. Multicoloured.

1069. 16 p. Type **291** .. .. 20 20
1070. 20 p. Girl playing piano (horiz.) .. .. 25 30

**292.** Harvesting.

**293.** Flowers.

**1982.** China–Bolivian Agricultural Co-operation.

1071. **292.** 30 p. multicoloured .. 50 20

**1982.** First Bolivian–Japanese Gastro-enterological Days.

1072. **293.** 22 p. multicoloured .. 25 20

**294.** Bolivian Stamps.

**295.** Hernando Siles.

**1982.** 10th Anniv. of Bolivian Philatelic Federation.

1073. **294.** 19 p. multicoloured 35 15

**1982.** Birth Centenary of Hernando Siles. (former President).

1074. **295.** 20 p. buff and brown 40 20

**296.** Baden-Powell.

**297.** "Liberty", Cochabamba.

**1982.** 125th Birth Anniv. of Lord Baden-Powell and 75th Anniv. of Boy Scout Movement.

1075. **296.** 5 p. multicoloured .. 15 10

**1982.** 25th Anniv. of Cochabamba Philatelic Centre.

1076. **297.** 3 p. buff, blk. & bl. 10 10

**298.** High Court, Cochabamba.

**299.** Virgin of Copacabana.

**1982.** 150th Anniv. of High Court, Cochabamba.

1077. **298.** 10 p. black, red and bronze .. .. 25 10

**1982.** 400th Anniv. of Enthronement of Virgin of Copacabana.

1078. **299.** 13 p. multicoloured 30 15

**300.** Puerto Busch Naval Base.

**1982.** Navy Day.

1079. **300.** 14 p. multicoloured .. 60 20

**1982.** Christmas. Design as Type **285**, inscribed "NAVIDAD 1982".

1080. **285.** 10 p. grey and green 20 10

**301.** Footballer and Emblem.

**1983.** Tenth American Youth Football Championships.

1081. **301.** 50 p. multicoloured .. 55 45

**302.** Sun Gate.

**1983.** "Exfivia 83" Stamp Exhibition.

1082. **302.** 150 p. red .. .. 90 35

**303.** Presidents Figueiredo and Zuazo.

**1984.** Visit of President of Brazil.

1083. **303.** 150 p. multicoloured .. 40 15

**1984.** Various stamps surch.

1084. **276.** 40 p. on 2 p.80 light grey, black and grey 15 10
1085. – 60 p. on 1 p.50 green and black (1026) .. 15 10
1086. **265.** 60 p. on 2 p.50 blue and red .. .. 15 10
1087. **274.** 100 p. on 2 p. blue, black and light blue 30 15
1088. **174.** 200 p. on 350 b. blue and light blue .. 2·75 1·50

**1984.** "Mladost 84". No. 1035 surch.

1089. **273.** 40 p. on 2 p.50 black, yellow and light yellow .. .. 15 10

**306.** "Simon Bolivar" (Mulato Gil de Quesada).

**308.** Pedestrian walking in Road.

**1984.** Birth Bicentenary of Simon Bolivar. Multicoloured.

1090. 50 p. Type **306** .. .. 15 10
1091. 200 p. "Simon Bolivar entering La Paz" (Carmen Baptista) .. .. 35 20

**1984.** Various stamps surch.

1092. **297.** 500 p. on 3 p. buff, black and blue (postage) .. 45 30
1093. **290.** 1000 p. on 4 p. multicoloured .. .. 90 65
1094. **285.** 2000 p. on 10 p. grey and green .. .. 2·00 85
1095. **296.** 5000 p. on 5 p. multicoloured .. .. 5·00 2·00
1096. – 10000 p. on 3 p. 80 multicoloured (No. 940) (air) .. .. .. 6·75 4·00

**1984.** Road Safety Campaign. Multicoloured.

1097. 80 p. Type **308** .. .. 10 10
1098. 120 p. Police motorcyclist and patrol car 10 10

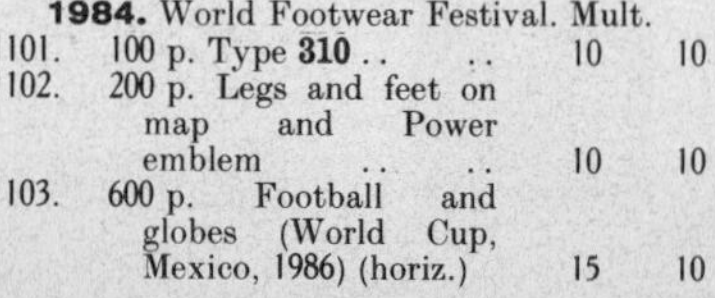


**309.** "Mendez's Birthplace" (Jorge Campos).

**310.** Legs and Feet on Map and Bata Emblem.

**1984.** Birth Bicentenary of Jose Eustaquio Mendez. Multicoloured.

1099. 300 p. Type **309** .. .. 15 10
1100. 500 p. "Battle of La Tablada" (M. Villegas) 20 10

**1984.** World Footwear Festival. Mult.

1101. 100 p. Type **310** .. .. 10 10
1102. 200 p. Legs and feet on map and Power emblem .. .. 10 10
1103. 600 p. Football and globes (World Cup, Mexico, 1986) (horiz.) 15 10

**311.** Inca Postal Runner.

**312.** Vicuna.

**1985.**

1104. **311.** 11000 p. blue .. 30 15

**1985.** Endangered Animals.

1105. **312.** 23000 p. brown and deep brown .. 35 15
1106. – 25000 p. brown, blue and orange .. 1·25 20
1107. – 30000 p. red and green .. .. 45 20
DESIGNS:—VERT. 25000 p. Andean condor. 30000 p. Marsh deer.

**313.** National Work Education Service Emblem.

**314.** Hand with Syringe, Victim in Droplet and Campaign Emblem.

**1985.** International Professional Education Year.

1108. **313.** 2000 p. blue and red. 10 10

**1985.** Anti-polio Campaign.

1109. **314.** 20000 p. blue and violet .. .. 30 15

**315.** Vicenta Juaristi Eguino.

**316.** U.N. Emblem.

**1985.** Birth Bicentenary of Vicenta Juaristi Eguino (Independence heroine).

1110 **315** 300000 p. multicoloured 30 15

**1985.** 40th Anniversary of U.N.O.

1111 **316** 1000000 p. blue & gold 45 30

**317.** Emblem.

**318.** Emblem, Envelope and Posthorn.

**1985.** 75th Anniv of "The Strongest" Football Club.

1112 **317** 200000 p. multicoloured 20 10

**1986.** Cent of Bolivian U.P.U. Membership.

1113 **318** 800000 p. multicoloured 65 30

**319.** Bull and Rider.

**321.** Footballs as Globes.

**1986.** 300th Anniv of Trinidad City.

1114 **319** 1400000 p. mult .. 1·00 45

**1986.** No. 1108 surch.

1115 **313** 200000 p. on 2000 p. blue and red .. 15 10
1116 5000000 p. on 2000 p. blue and red .. 3·50 1·60

**1986.** World Cup Football Championship, Mexico.
1117 **321** 300000 p. red & black 25 10
1118 – 550000 p. mult .. 45 20
1119 – 1000000 p. black and green (horiz) .. 80 40
1120 – 2500000 p. grn & yell 1·90 85
DESIGNS—VERT. 550000 p. Pique (mascot). 2500000 p. Trophy. HORIZ. 1000000 p. Azteca Stadium, Mexico City.

**322.** Alfonso Subieta Viaduct. **323.** Envelope.

**1986.** 25th Anniv of American Development Bank.
1121 **322** 400000 p. blue .. 35 15

**1986.** 50th Anniv of Society of Postmen.
1122 **323** 2000000 p. brown .. 1·60 70

**324.** Emblem and Dove. **325.** Emblem.

**1986.** International Peace Year.
1123 **324** 200000 p. green .. 15 10

**1986.** International Youth Year (1985).
1124 **325** 150000 p. red .. 15 10
1125 500000 p. green .. 45 30
1126 – 3000000 p. mult .. 2·10 1·00
DESIGNS: 3000000 p. Child clutching trophy and flag (25th anniv of Enrique Happ Sports Club, Cochabamba).

**326.** Zampa (after F. Diaz de Ortega). **328.** Refinery.

**327.** 1870 500 c. Stamp.

**1986.** 50th Death Anniv. of Friar Jose Antonio Zampa.
1127 **326** 400000 p. multicoloured 35 15

**1986.** 15th Anniv. of Bolivian Philatelic Federation.
1128 **327** 600000 p. brown .. 50 20

**1986.** 50th Anniv. of National Petroleum Refining Corporation.
1129 **328** 1000000 p. mult .. 1·00 30

**329.** Demon Mask.

**330.** Flags.

**1987.** Centenary of 10th February Society, Oruro.
1130. **329.** 20 c. multicoloured .. 10 10

**1987.** State Visit of President Richard von Weizsacker of German Federal Republic.
1131. **330.** 30 c. multicoloured .. 15 15

**331.** National Arms.

**1987.** Visit of King Juan Carlos of Spain.
1132. **331.** 60 c. multicoloured .. 60 20

**332.** Andean Condor. **333.** Modern View of Potosi.

**1987.** Endangered Animals. Multicoloured.
1133 20 c. Type **332** .. .. 60 15
1134 20 c. Tapir .. .. 10 10
1135 30 c. Vicuna (new-born) 15 15
1136 30 c. Armadillo .. .. 15 15
1137 40 c. Spectacled bear .. 25 20
1138 60 c. Keel-billed toucans 1·00 40

**1987.** "Exfivia 87" Stamp Exhibition, Potosi. Multicoloured.
1139. 40 c. Type **333** .. .. 25 20
1140. 50 c. 18th-century engraving of Potosi .. 30 25

**334.** "Nina" and Stern of "Santa Maria".

**1987.** "Espamer '87" Stamp Exhibition, La Coruna. Multicoloured.
1141. 20 c. Type **334** .. .. 30 15
1142. 20 c. "Pinta" and bow of "Santa Maria" .. 30 15
Nos. 1141/2 were printed together, se-tenant, forming a composite design.

**335.** Pan-pipes and Indian Flute.

**1987.** Musical Instruments. Multicoloured.
1143. 50 c. Type **335** .. .. 30 20
1144. 1 b. Indian guitars .. 1·00 35

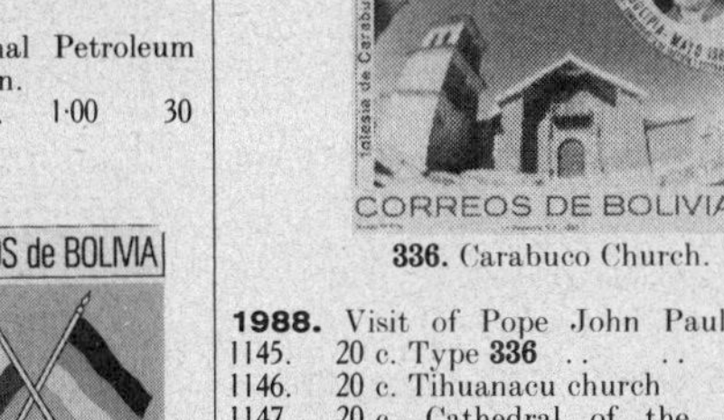

**336.** Carabuco Church.

**1988.** Visit of Pope John Paul II. Mult.
1145. 20 c. Type **336** .. .. 10 10
1146. 20 c. Tihuanacu church 10 10
1147. 20 c. Cathedral of the Kings, Beni .. .. 10 10
1148. 30 c. St. Joseph church, Chiquitos .. .. 15 15
1149. 30 c. St. Francis's church, Sucre .. .. 15 15
1150. 40 c. Cobija chapel (vert.) 20 15
1151. 50 c. Cochabamba cathedral (vert.) .. 25 20
1152. 50 c. Jayu Kcota church 25 20
1153. 60 c. St. Francis's Basilica, La Paz (vert.) 30 25
1154. 70 c. Church of Jesus, Machaca .. .. 60 30
1155. 70 c. St. Lawrence's church, Potosi (vert.) 60 30
1156. 80 c. Vallegrande church 70 35
1157. 80 c. Copacabana Virgin (vert.) .. .. 70 35
1158. 80 c. "The Holy Family" (Peter Paul Rubens) (vert.) .. .. .. 70 35
1159. 1 b. 30 Concepcion church .. .. .. 1·10 55
1160. 1 b. 30 Tarija cathedral (vert.) .. .. 1·10 55
1161. 1 b. 50 Pope and Arms of John Paul II and Bolivia .. .. 1·40 65

**337** Handshake and Flags

**1988.** Visit of President Jose Sarney of Brazil.
1162 **337** 50 c. multicoloured .. 25 20

**338** St. John Bosco **339** La Paz–Beni Steam Locomotive

**1988.** Death Centenary of St. John Bosco (founder of Salesian Brothers).
1163 **338** 30 c. multicoloured .. 15 15

**1988.** Centenary of Bolivian Railways.
1164 **339** 1 b. multicoloured .. 85 60

**340** Aguirre **341** "Column of the Future" (Battle of Bahia Monument)

**1988.** Death Cent of Nataniel Aguirre (writer).
1165 **340** 1 b. black and brown 80 35

**1988.** 50th Anniv of Pando Department. Mult.
1166 40 c. Type **341** .. .. 15 10
1167 60 c. Rubber production 50 20

**342** Athlete

**343** Mother Rosa Gattorno

**1988.** Olympic Games, Seoul.
1168 **342** 1 b. 50 multicoloured 1·25 55

**1988.** 88th Death Anniv of Mother Rosa Gattorno (Founder of the Daughters of St. Anne).
1169 **343** 80 c. multicoloured .. 70 30

**344** Bernardino de Cardenas

**345** Ministry Building

**1988.** 220th Death Anniv of Br. Bernardino de Cardenas (first Bishop of La Paz).
1170 **344** 70 c. black and brown 60 25

**1988.** Ministry of Transport and Communications.
1171 **345** 2 b. black, grn & red 1·60 70

**346** Arms **347** Rally Car

**1988.** 50th Anniv of Army Communications Corps.
1172 **346** 70 c. multicoloured .. 65 25

**1988.** 50th Anniv of Bolivian Automobile Club.
1173 **347** 1 b. 50 multicoloured 1·00 55

**348** Microphone and Emblem

**1989.** 50th Anniv of Radio Fides.
1174 **348** 80 c. multicoloured .. 65 30

**349** Obverse and Reverse of 1852 Gold Cuartillo

**1989.** Coins.
1175 **349** 1 b. multicoloured .. 80 35

**350** "Bulgaria '89" Stamp Exhibition Emblem and Orchid

**351** Birds

**1989.** Events and Plants. Multicoloured.
1176 50 c. Type **350** .. .. 20 15
1177 60 c. "Italia '90" World Cup football championship emblem and kantuta (national flower) (horiz) .. .. 50 20
1178 70 c. "Albertville 1986" emblem and "Heliconia humilis" .. .. 55 25
1179 1 b. Olympic Games, Barcelona emblem and "Hoffmanseggia" .. 80 35
1180 2 b. Olympic Games, Seoul emblem and bromeliad .. .. 1·60 70

**1989.** Bicentenary of French Revolution.
1181 **351** 70 c. multicoloured .. 60 25

**352** Clock Tower and Locomotive

**1989.** Centenary of Uyuni.
1182 **352** 30 c. grey, black & bl 15 10

**353** Federico Ahlfeld Waterfall, River Pauserna

**354** Making Metal Articles

**1989.** Noel Kempff Mercado National Park. Multicoloured.
1183 1 b. 50 Type **353** .. 1·25 60
1184 3 b. Pampas deer .. 2·40 1·00

**1989.** America. Tiahuanacu Culture. Mult.
1185 50 c. Type **354** .. .. 20 15
1186 1 b. Kalasasaya Temple 70 35

**355** Dr. Carlos Perez and Jaime Zamora

**356** Cobija Arch

**1989.** Meeting of Presidents of Bolivia and Venezuela.
1187 **355** 2 b. multicoloured .. 1·40 70

**1989.** World Heritage Site. Potosi. Mult.
1188 60 c. Type **356** .. .. 50 15
1189 80 c. Mint .. .. 60 20

**357** "Andean Lake" (Arturo Borda)

**1989.** Christmas. Paintings. Multicoloured.
1190 40 c. Type **357** .. .. 15 10
1191 60 c. "Virgin of the Roses" (anon) .. 45 15
1192 80 c. "Conquistador" (Jorge de la Reza) .. 55 20
1193 1 b. "Native Harmony" (Juan Rimsa) .. .. 70 25
1194 1 b. 50 "Woman with Pitcher" (Cecilio Guzman de Rojas) .. 1·10 40
1195 2 b. "Flower of Tenderness" (Gil Imana) .. 1·40 55

**358** Foot crushing Syringe

**359** Map of Americas

**1990.** Anti-drugs Campaign.
1196 **358** 80 c. multicoloured .. 60 20

**1990.** Centenary of Organization of American States.
1197 **359** 80 c. blue & deep blue 55 20

**360** Colonnade

**361** Penny Black, Sir Rowland Hill and Bolivian 5 c. Condor Stamp

**1990.** 450th Anniv of White City.
1198 **360** 1 b. 20 multicoloured 85 35

**1990.** 150th Anniv of the Penny Black.
1199 **361** 4 b. multicoloured .. 2·75 1·25

**362** Giuseppe Meaza Stadium, Milan

**363** Emblem

**1990.** World Cup Football Championship, Italy. Multicoloured.
1200 2 b. Type **362** .. .. 1·40 55
1201 6 b. Match scene .. 4·00 1·50

**1990.** Cent of Bolivian Chamber of Commerce.
1202 **363** 50 c. black, bl & gold 40 10

**364** Satellite, Map and Globe

**366** Chipaya Village, Oruro

**365** Hall

**1990.** Telecommunications Development Year.
1203 **364** 70 c. multicoloured .. 50 15

**1990.** Centenary of Cochabamba Social Club.
1204 **365** 40 c. multicoloured .. 15 10

**1990.** America. Multicoloured.
1205 80 c. Type **366** .. .. 50 15
1206 1 b. Nevado Huayna, Cordillera Real (mountain) (vert) .. 65 20

**367** Emblem

**368** Trees and Mountains

**1990.** "Meeting of Two Worlds, United towards Progress". 500th Anniv (1992) of Discovery of America by Columbus.
1207 **367** 2 b. multicoloured .. 1·25 40

**1990.** 400th Anniv of Larecaja District.
1208 **368** 1 b. 20 multicoloured 70 25



**369** Dove and German National Colours

**370** Boys playing Football (Omar Espana)

**1990.** Unification of Germany.
1209 **369** 2 b. multicoloured .. 1·25 55

**1990.** Christmas. Rights of the Child.
1210 **370** 50 c. multicoloured .. 15 10

**371** Arms of Bolivia and Ecuador

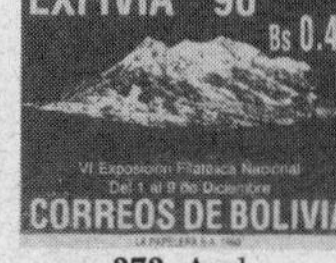

**373** Andes

**372** Flags and Andes

**1990.** Visit of Pres. Rodrigo Borja Cevallos of Ecuador.
1211 **371** 80 c. multicoloured .. 60 15

**1990.** 4th Andean Presidents' Council, La Paz.
1212 **372** 1 b. 50 multicoloured 90 30

**1990.** "Exfivia 90" National Stamp Exhibition.
1213 **373** 40 c. blue .. .. 15 10

**374** Arms of Bolivia and Mexico

**376** Emblem

**375** Emblem, Globe and Flags

**1990.** Visit of Pres. Carlos Salinas de Gortari of Mexico.
1214 **374** 60 c. multicoloured .. 50 15

**1990.** Express Mail Service.
1215 **375** 1 b. multicoloured .. 60 20

**1991.** 50th Anniv of Bolivian Radio Club.
1216 **376** 2 b. 40 multicoloured 1·40 50

**377** Head of Bear

**378** National Museum of Archaeology

**1991.** The Spectacled Bear. Multicoloured.
1217 30 c. Type **377** .. .. 10 10
1218 30 c. Bear on branch .. 10 10
1219 30 c. Bear and cub at water's edge .. .. 10 10
1220 30 c. Bear and cubs on branches .. .. 10 10

**1991.** "Espamer '91" Spain–Latin America Stamp Exhibition, Buenos Aires. Mult.
1221 50 c. Type **378** .. .. 15 10
1222 50 c. National Art Museum .. .. 15 10
1223 1 b. National Museum of Ethnography and Folklore .. .. .. 60 20

**379** Map

**380** Statue of Our Lady of La Paz and Cathedral

**1991.** 56th Anniv of Ending of Chaco War and Beginning of Construction of "Heroes of Chaco" Road.
1224 **379** 60 c. multicoloured .. 20 15

**1991.** La Paz Cathedral.
1225 **380** 1 b. 20 multicoloured 80 25

**381** Presidents Lacalle and Paz Zamora

**1991.** Meeting of Uruguayan and Bolivian Presidents.
1226 **381** 1 b. multicoloured .. 60 20

**382** Presidents Paz Zamora and Menem

**1991.** Meeting of Bolivian and Argentine Presidents.
1227 **382** 1 b. multicoloured .. 60 20

**383** "Exfivia 83", "87" and "90" Stamps

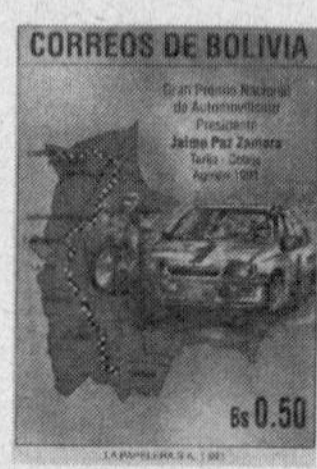

**385** Route Map, Motor Cycle and Rally Car

**384** Presidents Fujimori and Paz Zamora

**1991.** 20th Anniv of Bolivian Philatelic Federation.
1228 **383** 70 c. multicoloured .. 45 10

**1991.** Presidential Summit of Bolivia and Peru.

1229 **384** 50 c. multicoloured .. 15 10

**1991.** Pres. Jaime Paz Zamora National Grand Prix Motor Rally, Tarija–Cobija.

1230 **385** 50 c. multicoloured .. 15 10

**386** Data Retrieval Systems

**1991.** "Ecobol" Postal Security.

1231 **386** 1 b. 40 multicoloured 90 30

**387** "First Discovery of Chuquiago" (Arturo Reque)

**388** Stylized Figures and City Skyline

**1991.** America. Voyages of Discovery. Mult.

1232 60 c. Type **387** .. .. 20 10

1233 1 b. 20 "Foundation of City of Our Lady of La Paz" (J. Rimsa) (vert) 80 30

**1991.** National Population and Housing Census.

1234 **388** 50 c. multicoloured .. 15 10

**389** "Landscape" (Daniel Pena y Sarmiento)

**1991.** Christmas. Multicoloured.

1235 2 b. Type **389** .. .. 1·00 40

1236 5 b. "Fruit Seller" (Cecilio Guzman de Rojas) .. 2·50 1·00

1237 15 b. "Native Mother" (Crespo Gastelu) .. 7·50 3·00

**390** Camp-site and Emblem

**1992.** 75th Anniv (1990) of Bolivian Scout Movement and Los Andes Jamboree, Cochabamba.

1238 **390** 1 b. 20 multicoloured 80 30

**391** Simon Bolivar

**392** Raising Flag

**1992.** "Exfilbo 92" National Stamp Exhibition, La Paz.

1239 **391** 1 b. 20 deep brown, brown and stone .. 80 30

**1992.** Creation of Bolivian Free Zone in Ilo, Peru. Multicoloured.

1240 1 b. 20 Type **392** .. 65 30

1241 1 b. 50 Presidents Fujimori (Peru) and Paz Zamora (horiz) .. 80 30

1242 1 b. 80 Beach at Ilo (horiz) .. .. 95 35

**393** Logotype of Pavilion

**1992.** "Expo '92" World's Fair, Seville, and "Granada '92" Int Stamp Exn. Mult.

1243 30 c. Type **393** .. .. 10 10

1244 50 c. Columbus's fleet .. 30 10

**394** Rotary International Emblem and Prize

**1992.** Rotary Club Miraflores District 4690 "Illimani de Oro" Prize.

1245 **394** 90 c. gold, blue & blk 30 20

**395** School and Perez

**1992.** Birth Centenary of Elizardo Perez (founder of Ayllu School, Warisata).

1246 **395** 60 c. blue, black & yell 50 10

**396** Government Palace

**1992.** U.N.E.S.C.O. World Heritage Site, Sucre.

1247 **396** 50 c. multicoloured .. 15 10

**397** Mario Martinez Guzman

**398** Front Page

**1992.** Olympic Games, Barcelona.

1248 **397** 1 b. 50 multicoloured 80 30

**1992.** 25th Anniv of "Los Tiempos" (newspaper).

1249 **398** 50 c. multicoloured .. 15 10

**399** Canoeing

**400** Columbus leaving Palos (after Bejarano)

**1992.** 1st International River Bermejo Canoeing Championship.

1250 **399** 1 b. 20 multicoloured 75 30

**1992.** America. 500th Anniv of Discovery of America by Columbus.

1251 **400** 60 c. brown and black 20 10

1252 – 2 b. multicoloured .. 95 40

DESIGN—HORIZ. 2 b. "Columbus meeting the Caribisis Tribe" (Luis Vergara).

**401** Football Match

**402** "Chenopodium quinoa"

**1992.** World Cup Football Championship U.S.A. (1994).

1253 **401** 1 b. 20 multicoloured 1·25 30

**1992** 50th Anniv of Interamerican Institute for Agricultural Co-operation.

1254 **402** 1 b. 20 multicoloured 80 30

**403** University Arms and Minerals

**1992.** Cent of Oruro Technical University.

1255 **403** 50 c. multicoloured .. 15 10

**404** Mascots

**1992.** 12th Bolivarian Games, Cochabamba and Santa Cruz (1st issue).

1256 **404** 2 b. multicoloured .. 1·00 40

See also No. 1271.

**405** Cayman

**1992.** Ecology and Conservation. Mult.

1257 20 c. Type **405** .. .. 10 10

1258 50 c. Spotted cavy .. 15 10

1259 1 b. Chinchilla .. .. 30 20

1260 2 b. Anteater .. .. 1·00 40

1261 3 b. Jaguar .. .. 1·50 65

1262 4 b. Hummingbird (vert) 2·00 90

1263 5 b. Piranhas .. .. 2·50 1·10

Each stamp also bears the emblem of an anniversary or event.

**406** Battle Scene

**1992.** 150th Anniv of Battle of Ingavi.

1264 **406** 1 b. 20 brown & black 65 30

**407** Man following Star in Boat

**1992.** Christmas. Multicoloured.

1265 1 b. 20 Type **407** .. 60 20

1266 2 b. 50 Star over church 1·40 50

1267 6 b. Infant in manger and church .. .. 3·00 1·25

**408** Nicolas Copernicus (450th death anniv)

**409** Mother Nazaria (after Victor Eusebio Choque)

**1993.** Astronomy.

1268 **408** 50 c. multicoloured .. 15 10

1269 – 2 b. black .. .. 1·00 35

DESIGNS—HORIZ. 50 c. Santa Ana International Astronomical Observatory, Tarija (10th anniv (1992)).

**1993.** Beatification (1992) of Mother Nazaria Ignacia March Meza.

1270 **409** 60 c. multicoloured .. 40 10

**410** Pictograms and Flags of Ecuador, Venezuela, Peru, Bolivia, Colombia and Panama

**1993.** 12th Bolivarian Games, Cochabamba and Santa Cruz (2nd issue).

1271 **410** 2 b. 30 multicoloured 1·10 35

**411** Bolivia 1962 10000 b. Kantuta and Brazil 90 r. "Bull's Eye" Stamps

**1993.** 150th Anniv of First Brazilian Stamps.

1272 **411** 2 b. 30 multicoloured 1·10 35

**412** "Morpho sp."

**1993.** Butterflies. Multicoloured.

1273 60 c. Type **412** .. .. 15 10

1274 60 c. "Archaeoprepona demophon" .. .. 15 10

1275 80 c. "Papilio sp." .. 20 10

1276 80 c. Orion ("Historis odius") .. .. 20 10

1277 80 c. Mexican fritillary ("Euptoieta hegesia") 20 10

1278 1 b. 80 "Morpho deidamia" .. .. 85 30

1279 1 b. 80 Orange swallowtail ("Papilio thoas") .. 85 30

1280 1 b. 80 Monarch ("Danaus plexippus") .. .. 85 30

1281 2 b. 30 Scarlet emperor ("Anaea marthesia") .. 1·00 35

1282 2 b. 30 "Caligo sp." .. 1·00 35

1283 2 b. 30 "Rothschildia sp." 1·00 35

1284 2 b. 70 "Heliconius sp." 1·25 45

1285 2 b. 70 "Marpesia corinna" .. .. 1·25 45

1286 2 b. 70 "Prepona chromus" .. .. 1·25 45

1287 3 b. 50 Rusty-tipped page ("Siproeta epaphus") .. 1·50 60

1288 3 b. 50 "Heliconius sp." 1·50 60

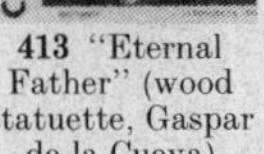

413 "Eternal Father" (wood statuette, Gaspar de la Cueva)

414 "Virgin of Urkupina"

**1993.**

1289 **413** 1 b. 80 multicoloured 90 30

**1993.** 400th Anniv of Quillacollo.

1290 **414** 50 c. multicoloured .. 15 10

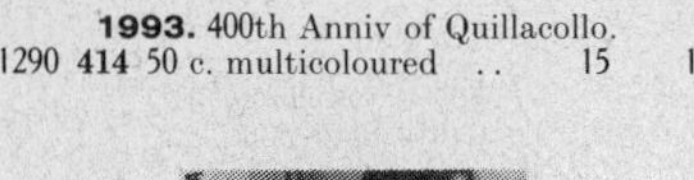

415 Student, Machinery and Emblem

**1993.** 50th Anniv (1992) of Pedro Domingo Murillo Technical College.

1291 **415** 60 c. multicoloured .. 15 10

416 Owl (painting, Chuquisaca)

417 Common Squirrel-monkeys

**1993.** Cave Art. Multicoloured.

1292 80 c. Type **416** .. .. 20 10
1293 80 c. Animals (painting, Cochabamba) .. .. 20 10
1294 80 c. Geometric patterns (engraving, Chuquisaca) (vert) .. .. .. 20 10
1295 80 c. Sun (engraving, Beni) (vert) .. .. 20 10
1296 80 c. Llama (painting, Oruro) .. .. 20 10
1297 80 c. Human figure (engraving, Potosi) .. 20 10
1298 80 c. Church and tower (painting, La Paz) (vert) .. .. .. 20 10
1299 80 c. Warrior (engraving, Tarija) (vert) .. .. 20 10
1300 80 c. Religious mask (engraving, Santa Cruz) (vert) .. .. .. 20 10

**1993.** America. Endangered Animals. Mult.

1301 80 c. Type **417** .. .. 20 10
1302 2 b. 30 Ocelot .. .. 1·00 35

418 Emblems and Map

419 Yolanda Bedregal (poet)

**1993.** 90th Anniv (1992) of Pan-American Health Organization. Anti-AIDS Campaign.

1303 **418** 80 c. multicoloured .. 20 10

**1993.** Personalities. Each brown.

1304 50 c. Type **419** .. .. 15 10
1305 70 c. Simon Martinic (President of Cochabamba Philatelic Centre) .. .. 20 10
1306 90 c. Eugenio von Boeck (politician and President of Bolivian Philatelic Federation) 25 15
1307 1 b. Marina Nunez del Prado (sculptor) .. 25 15

420 "Virgin with Child and Saints" (anonymous)

421 Riberalta Square

**1993.** Christmas. Multicoloured.

1308 2 b. 30 "Adoration of the Shepherds" (Leonardo Flores) .. .. 95 35
1309 3 b. 50 Type **420** .. 1·50 60
1310 6 b. "Virgin of the Milk" (Melchor Perez de Holguin) .. .. 2·50 1·00

**1994.** Centenary of Riberalta.

1311 **421** 2 b. multicoloured .. 85 35

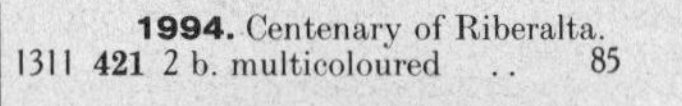

422 "Population and Our World" (Mayari Rodriguez)

**1994.** 2nd Prize-winning Design (6–8 year group) in United Nations Fund for Population Activities International Design Contest.

1312 **422** 2 b. 30 multicoloured 1·00 35

423 Sanchez de Lozada

424 Mascot

**1994.** Presidency of Gonzalo Sanchez de Lozada.

1313 **423** 2 b. multicoloured .. 85 35
1314 2 b. 30 multicoloured 1·00 35

**1994.** World Cup Football Championship, U.S.A. Multicoloured.

1315 80 c. Type **424** .. .. 20 10
1316 1 b. 80 Bolivia v Uruguay 75 30
1317 2 b. 30 Bolivia v Venezuela .. .. 95 35
1318 2 b. 50 Bolivian team (left half) .. .. .. 1·00 35
1319 2 b. 50 Bolivian team (right half) .. .. 1·00 35
1320 2 b. 70 Bolivia v Ecuador 1·10 45
1321 3 b. 50 Bolivia v Brazil .. 1·50 60

Nos. 1318/19 were issued together, se-tenant, forming a composite design.

425 Child

427 "Buddleja coriacea"

426 St. Peter's Church and Mgr. Jorge Manrique Hurtado (Archbishop, 1967–87)

**1994.** S.O.S. Children's Villages.

1322 **425** 2 b. 70 multicoloured 1·10 45

**1994.** 50th Anniv (1993) of Archdiocese of La Paz. Multicoloured.

1323 1 b. 80 Type **426** .. 75 30
1324 2 b. Church of the Sacred Heart of Mary and Mgr. Abel Antezana y Rojas (first Archbishop, 1943–67) (vert) .. 85 35
1325 3 b. 50 Santo Domingo Church and Mgr. Luis Sainz Hinojosa (Archbishop since 1987) (vert) 1·50 60

**1994.** Environmental Protection. Trees. Mult.

1326 60 c. Type **427** .. .. 15 10
1327 1 b. 80 "Bertholletia exelsa" .. .. 50 30
1328 2 b. "Schinus molle" (horiz) .. .. 55 35
1329 2 b. 70 "Polylepis racemosa" .. .. 70 45
1330 3 b. "Tabebuia chrysantha" .. .. 80 50
1331 3 b. 50 "Erythrina falcata" (horiz) .. 90 60

428 Paz

429 Tram and Mail Van

**1994.** Dr. Victor Paz Estenssoro (former President).

1332 **428** 2 b. multicoloured .. 55 35

**1994.** America. Postal Transport. Mult.

1333 1 b. Type **429** .. .. 25 15
1334 5 b. Airplane and ox cart 1·25 80

430 Coral Tree

431 Diagram of Eclipse

**1994.** 300th Anniv of San Borja.

1335 **430** 1 b. 60 multicoloured 40 25

**1994.** Solar Eclipse.

1336 **431** 3 b. 50 multicoloured 90 60

432 1894 100 c. Stamp

433 Col. Marzana and Soldiers

**1994.** Centenary of Arms Issue of 1894.

1337 **432** 1 b. 80 multicoloured 50 30

**1994.** 62nd Anniv of Defence of Fort Boqueron.

1338 **433** 80 c. multicoloured .. 20 10

434 "Delicate Flower of Tarija"

435 Emblem

**1994.** Christmas. Pastels of children by Maria Susana Castillo. Multicoloured.

1339 2 b. Type **434** .. .. 55 35
1340 5 b. "Child of the High Plateau" .. .. 1·25 80
1341 20 b. "Shoot of the Bolivian East" .. 5·25 3·50

**1994.** Pan-American Scout Jamboree, Cochabamba.

1342 **435** 1 b. 80 multicoloured 50 30

436 Sucre

437 Santa Ana Cathedral

**1995.** Birth Bicentenary of General Antonio Jose de Sucre. Multicoloured.

1343 1 b. 80 Type **436** .. 50 30
1344 3 b. 50 Sucre and national colours .. .. 90 60

**1995.** Centenary (1994) of Yacuma Province, Beni Department.

1345 **437** 1 b. 90 multicoloured 55 35
1346 2 b. 90 multicoloured 75 50

438 "Holy Virgin of Copacabana", Sanctuary and Franciscans

**1995.** Centenary of Franciscan Presence at Copacabana Sanctuary.

1347 **438** 60 c. multicoloured .. 15 10
1348 80 c. multicoloured .. 20 10

## POSTAGE DUE STAMPS

D 81.

D 93. " Youth ".

**1931.**

D 265. D 81. 5 c. blue .. .. 70 85
D 266. 10 c. red .. .. 70 85
D 267. 15 c. yellow .. 1·00 85
D 268. 30 c. green .. .. 1·00 85
D 269. 40 c. violet .. 1·75 1·75
D 270. 50 c. sepia .. 2·40 2·40

**1938.** Triangular designs.

D 346. D 93. 5 c. red .. .. 50 50
D 347. – 10 c. green .. .. 50 50
D 348. – 30 c. blue .. .. 50 50

**DESIGNS:** 10 c. Torch of Knowledge. 30 c. Date and Symbol of 17 May, 1936, Revolution.

## BOSNIA AND HERZEGOVINA — Pts. 2, 3

Turkish provinces administered by Austria from 1878 and annexed by her in 1908. In 1918 it became part of Yugoslavia.

In 1992 Bosnia and Herzegovina declared itself independent. Hostilities subsequently broke out between the Croat, Moslem and Serbian inhabitants, which ultimately led to the establishment of three de facto administrations: the mainly Moslem Bosnian government, based in Sarajevo; the Croats in Mostar; and the Serbian Republic in Pale. Under the Dayton Agreement in November 1995 the Republic was split between a Moslem–Croat Federation and the Serbian Republic.

1879. 100 kreuzer = 1 gulden.
1900. 100 heller = 1 krone.
1993. 100 para = 1 dinar.

### A. AUSTRO-HUNGARIAN MILITARY POST

1. Value at top.

2. Value at bottom.

**1879.**

| | | | | |
|---|---|---|---|---|
| 106 | 1 | ½ k. black | 16·00 | 23·00 |
| 135 | | 1 k. grey | 3·00 | 90 |
| 136 | | 2 k. yellow | 2·00 | 35 |
| 137 | | 3 k. green | 3·25 | 1·10 |
| 146 | | 5 k. red | 3·00 | 25 |
| 139 | | 10 k. blue | 5·50 | 35 |
| 140 | | 15 k. brown | 4·50 | 2·75 |
| 141 | | 20 k. green | 6·50 | 3·50 |
| 142 | | 25 k. purple | 7·00 | 5·50 |

**1900.**

| | | | | |
|---|---|---|---|---|
| 148 | 2 | 1 h. black | 20 | 10 |
| 149 | | 2 h. grey | 20 | 10 |
| 151 | | 3 h. yellow | 25 | 10 |
| 152 | | 5 h. green | 20 | 10 |
| 154 | | 6 h. brown | 55 | 10 |
| 155 | | 10 h. red | 30 | 10 |
| 156 | | 20 h. pink | £100 | 6·50 |
| 158 | | 25 h. blue | 1·00 | 20 |
| 159 | | 30 h. brown | £110 | 7·00 |
| 160 | | 40 h. orange | £170 | 10·00 |
| 161 | | 50 h. purple | 90 | 25 |

Larger stamps with value in each corner.

| | | | | |
|---|---|---|---|---|
| 162. | | 1 k. red | 1·00 | 60 |
| 163. | | 2 k. blue | 1·40 | 1·25 |
| 164. | | 5 k. green | 3·00 | 4·00 |

**1901.** Black figures of value.

| | | | | |
|---|---|---|---|---|
| 177. | 2. | 20 h. pink and black | 60 | 25 |
| 178. | | 30 h. brown and black | 60 | 30 |
| 180. | | 35 h. blue and black | 80 | 45 |
| 181. | | 40 h. orange and black | 80 | 50 |
| 182. | | 45 h. turquoise and black | 80 | 50 |

4. View of Doboj.

5. In the Carshija (business quarter) Sarajevo.

**1906.**

| | | | | |
|---|---|---|---|---|
| 186 | 4 | 1 h. black | 10 | 10 |
| 187 | – | 2 h. violet | 15 | 10 |
| 188 | – | 3 h. yellow | 15 | 10 |
| 189 | – | 5 h. green | 20 | 10 |
| 190 | – | 6 h. brown | 15 | 20 |
| 191 | – | 10 h. red | 25 | 10 |
| 192 | – | 20 h. brown | 45 | 15 |
| 193 | – | 25 h. blue | 1·00 | 85 |
| 194 | – | 30 h. green | 90 | 30 |
| 195 | – | 35 h. green | 90 | 30 |
| 196 | – | 40 h. orange | 90 | 30 |
| 197 | – | 45 h. red | 1·00 | 90 |
| 198 | – | 50 h. brown | 1·10 | 70 |
| 199 | 5 | 1 k. red | 3·00 | 2·25 |
| 200 | – | 2 k. green | 6·00 | 8·50 |
| 201 | – | 5 k. blue | 3·75 | 6·00 |

DESIGNS—As Type 4: 2 h. Mostar. 3 h. The old castle, Jajce. 5 h. Naretva pass and Prenz Planina. 6 h. Valley of the Rama. 10 h. Valley of the Vrbas. 20 h. Old Bridge, Mostar. 25 h. The Begova Djamia (Bey's Mosque), Sarajevo. 30 h. Post by beast of burden. 35 h. Village and lake, Jezero. 40 h. Mail wagon. 45 h. Bazaar at Sarajevo. 50 h. Postal motor-car. As Type 5: 2 k. St. Luke's Campanile at Jajce. 5 k. Emperor Francis Joseph I.

See also Nos. 359/61.

**1910.** 80th Birthday of Francis Joseph I. As stamps of 1906 but with date-label at foot.

| | | | |
|---|---|---|---|
| 343 | 1 h. black | 30 | 20 |
| 344 | 2 h. violet | 40 | 20 |
| 345 | 3 h. yellow | 40 | 20 |
| 346 | 5 h. green | 45 | 15 |
| 347 | 6 h. brown | 60 | 40 |
| 348 | 10 h. red | 45 | 10 |
| 349 | 20 h. brown | 1·25 | 1·50 |
| 350 | 25 h. blue | 2·25 | 3·00 |
| 351 | 30 h. green | 1·50 | 2·25 |
| 352 | 35 h. green | 2·25 | 2·25 |
| 353 | 40 h. orange | 2·25 | 3·00 |
| 354 | 45 h. red | 4·00 | 6·00 |
| 355 | 50 h. brown | 4·00 | 6·00 |
| 356 | 1 k. red | 4·00 | 6·00 |
| 357 | 2 k. green | 17·00 | 23·00 |
| 358 | 5 k. blue | 2·25 | 6·00 |

**1912.** As T 4 (new values and views).

| | | | |
|---|---|---|---|
| 359 | 12 h. blue | 4·00 | 5·00 |
| 360 | 60 h. grey | 2·75 | 4·00 |
| 361 | 72 h. red | 11·00 | 16·00 |

DESIGNS: 12 h. Jajce. 60 h. Konjica. 72 h. Vishegrad.

25. Francis Joseph I. 26.

**1912.** Various frames. Nos. 378/82 are larger (27 × 22 mm).

| | | | | |
|---|---|---|---|---|
| 362. | 25. | 1 h. olive | 30 | 10 |
| 363. | | 2 h. blue | 30 | 10 |
| 364. | | 3 h. lake | 30 | 10 |
| 365. | | 5 h. green | 30 | 10 |
| 366. | | 6 h. black | 30 | 10 |
| 367. | | 10 h. red | 30 | 10 |
| 368. | | 12 h. green | 70 | 20 |
| 369. | | 20 h. brown | 3·50 | 10 |
| 370. | | 25 h. blue | 1·75 | 10 |
| 371. | | 30 h. red | 1·75 | 10 |
| 372. | 26. | 35 h. green | 1·75 | 10 |
| 373. | | 40 h. violet | 6·00 | 10 |
| 374. | | 45 h. brown | 3·00 | 20 |
| 375. | | 50 h. blue | 2·50 | 10 |
| 376. | | 60 h. brown | 2·25 | 10 |
| 377. | | 72 h. blue | 3·00 | 3·25 |
| 378. | 25. | 1 k. brown on cream | 12·00 | 30 |
| 379. | | 2 k. blue on blue | 7·00 | 45 |
| 380. | 26. | 3 k. red on green | 12·00 | 11·00 |
| 381. | | 5 k. lilac and grey | 20·00 | 25·00 |
| 382. | | 10 k. blue on grey | 70·00 | 95·00 |

**1914.** Nos. 189 and 191 surch **1914.** and new value.

| | | | |
|---|---|---|---|
| 383 | 7 h. on 5 h. green | 30 | 30 |
| 384 | 12 h. on 10 h. red | 30 | 30 |

**1915.** Nos. 189 and 191 surch **1915.** and new value.

| | | | |
|---|---|---|---|
| 385 | 7 h. on 5 h. green | 9·00 | 9·00 |
| 386 | 12 h. on 10 h. red | 30 | 45 |

**1915.** Surch **1915.** and new value.

| | | | | |
|---|---|---|---|---|
| 387 | 25 | 7 h. on 5 h. green | 60 | 90 |
| 388 | | 12 h. on 10 h. red | 1·50 | 1·75 |

**1916.** Surch **1916.** and new value.

| | | | | |
|---|---|---|---|---|
| 389 | 25 | 7 h. on 5 h. green | 40 | 80 |
| 390 | | 12 h. on 10 h. red | 40 | 80 |

31.

**1916.** War Invalids' Fund.

| | | | | |
|---|---|---|---|---|
| 391 | 31 | 5 h. (+2 h.) green | 60 | 80 |
| 392 | – | 10 h. (+2 h.) purple | 90 | 1·40 |

DESIGN: 10 h. Blind soldier and girl.

See also Nos. 434/5.

33. Francis Joseph I. 34.

**1916.**

| | | | | |
|---|---|---|---|---|
| 393. | 33. | 3 h. black | 20 | 25 |
| 394. | | 5 h. olive | 25 | 35 |
| 395. | | 6 h. violet | 30 | 25 |
| 396. | | 10 h. bistre | 1·60 | 2·00 |
| 397. | | 12 h. grey | 30 | 50 |
| 398. | | 15 h. red | 10 | 10 |
| 399. | | 20 h. brown | 30 | 60 |
| 400. | | 25 h. blue | 25 | 50 |
| 401. | | 30 h. green | 25 | 50 |
| 402. | | 40 h. red | 25 | 50 |
| 403. | | 50 h. green | 25 | 50 |
| 404. | | 60 h. lake | 30 | 55 |
| 405. | | 80 h. brown | 1·10 | 35 |
| 406. | | 90 h. purple | 70 | 55 |
| 407. | 34. | 2 k. red on yellow | 40 | 75 |
| 408. | | 3 k. green on blue | 1·25 | 2·00 |
| 409. | | 4 k. red on green | 6·00 | 8·50 |
| 410. | | 10 k. violet on grey | 14·00 | 27·00 |

**1917.** War Widows' Fund. Optd **WITWEN. UND WAISENWOCHE 1917.**

| | | | | |
|---|---|---|---|---|
| 411 | 33 | 10 h. (+2 h.) bistre | 10 | 15 |
| 412 | | 15 h. (+2 h.) pink | 10 | 15 |

36. Design for Memorial Church, Sarajevo.

39. Emperor Charles.

**1917.** Assassination of Archduke Ferdinand. Fund for Memorial Church at Sarajevo.

| | | | | |
|---|---|---|---|---|
| 413 | 36 | 10 h. (+2 h.) black | 10 | 25 |
| 414 | – | 15 h. (+2 h.) red | 10 | 25 |
| 415 | – | 40 h. (+2 h.) blue | 10 | 25 |

PORTRAITS—HORIZ. 40 h. Francis Ferdinand and Sophie. VERT. 15 h. Archduke Francis Ferdinand.

**1917.**

| | | | | |
|---|---|---|---|---|
| 416. | 39. | 3 h. grey | 15 | 20 |
| 417. | | 5 h. olive | 10 | 15 |
| 418. | | 6 h. violet | 40 | 80 |
| 419. | | 10 h. brown | 15 | 10 |
| 420. | | 12 h. blue | 45 | 80 |
| 421. | | 15 h. red | 10 | 10 |
| 422. | | 20 h. brown | 10 | 10 |
| 423. | | 25 h. blue | 80 | 60 |
| 424. | | 30 h. green | 20 | 15 |
| 425. | | 40 h. bistre | 20 | 15 |
| 426. | | 50 h. green | 80 | 55 |
| 427. | | 60 h. red | 80 | 40 |
| 428. | | 80 h. blue | 20 | 30 |
| 429. | | 90 h. lilac | 1·00 | 1·40 |
| 430. | – | 2 k. red on yellow | 55 | 40 |
| 431. | – | 3 k. green on blue | 15·00 | 19·00 |
| 432. | – | 4 k. red on green | 5·50 | 8·00 |
| 433. | – | 10 k. violet on grey | 3·50 | 6·00 |

The kronen values are larger (25 × 25 mm) and with different border.

**1918.** War Invalids' Fund.

| | | | | |
|---|---|---|---|---|
| 434 | – | 10 h. (+2 h.) green (as No. 392) | 45 | 60 |
| 435 | 31 | 15 h. (+2 h.) brown | 45 | 60 |

40. Emperor Charles.

**1918.** Emperor's Welfare Fund.

| | | | | |
|---|---|---|---|---|
| 436. | 40. | 10 h. (+10 h.) green | 30 | 70 |
| 437. | – | 15 h. (+10 h.) brown | 30 | 70 |
| 438. | 40. | 40 h. (+10 h.) purple | 30 | 70 |

DESIGN—15 h. Empress Zita.

**1918.** Optd. **1918.**

| | | | | |
|---|---|---|---|---|
| 439. | – | 2 h. violet (No. 344) | 40 | 1·25 |
| 440. | 25. | 2 h. blue | 40 | 1·25 |

### NEWSPAPER STAMPS

N. 27 Girl in Bosnian Costume. N 35. Mercury.

**1913.** Imperf.

| | | | | |
|---|---|---|---|---|
| N 383. | N 27. | 2 h. blue | 40 | 70 |
| N 384. | | 6 h. mauve | 1·50 | 2·00 |
| N 385. | | 10 h. red | 1·75 | 2·25 |
| N 386. | | 20 h. green | 2·00 | 2·50 |

For these stamps perforated see **Yugoslavia**, Nos. 25 to 28.

**1916.** For Express.

| | | | | |
|---|---|---|---|---|
| N 411. | N 35. | 2 h. red | 20 | 40 |
| N 412. | | 5 h. green | 35 | 60 |

### POSTAGE DUE STAMPS

D 4.

D 35.

**1904.** Imperf. or perf.

| | | | | |
|---|---|---|---|---|
| D 183. | D 4. | 1 h. black, red & yell. | 40 | 10 |
| D 184. | | 2 h. black, red & yell. | 40 | 10 |
| D 185. | | 3 h. black, red & yell. | 40 | 10 |
| D 186. | | 4 h. black, red & yell. | 40 | 10 |
| D 187. | | 5 h. black, red & yell. | 1·25 | 10 |
| D 188. | | 6 h. black, red & yell. | 25 | 10 |
| D 189. | | 7 h. black, red & yell. | 2·50 | 2·00 |
| D 190. | | 8 h. black, red & yell. | 2·50 | 70 |
| D 191. | | 10 h. blk., red & yell. | 60 | 10 |
| D 192. | | 15 h. blk., red & yell. | 50 | 10 |
| D 193. | | 20 h. blk., red & yell. | 3·00 | 15 |
| D 194. | | 50 h. blk., red & yell. | 2·25 | 15 |
| D 195. | | 200 h. blk., red & grn. | 11·00 | 2·00 |

**1916.**

| | | | | |
|---|---|---|---|---|
| D 411. | D 35. | 2 h. red | 35 | 45 |
| D 412. | | 4 h. red | 30 | 35 |
| D 413. | | 5 h. red | 35 | 45 |
| D 414. | | 6 h. red | 30 | 55 |
| D 415. | | 10 h. red | 30 | 35 |
| D 416. | | 15 h. red | 2·75 | 3·50 |
| D 417. | | 20 h. red | 30 | 40 |
| D 418. | | 25 h. red | 1·00 | 1·25 |
| D 419. | | 30 h. red | 90 | 90 |
| D 420. | | 40 h. red | 7·00 | 8·50 |
| D 421. | | 50 h. red | 24·00 | 26·00 |
| D 422. | | 1 k. blue | 3·00 | 3·50 |
| D 423. | | 3 k. blue | 14·00 | 17·00 |

### B. INDEPENDENT REPUBLIC

The following issues were used in those areas controlled by the Sarajevo government.

50 State Arms

51 Games Emblem

**1993.** Imperf.

| | | | | |
|---|---|---|---|---|
| 450 | 50 | 100 d. blue, lemon & yell | 10 | 10 |
| 451 | | 500 d. blue, yell & pink | 15 | 15 |
| 452 | | 1000 d. ultramarine, yellow and blue | 25 | 25 |
| 453 | | 5000 d. blue, yell & grn | 75 | 75 |
| 454 | | 10000 d. bl, lemon & yell | 1·50 | 1·50 |
| 455 | | 20000 d. bl, yell & bistre | 3·00 | 3·00 |
| 456 | | 50000 d. blue, yell & grey | 7·50 | 7·50 |

**1994.** 10th Anniv of Winter Olympic Games, Sarajevo. Multicoloured. Imperf.

| | | | | |
|---|---|---|---|---|
| 457 | 51 | 50000 d. black & orange | 5·00 | 5·00 |

Currency Reform
10000 (old) dinar = 1 (new) dinar

53 Facade

55 Postman and Globe

54 Historical Map, 10th–15th Centuries

**1995.** Sarajevo Head Post Office. Mult.

| | | | |
|---|---|---|---|
| 460 | 10 d. Type **53** | 10 | 10 |
| 461 | 20 d. Interior | 15 | 15 |
| 462 | 30 d. As No. 461 | 25 | 25 |
| 463 | 35 d. Before conflict | 30 | 30 |
| 464 | 50 d. As No. 463 | 40 | 40 |
| 465 | 100 d. Present day | 80 | 80 |
| 466 | 200 d. As No. 465 | 1·60 | 1·60 |

**1995.** Bosnian History. Multicoloured.
467 35 d. Type **54** .. .. 30 30
468 100 d. 15th-century Bogomil tomb, Oplicici (vert) .. .. .. 80 80
469 200 d. Arms of Kotromanic Dynasty (14th–15th centuries) (vert) .. 1·60 1·60
470 300 d. Charter by Ban Kulin of Bosnia, 1189 .. 2·50 2·50

**1995.** World Post Day.
471 **55** 100 d. multicoloured .. 4·25 4·25

**56** Dove with Olive Branch

**1995.** Europa. Peace and Freedom.
472 **56** 200 d. multicoloured .. 1·75 1·75

**57** Children and Buildings (A. Softic)

**1995.** Children's Week.
473 **57** 100 d. multicoloured .. 95 95

**58** Tram, 1895

**59** "Simphyandra hofmannii"

**1995.** Centenary of Sarajevo Electric Tram System.
474 **58** 200 d. multicoloured .. 1·75 1·75

**1995.** Flowers. Multicoloured.
475 100 d. Type **59** .. .. 95 95
476 200 d. Turk's-head lily .. 1·90 1·90

**60** "Aulopyge huegeli"

**1995.** Fishes. Multicoloured.
477 100 d. Type **60** .. .. 95 95
478 200 d. "Paraphoxinus alepidotus" .. .. 1·90 1·90

**61** Kozija Bridge, Sarajevo

**1995.** Bridges. Multicoloured.
479 20 d. Type **61** .. .. 15 15
480 30 d. Arslanagica Bridge, Trebinje .. .. 25 25
481 35 d. Latinska Bridge, Sarajevo .. .. 35 35
482 50 d. Old bridge, Mostar .. 45 45
483 100 d. Visegrad .. .. 90 90

**HAVE YOU READ THE NOTES AT THE BEGINNING OF THIS CATALOGUE?**
These often provide answers to the enquiries we receive.

**62** Visiting Friends

**1995.** Christmas. Multicoloured.
484 100 d. Type **62** .. .. 1·00 1·00
485 200 d. Madonna and Child (vert) .. .. .. 2·00 2·00

**63** Queen Jelena of Bosnia and Tomb

**1995.** Personalities. Multicoloured.
486 30 d. Type **63** .. .. 20 20
487 35 d. Husein Gradascevic 30 30
488 100 d. Mirza Safvet Basagic (horiz) .. .. .. 95 95

**64** Places of Worship and Graveyards

**1995.** Religious Pluralism.
489 **64** 35 d. multicoloured .. 35 35

**65** Stadium and Sports

**1995.** Destruction of Olympic Stadium, Sarajevo. Multicoloured.
490 35 d. Type **65** .. .. 30 30
491 100 d. Stadium aflame (vert) .. .. .. 95 95

**66** Bahrija Hadzic (opera singer)

**67** Child's Handprint

**1996.** Europa. Famous Women. Mult.
492 80 d. Type **66** .. .. 75 75
493 120 d. Nasiha Hadzic (children's writer and radio presenter) .. 1·10 1·10

**1996.** 50th Anniv of U.N.I.C.E.F. Mult.
494 50 d. Child stepping on landmine (P. Mirna and K. Princes) .. .. 65 65
495 150 d. Type **67** .. .. 1·25 1·25

**68** Bobovac Castle

**69** Pagoda and Extract from Holy Koran

**1996.**
496 **68** 35 d. black, blue & violet 35 35

**1996.** Bairam Festival.
497 **69** 80 d. multicoloured .. 75 75

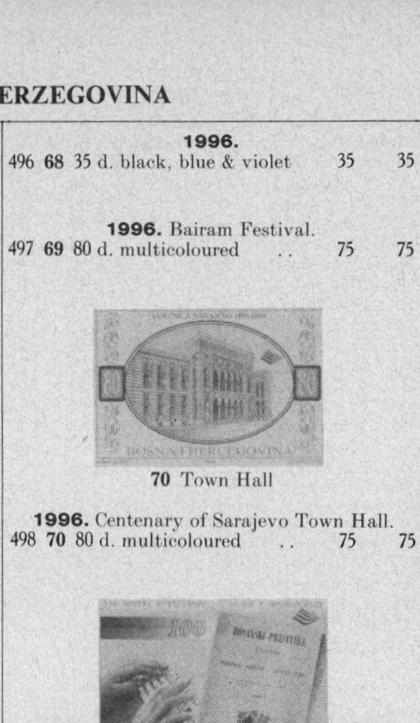

**70** Town Hall

**1996.** Centenary of Sarajevo Town Hall.
498 **70** 80 d. multicoloured .. 75 75

**71** Hands on Computer Keyboard and Title Page of "Bosanki Prijatelj"

**1996.** 150th Anniv of Journalists' Association.
499 **71** 100 d. multicoloured .. 95 95

**72** Essen

**1996.** "Essen 96" Int Stamp Fair, Essen.
500 **72** 200 d. multicoloured .. 1·75 1·75

**73** Running

**74** "Campanula hercegovina"

**1996.** Centenary of Modern Olympic Games and Olympic Games, Atlanta. Multicoloured.
501 30 d. Type **73** .. .. 25 25
502 35 d. Games emblem .. 30 30
503 80 d. Torch bearer and Olympic flag .. .. 75 75
504 120 d. Pierre de Coubertin (founder) .. .. 1·10 1·10

Nos. 501/4 were issued together, se-tenant, with the backgrounds of which form a composite design of athletes.

**1996.** Flowers. Multicoloured.
505 30 d. Type **74** .. .. 30 30
506 35 d. "Iris bosniaca" .. 35 35

**75** Barak

**1996.** Dogs. Multicoloured.
507 35 d. Type **75** .. .. 35 35
508 80 d. Tornjak .. .. 85 85

**76** Globe, Telephone and Alexander Bell

**1996.** Anniversaries. Multicoloured.
509 80 d. Type **76** (120th anniv of Bell's invention of telephone) .. .. 80 80
510 120 d. 1910 50 h. stamp (cent of post vans in Bosnia and Herzegovina) 1·10 1·10

**77** Charter with Seal

**78** Hot-air Balloons

**1996.** Granting of Privileges to Dubrovnik by Ban Stepan II Kotromanic, 1333.
511 **77** 100 d. multicoloured .. 95 95

**1996.** SOS Children's Village, Sarajevo.
512 **78** 100 d. multicoloured .. 95 95

**79** Muslim Costume of Bjelasnice

**80** Bogomil Soldier

**1996.** Traditional Costumes. Multicoloured.
513 50 d. Type **79** .. .. 40 40
514 80 d. Croatian .. .. 75 75
515 100 d. Muslim costume of Sarajevo .. .. 1·10 1·10

**1996.** Military Uniforms. Multicoloured.
516 35 d. Type **80** .. .. 30 30
517 80 d. Austro-Hungarian rifleman .. .. 75 75
518 100 d. Turkish light cavalryman .. .. 1·10 1·10
519 120 d. Medieval Bosnian king .. .. .. 1·25 1·25

## BOYACA — Pt. 20

One of the states of the Granadine Confederation.

A Department of Colombia from 1886, now uses Colombian stamps.

100 centavos = 1 peso.

1. Mendoza Perez.

**1899.** Imperf. or perf.

1. 1. 5 c. green .. .. .. 60 1·50

2.

6. Battle of Boyaca Monument.

**1903.** Imperf. or perf.

3. 2. 10 c. grey .. .. .. 15 15
4. 10 c. blue .. .. .. 60 60
12. – 10 c. orange .. .. 20 15
5. 2. 20 c. brown .. .. 20 20
5a. 20 c. lake .. .. .. 25 25
6. – 50 c. turquoise .. .. 15 15
8. – 1 p. red .. .. .. 20 15
9. – 1 p. red .. .. .. 1·40 1·40
10. 6. 5 p. black on red .. .. 50 35
11. – 10 p. black on buff .. 50 40

DESIGNS—As Type 2: 10 c. orange, Building. 50 c. Gen. Pinzon. 1 p. Figure of value. As Type 6: 10 p. Pres. Marroquin.

## BRAZIL — Pt. 20

A country in the N.E. of S. America. Portuguese settlement, 1500. Kingdom, 1815. Empire, 1822. Republic from 1889.

1843. 1000 reis = 1 milreis.
1942. 100 centavos = 1 cruzeiro.
1986. 100 centavos = 1 cruzado
1990. 100 centavos = 1 cruzeiro.
1994. 100 centavos = 1 real.

1. "Bull's Eye".

**1843.** Imperf.

4. 1. 30 r. black .. .. £1400 £350
5. 60 r. black .. .. £475 £160
6. 90 r. black .. .. £2250 £1000

2. 3. 4.

**1844.** Imperf.

10. 2. 10 r. black .. .. 95·00 19·00
11. 30 r. black .. .. £130 32·00
12. 60 r. black .. .. 95·00 19·00
13. 90 r. black .. .. £600 £130
14. 180 r. black .. .. £3500 £1100
15. 300 r. black .. .. £4750 £1500
16. 600 r. black .. .. £4250 £1700

**1850.** Imperf.

17. 3. 10 r. black .. .. 25·00 16·00
18. 20 r. black .. .. 60·00 80·00
19. 30 r. black .. .. 9·50 3·25
20. 60 r. black .. .. 9·50 2·50
21. 90 r. black .. .. 75·00 10·00
22. 180 r. black .. .. 75·00 45·00
23. 300 r. black .. .. £300 60·00
24. 600 r. black .. .. £400 75·00

**1854.** Imperf.

25. 3. 10 r. blue .. .. 11·50 9·50
26. 30 r. blue .. .. 28·00 50·00
27. 4. 280 r. red .. .. £160 95·00
28. 430 r. yellow .. .. £250 £130

5. 6. 17. Emperor Dom Pedro II.

**1866.** Various frames, but in T 5 the Emperor has a dark beard. Perf or roul.

43 5 10 r. red .. .. 6·25 3·25
44a 6 20 r. purple .. .. 7·50 1·90
45 5 50 r. blue .. .. 16·00 1·25
46a 80 r. purple .. .. 38·00 3·75
47a 100 r. green .. .. 14·50 60
55 6 200 r. black .. .. 55·00 3·75
67 17 300 r. green and orange 48·00 13·00
56 5 500 r. orange .. .. £140 19·00

12.

13.

**1878.** Various frames, but in T 13 the Emperor's beard is white. Roulette.

57 12 10 r. red .. .. 5·00 1·90
58 13 20 r. mauve .. .. 7·50 1·90
59 12 50 r. blue .. .. 11·50 1·25
60 80 r. red .. .. 13·00 7·50
61 100 r. green .. .. 13·00 60
62 200 r. black .. .. 80·00 9·50
63 260 r. brown .. .. 45·00 15·00
64 300 r. brown .. .. 45·00 3·75
65 700 r. red .. .. £100 70·00
66 1000 r. grey .. .. £130 28·00

21.

27. Pedro II.

**1881.** Various frames. Perf.

71. 21. 10 r. black .. .. 4·50 14·00
72. 10 r. orange .. .. 1·25 1·25
73. 50 r. blue .. .. 12·50 2·50
74. 100 r. olive .. .. 25·00 2·50
77. 100 r. lilac .. .. 55·00 1·25
75a. 200 r. red .. .. 25·00 3·25

No. 77 is inscr. "CORREIO".

**1884.**

81. 27. 100 r. lilac .. .. 55·00 1·25

25.

26.

29.

30. Southern Cross.

31.

32.

33. Entrance to Bay of Rio de Janeiro.

35. Southern Cross.

**1884.**

78. 25. 20 r. green .. .. 16·00 1·25
80. 26. 50 r. blue .. .. 12·50 2·50
83. 29. 100 r. lilac .. .. 28·00 60
84. 30. 300 r. blue .. .. £130 16·00
85a. 31. 500 r. olive .. .. 55·00 9·50
86. 32. 700 r. lilac .. .. 38·00 60·00
87. 33. 1000 r. blue .. .. £160 60·00

**1890.**

97a. 35. 20 r. green .. .. 1·90 1·25
89. 50 r. green .. .. 2·50 1·25
110a. 100 r. purple .. .. 16·00 60
91. 200 r. violet .. .. 7·50 95
100. 300 r. slate .. .. 38·00 3·25
92. 300 r. blue .. .. 38·00 3·25
93. 500 r. buff .. .. 14·50 6·25
94. 500 r. grey .. .. 14·50 9·50
95. 700 r. brown .. .. 19·00 19·00
96. 1000 r. yellow .. .. 11·50 2·50

37. Head of Liberty.

38. Head of Liberty.

**1891.**

111d. 37. 100 r. red and blue .. 22·00 50

**1893.**

114. 38. 100 r. red .. 48·00 60

39. Sugar-loaf Mountain.

41. Head of Liberty.

43. Head of Mercury.

**1894.**

124. 39. 10 r. blue and red .. 1·90 15
125. 20 r. blue and orange .. 1·60 45
126. 50 r. blue .. .. 9·50 95
232. 50 r. green .. .. 25·00 3·75
127. 41. 100 r. black and red .. 9·50 15
239. 100 r. red .. .. 16·00 10
128. 200 r. black and orange 1·25 10
234. 200 r. blue .. .. 9·25 10
129. 300 r. black and green .. 12·50 35
153. 500 r. black and blue .. 25·00 1·25
131a. 700 r. black and mauve 16·00 2·75
132. 43. 1000 r. mauve and green 50·00 1·25
133. 2000 r. purple and grey £130 22·00

**1897.** As T 39. but "REIS REIS" instead of "DEZ REIS".

165a. 10 r. blue and red .. 1·60 30

**1898.** Newspaper stamps of 1889 surch. **1898** between value twice in figures.

168. N 34. 100 r. on 50 r. orange 1·90 55·00
169. 200 r. on 100 r. mauve 2·50 95
170. 300 r. on 200 r. black 3·25 95
171. 500 r. on 300 r. red .. 4·50 2·50
173. 700 r. on 500 r. green .. 6·25 9·50
172. 700 r. on 500 r. orange 19·00 4·50
174. 1000 r. on 700 r. orange 28·00 28·00
175. 1000 r. on 700 r. blue .. 25·00 13·00
176. 2000 r. on 1000 r. orge. 19·00 11·50
177. 2000 r. on 1000 r. brn. 16·00 5·50

**1898.** Newspaper stamp of 1890 surch. **200** over **1898**.

180. N 37. 200 r. on 100 r. mauve 9·50 5·50

**1898.** Newspaper stamps of 1890 surch. **1898** over new value.

182. N 38. 20 r. on 10 r. blue .. 1·25 2·50
183. 50 r. on 20 r. green .. 3·25 5·50
184. 100 r. on 50 r. green .. 8·25 9·50

**1899.** Postage stamps of 1890 surch. **1899** over new value.

194. 35. 50 r. on 20 r. green .. 95 1·25
195. 100 r. on 50 r. green .. 1·25 1·25
196. 300 r. on 200 r. violet .. 5·50 9·50
190b. 500 r. on 300 r. slate .. 25·00 7·50
190. 500 r. on 300 r. blue .. 32·00 13·00
191. 700 r. on 500 r. buff .. 19·00 4·50
192a. 1,000 r. on 700 r. brown 14·00 4·50
193. 2,000 r. on 1,000 r. yell. 25·00 3·25

50. Discovery of Brazil.

52. Emancipation of Slaves.

**1900.** 400th Anniv. of Discovery of Brazil.

226. 50. 100 r. red .. .. 2·50 2·50
227. – 200 r. green and yellow 2·50 2·50
228. 52. 500 r. blue .. .. 2·50 2·50
229. – 700 r. green .. .. 2·50 2·50

DESIGNS—HORIZ. 200 r. Declaration of Independence. VERT. 700 r. Allegory of Republic.

56. Pan-American Congress.

**1906.**

259a. 56. 100 r. red .. .. 32·00 28·00
259b. 200 r. blue .. .. 70·00 8·25

57. Aristides Lobo.

61. Liberty.

**1906.**

260 57 10 r. grey .. .. 30 10
261 – 20 r. violet .. .. 20 10
262 – 50 r. green .. .. 60 10
264 – 100 r. red .. .. 4·75 10
265 – 200 r. blue .. .. 1·25 10
267 – 300 r. brown .. .. 3·25 35
268 – 400 r. olive .. .. 22·00 1·25
269 – 500 r. violet .. .. 4·75 10
272 – 600 r. olive .. .. 1·90 45
273 – 700 r. brown .. .. 4·75 1·90
274 61 1000 r. red .. .. 32·00 50
275 – 1000 r. green .. .. 1·90 35
276 – 1000 r. grey .. .. 14·00 20
277 61 2000 r. green .. .. 14·00 30
278 2000 r. blue .. .. 8·25 55
279 5000 r. pink .. .. 6·25 1·10
280 – 5000 r. brown .. .. 48·00 5·50
281 – 10000 r. brown .. .. 6·25 1·25

PORTRAITS: 20 r. B. Constant. 50 r. A. Cabral. 100 r. Wandenkolk. 200 r. D. da Fonseca. 300 r. F. Peixoto. 400 r., 600 r. P. de Moraes. 500 r. C. Salles. 700 r., 5000 r. (No. 280) R. Alves. 1000 r. (Nos. 275/6) B. do Rio Branco. 10000r. N. Pecanha.

64. King Carlos and Pres. Affonso Penna and Emblems of Portuguese-Brazilian Amity.

65. Emblems of Peace, Commerce and Industry.

**1908.** Centenary of Opening of Brazilian Ports to Foreign Commerce.

282. 64. 100 r. red .. .. 3·25 60

**1908.** National Exn., Rio de Janeiro.

283. 65. 100 r. red .. .. 17·00 95

66. Bonifacio, San Martin, Hidalgo, Washington, O'Higgins, Bolivar.

67. Cape Frio.

**1909.** Pan-American Congress, Rio de Janeiro.

284. 66. 200 r. blue .. .. 3·75 35

**1915.** 300th Anniv. of Discovery of Cape Frio.

285. 67. 100 r. turquoise on yell. 2·50 2·50

69. Bay of Guajara.

**1916.** 300th Anniv. of City of Belem.

286. 69. 100 r. red .. .. 7·00 3·75

70. Revolutionary Flag.

**1917.** Cent. of Pernambuco Revolution.

287. 70. 100 r. blue .. .. 12·50 7·50

71. Liberty. 72. 74. Inscr. "BRAZIL".

**1918.** Various frames.

288. 71. 10 r. brown .. .. 15 10
289. 20 r. violet .. .. 15 10
290. 25 r. grey .. .. 15 10
291. 50 r. green .. .. 95 30
292. 72. 100 r. red .. .. 55 10
293. 200 r. blue .. .. 5·00 20
294. 300 r. orange .. .. 15·00 1·90
295. 500 r. purple .. .. 13·50 1·90
296. 600 r. orange .. .. 1·90 7·00
297. 74. 1000 r. blue .. .. 3·25 10
298. 2000 r. brown .. .. 19·00 4·75
299. 5000 r. lilac .. .. 5·50 5·50
301. 10,000 r. red .. .. 26·00 1·25

77. Steam Locomotive. 78. "Industry". 79. "Agriculture".

80. "Aviation". 81. Mercury. 82. "Shipping".

**1920.** T 74 inscr "BRASIL".

317 77 10 r. purple .. .. 10 10
387 80 10 r. brown .. .. 10 10
318 77 20 r. grey .. .. 10 10
388 80 20 r. violet .. .. 10 10
389 78 25 r. purple .. .. 10 1·10
354 79 40 r. brown .. .. 20 10
306 78 50 r. green .. .. 35 10
323 50 r. brown .. .. 10 10
390 80 50 r. purple .. .. 10 10
391 50 r. green .. .. 10 10
308 79 80 r. green .. .. 20 6·25
309 80 100 r. red .. .. 95 10
392 100 r. orange .. .. 15 10
367 100 r. green .. .. 15 10
420 100 r. yellow .. .. 15 10
311 150 r. violet .. .. 55 15
312 200 r. blue .. .. 1·25 10
330 200 r. red .. .. 1·25 60
383 200 r. green .. .. 1·90 25
405 81 300 r. grey .. .. 15 10
394 300 r. green .. .. 95 10
333 300 r. red .. .. 95 10
406 400 r. blue .. .. 95 10
335 400 r. orange .. .. 1·60 15
407 500 r. brown .. .. 95 10
385 500 r. blue .. .. 95 10
408 600 r. brown .. .. 5·00 30
422 600 r. orange .. .. 70 10
361 82 600 r. orange .. .. 1·25 60
409 81 700 r. violet .. .. 1·90 10
342 82 1000 r. purple .. .. 2·50 10
410 81 1000 r. blue .. .. 3·75 10
362c 74 2000 r. blue .. .. 9·50 60
411 2000 r. violet .. .. 5·50 10
363a 5000 r. brown .. .. 12·50 95
364 10000 r. purple .. 9·50 60

93. King Albert and Pres. Pessoa.

**1920.** Visit of King of the Belgians.

431. 93. 100 r. red .. .. 70 50

94. Declaration of Ypiranga. 97. Brazilian Army entering Bahia.

**1922.** Cent. of Independence.

432. 94. 100 r. blue .. .. 1·00 25
433. – 200 r. red .. .. 1·90 20
434. – 300 r. green .. .. 2·75 20

DESIGNS: 200 r. Dom Pedro I and J. Bonifacio 300 r. National Exn. and Pres. Pessoa.

**1923.** Centenary of Capture of Bahia from the Portuguese.

435. 97. 200 r. red .. .. 5·50 4·50

98. Arms of the Confederation. 99. Ruy Barbosa.

**1924.** Cent. of Confederation of the Equator.

436 98 200 r. multicoloured .. 1·90 1·90

**1927.**

438b. 99. 1000 r. red .. .. 1·25 10

100. "Justice".

DESIGN: 200 r. Map and Balances.

**1927.** Centenary of Law Courses.

439. 100. 100 r. blue .. .. 75 35
440. – 200 r. red .. .. 65 35

**1928.** Air. Official stamps of 1913, Type O 67. surch. **SERVICO AEREO** and new value. Centres in black.

441. 50 r. on 10 r. grey .. 10 10
442. 200 r. on 1000 r. brown .. 1·90 4·00
443. 200 r. on 2000 r. brown .. 1·00 10·00
444. 200 r. on 5000 r. bistre .. 1·25 1·25
445. 300 r. on 500 r. yellow .. 1·25 1·90
446. 300 r. on 600 r. purple .. 65 65
447. 500 r. on 50 r. grey .. 1·25 65
448. 1000 r. on 20 r. olive .. 95 10
449. 2000 r. on 100 r. red .. 2·25 1·10
450. 2000 r. on 200 r. blue .. 2·75 1·60
451. 2000 r. on 10,000 r. black 2·25 65
452. 5000 r. on 20,000 r. blue 7·50 3·75
453. 5000 r. on 50,000 r. green 7·50 3·75
454. 5000 r. on 100,000 r. red 21·00 25·00
455. 10,000 r. on 500,000 r. brn. 25·00 19·00
456. 10,000 r. on 1,000,000 r. sepia .. .. .. 20·00 20·00

104. Liberty holding Coffee Leaves. 106. Ruy Barbosa.

**1928.** Bicentenary of Introduction of the Coffee Plant.

457. 104. 100 r. green .. .. 1·00 40
458. 200 r. red .. .. 70 35
459. 300 r. black .. .. 6·25 25

**1928.** Official stamps of 1919 surch.

460. O 77. 700 r. on 500 r. orange 3·25 3·25
461. 1000 r. on 100 r. red .. 2·50 20
462. 2000 r. on 200 r. blue .. 3·25 65
463. 5000 r. on 50 r. green .. 3·25 1·25
464. 10,000 r. on 10 r. brown 19·00 1·25

**1929.**

465 106 5000 r. blue .. .. 3·25 40

**MORE DETAILED LISTS**
are given in the Stanley Gibbons Catalogues referred to in the country headings.
For lists of current volumes see Introduction.

108. Santos Dumont's Airship "Ballon No. 6". 109. Santos Dumont.

**1929.** Air.

469. – 50 r. green .. .. 15 10
470. 108. 200 r. red .. .. 1·90 15
471. – 300 r. blue .. .. 1·60 15
472. – 500 r. purple .. .. 1·90 15
473. – 1000 r. brown .. .. 12·50 25
479. – 2000 r. green .. .. 10·00 65
480. – 5000 r. red .. .. 12·50 95
481. 109. 10,000 r. grey .. .. 12·50 1·25

DESIGNS: 50 r. De Gusmao's monument. 300 r. A. Severo's airship "Pax". 500 r. Santos Dumont's biplane "14 bis". 1000 r. R. de Barros's flying boat "Jahu". 2000 r. De Gusmao. 5000 r. A. Severo.

110. 112.

**1930.** Air.

486. 110. 3000 r. violet .. .. 1·25 1·25

**1930.** 4th Pan-American Architectural Congress.

487. – 100 r. turquoise .. 1·25 1·25
488. 112. 200 r. grey .. .. 2·00 95
489. – 300 r. red .. .. 3·75 1·25

DESIGNS: 100 r. Sun rays inscr. "ARCHITECTOS". 300 r. Architrave and Southern Cross.

113. G. Vargas and J. Pessoa – "Redemption of Brazil". 114. O. Aranha—"What is the matter?".

**1931.** Charity. Revolution of 3rd Oct., 1930.

490. 113. 10 r.+10 r. blue .. 15 9·50
491. 20 r.+20 r. brown .. 15 7·50
492. 114. 50 r.+50 r. green, red and yellow .. 15 15
493. 113. 100 r.+50 r. orange .. 25 25
494. 200 r.+100 r. green .. 25 25
495. – 300 r.+150 r. mult. .. 25 25
496. 113. 400 r.+200 r. red .. 1·00 95
497. 500 r.+250 r. blue .. 95 55
498. 600 r.+300 r. purple .. 45 9·50
499. – 700 r.+350 r. mult. .. 1·25 50
500. 1 \$+500 r. green, red and yellow .. .. 2·00 20
501. – 2 \$+1 \$ grey and red .. 11·50 50
502. – 5 \$+2 \$ 500 r. blk. & red 23·00 10·00
503. – 10 \$+5 \$ green and yell. 50·00 19·00

DESIGNS: 300 r., 700 r. as Type 113, but portraits in circles and frames altered. Milreis values as Type 114 with different portraits and frames.

**1931.** No. 333 surch **1931 200 Reis.**

507 81 200 r. on 300 r. red .. 60 10

**1931.** Zeppelin Air Stamps. Surch. **ZEPPELIN** and value.

508 108. 2\$500 on 200 r. red (No. 470) .. .. 19·00 19·00
511. 106. 3\$500 on 5000 r. blue (No. 468b) .. .. 19·00 19·00
509. – 5\$000 on 300 r. blue (No. 471) .. .. 25·00 25·00
512. 74. 7\$000 on 10,000 r. red (No. 364) .. .. 19·00 19·00

**1931.** Air. No. 486 surch **2.500 REIS.**

510. 110. 2500 r. on 3000 r. violet 14·00 28·00

121. Brazil.

**1932.** 400th Anniv. of Colonization of Sao Vicente.

513. 121. 20 r. purple .. .. 10 10
514. – 100 r. black .. .. 35 50
515. – 200 r. violet .. .. 85 10
516. – 600 r. brown .. .. 1·40 1·25
517. – 700 r. blue .. .. 2·50 1·90

DESIGNS: 100 r. Natives. 200 r. M. Afonso de Souza. 600 r. King John III of Portugal. 700 r. Founding of Sao Vicente.

125. Soldier and Flag. 130. "Justice".

**1932.** Sao Paulo Revolutionary Government issue.

518. – 100 r. brown .. .. 50 2·50
519. 125. 200 r. red .. .. 20 65
520. – 300 r. green .. .. 1·90 6·25
521. – 400 r. blue .. .. 4·50 9·50
522. – 500 r. sepia .. .. 4·50 9·50
523. – 600 r. red .. .. 4·50 9·50
524. 125. 700 r. violet .. .. 3·25 9·50
525. – 1000 r. orange .. .. 1·90 9·50
526. – 2000 r. brown .. .. 17·00 38·00
527. – 5000 r. green .. .. 25·00 60·00
528. 130. 10,000 r. purple .. 25·00 75·00

DESIGNS—As Type **125:** 100 r., 500 r. Map of Brazil. 300 r., 600 r. Symbolical of freedom, etc., 400 r., 1000 r. Soldier in tin helmet. As Type **130:** 2000 r. "LEX" and sword. 5000 r. "Justice" and soldiers with bayonets.

131. Campo Bello Square and memorial. Vassouras.

**1933.** Centenary of Vassouras.

529. 131. 200 r. red .. .. 75 75

132. Flag and Dornier Wal Flying Boat.

**1933.** Air.

530 132 3500 r. blue, grn & yell 3·75 95

**1933.** Surch. **200 REIS.**

536 81. 200 r. on 300 r. red .. 60 60

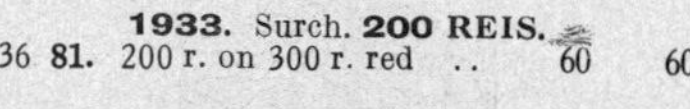

134. Flag of the Race.

**1933.** 441st Anniv. of Departure of Columbus from Polos.

537. 134. 200 r. red .. .. 70 40

136. From Santos Dumont Statue, St. Cloud.

135. Christian Symbols. 137. Faith and Energy.

**1933.** 1st Eucharistic Congress, Sao Salvador.

538 135 200 r. red .. .. 70 40

**1933.** Obligatory Tax for Airport Fund.

539. 136. 100 r. purple .. .. 20 10

**1933.**

540. 137. 200 r. red .. .. 60 10
543. 200 r. violet .. .. 1·25 10

138. "Republic" and Flags. 139. Santos Dumont Statue, St. Cloud.

**1933.** Visit of Pres. Justo of Argentina.

545. 138. 200 r. blue .. .. 40 25

546. 400 r. green .. .. 95 95

547. 600 r. red .. .. 3·75 5·00

548 1000 r. violet .. .. 5·00 3·75

**1934.** 1st National Aviation Congress, Sao Paulo.

549. 139. 200 r. blue .. .. 50 70

140. Exhibition Building. 141. Brazilian Stamp of 1845–46.

**1934.** 7th Int Sample Fair, Rio de Janeiro.

550 140 200 r. brown .. .. 65 65

551 400 r. red .. .. 2·50 2·50

552 700 r. blue .. .. 3·25 1·60

553 1000 r. orange .. 5·00 1·00

**1934.** National Philatelic Exhibition, Rio. Imperf.

555 141 200 r. + 100 r. purple .. 50 3·25

556 300 r. + 100 r. red .. 50 3·25

557 700 r. + 100 r. blue .. 4·50 25·00

558 1000 r. + 100 r. black 4·50 25·00

142. Christ of Mt. Corcovado. 143. Jose de Anchieta.

**1934.** Visit of Cardinal Pacelli.

559. 142. 300 r. red .. .. 3·25 3·25

560. 700 r. blue .. .. 12·50 12·50

**1934.** 400th Anniv. of Founding of Sao Paulo by Anchieta.

561. 143. 200 r. brown .. .. 50 40

562. 300 r. violet .. .. 40 20

563. 700 c. blue .. .. 1·90 1·90

564. 1000 r. green .. .. 3·75 1·40

145. "Brazil" and "Uruguay". 146. Town of Igarassu.

**1935.** Visit of President Terra of Uruguay.

565. – 200 r. orange .. .. 65 60

566. 145. 300 r. yellow .. .. 85 1·25

567. 700 r. blue .. .. 4·75 9·50

568. – 1000 r. violet .. .. 12·50 7·50

DESIGN—HORIZ. 200 r., 1000 r. Female figures as in Type 145 and bridge.

**1935.** 400th Anniv. of Founding of Pernambuco.

569. 146. 200 r. brown and red .. 1·00 95

570. 300 r. olive and violet .. 1·00 40

147. Nurse and Patient.

**1935.** 3rd Pan-American Red Cross Conference.

571. 147. 200 r. + 100 r. violet .. 75 95

572. 300 r. + 100 r. brown .. 75 55

573. 700 r. + 100 r. blue .. 8·50 8·50

DESIGNS: 200 r., 300 r. Mounted Gaucho. 1000 r. Marshal Caxias.

149. Gen. da Silva.

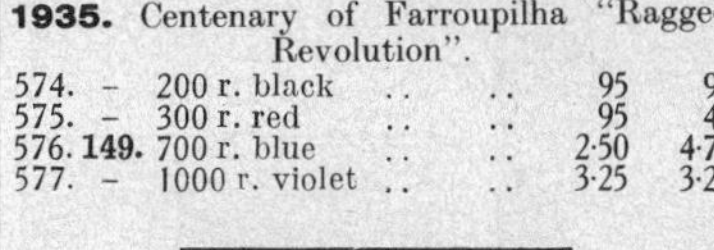

**1935.** Centenary of Farroupilha "Ragged Revolution".

574. – 200 r. black .. .. 95 95

575. – 300 r. red .. .. 95 40

576. 149. 700 r. blue .. .. 2·50 4·75

577. – 1000 r. violet .. .. 3·25 3·25

151. Gavea.

**1935.** Children's Day.

578. 151. 300 r. violet and brown 1·40 1·60

579. 300 r. turquoise & black 1·40 1·60

580. 300 r. blue and green 1·40 1·60

581. 300 r. black and red .. 1·40 1·60

152. Federal District Coat of Arms.

**1935.** 8th Int. Fair.

582. 152. 200 r. blue .. .. 2·75 2·75

153. Coutinho's ship "Gloria", 1535.

**1935.** 400th Anniv. of Colonization of State of Espirito Santo.

583. 153. 300 r. red .. .. 1·25 95

584. – 700 r. blue .. .. 3·75 2·50

DESIGN—VERT. 700 r. Arms of Coutinho.

154a. Viscount Cairu. 155. Cameta.

**1936.** Death Cent. of Cairu.

585. 154a. 1200 r. violet .. 5·00 4·75

**1936.** Tercentenary of Founding of Cameta.

586. 155. 200 r. buff .. .. 1·25 85

587. 500 r. green .. .. 1·25 50

156. Coin Press. 157. Scales of "Justice".

**1936.** Numismatic Congress, Sao Paulo.

588 156 300 r. brown .. .. 85 50

**1936.** First National Juridical Congress, Rio.

589 157 300 r. red .. .. 95 60

158. A. Carlos Gomes.

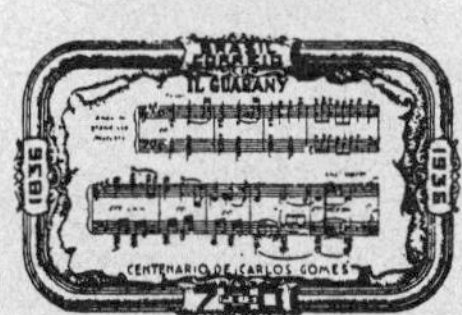

159. "Il Guarany".

**1936.** Birth Cent of C. Gomes (composer).

590 158 300 r. red .. .. 60 40

591 300 r. brown .. .. 60 40

592 159 700 r. blue .. .. 2·10 1·50

593 700 r. buff .. .. 2·50 2·10

**1936.** 9th International Sample Fair, Rio. As T 152 with inscription and date altered.

594 152 200 r. red .. .. 85 70

160. Congress Seal. 161. Botafogo Bay.

**1936.** 2nd National Eucharistic Congress, Belo Horizonte.

595 160 300 r. multicoloured .. 85 70

**1937.** Birth Centenary of Dr. Francisco Pereira Passos.

596. 161. 700 r. blue .. .. 75 50

597. 700 r. black .. .. 75 50

162. Esperanto Star and National Flags.

**1937.** 9th Brazilian Esperanto Congress, Rio de Janeiro.

598 162 300 r. green .. .. 1·25 75

163. Bay of Rio de Janeiro. 164. Globe.

**1937.** 2nd S. American Radio Conference.

599. 163. 300 r. black and orange 95 95

600. 700 r. brown and blue 2·50 95

**1937.** Golden Jubilee of Esperanto.

601. 164. 300 r. green .. .. 1·25 75

DESIGNS—HORIZ. 200 r., 2000 r. Monroe Palace, Rio. VERT. 300 r., 10,000 r. Botanical Gardens, Rio.

166. Iguazu Falls.

**1937.** Tourist Propaganda.

602. – 200 r. blue and brown 75 60

603. – 300 r. green & orange 75 60

604. 166. 1000 r. brown & sepia 2·50 1·90

605. – 2000 r. red and green 8·75 16·00

606. 166. 5000 r. green & black 28·00 28·00

607. – 10,000 r. blue and red 55·00 60·00

168. J. Da Silva Paes. 169. Eagle and Shield.

**1937.** Bicentenary of Founding of Rio Grande do Sul.

608 168 300 r. blue .. .. 75 25

**1937.** 150th Anniv. of U.S. Constitution.

609. 169. 400 r. blue .. .. 85 35

170. Coffee. 171. "Grito" Memorial.

**1938.** Coffee Propaganda.

610. 170. 1200 r. multicoloured 3·75 35

**1938.** Commem. of Abortive Proclamation of Republic.

611. 171. 400 r. brown .. .. 70 25

172. Arms of Olinda.

**1938.** 4th Cent. of Olinda.

612. 172. 400 r. violet .. .. 50 25

173. Couto de Magalhaes. 174. National Archives.

**1938.** Birth Cent. of De Magalhaes.

613. 173. 400 r. green .. .. 50 20

**1938.** Cent of Founding of National Archives.

614 174 400 r. brown .. .. 50 20

175. Rio de Janeiro. 176. Santos.

**1939.**

615. 175. 1200 r. purple .. 1·40 15

**1939.** Cent. of Santos City.

616. 176. 400 r. blue .. .. 40 20

177. Chalice-vine and Cup-of-gold Blossoms. 178. Seal of Congress.

**1939.** 1st S. American Botanical Congress, Rio.

617. 177. 400 r. green .. .. 95 35

**1939.** 3rd National Eucharistic Congress, Recife.

618. 178. 400 r. red .. .. 40 20

179. Duke of Caxias. 180. Washington.

**1939.** Soldiers' Day.

619. 179. 400 r. blue .. 40 25

**1939.** New York World's Fair. Inscr. "FEIRA MUNDIAL DE NOVA YORK".

620. 180. 400 r. orange .. .. 50 25

621. – 800 r. green .. .. 30 15

633. – 1 m. violet .. .. 2·00 2·10

622. – 1200 r. red .. .. 35 15

623. – 1600 r. blue .. .. 35 25

634. – 5 m. red .. .. 11·50 9·50

635. – 10 m. slate .. .. 12·50 4·75

DESIGNS—HORIZ. 1200 r. Grover Cleveland. VERT. 800 r. Dom Pedro II. 1 m. Water lily. 1600 r. Statue of Liberty, Rio de Janeiro. 5 m. Bust of Pres. Vargas. 10 m. Relief map of Brazil.

184. Benjamin Constant. 188. Child and Southern Cross.

**1939.** 50th Anniv. of Constitution.

624. 184. 400 r. green .. .. 40 20

625. – 800 r. black .. .. 30 30

626. – 1200 r. brown .. 60 25

DESIGNS—VERT: 800 r. Marshal da Fonseca. HORIZ. 1200 r. Marshal da Fonseca and Pres. Vargas.

**1940.** Child Welfare.

627. – 100 r. + 100 r. violet .. 35 35

628. – 200 r. + 100 r. blue .. 75 70

629. 188. 400 r. + 200 r. olive .. 70 15

630. – 1,200 r. + 400 r. red .. 2·75 1·60

DESIGNS: 100 r. Three Wise Men. 200 r. Angel and Child. 1,200 r. Mother and Child.

**189.** Roosevelt, Vargas and American Continents. **190.** Map of Brazil.

**1940.** 50th Anniv. of Pan-American Union.
631. **189.** 400 r. blue .. .. 60 40

**1940.** 9th National Geographical Congress, Florianopolis.
632. **190.** 400 r. red .. .. 35 15

**1940.** Birth Centenary of Machado de Assis (poet and novelist). As T **173** but portrait of de Assis, dated "1839-1939".
636 400 r. black .. .. 50 25

**193.** Two Workers. **195.** Brazilian Flags and Head of Liberty.

**194.** Acclaiming King John IV of Portugal.

**1940.** Bicent. of Colonization of Porto Alegre.
637. **193.** 400 r. green .. .. 40 25

**1940.** Centenaries of Portugal (1140–1640–1940). (1st issue.)
638. **194.** 1200 r. grey .. .. 1·40 35
See also Nos. 642/5.

**1940.** 10th Anniv. of Govt. of President Vargas.
639. **195.** 400 r. purple .. 50 25

**196.** Date of Fifth Census. **197.** Globe showing Spotlight on Brazil.

**1941.** 5th General Census.
640. **196.** 400 r. blue & red (post.) 30 10
641. **197.** 1200 r. brown (air) .. 2·50 50

**199.** Father Antonio Vieira. **202.** Father Jose Anchieta.

**1941.** Centenaries of Portugal (2nd issue).
642. – 200 r. pink .. .. 15 10
643. **199.** 400 r. blue .. .. 15 10
644. – 800 r. violet .. .. 20 10
645. – 5400 r. green .. .. 1·40 55
DESIGNS-VERT. 200 r. Alfonso Henriques. 800 r. Governor-Gen. Benevides. HORIZ. 5,400 r. Carmona and Vargas.

**1941.** 400th Anniv. of Order of Jesuits.
646. **202.** 1 m. violet .. .. 95 70

**205.** Oil Wells. **210.** Count of Porto Alegre.

**1941.** Value in reis.
647. **205.** 10 r. orange .. .. 30 10
648. 20 r. olive .. .. 30 10
649. 50 r. brown .. .. 30 10
650. 100 r. turquoise .. 10 10
651. – 200 r. brown .. .. 15 10
652. – 300 r. red .. .. 15 10
653. – 400 r. blue .. .. 20 10
654. – 500 r. red .. .. 15 10
655. – 600 r. violet .. .. 95 10
656. – 700 r. red .. .. 25 10
657. – 1000 r. grey .. .. 95 10
658. – 1200 r. blue .. .. 1·25 10
659. – 2000 r. purple .. 3·25 10
660. – 5000 r. blue .. .. 6·25 10
661. **210.** 10,000 r. red .. .. 9·50 10
662. – 20,000 r. brown .. 9·50 30
663. – 50 m. red .. .. 28·00 10·00
664. – 100 m. blue .. .. 60 3·75
DESIGNS: 200 r. to 500 r. Wheat harvesting machinery. 600 r. to 1200 r. Smelting works. 2000 r. "Commerce". 5000 r. Marshal F. Peixoto. 20,000 r. Admiral Maurity. 50 m. "Armed Forces". 100 m. Pres. Vargas.
For stamps with values in centavos and cruzeiros see Nos. 751, etc.

**213.** Amador Bueno. **214.** Brazilian Air Force Emblem.

**1941.** 300th Anniv of Amador Bueno as King of Sao Paulo.
665 **213** 400 r. black .. .. 55 35

**1941.** Aviation Week.
666. **214.** 5400 r. green .. .. 4·00 2·40

**1941.** Air. 4th Anniv of President Vargas's New Constitution. Optd **AEREO "10 Nov." 937-941.**
667 5400 r. green (No. 645) .. 1·40 70

**215.** Indo-Brazilian Cow **216.** Bernardino de Campos.

**1942.** 2nd Agriculture and Cattle Show, Uberaba.
668a. **215.** 200 r. blue .. .. 40 25
669a. 400 r. brown .. 40 25

**1942.** Birth Cents. of B. de Campos and P. de Morais (lawyers and statesmen).
670. **216.** 1000 r. red .. .. 1·90 95
671. – 1200 r. blue .. .. 4·75 65
PORTRAIT: 1200 r. Prudente de Morais.

**217.** Torch of Learning. **218.** Map of Brazil showing Goiania.

**1942.** 8th National Education Congress, Goiania.
672. **217.** 400 r. brown .. .. 45 25

**1942.** Founding of Goiania City.
673. **218.** 400 r. violet .. .. 45 25

**219.** Congressional Seal. **221.** Tributaries of R. Amazon.

**1942.** 4th National Eucharistic Congress, Sao Paulo.
674. **219.** 400 r. brown .. .. 35 15

**1942.** Air. 5th Anniv of President Vargas's New Constitution. No. 645 surch **AEREO "10 Nov." 937-942** and value.
675 5 cr. 40 on 5400 r. green .. 2·25 1·90

**1943.** 400th Anniv. of Discovery of River Amazon.
676. **221.** 40 c. brown .. .. 35 35

**222.** Early Brazilian Stamp. **223.** Memorial Tablet.

**1943.** Centenary of Petropolis.
677. **222.** 40 c. violet .. .. 50 25

**1943.** Air. Visit of Pres. Morinigo of Paraguay.
678. **223.** 1 cr. 20 blue .. .. 1·25 95

**224.** Map of S. America showing Brazil and Bolivia.

**1943.** Air. Visit of President Penaranda of Bolivia.
679. **224.** 1 cr. 20 multicoloured 95 65

**225.** " Bull's-eye ". **226.**

**1943.** Centenary of 1st Brazilian Postage Stamps.
(a) Postage. Imperf.
680. **225.** 30 c. black .. .. 70 35
681. 60 c. black .. .. 85 35
682. 90 c. black .. .. 45 35

(b) Air. Perf.
683. **226.** 1 cr. black and yellow 1·25 95
684. 2 cr. black and green .. 1·90 95
685. 5 cr. black and red .. 2·10 1·25

**227.** Book of the Law. **228.** Ubaldino do Amaral.

**1943.** Air. Inter-American Advocates Conference.
686 **227.** 1 cr. 20 red and brown 65 15

**1943.** Birth Cent. of Ubaldino do Amaral.
687. **228.** 40 c. grey .. .. 35 20

**229.** Indo-Brazilian Cow.

**1943.** 9th Cattle Show, Bahia.
688. **229.** 40 c. brown .. .. 60 50

**230.** Justice and Seal. **231.** Santa Casa de Misericordia Hospital.

**1943.** Cent. of Institute of Brazilian Lawyers.
689. **230.** 2 cr. red .. .. 1·60 95

**1943.** 400th Anniv. of Santa Casa de Misericordia de Santos.
690. **231.** 1 cr. blue .. .. 50 25

**232.** Barbosa Rodrigues. **233.** Pedro Americo.

**1943.** Birth Centenary of B. Rodrigues (botanist).
691. **232.** 40 c. green .. .. 40 15

**1943.** Birth Centenary of Americo (artist and author).
692. **233.** 40 c. brown .. .. 35 20

**1944.** Air. No. 629 surch. **AEREO** and value.
693. **188.** 20 c. on 400 r. + 200 r. 35 65
694. 40 c. on 400 r. + 200 r. 70 25
695. 60 c. on 400 r. + 200 r. 70 15
696. 1 cr. on 400 r. + 200 r. 85 50
697. 1 cr. 20 on 400 r. + 200 r. 1·25 20

**235.** Gen. Carneiro and Defenders of Lapa. **236.** Baron do Rio Branco.

**1944.** 50th Anniv. of Siege of Lapa.
698. **235.** 1 cr. 20 c. red .. 70 35

**1944.** Inauguration of Monument to Baron do Rio Branco.
699. **236.** 1 cr. blue .. .. 50 25

**237.** Duke of Caxias. **238.** Emblems of Y.M.C.A.

**1944.** Centenary of Pacification of Revolutionary Uprising of 1842.
700. **237.** 1 cr. 20 green & yellow 60 35

**1944.** Centenary of Y.M.C.A.
701. **238.** 40 c. blue, red & yell. 25 20

**239.** Rio Grande Chamber of Commerce. **240.** "Bartolomeo de Gusmao and the Aerostat". (Bernardino de Souza Pereira).

**1944.** Centenary of Founding of Rio Grande Chamber of Commerce.
702. **239.** 40 c. brown .. .. 25 25

**1944.** Air. Air Week.
703. **240.** 1 cr. 20 red .. .. 30 15

**241.** Ribeiro de Andrada. **242.** Meeting between Caxias and Canabarro.

**1945.** Death Centenary of M. de Andrada (statesman).
704. **241.** 40 c. blue .. .. 20 15

**1945.** Centenary of Pacification of Rio Grande do Sul.
705. **242.** 40 c. blue .. .. 20 15

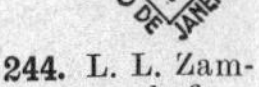

**244.** L. L. Zamenhof.　**247.** Baron do Rio Branco (statesman).

**1945.** 10th Brazilian Esperanto Congress, Rio de Janeiro.
706. – 40 c. green (postage).. 40 20
707. **244.** 1 cr. 20 brown (air) .. 40 20
DESIGN: 40 c. Woman and map.

**1945.** Birth Cent. of Baron do Rio Branco.
708. – 40 c. blue (postage) .. 20 15
709. – 1 cr. 20 purple (air) .. 45 15
710. **247.** 5 cr. purple .. .. 1·90 20
DESIGNS—HORIZ. 40 c. Bookplate VERT. 1 cr. 20, S. America.

**248.** " Glory ".　**250.** " Co-operation ".

**1945.** Victory of Allied Nations in Europe. Roul.
711. – 20 c. violet .. .. 15 10
712. **248.** 40 c. red .. .. 15 10
713. – 1 cr. orange .. .. 40 35
714. – 2 cr. blue .. .. 65 50
715. **250.** 5 cr. green .. .. 1·25 95
SYMBOLICAL DESIGNS—VERT. 20 c. Tranquility (inscr. "SAUDADE"), HORIZ. 1 cr. "Victory". (inscr. "VITORIA"), 2 cr. "Peace" (inscr. "PAZ"), ·

**251.** F. M. da Silva.　**252.** Bahia Institute.

**1945.** 150th Birth Anniv. of Francisco Manoel da Silva (composer of Brazilian National Anthem).
716. **251.** 40 c. red .. .. 50 25

**1945.** 50th Anniv. of Founding of Bahia Institute of Geography and History.
717. **252.** 40 c. blue .. .. 65 15

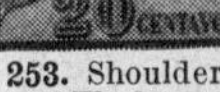

**253.** Shoulder Flash.　**255.** " V " Sign and Flashes.

**1945.** Return of Brazilian Expeditionary Force.
718. **253.** 20 c. blue, red & grn. 15 15
719. – 40 c. multicoloured .. 15 15
720. – 1 cr. multicoloured .. 85 50
721. – 2 cr. multicoloured .. 95 95
722. **255.** 5 cr. multicoloured .. 3·25 85
DESIGNS (embodying shoulder flashes) As Type **253**: 40 c. B.E.F. flash. As Type **255.** HORIZ. 1 cr. U.S.A. flag. 2 cr. Brazilian flag.

**256.** Wireless Mast and Map.　**257.** Admiral Saldanha da Gama.

**1945.** 3rd Inter-American Radio Communication Conference.
723. **256.** 1 cr. 20 black.. .. 40 15

**1946.** Birth Cent. of Admiral S. da Gama.
724. **257.** 40 c. grey .. .. 15 95

**258.** Princess Isabel d'Orleans-Braganza.　**261.** P.O., Rio de Janeiro.

**260.** Lockheed Super Electra over Bay of Rio de Janiero.

**1946.** Birth Centenary of Princess Isabel d'Orleans-Braganza.
725. **258.** 40 c. black .. .. 20 1·25

**1946.** 5th P.U. Congress of the Americas and Spain.
726. – 40 c. orange and black 20 15
727. **260.** 1 cr. 30 orge. & green 65 30
728. 1 cr. 70 orange and red 95 30
729. **261.** 2 cr. blue and slate .. 1·25 15
730. **260.** 2 cr. 20 orange & blue 95 40
731. **261.** 5 cr. blue and brown.. 5·00 75
732. 10 cr. blue and violet.. 5·00 60
DESIGN (25×37 mm.): 40 c. Post-horn, V and envelope.

**262.** Proposed Columbus Lighthouse.　**263.** " Liberty ".

**1946.** Construction of Columbus Lighthouse, Dominican Republic.
733. **262.** 5 cr. blue .. .. 9·50 2·50

**1946.** New Constitution.
734. **263.** 40 c. grey .. .. 10 10



**264.** Orchid.

**1946.** 4th National Exn. of Orchids, Rio de Janeiro.
735. **264.** 40 c. blue, red & yellow 65 10

**265.** Gen. A. E. Gomes Carneiro.　**266.** Academy of Arts.

**1946.** Birth Centenary of Gen. A. E. Gomes Carneiro.
736. **265.** 40 c. green .. .. 35 10

**1946.** 50th Anniv. of Brazilian Academy of Arts.
737. **266.** 40 c. blue .. .. 35 10

**267.** Antonio de Castro Alves.　**268.** Pres. Gonzalez.

**1947.** Birth Cent. of Castro Alves (poet).
738. **267.** 40 c. turquoise .. .. 35 10

**1947.** Visit of Chilean President.
739. **268.** 40 c. brown .. .. 35 10

**269.** " Peace and Security ".　**270.** " Dove of Peace ".

**1947.** Inter-American Defence Conference, Rio de Janeiro.
740. **269.** 1 cr. 20 blue (postage) 65 10
741. **270.** 2 cr. 20 green (air) .. 65 10

**271.** Pres. Truman, Map of S. America and Statue of Liberty.

**1947.** Visit of President Truman.
742. **271.** 40 c. blue .. .. 15 10

**272.** Pres. Enrico Gaspar Dutra.　**273.** Woman and Child.

**1947.** Commemorating Pres. Dutra.
743. **272.** 20 c. green .. .. 10 10
744. 40 c. red .. .. 15 10
745. 1 cr. 20 blue .. .. 30 10

**1947.** Children's Week. 1st Brazilian Infant Welfare Convention and Paediatrics.
747. **273.** 40 c. blue .. .. 15 10

**274.** Icarus.

**1947.** Obligatory Tax. " Week of the Wing " Aviation Fund.
748. **274.** 40 c.+10 c. orange .. 25 10

**275.** Santos Dumont Monument, St. Cloud, France.　**276.** Arms of Belo Horizonte.

**1947.** Air. Homage to Santos Dumont (aviation pioneer).
749. **275.** 1 cr. 20 c. brn. & grn. 65 10

**1947.** 50th Anniv. of Founding of City of Belo Horizonte.
750. **276.** 1 cr. 20 c. red.. .. 65 10

**1947.** As postage stamps of 1941, but values in centavos or cruzeiros.
751. **205.** 2 c. olive .. .. 10 10
752. 5 c. brown .. .. 10 10
753. 10 c. turquoise .. 10 10
754. – 20 c. brown (No. 651).. 15 10
755. – 30 c. red (No. 652) .. 65 10
756. – 40 c. blue (No. 653) .. 20 10
757. – 50 c. red (No. 654) .. 45 10
758. – 60 c. violet (No. 655).. 95 10
759. – 70 c. red (No. 656) .. 25 10
760. – 1 cr. grey (No. 657) .. 1·25 10
761. – 1 cr. 20 blue (No. 658) 3·75 10
762. – 2 cr. purple (No. 659).. 4·75 10
763. – 5 cr. blue (No. 660) .. 9·50 10
764. **210.** 10 cr. red .. .. 9·50 10
765. – 20 cr. brown (No. 662) 16·00 10
766. – 50 cr. red (No. 663) .. 28·00 10

**277.** Rio de Janeiro and Rotary Emblem.　**278.** Globe.

**279.** Quitandinha Hotel.

**1948.** Air. 39th Rotary Congress Rio de Janeiro.
769. **277.** 1 cr. 20 red .. .. 45 10
770. 3 cr. 80 violet.. .. 1·90 15

**1948.** Int. Industrial and Commercial Exn. Quitandinha.
771. **278.** 40 c. grn. & mve. (post) 15 10
772. **279.** 1 cr. 20 brown (air) .. 25 15
773. 3 cr. 80 violet .. 95 15

**280.** Arms of Paranagua.　**281.** Girl Reading.

**1948.** Tercent. of Founding of Paranagua.
774. **280.** 5 cr. brown .. .. 3·75 95

**1948.** National Children's Campaign.
775. **281.** 40 c. green .. .. 15 35

**282.** Three Muses. (after Henrique Bernardelli).

**1948.** Air. Cent. of National School of Music.
776. **282.** 1 cr. 20 blue .. .. 65 10

**283.** President Berres.

**1948.** Air. Visit of Uruguayan President.
777. **283.** 1 cr. 70 blue .. .. 50 10

**284.** Merino Ram.

**1948.** Air. Int. Livestock Show, Bage.
778. **284.** 1 cr. 20 orange .. 1·25 15

**285.** Congress Seal.　**286.** " Tiradentes " (trans. " Tooth-puller ").

**1948.** Air. 5th National Eucharistic Congress, Porto Alegre.
779. **285.** 1 cr. 20 purple .. 50 10

**1948.** Birth Bicentenary of A. J. J. da Silva Xavier (patriot).
780. **286.** 40 c. orange .. .. 10 10

287. Crab and Globe. 288. Adult Student.

**1948.** Anti-Cancer Campaign.
781. **287.** 40 c. purple .. .. 15 35

**1949.** Campaign for Adult Education.
782. **288.** 60 c. purple .. .. 15 10

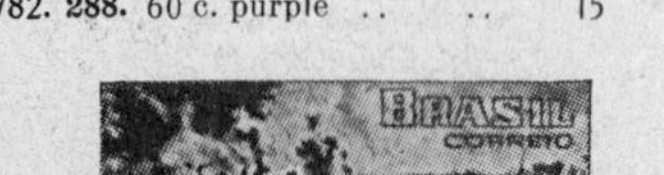

289. Battle of Guararapes.

**1949.** 300th Anniv of 2nd Battle of Guararapes.
783 **289** 60 c. blue (postage) .. 1·90 25
784 – 1 cr. 20 pink (air) .. 3·75 1·60
DESIGN: 1 cr. 20, View of Guararapes.

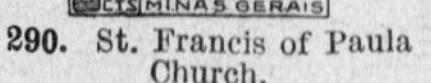

290. St. Francis of Paula Church. 291. Father Nobrega.

292. De Souza meeting Indians. 293. Franklin D. Roosevelt.

**1949.** Bicent. of Ouro Fino.
785. **290.** 60 c. brown .. .. 15 10

**1949.** 4th Cent. of Founding of Bahia.
(a) Postage. Imperf.
786. **291.** 60 c. violet .. .. 15 10

(b) Air. Perf.
787. **292.** 1 cr. 20 c. blue .. 95 15

**1949.** Air. Homage to Franklin D. Roosevelt. Imperf.
788. **293.** 3 cr. 80 c. blue .. 1·90 30

294. Douglas DC-3 and Air Force Badge.

**1949.** Homage to Brazilian Air Force. Imperf.
789 **294** 60 c. violet .. .. 15 10

295. Joaquim Nabuco. 296. "Revelation".

**1949.** Air. Birth Centenary of J. Nabuco (lawyer and author).
790. **295.** 3 cr. 80 c. purple .. 1·25 10

**1949.** 1st Sacerdotal Vocational Congress, Bahia.
791. **296.** 60 c. purple .. .. 15 10

297. Globe.

**1949.** 75th Anniv. of U.P.U.
792. **297.** 1 cr. 50 blue .. .. 65 10

298. Ruy Barbosa. 299. Cardinal Arcoverde.

300. "Agriculture and Industry". 301. Virgin of the Globe.

**1949.** Birth Cent. of Ruy Barbosa (statesman).
793. **298.** 1 cr. 20 red .. .. 95 15

**1950.** Birth Centenary of Cardinal Joaquim Arcoverde's
794. **299.** 60 c. pink .. .. 50 10

**1950.** 75th Anniv. of Arrival of Italian Immigrants.
795. **300.** 60 c. red .. .. 35 10

**1950.** Centenary of Establishment of Daughters of Charity of St. Vincent de Paul.
796. **301.** 60 c. blue and black .. 15 10

302. Globe and Footballers. 303. Stadium.

**1950.** 4th World Football Championship, Rio de Janeiro.
797. **302.** 60 c. grey & bl. (post) 95 15
798. **303.** 1 cr. 20 orange and blue (air) .. 1·60 25
799. – 5 cr. 80 yellow, green and blue .. 6·25 30
DESIGN—VERT. 5 cr. 80 Linesman and flag.

304. Three Heads, Map and Graph. 305. Line of People and Map.

**1950.** Sixth Brazilian Census, 1950.
800. **304.** 60 c. red (postage) .. 15 10
801. **305.** 1 cr. 20 brown (air) .. 95 10

306. Oswaldo Cruz. 307. Blumenau and Itajai River.

**1950.** 5th Int. Microbiological Congress, Rio de Janeiro.
802. **306.** 60 c. brown .. .. 50 10

**1950.** Cent. of Founding of Blumenau.
803. **307.** 60 c. pink .. .. 50 10

308. Government Offices. 309. Arms.

**1950.** Cent. of Amazon Province.
804. **308.** 60 c. red .. .. 35 10

**1950.** Cent. of Juiz de Fora City.
805. **309.** 60 c. red .. .. 35 10

310. P.O. Building, Recife.

**1951.** Inauguration of Head Post Office, Pernambuco Province.
806. **310.** 60 c. red .. .. 10 10
807. 1 cr. 20 red .. .. 35 10

311. Arms of Joinville. 312. S. Romero.

**1951.** Cent. of Founding of Joinville.
808. **311.** 60 c. brown .. .. 35 10

**1951.** Birth Cent. of Sylvio Romero (poet).
809. **312.** 60 c. brown .. .. 35 10

313. De La Salle. 314. Heart and Flowers.

**1951.** Birth Tricentenary of Jean-Baptiste de la Salle (educational reformer).
810. **313.** 60 c. blue .. .. 65 10

**1951.** Mothers' Day.
811. **314.** 60 c. purple .. .. 50 50

315. J. Caetano and Stage. 316. O. A. Derby.

317. Crucifix and Congregation. 318. E. P. Martins and Map.

**1951.** 1st Brazilian Theatrical Congress.
812. **315.** 60 c. blue .. .. 50 10

**1951.** Birth Cent. of Derby (geologist).
813. **316.** 2 cr. slate .. .. 65 35

**1951.** 4th Inter-American Catholic Education Congress, Rio de Janeiro.
814. **317.** 60 c. brown and buff 65 10

**1951.** 29th Anniv. of First Rio-New York Flight.
815. **318.** 3 cr. 80 c. brn. & lemon 3·25 15

## MORE DETAILED LISTS

are given in the Stanley Gibbons Catalogues referred to in the country headings.
For lists of current volumes see Introduction.

319. Penha Convent. 320. Santos Dumont and Boys with Model Aircraft.

321. Wheat Harvesters. 322. Bible and Map.

**1951.** 400th Anniv. of Founding of Vitoria.
816. **319.** 60 c. brown and buff 65 10

**1951.** "Week of the Wing" and 50th Anniv of Santos Dumont's Flight over Paris.
817 **320** 60 c. brn & orge (post) 65 15
818 – 3 cr. 80 violet (air) .. 1·90 20
DESIGN: 3 cr. 80, "Ballon No. 6" airship over Eiffel Tower.

**1951.** Wheat Festival, Bage.
819 **321** 60 c. green and grey .. 50 50

**1951.** Bible Day.
820. **322.** 1 cr. 20 brown .. 1·25 35

323. Isabella the Catholic. 324. Henrique Oswald.

**1952.** 500th Birth Anniv. of Isabella the Catholic.
821. **323.** 3 cr. 80 blue .. .. 1·90 10

**1952.** Birth Cent. of Oswald (composer).
822. **324.** 60 c. brown .. .. 65 10

325. Map and Symbol of Labour. 326. Dr. L. Cardoso.

**1952.** 5th Conf. of American Members of Int. Labour Organization.
823. **325.** 1 cr. 50 c. red .. .. 65 10

**1952.** Birth Centenary of Cardoso (scientist) and 4th Brazilian Homoeopathic Congress, Porto Alegre.
824. **326.** 60 c. blue .. .. 15 15

327. Gen. da Fonseca. 328. L. de Albuquerque.

330. Councillor J. A. Saraiva. 329. Olympic Flame and Athletes.

**1952.** Centenary of Telegraphs in Brazil.
825. **327.** 2 cr. 40 red .. .. 65 15
826. – 5 cr. blue .. .. 3·75 15
827. – 10 cr. turquoise .. 3·75 15
PORTRAITS—VERT. 5 cr. Baron de Capanema. 10 cr. E. de Queiros.

**1952.** Bicent. of Mato Grosso City.
828. **328.** 1 cr. 20 violet .. 65 10

**1952.** 50th Anniv. of Fluminense Football Club.
829. **329.** 1 cr. 20 blue .. .. 1·25 35

**1952.** 100th Anniv. of Terezina City.
830. **330.** 60 c. mauve .. .. 65 10

**331.** Emperor Dom Pedro II.  **332.** Globe, Staff and Rio de Janeiro Bay.

**1952.** Stamp Day and 2nd Philatelic Exn., Sao Paulo.
831. **331.** 60 c. black and blue .. 65 10

**1952.** 2nd American Congress of Industrial Medicine.
832. **332.** 3 cr. 80 green & brown 1·60 35

**333.** Dove, Globe and Flags.

**1952.** United Nations Day.
833. **333.** 3 cr. 80 blue .. .. 1·90 50

**334.** Compasses and Modern Buildings, Sao Paulo.  **335.** D. A. Feijo (Statesman).

**1952.** City Planning Day.
834. **334.** 60 c. yell., grn. & blue 50 10

**1952.** Homage to D. A. Feijo.
835. **335.** 60 c. brown .. .. 35 10

**336.** Father Damien. **337.** R. Bernardelli.

**1952.** Obligatory Tax. Leprosy Research Fund.
836. **336.** 10 c. brown .. .. 15 15
837. 10 c. green .. .. 15 10

**1952.** Birth Cent. of Bernardelli (sculptor).
838. **337.** 60 c. blue .. .. 65 10

**338.** Arms of Sao Paulo and Settler.  **339.** "Expansion".

**1953.** 400th Anniv. of Sao Paulo. (1st issue).
839. **338.** 1 cr. 20 black & brown 95 20
840. – 2 cr. green and yellow 2·50 20
841. – 2 cr. 80 brown & orange 1·90 15
842. **339.** 3 cr. 80 brown & green 1·90 15
843. 5 cr. 80 blue and green 1·25 15
DESIGNS—VERT. (Inscr. as Type **339**): 2 cr. Coffee blossom and berries. 2 cr. 80, Monk planting tree.
See also Nos. 875/9.

**340.**  **341.** J. Ramalho.

**1953.** 6th Brazilian Accountancy Congress, Port Alegre.
844. **340.** 1 cr. 20 brown .. 95 10

**1953.** 4th Cent. of Santo Andre.
845. **341.** 60 c. blue .. .. 10 10

**342.** A. Reis and Plan of Belo Horizonte.  **343.** "Almirante Saldanha" (cadet ship).

**1953.** Birth Cent. of A. Reis (engineer).
846. **342.** 1 cr. 20 brown .. 15 10

**1953.** 4th Voyage of Circumnavigation by Training Ship "Admiral Saldanha".
847. **343.** 1 cr. 50 blue .. .. 70 20

**344.** Viscount de Itaborahy.  **345.** Lamp and Rio-Petropolis Highway.

**1953.** Cent. of Bank of Brazil.
848. **344.** 1 cr. 20 violet .. 15 10

**1953** 10th Int. Nursing Congress, Petropolis.
849. **345.** 1 cr. 20 grey .. .. 15 10

**346.** Bay of Rio de Janeiro.

**1953.** 4th World Conf. of Young Baptists.
850. **346.** 3 cr. 80 c. turquoise .. 95 10

**347.** Ministry of Health and Education.  **348.** Arms and Map.

**1953.** Stamp Day and 1st National Philatelic Exn. of Education, Rio de Janeiro.
851. **347.** 1 cr. 20 turquoise .. 15 10

**1953.** Centenary of Jau City.
852. **348.** 1 cr. 20 violet .. 15 10

**349.** Maria Quiteria de Jesus.  **350.** Pres. Odria.

**1953.** Death Cent. of Maria Quiteria de Jesus.
853. **349.** 60 c. blue .. .. 10 10

**1953.** Visit of President of Peru.
854. **350.** 1 cr. 40 purple .. 15 10

**351.** Caxias leading Troops.  **352.** Quill-pen and Map.

**1953.** 150th Birth Anniv. of Duke of Caxias.
855. **351.** 60 c. turquoise .. 35 15
856. – 1 cr. 20 purple .. 50 15
857. – 1 cr. 70 blue .. .. 50 15
858. – 3 cr. 80 brown .. 1·60 15
859. – 5 cr. 80 violet.. .. 85 15
DESIGNS: 1 cr. 20, Tomb. 1 cr. 70, 5 cr. 80, Portrait of Caxias. 3 cr. 80, Coat of arms.

**1953.** 5th National Congress of Journalists, Curitiba.
860. **352.** 60 c. blue .. .. 10 10

**353.** H. Hora.  **354.** President Somoza.

**1953.** Birth Cent. of H. Hora (painter).
861. **353.** 60 c. purple and orange 35 10

**1953.** Visit of President Somoza of Nicaragua.
862. **354.** 1 cr. 40 purple .. 20 15

**355.** A. de Saint-Hilaire.  **356.** J. do Patrocinio and "Spirit of Emancipation" (after R. Amoedo).

**1953.** Death Centenary of A. de Saint-Hilaire (explorer and botanist).
863. **355.** 1 cr. 20 lake .. .. 20 10

**1953.** Death Centenary of J. do Patrocinio (slavery abolitionist).
864. **356.** 60 c. slate .. .. 10 10

**357.** Clock Tower, Crato.  **358.** C. de Abreu.

**1953.** Centenary of Crato City.
865. **357.** 60 c. green .. .. 15 10

**1953.** Birth Cent. of Abreu (historian).
866. **358.** 60 c. blue .. .. 20 10
867. 5 cr. violet .. .. 1·90 20

**359.** "Justice".  **360.** Harvesting.

**1953.** 50th Anniv. of Treaty of Petropolis.
868. **359.** 60 c. blue .. .. 15 10
869. 1 cr. 20 purple .. 15 10

**1953.** 3rd National Wheat Festival, Erechim.
870. **360.** 60 c. turquoise .. 15 10

**361.** Teacher and Pupils.  **362.** Porters with Trays of Coffee Beans.

**1953.** 1st National Congress of Elementary School-teachers, Salvador.
871. **361.** 60 c. red .. .. 15 10

**1953.** Cent. of State of Parana.
872a. – 2 cr. brown and black 95 35
873. **362.** 5 cr. orange and black 1·90 35
DESIGN: 2 cr. Portrait of Z. de Gois e Vasconcellos.

**363.** A. de Gusmao.  **364.** Growth of Sao Paulo.

**365.** Sao Paulo and Arms.

**1954.** Death Bicent. of Gusmao (statesman).
874. **363.** 1 cr. 20 purple .. 15 10

**1954.** 400th Anniv of Sao Paulo (2nd issue).
875 **364** 1 cr. 20 brown .. 1·25 45
876 – 2 cr. mauve .. .. 1·90 40
877 – 2 cr. 80 violet .. 2·10 30
878 **365** 3 cr. 80 green .. 2·50 20
879 5 cr. 80 red .. .. 2·50 40
DESIGNS—VERT. 2 cr. Priest, pioneer and Indian. 2 cr. 80, J. de Anchieta.

**366.** J. F. Vieira, A. V. de Negreiros, A. F. Camarao and H. Dias.

**1954.** 300th Anniv. of Recovery from the Dutch of Pernambuco.
880. **366.** 1 cr. 20 blue .. .. 50 10

**367.** Sao Paulo and Allegorical Figure.

**1954.** 10th Int. Congress of Scientific Organization, Sao Paulo.
881. **367.** 1 cr. 50 purple .. 15 10

**368.** Grapes and Winejar.  **369.** Immigrants' Monument.

**1954.** Grape Festival, Rio Grande do Sul.
882. **368.** 40 c. lake .. .. 15 10

**1954.** Immigrants' Monument, Caxias do Sul.
883. **369.** 60 c. violet .. .. 15 10

**370.** "Baronesa" (first locomotive used in Brazil).  **371.** Pres. Chamoun.

**1954.** Cent. of Brazilian Railways.
884. **370.** 40 c. red .. .. 80 40

**1954.** Visit of President of Lebanon.
885. **371.** 1 cr. 50 lake .. 20 10

**372.** Sao Jose College, Rio de Janeiro.

**373.** Vel Marcelino Champagnat.

**374.** Apolonia Pinto.

**375.** Admiral Tamandare.

**1954.** 50th Anniv. of Marists in Brazil.
886. **372.** 60 c. violet .. .. 20 15
887. **373.** 1 cr. 20 blue .. .. 20 15

**1954.** Birth Cent. of Apolonia Pinto (actress).
888. **374.** 1 cr. 20 green .. .. 10 10

**1954.** Portraits.
889. **375.** 2 c. blue .. .. 15 15
890. 5 c. red .. .. 15 10
891. 10 c. green .. .. 15 10
892. – 20 c. red .. .. 20 10
893. – 30 c. slate .. .. 30 10
894. – 40 c. red .. .. 50 10
895. – 50 c. lilac .. .. 65 10
896. – 60 c. turquoise .. .. 30 10
897. – 90 c. salmon .. .. 50 15
898. – 1 cr. brown .. .. 20 10
899. – 1 cr. 50 blue .. .. 25 10
900. – 2 cr. green .. .. 90 10
901. – 5 cr. purple .. .. 55 10
902. – 10 cr. green .. .. 1·90 10
903. – 20 cr. red .. .. 2·75 65
904. – 50 cr. blue .. .. 9·50 10
PORTRAITS—20 c., 30 c., 40 c. O. Cruz. 50 c. to 90 c. J. Murtinho. 1 cr., 1 cr. 50 c., 2 cr. Duke of Caxias. 5 cr., 10 cr. R. Barbosa. 20 cr., 50 cr. J. Bonifacio.

**376.** Boy Scout. **377.** B. Fernandes. **378.** Cardinal Piazza.

**1954.** Int. Scout Encampment, Sao Paulo.
905. **376.** 1 cr. 20 blue .. .. 95 15

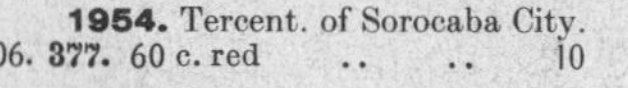

**1954.** Tercent. of Sorocaba City.
906. **377.** 60 c. red .. .. 10 10

**1954.** Visit of Cardinal Piazza (Papal Legate).
907. **378.** 4 cr. 20 red .. .. 95 10

**379.** Virgin and Map.

**380.** Benjamin Constant and Braille Book.

**1954.** Marian Year. Inscr. "ANO MARIANO".
908. **379.** 60 c. lake .. .. 30 10
909. – 1 cr. 20 blue .. .. 65 10
DESIGN: 1 cr. 20, Virgin and globe.
No. 909 also commemorates the Centenary of the Proclamation of the Dogma of the Immaculate Conception.

**1954.** Centenary of Education for the Blind in Brazil.
910 **380** 60 c. green .. .. 15 10

**381.** River Battle of Riachuelo.

**382.** Admiral Barroso.

**1954.** 150th Birth Anniv of Admiral Barroso.
911 **381** 40 c. brown .. .. 70 15
912 **382** 60 c. violet .. .. 25 10

**383.** S. Hahnemann (physician). **384.** Nisia Floresta (suffragist). **385.** Ears of Wheat.

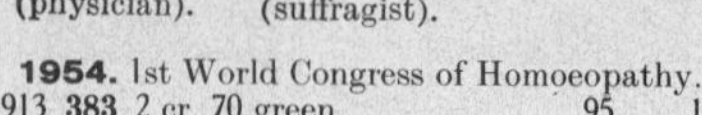

**1954.** 1st World Congress of Homoeopathy.
913 **383** 2 cr. 70 green .. .. 95 10

**1954.** Removal of Ashes of Nisia Floresta (suffragist) from France to Brazil.
914. **384.** 60 c. mauve .. .. 10 10

**1954.** 4th Wheat Festival, Carazinho.
915. **385.** 60 c. olive .. .. 15 10

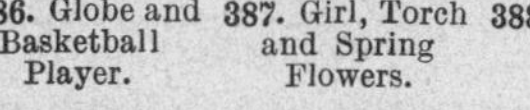

**386.** Globe and Basketball Player. **387.** Girl, Torch and Spring Flowers. **388.** Father Bento.

**1954.** 2nd World Basketball Championship.
916. **386.** 1 cr. 40 red .. .. 95 15

**1954.** 6th Spring Games.
917. **387.** 60 c. brown .. .. 20 10

**1954.** Obligatory Tax. Leprosy Research Fund.
918. **388.** 10 c. blue .. .. 15 10
919. 10 c. mauve .. .. 15 10
919a. 10 c. salmon .. .. 15 10
919b. 10 c. green .. .. 15 10
919c. 10 c. lilac .. .. 15 10
919d. 10 c. brown .. .. 15 10
919e. 10 c. slate .. .. 15 10
919f. 2 cr. lake .. .. 15 10
919g. 2 cr. lilac .. .. 15 10
919h. 2 cr. orange .. .. 15 10
See also Nos. 1239/40.

**389.** Sao Francisco Power Station.

**1955.** Inauguration of Sao Francisco Hydro-Electric Station
920. **389.** 60 c. orange .. .. 15 10

**390.** Itutinga Power Plant.

**1955.** Inaug. of Itutinga Hydro-Electric Station.
921. **390.** 40 c. blue .. .. 15 10

**391.** Rotary Symbol and Rio Bay. **392.** Aviation Symbols.

**1955.** 50th Anniv of Rotary International.
922 **391** 2 cr. 70 green and black 1·60 10

**1955.** 3rd Aeronautical Congress, Sao Paulo.
923 **392** 60 c. grey and black .. 15 10

**393.** Fausto Cardoso Palace.

**1955.** Centenary of Aracaju.
924. **393.** 40 c. brown .. .. 10 10

**394.** Arms of Botucatu.

**1955.** Centenary of Botucatu.
925. **394.** 60 c. brown .. .. 10 10
926. 1 cr. 20 green .. .. 15 10

**395.** Young Athletes.

**396.** Marshal da Fonseca.

**1955.** 5th Children's Games, Rio de Janeiro.
927. **395.** 60 c. brown .. .. 20 10

**1955.** Birth Cent. of Marshal da Fonseca.
928 **396.** 60 c. violet .. .. 10 10

**397.** Congress Altar, Sail and Sugar-loaf Mountain.

**398.** Cardinal Masella.

**1955.** 36th Int. Eucharistic Congress.
929. **397.** 1 cr. 40 green .. .. 10 10
930. – 2 cr. 70 lake (St. Pascoal) 65 65

**1955.** Visit of Cardinal Masella (Papal Legate) to Eucharistic Congress.
931. **398.** 4 cr. 20 blue .. .. 1·25 15

**399.** Gymnasts.

**1955.** 7th Spring Games.
932. **399.** 60 c. mauve .. .. 20 10

**400.** Monteiro Lobato.

**401.** A. Lutz.

**1955.** Honouring M. Lobato (author).
933. **400.** 40 c. green .. .. 10 10

**1955.** Birth Centenary of Lutz (public health pioneer).
934. **401.** 60 c. green .. .. 15 10

**402.** Lt.-Col. T. C. Vilagran Cabrita.

**403.** Salto Grande Dam.

**1955.** Cent. of 1st Battalion of Engineers.
935. **402.** 60 c. blue .. .. 15 10

**1956.** Salto Grande Dam.
936. **403.** 60 c. red .. .. 15 10

**404.** **405.** Arms of Mococa.

**1956.** 18th Int. Geographical Congress Rio de Janeiro.
937. **404.** 1 cr. 20 blue .. .. 15 10

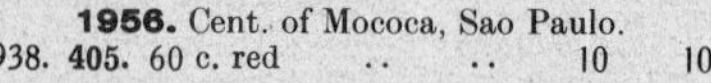

**1956.** Cent. of Mococa, Sao Paulo.
938. **405.** 60 c. red .. .. 10 10

**406.** Girls Running. **407.** Douglas DC-3 and Map.

**1956.** Sixth Children's Games.
939. **406.** 2 cr. 50 blue .. .. 65 10

**1956.** 25th Anniv. of National Air Mail.
940. **407.** 3 cr. 30 blue .. .. 95 10

**408.** Rescue Work.

**1956.** Centenary of Firemen's Corps, Rio de Janeiro.
941. **408.** 2 cr. 50 red .. .. 65 10

**409.** Franca Cathedral.

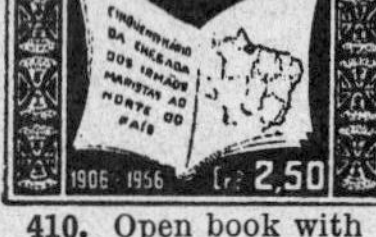

**410.** Open book with Inscription and Map.

**1956.** Centenary of City of Franca.
942. **409.** 2 cr. 50 blue .. .. 15 10

**1956.** 50th Anniv. of Arrival of Marist Brothers in N. Brazil.
943. **410.** 2 cr. 50 blue (postage) 15 10
944. – 3 cr. 30 purple (air) .. 15 10
DESIGN—VERT. 3 cr. 30, Father J. B. Marcelino Champagnat.

**411.** Hurdler.

**412.** Forest and Map of Brazil.

**414.** Commemorative Stamp from Panama. **413.** Baron da Bocaina and Express Letter.

**1956.** 8th Spring Games.
945. **411.** 2 cr. 50 red .. .. 95 10

**1956.** Afforestation Campaign.
946. **412.** 2 cr. 50 green .. .. 15 10

**1956.** Birth Cent. of Baron da Bocaina.
947. **413.** 2 cr. 50 brown .. .. 15 10

**1956.** Pan-American Congress. Panama.
948. **414.** 3 cr. 30 black & green 95 15

415. Santos Dumont's Biplane "14 bis".

**1956.** Air. Alberto Santos Dumont (aviation pioneer) Commemoration.

| | | | | |
|---|---|---|---|---|
| 949 | 415 | 3 cr. green .. .. | 1·60 | 15 |
| 950 | | 3 cr. 30 blue .. .. | 20 | 10 |
| 951 | | 4 cr. purple .. .. | 95 | 10 |
| 952 | | 6 cr. 50 brown .. | 20 | 10 |
| 953 | | 11 cr. 50 orange .. | 2·50 | 30 |

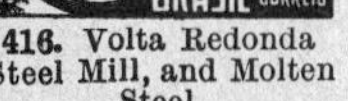

416. Volta Redonda Steel Mill, and Molten Steel. 417. J. E. Gomes da Silva (civil engineer).

**1957.** National Steel Company's Expansion Campaign.
955. **416.** 2 cr. 50 brown .. 25 10

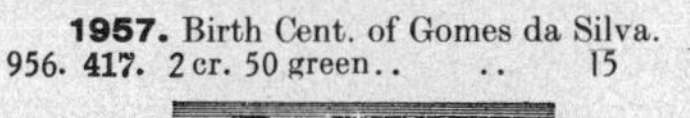

**1957.** Birth Cent. of Gomes da Silva.
956. **417.** 2 cr. 50 green .. .. 15 10

418. Allan Kardec, Code and Globe.

**1957.** Centenary of Spiritualism Code.
957. **418.** 2 cr. 50 brown .. 15 10

419. Young Gymnast. 420. Gen. Craveiro Lopes.

**1957.** Seventh Children's Games.
958. **419.** 2 cr. 50 lake .. .. 95 10

**1957.** Visit of President of Portugal.
959. **420.** 6 cr. 50 blue .. .. 95 10

421. Stamp of 1932. 422. Lord Baden-Powell.

**1957.** 25th Anniv. of Sao Paulo Revolutionary Government.
960. **421.** 2 cr. 50 red .. .. 10 10

**1957.** Air. Birth Cent. of Lord Baden-Powell.
961. **422.** 3 cr. 30 lake .. .. 95 10

423. Convent of Santo Antonio.

**1957.** 300th Anniv of Emancipation of Santo Antonio Province.
962 **423** 2 cr. 50 purple .. 15 10

424. Volleyball. 425. Basketball.

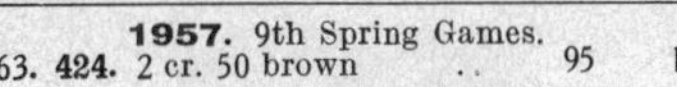

**1957.** 9th Spring Games.
963. **424.** 2 cr. 50 brown .. 95 10

**1957.** 2nd Women's World Basketball Championships.
964. **425.** 3 cr. 30 green & brown 95 10

426. U.N. Emblem, Map of Suez Canal and Soldier.

**1957.** Air. United Nations Day.
965. **426.** 5 cr. 30 blue .. .. 15 30

427. Count of Pinhal (founder), Arms and Locomotive. 428. Auguste Comte (philosopher).

**1957.** Cent. of City of San Carlos.
966. **427.** 2 cr. 50 red .. .. 60 30

**1957.** Death Centenary of Comte.
967. **428.** 2 cr. 50 brown .. 15 10

429. Sarapui Radio Station.

**1957.** Inaug. of Sarapui Radio Station.
968. **429.** 2 cr. 50 myrtle .. 15 10

430. Admiral Tamandare (founder) and "Almirante Tamandare" (cruiser). 431. Coffee Beans and Emblem.

**1957.** 150th Anniv. of Brazilian Navy.
969. **430.** 2 cr. 50 blue .. .. 50 10
970. – 3 cr. 30 green .. .. 60 10
DESIGN: 3 cr. 30, Aircraft-carrier "Minas Gerais".

**1957.** Cent. of City of Ribeirao Preto.
971. **431.** 2 cr. 50 red .. .. 35 10

432. King John VI of Portugal and Sail Merchantman.

**1958.** 150th Anniv. of Opening of Ports to Foreign Trade.
972. **432.** 2 cr. 50 purple .. 60 10

433. Bugler. 434. "Baronesa" Locomotive and Dom Pedro II Station, Rio de Janeiro.

**1958.** 150th Anniversary of Corps of Brazilian Marines.
973. **433.** 2 cr. 50 red .. .. 50 10

**1958.** Cent. of Central Brazil Railway.
974. **434.** 2 cr. 50 brown .. 60 20

435. High Court Building. 436. Brazilian Pavilion.

**1958.** 150th Anniv. of Military High Courts.
975. **435.** 2 cr. 50 green .. 15 10

**1958.** Brussels Int. Exn.
976. **436.** 2 cr. 50 blue .. .. 10 10

437. Marshal C. M. da Silva Ronden. 438. Jumping.

**1958.** Rondon Commem. and "Day of the Indian".
977. **437.** 2 cr. 50 purple .. 15 10

**1958.** Eighth Children's Games, Rio de Janeiro.
978. **438.** 2 cr. 50 red .. .. 50 10

439. Hydro-electric Station.

**1958.** Inauguration of Salto Grande Hydro-Electric Station.
979. **439.** 2 cr. 50 purple .. 15 10

440. National Printing Works. 441 Marshal Osorio.

**1958.** 150th Anniv. of National Printing Works.
980. **440.** 2 cr. 50 brown .. 10 10

**1958.** 150th Birth Anniv. of Marshal Osorio.
981. **441.** 2 cr. 50 violet .. 10 10

442. Pres. Morales of Honduras. 443. Botanical Gardens, Rio de Janeiro.

**1958.** Visit of President of Honduras.
982. **442.** 6 cr. 50 green .. .. 3·25 45

**1958.** 150th Anniv. of Botanical Gardens, Rio de Janeiro.
983. **443.** 2 cr. 50 green .. .. 10 10

444. Hoe, Rice and Cotton. 445. Prophet Joel.

**1958.** 50th Anniv. of Japanese Immigration.
984. **444.** 2 cr. 50 red .. .. 10 10

**1958.** Bicentenary of Basilica of the Good Jesus, Matosinhos.
985. **445.** 2 cr. 50 blue .. .. 35 10

446. Brazil on Globe.

**1958.** Int. Investments Conf., Belo Horizonte.
986. **446.** 2 cr. 50 brown .. 10 10

447. Tiradentes Palace, Rio de Janeiro. 448. J. B. Brandao (statesman).

**1958.** 47th Inter-Parliamentary Union Conf.
987. **447.** 2 cr. 50 brown .. 10 10

**1958.** Centenary of Brandao.
988. **448.** 2 cr. 50 brown .. 10 10

449. Dawn Palace, Brasilia.

**1958.** Construction of Presidential Palace.
989. **449.** 2 cr. 50 blue .. .. 10 10

450. Freighters.

**1958.** Govt. Aid for Brazilian Merchant Navy.
990. **450.** 2 cr. 50 blue .. .. 55 10

451. J. C. da Silva. 452. Pres. Gronchi.

**1958.** Birth Cent. of Da Silva (author).
991. **451.** 2 cr. 50 brown .. 10 10

**1958.** Visit of President of Italy.
992. **452.** 7 cr. blue .. .. 1·25 10

453. Archers. 454. Old People within Hour-glass.

**1958.** 10th Spring Games, Rio de Janeiro.
993. **453.** 2 cr. 50 orange .. 65 10

**1958.** Old People's Day.
994. **454.** 2 cr. 50 lake .. .. 15 10

455. Machado de Assis (writer). 456. Pres. Vargas with oily Hand.

**1958.** 50th Death Anniv. of Machado de Assis.
995. **455.** 2 cr. 50 brown .. 10 10

**1958.** 5th Anniv. of State Petroleum Law.
996. **456.** 2 cr. 50 blue .. .. 10 10

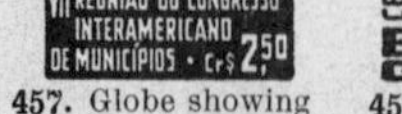

**457.** Globe showing Brazil and the Americas.

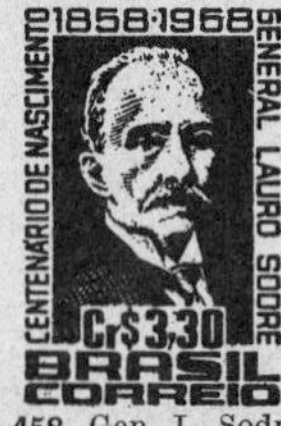

**458.** Gen. L. Sodre.

**1958.** 7th Inter-American Municipalities Congress, Rio de Janeiro.
997. **457.** 2 cr. 50 blue .. .. 50 10

**1958.** Birth Centenary of Sodre.
998. **458.** 3 cr. 30 green .. .. 10 10

**459.** U.N. Emblem.

**460.** Footballer.

**1958.** 10th Anniv. of Human Rights Declaration.
999. **459.** 2 cr. 50 blue .. .. 10 10

**1959.** World Football Cup Victory, 1958.
1000. **460.** 3 cr. 30 brown & green 95 10

**461.** Map and Railway Line.

**462.** Pres. Sukarno.

**1959.** Centenary of Opening of Patos-Campina Grande Railway.
1001. **461.** 2 cr. 50 brown .. 20 15

**1959.** Visit of President of Indonesia.
1002. **462.** 2 cr. 50 blue .. .. 10 10

**463.** Basketball Player.

**464.** King John VI of Portugal.

**465.** Polo Players.

**1959.** Air. World Basketball Championships 1959.
1003. **463.** 3 cr. 30 brown & blue 65 10

**1959.**
1004. **464.** 2 cr. 50 red .. .. 15 10

**1959.** Children's Games.
1005. **465.** 2 cr. 50 brown .. 20 10

**466.** Dockside Scene.

**467.** Church Organ, Diamantina.

**1959.** Rehabilitation of National Ports Law.
1006. **466.** 2 cr. 50 green .. 15 10

**1959.** Bicent. of Carmelite Order in Brazil.
1007. **467.** 3 cr. 30 lake .. .. 10 10

**468.** Dom J. S. de Souza (First Archbishop).

**469.** Sugar-loaf Mountain and Road.

**1959.** Birth Cent. of Archbishop of Diamantina.
1008. **468.** 2 cr. 50 brown .. 10 10

**1959.** 11th Int. Roads Congress.
1009. **469.** 3 cr. 30 blue and green 15 10

**470.** Londrina and Parana.

**471.** Putting the Shot.

**473.** Globe and "Snipe" Class Yachts.

**472.** Daedalus.

**1959.** 25th Anniv. of Londrina.
1010. **470.** 2 cr. 50 green .. 10 10

**1959.** Spring Games.
1011. **471.** 2 cr. 50 mauve .. 65 10

**1959.** Air. Aviation Week.
1012 **472** 3 cr. 30 blue .. .. 10 10

**1959.** World Sailing Championships, Porto Alegre.
1013. **473.** 6 cr. 50 green .. 10 10

**474.** Lusignan Cross and Arms of Salvador, Bahia.

**475.** Gunpowder Factory.

**1959.** 4th Int. Brazilian-Portuguese Study Conference, Bahia University.
1014. **474.** 6 cr. 50 blue .. .. 10 10

**1959.** 50th Anniv. of President Vargas Gunpowder Factory.
1015. **475.** 3 cr. 30 brown .. 10 10

**476.**

**477.** Sud Aviation Caravelle.

**1959.** Thanksgiving Day.
1016. **476.** 2 cr. 50 blue .. 50 10

**1959.** Air. Inaug. of "Caravelle" Airliners by Brazilian National Airlines.
1017. **477.** 6 cr. 50 blue .. .. 15 10

**478.** Burning Bush.

**1959.** Cent. of Presbyterian Work in Brazil.
1018. **478.** 3 cr. 30 green .. 10 10

**479.** P. da Silva and "Schistosoma mansoni".

**1959.** 50th Anniv. of Discovery and Identification of "Schistosoma Mansoni" (Fluke).
1019. **479.** 2 cr. 50 purple. .. 50 10

**480.** L. de Matos and Church.

**481.** Pres. Lopez Mateos of Mexico.

**1960.** Birth Centenary of Luiz de Matos (Christian evangelist).
1020. **480.** 3 cr. 30 brown .. 10 10

**1960.** Air. Visit of Mexican President.
1021. **481.** 6 cr. 50 brown .. 10 10

**482.** Pres. Eisenhower.

**483.** Dr. L. Zamenhof.

**1960.** Air. Visit of United States President.
1022. **482.** 6 cr. 50 brown .. 15 10

**1960.** Birth Centenary of Zamenhof (inventor of Esperanto).
1023. **483.** 6 cr. 50 green .. 35 10

**484.** Adel Pinto (engineer).

**485.** "Care of Refugees".

**1960.** Birth Cent. of Adel Pinto.
1024. **484.** 11 cr. 50 red .. .. 15 10

**1960.** Air. World Refugee Year.
1025. **485.** 6 cr. 50 blue .. .. 20 10

**486.** Plan of Brasilia.

**1960.** Inaug. of Brasilia as Capital.
1026. – 2 cr. 50 green (postage) 15 10
1027. – 3 cr. 30 violet (air) .. 10 10
1028. – 4 cr. blue .. .. 1·25 10
1029. – 6 cr. 50 mauve .. 10 10
1030. **486.** 11 cr. 50 brown .. 15 10

DESIGNS—Outlines representing: HORIZ. 2 cr. 50, President's Palace of the Plateau. 3 cr. 30, Parliament Buildings. 4 cr. Cathedral. VERT. 6 cr. 50, Tower. HORIZ. (105×47 mm.)

**487.** Congress Emblem.

**1960.** Air. 7th National Eucharistic Congress, Curitiba.
1032. **487.** 3 cr. 30 mauve .. 10 10

**488.** Congress Emblem, Sugar-loaf Mountain and Cross.

**489.** Boy Scout.

**1960.** Air. 10th Baptist World Alliance Congress, Rio de Janeiro.
1033. **488.** 6 cr. 50 blue .. .. 10 10

**1960.** Air. 50th Anniv. of Scouting in Brazil.
1034. **489.** 3 cr. 30 orange .. 10 10

**490.** "Agriculture". **491.** Caravel. **492.** P. de Frontin.

**1960.** Centenary of Brazilian Ministry of Agriculture.
1035. **490.** 2 cr. 50 brown .. 15 10

**1960.** Air. 5th Death Cent. of Prince Henry the Navigator.
1036. **491.** 6 cr. 50 black .. 30 10

**1960.** Birth Centenary of Paulo de Frontin (engineer).
1037. **492.** 2 cr. 50 orange .. 10 10

**493.** Locomotive Piston Gear.

**494.** Athlete.

**495.**

**1960.** 10th Pan-American Railways Congress.
1038. **493.** 2 cr. 50 blue .. .. 30 10

**1960.** 12th Spring Games.
1039. **494.** 2 cr. 50 turquoise .. 15 10

**1960.** World Volleyball Championships.
1040. **495.** 11 cr. blue .. .. 30 10

**496.** Maria Bueno in play.

**1960.** Air. Maria Bueno's Wimbledon Tennis Victories, 1959–60.
1041. **496.** 6 cr. brown .. .. 15 10

**497.** Exhibition Emblem.

**1960.** Int. Industrial and Commercial Exn., Rio de Janeiro.
1042. **497.** 2 cr. 50 brown & yell. 10 10

498. War Memorial, Rio do Janeiro. 499. Pylon and Map.

**1960.** Air. Return of Ashes of World War II Heroes from Italy.
1043. **498.** 3 cr. 30 lake .. .. 15 10

**1961.** Air. Inauguration of Tres Marias Hydro-electric Station.
1044. **499.** 3 cr. 30 mauve .. 15 10

500. Emperor Haile Selassie. 501. Sacred Book and Map of Brazil.

**1961.** Visit of Emperor of Ethiopia.
1045. **500.** 2 cr. 50 brown .. 10 10

**1961.** 50th Anniv. of Sacre-Coeur de Marie College.
1046. **501.** 2 cr. 50 blue .. .. 15 10

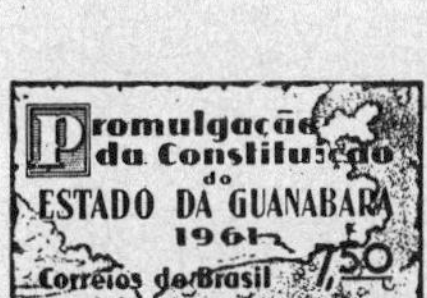
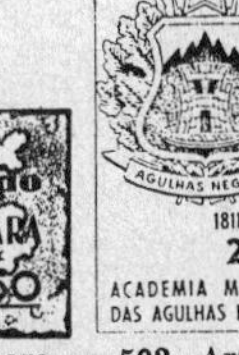
502. Map of Guanabara State. 503. Arms of Academy.

**1961.** Promulgation of Guanabara Constitution.
1047. **502.** 7 cr. 50 brown .. 35 10

**1961.** 150th Anniv. of Agulhas Negras Military Academy.
1048. **503.** 2 cr. 50 green .. 20 10
1049. – 3 cr. 30 red .. .. 10 10
DESIGN: 3 cr. 30, Military cap and sabre.

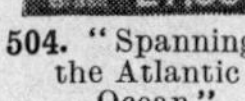

504. "Spanning the Atlantic Ocean". 505. View of Ouro Preto.

**1961.** Visit of Foreign Minister to Senegal.
1050. **504.** 27 cr. blue .. .. 95 10

**1961.** 250th Anniv. of Ouro Preto.
1051. **505.** 1 cr. orange .. .. 10 10

506. Arsenal. Rio de Janeiro.

507. Coffee Plant.

508. Tagore. 509. 280 r. Stamp of 1861 and Map of France.

**1961.** 150th Anniv. of Rio de Janeiro Arsenal.
1052. **506.** 5 cr. brown .. .. 45 10

**1961.** Int. Coffee Convention, Rio de Janeiro.
1053. **507.** 20 cr. brown .. .. 1·90 10

**1960.** Birth Centenary of Rabindranath Tagore (poet).
1054. **508.** 10 cr. mauve .. 50 10

**1961.** "Goat's Eyes" Stamp Centenary.
1055. **509.** 10 cr. red .. .. 1·25 10
1056. – 20 cr. orange .. 3·75 10
DESIGN: 20 cr. 430 r. stamp and map of the Netherlands.

510. Cloudburst. 511. Pinnacle, Rope and Haversack.

**1962.** World Meteorological Day.
1057. **510.** 10 cr. brown .. .. 1·25 10

**1962.** 50th Anniv. of 1st Ascent of "Finger of God" Mountain.
1058. **511.** 8 cr. green .. .. 10 10

512. Dr. G. Vianna and parasites.

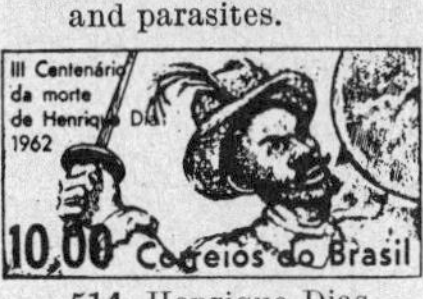
514. Henrique Dias (patriot). 513. Campaign Emblem.

**1962.** 50th Anniv. of Vianna's Cure for Leishman's Disease.
1059. **512.** 8 cr. blue .. .. 20 10

**1962.** Air. Malaria Eradication.
1060. **513.** 21 cr. blue .. .. 10 10

**1962.** 300th Death Anniv. of Dias.
1061. **514.** 10 cr. purple .. .. 15 10

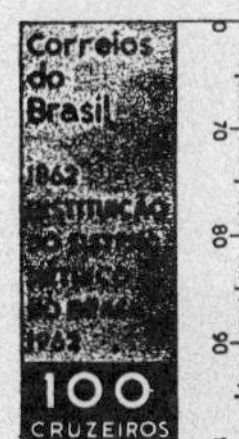

515. Metric Measure. 516. "Snipe" Sailing-boats.

**1962.** Centenary of Brazil's Adoption of Metric System.
1062. **515.** 100 cr. red .. .. 95 10

**1962.** 13th "Snipe" Class Sailing Championships, Rio de Janeiro.
1063. **516.** 8 cr. turquoise .. 20 10

517. J. Mesquita and Newspaper "O Estado de Sao Paulo".

519. Brasilia. 518. Empress Leopoldina.

**1962.** Birth Cent. of Mesquita (journalist and founder of "O Estado de Sao Paulo").
1064. **517.** 8 cr. bistre .. .. 65 10

**1962.** 140th Anniv. of Independence.
1065. **518.** 8 cr. mauve .. .. 15 10

**1962.** 51st Interparliamentary Conference, Brasilia.
1066. **519.** 10 cr. orange .. 40 10

520. Foundry Ladle. 521. U.P.A.E. Emblem.

**1962.** Inaug. of "Usiminas" (national iron and steel foundry).
1067. **520.** 8 cr. orange .. .. 10 10

**1962.** 50th Anniv. of Postal Union of the Americas and Spain.
1068. **521.** 8 cr. mauve .. .. 10 10

522. Emblems of Industry. 523. Q. Bocaiuva. 524. Footballer.

**1962.** 10th Anniv. of National Bank.
1069. **522.** 10 cr. turquoise .. 15 10

**1962.** 50th Death Anniv. of Bocaiuva (journalist and patriot).
1070. **523.** 8 cr. brown .. .. 10 10

**1962.** Brazil's Victory in World Football Championships, 1962.
1071. **524.** 10 cr. turquoise .. 1·25 10

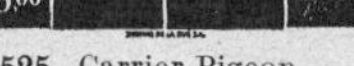

525. Carrier Pigeon. 526. Dr. S. Neiva (first Brazilian P.M.G.).

**1962.** Tercent. of Brazilian Posts.
1072. **525.** 8 cr. multicoloured .. 10 10

**1963.**
1073. **526.** 8 cr. violet .. .. 20 10
1073a. – 30 cr. turquoise (Euclides da Cunha) 2·50 10
1073b. – 50 cr. brown (Prof. A. Moreira da Costa Lima) 1·90 10
1073c. – 100 cr. blue (G. Dias) 75 10
1073d. – 200 cr. red (Tiradentes) 3·75 10
1073e. – 500 cr. brown (Emperor Pedro I) 15·00 20
1073f. – 1000 cr. blue (Emperor Pedro II) 19·00 25

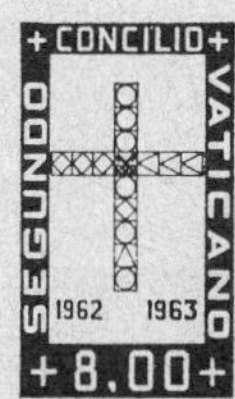
527. Rockets and "Dish" Aerial. 528. Cross.

**1963.** Int. Aeronautics and Space Exn., Sao Paulo.
1074. **527.** 21 cr. blue .. .. 15 10

**1963.** Ecumenical Council, Vatican City.
1075. **528.** 8 cr. purple .. .. 10 10

529. "abc" Symbol. 530. Basketball. 531. Torch Emblem.

**1963.** National Education Week.
1076. **529.** 8 cr. blue .. .. 10 10

**1963.** 4th World Basketball Championships.
1077. **530.** 8 cr. mauve .. .. 50 10

**1963.** 4th Pan-American Games, Sao Paulo.
1078. **531.** 10 cr. red .. .. 65 10

532. "OEA" and Map. 533. J. B. de Andrada e Silva.

**1963.** 15th Anniv. of Organization of American States.
1079. **532.** 10 cr. orange .. 50 10

**1963.** Birth Bicent. of Jose B. de Andrada e Silva ("Father of Independence")
1080. **533.** 8 cr. bistre .. .. 10 10

534. Campaign Emblem.

**1963.** Freedom from Hunger.
1081. **534.** 10 cr. blue .. .. 50 10

535. Centenary Emblem. 536. J. Caetano. 537. "Atomic" Development.

**1963.** Red Cross Cent.
1082. **535.** 8 cr. red and yellow .. 20 10

**1963.** Death Cent. of Joao Caetano (actor).
1083. **536.** 8 cr. black .. .. 10 10

**1963.** 1st Anniv. of Nat. Nuclear Energy Commission.
1084. **537.** 10 cr. mauve .. 50 10

538. Throwing the Hammer. 539. Pres. Tito. 540. Cross and Map.

**1963.** Int. Students' Games, Porto Alegre.
1085. **538.** 10 cr. black and grey 65 10

**1963.** Visit of President Tito of Yugoslavia.
1086. **539.** 80 cr. drab .. 1·25 10

**1963.** 8th Int. Leprology Congress, Rio de Janeiro.
1087. **540.** 8 cr. turquoise .. 10 10

541. Petroleum Installations.

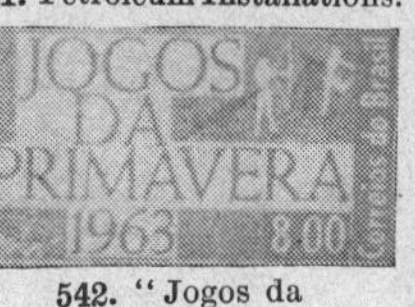
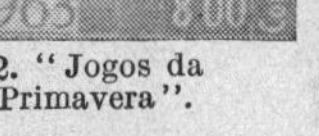

542. "Jogos da Primavera". 543. A. Borges de Medeiros.

**1963.** 10th Anniv. of Nat. Petroleum Industry.
1088. **541.** 8 cr. green .. .. 10 10

**1963.** Spring Games.
1089. **542.** 8 cr. yellow .. 10 10

**1963.** Birth Centenary of A. Borges de Medeiros (politician).
1090. **543.** 8 cr. brown .. .. 10 10

544. Bridge of Sao Joao del Rey.

545. Dr. A. Alvim.

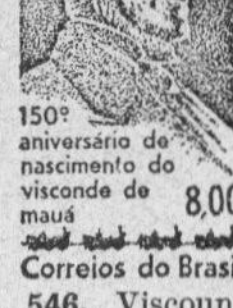
546. Viscount de Maua.

**1963.** 250th Anniv. of Sao Jao del Rey.
1091. **544.** 8 cr. blue .. .. 10 10

**1963.** Birth Centenary of Dr. Alvaro Alvim (scientist).
1092. **545.** 8 cr. slate .. .. 10 10

**1963.** 150th Birth Anniv. of Viscount de Maua (founder of Brazilian Railway).
1093. **546.** 8 cr. mauve .. .. 30 20

547. Cactus.

548. C. Netto.

**1964.** 10th Anniv. of North-East Bank.
1094. **547.** 8 cr. green .. .. 10 10

**1964.** Birth Cent. of Coelho Netto (author).
1095. **548.** 8 cr. violet .. .. 10 10

549. L. Muller.

550. Child with Spoon.

**1964.** Birth Cent. of Lauro Muller (patriot).
1096. **549.** 8 cr. red .. .. 10 10

**1964.** Schoolchildren's Nourishment Week.
1097. **550.** 8 cr. yellow and brown 10 10

551. "Chalice" (carved rock), Vila Velha, Parana.

552. A. Kardec (author).

**1964.** Tourism.
1098. **551.** 80 cr. red .. .. 65 10

**1964.** Cent. of Spiritual Code, "O Evangelho".
1099. **552.** 30 cr. green .. .. 95 10

553. Pres. Lubke.

554. Pope John XXIII.

**1964.** Visit of President Lubke of West Germany.
1100. **553.** 100 cr. brown .. 1·25 10

**1964.** Pope John Commem.
1101. **554.** 20 cr. lake .. .. 20 10

555. Pres. Senghor.

556. "Visit Rio de Janeiro".

**1964.** Visit of Pres. Senghor of Senegal.
1102. **555.** 20 cr. sepia .. .. 15 10

**1964.** 400th Anniv. (1965) of Rio de Janeiro.
1103. **556.** 15 cr. blue and orange 25 10
1104. – 30 cr. red and blue .. 40 10
1105. – 30 cr. black and blue 1·00 40
1106. – 35 cr. black and orange 15 10
1107. – 100 cr. brown and green on yellow .. .. 65 10
1108. – 200 cr. red and green 3·75 10

DESIGNS: As Type **556**—HORIZ. 30 cr. (No. 1105), Tramway viaduct. 200 cr. Copacabana Beach. VERT. 35 cr. Estacio de Sa's statue. 100 cr. Church of Our Lady of the Rock. SMALLER. (24½×37 mm.): 30 cr. (No. 1104), Statue of St. Sebastian.

558. Pres. De Gaulle.

559. Pres. Kennedy.

560. Nahum (statue).

**1964.** Visit of Pres. De Gaulle.
1110. **558.** 100 cr. brown .. 65 10

**1964.** Pres. Kennedy Commem.
1111. **559.** 100 cr. black .. 15 15

**1964.** 150th Death Anniv. of A. F. Lisboa (sculptor).
1112. **560.** 10 cr. black .. .. 30 10

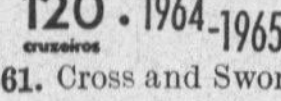
561. Cross and Sword.

562. V. Brazil (scientist).

**1965.** 1st Anniv. of Democratic Revolution.
1113. **561.** 120 cr. grey .. .. 15 10

**1965.** Birth Centenary of Vital Brazil.
1114. **562.** 120 cr. orange .. 1·25 10

563. Shah of Iran.

564. Marshal Rondon and Map.

**1965.** Visit of Shah of Iran.
1115. **563.** 120 cr. red .. .. 65 10

**1965.** Birth Centenary of Marshal C. M. da S. Rondon.
1116. **564.** 30 cr. purple .. .. 20 10

565. Lions Emblem.

566. I.T.U. Emblem and Symbols.

**1965.** Brazilian Lions Clubs National Convention, Rio de Janeiro.
1117. **565.** 35 cr. black and lilac 15 10

**1965.** I.T.U. Cent.
1118. **566.** 120 cr. green & yellow 65 10

567. E. Pessoa.

568. Barroso's Statue.

**1965.** Birth Cent. of Epitacio Pessoa.
1119. **567.** 35 cr. slate .. .. 10 10

**1965.** Cent. of Naval Battle of Riachuelo.
1120. **568.** 30 cr. blue .. .. 15 10

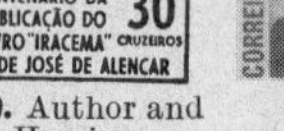
569. Author and Heroine.

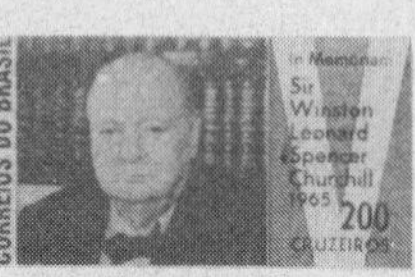
570. Sir Winston Churchill.

**1965.** Centenary of Publication of Jose de Alencar's "Iracema".
1121. **569.** 30 cr. purple .. .. 15 10

**1965.** Churchill Commem.
1122. **570.** 200 cr. slate .. .. 1·25 10

571. Scout Badge and Emblem of Rio's 400th Anniv.

572. I.C.Y. Emblem.

**1965.** 1st Pan-American Scout Jamboree, Rio de Janeiro.
1123 **571** 30 r. multicoloured .. 1·10 10

**1965.** Int. Co-operation Year.
1124. **572.** 120 cr. black & blue .. 95 10

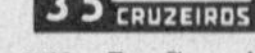
573. L. Correia.

574. Exhibition Emblem.

**1965.** Birth Cent. of Leoncia Correia (poet).
1125. **573.** 35 cr. green .. .. 10 10

**1965.** Sao Paulo Biennale (Art Exn.).
1126. **574.** 30 cr. red .. .. 10 10

575. President Saragat.

576. Grand Duke and Duchess of Luxembourg.

**1965.** Visit of President of Italy.
1127. **575.** 100 cr. green on pink 15 10

**1965.** Visit of Grand Duke and Duchess of Luxembourg.
1128. **576.** 100 cr. brown .. 15 10

577. Curtiss Fledgling on Map.

578. O.E.A. Emblem.

**1965.** Aviation Week and 3rd Philatelic Exn.
1129. **577.** 35 cr. blue .. .. 15 10

**1965.** Inter-American Conf., Rio de Janeiro.
1130. **578.** 100 cr. black and blue 45 10

579. King Baudouin and Queen Fabiola.

580. Coffee Beans.

**1965.** Visit of King and Queen of the Belgians.
1131. **579.** 100 cr. slate .. .. 50 10

**1965.** Brazilian Coffee.
1132. **580.** 30 cr. brown on cream 65 10

581. F. A. Varnhagen.

583. Sister and Globe.

582. Emblem and Map.

**1965.** Air. 150th Birth Anniv. of Francisco Varnhagen (historian).
1133. **581.** 45 cr. brown .. .. 15 10

**1966.** Air. 5th Anniv. of "Alliance for Progress".
1134. **582.** 120 cr. bl. & turq. .. 95 10

**1966.** Air. Centenary of Dorothean Sisters Educational Work in Brazil.
1135. **583.** 35 cr. violet .. .. 10 10

584. Loading Ore at Quayside.

585. "Steel".

**1966.** Inauguration of Rio Doce Iron-ore Terminal Tubarao, Espirito Santo.
1136. **584.** 110 cr. blk. & bis. .. 50 10

**1966.** Silver Jubilee of National Steel Company.
1137. **585.** 30 cr. black on orange .. .. 25 10

586. Prof. Rocha Lima.

587. Battle Scene.

**1966.** 50th Anniv. of Professor Lima's Discovery of the Characteristics of "Rickettsia prowazeki" (cause of typhus fever).
1138. **586.** 30 cr. turquoise .. 65 10

**1966.** Cent. of Battle of Tuiuti.
1139. **587.** 30 cr. green .. .. 65 10

588. " The Sacred Face ". 589. Mariz e Barros.

**1966.** Air. "Concilio Vaticano II".
1140. **588.** 45 cr. brown.. .. 10 10

**1966.** Air. Death Centenary of Commander Mariz e Barros.
1141. **589.** 35 cr. brown.. .. 15 10

590. Decade Symbol. 591. Pres. Shazar.

**1966.** Int. Hydrological Decade.
1142. **590.** 100 cr. blue & brown 65 10

**1966.** Visit of President Shazar of Israel.
1143. **591.** 100 cr. blue .. .. 95 10

592. "Youth". 593. Imperial Academy of Fine Arts.

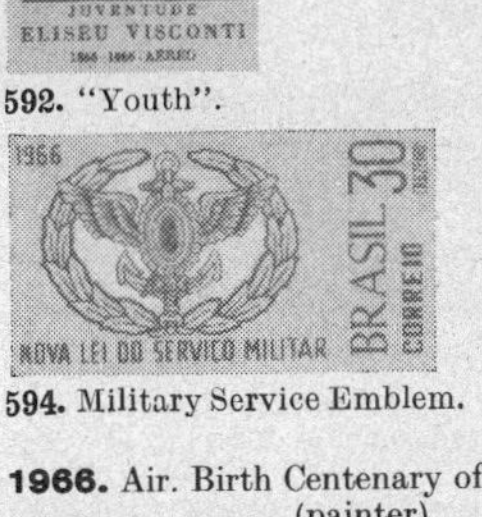


594. Military Service Emblem. 595. R. Dario.

**1966.** Air. Birth Centenary of Eliseu Visconti (painter).
1144. **592.** 120 cr. brown .. 1·90 10

**1966.** 150th Anniv. of French Art Mission's Arrival in Brazil.
1145. **593.** 100 cr. brown .. 1·25 10

**1966.** New Military Service Law.
1146. **594.** 30 cr. blue & yellow.. 15 10

**1966.** 50th Death Anniv. of Ruben Dario (Nicaraguan poet).
1148. **595.** 100 cr. purple .. 65 10

596. Santarem Candlestick. 597. Arms of Santa Cruz do Sul.

**1966.** Cent. of Goeldi Museum.
1149. **596.** 30 cr. brown on salmon 15 10

**1966.** 1st National Tobacco Exn., Santa Cruz.
1150. **597.** 30 cr. green .. .. 15 10

598. U.N.E.S.C.O. Emblem. 599. Capt. A. C. Pinto and Map.

**1966.** 20th Anniv. of U.N.E.S.C.O.
1151. **598.** 120 cr. black .. 40 10

**1966.** Bicent. of Arrival of Captain A. C. Pinto.
1153. **599.** 30 cr. red .. .. 15 10

600. Lusignan Cross and Southern Cross. 601. Madonna and Child.

**1966.** "Lubrapex 1966". Stamp Exn. Rio de Janeiro.
1154. **600.** 100 cr. green .. 25 10

**1966.** Christmas.
1155. **601.** 30 cr. green .. .. 20 10
1156. – 35 cr. blue & salmon 20 15
1157. – 150 cr. pink and blue 85 85
DESIGN—DIAMOND—(34 × 34 mm.). 35 cr. Madonna and child (different). VERT. (46 × 103 mm.). 150 cr. As 35 cr. inscr. " Pax Hominibus " but not " Brazil Correio ".

602. Arms of Laguna.

**1967.** Centenary of Laguna Postal and Telegraphic Agency.
1158. **602.** 60 cr. sepia .. .. 10 10

603. Railway Bridge.

**1967.** Cent. of Santos-Jundiai Railway.
1159. **603.** 50 cr. orange .. 75 15

604. Polish Cross and "Black Madonna".

**1967.** Polish Millennium.
1160. **604.** 50 cr. red, bl. & yell... 50 10

605. Research Rocket. 606. Anita Garibaldi.

**1967.** World Meteorological Day.
1161. **605.** 50 cr. black and blue 95 10

Currency reform. 100 (old) cruzeiros = 1 (new) cruzeiro.

**1967.**
1162. – 1 c. blue .. .. 10 10
1163. – 2 c. red .. .. 10 10
1164. – 3 c. green .. .. 15 10
1165. **606.** 5 c. black .. .. 15 10
1166. – 6 c. brown .. .. 15 10
1167. – 10 c. green .. 1·00 10
PORTRAITS: 1 c. Mother Angelica. 2 c. Marilia de Dirceu. 3 c. Dr. R. Lobato. 6 c. Ana Neri. 10 c. Darci Vargas.

607. " VARIG 40 Years". 608. Lions Emblem and Globes.

**1967.** 40th Anniv. of Varig Airlines.
1171. **607.** 6 c. black and blue.. 15 10

**1967.** 50th Anniv. of Lions Int.
1172. **608.** 6 c. green .. .. 25 10

609. "Madonna and Child". 610. Prince Akihito and Princess Michiko.

**1967.** Mothers' Day.
1174. **609.** 5 c. violet .. .. 10 10

**1967.** Visit of Crown Prince and Princess of Japan.
1176. **610.** 10 c. black and red 15 10

611. Radar Aerial and Pigeon. 612. Brother Vicente do Salvador.

**1967.** Inauguration of Communications Ministry, Brasilia.
1177. **611.** 10 c. blk. & mve. .. 15 10

**1967.** 400th Birth. Anniv. of Brother Vicente do Salvador (founder of Franciscan Brotherhood, Rio de Janeiro).
1178. **612.** 5 c. brown .. .. 15 10

613. Emblem and Members. 614. Mobius Symbol.

**1967.** National 4-S (" 4-H ") Clubs Day.
1179. **613.** 5 c. green and black.. 15 10

**1967.** 6th Brazilian Mathematical Congress. Rio de Janeiro.
1180. **614.** 5 c. black and blue .. 15 10

615. Fish and " Waves ".

**1967.** Bicentenary of Piracicaba.
1181. **615.** 5 c. black and blue.. 20 10

616. Papal Arms and " Golden Rose ". 617. General A. de Sampaio.

**1967.** Pope Paul's " Golden Rose " Offering to Our Lady of Fatima.
1182. **616.** 20 c. mauve & yellow 95 10

**1967.** Gen. Sampaio Commem.
1183. **617.** 5 c. blue .. .. 15 10

618. King Olav of Norway. 619. Sun and Rio de Janeiro.

**1967.** Visit of King Olav.
1184. **618.** 10 c. brown .. .. 15 10

**1967.** Meeting of Int. Monetary Fund, Rio de Janeiro.
1185. **619.** 10 c. black and red.. 15 10

620. N. Pecanha (statesman). 621. Our Lady of the Apparition and Basilica.

**1967.** Birth Cent. of Nilo Pecanha.
1186. **620.** 5 c. purple .. .. 10 10

**1967.** 250th Anniv. of Discovery of Statue of Our Lady of the Apparition.
1187. **621.** 5 c. blue and ochre.. 15 10

622. "Song Bird". 623. Balloon, Rocket and Airplane.

**1967.** Int. Song Festival.
1189. **622.** 20 c. multicoloured.. 30 10

**1967.** Aviation Week.
1190. **623.** 10 c. blue .. .. 30 10

624. Pres. Venceslau Braz. 625. Rio Carnival.

**1967.**
1192. – 10 c. blue .. .. 15 10
1193. – 20 c. brown .. 85 10
1195. **624.** 50 c. black .. .. 9·50 10
1198. – 1 cr. purple.. .. 15·00 10
1199. – 2 cr. green .. .. 1·90 10
Portraits of Brazilian Presidents: 10 c. Arthur Bernardes. 20 c. Campos Salles. 1 cr. Washington Luiz. 2 cr. Castello Branco.

**1967.** Int. Tourist Year.
1200. **625.** 10 c. multicoloured.. 15 10

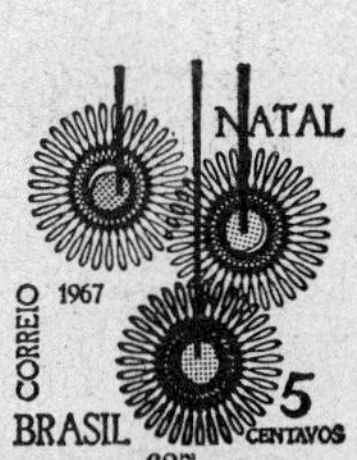


626. Sailor, Anchor and "Almirante Tamandare" (cruiser). 627. Christmas Decorations.

**1967.** Navy Week.
1202. **626.** 10 c. blue .. .. 30 15

**1967.** Christmas.
1203. **627.** 5 c. multicoloured .. 15 10

**628.** O. Bilac (poet), Aircraft, Tank and Aircraft-carrier "Minas Gerais".

**629.** J. Rodrigues de Carvalho.

**1967.** Reservists Day.
1204. **628.** 5 c. blue and yellow .. 30 15

**1967.** Birth Centenary of Jose Rodriques de Carvalho (jurist and writer).
1205. **629.** 10 c. green .. .. 10 10

**630.** O. Rangel.

**1968.** Birth Cent. of Orlando Rangel (chemist).
1206. **630.** 5 c. black and blue .. 15 10

**631.** Madonna and Diver.

**632.** Map of Free Zone.

**1968.** 250th Anniv. of Paranagua Underwater Exploration.
1207. **631.** 10 c. green and slate 20 10

**1968.** Manaus Free Zone.
1208. **632.** 10 c. red, grn. & yellow 15 10

**633.** Human Rights Emblem.

**634.** Paul Harris.

**1968.** 20th Anniv. of Declaration of Human Rights.
1209. **633.** 10 c. red and blue .. 10 10

**GUM.** All the following issues to No. 1425 are without gum, except where otherwise stated.

**1968.** Birth Centenary of Paul Harris (founder of Rotary International).
1210. **634.** 20 c. brown and green 50 20

**635.** College Arms.

**1968.** Cent. of St. Luiz College. With gum.
1211. **635.** 10 c. gold, blue & red 25 10

**636.** Cabral and his Fleet, 1500

**1968.** 500th Birth Anniv. of Pedro Cabral (discoverer of Brazil).
1212. **636.** 10 c. multicoloured .. 30 15
1213. – 20 c. multicoloured .. 45 20
DESIGN: 20 c. "The First Mass" (C. Portinari).

**637.** "Maternity" (after H. Bernardeli).

**638.** Harpy Eagle.

**1968.** Mother's Day.
1214. **637.** 5 c. multicoloured .. 20 15

**1968.** 150th Anniv. of National Museum. With gum.
1215. **638.** 20 c. black and blue 90 20

**639.** Women of Brazil and Japan.

**1968.** Inauguration of "VARIG" Brazil–Japan Air Service.
1216. **639.** 10 c. multicoloured 25 15

**640.** Horse-racing.

**1968.** Cent. of Brazilian Jockey Club.
1217. **640.** 10 c. multicoloured .. 20 10

**641.** Quadrille Wren.

**1968.** Birds.
1218. – 10 c. multicoloured .. 50 25
1219. **641.** 20 c. brown, green and blue .. .. 1·50 25
1220. – 50 c. multicoloured .. 1·90 40
DESIGNS–VERT. 10 c. Red-crested cardinal. 50 c. Amazonian royal flycatcher.

**642.** Ancient Post-box.

**643.** Marshal E. Luiz Mallet.

**1968.** Stamp Day. With gum.
1221. **642.** 5 c. black green and yellow .. .. 10 10

**1968.** Mallet Commem. With gum.
1222. **643.** 10 c. lilac .. .. 10 10

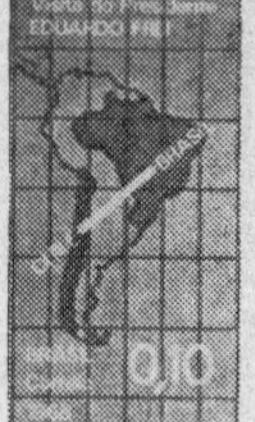

**644.** Map of South America.

**645.** Lyceum Badge.

**1968.** Visit of Chilean President. With gum.
1223. **644.** 10 c. orange .. .. 10 10

**1968.** Centenary of Portuguese Literacy Lyceum (High School). With gum.
1224. **645.** 5 c. green and pink 10 10

**646.** Map and Telex Tape.

**1968.** "Telex Service for 25th City (Curitiba)". With gum.
1225. **646.** 20 c. green and yell. 20 10

**647.** Soldiers on Medallion.

**648.** "Cock" shaped as Treble Clef.

**1968.** 8th American Armed Forces Conf.
1226. **647.** 5 c. black and blue .. 15 10

**1968.** 3rd. Int. Song Festival, Rio de Janeiro.
1227. **648.** 6 c. multicoloured .. 25 15

**649.** "Petrobras" Refinery.

**650.** Boy walking towards Rising Sun.

**1968.** 15th Anniv. of National Petroleum Industry.
1228. **649.** 6 c. multicoloured .. 25 15

**1968.** U.N.I.C.E.F.
1229. **650.** 5 c. black and blue .. 20 15
1230. – 10 c. blk., red & blue 20 15
1231. – 20 c. multicoloured .. 25 15
DESIGNS–HORIZ. 10 c. Hand protecting child. VERT. 20 c. Young girl in plaits.

**651.** Children with Books.

**1968.** Book Week.
1232. **651.** 5 c. multicoloured .. 15 10

**652.** W.H.O. Emblem and Flags.

**1968.** 20th Anniv. of W.H.O.
1233. **652.** 20 c. multicoloured .. 30 15

**653.** J. B. Debret (painter).

**1968.** Birth Bicentenary of Jean Baptiste Debret (1st issue).
1234. **653.** 10 c. black and yellow 20 10
See Nos. 1273/4.

**654.** Queen Elizabeth II.

**1968.** State Visit of Queen Elizabeth II.
1235. **654.** 70 c. multicoloured .. 1·25 50

**655.** Brazilian Flag.

**656.** F. Braga and part of "Hymn of National Flag".

**1968.** Brazilian Flag Day.
1236. **655.** 10 c. multicoloured .. 20 15

**1968.** Birth Centenary of Francisco Braga (composer).
1237. **656.** 5 c. purple .. .. 25 10

**657.** Clasped Hands.

**1968.** Blood Donors' Day.
1238. **657.** 5 c. red, black & blue 15 10

**1968.** Obligatory Tax. Leprosy Research Fund. Revalued currency. With gum.
1239. **388.** 5 c. green .. .. 1·90 55
1240. 5 c. red .. .. 95 30

**658.** Steam Locomotive of 1868.

**1968.** Cent. of Sao Paulo Railway.
1241. **658.** 5 c. multicoloured .. 2·50 70

**659.** Angelus Bell.

**660.** F.A.V. Caldas Jr.

**1968.** Christmas. Multicoloured.
1242. 5 c. Type **659** .. .. 15 10
1243. 6 c. Father Christmas giving present .. .. 15 10

**1968.** Birth Centenary of Francisco Caldas Junior (founder of "Correio do Povo" newspaper).
1244. **660.** 10 c. blk., pink & red 15 10

**661.** Reservists' Emblem and Memorial.

**1968.** Reservists' Day. With gum.
1245. **661.** 5 c. green and brown 15 10

**662.** Dish Aerial. **663.** Viscount do Rio Branco.

**1969.** Inauguration of Satellite Communications System.
1246. **662.** 30 c. black and blue 45 20

**1969.** 150th Birth Anniv. of Viscount do Rio Branco.
1247. **663.** 5 c. sepia and drab.. 15 10

**665.** Shoemaker's Last and Globe.

**664.** St. Gabriel. **666.** Kardec and Monument.

**1969.** St. Gabriel's Day (Patron Saint of Telecommunications).
1248. **664.** 5 c. multicoloured .. 15 10

**1969.** 4th Int. Shoe Fair, Novo Hamburgo.
1249. **665.** 5 c. multicoloured .. 15 10

**1969.** Death Centenary of "Allan Kardec" (Professor H. Rivail) (French educationalist and spiritualist).
1250. **666.** 5 c. brown and green 15 10

**667.** Men of Three Races and Arms of Cuiaba.

**1969.** 250th Anniv. of Cuiaba (capital of Mato Grosso state).
1251. **667.** 5 c. multicoloured .. 10 10

**668.** Mint and Banknote Pattern.

**1969.** Opening of New State Mint Printing Works.
1252. **668.** 5 c. bistre and orange 20 15

**669.** Society Emblem and Stamps.

**1969.** 50th Anniv. of Sao Paulo Philatelic Society.
1253. **669.** 5 c. multicoloured .. 10 10

**670.** "Our Lady of Santana" (statue).

**1969.** Mothers' Day.
1254. **670.** 5 c. multicoloured .. 20 15

**671.** ILO Emblem.

**1969.** 50th Anniv. of I.L.O. With gum.
1255. **671.** 5 c. gold and red .. 10 10

**672.** Diving Platform and Swimming Pool. **673.** "Mother and Child at Window" (after Di Cavalcanti).

**1969.** 40th Anniv. of Cearense Water Sports Club, Fortaleza.
1256. **672.** 20 c. blk., grn. and brn. 40 15

**1969.** 10th Art Exhibition, Biennale. Sao Paulo. Multicoloured.
1257 10 c. Type **673** .. .. 35 15
1258 20 c. Modern sculpture (F. Leirner) .. .. 50 30
1259 50 c. "Sunset in Brasilia" (D. di Prete) .. .. 1·25 70
1260 1 cr. "Angelfish" (A. Martins) .. .. 1·75 80
No. 1258 is square, size 33 × 33 mm. and Nos. 1259/60 vertical, size 33 × 53 mm.

**674.** Angelfish. **675.** I. O. Teles de Manezes (founder).

**1969.** A.C.A.P.I. Fish Preservation and Development Campaign.
1261. **674.** 20 c. multicoloured .. 45 15

**1969.** Cent. of Spiritualist Press. With gum.
1263. **675.** 50 c. green and orange 95 60

**676.** Postman delivering Letter. **677.** General Fragoso.

**1969.** Stamp Day. With gum.
1264. **676.** 30 c. blue .. .. 70 30

**1969.** Birth Cent. of General Tasso Fragoso. With gum.
1265. **677.** 20 c. green .. .. 30 15

**678.** Map of Army Bases. **679.** Jupia Dam.

**1969.** Army Week. Multicoloured.
1266. 10 c. Type **678** .. .. 25 15
1267. 20 c. Monument and railway bridge (39 × 22 mm.) 1·25 40

**1969.** Inauguration of Jupia Dam.
1268. **679.** 20 c. multicoloured.. 20 20

**680.** Mahatma Gandhi and Spinning-wheel.

**1969.** Birth Cent. of Mahatma Gandhi.
1269. **680.** 20 c. black and yellow 95 20

**681.** Alberto Santos Dumont, "Ballon No. 6", Eiffel Tower and Moon Landing.

**1969.** 1st Man on the Moon and Santos Dumont's Flight (1906). Commem.
1270. **681.** 50 c. multicoloured.. 1·40 80

**682.** Smelting Plant.

**1969.** Expansion of USIMINAS Steel Consortium.
1271. **682.** 20c. multicoloured .. 20 15

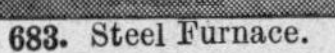

**683.** Steel Furnace. **685.** Exhibition Emblem.

**684.** "The Water Cart" (after Debret).

**1969.** 25th Anniv. of ACESITA Steel Works.
1272. **683.** 10 c. multicoloured.. 20 15

**1969.** Birth Cent. of J. B. Debret (painter). (2nd issue). Multicoloured. No. 1274 dated "1970".
1273. 20 c. Type **684** .. .. 75 25
1274. 30 c. "Street Scene" .. 75 70

**1969.** "Abuexpo 69" Stamp Exn.
1275. **685.** 10 c. multicoloured.. 20 15

**686.** Embraer Bandeirante Airplane.

**1969.** Brazilian Aeronautical Industry Expansion Year.
1276. **686.** 50 c. multicoloured.. 1·40 75

**687.** Pele scoring Goal. **688.** "Madonna and Child" (painted panel).

**1969.** Footballer Pele's 1,000th Goal.
1277. **687.** 10 c. multicoloured.. 40 95

**1969.** Christmas.
1279. **688.** 10 c. multicoloured.. 20 10

**689.** "Pernambuco" (destroyer) and "Bahia" (submarine).

**1969.** Navy Day. With gum.
1281. **689.** 5 c. blue .. .. 50 15

**690.** Dr. H. Blumenau.

**1969.** 150th Birth Anniv. of Dr. Hermann Blumenau (German immigrant leader). With gum.
1282. **690.** 20 c. green .. .. 35 15

**691.** Carnival Dancers.

**1969.** Carioca Carnival, Rio de Janeiro, (1970). Multicoloured.
1283. 5 c. Type **691** .. .. 25 20
1284. 10 c. Samba dancers .. 25 20
1285. 20 c. Clowns .. .. 25 30
1286. 30 c. Confetti and mask.. 1·40 1·10
1287. 50 c. Tambourine-player 1·25 95
Nos. 1284 and 1285 are horiz.

**692.** Carlos Gomes conducting.

**1970.** Centenary of Opera "O. Guarani" by A. Carlos Gomes.

1288. **692.** 20 c. multicoloured .. 30 20

**693.** Monastery.

**1970.** 400th Anniv. of Penha Monastery, Vilha Velha.

1289. **693.** 20 c. multicoloured 25 15

**694.** National Assembly Building.

**1970.** 10th Anniv. of Brasilia. Multicoloured.

1290. 20 c. Type **694** .. .. 25 15

1291. 50 c. Reflecting Pool .. 1·40 1·10

1292. 1 cr. Presidential Palace 1·40 1·10

**695.** Emblem on Map.

**1970.** Rondon Project (students' practical training scheme).

1293. **695.** 50 c. multicoloured 95 1·10

**696.** Marshal Osorio and Arms.

**1970.** Opening of Marshal Osorio Historical Park.

1294. **696.** 20 c. multicoloured .. 80 45

**697.** "Madonna and Child" (San Antonio Monastery). **698.** Brasilia Cathedral (stylised).

**1970.** Mothers' Day

1295. **697.** 20 c. multicoloured .. 30 20

**1970.** 8th National Eucharistic Congress, Brasilia. With gum.

1296. **698.** 20 c. green .. .. 15 15

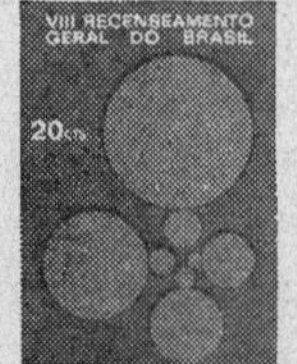

**699.** Census Symbol. **700.** Jules Rimet Cup, and Map.

**1970.** 8th National Census.

1297. **699.** 20 c. yellow and green 30 25

**1970.** World Cup Football Championships Mexico.

1298. **700.** 50 c. blk., gold & blue 50 40

**701.** Statue of Christ.

**1970.** Marist Students. 6th World Congress.

1299. **701.** 50 c. multicoloured .. 95 95

**702.** Bellini and Swedish Flag (1958).

**1970.** Brazil's Third Victory in World Cup Football Championships. Multicoloured.

1300. 1 cr. Type **702** .. .. 1·00 45

1301. 2 cr. Garrincha and Chilean flag (1962) .. 1·90 65

1302. 3 cr. Pele and Mexican flag (1970) .. .. 1·60 20

**703.** Pandia Calogeras. **704.** Brazilian Forces Badges and Map.

**1970.** Birth Centenary of Calogeras (author and politician).

1303. **703.** 20 c. green .. .. 35 20

**1970.** 25th Anniv. of World War II. Victory.

1304. **704.** 20 c. multicoloured .. 25 15

**705.** "The Annunciation" (Cassio M'Boy).

**1970.** St. Gabriel's Day (Patron Saint of Telecommunications).

1305. **705.** 20 c. multicoloured .. 60 40

**706.** Boy in Library. **707.** U.N. Emblem.

**1970.** Book Week.

1306. **706.** 20 c. multicoloured.. 50 35

**1970.** 25th Anniv. of United Nations.

1307. **707.** 50 c. blue, silver and ultram. .. .. 65 50

**708.** "Rio de Janeiro, circa 1820".

**1970.** 3rd Brasilian-Portuguese Stamp Exhib. "Lubrapex 70". Rio de Janeiro.

1308. **708.** 20 c. multicoloured 30 30

1309. – 50 c. brown and black 1·25 60

1310. – 1 cr. multicoloured .. 1·60 1·25

DESIGNS: 50 c. Post Office Symbol. 1 cr. Rio de Janeiro (modern view).

**709.** "The Holy Family" (C. Portinari). **710.** Destroyer.

**1970.** Christmas.

1312. **709.** 50 c. multicoloured .. 55 45

**1970.** Navy Day.

1314. **710.** 20 c. multicoloured 1·75 80

**711.** Congress Emblem. **712.** Links and Globe.

**1971.** 3rd Inter-American Housing Congress, Rio de Janeiro.

1315. **711.** 50 c. red and black .. 80 80

**1971.** Racial Equality Year.

1316. **712.** 20 c. multicoloured .. 30 30

**713.** "Morpho melacheilus".

**1971.** Butterflies. Multicoloured.

1317. 20 c. Type **713** .. .. 1·25 35

1318. 1 cr. "Papilio thoas brasiliensis" .. .. .. 6·00 2·10

**714.** Madonna and Child. **715.** Hands reaching for Ball.

**1971.** Mothers' Day.

1319. **714.** 20 c. multicoloured .. 30 15

**1971.** 6th Women's Basketball World Championships.

1320. **715.** 70 c. multicoloured .. 75 70

**716.** Eastern Part of Highway Map.

**1971.** Trans-Amazon Highway Project. Multicoloured.

1321. 40 c. Type **716** .. .. 6·25 3·75

1322. 1 cr. Western part of Highway Map .. .. 6·25 5·75

Nos. 1321/2 were issued together se-tenant, forming a composite design.

**717.** "Head of Man" (V. M. Lima).

**1971.** Stamp Day. Multicoloured.

1323. 40 c. Type **717** .. .. 75 45

1324. 1 cr. "Arab Violinist" (Pedro Americo) .. 2·00 95

**718.** General Caxias and Map. **719.** Anita Garibaldi.

**1971.** Army Week.

1325. **718.** 20 c. red and green.. 25 15

**1971.** 150th Birth Anniv. of Anita Garibaldi.

1326. **719.** 20 c. multicoloured .. 20 15

**720.** Xavante and Santos Dumont's Biplane "14 bis".

**1971.** First Flight of Embraer Xavante Jet Fighter.

1327 **720** 40 c. multicoloured .. 95 45

**721.** Flags of Central American Republics. **722.** Exhibition Emblem.

**1971.** 150th Anniv. of Central American Republics' Independence.

1328. **721.** 40 c. multicoloured .. 55 40

**1971.** "Franca 71" Industrial, Technical and Scientific Exhibition, Sao Paulo.

1329. **722.** 1 cr. 30 multicoloured 75 65

**723.** "The Black Mother" (L. de Albuquerque). **724.** Archangel Gabriel.

**1971.** Cent. of Slaves Emancipation Law.

1330. **723.** 40 c. multicoloured .. 40 20

**1971.** St. Gabriel's Day (Patron Saint of Communications).

1331. **724.** 40 c. multicoloured .. 45 50

**725.** "Couple on Bridge" (Marisa da Silva Chaves).

**1971.** Children's Day. Multicoloured.
1332. 35 c. Type **725** .. .. 35 30
1333. 45 c. "Couple on Riverbank" (Mary Rosa e Silva) 65 30
1334. 60 c. "Girl in Hat" (Teresa A. P. Ferreira) 35 30

**726.** "Laelia purpurata Werkhauserii superba".
**727.** Eunice Weaver.

**1971.** Brazilian Orchids.
1335. **726.** 40 c. multicoloured .. 95 50

**1971.** Obligatory Tax. Leprosy Research Fund.
1336. **727.** 10 c. green .. .. 95 65
1337. 10 c. purple .. .. 20 15

**728.** "25 Senac".

**1971.** 25th Annivs of SENAC (apprenticeship scheme) and SESC (workers' social service).
1338 **728** 20 c. blue & black .. 60 35
1339 – 40 c. orange and black 60 35
DESIGN: 40 c. As Type **728**, but inscribed "25 SESC".

**729.** "Parati" (gunboat). **730.** Cruciform Symbol.

**1971.** Navy Day.
1340. **729.** 20 c. multicoloured .. 1·40 30

**1971.** Christmas.
1341. **730.** 20 c. lilac, red and blue 30 15
1342. 75 c. black on silver .. 30 95
1343. 1 cr. 30 multicoloured 1·90 95

**731.** Washing Bomfim Church.

**1972.** Tourism. Multicoloured.
1344. 20 c. Type **731** .. .. 50 30
1345. 40 c. Cogwheel and grapes (Grape Festival, Rio Grande do Sul) .. 1·25 20
1346. 75 c. Nazareth Festival procession, Belem .. 1·25 1·25
1347. 1 cr. 30 Street scene (Winter Festival of Ouro Preto) .. .. 2·75 1·25

**732.** Pres. Lanusse.

**1972.** Visit of President Lanusse of Argentina.
1348. **732.** 40 c. multicoloured .. 90 75

**733.** Presidents Castello Branco, Costa e Silva and Medici. **734.** Post Office Symbol.

**1972.** 8th Anniv. of 1964 Revolution.
1349. **733.** 20 c. multicoloured .. 40 30

**1972.**
1350. **734.** 20 c. brown .. .. 1·50 10

**735.** Pres. Tomas.

**1972.** Visit of Pres. Tomas of Portugal.
1351. **735.** 75 c. multicoloured 1·25 95

**736.** Exploratory Borehole (C.P.R.M.)

**1972.** Mineral Resources. Multicoloured.
1352 20 c. Type **736** .. .. 60 15
1353 40 c. Oil rig (PETROBRAS) (vert) 2·25 50
1354 75 c. Power station and dam (ELECTROBRAS) 70 95
1355 1 cr. 30 Iron ore production (Vale do Rio Doce Co.) .. .. 2·75 1·25

**738.** Postman and Map (Post Office).

**1972.** Communications. Multicoloured.
1357. 35 c. Type **738** .. .. 50 20
1358. 45 c. Microwave Transmitter (Telecommunications) (vert.) .. .. 50 50
1359. 60 c. Symbol and diagram of Amazon microwave system .. .. 55 45
1360. 70 c. Worker and route map (Amazon Basin development) .. 65 45

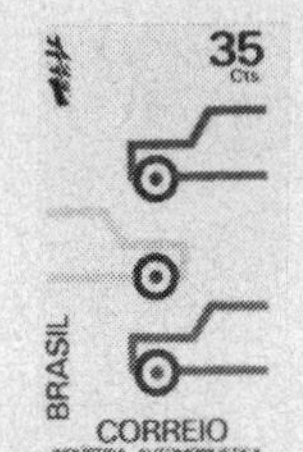


**739.** Motor Cars. **740.** Footballer (Independence Cup Championships).

**1972.** Major Industries.
1361. **739.** 35 c. orge., red & blk. 45 25
1362. – 45 c. multicoloured .. 45 40
1363. – 70 c. multicoloured .. 45 25
DESIGNS—HORIZ. 45 c. Three hulls (Shipbuilding). 70 c. Metal Blocks (Iron and Steel Industry).

**1972.** "Sports and Pastimes".
1364. **740.** 20 c. black and brown 40 15
1365. – 75 c. black and red .. 80 1·25
1366. – 1 cr. 30 black and blue 1·25 1·25
DESIGNS: 75 c. Treble clef in open mouth ("Popular Music"). 1 cr. 30, Hand grasping plastic ("Plastic Arts").

**741.** Diego Homem's Map of Brazil, 1568.

**1972.** "EXFILBRA 72" 4th Int. Stamp Exhib., Rio de Janeiro. Multicoloured.
1367. 70 c. Type **741** .. .. 35 35
1368. 1 cr. Nicolau Visscher's Map of Americas, c.1652 3·25 60
1369. 2 cr. Lopo Homem's World Map, 1519 .. 1·40 60

**742.** Figurehead, Sao Francisco River. **743.** "Institution of Brazilian Flag".

**1972.** Brazilian Folklore. Multicoloured.
1371. 45 c. Type **742** .. .. 45 15
1372. 60 c. Frandango, Rio Grande do Sul .. .. 75 50
1373. 75 c. Capoeira (game), Bahia .. .. 30 15
1374. 1 cr. 15 Karaja statuette 30 25
1375. 1 cr. 30 "Bumba-Meu-Boi" (folk play) .. 1·90 80

**1972.** 150th Anniv. of Independence.
1376. **743.** 30 c. green & yellow 75 75
1377. – 70 c. mauve & pink 75 30
1378. – 1 cr. red and brown 3·25 60
1379. – 2 cr. black & brown 1·90 60
1380. – 3 cr. 50 black & grey 3·25 1·90
DESIGNS—HORIZ. 70 c. "Proclamation of Emperor Pedro I" (lithograph after Debret). 2 cr. Commemorative gold coin of Pedro I. 3 cr. 50, Declaration of Ypiranga monument. VERT. 1 cr. "Emperor Pedro I" (H. J. da Silva).

**744.** Numeral and P.T.T. Symbol. **747.** Writing Hand and People ("Mobral" Literacy Campaign).

**745.** Scroll.

**1972.**
1383. **744.** 5 c. orange .. .. 30 10
1384. 10 c. brown .. .. 15 10
1394. 15 c. blue .. .. 15 10
1385. 20 c. blue .. .. 1·50 10
1396. 25 c. brown .. .. 15 10
1386. 30 c. red .. .. 95 10
1387. 40 c. green .. .. 15 10
1388. 50 c. green .. .. 75 10
1398. 70 c. purple .. .. 30 10
1389. **745.** 1 cr. purple .. .. 35 10
1390. 2 cr. blue .. .. 75 10
1391. 4 cr. orange and lilac 1·90 35
1392. 5 cr. brn., cinnamon and red .. .. 1·90 10
1393. 10 cr. grn., brn., & blk. 3·75 10
Nos. 1392/3 have a background of multiple P.T.T. symbols.

**1972.** Social Development. Multicoloured.
1412. 10 c. Type **747** .. .. 20 20
1413. 20 c. Graph and people (National Census Cent.) 50 40
1414. 1 cr. House in hand (Pension Fund system) 5·50 20
1415. 2 cr. Workers and factory (Gross National Product) 1·25 45

**748.** Legislative Building, Brasilia.

**1972.** National Congress Building, Brasilia.
1416. **748.** 1 cr. blk., orge. & blue 5·50 2·75

**749.** Pottery Crib. **750.** Farm-worker and Pension Book (Rural Social Security Scheme).

**1972.** Christmas.
1417. **749.** 20 c. black and brown 40 20

**1972.** Government Services.
1418. **750.** 10 c. blk., orge. & bl. 25 20
1419. – 10 c. multicoloured .. 60 60
1420. – 70 c. blk., brown & red 2·75 1·75
1421. – 2 cr. multicoloured .. 5·50 2·50
DESIGNS—VERT 70 c. Dr. Oswald Cruz, public health pioneer (birth cent.). HORIZ. 10 c. (No. 1419), Children and traffic lights (Transport system development). 2 cr. Bull, fish and produce (Agricultural exports).

**751.** Brazilian Expeditionary Force Monument.

**1972.** Armed Forces' Day.
1422 **751** 10 c. black, purple and brown .. 1·40 85
1423 – 30 c. multicoloured .. 1·75 85
1424 – 30 c. multicoloured .. 1·40 85
1425 – 30 c. black, brown and lilac .. .. 1·40 85
DESIGNS: No. 1423, Sail-training ship (Navy). No. 1424, Trooper (Army). No. 1425, Dassault Mirage IIIC jet fighter (Air Force).

**GUM.** All the following issues are with gum, except where otherwise stated.

**752.** Emblem and Cogwheels.

**1973.** 50th Anniv. of Rotary in Brazil.
1426 **752** 1 cr. blue, lt bl & yell 1·25 75

**753.** Swimming.

**1973.** Sporting Events.
1427 **753** 40 c. brown and blue 25 20
1428 – 40 c. red and green .. 1·60 55
1429 – 40 c. brown & purple 50 45
DESIGNS AND EVENTS—HORIZ. No. 1427, ("Latin Cup" Swimming Championships). No. 1428, Gymnast (Olympic Festival of Gymnastics, Rio de Janeiro). VERT. No. 1429, Volleyball player (Internation Volleyball Championships, Rio de Janeiro).

**754.** Paraguayan Flag.

**1973.** Visit of Pres. Stroessner of Paraguay.
1430. **754.** 70 c. multicoloured .. 95 80

**755.** "Communications".

**1973.** Inauguration of Ministry of Communications Building, Brasilia.
1431. **755.** 70 c. multicoloured .. 50 50

756. Neptune and Map.

**1973.** Inauguration of "Bracan 1" Underwater Cable, Recife to Canary Islands.
1432. 756. 1 cr. multicoloured .. 1·90 95

757. Congress Emblem.

758. Swallow-tailed Manakin and "Acacia decurrens".

**1973.** 24th Int. Chamber of Commerce Congress.
1433. 757. 1 cr. purple and orge. 2·25 95

**1973.** Tropical Birds and Plants. Mult.
1434. 20 c. Type 758 .. .. 65 30
1435. 20 c. Troupial and "Cereus peruvianus" .. .. 65 30
1436. 20 c. Brazilian Ruby and "Tecoma umbellata" 65 30

759. "Tourism".

760. "Caboclo" Festival Cart.

**1973.** National Tourism Year.
1437. 759. 70 c. multicoloured.. 60 30

**1973.** Anniversaries. Multicoloured
1438. 20 c. Type 760 .. .. 35 30
1439. 20 c. Arariboia (Indian chief) .. .. .. 35 30
1440. 20 c. Convention delegates 35 30
1441. 20 c. "The Graciosa Road" 35 30
EVENTS: No. 1438, 150th anniv. of Liberation Day. No. 1439, 400th anniv. of Niteroi. No. 1440, Cent. of Itu Convention. No. 1441, Cent. of Nhundiaquara highway.

761. "Institute of Space Research".

**1973.** Scientific Research Institute. Mult.
1442. 20 c. Type 761 .. .. 50 25
1443. 70 c. "Federal Engineering School", Itajuba .. 95 50
1444. 1 cr. "Institute for Pure and Applied Mechanics" 1·60 45

762. Santos Dumont and Biplane "14 bis".

**1973.** Birth Centenary of Alberto Santos Dumont (aviation pioneer).
1445. 762. 20 c. brown, green and pale green .. .. 50 20
1446. – 70 c. brown, red & yell. 95 95
1447. – 2 cr. brn., ultram. & bl. 1·60 1·25
DESIGNS: 70 c. Airship "Ballon No. 6". 2 cr. Monoplane No. 20 "Demoiselle".

764. G. Dias.

766. Festival Banner.

**1973.** 150th Birth Anniv of Goncalves Dias (poet).
1450 764 40 c. black and violet 35 30
See also Nos. 1459 and 1477.

**1973.** National Folklore Festival.
1452. 766. 40 c. multicoloured.. 35 20

767. Masonic Emblems.

**1973.** 150th Anniv. of Masonic Grand Orient Lodge of Brazil.
1453. 767. 1 cr. blue .. .. 1·25 95

768. Fire Protection.

**1973.** National Protection Campaign. Mult.
1454. 40 c. Type 768 .. .. 35 20
1455. 40 c. Cross and cornice (cultural protection) .. 35 20
1456. 40 c. Winged emblem (protection in flight) .. 35 20
1457. 40 c. Leaf (protection of nature) .. .. 35 20

**1973.** Birth Centenary of St. Theresa of Lisieux. As Type 764.
1459. – 2 cr. brown and orange 1·75 1·10
DESIGN: Portrait of St. Theresa.

770. M. Lobato and "Emilia".

**1973.** Monteiro Lobato's Children's Stories. Multicoloured.
1460 40 c. Type 770 .. .. 25 25
1461 40 c. "Aunt Nastasia" .. 25 25
1462 40 c. "Nazarinho", "Pedrinho" and "Quindim" .. .. 25 25
1463 40 c. "Visconde de Sabugosa" .. .. 25 25
1464 40 c. "Dona Benta" .. 25 25

771. Father J. M. Nunes Garcia.

**1973.** "The Baroque Age". Mult.
1465. 40 c. Wood carving, Church of St. Francia, Bahia .. 35 20
1466. 40 c. "Prophet Isaiah" (detail, sculpture by Aleijadinho) .. .. 35 20
1467. 70 c. Type 771 .. .. 80 80
1468. 1 cr. Portal, Church of Conceicao da Praia .. 3·75 1·60
1469. 2 cr. "Glorification of Holy Virgin", ceiling, St. Francis Assisi Church, Ouro Preto .. .. 3·25 1·60

772. Early Telephone and Modern Instruments.

**1973.** 50th Anniv. of Brazilian Telephone Company.
1470. 772. 40 c. multicoloured.. 35 15

773. "Angel" (J. Köpke).

**1973.** Christmas.
1471. 773. 40 c. multicoloured.. 25 10

774. "Gailora" (river steamboat).

**1973.** Brazilian Boats. Multicoloured.
1472 40 c. Type 774 .. .. 40 25
1473 70 c. "Regatao" (river trading boat) .. .. 1·00 75
1474 1 cr. "Jangada" (coastal raft) .. .. .. 3·25 1·50
1475 2 cr. "Saveiro" (passenger boat) .. .. .. 3·00 1·50

775. Scales of Justice.

**1973.** Judiciary Power.
1476. 775. 40 c. violet & mauve 30 15

**1973.** Birth Centenary of Placido de Castro. As Type 764.
1477. – 40 c. black and red .. 30 20
DESIGN: Portrait of Castro.

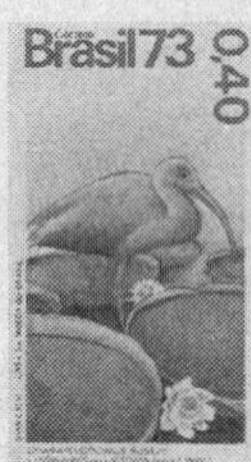
776. Scarlet Ibis and "Victoria Regia" Lilies.

777. Saci Perere (goblin).

**1973.** Brazilian Flora and Fauna. Mult.
1478. 40 c. Type 776 .. .. 1·75 30
1479. 70 c. Jaguar and Indian tulip .. .. .. 3·00 1·25
1480. 1 cr. Scarlet Macaw and palm .. .. .. 6·00 30
1481. 2 cr. Greater Rhea and mulunga plant .. 9·50 2·75

**1974.** Brazilian Folk Tales. Multicoloured.
1482. 40 c. Type 777 .. .. 35 15
1483. 80 c. Zumbi (warrior) .. 50 40
1484. 1 cr. Chico Rei (African king) .. .. .. 95 20
1485. 1 cr. 30 Little black boy of the pasture (32 × 33 mm.) .. .. .. 1·90 80
1486. 2 cr. 50 Iara, queen of the waters (32 × 33 mm.) 5·50 2·00

778. View of Bridge.

**1974.** Inauguration of President Costa e Silva (Rio de Janeiro–Niteroi) Bridge.
1487 778 40 c. multicoloured .. 35 20

779. "Press".

**1974.** Brazilian Communications Pioneers.
1488 779 40 c. red, blue & bis 30 15
1489 – 40 c. brown, bl & bis 25 15
1490 – 40 c. blue, pink & brn 30 15
DESIGNS AND EVENTS: No. 1488, Birth bicentenary of Hipolito da Costa (founder of newspaper "Correio Brasiliense", 1808). No. 1489, "Radio waves" (Edgar R. Pinto, founder of Radio Sociedade do Rio de Janeiro, 1923). No. 1490, "Television screen" (F. de Assis Chateaubriand, founder of first T.V. station, Sao Paulo, 1950).

780. "Construction".

**1974.** 10th Anniv. of March Revolution.
1491. 780. 40 c. multicoloured .. 25 20

781. Christ of the Andes.

**1974.** Birth Centenary of G. Marconi (radio pioneer).
1492 781 2 cr. 50 multicoloured 3·75 2·00

782. Heads of Three Races.

**1974.** Ethnical Origins and Immigration. Multicoloured.
1493 40 c. Type 782 .. .. 25 20
1494 40 c. Heads of many races 10 20
1495 2 cr. 50 German immigration .. .. .. 2·50 1·25
1496 2 cr. 50 Italian immigration .. .. .. 3·75 1·25
1497 2 cr. 50 Japanese immigration .. .. 1·90 95

783. Artwork and Stamp-printing Press.

**1974.** State Mint.
1498 783 80 c. multicoloured .. 95 20

784. Sete Cidades National Park.

**1974.** Tourism. Multicoloured.
1499. 40 c. Type 784 .. .. 60 25
1500. 80 c. Ruins of church of St. Michael of the Missions 60 25

786. Caraca College.

**1974.** Bicent. of Caraca College.
1502. 786. 40 c. multicoloured .. 20 15

763. Map of the World.

**1973.** Stamp Day.
1448. 763. 40 c. black and red .. 1·90 1·25
1449. – 40 c. black and red .. 1·90 1·25
The design of No. 1449 differs from Type 763 in that the red portion is to the top and right, instead of to the top and left.

787. Wave Pattern.

**1974.** Third Brazilian Telecommunications Congress, Brasilia.
1503. **787.** 40 c. black and blue .. 15 15

788. Fernao Dias Paes.

**1974.** 300th Anniv. of Paes Expedition.
1504. **788.** 20 c. multicoloured.. 15 15

**1974.** Visit of President Alvarez of Mexico. As Type **754.** Multicoloured.
1505. 80 c. Mexican Flag .. 1·25 70

789. Flags and Crowd in Stadium.

791. Pederneiras (after J. Carlos).

**1974.** World Cup Football Championships, West Germany (2nd issue).
1506. **789.** 40 c. multicoloured.. 50 25

**1974.** Birth Centenary of Raul Pederneiras (lawyer, author and artist).
1508. **791.** 40 c. blk. & yell. on brn. 20 20

792. Emblem and Seascape.

**1974.** 13th Int., Union of Building Societies and Savings Associations Congress, Rio de Janeiro.
1509. **792.** 1 cr. 30 multicoloured 75 35

794. "UPU" on World Map.

**1974.** Cent. of U.P.U.
1511. **794.** 2 cr. 50 black & blue 3·25 1·60

795. Aruak Hammock.

**1974.** "Popular Culture".
1512. **795.** 50 c. purple .. .. 75 30
1513. – 50 c. light blue & blue 95 30
1514. – 50 c. brn., red & yell. 40 30
1515. – 50 c. brown & yellow 50 30
DESIGNS—SQUARE No. 1513, Bilro Lace. VERT. (24 × 37 mm.), No. 1514, Guitar player (folk literature). No. 1515, Horseman (statuette by Vitalino).

796. Coffee Beans.

**1974.** Bicent. of City of Campinas.
1516. **796.** 50 c. multicoloured .. 50 20

797. Hornless Tabapua.

**1974.** Domestic Animals. Multicoloured.
1517. 80 c. Type **797** .. .. 95 60
1518. 1 cr. 30 Creole horse .. 90 70
1519. 2 cr. 50 Brazilian mastiff 4·75 1·75

798. Ilha Solteira Dam.

799. Herald Angel.

**1974.** Ilha Solteira Hydro-electric Power Project.
1520. **798.** 50 c. brn., grey & yell. 65 20

**1974.** Christmas.
1521. **799.** 50 c. multicoloured .. 30 15

800. "The Girls" (Carlos Reis).

802. Athlete.

801. "Justice for Juveniles".

**1974.** "Lubrapex 74" Stamp Exhibition, Sao Paulo (2nd issue).
1522. **800.** 1 cr. 30 multicoloured 40 25

**1974.** 50th Anniv. of Brazilian Juvenile Court.
1523. **801.** 90 c. multicoloured .. 20 20

**1974.** 50th Anniv. of Sao Silvestre Long-distance Race.
1524. **802.** 3 cr. 30 multicoloured 50 30

803. Mounted Newsvendor and Newspaper Masthead.

**1975.** Centenary of Newspaper "O Estado de S. Paulo".
1525. **803.** 50 c. multicoloured .. 60 30

804. Industrial Complex, Sao Paulo.

**1975.** Economic Resources.
1526. **804.** 50 c. yellow and blue 95 25
1527. – 1 cr. 40 yell. & brn... 35 35
1528. – 4 cr. 50 yell. & blk... 3·75 25
DESIGNS: 1 cr. 40 Rubber industry, Acre. 4 cr. 50 Manganese industry, Amapa.

805. Santa Cruz Fortress, Rio de Janeiro.

**1975.** Colonial Forts. Each brown on yellow.
1529 50 c. Type **805** .. .. 10 15
1530 50 c. Reis Magos Fort, Rio Grande do Norte .. 30 15
1531 50 c. Monte Serrat Fort, Bahia .. .. .. 50 15
1532 90 c. Nossa Senhora dos Remedios Fort, Fernando de Noronha 10 25

806. "Palafita" House, Amazonas.

**1975.** Brazilian Architecture. Multicoloured.
1533. 50 c. Modern Architecture, Brasilia .. .. 1·00 1·00
1534. 50 c. Modern Architecture, Brasilia. (yellow line at left) .. .. 9·50 4·75
1535. 1 cr. Type **806** .. .. 30 15
1536. 1 cr. 40 Indian hut, Rondonia (yellow line at left) .. 3·25 3·25
1537. 1 cr. 40 As No. 1536 but yellow line at right .. 55 60
1538. 3 cr. 30 "Enxaimel" house, Santa Catarina (yellow line at right) .. .. 95 95
1539. 3 cr. 30 As No. 1538 but yellow line at left .. 4·75 4·75

807. Marbled Cichlid.

**1975.** Freshwater Fishes. Multicoloured.
1540 50 c. Type **807** .. .. 1·00 20
1541 50 c. Puffer fish .. .. 40 30
1542 50 c. One-spot firebearer 40 35
1543 50 c. Discus fish .. .. 70 30

808. Flags forming Serviceman's Head.

809. Brazilian Pines.

**1975.** Honouring Ex-Servicemen of Second World War.
1544. **808.** 50 c. multicoloured .. 25 15

**1975.** Fauna and Flora Preservation. Mult.
1545. 70 c. Type **809** .. .. 1·60 20
1546. 1 cr. Giant otter (vert.) 1·00 40
1547. 3 cr. 30 Marsh cayman .. 95 40

810. Inga Carved Stone, from Paraiba.

811. Statue of the Virgin Mary.

**1975.** Archaeology. Multicoloured.
1548. 70 c. Type **810** .. .. 95 20
1549. 1 cr. Marajoara pot from Para .. .. .. 25 20
1550. 1 cr. Fossilized fish from Ceara (horiz.) .. .. 30 20

**1975.** Holy Year. 300th Anniv. of Franciscan Province of Our Lady of the Immaculate Conception.
1551. **811.** 3 cr. 30 multicoloured 95 60

812. Ministry of Communications Building, Rio de Janeiro.

813. "Congada" Sword Dance, Minas Gerais.

**1975.** Stamp Day.
1552. **812.** 70 c. red .. .. 45 15

**1975.** Folk Dances. Multicoloured.
1553. 70 c. Type **813** .. .. 25 30
1554. 70 c. "Frevo" umbrella dance, Pernambuco .. 25 30
1555. 70 c. "Warrior" dance, Alagoas.. .. .. 25 30

814. Stylised Trees.

**1975.** Tree Festival.
1556. **814.** 70 c. multicoloured .. 25 10

815. Dish Aerial and Globe.

816. Woman holding Globe.

**1975.** Inauguration of Tangua Satellite Telecommunications Station.
1557. **815.** 3 cr. 30 multicoloured 60 35

**1975.** International Women's Year.
1558. **816.** 3 cr. 30 multicoloured 80 45

817. Tile, Balcony Rail and Memorial Column, Alcantara.

**1975.** Historic Towns. Multicoloured.
1559. 70 c. Type **817** .. .. 40 25
1560. 70 c. Belfry, weather vane and jug, Goias (26 × 38 mm.) 40 25
1561. 70 c. Sao Francisco Convent, Sao Cristovao (40 × 22 mm.) 40 25

818. Crowd welcoming Walking Book.

**1975.** Day of the Book.
1562. **818.** 70 c. multicoloured .. 20 15

819. ASTA Emblem and Arrows.

**1975.** 45th American Society of Travel Agents Congress.

| | | | | |
|---|---|---|---|---|
| 1563. | 819. | 70 c. multicoloured .. | 20 | 15 |

820. Two Angels. 821. Aerial, and Map of America.

**1975.** Christmas.

| | | | | |
|---|---|---|---|---|
| 1564. | 820. | 70 c. brown and red | 15 | 10 |

**1975.** 2nd International Telecommunications Conference Rio de Janeiro.

| | | | | |
|---|---|---|---|---|
| 1565. | 821. | 5 cr. 20 multicoloured | 1·50 | 75 |

822. Friar Nicodemus 823. People in front of Cross.

**1975.** Obligatory Tax. Leprosy Research Fund.

| | | | | |
|---|---|---|---|---|
| 1566. | 822. | 10 c. brown .. .. | 20 | 10 |

**1975.** Thanksgiving Day.

| | | | | |
|---|---|---|---|---|
| 1567. | 823. | 70 c. turquoise & blue | 30 | 25 |

824. Emperor Pedro II in Naval Uniform (after P. P. da Silva Manuel). 825. Sal Stone Beach, Piaui.

**1975.** 150th Birth Anniv. of Emperor Pedro II.

| | | | | |
|---|---|---|---|---|
| 1568. | 824. | 70 c. brown .. .. | 40 | 20 |

**1975.** Tourism. Multicoloured.

| | | | |
|---|---|---|---|
| 1569 | 70 c. Type **825** .. .. | 30 | 20 |
| 1570 | 70 c. Guarapari Beach, Espirito Santo .. | 30 | 20 |
| 1571 | 70 c. Torres Cliffs, Rio Grande do Sul .. | 30 | 20 |

826. Triple Jump.

**1975.** 7th Pan-American Games, Santo Domingo, Dominican Republic.

| | | | | |
|---|---|---|---|---|
| 1572. | 826. | 1 cr. 60 turquoise & black | 20 | 20 |

827. U.N. Emblem and H.Q. Building, New York.

**1975.** 30th Anniv. of United Nations.

| | | | | |
|---|---|---|---|---|
| 1573. | 827. | 1 cr. 30 violet on blue | 15 | 15 |

828. Light Bulbs and House.

**1976.** "Preservation of Fuel Resources". Multicoloured.

| | | | |
|---|---|---|---|
| 1574. | 70 c. Type **828** .. .. | 25 | 10 |
| 1575. | 70 c. Drops of petrol and car | 25 | 10 |

829. Concorde.

**1976.** Concorde's First Commercial Flight, Paris–Rio de Janeiro.

| | | | | |
|---|---|---|---|---|
| 1576 | 829 | 5 cr. 20 black & grey | 1·10 | 40 |

831. Early and Modern Telephone Equipment.

**1976.** Telephone Centenary.

| | | | | |
|---|---|---|---|---|
| 1578. | 831. | 5 cr. 20 black & orange | 30 | 35 |

832. "Eye"-part of Exclamation Mark. 833. Kaiapo Body-painting.

**1976.** World Health Day.

| | | | | |
|---|---|---|---|---|
| 1579. | 832. | 1 cr. lake, brn. & violet | 30 | 25 |

**1976.** Brazil's Indigenous Culture. Mult.

| | | | |
|---|---|---|---|
| 1580. | 1 cr. Type **833** .. .. | 20 | 10 |
| 1581. | 1 cr. Bakairi ceremonial mask .. .. .. | 20 | 10 |
| 1582. | 1 cr. Karaja feather head-dress .. .. .. | 20 | 10 |

834. Itamaraty Palace, Brasilia.

**1976.** Diplomats' Day.

| | | | | |
|---|---|---|---|---|
| 1583. | 834. | 1 cr. multicoloured .. | 35 | 35 |

835. "The Sprinkler" (3D composition by J. Tarcisio). 836. Basketball.

**1976.** Modern Brazilian Art. Multicoloured.

| | | | |
|---|---|---|---|
| 1584. | 1 cr. Type **835** .. .. | 15 | 10 |
| 1585. | 1 cr. "Beribboned Fingers" (P. Checcacci) (horiz.) | 15 | 10 |

**1976.** Olympic Games, Montreal.

| | | | | |
|---|---|---|---|---|
| 1586. | 836. | 1 cr. black and green | 10 | 10 |
| 1587. | – | 1 cr. 40 black & blue | 25 | 10 |
| 1588. | – | 5 cr. 20 black & orge. | 35 | 30 |

Designs: 1 cr. 40, Olympic yachts. 5 cr. 20, Judo.

837. Golden Lion-Tamarin. 838. Cine Camera on Screen.

**1976.** Nature Protection. Multicoloured.

| | | | |
|---|---|---|---|
| 1589. | 1 cr. Type **837** .. .. | 25 | 20 |
| 1590. | 1 cr. Orchid ("Acacallis cyanea") .. .. | 25 | 30 |

**1976.** Brazilian Cinematograph Industry.

| | | | | |
|---|---|---|---|---|
| 1591. | 838. | 1 cr. multicoloured .. | 20 | 10 |

839. Ox-cart Driver.

**1976.**

| | | | | |
|---|---|---|---|---|
| 1592 | 839 | 10 c. red .. .. | 10 | 10 |
| 1593 | – | 15 c. brown .. .. | 25 | 10 |
| 1594 | – | 20 c. blue .. .. | 15 | 10 |
| 1595 | – | 30 c. red .. .. | 20 | 10 |
| 1596 | – | 40 c. orange .. | 20 | 10 |
| 1597a | – | 50 c. brown .. .. | 25 | 10 |
| 1598 | – | 70 c. black .. .. | 15 | 10 |
| 1599 | – | 80 c. green .. .. | 65 | 10 |
| 1600a | – | 1 cr. black .. .. | 20 | 10 |
| 1601 | – | 1 cr. 10 purple .. | 20 | 10 |
| 1602 | – | 1 cr. 30 red .. .. | 20 | 10 |
| 1603a | – | 1 cr. 80 violet .. | 20 | 10 |
| 1604a | – | 2 cr. brown .. .. | 30 | 10 |
| 1605 | – | 2 cr. 50 brown .. | 25 | 10 |
| 1605a | – | 3 cr. 20 blue .. | 25 | 10 |
| 1606a | – | 5 cr. lilac .. .. | 95 | 10 |
| 1607 | – | 7 cr. vilolet .. .. | 2·50 | 10 |
| 1608a | – | 10 cr. green .. | 95 | 10 |
| 1609 | – | 15 cr. green .. .. | 95 | 10 |
| 1610 | – | 20 cr. blue .. .. | 95 | 10 |
| 1611 | – | 21 cr. purple .. | 65 | 10 |
| 1612 | – | 27 cr. brown .. | 65 | 10 |

Designs—horiz. 20 c. Pirogue fisherman. 40 c. Cowboy. 3 cr. 20, Sao Francisco boatman. 27 cr. Muleteer. vert. 15 c. Bahia woman. 30 c. Rubber gatherer. 50 c. Gaucho. 70 c. Women breaking Babacu chestnuts. 80 c. Gold-washer. 1 cr. Banana gatherer. 1 cr. 10, Grape harvester. 1 cr. 30, Coffee harvester. 1 cr. 80, Carnauba cutter. 2 cr. Potter. 2 cr. 50, Basket maker. 5 cr. Sugar-cane cutter. 7 cr. Salt worker. 10 cr. Fisherman. 15 cr. Coconut vendor. 20 cr. Lace maker. 21 cr. Ramie cutter.

840. Neon Tetra.

**1976.** Brazilian Freshwater Fishes. Mult.

| | | | |
|---|---|---|---|
| 1613 | 1 cr. Type **840** .. .. | 40 | 40 |
| 1614 | 1 cr. "Copeina arnoldi" .. | 40 | 40 |
| 1615 | 1 cr. "Prochilodus insignis" .. .. | 40 | 40 |
| 1616 | 1 cr. Pike cichlid .. | 40 | 40 |
| 1617 | 1 cr. "Ageneiosus sp." .. | 40 | 40 |
| 1618 | 1 cr. Catfish .. .. | 40 | 40 |

841. Santa Marta Lighthouse. 842. Postage Stamps as Magic Carpet.

**1976.** 300th Anniv. of Laguna.

| | | | | |
|---|---|---|---|---|
| 1619. | 841. | 1 cr. blue .. .. | 40 | 15 |

**1976.** Stamp Day.

| | | | | |
|---|---|---|---|---|
| 1620. | 842. | 1 cr. multicoloured .. | 15 | 10 |

843. Oil Lamp and Profile.

**1976.** 50th Anniv of Brazilian Nursing Ass.

| | | | | |
|---|---|---|---|---|
| 1621 | 843 | 1 cr. multicoloured .. | 20 | 10 |

844. Puppet Soldier. 845. Winner's Medal.

**1976.** Mamulengo Puppet Theatre. Mult.

| | | | |
|---|---|---|---|
| 1622. | 1 cr. Type **844** .. .. | 20 | 15 |
| 1623. | 1 cr. 30 Puppet girl .. | 20 | 15 |
| 1624. | 1 cr. 60 Finger puppets .. (horiz.) | 20 | 15 |

**1976.** 27th International Military Athletics Championships, Rio de Janeiro.

| | | | | |
|---|---|---|---|---|
| 1625. | 845. | 5 cr. 20 multicoloured | 45 | 20 |

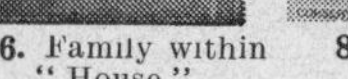

846. Family within "House". 847. Rotten Tree.

**1976.** SESC and SENAC National Organizations for Appenticeship and Welfare.

| | | | | |
|---|---|---|---|---|
| 1626. | 846. | 1 cr. blue .. .. | 15 | 10 |

**1976.** Conservation of the Environment.

| | | | | |
|---|---|---|---|---|
| 1627. | 847. | 1 cr. multicoloured .. | 15 | 10 |

848. Electron Orbits and Atomic Agency Emblem.

**1976.** 20th International Atomic Energy Conference, Rio de Janeiro.

| | | | | |
|---|---|---|---|---|
| 1628. | 848. | 5 cr. 20 multicoloured | 45 | 25 |

849. Metro Train. 851. School Building.

850. St. Francis.

**1976.** Inauguration of Sao Paulo Underground Railway.

| | | | | |
|---|---|---|---|---|
| 1629. | 849. | 1 cr. 60 multicoloured | 35 | 15 |

**1976.** 750th Death Anniv. of St. Francis of Assisi.

| | | | | |
|---|---|---|---|---|
| 1630. | 850. | 5 cr. 20 multicoloured | 45 | 20 |

**1976.** Cent. of Ouro Preto Mining School.

| | | | | |
|---|---|---|---|---|
| 1631. | 851. | 1 cr. violet .. .. | 25 | 30 |

852. "Three Kings" (J. A. da Silva).

**1976.** Christmas. Multicoloured.

| | | | |
|---|---|---|---|
| 1632 | 80 c. Type **852** .. .. | 30 | 20 |
| 1633 | 80 c. "Father Christmas" (T. Onivaldo Cogo) .. | 30 | 20 |
| 1634 | 80 c. "Nativity Scene" (R. Yabe) .. .. .. | 30 | 20 |
| 1635 | 80 c. "Angels" (E. Folchini) .. .. | 30 | 20 |
| 1636 | 80 c. "Nativity" (A.L. Cintra) .. .. | 30 | 20 |

854. "Our Lady of Monte Serrat" (Friar A. da Piedade).

**1976.** Brazilian Sculpture. Multicoloured.

| | | | |
|---|---|---|---|
| 1638. | 80 c. Type **854** .. .. | 15 | 10 |
| 1639. | 5 cr. "St. Joseph" (unknown artist) (25×37 mm.) .. .. .. | 40 | 20 |
| 1640. | 5 cr. 60 "The Dance" (J. Bernardelli) (square) | 45 | 20 |
| 1641. | 6 cr. 50 "The Caravel" (B. Giorgi) (As 5 cr.) .. | 35 | 20 |

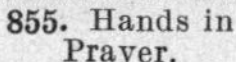

855. Hands in Prayer. 856. Sailor of 1840.

**1976** Thanksgiving Day.
1642. **855.** 80 c. multicoloured .. 15 10

**1976.** Brazilian Navy Commemoration. Multicoloured.
1643. 80 c. Type **856** .. .. 20 10
1644. 2 cr. Marine of 1808 .. 25 15

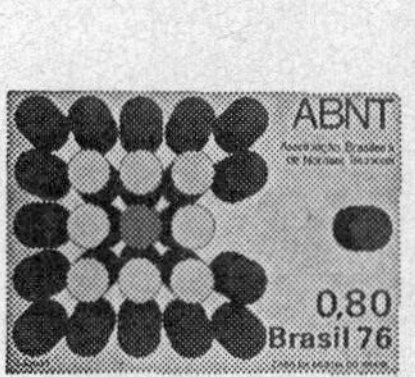


857. " Natural Resources ". 858. " Wheel of Life" (wood-carving, G. T. de Oliveira).

**1976.** Brazilian Bureau of Standards.
1645. **857.** 80 c. multicoloured .. 15 10

**1977.** 2nd World Black and African Festival of Arts and Culture, Lagos (Nigeria). Multicoloured.
1646. 5 cr. Type **858** .. .. 50 20
1647. 5 cr. 60 " The Beggar " (wood-carving, A. dos Santos) .. .. 50 20
1648. 6 cr. 50 Benin pectoral mask .. .. .. 90 20

859. Airport Layout. 860. Seminar Emblem.

**1977.** Inauguration of Operation of International Airport, Rio de Janeiro.
1649 **859** 6 c. 50 multicoloured 60 25

**1977.** 6th InterAmerican Budget Seminar.
1650. **860.** 1 cr. 10 turquoise, blue and stone .. .. 20 10

861. Salicylic Acid Crystals. 862. Emblem of Lions Clubs.

**1977.** World Rheumatism Year.
1651. **861.** 1 cr. 10 multicoloured 20 10

**1977.** 25th Anniv. of Brazilian Lions Clubs.
1652. **862.** 1 cr. 10 multicoloured 20 10

863. H. Villa-Lobos and Music.

**1977.** Brazilian Composers. Multicoloured.
1653. 1 cr. 10 Type **863** .. 25 10
1654. 1 cr. 10 Chiquinha Gonzaga and guitar .. .. 25 10
1655. 1 cr. 10 Noel Rosa and guitar .. .. .. 25 10

864. Rural and Urban Workers. 865. Memorial, Porto Seguro.

**1977.** Industrial Protection and Safety. Mult.
1656. 1 cr. 10 Type **864** .. 15 10
1657. 1 cr. 10 Laboratory vessels 15 10

**1977.** Cent. of U.P.U. Membership. Views of Porto Seguro. Multicoloured.
1658. 1 cr. 10 Type **865** .. 15 10
1659. 5 cr. Beach .. .. 1·25 20
1660. 5 cr. 60 Old houses .. 55 20
1661. 6 cr. 50 Post Office .. 50 25

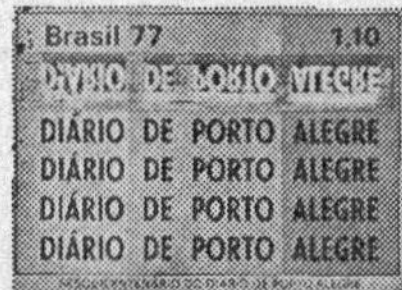


866. Newspaper Title in Linotype and Print.

**1977.** 150th Anniv. of Brazilian Newspaper "Diario de Porto Allegre".
1662. **866.** 1 cr. 10 blk. and pur. 15 10

867. Blue Whale. 868. " Cell System ".

**1977.** Fauna Preservation.
1663. **867.** 1 cr. 30 multicoloured 30 10

**1977.** 25th Anniv. of National Economic Development Bank.
1664. **868.** 1 cr. 30 multicoloured 15 10

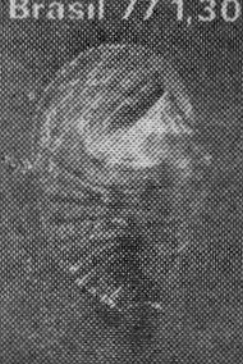


869. Locomotive leaving Tunnel. 870. Goliath Conch.

**1977.** Centenary of Rio de Janeiro-Sao Paulo Railway.
1665. **869.** 1 c. 30 black .. .. 30 10

**1977.** Brazilian Molluscs. Multicoloured.
1666 1 cr. 30 Type **870** .. 30 15
1667 1 cr. 30 Thin-bladed murex ("Murex tenuivaricosus") .. 30 15
1668 1 cr. 30 Helmet vase ("Vasum cassiforme") 30 15

871. Caduceus. 872. Masonic Symbols.

**1977.** 3rd Int Congress of Odontology.
1669 **871** 1 cr. 30 brn, bis & orge 20 10

**1977.** 50th Anniv. of Brazilian Grand Masonic Lodge.
1670. **872.** 1 cr. 30 blue, deep blue and black .. .. 25 10

873. " Sailboat ". 874. Law Proclamation.

**1977.** Stamp Day.
1671. **873.** 1 cr. 30 multicoloured 15 10

**1977.** 150th Anniv. of Juridical Courses.
1672. **874.** 1 cr. 30 multicoloured 15 10

875. " Cavalhada " (horsemen). 876. Doubloon.

**1977.** Folklore. Multicoloured.
1673. 1 cr. 30 Type **875** 20 10
1674. 1 cr. 30 Horseman with flag .. .. 20 10
1675. 1 cr. 30 Jousting (horiz.) 20 10

**1977.** Brazilian Colonial Coins. Multicoloured.
1676. 1 cr. 30 Type **876** .. 20 10
1677. 1 cr. 30 Pataca .. .. 20 10
1678. 1 cr. 30 Vintem .. .. 20 10

877. Toy Windmill. 878. " Neoregelia carolinae ".

**1977.** National Day.
1679. **877.** 1 cr. 30 multicoloured 15 10

**1977.** Nature Conservation.
1680. **878.** 1 cr. 30 multicoloured 20 10

879. Pen, Pencil and writing. 880. Observatory and Electrochromograph of Supernova.

**1977.** 150th Anniv. of Official Elementary Schooling.
1681. **879.** 1 cr. 30 multicoloured 15 10

**1977.** 150th Anniv. of National Observatory.
1682. **880.** 1 cr. 30 multicoloured 20 10

881. Airship "Pax". 882. Text from " O Guarani " and Ceci.

**1977.** Aviation Anniversaries. Multicoloured.
1683 1 cr. 30 Type **881** .. 20 10
1684 1 cr. 30 Savoia Marchetti flying boat "Jahu" .. 20 10

ANNIVERSARIES: No. 1683, 75th anniv of "Pax" flight. No. 1684, 50th anniv of "Jahu" South Atlantic crossing.

**1977.** Day of the Book and Jose de Alencar Commemoration.
1685. **882.** 1 cr. 30 multicoloured 15 10

883. Radio Waves. 884. Nativity (in carved gourd).

**1977.** Amateur Radio Operators' Day.
1686. **883.** 1 cr. 30 multicoloured 15 10

**1977.** Christmas. Multicoloured.
1687. 1 cr. 30 Type **884** .. 15 10
1688. 2 cr. The Annunciation .. 25 10
1689. 5 cr. Nativity .. .. 55 15

885. Emerald. 886. Angel holding Cornucopia.

**1977.** " Portucale 77 " Thematic Stamp Exhibition. Multicoloured.
1690. 1 cr. 30 Type **885** .. 20 10
1691. 1 cr. 30 Topaz .. .. 20 10
1692. 1 cr. 30 Aquamarine .. 20 10

**1977.** Thanksgiving Day.
1693. **886.** 1 cr. 30 multicoloured 15 10

887. Curtiss Fledgling, Douglas DC-3 and Badge (National Airmail Service).

**1977.** National Integration. Multicoloured.
1694. 1 cr. 30 Type **887** .. 30 10
1695. 1 cr. 30 Amazon River naval patrol boat and badge (Amazon Fleet) 30 10
1696. 1 cr. 30 Train crossing bridge and badges (Engineering Corps and Railway Battalion) .. 30 10

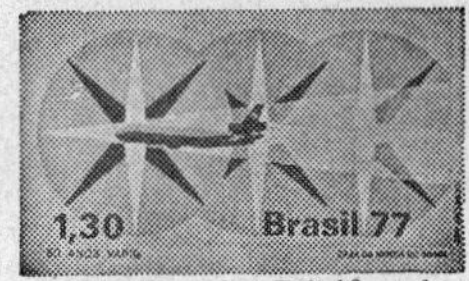


888. Douglas DC-10 and Varig Airline Emblems.

**1977.** 50th Anniv. of Varig State Airline.
1697. **888.** 1 cr. 30 blk., pale blue and blue .. .. 15 10

889. Sts. Cosmus and Damian Church, Igaracu. 890. Woman with Wheat Sheaf.

**1977.** Regional Architecture, Churches. Mult.
1698. 2 cr. 70 Type **889** .. 20 10
1699. 7 cr. 50 St. Bento Monastery Church, Rio de Janeiro .. .. 60 25
1700. 8 cr. 50 St. Francis Assisi Church, Ouro Preto .. 65 25
1701. 9 cr. 50 St. Anthony Convent Church, Joao Pessoa .. .. .. 80 30

**1977.** Diplomats' Day.
1702. **890.** 1 cr. 30 multicoloured 15 10

**891.** Scene from "Fosca" and Carlos Gomes (composer).

**892.** Foot kicking Ball.

**1978.** Bicentenary of La Scala Opera House, Milan, and Carlos Gomes Commemoration.
1703 **891** 1 cr. 80 multicoloured 30 10

**1978.** World Cup Football Championship, Argentina. Multicoloured.
1704 1 cr. 80 Type **892** .. 20 10
1705 1 cr. 80 Ball in net .. 20 10
1706 1 cr. 80 Stylized player with cup .. .. 20 10

**893.** " Postal Efficiency ".

**894.** Electro-cardiogram.

**1978.** Postal Staff College.
1707. **893.** 1 cr. 80 multicoloured 15 10

**1978.** World Hypertension Month.
1708. **894.** 1 cr. 80 mult. .. 20 10

**895.** World Map and Antenna.

**896.** Saffron Finch.

**1978.** World Telecommunications Day.
1709. **895.** 1 cr. 80 multicoloured 15 10

**1978.** Birds. Multicoloured.
1710. 7 cr. 50 Type **896** .. 1·25 50
1711. 8 cr. 50 Banded Cotinga 1·60 60
1712. 9 cr. 50 Seven-coloured Tanager .. .. 1·90 85

**897.** " Discussing the Opening Speech " (G. Mondin).

**1978.** 85th Anniv. of Union Court of Audit.
1713. **897.** 1 cr. 80 multicoloured 15 10

**898.** Post and Telegraph Headquarters, Brasilia.

**1978.** Opening of Post and Telegraph Headquarters.
1714. **898.** 1 cr. 80 multicoloured 15 10

**899.** President Geisel.

**900.** Savoia Marchetti S-64 and Map.

**1978.** President Geisel Commemoration.
1716. **899.** 1 cr. 80 olive .. 20 10

**1978.** 50th Anniv. of South Atlantic Flight by del Prete and Ferrarin.
1717. **900.** 1 cr. 80 multicoloured 25 10

**901.** " Smallpox ".

**902.** 10 r. Pedro II " White Beard " Stamp of 1878.

**1978.** Global Eradication of Smallpox.
1718. **901.** 1 cr. 80 multicoloured 20 10

**1978.** Stamp Day.
1719. **902.** 1 cr. 80 multicoloured 15 10

**903.** " Jangadeiros ".

**1978.** Birth Centenary of Helios Seelinger (painter).
1720 **903** 1 cr. 80 multicoloured 15 10

**904.** Musicians with Violas.

**1978.** Folk Musicians. Multicoloured.
1721. 1 cr. 80 Type **904**. .. 20 10
1722. 1 cr. 80 Two fife players 20 10
1723. 1 cr. 80 Berimbau players 20 10

**905.** Children playing Football.

**1978.** National Week.
1724. **905.** 1 cr. 80 multicoloured 20 10

**906.** Patio de Colegio Church.

**1978.** Restoration of Patio de Colegio Church, Sao Paulo.
1725. **906.** 1 cr. 80 brown .. 15 10

**907.** " Justice " (A. Ceschiatti).

**1978.** 150th Anniv. of Federal Supreme Court.
1726. **907.** 1 cr. 80 black & bistre 15 10

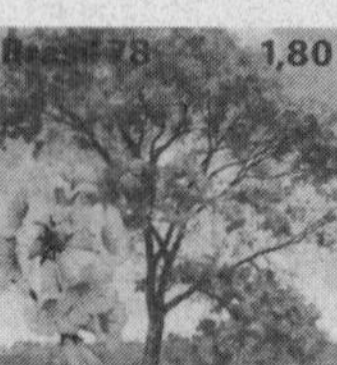

**908.** Ipe (flowering tree).

**909.** Stages of " Intelsat " Assembly.

**1978.** Environment Protection. Iguacu Falls National Park. Multicoloured.
1727. 1 cr. 80 Type **908** .. 25 10
1728. 1 cr. 80 Iguacu Falls .. 25 10

**1978.** 3rd Assembly. Users of " Intelsat " Telecommunications Satellite.
1729. **909.** 1 cr. 80 multicoloured 15 10

**910.** Flag of the Order of Christ.

**1978.** "Lubrapex 78" Stamp Exhibition. Flags. Multicoloured.
1730. 1 cr. 80 Type **910** .. 60 30
1731. 1 cr. 80 Principality of Brazil .. .. .. 60 30
1732. 1 cr. 80 United Kingdom of Brazil .. .. 60 30
1733. 8 cr. 50 Empire of Brazil 60 30
1734. 8 cr. 50 National Flag of Brazil .. .. .. 60 30

**911.** Postal Tramcar.

**1978.** 18th U.P.U. Congress, Rio de Janeiro.
1735. **911.** 1 cr. 80 brn., blk. & bl. 60 60
1736. – 1 cr. 80 brn., blk. & bl. 60 60
1737. – 1 cr. 80 grey, blk. & rose 60 60
1738. – 7 cr. 50 grey, blk. & rose 1·00 60
1739. – 8 cr. 50 brn., blk. & grn. 1·00 60
1740. – 9 cr. 50 brn., blk. & grn. 1·00 60

DESIGNS: No. 1736, Mail container truck. No. 1737, Mail van, 1914. No. 1738, Travelling post office. No. 1739, Mail coach. No. 1740, Mule caravan.

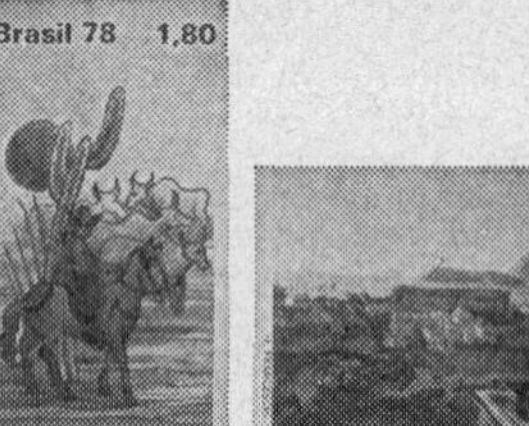

**912.** Gaucho.

**913.** " Morro de Santo Antonio " (Nicolas Antoine Taunay).

**1978.** Day of the Book and J. Guimaraes Rosa Commemoration.
1741 **912** 1 cr. 80 multicoloured 20 10

**1978.** Landscape Paintings. Multicoloured.
1742. 1 cr. 80 Type **913** .. 20 10
1743. 1 cr. 80 " View of Pernambuco " (Frans Post) .. 20 10
1744. 1 cr. 80 " Morro de Castelo " (Victor Meirelles) .. 20 10
1745. 1 cr. 80 " Landscape at Sabara " (Alberto da Veiga Guignard) .. 20 10

**914.** Angel with Lute.

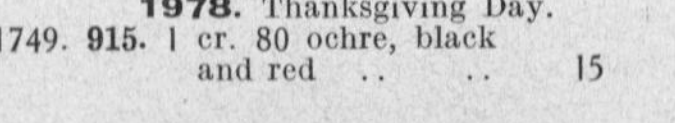
**915.** " Thanksgiving ".

**1978.** Christmas. Multicoloured.
1746. 1 cr. 80 Type **914**. .. 15 10
1747. 1 cr. 80 Angel with lyre .. 15 10
1748. 1 cr. 80 Angel with trumpet 15 10

**1978.** Thanksgiving Day.
1749. **915.** 1 cr. 80 ochre, black and red .. .. 15 10

**916.** Red Cross Services.

**1978.** 70th Anniv. of Brazilian Red Cross.
1750. **916.** 1 cr. 80 red and black 15 10

**917.** Peace Theatre, Belem.

**918.** Underground Trains.

**1978.** Brazilian Theatres. Multicoloured.
1751. 10 cr. 50 Type **917** .. 50 15
1752. 12 cr. Jose de Alencar Theatre, Fortaleza . 55 20
1753. 12 cr. 50 Rio de Janeiro Municipal Theatre .. 60 20

**1979.** Inauguration of Rio de Janeiro Underground Railway.
1754. **918.** 2 cr. 50 multicoloured 40 10

**919.** Old and New Post Offices.

**1979.** 10th Anniv of Post & Telegraph Department and 18th U.P.U. Congress (2nd issue). Multicoloured.
1755 2 cr. 50 Type **919** .. 25 15
1756 2 cr. 50 Mail boxes .. 25 15
1757 2 cr. 50 Mail sorting .. 25 15
1758 2 cr. 50 Mail planes .. 25 15
1759 2 cr. 50 Telegraph and telex machines .. 25 15
1760 2 cr. 50 Postmen .. 25 15

**920.** "O'Day 23" Class Yacht.

**1979.** "Brasiliana 79" 3rd World Thematic Stamp Exhibition (1st issue). Mult.
1761 2 cr. 50 Type **920** .. 20 10
1762 10 cr. 50 "Penguin" class dinghy .. .. 50 20
1763 12 cr. "Hobie Cat" class catamaran .. .. 50 20
1764 12 cr. 50 "Snipe" class dinghy .. .. 50 25
See Nos. 1773/6 and 1785/90.

**921.** Joao Bolinha (characters from childrens' story).

**1979.** Childrens' Book Day.
1765. **921.** 2 cr. 50 multicoloured 20 10

**922.** "Victoria amazonica".

**1979.** 18th U.P.U. Congress (3rd issue). Amazon National Park. Multicoloured.
1766 10 cr. 50 Type **922** .. 35 20
1767 12 cr. Amazon manatee .. 65 25
1768 12 cr. 50 Tortoise .. 70 25

**923.** Bank Emblem.

**1979.** 25th Anniv. of Northeast Bank of Brazil.
1769. **923.** 2 cr. 50 multicoloured 15 10

**924.** Physicians and Patient (15th cent. woodcut).

**1979.** 150th Anniv. of National Academy of Medicine.
1770. **924.** 2 cr. 50 yellow & black 15 10

**925.** Clover with Hearts as Leaves.

**1979.** 35th Brazilian Cardiology Congress.
1771. **925.** 2 cr. 50 multicoloured 15 10

**927.** " Cithaerias aurora ".

**1979.** " Brasiliana 79 ". (2nd issue). Butterflies. Multicoloured.
1773. 2 cr. 50 Type **927** .. 30 15
1774. 10 cr. 50 " Evenus regalis " 90 25
1775. 12 cr. " Caligo eurilochus " 1·00 35
1776. 12 cr. 50 " Diaethria clymena janeira " .. 1·10 40

**928.** Embraer Xingu. **929.** Globe illuminating Land.

**1979.** 10th Anniv of Brazilian Aeronautical Industry
1777 **928** 2 cr. 50 dp blue & blue 15 10

**1979.** National Week.
1778 **929** 3 cr. 20 blue, grn & yell 15 10

**930.** Our Lady Aparecida. **931.** Envelope and Transport.

**1979.** 75th Anniv. of Coronation of Our Lady Aparecida.
1779. **930.** 2 cr. 50 multicoloured 15 10

**1979.** 18th U.P.U. Congress, Rio de Janeiro (4th issue). Multicoloured.
1780 2 cr. 50 Type **931** .. 20 10
1781 2 cr. 50 Post Office emblems .. .. 20 10
1782 10 cr. 50 Globe .. .. 35 20
1783 12 cr. Flags of Brazil and U.P.U .. .. 40 20
1784 12 cr. 50 U.P.U. emblem 40 20

**932.** " Igreja da Gloria ". **933.** Pyramid Fountain, Rio de Janeiro.

**1979.** " Brasiliana 79 " Third World Thematic Stamp Exhibition (3rd issue). Paintings by Leandro Joaquim. Mult.
1785. 2 cr. 50 Type **932** .. 15 10
1786. 12 cr. " Fishing on Guanabara Bay " .. .. 35 20
1787. 12 cr. 50 " Boqueirao Lake and Carioca Arches " 45 25

**1979.** " Brasiliana 79 " (4th issue). 1st International Exhibition of Classical Philately. Fountains.
1788. **933.** 2 cr. 50 black, green and emerald .. 10 10
1789. – 10 cr. 50 black, turq. and blue .. .. 35 20
1790. – 12 cr. black, red and pink .. .. 40 25

DESIGNS—VERT. 12 cr. Boa Vista, Recife. HORIZ. 10 cr. 50, Marilia Fountain, Ouro Preto.

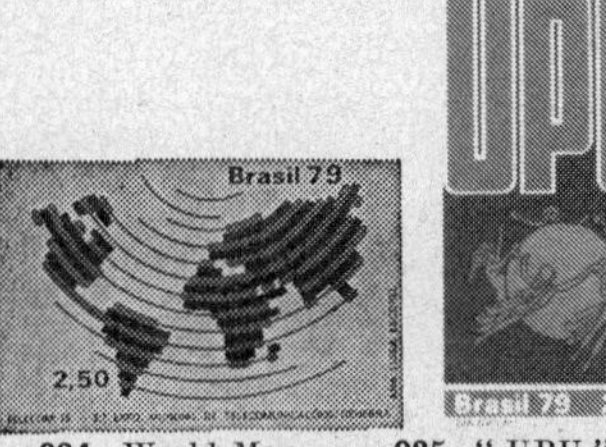


**934.** World Map. **935.** " UPU " and Emblem.

**1979.** Third World Telecommunications Exhibition, Geneva.
1791. **934.** 2 cr. 50 multicoloured 15 10

**1979.** U.P U. Day.
1792. **935.** 2 cr. 50 multicoloured 15 10
1793. 10 cr. 50 multicoloured 35 15
1794. 12 cr. multicoloured 35 15
1795. 12 cr. 50 multicoloured 35 20

**936.** " Peteca " (shuttlecock).

**1979.** International Year of the Child. Multicoloured.
1796. 2 cr. 50 Type **936** .. 20 10
1797. 3 cr. 20 Spinning top .. 20 10
1798. 3 cr. 20 Jumping Jack .. 20 10
1799. 3 cr. 20 Rag doll .. 20 10

**937.** " The Birth of Jesus ".

**1979.** Christmas. Tiles from the Church of Our Lady of Health and Glory, Salvador. Multicoloured.
1800. 3 cr. 20 Type **937** .. 15 10
1801. 3 cr. 20 " Adoration of the Kings " .. .. 15 10
1802. 3 cr. 20 " The Boy Jesus among the Doctors " 15 10

**939.** Woman with Wheat. **940.** Steel Mill.

**1979.** Thanksgiving Day.
1804. **939.** 3 cr. 20 multicoloured 15 10

**1979.** 25th Anniv. of Cosipa Steel Works, Sao Paulo.
1805. **940.** 3 cr. 20 multicoloured 15 10

**941.** Plant within Raindrop. **942.** Coal Trucks.

**1980.** Energy Conservation. Multicoloured.
1806. 3 cr. 20 Type **941** .. 25 10
1807. 17 cr.+7 cr. Sun and lightbulb .. .. 35 10
1808. 20 cr.+8 cr. Windmill and lightbulb .. .. 60 55
1809. 21 cr.+9 cr. Dam and lightbulb .. .. 1·90 30

**1980.** Coal Industry.
1810. **942.** 4 cr. blk., orge. & red 25 15

**943.** Coconuts.

**1980.**
1811 **943** 2 cr. brown .. .. 15 10
1812 – 3 cr. red .. .. 15 10
1813 – 4 cr. orange .. 15 10
1814 – 5 cr. violet .. .. 15 10
1815 – 7 cr. orange .. 35 10
1816 – 10 cr. green .. .. 15 10
1817 – 12 cr. green .. .. 10 10
1818 – 15 cr. brown .. 15 10
1819 – 17 cr. red .. .. 35 10
1820 – 20 cr. brown .. 15 10
1821 – 24 cr. orange .. 50 10
1822 – 30 cr. black .. .. 25 10
1823 – 34 cr. brown .. 3·75 65
1824 – 38 cr. red .. 2·25 15
1825 – 42 cr. green .. .. 4·75 65
1825a – 45 cr. brown .. 10 10
1826 – 50 cr. orange .. 20 10
1826a – 57 cr. brown .. 1·60 95
1826b – 65 cr. purple .. 15 10
1827 – 66 cr. violet .. 3·75 95
1827a – 80 cr. red .. .. 50 45
1828 – 100 cr. brown .. 30 10
1828a – 120 cr. blue .. .. 20 10
1829 – 140 cr. red .. .. 4·75 10
1829a – 150 cr. green .. 20 10
1830 – 200 cr. green .. 40 10
1830a – 300 cr. purple .. 20 10
1831 – 500 cr. brown .. 1·60 10
1832 – 800 cr. green .. 75 10
1833 – 1000 cr. olive .. 20 10
1834 – 2000 cr. orange .. 20 10

DESIGNS: 3 cr. Mangoes. 4 cr. Corn. 5 cr. Onions. 7 cr. Oranges. 10 cr. Passion fruit. 12 cr. Pineapple. 15 cr. Bananas. 17 cr. Guarana. 20 cr. Sugar cane. 24 cr. Bee and honeycomb. 30 cr. Silkworm and mulberry. 34 cr. Cocoa beans. 38 cr. Coffee. 42 cr. Soya bean. 45 cr. Manioc. 50 cr. Wheat. 57 cr. Peanuts 65 cr. Rubber. 66 cr. Grapes. 80 cr. Brazil nuts. 100 cr. Cashews. 120 cr. Rice. 140 cr. Tomatoes. 150 cr. Eucalyptus. 200 cr. Castor-oil bean. 300 cr. Parana pine. 500 cr. Cotton. 800 cr. Carnauba palm. 1000 cr. Babassu palm. 2000 cr. Sunflower.

**944.** Banknote with Development Symbols.

**1980.** 21st Inter-American Bank of Development Directors' Annual Assembly Meeting, Rio de Janeiro.
1836. **944.** 4 cr. blue, brn. & blk. 15 10

**945.** Tapirape Mask.

**1980.** Indian Art. Ritual Masks. Mult.
1837. 4 cr. Type **945** .. .. 20 10
1838. 4 cr. Tukuna mask (vert.) 20 10
1839. 4 cr. Kanela mask (vert.) 20 10

**946.** Geometric Head. **947.** Duke of Caxias (after Miranda Junior).

**1980.** 30th Anniv. of Brazilian Television.
1840. **946.** 4 cr. multicoloured .. 15 10

**1980.** Death Centenary of Duke de Caxias (General and statesman).
1841. **947.** 4 cr. multicoloured .. 15 10

**948.** " The Labourer " (Candido Portinari).

**1980.** Art in Brazilian Museums. Mult.
1842. 24 cr. Type **948** .. .. 75 25
1843. 28 cr. " Mademoiselle Pogany " (statuette, Constantin Brancusi) 75 25
1844. 30 cr. " The Glass of Water " (A. de Figueiredo) .. 95 30

MUSEUMS. 24 cr. Sao Paulo Museum of Art. 28 cr. Rio de Janeiro Museum of Modern Art. 30 cr. Rio de Janeiro Museum of Fine Art.

**949.** " Graf Zeppelin " flying through " 50 ".

**1980.** 50th Annivs. of "Graf Zeppelin" and First South Atlantic Air Mail Flight.
1845. **949.** 4 cr. blk., blue & violet 20 15
1846. – 4 cr. multicoloured .. 20 15

DESIGN: No. 1846, Latecoere seaplane "Comte de la Vaulx".

**951.** Pope John Paul II and Fortaleza Cathedral. **952.** Shooting.

**1980.** Papal Visit and 10th National Eucharistic Congress. Pope John Paul II and cathedrals. Multicoloured.
1848 4 cr. Type **951** .. .. 25 15
1849 4 cr. St. Peter's, Rome (horiz) .. .. 25 15
1850 24 cr. Apericida (horiz) .. 65 40
1851 28 cr. Rio de Janeiro (horiz) 65 20
1852 30 cr. Brasilia (horiz) 1·50 25

**1980.** Olympic Games, Moscow. Mult.
1853. 4 cr. Type **952** .. .. 20 10
1854. 4 cr. Cycling .. .. 20 10
1855. 4 cr. Rowing .. .. 20 10

**953.** Classroom.

**1980.** Rondon Project (voluntary student work in rural areas).
1856 **953** 4 cr. multicoloured .. 20 10

**954.** Helen Keller and Anne Sullivan. **956.** Houses and Microscope.

**1980.** Birth Centenary of Helen Keller, and 4th Brazilian Congress on Prevention of Blindness, Belo Horizonte.
1857 **954** 4 cr. multicoloured .. 20 10

**1980.** National Health Day. Campaign against Chagas Disease (barber bug fever).
1859 **956** 4 cr. multicoloured .. 20 10

**957.** Communications Equipment.

**1980.** 15th Anniv. of National Telecommunications System.
1860. **957.** 5 cr. stone, blue and green .. .. 20 10

**959.** "Cattleya amethystoglossa". **960.** Vinaceous Amazon.

**1980.** " Espamer 80 ". International Stamp Exhibition, Madrid. Orchids. Multicoloured.

1862. 5 cr. Type **959** .. .. 30 10
1863. 5 cr. " Laelia cinnabarina " .. .. .. 30 10
1864. 24 cr. " Zygopetalum crinitum " .. .. 75 35
1865. 28 cr. " Laelia tenebrosa " 75 40

**1980.** " Lubrapex 80 " Portuguesse–Brazilian Stamp Exhibition, Lisbon. Parrots. Multicoloured.

1866. 5 cr. Type **960** .. .. 60 40
1867. 5 cr. Red-tailed Amazon 60 40
1868. 28 cr. Red-spectacled Amazon .. .. 2·75 1·00
1869. 28 cr. Brown backed Parrotlet .. .. .. 2·75 1·00

**961.** Captain Rodrigo. (fictional character). **962.** Flight into Egypt.

**1980.** Book Day and Erico Verissimo (writer). Commemoration.

1870. **961.** 5 cr. multicoloured .. 20 10

**1980.** Christmas.

1871. **962.** 5 cr. multicoloured .. 20 10

**963.** Wave-form.

**1980.** Inauguration of Telecommunications Centre for Research and Development, Campanas City.

1872. **963.** 5 cr. multicoloured .. 20 10

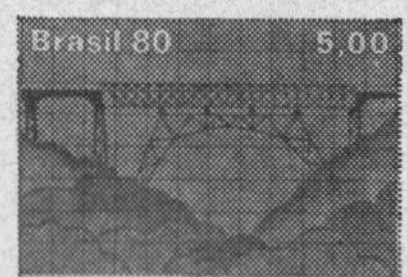


**964.** Carvalho Viaduct.

**1980.** Centenary of Engineering Club.

1873. **964.** 5 cr. multicoloured .. 35 15

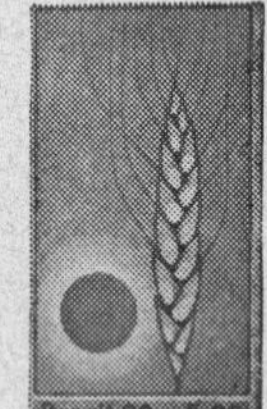


**965.** Postal Chess-board. **966.** Sun and Wheat.

**1980.** Postal Chess.

1874. **965.** 5 cr. multicoloured .. 55 20

**1980.** Thanksgiving Day.

1875. **966.** 5 cr. multicoloured .. 20 15

**967.** Father Anchieta writing Poem in Sand.

**1980.** Beatification of Father Jose de Anchieta.

1876. **967.** 5 cr. multicoloured .. 20 10

**968.** Christ on the Mount of Olives.

**1980.** 250th Birth Anniv of Antonio Lisboa (Aleijadinho) (sculptor). Wood sculptures of Christ's head. Multicoloured.

1877 5 cr. Type **968** .. .. 30 30
1878 5 cr. The Arrest in the Garden .. .. 30 30
1879 5 cr. Flagellation .. 30 30
1880 5 cr. Wearing Crown of Thorns .. .. 30 30
1881 5 cr. Carrying the cross .. 30 30
1882 5 cr. Crucifixion .. .. 30 30

**969.** Agricultural Produce.

**1981.** Agricultural Development. Mult.

1883. 30 cr. Type **969** .. .. 1·25 25
1884. 35 cr. Shopping .. .. 80 30
1885. 40 cr. Exporting .. .. 80 30

**970.** Scout sitting by Camp Fire.

**1981.** Fourth Pan-American Jamboree. Multicoloured.

1886 5 cr. Type **970** .. .. 25 10
1887 5 cr. Troop cooking .. 25 10
1888 5 cr. Scout with totem pole .. .. .. 25 10

**973.** Lima Barreto and Rio de Janeiro Street Scene.

**1981.** Birth Cent. of Lima Barreto (author).

1891. **973.** 7 cr. multicoloured .. 20 10

**974.** Tupi-Guarani Ceramic Funeral Urn.

**1981.** Artefacts from Brazilian Museums. Multicoloured.

1892 7 cr. Type **974** (Archaeology and Popular Arts Museum, Paranagua) .. .. 20 15
1893 7 cr. Marajoara "tanga" ceramic loincloth (Emilio Goeldi Museum, Para) .. .. 20 15
1894 7 cr. Maraca tribe funeral urn (National Museum, Rio de Janeiro) .. 20 15

**975.** Ruby-topaz Hummingbird.

**1981.** Hummingbirds. Multicoloured.

1895. 7 cr. Type **975** .. .. 85 25
1896. 7 cr. Horned Sungem .. 85 25
1897. 7 cr. Frilled Coquette .. 85 25
1898. 7 cr. Planalto Hermit .. 85 25

**976.** Hands and Cogwheels.

**1981.** 72nd International Rotary Convention, Sao Paulo.

1899 **976** 7 cr. red and black .. 15 10
1900 – 35 cr. multicoloured 75 30

Design: 35 cr. Head and cogwheels.

**977.** "Protection of the Water".

**1981.** Environment Protection. Multicoloured.

1901. 7 cr. Type **977** .. .. 25 15
1902. 7 cr. " Protection of the forests " .. .. 25 15
1903. 7 cr. " Protection of the air " .. .. .. 25 15
1904. 7 cr. " Protection of the soil " .. .. .. 25 15

**978.** Curtiss Fledgling.

**1981.** 50th Anniv. of National Air Mail Service.

1905. **978.** 7 cr. multicoloured .. 20 10

**979.** Locomotive " Colonel Church " and Map of Railway.

**1981.** 50th Anniv. of Madeira-Mamore Railway Nationalization.

1906. **979.** 7 cr. multicoloured .. 40 20

**980.** Esperanto Star and Arches of Alvorada Governmental Palace, Brasilia.

**1981.** 66th World Esperanto Congress, Brasilia.

1907. **980.** 7 cr. grn., grey & blk. 15 10

**981.** Pedro II and 50 r. " Small Head " Stamp.

**1981.** Cent. of Pedro II "Small Head" Stamps.

1908. **981.** 50 cr. brn., blk. & blue 1·10 25
1909. – 55 cr. mauve and green 1·10 25
1910. – 60 cr. blue, blk. & orge. 95 30

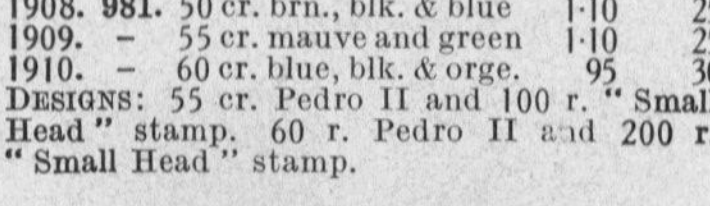

Designs: 55 cr. Pedro II and 100 r. " Small Head " stamp. 60 r. Pedro II and 200 r. " Small Head " stamp.

**982.** Military Institute of Engineering.

**1981.** 50th Anniv. of Military Institute of Engineering.

1911. **982.** 12 cr. multicoloured 15 10

**983.** Caboclinhos Folkdance.

**1981.** Festivities. Multicoloured.

1912. 50 cr. Type **983** .. .. 55 15
1913. 55 cr. Marujada folk festival .. .. 55 15
1914. 60 cr. Resado parade .. 55 20

**984.** Sun and Erect, Drooping, and Supported Flowers.

**1981.** International Year of Disabled Persons.

1915 **984** 12 cr. multicoloured .. 20 10

**985.** " Dalechampia caperoniodes ". **986.** Image of Our Lady of Nazareth.

**1981.** Flowers of the Central Plateau. Multicoloured.

1916. 12 cr. Type **985** .. .. 20 15
1917. 12 cr. " Palicourea rigida " 20 15
1918. 12 cr. " Eremanthus sphaerocephalus " (vert.) 20 15
1919. 12 cr. " Cassia clausseni " (vert.) .. .. .. 20 15

**1981.** Festival of Our Lady of Nazareth, Belem.

1920. **986.** 12 cr. multicoloured 15 10

**987.** Christ the Redeemer Monument. **988.** Farmhands seeding the Land.

**1981.** 50th Anniv. of Christ the Redeemer Monument, Rio de Janeiro.

1921. **987.** 12 cr. multicoloured 15 10

**1981.** World Food Day.

1922. **988.** 12 cr. multicoloured 15 10

**989.** Santos Dumont and Biplane "14 bis" landing at Paris.

**1981.** 75th Anniv. of Santos Dumont's First Powered Flight.

1923. **989.** 60 cr. multicoloured 75 20

**990.** Friar Santos Rita Durao, Title Page and Scene from "Caramuru".

**1981.** Book Day and Bicentenary of Publication of Epic Poem " Caramuru ".

1924. **990.** 12 cr. multicoloured 15 10

**991.** Crib, Juazeiro de Norte, (Cica.)

**1981.** Christmas. Various designs showing Cribs. Multicoloured.

1925. 12 cr. Type **991** .. .. 15 10
1926. 50 cr. Caruaru, (Vitalino Filho) .. .. .. 75 15
1927. 55 cr. Sao Jose dos Campos, (Eugenia) (vert.) .. 75 15
1928. 60 cr. Taubate, (Candida) (vert.) .. .. .. 1·10 20

**992.** Alagoas.

**1981.** State Flags (1st series). Multicoloured.

| | | | |
|---|---|---|---|
| 1929 | 12 cr. Type **992** .. .. | 25 | 25 |
| 1930 | 12 cr. Bahia .. .. | 25 | 25 |
| 1931 | 12 cr. Federal District .. | 25 | 25 |
| 1932 | 12 cr. Pernambuco .. | 25 | 25 |
| 1933 | 12 cr. Sergipe .. .. | 25 | 25 |

See also Nos. 1988/92, 2051/5, 2113/17, 2204/7 and 2432.

**993.** Girls with Wheat. **994.** Heads and Symbols of Occupations.

**1981.** Thanksgiving Day.

1934 **993** 12 cr. multicoloured .. 15 10

**1981.** 50th Anniv. of Ministry of Labour.

1935. **994.** 12 cr. multicoloured 15 10

**995.** Federal Engineering School, Itajuba.

**1981.** Birth Cent. of Theodomiro Carneiro Santiago (founder of Federal Engineering School).

1936. **995.** 15 cr. green and mauve 15 10

**996.** Musician of Police Military Band and Headquarters. **997.** Army Library " Ex Libris ".

**1981.** 150th Anniv. of Sao Paulo Military Police. Multicoloured.

| | | | |
|---|---|---|---|
| 1937. | 12 cr. Type **996** .. .. | 25 | 10 |
| 1938. | 12 cr. Lancers of Ninth of July Regiment, Mounted Police .. .. | 25 | 10 |

**1981.** Centenary of Army Library.

1939. **997.** 12 cr. multicoloured 15 10

**999.** Brigadier Eduardo Gomes.

**1982.** Brigadier Eduardo Gomes Commem.

1941. **999.** 12 cr. blue and black 15 10

**1000.** Lage, Trucks, "Ita" Freighter and HL-1 Airplane.

**1982.** Birth Centenary of Henrique Lage (industrialist).

1942. **1000.** 17 cr. multicoloured 1·10 20

**1001.** Tackle. **1002** Microscope, Bacillus and Lung.

**1982.** World Cup Football Championship, Spain. Multicoloured.

| | | | |
|---|---|---|---|
| 1943. | 75 cr. Type **1001** .. .. | 90 | 20 |
| 1944. | 80 cr. Kicking ball .. | 90 | 20 |
| 1945. | 85 cr. Goalkeeper .. | 90 | 20 |

**1982.** Centenary of Robert Koch's Discovery of Tubercle Bacillus. Multicoloured.

| | | | |
|---|---|---|---|
| 1947. | 90 cr. Type **1002** .. .. | 1·90 | 75 |
| 1948. | 100 cr. Flasks, tablets, syringe, bacillus and lung .. .. .. | 1·90 | 75 |

**1004.** Oil Rig Workers.

**1982.** Birth Centenary of Monteiro Lobato (writer).

1950. **1004.** 17 cr. multicoloured 20 10

**1005.** St. Vincent de Paul.

**1982.** 400th Birth Anniv. of St. Vincent de Paul.

1951. **1005.** 17 cr. multicoloured 15 10

**1006.** Fifth Fall.

**1982.** Guaira's Seven Falls. Multicoloured.

| | | | |
|---|---|---|---|
| 1952. | 17 cr. Type **1006** .. .. | 20 | 10 |
| 1953. | 21 cr. Seventh fall .. | 25 | 10 |

**1007.** Envelope, Telephone, Antenna and Postcode.

**1982.** 15th Anniv. of Ministry of Communications.

1954. **1007.** 21 cr. multicoloured 15 10

**1008.** House of the Train (National Historical Museum).

**1982.** 50th Anniv. of Museology Course.

1955. **1008.** 17 cr. black and pink 15 10

**1009.** Cogwheels and Ore Mountains.

**1982.** 40th Anniv. of Vale do Rio Doce Company.

1956. **1009.** 17 cr. multicoloured 15 10

**1010.** Martim Afonso de Souza proclaiming Sao Vicente a Town.

**1982.** 450th Anniv. of Sao Vicente.

1957. **1010.** 17 cr. multicoloured 15 10

**1011.** Giant Anteater.

**1982.** Animals. Multicoloured.

| | | | |
|---|---|---|---|
| 1958. | 17 cr. Type **1011** .. | 40 | 10 |
| 1959. | 21 cr. Maned wolf .. | 60 | 15 |
| 1960. | 30 cr. Pampas deer .. | 1·10 | 25 |

**1012.** Film and " Golden Palm ". **1014.** Church of Our Lady of O, Sabara.

**1982.** 20th Anniv. of "Golden Palm" Film Award to "The Given World".

1961. **1012.** 17 cr. multicoloured 20 10

**1982.** Baroque-style Architecture in Minas Gerais. Multicoloured.

| | | | |
|---|---|---|---|
| 1963. | 17 cr. Type **1014** .. .. | 20 | 10 |
| 1964. | 17 cr. Church of Our Lady of Carmo, Mariana (horiz.) .. .. | 20 | 10 |
| 1965. | 17 cr. Church of Our Lady of Rosary, Diamantina (horiz.) .. .. | 20 | 10 |

**1015.** St. Francis of Assisi. **1016.** " Large Head " Stamp of 1882.

**1982.** 800th Birth Anniv. of St. Francis of Assisi.

1966. **1015.** 21 cr. multicoloured 15 10

**1982.** Centenary of Pedro II "Large Head" Stamps.

1967. **1016.** 21 cr. yellow, brown and black .. 15 10

**1017.** Amazon River and Hands holding Scion, Screw and Coin.

**1982.** Manaus Free Trade Zone.

1968. **1017.** 75 cr. multicoloured 95 20

**1019.** Xango.

**1982.** Orixas Religious Costumes. Mult.

| | | | |
|---|---|---|---|
| 1970. | 20 cr. Type **1019** .. | 20 | 10 |
| 1971. | 20 cr. Iemanja .. .. | 20 | 10 |
| 1972. | 20 cr. Oxumare .. .. | 20 | 10 |

**1020.** XII Florin.

**1982.** 10th Anniv. of Brazilian Central Bank Values Museum. Multicoloured.

| | | | |
|---|---|---|---|
| 1973. | 25 cr. Type **1020** .. | 20 | 10 |
| 1974. | 25 cr. Pedro I Coronation piece .. .. .. | 20 | 10 |

**1021.** " Ipiranga Cry " (Dom Pedro proclaiming independence). **1022.** St. Theresa of Jesus.

**1982.** Independence Week.

1975. **1021.** 25 cr. multicoloured 20 10

**1982.** 400th Death Anniv. of St. Theresa of Jesus.

1976. **1022.** 85 cr. multicoloured 95 15

**1023.** Musical Instrument Maker. **1024.** Embraer Tucano Trainers.

**1982.** " Lubrapex 82 " Brazilian–Portuguese Stamp Exhibition, Curitiba. The Paranaense Fandango. Multicoloured.

| | | | |
|---|---|---|---|
| 1977. | 75 cr. Type **1023** .. | 75 | 20 |
| 1978. | 80 cr. Dancers .. .. | 75 | 20 |
| 1979. | 85 cr. Musicians .. .. | 75 | 20 |

**1982.** Aeronautical Industry Day.

1981. **1024.** 24 cr. multicoloured 20 25

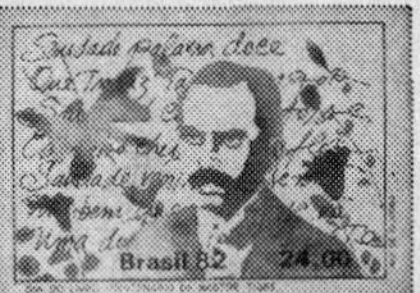


**1025.** Bastos Tigre and Verse from " Saudade ".

**1982.** Day of the Book and Birth Centenary of Bastos Tigre (poet).

1982. **1025.** 24 cr. multicoloured 15 10

**1026.** Telephone Dial on Map of Brazil.

**1982.** 10th Anniv. of Telebras (Brazilian Telecommunications Corporation).

1983. **1026.** 24 cr. multicoloured 15 10

**1027.** " Nativity " (C.S. Miyaba).

**1982.** Christmas. Children's Paintings. Multicoloured.

| | | | |
|---|---|---|---|
| 1984. | 24 cr. Type **1027** .. | 95 | 10 |
| 1985. | 24 cr. " Choir of Angels " (N. N. Aleluia) .. | 95 | 10 |
| 1986. | 30 cr. " Holy Family " (F. T. Filho) .. .. | 95 | 15 |
| 1987. | 30 cr. " Nativity with Angel " (N. Arand) .. | 95 | 15 |

**1982.** State Flags (2nd series). As T **992.** Multicoloured.

| | | | |
|---|---|---|---|
| 1988. | 24 cr. Ceara .. .. | 70 | 20 |
| 1989. | 24 cr. Espirito Santo .. | 70 | 20 |
| 1990. | 24 cr. Paraiba .. .. | 70 | 20 |
| 1991. | 24 cr. Rio Grande do Norte | 70 | 20 |
| 1992. | 24 cr. Rondonia .. .. | 70 | 20 |

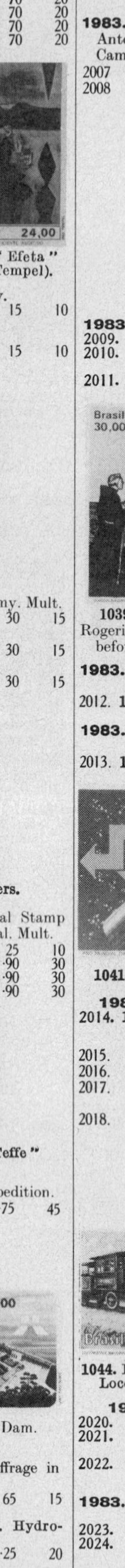

**1028.** " Germination ". **1029.** " Efeta " (S. Tempel).

**1982.** Thanksgiving Day.
1993. **1028.** 24 cr. multicoloured 15 10

**1982.** The Hard of Hearing.
1994. **1029.** 24 cr. multicoloured 15 10

**1030.** "Benjamin Constant" (cadet ship).

**1982.** Bicentenary of Naval Academy. Mult.

| | | | |
|---|---|---|---|
| 1995 | 24 cr. Type **1030** .. | 30 | 15 |
| 1996 | 24 cr. "Almirante Saldanha" (cadet ship) | 30 | 15 |
| 1997 | 24 cr. "Brasil" (training frigate) .. .. | 30 | 15 |

**1032.** Samba Parade Drummers.

**1983.** "Brasiliana 83" International Stamp Exhibition, Rio de Janeiro. Carnival. Mult.

| | | | |
|---|---|---|---|
| 1999. | 24 cr. Type **1032** .. | 25 | 10 |
| 2000. | 130 cr. Masked clowns .. | 1·90 | 30 |
| 2001. | 140 cr. Dancer .. .. | 1·90 | 30 |
| 2002. | 150 cr. Indian .. .. | 1·90 | 30 |

**1033.** Support Ship " Barao de Teffe " in Antarctic.

**1983.** First Brazilian Antarctic Expedition.
2003. **1033.** 150 cr. multicoloured 1·75 45

**1034.** Woman with Ballot Paper. **1035.** Itaipu Dam.

**1983.** 50th Anniv. of Women's Suffrage in Brazil.
2004. **1034.** 130 cr. multicoloured 65 15

**1983.** Itaipu Brazilian-Paraguayan. Hydro-electric Project.
2005. **1035.** 140 cr. multicoloured 1·25 20

**1036.** Luther. **1037.** Microscope and Crab.

**1983.** 500th Anniv. of Martin Luther. (Protestant reformer).
2006. **1036.** 150 cr. deep green, green and black 1·60 30

**1983.** Cancer Prevention. 30th Anniv. of Antonio Prudente Foundation and A.C. Camargo Hospital. Multicoloured.

| | | | |
|---|---|---|---|
| 2007 | 30 cr. Type **1037** .. | 25 | 20 |
| 2008 | 38 cr. Antonio Prudente, hospital and crab .. | 25 | 20 |

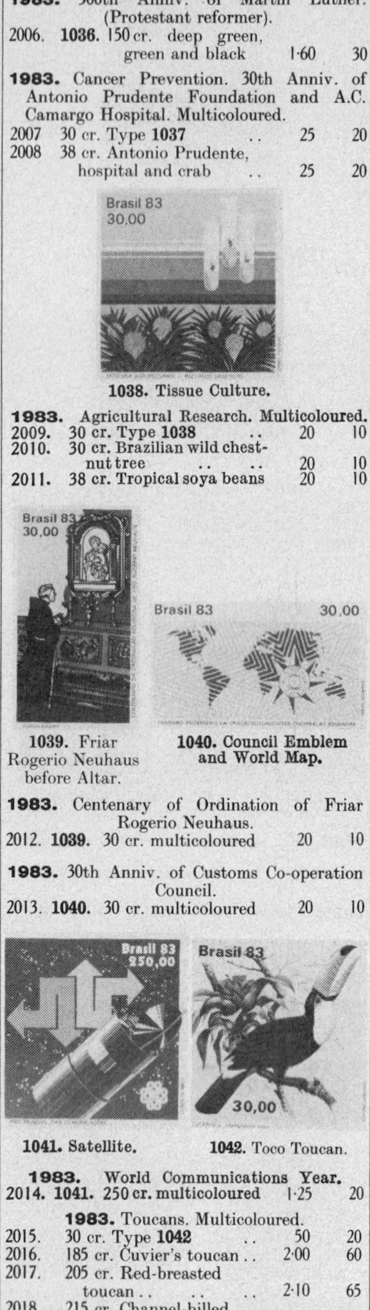

**1038.** Tissue Culture.

**1983.** Agricultural Research. Multicoloured.

| | | | |
|---|---|---|---|
| 2009. | 30 cr. Type **1038** .. | 20 | 10 |
| 2010. | 30 cr. Brazilian wild chest-nut tree | 20 | 10 |
| 2011. | 38 cr. Tropical soya beans | 20 | 10 |

**1039.** Friar Rogerio Neuhaus before Altar. **1040.** Council Emblem and World Map.

**1983.** Centenary of Ordination of Friar Rogerio Neuhaus.
2012. **1039.** 30 cr. multicoloured 20 10

**1983.** 30th Anniv. of Customs Co-operation Council.
2013. **1040.** 30 cr. multicoloured 20 10

**1041.** Satellite. **1042.** Toco Toucan.

**1983.** World Communications Year.
2014. **1041.** 250 cr. multicoloured 1·25 20

**1983.** Toucans. Multicoloured.

| | | | |
|---|---|---|---|
| 2015. | 30 cr. Type **1042** | 50 | 20 |
| 2016. | 185 cr. Cuvier's toucan .. | 2·00 | 60 |
| 2017. | 205 cr. Red-breasted toucan .. .. .. | 2·10 | 65 |
| 2018. | 215 cr. Channel-billed toucan .. .. .. | 2·10 | 80 |

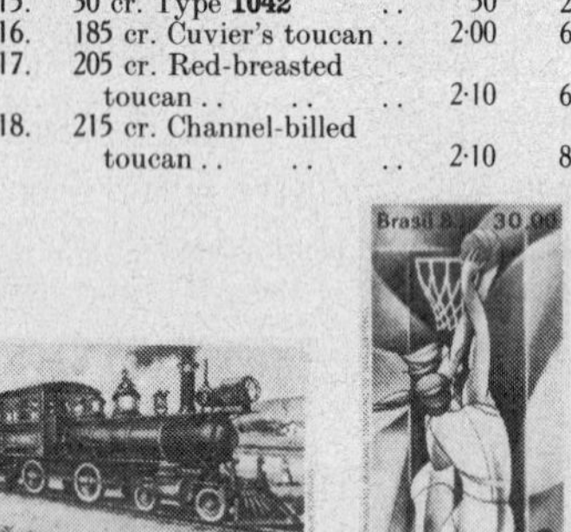

**1044.** Baldwin " No. 1 " Locomotive, 1880. **1045.** Basketball Players.

**1983.** Locomotives. Multicoloured.

| | | | |
|---|---|---|---|
| 2020. | 30 cr. Type **1044** .. | 25 | 10 |
| 2021. | 30 cr. Hohenzollern " No. 980 ", 1889 .. | 25 | 10 |
| 2022. | 38 cr. Fowler " No. 1 ", 1871 .. .. .. | 25 | 10 |

**1983.** Ninth Women's World Basketball Championship, Sao Paulo.

| | | | |
|---|---|---|---|
| 2023. | 30 cr. Type **1045** .. | 25 | 10 |
| 2024. | 30 cr. Basketball players (different) .. .. | 25 | 10 |

**1046.** Bolivar (after Tito Salas).

**1983.** Birth Bicent. of Simon Bolivar.
2025. **1046.** 30 cr. multicoloured 20 10

**1047.** Boy with Kite and Boy waiting for Polio Vaccination. **1048.** Minerva and Computer Punched Tape.

**1983.** Polio and Measles Vaccination Campaign. Multicoloured.

| | | | |
|---|---|---|---|
| 2026. | 30 cr. Type **1047** .. .. | 30 | 10 |
| 2027. | 30 cr. Girl on bicycle and girl receiving measles vaccination .. .. | 30 | 10 |

**1983.** 20th Anniv. of Post-graduate Master's Programmes in Engineering.
2028. **1048.** 30 cr. light brown, blue and brown .. 20 10

**1049.** 30 r. "Bull's Eye" Stamp and Rio de Janeiro Bay.

**1983.** "Brasiliana 83" International Stamp Exhibition, Rio de Janeiro. 140th Anniv. of "Bull's Eye" Stamps.

| | | | | |
|---|---|---|---|---|
| 2029 | **1049** | 185 cr. black & bl | 1·25 | 20 |
| 2030 | – | 205 cr. black & bl | 1·25 | 20 |
| 2031 | – | 215 cr. black & vio | 1·25 | 20 |

DESIGNS: Nos. 2030/1, As Type **1049** but showing 60 r. and 90 r. "Bull's Eye" stamp respectively.

**1052.** Embraer EMB-120.

**1983.** Brazilian Aeronautics Industry.
2035. **1052.** 30 cr. multicoloured 25 10

**1053.** Bosco and State Departments Esplanade, Brasilia.

**1983.** Dom Bosco's Dream of Brazil.
2036. **1053.** 130 cr. multicoloured 75 10

**1054.** " Council of State decides on Independence " (detail, Georgina de Albuquerque).

**1983.** National Week.
2037 **1054** 50 cr. multicoloured 15 10

**1055.** Iron and Steel Production. **1056.** " Pilosocereus gounellei ".

**1983.** 10th Anniv. of Siderbras (Brazilian Steel Corporation).
2038. **1055.** 45 cr. multicoloured 15 10

**1983.** Cacti. Multicoloured.

| | | | |
|---|---|---|---|
| 2039. | 45 cr. Type **1056** .. | 95 | 10 |
| 2040. | 45 cr. "Melocactus bahiensis" .. .. | 95 | 10 |
| 2041. | 57 cr. "Cereus jamacari" | 95 | 10 |

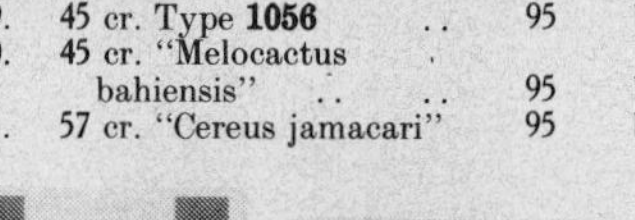

**1057.** Monstrance. **1058.** Mouth and Wheat.

**1983.** 50th Anniv. of National Eucharistic Congress.
2042. **1057.** 45 cr. multicoloured 15 10

**1983.** 20th Anniv of World Food Programme. Fishery Resources. Multicoloured.

| | | | |
|---|---|---|---|
| 2043. | 45 cr. Type **1058** .. | 20 | 15 |
| 2044. | 57 cr. Fish and fishing pirogue .. .. | 50 | 15 |

**1060.** "Our Lady of Angels" (wood, Fransico Xavier de Brito).

**1983.** Christmas. Statues of the Madonna. Multicoloured.

| | | | |
|---|---|---|---|
| 2046 | 45 cr. Type **1060** .. | 30 | 10 |
| 2047 | 315 cr. "Our Lady of Birth" .. .. | 2·25 | 20 |
| 2048 | 335 cr. "Our Lady of Joy" (fired clay, Agostinho de Jesus) .. .. | 2·25 | 20 |
| 2049 | 345 cr. "Our Lady of Presentation" .. | 2·25 | 20 |

**1061.** Moraes and Map of Italian Campaign.

**1983.** Birth Centenary of Marshal Mascarenhas de Moraes.
2050 **1061** 45 cr. pink, grn & pur 20 15

**1983.** State Flags (3rd series). As Type **992.** Multicoloured.

| | | | |
|---|---|---|---|
| 2051. | 45 cr. Amazonas .. | 30 | 15 |
| 2052. | 45 cr. Goias .. .. | 30 | 15 |
| 2053. | 45 cr. Rio de Janeiro .. | 30 | 15 |
| 2054. | 45 cr. Mato Grosso do Sul | 30 | 15 |
| 2055. | 45 cr. Parana .. .. | 30 | 15 |

**1062.** Praying Figure and Wheat.

**1983.** Thanksgiving Day.
2056. **1062.** 45 cr. multicoloured 15 10

**1063.** Friar Vincente Borgard. **1064.** Montgolfier Balloon.

**1983.** Obligatory Tax. Anti-Leprosy Week.
2057 **1063** 10 cr. brown .. 95 65

**1983.** Bicentenary of Manned Flight.
2058. **1064.** 345 cr. multicoloured 2·25 95

**1065.** Indian, Portuguese Navigator and Negro.

**1984.** 50th Anniv of Publication of "Masters and Slaves" by Gilberto Freyre.
2059 **1065** 45 cr. multicoloured 60 10

**1066.** Crystal Palace.

**1984.** Centenary of Crystal Palace, Petropolis.
2060 **1066** 45 cr. multicoloured 25 10

**1068.** "Don Afonso" (sail/steam warship) and Figurehead.

**1984.** Cent. of Naval Oceanographic Museum.
2062. **1068.** 620 cr. multicoloured 1·25 35

**1069.** Manacled Hands and Beached Fishing Pirogue.

**1984.** Centenary of Abolition of Slavery in Ceara and Amazonas. Multicoloured.
2063. 585 cr. Type **1069** .. 95 40
2064. 610 cr. Emancipated slave .. .. .. 95 40

**1071.** Long Jumping.

**1984.** Olympic Games, Los Angeles. Mult.
2066 65 cr. Type **1071** .. 65 20
2067 65 cr. 100 metres .. 65 20
2068 65 cr. Relay .. .. 65 20
2069 585 cr. Pole vaulting .. 65 20
2070 610 cr. High jumping .. 65 20
2071 620 cr. Hurdling .. 65 20

**1072.** Oil Rigs and Blast Furnace.

**1073.** Pedro Alvares Cabral.

**1984.** Birth Cent (1983) of Getulio Vargas (President 1930–45 and 1951–54). Mult.
2072 65 cr. Type **1072** .. 15 10
2073 65 cr. Ballot boxes and symbols of professions and trades .. .. 15 10
2074 65 cr. Sugar refinery and electricity pylons .. 15 10

**1984.** "Espana 84" International Stamp Exhibition, Madrid. Explorers. Multicoloured.
2075 65 cr. Type **1073** .. 15 10
2076 610 cr. Christopher Columbus .. .. 1·25 20

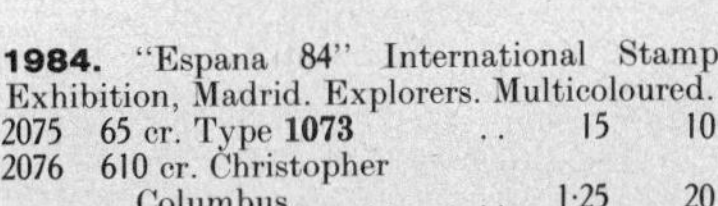

**1074.** Heads and Map of Americas.

**1075.** Chinese Painting.

**1984** 8th Pan-American Surety Association General Assembly.
2077 **1074** 65 cr. multicoloured 15 10

**1984.** "Lubrapex 84" Brazillian–Portuguese Stamp Exhibition, Lisbon.
2078. **1075.** 65 cr. multicoloured 15 10
2079. – 585 cr. mult. .. 65 15
2080. – 610 cr. mult. .. 65 15
2081. – 620 cr. mult. .. 65 15
DESIGNS: 585 to 620 cr. Chinese paintings from Mariana Cathedral.

**1077.** Marsh Deer and Great Egret.

**1984.** Mato Grosso Flood Plain. Mult.
2083 65 cr. Type **1077** .. 80 50
2084 65 cr. Jaguar, capybara and roseate spoonbill .. 80 50
2085 80 cr. Alligator, jabiru and red-cowled cardinals .. .. 85 55

**1078.** "The First Letter Sent from Brazil" (Guido Mondin).

**1079.** Route Map and Dornier Wal Flying Boat.

**1984.** 1st Anniv of Postal Union of the Americas and Spain H.Q, Montevideo, Uruguay.
2086 **1078** 65 cr. multicoloured 40 15

**1984.** 50th Anniv. of First Trans-Oceanic Air Route. Multicoloured.
2087. 610 cr. Type **1079** .. 1·60 50
2088. 620 cr. Support ship "Westfalen" and Dornier Wal .. .. 1·60 35

**1080.** Mother and Baby.

**1081.** Murrah Buffaloes.

**1984.** Wildlife Preservation Woolley Spider Monkey. Multicoloured.
2089 65 cr. Type **1080** .. 25 10
2090 80 cr. Monkey in tree .. 25 10

**1984.** Marajo Island Water Buffaloes. Designs showing different races. Multicoloured.
2091 65 cr. Type **1081** .. 40 30
2092 65 cr. Carabao buffaloes 40 30
2093 65 cr. Mediterranean buffaloes .. .. 30 25
Nos. 201/3 were issued together se-tenant forming a composite design.

**1082.** Headquarters, Salvador.

**1984.** 150th Anniv. of Economic Bank.
2094. **1082.** 65 cr. multicoloured 15 10

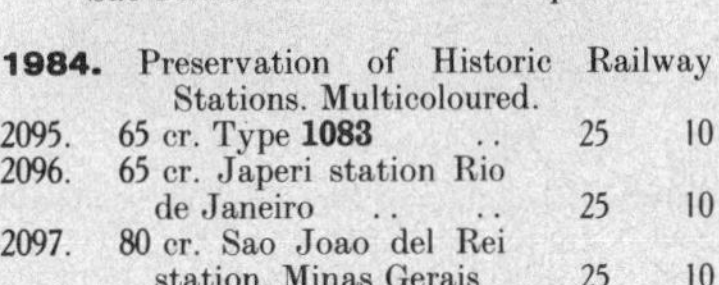

**1083.** Da Luz Station, Sao Paulo.

**1085.** Roof protecting Couple.

**1984.** Preservation of Historic Railway Stations. Multicoloured.
2095. 65 cr. Type **1083** .. 25 10
2096. 65 cr. Japeri station Rio de Janeiro .. .. 25 10
2097. 80 cr. Sao Joao del Rei station, Minas Gerais 25 10

**1984.** 20th Anniv. of National Housing Bank.
2099. **1085.** 65 cr. multicoloured 10 10

**1086.** "Pedro I" (Solano Peixoto Machado).

**1984.** National Week. Designs showing children's paintings. Multicoloured.
2100. 100 cr. Type **1086** .. 15 10
2101. 100 cr. Girl painting word "BRASIL" (Juruce Maria Klein) 15 10
2102. 100 cr. Children of different races under rainbow (Priscela Barreto da Fonseca Bara) .. 15 10
2103. 100 cr. Caravels (Carlos Peixoto Mangueira) .. 15 10

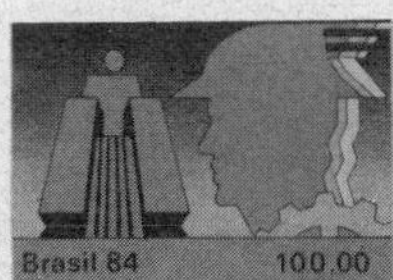

**1087.** Headquarters, Mercury and Cogwheel.

**1984.** 150th Anniv. of Rio de Janeiro Commercial Association.
2104. **1087.** 100 cr. multicoloured 15 10

**1088.** Pedro I.

**1984.** 150th Death Anniv of Emperor Pedro I.
2105 **1088** 1000 cr. multicoloured 2·50 15

**1089.** "Pycnoporus sanguineus".

**1090.** Child stepping from Open Book.

**1984.** Fungi. Multicoloured.
2106. 120 cr. Type **1089** .. 40 15
2107. 1050 cr. "Calvatia" sp. .. 2·25 25
2108. 1080 cr. "Pleurotus" sp. (horiz.) .. .. 2·25 25

**1984.** Book Day. Children's Literature.
2109 **1090** 120 cr. multicoloured 20 10

**1091.** New State Mint and 17th-century Minter.

**1092.** Computer Image of Eye.

**1984.** Inauguration of New State Mint, Santa Cruz, Rio de Janeiro.
2110. **1091.** 120 cr. bl. & deep bl. 15 10

**1984.** "Informatica 84" 17th National Information Congress and 4th International Informatics Fair, Rio de Janeiro.
2111 **1092** 120 cr. multicoloured 15 10

**1093.** Sculpture by Bruno Giorgi and Flags.

**1094.** Brasilia Cathedral and Wheat.

**1984.** 14th General Assembly of Organization of American States, Brasilia.
2112. **1093.** 120 cr. multicoloured 15 10

**1984.** State Flags (4th series). As T **992.**
2113. 120 cr. red, blk. & buff .. 45 15
2114. 120 cr. multicoloured .. 45 15
2115. 120 cr. multicoloured .. 45 15
2116. 120 cr. multicoloured .. 45 15
2117. 120 cr. multicoloured .. 45 15
DESIGNS: No. 2113, Minas Gerais. 2114, Mato Grosso. 2115, Piaui. 2116, Maranhao. 2117, Santa Catarina.

**1984.** Thanksgiving Day.
2118. **1094.** 120 cr. multicoloured 15 10

**1095.** Father Bento Dias Pacheco.

**1096.** "Nativity" (Djanira da Mota e Silva).

**1984.** Obligatory Tax. Anti-leprosy Week.
2119 **1095** 30 cr. blue .. 10 10
See also Nos. 2208, 2263 and 2291.

**1984.** Christmas. Paintings from Federal Savings Bank collection. Multicoloured.
2120 120 cr. Type **1096** .. 15 10
2121 120 cr. "Virgin and Child" (Glauco Rodrigues) .. 75 25
2122 1050 cr. "Flight into Egypt" (Paul Garfunkel) .. .. 1·90 15
2123 1080 cr. "Nativity" (Emiliano Augusto di Cavalcanti) .. .. 1·90 15

**1097.** Airbus Industrie A300.

**1984.** 40th Anniv. of I.C.A.O.
2124. **1097.** 120 cr. multicoloured 15 10

**1098.** Symbols of Agriculture and Industry on Hat.

**1984.** 25th Anniv. of North-east Development Office.

| | | | | |
|---|---|---|---|---|
| 2125. | **1098.** | 120 cr. multicoloured | 15 | 10 |

**1099.** "Virgin of Safe Journeys Church" (detail).

**1985.** 77th Death Anniv of Emilio Rouede (artist).

| | | | | |
|---|---|---|---|---|
| 2126 | **1099** | 120 cr. multicoloured | 20 | 10 |

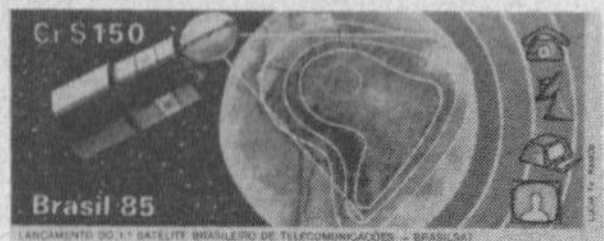

**1100.** "Brasilsat" over Brazil.

**1985.** Launch of "Brasilsat" (first Brazilian telecommunications satellite).

| | | | | |
|---|---|---|---|---|
| 2127 | **1100** | 150 cr. multicoloured | 25 | 10 |

**1101.** Trains and Station Plan.

**1985.** Inauguration of Metropolitan Surface Railway, Recife and Porto Alegre.

| | | | | |
|---|---|---|---|---|
| 2128 | **1101** | 200 cr. multicoloured | 40 | 10 |

**1102.** Butternut Tree. **1103.** Parachutist.

**1985.** Opening of Botanical Gardens, Brasilia.

| | | | | |
|---|---|---|---|---|
| 2129. | **1102.** | 200 cr. multicoloured | 20 | 10 |

**1985.** 40th Anniv. of Military Parachuting.

| | | | | |
|---|---|---|---|---|
| 2130. | **1103.** | 200 cr. multicoloured | 20 | 10 |

**1104.** Map, Temperature Graph and Weather Scenes.

**1985.** National Climate Programme

| | | | | |
|---|---|---|---|---|
| 2131. | **1104.** | 500 cr. multicoloured | 20 | 10 |

**1105.** Campolina. **1107.** "Polyvolume" (Mary Vieira).

**1106.** Ouro Preto.

**1985.** Brazilian Horses. Multicoloured.

| | | | |
|---|---|---|---|
| 2132 | 1000 cr. Type **1105** | 1·25 | 15 |
| 2133 | 1500 cr. Marajoara | 95 | 15 |
| 2134 | 1500 cr. Mangalarga pacer | 95 | 15 |

**1985.** U.N.E.S.C.O. World Heritage Sites. Multicoloured.

| | | | |
|---|---|---|---|
| 2135 | 220 cr. Type **1106** | 15 | 10 |
| 2136 | 220 cr. Sao Miguel das Missoes | 15 | 10 |
| 2137 | 220 cr. Olinda | 15 | 10 |

**1985.** 40th Anniv. of Rio-Branco Institute (diplomatic training academy).

| | | | | |
|---|---|---|---|---|
| 2138. | **1107.** | 220 cr. multicoloured | 10 | 10 |

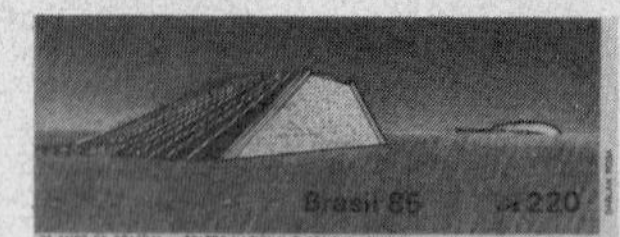

**1108.** National Theatre.

**1985.** 25th Anniv. of Brasilia. Multicoloured.

| | | | |
|---|---|---|---|
| 2139 | 220 cr. Type **1108** | 10 | 10 |
| 2140. | 220 cr. Catetinho (home of former President Juscelino Keubitschek) and memorial | 10 | 15 |

**1109.** Rondon and Morse Telegraph. **1110.** Fontoura and Pharmaceutical Equipment.

**1985.** 120th Birth Anniv. of Marshal Candido Mariano da Silva Rondon (military engineer and explorer).

| | | | | |
|---|---|---|---|---|
| 2141. | **1109.** | 220 cr. multicoloured | 10 | 10 |

**1985.** Birth Centenary of Candido Fontoura (pharmacist).

| | | | | |
|---|---|---|---|---|
| 2142. | **1110.** | 220 cr. multicoloured | 15 | 10 |

**1111.** Lizards. **1112.** Numeral. **1113.** Numeral.

**1985.** Rock Paintings. Multicoloured.

| | | | |
|---|---|---|---|
| 2143 | 300 cr. Type **1111** | 10 | 10 |
| 2144 | 300 cr. Deer | 10 | 10 |
| 2145 | 2000 cr. Various animals | 75 | 15 |

**1985.**

| | | | | |
|---|---|---|---|---|
| 2147 | **1112** | 50 cr. red | 10 | 10 |
| 2148 | | 100 cr. purple | 10 | 10 |
| 2149 | | 150 cr. lilac | 10 | 10 |
| 2150 | | 200 cr. blue | 10 | 10 |
| 2151 | | 220 cr. green | 10 | 10 |
| 2152 | | 300 cr. blue | 10 | 10 |
| 2153 | | 500 cr. black | 10 | 10 |
| 2154 | **1113** | 1000 cr. brown | 10 | 10 |
| 2155 | | 2000 cr. green | 15 | 10 |
| 2156 | | 3000 cr. lilac | 15 | 10 |
| 2157 | | 5000 cr. brown | 50 | 10 |

**1114.** Common Noddies

**1985.** National Marine Park, Abrolhos. Mult.

| | | | |
|---|---|---|---|
| 2168 | 220 cr. Type **1114** | 55 | 35 |
| 2169 | 220 cr. Magnificent frigate birds and blue-faced booby | 55 | 35 |
| 2170 | 220 cr. Blue-faced boobies and red-billed tropic bird | 55 | 35 |
| 2171 | 2000 cr. Grey plovers | 2·75 | 65 |

**1115.** Breast-feeding. **1116.** Bell 47J Ranger Helicopter rescuing Man, Corvette and Diver.

**1985.** United Nations Children's Fund Child Survival Campaign. Multicoloured.

| | | | |
|---|---|---|---|
| 2172 | 220 cr. Type **1115** | 15 | 10 |
| 2173 | 220 cr. Growth chart and oral rehydration | 15 | 10 |

**1985.** International Sea Search and Rescue Convention, Rio de Janeiro.

| | | | | |
|---|---|---|---|---|
| 2174 | **1116** | 220 cr. multicoloured | 65 | 30 |

**1118.** Children holding Hands. **1119.** Hands holding Host.

**1985.** International Youth Year.

| | | | | |
|---|---|---|---|---|
| 2176 | **1118** | 220 cr. multicoloured | 15 | 10 |

**1985.** 11th National Eucharistic Congress, Aparecida.

| | | | | |
|---|---|---|---|---|
| 2177 | **1119** | 2000 cr. multicoloured | 75 | 10 |

**1120.** Scene from "Mineiro Blood", Camera and Mauro.

**1985.** 60th Anniv of Humberto Mauro's Cataguases Cycle of Films.

| | | | | |
|---|---|---|---|---|
| 2178 | **1120** | 300 cr. multicoloured | 15 | 10 |

**1121.** Escola e Sacro Museum. **1122.** Inconfidencia Museum, Ouro Preto.

**1985.** 400th Anniv. of Paraiba State.

| | | | | |
|---|---|---|---|---|
| 2179 | **1121** | 330 cr. multicoloured | 15 | 10 |

**1985.** Museums. Multicoloured.

| | | | |
|---|---|---|---|
| 2180 | 300 cr. Type **1122** | 15 | 10 |
| 2181 | 300 cr. Historical and Diplomatic Museum Itamaraty | 15 | 10 |

**1123.** "Cabano" (Guido Mondin). **1124.** Aeritalia/Aermacchi AM-X Fighter.

**1985.** 150th Anniv. of Cabanagem Insurrection, Belem City.

| | | | | |
|---|---|---|---|---|
| 2182 | **1123** | 330 cr. multicoloured | 15 | 10 |

**1985.** AM-X (military airplane) Project.

| | | | | |
|---|---|---|---|---|
| 2183 | **1124** | 330 cr. multicoloured | 15 | 10 |

**1125.** Captain and Crossbowman (early 16th century).

**1985.** Military Dress. Multicoloured.

| | | | |
|---|---|---|---|
| 2184 | 300 cr. Type **1125** | 15 | 10 |
| 2185 | 300 cr. Arquebusier and sergeant (late 16th cent) | 15 | 10 |
| 2186 | 300 cr. Musketeer and pikeman (early 17th century) | 15 | 10 |
| 2187 | 300 cr. Mulatto fusilier and pikeman with scimitar (early 17th century) | 15 | 10 |

**1126.** "Farroupilha Rebels" (Guido Mondin).

**1985.** 150th Anniv of Farroupilha Revolution.

| | | | | |
|---|---|---|---|---|
| 2188 | **1126** | 330 cr. multicoloured | 15 | 10 |

**1127.** Itaimbezinho Canyon.

**1985.** Aparados da Serra National Park. Mult.

| | | | |
|---|---|---|---|
| 2189 | 3100 cr. Type **1127** | 95 | 15 |
| 2190 | 3320 cr. Mountain range | 95 | 15 |
| 2191 | 3480 cr. Pine forest | 95 | 15 |

**1128.** Neves and Brasilia Buildings.

**1985.** Tancredo Neves (President-elect) Commemoration.

| | | | | |
|---|---|---|---|---|
| 2192 | **1128** | 330 cr. black & orange | 15 | 10 |

**1129.** "FEB" on Envelope.

**1985.** 40th Anniv. (1984) of Brazilian Expeditionary Force Postal Service.

| | | | | |
|---|---|---|---|---|
| 2193 | **1129** | 500 cr. multicoloured | 15 | 10 |

**1130.** "Especuladora", 1835.

**1985.** 150th Anniv. of Rio de Janeiro–Niteroi Ferry Service. Multicoloured.

2194 500 cr. Type **1130** .. 35 10
2195 500 cr. "Segunda", 1862 .. 35 10
2196 500 cr. "Terceira", 1911 .. 35 10
2197 500 cr. "Urca", 1981 .. 35 10

**1131.** Muniz M-7.

**1985.** 50th Anniv of Muniz M-7 Biplane's Maiden Flight.

2198 **1131** 500 cr. multicoloured 30 15

**1132.** Dove Emblem and Stylized Flags.
**1133.** Front Page of First Edition.

**1985.** 40th Anniv. of U.N.O.

2199 **1132** 500 cr. multicoloured 15 10

**1985.** 160th Anniv. of "Pernambuco Daily News".

2200 **1133** 500 cr. multicoloured 15 10

**1134.** Adoration.
**1135.** Child holding Wheat.

**1985.** Christmas. Multicoloured.

2201 500 cr. Type **1134** .. 15 10
2202 500 cr. Adoration of the Magi .. .. .. 15 10
2203 500 cr. Flight into Egypt 15 10

**1985.** State Flags (5th series). As T **992**. Multicoloured.

2204. 500 cr. Para .. .. 15 10
2205. 500 cr. Rio Grande do Sul 15 10
2206. 500 cr. Acre .. .. 15 10
2207. 500 cr. Sao Paulo .. .. 15 10

**1985.** Obligatory Tax. Anti-leprosy Week.

2208 **1095** 100 cr. red .. .. 25 25

**1985.** Thanksgiving Day.

2209 **1135** 500 cr. multicoloured 10 10

**1136.** Transport, Mined Ore and Trees.

**1985.** Carajas Development Programme.

2210 **1136** 500 cr. multicoloured 10 10

**1137.** Gusmao and Balloons.

**1985.** 300th Birth Anniv. of Bartolomeu Lourenco de Gusmao (inventor).

2211 **1137** 500 cr. multicoloured 10 10

**1138.** "The Trees".

**1985.** Birth Centenary of Antonio Francisco da Costa e Silva (poet).

2212 **1138** 500 cr. multicoloured 10 10

**1140.** Comet.

**1986.** Appearance of Halley's Comet.

2214 **1140** 50 c. multicoloured 35 15

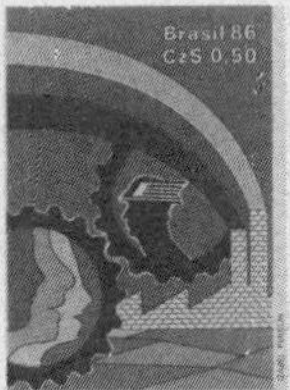

**1141.** Flags and Station.
**1142.** Symbols of Industry, Agriculture and Commerce.

**1986.** Second Anniv. of Commander Ferraz Antarctic Station.

2215 **1141** 50 c. multicoloured .. 10 15

**1986.** Labour Day.

2216 **1142** 50 c. multicoloured .. 10 10

**1143.** "Maternity".
**1144.** Broken Chain Links as Birds.

**1986.** 50th Death Anniv. of Henrique Bernardelli (artist).

2217 **1143** 50 c. multicoloured .. 10 10

**1986.** 25th Anniv. of Amnesty International.

2218 **1144** 50 c. multicoloured .. 10 10

**1145.** "Pyrrhopyge ruficauda".

**1986.** Butterfiles. Multicoloured.

2219 50 c. Type **1145** .. .. 85 30
2220 50 c. "Pierriballia mandela molione" .. 85 30
2221 50 c. "Prepona eugenes diluta" .. .. 85 30

**1146.** Gomes Peri, and Score of "O Guarani".
**1147.** Man in Safety Harness.

**1986.** 150th Birth Anniv. of Antonio Carlos Gomes (composer).

2222 **1146** 50 c. multicoloured .. 15 10

**1986.** Prevention of Industrial Accidents.

2223 **1147** 50 c. multicoloured .. 15 10

**1149.** Garcia D'Avila's House Chapel, Nazare de Mata.
**1150.** Kubitschek and Alvorada Palace.

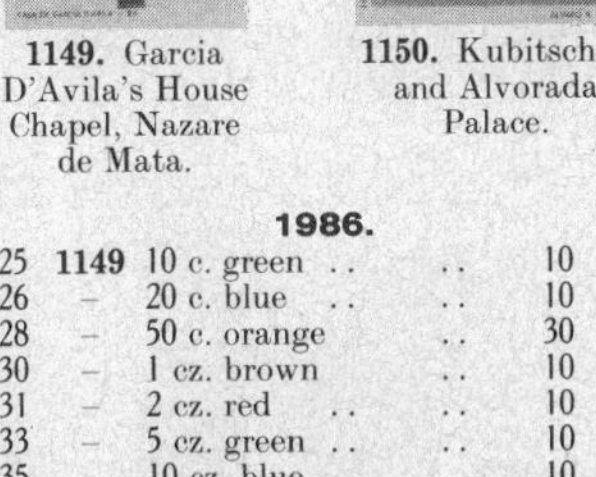

**1986.**

2225 **1149** 10 c. green .. .. 10 10
2226 – 20 c. blue .. .. 10 10
2228 – 50 c. orange .. 30 10
2230 – 1 cz. brown .. 10 10
2231 – 2 cz. red .. .. 10 10
2233 – 5 cz. green .. .. 10 10
2235 – 10 cz. blue .. .. 10 10
2236 – 20 cz. red .. .. 10 10
2238 – 50 cz. orange .. 15 15
2240 – 100 cz. green .. 30 25
2241 – 200 cz. blue .. 10 30
2242 – 500 cz. brown .. 10 10

DESIGNS—HORIZ. 20 c. Church of Our Lady of the Assumptiom, Anchieta. 50 c. Reis Magos Fortress, Natal. 1 cz. Pelourinho, Alcantara. 2 cz. St. Francis's Monastery, Olinda. 5 cz. St. Anthony's Chapel, Sao Roque. 10 cz. St Lawrence of the Indians Church, Niteroi. 20 cz. Principe da Beira Fortress, Costa Marques, Rondobua. 100 cz. Church of Our Lady of Sorrows, Campanha. 200 cz. Counting House, Ouro Preto. 500 cz. Customs building, Belem. VERT. 50 cz. Church of the Good Jesus, Matasinhos.

**1986.** 10th Death Anniv of Juscelino Kubitschek (President 1956–61).

2244 **1150** 50 c. multicoloured .. 25 10

**1151** Mangabeira and Itamaraty Palace, Rio de Janeiro

**1986.** Birth Centenary of Octavio Mangabeira (politician).

2245 **1151** 50 c. multicoloured .. 10 10

**1152** Congress Emblem and Sao Paulo
**1153** Microphone and Radio Waves

**1986.** 8th World Gastroenterology Congress, Sao Paulo.

2246 **1152** 50 c. multicoloured .. 10 10

**1986.** 50th Annivs. of National Radio and Education and Culture Ministry Radio.

2247 **1153** 50 c. multicoloured .. 10 10

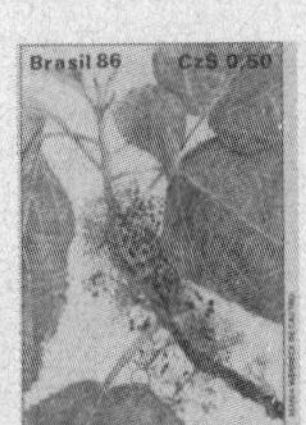

**1154** "Peace" (detail, Candido Portinari)
**1155** "Urera mitis"

**1986.** International Peace Year.

2248 **1154** 50 c. multicoloured .. 10 10

**1986.** Flowers. Multicoloured.

2249 50 c. Type **1155** .. 15 10
2250 6 cz. 50 "Couroupita guyanensis" .. .. 50 20
2251 6 cz. 90 Mountain ebony (horiz) .. .. 55 20

**1156** Simoes Filho and Newspaper
**1157** Title Page of Gregorio de Matto's MS

**1986.** Birth Centenary of Ernesto Simoes Filho (politician and founder of "A Tarde").

2252 **1156** 50 c. multicoloured .. 10 10

**1986.** Book Day. Poets' Birth Anniversaries.

2253 **1157** 50 c. brown & lt brn 10 10
2254 – 50 c. green and red 10 10

DESIGNS: No. 2253, Type **1157** (350th anniv). 2254, Manuel Bandeira and last verse of "I'll Return to Pasargada" (centenary).

**1158** Head Office, Brasilia
**1159** Birds around Baby lying in Nest

**1986.** 125th Anniv of Federal Savings Bank.

2255 **1158** 50 c. multicoloured .. 10 10

**1986.** Christmas. Multicoloured.

2256 50 c. Type **1159** .. 75 15
2257 6 cz. 50 Birds around tree with Christmas decorations .. .. 1·00 25
2258 7 cz. 30 Birds wearing Santa Claus caps .. 60 30

**1160** Rocha on Strip of Film
**1161** "History of Empress Porcina"

**1986.** 5th Death Anniv. of Glauber Rocha (film producer).

2259 **1160** 50 c. multicoloured .. 10 10

**1986.** "Lubrapex 86" Brazilian-Portuguese Stamp Exhibition, Rio de Janeiro. Design showing scenes from Cordel Literature. Multicoloured.

2260 6 cz. 90 Type **1161** .. 30 15
2261 6 cz. 90 "Romance of the Mysterious Peacock" .. 30 15

**1986.** Obligatory Tax. Anti-leprosy Week.

2263 **1095** 10 c. brown .. 10 10

**1162** Lieutenant Commander, 1930
**1163** "Graf Zeppelin" over Hangar

**1986.** Military Uniforms. Multicoloured.
2264 50 c. Type **1162** .. 20 10
2265 50 c. Military Aviation flight lieutenant, 1930 10 10

**1986.** 50th Anniv of Bartolomeu de Gusmao Airport, Santa Cruz.
2266 **1163** 1 cz. multicoloured .. 10 10

**1164** Museum

**1987.** 50th Anniv of National Fine Arts Museum, Rio de Janeiro.
2267 **1164** 1 cz. multicoloured .. 10 10

**1165** Villa-Lobos conducting and Musical Motifs

**1167** Landscape on Open Envelope (Rural Post Office Network).

**1166** Flag, Lockheed Hercules Aircraft and Antarctic Landscape

**1987.** Birth Centenary of Heitor Villa-Lobos (composer).
2268 **1165** 1 cz. 50 multicoloured 30 10

**1987.** Air Force Participation in Brazilian Antarctic Programme.
2269 **1166** 1 cz. multicoloured .. 90 20

**1987.** Special Mail Services. Multicoloured.
2270 1 cz. Type **1167** .. 10 10
2271 1 cz. Satchel and globe (International Express Mail Service) .. .. 10 10

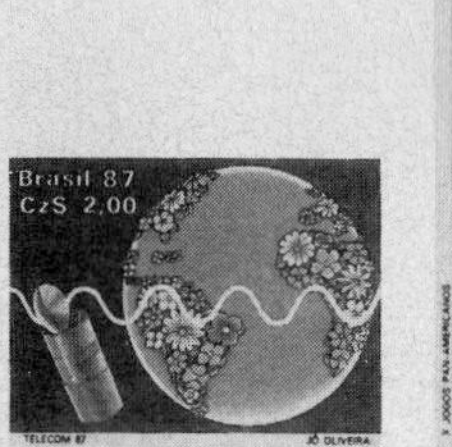

**1168.** "Brasilsat" Satellite, Radio Wave and Globe.

**1169.** Modern Pentathlon.

**1987.** "Telecom 87" World Telecommunications Exhibition, Geneva.
2272 **1168** 2 cz. multicoloured 10 10

**1987.** 10th Pan-American Games, Indianapolis, U.S.A.
2273 **1169** 18 cz. multicoloured 95 20

**1170** Hawksbill Turtle

**1987.** Endangered Animals. Multicoloured.
2274 2 cz. Type **1170** .. 10 10
2275 2 cz. Right whale .. 10 10

**1171** Old and New Court Buildings and Symbol of Justice

**1172** Arms

**1987.** 40th Anniv. of Federal Appeal Court.
2276 **1171** 2 cz. multicoloured .. 10 10

**1987.** Centenary of Military Club.
2277 **1172** 3 cz. multicoloured .. 10 10

**1173** Institute and Foodstuffs.

**1987.** Centenary of Agronomic Institute, Campinas.
2278 **1173** 2 cz. multicoloured .. 10 10

**1174** "Fulgora servillei"

**1987.** 50th Anniv of Brazilian Entomology Society. Multicoloured.
2279 3 cz. Type **1174** .. .. 15 10
2280 3 cz. "Zoolea lopiceps" .. 15 10

**1175** Features of Northern and North-east Regions

**1176** Main Tower

**1987.** National Tourism Year. Multicoloured.
2281 3 cz. Type **1175** .. 50 15
2282 3 cz. Features of mid-west, south-east and south regions .. 10 10

**1987.** 150th Anniv. of Royal Portuguese Reading Cabinet, Rio de Janeiro.
2283 **1176** 30 cz. green and red 25 20

**1177** International Sport Club (1975, 1976, 1979)

**1987.** Brazilian Football Championship Gold Cup Winners (1st series). Designs showing footballers and Club emblems.
2284 **1177** 3 cz. red, blk & yell 10 10
2285 – 3 cz. red, yell & blk 10 10
2286 – 3 cz. multicoloured 10 10
2287 – 3 cz. red, blk & yell 10 10

DESIGNS: No. 2285, Sao Paulo Football Club (1977, 1986); 2286, Guarani Football Club (1978); 2287, Regatas do Flamengo Club (1980, 1982, 1983).

See also Nos. 2322/5, 2398 and 2408.

**1178** St. Francis's Church and Tiled Column

**1987.** 400th Anniv of St. Francis's Monastery, Salvador.
2288 **1178** 4 cz. multicoloured .. 10 10

**1179** Almeida and Scenes from "A Bagaceira"

**1987.** Birth Centenary of Jose Americo de Almeida (writer).
2289 **1179** 4 cz. multicoloured .. 10 10

**1180** Barra do Picao

**1987.** 450th Anniv. of Recife.
2290 **1180** 5 cz. multicoloured .. 20 10

**1987.** Obligatory Tax. Anti-leprosy Week.
2291 **1095** 30 cz. green .. 15 15

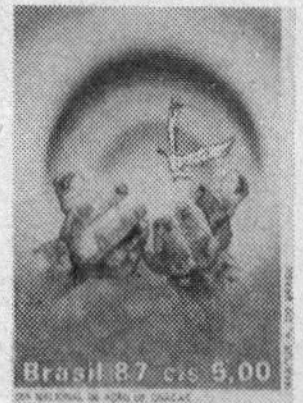

**1181.** Rainbow, Dove and Open Hands.

**1182.** Angels.

**1987.** Thanksgiving Day.
2292. **1181.** 5 cz. multicoloured 10 10

**1987.** Christmas. Multicoloured.
2293. 6 cz. Type **1182** .. .. 10 10
2294. 6 cz. Dancers on stage .. 10 10
2295. 6 cz. Shepherd playing flute .. .. .. 10 10

**1183.** Bernardo Pereira de Vasconcelos (founder) and Pedro II.

**1987.** 150th Anniv. of Pedro II School, Rio de Janeiro.
2296. **1183.** 6 cz. yellow, black and red .. .. 10 10

**1184.** "Cattleya guttata".

**1987.** 50th Anniv. of Brazilian Orchid Growers Society. Multicoloured.
2297. 6 cz. Type **1184** .. .. 10 10
2298. 6 cz. "Laelia lobata" .. 10 10

## INDEX

Countries can be quickly located by referring to the index at the end of this volume.

**1185.** Statue and Fatima Basilica, Portugal.

**1987.** Marian Year. Visit to Brazil of Statue of Our Lady of Fatima.
2299. **1185.** 50 cz. multicoloured 30 25

**1186.** Sousa, Indians and Fauna.

**1987.** 400th Anniv of "Descriptive Treaties of Brazil" by Gabriel Soares de Sousa.
2300 **1186** 7 cz. multicoloured .. 30 15

**1187.** Page from Book of Gregorian Chants and Computer Terminal.

**1988.** 150th Anniv. of National Archives.
2301. **1187.** 7 cz. multicoloured 10 10

**1188.** National Colours, Caravel and Modern Ship.

**1988.** 180th Anniv. of Opening of Brazilian Ports to Free Trade.
2302. **1188.** 7 cz. multicoloured 10 10

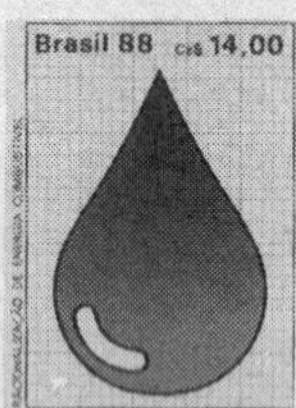

**1190.** Petrol Droplet.

**1192.** Bonifacio and Emblems of his Life.

**1988.** Energy Conservation. Multicoloured.
2304 14 cz. Type **1190** .. 10 10
2305 14 cz. Flash of electricity

**1988.** 150th Death Anniv. of Jose Bonifacio de Andrada e Silva (scientist, writer and "Patriarch of the Independence").
2307. **1192.** 20 cz. multicoloured 10 10

**1193.** Quill Pen on Page of Aurea Law.

**1988.** Cent. of Abolition of Slavery. Mult.
2308. 20 cz. Type **1193** .. 10 10
2309. 50 cz. Norris map of Africa, 1773, slave ship and plan of trading routes .. .. .. 10 10

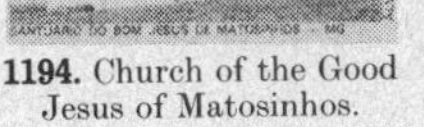

**1194.** Church of the Good Jesus of Matosinhos. **1195.** Concentric Circles on Map of Americas.

**1988.** U.N.E.S.C.O. World Heritage Sites. Multicoloured.
2310. 20 cz. Type **1194** .. 10 10
2311. 50 cz. Brasilia .. .. 15 15
2312. 100 cz. Pelourinho, Salvador .. .. 15 15

**1988.** "Americas Telecom 88" Telecommunications Exhibition, Rio de Janeiro.
2313. **1195.** 50 cz. multicoloured 15 15

BRASIL TARIFA POSTAL NACIONAL 1º PORTE SÉRIE A

**1196.** "Kasato Maru" (first immigrant ship) and Japanese Family. **1197.** Postal Authority Emblem.

**1988.** 80th Anniv. of Japanese Immigration into Brazil.
2314. **1196.** 100 cz. mult. .. 30 25

**1988.** No value expressed.
2315. **1197.** (-) blue .. .. 10 10
No. 2315 was valid for use at the current first class inland letter rate. It could not be used to pay postage to foreign countries.

**1198.** Judo. **1199.** Giant Anteater.

**1988.** Olympic Games, Seoul.
2316. **1198.** 20 cz. multicoloured 10 1C

**1988.** Endangered Mammals. Multicoloured.
2317. 20 cz. Type **1199** .. 10 10
2318. 50 cz. Thin-spined porcupine .. .. 15 15
2319. 100 cz. Bush dog .. 30 25

**1201** Industrial Symbols

**1988.** 50th Anniv of National Confederation of Industry.
2321 **1201** 50 cz. multicoloured 15 15

**1988.** Brazilian Football Championship Gold Cup Winners (2nd series). As T **1177**. Multicoloured.
2322 50 cz. Sport Club do Recife (1987) .. 15 15
2323 50 cz. Coritiba Football Club (1985) .. .. 15 15
2324 100 cz. Gremio Football Porto Alegrense (1981) 30 25
2325 200 cz. Fluminense Football Club (1984) .. 50 40

**1203** Raul Pompeia and Lines from "O Ateneu"

**1988.** Book Day. Centenaries of Publication of "O Ateneu" and "Verses". Mult.
2327 50 cz. Type **1203** .. 15 15
2328 100 cz. Olavo Bilac and lines from "Verses" .. 30 25

**1204** Church **1205** Father Santiago Uchoa

**1988.** Christmas. Origami by Marcia Bloch. Multicoloured.
2329 50 cz. Type **1204** .. 15 15
2330 100 cz. Nativity .. .. 30 25
2331 200 cz. Santa Claus and parcels .. .. 55 45

**1988.** Obligatory Tax. Anti-leprosy Week.
2332 **1205** 1 cz. 30 brown .. 10 10
See also Nos. 2614 and 2686.

**1206** Mate and Rodeo Rider

**1988.** "Abrafex" Argentine–Brazilian Stamp Exhibition, Buenos Aires.
2333 **1206** 400 cz. multicoloured 1·00 25

**1207** "Gasteropelecus" sp.

**1988.** Fresh-water Fishes. Multicoloured.
2334 55 cz. Type **1207** .. 15 15
2335 55 cz. "Osteoglossum ferreirai" .. .. 15 15
2336 55 cz. Green neon .. 15 15
2337 55 cz. "Cynolebia xavantei" .. .. 15 15
2338 55 cz. "Ancistrus hoplogenys" .. .. 15 15
2339 55 cz. "Brochis splendens" 15 15

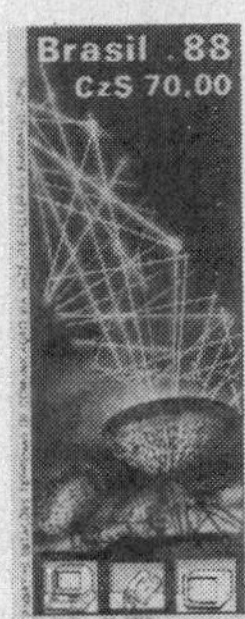

**1209** Dish Aerials **1210** "Four Arts"

**1988.** 10th Anniv of Ansat 10 (first Brazilian dish aerial), Macapa.
2341 **1209** 70 cz. multicoloured 20 15

**1988.** Establishment of National Foundation of Scenic Arts.
2342 **1210** 70 cz. multicoloured 20 15

**1211** Court Building

**1989.** 380th Anniv of Bahia Court of Justice.
2343 **1211** 25 c. multicoloured .. 10 10

**1212** Library Building and Detail of Main Door

**1989.** Public Library Year. 178th Anniv of First Public Library, Bahia.
2344 **1212** 25 c. multicoloured .. 10 10

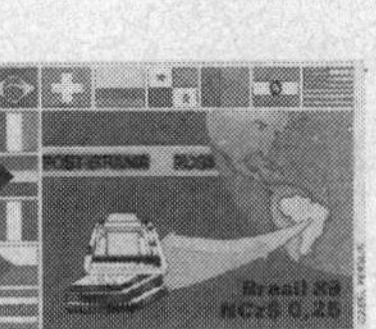

**1213** Facsimile Machine **1215** Emblem

**1989.** 20th Anniv of Post and Telegraph Department. Postal Services. Multicoloured.
2345 25 c. Type **1213** .. .. 10 10
2346 25 c. Hand holding parcel (Express Mail Service) 10 10
2347 25 c. Airbus Industrie 300 airplane on runway (SEDEX express parcel service) .. .. 10 10
2348 25 c. Putting coin in savings box (CEF postal savings) .. 10 10

**1989.** "Our Nature" Programme.
2350 **1215** 25 c. multicoloured .. 10 10

**1216** Hand reaching for Symbol of Freedom

**1989.** Bicentenary of Inconfidencia Mineira (independence movement). Multicoloured.
2351 30 c. Type **1216** .. .. 10 10
2352 30 c. Man's profile and colonial buildings .. 10 10
2353 40 c. Baroque buildings in disarray .. .. 10 10

**1217** School

**1989.** Cent of Rio de Janeiro Military School.
2354 **1217** 50 c. multicoloured .. 10 10

**1218** "Pavonia alnifolia"

**1989.** Endangered Plants. Multicoloured.
2355 50 c. Type **1218** .. .. 10 10
2356 1 cz. "Worsleya rayneri" (vert) .. .. 10 10
2357 1 cz. 50 "Heliconia farinosa" (vert) .. 15 10

**1219** Barreto and Pedro II Square, Recife Law School **1220** "Quiabentia zehntneri"

**1989.** 150th Birth Anniv of Tobias Barreto (writer).
2358 **1219** 50 c. multicoloured .. 10 10

**1989.** Flowers. Currency expressed as "NCz $". Multicoloured.
2359 10 c. "Dichorisandra sp." 10 10
2360 20 c. Type **1220** .. .. 10 10
2361 50 c. "Bougainvillea glabra" .. .. 10 10
2363 1 cz. "Impatiens sp." .. 10 10
2364 2 cz. "Chorisia crispiflora" (vert) .. .. 10 15
2366 5 cz. "Hibiscus trilineatus" .. .. 10 10
See also Nos. 2413/24.

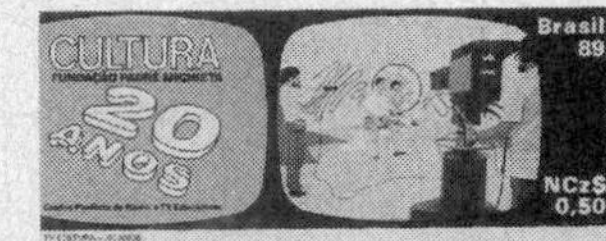


**1221** Shooting of "Revistinha"

**1989.** 20th Anniv of TV Cultura.
2371 **1221** 50 c. multicoloured .. 10 10

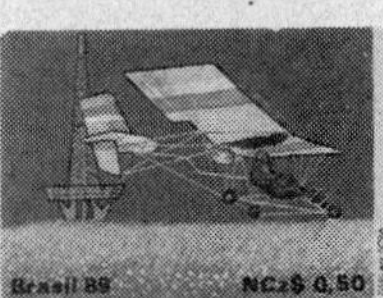


**1222** Postal Authority Emblem **1223** Brasilia T.V. Tower and Microlight

**1989.** No value expressed.
2372 **1222** (-) blue and orange .. 10 10
No. 2372 was sold at the current rate for first class internal postage.

**1989.** Aerosports and 80th Anniv of Santos Dumont's Flight in "Demoiselle". Mult.
2373 50 c. Type **1223** .. .. 10 10
2374 1 cz. 50 Eiffel Tower and "Demoiselle" .. .. 15 10

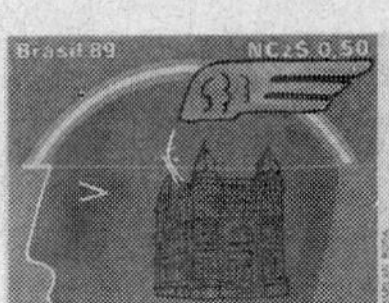


**1225** Tourmaline **1226** Rainbow and Association H.Q. Mercury

**1989.** Precious Stones. Multicoloured.
2376 50 c. Type **1225** .. .. 10 10
2377 1 cz. 50 Amethyst .. 15 10

**1989.** 150th Anniv of Pernambuco Trade Association.
2379 **1226** 50 c. multicoloured .. 10 10

**1228** Pioneers' Names and 19th-century to Modern Photographs

**1989.** International Photography Year.
2380 **1228** 1 cz. 50 multicoloured 15 10

**1229** Power Station

**1989.** Centenary of Marmelos-o Power Station (first South American hydro-electric power station).
2381 **1229** 50 c. multicoloured .. 10 10

1230 Hebrew Volute 1231 Muiraquita

**1989.** Molluscs. Multicoloured.

2382 50 c. Type **1230** .. .. 10 10
2383 1 cz. Matthew's morum .. 20 15
2384 1 cz. 50 Travasso's ancilla 30 20

**1989.** America. Pre-Columbian Artefacts. Multicoloured.

2385 1 cz. Type **1231** .. .. 10 10
2386 4 cz. Caryatid vase (horiz) 10 10

1233 Casimiro de Abreu 1234 Postal Authority Emblem

**1989.** Book Day. Writers' Birth Annivs. Multicoloured.

2388 1 cz. Type **1233** (150th anniv) .. .. 10 10
2389 1 cz. Machado de Assis (150th anniv) .. .. 10 10
2390 1 cz. Cora Coralina (cent) 10 10

**1989.** No value expressed. Burelage in second colour.

2391 **1234** (–) red and orange .. 10 10

No. 2391 was sold at the current rate for first class international postage.

1235 Police Emblem

**1989.** 25th Anniv of Federal Police Department.

2392 **1235** 1 cz. multicoloured .. 10 10

1237 Angel 1238 Candle Flame as Dove

**1989.** Christmas. Multicoloured.

2394 70 c. Type **1237** .. .. 10 10
2395 1 cz. Nativity .. .. 10 10

**1989.** Thanksgiving Day.

2396 **1238** 1 cz. multicoloured .. 10 10

1239 Fr. Damien de Veuster 1240 "The Yellow Man"

**1989.** Obligatory Tax. Anti-Leprosy Week.

2397 **1239** 2 c. red .. .. 10 10

See also Nos. 2458, 2509 and 2565.

**1989.** Football Clubs. As T **1177**. Mult.

2398 50 c. Bahia Sports Club .. 10 10

**1989.** Birth Cent of Anita Malfatti (painter).

2399 **1240** 1 cz. multicoloured .. 10 10

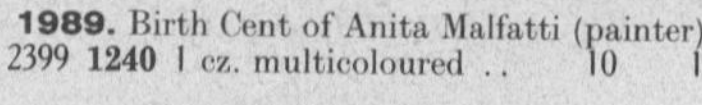

1241 Archive and Proclamation by Bento Goncalves

**1990.** Cent of Bahia State Public Archive.

2400 **1241** 2 cz. multicoloured .. 20 15

1242 "Mimosa caesalpiniifolia"

**1990.** 40th Anniv of Brazilian Botanical Society. Multicoloured.

2401 2 cz. Type **1242** .. .. 10 10
2402 13 cz. "Caesalpinia echinata" .. .. 10 10

1243 Cathedral of St. John the Baptist, Santa Cruz do Sul 1244 Sailing Barque and Modern Container Ship

**1990.** Churches. Multicoloured.

2403 2 cz. Type **1243** .. .. 10 10
2404 3 cz. Our Lady of Victory Church, Oeiras (horiz) 10 10
2405 5 cz. Our Lady of the Rosary Church, Ouro Preto .. .. .. 10 10

**1990.** Centenary of Lloyd Brasileiro Navigation Company.

2406 **1244** 3 cz. multicoloured .. 10 10

**1990.** Brazilian Football Clubs. As T **1177**. Multicoloured.

2408 10 cz. Vasco da Gama Regatas Club .. .. 15 10

1246 Collor and Newspaper Mastheads 1247 Sarney

**1990.** Birth Centenary of Lindolfo Collor (journalist).

2409 **1246** 20 cz. multicoloured 25 20

**1990.** Tribute to Jose Sarney (retiring President).

2410 **1247** 20 cz. blue .. .. 25 20

1248 Gold Coin, Anniversary Emblem and Bank Headquarters, Brasilia 1249 Hearts sprouting in Flask

**1990.** 25th Anniv of Brazil Central Bank.

2411 **1248** 20 cr. multicoloured 25 20

**1990.** World Health Day. Anti-AIDS Campaign.

2412 **1249** 20 cr. multicoloured 25 20

**1990.** Flowers. As T **1220** but with currency expressed as "Cr$".

2413 1 cr. "Impatiens sp" .. 10 10
2414 2 cr. "Chorisia crispiflora" (vert) .. 10 10
2415 5 cr. "Hibiscus trilineatus" .. .. 10 10
2417 10 cr. "Tibouchina granulosa" (vert) .. 15 10
2418 20 cr. "Cassia micranthera" (vert) .. 25 20
2420 50 cr. "Clitoria fairchildiana" (vert) 30 10
2421 50 cr. "Tibouchina mutabilis" (vert) .. 75 65
2422 100 cr. "Erythrina cristagalli" (vert) .. 65 10
2423 200 cr. "Jacaranda mimosifolia" (vert) .. 40 35
2424 500 cr. "Caesalpinia peltophoroides" (vert) 1·00 90
2424a 1000 cr. "Pachira aquatica" (vert) .. 15 10
2424b 2000 cr. "Hibiscus pernambucensis" (vert) 25 20
2424c 5000 cr. "Triplaris surinamensis" (vert) 65 55
2424d 10000 cr. "Tabebuia heptaphylia" (vert) .. 1·25 1·10
2424e 20000 cr. "Erythrina speciosa" (vert) .. 2·50 2·25

1250 Amazon Post Launch

**1990.** River Post Network.

2425 **1250** 20 cr. multicoloured 35 25

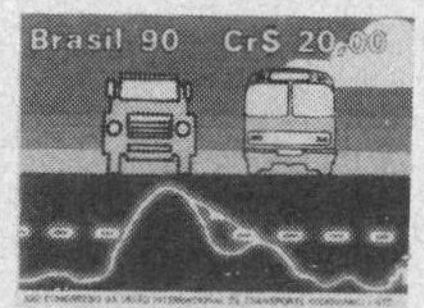

1253 Lorry and Coach

**1990.** 22nd World Congress of Int. Road Transport Union, Rio de Janeiro. Mult.

2428 20 cr. Type **1253** .. 25 20
2429 80 cr. Van and motor car 75 20

Nos. 2428/29 were printed together, se-tenant, forming a composite design.

1254 Imperial Crown (Imperial Museum, Petropolis)

**1990.** Museum 50th Anniversaries. Mult.

2430 20 cr. Type **1254** .. 25 20
2431 20 cr. "Our Lady of the Immaculate Conception" (woodcarving) (Missionary Museum, Sao Miguel das Missoes) 25 20

**1990.** Creation of State of Tocantins. As T **992** showing state flag.

2432 20 cr. yellow, blue & black 25 20

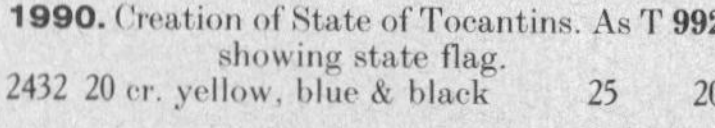

1255 Service Building, Hildebrand Theodolite and Map of Rio de Janeiro

**1990.** Centenary of Army Geographic Service.

2433 **1255** 20 cr. multicoloured 25 20

1256 Adhemar Gonzaga (producer)

**1990.** Brazilian Film Industry. Each maroon and purple.

2434 25 cr. Type **1256** .. 30 25
2435 25 cr. Carmen Miranda (actress) .. .. 30 25
2436 25 cr. Carmen Santos (actress) .. .. 30 25
2437 25 cr. Oscarito (actor) .. 30 25

1257 Aerial View of House 1258 Ball and Net

**1990.** 5th Anniv of France–Brazil House, Rio de Janeiro.

2438 **1257** 50 cr. multicoloured 60 10

**1990.** 12th World Men's Volleyball Championship, Brazil.

2439 **1258** 10 cr. multicoloured 15 10

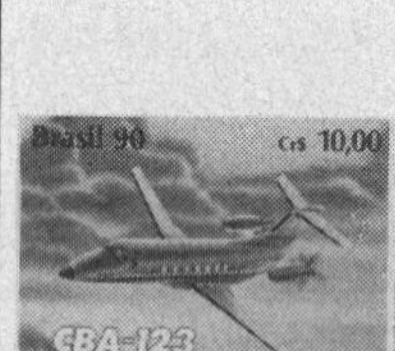

1259 Embraer/FMA Vector 1260 Globe, Pencil and Alphabet

**1990.** Aeronautics Industry.

2440 **1259** 10 cr. multicoloured 15 10

**1990.** International Literacy Year.

2441 **1260** 10 cr. multicoloured 15 10

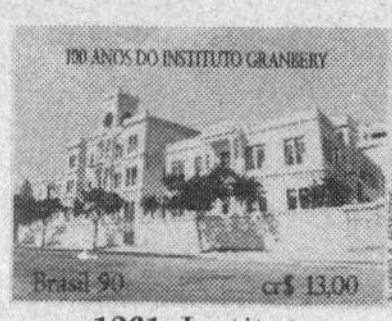

1261 Institute

**1990.** Cent of Granbery Institute, Juiz de Fora.

2442 **1261** 13 cr. multicoloured 15 10

1262 Map, Track and Diesel Locomotive

**1990.** 18th Pan-American Railways Congress, Rio de Janeiro.

2443 **1262** 95 cr. multicoloured 95 95

**1263** Satellite and Computer Communication

**1990.** 25th Anniv of Embratel (Telecommunications Enterprise).
2444 **1263** 13 cr. multicoloured 15 10

**1264** "Bathers" (Alfredo Ceschiatti)

**1990.** "Lubrapex 90" Brazilian–Portuguese Stamp Exhibition, Brasilia. Brasilia Sculptures. Multicoloured.
2445 25 cr. Type **1264** .. 30 25
2446 25 cr. "Warriors" (Bruno Giorgi) .. .. 30 25
2447 100 cr. "St. John" (Ceschiatti) .. .. 95 50
2448 100 cr. "Justice" (Ceschiatti) .. .. 95 50

**1265** "Bromelia antiacantha"

**1990.** America. 500th Anniv of Discovery of America by Columbus. Praia do Sul Nature Reserve. Multicoloured.
2450 15 cr. Type **1265** .. 15 10
2451 105 cr. Wooded shoreline of Lagoa do Sul .. 1·25 50
Nos. 2450/1 were printed together, se-tenant, forming a composite design.

**1266** Oswald de Andrade (birth centenary) and Illustration from "Anthropophagic Manifesto"

**1990.** Book Day. Anniversaries. Mult.
2452 15 cr. Type **1266** .. 15 10
2453 15 cr. Guilherme de Almeida (birth cent) and illustration of "Greek Songs" .. 15 10
2454 15 cr. National Library (180th anniv) and illuminated book .. 15 10

**1267** Emblem and Tribunal Offices, Brasilia

**1990.** Centenary of National Accounts Tribunal.
2455 **1267** 15 cr. multicoloured 15 10

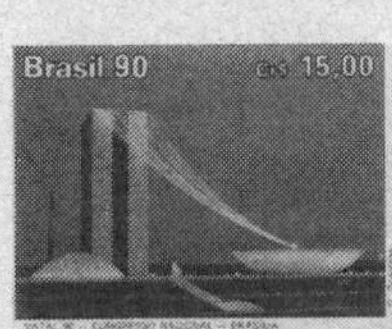

**1268** National Congress Building

**1269** Fingers touching across Map of Americas

**1990.** Christmas. Brasilia Lights. Mult.
2456 15 cr. Type **1268** .. 15 10
2457 15 cr. Television Tower .. 15 10

**1990.** Obligatory Tax. Anti-Leprosy Week. As No. 2397 but value and colour changed.
2458 **1239** 50 c. blue .. 10 10

**1990.** Centenary of Organization of American States.
2459 **1269** 15 cr. multicoloured 15 10

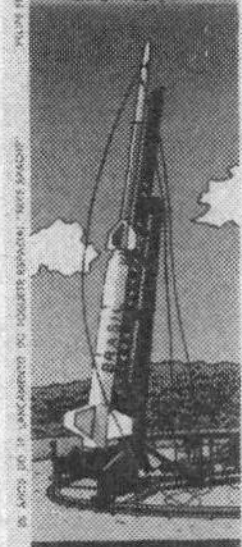


**1270** "Nike Apache" Rocket on Launch Pad

**1271** Sao Cristovao City

**1990.** 25th Anniv of Launch of "Nike Apache" Rocket.
2460 **1270** 15 cr. multicoloured 15 10

**1990.** 400th Anniv of Colonization of Sergipe State.
2461 **1271** 15 cr. multicoloured 15 10

**1272** Gymnasts

**1991.** World Congress on Physical Education, Sports and Recreation, Foz do Iguacu.
2462 **1272** 17 cr. multicoloured 20 15

**1273** Cazuza

**1991.** "Rock in Rio" Concert. Multicoloured.
2463 25 cr. Type **1273** .. 30 25
2464 185 cr. Raul Seixas .. 2·25 2·00
Nos. 2463/4 were printed together, se-tenant, forming a composite design.

**1274** Aeritalia/Aermacchi AM-X and Republic Thunderbolt

**1991.** 50th Anniv of Aeronautics Ministry.
2465 **1274** 17 cr. multicoloured 20 15

**1275** Effigies of Day Woman and Midnight Man, Olinda

**1276** Antarctic Wildlife

**1991.** Carnival. Multicoloured.
2466 25 cr. Type **1275** .. 10 10
2467 30 cr. Electric trio on truck, Salvador 10 10
2468 280 cr. Samba dancers, Rio de Janeiro .. 55 45

**1991.** Visit of President Collor to Antarctica.
2469 **1276** 300 cr. multicoloured 2·75 1·00

**1277** Hang-gliders

**1991.** 8th World Free Flight Championships, Governador Valadares.
2470 **1277** 36 cr. multicoloured 15 10

**1278** Yachting

**1991.** 11th Pan-American Games, Cuba, and Olympic Games, Barcelona (1992). Mult.
2471 36 cr. Type **1278** .. 10 10
2472 36 cr. Rowing .. .. 10 10
2473 300 cr. Swimming .. 60 50

**1279** Cross over Bottle (alcoholism)

**1991.** Anti-addiction Campaign. Mult.
2474 40 cr. Type **1279** .. 10 10
2475 40 cr. Cross over cigarette (smoking) .. .. 10 10
2476 40 cr. Cross over syringe (drug abuse) .. .. 10 10

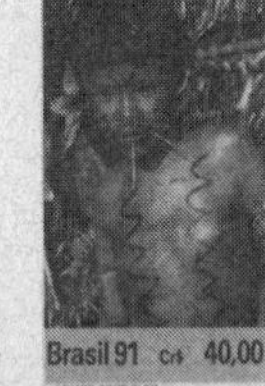


**1280** Old and Present Offices and Mastheads

**1281** Yanomami Youth in Ceremonial Paint

**1991.** Cent of "Jornal do Brasil" (newspaper).
2477 **1280** 40 cr. multicoloured 10 10

**1991.** Indian Culture. The Yanomami. Mult.
2478 40 cr. Type **1281** .. 10 10
2479 400 cr. Hunter (horiz) .. 80 70

**1282** Orinoco Goose

**1991.** United Nations Conference on Environment and Development.
2480 **1282** 45 cr. multicoloured 55 20

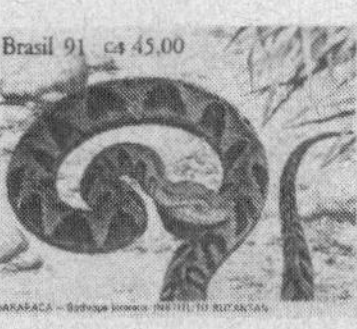

**1283** Jararaca

**1284** National Flag

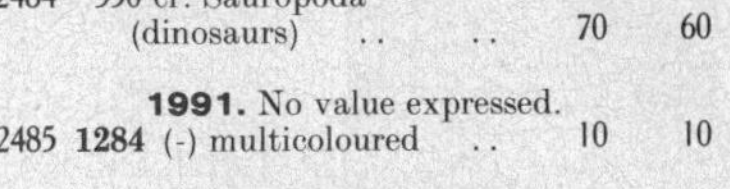

**1991.** 90th Anniv of Butantan Institute (2481/2) and 173rd Anniv of National Museum (others). Multicoloured.
2481 45 cr. Type **1283** .. 10 10
2482 45 cr. Green tree boa .. 10 10
2483 45 cr. Theropoda (dinosaurs) .. .. 10 10
2484 350 cr. Sauropoda (dinosaurs) .. .. 70 60

**1991.** No value expressed.
2485 **1284** (-) multicoloured .. 10 10

**1285** Early Steam Pump and Santos City 6th Fire Group's Headquarters

**1991.** Fire Fighting.
2486 **1285** 45 cr. multicoloured 10 10

**1286** Pedra Pintada, Boa Vista, Roraima

**1991.** Tourism. Centenaries of Boa Vista (1990) and Teresopolis. Multicoloured.
2487 45 cr. Type **1286** .. 10 10
2488 350 cr. God's Finger, Teresopolis, Rio de Janeiro .. .. 70 60

**1287** Welder, "Justice" and Farmer

**1991.** 50th Anniv of Labour Justice Legal System.
2489 **1287** 45 cr. multicoloured 10 10

**1288** Folklore Characters, Singers and Mota

**1991.** 5th International Festival of Folklore and Birth Cent of Leonardo Mota (folklorist).
2490 **1288** 45 cr. red, ochre & blk 10 10

**1289** Jose Basilio da Gama (poet)

**1290** Pope John Paul II

**1991.** Writers' Birth Anniversaries. Mult.
2491 45 cr. Type **1289** (250th anniv) .. .. 10 10
2492 50 cr. Luis Nicolau Fagundes Varela (poet, 150th anniv) .. .. 10 10
2493 50 cr. Jackson de Figueiredo (essayist and philosopher, centenary) 10 10

**1991.** Papal Visit and 12th National Eucharistic Congress, Natal. Multicoloured.
2494 50 cr. Type **1290** .. 10 10
2495 400 cr. Congress emblem 80 70
Nos. 2494/5 were issued together, se-tenant, forming a composite design.

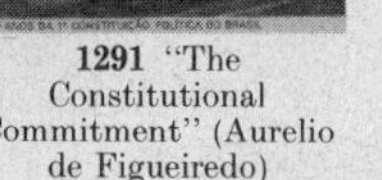

**1291** "The Constitutional Commitment" (Aurelio de Figueiredo)

**1292** Exhibition Emblem and dish Aerial

**1991.** Centenary of 1891 Constitution.
2496 **1291** 50 cr. multicoloured 10 10

**1991.** "Telecom 91" International Telecommunications Exhibition, Geneva.
2497 **1292** 50 cr. multicoloured 10 10

**1293** Ferdinand Magellan

**1294** White-vented Violetear and "Cattleya warneri"

**1991.** America. Voyages of Discovery. Mult.
2498 50 cr. Type **1293** .. 15 10
2499 400 cr. Francisco de Orellana on River Amazon .. .. 1·10 75

**1991.** "Brapex 91" National Stamp Exhibition, Vitoria. Humming Birds and Orchids in Mata Atlantica Forest. Multicoloured.
2500 50 cr. Type **1294** .. 60 15
2501 65 cr. Glittering-bellied emerald and "Rodriguezia venusta" .. 80 35
2502 65 cr. Brazilian ruby and "Zygopetalum intermedium" .. .. 80 35

**1295** "Self-portrait III"

**1296** Agricultural Projects

**1991.** Birth Cent of Lasar Segall (artist).
2504 **1295** 400 cr. multicoloured 80 70

**1991.** Centenary of Bureau of Agriculture and Provision, Sao Paulo.
2505 **1296** 70 cr. multicoloured 10 10

**1297** Dr. Manuel Ferraz de Campos Salles (President, 1898–1902)

**1298** Madonna and Child

**1991.** 150th Birth Anniversaries. Mult.
2506 70 cr. Type **1297** .. 10 10
2507 90 cr. Dr. Prudente de Moraes (President, 1894–98) and Catete Palace, Rio de Janeiro (former Executive Headquarters) .. 10 10
Nos. 2506/7 were issued together, se-tenant, forming a composite design.

**1991.** Christmas.
2508 **1298** 70 cr. multicoloured 10 10

**1991.** Obligatory Tax. Anti-Leprosy Week.
2509 **1239** 3 cr. green .. .. 10 10

**1299** Hand holding Prayer Book

**1991.** Thanksgiving Day.
2510 **1299** 70 cr. multicoloured 10 10

**1301** Policeman in Historic Uniform and Tobias de Aguiar Battalion Building, Sao Paulo

**1302** First Baptist Church, Niteroi (centenary)

**1991.** Military Police.
2512 **1301** 80 cr. multicoloured 10 10

**1992.** Church Anniversaries. Multicoloured.
2513 250 cr. Type **1302** .. 20 15
2514 250 cr. Presbyterian Cathedral, Rio de Janeiro (130th anniv) .. 20 15

**1303** Afranio Costa (silver, free pistol)

**1992.** Olympic Games, Barcelona (1st issue). 1920 Olympics Shooting Medal Winners. Multicoloured.
2515 300 cr. Type **1303** .. 25 20
2516 2500 cr. Guilherme Paraense (gold, 30 m. revolver) .. .. 2·00 1·90
See also No. 2526.

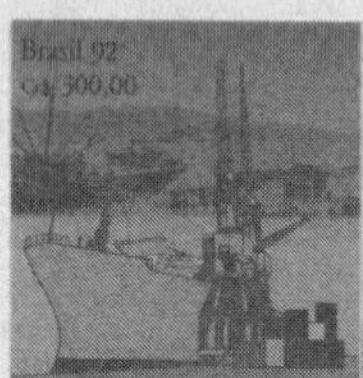


**1304** Old and Modern Views of Port

**1992.** Centenary of Port of Santos.
2517 **1304** 300 cr. multicoloured 25 20

**1305** White-tailed Tropic Birds

**1992.** 2nd United Nations Conference on Environment and Development, Rio de Janeiro (1st issue). Multicoloured.
2518 400 cr. Type **1305** .. 1·25 85
2519 2500 cr. Spinner dolphins 2·00 1·90
See also Nos. 2532/5, 2536/8, 2539/42 and 2543/6.

**1306** Ipe

**1307** Hunting using Boleadeira

**1992.** No value expressed.
2520 **1306** (–) multicoloured .. 10 10
No. 2520 was valid for use at the second class inland letter rate.

**1992.** "Abrafex '92" Argentinian–Brazilian Stamp Exhibition, Porto Alegre. Mult.
2521 250 cr. Type **1307** .. 20 15
2522 250 cr. Traditional folk dancing .. .. 20 15
2523 250 cr. Horse and cart .. 20 15
2524 1000 cr. Rounding-up cattle .. .. .. 85 75

**1308** Sportsmen on Globe

**1310** Columbus's Fleet

**1992.** Olympic Games, Barcelona (2nd issue).
2526 **1308** 300 cr. multicoloured 20 15

**1992.** America. 500th Anniv of Discovery of America by Columbus. Multicoloured.
2528 500 cr. Type **1310** .. 30 25
2529 3500 cr. Columbus, route map and quadrant .. 2·10 1·90
Nos. 2528/9 were issued together, se-tenant, forming a composite design.

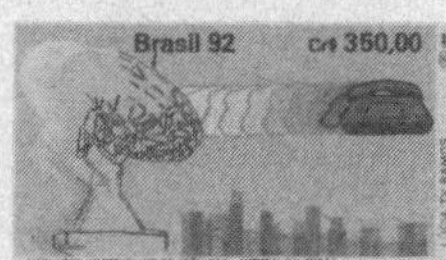


**1311** Dish Aerial, Telephone and City

**1992.** Installation of 10,000,000th Telephone Line in Brazil.
2530 **1311** 350 cr. multicoloured 15 10

**1313** Hercule Florence (botanist)

**1992.** 2nd U.N. Conference on Environment and Development (2nd issue). 170th Anniv of Langsdorff Expedition. Multicoloured.
2532 500 cr. Type **1313** .. 20 15
2533 500 cr. Aime-Adrien Taunay (ethnographer) and Amerindians .. 20 15
2534 500 cr. Johann Moritz Rugendas (zoologist) .. 20 15
2535 3000 cr. Gregory Ivanovich Langsdorff and route map .. 1·10 1·00

**1314** Urban and Rural Symbols

**1992.** 2nd U.N. Conference on Environment and Development (3rd issue). Multicoloured.
2536 450 cr. Type **1314** .. 20 15
2537 450 cr. Flags of Sweden (host of first conference) and Brazil around globe .. .. 20 15
2538 3000 cr. Globe, map, flora and fauna .. .. 1·10 1·00

**1315** Monica sitting by Waterfall

**1992.** 2nd U.N. Conf on Environment and Development (4th issue). Ecology. Designs showing cartoon characters. Multicoloured.
2539 500 cr. Type **1315** .. 20 15
2540 500 cr. Cebolinha in canoe 20 15
2541 500 cr. Cascao photographing wildlife 20 15
2542 500 cr. Magali picking wild fruit .. .. 20 15
Nos. 2539/42 were issued together, se-tenant, forming a composite design.

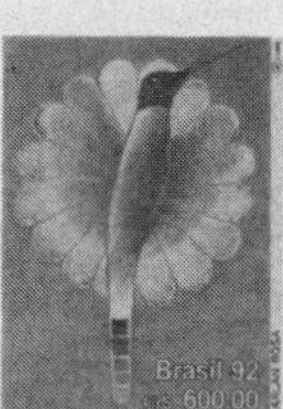


**1316** "Nidularium innocentii"

**1317** Humming-bird's Wings forming Flower

**1992.** 2nd U.N. Conference on Environment and Development (5th issue). 3rd Anniv of Margaret Mee Brazilian Botanical Foundation. Flower paintings by Margaret Mee. Multicoloured.
2543 600 cr. Type **1316** .. 25 20
2544 600 cr. "Canistrum exiguum" .. .. 25 20
2545 700 cr. "Nidularium rubens" .. .. 25 20
2546 700 cr. "Canistrum cyathiforme" .. .. 25 20

**1992.** National Diabetes Day.
2547 **1317** 600 cr. multicoloured 20 15

**1318** Training Tower and First Manual Pump

**1319** Animals, Cave Paintings and Map of Piaui State

**1992.** Centenary of Joinville Volunteer Fire Service.
2548 **1318** 550 cr. multicoloured 20 15

**1992.** 13th Anniv of Capivara Mountain National Park. Multicoloured.
2549 550 cr. Type **1319** .. 20 15
2550 550 cr. Canyons and map of Brazil .. .. 20 15
Nos. 2549/50 were issued together, se-tenant, forming a composite design.

**1320** Projects within Flask

**1322** Santa Cruz Fortress, Anhatomirim Island

**1321** Students at Work

**1992.** 24th Anniv of Financing Agency for Studies and Projects.
2551 **1320** 550 cr. multicoloured 20 15

**1992.** 50th Anniv of National Industrial Training Service.
2552 **1321** 650 cr. multicoloured 15 10

**1992.** Santa Catarina Fortresses. Mult.
2553 650 cr. Type **1322** .. 15 10
2554 3000 cr. Santo Antonio Fort, Ratones Grande island .. .. .. 65 60

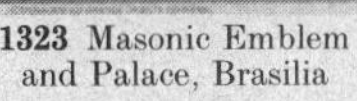

**1323** Masonic Emblem and Palace, Brasilia

**1324** Profiles of Child and Man forming Hourglass

**1992.** 170th Anniv of Grande Oriente (Federation of Brazil's Freemasonry Lodges).
2555 **1323** 650 cr. multicoloured 10 10

**1992.** 50th Anniv of Brazilian Legion of Assistance.
2556 **1324** 650 cr. multicoloured 10 10

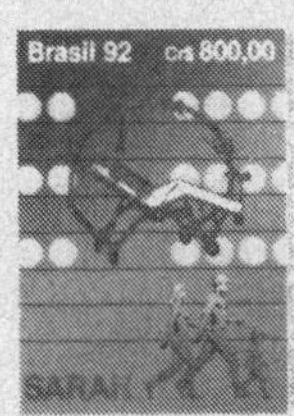

**1325** Medical Equipment and Patients

**1326** Menotti del Picchia

**1992.** Sarah Locomotor Hospital, Brasilia.
2557 **1325** 800 cr. multicoloured 10 10

**1992.** Book Day. Writers' Birth Centenaries. Multicoloured.
2558 900 cr. Type **1326** .. 10 10
2559 900 cr. Graciliano Ramos 10 10
2560 1000 cr. Assis Chateaubriand (journalist) (horiz) .. .. 15 10

**1327** Meridian Circle, Map, Cruls and Tent

**1992.** Centenary of Luiz Cruls's Exploration of Central Plateau.
2561 **1327** 900 cr. multicoloured 10 10

**1328** Productivity Graph on Flag

**1992.** 2nd Anniv of Brazilian Quality and Productivity Programme.
2562 **1328** 1200 cr. multicoloured 15 10

**1330** Father Christmas

**1992.** Christmas. No value expressed.
2564 **1330** (–) multicoloured .. 10 10

**1992.** Obligatory Tax. Anti-leprosy Week.
2565 **1239** 30 cr. brown .. 10 10

**1331** Sister Dulce, Patients and Lacerda Lift, Salvador

**1993.** Sister Dulce (founder of Santo Antonio Hospital and Simoes Filho Educational Centre) Commemoration.
2566 **1331** 3500 cr. multicoloured 20 20

**1333** Tube Station, Pine Trees and Church of the Third Order of St. Francis of Assisi and Stigmata

**1993.** 300th Anniv of Curitiba.
2568 **1333** 4500 cr. multicoloured 25 20

**1334** Heart dripping Blood onto Flowers

**1335** "Night with the Geniuses of Study and Love"

**1993.** Health and Preservation of Life. Multicoloured.
2569 4500 cr. Type **1334** (blood donation) .. .. 20 20
2570 4500 cr. Crab attacking healthy cell (anti-cancer campaign) .. .. 20 20
2571 4500 cr. Rainbow, head and encephalogram (mental health) .. 20 20

**1993.** 150th Birth Anniv of Pedro Americo (painter). Multicoloured.
2572 5500 cr. Type **1335** .. 20 20
2573 36000 cr. "David and Abizag" (horiz) .. 1·50 1·25
2574 36000 cr. "A Carioca" .. 1·50 1·25

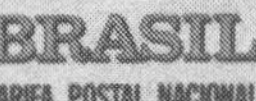

**1336** Flag

**1337** "Dynastes hercules"

**1993.** No value expressed. Self-adhesive. Die-cut.
2575 **1336** (–) blue, yellow & grn 20 20
No. 2575 was valid for use at the current first class inland letter rate. It could not be used to pay postage to foreign countries.

**1993.** World Environment Day. Beetles. Multicoloured.
2576 8000 cr. Type **1337** .. 30 25
2577 55000 cr. "Batus barbicornis" .. .. 1·90 1·60

**1338** Map, Flags and Discussion Themes

**1993.** Third Iberian–American Summit Conference, Salvador.
2578 **1338** 12000 cr. mult .. 25 20

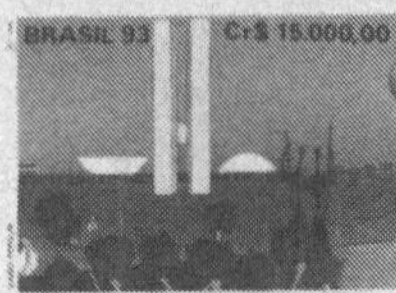


**1339** Lake, Congress Building and "Os Candangos" (statue), Brasilia

**1993.** Union of Portuguese-speaking Capital Cities. Multicoloured.
2579 15000 cr. Type **1339** .. 30 25
2580 71000 cr. Copacabana beach and "Christ the Redeemer" (statue), Rio de Janeiro .. 1·40 1·25
Nos. 2579/80 were issued together, se-tenant, forming a composite design.

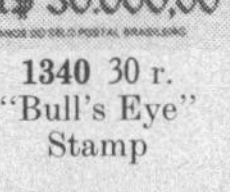

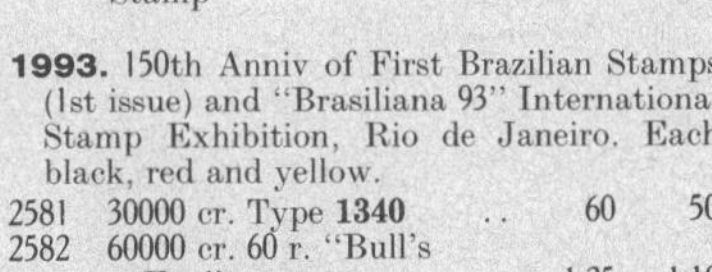


**1340** 30 r. "Bull's Eye" Stamp

**1341** Cebolinha designing Stamp

**1993.** 150th Anniv of First Brazilian Stamps (1st issue) and "Brasiliana 93" International Stamp Exhibition, Rio de Janeiro. Each black, red and yellow.
2581 30000 cr. Type **1340** .. 60 50
2582 60000 cr. 60 r. "Bull's Eye" stamp .. .. 1·25 1·10
2583 90000 cr. 90 r. "Bull's Eye" stamp .. .. 1·75 1·60
See also Nos. 2585/8.

**1993.** 150th Anniv of First Brazilian Stamps (2nd issue). No value expressed. Cartoon characters. Multicoloured.
2585 (–) Type **1341** .. .. 20 15
2586 (–) Cascao as king and 30 r. "Bull's Eye" stamp .. .. .. 20 15
2587 (–) Monica writing letter and 60 r. "Bull's Eye" stamp .. .. .. 20 15
2588 (–) Magali receiving letter and 90 r. "Bull's Eye" stamp .. .. .. 20 15
Nos. 2585/8 were issued together, se-tenant, forming a composite design.
Nos. 2585/8 were valid for use at the current first class inland letter rate. They could not be used to pay postage to other countries.

**1342** Imperial Palace (former postal H.Q.), Rio de Janeiro

**1344** Forest Mound and Tools

**1343** Polytechnic School, Sao Paulo University

**1993.** 330th Anniv of Postal Service. Mult.
2589 20000 cr. Type **1342** .. 40 35
2590 20000 cr. Petropolis post office .. .. 40 35
2591 20000 cr. Main post office, Rio de Janeiro .. 40 35
2592 20000 cr. Niteroi post office .. .. .. 40 35

Currency Reform
1 (new) cruzeiro real = 1000 (old) cruzeiros

**1993.** Engineering Schools. Multicoloured.
2593 17 cr. Type **1343** (centenary, 1994) .. 30 25
2594 17 cr. Old and new engineering schools, Rio de Janeiro Federal University (bicent, 1992) .. .. .. 30 25

**1993.** Preservation of Archaeological Sites. Multicoloured.
2595 17 cr. Type **1344** .. 20 15
2596 17 cr. Coastal mound, shells and tools .. 20 15

**1345** Guimaraes and National Congress

**1993.** Ulysses Guimaraes (politician).
2597 **1345** 22 cr. multicoloured 25 20

**1346** Hands holding Candles and Rope around Statue

**1347** Spix's Macaw

**1993.** Bicentenary of Procession of "Virgin of Nazareth", Belem.
2598 **1346** 22 cr. multicoloured 25 20

**1993.** America. Endangered Macaws. Mult.
2599 22 cr. Hyacinth macaw, glaucous macaw and Lear's macaw .. .. 25 20
2600 130 cr. Type **1347** .. 1·10 90

**1348** Vinicius de Moraes

**1349** Liberty

**1993.** Composers' Anniversaries. Mult.
2601 22 cr. Type **1348** (80th birth anniv) .. .. 25 20
2602 22 cr. Alfredo da Rocha Vianna (pseud. Pixinguinha) and score of "Carinhoso" (20th death anniv) .. .. 25 20

**1993.** No value expressed.
2603 **1349** (–) blue, turquoise and yellow .. 50 45
No. 2603 was sold at the current rate for first class international postage.

**1350** Mario de Andrade

**1351** Knot

**1993.** Book Day. Writers' Birth Centenaries. Multicoloured.

2604 30 cr. Type **1350** .. 30 25
2605 30 cr. Alceu Amoroso Lima (pseud. Tristao de Athayde) .. .. 30 25
2606 30 cr. Gilka Machado (poet) .. .. .. 30 25

**1993.** 40th Anniv of Brazil–Portugal Consultation and Friendship Treaty.

2607 **1351** 30 cr. multicoloured 30 25

**1352** Nho-Quim

**1993.** 2nd International Comic Strip Biennial. No value expressed. Multicoloured.

2608 (–) Type **1352** .. .. 30 25
2609 (–) Benjamin (Louneiro) 30 25
2610 (–) Lamparina .. .. 30 25
2611 (–) Reco-Reco, Bolao and Azeitona (Luiz Sa) .. 30 25
See note below Nos. 2585/8.

**1353** Diagram and Submarine

**1993.** Launch of First Brazilian-built Submarine.

2612 **1353** 240 cr. multicoloured 80 70

**1354** Nativity

**1993.** Christmas. No value expressed.

2613 **1354** (–) multicoloured .. 30 25
See note below Nos. 2585/8.

**1993.** Obligatory Tax. Anti-Leprosy Week.

2614 **1205** 50 c. blue .. .. 20 15

**1355** Republic P-47 Thunderbolt Fighters over Tarquinia Camp, Italy

**1356** Flag

**1993.** 50th Anniv of Formation of 1st Fighter Group, Brazilian Expeditionary Force.

2615 **1355** 42 cr. multicoloured 30 25

**1994.** No value expressed. Self-adhesive. Imperf.

2616 **1356** (–) blue, yellow & grn 35 30
See note below Nos. 2585/8.

**1357** Foundation of Republican Memory, Convent and Cloisters

**1994.** 340th Anniv of Convent of Merces (now Cultural Centre), Sao Luis.

2617 **1357** 58 cr. multicoloured 40 35

**1358** "Mae Menininha"

**1994.** Birth Centenary of Mae Menininha do Gantois (Escolastica Maria da Conceiao Nazare).

2618 **1358** 80 cr. multicoloured 55 45

**1359** Olympic Rings and Rower

**1360** Blue and White Swallow

**1994.** Centenaries of International Olympic Committee and Rowing Federation, Rio Grande do Sul. No value expressed.

2619 **1359** (–) multicoloured .. 70 60
See note below No. 2603.

**1994.** Birds. Multicoloured.

2620 10 cr. Type **1360** .. 10 10
2621 20 cr. Large-billed hawk 10 10
2622 50 cr. Rufous-bellied thrush .. .. 10 10
2623 100 cr. Ruddy ground dove .. .. .. 15 10
2624 200 cr. Chilian lapwing .. 30 25
2625 500 cr. Rufous-collared sparrow .. .. 80 70
See after Nos. 2649/61.

**1361** Map and Prince Henry

**1994.** 600th Birth Anniv of Prince Henry the Navigator.

2626 **1361** 635 cr. multicoloured 1·00 90

**1362** Bicycle

**1994.** America. Postal Vehicles. Mult.

2627 110 cr. Type **1362** .. 15 10
2628 635 cr. Motor cycle .. 1·00 90

**1363** Statue, Grain Store and Chapel of Help, Juazeiro do Norte

**1994.** 150th Anniv of Birth of Father Cicero Romao Batista. With service indicator.

2629 **1363** (–) multicoloured .. 20 15
See note below Nos. 2585/8.

**1364** Sabin and Children

**1994.** 1st Death Anniv of Albert Sabin (developer of oral polio vaccine).

2630 **1364** 160 cr. multicoloured 25 20

**HAVE YOU READ THE NOTES AT THE BEGINNING OF THIS CATALOGUE?**
These often provide answers to the enquiries we receive.

**1365** Castello Branco and Brasilia

**1994.** Carlos Castello Branco (journalist).

2631 **1365** 160 cr. multicoloured 25 20

**1366** "Euterpe oleracea"

**1367** "Brazil"

**1994.** Birth Bicentenary of Karl Friedrich Phillip von Martius (botanist). With service indicator. Multicoloured. (a) Inscr "1. PORTE NACIONAL".

2632 (–) Type **1366** .. .. 20 15
2633 (–) "Jacaranda paucifoliolata" .. 20 15

(b) Inscr "1. PORTE INTERNACIONAL TAXE PERCUE"

2634 (–) "Barbacenia tomentosa" .. .. 1·25 1·00

Nos. 2632/3 were for use at the current first class inland letter rate and Nos. 2634 for first class international postage.

**1994.** With service indicator. (a) Size 21 × 28 mm. Self-adhesive. Rouletted. (i) PRINTED MATTER. Inscr "1. PORTE IMPRESSO CATEGORIA II"

2635 **1367** (–) blue .. .. 10 10

(ii) INLAND POSTAGE. Inscr "3. PORTE NACIONAL"

2636 **1367** (3rd) red .. .. 30 20

(b) INLAND POSTAGE. Inscr "PORTE NACIONAL". Size 26 × 35 mm.

2637 **1367** (4th) green .. .. 40 30
2638 (5th) red .. .. 75 65

Nos. 2635/8 were valid for internal use in the category described.

**1368** Brazilian Player wearing "100"

**1994.** Centenary of Football in Brazil and World Cup Football Championship, U.S.A. With service indicator.

2639 **1368** (–) multicoloured .. 2·00 1·75
See note below No. 2603.

**1369** Emperor Tamarin ("Saguinus imperator")

**1371** Pencils Crossing over Fingerprint

**1994.** Endangered Mammals. With service indicator. Multicoloured.

2640 (–) Type **1369** .. .. 20 15
2641 (–) Bare-faced tamarin ("Saguinus bicolor") .. 20 15
2642 (–) Golden lion tamarin ("Leontopithecus rosalia") .. .. 20 15
See note below Nos. 2585/8

**1994.** 10 Year Education Plan. With service indicator. Multicoloured.

2644 (–) Type **1371** (literacy campaign) .. .. 20 15
2645 (–) PRONAICA pencil and school (National Programme of Integral Care to Children and Teenagers) .. .. 20 15
2646 (–) Lecture scene and graph (increase in qualified teachers) .. 20 15
2647 (–) Pencil and "lecturers" on television (distance learning by video) .. 20 15
See note below Nos. 2585/8.

**1994.** Birds. As T **1360** but with value expressed as "R$". Multicoloured.

2649 1 c. Type **1360** .. .. 10 10
2650 2 c. As No. 2621 .. .. 10 10
2652 5 c. As No. 2622 .. .. 10 10
2654 10 c. As No. 2623 .. 15 10
2655 15 c. Saffron finch .. 20 15
2656 20 c. As No. 2624 .. 30 25
2658 50 c. As No. 2625 .. 75 65
2661 1 r. Rufous hornero .. 1·50 1·25

**1373** Edgard Santos (founder of Bahia University)

**1374** "Petrobras X" (drilling platform), Campos Basin, Rio de Janeiro

**1994.** Anniversaries. With service indicator. Multicoloured.

2662 (–) Type **1373** (birth centenary) .. .. 20 15
2663 (–) Oswaldo Aranha (politician, birth centenary) .. .. 20 15
2664 (–) Otto Lara Resende (author and journalist, 2nd death anniv) .. 20 15
See note below Nos. 2585/8.

**1994.** 40th Anniv of Petrobras (state oil company).

2665 **1374** 12 c. multicoloured .. 20 15

**1375** 17th-century Coin Production

**1376** Loaf of Bread

**1994.** 300th Anniv of Brazilian Mint.

2666 **1375** 12 c. multicoloured .. 20 15

**1994.** Campaign against Famine and Misery. With service indicator.

2667 **1376** (–) multicoloured .. 20 15
2668 – (–) black and blue .. 20 15
DESIGN: No. 2668, Fish.
See note below Nos. 2585/8.

**1377** Writing with Quill and Scales of Justice

**1994.** 150th Anniv of Brazilian Lawyers Institute.

2669 **1377** 12 c. multicoloured .. 20 15

**1378** Family within Heart

**1994.** International Year of the Family.

2670 **1378** 84 c. multicoloured .. 1·25 1·10

1379 Hospital, White Stork and Babies forming "1000000"

**1994.** Centenary of Sao Paulo Maternity Hospital. Its Millionth Birth.
2671 **1379** 12 c. multicoloured .. 20 15

1380 Celestino performing and "Maternal Heart" (record sleeve)

**1994.** Birth Centenary of Vicente Celestino (singer).
2672 **1380** 12 c. multicoloured .. 20 15

1381 Fernando de Azevedo (educationist)

**1994.** Writers' Birth Anniversaries. Mult.
2673 12 c. Type **1381** (cent) .. 20 15
2674 12 c. Tomas Antonio Gonzaga (poet, 250th) 20 15

1382 "Joao and Maria" (Hansel and Gretel)

**1994.** Centenary of Publication of "Fairy Tales" by Alberto Figueiredo Pimentel (first Brazilian children's book). Multicoloured.
2675 12 c. Type **1382** .. .. 20 15
2676 12 c. "Dona Baratinha" (Little Mrs Cockroach) 20 15
2677 84 c. "Puss in Boots" .. 1·25 1·10
2678 84 c. "Tom Thumb" .. 1·25 1·10

1383 St. Clare, St. Damian's Convent and Statue of St. Francis

**1994.** 800th Birth Anniv of St. Clare of Assisi (founder of order of Poor Clares).
2679 **1383** 12 c. multicoloured .. 20 15

1384 Racing Car and Brazilian Flag

**1994.** Ayrton Senna (racing driver) Commemoration. Multicoloured.
2680 12 c. Type **1384** .. .. 20 15
2681 12 c. Senna and crowd waving farewell .. 20 15
2682 84 c. Brazilian and chequered flags, racing cars and Senna giving victory salute .. .. 1·25 1·10
Nos. 2680/2 were issued together, se-tenant, forming a composite design.

1385 Books and Globe

**1994.** Centenary of Historical and Geographical Institute, Sao Paulo.
2683 **1385** 12 c. multicoloured .. 20 15

1386 Adoniran Barbosa and "11 o'Clock Train"

**1994.** Composers. Multicoloured.
2684 12 c. Type **1386** .. .. 20 15
2685 12 c. Score of "The Sea" (Dorival Caymmi) .. 20 15

**1994.** Obligatory Tax. Anti-Leprosy Week.
2686 **1205** 1 c. purple .. .. 10 10

1387 Maggot wearing Santa Claus Hat in Apple

**1994.** Christmas. Multicoloured.
2687 12 c. Type **1387** .. .. 20 15
2688 12 c. Carol singers .. 20 15
2689 12 c. Boy smoking pipe and letter in boot .. 20 15
2690 84 c. Boy wearing saucepan on head and Santa Claus cloak .. 1·25 1·10

1389 Pasteur

**1995.** Death Centenary of Louis Pasteur (chemist).
2692 **1389** 84 c. multicoloured .. 1·10 95

1390 Duke of Caxias and Soldiers

1391 Pres. Franco

**1995.** 150th Anniv of Peace of Ponche Verde (pacification of Farroupilha Revolution) (2693) and 50th Anniv of Battle of Monte Castello (2694). Multicoloured.
2693 12 c. Type **1390** .. .. 15 10
2694 12 c. Soldier, Brazilian flag and battle scene .. 15 10

**1995.** Itamar Franco (President 1992–94).
2695 **1391** 12 c. multicoloured .. 15 10

1392 Meal before Child

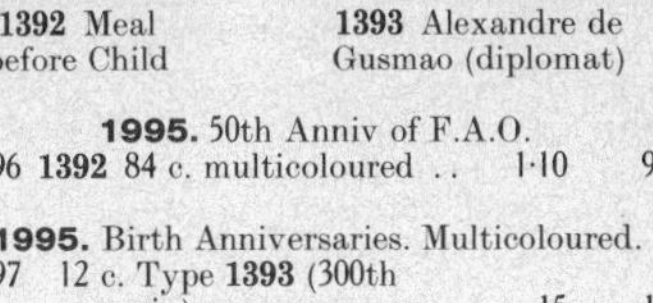
1393 Alexandre de Gusmao (diplomat)

**1995.** 50th Anniv of F.A.O.
2696 **1392** 84 c. multicoloured .. 1·10 95

**1995.** Birth Anniversaries. Multicoloured.
2697 12 c. Type **1393** (300th anniv) .. .. 15 10
2698 12 c. Visconde (Viscount) de Jequitinhonha (lawyer, bicent (1994)) 15 10
2699 15 c. Barao (Baron) do Rio Branco (diplomat, 150th anniv) .. .. 20 15

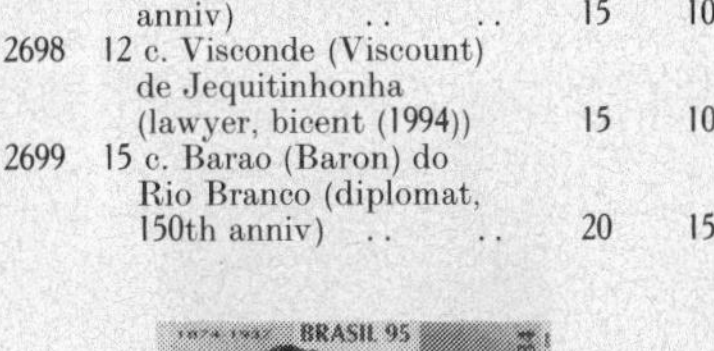

1394 Guglielmo Marconi and his Transmitter

**1995.** Centenary of First Radio Transmission.
2700 **1394** 84 c. multicoloured 1·10 95

1395 Ipe-amarelo and Cherry Blossom

1396 Solitary Tinamou ("Tinamus solitarius")

**1995.** Centenary of Brazil–Japan Friendship Treaty.
2701 **1395** 84 c. multicoloured .. 1·10 95

**1995.** Birds. Multicoloured.
2702 12 c. Type **1396** .. .. 15 10
2703 12 c. Razor-billed curassow ("Mitu mitu") 15 10

1397 St. John's Party, Campina Grande

**1995.** June Festivals. Multicoloured.
2704 12 c. Type **1397** .. .. 15 10
2705 12 c. Country wedding, Caruaru .. .. 15 10

1398 St. Antony holding Child Jesus (painting, Vieira Lusitano)

**1995.** 800th Birth Anniv of St. Antony of Padua.
2706 **1398** 84 c. multicoloured .. 1·10 95

**MINIMUM PRICE**

The minimum price quoted is 10p which represents a handling charge rather than a basis for valuing common stamps. For further notes about prices see introductory pages.

1400 Laurel and "Republic"

1401 Player, Net and Anniversary Emblem

**1995.** 1st Anniv of Real Currency.
2708 **1400** 12 c. brn, grn & blk 15 10

**1995.** Centenary of Volleyball.
2709 **1401** 15 c. multicoloured .. 20 15

1402 "Angaturama limai"

**1995.** 14th Brazilian Palaeontology Society Congress, Uberaba. Dinosaurs. Mult.
2710 15 c. Type **1402** .. .. 20 10
2711 1 r. 50 Titanosaurus .. 2·00 1·75

1403 Crash Test Dummies in Car

**1995.** Road Safety Campaign. Multicoloured.
2712 12 c. Type **1403** .. .. 15 10
2713 71 c. Car crashing into glass of whisky .. 95 85

1404 "Calathea burle-marxii"

1405 Paratroopers

**1995.** "Singapore'95" International Stamp Exhibition. 10th Anniv of Donation to Nation by Roberto Burle Marx of his Botanical Collection. Multicoloured.
2714 15 c. Type **1404** .. .. 20 15
2715 15 c. "Vellozia burle-marxii" .. .. 20 15
2716 1 r. 50 "Heliconia aemygdiana" .. .. 2·00 1·75

**1995.** 50th Anniv of Parachutist Infantry Brigade.
2717 **1405** 15 c. multicoloured .. 20 15

1406 Paulista Museum and "Fernao Dias Paes Leme" (statue, Luigi Brizzolara)

**1995.** Centenary of Paulista Museum of the University of Sao Paulo.
2718 **1406** 15 c. multicoloured .. 20 15

1407 Olinda

1408 Scarlet Ibis and Stoat catching Fish

**1995.** Lighthouses. Multicoloured.
2719 15 c. Type **1407** .. .. 20 15
2720 15 c. Sao Joao .. .. 20 15
2721 15 c. Santo Antonio da Barra .. .. .. 20 15

**1995.** "Lubrapex 95" Brazilian–Portuguese Stamp Exhibition, Sao Paulo. Fauna of the Tiete River Valley. Multicoloured.
2722 15 c. Type **1408** .. .. 20 15
2723 84 c. Heron flying over canoe .. .. .. 1·10 95

1409 X-Ray of Hand

**1995.** 150th Birth Anniv of Wilhelm Rontgen and Centenary of his Discovery of X-Rays.
2725 **1409** 84 c. multicoloured .. 1·10 95

1410 Arms and Crowd

**1995.** Centenary of Flamengo Regatta Club.
2726 **1410** 15 c. multicoloured .. 20 15

1411 Fungi and Alligator

**1995.** America. Environmental Protection. Multicoloured.
2727 15 c. Type **1411** .. .. 20 15
2728 84 c. Black-necked swans on lake .. .. 1·10 95
Nos. 2727/8 were issued together, se-tenant, forming a composite design.

1412 Dove over World Map (left detail)

1413 Jose Maria Eca de Queiroz

**1995.** 50th Anniv of U.N.O. Multicoloured.
2729 1 r. 05 Type **1412** .. 1·40 1·25
2730 1 r. 05 Dove over world map (right detail) .. 1·40 1·25
Nos. 2729/30 were issued together, se-tenant, forming a composite design.

**1995.** Book Day. Writers' Anniversaries. Multicoloured.
2731 15 c. Type **1413** (150th birth) .. .. .. 20 15
2732 15 c. Rubem Braga (5th death) .. .. 20 15
2733 23 c. Carlos Drummond de Andrade (8th death) .. 30 25

1415 Front Crawl (Freestyle)

**1995.** 11th World Short-course Swimming Championships, Rio de Janeiro. Mult.
2735 23 c. Type **1415** .. .. 30 25
2736 23 c. Backstroke .. 30 25
2737 23 c. Butterfly .. .. 30 25
2738 23 c. Breaststroke .. 30 25
Nos. 2735/8 were issued together, se-tenant, forming a composite design of a swimming pool.

1416 Cherub

**1995.** Christmas. Multicoloured.
2739 15 c. Type **1416** .. .. 20 15
2740 23 c. Cherub (different) .. 30 25
Nos. 2739/40 were issued together, se-tenant, forming a composite design.

1417 Flag, Former Headquarters and "Manequinho" (statue)

**1995.** Centenary (1994) of Botafogo Football and Regatta Club.
2741 **1417** 15 c. multicoloured .. 20 15

1418 Computer, Mouse and Masthead

**1995.** 170th Anniv of "Diario de Pernambuco" (newspaper).
2742 **1418** 23 c. multicoloured .. 30 25

1420 Prestes Maia and Sao Paulo

**1996.** Birth Centenary of Francisco Prestes Maia (Mayor of Sao Paulo).
2744 **1420** 18 c. multicoloured .. 20 15

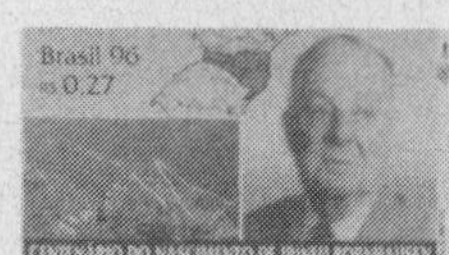

1421 Bornhausen and Santa Catarina

**1996.** Birth Centenary of Irineu Bornhausen (Governor of State of Santa Catarina).
2745 **1421** 27 c. multicoloured 35 30

1422 "Ouro Preto Landscape" (Alberto da Veiga Guignard)

1423 Doll

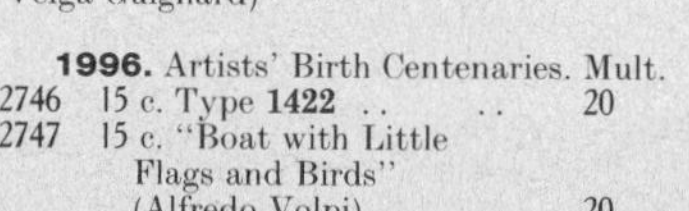
**1996.** Artists' Birth Centenaries. Mult.
2746 15 c. Type **1422** .. .. 20 15
2747 15 c. "Boat with Little Flags and Birds" (Alfredo Volpi) .. 20 15

**1996.** 50th Anniv of United Nations Children's Fund. Campaign against Sexual Abuse.
2748 **1423** 23 c. multicoloured .. 30 25

1424 Anniversary Emblem

1426 Pantanal

1425 Pinheiro da Silva and National Congress

**1996.** 500th Anniv (2000) of Discovery of Brazil.
2749 **1424** 1 r. 05 multicoloured 1·25 1·10

**1996.** Birth Centenary of Israel Pinheiro da Silva (politician).
2750 **1425** 18 c. multicoloured 20 15

**1996.** Tourism. Multicoloured. Self-adhesive. Imperf (backing paper rouletted).
2751 23 c. Amazon River .. 30 25
2752 23 c. Type **1426** .. .. 30 25
2753 23 c. Jangada raft .. 30 25
2754 23 c. "The Sugarloaf", Guanabara Bay .. 30 25
2755 23 c. Iguau Falls .. 30 25

1427 Crimson Topaz

**1996.** "Espamer 96" Spanish and Latin-American Stamp Exhibition, Seville, Spain. Hummingbirds. Multicoloured.
2756 15 c. Type **1427** .. .. 20 15
2757 1 r. 05 Black-breasted plovercrest .. .. 1·25 1·10
2758 1 r. 15 Swallow-tailed hummingbird .. .. 1·40 1·25

1428 Marathon Runners

**1996.** Centenary of Modern Olympic Games. Multicoloured.
2759 18 c. Type **1428** .. .. 20 15
2760 23 c. Gymnastics .. 30 25
2761 1 r. 05 Swimming .. 1·25 1·10
2762 1 r. 05 Beach volleyball .. 1·25 1·10

1430 Dish Aerial, Satellite over Earth and Sports

**1996.** "Americas Telecom 96" International Telecommunications Exn, Rio de Janeiro.
2764 **1430** 1 r. 05 multicoloured 1·25 1·10

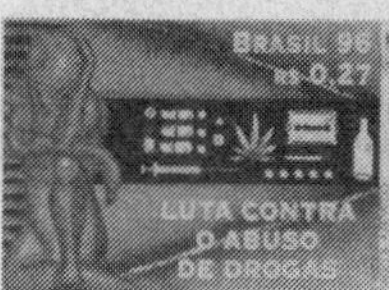

1432 Addict and Drugs

**1996.** Anti-drug Abuse Campaign.
2766 **1432** 27 c. multicoloured .. 35 30

1433 Coloured Pencils

1435 Gomes and Peace Theatre

1434 Princess Isabel and Aurea Law

**1996.** Education Year.
2767 **1433** 23 c. multicoloured .. 30 25

**1996.** 150th Birth Anniv of Princess Isabel the Redeemer.
2768 **1434** 18 c. multicoloured .. 20 15
The Aurea Law abolished slavery in Brazil.

**1996.** Death Centenary of Carlos Gomes (opera composer).
2769 **1435** 50 c. multicoloured .. 60 50

1436 "Cattleya eldorado"

**1996.** 15th International Orchid Conference, Rio de Janeiro. Multicoloured.
2770 15 c. Type **1436** .. .. 20 15
2771 15 c. "Cattleya loddigesii" 20 15
2772 15 c. "Promenaea stapellioides" .. .. 20 15

1437 Melania and Maximino and Virgin Mary

**1996.** 150th Anniv of Apparition of Our Lady at La Salette, France.
2773 **1437** 1 r. multicoloured .. 1·25 1·10

1439 Vaqueiro

1440 Poinsettia and Lighted Candle

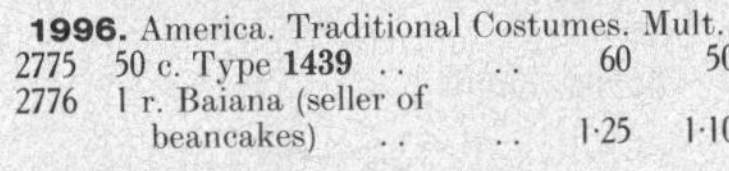

**1996.** America. Traditional Costumes. Mult.

| | | | | |
|---|---|---|---|---|
| 2775 | | 50 c. Type **1439** .. .. | 60 | 50 |
| 2776 | | 1 r. Baiana (seller of beancakes) .. .. | 1·25 | 1·10 |

**1996.** Christmas.

| | | | | |
|---|---|---|---|---|
| 2777 | **1440** | (–) multicoloured .. | 20 | 15 |

See second note below No. 2588.

1441 "Melindrosa" (cover of 1931 "O Cruzeiro" magazine)

**1996.** 46th Death Anniv of Jose Carlos (caricaturist).

| | | | | |
|---|---|---|---|---|
| 2778 | **1441** | (–) multicoloured .. | 20 | 15 |

See second note below No. 2588.

## EXPRESS STAMP

**1930.** Surch. **1000 REIS EXPRESSO** and bars.

| | | | | |
|---|---|---|---|---|
| E490. | **66.** | 1000 r. on 200 r. blue | 2·00 | 1·00 |

## NEWSPAPER STAMPS

N 34.

N 37.

**1889.** Roul.

| | | | | |
|---|---|---|---|---|
| N 88. | N **34.** | 10 r. orange .. .. | 1·25 | 60 |
| N 89. | | 20 r. orange .. .. | 4·00 | 1·75 |
| N 90. | | 50 r. orange .. .. | 6·00 | 3·00 |
| N 91. | | 100 r. orange .. | 2·50 | 1·50 |
| N 92. | | 200 r. orange .. | 1·25 | 70 |
| N 93. | | 300 r. orange .. | 1·25 | 70 |
| N 94. | | 500 r. orange .. | 10·00 | 5·00 |
| N 95. | | 700 r. orange .. | 1·40 | 1·25 |
| N 96. | | 1000 r. orange .. | 2·75 | 2·00 |

**1889.** Roul.

| | | | | |
|---|---|---|---|---|
| N 97. | N **34.** | 10 r. green .. .. | 15 | 15 |
| N 98. | | 20 r. green .. .. | 20 | 15 |
| N 99. | | 50 r. buff .. .. | 25 | 15 |
| N 100a. | | 100 r. mauve .. | 25 | 15 |
| N 101. | | 200 r. black .. .. | 60 | 35 |
| N 102. | | 300 r. red .. .. | 2·50 | 2·00 |
| N 103. | | 500 r. green .. .. | 15·00 | 12·00 |
| N 104. | | 700 r. blue .. .. | 9·00 | 9·00 |
| N 105. | | 1000 r. brown .. | 4·00 | 4·00 |

**1890.** Perf.

| | | | | |
|---|---|---|---|---|
| N 111 | N **37** | 10 r. blue .. .. | 2·00 | 1·50 |
| N 112 | | 20 r. green .. | 6·00 | 2·50 |
| N 113 | | 100 r. mauve .. | 2·75 | 2·50 |

N 38. Southern Cross and Sugar-loaf Mountain.

**1890.** Perf.

| | | | | |
|---|---|---|---|---|
| N 119. | N**38**. | 10 r. blue .. .. | 20 | 15 |
| N 123a. | | 20 r. green .. .. | 50 | 40 |
| N 127. | | 50 r. green .. .. | 2·50 | 2·50 |

## OFFICIAL STAMPS

**O 64.** Pres. Affonso Penna. **O 67.** Pres. Hermes de Fonseca. **O 77.** Pres. Wenceslao Braz.

**1906.** Various frames.

| | | | | |
|---|---|---|---|---|
| O 282 | O **64** | 10 r. green & orge | 15 | 10 |
| O 283 | | 20 r. green & orge | 25 | 10 |
| O 284 | | 50 r. green & orge | 80 | 10 |
| O 285 | | 100 r. green & orge | 25 | 10 |
| O 286 | | 200 r. green & orge | 45 | 10 |
| O 287 | | 300 r. green & orge | 1·25 | 20 |
| O 288 | | 400 r. green & orge | 2·50 | 45 |
| O 289 | | 500 r. green & orge | 1·40 | 35 |
| O 290 | | 700 r. green & orge | 2·00 | 1·40 |
| O 291 | | 1000 r. green & orge | 1·40 | 50 |
| O 292 | | 2000 r. green & orge | 1·60 | 60 |
| O 293 | | 5000 r. green & orge | 4·75 | 60 |
| O 294 | | 10000 r. grn & orge | 6·00 | 35 |

**1913.** Various frames.

| | | | | |
|---|---|---|---|---|
| O 295 | O **67** | 10 r. black & grey | 20 | 10 |
| O 296 | | 20 r. black & olive | 20 | 10 |
| O 297 | | 50 r. black & grey | 25 | 10 |
| O 298 | | 100 r. black & red | 45 | 10 |
| O 299 | | 200 r. black & blue | 50 | 10 |
| O 300 | | 500 r. black & yell | 1·60 | 20 |
| O 301 | | 600 r. black & pur | 2·40 | 30 |
| O 302 | | 1000 r. black & brn | 2·50 | 50 |
| O 303 | | 2000 r. black & brn | 3·00 | 50 |
| O 304 | | 5000 r. black & bis | 3·25 | 70 |
| O 305 | | 10000 r. black .. | 4·00 | 2·50 |
| O 306 | | 20000 r. black & bl | 17·00 | 17·00 |
| O 307 | | 50000 r. black & grn | 24·00 | 24·00 |
| O 308 | | 100000 r. black & red | 65·00 | 65·00 |
| O 309 | | 500000 r. blk & brn | £110 | £110 |
| O 310 | | 1000000 r. blk & brn | £120 | £120 |

**1919.**

| | | | | |
|---|---|---|---|---|
| O 311. | O **77.** | 10 r. brown .. | 25 | 70 |
| O 312. | | 50 r. green .. .. | 35 | 35 |
| O 313. | | 100 r. red .. .. | 50 | 25 |
| O 314. | | 200 r. blue .. .. | 70 | 25 |
| O 315. | | 500 r. orange .. | 4·25 | 5·00 |

## POSTAGE DUE STAMPS

D 34. D 45. D 64.

**1889.** Roul.

| | | | | |
|---|---|---|---|---|
| D 88. | D **34.** | 10 r. red .. .. | 40 | 25 |
| D 89. | | 20 r. red .. .. | 40 | 25 |
| D 90. | | 50 r. red .. .. | 90 | 30 |
| D 91. | | 100 r. red .. .. | 35 | 20 |
| D 92. | | 200 r. red .. .. | 12·00 | 5·00 |
| D 93. | | 300 r red .. .. | 1·60 | 1·00 |
| D 94. | | 500 r. red .. .. | 1·25 | 70 |
| D 95. | | 700 r. red .. .. | 1·50 | 1·00 |
| D 96. | | 1000 r. red .. .. | 2·25 | 2·00 |

**1890.** Roul.

| | | | | |
|---|---|---|---|---|
| D 97. | D **34.** | 10 r. orange .. | 15 | 10 |
| D 98. | | 20 r. blue .. .. | 15 | 10 |
| D 99. | | 50 r. olive .. .. | 15 | 10 |
| D 100. | | 200 r. red .. .. | 50 | 20 |
| D 101. | | 300 r. green .. | 50 | 25 |
| D 102. | | 500 r. grey .. .. | 60 | 40 |
| D 103. | | 700 r. violet .. | 1·25 | 1·00 |
| D 104. | | 1000 r. purple .. | 2·00 | 1·50 |

**1895.** Perf.

| | | | | |
|---|---|---|---|---|
| D 172. | D **45.** | 10 r. blue .. .. | 30 | 25 |
| D 173. | | 20 r. green .. .. | 50 | 35 |
| D 174. | | 50 r. green .. .. | 65 | 40 |
| D 175. | | 100 r. red .. .. | 90 | 20 |
| D 176b. | | 200 r. lilac .. .. | 45 | 25 |
| D 177a. | | 300 r. blue .. .. | 1·25 | 40 |
| D 178. | | 2000 r. brown .. | 5·50 | 4·00 |

**1906.**

| | | | | |
|---|---|---|---|---|
| D 282. | D**64.** | 10 r. slate .. .. | 10 | 10 |
| D 283. | | 20 r. violet .. .. | 10 | 10 |
| D 284. | | 50 r. green .. .. | 15 | 10 |
| D 285. | | 100 r. red .. .. | 1·00 | 35 |
| D 286. | | 200 r. blue .. .. | 45 | 15 |
| D 287. | | 300 r. grey .. .. | 15 | 35 |
| D 288. | | 400 r. deep olive .. | 55 | 50 |
| D 289. | | 500 r. lilac .. .. | 20·00 | 20·00 |
| D 290. | | 600 r. purple .. | 70 | 70 |
| D 291. | | 700 r. brown .. | 17·00 | 17·00 |
| D 292. | | 1000 r. red .. .. | 85 | 1·25 |
| D 293. | | 2000 r. green .. | 2·50 | 3·00 |
| D 294. | | 5000 r. brown .. | 50 | 3·25 |

D 77.

**1919.**

| | | | | |
|---|---|---|---|---|
| D 345. | D**77.** | 5 r. brown .. .. | 15 | 15 |
| D 403. | | 10 r. mauve .. .. | 10 | 10 |
| D 365. | | 20 r. olive .. .. | 15 | 15 |
| D 404. | | 20 r. black .. .. | 15 | 10 |
| D 405. | | 50 r. green .. .. | 20 | 20 |
| D 375. | | 100 r. red .. .. | 15 | 15 |
| D 407. | | 200 r. blue .. .. | 25 | 25 |
| D 408. | | 400 r. brown .. | 1·25 | 1·25 |
| D 401. | | 600 r. violet .. | 20 | 15 |
| D 350. | | 600 r. orange .. | 35 | 35 |
| D 409. | | 1000 r. turquoise .. | 35 | 25 |
| D 439. | | 2000 r. brown .. | 35 | 35 |
| D 411. | | 5000 r. blue .. .. | 85 | 85 |

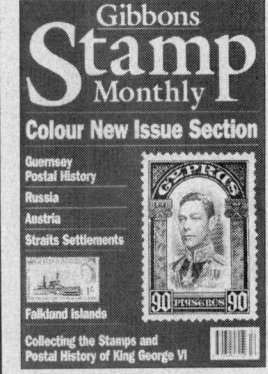

## BREMEN Pt. 7

A free city of the Hanseatic League, situated on the R. Weser in northern Germany. Joined the North German Confederation in 1868.

22 grote = 10 silbergroschen.
72 grote = 1 thaler.

1. 2. 3.

**1855.** Imperf.
1 1 3 g. black on blue .. .. £160 £225

**1856.** Imperf.
3. **2.** 5 g. black on red .. .. £150 £250
4. 7 g. black on yellow .. £190 £600
5. **3.** 5 sg. green .. .. .. £120 £200

4. 5.

**1861.** Zigzag roulette or perf.
17 4 2 g. orange .. .. 55·00 £275
19 1 3 g. black on blue .. 60·00 £275
20 2 5 g. black on red .. .. £110 £160
21 7 g. black on yellow .. £110 £2750
22 5 10 g. black .. .. £170 £900
24 3 5 sg. green .. .. £140 £140

## BRUNSWICK Pt. 7

Formerly a duchy of N. Germany. Joined North German Confederation in 1868.

30 silbergroschen = 1 thaler.

1.

**1852.** Imperf.
1. **1.** 1 sg. red .. .. .. £4500 £275
2. 2 sg. blue .. .. .. £2750 £225
3. 3 sg. red .. .. .. £2750 £225

**1853.** Imperf.
4 1 ¼ g. black on brown .. £250 £250
5 ⅓ g. black .. .. £100 £325
15 ½ sg. black on green .. 24·00 £225
7 1 sg. black on buff .. £110 55·00
9 2 sg. black on blue .. 60·00 55·00
10 3 sg. black on red .. £170 75·00

3. 4.

**1857.** Imperf.
12. **3.** 4/4 g. black on brown .. 28·00 £100

**1864.** Rouletted.
22 1 ⅓ g. black .. .. £400 £1900
23 ½ g. black on green .. £325 £2250
25 1 g. yellow .. .. £140 £110
24 1 g. black on yellow .. £1700 £1300
26 2 g. black on blue .. £225 £300
27 3 g. pink .. .. £650 £450

**1865.** Roul.
28. **4.** ½ g. black .. .. .. 25·00 £350
29. 1 g. red .. .. .. 1·75 42·00
32. 2 g. blue .. .. .. 7·50 £110
34. 3 g. brown .. .. 6·00 £150

## BUENOS AIRES Pt. 20

A province of the Argentine Republic. Issued its own stamps from 1858–1862.

8 reales = 1 peso.

1. Steamship. 2. Head of Liberty.

**1858.** Imperf.
P 13. **1.** 4 r. brown .. .. £100 80·00
P 17. 1 (IN) p. brown .. £125 80·00
P 20. 1 (IN) p. blue .. .. 65·00 50·00
P 25. 1 (TO) p. blue .. .. £150 £100
P 1. 2 p. blue .. .. 90·00 50·00
P 4. 3 p. green .. .. £450 £250
P 7. 4 p. red .. .. £1500 £900
P 10. 5 p. yellow .. .. £1500 £900

**1859.** Imperf.
P 37. **2.** 4 r. green on blue .. 90·00 50·00
P 38. 1 p. blue .. .. 12·00 7·50
P 45. 1 p red .. .. 60·00 30·00
P 43. 2 p. red .. .. £120 80·00
P 48. 2 p. blue .. .. £120 45·00

## BULGARIA Pt. 3

Formerly a Turkish province; a principality under Turkish suzerainty from 1878 to 1908, when an independent kingdom was proclaimed. A People's Republic since 1946.

1879. 100 centimes = 1 franc.
1881. 100 stotinki = 1 lev.

1. Large Lion 2a.

**1879.** Value in centimes and franc.
1. **1.** 5 c. black and yellow .. £170 50·00
3. 10 c. black and green .. £700 £150
5. 25 c. black and purple .. £400 30·00
7. 50 c. black and blue .. £650 £130
8. 1 f. black and red .. £100 42·00

**1881.** Value in stotinki.
10. **2a.** 3 s. red and grey .. 32·00 6·75
11. 5 s. black and yellow .. 32·00 6·75
14. 10 s. black and green .. £170 20·00
15. 15 s. red and green .. £170 23·00
18. 25 s. black and purple .. £750 75·00
19. 30 s. blue and brown .. 32·00 17·00
See also Nos. 275/9.

A. B.

C. D.

**1882.**
46 2a 1 s. violet (Type A) .. 25·00 8·25
48 1 s. violet (Type B) .. 1·75 15
47 2 s. green (Type C) .. 23·00 6·75
49 2 s. green (Type D) .. 1·75 15
22 3 s. orange and yellow .. 1·75 50
23 5 s. green .. .. 13·50 85
26 10 s. red .. .. 17·00 1·25
28 15 s. purple and mauve 13·00 40
31 25 s. blue .. .. 13·00 65
33 30 s. lilac and green .. 13·00 1·00
34 50 s. blue and red .. 13·00 1·00
50 1 l. black and red .. 50·00 6·75

**1884.** Surch. with large figure of value.
38. **2a.** 3 on 10 s. red .. .. 85·00 65·00
43. 5 on 30 s. blue and brown 85·00 85·00
45. 15 on 25 s. blue .. .. £130 £100
40. 50 on 1 f. black and red .. £550 £375

7.

11. Arms of Bulgaria.

13. Cherry wood Cannon used against the Turks.

**1889.**
51. **7.** 1 s. mauve .. .. 25 10
52. 2 s. grey .. .. 1·10 45
53. 3 s. brown .. .. 85 20
54. 5 s. green .. .. 8·25 10
55. 10 s. red .. .. 8·25 20
56. 15 s. orange .. .. 50·00 10
57. 25 s. blue .. .. 10·00 10
58. 30 s. brown .. .. 17·00 10
59. 50 s. green .. .. 80 10
60. 1 l. red .. .. .. 75 40
83. 2 l. red and pink .. .. 3·25 2·75
84. 3 l. black and buff .. 6·00 5·00

**1892.** Surch. **15.**
61. **7.** 15 on 30 s. brown .. 17·00 1·40

**1895.** Surch. **01.**
74. **2a.** 01 on 2 s. green (No. 49) 1·25 30

**1896.** Baptism of Prince Boris.
78. **11.** 1 s. green .. .. .. 60 20
79. 5 s. blue .. .. .. 60 20
81. 15 s. violet .. .. 85 30
82. 25 s. red .. .. .. 8·00 2·00

**1901.** Surch. in figures.
102. **7.** 5 on 3 s. brown .. .. 3·25 1·40
103. 10 on 50 s. green .. 3·25 1·40

**1901.** 25th Anniv. of Uprising against Turkey.
104. **13.** 5 s. red .. .. .. 2·00 1·60
105. 15 s. green .. .. 2·00 1·60

14. Prince Ferdinand. 16. Fighting at Shipka Pass.

**1901.**
106. **14.** 1 s. black and purple .. 15 10
107. 2 s. blue and green .. 25 10
108. 3 s. black and orange .. 25 10
109. 5 s. brown and green .. 3·00 10
110. 10 s. brown and red .. 1·75 10
113. 15 s. black and lake .. 1·00 10
114. 25 s. black and blue .. 1·00 10
116. 30 s. black and brown .. 32·00 40
117. 50 s. brown and blue .. 1·75 20
118. 1 l. green and red .. 4·00 20
120. 2 l. black and red .. 7·75 1·00
123. 3 l. red and grey .. 11·50 5·00

**1902.** 25th Anniv. of Battle of Shipka Pass.
124. **16.** 5 s. red .. .. .. 2·40 85
125. 10 s. green .. .. 2·40 85
126. 15 s. blue .. .. 8·75 3·25

**1903.** Surch.
140. **14.** 5 on 15 s. black and lake 2·50 1·50
127. 10 on 15 s. blk. and lake 5·00 65
143. 25 on 30 s. blk. & brown 15·00 1·60

18. Ferdinand I in 1887 and 1907.

**1907.** 20th Anniv. of Prince Ferdinand's Accession.
132. **18.** 5 s. green .. .. 13·50 1·75
134. 10 s. brown .. .. 23·00 1·75
137. 25 s. blue .. .. 48·00 3·50

**1909.** Optd. **1909.**
146. **7.** 1 s. mauve .. .. 1·90 45
149. 5 s. green .. .. 1·90 45

**1909.** Surch. **1909** and new value.
151. **7.** 5 on 30 s. brown .. 2·75 35
154. 10 on 15 s. orange .. 2·75 85
156. 10 on 50 s. green .. 2·75 85

**1910.** Surch. **1910** and new value.
157. **14.** 1 on 3 s. black and orange 6·50 1·40
158. 5 on 15 s. black and lake 2·00 1·10

23. King Asen Tower.

24. Tsar in General's Uniform.

25. Tirnovo City.

**1911.**
159. **23.** 1 s. green .. .. 15 10
182a. 1 s. slate .. .. 10 10
160. **24.** 2 s. black and red .. 15 10
161. **25.** 3 s. black and lake .. 60 10
162. – 5 s. black and green .. 1·00 10
181. – 5 s. purple and green .. 2·00 10
163. – 10 s. black and red .. 1·75 10
181a. – 10 s. sepia and brown .. 15 10
164. – 15 s. bistre .. .. 5·00 20
183. – 15 s. olive .. .. 50 15
165. – 25 s. black and blue .. 50 10
166. – 30 s. black and blue .. 5·00 15
182. – 30 s. brown and olive .. 25 15
167. – 50 s. black and yellow .. 32·00 20
168. – 1 l. brown .. .. 8·25 15
169. – 2 l. black and purple .. 2·00 80
170. – 3 l. black and violet .. 17·00 5·00
DESIGNS—VERT. 5 s., 10 s., 25 s., 1 l. Portraits of Tsar Ferdinand. HORIZ. 15 s. R. Isker. 30 s. Rila Monastery. 50 s. Tsars and Princes. 2 l. Monastery of the Holy Trinity. 3 l. Varna.
See also Nos. 229/30 and 236/7.

35. Tsar Ferdinand.

**1912.** 25th Year of the Reign.
171. **35.** 5 s. grey .. .. 4·25 1·25
172. 10 s. lake .. .. 6·75 2·50
173. 25 s. blue .. .. 9·00 3·75

**ОСВОБ. ВОЙНА**
**1912-1913**
(36.) " War of Liberation " 1912–13.

**3**
**СТОТИНКИ**
(37a.)

**1913.** Victory over Turks. Stamps of 1911 optd. as T **36.**
174. **23.** 1 s. green .. .. 35 15
175. **24.** 2 s. black and red .. 35 15
176. **25.** 3 s. black and lake .. 35 15
177. – 5 s. black and green .. 35 10
178. – 10 s. black and red .. 40 10
179. – 15 s. bistre .. .. 1·10 30
180. – 25 s. black and blue .. 3·25 70

**1915.** No. 165 surch. **10 CT.** and bar.
180a. – 10 s. on 25 s. blk. & blue 85 15

**1916.** Red Cross Fund. Surch. with T **37a.**
185. **7.** 3 s. on 1 s. mauve .. 7·25 7·25
Nos. 186/9 formerly listed here will now be found under Bulgarian Occupation of Rumania.

45. Veles. 46. Bulgarian Ploughman.

38. 39. Bulgarian peasant.

**1917.** Liberation of Macedonia.
193. **45.** 1 s. grey .. .. 10 10
194. **46.** 1 s. green .. .. 10 10
195. – 5 s. green .. .. 10 10
186. **38.** 5 s. green .. .. 45 20
187. **39.** 15 s. grey .. .. 15 15
188. – 25 s. blue .. .. 15 15
189. – 30 s. orange .. .. 15 20
190. – 50 s. violet .. .. 65 40
191. – 2 l. brown .. .. 70 40
192. – 3 l. red .. .. 1·40 65
DESIGNS—As Type **45:** 5 s. Monastery of St. John, Ochrid. As Type **38:** 25 s. Soldier and Mt. Sonichka. 50 s. Ochrid and Lake. As Type **39:** 30 s. Nish. 2 l. Demir kapija. 3 l. Gevgeli.

48.

**1918.** 30th Anniv. of Tsar's Accession.
196. **48.** 1 s. slate .. .. 10 10
197. 2 s. brown .. .. 10 10
198. 3 s. blue .. .. 40 25
199. 10 s. red .. .. 40 25

49. Parliament Building.

50. King Boris III

**1919.**
201. **49.** 1 s. black .. .. 10 10
202. 2 s. olive .. .. 10 10

**1919.** 1st Anniv. of Enthronement of King Boris III.
203. **50.** 3 s. brown .. .. 10 10
204. 5 s. green .. .. 10 10
205. 10 s. red .. .. 10 10
206. 15 s. violet .. .. 10 10
207. 25 s. blue .. .. 10 10
208. 30 s. brown .. .. 10 10
209. 50 s. brown .. .. 10 10

ЗА НАШИТЬ ПЛѢННИЦИ 2½ (52.)  ЗА НАШИТЬ ПЛѢННИЦИ 50 (53.)

**1920.** Prisoners of War Fund. Surch. as T **52/53.**

| | | | | |
|---|---|---|---|---|
| 210. | **49.** | 1 on 2 s. olive .. .. | 10 | 10 |
| 211. | **50.** | 2½ on 5 s. green .. | 10 | 10 |
| 212. | | 5 on 10 s. red .. .. | 10 | 10 |
| 213. | | 7½ on 15 s. violet .. | 10 | 10 |
| 214. | | 12½ on 25 s. blue .. | 10 | 10 |
| 215. | | 15 on 30 s. brown .. | 10 | 10 |
| 216. | | 25 on 50 s. brown .. | 10 | 10 |
| 217. | – | 50 on 1 l. brn. (No. 168) | 15 | 15 |
| 218. | – | 1 on 2 l. brn. (No. 191) | 15 | 25 |
| 219. | – | 1½ on 3 l. red (No. 192) | 65 | 65 |

**54.** Vazov's Birthplace at Sopot and Cherry-wood Cannon. **55.** "The Bear-fighter", character from "Under the Yoke".

**1920.** 70th Birth Anniv. of Ivan Vazov (writer).

| | | | | |
|---|---|---|---|---|
| 220. | **54.** | 30 s. red .. .. | 15 | 10 |
| 221. | **55.** | 50 s. green .. .. | 20 | 15 |
| 222. | – | 1 l. sepia .. .. | 40 | 25 |
| 223. | – | 2 l. brown .. .. | 1·40 | 75 |
| 224. | – | 3 l. violet .. .. | 1·75 | 1·25 |
| 225. | – | 5 l. blue .. .. | 2·40 | 1·50 |

DESIGNS—HORIZ. 1 l. Ivan Vazov in 1870 and 1920. 3 l. Vazov's Houses in Plovdiv and Sofia. VERT. 2 l. Vazov. 5 l. Monk Paissi quoted by Vazov.

**59.** Sofia.

**62.** King Boris III.

**1921.**

| | | | | |
|---|---|---|---|---|
| 226. | **59.** | 10 s. violet .. .. | 10 | 10 |
| 227. | – | 20 s. green .. .. | 10 | 10 |
| 228. | **62.** | 25 s. blue .. .. | 10 | 10 |
| 229. | **25.** | 50 s. orange .. .. | 40 | 10 |
| 230. | | 50 s. blue .. .. | 6·00 | 2·50 |
| 231. | – | 75 s. purple .. .. | 15 | 10 |
| 232. | – | 75 s. blue .. .. | 40 | 10 |
| 233. | **62.** | 1 l. red .. .. | 25 | 15 |
| 234. | | 1 l. blue .. .. | 15 | 10 |
| 235. | – | 2 l. brown .. .. | 50 | 10 |
| 236. | – | 3 l. purple .. .. | 1·40 | 10 |
| 237. | – | 5 l. blue .. .. | 5·00 | 30 |
| 238. | **62.** | 10 l. red .. .. | 17·00 | 4·25 |

DESIGNS—HORIZ. 20 s. Alexander II "The Liberator" Monument Sofia. 75 s. Shipka Pass Monastery. 5 l. Rila Monastery. VERT. 2 l. Girl with wheatsheaf. 3 l. King Aen Tower.

**66.**

**68.** Mt. Shar.

**1921.**

| | | | | |
|---|---|---|---|---|
| 239. | **66.** | 10 s. red .. .. | 10 | 10 |
| 240. | – | 10 s. red .. .. | 10 | 10 |
| 241. | **68.** | 10 s. red .. .. | 10 | 10 |
| 242. | – | 10 s. mauve .. .. | 15 | 10 |
| 243. | – | 20 s. blue .. .. | 45 | 10 |

DESIGNS—VERT. No. 240, King and Lion. HORIZ. No. 242, Bridge over Vardar, at Skopje. No. 243, Lake Ochrid.

**71.** Bourchier in Bulgarian Costume.

**72.** J. D. Bourchier.

**73.** Rila Monastery, Bourchier's Resting-place.

**1921.** J. D. Bourchier ("Times" Correspondent). Commemoration.

| | | | | |
|---|---|---|---|---|
| 244. | **71.** | 10 s. red .. .. | 10 | 10 |
| 245. | | 20 s. orange .. .. | 10 | 10 |
| 246. | **72.** | 30 s. slate .. .. | 10 | 10 |
| 247. | | 50 s. lilac .. .. | 10 | 10 |
| 248. | | 1 l. purple .. .. | 25 | 10 |
| 249. | **73.** | 1½ l. olive .. .. | 20 | 20 |
| 250. | | 2 l. green .. .. | 25 | 15 |
| 251. | | 3 l. blue.. .. .. | 85 | 25 |
| 252. | | 5 l. red .. .. | 1·50 | 85 |

**1924.** Surch.

| | | | | |
|---|---|---|---|---|
| 253. | **49.** | 10 s. on 1 s. black .. | 10 | 10 |
| 254. | **D 37.** | 10 s. on 20 s. orange .. | 10 | 10 |
| 255. | | 20 s. on 5 s. green .. | 11·50 | 11·50 |
| 256. | | 20 s. on 10 s. violet .. | 3·50 | 3·50 |
| 257. | | 20 s. on 30 s. orange .. | 10 | 10 |
| 258. | **50.** | 1 l. on 5 s. green .. | 10 | 10 |
| 259. | **25.** | 3 l. on 50 s. blue .. | 60 | 25 |
| 260. | **62.** | 6 l. on 1 l. red .. .. | 50 | 30 |

**77.** **78.**

**79.** King Boris III.

**81.** Nevski Church, Sofia.

**82.** Harvesters. **83.** Proposed Rest-home.

**1925.**

| | | | | |
|---|---|---|---|---|
| 261 | **77** | 10 s. blue & red on rose | 20 | 10 |
| 262 | | 15 s. orange & red on bl | 35 | 10 |
| 263 | | 30 s. buff and black .. | 20 | 10 |
| 264 | **78** | 50 s. brown on green .. | 20 | 10 |
| 265 | **79** | 1 l. olive .. .. | 45 | 10 |
| 266 | | 1 l. green .. .. | 75 | 10 |
| 267 | **81** | 2 l. green and buff .. | 2·25 | 10 |
| 267a | **79** | 2 l. yellow .. .. | 80 | 10 |
| 268 | **82** | 4 l. red and yellow .. | 1·90 | 10 |

**1925.** Sunday Delivery Stamps.

| | | | | |
|---|---|---|---|---|
| 268a. | **83.** | 1 l. black on green .. | 3·75 | 15 |
| 268b. | | 1 l. brown .. .. | 3·75 | 15 |
| 268c. | | 1 l. orange .. .. | 3·50 | 15 |
| 268d. | | 1 l. pink .. .. | 5·00 | 15 |
| 268e. | | 1 l. violet on red .. | 4·50 | 15 |
| 268f. | – | 2 l. green .. .. | 40 | 15 |
| 268g. | – | 2 l. violet .. .. | 40 | 20 |
| 268h. | – | 5 l. blue .. .. | 3·25 | 55 |
| 268j. | – | 5 l. red .. .. | 3·00 | 45 |

DESIGN: 2 l. 5 l Proposed Sanatorium.

**85.** Sveta Nedelya Cathedral, Sofia after Bomb Outrage.

**86.** C. Botev (poet).

**1926.**

| | | | | |
|---|---|---|---|---|
| 269. | **85.** | 50 s. black .. .. | 10 | 10 |

**1926.** Botev Commem.

| | | | | |
|---|---|---|---|---|
| 270. | **86.** | 1 l. green .. .. | 85 | 15 |
| 271. | | 2 l. lilac.. .. | 1·75 | 15 |
| 272. | | 4 l. red .. .. | 2·40 | 1·75 |

**87.** **89.** King Boris III.

**90.** Saint Clement of Ochrid.

**1926.**

| | | | | |
|---|---|---|---|---|
| 273. | **87.** | 6 l. olive and blue .. | 2·00 | 15 |
| 274. | | 10 l. orange and sepia.. | 8·00 | 2·00 |

**1927.** As T **2a** in new colours.

| | | | | |
|---|---|---|---|---|
| 275. | | 10 s. red and green .. | 15 | 10 |
| 276. | | 15 s. black and yellow .. | 15 | 10 |
| 277. | | 30 s. slate and buff .. | 15 | 10 |
| 278. | | 30 s. blue and buff .. | 15 | 10 |
| 279. | | 50 s. black and red .. | 15 | 10 |

**1927.** Air. Various stamps optd with Albatros biplane and 6 l. surch also.

| | | | | |
|---|---|---|---|---|
| 281 | **87** | 1 l. on 6 l. green & blue | 2·00 | 1·75 |
| 282 | **79** | 2 l. yellow .. .. | 2·00 | 1·75 |
| 283 | **82** | 4 l. red and yellow .. | 3·00 | 1·75 |
| 284 | **87** | 10 l. orange and brown | 50·00 | 32·00 |

**1928.**

| | | | | |
|---|---|---|---|---|
| 285. | **89.** | 1 l. green .. .. | 1·90 | 10 |
| 286. | | 2 l. brown .. .. | 3·00 | 10 |

**1929.** 50th Anniv. of Liberation of Bulgaria and Millenary of Tsar Simeon. Various sizes.

| | | | | |
|---|---|---|---|---|
| 287. | **90.** | 10 s. violet .. .. | 15 | 10 |
| 288. | – | 15 s. purple .. .. | 15 | 10 |
| 289. | – | 30 s. red .. .. | 15 | 10 |
| 290. | – | 50 s. olive .. .. | 50 | 10 |
| 291. | – | 1 l. brown .. .. | 1·40 | 15 |
| 292. | – | 2 l. blue.. .. .. | 1·40 | 15 |
| 293. | – | 3 l. green .. .. | 3·25 | 50 |
| 294. | – | 4 l. brown .. .. | 6·75 | 25 |
| 295. | – | 5 l. brown .. .. | 3·00 | 55 |
| 296. | – | 6 l. turquoise .. .. | 6·75 | 1·90 |

DESIGNS: 15 s. Miladinov. 30 s. George S. Rakovski. 50 s. Drenovo Monastery. 1 l. Father Paissi. 2 l. Tsar Simeon. 3 l. Liuben Karavelov. 4 l. Vasil Levski. 5 l. George Benkovski. 6 l. Tsar Alexander II of Russia.

**98.** Convalescent Home, Varna.

**1930.** Sunday Delivery stamps.

| | | | | |
|---|---|---|---|---|
| 297. | **98.** | 1 l. green and purple .. | 6·00 | 15 |
| 298. | | 1 l. yellow and green .. | 70 | 15 |
| 299. | | 1 l. brown and red .. | 70 | 15 |

**99.**

**101.** King Boris III.

**1930.** Marriage of King Boris and Princess Giovanna.

| | | | | |
|---|---|---|---|---|
| 300. | **99.** | 1 l. green .. .. | 30 | 20 |
| 301. | – | 2 l. purple .. .. | 45 | 20 |
| 302. | **99.** | 4 l. red .. .. | 45 | 30 |
| 303. | – | 6 l. blue .. .. | 55 | 35 |

DESIGN: 2 l., 6 l. Portraits in separate ovals.

**1931.** The 20 l. is 24½ × 33½ mm.

| | | | | |
|---|---|---|---|---|
| 304. | **101.** | 1 l. green (A) .. | 55 | 10 |
| 305. | | 2 l. red (A) .. .. | 85 | 10 |
| 306. | | 4 l. orange (A) .. | 1·10 | 10 |
| 308a. | | 4 l. orange (B) .. | 70 | 10 |
| 307. | | 6 l. blue (A) .. .. | 85 | 10 |
| 308b. | | 6 l. blue (B) .. .. | 1·90 | 10 |
| 308c. | | 7 l. blue (B) .. .. | 25 | 20 |
| 308d. | | 10 l. slate (B) .. .. | 22·00 | 1·10 |
| 308. | | 12 l. brown (A) .. | 45 | 10 |
| 308e. | | 14 l. brown (B) .. | 35 | 20 |
| 308f. | – | 20 l. brown & purple (B) | 1·75 | 70 |

(A) Without coloured frame-lines at top and bottom: (B) with frame-lines.

**103.** Gymnastics.

**1931.** Balkan Olympic Games.

| | | | | |
|---|---|---|---|---|
| 309. | **103.** | 1 l. green .. .. | 1·40 | 1·00 |
| 326. | | 1 l. turquoise .. .. | 3·25 | 2·75 |
| 310. | – | 2 l. lake.. .. .. | 2·00 | 1·40 |
| 327. | – | 2 l. blue.. .. .. | 5·00 | 2·75 |
| 311. | – | 4 l. red .. .. .. | 3·00 | 1·40 |
| 328. | – | 4 l. purple .. .. | 6·75 | 2·75 |
| 312. | – | 6 l. turquoise .. .. | 10·00 | 3·25 |
| 329. | – | 6 l. red .. .. .. | 13·50 | 6·75 |
| 313. | – | 10 l. orange .. .. | 25·00 | 8·25 |
| 330. | – | 10 l. brown .. .. | 85·00 | 32·00 |
| 314. | – | 12 l. blue .. .. | 85·00 | 23·00 |
| 331. | – | 12 l. orange .. .. | £170 | 60·00 |
| 315. | – | 50 l. brown .. .. | 80·00 | 55·00 |
| 332. | – | 50 l. red.. .. .. | £475 | £325 |

DESIGNS—VERT. (23 × 28 mm.): 2 l. Footballer. 4 l. Horse-riding. As Type **103**—HORIZ. 6 l. Fencing. 10 l. Cycling. VERT. 12 l. Diving. 50 l. Spirit of Victory.

**108.**

**109.** Rila Monastery.

**1931.** Air.

| | | | | |
|---|---|---|---|---|
| 316. | **108.** | 1 l. green .. .. | 60 | 15 |
| 316a. | | 1 l. purple .. .. | 20 | 15 |
| 317. | | 2 l. red .. .. | 60 | 15 |
| 317a. | | 2 l. green .. .. | 20 | 15 |
| 318. | | 6 l. blue.. .. .. | 50 | 25 |
| 318a. | | 6 l. red .. .. | 1·10 | 50 |
| 319. | | 12 l. red .. .. | 1·40 | 55 |
| 319a. | | 12 l. blue .. .. | 1·10 | 50 |
| 320. | | 20 l. violet .. .. | 1·40 | 85 |
| 321. | | 30 l. orange .. .. | 3·25 | 2·40 |
| 322. | | 50 l. brown .. .. | 4·25 | 2·40 |

**1932.** Air.

| | | | | |
|---|---|---|---|---|
| 323. | **109.** | 18 l. green .. .. | 60·00 | 40·00 |
| 324. | | 24 l. red .. .. | 60·00 | 32·00 |
| 325. | | 28 l. blue .. .. | 30·00 | 27·00 |

**1934.** Surch. **2.**

| | | | | |
|---|---|---|---|---|
| 333. | **101.** | 2 on 3 l. olive.. .. | 8·25 | 35 |

**111.** Defending the pass.

**113.** Convalescent Home, Troyan.

**1934.** Unveiling of Shipka Pass Memorial.

| | | | | |
|---|---|---|---|---|
| 334. | **111.** | 1 l. green .. .. | 1·00 | 85 |
| 340. | | 1 l. green .. .. | 1·00 | 85 |
| 335. | – | 2 l. red .. .. | 1·00 | 20 |
| 341. | – | 2 l. orange .. .. | 1·00 | 20 |
| 336. | – | 3 l. brown .. .. | 3·25 | 2·00 |
| 342. | – | 3 l. yellow .. .. | 3·25 | 2·00 |
| 337. | – | 4 l. red .. .. | 3·00 | 45 |
| 343. | – | 4 l. red .. .. | 3·00 | 45 |
| 338. | – | 7 l. blue.. .. .. | 4·25 | 2·75 |
| 344. | – | 7 l. light blue .. | 4·25 | 2·75 |
| 339. | – | 14 l. purple .. .. | 17·00 | 13·50 |
| 345. | – | 14 l. bistre .. .. | 17·00 | 13·50 |

DESIGNS—VERT. (dated "1934"): 2 l. Shipka Memorial. 3 l., 7 l. Veteran standard-bearer. 14 l. Widow showing orphans memorial. HORIZ. 4 l. Bulgarian Veteran.

**1935.** Sunday Delivery stamps.

| | | | | |
|---|---|---|---|---|
| 346. | **113.** | 1 l. red and brown .. | 45 | 15 |
| 347. | | 1 l. blue and green .. | 75 | 15 |
| 348. | – | 5 l. blue and red .. | 1·90 | 45 |

DESIGN: 5 l. Convalescent Home, Banya.

**114.** Capt. Mamarchef.

**115.** Cathedral.

**1935.** Centenary of Tirnovo Insurrection.

| | | | | |
|---|---|---|---|---|
| 349. | – | 1 l. blue.. .. .. | 2·40 | 35 |
| 350. | **114.** | 2 l. red .. .. | 2·40 | 85 |

DESIGN: 1 l. Velcho A. Djamdjyata.

**1935.** 5th Balkan Football Tournament.

| | | | | |
|---|---|---|---|---|
| 351. | – | 1 l. green .. .. | 3·25 | 3·25 |
| 352. | **115.** | 2 l. grey .. .. | 8·25 | 5·00 |
| 353. | – | 4 l. red .. .. | 13·50 | 6·75 |
| 354. | – | 7 l. blue .. .. | 27·00 | 10·00 |
| 355. | – | 14 l. orange .. .. | 23·00 | 11·50 |
| 356. | – | 50 l. brown .. .. | £300 | £275 |

DESIGNS—HORIZ. 1 l. Match in progress. 4 l. Footballers. VERT. 7 l. Herald and map. 14 l. Footballer and trophy. 50 l. Football trophy.

**116.** Girl Gymnast.

**117.** Janos Hunyadi.

**1935.** 8th Bulgarian Gymnastic Tournament. Dated "12–14. VII. 1935".

| | | | | |
|---|---|---|---|---|
| 357. | – | 1 l. green .. .. | 3·25 | 3·25 |
| 358. | – | 2 l. blue .. .. | 5·00 | 3·25 |
| 359. | **116.** | 4 l. red .. .. | 11·50 | 6·75 |
| 360. | – | 7 l. blue .. .. | 13·50 | 10·00 |
| 361. | – | 14 l. brown .. .. | 11·50 | 6·75 |
| 362. | – | 50 l. orange .. .. | £170 | £150 |

DESIGNS—VERT. 1 l. Parallel bars. 2 l. Male gymnast in uniform. 7 l. Pole vault. 50 l. Athlete and lion. HORIZ. 14 l. Stadium, Sofia.

**1935.** Unveiling of Monument to Ladislas III of Poland at Varna. Inscr. "WARNENCZYK(A)", etc.

| | | | | |
|---|---|---|---|---|
| 363. | **117.** | 1 l. orange .. .. | 2·00 | 45 |
| 364. | – | 2 l. red .. .. | 3·25 | 1·40 |
| 365. | – | 4 l. red .. .. | 23·00 | 5·00 |
| 366. | – | 7 l. blue .. .. | 5·00 | 2·75 |
| 367. | – | 14 l. green .. .. | 5·00 | 2·40 |

DESIGNS—VERT. 2 l. King Ladislas of Hungary enthroned (22 × 32 mm.). 7 l. King Ladislas in armour (20 × 31 mm.). HORIZ. 4 l. Varna Memorial (33 × 24 mm.). 14 l. Battle scene (30 × 25 mm.).

**118.** H. Dimitr.

**119.**

**120.**

**1935.** 67th Death Anniv. of Hadji Dimitr.

| | | | | |
|---|---|---|---|---|
| 368. | – | 1 l. green .. .. | 2·75 | 1·00 |
| 369. | **118.** | 2 l. brown .. .. | 4·00 | 1·60 |
| 370. | – | 4 l. red .. .. | 8·25 | 4·00 |
| 371. | – | 7 l. blue .. .. | 17·00 | 8·25 |
| 372. | – | 14 l. orange .. .. | 18·00 | 8·25 |

DESIGNS—VERT. 1 l. H. Dimitr's monument at Sliven. 7 l. Revolutionary group (dated 1868). HORIZ. 4 l. H. Dimitr and S. Karadzha. 14 l. Dimitr's birthplace at Silven.

**1936.**

373. 119. 10 s. red .. .. 10 10
373a. 15 s. green .. .. 10 10
374. 120. 30 s. red .. .. 15 10
374a. 30 s. red .. .. 10 10
374b. 30 s. blue .. .. 10 10
375. 50 s. blue .. .. 20 10
375a. 50 s. red .. .. 15 10
375b. 50 s. green .. .. 10 10

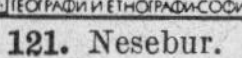

**121.** Nesebur. **122.** St. Cyril and St. Methodius.

**1936.** Slav Geographical and Ethnographical Congress, Sofia.

376. – 1 l. violet .. .. 2·75 2·00
377. – 2 l. blue .. .. 2·75 1·60
378. 121. 7 l. blue .. .. 6·75 3·25
DESIGNS—VERT. 1 l. Meteorological Bureau, Mt. Mousala. 2 l. Peasant Girl.

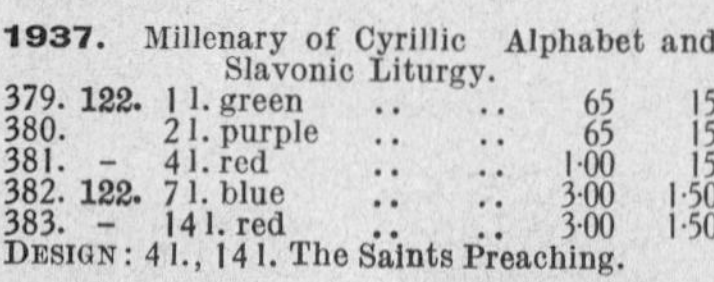

**1937.** Millenary of Cyrillic Alphabet and Slavonic Liturgy.

379. 122. 1 l. green .. .. 65 15
380. 2 l. purple .. .. 65 15
381. – 4 l. red .. .. 1·00 15
382. 122. 7 l. blue .. .. 3·00 1·50
383. – 14 l. red .. .. 3·00 1·50
DESIGN: 4 l., 14 l. The Saints Preaching.

**124.** Princess Marie Louise. **125.** King Boris III.

**1937.**

384. 124. 1 l. green .. .. 35 10
385. 2 l. red .. .. 40 15
386. 4 l. red .. .. 40 20

**1937.** 19th Anniv. of Accession.

387. 125. 2 l. red .. .. 35 25

**126.** Harvesting. **129.** Prince Simeon.

**1938.** Trade Propaganda.

388. 126. 10 s. orange .. .. 10 10
389. 10 s. red .. .. 10 10
390. – 15 s. red .. .. 30 10
391. – 15 s. purple .. .. 30 10
392. – 30 s. brown .. .. 15 10
393. – 30 s. brown .. .. 15 10
394. – 50 s. blue .. .. 85 10
395. – 50 s. black .. .. 85 10
396. – 1 l. green .. .. 85 10
397. – 1 l. green .. .. 85 10
398. – 2 l. red .. .. 85 10
399. – 2 l. brown .. .. 85 10
400. – 3 l. purple .. .. 1·60 85
401. 126. 3 l. purple .. .. 1·60 85
402. – 4 l. brown .. .. 1·25 20
403. – 4 l. purple .. .. 1·25 20
404. – 7 l. violet .. .. 2·00 85
405. – 7 l. blue .. .. 2·00 85
406. – 14 l. brown .. .. 3·75 1·75
407. – 14 l. brown .. .. 3·75 1·75
DESIGNS—VERT. 15 s. Sunflower. 30 s. Wheat. 50 s. Chickens and eggs. 1 l. Grapes. 3 l. Strawberries. 4 l. Girl carrying grapes. 7 l. Roses. 14 l. Tobacco leaves. HORIZ. 2 l. "Attar of Roses".

**1938.** First Birthday of Heir Apparent.

408. 129. 1 l. green .. .. 10 10
409. 2 l. red .. .. 15 10
410. – 4 l. orange .. .. 25 10
411. 129. 7 l. blue .. .. 1·10 35
412. – 14 l. brown .. .. 1·10 35
DESIGN: 4 l., 14 l. Another portrait.

**131.** King Boris III. **132.** First Bulgarian Locomotive.

**1938.** 20th Anniv. of King's Accession. Portraits of King in various uniforms.

413. 131. 1 l. green .. .. 15 10
414. – 2 l. red .. .. 75 10
415. – 4 l. brown .. .. 15 10
416. – 7 l. blue .. .. 35 25
417. – 14 l. mauve .. .. 35 25

**1939.** Bulgarian Railways' Jubilee, Locomotive types dated "1888–1938".

418. 132. 1 l. green .. .. 55 20
419. – 2 l. brown .. .. 70 20
420. – 4 l. orange .. .. 2·00 60
421. – 7 l. blue .. .. 5·75 2·75
DESIGNS: 2 l. Modern express train. 4 l. Train crossing viaduct. 7 l. King Boris as engine-driver.

**133.** P.O. Emblem. **135.** Gymnast.

**1939.** 60th Anniv. of Bulgarian P.O. Inscr. "1879 1939".

422. 133. 1 l. green .. .. 15 10
423. – 2 l. red (G.P.O., Sofia) 20 10

**1939.** Yunak Gymnastic Society's Rally.

424. 135. 1 l. green .. .. 50 15
425. – 2 l. red .. .. 50 15
426. – 4 l. brown .. .. 85 50
427. – 7 l. blue .. .. 2·50 1·10
428. – 14 l. mauve .. .. 12·50 9·25
DESIGNS: 2 l. Yunak badge. 4 l. Throwing discus. 7 l. Rhythmic dancer. 14 l. Weight-lifting.

**1939.** Sevlievo and Tirnovo Floods' Relief Fund. Surch. **Наводнението** (=Inundation) **1939** and value.

429. 39. 1 l.+1 l. on 15 s. grey .. 15 15
430. 73. 2 l.+1 l. on 1½ l. olive 15 15
431. 4 l.+2 l. on 2 l. green .. 20 20
432. 7 l.+4 l. on 3 l. blue .. 55 55
433. 14 l.+7 l. on 5 l. red .. 95 95

**137.** Mail Plane. **138.** King Boris III.

**1940.** Air.

434. 137. 1 l. green .. .. 10 10
435. – 2 l. red .. .. 2·00 10
436. – 4 l. orange .. .. 15 10
437. – 6 l. blue .. .. 15 10
438. – 10 l. brown .. .. 45 20
439. – 12 l. brown .. .. 65 30
440. – 16 l. violet .. .. 1·00 45
441. – 19 l. blue .. .. 1·25 60
442. – 30 l. mauve .. .. 1·90 90
443. – 45 l. violet .. .. 5·00 2·40
444. – 70 l. red .. .. 4·00 3·00
445. – 100 l. blue .. .. 17·00 9·00
DESIGNS—VERT. Aircraft over: King Asen's Tower (2 l.), Bachovo Monastery (4 l.), Nevski Church, Sofia (45 l.), Shipka Pass Memorial (70 l.). 10 l. Airplane, mail train and express motor cycle. 30 l. Airplane and swallow. 100 l. Airplane and Royal cypher. HORIZ. 6 l. Loading mails at aerodrome. Aircraft over: Sofia Palace (12 l.), Mt. El Tepe (16 l.), Rila Lakes and mountains (19 l.).

**1940.**

445a. 138. 1 l. green .. .. 15 10
446. 2 l. red .. .. 50 10

**139.** First Bulgarian Postage Stamp. **140.** Peasant Couple and King Boris.

**141.** King Boris and Map of Dobrudja.

**1940.** Cent. of 1st Adhesive Postage Stamp.

447. 139. 10 l. olive .. .. 2·50 1·90
448. – 20 l. blue .. .. 2·50 1·90
DESIGN: 20 l. has scroll dated "1840–1940".

**1940.** Recovery of the Dobrudja from Rumania. Designs incorporating miniature portrait of King Boris.

449. 140. 1 l. green .. .. 15 10
450. – 2 l. red .. .. 15 10
451. 141. 4 l. brown .. .. 15 10
452. 7 l. blue .. .. 55 30
DESIGN—VERT. 2 l. Bulgarian flags and wheat-field.

**142.** Grapes. **143.** Ploughing.

**1940.**

453. 142. 10 s. orange .. .. 10 10
454. – 15 s. blue .. .. 10 10
455. 143. 30 s. brown .. .. 10 10
456. – 50 s. violet .. .. 10 10
456a. – 50 s. green .. .. 10 10
DESIGNS—As Type 142: 15 s. Beehive. As Type 143.: 50 s. Shepherd and flock.

**144.** King Boris III. **145.** Bee-keeping.

**1940.**

457. 144. 1 l. green .. .. 10 10
458. 2 l. red .. .. 10 10
459. 4 l. orange .. .. 10 10
460. 6 l. violet .. .. 20 10
461. 7 l. blue .. .. 25 10
462. 10 l. green .. .. 25 10

**1940.** Agricultural Scenes.

468. – 10 s. purple .. .. 10 10
469. – 10 s. blue .. .. 10 10
470. – 15 s. green .. .. 10 10
471. – 15 s. olive .. .. 10 10
472. 145. 30 s. orange .. .. 10 10
473. 30 s. green .. .. 10 10
474. – 50 s. violet .. .. 10 10
475. – 50 s. purple .. .. 10 10
476. – 3 l. brown .. .. 55 15
477. – 3 l. black .. .. 1·50 65
478. – 5 l. brown .. .. 1·00 40
479. – 5 l. blue .. .. 1·50 55
DESIGNS: 10 s. Threshing. 15 s. Ploughing with oxen. 50 s. Picking apples. 3 l. Shepherd. 5 l. Cattle.

**146.** P. R. Slaveykov. **147.** St. Ivan Rilski.

**1940.** National Relief. Patriots.

480. 146. 1 l. green .. .. 10 10
481. – 2 l. red .. .. 15 10
482. 147. 3 l. brown .. .. 15 10
483. – 4 l. orange .. .. 15 10
484. – 7 l. blue .. .. 1·75 1·40
485. – 10 l. brown .. .. 2·50 1·40
DESIGNS: 2 l. Bishop Sofroni of Vratsa. 4 l. M. S. Drinov. 7 l. Chernorisev the Brave. 10 l. K. Ficheto.

**148.** J. Gutenberg. **149.** N. Karastoyanov.

**1940.** 500th Anniv. of Invention of Printing and Cent. of Bulgarian printer, Karastoyanov.

486. 148. 1 l. green .. .. 15 10
487. 149. 2 l. brown .. .. 15 10

**150.** C. Botev. **151.** Arrival in Koslodul.

**1941.** 65th Death Anniv. of Botev.

488. 150. 1 l. green .. .. 10 10
489. 151. 2 l. red .. .. 15 10
490. – 3 l. brown .. .. 1·40 1·00
DESIGN—VERT. 3 l. Botev Memorial Cross.

**152.** Palace of Justice.

**1941.**

491. 152. 14 l. brown .. .. 55 35
492. – 20 l. green .. .. 85 50
493. – 50 l. blue .. .. 2·40 1·75
DESIGNS: 20 l. Workers' Hospital. 50 l. National Bank, Sofia.

**153.** Thasos Island. **154.** Ochrid.

**1941.** Reacquisition of Macedonia.

494. – 1 l. green .. .. 10 10
495. 153. 2 l. orange .. .. 10 10
496. – 2 l. red .. .. 10 10
497. – 4 l. brown .. .. 15 10
498. 154. 7 l. blue .. .. 45 30
DESIGNS—VERT. 1 l. Macedonian Girl. HORIZ. 2 l. (No. 496) King Boris and map dated "1941". 4 l. Cloister of Poganowski.

**155.** Children on Beach.

**1942.** Sunday Delivery. Insc. as in T **155**.

499. – 1 l. olive .. .. 10 10
500. 155. 2 l. orange .. .. 15 10
501. – 5 l. blue .. .. 30 25
DESIGNS: 1 l. Sanatorium. 5 l. Sun-bathing.

**156.** Bugler at Camp. **157.** Folk Dancers.

**1942.** "Work and Joy". Inscr. as at foot of T **157**.

502. – 1 l. green .. .. 15 10
503. – 2 l. red .. .. 15 10
504. – 4 l. black .. .. 15 10
505. 156. 7 l. blue .. .. 20 15
506. 157. 14 l. brown .. .. 60 20
DESIGNS—VERT. 1 l. Girl with guitar. 2 l. Camp orchestra. 4 l. Hoisting the flag.

**158.** Wounded Soldier. **159.** Queen visiting Wounded.

**1942.** War Invalids. Inscr. as T**158/9**.

507. 158. 1 l. green .. .. 10 10
508. – 2 l. red .. .. 10 10
509. – 4 l. orange .. .. 10 10
510. – 7 l. blue .. .. 10 10
511. – 14 l. brown .. .. 15 10
512. 159. 20 l. black .. .. 30 15
DESIGNS—HORIZ. 2 l. Soldier and family. 4 l. First aid on battlefield. 7 l. Widow and orphans at grave. 14 l. Unknown Soldiers Memorial.

160. Legend of Kubrat.

161. King Boris III.

**1942.** Historical series.

| No. | Type | Description | Unused | Used |
|---|---|---|---|---|
| 513. | 160. | 10 s. black | 10 | 10 |
| 514. | – | 15 s. blue | 10 | 10 |
| 515. | – | 30 s. mauve | 10 | 10 |
| 516. | – | 50 s. blue | 10 | 10 |
| 517. | – | 1 l. green | 10 | 10 |
| 518. | – | 2 l. red | 10 | 10 |
| 519. | – | 3 l. brown | 10 | 10 |
| 520. | – | 4 l. orange | 10 | 10 |
| 521. | – | 5 l. green | 15 | 10 |
| 522. | – | 7 l. blue | 15 | 10 |
| 523. | – | 10 l. black | 15 | 10 |
| 524. | – | 14 l. olive | 15 | 10 |
| 525. | – | 20 l. brown | 55 | 30 |
| 526. | – | 30 l. black | 1·40 | 40 |

Designs: 15 s. Cavalry charge. 30 s. Equestrian statue. 50 s. Baptism of King Boris I. 1 l. St. Naum's School. 2 l. Coronation of Tsar Simeon. 3 l. Golden Era of Bulgarian literature. 4 l. Trial of Bogomil Vasili. 5 l. Proclamation of Second Bulgarian Empire. 7 l. Ivan Asen II at Trebizond. 10 l. Expulsion of Patriarch Ertimi. 14 l. Wandering minstrels. 20 l. Father Paissi. 30 l. Shipka Pass Memorial.

**1944.** King Boris Mourning Issue. Portraits dated "1894–1943". Perf. or imperf.

| No. | Type | Description | Unused | Used |
|---|---|---|---|---|
| 527. | 161. | 1 l. olive | 10 | 10 |
| 528. | – | 2 l. brown | 15 | 15 |
| 529. | – | 4 l. brown | 15 | 15 |
| 530. | – | 5 l. violet | 60 | 55 |
| 531. | – | 7 l. blue | 60 | 55 |

163. King Simeon II.

167.

**1944.**

| No. | Type | Description | Unused | Used |
|---|---|---|---|---|
| 532. | 163. | 3 l. orange | 10 | 10 |

**1945.** "All for the Front". Parcel Post stamps optd. ВСИЧКО ЗА ФРОНТА or surch. also.

| No. | Type | Description | Unused | Used |
|---|---|---|---|---|
| 533.P | 163. | 1 l. red | 10 | 10 |
| 534. | | 4 l. on 1 l. red | 10 | 10 |
| 535. | | 7 l. mauve | 10 | 10 |
| 536. | | 20 l. brown | 25 | 10 |
| 537. | | 30 l. purple | 35 | 10 |
| 538. | | 50 l. orange | 40 | 20 |
| 539. | | 100 l. blue | 1·40 | 45 |

**1945.** Air. Optd with airplane or surch also.

| No. | Type | Description | Unused | Used |
|---|---|---|---|---|
| 540. | 144. | 1 l. green | 10 | 10 |
| 541. | | 4 l. orange | 10 | 10 |
| 542.P | 163. | 10 l. on 100 l. yellow | 20 | 15 |
| 543. | | 45 l. on 100 l. yellow | 20 | 15 |
| 544. | | 75 l. on 100 l. yellow | 50 | 30 |
| 545. | | 100 l. yellow | 1·10 | 40 |

Nos. 540/1 are perf.; the rest imperf.

**1945.** Slav Congress. Perf. or imperf.

| No. | Type | Description | Unused | Used |
|---|---|---|---|---|
| 546. | 167. | 4 l. red | 10 | 10 |
| 547. | | 10 l. blue | 10 | 10 |
| 548. | | 50 l. red | 20 | 20 |

СЪБИРАЙТЕ
ВСЪКАКВИ
ПАРЦАЛИ
(168.) "Collect All Rags".

СЪБИРАЙТЕ
СТАРО
ЖЕЛЪЗО
(169.) "Collect Old Iron".

СЪБИРАЙТЕ
ХАРТИЕНИ
ОТПАДЪЦИ
(170.) "Collect Wastepaper".

**1945.** Salvage Campaign. Nos. 457/9 optd. with T 168/70

| No. | Type | Description | Unused | Used |
|---|---|---|---|---|
| 549. | 144. | 1 l. green | 15 | 10 |
| 550. | | 2 l. red | 40 | 15 |
| 551. | | 4 l. orange | 65 | 10 |

Prices are the same for these stamps with any one of the overprints illustrated.

171. Lion Rampant.

172.

**1945.** Lion Rampant, in various frames.

| No. | Type | Description | Unused | Used |
|---|---|---|---|---|
| 552. | – | 30 s. green | 10 | 10 |
| 553. | – | 50 s. blue | 10 | 10 |
| 554. | 171. | 1 l. green | 10 | 10 |
| 555. | – | 2 l. brown | 10 | 10 |
| 556. | – | 4 l. blue | 10 | 10 |
| 557. | – | 5 l. violet | 10 | 10 |
| 558. | 172. | 9 l. grey | 10 | 10 |
| 559. | – | 10 l. blue | 10 | 10 |
| 560. | – | 15 l. brown | 20 | 10 |
| 561. | – | 20 l. black | 20 | 10 |
| 562. | – | 20 l. red | 20 | 10 |

173. Chain-breaker.

174. "VE Day".

**1945** Liberty Loan. Imperf.

| No. | Type | Description | Unused | Used |
|---|---|---|---|---|
| 563. | 173. | 50 l. orange | 15 | 10 |
| 564. | | 50 l. lake | 15 | 10 |
| 565. | – | 100 l. blue | 20 | 15 |
| 566. | – | 100 l. brown | 20 | 15 |
| 567. | – | 150 l. red | 45 | 30 |
| 568. | – | 150 l. green | 45 | 30 |
| 569. | – | 200 l. olive | 1·00 | 55 |
| 570. | – | 200 l. blue | 1·00 | 55 |

Designs: 100 l. Hand holding coin. 150 l. Water-mill. 200 l. Coin and symbols of industry and agriculture.

**1945.** VE Day.

| No. | Type | Description | Unused | Used |
|---|---|---|---|---|
| 571. | 174. | 10 l. green and brown | 10 | 10 |
| 572. | | 50 l. green and red | 30 | 15 |

175.

176.

**1945.** 1st Anniv. of Fatherland Front.

| No. | Type | Description | Unused | Used |
|---|---|---|---|---|
| 573. | 175. | 1 l. olive | 10 | 10 |
| 574. | | 4 l. blue | 10 | 10 |
| 575. | | 5 l. mauve | 10 | 10 |
| 576. | 176. | 10 l. blue | 10 | 10 |
| 577. | | 20 l. red | 25 | 15 |
| 578. | 175. | 50 l. green | 50 | 35 |
| 579. | | 100 l. brown | 85 | 45 |

177. Refugee Children.

178. Red Cross Train.

**1946.** Red Cross.

| No. | Type | Description | Unused | Used |
|---|---|---|---|---|
| 580. | 177. | 2 l. olive | 10 | 10 |
| 645d. | | 2 l. brown | 10 | 10 |
| 581. | – | 4 l. violet | 10 | 10 |
| 645e. | – | 4 l. black | 10 | 10 |
| 582. | 177. | 10 l. purple | 10 | 10 |
| 645f. | | 10 l. green | 15 | 10 |
| 583. | – | 20 l. dark blue | 10 | 10 |
| 645g. | – | 20 l. light blue | 25 | 15 |
| 584. | – | 30 l. brown | 15 | 15 |
| 645h. | – | 30 l. green | 35 | 25 |
| 585. | 178. | 35 l. black | 1·25 | 75 |
| 645i. | | 35 l. green | 1·25 | 75 |
| 586. | – | 50 l. purple | 35 | 25 |
| 645j. | – | 50 l. lake | 60 | 45 |
| 587. | 178. | 100 l. brown | 2·75 | 1·75 |
| 645k. | | 100 l. blue | 2·75 | 1·75 |

Designs—horiz. 4 l. 20 l. Soldier on stretcher. vert. 30 l., 50 l. Nurse and wounded soldier.

179. Postal Savings Emblem.

180. Savings Bank-Note.

**1946.** 50th Anniv. of Savings Bank.

| No. | Type | Description | Unused | Used |
|---|---|---|---|---|
| 588. | 179. | 4 l. red | 15 | 10 |
| 589. | 180. | 10 l. olive | 15 | 10 |
| 590. | – | 20 l. blue | 15 | 10 |
| 591. | – | 50 l. black | 1·00 | 95 |

Designs—vert. 20 l. Child filling money-box. 50 l. Postal Savings Bank.

181. Arms of Russia and Bulgaria and Spray of Oak.

182. Lion Rampant.

**1946.** Bulgo-Russian Congress.

| No. | Type | Description | Unused | Used |
|---|---|---|---|---|
| 592. | 181. | 4 l. red | 6·75 | 6·75 |
| 593. | | 4 l. orange | 15 | 10 |
| 594. | | 20 l. blue | 6·75 | 6·75 |
| 595. | | 20 l. green | 15 | 15 |

**1946.** Stamp Day. Imperf.

| No. | Type | Description | Unused | Used |
|---|---|---|---|---|
| 596. | 182. | 20 l. blue | 35 | 35 |

183.

190.

**1946.** Air. Inscr. "PAR AVION".

| No. | Type | Description | Unused | Used |
|---|---|---|---|---|
| 597. | 183. | 1 l. lilac | 15 | 10 |
| 598. | | 2 l. grey | 15 | 10 |
| 599. | – | 4 l. black | 30 | 15 |
| 600. | – | 6 l. blue | 40 | 30 |
| 601. | – | 10 l. green | 10 | 10 |
| 602. | – | 12 l. brown | 10 | 10 |
| 603. | – | 16 l. purple | 10 | 10 |
| 604. | – | 19 l. red | 10 | 10 |
| 605. | – | 30 l. orange | 15 | 10 |
| 606. | – | 45 l. green | 45 | 15 |
| 607. | – | 75 l. brown | 55 | 15 |
| 608. | 190. | 100 l. red | 1·10 | 25 |
| 609. | – | 100 l. slate | 1·10 | 25 |

Designs—horiz. 4 l. Bird and envelope. 100 l. (No. 609), Aeroplane. vert. 6 l. Aeroplane and envelope. 10 l., 12 l. and 19 l. Wings and posthorn. 16 l. Wings and envelope. 30 l. Aeroplane. 45 l., 75 l. Dove and posthorn.

192. Alexander Stamboliiski.

193. Flags of Albania, Bulgaria, Yugoslavia and Rumania.

**1946.** 25th Death Anniv. of A. Stamboliiski (Agrarian Leader).

| No. | Type | Description | Unused | Used |
|---|---|---|---|---|
| 610. | 192. | 100 l. orange | 6·75 | 6·75 |

**1946.** Balkan Games.

| No. | Type | Description | Unused | Used |
|---|---|---|---|---|
| 611. | 193. | 100 l. brown | 1·25 | 1·25 |

196. Artillery.

195. Junkers Ju87B "Stuka" Dive Bombers.

**1946.** Military and Air Services.

| No. | Type | Description | Unused | Used |
|---|---|---|---|---|
| 612. | – | 2 l. red | 10 | 10 |
| 613. | – | 4 l. grey | 10 | 10 |
| 614. | 196. | 5 l. red | 10 | 10 |
| 615. | 195. | 6 l. brown | 10 | 10 |
| 616. | – | 9 l. mauve | 10 | 10 |
| 617. | – | 10 l. violet | 10 | 10 |
| 618. | – | 20 l. blue | 35 | 15 |
| 619. | – | 30 l. orange | 35 | 15 |
| 620. | – | 40 l. olive | 40 | 20 |
| 621. | – | 50 l. green | 50 | 30 |
| 622. | – | 60 l. brown | 75 | 50 |

Designs—horiz. 2 l., 20 l. Grenade thrower and machine-gunner. 9 l. Pontoon-bridge builders. 10 l., 30 l. Cavalry charge. 40 l. Supply column. 50 l. Motor convoy. 60 l. Tanks. vert. 4 l. Grenade thrower.

203. St. Ivan Rilski.

208. "New Republic".

**1946.** Millenary of St. Ivan Rilski.

| No. | Type | Description | Unused | Used |
|---|---|---|---|---|
| 623. | 203. | 1 l. brown | 10 | 10 |
| 624. | – | 4 l. sepia | 10 | 10 |
| 625. | – | 10 l. green | 25 | 10 |
| 626. | – | 20 l. blue | 30 | 10 |
| 627. | – | 50 l. red | 1·25 | 55 |

Designs—horiz. 4 l. 10 l., 50 l. Views of Rila Monastery. vert. 20 l. Aerial view of Monastery.

**1946.** Referendum.

| No. | Type | Description | Unused | Used |
|---|---|---|---|---|
| 628. | 208. | 4 l. red | 10 | 10 |
| 629. | | 20 l. blue | 10 | 10 |
| 630. | | 50 l. brown | 25 | 15 |

209. Assault.

210. Ambuscade.

211. Nurse and Children.

**1946.** Partisan Activities.

| No. | Type | Description | Unused | Used |
|---|---|---|---|---|
| 631. | 209. | 1 l. purple | 10 | 10 |
| 632. | 210. | 4 l. green | 10 | 10 |
| 633. | – | 5 l. brown | 10 | 10 |
| 634. | 210. | 10 l. red | 10 | 10 |
| 635. | 209. | 20 l. blue | 30 | 10 |
| 636. | – | 30 l. brown | 30 | 15 |
| 637. | – | 50 l. black | 40 | 25 |

Designs—vert. 5 l., 50 l. Partisan riflemen. 30 l. Partisan leader.

**1947.** Winter Relief.

| No. | Type | Description | Unused | Used |
|---|---|---|---|---|
| 638. | 211. | 1 l. violet | 10 | 10 |
| 639. | – | 4 l. red | 10 | 10 |
| 640. | – | 9 l. olive | 10 | 10 |
| 641. | 211. | 10 l. grey | 10 | 10 |
| 642. | – | 20 l. blue | 15 | 10 |
| 643. | – | 30 l. brown | 15 | 10 |
| 644. | – | 40 l. red | 30 | 25 |
| 645. | 211. | 50 l. green | 50 | 35 |

Designs: 4 l., 9 l. Child carrying gifts. 20 l., 40 l. Hungry child. 30 l. Destitute mother and child.

212a. Partisans.

213. Olive Branch.

214. Dove of Peace.

**1947.** Anti-fascists of 1923, 1941 and 1944 Commem.

| No. | Type | Description | Unused | Used |
|---|---|---|---|---|
| 645a. | – | 10 l. brown & orange | 35 | 30 |
| 645b. | 212a. | 20 l. deep blue and pale blue | 35 | 30 |
| 645c. | – | 70 l. brown and red | 32·00 | 32·00 |

Designs—horiz. 10 l. Group of fighters. 70 l. Soldier addressing crowd.

**1947.** Peace.

| No. | Type | Description | Unused | Used |
|---|---|---|---|---|
| 646. | 213. | 4 l. olive | 10 | 10 |
| 647. | 214. | 10 l brown | 10 | 10 |
| 648. | | 20 l. blue | 20 | 15 |

"BULGARIA" is in Roman characters on the 20 l.

215. "U.S.A." and "Bulgaria".

216. Esperanto Emblem and Map of Bulgaria.

**1947.** Air. Stamp Day and New York Int. Philatelic Exn.

| No. | Type | Description | Unused | Used |
|---|---|---|---|---|
| 649. | 215. | 70 l. + 30 l. brown | 1·50 | 1·50 |

**1947.** 30th Esperanto Jubilee Congress, Sofia.

| No. | Type | Description | Unused | Used |
|---|---|---|---|---|
| 650. | 216. | 20 l. + 10 l. pur. & grn. | 75 | 75 |

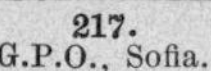

217. G.P.O., Sofia. 218. National Theatre, Sofia.

219. Parliament Building. 220. President's Palace. 221. G.P.O., Sofia.

**1947.** Government Buildings.

(a) T 217.

| | | | | |
|---|---|---|---|---|
| 651. | | 1 l. green | 10 | 10 |

(b) T 218.

| | | | | |
|---|---|---|---|---|
| 652. | | 50 s. green | 10 | 10 |
| 653. | | 2 l. red | 10 | 10 |
| 654. | | 4 l. blue | 10 | 10 |
| 655. | | 9 l. red | 25 | 10 |

(c) T 219.

| | | | | |
|---|---|---|---|---|
| 656. | | 50 s. green | 10 | 10 |
| 657. | | 2 l. blue | 10 | 10 |
| 658. | | 4 l. blue | 10 | 10 |
| 659. | | 20 l. blue | 85 | 30 |

(d) T 220.

| | | | | |
|---|---|---|---|---|
| 660. | | 1 l. green | 10 | 10 |

(e) T 221.

| | | | | |
|---|---|---|---|---|
| 661. | | 1 l. green | 10 | 10 |
| 662. | | 2 l. red | 10 | 10 |
| 663. | | 4 l. blue | 10 | 10 |

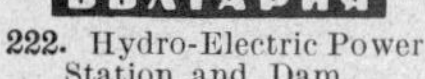

222. Hydro-Electric Power Station and Dam. 223. Emblem of Industry.

**1947.** Reconstruction.

| | | | | |
|---|---|---|---|---|
| 664. | 222. | 4 l. green | 15 | 15 |
| 665. | – | 9 l. brown (Miner) | 15 | 15 |
| 666. | 223. | 20 l. blue | 25 | 25 |
| 667. | – | 40 l. ol. (Motor plough) | 80 | 80 |

224. Exhibition Building. 225. Former Residence of the French Poet Lamartine.

226. Rose and Grapes. 227. Airplane over City.

**1947.** Plovdiv Fair. (a) Postage.

| | | | | |
|---|---|---|---|---|
| 668. | 224. | 4 l. red | 10 | 10 |
| 669. | 225. | 9 l. red | 10 | 10 |
| 670. | 226. | 20 l. blue | 25 | 15 |

(b) Air. Imperf.

| | | | | |
|---|---|---|---|---|
| 671. | 227. | 40 l. green | 1·00 | 1·00 |

228. Cycle Racing.

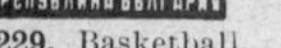

229. Basketball. 231. V. E. Aprilov.

**1947.** Balkan Games.

| | | | | |
|---|---|---|---|---|
| 672. | 228. | 2 l. lilac | 30 | 15 |
| 673. | 229. | 4 l. green | 30 | 15 |
| 674. | – | 9 l. brown | 80 | 25 |
| 675. | – | 20 l. blue | 1·00 | 35 |
| 676. | – | 60 l. red | 2·50 | 1·90 |

DESIGNS—VERT. 9 l. Chess. 20 l. Football. 60 l. Balkan flags.

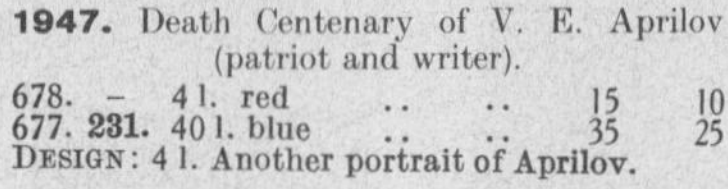

**1947.** Death Centenary of V. E. Aprilov (patriot and writer).

| | | | | |
|---|---|---|---|---|
| 678. | – | 4 l. red | 15 | 10 |
| 677. | 231. | 40 l. blue | 35 | 25 |

DESIGN: 4 l. Another portrait of Aprilov.

233. Postman. 235.

**1947.** Postal Employees' Relief Fund.

| | | | | |
|---|---|---|---|---|
| 679. | 233. | 4 l.+2 l. olive | 10 | 10 |
| 680. | – | 10 l.+5 l. red | 15 | 15 |
| 681. | – | 20 l.+10 l. blue | 20 | 20 |
| 682. | – | 40 l.+20 l. brown | 1·00 | 1·00 |

DESIGNS: 10 l. Linesman. 20 l. Telephonists. 40 l. Wireless masts.

**1947.** Theatrical Artists' Benevolent Fund.

| | | | | |
|---|---|---|---|---|
| 683. | 235. | 50 s. brown | 10 | 10 |
| 684. | – | 1 l. green | 10 | 10 |
| 685. | – | 2 l. green | 10 | 10 |
| 686. | – | 3 l. blue | 10 | 10 |
| 687. | – | 4 l. red | 10 | 10 |
| 688. | – | 5 l. purple | 10 | 10 |
| 689. | – | 9 l.+5 l. blue | 15 | 15 |
| 690. | – | 10 l.+6 l. red | 20 | 20 |
| 691. | – | 15 l.+7 l. violet | 25 | 25 |
| 692. | – | 20 l.+15 l. blue | 50 | 25 |
| 693. | – | 30 l.+20 l. purple | 1·00 | 85 |

PORTRAITS: 50 s. Kirov. 1 l. Nedeva. 2 l. Popov. 3 l. Kirchev. 4 l. Snezhina. 5 l. Buchvarov. 9 l. Ganchev. 10 l. Budevska. 15 l. Kirkov. 20 l. Orgnianov. 30 l. Sarafov.

236. "Rodina" (freighter).

**1947.** National Shipping Revival.

| | | | | |
|---|---|---|---|---|
| 694. | 236. | 50 l. blue | 90 | 35 |

237. Worker and Flag. 238. Worker and Globe.

**1948.** 2nd General Workers' Union Congress.

| | | | | |
|---|---|---|---|---|
| 695. | 237. | 4 l. blue (postage) | 15 | 10 |
| 696. | 238. | 60 l. brown (air) | 65 | 50 |

239. 240.

**1948.** Leisure and Culture.

| | | | | |
|---|---|---|---|---|
| 697. | 239. | 4 l. red | 15 | 10 |
| 698. | 240. | 20 l. blue | 25 | 15 |
| 699. | – | 40 l. green | 40 | 20 |
| 700. | – | 60 l. brown | 65 | 40 |

DESIGNS—VERT. 40 l. Workers' musical interlude. 60 l. Sports Girl.

241. Vaptsarov. 242. Petlyakov Pe-2 Bomber over Fortress.

**1948.** Poets and Writers.

| | | | | |
|---|---|---|---|---|
| 701. | 241. | 4 l. red on cream | 10 | 10 |
| 702. | – | 9 l. brown on cream | 15 | 10 |
| 703. | – | 15 l. purple on cream | 15 | 15 |
| 704. | – | 20 l. blue on cream | 20 | 15 |
| 705. | – | 45 l. green on cream | 55 | 75 |

PORTRAITS: 9 l. Yavorov. 15 l. Smirnensky. 20 l. Vazov. 45 l. Slaveykov.

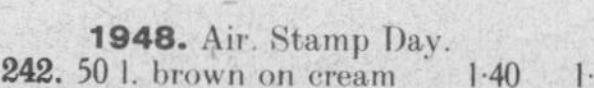

**1948.** Air. Stamp Day.

| | | | | |
|---|---|---|---|---|
| 706. | 242. | 50 l. brown on cream | 1·40 | 1·10 |

243. Soldier. 244. Peasants and Soldiers.

**1948.** Soviet Army Monument.

| | | | | |
|---|---|---|---|---|
| 707. | 243. | 4 l. red on cream | 10 | 10 |
| 708. | 244. | 10 l. green on cream | 15 | 10 |
| 709. | – | 20 l. blue on cream | 25 | 15 |
| 710. | – | 60 l. olive on cream | 75 | 45 |

DESIGNS—HORIZ. 20 l. Soldiers of 1878 and 1944. VERT. 60 l. Stalin and Spasski Tower, Kremlin.

245. Bath, Gorna Banya. 246. Lion Emblem.

**1948.** Bulgarian Health Resorts.

| | | | | |
|---|---|---|---|---|
| 711. | 245. | 2 l. red | 10 | 10 |
| 712. | – | 3 l. orange | 10 | 10 |
| 713. | – | 4 l. blue | 15 | 10 |
| 714. | – | 5 l. brown | 15 | 10 |
| 715. | – | 10 l. purple | 15 | 10 |
| 716. | – | 15 l. olive | 25 | 10 |
| 717. | 245. | 20 l. blue | 1·00 | 15 |
| 718. | – | 20 l. blue | 1·50 | 15 |

DESIGNS: 3 l., 10 l. Bath, Bankya, 4 l., 20 l. (No. 716), Mineral bath, Sofia. 5 l., 15 l. Malyovitsa Peak.

**1948.**

| | | | | |
|---|---|---|---|---|
| 719. | 246. | 50 s. orange | 10 | 10 |
| 719a. | | 50 s. brown | 10 | 10 |
| 720. | | 1 l. green | 10 | 10 |
| 721. | | 9 l. black | 15 | 10 |

247. D. Blagoev. 248. Youths marching.

**1948.** 25th Anniv. of September Uprising.

| | | | | |
|---|---|---|---|---|
| 722. | 247. | 4 l. brown | 10 | 10 |
| 723. | – | 9 l. orange | 10 | 10 |
| 724. | – | 20 l. blue | 15 | 15 |
| 725. | 248. | 60 l. brown | 1·00 | 85 |

DESIGNS—VERT. 9 l. Genov. HORIZ. 20 l. Bishop Andrey Monument.

249. Christo Smirnenski. 250. Miner. 251. Battle of Grivitza.

**1948.** 500th Birth Anniv. of Smirnenski (poet and revolutionary).

| | | | | |
|---|---|---|---|---|
| 726. | 249. | 4 l. blue | 10 | 10 |
| 727. | | 16 l. brown | 15 | 10 |

**1948.**

| | | | | |
|---|---|---|---|---|
| 728. | 250. | 4 l. blue | 20 | 10 |

**1948.** Treaty of Friendship with Rumania.

| | | | | |
|---|---|---|---|---|
| 729. | 251. | 20 l. blue (postage) | 20 | 10 |
| 730. | – | 40 l. black (air) | 25 | 15 |
| 731. | – | 100 l. mauve | 95 | 85 |

DESIGNS: 40 l. Parliament Buildings in Sofia and Bucharest. 100 l. Projected Danube Bridge.

252. Botev's House, Kalofer. 253. Christo Botev (poet).

**1948.** Birth Cent. of Botev. Inscr. "1848–1948".

| | | | | |
|---|---|---|---|---|
| 732. | 252. | 1 l. green | 10 | 10 |
| 733. | 253. | 4 l. brown | 10 | 10 |
| 734. | | 4 l. purple | 10 | 10 |
| 735. | – | 9 l. violet | 20 | 10 |
| 736. | – | 15 l. brown | 10 | 10 |
| 737a. | – | 20 l. blue | 15 | 10 |
| 738. | – | 40 l. brown | 35 | 20 |
| 739. | – | 50 l. black | 65 | 30 |

DESIGNS—HORIZ. 9 l. River paddle-steamer "Radetski". 15 l. Village of Kalofer. 40 l. Botev's mother and verse of poem. VERT. 20 l. Botev in uniform. 50 l. Quill, pistol and laurel wreath.

254. V. I. Lenin. 255. Road Construction.

**1949.** 25th Death Anniv. of Lenin. Inscr. "1924–1949".

| | | | | |
|---|---|---|---|---|
| 740. | 254. | 4 l. brown | 15 | 10 |
| 741. | – | 20 l. red | 40 | 25 |

DESIGN—(27×37 mm.): 20 l. Lenin as an orator.

**1949.** National Youth Movement.

| | | | | |
|---|---|---|---|---|
| 742. | 255. | 4 l. red | 15 | 10 |
| 743. | – | 5 l. brown | 25 | 20 |
| 744. | – | 9 l. green | 50 | 10 |
| 745. | – | 10 l. violet | 30 | 20 |
| 746. | – | 20 l. blue | 85 | 45 |
| 747. | – | 40 l. brown | 1·75 | 1·00 |

DESIGNS—HORIZ. 5 l. Tunnel construction. 9 l. Locomotive. 10 l. Textile workers. 20 l. Girl driving tractor. 40 l. Workers in lorry.

256. Lisunov Li-2 over Pleven Mausoleum.

**1949.** Air. 7th Philatelic Congress, Pleven.

| | | | | |
|---|---|---|---|---|
| 748. | 256. | 50 l. bistre | 4·50 | 3·75 |

257. G. Dimitrov. 258.

**1949.** Death of G. Dimitrov (statesman).

| | | | | |
|---|---|---|---|---|
| 749. | 257. | 4 l. red | 15 | 10 |
| 750. | 258. | 20 l. blue | 1·00 | 25 |

259. Hydro-electric Power Station. 260. Symbols of Agriculture and Industry.

**1949.** 5 Year Industrial and Agricultural Plan.

| | | | | |
|---|---|---|---|---|
| 751. | 259. | 4 l. olive (postage) | 15 | 10 |
| 752. | – | 9 l. red | 20 | 15 |
| 753. | – | 15 l. violet | 25 | 15 |
| 754. | – | 20 l. blue | 1·00 | 40 |
| 755. | 260. | 50 l. brown (air) | 2·75 | 1·50 |

DESIGNS—VERT. 9 l. Cement works. 15 l. Tractors in garage. HORIZ. 20 l. Tractors in field.

261. Javelin and Grenade Throwing. 262. Motor-cyclist and Tractor.

**1949.** Physical Culture Campaign.

| | | | | |
|---|---|---|---|---|
| 756. | 261. | 4 l. red | 30 | 15 |
| 757. | – | 9 l. olive | 1·40 | 60 |
| 758. | 262. | 20 l. blue | 2·00 | 1·10 |
| 759. | – | 50 l. red | 5·00 | 2·75 |

DESIGNS—HORIZ. 9 l. Hurdling and leaping barbed-wire. VERT. 50 l. Two athletes marching.

263. Globe. 265. Guardsman with Dog.

264. Guardsman and Peasant.

**1949.** Air. 75th Anniv. of U.P.U.
760. **263.** 50 l. blue .. .. 2·40 1·10

**1949.** Frontier Guards.
761 **264** 4 l. brown (postage) .. 15 35
762 – 20 l. blue .. .. 1·00 1·00
763 **265** 60 l. green (air) .. 2·75 2·75
DESIGN—VERT: 20 l. Guardsman on coast.

**266.** G. Dimitrov. **267.** "Unanimity". **268.** Joseph Stalin.

**1949.** Fatherland Front.
764. **266.** 4 l. brown .. .. 15 10
765. **267.** 9 l. violet .. .. 20 10
766. – 20 l. blue .. .. 30 20
767. – 50 l. red .. .. 1·00 1·00
DESIGNS: 20 l. Man and woman with wheel-barrow and spade. 50 l. Young people marching with banners.

**1949.** 70th Birthday of Stalin.
768. **268.** 4 l. orange .. .. 25 10
769. – 40 l. red .. .. 80 75
DESIGN—VERT. (25×37 mm.): 40 l. Stalin as an orator.

**269.** Haralampi Stoyanov. **270.** Strikers and Train.

**272.** Steam Locomotive. **271.** Miner.

**1950.** 30th Anniv. of Railway Strike.
770. **269.** 4 l. brown .. .. 15 10
771. **270.** 20 l. blue .. .. 60 30
772. – 60 l. olive .. .. 1·50 90
DESIGN—VERT. 60 l. Two workers and flag.

**1950.**
773. **271.** 1 l. olive .. .. 10 10
773a. 1 l. violet .. .. 15 10
774. **272.** 2 l. black .. .. 35 10
774a. 2 l. brown .. .. 35 10
775. – 3 l. blue .. .. 35 10
776a. – 4 l. green .. .. 40 10
777. – 5 l. red.. .. .. 40 10
778. – 9 l. grey .. .. 20 10
779. – 10 l. purple .. .. 25 10
780. – 15 l. red .. .. 45 15
781. – 20 l. blue .. .. 80 45
DESIGNS—VERT. 3 l. Ship under construction. 10 l. Power station. 15 l., 20 l. Woman in factory. HORIZ. 4 l. Tractor. 5 l., 9 l. Threshing machines.

**273.** Vasil Kolarov.

**1950.** Death of Vasil Kolarov (statesman). Inscr. "1877–1950".
782. **273.** 4 l. brown .. .. 10 10
783. – 20 l. blue .. .. 40 35
DESIGN—(27½×39½ mm.): 20 l. Portrait as Type **273**, but different frame.

**274.** Dospevski (self-portrait). **274a.** Peasant (Stanchev).

**275.** Ivan Vazov and Birthplace. **276a.** Dimitrov (statesman).

**1950.** Painters and paintings.
784. **274.** 1 l. green .. .. 30 15
785. – 4 l. orange .. .. 1·40 25
786. – 9 l. brown .. .. 2·00 25
787. **274a.** 15 l. brown .. .. 2·75 70
788. 20 l. blue .. .. 4·50 2·00
789. – 40 l. brown .. .. 5·25 2·75
790. – 60 l. orange .. .. 5·75 4·00
DESIGNS—VERT. 4 l. King Kaloyan and Desislava. 9 l. Pavlovich. 40 l. Debeyanov Statue (I. Lazarov). 60 l. Peasant (Dimitrov).

**1950.** Birth Cent. of Vazov (poet).
791. **275.** 4 l. olive .. .. 15 10

**1950.** 1st Death Anniv. of G. Dimitrov.
792. – 50 s. brown (postage) 15 10
793. – 50 s. green .. .. 15 10
794. **276a.** 1 l. brown .. .. 15 10
795. – 2 l. slate .. .. 15 10
796. – 4 l. purple .. .. 65 20
797. – 9 l. red .. .. 1·10 40
798. – 10 l. red .. .. 1·75 85
799. – 15 l. grey .. .. 1·75 85
800. – 20 l. blue .. .. 2·75 1·75
801. – 40 l. brown (air) .. 5·25 3·25
DESIGNS—HORIZ. 50 s. green, Dimitrov and birthplace. 2 l. Dimitrov's house, Sofia. 15 l. Dimitrov signing new constitution. 20 l. Dimitrov. 40 l. Mausoleum. VERT. 50 s. brown, 4 l., 9 l., 10 l. Dimitrov in various poses.

**277.** Runners. **278.** Workers and Tractor.

**1950.**
802. **277.** 4 l. green .. .. 65 20
803. – 9 l. brown (Cycling) .. 85 40
804. – 20 l. blue (Putting the shot) 1·10 85
805. – 40 l. purple (Volley-ball) 2·40 2·00

**1950.** 2nd National Peace Congress.
806. **278.** 4 l. red .. .. 10 10
807. – 20 l. blue .. .. 40 25
DESIGN—VERT. 20 l. Stalin on flag and three heads.

**278b.** **279.** Children on Beach.

**1950.** Arms designs.
807a. – 2 l. brown .. .. 10 10
807b. – 3 l. red .. .. 10 10
807c. **278b.** 5 l. red .. .. 10 10
807d. – 9 l. blue .. .. 20 10
Although inscribed "OFFICIAL MAIL", the above were issued as regular postage stamps.

**1950.** Sunday Delivery.
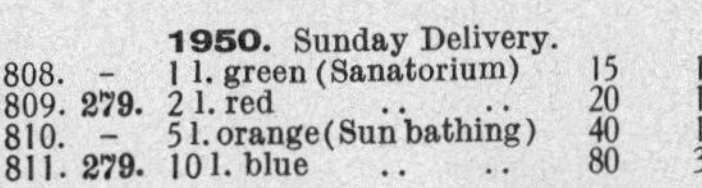
808. – 1 l. green (Sanatorium) 15 10
809. **279.** 2 l. red .. .. 20 10
810. – 5 l. orange (Sun bathing) 40 15
811. **279.** 10 l. blue .. .. 80 35

**280.** Molotov, Kolarov, Stalin and Dimitrov. **281.** Russian and Bulgarian Girls.

**1950.** 2nd Anniv. of Soviet-Bulgarian Treaty of Friendship.
812. **280.** 4 l. brown .. .. 10 10
813. – 9 l. red .. .. 15 10
814. **281.** 20 l. blue .. .. 30 25
815. – 50 l. green .. .. 2·00 75
DESIGNS—VERT. 9 l. Spasski Tower and flags. 50 l. Freighter and tractor.

**282.** Marshal Tolbukhin. **284.** A. S. Popov. **286.** Kirkov.

**1950.** Honouring Marshal Tolbukhin.
816. **282.** 4 l. mauve .. .. 15 10
817. – 20 l. blue .. .. 1·00 30
DESIGN—HORIZ. 20 l. Bulgarians greeting Tolbukhin.

**1951.** Honouring A. S. Popov (inventor).
818. **284.** 4 l. brown .. .. 25 15
819. 20 l. blue .. .. 85 30

**1951.** Anti-Fascist Heroes.
823. – 1 l. mauve .. .. 15 10
824. – 2 l. plum .. .. 15 10
825. **286.** 4 l. red .. .. 15 10
826. – 9 l. brown .. .. 55 40
827. – 15 l. olive .. .. 1·75 65
828. – 20 l. blue .. .. 1·75 1·00
829. – 50 l. grey .. .. 4·00 1·40
PORTRAITS: 1 l. Chankova, Antonov-Malchika, Sasho Dimitrov and Lilyana Dimitrova. 2 l. Stanke Dimitrov. 9 l. Ivanov. 15 l. Mihailov. 20 l. Dimitrov at Leipzig. 50 l. Ivanov and Stoyanov.

**285.** First Bulgarian Truck. **289.** Embroidery.

**1951.** National Occupations.
(a) As T **285**.
820. – 1 l. violet (Tractor) .. 15 10
821. – 2 l. grn. (Steam-roller) 20 10
822. **285.** 4 l. brown .. .. 25 10

(b) As T **289**.
830. – 1 l. brown (Tractor) .. 15 10
831. – 2 l. vio. (Steam-roller) 20 10
832. – 4 l. brown (Truck) .. 35 40
833. **289.** 9 l. violet .. .. 85 30
834. – 15 l. purple (Carpets) .. 1·50 1·00
835. – 20 l. blue (Roses and Tobacco) .. 3·25 1·50
836. – 40 l. green (Fruit) .. 5·00 2·10
The 9 l. and 20 l. are vert., the remainder horiz.

**290.** Turkish Attack.

**1951.** 75th Anniv. of April Uprising.
837. **290.** 1 l. brown .. .. 50 15
838. – 4 l. green .. .. 50 15
839. – 9 l. purple .. .. 85 45
840. – 20 l. blue .. .. 1·25 80
841. – 40 l. lake .. .. 1·75 1·50
DESIGNS—HORIZ. 4 l. Proclamation of Uprising. 9 l. Cannon and cavalry. 20 l. Patriots in 1876 and 1944. 40 l. G. Benkovsky and G. Dimitrov.

**291.** Blagoev as Orator.

**1951.** 60th Anniv. of First Bulgarian Social Democratic Party Congress, Buzludzha.
842. **291.** 1 l. violet .. .. 20 10
843. 4 l. green .. .. 40 15
844. 9 l. purple .. .. 1·10 80

**292.** Babies in Creche.

**1951.** Children's Day.
845. **292.** 1 l. brown .. .. 20 10
846. – 4 l. purple .. .. 40 15
847. – 9 l. green .. .. 95 35
848. – 20 l. blue .. .. 2·00 1·40
DESIGNS: 4 l. Children building models. 9 l. Girl and children's playground. 20 l. Boy bugler and children marching.

**293.** Workers. **294.** Labour medal (Obverse). **295.** Labour medal (Reverse).

**1951.** 3rd General Workers' Union Congress.
849. **293.** 1 l. black .. .. 10 10
850. – 4 l. brown .. .. 15 10
DESIGN inscr. "16 XII 1951". 4 l. Dimitrov and Chervenkov.

**1952.** Order of Labour.
851. **294.** 1 l. red .. .. 10 10
852. **295.** 1 l. brown .. .. 10 10
853. **294.** 4 l. green .. .. 10 10
854. **295.** 4 l. green .. .. 10 10
855. **294.** 9 l. violet .. .. 35 15
856. **295.** 9 l. blue .. .. 35 15

**296.** Kolarov Dam.

**297.** G. Dimitrov and Chemical Works.

**299.** N. Vaptsarov (revolutionary). **298.** Republica Power Station.

**1952.**
857. **296.** 4 s. green .. .. 15 10
858. 12 s. violet .. .. 20 10
859. 16 s. brown .. .. 25 10
860. 44 s. red .. .. 60 10
861. 80 s. blue .. .. 2·75 25

**1952.** 70th Birth Anniv. of Dimitrov (statesman). Dated "1882–1952".
862. **297.** 16 s. brown .. .. 40 20
863. – 44 s. brown .. .. 1·00 35
864. – 80 s. blue .. .. 1·75 1·00
DESIGNS—HORIZ. 44 s. Dimitrov and Chervenkov. VERT. 80 s. Dimitrov full-face.

**1952.**
866. **298.** 16 s. sepia .. .. 40 10
867. 44 s. purple .. .. 1·25 15

**1952.** 10th Death Anniv of Vaptsarov (revolutionary).
869. **299.** 16 s. lake .. .. 30 45
870. – 44 s. brown .. .. 1·10 90
871. – 80 s. sepia .. .. 2·10 90
PORTRAITS: 44 s. Facing bayonets. 80 s. Full-face.

**300.** Congress Delegates.

**1952.** 40th Anniv. of First Workers' Social Democratic Youth League Congress.
872. **300.** 2 s. lake .. .. 15 10
873. – 16 s. violet .. .. 25 15
874. – 44 s. green .. .. 80 40
875. – 80 s. sepia .. .. 1·75 1·40
DESIGNS: 16 s. Young partisans. 44 s. Factory and guards. 80 s. Dimitrov addressing young workers.

**301.** Attack on Winter Palace, St. Petersburg.

**1952.** 35th Anniv. of Russian Revolution. Dated "1917 1952".
876. **301.** 4 s. lake .. .. 10 10
877. – 8 s. green .. .. 15 10
878. – 16 s. blue .. .. 15 10
879. – 44 s. sepia .. .. 35 20
880. – 80 s. olive .. .. 90 40
DESIGNS: 8 s. Volga - Don canal. 16 s. Dove and globe. 44 s. Lenin and Stalin. 80 s. Lenin, Stalin and Himlay hydro-electric station.

302. 303. Vintagers and Grapes.

**1952.** Wood Carvings depicting National Products.

881 – 2 s. brown .. .. 10 10
882 – 8 s. green .. .. 10 10
883 – 12 s. brown .. .. 20 10
884 – 16 s. purple .. .. 45 10
885 302 28 s. green .. .. 85 15
886 – 44 s. brown .. .. 90 15
887 303 80 s. blue .. .. 1·50 15
888 1 l. violet .. .. 3·25 30
889 4 l. red .. .. 4·25 2·10

DESIGNS—VERT: 2 s. Numeral in carved frame. HORIZ: 8 s. Gift-offering to idol. 12 s. Birds and grapes. 16 s. Rose-gathering. 44 s. "Attar of Roses."

304. V. Levski.

**1953.** 80th Anniv. of Execution of V. Levski (revolutionary).

890. 304. 16 s. brown on cream .. 15 10
891. – 44 s. brown on cream .. 30 15

DESIGN: 44 s. Levski addressing crowd

305. Russian Army Crossing R. Danube. 306. Mother and Children.

**1953.** 75th Anniv. of Liberation from Turkey.

892. 305. 8 s. blue .. .. 30 10
893. – 16 s. brown .. .. 25 10
894. – 44 s. green .. .. 55 20
895. – 80 s. lake .. .. 1·60 1·00
896. – 1 l. black .. .. 2·00 1·60

DESIGNS—VERT. 16 s. Battle of Shipka Pass. HORIZ. 44 s. Peasants welcoming Russian soldiers. 80 s. Bulgarians and Russians embracing. 1 l. Shipka Pass memorial and Dimitrovgrad.

**1953.** Int. Women's Day.

897. 306. 16 s. blue .. .. 10 10
898. 16 s. green .. .. 10 10

307. Karl Marx. 308. May Day Parade.

**1953.** 70th Death Anniv. of Karl Marx.

899. 307. 16 s. blue .. .. 15 15
900. – 44 s. brown .. .. 40 25

DESIGN—VERT. 44 s. Book "Das Kapital".

**1953.** Labour Day.

901. 308. 16 s. red .. .. 20 10

309. Stalin. 310. G. Dlechev.

**1953.** Death of Stalin.

902. 309. 16 s. brown .. .. 25 10
903. 16 s. black .. .. 25 15

**1953.** 50th Anniv. of Ilinden–Preobrazhenie Rising.

904. 310. 16 s. brown .. .. 10 10
905. – 44 s. violet .. .. 40 25
906. – 1 l. purple .. .. 55 30

DESIGNS. 44 s. Insurgents and flag facing left. HORIZ. 1 l. Insurgents and flag facing right.

311. Soldier and Insurgents. 312. D. Blagoev.

**1953.** Army Day.

907. 311. 16 s. red .. .. 25 10
908. – 44 s. blue .. .. 65 15

DESIGN: 44 s. Soldier, factories and combine-harvester.

**1953.** 50th Anniv. of Bulgarian Workers' Social Democratic Party.

909. 312. 16 s. brown .. .. 30 15
910. – 44 s. red .. .. 65 20

DESIGN: 44 s. Dimitrov and Blagoev.

313. G. Dimitrov and Y. Kolarov. 314. Railway Viaduct.

**1953.** 30th Anniv. of September Uprising.

911. 313. 8 s. black .. .. 25 10
912. – 16 s. brown .. .. 15 10
913. – 44 s. red .. .. 80 30

DESIGNS: 16 s. Insurgent and flag. 44 s. Crowd of Insurgents.

**1953.** Bulgarian-Russian Friendship.

914. 314. 8 s. blue .. .. 20 20
915. – 16 s. slate .. .. 10 10
916. – 44 s. brown .. .. 30 15
917. – 80 s. orange .. .. 90 30

DESIGNS—HORIZ. 16 s. Welder and industrial plant. 80 s. Combine-harvester. VERT. 44 s. Iron foundry.

315. Wild Rose. 316. Kolarov Library

**1953.** Medicinal Flowers.

918. – 2 s. blue .. .. 10 10
919. – 4 s. orange .. .. 10 10
920. – 8 s. turquoise .. .. 15 10
921. 315. 12 s. green .. .. 15 10
922. – 12 s. red .. .. 15 10
923. – 16 s. blue .. .. 25 10
924. – 16 s. purple .. .. 25 10
925. – 20 s. red .. .. 50 10
926. – 28 s. green .. .. 50 15
927. – 40 s. blue .. .. 55 25
928. – 44 s. brown .. .. 75 25
929. – 80 s. brown .. .. 1·25 55
930. – 1 l. brown .. .. 3·00 1·00
931. – 2 l. purple .. .. 6·00 2·50

FLOWERS: 2 s. Deadly Nightshade. 4 s. Thorn-apple. 8 s. Sage. 16 s. Gentian. 20 s. Opium Poppy. 28 s. Peppermint. 40 s. Bear berry. 44 s. Coltsfoot. 30 s. Cowslip. 1 l. Dandelion. 2 l. Foxglove.

**1953.** 75th Anniv. of Kolarov Library, Sofia.

932. 316. 44 s. brown .. .. 30 15

317. Singer and Musician. 318. Airplane over Mountains.

**1953.** Amateur Theatricals.

933. 317. 16 s. brown .. .. 15 10
934. – 44 s. green .. .. 40 20

DESIGN: 44 s. Folk-Dancers.

**1954.** Air.

935. 318. 8 s. green .. .. 10 10
936. – 12 s. lake .. .. 10 10
937. – 16 s. brown .. .. 15 10
938. – 20 s. salmon .. .. 15 10
939. – 28 s. blue .. .. 20 10
940. – 44 s. purple .. .. 25 10
941. – 60 s. brown .. .. 45 10
942. – 80 s. green .. .. 55 20
943. – 1 l. green .. .. 2·10 40
944. – 4 l. blue .. .. 4·25 1·60

DESIGNS—VERT. 12 s. Exhibition buildings, Plovdiv. 80 s. Tirnovo. 4 l. Partisans' Monument. HORIZ. 16 s. Seaside promenade, Varna. 20 s. Combine-harvester in cornfield. 28 s. Rila Monastery. 44 s. Studena hydro-electric barrage. 60 s. Dimitrovgrad. 1 l. Sofia University and equestrian statue.

319. Lenin and Stalin. 320. D. Blagoev and Crowd.

**1954.** 30th Death Anniv. of Lenin.

945. 319. 16 s. brown .. .. 15 10
946. – 44 s. lake .. .. 30 10
947. – 80 s. blue .. .. 70 20
948. – 1 l. green .. .. 95 75

DESIGNS—VERT. 44 s. Lenin statue. 80 s. Lenin–Stalin Mausoleum and Kremlin. 1 l. Lenin.

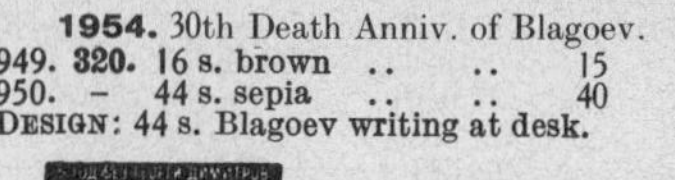

**1954.** 30th Death Anniv. of Blagoev.

949. 320. 16 s. brown .. .. 15 10
950. – 44 s. sepia .. .. 40 15

DESIGN: 44 s. Blagoev writing at desk.

321. Dimitrov Speaking. 322. Steam Locomotive.

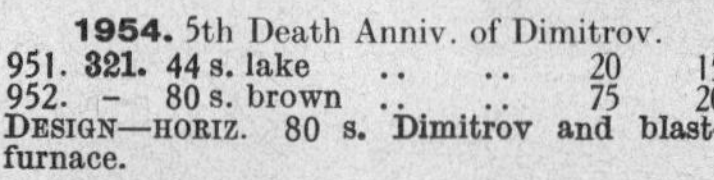

**1954.** 5th Death Anniv. of Dimitrov.

951. 321. 44 s. lake .. .. 20 15
952. – 80 s. brown .. .. 75 20

DESIGN—HORIZ. 80 s. Dimitrov and blast-furnace.

**1954.** Railway Workers' Day.

953. 322. 44 s. turquoise .. 1·25 20
954. 44 s. black .. .. 1·25 20

323. Miner Operating Machinery. 324. Marching Soldiers.

**1954.** Miners' Day.

955. 323. 44 s. green .. .. 25 15

**1954.** 10th Anniv. of Fatherland Front Government.

956. 324. 12 s. lake .. .. 10 10
957. – 16 s. red .. .. 10 10
958. – 28 s. slate .. .. 20 10
959. – 44 s. brown .. .. 25 10
960. – 80 s. blue .. .. 70 30
961. – 1 l. green .. .. 1·00 30

DESIGNS—VERT. 16 s. Soldier and parents. 80 s. Girl and boy pioneers. 1 l. Dimitrov. HORIZ. 28 s. Industrial plant. 44 s. Dimitrov and workers.

325. Academy Building. 326. Gymnast.

**1954.** 85th Anniv. of Academy of Sciences.

962. 325. 80 s. black .. .. 1·00 50

**1954.** Sports. Cream paper.

963. 326. 16 s. green .. .. 1·40 20
964. – 44 s. red .. .. 1·50 65
965. – 80 s. brown .. .. 2·40 1·00
966. – 2 l. blue .. .. 4·25 3·25

DESIGNS—VERT. 44 s. Wrestlers. 2 l. Ski-jumper. HORIZ. 80 s. Horse-jumper.

327. Velingrad Rest Home.

**1954.** 50th Anniv. of Trade Union Movement.

967. 327. 16 s. green .. .. 15 10
968. – 44 s. brown .. .. 15 15
969. – 80 s. blue .. .. 85 30

DESIGNS—VERT. 44 s. Foundryman. HORIZ. 80 s. Dimitrov, Blagoev and Kirkov.

328. Geese. 329. Communist Party Building.

**1955.**

970. 328. 2 s. green .. .. 10 10
971. – 4 s. olive .. .. 20 10
972. – 12 s. brown .. .. 35 10
973. – 16 s. brown .. .. 60 10
974. – 28 s. blue .. .. 30 10
975. 329. 44 s. red .. .. 10·00 20
976. – 80 s. brown .. .. 70 20
977. – 1 l. green .. .. 1·75 30

DESIGNS: 4 s. Rooster and hens. 12 s. Sow and piglets. 16 s. Ewe and lambs. 28 s. Telephone exchange. 80 s. Flats. 1 l. Cellulose factory.

330. Mill Girl. 332. Rejoicing Crowds.

**1955.** Int. Women's Day.

978. 330. 12 s. brown .. .. 10 10
979. – 16 s. green .. .. 20 10
980. – 44 s. blue .. .. 75 10
981. – 44 s. red .. .. 75 10

DESIGNS—HORIZ. 16 s. Girl feeding cattle. VERT. 44 s. Mother and baby.

**1955.** As Nos. 820 and 822 surch. **16 CT.**

981a. – 16 s. on 1 l. violet .. 20 10
982. 285. 16 s. on 4 l. brown .. 75 10

**1955.** Labour Day.

983. 332. 16 s. red .. .. 10 10
984. – 44 s. blue .. .. 50 15

DESIGN: 44 s. Three workers and globe.

333. St. Cyril and St. Methodius. 334. S. Rumyantsev.

**1955.** 1100th Anniv. of 1st Bulgarian Literature. On cream paper.

985. 333. 4 s. blue .. .. 10 10
986. – 8 s. olive .. .. 10 10
987. – 16 s. black .. .. 10 10
988. – 28 s. red .. .. 20 15
989. – 44 s. brown .. .. 30 20
990. – 80 s. red .. .. 95 75
991. – 2 l. black .. .. 2·40 1·50

DESIGNS: 8 s. Monk writing. 16 s. Early printing press. 28 s. Christo Botev. 44 s. Ivan Vazov. 80 s. D. Blagoev and Books. 2 l. Building.

**1955.** 30th Death Annivs. of Bulgarian Poets. On cream paper.

992. 334. 12 s. brown .. .. 15 10
993. – 16 s. brown (Jasenov) 40 15
994. – 44 s. green (Milev) .. 65 25

335. F. Engels and Book. 336. Mother and Children.

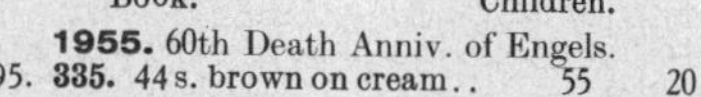

**1955.** 60th Death Anniv. of Engels.

995. 335. 44 s. brown on cream .. 55 20

**1955.** World Mothers' Congress, Lausanne.

996. 336. 44 s. lake on cream .. 35 10

337. "Youth of the World." 338. Main Entrance in 1892.

**1955.** 5th World Youth Festival, Warsaw.

997. 337. 44 s. blue on cream .. 30 25

**1955.** 16th Int. Fair, Plovdiv. On cream paper.

998. 338. 4 s. brown .. .. 10 10
999. – 16 s. red .. .. 10 10
1000. – 44 s. olive .. .. 20 15
1001. – 80 s. blue .. .. 85 15

DESIGNS—VERT. 16 s. Sculptured group. 80 s. Fair poster. HORIZ. 44 s. Fruit.

339. Schiller. 340. Industrial Plant.

**1955.** Cultural Annivs. Writers. On cream paper.

1002. 339. 16 s. brown .. .. 20 15
1003. – 44 s. red .. .. 75 15
1004. – 60 s. blue .. .. 80 15
1005. – 80 s. black .. .. 1·25 15
1006. – 1 l. purple .. .. 2·40 1·00
1007. – 2 l. olive .. .. 3·25 2·10

PORTRAITS: 44 s. Mickiewicz. 60 s. Hans Anderson. 80 s. Montesquieu. 1 l. Cervantes. 2 l. Walt Whitman.

**1955.** Bulgarian-Russian Friendship. On cream paper.

1008. 340. 2 s. slate .. .. 10 10
1009. – 4 s. blue .. .. 10 10
1010. – 16 s. green .. .. 15 10
1011. – 44 s. brown .. .. 25 10
1012. – 80 s. green .. .. 65 15
1013. – 1 l. black .. .. 70 30

DESIGNS—HORIZ. 4 s. Dam. 16 s. Danube Bridge. VERT. 44 s. Monument. 80 s. Michurin. 1 l. V. Mayakovsky.

**341.** Emblem.

**342.** Quinces.

**1956.** Cent. of Library Reading Rooms. On cream paper.

1014. **341.** 12 s. red .. .. 10 10
1015. – 16 s. brown .. .. 10 10
1016. – 44 s. myrtle .. .. 40 20

DESIGNS: 16 s K. Pshourka writing. 44 s. B. Kiro reading.

**1956.** Fruits.

1017. **342.** 4 s. red .. .. 1·40 10
1017a. 4 s. green .. .. 10 10
1018. – 8 s. green (Pears) .. 60 15
1018a. – 8 s. brown (Pears) .. 15 10
1019. – 16 s. dark red (Apples) 1·25 15
1019a. – 16 s. red (Apples) .. 35 10
1020. – 44 s. violet (Grapes) 1·40 30
1020a. – 44 s. ochre (Grapes) 70 25

**343.** Artillerymen.

**344.** Blagoev and Birthplace.

**1956.** 80th Anniv. of April Uprising.

1021. **343.** 16 s. brown .. .. 25 25
1022. – 44 s. green (Cavalry charge) .. .. 30 25

**1956.** Birth Cent. of Blagoev (socialist).

1023. **344.** 44 s. turquoise .. 30 15

**345.** Cherries.

**346.** Football.

**1956.** Fruits.

1024. **345.** 2 s. lake .. .. 15 10
1025. – 12 s. blue (Plums) .. 20 10
1026. – 28 s. buff (Greengages) 35 10
1027. – 80 s. red (Strawberries) 1·00 35

**1956.** Olympic Games.

1028. – 4 s. blue .. .. 40 15
1029. – 12 s. red .. .. 50 10
1030. – 16 s. brown .. .. 60 10
1031. **346.** 44 s. green .. .. 1·00 30
1032. – 80 s. brown .. .. 1·60 1·00
1033. – 1 l. lake .. .. 2·40 1·40

DESIGNS—VERT. 4 s. Gymnastics. 12 s. Throwing the discus. 80 s. Basketball. HORIZ. 16 s. Pole-vaulting. 1 l. Boxing.

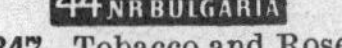

**347.** Tobacco and Rose.

**348.** Glider.

**1956.** 17th Int. Fair, Plovdiv.

1034. **347.** 44 s. red .. .. 55 40
1035. 44 s. green .. .. 55 40

**1956.** Air. 30th Anniv. of Gliding Club.

1036. – 44 s. blue .. .. 30 15
1037. – 60 s. violet .. .. 55 15
1038. **348.** 80 s. green .. .. 80 25

DESIGNS: 44 s. Launching glider. 60 s. Glider over hangar.

**349.** National Theatre.

**350.** Mozart.

**1956.** Centenary of National Theatre.

1039. **349.** 16 s. brown .. .. 15 10
1040. – 44 s. turquoise .. 40 15

DESIGN: 44 s. D. Voinikov and S. Dobroplodni.

**1956.** Cultural Anniversaries.

1041. – 16 s. olive .. .. 15 10
1042. – 20 s. brown .. .. 25 10
1043. **350.** 40 s. red .. .. 50 15
1044. – 44 s. brown .. .. 40 15
1045. – 60 s. slate .. .. 70 15
1046. – 80 s. brown .. .. 65 15
1047. – 1 l. green .. .. 1·25 50
1048. – 2 l. green .. .. 2·40 1·40

PORTRAITS: 16 s. Franklin. 20 s. Rembrandt. 44 s. Heine. 60 s. Shaw. 80 s. Dostoevsky. 1 l. Ibsen. 2 l. Curie.

**351.** Cyclists.

**352.** Woman with Microscope.

**1957.** Tour of Egypt Cycle Race.

1049. **351.** 80 s. brown .. .. 90 30
1050. 80 s. turquoise .. 90 30

**1957.** Int. Women's Day. Inscr. as in T **352.**

1051. **352.** 12 s. blue .. .. 10 10
1052. – 16 s. brown .. .. 15 10
1053. – 44 s. green .. .. 35 15

DESIGNS: 16 s. Woman and children. 44 s. Woman feeding poultry.

**353.** The "New Times".

**354.** Lisunov Li-2.

**1957.** 60th Anniv. of "New Times" (book).

1054. **353.** 16 s. red .. .. 20 10

**1957.** Air. 10th Anniv. of Bulgarian Airways.

1055. **354.** 80 s. blue .. .. 1·00 30

**355.** St. Cyril and St. Methodius.

**356.** Basketball.

**1957.** Cent. of Canonization of Saints Cyril and Methodius (founders of Cyrillic alphabet).

1056. **355.** 44 s. olive and buff .. 85 20

**1957.** 10th European Basketball Championships.

1057. **356.** 44 s. green .. .. 1·60 30

**357.** Girl in National Costume.

**358.** G. Dimitrov.

**1957.** 6th World Youth Festival, Moscow.

1058. **357.** 44 s. blue .. .. 50 15

**1957.** 75th Birth Anniv. of G. Dimitrov (statesman).

1059. **358.** 44 s. red .. .. 1·00 15

**359.** V. Levski.

**360.** View of Tirnovo and Dr. Zamenhof.

**1957.** 120th Birth Anniv. of Levski (revolutionary).

1060. **359.** 44 s. green .. .. 85 15

**1957.** 70th Anniv. of Esperanto and 50th Anniv. of Bulgarian Esperanto Assn.

1061. **360.** 44 s. green .. .. 1·00 20

**361.** Soldiers in Battle.

**362.** Woman Planting Tree.

**1957.** 80th Anniv. of Liberation from Turkey.

1062. – 16 s. green .. .. 20 10
1063. **361.** 44 s. brown .. 55 15

DESIGN: 16 s. Old and young soldiers.

**1957.** Reafforestation Campaign.

1064. **362.** 2 s. green .. .. 10 10
1065. – 12 s. brown .. .. 10 10
1066. – 16 s. blue .. .. 10 10
1067. – 44 s. turquoise .. 35 10
1068. – 80 s. green .. .. 85 25

DESIGNS—HORIZ. 12 s. Red deer in forest. 16 s. Dam and trees. 44 s. Polikarpov Po-2 biplane over forest. 80 s. Trees and cornfield.

**363.** Two Hemispheres.

**364.** Lenin.

**1957.** 4th World T.U.C., Leipzig.

1069. **363.** 44 s. blue .. .. 45 15

**1957.** 40th Anniv. of Russian Revolution. Inscr. "1917–1957".

1070. **364.** 12 s. brown .. .. 20 10
1071. – 16 s. turquoise .. 85 10
1072. – 44 s. blue .. .. 1·10 25
1073. – 60 s. red .. .. 1·50 20
1074. – 80 s. green .. .. 2·40 30

DESIGNS: 16 s. Cruiser "Aurora". 44 s. Dove of Peace over Europe. 60 s. Revolutionaries. 80 s. Oil refinery.

**365.** Youth and Girl.

**366.** Partisans.

**1957.** 10th Anniv. of Dimitrov National Youth Movement.

1075. **365.** 16 s. red .. .. 15 10

**1957.** 15th Anniv. of Fatherland Front.

1076. **366.** 16 s. brown .. .. 15 10

**367.** Glinka.

**368.** Kolarov.

**1957.** Cultural Celebrities.

1077. **367.** 12 s. brown .. .. 30 10
1078. – 16 s. green (Comenius) 30 10
1079. – 40 s. blue (Linnaeus) 1·25 25
1080. – 44 s. brown (Blake) .. 1·25 25
1081. – 60 s. brown (Goldoni) 1·40 50
1082. – 80 s. purple (Comte) 1·90 2·10

**1958.** Holiday Resorts.

1083. – 4 s. blue .. .. 10 10
1084. – 8 s. brown .. .. 10 10
1085. – 12 s. green .. .. 10 10
1086. **368.** 16 s. green .. .. 15 10
1087. – 44 s. turquoise .. 30 15
1088. – 60 s. blue .. .. 40 20
1089. – 80 s. brown .. .. 50 25
1090. – 1 l. brown .. .. 60 25

DESIGNS—HORIZ. 4 s. Skis and Pirin Mts. 8 s. Old house in Koprivshtita. 12 s. Hostel at Velingrad. 44 s. Hotel at Momin-Prohod. 60 s. Seaside hotel and peninsula, Nesebur. 80 s. Beach scene, Varna. 1 l. Modern hotels, Varna.

**369.** Brown Hare.

**370.** Marx and Lenin.

**371.** Wrestlers.

**1958.** Forest Animals.

1091 **369** 2 s. dp green & green 15 10
1092 – 12 s. brown and green 15 15
1093 – 16 s. brown and green 50 10
1094 – 44 s. brown and blue 55 15
1095 – 80 s. brown and ochre 85 35
1096 – 1 l. brown and blue .. 1·90 65

DESIGNS—VERT. 12 s. Roe doe. HORIZ. 16 s. Red deer. 44 s. Chamois. 80 s. Brown bear. 1 l. Wild boar.

**1958.** 7th Bulgarian Communist Party Congress. Inscr. as in T **370.**

1097. **370.** 12 s. brown .. .. 30 10
1098. – 16 s. red .. .. 60 15
1099. – 44 s. blue .. .. 1·25 15

DESIGNS: 16 s. Workers marching with banners. 44 s. Lenin blast furnaces.

**1958.** Wrestling Championships.

1100. **371.** 60 s. lake .. .. 1·50 1·00
1101. 80 s. sepia .. .. 1·40 1·25

**372.** Chessmen and "Oval Chessboard".

**1958.** 5th Students' World Chess Championship, Varna.

1102 **372** 80 s. green .. .. 6·75 6·75

**373.** Russian Pavilion.

**1958.** 18th Int. Fair, Plovdiv.

1103. **373.** 44 s. red .. .. 45 25

**374.** Swimmer.

**1958.** Bulgarian Students' Games.

1104. **374.** 16 s. blue .. .. 15 10
1105. – 28 s. brown .. .. 30 15
1106. – 44 s. green .. .. 50 15

DESIGNS. 28 s. Dancer. 44 s. Volleyball players at net.

**375.** Onions.

**376.** Insurgent with Rifle.

**1958** "Agricultural Propaganda".

1107. **375.** 2 s brown .. .. 10 10
1108. – 12 s. lake (Garlic) .. 10 10
1109. – 16 s. myrtle (Peppers) 15 10
1110. – 44 s. red (Tomatoes) 20 10
1111. – 80 s. green (Cucumbers) 50 20
1112. – 1 l. violet (Aubergines) 1·00 20

**1958.** 35th Anniv. of September Uprising.

1113. **376.** 16 s. orange .. .. 15 10
1114. – 44 s. lake .. .. 40 20

DESIGN—HORIZ.: 44 s. Insurgent helping wounded comrade.

**377.** Conference Emblem.

**1958.** 1st. World T.U. Young Workers' Conf., Prague.
1115. **377.** 44 s. blue .. .. 65 45

**378.** Exhibition Emblem.

**1958.** Brussels Int. Exn.
1116. **378.** 1 l. blue and black .. 10·00 8·25

**379.** Sputnik over Globe. **380.** Running.

**1958.** Air. I.G.Y.
1117. **379.** 80 s. turquoise .. 5·25 4·00

**1958.** Balkan Games. Inscr. "1958".
1118. **380.** 16 s. brown .. 60 15
1119. – 44 s. olive .. .. 65 20
1120. – 60 s. blue .. .. 1·10 25
1121. – 80 s. green .. .. 1·60 65
1122. – 4 l. lake .. .. 9·25 6·75
DESIGNS—HORIZ. 44 s. Throwing the javelin. 60 s. High-jumping. 80 s. Hurdling. VERT. 4 l. Putting the shot.

**381.** Young Gardeners. **382.** Christo Smirnenski.

**1958.** 4th Dimitrov National Youth Movement Congress. Inscr. as in T **381**.
1123. **381.** 8 s. myrtle .. .. 10 10
1124. – 12 s. brown .. .. 10 10
1125. – 16 s. purple .. .. 15 10
1126. – 40 s. blue .. .. 30 15
1127. – 44 s. red .. .. 75 25
DESIGNS—HORIZ. 12 s. Farm girl with cattle. 40 s. Youth with wheel-barrow. VERT. 16 s. Youth with pickaxe and girl with spade. 44 s. Communist Party Building.

**1958.** 60th Birth Anniv of Smirnenski (poet and revolutionary).
1128 382 16 s. red .. .. 15 15

**383.** First Cosmic Rockets. **384.** Footballers.

**1959.** Air. Launching of First Cosmic Rocket.
1129. **383.** 2 l. brown and blue.. 8·25 8·25

**1959.** Youth Football Games, Sofia.
1130. **384.** 2 l. brown on cream 2·40 1·75

**385.** U.N.E.S.C.O. Headquarters, Paris. **386.** Skier.

**1959.** Inauguration of U.N.E.S.C.O. Headquarters Building.
1131. **385.** 2 l. purple on cream 2·40 1·90

**1959.** 40 Years of Skiing in Bulgaria.
1132. **386.** 1 l. blue on cream .. 1·50 85

**1959.** No. 1110 surch. **45 CT.**
1133. – 45 s. on 44 s. red .. 1·00 15

**388.** Military Telegraph Linesman.

**1959.** 80th Anniv. of 1st Bulgarian Postage Stamps.
1134. **388.** 12 s. yellow and green 15 10
1135. – 16 s. mauve & purple 35 10
1136. – 60 s. yellow & brown 65 25
1137. – 80 s. salmon and red 85 25
1138. – 1 l. blue .. .. 1·00 40
1139. – 2 l. brown .. .. 2·75 1·90
DESIGNS—HORIZ. 16 s. 19th-cent. mail-coach. 80 s. Early postal car. 2 l. Striking railway workers. VERT. 60 s. Bulgarian 1879 stamp. 1 l. Radio tower.

**389.** Great Tits. **390.** Cotton-picking

**1959.** Birds.
1140. **389.** 2 s. slate and yellow 15 10
1141. – 8 s. green and brown 15 15
1142. – 16 s. sepia and brown 45 20
1143. – 45 s. myrtle & brown 80 30
1144. – 60 s. grey and blue .. 2·10 35
1145. – 80 s. drab & turquoise 3·50 55
DESIGNS—HORIZ. 8 s. Hoopoe. 60 s. Rock partridge, 80 s. European cuckoo. VERT. 16 s. Great spotted woodpecker. 45 s. Grey partridge.

**1959.** Five Year Plan.
1146. – 2 s. brown .. .. 10 10
1147. – 4 s. bistre .. .. 20 10
1148. **390.** 5 s. green .. .. 20 10
1149. – 10 s. brown .. .. 20 10
1150. – 12 s. brown .. .. 15 10
1151. – 15 s. mauve .. .. 20 10
1152. – 16 s. violet .. .. 20 10
1153. – 20 s. orange .. .. 30 10
1154. – 25 s. blue .. .. 25 10
1155. – 28 s. green .. .. 35 10
1156. – 40 s. blue .. .. 45 10
1157. – 45 s. brown .. .. 35 15
1158. – 60 s. red .. .. 60 20
1159. – 80 s. olive .. .. 1·25 20
1160. – 1 l. lake .. .. 90 20
1161. – 1 l. 25 blue .. .. 2·25 75
1162. – 2 l. red .. .. 1·25 35
DESIGNS—HORIZ. 2 s. Children at play. 10 s. Dairymaid milking cow. 16 s. Industrial plant. 20 s. Combine-harvester. 40 s. Hydro-electric barrage. 60 s. Furnaceman. 1 l. 25, Machinist. VERT. 4 s. Woman doctor examining child. 12 s. Tobacco harvesting. 15 s. Machinist. 25 s. Power linesman. 28 s. Tending sunflowers. 45 s. Miner. 80 s. Fruit-picker. 1 l. Workers with symbols of agriculture and industry. 2 l. Worker with banner.

**391.** Patriots. **392.** Piper.

**1959.** 300th Anniv of Batak.
1163 391 16 s. brown .. .. 25 10

**1959.** Spartacist Games. Inscr. "1958–1959".
1164. **392.** 4 s. olive on cream .. 20 15
1165. – 12 s. red on yellow .. 20 15
1166. – 16 s. lake on salmon 20 15
1167. – 20 s. blue on blue .. 25 15
1168. – 80 s. green on green 85 25
1169. – 1 l. brown on orange 1·25 75
DESIGNS—VERT. 12 s. Gymnastics. 1 l. Urn. HORIZ. 16 s. Girls exercising with hoops. 20 s. Dancers leaping. 80 s. Ballet dancers.

**393.** Soldiers in Lorry.

**1959.** 15th Anniv. of Fatherland Front Government.
1170. **393.** 12 s. blue and red .. 10 10
1171. – 16 s. black and red .. 10 10
1172. – 45 s. blue and red .. 20 10
1173. – 60 s. green and red .. 25 20
1174. – 80 s. brown and red .. 45 25
1175. – 1 l. 25 brown and red 95 45
DESIGNS—HORIZ. 16 s. Partisans meeting Red Army soldiers. 45 s. Blast furnaces. 60 s. Tanks. 80 s. Combine-harvester in cornfield. VERT. 1 l. 25, Pioneers with banner.

**394.** Footballer.

**1959.** 50th Anniv. of Football in Bulgaria.
1176. **394.** 1 l. 25 grn, on yell. .. 6·75 5·00

**395.** Tupolev Tu-104A Airplane and Statue of Liberty. **396.** Globe and Letter.

**1959.** Air. Visit of Russian Prime Minister to U.S.A.
1177. **395.** 1 l. pink and blue .. 3·00 2·75

**1959.** Int. Correspondence Week.
1178. **396.** 45 s. black and green 60 15
1179. – 1 l. 25 red, blk. & blue 85 25
DESIGN: 1 l. 25, Pigeon and letter.

**397.** Parachutist. **398.** N. Vaptsarov.

**1960.** 3rd Voluntary Defence Congress.
1180. **397.** 1 l. 25 cream & turq. 2·40 1·10

**1960.** 50th Birth Anniv. of Vaptsarov (poet).
1181. **398.** 80 st. brn. & grn. .. 45 15

**399.** Dr. L. Zamenhof. **400.**

**1960.** Birth Cent. of Zamenhof (inventor of Esperanto).
1182. **399.** 1l. 25 green & apple 1·40 85

**1960.** 50th Anniv. of State Opera.
1183. **400.** 80 s. black and green 85 25
1184. – 1 l. 25 black and red 1·25 30
DESIGN: 1 l. 25, Lyre.

**401.** Track of Lunik 3 around the Moon.

**1960.** Flight of Lunik 3.
1185. **401.** 1 l. 25 grn., yell. & bl. 6·75 5·00

**402.** Skier.

**1960.** Winter Olympic Games.
1186. **402.** 2 l. brn., blue & black 1·60 1·00

**HAVE YOU READ THE NOTES AT THE BEGINNING OF THIS CATALOGUE?**
These often provide answers to the enquiries we receive.

**403.** Vela Blagoeva. **404.** Lenin.

**1960.** 50th Anniv. of Int. Women's Day. Inscr. "1910–1960".
1187. **403.** 16 s. brown and pink 10 10
1188. – 28 s. olive and yellow 20 10
1189. – 45 s. green & olive .. 20 10
1190. – 60 s. blue & pale blue 30 20
1191. – 80 s. brown and red .. 35 15
1192. – 1 l. 25 olive and ochre 70 30
PORTRAITS: 28 s. Anna Maimunkowa. 45 s. Vela Piskova. 60 s. Rosa Luxemburg. 80 s. Clara Zetkin. 1 l. 25, N. K. Krupskaya.

**1960.** 90th Birth Anniv. of Lenin.
1193. **404.** 16 s. flesh and brown 1·00 25
1194. – 45 s. black and pink 1·75 30
DESIGN: 45 s. "Lenin at Smolny" (writing in chair).

**406.** Basketball Players. **407.** Moon Rocket.

**1960.** 7th European Women's Basketball Championships.
1195. **406.** 1 l. 25 black and yell. 1·50 45

**1960.** Air. Landing of Russian Rocket on Moon.
1196. **407.** 1 l. 25 blk. yell. & blue 8·25 5·00

**408.** Parachutist. **409.** "Gentiana lutea".

**1960.** World Parachuting Championships, 1960.
1197. **408.** 16 s. blue and lilac .. 60 55
1198. – 1 l. 25 red and blue .. 2·75 85
DESIGN: 1 l. 25, Parachutes descending.

**1960.** Flowers.
1199. **409.** 2 s. orge., grn. & drab 15 10
1200. – 5 s. red, green and yellow .. .. 15 10
1201. – 25 s. orange, green & salmon .. .. 50 10
1202. – 45 s. mauve, green and lilac .. .. 65 15
1203. – 60 s. red, green and buff .. .. 1·10 15
1204. – 80 s. blue, grn. & drab 1·10 65
FLOWERS: 5 s. "Tulipa rhodopea". 25 s. "Lilium jankae". 45 s. "Rhododendron ponticum". 60 s. "Cypripedium calceolus". 80 s. "Haberlea rhodopenis".

**410.** Football.

**1960.** Olympic Games.
1205. **410.** 8 s. pink and brown 10 10
1206. – 12 s. pink and violet 15 10
1207. – 16 s. pink & turq. .. 25 15
1208. – 45 s. pink and purple 50 15
1209. – 80 s. pink and blue .. 85 30
1210. – 2 l. pink and green .. 1·60 55
DESIGNS: 12 s. Wrestling. 16 s. Weightlifting. 45 s. Gymnastics. 80 s. Canoeing. 2 l. Running.

**411.** Racing Cyclists.

**1960.** Tour of Bulgaria Cycle Race.
1211. **411.** 1 l. blk., yell. & red 1·75 1·10

412. Globes.

**1960.** W.F.T.U. 15th Anniv.
1212. **412.** 1 l. 25 cobalt and blue 60 30

413. Popov. 414. Y. Veshin.

**1960.** Birth Cent. of Popov (Russian inventor).
1213. **413.** 90 s. black and blue 1·10 30

**1960.** Birth Cent. of Veshin (painter).
1214. **414.** 1 l. olive and yellow 5·00 2·40

415. U.N. Headquarters, New York. 416. Boyana Church.

**1961.** 15th Anniv. of U.N.O.
1215. **415.** 1 l. cream and brown 2·00 1·50

**1961.** 700th Anniv. of Boyana Murals (1959).
1216. **416.** 60 s. black, emerald and green .. .. 85 15
1217. – 80 s. green, cream and orange .. .. 95 25
1218. – 1 l. 25 red, cream and green .. .. 1·50 65
DESIGNS (Frescoes of): 80 s. Theodor Tiron. 1 l. 25, Desislava.

417. Cosmic Rocket.

**1961.** Russian Cosmic Rocket Flight of August, 1960.
1219. **417.** 1 l. 25 blue and red 8·25 5·75

419. Pleven Costume. 420. Clock Tower, Vratsa.

**1961.** Provincial Costumes.
1220. – 12 s. yell., grn. & sal. 15 10
1221. **419.** 16 s. brn., buff & lilac 15 10
1222. – 28 s. red, blk., & grn. 25 10
1223. – 45 s. blue and red .. 40 15
1224. – 60 s. yell., blue & turq. 70 20
1225. – 80 s. red, grn. & yell. 90 30
COSTUMES: 12 s. Kyustendil. 28 s. Sliven. 45 s. Sofia. 60 s. Rhodope. 80 c. Karnobat.

**1961.** Museums and Monuments. Values and star in red.
1226. **420.** 8 s. green .. .. 10 10
1227. – 12 s. violet .. .. 10 10
1228. – 16 s. brown .. .. 40 10
1229. – 20 s. blue .. .. 10 10
1230. – 28 s. turquoise .. 25 15
1231. – 40 s. brown .. .. 15 15
1232. – 45 s. olive .. .. 20 20
1233. – 60 s. slate .. .. 65 25
1234. – 80 s. brown .. .. 85 15
1235. – 1 l. turquoise .. 1·10 30
DESIGNS—As Type **420**. VERT. 12 s. Clock Tower, Bansko. 20 s. "Agushev" building, Mogilitsa (Smolensk). HORIZ. 28 s. Oslekoff House, Koprivshtitsa. 40 s. Pasha's House, Melnik. SQUARE (27×27mm.). 16 s. Wine jug. 45 s. Lion (bas-relief). 60 s. "Horseman of Madara". 80 s. Fresco, Bachkovo Monastery. 1 l. Coin of Tsar Konstantin-Asen (13th cent).

421. Dalmatian Pelican. 422. "Communications and Transport".

**1961.** Birds.
1236. 2 s. turq., black and red 10 10
1237. 4 s. orge., black & green 15 10
1238. 16 s. orge., brn. and grn. 15 10
1239. 80 s. yell., brn. & turq. 1·75 30
1240. 1 l. yellow, sepia and blue 1·75 75
1241. 2 l. yell., brn. and blue .. 2·75 65
BIRDS: 2 s. Capercaillie. 4 s. Type **421**. 16 s. Ring-necked pheasant. 80 s. Great Bustard. 1 l. Lammergeier. 2 l. Hazel grouse.

**1961.** 50th Anniv. of Transport Workers' Union.
1242. **422.** 80 s. green and black 85 20

423. Gagarin and Rocket.

**1961.** World's First Manned Space Flight.
1243. **423.** 4 l. turq., blk. & red 5·00 3·25

424. Shevchenko (poet).

**1961.** Shevchenko Commem.
1244. **424.** 1 l. sepia and olive .. 4·75 2·40

425. Throwing the Discus.

**1961.** World Students' Games. Values and inscr. in black.
1245. – 4 s. blue .. .. 10 10
1246. – 5 s. red .. .. 20 10
1247. – 16 s. olive .. .. 30 10
1248. **425.** 45 s. blue .. .. 45 20
1249. – 1 l. 25 brown .. 1·00 35
1250. – 2 l. mauve .. .. 1·40 80
DESIGNS—VERT. 4 s. Water polo. 2 l. Basket-ball. HORIZ. 5 s. Tennis. 16 s. Fencing. 1 l. 25, Sports Palace, Sofia.

426. Sea-horse. 427. "Space" Dogs.

**1961.** Black Sea Fauna.
1251. – 2 s. sepia and green 10 10
1252. – 12 s. pink and blue .. 10 10
1253. – 16 s. violet and blue 10 10
1254. **426.** 45 s. brown and blue 65 10
1255. – 1 l. blue and green .. 1·50 50
1256. – 1 l. 25 brown and blue .. .. 2·50 85
DESIGNS—HORIZ. 2 s. Mediterranean monk seal. 12 s. Lung jellyfish. 16 s. Common dolphins. 1 l. Starred sturgeons. 1 l. 25, Thornback ray.

**1961.** Air. Space Exploration.
1257. **427.** 2 l. slate and purple .. 4·00 3·00
1258. – 2 l. blue, yell. & orge. 8·25 5·00
DESIGN: No. 1258, "Venus" rocket in flight (24×41½ mm.).

428. Blagoev as Orator.

**1961.** 70th Anniv. of First Bulgarian Social Democratic Party Congress, Buzludzha.
1259. **428.** 45 s. red and cream 25 15
1260. – 80 s. blue and pink .. 40 15
1261. – 2 l. sepia and green .. 1·40 45

429. Hotel. 430. "The Golden Girl".

**1961.** Tourist issue. Inscr. in black; designs green. Background colours given.
1262. **429.** 4 s. green .. .. 10 10
1263. – 12 s. blue (Hikers) .. 10 10
1264. – 16 s. green (Tents) .. 10 10
1265. – 1 l. 25 bistre (Climber) 85 15
Nos. 1263/5 are vert.

**1961.** Bulgarian Fables.
1266. **430.** 2 s. multicoloured .. 15 10
1267. – 8 s. grey, black & pur. 20 10
1268. – 12 s. pink, blk. & grn. 25 10
1269. – 16 s. multicoloured .. 85 20
1270. – 45 s. multicoloured .. 1·50 30
1271. – 80 s. multicoloured .. 2·00 45
DESIGNS: 8 s. Man and woman ("The Living Water"). 12 s. "The Golden Apple"). 16 s. Horseman ("Krali Marko"; national hero). 45 s. Female archer on stag ("Samovila-Vila", fairy). 80 s. "Tom Thumb" and cockerel.

431. Major Titov in Space-suit. 432. "Amanita caesarea".

**1961.** Air. 2nd Russian Manned Space Flight.
1272. **431.** 75 s. flesh, blue & ol. 3·25 2·50
1273. – 1 l. 25 pink, blue and violet .. .. 4·25 3·75
DESIGN: 1 l. 25, "Vostok-2" in flight.

**1961.** Mushrooms.
1274. **432.** 2 s. red, bistre & blk. 10 10
1275. – 4 s. brn., grn. & blk. 10 10
1276. – 12 s. brn., bistre & blk. 15 10
1277. – 16 s. brn., mve. & blk. 20 10
1278. – 45 s. multicoloured .. 40 15
1279. – 80 s. orge., sepia & blk. 70 15
1280. – 1 l. 25 lav., brn. & blk. 1·00 30
1281. – 2 l. brown, bistre & blk. 1·90 1·00
MUSHROOMS: 4 s. "Psalliota silvatica". 12 s. "Boletus elegans". 16 s. "Boletus edulis". 45 s. "Lactarius deliciosus". 80 s. "Lepiota procera". 1 l. 25, "Pleurotus ostreatus". 2 l. "Armillariella mellea".

433. Miladinov Brothers (authors). 436. Isker River.

**1961.** Publication Cent. of "Collected Folk-songs".
1282. **433.** 1 l. 25 black and olive 1·00 30

**(Currency revaluation.)**

**1962.** Surch.
1283 1 s. on 10 s. brown (1149) 10 10
1284 1 s. on 12 s. brown (1150) 10 10
1285 2 s. on 15 s. mauve (1151) 10 10
1286 2 s. on 16 s. violet (1152) 10 10
1287 2 s. on 20 s. orge (1153)(A) 10 10
1288 2 s. on 20 s. orge (1153)(B) 25 10
1289 3 s. on 25 s. blue (1154) .. 20 10
1290 3 s. on 28 s. green (1155) 20 10
1291 5 s. on 44 s. green (1087) 25 10
1292 5 s. on 44 s. red (1110) .. 25 10
1293 5 s. on 45 s. brown (1157) 25 10
1294 10 s. on 1 l. red (1160) .. 45 15
1295 20 s. on 2 l. red (1162) .. 75 40
1296 40 s. on 4 l. red (889) .. 2·00 75
(A) Surch in one line; (B) in two lines.

**1962.** Air.
1297. **436.** 1 s. blue and violet .. 10 10
1298. – 2 s. blue and pink .. 20 10
1299. – 3 s. brown & chestnut 20 10
1300. – 10 s. black and bistre 50 15
1301. – 40 s. black and green 1·90 45
DESIGNS: 2 s. Yacht at Varna. 3 s. Melnik. 10 s. Tirnovo. 40 s. Pirin Mountains.

## INDEX
Countries can be quickly located by referring to the index at the end of this volume.

437. Freighter "Varna". 438. Rila Mountains.

**1962.** Bulgarian Merchant Navy.
1302. **437.** 1 s. green and blue .. 10 10
1303. – 5 s. pale blue, & green 60 10
1304. – 20 s. violet and blue 1·75 25
SHIPS: 5 s. Tanker "Komsomols". 20 s. Liner "Georgi Dimitrov".

**1962.** Views.
1305. **438.** 1 s. turquoise .. 10 10
1306. – 2 s. blue .. .. 10 10
1307. – 6 s. turquoise .. 60 10
1308. – 8 s. purple .. .. 80 20
1309. – 13 s. green .. .. 55 15
1310. – 1 l. deep green .. 5·25 40
VIEWS: 2 s. Pirin Mts. 6 s. Fishing boats, Nesebur. 8 s. Danube shipping. 13 s. Viden Castle. 1 l. Rhodope Mts.

439. Dimitrov as Printer. 440. Pink Roses.

**1962.** 80th Anniv. of State Printing Office.
1311. **439.** 2 s. red, black & yell. 10 10
1312. – 13 s. blk., orge. & yell. 75 15
DESIGN: 13 s. Emblem of Printing Office.

**1962.** Bulgarian Roses. T **440** and similar designs.
1313. 1 s. pink, green and violet 10 10
1314. 2 s. red, green and buff .. 10 10
1315. 3 s. red, green and blue .. 25 10
1316. 4 s. yell., turq. and grn. 20 10
1317. 5 s. pink, green and blue 30 15
1318. 6 s. red, green & turquoise 50 25
1319. 8 s. red, green & yellow 2·00 35
1320. 13 s. yellow, green & blue 3·75 1·90

441. "The World United against Malaria".

**1962.** Malaria Eradication.
1321. **441.** 5 s. yell., blk. & brn. 60 15
1322. – 20 s. yell., grn. & blk. 1·40 60
DESIGN: 20 s. Campaign emblem.

442. Lenin and Front Page of "Pravda". 443. Text-book and Blackboard.

**1962.** 50th Anniv. of "Pravda" Newspaper.
1323. **442.** 5 s. blue, red & black 90 25

**1962.** Bulgarian Teachers' Congress.
1324. **443.** 5 s. black, yell. & blue 15 10

444. Footballer. 445. Dimitrov.

**1962.** World Football Championships, Chile.
1325. **444.** 13 s. brn., grn. & blk. 1·10 35

**1962.** 80th Birth Anniv. Dimitrov.
1326. **445.** 2 s. green .. .. 15 10
1327. – 5 s. blue .. .. 75 45

446. Bishop. 448. Festival Emblem.

**1962.** 15th Chess Olympiad, Varna. Inscr. "1962". Inscr. in black.
1328. **446.** 1 s. green and grey .. 15 10
1329. – 2 s. bistre and grey .. 15 10
1330. – 3 s. purple and grey 15 10
1331. – 13 s. orange and grey 1·50 40
1332. – 20 s. blue and grey .. 2·00 1·00
CHESS PIECES: 2 s. Rook. 3 s. Queen. 14 s. Knight. 20 s. Pawn.

**1962.** 35th Esperanto Congress, Burgas. Surch. **XXXV КОНГРЕС 1962 13** and bars.
1333. **360.** 13 s. on 44 s. green .. 4·75 3·00

**1962.** World Youth Festival, Helsinki. Inscr. "1962".
1334. **448.** 5 s. blue, pink & green 20 10
1335. – 13 s. blue, pur. & grey 50 20
DESIGN: 13 s. Girl and emblem.

**449.** Ilyushin Il-18 Airliner.

**1962.** Air. 13th Anniv. of TABSO Airline.
1336. **449.** 13 s. bl., ultram. & blk. .. .. 1·25 20

**450.** "Parnassius apollo".

**1962.** Butterflies and Moths. Multicoloured.
1337 1 s. Type **450** .. .. 10 10
1338 2 s. "Thais cerisyi" .. 10 10
1339 3 s. "Meleageria daphnis" 10 10
1340 4 s. "Nymphalis antiopa" 20 10
1341 5 s. "Astiotes dilecta" .. 25 10
1342 6 s. "Eucharia festive" .. 45 10
1343 10 s. "Colias myrmidone" 2·40 40
1344 13 s. "Pandoriana pandora" .. .. 2·75 90

**451.** K. E. Tsiolkovsky (scientist).

**1962.** Air. 13th Int. Astronautics Congress. Inscr. "1962".
1345. **451.** 5 s. drab and green .. 4·00 1·50
1346. – 13 s. blue and yellow 2·00 75
DESIGN: 13 s. Moon rocket.

**452.** Combine Harvester. **453.** Cover of "History of Bulgaria".

**1962.** 8th Bulgarian Communist Party Congress.
1347. **452.** 1 s. olive & turquoise 10 10
1348. – 2 s. turquoise & blue 10 15
1349. – 3 s. brown and red .. 20 10
1350. – 13 s. sepia, red & pur. 1·00 30
DESIGNS: 2 s. Electric train. 3 s. Steel furnace. 13 s. Blagoev and Dimitrov.

**1962.** Bicent. of Paissi's "History of Bulgaria".
1351. **453.** 2 s. black and olive .. 10 10
1352. – 5 s. sepia and brown 25 10
DESIGN—HORIZ. 5 s. Father Paissi at work on book.

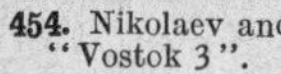
**454.** Nikolaev and "Vostok 3". **455.** Parachutist.

**1962.** Air. 1st "Team" Manned Space Flight.
1353. **454.** 1s. olive, blue & black 15 10
1354. – 2 s. olive, green & blk. 30 15
1355. – 40s. pink, turq. & blk. 3·25 2·10
DESIGNS: 2 s. Popovich and "Vostok 4". 40 s. "Vostoks 3 and 4" in flight.

**1963.**
1356. – 1 s. lake .. .. 10 10
1357. – 1 s. brown .. .. 10 10
1358. – 1 s. turquoise .. 10 10
1359. – 1 s. green .. .. 10 10
1360. **455.** 1 s. blue .. .. 10 10
DESIGNS—VERT. No. 1356, State crest. HORIZ. No. 1357, Sofia University. No. 1358, "Vasil Levski" Stadium, Sofia. No. 1359, "The Camels" (archway). Hisar.

**456.** Aleko Konstantinov.

**1963.** Birth Cent. of Konstantinov (author).
1361. **456.** 5 s. green and red. .. 20 15

**457.** Mars and Space Station.

**1963.** Air. Launching of Soviet Space Station, "Mars 1".
1362. **457.** 5 s. vio., turq., red & blk. 70 30
1363. – 13 s. turq., red. & blk. 1·40 75
DESIGN: 13 s. Release of station from rocket.

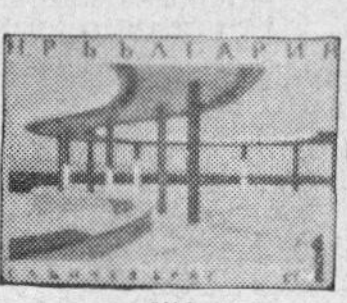
**458.** Orpheus Restaurant, "Sunny Beach". **459.** V. Levski.

**1963.** Black Sea Coast Resorts.
1364 458 1 s. blue .. .. 10 10
1365a – 2 s. red .. .. 50 15
1366 – 3 s. bistre .. .. 25 10
1367 – 5 s. purple .. .. 35 10
1368 – 13 s. turquoise .. 1·25 20
1369 – 20 s. green .. .. 1·75 30
VIEWS ("Sunny Beach"): 5 s. The Dunes Restaurant. 20 s. Hotel, "Golden Sands". 2 s., 3 s., 13 s. Various hotels.

**1963.** 90th Anniv. of Execution of Vasil Levski (revolutionary).
1370. **459.** 13 s. blue and yellow 1·50 30

**460.** Dimitrov, Boy and Girl. **461.** Eurasian Red Squirrel.

**1963.** 10th Dimitrov Communist Youth League Congress, Sofia.
1371. **460.** 2 s. brown, red & blk. 15 10
1372. – 13 s. brn., turq. & blk. 45 20
DESIGN: 13 s. Girl and youth holding book and hammer aloft.

**1963.** Woodland Animals.
1373. **461.** 1 s. brown, red & green on turquoise 10 10
1374. – 2 s. black, red & green on yellow .. 15 10
1375. – 3 s. sepia, red & olive on drab .. .. 10 10
1376. – 5 s. brown, red & blue on violet 50 10
1377. – 13 s. blk., red & brown on pink .. 1·60 25
1378. – 20 s. sepia, red & blue on blue .. 2·50 40
ANIMALS—HORIZ. 2 s. East European Hedgehog. 3 s. Marbled polecat. 5 s. Beech Marten. 13 s. Eurasian Badger. VERT. 20 s. European Otter.

**MINIMUM PRICE**
The minimum price quoted is 10p which represents a handling charge rather than a basis for valuing common stamps. For further notes about prices see introductory pages.

**462.** Wrestling.

**1963.** 15th Int. Open Wrestling Championships, Sofia.
1379. **462.** 5 s. bistre and black .. 20 15
1380. – 20 s. brown and black 1·25 30
DESIGN—HORIZ 20 s. As Type **462** but different hold.

**463.** Congress Emblem and Allegory. **464.** Esperanto Star and Sofia Arms.

**1963.** World Women's Congress, Moscow.
1381. **463.** 20 s. blue and black .. 1·00 25

**1963.** 48th World Esperanto Congress, Sofia.
1382. **464.** 13 s. multicoloured .. 1·00 25

**465.** Rocket, Globe and Moon. **466.** Bykovsky in Space-suit.

**1963.** Launching of Soviet Moon Rocket "Luna 4". Inscr. "2.IV.1963".
1383. **465.** 1 s. blue .. .. 10 10
1384. – 2 s. purple .. .. 10 10
1385. – 3 s. turquoise .. 15 10
DESIGNS: 2 s. Tracking equipment. 3 s. Sputniks.

**1963.** Air. Second "Team" Manned Space Flights. Inscr. "14.VI.1963".
1386. **466.** 1 s. turquoise and lilac 10 10
1387. – 2 s. brown and yellow 15 10
1388. – 5 s. red and light red 25 10
1389. – 20 s. + 10 s. green and light blue .. 2·10 80
DESIGNS: 2 s. Tereshkova in space-suit. 5 s. Globe. 20 s. Bykovsky and Tereshkova.

**1963.** Europa Fair, Riccione. Nos. 1314/5 and 1318 (Roses) optd. **MOSTRA EUROPEISTICA. 1963 RICCIONE** and sailing boat motif or additionally surch.
1390. 2 s. red, grn. & buff .. 30 15
1391. 5 s. on 3 s. red, green and blue .. 40 15
1392. 13 s. on 6 s. red, green and turquoise .. 1·40 40

**468.** Relay-racing.

**1963.** Balkan Games. Flags in red, yellow, blue, green and black.
1393. **468.** 1 s. green .. .. 10 10
1394. – 2 s. violet .. .. 15 10
1395. – 3 s. turquoise .. 20 10
1396. – 5 s. red .. .. 50 20
1397. – 13 s. brown .. .. 3·00 2·40
DESIGNS: 2 s. Throwing the hammer. 3 s. Long-jump. 5 s. High jump. 13 s. Throwing the discus. Each design includes the flags of the competing countries.

**469.** Slavonic Scroll. **470.** Insurgents.

**1963.** 5th Int. Slav Congress, Sofia.
1398. **469.** 5 s. red, yellow and deep green .. 20 10

**1963.** 40th Anniv. of September Uprising.
1399. **470.** 2 s. black and red .. 15 10

**471.** Aquilegia. **472.** Christo Smirnenski.

**1963.** Nature Protection. Flowers in natural colours; background colours given.
1400. **471.** 1 s. turquoise .. 10 10
1401. – 2 s. olive .. .. 10 10
1402. – 3 s. yellow .. .. 15 10
1403. – 5 s. blue .. .. 20 10
1404. – 6 s. purple .. .. 25 15
1405. – 8 s. light grey .. 45 20
1406. – 10 s. mauve .. .. 1·25 25
1407. – 13 s. olive .. .. 1·75 35
FLOWERS: 2 s. Edelweiss. 3 s. Primula. 5 s. Water-lily. 6 s. Tulip. 8 s. Viola. 10 s. Clematis. 13 s. Anemone.

**1963.** 65th Birth Anniv. of Smirnenski (poet and revolutionary).
1408. **472.** 13 s. black and lilac 75 15

**473.** Chariot Horses (wall-painting). **474.** Hemispheres and Centenary Emblem.

**1963.** Thracian Tombs, Kazanilk.
1409. **473.** 1 s. red, yell. & grey 10 10
1410. – 2 s. violet, yell. & grey 20 10
1411. – 3 s. turquoise, yellow and grey .. .. 15 15
1412. – 5 s. brn., yell & grn. 25 15
1413. – 13 s. blk., yell. & grn. 60 15
1414. – 20 s. red, yell. & grn. 1·40 55
DESIGNS (wall paintings on tombs): 2 s. Chariot race. 3 s. Flautists. 5 s. Tray-bearer. 13 s. Funeral feast. 20 s. Seated woman.

**1964.** Centenary of Red Cross.
1415. **474.** 1 s. yell., red and blk. 10 10
1416. – 2 s. blue, red & black 10 10
1417. – 3 s. multicoloured .. 10 10
1418. – 5 s. turq., red & black 25 10
1419. – 13 s. blk., red & orge. 85 25
DESIGNS: 2 s. Blood donation. 3 s. Bandaging wrist. 5 s. Nurse. 13 s. Henri Dunant.

**475.** Speed-skating.

**1964.** Winter Olympic Games, Innsbruck.
1420. **475.** 1 s. indigo, brn. & blue 10 10
1421. – 2 s. olive, mve. & blk. 10 10
1422. – 3 s. grn., brn. & blk. 15 10
1423. – 5 s. multicoloured .. 20 15
1424. – 10 s. orge., blk. & grey 85 15
1425. – 13 s. mauve, violet and black .. .. 1·00 25
DESIGNS: 2 s. Figure skating. 3 s. Cross-country skiing. 5 s. Ski-jumping. Ice-hockey: 10 s. Goalkeeper. 13 s. Players.

**476.** Head (2nd cent.). **477.** "The Unborn Maid".

**1964.** 2500 years of Bulgarian Art. Borders in grey.
1426. **476.** 1 s. turquoise and red 10 10
1427. – 2 s. sepia and red .. 10 10
1428. – 3 s. bistre and red .. 10 10
1429. – 5 s. blue and red .. 25 10
1430. – 6 s. brown and red .. 35 10
1431. – 8 s. brown & red .. 50 15
1432. – 10 s. olive and red .. 60 15
1433. – 13 s. olive and red .. 1·10 55
DESIGNS: 2 s. Horseman (1st to 4th cent.). 3 s. Jug (19th cent.). 5 s. Buckle (19th cent.). 6 s. Pot (19th cent.). 8 s. Angel (17th cent.). 10 s. Animals (8th to 10th cent.). 13 s. Peasant woman (20th cent.).

**1964.** Folk Tales. Multicoloured.
1434. 1 s. Type **477**. .. .. 10 10
1435. 2 s. "Grandfather's Glove" 10 10
1436. 3 s. "The Big Turnip" .. 10 10
1437. 5 s. "The Wolf and the Seven Kids" .. .. 25 10
1438. 8 s. "Cunning Peter" .. 40 15
1439. 13 s. "The Loaf of Corn" 1·25 30

478. "Ascalaphus ottomanus".

**1964.** Insects.
1440. 1 s. black, yellow & brown 10 10
1441. 2 s. black, ochre & turq. 15 10
1442. 3 s. green, black & drab 20 10
1443. 5 s. violet, black and olive 65 10
1444. 13 s. brown, black & violet 1·40 25
1445. 20 s. yellow, black & blue 2·40 35
DESIGNS—HORIZ. 1 s. Type **478**. 3 s. "Nemoptera coa". 20 s. "Saga natoliae". VERT. 2 s. "Rosalia alpina". 5 s. "Anisoplia austriaca". 13 s. "Scolia flavifrons".

479. Football.

**1964.** 50th Anniv. of Levski Physical Culture Association.
1446. 2 s. Type **479** .. .. 15 10
1447. 13 s. Handball .. .. 95 30

480. Title Page and P. Beron (author).

**1964.** 40th Anniv. of First Bulgarian Primer.
1448. **480.** 20 s. blk. & brn. .. 1·75 1·75

481. Stephenson's "Rocket".

**1964.** Railway Transport. Multicoloured.
1449. 1 s. Type **481** .. .. 10 10
1450. 2 s. Steam loco. .. .. 10 10
1451. 3 s. Diesel loco. .. .. 15 10
1452. 5 s. Electric loco. .. 50 10
1453. 8 s. Steam train on bridge 65 15
1454. 13 s. Diesel train emerging from tunnel .. .. 80 20

482. Alsatian.

МЕЖДУНАРОДНА КОСМИЧЕСКА ИЗЛОЖБА РИЧИОНЕ-1964 ST 10

(483.)

**1964.** Dogs. Multicoloured.
1455. 1 s. Type **482** .. .. 10 10
1456. 2 s. Setter .. .. 20 10
1457. 3 s. Poodle .. .. 25 10
1458. 4 s. Pomeranian .. .. 15 10
1459. 5 s. St. Bernard .. .. 25 15
1460. 6 s. Fox terrier .. .. 65 15
1461. 10 s. Pointer .. .. 2·75 45
1462. 13 s. Dachshund .. .. 3·25 1·40

**1964.** Air. Int. Cosmic Exn., Riccione. No. 1386 surch. with T **483** and No. 1387 surch. as T **483**, but in Italian.
1463. **466.** 10 s. on 1 s. turquoise and lilac .. .. 35 20
1464. – 20 s. on 2 s. brn. & yell. 1·00 30

484. Partisans and Flag.

**1964.** 20th Anniv. of Fatherland Front Government. Flag in red.
1465. **484.** 1 s. blue and light blue 10 10
1466. – 2 s. olive and bistre .. 10 10
1467. – 3 s. lake and mauve .. 10 10
1468. – 4 s. violet and lavender 15 10
1469. – 5 s. brown and orange 20 10
1470. – 6 s. blue & light blue 25 10
1471. – 8 s. green & light green 70 10
1472. – 13 s. brown & salmon 1·00 50
DESIGNS: 2 s. Greeting Soviet troops. 3 s. Soviet aid—arrival of goods. 4 s. Industrial plant, Kremikovtsi. 5 s. Combine-harvester. 6 s. "Peace" campaigners. 8 s. Soldier of National Guard. 3 s. Blagoev and Dimitrov. All with flag as Type **484**.

(485.) 486. Transport.

**1964.** 21st Int. Fair, Plovdiv. Surch. with T **485**.
1473. 20 s. on 44 s. ochre (No. 1020a) .. .. .. 1·90 35

**1964.** 1st National Stamp Exn., Sofia.
1474. **486.** 20 s. blue .. .. 2·75 1·00

487. Gymnastics.

488. Vratsata.

**1964.** Olympic Games, Tokyo. Rings and values in red.
1475. **487.** 1 s. green & light green 10 10
1476. – 2 s. blue and lavender 10 10
1477. – 3 s. blue and turquoise 15 10
1478. – 5 s. violet and red .. 15 10
1479. – 13 s. blue & light blue 1·00 15
1480. – 20 s. green and buff .. 1·40 25
DESIGNS: 2 s. Long-jump. 3 s. Swimmer on starting block. 5 s. Football. 13 s. Volleyball. 20 s. Wrestling.

**1964.** Landscapes.
1481. **488.** 1 s. green .. .. 10 10
1482. – 2 s. brown .. .. 10 10
1483. – 3 s. blue .. .. 15 10
1484. – 4 s. brown .. .. 20 10
1485. – 5 s. green .. .. 30 10
1486. – 6 s. violet .. .. 40 10
DESIGNS: 2 s. The Ritli. 3 s. Maliovitsa. 4 s. Broken Rocks. 5 s. Erkyupria. 6 s. Rhodope mountain pass.

489. Paper and Cellulose Factory, Bukovtsi.

**1964.** Air. Industrial Buildings.
1487. **489.** 8 s. turquoise .. 25 10
1488. – 10 s. purple .. .. 35 10
1489. – 13 s. violet .. .. 40 10
1490. – 20 s. blue .. .. 1·00 15
1491. – 40 s. green .. .. 1·90 60
DESIGNS: 10 s. Metal works, Plovdiv. 13 s. Metallurgical works, Kremikovtzi. 20 s. Petrol refinery, Burgas. 40 s. Fertiliser factory, Stara-Zagora.

490. Rila Monastery.

**1964.** Philatelic Exn. for Franco-Bulgarian Amity.
1492. **490.** 5 s. black and drab .. 30 15
1493. – 13 s. black and blue .. 1·10 30
DESIGN: 13 s. Notre-Dame, Paris (inscr. in French).

**MORE DETAILED LISTS**
are given in the Stanley Gibbons Catalogues referred to in the country headings.
For lists of current volumes see Introduction.

491. 500-year-old Walnut.

492.

**1964.** Ancient Trees. Values and inscr. in black.
1494. **491.** 1 s. brown .. .. 10 10
1495. – 2 s. purple .. .. 10 10
1496. – 3 s. sepia .. .. 15 10
1497. – 4 s. blue .. .. 15 10
1498. – 10 s. green .. .. 45 20
1499. – 13 s olive .. .. 80 25
TREES: 2 s. Plane (1000 yrs.). 3 s. Plane (600 yrs.). 4 s. Poplar (800 yrs.). 10 s. Oak (800 yrs.). 13 s. Fir (1200 yrs.).

**1964.** 8th Congress of Int. Union of Students, Sofia.
1500. **492.** 13 s. black and blue 80 15

493. Bulgarian Veteran and Soviet Soldier. (Sculpture by T. Zlatarev).

494. "Gold Medal".

**1965.** 30 Years of Bulgarian–Russian Friendship.
1501. **493.** 2 s. red and black .. 20 10

**1965.** Olympic Games, Tokyo (1964).
1502. **494.** 20 s. blk., gold & brn. 1·00 30

495. Komarov.

**1965.** Flight of "Voskhod 1". Multicoloured.
1503. 1 s. Type **495** .. .. 10 10
1504. 2 s. Feoktistov .. .. 10 10
1505. 5 s. Yegorov .. .. 15 10
1506. 13 s. The three astronauts 85 15
1507. 20 s. "Voskhod 1" .. 1·40 25

496. Corn-cob.

497. "Victory against Fascism".

**1965.** Agricultural Products.
1508. **496.** 1 s. yellow .. .. 10 10
1509. – 2 s. green .. .. 10 10
1510. – 3 s. orange .. .. 15 10
1511. – 4 s. olive .. .. 20 10
1512. – 5 s. red .. .. 30 10
1513. – 10 s. blue .. .. 50 20
1514. – 13 s. bistre .. .. 1·25 25
DESIGNS: 2 s. Ears of Wheat. 3 s. Sunflowers. 4 s. Sugar beet. 5 s. Clover. 10 s. Cotton. 13 s. Tobacco.

**1965.** 20th Anniv. of "Victory of 9 May, 1945".
1515. **497.** 5 s. black, bistre & grey 15 10
1516. – 13 s. blue, black & grey 40 20
DESIGN: 13 s. Globes on dove ("Peace").

498. Bullfinch. 499. Transport, Globe and Whale.

**1965.** Song Birds. Multicoloured.
1517. 1 s. Type **498** .. .. 10 10
1518. 2 s. Golden oriole .. 10 10
1519. 3 s. Rock thrush .. 10 10
1520. 5 s. Barn swallows .. 60 10
1521. 8 s. Common roller .. 95 15
1522. 10 s. Goldfinch .. .. 3·50 25
1523. 13 s. Rose-coloured starling .. .. 3·50 55
1524. 20 s. Nightingale .. 3·50 1·25

**1965.** 4th Int. Transport Conf., Sofia.
1525. **499.** 13 s. multicoloured .. 80 20

500. I.C.Y. Emblem. 501. I.T.U. Emblem and Symbols.

**1965.** Int. Co-operation Year.
1526. **500.** 20 s. orge., olive & blk. 90 25

**1965.** Centenary of I.T.U.
1527. **501.** 20 s. yell., grn. & bl. 1·25 30

502. Beliaiev and Leonov.

**1965.** "Voskhod 2" Space Flight.
1528. **502.** 2 s. pur., grn. & drab 30 10
1529. – 20 s. multicoloured .. 3·00 1·10
DESIGN: 20 s. Leonov on space.

503. Sting-ray.

504. Marx and Lenin.

**1965.** Fishes. Borders in grey.
1530. **503.** 1 s. gold, black & orge. 10 10
1531. – 2 s. silver, indigo & bl. 10 10
1532. – 3 s. gold, black & grn. 20 10
1533. – 5 s. gold, black & red 25 10
1534. – 10 s. silver, blue and turquoise .. 1·40 25
1535. – 13 s. gold, blk. & brn. 1·40 45
FISHES: 2 s. Belted bonito. 3 s. Scorpion-fish. 5 s. Gurnard. 10 s. Horse mackerel. 13 s. Turbot.

**1965.** Postal Ministers' Congress, Peking.
1536. **504.** 13 s. brown and red .. 1·10 20

505. Film and Screen.

506. Quinces.

**1965.** Balkan Film Festival, Varna.
1537. **505.** 13 s. black, silver & bl. 85 20

**1965.** Fruits.
1538. **506.** 1 s. orange .. .. 10 10
1539. – 2 s. olive (Grapes) .. 10 10
1540. – 3 s. bistre (Pears) .. 15 10
1541. – 4 s. orange (Plums) .. 15 10
1542. – 5 s. red (Strawberries) 30 10
1543. – 6 s. brown (Walnuts) 50 15

507. Ballerina. 508. Dove, Emblem and Map.

**1965.** Ballet Competitions, Varna.
1544 **507** 5 s. black and mauve 85 30

**1965.** "Balkanphila" Stamp Exn., Varna.
1545. **508.** 1 s. silver, blue & yell. 10 10
1546. – 2 s. silver, violet & yell. 10 10
1547. – 3 s. gold, green & yell. 15 10
1548. – 13 s. gold, red & yell. 1·00 85
1549. – 20 s. brn., bl. & silver 1·40 1·00
DESIGNS: 2 s. Yacht emblem. 3 s. Stylised fish and flowers. 13 s. Stylised Sun, planet and rocket. LARGER (45×25½ mm.): 20 s. Cosmonauts Beliaiev and Leonov.

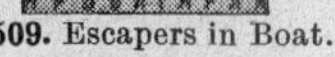
**509.** Escapers in Boat.

**511.** Gymnast.

(510.)

**1965.** 40th Anniv. of Political Prisoners' Escape from "Bolshevik Island".
1551. **509.** 2 s. black and slate 20 15

**1965.** National Folklore Competition. No. 1084 surch. with T **510.**
1552. – 2 s. on 8 s. brown .. 1·40 1·40

**1965.** Balkan Games.
1553. **511.** 1 s. black and red .. 10 10
1554. – 2 s. purple and black 10 10
1555. – 3 s. pur., blk. & red 10 10
1556. – 5 s. brown, black & red 20 10
1557. – 10 s. purple, blk. & mauve 1·00 20
1558. – 13 s. purple and black 80 25
DESIGNS: 2 s. Gymnastics on bars. 3 s. Weight-lifting. 5 s. Rally car and building. 10 s. Basketball. 13 s. Rally car and map.

**512.** Dressage.

**1965.** Horsemanship.
1559. **512.** 1 s. plum, blk. & blue 10 10
1560. – 2 s. brn., blk. & ochre 10 10
1561. – 3 s. red, blk. and pur. 10 10
1562. – 5 s. brown and green 50 10
1563. – 10 s. brn., blk. & grey 2·00 25
1564. – 13 s. brn., grn. & buff 2·10 35
DESIGNS: 5 s. Horse-racing. Others, Horse-jumping (various).

**513.** Young Pioneers.

**1965.** Dimitrov. September Pioneers Organization.
1566. **513.** 1 s. green & turquoise 10 10
1567. – 2 s. mauve and violet 10 10
1568. – 3 s. bistre and olive .. 10 10
1569. – 5 s. ochre and blue .. 15 10
1570. – 8 s. orange and brown 50 15
1571. – 13 s. violet and red .. 95 30
DESIGNS: 2 s. Admitting recruit. 3 s. Camp bugler. 5 s. Flying model aircraft. 8 s. Girls singing. 13 s. Young athlete.

**514.** Junkers Ju 52/3m over Tirnovo.

**515.** Women of N. and S. Bulgaria.

**1965.** Bulgarian Civil Aviation. Mult.
1572 1 s. Type **514** .. .. 10 10
1573 2 s. Ilyushin Il-14 over Plovdiv .. .. 10 10
1574 3 s. Mil Mi-4 helicopter over Dimitrovgrad .. 10 10
1575 5 s. Tupolev Tu-104A over Ruse .. .. 25 10
1576 13 s. Ilyushin Il-18 over Varna .. .. 1·40 15
1577 20 s. Tupolev Tu-114 over Sofia .. .. 1·75 45

**1965.** 80th Anniv. of North and South Bulgarian Union.
1578. **515.** 13 s. black and green 85 30

**516.** I.Q.S.Y. Emblem and Earth's Radiation Zones.

**517.** "Spring Greetings".

**1965.** Int. Quiet Sun Year.
1579. **516.** 1 s. yell., grn. & blue 10 10
1580. – 2 s. multicoloured .. 10 10
1581. – 13 s. multicoloured .. 90 20
DESIGNS (I.Q.S.Y. emblem and): 2 s. Sun and solar flares. 13 s. Total eclipse of the Sun.

**1966.** "Spring". National Folklore.
1582. **517.** 1 s. mve., blue & drab 10 10
1583. – 2 s. red, black & drab 10 10
1584. – 3 s. violet, red & grey 10 10
1585. – 5 s. red, violet & black 15 15
1586. – 8 s. pur., brn. & mve. 35 15
1587. – 13 s. mve., blk. & blue 70 15
DESIGNS: 2 s. Drummer. 3 s. "Birds" (stylised). 5 s. Folk dancer. 8 s. Vase of flowers. 13 s. Bagpiper.

**518.** Byala Bridge.

DESIGNS: No. 1589, Svilengrad Bridge. No. 1590, Fountain, Samokov. No. 1591, Ruins of Matochina Castle. No. 1592, Cherven Castle. No. 1593, Cafe, Bozhentsi.

**1966.** Ancient Monuments.
1588. **518.** 1 s. turquoise .. 10 10
1589. – 1 s. green .. .. 10 10
1590. – 2 s. green .. .. 10 10
1591. – 2 s. purple .. .. 10 10
1592. – 8 s. brown .. .. 40 15
1593. – 13 s. blue .. .. 65 15

**519.** "Christ" (from fresco Boyana Church).

**1966.** "2,500 Years of Culture". Mult.
1594. 1 s. Type **519** .. 5·00 4·00
1595. 2 s. "Destruction of the Idols" (from fresco, Boyana Church) (horiz.) 25 15
1596. 3 s. Bachkovo Monastery 50 15
1597. 4 s. Zemen Monastery (horiz.) .. 50 15
1598. 5 s. John the Baptist Church, Nesebur .. 50 25
1599. 13 s. "Nativity" (icon, Monumental Church of Alexander Nevski, Sofia) 1·00 85
1600. 20 s. "Virgin and Child" (icon, Archaeological Museum, Sofia) .. 1·50 1·00

**520.** "The First Gunshot" at Koprivshtitsa.

**1966.** 90th Anniv. of April Uprising.
1601. **520.** 1 s. black, brn. & gold 10 10
1602. – 2 s. black, red & gold 10 10
1603. – 3 s. black, green & gold 10 10
1604. – 5 s. black, blue & gold 20 10
1605. – 10 s. black, pur. & gold 60 10
1606. – 13 s. black, vio. & gold 60 15
DESIGNS: 2 s. G. Benkovski and T. Kableskov. 3 s. "Showing the Flag" at Panagyurishte. 5 s. V. Petleshkov and Z. Dyustabanov. 10 s. Landing of Botev's detachment at Kozlodui. 13 st. P. Volov and I. Dragostinov.

**522.** W.H.O. Building.

**1966.** Inaug. of W.H.O. Headquarters, Geneva.
1608. **522.** 13 s. blue and silver 1·00 20

**523.** Worker.

**1966.** 6th Trades Union Congress, Sofia
1609. **523.** 20 s. black and pink 1·10 20

**524.** Indian Elephant.

**525.** Boy and Girl holding Banners.

**1966.** Sofia Zoo Animals. Multicoloured.
1610. 1 s. Type **524** .. .. 10 10
1611. 2 s. Tiger .. .. .. 10 10
1612. 3 s. Chimpanzee .. .. 10 10
1613. 4 s. Ibex .. .. .. 20 10
1614. 5 s. Polar bear .. .. 30 10
1615. 8 s. Lion .. .. .. 65 20
1616. 13 s. American bison .. 2·10 35
1617. 20 s. Eastern grey kangaroo .. .. 2·75 55

**1966.** 3rd Congress of Bulgarian Sports Federation.
1618. **525.** 13 s. bl., orge. & cobalt 45 20

**526.** "Radetski" and Pioneer.

**527.** Standard-bearer B.N. Simov-Kuruto.

**1966.** 90th Anniv of Botev's Seizure of River Paddle-steamer "Radetski".
1619 **526** 2 s. multicoloured .. 20 10

**1966.** 90th Anniv. of Simov-Kuruto (hero of the Uprising against Turkey).
1620. **527.** 5 s. multicoloured .. 30 15

**528.** Federation Emblem.

**1966.** 7th Int. Youth Federation Assembly, Sofia.
1621. **528.** 13 s. blue and black .. 65 15

**529.** U.N.E.S.C.O. Emblem.

**1966.** 20th Anniv. of U.N.E.S.C.O.
1622. **529.** 20 s. ochre, red & black .. .. 85 30

**530.** Footballer with Ball.

**1966.** World Cup Football Championships, London. Showing players in action. Borders in grey.
1623. **530.** 1 s. black and brown 10 10
1624. – 2 s. black and red .. 10 10
1625. – 5 s. black and bistre 15 10
1626. – 13 s. black and blue .. 65 15
1627. – 20 s. black and blue .. 1·00 30

**532.** Wrestling.

**1966.** 3rd Int. Wrestling Championships, Sofia.
1629. **532.** 13 s. sepia, grn & brn. 45 20

**533.** Throwing the Javelin.

**1966.** 3rd Republican Spartakiade.
1630. **533.** 2 s. green, red & yellow 10 10
1631. – 13 s. green, red & yell. 65 25
DESIGN: 13 s. Running.

**534.** Map of Balkans, Globe and U.N.E.S.C.O. Emblem.

**1966.** Int. Balkan Studies Congress, Sofia.
1632. **534.** 13 s. green, pink & blue 65 15


**535.** Children with Construction Toy.

DESIGNS: 2 s. Rabbit and Teddy Bear. 3 s. Children as astronauts. 13 s. Children with gardening equipment.

**1966.** Children's Day.
1633. **535.** 1 s. blk., yellow & red 10 10
1634. – 2 s. black, brn. & grn. 10 10
1635. – 3 s. blk., yell. & blue 10 10
1636. – 13 s. blk., mve. & blue 1·00 15

**536.** Gagarin and "Vostok 1".

**1966.** Russian Space Exploration.
1637. **536.** 1 s. slate and grey .. 10 10
1638. – 2 s. purple and grey .. 10 10
1639. – 3 s. brown and grey .. 10 10
1640. – 5 s. lake and grey .. 15 10
1641. – 8 s. blue and grey .. 20 10
1642. – 13 s. turquoise & grey 80 10
1643. – 20 s. + 10 s. violet & grey 1·75 55
DESIGNS: 2 s. Titov and "Vostok 2". 3 s. Nikolaev, Popovich and "Vostoks 3" and "4". 5 s. Tereshkova, Bykovsky and "Vostoks 5" and "6". 8 s. Komarov, Yegorov, Feoktistov and "Voskhod 1". 13 s. Beliaiev, Leonov and "Voskhod 2". 20 s. Gagarin, Leonov and Tereshkova.

**537.** St. Clement (14th-cent. wood-carving).

**538.** M. Shatorov.

**1966.** 1050th Death Anniv. of St. Clement of Ochrid.
1645. **537.** 5 s. brn., red & drab 65 35

**1966.** Anti-Fascist Fighters. Frames in gold; value in black.
1646. **538.** 2 s. violet and red .. 10 10
1647. – 3 s. brown and mauve 15 10
1648. – 5 s. blue and red .. 20 10
1649. – 10 s. brown & orange 35 15
1650. – 13 s. brown and red .. 70 15
PORTRAITS: 3 s. V. Trichkov. 5 s. V. Ivanov. 10 s. R. Daskalov. 13 s. Gen. V. Zaimov.

**539.** G. Dimitrov (statesman).

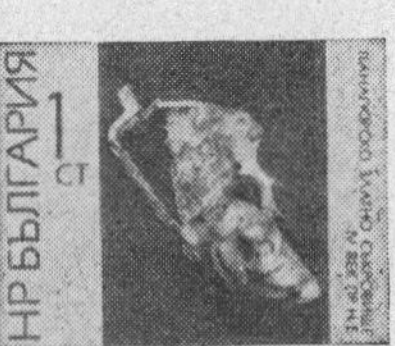

**540.** Deer's head Vessel.

**1966.** 9th Bulgarian Communist Party Congress, Sofia.
1651. **539.** 2 s. black and red .. 20 10
1652. – 20 s. black, red & grey 1·10 20
DESIGN: 20 s. Furnaceman and steelworks.

**1966.** The Gold Treasures of Panagyurishte. Multicoloured.
1653. 1 s. Type **540** .. .. 10 10
1654. 2 s. Amazon .. .. 20 10
1655. 3 s. Ram .. .. .. 20 10
1656. 5 s. Plate .. .. 25 10
1657. 6 s. Venus .. .. 25 10
1658. 8 s. Roe-buck .. .. 1·10 15
1659. 10 s. Amazon (different) 1·10 15
1660. 13 s. Amphora .. .. 1·40 30
1661. 20 s. Goat .. .. 2·00 65
Except for the 5 s. and 13 s. the designs show vessels with animal heads.

**541.** Bansko Hotel. **542.** Christmas Tree.

**1966.** Tourist Resorts.
1662. **541.** 1 s. blue .. .. 10 10
1663. – 2 s. grn. (Belogradchik) 10 10
1664. – 2 s. lake (Triavna) .. 10 10
1665. – 20 s. purple (Maliovitsa, Rila) .. 70 15

**1966.** New Year. Multicoloured.
1666. 2 s. Type **542** .. .. 10 10
1667. 13 s. Money-box .. 45 15

**543.** P. Slaveikov (writer). **544.** Dahlias.

**1966.** Cultural Celebrities.
1668. **543.** 1 s. bistre, blue & orge. 10 10
1669. – 2 s. brown, orge. & grey 10 10
1670. – 3 s. blue, bistre & orge. 10 10
1671. – 5 s. purple, drab & orge. 20 10
1672. – 8 s. grey, purple & blue 55 15
1673. – 13 s. violet, blue & pur. 65 15
CELEBRITIES, Writers (with pen emblem): 2 s. D. Debelyanov. 3 s. P. Todorov. Painters (with brush emblem): 5 s. D. Dobrovich. 8 s. I. Murkvichka. 13 s. I. Beshkov.

**1966.** Flowers. Multicoloured.
1674. 1 s. Type **544** .. .. 10 10
1675. 1 s. Clematis .. .. 10 10
1676. 2 s. Narcissi .. .. 15 10
1677. 2 s. Foxgloves .. .. 15 10
1678. 3 s. Snowdrops .. .. 25 10
1679. 5 s. Petunias .. .. 25 10
1680. 13 s. Tiger lilies .. 1·00 15
1681. 20 s. Campanulas .. 1·40 30

**545.** Ring-necked Pheasant.

**1967.** Hunting. Multicoloured.
1682 1 s. Type **545** .. .. 30 10
1683 2 s. Chukar partridge .. 30 10
1684 3 s. Grey partridge .. 30 10
1685 5 s. Brown hare .. .. 65 10
1686 8 s. Roe deer .. .. 1·90 20
1687 13 s. Red deer .. .. 2·00 40

**546.** "Philately". **547.** 6th-cent. B.C. Coin of Thrace.

**1967.** 10th Bulgarian Philatelic Federation Congress, Sofia.
1688. **546.** 10 s. yell., blk. & grn. 1·40 1·00

**1967.** Ancient Bulgarian Coins. Coins in silver on black background except 13 s. (gold on black). Frame colours given.
1689. **547.** 1 s. brown .. .. 10 10
1690. – 2 s. purple .. .. 10 10
1691 – 3 s. green .. .. 15 10
1692. – 5 s. brown .. .. 25 15
1693. – 13 s. turquoise .. 1·25 40
1694. – 20 s. violet .. .. 1·60 1·40
COINS—SQUARE. 2 s. 2nd-cent. B.C. Macedonian tetradrachm. 3 s. 2nd-cent. B.C. Odessos (Varna) tetradrachm. 5 s. 4th-cent. B.C. Macedonian coin of Philip II. HORIZ. (38 × 25 mm.): 13 s. Obverse and reverse of 4th-cent. B.C. coin of King Sevt (Thrace). 20 s. Obverse and reverse of 5th-cent. B.C. coin of Apollonia (Sozopol)

**548.** Partisans listening to radio.

**1967.** 25th Anniv. of Fatherland Front. Multicoloured.
1695. 1 s. Type **548** .. .. 10 10
1696. 20 s. Dimitrov speaking at rally .. .. 1·00 25

**549.** Nikola Kofardzhiev. **550.** "Cultural Development".

**1967.** Anti-Fascist Fighters.
1697. **549.** 1 s. lake, black & blue 10 10
1698. – 2 s. green, black & blue 10 10
1699. – 5 s. ochre, black & blue 15 10
1700. – 10 s. blue, blk. & lilac 50 15
1701. – 13 s. pur., black & grey 65 15
PORTRAITS: 2 s. P. Napetov. 5 s. P. D. Petkov. 10 s. E. Markov. 13 s. T. Kostov.

**1967.** 1st Cultural Conf., Sofia.
1702. **550.** 13 s. yell., grn. & gold 80 15

**551.** Angora Kitten. **552.** "Golden Sands" Resort.

**1967.** Cats. Multicoloured
1703. 1 s. Type **551** .. .. 10 10
1704. 2 s. Siamese (horiz.) .. 15 10
1705. 3 s. Abyssinian .. .. 20 10
1706. 5 s. European black and white .. .. 1·00 10
1707. 13 s. Persian (horiz.) .. 1·40 25
1708. 20 s. European tabby .. 2·00 90

**1967.** Int. Tourist Year. Multicoloured.
1709. 13 s. Type **552** .. .. 35 15
1710. 20 s. Pamporovo .. .. 85 20
1711. 40 s. Old Church, Nesebur 1·60 60

**553.** Scene from Iliev's Opera, "The Master of Boyana".

**1967.** 3rd Int. Young Opera singers' Competition, Sofia.
1712. **553.** 5 s. red, blue and grey 20 10
1713. – 13 s. red, blue & grey 60 15
DESIGN—VERT. 13 s. "Vocal Art" (song-bird on piano-keys).

**554.** G. Kirkov.

**1967.** Birth Cent. of Georgi Kirkov (patriot).
1714. **554.** 2 s. bistre and red .. 15 10

**555.** Roses and Distillery.

**1967.** Economic Achievements. Mult.
1715. 1 s. Type **555** .. .. 10 10
1716. 1 s. Chick and incubator 10 10
1717. 2 s. Cucumber and glass-houses .. .. 10 10
1718. 2 s. Lamb and farm building 10 10
1719. 3 s. Sunflower and oil-extraction plant .. 10 10
1720. 4 s. Pigs and piggery .. 10 10
1721. 5 s. Hops and vines .. 10 10
1722. 6 s. Grain and irrigation canals .. .. 20 10
1723. 8 s. Grapes and "Bulgar" tractor .. .. 15 10
1724. 10 s. Apples and tree .. 30 15
1725. 13 s. Bees and honey .. 55 15
1726. 20 s. Bee on flower, and hives .. .. 1·10 25

**556.** D.K.M.S. Emblem. **557.** Map and Spasski Tower, Kremlin.

**1967.** 11th Anniv. of Dimitrov Communist Youth League.
1727. **556.** 13 s. blk., red & bl. 70 15

**1967.** 50th Anniv. of October Revolution.
1728. **557.** 1 s. multicoloured .. 10 10
1729. – 2 s. olive and purple 10 10
1730. – 3 s. violet and purple 10 10
1731. – 5 s. red and purple .. 15 10
1732. – 13 s. blue and purple 30 15
1733. – 20 s. blue and purple 1·00 20
DESIGNS: 2 s. Lenin directing revolutionaries. 3 s. Bulgarian revolutionaries. 5 s. Marx, Engels and Lenin. 13 s. Soviet oil refinery. 20 s. "Molyna" satellite and Moon (Soviet space research).

**558.** Scenic "Fish" and Rod. **560.** Bogdan Peak, Sredna Mts.

**559.** Ski-walking.

**1967.** 7th World Angling Championships, Varna.
1734. **558.** 10 s. multicoloured .. 40 15

**1967.** Winter Olympic Games, Grenoble (1968).
1735. **559.** 1 s. black, red & turq. 10 10
1736. – 2 s. black, bistre & bl. 10 10
1737. – 3 s. black, blue & pur. 10 10
1738. – 5 s. black, yell. & grn. 15 10
1739. – 13 s. blk., buff & blue 1·00 25
1740. – 20 s.+10 s. mult. .. 1·90 50
DESIGNS: 2 s. Ski-jumping. 3 s. Biathlon 5 s. Ice-hockey. 13 s. Pair dancing. 20 s. Men's slalom.

**1967.** Tourism. Mountain Peaks.
1742. **560.** 1 s. green and yellow 10 10
1743. – 2 s. sepia and blue .. 10 10
1744. – 3 s. indigo and blue .. 10 10
1745. – 5 s. green and blue .. 15 10
1746. – 10 s. brown and blue 30 10
1747. – 13 s. black and blue 40 15
1748. – 20 s. blue and purple 70 25
DESIGNS—HORIZ. 2 s. Cherni Vruh, Vitosha. 5 s. Persenk, Rhodopes. 10 s. Botev, Stara-Planina. 20 s. Vihren, Pirin. VERT. 3 s. Ruen, Osogovska Planina. 13 s. Musala, Rila.

**561.** G. Rakovski.

**1967.** Death Centenary of G. Rakovski (revolutionary).
1749. **561.** 13 s. black and green 45 15

**562.** Gagarin, Tereshkova and Leonov.

**1967.** Space Exploration. Multicoloured.
1750. 1 s. Type **562** .. .. 10 10
1751. 2 s. Glenn and White .. 15 10
1752. 5 s. "Molyna 1" .. 25 10
1753. 10 s. "Gemini 6 and 7" .. 65 15
1754. 13 s. "Luna 13" .. 85 20
1755. 20 s. "Gemini 10" .. 1·10 35

**563.** Railway Bridge over Yantra River.

**1967.** Views of Tirnova (Ancient Capital).
1756. **563.** 1 s. black, drab & blue 10 10
1757. – 2 s. multicoloured .. 10 10
1758. – 3 s. multicoloured .. 10 10
1759. – 5 s. black, slate & red 20 10
1760. – 13 s. multicoloured .. 65 15
1761. – 20 s. blk., orge. & lav. 1·00 25
DESIGNS: 2 s. Hadji Nikola's Inn. 3 s. Houses on hillside. 5 s. Town and river. 13 s. "House of the Monkeys". 20 s. Gurko street.

**564.** "The Ruchenitsa" (folk dance, from painting by Murkvichka).

**1967.** Belgian-Bulgarian "Painting and Philately" Exn., Brussels.
1762. **564.** 20 s. green and gold 1·90 1·50

**565.** "The Shepherd" (Z. Boyadzhiev).

**1967.** Paintings in the National Gallery, Sofia. Multicoloured.
1763. 1 s. Type **565** .. .. 10 10
1764. 2 s. "The Wedding" (V Dimitrov) .. .. 10 10
1765. 3 s. "The Partisans" (I. Petrov) .. .. 20 10
1766. 5 s. "Anastasia Penchovich" (N. Pavlovich) .. 85 25
1767. 13 s. "Self-Portrait" (Z. Zograf) .. .. 1·50 60
1768. 20 s. "Old Town of Plovdiv" (T. Lavrenov) .. .. 2·00 1·00
The 3 s. design is 55 × 35 mm. and those of the 2, 5 and 13 s. are vert.

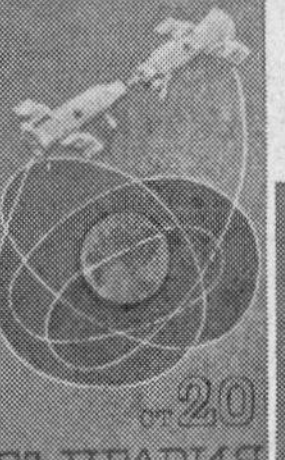

**566.** Linked Satellites "Cosmos 186" and "188". **567.** "Crossing the Danube" (Orenburgski).

**1968.** "Cosmic Activities". Multicoloured.
1770. 20 s. Type **566** .. .. 1·00 25
1771. 40 s. "Venus 4" and orbital diagram (horiz.) 1·90 75

**1968.** 90th Anniv. of Liberation from Turkey. Paintings. Inscr. and frames in black and gold; centre colours below.
1772. **567.** 1 s. green .. .. 25 10
1773. – 2 s. blue .. .. 10 10
1774. – 3 s. brown .. .. 15 10
1775. – 13 s. blue .. .. 60 40
1776. – 20 s. turquoise .. 1·00 40
DESIGNS—VERT. 2 s. "Flag of Samara" (Veschin). 13 s. "Battle of Orlovo Gnezdo" (Popov). HORIZ. 3 s. "Battle of Pleven" (Orenburgski). 20 s. "Greeting Russian Soldiers" (Goudienov).

**568.** Karl Marx. **569.** Maxim Gorky.

**1968.** 150th Birth Anniv. of Karl Marx.
1777. **568.** 13 s. grey, red & blk. 65 25

**1968.** Birth Cent of Maxim Gorky (writer).
1778 **569** 13 s. green, orge & blk 65 15

**570.** Dancers.

**1968.** 9th World Youth and Students' Festival. Sofia. Multicoloured.
1779. 2 s. Type **570** .. .. 10 10
1780. 5 s. Running .. .. 10 10
1781. 13 s. "Doves" .. .. 65 10
1782. 20 s. "Youth" (symbolic design) .. .. 85 25
1783. 40 s. Bulgarian 5 c. stamp of 1879 under magnifier and Globe .. .. 1·50 80

**571.** "Campanula alpina". **572.** "The Unknown Hero" (Ran Bosilek).

**1968.** Wild Flowers. Multicoloured.
1784. 1 s. Type **571** .. .. 10 10
1785. 2 s. "Gentiana clusii" (wrongly inscr. "acaulis") 10 10
1786. 3 s. "Crocus veluchensis" 15 10
1787. 5 s. "Iris sibirica" .. 20 10
1788. 10 s. "Erythronium dens-canis" .. .. 30 15
1789. 13 s. "Sempervivum eucanthum" .. .. 1·00 20
1790. 20 s. "Dictamnus albus" 1·40 30

**1968.** Bulgarian—Danish Stamp Exn. Fairy Tales. Multicoloured.
1791. 13 s. Type **572** .. .. 45 20
1792. 20 s. "The Witch and the Young Men" (Hans Andersen) .. .. 55 35

**573.** Memorial Temple. Shipka. **574.** Copper Rolling-mill, Medet.

**1968.** Bulgarian—West Berlin Stamp Exn.
1793. **573.** 13 s. multicoloured 1·00 35

**1968.** Air.
1794. **574.** 1 l. red .. .. 2·75 35

**575.** Lake Smolyan. **576.** Gymnastics.

**1968**
1795. **575.** 1 s. green .. .. 10 10
1796. – 2 s. myrtle .. .. 10 10
1797. – 3 s. sepia .. .. 10 10
1798. – 8 s. green .. .. 25 10
1799. – 10 s. brown .. .. 55 10
1800. – 13 s. olive .. .. 45 15
1801. – 40 s. blue .. .. 1·25 35
1802. – 2 l. brown .. .. 6·00 1·40
DESIGNS: 2 s. Ropotamo River. 3 s. Lomnitza Gorge, Erma River. 8 s. Isker River. 10 s. Cruise ship "Die Fregatte". 13 s. Cape Kaliakra. 40 s. Sozopol. 2 l. Mountain road, Kamchia River.

**1968.** Olympic Games, Mexico.
1803. **576.** 1 s. black and red .. 10 10
1804. – 2 s. black, brn. & grey 10 10
1805. – 3 s. black & mauve .. 15 10
1806. – 10 s. blk., yell. & turq. 50 10
1807. – 13 s. blk., pink & blue 1·00 20
1808. – 20 s. + 10 s. grey, pink and blue .. .. 1·60 40
DESIGNS: 2 s. Horse-jumping. 3 s. Fencing. 10 s. Boxing. 13 s. Throwing the discus. 20 s. Rowing.

**577.** Dimitr on Mt. Buzludzha. **578.** Human Rights Emblem.

**1968.** Cent. of Exploits of Hadji Dimitr and Stefan Karadzha (partisan leaders).
1810. **577.** 2 s. brown and drab .. 15 10
1811. – 13 s. green and gold .. 35 15
DESIGN: 13 s. Hadji Dimitr and Stefan Karadzha.

**1968.** Human Rights Year.
1812. **578.** 20 s. gold and blue .. 1·00 15

**579.** European Black Vulture. **580.** Battle Scene.

**1968.** 80th Anniv. of Sofia Zoo.
1813. **579.** 1 s. black, brown and blue .. .. 50 10
1814. – 2 s. blk., yell. & brn. 50 10
1815. – 3 s. black and green 20 10
1816. – 5 s. blk., yell. & lake 40 10
1817. – 13 s. black, bistre and green .. .. 1·60 15
1818. – 20 s. blk., grn. & blue 2·40 55
DESIGNS: 2 s. South African crowned crane. 3 s. Common zebra. 5 s. Leopard. 13 s. Python. 20 s. Crocodile.

**1968.** 280th Anniv. of Chiprovtsi Rising.
1819. **580.** 13 s. multicoloured .. 80 15

**581.** "Calosoma sycophanta". **582.** Flying Swans.

**1968.** Insects.
1820. **581.** 1 s. green .. .. 15 10
1821. – 1 s. brown .. .. 15 10
1822. – 1 s. blue .. .. 15 10
1823. – 1 s. brown .. .. 15 10
1824. – 1 s. purple .. .. 35 20
DESIGNS—VERT. No. 1821, "Lucanus cervus". No. 1822, "Procerus scabrosus". HORIZ. No. 1823, "Oryctes nasicornis". No. 1824, "Perisomena caecigena".

**1968.** "Co-operation with Scandinavia".
1825. – 2 s. ochre and gree 1·25 1·25
1826. **582.** 5 s. bl., grey & blk. .. 1·25 1·25
1827. – 13 s. purple & maroon 1·25 1·25
1828. – 20 s. grey & violet .. 1·00 85
DESIGNS: 2 s. Wooden flask. 13 s. Rose. 20 s. "Viking ships".

**583.** Congress Building and Emblem.

**1968.** Int. Dental Congress, Varna.
1829. **583.** 20 s. gold, grn. & red 85 15

**584.** C. Smirnenski and Part of poem "Red Squadrons".

**1968.** 70th Birth Anniv. of Christo Smirnenski (poet).
1830. **584.** 13 s. black, orange & gold .. .. 45 20

**585.** Dove with Letter.

**1968.** National Stamp Exn., Sofia and 75th Anniv. of "National Philately".
1831. **585.** 20 s. green .. 1·10 85

**586.** Dalmatian Pelican.

**1968.** Srebirna Wildlife Reservation. Birds. Multicoloured.
1832. 1 s. Type **586** .. .. 10 10
1833. 2 s. Little Egret .. 10 10
1834. 3 s. Great Crested Grebe 15 10
1835. 5 s. Common Tern .. 40 15
1836. 13 s. White Spoonbill .. 1·25 50
1837. 20 s. Glossy Ibis .. 2·40 85

**587.** Silistra Costume.

**1968.** Provincial Costumes. Multicoloured.
1838. 1 s. Type **587** .. .. 10 10
1839. 2 s. Lovech .. .. 10 10
1840. 3 s. Yamboi .. .. 15 10
1841. 13 s. Chirpan .. .. 45 25
1842. 20 s. Razgrad .. .. 1·00 25
1843. 40 s. Ikhtiman .. .. 2·00 50

**588.** "St. Arsenius" (icon).

**1968.** Rila Monastery. Icons and murals. Multicoloured.
1844. 1 s. Type **588** .. .. 10 10
1845. 2 s. "Carrying St. Ivan Rilski's Relics" (horiz.) 10 10
1846. 3 s. "St. Michael torments the Rich Man's Soul" 15 10
1847. 13 s. "St. Ivan Rilski" 1·00 15
1848. 20 s. "Prophet Iona" .. 1·40 30
1849. 40 s. "St. George" .. 2·40 1·00

**589.** "Matricaria chamomilla".

**1968.** Medicinal Plants. Multicoloured.
1851. 1 s. Type **589** .. .. 10 10
1852. 1 s. "Mespilus oxyacantha" .. 10 10
1853. 2 s. "Convallaria majalis" .. .. 10 10
1854. 3 s. "Atropa belladonna" 15 10
1855. 5 s. "Malva silvestris" 20 10
1856. 10 s. "Adonis vernalis" 50 10
1857. 13 s. "Papaver rhoeas" 40 15
1858. 20 s. "Thymus serpyllum" .. .. 1·00 25

**590.** Silkworms and Spindles.

**1969.** Silk Industry. Multicoloured.
1859. 1 s. Type **590** .. .. 10 10
1860. 2 s. Worm, cocoons and pattern .. .. 10 10
1861. 3 s. Cocoons and spinning wheel .. .. 10 10
1862. 5 s. Cocoons and patter 15 10
1863. 13 s. Moth, cocoon and spindles .. .. 40 15
1864. 20 s. Moth, eggs and shuttle .. .. 85 25

**591.** "Death of Ivan Asen". **592.** "Saints Cyril and Methodius" (mural, Troyan Monastery).

**1969.** Manasses Chronicle (1st series). Multicoloured.
1865. 1 s. Type **591** .. .. 10 10
1866. 2 s. "Emperor Nicephorus invading Bulgaria" .. 10 10
1867. 3 s. "Khan Krum's Feast" .. .. 15 10
1868. 13 s. "Prince Sviatoslav invading Bulgaria" .. 85 35
1869. 20 s. "The Russian invasion" .. .. 1·10 25
1870. 40 s. "Jesus Christ, Tsar Ivan Alexander and Constantine Manasses" 2·00 85
See also Nos. 1911/16.

**1969.** Saints Cyril and Methodius Commem.
1871. **592.** 28 s. multicoloured .. 1·40 45

**593.** Galleon. **594.** Posthorn Emblem.

**1969.** Air. "SOFIA 1969" International Stamp Exhibition. "Transport". Multicoloured.
1872 1 s. Type **593** .. .. 10 10
1873 2 s. Mail coach .. .. 10 10
1874 3 s. Steam locomotive .. 10 10
1875 5 s. Early motor-car .. 10 10
1876 10 s. Montgolfier's balloon and Henri Giffard's steam-powered dirigible airship, 1852 .. .. 20 10
1877 13 s. Early flying machines .. .. 30 15
1878 20 s. Modern aircraft .. 85 25
1879 40 s. Rocket and planets 1·50 75

**1969.** 90th Anniv. of Bulgarian Postal Services.
1881. **594** 2 s. yellow and green 10 10
1882. – 13 s. multicoloured .. 45 10
1883. – 20 s. blue .. .. 85 25
DESIGNS: 13 s. Bulgarian Stamps of 1879 and 1946. 20 s. Post Office workers' strike, 1919.

595. ILO Emblem.

596. "Fox" and "Rabbit".

**1969.** 50th Anniv. of Int. Labour Organization.
1884. 595. 13 s. black and green 35 15

**1969.** Children's Book Week.
1885. 596. 1 s. blk., orge. & grn. 10 10
1886. – 2 s. black, blue & red 10 10
1887. – 13 s. black, olive & bl. 65 15
DESIGNS: 2 s. Boy with "hedgehog" and "squirrel". 13 s. "The Singing Lesson".

597. Hand with Seedling. 598. "St. George" (14th Century).

**1969.** "10,000,000 Hectares of New Forests".
1888. 597. 2 s. black, grn. & pur. 15 10

**1969.** Religious Art. Multicoloured.
1889. 1 s. Type 598 .. .. 10 10
1890. 2 s. "The Virgin and St. John Bogoslov" (14th century) .. .. 10 10
1891. 3 s. "Archangel Michael" (17th century) .. 15 10
1892. 5 s. "Three Saints" (17th century) .. 25 10
1893. 8 s. "Jesus Christ" (17th century) .. .. 15 10
1894. 13 s. "St. George and St. Dimitr" (19th century) 75 15
1895. 20 s. "Christ the Universal" (19th century) .. 1·10 15
1896. 60 s. "The Forty Martyrs" (19th century) .. .. 3·25 90
1897. 80 s. "The Transfiguration" (19th century) .. 4·00 1·60

599. Roman Coin. 600. St. George and the Dragon.

**1969.** "SOFIA 1969" Int. Stamp Exhibition. "Sofia Through the Ages".
1899. 599. 1 s. silver, blue & gold 10 10
1900. – 2 s. silver, grn. & gold 10 10
1901. – 3 s. silver, lake & gold 10 10
1902. – 4 s. silver, vio. & gold 15 10
1903. – 5 s. silver, pur. & gold 15 10
1904. – 13 s. silver, grn. & gold 50 10
1905. – 20 s. silver, bl. & gold 1·00 15
1906. – 40 s. silver, red & gold 2·00 35
DESIGNS: 2 s. Roman Coin showing Temple of Aesculapius. 3 s. Church of St. Sophia. 4 s. Boyana Church. 5 s. Parliament Building. 13 s. National Theatre. 20 s. Alexander Nevsky Church. 40 s. Sofia University.

**1969.** F.I.P. Congress, Sofia.
1908. 600. 40 s. blk., orge. & silver 2·00 85

601. St. Cyril.

**1969.** 1,100th Death Anniv. of St. Cyril.
1909. 601. 2 s. grn. & red on silver 15 10
1910. – 28 s. bl. & red on silver 1·40 35
DESIGN: 28 s. St. Cyril and procession.

**1969.** Manasses Chronicle (2nd series). Designs at T 591, but all horiz. Mult.
1911. 1 s. "Nebuchadnezzar II and Balthasar of Babylon, Cyrus and Darius of Persia" .. .. 10 10
1912. 2 s. "Cambyses, Gyges and Darius of Persia" 10 10
1913. 5 s. "Prophet David and Tsar Ivan Alexander" 15 10
1914. 13 s. "Rout of the Byzantine Army, 811" 85 15
1915. 20 s. "Christening of Khan Boris" .. 1·60 20
1916. 60 s. "Tsar Simeon's attack on Constantinople" .. .. .. 3·25 1·10

602. Partisans.

**1969.** 25th Anniv. of Fatherland Front Government.
1917. 602. 1 s. lilac, red & black 10 10
1918. – 2 s. brn., red & black 10 10
1919. – 3 s. green, red & black 10 10
1920. – 5 s. brn., red & black 20 10
1921. – 13 s. blue, red & blk. 35 10
1922. – 20 s. brown, green, red and black .. 1·00 25
DESIGNS: 2 s. Combine-harvester. 3 s. Dam. 5 s. Folk singers. 13 s. Petroleum Refinery. 20 s. Lenin, Dimitrov and flags.

603. Gymnastics.

**1969.** Third Republican Spartakiad. Mult.
1923. 2 s. Type 603 .. .. 10 10
1924. 20 s. Wrestling .. .. 85 25

604. "Construction" and soldier. 605. T. Tserkovski.

**1969.** 25th Anniv. of Army Engineers.
1925. 604. 6 s. black and blue .. 15 10

**1969.** Birth Cent. of Tsanke Tserkovski (poet).
1926. 605. 13 s. multicoloured .. 35 20

606. "Woman" (Roman Statue). 607. Skipping-rope Exercise.

**1969.** 1,800th Anniv. of Silistra.
1927. 606. 2 s. grey, blue & silver 15 10
1928. – 13 s. brn., grn. & silver 75 15
DESIGN—HORIZ. 13 st. "Wolf" (bronze statue).

**1969.** World Gymnastics Competition, Varna.
1929. 607. 1 s. grey, blue & grn. 10 10
1930. – 2 s. grey and blue .. 10 10
1931. – 3 s. grey, grn. & emer. 10 10
1932. – 5 s. grey, pur. & red 10 10
1933. – 13 s.+5 s. grey, blue and red .. .. 85 25
1934. – 20 s.+10 s. grey, green and yellow 1·40 40
DESIGNS: 2 s. Hoop exercise (pair). 3 s. Hoop exercise (solo). 5 s. Ball exercise (pair). 13 s. Ball exercise (solo). 20 s. Solo gymnast.

608. Marin Drinov (founder).

**1969.** Cent. of Bulgarian Academy of Sciences.
1935. 608. 20 s. black and red .. 45 15

609. "Neophit Rilski" (Z. Zograf).

**1969.** Paintings in National Gallery, Sofia. Multicoloured.
1936. 1 s. Type 609 .. .. 10 10
1937. 2 s. "German's Mother" (V. Stoilov) .. .. 10 10
1938. 3 s. "Workers' Family" (Balkanski) (horiz.) .. 20 10
1939. 4 s. "Woman Dressing" (I. Nenov) .. .. 30 10
1940. 5 s. "Portrait of a Woman" (N. Pavlovich) 30 10
1941. 13 s. "Sarafov as Falstaff" (D. Uzunov) .. 85 15
1942. 20 s. "Artist's Wife" (N. Michailov) (horiz.) 1·00 25
1943. 20 s. "Worker's Lunch" (S. Sotirov) (horiz.) .. 1·10 30
1944. 40 s. "Self portrait" (Ts. Todorov) (horiz.) 1·60 80

610. Pavel Banya.

**1969.** Sanatoria.
1945. 610. 2 s. blue .. .. 10 10
1946. – 5 s. blue .. .. 10 10
1947. – 6 s. green .. .. 20 10
1948. – 20 s. green .. .. 55 20
SANATORIA: 5 s. Khisar. 6 s. Kotel. 20 s. Narechen Polyclinic.

611. Deep-sea Trawler.

**1969.** Ocean Fisheries.
1949. 611. 1 s. grey and blue .. 20 10
1950. – 1 s. green and black 10 10
1951. – 2 s. violet and black 10 10
1952. – 3 s. blue and black .. 20 10
1953. – 5 s. mauve and black 20 10
1954. – 10 s. grey and black 1·00 15
1955. – 13 s. flesh, orge. & blk. 1·50 25
1956. – 20 s. brn., ochre & blk. 2·00 25
DESIGNS: 1 s. (No. 1950), Cape hake. 2 s. Scad. 3 s. Pilchard. 5 s. Sea bream. 10 s. Chub-mackerel. 13 s. Salmon-bass. 20 s. Leer-fish.

612. Trapeze Act. 613. Cosmonauts and "Soyuz 6".

**1969.** Circus. Multicoloured.
1957. 1 s. Type 612 .. .. 10 10
1958. 2 s. Acrobats .. .. 10 10
1959. 3 s. Balancing act with hoops .. .. .. 10 10
1960. 5 s. Juggler, and bear on cycle .. .. .. 15 10
1961. 13 s. Equestrian act .. 40 15
1962. 20 s. Clowns .. .. 1·00 35

**1970.** Space Flights of "Soyuz 6, 7 and 8".
1963. 613. 1 s. multicoloured .. 10 10
1964. – 2 s. multicoloured .. 10 10
1965. – 3 s. multicoloured .. 15 10
1966. – 28 s. pink and blue .. 1·40 30
DESIGNS: 2 s. Cosmonauts and "Soyuz 7". 3 s. Cosmonauts and "Soyuz 8". 28 s. Three "Soyuz" spacecraft in orbit.

614. Khan Asparerch and "Old-Bulgars" crossing the Danube, 679.

**1970.** History of Bulgaria. Multicoloured.
1967. 1 s. Type 614 .. .. 10 10
1968. 2 s. Khan Krum and defeat of Emperor Nicephorus, 811 .. 10 10
1969. 3 s. Conversion of Khan Boris I to Christianity, 865 .. .. .. 15 10
1970. 5 s. Tsar Simeon and Battle of Akhelo, 917 20 10
1971. 8 s. Tsar Samuel and defeat of Byzantines, 976 .. .. .. 20 10
1972. 10 s. Tsar Kaloyan and victory over Emperor Baldwin, 1205 .. 30 15
1973. 13 s. Tsar Ivan Assen II and defeat of Komnine of Epirus, 1230 .. 85 15
1974. 20 s. Coronation of Tsar Ivailo, 1277 .. .. 1·40 25

615. Bulgarian Pavilion.

**1970.** "Expo 70" World's Fair, Osaka, Japan (1st. issue).
1975. 615. 20 s. silver, yell. & brn. 1·40 85
See Nos. 2009/12

616. Footballers.

**1970.** World Football Cup, Mexico.
1976. 616. 1 s. multicoloured .. 10 10
1977. – 2 s. multicoloured .. 10 10
1978. – 3 s. multicoloured .. 15 10
1979. – 5 s. multicoloured .. 15 10
1980. – 20 s. multicoloured 1·10 35
1981. – 40 s. multicoloured 2·00 60
DESIGNS: 2 s. to 40 s. various football scenes.

617. Lenin. 618. "Tephrocactus Alexanderi v. bruchi".

**1970.** Birth Cent. of Lenin. Multicoloured.
1983. 2 s. Type 617 .. .. 10 10
1984. 13 s. Full-face portrait .. 40 15
1985. 20 s. Lenin writing .. 1·10 25

**1970.** Flowering Cacti. Multicoloured.
1986. 1 s. Type 618 .. .. 10 10
1987. 2 s. "Opuntia drummondii" 10 10
1988. 3 s. "Hatiora cilindrica" 10 10
1989. 5 s. "Gymnocalycium vatteri" .. .. 15 10
1990. 8 s. "Heliantho cereus grandiflorus" .. 30 10
1991. 10 s. "Neochilenia andreaeana" .. .. 1·40 20
1992. 13 s. "Peireskia vargasii v. longispina" .. 1·40 25
1993. 20 s. "Neobesseya rosiflora" 2·00 40

619. Rose. 620. Union Badge.

**1970.** Bulgarian Roses.
1994. **619.** 1 s. multicoloured .. 10 10
1995. – 2 s. multicoloured .. 10 10
1996. – 3 s. multicoloured .. 25 10
1997. – 4 s. multicoloured .. 20 10
1998. – 5 s. multicoloured .. 25 10
1999. – 13 s. multicoloured 45 15
2000. – 20 s. multicoloured .. 1·50 35
2001. – 28 s. multicoloured .. 2·75 85
DESIGNS: 2 s. to 28 s. various roses.

**1970.** 70th Anniv. of Agricultural Union.
2002. **620.** 20 s. blk., gold & red 1·00 25

**621.** Gold Bowl.

**1970.** Gold Treasures of Thrace.
2003. **621.** 1 s. blk., blue & gold 10 10
2004. – 2 s. blk., lilac & gold 10 10
2005. – 3 s. blk., red & gold .. 15 10
2006. – 5 s. blk., green & gold 20 10
2007. – 13 s. blk., orge. & gold 1·00 15
2008. – 20 s. blk., violet & gold 1·50 30
DESIGNS: 2 s. Three small bowls. 3 s. Plain lid. 5 s. Pear shaped ornaments. 13 s. Large lid with pattern. 20 s. Vase.

**622.** Rose and Woman with Baskets of Produce.

**1970.** "Expo 70" World's Fair, Osaka, Japan (2nd issue). Multicoloured.
2009. 1 s. Type **622** .. 10 10
2010. 2 s. Three Dancers .. 10 10
2011. 3 s. Girl in National costume .. .. 10 10
2012. 28 s. Dancing couples .. 1·40 30

**623.** U.N. Emblem.

**1970.** 25th Anniv. of United Nations.
2014. **623.** 20 s. gold and blue .. 85 15

**624.** I. Vasov. **625.** Edelweiss Sanatorium, Borovets.

**1970.** 120th Birth Anniv. of Ivan Vasov (poet).
2015. **624.** 13 s. blue .. .. 45 25

**1970.** Health Resorts.
2016. **625.** 1 s. green .. .. 10 10
2017. – 2 s. olive .. .. 10 10
2018. – 4 s. blue .. .. 20 10
2019. – 8 s. blue .. .. 30 10
2020. – 10 s. blue .. .. 35 10
DESIGNS: 2 s. Panorama Hotel, Pamporovo. 4 s. Yachts, Albena. 8 s. Harbour scene, Rousalka. 10 s. Shtastlivetsa Hotel, Mt. Vitosha.

**626.** Golden Retriever.

**1970.** Dogs. Multicoloured.
2021. 1 s. Type **626** .. .. 10 10
2022. 2 s. Retriever (vert.) .. 15 10
2023. 3 s. Great Dane (vert.) 25 10
2024. 4 s. Boxer (vert.) .. 35 10
2025. 5 s. Cocker spaniel (vert.) 40 10
2026. 13 s. Dobermann pinscher (vert.) .. .. 1·00 15
2027. 20 s. Scottish terrier (vert.) 1·90 35
2028. 28 s. Collie .. .. 2·10 45

**627.** Fireman with Hose. **628.** Congress Emblem.

**1970.** Fire Protection.
2029. **627.** 1 s. grey, yell. & blk. 10 10
2030. – 3 s. red, grey & blk. 15 10
DESIGN. 3 s. Fire-engine.

**1970.** 7th World Sociological Congress, Varna.
2031. **628.** 13 s. multicoloured .. 40 15

**629.** Two Male Players. **630.** Cyclists.

**1970.** World Volleyball Championships.
2032. **629.** 2 s. black and brown 10 10
2033. – 2 s. orge., blk. & blue 15 10
2034. – 20 s. yell., blk. & green 1·00 20
2035. – 20 s. multicoloured .. 1·00 20
DESIGNS: No. 2033, Two female players. No. 2034, Male player. No. 2035, Female player.

**1970.** 20th Round-Bulgaria Cycle Race.
2036. **630.** 20 s. mauve, yell. & grn. 75 20

**631.** Caruso and Scene from "Il Pagliacci".

**1970.** Opera Singers. Multicoloured.
2037. 1 s. Type **631** .. .. 10 10
2038. 2 s. C. Morfova and "The Bartered Bride" .. 10 10
2039. 3 s. P. Raichev and "Tosca" .. .. 10 10
2040. 10 s. S. Tabakova and "The Flying Dutchman" .. .. .. 25 15
2041. 13 s. K. Popova and "The Masters of Nuremberg" 45 15
2042. 20 s. Chaliapin and "Boris Godunov" .. .. 1·75 80

**632.** Beethoven.

**1970.** Birth Bicent. of Beethoven.
2043. **632.** 28 s. blue and purple 2·00 1·40

**633.** Ivan Asen II Coin.

**1970.** Bulgarian Coins of the 14th century. Multicoloured.
2044. 1 s. Type **633** .. .. 10 10
2045. 2 s. Theodor Svetoslav .. 10 10
2046. 3 s. Mikhail Shishman .. 10 10
2047. 13 s. Ivan Alexander and Mikhail Asen .. .. 45 10
2048. 20 s. Ivan Sratsimir .. 1·00 20
2049. 28 s. Ivan Shishman (initials) .. .. 1·25 30

**INDEX**
Countries can be quickly located by referring to the index at the end of this volume.

**635.** Engels. **636.** Snow Crystal.

**1970.** 150th Birth Anniv. of Friedrich Engels.
2051. **635.** 13 s. brown and red 45 15

**1970.** New Year.
2052. **636.** 2 s. multicoloured .. 15 10

**638.** "Girls' Head" (Z. Spiridonov.)

**1971.** Modern Bulgarian Sculpture.
2054. **638.** 1 s. violet and gold .. 10 10
2055. – 2 s. green and gold .. 15 10
2056. – 3 s. brown and gold .. 10 10
2057. – 13 s. green and gold .. 40 15
2058. – 20 s. red and gold .. 1·00 20
2059. – 28 s. brown and gold 1·40 30
SCULPTURES: 2 s. "Third Class Carriage" (I. Funev). 3 s. "Elin Pelin" (M. Markov). 13 s. "Nina" (A. Nikolov). 20 s. "Kneeling Woman" (Yavorov monument, I. Lazarov). 28 s. "Engineer" (I. Funev).

**639.** Birds and Flowers.

**1971.** Spring.
2061. **639.** 1 s. multicoloured .. 10 10
2062. – 2 s. multicoloured .. 10 10
2063. – 3 s. multicoloured .. 10 10
2064. – 5 s. multicoloured .. 10 10
2065. – 13 s. multicoloured .. 25 10
2066. – 20 s. multicoloured .. 1·10 20
DESIGNS: 2 s. to 20 s. Various designs of birds and flowers similar to Type **639**.

**640.** "Khan Asparuch Crossing Danube" (B. Angelushev).

**1971.** Bulgarian History. Paintings. Mult.
2067. 2 s. Type **640** .. .. 10 10
2068. 3 s. "Ivajlo Meeting Tirnovo" (I. Petrov) 15 10
2069. 5 s. "Cavalry Charge, Benkovski" (P. Morosov) .. .. 50 10
2070. 8 s. "Gen. Gzrko entering Sofia, 1878" (D. Gyudzhenov) .. .. 85 10
2071. 28 s. "Greeting Red Army" (S. Venev) .. 4·25 1·60

**641.** Running.

**1971.** 2nd European Indoor Track and Field Championships. Multicoloured.
2073. 2 s. Type **641** .. .. 15 10
2074. 20 s. Putting the shot .. 1·60 25

**642.** School Building.

**1971.** Foundation of First Bulgarian Secondary School, Bolgrad.
2075. **642.** 2 s. grn., brn. & silver 10 10
2076. – 20 s. vio., brn. & silver 95 20
DESIGN: 20 s. Prince Bogoridi, Dimitr Mutev and Sada Radulov (founders).

**643.** Communards.

**1971.** Centenary of Paris Commune.
2077. **643.** 20 s. black and red .. 65 25

**644.** Dimitrov challenging Goering. **646.** G. Rakovski.

**1971.** 20th Anniv. of "Federation Internationale des Resistants".
2078. **644.** 2 s. multicoloured .. 15 10
2079. 13 s. multicoloured .. 1·10 25

**1971.** 150th Birth Anniv. of Georgi Rakovski (politician and Revolutionary).
2081. **646.** 13 s. brn., cream & green .. .. 35 15

**647.** Worker and Banner ("People's Progress"). **648.** Pipkov and Music.

**1971.** 10th Bulgarian Communist Party Congress. Multicoloured.
2082. 1 s. Type **647** .. .. 10 10
2083. 2 s. Symbols of "Technical Progress" (horiz.) 10 10
2084. 12 s. Men clasping hands ("Bulgarian-Soviet Friendship") .. 1·00 20

**1971.** Birth Cent. of Panayot Pipokov.
2085. **648.** 13 s. black, green and silver .. .. 60 20

**649.** "Three Races". **650.** Mammoth.

**1971.** Racial Equality Year.
2086. **649.** 13 s. multicoloured .. 45 15

**1971.** Prehistoric Animals. Multicoloured.
2087. 1 s. Type **650** .. .. 10 10
2088. 2 s. Bear (vert.) .. .. 10 10
2089. 3 s. Hipparion .. .. 15 10
2090. 13 s. Mastodon .. .. 90 15
2091. 20 s. Dinotherium (vert.) 1·40 25
2092. 28 s. Sabre-toothed tiger 1·90 35

**651.** Facade of Ancient Building. **652.** Weights Emblem on Map of Europe.

**1971.** Ancient Buildings of Koprivshitsa.
2093. **651.** 1 s. grn., brn. & grn. 10 10
2094. – 2 s. brn., grn. & buff 10 10
2095. – 6 s. violet, brn. & blue 20 10
2096. – 13 s. red, blue & orge. 65 25
DESIGNS: 1 s. to 13 s. Different facades.

**1971.** 30th European Weightlifting Championships, Sofia. Multicoloured.
2097. 2 s. Type **652** .. .. 10 10
2098. 13 s. Figures supporting weights .. .. 80 20

653. Frontier Guard and Dog.

654. Tweezers, Magnifying Glass and "Stamp".

**1971.** 25th Anniv. of Frontier Guards.
2099. **653.** 2 s. ol., grn. & turq. 10 10

**1971.** 9th Congress of Bulgarian Philatelic Federation.
2100. **654.** 20 s.+10 s. brown, black and red .. .. 1·50 50

655. Congress Meeting (sculpture).

**1971.** 80th Anniv. of Bulgarian Social Democratic Party Congress, Buzludzha.
2101. **655.** 2 s. grn., cream & red 15 10

656. "Mother" (I. Nenov).

657. Factory, Botevgrad.

**1971.** Paintings from the National Art Gallery (1st series). Multicoloured.
2102. 1 s. Type **656** .. .. 10 10
2103. 2 s. "Lazorova" (S. Ivanov) .. .. 10 10
2104. 3 s. "Portrait of Yu. Kh." (C. Tsonev) .. 15 10
2105. 13 s. "Portrait of a Lady" (D. Uzunov).. 85 25
2106. 30 s. "Young Woman from Kalotina" (V. Dimitrov) .. .. 1·10 35
2107. 40 s. "Goryanin" (S. Venev).. .. .. 2·00 60
See also Nos. 2145/50.

**1971.** Industrial Buildings.
2108. **657.** 1 s. violet .. .. 10 10
2109. – 2 s. red .. .. 10 10
2110. – 10 s. violet .. .. 25 10
2111. – 13 s. red .. .. 30 15
2112. – 40 s. brown .. .. 1·40 15
DESIGNS—VERT. 2 s. Petro-chemical plant, Pleven. HORIZ. 10 s. Chemical works, Vratsa. 13 s. "Maritsa-Istok" plant, Dimitrovgrad. 40 s. Electronics factory, Sofia.

658. Free Style Wrestling.

659. Posthorn Emblem.

**1971.** European Wrestling Championships, Sofia.
2113. **658.** 2 s. grn., blk. and blue 10 10
2114. – 13 s. blk., red & blue 85 25
DESIGN: 13 s. Greco-Roman wrestling.

**1971.** Organization of Socialist Countries' Postal Administrations Congress.
2115. **659.** 20 s. gold and green 65 25

660 Entwined Ribbons.

**1971.** 7th European Biochemical Congress, Varna.
2116. **660.** 13 s. red, brn. & blk. 65 25

661. "New Republic" Statue.

662. Cross-country Skiing.

**1971.** 25th Anniv. of People's Republic.
2117. **661.** 2 s. red, yell. & gold 10 10
2118. – 13 s. grn., red & gold 50 20
DESIGN: 13 s. Bulgarian flag.

**1971.** Winter Olympic Games, Sapporo, Japan. Multicoloured.
2119. 1 s. Type **662** .. .. 10 10
2120. 2 s. Downhill skiing .. 10 10
2121. 3 s. Ski-jumping .. 10 10
2122. 4 s. Figure-skating .. 15 10
2123. 13 s. Ice-hockey .. 85 40
2124. 28 s. Slalom skiing .. 1·50 40

663. Brigade Members.

664. U.N.E.S.C.O. Emblem and Wreath.

**1971.** 25th Anniv. of Youth Brigades Movement.
2126. **663.** 2 s. blue .. .. 15 10

**1971.** 25th Anniv. of U.N.E.S.C.O.
2127. **664.** 20 s. multicoloured .. 85 25

665. "The Footballer".

**1971.** Paintings by Kiril Tsonev. Mult.
2128. 1 s. Type **665** .. .. 10 10
2129. 2 s. "Landscape" (horiz.) 10 10
2130. 3 s. Self-portrait .. 25 10
2131. 13 s. "Lilies" .. .. 60 20
2132. 20 s. "Woodland Scene" (horiz.) .. .. 1·10 30
2133. 40 s. "Portrait of a Young Woman" .. .. 1·90 40

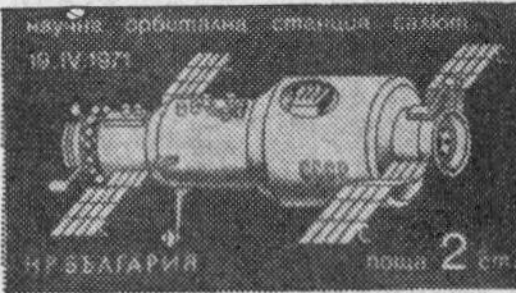


666. "Salyut" Space-station.

**1971.** Space Flights of "Salyut" and "Soyuz 11". Multicoloured.
2134. 2 s. Type **666** .. .. 10 10
2135. 13 s. "Soyuz 11" .. 40 15
2136. 40 s. "Salyut" and "Soyuz 11" joined together .. 1·90 45

667. Ore Carrier "Vikhren".

**1972.** "One Million Tons of Bulgarian Shipping".
2138. **667.** 18 s. lilac, red & blk. 1·25 20

---

## MINIMUM PRICE

The minimum price quoted is 10p which represents a handling charge rather than a basis for valuing common stamps. For further notes about prices see introductory pages.

---

668. Gotse Delchev.

**1972.** Bulgarian Patriots' Birth Cents. Centenary year in brackets.
2139. **668.** 2 s. black and red .. 10 10
2140. – 5 s. black and green 10 10
2141. – 13 s. black and yell. 45 15
PATRIOTS: 5 s. J. Sandanski (1972). 13 s. D. Gruev (1971).

669. Gymnast with Ball.

**1972.** World Gymnastics Championships, Havana (Cuba). Multicoloured.
2142. 13 s. Type **669** .. .. 85 15
2143. 18 s. Gymnast with hoop 1·00 25

**1972.** Paintings in Bulgarian National Gallery (2nd series). As T **656** but horiz. Multicoloured.
2145. 1 s. "Melnik" (Mladenov) 10 10
2146. 2 s. "Ploughman" (Georgiev) .. .. 10 10
2147. 3 s. "By the Death-bed" (Zhendov) .. .. 20 10
2148. 13 s. "Family" (Dimitrov) .. .. 85 15
2149. 20 s. "Family" (Balkanski) .. .. 1·40 25
2150. 40 s. "Paisi" (Denchev) 2·00 65

670. Bulgarian Worker.

671. "Singing Harvesters" (V. Dimitrov).

**1972.** 7th Bulgarian Trade Unions Congress.
2151. **670.** 13 s. multicoloured .. 35 15

**1972.** 90th Birth Anniv. of Vladimir Dimitrov (painter). Multicoloured
2152. 1 s. Type **671** .. 10 10
2153. 2 s. "Farm Worker" .. 10 10
2154. 3 s. "Women Cultivators" (horiz.) .. .. 25 10
2155. 13 s. "Peasant Girl" (horiz.) .. .. 70 10
2156. 20 s. "My Mother" .. 1·10 30
2157. 40 s. Self-portrait .. 2·00 40

672. Heart and Tree Emblem.

673. St. Mark's Cathedral.

**1972.** World Heart Month.
2158. **672.** 13 s. multicoloured .. 1·10 50

**1972.** U.N.E.S.C.O. "Save Venice" Campaign.
2159. **673.** 2 s. grn., turq. & blue 10 10
2160. – 13 s. brn., violet & grn. 70 20
DESIGN: 13 s. Doge's Palace.

674. Dimitrov and Printing-press.

**1972.** 90th Birth Anniv. of Georgi Dimitrov (statesman). Multicoloured.
2161. 1 s. Type **674** .. .. 10 10
2162. 2 s. Dimitrov leading uprising of 1923.. .. 10 10
2163. 3 s. Dimitrov at Leipzig Trial .. .. .. 10 10
2164. 5 s. Dimitrov addressing workers .. .. 15 10
2165. 13 s. Dimitrov with Bulgarian crowd .. 25 20
2166. 18 s. Addressing young people .. .. 1·00 15
2167. 28 s. Dimitrov with children .. .. 1·25 25
2168. 40 s. Dimitrov's mausoleum 2·00 60
2169. 80 s. Portrait head (green and gold) .. .. 5·75 1·25
2173. 80 s. As No. 2169 .. 10·00 10·00
No. 2173 has the centre in red and gold, and is imperforate.

675. "Lamp of Learning" and Quotation.

**1972.** Father Paissi (monastic historian). 250th Birth Anniv.
2171. **675.** 2 s. brn., grn. & gold 15 10
2172. – 13 s. brn., grn. & gold 85 20
DESIGN: 13 s. Paissi writing.

676. Canoeing.

**1972.** Olympic Games, Munich. Multicoloured.
2174. 1 s. Type **676** .. .. 10 10
2175. 2 s. Gymnastics .. .. 10 10
2176. 3 s. Swimming .. .. 10 10
2177. 13 s. Volleyball .. .. 35 15
2178. 18 s. Hurdling .. .. 85 25
2179. 40 s. Wrestling .. .. 1·50 45

677. Angel Kunchev.

**1972.** Death Cent. of Angel Kunchev (patriot).
2181. **677.** 2 s. mve., gold & pur. 15 10

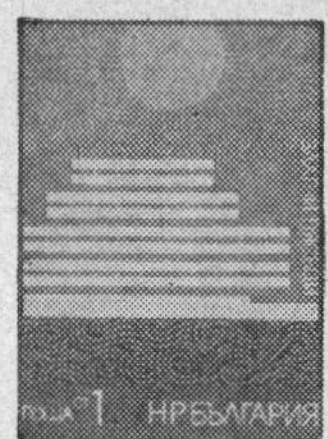


678. "Golden Sands".

**1972.** Black Sea Resorts. Hotels. Mult.
2182. 1 s. Type **678** .. .. 10 10
2183. 2 s. Druzhba .. .. 10 10
2184. 3 s. "Sunny Beach" .. 10 10
2185. 13 s. Primorsko .. .. 25 15
2186. 28 s. Rusalka .. .. 1·00 30
2187. 40 s. Albena .. .. 1·40 40

679. Canoeing (Bronze Medal).

**1972.** Bulgarian Medal Winners, Olympic Games, Munich. Multicoloured.
2188. 1 s. Type **679** .. 10 10
2189. 2 s. Long jumping (Silver Medal) .. 15 10
2190. 3 s. Boxing (Gold Medal) .. .. 15 10
2191. 18 s. Wrestling (Gold Medal) .. .. 1·00 30
2192. 40 s. Weightlifting (Gold Medal) .. 1·60 40

680. Subi Dimitrov.

682. " Lilium rhodopaeum ".

681. Commemorative Text.

**1972.** Resistance Heroes. Multicoloured.
2193. 1 s. Type **680** .. .. 10 10
2194. 2 s. T. Radoinov .. .. 10 10
2195. 3 s. Y. Lyutibrodski .. 10 10
2196. 5 s. M. Ganev .. .. 10 10
2197. 13 s. N. Nikolov .. 35 15

**1972.** 50th Anniv. of U.S.S.R.
2198. **681.** 13 s. red, yellow & gold .. .. 60 15

**1972.** Protected Flowers. Multicoloured.
2199. 1 s. Type **682** .. .. 10 10
2200. 2 s. " Gentiana pneumonanthe " .. 10 10
2201. 3 s. " Pancratium maritimum " .. .. 15 10
2202. 4 s. " Trollius europaeus " 20 10
2203. 18 s. " Primula frondosa " 70 25
2204. 23 s. " Pulsatilla vernalis " .. .. 1·00 35
2205. 40 s. " Fritillaria stribrnyi " .. .. 2·00 60

СВЕТОВЕН ПЪРВЕНЕЦ

(683.) 684. Dobri Chintulov.

**1972.** " Bulgaria, World Weightlifting Champions ". No. 2192 optd. with T **683**.
2206. 40 s. multicoloured .. 1·90 55

**1972.** 150th Birth Anniv. of Dobri Chintulov.
2207. **684.** 2 s. multicoloured .. 20 10

685. Forehead Ornament (19th-century).
686. Divers with Cameras.

**1972.** Antique Ornaments.
2208. **685.** 1 s. black and brown 10 10
2209. – 2 s. black and green 10 10
2210. – 3 s. black and blue .. 10 10
2211. – 8 s. black and red .. 25 10
2212. – 23 s. black and brown 75 30
2213. – 40 s. black and violet 1·40 85
DESIGNS: 2 s. Belt-buckle (19th-century). 3 s. Amulet (18th-century). 8 s. Pendant (18th-century). 23 s. Earrings (14th-century). 40 s. Necklace (18th-century).

**1973.** Underwater Research in the Black Sea.
2214. **686.** 1 s. blk., yell. and blue 10 10
2215. – 2 s. blk., yell. and blue 10 10
2216. – 18 s. blk., yell. & blue 85 35
2217. – 40 s. blk., yell. & blue 1·40 55
DESIGNS—HORIZ. 2 s. Divers with underwater research vessel "Shelf 1". VERT. 18 s. Diver and "NIV 100" diving bell. 40 s. Lifting balloon.

687. " The Hanging of Vasil Levski " (B. Angelushev).
688. Elhovo Mask.

**1973.** Death Cent. of Vasil Levski (patriot).
2219. **687.** 2 s green and red .. 10 10
2220. – 20 s. brn., cream & green .. .. 1·50 40
DESIGN: 20 s. "Vasil Levski" (G. Danchov).

**1973.** Koukeris' Festival Masks. Mult.
2221. 1 a. Type **688** .. .. 10 10
2222. 2 s. Breznik .. .. 10 10
2223. 3 s. Khisar .. .. 10 10
2224. 13 s. Radomir .. .. 35 15
2225. 20 s. Karnobat .. .. 40 25
2226. 40 s. Pernik .. .. 4·25 3·25

689. Copernicus. 690. Vietnamese "girl".

**1973.** 500th Birth Anniv. of Copernicus.
2227. **689.** 28 s. pur., blk. & brn. 2·00 1·00

**1973.** Vietnam Peace Treaty.
2229. **690.** 18 s. multicoloured .. 40 15

691. Poppy. 692. C. Botev (T. Todorov).

**1973.** Wild Flowers. Multicoloured.
2231. 1 s. Type **691** .. .. 10 10
2232. 2 s. Marguerite .. .. 10 10
2233. 3 s. Peony .. .. 15 10
2234. 13 s. Centaury .. .. 40 15
2235. 18 s. Corn-cockle .. 4·75 2·75
2236. 28 s. Ranunculas .. 1·25 65

**1973.** 125th Birth Anniv. of Christo Botev.
2237. **692.** 2 s. yellow, brown and green .. .. 15 10
2238. 18 s. green, pale green and brown .. 1·10 65

693. Asen Khalachev and insurgents.

**1973.** 50th Anniv. of June Uprising.
2239. **693.** 1 s. blk., red and gold 10 10
2240. – 2 s. blk., orge. & gold 10 10
DESIGNS: 2 s. Crawling Worker, ("September", B. Angelushev).

694. A. Stamboliisky (from sculpture by A. Nikolov).

**1973.** 50th Death Anniv. of Alexander Stamboliisky.
2241. **694.** 18 s. light-brown, brown and orange 40 30
2242. 18 s. orange .. .. 4·50 3·25

695. Muskrat.

**1973.** Bulgarian Fauna. Multicoloured.
2243. 1 s. Type **695** .. .. 10 10
2244. 2 s. Racoon-dog .. .. 10 10
2245. 3 s. Mouflon (vert.) .. 15 10
2246. 12 s. Fallow deer (vert.) 45 25
2247. 18 s. European bison 1·00 65
2248. 40 s. Elk .. .. 4·25 2·75

696. Tirnovo. 698. Congress Emblem.

697. Insurgents on the March (B. Angelushev).

**1973.** Air. Tourism. Views of Bulgarian Towns and Cities. Multicoloured.
2249. 2 s. Type **696** .. .. 10 10
2250. 13 s. Rusalka .. .. 30 15
2251. 20 s. Plovdiv .. .. 2·75 2·10
2252. 28 s. Sofia .. .. 80 55

**1973.** 50th Anniv. of September Uprising.
2253. **697.** 2 s. multicoloured .. 10 10
2254. 5 s. violet, pink & lake 40 15
2255. 13 s. multicoloured .. 35 15
2256. 18 s. olive, cream & lake 1·40 1·00
DESIGNS—HORIZ. 5 s. " Armed Train " (B. Angelushev). VERT. 13 s. Patriotic poster by N. Mirchev. HORIZ. 18 s. Georgi Dimitrov and Vasil Kolarov.

**1973.** 8th World Trade Union Congress, Varna.
2257. **698.** 2 s. multicoloured .. 10 10

699. " Sun " Emblem and Olympic Rings. 700. "Prince Kaloyan".

**1973.** Olympic Congress, Varna. Mult.
2258. 13 s. Type **699** .. 1·40 50
2259. 28 s. Lion Emblem of Bulgarian Olympic Committee (vert.) .. .. 2·00 1·00

**1973.** Fresco Portraits, Boyana Church. Multicoloured.
2261. 1 s. Type **700** .. .. 10 10
2262. 2 s. " Desislava " .. 15 10
2263. 3 s. " Saint " .. .. 20 10
2264. 5 s. " St. Eustratius " .. 25 10
2265. 10 s. " Tsar Constantine-Asen " .. .. 75 35
2266. 13 s. " Deacon Laurentius " 1·00 50
2267. 18 s. " Virgin Mary " .. 1·40 55
2268. 20 s. " St. Ephraim " .. 1·50 65
2269. 28 s. " Jesus Christ " .. 5·00 1·40

701. Smirnenski and Cavalry Charge.

**1973.** 75th Birth Anniv. of Christo Smirnenski (poet and revolutionary).
2271. **701.** 1 s. blue, red and gold 10 10
2272. 2 s. blue, red and gold 25 10

702. Human Rights Emblem. 704. " Finn " Class Yacht.

703. Tsar Todor Svetoslav meeting the Byzantine Embassy, 1307.

**1973.** 25th Anniv. of Declaration of Human Rights.
2273. **702.** 13 s. gold, red and blue 35 25

**1973.** Bulgarian History. Multicoloured.
2274. 1 s. Type **703** .. .. 10 10
2275. 2 s. Tsar Mikhail Shishman in battle against Byzantines, 1328 .. 10 10
2276. 3 s. Battle of Rosokastro, 1332, and Tsar, Ivan Alexander .. 15 10
2277. 4 s. Defence of Tirnovo, 1393 and Patriarch Evtimi .. .. 10 10
2278. 5 s. Tsar Ivan Shisman's attack on the Turks .. 10 10
2279. 13 s. Momchil attacks Turkish ships at Umur, 1344 .. .. 50 15
2280. 18 s. Meeting of Tsar Ivan Sratsimir and Crusaders, 1396 .. 65 20
2281. 28 s. Embassy of Empress Anne of Savoy meets Boyar Balik .. .. 2·00 1·40

**1973.** Sailing. Various Yachts. Multicoloured.
2282. 1 s. Type **704** .. .. 10 10
2283. 2 s. " Flying Dutchman " class .. .. 10 10
2284. 3 s. " Soling " class .. 10 10
2285. 13 s. " Tempest " class 50 10
2286. 20 s. " 470 " class .. 75 35
2287. 40 s. " Tornado " class .. 3·50 2·00

705. " Balchik " (B. Obreshkov).

**1973.** 25th Anniv. of National Art Gallery, Sofia and 150th Birth Anniv. of Stanislav Dospevski (painter). Multicoloured.
2288. 1 s. Type **705** .. .. 10 10
2289. 2 s. " Mother and Child " (S. Venev) .. .. 10 10
2290. 3 s. " Rest " (Ts. Boyadzhiev) .. .. 10 10
2291. 13 s. " Vase with Flowers " (S. Skitnik) (vert.) .. 60 15
2292. 18 s. " Mary Kuneva " (I. Petrov) (vert.) .. 65 20
2293. 40 s. " Winter in Plovdiv " (Z. Boyadzhiev) (vert.) 3·75 2·50



707. Old Testament Scene. (Wood-carving).

**1974.** Wood-Carvings from Rozhen Monastery.
2296. **707.** 1 s. dark brn., cream and brown .. 10 10
2297. – 2 s. dark brown, cream and brown .. 10 10
2298. – 3 s. dark brown, cream and brown .. 15 10
2299. – 5 s. olive, cream & grn. 15 10
2300. – 8 s. olive, cream & grn. 20 20
2301. – 13 s. brn., cream and chestnut .. .. 40 30
2302. – 28 s. brn., cream and chestnut .. .. 1·00 75
DESIGNS: No. 2296/8, " Passover Table ". No. 2299/2300, " Abraham and the Angel ". No. 2301/2, " The Expulsion from Eden ".
Nos. 2296/8, 2299/300 and 2301/2 form three composite designs.

708. " Lenin " (N. Mirchev).

**1974.** 50th Death Anniv. of Lenin. Mult.
2303. 2 s. Type **708** 10 10
2304. 18 s. "Lenin with Workers" (W. A. Serov) 85 25

**709.** "Blagoev addressing Meeting" (G. Kovachev).

**1974.** 50th Death Anniv. of D. Blagoev (founder of Bulgarian Communist Party).
2305. **709.** 2 s. multicoloured 15 10

**710.** Sheep.

**1974.** Domestic Animals.
2306. **710.** 1 s. brn., buff & grn. 10 10
2307. – 2 s. pur., vio. & red 10 10
2308. – 3 s. brn., pink & grn. 10 10
2309. – 5 s. brn., buff & blue 15 10
2310. – 13 s. blk., bl. & brn. 30 15
2311. – 20 s. brn., pink & blue 1·90 80
DESIGNS: 2. s. Goat. 3 s. Pig. 5 s. Cow. 13 s. Buffalo. 20 s. Horse.

**711.** Social Economic Integration Emblem.

**1974.** 25th Anniv. of Council for Mutual Economic Aid.
2312. **711.** 13 s. multicoloured 65 15

**712.** Footballers.

**1974.** World Cup Football Championship.
2313. **712.** 1 s. multicoloured 10 10
2314. – 2 s. multicoloured 10 10
2315. – 3 s. multicoloured 15 10
2316. – 13 s. multicoloured 50 10
2317. – 28 s. multicoloured 85 25
2318. – 40 s. multicoloured 2·75 1·60
DESIGNS: Nos. 2314/18, various designs similar to Type **712**.

**713.** Folk-singers. **714.** "Cosmic Research" (P. Barnbov).

**1974.** Amateur Arts and Sports Festival. Multicoloured.
2320. 1 s. Type **713** 10 10
2321. 2 s. Folk-dancers 10 10
2322. 3 s. Piper and drummer 10 10
2323. 5 s. Wrestling 10 10
2324. 13 s. Athletics 1·00 80
2325. 18 s. Gymnastics 55 20

**1974.** "Mladost '74" Youth Stamp Exhibition, Sofia. Multicoloured.
2326. 1 s. Type **714** 10 10
2327. 2 s. "Salt Production" (M. Bliznakaa) 10 10
2328. 3 s. "Fire-dancer" (D. Lalova) 10 10
2329. 28 s. "Friendship" (V. Boyanova) 3·00 2·00

**715.** Motor-cars.

**1974.** World Automobile Federation's Spring Congress, Sofia.
2331. **715.** 13 s. multicoloured 30 20

**716.** Period Architecture.

**1974.** U.N.E.S.C.O. Executive Council's 94th Session, Varna.
2332. **716.** 18 s. multicoloured 30 20

**717.** Chinese Aster.

**1974.** Bulgarian Flowers. Multicoloured.
2333. 1 s. Type **717** 10 10
2334. 2 s. Mallow 10 10
2335. 3 s. Columbine 15 10
2336. 18 s. Tulip 65 15
2337. 20 s. Marigold 85 20
2338. 28 s. Pansy 2·40 1·10

**718.** 19th Century Post-boy.

**1974.** Cent. of Universal Postal Union.
2340. **718.** 2 s. vio. & blk. on orge. 10 10
2341. – 18 s. grn. & blk. on orge. 50 25
DESIGN: 18 s. First Bulgarian mail-coach.

**719.** Young Pioneer and Komsomol Girl. **720.** Communist soldiers with Flag.

**1974.** 30th Anniv. of Dimitrov's Septembrist Pioneers Organization. Multicoloured.
2343. 1 s. Type **719** 10 10
2344. 2 s. Pioneer with doves 10 10

**1974.** 30th Anniv. of Fatherland Front Government. Multicoloured.
2346. 1 s. Type **720** 10 10
2347. 2 s. "Soviet Liberators" 10 10
2348. 5 s. "Industrialisation" 15 10
2349. 13 s. "Modern Agriculture" 20 10
2350. 18 s. "Science and Technology" 75 40

**722.** Gymnast on Beam. **724.** Envelope with arrow pointing to Postal Code.

**1974.** 18th World Gymnastic Championships, Varna. Multicoloured.
2352. 2 s. Type **722** 10 10
2353. 13 s. Gymnast on horse 40 25

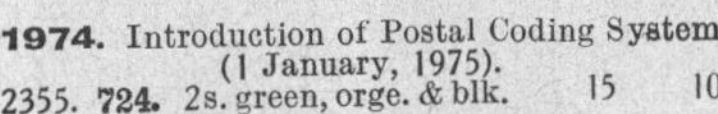

**1974.** Introduction of Postal Coding System (1 January, 1975).
2355. **724.** 2s. green, orge. & blk. 15 10

**725.** "Sourovachka" (twig decorated with coloured ribbons).

**1974.** New Year.
2356. **725.** 2 s. multicoloured 15 10

**726.** Icon of St. Theodore. **727.** Apricot.

**1974.** Bulgarian History.
2357. **726.** 1 s. multicoloured 10 10
2358. – 2 s. grey, mve. & blk. 10 10
2359. – 3 s. grey, blue & blk. 10 10
2360. – 5 s. grey, lilac & blk. 10 10
2361. – 8 s. black, buff & brn. 20 10
2362. – 13 s. grey, grn. & blk. 25 15
2363. – 18 s. blk., gold & red 35 20
2364. – 28 s. grey, blue & blk. 1·90 1·50
DESIGNS: 2 s. Bronze medallion. 3 s. Carved capital. 5 s. Silver bowl of Sivin Jupan. 8 s. Clay goblet. 13 s. Lioness (torso). 18 s. Gold tray. 28 s. Double-headed eagle.

**1975.** Fruit-tree Blossoms. Multicoloured.
2365. 1 s. Type **727** 10 10
2366. 2 s. Apple 10 10
2367. 3 s. Cherry 10 10
2368. 19 s. Pear 35 15
2369. 28 s. Peach 1·10 50

**730.** Star and Arrow. **731.** "Weights and Measures".

**1975.** 30th Anniv. of "Victory in Europe" Day.
2372. **730.** 2 s. red, blk. & brn. 10 10
2373. – 13 s. blk., brn. & blue 35 20
DESIGNS: 13 s. Peace dove and broken sword.

**1975.** Centenary of Metre Convention.
2374. **731.** 13 s. violet, black & silver 20 15

**732.** Tree and open book.

**1975.** 50th Anniv. of Forestry School.
2375. **732.** 2 s. multicoloured 10 10

**733.** Michelangelo. **734.** Festival Emblem.

**1975.** 500th Birth Anniv. of Michelangelo.
2376. **733.** 2 s. purple and blue 10 10
2377. – 13 s. violet and purple 30 10
2378. – 18 s. brown and green 85 15
DESIGNS—HORIZ. Sculptures from Giuliano de Medici's tomb: 13 s. "Night". 18 s. "Day".

**1975.** Festival of Humour and Satire, Gabrovo.
2380. **734.** 2 s. multicoloured 10 10

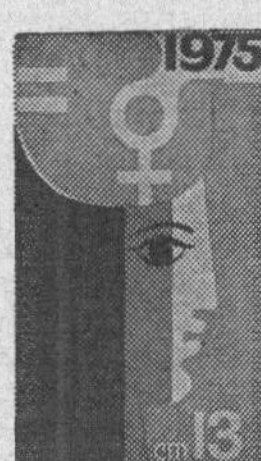

**735.** Women's Head and Emblem.

**1975.** International Women's Year.
2381. **735.** 13 s. multicoloured 20 15

**736.** Vasil and Sava Kokareshkov.

**1975.** "Young Martyrs to Fascism".
2382. **736.** 1 s. blk., grn. & gold 10 10
2383. – 2 s. blk., mve. & gold 10 10
2384. – 5 s. blk., red & gold 15 10
2385. – 13 s. blk., bl. & gold 35 35
DESIGNS—HORIZ: 2 s. Mitko Palauzov and Ivan Vasilev. 5 s. Nikola Nakev and Stefcho Kraychev. 13 s. Ivanka Pashkolouva and Detelina Mincheva.

**737.** "Mother feeding Child" (Millais). **738.** Gabrovo Costume.

**1975.** World Graphics Exhibition, Sofia. Celebrated Drawings and Engravings. Mult.
2386. 1 s. Type **737** 10 10
2387. 2 s. "Mourning a Dead Daughter" (Goya) 10 10
2388. 3 s. "The Reunion" (Beshkov) 10 10
2389. 13 s. "Seated Nude" (Renoir) 20 10
2390. 20 s. "Man in a Fur Hat" (Rembrandt) 50 15
2391. 40 s. "The Dream" (Daumier) (horiz.) 2·00 45

**1975.** Women's Regional Costumes. Mult.
2393. 2 s. Type **738** 10 10
2394. 3 s. Trin Costume 10 10
2395. 5 s. Vidin Costume 10 10
2396. 13 s. Gotse Delchev Costume 65 20
2397. 18 s. Ruse Costume 1·40 35

**739.** "Bird" (manuscript illumination). **740.** Ivan Vasov.

**1975.** Original Bulgarian Manuscripts. Mult.
2398. 1 s. Type **739** 10 10
2399. 2 s. "Head" 10 10
2400. 3 s. Abstract design 10 10
2401. 8 s. "Pointing finger" 10 10
2402. 13 s. "Imaginary creature" 50 10
2403. 18 s. Abstract design 1·10 35

**1975.** 125th Anniv. of Ivan Vasov (writer). Multicoloured.
2404. 2 s. Type **740** 10 10
2405. 13 s. Vasov seated 20 15

**741.** "Soyuz" and Leonov.

**1975.** "Apollo-Soyuz" Space Link. Mult.
2406. 13 s. Type **741** 50 10
2407. 18 s. "Apollo" and Stafford 65 10
2408. 28 s. Linking manoeuvre 1·60 40

**742.** Ryukyu Sailing Boat, Map and Emblems.

**1975.** International Exposition, Okinawa.
2410. **742.** 13 s. multicoloured 20 10

**743.** St. Cyril and St. Methodius. **744.** Footballer.

**1975.** " Balkanphila V " Stamp Exhibition, Sofia.
2411. **743.** 2 s. brn., lt. brn. & red .. 10 10
2412. – 13 s. brn., lt. brn. & grn. 25 15
DESIGN: 13 s. St. Constantine and St. Helene.

**1975.** 8th Inter-Toto (Football Pools) Congress, Varna.
2414. **744.** 2 s. multicoloured .. 10 10

**745.** " Acherontia atropos ".

**1975.** Moths. Multicoloured.
2415. 1 s. Type **745** .. .. 10 10
2416. 2 s. " Daphnis neri " .. 10 10
2417. 3 s. " Smerinthus ocellata " 10 10
2418. 10 s. " Deilaphila nicea " 15 10
2419. 13 s. " Choerocampa elpenor " .. .. 50 20
2420. 18 s. " Macroglossum fuciformis " .. 95 40

**746.** U.N. Emblem. **747.** Map of Europe on Peace Dove.

**1975.** 30th Anniv. of U.N.O.
2421. **746.** 13 s. red, brn. & blk. 20 10

**1975.** European Security and Co-operation Conference, Helsinki.
2422. **747.** 18 s. lilac, blue & yell. 60 60

**748.** D. Khristov.

**1975.** Birth Cent. of Dobri Khristov (composer).
2423. **748.** 5 s. brn., yell. & grn. 15 10

**749.** Constantine's Rebellion against the Turks.

**1975.** Bulgarian History. Multicoloured.
2424. 1 s. Type **749** .. .. 10 10
2425. 2 s. Vladislav III's campaign .. .. 10 10
2426. 3 s. Battle of Tirnovo .. 10 10
2427. 10 s. Battle of Chiprovtsi 15 10
2428. 13 s. 17th-century partisans .. .. 50 20
2429. 18 s. Return of banished peasants .. .. 70 40

**750.** " First Aid ".

**1975.** 90th Anniv. of Bulgarian Red Cross.
2430. **750.** 2 s. brn., blk. and red 10 10
2431. – 13 s. grn., blk. & red 35 10
DESIGN: 13 s. " Peace and international Co-operation ".

**751.** Ethnographical Museum, Plovdiv.

**1975.** European Architectural Heritage Year.
2432. **751.** 80 s. brn., yell. & grn. 2·40 2·00

**752.** Christmas Lanterns.

**1975.** Christmas and New Year. Mult.
2433. 2 s. Type **752** .. .. 10 10
2434. 13 s. Stylised peace dove 15 20

**753.** Egyptian Galley.

**1975.** Historic Ships (1st series). Multicoloured.
2435 1 s. Type **753** .. .. 10 10
2436 2 s. Phoenician galley .. 10 10
2437 3 s. Greek trireme .. 10 10
2438 5 s. Roman galley .. 10 10
2439 13 s. "Mora" (Norman ship) .. .. .. 40 10
2440 18 s. Venetian galley .. 75 45
See also Nos. 2597/2602, 2864/9, 3286/91 and 3372/7.

**754.** Modern Articulated Tram-car.

**1976.** 75th Anniv. of Sofia Tramways. Mult.
2441. 2 s. Type **754** .. .. 20 10
2442. 13 s. Early 20th-century tram-car .. .. 65 30

**755.** Skiing.

**1976.** Winter Olympic Games, Innsbruck. Multicoloured.
2443. 1 s. Type **755** .. .. 10 10
2444. 2 s. Cross-country skiing (vert.) .. .. .. 10 10
2445. 2 s. Ski-jumping .. 15 10
2446. 13 s. Biathlon (vert.) .. 15 25
2447. 18 s. Ice-hockey (vert.) .. 65 25
2448. 18 s. Speed-skating (vert.) 1·40 45

**756.** Stylised Bird.

**1976.** 11th Bulgarian Communists Party Congress. Multicoloured.
2450. 2 s. Type **756** .. .. 10 10
2451. 5 s. " 1956–1976, Fulfilment of the Five Year Plans " .. .. 10 10
2452. 13 s. Hammer and Sickle 35 15

**757.** Alexander Graham Bell and early Telephone.

**1976.** Telephone Centenary.
2454. **757.** 18 s. light brown, brown and purple .. 35 20

**758.** Mute Swan.

**1976.** Waterfowl. Multicoloured.
2455. 1 s. Type **758** .. .. 10 10
2456. 2 s. Ruddy Shelduck .. 15 10
2457. 3 s. Common Shelduck .. 30 15
2458. 5 s. Garganey .. .. 45 20
2459. 13 s. Mallard .. .. 1·00 30
2460. 18 s. Red-crested Pochard 2·10 80

**759.** Guerillas' Briefing.

**1976.** Cent. of April Uprising. Multicoloured.
2461. 1 s. Type **759** .. .. 10 10
2462. 2 s. Peasants briefing .. 10 10
2463. 5 s. Krishina, horse and guard .. .. .. 10 10
2464. 13 s. Rebels with cannon 30 20

**760.** New Industrial Building Complex.

**1976.** Modern Industrial Installations.
2465. **760.** 5 s. green .. .. 15 10
2466. – 8 s. red .. .. 25 10
2467. – 10 s. green .. .. 15 15
2468. – 13 s. violet .. .. 50 10
2469. – 20 s. green .. .. 65 15
DESIGNS: 8 s. Factory. 10 s. Office block. 13 s. Chemical works. 20 s. Saw-mill.

**761.** Guard with Patrol-dog.

**1976.** 30th Anniv. of Frontier Guards. Mult.
2470. 2 s. Type **761** .. .. 10 10
2471. 13 s. Mounted guards .. 25 15

**762.** Worker with Spade. **763.** Christo Botev.

**1976.** 30th Anniv. of Youth Brigades Movement.
2472. **762.** 2 s. multicoloured .. 15 10

**1976.** Death Cent. of Christo Botev (poet).
2473. **763.** 13 s. grn. & brn. .. 20 10

**764.** " Martyrs of First Congress " (relief). **765.** Dimitur Blagoev.

**1976.** 85th Anniv. of 1st Bulgarian Social Democratic Party Congress, Buzludzha. Multicoloured.
2474. 2 s. Type **764** .. .. 10 10
2475. 5 s. Modern memorial, Buzludzha Peak .. 10 10

**1976.** 120th Birth Anniv. of Dimitur Blagoev (socialist).
2476. **765.** 13 s. blk., red & gold 50 10

**767.** Children Playing.

**1976.** Child Welfare.
2478. **767.** 1 s. multicoloured .. 10 10
2479. – 2 s. multicoloured .. 10 10
2480. – 5 s. multicoloured .. 10 10
2481. – 23 s. multicoloured .. 75 25
DESIGNS: 2 s. Girls with pram and boy on rocking horse. 5 s. Playing ball. 23 s. Dancing.

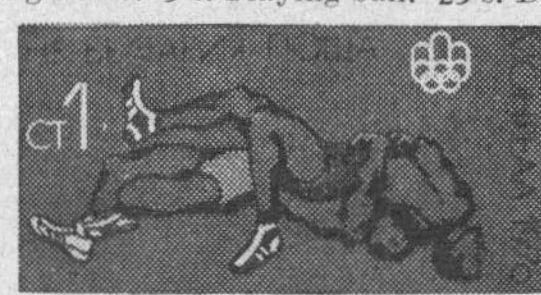

**768.** Wrestling.

**1976.** Olympic Games, Montreal. Mult.
2482. 1 s. Type **768** .. .. 10 10
2483. 2 s. Boxing .. .. 10 10
2484. 3 s. Weight-lifting .. 10 10
2485. 13 s. Canoeing .. 20 15
2486. 18 s. Gymnastics .. 30 10
2487. 28 s. Diving .. 75 20
2488. 40 s. Athletics .. .. 1·00 25
Nos. 2483/8 are vert.

**769.** Belt Buckle, Vidin. **772.** Fish on line.

**770.** " Partisans at Night " (Petrov).

**1976.** Thracian Art (8th-4th-Century BC). Multicoloured.
2490. 1 s. Type **769** .. .. 10 10
2491. 2 s. Brooch, Durzhanitsa 10 10
2492. 3 s. Mirror handle, Chukarka .. .. .. 10 10
2493. 5 s. Helmet cheek guard, Gurlo .. .. .. 15 10
2494. 13 s. Gold decoration, Orizovo .. .. 25 10
2495. 18 s. Decorated horse-harness, Brezovo .. 30 15
2496. 20 s. Greave, Mogilanska Mogila .. .. .. 65 20
2497. 28 s. Pendant, Bukovtsi 85 25

**1976.** Paintings by Iliya Petrov and Tsanko Lavrenov from the National Gallery. Multicoloured.
2498. 2 s. Type **770** .. .. 10 10
2499. 5 s. " Townscape " (Lavrenov) .. .. 10 10
2500. 13 s. " Seated Woman " (Petrov) .. .. 25 15
2501. 18 s. " Boy seated in chair " (Petrov) .. 65 25
2502. 28 s. " Old Plovdiv " (Lavrenov) .. .. 1·00 30
The 18 s. and 28 s. are vert.

**1976.** World Sports Fishing Congress, Varn.
2505. **772.** 5 s. multicoloured .. 20 10

**773.** " The Pianist ". **774.** St. Theodor.

**1976.** 75th Birth Anniv. of Alex Jhendov (caricaturist).
2506. **773.** 2 s. deep green, cream and green .. .. 10 10
2507. – 5 s. deep violet, violet and lilac .. .. 20 10
2508. – 13 s. blk., pink and red 30 15
DESIGNS: 5 s. " Trick or Treat ". 13 s. " The Leader ".

**1976.** Zemen Monastery. Frescoes. Mult.
2509. 2 s. Type **774** .. .. 10 10
2510. 3 s. St. Paul and Apostle 15 10
2511. 5 s. St. Joachim .. .. 10 10
2512. 13 s. Prophet Melchisadek 50 10
2513. 19 s. St. Porphyr us .. 65 15
2514. 28 s. Queen Doya .. 1·00 25

775. Legal Document. 776. " Aesculus hippocastanum ".

**1976.** 25th Anniv. of State Archives.
2516. **775.** 5 s. multicoloured .. 20 10

**1976.** Wild Flowers. Multicoloured.
2517 1 s. Type **776** .. .. 10 10
2518 2 s. "Potentilla fruticosa" .. 10 10
2519 5 s. "Ilex aquifolium" .. 10 10
2520 8 s. "Taxus baccata" .. 20 10
2521 13 s. "Daphne pontica" .. 20 15
2522 23 s. "Cercis siliquastrum" 1·00 30

777. Cloud over Sun.

**1976.** Protection of the Environment. Mult.
2523. 2 s. Cloud over Tree .. 10 10
2524. 18 s. Type **777** .. .. 35 15

778. Dimitur Polyanov.

**1976.** Birth Cent. of Dimitur Polyanov.
2525. **778.** 2 s. orange and lilac 15 10

779. Congress Emblem.

**1976.** 33rd Bulgarian People's Agrarian Union Congress. Multicoloured.
2526. 2 s. Type **779** .. .. 10 10
2527. 13 s. Flags .. .. 20 15

781. " Khristo Botev " (Zlatyu Boyad Zhiev).

**1976.** Centenary of April Uprising. Mult.
2529. 1 s. Type **781** .. .. 10 10
2530. 2 s. " Partisan carrying Cherrywood Cannon " (Iliya Petrov).. .. 10 10
2531. 3 s. " Necklace of Immortality " (Dechko Uzunov) 10 10
2532. 13 s. " April 1876 " (Georgi Popov) .. 25 10
2533. 18 s. " Partisans " (Stoyan Venev) .. .. .. 45 20

782. Tobacco Workers.

**1976.** 70th Birth Anniv. of Veselin Staikov (artist). Multicoloured.
2535. 1 s. Type **782** .. .. 10 10
2536. 2 s. " Melnik " .. .. 10 10
2537. 13 s. " Boat Builders ".. 35 15

783. " Snowflake ". 784. Zakhari Stojanov.

**1976.** New Year.
2538. **783.** 2 s. multicoloured .. 15 10

**1976.** 125th Anniv of Zakhari Stojanov.
2539 **784** 2 s. brown, red & gold 15 10

785. Bronze Coin of Septimus Severus.

**1977.** Roman Coins struck in Serdica. Multicoloured.
2540. 1 s. Type **785** .. .. 10 10
2541. 2 s. Bronze coin of Caracalla 10 10
2542. 13 s. Bronze coin of Caracalla (diff.) .. 25 10
2543. 18 s. Bronze coin of Caracalla (diff.) .. 30 15
2544. 23 s. Copper coin of Diocletian .. .. 85 30

786. Championships Emblem. 787. Congress Emblem.

**1977.** World Ski-Orienteering Championships.
2545. **786.** 13 s. blue, red and ultramarine .. 25 15

**1977.** Fifth Congress of Bulgarian Tourist Associations.
2546. **787.** 2 s. multicoloured .. 15 10

788. " Symphyandra wanneri ". 789. V. Kolarov.

**1977.** Mountain Flowers. Multicoloured.
2547. 1 s. Type **788** .. .. 10 10
2548. 2 s. " Petcovia orphanidea " .. .. 10 10
2549. 3 s. " Campanula lanatra " .. .. 15 10
2550. 13 s. " Campanula scutellata " .. .. 50 10
2551. 43 s. " Campanula trachelium " .. .. 1·50 30

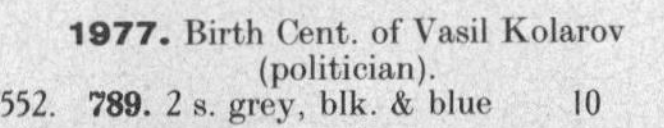

**1977.** Birth Cent. of Vasil Kolarov (politician).
2552. **789.** 2 s. grey, blk. & blue 10 10

790. Congress Emblem. 791. Joint.

**1977.** Eighth Bulgarian Trade Unions Congress.
2553. **790.** 2 s. multicoloured .. 15 10

**1977.** World Rheumatism Year.
2554. **791.** 23 s. multicoloured .. 45 20

792. Wrestling.

793. National Theatre. 794. Congress Emblem.

**1977.** World University Games, Sofia. Multicoloured.
2555. 2 s. Type **792** .. .. 10 10
2556. 13 s. Running .. .. 20 10
2557. 23 s. Handball .. .. 40 20
2558. 43 s. Gymnastics .. 1·40 60

**1977.** Buildings in Sofia. Pale brown backgrounds.
2559. **793.** 12 s. red .. .. 20 10
2560. – 13 s. brown .. .. 20 10
2561. – 23 s. blue .. .. 35 15
2562. – 30 s. green .. .. 75 20
2563. – 80 s. violet .. .. 1·75 55
2564. – 1 l. brown .. .. 2·40 95

DESIGNS: 13 s. Party Building. 23 s. People's Army Building. 30 s. Kliment Okhridski University. 80 s. National Art Gallery. 1 l. National Assembly Building.

**1977.** 13th Dimitrov Communist Youth League Congress.
2565. **794.** 2 s. red, green & gold 15 10

795. " St. Nicholas " Nesebur.

**1977.** Bulgarian Icons. Multicoloured.
2566. 1 s. Type **795** .. .. 10 10
2567. 2 s. " Old Testament Trinity ", Sofia .. 10 10
2568. 3 s. " The Royal Gates ", Veliko Tirnovo .. 10 10
2569. 5 s. " Deisis ", Nesebur 10 10
2570. 13 s. " St. Nicholas ", Elena .. .. 25 10
2571. 23 s. " The Presentation of the Blessed Virgin ", Rila Monastery .. 45 15
2572. 35 s. " The Virgin Mary with Infant ", Varna 85 30
2573. 40 s. " St. Demetrius on Horseback ", Provadya 2·75 45

796. Wolf.

**1977.** Wild Animals. Multicoloured.
2575. 1 s. Type **796** .. .. 10 10
2576. 2 s. Red fox .. .. 10 10
2577. 10 s. Weasel .. .. 30 10
2578. 13 s. Wild cat .. .. 35 15
2579. 23 s. Golden jackal .. 1·10 25

797. Congress Emblem. 798. " Crafty Peter riding a Donkey " (drawing by Iliya Beshkov).

**1977.** Third Bulgarian Culture Congress.
2580. **797.** 13 s. multicoloured .. 20 10

**1977.** 11th Festival of Humour and Satire, Gabrovo.
2581. **798.** 2 s. multicoloured .. 15 10

799. Congress Emblem. 800. Newspaper Masthead.

**1977.** Eighth Congress of the Popular Front, Sofia.
2582. **799.** 2 s. multicoloured .. 15 10

**1977.** Cent. of Bulgarian Daily Press.
2583. **800.** 2 s. multicoloured .. 15 10

802. Conference Emblem.

**1977.** International Writers Conference, Sofia.
2585. **802.** 23 s. bl., pale bl. & grn. 1·00 55

803. Map of Europe.

**1977.** 21st Congress of European Organization for Quality Control, Varna.
2586. **803.** 23 s. multicoloured .. 45 20

804. Basketball. 805. Weightlifter.

**1977.** Women's European Basketball Championships.
2587. **804.** 23 s. multicoloured .. 85 20

**1977.** World Junior Weightlifting Championships.
2588. **805.** 13 s. multicoloured .. 30 15

806. Georgi Dimitrov. 807. Tail Section of Tupolev " TU-154 ".

**1977.** 95th Birth Anniv. of Georgi Dimitrov (statesman).
2589. **806.** 13 s. brown and red 50 20

**1977.** Air. 30th Anniv. of Bulgarian Airline "Balkanair".
2590. **807.** 35 s. multicoloured .. 1·50 50

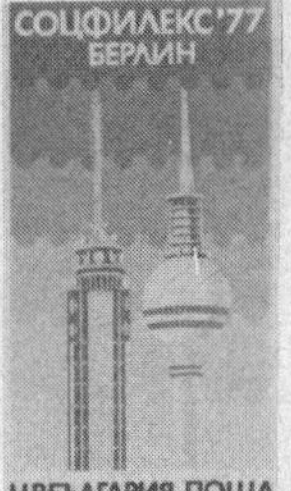

809. T.V. Towers, Berlin and Sofia. 810. Elin Pelin alias Dimitur Stoyanov (writer).

**1977.** "Sozphilex 77" Stamp Exhibition, East Berlin.
2592. **809.** 25 s. blue & deep blue 75 20

**1977.** Writers and Painters.
2593. **810.** 2 s. brown and gold .. 10 10
2594. – 5 s. olive and gold .. 10 10
2595. – 13 s. red and gold .. 20 10
2596. – 23 s. blue and gold .. 80 30
DESIGNS: 5 s. Peyo Kratscholov Yavorov (writer). 13 s. Boris Angelushev (painter and illustrator). 23 s. Iseno Todorov (painter).

**1977.** Historic Ships (2nd series). As T **753**. Multicoloured.
2597. 1 s. Hansa Kogge .. 10 10
2598. 2 s. "Santa Maria" .. 10 10
2599. 3 s. "Golden Hind" .. 10 10
2600. 12 s. Carrack "Santa Catherina" .. .. 30 10
2601. 13 s. Galleon "La Corona" .. .. 30 10
2602. 43 s. Mediterranean galley .. .. .. 1·10 40

**811.** Women Canoeists.

**1977.** World Canoe Championships.
2603. **811.** 2 s. blue and yellow .. 10 10
2604. – 23 s. blue & turquoise 45 20
DESIGN: 23 s. Men canoeists.

**812.** Balloon over Plovdiv. **813.** Presidents Zhivkov and Brezhnev.

**1977.** Air. 85th Anniv. "Panair" International Aviation exhibition. Plovdiv.
2605. **812.** 25 s. orange, yellow and brown .. 85 20

**1977.** Soviet-Bulgarian Friendship.
2606. **813.** 18 s. brn., red & gold 25 20

**814.** Conference Building.

**1977.** 64th International Parliamentary Conference, Sofia.
2607. **814.** 23 s. grn., pink & red 70 25

**815.** Newspaper Mastheads. **816.** "The Union of Earth and Water".

**1977.** 50th Anniv. of Official Newspaper "Rabotnichesko Delo" (Workers' Press).
2608. **815.** 2 s. red, green & grey 15 10

**1977.** 400th Birth Anniv. of Rubens. Mult.
2609. 13 s. Type **816** .. .. 50 10
2610. 23 s. "Venus and Adonis" (detail) .. .. 85 20
2611. 40 s. "Amorous Shepherd" (detail) .. .. 2·00 30

**817.** Cossack with Bulgarian Child (Angelushev). **818.** Albena, Black Sea.

**1977.** Centenary of Liberation from Turkey. (1978). Posters.
2613. **817.** 2 s. multicoloured .. 10 10
2614. – 13 s. grn., blue & red 25 10
2615. – 23 s. blue, red & grn. 50 20
2616. – 25 s. multicoloured .. 1·00 25
DESIGNS: 13 s. Bugler (Cheklarov). 23 s. Mars (god of war) and Russian soldiers (Petrov). 25 s. Flag of Russian Imperial Army.

**1977.** Tourism.
2617. **818.** 35 s. blue, turq. & brn. 1·25 40
2618. – 43 s. yell., grn. & blue 1·25 40
DESIGN: 43 s. Rila Monastery.

**819.** Dr. Nikolai Pirogov (Russian surgeon). **821.** Soviet Emblems and Decree.

**820.** Space walking.

**1977.** Cent. of Dr. Pirogov's Visit to Bulgaria.
2619. **819.** 13 s. brn., buff & grn. 20 10

**1977.** Air. 20th Anniv. of First Artificial Satellite. Multicoloured.
2620. 12 s. Type **820** .. .. 20 15
2621. 25 s. Space probe over Mars .. .. .. 65 20
2622. 35 s. Space probe "Venus-4" over Venus .. 1·10 30

**1977.** 60th Anniv. of Russian Revolution.
2623. **821.** 2 s. red, blk. & stone 10 10
2624. – 13 s. red and purple .. 20 10
2625. – 23 s. red and violet .. 75 15
DESIGNS: 13 s. Lenin. 23 s. "1977" as flame.

**822.** Diesel Train on Bridge.

**1977.** 50th Anniv. of Transport, Bridges and Highways Organization.
2626. **822.** 13 s. yellow, green and olive .. .. 45 10

**1977.** 150th Birth Anniv. of Petko Ratshev Slaveikov (poet). As T **810**.
2627. 8 s. brown and gold .. 20 15

**824.** Decorative Initials of New Year Greeting. **825.** Footballer.

**1977.** New Year. Multicoloured.
2628. 2 s. Type **824** .. .. 10 10
2629. 13 s. "Fireworks" .. .. 20 10

**1978.** World Cup Football Championship, Argentina. Multicoloured.
2630. 13 s. Type **825** .. .. 50 20
2631. 23 s. Shooting the ball .. 70 60

**826.** Baba Vida Fortress, Vidin.

**1977.** Air. "The Danube—European River". Multicoloured.
2633. 25 s. Type **826** .. .. 75 75
2634. 35 s. Friendship Bridge .. 80 80

**827.** Television Mast, Moscow. **829.** Red Cross in Laurel Wreath.

**1978.** 20th Anniv. of Organization of Socialist Postal Administrations (O.S.S.).
2635. **827.** 13 s. multicoloured .. 20 10

**1978.** Cent. of Bulgarian Red Cross.
2637. **829.** 25 s. red, brn. & blue 85 20

**830.** "XXX" formed from Bulgarian and Russian National Colours.

**1978.** 30th Anniv. of Bulgarian–Soviet Friendship.
2638. **830.** 2 s. multicoloured .. 15 10

**831.** Leo Tolstoy. **832.** Nikolai Roerich (artist).

**1978.** Famous Personalities.
2639. **831.** 2 s. green and yellow 10 10
2640. – 5 s. brown and bistre 10 10
2641. – 13 s. green and mauve 20 10
2642. – 23 s. brown and grey 35 20
2643. – 25 s. brown and green 40 20
2644. – 35 s. violet and blue .. 1·10 30
DESIGNS: 5 s. F. Dostoevsky. 13 s. I. Turgenev. 23 s. V. Vereshchagin. 25 s. Garibaldi. 35 s. Victor Hugo.

**1978.** Nikolai Roerich Exhibition, Sofia.
2645. **832.** 8 s. brown, grn. & red 20 10

**833.** Bulgarian Flag and Red Star.

**1978.** Communist Party National Conference, Sofia.
2646. **833.** 2 s. multicoloured .. 15 10

**834.** Goddess. **835.** "Spirit of Nature".

**1978.** "Philaserdica 79" International Stamp Exhibition (1st issue). Ancient Ceramics. Multicoloured.
2647. 2 s. Type **834** .. .. 10 10
2648. 5 s. Mask with beard .. 10 10
2649. 13 s. Decorated vase .. 25 15
2650. 23 s. Vase with scallop design .. .. .. 45 25
2651. 35 s. Head of Silenus .. 85 60
2652. 53 s. Cockerel .. .. 2·75 90
See also Nos. 2674/9, 2714/18, 2721/5 and 2753/4.

**1978.** Birth Cent. of A. Nikolov (sculptor).
2653. **835.** 13 s. blue, mauve and violet .. .. 20 10

**836.** Heart and Arrows.

**1978.** World Hypertension Month.
2654. **836.** 23 s. red, oran. & grey 45 15

**837.** "Kor Karoli" and Map of Route.

**1978.** Georgi Georgiev's World Voyage.
2655. **837.** 23 s. blue, mauve and green .. .. 55 25

**838.** Doves.

**1978.** 11th World Youth and Students, Festival, Havana.
2656. **838.** 13 s. multicoloured .. 20 10

**839.** "Portrait of a Young Man" (Durer). **840.** "Fritillaria stribrnyi".

**1978.** Paintings. Multicoloured.
2657. 13 s. Type **839** .. .. 20 10
2658. 23 s. "Bathsheba at the Fountain" (Rubens) .. 35 15
2659. 25 s. "Signor de Moret" (Hans Holbein the Younger) .. .. 35 15
2660. 35 s. "Self portrait with Saskia" (Rembrandt) 50 25
2661. 43 s. "Lady in Mourning" (Tintoretto) .. 60 30
2662. 60 s. "Old Man with a Beard" (Rembrandt) 1·10 40
2663. 80 s. "Man in Armour" (Van Dyck) .. .. 2·40 1·10

**1978.** Flowers. Multicoloured.
2664. 1 s. Type **840** .. .. 10 10
2665. 2 s. "Fritillaria drenovskyi" .. .. .. 10 10
2666. 3 s. "Lilium rhodopaeum" 10 10
2667. 13 s. "Tulipa urumoffii" 25 10
2668. 23 s. "Lilium jankae" 65 10
2669. 43 s. "Tulipa rhodopaea" 1·60 65

**841.** Varna.

**1978.** 63rd Esperanto Congress, Varna.
2670. **841.** 13 s. orange, red and green .. .. 50 25

## INDEX

Countries can be quickly located by referring to the index at the end of this volume.

842. Gotse Delchev.

**1978.** 75th Death Anniv. of Gotse Delchev (freedom fighter).
2671. 842. 13 s. multicoloured .. 20 10

843. Freedom Fighters.

**1978.** 75th Anniv. of Ilinden-Preobrazhenie Rising.
2672. 843. 5 s. black and red .. 15 10

845. " Market " (N. Petkov).

**1978.** " Philaserdica 79 " International Stamp Exhibition (2nd issue). Paintings of Sofia. Multicoloured.
2674. 2 s. Type 845 .. .. 10 10
2675. 5 s. " View of Sofia " E. Stoichev) .. .. 10 10
2676. 13 s. " View of Sofia " (B. Ivanov) .. .. 20 10
2677. 23 s. " Tolbukhin Boulevard " (N. Tanev) .. 35 15
2678. 35 s. " National Theatre " (N. Petrov) .. 50 25
2679. 53 s. " Market " (A. Mitov) 1·40 80

846. Black Woodpecker. 848. " Elka 55 " Computer.

**1978.** Woodpeckers. Multicoloured.
2680. 1 s. Type 846 .. .. 15 10
2681. 2 s. Syrian Woodpecker .. 20 10
2682. 3 s. Three-toed Woodpecker .. .. 25 10
2683. 13 s. Middle Spotted Woodpecker .. .. 70 25
2684. 23 s. Lesser Spotted Woodpecker .. .. 1·10 40
2685. 43 s. Green Woodpecker 2·25 1·10

**1978.** Plovdiv International Fair.
2687. 848. 2 s. multicoloured .. 15 10

849. " September 1923 " (B. Angelushev). 850. Khristo Danov.

**1978.** 55th Anniv. of September Uprising.
2688. 849. 2 s. red and brown .. 15 10

**1978.** 150th Birth Anniv. of Khristo Danov (first Bulgarian publisher).
2689. 850. 2 s. orange and lake 15 10

851. " The People of Vladaya " (Todor Panayotov). 852. Hands supporting Rainbow.

**1978.** 60th Anniv. of Vladaya Mutiny.
2690. 851. 2 s. lilac, brn. & red 15 10

**1978.** International Anti-Apartheid Year.
2691. 852. 13 s. multicoloured .. 20 10

853. Pipeline and Flags. 854. Acrobats.

**1978.** Inauguration of Orenburg–U.S.S.R. Natural Gas Pipeline.
2692. 853. 13 s. multicoloured .. 20 10

**1978.** 3rd World Sports Acrobatics Championships, Sofia.
2693 854 13 s. multicoloured .. 25 10

855. Salvador Allende. 856. Human Rights Emblem.

**1978.** 70th Birth Anniv. of Salvador Allende (Chilean politician).
2694. 855. 13 s. brown and red 25 10

**1978.** 30th Anniv. of Declaration of Human Rights.
2695. 856. 23 s. yell., red & blue 85 20

857. " Levski and Matei Mitkaloto " (Kalina Taseva). 858. Tourist Home, Plovdiv.

**1978.** History of Bulgaria. Paintings. Multicoloured.
2696. 1 s. Type 857 .. .. 10 10
2697. 2 s. " Give Strength to my Arm " (Zlatyu Boyadzhiev) .. .. .. 10 10
2698. 3 s. " Rumena Voevoda " (Nikola Mirchev) (horiz.) 15 10
2699. 13 s. " Kolya Ficheto " (Elza Goeva) .. .. 20 10
2700. 23 s. " A Family of the National Revival Period " (Naiden Petkov) .. 75 15

**1978.** European Architectural Heritage. Multicoloured.
2701. 43 s. Type 858 .. .. 60 30
2702. 43 s. Tower of the Prince, Rila Monastery .. 60 30

859. "Geroi Plevny" and Route Map. 860. Mosaic Bird (Santa Sofia Church).

**1978.** Opening of the Varna–Ilichovsk Ferry Service.
2703. 859. 13 s. blue, red & grn. 40 10

**1978.** " Bulgaria 78 " National Stamp Exhibition, Sofia.
2704. 860. 5 s. multicoloured .. 15 10

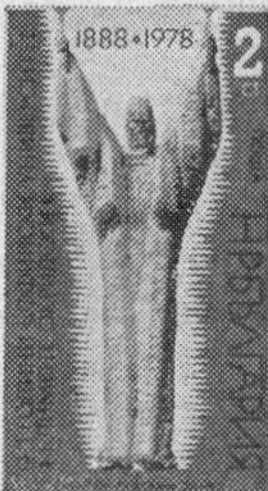

861. Monument to Kliment Okhridski (university patron) (Lyubemir Dalcher). 862. Nikola Karastoyanov.

**1978.** 90th Anniv. of Sofia University.
2705. 861. 2 s. lilac, blk. & olive 15 10

**1978.** Birth Bicentenary of Nikola Karastoyanov (first Bulgarian printer).
2706. 862. 2 s. brown, yellow and chestnut .. 10 10

863. Initial from 13th Century Bible Manuscript. 864. Ballet Dancers.

**1978.** Centenary of Cyril and Methodius People's Library. Multicoloured.
2707. 2 s. Type 863 .. .. 10 10
2708. 13 s. Monk writing (from a 1567 manuscript) .. 20 10
2709. 23 s. Decorated page from 16th century manuscript Bible .. 60 25

**1978.** 50th Anniv. of Bulgarian Ballet.
2711. 864. 13 s. olive, mauve and lavender .. 35 20

865. Tree of Birds.

**1978.** New Year. Multicoloured.
2712. 2 s. Type 865 .. .. 10 10
2713. 13 s. Posthorn .. .. 20 10

866. 1961 Communist Congress Stamp.

**1978.** " Philaserdica 79 " International Stamp Exhibition (3rd issue) and Bulgarian Stamp Centenary (1st issue).
2714. – 2 s. red and green .. 10 10
2715. – 13 s. claret and blue 20 10
2716. – 23 s. green & magenta 35 15
2717. 866. 35 s. grey and blue .. 80 25
2718. – 53 s. green and red .. 1·40 50

DESIGNS—HORIZ. 2 s. 1901 " Cherrywood Cannon " Stamp. 13 s. 1946 " New Republic " stamp. 23 s. 1957 Canonisation of St. Cyril and St. Methodius stamp. VERT. 53 s. 1962 Dimitrov stamp.

867. Council Building, Moscow and Flags.

**1979.** 30th Anniv. of Council of Mutual Economic Aid.
2720. 867. 13 s. multicoloured .. 20 10

**1979.** " Philaserdica 79 " Int. Stamp Exhib. (4th issue) and Bulgarian Stamp Cent. (2nd issue). As Nos. 2714/18 but inscr. "1979" and colours changed.
2721. – 2 s. red and blue .. 10 10
2722. – 13 s. claret and green 20 10
2723. – 23 s. green, yell. & red 35 15
2724. 866. 35 s. grey and red .. 75 25
2725. – 53 s. brown and violet 1·40 50

868. National Bank. 868a.

**1979.** Cent. of Bulgarian National Bank.
2726. 868. 2 s. grey and yellow 15 10

**1979.** Coil stamps.
2726a. 868a. 2 s. blue .. .. 10 10
2726b. 5 s. red .. .. 15 10
5 s. is as T 868a but different pattern.

869. Aleksander Stamboliiski. 870. Child's Head as Flower.

**1979.** Birth Cent. of Alexander Stamboliiski (leader of Agrarian Party).
2727. 869. 2 s. brown and yellow 15 10

**1979.** International Year of the Child.
2728. 870. 23 s. multicoloured .. 65 20

871. Profiles. 872. " 75 " and Emblem.

**1979.** Eighth World Congress for the Deaf, Varna.
2729. 871. 13 s. green and blue 25 10

**1979.** 75th Anniv. of Bulgarian Trade Unions.
2730. 872. 2 s. green and orange 15 10

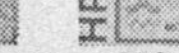

874. Rocket. 876. Running.

875. Carrier Pigeon and Tupolev Tu-154 Jet.

**1979.** Soviet–Bulgarian Space Flight. Multicoloured.
2732. 2 s. Georgi Ivanov (horiz.) 15 10
2733. 12 s. Type 874 .. .. 20 10
2734. 13 s. Nikolai Rukavishnikov and Ivanov (horiz.) 50 10
2735. 25 s. Link-up with "Salyut" space station (horiz.) .. 65 20
2736. 35 s. Capsule descending by parachute .. .. 1·10 25

**1979.** Centenary of Bulgarian Post and Telegraph Services. Multicoloured.
2738. 2 s. Type 875 .. .. 10 10
2739. 5 s. Old and new telephones 15 10
2740. 13 s. Morse key and teleprinter .. .. .. 20 10
2741. 23 s. Old radio transmitter and aerials .. 35 15
2742. 35 s. T.V. tower and satellite .. .. 85 25

**1979.** Olympic Games. Moscow (1980) (1st issue). Athletics. Multicoloured.
2744. 2 s. Type 876 .. .. 15 10
2745. 13 s. Pole vault (horiz.) .. 30 15
2746. 25 s. Discus .. .. 1·00 50
2747. 35 s. Hurdles (horiz.) .. 1·40 65
2748. 43 s. High jump (horiz.) 1·60 85
2749. 1 l. Long jump .. .. 3·25 2·00
See also Nos. 2773/78, 2803/8, 2816/21, 2834/9 and 2851/6.

879. Hotel Vitosha–New Otani.

**1979.** "Philaserdica 79" International Stamp Exhibition, Sofia (5th issue) and Bulgaria Day.
2753. 879. 2 s. pink and blue .. 15 10

**880.** "Good Morning, Little Brother" (illus. by Kukuliev of folktale).

**1979.** "Philaserdica 79" International Stamp Exhibition, Sofia (6th issue) and Bulgarian-Russian Friendship Day.
2754. **880.** 2 s. multicoloured .. 15 10

**882.** "Man on Donkey" (Boris Angelushev). **883.** "Four Women".

**1979.** 12th Festival of Humour and Satire, Grabovo.
2756. **882.** 2 s. multicoloured .. 15 10

**1979.** 450th Death Anniv. of Albrecht Durer (artist). Multicoloured.
2757. 13 s. Type **883** .. .. 20 10
2758. 23 s. "Three Peasants Talking" .. .. 55 20
2759. 25 s. "The Cook and his Wife" .. .. 65 20
2760. 35 s. "Portrait of Eobanus Hessus" .. .. 1·00 25

**884.** Clocktower, Byala Cherkva. **885.** P. Yu. Todorov. (Birth Centenary).

**1979.** Air. Clocktowers (1st series). Mult.
2762. 13 s. Type **884** .. .. 25 10
2763. 23 s. Botevgrad .. .. 40 15
2764. 25 s. Pazardzhik .. .. 50 20
2765. 35 s. Gabrovo .. .. 65 30
2766. 53 s. Tryavna .. .. 90 45
See also Nos. 2891/5.

**1979.** Bulgarian Writers.
2767. **885.** 2 s. black, brown and yellow .. .. 15 10
2768. – 2 s. green and yellow 15 10
2769. – 2 s. red and yellow .. 15 10
DESIGNS: No. 2768, Dimitur Dimov (70th birth anniv.). No. 2769, S. L. Kostov (birth centenary).

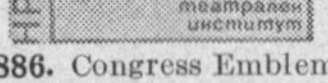

**886.** Congress Emblem. **887.** House of Journalists, Varna.

**1979.** 18th Congress of International Theatrical Institute, Sofia.
2770. **886.** 13 s. cobalt, blue and black .. .. 20 10

**1979.** 20th Anniv. of House of Journalists (holiday home), Varna.
2771. **887.** 8 s. orge., blk. & blue 15 10

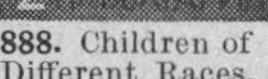

**888.** Children of Different Races. **889.** Parallel Bars.

**1979.** "Banners for Peace" Children's Meeting, Sofia.
2772. **888.** 2 s. multicoloured .. 10 10

**1979.** Olympic Games, Moscow (1980) 2nd issue). Gymnastics. Multicoloured.
2773. 2 s. Type **889** .. .. 10 10
2774. 13 s. Horse exercise (horiz.) 35 15
2775. 25 s. Rings exercise .. 1·00 50
2776. 35 s. Beam exercise .. 1·40 65
2777. 43 s. Uneven bars .. 1·75 95
2778. 1 l. Floor exercise .. 3·25 2·00

**890.** "Virgin and Child" (Nesebur).

**1979.** Icons of the Virgin and Child. Mult.
2780. 13 s. Type **890** .. .. 20 10
2781. 23 s. Nesebur (diff.) .. 35 15
2782. 35 s. Sozopol .. .. 55 25
2783. 43 s. Sozopol (diff.) .. 65 30
2784. 53 s. Samokov .. .. 1·40 1·10

**891.** Anton Bezenshek. **892.** Mountaineer.

**1979.** Cent. of Bulgarian Stenography.
2785. **891.** 2 s. yellow and grey 15 10

**1979.** 50th Anniv. of Bulgarian Alpine Club.
2786. **892.** 2 s. multicoloured .. 15 10

**893.** Commemorative Inscription.

**1979.** Centenary of Bulgarian Public Health Services.
2787. **893.** 2 s. blk., silver & grn. 15 10

**894.** Rocket and Flowers. **896.** Games Emblem.

**895.** "IZOT–0250" Computer.

**1979.** 35th Anniv. of Fatherland Front Government. Multicoloured.
2788. 2 s. Type **894** .. .. 10 10
2789. 5 s. Russian and Bulgarian flags .. .. 10 10
2790. 13 s. "35" in national colours .. .. 20 10

**1979.** 35th Plovdiv Fair.
2791. **895.** 2 s. multicoloured .. 15 10

**1979.** World University Games, Mexico.
2792. **896.** 5 s. red, yell. and blue 15 10

**897.** Footballer.

**1979.** 50th Anniv. of DFS Lokomotiv Football Team.
2793. **897.** 2 s. red and black .. 15 10

**898.** Lyuben Karavelov. **899.** Cross-country Skiing.

**1979.** Death Cent. of Lyuben Karavelov.
2794. **898.** 2 s. olive and blue .. 15 10

**1979.** Winter Olympic Games, Lake Placid. (1980).
2795. **899.** 2 s. red, pur. and blk. 10 10
2796. – 13 s. orge., blue & blk. 20 10
2797. – 23 s. turq., blue & blk. 35 15
2798. – 43 s. pur., turq. & blk. 1·40 65
DESIGNS: 13 s. Speed skating. 23 s. Skiing. 43 s. Luge.

**900.** "Woman from Thrace". **901.** Canoeing (Canadian pairs).

**1979.** 80th Birth Anniv. of Dechko Uzunov (artist). Multicoloured.
2800. 12 s. "Figure in Red" .. 20 10
2801. 13 s. Type **900** .. .. 20 10
2802. 23 s. "Composition II" .. 85 20

**1979.** Olympic Games, Moscow (1980) (3rd issue.) Water Sports. Multicoloured.
2803. 2 s. Type **901** .. .. 15 10
2804. 13 s. Swimming (freestyle) 30 15
2805. 25 s. Swimming (back-stroke) (horiz.) .. 1·00 50
2806. 35 s. Kayak (horiz.) .. 1·40 65
2807. 43 s. Diving .. .. 1·60 85
2808. 1 l. Springboard diving .. 3·25 2·00

**902.** Nikola Vaptsarov.

**1979.** 70th Birth Anniv. of Nikola Vaptsarov (writer).
2810. **902.** 2 s. pink and red .. 15 10

**903.** "Dawn in Plovdiv" (Yoan Leviev).

**1979.** History of Bulgaria. Paintings. Mult.
2811. 2 s. "The First Socialists" (Boyan Petrov) (horiz.) 10 10
2812. 13 s. "Dimitur Blagoev as Editor of "Rabotnik" (Dimitur Gyvdzhenov) (horiz.) .. 25 10
2813. 25 s. "Workers' Party March" (Stoyan Sotirov) (horiz.) .. 45 20
2814. 35 s. Type **903** .. .. 65 40

**904.** Doves in a Girl's Hair.

**1979.** New Year.
2815. **904.** 13 s. multicoloured .. 20 10

**905.** Shooting. **906.** Procession with Relics of Saints.

**1979.** Olympic Games, Moscow (1980) (4th issue). Multicoloured.
2816. 2 s. Type **905** .. .. 15 10
2817. 13 s. Judo (horiz.) .. 30 15
2818. 25 s. Wrestling (horiz.) .. 1·00 50
2819. 35 s. Archery .. .. 1·40 70
2820. 43 s. Fencing (horiz.) .. 1·60 75
2821. 1 l. Fencing (different) .. 3·25 2·00

**1979.** Frescoes of Saints Cyril and Methodius in St. Clement's Basilica, Rome. Multicoloured.
2823. 2 s. Type **906** .. .. 10 10
2824. 13 s. Cyril and Methodius received by Pope Adrian II .. .. 20 10
2825. 23 s. Burial of Cyril the Philosopher .. .. 35 15
2826. 25 s. St. Cyril .. .. 65 20
2827. 35 s. St. Methodius .. 1·00 35

**907.** Television Screen showing Emblem. **908.** Puppet of Krali Marko (national hero).

**1979.** 25th Anniv. of Bulgarian Television.
2828. **907.** 5 s. blue & dp. blue 15 10

**1980.** 50th Anniv. of International Puppet Theatre Organization. (U.N.I.M.A.).
2829. **908.** 2 s. multicoloured .. 15 10

**909.** Thracian Rider (3rd-cent. votive tablet). **910.** "Meeting of Lenin and Dimitrov" (A. Poplilov).

**1980.** Centenary of National Archaeological Museum Sofia.
2830. **909.** 2 s. brn., gold & pur. 10 10
2831. – 13 s. brn., gold & grn. 20 10
DESIGN: 13 s. Grave stele of Deines (5th–6th cent.).

**1980.** 110th Birth Anniv. of Lenin.
2832. **910.** 13 s. multicoloured .. 20 10

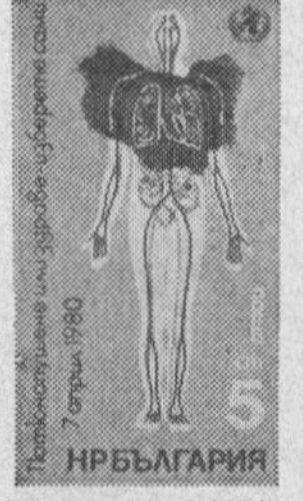

**911.** Diagram of Blood Circulation and Lungs obscured by Smoke. **912.** Basketball.

**1980.** World Health Day. Anti-smoking Campaign.
2833. **911.** 5 s. multicoloured .. 15 10

**1980.** Olympic Games, Moscow (5th issue). Multicoloured.
2834. 2 s. Type **912** .. .. 15 10
2835. 13 s. Football .. .. 30 15
2836. 25 s. Hockey .. .. 1·00 50
2837. 35 s. Cycling .. .. 1·40 70
2838. 43 s. Handball .. .. 1·60 75
2839. 1 l. Volleyball .. .. 3·25 2·00

**914.** Penyo Penev. **915.** Penny Black.

**1980.** 50th Birth Anniv. of Penyo Penev (poet).
2842. **914.** 5 s. brn., red & turq. 15 10

**1980.** "London 1980" International Stamp Exhibition.
2843. **915.** 25 s. black and red .. 1·00 1·00

**916.** Dimitur Khv. Chorbadzhuski-Chudomir (self-portrait).

**1980.** 90th Birth Anniv. of Dimitur Khv. Chorbadzhusk-Chudomir (artist).
2844. **916.** 5 s. pink, brown and turquoise .. .. 15 15
2845. – 13 s. black, blue and turquoise .. .. 20 10
DESIGN: 13 s. " Our People ".

**917.** Nikolai Gyaurov. **918.** Soviet Soldiers raising Flag on Berlin Reichstag.

**1980.** 50th Birth Anniv. of Nikolai Gyaurov (opera singer).
2846. **917.** 5 s. yell., brn. & grn. 20 10

**1980.** 35th Anniv. of "Victory in Europe" Day.
2847. **918.** 5 s. gold, brn. & blk. 15 10
2848. – 13 s. gold, brn. & blk. 25 20
DESIGN: 13 s. Soviet Army memorial, Berlin–Treptow.

**919.** Open Book and Sun. **920.** Stars representing Member Countries.

**1980.** 75th Anniv. Bulgarian Teachers' Union.
2849. **919.** 5 s. purple & yellow 15 10

**1980.** 25th Anniv. of Warsaw Pact.
2850. **920.** 13 s. multicoloured .. 20 10

**921.** Greek Girl with Olympic Flame. **922.** Ballerina.

**1980.** Olympic Games, Moscow (6th issue). Multicoloured.
2851. 2 s. Type **921** .. .. 15 10
2852. 13 s. Spartacus monument, Sandanski .. 30 15
2853. 25 s. Liberation monument, Sofia (detail) .. 1·00 50
2854. 35 s. Liberation monument, Plovdiv .. 1·40 70
2855. 43 s. Liberation monument, Shipka Pass .. 1·60 75
2856. 1 l. Liberation monument, Ruse .. 3·25 2·00

**1980.** 10th International Ballet Competition, Varna.
2858. **922.** 13 s. multicoloured .. 30 10

**923.** Europa Hotel, Sofia. **924.** Parachute Descent.

**1980.** Hotels. Multicoloured.
2859. 23 s. Type **923** .. .. 35 20
2860. 23 s. Bulgaria Hotel, Burgas (vert.) .. 35 20
2861. 23 s. Plovdiv Hotel, Plovdiv .. .. .. 35 20
2862. 23 s. Riga Hotel, Ruse (vert.) .. .. .. 35 20
2863. 23 s. Varna Hotel, Prazhba .. .. .. 35 20

**1980.** Historic Ships (3rd series). As T **753**. Multicoloured.
2864 5 s. Hansa kogge "Jesus of Lubeck" .. .. 10 10
2865 8 s. Roman galley .. 20 10
2866 13 s. Galleon "Eagle" .. 30 10
2867 23 s. "Mayflower" .. 45 15
2868 35 s. Maltese galleon .. 60 25
2869 53 s. Galleon "Royal Louis" .. .. 95 35

**1980.** 15th World Parachute Championships, Kazanluk. Multicoloured.
2870. 13 s. Type **924** .. .. 30 10
2871. 25 s. Parachutist in free fall .. .. .. 50 20

**925.** Clown and Children.

**1980.** 1st Anniv. of "Banners for Peace" Children's Meeting. Multicoloured.
2872. 3 s. Type **925** .. .. 10 10
2873. 5 s." Cosmonauts in Spaceship " (vert.) .. 10 10
2874. 8 s. " Picnic " .. .. 15 10
2875. 13 s. " Children with Ices " 20 10
2876. 25 s. " Children with Cat " (vert.) .. .. 40 20
2877. 35 s. " Crowd " .. .. 60 25
2878. 43 s. " Banners for Peace " monument (vert.) .. 1·40 30

**926.** Assembly Emblem. **927.** Yordan Yovkov.

**1980.** Assembly of Peoples' Parliament for Peace, Sofia.
2879. **926.** 25 s. multicoloured .. 40 20

**1980.** Birth Centenary of Yordan Yovkov (writer).
2880. **927.** 5 s. multicoloured .. 15 10

**928.** Yakovlev Yak-24 Helicopter, Missile Launcher and Tank.

**1980.** Bulgarian Armed Forces. Mult.
2881 3 s. Type **928** .. .. 15 10
2882 5 s. Mikoyan Gurevich MiG-21 bomber, radar antennae and missile transporter .. .. 25 10
2883 8 s. Mil Mi-24 helicopter, missile boat and landing ship "Ropucha" .. 45 15

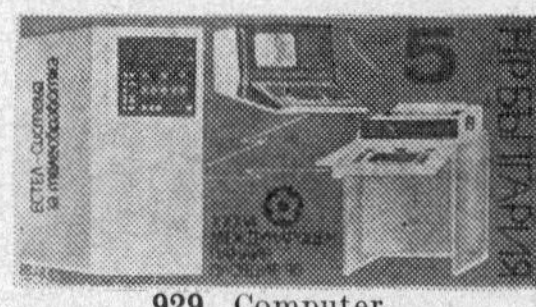
**929.** Computer.

**1980.** 36th Plovdiv Fair.
2884. **929.** 5 s. multicoloured .. 15 10

**930.** " Virgin and Child with St. Anne " **931.** " Parodia saint-pieana ".

**1980.** Paintings by Leonardo da Vinci. Multicoloured.
2885. 5 s. Type **930** .. .. 10 10
2886. 8 s. Angel (detail, " The Annunciation ") .. 15 10
2887. 13 s. Virgin (detail, " The Annunciation ") .. 20 10
2888. 25 s. " Adoration of the Kings " (detail) .. 40 20
2889. 35 s. " Woman with Ermine " .. .. 50 25

**1980.** Air. Clocktowers (2nd series). As T **884**. Multicoloured.
2891. 13 s. Byala .. .. 25 10
2892. 23 s. Razgrad .. .. 40 15
2893. 25 s. Karnobat .. .. 45 20
2894. 35 s. Sevlievo .. .. 60 25
2895. 53 s. Berkovitsa .. .. 1·40 50

**1980.** Cacti. Multicoloured.
2896. 5 s. Type **931** .. .. 10 10
2897. 13 s. " Echinopsis bridgesii " .. .. 25 10
2898. 25 s. " Echinocereus purpureus " .. .. 50 20
2899. 35 s. " Opuntia bispinosa " 65 25
2900. 53 s. " Mamillopsis senilis " .. .. 1·40 35

**933.** Wild Horse.

**1980.** Horses. Multicoloured.
2902. 3 s. Type **933** .. .. 15 10
2903. 5 s. Tarpan .. .. 15 10
2904. 13 s. Arabian .. .. 25 10
2905. 23 s. Anglo-Arabian .. 45 15
2906. 35 s. Draught horse .. 1·40 25

**934.** Vasil Stoin.

**1980.** Birth Centenary of Vasil Stoin (collector of folk songs).
2907. **934.** 5 s. vio., yell. & gold 15 10

**935.** Armorial Lion. **936.** Red Star.

**1980.** New Year. 1300th Anniv. of Bulgarian State. Multicoloured.
2908. 5 s. Type **935** .. .. 10 10
2909. 13 s. Dish and dates " 681–1981 " .. .. .. 20 10

**1980.** 12th Bulgarian Communist Party Congress (1st issue).
2910. **936.** 5 s. yellow and red .. 15 10
See also Nos. 2920/2.

**937.** Cross-country Skier.

**1981.** World Ski-racing Championship, Velingrad.
2911. **937.** 43 s. orge., blue & blk. 80 35

**938.** Whitethorn " Crataegus oxpacantha ". **939.** Skier.

**1981.** Useful Plants. Multicoloured.
2912. 3 s. Type **938** .. .. 10 10
2913. 5 s. Perforate St. John's wort " Hypericum perforatum " .. .. 15 10
2914. 13 s. Elder " Sambucus nigra " .. .. 30 10
2915. 25 s. Dewberry " Rubus caesius " .. .. 55 20
2916. 35 s. Lime " Tilia argentea " .. .. .. 65 30
2917. 43 s. Dog rose " Rosa canina " .. .. 1·10 40

**1981.** Alpine Skiing World Championships, Borovets.
2918. **939.** 43 s. yell., blk. & blue 80 35

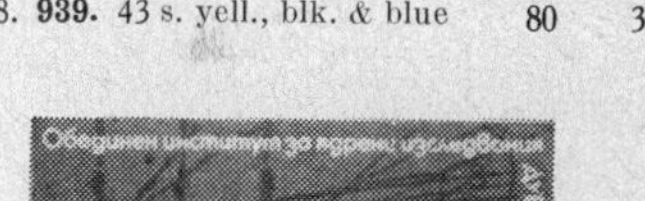

**940.** Nuclear Traces.

**1981.** 25th Anniv. of Nuclear Research Institute, Dubna, U.S.S.R.
2919. **940.** 13 s. black & silver .. 25 10

**941.** " XII " formed from Flag.

**1981.** 12th Bulgarian Communist Party Congress (2nd issue)
2920. **941.** 5 s. multicoloured 10 10
2921. – 13 s. red, black & blue 20 10
2922. – 23 s. red, black & blue 35 15
DESIGNS: 13 s. Stars, 23 s. Computer tape.

**942.** Palace of Culture.

**1981.** Opening of Palace of Culture, Sofia.
2924. **942.** 5 s. deep green, green and red .. .. 15 10

**943.** " Self-portrait ".

**1981.** 170th Birth Anniv. (1980) of Zakharu Zograf (artist). Multicoloured.

| | | | |
|---|---|---|---|
| 2925. | 5 s. Type **943** .. .. | 15 | 10 |
| 2926. | 13 s. " Portrait of Khristionia Zografska " .. | 20 | 10 |
| 2927. | 23 s. " The Transfiguration " (icon from Preobrazhenie Monastery) .. .. | 35 | 15 |
| 2928. | 25 s. " Doomsday " (detail) (horiz.) .. .. | 65 | 25 |
| 2929. | 35 s. " Doomsday " (detail — different) (horiz.) .. | 1·40 | 35 |

**944.** Squacco Heron.

**1981.** Birds. Multicoloured.

| | | | |
|---|---|---|---|
| 2930. | 5 s. Type **944** .. .. | 25 | 10 |
| 2931. | 8 s. Eurasian Bittern .. | 35 | 15 |
| 2932. | 13 s. Cattle Egret .. | 70 | 25 |
| 2933. | 25 s. Great Egret .. | 1·25 | 50 |
| 2934. | 53 s. Black Stork .. | 2·50 | 90 |

**945.** Liner " Georgi Dimitrov ".

**1981.** Centenary of Bulgarian Shipbuilding. Multicoloured.

| | | | |
|---|---|---|---|
| 2935 | 35 s. Type **945** .. .. | 1·00 | 30 |
| 2936 | 43 s. Freighter "Petimata of RMS" .. .. | 1·25 | 40 |
| 2937 | 53 s. Tanker "Khan Asparuch" .. .. | 1·90 | 70 |

**946.** Hofburg Palace, Vienna.

**1981.** " WIPA 1981 " International Stamp Exhibition, Vienna.

| | | | |
|---|---|---|---|
| 2938. **946.** | 35 s. bright red, red and green .. .. | 85 | 35 |

**947.** " XXXIV ".

**1981.** 34th Bulgarian People's Agrarian Union Congress.

| | | | |
|---|---|---|---|
| 2939. **947.** | 5 s. multicoloured .. | 10 | 10 |
| 2940. – | 8 s. orge., blk. & bl. | 15 | 10 |
| 2941. – | 13 s. multicoloured .. | 25 | 20 |

DESIGNS: 8 s. Flags. 13 s. Bulgarian Communist Party and Agrarian Union flags.

**948.** Wild Cat.

**1981.** International Hunting Exhibition, Plovdiv.

| | | | |
|---|---|---|---|
| 2942. **948.** | 5 s. stone, blk. & brn. | 15 | 10 |
| 2943. – | 13 s. black, brown and stone .. .. | 30 | 15 |
| 2944. – | 23 s. brown, black and orange .. | 50 | 20 |
| 2945. – | 25 s. black, brown and mauve .. | 85 | 40 |
| 2946. – | 35 s. light brown, black and brown .. | 85 | 35 |
| 2947. – | 53 s. brn., blk. & grn. | 1·60 | 50 |

DESIGNS: 13 s. Wild boar. 23 s. Mouflon. 25 s. Chamois. 35 s. Roe deer. 53 s. Fallow deer.

**949.** " Crafty Peter " (sculpture, Georgi Chapkanov).

**950.** Bulgarian Arms and U.N.E.S.C.O. Emblem.

**1981.** Festival of Humour and Satire, Gabrovo.

| | | | |
|---|---|---|---|
| 2949. **949.** | 5 s. multicoloured .. | 10 | 10 |

**1981.** 25th Anniv. of U.N.E.S.C.O. Membership.

| | | | |
|---|---|---|---|
| 2950. **950.** | 13 s. multicoloured .. | 30 | 10 |

**951.** Deutsche Flugzeugwerke D.F.W. C.V. Biplane.

**1981.** Air. Aircraft. Multicoloured.

| | | | |
|---|---|---|---|
| 2951 | 5 s. Type **951** .. .. | 15 | 10 |
| 2952 | 12 s. LAS-7 monoplane .. | 35 | 10 |
| 2953 | 25 s. LAS-8 monoplane .. | 65 | 30 |
| 2954 | 35 s. DAR-1 biplane .. | 85 | 40 |
| 2955 | 45 s. DAR-3 biplane .. | 1·10 | 55 |
| 2956 | 55 s. DAR-9 biplane .. | 1·40 | 80 |

**952.** " Eye ".

**1981.** Cent. of State Statistical Office.

| | | | |
|---|---|---|---|
| 2957. **952.** | 5 s. multicoloured .. | 15 | 10 |

**953.** Veliko Tirnovo Hotel.

**1981.** Hotels.

| | | | |
|---|---|---|---|
| 2958. **953.** | 23 s. multicoloured .. | 35 | 15 |

**954.** " Flying Figure "

**1981.** 90th Anniv. of First Bulgarian Social Democratic Party Congress, Buzludzha. Sculptures, by Velichko Minekov.

| | | | |
|---|---|---|---|
| 2959. **954.** | 5 s. blue, blk. and grn. | 10 | 10 |
| 2960. – | 13 s. brown, blk. & orge. | 20 | 10 |

DESIGN: 13 s. " Advancing Female ".

**955.** Animal-shaped Dish.

**1981.** Golden Treasure of Old St. Nicholas. Multicoloured.

| | | | |
|---|---|---|---|
| 2961. | 5 s. Type **955** .. .. | 10 | 10 |
| 2962. | 13 s. Jug with decorated neck .. .. | 25 | 10 |
| 2963. | 23 s. Jug with loop pattern | 45 | 20 |
| 2964. | 25 s. Jug with bird pattern | 55 | 25 |
| 2965. | 35 s. Decorated vase .. | 70 | 35 |
| 2966. | 53 s. Decorated dish | 1·40 | 70 |

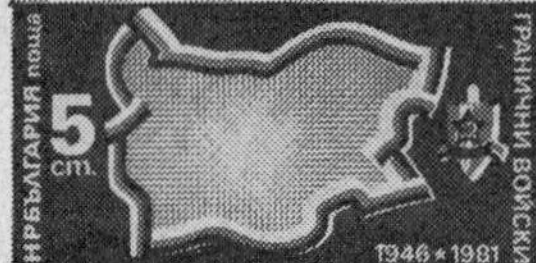


**956.** Badge and Map of Bulgaria.

**1981.** 35th Anniv. of Frontier Guards.

| | | | |
|---|---|---|---|
| 2967. **956.** | 5 s. multicoloured .. | 15 | 10 |

**957.** Saints Cyril and Methodius (9th century.)

**1981.** 1300th Anniv. of Bulgarian State.

| | | | |
|---|---|---|---|
| 2968. – | 5 s. green and grey .. | 10 | 10 |
| 2969. **957.** | 5 s. brown and yellow | 10 | 10 |
| 2970. – | 8 s. violet and lilac .. | 15 | 10 |
| 2971. – | 12 s. mauve and purple | 20 | 10 |
| 2972. – | 13 s. purple & brown | 20 | 10 |
| 2973. – | 13 s. green and black | 20 | 10 |
| 2974. – | 16 s. green and dp. grn. | 25 | 15 |
| 2975. – | 23 s. black and blue | 35 | 15 |
| 2976. – | 25 s. grn. and light grn. | 40 | 20 |
| 2977. – | 35 s. brn. and light brn. | 55 | 25 |
| 2978. – | 41 s. red and pink .. | 90 | 30 |
| 2979. – | 43 s. red and pink .. | 1·00 | 30 |
| 2980. – | 53 s. dp. brn. and brn. | 1·10 | 35 |
| 2981. – | 55 s. dp. grn. and grn. | 1·40 | 65 |

DESIGNS: No. 2968, Madara horsemen (8th century). No. 2970, Plan of Round Church at Veliki Preslav (10th century). No. 2971, Four Evangelists of King Ivan, 1356. No. 2972, Column of Ivan Asen II (13th century.) No. 2973, Manasiev Chronicle (14th century). No. 2974, Rising of April 1876. No. 2975, Arrival of Russian liberation troops. No. 2976, Foundation ceremony of Bulgarian Social Democratic Party 1891. No. 2977 Rising of September 1923. No. 2978, Formation of Fatherland Front Government, 9 September 1944. No. 2979, Bulgarian Communist Party Congress 1948. No. 2980, 10th Communist Party Congress 1971. No. 2981, Kremikovski metallurgical combine.

**958.** Volleyball Players.

**959.** " Pegasus " (bronze sculpture).

**1981.** European Volleyball Championships.

| | | | |
|---|---|---|---|
| 2983. **958.** | 13 s. red, blue & blk. | 25 | 10 |

**1981.** Day of the Word.

| | | | |
|---|---|---|---|
| 2984. **959.** | 5 s. green .. .. | 10 | 10 |

**960.** Loaf of Bread.

**961.** Mask.

**1981.** World Food Day.

| | | | |
|---|---|---|---|
| 2985. **960.** | 13 s. brn., blk. and grn. | 25 | 10 |

**1981.** Cent. of Bulgarian Professional Theatre.

| | | | |
|---|---|---|---|
| 2986. **961.** | 5 s. multicoloured .. | 15 | 10 |

**962.** Examples of Bulgarian Art.

**1981.** Cultural Heritage Day.

| | | | |
|---|---|---|---|
| 2987. **962.** | 13 s. green and brn .. | 20 | 10 |

**963.** Footballer.

**1981.** World Cup Football Championship, Spain (1982). Multicoloured.

| | | | |
|---|---|---|---|
| 2988. | 5 s. Type **963** .. .. | 10 | 10 |
| 2989. | 13 s. Heading ball .. | 25 | 10 |
| 2990. | 43 s. Saving a goal .. | 70 | 40 |
| 2991. | 53 s. Running with ball .. | 90 | 60 |

**964.** Dove encircled by Barbed Wire.

**1981.** Anti-Apartheid Campaign.

| | | | |
|---|---|---|---|
| 2992. **964.** | 5 s. red, blk. and yell | 15 | 10 |

**965.** " Mother ". (L. Ruseva).

**1981.** 35th Anniv. of U.N.I.C.E.F. Various designs showing mother and child paintings by named artists. Multicoloured.

| | | | |
|---|---|---|---|
| 2994. | 53 s. Type **965** .. | 1·40 | 45 |
| 2995. | 53 s. " Bulgarian Madonna " (V. Stoilov) .. | 1·40 | 45 |
| 2996. | 53 s. " Village Madonna " (I. Milev) .. .. | 1·40 | 45 |
| 2997. | 53 s. " Mother " (V. Dimitrov) .. .. | 1·40 | 45 |

**966.** 8th century Ceramic from Pliska.

**1981.** New Year. Multicoloured.

| | | | |
|---|---|---|---|
| 2998. | 5 s. Armorial lion .. | 10 | 10 |
| 2999. | 13 s. Type **966** .. .. | 20 | 10 |

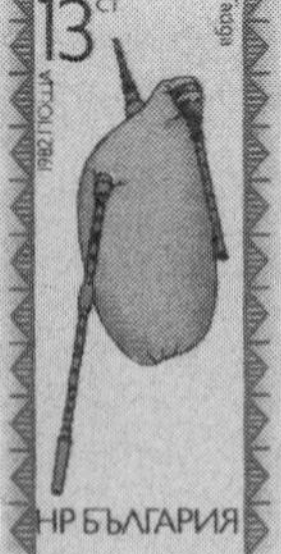

**967.** Bagpipes

**968.** Open Book.

**1982.** Musical Instruments. Multicoloured.

| | | | |
|---|---|---|---|
| 3000. | 13 s. Type **967** .. .. | 25 | 10 |
| 3001. | 25 s. Single and double flutes .. .. .. | 45 | 20 |
| 3002. | 30 s. Rebec .. .. | 55 | 25 |
| 3003. | 35 s. Flute and pipe .. | 65 | 25 |
| 3004. | 44 s. Mandolin .. | 1·40 | 30 |

**1982.** 125th Anniv. of Public Libraries.

| | | | |
|---|---|---|---|
| 3005. **968.** | 5 s. green .. .. | 15 | 10 |

**969.** " Sofia Plains ".

**1982.** Birth Centenary of Nikola Petrov (artist).

3006. 5 s. Type **969** .. .. 10 10
3007. 13 s. " Girl Embroidering " 25 10
3008. 30 s. " Fields of Peshtera " 55 30

**971.** " Peasant Woman ".

**1982.** Birth Centenary of Valadimir Dimitrov (artist). Multicoloured.

3010. 5 s. Figures in a landscape (horiz.) .. .. 10 10
3011. 8 s. Town and harbour (horiz.) .. .. 15 10
3012. 13 s. Town scene (horiz.) 20 10
3013. 25 s. " Reapers " .. 40 20
3014. 30 s. Woman and child .. 45 25
3015. 35 s. Type **971** .. .. 55 25

**972.** Georgi Dimitrov.

**1982.** Ninth Bulgarian Trade Unions Congress, Sofia.

3017. **972.** 5 s. light brown, deep brown and brown .. 15 10
3018. – 5 s. brown and blue .. 15 10

DESIGN: No. 3018, Palace of Culture, Sofia.

**973.** Summer Snowflake.

**1982.** Medicinal Plants. Multicoloured.

3019. 3 s. Type **973** .. .. 10 10
3020. 5 s. Chicory .. .. 15 10
3021. 8 s. Rosebay willowherb 15 10
3022. 13 s. Solomon's seal .. 20 10
3023. 25 s. Sweet violet .. 65 20
3024. 35 s. "Ficaria verna" .. 1·10 50

**974.** Russian Space Station.

**1982.** 25th Anniv. of First Soviet Artificial Satellite.

3025. **974.** 13 s. multicoloured .. 20 10

**976.** Dimitrov and Congress Emblem.

**1982.** 14th Dimitrov Communist Youth League Congress, Sofia.

3027. **976.** 5 s. blue, red and yell. 15 10

**977.** First French and Bulgarian Stamps.

**1982.** " Philexfrance 82 " International Stamp Exhibition, Paris.

3028. **977.** 42 s. multicoloured .. 65 30

**978.** Abstract with Birds.

**980.** Georgi Dimitrov.

**1982.** Alafrangi Frescoes from 19th-century Houses.

3029. **978.** 5 s. multicoloured .. 10 10
3030. – 13 s. multicoloured .. 20 10
3031. – 25 s. multicoloured .. 40 20
3032. – 30 s. multicoloured .. 45 25
3033. – 42 s. multicoloured .. 65 30
3034. – 60 s. multicoloured .. 1·60 40

DESIGNS: 13 s. to 60 s. Various flower and bird patterns.

During 1982 sets were issued for World Cup Football Championship, Spain (5, 13, 30 s.). Tenth Anniv. of First European Security and Co-operation Conference (5, 13, 25, 30 s.). World Cup Results (5, 13, 30 s.) and 10th Anniv. (1983) of European Security and Co-operation Conference, Helsinki (5, 13, 25, 30 s.). Supplies and distribution of these stamps were restricted and it is understood they were not available at face value.

**1982.** Ninth Fatherland Front Congress, Sofia.

3036. **980.** 5 s. multicoloured .. 15 10

**981.** Airplane.

**1982.** 35th Anniv. of Balkan air (state airline).

3037. **981.** 42 s. blue, grn. & red 65 30

**982.** Atomic Bomb Mushroom-cloud. **983.** Lyudmila Zhivkova.

**1982.** Nuclear Disarmament Campaign.

3038. **982.** 13 s. multicoloured .. 20 10

**1982.** 40th Birth Anniv. of Lyudmila Zhivkova (founder of "Banners for Peace" Children's Meetings).

3039. **983.** 5 s. multicoloured .. 10 10
3040. 13 s. multicoloured .. 20 10

**984.** Emblem.

**1982.** 10th Anniv. of U.N. Environment Programme.

3042. **984.** 13 s. green and blue 20 10

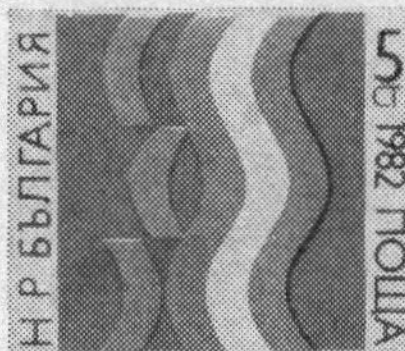


**985.** Wave Pattern.

**1982.** 5th Bulgarian Painters' Association Congress.

3043. **985.** 5 s. multicoloured .. 15 10

**986.** Child Musicians.

**1982.** 2nd "Banners for Peace". Children's Meeting (1st issue). Children's Paintings. Multicoloured.

3044. 3 s. Type **986** .. .. 10 10
3045. 5 s. Children skating .. 15 10
3046. 8 s. Adults, children and flowers .. .. .. 15 10
3047. 13 s. Children with flags 20 10

See also Nos. 3057/62.

**987.** Moscow Park Hotel, Sofia.

**988.** Cruiser " Aurora " and Satellite.

**1982.** Hotels. Multicoloured.

3049 32 s. Type **987** .. .. 50 25
3050 32 s. Black Sea Hotel, Varna .. .. .. 50 25

**1982.** 65th Anniv. of Russian October Revolution.

3051. **988.** 13 s. red and blue .. 45 10

**989.** Hammer and Sickle.

**1982.** 60th Anniv. of U.S.S.R.

3052. **989.** 13 s. red, gold & vio. 20 10

**990.** " The Piano ".

**1982.** Birth Centenary of Pablo Picasso (artist). Multicoloured.

3053. 13 s. Type **990** .. .. 20 10
3054. 30 s. " Portrait of Jacqueline " .. .. .. 45 20
3055. 42 s. " Maternity " .. 1·10 30

**991.** Boy and Girl.

**1982.** 2nd "Banners for Peace" Children's Meeting (2nd issue). Multicoloured.

3057. 3 s. Type **991** .. .. 10 10
3058. 5 s. Market place .. 10 10
3059. 8 s. Children in fancy dress (vert.) .. .. 15 10
3060. 13 s. Chickens (vert.) .. 20 10
3061. 25 s. Interlocking heads 40 20
3062. 30 s. Lion .. .. 45 20

**992.** Lions.

**1982.** New Year. Multicoloured.

3064 5 s. Type **992** .. .. 15 10
3065 13 s. Decorated letters .. 20 10

**993.** Broadcasting Tower. **994.** Dr. Robert Koch.

**1982.** 60th Anniv. of Avram Stoyanov Broadcasting Institute.

3066. **993.** 5 s. blue .. .. 15 10

**1982.** Cent. of Discovery of Tubercle Bacillus.

3067. **994.** 25 s. brn. & grn. .. 40 20

**995.** Simon Bolivar. **996.** Vasil Levski.

**1982.** Birth Annivs.

3068. **995.** 30 s. green and grey 45 20
3069. – 30 s. yellow & brown 45 20

DESIGN: No. 3068. Type **995** (bicent). No. 3069. Rabindranath Tagore (philosopher, 120th anniv.).

**1983.** 110th Death Anniv. of Vasil Levski (revolutionary).

3070. **996.** 5 s. brown & green .. 10 10

**997.** Skier.

**1983.** "Universiade 83" University Games, Sofia.

3071. **997.** 30 s. multicoloured .. 45 20

**998.** Pike.

**1983.** Freshwater Fishes. Multicoloured.

3072. 3 s. Type **998** .. .. 10 10
3073. 5 s. Sturgeon .. .. 10 10
3074. 13 s. Chub .. .. 20 10
3075. 25 s. Perch .. .. 40 20
3076. 30 s. Catfish .. .. 45 20
3077. 42 s. Trout .. .. 1·90 30

**999.** Karl Marx.

**1983.** Death Cent. of Karl Marx.

3078. **999.** 13 s. red, pur. & yell. 20 10

**1000.** Hasek and Illustrations from "The Good Soldier Schweik".

**1983.** Birth Centenary of Jaroslav Hasek (Czech writer).
3079. **1000.** 13 s. brown, grey and green .. 20 10

**1001.** Martin Luther.

**1983.** 500th Birth Anniv. of Martin Luther (Protestant reformer).
3080. **1001.** 13 s. grey, blk. & brown .. .. 45 10

**1002.** Figures forming Initials.

**1983.** 55th Anniv. of Young Workers' Union.
3081. **1002.** 5 s. red, black and orange .. .. 10 10

**1003.** Khaskovo. Costume.
**1004.** Old Man feeding a Chicken.

**1983.** Folk Costumes. Multicoloured.
3082. 5 s. Type **1003** .. .. 10 10
3083. 8 s. Pernik .. .. 15 10
3084. 13 s. Burgas .. .. 20 10
3085. 25 s. Tolbukhin .. .. 40 20
3086. 30 s. Blagoevgrad .. 45 20
3087. 42 s. Topolovgrad .. 1·75 30

**1983.** 6th International Festival of Humour and Satire, Gabrovo.
3088. **1004.** 5 s. multicoloured .. 15 10

During 1983 sets were issued for European Security and Co-operation Conference, Budapest (5, 13, 25, 30 s.), Olympic Games, Los Angeles (5, 13, 30, 42 s), Winter Olympic Games, Sarajevo (horiz. designs, 5, 13, 30, 42 s) and European Security and Co-operation Conference, Madrid (5, 13, 30, 42 s.). Supplies and distribution of these stamps were restricted, and it is understood they were not available at face value.

**1005.** Smirnenski.

**1983.** 85th Birth Anniv. of Khristo Smirnenski (poet).
3089. **1005.** 5 s. red, brown and yellow .. .. 25 10

**MORE DETAILED LISTS**
are given in the Stanley Gibbons Catalogues referred to in the country headings.
For lists of current volumes see Introduction.

**1006.** Emblem.

**1983.** 17th International Geodesy Federation Congress.
3090. **1006.** 30 s. grn., bl. & yell. 45 20

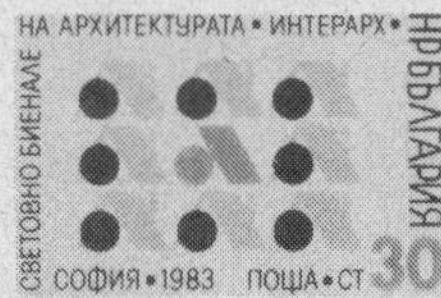

**1007.** Stylized Houses.

**1983.** "Interarch 83" World Architecture Biennale, Sofia.
3091. **1007.** 30 s. multicoloured 45 20

**1008.** Staunton Chess Pieces on Map of Europe.
**1011.** Television Mast, Tolbukhin.

**1983.** 8th European Chess Team Championship, Plovdiv.
3092 **1008** 13 s. multicoloured .. 20 10

**1983.** Air. World Communications Year.
3095. **1011.** 5 s. blue & red .. 15 10
3096. – 13 s. mauve & red .. 20 10
3097. – 30 s. yellow & red .. 45 20
DESIGNS: 13 s. Postwoman. 30 s. Radio tower, Mount Botev.

**1012.** Lenin addressing Congress.

**1983.** 80th Anniv. of 2nd Russian Social Democratic Workers' Party Congress.
3098. **1012.** 5 s. purple, deep purple and yellow 15 10

**1013.** Pistol and Dagger on Book.

**1983.** 80th Anniv. of Ilinden-Preobrazhenie Rising.
3099. **1013.** 5 s. yellow & green .. 10 10

**1014.** Crystals and Hammers within Gearwheels.

**1983.** 30th Anniv. of Mining and Geology Institute, Sofia.
3100. **1014.** 5 s. grey, pur. & bl. 10 10

**1015.** Dimitrov and Revolution Scenes.

**1983.** 60th Anniv. of September Uprising. Multicoloured.
3101. 5 s. Type **1015** .. .. 10 10
3102. 13 s. Wreath and revolution scenes .. 20 10

**1016.** Animated Drawings.
**1017.** Angora.

**1983.** 3rd Animated Film Festival, Varna.
3101. **1016.** 5 s. multicoloured .. 10 10

**1983.** Cats. Multicoloured.
3104. 5 s. Type **1017** .. .. 15 10
3105. 13 s. Siamese .. .. 20 10
3106. 20 s. Abyssinian (vert.) 30 10
3107. 25 s. European .. .. 65 15
3108. 30 s. Persian (vert.) .. 85 15
3109. 42 s. Khmer .. .. 1·50 25

**1018.** Trevithick's Locomotive, 1803.

**1983.** Locomotives (1st series). Multicoloured.
3110. 5 s. Type **1018** .. .. 15 10
3111. 13 s. Blenkinsop's rack locomotive "Prince Royal", 1810 .. .. 20 15
3112. 42 s. Hedley's "Puffing Billy", 1812 .. .. 1·50 55
3113. 60 s. "Der Adler" (first German locomotive, 1835 .. .. .. 2·40 70
See also Nos. 3159/63.

**1020.** Mask and Laurel as Lyre.
**1021.** Ioan Kukuzel.

**1983.** 75th Anniv. of National Opera, Sofia.
3115. **1020.** 5 s. red, blk. & gold 10 10

**1983.** Bulgarian Composers.
3116. **1021.** 5 s. yellow, brown & green .. .. 10 10
3117. – 8 s. yellow, brown and red .. .. 15 10
3118. – 13 s. yellow, brown & green .. .. 20 10
3119. – 20 s. yellow, brown & blue .. .. 30 15
3120. – 25 s. yellow, brown & grey .. .. 40 20
3121. – 30 s. yellow, deep brown & brown .. 45 20
DESIGNS: 8 s. Georgi Atanasov. 13 s. Petko Stainov. 20 s. Veselin Stoyanov. 25 s. Lyubomir Pipkov. 30 s. Pancho Vladigerov.

**1022.** Snowflake.

**1983.** New Year.
3122. **1022.** 5 s. grn., bl. & gold 10 10

**1023.** "Angelo Donni".

**1983.** 500th Birth Anniv. of Raphael (artist). Multicoloured.
3123. 5 s. Type **1023** .. .. 10 10
3124. 13 s. "Portrait of a Cardinal" .. .. 20 10
3125. 30 s. "Baldassare Castiglioni" .. .. 45 20
3126. 42 s. "Woman with a Veil" .. .. .. 1·00 30

**1024.** Eurasian Common Shrew.

**1983.** Protected Mammals. Mult.
3128. 12 s. Type **1024** .. .. 25 20
3129. 13 s. Greater Horseshoe bat .. .. .. 30 20
3130. 20 s. Common long-eared bat .. .. .. 40 30
3131. 30 s. Forest dormouse .. 60 40
3132. 42 s. Fat dormouse .. 90 60

**1025.** Karavelov.

**1984.** 150th Birth Anniv. of Lyuben Karavelov (poet).
3133. **1025.** 5 s. blue, bistre and brown .. .. 10 10

During 1984 sets were issued for European Confidence- and Security-building Measures and Disarmament Conference, Stockholm (5, 13, 30, 42 s.) and Winter Olympic Games, Sarajevo (vert designs, 5, 13, 30, 42 s.). Supplies and distribution of these stamps were restricted and it is understood that they were not available at face value.

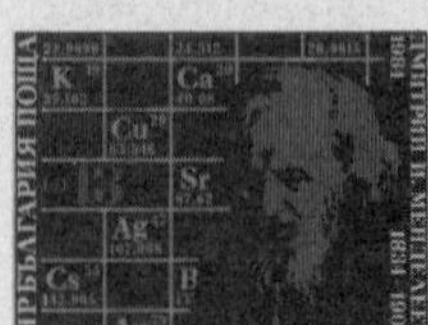

**1026.** Mendeleev and Formulae.

**1984.** 150th Birth Anniv. of Dmitry Mendeleev (chemist).
3134. **1026.** 13 s. multicoloured 20 10

**1027.** Bulk Carrier "Gen. Vl. Zaimov".

**1984.** Ships. Multicoloured.
3135. 5 s. Type **1027** .. .. 20 10
3136. 13 s. Tanker "Mesta" .. 45 15
3137. 25 s. Tanker "Veleka" .. 85 30
3138. 32 s. Ferry "Geroite na Odesa" .. .. 90 40
3139. 42 s. Bulk carrier "Rozhen" .. .. 1·10 45

1029. Pigeon with Letter over Globe.

1030. Cherries.

**1984.** "Mladost '84" Youth Stamp Exhibition, Pleven (1st issue).

3141. **1029.** 5 s. multicoloured .. 15 10

See also Nos. 3171/2.

**1984.** Fruits. Multicoloured.

3142. 5 s. Type **1030** .. .. 10 10
3143. 8 s. Strawberries .. 15 10
3144. 13 s. Dewberries .. 20 10
3145. 20 s. Raspberries .. 30 15
3146. 42 s. Medlars .. .. 1·00 30

1031. "Vitosha Conference" (K. Buyukliiski and P. Petrov).

**1984.** 60th Anniv. of Bulgarian Communist Party Conference, Vitosha.

3147. **1031.** 5 s. purple, brown and red .. .. 10 10

1033. Athletes and Doves.

1034. Mt. Everest.

**1984.** Sixth Republican Spartakiad.

3149. **1033.** 13 s. multicoloured 20 10

**1984.** Bulgarian Expedition to Mt. Everest.

3150. **1034.** 5 s. multicoloured .. 10 10

1036. Drummer.

**1984.** 6th Amateur Performers Festival.

3152. **1036.** 5 s. multicoloured .. 10 10

1037. Seal.

**1984.** 50 Years of Bulgarian–U.S.S.R. Diplomatic Relations.

3153. **1037.** 13 s. multicoloured 20 10

1038. Rock Dove.

1039. Production Quality Emblem.

**1984.** Pigeons and Doves. Multicoloured.

3154. 5 s. Type **1038** .. .. 20 15
3155. 13 s. Stock dove .. 45 20
3156. 20 s. Wood pigeon .. 80 30
3157. 30 s. Turtle dove .. 1·25 40
3158. 42 s. Domestic pigeon .. 1·75 50

**1984.** Locomotives (2nd series). As T **1018**. Multicoloured.

3159. 13 s. "Best Friend", Charleston, U.S.A., 1830 .. .. .. 35 15
3160. 25 s. "Saxonia", Dresden, 1836 .. .. 55 30
3161. 30 s. "Lafayette", U.S.A., 1837 .. .. 60 35
3162. 42 s. "Borsig", Germany, 1841 .. .. .. 85 55
3163. 60 s. "Philadelphia", U.S.A., 1843 .. .. 1·50 75

**1984.** 40th Anniv. of Fatherland Front Government.

3164. **1039.** 5 s. red, light green and green .. 10 10
3165. – 20 s. red and violet 30 15
3166. – 30 s. red and blue .. 45 20

DESIGNS: 20 s. Monument to Soviet Army, Sofia. 30 s. Figure nine and star.

1040. "Boy with Harmonica".

1041. Mausoleum of Russian Soldiers.

**1984.** Paintings by Nenko Balkanski. Multicoloured.

3167. 5 s. Type **1040** .. .. 10 10
3168. 30 s. "Window in Paris" 45 20
3169. 42 s. "Portrait of Two Women" (horiz.) .. 1·10 30

**1984.** "Mladost '84" Youth Stamp Exhibition, Pleven (2nd issue).

3171. **1041.** 5 s. multicoloured .. 10 10
3172. – 13 s. black, green and red .. .. 20 10

DESIGN: 13 s. Panorama building.

1042. Pioneers saluting.

**1984.** 40th Anniv. of Dimitrov Septembrist Pioneers Organization.

3173. **1042.** 5 s. multicoloured .. 10 10

1043. Vaptsarov (after D. Nikolov).

**1984.** 75th Birth Anniv. of Nikola I. Vaptsarov (poet).

3174. **1043.** 5 s. yellow and red 10 10

1044. Goalkeeper saving Goal.

**1984.** 75th Anniv. of Bulgarian Football.

3175. **1044.** 42 s. multicoloured 65 30

1046. Devil's Bridge, R. Arda.

**1984.** Bridges. Multicoloured.

3177. 5 s. Type **1046** .. .. 10 10
3178. 13 s. Kolo Ficheto Bridge, Byala .. 25 25
3179. 30 s. Asparukhov Bridge, Varna .. .. .. 1·00 50
3180. 42 s. Bebresh Bridge, Botevgrad .. .. 1·60 95

1047. Olympic Emblem.

**1984.** 90th Anniv. of International Olympic Committee.

3181. **1047.** 13 s. multicoloured 20 10

1049. Dalmatian Pelican with Chicks.

1050. Anton Ivanov.

**1984.** Wildlife Protection. Dalmatian Pelican.

3183. **1049.** 5 s. multicoloured .. 25 15
3184. – 13 s. lavender, black and brown .. 70 25
3185. – 20 s. multicoloured 1·25 40
3186. – 32 s. multicoloured 2·25 75

DESIGNS: 13 s. Two pelicans. 20 s. Pelican on water. 32 s. Pelican in flight.

**1984.** Birth Centenary of Anton Ivanov (revolutionary).

3187. **1050.** 5 s. yell., brn. & red 10 10

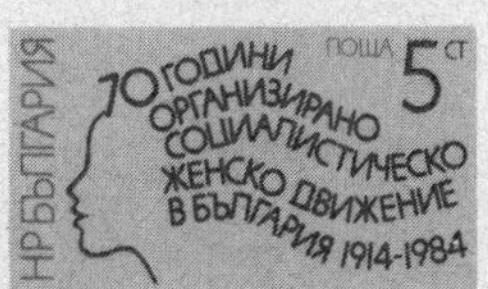


1051. Girl's Profile with Text as Hair.

**1984.** 70th Anniv of Bulgarian Women's Socialist Movement.

3188. **1051.** 5 s. multicoloured .. 10 10

1052. Snezhanka Television Tower.

**1984.** Television Towers.

3189. **1052.** 5 s. bl., grn. & mve. 10 10
3190. – 1 l. brown, mauve and bistre .. 2·00 65

DESIGN: 1 l. Orelek television tower.

1053. Birds and Posthorns.

**1984.** New Year. Multicoloured.

3191. 5 s. Type **1053** .. .. 10 10
3192. 13 s. Decorative pattern 20 10

1054. "September Nights".

**1984.** 80th Birth Anniv. of Stoyan Venev (artist). Multicoloured.

3193. 5 s. Type **1054** .. .. 10 10
3194. 30 s. "Man with Three Orders" .. .. 45 20
3195. 42 s. "The Hero" .. 1·00 30

1055. "Inachis io".

1056. Augusto Sandino.

**1984.** Butterflies. Multicoloured.

3196 13 s. Type **1055** .. .. 25 15
3197 25 s. "Papilio machaon" 45 25
3198 30 s. "Brintesia circe" .. 50 25
3199 42 s. "Anthocharis cardamines" .. .. 70 40
3200 60 s. "Vanessa atalanta" 1·50 50

**1984.** 50th Death Anniv. of Augusto Sandino (Nicaraguan revolutionary).

3202. **1056.** 13 s. black, red and yellow .. .. 20 10

1057. Tupolev Tu-154 Airplane.

**1984.** 40th Anniv. of I.C.A.O.

3203. **1057.** 42 s. multicoloured 90 35

1058. "The Three Graces" (detail).

**1984.** 500th Birth Anniv. (1983) of Raphael (artist) (2nd issue). Multicoloured.

3204. 5 s. Type **1058** .. .. 10 10
3205. 13 s. "Cupid and the Three Graces" (detail) 20 10
3206. 30 s. "Original Sin" (detail) .. .. 45 20
3207. 42 s. "La Fornarina" .. 1·10 30



1059. "Sofia".

**1984.** Maiden Voyage of Danube Cruise Ship "Sofia".

3209 **1059** 13 s. dp bl, bl & yell 65 10

**1060.** Eastern Hog-nosed Skunk.

**1985.** Mammals.

3210. **1060.** 13 s. black, blue and orange . . . . 20 10
3211. – 25 s. black, brown and green . . 35 20
3212. – 30 s. black, brown and yellow . . 45 20
3213. – 42 s. multicoloured 60 25
3214. – 60 s. multicoloured 1·40 40

DESIGNS: 25 s. Banded linsang. 30 s. Zorilla. 42 s. Banded palm civet. 60 s. Broad-striped galidia.

**1061.** Nikolai Liliev.

**1985.** Birth Cent. of Nikolai Liliev (poet).

3215. **1061.** 30 s. light brown, brown and gold . . 45 20

**1062.** Tsvyatko Radoinov.

**1985.** 90th Birth Anniv. of Tsvyatko Radoinov (resistance fighter).

3216. **1062.** 5 s. brown and red 10 10

**1063.** Asen Zlatarov. **1066.** Olive Branch and Sword Blade.

**1985.** Birth Centenary of Asen Zlatarov (biochemist).

3217. **1063.** 5 s. pur., yell. & grn. 10 10

**1985.** 30th Anniv. of Warsaw Pact.

3220. **1066.** 13 s. multicoloured 20 10

**1067.** Bach. **1069.** Saint Methodius.

**1068.** Girl with Birds.

**1985.** Composers.

3221. **1067.** 42 s. blue and red . . 1·00 25
3222. – 42 s. violet & green 1·00 25
3223. – 42 s. yellow, brown & orange . . 1·00 25
3224. – 42 s. yellow, brown and red . . . . 1·00 25
3225. – 42 s. yellow, green and blue . . . . 1·00 25
3226. – 42 s. yellow, red and green . . . . 1·00 25

DESIGNS: No. 3222, Mozart. 3223, Tchaikovsky. 3224, Modest Petrovich Musorgsky. 3225, Giuseppe Verdi. 3226, Filip Kutev.

**1985.** 3rd "Banners for Peace" Children's Meeting, Sofia. Multicoloured.

3227. 5 s. Type **1068** . . . . 10 10
3228. 8 s. Children painting . . 15 10
3229. 13 s. Girl among flowers 20 10
3230. 20 s. Children at market stall . . . . 30 15
3231. 25 s. Circle of children . . 35 20
3232. 30 s. Nurse . . . . 45 20

**1985.** 1100th Death Anniv. of Saint Methodius.

3234. **1069.** 13 s. multicoloured 50 15

**1070.** Soldiers and Nazi Flags.

**1985.** 40th Anniv. of V.E. ("Victory in Europe") Day. Multicoloured.

3235. 5 s. Type **1070** . . . . 10 10
3236. 13 s. 11th Infantry parade, Sofia . . . . 20 10
3237. 30 s. Soviet soldier with orphan . . . . 45 20

**1071.** Woman carrying Child and Man on Donkey.

**1985.** 7th International Festival of Humour and Satire, Gabrovo.

3239. **1071.** 13 s. black, yellow and red . . . . 20 10

**1072.** Profiles and Flowers.

**1985.** International Youth Year.

3240. **1072.** 13 s. multicoloured 20 10

**1073.** Ivan Vazov.

**1985.** 135th Birth Anniv. of Ivan Vazov (poet).

3241. **1073.** 5 s. brown and stone 10 10

**1074.** Monument to Unknown Soldiers and City Arms.

**1985.** Millenary of Khaskovo.

3242. **1074.** 5 s. multicoloured . . 10 10

**1075.** Festival Emblem. **1077.** Vasil E. Aprilov (founder).

**1076.** Indira Gandhi.

**1985.** 12th World Youth and Students' Festival, Moscow.

3243. **1075.** 13 s. multicoloured 20 10

**1985.** Indira Gandhi (Indian Prime Minister) Commemoration.

3244. **1076.** 30 s. brown, orange and yellow . . 45 20

**1985.** 150th Anniv. of New Bulgarian School, Gabrovo.

3245. **1077.** 5 s. blue, purple and green . . . . 10 10

**1078.** Congress Emblem.

**1985.** 36th International Shorthand and Typing Federation Congress ("Intersteno"), Sofia.

3246. **1078.** 13 s. multicoloured 20 10

**1079.** Alexandr Nevski Cathedral, Sofia.

**1985.** Sixth General Assembly of World Tourism Organization, Sofia.

3247. **1079.** 42 s. green, blue and orange . . . . 60 30

**1080.** State Arms and U.N. Flag. **1081.** Rosa "Trakijka".

**1985.** 40th Anniv. of U.N.O. (3248) and 30th Anniv. of Bulgaria's Membership (3249). Multicoloured.

3248. 13 s. Dove around U.N. emblem . . . . 20 10
3249. 13 s. Type **1080** . . . . 20 10

**1985.** Roses. Multicoloured.

3250. 5 s. "Rosa damascena" 10 10
3251. 13 s. Type **1081** . . . . 20 10
3252. 20 s. "Radiman" . . 30 15
3253. 30 s. "Marista" . . 45 20
3254. 42 s. "Valentina" . . 60 25
3255. 60 s. "Maria" . . . . 1·50 40

**1082.** Peace Dove.

**1985.** 10th Anniv. of European Security and Co-operation Conference, Helsinski.

3256. **1082.** 13 s. multicoloured 20 10

**1083.** Water Polo.

**1985.** European Swimming Championships, Sofia. Multicoloured.

3257. 5 s. Butterfly stroke (horiz.) . . . . 10 10
3258. 13 s. Type **1083** . . . . 20 10
3259. 42 s. Diving . . . . 65 25
3260. 60 s. Synchronised swimming (horiz.) . . . . 1·50 40

**1084.** Edelweiss.

**1985.** 90th Anniv. of Bulgarian Tourist Organization.

3261. **1084.** 5 s. multicoloured . . 10 10

**1085.** State Arms. **1086.** Footballers.

**1985.** Centenary of Union of E. Roumelia and Bulgaria.

3262. **1085.** 5 s. black, orange and green . . 10 10

**1985.** World Cup Football Championship, Mexico (1986) (1st issue).

3263. **1086.** 5 s. multicoloured . . 10 10
3264. – 13 s. multicoloured 20 10
3265. – 30 s. multicoloured 45 20
3266. – 42 s. multicoloured 1·10 25

DESIGNS: 13 s. to 42 s. Various footballers.

See also Nos. 3346/51.

**1087.** Computer Picture of Boy.

**1985.** International Young Inventors' Exhibition, Plovdiv. Multicoloured.

3268. 5 s. Type **1087** . . . . 10 10
3269. 13 s. Computer picture of youth . . . . . . 20 10
3270. 30 s. Computer picture of cosmonaut . . . . 45 20

**1088.** St. John's Church, Nesebur.

**1985.** 40th Anniv of U.N.E.S.C.O. Mult.
3271 5 s. Type **1088** .. .. 10 10
3272 13 s. Rila Monastery .. 20 10
3273 35 s. Soldier (fresco, Ivanovo Rock Church) 50 25
3274 42 s. Archangel Gabriel (fresco, Boyana Church) 60 25
3275 60 s. Thracian woman (fresco, Kazanlak tomb) 1·50 40

**1090.** Colosseum, Rome. **1091.** "Gladiolus".

**1985.** "Italia '85" International Stamp Exhibition, Rome.
3278. **1090.** 42 s. multicoloured 60 25

**1985.** Flowers.
3279. **1091.** 5 s. pink and red .. 10 10
3280. – 5 s. blue and light blue .. .. 10 10
3281. – 5 s. light violet and violet .. .. 10 10
3282. – 8 s. light blue and blue .. .. 15 10
3283. – 8 s. orange and red 15 10
3284. – 32 s. orge. and brn. 40 20
Designs: No. 3280, "Iris germanica". 3281, "Convolvulus tricolor". 3282, "Ipomea tricolor". 3283, "Anemone coronaria". 3284, "Lilium auratum".

**1985.** Historic Ships (4th series). As T **753**. Multicoloured.
3286 5 s. 17th-century Dutch fly .. .. .. 10 10
3287 12 s. Galleon "Sovereign of the Seas" .. .. 35 10
3288 20 s. Mediterranean polacca .. .. 45 25
3289 25 s. Warship "Prince Royal" .. .. 55 25
3290 42 s. Xebec .. .. 85 35
3291 60 s. 17th-century English warship .. .. 1·00 50

**1094.** Bacho Kiro. **1095.** Hands, Sword and Bible.

**1985.** Revolutionaries.
3293. **1094.** 5 s. light brown, brown and blue .. 10 10
3294. – 5 s. grn., pur. & brn. 10 10
Design: No. 3294, Georgi S. Rakovski.

**1985.** 150th Anniv. of Tirnovo Uprising.
3295. **1095.** 13 s. brown, blue and purple .. 20 10

**1096.** "1185 Revolution" (G. Bogdanov).

**1985.** 800th Anniv. of Liberation from Byzantine Empire. Multicoloured.
3296. 5 s. Type **1096** .. .. 10 10
3297. 13 s. "1185 Revolution" (Al. Terziev) .. .. 20 10
3298. 30 s. "Battle of Klakotnitsa, 1230" (B. Grigorov and M. Ganovski) .. .. 40 20
3299. 42 s. "Veliko Tirnovo" (Ts. Lavrenov) .. 1·10 25

**1098.** Emblem and Globe.

**1985.** International Development Programme for Posts and Telecommunications.
3302. **1098.** 13 s. multicoloured 20 10

**1099.** Popov.

**1985.** 70th Birth Anniv. of Anton Popov (revolutionary).
3303. **1099.** 5 s. red .. .. 10 10

**1100.** Doves around Snowflake.

**1985.** New Year. Multicoloured.
3304 5 s. Type **1100** .. .. 10 10
3305 13 s. Circle of stylized doves .. .. .. 20 10

**1101.** Pointer and Chukar Partridge.

**1985.** Hunting Dogs. Multicoloured.
3306 5 s. Type **1101** .. .. 50 15
3307 8 s. Irish setter and European pochard .. 65 15
3308 13 s. English setter and mallard .. .. 85 15
3309 20 s. Cocker spaniel and woodcock .. .. 1·25 20
3310 25 s. German pointer and rabbit .. .. .. 35 15
3311 30 s. Bulgarian bloodhound and boar 40 20
3312 42 s. Dachshund and fox 1·10 25

**1102.** Person in Wheelchair and Runners.

**1985.** International Year of Disabled Persons (1984).
3313. **1102.** 5 s. multicoloured .. 10 10

**1103.** Georgi Dimitrov (statesman).

**1985.** 50th Anniv. of 7th Communist International Congress, Moscow.
3314. **1103.** 13 s. red .. .. 20 10

**1104.** Emblem within "40".

**1986.** 40th Anniv. of U.N.I.C.E.F.
3315. **1104.** 13 s. blue, gold and black .. .. 20 10

**1105.** Blagoev. **1106.** Hands and Dove within Laurel Wreath.

**1986.** 130th Birth Anniv. of Dimitur Blagoev (founder of Bulgarian Communist Party).
3316. **1105.** 5 s. purple & orange 10 10

**1986.** International Peace Year.
3317. **1106.** 5 s. multicoloured .. 10 10

**1107.** "Dactylorhiza romana".

**1986.** Orchids. Multicoloured.
3318. 5 s. Type **1107** .. .. 10 10
3319. 13 s. "Epipactis palustris" .. .. 20 10
3320. 30 s. "Ophrys cornuta" 40 20
3321. 32 s. "Limodorum abrotivum" .. .. 40 20
3322. 42 s. "Cypripedium calceolus" .. .. 55 25
3323. 60 s. "Orchis papilionacea" .. .. 1·40 35

**1108.** Angora Rabbit.

**1986.** Rabbits.
3324 – 5 s. grey, blk & brn 10 10
3325 **1108** 25 s. red and black .. 35 15
3326 – 30 s. brn, yell & blk 40 20
3327 – 32 s. orange & black 40 20
3328 – 42 s. red and black .. 55 25
3329 – 60 s. blue and black 1·50 35
Designs: 5 s. French grey. 30 s. English lop-eared. 32 s. Belgian. 42 s. English spotted. 60 s. Dutch black and white rabbit.

**HAVE YOU READ THE NOTES AT THE BEGINNING OF THIS CATALOGUE?**
These often provide answers to the enquiries we receive.

**1109.** Front Page and Ivan Bogorov.

**1986.** 140th Anniv. of "Bulgarian Eagle".
3330. **1109.** 5 s. multicoloured .. 10 10

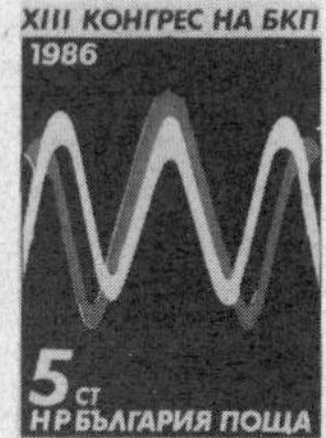


**1111.** Bashev. **1112.** Wave Pattern.

**1986.** 50th Birth Anniv. (1985) of Vladimir Bashev (poet).
3332. **1111.** 5 s. blue & lt. blue 10 10

**1986.** 13th Bulgarian Communist Party Congress.
3333. **1112.** 5 s. blue, grn. & red 10 10
3334. – 8 s. blue and red .. 15 10
3335. – 13 s. blue, red and light blue .. 20 10
Designs: 8 s. Printed circuit as tail of shooting star. 13 s. Computer picture of man.

**1114.** Monument, Panagyurishte. **1116.** Stylized Ear of Wheat.

**1986.** 110th Anniv. of April Uprising.
3338. **1114.** 5 s. black, stone and green .. .. 10 10
3339. – 13 s. black, stone and red .. .. 20 10
Design: 13 s. Statue of Khristo Botev, Vratsa.

**1986.** 35th Bulgarian People's Agrarian Union Congress.
3341. **1116.** 5 s. gold, orange and black .. .. 10 10
3342. – 8 s. gold, blue and black .. 15 10
3343. – 13 s. multicoloured 20 10
Designs: 8 s. Stylized ear of wheat on globe. 13 s. Flags.

**1117.** Transport Systems. **1118.** Emblem.

**1986.** Socialist Countries' Transport Ministers Conference.
3344. **1117.** 13 s. multicoloured 20 10

**1986.** 17th International Book Fair, Sofia.
3345. **1118.** 13 s. grey, red and black .. .. 20 10

**1119.** Player with Ball.

**1986.** World Cup Football Championship, Mexico (2nd issue). Multicoloured.

3346 5 s. Type **1119** .. .. 10 10
3347 13 s. Player tackling (horiz) .. .. 20 10
3348 20 s. Player heading ball (horiz) .. .. 30 15
3349 30 s. Player kicking ball (horiz) .. .. 40 20
3350 42 s. Goalkeeper (horiz) .. 55 25
3351 60 s. Player with Trophy 1·40 35

**1120.** Square Brooch.

**1986.** Treasures of Preslav. Multicoloured.

3353. 5 s. Type **1120** .. .. 10 10
3354. 13 s. Pendant (vert.) .. 20 10
3355. 20 s. Wheel-shaped pendant .. .. 30 15
3356. 30 s. Breast plate decorated with birds and chalice .. .. 40 20
3357. 42 s. Pear-shaped pendant (vert.) .. 55 25
3358. 60 s. Enamelled cockerel on gold base .. .. 80 35

**1121.** Fencers with Sabres.

**1986.** World Fencing Championships, Sofia. Multicoloured.

3359. 5 s. Type **1121** .. .. 10 10
3360. 13 s. Fencers .. .. 20 10
3361. 25 s. Fencers with rapiers 40 20

**1122.** Stockholm Town Hall.

**1986.** "Stockholmia 86" International Stamp Exhibition.

3362. **1122.** 42 s. brown, red and deep red .. .. 60 25

**1124.** Arms and Parliament Building, Sofia.

**1986.** 40th Anniv. of People's Republic.

3364. **1124.** 5 s. green, red and light green .. 10 10

**1125.** Posthorn.

**1986.** 15th Organization of Socialist Countries' Postal Administrations Session, Sofia.

3365. **1125.** 13 s. multicoloured 20 10

**1126.** "All Pull Together".

**1127.** Dove and Book as Pen Nib.

**1986.** 40th Anniv. of Voluntary Brigades.

3366. **1126.** 5 s. multicoloured .. 15 10

**1986.** 10th International Journalists Association Congress, Sofia.

3367. **1127.** 13 s. bl. & deep bl. 20 10

**1128.** Wrestlers.

**1986.** 75th Anniv. of Levski-Spartak Sports Club.

3368. **1128.** 5 s. multicoloured .. 10 10

**1129.** Saints Cyril and Methodius with Disciples (fresco).

**1986.** 1100th Anniv. of Arrival in Bulgaria of Pupils of Saints Cyril and Methodius.

3369. **1129.** 13 s. brown and buff 20 10

**1130.** Old and Modern Telephones.

**1986.** Centenary of Telephone in Bulgaria.

3370. **1130.** 5 s. multicoloured .. 10 10

**1131.** Weightlifter.

**1986.** World Weightlifting Championships, Sofia.

3371. **1131.** 13 s. multicoloured 20 10

**1986.** Historic Ships (5th series). 18th-century ships. As T **753**. Multicoloured.

3372 5 s. Galleon "King of Prussia" .. .. 15 10
3373 13 s. East Indiaman .. 25 10
3374 25 s. Xebec .. .. 50 25
3375 30 s. Russian ship of the line "Sv. Paul" .. 65 30
3376 32 s. Topsail schooner .. 65 30
3377 42 s. Russian ship of the line "Pobeda" .. 80 30


**1133.** Silver Jug decorated with Seated Woman.

**1986.** 14th Congress of Bulgarian Philatelic Federation and 60th Anniv. of International Philatelic Federation. Repousse work found at Rogozen.

3379. **1133.** 10 s. grey, black and blue .. .. 15 15
3380. – 10 s. green, black and red .. .. 15 15

DESIGN: No. 3380, Silver jug decorated with sphinx.

**1134.** Doves between Pine Branches.

**1986.** New Year.

3381. **1134.** 5 s. red, green and blue .. .. 10 10
3382. – 13 s. mauve, blue and violet .. 20 10

DESIGN: 13 s. Fireworks and snowflakes.

**1135.** Earphones as "60" on Globe.

**1986.** 60th Anniv. of Bulgarian Amateur Radio.

3383. **1135.** 13 s. multicoloured 20 10

**1137.** Gen. Sandino and Flag.

**1986.** 25th Anniv. of Sandinista Movement of Nicaragua.

3385. **1137.** 13 s. multicoloured 20 10

**1138.** Miladinovits Brothers (authors).


**1139.** Pencho Slaveikov.

**1986.** 125th Anniv. of "Bulgarian Popular Songs".

3386. **1138.** 10 s. blue, brown and red .. .. 15 10

**1986.** Writers' Birth Annivs. Multicoloured.

3387. 5 s. Type **1139** (125th anniv.) .. .. 10 10
3388. 5 s. Stoyan Mikhailovski (130th anniv.) .. .. 10 10
3389. 8 s. Nikola Atanasov (centenary) .. .. 10 10
3390. 8 s. Ran Bosilek (centenary) .. .. 10 10

**1140.** Raiko Daskalov.

**1141.** "Girl with Fruit".

**1986.** Birth Centenary of Raiko Daskalov (politician).

3391. **1140.** 5 s. brown .. .. 10 10

**1986.** 500th Birth Anniv. of Titian (painter). Multicoloured.

3392. 5 s. Type **1141** .. .. 10 10
3393. 13 s. "Flora" .. .. 20 10
3394. 20 s. "Lucretia and Tarquin" .. .. 30 15
3395. 30 s. "Caiphas and Magdelena" .. .. 50 25
3396. 32 s. "Toilette of Venus" (detail) .. .. 50 25
3397. 42 s. "Self-portrait" .. .. 1·10 25

**1142.** Fiat, 1905.

**1986.** Racing Cars.

3399. **1142.** 5 s. brown, red and black .. .. 10 10
3400. – 10 s. red, orange and black .. .. 15 10
3401. – 25 s. green, red and black .. .. 40 20
3402. – 32 s. brown, red and black .. .. 50 25
3403. – 40 s. violet, red and black .. .. 60 25
3404. – 42 s. grey, black and red .. .. 1·10 25

DESIGNS: 10 s. Bugatti, 1928. 25 s. Mercedes, 1936. 32 s. Ferrari, 1952. 40 s. Lotus, 1985. 42 s. Maclaren, 1986.

**1143.** Steam Locomotive.

**1987.** 120th Anniv. of Ruse–Varna Railway.

3405. **1143.** 5 s. multicoloured .. 10 10

**1144.** Debelyanov.

**1987.** Birth Centenary of Dimcho Debelyanov (poet).

3406. **1144.** 5 s. deep blue, yellow and blue .. 10 10

**1145.** Lazarus Ludwig Zamenhof (inventor).

**1987.** Centenary of Esperanto (invented language).

3407. **1145.** 13 s. blue, yellow and green .. 20 10

**1146.** "Amanita rubescens". **1147.** Worker.

**1987.** Edible Fungi. Multicoloured.

3408. 5 s. Type **1146** .. .. 10 10
3409. 20 s. "Boletus regius" .. 40 20
3410. 30 s. "Leccinum aurantiacum" .. 65 25
3411. 32 s. "Coprinus comatus" 65 30
3412. 40 s. "Russula vesca" .. 80 35
3413. 60 s. "Cantharellus cibarius" .. .. 1·25 70

**1987.** 10th Trade Unions Congress.
3414. **1147.** 5 s. violet and red . . 10 10

**1148.** Silver-gilt Plate with Design of Hercules and Auge.

**1987.** Treasure of Rogozen. Multicoloured.
3415. 5 s. Type **1148** . . . . 10 10
3416. 8 s. Silver-gilt jug with design of lioness attacking stag . . 10 10
3417. 20 s. Silver-gilt plate with quatrefoil design 30 15
3418. 30 s. Silver-gilt jug with design of horse rider . . 50 25
3419. 32 s. Silver-gilt pot with palm design . . . . 50 25
3420. 42 s. Silver jug with chariot and horses design . . . . . . 60 25

**1150.** Wrestlers. **1152.** "X" and Flags.

**1151.** Totem Pole.

**1987.** 30th European Freestyle Wrestling Championships, Turnovo.
3422. **1150.** 5 s. lilac, red and violet . . . . 10 10
3423. – 13 s. deep blue, red and blue . . 20 10
DESIGNS: 13 st. Wrestlers (different).

**1987.** "Capex '87" International Stamp Exhibition, Toronto.
3424. **1151.** 42 s. multicoloured 60 25

**1987.** 10th Fatherland Front Congress.
3425. **1152.** 5 s. green, orange and blue . . . . 10 10

**1153.** Georgi Dimitrov and Profiles.

**1987.** 15th Dimitrov Communist Youth League Congress.
3426. **1153.** 5 s. purple, green and red . . . . 10 10

**1154.** Mask. **1156.** Mariya Gigova.

**1155.** Mastheads.

**1987.** 8th International Festival of Humour and Satire, Gabrovo.
3427. **1154.** 13 s. multicoloured 20 10

**1987.** 60th Anniv. of "Rabotnichesko Delo" (newspaper).
3428. **1155.** 5 s. red and black . . 10 10

**1987.** 13th World Rhythmic Gymnastics Championships, Varna.
3429. **1156.** 5 s. blue and yellow 10 10
3430. – 8 s. red and yellow 10 10
3431. – 13 s. blue and stone 20 10
3432. – 25 s. red and yellow 40 20
3433. – 30 s. blk. & yellow 50 25
3434. – 42 s. mauve & yell. 60 25
DESIGNS: 8 s. Iliana Raeva. 13 s. Aneliya Ralenkova. 25 s. Dilyana Georgieva. 30 s. Liliya Ignatova. 42 s. Bianka Panova.

**1157.** Man breaking Chains around Globe and Kolarov.

**1987.** 110th Birth Anniv. of Vasil Kolarov.
3436. **1157.** 5 s. multicoloured . . 10 10

**1158.** Stela Blagoeva. **1160.** Roe Deer.

**1159.** Levski.

**1987.** Birth Centenary of Stela Blagoeva.
3437. **1158.** 5 s. brown and pink 10 10

**1987.** 150th Birth Anniv. of Vasil Levski (revolutionary).
3438. **1159.** 5 s. brown & green 10 10
3439. – 13 s. green & brown 20 10
DESIGN: 13 s. Levski and Bulgarian Revolutionary Central Committee emblem.

**1987.** Stags. Multicoloured.
3440. 5 s. Type **1160** . . . . 10 10
3441. 10 s. Elk (horiz.) . . 15 10
3442. 32 s. Fallow deer . . 50 25
3443. 40 s. Sika deer . . . . 60 25
3444. 42 s. Red deer (horiz.) . . 60 25
3445. 60 s. Reindeer . . . . 90 40

**1161.** Barbed Wire as Dove.

**1987.** International Namibia Day.
3446. **1161.** 13 s. black, red and orange . . . . 20 10

**1162.** "Phacelia tanacetifolia". **1164.** Kirkov.

**1163.** Mil Mi-8 Helicopter, Tupolev Tu-154 and Antonov An-12 Aircraft.

**1987.** Flora. Multicoloured.
3447. 5 s. Type **1162** . . . . 10 10
3448. 10 s. Sunflower . . . . 15 10
3449. 30 s. "Robinia pseudoacacia" . . 50 25
3450. 32 s. Lavender . . . . 50 25
3451. 42 s. Lime . . . . 60 25
3452. 60 s. "Onobrychis sativa" . . . . 90 40

**1987.** 40th Anniv. of Balkanair.
3453. **1163.** 25 s. multicoloured 70 30

**1987.** 120th Birth Anniv. of Georgi Kirkov (politician).
3454. **1164.** 5 s. red and pink . . 10 10

**1165.** 1879 5 st. Stamp.

**1987.** "Bulgaria '89" International Stamp Exhibiton, Sofia (1st issue).
3455 **1165** 13 s. multicoloured . . 20 10
See also Nos. 3563, 3573/6 and 3596/9.

**1166.** Copenhagen Town Hall. **1167.** "Portrait of Girl" (Stenaf Ivanov).

**1987.** "Hafnia '87" International Stamp Exhibition, Copenhagen.
3456. **1166.** 42 s. multicoloured 60 25

**1987.** Paintings in Sofia National Gallery. Multicoloured.
3457. 5 s. Type **1167.** 10 10
3458. 8 s. "Woman carrying Grapes" (Bencha Obreshkov) . . 10 10
3459. 20 s. "Portrait of a Woman wearing a Straw Hat" (David Perets) . . . . . . 30 10
3460. 25 s. "Women listening to Marimba" (Kiril Tsonev) . . . . 40 20
3461. 32 s. "Boy with Harmonica" (Nenko Balkanski) . . . . 50 25
3462. 60 s. "Rumyana" (Vasil Stoinov) . . . . 90 40

**1168.** Battle Scene.

**1987.** 75th Anniv. of Balkan War.
3463. **1168.** 5 s. black, stone and red . . . . 10 10

**1169.** Emblem.

**1987.** 30th Anniv. of International Atomic Energy Agency.
3464. **1169.** 13 s. blue, green and red . . . . 20 10

**1170.** Mastheads.

**1987.** 95th Anniv. of "Rabotnik", 90th Anniv. of "Rabotnicheski Vestnik" and 60th Anniv. of "Rabotnichesko Delo" Newspapers.
3465. **1170.** 5 s. red, blue and gold . . . . 10 10

**1171.** Winter Wren. **1174.** Biathlon.

**1173.** Lenin and Revolutionary.

**1987.** Birds. Multicoloured.
3466. 5 s. Type **1171** . . . . 10 10
3467. 13 s. Yellowhammer . . 30 15
3468. 20 s. European nuthatch 40 20
3469. 30 s. Blackbird . . . . 60 35
3470. 42 s. Hawfinch . . . . 90 40
3471. 60 s. Dipper . . . . 1·25 55

**1987.** 70th Anniv. of Russian Revolution.
3473. **1173.** 5 s. purple and red 10 10
3474. – 13 s. blue and red . . 20 10
DESIGN: 13 s. Lenin and cosmonaut.

**1987.** Winter Olympic Games, Calgary. Multicoloured.
3475. 5 s. Type **1174** . . . . 10 10
3476. 13 s. Slalom . . . . 20 10
3477. 30 s. Figure skating (women's) . . . . 40 20
3478. 42 s. Four-man bobsleigh 60 25

**1175.** "Socfilex" Emblem within Folk-design Ornament.

**1987.** New Year. Multicoloured.
3480. 5 s. Type **1175** . . . . 10 10
3481. 13 s. Emblem within flower ornament . . 20 10

**1177.** Kabakchiev. **1178.** "Scilla bythynica".

**1988.** 110th Birth Anniv. of Khristo Kabakchiev (Communist Party official).
3483. **1177** 5 s. multicoloured . . 10 10

**1988.** Marsh Flowers. Multicoloured.
3484. 5 s. Type **1178** . . . . 10 10
3485. 10 s. "Geum rhodopaeum" . . . . 15 10
3486. 13 s. "Caltha polypetala" 20 10
3487. 25 s. "Nymphoides peltata" . . . . 35 15
3488. 30 s. "Cortusa matthioli" 40 20
3489. 42 s. "Striatiotes aloides" 60 25

**1179.** Commander on Horseback.

**1988.** 110th Anniv. of Liberation from Turkey. Multicoloured.
3490. 5 s. Type **1179** . . . . 10 10
3491. 13 s. Soldiers . . . . 20 10

**1180.** Emblem.

**1988.** Public Sector Workers' 8th International Congress, Sofia.
3492. **1180.** 13 s. multicoloured 20 10

**1181.** "Yantra", 1888.

**1988.** Cent. of State Railways. Locomotives. Multicoloured.
3493. 5 s. Type **1181** . . . . 10 10
3494. 13 s. Kh. Botoav, 1905 . . 20 10
3495. 25 s. "807", 1918 . . . . 35 15
3496. 32 s. Steam locomotive, 1943 . . . . . . 45 20
3497. 42 s. Diesel locomotive, 1964 . . . . . . 60 25
3498. 60 s. Electric locomotive, 1979 . . . . . . 85 35

**1182.** Ivan Nedyalkov (Shablin).

НР БЪЛГАРИЯ 5 cm 1898–1988 ГЕОРГИ ТРАЙКОВ

**1183.** Traikov.

**1988.** Post Office Revolutionary Heroes.
3499. **1182.** 5 s. light brown and brown . . . . 10 10
3500. – 8 s. grey and blue . . 10 10
3501. – 10 s. green and olive 15 10
3502. – 13 s. pink and red . . 20 10

Designs: 8 s. Delcho Spasov. 10 s. Nikola Ganchev (Gudzho). 13 s. Ganka Rasheva (Boika).

**1988.** 90th Birth Anniv. of Georgi Traikov (politician).
3503. **1183.** 5 s. orge. and brn. 10 10

**1184.** Anniversary Emblem.

**1185.** Girl.

**1988.** 125th Anniv. of Red Cross.
3504. **1184.** 13 s. multicoloured 20 10

**1988.** 4th "Banners for Peace" Children's Meeting, Sofia. Children's paintings. Multicoloured.
3505. 5 s. Type **1185** . . . . 10 10
3506. 8 s. Artist at work . . 10 10
3507. 13 s. Circus (horiz.) . . 20 10
3508. 20 s. Kite flying (horiz.) . . 30 15
3509. 32 s. Accordian player . . 45 20
3510. 42 s. Cosmonaut . . 60 25

**1186.** Marx.

**1988.** 170th Birth Anniv. of Karl Marx.
3512. **1186.** 13 s. red, black and yellow . . . . 20 10

**1187** Herring Gull

**1189** "Soyuz TM" Spacecraft, Flags and Globe

**1188** African Elephant

**1988.** Birds. Multicoloured.
3513 5 s. Type **1187** . . . . 25 10
3514 5 s. White stork . . . . 25 10
3515 8 s. Grey heron . . . . 40 15
3516 8 s. Carrion crow . . . . 40 15
3517 10 s. Northern goshawk . . 50 20
3518 42 s. Eagle owl . . . . 1·00 30

**1988.** Centenary of Sofia Zoo. Multicoloured.
3519 5 s. Type **1188** . . . . 10 10
3520 13 s. White rhinoceros . . 20 10
3521 25 s. Hunting dog . . 35 15
3522 30 s. Eastern white pelican . . . . 70 30
3523 32 s. Abyssinian ground hornbill . . . . 75 35
3524 42 s. Snowy owl . . 1·50 55

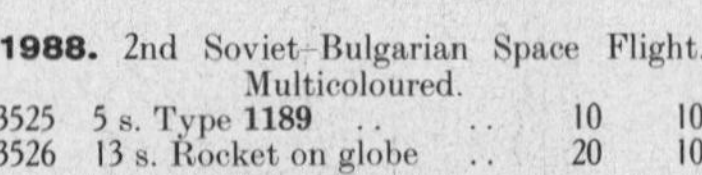

**1988.** 2nd Soviet–Bulgarian Space Flight. Multicoloured.
3525 5 s. Type **1189** . . . . 10 10
3526 13 s. Rocket on globe . . 20 10

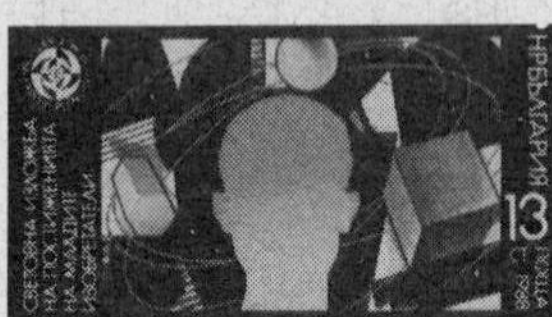

**1190** Young Inventor

**1988.** International Young Inventors' Exhibition, Plovdiv.
3527 **1190** 13 s. multicoloured . . 20 10

**1191** 1856 Handstamp of Russian Duchy of Finland

**1988.** "Finlandia '88" International Stamp Exhibition, Helsinki.
3528 **1191** 30 s. blue and red . . 40 20

**1192** Player taking Corner

**1193** "Portrait of Child"

**1988.** 8th European Football Championship, West Germany. Multicoloured.
3529 5 s. Type **1192** . . . . 10 10
3530 13 s. Goalkeeper and player . . . . . . 20 10
3531 30 s. Referee and player 40 20
3532 42 s. Player with trophy 60 25

**1988.** 2nd Death Anniv. of Dechko Uzunov (painter). Multicoloured.
3534 5 s. Type **1193** . . . . 10 10
3535 13 s. "Portrait of Mariya Vasileva" . . . . 20 10
3536 30 s. "Self-portrait" . . 40 20

**1195** "St. John"

**1196** High Jumping

**1988.** Icons from Kurdzhali. Multicoloured.
3538 5 s. Type **1195** . . . . 10 10
3539 8 s. "St. George and Dragon" . . . . 10 10

**1988.** Olympic Games, Seoul. Multicoloured.
3540 5 s. Type **1196** . . . . 10 10
3541 13 s. Weightlifting . . 20 10
3542 30 s. Wrestling . . . . 40 20
3543 42 s. Gymnastics . . 60 25

**1197** Dimitur and Stefan Karadzha

**1988.** 120th Death Anniv of Dimitur and Stefan Karadzha (revolutionaries).
3545 **1197** 5 s. green, blk & brn 10 10

**1198** Mastheads

**1988.** 30th Anniv of "Problems of Peace and Socialism" (magazine).
3546 **1198** 13 s. multicoloured . . 20 10

**1199** "The Dead Tree" (Roland Udo)

**1988.** Paintings in L. Zhivkova Art Gallery. Multicoloured.
3547 30 s. Type **1199** . . . . 45 20
3548 30 s. "Algiers Harbour" (Albert Marque) . . 45 20
3549 30 s. "Potrait of Hermine David" (Jule Pasquin) 45 20
3550 30 s. "Madonna and Child with Two Saints" (Giovanni and Rosso) 45 20

**1200** University Building

**1988.** Centenary of St. Clement of Ohrid University, Sofia.
3551 **1200** 5 s. black, yell & grn 10 10

**1201** Czechoslovakia 1918 5 h. Stamp

**1988.** "Praga '88" International Stamp Exhibition, Prague.
3552 **1201** 25 s. red and blue . . 35 15

**1202** Korea 1884 5 m. Stamp

**1988.** "Olymphilex' 88" Olympic Stamps Exhibition, Seoul.
3553 **1202** 62 s. red and green . . 90 40

**1203** Anniversary Emblem

**1204** Parliment Building, Sofia, and Map

**1988.** 25th Anniv of Kremikovtsi Steel Mills.
3554 **1203** 5 s. violet, red & blue 10 10

**1988.** 80th Interparliamentary Conference, Sofia.
3555 **1204** 13 s. blue and red . . 20 10

**1205** Chalice, Glinena

**1988.** Kurdzhali Culture. Multicoloured.
3556 5 s. Type **1205** .. .. 10 10
3557 8 s. Part of ruined fortifications .. .. 10 10

**1206** Soldiers

**1988.** 300th Anniv of Chiprovtsi Rising.
3558 **1206** 5 s. multicoloured .. 10 10

**1207** Brown Bear

**1988.** Bears. Multicoloured.
3559 5 s. Type **1207** .. .. 10 10
3560 8 s. Polar bear .. .. 10 10
3561 13 s. Sloth bear .. .. 20 10
3562 20 s. Sun bear .. .. 30 15
3563 32 s. Asiatic black bear .. 45 20
3564 42 s. Spectacled bear .. 60 25

**1208** Emblem

**1988.** 80th Council of Mutual Economic Aid Transport Commission Meeting, Sofia.
3565 **1208** 13 s. red and black .. 20 10

**1209** Emblem

**1988.** World Ecoforum.
3566 **1209** 20 s. multicoloured .. 30 15

**1210** Amphitheatre, Plovdiv

**1988.** "Plovdiv '88" National Stamp Exn.
3567 **1210** 5 s. multicoloured .. 10 10

**1211** Transmission Towers

**1988.** 25th Anniv of Radio and Television.
3568 **1211** 5 s. green, blue & brn 10 10

**1212** 1879 5 c. Stamp

**1988.** "Bulgaria '89" International Stamp Exhibition (2nd issue).
3569 **1212** 42 s. orge, blk & mve 60 25

**1214** Children and Cars

**1988.** Road Safety Campaign.
3571 **1214** 5 s. multicoloured .. 10 10

**1215** Rila Hotel, Borovets

**1988.** Hotels. Multicoloured.
3572 5 s. Type **1215** .. .. 10 10
3573 8 s. Pirin Hotel, Bansko 10 10
3574 13 s. Shchastlivetsa Hotel, Vitosha .. .. 20 10
3575 30 s. Perelik Hotel, Pamporovo .. .. 45 20

**1216** Tree Decoration

**1988.** New Year. Multicoloured.
3576 5 s. Type **1216** .. .. 10 10
3577 13 s. "Bulgaria '89" emblem, tree and decorations .. .. 20 10

**1218** Mail Coach

**1988.** "Bulgaria '89" International Stamp Exhibition, Sofia (3rd issue). Mail Transport. Multicoloured.
3579 25 s. Type **1218** .. .. 35 15
3580 25 s. Paddle-steamer .. 35 15
3581 25 s. Lorry .. .. 35 15
3582 25 s. Biplane .. .. 45 15

**1219** India 1947 1½ a. Independence Stamp

**1989.** "India 89" International Stamp Exhibition, New Delhi.
3583 **1219** 62 s. green and orange 90 40

**1220** France 1850 10 c. Ceres Stamp

**1989.** "Philexfrance '89" International Stamp Exhibition, Paris.
3584 **1220** 42 s. brown and blue 60 25

**1222** Don Quixote

**1223** "Ramonda serbica"

**1989.** International Festival of Humour and Satire, Gabrovo.
3586 **1222** 13 s. multicoloured .. 20 10

**1989.** Flowers. Multicoloured.
3587 5 s. Type **1223** .. .. 10 10
3588 10 s. "Paeonia maskula" 15 15
3589 25 s. "Viola perinensis" .. 35 15
3590 30 s. "Dracunculus vulgaris" .. .. 45 45
3591 42 s. "Tulipa splendens" 60 60
3592 60 s. "Rindera umbellata" 90 85

**1224** Common Noctule Bat

**1989.** Bats. Multicoloured.
3593 5 s. Type **1224** .. .. 10 10
3594 13 s. Greater horseshoe bat .. .. .. 20 10
3595 30 s. Large mouse-eared bat .. .. .. 45 20
3596 42 s. Particoloured frosted bat .. .. .. 60 25

**1225** Stamboliiski

**1989.** 110th Birth Anniv of Aleksandur Stamboliiski (leader of People's Agrarian Union).
3597 **1225** 5 s. black and orange 10 10

**1227** Young Inventor

**1989.** International Young Inventors' Exhibition, Plovdiv.
3599 **1227** 5 s. multicoloured .. 10 10

**1228** Stanke Dimitrov-Marek (Party activist)

**1229** "John the Baptist" (Toma Vishanov)

**1989.** Birth Centenaries.
3600 **1228** 5 s. red and black .. 10 10
3601 – 5 s. red and black .. 10 10
DESIGN: No. 3601, Petko Yenev.

**1989.** "Bulgaria 89" International Stamp Exhibition, Sofia (4th issue). Icons. Mult.
3602 30 s. Type **1229** .. .. 45 20
3603 30 s. "St. Dimitur" (Ivan Terziev) .. .. 45 20
3604 30 s. "Archangel Michael" (Dimitur Molerov) .. 45 20
3605 30 s. "Madonna and Child" (Toma Vishanov) .. .. 45 20

**1230** Fax Machine and Woman reading letter

**1989.** 110th Anniv of Bulgarian Post and Telegraph Services. Multicoloured.
3606 5 s. Type **1230** .. .. 10 10
3607 8 s. Telex machine and old telegraph machine 10 10
3608 35 s. Modern and old telephones .. .. 50 25
3609 42 s. Dish aerial and old radio .. .. .. 60 25

**1232** A. P. Aleksandrov, A.Ya. Solovov and V. P. Savinikh

**1989.** Air. "Soyuz TM5" Soviet–Bulgarian Space Flight.
3611 **1232** 13 s. multicoloured .. 20 10

**1233** Party Programme

**1234** Sofronii Vrachanski (250th anniv)

**1989.** 70th Anniv of First Bulgarian Communist Party Congress, Sofia.
3612 **1233** 5 s. blk, red & dp red 10 10

**1989.** Birth Anniversaries.
3613 **1234** 5 s. green, brn & blk 10 10
3614 – 5 s. green, brn & blk 10 10
DESIGN: No. 3614, Iliya Bluskov (150th anniv).

**1235** Birds

**1989.** Bicentenary of French Revolution. Each black, red and blue.
3615 13 s. Type **1235** .. 20 10
3616 30 s. Jean-Paul Marat .. 45 20
3617 42 s. Robespierre .. 60 25

**1236** Gymnastics

**1989.** 7th Friendly Armies Summer Spartakiad. Multicoloured.
3618 5 s. Type **1236** .. .. 10 10
3619 13 s. Show jumping .. 20 10
3620 30 s. Long jumping .. 45 20
3621 42 s. Shooting .. 60 25

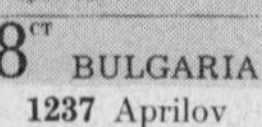

**1237** Aprilov

**1238** Zagorchinov

**1989.** Birth Bicentenary of Vasil Aprilov (educationalist).
3622 **1237** 8 s. lt blue, bl & blk 10 10

**1989.** Birth Centenary of Stoyan Zagorchinov.
3623 **1238** 10 s. turq, brn & blk 15 10

**1239** Woman in Kayak

**1989.** Canoeing and Kayak Championships, Plovdiv. Multicoloured.
3624 13 s. Type **1239** .. .. 20 10
3625 30 s. Man in kayak .. 45 20

**1240** Nadar in Balloon "Le Geant" and Photograph of Airship "Graf Zeppelin" over Cathedral

**1989.** 150th Anniv of Photography.
3626 **1240** 42 s. blk, stone & yell 80 30

**1241** Lammergeier and Lynx

**1989.** Centenary of Natural History Museum.
3627 **1241** 13 s. multicoloured .. 1·00 20

**1242** Soldiers

**1243** Lyubomir D. Dardzhidov

**1989.** 45th Anniv of Fatherland Front Government. Multicoloured.
3628 5 s. Type **1242** .. .. 10 10
3629 8 s. Welcoming officers .. 10 10
3630 13 s. Crowd of youths .. 20 10

**1989.** 48th Death Anniversaries of Post Office War Heroes. Multicoloured.
3631 5 s. Type **1243** .. .. 10 10
3632 8 s. Ivan Bankov Dobrev 10 10
3633 13 s. Nestor P. Antonov 20 10

**1244** Yasenov

**1246** Nehru

**1245** Lorry leaving Weighbridge

**1989.** Birth Cent of Khristo Yasenov (writer).
3634 **1244** 8 s. grey, brn & blk 10 10

**1989.** 21st Transport Congress, Sofia.
3635 **1245** 42 s. blue & deep blue 60 25

**1989.** Birth Centenary of Jawaharlal Nehru (Indian statesman).
3636 **1246** 13 s. yell, brn & blk 20 10

**1248** Javelin Sand Boa

**1989.** Snakes. Multicoloured.
3638 5 s. Type **1248** .. .. 10 10
3639 10 s. Aesculapian snake .. 15 10
3640 25 s. Leopard snake .. 35 15
3641 30 s. Four-lined rat snake 45 20
3642 42 s. Cat snake .. .. 60 25
3643 60 s. Whip snake .. 90 40

**1249** Tiger and Balloon of Flags

**1251** Goalkeeper saving Ball

**1989.** Young Inventors' Exhibition, Plovdiv.
3644 **1249** 13 s. multicoloured .. 20 10

**1989.** World Cup Football Championship, Italy (1990). Multicoloured.
3646 5 s. Type **1251** .. .. 10 10
3647 13 s. Player tackling .. 20 15
3648 30 s. Player heading ball 50 30
3649 42 s. Player kicking ball 70 40

**1252** Gliders

**1989.** 82nd Int. Airsports Federation General Conference, Varna. Aerial Sports. Mult.
3651 5 s. Type **1252** .. .. 10 10
3652 13 s. Hang gliding .. 20 15
3653 30 s. Parachutist landing 50 30
3654 42 s. Free falling parachutist .. .. 70 40

**MORE DETAILED LISTS**
are given in the Stanley Gibbons Catalogues referred to in the country headings.
For lists of current volumes see Introduction.

**1253** Children on Road Crossing

**1989.** Road Safety.
3655 **1253** 5 s. multicoloured .. 10 10

**1254** Santa Claus's Sleigh

**1255** European Shorthair

**1989.** New Year. Multicoloured.
3656 5 s. Type **1254** .. .. 10 10
3657 13 s. Snowman .. .. 20 15

**1989.** Cats.
3658 **1255** 5 s. black and yellow 10 10
3659 – 5 s. black and grey 10 10
3660 – 8 s. black and yellow 15 10
3661 – 10 s. black & brown 15 10
3662 – 10 s. black and blue 15 10
3663 – 13 s. black and red 20 15
DESIGNS—HORIZ. No. 3659, Persian; 3660, European shorthair (different); 3662, Persian (different). VERT. 3661, Persian (different); 3663, Siamese.

**1256** Christopher Columbus

**1990.** Navigators. Multicoloured.
3664 5 s. Type **1256** .. .. 20 10
3665 8 s. Vasco da Gama .. 20 10
3666 13 s. Ferdinand Magellan 20 10
3667 32 s. Francis Drake .. 20 10
3668 42 s. Henry Hudson .. 25 10
3669 60 s. James Cook .. 35 10

**1257** Banner

**1990.** Centenary of Esperanto (invented language) in Bulgaria.
3670 **1257** 10 s. stone, grn & blk 15 10

**1258** "Portrait of Madeleine Rono" (Maurice Brianchon)

**1990.** Paintings. Multicoloured.
3671 30 s. Type **1258** .. .. 50 30
3672 30 s. "Still Life" (Suzanne Valadon) .. .. 50 30
3673 30 s. "Portrait of a Woman" (Moise Kisling) .. .. 50 30
3674 30 s. "Portrait of a Woman" (Giovanni Boltraffio) .. .. 50 30

**1259** Players

**1990.** World Cup Football Championship, Italy. Designs showing various match scenes.
3675 **1259** 5 s. multicoloured .. 10 10
3676 – 13 s. multicoloured 20 15
3677 – 30 s. multicoloured 50 30
3678 – 42 s. multicoloured 70 40
DESIGNS: 13 to 42 s. Various match scenes.

**1260** Bavaria 1849 1 k. Stamp

**1990.** "Essen 90" International Stamp Fair.
3680 **1260** 42 s. black and red .. 70 40

**1262** "100" and Rainbow

**1990.** Centenary of Co-operative Farming.
3682 **1262** 5 s. multicoloured .. 10 10

**1263** "Elderly Couple at Rest"

**1990.** Birth Cent of Dimitur Chorbadzhiiski-Chudomir (artist).
3683 **1263** 5 s. multicoloured .. 10 10

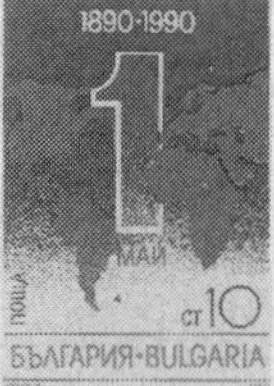

**1264** Map

**1990.** Centenary of Labour Day.
3684 **1264** 10 s. multicoloured .. 15 10

**1265** Emblem

**1990.** 125th Anniv of I.T.U.
3685 **1265** 20 s. blue, red & black 35 20

**1266** Belgium 1849 10 c. "Epaulettes" Stamp

**1990.** "Belgica 90" International Stamp Exhibition, Brussels.
3686 **1266** 30 s. brown and green 50 35

**1267** Lamartine and his House

**1990.** Birth Bicentenary of Alphonse de Lamartine (poet).
3687 **1267** 20 s. multicoloured .. 35 20

**1268** Brontosaurus

**1990.** Prehistoric Animals. Multicoloured.
3688 5 s. Type **1268** .. .. 10 10
3689 8 s. Stegosaurus .. .. 15 10
3690 13 s. Edaphosaurus .. .. 20 15
3691 25 s. Rhamphorhynchus 40 25
3692 32 s. Protoceratops .. 55 35
3693 42 s. Triceratops .. 70 40

**1269** Swimming

**1990.** Olympic Games, Barcelona (1992). Mult.
3694 5 s. Type **1269** .. .. 10 10
3695 13 s. Handball .. .. 20 15
3696 30 s. Hurdling .. .. 50 30
3697 42 s. Cycling .. .. 70 40

**1270** "Zerynthia polyxena"

**1990.** Butterflies and Moths. Multicoloured.
3699 5 s. Type **1270** .. .. 10 10
3700 10 s. "Panaxia quadripunctaria" .. .. 10 10
3701 20 s. "Proserpinus proserpina" .. .. 10 10
3702 30 s. "Hyles lineata" .. 45 10
3703 42 s. "Thecla betulae" .. 60 35
3704 60 s. "Euphydryas cynthia" .. .. 90 55

**1271** Airbus Industrie A310

**1990.** Airplanes. Multicoloured.
3705 5 s. Type **1271** .. .. 10 10
3706 10 s. Tupolev Tu-204 .. 15 10
3707 25 s. Concorde .. .. 40 25
3708 30 s. Douglas DC-9 .. 45 30
3709 42 s. Ilyushin Il-86 .. 60 35
3710 60 s. Boeing 747 .. .. 90 55
No. 3705 is wrongly inscribed Airbus "A300".

**1272** Iosif I

**1274** Putting the Shot

**1273** Road and U.N. Emblem within Triangles

**1990.** 150th Birth Anniv of Exarch Iosif I.
3711 **1272** 5 s. mauve, blk & grn 10 10

**1990.** International Road Safety Year.
3712 **1273** 5 s. multicoloured .. 10 10

**1990.** "Olymphilex '90" Olympic Stamps Exhibition, Varna. Multicoloured.
3713 5 s. Type **1274** .. .. 10 10
3714 13 s. Throwing the discus 20 10
3715 42 s. Throwing the hammer .. .. 65 40
3716 60 s. Throwing the javelin 90 55

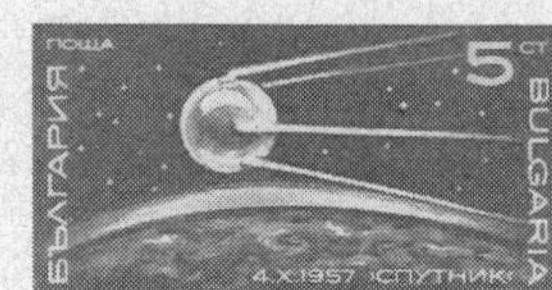


**1275** "Sputnik"

**1990.** Space Research. Multicoloured.
3717 5 s. Type **1275** .. .. 10 10
3718 8 s. "Vostok" .. .. 10 10
3719 10 s. Spacewalker from "Voskhod 2" .. 15 10
3720 20 s. "Soyuz"–"Apollo" link .. .. 30 20
3721 42 s. Space shuttle "Columbia" .. .. 65 40
3722 60 s. Space probe "Galileo" .. .. 90 55

**1276** St. Clement of Ohrid

**1277** Tree

**1990.** 1150th Birth Anniv of St. Clement of Ohrid.
3724 **1276** 5 s. brown, blk & grn 10 10

**1990.** Christmas. Multicoloured.
3725 5 s. Type **1277** .. .. 10 10
3726 20 s. Father Christmas .. 30 20

**1278** Skaters

**1991.** European Figure Skating Championships, Sofia.
3727 **1278** 15 s. multicoloured .. 25 15

**1279** Chicken

**1281** "Good Day" (Paul Gauguin)

**1280** Deadly Amanite

**1991.** Farm Animals.
3730 – 20 s. brown and black 10 10
3731 – 25 s. blue and black 10 10
3732 **1279** 30 s. brown and black 10 10
3733 – 40 s. brown and black 10 10
3735 – 62 s. green and black 40 10
3737 – 86 s. red and black .. 55 35
3738 – 95 s. mauve and black 40 10
3739 – 1 l. brown and black 65 40
3740 – 2 l. green and black 1·40 85
3742 – 5 l. violet and black 3·25 2·10
3745 – 10 l. blue and black 6·75 4·25
DESIGNS: 20 s. Sheep; 25 s. Goose; 40 s. Horse; 62 s. Goat; 86 s. Sow; 95 s. Billy goat; 1 l. Donkey; 2 l. Bull; 5 l. Turkey; 10 l. Cow.

**1991.** Fungi. Multicoloured.
3746 5 s. Type **1280** .. .. 15 10
3747 10 s. "Amanita verna" .. 25 10
3748 20 s. False blusher .. 55 15
3749 32 s. Fly agaric .. .. 95 25
3750 42 s. Beefsteak morel .. 1·25 35
3751 60 s. Devil's boletus .. 1·90 50

**1991.** Paintings. Multicoloured.
3752 20 s. Type **1281** .. .. 10 10
3753 43 s. "Madame Dobini" (Edgar Degas) .. 10 10
3754 62 s. "Peasant Woman" (Camille Pissarro) .. 40 10
3755 67 s. "Woman with Black hair" (Edouard Manet) 45 10
3756 80 s. "Blue Vase" (Paul Cezanne) .. .. 55 35
3757 2 l. "Madame Samari" (Pierre Auguste Renoir) 1·40 85

**1282** Map

**1991.** 700th Anniv of Swiss Confederation.
3759 **1282** 62 s. red and violet .. 40 10

**1283** Postman on Bicycle, Envelopes and Paper

**1991.** 100 Years of Philatelic Publications in Bulgaria.
3760 **1283** 30 s. multicoloured .. 10 10

**1284** "Meteosat" Weather Satellite

**1991.** Europa. Europe in Space. Mult.
3761 43 s. Type **1284** .. .. 10 10
3762 62 s. "Ariane" rocket .. 40 10

**1285** Przewalski's Horse

**1991.** Horses. Multicoloured.
3763 5 s. Type **1285** .. .. 10 10
3764 10 s. Tarpan .. .. 10 10
3765 25 s. Black arab .. .. 10 10
3766 35 s. White arab .. 10 10
3767 42 s. Shetland pony .. 10 10
3768 60 s. Draught horse .. 40 10

**1286** "Expo '91"

**1991.** "Expo '91" Exhibition, Plovdiv.
3769 **1286** 30 s. multicoloured .. 10 10

**1287** Mozart

**1991.** Death Bicentenary of Wolfgang Amadeus Mozart (composer).
3770 **1287** 62 s. multicoloured .. 40 10

**1288** Astronaut and Rear of Space Shuttle "Columbia"

**1991.** Space Shuttles. Multicoloured.
3771 12 s. Type **1288** .. .. 10 10
3772 32 s. Satellite and "Challenger" .. .. 10 10
3773 50 s. "Discovery" and satellite .. 35 10
3774 86 s. Satellite and "Atlantis" (vert) .. 60 35
3775 1 l. 50 Launch of "Buran" (vert) .. .. .. 1·00 65
3776 2 l. Satellite and "Atlantis" (vert) .. 1·40 85

**1289** Luge

**1291** Japanese Chin

**1290** Sheraton Hotel, Sofia

**1991.** Winter Olympic Games, Albertville (1992). Multicoloured.

3778 30 s. Type **1289** .. .. 10 10
3779 43 s. Slalom skiing .. 10 10
3780 67 s. Ski jumping .. 45 10
3781 2 l. Biathlon .. .. 1·40 85

**1991.**

3783 **1290** 62 s. multicoloured .. 15 20

**1991.** Dogs. Multicoloured.

3784 30 s. Type **1291** .. .. 10 10
3785 43 s. Chihuahua .. .. 10 10
3786 62 s. Miniature pinscher 35 10
3787 80 s. Yorkshire terrier .. 50 10
3788 1 l. Mexican hairless .. 60 30
3789 3 l. Pug .. .. .. 1·75 90

**1292** Arms

**1991.** "Philatelia '91" Stamp Fair, Cologne.

3790 **1292** 86 s. multicoloured .. 50 10

**1294** Japan 1871 48 mon "Dragon" Stamp

**1991.** "Phila Nippon '91" International Stamp Exhibition, Tokyo.

3792 **1294** 62 s. black, brn & bl 10 10

**1295** Small Pasque Flower

**1991.** Medicinal Plants. Multicoloured.

3793 30 s. (+15 s.) Pale pasque flower .. .. .. 10 10
3794 40 s. Type **1295** .. .. 10 10
3795 55 s. "Pulsatilla halleri" 10 10
3796 60 s. "Aquilegia nigricans" .. .. 10 10
3797 1 l. Sea buckthorn .. 40 10
3798 2 l. Blackcurrant .. 85 40

No. 3793 includes a se-tenant premium-carrying label for 15 s. inscribed "ACTION 2000. For Environment Protection".

**1296** Steam Locomotive and Tender

**1991.** 125th Anniv of the Railway in Bulgaria. Multicoloured.

3799 30 s. Type **1296** .. .. 10 10
3800 30 s. Passenger carriage .. 10 10

**1297** Ball ascending to Basket

**1298** "Christ carrying the Cross"

**1991.** Centenary of Basketball. Multicoloured.

3801 43 s. Type **1297** .. .. 10 10
3802 62 s. Ball level with basket mouth .. .. 10 10
3803 90 s. Ball entering basket 40 10
3804 1 l. Ball in basket .. 40 10

**1991.** 450th Birth Anniv of El Greco (painter). Multicoloured.

3805 43 s. Type **1298** .. .. 10 10
3806 50 s. "Holy Family with St. Anna" .. .. 10 10
3807 60 s. "St. John of the Cross and St. John the Evangelist" .. .. 10 10
3808 62 s. "St. Andrew and St. Francis" .. .. 10 10
3809 1 l. "Holy Family with Magdelene" .. .. 40 10
3810 2 l. "Cardinal Fernando Nino de Guevara" .. 85 40

**1299** Snowman, Moon, Candle, Bell and Heart

**1991.** Christmas. Multicoloured.

3812 30 s. Type **1299** .. 10 10
3813 62 s. Star, clover, angel, house and Christmas tree .. .. .. 10 10

**1300** Greenland Seals

**1991.** Marine Mammals. Multicoloured.

3814 30 s. Type **1300** .. .. 10 10
3815 43 s. Killer whales .. 10 10
3816 62 s. Walruses .. .. 10 10
3817 68 s. Bottle-nosed dolphins .. .. 10 10
3818 1 l. Mediterranean monk seals .. .. .. 40 10
3819 2 l. Common porpoises .. 85 40

**1301** Synagogue

**1992.** 500th Anniv of Jewish Settlement in Bulgaria.

3820 **1301** 1 l. multicoloured .. 40 10

**1302** Rossini, "The Barber of Seville" and Figaro

**1992.** Birth Bicentenary of Gioacchino Rossini (composer).

3821 **1302** 50 s. multicoloured .. 10 10

**1303** Plan of Fair

**1992.** Centenary of Plovdiv Fair.

3822 **1303** 1 l. black and stone 40 10

**1304** Volvo "740"

**1992.** Motor Cars. Multicoloured.

3823 30 s. Type **1304** .. .. 10 10
3824 45 s. Ford "Escort" .. 10 10
3825 50 s. Fiat "Croma" .. 10 10
3826 50 s. Mercedes Benz "600" 10 10
3827 1 l. Peugeot "605" .. 40 10
3828 2 l. B.M.W. "316" .. 85 10

**1305** Amerigo Vespucci

**1992.** Explorers. Multicoloured.

3829 50 s. Type **1305** .. .. 20 10
3830 50 s. Francisco de Orellana .. .. 20 10
3831 1 l. Ferdinand Magellan 40 10
3832 1 l. Jimenez de Quesada 40 10
3833 2 l. Sir Francis Drake .. 80 35
3834 3 l. Pedro de Valdivia .. 1·25 50

**1306** Granada

**1992.** "Granada '92" Int Stamp Exn.

3836 **1306** 62 s. multicoloured .. 10 10

**1307** "Santa Maria"

**1992.** Europa. 500th Anniv of Discovery of America by Columbus. Multicoloured.

3837 1 l. Type **1307** .. .. 40 10
3838 2 l. Christopher Columbus 80 35

Nos. 3837/8 were issued together, se-tenant, forming a composite design.

**1308** House

**1992.** S.O.S. Children's Village.

3839 **1308** 1 l. multicoloured .. 40 10

**1309** Long Jumping

**1992.** Olympic Games, Barcelona. Mult.

3840 50 s. Type **1309** .. .. 10 10
3841 50 s. Swimming .. .. 10 10
3842 1 l. High jumping .. 40 10
3843 3 l. Gymnastics .. .. 1·25 50

**1310** 1902 Laurin and Klement Motor Cycle

**1992.** Motor Cycles. Multicoloured.

3845 30 s. Type **1310** .. .. 10 10
3846 50 s. 1928 Puch "200 Luxus" .. .. .. 10 10
3847 50 s. 1931 Norton "CS 1" 10 10
3848 70 s. 1950 Harley Davidson .. .. 10 10
3849 1 l. 1986 Gilera "SP 01" .. 40 10
3850 2 l. 1990 BMW "K 1" .. 80 10

**1311** Genoa

**1992.** "Genova '92" International Thematic Stamp Exhibition.

3851 **1311** 1 l. multicoloured .. 40 10

**1312** Grasshopper

**1313** Silhouette of Head on Town Plan

**1992.** Insects. Multicoloured.

3852 1 l. Four-spotted libellula 25 10
3853 2 l. "Raphidia notata" .. 50 20
3854 3 l. Type **1312** .. .. 75 35
3855 4 l. Stag beetle .. .. 1·00 40
3856 5 l. Fire bug .. .. 1·25 50
3857 7 l. Ant .. .. .. 2·40 1·10
3860 20 l. Wasp .. .. 6·75 3·25
3863 50 l. Praying mantis .. 12·50 4·25

**1992.** 50th Anniv of Institute of Architecture and Building.

3862 **1313** 1 l. red and black .. 40 10

**1314** Oak ("Quercus mestensis")

**1992.** Trees. Multicoloured.

3863 50 s. Type **1314** .. .. 10 10
3864 50 s. Horse chestnut ("Aesculus hippocastanum") .. .. 10 10
3865 1 l. Oak ("Quercus thracica") .. .. 40 10
3866 1 l. Macedonian pine ("Pinus peuce") .. 40 10
3867 2 l. Maple .. .. 80 10
3868 3 l. Pear .. .. .. 1·25 40

**1315** Embroidered Flower

**1992.** Centenary of Folk Museum, Sofia.

3869 **1315** 1 l. multicoloured .. 40 10

**1316** "Bulgaria" (freighter)

**1992.** Centenary of National Shipping Fleet. Multicoloured.

| No. | Description | Unused | Used |
|---|---|---|---|
| 3870 | 30 s. Type **1316** .. .. | 10 | 10 |
| 3871 | 50 s. "Kastor" (tanker) .. | 20 | 10 |
| 3872 | 1 l. "Geroite na Sebastopol" (ferry) .. | 40 | 15 |
| 3873 | 2 l. "Aleko Konstantinov" (tanker) .. .. | 80 | 30 |
| 3874 | 2 l. "Bulgaria" (tanker) | 80 | 30 |
| 3875 | 3 l. "Varna" (container ship) .. .. .. | 1·25 | 45 |

**1317** Council Emblem

**1992.** Admission to Council of Europe.

| No. | Description | Unused | Used |
|---|---|---|---|
| 3876 | **1317** 7 l. multicoloured .. | 2·75 | 1·00 |

**1319** "Santa Claus" (Ani Bacheva)

**1992.** Christmas. Children's Drawings. Mult.

| No. | Description | Unused | Used |
|---|---|---|---|
| 3878 | 1 l. Type **1319** .. .. | 35 | 10 |
| 3879 | 7 l. "Madonna and Child" (Georgi Petkov) .. | 2·75 | 1·00 |

**1320** Leopard ("Pathera pardus") **1322** Tengmalm's Owl

**1321** Cricket

**1992.** Animals. Multicoloured.

| No. | Description | Unused | Used |
|---|---|---|---|
| 3880 | 50 s. Type **1320** .. .. | 10 | 10 |
| 3881 | 50 s. Cheetah ("Acinonyx jubatus") .. .. | 10 | 10 |
| 3882 | 1 l. Jaguar .. .. | 40 | 10 |
| 3883 | 2 l. Puma ("Felis concolor") .. .. | 80 | 35 |
| 3884 | 2 l. Tiger ("Panthera tigris") .. .. | 80 | 35 |
| 3885 | 3 l. Lion .. .. .. | 1·25 | 50 |

**1992.** Sport. Multicoloured.

| No. | Description | Unused | Used |
|---|---|---|---|
| 3886 | 50 s. Type **1321** .. .. | 10 | 10 |
| 3887 | 50 s. Baseball .. .. | 10 | 10 |
| 3888 | 1 l. Pony and trap racing | 40 | 10 |
| 3889 | 1 l. Polo .. .. .. | 40 | 10 |
| 3890 | 2 l. Hockey .. .. | 80 | 35 |
| 3891 | 3 l. American football .. | 1·25 | 50 |

**1992.** Owls. Multicoloured.

| No. | Description | Unused | Used |
|---|---|---|---|
| 3892 | 30 s. Type **1322** .. .. | 10 | 10 |
| 3893 | 50 s. Tawny owl (horiz) .. | 10 | 10 |
| 3894 | 1 l. Long-eared owl .. | 40 | 10 |
| 3895 | 2 l. Short-eared owl ("Asio flammeus") .. | 80 | 35 |
| 3896 | 2 l. Scops owl ("Otus scops") (horiz) | 80 | 35 |
| 3897 | 3 l. Barn owl .. .. | 1·25 | 50 |

**1323** "Khan Kubrat" (Dimitr Gyudzhenov)

**1992.** Historical Paintings. Multicoloured.

| No. | Description | Unused | Used |
|---|---|---|---|
| 3898 | 50 st. Type **1323** .. | 25 | 10 |
| 3899 | 1 l. "Khan Asparukh" (Nicolai Pavlovich) .. | 50 | 20 |
| 3900 | 2 l. "Khan Terval at Tsarigrad" (Dimitr Panchev) .. .. | 1·00 | 40 |
| 3901 | 3 l. "Prince Boris" (Nicolai Pavlovich) .. | 1·60 | 65 |

**1324** Sculpted Head **1325** Shooting

**1993.** Centenary of National Archaeological Museum, Sofia.

| No. | Description | Unused | Used |
|---|---|---|---|
| 3903 | **1324** 1 l. multicoloured .. | 50 | 20 |

**1993.** "Borovets '93" Biathlon Championship. Multicoloured.

| No. | Description | Unused | Used |
|---|---|---|---|
| 3904 | 1 l. Type **1325** .. .. | 50 | 20 |
| 3905 | 7 l. Skiing .. .. | 3·50 | 1·40 |

**1326** Rilski **1327** "Morning" (sculpture, Georgi Chapkunov)

**1993.** Birth Bicentenary of Neofit Rilski (compiler of Bulgarian grammar and dictionary).

| No. | Description | Unused | Used |
|---|---|---|---|
| 3906 | **1326** 1 l. bistre and red .. | 50 | 20 |

**1993.** Europa. Contemporary Art. Mult.

| No. | Description | Unused | Used |
|---|---|---|---|
| 3907 | 3 l. Type **1327** .. .. | 60 | 25 |
| 3908 | 8 l. "Composition" (D. Buyukliiski) .. | 1·60 | 65 |

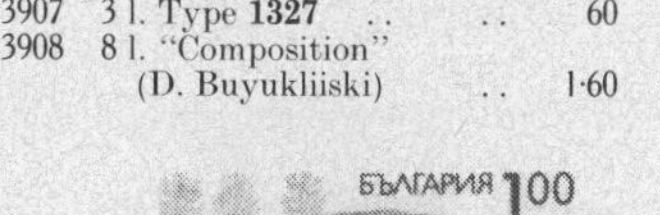

**1328** Goldfish

**1993.** Fishes. Multicoloured.

| No. | Description | Unused | Used |
|---|---|---|---|
| 3909 | 1 l. Type **1328** .. .. | 20 | 10 |
| 3910 | 2 l. Yucatan sailfish .. | 40 | 20 |
| 3911 | 3 l. Two-striped killifish | 60 | 25 |
| 3912 | 3 l. Angelfish .. .. | 60 | 25 |
| 3913 | 4 l. Discus .. .. | 85 | 35 |
| 3914 | 8 l. Pearl gourami .. | 1·60 | 65 |

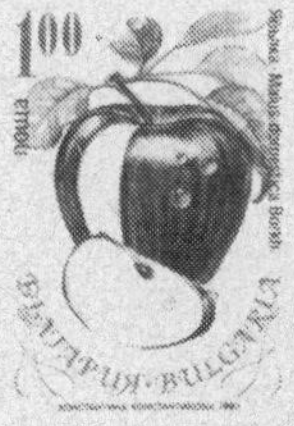

**1329** Apple **1330** Monteverdi

**1993.** Fruits. Multicoloured.

| No. | Description | Unused | Used |
|---|---|---|---|
| 3915 | 1 l. Type **1329** .. .. | 20 | 10 |
| 3916 | 2 l. Peach .. .. | 40 | 15 |
| 3917 | 2 l. Pear .. .. .. | 40 | 15 |
| 3918 | 3 l. Quince .. .. | 60 | 25 |
| 3919 | 5 l. Pomegranate .. | 1·00 | 40 |
| 3920 | 7 l. Fig .. .. .. | 1·50 | 60 |

**1993.** 350th Death Anniv of Claudio Monteverdi (composer).

| No. | Description | Unused | Used |
|---|---|---|---|
| 3921 | **1330** 1 l. green, yell & red | 50 | 20 |

**1331** High Jumping

**1993.** Int Games for the Deaf, Sofia. Mult.

| No. | Description | Unused | Used |
|---|---|---|---|
| 3922 | 1 l. Type **1331** .. .. | 25 | 10 |
| 3923 | 2 l. Swimming .. .. | 45 | 20 |
| 3924 | 3 l. Cycling .. .. | 65 | 30 |
| 3925 | 4 l. Tennis .. .. | 85 | 35 |

**1333** Prince Alexander **1334** Tchaikovsky

**1993.** Death Centenary of Prince Alexander I.

| No. | Description | Unused | Used |
|---|---|---|---|
| 3928 | **1333** 3 l. multicoloured .. | 65 | 30 |

**1993.** Death Centenary of Pyotr Tchaikovsky (composer).

| No. | Description | Unused | Used |
|---|---|---|---|
| 3929 | **1334** 3 l. multicoloured .. | 65 | 30 |

**1335** Crossbow **1336** Newton

**1993.** Weapons. Multicoloured.

| No. | Description | Unused | Used |
|---|---|---|---|
| 3930 | 1 l. Type **1335** .. .. | 20 | 10 |
| 3931 | 2 l. 18th-century flintlock pistol .. .. | 40 | 15 |
| 3932 | 3 l. Revolver .. .. | 60 | 25 |
| 3933 | 3 l. Luger pistol .. .. | 60 | 25 |
| 3934 | 5 l. Mauser rifle .. .. | 1·00 | 40 |
| 3935 | 7 l. Kalashnikov assault rifle .. .. .. | 1·50 | 60 |

**1993.** 350th Birth Anniv of Sir Isaac Newton (mathematician).

| No. | Description | Unused | Used |
|---|---|---|---|
| 3936 | **1336** 1 l. multicoloured .. | 25 | 10 |

**1337** "100" on Stamps and Globe

**1993.** Centenary of Bulgarian Philately.

| No. | Description | Unused | Used |
|---|---|---|---|
| 3937 | **1337** 1 l. multicoloured .. | 25 | 10 |

**1338** "Ecology" in Cyrillic

**1993.** Ecology. Multicoloured.

| No. | Description | Unused | Used |
|---|---|---|---|
| 3938 | 1 l. Type **1338** .. .. | 25 | 10 |
| 3939 | 7 l. "Ecology" in English | 1·40 | 60 |

**1339** Mallard

**1993.** Hunting. Multicoloured.

| No. | Description | Unused | Used |
|---|---|---|---|
| 3940 | 1 l. Type **1339** .. .. | 20 | 10 |
| 3941 | 1 l. Ring-necked pheasant | 20 | 10 |
| 3942 | 2 l. Red fox .. .. | 40 | 15 |
| 3943 | 3 l. Roe deer .. .. | 60 | 25 |
| 3944 | 6 l. European brown hare | 1·25 | 50 |
| 3945 | 8 l. Wild boar .. .. | 1·50 | 60 |

**1340** "Taurus", "Gemini" and "Cancer" **1341** Sofia Costume

**1993.** Christmas. Signs of the Zodiac. Mult.

| No. | Description | Unused | Used |
|---|---|---|---|
| 3946 | 1 l. Type **1340** .. .. | 25 | 10 |
| 3947 | 1 l. "Leo", "Virgo" and "Libra" .. .. | 25 | 10 |
| 3948 | 7 l. "Aquarius", "Pisces" and "Aries" .. .. | 1·40 | 60 |
| 3949 | 7 l. "Scorpio", "Sagittarius" and "Capricorn" .. .. | 1·40 | 60 |

Nos. 3946/7 and 3948/9 were each issued together, se-tenant; when placed together the four stamps form a composite design.

**1993.** Costumes. Multicoloured.

| No. | Description | Unused | Used |
|---|---|---|---|
| 3950 | 1 l. Type **1341** .. .. | 20 | 10 |
| 3951 | 1 l. Plovdiv .. .. | 20 | 10 |
| 3952 | 2 l. Belograd .. .. | 40 | 15 |
| 3953 | 3 l. Oryakhovo .. .. | 60 | 25 |
| 3954 | 3 l. Shumen .. .. | 60 | 25 |
| 3955 | 8 l. Kurdzhali .. .. | 1·60 | 65 |

**1342** Freestyle Skiing **1343** "Self-portrait" and "Tsar Simeon"

**1994.** Winter Olympic Games, Lillehammer, Norway. Multicoloured.

| No. | Description | Unused | Used |
|---|---|---|---|
| 3956 | 1 l. Type **1342** .. .. | 20 | 10 |
| 3957 | 2 l. Speed skating .. | 45 | 20 |
| 3958 | 3 l. Two-man luge .. | 65 | 30 |
| 3959 | 4 l. Ice hockey .. .. | 90 | 40 |

**1994.** Death Centenary of Nikolai Pavlovich (artist).

| No. | Description | Unused | Used |
|---|---|---|---|
| 3961 | **1343** 3 l. multicoloured .. | 50 | 20 |

**1344** Plesiosaurus

**1994.** Prehistoric Animals. Multicoloured.

| No. | Description | Unused | Used |
|---|---|---|---|
| 3962 | 2 l. Type **1344** .. .. | 35 | 15 |
| 3963 | 3 l. Archaeopteryx .. | 50 | 20 |
| 3964 | 3 l. Iguanodon .. .. | 50 | 20 |
| 3965 | 4 l. Edmontonia .. | 70 | 30 |
| 3966 | 5 l. Styracosaurus .. | 85 | 35 |
| 3967 | 7 l. Tyrannosaurus .. | 1·10 | 45 |

**1345** Players (Chile, 1962)

**1994.** World Cup Football Championship, U.S.A. Multicoloured.

| No. | Description | Unused | Used |
|---|---|---|---|
| 3968 | 3 l. Type **1345** .. .. | 50 | 20 |
| 3969 | 6 l. Players (England, 1966) .. .. | 1·00 | 40 |
| 3970 | 7 l. Goalkeeper making save (Mexico, 1970) .. | 1·25 | 50 |
| 3971 | 9 l. Player kicking (West Germany, 1974) .. | 1·50 | 60 |

1346 Photoelectric Analysis (Georgi Nadzhakov)

**1994.** Europa. Discoveries. Multicoloured.

| | | | |
|---|---|---|---|
| 3973 | 3 l. Type **1346** . . . . | 50 | 20 |
| 3974 | 15 l. Cardiogram and heart (Prof. Ivan Mitev) . . . . | 2·40 | 1·00 |

1347 Khristov

**1994.** 80th Birth Anniv of Boris Khristov (actor).

| | | | | |
|---|---|---|---|---|
| 3975 | 1347 | 3 l. multicoloured . . | 50 | 20 |

1348 Sleeping Hamster

1349 Space Shuttle, Satellite and Dish Aerial

**1994.** The Common Hamster Multicoloured.

| | | | |
|---|---|---|---|
| 3976 | 3 l. Type **1348** . . . . | 50 | 20 |
| 3977 | 7 l. Hamster looking out of burrow . . . . | 1·25 | 50 |
| 3978 | 10 l. Hamster sitting up in grass . . . . | 2·00 | 80 |
| 3979 | 15 l. Hamster approaching berry . . . . | 2·40 | 1·00 |

**1994.** North Atlantic Co-operation Council (North Atlantic Treaty Organization and Warsaw Pact members).

| | | | | |
|---|---|---|---|---|
| 3980 | 1349 | 3 l. multicoloured . . | 50 | 20 |

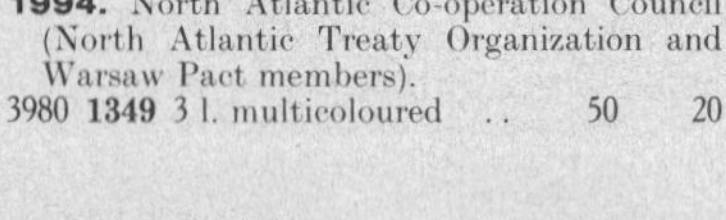

1350 Baron Pierre de Coubertin (founder of modern games)

1351 "Christ Pantocrator"

**1994.** Centenary of International Olympic Committee.

| | | | | |
|---|---|---|---|---|
| 3981 | 1350 | 3 l. multicoloured . . | 50 | 20 |

**1994.** Icons. Multicoloured.

| | | | |
|---|---|---|---|
| 3982 | 2 l. Type **1351** . . . . | 35 | 15 |
| 3983 | 3 l. "Raising of Lazarus" | 50 | 20 |
| 3984 | 5 l. "Passion of Christ" . . | 85 | 35 |
| 3985 | 7 l. "Archangel Michael" | 1·25 | 50 |
| 3986 | 8 l. "Sts. Cyril and Methodius" . . . . | 1·60 | 65 |
| 3987 | 15 l. "Madonna on the Throne" . . . . | 2·40 | 1·00 |

1352 Vechernik

**1994.** Christmas. Breads. Multicoloured.

| | | | |
|---|---|---|---|
| 3988 | 3 l. Type **1352** . . . . | 50 | 20 |
| 3989 | 15 l. Bogovitsa . . . . | 2·50 | 1·00 |

1353 "Golden Showers"

**1994.** Roses. Multicoloured.

| | | | |
|---|---|---|---|
| 3990 | 2 l. Type **1353** . . . . | 35 | 15 |
| 3991 | 3 l. "Kaen Lape" . . | 50 | 20 |
| 3992 | 5 l. "Theresa of Lisieux" | 85 | 25 |
| 3993 | 7 l. "Zambra 93" . . | 1·40 | 60 |
| 3994 | 10 l. "Gustave Courbet" | 2·00 | 80 |
| 3995 | 15 l. "Honore de Balzac" | 2·60 | 1·10 |

1355 "AM/ASES", 1912

**1994.** Trams. Multicoloured.

| | | | |
|---|---|---|---|
| 3997 | 1 l. Type **1355** . . . . | 10 | 10 |
| 3998 | 2 l. "AM/ASES", 1928 . . | 35 | 15 |
| 3999 | 3 l. "M.A.N./AEG", 1931 | 50 | 20 |
| 4000 | 5 l. "D.T.O.", 1942 . . | 85 | 35 |
| 4001 | 8 l. "Republika", 1951 . . | 1·75 | 70 |
| 4002 | 10 l. "Kosmonavt", 1961 | 1·90 | 80 |

1356 Petleshkov and Flag

1357 Daisy growing through Cracked Helmet

**1995.** 150th Birth Anniv of Vasil Petleshkov (leader of 1876 April uprising).

| | | | | |
|---|---|---|---|---|
| 4003 | 1356 | 3 l. multicoloured . . | 50 | 20 |

**1995.** Europa. Peace and Freedom. Mult.

| | | | |
|---|---|---|---|
| 4004 | 3 l. Type **1357** . . . . | 50 | 20 |
| 4005 | 15 l. Dove with olive branch on rifle barrel . . | 2·40 | 1·00 |

1360 "Euphausia superba"

**1995.** Antarctic Animals. Multicoloured.

| | | | |
|---|---|---|---|
| 4008 | 1 l. Type **1360** . . . . | 10 | 10 |
| 4009 | 2 l. Ice fish . . . . | 35 | 15 |
| 4010 | 3 l. Sperm whale . . | 50 | 20 |
| 4011 | 5 l. Weddell's seal . . | 85 | 35 |
| 4012 | 8 l. Arctic skua . . . . | 1·75 | 70 |
| 4013 | 10 l. Emperor penguin (vert) . . . . | 2·00 | 80 |

1361 Stambolov

**1995.** Death Centenary of Stefan Stambolov (politician).

| | | | | |
|---|---|---|---|---|
| 4014 | 1361 | 3 l. multicoloured . . | 55 | 25 |

1362 Pole Vaulting

**1995.** Olympic Games, Atlanta (1996). Mult.

| | | | |
|---|---|---|---|
| 4015 | 3 l. Type **1362** . . . . | 45 | 20 |
| 4016 | 7 l. High jumping . . | 1·10 | 45 |
| 4017 | 10 l. Long jumping . . | 1·75 | 70 |
| 4018 | 15 l. Triple jumping . . | 2·50 | 1·00 |

1363 Pea

1365 "Ivan Nikolov"

1364 "100"

**1995.** Food Plants. Multicoloured.

| | | | |
|---|---|---|---|
| 4019 | 2 l. Type **1363** . . . . | 30 | 15 |
| 4020 | 3 l. Chickpea . . . . | 40 | 20 |
| 4021 | 3 l. Soya bean . . . . | 40 | 20 |
| 4022 | 4 l. Spinach . . . . | 55 | 25 |
| 4023 | 5 l. Peanut . . . . | 70 | 30 |
| 4024 | 15 l. Lentil . . . . | 2·00 | 80 |

**1995.** Centenary of Organized Tourism.

| | | | | |
|---|---|---|---|---|
| 4025 | 1364 | 1 l. multicoloured . . | 50 | 50 |

**1995.** Birth Centenary of Vasil Zakhariev (painter).

| | | | | |
|---|---|---|---|---|
| 4026 | 1365 | 2 l. multicoloured . . | 35 | 15 |
| 4027 | – | 3 l. multicoloured . . | 45 | 20 |
| 4028 | – | 5 l. black, brn & grn | 80 | 35 |
| 4029 | – | 10 l. multicoloured . . | 1·75 | 70 |

DESIGNS: 3 l. "Rila Monastery"; 5 l. "Self-portrait"; 10 l. "Raspberry Collectors".

1366 "Dove-Hands" holding Globe

**1995.** 50th Anniv of U.N.O.

| | | | | |
|---|---|---|---|---|
| 4030 | 1366 | 3 l. multicoloured . . | 35 | 15 |

1367 Polikarpov Po-2 Biplane

**1995.** Aircraft. Multicoloured.

| | | | |
|---|---|---|---|
| 4031 | 3 l. Type **1367** . . . . | 25 | 10 |
| 4032 | 5 l. Lisunov Li-2 . . | 40 | 20 |
| 4033 | 7 l. Junkers Ju 52 . . | 80 | 35 |
| 4034 | 10 l. Focke Wulf Fw 58 . . | 1·10 | 45 |

1368 Charlie Chaplin and Mickey Mouse

**1995.** Centenary of Motion Pictures. Mult.

| | | | |
|---|---|---|---|
| 4035 | 2 l. Type **1368** . . . . | 15 | 10 |
| 4036 | 3 l. Marilyn Monroe and Marlene Dietrich . . | 30 | 15 |
| 4037 | 5 l. Nikolai Cherkasov and Humphrey Bogart . . | 55 | 25 |
| 4038 | 8 l. Sophia Loren and Liza Minelli . . . . | 65 | 30 |
| 4039 | 10 l. Gerard Philipe and Toshiro Mifune . . | 1·25 | 50 |
| 4040 | 15 l. Katya Paskaleva and Nevena Kokanova . . | 1·40 | 60 |

1369 Agate

**1995.** Minerals. Multicoloured.

| | | | |
|---|---|---|---|
| 4041 | 1 l. Type **1369** . . . . | 10 | 10 |
| 4042 | 2 l. Sphalerite . . . . | 20 | 10 |
| 4043 | 5 l. Calcite . . . . | 45 | 20 |
| 4044 | 7 l. Quartz . . . . | 65 | 25 |
| 4045 | 8 l. Pyromorphite . . | 75 | 30 |
| 4046 | 10 l. Almandine . . . . | 90 | 40 |

1370 Mary and Joseph

**1995.** Christmas. Multicoloured.

| | | | |
|---|---|---|---|
| 4047 | 3 l. Type **1370** . . . . | 30 | 15 |
| 4048 | 15 l. Three wise men approaching stable . . | 1·40 | 60 |

1371 "Polynesian Woman with Fruit"

**1996.** Birth Centenary of Kirul Tsonev (painter).

| | | | | |
|---|---|---|---|---|
| 4049 | 1371 | 3 l. multicoloured . . | 30 | 15 |

1372 Luther

**1996.** 450th Death Anniv of Martin Luther (Protestant reformer).

| | | | | |
|---|---|---|---|---|
| 4050 | 1372 | 3 l. multicoloured . . | 30 | 15 |

1373 Preobrazhenie

1374 Bulgarian National Bank

**1996.** Monasteries.

| | | | | |
|---|---|---|---|---|
| 4053 | 1373 | 3 l. green . . . . | 15 | 10 |
| 4054 | – | 5 l. red . . . . | 25 | 10 |
| 4056 | – | 10 l. blue . . . . | 45 | 20 |
| 4058 | – | 20 l. orange . . | 95 | 40 |
| 4059 | – | 25 l. brown . . | 1·25 | 50 |
| 4061 | – | 40 l. purple . . | 1·90 | 80 |

DESIGNS: 5 l. Arapov; 10 l. Dryanovo; 20 l. Bachkov; 25 l. Troyan; 40 l. Zograf.

**1996.** 5th Anniv of European Reconstruction and Development Bank.

| | | | | |
|---|---|---|---|---|
| 4063 | 1374 | 7 l. green, red & blue | 30 | 15 |
| 4064 | – | 30 l. blue, red & pur | 1·25 | 50 |

DESIGN: 30 l. European Bank.

1375 Yew

**1996.** Conifers. Multicoloured.

4065 5 l. Type **1375** .. .. 20 10
4066 8 l. European silver fir .. 35 15
4067 10 l. Norway spruce .. 45 20
4068 20 l. Scots pine .. .. 90 40
4069 25 l. "Pinus heldreichii" 1·10 45
4070 40 l. Juniper .. .. 1·75 70

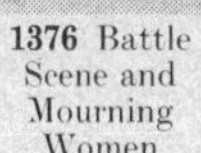

1376 Battle Scene and Mourning Women

1377 Modern Officer's Parade Uniform

**1996.** 120th Anniversaries. Multicoloured.

4071 10 l. Type **1376** (April uprising) .. .. 45 20
4072 40 l. Khristo Botev and script (poet, death anniv) (horiz) .. .. 1·75 70

**1996.** Military Uniforms. Multicoloured.

4073 5 l. Type **1377** .. .. 20 10
4074 8 l. Second World War combat uniform .. .. 35 15
4075 10 l. Balkan War uniform 45 20
4076 20 l. Guard officer's ceremonial uniform .. 90 40
4077 25 l. Serbo-Bulgarian War officer's uniform .. 1·10 45
4078 40 l. Russo-Turkish War soldier's uniform .. 1·75 70

1378 Monument

**1996.** 50th Anniv of the Republic.

4079 **1378** 10 l. multicoloured .. 45 20

1379 Elisaveta Bagryana (poet)

**1996.** Europa. Famous Women. Mult.

4080 10 l. Type **1379** .. .. 60 25
4081 40 l. Katya Popova (opera singer) .. .. 2·50 1·00

EXPRESS STAMPS

E 137. Express Delivery Van.

DESIGNS—VERT. 5 l., 20 l. Bicycle messenger. 7 l. Motorcyclist and sidecar.

**1939.**

E 429. – 5 l. blue .. 1·10 25
E 430. E **137.** 6 l. brown .. 40 25
E 431. – 7 l. brown .. 85 30
E 432. E **137.** 8 l. red .. 1·00 30
E 433. – 20 l. red .. .. 1·75 65

OFFICIAL STAMPS.

O 158. O 177.

**1942.**

O 507. O **158.** 10 s. green .. 10 10
O 508. 30 s. orange .. 10 10
O 509. 50 s. brown .. 10 10
O 510. – 1 l. blue .. .. 10 10
O 511. – 2 l. green .. 10 10
O 534. – 2 l. red .. 50 20
O 512. – 3 l. mauve .. 10 10
O 513. – 4 l. pink .. 15 10
O 514. – 5 l. red .. 35 15

The 1 l. to 5 l. are larger (19 × 23 mm.).

**1945.** Arms designs. Imperf. or perf.

O 580. – 1 l. mauve .. 10 10
O 581. O **177.** 2 l. green .. 10 10
O 582. – 3 l. brown .. 10 10
O 583. – 4 l. blue .. .. 10 10
O 584. – 5 l. red .. .. 15 10

PARCEL POST STAMPS

P **153.** Weighing Machine.

P **154.** Loading Motor Lorry.

**1941.**

P 494. P **153.** 1 l. green .. 10 10
P 495. A. 2 l. red .. 10 10
P 496. P **154.** 3 l. brown .. 10 10
P 497. B. 4 l. orange .. 10 10
P 498. P **153.** 5 l. blue .. 10 10
P 506. 5 l. green .. 15 10
P 499. B. 6 l. purple .. 10 10
P 507. 6 l. brown .. 10 10
P 500. P **153.** 7 l. blue .. 10 10
P 508. 7 l. sepia .. 10 10
P 501. P **154.** 8 l. turquoise .. 20 10
P 509. 8 l. green .. 10 10
P 502. A. 9 l. olive .. 15 10
P 503. B. 10 l. orange .. 15 10
P 504. P **154.** 20 l. violet .. 35 10
P 513. A. 30 l. black .. 35 10

DESIGNS—HORIZ. A, Loading mail coach. B, Motor-cycle combination.

P 163.

**1944.** Imperf.

P 532. P **163.** 1 l. red .. 15 10
P 533. 3 l. green .. 15 10
P 534. 5 l. green .. 15 10
P 535. 7 l. mauve .. 15 10
P 536. 10 l. blue .. 15 10
P 537. 20 l. brown .. 15 10
P 538. 30 l. purple .. 15 10
P 539. 50 l. orange .. 35 15
P 540. 100 l. blue .. 95 25

POSTAGE DUE STAMPS

D 7. D 12.  D 16.

**1884.** Perf.

D 53. D **7.** 5 s. orange .. .. 17·00 4·00
D 54. 25 s. lake .. .. 13·50 4·25
D 55. 50 s. blue .. .. 6·75 5·00

**1886.** Imperf.

D 50. D **7.** 5 s. orange .. .. £275 13·50
D 51. 25 s. lake .. .. £400 11·50
D 52. 50 s. blue .. .. 13·50 13·50

**1893.** Surch. with bar and **30.**

D 78. D **7.** 30 s. on 50 s. bl. (perf.) 17·00 8·25
D 79. 30 s. on 50 s. blue (imperf.) .. .. 15·00 8·25

**1896.** Perf.

D 83. D **12.** 5 s. orange .. .. 10·00 2·40
D 84. 10 s. violet .. .. 6·75 2·00
D 85. 30 s. green .. .. 5·00 1·60

**1901.**

D 124. D **16.** 5 s. red .. .. 65 20
D 125. 10 s. green .. .. 1·40 25
D 126. 20 s. blue .. .. 10·00 25
D 127. 30 s. red .. .. 1·00 30
D 128. 50 s. orange .. 14·00 8·75

D 37.  D 110.

**1915.**

D 181. D **37.** 5 s. green .. 20 10
D 240. 10 s. violet .. 10 10
D 202. 20 s. red .. 20 15
D 241. 20 s. orange .. 10 10
D 203a. 30 s. red .. 20 10
D 242. 50 s. blue .. 10 10
D 243. 1 l. green .. 35 10
D 244. 2 l. red .. .. 35 15
D 245. 3 l. brown .. 65 20

**1932.**

D 326. D **110.** 1 l. bistre .. 1·00 85
D 327. 2 l. red .. .. 1·00 85
D 328. 6 l. purple .. 2·10 1·00

D 111. D 112.  D 293.

**1933.**

D 333. D **111.** 20 s. sepia .. 10 10
D 334. 40 s. blue .. 10 10
D 335. 80 s. red .. 10 10
D 336. D **112.** 1 l. brown .. 60 30
D 337. 2 l. olive .. 65 40
D 338. 6 l. violet .. 20 20
D 339. 14 l. blue .. 55 30

**1947.** As Type D **112**, but larger (18 × 24 mm.).

D 646. 1 l. brown .. 10 10
D 647. 2 l. red .. .. 10 10
D 648. 8 l. orange .. 15 10
D 649. 20 l. blue .. 25 15

**1951.**

D 849. D **293.** 1 l. brown .. 10 10
D 850. 2 l. purple .. 15 10
D 851. 8 l. orange .. 30 30
D 852. 20 l. blue .. 1·10 90

## BULGARIAN OCCUPATION OF RUMANIA Pt. 3

(DOBRUJA DISTRICT)

100 stotinki = 1 leva.

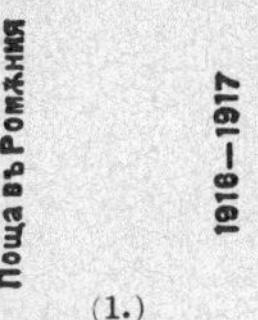


(1.)

**1916.** Bulgarian stamps of 1911 optd. with T **1.**

1. **23.** 1 s. slate .. .. .. 10 10
2. – 5 s. purple and green .. 2·75 1·90
3. – 10 s. sepia and brown .. 15 10
4. – 25 s. black and blue .. 15 10

## BURKINA FASO Pt. 12

A country in W. Africa, formerly known as Upper Volta. The name was changed in August 1984.

100 centimes = 1 franc.

**249.** "Graphium pylades".

**1984.** Air. Butterflies. Multicoloured.

738. 10 f. Type **249** .. .. 10 10
739. 120 f. "Hyploimnas misippus" .. .. 65 40
740. 400 f. "Danaus chrysippus" .. .. 2·10 1·50
741. 450 f. "Papilio demodocus" 2·40 1·60

**250.** Soldier with Gun.

**1984.** 1st Anniv of Captain Thomas Sankara's Presidency. Multicoloured.

742 90 f. Type **250** .. .. 40 25
743 120 f. Capt. Sankara and crowd .. .. 50 35

**1985.** Nos. 716/21 of Upper Volta optd **BURKINA FASO**.

744 25 f. Type **246** (postage) .. 15 10
745 185 f. "Pterocarpus lucens" 80 65
746 200 f. "Phlebopus colossus sudanicus" .. .. 1·50 85
747 250 f. "Cosmos sulphureus" 1·10 90
748 300 f. "Trametes versicolor" (air) .. 1·75 1·25
749 400 f. "Ganoderma lucidum" .. .. 2·25 1·75

**252.** National Flag.

**1985.** National Symbols. Multicoloured.

750. 5 f. Type **252** (postage) .. 10 10
751. 15 f. National arms (vert.) 10 10
752. 90 f. Maps of Africa and Burkina Faso .. .. 40 25
753. 120 f. Type **252** (air) .. 50 35
754. 150 f. As No. 751 .. .. 65 50
755. 185 f. As No. 752 .. .. 80 65

## MINIMUM PRICE

The minimum price quoted is 10p which represents a handling charge rather than a basis for valuing common stamps. For further notes about prices see introductory pages.

**253.** Footballers and Statue.

**1985.** World Cup Football Championship, Mexico.

756. **253.** 25 f. mult. (post.) .. 15 10
757. – 45 f. multicoloured .. 20 15
758. – 90 f. multicoloured .. 40 25
759. – 100 f. mult. (air) .. 45 30
760. – 150 f. multicoloured .. 65 50
761. – 200 f. mult. (horiz.) .. 90 75
762. – 250 f. mult. (horiz.) .. 1·10 90

DESIGNS: 45 f. to 250 f. Mexican statues and various footballing scenes.

**254.** Children playing and Boy.

**1985.** Air "Philexafrique" International Stamp Exhibition, Lome, Togo (1st issue). Multicoloured.

764. 200 f. Type **254** .. .. 90 75
765. 200 f. Solar panels, transmission mast, windmill, dish aerial and tree .. 90 75

See also Nos. 839/40.

**255.** G. A. Long's Steam Tricycle.

**1985.** Centenary of Motor Cycle. Mult.

766. 50 f. Type **255** (postage) .. 20 15
767. 75 f. Pope .. .. .. 30 20
768. 80 f. Manet .. .. .. 35 25
769. 100 f. Ducati (air) .. .. 45 30
770. 150 f. Jawa .. .. .. 65 50
771. 200 f. Honda .. .. 90 75
772. 250 f. B.M.W. .. .. 1·10 90

**256.** "Chamaeleon dilepis".

**1985.** Reptiles and Amphibians. Mult.

773. 5 f. Type **256** (postage) .. 10 10
774. 15 f. "Agama stellio" .. 10 10
775. 35 f. "Lacerta lepida" (horiz.) .. .. .. 15 10
776. 85 f. "Hiperolius marmoratus" (horiz.) .. 35 25
777. 100 f. "Echis leucogaster" (horiz.) (air) .. .. 45 30
778. 150 f. "Kinixys erosa" (horiz.) .. .. .. 65 50
779. 250 f. "Python regius" (horiz.) .. .. .. 1·10 90

**257.** Benz "Victoria", 1893.

**1985.** Motor Cars and Aircraft. Multicoloured.

780 5 f. Type **257** (postage) .. 10 10
781 25 f. Peugeot "174", 1927 15 10
782 45 f. Bleriot XI airplane .. 40 15
783 50 f. Breguet 14T biplane 40 15
784 500 f. Bugatti "Napoleon T41 Royale" (air) .. 2·75 2·25
785 500 f. Airbus Industrie A300 .. .. .. 2·75 2·25
786 600 f. Mercedes-Benz "540 K", 1938 .. .. 3·00 2·50
787 600 f. Airbus Industrie A300 .. .. .. 3·00 2·50

**258.** Wood Duck.

**1985.** Birth Bicentenary of John J. Audubon (ornithologist). Multicoloured.

789. 60 f. Type **258** (postage) .. 60 35
790. 100 f. Northern mockingbird .. .. 1·25 55
791 300 f. Northern oriole .. 3·00 1·75
[illegible] f. White-breasted [illegible] .. .. 4·00 2·50
793. [illegible] mon flicker (air) 5·50 3·25
794. 600 f. Rough-legged buzzard .. .. .. 5·75 3·75

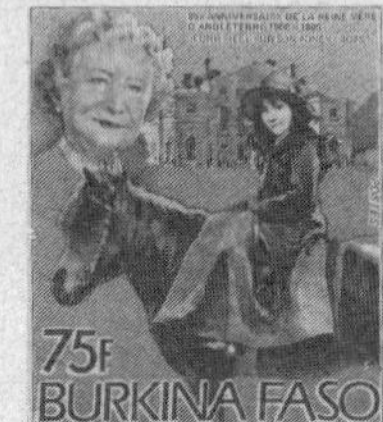


**259.** Young Lady Elizabeth Bowes-Lyon on Pony.

**1985.** 85th Birthday of Queen Elizabeth the Queen Mother. Multicoloured.

796. 75 f. Type **259** (postage) .. 30 20
797. 85 f. Marriage of Lady Elizabeth Bowes-Lyon and Albert, Duke of York .. .. .. 35 25
798. 500 f. Duke and Duchess of York with Princess Elizabeth (air) .. .. 2·25 1·90
799. 600 f. Royal family in Coronation robes .. 2·50 2·25

**260.** Gaucho on Piebald Horse.

**1985.** "Argentina '85" International Stamp Exhibition, Buenos Aires. Horses. Mult.

801. 25 f. Type **260** (postage) .. 15 10
802. 45 f. Gaucho on horse .. 20 15
803. 90 f. Rodeo rider .. .. 45 30
804. 100 f. Rider hunting gazelle (air) .. .. .. 45 30
805. 150 f. Horses and gauchos at camp fire .. .. 65 50
806. 200 f. Horse and man sitting on steps .. .. 90 75
807. 250 f. Riding contest .. 1·10 90

**261.** Electric Locomotive "105-30" and Tank Wagon.

**1985.** Trains. Multicoloured.

809. 50 f. Type **261** (postage) .. 30 20
810. 75 f. Diesel shunting locomotive .. .. 40 30
811. 80 f. Diesel passenger locomotive .. .. 45 35
812. 100 f. Diesel railcar (air) .. 55 40
813. 150 f. Diesel locomotive "6093" .. .. .. 75 60
814. 200 f. Diesel railcar "105" 1·00 90
815. 250 f. Diesel locomotive and passenger train .. 1·50 1·10

**262.** Pot (Tikare).

**263.** "Pholiota mutabilis".

**1985.** Handicrafts. Multicoloured.

816. 10 f. Type **262** (postage) .. 10 10
817. 40 f. Pot with lid decorated with birds (P. Bazega) .. 20 15
818. 90 f. Bronze statuette of mother with child (Ouagadougou) .. .. 40 25
819. 120 f. Bronze statuette of drummer (Ouagadougou) (air) .. 50 35

**1985.** Fungi. Multicoloured.

820. 15 f. Type **263** (postage) .. 15 10
821. 20 f. "Hypholoma (nematoloma) fasciculare" .. .. 20 10
822. 30 f. "Ixocomus granulatus" .. .. 25 10
823. 60 f. "Agaricus campestris" .. .. 50 20
824. 80 f. "Trachypus scaber" 70 40
825. 250 f. "Marasmius scorodonius" .. .. 2·25 1·40
826. 150 f. "Armillaria mellea" (air) .. .. .. 1·10 60

**264.** "Virgin and Child".

**1985.** "Italia '85" International Stamp Exhibition, Rome. Paintings by Botticelli.

827. 25 f. Type **264** (postage) .. 15 10
828. 45 f. Portrait of an Unknown Man" .. 20 15
829. 90 f. "Mars and Venus" .. 50 30
830. 100 f. "Birth of Venus (air) 55 40
831. 150 f. "Allegory of Calumny" .. .. 75 60
832. 200 f. "Pallas and the Centaur" .. .. 90 75
833. 250 f. "Allegory of Spring" 1·10 90

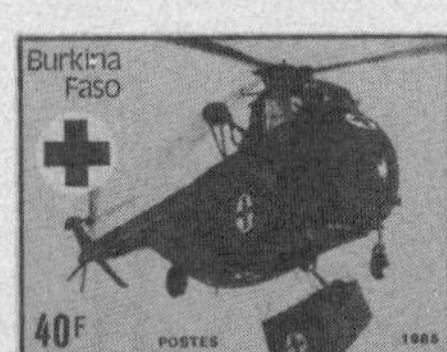


**265.** Sikorsky S-55 Helicopter.

**1985.** Red Cross. Multicoloured.

835. 40 f. Type **265** (postage) .. 30 15
836. 85 f. Ambulance .. .. 35 25
837. 150 f. Henri Dunant (founder) (vert.) (air) .. 65 50
838. 250 f. Nurse attending patient (vert.) .. .. 1·10 90

**266.** Transport and Communications (development).

**1985.** Air. "Philexafrique" International Stamp Exhibition, Lome, Togo (2nd issue). Multicoloured.

839. 250 f. Type **266** .. .. 2·00 1·75
840. 250 f. Youth activities (youth) .. .. .. 1·10 90

**267.** Girls drumming and clapping.

**1986.** Dodo Carnival. Multicoloured.

841. 20 f. Type **267** .. .. 10 10
842. 25 f. Masked lion dancers 15 10
843. 40 f. Masked stick dancers and drummers .. .. 20 15
844. 45 f. Stick dancers with elaborate headdresses .. 20 15
845. 90 f. Masked elephant dancer .. .. .. 40 25
846. 90 f. Animal dancers .. 40 25

**268.** Mother breast-feeding Baby.

**1986.** Child Survival Campaign.

847. **268.** 90 f. multicoloured .. 40 25

**269.** Couple carrying Rail.

**1986.** Railway Construction. Multicoloured.

848. 90 f. Type **269** (postage) .. 40 25
849. 120 f. Laying tracks .. 50 35
850. 185 f. Workers waving to passing train .. .. 85 65
851. 500 f. "Inauguration of First German Railway" (Heim) (air) .. .. 2·25 1·90

No. 851 commemorates the 150th anniv. of German railways.

**270.** Columbus before King of Portugal, and "Nina".

**271.** Village and First Aid Post.

**1986.** 480th Death Anniv. of Christopher Columbus (explorer). Multicoloured.

853. 250 f. Type **270** (postage) 1·50 90
854. 300 f. "Santa Maria" and Columbus with astrolabe 1·75 1·00
855. 400 f. Columbus imprisoned and "Santa Maria" .. 2·40 1·40
856. 450 f. Landing at San Salvador and "Pinta" (air) .. .. .. 2·75 1·50

**1986.** "Health For All by Year 2000". Multicoloured.
858. 90 f. Type **271** .. .. 40 25
859. 100 f. Man receiving first aid (26×36 mm.) .. 40 25
860. 120 f. People queuing for vaccinations (26×36 mm.) .. .. 50 35

**272.** "Phryneta aurocinta".
**273.** Woman feeding Child and Fresh Foods.

**1986.** Insects. Multicoloured.
861. 15 f. Type **272** .. .. 10 10
862. 20 f. "Sternocera interrupta" .. .. 10 10
863. 40 f. "Prosoprocera lactator" .. .. 35 15
864. 45 f. "Gonimbrasia hecate" .. .. 40 15
865. 85 f. "Charaxes epijasius" .. .. 70 50

**1986.** Gobi Health Strategy. Multicoloured.
866. 30 f. Type **273** .. .. 15 10
867. 60 f. Ingredients of oral re-hydration therapy .. 25 15
868. 90 f. Mother holding child for vaccination .. .. 40 25
869. 120 f. Doctor weighing child .. .. .. 50 35

**274.** U.P.U. Emblem on Dove.
**275.** Emblem.

**1986.** World Post Day.
870. **274.** 120 f. multicoloured .. 50 35

**1986.** International Peace Year.
871. **275.** 90 f. blue .. .. 40 25

**276.** Namende Dancers.
**277.** Warthog.

**1986.** National Bobo Culture Week. Mult.
872. 10 f. Type **276** .. .. 10 10
873. 25 f. Mouhoun dancers .. 10 10
874. 90 f. Houet dancer .. 40 25
875. 105 f. Seno musicians .. 40 25
876. 120 f. Ganzourgou dancers 50 35

**1986.** Wildlife. Multicoloured.
877. 50 f. Type **277** .. .. 20 15
878. 65 f. Spotted hyena .. 25 15
879. 90 f. Antelope .. .. 40 25
880. 100 f. Red-fronted gazelle 40 25
881. 120 f. Harnessed antelope 50 35
882. 145 f. Hartebeest .. .. 60 45
883. 500 f. Kob .. .. .. 2·00 1·50

**278.** Peul.
**279.** Charlie Chaplin within Film Frame (10th death anniv.).

**1986.** Traditional Hairstyles. Multicoloured.
884. 35 f. Type **278** .. .. 25 15
885. 75 f. Dafing .. .. 30 20
886. 90 f. Peul (different) .. 55 30
887. 120 f. Mossi .. .. 60 35
888. 185 f. Peul (different) .. 1·00 80

**1987.** 10th Fespaco Film Festival.
889 – 90 f. mauve, blk & brn 40 25
890 – 120 f. multicoloured .. 50 35
891 **279** 185 f. multicoloured .. 75 60
DESIGNS: 90 f. Camera on map in film frame. 120 f. Cameraman and soundman (60th anniv. of first talking film "The Jazz Singer").

**280.** Woman trimming Rug.
**281.** "Calotripis procera".

**1987.** International Woman's Day.
892. **280.** 90 f. multicoloured .. 40 25

**1987.** Flowers. Multicoloured.
893. 70 f. Type **281** .. .. 30 20
894. 75 f. "Acacia seyal" .. 30 20
895. 85 f. "Parkia biglobosa" .. 35 25
896. 90 f. "Sterospernum kunthianum" .. .. 40 25
897. 100 f. "Dichrostachys cinerea" .. .. 40 25
898. 300 f. "Combretum paniculatum" .. .. 1·25 1·00

**282.** High Jumping.

**1987.** Olympic Games, Seoul (1988). 50th Death Anniv. of Pierre de Coubertin (founder of modern Olympic Games). Multicoloured.
899. 75 f. Type **282** .. .. 30 20
900. 85 f. Tennis (vert.) .. 35 25
901. 90 f. Ski jumping .. .. 40 25
902. 100 f. Football .. .. 40 25
903. 145 f. Running .. .. 60 45
904. 350 f. Pierre de Coubertin and tennis game (vert.) 1·50 1·25

**283.** Follereau and Doctor treating Patient.
**285.** Globe in Envelope.

**284.** Woman sweeping.

**1987.** Anti-leprosy Campaign. 10th Death Anniv. of Raoul Follereau (pioneer). Mult.
905. 90 f. Type **283** .. .. 40 25
906. 100 f. Laboratory technicians .. .. 40 25
907. 120 f. Gerhard Hansen (discoverer of bacillus) .. 50 35
908. 300 f. Follereau kissing patient .. .. 1·25 1·00

**1987.** World Environment Day. Mult.
909. 90 f. Type **284** .. .. 40 25
910. 145 f. Emblem .. .. 60 45

**1987.** World Post Day.
911. **285.** 90 f. multicoloured .. 35 25

**286.** Luthuli and Open Book.

**1987.** Anti-Apartheid Campaign. 20th Death Anniv. of Albert John Luthuli (anti-apartheid campaigner). Multicoloured.
912. 90 f. Barbed wire and apartheid victims .. 35 25
913. 100 f. Type **286** .. .. 40 25

**287.** Dagari.
**288.** Balafon (16 key xylophone).

**1987.** Traditional Costumes. Multicoloured.
914. 10 f. Type **287** .. .. 10 10
915. 30 f. Peul .. .. .. 15 10
916. 90 f. Mossi (female) .. 35 25
917. 200 f. Senoufo .. .. 80 60
918. 500 f. Mossi (male) .. 1·90 1·40

**1987.** Traditional Music Instruments. Multicoloured.
919. 20 f. Type **288** .. .. 10 10
920. 25 f. Kunde en more (3 stringed lute (vert.) .. 10 10
921. 35 f. Tiahoun en bwaba (zither) .. .. .. 15 10
922. 90 f. Jembe en dioula (conical drum) .. .. 35 25
923. 1000 f. Bendre en more (calabash drum) (vert.) 3·75 2·40

**289.** Dwellings.

**1987.** International Year of Shelter for the Homeless.
924. **289.** 90 f. multicoloured .. 35 25

**290.** Small Industrial Units.
**291.** People with Candles.

**1987.** Five Year Plan for Popular Development. Multicoloured.
925. 40 f. Type **290** .. .. 15 10
926. 55 f. Management of dams 20 15
927. 60 f. Village community building primary school 25 15
928. 90 f. Bus (Transport and communications) .. 35 25
929. 100 f. National education: literacy campaign .. 40 25
930. 120 f. Intensive cattle farming .. .. .. 45 30

**1988.** 40th Anniv. of W.H.O.
931. **291.** 120 f. multicoloured .. 45 30

**292.** Exhibition Emblem and Games Mascot.
**293.** Houet "Sparrow Hawk" Mask.

**1988.** Olympic Games, Seoul, and "Olymphilex '88" Olympic Stamps Exhibition, Rome (932). Multicoloured.
932. 30 f. Type **292** .. .. 15 10
933. 160 f. Olympic flame (vert.) 60 45
934. 175 f. Football .. .. 65 45
935. 235 f. Volleyball (vert.) .. 90 65
936. 450 f. Basketball (vert.) .. 1·75 1·25

**1988.** Masks. Multicoloured.
938. 10 f. Type **293** .. .. 10 10
939. 20 f. Ouillo "Young Girls" mask .. .. .. 10 10
940. 30 f. Houet "Hartebeest" mask .. .. .. 15 10
941. 40 f. Mouhoun "Blacksmith" mask .. 15 10
942. 120 f. Ouri "Nanny" mask 45 30
943. 175 f. Ouri "Bat" mask (horiz.) .. .. .. 65 45

**294** Kieriba Jug
**295** Envelopes forming Map

**1988.** Handicrafts. Multicoloured.
944 5 f. Type **294** .. .. 10 10
945 15 f. Mossi basket (horiz) 10 10
946 25 f. Gurunsi chair (horiz) 10 10
947 30 f. Bissa basket (horiz) .. 15 10
948 45 f. Ouagadougou hide box (horiz) .. .. 15 10
949 85 f. Ouagadougou bronze statuette .. .. 35 20
950 120 f. Ouagadougou hide travelling bag (horiz) .. 45 30

**1988.** World Post Day.
951 **295** 120 f. blue, black & yell 45 30

**296** White-collared Kingfisher

**1988.** Aquatic Wildlife. Multicoloured.
952 70 f. Type **296** .. .. 75 30
953 100 f. "Mormyrus rume" (fish) .. .. .. 60 25
954 120 f. Frog .. .. 55 30
955 160 f. White-faced whistling duck .. .. 2·25 1·25

**297** Mohammed Ali Jinnah (first Pakistan Governor-General)
**298** Shepherds adoring Child

**1988.** Death Anniversaries. Multicoloured.
956 80 f. Type **297** (40th anniv) (postage) .. .. 30 20
957 120 f. Mahatma Gandhi (Indian human rights activist, 40th anniv) .. 45 30
958 160 f. John Fitzgerald Kennedy (U.S. President, 25th anniv) .. 60 45
959 235 f. Martin Luther King (human rights activist, 20th anniv) (air) .. 90 65

**1988.** Christmas. Stained Glass Windows. Multicoloured.
960 120 f. Type **298** .. .. 45 30
961 160 f. Wise men presenting gifts to Child .. .. 60 45
962 450 f. Virgin and Child .. 1·75 1·25
963 1000 f. Flight into Egypt 3·75 2·75

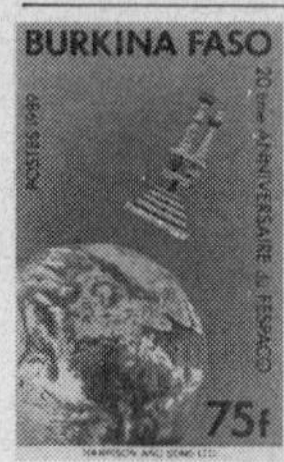

**299** Satellite and Globe **300** W.H.O. and Aids Emblems

**1989.** 20th Anniv of FESPACO Film Festival. Multicoloured.
964 75 f. Type **299** (postage) .. 30 20
965 500 f. Ababacar Samb Makharam (air) .. 1·90 1·40
966 500 f. Jean Michel Tchissoukou .. .. 1·90 1·40
967 500 f. Paulin Soumanou Vieyra .. .. .. 1·90 1·40

**1989.** Campaign against Aids.
969 **300** 120 f. multicoloured .. 45 30

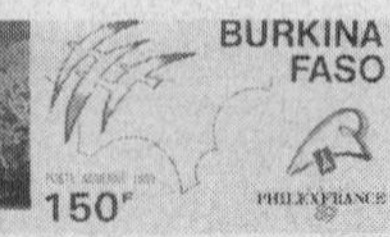


**301** "Oath of the Tennis Court" (Jacques Louis David) (Illustration reduced. Actual size 80 × 36 mm)

**1989.** Air. "Philexfrance 89" International Stamp Exhibition, Paris, and Bicentenary of French Revolution. Multicoloured.
970 150 f. Type **301** .. .. 60 45
971 200 f. "Storming of the Bastille" (Thevenin) .. 75 50
972 600 f. "Rouget de Lisle singing La Marseillaise" (Pils) .. .. .. 2·25 1·60

**302** Map and Tractor

**1989.** 30th Anniv of Council of Unity.
973 **302** 75 f. multicoloured .. 30 20

**303** "Striga generioides" **304** Sahel Dog

**1989.** Parasitic Plants. Multicoloured.
974 20 f. Type **303** .. .. 10 10
975 50 f. "Striga hermonthica" 20 15
976 235 f. "Striga aspera" .. 90 65
977 450 f. "Alectra vogelii" .. 1·75 1·25

**1989.** Dogs. Multicoloured.
978 35 f. Type **304** .. .. 10 10
979 50 f. Young dog .. .. 20 15
980 60 f. Hunting dog .. 20 15
981 350 f. Guard dog .. .. 1·50 1·00

BURKINA FASO
120f

**305** Statue **307** Pilgrims at Shrine of Our Lady of Yagma

**1989.** Solidarity with Palestinian People.
982 **305** 120 f. multicoloured .. 45 30

**1989.** Nos. 647/9 of Upper Volta optd **BURKINA FASO**.
983 **229** 90 f. multicoloured .. 35 20
984 120 f. multicoloured .. 50 35
985 170 f. multicoloured .. 70 50

**1990.** Visit of Pope John Paul II. Mult.
986 120 f. Type **307** .. .. 50 35
987 160 f. Pope and crowd .. 65 45

**308** Mail Steamer, Globe and Penny Black **309** Goalkeeper catching Ball

**1990.** 150th Anniv of Penny Black and "Stamp World London 90" International Stamp Exhibition.
988 **308** 120 f. multicoloured .. 70 45

**1990.** World Cup Football Championship, Italy. Multicoloured.
990 30 f. Type **309** .. .. 15 10
991 150 f. Footballers .. 60 45

**310** "Cantharellus cibarius" **311** Open Book

**1990.** Fungi. Multicoloured.
993 10 f. Type **310** .. .. 10 10
994 15 f. "Psalliota bispora" .. 15 10
995 60 f. "Amanita caesarea" 75 35
996 190 f. "Boletus badius" .. 2·40 1·25

**1990.** International Literacy Year.
998 **311** 40 f. multicoloured .. 15 10
999 130 f. multicoloured .. 50 35

**312** Maps, Emblem and Native Artefacts **313** De Gaulle

**1990.** 2nd International Salon of Arts and Crafts, Ouagadougou. Multicoloured.
1000 35 f. Type **312** .. .. 15 10
1001 45 f. Pottery (horiz) .. 20 15
1002 270 f. Cane chair .. 1·10 75

**1990.** Birth Centenary of Charles de Gaulle (French statesman).
1003 **313** 200 f. multicoloured .. 80 55

**314** Quartz **315** Hand Holding Cigarette, Syringe and Tablets

**1991.** Rocks. Multicoloured.
1004 20 f. Type **314** .. .. 10 10
1005 50 f. Granite .. 20 15
1006 280 f. Amphibolite .. 1·10 75

**1991.** Anti-Drugs Campaign.
1007 **315** 130 f. multicoloured .. 50 35

**316** Film and Landscape **318** Traditional Hairstyle

**317** Morse and Key

**1991.** 12th "Fespaco 91" Pan-African Cinema and Television Festival. Multicoloured.
1008 **316** 150 f. multicoloured .. 60 40

**1991.** Birth Bicentenary of Samuel Morse (inventor of signalling system).
1010 **317** 200 f. multicoloured .. 80 55

**1991.**
1011 **318** 5 f. multicoloured .. 10 10
1012 10 f. multicoloured .. 10 10
1013 25 f. multicoloured .. 10 10
1014 50 f. multicoloured .. 10 10
1018 130 f. multicoloured .. 30 20
1019 150 f. multicoloured .. 60 40
1020 200 f. multicoloured .. 80 55
1021 330 f. multicoloured .. 80 55

**319** "Grewia tenax" **320** Warba

**1991.** Flowers. Multicoloured.
1025 5 f. Type **319** .. .. 10 10
1026 15 f. "Hymenocardia acide" .. .. 10 10
1027 60 f. "Cassia sieberiana" (vert) .. .. .. 25 20
1028 100 f. "Adenium obesum" 40 30
1029 300 f. "Mitragyna inermis" .. .. 1·25 85

**1991.** Dance Costumes. Multicoloured.
1030 75 f. Type **320** .. .. 40 25
1031 130 f. Wiskamba .. 65 40
1032 280 f. Pa-Zenin .. .. 1·40 85

**321** Pillar Box and Globe **322** Cake Tin

**1991.** World Post Day.
1033 **321** 130 f. multicoloured .. 50 35

**1992.** Cooking Utensils.
1034 45 f. Type **322** .. .. 20 15
1035 130 f. Cooking pot (vert) 60 40
1036 310 f. Pestle and mortar (vert) .. .. .. 1·50 1·00
1037 500 f. Ladle and bowl .. 2·40 1·60

**323** Yousouf Fofana **324** Disabled Man at Potter's Wheel

**1992.** African Nations Cup Football Championship, Senegal. Multicoloured.
1038 50 f. Type **323** .. .. 25 20
1039 100 f. Franois-Jules Bocande .. .. 50 35

**1992.** U.N. Decade of the Handicapped.
1041 **324** 100 f. multicoloured .. 50 35

**325** Child and Cardiograph **326** Columbus and "Santa Maria"

**1992.** World Health Day. "Health in Rhythm with the Heart".
1042 **325** 330 f. multicoloured .. 1·60 1·10

**1992.** "Genova '92" International Thematic Stamp Exhibition and 500th Anniv of Discovery of America by Columbus. Mult.
1043 50 f. Type **326** .. .. 25 20
1044 150 f. Amerindians watching Columbus's fleet off San Salvador 75 55

**327** "Dysdercus voelkeri" (fire bug) on Cotton Boll **328** Crib

**1992.** Insects. Multicoloured.
1046 20 f. Type **327** .. .. 10 10
1047 40 f. "Rhizopertha dominica" (beetle) on leaf .. .. .. 20 15
1048 85 f. "Orthetrum microstigma" (dragonfly) on stem .. .. 40 30
1049 500 f. Honey bee on flower 2·40 1·60

**1992.** Christmas. Multicoloured.
1050 10 f. Type **328** .. .. 10 10
1051 130 f. Children decorating crib .. .. .. 60 40
1052 1000 f. Boy with christmas card .. .. .. 4·50 3·00

BURKINA FASO
250F

BURKINA FASO
100F
LES ECHASSIERS

**329** Film Makers' Monument **330** Yellow-billed Stork

**1993.** 13th "Fespaco" Pan-African Film Festival, Ouagadougou. Multicoloured.
1053 250 f. Type **329** .. .. 1·10 75
1054 750 f. Douta Seck (comedian) (horiz) .. 3·50 2·40

**1993.** Birds. Multicoloured.
1055 100 f. Type **330** .. .. 45 30
1056 200 f. Marabou stork .. 90 60
1057 500 f. Saddle-bill stork .. 2·25 1·50

**331** Statue of Liberty, Globe and Ball

**1993.** World Cup Football Championship, U.S.A. (1994). Multicoloured.
1059 500 f. Type **331** .. .. 2·25 1·50
1060 1000 f. Players, map of world and U.S. flag .. 4·50 3·00

**332** Peterbilt Canadian Hauler and "BB 852" Type Locomotive

**333** "Saba senegalensis"

**1993.** Centenary of Invention of Diesel Engine.
1061 **332** 1000 f. multicoloured .. 4·50 3·00

**1993.** Wild Fruits. Multicoloured.
1062 150 f. Type **333** .. .. 70 50
1063 300 f. Karite (horiz) .. 1·40 95
1064 600 f. Baobab .. .. 2·75 1·90

**334** Flowers, "Stamps" and Sights of Paris

**1993.** 1st European Stamp Salon, Flower Gardens, Paris (1994). Multicoloured.
1065 400 f. Type **334** .. .. 95 65
1066 650 f. "Stamps", sights of Paris, daffodils and irises .. .. .. 1·50 1·00

**335** Peulh Copper Hair Ornament

**1993.** Jewellery. Multicoloured.
1067 200 f. Type **335** .. .. 50 35
1068 250 f. Mossi agate necklace (vert) .. .. 60 40
1069 500 f. Gourounsi copper bracelet .. .. 1·25 85

**336** Gazelle

**337** Woodland Kingfisher

**1993.** The Red-fronted Gazelle. Mult.
1070 30 f. Type **336** .. .. 10 10
1071 40 f. Two gazelle .. .. 10 10
1072 60 f. Two gazelle (different) .. .. 15 10
1073 100 f. Gazelle .. .. 25 20

**1994.** Kingfishers.
1075 600 f. Type **337** .. .. 1·50 1·00
1076 1200 f. Striped kingfisher 3·00 2·00

**338** Players

**1994.** World Cup Football Championship, United States. Multicoloured.
1078 1000 f. Type **338** .. 2·40 1·60
1079 1800 f. Goalkeeper saving ball .. .. .. 4·25 3·00

**339** Dog with Puppy

**1994.** 1st European Stamp Salon, Flower Gardens, Paris, France.
1081 **339** 1500 f. multicoloured 3·75 2·50

**340** Astronaut planting Flag on Moon

**341** Guinea Sorrel

**1994.** 25th Anniv of First Manned Moon Landing. Multicoloured.
1083 750 f. Type **340** .. .. 1·75 1·25
1084 750 f. Landing module on Moon .. .. .. 1·75 1·25
Nos. 1083/4 were issued together, se-tenant, forming a composite design.

**1994.** Vegetables. Multicoloured.
1085 40 f. Type **341** .. .. 10 10
1086 45 f. Aubergine .. .. 10 10
1087 75 f. Aubergine .. .. 20 15
1088 100 f. Okra .. .. 25 20

**342** Pig

**343** Pierre de Coubertin (founder) and Anniversary Emblem

**1994.** Domestic Animals. Multicoloured.
1089 150 f. Type **342** .. .. 35 25
1090 1000 f. Goat (vert) .. 2·40 1·60
1091 1500 f. Sheep .. .. 3·75 2·50

**1994.** Centenary of Int Olympic Committee.
1092 **343** 320 f. multicoloured .. 80 55

**APPENDIX.**

The following stamps have either been issued in excess of postal needs or have not been available to the public in reasonable quantities at face value. Such stamps may later be given full listing if there is evidence of regular postal use.

**1985.**

85th Birthday of Queen Elizabeth the Queen Mother. 1500 f.

## BURMA Pt. 21

A territory in the east of India which was granted independence by the British in 1948. From May 1990 it was known as Myanmar.

For stamps issued before 1948, see volume 3.

1948. 12 pies = 1 anna; 16 annas = 1 rupee.
1953. 100 pyas = 1 kyat.

**20.** Gen. Aung San, Chinthe and Map of Burma.

**21.** Martyrs' Memorial.

**1948.** Independence Day.
83. **20.** $\frac{1}{2}$ a. green .. .. 10 10
84. 1 a. pink .. .. 10 10
85. 2 a. red .. .. 15 15
86. $3\frac{1}{2}$ a. blue .. .. 20 15
87. 8 a. brown .. .. 25 25

**1948.** 1st Anniv. of Murder of Aung San and his Ministers.
88. **21.** 3 p. blue .. .. 10 10
89. 6 p. green .. .. 10 10
90. 9 p. red .. .. 10 10
91. 1 a. violet .. .. 10 10
92. 2 a. mauve .. .. 10 10
93. $3\frac{1}{2}$ a. green .. .. 15 15
94. 4 a. brown .. .. 15 15
95. 8 a. red .. .. 20 15
96. 12 a. purple .. .. 25 20
97. 1 r. green .. .. 35 20
98. 2 r. blue .. .. 60 40
99. 5 r. brown .. .. 1·90 1·10

**22.** Playing Cane-ball.

**25.** Bell, Mingun Pagoda.

**27.** Transplanting Rice.

**28.** Lion Throne.

**1949.** 1st Anniv of Independence.
100 **22** 3 p. blue .. .. 95 25
120 3 p. orange .. .. 65 25
101 – 6 p. green .. .. 10 10
121 – 6 p. purple .. .. 10 10
102 – 9 p. red .. .. 10 10
122 – 9 p. blue .. .. 10 10
103 **25** 1 a. red .. .. 15 10
123 1 a. blue .. .. 10 10
104 – 2 a. orange .. .. 45 10
124 – 2 a. green .. .. 40 20
105 **27** 2 a. 6 p. mauve .. 20 15
125 2 a. 6 p. green .. 20 15
106 – 3 a. violet .. .. 20 15
126 – 3 a. red .. .. 20 15
107 – 3 a. 6 p. green .. 25 15
127 – 3 a. 6 p. orange .. 25 15
108 – 4 a. brown .. .. 25 15
128 – 4 a. red .. .. 25 15
109 – 8 a. red .. .. 35 15
129 – 8 a. blue .. .. 25 20
110 **28** 1 r. green .. .. 50 15
130 1 r. violet .. .. 50 35
111 2 r. blue .. .. 1·25 40
131 2 r. green .. .. 85 75
112 5 r. brown .. .. 2·50 1·25
132 5 r. blue .. .. 2·25 2·25
113 10 r. orange .. .. 4·25 1·90
133 10 r. blue .. .. 5·50 4·25

DESIGNS—As Type **22**: 6 p. Dancer. 9 p. Girl playing saunggaut (string instrument). 2 a. Hintha (legendary bird). As Type **25**: 4 a. Elephant hauling log. As Type **27**: 3 a. Girl weaving. 3 a. 6 p. Royal Palace. 8 a. Ploughing paddy field with oxen.

See also Nos. 137/50.

**29.** U.P.U. Monument, Berne.

**30.** Independence Monument, Rangoon, and Map.

**1949.** 75th Anniversary of U.P.U.
114. **29.** 2 a. orange .. .. 15 15
115. $3\frac{1}{2}$ a. green .. .. 20 15
116. 6 a. violet .. .. 25 25
117. 8 a. red .. .. 40 25
118. $12\frac{1}{2}$ a. blue .. .. 70 40
119. 1 r. green .. .. 90 50

**1953.** 5th Anniversary of Independence.
134. **30.** 14 p. grn. (22 × 18 mm.) 20 10
135. 20 p. red ($36\frac{1}{2}$ × $26\frac{1}{2}$ mm.) 25 15
136. 25 p. blue ($36\frac{1}{2}$ × $26\frac{1}{2}$ mm.) 35 20

**1954.** New Currency. As 1949 issue but values in pyas and kyats.
137 **22** 1 p. orange .. .. 65 10
138 – 2 p. purple (as 6 p.) .. 10 10
139 – 3 p. blue (as 9 p.) .. 10 10
140 **25** 5 p. blue .. .. 10 10
141 **27** 10 p. green .. .. 10 10
142 – 15 p. green (as 2 a.) .. 25 10
143 – 20 p. red (as 3 a.) .. 15 10
144 – 25 p. orange (as 3 a. 6 p.) 15 10
145 – 30 p. red (as 4 a.) .. 25 15
146 – 50 p. blue (as 8 a.) .. 25 15
147 **28** 1 k. violet .. .. 75 25
148 2 k. green .. .. 1·25 35
149 5 k. blue .. .. 3·75 70
150 10 k. blue .. .. 6·50 1·25

**31.** Sangiti Mahapasana Rock Cave in Grounds of Kaba-Aye Pagoda.

**1954.** 6th Buddhist Council, Rangoon.
151. – 10 p. blue .. .. 10 10
152. – 15 p. purple .. .. 15 15
153. **31.** 35 p. brown .. .. 25 20
154. – 50 p. green .. .. 40 25
155. – 1 k. red .. .. 90 50
156. – 2 k. violet .. .. 1·40 1·00

DESIGNS: 10 p. Rock caves and Songha of Cambodia. 15 p. Buddhist priests and Kuthodaw Pagoda, Mandalay. 50 p. Rock cave and Songha of Thailand. 1 k. Rock cave and Songha of Ceylon. 2 k. Rock cave and Songha of Laos.

**32.** Fifth Buddhist Council Monuments.

**1956.** Buddha Jayanti.
157 **32** 20 p. green and blue .. 20 15
158 – 40 p. green and blue .. 25 20
159 – 60 p. yellow and green 45 35
160 – 1 k. 25 blue and yellow 85 70

DESIGNS: 40 p. Thatbyinnyu Pagoda, Pagan. 60 p. Shwedagan Pagoda, Rangoon. 1 k. 25, Sangiti Mahapasana Rock Cave and Kaba-Aye Pagoda, Rangoon (venue of 6th Buddhist Council).

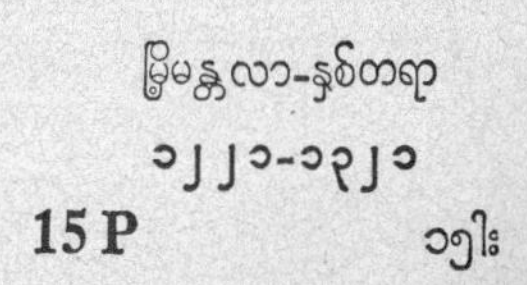

15 P

(**33**).
("Mandalay Town—100 Years/1221–1321").

**1959.** Cent of Mandalay. No. 144 surch with T **33** and Nos. 147/8 with two-line opt only.
161 – 15 p. on 25 p. orange .. 15 20
162 **28** 1 k. violet .. .. 70 60
163 2 k. green .. .. 1·50 1·25

**1961.** No. 134 surch as right-hand characters in third line of T **33**.
164 **30** 15 p. on 14 p. green .. 60 25

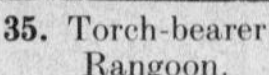

**35.** Torch-bearer in Rangoon. **36.** Children at Play.

**1961.** 2nd South-East Asia Peninsula Games, Rangoon.
165 **35** 15 p. blue and red .. 20 10
166 – 25 p. green and brown 25 15
167 – 50 p. mauve and blue .. 50 25
168 – 1 k. yellow and green .. 95 75
DESIGNS—VERT. 25 p. Contestants. 50 p. Women sprinting in Aung San Stadium, Rangoon. HORIZ. 1 k. Contestants.

**1961.** 15th Anniversary of U.N.I.C.E.F.
169. **36.** 15 p. red and pink .. 30 10

အလုပ်သမားနေ့
၁၉၆၃

**37.** Flag and Map. **(39.)**

**1963.** 1st Anniv. of Military Coup by General Ne Win.
170. **37.** 15 p. red .. .. 30 20

**1963.** Freedom from Hunger. Nos. 141 and 146 optd. **FREEDOM FROM HUNGER.**
171. **27.** 10 p. green .. .. 40 35
172. – 50 p. blue .. .. 75 65

**1963.** Labour Day. No. 143 optd. with T **39.**
173. 20 p. red .. .. .. 35 20

**40.** White-browed Fantail. **41.** I.T.U. Emblem and Symbols.

**1964.** Burmese Birds (1st series).
174 **40** 1 p. black .. .. 15 15
175 2 p. red .. .. 20 15
176 3 p. green .. .. 20 15
177 – 5 p. blue .. .. 25 20
178 – 10 p. brown .. .. 25 20
179 – 15 p. green .. .. 25 20
180 – 20 p. brown and red .. 45 25
181 – 25 p. brown and yellow 45 25
182 – 50 p. blue and red .. 85 30
183 – 1 k. blue, yellow & grey 2·40 70
184 – 2 k. blue, green and red 4·75 1·75
185 – 5 k. multicoloured .. 9·75 4·50
BIRDS—22 × 26 mm: 5 to 15 p. Indian roller. 27 × 37 mm: 25 p. Crested serpent eagle. 50 p. Sarus crane. 1 k. Indian pied hornbill. 5 k. Green peafowl. 35½ × 25 mm: 20 p. Red-whiskered bulbul. 37 × 27 mm: 2 k. Kalij pheasant.
See also Nos. 195/206.

**1965.** Centenary of I.T.U.
186. **41.** 20 p. mauve .. .. 15 15
187. 50 p. grn. (34 × 24½ mm.) 40 40

**42.** I.C.Y. Emblem. **43.** Harvesting.

**1965.** Int. Co-operation Year.
188. **42.** 5 p. blue .. .. 10 10
189. 10 p. brown .. .. 20 10
190. 15 p. olive .. .. 25 10

**1966.** Peasants' Day
191. **43.** 15 p. multicoloured .. 25 15

**44.** Cogwheel and Hammer. **45.** Aung San and Agricultural Cultivation.

**1967.** May Day.
192. **44.** 15 p. yell., black & blue 25 20

**1968.** 20th Anniversary of Independence.
193. **45.** 15 p. multicoloured .. 25 20

**46.** Burma Pearls. **47.** Spike of Paddy.

**1968.** Burmese Gems, Jades and Pearls Emporium, Rangoon.
194. **46.** 15 p. ultram., blue & yell. 40 15

**1968.** Burmese Birds (2nd series). Designs and colours as Nos. 174/85 but formats and sizes changed.
195 **40** 1 p. black .. .. 15 15
196 2 p. red .. .. 15 15
197 3 p. green .. .. 20 15
198 – 5 p. blue .. .. 20 15
199 – 10 p. brown .. .. 20 15
200 – 15 p. yellow .. .. 25 20
201 – 20 p. brown and red .. 25 20
202 – 25 p. brown and yellow 30 25
203 – 50 p. blue and red .. 55 45
204 – 1 k. blue, yellow & grey 1·60 45
205 – 2 k. blue, green and red 4·50 1·10
206 – 5 k. multicoloured .. 9·50 4·50
NEW SIZES—21 × 17 mm: 1, 2, 3 p. 39 × 21 mm: 20 p., 2 k. 23 × 28 mm: 5, 10, 15 p. 21 × 39 mm: 25, 50 p., 1, 5 k.

**1969.** Peasants' Day.
218. **47.** 15 p. yellow, blue & grn. 25 10

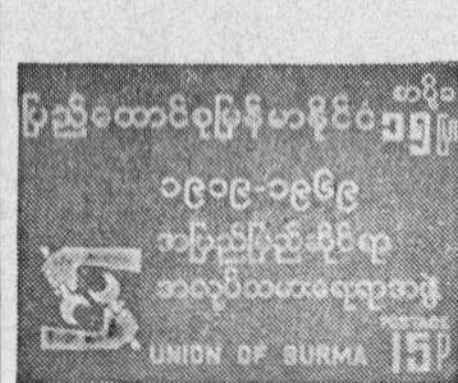

**48.** I.L.O. Emblem. **49.** Football.

**1969.** 50th Anniv of I.L.O.
219 **48** 15 p. gold and green .. 15 10
220 50 p. gold and red .. 40 25

**1969.** 5th South-East Asian Peninsula Games, Rangoon.
221. **49.** 15 p. multicoloured .. 20 10
222. – 25 p. multicoloured .. 25 15
223. – 50 p. multicoloured .. 50 20
224. – 1 k. blk., grn. & blue.. 95 50
DESIGNS–HORIZ. 25 p. Running. VERT. 50 p. Weightlifting. 1 k. Volleyball.

**50.** Marchers with Independence, Resistance and Union Flags.

**1970.** 25th Anniv. of Burmese Armed Forces.
225. **50.** 15 p. multicoloured .. 20 15

**51.** " Peace and Progress ".

**1970.** 25th Anniversary of United Nations.
226. **51.** 15 p. multicoloured .. 25 20

**52.** Boycott Declaration and Marchers.

**1970.** National Day and 50th Anniv. of University Boycott. Multicoloured.
227. 15 p. Type **52** .. .. 10 10
228. 25 p. Students on boycott march .. .. 20 10
229. 50 p. Banner and demonstrators .. .. .. 40 20

**53.** Burmese Workers.

**1971.** First Burmese Socialist Programme Party Congress. Multicoloured.
230 5 p. Type **53** .. .. 10 10
231 15 p. Burmese races and flags .. .. .. 15 10
232 25 p. Hands holding scroll 25 15
233 50 p. Party flag .. .. 50 30

**54.** Child drinking Milk.

**1971.** 25th Anniv. of U.N.I.C.E.F. Mult.
235. 15 p. Type **54** .. .. 25 15
236. 50 p. Marionettes .. .. 55 40

**55.** Aung San and Independence Monument, Panglong.

**1972.** 25th Anniv. of Independence. Mult.
237. 15 p. Type **55** .. .. 10 10
238. 50 p. Aung San and Burmese in national costumes.. 25 20
239. 1 k. Flag and map (vert.) 60 40

**56.** Burmese and Stars.

**1972.** 10th Anniv. of Revolutionary Council.
240. **56.** 15 p. multicoloured .. 20 10

**57.** Human Heart **59.** Casting Vote.

**58.** Ethnic Groups.

**1972.** World Health Day.
241. **57.** 15 p. red, blk. & yellow 20 15

**1973.** National Census.
242. **58.** 15 p. multicoloured .. 20 10

**1973.** National Constitutional Referendum.
243. **59.** 5 p. red and black .. 15 10
244. – 10 p. multicoloured .. 15 10
245. – 15 p. multicoloured .. 15 10
DESIGNS—HORIZ. 10p. Voter supporting map. VERT. 15 p. Burmese with ballot papers.

**60.** Open-air Meeting.

**1974.** Opening of 1st Pyithu Hluttaw (People's Assembly). Multicoloured.
246 15 p. Burmese flags, 1752–1974 (80 × 26 mm) 20 15
247 50 p. Type **60** .. .. 40 25
248 1 k. Burmese badge .. 80 55

**61.** U.P.U. Emblem and Carrier Pigeon.

**1974.** Cent. of Universal Postal Union. Mult.
249. 15 p. Type **61** .. .. 15 10
250. 20 p. Woman reading letter (vert.) .. .. .. 20 10
251. 50 p. U.P.U. emblem on "stamps" (vert.) .. 45 20
252. 1 k. Stylized doll (vert.) .. 75 35
253. 2 k. Postman delivering letter to family .. .. 1·75 75

**62.** Kachin Couple. **63.** Bamar Couple.

**1974.** Burmese Costumes. Inscr "SOCIALIST REPUBLIC OF THE UNION OF BURMA".
254 **62** 1 p. mauve .. .. 10 10
255 3 p. brown and mauve 10 10
256 5 p. violet and mauve .. 10 10
257 10 p. blue .. .. 10 10
258 15 p. green and lt green 10 10
259 **63** 20 p. black, brown & bl 15 10
260 – 50 p. violet, brn & ochre 40 15
261 – 1 k. violet, mauve & blk 1·10 60
262 – 5 k. multicoloured .. 4·00 2·25
DESIGNS—As Type **62**: 3 p. Kayah girl. 5 p. Kayin couple and bronze drum. 15 p. Chin couple. As Type **63**: 50 p. Mon woman. 1 k. Rakhine woman. 5 k. Musician.
For 15, 50 p. and 1 k. stamps in these designs, but inscr "UNION OF BURMA", see Nos. 309/11.

**64.** Woman on Globe and I.W.Y. Emblem.

**1975.** International Women's Year
263. **64.** 50 p. black and green 30 20
264. – 2 k. black and blue .. 1·25 95
DESIGN—VERT. 2 k. Globe on flower and I.W.Y. emblem.

**65.** Burmese and Flag. **66.** Emblem and Burmese learning Alphabet.

**1976.** Constitution Day.
265. **65.** 20 p. black and blue .. 15 10
266. – 50 p. brown and blue 35 30
267. – 1 k. multicoloured .. 1·00 60
DESIGNS—As Type **65**: 50 p. Burmese with banners and flag. 57 × 21 mm. 1 k. Map of Burma, Burmese and flag.

**1976.** International Literacy Year.
268 **66** 10 p. brown and red .. 10 10
269 – 15 p. turq, grn & blk .. 10 10
270 – 50 p. blue, orange & blk 40 20
271 – 1 k. multicoloured .. 75 50
DESIGNS—HORIZ: 15 p. Abacus and open books. 50 p. Emblem. VERT: 1 k. Emblem, open book and globe.

**67.** Early Train and Ox-cart.

**1977.** Centenary of Railway.

| | | | | |
|---|---|---|---|---|
| 272 | – | 15 p. green, black & mve | 90 | 40 |
| 273 | **67** | 20 p. multicoloured .. | 30 | 15 |
| 274 | – | 25 p. multicoloured .. | 45 | 25 |
| 275 | – | 50 p. multicoloured .. | 55 | 40 |
| 276 | – | 1 k. multicoloured .. | 1·25 | 75 |

DESIGNS—26 × 17 mm: 15 p. Early steam locomotive. As Type **67**—HORIZ: 25 p. Train approaching railway station. 50 p. Railway bridge. VERT: Diesel train emerging from tunnel.

**68.** Karaweik Hall

**1978.**

| | | | | |
|---|---|---|---|---|
| 277. | **68.** | 50 p. brown .. .. | 35 | 25 |
| 278. | – | 1 k. multicoloured .. | 95 | 60 |

DESIGN—$79\frac{1}{2} \times 25$ mm: 1 k. Side view of Karaweik Hall.

**69.** Jade Naga and Gem. **70.** "Intelsat IV" Satellite over Burma.

**1979.** 16th Gem Emporium.

| | | | | |
|---|---|---|---|---|
| 279 | **69** | 15 p. green & turquoise | 15 | 10 |
| 280 | – | 20 p. blue, yellow & mve | 35 | 15 |
| 281 | – | 50 p. blue, brown & grn | 65 | 40 |
| 282 | – | 1 k. multicoloured .. | 1·25 | 70 |

DESIGNS—As T **69**: 20 p. Hintha (legendary bird) holding pearl in beak. 50 p. Hand holding pearl and amethyst pendant. 55 × 20 mm: 1 k. Gold jewel-studded dragon.

**1979.** Introduction of Satellite Communications System.

| | | | | |
|---|---|---|---|---|
| 283. | **70.** | 25 p. multicoloured .. | 25 | 15 |

**71.** I.Y.C. Emblem on Map of Burma. **72.** Weather Balloon.

**1979.** International Year of the Child.

| | | | | |
|---|---|---|---|---|
| 284. | **71.** | 25 p. orange and blue .. | 35 | 25 |
| 285. | | 50 p. red and violet .. | 65 | 40 |

**1980.** World Meteorological Day.

| | | | | |
|---|---|---|---|---|
| 286. | **72.** | 25 p. blue, yellow and black .. | 25 | 15 |
| 287. | – | 50 p. green, black and red .. .. .. | 50 | 35 |

DESIGN: 50 p. Meteorological satellite and W.M.O. emblem.

**73.** Weightlifting.

**1980.** Olympic Games, Moscow.

| | | | | |
|---|---|---|---|---|
| 288 | **73** | 20 p. green, orge & blk | 20 | 10 |
| 289 | – | 50 p. black, orge & red | 45 | 25 |
| 290 | – | 1 k. black, orange & bl | 90 | 50 |

DESIGNS: 50 p. Boxing. 1 k. Football.

**74.** I.T.U. and W.H.O. Emblems with Ribbons forming Caduceus.

**1981.** World Telecommunications Day.

| | | | | |
|---|---|---|---|---|
| 291. | **74.** | 25 p. orange and black | 20 | 10 |

**75.** Livestock and Vegetables.

**1981.** World Food Day. Multicoloured.

| | | | |
|---|---|---|---|
| 292. | 25 p. Type **75** .. .. | 25 | 10 |
| 293. | 50 p. Farm produce and farmer holding wheat .. | 40 | 20 |
| 294. | 1 k. Globe and stylized bird .. .. .. | 75 | 45 |

**76.** Athletes and Person in Wheelchair.

**1981.** International Year of Disabled Persons.

| | | | | |
|---|---|---|---|---|
| 295. | **76.** | 25 p. multicoloured .. | 25 | 15 |

**77.** Telephone, Satellite and Antenna.

**1983.** World Communications Year.

| | | | | |
|---|---|---|---|---|
| 296. | **77.** | 15 p. blue and black .. | 10 | 10 |
| 297. | | 25 p. mauve and black | 30 | 15 |
| 298. | | 50 p. green, black and red .. .. .. | 50 | 35 |
| 299. | | 1 k. brn., blk and grn. | 1·25 | 70 |

**78.** Fish and Globe.

**1983.** World Food Day.

| | | | | |
|---|---|---|---|---|
| 300. | **78.** | 15 p. yell,. blue & blk.. . | 10 | 10 |
| 301. | | 25 p. orge., grn & blk .. | 15 | 10 |
| 302. | | 50 p. grn., yell. & blk .. | 40 | 40 |
| 303. | | 1 k. blue, yell. & blk. .. | 90 | 80 |

**79.** Globe and Log.

**1984.** World Food Day.

| | | | | |
|---|---|---|---|---|
| 304 | **79** | 15 p. blue, yellow & blk | 10 | 10 |
| 305 | | 25 p. violet, yell & blk | 15 | 10 |
| 306 | | 50 p. green, pink & blk | 50 | 40 |
| 307 | | 1 k. mauve, yell & blk | 1·00 | 90 |

**80.** Potted Plant.

**1985.** International Youth Year.

| | | | | |
|---|---|---|---|---|
| 308. | **80.** | 15 p. multicoloured .. | 25 | 20 |

**1989.** As Nos. 258/9 and 260/1 but inscribed "UNION OF BURMA".

| | | | | |
|---|---|---|---|---|
| 309 | **62** | 15 p. dp green & green | 25 | 20 |
| 309a | – | 20 p. black, brown & bl | 5·00 | |
| 310 | – | 50 p. violet and brown | 50 | 30 |
| 311 | – | 1 k. violet, mve & blk | 85 | 65 |

OFFICIAL STAMPS

ဘစိုးရကိစ္စ

(O **29.**) (size of opt varies).

**1949.** 1st Anniv. of Independence. Nos. 100/4 and 107/113 optd. as Type O **29.**

| | | | | |
|---|---|---|---|---|
| O 114. | **22.** | 3 p. blue .. .. | 40 | 10 |
| O 115. | – | 6 p. green .. .. | 10 | 15 |
| O 116. | – | 9 p. red .. .. | 10 | 15 |
| O 117. | **25.** | 1 a. red .. .. | 10 | 15 |
| O 118. | – | 2 a. orange .. .. | 15 | 15 |
| O 119. | – | 3 a.6 p. green .. | 15 | 15 |
| O 120. | – | 4 a. brown .. .. | 15 | 15 |
| O 121. | – | 8 a. red .. .. | 15 | 15 |
| O 122. | **28.** | 1 r. green .. .. | 40 | 25 |
| O 123. | | 2 r. blue .. .. | 65 | 45 |
| O 124. | | 5 r. brown .. .. | 2·25 | 1·50 |
| O 125. | | 10 r. orange .. .. | 5·00 | 3·75 |

**1954.** Nos. 137/40 and 142/50 optd as Type O **29**.

| | | | | |
|---|---|---|---|---|
| O151 | **22** | 1 p. orange .. .. | 10 | 10 |
| O152 | – | 2 p. purple .. .. | 10 | 10 |
| O153 | – | 3 p. blue .. .. | 10 | 10 |
| O154 | **25** | 5 p. blue .. .. | 10 | 10 |
| O155 | – | 15 p. green .. .. | 10 | 10 |
| O156 | – | 20 p. red .. .. | 15 | 10 |
| O157 | – | 25 p. orange .. .. | 15 | 10 |
| O158 | – | 30 p. red .. .. | 15 | 10 |
| O159 | – | 50 p. blue .. .. | 25 | 20 |
| O160 | **28** | 1 k. violet .. .. | 45 | 20 |
| O161 | | 2 k. green .. .. | 1·25 | 35 |
| O162 | | 5 k. blue .. .. | 2·50 | 90 |
| O163 | | 10 k. blue .. .. | 6·00 | 2·50 |

**1964.** No. 139 optd **Service**.

| | | | | |
|---|---|---|---|---|
| O174 | – | 3 p. blue .. .. | 9·50 | 6·50 |

**1966.** Nos. 174/7 and 179/85 optd as Type O **29**.

| | | | | |
|---|---|---|---|---|
| O196 | **40** | 1 p. black .. .. | 20 | 15 |
| O197 | | 2 p. red .. .. | 30 | 25 |
| O198 | | 3 p. green .. .. | 30 | 25 |
| O199 | – | 5 p. blue .. .. | 35 | 30 |
| O200 | – | 15 p. green .. .. | 35 | 30 |
| O201 | – | 20 p. brown and red .. | 65 | 60 |
| O202 | – | 25 p. brown and yellow | 70 | 65 |
| O203 | – | 50 p. blue and red .. | 1·25 | 80 |
| O204 | – | 1 k. blue, yell & grey | 3·50 | 1·90 |
| O205 | – | 2 k. blue, green & red | 4·75 | 1·75 |
| O206 | – | 5 k. multicoloured .. | 14·00 | 12·00 |

**1968.** Nos. 195/8 and 200/6 optd as Type O **29**.

| | | | |
|---|---|---|---|
| O207 | 1 p. black .. .. | 20 | 15 |
| O208 | 2 p. red .. .. | 25 | 20 |
| O209 | 3 p. green .. .. | 30 | 25 |
| O210 | 5 p. blue .. .. | 30 | 25 |
| O211 | 15 p. green .. .. | 30 | 25 |
| O212 | 20 p. brown and red .. | 40 | 30 |
| O213 | 25 p. brown and yellow | 30 | 25 |
| O214 | 50 p. blue and red .. | 30 | 25 |
| O215 | 1 k. blue, yellow and grey | 1·75 | 45 |
| O216 | 2 k. blue, green and red | 3·50 | 1·10 |
| O217 | 5 k. multicoloured .. | 5·00 | 4·50 |

For later issues see **MYANMAR**.



## BURUNDI Pt. 12

Once part of the Belgian territory, Ruanda-Urundi. Independent on 1 July 1962, when a monarchy was established. After a revolution in 1967 Burundi became a republic.

Currency: Belgian.

**1962.** Stamps of Ruanda-Urundi optd. **Royaume du Burundi** and bar or surch. also.

(a) Flowers. (Nos. 167, etc.).

| | | | |
|---|---|---|---|
| 1. | 25 c. orange and green .. | 15 | 15 |
| 2. | 40 c. salmon and green .. | 15 | 15 |
| 3. | 60 c. purple and green .. | 35 | 35 |
| 4. | 1 f. 25 blue and green .. | 16·00 | 16·00 |
| 5. | 1 f. 50 green and violet .. | 60 | 60 |
| 6. | 5 f. green and purple .. | 90 | 90 |
| 7. | 7 f. brown and green .. | 1·40 | 1·40 |
| 8. | 10 f. olive and purple .. | 2·50 | 2·50 |

(b) Animals (Nos. 192, etc.).

| | | | |
|---|---|---|---|
| 9. | 10 c. black, red and brown | 10 | 10 |
| 10. | 20 c. black and green .. | 10 | 10 |
| 11. | 40 c. black, olive & mauve | 10 | 10 |
| 12. | 50 c. brown, yellow & green | 10 | 10 |
| 13. | 1 f. black, blue and brown | 15 | 15 |
| 14. | 1 f. 50 black and orange .. | 15 | 15 |
| 15. | 2 f. black, brown and turq. | 15 | 15 |
| 16. | 3 f. black, red and brown .. | 15 | 15 |
| 17. | 3 f. 50on 3 f. blk., red & brn. | 20 | 20 |
| 18a. | 4 f. on 10 f. multicoloured | 25 | 25 |
| 19. | 5 f. multicoloured .. .. | 25 | 25 |
| 20. | 6 f. 50 brown, yellow & red | 40 | 30 |
| 21. | 8 f. black, mauve and blue | 55 | 40 |
| 23. | 10 f. multicoloured .. | 55 | 40 |

(c) Animals (Nos. 211/12).

| | | | |
|---|---|---|---|
| 24. | 20 f. multicoloured .. | 1·00 | 80 |
| 25. | 50 f. multicoloured .. | 1·90 | 1·50 |

**10.** King Mwambutsa IV and Royal Drummers.

**1962.** Independence. Inscr. "1.7.1962".

| | | | | |
|---|---|---|---|---|
| 26. | **10.** | 50 c. sepia and lake .. | 10 | 10 |
| 27. | A. | 1 f. green, red & deep grn. | 10 | 10 |
| 28. | B. | 2 f. sepia and olive .. | 10 | 10 |
| 29. | **10.** | 3 f. sepia and red .. | 10 | 10 |
| 30. | A. | 4 f. green, red and blue .. | 15 | 10 |
| 31. | B. | 8 f. sepia and violet .. | 30 | 15 |
| 32. | **10.** | 10 f. sepia and green .. | 40 | 15 |
| 33. | A. | 20 f. green, red and sepia | 45 | 20 |
| 34. | B. | 50 f. sepia and mauve .. | 1·25 | 45 |

DESIGNS—VERT. A, Burundi flag and arms. HORIZ. B, King and outline map of Burundi.

**1962.** Dag Hammarskjold Commem. No. 204 of Ruanda-Urundi surch. **HOMMAGE A DAG HAMMARSKJOLD ROYAUME DU BURUNDI** and new value. U.N. emblem and wavy pattern at foot. Inscr. in French or Flemish.

| | | | |
|---|---|---|---|
| 35. | 3 f. 50 on 3 f. salmon & bl. | 35 | 35 |
| 36. | 6 f. 50 on 3 f. salmon & bl. | 65 | 45 |
| 37. | 10 f. on 3 f. salmon & blue | 1·25 | 1·10 |

**1962.** Malaria Eradication. As Nos. 31 and 34 but colours changed and with campaign emblem superimposed on map.

| | | | | |
|---|---|---|---|---|
| 38. | B. | 8 f. sepia turq. & bistre | 55 | 35 |
| 39. | | 50 f. sepia turq. & olive | 1·40 | 35 |

**12.** Prince Louis Rwagasore. **13.** "Sowing".

**1963.** Prince Rwagasore Memorial and Stadium Fund.

| | | | | |
|---|---|---|---|---|
| 40. | **12.** | 50 c. + 25 c. violet .. | 10 | 10 |
| 41. | – | 1 f. + 50 c. blue and orange | 10 | 10 |
| 42. | – | 1 f. 50 + 75 c. vio. & bistre | 10 | 10 |
| 43. | **12.** | 3 f. 50 + 1 f. 50 mauve .. | 20 | 10 |
| 44. | – | 5 f. + 2 f. blue and pink .. | 20 | 10 |
| 45. | – | 6 f. 50 + 3 f. violet & olive | 25 | 10 |

DESIGNS—HORIZ. 1 f., 5 f. Prince and stadium. 1 f. 50, 6 f. 50 Prince and memorial.

**1963.** Freedom from Hunger.

| | | | | |
|---|---|---|---|---|
| 46. | **13.** | 4 f. purple and olive .. | 15 | 15 |
| 47. | | 8 f. purple and olive .. | 20 | 15 |
| 48. | | 15 f. purple and green .. | 35 | 15 |

**1963.** "Peaceful Uses of Outer Space" Nos. 28 and 34 optd. **UTILISATIONS PACIFIQUES DE L'ESPACE** around globe encircled by rocket.

| | | | | |
|---|---|---|---|---|
| 49. | B. | 2 f. sepia and olive .. | 2·25 | 2·25 |
| 50. | | 50 f. sepia and mauve .. | 3·50 | 3·50 |

**1963.** 1st Anniv. of Independence. Nos. 30/3 but with colours changed and optd. **Premier Anniversaire.**
51. A. 4 f. green, red and olive .. 20 10
52. B. 8 f. sepia and orange .. 30 10
53. **10.** 10 f. sepia and mauve .. 40 20
54. A. 20 f. green, red and grey 90 30

**1963.** Nos. 27 and 33 surch.
55. A. 6 f. 50 on 1 f. green, red and deep green .. 55 10
56. 15 f. on 20 f. green, red and sepia .. .. 85 35

**17.** Globe and Red Cross Flag. **18.** " 1962 " and U.N.E.S.C.O. Emblem.

**1963.** Centenary of Red Cross.
57. **17.** 4 f. green, red and grey .. 20 10
58. 8 f. brown, red and grey .. 40 20
59. 10 f. blue, red and grey .. 50 20
60. 20 f. violet, red and grey .. 1·10 40

**IMPERF. STAMPS.** Many Burundi stamps from No. 61 onwards exist imperf. from limited printings and/or miniature sheets.

**1963.** 1st Anniv. of Admission to U.N.O. Emblems and values in black.
61. **18.** 4 f. olive and yellow .. 15 10
62. – 8 f. blue and lilac .. 25 10
63. – 10 f. violet and blue .. 40 10
64. – 20 f. green & yellow .. 65 20
65. – 50 f. brown and ochre .. 1·75 35
EMBLEMS: 8 f. I.T.U.; 10 f. W.M.O.; 20 f. U.P.U ; 50 f. F.A.O.

**19.** U.N.E.S.C.O. Emblem and Scales of Justice.

**1963.** 15th Anniv. of Declaration of Human Rights.
66. **19.** 50 c. blk., blue and pink .. 10 10
67. – 1 f. 50 black, blue & oran. 10 10
68. – 3 f. 50 black, green & brn. 15 10
69. – 6 f. 50 black, green & lilac 25 10
70. – 10 f. black, bistre & blue 40 15
71. – 20 f. multicoloured .. 70 25
DESIGNS: 3 f. 50, 6 f. 50, Scroll. 10 f., 20 f. Lincoln.

**20.** Ice-hockey. **22.** Burundi Dancer

**21.** Hippopotamus.

**1964.** Winter Olympic Games, Innsbruck.
72. **20.** 50 c. black, gold & olive .. 15 10
73. – 3 f. 50 black, gold & brn. 20 10
74. – 6 f. 50 black, gold and grey 45 20
75. – 10 f. black, gold and grey 90 35
76. – 20 f. blk., gold & bistre .. 2·10 65
DESIGNS: 3 f. 50, Figure-skating. 6 f. 50, Olympic flame. 10 f. Speed-skating. 20 f. Skiing (slalom).

**1964.** Burundi Animals. Multicoloured.
(i) Postage. (a) Size as T **21**
77. 50 c. Impala .. .. 10 10
78. 1 f. Type **21** .. .. 10 10
79. 1 f. 50 Giraffe .. .. 10 10
80. 2 f. African buffalo .. 15 10
81. 3 f. Common zebra .. 15 10
82. 3 f. 50 Waterbuck .. 15 10
(b) Size 16 × 42½ mm. or 42½ × 26 mm.
83. 4 f. Impala .. .. 20 10
84. 5 f. Hippopotamus .. 25 10
85. 6 f. 50 Common zebra 25 10
86. 8 f. African buffalo .. 45 15
87. 10 f. Giraffe .. .. 50 15
88. 15 f. Waterbuck .. .. 70 25
(c) Size 53½ × 33½ mm.
89. 20 f. Cheetah .. 1·25 35
90. 50 f. African elephant .. 3·25 55
91. 100 f. Lion .. .. 5·25 90
(ii) Air. Inscr. "POSTE AERIENNE" and optd. with gold border.
(a) Size 26 × 42½ mm. or 42½ × 26 mm.
92. 6 f. Common zebra .. .. 30 10
93. 8 f. African buffalo .. 50 10
94. 10 f. Impala .. .. 55 10
95. 14 f. Hippopotamus .. 70 15
96. 15 f. Waterbuck .. 1·10 30
(b) Size 53½ × 33½ mm.
97. 20 f. Cheetah .. 1·40 35
98. 50 f. African elephant .. 3·25 80
The impala, giraffe and waterbuck stamp are all vert. designs, and the remainder are horiz.

**1964.** World's Fair, New York (1st series). Gold backgrounds.
99. **22.** 50 c. multicoloured .. 10 10
100. – 1 f. multicoloured .. 10 10
101. – 4 f. multicoloured .. 15 10
102. – 6 f. 50 multicoloured .. 20 10
103. – 10 f. multicoloured .. 40 15
104. – 15 f. multicoloured .. 70 20
105. – 20 f. multicoloured .. 90 30
DESIGNS: 1 f. to 20 f. Various dancers and drummers as Type **22**.
See also Nos. 175/81.

**23.** Pope Paul and King Mwambutsa IV.

**1964.** Canonisation of 22 African Martyrs. Inscriptions in gold.
106. **23.** 50 c. lake and blue .. 15 10
107. – 1 f. blue and purple .. 15 10
108. – 4 f. sepia and mauve .. 25 10
109. – 8 f. brown and red .. 40 15
110. – 14 f. brown & turquoise 40 20
111. **23.** 20 f. green and red .. 65 40
DESIGNS—VERT. 1 f., 8 f. Group of martyrs. HORIZ. 4 f., 14 f. Pope John XXIII and King Mwambutsa IV.

**24.** Putting the Shot.

**1964.** Olympic Games Tokyo. Inscr. "TOKYO 1964". Multicoloured.
112. 50 c. Type **24** .. .. 10 10
113. 1 f. Throwing the discus .. 10 10
114. 3 f. Swimming .. .. 10 10
115. 4 f. Relay-racing .. 10 10
116. 6 f. 50 Throwing the javelin 30 20
117. 8 f. Hurdling .. .. 35 20
118. 10 f. Long-jumping .. 40 20
119. 14 f. High-diving .. .. 55 20
120. 18 f. High-jumping .. 65 35
121. 20 f. Gymnastics .. 85 35
The 3, 8, 10, 18, and 20 f. are horiz. designs.

**25.** Scientist, Map and Emblem.

**1965.** Anti-T.B. Campaign. Country name values and Lorraine Cross in red.
122. **25.** 2 f. + 50 c. sepia & drab 10 10
123. 4 f. + 1 f. 50 grn. & pink 25 10
124. 5 f. + 2 f. 50 vio. & buff 30 15
125. 8 f. + 3 f. blue & grey .. 40 20
126. 10 f. + 5 f. red & green .. 55 30

**26.** Purple Swamphen. **27.** " Relay " Satellite and Telegraph Key.

**1965.** Birds. Multicoloured.
(i) Postage. (a) Size, as T **26**.
127 50 c. Type **26** .. .. 15 10
128 1 f. Little bee eater .. 15 10
129 1 f. 50 Secretary birdd .. 15 10
130 2 f. Painted stork .. 30 10
131 3 f. Congo peafowl .. 40 10
132 3 f. 50 African darter .. 45 10
(b) Size 26 × 42½ mm.
133 4 f. Type **26** .. .. 60 10
134 5 f. Little bee eater .. 70 15
135 6 f. Secretary bird .. 90 15
136 8 f. Painted stork .. 90 15
137 10 f. Congo peafowl .. 1·00 15
138 15 f. African darter .. 1·25 30
(c) Size 33½ × 53 mm.
139. 20 f. Saddle-bill stork .. 1·75 30
140. 50 f. Abyssinian ground hornbill .. .. .. 3·50 60
141. 100 f. South African crowned crane .. .. 6·00 1·10
(ii) Air. Inscr "POSTE AERIENNE" optd with gold border.
(a) Size 26 × 42½ mm.
142 6 f. Secretary bird .. 75 10
143 8 f. African darter .. 90 15
144 10 f. Congo peafowl .. 1·00 20
145 14 f. Little bee eater .. 1·10 25
146 15 f. Painted stork .. 1·25 25
(b) Size 33½ × 53 mm.
147. 20 f. Saddle-bill stork .. 1·75 35
148. 50 f. Abyssinian ground hornbill .. .. .. 3·25 95
149. 75 f. Martial eagle .. .. 3·75 1·25
150. 130 f. Lesser flamingo .. 6·75 2·00

**1965.** Cent. of I.T.U. Multicoloured.
151. 1 f. Type **27** .. .. 10 10
152. 3 f. "Telstar 1" and hand telephone .. .. 10 10
153. 4 f. "Lunik 3" and wall telephone .. .. 10 10
154. 6 f. 50 Weather satellite and tracking station .. 15 10
155. 8 f. "Telstar 2" and head-phones .. .. 15 15
156. 10 f. "Sputnik" and radar scanner .. .. 20 15
157. 14 f. "Syncom" and aerial 30 20
158. 20 f. "Pioneer 5" space probe and radio aerial .. 35 30

**28.** Arms (reverse of 10 f. coin).

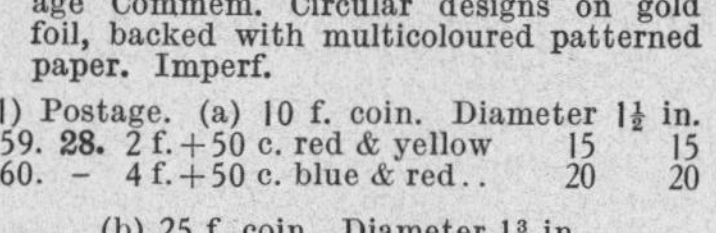
**1956.** 1st Independence Anniv. Gold Coinage Commem. Circular designs on gold foil, backed with multicoloured patterned paper. Imperf.
(I) Postage. (a) 10 f. coin. Diameter 1½ in.
159. **28.** 2 f. + 50 c. red & yellow 15 15
160. – 4 f. + 50 c. blue & red .. 20 20
(b) 25 f. coin. Diameter 1⅞ in.
161. **28.** 6 f. + 50 c. orange & grey 50 30
162. – 8 f. + 50 c. blue & purple 60 60
(c) 50 f. coin. Diameter 2¼ in.
163. **28.** 12 f. + 50 c. green & pur. 60 60
164. – 15 f. + 50 c. green & lilac 65 65
(d) 100 f. coin. Diameter 2 in.
165. **28.** 25 f. + 50 c. blue & flesh 1·25 1·25
166. – 40 f. + 50 c. mauve & brn. 1·75 1·75
(ii) Air. (a) 10 f. coin. Diameter 1½ in.
167. **28.** 3 f. + 1 f. violet & lav. 30 30
168. – 5 f. + 1 f. red & turquoise 40 40
(b) 25 f. coin. Diameter 1⅞ in.
169. **28.** 11 f. + 1 f. pur. & yellow 60 60
170. – 14 f. + 1 f. green & red 60 60
(c) 50 f. coin. Diameter 2¼ in.
171. **28.** 20 f. + 1 f. black & blue 85 85
172. – 30 f. + 1 f. lake & orange 1·10 1·10
(d) 100 f. coin. Diameter 2⅝ in.
173. **28.** 50 f. + 1 f. violet & blue 1·25 1·25
174. – 100 f. + 1 f. pur. & mve. 3·00 3·00
DESIGNS: The 4, 5, 8, 14, 15, 30, 40 and 100 f. each show the obverse side of the coin (King Mwambutsa IV).

**1965.** Worlds Fair, New York (2nd series). As Nos. 99/105, but with silver backgrounds.
175. **22.** 50 c. multicoloured .. 10 10
176. – 1 f. multicoloured .. 10 10
177. – 4 f. multicoloured .. 15 10
178. – 6 f. 50 multicoloured .. 25 10
179. – 10 f. multicoloured .. 45 20
180. – 15 f. multicoloured .. 55 30
181. – 20 f. multicoloured .. 70 35

**29.** Globe and I.C.Y. Emblem.

**1965.** Int. Co-operation Year. **Multicoloured.**
182. 1 f. Type **29** .. .. 10 10
183. 4 f. Map of Africa and cog-wheel emblem of U.N. Science and Technology Conference .. .. 15 10
184. 8 f. Map of South-East Asia and Colombo Plan emblem 20 10
185. 10 f. Globe & U.N. emblem 25 10
186. 18 f. Map of Americas and " Alliance for Progress " emblem .. .. .. 40 10
187. 25 f. Map of Europe and C.E.P.T. emblems .. 60 30
188. 40 f. Space map and satellite (U.N.—"Peaceful Uses of Outer Space") 1·00 50

**30.** Prince Rwagasore and Memorial.

**1966.** Prince Rwagasore and Pres. Kennedy Commem.
189. **30.** 4 f. + 1 f. brown & blue 20 10
190. – 10 f. + 1 f. blue, brown and green .. .. 30 10
191. – 20 f. + 2 f. green & lilac 65 15
192. – 40 f. + 2 f. brown & grn. 75 30
DESIGNS—HORIZ. 10 f. Prince Rwagasore and Pres. Kennedy. 20 f. Pres. Kennedy and memorial library. VERT. 40 f. King Mwambutsa at Pres. Kennedy's grave.

**31.** Protea.

**1966.** Flowers. Multicoloured.
(i) Postage. (a) Size as T **31.**

194. 50 c. Type **31** .. .. 15 10
195. 1 f. Crossandra .. .. 15 10
196. 1 f. 50 Ansellia .. .. 15 10
197. 2 f. Thunbergia .. .. 15 10
198. 3 f. Schizoglossum .. 20 10
199. 3 f. 50 Dissotis .. .. 20 10

(b) Size 41 × 41 mm.

200. 4 f. Type **31** .. .. 20 10
201. 5 f. Crossandra .. .. 30 10
202. 6 f. 50 Ansellia .. .. 40 10
203. 8 f. Thunbergia .. .. 55 10
204. 10 f. Schizoglossum .. 60 10
205. 15 f. Dissotis .. .. 75 10

(c) Size 50 × 50 mm.

206. 20 f. Type **31** .. .. 95 15
207. 50 f. Gazania .. .. 2·25 30
208. 100 f. Hibiscus .. .. 3·50 50
209. 150 f. Markhamia .. 5·50 65

(ii) Air. (a) Size 41 × 41 mm.

210. 6 f. Dissotis .. .. 25 10
211. 8 f. Crossandra .. .. 30 10
212. 10 f. Ansellia .. .. 30 10
213. 14 f. Thunbergia .. .. 35 10
214. 15 f. Schizoglossum .. 35 10

(b) Size 50 × 50 mm.

215. 20 f. Gazania .. .. 60 15
216. 50 f. Type **31** .. .. 1·60 30
217. 75 f. Hibiscus .. .. 2·25 75
218. 130 f. Markhamia .. 3·50 1·10

**1967.** Various stamps optd.
(i) Nos. 127, etc. (Birds) optd. **REPUBLIQUE DU BURUNDI** and bar. (a) Postage.

221. 50 c. multicoloured .. 1·50 15
222. 1 f. 50 multicoloured .. 30 15
223. 3 f. 50 multicoloured .. 40 20
224. 5 f multicoloured.. .. 55 30
225. 6 f. 50 multicoloured .. 55 40
226. 8 f. multicoloured.. .. 65 50
227. 10 f. multicoloured .. 75 55
228. 15 f. multicoloured .. 1·00 75
229. 20 f. multicoloured .. 2·40 1·10
230. 50 f. multicoloured .. 4·75 2·40
231. 100 f. multicoloured .. 7·75 4·25

(b) Air.

232. 6 f. multicoloured.. .. 50 15
233. 8 f. multicoloured.. .. 65 25
234. 10 f. multicoloured .. 75 40
235. 14 f. multicoloured .. 1·00 40
236. 15 f. multicoloured .. 1·10 50
237. 20 f. multicoloured .. 1·60 60
238. 50 f. multicoloured .. 5·75 1·75
239. 75 f. multicoloured .. 7·75 2·10
240. 130 f. multicoloured .. 11·00 3·50

(ii) Nos. 194, etc. (Flowers) optd. as Nos. 221, etc., but with two bars. (a) Postage.

241. 50 c. multicoloured .. 15 15
242. 1 f. multicoloured.. .. 15 15
243. 1 f. 50 multicoloured .. 15 15
244. 2 f. multicoloured .. 15 15
245. 3 f. multicoloured.. .. 20 15
246. 3 f. 50 multicoloured .. 30 15
247. 4 f. multicoloured .. 1·75 15
248. 5 f. multicoloured.. .. 45 20
249. 6 f. 50 multicoloured .. 40 30
250. 8 f. multicoloured.. .. 40 30
251. 10 f. multicoloured .. 55 35
252. 15 f. multicoloured .. 70 40
253. 50 f. multicoloured .. 3·50 60
254. 100 f. multicoloured .. 8·25 2·40
255. 150 f. multicoloured .. 7·75 8·50

(b) Air.

256. 6 f. multicoloured.. .. 20 15
257. 8 f. multicoloured.. .. 30 15
258. 10 f. multicoloured .. 35 15
259. 14 f. multicoloured .. 45 30
260. 15 f. multicoloured .. 55 30
261. 20 f. multicoloured .. 1·75 40
262. 50 f. multicoloured .. 3·75 65
263. 75 f. multicoloured .. 5·75 90
264. 130 f. multicoloured .. 5·75 1·50

**35.** Sir Winston Churchill and St. Paul's Cathedral.

**1967.** Churchill Commem.

265. **35.** 4 f.+1 f. multicoloured 30 10
266. – 15 f.+2 f. multicoloured 50 25
267. – 20 f.+3 f. multicoloured 60 35

DESIGNS (Churchill and): 15 f. Tower of London. 20 f. Big Ben and Boadicea statue, Westminster.



**36.** Egyptian Mouthbreeder.

**1967.** Fishes. Multicoloured.
(a) Postage. (i) Size as T **36.**

269. 50 c. Type **36** .. .. 15 10
270. 1 f. Spotted Climbing Perch 15 10
271. 1 f. 50 Six Banded Panchax 15 10
272. 2 f. Congo Tetra .. .. 15 10
273. 3 f. Red Jewel Fish .. 15 10
274. 3 f. 50 White Spotted Cichlid 15 10

(ii) Size 53½ × 27 mm.

275. 4 f. Type **36** .. .. 40 10
276. 5 f. As 1 f. .. .. 40 10
277. 6 f. 50. As 1 f. 50.. .. 50 10
278. 8 f. As 2 f. .. .. 50 10
279. 10 f. As 3 f. .. .. 75 10
280. 15 f. As 3 f. 50 .. .. 85 10

(iii) Size 63½ × 31½ mm.

281. 20 f. Type **36** .. .. 1·40 15
282. 50 f. Snakehead .. .. 2·75 25
283. 100 f. Tooth Carp.. .. 5·50 30
284. 150 f. African Tetra .. 5·50 50

(b) Air. (i) Size 50 × 23 mm.

285. 6 f. Type **36** .. .. 25 10
286. 8 f. As 1 f.. .. .. 35 10
287. 10 f. As 1 f. 50 .. .. 40 10
288. 14 f. As 2 f. .. .. 50 10
289. 15 f. As 3 f. .. .. 60 10

(ii) Size 59 × 27 mm.

290. 20 f. As 3 f. 50 .. .. 70 10
291. 50 f. As 50 f. (postage) .. 3·50 15
292. 75 f. As 100 f. .. .. 4·75 25
293. 130 f. As 150 f. .. .. 8·00 40

**37.** Baule Ancestral Figures.

**1967.** "African Art". Multicoloured.

294. 50 c. Type **37** (postage) .. 10 10
295. 1 f. "Master of Buli's" carved seat .. .. 10 10
296. 1 f. 50, Karumba antelope's head .. .. 10 10
297. 2 f. Bobo buffalo's head .. 10 10
298. 4 f. Guma-Goffa funeral figures .. .. 15 10
299. 10 f. Bakoutou "spirit" (carving) (air) .. .. 30 20
300. 14 f. Bamum sultan's throne 40 20
301. 17 f. Bebin bronze head .. 45 20
302. 24 f. Statue of 109th Bakouba king .. .. 55 30
303. 26 f. Burundi basketwork and lances .. .. 60 35

**1967.** 50th Anniv. of Lions Int. Nos. 265/7 optd. **1917 1967** and emblem.

304. 4 f.+1 f. multicoloured .. 50 20
305. 15 f.+2 f. multicoloured.. 80 35
306. 20 f.+3 f. multicoloured.. 95 35

**39.** Lord Baden-Powell (founder).

**1967.** 60th Anniv. of Scout Movement and World Scout Jamboree, Idaho.

308. 50 c. Scouts climbing (post.) 20 10
309. 1 f. Scouts preparing meal 20 10
310. 1 f. 50, Type **39** .. .. 20 10
311. 2 f. Two scouts .. .. 20 10
312. 4 f. Giving first aid .. 30 10
313. 10 f. As 50 c. (air) .. 60 15
314. 14 f. As 1 f. .. .. 70 15
315. 17 f. Type **39** .. .. 85 15
316. 24 f. As 2 f. .. .. 1·10 35
317. 26 f. As 4 f. .. .. 1·25 40

**40.** "The Gleaners" (Millet).

**1967.** World Fair, Montreal. Multicoloured.

318. 4 f. Type **40** .. .. 15 10
319. 8 f. "The Water-carrier of Seville" (Velasquez) .. 15 10
320. 14 f. "The Triumph of Neptune and Amphitrite" (Poussin).. .. .. 35 15
321. 18 f. "Acrobat with a ball" (Picasso) .. .. .. 35 15
322. 25 f. "Margaret van Eyck" (Van Eyck) .. .. 95 25
323. 40 f. "St. Peter denying Christ" (Rembrandt) .. 1·10 50

41. Boeing 707.

**1967.** Air. Opening of Bujumbura Airport. Aircraft and inscr. in black and silver.

325. **41.** 10 f. green .. .. 25 10
326. – 14 f. yellow .. .. 40 20
327. – 17 f. blue .. .. 60 20
328. – 26 f. purple .. .. 1·00 30

AIRCRAFT: 14 f. Boeing 727 over lakes. 17 f. Vickers Super VC-10 over lake. 26 f. Boeing 727 over Bujumbura Airport.

**42.** Pres. Micombero and Flag.

**1967.** 1st Anniv. of Republic. Multicoloured.

329. 5 f. Type **42** .. .. 25 10
330. 14 f. Memorial and Arms.. 35 15
331. 20 f. View of Bujumbura and Arms .. .. 50 20
332. 30 f. "Place de la Revolution" and President Micombero .. .. 90 30

**43.** "The Adoration of the Shepherds" (J. B. Mayno).

**45.** Downhill Skiing.

**1967.** Christmas. Religious Paintings. Multicoloured.

333. 1 f. Type **43** .. .. 10 10
334. 4 f. "The Holy Family" (A. van Dyck) .. .. 15 10
335. 14 f. "The Nativity" (Maitre de Moulins) .. 40 20
336. 26 f. "Madonna and Child" (C. Crivelli) .. .. 75 30

**1968.** Winter Olympic Games. Grenoble. Multicoloured.

339. 5 f. Type **45** .. .. 20 10
340. 10 f. Ice-hockey .. .. 25 10
341. 14 f. Figure-skating .. 40 10
342. 17 f. Bobsleighing .. 50 10
343. 26 f. Ski-jumping .. 65 10
344. 40 f. Speed-skating .. 1·10 25
345. 60 f. Olympic torch .. 1·75 30

**46.** "Portrait of a Young Man" (Botticelli).

**1968.** Famous Paintings. Multicoloured.

347. 1 f. 50 Type **46** (postage) 10 10
348. 2 f. "La Maja Vestida" (Goya) (horiz.) .. 10 10
349. 4 f. "The Lacemaker" (Vermeer) .. .. 15 10
350. 17 f. "Woman and Cat" (Renoir) (air) .. .. 40 20
351. 24 f. "The Jewish Bride" (Rembrandt) (horiz.) .. 55 30
352. 26 f. "Pope Innocent X" (Velasquez) .. .. 80 40

**47.** Module landing on Moon.

**1968.** Space Exploration. Multicoloured.

353. 4 f. Type **47** (postage) .. 20 10
354. 6 f. Russian cosmonaut in Space .. .. 30 10
355. 8 f. Weather satellite .. 30 10
356. 10 f. American astronaut in Space .. .. 45 15
357. 14 f. Type **47** (air) .. 40 15
358. 18 f. As 6 f. .. .. 50 15
359. 25 f. As 8 f. .. .. 80 25
360. 40 f. As 10 f. .. .. 1·10 40

**48.** "Salamis aethiops".

**1968.** Butterflies. Multicoloured.
(a) Postage. (i) Size 30½ × 34 mm.

362. 50 c. Type **48** .. .. 10 10
363. 1 f. "Graphium ridleyanus" .. .. 15 10
364. 1 f. 50 "Cymothoe" .. 20 10
365. 2 f. "Charaxes eupale".. 25 10
366. 3 f. "Papilio bromius" .. 30 10
367. 3 f. 50 "Teracolus annae" 35 10

(ii) Size 34 × 38 mm.

368. 4 f. Type **48** .. .. 35 10
369. 5 f. As 1 f. .. .. 40 10
370. 6 f. 50 As 1 f. 50 .. .. 45 10
371. 8 f. As 2 f. .. .. 65 15
372. 10 f. As 3 f. .. .. 80 15
373. 15 f. As 3 f. 50 .. .. 1·00 20

(iii) Size 41 × 46 mm.

374. 20 f. Type **48** .. .. 1·90 25
375. 50 f. "Papilio zenobia".. 3·25 60
376. 100 f. "Danais chrysippus" .. .. 6·00 1·00
377. 150 f. "Salamis temora" 10·50 1·60

(b) Air. With gold frames.
(i) Size 33 × 37 mm.

378. 6 f. As 3 f. 50 .. .. 35 10
379. 8 f. As 1 f. .. .. 40 10
380. 10 f. As 1 f. 50 .. .. 45 10
381. 14 f. As 2 f. .. .. 50 15
382. 15 f. As 3 f. .. .. 75 15

(ii) Size 39 × 44 mm.

383. 20 f. As 50 f. (postage) .. 1·75 20
384. 50 f. Type **48** .. .. 4·00 40
385. 75 f. As 100 f. .. .. 5·00 70
386. 130 f. As 150 f. .. .. 9·00 85

**49.** " Woman by the Manzanares " (Goya).

**1968.** Int. Letter-writing Week. Mult.

387. 4 f. Type **49** (postage) .. 25 10
388. 7 f. " Reading a Letter " (De Hooch) .. .. 35 10
389. 11 f. " Woman reading a Letter " (Terborch) .. 40 10
390. 14 f. " Man writing a Letter " (Metsu) .. 45 10
391. 17 f. " The Letter " (Fragonard) (air) .. .. 60 10
392. 26 f. " Young Woman reading Letter " (Vermeer) .. 80 20
393. 40 f. " Folding a Letter " (Vigee-Lebrun) .. 90 25
394. 50 f. " Mademoiselle Lavergne " (Liotard) .. 95 35

**50.** Football.

**1968.** Olympic Games, Mexico. Mult.

396. 4 f. Type **50** (postage) .. 25 10
397. 7 f. Basketball .. .. 30 10
398. 13 f. High jumping .. 35 10
399. 24 f. Relay racing .. .. 55 20
400. 40 f. Throwing the javelin 1·25 40
401. 10 f. Putting the shot (air) 25 15
402. 17 f. Running .. .. 45 15
403. 26 f. Throwing the hammer 70 25
404. 50 f. Hurdling .. .. 1·40 45
405. 75 f. Long jumping .. 2·25 60

**51.** " Virgin and Child " (Lippi).

**1968.** Christmas. Paintings. Multicoloured.

407. 3 f. Type **51** (postage) .. 20 10
408. 5 f. " The Magnificat " (Botticelli) .. .. 25 10
409. 6 f. " Virgin and Child " (Durer) .. .. .. 40 10
410. 11 f. " Virgin and Child " (Raphael) .. .. 40 10
411. 10 f. " Madonna " (Correggio) (air) .. 25 10
412. 14 f. " The Nativity " (Baroccio) .. .. 35 15
413. 17 f. " The Holy Family " (El Greco) .. .. 55 20
414. 26 f. " Adoration of the Magi " (Maino) .. .. 75 35

**52.** W.H.O. Emblem and Map.

**1969.** 20th Anniv. of World Health Organization Operation in Africa.

416. **52.** 5 f. multicoloured .. 15 10
417. 6 f. multicoloured .. 20 10
418. 11 f. multicoloured .. 25 15

**53.** Hand holding Flame.

**1969.** Air. Human Rights Year.

419. **53.** 10 f. multicoloured .. 35 10
420. 14 f. multicoloured .. 45 10
421. 26 f. multicoloured .. 65 25

**1969.** Space Flight of " Apollo 8 ". Nos. 407/14 optd. *VOL DE NOEL APOLLO 8* and space module.

422. 3 f. multicoloured (postage) 15 10
423. 5 f. multicoloured .. .. 25 10
424. 6 f. multicoloured .. .. 40 10
425. 11 f. multicoloured .. 50 20
426. 10 f. multicoloured (air) .. 30 15
427. 14 f. multicoloured .. 35 20
428. 17 f. multicoloured .. 55 25
429. 26 f. multicoloured .. 70 35

**55.** Map showing African Members.

**56.** " Resurrection " (Isenmann).

**1969.** 5th Anniv. of Yaounde Agreement between Common Market Countries and African-Malagasy Economic Community. Multicoloured.

430. 5 f. Type **55** .. .. 20 10
431. 14 f. Ploughing with tractor .. .. .. 40 15
432. 17 f. Teacher and pupil .. 55 20
433. 26 f. Maps of Africa and Europe (horiz.) .. 75 25

**1969.** Easter. Multicoloured.

434. 11 f. Type **56** .. .. 30 10
435. 14 f. " Resurrection " (Caron) .. .. .. 40 15
436. 17 f. " Noli me Tangere " (Schongauer) .. .. 45 20
437. 26 f. " Resurrection " (El Greco) .. .. 75 30

**57.** Potter.

**1969.** 50th Anniv. of Int. Labour Organization. Multicoloured.

439. 3 f. Type **57** .. .. 10 10
440. 5 f. Farm workers .. 10 10
441. 7 f. Foundry worker .. 25 10
442. 10 f. Harvester .. .. 25 15

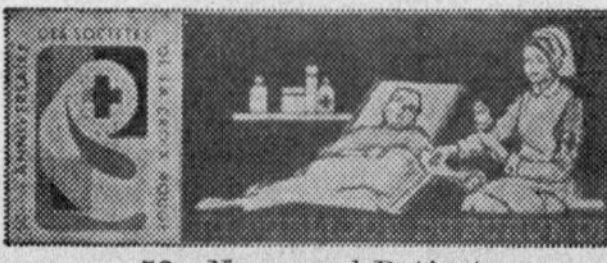

**58.** Nurse and Patient.

**1969.** 50th Anniv. of League of Red Cross Societies. Multicoloured.

443. 4 f.+1 f. Type **58** (postage) 15 10
444. 7 f.+1 f. Stretcher bearers 35 10
445. 11 f.+1 f. Operating theatre 50 15
446. 17 f.+1 f. Blood bank .. 60 25
447. 26 f.+3 f. Laboratory (air) 75 25
448. 40 f.+3 f. Red Cross truck in African village .. 1·10 45
449. 50 f.+3 f. Nurse and woman patient .. .. .. 1·60 50

**59.** Steel Works.

**1969.** 5th Anniv. of African Development Bank. Multicoloured.

451. 10 f. Type **59** .. .. 30 30
452. 17 f. Broadcaster .. .. 50 50
453. 30 f. Language laboratory 70 70
454. 50 f. Tractor and harrow 1·25 1·25

**60.** Pope Paul VI.

**61.** " Girl reading Letter " (Vermeer).

**1969.** 1st Papal Visit to Africa. Mult.

456. 3 f.+2 f. Type **60** .. .. 15 10
457. 5 f.+2 f. Pope Paul and map of Africa .. .. 30 10
458. 10 f.+2 f. Pope Paul and African flags .. .. 30 10
459. 14 f.+2 f. Pope Paul and the Vatican .. .. 55 10
460. 17 f.+2 f. Type **60** .. 60 10
461. 40 f.+2 f. Pope Paul and Uganda Martyrs .. 1·25 30
462. 50 f.+2 f. Pope Paul enthroned .. .. 1·60 35

Nos. 457/59 and 461/62 are horiz.

**1969.** Int. Letter-writing Week. Mult.

464. 4 f. Type **61** .. .. 15 10
465. 7 f. " Graziella " (Renoir) 20 10
466. 14 f. " Woman writing a Letter " (Terborch) .. 30 10
467. 26 f. " Galileo " (unknown painter) .. .. 55 15
468. 40 f. " Beethoven " (unknown painter) .. 1·10 35

**62.** Blast-off.

**63.** " Adoration of the Magi " (detail, Rubens).

**1969.** 1st Man on the Moon. Multicoloured.

470. 4 f. Type **62** (postage) .. 30 10
471. 6 f. 50 Rocket in Space .. 40 10
472. 7 f. Separation of lunar module .. .. .. 50 10
473. 14 f. Module landing on Moon .. .. .. 80 15
474. 17 f. Command module in orbit .. .. .. 1·10 25
475. 26 f. Astronaut descending ladder (air) .. .. 1·25 20
476. 40 f. Astronaut on Moon's surface .. .. 2·00 25
477. 50 f. Module in sea .. 3·00 45

**1969.** Christmas. Multicoloured.

479. 5 f. Type **63** (postage) .. 15 10
480. 6 f. " Virgin and Child with St. John " (Romano) 15 10
481. 10 f. " Madonna of the Magnificat " (Botticelli) 40 15
482. 17 f. " Virgin and Child " (Garofalo) (air) .. .. 60 15
483. 26 f. " Madonna and Child " (Negretti) .. .. 80 20
484. 50 f. " Virgin and Child " (Barbarelli) .. .. 1·60 35

Nos. 482/4 are horiz.

**64.** " Chelorrhina polyphemus ".

**1970.** Beetles. Multicoloured.

(a) Postage. (i) Size 39 × 28 mm.

486. 50 c. " Sternotomis bohemani " .. .. 15 10
487. 1 f. " Tetralobus flabellicornis " .. .. 15 10
488. 1 f. 50 Type **64** .. .. 15 10
489. 2 f. " Brachytritus hieroglyphicus " .. 15 10
490. 3 f. " Goliathus goliathus " 15 10
491. 3 f. 50 " Homoderus mellyi " 25 10

(ii) Size 46 × 32 mm.

492. 4 f. As 50 c. .. .. 40 10
493. 5 f. As 1 f. .. .. 50 10
494. 6 f. 50 Type **64** .. .. 50 10
495. 8 f. As 2 f. .. .. 50 10
496. 10 f. As 3 f. .. .. 60 10
497. 15 f. As 3 f. 50 .. .. 95 15

(iii) Size 62 × 36 mm.

498. 20 f. As 50 c. .. .. 1·25 30
499. 50 f. " Stephanorrhina guttata " .. .. 3·50 40
500. 100 f. " Phyllocnema viridocostata " .. .. 5·75 85
501. 150 f. " Mecynorrhina oberthueri " .. .. 7·00 1·60

(b) Air. (i) Size 46 × 32 mm.

502. 6 f. As 3 f. 50 .. .. 30 10
503. 8 f. As 1 f. .. .. 40 10
504. 10 f. Type **64** .. .. 50 15
505. 14 f. As 2 f. .. .. 60 15
506. 15 f. As 3 f. .. .. 65 20

(ii) Size 52 × 36 mm.

507. 20 f. As 50 f. (No. 499) .. 1·10 25
508. 50 f. As 50 c. .. .. 3·50 35
509. 75 f. As 100 f. .. .. 4·25 55
510. 130 f. As 150 f. .. .. 6·75 80

**65.** " Jesus Condemned to Death ".

**1970.** Easter. " The Stations of the Cross " (Carredano). Multicoloured.

511. 1 f. Type **65** (postage) .. 10 10
512. 1 f. 50 " Carrying the Cross " 10 10
513. 2 f. " Jesus falls for the First Time " .. .. 10 10
514. 3 f. " Jesus meets His Mother " .. .. 10 10
515. 3 f. 50 " Simon of Cyrene takes the Cross " .. 15 10
516. 4 f. " Veronica wipes the face of Christ " .. 15 10
517. 5 f. " Jesus falls for the Second Time " .. .. 15 10
518. 8 f. " The Women of Jerusalem " (air) .. 20 10
519. 10 f. " Jesus falls for the Third Time " .. .. 25 15
520. 14 f. " Christ stripped " .. 30 25
521. 15 f. " Jesus nailed to the Cross " .. .. 40 25
522. 18 f. " The Crucifixion " .. 40 30
523. 20 f. " Descent from the Cross " .. .. 50 30
524. 50 f. " Christ laid in the Tomb " .. .. 1·25 45

**66.** Japanese Parade.

**1970.** World Fair, Osaka, Japan (EXPO '70). Multicoloured.

526. 4 f. Type **66** .. .. 15 10
527. 6 f. 50 Exhibition site from the air .. .. 20 10
528. 7 f. African pavilions .. 20 10
529. 14 f. Pagoda (vert.) .. 30 10
530. 26 f. Recording pavilion and pool .. .. 60 15
531. 40 f. Tower of the Sun (vert.) .. .. .. 1·00 30
532. 50 f. National flags (vert.) 1·25 35

**67.** Burundi Cow.

**1970.** Source of the Nile. Multicoloured.

534. 7 f. Any design (postage) 80 25
535. 14 f. Any design (air) .. 80 30

Nos. 534 and 535 were each issued in se-tenant sheets of 18 stamps as Type **67**, showing map sections, animals and birds, forming a map of the Nile from Cairo to Burundi.

**68.** Redstart.

**1970.** Birds. Multicoloured.

(a) Postage. Size 44 × 33 or 33 × 44 mm.

536. 2 f. Great grey shrike (vert.) 20 10
537. 2 f. Common starling (vert.) 20 10
538. 2 f. Yellow wagtail (vert.) 20 10
539. 2 f. Sand martin (vert.) .. 35 10
540. 3 f. Winter wren .. .. 50 10
541. 3 f. Firecrest .. .. 50 10
542. 3 f. Skylark .. .. 50 10
543. 3 f. Crested lark .. .. 50 10
544. 3 f. 50 Woodchat shrike (vert.) .. .. .. 55 10
545. 3 f. 50 Rock thrush (vert.) 55 10
546. 3 f. 50 Black redstarts (vert.) .. .. .. 55 10
547. 3 f. 50 Ring ousel (vert.) .. 55 10
548. 4 f. Type **68** .. .. 80 20
549. 4 f. Dunnock .. .. 80 20
550. 4 f. Grey wagtail .. .. 80 20
551. 4 f. Meadow pipit .. .. 80 20
552. 5 f. Hoopoe (vert.) .. 1·00 25
553. 5 f. Pied flycatcher (vert.) 1·00 25
554. 5 f. Great reed warbler (vert.) .. .. 1·00 25
555. 5 f. Common kingfisher (vert.) .. .. .. 1·00 25
556. 6 f. 50 House martin .. 1·10 40
557. 6 f. 50 Sedge warbler .. 1·10 40
558. 6 f. 50 Fieldfare .. .. 1·10 40
559. 6 f. 50 Golden oriole .. 1·10 40

(b) Air. Size 52 × 44 mm. or 44 × 52 mm.

560. 8 f. As No. 536 .. .. 1·25 40
561. 8 f. As No. 537 .. .. 1·25 40
562. 8 f. As No. 538 .. .. 1·25 40
563. 8 f. As No. 539 .. .. 1·25 40
564. 10 f. As No. 540 .. .. 1·40 50
565. 10 f. As No. 541 .. .. 1·40 50
566. 10 f. As No. 542 .. .. 1·40 50
567. 10 f. As No. 543 .. .. 1·40 50
568. 14 f. As No. 544 .. .. 1·50 50
569. 14 f. As No. 545 .. .. 1·50 50
570. 14 f. As No. 546 .. .. 1·50 50
571. 14 f. As No. 547 .. .. 1·50 50
572. 20 f. Type **68** .. .. 1·75 55
573. 20 f. As No. 549 .. .. 1·75 55
574. 20 f. As No. 550 .. .. 1·75 55
575. 20 f. As No. 551 .. .. 1·75 55
576. 30 f. As No. 552 .. .. 1·90 55
577. 30 f. As No. 553 .. .. 1·90 55
578. 30 f. As No. 554 .. .. 1·90 55
579. 30 f. As No. 555 .. .. 1·90 55
580. 50 f. As No. 556 .. .. 3·25 60
581. 50 f. As No. 557 .. .. 3·25 60
582. 50 f. As No. 558 .. .. 3·25 60
583. 50 f. As No. 559 .. .. 3·25 60

**69.** Library.

**1970.** Int. Educational Year. Multicoloured.

584. 3 f. Type **69** .. .. 10 10
585. 5 f. Examination .. .. 15 10
586. 7 f. Experiments in the laboratory .. .. 25 10
587. 10 f. Students with electron microscope .. .. 30 10

**70.** United Nations Building, New York.

**1970.** Air. 25th Anniv. of United Nations. Multicoloured.

588. 7 f. Type **70** .. .. 25 10
589. 11 f. Security Council in session .. .. .. 30 10
590. 26 f. Paul VI and U Thant 70 20
591. 40 f. U.N. and National flags .. .. .. 1·00 30

**71.** Pres. Micombero and Wife.

**1970.** 4th Anniv. of Republic.

593. 4 f. Type **71** .. .. 10 10
594. 7 f. Pres. Micombero and flag .. .. .. 25 10
595. 11 f. Revolution Memorial 35 15

**72.** King Baudouin and Queen Fabiola.

**1970.** Air. Visit of King and Queen of the Belgians. Each brown, purple and gold.

597. 6 f. Type **72** .. .. 65 15
598. 20 f. Pres. Micombero and King Baudouin .. 1·50 40
599. 40 f. Pres. Micombero in evening dress .. .. 3·00 70

**73.** " Adoration of the Magi " (Durer).

**1970.** Christmas. Multicoloured.

601. 6 f. 50 + 1 f. Type **73** (post). 50 15
602. 11 f. + 1 f. " The Virgin of the Eucharist " (Botticelli) 60 25
603. 20 f. + 1 f. " The Holy Family " (El Greco) .. 90 30
604. 14 f. + 3 f. " The Adoration of the Magi " (Velasquez) (air) .. .. .. 50 25
605. 26 f. + 3 f. " The Holy Family " (Van Cleve) .. 85 40
606. 40 f. + 3 f. " Virgin and Child " (Van der Weyden) 1·40 60

**74.** Lenin in Discussion.

**76.** " The Resurrection " (Il Sodoma).

**75.** Lion.

**1970.** Birth Cent. of Lenin. Each brown and gold.

608. 3 f. 50 Type **74** .. .. 20 15
609. 5 f. Lenin addressing Soviet 30 15
610. 6 f. 50 Lenin with soldier and sailor .. .. 40 15
611. 15 f. Lenin speaking to crowd .. .. .. 60 25
612. 50 f. Lenin .. .. 2·00 55

**1971.** African Animals (1st series). Mult.

(a) Postage. Size 38 × 38 mm.

613. 1 f. Type **75** .. .. 20 10
614. 1 f. African buffalo .. 20 10
615. 1 f. Hippopotamus .. 20 10
616. 1 f. Giraffe .. .. .. 20 10
617. 2 f. Topi .. .. .. 30 15
618. 2 f. Black rhinoceros .. 30 15
619. 2 f. Common zebra .. 30 15
620. 2 f. Leopard .. .. 30 15
621. 3 f. Grant's gazelle .. 50 25
622. 3 f. Cheetah .. .. 50 25
623. 3 f. African White-backed Vultures .. .. .. 70 30
624. 3 f. Okapi .. .. .. 50 25
625. 5 f. Chimpanzee .. .. 60 25
626. 5 f. African elephant .. 60 25
627. 5 f. Spotted hyena .. 60 25
628. 5 f. Gemsbok .. .. 60 25
629. 6 f. Gorilla .. .. .. 80 25
630. 6 f. Blue wildebeest .. 80 25
631. 6 f. Warthog .. .. 80 25
632. 6 f. Hunting dog .. .. 80 25
633. 11 f. Stable antelope .. 1·40 30
634. 11 f. Caracal .. .. 1·40 30
635. 11 f. Ostriches .. .. 2·25 50
636. 11 f. Bongo .. .. 1·40 30

(b) Air. Size 44 × 44 mm.

637. 10 f. Type **75** .. .. 65 25
638. 10 f. As No. 614 .. .. 65 25
639. 10 f. As No. 615 .. .. 65 25
640. 10 f. As No. 616 .. .. 65 25
641. 14 f. As No. 617 .. .. 75 30
642. 14 f. As No. 618 .. .. 75 30
643. 14 f. As No. 619 .. .. 75 30
644. 14 f. As No. 620 .. .. 75 30
645. 17 f. As No. 621 .. .. 85 30
646. 17 f. As No. 622 .. .. 85 30
647. 17 f. As No. 623 .. .. 2·50 50
648. 17 f. As No. 624 .. .. 85 30
649. 24 f. As No. 625 .. .. 1·25 40
650. 24 f. As No. 626 .. .. 1·25 40
651. 24 f. As No. 627 .. .. 1·25 40
652. 24 f. As No. 628 .. .. 1·25 40
653. 26 f. As No. 629 .. .. 1·40 40
654. 26 f. As No. 630 .. .. 1·40 40
655. 26 f. As No. 631 .. .. 1·40 40
656. 26 f. As No. 632 .. .. 1·40 40
657. 31 f. As No. 633 .. .. 1·50 50
658. 31 f. As No. 634 .. .. 1·50 50
659. 31 f. As No. 635 .. .. 3·50 90
660. 31 f. As No. 636 .. .. 1·50 50

See also Nos. 1028/75, 1178/1225 and 1385/97.

**1971.** Easter. Multicoloured.

661. 3 f. Type **76** (postage) .. 15 10
662. 6 f. " The Resurrection " (Del Castagno) .. .. 30 10
663. 11 f. " Noli Me Tangere " (Correggio) .. .. 45 15
664. 14 f. " The Resurrection " (Borrassa) (air) .. .. 50 20
665. 17 f. " The Resurrection " (Della Francesca) .. 65 20
666. 26 f. " The Resurrection " (Pleydenwyurff) .. 85 30

**1971.** Air. United Nations Campaigns. Nos. 637/48 optd. or surch.

(a) Optd. **LUTTE CONTRE LE RACISME ET LA DISCRIMINATION RACIALE** and Racial Equality Year emblem.

668. 10 f. multicoloured .. 50 10
669. 10 f. multicoloured .. 50 10
670. 10 f. multicoloured .. 50 10
671. 10 f. multicoloured .. 50 10

(b) Surch. **LUTTE CONTRE L'ANALPHABETISME,** U.N.E.S.C.O. emblem and premium (Campaign against Illiteracy).

672. 14 f. + 2 f. multicoloured .. 75 15
673. 14 f. + 2 f. multicoloured .. 75 15
674. 14 f. + 2 f. multicoloured .. 75 15
675. 14 f. + 2 f. multicoloured .. 75 15

(c) Surch. **AIDE INTERNATIONALE AUX REFUGIES,** emblem and premium (Int. Help for Refugees).

676. 17 f. + 1 f. multicoloured .. 1·25 25
677. 17 f. + 1 f. multicoloured .. 1·25 25
678. 17 f. + 1 f. multicoloured .. 2·75 30
679. 17 f. + 1 f. multicoloured .. 1·25 25

**1971.** Air. Olympic Commems. Nos. 653/56 surch.

(a) Surch. **75eme ANNIVERSAIRE DES JEUX OLYMPIQUES MODERNES (1896-1971),** Olympic rings and premium.

680. 26 f. + 1 f. multicoloured .. 90 35
681. 26 f + 1 f. multicoloured .. 90 35
682. 26 f. + 1 f. multicoloured .. 90 35
683. 26 f. + 1 f. multicoloured .. 90 35

(b) Surch. **JEUX PRE-OLYMPIQUES MUNICH 1972,** rings and premium (Olympic Games, Munich (1972)).

684. 31 f. + 1 f. multicoloured .. 1·75 1·00
685. 31 f. + 1 f. multicoloured .. 1·75 1·00
686. 31 f. + 1 f. multicoloured .. 2·25 1·00
687. 31 f. + 1 f. multicoloured .. 1·75 1·00

**79.** " Venetian Girl ".

**81.** " The Virgin and Child " (Il Perugino).

**1971.** Int. Letter-writing Week. Paintings by Durer. Multicoloured.

688. 6 f. Type **79** .. .. 30 30
689. 11 f. " Jerome Holzschuhers " 35 35
690. 14 f. " Emperor Maximilian " 40 40
691. 17 f. Altar painting, Paumgartner .. .. 65 65
692. 26 f. " The Halle Madonna " 80 80
693. 31 f. Self portrait .. .. 1·00 1·00

**1971.** 6th Congress of Int. Institute of French Law, Bujumbura. Nos. 668/693 optd. **VIeme CONGRES DE L'INSTITUT INTERNATIONAL DE DROIT D'EXPRESSION FRANCAISE.**

695. 6 f. multicoloured .. 30 10
696. 11 f. multicoloured .. 35 10
697. 14 f. multicoloured .. 45 20
698. 17 f. multicoloured .. 65 20
699. 26 f. multicoloured .. 75 25
700. 31 f. multicoloured .. 1·00 25

**1971.** Christmas. Paintings of " Virgin and Child " by following artists. Mult.

702. 3 f. Type **81** (postage) .. 15 10
703. 5 f. Del Sarto .. .. 25 10
704. 6 f. Morales .. .. 50 10
705. 14 f. Da Conegliano (air) .. 55 15
706. 17 f. Lippi .. .. .. 60 20
707. 31 f. Leonardo da Vinci .. 1·10 45

**1971.** 25th Anniv. of U.N.I.C.E.F. Nos. 702/707 surch. **UNICEF XXVe ANNIVERSAIRE 1946–1971,** emblem and premium.

709. 3 f. + 1 f. mult. (postage) .. 30 10
710. 5 f. + 1 f. multicoloured .. 50 20
711. 6 f. + 1 f. multicoloured .. 60 30
712. 14 f. + 1 f. mult. (air) .. 40 20
713. 17 f. + 1 f. multicoloured .. 95 25
714. 31 f. + 1 f. multicoloured .. 1·50 45

83. "Archangel Michael" (icon, St. Mark's).

**1971.** U.N.E.S.C.O. "Save Venice" Campaign. Multicoloured.
716. 3 f.+1 f. Type **83** (postage) 25 10
717. 5 f.+1 f. "La Polenta" (Longhi) .. .. 35 15
718. 6 f.+1 f. "Gossip" (Longhi) 35 15
719. 11 f.+1 f. "Diana's Bath" (Pittoni) .. .. 45 25
720. 10 f.+1 f. Casa d'Oro (air) 45 10
721. 17 f.+1 f. Doge's Palace .. 65 15
722. 24 f.+1 f. St. John and St. Paul Church .. .. 90 25
723. 31 f.+1 f. "Doge's Palace and Piazzetta" (Canaletto) 2·00 40

84. "Lunar Orbiter". 86. "Ecce Homo" (Metzys).

85. Slalom skiing.

**1972.** Conquest of Space. Multicoloured.
725. 6 f. Type **84** .. .. 15 15
726. 11 f. "Vostok" spaceship 40 15
727. 14 f. "Luna 1" .. 45 30
728. 17 f. First Man on Moon .. 65 30
729. 26 f. "Soyuz 11" space flight .. .. 80 40
730. 40 f. "Lunar Rover" .. 1·60 95

**1972.** Winter Olympic Games, Sapporo, Japan. Multicoloured.
732. 5 f. Type **85** .. .. 15 10
733. 6 f. Pair skating .. .. 20 10
734. 11 f. Figure-skating .. 35 10
735. 14 f. Ski-jumping .. 35 20
736. 17 f. Ice-hockey .. .. 50 20
737. 24 f. Speed skating .. 60 25
738. 26 f. Snow scooting .. 60 25
739. 31 f. Downhill skiing .. 75 25
740. 50 f. Bobsleighing .. 1·50 35

**1972.** Easter. Paintings. Multicoloured.
742. 3 f. 50 Type **86** .. .. 20 10
743. 6 f. 50 "The Crucifixion" (Rubens) .. .. 30 10
744. 10 f. "The Descent from the Cross" (Portormo) .. 40 10
745. 18 f. "Pieta" (Gallegos) 70 15
746. 27 f. "The Trinity" (El Greco) .. .. .. 1·40 30

87. Gymnastics.

**1972.** Olympic Games. Munich. Mult.
748. 5 f. Type **87** (postage) .. 20 10
749. 6 f. Throwing the javelin .. 20 10
750. 11 f. Fencing .. .. 35 15
751. 14 f. Cycling .. .. 50 20
752. 17 f. Pole-vaulting .. 75 20
753. 24 f. Weightlifting (air) .. 65 25
754. 26 f. Hurdling .. .. 90 25
755. 31 f. Throwing the discus .. 1·40 40
756. 40 f. Football .. .. 1·50 50

88. Prince Rwagasore, Pres. Micombero and Drummers.

**1972.** 10th Anniv. of Independence. Mult.
758. 5 f. Type **88** (postage) .. 15 10
759. 7 f. Rwagasore, Micombero and map .. .. 25 10
760. 13 f. Pres. Micombero and Burundi flag. .. .. 40 15
761. 15 f. Type **65** (air) .. 30 15
762. 18 f. As 7 f. .. .. 35 15
763. 27 f. As 13 f. .. .. 60 30

89. "Madonna and Child" (A. Solario).

**1972.** Christmas. "Madonna and Child" paintings by artists given below. Mult.
765. 5 f. Type **89** (postage) .. 30 10
766. 10 f. Raphael .. .. 50 10
767. 15 f. Botticelli .. .. 75 15
768. 18 f. S. Mainardi (air) .. 50 15
769. 27 f. H. Memling .. .. 1·00 25
770. 40 f. Lotto .. .. .. 1·50 40

90. "Platycoryne crocea".

**1972.** Orchids. Multicoloured.
772. 50 c. Type **90** (postage) .. 20 10
773. 1 f. "Cattleya trianaei" .. 20 10
774. 2 f. "Eulophia cucullata" 20 10
775. 3 f. "Cymbidium hamsey" 20 10
776. 4 f. "Thelymitra pauciflora" 20 10
777. 5 f. "Miltassia" .. .. 20 10
778. 6 f. "Miltonia" .. .. 80 10
779. 7 f. Type **90** .. .. 80 10
780. 8 f. As 1 f. .. .. 90 10
781. 9 f. As 2 f. .. .. 90 15
782. 10 f. As 3 f. .. .. 1·25 15
783. 13 f. As 4 f. (air) .. 1·00 15
784. 14 f. As 5 f. .. .. 1·00 15
785. 15 f. As 6 f. .. .. 1·25 20
786. 18 f. Type **90** .. .. 1·25 20
787. 20 f. As 1 f. .. .. 1·25 25
788. 27 f. As 2 f. .. .. 2·25 30
789. 36 f. As 3 f. .. .. 3·50 40

Nos. 779/89 are size 53×53 mm.

**1972.** Christmas Charity. Nos. 765/770 surch.
790. 5 f.+1 f. mult. (postage) .. 35 15
791. 10 f.+1 f. multicoloured .. 65 20
792. 15 f.+1 f. multicoloured .. 75 25
793. 18 f.+1 f. mult. (air) .. 60 20
794. 27 f.+1 f. multicoloured .. 90 25
795. 40 f.+1 f. multicoloured .. 1·50 45

92. H. M. Stanley.

**1973.** Centenary of Stanley/Livingstone African Exploration. Multicoloured.
797. 5 f. Type **92** (postage) .. 20 10
798. 7 f. Expedition bearers .. 25 10
799. 13 f. Stanley directing foray 45 15
800. 15 f. Dr. Livingstone (air) 35 20
801. 18 f. Stanley meets Livingstone .. .. .. 55 20
802. 27 f. Stanley conferring with Livingstone .. 1·00 30

93. "The Scourging" (Caravaggio).

**1973.** Easter. Multicoloured.
804. 5 f. Type **93** (postage) .. 15 10
805. 7 f. "Crucifixion" (Van der Weyden) .. .. 25 10
806. 13 f. "The Deposition" (Raphael) .. .. 50 15
807. 15 f. "Christ bound to the Pillar" (Guido Reni) (air) .. .. .. 45 25
808. 18 f. "Crucifixion" (M. Grunewald) .. .. 70 25
809. 27 f. "The Descent from the Cross" (Caravaggio) 1·10 30

94. Interpol Emblem.

**1973.** 50th Anniv. of Interpol. Multicoloured.
811. 5 f. Type **94** (postage) .. 25 10
812. 10 f. Burundi flag .. .. 40 10
813. 18 f. Interpol H.Q., Paris 60 15
814. 27 f. As 5 f. (air) .. 75 25
815. 40 f. As 10 f. .. .. 1·25 35

95. Capricorn, Aquarius, and Pisces.

**1973.** 500th Birth Anniv. of Copernicus.
816. **95.** 3 f. gold, red & blk. (post.) 20 10
817. – 3 f. gold, red and black 20 10
818. – 3 f. gold, red and black 20 10
819. – 3 f. gold, red and black 20 10
820. – 5 f. multicoloured .. 30 10
821. – 5 f. multicoloured .. 30 10
822. – 5 f. multicoloured .. 30 10
823. – 5 f. multicoloured .. 30 10
824. – 7 f. multicoloured .. 40 10
825. – 7 f. multicoloured .. 40 10
826. – 7 f. multicoloured .. 40 10
827. – 7 f. multicoloured .. 40 10
828. – 13 f. multicoloured .. 60 10
829. – 13 f. multicoloured .. 60 10
830. – 13 f. multicoloured .. 60 10
831. – 13 f. multicoloured .. 60 10
832. – 15 f. multicoloured (air) 40 15
833. – 15 f. multicoloured .. 40 15
834. – 15 f. multicoloured .. 40 15
835. – 15 f. multicoloured .. 40 15
836. – 18 f. multicoloured .. 55 15
837. – 18 f. multicoloured .. 55 15
838. – 18 f. multicoloured .. 55 15
839. – 18 f. multicoloured .. 55 15
840. – 27 f. multicoloured .. 95 25
841. – 27 f. multicoloured .. 95 25
842. – 27 f. multicoloured .. 95 25
843. – 27 f. multicoloured .. 95 25
844. – 36 f. multicoloured .. 2·10 40
845. – 36 f. multicoloured .. 2·10 40
846. – 36 f. multicoloured .. 2·10 40
847. – 36 f. multicoloured .. 2·10 40

DESIGNS: No. 816, Type **95**. No. 817, Aries, Taurus and Gemini. No. 818, Cancer, Leo and Virgo. No. 819, Libra, Scorpio and Sagittarius. Nos. 820/23, Greek and Roman Gods. Nos. 824/7, Ptolemy and Ptolemaic System. Nos. 828/31, Copernicus and Solar System. Nos. 823/5, Copernicus, Earth, Pluto and Jupiter. Nos. 836/39, Copernicus, Venus, Saturn and Mars. Nos. 840/43, Copernicus, Uranus, Neptune and Mercury. Nos. 844/7, Earth and spacecraft.

The four designs of each value were issued se-tenant in blocks of four within the sheet, forming composite designs.

96. "Protea cynaroides".

97. "Virgin and Child" (G. Bellini).

**1973.** Flora and Butterflies. Multicoloured.
849 1 f. Type **96** (postage) .. 40 10
850 1 f. "Precis octavia" .. 40 10
851 1 f. "Epiphora bauhiniae" .. 40 10
852 1 f. "Gazania longiscapa" .. 40 10
853 2 f. "Kniphofia"–"Royal Standard" .. .. 40 10
854 2 f. "Cymothoe coccinata hew" .. .. .. 60 15
855 2 f. "Nudaurelia zambesina" .. .. 60 15
856 2 f. "Freesia refracta" .. 40 10
857 3 f. "Calotis eupompe" .. 60 15
858 3 f. Narcissus .. .. 40 10
859 3 f. "Cineraria hybrida" .. 40 10
860 3 f. "Cyrestis camillus" .. 60 15
861 5 f. "Iris tingitana" .. 80 10
862 5 f. "Papilio demodocus" 1·25 15
863 5 f. "Catopsilia avelaneda" 1·25 15
864 5 f. "Nerine sarniensis" .. 80 10
865 6 f. "Hypolimnas dexithea" .. .. 1·25 15
866 6 f. "Zantedeschia tropicalis" .. .. 80 10
867 6 f. "Sandersonia aurantiaca" .. .. 80 10
868 6 f. "Drurya antimachus" 1·25 15
869 11 f. "Nymphaea capensis" 1·00 15
870 11 f. "Pandoriana pandora" .. .. 1·60 20
871 11 f. "Precis orythia" .. 1·60 20
872 11 f. "Pelargonium domesticum"–"Aztec" 1·00 15
873 10 f. Type **96** (air) .. 60 15
874 10 f. As No. 850 .. 1·10 15
875 10 f. As No. 851 .. 1·10 15
876 10 f. As No. 852 .. 60 15
877 14 f. As No. 853 .. 75 15
878 14 f. As No. 854 .. 1·25 20
879 14 f. As No. 855 .. 1·25 20
880 14 f. As No. 856 .. 50 15
881 17 f. As No. 857 .. 1·60 25
882 17 f. As No. 858 .. 1·10 20
883 17 f. As No. 859 .. 1·10 20
884 17 f. As No. 860 .. 1·60 25
885 24 f. As No. 861 .. 1·75 25
886 24 f. As No. 862 .. 2·10 30
887 24 f. As No. 863 .. 2·10 30
888 24 f. As No. 864 .. 1·40 25
889 26 f. As No. 865 .. 2·10 30
890 26 f. As No. 866 .. 1·40 30
891 26 f. As No. 867 .. 1·40 30
892 26 f. As No. 868 .. 2·10 30
893 31 f. As No. 869 .. 1·60 35
894 31 f. As No. 870 .. 2·40 45
895 31 f. As No. 871 .. 2·40 45
896 31 f. As No. 872 .. 1·60 35

Nos. 849, 852/3, 856, 858/9, 861, 864, 866/7, 869, 872, 876/7, 880, 882/3, 885, 888, 890/1, 893 and 896 depict flora and the remainder butterflies.

The four designs of each value were issued se-tenant in blocks of four within the sheet, forming composite designs.

**1973.** Christmas. Various paintings of "The Virgin and Child" by artists listed below. Multicoloured.
897. 5 f. Type **97** (postage) .. 45 10
898. 10 f. Van Eyck .. .. 55 15
899. 15 f. G. A. Boltraffio .. 75 20
900. 18 f. Raphael (air) .. 35 10
901. 27 f. P. Perugino .. .. 1·10 30
902. 40 f. Titian .. .. 1·60 40

**1973.** Christmas Charity. Nos. 897/902 surch.
904. **97.** 5 f.+1 f. mult. (postage) 50 15
905. – 10 f.+1 f. multicoloured 80 20
906. – 15 f.+1 f. multicoloured 95 25
907. – 18 f.+1 f. multicoloured (air) 70 15
908. – 27 f.+1 f. multicoloured 1·10 35
909. – 40 f.+1 f. multicoloured 1·60 50

98. "The Pieta" (Veronese).

**1974.** Easter. Religious Paintings. Mult.

| No. | Description | Mint | Used |
|---|---|---|---|
| 911. | 5 f. Type 98 .. .. | 15 | 10 |
| 912. | 10 f. "The Virgin and St. John" (Van der Weyden) | 30 | 15 |
| 913. | 18 f. "The Crucifixion" (Van der Weyden) .. | 60 | 20 |
| 914. | 27 f. "The Entombment" (Titian) .. .. .. | 85 | 30 |
| 915. | 40 f. "The Pieta" (El Greco) | 2·10 | 50 |

99. "Haplochromis multicolor".

**1974.** Fishes. Multicoloured.

| No. | Description | Mint | Used |
|---|---|---|---|
| 917. | 1 f. Type 99 (postage) .. | 30 | 10 |
| 918. | 1 f. "Tropheus duboisi" .. | 30 | 10 |
| 919. | 1 f. "Pantodon buchholzi" | 30 | 10 |
| 920. | 1 f. "Distichodus sexfasciatus" | 30 | 10 |
| 921. | 2 f. "Pelmatochromis kribensis" | 30 | 10 |
| 922. | 2 f. "Polycentropsis abbreviata" | 30 | 10 |
| 923. | 2 f. "Nannaethiops tritaeniatus" | 30 | 10 |
| 924. | 2 f. "Hemichromis bimaculatus" | 30 | 10 |
| 925. | 3 f. "Ctenopoma acutirostre" | 30 | 10 |
| 926. | 3 f. "Tilapia melanopleura" | 30 | 10 |
| 927. | 3 f. "Synodontis angelicus" | 30 | 10 |
| 928. | 3 f. "Aphyosemion bivittatum" | 30 | 10 |
| 929. | 5 f. "Monodactylus argenteus" | 45 | 10 |
| 930. | 5 f. "Pygoplites diacanthus" | 45 | 10 |
| 931. | 5 f. "Zanclus canescens" .. | 45 | 10 |
| 932. | 5 f. "Cephalopholis argus" | 45 | 10 |
| 933. | 6 f. "Priacanthus arenatus" | 1·25 | 10 |
| 934. | 6 f. "Scarus guacamaia" .. | 1·25 | 10 |
| 935. | 6 f. "Pomacanthus arcuatus" | 1·25 | 10 |
| 936. | 6 f. "Zeus faber" .. | 1·25 | 10 |
| 937. | 11 f. "Lactophrys quadricornis" .. .. | 1·50 | 15 |
| 938. | 11 f. "Acanthurus bahianus" | 1·50 | 15 |
| 939. | 11 f. "Balistes vetula" .. | 1·50 | 15 |
| 940. | 11 f. "Holocanthus ciliaris" | 1·50 | 15 |
| 941. | 10 f. Type 99 (air) .. | 35 | 10 |
| 942. | 10 f. As No. 918 .. .. | 35 | 10 |
| 943. | 10 f. As No. 919 .. .. | 35 | 10 |
| 944. | 10 f. As No. 920 .. .. | 35 | 10 |
| 945. | 14 f. As No. 921 .. .. | 70 | 10 |
| 946. | 14 f. As No. 922 .. .. | 70 | 10 |
| 947. | 14 f. As No. 923 .. .. | 70 | 10 |
| 948. | 14 f. As No. 924 .. .. | 70 | 10 |
| 949. | 17 f. As No. 925 .. .. | 70 | 10 |
| 950. | 17 f. As No. 926 .. .. | 70 | 10 |
| 951. | 17 f. As No. 927 .. .. | 70 | 10 |
| 952. | 17 f. As No. 928 .. .. | 70 | 10 |
| 953. | 24 f. As No. 929 .. .. | 1·60 | 10 |
| 954. | 24 f. As No. 930 .. .. | 1·60 | 10 |
| 955. | 24 f. As No. 931 .. .. | 1·60 | 10 |
| 956. | 24 f. As No. 932 .. .. | 1·60 | 10 |
| 957. | 26 f. As No. 933 .. .. | 2·25 | 15 |
| 958. | 26 f. As No. 934 .. .. | 2·25 | 15 |
| 959. | 26 f. As No. 935 .. .. | 2·25 | 15 |
| 960. | 26 f. As No. 936 .. .. | 2·25 | 15 |
| 961. | 31 f. As No. 937 .. .. | 2·40 | 25 |
| 962. | 31 f. As No. 938 .. .. | 2·40 | 25 |
| 963. | 31 f. As No. 939 .. .. | 2·40 | 25 |
| 964. | 31 f. As No. 940 .. .. | 2·40 | 25 |

The four designs of each value are arranged together in se-tenant blocks of four within the sheet, forming composite designs.

100. Footballers and World Cup Trophy.

**1974.** World Cup Football Championships.

| No. | Description | Mint | Used |
|---|---|---|---|
| 965. 100. | 5 f. multicoloured (postage) | 25 | 10 |
| 966. – | 6 f. multicoloured .. | 30 | 10 |
| 967. – | 11 f. multicoloured .. | 40 | 20 |
| 968. – | 14 f. multicoloured .. | 50 | 25 |
| 969. – | 17 f. multicoloured .. | 55 | 25 |
| 970. – | 20 f. multicoloured (air) | 70 | 35 |
| 971. – | 26 f. multicoloured .. | 90 | 45 |
| 972. – | 40 f. multicoloured .. | 1·40 | 60 |

DESIGNS: Nos. 966/72, Football scenes as Type 100.

101. Burundi Flag.

**1974.** Cent. of U.P.U. Multicoloured.

| No. | Description | Mint | Used |
|---|---|---|---|
| 974. | 6 f. Type 101 (postage) .. | 20 | 10 |
| 975. | 6 f. Burundi P.T.T. Building | 20 | 10 |
| 976. | 11 f. } Postmen carrying .. | 30 | 10 |
| 977. | 11 f. } letters .. .. | 30 | 10 |
| 978. | 14 f. U.P.U. Monument .. | 1·25 | 50 |
| 979. | 14 f. Mail transport .. | 1·25 | 50 |
| 980. | 17 f. Burundi on map .. | 55 | 10 |
| 981. | 17 f. Dove and letter .. | 55 | 10 |
| 982. | 24 f. Type 101 (air) .. | 80 | 20 |
| 983. | 24 f. As No. 975 .. .. | 80 | 20 |
| 984. | 26 f. As No. 976 .. .. | 1·10 | 30 |
| 985. | 26 f. As No. 977 .. .. | 1·10 | 30 |
| 986. | 31 f. As No. 978 .. .. | 4·50 | 70 |
| 987. | 31 f. As No. 979 .. .. | 4·50 | 70 |
| 988. | 40 f. As No. 980 .. .. | 3·50 | 45 |
| 989. | 40 f. As No. 981 .. .. | 3·50 | 45 |

The two designs in each denomination were arranged together in se-tenant pairs within the sheet, each pair forming a composite design.

102. "St. Ildefonse writing a letter" (El Greco).

**1974.** International Letter-writing Week. Multicoloured.

| No. | Description | Mint | Used |
|---|---|---|---|
| 991. | 6 f. Type 102 .. .. | 30 | 15 |
| 992. | 11 f. "Lady sealing a letter" (Chardin) .. .. | 50 | 20 |
| 993. | 14 f. "Titus at desk" (Rembrandt) .. | 55 | 30 |
| 994. | 17 f. "The Love-letter" (Vermeer) .. | 60 | 30 |
| 995. | 26 f. "The Merchant G. Gisze" (Holbein) | 65 | 50 |
| 996. | 31 f. "A. Lenoir" (David) | 90 | 55 |

103. "Virgin and Child". (Van Orley).

**1974.** Christmas. Showing "Virgin and Child" paintings by artists named. Mult.

| No. | Description | Mint | Used |
|---|---|---|---|
| 998. | 5 f. Type 103 (postage) .. | 25 | 10 |
| 999. | 10 f. Hans Memling .. | 45 | 15 |
| 1000. | 15 f. Botticelli .. .. | 1·00 | 20 |
| 1001. | 18 f. Hans Memling (different) (air) .. | 35 | 20 |
| 1002. | 27 f. F. Lippi .. .. | 1·10 | 35 |
| 1003. | 40 f. L. di Gredi .. .. | 1·50 | 45 |

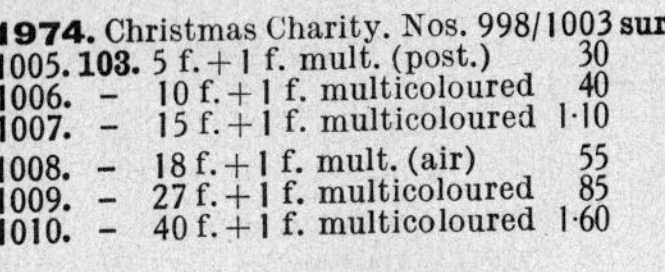
**1974.** Christmas Charity. Nos. 998/1003 surch.

| No. | Description | Mint | Used |
|---|---|---|---|
| 1005. 103. | 5 f. + 1 f. mult. (post.) | 30 | 10 |
| 1006. – | 10 f. + 1 f. multicoloured | 40 | 25 |
| 1007. – | 15 f. + 1 f. multicoloured | 1·10 | 30 |
| 1008. – | 18 f. + 1 f. mult. (air) | 55 | 20 |
| 1009. – | 27 f. + 1 f. multicoloured | 85 | 35 |
| 1010. – | 40 f. + 1 f. multicoloured | 1·60 | 45 |

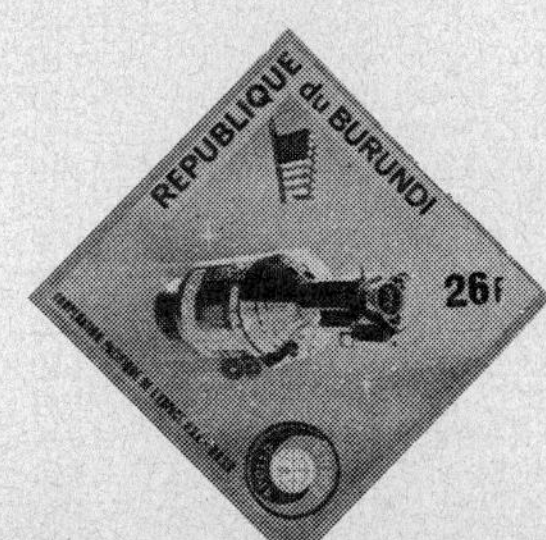

104. "Apollo" Spacecraft with Docking Tunnel.

**1975.** "Apollo-Soyuz" Space Project.

| No. | Description | Mint | Used |
|---|---|---|---|
| 1012. | 26 f. Type 104 (postage) | 45 | 30 |
| 1013. | 26 f. Leonov and Kubasov | 45 | 30 |
| 1014. | 26 f. "Soyuz" Spacecraft | 45 | 30 |
| 1015. | 26 f. Slayton, Brand and Stafford .. .. | 45 | 30 |
| 1016. | 31 f. "Soyuz" launch .. | 55 | 40 |
| 1017. | 31 f. "Apollo" and "Soyuz" spacecraft .. .. | 55 | 40 |
| 1018. | 31 f. "Apollo" third stage separation .. .. | 55 | 40 |
| 1019. | 31 f. Slayton, Brand, Stafford, Leonov and Kubasov | 55 | 40 |
| 1020. | 27 f. Type 104 (air) .. | 60 | 45 |
| 1021. | 27 f. As No. 1012 .. | 60 | 45 |
| 1022. | 27 f. As No. 1013 .. | 60 | 45 |
| 1023. | 27 f. As No. 1014 .. | 60 | 45 |
| 1024. | 40 f. As No. 1015 .. | 80 | 60 |
| 1025. | 40 f. As No. 1016 .. | 80 | 60 |
| 1026. | 40 f. As No. 1017 .. | 80 | 60 |
| 1027. | 40 f. As No. 1018 .. | 80 | 60 |

The four designs in each value were issued together in se-tenant blocks of four within the sheet.

105. Addax.

**1975.** African Animals (2nd series). Mult.

| No. | Description | Mint | Used |
|---|---|---|---|
| 1028. | 1 f. Type 105 (postage) .. | 20 | 10 |
| 1029. | 1 f. Roan antelope .. | 20 | 10 |
| 1030. | 1 f. Nyala .. .. | 20 | 10 |
| 1031. | 1 f. White rhinoceros .. | 20 | 10 |
| 1032. | 2 f. Mandrill .. .. | 20 | 10 |
| 1033. | 2 f. Eland .. .. | 20 | 10 |
| 1034. | 2 f. Salt's dik-dik .. | 20 | 10 |
| 1035. | 2 f. Thomson's gazelles .. | 20 | 10 |
| 1036. | 3 f. African claw-less otter .. .. | 30 | 10 |
| 1037. | 3 f. Bohar reedbuck .. | 30 | 10 |
| 1038. | 3 f. African civet .. | 30 | 10 |
| 1039. | 3 f. African buffalo .. | 30 | 10 |
| 1040. | 5 f. Black wildebeest .. | 30 | 10 |
| 1041. | 5 f. African asses .. | 30 | 10 |
| 1042. | 5 f. Angolan black and white colobus .. | 30 | 10 |
| 1043. | 5 f. Gerenuk .. .. | 30 | 10 |
| 1044. | 6 f. Addra gazelle .. | 50 | 15 |
| 1045. | 6 f. Black-backed jackal | 50 | 15 |
| 1046. | 6 f. Sitatungas .. .. | 50 | 15 |
| 1047. | 6 f. Banded duiker .. | 50 | 15 |
| 1048. | 11 f. Fennec fox .. .. | 70 | 15 |
| 1049. | 11 f. Lesser kudus .. | 70 | 15 |
| 1050. | 11 f. Blesbok .. .. | 70 | 15 |
| 1051. | 11 f. Serval .. .. | 70 | 15 |
| 1052. | 10 f. Type 105 (air) .. | 65 | 10 |
| 1053. | 10 f. As No. 1029 .. | 65 | 10 |
| 1054. | 10 f. As No. 1030 .. | 65 | 10 |
| 1055. | 10 f. As No. 1031 .. | 65 | 10 |
| 1056. | 14 f. As No. 1032 .. | 75 | 15 |
| 1057. | 14 f. As No. 1033 .. | 75 | 15 |
| 1058. | 14 f. As No. 1034 .. | 75 | 15 |
| 1059. | 14 f. As No. 1035 .. | 75 | 15 |
| 1060. | 17 f. As No. 1036 .. | 1·25 | 15 |
| 1061. | 17 f. As No. 1037 .. | 1·25 | 15 |
| 1062. | 17 f. As No. 1038 .. | 1·25 | 15 |
| 1063. | 17 f. As No. 1039 .. | 1·25 | 15 |
| 1064. | 24 f. As No. 1040 .. | 2·00 | 25 |
| 1065. | 24 f. As No. 1041 .. | 2·00 | 25 |
| 1066. | 24 f. As No. 1042 .. | 2·00 | 25 |
| 1067. | 24 f. As No. 1043 .. | 2·00 | 25 |
| 1068. | 26 f. As No. 1044 .. | 2·10 | 25 |
| 1069. | 26 f. As No. 1045 .. | 2·10 | 25 |
| 1070. | 26 f. As No. 1046 .. | 2·10 | 25 |
| 1071. | 26 f. As No. 1047 .. | 2·10 | 25 |
| 1072. | 31 f. As No. 1048 .. | 2·40 | 30 |
| 1073. | 31 f. As No. 1049 .. | 2·40 | 30 |
| 1074. | 31 f. As No. 1050 .. | 2·40 | 30 |
| 1075. | 31 f. As No. 1051 .. | 2·40 | 30 |

The four designs in each value were issued together in horiz. se-tenant strips within the sheet, forming composite designs.

**1975.** Air. International Women's Year. Nos. 1052/9 optd. with **ANNEE INTERNATIONALE DE LA FEMME.**

| No. | Description | Mint | Used |
|---|---|---|---|
| 1076. 105. | 10 f. multicoloured .. | 40 | 30 |
| 1077. – | 10 f. multicoloured .. | 40 | 30 |
| 1078. – | 10 f. multicoloured .. | 40 | 30 |
| 1079. – | 10 f. multicoloured .. | 40 | 30 |
| 1080. – | 14 f. multicoloured .. | 70 | 35 |
| 1081. – | 14 f. multicoloured .. | 70 | 35 |
| 1082. – | 14 f. multicoloured .. | 70 | 35 |
| 1083. – | 14 f. multicoloured .. | 70 | 35 |

**1975.** Air. 30th Anniv. of United Nations. Nos. 1068/75. optd. with **30eme ANNIVERSAIRE DES NATIONS UNIES.**

| No. | Description | Mint | Used |
|---|---|---|---|
| 1084. | 26 f. multicoloured .. | 90 | 70 |
| 1085. | 26 f. multicoloured .. | 90 | 70 |
| 1086. | 26 f. multicoloured .. | 90 | 70 |
| 1087. | 26 f. multicoloured .. | 90 | 70 |
| 1088. | 31 f. multicoloured .. | 1·50 | 1·10 |
| 1089. | 31 f. multicoloured .. | 1·50 | 1·10 |
| 1090. | 31 f. multicoloured .. | 1·50 | 1·10 |
| 1091. | 31 f. multicoloured .. | 1·50 | 1·10 |

108. "Jonah".

**1975.** Christmas. 500th Birth Anniv. of Michaelangelo. Multicoloured.

| No. | Description | Mint | Used |
|---|---|---|---|
| 1092. | 5 f. Type 108 .. .. | 25 | 10 |
| 1093. | 5 f. "Libyan Sibyl" .. | 25 | 10 |
| 1094. | 13 f. "Daniel" .. .. | 90 | 10 |
| 1095. | 13 f. "Cumaean Sybil" | 90 | 10 |
| 1096. | 27 f. "Isaiah" .. .. | 1·25 | 15 |
| 1097. | 27 f. "Delphic Sybil" (different) .. | 1·25 | 15 |
| 1098. | 18 f. "Zachariah" (air) | 90 | 10 |
| 1099. | 18 f. "Joel" .. .. | 90 | 10 |
| 1100. | 31 f. "Erythraean Sybil" | 1·60 | 30 |
| 1101. | 31 f. "Ezekiel" .. .. | 1·60 | 30 |
| 1102. | 40 f. "Persian Sybil" .. | 2·00 | 35 |
| 1103. | 40 f. "Jeremiah" .. | 2·00 | 35 |

**1975.** Christmas Charity. Nos. 1092/1103 surch. with premium.

| No. | Description | Mint | Used |
|---|---|---|---|
| 1105. 108. | 5 f. + 1 f. mult. (postage) | 45 | 10 |
| 1106. – | 5 f. + 1 f. multicoloured | 45 | 10 |
| 1107. – | 13 f. + 1 f. multicoloured | 75 | 10 |
| 1108. – | 13 f. + 1 f. multicoloured | 75 | 10 |
| 1109. – | 27 f. + 1 f. multicoloured | 1·25 | 15 |
| 1110. – | 27 f. + 1 f. multicoloured | 1·25 | 15 |
| 1111. – | 18 f. + 1 f. mult. (air) | 1·00 | 10 |
| 1112. – | 18 f. + 1 f. multicoloured | 1·00 | 10 |
| 1113. – | 31 f. + 1 f. multicoloured | 1·60 | 30 |
| 1114. – | 31 f. + 1 f. multicoloured | 1·60 | 30 |
| 1115. – | 40 f. + 1 f. multicoloured | 1·90 | 35 |
| 1116. – | 40 f. + 1 f. multicoloured | 1·90 | 35 |

110. Speed Skating.

111. Basketball.

**1976.** Winter Olympic Games, Innsbruck. Multicoloured.

| No. | Description | Mint | Used |
|---|---|---|---|
| 1118. | 17 f. Type 110 (postage) | 45 | 20 |
| 1119. | 24 f. Figure-skating .. | 50 | 20 |
| 1120. | 26 f. Two-man bobsleigh | 60 | 20 |
| 1121. | 31 f. Cross-country skiing | 70 | 30 |
| 1122. | 18 f. Ski-jumping (air) .. | 40 | 25 |
| 1123. | 36 f. Skiing (slalom) .. | 1·50 | 40 |
| 1124. | 50 f. Ice-hockey .. .. | 1·60 | 60 |

**1976.** Olympic Games, Montreal. Mult.

| No. | Description | Mint | Used |
|---|---|---|---|
| 1126. | 14 f. Type 111 (postage) | 40 | 30 |
| 1127. | 14 f. Pole-vaulting .. | 40 | 30 |
| 1128. | 17 f. Running .. .. | 60 | 45 |
| 1129. | 17 f. Football .. .. | 60 | 45 |
| 1130. | 28 f. As No. 1127 .. | 90 | 65 |
| 1131. | 28 f. As No. 1128 .. | 90 | 65 |
| 1132. | 40 f. As No. 1129 .. | 1·50 | 1·10 |
| 1133. | 40 f. Type 111 .. .. | 1·50 | 1·10 |
| 1134. | 27 f. Hurdling (air) .. | 90 | 65 |
| 1135. | 27 f. High-jumping (horiz.) | 90 | 65 |
| 1136. | 31 f. Gymnastics (horiz.) | 1·25 | 90 |
| 1137. | 31 f. As No. 1134 (horiz.) | 1·25 | 90 |
| 1138. | 50 f. As No. 1135 (horiz.) | 1·90 | 1·40 |
| 1139. | 50 f. As No. 1136 (horiz.) | 1·90 | 1·40 |

112. "Battle of Bunker Hill" (detail, John Trumbull).

113. "Virgin and Child" (Dirk Bouts).

**1976.** Air. Bicent. of American Revolution. Multicoloured.

| No. | Description | Mint | Used |
|---|---|---|---|
| 1141. | 18 f. } Type 112 .. .. | 55 | 15 |
| 1142. | 18 f. } | 55 | 15 |
| 1143. | 26 f. } Franklin, Jefferson | 75 | 25 |
| 1144. | 26 f. } and John Adams | 75 | 25 |
| 1145. | 36 f. } "Signing of Declar- | 1·25 | 35 |
| 1146. | 36 f. } ation of Independence" (Trumbull) | 1·25 | 35 |

The two designs of each value form composite pictures. Type 112 is the left-hand portion of the painting.

**1976.** Christmas. Multicoloured.

1148. 5 f. Type **113** (postage) 35 10
1149. 13 f. " Virgin of the Trees " (Bellini) 65 10
1150. 27 f. " Virgin and Child " (C. Crivelli) 1·00 25
1151. 18 f. " Virgin and Child with St. Anne " (Leonardo) (air) 80 30
1152. 31 f. " Holy Family with Lamb " (Raphael) 1·10 60
1153. 40 f. " Virgin with Basket " (Correggio) 1·60 70

**1976.** Christmas Charity. Nos. 1148/53 surch. **+1F.**

1155. **113.** 5 f. + 1 f. multicoloured (postage) 25 10
1156. – 13 f. + 1 f. multicoloured 70 30
1157. – 27 f. + 1 f. multicoloured 1·10 50
1158. – 18 f. + 1 f. multicoloured (air) 60 30
1159. – 31 f. + 1 f. multicoloured 1·00 45
1160. – 40 f. + 1 f. multicoloured 1·90 65

**115.** " The Ascent of Calvary " (Rubens).

**1977.** Easter. 400th Birth Anniv. of Peter Paul Rubens.

1162. 10 f. Type **115** 35 25
1163. 21 f. " Christ Crucified " 95 70
1164. 27 f. " The Descent from the Cross " 1·10 80
1165. 35 f. " The Deposition " 1·50 1·10

**116.** Alexander Graham Bell.

**117.** Kobs.

**1977.** Telephone Centenary and World Telecommunications Day. Multicoloured.

1167. 10 f. Type **116** (postage) 25 15
1168. 10 f. Satellite, Globe and telephones 25 15
1169. 17 f. Switchboard operator and wall telephone 45 30
1170. 17 f. Satellite transmitting to Earth 45 30
1171. 26 f. A. G. Bell and first telephone 80 60
1172. 26 f. Satellites circling Globe, and videophone 80 60
1173. 18 f. Type **116** (air) 40 30
1174. 18 f. As No. 1172 40 30
1175. 36 f. As No. 1169 1·10 80
1176. 36 f. As No. 1168 1·10 80

**1977.** African Animals (3rd series). Mult.

1178. 2 f. Type **117** (postage) 40 25
1179. 2 f. Marabou storks 60 30
1180. 2 f. Blue wildebeest 40 25
1181. 2 f. Bush pig 40 25
1182. 5 f. Grevy's zebras 45 25
1183. 5 f. Whale-headed stork 80 30
1184. 5 f. Striped hyenas 45 25
1185. 5 f. Pygmy chimpanzee 45 25
1186. 8 f. Greater flamingoes 90 30
1187. 8 f. Nile crocodiles 50 25
1188. 8 f. Green tree snake 50 25
1189. 8 f. Greater kudus 50 25
1190. 11 f. Large-toothed rock hyrax 55 30
1191. 11 f. Cobra 55 30
1192. 11 f. Golden jackals 55 30
1193. 11 f. Verreaux eagles 1·10 35
1194. 21 f. Ratel 65 40
1195. 21 f. Bushbuck 65 40
1196. 21 f. Secretary bird 1·75 60
1197. 21 f. Klipspringer 65 40
1198. 27 f. Bat-eared fox 85 45
1199. 27 f. African elephants 85 45
1200. 27 f. Vulturine guinea-fowl 2·00 65
1201. 27 f. Impalas 85 45
1202. 9 f. Type **117** (air) 45 25
1203. 9 f. As No. 1179 90 30
1204. 9 f. As No. 1180 45 25
1205. 9 f. As No. 1181 45 25
1206. 13 f. As No. 1182 65 30
1207. 13 f. As No. 1183 1·25 30
1208. 13 f. As No. 1184 65 30
1209. 13 f. As No. 1185 65 30
1210. 30 f. As No. 1186 2·25 70
1211. 30 f. As No. 1187 1·00 50
1212. 30 f. As No. 1188 1·00 50
1213. 30 f. As No. 1189 1·00 50
1214. 35 f. As No. 1190 1·10 60
1215. 35 f. As No. 1191 1·10 60
1216. 35 f. f. As No. 1192 1·10 60
1217. 35 f. As No. 1193 2·50 80
1218. 54 f. As No. 1194 1·90 75
1219. 54 f. As No. 1195 1·90 75
1220. 54 f. As No. 1196 3·25 1·00
1221. 54 f. As No. 1197 1·90 75
1222. 70 f. As No. 1198 2·50 90
1223. 70 f. As No. 1199 2·50 90
1224. 70 f. As No. 1200 4·25 1·40
1225. 70 f. As No. 1201 2·50 90

The four designs in each value were issued together se-tenant in horizontal strips within the sheet, forming composite designs.

**118.** " The Man of Iron " (Grimm).

**119.** U.N. General Assembly and U.N. 3 c. Stamp, 1954.

**1977.** Fairy Tales. Multicoloured.

1226 5 f. Type **118** 20 10
1227 5 f. "Snow White and Rose Red" (Grimm) 20 10
1228 5 f. "The Goose Girl" (Grimm) 20 10
1229 5 f. "The Two Wanderers" (Grimm) 20 10
1230 11 f. "The Hermit and the Bear" (Aesop) 60 10
1231 11 f. "The Fox and the Stork" (Aesop) 60 10
1232 11 f. "The Litigious Cats" (Aesop) 60 10
1233 11 f. "The Blind and the Lame" (Aesop) 60 10
1234 14 f. "The Ice Maiden" (Andersen) 70 10
1235 14 f. "The Old House" (Andersen) 70 10
1236 14 f. "The Princess and the Pea" (Andersen) 70 10
1237 14 f. "The Elder Tree Mother" (Andersen) 70 10
1238 17 f. "Hen with the Golden Eggs" (La Fontaine) 80 15
1239 17 f. "The Wolf Turned Shepherd" (La Fontaine) 80 15
1240 17 f. "The Oyster and Litigants" (La Fontaine) 80 15
1241 17 f. "The Wolf and the Lamb" (La Fontaine) 80 15
1242 26 f. "Jack and the Beanstalk" (traditional) 1·60 25
1243 26 f. "Alice in Wonderland) (Lewis Carroll) 1·60 25
1244 26 f. "Three Heads in the Well" (traditional) 1·60 25
1245 26 f. "Tales of Mother Goose" (traditional) 1·60 25

**1977.** 25th Anniv. of United Nations Postal Administration. Multicoloured.

1246. 8 f. Type **119** (postage) 40 30
1247. 8 f. U.N. 4 c. stamp, 1957 40 30
1248. 8 f. U.N. 3 c. stamp, 1954 (FAO) 40 30
1249. 8 f. U.N. 1½ c. stamp, 1951 40 30
1250. 10 f. Security Council and U.N. 8 c. red, 1954 50 35
1251. 10 f. U.N. 8 c. green, 1956 50 35
1252. 10 f. U.N. 8 c. black, 1955 50 35
1253. 10 f. U.N. 7 c. stamp, 1959 50 35
1254. 21 f. Meeting hall and U.N. 3 c. grey, 1956 80 60
1255. 21 f. U.N. 8 c. stamp, 1956 80 60
1256. 21 f. U.N. 3 c. brown, 1953 80 60
1257. 21 f. U.N. 3 c. green, 1952 80 60
1258. 24 f. Building by night and U.N. 4 c. red, 1957 (air) 80 60
1259. 24 f. U.N. 8 c. brn. & grn. 1960 80 60
1260. 24 f. U.N. 8 c. green, 1955 80 60
1261. 24 f. U.N. 8 c. red, 1955 80 60
1262. 27 f. Aerial view of U.N. 8 c. red, 1957 90 65
1263. 27 f. U.N. 3 c. stamp, 1953 90 65
1264. 27 f. U.N. 8 c. green, 1954 90 65
1265. 27 f. U.N. 8 c. brown, 1956 90 65
1266. 35 f. U.N. Building by day and U.N. 5 c. stamp, 1959 1·40 1·00
1267. 35 f. U.N. 3 c. stamp, 1962 1·40 1·00
1268. 35 f. U.N. 3 c. bl. & pur., 1951 1·40 1·00
1269. 35 f. U.N. 1 c. stamp, 1951 1·40 1·00

The four designs in each value were issued together in se-tenant blocks of four, each design in the block having the same background.

**120.** " Virgin and Child " (Jean Lambardos).

**121.** Cruiser "Aurora" and Russian 5 r. Stamp, 1922.

**1977.** Christmas. Paintings of Virgin and Child by artists named. Multicoloured.

1271. 5 f. Type **120** (postage) 15 10
1272. 13 f. Melides Toscano 65 50
1273. 27 f. Emmanuel Tzanes 95 70
1274. 18 f. Master of Moulins (air) 50 35
1275. 31 f. Lorenzo di Credi 1·00 75
1276. 40 f. Palma the Elder 1·25 90

**1977.** 60th Anniv. of Russian Revolution. Multicoloured.

1278. 5 f. Type **121** 40 10
1279. 5 f. Russia S.G. 455 40 10
1280. 5 f. Russia S.G. 1392 40 10
1281. 5 f. Russia S.G. 199 40 10
1282. 8 f. Decemberists' Square, Leningrad and Russia S.G. 983 25 10
1283. 8 f. Russia S.G. 2122 25 10
1284. 8 f. Russia S.G. 1041 25 10
1285. 8 f. Russia S.G. 2653 25 10
1286. 11 f. Pokrovski Cathedral, Moscow and Russia S.G. 3929 45 10
1287. 11 f. Russia S.G. 3540 45 10
1288. 11 f. Russia S.G. 3468 45 10
1289. 11 f. Russia S.G. 3921 45 10
1290. 13 f. May Day celebrations, Moscow and Russia S.G. 4518 60 15
1291. 13 f. Russia S.G. 3585 60 15
1292. 13 f. Russia S.G. 3024 60 15
1293. 13 f. Russia S.G. 2471 60 15

The four designs in each value were issued in se-tenant blocks of four, each design in the block having the same background.

**122.** Tanker Unloading (Commerce).

**1977.** 15th Anniv. of Independence. Mult.

1294. 1 f. Type **122** 20 15
1295. 5 f. Assembling electric armatures (Economy) 20 15
1296. 11 f. Native dancers (Tourism) 30 20
1297. 14 f. Picking coffee (Agriculture) 45 30
1298. 17 f. National Palace, Bujumbura 55 40

**1977.** Christmas Charity. Nos. 1271/6 surch. **+ 1F.**

1299. **120.** 5 f. + 1 f. multicoloured (postage) 30 15
1300. – 13 f. + 1 f. multicoloured 65 20
1301. – 27 f. + 1 f. multicoloured 95 45
1302. – 18 f. + 1 f. multicoloured (air) 65 25
1303. – 31 f. + 1 f. multicoloured 1·00 45
1304. – 40 f. + 1 f. multicoloured 1·60 60

**123.** " Madonna and Child " (Solario).

**124.** Abyssinian Ground Hornbill.

**1979.** Christmas (1978). Paintings of Virgin and Child by named artists. Multicoloured.

1306. 13 f. Rubens 85 85
1307. 17 f. Type **123** 90 90
1308. 27 f. Tiepolo 1·40 1·40
1309. 31 f. Gerard David 1·60 1·60
1310. 40 f. Bellini 2·00 2·00

**1979.** Christmas Charity. Nos. 1306/10 surch. **+1F.**

1312. – 13 f. + 1 f. multicoloured 85 85
1313. **123.** 17 f. + 1 f. multicoloured 90 90
1314. – 27 f. + 1 f. multicoloured 1·40 1·40
1315. – 31 f. + 1 f. multicoloured 1·60 1·60
1316. – 40 f. + 1 f. multicoloured 2·00 2·00

**1979.** Birds. Multicoloured.

1318 1 f. Type **124** (postage) 60 30
1319 2 f. African darter 60 30
1320 3 f. Little bee eater 60 30
1321 5 f. Lesser flamingo 80 40
1322 8 f. Congo peafowl 1·00 55
1323 10 f. Purple swamphen 1·10 60
1324 20 f. Martial eagle 1·25 70
1325 27 f. Painted stork 1·50 85
1326 50 f. Saddle-bill stork 2·50 1·25
1327 6 f. Type **124** (air) 90 50
1328 13 f. As No. 1319 1·10 65
1329 18 f. As No. 1320 1·25 70
1330 26 f. As No. 1321 1·40 80
1331 31 f. As No. 1322 1·50 85
1332 36 f. As No. 1323 1·60 90
1333 40 f. As No. 1324 1·90 1·10
1334 54 f. As No. 1325 2·10 1·20
1335 70 f. As No. 1326 2·75 1·50

**125.** Mother and Child.

**1979.** International Year of the Child. Mult.

1336. 10 f. Type **125** 90 90
1337. 20 f. Baby 1·40 1·40
1338. 27 f. Child with doll 1·50 1·50
1339. 50 f. S.O.S. village, Gitega 2·00 2·00

**126.** " Virgin and Child " (Raffaellino Del Garbo).

**127.** Sir Rowland Hill and Penny Black.

**1979.** Christmas. " Virgin and Child " paintings by named artists. Multicoloured.

1341. 20 f. Type **126** 90 90
1342. 27 f. Giovanni Penni 1·10 1·10
1343. 31 f. Giulio Romano 1·25 1·25
1344. 50 f. Detail of " Adoration of the Shepherds " (Jacopo Bassano) 1·75 1·75

**1979.** Death Centenary of Sir Rowland Hill. Multicoloured.

1346. 20 f. Type **127** 80 80
1347. 27 f. German East Africa 25 p. stamp and Ruanda-Urundi 5 c. stamp 95 95
1348. 31 f. Burundi 1 f. 25 and 50 f. stamps of 1962 1·10 1·10
1349. 40 f. 4 f. (1962) and 14 f. (1969) stamps of Burundi 1·25 1·25
1350. 60 f. Heinrich von Stephan (founder of U.P.U.) and Burundi 14 f. U.P.U. stamps of 1974 2·75 2·75

**1979.** Christmas Charity. Nos. 1341/4 additionally inscr. with premiums.

1352. 20 f. + 1 f. multicoloured 65 65
1353. 27 f. + 1 f. multicoloured 1·40 1·40
1354. 31 f. + 1 f. multicoloured 1·60 1·60
1355. 50 f. + 1 f. multicoloured 2·10 2·10

**128.** Approaching Hurdle (110 Metres Hurdles, Thomas Munkelt).

**1980.** Olympic Medal Winners. Multicoloured.

1357. 20 f. Type **128** 95 95
1358. 20 f. Jumping hurdle 95 95
1359. 20 f. Completing jump 95 95
1360. 30 f. Discus—beginning to throw 1·40 1·40
1361. 30 f. Continuing throw 1·40 1·40
1362. 30 f. Releasing discus 1·40 1·40
1363. 40 f. Football—running for goal (Czechoslovakia) 1·50 1·50
1364. 40 f. Kicking ball 1·50 1·50
1365. 40 f. Saving ball 1·50 1·50

**129.** " The Virgin and Child " (Sebastiano Mainardi).

**1980.** Christmas. Multicoloured.

1367. 10 f. Type **129** 90 90
1368. 30 f. " Doni Tondo " (Michelangelo) 1·50 1·50
1369. 40 f. " The Virgin and Child " (Piero di Cosimo) 2·10 2·10
1370. 45 f. " The Holy Family " (Fra Bartolomeo) 2·25 2·25

130. Congress Emblem.

131. Kepler and Dish Aerial

**1980.** First National Party Congress, Uprona.
1372. **130.** 10 f. multicoloured .. 30 30
1373. 40 f. multicoloured .. 1·50 1·50
1374. 45 f. multicoloured .. 1·60 1·60

**1981.** Christmas Charity. Nos. 1367/70 additionally inscr. with premiums.
1376. 10 f.+1 f. multicoloured 75 75
1377. 30 f.+1 f. multicoloured 1·75 1·75
1378. 40 f.+1 f. multicoloured 2·25 2·25
1379. 50 f.+1 f. multicoloured 2·50 2·50

**1981.** 350th Death Anniv. of Johannes Kepler (astronomer). First Earth Satellite Station in Burundi. Multicoloured.
1381. 10 f. Type **131** .. .. 60 60
1382. 40 f. Satellite and antenna 1·50 1·50
1383. 45 f. Satellite (different) and antenna .. .. 1·90 1·90

132. Giraffes

**1982.** African Animals (4th series). Mult.
1385. 2 f. Lion .. .. .. 45 45
1386. 3 f. Type **132** .. .. 45 45
1387. 5 f. Black rhinoceros .. 45 45
1388. 10 f. African buffalo .. 1·40 1·40
1389. 20 f. African elephant .. 2·25 2·25
1390. 25 f. Hippopotamus .. 2·50 2·50
1391. 30 f. Common zebra .. 2·75 2·75
1392. 50 f. Warthog .. .. 5·25 5·25
1393. 60 f. Eland .. .. 6·50 6·50
1394. 65 f. Black-backed jackal .. .. .. 8·00 8·00
1395. 70 f. Cheetah .. .. 9·00 9·00
1396. 75 f. Blue Wildebeest .. 9·50 9·50
1397. 85 f. Spotted hyena .. 11·50 11·50

**1983.** Animal Protection Year. Nos. 1385/97 optd. with World Wildlife Fund emblem.
1398. 2 f. Type **131** .. .. 70 70
1399. 3 f. Giraffe .. .. 70 70
1400. 5 f. Black rhinoceros .. 70 70
1401. 10 f. African buffalo .. 2·10 2·10
1402. 20 f. African elephant .. 3·25 3·25
1403. 25 f. Hippopotamus .. 3·75 3·75
1404. 30 f. Common zebra .. 4·00 4·00
1405. 50 f. Warthog .. .. 7·75 7·75
1406. 60 f. Eland .. .. 9·75 9·75
1407. 65 f. Jackal ("Canis mesomelas") .. .. 12·00 12·00
1408. 70 f. Cheetah .. .. 13·00 13·00
1409. 75 f. Blue wildebeest .. 14·00 14·00
1410. 85 f. Spotted Hyena .. 17·00 17·00

133. Flag and National Party Emblem.

**1983.** 20th Anniv. (1982) of Independence. Multicoloured.
1411. 10 f. Type **133** .. .. 65 65
1412. 25 f. Flag and arms .. 1·00 1·00
1413. 30 f. Flag and map of Africa .. .. .. 1·10 1·10
1414. 50 f. Flag and emblem .. 1·50 1·50
1415. 65 f. Flag and President Bagaza .. .. 2·00 2·00

134. "Virgin and Child" (Lucas Signorelli).

**1983.** Christmas. Multicoloured.
1416. 10 f. Type **134** .. .. 1·10 1·10
1417. 25 f. E. Murillo .. .. 1·50 1·50
1418. 30 f. Carlo Crivelli .. 1·75 1·75
1419. 50 f. Nicolas Poussin .. 2·40 2·40
Designs: Virgin and Child paintings by named artists.

**1983.** Christmas Charity. Nos. 1416/19 additionally inscr. with premiums.
1421. 10 f.+1 f. multicoloured 1·10 1·10
1422. 25 f.+1 f. multicoloured 1·50 1·50
1423. 30 f.+1 f. multicoloured 1·75 1·75
1424. 50 f.+1 f. multicoloured 2·40 2·40

135. "Papilio zalmoxis".

**1984.** Butterflies. Multicoloured.
1426. 5 f. Type **135** .. .. 45 45
1427. 5 f. "Cymothoe coccinata" 45 45
1428. 10 f. "Papilio antimachus" 1·10 1·10
1429. 10 f. "Asterope pechueli" 1·10 1·10
1430. 30 f. "Bebearia mardania" 2·10 2·10
1431. 30 f. "Papilio hesperus" 2·10 2·10
1432. 35 f. "Euphaedra perseis" 2·75 2·75
1433. 35 f. "Euphaedra neophron" .. .. 2·75 2·75
1434. 65 f. "Pseudacraea striata' 5·00 5·00
1435. 65 f. "Euphaedra imperialis" .. .. 5·00 5·00

136. Stamps of German East Africa and Belgian Occupation.

**1984.** 19th U.P.U. Congress, Hamburg. Multicoloured.
1436. 10 f. Type **136** .. .. 65 65
1437. 30 f. 1962. Burundi overprinted stamps .. 1·10 1·10
1438. 35 f. 1969 14 f. Letter-writing Week and 1982 30 f. Zebra stamps .. 1·25 1·25
1439. 65 f. Heinrich von Stephan (founder of U.P.U.) and 1974 14 f. U.P.U. Centenary stamps.. .. .. 2·75 2·75

137. Jesse Owens (runner).

**1984.** Olympic Games, Los Angeles. Mult.
1441. 10 f. Type **137** .. .. 1·10 1·10
1442. 30 f. Rafer Johnson (discus thrower) .. 1·60 1·60
1443. 35 f. Bob Beamon (long jumper) .. .. 1·75 1·75
1444. 65 f. K. Keino (sprinter) 2·25 2·25

138. "Virgin and Child" (Botticelli).

**1984.** Christmas. Multicoloured.
1446. 10 f. "Rest on the Flight into Egypt" (Murillo) 30 30
1447. 25 f. "Virgin and Child" (R. del Garbo) .. 1·10 1·10
1448. 30 f. Type **138** .. .. 1·60 1·60
1449. 50 f. "Adoration of the Shepherds" (J. Bassano) .. .. 2·00 2·00

**1984.** Christmas Charity. As Nos. 1446/49 but with additional premium.
1451. 10 f.+1 f. multicoloured 30 30
1452. 25 f.+1 f. multicoloured 1·10 1·10
1453. 30 f.+1 f. multicoloured 1·60 1·60
1454. 50 f.+1 f. multicoloured 2·00 2·00

139. Thunbergia.

140. Bombs as Flats.

**1986.** Flowers. Multicoloured.
1456. 2 f. Type **139** (postage).. 45 45
1457. 3 f. African violets .. 45 45
1458. 5 f. "Clivia" .. .. 45 45
1459. 10 f. "Cassia" .. .. 45 45
1460. 20 f. Bird of Paradise flower .. .. .. 90 90
1461. 35 f. "Gloriosa" .. .. 1·60 1·60
1462. 70 f. Type **139** (air.) .. 1·40 1·40
1463. 75 f. As No. 1457 .. 1·50 1·50
1464. 80 f. As No. 1458 .. 1·60 1·60
1465. 85 f. As No. 1459 .. 1·75 1·75
1466. 100 f. As No. 1460 .. 2·00 2·00
1467. 150 f. As No. 1461 .. 3·25 3·25

**1987.** International Peace Year (1986). Multicoloured.
1468. 10 f. Type **140** .. .. 20 20
1469. 20 f. Molecular diagrams as flower .. .. 40 40
1470. 30 f. Clasped hands across globe .. .. 1·10 1·10
1471. 40 f. Chicks in split globe 1·25 1·25

141. Map, Airplane and Emblem.

**1987.** 10th Anniv. of Great Lakes Countries Economic Community. Multicoloured.
1473. 5 f. Type **141** .. .. 55 55
1474. 10 f. Map, ear of wheat, cogwheel and emblem 65 65
1475. 15 f. Map, factory and emblem .. .. 75 75
1476. 25 f. Map, electricity pylons and emblem .. 1·60 1·60
1477. 35 f. Map, flags and emblem .. .. 2·25 2·25

142. Leaves and Sticks Shelter.

**1988.** International Year of Shelter for the Homeless (1987). Multicoloured.
1479. 10 f. Type **142** .. .. 55 55
1480. 20 f. People living in concrete pipes .. 70 70
1481. 80 f. Boys mixing mortar 1·50 1·50
1482. 150 f. Boys with model house .. .. .. 3·00 3·00

143 Skull between Cigarettes

144 Pope John Paul II

**1989.** Anti-smoking Campaign. Multicoloured.
1484 5 f. Type **143** .. .. 70 70
1485 20 f. Cigarettes, lungs and skull .. .. .. 1·40 1·40
1486 80 f. Cigarettes piercing skull .. .. .. 2·25 2·25

**1990.** Papal Visit.
1488 **144** 5 f. multicoloured .. 45 45
1489 10 f. multicoloured .. 45 45
1490 20 f. multicoloured .. 70 70
1491 30 f. multicoloured .. 70 70
1492 50 f. multicoloured .. 1·40 1·40
1493 80 f. multicoloured .. 2·00 2·00

145 Hippopotamus

**1991.** Animals. Multicoloured.
1495 5 f. Type **145** .. .. 65 65
1496 10 f. Hen and cockerel .. 65 65
1497 20 f. Lion .. .. 65 65
1498 30 f. Elephant .. .. 90 90
1499 50 f. Helmet guineafowl 1·90 1·90
1500 80 f. Crocodile .. .. 2·75 2·75

146 Drummer

147 "Impatiens petersiana"

**1992.** Traditional Dancing. Multicoloured.
1502 15 f. Type **146** .. .. 25 25
1503 30 f. Men dancing .. 40 40
1504 115 f. Group of drummers (horiz) .. .. 1·90 1·90
1505 200 f. Men dancing in fields (horiz) .. .. 3·25 3·25

**1992.** Flowers. Multicoloured.
1507 15 f. Type **147** .. .. 40 40
1508 20 f. ."Lachenalia aloides" "Nelsonii" .. .. 40 40
1509 30 f. Egyptian lotus .. 60 60
1510 50 f. Kaffir lily .. .. 1·40 1·40

148 Pigtail Macaque

**1992.** Air. Animals. Multicoloured.
1512 100 f. Type **148** .. .. 1·50 1·50
1513 115 f. Grevy's zebra .. 1·75 1·75
1514 200 f. Ox .. .. 2·50 2·50
1515 220 f. Eastern white pelican .. .. 3·25 3·25

149 People holding Hands and Flag

**1992.** 30th Anniv of Independence. Mult.
1517 30 f. Type **149** .. .. 20 20
1518 85 f. State flag .. .. 80 80
1519 110 f. Independence monument (vert) .. 1·10 1·10
1520 115 f. As No. 1518 .. 1·10 1·10
1521 120 f. Map (vert) .. 1·40 1·40
1522 140 f. Type **149** .. .. 1·50 1·50
1523 200 f. As No. 1519 .. 2·10 2·10
1524 250 f. As No. 1521 .. 2·75 2·75

150 "Russula ingens"

**1992.** Fungi. Multicoloured.
1525 10 f. Type **150** .. .. 15 10
1526 15 f. "Russula brunneorigida" .. .. 20 15
1527 20 f. "Amanita zambiana" 25 20
1528 30 f. "Russula subfistulosa" .. .. 40 30

| | | | |
|---|---|---|---|
| 1529 | 75 f. "Russula meleagris" | 95 | 65 |
| 1530 | 85 f. As No. 1529 .. | 1·10 | 75 |
| 1531 | 100 f. "Russula immaculata" .. .. | 1·25 | 90 |
| 1532 | 110 f. Type **150** .. .. | 1·40 | 1·00 |
| 1533 | 115 f. As No. 1526 .. | 1·40 | 1·00 |
| 1534 | 120 f. "Russula sejuncta" | 1·50 | 1·10 |
| 1535 | 130 f. As No. 1534 .. | 1·60 | 1·10 |
| 1536 | 250 f. "Afroboletus luteolus" .. .. | 3·25 | 2·25 |

**151** Columbus's Fleet, Treasure and Globes

**1992.** 500th Anniv of Discovery of America by Columbus. Multicoloured.

| | | | |
|---|---|---|---|
| 1541 | 200 f. Type **151** .. .. | 2·00 | 2·00 |
| 1542 | 400 f. American produce, globes and Columbus's fleet .. .. .. | 4·25 | 4·25 |

**152** Serval

**1992.** The Serval. Multicoloured.

| | | | |
|---|---|---|---|
| 1543 | 30 f. Type **152** .. .. | 40 | 40 |
| 1544 | 130 f. Pair sitting and crouching .. .. | 1·60 | 1·60 |
| 1545 | 200 f. Pair, one standing over the other .. | 2·50 | 2·50 |
| 1546 | 220 f. Heads of pair .. | 2·75 | 2·75 |

**153** Running

**154** Emblems

**1992.** Olympic Games, Barcelona. Mult.

| | | | |
|---|---|---|---|
| 1547 | 130 f. Type **153** .. .. | 1·50 | 1·50 |
| 1548 | 500 f. Hurdling .. .. | 5·25 | 5·25 |

**1992.** International Nutrition Conference, Rome. Multicoloured.

| | | | |
|---|---|---|---|
| 1549 | 200 f. Type **154** .. .. | 2·00 | 2·00 |
| 1550 | 220 f. Woman's face made from vegetables (G. Arcimbolo) .. .. | 2·40 | 2·40 |

**155** Horsemen

**156** Flags of Member Countries and European Community Emblem

**1992.** Christmas. Details of "Adoration of the Magi" by Gentile da Fabriano. Mult.

| | | | |
|---|---|---|---|
| 1551 | 100 f. Type **155** .. .. | 90 | 90 |
| 1552 | 130 f. Three Kings .. | 1·10 | 1·10 |
| 1553 | 250 f. Holy family .. | 2·50 | 2·50 |

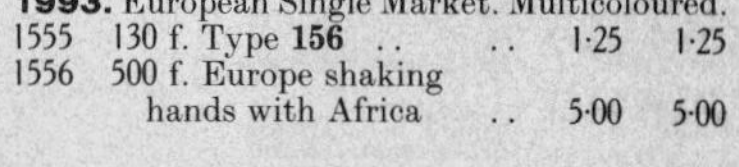

**1993.** European Single Market. Multicoloured.

| | | | |
|---|---|---|---|
| 1555 | 130 f. Type **156** .. .. | 1·25 | 1·25 |
| 1556 | 500 f. Europe shaking hands with Africa .. | 5·00 | 5·00 |

**157** Indonongo

**1993.** Musical Instruments. Multicoloured.

| | | | |
|---|---|---|---|
| 1557 | 200 f. Type **157** .. .. | 2·00 | 2·00 |
| 1558 | 220 f. Ingoma (drum) .. | 2·25 | 2·25 |
| 1559 | 250 f. Ikembe (xylophone) | 2·50 | 2·50 |
| 1560 | 300 f. Umuduri (musical bow) .. .. .. | 3·25 | 3·25 |

**158** Broad Blue-banded Swallowtail

**159** Players, Stadium, United States Flag and Statue of Liberty

**1993.** Butterflies. Multicoloured.

| | | | |
|---|---|---|---|
| 1561 | 130 f. Type **158** .. .. | 1·25 | 1·25 |
| 1562 | 200 f. Green charaxes .. | 2·00 | 2·00 |
| 1563 | 250 f. Migratory glider .. | 2·50 | 2·50 |
| 1564 | 300 f. Red swallowtail .. | 3·25 | 3·25 |

**1993.** World Cup Football Championship, U.S.A. (1994). Multicoloured.

| | | | |
|---|---|---|---|
| 1566 | 130 f. Type **159** .. .. | 1·25 | 1·25 |
| 1567 | 200 f. Players, stadium, United States flag and Golden Gate Bridge .. | 2·50 | 2·50 |

**160** Cattle

**161** Woman with Baby and Two Men

**1993.** Domestic Animals. Multicoloured.

| | | | |
|---|---|---|---|
| 1568 | 100 f. Type **160** .. .. | 1·00 | 1·00 |
| 1569 | 120 f. Sheep .. .. | 1·10 | 1·10 |
| 1570 | 130 f. Pigs .. .. | 1·25 | 1·25 |
| 1571 | 250 f. Goats .. .. | 2·50 | 2·50 |

**1993.** Christmas. Each orange and black.

| | | | |
|---|---|---|---|
| 1572 | 100 f. Type **161** .. | 1·25 | 1·25 |
| 1573 | 130 f. Nativity .. .. | 1·50 | 1·50 |
| 1574 | 250 f. Woman with baby and three men .. | 3·00 | 3·00 |

**162** Elvis Presley

**163** "The Discus Thrower" (statue)

**1994.** Entertainers. Multicoloured.

| | | | |
|---|---|---|---|
| 1576 | 60 f. Type **162** .. .. | 30 | 30 |
| 1577 | 115 f. Mick Jagger .. | 55 | 55 |
| 1578 | 120 f. John Lennon .. | 60 | 60 |
| 1579 | 200 f. Michael Jackson .. | 1·00 | 1·00 |

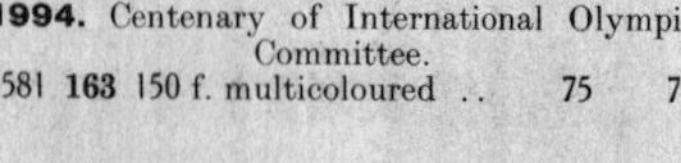

**1994.** Centenary of International Olympic Committee.

| | | | |
|---|---|---|---|
| 1581 | **163** 150 f. multicoloured .. | 75 | 75 |

**164** Pres. Buyoya handing over Baton of Power to Pres. Ndadaye

**165** Madonna, China

**1994.** 1st First Anniv of First Multi-party Elections in Burundi. Multicoloured.

| | | | |
|---|---|---|---|
| 1582 | 30 f. + 10 f. Type **164** .. | 20 | 20 |
| 1583 | 110 f. + 10 f. Pres. Ndadaye (first elected President) giving inauguration speech .. | 60 | 60 |
| 1584 | 115 f. + 10 f. Arms on map | 60 | 60 |
| 1585 | 120 f. + 10 f. Warrior on map .. .. .. | 65 | 65 |

**1994.** Christmas. Multicoloured.

| | | | |
|---|---|---|---|
| 1586 | 115 f. Type **165** .. .. | 55 | 55 |
| 1587 | 120 f. Madonna, Japan .. | 60 | 60 |
| 1588 | 250 f. Black Virgin, Poland .. .. | 1·25 | 1·25 |

**166** Emblem and Earth

**167** "Cassia didymobotrya"

**1995.** 50th Anniversaries. Multicoloured.

| | | | |
|---|---|---|---|
| 1590 | 115 f. Type **166** (F.A.O.) | 55 | 55 |
| 1591 | 120 f. U.N.O. emblems and dove .. .. | 60 | 60 |

**1995.** Flowers. Multicoloured.

| | | | |
|---|---|---|---|
| 1592 | 15 f. Type **167** .. .. | 10 | 10 |
| 1593 | 20 f. "Mitragyna rubrostipulosa" .. | 10 | 10 |
| 1594 | 30 f. "Phytolacca dodecandra" .. | 15 | 15 |
| 1595 | 85 f. "Acanthus pubescens" .. | 40 | 40 |
| 1596 | 100 f. "Bulbophyllum comatum" .. | 50 | 50 |
| 1597 | 110 f. "Angraecum evrardianum" .. | 55 | 55 |
| 1598 | 115 f. "Eulophia burundiensis" .. | 55 | 55 |
| 1599 | 120 f. "Habenaria adolphii" .. .. | 60 | 60 |

**168** Otraca Bus

**169** Boy with Panga

**1995.** Transport. Multicoloured.

| | | | |
|---|---|---|---|
| 1600 | 30 f. Type **168** .. .. | 15 | 15 |
| 1601 | 115 f. Transintra lorry .. | 65 | 65 |
| 1602 | 120 f. Arnolac ferry .. | 70 | 70 |
| 1603 | 250 f. Air Burundi airplane .. .. | 1·40 | 1·40 |

**1995.** Christmas. Multicoloured.

| | | | |
|---|---|---|---|
| 1604 | 100 f. Type **169** .. .. | 55 | 55 |
| 1605 | 130 f. Boy with sheaf of wheat .. .. .. | 75 | 75 |
| 1606 | 250 f. Mother and children | 1·40 | 1·40 |

# CAMBODIA Pt. 21

A Kingdom in south-east Asia.

From 1887 Cambodia was part of the Union of Indo-China. In 1949 it became an Assiociated State of the French Union, in 1953 it attained sovereign independence and in 1955 it left the Union.

Following the introduction of a republican constitution in 1970 the name of the country was changed to Khmer Republic and in 1975 to Kampuchea.

In 1989 it reverted to the name of Cambodia. Under a new constitution in 1993 it became a parliamentary monarchy.

1951. 100 cents = 1 piastre.
1955. 100 cents = 1 riel.

**1.** " Apsara " or Dancing Nymph.

**2.** Throne Room, Phnom-Penh.

**3.** King Norodom Sihanouk.

**5.** " Kinnari ".

**1951.**

| | | | | |
|---|---|---|---|---|
| 1 | **1** | 10 c. green and deep green | 85 | 85 |
| 2 | | 20 c. brown and red .. | 70 | 55 |
| 3 | | 30 c. blue and violet .. | 70 | 55 |
| 4 | | 40 c. blue and ultramarine | 70 | 55 |
| 5 | **2** | 50 c. green and deep green | 60 | 55 |
| 6 | **3** | 80 c. green and blue .. | 85 | 90 |
| 7 | **2** | 1 p. violet and blue .. | 1·25 | 1·10 |
| 8 | **3** | 1 p. 10 red and lake .. | 1·40 | 1·10 |
| 9 | **1** | 1 p. 50 red and lake .. | 1·75 | 1·25 |
| 10 | **2** | 1 p. 50 blue and indigo .. | 1·60 | 1·25 |
| 11 | **3** | 1 p. 50 brown & chocolate | 1·60 | 1·25 |
| 12 | | 1 p. 90 blue and indigo .. | 2·75 | 2·25 |
| 13 | **2** | 2 p. brown and red .. | 2·75 | 1·50 |
| 14 | **3** | 3 p. brown and red .. | 3·25 | 2·75 |
| 15 | **1** | 5 p. violet and blue .. | 12·00 | 5·25 |
| 16 | **2** | 10 p. blue and violet .. | 24·00 | 12·00 |
| 17 | **3** | 15 p. violet & deep violet | 30·00 | 18·00 |

**1952.** Students' Aid Fund. Surch **AIDE A L'ETUDIANT** and premium.

| | | | | |
|---|---|---|---|---|
| 18 | **3** | 1 p. 10 + 40 c. red and lake | 3·75 | 4·00 |
| 19 | | 1 p. 90 + 60 c. bl & indigo | 3·75 | 4·00 |
| 20 | | 3 p. + 1 p. brown and red | 3·75 | 4·00 |
| 21 | **1** | 5 p. + 2 p. violet and blue | 3·75 | 4·00 |

**1953.** Air.

| | | | | |
|---|---|---|---|---|
| 22 | **5** | 50 c. green .. .. | 85 | 80 |
| 23 | | 3 p. red .. .. | 95 | 85 |
| 24 | | 3 p. 30 violet .. | 1·40 | 1·25 |
| 25 | | 4 p. blue and brown .. | 1·60 | 1·50 |
| 26 | | 5 p. 10 ochre, red & brown | 2·75 | 2·25 |
| 27 | | 6 p. 50 purple and brown | 2·75 | 2·75 |
| 28 | | 9 p. green and mauve .. | 3·75 | 4·00 |
| 29 | | 11 p. 50 multicoloured .. | 8·00 | 6·50 |
| 30 | | 30 p. ochre, brown & green | 15·00 | 11·00 |

**6.** Arms of Cambodia.

**7.** " Postal Transport ".

**1954.**

| | | | | |
|---|---|---|---|---|
| 31. | – | 10 c. red .. .. .. | 30 | 30 |
| 32. | – | 20 c. green .. .. | 30 | 20 |
| 33. | – | 30 c. blue .. .. .. | 30 | 20 |
| 34. | – | 40 c. violet .. .. | 30 | 20 |
| 35. | – | 50 c. purple .. .. | 30 | 20 |
| 36. | – | 70 c. brown .. .. | 40 | 30 |
| 37. | – | 1 p. violet .. .. .. | 50 | 30 |
| 38. | – | 1 p. 50 red .. .. | 50 | 30 |
| 39. | **6.** | 2 p. red .. .. .. | 50 | 50 |
| 40. | – | 2 p. 50 green .. .. | 80 | 70 |
| 41. | **7.** | 2 p. 50 green .. .. | 1·00 | 90 |
| 42. | **6.** | 3 p. blue .. .. .. | 1·50 | 1·40 |
| 43. | **7.** | 4 p. sepia .. .. .. | 1·60 | 1·40 |
| 44. | **6.** | 4 p. 50 violet .. .. | 1·90 | 1·40 |

| | | | | |
|---|---|---|---|---|
| 45. | 7. | 5 p. red .. .. .. | 2·00 | 1·75 |
| 46. | 6. | 6 p. brown .. .. | 2·25 | 1·90 |
| 47. | 7. | 10 p. violet .. .. | 2·50 | 2·25 |
| 48. | | 15 p. blue .. .. .. | 3·25 | 2·75 |
| 49. | – | 20 p. blue .. .. .. | 8·25 | 5·50 |
| 50. | – | 30 p. green .. .. | 13·00 | 9·75 |

DESIGNS—VERT: 10 c. to 50 c. View of Phnom Daun Penah. HORIZ: 70 c., 1, 1 p. 50, 20, 30 p. East Gate, Temple of Angkor.

8. King Norodom Suramarit.

9. King and Queen of Cambodia.

**1955.**

| | | | | |
|---|---|---|---|---|
| 51. | – | 50 c. blue .. .. .. | 25 | 25 |
| 52. | 8. | 50 c. violet .. .. | 25 | 25 |
| 53. | | 1 r. red .. .. .. | 40 | 25 |
| 54. | | 2 r. blue .. .. .. | 45 | 40 |
| 55. | – | 2 r. 50 brown .. .. | 60 | 50 |
| 56. | – | 4 r. green .. .. .. | 90 | 80 |
| 57. | – | 6 r. lake .. .. .. | 1·40 | 1·10 |
| 58. | 8. | 7 r. brown .. .. .. | 1·75 | 1·25 |
| 59. | – | 15 r. lilac .. .. .. | 2·75 | 2·10 |
| 60. | 8. | 20 r. green .. .. | 4·00 | 3·00 |

PORTRAIT: Nos. 51, 55/7 and 59, Queen Kosssamak.

For stamps as Nos. 58 and 60, but with black border, see Nos. 101/2.

**1955.** Coronation (1st issue).

| | | | | |
|---|---|---|---|---|
| 61 | 9 | 1 r. 50 sepia and brown | 55 | 35 |
| 62 | | 2 r. black and blue .. | 55 | 35 |
| 63 | | 3 r. red and orange .. | 70 | 55 |
| 64 | | 5 r. black and green .. | 1·10 | 90 |
| 65 | | 10 r. purple and violet .. | 1·90 | 1·10 |

See Nos. 66/71.

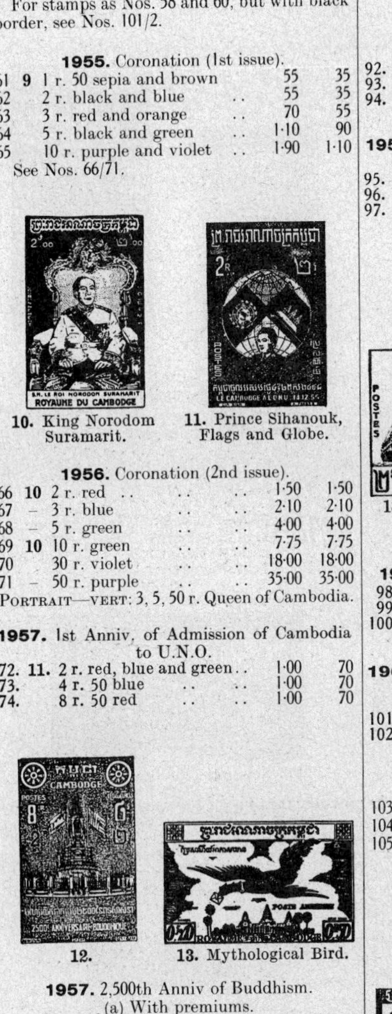

10. King Norodom Suramarit.

11. Prince Sihanouk, Flags and Globe.

**1956.** Coronation (2nd issue).

| | | | | |
|---|---|---|---|---|
| 66 | 10 | 2 r. red .. .. .. | 1·50 | 1·50 |
| 67 | – | 3 r. blue .. .. .. | 2·10 | 2·10 |
| 68 | – | 5 r. green .. .. .. | 4·00 | 4·00 |
| 69 | 10 | 10 r. green .. .. | 7·75 | 7·75 |
| 70 | | 30 r. violet .. .. | 18·00 | 18·00 |
| 71 | – | 50 r. purple .. .. | 35·00 | 35·00 |

PORTRAIT—VERT: 3, 5, 50 r. Queen of Cambodia.

**1957.** 1st Anniv. of Admission of Cambodia to U.N.O.

| | | | | |
|---|---|---|---|---|
| 72. | 11. | 2 r. red, blue and green .. | 1·00 | 70 |
| 73. | | 4 r. 50 blue .. .. | 1·00 | 70 |
| 74. | | 8 r. 50 red .. .. | 1·00 | 70 |

12.

13. Mythological Bird.

**1957.** 2,500th Anniv of Buddhism.

(a) With premiums.

| | | | | |
|---|---|---|---|---|
| 75 | 12 | 1 r. 50+50 c. bis, red & bl | 1·25 | 1·25 |
| 76 | | 6 r. 50+1 r. 50 bistre, red and purple .. .. | 2·00 | 2·00 |
| 77 | | 8 r.+2 r. bistre, red & bl | 3·25 | 3·25 |

(b) Colours changed and premiums omitted.

| | | | | |
|---|---|---|---|---|
| 78 | 12 | 1 r. 50 red .. .. | 85 | 85 |
| 79 | | 6 r. 50 violet .. .. | 1·00 | 1·00 |
| 80 | | 8 r. green .. .. | 1·00 | 1·00 |

**1957.** Air.

| | | | | |
|---|---|---|---|---|
| 81. | 13. | 50 c. lake .. .. | 30 | 15 |
| 82. | | 1 r. green .. .. | 40 | 20 |
| 83. | | 4 r. blue .. .. .. | 1·40 | 95 |
| 84. | | 50 r. red .. .. .. | 6·00 | 5·50 |
| 85. | | 100 r. red, green and blue | 10·50 | 7·75 |

## MINIMUM PRICE

The minimum price quoted is 10p which represents a handling charge rather than a basis for valuing common stamps. For further notes about prices see introductory pages.

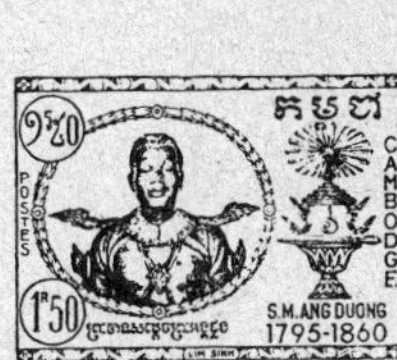

14. King Ang Duong.

15. King Norodom I.

**1958.** King Ang Duong Commem.

| | | | | |
|---|---|---|---|---|
| 86. | 14. | 1 r. 50 brown and violet | 35 | 35 |
| 87. | | 5 r. bistre and black .. | 45 | 45 |
| 88. | | 10 r. sepia and purple .. | 90 | 90 |

**1958.** King Norodom I Commem.

| | | | | |
|---|---|---|---|---|
| 89 | 15 | 2 r. brown and blue .. | 30 | 30 |
| 90 | | 6 r. green and orange .. | 45 | 45 |
| 91 | | 15 r. brown and green .. | 90 | 90 |

16. Children.

**1959.** Children's World Friendship.

| | | | | |
|---|---|---|---|---|
| 92. | 16. | 20 c. purple .. .. | 25 | 25 |
| 93. | | 50 c. blue .. .. | 40 | 40 |
| 94. | | 80 c. red .. .. .. | 90 | 90 |

**1959.** Red Cross Fund. Nos. 92/4 surch with red cross and premium.

| | | | | |
|---|---|---|---|---|
| 95. | 16. | 20 c.+20 c. purple .. | 25 | 25 |
| 96. | | 50 c.+30 c. blue .. | 50 | 50 |
| 97. | | 80 c.+50 c. red .. .. | 95 | 95 |

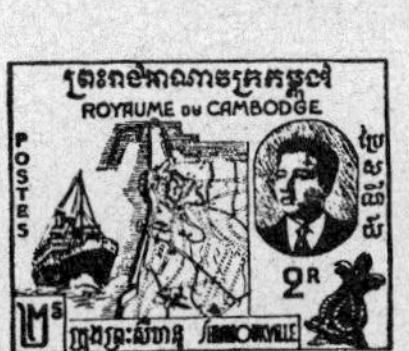

18. Prince Sihanouk, Plan of Port and Freighter.

19. Sacred Plough in Procession.

**1960.** Inauguration of Sihanoukville Port.

| | | | | |
|---|---|---|---|---|
| 98. | 18. | 2 r. sepia and red .. | 50 | 50 |
| 99. | | 5 r. brown and blue .. | 50 | 50 |
| 100. | | 20 r. blue and violet .. | 1·75 | 1·75 |

**1960.** King Norodom Suramarit Mourning issue. Nos. 58 and 60 reissued with black border.

| | | | | |
|---|---|---|---|---|
| 101. | 8. | 7 r. brown and black .. | 3·00 | 3·00 |
| 102. | | 20 r. green and black .. | 3·00 | 3·00 |

**1960.** Festival of the Sacred Furrow.

| | | | | |
|---|---|---|---|---|
| 103 | 19 | 1 r. purple .. .. | 40 | 40 |
| 104 | | 2 r. brown .. .. | 50 | 50 |
| 105 | | 3 r. green .. .. | 75 | 75 |

20. Child and Book ("Education").

21. Flag and Dove of Peace.

**1960.** "Works of the Five Year Plan".

| | | | | |
|---|---|---|---|---|
| 106 | 20 | 2 r. brown, blue & green | 35 | 25 |
| 107 | – | 3 r. green and brown .. | 45 | 30 |
| 108 | – | 4 r. violet, green & pink | 45 | 35 |
| 109 | – | 6 r. brown, orange & grn | 55 | 45 |
| 110 | – | 10 r. blue, green & bistre | 1·25 | 85 |
| 111 | – | 25 r. red and lake .. | 2·75 | 2·40 |

DESIGNS—HORIZ. 3 r. Chhouksar Barrage ("Irrigation"). 6 r. Carpenter and huts ("Construction"). 10 r. Rice-field ("Agriculture"). VERT. 4 r. Industrial scene and books ("National balance-sheet"). 25 r. Anointing children ("Child welfare").

**1961.** Peace. Flag in red and blue.

| | | | | |
|---|---|---|---|---|
| 112. | 21. | 1 r. 50 green and brown | 35 | 35 |
| 113. | | 5 r. red .. .. .. | 50 | 50 |
| 114. | | 7 r. blue and green .. | 65 | 65 |

23. Frangipani.

24. "Rama" (from temple door, Baphoun).

**1961.** Cambodian Flowers.

| | | | | |
|---|---|---|---|---|
| 115 | 23 | 2 r. yellow, green & mve | 45 | 45 |
| 116 | – | 5 r. mauve, green & blue | 70 | 70 |
| 117 | – | 10 r. red, green and blue | 2·00 | 2·00 |

FLOWERS: 5 r. Oleander. 10 r. Amaryllis.

**1961.** Cambodian Soldiers Commemoration.

| | | | | |
|---|---|---|---|---|
| 118 | 24 | 1 r. mauve .. .. | 40 | 25 |
| 118a | | 2 r. blue .. .. | 2·50 | 1·50 |
| 119 | | 3 r. green .. .. | 50 | 35 |
| 120 | | 6 r. orange .. .. | 70 | 45 |

25. Prince Norodom Sihanouk and Independence Monument.

**1961.** Independence Monument.

| | | | | |
|---|---|---|---|---|
| 121. | 25. | 2 r. green (postage) .. | 65 | 50 |
| 122. | | 4 r. sepia .. .. | 65 | 50 |
| 123. | | 7 r. multicoloured (air) | 60 | 50 |
| 124. | | 30 r. red, blue and green | 2·00 | 1·60 |
| 125. | | 50 r. multicoloured .. | 3·00 | 2·75 |

**1961.** 6th World Buddhist Conf. Optd. **VIe CONFERENCE MONDIALE BOUDDHIQUE 12-11-1961.**

| | | | | |
|---|---|---|---|---|
| 126. | 6. | 2 p. 50 (2 r. 50) green .. | 50 | 50 |
| 127. | | 4 p. 50 (4 r. 50) violet .. | 70 | 70 |

27. Power Station (Czech Aid).

28. Campaign Emblem.

**1962.** Foreign Aid Programme.

| | | | | |
|---|---|---|---|---|
| 128 | 27 | 2 r. lake and red .. | 25 | 15 |
| 129 | – | 3 r. brown, green & blue | 30 | 15 |
| 130 | – | 4 r. brown, red and blue | 30 | 15 |
| 131 | – | 5 r. purple and green .. | 40 | 35 |
| 132 | – | 6 r. brown and blue .. | 80 | 50 |

DESIGNS: 3 r. Motorway (American Aid). 4 r. Textile Factory (Chinese Aid). 5 r. Friendship Hospital (Soviet Aid). 6 r. Airport (French Aid).

**1962.** Malaria Eradication.

| | | | | |
|---|---|---|---|---|
| 133 | 28 | 2 r. purple and brown .. | 35 | 20 |
| 134 | | 4 r. green and brown .. | 40 | 40 |
| 135 | | 6 r. violet and bistre .. | 50 | 35 |

29. Curucmas.

**1962.** Cambodian Fruits (1st issue).

| | | | | |
|---|---|---|---|---|
| 136 | 29 | 2 r. yellow and brown .. | 45 | 40 |
| 137 | – | 4 r. green and turquoise | 65 | 45 |
| 138 | – | 6 r. red, green and blue | 80 | 60 |

FRUITS: 4 r. Lychees. 6 r. Mangosteens.

**1962.** Cambodian Fruits (2nd issue).

| | | | | |
|---|---|---|---|---|
| 139 | | 2 r. brown and green .. | 40 | 30 |
| 140 | | 5 r. green and brown .. | 55 | 40 |
| 141 | | 9 r. brown and green .. | 70 | 45 |

DESIGNS—VERT: 2 r. Pineapples. 5 r. Sugarcane. 9 r. "Bread" trees.

**1962.** Surch.

| | | | | |
|---|---|---|---|---|
| 142. | 16. | 50 c. on 80 c. red .. | 60 | 35 |
| 150. | – | 3 r. on 2 r. 50 brown (No. 55) .. .. | 45 | 40 |

**1962.** Inauguration of Independence Monument. Surch **INAUGURATION DU MONUMENT** and new value.

| | | | | |
|---|---|---|---|---|
| 143. | 25. | 3 r. on 2 r. green (post.) | 50 | 30 |
| 144. | | 12 r. on 7 r. multicoloured (air) .. .. | 1·40 | 1·00 |

32. Campaign Emblem, Corn and Maize.

33. Temple Preah Vihear.

**1963.** Freedom from Hunger.

| | | | | |
|---|---|---|---|---|
| 145 | 32 | 3 r. chestnut, brn & bl | 50 | 40 |
| 146 | | 6 r. chestnut, brn & bl | 50 | 40 |

**1963.** Reunification of Preah Vihear Temple with Cambodia.

| | | | | |
|---|---|---|---|---|
| 147 | 33 | 3 r. brown, purple & grn | 30 | 20 |
| 148 | | 6 r. green, orange & blue | 50 | 40 |
| 149 | | 15 r. brown, blue & grn | 80 | 65 |

35. Kep sur Mer.

**1963.** Cambodian Resorts. Multicoloured.

| | | | |
|---|---|---|---|
| 151. | 3 r. Koh Tonsay .. .. | 35 | 25 |
| 152. | 7 r. Popokvil (waterfall) .. | 50 | 30 |
| 153. | 20 r. Type 35 .. .. | 1·60 | 70 |

The 3 r. and 7 r. are vert.

**1963.** Red Cross Centenary. Surch **1863 1963 CENTENAIRE DE LA CROIX-ROUGE** and premium.

| | | | | |
|---|---|---|---|---|
| 154 | 28 | 4 r.+40 c. green & brn | 60 | 60 |
| 155 | | 6 r.+60 c. violet & bistre | 95 | 95 |

37. Scales of Justice.

**1963.** 15th Anniv. of Declaration of Human Rights.

| | | | | |
|---|---|---|---|---|
| 156. | 37. | 1 r. green, red and blue | 30 | 30 |
| 157. | | 3 r. red, blue and green | 50 | 50 |
| 158. | | 12 r. blue, green & red | 95 | 95 |

38. Kouprey.

39. Magpie.

**1964.** Wild Animal Protection.

| | | | | |
|---|---|---|---|---|
| 159. | 38. | 50 c. brn., grn. & chest. | 40 | 25 |
| 160. | | 3 r. brn., chest. & grn. | 55 | 35 |
| 161. | | 6 r. brown, blue & green | 85 | 55 |

**1964.** Birds.

| | | | | |
|---|---|---|---|---|
| 162 | 39 | 3 r. blue, green & indigo | 60 | 40 |
| 163 | – | 6 r. orange, purple & bl | 95 | 65 |
| 164 | – | 12 r. green and purple .. | 1·75 | 95 |

BIRDS: 6 r. Common kingfisher. 12 r. Grey heron.

40. "Hanuman".

42. Airline Emblem.

**1964.** Air.

| | | | | |
|---|---|---|---|---|
| 165 | 40 | 5 r. mauve, brown & bl | 60 | 40 |
| 166 | | 10 r. bistre, mve & grn | 95 | 40 |
| 167 | | 20 r. bistre, violet & blue | 1·60 | 75 |
| 168 | | 40 r. bistre, blue and red | 3·50 | 1·50 |
| 169 | | 80 r. orange, green & pur | 5·75 | 3·75 |

**1964.** Air Olympic Games, Tokyo. Surch **JEUX OLYMPIQUES TOKYO–1964**, Olympic rings and value.

170 40 3 r. on 5 r. mauve, brown and blue .. 55 40
171 6 r. on 10 r. bistre, mauve and green .. 85 60
172 9 r. on 20 r. bis, vio & bl 95 70
173 12 r. on 40 r. bistre, blue and red .. .. 1·90 1·10

**1964.** 8th Anniv. of Royal Air Cambodia.

174. **42.** 1 r. 50 red and violet .. 20 15
175. 3 r. red and blue .. 30 20
176. 7 r. 50 red and blue .. 75 45

**43.** Prince Norodom Sihanouk.

**44.** Weaving.

**1964.** 10th Anniv of Foundation of Sangkum (Popular Socialist Community).

177. **43.** 2 r. violet .. .. 25 20
178. 3 r. brown .. .. 35 30
179. 10 r. blue .. .. 70 55

**1965.** Native Handicrafts.

180. **44.** 1 r. vio., brn. & bistre 25 25
181. – 3 r. brown, green & pur. 45 35
182. – 5 r. red, purple & green 75 50

DESIGNS: 3 r. Engraving. 5 r. Basket-making.

**1965.** Indo-Chinese People's Conference. Nos. 178/9 optd **CONFERENCE DES PEUPLES INDOCHINOIS**.

183 43 3 r. brown .. .. 40 35
184 10 r. blue .. .. 60 45

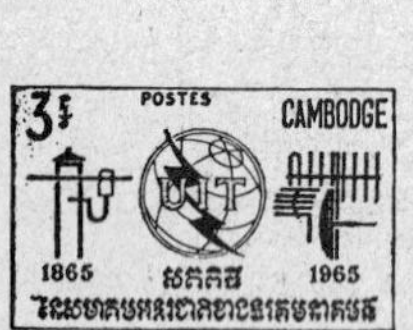


**46.** I.T.U. Emblem and Symbols.

**47.** Cotton.

**1965.** Centenary of I.T.U.

185. **46.** 3 r. bistre and green .. 35 30
186. 4 r. blue and red .. 45 30
187. 10 r. purple and violet .. 70 60

**1965.** Industrial Plants. Multicoloured.

188. 1 r. 50 Type **47** .. 30 20
189. 3 r. Groundnuts .. 45 25
190. 7 r. 50 Coconut palms .. 70 50

**48.** Preah Ko.

**1966.** Cambodian Temples.

191 48 3 r. green, turq & brn .. 50 30
192 – 5 r. brown, green & pur 60 40
193 – 7 r. brown, grn & ochre 80 50
194 – 9 r. purple, green & blue 1·25 70
195 – 12 r. red, green and vermilion .. .. 1·90 1·40

TEMPLES: 5 r. Baksei Chamkrong. 7 r. Banteay Srei. 9 r. Angkor Vat. 12 r. Bayon.

**49.** W.H.O. Building.

**50.** Tree-planting.

**1966.** Inauguration of W.H.O. Headquarters, Geneva.

196. **49.** 2 r. multicoloured .. 30 15
197. 3 r. multicoloured .. 35 25
198. 5 r. multicoloured .. 55 35

**1966.** Tree Day.

199 **50** 1 r. brown, grn & dp brn 20 15
200 3 r. brown, green & orge 35 25
201 7 r. brown, green & grey 60 40

**51.** U.N.E.S.C.O. Emblem.

**52.** Stadium.

**1966.** 20th Anniv. of U.N.E.S.C.O.

202. **51.** 3 r. multicoloured .. 35 25
203. 7 r. multicoloured .. 45 35

**1966.** "Ganefo" Games, Phnom Penh.

204. **52.** 3 r. blue .. .. 25 20
205. – 4 r. green .. .. 35 25
206. – 7 r. red .. .. 50 40
207. – 10 r. brown .. .. 70 60

DESIGNS: 4 r., 7 r., 10 r. Various bas-reliefs of ancient sports from Angkor Vat.

**53.** Wild Boar.

**56.** Ballet Dancer.

**1967.** Fauna.

208. **53.** 3 r. black, green & blue 50 25
209. – 5 r. multicoloured .. 60 30
210. – 7 r. multicoloured .. 90 50

FAUNA—VERT. 5 r. Hog-deer. HORIZ 7 r. Indian elephant.

**1967.** Int Tourist Year. Nos. 191/2, 194/5 and 149 optd **ANNEE INTERNATIONALE DU TOURISME 1967**.

211 48 3 r. green, turq & brn .. 45 35
212 5 r. brown, green & pur 55 35
213 – 9 r. purple, green & blue 65 55
214 – 12 r. red, grn & verm .. 90 70
215 33 15 r. brown, blue & grn 1·10 90

**1967.** Millenary of Banteay Srei Temple. No. 193 optd **MILLENAIRE DE BANTEAY SREI 967–1967**.

216 – 7 r. brown, green & ochre 50 35

**1967.** Cambodian Royal Ballet. Designs showing ballet dancers.

217. **56.** 1 r. orange .. .. 25 20
218. – 3 r. blue .. .. 40 30
219. – 5 r. blue .. .. 50 35
220. – 7 r. red .. .. 60 45
221. – 10 r. multicoloured .. 1·10 60

**1967.** Int Literacy Day. Surch **Journee Internationale de l'Alphabetisation 8–9–67** and new value.

222 37 6 r. on 12 r. bl, grn & red 50 35
223 15 7 r. on 15 r. brown & grn 60 40

**58.** Decade Emblem.

**59.** Royal University of Kompong-Cham.

**1967.** Int Hydrological Decade.

224 58 1 r. orange, blue & black 20 15
225 6 r. orange, blue & violet 40 30
226 10 r. orge, lt grn & grn 65 45

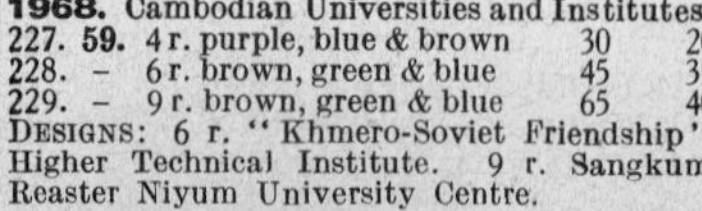

**1968.** Cambodian Universities and Institutes.

227. **59.** 4 r. purple, blue & brown 30 20
228. – 6 r. brown, green & blue 45 35
229. – 9 r. brown, green & blue 65 40

DESIGNS: 6 r. "Khmero-Soviet Friendship" Higher Technical Institute. 9 r. Sangkum Reaster Niyum University Centre.

**60.** Doctor tending child.

**1968.** 20th Anniv. of W.H.O.

230. **60.** 3 r. blue .. .. 30 20
231. – 7 r. blue .. .. 40 35

DESIGN: 7 r. Man using insecticide.

**61.** Stadium.

**1968.** Olympic Games, Mexico.

232. **61.** 1 r. brown, green & red 25 20
233. – 2 r. brown, red & blue .. 35 20
234. – 3 r. brn., blue & purple 40 25
235. – 5 r. violet .. .. 45 30
236. – 7 r. 50, brn., grn. & red 55 40

DESIGNS—HORIZ. 2 r. Wrestling. 3 r. Cycling. VERT. 5 r. Boxing. 7 r. 50, Runner with torch.

**62.** Stretcher-party.

**1968.** Cambodian Red Cross Fortnight.

237. **62.** 3 r. red, green & blue .. 40 25

**63.** Prince Norodom Sihanouk.

**1968.** 15th Anniv. of Independence.

238. **63.** 7 r. violet, green & blue 35 35
239. – 8 r. brown, green & blue 45 45

DESIGN: 8 r. Soldiers wading through stream.

**64.** Human Rights Emblem and Prince Norodom Sihanouk.

**1968.** Human Rights Year.

240. **64.** 3 r. blue .. .. 30 20
241. 5 r. purple .. .. 35 20
242. 7 r. black, orge. & grn. 65 30

**65.** I.L.O. Emblem.

**1969.** 50th Anniv. of I.L.O.

243. **65.** 3 r. blue .. .. 25 15
244. 6 r. red .. .. 40 20
245. 9 r. green .. .. 60 35

**66.** Red Cross Emblems around Globe.

**1969.** 50th Anniv. of League of Red Cross Societies.

246. **66.** 1 r. multicoloured .. 25 15
247. 3 r. multicoloured .. 30 20
248. 10 r. multicoloured .. 65 35

**67.** Golden Birdwing.

**1969.** Butterflies.

249 67 3 r. black, yellow & vio 70 45
250 – 4 r. black, green & verm 75 50
251 – 8 r. black, orange & grn 1·25 90

DESIGNS: 4 r. Tailed jay. 8 r. Orange tiger.

**68.** Diesel Train and Route Map.

**1969.** Opening of Phnom Penh–Sihanoukville Railway.

252 68 3 r. multicoloured .. 80 55
253 – 6 r. brown, black & grn 95 65
254 – 8 r. black .. 1·60 1·10
255 – 9 r. blue, turq & grn .. 1·60 1·10

DESIGNS: 6 r. Phnom Penh Station. 8 r. Diesel locomotive and rural station. 9 r. Steam locomotive at Sihanoukville Station.

**69.** Triple Tail.

**1970.** Fishes. Multicoloured.

256. 3 r. Type **69** .. .. 40 25
257. 7 r. Marbled Goby .. 80 50
258. 9 r. Striped Snakehead .. 1·25 60

**70.** Vat Tepthidaram.

**71.** Dish Aerial and Open Book.

**1970.** Buddhist Monasteries in Cambodia. Multicoloured.

259 2 r. Type **70** .. .. 20 15
260 3 r. Vat Maniratanaram (horiz) .. .. 25 15
261 6 r. Vat Patumavati (horiz) 45 20
262 8 r. Vat Unnalom (horiz) 55 40

**1970.** World Telecommunications Day.

263. **71.** 3 r. multicoloured .. 20 10
264. 4 r. multicoloured .. 30 15
265. 9 r. multicoloured .. 50 30

**72.** New Headquarters Building.

**1970.** Opening of New U.P.U. Headquarters Building, Berne.

266. **72.** 1 r. multicoloured .. 20 10
267. 3 r. multicoloured .. 25 15
268. 4 r. multicoloured .. 40 25
269. 10 r. multicoloured .. 65 35

**73.** "Nelumbium speciosum".

**1970.** Aquatic Plants. Multicoloured.

270 3 r. Type **73** .. .. 45 15
271 4 r. "Eichhornia crassipes" 70 20
272 13 r. "Nymphea lotus" .. 1·25 50

**74.** "Banteay-srei" (bas-relief).

**1970.** World Meteorological Day.

273. **74.** 3 r. red and green .. 20 10
274. 4 r. red, green and blue 30 15
275. 7 r. green, blue and black 40 20

75. Rocket, Dove and Globe.

**1970.** 25th Anniv. of United Nations.

| | | | | |
|---|---|---|---|---|
| 276. | 75. | 3 r. multicoloured .. | 20 | 15 |
| 277. | | 5 r. multicoloured .. | 40 | 20 |
| 278. | | 10 r. multicoloured .. | 60 | 40 |

76. I.E.Y. Emblem.

**1970.** International Education Year.

| | | | | |
|---|---|---|---|---|
| 279. | 76. | 1 r. blue .. .. | 15 | 10 |
| 280. | | 3 r. purple .. .. | 20 | 15 |
| 281. | | 8 r. green .. .. | 45 | 20 |

77. Samdech Chuon Nath.

**1971.** 2nd Death Anniv of Samdech Chuon-Nath (Khmer language scholar).

| | | | | |
|---|---|---|---|---|
| 282. | 77. | 3 r. multicoloured .. | 15 | 15 |
| 283. | | 8 r. multicoloured .. | 45 | 20 |
| 284. | | 9 r. multicoloured .. | 55 | 30 |

For issues between 1971 and 1989 see under KHMER REPUBLIC and KAMPUCHEA in volume 2.

203 17th-century Coach

**1989.** Coaches. Multicoloured.

| | | | |
|---|---|---|---|
| 1020 | 2 r. Type **203** .. .. | 10 | 10 |
| 1021 | 3 r. Paris–Lyon coach, 1720 .. .. | 20 | 10 |
| 1022 | 5 r. Mail coach, 1793 .. | 30 | 10 |
| 1023 | 10 r. Light mail coach, 1805 .. .. | 65 | 20 |
| 1024 | 15 r. Royal mail coach .. | 1·00 | 30 |
| 1025 | 20 r. Russian mail coach | 1·25 | 40 |
| 1026 | 35 r. Paris–Lille coupe, 1837 (vert) .. .. | 2·40 | 70 |

204 "Papilio zagreus"

**1989.** "Brasiliana 89" International Stamp Exn, Rio de Janeiro. Butterflies. Mult.

| | | | |
|---|---|---|---|
| 1028 | 2 r. Type **204** .. .. | 10 | 10 |
| 1029 | 3 r. "Morpho catenarius" | 20 | 10 |
| 1030 | 5 r. "Morpho aega" .. | 30 | 10 |
| 1031 | 10 r. "Callithea sapphira" ("wrongly inscr "saphhira") .. .. | 65 | 20 |
| 1032 | 15 r. "Catagramma sorana" .. .. | 1·00 | 30 |
| 1033 | 20 r. "Pierella nereis" .. | 1·25 | 40 |
| 1034 | 35 r. "Papilio brasiliensis" | 2·40 | 70 |



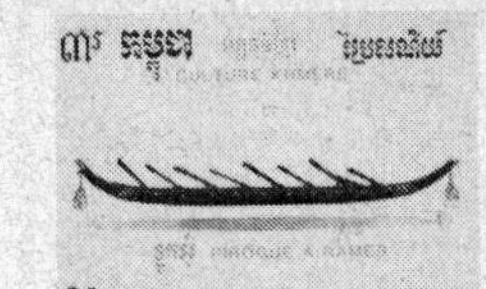


205 Pirogue

**1989.** Khmer Culture. Multicoloured.

| | | | |
|---|---|---|---|
| 1036 | 3 r. Type **205** .. .. | 25 | 10 |
| 1037 | 12 r. Pirogue (two sets of oars) .. .. .. | 90 | 30 |
| 1038 | 30 r. Pirogue with cabin | 2·40 | 70 |

206 Youth 207 Goalkeeper

**1989.** National Development. Multicoloured.

| | | | |
|---|---|---|---|
| 1039 | 3 r. Type **206** .. .. | 25 | 10 |
| 1040 | 12 r. Trade unions emblem (horiz) .. | 90 | 30 |
| 1041 | 30 r. National Front emblem (horiz) .. | 2·40 | 70 |

**1990.** World Cup Football Championship, Italy. Multicoloured.

| | | | |
|---|---|---|---|
| 1042 | 2 r. Type **207** .. .. | 10 | 10 |
| 1043 | 3 r. Dribbling ball .. | 20 | 10 |
| 1044 | 5 r. Controlling ball with thigh .. .. | 30 | 10 |
| 1045 | 10 r. Running with ball .. | 65 | 20 |
| 1046 | 15 r. Shooting .. .. | 1·00 | 30 |
| 1047 | 20 r. Tackling .. .. | 1·25 | 40 |
| 1048 | 35 r. Tackling (different) | 2·40 | 70 |

208 Two-horse Postal Van

**1990.** "Stamp World London 90" International Stamp Exhibition. Royal Mail Horse-drawn Transport. Multicoloured.

| | | | |
|---|---|---|---|
| 1050 | 2 r. Type **208** .. .. | 10 | 10 |
| 1051 | 3 r. One-horse cart .. | 20 | 10 |
| 1052 | 5 r. Rural post office cart | 30 | 10 |
| 1053 | 10 r. Rural post office van | 65 | 20 |
| 1054 | 15 r. Local post office van | 1·00 | 30 |
| 1055 | 20 r. Parcel-post cart .. | 1·25 | 40 |
| 1056 | 35 r. Two-horse wagon .. | 2·40 | 70 |

209 Rice Grains 210 Shooting

**1990.** Cultivation of Rice. Multicoloured.

| | | | |
|---|---|---|---|
| 1058 | 3 r. Type **209** .. .. | 25 | 10 |
| 1059 | 12 r. Transporting rice (horiz) .. .. | 90 | 30 |
| 1060 | 30 r. Threshing rice .. | 2·40 | 70 |

**1990.** Olympic Games, Barcelona (1992) (1st issue). Multicoloured.

| | | | |
|---|---|---|---|
| 1061 | 2 r. Type **210** .. .. | 10 | 10 |
| 1062 | 3 r. Putting the shot .. | 20 | 10 |
| 1063 | 5 r. Weightlifting .. | 30 | 10 |
| 1064 | 10 r. Boxing .. .. | 65 | 20 |
| 1065 | 15 r. Pole vaulting .. | 1·00 | 30 |
| 1066 | 20 r. Basketball .. .. | 1·25 | 40 |
| 1067 | 35 r. Fencing .. .. | 2·40 | 70 |

See also Nos. 1163/9, 1208/12 and 1241/5.

211 Four-man Bobsleighing

**1990.** Winter Olympic Games, Albertville (1992) (1st issue). Multicoloured.

| | | | |
|---|---|---|---|
| 1069 | 2 r. Type **211** .. .. | 10 | 10 |
| 1070 | 3 r. Speed skating .. | 20 | 10 |
| 1071 | 5 r. Figure skating .. | 30 | 10 |
| 1072 | 10 r. Ice hockey .. .. | 65 | 20 |
| 1073 | 15 r. Biathlon .. .. | 1·00 | 30 |
| 1074 | 20 r. Lugeing .. .. | 1·25 | 40 |
| 1075 | 35 r. Ski jumping .. | 2·40 | 70 |

See also Nos. 1152/8.

212 Facade of Banteay Srei

**1990.** Khmer Culture. Multicoloured.

| | | | |
|---|---|---|---|
| 1077 | 3 r. Type **212** .. .. | 25 | 10 |
| 1078 | 12 r. Ox-carts (12th-century relief) .. | 90 | 30 |
| 1079 | 30 r. Banon ruins (36×21 mm) .. .. | 2·40 | 70 |

213 "Zizina oxleyi"

**1990.** "New Zealand 1990" International Stamp Exn, Auckland. Butterflies. Mult.

| | | | |
|---|---|---|---|
| 1080 | 2 r. Type **213** .. .. | 10 | 10 |
| 1081 | 3 r. "Cupha prosope" .. | 10 | 10 |
| 1082 | 5 r. "Heteronympha merope" .. .. | 25 | 10 |
| 1083 | 10 r. "Dodonidia helmsi" | 50 | 15 |
| 1084 | 15 r. "Argirophenga antipodum" .. .. | 90 | 30 |
| 1085 | 20 r. "Tysonotis danis" | 1·40 | 45 |
| 1086 | 35 r. "Pyrameis gonnarilla" .. .. | 2·10 | 70 |

214 "Vostok"

**1990.** Spacecraft. Multicoloured.

| | | | |
|---|---|---|---|
| 1088 | 2 r. Type **214** .. .. | 15 | 10 |
| 1089 | 3 r. "Soyuz" .. .. | 20 | 10 |
| 1090 | 5 r. Satellite .. .. | 35 | 10 |
| 1091 | 10 r. "Luna 10" .. .. | 75 | 25 |
| 1092 | 15 r. "Mars 1" .. .. | 1·10 | 40 |
| 1093 | 20 r. "Venus 3" .. .. | 1·50 | 50 |
| 1094 | 35 r. "Mir" space station | 2·50 | 95 |

215 Poodle

**1990.** Dogs. Multicoloured.

| | | | |
|---|---|---|---|
| 1096 | 20 c. Type **215** .. .. | 10 | 10 |
| 1097 | 80 c. Shetland sheepdog | 10 | 10 |
| 1098 | 3 r. Samoyede .. .. | 25 | 10 |
| 1099 | 6 r. Springer spaniel .. | 50 | 15 |
| 1100 | 10 r. Wire-haired fox terrier .. .. | 90 | 30 |
| 1101 | 15 r. Afghan hound .. | 1·40 | 45 |
| 1102 | 25 r. Dalmatian .. .. | 2·10 | 70 |

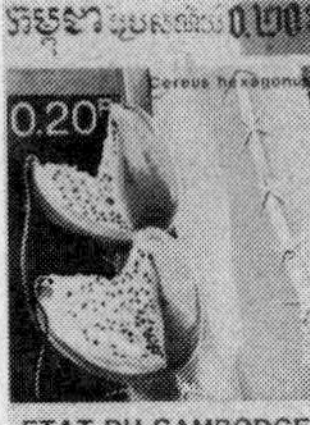

216 "Cereus hexagonus" 217 Learning to Write

**1990.** Cacti. Mulicoloured.

| | | | |
|---|---|---|---|
| 1104 | 20 c. Type **216** .. .. | 10 | 10 |
| 1105 | 80 c. "Arthrocereus rondonianus" .. .. | 10 | 10 |
| 1106 | 3 r. "Matucana multicolor" .. .. | 25 | 10 |
| 1107 | 6 r. "Hildewintera aureispina" .. .. | 50 | 15 |
| 1108 | 10 r. "Opuntia retrosa" .. | 90 | 30 |
| 1109 | 15 r. "Erdisia tenuicula" | 1·40 | 45 |
| 1110 | 25 r. "Mamillaria yaquensis" .. .. | 2·10 | 70 |

**1990.** International Literacy Year.

| | | | | |
|---|---|---|---|---|
| 1111 | 217 | 3 r. black and blue .. | 25 | 10 |
| 1112 | | 12 r. black and yellow | 95 | 30 |
| 1113 | | 30 r. black and pink | 2·50 | 70 |

218 English Nef, 1200

**1990.** Ships. Multicoloured.

| | | | |
|---|---|---|---|
| 1114 | 20 c. Type **218** .. .. | 10 | 10 |
| 1115 | 80 c. 16th-century Spanish galleon .. .. | 10 | 10 |
| 1116 | 3 r. Dutch jacht, 1627 .. | 25 | 10 |
| 1117 | 6 r. "La Couronne" (warship), 1638 .. | 50 | 15 |
| 1118 | 10 r. Dumont d'Urville's ship "L'Astrolabe", 1826 .. .. | 90 | 30 |
| 1119 | 15 r. "Louisiane" (steamer), 1864 .. | 1·40 | 45 |
| 1120 | 25 r. Clipper, 1900 (vert) | 2·10 | 70 |

No. 1118 is wrongly inscribed "d'Uville".

219 Phnom-Penh–Kampong Som Railway

**1990.** National Development. Multicoloured.

| | | | |
|---|---|---|---|
| 1122 | 3 r. Type **219** .. .. | 25 | 10 |
| 1123 | 12 r. Port, Kampong Som | 95 | 30 |
| 1124 | 30 r. Fishing boats, Kampong Som .. | 2·50 | 70 |

220 Sacre-Coeur de Montmartre and White Bishop 221 Columbus

**1990.** "Paris '90" World Chess Championship, Paris. Multicoloured.

1125 2 r. Type **220** .. .. 15 10
1126 3 r. "The Horse Trainer" (statue) and white knight .. .. 25 10
1127 5 r. "Victory of Samothrace" (statue) and white queen .. 40 10
1128 10 r. Azay-le-Rideau Chateau and white rook 80 25
1129 15 r. "The Dance" (statue) and white pawn .. .. 1·25 40
1130 20 r. Eiffel Tower and white king .. .. 1·60 50
1131 35 r. Arc de Triomphe and black chessmen .. 2·75 95

**1990.** 500th Anniv (1992) of Discovery of America by Columbus (1st issue). Mult.

1133 2 r. Type **221** .. .. 15 10
1134 3 r. Queen Isabella's jewel-chest .. .. 20 10
1135 5 r. Queen Isabella the Catholic .. .. 35 10
1136 10 r. "Santa Maria" (flagship) .. .. 75 25
1137 15 r. Juan de la Cosa .. 1·10 40
1138 20 r. Monument to Columbus .. .. 1·50 50
1139 35 r. Devin Pyramid, Yucatan .. .. 2·50 95

See also Nos. 1186/92.

222 Tyre Factory

223 Tackle

**1991.** National Festival. Multicoloured.

1141 100 r. Type **222** .. .. 55 25
1142 300 r. Rural hospital .. 1·60 75
1143 500 r. Freshwater fishing (27 × 40 mm) .. .. 2·75 1·25

**1991.** World Cup Football Championship, U.S.A. (1994) (1st issue).

1144 **223** 5 r. multicoloured .. 10 10
1145 – 25 r. multicoloured .. 10 10
1146 – 70 r. multicoloured .. 30 10
1147 – 100 r. multicoloured 40 15
1148 – 200 r. multicoloured 85 25
1149 – 400 r. multicoloured 1·60 45
1150 – 1000 r. multicoloured 4·25 1·25

DESIGNS: 25 r. to 1000 r. Different footballing scenes.

See also Nos. 1220/4, 1317/21 and 1381/5.

224 Speed Skating

**1991.** Winter Olympic Games, Albertville (1992) (2nd issue). Multicoloured.

1152 5 r. Type **224** .. .. 10 10
1153 25 r. Slalom skiing .. 10 10
1154 70 r. Ice hockey .. .. 30 10
1155 100 r. Bobsleighing .. 40 15
1156 200 r. Freestyle skiing .. 85 25
1157 400 r. Ice skating .. 1·60 45
1158 1000 r. Downhill skiing .. 4·25 1·25

225 "Torso of Vishnu Reclining" (11th cent)

**1991.** Sculpture. Multicoloured.

1160 100 r. "Garuda" (Koh Ker, 10th century) .. 55 25
1161 300 r. Type **225** .. 1·60 75
1162 500 r. "Reclining Nandin" (7th century) .. .. 2·75 1·25

226 Pole Vaulting

**1991.** Olympic Games, Barcelona (1992) (2nd issue). Multicoloured.

1163 5 r. Type **226** .. .. 10 10
1164 25 r. Table tennis .. 10 10
1165 70 r. Running .. .. 30 10
1166 100 r. Wrestling .. .. 40 15
1167 200 r. Gymnastics (bars) 85 25
1168 400 r. Tennis .. .. 1·60 45
1169 1000 r. Boxing .. .. 4·25 1·25

227 Douglas DC-10-30

**1991.** Airplanes. Multicoloured.

1171 5 r. Type **227** .. .. 10 10
1172 25 r. McDonnell Douglas MD-11 .. .. 10 10
1173 70 r. Ilyushin Il-96-300 .. 30 10
1174 100 r. Airbus Industrie A310 .. .. 40 15
1175 200 r. Yakovlev Yak-42 .. 85 25
1176 400 r. Tupolev Tu-154 .. 1·60 45
1177 1000 r. Douglas DC-9 .. 4·25 1·25

228 Diaguita Funerary Urn, Catamarca

**1991.** "Espamer '91" Iberia–Latin America Stamp Exhibition, Buenos Aires. Mult.

1178 5 r. Bareales glass pot, Catamarca (horiz) .. 10 10
1179 25 r. Type **228** .. .. 10 10
1180 70 r. Quiroga urn, Tucuman .. .. 30 10
1181 100 r. Round glass pot, Santiago del Estero (horiz) .. .. 40 15
1182 200 r. Pitcher, Santiago del Estero (horiz) .. 85 25
1183 400 r. Diaguita funerary urn, Tucuman .. 1·60 45
1184 1000 r. Bareales funerary urn, Catamarca (horiz) 4·25 1·25

229 "Pinta"

**1991.** 500th Anniv (1992) of Discovery of America by Columbus (2nd issue). Each brown, stone and black.

1186 5 r. Type **229** .. .. 10 10
1187 25 r. "Nina" .. .. 10 10
1188 70 r. "Santa Maria" .. 30 10
1189 100 r. Landing at Guanahani, 1492 (horiz) 40 15
1190 200 r. Meeting of two cultures (horiz) .. 85 25
1191 400 r. La Navidad (first European settlement in America) (horiz) .. 1·60 45
1192 1000 r. Amerindian village (horiz) .. .. 4·25 1·25

230 "Neptis pryeri"

**1991.** "Phila Nippon '91" International Stamp Exn, Tokyo. Butterflies. Mult.

1194 5 r. Type **230** .. .. 10 10
1195 25 r. "Papilio xuthus" .. 10 10
1196 70 r. Common map butterfly .. .. 30 10
1197 100 r. "Argynnis anadiomene" .. .. 40 15
1198 200 r. "Lethe marginalis" 85 25
1199 400 r. "Artopoetes pryeri" 1·60 45
1200 1000 r. "African monarch 4·25 1·25

231 Coastal Fishing Port

**1991.** National Development. Food Industry. Multicoloured.

1202 100 r. Type **231** .. .. 55 25
1203 300 r. Preparing palm sugar (29 × 40 mm) .. 1·60 75
1204 500 r. Picking peppers .. 2·75 1·25

232 Chakdomuk Costumes

233 Wrestling

**1992.** National Festival. Traditional Costumes. Multicoloured.

1205 150 r. Type **232** .. .. 55 30
1206 350 r. Longvek .. .. 1·25 70
1207 1000 r. Angkor .. .. 3·50 1·25

**1992.** Olympic Games, Barcelona (3rd issue). Multicoloured.

1208 5 r. Type **233** .. .. 10 10
1209 15 r. Football .. .. 10 10
1210 80 r. Weightlifting .. 20 10
1211 400 r. Archery .. .. 1·10 35
1212 1500 r. Gymnastics .. 4·25 1·40

234 Neon Tetra

**1992.** Fishes. Multicoloured.

1214 5 r. Type **234** .. .. 10 10
1215 15 r. Siamese fighting fish 10 10
1216 80 r. Kaiser tetra .. 20 10
1217 400 r. Dwarf gourami .. 1·10 35
1218 1500 r. Catfish .. .. 4·25 1·40

235 Germany v Columbia

236 Monument

**1992.** World Cup Football Championship, U.S.A. (1994) (2nd issue). Multicoloured.

1220 5 r. Type **235** .. .. 10 10
1221 15 r. Netherlands player (horiz) .. .. 10 10
1222 80 r. Uruguay v C.I.S. (ex-Soviet states) .. 20 10
1223 400 r. Cameroun v Yugoslavia .. .. 1·10 35
1224 1500 r. Italy v Sweden .. 4·25 1·40

**1992.** Khmer Culture. 19th-cent Architecture. Multicoloured.

1226 150 r. Type **236** .. .. 55 30
1227 350 r. Stupa .. .. 1·25 70
1228 1000 r. Mandapa library 3·50 1·25

237 Motor Car

**1992.** 540th Birth Anniv (1992) of Leonardo da Vinci (artist and inventor). Multicoloured.

1229 5 r. Type **237** .. .. 10 10
1230 15 r. Container ship .. 10 10
1231 80 r. Helicopter .. .. 20 10
1232 400 r. Scuba diver .. 1·10 35
1233 1500 r. Parachutists (vert) 4·25 1·40

238 Juan de la Cierva and Autogyro

**1992.** "Expo '92" World's Fair, Seville. Inventors. Multicoloured.

1235 5 r. Type **238** .. .. 10 10
1236 15 r. Thomas Edison and electric light bulb .. 10 10
1237 80 r. Samuel Morse and Morse telegraph .. 20 10
1238 400 r. Narciso Monturiol and submarine .. 1·10 35
1239 1500 r. Alexander Graham Bell and early telephone .. .. 4·25 1·40

239 Weightlifting

**1992.** Olympic Games, Barcelona (4th issue). Multicoloured.

1241 5 r. Type **239** .. .. 10 10
1242 15 r. Boxing .. .. 10 10
1243 80 r. Basketball .. .. 20 10
1244 400 r. Running .. .. 1·00 35
1245 1500 r. Water polo .. 4·00 1·40

240 Palm Trees

**1992.** Environmental Protection. Mult.

1247 5 r. Couple on riverside .. 10 10
1248 15 r. Pagoda .. .. 10 10
1249 80 r. Type **240** .. .. 20 10
1250 400 r. Boy riding water buffalo .. .. 1·00 35
1251 1500 r. Swimming in river 4·00 1·40

241 Louis de Bougainville and "La Boudeuse"

242 "Albatrellus confluens"

**1992.** "Genova '92" International Thematic Stamp Exhibition, Genoa. Multicoloured.

| | | | |
|---|---|---|---|
| 1253 | 5 r. Type **241** . . . . | 10 | 10 |
| 1254 | 15 r. James Cook and H.M.S. "Endeavour" | 10 | 10 |
| 1255 | 80 r. Charles Darwin and H.M.S. "Beagle" . . | 20 | 10 |
| 1256 | 400 r. Jacques Cousteau and "Calypso" . . | 1·00 | 35 |
| 1257 | 1500 r. Thor Heyerdahl and "Kon Tiki" . . | 4·00 | 1·40 |

**1992.** Fungi. Multicoloured.

| | | | |
|---|---|---|---|
| 1259 | 5 r. Type **242** . . . . | 10 | 10 |
| 1260 | 15 r. Scarlet-stemmed boletus . . . . | 10 | 10 |
| 1261 | 80 r. Verdigris agaric . . | 30 | 10 |
| 1262 | 400 r. "Telamonia armillata" . . . . | 1·50 | 60 |
| 1263 | 1500 r. Goaty smell cortinarius . . . . | 6·00 | 2·00 |

243 Bellanca Pacemaker Seaplane, 1930

**1992.** Aircraft. Multicoloured.

| | | | |
|---|---|---|---|
| 1264 | 5 r. Type **243** . . . . | 10 | 10 |
| 1265 | 15 r. Canadair CL-215 fire-fighting amphibian, 1965 . . . . | 10 | 10 |
| 1266 | 80 r. Grumman G-21 Goose amphibian, 1937 | 20 | 10 |
| 1267 | 400 r. Grumman SA-6 Sealand flying boat, 1947 . . . . | 95 | 30 |
| 1268 | 1500 r. Short S.23 Empire "C" Class flying boat, 1936 . . . . | 3·75 | 1·00 |

244 Dish Aerial

**1992.** National Development. Multicoloured.

| | | | |
|---|---|---|---|
| 1270 | 150 r. Type **244** . . . . | 40 | 20 |
| 1271 | 350 r. Dish aerial, flags and satellite . . . . | 90 | 45 |
| 1272 | 1000 r. Hotel Cambodiana | 2·25 | 1·10 |

245 Sociological Institute

**1993.** National Festival. Multicoloured.

| | | | |
|---|---|---|---|
| 1273 | 50 r. Type **245** . . . . | 15 | 10 |
| 1274 | 450 r. Motel Cambodiana | 1·00 | 50 |
| 1275 | 1000 r. Theatre, Bassac . . | 2·25 | 1·10 |

**HAVE YOU READ THE NOTES AT THE BEGINNING OF THIS CATALOGUE?**
These often provide answers to the enquiries we receive.

246 Bottle-nosed Dolphin and Submarine

**1993.** Wildlife and Technology. Mult.

| | | | |
|---|---|---|---|
| 1276 | 150 r. Type **246** . . . . | 40 | 10 |
| 1277 | 200 r. Supersonic jet airplane and Kleinschmidt's falcon | 50 | 10 |
| 1278 | 250 r. Eurasian beaver and dam . . . . | 65 | 15 |
| 1279 | 500 r. Satellite and Natterer's bat . . | 1·25 | 30 |
| 1280 | 900 r. Rufous humming-bird and helicopter . . | 2·25 | 55 |

247 "Datura suaveolens"

**1993.** Wild Flowers. Multicoloured.

| | | | |
|---|---|---|---|
| 1281 | 150 r. Type **247** . . . . | 40 | 10 |
| 1282 | 200 r. "Convolvulus tricolor" . . . . | 50 | 10 |
| 1283 | 250 r. "Hippeastrum" hybrid . . . . | 65 | 15 |
| 1284 | 500 r. "Camellia" hybrid | 1·25 | 30 |
| 1285 | 900 r. "Lilium speciosum" | 2·25 | 55 |

248 Vihear Temple

**1993.** Khmer Culture. Multicoloured.

| | | | |
|---|---|---|---|
| 1287 | 50 r. Sculpture of ox . . | 15 | 1C |
| 1288 | 450 r. Type **248** . . . . | 1·10 | 20 |
| 1289 | 1000 r. Offering to Buddha | 2·50 | 55 |

249 Philippine Flying Lemur

**1993.** Animals. Multicoloured.

| | | | |
|---|---|---|---|
| 1290 | 150 r. Type **249** . . . . | 40 | 10 |
| 1291 | 200 r. Red giant flying squirrel . . . . | 50 | 10 |
| 1292 | 250 r. Fringed gecko . . | 65 | 15 |
| 1293 | 500 r. Wallace's flying frog . . . . | 1·25 | 30 |
| 1294 | 900 r. Flying lizard . . | 2·25 | 55 |

250 "Symbrenthia hypselis"

**1993.** "Brasiliana '93" International Stamp Exn, Rio de Janeiro. Butterflies. Mult.

| | | | |
|---|---|---|---|
| 1295 | 250 r. Type **250** . . . . | 65 | 15 |
| 1296 | 350 r. "Sithon nedymond" | 90 | 20 |
| 1297 | 600 r. "Geitoneura minyas" . . . . | 1·50 | 35 |
| 1298 | 800 r. "Argyreus hyperbius" . . | 2·00 | 50 |
| 1299 | 1000 r. "Argyrophenga antipodum" . . | 2·50 | 60 |

251 Armed Cambodians reporting to U.N. Base

253 Santos-Dumont, Eiffel Tower and "Ballon No. 6", 1901

252 Venetian Felucca

**1993.** United Nations Transitional Authority in Cambodia Pacification Programme. Each black and blue.

| | | | |
|---|---|---|---|
| 1301 | 150 r. Type **251** . . . . | 40 | 10 |
| 1302 | 200 r. Military camp . . | 50 | 10 |
| 1303 | 250 r. Surrender of arms | 65 | 15 |
| 1304 | 500 r. Vocational training | 1·25 | 30 |
| 1305 | 900 r. Liberation . . | 2·25 | 50 |

**1993.** Sailing Ships. Multicoloured.

| | | | |
|---|---|---|---|
| 1307 | 150 r. Type **252** . . . . | 40 | 10 |
| 1308 | 200 r. Phoenician galley | 50 | 10 |
| 1309 | 250 r. Egyptian merchantman . . . . | 65 | 15 |
| 1310 | 500 r. Genoese merchantman . . . . | 1·25 | 30 |
| 1311 | 900 r. English merchantman . . . . | 2·25 | 50 |

**1993.** 120th Birth Anniv of Alberto Santos-Dumont (aviator). Multicoloured.

| | | | |
|---|---|---|---|
| 1312 | 150 r. Type **253** . . . . | 40 | 10 |
| 1313 | 200 r. "14 bis" (biplane), 1906 (horiz) . . . . | 50 | 10 |
| 1314 | 250 r. "Demoiselle" (monoplane), 1909 (horiz) . . . . | 65 | 15 |
| 1315 | 500 r. Embraer EMB-201 A (horiz) . . | 1·25 | 30 |
| 1316 | 900 r. Embraer EMB-111 (horiz) . . . . | 2·25 | 50 |

254 Footballer

**1993.** World Cup Football Championship, U.S.A. (1994) (3rd issue).

| | | | | |
|---|---|---|---|---|
| 1317 | **254** | 250 r. multicoloured | 65 | 10 |
| 1318 | – | 350 r. multicoloured | 90 | 15 |
| 1319 | – | 600 r. multicoloured | 1·50 | 30 |
| 1320 | – | 800 r. multicoloured | 2·00 | 40 |
| 1321 | – | 1000 r. mult (vert) . . | 2·50 | 50 |

DESIGNS: 350 r. to 1000 r. Various footballing scenes.

255 European Wigeon

**1993.** "Bangkok 1993" International Stamp Exhibition, Thailand. Ducks. Mult.

| | | | |
|---|---|---|---|
| 1323 | 250 r. Type **255** . . . . | 65 | 10 |
| 1324 | 350 r. Baikal teal . . | 90 | 15 |
| 1325 | 600 r. Mandarin . . . . | 1·50 | 30 |
| 1326 | 800 r. Wood duck . . | 2·00 | 40 |
| 1327 | 1000 r. Harlequin duck . . | 2·50 | 50 |

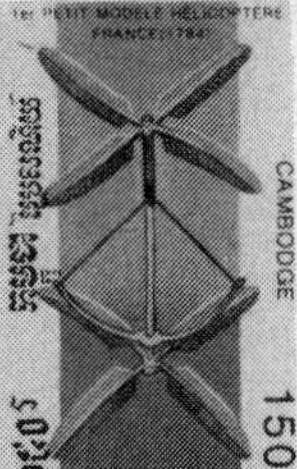
256 First Helicopter Model, France, 1784

257 "Cnaphalocrosis medinalis"

**1993.** Vertical Take-off Aircraft. Mult.

| | | | |
|---|---|---|---|
| 1329 | 150 r. Type **256** . . . . | 40 | 10 |
| 1330 | 200 r. Model of steam helicopter, 1863 . . | 50 | 10 |
| 1331 | 250 r. New York–Atlanta–Miami autogyro flight, 1927 (horiz) . . | 65 | 10 |
| 1332 | 500 r. Sikorsky helicopter, 1943 (horiz) . . . . | 1·25 | 20 |
| 1333 | 900 r. French vertical take-off jet . . . . | 2·25 | 40 |

**1993.** National Development. Harmful Insects. Multicoloured.

| | | | |
|---|---|---|---|
| 1335 | 50 r. Type **257** . . . . | 10 | 10 |
| 1336 | 450 r. Brown leaf-hopper | 1·10 | 15 |
| 1337 | 500 r. "Scirpophaga incertulas" . . . . | 1·25 | 20 |
| 1338 | 1000 r. Stalk-eyed fly . . | 2·50 | 40 |

258 Ministry of Posts and Telecommunications

**1993.** 40th Anniv of Independence.

| | | | | |
|---|---|---|---|---|
| 1340 | **258** | 300 r. multicoloured | 75 | 15 |
| 1341 | – | 500 r. multicoloured | 1·25 | 20 |
| 1342 | – | 700 r. blue, red & blk | 1·75 | 30 |

DESIGNS—VERT: 500 r. Independence monument. HORIZ: 700 r. National flag.

259 Boy with Pony

260 Figure Skating

**1993.** Figurines by M. J. Hummel. Mult.

| | | | |
|---|---|---|---|
| 1343 | 50 r. Type **259** . . . . | 10 | 10 |
| 1344 | 100 r. Girl and pram . . | 25 | 10 |
| 1345 | 150 r. Girl bathing doll . . | 40 | 10 |
| 1346 | 200 r. Girl holding doll . . | 50 | 10 |
| 1347 | 250 r. Boys playing . . | 65 | 10 |
| 1348 | 300 r. Girls pulling boy in cart . . . . | 75 | 15 |
| 1349 | 350 r. Girls playing ring-o-roses . . . . | 90 | 15 |
| 1350 | 600 r. Boys with stick and drum . . . . . . | 1·50 | 25 |

**1994.** Winter Olympic Games, Lillehammer, Norway. Multicoloured.

| | | | |
|---|---|---|---|
| 1351 | 150 r. Type **260** . . . . | 40 | 10 |
| 1352 | 250 r. Two-man luge (horiz) . . . . | 65 | 10 |
| 1353 | 400 r. Skiing (horiz) . . | 1·00 | 15 |
| 1354 | 700 r. Biathlon (horiz) . . | 1·75 | 30 |
| 1355 | 1000 r. Speed skating . . | 2·50 | 40 |

261 Opel, 1924

**1994.** Motor Cars. Multicoloured.

| | | | |
|---|---|---|---|
| 1357 | 150 r. Type **261** .. .. | 40 | 10 |
| 1358 | 200 r. Mercedes, 1901 .. | 50 | 10 |
| 1359 | 250 r. Ford Model "T", 1927 .. .. | 65 | 10 |
| 1360 | 500 r. Rolls Royce, 1907 | 1·25 | 20 |
| 1361 | 900 r. Hutton, 1908 .. | 2·25 | 35 |

**262** Gymnastics

**263** Siva and Uma (10th century, Banteay Srei)

**1994.** Olympic Games, Atlanta (1996) (1st issue). Multicoloured.

| | | | |
|---|---|---|---|
| 1363 | 150 r. Type **262** .. .. | 40 | 10 |
| 1364 | 200 r. Football .. .. | 50 | 10 |
| 1365 | 250 r. Throwing the javelin .. .. | 65 | 10 |
| 1366 | 300 r. Canoeing .. .. | 75 | 15 |
| 1367 | 600 r. Running .. .. | 1·50 | 25 |
| 1368 | 1000 r. Diving (horiz) .. | 2·50 | 40 |

See also Nos. 1437/41 and 1495/1500.

**1994.** Khmer Culture. Statues. Mult.

| | | | |
|---|---|---|---|
| 1370 | 300 r. Type **263** .. .. | 75 | 15 |
| 1371 | 500 r. Vishnu (6th cent, Tvol Dai-Buon) | 1·25 | 20 |
| 1372 | 700 r. King Jayavarman VII (12th–13th century, Krol Romeas Angkor) | 1·75 | 30 |

**264** Olympic Flag

**1994.** Centenary of International Olympic Committee. Multicoloured.

| | | | |
|---|---|---|---|
| 1373 | 100 r. Type **264** .. .. | 25 | 10 |
| 1374 | 300 r. Flag and torch .. | 75 | 15 |
| 1375 | 600 r. Flag and Pierre de Coubertin (reviver of modern Olympic Games) .. .. | 1·50 | 25 |

**265** Mesonyx

**1994.** Prehistoric Animals. Multicoloured.

| | | | |
|---|---|---|---|
| 1376 | 150 r. Type **265** .. .. | 40 | 10 |
| 1377 | 250 r. Doedicurus .. | 65 | 10 |
| 1378 | 400 r. Mylodon .. .. | 1·00 | 15 |
| 1379 | 700 r. Uintatherium .. | 1·75 | 30 |
| 1380 | 1000 r. Hyrachyus .. | 2·50 | 40 |

**266** Players

**267** "Soldiers in Combat"

**1994.** World Cup Football Championship, U.S.A. (4th issue).

| | | | | |
|---|---|---|---|---|
| 1381 | **266** | 150 r. multicoloured | 40 | 10 |
| 1382 | – | 250 r. multicoloured | 65 | 10 |
| 1383 | – | 400 r. multicoloured | 1·00 | 15 |
| 1384 | – | 700 r. multicoloured | 1·75 | 30 |
| 1385 | – | 1000 r. multicoloured | 2·50 | 40 |

DESIGNS: 250 r. to 1000 r. Different footballing scenes.

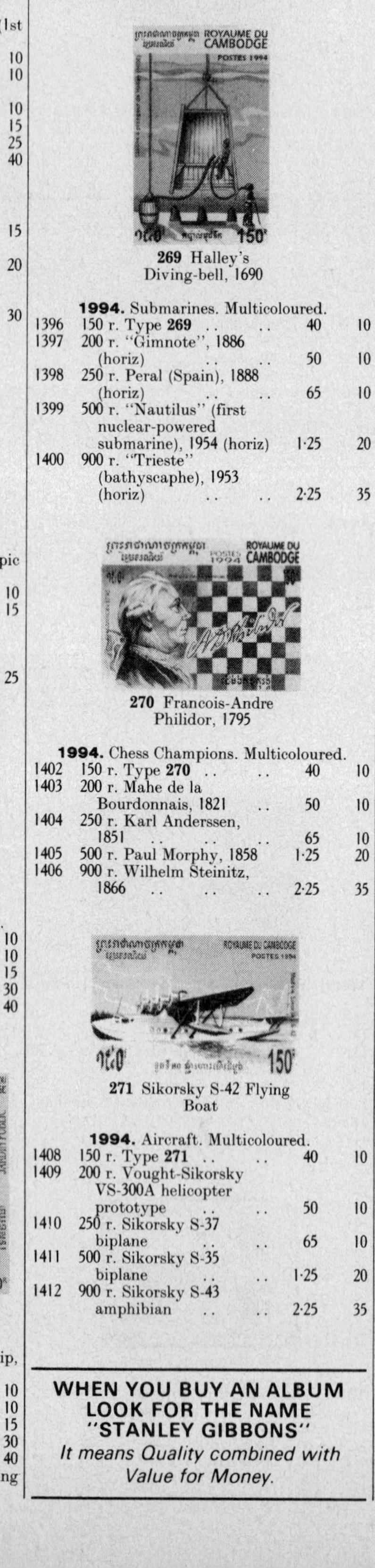

**1994.** Tourism. Statues in Public Gardens. Multicoloured.

| | | | |
|---|---|---|---|
| 1387 | 300 r. "Stag and Hind" .. | 75 | 15 |
| 1388 | 500 r. Type **267** .. .. | 1·25 | 20 |
| 1389 | 700 r. "Lions" .. .. | 1·75 | 30 |

**268** "Chlorophanus viridis"

**1994.** Beetles. Multicoloured.

| | | | |
|---|---|---|---|
| 1390 | 150 r. Type **268** .. .. | 40 | 10 |
| 1391 | 200 r. "Chrysochroa fulgidissima" .. .. | 50 | 10 |
| 1392 | 250 r. "Lytta vesicatoria" | 65 | 10 |
| 1393 | 500 r. "Purpuricenus kaehleri" .. .. | 1·25 | 20 |
| 1394 | 900 r. Herculese beetle .. | 2·25 | 25 |

**269** Halley's Diving-bell, 1690

**1994.** Submarines. Multicoloured.

| | | | |
|---|---|---|---|
| 1396 | 150 r. Type **269** .. .. | 40 | 10 |
| 1397 | 200 r. "Gimnote", 1886 (horiz) .. .. | 50 | 10 |
| 1398 | 250 r. Peral (Spain), 1888 (horiz) .. .. | 65 | 10 |
| 1399 | 500 r. "Nautilus" (first nuclear-powered submarine), 1954 (horiz) | 1·25 | 20 |
| 1400 | 900 r. "Trieste" (bathyscaphe), 1953 (horiz) .. .. | 2·25 | 35 |

**270** Francois-Andre Philidor, 1795

**1994.** Chess Champions. Multicoloured.

| | | | |
|---|---|---|---|
| 1402 | 150 r. Type **270** .. .. | 40 | 10 |
| 1403 | 200 r. Mahe de la Bourdonnais, 1821 .. | 50 | 10 |
| 1404 | 250 r. Karl Anderssen, 1851 .. .. .. | 65 | 10 |
| 1405 | 500 r. Paul Morphy, 1858 | 1·25 | 20 |
| 1406 | 900 r. Wilhelm Steinitz, 1866 .. .. .. | 2·25 | 35 |

**271** Sikorsky S-42 Flying Boat

**1994.** Aircraft. Multicoloured.

| | | | |
|---|---|---|---|
| 1408 | 150 r. Type **271** .. .. | 40 | 10 |
| 1409 | 200 r. Vought-Sikorsky VS-300A helicopter prototype .. .. | 50 | 10 |
| 1410 | 250 r. Sikorsky S-37 biplane .. .. | 65 | 10 |
| 1411 | 500 r. Sikorsky S-35 biplane .. .. | 1·25 | 20 |
| 1412 | 900 r. Sikorsky S-43 amphibian .. .. | 2·25 | 35 |

**272** Penduline Tit

**1994.** Birds. Multicoloured.

| | | | |
|---|---|---|---|
| 1414 | 150 r. Type **272** .. .. | 40 | 10 |
| 1415 | 250 r. Bearded reedling .. | 65 | 10 |
| 1416 | 400 r. Little bunting .. | 1·00 | 15 |
| 1417 | 700 r. Cirl bunting .. | 1·75 | 30 |
| 1418 | 1000 r. Goldcrest .. | 2·50 | 40 |

**273** Postal Service Float

**1994.** National Independence Festival. Mult.

| | | | |
|---|---|---|---|
| 1420 | 300 r. Type **273** .. .. | 80 | 15 |
| 1421 | 500 r. Soldiers marching | 1·40 | 25 |
| 1422 | 700 r. Women's army units on parade .. | 2·00 | 35 |

**274** Chruoi Changwar Bridge

**1994.** National Development. Multicoloured.

| | | | |
|---|---|---|---|
| 1423 | 300 r. Type **274** .. .. | 80 | 15 |
| 1424 | 500 r. Olympique Commercial Centre .. | 1·40 | 25 |
| 1425 | 700 r. Sakyamony Chedei Temple .. .. | 2·00 | 35 |

**275** Psittacosaurus

**1995.** Prehistoric Animals. Multicoloured.

| | | | |
|---|---|---|---|
| 1426 | 100 r. Type **275** .. .. | 30 | 10 |
| 1427 | 200 r. Protoceratops .. | 60 | 10 |
| 1428 | 300 r. Montanoceraptors | 80 | 15 |
| 1429 | 400 r. Centrosaurus .. | 1·10 | 20 |
| 1430 | 700 r. Styracosaurus .. | 2·00 | 35 |
| 1431 | 800 r. Triceratops .. | 2·25 | 40 |

**276** Orange-tip

**278** Death Cap

**277** Swimming

**1995.** Butterflies. Multicoloured.

| | | | |
|---|---|---|---|
| 1432 | 100 r. Type **276** .. .. | 30 | 10 |
| 1433 | 200 r. Scarce swallowtail | 60 | 10 |
| 1434 | 300 r. Dark green fritillary | 80 | 15 |
| 1435 | 600 r. Red admiral .. | 1·60 | 30 |
| 1436 | 800 r. Peacock .. .. | 2·25 | 40 |

**1995.** Olympic Games, Atlanta (1996) (2nd issue). Multicoloured.

| | | | |
|---|---|---|---|
| 1437 | 100 r. Type **277** .. .. | 30 | 10 |
| 1438 | 200 r. Callisthenics (vert) | 60 | 10 |
| 1439 | 400 r. Basketball (vert) .. | 1·10 | 20 |
| 1440 | 800 r. Football (vert) .. | 2·25 | 40 |
| 1441 | 1000 r. Cycling (vert) .. | 2·75 | 45 |

**1995.** Fungi. Multicoloured.

| | | | |
|---|---|---|---|
| 1443 | 100 r. Type **278** .. .. | 40 | 15 |
| 1444 | 200 r. Chanterelle .. | 75 | 20 |
| 1445 | 300 r. Honey fungus .. | 1·00 | 30 |
| 1446 | 600 r. Field mushroom .. | 2·10 | 60 |
| 1447 | 800 r. Fly agaric .. | 3·00 | 80 |

**279** Kneeling Ascetic

**281** Black-capped Lory

**280** Gaur

**1995.** Khmer Culture. Statues. Mult.

| | | | |
|---|---|---|---|
| 1448 | 300 r. Type **279** .. .. | 80 | 15 |
| 1449 | 500 r. Parasurama .. | 1·40 | 25 |
| 1450 | 700 r. Shiva .. .. | 2·00 | 35 |

**1995.** Protected Animals. Multicoloured.

| | | | |
|---|---|---|---|
| 1451 | 300 r. Type **280** .. .. | 80 | 15 |
| 1452 | 500 r. Kouprey (vert) .. | 1·40 | 25 |
| 1453 | 700 r. Saurus crane (vert) | 2·00 | 35 |

**1995.** Parrot Family. Multicoloured.

| | | | |
|---|---|---|---|
| 1454 | 100 r. Type **281** .. .. | 30 | 10 |
| 1455 | 200 r. Princess parrot .. | 60 | 10 |
| 1456 | 400 r. Eclectus parrot .. | 1·10 | 20 |
| 1457 | 800 r. Scarlet macaw .. | 2·25 | 40 |
| 1458 | 1000 r. Budgerigar .. | 2·75 | 45 |

**282** Bird (sculpture)

**1995.** Tourism. Public Gardens. Mult.

| | | | |
|---|---|---|---|
| 1460 | 300 r. Type **282** .. .. | 80 | 15 |
| 1461 | 500 r. Water feature .. | 1·40 | 25 |
| 1462 | 700 r. Mythical figures (sculpture) .. .. | 2·00 | 35 |

**283** Richard Trevithick's Steam Locomotive, 1804

**1995.** Steam Locomotives. Multicoloured.

| | | | |
|---|---|---|---|
| 1463 | 100 r. Type **283** .. .. | 25 | 10 |
| 1464 | 200 r. George Stephenson's "Rocket", 1830 .. | 65 | 20 |
| 1465 | 300 r. Stephenson's "Locomotion", 1825 .. | 90 | 30 |
| 1466 | 600 r. "Lafayette", 1837 | 1·75 | 60 |
| 1467 | 800 r. "Best Friend of Charleston", 1830 .. | 2·10 | 70 |

**284** Bristol Type 142 Blenheim Mk II Bomber

**1995.** Second World War Planes. Mult.
1469 100 r. Type **284** .. .. 25 10
1470 200 r. North American B-25B Mitchell bomber (horiz) .. .. 65 20
1471 300 r. Avro Type 652 Anson Mk I general purpose plane (horiz) .. 90 30
1472 600 r. Avro Manchester bomber (horiz) .. 1·75 55
1473 800 r. Consolidated B-24 Liberator bomber (horiz) .. .. 2·10 70

**285** Gathering Crops

**1995.** 50th Anniv of F.A.O. Multicoloured.
1475 300 r. Type **285** .. .. 1·00 30
1476 500 r. Transplanting crops 1·50 50
1477 700 r. Paddy field .. 2·50 80

**286** Bridge

**1995.** 50th Anniv of U.N.O. Preah Kunlorng Bridge. Multicoloured.
1478 300 r. Type **286** .. .. 85 25
1479 500 r. People on bridge 1·40 45
1480 700 r. Closer view of bridge .. .. .. 1·90 60

**287** Queen Monineath

**1995.** National Independence. Multicoloured.
1481 700 r. Type **287** .. .. 2·40 80
1482 800 r. King Norodom Sihanouk .. .. 2·75 90

**288** Pennant Coralfish

**1995.** Fishes. Multicoloured.
1483 100 r. Type **288** .. .. 25 10
1484 200 r. Coralfish .. .. 55 20
1485 400 r. Orange anemonefish 1·10 35
1486 800 r. Blue surgeon .. 2·25 75
1487 1000 r. Angel fish .. 2·75 90

**289** Post Office Building

**1995.** Cent of Head Post Office, Phnom Penh.
1489 **289** 300 r. multicoloured 80 25
1490 500 r. multicoloured 1·25 40
1491 700 r. multicoloured 1·90 60

**290** Independence Monument

**1995.** 40th Anniv of Admission of Cambodia to United Nations Organization. Mult.
1492 300 r. Type **290** .. .. 80 25
1493 400 r. Angkor Vat .. 1·10 35
1494 800 r. U.N. emblem and national flag (vert) .. 2·10 70

**291** Tennis **292** Kep State Chalet

**1996.** Olympic Games, Atlanta (3rd issue). Multicoloured.
1495 100 r. Type **291** .. .. 25 10
1496 200 r. Volleyball .. 45 15
1497 300 r. Football .. .. 70 20
1498 500 r. Running .. .. 1·10 35
1499 900 r. Baseball .. .. 2·10 70
1500 1000 r. Basketball .. 2·25 75

**1996.**
1502 **292** 50 r. blue and black .. 10 10
1503 – 100 r. red and black .. 15 10
1504 – 200 r. yellow & black 25 10
1505 – 500 r. blue and black 70 20
1506 – 800 r. mauve & black 1·10 35
1507 – 1000 r. yellow & black 1·50 50
1508 – 1500 r. green & black 2·25 75
DESIGNS—HORIZ: 100 r. Power station; 200 r. Wheelchair; 500 c. Handicapped basketball team; 1000 r. Kep beach; 1500 r. Serpent Island. VERT: 800 r. Man making crutches.

**293** European Wild Cat

**1996.** Wild Cats. Multicoloured.
1509 100 r. "Felis libyca" (vert) 25 10
1510 200 r. Type **293** .. .. 45 15
1511 300 r. Caracal .. .. 70 20
1512 500 r. Geoffroy's cat .. 1·10 35
1513 900 r. Black-footed cat .. 2·10 70
1514 1000 r. Flat-headed cat .. 2·25 75

**294** Player dribbling Ball

**1996.** World Cup Football Championship, France (1998). Multicoloured.
1515 **294** 100 r. multicoloured 25 10
1516 – 200 r. multicoloured 45 15
1517 – 300 r. multicoloured 70 20
1518 – 500 r. multicoloured 1·10 35
1519 – 900 r. multicoloured 2·10 70
1520 – 1000 r. mult (horiz) .. 2·25 75
DESIGNS: 200 r. to 1000 r. Different players.

POSTAGE DUE STAMPS

**D 13.**

**1957.**
D 81. **D 13.** 10 c. red, blue & black 20 20
D 82. 50 c. red, blue & black 40 40
D 83. 1 r. red, blue & black 55 55
D 84. 3 r. red, blue & black 70 70
D 85. 5 r. red, blue & black 1·40 1·40

For later issues see **KHMER REPUBLIC.**

# CAMEROUN

**Pt. 7; Pt. 6; Pt. 12**

Territory in western Africa which became a German Protectorate in 1884. During 1914–16 it was occupied by allied troops and in 1922 Britain and France were granted separate United Nations mandates. Issues made by the British administration are listed in volume 3 under CAMEROON.

In 1960 the French trust territory became an independent republic and, following a plebiscite, in September 1961 the southern part of the area under British control joined the Cameroun Republic. In November 1995 the republic joined the Commonwealth.

## A. GERMAN COLONY OF KAMERUN.

100 pfennig = 1 mark.

**1897.** Stamps of Germany optd. **Kamerun.**
K1a **8** 3 pf. brown .. .. 10·00 17·00
K2 5 pf. green .. .. 5·00 6·00
K3 **9** 10 pf. red .. .. 3·00 6·00
K4 20 pf. blue .. .. 3·50 8·00
K5 25 pf. orange .. .. 20·00 35·00
K6a 50 pf. brown .. .. 15·00 35·00

**1900.** "Yacht" key-types inscr. "KAMERUN".
K 7 N 3 pf. brown .. .. 1·00 1·25
K21 5 pf. green .. .. 60 1·50
K22 10 pf. red .. .. 60 90
K10 20 pf. blue .. .. 26·00 2·00
K11 25 pf. blk. & red on yell. 1·00 5·50
K12 30 pf. blk. & orge. on buff 1·25 4·50
K13 40 pf. black and red .. 1·25 4·50
K14 50 pf. blk. & pur. on buff 1·60 6·00
K15 80 pf. blk. & red on rose 2·00 12·00
K16 O 1 m. red .. .. 75·00 80·00
K17 2 m. blue .. .. 4·50 80·00
K18 3 m. black .. .. 4·75 £120
K19 5 m. red and black .. £110 £500

## B. FRENCH ADMINISTRATION OF CAMEROUN.

100 centimes = 1 franc.

**1915.** Stamps of Gabon with inscription "AFRIQUE EQUATORIALE-GABON" optd. **Corps Expeditionnaire Franco-Anglais CAMEROUN.**
1 **7** 1 c. brown and orange .. 48·00 19·00
2 2 c. black and brown .. £100 85·00
3 4 c. violet and blue .. £100 85·00
4 5 c. olive and green .. 18·00 9·25
5 10 c. red and lake (on No. 37 of Gabon) .. 19·00 9·50
6 20 c. brown and violet £100 95·00
7 **8** 25 c. brown and blue .. 35·00 16·00
8 30 c. red and grey .. £100 85·00
9 35 c. green and violet .. 35·00 16·00
10 40 c. blue and brown .. £100 95·00
11 45 c. violet and red .. £100 95·00
12 50 c. grey and green .. £100 £100
13 75 c. brown and orange .. £150 £100
14 **9** 1 f. yellow and brown .. £150 £110
15 2 f. brown and red .. £160 £130

**1916.** Optd **Occupation Francaise du Cameroun**. (a) On stamps of Middle Congo.
16 **1** 1 c. olive and brown .. 50·00 50·00
17 2 c. violet and brown .. 65·00 55·00
18 4 c. blue and brown .. 65·00 55·00
19 5 c. green and blue .. 20·00 16·00
20 **2** 35 c. brown and blue .. 75·00 50·00
21 45 c. violet and orange .. 48·00 42·00

(b) On stamps of French Congo
22 **6** 15 c. violet and green .. 65·00 60·00
23 **8** 20 c. green and red .. £110 60·00
24 30 c. red and yellow .. 60·00 42·00
25 40 c. brown and green .. 48·00 42·00
26 50 c. violet and lilac .. 60·00 45·00
27 75 c. purple and orange .. 60·00 40·00
28 – 1 f. drab and grey (48) .. 80·00 50·00
29 – 2 f. red and brown (49) .. 80·00 50·00

**1916.** Stamps of Middle Congo optd **CAMEROUN Occupation Francaise**.
30 **1** 1 c. olive and brown .. 10 25
31 2 c. violet and brown .. 10 25
32 4 c. blue and brown .. 10 25
33 5 c. green and blue .. 15 30
34 10 c. red and blue .. 50 60
34a 15 c. purple and red .. 50 65
35 20 c. brown and blue .. 40 50
36 **2** 25 c. blue and green .. 40 60
37 30 c. pink and green .. 50 65
38 35 c. brown and blue .. 40 60
39 40 c. green and brown .. 60 90
40 45 c. violet and orange .. 80 1·00
41 50 c. green and orange .. 80 1·00
42 75 c. brown and blue .. 90 1·00
43 **3** 1 f. green and violet .. 80 1·00
44 2 f. violet and green .. 4·75 5·00
45 5 f. blue and pink .. 6·00 6·50

**1921.** Stamps of Middle Congo (colours changed) optd **CAMEROUN**.
46 **1** 1 c. orange and green .. 10 25
47 2 c. red and brown .. 10 25
48 4 c. green and grey .. 15 30
49 5 c. orange and red .. 15 30
50 10 c. light green and green 25 40
51 15 c. orange and blue .. 40 50
52 20 c. grey and purple .. 40 50

53 2 25 c. orange and grey .. 40 55
54 30 c. red and carmine .. 40 60
55 35 c. blue and grey .. 45 60
56 40 c. orange and green .. 45 55
57 45 c. red and brown .. 45 60
58 50 c. ultramarine and blue 30 55
59 75 c. green and purple .. 45 60
60 3 1 f. orange and grey .. 90 1·25
61 2 f. red and green .. 3·50 4·00
62 5 f. grey and red .. 4·00 6·00

**1924.** Stamps of 1921 surch.
63. **1.** 25 c. on 15 c. orge. & bl. 40 60
64. **3.** 25 c. on 2 f. red & olive 40 60
65. 25 c. on 5 f. grey and red 50 75
66. **2.** "65" on 45 c. red & brown 90 1·10
67. "85" on 75 c. grn. & red 90 1·25

**5.** Cattle fording River.

**1925.**
68. **5.** 1 c. mauve and olive .. 10 25
69. 2 c. green & red on grn. 10 25
70. 4 c. black and blue .. 10 25
71. 5 c. mauve and yellow 10 15
72. 10 c. orge. & pur. on yell. 15 10
73. 15 c. green .. .. 25 30
88. 15 c. red and lilac .. 30 55
74. **A.** 20 c. brown and olive 30 40
89. 20 c. green .. .. 40 50
90. 20 c. brown and red .. 20 20
75. 25 c. black and green .. 25 20
76. 30 c. red and green .. 25 25
91. 30 c. green and olive .. 30 40
77. 35 c. black and brown 40 50
91a. 35 c. green .. .. 60 75
78. 40 c. violet and orange 60 95
79. 45 c. red .. .. 30 45
92. 45 c. brown and mauve 1·10 1·25
80. 50 c. red and green .. 45 50
93. 55 c. red and blue .. 80 1·00
81. 60 c. black and mauve 50 45
94. 60 c. red .. .. 20 30
82. 65 c. brown and blue 30 30
83. 75 c. blue .. .. 25 45
95. 75 c. mauve and brown 35 45
95a. 80 c. brown and red 60 75
84. 85 c. blue and red .. 40 60
96. 90 c. red .. .. 1·00 1·10
85. **B.** 1 f. brown and blue .. 25 60
97. 1 f. blue .. .. 30 40
98. 1 f. mauve and brown 35 50
99. 1 f. brown and green 80 80
100. 1 f. 10 brown and red .. 2·50 2·50
100a. 1 f. 25 blue and brown 3·50 3·00
101. 1 f. 50 blue .. .. 60 25
101a. 1 f. 75 red and brown .. 60 60
101b. 1 f. 75 blue .. .. 75 75
86. 2 f. orange and olive .. 1·00 35
102. 3 f. mauve and brown 2·75 3·00
87. 5 f. blk. & brn. on blue 1·75 70
103. 10 f. mauve and orange 6·00 6·00
104. 20 f. green and red .. 11·50 11·00
DESIGNS—VERT. A, Tapping for rubber. HORIZ. B, Liana suspension bridge.

**1926.** Surch. with new value.
105. **B.** 1 f. 25 on 1 f. blue .. 30 45

**1931.** "Colonial Exhibition" key-types inscribed "CAMEROUN".
106. E. 40 c. green .. .. 2·00 2·00
107. F. 50 c. mauve .. .. 2·25 2·25
108. G. 90 c. orange .. .. 2·25 2·25
109. H. 1 f. 50 blue .. .. 3·00 2·25

**14.** Sailing Ships.

**1937.** Paris International Exn. Inscr. "EXPOSITION INTERNATIONALE PARIS 1937".
110. – 20 c. violet .. .. 90 1·25
111. **14.** 30 c. green .. .. 75 1·00
112. – 40 c. red .. .. 65 90
113. – 50 c. brn. and deep brn. 65 90
114. – 90 c. red .. .. 75 1·10
115. – 1 f. 50 blue .. .. 75 1·10
DESIGNS—VERT. 20 c. Allegory of Commerce. 50 c. Allegory of Agriculture. HORIZ. 40 c. Berber, Negress and Annamite. 90 c. France with torch of Civilization. 1 f. 50, Diane de Poitiers.

**19.** Pierre and Marie Curie.

**1938.** International Anti-Cancer Fund.
116. **19.** 1 f. 75 + 50 c. blue .. 4·00 5·50

**20.**

**1939.** New York World's Fair.
117. **20.** 1 f. 25 red .. .. 70 80
118. 2 f. 25 blue .. .. 65 80

**21.** Lamido Woman.

**1939.**
119. **21.** 2 c. black .. .. 10 25
120. 3 c. mauve .. .. 10 25
121. 4 c. blue .. .. 15 25
122. 5 c. brown .. .. 10 25
123. 10 c. green .. .. 10 25
124. 15 c. red .. .. 10 25
125. 20 c. purple .. .. 10 25
126. **A.** 25 c. black .. .. 30 45
127. 30 c. orange .. .. 30 45
128. 40 c. blue .. .. 40 55
129. 45 c. green .. .. 1·25 1·50
130. 50 c. brown .. .. 40 50
131. 60 c. blue .. .. 35 50
132. 70 c. purple .. .. 1·75 2·00
133. **B.** 80 c. blue .. .. 1·25 1·50
134. 90 c. blue .. .. 45 60
135. 1 f. red .. .. 65 75
135a. 1 f. brown .. .. 60 75
136. 1 f. 25 red .. .. 2·50 3·00
137. 1 f. 40 orange .. .. 65 80
138. 1 f. 50 brown .. .. 50 65
139. 1 f. 60 brown .. .. 1·25 1·40
140. 1 f. 75 blue .. .. 50 60
141. 2 f. green .. .. 55 65
142. 2 f. 25 blue .. .. 45 65
143. 2 f. 50 purple .. .. 65 80
144. 3 f. violet .. .. 40 60
145. **C.** 5 f. brown .. .. 45 60
146. 10 f. purple .. .. 1·00 1·25
147. 20 f. green .. .. 1·75 2·00
DESIGNS—VERT. A, Banyo Waterfall. C, African Boatman. HORIZ. B, African elephants.

**25.** Storming the Bastille.

**1939.** 150th Anniv. of Revolution.
148. **25.** 45 c. + 25 c. green .. 4·25 5·00
149. 70 c. + 30 c. brown .. 4·25 5·00
150. 90 c. + 35 c. orange .. 4·25 5·00
151. 1 f. 25 + 1 f. red .. 5·25 6·25
152. 2 f. 25 + 2 f. blue .. 6·75 7·75

**1940.** Adherence to General de Gaulle. Optd **CAMEROUN FRANCAIS 27-8-40.**
153 **21** 2 c. black .. .. 45 50
154 3 c. mauve .. .. 40 50
155 4 c. blue .. .. 40 50
156 5 c. brown .. .. 1·40 1·40
157 10 c. green .. .. 40 40
158 15 c. red .. .. 50 50
159 20 c. purple .. .. 5·25 5·00
160 A 25 c. black .. .. 40 50
161 30 c. orange .. .. 4·50 4·50
162 40 c. blue .. .. 1·90 2·00
163 45 c. green .. .. 1·25 1·40
164 – 50 c. red & grn (No. 80) 50 60
165 A 60 c. blue .. .. 1·75 1·75
166 70 c. purple .. .. 55 60
167 B 80 c. blue .. .. 2·50 2·50
168 90 c. blue .. .. 40 50
169 **20** 1 f. 25 red .. .. 1·90 1·90
170 B 1 f. 25 red .. .. 60 70
171 1 f. 40 orange .. .. 1·10 1·25
172 1 f. 50 brown .. .. 40 50
173 1 f. 60 brown .. .. 65 70
174 1 f. 75 blue .. .. 1·00 1·25
175 **20** 2 f. 25 blue .. .. 1·90 2·00
176 B 2 f. 25 blue .. .. 50 50
177 2 f. 50 purple .. .. 45 50
178 – 5 f. black and brown on blue (No. 87) .. 9·00 9·00
179 C 5 f. brown .. .. 9·75 10·00
180 – 10 f. mauve and orange (No. 103) .. .. 12·00 9·50
181 C 10 f. purple .. .. 24·00 18·00
182 – 20 f. grn & red (No. 104) 25·00 21·00
183 C 20 f. green .. .. £110 £140

**1940.** War Relief Fund. Nos. 100a, 101a and 86 surch. **OEUVRES DE GUERRE** and premium.
184. 1 f. 25 + 2 f. blue & brn. 8·75 8·75
185. 1 f. 75 + 3 f. red & brn. 8·75 9·00
186. 2 f. + 5 f. orange & olive 9·00 8·75

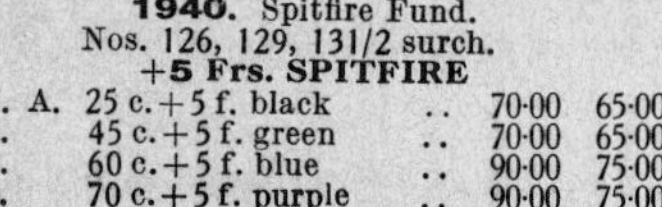

**1940.** Spitfire Fund. Nos. 126, 129, 131/2 surch. **+5 Frs. SPITFIRE**
187. A. 25 c. + 5 f. black .. 70·00 65·00
188. 45 c. + 5 f. green .. 70·00 65·00
189. 60 c. + 5 f. blue .. 90·00 75·00
190. 70 c. + 5 f. purple .. 90·00 75·00

**1941.** Spitfire Fund. Surch. **SPITFIRE 10 fr. General de GAULLE.**
190a. **20.** 1 f. 25 + 10 f. red .. 65·00 55·00
190b. 2 f. 25 + 10 f. blue .. 65·00 55·00

**29b.** Sikorsky S-43 over Map.

**29c.** Sikorsky S-43 Amphibian.

**1941.** Air.
190c. **29b.** 25 c. red .. .. 30 45
190d. 50 c. green .. .. 35 45
190e. 1 f. purple .. .. 35 45
190f. **29c.** 2 f. olive .. .. 35 45
190g. 3 f. brown .. .. 40 50
190h. 4 f. blue .. .. 35 45
190i. 6 f. myrtle .. .. 40 50
190j. 7 f. purple .. .. 40 50
190k. 12 f. orange .. .. 2·50 2·75
190l. 20 f. red .. .. 65 80
190m. – 50 f. blue .. .. 85 90
DESIGN: 50 f. Latecoere 631 flying boat over harbour.

**1941.** Laquintinie Hospital Fund. Surch. **+10 Frs. AMBULANCE LAQUINTINIE.**
191. **20.** 1 f. 25 + 10 f. red .. 13·50 11·00
192. 2 f. 25 + 10 f. blue .. 14·00 11·00

**31.** Cross of Lorraine, Sword and Shield.

**32.** Fairey FC-1.

**1942.** Free French Issue.
193. **31.** 5 c. brown (postage) .. 10 25
194. 10 c. blue .. .. 10 15
195. 25 c. green .. .. 10 25
196. 30 c. red .. .. 10 25
197. 40 c. green .. .. 10 25
198. 80 c. purple .. .. 10 25
199. 1 f. mauve .. .. 10 15
200. 1 f. 50 red .. .. 10 15
201. 2 f. black .. .. 25 25
202. 2 f. 50 blue .. .. 25 35
203. 4 f. violet .. .. 30 40
204. 5 f. yellow .. .. 30 50
205. 10 f. brown .. .. 30 55
206. 20 f. green .. .. 60 90
207. **32.** 1 f. orange (air) .. 30 40
208. 1 f. 50 red .. .. 30 40
209. 5 f. purple .. .. 30 40
210. 10 f. black .. .. 40 60
211. 25 f. blue .. .. 55 65
212. 50 f. green .. .. 80 85
213. 100 f. red .. .. 85 1·25

**1943.** Surch **Valmy + 100 frs.**
213a – 1 f. 25 + 100 f. blue and brown (No. 100a) .. 11·50 13·00
213b **20** 1 f. 25 + 100 f. red .. 6·50 13·00
213c – 1 f. 25 + 100 f. red (No. 136) .. .. 11·50 13·00
213d – 1 f. 50 + 100 f. brown (No. 138) .. .. 11·50 13·00
213e **20** 2 f. 25 + 100 f. blue .. 6·75 13·00

**33.**

**34.** Felix Eboue.

**1944.** Mutual Aid and Red Cross Funds.
214. **33.** 5 f. + 20 f. red .. .. 90 1·50

**1945.** Surch.
215. **31.** 50 c. on 5 c. brown .. 30 40
216. 60 c. on 5 c. brown .. 35 45
217. 70 c. on 5 c. brown .. 35 45
218. 1 f. 20 on 5 c. brown .. 35 45
219. 2 f. 40 on 25 c. green .. 30 40
220. 3 f. on 25 c. green .. 45 55
221. 4 f. 50 on 25 c. green .. 70 85
222. 15 f. on 2 f. 50 blue .. 70 85

**1945.**
223. **34.** 2 f. black .. .. 25 35
224. 25 f. green .. .. 65 80

**35.** "Victory".

**1946.** Air. Victory.
225. **35.** 8 f. purple .. .. 35 50

**36.** Chad.

**1946.** Air. From Chad to the Rhine. Inscr. "DU TCHAD AU RHIN".
226. **36.** 5 f. blue .. .. 55 75
227. – 10 f. purple .. .. 50 75
228. – 15 f. red .. .. 65 80
229. – 20 f. blue .. .. 60 80
230. – 25 f. brown .. .. 85 1·00
231. – 50 f. black .. .. 90 1·25
DESIGNS: 10 f. Koufra. 15 f. Mareth. 20 f. Normandy. 25 f. Paris. 50 f. Strasbourg.

**37.** Zebu and Herdsman.

**45.** Aeroplane, African and Mask.

**1946.**
232. **37.** 10 c. green (postage) .. 15 30
233. 30 c. orange .. .. 15 30
234. 40 c. blue .. .. 15 30
235. – 50 c. sepia .. .. 15 30
236. – 60 c. purple .. .. 10 25
237. – 80 c. brown .. .. 25 30
238. – 1 f. orange .. .. 15 15
239. – 1 f. 20 green .. .. 30 45
240. – 1 f. 50 red .. .. 85 95
241. – 2 f. black .. .. 10 10
242. – 3 f. red .. .. 10 10
243. – 3 f. 60 red .. .. 45 65
244. – 4 f. blue .. .. 15 15
245. – 5 f. red .. .. 30 30
246. – 6 f. blue .. .. 30 30
247. – 10 f. green .. .. 30 30
248. – 15 f. blue .. .. 30 30
249. – 20 f. green .. .. 40 40
250. – 25 f. black .. .. 60 70
DESIGNS—VERT. 50 c. to 80 c. Tikar women. 1 f. to 1 f. 50, Africans carrying bananas. 2 f. to 4 f. Bowman. 5 f. to 10 f. Lamido horsemen. 15 f. to 25 f. Native head.
251. – 50 f. green (air) .. 75 90
252. – 100 f. brown .. .. 1·25 1·50
253. **45.** 200 f. olive .. .. 2·75 2·75
DESIGNS—HORIZ. 50 f. Birds over mountains. 100 f. African horsemen and Dewoitine D-333 trimotor airplane.

**46.** People of Five Races, Lockheed Constellation Airplane and Globe.

**1949.** Air. 75th Anniv. of U.P.U.
254. **46.** 25 f. multicoloured .. 3·00 3·50

**47.** Doctor and Patient.

**1950.** Colonial Welfare Fund.
255 **47** 10 f. + 2 f. green & turq 2·50 3·00

48. Military Medal. 49. Porters Carrying Bananas.

50. Transporting Logs.

**1952.** Military Medal Centenary.
256. **48.** 15 f. red, yellow & green 3·00 3·00

**1953.**
257. **49.** 8 f. violet, orange and purple (postage) .. 35 15
258. 15 f. brown, yell. & red 70 50
259. – 40 f. brown, pink & choc. 65 40
260. **50.** 50 f. ol., brn. & sep. (air) 1·25 60
261. – 100 f. sepia, brn. & turq. 3·25 75
262. – 200 f. brn., blue & grn. 6·00 3·50
262a. – 500 f. indigo, bl. and lilac 10·00 6·50
DESIGNS—As Type **49**: 40 f. Woman gathering coffee. As Type **50**: HORIZ. 100 f. Airplane over giraffes. 200 f. Freighters, Douala Port. VERT. 500 f. Sud Ouest Corse II over Piton d'Humsiki.

51. Edea Barrage.

**1953.** Air. Opening of Edea Barrage.
263. **51.** 15 f. blue, lake & brown 2·50 1·50

52. "D-Day".

**1954.** Air. 10th Anniv. of Liberation.
264. **52.** 15 f. green and turquoise 2·25 2·50

53. Dr. Jamot and Students.

**1954.** Air. 75th Birthday of Dr. Jamot (physician).
265. **53.** 15 f. brn., blue & green 2·50 2·00

54. Native Cattle.

DESIGNS: 15 f. R. Wouri bridge. 20 f. Technical education. 25 f. Mobile medical unit.

**1956.** Economic and Social Development Fund. Inscr. "F.I.D.E.S.".
266. **54.** 5 f. brown and sepia .. 45 40
267. – 15 f. turq., blue & black 65 45
268. – 20 f. turquoise and blue 60 50
269. – 25 f. blue .. .. 95 65

**1956.** Coffee. As T **51** of French Equatorial Africa.
270 15 f. vermilion and red .. 60 25

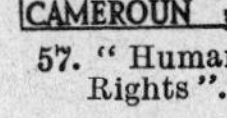


56. Woman, Child and Flag. 57. "Human Rights".

**1958.** 1st Anniv. of First Cameroun Govt.
271. **56.** 20 f. multicoloured .. 50 40

**1958.** 30th Anniv. of Declaration of Human Rights.
272. **57.** 20 f. brown and red .. 75 70

**1958.** Tropical Flora. As T **56** of French Equatorial Africa.
273. 20 f. multicoloured .. 80 70
DESIGN—VERT. "Randia malleifera".

59. Loading Bananas on Ship. 60. Prime Minister A. Ahidjo.

**1959.**
274. **59.** 20 f. multicoloured .. 60 50
275. – 25 f. grn., brn. and pur. 65 55
DESIGN—VERT. 25 f. Bunch of bananas and native bearers in jungle path.

## C. INDEPENDENT REPUBLIC.

**1960.** Proclamation of Independence. Inscr. "1 ER JANVIER 1960".
276. – 20 f. multicoloured .. 55 15
277. **60.** 25 f. grn., bistre & black 55 15
DESIGN: 20 f. Cameroun flag and map.

61. "Uprooted Tree". 62. C.C.T.A. Emblem.

**1960.** World Refugee Year.
278. **61.** 30 f. green, blue & brown 1·00 50

**1960.** 10th Anniv. of African Technical Co-operation Commission.
279. **62.** 50 f. black and purple 1·10 60

63. Map and Flag. 64. U.N. Headquarters, Emblem and Cameroun Flag.

**1961.** Red Cross Fund. Flag in green, red and yellow; cross in red; background colours given.
280. **63.** 20 f. + 5 f. green & red .. 70 70
281. 25 f. + 10 f. red & green 95 95
282. 30 f. + 15 f. red & green 1·75 1·75

**1961.** Admission to U.N.O. Flag in green, red and yellow; emblem in blue, buildings and inscr. in colours given.
283. **64.** 15 f. brown and green .. 45 30
284. 25 f. green and blue .. 55 30
285. 85 f. purple, blue & red 2·10 1·10

**1961.** Surch. **REPUBLIQUE FEDERALE** and value in sterling currency.
286. – ½d. on 1 f. orge. (238) (postage) .. 35 25
287. – 1d. on 2 f. black (241) 45 30
288. **54.** 1½d. on 5 f. brn. & sepia 50 40
289. – 2d. on 10 f. green (247) 95 50
290. – 3d. on 15 f. turq., indigo and black (267) .. 90 55
291. – 4d. on 15 f. vermilion and red (270) .. 1·10 85
292. – 6d. on 20 f. multicoloured (274) .. .. 1·40 95
293. **60.** 1s. on 25 f. grn., bistre and black .. 2·75 2·00
294a. **61.** 2s. 6d. on 30 f. green, blue and brown .. 4·75 4·75
295a. – 5s. on 100 f. sepia, brn. and turq. (264) (air) .. 9·00 9·00
296a. – 10s. on 200 f. brn., blue and green (265) .. 18·00 18·00
297a. – £1 on 500 f. indigo, blue and lilac (253a) .. 30·00 30·00

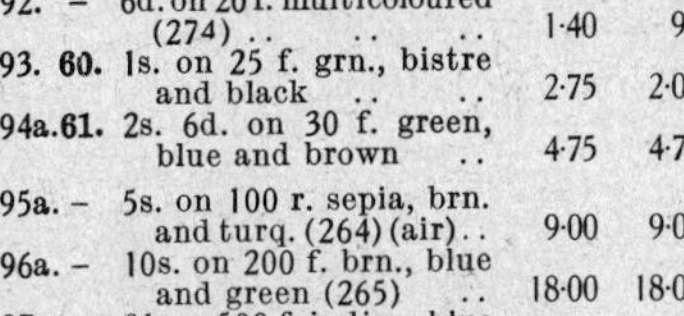

The above were for use in the former British Cameroon Trust Territory pending the introduction of the Cameroun franc.

66. Pres. Ahidjo and Prime Minister Foncha.

**1962.** Reunification. (a) T **66**.
298. 20 f. brown and violet .. 16·00 14·00
299. 25 f. brown and green .. 16·00 14·00
300. 60 f. green and red .. 16·00 14·00

(b) T **66** surch. in sterling currency.
301. 3d. on 20 f. brn. & violet
302. 6d. on 25 f. brn. and grn.
303. 2s. 6d. on 60 f. grn. & red
Set of 3 .. .. £375 £375

68. Lions International Badge, Doctor and Leper.

**1962.** World Leprosy Day. Lions International Relief Fund.
304. **68.** 20 f. + 5 f. pur. and brn. 60 60
305. 25 f. + 10 f. pur. and blue 70 70
306. 50 f. + 15 f. pur. and grn. 1·40 1·40

69. European, African and Boeing 707 Airliners.

**1962.** Air. Foundation of "Air Afrique" Airline.
307. **69.** 25 f. purple, vio. & grn. 65 40

70. Campaign Emblem. 71. Giraffes and Waza Camp.

**1962.** Malaria Eradication.
308. **70.** 25 f. + 5 f. mauve .. 65 60

**1962.** (a) Postage. Animals.
309. A. 50 c. sepia, blue & turq. 10 10
310. B. 1 f. black, turq. & oran. 10 10
311. C. 1 f. 50 brn., sage & blk. 10 10
312. D. 2 f. black, blue & green 15 10
313. C. 3 f. brown, orange & pur. 15 10
314. B. 4 f. sepia, green & turq. 20 10
315. D. 5 f. purple, green & brn. 20 10
316. A. 6 f. sepia, blue & lemon 30 15
317. E. 8 f. blue, red and green 65 45
318. F. 10 f. black, orange & blue 50 15
319. A. 15 f. brown, blue & turq. 65 35
320. **71.** 20 f. brown and grey .. 85 35
321. F. 25 f. brown, yell. & grn. 2·10 85
322. E. 30 f. black, blue & brn. 2·50 90
323. **71.** 40 f. lake and green .. 4·75 1·40

(b) Air.
324. – 50 f. brn., myrtle & blue 90 40
325. – 100 f. multicoloured .. 2·75 85
326. – 200 f. blk., brn. & turq. 9·00 1·75
327. – 500 f. buff, purple & blue 9·50 3·00
DESIGNS—HORIZ. As Type **71**: A, Moustached monkey, B, African elephant and Ntem Falls. C, Kob, Dschang. D, Hippopotamus, Hippo Camp. E, African manatee, Lake Ossa. F, Buffalo, Batoun Region (48 × 27 mm.): 50 f. Cocotiers Hotel, Douala. 100 f. "Cymothoe sangaris" (butterfly). 200 f. Ostriches. 500 f. Kapsikis, Mokolo (landscape).

72. Union Flag.

**1962.** 1st Anniv. of Union of African and Malagasy States. Flag in green, red and gold.
328. **72.** 30 f. brown .. .. 1·40 65

73. Map and View. 74. "The School Under the Tree".

**1962.** 1st Anniv. of Reunification.
329. **73.** 9 f. bistre, violet & brn. 30 20
330. 18 f. red, green & blue .. 40 30
331. – 20 f. bistre, blue & purple 45 30
332. – 25 f. orge., sepia & blue 45 35
333. – 50 f. blue, sepia and red 1·25 80
DESIGNS: 20 f., 25 f. Sunrise over Cameroun. 50 f. Commemorative scroll.

**1962.** Literacy and Popular Education Plan.
334. **74.** 20 f. red, yellow & green 65 35

75. Globe and "Telstar".

**1963.** 1st Trans-Atlantic Television Satellite Link.
335. **75.** 1 f. ol., vio. & blue (post.) 10 10
336. 2 f. lake, green and blue 15 15
337. 3 f. olive purple & green 20 20
338. 25 f. blue and green .. 85 85
339. 100 f. brown and green (air) (48 × 27 mm.) .. 1·90 1·10

76. Globe and Emblem. 77. VHF Station, Mt. Bankolo, Yaounde.

**1963.** Freedom from Hunger.
340. **76.** 18 f. + 5 f. blue, brown and green .. .. 70 40
341. 25 f. + 5 f. grn. & brown 85 45

**1963.** Inauguration of Doala-Yaounde VHF Radio Service.
342. **77.** 15 f. multicoloured (post.) 35 30
343. – 20 f. multicoloured .. 45 35
344. – 100 f. multicoloured (air) 1·90 1·10
DESIGNS: 20 f. Aerials and control panel. 100 f. Edea relay station (26 × 44 mm.).

78. "Centre regional . . .". 80. Pres. Ahidjo.

**1963.** Inauguration of U.N.E.S.C.O. Regional Schoolbooks Production Centre. Yaounde.
345. **78.** 20 f. red, black & green 35 20
346. 25 f. red, black & orange 40 20
347. 100 f. red, black & gold 1·50 85

**1963.** Air. African and Malagasian Posts and Telecommunications Union. As T **18** of Central African Republic.
348. 85 f. multicoloured .. 1·60 1·10

**1963.** 2nd Anniv. of Reunification. Mult.
349. 9 f. Type **80** .. .. 30 20
350. 18 f. Map and flag .. 40 20
351. 20 f. Type **80** .. .. 45 30

**1963.** Air. Inauguration of "DC-8" Service. As T **11** of Congo Republic.
352. 50 f. multicoloured .. 90 45

82. Globe and Scales of Justice.

**1963.** 15th Anniv. of Declaration of Human Rights.
353. 82. 9 f. brown, black & blue 35 15
354. 18 f. red, black & green 40 20
355. 25 f. green, black & red 50 30
356. 75 f. blue, black & yell. 1·60 65

83. Lion.

**1964.** Waza National Park.
357. 83. 10 f. bistre green & brown 1·25 35
358. 25 f. bistre and green .. 2·40 80

84. Football Stadium, Yaounde.

DESIGNS: 18 f. Sports Equipment. 30 f. Stadium Entrance. Yaounde.

**1964.** Tropics Cup. Inscr. as in T 84.
359. 84. 10 f. brown, turq. & grn. 35 20
360. – 18 f. green, red & violet 40 30
361. – 30 f. blue, brown & black 70 40

85. Palace of Justice, Yaounde.

**1964.** 1st Anniv. of European-African Economic Convention. Multicoloured
362. 15 f. Type 85 .. .. 1·25 55
363. 40 f. Sun, moon and economic emblems (vert.) .. 2·10 1·10

86. Olympic Flame and Hurdling.

**1964.** Olympic Games, Toyko.
364. 86. 9 f. red, blk. & grn. (post.) 1·75 1·40
365. – 10 f. brown, violet & red 1·90 1·40
366. – 300 f. turquoise, brown and red (air) .. 7·75 4·25
DESIGNS—VERT. 10 f. Running. HORIZ. 300 f. Wrestling.

87. Ntem Falls.

90. Inscription recording laying of First Rail.

89. Pres. Kennedy.

**1964.** Folklore and Tourism.
367. – 9 f. red, bl. & grn. (post.) 45 20
368. – 18 f. blue, brown & red 55 35
369. 87. 20 f. drab, green & red 65 35
370. – 25 f. red, brown & oran. 1·40 55
371. – 50 f. brn., grn. & bl. (air) 90 55
372. – 250 f. sep., grn. & brn. 9·75 3·25
DESIGNS—As Type 87. VERT. 9 f. Bamileke dance costume. 18 f. Bamenda dance mask. HORIZ. 25 f. Fulani horseman. LARGER (43×27½ mm.): 50 f. View of Kribi and Longji. 250 f. Black rhinoceros.

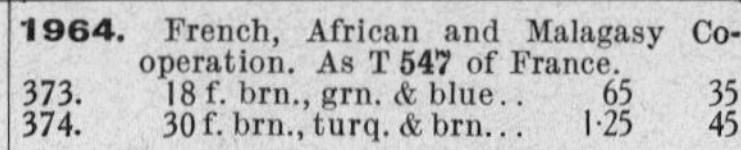
**1964.** French, African and Malagasy Cooperation. As T 547 of France.
373. 18 f. brn., grn. & blue .. 65 35
374. 30 f. brn., turq. & brn. .. 1·25 45

**1964.** Air. Pres. Kennedy Commem.
375. 89. 100 f. sepia, grn. & apple 2·00 2·00

**1965.** Opening of Mbanga-Kumba Railway.
376. 90. 12 f. indigo, grn. & blue 65 40
377. – 20 f. yellow, grn. & red 1·75 80
DESIGN—HORIZ. (36×22 mm.): 20 f. Diesel locomotive.

91. Abraham Lincoln.

**1965.** Air. Death Cent. of Abraham Lincoln.
378. 91. 100 f. multicoloured .. 2·00 1·40

92. Ambulance and First Aid Post.

DESIGN — VERT. 50 f. Nurse and child.

**1965.** Cameroun Red Cross.
379. 92. 25 f. yellow, green & red 50 30
380. – 50 f. brown, red and grey 1·25 45

93. "Syncom" and I.T.U. Emblem.

**1965.** Air. Centenary of I.T.U.
381. 93. 70 f. black, blue & red 1·40 70

94. Churchill giving "V" Sign.

95. "Map" Savings Bank.

**1965.** Air. Churchill Commem. Mult.
382. 12 f. Type 94 .. .. 1·00 55
383. 18 f. Churchill, oak spray and cruiser "De Grasse" 1·10 60

**1965.** Federal Postal Savings Bank.
384. 95. 9 f. yellow, red & green 30 15
385. – 15 f. brown, green & blue 40 20
386. – 20 f brn., chest. & turq. 45 30
DESIGNS—HORIZ. (48×27 mm.): 15 f. Savings Bank building. VERT. (27×48 mm.): 20 f. "Cocoa-bean" savings bank.

96. Africa Cup and Players.

**1965.** Winning of Africa Cup by Oryx Football Club.
387. 96. 9 f. brown, yellow & red 55 35
388. 20 f. blue, yellow and red 1·40 45

97. Map of Europe and Africa.

98. U.P.U. Monument, Berne and Doves.

**1965.** "Europafrique".
389. 97. 5 f. red, lilac and black 20 15
390. – 40 f. multicoloured .. 90 60
DESIGN: 40 f. Yaounde Conference.

**1965.** 5th Anniv. of Admission to U.P.U.
391. 98. 30 f. purple and red .. 60 45

99. I.C.Y. Emblem.

**1965.** Int. Co-operation Year.
392. 99. 10 f. red & blue (postage) 35 30
393. 100 f. blue and red (air) 1·60 90

100. Pres. Ahidjo and Government House.

**1965.** Re-election of Pres. Ahidjo. Mult.
394. 9 f. Pres. Ahidjo wearing hat, and Government House (vert.) .. .. .. 20 10
395. 18 f. Type 100 .. .. 35 15
396. 20 f. As 9 f. .. .. 45 20
397. 25 f. Type 100 .. .. 55 30

101. Musgum Huts, Pouss.

**1965.** Folklore and Tourism.
398. 101. 9 f. green, brown and red (postage) .. .. 35 15
399. – 18 f. brown, green & blue 50 30
400. – 20 f. brown and blue .. 70 30
401. – 25 f. grey, lake & green 95 30
402. – 50 f. brown, blue & green (48×27 mm.) (air).. 2·00 80
DESIGNS—HORIZ. 18 f. Great Calao's dance (N. Cameroons). 25 f. National Tourist office, Yaounde. 50 f. Racing pirogue on Sanaga River, Edea. VERT. 20 f. Sultan's palace gate Foumban.

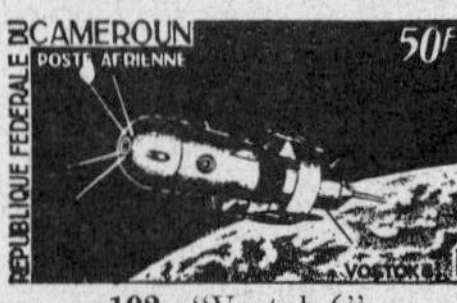

102. "Vostok 6".

**1966.** Air. Spacecraft.
403. 102. 50 f. green and lake .. 80 45
404. – 100 f. blue and purple .. 2·00 85
405. – 200 f. violet and blue .. 3·50 2·10
406. – 500 f. blue and indigo.. 8·50 4·25
DESIGNS: 100 f. "Gemini 4", and White in space. 200 f. "Gemini 5". 500 f. "Gemini 6" and "Gemini 7" making rendezvous.

103. Mountain's Hotel, Buea.

**1966.** Cameroun Hotels.
407. 103. 9 f. bistre, green and red (postage) .. .. 30 15
408. – 20 f. black, green & blue 35 20
409. – 35 f. red, brown & green 60 40
410. 103. 18 f. blk., grn. & bl. (air) 35 20
411. – 25 f. indigo, red and blue 55 20
412. – 50 f. brn., oran. & green 2·10 90
413. – 60 f. brn., green & blue 1·40 55
414. – 85 f. blue, red and green 1·75 65
415. – 100 f. pur., blue & grn. 2·40 95
416. – 150 f. orge., brn. & blue 3·25 1·60
HOTELS—HORIZ. 20 f. Deputies, Yaounde. 25 f. Akwa Palace, Douala. 35 f. Dschang. 50 f. Terminus, Yaounde. 60 f. Imperial, Yaounde. 85 f. Independence, Yaounde. 150 f. Huts, Waza Camp. VERT. 100 f. Hunting Lodge, Mora.

104. Foumban Bas-relief.

**1966.** World Festival of Negro Arts, Dakar
417. 104. 9 f. black and red .. 55 15
418. – 18 f. pur., brn. and grn. 55 30
419. – 20 f. brown, blue & violet 80 30
420. – 25 f. brown and plum.. 90 30
DESIGNS—VERT. 18 f. Ekoi mask. 20 f. Bamileke statue. HORIZ. 25 f. Bamoun stool.

105. W.H.O. Headquarters, Geneva.

106. "Phaeomeria magnifica".

**1966.** U.N. Agency Buildings.
421 105. 50 f. lake, blue & yellow 90 50
422. – 50 f. yellow, blue & grn. 90 50
DESIGN: No. 422, I.T.U. Headquarters, Geneva.

**1966.** Flowers. Multicoloured.
(a) Postage. Size as T 106.
423. 9 f. Type 106 .. .. 45 15
424. 15 f. "Strelitzia reginae" 65 15
425. 18 f. "Hibiscus schizopetalus X, rosa sinensis" .. 55 20
426. 20 f. "Antigonon leptopus" 55 15
(b) Air. Size 26×45½ mm.
427. 25 f. "Hibiscus mutabilis" ("Caprice des dames") 80 20
428. 50 f. "Delonix regia" .. 1·40 30
429. 100 f. "Bougainvillea glabra" .. .. .. 2·50 50
430. 200 f. "Thevetia peruviana" 3·75 1·50
431. 250 f. "Hippeastrum equestre" .. .. 4·50 1·90
For stamps as Type 106 but showing fruits, see Nos. 463/71.

107. Mobile Gendarmerie.

**1966.** Air. Cameroun Armed Forces.
432. 107. 20 f. blue, brown & plum 45 20
433. – 25 f. green, violet & brn. 45 20
434. – 60 f. indigo, green & blue 1·60 80
435. – 100 f. blue, red & purple 2·40 95
DESIGNS: 25 f. Paratrooper. 60 f. Gunboat "Vigilant". 100 f. Dassault MD-315 Flamant airplane.

108. Wembley Stadium.

**1966.** Air. World Cup Football Championships.
436. 108. 50 f. green, blue & red 1·40 45
437. – 200 f. red, blue & green 3·75 2·10
DESIGN: 200 f. Footballers.

109. Douglas DC-8F Jet Trader and "Air Afrique" Emblem.

**1966.** Air. Inaug of DC-8 Air Service.
438 109 25 f. grey, black & pur 60 35

**110.** U.N. General Assembly

**1966.** 6th Anniv. of Admission to U.N.
439. **110.** 50 f. pur., green & blue 65 20
440. – 100 f. blue, brown & grn. 1·40 65
DESIGN—VERT. 100 f. Africans encircling U.N. emblem within figure "6".

**111.** 1st Minister's Residency, Buea (side view).

**1966.** 5th Anniv of Cameroun's Reunification. Multicoloured.
441. 9 f. Type **111** .. .. .. 30 15
442. 18 f. Prime Minister's Residency, Yaounde (front view) .. .. .. 40 20
443. 20 f. As 18 f. but side view 45 30
444. 25 f. As Type **111** but front view .. .. .. 55 30

**112.** Learning to Write.

**1966.** 20th Anniv. of U.N.E.S.C.O. and U.N.I.C.E.F.
445. **112.** 50 f. brown, pur. & blue 90 45
446. – 50 f. black, blue & pur. 90 45
DESIGN: No. 446, Cameroun children.

**113.** Buea Cathedral.

**1966.** Air. Religious Buildings.
447. **113.** 18 f. purple, blue & grn. 35 20
448. – 25 f. violet, brown & grn. 45 20
449. – 30 f. lake, green & purple 55 30
450. – 60 f. green, lake & turq. 1·10 50
BUILDINGS: 25 f. Yaounde Cathedral. 30 f. Orthodox Church, Yaounde. 60 f. Garoua Mosque.

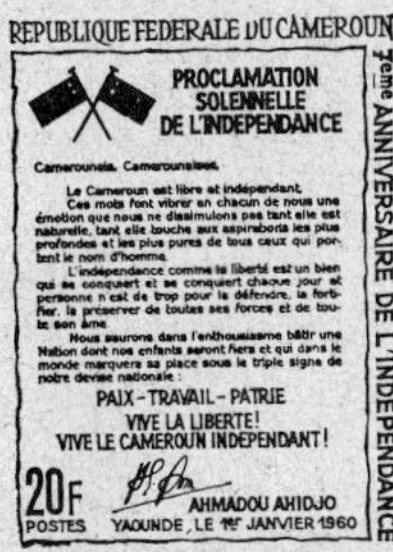

**114.** Proclamation.

**1967.** 7th Anniv. of Independence.
451. **114.** 20 f. red, green & yellow .. .. 1·90 1·10

**115.** Map of Africa, Railway Lines and Signals.

**117.** Aircraft and I.C.A.O. Emblem.

**116.** Lions Emblem and Jungle.

**1967.** 5th African and Malagasy Railway Technicians Conf., Yaounde. Multicoloured.
452. 20 f. Type **115** .. .. 1·25 75
453. 20 f. Map of Africa and diesel train .. .. 1·75 80

**1967.** 50th Anniv. of Lions Int. Mult.
454. 50 f. Type **116** .. .. 80 45
455. 100 f. Lions emblem and palms .. .. .. 1·75 95

**1967.** Int. Civil Aviation Organization.
456. **117.** 50 f. multicoloured .. 90 45

**118.** Dove and I.A.E.A. Emblem.

**1967.** Int. Atomic Energy Agency.
457. **118.** 50 f. blue and green .. 90 45

**119.** Rotary Banner and Emblem.

**1967.** 10th Anniv. of Cameroun Branch, Rotary Int.
458. **119.** 25 f. red, gold & blue 80 45

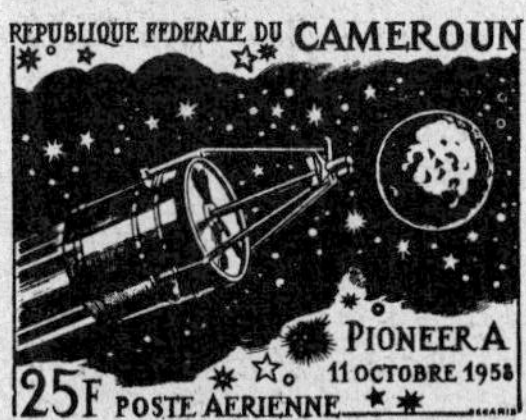

**120.** "Pioneer A".

**1967.** Air. "Conquest of the Moon".
459. **120.** 25 f. green, brown & blue 40 20
460. – 50 f. violet, pur. & grn. 85 35
461. – 100 f. purple, brn. & bl. 2·00 85
462. – 250 f. purple, grey & brn. 4·50 2·50
DESIGNS: 50 f. "Ranger 6". 100 f. "Luna 9". 250 f. "Luna 10".

**121.** Grapefruit.

**122.** Sanaga Waterfalls.

**1967.** Fruits. Multicoloured.
463 1 f. Type **121** .. .. 10 10
464 2 f. Papaw .. .. 10 10
465 3 f. Custard-apple .. .. 15 15
466 4 f. Breadfruit .. .. 15 15
467 5 f. Coconut .. .. 30 15
468 6 f. Mango .. .. 35 15
469 8 f. Avocado .. .. 65 30
470 10 f. Pineapple .. .. 1·10 40
471 30 f. Bananas .. .. 3·00 1·25

**1967.** Int. Tourist Year.
472. **122.** 30 f. multicoloured .. 55 30

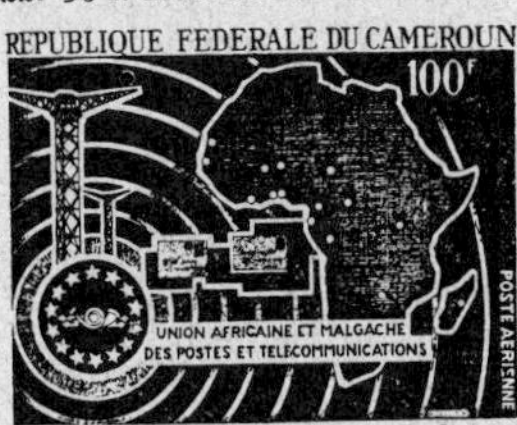

**123.** Map, Letters and Pylons.

**1967.** Air. 5th Anniv. of African and Malagasy Posts and Telecommunications Union (U.A.M.P.T.).
473. **123.** 100 f. purple, lake and turquoise .. .. 2·00 85

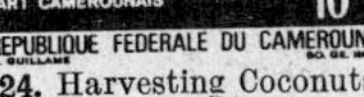

**124.** Harvesting Coconuts (carved box).

**125.** Crossed Skis.

**1967.** Cameroun Art.
474. **124.** 10 f. brown, red & blue 30 15
475. – 20 f. brown, green & yell. 45 30
476. – 30 f. brown, red & green 65 30
477. – 100 f. brown, red & grn. 2·00 70
DESIGNS (Carved boxes): 20 f. Lion-hunting. 30 f. Harvesting coconuts (different). 100 f. Carved chest.

**1967.** Air. Winter Olympic Games, Grenoble.
478. **125.** 30 f. brown and blue .. 1·40 65

**126.** Cameroun Exhibit.

**1967.** Air. World Fair, Montreal.
479. **126.** 50 f. brown, chest. & pur. 90 35
480. – 100 f. brn., pur. and grn. 2·75 95
481. – 200 f. grn., pur. & brn. 3·75 1·90
DESIGNS: 100 f. Totem poles. 200 f. African pavilion.

For No. 481 optd., **PREMIER HOMME SUR LA LUNE 20 JUILLET 1969/FIRST MAN LANDING ON MOON 20 JULY 1969** see note below Nos. 512/17.

**127.** Chancellor Adenauer and Cologne Cathedral.

**128.** Arms of the Republic.

**1967.** Air. Adenauer Commem. Mult.
482. 30 f. Type **127** .. .. 80 30
483. 70 f. Adenauer and Chancellor's residence, Bonn .. 1·75 55

**1968.** 8th Anniv. of Independence.
484. **128.** 30 f. multicoloured 65 35

**129.** Pres. Ahidjo and King Faisal of Saudi Arabia.

**1968.** Air. Pres. Ahidjo's Pilgrimage to Mecca and Visit to the Vatican. Multicoloured.
485. 30 f. Type **129** .. .. 65 35
486. 60 f. Pope Paul VI greeting Pres. Ahidjo .. .. 1·60 55

**130.** "Explorer VI" (televised picture of Earth).

**1968.** Air. Telecommunications Satellites.
487. **130.** 20 f. grey, red and blue 40 20
488. – 30 f. blue, indigo & red 55 30
489. – 40 f. green, red & plum 80 40
DESIGNS: 30 f. "Molnya". 40 f. "Molnya" (televised picture of Earth).

**131.** Douala Port.

**1968.** Air. Five-Year Development Plan.
490. – 20 f. blue, red & green 35 20
491. – 30 f. blue, green & brn. 2·00 65
492. – 30 f. blue, brown & grn. 65 30
493. – 40 f. brn., grn. & turq. 65 30
494. **131.** 60 f. pur., indigo & blue 1·75 70
DESIGNS—VERT. 20 f. Steel forge. 30 f. (No. 491), "Transcamerounais" express train leaving tunnel. 30 f. (No. 492), Tea-harvesting. 40 f. Rubber-tapping.

**132.** Spiny Lobster.

**1968.** Fishes and Crustaceans.
495. **132.** 5 f. grn., brn. & violet 15 15
496. – 10 f. slate, brn. & blue 20 15
497. – 15 f. brn., chest. & pur. 40 15
498. – 20 f. brown and blue .. 50 15
499. – 25 f. blue, brn. and grn. 70 45
500. – 30 f. brn., blue and red 1·00 45
501. – 40 f. blue, brn. & oran. 1·10 55
502. – 50 f. red, slate & green 2·00 65
503. – 55 f. purple, brn. & blue 2·40 1·10
504. – 60 f. blue, purple & grn. 3·75 1·40
FISHES AND CRUSTACEANS—HORIZ. 10 f. Fresh water crayfish. 15 f. Nile mouthbreeder. 20 f. Sole. 25 f. Pike. 30 f. Swimming crab. 55 f. Snakehead. 60 f. Threadfin. VERT. 40 f. Sickle fish. 50 f. Prawn.

**133.** Refinery and Tanker.

**1968.** Inauguration of Petroleum Refinery, Port Gentil, Gabon.
505. **133.** 30 f. multicoloured .. 1·00 40

**134.** Boxing.

**135.** Human Rights Emblem.

**1968.** Air. Olympic Games, Mexico.
506. **134.** 30 f. brn., grn. & emer. 60 30
507. – 50 f. brn., red & green 1·25 50
508. – 60 f. brn., blue & green 1·50 55
DESIGNS: 50 f. Long-jumping. 60 f. Gymnastics.

**1968.** Human Rights Year.
510. **135.** 15 f. bl. & salmon (post.) 45 20
511. 30 f. grn. & pur. (air) .. 55 35

**136.** Mahatma Gandhi and Map of India.

**137.** "The Letter" (A. Cambon).

**1968.** Air. "Apostles of Peace".
512. **136.** 30 f. blk., yell. & blue 45 30
513. – 30 f. black and blue .. 45 30
514. – 40 f. black and pink .. 65 55
515. – 60 f. black and lilac .. 90 65
516. – 70 f. blk., blue & buff .. 1·25 80
517. – 70 f. black and green .. 1·25 80
PORTRAITS: No. 513, Martin Luther King. No. 514, J. F. Kennedy. No. 515, R. F. Kennedy. No. 516, Gandhi (full-face). No. 517, Martin Luther King (half-length).

During 1969, Nos. 481 and 512/17 were issued optd. **PREMIER HOMME SUR LA LUNE 20 JUILLET 1969/FIRST MAN LANDING ON MOON 20 JULY 1969** in very limited quantities.

**1968.** Air. "Philexafrique" Stamp Exn., Abidjan (in 1969). (1st issue).

519. **137.** 100 f. multicoloured 3·00 2·40

**138.** Wouri Bridge and 1 f. stamp of 1925.

**1969.** Air. "Philexafrique" Stamp Exn., Abidjan, Ivory Coast (2nd issue).

520. **138.** 50 f. blue, olive and grn. 1·40 1·40

**139.** President Ahidjo.

**1969.** 9th Anniv. of Independence.

521. **139.** 30 f. multicoloured .. 65 25

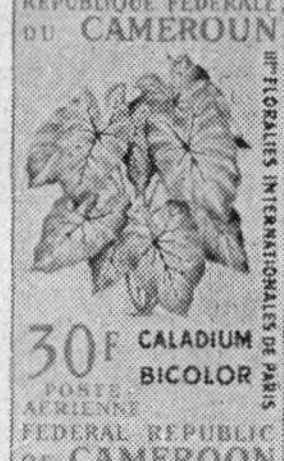


**140.** Vat of Chocolate. **141.** "Caladium bicolor".

**1969.** Chocolate Industry Development.

522. **140.** 15 f. blue, brown & red 30 20
523. – 30 f. brn., choc. & grn. 55 30
524. – 50 f. red, grn. & bistre 80 35

DESIGNS—HORIZ. 30 f. Chocolate factory. VERT. 50 f. Making confectionery.

**1969.** Air. 3rd Int. Flower Show, Paris. Multicoloured.

525. 30 f. Type **141** .. .. 65 45
526. 50 f. "Aristolochia elegans" 1·40 65
527. 100 f. "Gloriosa simplex" 3·00 1·40

**142.** Reproduction Symbol.

**1969.** Abbia Arts and Folklore.

528. **142.** 5 f. purple, turquoise and blue .. .. 20 15
529. – 10 f. orge., olive & blue 30 15
530. – 15 f. indigo, red & blue 40 20
531. – 30 f. green, brn. & blue 60 30
532. – 70 f. red, green and blue 1·50 70

DESIGNS—HORIZ. 10 f. "Two Toucans". 30 f. "Vulture attacking Monkey". VERT. 15 f. Forest Symbol. 70 f. Oliphant-player.

**143.** Post Office, Douala.

**1969.** Air. New Post Office Buildings.

533. **143.** 30 f. brn., blue & green 40 20
534. – 50 f. red, slate & turq. 65 35
535. – 100 f. brn. and turq... 1·40 65

DESIGNS: 50 f. G.P.O., Buea. 100 f. G.P.O., Bafoussam.

**144.** "Coronation of Napoleon" (David).

**1969.** Air. Birth Bicent. of Napoleon Bonaparte.

536. **144.** 30 f. multicoloured .. 90 55
537. – 1,000 f. gold .. .. 35·00

DESIGN: 1,000 f. "Napoleon crossing the Alps".

No. 537 is embossed on gold foil.

**145.** Kumba Station. **146.** Bank Emblem.

**1969.** Opening of Mbanga-Kumba Railway. Multicoloured.

538. 30 f. Type **145** .. .. 95 50
539. 50 f. Diesel train on bridge (vert.) .. .. 2·25 80

**1969.** 5th Anniv. of African Development Bank.

540. **146.** 30 f. brn., grn. & vio. 60 30

**1969.** Air. Negro Writers. Portrait designs as T **136**.

541. 15 f. brown and blue .. 40 20
542. 30 f. brown and purple .. 50 20
543. 30 f. brown and yellow .. 50 20
544. 50 f. brown and green .. 70 40
545. 50 f. brown and agate .. 70 40
546. 100 f. brown and yellow.. 1·75 1·10

DESIGNS—VERT. No. 541, Dr. P. Mars (Haiti). No. 542, W. Dubois (U.S.A.). No. 543, A. Cesaire (Martinique). No. 544, M. Garvey (Jamaica). No. 545, L. Hughes (U.S.A.) No. 546, R. Maran (Martinique).

**148.** I.L.O. Emblem.

**1969.** Air. 50th Anniv. of I.L.O.

548. **148.** 30 f. black and turq... 55 30
549. 50 f. black and mauve 90 40

**149.** Astronauts and "Apollo II" in Sea.

**1969.** Air. 1st Man on the Moon. Mult.

550. 200 f. Type **149** .. .. 3·25 1·75
551. 500 f. Astronaut and module on Moon.. .. .. 7·75 3·50

**150.** Airplane, Map and Airport.

**1969.** 10th Anniv. of Aerial Navigation Security Agency for Africa and Madagascar (ASECNA).

552. **150.** 100 f. green .. .. 1·50 70

**151.** President Ahidjo, Arms and Map.

**1970.** Air. 10th Anniv. of Independence.

553. **151.** 1,000 f. gold and mult. 21·00

No. 553 is embosed on gold foil.

**152.** Mont Febe Hotel, Yaounde.

**1970.** Air. Tourism.

554. **152.** 30 f. grey, grn. & brn. 60 30

**153.** Lenin. **154.** "Lantana camara".

**1970.** Air. Birth Cent. of Lenin.

555. **153.** 50 f. brown and yellow 1·40 35

**1970.** African Climbing Plants. Mult.

556. 15 f. Type **154** (postage).. 35 15
557. 30 f. "Passiflora quadrangularis" .. .. 80 20
558. 50 f. "Cleome speciosa" (air) .. .. .. 1·40 55
559. 100 f. "Mussaenda erythrophylla" .. .. 2·50 1·40

**155.** Lions' Emblem and Map of Africa.

**1970.** Air. 13th Congress of Lions Int. District 403, Yaounde.

560. **155.** 100 f. multicoloured .. 1·90 80

**156.** New U.P.U. H.Q.

**1970.** New U.P.U. Headquarters Building, Berne.

561. **156.** 30 f. green, violet & bl. 55 20
562. 50 f. blue, red & grey.. 80 30

**157.** U.N. Emblem and Stylised Doves.

**1970.** Air. 25th Anniv. of United Nations.

563. **157.** 30 f. brown and orange 65 30
564. – 50 f. indigo and blue.. 90 40

DESIGN—VERT. 50 f. U.N. emblem and stylised dove.

**158.** Fermenting Vats.

**1970.** Brewing Industry.

565. **158.** 15 f. brn., grn. & slate 35 20
566. – 30 f. red, brown & blue 65 30

DESIGN: 30 f. Storage tanks.

**159.** Japanese Pavilion.

**1970.** Air. Expo 70.

567. **159.** 50 f. blue, red and green 90 45
568. – 100 f. red, blue and grn. 1·90 80
569. – 150 f. brn., slate and bl. 3·00 1·50

DESIGNS—VERT. 100 f. Expo Emblem and Map of Japan. HORIZ. 150 f. Australian Pavilion.

**160.** Gen. De Gaulle in Tropical Kit. **162.** Dancers.

**161.** Aztec Stadium, Mexico City.

**1970.** Air. "Homage to General De Gaulle".

570. **160.** 100 f. brown, blue and green .. .. 2·50 1·60
571. – 200 f. blue, green and brown .. .. 4·50 2·25

DESIGN: 200 f. Gen. De Gaulle in military uniform.

Nos. 570/1 were issued together as a triptych, separated by a stamp-size label showing Maps of France and Cameroun.

**1970.** Air. World Cup Football Championships, Mexico. Multicoloured.

572. 50 f. Type **161** .. .. 80 40
573. 100 f. Mexican team .. 1·75 1·00
574. 200 f. Pele and Brazilian team with World Cup (vert.) .. .. .. 3·00 1·40

**1970.** Ozila Dancers.

575. **162.** 30 f. red, orge. & grn. 70 35
576. 50 f. red, brown and scarlet .. .. 1·90 80

**163.** Doll in National Costume. **164.** Beethoven (after Stieler).

**1970.** Cameroun Dolls.

577. **163.** 10 f. grn., black and red 45 35
578. 15 f. red, grn. and yell. 55 45
579. 30 f. brn., grn. and blk. 1·50 55

**1970.** Air. Birth Bicent. of Beethoven.

580. **164.** 250 f. multicoloured.. 3·75 1·90

**1970.** Air. Rembrandt Paintings. Horiz. designs similar to T **144**. Multicoloured.

581. 70 f. "Christ at Emmaus" 1·40 45
582. 150 f. "The Anatomy Lesson" .. .. 2·50 95

**166.** "Industry and Agriculture". **167.** Bust of Dickens.

**1970.** "Europafrique" Economic Community.

583. **166.** 30 f. multicoloured .. 60 30

**1970.** Air. Death Cent. of Charles Dickens.

584. **167.** 40 f. brown and red .. 65 30
585. – 50 f. multicoloured .. 80 35
586. – 100 f. multicoloured.. 1·40 90

DESIGNS: 50 f. Characters from David Copperfield. 100 f. Dickens writing.

**1971.** Air. De Gaulle Memorial Issue. Nos. 570/1 opted. **IN MEMORIAM 1890-1970.**

587. **160.** 100 f. brn., blue & grn. 2·50 1·40
588. – 200 f. blue, grn. & brn. 4·50 2·00

169. University Buildings.

**1971.** Inaug. of Federal University, Yaounde.

589. 169. 50 f. grn., blue & brn. 65 30

170. Presidents Ahidjo and Pompidou.

**1971.** Visit of Pres. Pompidou of France.

590. 170. 30 f. multicoloured .. 90 55

171. " Cameroun Youth ".

**1971.** 5th National Youth Festival.

591. 171. 30 f. multicoloured .. 55 30

172. Timber Yard, Douala.

**1971.** Air. Industrial Expansion.

592. 172. 40 f. brn., grn. & red .. 40 20

593. – 70 f. brn., grn. & blue 90 40

594. – 100 f. red, blue & grn. 1·50 50

DESIGNS—VERT. 70 f. " Alucam " aluminium plant, Edea. HORIZ. 100 f. Mbakaou Dam.

173. "Gerbera hybrida". 174. "World Races".

**1971.** Flowers. Multicoloured.

595. 20 f. Type 173 .. .. 45 35

596. 40 f. "Opuntia polyantha" 1·00 45

597. 50 f. "Hemerocallis hybrida" 1·40 55

For similar designs inscr. " United Republic of Cameroun " etc., see Nos. 648/52.

**1971.** Racial Equality Year. Multicoloured.

598. 20 f. Type 174 .. .. 35 15

599. 30 f. Hands of four races clasping globe .. .. 50 20

175. Crowned Cranes, Camp de Waza.

**1971.** Landscapes.

600. 175. 10 f. blue, red & green 1·25 30

601. – 20 f. red, brn. & grn... 40 25

602. – 30 f. grn., blue & brn. 55 25

DESIGNS: 20 f. African pirogue. 30 f. Sanaga River.

176. Relay-racing.

**1971.** Air. 75th Anniv. of Modern Olympic Games.

603. 176. 30 f. blue, red & brn. 45 30

604. – 50 f. purple and blue.. 65 30

605. – 100 f. blk., grn. & red 1·40 55

DESIGNS—VERT. 50 f. Olympic runner with torch. HORIZ. 100 f. Throwing the discus.

177. "Villalba" (deep-sea trawler).

**1971.** Air. Fishing Industry.

606. 177. 30 f. brn., grn. & blue 65 45

607. – 40 f. purple, blue & grn. 80 45

608. – 70 f. brown, red & blue 1·40 65

609. – 150 f. multicoloured .. 3·75 1·75

DESIGNS: 40 f. Traditional fishing method, Northern Cameroun. 70 f. Fish quay, Douala. 150 f. Shrimp-boats, Douala.

178. Peace Palace, The Hague.

**1971.** 25th Anniv. of Int. Court of Justice, The Hague.

610. 178. 50 f. brn., bl. & green 65 30

179. 1916 French Occupation 20 c. and 1914–18 War Memorial, Yaounde.

**1971.** Air. " Philatecam 71 " Stamp Exhibition, Yaounde (1st issue).

611. 179. 20 f. brn., ochre & grn. 35 20

612. – 25 f. brn., grn. & blue 40 20

613. – 40 f. grn., grey & brn. 65 20

614. – 50 f. black, red, sepia and brown .. .. 85 35

615. – 100 f. grn., brn. & orge. 2·00 65

DESIGNS: 25 f. 1954 15 f. Jamot stamp and memorial. 40 f. 1965 25 f. Tourist Office stamp and public buildings, Yaounde. 50 f. German stamp and Imperial German postal emblem. 100 f. 1915 Expeditionary Force optd., error, and Expeditionary Force memorial. See also No. 620.

180. Rope Bridge. 181. Bamoun Horseman (carving).

**1971.** " Rural Life ". Multicoloured.

616. 40 f. Type 180 .. .. 70 20

617. 45 f. Local market (horiz.) 85 30

**1971.** Cameroun Carving.

618. 181. 10 f. brown and yellow 35 15

619. – 15 f. brown and yellow 35 20

DESIGN: 15 f. Fetish statuette.

182. Pres. Ahidjo, Flag and " Reunification " Road.

**1971.** Air. " Philatecam 71 " Stamp Exhib., Yaounde (2nd issue).

620. 182. 250 f. multicoloured.. 5·25 3·75

183. Satellite and Globe.

**1971.** Pan-African Telecommunications Network.

621. 183. 40 f. multicoloured. .. 55 35

184. U.A.M.P.T. Headquarters, Brazzaville and Carved Stool.

**1971.** Air. 10th Anniv. of African and Malagasy Posts and Telecommunications Union.

622. 184. 100 f. multicoloured .. 1·40 65

185. Children acclaiming Emblem.

**1971.** 25th Anniv. of U.N.I.C.E.F.

623. 185. 40 f. pur., blue & slate 60 20

624. - 50 f. red green & blue 70 35

DESIGN—VERT. 50 f. Ear of Wheat and Emblem.

186. " The Annunciation " (Fra Angelico).

**1971.** Air. Christmas. Paintings. Mult.

625. 40 f. Type 186 .. .. 45 15

626. 45 f. " Virgin and Child " (Del Sarto) .. .. 55 30

627. 150 f. " The Holy Family with the Lamb " (detail Raphael) (vert.) .. 2·75 95

187. Cabin, South-Central Region.

**1972.** Traditional Cameroun Houses. Mult.

628. 10 f. Type 187 .. .. 20 15

629. 15 f. Adamaoua round house .. .. .. 35 20

188. Airline Emblem.

**1972.** Air. Cameroun Airlines' Inaugural Flight.

630. 188. 50 f. multicoloured .. 55 20

189. Giraffe and Palm Tree. 190. Africa Cup.

**1972.** Festival of Youth. Multicoloured.

631. 2 f. Type 189 .. .. 15 10

632. 5 f. Domestic scene .. 15 10

633. 10 f. Blacksmith (horiz.).. 20 15

634. 15 f. Women .. .. 20 15

**1972.** African Football Cup Championships. Multicoloured.

635. 20 f. Type 190 .. .. 45 20

636. 40 f. Players with ball (horiz.) 65 35

637. 45 f. Team captains .. 1·10 35

191. " St. Mark's Square and Doge's Palace " (detail-Caffi).

**1972.** Air. U.N.E.S.C.O. " Save Venice " Campaign, Multicoloured.

638. 40 f. Type 191 .. .. 55 30

639. 100 f. " Regatta on the Grand Canal " (detail - Canaletto) .. .. 1·75 55

640. 200 f. " Regatta on the Grand Canal " (detail - Canalette) (different) .. 3·50 1·40

192. Assembly Building, Yaounde.

**1972.** 110th Session of Inter-Parliamentary Council, Yaounde.

641. 192. 40 f. multicoloured .. 55 30

193. Horseman, North Cameroun.

**1972.** Traditional Life and Folklore. Mult.

642. 15 f. Type 193 .. .. 30 15

643. 20 f. Bororo woman (vert.) 35 15

644. 40 f. Wouri River and Mt. Cameroun .. .. 1·40 45

194. Pataiev, Dobrovolsky and Volkov.

**1972.** Air. " Soyuz 11 " Cosmonauts. Memorial Issue.

645. 194. 50 f. multicoloured .. 65 35

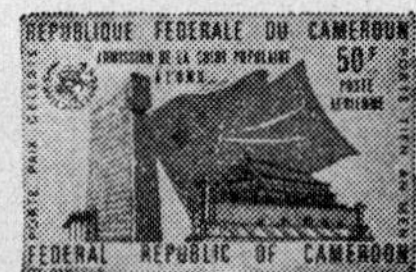


195. U.N. Building, New York, Gate of Heavenly Peace, Peking and Chinese Flag.

**1972.** Air. Admission of Chinese People's Republic to U.N.

646. 195. 50 f. multicoloured .. 55 20

196. Chemistry Laboratory, Federal University.

**1972.** Pres. Ahidjo Prize.

647. 196. 40 f. red, green & purple 55 35

**1972.** Flowers. As T 173, but inscr. " UNITED REPUBLIC OF CAMEROON ", etc. Multicoloured.

648. 40 f. "Solanum macranthum" 55 20

649. 40 f. " Kaempferia aethiopica " .. .. 65 20

650. 45 f. " Hoya carnosa " .. 65 35

651. 45 f. " Cassia alata " .. 65 20

652. 50 f. "Crinum sanderianum" 90 35

197. Swimming.

**1972.** Air. Olympic Games, Munich.

653. **197.** 50 f. grn., brn. & lake 80 35
654. – 50 f. brn., blue and sepia .. .. 80 35
655. – 200 f. lake, grey & pur. 3·25 1·40

DESIGNS—HORIZ. No. 655, Horse-jumping. VERT. No. 654, Boxing.

**198.** " Charaxes ameliae ".

**201.** Great Blue Turacos.

**1972.** Butterflies. Multicoloured.

657. 40 f. Type **198** .. .. 2·00 55
658. 45 f. " Papiliotynderaeus " 2·50 1·10

**1972.** No. 471 surch.

659. 40 f. on 30 f. multicoloured 60 40

**1972.** Air. Olympic Gold Medal Winners. Nos. 653/5 optd. as listed below.

660. 50 f. green, brown & lake 80 35
661. 50 f. brown, blue and sepia .. .. .. 80 35
662. 200 f. lake, grey and purple 3·25 1·40

OVERPRINTS: No. 660, **NATATION MARK SPITZ 7 MEDAILLES D'OR.** No. 661, **SUPER-WELTER KOTTYSCH MEDAILLE D'OR.** No. 662, **CONCOURS COMPLET MEADE MEDAILLE D'OR.**

**1972.** Birds. Multicoloured.

663. 10 f. Type **201** .. .. 50 25
664. 45 f. Red-faced Lovebirds (horiz.) .. .. 1·75 65

**202.** " The Virgin with Angels " (Cimabue).

**203.** St. Theresa.

**1972.** Air. Christmas. Multicoloured.

665. 45 f. Type **202** .. .. 80 35
666. 140 f. "The Madonna of the Rose Arbour" (S. Lochner) 2·25 1·25

**1973.** Air. Birth Cent. of St. Theresa of Lisieux.

667. **203.** 45 f. blue, brn. & violet 55 20
668. – 100 f. mauve, brn. & bl. 1·40 55

DESIGN: 100 f. Lisieux Basilica.

**204.** Emperor Haile Selassie and " Africa Hall ", Addis Ababa.

**1973.** Air. 80th Birthday of Emperor Haile Selassie of Ethiopia.

669. **204.** 45 f. multicoloured .. 60 35

**205.** Cotton Cultivation, North Cameroun.

**207.** Human Hearts.

**206.** " Food for All ".

**1973.** 3rd Five Year Plan. Multicoloured.

670. 5 f. Type **205** .. .. 10 10
671. 10 f. Cacao pods, South-central region .. .. 10 10
672. 15 f. Forestry, South-eastern area .. .. 20 10
673. 20 f. Coffee plant, West Cameroun .. .. 45 15
674. 45 f. Tea-picking, West Cameroun .. .. 95 30

**1973.** Air. 10th Anniv. of World Food Programme.

675. **206.** 45 f. multicoloured .. 60 35

**1973.** Air. 25th Anniv. of W.H.O.

676. **207.** 50 f. red and blue .. 60 30

**208.** Pres. Ahidjo, Map, Flag and Cameroun Stamp.

**1973.** 1st Anniv. of United Republic. Mult.

677. 10 f. Type **208** (postage).. 45 20
678. 20 f. Pres. Ahidjo, proclamation and stamp .. 65 35
679. 45 f. Pres. Ahidjo, map of Cameroun, rivers & stamp (air) .. .. 55 20
680. 70 f. Significant dates on Cameroun flag .. .. 80 50

**209.** Mask.

**210.** Dr. G. A. Hansen.

**1973.** Bamoun Masks.

681. **209.** 5 f. blk., brn. & green 10 10
682. – 10 f. brn., blk. & purple 20 10
683. – 45 f. brn., black & red 55 30
684. – 100 f. brn., blk. & blue 1·40 55

DESIGNS: 10 f., 45 f., 100 f., as Type **209**, but different masks.

**1973.** Centenary of Hansen's Identification of Leprosy Bacillus.

685. **210.** 45 f. bl., light bl. & brn. 55 30

**211.** Scout Emblem and Flags.

**213.** Folk-dancers.

**1973.** Air. Admission of Cameroun to 24th World Scout Conference.

686. **211.** 40 f. multicoloured .. 50 30
687. 45 f. multicoloured .. 60 35
688. 100 f. multicoloured.. 1·40 60

**1973.** African Solidarity " Drought Relief ". No. 670 surch. **SECHERESSE SOLIDARITE AFRICAINE** and value.

689. **205.** 100 f. on 5 f. mult. .. 1·25 90

**1973.** Folklore Dances of South-west Cameroun. Multicoloured.

690. 10 f. Type **213** .. .. 15 10
691. 25 f. Dancer in plumed hat 45 15
692. 45 f. Dancers with "totem" 80 30

**214.** W.M.O. Emblem.

**1973.** Centenary of W.M.O.

693. **214.** 45 f. blue and green .. 55 30

**215.** Garoua Party H.Q. Building.

**1973.** 7th Anniv. of Cameroun National Union.

694. **215.** 40 f. multicoloured .. 55 30

**216.** Crane with Letter and Telecommunications Emblem.

**1973.** 12th Anniv. of U.A.M.P.T.

695. **216.** 100 f. bl., light bl. & grn. 1·40 55

**217.** African Mask and Old Town Hall, Brussels.

**218.** Avocado.

**1973.** Air. African Fortnight Brussels.

696. **217.** 40 f. brown and purple 55 30

**1973.** Cameroun Fruits. Multicoloured.

697. 10 f. Type **218** .. .. 30 15
698. 20 f. Mango .. .. 35 15
699. 45 f. Plum .. .. 85 20
700. 50 f. Custard-apple .. 1·25 35

**219.** Map of Africa.

**1973.** Air. Aid for Handicapped Children.

701. **219.** 40 f. red, brn. & grn... 55 35

**220.** Kirdi Village.

**1973.** Cameroun Villages.

702. **220.** 15 f. blk., grn. & brn. 20 15
703. – 45 f. brn., red & orge. 50 30
704. – 50 f. blk., grn. & orge. 70 35

DESIGNS: 45 f. Mabas village. 50 f. Fishing village.

**221.** Earth Station.

**1973.** Air. Inauguration of Satellite Earth Station, Zamengoe.

705. **221.** 100 f. brn., blue & grn. 1·10 55

**222.** " The Madonna with Chancellor Rolin " (Van Eyck).

**223.** Handclasp on Map of Africa.

**1973.** Air. Christmas. Multicoloured.

706. 45 f. Type **222** .. .. 80 40
707. 140 f. " The Nativity " (Federico Fiori–Il Barocci) 2·25 1·50

**1974.** 10th Anniv. of Organization of African Unity.

708. **223.** 40 f. blue, red & green 40 20
709. 45 f. green, blue & red 50 20

**224.** Mill-worker.

**1974.** C.I.C.A.M. Industrial Complex.

710. **224.** 45 f. brown, green & red 55 20

**225.** Bilinga Carved Panel. (detail).

**1974.** Cameroun Art.

711. **225.** 10 f. brown and green 20 15
712. – 40 f. brown and red .. 50 20
713. – 45 f. red and blue .. 70 30

DESIGNS: 40 f. Tubinga carving (detail). 45 f. Acajou Ngollon carved panel (detail).

**1974.** No. 469 surch.

714. 40 f. on 8 f. multicoloured 60 30

**227.** Cameroun Cow.

**228.** Route-map and Track.

**1974.** Cattle-raising in North Cameroun. Multicoloured.

715. 40 f. Type **227** (postage).. 65 30
716. 45 f. Cattle in pen (air) .. 65 35

**1974.** Trans-Cameroun Railway. Inauguration of Yaounde–Ngaoundere Line.

717. **228.** 5 f. brown, blue & green 55 30
718. – 20 f. brn., bl. & violet 75 40
719. – 40 f. red, blue & green 1·25 65
720. – 100 f. green, bl. & brn. 2·40 1·10

DESIGNS—HORIZ. 20 f. Laying track. 100 f. Railway bridge over Djerem River. VERT. 40 f. Welding rails.

**229.** Sir Winston Churchill.

**1974.** Air. Birth Cent. of Sir Winston Churchill.

721. **229.** 100 f. black, red & bl. 1·10 55

**230.** Footballer and City Crests.

**1974.** Air. World Cup Football Championships.
722. **230.** 45 f. orange, slate & grey 55 20
723. – 100 f. orge., slate & grey 1·00 50
724. – 200 f. bl., orge. & blk. 2·00 1·25
DESIGNS: 100 f. Goalkeeper and city crests. 200 f. World Cup.

**1974.** Air. West Germany's Victory in World Cup Football Championships. Nos. 722/4 optd. **7th JULY 1974 R.F.A. 2 HOLLANDE 1 7 JUILLET 1974.**
725. **230.** 45 f. orge., slate & grey 55 20
726. – 100 f. orge., slate & grey 1·25 50
727. – 200 f. bl., orge. & blk. 2·40 1·50

**232.** U.P.U. Emblem and Hands with Letters.

**1974.** Cent. of Universal Postal Union.
728. **232.** 40 f. red, bl. & grn. (post.) 65 35
729. – 100 f. grn., vio. & bl. (air) 1·40 65
730. – 200 f. green, red & blue 2·25 1·40
DESIGNS: 100 f. Cameroun U.P.U. headquarters stamps of 1970. 200 f. Cameroun U.P.U. 75th anniv. stamps of 1949.

**233.** Copernicus and Solar System.

**1974.** Air. 500th Birth Anniv. (1973) of Copernicus.
731. **233.** 250 f. blue, red & brown .. .. 3·50 2·25

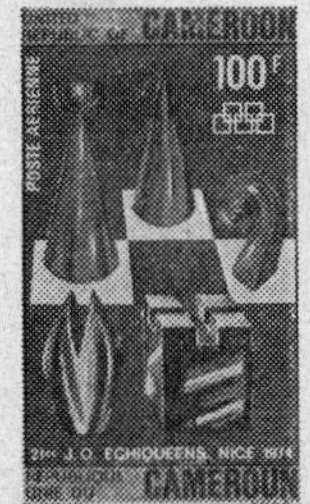

**234.** Modern Chess Pieces.

**1974.** Air. Chess Olympics, Nice.
732. **234.** 100 f. multicoloured .. 2·75 1·10

**235.** African Mask and "Arphila" Emblem.

**1974.** Air. "Arphila 75" Stamp Exhibition, Paris.
733. **235.** 50 f. brown and red .. 45 30

**236.** African Leaders, U.D.E.A.C. H.Q. and Flags.

**1974.** 10th Anniv. of Central African Customs and Economics Union.
734. **236.** 40 f. multicoloured (post.) 55 30
735. – 100 f. multicoloured (air) 1·40 50
DESIGN: 100 f. Similar to Type **236.**

**1974.** No. 717 surch. **10 DECEMBRE 1974** and value.
736. **228.** 100 f. on 5 f. brown, blue and green .. 1·40 90

**238.** "Apollo" Emblem, Astronaut, Module and Astronaut's Boots.

**1974.** Air. 5th Anniv. of 1st Landing on Moon.
737. **238.** 200 f. brown, red & blue 2·75 1·40

**1974.** Christmas. VERT. designs as T. **222.** Multicoloured.
738. 40 f. "Virgin of Autumn" (15th-century sculpture) 60 35
739. 45 f. "Virgin and Child" (Luis de Morales) .. 80 45

**239.** De Gaulle and Eboue.

**1975.** Air. 30th Anniv. of Felix Eboue ("Free French" leader).
740. **239.** 45 f. multicoloured .. 1·40 55
741. 200 f. multicoloured .. 4·50 2·50

**240.** "Celosia cristata".

**242.** Afo Akom Statue.

**241.** Fish and Fishing-boat.

**1975.** Flowers of North Cameroun. Mult.
742. 5 f. Type **240** .. .. 15 10
743. 40 f. "Costus spectabilis" 60 20
744. 45 f. "Mussaenda erythrophylla" .. 80 30

**1975.** Offshore Fishing.
745. **241.** 40 f. brn., blue & choc. 60 20
746. – 45 f. brn., bistre & blue 70 35
DESIGN: 45 f. Fishing-boat and fish in net.

**1975.**
747. **242.** 40 f. multicoloured .. 45 20
748. 45 f. multicoloured .. 55 35
749. 200 f. multicoloured .. 2·10 1·50

**243.** "Polypore" (fungus).

**245.** Presbyterian Church, Elat.

**244.** View of Building.

**1975.** Natural History. Multicoloured.
750. 15 f. Type **243** .. .. 3·25 1·25
751. 40 f. "Nymphalis Chrysalis" .. .. 2·00 55

**1975.** Inaug. of New Ministry of Posts Building.
752. **244.** 40 f. blue, grn. & brn. 45 15
753. 45 f. brn., grn. & blue 65 35

**1975.** Churches and Mosque.
754. **245.** 40 f. brn., blue & blk. 35 15
755. – 40 f. brn., blue & slate 35 15
756. – 45 f. brn., grn. & blk. 45 20
DESIGNS: No. 755, Foumban Mosque. No. 756, Catholic Church, Ngaoundere.

**246.** Marquis de Lafayette (after Chappel) and Naval Battle.

**247.** Harvesting Maize.

**1975.** Air. Bicentenary (1976) of American Revolution.
757. **246.** 100 f. bl., turq. & brn. 1·75 85
758. – 140 f. bl., brn. & grn... 1·90 90
759. – 500 f. green, brn. & bl. 6·00 1·25
DESIGNS: 140 f. George Washington (after Stuart) and Continental Infantry (after Ogden). 500 f. Benjamin Franklin (after Peale and Nee) and Boston.

**1975.** "Green Revolution". Multicoloured.
760. 40 f. Type **247** .. .. 45 15
761. 40 f. Ploughing with oxen (horiz.) .. .. .. 40 20

**248.** "The Burning Bush" (N. Froment).

**1975.** Air. Christmas. Multicoloured.
762. 50 f. Type **248** .. .. 55 45
763. 500 f. "Adoration of the Magi" (Gentile da Fabriano) (horiz.) .. 6·50 4·75

**249.** Tracking Aerial.

**1976.** Inauguration of Satellite Monitoring Station, Zamengoe. Multicoloured.
764. 40 f. Type **249** .. .. 35 15
765. 100 f. Close-up of tracking aerial (vert.) .. .. 65 40

**250.** Porcelain Rose.

**252.** Masked Dancer.

**251.** Concorde.

**1976.** Flowers. Multicoloured.
766. 40 f. Type **250** .. .. 55 15
767. 50 f. Flower of North Cameroun .. .. 85 20

**1976.** Air. Concorde's First Commercial Flight, Paris to Rio de Janeiro.
768 **251** 500 f. multicoloured .. 4·50 2·40

**1976.** Cameroun Dances. Multicoloured.
770. 40 f. Type **252** (postage).. 55 35
771. 50 f. Drummers and two dancers (air) .. .. 45 20
772. 100 f. Female dancer .. 90 35

**253.** Telephone Exchange.

**255.** Dr. Adenauer and Cologne Cathedral.

**254.** Young Men Building House.

**1976.** Air. Telephone Cent.
773. **253.** 50 f. multicoloured .. 40 30

**1976.** 10th Anniv. of National Youth Day. Multicoloured.
774. 40 f. Type **254** .. .. 30 15
775. 45 f. Gathering palm leaves 40 15

**1976.** Birth Centenary of Dr. Konrad Adenauer (Statesman).
776. **255.** 100 f. multicoloured .. 65 35

**256.** "Adoration of the Shepherds" (Charles Le Brun).

**1976.** Air. Christmas.
777. 30 f. Type **256** .. .. 45 15
778. 60 f. "Adoration of the Magi" (Rubens) .. 55 30
779. 70 f. "Virgin and Child" (Bellini).. .. 80 40
780. 500 f. "The New-born" (G. de la Tour).. .. 5·75 3·50

**257.** Pres. Ahidjo and Douala Party H.Q.

**1976.** 10th Anniv. of Cameroun National Union. Multicoloured.
782. 50 f. Type **257** .. .. 35 15
783. 50 f. Pres. Ahidjo and Yaounde Party H.Q. .. 35 15

**258.** Bamoun Copper Pipe.

**259.** Crowned Cranes.

**1977.** 2nd World Festival of Negro Arts, Nigeria. Multicoloured.
784. 50 f. Type **258** (postage).. 55 30
785. 60 f. Traditional chief on throne (sculpture) (air) 85 35

**1977.** Cameroun Birds. Multicoloured.
786. 30 f. Ostrich .. .. 1·10 30
787. 50 f. Type **259** .. .. 1·40 45

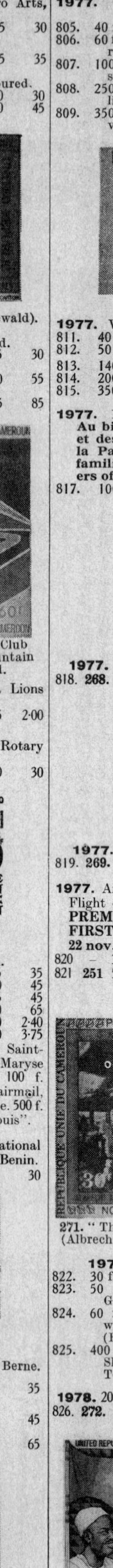

**260.** "Christ on the Cross" (Issenheim Altarpiece, Mathias Grunewald).

**1977.** Air. Easter. Multicoloured.
788. 50 f. Type **260** .. .. 65 30
789. 125 f. "Christ on the Cross" (Veslasquez) (vert.) .. 1·40 55
790. 150 f. "The Entombment" (Titian) .. .. .. 2·25 85

**261.** Lions Club Emblem. **262.** Rotary Club Emblem, Mountain and Road.

**1977.** Air. 19th Congress of Douala Lions Club.
792. **261.** 250 f. multicoloured .. 3·25 2·00

**1977.** Air. 20th Anniv. of Douala Rotary Club.
793. **262.** 60 f. red and blue .. 50 30

**263.** Jean Mermoz and Seaplane "Comte de la Vaulx".

**1977.** Air. History of Aviation.
794. **263.** 50 f. blue, oran. & brn. 65 35
795. – 60 f. purple and orange 70 45
796. – 80 f. lake and blue .. 85 45
797. – 100 f. green and yellow 1·40 65
798. – 300 f. blue, red & pur. 4·50 2·40
799. – 500 f. pur., grn. & plum 6·50 3·75
DESIGNS—VERT. 60 f. Antoine de Saint-Exupery and Latecoere 2b. HORIZ. 80 f. Maryse Bastie and Caudron C-635 Simoun. 100 f. Sikorski S-43 amphibian (1st airmail, Marignane–Douala, 1937). 300 f. Concorde. 500 f. Charles Lindbergh and "Spirit of St. Louis".

**1977.** Air. 10th Anniv. of International French Language Council. As T **204** of Benin.
801. 70 f. multicoloured .. 55 30

**264.** Cameroun 40 f. and Basle 2½ r. Stamps.

**1977.** "Jufilex" Stamp Exhibition, Berne. Multicoloured.
802. 50 f. Type **264** (postage).. 65 35
803. 70 f. Zurich 4 r. and Kamerun 1 m. stamps (air) 90 45
804. 100 f. Geneva 5 + 5 c. & Cameroun 20 f. stamps 1·90 65

**265.** Stafford and "Apollo" Rocket.

**1977.** U.S.A.–U.S.S.R. Space Co-operation. Multicoloured.
805. 40 f. Type **265** (postage).. 35 15
806. 60 f. Leonov and "Soyuz" rocket .. .. .. 45 20
807. 100 f. Brand & "Apollo" space vehicle (air) .. 65 35
808. 250 f. "Apollo–Soyuz" link-up .. .. .. 2·00 1·10
809. 350 f. Kubasov & "Soyuz" vehicle .. .. .. 2·75 1·40

**266.** Luge Sledging.

**1977.** Winter Olympics. Innsbruck. Mult.
811. 40 f. Type **266** (postage).. 30 15
812. 50 f. Ski-jumping.. .. 40 15
813. 140 f. Ski-marathon (air) 90 45
814. 200 f. Ice-hockey.. .. 1·40 65
815. 350 f. Figure-skating .. 2·75 1·10

**1977.** Palestinian Welfare. No. 765 optd. **Au bien-etre des familles des martyrs et des combattants pour la liberte de la Palestine. To the Welfare of the families of martyrs and freedom fighters of Palestine.**
817. 100 f. multicoloured .. 65 45

**268.** Mao Tse-Tung and Great Wall of China.

**1977.** 1st Death Anniv. of Mao Tse-tung.
818. **268.** 100 f. brown and green 1·50 65

**269.** Knee Joint.

**1977.** Air. World Rheumatism Year.
819. **269.** 70 f. brn., red & blue 55 20

**1977.** Air. 1st Paris–New York Commercial Flight of Concorde. Nos. 798 and 768 optd **PREMIER VOL PARIS-NEW YORK FIRST FLIGHT PARIS-NEW YORK 22 nov. 1977 — 22nd Nov. 1977.**
820 – 300 f. blue, red & pur 2·75 1·40
821 **251** 500 f. multicoloured .. 4·25 2·25

**271.** "The Nativity" (Albrecht Altdorfer). **272.** Club Flag and Rotary Emblem.

**1977.** Christmas. Multicoloured.
822. 30 f. Type **271** (postage).. 40 15
823. 50 f. "Madonna of the Grand Duke" (Raphael) 70 30
824. 60 f. "Virgin and Child with Four Saints" (Belini) (horiz.) (air) .. 80 30
825. 400 f. "Adoration of the Shepherds" (G. de la Tour) (horiz.) .. .. 4·50 2·25

**1978.** 20th Anniv. of Yaounde Rotary Club.
826. **272.** 50 f. multicoloured .. 60 30

**273.** Pres. Ahidjo, Flag and Map. **274.** "Cardioglossa escalerae".

**1978.** New Cameroun Flag. Multicoloured.
827. 50 f. Type **273** (postage).. 55 20
828. 60 f. President, Flag and arms (air) .. .. 30 20

**1978.** Cameroun Frogs. Multicoloured.
829. 50 f. Type **274** (postage).. 50 35
830. 60 f. "Cardioglossa elegans" 1·00 45
831. 100 f. "Cardiglossa trifasciata" (air) .. .. 1·25 35

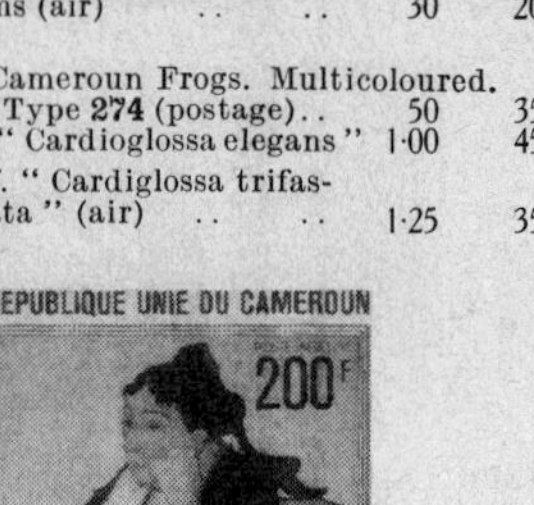

**275.** "L'Arlesienne" (Van Gogh).

**1978.** Air. Paintings. Multicoloured.
832. 200 f. Type **275** .. .. 3·00 1·40
833. 200 f. "Deposition of Christ" (Durer) .. 2·25 65

**276.** Raoul Follereau and Leprosy Distribution Map.

**1978.** Air. World Leprosy Day.
834. **276.** 100 f. multicoloured .. 80 45

**277.** Capt. Cook and the Siege of Quebec.

**1978.** Air. 250th Birth Anniv. of Capt. James Cook.
835. **277.** 100 f. grn., blue & lilac 1·40 55
836. – 250 f. brown, red & lilac 3·25 1·40
DESIGN: 250 f. Capt. Cook, H.M.S. "Adventure" and H.M.S. "Resolution".

**278.** Footballers.

**1978.** Air. World Cup Football Championship, Argentina. Multicoloured.
837. 100 f. Argentinian Team (horiz.) .. .. .. 70 35
838. 200 f. Type **278** .. .. 1·50 65
839. 1000 f. Football illuminating globe .. .. 9·00 4·50

**279.** Jules Verne and scene from "From the Earth to the Moon".

**1978.** 150th Birth Anniv. of Jules Verne (novelist). Multicoloured.
840. 250 f. Type **279** (postage) 1·90 55
841. 400 f. Portrait and "20,000 Leagues under the Sea" (horiz.) (air) .. .. 3·25 1·40

**280.** "Hypolimnas salmacis".

**1978.** Butterflies. Multicoloured.
842. 20 f. Type **280** .. .. 35 20
843. 25 f. "Euxanthe trajanus" 35 20
844. 30 f. "Euphaedra cyparissa" 45 20

**281.** Planting Trees. **282.** Carved Bamoun Drum.

**1978.** Protection against Saharan Encroachment.
845. **281.** 10 f. multicoloured .. 15 10
846. 15 f. multicoloured .. 20 10

**1978.** Musical Instruments. Multicoloured.
847. 50 f. Type **282** (postage).. 35 20
848. 60 f. Gueguerou (horiz.).. 50 30
849. 100 f. Mvet Zither (air) .. 80 35

**283.** Presidents of Cameroun and France with Independence Monument, Douala.

**1978.** Visit of President Giscard d'Estaing.
850. **283.** 60 f. multicoloured .. 85 40

**284.** African, Human Rights Charter and Emblem.

**1979.** 30th Anniv. of Declaration of Human Rights.
851. **284.** 5 f. mult. (postage) .. 15 10
852. 500 f. multicoloured (air) 5·25 2·50
See also No. 1070.

**285.** Lions Emblem & Map of Cameroun. **286.** Globe, Emblem & Waving Children.

**1979.** Air. Lions International Congress.
853. **285.** 60 f. multicoloured .. 60 30

**1979.** International Year of the Child.
854. **286.** 50 f. multicoloured .. 55 20

**287.** Penny Black, Rowland Hill and German Cameroun 10 pf. Stamp.

**1979.** Air. Death Cent. of Sir Rowland Hill.
855. **287.** 100 f. black, red & turq. 1·10 45

288. Black Rhinoceros.

289. "Telecom 79".

**1979.** Endangered Animals (1st series). Mult.
856 50 f. Type **288** .. .. 65 30
857 60 f. Giraffe (vert) .. 80 45
858 60 f. Gorilla .. .. 80 35
859 100 f. African elephant (vert) .. .. .. 2·50 1·00
860 100 f. Leopard .. .. 1·75 75
See also Nos. 891/2, 904/6, 975/7, 939/40 and 1007/8.

**1979.** Air. Third World Telecommunications Exhibition, Geneva.
861. **289.** 100 f. orge., blue & grey 90 45

290. Pope John Paul II.

291. Dr. Jamot, Map and "Glossina palpalis".

**1979.** Air. Popes.
862. **290.** 100 f. blue, vio. & grn. 1·90 55
863. – 100 f. brn., red & grn. 1·90 55
864. – 100 f. chest., olive & grn. 1·90 55
DESIGNS: No. 863, Pope John Paul I. No. 864, Pope Paul VI.

**1979.** Birth Centenary of Dr. Eugene Jamot (discoverer of sleeping sickness cure).
865. **291.** 50 f. brown, blue & red 60 30

292. " The Annunciation " (Fra Filippo Lippi).

**1979.** Christmas. Multicoloured.
866. 10 f. Type **292** .. .. 10 10
867. 50 f. " Rest during the Flight into Egypt " (Antwerp Master) .. 35 10
868. 60 f. " The Nativity " (Kalkar) .. .. 50 15
869. 60 f. " The Flight into Egypt " (Kalkar) .. 50 15
870. 100 f. " The Nativity " (Boticelli) .. .. 1·25 35

293. " Double Eagle II " and Balloonists.

**1979.** Air. First Atlantic Crossing by Balloon. Multicoloured.
871. 500 f. Type **293** .. .. 4·50 1·40
872. 500 f. " Double Eagle II " over Atlantic and balloonists in basket .. 4·50 1·40

294. " Piper capense ".

**1979.** Medicinal Plants. Multicoloured.
873. 50 f. Type **294** .. .. 65 15
874. 60 f. " Pteridium aquilinum " 70 20

295. Pres. Ahidjo, Map, Independence Stamp and Arms.

**1980.** 20th Anniv. of Independence.
875. **295.** 50 f. multicoloured .. 45 20

296. Congress Building.

**1980.** 3rd Ordinary Congress of Cameroun National Union, Bafoussam.
876. **296.** 50 f. multicoloured .. 45 20

297. Globe.

**1980.** 75th Anniv. of Rotary International. Multicoloured.
877. 200 f. Type **297** .. .. 2·00 65
878. 200 f. Map of Cameroun .. 2·00 65

298. Voacanga Fruit and Seeds.

299. " Dissotis perkinsiae ".

**1980.** Medicinal Plants. Multicoloured.
880. 50 f. Type **298** .. .. 45 10
881. 60 f. Voacanga tree .. 45 15
882. 100 f. Voacanga flowers .. 80 20

**1980.** Flowers. Multicoloured.
883. 50 f. Type **299** .. .. 45 10
884. 60 f. " Brillantaisia sp " 65 15
885. 100 f. " Clerodendron splendens " .. .. 1·40 20

300. Ka'aba, Mecca.

**1980.** 1350th Anniv. of Mohammed's Occupation of Mecca.
886. **300.** 50 f. multicoloured .. 65 35

301. Ice Skating.

**1980.** Air. Olympic Games, Moscow and Lake Placid.
887. – 100 f. brown and ochre 65 30
888. **301.** 150 f. brown and blue 1·00 45
889. – 200 f. brown and green 1·75 55
890. – 300 f. brown and red 2·25 95
DESIGNS: 100 f. Running, 200 f. Throwing the Javelin. 300 f. Wrestling.

302. Crocodile.

**1980.** Endangered Animals (2nd series). Multicoloured.
891. 200 f. Type **302** .. .. 2·50 55
892. 300 f. Kob .. .. .. 3·25 90

303. Bororo Girls and Roumsiki Peak.

**1980.** Tourism. Multicoloured.
893. 50 f. Type **303** .. .. 40 15
894. 60 f. Dschang tourist centre .. .. .. 45 20

304. Banana Trees.

**1981.** Bertona Agricultural Research Station. Multicoloured.
895. 50 f. Type **304** .. .. 45 10
896. 60 f. Cattle in watering hole 55 15

305. Girl on Crutches.

**1981.** International Year of Disabled People. Multicoloured.
897. 60 f. Type **305** .. .. 40 20
898. 150 f. Boy in wheelchair .. 1·00 50

306. Camair Headquarters, Douala.

**1981.** 10th Anniv. of Cameroun Airlines. Multicoloured.
899 100 f. Type **306** .. .. 65 20
900 200 f. Boeing 747 "Mount Cameroun" .. .. 1·60 45
901 300 f. Douala International Airport .. .. 2·50 65

307. Presentation African Club Champions Cup.

308. African Buffalo.

**1981.** Football Victories of Cameroun Clubs. Multicoloured.
902. 60 f. Type **307** .. .. 65 35
903. 60 f. Cup presentation (African Cup Winner's Cup) .. .. 65 35

**1981.** Endangered Animals (3rd series). Multicoloured.
904. 50 f. Type **308** .. .. 65 20
905. 50 f. Cameroun tortoise .. 65 20
906. 100 f. Long-tailed pangolin 1·40 35

309. Prince Charles, Lady Diana Spencer and St. Paul's Cathedral.

310. Bafoussam-Bamenda Road.

**1981.** Wedding of Prince of Wales. Multicoloured.
907. 500 f. Type **309** .. .. 3·75 1·75
908. 500 f. Prince Charles, Lady Diana and Royal Coach 3·75 1·75

**1981.** Tourism.
910. **310.** 50 f. multicoloured .. 45 15

311. Yuri Gagarin and " Vostok 1 ".

**1981.** 20th Anniv. of 1st Men in Space. Mult.
911. 500 f. Type **311** .. .. 4·50 1·40
912. 500 f. Alan Shepard and "Freedom 7" .. .. 4·50 1·40

312. "Cam Iroko" (freighter) in Harbour.

**1981.** Cameroun Shipping Lines.
913. **312.** 60 f. multicoloured .. 65 30

313. Scout Salute and Badge within Knotted Rope, and National Flag.

314. Unity Monument.

**1981.** Air. Fourth African Scouting Conference, Abidjan. Multicoloured.
914. 100 f. Type **313** .. .. 55 30
915. 500 f. Saluting Girl Guide 3·75 1·40

**1981.** 20th Anniv. of Reunification.
916. **314.** 50 f. multicoloured .. 45 20

315. " L'Estaque " (Cezanne).

**1981.** Air. Paintings. Multicoloured.
917. 500 f. Type **315** .. .. 5·25 1·50
918. 500 f. " Guernica " (detail) (Picasso) .. .. 5·25 1·50

316. " Virgin and Child " (detail of San Zeno altarpiece, Mantegna).

**1981.** Air. Christmas. Paintings. Mult.
919. 50 f. " Virgin and Child " (detail, " The Burning Bush ") (Nicholas Froment) .. .. 30 10
920. 60 f. Type **316** .. .. 45 15
921. 400 f. " The Flight into Egypt " (Giotto) (horiz.) 3·00 1·25

317. " Voacanga thouarsii ".

**1981.** Medicinal Plants. Multicoloured.
923 60 f. Type **317** .. .. 55 15
924 70 f. "Cassia alata" .. 65 20

318. " Descent from the Cross " (detail, Giotto).

**1982.** Easter. Paintings. Multicoloured.
925. 100 f. " Christ in the Garden of Olives " (Eugene Delacroix) .. 65 20
926. 200 f. Type **318** .. .. 1·40 45
927. 250 f. " Pieta in the Countryside " (Bellini) 2·00 55

319. Carving, Giraffes and Map.

**1982.** " Philexfrance 82 " International Stamp Exhibition, Paris.
928. **319.** 90 f. multicoloured .. 80 20

320. Clay Water Jug.

**1982.** Local Handicrafts. Multicoloured.
929. 60 f. Python-skin handbag 45 15
930. 70 f. Type **320** .. .. 55 20

321. Pres. Ahidjo, Map and Arms.

**1982.** 10th Anniv. of United Republic.
931. **321.** 500 f. multicoloured .. 4·50 1·40

322. Douala Town Hall.

**1982.** Town Halls. Multicoloured.
932. 40 f. Type **322** .. .. 35 10
933. 60 f. Yaounde town hall .. 45 15
See also No. 1139.

323. Cameroun Football Team.

**1982.** World Cup Football Championship, Spain. Multicoloured.
934. 100 f. Type **323** .. .. 1·40 35
935. 200 f. Cameroun and Algerian teams .. 2·50 55
936. 300 f. Nkono Thomas, Cameroun goalkeeper .. 3·75 80
937. 400 f. Cameroun team (different) .. .. 5·25 1·40

324. Bongo. 325. Cameroun Mountain Francolin.

**1982.** Endangered Animals (4th series). Multicoloured.
939. 200 f. Type **324** .. .. 2·40 85
940. 300 f. Black colobus .. 3·50 1·40

**1982.** Birds. Multicoloured.
941. 10 f. Type **325** .. .. 40 15
942. 15 f. Red-eyed dove .. 40 20
943. 20 f. Barn swallow .. 1·40 55
See also No. 1071.

326. Scouts round Campfire.

**1982.** 75th Anniv. of Boy Scout Movement. Multicoloured.
944. 200 f. Type **326** .. .. 2·00 55
945. 400 f. Lord Baden-Powell 3·50 1·40

327. I.T.U. Emblem. 328. Nyasoso Chapel.

**1982.** I.T.U. Delegates' Conference, Nairobi.
946. **327.** 70 f. multicoloured .. 55 20

**1982.** 25th Anniv. of Presbyterian Church. Multicoloured.
947. 45 f. Buea Chapel .. 40 15
948. 60 f. Type **328** .. .. 50 20

329. World Cup, Footballers and Globe.

**1982.** World Cup Football Championship Result.
949. **329.** 500 f. multicoloured .. 4·50 1·90
950. 1000 f. multicoloured 8·50 3·25

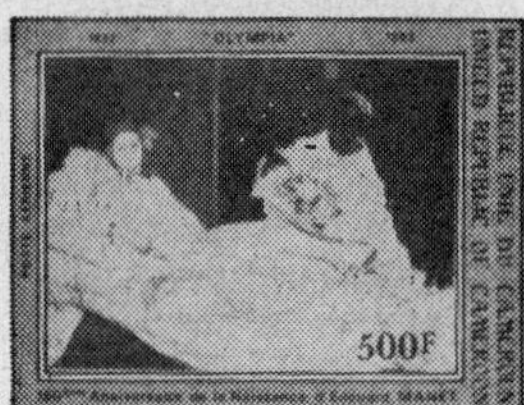


330. " Olympia " (Edouard Manet).

**1982.** Air. Artists' Anniversaries. Multicoloured.
951. 500 f. Type **330** (150th birth anniv.) .. .. .. 4·50 1·75
952. 500 f. " Still-life " (Georges Braque, birth centenary) 4·50 1·75

331. Council Headquarters, Brussels.

**1983.** 30th Anniv. of Customs Co-operation Council. Multicoloured.
953. 250 f. Type **331** .. .. 1·90 1·10
954. 250 f. Council emblem .. 1·90 1·10

332. Yaounde University Hospital.

**1983.** Second Yaounde Medical Days.
955. **332.** 60 f. multicoloured .. 55 15
956. 70 f. multicoloured .. 65 20

333. Pres. Kennedy.

**1983.** Air. 20th Death Anniv. of John F. Kennedy (U.S. President).
957. **333.** 500 f. multicoloured .. 4·50 2·00

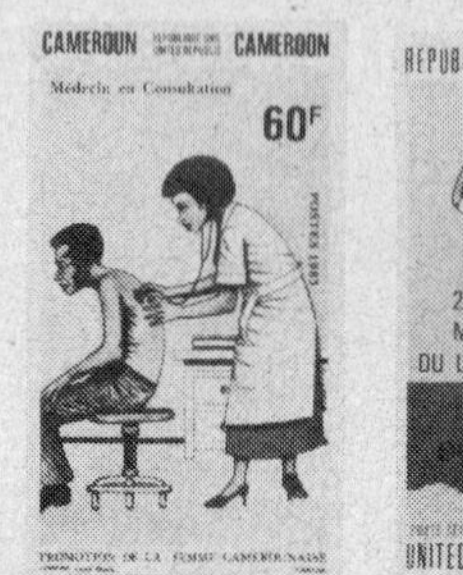


334. Woman Doctor. 335. Lions Emblem and Map.

**1983.** Cameroun Women. Multicoloured.
958. 60 f. Type **334** .. .. 55 20
959. 70 f. Woman lawyer .. 55 20

**1983.** Air. District 403 of Lions International Convention, Douala.
960. **335.** 70 f. multicoloured .. 45 20
961. 150 f. multicoloured .. 1·25 55

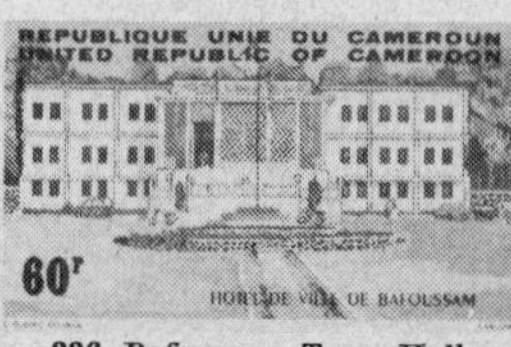


336. Bafoussam Town Hall.

**1983.** Town Halls. Multicoloured.
962. 60 f. Type **336** .. .. 45 15
963. 70 f. Garoua town hall .. 55 20

337. President Biya and National Flag.

**1983.** 11th Anniv. of United Republic. Multicoloured.
964. 60 f. Type **337** .. .. 45 15
965. 70 f. Pres. Biya and national arms .. .. 55 20

338. Container Ship and Buoy.

**1983.** 25th Anniv. of I.M.O.
966. **338.** 500 f. multicoloured .. 4·50 2·00

339. Martial Eagle.

**1983.** Birds. Multicoloured.
967. 25 f. Type **339** .. .. 60 35
968. 30 f. Rufous-breasted sparrowhawk .. .. 90 50
969. 50 f. Purple heron .. .. 1·75 70
See also Nos. 1157 and 1169.

340. Bread Mask (" Wery-Nwen-Nto ").

**1983.** Cameroun Artists. Multicoloured.
970. 60 f. Type **340** .. .. 55 15
971. 70 f. Basket with lid (" Chechia Bamoun ") 65 20

341. Mobile Rural Post Office.

**1983.** World Communications Year. Multicoloured.
972. 90 f. Type **341** .. .. 65 20
973. 150 f. Radio operator with morse key .. .. 1·40 35
974. 250 f. Tom-tom drums .. 2·40 55

342. African Civet.

**1983.** Endangered Animals (5th series). Mult.
975 200 f. Type **342** .. .. 2·40 65
976 200 f. Gorilla .. .. 2·40 65
977 350 f. Guinea-pig (vert) .. 3·75 1·25
See also No. 1170.

**343.** "Jeanne d'Aragon" (Raphael).

**1983.** Air. Paintings. Multicoloured.

978. 500 f. Type **343** .. .. 4·50 1·75
979. 500 f. "Massacre of Scio" (Delacroix) .. .. 4·50 1·75

**344.** Lake Tizon.

**1983.** Landscapes. Multicoloured.

980. 60 f. Type **344** .. .. 45 15
981. 70 f. Mount Cameroun in eruption .. .. 55 15

**345.** Boy and Girl holding Hands. **346.** Christmas Tree.

**1983.** 35th Anniv. of Declaration of Human Rights.

982. **345.** 60 f. multicoloured .. 45 15
983. – 70 f. multicoloured .. 55 15

**1983.** Christmas. Multicoloured.

984. 60 f. Type **346** .. .. 35 15
985. 200 f. Stained-glass window, Yaounde Cathedral .. 1·40 55
986. 500 f. Statue of angel, Reims Cathedral .. 3·75 1·40
987. 500 f. "The Rest on the Flight into Egypt" (Philipp Otto Runge) (horiz.) .. .. .. 3·75 1·40

**348.** "Pieta" (G. Hernandez).

**1984.** Air. Easter. Multicoloured.

992. 200 f. Type **348** .. .. 1·75 55
993. 500 f. "Martyrdom of St. John the Evangelist" (C. le Brun) .. .. .. 4·00 2·00

**349.** Urban Council Building, Bamenda.

**1984.** Town Halls. Multicoloured.

995. 60 f. Type **349** .. .. 45 15
996. 70 f. Mbalmayo .. .. 55 20

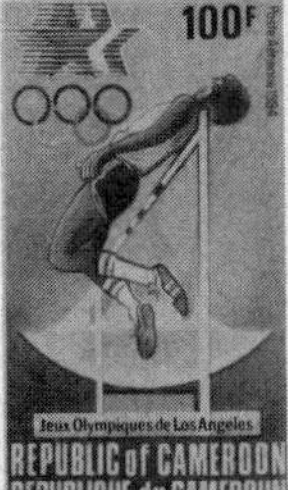

**350.** High Jump. **351.** Running with Ball.

**1984.** Air. Olympic Games, Los Angeles. Mult.

997. 100 f. Type **350** .. .. 65 30
998. 150 f. Volleyball .. .. 1·25 45
999. 250 f. Basketball .. .. 2·00 65
1000. 500 f. Cycling .. .. .. 3·75 1·40

**1984.** Air. European Football Championship. Multicoloured.

1001. 250 f. Type **351** .. .. 2·00 65
1002. 250 f. Heading ball .. .. 2·00 65
1003. 500 f. Tackle .. .. .. 3·75 1·40

**352.** Catholic Church, Zoetele.

**1984.** Churches. Multicoloured.

1005. 60 f. Type **352** .. .. 45 15
1006. 70 f. Marie Gocker Protestant Church, Yaounde .. .. 55 20

**353.** Antelope.

**1984.** Endangered Animals (6th series). Multicoloured.

1007. 250 f. Type **353** .. .. 2·50 1·10
1008. 250 f. Wild boar .. .. 2·50 1·10

**354.** Pres. Biya and Arms.

**1984.** Air. President's Oath-taking Ceremony.

(a) Inscr. in French.

1009. **354.** 60 f. multicoloured .. 40 15
1010. 70 f. multicoloured .. 45 15
1011. 200 f. multicoloured 1·40 40

(b) Inscr. in English.

1012. **354.** 60 f. multicoloured .. 40 15
1013. 70 f. multicoloured .. 45 15
1014. 200 f. multicoloured 1·40 40

**355.** "Diana Bathing" (Watteau).

**1984.** Air. Anniversaries. Multicoloured.

1015. 500 f. Type **355** (300th birth anniv.) (wrongly inscr. "1624") .. .. 4·75 1·40
1016. 500 f. Diderot (encyclopedist, death bicentenary) .. 4·75 1·40

**1984.** Air. Olympic Games Medal Winners. Nos. 997/1000 optd.

1017. 100 f. **MOEGENBURG (R.F.A.) 11-08-84** .. 65 35
1018. 150 f. **U.S.A. 11-08-84** .. 1·25 50
1019. 250 f. **YOUGOSLAVIE 9-08-84** .. .. .. 2·00 1·10
1020. 500 f. **GORSKI (U.S.A.) 3-08-84** .. .. 3·75 1·90

**357.** Nightingale. **358.** Neil Armstrong.

**1984.** Birds. Multicoloured.

1021. 60 f. Type **357** .. .. 1·60 70
1022. 60 f. Ruppell's Griffon .. 1·60 70

See also No. 1158.

**1984.** Air. 15th Anniv. of 1st Man on the Moon. Multicoloured.

1023. 500 f. Type **358** .. 4·50 1·75
1024. 500 f. Launching of "Apollo 12" .. .. 4·50 1·75

**359.** Maize and Young Plants.

**1984.** Agro-pastoral Fair. Bamenda. Mult.

1025. 60 f. Type **359** .. .. 45 15
1026. 70 f. Zebus .. .. 55 20
1027. 300 f. Potatoes .. .. 2·50 85

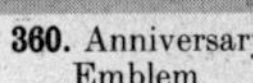


**360.** Anniversary Emblem. **362.** Balafons (xylophone).

**361.** Wrestling.

**1984.** 40th Anniv. of I.C.A.O.

1028. – 200 f. multicoloured 1·40 55
1029. **360.** 200 f. bl & deep bl. .. 1·40 55
1030. – 300 f. multicoloured 2·40 85
1031. – 300 f. multicoloured 3·00 1·40

DESIGNS: No. 1028, "Icarus" (Hans Herni). 1030, Cameroun Airlines Boeing 737. 1031, "Solar Princess" (Sadiou Diouf).

**1985.** "Olyphilex '85" International Thematic Stamps Exhibition, Lausanne.

1032. **361.** 150 f. multicoloured 1·40 55

**1985.** Musical Instruments. Multicoloured.

1033. 60 f. Type **362** .. .. 45 10
1034. 70 f. Mvet (stringed instrument) .. .. .. 55 15
1035. 100 f. Flute .. .. 1·10 20

**363.** Intelcam Headquarters, Yaounde.

**1985.** 20th Anniv. of International Telecommunications Satellite Consortium.

1036. – 125 f. black, orange and blue .. .. 1·40 45
1037. **363.** 200 f. multicoloured 1·75 50

DESIGN—125 f. "Intelsat V" satellite.

**365.** U.N. Emblem and Headquarters.

**1985.** 40th Anniv. of U.N.O.

1038. **365.** 250 f. multicoloured 2·40 65
1039. 500 f. multicoloured 4·50 1·40

**366.** French and Cameroun Flags and Presidents.

**1985.** President Mitterrand of France's Visit to Cameroun.

1040. **366.** 60 f. multicoloured .. 55 30
1041. 70 f. multicoloured .. 65 30

**367.** U.N.I.C.E.F. Emblem.

**1985.** Child Survival Campaign.

1042. **367.** 60 f. black, blue and yellow .. .. 45 15
1043. – 300 f. multicoloured 2·40 80

DESIGN:—Doctor inoculating babies.

**368.** Lake Barumbi, Kumba.

**1985.** Landscapes. Multicoloured.

1044. 60 f. Type **368** .. .. 55 10
1045. 70 f. Pygmy village, Bonando .. .. 55 15
1046. 150 f. River Cameroun .. 1·40 35

**369.** Ebolowa Town Hall.

**1985.** Town Halls. Multicoloured.

1047. 60 f. Type **369** .. .. 45 15
1048. 60 f. Ngaoundere town hall .. .. .. 45 15

**370.** Pope John Paul II.

**371.** Porcupine.

**1985.** Papal Visit to Cameroun. Mult.

1049. 60 f. Type **370** .. .. 60 30
1050. 70 f. Pope John Paul II holding crucifix .. 80 30
1051. 200 f. Pres. Biya and Pope John Paul II .. 2·25 1·25

**1985.** Animals. Multicoloured.

1053. 125 f. Type **371** .. .. 1·25 35
1054. 200 f. Squirrel .. .. 1·75 55
1055. 350 f. Greater cane rat .. 2·75 90

**372.** Wooden Mask.

**373.** "Tomb of Henri Claude d'Harcourt" (detail).

**1985.** Cameroun Art (1st series). Mult.

1056. 60 f. Type **372** .. .. 45 15
1057. 70 f. Wooden mask (different) .. .. 55 20
1058. 100 f. Men using pestle and mortar (wooden bas-relief) .. .. 80 30

See also Nos. 1081/3.

**1985.** Air. Death Anniversaries. Mult.

1059. 500 f. Type **373** (bicentenary Jean Baptiste Pigalle (sculptor)) .. .. 4·75 1·40
1060. 500 f. Louis Pasteur (bacteriologist, 90th anniv.) (after Edelfelt) 4·75 1·40

**374.** Yellow-casqued Hornbill.

**375.** Child's Toys.

**1985.** Birds. Multicoloured.

1061. 140 f. Type **374** .. .. 1·75 60
1062. 150 f. Cock .. .. 1·75 60
1063. 200 f. European robins .. 2·50 95

See also No. 1156.

**1985.** Air. Christmas. Multicoloured.

1064. 250 f. Type **375** .. .. 1·90 65
1065. 300 f. Akono church .. 2·25 80
1066. 400 f. Christmas crib .. 2·75 1·10
1067. 500 f. "The Virgin of the Blue Diadem" (Raphael) .. .. 4·50 1·40

**376.** Emblem, Flag and Volunteers.

**1986.** 25th Anniv. of American Peace Corps in Cameroun.

1068. **376.** 70 f. multicoloured .. 55 20
1069. 100 f. multicoloured 80 35

**1986.** As Nos. 851 and 941 but inscr. "Republique du Cameroun/Republic of Cameroon".

1070. **284.** 5 f. multicoloured .. 10 10
1071. **325.** 10 f. multicoloured .. 80 40

**377.** "Virgin Mary" (Pierre Prud'hon).

**1986.** Easter. Multicoloured.

1072 210 f. Type **377** .. .. 1·40 65
1073 350 f. "Stoning of St. Stephen" (Van Scorel) 2·50 1·25

**378.** "Anax sp.".

**1986.** Insects. Multicoloured.

1074. 70 f. Type **378** .. .. 60 40
1075. 70 f. Bee on flower (vert.) 60 40
1076. 100 f. Grasshopper .. 90 55

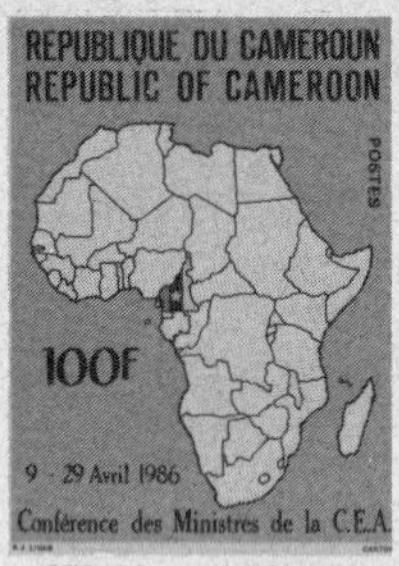

**379.** Map of Africa.

**1986.** Economic Commission for Africa Ministers' Conference. Multicoloured.

1077. 100 f. Type **379** .. .. 80 45
1078. 175 f. Members' flags .. 1·40 65

**380.** Azteca Stadium.

**1986.** Air. World Cup Football Championship, Mexico. Multicoloured.

1079. 300 f. Type **380** .. .. 2·25 1·10
1080. 400 f. Mexico team .. 3·00 1·40

**1986.** Cameroun Art (2nd series). As Type **372**. Multicoloured.

1081. 70 f. Copper Statuette .. 45 15
1082. 100 f. Wooden ash-tray 70 20
1083. 130 f. Wooden horseman 1·40 35

**381.** Queen Elizabeth.

**1986.** 60th Birthday of Queen Elizabeth II. Multicoloured.

1084. 100 f. Type **381** .. .. 80 35
1085. 175 f. Queen and President Biya .. 1·40 55
1086. 210 f. Queen Elizabeth (different) .. .. 1·75 80

**382.** President Biya.

**1986.** 1st Anniv. of Cameroun Republic Democratic Party. Multicoloured.

1087. 70 f. Type **382** .. .. 50 20
1088. 70 f. Bamenda Party headquarters (horiz.) 50 20
1089. 100 f. President Biya making speech .. 65 30

**383.** Argentine Team.

**384.** Mask Dancer with Sword.

**1986.** Air. World Cup Football Championship Winners.

1090. **383.** 250 f. multicoloured 2·50 1·10

**1986.** Traditional Dances of North-west Kwem. Multicoloured.

1091. 100 f. Type **384** .. .. 70 45
1092. 130 f. Mask dancer with rattle .. .. .. 1·25 55

**385.** Cheetah.

**386.** Bishop Desmond Tutu (Nobel Peace Prize Winner).

**1986.** Endangered Animals (7th series). Mult.

1093 300 f. Type **385** .. .. 2·50 1·40
1094 300 f. Varan .. .. 2·50 1·40

**1986.** International Peace Year. Mult.

1095. 175 f. Type **386** .. .. 1·40 55
1096. 200 f. Type **386** .. .. 1·75 65
1097. 250 f. I.P.Y. and U.N. emblems .. .. 2·00 1·10

**387.** Pierre Curie (physicist).

**1986.** Air. Death Anniversaries. Mult.

1098. 500 f. Type **387** (80th anniv.) .. .. .. 5·25 2·25
1099. 500 f. Jean Mermoz and "Arc en Ciel" (aviation pioneer, 50th anniv.) .. 5·25 2·25

**388.** Emblem.

**389.** Man holding Syringe and National Flag "Umbrella" over Woman and Child.

**1986.** National Federation of Cameroun Handicapped Associations.

1100. **388.** 70 f. yellow and red 50 20

**1986.** African Vaccination Year.

1101. 70 f. Type **389** .. .. 50 15
1102. 100 f. Flag behind woman holding child being immunised .. 65 30

**390.** Trees on Map.

**391.** Loading Palm Nuts onto Truck at Dibombari.

**1986.** National Tree Day.

1103. 70 f. Type **390** .. .. 50 15
1104. 100 f. Hands holding clump of earth and seedling .. .. 65 30

**1986.** Agricultural Development. Mult.

1105. 70 f. Type **391** .. .. 50 20
1106. 70 f. Payment for produce harvested .. 50 20
1107. 200 f. Pineapple plantation .. .. 1·40 65

**392.** "Antestiopsis lineaticollis intricata".

**1987.** Harmful Insects. Multicoloured.

1108. 70 f. Type **392** .. .. 70 45
1109. 100 f. "Distantiella theobroma" .. .. 85 55

**393.** Millet.

**1987.** Agricultural Show, Maroua. Mult.

1110. 70 f. Type **393** .. .. 50 30
1111. 100 f. Cotton .. .. 65 40
1112. 150 f. Cattle .. .. 1·25 55

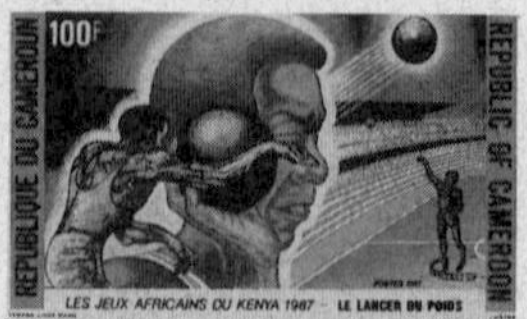

**394.** Shot-putting.

**1987.** 4th All-Africa Games, Kenya. Mult.

1113 100 f. Type **394** .. .. 65 35
1114 140 f. Pole-vaulting .. 1·25 45

**395** Drill Baboon

**1988.** Endangered Mammals. Drill Baboon. Multicoloured.

1115. 30 f. Type **395** .. .. 30 15
1116. 40 f. Adult baboons .. 35 15
1117. 70 f. Young baboon .. 60 35
1118. 100 f. Mother with baby 1·10 55

**396** National Assembly Building

**1989.** Cent of Interparliamentary Union.
1119 **396** 50 f. multicoloured .. 35 15

**397** Cameroun and Argentine Players

**1990.** World Cup Football Championship, Italy. Multicoloured.
1120 200 f. Type **397** .. .. 1·50 55
1121 250 f. Cameroun player and match scene .. 2·00 1·10
1122 250 f. Cameroun winning goal .. .. .. 2·00 1·10
1123 300 f. Cameroun first eleven .. .. .. 2·25 1·40

**1990.** Nos. 1062 and 1093 surch.
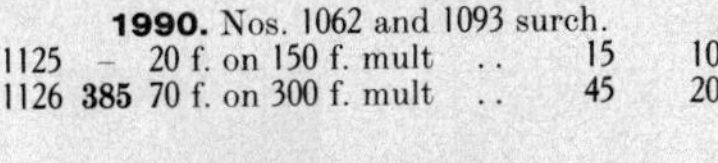
1125 – 20 f. on 150 f. mult .. 15 10
1126 **385** 70 f. on 300 f. mult .. 45 20

**399** Milla and Match Scene

**1990.** Roger Milla, Fourth Best Player in World Cup.
1127 **399** 500 f. multicoloured .. 3·75 2·50

**400** Anniversary Emblem

**1990.** 40th Anniv of United Nations Development Programme.
1129 **400** 50 f. multicoloured .. 35 20

**401** U.N.E.S.C.O. and I.L.Y. Emblems

**1990.** International Literacy Year.
1130 **401** 200 f. black, lt bl & bl 1·40 55

**402** Arms and Pres. Paul Biya

**1991.** 30th Anniv (1990) of Independence. Multicoloured.
1131 150 f. Type **402** .. .. 1·40 55
1132 1000 f. Flag, city and 1960 20 f. Independence stamp .. .. .. 7·75 3·75

**403** Treating Cacao Plantation

**1991.** Unissued stamps (for Ebolowa Agricultural Show) with bars over inscr and surch **125F**. Multicoloured.
1134 125 f. on 70 f. Type **403**
1135 125 f. on 100 f. Sheep ..

The stamps without surcharge were sold only by the Paris agency.

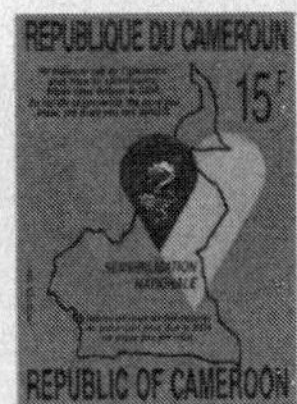

**405** Snake on National Colours and Map

**1991.** Anti-AIDS Campaign. Multicoloured.
1137 15 f. Type **405** .. .. 10 10
1138 25 f. Youth pushing back "AIDS" in French and English (horiz) .. 15 10

See also Nos. 1171/2.

**1991.** As No. 932 but inscr "Republic du Cameroun / Republic of Cameroun".
1139 **322** 40 f. multicoloured .. 30 15

**406** Oribi

**1991.** Sovereign Military Order of Malta Child Survival Project. Antelopes. Multicoloured.
1140 125 f. + 10 f. Type **406** .. 1·25 95
1141 250 f. + 20 f. Waterbucks 2·25 2·25

**407** Serle's Bush Shrike

**408** African Elephant

**1991.** Birds. Multicoloured.
1143 70 f. Type **407** .. .. 50 35
1144 70 f. Grey-necked bald crow (horiz) .. .. 50 35
1145 300 f. As No. 1144 .. 2·40 1·40
1146 350 f. Type **407** .. 2·75 1·40

**1991.** Animals. Multicoloured.
1148 125 f. Type **408** .. .. 1·10 55
1149 250 f. Buffalo .. .. 2·00 1·40

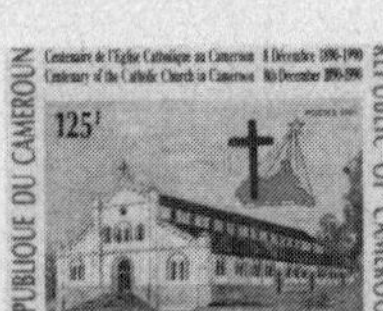

**409** Mvolye Church

**1991.** Centenary (1990) of Catholic Church in Cameroun. Multicoloured.
1151 125 f. Type **409** .. 1·10 55
1152 250 f. Akono church .. 2·00 1·40

**410** Emblems

**1991.** 7th African Group Meeting of Int Savings Banks Institute, Yaounde.
1154 **410** 250 f. multicoloured .. 2·00 1·10

**1992.** Birds. As previous designs but with values changed. Multicoloured.
1156 125 f. As No. 1063 .. 1·10 40
1157 200 f. As No. 968 .. 1·60 60
1158 350 f. Type **357** .. .. 2·50 1·40

**411** Columbus's Fleet

**412** Mbappe Lepe (footballer)

**1992.** 500th Anniv of Discovery of America by Columbus. Multicoloured.
1159 125 f. Type **411** .. .. 1·10 40
1160 250 f. Columbus kneeling on beach .. .. 2·10 1·40
1161 400 f. Meeting Amerindians .. .. 3·00 1·90
1162 500 f. Fleet crossing the Atlantic .. .. 4·25 2·75

**1992.** Cameroun Football. Multicoloured.
1163 125 f. Type **412** .. .. 1·10 40
1164 250 f. League emblem .. 2·10 1·40
1165 400 f. National Football Federation emblem (horiz) .. .. 3·00 1·90
1166 500 f. Ahmadou Ahidjo Stadium, Yaounde (horiz) .. .. 4·25 4·75

See also Nos. 1173/5.

**413** Crocodile

**1993.** Endangered Animals. Multicoloured. Self-adhesive.
1167 125 f. Type **413** .. .. 1·00 65
1168 250 f. Kob (vert) 2·00 1·40

**1993.** As Nos. 967 and 975 but inscr "REPUBLIQUE DU CAMEROUN REPUBLIC OF CAMEROON" and with values changed.
1169 **339** 370 f. multicoloured .. 2·50 1·60
1170 **342** 410 f. multicoloured .. 3·25 2·00

**1993.** Anti-AIDS Campaign. As Nos. 1137/8 but values changed. Multicoloured.
1171 100 f. Type **405** .. .. 80 55
1172 175 f. As No. 1138 .. 1·40 80

**1993.** As Nos. 1163/5 but values changed.
1173 10 f. As No. 1165 .. 10 10
1174 25 f. As No. 1164 .. 10 10
1175 50 f. Type **412** .. .. 15 10

**414** President Biya holding Football and Lion (national team mascot)

**1994.** World Cup Football Championship, United States. Multicoloured.
1176 125 f. Type **414** .. .. 50 40
1177 250 f. Emblem, lion, player and map of Cameroun .. .. 90 65
1178 450 f. Players, ball showing world map, national flag and trophy .. .. 1·75 1·25
1179 500 f. Eagle and lion supporting ball .. 1·90 1·50

**415** Grey Parrot

**417** Anniversary Emblem and Dove carrying Branch

**416** Chi-rho, Cross and Pope John Paul II

**1995.**
1181 **415** 125 f. multicoloured .. 50 35

**1995.** 2nd Papal Visit.
1182 **416** 55 f. black, pink & yell 25 20
1183 – 125 f. multicoloured .. 50 35

DESIGN: 125 f. Pope and open book.

**1995.** 50th Anniv of U.N.O. Multicoloured.
1184 200 f. Type **417** .. .. 55 40
1185 250 f. Anniversary emblem and figures joining hands .. .. 65 45

Cameroun joined the Commonwealth on 1st November 1995. Further issues appear in Part 1.

MILITARY FRANK STAMP

M 78. Arms and Crossed Swords.

**1963.** No value indicated.
M 1. M 78. (-) lake .. .. 3·25 3·25

POSTAGE DUE STAMPS

D 8. Felling Mahogany Tree. D 25. African Idols.

**1925.**
D 88. D 8. 2 c. black and blue .. 10 30
D 89. 4 c. purple and olive 10 30
D 90. 5 c. black and lilac .. 20 45
D 91. 10 c. black and red .. 25 45
D 92. 15 c. black and grey 25 50
D 93. 20 c. black and olive 25 50
D 94. 25 c. black & yellow 40 75
D 95. 30 c. orange & blue 45 75
D 96. 50 c. black & brown 65 80
D 97. 60 c. red and green 60 1·10
D 98. 1 f. grn. & red on grn. 1·25 1·40
D 99. 2 f. mauve and red 2·25 2·50
D 100. 3 f. blue and brown 3·75 3·75

**1939.**
D 148. D 25. 5 c. purple .. .. 10 25
D 149. 10 c. blue .. .. 30 60
D 150. 15 c. red .. .. 10 25
D 151. 20 c. brown .. .. 15 25
D 152. 30 c. blue .. .. 15 25
D 153. 50 c. green .. .. 25 35
D 154. 60 c. purple .. .. 25 35
D 155. 1 f. violet .. .. 45 60
D 156. 2 f. orange .. .. 60 90
D 157. 3 f. blue .. .. 60 1·40

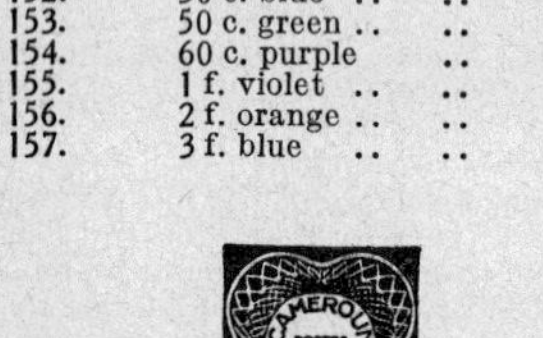

D 46.

**1947.**
D 254. D 46. 10 c. red .. .. 10 25
D 255. 30 c. orange .. .. 10 25
D 256. 50 c. black .. .. 10 25
D 257. 1 f. red .. .. 15 30
D 258. 2 f. green .. .. 20 40
D 259. 3 f. mauve .. .. 35 50
D 260. 4 f. blue .. .. 40 50
D 261. 5 f. brown .. .. 30 50
D 262. 10 f. blue .. .. 60 70
D 263. 20 f. sepia .. .. 65 1·25

D 77. "Hibiscus rosa sinensis".

**1983.** Flowers. Multicoloured.
D 342. 50 c. Type D 77 .. 10 10
D 343. 50 c. "Erythrine" .. 10 10
D 344. 1 f. "Plumeria lutea" .. 10 10
D 345 1 f. "Ipomoea sp." .. 10 10
D 346. 1 f. 50 "Grinum sp." .. 10 10
D 347. 1 f. 50 "Hoodia gordonii" .. 10 10
D 348. 2 f. "Ochna" .. 10 10
D 349. 2 f. "Gloriosa" .. 10 10
D 350. 5 f. "Costus spectabilis" 15 15
D 351. 5 f. "Bougainvillea spectabilis" .. 15 15
D 352. 10 f. "Delonix regia" .. 40 40
D 353. 10 f. "Haemanthus" .. 40 40
D 354. 20 f. "Titanopsis" .. 1·25 1·25
D 355. 20 f. "Ophthalmophyllum" 1·25 1·25
D 356. 40 f. "Zingiberacee" .. 1·75 1·75
D 357. 40 f. "Amorphophalus" 1·75 1·75



## CANAL ZONE Pt. 22

Territory adjacent to the Panama Canal leased by the U.S.A. from the Republic of Panama. The U.S. Canal Zone postal service closed on 30 September 1979.

1904. 100 centavos = 1 peso.
1906. 100 centesimos = 1 balboa.
1924. 100 cents = 1 dollar (U.S.)

**1904.** Stamps of Panama (with **PANAMA** optd. twice) optd. **CANAL ZONE** horiz. in one line.
1. 5. 2 c. red (No. 54) .. .. £300 £275
2. 5 c. blue (No. 55) .. .. £160 £140
3. 10 c. orange (No. 56) .. £350 £225

**1904.** Stamps of the United States of 1902 optd. **CANAL ZONE PANAMA.**
4 103 1 c. green .. .. 20·00 18·00
5a 117 2 c. red .. .. 18·00 14·00
6 107 5 c. blue .. .. 60·00 42·00
7 109 8 c. violet .. .. 95·00 80·00
8 110 10 c. brown .. .. £100 80·00
Stamps of Panama overprinted.

**1904.** 1905 stamps optd. **CANAL ZONE** in two lines.
9. 38. 1 c. green .. .. 1·75 1·40
10. 2 c. red .. .. 2·75 1·50

**1904.** Stamps with **PANAMA** optd. twice, optd. **CANAL ZONE** in two lines or surch. also.
11. 5. 2 c. red (No. 54) .. 4·50 3·00
12. 5 c. blue (No. 55) .. 5·00 2·50
14. 8 c. on 50 c. brn. (No. 65) 22·00 17·00
13. 10 c. orange (No. 56) .. 14·00 10·00

**1906.** 1892 stamps surch. **PANAMA** on both sides and **CANAL ZONE** and new value in centre between bars.
21 5 1 c. on 20 c. violet (No. 64) 1·00 90
22 2 c. on 1 p. red (No. 66) .. 1·75 1·75

**1906.** 1906 stamps optd. **CANAL ZONE** vert.
26. 42. 1 c. black and green .. 1·40 80
27. 43. 2 c. black and red .. 2·10 85
28. 45. 5 c. black and blue .. 4·50 1·50
29. 46. 8 c. black and purple .. 15·00 5·50
30. 47. 10 c. black and violet .. 15·00 5·00

**1909.** 1909 stamps optd. **CANAL ZONE** vert.
35 48 1 c. black and green .. 2·50 1·00
36 49 2 c. black and red .. 3·00 1·00
37 51 5 c. black and blue .. 9·50 2·25
38 52 8 c. black and purple .. 7·00 4·00
43 53 10 c. black and purple .. 38·00 7·00

**1911.** Surch. **CANAL ZONE 10 cts.**
53. 38. 10 c. on 13 c. grey .. 3·50 1·40

**1914.** Optd. **CANAL ZONE** vert.
54. 38. 10 c. grey .. .. 40·00 8·00

**1915.** 1915 and 1918 stamps optd. **CANAL ZONE** vert.
55. 1 c. black and green (No. 162) 6·00 4·00
56. 2 c. black and red (No. 163) 6·50 3·00
57. 5 c. black and blue (No. 166) 7·50 4·00
58. 10 c. blk. & orange (No. 167) 16·00 9·00
59. 12 c. blk. and violet (No. 178) 13·50 4·75
60. 15 c. blk. and blue (No. 179) 40·00 23·00
61. 24 c. blk. & brown (No. 180) 38·00 9·00
62. 50 c. blk. & orange (No. 181) £250 £150
63. 1 b. blk. and violet (No. 182) £130 50·00

**1921.** 1921 stamps optd. **CANAL ZONE** vert.
64. 65. 1 c. green .. .. 2·75 85
65. – 2 c. red (No. 186) .. 2·00 95
66. 68. 5 c. blue .. .. 7·00 2·75
67. – 10 c. violet (No. 191) .. 12·50 5·50
68. – 15 c. blue (No. 192) .. 45·00 11·00
69. – 24 c. sepia (No. 194) .. 50·00 16·00
70. – 50 c. black (No. 195) .. £100 80·00

**1924.** 1924 stamps optd. **CANAL ZONE** vert.
72. 72. 1 c. green .. .. 8·00 3·25
73. 2 c. red .. .. 6·50 2·25

**1924.** Stamps of the United States of 1922 optd. **CANAL ZONE** horiz.
74. ½ c. sepia (No. 559) .. 60 80
75. 1 c. green (No. 602) .. 1·10 45
76. 1½ c. brown (No. 603) .. 1·50 1·00
103. 2 c. red (No. 604) .. 1·75 65
87. 3 c. violet (No. 638a) .. 3·00 2·25
88. 5 c. blue (No. 640) .. 3·00 1·75
106. 10 c. orange (No. 645) .. 13·00 6·50
90. 12 c. purple (No. 693) .. 20·00 12·00
141. 14 c. blue (No. 695) .. 5·00 2·75
92. 15 c. grey (No. 696) .. 5·00 2·75
93. 17 c. black (No. 697) .. 3·00 2·40
94. 20 c. red (No. 698) .. 6·00 3·25
95. 30 c. sepia (No. 700) .. 4·75 2·75
84. 50 c. mauve (No. 701) .. 48·00 30·00
97. $1 brown (No. 579) .. £100 40·00

**1926.** Liberty Bell stamp of United States optd **CANAL ZONE**
101 177 2 c. red .. .. 3·25 2·75

22. Gen. Gorgas. 24. Panama Canal under Construction.

**1928.**
107 22 1 c. green .. .. 10 10
108 – 2 c. red .. .. 20 15
109 24 5 c. blue .. .. 1·50 60
110 – 10 c. orange .. .. 30 20
111 – 12 c. purple .. .. 75 60
112 – 14 c. blue .. .. 80 80
113 – 15 c. grey .. .. 60 40
114 – 20 c. brown .. .. 75 30
115 – 30 c. black .. .. 80 80
116 – 50 c. mauve .. .. 1·50 70
PORTRAITS: 2 c. Gen. Goethals, 10 c. H. F. Hodges. 12 c. Col. Gaillard. 14 c. Gen. Sibert. 15 c. Jackson Smith. 20 c. Admiral Rousseau. 30 c. Col. S. B. Williamson. 50 c. Governor Blackburn.

**1929.** Air. Stamps of 1928 surch. **AIR MAIL** and value.
124. – 10 c. on 50 c. mauve .. 9·00 7·50
117. 22. 15 c. on 1 c. green .. 9·50 4·50
125. – 20 c. on 2 c. red .. 6·50 1·50
119. – 25 c. on 2 c. red .. 3·00 1·75

36. Steamer, Panama Canal.

**1931.** Air.
126. 36. 4 c. purple .. .. 55 65
127. 5 c. green .. .. 45 30
128. 6 c. brown .. .. 60 35
129. 10 c. orange .. .. 70 30
130. 15 c. blue .. .. 1·00 25
131. 20 c. violet .. .. 2·00 25
132. 30 c. red .. .. 2·75 1·00
133. 40 c. yellow .. .. 2·50 1·00
134. $1 black .. .. 8·50 1·75

**1933.** No. 720 of United States optd. **CANAL ZONE.**
140. 3 c. violet .. .. .. 2·25 25

38. Gen. Goethals. 45. Balboa (before construction).

**1934.** 20th Anniv of Opening of Panama Canal.
142 38 3 c. violet .. .. 15 10

**1939.** 25th Anniv. of Opening of Panama Canal and 10th Anniv. of Canal Zone Airmail Service. (a) Postage. As T **45**. Inscr. "25TH ANNIVERSARY 1939 OPENING PANAMA CANAL 1914".
149. 45. 1 c. green .. .. 45 30
150. – 2 c. red .. .. 50 40
151. – 3 c. violet .. .. 45 20
152. – 5 c. blue .. .. 1·40 95
153. – 6 c. orange .. .. 2·00 1·60
154. – 7 c. black .. .. 2·75 1·40
155. – 8 c. green .. .. 2·50 2·50
156. – 10 c. blue .. .. 2·50 1·75
157. – 11 c. green .. .. 7·00 8·00
158. – 12 c. purple .. .. 7·00 5·50
159. – 14 c. violet .. .. 6·50 8·00
160. – 15 c. olive .. .. 15·00 12·50
161. – 18 c. red .. .. 8·00 9·00
162. – 20 c. brown .. .. 15·00 8·00
163. – 25 c. orange .. .. 12·00 12·00
164. – 50 c. purple .. .. 16·00 3·25
DESIGNS: 2 c. Balboa (after construction). 3 c., 5 c. Gaillard Cut. 6 c., 7 c. Bas Obispo. 8 c., 10 c. Gatun Locks. 11 c., 12 c. Canal Channel. 14 c., 15 c. Gamboa. 18 c., 20 c. Pedro Miguel Locks. 25 c., 50 c. Gatun Spillway.

(b) Air. Inscr. "TENTH ANNIVERSARY AIR MAIL" and "25TH ANNIVERSARY OPENING PANAMA CANAL".
143. 5 c. black .. .. 3·25 3·00
144. 10 c. violet .. .. 3·25 2·25
145. 15 c. brown .. .. 3·25 1·10
146. 25 c. blue .. .. 16·00 11·00
147. 30 c. red .. .. 12·00 8·00
148. $1 green .. .. 30·00 30·00
DESIGNS—HORIZ. As Type **45**: 5 c. Douglas DC-3 airplane over Sosa Hill. 10 c. Douglas DC-3 airplane, Sikorsky S-42A flying boat and map of Central America. 15 c. Sikorsky S-42A and Fort Amador. 25 c. Sikorsky S-42A at Cristobal Harbour, Manzanillo Island. 30 c. Sikorsky S-42A over Culebra Cut. $1 Sikorsky S-42A and palm trees.

**1939.** Stamps of United States (1938) optd. **CANAL ZONE.**
165. 276. ½ c. orange .. .. 15 10
166. – 1½ c. brown (No. 801) 15 10

67. John F. Stevens. 69. Northern Coati and Barro Colorado Island.

**1946.** Portraits.
188. – ½ c. red (Davis) .. .. 30 15
189. – 1½ c. brown (Magoon) .. 30 15
190. – 2 c. red (Theodore Roosevelt) .. .. 15 10
191. 67. 5 c. blue .. .. 30 10
192. – 25 c. green (Wallace) .. 1·10 60

**1948.** 25th Anniv of Establishment of Canal Zone Biological Area.
194 69 10 c. black .. .. 1·40 80

70. "Arriving at Chagres on the Atlantic Side." 74. Western Hemisphere.

**1949.** Centenary of the Gold Rush.
195. 70. 3 c. blue .. .. 70 30
196. – 6 c. violet .. .. 1·25 50
197. – 12 c. green .. .. 1·75 1·00
198. – 18 c. mauve .. .. 2·75 2·00
DESIGNS: 6 c. "Up the Chagres River to Las Cruces". 12 c. "Las Cruces Trail to Panama". 18 c. "Leaving Panama for San Francisco".

**1951.** Air.
199. 74. 4 c. purple .. .. 75 25
200. 5 c. green .. .. 1·00 60
201. 6 c. brown .. .. 50 15
202. 7 c. olive .. .. 1·00 35
210. 8 c. red .. .. 70 20
203. 10 c. orange .. .. 1·00 35
204. 15 c. purple .. .. 4·50 1·75
205. 21 c. blue .. .. 8·00 2·75
206. 25 c. yellow .. .. 9·50 2·25
207. 31 c. red .. .. 8·50 3·25
208. 35 c. blue .. .. 8·50 2·50
209. 80 c. black .. .. 4·50 90

75. Labourers in Gaillard Cut. 76. Early Train.

**1951.** West Indian Panama Canal Labourers.
211. 75. 10 c. red .. .. 3·50 1·75

**1955.** Cent. of Panama Railway.
212. 76. 3 c. violet .. .. 2·25 90

77. Gorgas Hospital.

**1957.** 75th Anniv. of Gorgas Hospital.
213. 77. 3 c. black on green .. 50 30

78. "Ancon II" (liner).

79. Roosevelt Medal and Map of Canal Zone. 80. "First Class" Scout Badge.

**1958.**
214. 78. 4 c. turquoise .. .. 55 20

**1958.** Birth Cent. of Theodore Roosevelt.
215. 79. 4 c. brown .. .. 45 30

**1960.** 50th Anniv. of American Boy Scout Movement.
216. 80. 4 c. ochre, red and blue 65 30

81. Administration Building, Balboa. 82. U.S. Army Caribbean School Crest.

**1960.**
217. 81. 4 c. purple .. .. 20 15

**1961.** Air.
221. 82. 15 c. blue and red .. 1·60 80

83. Girl Scout Badge and Camp on Lake Gatun.

**1962.** 50th Anniv. of U.S. Girl Scout Movement.
222. **83.** 4 c. ochre, green & blue 55 25

**84.** Campaign Emblem and Mosquito.

**1962.** Air. Malaria Eradication.
223. **84.** 7 c. black on yellow .. 45 40

**85.** Thatcher Ferry Bridge.

**1962.** Opening of Thatcher Ferry Bridge.
224. **85.** 4 c. black and silver .. 35 20

**86.** Torch of Progress

**1963.** Air. "Alliance for Progress".
225. **86.** 15 c. blue, green & black 1·40 85

**87.** Cristobal.

**1964.** Air. 50th Anniv of Panama Canal.
226. **87.** 6 c. black and green .. 45 30
227. – 8 c. black and red .. 55 25
228. – 15 c. black and blue .. 1·25 45
229. – 20 c. black and purple .. 2·00 85
230. – 30 c. black and brown .. 4·75 1·75
231. – 80 c. black and bistre .. 5·00 2·50
DESIGNS: 8 c. Gatun Locks. 15 c. Madden Dam. 20 c. Gaillard Cut. 30 c. Miraflores Locks. 80 c. Balboa.

**93.** Seal and Jetliner.

**1965.** Air.
232. **93.** 6 c. black and green .. 35 20
233. 8 c. black and red .. 40 10
234. 10 c. black and orange 30 10
235. 11 c. black and green .. 40 15
236. 13 c. black and green .. 95 20
237. 15 c. black and blue .. 40 15
238. 20 c. black and violet .. 60 25
239. 22 c. black and violet .. 1·00 55
240. 25 c. black and green .. 90 40
241. 30 c. black and brown .. 90 30
242. 35 c. black and red .. 1·25 65
243. 80 c. black and ochre .. 2·75 85

**94.** Goethal's Memorial, Balboa.
**96.** Dredger "Cascadas".

**1968.**
244. **94.** 6 c. blue and green .. 20 20
245. – 8 c. multicoloured .. 35 15
DESIGN: 8 c. Fort San Lorenzo.

**1976.**
249. **96.** 13 c. blk., grn. and blue 60 20

**97.** Electric Towing Locomotive.

**1978.**
251. **97.** 15 c. grn. and deep grn. 1·25 30

OFFICIAL STAMPS

**1941.** Air. Optd. **OFFICIAL PANAMA CANAL.**
O 167. **36.** 5 c. green .. .. 3·75 1·50
O 168. 6 c. brown .. .. 9·00 3·50
O 169. 10 c. orange .. .. 8·00 1·75
O 170. 15 c. blue .. .. 12·00 3·00
O 171. 20 c. violet .. .. 13·00 4·00
O 172. 30 c. red .. .. 15·00 4·00
O 173. 40 c. yellow .. .. 17·00 7·50
O 174. $1 black .. .. 20·00 10·00

**1941.** Optd. **OFFICIAL PANAMA CANAL.**
O 180 **22** 1 c. green .. .. 1·50 40
O 181 **38** 3 c. violet .. .. 3·25 70
O 182 **24** 5 c. blue .. .. — 28·00
O 183 – 10 c. orange .. .. 4·25 1·75
O 184 – 15 c. grey (No. 113) .. 9·00 2·00
O 185 – 20 c. brown (No. 114) 12·00 2·75
O 186 – 50 c. mauve (No. 116) 32·00 5·50

**1947.** No. 192 optd. **OFFICIAL PANAMA CANAL.**
O 193. **67.** 5 c. blue .. .. 8·50 3·25

POSTAGE DUE STAMPS

**1914.** Postage Due stamps of United States of 1894 optd. **CANAL ZONE** diag.
D 55. **D 87.** 1 c. red .. .. 55·00 13·00
D 56. 2 c. red .. .. £180 38·00
D 57. 10 c. red .. .. £475 38·00

**1915.** Postage Due stamps of Panama of 1915 optd. **CANAL ZONE** vert.
D 59. **D 58.** 1 c. brown .. .. 7·00 3·00
D 60. – 2 c. brown .. .. £100 12·00
D 61. – 10 c. brown .. .. 32·00 8·00

**1915.** Postage Due stamps of Panama of 1915 surch. **CANAL ZONE** vert. and value in figures.
D 62. **D 58.** 1 c. on 1 c. brown .. 70·00 9·50
D 63. – 2 c. on 2 c. brown .. 18·00 5·00
D 66. – 4 c. on 4 c. .. .. 24·00 11·00
D 64. – 10 c. on 10 c. brown .. 16·00 3·50

**1925.** Postage Due stamps of United States of 1894 optd. **CANAL ZONE** horiz. in two lines.
D 92. **D 87.** 1 c. red .. .. 8·00 2·50
D 93. 2 c. red .. .. 13·00 4·50
D 94. 10 c. red .. .. £110 17·00

**1925.** Stamps of Canal Zone of 1924. optd. **POSTAGE DUE.**
D 89. 1 c. green (No. 75) .. 85·00 17·00
D 90. 2 c. red (No. 103) .. 22·00 6·00
D 91. 10 c. orange (No. 106) .. 38·00 10·00

**1929.** No. 109 surch. **POSTAGE DUE** and value and bars.
D 120. **24.** 1 c. on 5 c. blue .. 3·50 2·50
D 121. 2 c. on 5 c. blue .. 6·50 3·50
D 122. 5 c. on 5 c. blue .. 6·50 4·25
D 123. 10 c. on 5 c. blue .. 6·50 3·75

D 37. Canal Zone Shield.

**1932.**
D 135. **D 37.** 1 c. red .. .. 15 20
D 136. 2 c. red .. .. 15 20
D 137. 5 c. red .. .. 40 25
D 138. 10 c. red .. .. 1·60 1·50
D 139. 15 c. red .. .. 1·25 1·10

## CANTON Pt. 17

A treaty port in S. China. Stamps issued at the French Indo-Chinese P.O. which was closed in 1922.

1901. 100 centimes = 1 franc.
1919. 100 cents = 1 piastre.

Stamps of Indo-China overprinted or surcharged.

CANTON
州廣
(1.)

**1901.** "Tablet" key-type, optd. with T 1. The Chinese characters represent "Canton" and are therefore the same on every value.
1. D. 1 c. black on blue .. 40 40
2. 2 c. brown on yellow .. 40 40
3. 4 c. red on grey .. .. 55 55
5. 5 c. green .. .. 55 55
6. 10 c. black on lilac .. 1·10 1·10
7. 15 c. blue .. .. 70 70
8. 15 c. grey .. .. 1·25 1·25
9. 20 c. red on green .. 2·50 2·50
10. 25 c. black on red .. 2·25 2·25
11. 30 c. brown .. .. 5·50 5·50
12. 40 c. red on yellow .. 6·00 6·50
13. 50 c. red on rose .. 9·50 8·00
14. 75 c. brown on orange .. 12·00 12·00
15. 1 f. olive .. .. 11·00 11·00
16. 5 f. mauve on lilac .. 85·00 85·00

**1903.** "Tablet" key-type, surch. as T 1. The Chinese characters indicate the value and therefore differ for each value.
17. D. 1 c. black on blue .. 80 80
18. 2 c. brown on yellow .. 85 80
19. 4 c. red on grey .. .. 85 80
20. 5 c. green .. .. 65 50
21. 10 c. red .. .. 65 50
22. 15 c. grey .. .. 1·10 80
23. 20 c. red on green .. 4·50 4·75
24. 25 c. blue .. .. 1·75 1·40
25. 25 c. black on red .. 1·75 1·25
26. 30 c. brown .. .. 5·50 4·75
27. 40 c. red on yellow .. 15·00 11·00
28. 50 c. red on rose .. £125 £110
29. 50 c. brown on blue .. 20·00 18·00
30. 75 c. brown on orange .. 22·00 18·00
31. 1 f. olive .. .. 20·00 16·00
32. 5 f. mauve on lilac .. 25·00 22·00

**1906.** Surch. **CANTON** (letters without serifs) and value in Chinese.
33. **8.** 1 c. olive .. .. 40 40
34. 2 c. red on yellow .. 40 40
35. 4 c. purple on grey .. 40 40
36. 5 c. green .. .. 50 40
37. 10 c. red .. .. 70 55
38. 15 c. brown on blue .. 80 80
39. 20 c. red on green .. 55 55
40. 25 c. blue .. .. 55 55
41. 30 c. brown on cream .. 1·00 95
42. 35 c. black on yellow .. 55 45
43. 40 c. black on grey .. 1·10 1·00
44. 50 c. olive on cream .. 1·50 1·40
45. D. 75 c. olive on orange .. 20·00 16·00
46. **8.** 1 f. green .. .. 3·00 2·75
47. 2 f. brown on yellow .. 15·00 10·00
48. D. 5 f. mauve on lilac .. 28·00 25·00
49. **8.** 10 f. red on green .. 25·00 22·00

**1908.** 1907 stamps surch. **CANTON** and value in Chinese.
50. **10.** 1 c. black and olive .. 30 25
51. 2 c. black and brown .. 30 25
52. 4 c. black and blue .. 40 35
53. 5 c. black and green .. 40 35
54. 10 c. black and red .. 40 35
55. 15 c. black and violet .. 80 80
56. **11.** 20 c. black and violet .. 80 80
57. 25 c. black and blue .. 80 85
58. 30 c. black and purple .. 2·00 1·60
59. 35 c. black and green .. 2·00 1·60
60. 40 c. black and brown .. 2·10 1·90
61. 50 c. black and red .. 3·25 2·50
62. **12.** 75 c. black and orange .. 3·25 2·50
63. – 1 f. black and red .. 4·00 4·50
64. – 2 f. black and green .. 14·00 12·00
65. – 5 f. black and blue .. 15·00 14·00
66. – 10 f. black and violet .. 28·00 25·00

**1919.** As last but additionally surch.
67. **10.** ⅖ c. on 1 c. blk. & olive .. 25 25
68. ⅘ c. on 2 c. black & brown 25 25
69. 1⅗ c. on 4 c. black & blue .. 30 25
70. 2 c. on 5 c. blk. & grn. .. 30 25
71. 4 c. on 10 c. black and red 30 25
72. 6 c. on 15 c. black & violet 60 40
73. **11.** 8 c. on 20 c. black & violet 70 60
74. 10 c. on 25 c. black & blue 80 30
75. 12 c. on 30 c. black & pur. 90 60
76. 14 c. on 35 c. black & grn. 1·00 60
77. 16 c. on 40 c. black & brn. 80 60
78. 20 c. on 50 c. black & red 90 70
79. **12.** 30 c. on 75 c. blk. & orge. 1·00 70
80. – 40 c. on 1 f. black and red 2·50 1·50
81. – 80 c. on 2 f. black & green 2·75 2·50
82. – 2 p. on 5 f. black and blue 3·50 3·25
83. – 4 p. on 10 f. black & violet 5·50 4·50

## CAPE JUBY Pt. 9

Former Spanish possession on the N.W. coast of Africa, ceded to Morocco in 1958.

100 centimos = 1 peseta.

**1916.** Stamps of Rio de Oro surch **CABO JUBI** and value.
1a **12** 5 c. on 4 p. red .. .. 75·00 24·00
2 10 c. on 10 p. violet .. 32·00 16·00
3 15 c. on 50 c. brown .. 32·00 16·00
4 40 c. on 1 p. lilac .. 55·00 22·00

**1919.** Stamps of Spain optd **CABO JUBY.**
5 **38a** ¼ c. green .. .. 15 10
18 **66** 1 c. green (imperf) .. 17·00 11·00
6 **64** 2 c. brown .. .. 15 10
7 5 c. green .. .. 40 10
8 10 c. red .. .. 45 10
9 15 c. yellow .. .. 2·25 15
10 20 c. green .. .. 13·50 4·00
19 20 c. violet .. .. 75·00 28·00
11 25 c. blue .. .. 2·00 30
12 30 c. green .. .. 2·00 40
13 40 c. orange .. .. 2·00 40
14 50 c. blue .. .. 2·50 40
15 1 p. red .. .. 7·00 4·00
16 4 p. purple .. .. 28·00 20·00
17 10 p. orange .. .. 38·00 24·00

**1925.** Stamps of Spain optd. **CABO JUBY.**
19a. **68.** 2 c. green .. .. £200 55·00
20. 5 c. purple .. .. 3·50 2·75
21. 10 c. green .. .. 9·25 2·75
22. 20 c. violet .. .. 19·00 8·50

**1926.** As Red Cross stamps of Spain of 1926 optd **CABO-JUBY.**
23 **70** 1 c. orange .. .. 9·75 9·75
24 – 2 c. red .. .. 9·75 9·75
25 – 5 c. brown .. .. 2·50 2·50
26 – 10 c. green .. .. 1·25 1·25
27 **70** 15 c. violet .. .. 85 85
28 – 20 c. purple .. .. 85 85
29 **71** 25 c. red .. .. 85 85
30 **70** 30 c. green .. .. 85 85
31 – 40 c. blue .. .. 30 30
32 – 50 c. red .. .. 30 30
33 – 1 p. red .. .. 30 30
34 – 4 p. bistre .. .. 1·10 1·10
35 **71** 10 p. violet .. .. 2·75 2·75

**1929.** Seville and Barcelona Exhibition stamps of Spain (Nos. 504/14) optd. **CABO JUBY.**
36. – 5 c. red .. .. 30 40
37. – 10 c. green .. .. 30 40
38. **83.** 15 c. blue .. .. 30 40
39. **84.** 20 c. violet .. .. 30 40
40. **83.** 25 c. red .. .. 30 40
41. – 30 c. brown .. .. 30 40
42. – 40 c. blue .. .. 30 40
43. **84.** 50 c. orange .. .. 35 55
44. – 1 p. grey .. .. 14·00 21·00
45. – 4 p. red .. .. 21·00 32·00
46. – 10 p. brown .. .. 21·00 32·00

**1934.** Stamps of Spanish Morocco optd **Cabo Juby.** (a) Stamps of 1928.
47 **11** 1 c. red .. .. 1·50 85
48 2 c. violet .. .. 3·00 55
49 5 c. blue .. .. 3·00 55
50 10 c. green .. .. 7·00 1·40
51 15 c. brown .. .. 16·00 9·00
52 **12** 25 c. red .. .. 3·00 3·25
53 – 1 p. green .. .. 29·00 18·00
54 – 2 p. 50 purple .. .. 65·00 38·00
55 – 4 p. blue .. .. 85·00 48·00

(b) Stamps of 1933.
56 **14** 1 c. red .. .. 35 35
57 – 10 c. green .. .. 2·25 2·25
58 **14** 20 c. black .. .. 6·25 5·00
59 – 30 c. red .. .. 6·25 5·00
60 **15** 40 c. blue .. .. 22·00 19·00
61 50 c. orange .. .. 42·00 30·00

**1935.** Stamps of Spanish Morocco of 1933 optd **CABO JUBY.**
62 **14** 1 c. red .. .. 15 15
63 – 2 c. green .. .. 50 15
64 – 5 c. mauve .. .. 1·90 15
65 – 10 c. green .. .. 11·00 3·00
66 – 15 c. yellow .. .. 4·25 1·90
67 **14** 20 c. black .. .. 4·00 3·00
68 – 25 c. red .. .. 48·00 30·00
73 – 25 c. violet .. .. 3·00 1·90
74 – 30 c. red .. .. 3·00 1·60
75 – 40 c. orange .. .. 4·00 1·90
76 – 50 c. blue .. .. 8·00 1·90
77 – 60 c. green .. .. 10·00 4·25
69 – 1 p. grey .. .. 6·75 6·00
78 – 2 p. brown .. .. 55·00 30·00
70 – 2 p. 50 brown .. .. 27·00 16·00
71 – 4 p. green .. .. 45·00 22·00
72 – 5 p. black .. .. 35·00 30·00

**1937.** 1st Anniv. of Civil War. Nos. 184/99 of Spanish Morocco optd. **CABO JUBY.**
79. 1 c. blue .. .. 30 30
80. 2 c. brown .. .. 30 30
81. 5 c. mauve .. .. 30 30
82. 10 c. green .. .. 30 30
83. 15 c. blue .. .. 30 30
84. 20 c. purple .. .. 30 30
85. 25 c. mauve .. .. 30 30
86. 30 c. red .. .. 30 30
87. 40 c. orange .. .. 85 85
88. 50 c. blue .. .. 85 85
89. 60 c. green .. .. 85 85
90. 1 p. violet .. .. 85 85
91. 2 p. blue .. .. 60·00 60·00
92. 2 p. 50 black .. .. 60·00 60·00
93. 4 p. brown .. .. 60·00 60·00
94. 10 p. black .. .. 60·00 60·00

**1938.** Air. Nos. 203/12 of Spanish Morocco optd **CABO JUBY.**
95. 5 c. brown .. .. 15 15
96. 10 c. green .. .. 1·00 50
97. 25 c. red .. .. 15 15
98. 40 c. blue .. .. 1·50 1·25
99. 50 c. mauve .. .. 15 15
100. 75 c. blue .. .. 15 20
101. 1 p. brown .. .. 15 20
102. 1 p. 50 violet .. .. 4·00 1·50
103. 2 p. red .. .. 2·10 1·75
104. 3 p. black .. .. 5·50 6·00

**1939.** As Nos. 213/16 of Spanish Morocco optd **CABO JUBY.**
105 5 c. red .. .. 35 35
106 10 c. green .. .. 35 35
107 15 c. purple .. .. 35 35
108 20 c. blue .. .. 35 35

**1940.** Nos. 217/32 of Spanish Morocco, but without "ZONA" on back, optd **CABO JUBY.**
109 1 c. brown .. .. 15 15
110 2 c. green .. .. 15 15
111 5 c. blue .. .. 15 15
112 10 c. mauve .. .. 15 15
113 15 c. green .. .. 15 15
114 20 c. violet .. .. 15 15
115 25 c. brown .. .. 15 15
116 30 c. green .. .. 15 15
117 40 c. green .. .. 40 15
118 45 c. red .. .. 40 15
119 50 c. brown .. .. 40 15
120 75 c. blue .. .. 1·40 60
121 1 p. brown and blue .. 2·75 60
122 2 p. 50 green and brown .. 7·50 4·00
123 5 p. brown and purple .. 7·50 4·00
124 10 p. brown & dp brown .. 22·00 15·00

**1942.** Air. Nos. 258/62 of Spanish Morocco, but without "Z" opt and inscr "CABO JUBY".
125 5 c. blue .. .. 15 15
126 10 c. brown .. .. 15 15
127 15 c. green .. .. 15 15
128 90 c. pink .. .. 35 30
129 5 p. black .. .. 1·40 95

**1944.** Nos. 269/82 (agricultural scenes) of Spanish Morocco optd **CABO JUBY.**
130 – 1 c. blue and brown .. 1·00 50
131 – 2 c. light green & green 15 15
132 **26** 5 c. green and brown .. 15 15
133 – 10 c. orange and blue .. 15 15
134 – 15 c. light green & green 15 15
135 – 20 c. black and purple 15 15
136 – 25 c. brown and blue .. 15 15
137 – 30 c. blue and green .. 1·50 50
138 – 40 c. purple and brown 15 15
139 **26** 50 c. brown and blue .. 15 15
140 – 75 c. blue and green .. 90 40
141 – 1 p. brown and blue .. 90 40
142 – 2 p. 50 blue and black .. 2·75 2·00
143 – 10 p. black and orange 18·00 13·00

**1946.** Nos. 285/94 (craftsmen) of Spanish Morocco optd. **CABO JUBY.**

| | | | |
|---|---|---|---|
| 144. – | 1 c. brown and purple | 15 | 15 |
| 145. 27. | 2 c. violet and green .. | 15 | 15 |
| 146. – | 10 c. blue and orange.. | 15 | 15 |
| 147. 27. | 15 c. green and blue .. | 15 | 15 |
| 148. – | 25 c. blue and green .. | 15 | 15 |
| 149. – | 40 c. brown and blue .. | 15 | 15 |
| 150. 27. | 45 c. red and black .. | 15 | 15 |
| 151. – | 1 p. blue and green .. | 1·10 | 45 |
| 152. – | 2 p. 50 green and orange | 3·25 | 2·10 |
| 153. – | 10 p. grey and blue .. | 10·00 | 7·00 |

**1948.** Nos. 307/17 (transport and commerce) of Spanish Morocco, but without "Z" on back, optd **CABO JUBY**.

| | | | |
|---|---|---|---|
| 154 30 | 2 c. brown and violet .. | 15 | 50 |
| 155 – | 5 c. violet and purple .. | 15 | 10 |
| 156 – | 15 c. green and blue .. | 15 | 10 |
| 157 – | 25 c. green and black .. | 15 | 10 |
| 158 – | 35 c. black and blue .. | 15 | 10 |
| 159 – | 50 c. violet and red .. | 15 | 10 |
| 160 – | 70 c. blue and green .. | 15 | 10 |
| 161 – | 90 c. green and mauve | 15 | 10 |
| 162 – | 1 p. violet and blue .. | 25 | 25 |
| 163 30 | 2 p. 50 green and purple | 5·50 | 4·50 |
| 164 – | 10 p. blue and black .. | 3·00 | 3·25 |

EXPRESS LETTER STAMPS

**1919.** Express letter stamp of Spain optd. **CABO JUBY.**

| | | | |
|---|---|---|---|
| E 18. E 53. | 20 c. red .. .. | 1·10 | 1·10 |

**1926.** Red Cross stamp. As Express letter stamp of Spain optd. **CABO-JUBY.**

| | | | |
|---|---|---|---|
| E 36. E 77. | 20 c. black and blue | 2·75 | 2·75 |

**1934.** Stamp of Spanish Morocco optd. **Cabo Juby.**

| | | | |
|---|---|---|---|
| E 62 E 12 | 20 c. black .. .. | 7·00 | 7·50 |

**1935.** Stamp of Spanish Morocco optd. **CABO JUBY.**

| | | | |
|---|---|---|---|
| E 79. E 16. | 20 c. red .. .. | 3·00 | 1·10 |

**1937.** No. E 200 of Spanish Morocco optd. **CABO JUBY.**

| | | | |
|---|---|---|---|
| E 95. E 19. | 20 c. red .. .. | 85 | 85 |

**1940.** No. E 233 Spanish Morocco optd. **CABO JUBY.**

| | | | |
|---|---|---|---|
| E 125. E 21. | 25 c. red .. .. | 30 | 30 |

# CAPE VERDE ISLANDS

**Pt. 9; Pt. 12**

Islands in the Atlantic. Formerly Portuguese; became independent on 5 July 1975.

1877. 1000 reis = 1 milreis.
1913. 100 centavos = 1 escudo.

**1877.** "Crown" key-type inscr "CABO VERDE".

| | | | |
|---|---|---|---|
| 1 P | 5 r. black .. .. | 1·25 | 95 |
| 2a | 10 r. yellow .. .. | 6·75 | 4·00 |
| 18 | 10 r. green .. .. | 1·00 | 80 |
| 3 | 20 r. bistre .. .. | 90 | 75 |
| 19 | 20 r. red .. .. | 1·90 | 1·40 |
| 4 | 25 r. pink .. .. | 90 | 60 |
| 20 | 25 r. lilac .. .. | 1·60 | 1·10 |
| 5 | 40 r. blue .. .. | 30·00 | 20·00 |
| 21 | 40 r. yellow .. .. | 90 | 85 |
| 15 | 50 r. green .. .. | 30·00 | 20·00 |
| 22 | 50 r. blue .. .. | 2·50 | 1·90 |
| 7b | 100 r. lilac .. .. | 3·00 | 1·40 |
| 8 | 200 r. orange .. .. | 1·60 | 1·10 |
| 9b | 300 r. brown .. .. | 2·10 | 1·90 |

**1886.** "Embossed" key-type inscribed "PROVINCIA DE CABO-VERDE".

| | | | |
|---|---|---|---|
| 33 Q. | 5 r. black .. .. .. | 1·50 | 1·00 |
| 34 | 10 r. green .. .. | 1·50 | 1·00 |
| 35 | 20 r. red .. .. .. | 2·75 | 1·90 |
| 26 | 25 r. mauve .. .. | 2·10 | 1·40 |
| 27 | 40 r. brown .. .. | 2·50 | 1·50 |
| 28 | 50 r. blue .. .. .. | 2·50 | 1·50 |
| 29 | 100 r. brown .. .. | 2·75 | 1·60 |
| 30 | 200 r. lilac .. .. | 6·00 | 3·75 |
| 31 | 300 r. orange .. .. | 6·50 | 4·25 |

**1894.** "Figures" key-type inscribed "CABO-VERDE".

| | | | |
|---|---|---|---|
| 37. R. | 5 r. orange .. .. | 55 | 45 |
| 38. | 10 r. mauve .. .. | 60 | 50 |
| 39. | 15 r. brown .. .. | 1·50 | 1·00 |
| 40. | 20 r. lilac .. .. | 1·50 | 1·00 |
| 41. | 25 r. green .. .. | 1·10 | 85 |
| 42. | 50 r. blue .. .. .. | 1·10 | 85 |
| 51. | 75 r. red .. .. .. | 3·75 | 2·50 |
| 43. | 80 r. green .. .. | 4·00 | 3·50 |
| 44. | 100 r. brown on buff .. | 3·25 | 1·25 |
| 58. | 150 r. red on rose .. | 5·25 | 4·00 |
| 59. | 200 r. blue on blue .. | 5·25 | 3·00 |
| 46. | 300 r. blue on buff .. | 8·50 | 4·75 |

**1898.** "King Carlos" key-type inscr. "CABO VERDE".

| | | | |
|---|---|---|---|
| 60. S. | 2½ r. grey .. .. .. | 20 | 15 |
| 61. | 5 r. orange .. .. | 20 | 15 |
| 62. | 10 r. green .. .. | 20 | 15 |
| 63. | 15 r. brown .. .. | 1·75 | 80 |
| 111. | 15 r. green .. .. | 55 | 40 |
| 64. | 20 r. lilac .. .. | 50 | 30 |
| 65. | 25 r. green .. .. | 1·10 | 50 |
| 112. | 25 r. red .. .. .. | 40 | 20 |
| 66. | 50 r. blue .. .. .. | 1·25 | 50 |
| 113. | 50 r. brown .. .. | 1·10 | 80 |
| 114. | 65 r. blue .. .. | 5·75 | 3·75 |
| 67. | 75 r. red .. .. .. | 2·10 | 1·10 |
| 115. | 75 r. purple .. .. | 95 | 75 |
| 68. | 80 r. mauve .. .. | 2·50 | 1·40 |
| 69. | 100 r. blue on blue .. | 1·10 | 65 |
| 116. | 115 r. brown on pink .. | 3·75 | 3·00 |
| 117. | 130 r. brown on yellow .. | 3·75 | 3·00 |
| 70. | 150 r. brown on yellow .. | 2·75 | 1·50 |
| 71. | 200 r. purple on pink .. | 1·25 | 90 |
| 72. | 300 r. blue on pink .. | 3·25 | 1·75 |
| 118. | 400 r. blue on yellow .. | 3·75 | 3·00 |
| 73. | 500 r. black on blue .. | 3·25 | 1·75 |
| 74. | 700 r. mauve on yellow .. | 8·50 | 7·00 |

**1902.** Key-types of Cape Verde Is. surch.

| | | | |
|---|---|---|---|
| 119 S. | 50 r. on 65 r. blue .. | 1·10 | 1·00 |
| 75 Q. | 65 r. on 5 r. black .. | 2·00 | 1·60 |
| 78 R. | 65 r. on 10 r. mauve .. | 2·50 | 1·50 |
| 79 | 65 r. on 20 r. lilac .. | 2·50 | 1·50 |
| 80 | 65 r. on 100 r. brn. on buff | 2·50 | 1·50 |
| 76 Q. | 65 r. on 200 r. lilac .. | 2·00 | 1·60 |
| 77 | 65 r. on 300 r. orange .. | 2·00 | 1·60 |
| 85 R. | 115 r. on 5 r. orange .. | 1·50 | 1·25 |
| 82 Q. | 115 r. on 10 r. green .. | 2·00 | 1·60 |
| 83 | 115 r. on 20 r. red .. | 2·10 | 1·60 |
| 87 R. | 115 r. on 25 r. green .. | 1·50 | 1·10 |
| 88 | 115 r. on 150 r. red on rose | 2·75 | 2·40 |
| 90 Q. | 130 r. on 50 r. blue .. | 2·00 | 1·60 |
| 93 R. | 130 r. on 75 r. red .. | 1·00 | 1·00 |
| 96 | 130 r. on 80 r. green .. | 1·10 | 95 |
| 92 Q. | 130 r. on 100 r. brown .. | 2·00 | 1·60 |
| 97 R. | 130 r. on 200 r. bl. on blue | 1·25 | 1·25 |
| 106 V. | 400 r. on 2½ r. brown .. | 55 | 45 |
| 98 Q. | 400 r. on 25 r. mauve .. | 1·10 | 95 |
| 99 | 400 r. on 40 r. brown .. | 1·50 | 1·40 |
| 101 R. | 400 r. on 50 r. blue .. | 1·75 | 1·60 |
| 103 | 400 r. on 300 r. blue on buff | 1·00 | 75 |

**1902.** "King Carlos" key-type of Cape Verde Is. optd. **PROVISORIO.**

| | | | |
|---|---|---|---|
| 107. S. | 15 r. brown .. .. | 75 | 55 |
| 108. | 25 r. green .. .. | 75 | 55 |
| 109. | 50 r. blue .. .. .. | 75 | 55 |
| 110. | 75 r. red .. .. .. | 1·25 | 85 |

**1911.** "King Carlos" key-type of Cape Verde Is. optd. **REPUBLICA.**

| | | | |
|---|---|---|---|
| 120. S. | 2½ r. grey .. .. .. | 15 | 15 |
| 121. | 5 r. orange .. .. | 15 | 15 |
| 122. | 10 r. green .. .. | 40 | 30 |
| 123. | 15 r. green .. .. | 25 | 15 |
| 124. | 20 r. lilac .. .. .. | 40 | 30 |
| 125. | 25 r. red .. .. .. | 30 | 20 |
| 126. | 50 r. brown .. .. | 3·00 | 2·25 |
| 127. | 75 r. purple .. .. | 45 | 30 |
| 128. | 100 r. blue on blue .. | 45 | 30 |
| 129. | 115 r. brown on pink .. | 40 | 35 |
| 130. | 130 r. brown on yellow .. | 40 | 35 |
| 131. | 200 r. purple on pink .. | 2·25 | 1·40 |
| 132. | 400 r. blue on yellow .. | 1·10 | 40 |
| 133. | 500 r. black on blue .. | 1·10 | 40 |
| 134. | 700 r. mauve on yellow .. | 1·10 | 65 |

**1912.** "King Manoel" key-type inscr. "CABO VERDE" and optd. **REPUBLICA.**

| | | | |
|---|---|---|---|
| 135. T. | 2½ r. lilac .. .. | 10 | 10 |
| 136. | 5 r. black .. .. | 10 | 10 |
| 137. | 10 r. green .. .. | 10 | 10 |
| 138. | 20 r. red .. .. .. | 90 | 60 |
| 139. | 25 r. brown .. .. | 15 | 10 |
| 140. | 50 r. blue .. .. | 1·40 | 1·25 |
| 141. | 75 r. brown .. .. | 40 | 35 |
| 142. | 100 r. brown on green .. | 40 | 35 |
| 143. | 200 r. green on pink .. | 60 | 35 |
| 144. | 300 r. black on blue .. | 60 | 35 |
| 145. | 400 r. blue and black .. | 1·25 | 1·10 |
| 146. | 500 r. brown and olive .. | 1·25 | 1·10 |

**1913.** Surch. **REPUBLICA CABO VERDE** and new value on "Vasco da Gama" issues of

(a) Portuguese Colonies.

| | | | |
|---|---|---|---|
| 147. | ¼ c. on 2½ r. green .. | 50 | 30 |
| 148. | ½ c. on 5 r. red .. .. | 50 | 30 |
| 149. | 1 c. on 10 r. purple .. | 35 | 30 |
| 150. | 2½ c. on 25 r. green .. | 35 | 30 |
| 151. | 5 c. on 50 r. blue .. | 70 | 60 |
| 152. | 7½ c. on 75 r. brown .. | 85 | 75 |
| 153. | 10 c. on 100 r. brown .. | 70 | 70 |
| 154. | 15 c. on 150 r. bistre | 90 | 75 |

(b) Macao.

| | | | |
|---|---|---|---|
| 155. | ¼ c. on ½ a. green .. | 50 | 40 |
| 156. | ½ c. on 1 a. red .. | 50 | 40 |
| 157. | 1 c. on 2 a. purple .. | 45 | 40 |
| 158. | 2½ c. on 4 a. green .. | 45 | 40 |
| 159. | 5 c. on 8 a. blue .. | 2·50 | 1·90 |
| 160. | 7½ c. on 12 a. brown .. | 1·60 | 90 |
| 161. | 10 c. on 16 a. brown .. | 80 | 70 |
| 162. | 15 c. on 24 a. bistre .. | 1·75 | 1·25 |

(c) Timor.

| | | | |
|---|---|---|---|
| 163. | ¼ c. on ½ a. green .. | 50 | 40 |
| 164. | ½ c. on 1 a. red .. .. | 50 | 40 |
| 165. | 1 c. on 2 a. purple .. | 45 | 40 |
| 166. | 2½ c. on 4 a. green .. | 45 | 40 |
| 167. | 5 c. on 8 a. blue .. | 2·50 | 1·90 |
| 168. | 7½ c. on 12 a. brown .. | 2·00 | 1·40 |
| 169. | 10 c. on 16 a. brown .. | 80 | 70 |
| 170. | 15 c. on 24 a. bistre .. | 1·00 | 80 |

**1913.** Stamps of 1902 optd **REPUBLICA**.

| | | | |
|---|---|---|---|
| 171 S | 75 r. red (No. 110) .. | 1·50 | 1·40 |
| 192 R | 115 r. on 5 r. (No. 85) .. | 30 | 20 |
| 193 Q | 115 r. on 10 r. (No. 82) | 50 | 40 |
| 195 | 115 r. on 20 r. (No. 83) .. | 60 | 50 |
| 198 R | 115 r. on 25 r. (No. 87) | 40 | 30 |
| 200 | 115 r. on 150 r. (No. 88) | 25 | 20 |
| 201 Q | 130 r. on 50 r. (No. 90) .. | 50 | 50 |
| 202 R | 130 r. on 75 r. (No. 93) .. | 40 | 30 |
| 204 | 130 r. on 80 r. (No. 96) | 40 | 30 |
| 206 Q | 130 r. on 100 r. (No. 92) | 40 | 30 |
| 208 R | 130 r. on 200 r. (No. 97) | 40 | 30 |

**1914.** "Ceres" key-type inscr "CABO VERDE". Name and value in black.

| | | | |
|---|---|---|---|
| 219 U | ¼ c. green .. .. | 10 | 10 |
| 220 | ½ c. black .. .. | 10 | 10 |
| 221 | 1 c. green .. .. | 10 | 10 |
| 222 | 1½ c. brown .. .. | 10 | 10 |
| 223 | 2 c. red .. .. | 10 | 10 |
| 224 | 2 c. grey .. .. | 15 | 15 |
| 180 | 2½ c. violet .. .. | 25 | 20 |
| 214 | 2½ c. mauve .. .. | 10 | 10 |
| 215 | 3 c. orange .. .. | 10 | 10 |
| 216 | 4 c. red .. .. .. | 10 | 15 |
| 228 | 4½ c. grey .. .. | 15 | 15 |
| 229 | 5 c. blue .. .. | 15 | 15 |
| 230 | 6 c. mauve .. .. | 15 | 15 |
| 231 | 7 c. blue .. .. | 15 | 15 |
| 232 | 7½ c. brown .. .. | 10 | 10 |
| 233 | 8 c. grey .. .. | 20 | 15 |
| 234 | 10 c. red .. .. | 10 | 10 |
| 235 | 12 c. green .. .. | 20 | 20 |
| 236 | 15 c. pink .. .. | 10 | 10 |
| 237 | 20 c. green .. .. | 15 | 10 |
| 238 | 24 c. blue .. .. | 40 | 35 |
| 239 | 25 c. brown .. .. | 40 | 35 |
| 188 | 30 c. brown on green .. | 1·50 | 1·25 |
| 240 | 30 c. green .. .. | 15 | 15 |
| 189 | 40 c. brown on pink .. | 90 | 80 |
| 241 | 40 c. turquoise .. | 15 | 15 |
| 190 | 50 c. orange on orange .. | 1·10 | 85 |
| 242 | 50 c. mauve .. .. | 30 | 20 |
| 243 | 60 c. blue .. .. | 40 | 30 |
| 244 | 60 c. red .. .. | 40 | 30 |
| 245 | 80 c. red .. .. | 1·50 | 55 |
| 191 | 1 e. green on blue .. | 1·10 | 85 |
| 246 | 1 e. pink .. .. | 1·90 | 1·00 |
| 247 | 1 e. blue .. .. | 1·75 | 1·10 |
| 248 | 2 e. purple .. .. | 1·90 | 1·10 |
| 249 | 5 e. brown .. .. | 4·00 | 3·50 |
| 250 | 10 e. pink .. .. | 7·00 | 6·25 |
| 251 | 20 e. green .. .. | 17·00 | 16·00 |

**1921.** Nos. 153/4 surch.

| | | | |
|---|---|---|---|
| 252 | 2 c. on 15 c. on 150 r. brn | 60 | 55 |
| 253 | 4 c. on 10 c. on 100 r. brn | 80 | 80 |

**1921.** No. 69 surch. **REPUBLICA 6 c.**

| | | | |
|---|---|---|---|
| 254. S. | 6 c. on 100 r. blue on blue | 80 | 80 |

**1921.** Charity Tax stamp of Portuguese Colonies (General issues) optd **CABO VERDE CORREIOS** or surch also.

| | | | |
|---|---|---|---|
| 255. | ¼ c. on 1 c. green .. | 15 | 15 |
| 256. | ½ c. on 1 c. green .. | 15 | 15 |
| 257. | 1 c. green .. .. | 20 | 15 |

**1922.** Provisionals of 1913 surch **$04**.

| | | | |
|---|---|---|---|
| 260 R | 4 c. on 130 r. on 75 r. red (No. 202) .. .. | 35 | 30 |
| 262 | 4 c. on 130 r. on 80 r. green (No. 204) .. | 45 | 40 |
| 265 | 4 c. on 130 r. on 200 r. blue (No. 208) .. | 35 | 30 |

**1925.** Provisional stamps of 1902 surch **Republica 40 C**.

| | | | |
|---|---|---|---|
| 267 V | 40 c. on 400 r. on 2½ r. brown (No. 106) .. | 20 | 20 |
| 268 R | 40 c. on 400 r. on 300 r. blue on buff (No. 103) | 30 | 30 |

**1931.** No. 245 surch **70 C**.

| | | | |
|---|---|---|---|
| 269 U | 70 c. on 80 c. red .. | 1·40 | 1·10 |

**1934.** As T17 of Angola (new "Ceres" type).

| | | | |
|---|---|---|---|
| 270. 17. | 1 c. brown .. .. | 10 | 10 |
| 271. | 5 c. sepia .. .. .. | 10 | 10 |
| 272. | 10 c. mauve .. .. | 10 | 10 |
| 273. | 15 c. black .. .. | 10 | 10 |
| 274. | 20 c. grey .. .. | 10 | 10 |
| 275. | 30 c. green .. .. | 10 | 10 |
| 276. | 40 c. red .. .. .. | 10 | 10 |
| 277. | 45 c. blue .. .. | 40 | 25 |
| 278. | 50 c. brown .. .. | 30 | 15 |
| 279. | 60 c. olive .. .. | 30 | 15 |
| 280. | 70 c. brown .. .. | 30 | 15 |
| 281. | 80 c. green .. .. | 30 | 15 |
| 282. | 85 c. red .. .. .. | 1·40 | 85 |
| 283. | 1 e. red .. .. | 95 | 15 |
| 284. | 1 e. 40 blue .. .. | 1·00 | 75 |
| 285. | 2 e. mauve .. .. | 1·60 | 75 |
| 286. | 5 e. green .. .. | 7·00 | 1·75 |
| 287. | 10 e. brown .. .. | 12·50 | 6·25 |
| 288. | 20 e. orange .. .. | 25·00 | 11·00 |

**1938.** As Nos. 383/409 of Angola.

| | | | |
|---|---|---|---|
| 289. | 1 c. olive (postage) .. | 10 | 10 |
| 290. | 5 c. brown .. .. | 10 | 10 |
| 291. | 10 c. red .. .. .. | 10 | 10 |
| 292. | 15 c. purple .. .. | 35 | 25 |
| 293. | 20 c. slate .. .. | 20 | 15 |
| 294. | 30 c. purple .. .. | 20 | 15 |
| 295. | 35 c. green .. .. | 20 | 15 |
| 296. | 40 c. brown .. .. | 20 | 15 |
| 297. | 50 c. mauve .. .. | 20 | 15 |
| 298. | 60 c. black .. .. | 20 | 15 |
| 299. | 70 c. violet .. .. | 20 | 15 |
| 300. | 80 c. orange .. .. | 20 | 15 |
| 301. | 1 e. red .. .. .. | 25 | 15 |
| 302. | 1 e. 75 blue .. .. | 60 | 40 |
| 303. | 2 e. green .. .. | 1·10 | 65 |
| 304. | 5 e. olive .. .. | 3·00 | 85 |
| 305. | 10 e. blue .. .. | 5·25 | 1·00 |
| 306. | 20 e. brown .. .. | 13·00 | 2·00 |
| 307. | 10 c. red (air) .. .. | 30 | 20 |
| 308. | 20 c. violet .. .. | 30 | 20 |
| 309. | 50 c. orange .. .. | 30 | 20 |
| 310. | 1 e. blue .. .. .. | 35 | 20 |
| 311. | 2 e. red .. .. .. | 65 | 30 |
| 312. | 3 e. green .. .. | 90 | 45 |
| 313. | 5 e. brown .. .. | 2·00 | 70 |
| 314. | 9 e. red .. .. .. | 4·75 | 1·50 |
| 315. | 10 e. mauve .. .. | 6·00 | 1·75 |

**14.** Route of President's Tour.

**16.** Machado Point, Sao Vicente.

**17.** Ribeira Brava, Sao Nicolau.

**1939.** Pres. Carmona's 2nd Colonial Tour.

| | | | |
|---|---|---|---|
| 316 14 | 80 c. violet on mauve .. | 1·90 | 1·40 |
| 317 | 1 e. 75 blue on blue .. | 12·00 | 8·00 |
| 318 | 20 e. brown on cream .. | 32·00 | 8·00 |

**1948.** Nos. 276 and 294 surch.

| | | | |
|---|---|---|---|
| 319. | 10 c. on 30 c. purple .. | 50 | 40 |
| 320. | 25 c. on 40 c. red .. | 65 | 40 |

**1948.**

| | | | |
|---|---|---|---|
| 321 16 | 5 c. purple and bistre .. | 25 | 25 |
| 322 – | 10 c. green & light green | 25 | 25 |
| 323 17 | 50 c. purple and lilac .. | 45 | 25 |
| 324 – | 1 e. purple .. .. | 1·60 | 75 |
| 325 – | 1 e. 75 blue and green | 1·90 | 1·10 |
| 326 – | 2 e. brown and ochre .. | 4·50 | 1·25 |
| 327 – | 5 e. green and yellow .. | 9·00 | 1·90 |
| 328 – | 10 e. red and orange .. | 14·00 | 9·50 |
| 329 – | 20 e. violet and buff .. | 35·00 | 16·00 |

DESIGNS—VERT. 10 c. Ribeira Grande. HORIZ. 1 e. Porto Grande, Sao Vicente. 1 e. 75, 5 e. Mindelo, Sao Vicente. 2 e. Joao de Evora beach, Sao Vicente. 10 e. Volcano, Fogo. 20 e. Paul.

**1948.** Honouring the Statue of Our Lady of Fatima. As T **33** of Angola.

| | | | |
|---|---|---|---|
| 330. | 50 c. blue .. .. | 6·75 | 3·25 |

**1949.** 75th Anniv. of U.P.U. As T **39** of Angola.

| | | | |
|---|---|---|---|
| 331. | 1 e. mauve .. .. | 4·75 | 2·75 |

**1950.** Holy Year. As T **41/2** of Angola.

| | | | |
|---|---|---|---|
| 332. | 1 e. brown .. .. | 55 | 40 |
| 333. | 2 e. blue .. .. .. | 2·50 | 1·25 |

**1951.** Surch. with figures and bars over old value.

| | | | |
|---|---|---|---|
| 334. | 10 c. on 35 c. (No. 295).. | 40 | 40 |
| 335. | 20 c. on 70 c. (No. 299).. | 55 | 50 |
| 336. | 40 c. on 70 c. (No. 299).. | 60 | 50 |
| 337. | 50 c. on 80 c. (No. 300).. | 60 | 50 |
| 338. | 1 e. on 1 e. 75 (No. 302).. | 60 | 50 |
| 339. | 2 e. on 10 e. (No. 305) .. | 3·50 | 1·25 |

**1951.** Termination of Holy Year. As T **44** of Angola.

| | | | |
|---|---|---|---|
| 340 | 2 e. violet and mauve .. | 1·00 | 70 |

**1952.** No. 302 surch. with figures and cross over old values.

| | | | |
|---|---|---|---|
| 341. | 10 c. on 1 e. 75 blue .. | 85 | 85 |
| 342. | 20 c. on 1 e. 75 blue .. | 85 | 85 |
| 343. | 50 c. on 1 e. 75 blue .. | 3·75 | 3·50 |
| 344. | 1 e. on 1 e. 75 blue .. | 45 | 15 |
| 345. | 1 e. 50 on 1 e. 75 blue .. | 45 | 15 |

**20.** Map, c. 1471.

**21.** V. Dias and G. de Cintra.

**1952.** Portuguese Navigators as T **20/21**. Mult.

| | | | |
|---|---|---|---|
| 346 | 5 c. Type **20** .. .. | 10 | 10 |
| 347 | 10 c. Type **21** .. .. | 10 | 10 |
| 348 | 30 c. D. Afonso and A. Fernandes .. .. | 10 | 10 |
| 349 | 50 c. Lancarote and S. da Costa .. .. .. | 10 | 10 |
| 350 | 1 e. D. Gomes and A. da Nola .. .. .. | 15 | 10 |
| 351 | 2 e. Princes Fernando and Henry the Navigator .. | 55 | 10 |
| 352 | 3 e. A. Goncalves and D. Dias .. .. .. | 5·50 | 80 |
| 353 | 5 e. A. Goncalves Baldaia and J. Fernandes .. | 1·75 | 40 |
| 354 | 10 e. D. Eanes da Gra and A. de Freitas .. .. | 3·75 | 1·10 |
| 355 | 20 e. Map, 1502 .. .. | 6·50 | 1·25 |

**22.** Doctor giving Injection.

**23.** Facade of Monastery.

**1952.** 1st Tropical Medicine Congress, Lisbon.

| | | | |
|---|---|---|---|
| 356. 22. | 20 c. black and green .. | 35 | 30 |

**1953.** Missionary Art Exhibition.

| | | | |
|---|---|---|---|
| 357. 23. | 10 c. brown and olive .. | 10 | 10 |
| 358. | 50 c. violet and salmon | 35 | 25 |
| 359. | 1 e. green and orange .. | 1·00 | 55 |

**1953.** Portuguese Stamp Centenary. As T **48** of Angola.

| | | | |
|---|---|---|---|
| 360 | 50 c. multicoloured .. | 1·00 | 55 |

**1954.** 4th Cent. of Sao Paulo. As T **49** of Angola.

| | | | |
|---|---|---|---|
| 361. | 1 e. black, green and buff | 30 | 25 |

24. Arms of Cape Verde Is. and Portuguese Guinea. 25. Arms of Praia. 26. Prince Henry the Navigator.

**1955.** Presidential Visit.
362. **24.** 1 e. multicoloured .. 30 25
363. 1 e. 60 c. multicoloured 50 40

**1958.** Cent of City of Praia. Multicoloured.
364 **25** 1 e. on yellow .. .. 30 20
365 2 e. 50 on salmon .. 45 50

**1958.** Brussels Int. Exn. As T **55** of Angola.
366. 2 e. multicoloured .. 40 20

**1958.** 6th International Congress of Tropical Medicine. As T **56** of Angola. Multicoloured.
367 3 c. "Aloe vera" (plant) .. 2·75 1·25

**1960.** 500th Death Anniv. of Prince Henry the Navigator.
368. **26.** 2 e. multicoloured .. 20 15

27. Antonio da Nola. 28. "Education".

**1960.** 500th Anniv of Colonization of Cape Verde Islands. Multicoloured.
369 1 e. Type **27** .. .. 30 25
370 2 e. 50 Diogo Gomes .. 80 60

**1960.** 10th Anniv. of African Technical Co-operation Commission.
371. **28.** 2 e. 50 multicoloured .. 55 30

29. Arms of Praia. 30. Militia Regiment Drummer, 1806.

**1961.** Urban Arms. As T **29.** Arms multicoloured; inscriptions in red and green; background colours given.
372. 5 c. buff .. .. .. 15 15
373. 15 c. blue .. .. .. 15 15
374. 20 c. yellow .. .. 15 15
375. 30 c. lilac .. .. .. 15 15
376. 1 e. green .. .. .. 35 15
377. 2 e. lemon .. .. .. 35 15
378. 2 e. 50 pink .. .. 50 15
379. 3 e. brown .. .. .. 75 25
380. 5 e. blue .. .. .. 75 25
381. 7 e. 50 olive .. .. 85 40
382. 15 e. mauve .. .. 1·40 60
383. 30 e. yellow .. .. 2·75 1·60
ARMS: 15 c. Nova Sintra. 20 c. Ribeira Brava. 30 c. Assomada. 1 e. Maio. 2 e. Mindelo. 2 e. 50 Santa Maria. 3 e. Pombas. 5 e. Sal-Rei. 7 e. 50, Tarrafal. 15 e. Maria Pia. 30 e. San Felipe.

**1962.** Sports. As T **62** of Angola. Mult.
384 50 c. Throwing the javelin 15 15
385 1 e. Discus thrower .. 50 15
386 1 e. 50 Batsman (cricket) 1·25 30
387 2 e. 50 Boxing .. .. 50 25
388 4 e. 50 Hurdler .. .. 80 55
389 12 e. 50 Golfers .. .. 1·60 1·00

**1962.** Malaria Eradication. Mosquito design as T **63** of Angola. Multicoloured.
390 2 e. 50 "Anopheles pretoriensis" .. .. 75 55

**1963.** 10th Anniv. of T.A.P. Airline. As T **69** of Angola.
391. 2 e. 50 multicoloured .. 45 30

**1964.** Centenary of National Overseas Bank. As T **71** of Angola but portrait of J. da S. M. Leal.
392 1 e. 50 multicoloured .. 50 40

**1965.** Cent. of I.T.U. As T **73** of Angola.
393. 2 e. 50 multicoloured .. 1·00 80

**1965.** Portuguese Military Uniforms. Mult.
394. 50 c. Type **30** .. .. 15 15
395. 1 e. Militiaman, 1806 .. 25 15
396. 1 e. 50 Infantry Grenadiers officer, 1833 .. .. 40 25
397. 2 e. 50 Infantry grenadier, 1833 .. .. .. 70 20
398. 3 e. Cavalry officer, 1834 .. 1·00 30
399. 4 e. Infantry grenadier, 1835 .. .. .. 70 40
400. 5 e. Artillery officer, 1848 70 40
401. 10 e. Infantry drum-major, 1856 .. .. .. 1·40 1·10

**1966.** 40th Anniv. of National Revolution. As T **77** of Angola, but showing different building. Multicoloured.
402. 1 e. Dr. A. Moreira's Academy and Public Assistance Building .. .. 30 20

**1967.** Centenary of Military Naval Assn. As T **79** of Angola. Multicoloured.
403 1 e. F. da Costa and gunboat "Mandovy" .. 45 25
404 1 e. 50 C. Araujo and minesweeper "Augusto Castilho" .. .. 75 40

**1967.** 50th Anniv. of Fatima Apparitions. As T **80** of Angola. Multicoloured.
405. 1 e. Image of Virgin Mary 15 15

33. President Tomas. 34. Port of Sao Vicente.

**1968.** Visit of President Tomas of Portugal.
406. **33.** 1 e. multicoloured .. 15 15

**1968.** 500th Birth Anniv. of Pedro Cabral (explorer). As T **84** of Angola. Multicoloured.
407. 1 e. Cantino's map, 1502 .. 40 25
408. 1 e. 50 Pedro Alvares Cabral (vert.) .. .. .. 60 40

**1968.** "Produce of Cape Verde Islands". Multicoloured.
409. 50 c. Type **34** .. .. 15 15
410. 1 e. "Purgueira" (Tatrophus curcus) .. .. 20 15
411. 1 e. 50 Groundnuts .. 20 15
412. 2 e. 50 Castor-oil Plant .. 20 15
413. 3 e. 50 "Inhame" (Dioscorea alata) .. .. 25 15
414. 4 e. Date Palm .. .. 25 15
415. 4 e. 50 "Goiabeira" (Psidium guajava) .. 35 20
416. 5 e. Tamarind .. .. 50 20
417. 10 e. Manioc .. .. 65 40
418. 30 e. Girl of Cape Verde .. 1·60 1·25
The 1 e. to 30 e. values are vert.

**1969.** Birth Centenary of Admiral Gago Coutinho. As T **86** of Angola. Multicoloured.
419 30 c. Fairey IIID seaplane "Lusitania" and map of Lisbon–Rio flight (vert) 15 15

**1969.** 500th Birth Anniv. of Vasco da Gama (explorer). Multicoloured. As T **87** of Angola.
420. 1 e. 50 Vasco da Gama (vert.) .. .. .. 15 15

**1969.** Centenary of Overseas Administrative Reforms. As T **88** of Angola.
421. 2 e. multicoloured .. .. 15 15

**1969.** 500th Birth Anniv of King Manoel I. As T **89** of Angola. Multicoloured.
422 3 e. Manoel I .. .. 20 15

**1970.** Birth Centenary of Marshal Carmona. As T **91** of Angola. Multicoloured.
423 2 e. 50 Half-length portrait 25 20

35. Desalination Installation. 37. Cabral, Flag and People.

**1971.** Inauguration of Desalination Plant, Mindelo.
424 **35** 4 e. multicoloured .. 55 45

**1972.** 400th Anniv. of Camoens' "Lusiad" (epic poem). As T **96** of Angola. Mult.
425. 5 e. Galleons at Cape Verde 50 20

**1972.** Olympic Games, Munich. As T **97** of Angola. Multicoloured.
426. 4 e. Basketball and boxing 30 20

**1972.** 50th Anniv of 1st Flight Lisbon–Rio de Janeiro. As T **98** of Angola. Multicoloured.
427 3 e. 50 Fairey IIID seaplane "Lusitania" near Sao Vicente .. 30 20

**1973.** Centenary of I.M.O./W.M.O. As Type **99** of Angola.
428. 2 e. 50 multicoloured .. 30 20

**1975.** Independence. No. 407 optd. **INDEPENDENCIA 5 Julho—75.**
430. 1 e. multicoloured .. .. 15 10

**1975.** 3rd Anniv. of Amilcar Cabral's Assassination.
431. **37.** 5 e. multicoloured .. 20 15

38. Islanders with Broken Shackles.

**1976.** First Anniv. of Independence.
432. **38.** 50 c. multicoloured .. 10 10
433. 3 e. multicoloured .. 15 10
434. 15 e. multicoloured .. 40 20
435. 50 e. multicoloured .. 1·25 65

**1976.** Nos. 428, 424 and 415 optd. **REPUBLICA DE.**
437. 2 e. 50 multicoloured (No. 428) .. .. .. 15 10
438. 4 e. multicoloured (No. 424) .. .. .. 11·00 1·75
439. 4 e. 50 multicoloured (No. 415) .. .. .. 1·00 1·00

40. Cabral and Map. 41. Map of Islands.

**1976.** 20th Anniv. of PAIGC (Revolutionary Party).
440. **40.** 1 e. multicoloured .. 10 10

**1977.** Red Cross.
441. **41.** 50 c. multicoloured .. 10 10

42. Printed Circuit. 43. Ashtray on Stand.

**1977.** International Telecommunications Day.
442. **42.** 5 e. 50 orge., brn. & blk. 15 10

**1977.** Craftsmanship in Coconut. Mult.
443. 20 c. Type **43** .. .. 10 10
444. 30 c. Ornamental bell .. 10 10
445. 50 c. Lamp .. .. 10 10
446. 1 e. Nativity .. .. 10 10
447. 1 e. 50 Desk lamp .. 10 10
448. 5 e. Storage jar .. .. 15 10
449. 10 e. Container with hinged lid .. .. 35 15
450. 20 e. Tobacco jar .. .. 65 20
451. 30 e. Stringed instrument 1·10 35

44. 5 r. Stamp, 1877. 45. Congress Emblem.

**1977.** Cent. of First Cape Verde Stamps.
452. **44.** 4 e. multicoloured .. 15 10
453. 8 e. multicoloured .. 25 10

**1977.** Third PAIGC Congress, Bissau.
454. **45.** 3 e. 50 multicoloured .. 15 10

**1978.** No. 419 surch **3$00.**
455. 3 e. on 30 c. multicoloured 15 10

47. Microwave Antenna.

**1978.** 10th World Telecommunications Day.
456. **47.** 3 c. 50 multicoloured .. 15 10

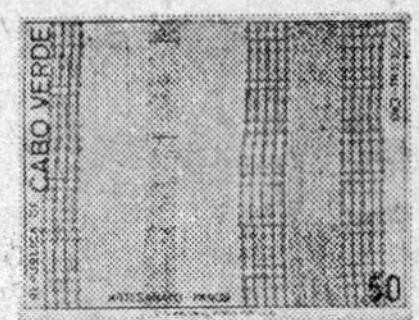

48. Textile Pattern.

**1978.** Handicrafts. Multicoloured.
457. 50 c. Type **48** .. .. 10 10
458. 1 e. 50, Carpet runner and map of Islands .. .. 10 10
459. 2 e. Woven ribbon & map of Islands .. .. 10 10
460. 3 e. Shoulder bag and map of Islands .. .. 10 10
461. 10 e. Woven Cushions (vert.) 30 20

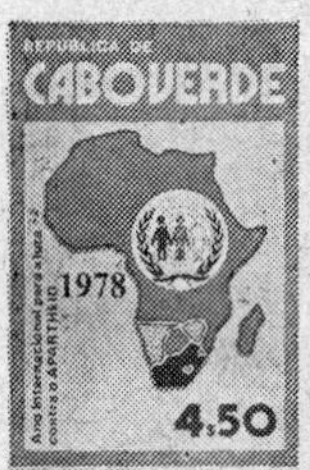

49. Map of Africa. 51. Human Rights Emblem.

50. Freighter "Cabo Verde".

**1978.** International Anti-Apartheid Year.
462. **49.** 4 e. 50 multicoloured .. 15 10

**1978.** 1st Cape Verde Merchant Ship.
463. **50.** 1 e. multicoloured .. 30 10

**1978.** 30th Anniv. of Declaration of Human Rights.
464. **51.** 1 e. 50 multicoloured .. 10 10
465. 2 e. multicoloured .. 10 10

52. Children with Flowers.

**1979.** International Year of the Child. Multicoloured.
466. 1 e. 50 Children with balloons and flags .. 10 10
467. 3 e. 50 Type **52** .. .. 10 10

53. Monument. 54. Poster.

**1979.** 20th Anniv. of Pindjiguiti Massacre.
468. **53.** 4 e. 50 multicoloured .. 15 10

**1979.** First National Youth Week.
469. **54.** 3 e. 50 multicoloured .. 15 10

55. Mindelo.

**1980.** Centenary of Mindelo City.
470. 55. 4 e. multicoloured .. 30 15

56. Family, Graph and Map. 57. National Flag.

**1980.** First Population and Housing Census.
471. 56. 3 e. 50 multicoloured .. 10 10
472. 4 e. 50 multicoloured .. 15 10

**1980.** 5th Anniv. of Independence (1st issue).
473. 57. 4 e. multicoloured .. 10 10
See also Nos. 481/3.

58. Running. 59. Stylized Bird.

**1980.** Olympic Games, Moscow. Multicoloured.
474. 1 e. Type 58 .. .. 10 10
475. 2 e. 50 Boxing .. .. 10 10
476. 3 e. Basketball .. .. 10 10
477. 4 e. Volleyball .. .. 10 10
478. 20 e. Swimming .. .. 55 25
479. 50 e. Tennis .. .. 1·25 50

**1980.** 5th Anniv. of Independence (2nd issue).
481. 59. 4 e. multicoloured .. 10 10
482. – 7 e. multicoloured .. 15 10
483. – 11 e. multicoloured .. 25 15

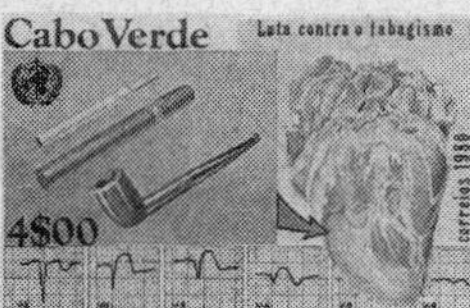


60. Cigarette, Cigar, Pipe and Diseased Heart.

**1980.** World Health Day. Anti-Smoking Campaign. Multicoloured.
484. 4 e. Type 60 .. .. 10 10
485. 7 e. Healthy lungs plus smoking equals diseased lungs .. .. .. 20 10

61. " Thunnus alalunga ".

**1980.** Marine Life. Multicoloured.
486. 50 c. Type 61 .. .. 10 10
487. 4 e. 50 " Trachurus trachurus " .. .. 10 10
488. 8 e. " Muraena helena " .. 25 10
489. 10 e. " Corvina nigra " .. 25 10
490. 12 e. " Katsuwonus pelamis " .. .. 30 15
491. 50 e. " Prionace glauca " 1·00 50

62. " Arca Verdel ".

**1980.** Freighters. Multicoloured.
492. 3 e. Type 62 .. .. 20 15
493. 5 e. 50 " Ilha do Maio " .. 25 15
494. 7 e. 50 " Ilha de Komo " 50 20
495. 9 e. " Boa Vista " .. 50 20
496. 12 e. " Santo Antao " .. 60 30
497. 30 e. " Santiago " .. 1·25 70

63. " Lochnera rosea ".

**1980.** Flowers. Multicoloured.
498. 50 c. Type 63 .. .. 10 10
499. 4 e. 50 " Pioncinana regia-Bojer " .. .. 10 10
500. 8 e. " Mirabilis jalapa " .. 25 10
501. 10 e. " Nerium oleander " 25 10
502. 12 e. " Bougainvillea litoralis " .. .. 30 10
503. 30 e. " Hibiscus rose sinenis " 70 30

64. Desert Scene and Hands holding plant.

**1981.** Desert Erosion Prevention. Mult.
504. 4 e. 50 Type 64 .. .. 15 10
505. 10 e. 50 Hands caring for plant and river scene .. 25 15

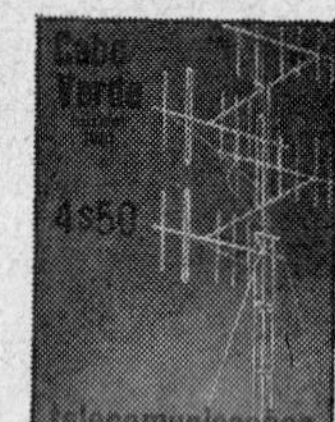


65. Map, Flag, and " Official Bulletin " announcing Constitution. 67. Antenna.

**1981.** 6th Anniv. of Constitution.
506. 65. 4 e. 50 multicoloured .. 15 10

**1981.** Telecommunications. Multicoloured.
508. 4 e. 50 Type 67 .. .. 10 10
509. 8 e. Dish antenna .. .. 25 10
510. 20 e. Dish antenna and satellite .. .. .. 50 30

68. Disabled Person in Wheelchair and I.Y.D.P. Emblem.

**1981.** International Year of Disabled Persons.
511. 68. 4 e. 50, multicoloured 15 10

69. Moorhens.

**1981.** Birds. Multicoloured.
512 1 e. Little egret (vert) .. 10 10
513 4 e. 50 Barn owl (vert) .. 35 25
514 8 e. Grey-headed king-fisher (vert) .. 75 40
515 10 e. Type 69 .. .. 1·00 45
516 12 e. Helmet guineafowls 1·40 45

**INDEX**

Countries can be quickly located by referring to the index at the end of this volume.

70. Map showing Member States.

**1982.** CILSS Congress, Praia.
518. 70. 11 e. 50 multicoloured .. 30 10

71. Tackle.

**1982.** " Amilcar Cabral " Football Cup Competition. Multicoloured.
519. 4 e. 50 Type 71 .. .. 15 10
520. 7 e. 50 Running with ball 20 10
521. 11 e. 50 Goalmouth scene 30 10

72. Militiawomen.

**1982.** 1st Anniv. of Cape Verde Women's Organization. Multicoloured.
522. 4 e. 50 Type 72 .. 15 10
523. 8 e. Women farmers .. 20 10
524. 12 e. Nursery teacher .. 30 10

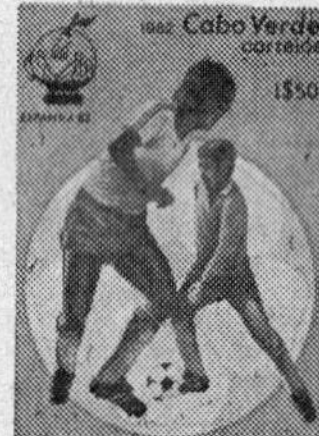


73. Footballers.

**1982.** World Cup Football Championship, Spain.
525. 73. 1 e. 50 multicoloured .. 10 10
526. – 4 e. 50 multicoloured .. 15 10
527. – 8 e. multicoloured .. 20 10
528. – 10 e. 50 multicoloured 25 10
529. – 12 e. multicoloured .. 30 10
530. – 20 e. multicoloured .. 50 30
DESIGNS: 4 e. 50 to 20 e. show various football scenes.

74. " Morrissey-Ernestina ".

**1982.** Return of Schooner "Morrissey-Ernestina".
532 74 12 e. multicoloured .. 1·00 30

75. San Vicente Shipyard.

**1982.** 7th Anniv. of Independence.
533. 75. 10 e. 50, multicoloured 75 30

76. " Hypolimnas misippus ".

**1982.** Butterflies. Multicoloured.
534 2 e. Type 76 .. .. 15 10
535 4 e. 50 "Melanitis lede" .. 25 15
536 8 e. "Catopsilia florella" .. 40 20
537 10 e. 50 "Colias electo" .. 55 20
538 11 e. 50 "Danaus chrysippus" .. .. 65 20
539 12 e. "Papilio demodecus" 65 20

77. Amilcar Cabral. 78. Francisco Xavier de Cruz (composer).

**1983.** Amilcar Cabral Symposium.
540. 77. 7 e. multicoloured .. 15 10
541. 10 e. 50 multicoloured .. 20 10

**1983.** Composers and Poets. Multicoloured.
543. 7 e. Type 78 .. .. 15 10
544. 14 e. Eugenio Tavares (poet) .. .. .. 30 10

79. "World Communications Network". 80. Cape Verde Cone.

**1983.** World Communications Year.
545. 79. 13 e. multicoloured .. 20 10

**1983.** Shells. Multicoloured.
546. 50 c. Type 80 .. .. 10 10
547. 1 e. "Conus decoratus" .. 10 10
548. 3 e. "Conus salreiensis" .. 15 10
549. 10 e. "Conus verdensis" .. 30 20
550. 50 e. "Conus cuneolus" .. 1·40 90

81. Arch and Cross. 82. Auster D5/160 Husky.

**1983.** 450th Anniv. of Christianity in Cape Verde Islands.
551. 81. 7 e. multicoloured .. 15 10

**1984.** 40th Anniv of I.C.A.O. Multicoloured.
552 50 c. Type 82 .. .. 10 10
553 2 e. De Havilland Dove .. 10 10
554 10 e. Hawker Siddeley HS748 .. .. .. 25 15
555 13 e. De Havilland Dragon Rapide .. .. .. 25 15
556 20 e. De Havilland Twin Otter .. .. .. 50 30
557 50 e. Britten-Norman Islander .. .. 1·10 65

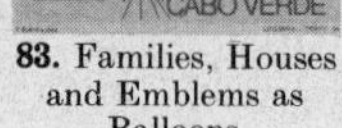

83. Families, Houses and Emblems as Balloons. 84. Figure rising from Nautilus Shell.

**1984.** National Solidarity Campaign.
558. 83. 6 e. 50 multicoloured .. 10 10
559. 13 e. 50 multicoloured 20 10

**1985.** 2nd Cape Verde Womens' Organization Conference.
560. 84. 8 e. multicoloured .. 25 15

**85.** Emblem. **87.** "Steamer".

**1985.** 10th Anniv. of Independence.
561. **85.** 8 e. multicoloured .. 15 10
562. 12 e. multicoloured .. 20 10

**1985.**
564. **87.** 30 e. on 10 c. mult. .. 40 40

**88.** "Mabuya vaillanti". **89.** Food in Pot over Fire.

**1986.** Endangered Reptiles. Multicoloured.
566. 8 e. Type **88** .. .. 30 10
567. 10 e. "Tarentola gigas brancoensis" .. .. 35 10
568. 15 e. "Tarentola gigas gigas" .. .. 45 10
569. 30 e. "Hemidactylus bouvieri" .. .. 90 20

**1986.** World Food Day. Multicoloured.
571. 8 e. Type **89** .. .. 15 10
572. 12 e. Women pounding food in mortar .. .. 15 10
573. 15 e. Woman rolling flat bread with stone .. 20 10

**90.** Dove and Olive Branch.

**1986.** International Peace Year.
574. **90.** 12 e. multicoloured .. 15 10
575. 30 e. multicoloured .. 40 20

**91.** Family Planning and Child Health Centre, Praia, and Woman breastfeeding Baby.

**1987.** Child Survival Campaign. Mult.
576. 8 e. Type **91** .. .. 15 10
577. 10 e. Assomada SOS children's village .. 15 10
578. 12 e. Family planning clinic, Mindelo, and nurse with child 15 10
579. 16 e. Children's home, Mindelo, and nurse with baby .. .. 25 10
580. 100 e. Calouste Gulbenkian kindergarten, Praia, and child writing .. .. 1·40 1·25

**92.** Mindelo City.

**1987.** Tourism. Multicoloured.
581. 1 e. Type **92** .. .. 10 10
582. 2 e. 50 Santo Antao island 10 10
583. 5 e. Fogo island .. .. 10 10
584. 8 e. Pillory, Velha City .. 15 10
585. 10 e. Boa Entrada valley, Santiago island .. .. 15 10
586. 12 e. Fishing boats, Santiago .. .. 30 15
587. 100 c. Furna harbour, Brava island .. .. 1·40 65

**93.** "Carvalho" (schooner).

**1987.** Sailing Ships. Multicoloured.
588. **93.** 12 e. black, mve. & bl. 35 15
589. – 16 e. black, bl. & mve. 55 15
590. – 50 e. black, blue and deep blue .. .. 1·60 55
DESIGNS: 16 e. "Nauta" (cutter). 50 e. "Maria Sony" (schooner).

**94.** Emblem.

**1987.** 2nd National Development Plan.
592. **94.** 8 e. multicoloured .. 15 10

**95.** Moths on Stem.

**1988.** Crop Protection. Multicoloured.
593. 50 c. Type **95** .. .. 10 10
594. 2 e. Caterpillars on plant treated with bio-insecticides .. .. 10 10
595. 9 e. Use of imported predators .. .. 20 10
596. 13 e. Use of imported predatorial insects .. 30 15
597. 16 e. Locust on stem .. 35 15
598. 19 e. Damaged wood .. 45 20

**96.** 17th-century Dutch Map.

**1988.** Antique Maps of Cape Verde Islands. Multicoloured.
600. 1 e. 50 Type **96** .. .. 10 10
601. 2 e. 50 18th-cent. Belgian map .. .. 10 10
602. 4 e. 50 18th-cent. French map 10 10
603. 9 e. 50 18th-cent. English map .. .. 15 10
604. 19 e. 50 19th-cent. English map .. .. 30 15
605. 20 e. 18th-cent. French map (vert.) .. .. 30 15

**97.** Church of the Abbot of the Holy Shelter, Tarrafal, Santiago.

**1988.** Churches. Multicoloured.
606. 5 e. Type **97** .. .. 10 10
607. 8 e. Church of Our Lady of Light, Maio .. .. 15 10
608. 10 e. Church of the Nazarene, Praia, Santiago .. 15 10
609. 12 e. Church of Our Lady of the Rosary, Sao Nicolau .. .. 20 10
610. 15 e. Church of the Nazarene, Mindelo, Sao Vicente .. .. 25 15
611. 20 e. Church of Our Lady of Grace, Praia, Santiago 30 15

**98** Boy filling Tin with Water

**1988.** Water Economy Campaign.
612 **98** 12 e. multicoloured .. 20 10

**99** Red Cross Workers

**1988.** 125th Anniv of Red Cross Movement.
613 **99** 7 e. multicoloured .. 10 10

**100** Group of Youths and Pres. Pereira

**1988.** 3rd Congress of African Party for the Independence of Cape Verde. Mult.
614 7 e. Type **100** .. .. 10 10
615 10 e. 50 Pres. Pereira and Perez de Cuellar (U.N. Secretary-General) .. 15 10
616 30 e. Emblem and Pres. Pereira .. .. 50 25

**101** Handball

**1988.** Olympic Games, Seoul. Multicoloured.
618 12 e. Type **101** .. .. 20 10
619 15 e. Tennis .. .. 25 15
620 20 e. Football .. .. 30 15
621 30 e. Boxing .. .. 50 25

**102** Hot-air Balloon "Pro Juventute"

**1989.** 2nd Pro Juventute Congress.
623 **102** 30 e. multicoloured .. 45 25

**103** Silva

**1989.** Death Centenary of Roberto Duarte Silva (chemist).
624 **103** 12 e. 50 multicoloured 20 10

**104** "Liberty guiding the People" (Eugene Delacroix)

**1989.** Bicentenary of French Revolution.
625 **104** 20 e. multicoloured .. 30 15
626 24 e. multicoloured .. 35 20
627 25 e. multicoloured .. 40 20

**105** Anniversary Emblem

**1989.** Centenary of Interparliamentary Union. Multicoloured.
629 2 e. Type **105** .. .. 10 10
630 4 e. Dove .. .. .. 10 10
631 13 e. National Assembly building .. .. 20 10

**106** Fonte Lima Women firing Pots

**1989.** Traditional Pottery. Multicoloured.
632 13 e. Type **106** .. .. 20 10
633 20 e. Terra di Monti women and children arranging pots to bake in sun (vert) .. .. 30 15
634 24 e. Terra di Monti woman shaping pot .. 35 20
635 25 e. Fonte Lima women kneading clay (vert) .. 40 20

**107** Boy and Truck **108** Pope John Paul II

**1989.** Christmas. Home-made Toys. Mult.
636 1 e. Type **107** .. .. 10 10
637 6 e. Boy with car on waste ground .. .. .. 10 10
638 8 e. Boy with truck on pavement .. .. 15 10
639 11 e. 50 Boys with various vehicles .. .. 15 10
640 18 e. Boys and sit-on scooter .. .. .. 30 15
641 100 e. Boy with boat .. 1·50 75

**1990.** Papal Visit.
642 **108** 13 e. multicoloured .. 20 10
643 20 e. multicoloured .. 30 15

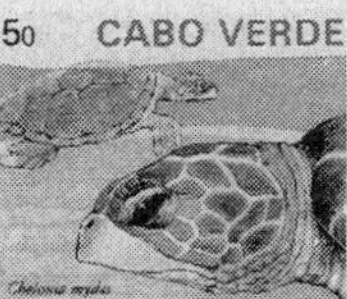


**109** Green Turtles

**1990.** Turtles. Multicoloured.
645 50 c. Type **109** .. .. 10 10
646 1 e. Leatherback turtles .. 10 10
647 5 e. Olive ridley turtles .. 10 10
648 10 e. Loggerhead turtles .. 15 10
649 42 e. Hawksbill turtles .. 65 35

**110** Footballers

**1990.** World Cup Football Championship, Italy.
650 **110** 4 e. multicoloured .. 10 10
651 – 7 e. 50 multicoloured .. 15 10
652 – 8 e. multicoloured .. 15 10
653 – 100 e. multicoloured 1·60 80
DESIGNS: 7 e. 50 to 100 e. Different footballing scenes.

**111** Face

**1990.** 1st Congress of Cape Verde Women's Movement.

655 **111** 9 e. multicoloured .. 15 10

**112** Teacher helping Boy to Read

**113** Diphtheria Treatment and Emile Roux (pioneer of antitoxic method)

**1990.** International Literacy Year. Mult.

656 2 e. Type **112** .. .. 10 10
657 3 e. Teacher with adult class .. .. .. 10 10
658 15 e. Teacher with flash-card .. .. .. 25 15
659 19 e. Adult student pointing to letters on blackboard .. .. .. 30 15

**1990.** Vaccination Campaign. Multicoloured.

660 5 e. Type **113** .. .. 10 10
661 13 e. Tuberculosis vaccination and Robert Koch (discoverer of tubercle bacillus) .. .. 20 10
662 20 e. Tetanus vaccination and Gaston Ramon .. 30 15
663 24 e. Poliomyelitis oral vaccination and Jonas Edward Salk (discoverer of vaccine) .. .. 40 20

**114** Musician on Bull's Back

**1990.** Traditional Stories. Multicoloured.

664 50 c. Type **114** .. .. 10 10
665 2 e. 50 Fisherman and mermaid ("Joao Piquinote") 10 10
666 12 e. Girl and snake .. 20 10
667 25 e. Couple and eggs ("Ti Lobo, Ti Lobo") .. 40 20

**115** World Map and Beam destroying AIDS Virus

**1991.** Anti-AIDS Campaign. Multicoloured.

668 13 e. Type **115** .. .. 20 10
669 24 e. Beam, AIDS virus and "SIDA" .. .. 40 20

**116** Fishing Boat at Sea and Fishermen on Shore

**1991.** Fishing Industry. Multicoloured.

670 10 e. Type **116** .. .. 20 15
671 24 e. Fisherman removing hook from fish .. .. 55 30
672 25 e. Fishing boats .. .. 55 30
673 50 e. Fishermen taking in lines .. .. .. 1·10 65

**117** Our Lady of the Rosary Church

**1991.** Tourism. Ruins of Ribeira Grande, Santiago Island. Multicoloured.

674 12 e. 50 Type **117** .. 20 10
675 15 e. Se Cathedral .. 25 15
676 20 e. Sao Filipe fortress .. 30 15
677 30 e. St. Francis's Convent 45 20

**118** "Lavandula rotundifolia"

**119** Guitar

**1991.** Medicinal Plants. Multicoloured.

679 10 e. Type **118** .. .. 15 10
680 15 e. "Micromeria forbesii" 25 15
681 21 e. "Sarcostemma daltonii" .. .. 30 15
682 24 e. "Periploca chevalieri" 40 20
683 30 e. "Echium hypertropicum" .. .. 45 20
684 35 e. "Erysimum caboverdeanum" .. .. 55 25

**1991.** Musical Instruments. Multicoloured.

685 10 e. Type **119** .. .. 20 10
686 20 e. Violin .. .. 40 25
687 29 e. Guitar with five double strings .. .. 60 30
688 47 e. Cimboa .. .. 90 55

**120** Crib (Tito Livio Goncalves)

**1991.** Christmas. Multicoloured.

690 31 e. Type **120** .. .. 50 25
691 50 e. Fonte-Lima crib .. 80 40

**121** Rose Apples

**1992.** Tropical Fruits. Multicoloured.

692 16 e. Type **121** .. .. 35 15
693 25 e. Mangoes .. .. 50 25
694 31 e. Cashews .. .. 65 30
695 32 e. Avocados .. .. 70 35

**122** Ships anchored in Bay

**1992.** 500th Anniv of Discovery of America by Columbus. Columbus's Landings in Cape Verde Islands. Multicoloured.

696 40 e. Type **122** .. .. 1·00 55
697 40 e. Caravel .. .. 1·00 55

**124** Throwing the Javelin

**1992.** Olympic Games, Barcelona. Mult.

700 16 e. Type **124** .. .. 35 15
701 20 e. Weightlifting .. 40 20
702 32 e. Pole vaulting .. 70 35
703 40 e. Putting the shot .. 85 40

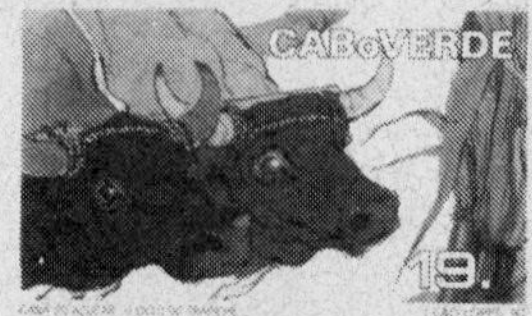


**125** Oxen and Sugar Cane

**1992.** Production of Molasses. Multicoloured.

705 19 e. Type **125** .. .. 35 15
706 20 e. Crushing cane .. 35 15
707 37 e. Feeding cane into mill 70 35
708 38 e. Cooking molasses .. 70 35

**126** Cat

**1992.** Domestic Animals. Multicoloured.

709 16 e. Type **126** .. .. 30 15
710 31 e. Chickens .. .. 55 25
711 32 e. Dog (vert) .. .. 60 30
712 50 e. Horse .. .. 90 45

**127** "Tubastrea aurea"

**1993.** Corals. Multicoloured.

713 5 e. Type **127** .. .. 10 10
714 31 e. "Corallium rubrum" 55 25
715 37 e. "Porites porites" .. 65 30
716 50 e. "Millepora alcicornis" 90 45

**129** King Ferdinand and Queen Isabella of Spain and Pope Alexander VI

**130** "Palinurus charlestoni"

**1993.** 500th Annivs of Pope Alexander VI's Bulls (on Portuguese and Spanish spheres of influence) and of Treaty of Tordesillas. Multicoloured.

718 37 e. Type **129** .. .. 65 30
719 37 e. King Joao II of Portugal and Pope Julius II .. .. 65 30
720 38 e. Astrolabe, quill and left-half of globe .. 70 35
721 38 e. Map of Iberian Peninsula and right-half of globe with Cape Verde Islands highlighted .. 70 35

Stamps of the same value were issued together in se-tenant pairs, each pair forming a composite design.

**1993.** Lobsters. Multicoloured.

722 2 e. Type **130** .. .. 10 10
723 10 e. Brown lobster .. 20 10
724 17 e. Royal lobster .. 30 15
725 38 e. Stone lobster .. 70 35

**131** Cory's Shearwater

**1993.** Nature Reserves. Multicoloured.

727 10 e. Type **131** (Branco and Raso Islets) .. .. 20 10
728 30 e. Brown booby (De Cima and Raso Islets) .. 55 25
729 40 e. Magnificent frigate bird (Curral Velho and Baluarte Islets) .. 70 35
730 41 e. Red-billed tropic bird (Raso and De Cima Islets) .. .. .. 75 35

**132** Rose

**1993.** Flowers. Multicoloured.

731 5 e. Type **132** .. .. 10 10
732 30 e. Bird of Paradise flower .. .. .. 55 25
733 37 e. Sweet William .. 65 30
734 50 e. Cactus dahlia .. 90 45

**133** Map and Prince Henry (½-size illustration)

**1994.** 600th Birth Anniv of Prince Henry the Navigator.

736 **133** 37 e. multicoloured .. 55 25

**134** Players and Giants Stadium, New York

**1994.** World Cup Football Championship, U.S.A. Multicoloured.

737 1 e. Type **134** .. .. 10 10
738 20 e. Referee showing red card and Rose Bowl, Los Angeles .. .. 30 15
739 37 e. Scoring goal and Foxboro Stadium, Boston .. .. .. 55 25
740 38 e. Linesman raising flag and Silverdome, Detroit 55 25

**135** Sand Shark

**136** "Prata" Bananas

**1994.** Sharks. Multicoloured.

742 21 e. Type **135** .. .. 30 15
743 27 e. Black-tip shark .. 40 20
744 37 e. Whale shark .. 55 25
745 38 e. Velvet belly shark .. 55 25

**1994.** Bananas. Multicoloured.

746 12 e. Type **136** .. .. 20 10
747 16 e. "Pao" bananas (horiz) .. .. .. 25 10
748 30 e. "Ana roberta" bananas .. .. .. 45 20
749 40 e. "Roxa" bananas .. 60 30

137 Fontes Pereira de Melo

**1994.** Lighthouses. Multicoloured.
751 2 e. Type **137** .. .. 10 10
752 37 e. Morro Negro .. 60 30
753 38 e. D. Amelia (vert) .. 60 30
754 50 e. D. Maria Pia (vert) .. 80 40

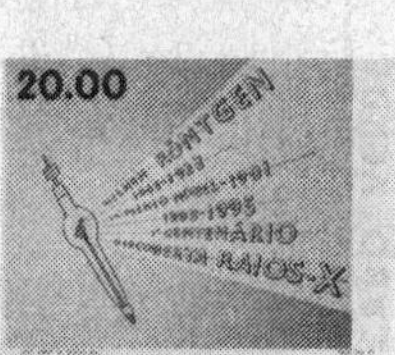

138 X-Ray Tube and Dates
139 Child with Fish

**1995.** Centenary of Discovery of X-Rays by Wilhelm Rontgen.
755 **138** 20 e. multicoloured .. 30 15
756 37 e. multicoloured .. 60 30

**1995.** 50th Anniv of F.A.O. Multicoloured.
758 37 e. Type **139** .. .. 60 30
759 38 e. Globe and wheat ear 60 30

140 Wire-haired Fox Terrier and "Two Foxhounds and Fox Terrier" (John Emms)
141 Communications

**1995.** Dogs. Heads of dogs and paintings. Multicoloured.
760 1 e. Type **140** .. .. 10 10
761 10 e. Cavalier King Charles and "Shooting Over Dogs" (Richard Ansdell) 15 10
762 40 e. German shepherd and rough collies .. .. 65 30
763 50 e. Bearded collie and "Hounds at Full Cry" (Thomas Blinks) .. 80 40

**1995.** 20th Anniv of Independence.
764 **141** 37 e. multicoloured .. 60 30

143 Horse Race

**1995.** St. Philip's Flag Festival, Fogo. Multicoloured.
766 2 e. Type **143** .. 10 10
767 10 e. Preparing for horse race .. .. 15 10
768 37 e. Preparing food and clapping to music .. 55 25
769 40 e. Crowd watching final horse race .. .. 60 30

144 Grasshopper playing Guitar
145 "Sonchus daltonii"

**1995.** Childrens' Stories. 300th Death Anniv of Jean de La Fontaine (writer). Scenes from "The Ant and the Grasshopper". Mult.
770 10 e. Type **144** .. .. 15 10
771 25 e. Grasshopper in snowstorm looking through ants' window .. 40 20
772 38 e. Ant laying-in supplies for winter .. .. 55 25
773 45 e. Ants welcoming grasshopper into their home .. .. .. 70 35

**1996.** Endangered Flowers. Multicoloured.
774 20 e. Type **145** .. .. 30 15
775 37 e. "Echium vulcanorum" .. .. 55 25
776 38 e. "Nauplius smithii" .. 55 25
777 50 e. "Campanula jacobaea" .. .. 75 35

146 Table Tennis

**1996.** Olympic Games, Atlanta. Mult.
778 1 e. Type **146** .. .. 10 10
779 37 e. Gymnastics .. .. 55 25
780 100 e. Athletics .. .. 1·50 75

CHARITY TAX STAMPS

The notes under this heading in Portugal also apply here.

**1925.** As Marquis de Pombal issue of Portugal but inscr "CABO VERDE".
C 266. C **73.** 15 c. violet .. .. 25 25
C 267. – 15 c. violet .. .. 25 25
C 268. C **75.** 15 c. violet .. .. 25 25

C **16.** St. Isabel. C **31.** C **32.**

**1948.**
C321 C **16** 50 c. green .. .. 1·25 85
C322 1 c. red .. .. 2·50 1·00

**1959.** Surch.
C368 C **16** 50 c. on 1 e. red 50 30

**1959.** Colours changed.
C369 C **16** 50 c. mauve .. 1·10 65
C370 1 e. blue .. .. 1·10 65

**1967.**
C406 C **31** 30 c. multicoloured 15 15
C407 50 c. mult (purple panel) 30 30
C408 50 c. mult (red panel) 15 15
C409 1 e. mult (brn panel) 45 45
C410 1 e. multicoloured (purple panel) .. 45 45

**1968.** Pharmaceutical Tax stamps surch as in Type C **32**.
C411a C **32** 50 c. on 1 c. black, orange and green 80 60
C412c 50 c. on 2 c. black, orange and green 40 25
C413 50 c. on 3 c. black, orange and green 55 40
C414 50 c. on 5 c. black, orange and green 55 40
C415 50 c. on 10 c. black, orange and green 65 55
C416 1 e. on 1 c. black, orange and green 1·50 1·00
C417a 1 e. on 2 c. black, orange and green 1·00 85

NEWSPAPER STAMP

**1893.** "Newspaper" key-type inscr. "CABO VERDE".
N 37. V. 2½ r. brown .. .. 55 35

POSTAGE DUE STAMPS

**1904.** "Due" key-type inscr. "CABO VERDE".
D 119. W. 5 r. green .. .. 15 15
D 120. 10 r. grey .. .. 15 15
D 121. 20 r. brown .. .. 15 15
D 122. 30 r. orange .. .. 40 20
D 123. 50 r. brown .. .. 20 15
D 124. 60 r. brown .. .. 3·00 1·75
D 125. 100 r. mauve .. .. 80 50
D 126. 130 r. blue .. .. 80 50
D 127. 200 r. red .. .. 85 75
D 128. 500 r. lilac .. .. 2·10 1·50

**1911.** Nos. D119/28 optd **REPUBLICA**.
D 135. W. 5 r. green .. .. 10 10
D 136. 10 r. grey .. .. 10 10
D 137. 20 r brown .. .. 15 10
D 138. 30 r. orange .. .. 15 10
D 139. 50 r. brown .. .. 15 10
D 140. 60 r. brown .. .. 30 20
D 141. 100 r. mauve .. .. 30 20
D 142. 130 r. blue .. .. 35 25
D 143. 200 r. red .. .. 75 60
D 144. 500 r. lilac .. .. 90 75

**1921.** "Due" key-type inscr. "CABO VERDE" with currency in **centavos.**
D 252. W. ½ c. green .. .. 10 10
D 253. 1 c. slate .. .. 10 10
D 254. 2 c. brown .. .. 10 10
D 255. 3 c. orange .. .. 10 10
D 256. 5 c. brown .. .. 10 10
D 257. 6 c. brown .. .. 10 10
D 258. 10 c. mauve .. 15 15
D 259. 13 c. blue .. .. 30 25
D 260. 20 c. red .. .. 30 25
D 261. 50 c. grey .. .. 60 45

**1925.** As Nos. C266/8 optd. **MULTA.**
D 266. C **73.** 30 c. violet .. 25 25
D 267. – 30 c. violet .. 25 25
D 268. C **75.** 30 c. violet .. 25 25

**1952.** As Type D **45** of Angola, but inscr "CABO VERDE". Numerals in red; name in black.
D356 10 c. brown and grey .. 10 10
D357 30 c. black, blue & mauve 10 10
D358 50 c. blue, green & yellow 10 10
D359 1 e. blue and pale blue .. 10 10
D360 2 e. brown and orange .. 20 20
D361 5 e. green and grey .. 45 45

# CAROLINE ISLANDS Pt. 7

A group of islands in the Pacific Ocean, formerly a German protectorate; under Japanese mandate after 1918. Now under United States trusteeship.

100 pfennig = 1 mark.

**1899.** Stamps of Germany optd. **Karolinen.**
7. **8.** 3 pf. brown .. .. 11·00 15·00
8. 5 pf. green .. .. 13·00 16·00
9. **9.** 10 pf. red .. .. .. 15·00 22·00
10. 20 pf. blue .. .. 19·00 28·00
11. 25 pf. orange .. .. 50·00 70·00
12. 50 pf. brown .. .. 45·00 65·00

**1901.** "Yacht" key-types inscr. "KAROLINEN".
13 N 3 pf. brown .. .. 65 1·50
14 5 pf. green .. .. 65 1·75
15 10 pf. red .. .. 65 4·00
16 20 pf. blue .. .. 1·00 7·50
17 25 f. black & red on yell 1·25 15·00
18 30 pf. blk & orge on buff 1·25 15·00
19 40 pf. black and red .. 1·25 17·00
20 50 pf. blk & pur on buff 1·50 18·00
21 80 pf. blk & red on rose 2·25 25·00
22 O 1 m. red .. .. 3·00 60·00
23 2 m. blue .. .. 6·00 80·00
24 3 m. black .. .. 8·00 £160
29b 5 m. red and black .. 17·00

**1910.** No. 13 surch **5 PF**.
26 N 5 pf. on 3 pf. brown .. — £2000

# CASTELROSSO Pt. 3

**One of the Aegean Is. Occupied by the French Navy on 27 December 1915. The French withdrew in August 1921 and, after a period of Italian Naval administration, the island was included in the Dodecanese territory.**

## A. FRENCH OCCUPATION.

100 centimes = 1 franc = 4 piastres.

**1920.** Stamps of 1902–20 of French Post Offices in Turkish Empire optd **B. N. F. CASTELLORIZO**.
F1 A 1 c. grey .. .. 18·00 18·00
F2 2 c. purple .. .. 18·00 18·00
F3 3 c. red .. .. 18·00 18·00
F4 5 c. green .. .. 18·00 18·00
F5 B 10 c. red .. .. 30·00 30·00
F6 15 c. red .. .. 40·00 40·00
F7 20 c. brown .. .. 40·00 40·00
F8 1 pi. on 20 c. blue .. 40·00 40·00
F9 30 c. lilac .. .. 50·00 50·00
F10 C 40 c. red and blue .. 95·00 95·00
F11 2 pi. on 50 c. brn & lilac 95·00 95·00
F12 4 pi. on 1 f. red & green 95·00 95·00
F13 20 pi. on 5 f. blue & brn £300 £300

**1920.** Optd **O. N. F. Castellorizo**. (a) On stamps of 1902–20 of French Post Offices in Turkish Empire.
F14 A 1 c. grey .. .. 15·00 15·00
F15 2 c. purple .. .. 15·00 15·00
F16 3 c. red .. .. 15·00 15·00
F17 5 c. green .. .. 15·00 15·00
F18 B 10 c. red .. .. 15·00 15·00
F19 15 c. red .. .. 30·00 30·00
F20 20 c. brown .. .. 60·00 60·00
F21 1 pi. on 25 c. blue .. 45·00 45·00
F22 30 c. lilac .. .. 45·00 45·00
F23 C 40 c. red and blue .. 45·00 45·00
F24 2 pi. on 50 c. brn & lilac 45·00 45·00
F25 4 pi. on 1 f. red and green 45·00 45·00
F26 20 pi. on 5 f. blue & brown £275 £275

(b) Nos. 334 and 341 of France.
F27 **18** 10 c. red .. .. 15·00 15·00
F28 25 c. blue .. .. 15·00 15·00

**1920.** Stamps of France optd **O F CASTELLORISO**.
F29 **18** 5 c. green .. .. £120 £120
F30 10 c. red .. .. £120 £120
F31 20 c. red .. .. £120 £120
F32 25 c. blue .. .. £120 £120
F33 **13** 50 c. brown and lilac .. £425 £425
F34 1 f. red and green .. £425 £425

## B. ITALIAN OCCUPATION.

100 centesimi = 1 lira.

**1922.** Stamps of Italy optd **CASTELROSSO**.
15 **37** 5 c. green .. .. 1·00 6·00
16 10 c. red .. .. 1·00 6·00
17 15 c. grey .. .. 1·00 6·00
18 **41** 20 c. orange .. .. 1·00 6·00
19 **39** 25 c. blue .. .. 1·00 6·00
20 40 c. brown .. .. 1·00 6·00
21 50 c. violet .. .. 1·00 6·00
22 60 c. red .. .. 1·00 6·00
23 85 c. brown .. .. 1·00 6·00
24 **34** 1 l. brown and green .. 1·00 6·00

2.

**1923.**

| | | | | |
|---|---|---|---|---|
| 10. | **2.** | 5 c. green .. | 1·50 | 4·75 |
| 11. | | 10 c. red | 1·50 | 4·75 |
| 12. | | 25 c. blue .. | 1·50 | 4·75 |
| 13. | | 50 c. purple | 1·50 | 4·75 |
| 14. | | 1 l. brown | 1·50 | 4·75 |

**1930.** Ferrucci stamps of Italy optd. **CASTELROSSO.**

| | | | | |
|---|---|---|---|---|
| 25. | **114.** | 20 c. violet | 80 | 3·00 |
| 26. | – | 25 c. green (No. 283) | 80 | 3·00 |
| 27. | – | 50 c. black (as No. 284) | 80 | 3·00 |
| 28. | – | 1 l. 25 blue (No. 285) | 80 | 3·00 |
| 29. | – | 5 l.+2 l. red (as No. 286) | 10·00 | 14·00 |

**1932.** Garibaldi stamps of Italy optd **CASTELROSSO.**

| | | | | |
|---|---|---|---|---|
| 30 | – | 10 c. brown | 6·50 | 10·00 |
| 31 | 128 | 20 c. brown | 6·50 | 10·00 |
| 32 | – | 25 c. green | 6·50 | 10·00 |
| 33 | 128 | 30 c. blue | 6·50 | 10·00 |
| 34 | – | 50 c. purple | 6·50 | 10·00 |
| 35 | – | 75 c. red | 6·50 | 10·00 |
| 36 | – | 1 l. 25 blue | 6·50 | 10·00 |
| 37 | – | 1 l. 75+25 c. brown | 6·50 | 10·00 |
| 38 | – | 2 l. 55+50 c. red | 6·50 | 10·00 |
| 39 | – | 5 l.+1 l. violet | 6·50 | 10·00 |

## CAUCA Pt. 20

A State of Colombia, reduced to a Department in 1886, now uses Colombian stamps.

100 centavos = 1 peso.

2.

**1902.** Imperf.

| | | | | |
|---|---|---|---|---|
| 2. | **2.** | 10 c. black on red | 1·00 | 1·00 |
| 3. | | 20 c. black on orange | 85 | 85 |

## CAVALLA (KAVALLA) Pt. 16

French P.O. in a former Turkish port, now closed.

100 centimes = 1 franc.
40 paras = 1 piastre.

**1893.** Stamps of France optd **Cavalle** or surch also in figures and words.

| | | | | |
|---|---|---|---|---|
| 41 | 10 | 5 c. green | 4·50 | 2·50 |
| 43 | | 10 c. black on lilac | 6·50 | 3·25 |
| 45 | | 15 c. blue | 6·50 | 3·75 |
| 46 | | 1 pi. on 25 c. black on pink | 8·50 | 4·25 |
| 47 | | 2 pi. on 50 c. red | 22·00 | 15·00 |
| 48a | | 4 pi. on 1 f. green | 28·00 | 25·00 |
| 49 | | 8 pi. on 2 f. brown on blue | 32·00 | 30·00 |

**1902.** "Blanc", "Mouchon" and "Merson" key-types inscr "CAVALLE". The four higher values surch also.

| | | | | |
|---|---|---|---|---|
| 50 | A | 5 c. green | 25 | 20 |
| 51 | B | 10 c. red | 30 | 25 |
| 52 | | 15 c. red | 2·25 | 1·50 |
| 53 | | 15 c. orange | 50 | 25 |
| 54 | | 1 pi. on 25 c. blue | 1·00 | 50 |
| 55 | C | 2 pi. on 50 c. brown & lilac | 2·25 | 1·00 |
| 56 | | 4 pi. on 1 f. red and green | 2·50 | 3·00 |
| 57 | | 8 pi. on 2 f. lilac and brown | 6·50 | 5·75 |

## CENTRAL AFRICAN EMPIRE Pt. 12

Central African Republic was renamed Central African Empire on 4th December, 1976, when Pres. Bokassa became Emperor.

The country reverted to Central African Republic on his overthrow in 1979.

100 centimes = 1 franc.

**1977.** Various stamps of Central African Republic optd. **EMPIRE CENTRAFRICAIN.**

| | | | | |
|---|---|---|---|---|
| 439. | **150.** | 3 f. multicoloured (postage) | 40 | 35 |
| 444. | **167.** | 10 f. multicoloured .. | 25 | 25 |
| 457. | – | 10 f. red and blue (386) | 25 | 25 |
| 459. | **172.** | 10 f. multicoloured .. | 35 | 35 |
| 460. | – | 15 f. multicoloured (391) | 45 | 45 |
| 465. | – | 15 f. brown, green and blue (397) .. | 25 | 25 |
| 445. | – | 20 f. multicoloured (366) | 25 | 25 |
| 461. | – | 20 f. multicoloured (392) | 40 | 40 |
| 446. | – | 25 f. multicoloured (367) | 25 | 25 |
| 451. | – | 25 f. multicoloured (376) | 25 | 25 |
| 449. | **168.** | 30 f. multicoloured .. | 40 | 40 |
| 452. | – | 30 f. multicoloured (377) | 40 | 40 |
| 462. | – | 30 f. multicoloured (393) | 45 | 45 |
| 447. | – | 40 f. multicoloured (370) | 40 | 40 |
| 450. | – | 40 f. multicoloured (373) | 45 | 45 |
| 453. | – | 40 f. multicoloured (378) | 40 | 40 |
| 454. | – | 40 f. multicoloured (380) | 45 | 45 |
| 455. | **170.** | 40 f. multicoloured .. | 40 | 40 |
| 456. | – | 40 f. multicoloured (384) | 40 | 40 |
| 458. | – | 40 f. multicoloured (389) | 40 | 35 |
| 482. | – | 40 f. multicoloured (423) | 65 | 55 |
| 466. | – | 50 f. blue, brown and green (398) .. | 55 | 55 |
| 440. | **163.** | 100 f. multicoloured .. | 5·00 | 5·00 |
| 441. | **164.** | 100 f. grn., red and brn. | 1·25 | 1·25 |
| 442. | **165.** | 100 f. brn., grn. & blue | 1·60 | 1·60 |
| 468. | **179.** | 100 f. black and yellow | 1·25 | 1·25 |
| 469. | **180.** | 100 f. pur., blue & grn. | 1·25 | 1·25 |
| 491. | **185.** | 100 f. multicoloured .. | 1·25 | 1·25 |
| 483. | – | 50 f. multicoloured (424) (air) .. | 45 | 30 |
| 448. | – | 100 f. multicoloured (371) | 85 | 85 |
| 463. | **173.** | 100 f. red and blue .. | 90 | 90 |
| 467. | **178.** | 100 f. multicoloured .. | 85 | 85 |
| 484. | – | 100 f. multicoloured (425) | 85 | 85 |
| 464. | **174.** | 200 f. multicoloured .. | 1·90 | 1·90 |
| 443. | **166.** | 500 f. red, grn. and brn. | 6·25 | 6·25 |

**1977.** "Apollo–Soyuz" Space Link optd. Nos. 410/14 of Central African Republic. **EMPIRE CENTRAFRICAIN.**

| | | | | |
|---|---|---|---|---|
| 470. | **181.** | 40 f. multicoloured (postage) .. | 50 | 50 |
| 471. | – | 50 f. multicoloured .. | 60 | 60 |
| 472. | – | 100 f. multicoloured (air) | 85 | 85 |
| 473. | – | 200 f. multicoloured.. | 1·90 | 1·90 |
| 474. | – | 300 f. multicoloured.. | 2·50 | 2·50 |

**1977.** Air. Bicent. of American Revolution. Nos. 416/20 of Central African Republic optd. **EMPIRE CENTRAFRICAIN.**

| | | | | |
|---|---|---|---|---|
| 476. | **182.** | 100 f. multicoloured.. | 75 | 45 |
| 477. | – | 125 f. multicoloured.. | 95 | 60 |
| 478. | – | 150 f. multicoloured.. | 1·25 | 70 |
| 479. | – | 200 f. multicoloured.. | 1·60 | 95 |
| 480. | – | 250 f. multicoloured.. | 1·90 | 1·25 |

**1977.** Winners of Winter Olympic Games, Innsbruck. Nos. 426/30 of Central African Republic optd. **EMPIRE CENTRAFRICAIN.**

| | | | | |
|---|---|---|---|---|
| 485. | – | 40 f. multicoloured (postage) .. | 40 | 35 |
| 486. | – | 60 f. multicoloured .. | 50 | 35 |
| 487. | **184.** | 100 f. multicoloured (air) | 65 | 45 |
| 488. | – | 200 f. multicoloured .. | 1·50 | 85 |
| 489. | – | 300 f. multicoloured .. | 2·25 | 1·25 |

**1977.** "Viking" Space Mission. Nos. 433/7 of Central African Republic optd. **EMPIRE CENTRAFRICAIN.**

| | | | | |
|---|---|---|---|---|
| 492. | **186.** | 40 f. multicoloured (postage) .. | 40 | 30 |
| 493. | – | 60 f. multicoloured .. | 50 | 35 |
| 494. | – | 100 f. multicoloured (air) | 65 | 45 |
| 495. | – | 200 f. multicoloured .. | 1·50 | 85 |
| 496. | – | 300 f. multicoloured .. | 2·25 | 1·25 |

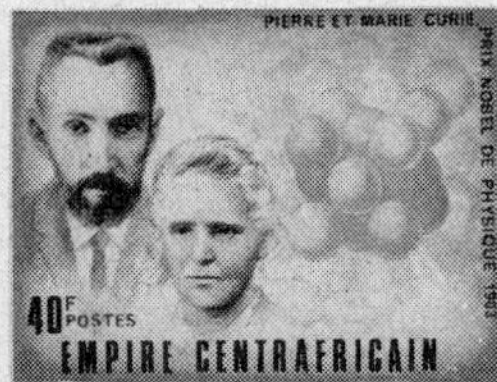


**189.** Pierre and Marie Curie (Physics, 1903).

**1977.** Nobel Prize-winners. Multicoloured.

| | | | |
|---|---|---|---|
| 503. | 40 f. Type **189** (postage).. | 60 | 25 |
| 504. | 60 f. W. C. Rontgen (Physics, 1901).. | 60 | 35 |
| 505. | 100 f. Rudyard Kipling (Literature, 1907) (air) | 75 | 35 |
| 506. | 200 f. Ernest Hemingway (Literature, 1954) .. | 1·50 | 65 |
| 507. | 300 f. L. Pirandello (Literature, 1934) .. | 2·25 | 75 |

**190.** Roman Temple and Italy 1933 3 l. stamp.

**1977.** "Graf Zeppelin" Flights. Multicoloured.

| | | | |
|---|---|---|---|
| 509. | 40 f. Type **190** (postage).. | 60 | 25 |
| 510. | 60 f. St. Basil's Cathedral, Moscow, and Russia 1930 40 k. stamp .. | 70 | 40 |
| 511. | 100 f. North Pole and Germany 1931 "Polarfahrt" stamp (air) .. | 1·10 | 45 |
| 512. | 200 f. Museum of Science and Industry, Chicago, and Germany 1933 "Chicagofahrt" stamp | 2·10 | 65 |
| 513. | 300 f. Brandenburg Gate, Berlin, and German 1931 stamp .. .. | 3·25 | 95 |

**191.** Charles Lindbergh and "Spirit of St. Louis".

**1977.** History of Aviation. Mult.

| | | | |
|---|---|---|---|
| 515 | 50 f. Type **191** .. .. | 45 | 20 |
| 516 | 60 f. Alberto Santos-Dumont and "14 bis" biplane .. .. | 55 | 25 |
| 517 | 100 f. Louis Bleriot and Bleriot XI .. .. | 95 | 40 |
| 518 | 200 f. Roald Amundsen and Dornier Wal flying boat .. .. | 1·60 | 60 |
| 519 | 300 f. Concorde .. .. | 3·00 | 1·25 |

**192.** Lily. **193.** Group of Africans and Rotary Emblem.

**1977.** Flowers. Multicoloured.

| | | | |
|---|---|---|---|
| 521. | 5 f. Type **192** .. .. | 35 | 35 |
| 522. | 10 f. Hibiscus .. .. | 65 | 60 |

**1977.** 20th Anniv. of Bangui Rotary Club.

| | | | | |
|---|---|---|---|---|
| 523. | **193.** | 60 f. multicoloured .. | 1·90 | 1·25 |

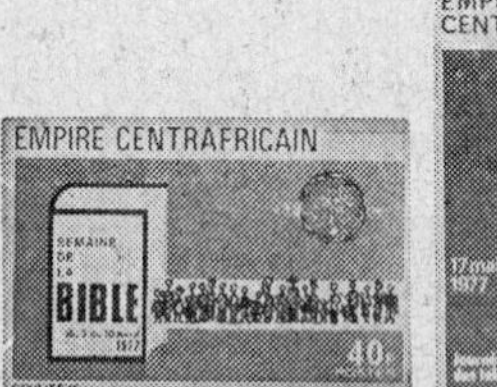


**194.** Africans queueing beside Bible. **195.** Printed Circuit.

**1977.** Bible Week.

| | | | | |
|---|---|---|---|---|
| 524. | **194.** | 40 f. multicoloured .. | 1·50 | 95 |

**1977.** World Telecommunications Day.

| | | | | |
|---|---|---|---|---|
| 525. | **195.** | 100 f. orge., brn. & blk. | 2·25 | 1·90 |

**196.** Doctor inoculating Child.

**1977.** Air. World Health Day.

| | | | | |
|---|---|---|---|---|
| 526. | **196.** | 150 f. multicoloured .. | 1·00 | 70 |

**197.** Goalkeeper.

**1977.** World Cup Football Championship (1978). Multicoloured.

| | | | |
|---|---|---|---|
| 527. | 50 f. Type **197** .. | 40 | 20 |
| 528. | 60 f. Goalmouth melee .. | 45 | 25 |
| 529. | 100 f. Mid-field play .. | 75 | 30 |
| 530. | 200 f. World Cup poster.. | 1·60 | 50 |
| 531. | 300 f. Mario Jorge Lobo Zagalo (Argentine trainer) and Buenos Aires stadium | 2·50 | 90 |

### MINIMUM PRICE

The minimum price quoted is 10p which represents a handling charge rather than a basis for valuing common stamps. For further notes about prices see introductory pages.

**198.** Emperor Bokassa I.

**1977.** Coronation of Emperor Bokassa.

| | | | | |
|---|---|---|---|---|
| 533. | **198.** | 40 f. mult. (postage) | 25 | 20 |
| 534. | | 60 f. multicoloured .. | 40 | 25 |
| 535. | | 100 f. multicoloured | 75 | 45 |
| 536. | | 150 f. mutlicoloured .. | 1·25 | 70 |
| 537. | | 200 f. mult. (air) .. | 1·50 | 75 |
| 538. | | 300 f. multicoloured .. | 2·25 | 1·25 |

No. 539 is horizontal, 47 × 38 mm., and printed on gold foil.

**199.** Bangui Telephone Exchange.

**1978.** Opening of Automatic Telephone Exchange, Bangui. Multicoloured.

| | | | |
|---|---|---|---|
| 541. | 40 f. Type **199** .. .. | 40 | 25 |
| 542. | 60 f. Bangui Telephone Exchange (different) .. | 50 | 35 |

**200.** Bokassa Sports Palace.

**1978.** Bokassa Sports Palace. Multicoloured.

| | | | |
|---|---|---|---|
| 543. | 40 f. Type **200** .. .. | 40 | 25 |
| 544. | 60 f. Sports Palace (different) .. .. .. | 50 | 35 |

**201.** "The Holy Family".

**1978.** 400th Birth Anniv. of Rubens. Mult.

| | | | |
|---|---|---|---|
| 545. | 60 f. Type **201** .. .. | 50 | 20 |
| 546. | 150 f. "Marie de Medici" | 1·10 | 40 |
| 547. | 200 f. "The Artist's Sons" | 1·60 | 60 |
| 548. | 300 f. "Neptune" (horiz.) | 2·50 | 75 |

**202.** Black Rhinoceros.

**1978.** Endangered Animals. Multicoloured.

| | | | |
|---|---|---|---|
| 550. | 40 f. Type **202** .. .. | 50 | 15 |
| 551. | 50 f. Crocodile .. .. | 65 | 20 |
| 552. | 60 f. Leopard (vert.) .. | 75 | 25 |
| 553. | 100 f Giraffe (vert.) .. | 1·25 | 40 |
| 554. | 200 f. African elephant .. | 3·25 | 60 |
| 555. | 300 f. Gorilla (vert.) .. | 3·75 | 1·00 |

**203.** Mail Coach and Satellite.

**1978.** 100 Years of Progress in Posts and Telecommunications. Multicoloured.

556 40 f. Type **203** (postage) .. 35 20
557 50 f. Steam locomotive and space communications 2·00 90
558 60 f. Paddle-steamer and ship-to-shore communications .. .. .. 45 25
559 80 f. Renault car and "Pioneer" satellite .. 65 25
560 100 f. Mail balloon and "Apollo"–"Soyuz" link-up (air) 75 40
561 200 f. Seaplane "Comte da la Vaulx" and Concorde 1·50 65

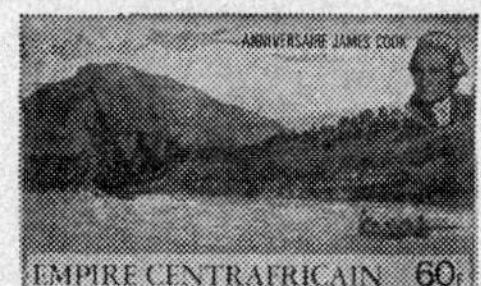


**205.** H.M.S. "Endeavour" under Repair (after W. Byrne).

**1978.** 250th Birth Anniv of Captain Cook. Multicoloured.

578 60 f. Type **205** .. .. 1·00 35
579 80 f. Cook on board "Endeavour" (vert) .. 75 25
580 200 f. Landing party in New Hebrides .. .. 1·90 65
581 350 f. Masked paddlers in canoe (after Webber) .. 3·75 1·25

**206.** Ife Bronze Head.

**1978.** 2nd World Festival of Negro Arts, Lagos.

582. **206.** 20 f. black and yellow 25 20
583. – 30 f. black and blue .. 25 20
584. – 60 f. multicoloured .. 65 40
585. – 100 f. multicoloured .. 1·10 65

DESIGNS—VERT. 30 f. Carved mask. HORIZ. 60 f. Dancers. 100 f. Dancers with musical instruments.

**207.** Clement Ader and "Avion III".

**1978.** Air. Aviation Pioneers. Multicoloured.

586 40 f. Type **207** .. .. 40 20
587 50 f. Wright Brothers and glider No. III .. .. 40 20
588 60 f. Alcock, Brown and Vickers Vimy .. .. 45 30
589 100 f. Sir Alan Cobham and De Havilland D.H.50 .. 90 45
590 150 f. Dr. Claude Dornier and Dornier Gsl flying boat .. .. .. 1·40 65

**208.** "Self-portrait".

**1978.** 450th Death Anniv. of Albrecht Durer (artist). Multicoloured.

592. 60 f. Type **208** .. .. 50 20
593. 80 f. "The Four Apostles" 75 25
594. 200 f. "The Virgin and Child" .. .. 1·90 80
595. 350 f. "The Emperor Maxillian I" .. .. 3·25 1·25

**1978.** Air. "Philexafrique" Stamp Exhibition, Gabon (1st issue). and International Stamp Fair, Essen. As T **237** of Benin. Multicoloured.

596. 100 f. Red Crossbills and Mecklenbefg-Schwerin, 1856 ¼ s. stamp .. 1·50 1·25
597. 100 f. Crocodile and Central African Republic, 1960, 500 f. stamp .. .. 1·50 1·25

See also Nos. 647/8.

**209.** Third Mummiform Coffin.

**1978.** Treasures of Tutankhamun. Mult.

598. 40 f. Type **209** .. .. 35 20
599. 60 f. Tutankhamun and Ankhesenamun (back of gilt throne) .. .. 45 25
600. 80 f. Ecclesiastical throne 65 35
601. 100 f. Head of Tutankhamun (wooden statuette) .. 75 35
602. 120 f. Lion's head (funerary bedhead) .. .. 95 40
603. 150 f. Life-size statue of Tutankhamun .. .. 1·25 45
604. 180 f. Gilt throne .. .. 1·50 55
605. 250 f. Canopic coffin .. 1·90 75

**210.** Lenin speaking at the Smolny Institute. **211.** Catherine Bokassa.

**1978.** 60th Anniv. of Russian Revolution.

606. **210.** 40 f. multicoloured .. 40 25
607. – 60 f. multicoloured .. 50 35
608. – 100 f. black, grey and gold .. .. .. 90 40
609. – 150 f. red, black & gold 1·40 65
610. – 200 f. multicoloured .. 1·90 95
611. – 300 f. multicoloured .. 2·50 1·25

DESIGNS—VERT. 60 f. Lenin addressing crowd in Red Square. 200 f. Lenin at Smolny Institute. 300 f. Lenin and banner. HORIZ. 100 f. Lenin, Krupskaya and family. 150 f. Lenin, Cruiser "Aurora" and revolutionaries.

**1978.** 1st Anniv. of Emperor Bokassa's Coronation. Multicoloured.

613. 40 f. Type **211** (postage) .. 40 20
614. 60 f. Emperor Bokassa .. 50 35
615. 150 f. The Emperor and Empress (horiz.) (air) .. 1·25 70

**212.** Rowland Hill, Letter-weighing Scale and Penny Black.

**1978.** Death Centenary of Sir Rowland Hill (1st issue). Multicoloured.

617 40 f. Type **212** (postage) .. 35 20
618 50 f. Postman on bicycle and U.S. 5 c. stamp, 1847 40 25
619 60 f. Danish postman and Austrian newspaper stamp, 1856 .. .. 45 30
620 80 f. Postilion, mail coach and Geneva 5+5 c. stamp, 1843 .. .. 65 25
621 100 f. Postman, mail train and Tuscan 3 l. stamp, 1860 (air) .. .. 1·50 90
622 200 f. Mail balloon and French 10 c. stamp, 1850 1·50 65

See also Nos. 671/4.

**1978.** Argentina's Victory in World Cup Football Championship. Nos. 527/31 optd. **VAINQUEUR ARGENTINE.**

625. 50 f. Type **197** .. .. 40 25
626. 60 f. Goalmouth melee .. 45 35
627. 100 f. Mid-field play .. 75 45
628. 200 f. World Cup poster .. 1·50 95
629. 300 f. Mario Jorge Lobo Zagalo and Buenos Aires Stadium .. .. 2·25 1·25

**214.** Children painting and Dutch Master.

**1979.** International Year of the Child (1st issue). Multicoloured.

631 40 f. Type **214** (postage) .. 40 15
632 50 f. Eskimo children and skier .. .. .. 50 20
633 60 f. Benz automobile and children with toy car .. 65 20
634 80 f. Satellite and children launching rocket .. 90 25
635 100 f. Dornier Do-X flying boat and Chinese child flying kite (air) .. 95 40
636 200 f. Hurdler and children playing leap-frog .. 1·90 45

See also Nos. 666/70.

**215.** High Jump.

**1979.** Pre-Olympic Year (1st issue). Mult.

639. 40 f. Type **215** (postage) .. 35 15
640. 50 f. Cycling .. .. 40 20
641. 60 f. Weightlifting .. 45 20
642. 80 f. Judo .. .. .. 65 30
643. 100 f. Hurdles (air) .. 75 35
644. 200 f. Long jump .. 1·50 50

See also Nos. 676/70 and 705.

**216.** Co-operation Monument, "Aurivillius arata" and Hibiscus.

**1979.** "Philexafrique" Exhibition (2nd issue). Multicoloured.

647. 60 f. Type **216** .. .. 1·60 1·10
648. 150 f. Envelopes, van, canoeist and U.P.U. emblem .. .. .. 3·25 2·10

**217.** School Teacher.

**1979.** 50th Anniv. of International Bureau of Education.

649. **217.** 70 f. multicoloured .. 65 40

**219.** Chicken.

**1979.** National Association of Farmers. Multicoloured.

651. 10 f. Type **219** (postage) .. 1·25 90
652. 20 f. Bullock .. .. 1·25 90
653. 40 f. Sheep .. .. 2·50 1·75
654. 60 f. Horse (air) .. .. 3·50 1·60

OFFICIAL STAMPS

**1977.** Official stamps of Central African Republic optd **EMPIRE CENTRAFRICAIN**.

O 498. **O 109.** 5 f. multicoloured 25 20
O 499. 40 f. multicoloured 40 20
O 500. 100 f. multicoloured 1·00 45
O 501. 140 f. multicoloured 1·25 70
O 502. 200 f. mult. .. 2·25 1·00

**O 204.** Coat of Arms.

**1978.**

O 564. **O 204.** 1 f. multicoloured 20 15
O 565. 2 f. multicoloured 15 15
O 566. 5 f. multicoloured 15 15
O 567. 10 f. mul icoloured 20 15
O 568. 15 f. multicoloured 20 15
O 569. 20 f. multicoloured 25 20
O 570. 30 f. multicoloured 35 25
O 571. 40 f. multicoloured 40 30
O 572. 50 f. multicoloured 50 35
O 673. 60 f. multicoloured 65 45
O 574. 100 f. mult .. 75 60
O 575. 130 f. mult. .. 1·25 90
O 576. 140 f. mult. .. 1·25 90
O 577. 200 f. mult. .. 2·50 1·25

## CENTRAL AFRICAN REPUBLIC
Pt. 12

Formerly Ubangi-Shari. An independent republic within the French Community.

100 centimes = 1 franc.

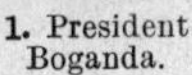

**1.** President Boganda. **3.** "Dactyloceras widenmanni".

**4.** Abyssinian Roller.

**1959.** Republic. 1st Annv. Centres multicoloured. Frame colours given.

1. **1.** 15 f. blue .. .. .. 35 25
2. – 25 f. red .. .. .. 45 25

DESIGN—HORIZ. 25 f. As Type **1** but flag behind portrait.

**1960.** 10th Anniv. of African Technical Co-operation Commission. As T **62** of Cameroun.

3. 50 f. blue and green .. 1·25 75

**1960.**

4. – 50 c. brown, red and turquoise (postage) .. 10 10
5. – 1 f. myrtle, brn. & violet 10 10
6. – 2 f. myrtle, brown & green 15 15
7. – 3 f. brown, red and olive 25 20
8. **3.** 5 f. brown and green .. 35 25
9. – 10 f. blue, black and green 70 45
10. – 20 f. red, black and green 1·50 65
11. – 85 f. red, black and green 5·75 1·60
12. – 50 f. turquoise, red and green (air) .. .. 4·25 1·40
13. **4.** 100 f. violet, brown & green 7·00 2·00
14. – 200 f. multicoloured .. 12·00 4·75
15. – 250 f. multicoloured .. 12·50 5·00
16. – 500 f. brown, blue & green 25·00 7·75

BUTTERFLIES—As Type **3**: 50 c., 3 f. "Cymothoe sangaris". 1 f., 2 f., "Charaxe mobilis" 10 f. "Charaxes ameliae". 20 f. "Charaxes zingha". 85 f. "Drurya antimachus". BIRDS—As Type **4**: 50 f. Great blue turaco. 200 f. Knysna turaco 250 f. Red-faced lovebirds. 500 f. African fish eagle.

See also Nos. 42/5.

**1960.** National Festival. No. 2 optd. **FETE NATIONALE 1-12-1960.**

17. 25 f. multicoloured .. 1·25 1·25

**1960.** Air. Olympic Games. No. 276 of French Equatorial Africa optd. with Olympic rings, **XVIIe OLYMPIADE 1960 REPUBLIQUE CENTRAFRICAINE** and surch. **250 F** and bars.

18. 250 f. on 500 f blue, black and green .. .. 7·50 7·50

**7.** Pasteur Institute, Bangui.

**1961.** Opening of Pasteur Institute, Bangui.

19 **7** 20 f. multicoloured .. 75 65

**8.** U.N. Emblem, Map and Flag.

**1961.** Admission into U.N.O.

20. **8.** 15 f. multicoloured .. 40 35
21. 25 f. multicoloured .. 45 35
22. 85 f. multicoloured .. 1·40 95

**1961.** National Festival. Optd. with star and **FETE NATIONALE 1-12-61.**

23. **8.** 25 f. multicoloured .. 1·75 1·75

**1962.** Air. "Air Afrique" Airline. As T **69** of Cameroun.

24. 50 f. violet, brown & green 95 60

**1962.** Union of African States and Madagascar Conference, Bangui. Surch. **U.A.M. CONFERENCE DE BANGUI 25-27 MARS 1962 50 F.**

25. **8.** 50 f. on 85 f. multicoloured 1·25 1·25

**1962.** Malaria Eradication. As T **70** of Cameroun.

26. 25 f. + 5 f. slate .. .. 85 85

**12.** Hurdling. **13.** Pres. Dacko.

**1962.** Sports.

27. **12.** 20 f. sepia, yellow & green (postage) .. .. 45 35
28. – 50 f. sepia, yellow & green 1·10 65
29. – 100 f. sepia, yellow and green (air) .. .. 2·10 1·40

DESIGNS—As Type **12**: 50 f. Cycling. VERT. (26×47 mm.): 100 f. Pole-vaulting.

**1962.**

30. **13.** 20 f. multicoloured .. 35 20
31. 25 f. multicoloured .. 45 20

**1962.** 1st Anniv. of Union of African and Malagasy States. As T **72** of Cameroun.

32. 30 f. green .. .. 65 45

**15.** Athlete.

**18.** "Posts and Telecommunications".

**17.** "National Army". **19.** "Telecommunications".

**1962.** Air. "Coupe des Tropiques" Games Bangui.

33. **15.** 100 f. brown, turq. & red .. 2·25 1·40

**1963.** Freedom from Hunger. As T **76** of Cameroun.

34. 25 f. + 5 f. turq., brn. & bistre 75 75

**1963.** 3rd Anniv. of Proclamation of Republic.

35. **17.** 20 f. multicoloured .. 60 40

**1963.** Air. African and Malagasy Posts and Telecommunications Union.

36. **18.** 85 f. multicoloured .. 1·60 80

**1963.** Space Telecommunications.

37. **19.** 25 f. green and purple .. 65 50
38. – 100 f. green, orge. & blue 1·60 1·40

DESIGN: 100 f. Radio waves and globe.

**20.** "Young Pioneers". **21.** Boali Falls.

**1963.** Young Pioneers.

39. **20.** 50 f. brown, blue & turq. 65 45

**1963.**

40. **21.** 30 f. purple, green & blue 65 40

**22.** Map of Africa and Sun.

**1963.** Air. "African Unity".

41. **22.** 25 f. ultram., yell. & blue 55 35

**23.** "Colotis evippe". **24.** "Europafrique".

**25.** Diesel Train. **26.** U.N.E.S.C.O. Emblem, Scales of Justice and Tree.

**1963.** Butterflies. Mult.

42. 1 f. Type **23** .. .. 20 15
43. 3 f. "Papilio dardanus" .. 30 25
44. 4 f. "Papilio lormieri" .. 40 30
45. 60 f. "Papilio zalmoxis" .. 3·00 2·25

**1963.** Air. European-African Economic Convention.

46. **24.** 50 f. multicoloured .. 2·25 1·75

**1963.** Air. Bangui-Douala Railway Project.

47. – 20 f. myrtle, pur. & brn. 75 70
48. **25.** 25 f. choc., blue & brown 90 85
49. – 50 f. violet, pur. & brown 3·00 2·75
50. – 100 f. purple, turq. & brown .. .. .. 3·50 3·25

DESIGNS: (Diesel rolling stock)—HORIZ. 20 f. Railcar. 100 f. Diesel locomotive. VERT. 50 f. Diesel shunter.

**1963.** 15th Anniv. of Declaration of Human Rights.

51. **26.** 25 f. bistre, grn. and brn. 70 50

**27.** Bangui Cathedral.

**1964.** Air.

52. **27.** 100 f. brown, green & blue 1·50 85

**28.** Cleopatra, Temple of Kalabsha. **30.** "Tree" and Sun Emblem.

**29.** Radar Scanner.

**1964.** Air. Nubian Monuments Preservation.

53. **28.** 25 f. + 10 f. mauve, blue and green .. .. 1·10 1·10
54. 50 f. + 10 f. brown, olive and turquoise .. .. 1·90 1·90
55. 100 f. + 10 f. purple, violet and green .. .. 3·00 3·00

**1964.** Air. World Meteorological Day.

56. **29.** 50 f. violet, brown & blue 95 95

**1964.** International Quiet Sun Years.

57. **30.** 25 f. orge., ochre & turq. 1·00 75

**31.** Map and African Heads of State. **33.** Pres. Kennedy.

**32.** Throwing the Javelin.

**1964.** Air. 5th Anniv. of Equatorial African Heads of State Conf.

58. **31.** 100 f. multicoloured .. 1·60 85

**1964.** Air. Olympic Games, Tokyo.

59. **32.** 25 f. brown, green & blue 40 30
60. – 50 f. red, black and green 85 40
61. – 100 f. brown, blue & green 1·90 85
62. – 250 f. black, green & red 5·00 2·50

DESIGNS: 50 f. Basketball. 100 f. Running. 250 f. Diving and swimming.

**1964.** Air. Pres. Kennedy Memorial Issue.

63. **33.** 100 f. brn., blk. & violet 1·90 1·40

**34.** African Child.

**35.** Silhouettes of European and African.

**1964.** Child Welfare. Different portraits of children. As T **34**.

64. **34.** 20 f. brown, green & pur. 35 25
65. – 25 f. brown, blue and red 40 35
66. – 40 f. brown, purple & grn. 60 45
67. – 50 f. brown, green & red 70 50

**1964.** French, African and Malagasy Co-operation. As T **547** of France.

68. 25 f. brown, red and green 60 40

**1964.** National Unity.

69. **35.** 25 f. multicoloured .. 65 40

**36.** "Economic Co-operation".

**1964.** Air. "Europafrique".

70. **36.** 50 f. green, red & yellow 95 65

**37.** Handclasp.

**1965.** Air. Int. Co-operation Year.

71. **37.** 100 f. multicoloured .. 1·60 85

**38.** Weather Satellite.

**1965.** Air. World Meteorological Day.

72. **38.** 100 f. blue and brown .. 1·60 85

**39.** Abraham Lincoln.

**1965.** Air. Death Cent. of Abraham Lincoln.

73. **39.** 100 f. flesh, blue & green 1·60 85

**40.** Team of Oxen.

**1965.** Harnessed Animals in Agriculture.

74. **40.** 25 f. red, brown & green 50 35
75. – 50 f. purple, green & blue 85 45
76. – 85 f. brown, green & blue 1·25 70
77. – 100 f. multicoloured .. 1·60 90

DESIGNS: 50 f. Ploughing with bullock. 85 f. Ploughing with oxen. 100 f. Oxen with hay cart.

**41.** Pouget-Maisonneuve Telegraph Instrument.

**1965.** I.T.U. Cent.
78. **41.** 25 f. bl., red & grn. (post.) 50 40
79. – 30 f. lake and green .. 60 45
80. – 50 f. red and violet .. 90 65
81. – 85 f. blue and purple .. 1·60 95
82. – 100 f. brown, blue & green (48½ × 27 mm.) (air) .. 1·90 1·10

DESIGNS—VERT. 30 f. Chappe's telegraph instrument. 50 f. Doignon regulator for Hughes telegraph. HORIZ. 85 f. Pouillet's telegraph apparatus. 100 f. "Relay" satellite and I.T.U. emblem.

**42.** Women and Loom ("To Clothe"). **43.** Coffee Plant, Hammer Grubs and "Epicampoptera strandi".

**1965.** "M.E.S.A.N" Welfare Campaign. Designs depicting "Five Aims".
83. **42.** 25 f. green, brown and blue (postage) .. .. 45 35
84. – 50 f. brown, blue & green 75 45
85. – 60 f. brown, blue & green 85 60
86. – 85 f. multicoloured .. 1·25 65
87. – 100 f. blue, brown & green (48 × 27 mm.) (air) .. 1·25 70

DESIGNS: 50 f. Doctor examining child, and hospital ("To care for"). 60 f. Student and school ("To instruct"). 85 f. Women and child, and harvesting scene ("To nourish"). 100 f. Village houses ("To house"). "M.E.S. A.N.—Mouvement Evolution Social Afrique Noire".

**1965.** Plant Protection.
88. **43.** 2 f. purple, red & green 10 10
89. – 3 f. red, green & black 25 15
90. – 30 f. purple, green & red 1·50 65

DESIGNS—HORIZ. 3 f. Coffee plant, caterpillar and hawk-moth. VERT. 30 f. Cotton plant caterpillar and rose-moth.

**1965.** Surch.
91. – 2 f. on 3 f. (No. 43) .. 2·50 2·50
92. **1.** 5 f. on 15 f. .. .. 2·50 2·50
93. – 5 f. on 85 f. (No. 76) .. 35 35
94. **13.** 10 f. on 20 f. .. .. 3·25 3·25
95. – 10 f. on 100 f. (No. 77) .. 45 45

**45.** Camp Fire.

**46.** U.N. and Campaign Emblems. **47.** "Industry and Agriculture".

**1965.** Scouting.
96. **45.** 25 f. red, purple and blue 75 25
97. – 50 f. brown and blue (Boy Scout) .. .. 1·00 60

**1965.** Freedom from Hunger.
98. **46.** 50 f. brown, blue & green 90 65

**1965.** Air. "Europafrique".
99. **47.** 50 f. multicoloured .. 80 50

**48.** Mercury (statue after Coysevox). **49.** Father and Child.

**1965.** Air. 5th Anniv. of Admission to U.P.U..
100. **48.** 100 f. black, blue & red 1·90 1·10

**1965.** Air. Red Cross.
101. **49.** 50 f. black, blue & red 1·00 50
102. – 100 f. brown, green & red (Mother and Child) .. 2·10 1·00

**50.** Grading Diamonds. **51.** Mbaka Porter.

**1966.** National Diamond Industry.
103. **50.** 25 f. brown, violet & red 75 40

**1966.** World Festival of Negro Arts, Dakar.
104. **51.** 25 f. multicoloured .. 65 40

**52.** W.H.O. Building. **53.** "Eulophia cucullata".

**1966.** W.H.O. Headquarters, Geneva. Inaug.
105. **52.** 25 f. violet, blue & yell. 65 40

**1966.** Flowers. Multicoloured.
106. 2 f. Type **53** .. .. 10 10
107. 5 f. "Lissochilus horsfalii" 20 10
108. 10 f. "Tridactyle bicaudata" 25 20
109. 15 f. "Polystachya" .. 50 25
110. 20 f. "Eulophia alta" .. 75 40
111. 25 f. "Microcelia macrorrhynchium" .. .. 1·00 50

**54.** Douglas DC-8F Aircraft and "Air Afrique" Emblem.

**1966.** Air. Inaug. of "DC–8" Air Services.
112. **54.** 25 f. multicoloured .. 60 30

**55.** Congo Forest Mouse.

**1966.** Rodents. Multicoloured.
113. 5 f. Type **55** .. .. 40 25
114. 10 f. Black-striped mouse 65 40
115. 20 f. Dollman's tree mouse 1·50 70

**56.** "Luna 9".

**1966.** Air. "Conquest of the Moon". Mult.
116. 130 f. Type **56** .. .. 1·60 95
117. 130 f. "Surveyor" .. 1·60 95
118. 200 f. "From the Earth to the Moon" (Jules Verne) 2·75 1·60

**57.** Cernan. **59.** U.N.E.S.C.O. Emblem.

**1966.** Air. Astronauts. Multicoloured.
120. 50 f. Type **57** .. .. 85 50
121. 50 f. Popovich .. .. 85 50

**1966.** Air. Launching of Satellite "D 1". As T **569** of France.
122. 100 f. purple and brown .. 1·60 80

**1966.** 20th Anniv. of U.N.E.S.C.O.
123. **59.** 30 f. multicoloured .. 65 40

**60.** Symbols of Industry and Agriculture. **61.** Pres. Bokassa.

**1966.** Air. Europafrique.
124. **60.** 50 f. multicoloured .. 1·10 75

**1967.**
125. **61.** 30 f. black, ochre & grn. 60 35

**1967.** Provisional Stamps. (a) Postage. No. 111 surch. **XX** and value.
126. 10 f. on 25 f. multicoloured 45 20

(b) Air. No. 112 with face value altered by obliteration of figure "2" in "25".
127. **54.** 5 f. multicoloured .. 25 20

**63.** Douglas DC-8 over Bangui M'Poko Airport.

**1967.** Air.
128. **63.** 100 f. blue, green & brown 2·10 1·00

**64.** Aerial View of Fair.

**1967.** Air. World Fair. Montreal.
129. **64.** 100 f. brn., ultram. & blue 1·50 70

**65.** Central Market, Bangui.

**1967.** Multicoloured.
130. 30 f. Type **65** .. .. 65 35
131. 30 f. Safari Hotel, Bangui 65 35

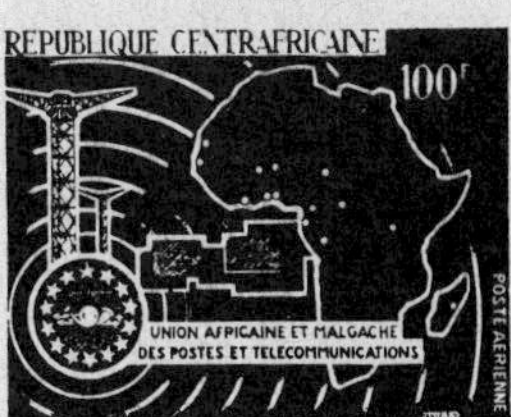


**66.** Map, Letters and Pylons.

**1967.** Air. 5th Anniv. of African and Malagasy Posts and Telecommunications Union (U.A.M.P.T.).
132. **66.** 100 f. pur. grn. & red 1·50 70

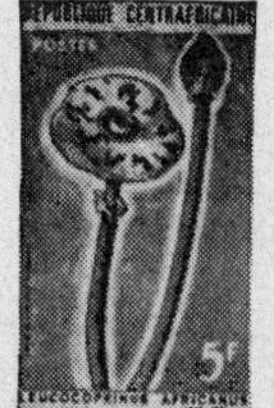

**67.** "Leucocoprinus africanus". **68.** Projector, Africans and Map.

**1967.** Mushrooms. Multicoloured.
133. 5 f. Type **67** .. .. 95 30
134. 10 f. "Synpodia arborescens" .. .. 1·25 60
135. 15 f. "Phlebopus sudanicus" 1·40 90
136. 30 f. "Termitomyces schimperi" .. .. 4·75 1·50
137. 50 f. "Psalliota sebedulis" 7·25 2·75

**1967.** "Radiovision" Service.
138. **68.** 30 f. blue, green & brown 65 40

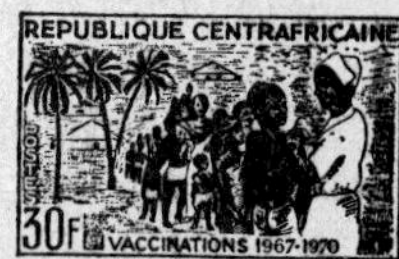


**69.** Coiffure. **70.** Inoculation Session.

**1967.** Female Coiffures. Showing different hairstyles.
139. **69.** 5 f. brown & blue 25 20
140. – 10 f. brown, brown & red 40 25
141. – 15 f. brn., brown & grn. 65 45
142. – 20 f. brn., brn. & orge. 75 45
143. – 30 f. brn., choc. & purple 1·25 60

**1967** Vaccination Programme, 1967-70.
144. **70.** 30 f. brown, green & lake 65 45

**71.** Douglas DC-3.

**1967.** Aircraft.
145. **71.** 1 f. slate, green & brown (post.) .. .. 20 10
146. – 2 f. black, blue & purple 20 10
147. – 5 f. black, green & blue 25 15
148. – 100 f. brn., grn. & bl. (air) 1·75 80
149. – 200 f. blue, brn. & grn. 3·75 1·75
150. – 500 f. slate, red & blue 11·00 4·50

DESIGNS—As T **71**: 2 f. Beechcraft Baron. 5 f. Douglas DC-4. 48 × 27 mm: 100 f. Potez 25-TOE. 200 f. Junkers 52/3m. 500 f. Sud Aviation Caravelle.

**72.** Presidents Boganda and Bokassa.

**1967.** Air. 9th Anniv. of Republic.
151. **72.** 130 f. multicoloured .. 1·60 1·10

**73.** Primitive Shelter, Toulou.

**1967.** 6th Pan-African Prehistory Congress Dakar.
152. **73.** 30 f. blue, purple & red 65 25
153. – 50 f. bistre, ochre & grn. 1·25 65
154. – 100 f. purple, brn. & blue 2·50 95
155. – 130 f. red, green & brn. 2·50 95

DESIGNS—VERT. 50 f. Kwe perforated stone. 100 f. Megaliths, Bouar. HORIZ. 130 f. Rock drawings, Toulou.

**74.** Pres. Bokassa.

**1968.** Air.
156. **74.** 30 f. multicoloured .. 60 35

**75.** Human Rights Emblem, Human Figures and Globe.

**1968.** Air. Human Rights Year.
157. **75.** 200 f. red, grn. & violet 3·25 1·50

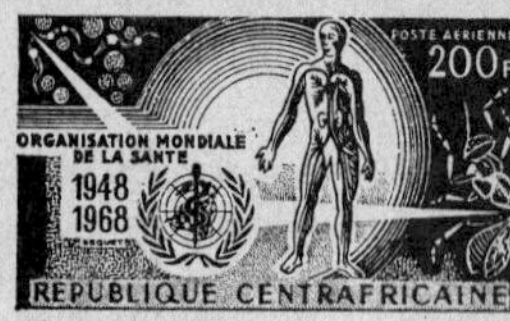
**76.** Human Figure and W.H.O. Emblem.

**1968.** Air. 20th Anniv. of W.H.O.
158. **76.** 200 f. red, bl. & brn. .. 3·50 1·90

**77.** Downhill Skiing

**78.** Parachute-landing on Venus.

**1968.** Air. Olympic Games, Grenoble and Mexico.
159. **77.** 200 f. brown, blue & red 4·25 2·50
160. – 200 f. brown, blue & red 4·25 2·50
DESIGN: No. 160, Throwing the javelin.

**1968.** Air. " Venus 4 ". Exploration of planet Venus.
161. **78.** 100 f. blue, turq. & grn. 1·60 80

**79.** Marie Curie and impaled Crab (of Cancer).

**1968.** Air. Marie Curie Commem.
162. **79.** 100 f. brn., violet & blue 1·90 1·00

**80.** Refinery and Tanker.

**1968.** Inauguration of Petroleum Refinery, Port Gentil, Gabon.
163. **80.** 30 f. multicoloured .. 70 30

**1968.** Air. Surch. Nos. 165/6 are obliterated with digit.
164. **56.** 5 f. on 130 f. (No. 116).. 15 10
165. – 10 f. (100 f. No. 148) .. 20 15
166. – 20 f. (200 f. No. 149) .. 35 25
167. – 50 f. on 130 f. (No. 117) 75 50

**82.** "CD-8" Bulldozer.

**1968.** Bokassa Project.
168. **82.** 5 f. brn., blk. & grn. .. 25 15
169. – 10 f. black, brn. & grn... 40 25
170. – 20 f. grn., yell. & brn... 65 25
171. – 30 f. bl., drab & brn. .. 95 45
172. – 30 f. red, bl. & grn. .. 95 50
DESIGNS: 10 f. Baoule cattle. 20 f. Spinning-machine. 30 f. (No. 171), Automatic looms. 30 f. (No. 172), "D4-C" bulldozer.

**83.** Bangui Mosque.

**1968.** 2nd Anniv. of Bangui Mosque.
173. **83.** 30 f. flesh, green & bl. 70 40

**84.** Za Throwing-knife.

**1968.** Hunting Weapons.
174. **84.** 10 f. blue and bistre .. 45 25
175. – 20 f. green, brown & bl. 60 35
176. – 30 f. green, orge. & blue 65 45
DESIGNS: 20 f. Kpinga-Gbengue Throwing-knife. 30 f. Mbano Cross-bow.

**85.** " Ville de Bangui " (1958).

**1968.** River Craft.
177. **85.** 10 f. blue, grn. & pur. (postage) .. .. 50 40
178. – 30 f. brown, bl. & grn... 90 50
179. – 50 f. black, brn. & grn. 1·40 65
180. – 100 f. brn., grn. & bl. (air) 2·10 95
181. – 130 f. blue, grn. & pur. 2·10 1·25
DESIGNS: 30 f. "J.B. Gouandjia" (1968). 50 f. "Lamblin" (1944). LARGER (48 × 27 mm.): 100 f. " Pie X " (Bangui, 1894). 130 f. "Ballay" (Bangui, 1891).

**86.** " Madame de Sevigne " (French School, 17th century).

**1968.** Air. " Philexafrique " Stamp Exn., Abidjan, Ivory Coast (1969) (1st issue).
182. **86.** 100 f. multicoloured .. 2·25 2·00

**87.** President Bokassa, Cotton Plantation, and Ubangui Chari stamp of 1930.

**1969.** Air. " Philexafrique " Stamp Exn. Abidjan, Ivory Coast (2nd issue).
183. **87.** 50 f. blk., grn. & brown 1·75 1·75

**88.** " Holocerina angulata ".

**1969.** Air. Butterflies. Multicoloured.
184. 10 f. Type **88** .. .. 50 25
185. 20 f. " Nudaurelia dione " 75 35
186. 30 f. " Eustera troglophylla " (vert.) .. 1·90 60
187. 50 f. " Aurivillius aratus " 3·00 1·60
188. 100 f. " Epiphora albida " 5·00 2·50

**89.** Throwing the Javelin.

**90.** Miner and Emblems.

**1969.** Sports. Multicoloured.
189. 5 f. Type **89** (postage) .. 20 10
190. 10 f. Start of race .. .. 25 15
191. 15 f. Football .. .. 40 20
192. 50 f. Boxing (air) .. .. 80 30
193. 100 f. Basketball .. 1·75 65
Nos. 192/3 are 48 × 28 mm.

**1969.** 50th Anniv. of I.L.O.
194. **90.** 30 f. multicoloured .. 50 25
195. 50 f. multicoloured .. 75 40

**INDEX**
Countries can be quickly located by referring to the index at the end of this volume.

**91.** " Apollo 8 " over Moon's Surface.

**1969.** Air. Flight of " Apollo 8 " Around Moon.
196. **91.** 200 f. multicoloured .. 3·00 1·60

**92.** Nuremberg Spire and Toys.

**1969.** Air. Int. Toy Fair, Nuremberg.
197. **92.** 100 f. blk., purple & grn. 1·50 1·00

**1969.** Air. Birth Bicent. of Napoleon Bonaparte. As T **144** of Cameroun. Mult.
198. 100 f. " Napoleon as First Consul " (Girodet-Trioson) (vert.) .. 1·90 1·25
199. 130 f. " Meeting of Napoleon and Francis II of Austria " (Gros) .. 2·50 1·40
200. 200 f. " Marriage of Napoleon and Marie-Louise " (Rouget) .. .. 3·75 2·50

**93.** President Bokassa in Military Uniform.

**94.** Pres. Bokassa, Flag and Map.

**1969.**
201. **93.** 30 f. multicoloured .. 50 25

**1969.** 10th Anniv. of A.S.E.C.N.A. As T **151** of Cameroun.
202. 100 f. blue .. .. .. 1·75 75

**1970.** Air. Die-stamped on gold foil.
203. **94.** 2000 f. gold .. .. 32·00 32·00

**95.** Garayah.

**97.** F. D. Roosevelt (25th Death Anniv.).

**96.** Flour Storage Depot.

**1970.** Musical Instruments.
204. **95.** 10 f. brown, sepia & grn. 40 15
205. – 15 f. brown and green .. 45 20
206. – 30 f. brown, lake & yellow 70 35
207. – 50 f. blue and red .. 1·00 40
208. – 130 f. brown, olive & blue 3·25 1·00
DESIGNS—VERT. 130 f. Gatta and Babylon. HORIZ. 15 f. Ngombi. 30 f. Xylohone. 50 f. Nadla.

**1970.** Societie Industrielle Centra-africaine des Produits Alimentaires et Derives (S.I.C.P.A.D.) Project. Mult.
209. 25 f. Type **96** .. 45 25
210. 50 f. Mill machinery .. 90 70
211. 100 f. View of flour mill .. 1·40 1·00

**1970.** Air. World Leaders. Multicoloured.
212. 100 f. Lenin (birth cent.) 2·50 1·10
213. 100 f. Type **97** .. .. 1·50 85

**1970.** New U.P.U. Headquarters Building, Berne. As T **156** of Cameroun.
214. 100 f. vermilion, red & blue 1·40 65

**1970.** Air. Moon Landing of " Apollo 12 ". No. 196 optd. **ATTERRISSAGE d'APOLLO 12 19 novembre 1969.**
215. **91.** 200 f. multicoloured .. 12·50 9·25

**99.** Pres. Bokassa.

**101.** Silkworm.

**100.** Cheese Factory, Sarki.

**1970.**
216. **99.** 30 f. multicoloured .. 5·00 3·75
217. 40 f. multicoloured .. 6·25 4·50

**1970.** " Operation Bokassa " Development Projects. Multicoloured.
218. 5 f. Type **100** (postage) .. 35 20
219. 10 f. M'Bali Ranch .. 4·75 3·75
220. 20 f. Zebu bull and herdsman (vert.) .. .. 65 45
221. 40 f. Type **101** .. .. 1·90 65
222. 140 f. Type **101** (air) . 3·00 1·25

**102.** African Dancer.

**1970.** Air. " Knokphila 70 " Stamp Exhib., Knokke, Belgium. Multicoloured.
223. 100 f. Type **102** .. .. 1·50 50
224. 100 f. African produce .. 1·50 50

**103.** Footballer.

**1970.** Air. World Cup Football Championships, Mexico.
225. **103.** 200 f. multicoloured .. 3·00 1·60

**104.** Central African Republic's Pavilion.

**1970.** Air. " EXPO 70 ", Osaka, Japan.
226. **104.** 200 f. multicoloured .. 3·50 1·75

**105.** Dove and Cogwheel.

**1970.** Air. 25th Anniv. of U.N.O.
227. **105.** 200 f. black, yell. & bl. 3·00 1·50

**106.** Presidents Mobutu, Bokassa and Tombalbaye.

**1970.** Air. Reconciliation with Chad and Zaire.
228. **106.** 140 f. multicoloured .. 1·90 80

**107.** Scaly Francolin and Helmet Guineafowl.

**1971.** Wildlife. Multicoloured.
229 5 f.+5 f. Type **107** .. 3·50 2·25
230 10 f. + 5 f. Common duiker and true achatina (snail) .. .. .. 4·75 2·75
231 20 f+5 f. Hippopotamus, African elephant and tortoise in tug-of-war 5·75 3·00
232 30 f.+10 f. Tortoise and Senegal coucal .. .. 8·25 7·00
233 50 f.+20 f. Monkey and leopard .. .. 12·50 10·50

**108.** Lengue Dancer.

**1971.** Traditional Dances. Multicoloured.
234. 20 f.+5 f. Type **108** .. 50 25
235. 40 f.+10 f. Lengue (diff.) 75 40
236. 100 f.+40 f. Teke.. .. 2·25 1·25
237. 140 f.+40 f. Englabolo .. 3·00 1·40

**110.** "Gnathonemus monteiri".

**1971.** Fishes. Multicoloured.
244. 10 f. Type **110** .. .. 25 20
245. 20 f. "Mormyrus proboscirostris" .. .. 50 25
246. 30 f. "Marcusenius wilverthi" .. .. 85 50
247. 40 f. "Gnathonemus elephas" .. .. 1·60 60
248. 50 f. "Gnathonemus curvirostris" .. 1·90 1·00

**111.** Satellite and Globe.

**1971.** Air. World Telecommunications Day.
249. **111.** 100 f. multicoloured 1·50 75

**112.** Berberati Cathedral. **113.** Gen. De Gaulle.

**1971.** Consecration of Roman Catholic Cathedral, Berberati.
250. **112.** 5 f. multicoloured .. 25 15

**1971.** 1st Death Anniv. of De Gaulle.
251. **113.** 100 f. multicoloured .. 3·25 1·90

**114.** Lesser Bushbaby.

**1971.** Animals: Primates. Multicoloured.
252. 30 f. Type **114** .. .. 65 60
253. 40 f. Western needle-clawed bushbaby .. 95 65
254. 100 f. Angwantibo (horiz.) 2·25 1·40
255. 150 f. Potto (horiz.) .. 3·75 2·40
256. 200 f. Red colobus (horiz.) 5·00 3·25

**1971.** Air. 10th Anniv. of African and Malagasy Posts and Telecommunications Union. Similar to T **184** of Cameroun. Mult.
257. 100 f. Headquarters and carved head .. .. 1·50 75

**115.** Shepard in Capsule.

**1971.** Space Achievements. Multicoloured.
258. 40 f. Type **115** .. .. 45 30
259. 40 f. Gagarin in helmet .. 45 30
260. 100 f. Aldrin in Space .. 1·10 45
261. 100 f. Leonov in Space .. 1·10 45
262. 200 f. Armstrong on Moon 2·25 1·00
263. 200 f. "Lunokhod 1" on Moon .. .. .. 2·25 1·00

**116.** Crab Emblem. **117.** "Operation Bokassa".

**1971.** Air. Anti-Cancer Campaign.
264. **116.** 100 f. multicoloured .. 1·90 95

**1971.** 12th Year of Independence.
265. **117.** 40 f. multicoloured .. 65 40

**118.** Racial Equality Year Emblem.

**1971.** Racial Equality Year.
266. **118.** 50 f. multicoloured .. 65 40

**119.** Int. I.E.Y. Emblem and Child with Toy Bricks.

**1971.** Air. 25th Anniv. of U.N.E.S.C.O.
267. **119.** 140 f. multicoloured .. 1·50 70

**120.** African Children.

**1971.** Air. 25th Anniv. of U.N.I.C.E.F.
268. **120.** 140 f.+50 f. mult. .. 2·50 1·60

**121.** Arms and Parade. **122.** Pres. G. Nasser.

**1972.** Bokassa Military School.
269. **121.** 30 f. multicoloured .. 65 45

**1972.** Air. Nasser Commem.
270. **122.** 100 f. ochre, brn. & red 1·60 80

**123.** Book Year Emblem. **124.** Heart Emblem.

**1972.** Int. Book Year.
271. **123.** 100 f. gold, yell. & brn. 1·60 95

**1972.** World Heart Month.
272. **124.** 100 f. red, blk. & yell. 1·40 80

**125.** First-Aid Post. **126.** Global Emblem.

**1972.** Red Cross Day.
273. **125.** 150 f. multicoloured .. 2·25 1·25

**1972.** World Telecommunications Day.
274. **126.** 50 f. blk., yellow & red 75 50

**127.** Boxing.

**1972.** Air. Olympic Games, Munich.
275. **127.** 100 f. bistre & brown 1·60 95
276. – 100 f. violet and green 1·60 1·10
DESIGN—VERT. No. 276, Long-jumping.

**128.** Pres. Bokassa and Family.

**1972.** Mothers' Day.
278. **128.** 30 f. multicoloured .. 75 40

**129.** Pres. Bokassa planting Cotton Bush. **130.** Savings Bank Building.

**1972.** "Operation Bokassa" Cotton Development.
279. **129.** 40 f. multicoloured .. 55 35

**1972.** Opening of New Postal Cheques and Savings Bank Building.
280. **130.** 30 f. multicoloured .. 50 35

**131.** "Le Pacifique" Hotel.

**1972** "Operation Bokassa" Completion of "Le Pacifique" Hotel
281. **131.** 30 f blue, red & green 35 25

**132.** Giraffe and Monkeys. **133.** Postal Runner.

**134.** Tiling's Postal Rocket, 1931.

**1972.** Clock-faces from Central African HORCEN Factory. Multicoloured.
282 5 f. Rhinoceros chasing African .. .. 20 20
283 10 f. Camp fire and Native warriors .. .. 25 20
284 20 f. Fishermen .. .. 60 30
285 30 f. Type **132** .. .. 65 45
286 40 f. Warriors fighting .. 90 65

**1972.** "CENTRAPHILEX" Stamp Exhibition, Bangui.
287. **133.** 10 f. mult. (postage).. 25 20
288. – 20 f. multicoloured .. 40 30
289. **134.** 40 f. orange, blue and slate (air) .. 55 45
290. – 50 f. blue, slate & orge. 70 50
291. – 150 f. grey, orge. & brn. 1·90 1·25
292. – 200 f. blue, orge. & brn. 2·75 1·90
DESIGNS—As Type **133**: HORIZ. Protestant Youth Centre. As Type **134**: VERT. 50 f. Douglas DC-3 and camel postman. 150 f. "Sirio" satellite and rocket. HORIZ. 200 f. "Intelstat 4" satellite and rocket.

**135.** University Buildings.

**1972.** Inaug. of Bokassa University.
294. **135.** 40 f. grey, blue & red 55 35

**136.** Mail Van.

**1972.** World U.P.U. Day.
295. **136.** 100 f. multicoloured .. 1·75 85

137. Paddy Field.

**1972.** Bokassa Plan. State Farms. Mult.
296. 5 f. Type **137** .. .. 20 15
297. 25 f. Rice cultivation .. 35 20

**138.** Four Linked Arrows. **140.** Hotel Swimming Pool.

**1972.** Air. "Europafrique".
298. **138.** 100 f. multicoloured.. 1·25 75

**1972.** Air. Munich Olympic Gold Medal Winners. Nos. 275/6 optd. as listed below.
299. **127.** 100 f. bistre and brown 1·25 80
300. – 100 f. violet and green 1·25 80
OVERPRINTS: No. 299, **POIDS MOYEN-LEMECHEV-MEDAILLE D'OR.** No. 300, **LONGUEUR - WILLIAMS - MEDAILLE D'OR.**

**1972.** Opening of Hotel St. Sylvestre.
302. **140.** 30 f. brn., turq. & grn. 40 30
303. – 40 f. pur., grn. & blue 40 30
DESIGN: 40 f. Facade of Hotel.

**141.** Landing Module and Lunar Rover on Moon.

**1972.** Air. Moon Flight of "Apollo 16".
304. **141.** 100 f. green, blue & grey 1·25 60

**142.** "Virgin and Child" (F. Pesellino).

**1972.** Air. Christmas. Multicoloured.
305. 100 f. Type **142** .. .. 1·60 95
306. 150 f. "Adoration of the Child" (F. Lippi) .. 2·25 1·25

**143.** Learning to Write.

**1972.** "Central African Mothers". Mult.
307. 5 f. Type **143** .. .. 15 10
308. 10 f. Baby-care .. .. 25 20
309. 15 f. Dressing hair .. 25 20
310. 20 f. Learning to read .. 40 25
311. 180 f. Suckling baby .. 2·40 1·25
312. 190 f. Learning to walk .. 2·40 1·25

**144.** Louys (marathon), Athens, 1896.

**1972.** Air. 75th Anniv. of Revival of Olympic Games.
313. **144.** 30 f. pur., brn. & green 30 25
314. – 40 f. green, blue & brn. 35 25
315. – 50 f. violet, blue & red 50 40
316. – 100 f. pur., brn. & grey 1·00 50
317. – 150 f. blk., blue & pur. 1·60 1·10
DESIGNS: 40 f. Barrelet (sculling), Paris, 1900. 50 f. Prinstein (triple-jump), St. Louis, U.S.A., 1904. 100 f. Taylor (400 m. freestyle swimming), London, 1908. 150 f. Johansson (Greco-Roman wrestling), Stockholm, 1912.

**145.** W.H.O. Emblem, Doctor and Nurse.

**1973.** Air. 25th Anniv. of W.H.O.
318. **145.** 100 f. multicoloured .. 1·25 70

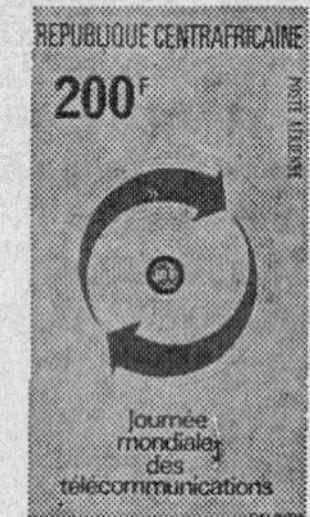


**146.** "Telecommunications".

**1973.** World Telecommunications Day.
319. **146.** 200 f. orge., blue & blk. 1·90 1·00

**147.** Harvesting.

**1973.** 10th Anniv. of World Food Programme.
320. **147.** 50 f. multicoloured .. 65 40

**148.** "Garcinia punctata".

**1973.** "Flora". Multicoloured.
321. 10 f. Type **148** .. .. 25 15
322. 20 f. "Bertiera racemosa" 35 20
323. 30 f. "Coryanthe pachyceras" .. .. .. 50 30
324. 40 f. "Combretodendron africanum" .. .. 70 30
325. 50 f. "Xylopia villosa" .. 85 45

**149.** Pygmy Chameleon.

**1973.**
326. **149.** 15 f. multicoloured .. 60 25

**150.** "Mboyo Ndili".

**1973.** Caterpillars. Multicoloured.
327. 3 f. Type **150** .. .. 25 20
328. 5 f. "Piwili" .. .. 40 25
329. 25 f. "Loulia Konga" .. 90 40

**1973.** African Solidarity "Drought Relief". No. 321 surch. **SECHERESSE SOLIDARITE AFRICAINE** and value.
330. **148.** 100 f. on 10 f. mult. .. 1·25 95

**1973.** U.A.M.P.T. As Type **216** of Cameroun.
331. 100 f. red, brown and olive 1·10 70

**1973.** Air. African Fortnight, Brussels. As Type **217** of Cameroun.
332. 100 f. brown and violet.. 1·00 60

**152.** African and Symbolic Map.

**1973.** Air. Europafrique.
333. **152.** 100 f. red, grn. & brn. 1·25 75

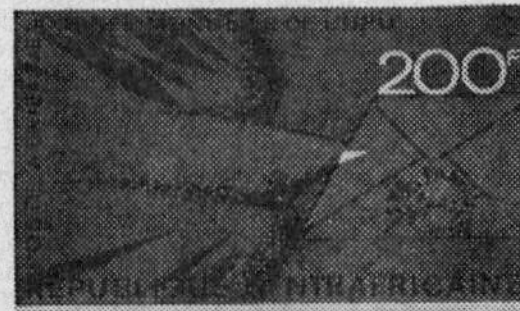


**153.** Bird with Letter.

**1973.** Air. World U.P.U. Day.
334. **153.** 200 f. multicoloured .. 2·25 1·40

**154.** Weather Map.

**1973.** Air. Cent. of I.M.O./W.M.O.
335. **154.** 150 f. multicoloured .. 1·90 85

**155.** Copernicus.

**1973.** Air. 500th Birth Anniv. of Copernicus.
336. **155.** 100 f. multicoloured .. 2·25 1·50

**156.** Pres. Bokassa. **158.** Launch.

**1973.**
337. **156.** 1 f. multicoloured (post.) 10 10
338. 2 f. multicoloured .. 10 10
339. 3 f. multicoloured .. 15 10
340. 5 f. multicoloured .. 15 10
341. 10 f. multicoloured .. 25 15
342. 15 f. multicoloured .. 25 20
343. 20 f. multicoloured .. 35 20
344. 30 f. multicoloured .. 35 25
345. 40 f. multicoloured .. 45 35
346. – 50 f. multicoloured (air) 50 35
347. – 100 f. multicoloured 1·00 50
DESIGNS-SQUARE (35×35 mm.). 50 f. Pres. Bokassa facing left. VERT. (26×47 mm.). 100 f. Pres. Bokassa in military uniform.

**1973.** Air. Moon Flight of "Apollo 17".
348. **158.** 50 f. red, grn. & brn. 50 30
349. – 65 f. grn., red & purple 60 35
350. – 100 f. blue, brn. & red 1·00 50
351. – 150 f. grn., brn. & red 1·50 70
352. – 200 f. grn., red and blue 2·00 1·10
DESIGNS—HORIZ. 65 f. Surveying lunar surfaces. 100 f. Descent on Moon. VERT. 150 f. Astronauts on Moon's surface. 200f. Splash-down.

**159.** Interpol Emblem within "Eye". **160.** St. Theresa.

**1973.** 50th Anniv. of Interpol.
353. **159.** 50 f. multicoloured .. 70 50

**1973.** Air. Birth Centenary of St. Theresa of Lisieux.
354. **160.** 500 f. blue & light blue 5·00 3·50

**161.** Main Entrance.

**1974.** Opening of "Catherine Bokassa" Mother-and-Child Centre.
355. **161.** 30 f. brn., red & blue 35 25
356. – 40 f. brn., blue & red 45 35
DESIGN: 40 f. General view of Centre.

**162.** Cigarette-packing Machine. **163.** "Telecommunications".

**1974.** "Centra" Cigarette Factory.
357. **162.** 5 f. pur., green & red.. 10 10
358. – 10 f. blue, green & brn. 25 15
359. – 30 f. blue, green & red 30 20
DESIGNS: 10 f. Administration block and factory building. 30 f. Tobacco warehouse.

**1974.** World Telecommunications Day.
360. **163.** 100 f. multicoloured .. 1·75 1·25

**164.** "Peoples of the World". **165.** Mother and Baby.

**1974.** World Population Year.
361. **164.** 100 f. green, red & brown 1·10 65

**1974.** 26th Anniv. of W.H.O.
362. **165.** 100 f. brn., bl. & grn. 1·25 65

**166.** Letter and U.P.U. Emblem. **168.** Modern Building.

**167.** Battle Scene.

**1974.** Cent. of U.P.U.
363. **166.** 500 f. red, grn. & brn. 4·00 3·00

**1974.** "Activities of Forces' Veterans". Multicoloured.
364. 10 f. Type **167** .. .. 15 10
365. 15 f. "Today" (Peace-time activities) .. .. 20 15
366. 20 f. Planting rice .. 20 15
367. 25 f. Cattle-shed .. .. 25 20
368. 30 f. Workers hoeing .. 25 20
369. 40 f. Veterans' houses .. 40 20

**1974.** 10th Anniv. of Central African Customs and Economics Union. As Nos. 734/5 of Cameroun.
370. 40 f. multicoloured (post.) 50 35
371. 100 f. multicoloured (air) 1·00 65

**1975.** "OCAM City" Project.

372. **168.** 30 f. multicoloured .. 25 20
373. – 40 f. multicoloured .. 35 25
374. – 50 f. multicoloured .. 40 30
375. – 100 f. multicoloured .. 75 50

DESIGNS: Nos. 373/5, Various views similar to Type **150**.

**1975.** "J. B. Bokassa Pilot Village Project". As T **168**, but inscr. "VILLAGE PILOTE J. B. BOKASSA".

376. 25 f. multicoloured .. 20 15
377. 30 f. multicoloured .. 30 20
378. 40 f. multicoloured .. 35 25

DESIGNS: Nos. 376/8, Various views similar to Type **168**.

**169.** President Bokassa's Sword.

**1975.** "Homage to President Bokassa". Multicoloured.

379. 30 f. Type **169.** (postage) .. 45 25
380. 40 f. President Bokassa's baton .. .. .. 45 30
381. 50 f. Bokassa in Pres. uniform (air) .. .. 50 35
382. 100 f. Pres. Bokassa in cap and cape .. .. .. 1·00 45

Nos. 381 and 382 are vertical, 36 × 49 mm.

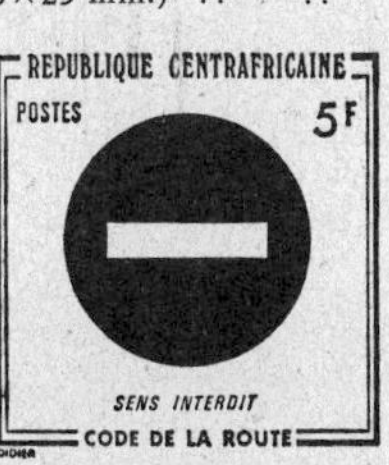

**170.** Foreign Minister and Ministry.

**1975.** Government Buildings. Mult.

383. 40 f. Type **170** .. .. 50 35
384. 40 f. Television Centre (36 × 23 mm.) .. .. 50 35

**171.** " No Entry ".

**1975.** Road Signs.

385. **171.** 5 f. red and blue .. 10 10
386. – 10 f. red and blue .. 15 10
387. – 20 f. red and blue .. 20 15
388. – 30 f. multicoloured .. 35 20
389. – 40 f. multicoloured .. 50 25

SIGNS: 10 f. " Stop ". 20 f. " No stopping ". 30 f. " School ". 40 f. " Crossroads ".

**172.** Kob.

**173.** Carved Wooden Mask.

**1975.** Wild Animals. Multicoloured.

390. 10 f. type **172** .. .. 25 20
391. 15 f. Warthog .. .. 35 20
392. 20 f. Waterbuck .. .. 50 25
393. 30 f. Lion .. .. .. 50 35

**1975.** Air. " Arphila " International Stamp Exhibition. Paris.

394. **173.** 100 f. red, rose & blue 1·00 60

**174.** Dr. Schweitzer and Dug-out Canoe.

**175.** Forest Scene.

**1975.** Air. Birth Centenary of Dr. Albert Schweitzer.

395. **174.** 200 f. blk., bl. & brn... 2·50 1·60

**1975.** Central African Woods.

396. **175.** 10 f. brn., grn. & lake 20 15
397. – 15 f. brn., grn. & bl... 25 15
398. – 50 f. bl., brn. & grn... 45 20
399. – 100 f. brn., bl. & grn... 95 55
400. – 150 f. bl., brn. & grn... 1·25 95
401. – 200 f. brn., red & grn. 1·75 1·25

DESIGNS—VERT. 15 f. Cutting sapeles. HORIZ. 50 f. Mobile crane. 100 f. Log stack. 150 f. Floating logs. 200 f. Timber-sorting yard.

**176.** Women's Heads and Women Working.

**1975.** International Women's Year.

402. **176.** 40 f. multicoloured .. 45 25
403. 100 f. multicoloured .. 1·25 65

**177.** River Vessel "Jean Bedel Bokassa".

**1976.** Air. Multicoloured.

404. 30 f. Type **177** .. .. 50 25
405. 40 f. Frontal view of " Jean Bedel Bokassa " .. 60 40

**178.** Co-operation Monument.

**1976.** Air. Central African-French Co-operation and Visit of President Giscard d'Estaing. Multicoloured.

406. 100 f. Type **178** .. .. 1·00 75
407. 200 f. Flags and President's Giscard d'Estaing and Bokassa .. .. 2·10 1·25

**179.** Alexander Graham Bell.

**1976.** Telephone Centenary.

408. **179.** 100 f. black and yellow 1·25 75

**180.** Telecommunications Satellite.

**1976.** World Telecommunications Day.

409. **180.** 100 f. pur., blue & grn. 1·40 95

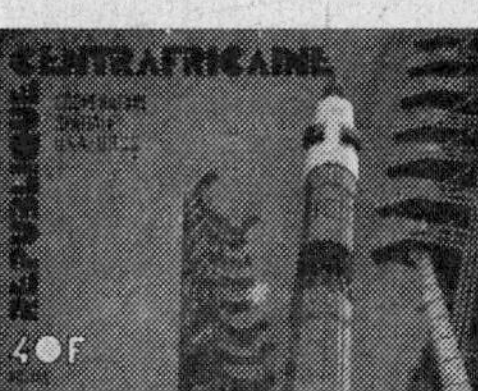

**181.** Rocket on Launch-pad.

**1976.** Apollo–Soyuz Space Link. Mult.

410. 40 f. Type **181** (postage) .. 45 25
411. 50 f. Blast-off .. .. 55 25
412. 100 f. " Soyuz " in flight (air) .. .. .. 75 25
413. 200 f. " Apollo " in flight 1·50 50
414. 300 f. Crew meeting in space 2·25 85

**182.** French Hussar.

**1976.** Air. American Revolution Bicent. Multicoloured.

416. 100 f. Type **182** .. .. 75 30
417. 125 f. Black Watch soldier 95 45
418. 150 f. German Dragoons' officer .. .. .. 1·10 50
419. 200 f. British Grenadiers' officer .. .. .. 1·90 55
420. 250 f. American Ranger .. 2·25 75

**183.** " Drurya antimachus ".

**1976.** Butterflies. Multicoloured.

422. 30 f. Type **183** (postage) .. 1·25 75
423. 40 f. " Argema mittrei " (vert.) .. .. .. 1·90 75
424. 50 f. " Acherontia atropos " and " Saturnia pyri " (air) .. .. .. 1·25 75
425. 100 f. " Papilio nireus " and " Heniocha marnois " 2·50 1·10

**184.** Dorothy Hamill of U.S.A. (figure skating).

**1976.** Medal Winners, Winter Olympic Games, Innsbruck. Multicoloured.

426. 40 f. Piero Gros of Italy (slalom) (horiz.) .. 45 25
427. 60 f. Karl Schnabl and Toni Innauer of Austria (ski-jumping) (horiz.) .. 55 35
428. 100 f. Type **184** (air) .. 70 35
429. 200 f. Alexandre Gorshkov and Ludmilla Pakhomova (figure-skating, pairs) (horiz.) .. .. .. 1·25 60
430. 300 f. John Curry of Great Britain (figure-skating) 2·25 95

**185.** U.P.U. Emblem, Letters, and Types of Mail Transport.

**1976.** World U.P.U. Day.

432. **185.** 100 f. multicoloured .. 1·60 95

**186.** Assembly of " Viking ".

**1976.** " Viking " Space Mission to Mars. Multicoloured.

433. 40 f. Type **186** (postage) .. 45 25
434. 60 f. Launch of " Viking " 55 35
435. 100 f. Parachute descent on Mars (air) .. .. 70 35
436. 200 f. " Viking " on Mars (horiz.) .. .. .. 1·25 60
437. 300 f. " Viking " operating gravel scoop .. .. 2·25 75

Issues between 1977 and 1979 are listed under **CENTRAL AFRICAN EMPIRE.**

**220.** Ski Jump.

**1979.** Air. Winter Olympic Games, Lake Placid (1980). multicoloured.

655. 60 f. Type **220** .. .. 45 20
656. 100 f. Downhill skiing .. 75 35
657. 200 f. Ice hockey .. .. 1·60 80
658. 300 f. Skiing (slalom) .. 2·25 1·10

**1979.** " Apollo 11 " Moon Landing. 10th Anniv. Nos. 433/7 optd. **ALUNISSAGE APOLLO XI JUILLET 1969.**

660. **186.** 40 f. multicoloured (postage) .. .. 40 35
661. – 60 f. multicoloured .. 45 40
662. – 100 f. multicoloured (air) 75 50
663. – 200 f. multicoloured .. 1·25 85
664. – 300 f. multicoloured .. 2·25 1·10

**222.** Thumbellina. (Andersen).

**224.** Basketball.

**223.** Locomotive, U.S. Stamp and Hill.

**1979.** International Year of the Child (2nd issue). Multicoloured.

666. 30 f. Type **222** .. .. 25 15
667. 40 f. Sleeping Beauty (horiz.) 35 20
668. 60 f. Hansel and Gretel .. 50 25
669. 200 f. The Match Girl (horiz.) .. .. .. 1·25 60
670. 250 f. The Little Mermaid 1·90 70

**1979.** Death Centenary of Sir Rowland Hill (2nd issue). Multicoloured.

671 60 f. Type **223** .. .. 60 20
672 100 f. Locomotive and French stamp and Hill 85 35
673 150 f. Locomotive and German stamp and Hill 1·25 45
674 250 f. Locomotive and British stamp and Hill 2·25 95

**1979.** Olympic Games, Moscow (2nd issue). Basketball.

676. **224.** 50 f. multicoloured .. 40 20
677. – 125 f. multicoloured .. 90 35
678. – 200 f. multicoloured .. 1·50 60
679. – 300 f. multicoloured .. 2·25 85
680. – 500 f. multicoloured .. 3·75 1·25

DESIGNS: 125 f. to 500 f. Views of different basketball matches.

**1980.** Various stamps, including one unissued, of Central African Empire optd. **REPUBLIQUE CENTRAFRICAINE.**

681. **192.** 5 f. multicoloured .. 10 10
682. – 10 f. multicoloured (No. 522) .. .. 10 10
683. – 20 f. multicoloured (Balambo (stand)) .. 15 10
684. **206.** 20 f. black and yellow 15 10
685. – 30 f. black and blue (No. 583) .. .. 25 15

## INDEX

Countries can be quickly located by referring to the index at the end of this volume.

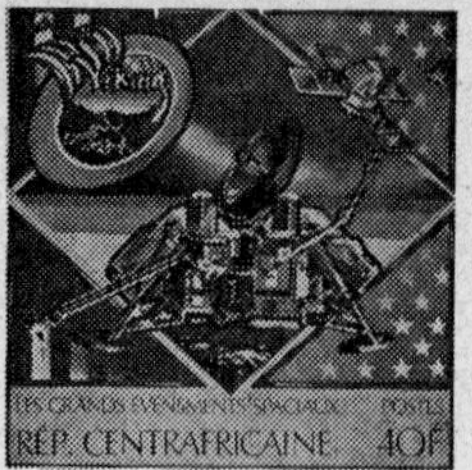

226. " Viking ".

**1980.** Space Exploration. Multicoloured.
686. 40 f. Type **226** (postage).. 35 15
687. 50 f. " Apollo "–" Soyuz " link .. .. .. 40 20
688. 60 f. " Voyager ".. .. 45 20
689. 100 f. European Space Agency .. .. .. 75 25
690. 150 f. Early satellites (air) 1·25 30
691. 200 f. Space shuttle .. 1·60 45

**1980.** Air. Winter Olympic Medal Winners. Nos. 655/8 optd. as listed below.
693. **220.** 60 f. multicoloured .. 45 20
694. – 100 f. multicoloured .. 75 35
695. – 200 f. multicoloured .. 1·60 80
696. – 300 f. multicoloured .. 2·25 1·10
OVERPRINTS: 60 f. **VAINQUEUR INNAVER AUTRICHE.** 100 f. **VAINQUEUR MOSERPROELI AUTRICHE.** 200 f. **VAINQUEUR ETATS-UNIS.** 300 f. **VAINQUEUR STENMARK SUEDE.**

228. Telephone and Sun.

**1980.** World Telecommunications Day. Multicoloured.
698. 100 f. Type **228** .. .. 90 50
699. 150 f. Telephone and sun (different) .. .. 1·25 65

229. Walking.

**1980.** Olympic Games, Moscow (3rd issue). Multicoloured.
700. 30 f. Type **229** (postage) 35 15
701. 40 f. Women's relay .. 40 20
702. 70 f. Running .. .. 60 20
703. 80 f. Women's high jump 65 30
704. 100 f. Boxing (air) .. 75 25
705. 150 f. Hurdles .. .. 1·10 30

229a. Fruit.

**1980.**
706a **229a** 40 f. multicoloured ..

230. Agriculture.

232. " Foligne Madonna ". (detail).

**1980.** European-African Co-operation. Mult.
707. 30 f. Type **230** (postage) 25 15
708. 40 f. Industry .. .. 40 15
709. 70 f. Communications .. 65 20
710. 100 f. Building construction and rocket .. .. 95 45
711. 150 f. Meteorological satellite (air) .. .. .. 1·25 30
712. 200 f. Space shuttle .. 1·50 45

**1980.** Olympic Medal Winners. Nos. 676/80 optd.
717. 50 f. " **MEDAILLE OR YOUGOSLAVIE** " .. 40 20
718. 125 f. " **MEDAILLE OR URSS** " .. .. 90 45
719. 200 f. " **MEDAILLE OR/ URSS** " .. .. 1·50 65
720. 300 f. " **MEDAILLE ARGENT/ITALIE** " 2·25 1·00
721. 500 f. " **MEDAILLE BRONZE/URSS** " .. 3·75 1·50

**1980.** Christmas. Multicoloured.
722. 60 f. Type **232** .. .. 50 20
723. 150 f. " Virgin and Saints " 1·25 50
724. 250 f. " Conestabile Madonna " .. .. .. 2·00 85

**1980.** 5th Anniv. of African Posts and Telecommunications Union. As T**269** of Benin.
725. 70 f. multicoloured .. 65 40

233. Peruvian Football Team.

**1981.** World Cup Football Championships, Spain (1982). Multicoloured.
726. 10 f. Type **233** (postage) 15 10
727. 15 f. Scottish team .. 20 15
728. 20 f. Mexican team .. 25 15
729. 25 f. Swedish team .. 25 15
730. 30 f. Austrian team .. 30 15
731. 40 f. Polish team .. 35 20
732. 50 f. French team .. 50 20
733. 60 f. Italian team .. 55 25
734. 70 f. West German team 75 30
735. 80 f. Brazilian team .. 75 30
736. 100 f. Dutch team (air) .. 75 25
737. 200 f. Spanish team .. 1·25 35

234. " Fight between Jacob and the Angel. "

236. I.T.U. and W.H.O. Emblems and Ribbons forming Caduceus.

**1981.** Air. 375th Birth Anniv. of Rembrandt. Multicoloured.
739. 60 f. Type **234** .. .. 50 20
740. 90 f. " Christ in the Tempest " 75 25
741. 150 f. " Jeremiah mourning the Destruction of Jerusalem " .. .. 1·25 50
742. 250 f. " Anna accused by Tobit of Theft of a Goat " 2·25 60

**1981.** Olympic Games Winners. Nos. 701/5 optd. with Events and names of Winners.
744. 30 f. Type **229** (postage) 25 15
745. 40 f. Women's relay .. 30 20
746. 70 f. Running .. .. 50 30
747. 80 f. Women's high jump 55 35
748. 100 f. Boxing (air) .. 45 30
749. 150 f. Hurdles .. .. 70 45
OPTS. 30 f. **50 K.M. MARCHE HARTWIG GAUDER – G.D.R.** 40 f. " **4×400 M. DAMES–U.R.S.S.**". 70 f. " **100 M. COURSE HOMMES/ALLAN WELLS – G.B.R.**". 80 f. " **SAUT EN HAUTEUR DAMES/ SARA SIMEONI – ITALIE** ". 100 f. " **BOXE – 71 KG/ARMANDO MARTINEZ – CUBA** ". 150 f. " **110 M. HAIES HOMMES/THOMAS MUNKELT – G.D.R.**".

**1981.** World Telecommunications Day.
751. **236.** 150 f. multicoloured .. 1·10 65

237. Boeing 747 carrying Space Shuttle "Enterprise".

**1981.** Conquest of Space. Multicoloured.
752 100 f. "Apollo 15" and jeep on the Moon .. .. 75 30
753 150 f. Type **237** .. .. 1·10 50
754 200 f. Space Shuttle launch 1·60 55
755 300 f. Space Shuttle performing experiment in space .. .. .. 2·50 90

238. " Family of Acrobats with a Monkey ".

**1981.** Birth Bicent. of Pablo Picasso. Mult.
757. 40 f. Type **238** (postage) .. 35 15
758. 50 f. "The Balcony " .. 50 20
759. 80 f. " The Artist's Son as Pierrot " .. .. 90 25
760. 100 f. " The Three Dancers " 1·10 35
761. 150 f. " Woman and Mirror with Self-portrait " (air) 1·75 40
762. 200 f. " Sleeping Woman, the Dream " .. .. 1·90 45

239. Tractor and Plough breaking Chain.

**1981.** 1st Anniv. of Zimbabwe's Independence.
764. **239.** 100 f. multicoloured .. 75 45
765. 150 f. multicoloured .. 1·10 50
766. 200 f. multicoloured .. 1·60 65

240. Prince Charles.

**1981.** Royal Wedding (1st issue). Mult.
767. 75 f. Type **240** .. .. 55 20
768. 100 f. Lady Diana Spencer 70 30
769. 150 f. St. Paul's Cathedral 1·10 45
770. 175 f. Couple and Prince's personal Standard .. 1·40 55
See also Nos. 772/7.

241. Lady Diana Spencer with Children.

**1981.** Royal Wedding (2nd issue). Mult.
772. 40 f. Type **241** (postage) .. 30 15
773. 50 f. Investiture of the Prince of Wales .. 35 20
774. 80 f. Lady Diana Spencer at Althorp House .. 60 25
775. 100 f. Prince Charles in naval uniform .. .. 75 30
776. 150 f. Prince of Wales's feathers (air) .. 1·10 35
777. 200 f. Highgrove House .. 1·40 45

242. C.V. Rietschoten.

**1981.** Navigators. Multicoloured.
779. 40 f. Type **242** (postage) .. 30 15
780. 50 f. M. Pajot .. .. 40 25
781. 60 f. L. Jaworski .. .. 50 30
782. 80 f. M. Birch .. .. 70 35
783. 100 f. O. Kersauson (air).. 75 40
784. 200 f. Sir Francis Chichester 1·60 75

243. Renault, 1906.

**1981.** 75th Anniv. of French Grand Prix Motor Race. Multicoloured.
786. 20 f. Type **243** .. .. 25 10
787. 40 f. Mercedes-Benz, 1937 45 15
788. 50 f. Matra-Ford, 1969 .. 50 25
789. 110 f. Tazio Nuvolari .. 1·10 45
790. 150 f. Jackie Stewart .. 1·25 65

244. Emperor's Crown pierced by Bayonet.

**1981.** Overthrow of the Empire. Mult.
792. 5 f. Type **244** .. .. 10 10
793. 10 f. Type **244** .. .. 15 10
794. 25 f. Axe splitting crown, and angel holding map 20 15
795. 60 f. As 25 f. .. .. 45 25
796. 90 f. Emperor Bokassa's statue being toppled and map of Republic .. 70 30
797. 500 f. As 90 f. .. .. 3·75 1·60

245. F.A.O. Emblem.

**1981.** World Food Day.
798. **245.** 90 f. green, brown and yellow .. .. 75 25
799. 110 f. green, brown and blue .. .. .. 90 30

246. Lizard.

247. Plumed Guineafowl.

**1981.** Air. Reptiles. Multicoloured.
800. 30 f. Type **246** .. .. 50 15
801. 60 f. Snake .. .. 55 20
802. 110 f. Crocodile .. .. 1·10 30

**1981.** Birds. Multicoloured.
803. 50 f. Type **247** .. .. 90 50
804. 90 f. Schlegel's francolin .. 1·40 60
805. 140 f. Black-headed bunting .. .. .. 2·40 1·10

248. Bank Building.

**1981.** Central African States' Bank.
806. **248.** 90 f. multicoloured .. 75 25
807. 110 f. multicoloured .. 90 30

**249.** " Madonna and Child " (Fra Angelico).

**1981.** Christmas. Various paintings showing Virgin and Child by named artists. **Mult.**

808. 50 f. Type **249** (postage) .. 35 20
809. 60 f. Cosme-Tura .. 45 25
810. 90 f. Bramantino .. .. 65 30
811. 110 f. Memling .. .. 80 45

812. 140 f. Corrège (air) .. 95 30
813. 200 f. Gentileschi .. 1·60 45

**250.** Scouts with Packs.

**1982.** 75th Anniv. of Boy Scout Movement Multicoloured.

815. 100 f. Type **250** .. .. 75 35
816. 150 f. Three scouts (horiz.) 1·10 55
817. 200 f. Scouts admiring mountain view (horiz.) 1·25 75
818. 300 f. Scouts taking oath 2·25 1·10

**251.** African Elephant.

**1982.** Animals. Multicoloured.

820. 60 f. Type **251** (postage) .. 50 35
821. 90 f. Giraffe .. .. 70 40
822. 100 f. Addax .. .. 75 45
823. 110 f. Okapi .. .. 85 50

824. 300 f. Mandrill (air) .. 2·25 1·25
825. 500 f. Lion .. .. 3·75 2·10

**252.** " Grandfather Snowman ".

**1982.** Norman Rockwell Illustrations. **Mult.**

827. 30 f. Type **252** .. .. 25 15
828. 60 f. " Croquet Players " 55 25
829. 110 f. " Women talking " 1·00 35
830. 150 f. " Searching " .. 1·25 50

**253.** Vickers Valentia biplane, 1928.

**1982.** Transport. Multicoloured.

831 5 f. Astra Torres AT-16 airship, 1919 (postage) .. 15 15
832 10 f. "Beyer-Garrat 1" locomotive .. .. 75 45
833 20 f. Bugatti "Royale" car, 1926 .. .. .. 20 15
834 110 f. Type **253** .. .. 80 40

835 300 f. Nuclear-powered freighter "Savannah" (air) .. .. .. 3·00 1·50
836 500 f. Space shuttle .. 4·25 1·25

**254.** George Washington.

**1982.** Anniversaries. Multicoloured.

838. 200 f. " Le Jardin de Bellevue " (E. Manet) (150th birth anniv.) (horiz.) .. 2·25 60
839. 300 f. Type **254** (250th birth anniv.) .. .. 2·25 85
840. 400 f. Goethe (150th death anniv.) .. .. .. 3·00 1·25
841. 500 f. Princess of Wales (21st Birthday) .. 3·75 1·90

**255.** Edward VII and Lady Diana Spencer with her Brother.

**1982.** 21st Birthday of Princess of Wales. Multicoloured.

843. 5 f. George II and portrait of Lady Diana as child (postage) .. .. 10 10
844. 10 f. Type **255** .. .. 15 10
845. 20 f. Charles I and Lady Diana with guinea pig .. 20 15
846. 110 f. George V and Lady Diana as student in Switzerland .. .. 80 25
847. 300 f. Charles II and Lady Diana in skiing clothes (air) 2·25 65
848. 500 f. George IV and Lady Diana as nursery teacher 3·75 1·25

**256.** Football.

**1982.** Olympic Games, Los Angeles. (1984). Multicoloured.

850. 5 f. Type **256** (postage) .. 10 10
851. 10 f. Boxing .. .. 15 10
852. 20 f. Running .. .. 20 15
853. 110 f. Hurdling .. .. 80 25

854. 300 f. Diving (air) .. 2·25 65
855. 500 f. Show jumping .. 3·75 1·25

**257.** Weather Satellite.

**259.** Pestle and Mortar, Chopping Board and Dish.

**1982.** Space Resources. Multicoloured.

857. 5 f. Space shuttle and scientist (Food resources) (postage) .. .. 10 10
858. 10 f. Type **257** .. .. 15 10
859. 20 f. Space laboratory (Industrial use) .. .. 20 15
860. 110 f. Astronaut on Moon (Lunar resources) .. 80 25

861. 300 f. Satellite and energy map (Planetary energy) (air) .. .. .. 2·25 65
862. 500 f. Satellite and solar panels (Solar energy) .. 3·75 1·25

**1982.** Birth of Prince William of Wales. Nos. 767/70 optd. **NAISSANCE ROYALE 1982.**

864. **240.** 75 f. multicoloured .. 50 25
865. – 100 f. multicoloured .. 60 35
866. – 150 f. multicoloured .. 1·10 50
867. – 175 f. multicoloured .. 1·50 75

**1982.** Utensils. Multicoloured.

869. 5 f. Basket of vegetables (horiz.) .. .. .. 10 10
870. 10 f. As. No. 869 .. .. 15 10
871. 25 f. Flagon made from decorated gourd .. 20 15
872. 60 f. As No. 871 .. .. 40 20
873. 120 f. Clay jars (horiz.) .. 1·00 35
874. 175 f. Decorated bowls (horiz.) .. .. .. 1·25 50
875. 300 f. Type **259** .. .. 2·50 1·10

**260.** Footballers.

**1982.** World Cup Football Championship Results. Unissued stamps optd. as T **260.** Multicoloured.

876. 60 f. "ITALIE 1er/ALLEMAGNE 2e/(R.F.A.)" .. 50 25
877. 150 f. "POLOGNE 3e" .. 1·10 50
878. 300 f. "FRANCE 4e" .. 2·50 1·10

**261.** Jean Tubind. **262.** Globe and U.P.U. Emblem.

**1982.** Painters. Multicoloured.

880. 40 f. Type **261** .. .. 35 15
881. 70 f. Pierre Ndarata and 10 f. stamp .. .. .. 55 25
882. 90 f. As No. 881 .. .. 75 30
883. 140 f. Type **261** .. .. 1·10 45

**1982.** U.P.U. Day.

884. **262.** 60 f. vio., blue & red .. 50 25
885. 120 f. vio., yell. & red 1·00 45

**263.** Hairpins and Comb.

**1983.** Hair Accessories.

886. **263.** 20 f. multicoloured .. 10 10
887. 30 f. multicoloured .. 25 15
888. 70 f. multicoloured .. 50 25
889. 80 f. multicoloured .. 70 30
890. 120 f. multicoloured .. 95 35

**264.** Koch and Microscope.

**1982.** Centenary of Discovery of Tubercle Bacillus by Dr. Robert Koch.

891. **264.** 100 f. mauve and black 85 30
892. 120 f. red and black .. 1·00 45
893. 175 f. blue and black .. 1·60 60

**265.** Emblem.

**1982.** 10th Anniv. of United Nations Environment Programme.

894. **265.** 120 f. bl., orge. & blk. 1·00 35
895. 150 f. bl., yell. & blk. 1·10 50
896. 300 f. bl., grn. & blk. 2·25 1·00

**266.** Granary.

**1982.**

897. **266.** 60 f. multicoloured .. 50 25
898. 80 f. multicoloured .. 75 35
899. 120 f. multicoloured .. 1·00 50
900. 200 f. multicoloured .. 1·75 85

**267.** " The Beautiful Gardener ". **268.** Stylized Transmitter.

**1982.** Air. Christmas. Paintings by Raphael. Multicoloured.

901. 150 f. Type **267** .. .. 1·60 35
902. 500 f. " The Holy Family " 4·00 1·25

**1983.** I.T.U. Delegates' Conference, Nairobi (1982).

903. **268.** 100 f. multicoloured .. 75 30
904. 120 f. multicoloured .. 1·00 45

**269.** Steinitz.

**1983.** Chess Masters. Multicoloured.

905. 5 f. Type **269** (postage) .. 10 10
906. 10 f. Aaron Niemsovich .. 10 10
907. 20 f. Aleksandr Alekhine .. 15 10
908. 110 f. Botvinnik .. .. 1·10 30

909. 300 f. Boris Spassky (air) .. 2·50 75
910. 500 f. Bobby Fischer .. 4·00 1·40

**270.** George Washington.

**1983.** Celebrities. Multicoloured.

912. 20 f. Type **270** (postage) .. 15 10
913. 110 f. Pres. Tito of Yugoslavia .. .. .. 90 25

914. 500 f. Princess of Wales with Prince William (air) 3·75 1·00

**271.** Telephone, Satellite and Globe. **272.** Billy Hamilton and Bruno Pezzey.

**1983.** U.N. Decade for African Transport and Communications. Multicoloured.

916. 5 f. Type **271** .. .. 15 15
917. 60 f. Type **271** .. .. 50 20
918. 120 f. Radar screen and map of Africa .. .. 95 40
919. 175 f. As No. 918 .. .. 1·25 60

**1983.** World Cup Football Championship, Spain. Multicoloured.

920. 5 f. Type **272** (postage) .. 10 10
921. 10 f. Sergeij Borovski and Zbigniew Boniek .. 10 10
922. 20 f. Pierre Littbarski and Jesus Maria Zamora .. 15 10
923. 110 f. Zico and Alberto Pajsarella 85 25
924. 300 f. Paolo Rossi and Smolarek (air) .. .. 2·25 60
925. 500 f. Rummenigge and Alain Giresse .. .. 3·75 95

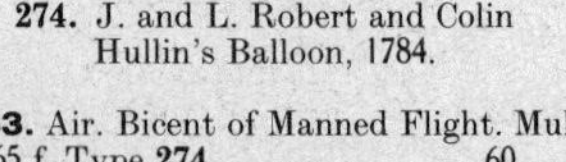

**273.** " Entombment ".

**1983.** Easter. Paintings by Rembrandt. Multicoloured.

927. 100 f. Type **273** .. .. 75 35
928. 300 f. " Christ on the Cross " .. .. 2·25 1·10
929. 400 f. " Descent from the Cross " .. .. .. 3·00 1·50

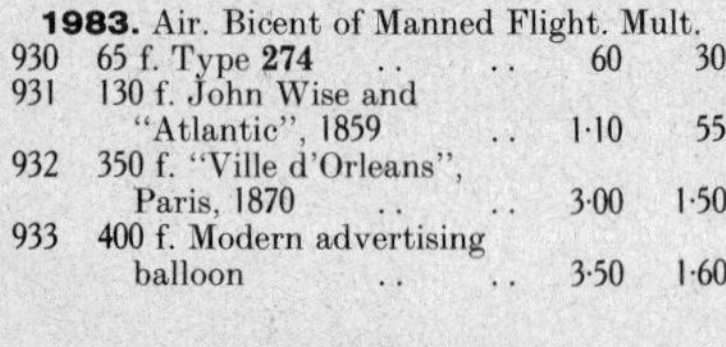

**274.** J. and L. Robert and Colin Hullin's Balloon, 1784.

**1983.** Air. Bicent of Manned Flight. Mult.

930 65 f. Type **274** .. .. 60 30
931 130 f. John Wise and "Atlantic", 1859 .. 1·10 55
932 350 f. "Ville d'Orleans", Paris, 1870 .. .. 3·00 1·50
933 400 f. Modern advertising balloon .. .. 3·50 1·60

**275.** Emile Levassor, Rene Panhard and Panhard-Levassor Car, 1895.

**276.** I.M.O. Emblem.

**1983.** Car Manufacturers. Multicoloured.

935. 10 f. Type **275** (postage) .. 10 10
936. 20 f. Henry Ford and first Ford car, 1896 .. 15 10
937. 30 f. Louis Renault and first Renault car, 1899 .. 20 15
938. 80 f. Ettore Bugatti and Bugatti " Type 37 ", 1925 .. .. 70 25
939. 400 f. Enzo Ferrari and Ferrari " 815 Sport ", 1940 (air) 3·25 85
940. 500 f. Ferdinand Porsche and Porsche " 356 Coupe ", 1951 .. .. .. 3·75 1·00

**1983.** 25th Anniv. of International Maritime Organization.

942. **276.** 40 f. bl., lt. bl. & turq. 35 15
943. 100 f. multicoloured .. 85 35

**277.** Gymnastics.

**1983.** Olympic Games, Los Angeles. Mult.

944. 5 f. Type **277** (postage) .. 15 15
945. 40 f. Javelin .. .. 25 15
946. 60 f. High jump .. .. 45 20
947. 120 f. Fencing .. .. 95 25
948. 200 f. Cycling (air) .. 1·50 35
949. 300 f. Sailing .. .. 2·25 60

**278.** W.C.Y. Emblem and Satellite.

**1983.** World Communications Year. Mult.

951. 50 f. Type **278** .. .. 40 20
952. 130 f. W.C.Y. emblem and satellite (different) .. 1·00 45

**279.** Horse Jumping.

**1983.** Air. Pre-Olympic Year. Multicoloured.

953. 100 f. Type **279** .. .. 80 40
954. 200 f. Dressage .. .. 80 65
955. 300 f. Jumping double jump 2·50 75
956. 400 f. Trotting .. .. 3·00 1·00

**280.** Andre Kolingba.

**281.** Antenna, Bangui M'Poko Earth Station.

**1983.** 2nd Anniv. of Military Committee for National Recovery.

958. **280.** 65 f. multicoloured .. 55 20
959. 130 f. multicoloured .. 1·10 40

**1983.** Bangui M'Poko Earth Station.

960. **281.** 130 f. multicoloured .. 1·10 50

**282.** Flower and Broken Chain on Map of Africa.

**1983.** Namibia Day.

961. **282.** 100 f. grn., lt. grn. & red 75 35
962. 200 f. multicoloured .. 1·50 75

**283.** J. Montgolfier and Balloon.

**1983.** Bicent of Manned Flight. Mult.

963 50 f. Type **283** (postage) .. 35 15
964 100 f. J. Blanchard and Channel crossing, 1785 .. 75 35
965 200 f. Joseph Gay-Lussac and ascent to 4000 metres, 1804 .. .. 1·60 65
966 300 f. Henri Giffard and steam-powered dirigible airship, 1852 .. .. 2·25 1·00
967 400 f. Santos-Dumont and airship "Ballon No. 6", Paris, 1901 (air) .. 3·00 1·25
968 500 f. A. Laquot and captive observation balloon, 1914 .. .. 3·75 1·50

**284.** "Global Communications".

**1983.** World Communications Year. U.P.U. Day.

970. **284.** 205 f. multicoloured .. 1·75 90

**285.** Black Rhinoceros.

**1983.** Endangered Animals. Multicoloured.

971. 10 f. Type **285** (postage) .. 10 10
972. 40 f. Two rhinoceros .. 65 20
973. 70 f. Black rhinoceros (different) .. .. .. 75 20
974. 180 f. Black rhinoceros and young .. .. .. 3·50 1·25
975. 400 f. Rangers attending sick rhinoceros (air) .. 7·50 3·25
976. 500 f. Wild animals and flag .. .. .. 8·50 3·75

**286.** Handicapped Person and Old Man.

**1983.** National Day of the Handicapped and Old.

978. **286.** 65 f. orange and mauve 50 25
979. 130 f. orange and blue 1·00 50
980. 250 f. orange and green 1·50 75

**287.** Fish Pond.

**1983.** Fishery Resources. Multicoloured.

981. 25 f. Type **287** .. .. 10 10
982. 65 f. Net fishing .. .. 45 25
983. 100 f. Traditional fishing .. 80 35
984. 130 f. Fish on plate .. 1·10 45
985. 205 f. Weir basket .. .. 1·60 70

**288.** "The Annunciation" (Leonardo da Vinci).

**1984.** Air. Christmas. Multicoloured.

986. 130 f. Type **288** .. .. 95 25
987. 205 f. "The Virgin of the Rocks" (Leonardo da Vinci) .. .. 1·60 45
988. 350 f. "Adoration of the Shepherds" (Rubens) .. 2·50 80
989. 500 f. "A. Goubeau before the Virgin" (Rubens) .. 3·75 1·00

**289.** Bush Fire.

**1984.** Nature Protection. Multicoloured.

990. 30 f. Type **289** .. .. 75 25
991. 130 f. Soldiers protecting wildlife from hunters .. 1·10 70

**290.** Goethe and Scene from "Faust".

**1984.** Celebrities. Multicoloured.

992. 50 f. Type **290** (postage) .. 40 15
993. 100 f. Henri Dunant and battle scene .. .. 75 35
994. 200 f. Alfred Nobel .. 1·60 55
995. 300 f. Lord Baden-Powell and scout camp .. .. 2·25 90
996. 400 f. President Kennedy and first foot-print on Moon (air) .. .. 3·00 90
997. 500 f. Prince and Princess of Wales .. .. .. 3·75 1·00

**291.** Fixed Bar.

**1984.** Air. Olympic Games, Los Angeles. Gymnastics. Multicoloured.

999. 65 f. Type **291** .. .. 50 20
1000. 100 f. Parallel bars .. 85 25
1001. 130 f. Ribbon (horiz.) .. 1·10 30
1002. 205 f. Cord .. .. 1·90 45
1003. 350 f. Hoop .. .. 3·00 85

**292.** "Madonna and Child" (Raphael).

**1984.** Paintings. Multicoloured.

1005. 50 f. Type **292** (postage) 35 15
1006. 100 f. "The Madonna of the Pear" (Durer) .. 75 20
1007. 200 f. "Aldobrandini Madonna" (Raphael) 1·60 35
1008. 300 f. "Madonna of the Pink" (Durer) 2·25 70
1009. 400 f. "Virgin and Child" (Correggio) (air) .. 3·00 1·50
1010. 500 f. "The Bohemian" (Modigliani) .. 3·75 2·10

**293.** "Le Pericles" (mail ship).

**1984.** Transport. Multicoloured. (a) Ships.

1012 65 f. Type **293** .. .. 50 25
1013 120 f. "Pereire" (steamer) 90 50
1014 250 f. "Admella" (passenger steamer) .. 1·75 85
1015 400 f. "Royal William" (paddle-steamer) .. 3·00 1·50
1016 500 f. "Great Britain" (steam/sail) .. .. 3·75 2·10

(b) Locomotives.

1017. 110 f. "CC–1500 ch" .. 75 35
1018. 240 f. "PLM Series 210", 1968 .. .. .. 1·75 80
1019. 350 f. "231–726" 1937 .. 2·50 1·10
1020. 440 f. "Pacific S3/6" 1908 3·50 1·50
1021. 500 f. Henschel "151 Series 45" 1937 .. 3·75 1·75

Nos. 1017/21 each include an inset portrait of George Stephenson in the design.

**294.** Forest.

**295.** Weighing Baby and Emblem.

**1984.** Forest Resources. Multicoloured.
1022. 70 f. Type **294** .. .. 65 25
1023. 130 f. Log cabin and timber .. .. .. 1·25 50

**1984.** Infant Survival Campaign. Mult.
1024. 10 f. Type **295** .. .. 15 10
1025. 30 f. Vaccinating baby .. 30 25
1026. 65 f. Feeding dehydrated baby .. .. .. 50 30
1027. 100 f. Mother, healthy baby and foodstuffs .. 95 50

**296.** Bangui-Kette Conical Trap.

**1984.** Fish Traps. Multicoloured.
1028 50 f. Type **296** .. .. 60 30
1029 80 f. Mbres fish trap .. 85 50
1030 150 f. Bangui-Kette round fish trap .. .. 1·60 50

**297.** Galileo and "Ariane" Rocket.

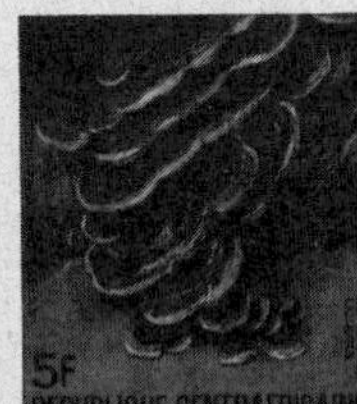

**298.** "Leptoporus lignosus".

**1984.** Space Technology. Multicoloured.
1031 20 f. Type **297** (postage) 15 10
1032 70 f. Auguste Piccard and stratosphere balloon "F.N.R.S." .. .. 50 20
1033 150 f. Hermann Oberth and satellite .. .. 1·10 45
1034 205 f. Albert Einstein and "Giotto" satellite .. 1·50 55
1035 300 f. Marie Curie and "Viking I" and "II" (air) .. .. .. 2·50 65
1036 500 f. Dr. U. Merbold and "Navette" space laboratory .. .. 3·75 95

**1984.** Fungi. Multicoloured.
1038. 5 f. Type **298** (postage) .. 10 10
1039. 10 f. "Phlebopus sudanicus" .. .. 20 10
1040. 40 f. "Termitomyces letestui" .. .. 45 20
1041. 130 f. "Lepiota esculenta" .. .. 1·25 60
1042. 300 f. "Termitomyces aurantiacus" (air) .. 3·25 1·40
1043. 500 f. "Termitomyces robustus" .. .. 5·75 2·25

**299.** Hibiscus.

**300.** G. Boucher (speed skating).

**1984.** Flowers. Multicoloured.
1045. 65 f. Type **299** .. .. 60 35
1046. 130 f. Canna .. .. 1·10 50
1047. 205. f. Water hyacinth .. 1·75 85

**1984.** Winter Olympic Gold Medallists. Multicoloured.
1048. 30 f. Type **300** (postage) 20 15
1049. 90 f. W. Hoppe, R. Wetzig, D. Schauerhammer and A. Kirchner (bobsleigh) .. 70 25
1050. 140 f. P. Magoni (ladies' slalom) .. .. 1·10 35
1051. 200 f. J. Torvill and C. Dean (ice skating) .. 1·50 50
1052. 400 f. M. Nykanen (90 metre ski jump) (air) 3·00 90
1053. 400 f. Russia (ice hockey) 3·75 1·00

**301.** Workers sowing Cotton Seeds.

**1984.** Economic Campaign. Multicoloured.
1055. 25 f. Type **301** .. .. 25 20
1056. 40 f. Selling cotton .. 45 30
1057. 130 f. Cotton market .. 1·25 50

**302.** Woman picking corn.

**1984.** World Food Day.
1058. **302.** 205 f. multicoloured 1·75 85

**303.** Abraham Lincoln.

**1984.** Celebrities. Multicoloured.
1059. 50 f. Type **303** (postage) 45 15
1060. 90 f. Auguste Piccard (undersea explorer) .. 80 30
1061. 120 f. Gottlieb Daimler (automobile designer) 1·25 35
1062. 200 f. Louis Blériot (pilot) .. .. .. 1·90 55
1063. 350 f. A. Karpov (chess champion) (air) .. 3·00 75
1064. 400 f. Henri Dunant (founder of Red Cross) 3·00 85

**304.** Profile, Water and Emblem.

**1984.** Bangui Rotary Club and Water.
1066. **304.** 130 f. multicoloured 1·25 35
1067. 205 f. multicoloured 1·90 60

**305.** United States (4 × 400 metres relay).

**1985.** Air Olympic Games Gold Medallists. Multicoloured.
1068. 60 f. Type **305** .. .. 45 20
1069. 140 f. E. Moses (400 metres hurdles) .. 1·10 30
1070. 300 f. S. Aouita (5,000 metres) .. .. 2·50 75
1071. 440 f. D. Thompson (decathlon) .. .. 3·50 1·00

**306.** "Virgin and Infant Jesus" (Titian).

**1985.** Air. Christmas (1984). Multicoloured.
1073. 130 f. Type **306** .. .. 95 45
1074. 350 f. "Virgin with Rabbit" (Titian) .. 2·50 1·10
1075. 400 f. "Virgin and Child" (Titian) .. .. 3·00 1·25

**307.** Screech Owls.

**1985.** Air. Birth Bicent. of John J. Audubon (ornithologist). (1st issue). Multicoloured.
1076. 60 f. Type **307** .. .. 90 60
1077. 110 f. Mangrove cuckoo (vert.) .. .. .. 1·40 95
1078. 200 f. Mourning doves (vert.) .. .. .. 2·50 1·60
1079. 500 f. Wood ducks .. 6·25 4·00
See also Nos. 1099/1104.

**1985.** International Exhibitions. Nos. 1014/15 and 1019/20 overprinted as listed below.
1083. 250 f. multicoloured .. 1·90 95
1084. 350 f. multicoloured .. 2·50 1·60
1085. 400 f. multicoloured .. 3·75 1·90
1086. 440 f. multicoloured .. 3·75 1·90
Overprints: 250 f. **ARGENTINA '85 BUENOS AIRES** and emblem. 350 f. **TSUKUBA EXPO '85** 400 f. **Italia '85 ROME** and emblem. 440 f. **MOPHILA '85 HAMBOURG.**

**310.** "Chelorrhina polyphemus".

**312.** Blue Jay.

**311.** Olympic Games Poster and Stockholm.

**1985.** Beetles. Multicoloured.
1088. 15 f. Type **310** .. .. 20 15
1089. 20 f. "Fornasinius russus" .. .. 25 15
1090. 25 f. "Goliathus giganteus" .. .. 30 15
1091. 65 f. "Goliathus meleagris" .. .. 80 50



**1985.** "Olymphilex '85" Olympic Stamps Exhibition, Lausanne. Multicoloured.
1092. 5 f. Type **311** (postage) .. 15 10
1093. 10 f. Olympic Games poster and Paris .. 20 15
1094. 20 f. Olympic Games poster and London .. 20 15
1095. 100 f. Olympic Games poster and Tokyo .. 75 25
1096. 400 f. Olympic Games poster and Mexico (air) 3·25 85
1097. 500 f. Olympic Games poster and Munich .. 3·75 1·00

**1985.** Birth Bicent. of John J. Audubon (ornithologist). (2nd issue). Multicoloured.
1099. 40 f. Type **312** (postage) 45 25
1100. 80 f. Chuck Will's widow 85 55
1101. 130 f. Ivory-billed woodpecker .. .. .. 1·10 80
1102. 250 f. Collie's magpie-jay .. .. 2·50 1·75
1103. 300 f. Mangrove cuckoo (horiz.) (air) .. 2·75 1·90
1104. 500 f. Barn swallow (horiz.) .. .. 5·50 3·75

**313.** Delivering Post by Van.

**1985.** "Philexafrique" Stamp Exhibition, Lome, Togo (1st issue). Multicoloured.
1106. 200 f. Type **313** .. .. 1·90 1·00
1107. 200 f. Scouts and flag .. 1·90 1·00
See also Nos. 1154/5.

**314.** Tiger and Rudyard Kipling.

**1985.** International Youth Year (1st issue). Multicoloured.
1108. 100 f. Type **314** .. .. 1·00 30
1109. 200 f. Men on horseback and Joseph Kessel .. 1·90 55
1110. 300 f. Submarine gripped by octopus and Jules Verne .. .. .. 2·25 1·10
1111. 400 f. Mississippi sternwheeler, Huckleberry Finn and Mark Twain 3·00 1·75
See also Nos. 1163/68.

**315.** Louis Pasteur.

**1985.** Anniversaries. Multicoloured.
1112. 150 f. Type **315** (centenary of discovery of anti-rabies vaccine) (postage) .. .. 1·75 40
1113. 200 f. Henri Dunant (founder of Red Cross) and 125th anniv. of Battle of Solferino (horiz.) .. .. 1·90 50
1114. 300 f. Girl guides (75th anniv. of Girl Guide Movement) (air) .. 1·90 75
1115. 450 f. Queen Elizabeth, the Queen Mother (85th birthday) .. 3·25 1·25
1116. 500 f. Statue of Liberty (centenary) .. .. 3·75 1·50

**316.** Pele and Footballers.

**1985.** World Cup Football Championship, Mexico. Multicoloured.

1117. 5 f. Type **316** (postage) .. 10 10
1118. 10 f. Harald "Tony" Schumacher .. .. 15 10
1119. 20 f. Paolo Rossi .. 15 15
1120. 350 f. Kevin Keegan (wrongly inscr. "Kervin") .. .. 2·75 90
1121. 400 f. Michel Platini (air) 3·00 90
1122. 500 f. Karl Heinz Rummenigge .. .. 3·75 1·00

**317.** La Kotto Waterfalls.

**318.** Pope with Hand raised in Blessing.

**1985.**

1124. **317.** 65 f. multicoloured .. 60 25
1125. 90 f. multicoloured .. 75 30
1126. 130 f. multicoloured 1·10 50

**1985.** Papal Visit. Multicoloured.

1127. 65 f. Type **318** .. .. 55 25
1128. 130 f. Pope John Paul II in Communion robes .. 1·10 50

**319.** Soldier using Ox-drawn Plough.

**1985.** Economic Campaign. Multicoloured.

1129. 5 f. Type **319** .. .. 15 10
1130. 60 f. Soldier sowing cotton .. .. .. 35 20
1131. 130 f. Soldier sowing cotton (different) .. 1·00 35

**320.** As Young Girl with her Brother.

**1985.** 85th Birthday of Queen Elizabeth the Queen Mother. Multicoloured.

1132. 100 f. Type **320** (postage) 60 20
1133. 200 f. Queen Mary with Duke and Duchess of York .. .. .. 1·50 35
1134. 300 f. Duchess of York inspecting Irish Guards .. .. 2·25 70
1135. 350 f. Duke and Duchess of York with the young Princesses .. 2·50 80
1136. 400 f. In the Golden State Coach at Coronation of King George VI (air) 3·00 90
1137. 500 f. At the service for her Silver Wedding .. 3·75 1·00

**321.** Dr. Labusquiere and Map of Republic.

**1985.** 8th Death Anniv. of General Doctor Labusquiere. Multicoloured.

1139. **321.** 10 f. multicoloured .. 15 10
1140. 45 f. multicoloured .. 35 20
1141. 110 f. multicoloured 1·00 35

**322.** Mail Van delivering Parcels to Local Post Office.

**1985.** Postal Service. Multicoloured.

1142. 15 f. Type **322** .. .. 15 10
1143. 60 f. Van collecting mail from local post office 45 20
1144. 150 f. Vans at main post office .. .. .. 1·10 50

**323.** Gagarin, Korolev and Space Station Complex.

**1985.** Space Research. Multicoloured.

1145. 40 f. Type **323** (postage) 20 10
1146. 110 f. Copernicus and "Cassini" space probe 75 25
1147. 240 f. Galileo and "Viking" orbiter .. 1·75 50
1148. 300 f. T. von Karman and astronaut recovering satellite .. .. 2·25 70
1149. 450 f. Percival Lowell and "Viking" space probe (air) .. .. 3·50 90
1150. 500 f. Dr. U. Merbold and "Columbus" space station .. .. .. 3·75 1·00

**324.** Damara Solar Energy Plant.

**1985.**

1152. **324.** 65 f. multicoloured .. 55 25
1153. 130 f. multicoloured 1·10 50

**325.** Ouaka Sugar Refinery.

**1985.** "Philexafrique" Stamp Exhibition, Lome, Togo (2nd issue). Multicoloured.

1154. 250 f. Nature studies .. 3·25 1·60
1155. 250 f. Type **325** .. .. 2·10 1·40

**326.** Pres. Mitterrand, Gen. Kolingba and Flags.

**1985.** Visit of President Mitterrand of France.

1156. **326.** 65 f. multicoloured .. 50 20
1157. 130 f. multicoloured 1·00 45
1158. 160 f. multicoloured 1·40 60

**327.** Map and U.N. Emblem. **328.** "Virgin and Angels" (Master of Burgo de Osma).

**1985.** 40th Anniv. of U.N.O. and 25th Anniv. of Central African Republic Membership.

1159. **327.** 140 f. multicoloured 1·10 50

**1985.** Air. Christmas. Multicoloured.

1160. 100 f. Type **328** .. .. 80 25
1161. 200 f. "Nativity" (Louis Le Nain) .. .. 1·75 1·00
1162. 400 f. "Virgin and Child with Dove (Piero di Cosimo) .. .. 3·25 1·00

**329.** Leonardo da Vinci and "Madonna of the Eyelet".

**1985.** International Youth Year (2nd issue). Multicoloured.

1163. 40 f. Type **329** (postage) 30 15
1164. 80 f. Johann Sebastian Bach .. .. .. 75 20
1165. 100 f. Diego Velasquez and "St. John of Patmos" .. .. 1·00 20
1166. 250 f. Franz Schubert and illustration of "King of Aulnes" .. 2·00 50
1167. 400 f. Francisco Goya and "Vicente Osario de Moscoso" (air) .. 3·50 90
1168. 500 f. Wolfgang Amadeus Mozart .. .. .. 4·00 1·00

**330.** Halley and "Comet".

**1985.** Appearance of Halley's Comet (1st issue). Multicoloured.

1170. 100 f. Type **330** (postage) 60 20
1171. 200 f. Newton's telescope 1·50 35
1172. 300 f. Halley and Newton observing comet .. 2·25 45
1173. 350 f. American space probe and comet .. 2·50 80
1174. 400 f. Sun, Russian space probe and diagram of comet trajectory (air) 3·00 90
1175. 500 f. Infra-red picture of comet .. .. .. 3·75 1·00

See also Nos. 1184/8.

**331.** Columbus with Globe.

**1986.** 480th Death Anniv. of Christopher Columbus (explorer). Multicoloured.

1177. 90 f. Type **331** (postage) 70 20
1178. 110 f. Receiving blessing 85 25
1179. 240 f. Crew going ashore in rowing boat .. 2·00 1·25
1180. 300 f. Columbus with American Indians .. 2·50 60
1181. 400 f. Ships at sea in storm (air) .. .. 3·50 2·00
1182. 500 f. Sun breaking through clouds over fleet .. .. .. 4·00 2·25

**332.** Halley and Comet.

**1986.** Air. Appearance of Halley's Comet (2nd issue). Multicoloured.

1184 110 f. Type **332** .. .. 80 25
1185 130 f. "Giotto" space probe .. .. .. 1·00 25
1186 200 f. Comet and globe .. 1·50 45
1187 300 f. "Vega" space probe 2·25 60
1188 400 f. Space shuttle .. 3·25 95

**1986.** Nos. 874/5 surch.

1188a – 30 f. on 175 f. mult
1188b **259** 65 f. on 300 f. mult

**333.** Spiky Hair Style.

**334.** Communications.

**1986.** Traditional Hair Styles. Multicoloured.

1189. 20 f. Type **333** .. .. 20 10
1190. 30 f. Braids around head 25 15
1191. 65 f. Plaits .. .. 30 25
1192. 160 f. Braids from front to back of head .. 1·50 50

**1986.** Franco-Central African Week. Mult.

1193. 40 f. Type **334** .. .. 30 15
1194. 60 f. Youth .. .. 50 20
1195. 100 f. Basket weaver (craft) .. .. .. 75 30
1196. 130 f. Cyclists (sport) .. 1·25 50

**335.** "Allamanda neriifolia".

**1986.** Flora and Fauna. Multicoloured.

1197. 25 f. Type **335** (postage) 20 15
1198. 65 f. Bongo (horiz.) .. 50 20
1199. 160 f. "Plumieria acuminata" .. .. 1·10 40
1200. 300 f. Cheetah (horiz.) .. 2·25 1·00
1201. 400 f. "Eulophia erthoplata" (air) .. 2·75 90
1202. 500 f. Leopard (horiz.) .. 3·75 1·75

**336.** Palm Tree and Bossongo Oil Refinery.

**1986.** Centrapalm. Multicoloured.

1204. 25 f. Type **336** .. .. 20 15
1205. 65 f. Type **336** .. .. 50 30
1206. 120 f. Palm tree and Bossongo agro-industrial complex .. 85 60
1207. 160 f. As No. 1206 .. 1·25 50

**337.** Pointer.

**1986.** Dogs and Cats. Multicoloured.

1208. 10 f. Type **337** (postage) 15 10
1209. 20 f. Egyptian mau .. 25 15
1210. 200 f. Newfoundland .. 1·75 50
1211. 300 f. Borzoi (air) .. 2·50 60
1212. 400 f. Persian red .. 3·50 80

**338.** Map of Africa showing Member Countries.

**1986.** 25th Anniv. of African and Malagasy Coffee Producers Organization.

1214. **338.** 160 f. multicoloured 1·40 60

**339.** Trophy, Brazilian flag, L.-A. Muller and Socrates.

**1986.** World Cup Football Championships, Mexico. Multicoloured.

1215. 30 f. Type **339** (postage) 20 15
1216. 110 f. Trophy, Belgian flag, V. Scifo and F. Ceulemans .. .. 70 20
1217. 160 f. Trophy, French flag, Y. Stopyra and M. Platini .. .. 1·00 25
1218. 350 f. Trophy, West German flag, A. Brehme and H. Schumacher .. .. 2·50 70
1219. 450 f. Trophy, Argentinian flag and Diego Maradona (air) .. 3·00 1·00

**340.** Judith Resnik and Astronaut.

**341.** People around Globe within Emblem.

**1986.** Anniversaries and "Challenger" Astronauts Commemoration. Multicoloured.

1221. 15 f. Type **340** (postage) 15 10
1222. 25 f. Frederic Bartholdi and torch (centenary of Statue of Liberty) 25 15
1223. 70 f. Elvis Presley (ninth death anniv.) .. .. 95 20
1224. 300 f. Ronald MacNair and man watching astronaut on screen .. 2·10 65
1225. 485 f. on 70 f. No. 1223 .. 5·25 1·00
1226. 450 f. Christa McAulife and Shuttle lifting off (air) .. .. 3·25 1·10

**1986.** International Peace Year.

1228. **341.** 160 f. multicoloured 1·40 65

**342.** Globe, Douglas DC-10 and "25".

**343.** Emblem and Flag as Map.

**1986.** 25th Anniv. of Air Afrique.

1229. **342.** 200 f. multicoloured 1·50 85

**1986.** U.N.I.C.E.F. Child Survival Campaign. Multicoloured.

1230. 15 f. Type **343** .. .. 15 10
1231. 130 f. Doctor vaccinating child .. .. .. 1·10 50
1232. 160 f. Basket of fruit and boy holding fish on map .. .. .. 1·25 65

**344.** "Nativity" (detail, Giotto).

**1986.** Air. Christmas. Multicoloured.

1233. 250 f. Type **344** .. .. 1·90 60
1234. 440 f. "Adoration of the Magi" (detail, Sandro Botticelli) (vert.) .. 3·25 1·10
1235. 500 f. "Nativity" (detail, Giotto) (different) .. 4·00 1·10

**345.** Transmission Mast, People with Radios and Baskets of Produce.

**1986.** African Telecommunications Day. Telecommunications and Agriculture. Mult.

1236. 170 f. Type **345** (Rural Radio Agriculture Project) .. .. 1·40 75
1237. 265 f. Lorry, satellite, men using telephones and sacks of produce 2·10 1·10

**346.** Steam Locomotive DH 2 "Green Elephant" and Alfred de Glehn.

**1986.** 150th Anniv. of German Railways. Multicoloured.

1238. 40 f. Type **346** (postage) 35 15
1239. 70 f. Rudolf Diesel (engineer) and steam locomotive No. 1829 Rheingold", series "S 3/6" .. .. .. 55 25
1240. 160 f. Electric locomotive type "103" "Rapide" and Carl Golsdorf .. 1·25 50
1241. 300 f. Wilhelm Schmidt and Beyer–Garratt steam locomotive .. 2·25 1·10
1242. 400 f. De Bousquet and compound locomotive, series "3500" (air) .. 3·25 1·40

**347.** Player returning Ball.

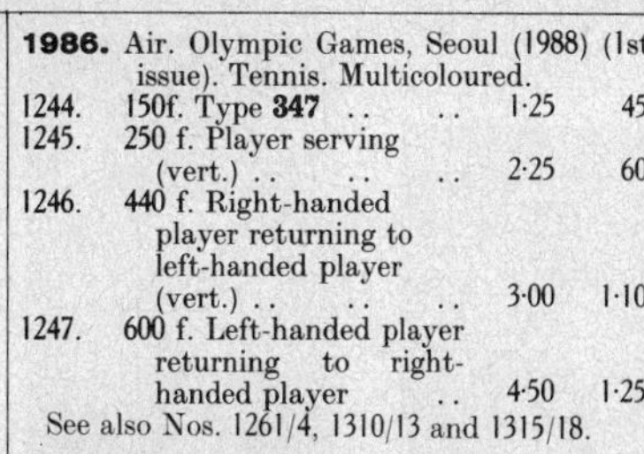

**1986.** Air. Olympic Games, Seoul (1988) (1st issue). Tennis. Multicoloured.

1244. 150f. Type **347** .. .. 1·25 45
1245. 250 f. Player serving (vert.) .. .. .. 2·25 60
1246. 440 f. Right-handed player returning to left-handed player (vert.) .. .. .. 3·00 1·10
1247. 600 f. Left-handed player returning to right-handed player .. 4·50 1·25

See also Nos. 1261/4, 1310/13 and 1315/18.

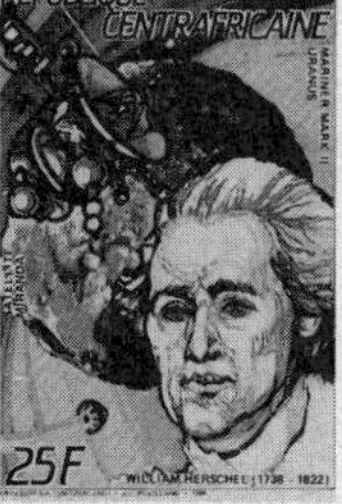


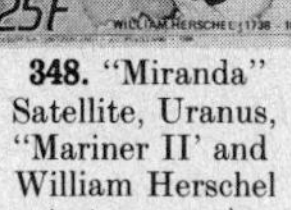

**348.** "Miranda" Satellite, Uranus, "Mariner II" and William Herschel (astronomer).

**349.** Footballer and "Woman with Umbrella" Fountain.

**1987.** Space Research. Multicoloured.

1248. 25 f. Type **348** (postage) 20 15
1249. 65 f. Mars Rover vehicle and Werner von Braun (rocket pioneer) .. 45 20
1250. 160 f. "Mariner II", Titan and Rudolf Hanel .. .. .. 1·25 35
1251. 300 f. Space ship "Hermes", space platform "Eureka" and Patrick Baudry .. 2·25 70
1252. 400 f. Halley's Comet, "Giotto" space probe and Dr. U. Keller (air) 2·75 85
1253. 500 f. European space station "Columbus", Wubbo Ockels and Ulf Merbold .. .. 3·25 1·00

**1987.** Olympic Games, Barcelona (1992). Multicoloured.

1255. 30 f. Type **349** (postage) 25 15
1256. 150 f. Judo competitors and Barcelona Cathedral .. .. 1·00 40
1257. 265 f. Cyclist and Church of the Holy Family .. 1·90 65
1258. 350 f. Diver and Christopher Columbus's tomb (air) 2·50 85
1259. 495 f. Runner and human tower .. .. 3·75 1·10

**350.** Triple Jumping.

**1987.** Air. Olympic Games, Seoul (1988) (2nd issue). Multicoloured.

1261. 100 f. Type **350** .. .. 75 25
1262. 200 f. Highjumping (horiz.) .. .. 1·50 50
1263. 300 f. Long jumping (horiz.) .. .. 2·25 75
1264. 400 f. Pole vaulting .. 3·00 1·00

**351.** Two-man Luge.

**352.** Peace Medal.

**1987.** Winter Olympic Games, Calgary (1988) (1st issue). Multicoloured.

1266. 20 f. Type **351** .. .. 20 15
1267. 140 f. Cross-country skiing .. .. .. 1·10 40
1268. 250 f. Figure skating .. 1·90 65
1269. 300 f. Ice hockey (air) .. 2·25 75
1270. 400 f. Slalom .. .. 2·75 1·00

See also Nos. 1320/3.

**1987.** International Peace Year (1986).

1272. **352.** 50 f. brown, blue and black .. .. 35 25
1273. 160 f. brown, green and black .. .. 1·25 65

**1987.** 10th Death Anniv of Elvis Presley (singer). Nos. 1223 and 1225 optd **Elvis Presley 1977–1987**.

1274 70 f. multicoloured .. 65 20
1275 485 f. on 70 f. mult .. 4·25 1·10

**354** Woman at Village Pump

**1987.** International Decade of Drinkable Water. Multicoloured.

1276 5 f. Type **354** .. ..
1277 10 f. Woman at village pump (different) ..
1278 200 f. Three women at village pump .. ..

**355** "Charaxes candiope"

**1987.** Butterflies. Multicoloured.

1279 100 f. Type **355** .. .. 75 55
1280 120 f. "Graphium leonidas" .. .. 95 60
1281 130 f. "Charaxes brutus" 1·10 60
1282 160 f. "Salamis aetiops" 1·25 70

**356** Nola Football Team

**1987.** Campaign for Integration of Pygmies.

1283 **356** 90 f. multicoloured .. 1·10 75
1284 160 f. multicoloured 1·75 1·10

**357** James Madison (U.S. President, 1809-17)

**1987.** Anniversaries and Celebrities. Mult.

1285 40 f. Type **357** (bicent of U.S. constitution) (post) 30 15
1286 160 f. Queen Elizabeth II and Prince Philip (40th wedding anniv) .. 1·25 25
1287 200 f. Steffi Graf (tennis player) .. .. 1·60 45
1288 300 f. Gary Kasparov (chess champion) and "The Chess Players" (after Honore Daumier) (air) 2·50 75
1289 400 f. Boris Becker (tennis player) .. .. 3·00 1·00

**358** Brontosaurus

**1988.** Prehistoric Animals. Multicoloured.

| No. | Description | Unused | Used |
|---|---|---|---|
| 1291 | 50 f. Type **358** | 35 | 15 |
| 1292 | 65 f. Triceratops | 50 | 15 |
| 1293 | 100 f. Ankylosaurus | 75 | 25 |
| 1294 | 160 f. Stegosaurus | 1·25 | 45 |
| 1295 | 200 f. Tyrannosaurus rex | 1·50 | 50 |
| 1296 | 240 f. Corythosaurus | 1·90 | 65 |
| 1297 | 300 f. Allosaurus | 2·25 | 75 |
| 1298 | 350 f. Brachiosaurus | 2·75 | 95 |

Nos. 1295/8 are vert.

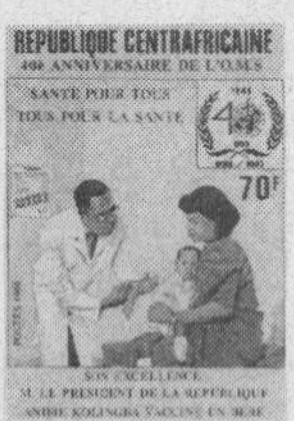

**359** Pres. Kolingba vaccinating Baby

**360** Carmine Bee Eater

**1988.** 40th Anniv of W.H.O.

| No. | Description | Unused | Used |
|---|---|---|---|
| 1299 | **359** 70 f. multicoloured | 60 | 40 |
| 1300 | 120 f. multicoloured | 1·60 | 45 |

**1988.** Scouts and Birds. Multicoloured.

| No. | Description | Unused | Used |
|---|---|---|---|
| 1301 | 25 f. Type **360** (postage) | 15 | 10 |
| 1302 | 170 f. Red-crowned bishop | 1·10 | 80 |
| 1303 | 300 f. Lesser pied king-fisher | 2·40 | 1·75 |
| 1304 | 400 f. Red-cheeked cordonbleu (air) | 2·75 | 2·40 |
| 1305 | 450 f. Lizard buzzard | 3·50 | 2·75 |

**361** Schools replanting Campaign

**1988.** National Tree Day. Multicoloured.

| No. | Description | Unused | Used |
|---|---|---|---|
| 1307 | 50 f. Type **361** | 35 | 25 |
| 1308 | 100 f. Type **361** | 75 | 50 |
| 1309 | 130 f. Felling tree and planting saplings | 1·10 | 60 |

**362** 1972 100 f. Stamp and Beam Exercise

**1988.** Air. Olympic Games, Seoul (3rd issue). Gymnastics. Multicooured.

| No. | Description | Unused | Used |
|---|---|---|---|
| 1310 | 90 f. Type **362** | 75 | 25 |
| 1311 | 200 f. 1964 50 f. stamp and beam exercise (horiz) | 1·50 | 35 |
| 1312 | 300 f. 1964 100 f. stamp and vault exercise (horiz) | 2·25 | 75 |
| 1313 | 400 f. 1964 250 f. stamp and parallel bars exercise (horiz) | 3·00 | 1·10 |

**363** Running

**364** Cross-country Skiing

**1988.** Olympic Games, Seoul (4th issue). Mult.

| No. | Description | Unused | Used |
|---|---|---|---|
| 1315 | 150 f. Type **363** (postage) | 1·10 | 25 |
| 1316 | 300 f. Judo | 2·25 | 60 |
| 1317 | 400 f. Football (air) | 2·75 | 85 |
| 1318 | 450 f. Tennis | 3·00 | 1·00 |

**1988.** Winter Olympic Games, Calgary (2nd issue). Multicoloured.

| No. | Description | Unused | Used |
|---|---|---|---|
| 1320 | 170 f. Type **364** (postage) | 1·25 | 30 |
| 1321 | 350 f. Ice hockey | 2·25 | 60 |
| 1322 | 400 f. Downhill skiing (air) | 2·75 | 85 |
| 1323 | 450 f. Slalom | 3·00 | 1·00 |

**1988.** Nos. 1302/5 surch.

| No. | Description | Unused | Used |
|---|---|---|---|
| 1325 | 30 f. on 170 f. mult (post) | 40 | 20 |
| 1326 | 70 f. on 300 f. mult | 1·25 | 65 |
| 1327 | 160 f. on 400 f. mult (air) | 2·50 | 1·40 |
| 1328 | 200 f. on 450 f. mult | 3·00 | 1·90 |

**366** Hospital and Grounds

**1988.** 1st Anniv of L'Amitie Hospital. Mult.

| No. | Description | Unused | Used |
|---|---|---|---|
| 1329 | 5 f. Type **366** | 15 | 10 |
| 1330 | 60 f. Aerial view of hospital complex | 50 | 35 |
| 1331 | 160 f. Hospital entrance | 1·25 | 75 |

**367** Buildings Complex

**1988.** 30th Anniv of Republic. Multicoloured.

| No. | Description | Unused | Used |
|---|---|---|---|
| 1332 | 65 f. Family on map, flags and dove | | |
| 1334 | 240 f. Type **367** | | |

**368** Kristine Otto (East Germany)

**369** Hebmuller and Volkswagen Cabriolet, 1953

**1989.** Olympic Games, Seoul, Gold Medal Winners. Multicoloured.

| No. | Description | Unused | Used |
|---|---|---|---|
| 1335 | 150 f. Type **368** (100 m. butterfly and 100 m. backstroke) (postage) | 1·00 | 35 |
| 1336 | 240 f. Matt Biondi (100 m. freestyle) | 1·50 | 50 |
| 1337 | 300 f. Florence Griffith-Joyner (U.S.A.) (100 and 200 m. sprints) | 1·90 | 75 |
| 1338 | 450 f. Pierre Durand (France) (show jumping) (air) | 3·00 | 1·10 |

**1989.** Transport. Multicoloured.

| No. | Description | Unused | Used |
|---|---|---|---|
| 1340 | 20 f. Type **369** (postage) | 20 | 15 |
| 1341 | 205 f. Werner von Siemens and "B" locomotive, 1879 | 1·75 | 50 |
| 1342 | 300 f. Dennis Conner and "Stars and Stripes" (winner of Americas Cup yacht races) | 2·25 | 65 |
| 1343 | 400 f. Andre Citroen and "16 Six" car, 1955 | 3·00 | 1·00 |
| 1344 | 450 f. Marc Seguin and Decauville-Mallet "020 + 020" locomotive, 1895 (air) | 3·25 | 1·10 |

**370** Allegory in Honour of Liberty

**1989.** Bicentenary of French Revolution and "Philexfrance 89" International Stamp Exhibition, Paris (1st issue). Multicoloured.

| No. | Description | Unused | Used |
|---|---|---|---|
| 1346 | 200 f. Type **370** | 1·75 | 60 |
| 1347 | 300 f. Declaration of Rights of Man | 2·50 | 1·25 |

See also Nos. 1366/9.

**REPUBLIQUE CENTRAFRICAINE**

**371** Statue of Liberty at Night

**1989.** Centenary of Statue of Liberty. Mult.

| No. | Description | Unused | Used |
|---|---|---|---|
| 1349 | 150 f. Type **371** | 1·10 | 60 |
| 1350 | 150 f. Maintenance worker | 1·10 | 60 |
| 1351 | 150 f. Close-up of face | 1·10 | 60 |
| 1352 | 200 f. Maintenance worker (different) | 1·40 | 95 |
| 1353 | 200 f. Colour party in front of statue | 1·40 | 95 |
| 1354 | 200 f. Close-up of head at night | 1·40 | 95 |

**373** "Apollo 11" Astronaut on Moon

**1989.** Air. 20th Anniv of First Manned Landing on Moon. Multicoloured.

| No. | Description | Unused | Used |
|---|---|---|---|
| 1355 | 40 f. Type **373** | 30 | 20 |
| 1356 | 80 f. "Apollo 15" astronaut and moon buggy | 55 | 25 |
| 1357 | 130 f. "Apollo 16" module landing in sea | 1·00 | 50 |
| 1358 | 1000 f. "Apollo 17" astronaut on Moon | 7·50 | 2·25 |

**374** Champagnat, Map and "Madonna and Child"

**1989.** Birth Bicentenary of Marcelino Champagnat (founder of Marist Brothers). Multicoloured.

| No. | Description | Unused | Used |
|---|---|---|---|
| 1359 | 15 f. Type **374** | 15 | 15 |
| 1360 | 50 f. Champagnat, cross, globe and emblem | 35 | 25 |
| 1361 | 160 f. Champagnat and flags (horiz) | 1·40 | 1·00 |

**375** Food Products

**1989.** Bambari Harvest Festival. Mult.

| No. | Description | Unused | Used |
|---|---|---|---|
| 1362 | 100 f. Type **375** | 80 | 50 |
| 1363 | 160 f. Ploughing with oxen | 1·25 | 60 |

**376** Raising of Livestock

**1989.** World Food Day. Multicoloured.

| No. | Description | Unused | Used |
|---|---|---|---|
| 1364 | 60 f. Type **376** | 50 | 35 |
| 1365 | 240 f. Soldiers catching poachers | 2·00 | 1·10 |

**377** Gen. Kellermann and Battle of Valmy

**1989.** Bicentenary of French Revolution and "Philexfrance 89" International Stamp Exhibition, Paris (2nd issue). Multicoloured.

| No. | Description | Unused | Used |
|---|---|---|---|
| 1366 | 160 f. Type **377** (postage) | 1·25 | 35 |
| 1367 | 200 f. Gen. Dumouriez and Battle of Jemappes (wrongly inscr "JEMMAPES") | 1·60 | 50 |
| 1368 | 500 f. Gen. Pichegru and capture of Dutch fleet (air) | 3·75 | 85 |
| 1369 | 600 f. Gen. Hoche and Royalist landing at Quiberon | 4·25 | 1·00 |

**378** Players and Trophy

**1989.** Victory in 1987 African Basketball Championships, Tunis (1st issue). Mult.

| No. | Description | Unused | Used |
|---|---|---|---|
| 1371 | 160 f. Type **378** | 1·25 | 60 |
| 1372 | 240 f. National team with medals and trophy (horiz) | 1·60 | 80 |
| 1373 | 500 f. Type **378** | 4·00 | 1·75 |

See also Nos. 1383/4.

**379** Governor's Palace, 1906

**1989.** Centenary of Bangui. Multicoloured.

1374 100 f. Type **379** .. .. 75 35
1375 160 f. Bangui post office 1·10 90
1376 200 f. A. Dosilie (founder of Bangui post office) (vert) .. .. .. 1·50 85
1377 1000 f. Michel Dolisie and Chief Gbembo agreeing peace pact (vert) .. 7·25 3·75

**380** Footballer and Palermo Cathedral Belltower

**381** Trophy and Map of Africa

**1989.** World Cup Football Championship, Italy (1990) (1st issue). Multicoloured.

1378 20 f. Type **380** (postage) 20 15
1379 160 f. Footballer and St. Francis's church, Bologna .. .. 1·10 35
1380 200 f. Footballer and Old Palace, Florence .. 1·50 50
1381 120 f. Footballer and Church of Trinita dei Monti, Rome (air) .. 90 35

See also Nos. 1405/8.

**1990.** Victory in 1987 African Basketball Championships, Tunis (2nd issue).

1383 **381** 100 f. multicoloured .. 80 35
1384 130 f. multicoloured .. 1·10 60

**382** Tree with Map as Foliage

**383** Speed Skating

**1990.** Inauguration (1989) of Forest Conservation Organization.

1385 **382** 160 f. multicoloured .. 1·40 65

**1990.** Winter Olympic Games, Albertville (1992). Multicoloured.

1386 10 f. Type **383** (postage) 15 15
1387 60 f. Cross-country skiing 45 25
1388 500 f. Slalom skiing (air) 3·75 95
1389 750 f. Ice dancing .. 5·50 1·25

**384** "Euphaera eusemoides"

**385** Throwing the Javelin

**1990.** Scouts and Butterflies. Multicoloured.

1391 25 f. Type **384** .. .. 20 15
1392 65 f. Becker's glider .. 45 15
1393 160 f. "Pseudacraea clarki" .. .. 1·10 25
1394 250 f. Giant charaxes 1·75 50
1395 300 f. "Euphaedra gausape" .. 2·25 60
1396 500 f. Red swallowtail .. 3·75 85

**1990.** Olympic Games, Barcelona (1992). Mult.

1398 10 f. Type **385** (postage) 15 15
1399 40 f. Running .. .. 35 15
1400 130 f. Tennis .. .. 95 25
1401 240 f. Hurdling (horiz) .. 1·75 50
1402 400 f. Yachting (horiz) (air) .. .. 3·00 85
1403 500 f. Football (horiz) .. 3·75 1·00

**386** Footballers and Globe

**1990.** Air. World Cup Football Championship, Italy (2nd issue).

1405 **386** 5 f. multicoloured .. 10 10
1406 – 30 f. multicoloured .. 20 15
1407 – 500 f. multicoloured .. 3·25 1·00
1408 – 1000 f. multicoloured 7·50 1·60

DESIGNS: 30 to 1000 f. Various footballing scenes.

**387** Pres. Gorbachev of U.S.S.R., Map of Malta and Pres. Bush of U.S.A.

**1990.** Anniversaries and Events. Mult.

1409 120 f. Type **387** (summit conference, Malta) (postage) .. .. 85 20
1410 130 f. Sir Rowland Hill and Penny Black (150th anniv of first postage stamps) .. .. 85 20
1411 160 f. Galileo space probe and planet Jupiter .. 1·10 25
1412 200 f. Pres. Gorbachev meeting Pope John Paul II, statue of Saturn and dove .. 1·50 35
1413 240 f. Neil Armstrong and eagle (21st anniv of first manned landing on Moon) .. .. .. 1·90 45
1414 250 f. Concorde, "Transrapid" (German train) and Rotary International emblem 1·90 50
1415 300 f. Don Mattingly (baseball player) and New York Yankees club badge (air) .. 2·25 60
1416 500 f. Charles de Gaulle (French statesman, birth centenary) .. 3·75 85

**388** AIDS Information on Radio, Television and Leaflets

**1991.** Anti-AIDS Campaign. Multicoloured.

1418 5 f. Type **388** .. .. 15 10
1419 70 f. Type **388** .. .. 55 35
1420 120 f. Lecture on AIDS (vert) .. .. .. 85 50

**389** Demonstrators

**1991.** Protection of Animals. Multicoloured.

1421 15 f. Type **389** .. .. 15 10
1422 60 f. Type **389** .. .. 50 25
1423 100 f. Decrease in elephant population, 1945–2045 (vert) .. .. .. 75 35

**HAVE YOU READ THE NOTES AT THE BEGINNING OF THIS CATALOGUE?**
These often provide answers to the enquiries we receive.

**390** Catfish

**1991.** Fishes. Multicoloured.

1424 50 f. Type **390** .. .. 35 25
1425 160 f. Type **390** .. .. 1·25 60
1426 240 f. "Distichodus" sp. 1·90 1·00

**391** President Kolingba

**1992.** 10th Anniv (1991) of Assumption of Power by Military Committee under Andre Kolingba.

1427 **391** 160 f. multicoloured .. 1·25 50

**392** Count Ferdinand von Zeppelin (airship pioneer)

**1992.** Celebrities, Anniversaries and Events. Multicoloured.

1428 80 f. Type **392** (75th death anniv) (postage) .. 40 10
1429 140 f. Henri Dunant (founder of Red Cross) 95 15
1430 160 f. Michael Schumacher (racing driver) .. 1·10 25
1431 350 f. Brandenburg Gate (bicent) and Konrad Adenauer (German Federal Republic Chancellor) signing 1949 constitution .. .. 2·50 75
1432 500 f. Pope John Paul II (tour of West Africa) (air) .. .. 3·50 90
1433 600 f. Wolfgang Amadeus Mozart (composer, death bicent (1991)) .. 4·50 1·00

**393** Dam

**395** Breastfeeding

**394** Compass Rose and Organization Emblem

**1993.** River M'Bali Dam. Multicoloured.

1435 160 f. Type **393** .. .. 80 15
1436 200 f. People fishing near dam (self-sufficiency in food) .. .. .. 1·00 25

**1993.** International Customs Day and 40th Anniv of Customs Co-operation Council.

1437 **394** 240 f. multicoloured .. 1·10 25

**1993.** International Nutrition Conference, Rome (1992). Multicoloured.

1438 90 f. Type **395** .. .. 40 10
1439 140 f. Foodstuffs .. 70 15

**396** Bangui University

**1993.**

1440 **396** 100 f. multicoloured .. 50 15

**397** Masako Owada as Baby

**1993.** Wedding of Crown Prince Naruhito of Japan and Masako Owada. Multicoloured.

1441 50 f. Type **397** (postage) 10 10
1442 65 f. Prince Naruhito as child with parents .. 25 10
1443 160 f. Masako Owada at Harvard University, U.S.A. .. .. 70 15
1444 450 f. Prince Naruhito at Oxford University (air) 1·75 50

**398** Presley singing "Heartbreak Hotel" (1956)

**1993.** 16th Death Anniv of Elvis Presley (entertainer). Multicoloured.

1446 200 f. Type **398** .. .. 75 15
1447 300 f. "Love Me Tender", 1957 .. .. .. 1·00 25
1448 400 f. "Jailhouse Rock", 1957 .. .. .. 1·25 30
1449 "Harum Scarum", 1965 (air) .. .. .. 2·00 50

**399** First World Cup Final, 1928, and Uruguay v Argentina, 1930

**1993.** World Cup Football Championship, U.S.A. (1994). History of the World Cup. Multicoloured.

1451 40 f. Type **399** .. .. 10 10
1452 50 f. Italy v Czechoslovakia, 1934, and Italy v Hungary, 1938 .. .. 10 10
1453 60 f. Uruguay v Brazil, 1950, and Germany v Hungary, 1954 .. 15 10
1454 80 f. Brazil v Sweden, 1958, and Brazil v Czechoslovakia, 1962 .. 20 10
1455 160 f. England v West Germany, 1966, and Brazil v Italy, 1970 .. 40 15
1456 200 f. West Germany v The Netherlands, 1974, and Argentina v The Netherlands, 1978 .. 55 20

1457 400 f. Italy v West Germany, 1982, and Argentina v West Germany, 1986 .. 1·00 35
1458 500 f. West Germany v Argentina, 1990, and 1994 Championship emblem and player .. 1·40 45

**400** Baron Pierre de Coubertin (founder of modern games)

**1993.** Centenary (1996) of Modern Olympic Games. Multicoloured.

| | | | |
|---|---|---|---|
| 1460 | 90 f. Ancient Greek athlete .. .. | 25 | 10 |
| 1461 | 90 f. Type **400** .. .. | 25 | 10 |
| 1462 | 90 f. Charles Bennett (running), Paris, 1900 .. | 25 | 10 |
| 1463 | 90 f. Etienne Desmarteau (stone throwing), St. Louis, 1904 .. .. | 25 | 10 |
| 1464 | 90 f. Harry Porter (high jump), London, 1908 .. | 25 | 10 |
| 1465 | 90 f. Patrick MacDonald (putting the shot), Stockholm, 1912 .. | 25 | 10 |
| 1466 | 90 f. Coloured and black Olympic rings (1916) .. | 25 | 10 |
| 1467 | 90 f. Frank Loomis (400 m. hurdles), Antwerp, 1920 .. | 25 | 10 |
| 1468 | 90 f. Albert White (diving), Paris, 1924 .. | 25 | 10 |
| 1469 | 100 f. El Ouafi (marathon), Amsterdam, 1928 .. | 25 | 10 |
| 1470 | 100 f. Eddie Tolan (100 m.), Los Angeles, 1932 .. .. .. | 25 | 10 |
| 1471 | 100 f. Jesse Owens (100 m., long jump and 200 m. hurdles), Berlin, 1936 .. | 25 | 10 |
| 1472 | 100 f. Coloured and black Olympic rings (1940) .. | 25 | 10 |
| 1473 | 100 f. Coloured and black Olympic rings (1944) .. | 25 | 10 |
| 1474 | 100 f. Tapio Rautavaara (throwing the javelin), London, 1948 .. .. | 25 | 10 |
| 1475 | 100 f. Jean Boiteux (400 m. freestyle swimming), Helsinki, 1952 .. .. .. | 25 | 10 |
| 1476 | 100 f. Petrus Kasterman (three-day equestrian event), Melbourne, 1956 | 25 | 10 |
| 1477 | 100 f. Sante Gaiardoni (cycling), Rome, 1960 .. | 25 | 10 |
| 1478 | 160 f. Anton Geesink (judo), Tokyo, 1964 .. | 40 | 15 |
| 1479 | 160 f. Bob Beamon (long jump), Mexico, 1968 .. | 40 | 15 |
| 1480 | 160 f. Mark Spitz (swimming), Munich, 1972 .. .. .. | 40 | 15 |
| 1481 | 160 f. Nadia Comaneci (gymnastics (beam)), Montreal, 1976 .. | 40 | 15 |
| 1482 | 160 f. Aleksandre Ditjatin (gymnastics (rings) and dressage), Moscow, 1980 | 40 | 15 |
| 1483 | 160 f. J. F. Lamour (sabre), Los Angeles, 1984 .. .. .. | 40 | 15 |
| 1484 | 160 f. Pierre Durand (show jumping), Seoul, 1988 .. .. .. | 40 | 15 |
| 1485 | 160 f. Michael Jordan (basketball), Barcelona, 1992 .. .. .. | 40 | 15 |
| 1486 | 160 f. Footballer and Games emblem, Atlanta, 1996 .. .. | 40 | 15 |

**401** Man planting Sapling, and Animals

**402** Woman selling Foodstuffs

**1993.** Biodiversity. Multicoloured.

| | | | |
|---|---|---|---|
| 1487 | 100 f. Type **401** .. | 25 | 10 |
| 1488 | 130 f. Man amongst flora and fauna (vert) .. | 35 | 15 |

**1993.** The Environment and Sustainable Development. Multicoloured.

| | | | |
|---|---|---|---|
| 1489 | 160 f. Type **402** .. | 40 | 15 |
| 1490 | 240 f. Woman tending cooking pot .. .. | 60 | 20 |

**403** Saltoposuchus

**1993.** Prehistoric Animals. Multicoloured.

| | | | |
|---|---|---|---|
| 1491 | 25 f. Type **403** .. .. | 10 | 10 |
| 1492 | 25 f. Rhamphorhynchus | 10 | 10 |
| 1493 | 25 f. Dimorphodon .. | 10 | 10 |
| 1494 | 25 f. Archaeopteryx .. | 10 | 10 |
| 1495 | 30 f. "Compsognathos longipes" .. .. | 10 | 10 |
| 1496 | 30 f. "Cryptocleidus oxoniensis" .. .. | 10 | 10 |
| 1497 | 30 f. Stegosaurus .. | 10 | 10 |
| 1498 | 30 f. Cetiosaurus .. | 10 | 10 |
| 1499 | 50 f. Brontosaurus .. | 10 | 10 |
| 1500 | 50 f. "Corythosaurus casuarius" .. .. | 10 | 10 |
| 1501 | 50 f. Styracosaurus .. | 10 | 10 |
| 1502 | 50 f. Gorgosaurus .. | 10 | 10 |
| 1503 | 500 f. Scolosaurus .. | 1·40 | 45 |
| 1504 | 500 f. Trachodon .. | 1·40 | 45 |
| 1505 | 500 f. Struthiomimus .. | 1·40 | 45 |
| 1506 | 500 f. "Tarbosaurus bataar" | 1·40 | 45 |

Nos. 1491/1506 were issued together, se-tenant, forming a composite design of a volcanic landscape.

**404** Th. Haug (combined skiing, Chamonix, 1924)

**1994.** Winter Olympic Games, Lillehammer, Norway. Previous Medal Winners. Mult.

| | | | |
|---|---|---|---|
| 1508 | 100 f. Type **404** .. .. | 25 | 10 |
| 1509 | 100 f. J. Heaton (luge, St. Moritz, 1928) .. .. | 25 | 10 |
| 1510 | 100 f. B. Ruud (ski jumping, Lake Placid, 1932) .. .. .. | 25 | 10 |
| 1511 | 100 f. I. Ballangrud (speed skating, Garmisch-Partenkirchen, 1936) .. | 25 | 10 |
| 1512 | 100 f. G. Fraser (slalom, St. Moritz, 1948) .. | 25 | 10 |
| 1513 | 100 f. West German 4-man bobsleigh team (Oslo, 1952) .. .. .. | 25 | 10 |
| 1514 | 100 f. U.S.S.R. ice hockey team (Cortina d'Ampezzo, 1956) .. | 25 | 10 |
| 1515 | 100 f. J. Vuarnet (downhill skiing, Squaw Valley, 1960) .. .. | 25 | 10 |
| 1516 | 200 f. M. Goitschel (giant slalom, Innsbruck, 1964) | 50 | 15 |
| 1517 | 200 f. Jean-Claud Killy (special slalom, Grenoble, 1968) .. | 50 | 15 |
| 1518 | 200 f. U. Wehling (cross-country skiing, Sapporo, 1972) .. | 50 | 15 |
| 1519 | 200 f. Irina Rodnina and Aleksandr Zaitsev (figure skating, Innsbruck, 1976) .. | 50 | 15 |
| 1520 | 200 f. E. Heiden (speed skating, Lake Placid, 1980) .. .. | 50 | 15 |
| 1521 | 200 f. Katarina Witt (figure skating, Sarajevo, 1984) .. | 50 | 15 |
| 1522 | 200 f. J. Mueller (single luge, Calgary, 1988) .. | 50 | 15 |
| 1523 | 200 f. E. Grospiron (acrobatic skiing, Albertville, 1992) .. | 50 | 15 |
| 1524 | 200 f. Speed skiing, Lillehammer, 1994 .. | 50 | 15 |

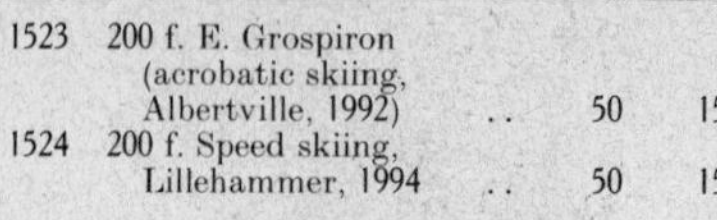

**405** "Ansellia africa"

**1994.** Flowers, Vegetables, Fruit and Fungi. Multicoloured.

| | | | |
|---|---|---|---|
| 1525 | 25 f. Type **405** .. .. | 10 | 10 |
| 1526 | 30 f. Yams .. .. | 10 | 10 |
| 1527 | 40 f. Oranges .. .. | 10 | 10 |
| 1528 | 50 f. Termite mushroom | 10 | 10 |
| 1529 | 60 f. "Polystachia bella" (flower) .. .. | 15 | 10 |
| 1530 | 65 f. Manioc .. .. | 15 | 10 |
| 1531 | 70 f. Banana .. .. | 15 | 10 |
| 1532 | 80 f. "Synpodia arborescens" (wrongly inscr "Sympodia") (fungi) .. .. | 20 | 10 |
| 1533 | 90 f. "Aerangis rhodosticta" (flower) .. | 20 | 10 |
| 1534 | 100 f. Maize .. .. | 25 | 10 |
| 1535 | 160 f. Mango .. .. | 40 | 15 |
| 1536 | 200 f. "Phlebopus sudanicus" (fungi) .. | 50 | 15 |
| 1537 | 300 f. Coffee beans .. | 75 | 25 |
| 1538 | 400 f. Sweet potato .. | 95 | 30 |
| 1539 | 500 f. "Angraecum eburneum" (flower) .. | 1·25 | 40 |
| 1540 | 600 f. "Leucocoprinus africanus" (fungi) .. | 1·50 | 50 |

Nos. 1525/40 were issued together, se-tenant, the backgrounds forming a composite design.

## MILITARY FRANK STAMPS

**1963.** Optd. **FM.** No. M1 also has the value obliterated with two bars. Centre multicoloured; frame colour given.

| | | |
|---|---|---|
| M 35. | **1.** (–) on 15 f. blue .. | 4·50 |
| M 36. | 15 f. blue .. .. | 3·00 |

## OFFICIAL STAMPS

**O 41.** Arms.

**O 109.** Arms.

**1965.**

| | | | | |
|---|---|---|---|---|
| O 78. | **O 41.** | 1 f. multicoloured .. | 15 | 10 |
| O 79. | | 2 f. multicoloured .. | 10 | 10 |
| O 80. | | 5 f. multicoloured .. | 10 | 10 |
| O 81. | | 10 f. multicoloured .. | 25 | 10 |
| O 82. | | 20 f. multicoloured .. | 35 | 30 |
| O 83. | | 30 f. multicoloured .. | 70 | 50 |
| O 84. | | 50 f. multicoloured .. | 80 | 70 |
| O 85. | | 100 f. multicoloured | 2·10 | 1·00 |
| O 86. | | 130 f. multicoloured | 3·00 | 1·90 |
| O 87. | | 200 f. multicoloured | 4·75 | 2·25 |

**1971.**

| | | | | |
|---|---|---|---|---|
| O 238. | **O 109.** | 5 f. multicoloured | 10 | 10 |
| O 239. | | 30 f. multicoloured | 30 | 20 |
| O 240. | | 40 f. multicoloured | 50 | 25 |
| O 241. | | 100 f. multicoloured | 1·25 | 55 |
| O 242. | | 140 f. multicoloured | 2·25 | 75 |
| O 243. | | 200 f. multicoloured | 2·75 | 1·25 |

## POSTAGE DUE STAMPS

**D 15.** " Sternotomis gama " (Beetle).

**1962.** Beetles.

| | | | |
|---|---|---|---|
| D 33. | 50 c. brown and turquoise | 10 | 10 |
| D 34. | 50 c. turquoise and brown | 10 | 10 |
| D 35. | 1 f. brown and green .. | 10 | 10 |
| D 36. | 1 f. green and brown .. | 10 | 10 |
| D 37. | 2 f. pink and black .. | 10 | 10 |
| D 38. | 2 f. green, black and pink | 10 | 10 |
| D 39. | 5 f. green and brown .. | 25 | 25 |
| D 40. | 5 f. green and brown .. | 25 | 25 |
| D 41. | 10 f. green, black & drab | 50 | 50 |
| D 42. | 10 f. drab, black & green | 50 | 50 |
| D 43. | 25 f. brown, blk. & green | 1·40 | 1·40 |
| D 44. | 25 f. brown, green & black | 1·40 | 1·40 |

DESIGNS: Nos. D 33, Type **D 15.** D 34, "Sternotomis virescens". D 35, "Augosoma centaurus". D 36, "Phosphorus virescens" and "Ceroplesis carabarica". D 37, "Ceroplesis S.P.". D 38, "Cetoine scaraboidae". D 39, "Cetoine scaraboidae". D 40, "Macrorhina S.P.". D 41, "Taurina longiceps". D 42, "Phryneta leprosa". D 43, "Monohamus griseoplagiatus". D 44, "Jambonus trifasciatus".

**D 308.** Giant Pangolin ("Manis gigantea").

**1985.**

| | | | | |
|---|---|---|---|---|
| D1080. | **D 308.** | 5 f. multicoloured | 10 | 10 |
| D1081. | | 20 f. multicoloured | 20 | 20 |
| D1082. | | 30 f. multicoloured | 25 | 25 |

## APPENDIX

The following stamps have either been issued in excess of postal needs or have not been availble to the public in reasonable quantities at face value. Such stamps may later be given full listing if there is evidence of regular postal use.

All the stamps listed below are embossed on gold foil.

**1977.**

Coronation of Emperor Bokassa. **Air 2500 f.**

**1978.**

100 Years of Progress in Posts and Telecommunications. Air 1500 f.

Death Centenary of Sir Rowland Hill. Air 1500 f.

**1979.**

International Year of the Child. **Air 1500 f.**

Olympic Games, Moscow. Air 1500 f. (" The Discus-thrower ")

Space Exploration. Air 1500 f.

**1980.**

Olympic Games, Moscow. **Air 1500 f. (Relay)**

European-African Co-operation. **Air 1500 f.**

World Cup Football Championship, Spain. **Air 1500 f.**

**1981.**

Olympic Games Medal Winners. 1980 Olympic Games issue optd. Air 1500 f.

Birth Centenary of Pablo Picasso. Air 1500 f.

Wedding of Prince of Wales. Air 1500 f.

Navigators. Air 1500 f.

Christmas. Air. 1500 f.

**1982.**

Animals and Rotary International. Air 1500 f.

Transport. Air 1500 f.

21st Birthday of Princess of Wales. Air 1500 f.

Olympic Games, Los Angeles. Air 1500 f. (horiz.)

Spaces Resources. Air 1500 f.

**1983.**

Chess Masters. Air 1500 f.

World Cup Football Championship, Spain. Air 1500 f.

Car Manufacturers. Air 1500 f.

Olympic Games, Los Angeles. Air 1500 f. (vert.)

Bicentenary of Manned Flight. Air 1500 f.

**1984.**

Winter Olympic Gold Medalists. Air 1500 f.

Celebrities. Air 1500 f.

**1985.**

85th Birthday of Queen Elizabeth the Queen Mother. Air 1500 f.

Appearance of Halley's Comet. Air 1500 f.

480th Death Anniv. of Christopher Columbus. Air 1500 f.

**1988.**

Olympic Games, Seoul. Air 1500 f.

Scouts and Birds. Air 1500 f.

**1989.**

Olympic Games, Seoul, Gold Medal Winner. Air 1500 f.

Bicentenary of French Revolution. Air 1500 f.

World Cup Football Championship, Italy. Air 1500 f.

**1990.**
Winter Olympic Games, Albertville (1992). Air 1500 f.
Scouts and Butterflies. Air 1500 f.
Birth Centenary of Charles de Gaulle. Air 1500 f.

**1993.**
Wedding of Crown Prince Naruhito of Japan and Masako Owada. Air 1500 f.
16th Death Anniv of Elvis Presley. Air 1500 f.
World Cup Football Championship, U.S.A. (1994). Air 1500 f.
Visit of Pope John Paul II to Africa. Air 1500 f.

**1994.**
Winter Olympic Games, Lillehammer. Air 1500 f.

## CENTRAL LITHUANIA — Pt. 10

Became temporarily independent in 1918 and was subsequently absorbed by Poland.

100 fenigi = 1 mark.

1.

3. Girl.

**1920.** Imperf. or perf.
1. 1. 25 f. red .. .. .. 10 10
20. 25 f. green .. .. 10 10
2. 1 m. blue .. .. .. 10 10
21. 1 m. brown .. .. 10 10
3. 2 m. violet .. .. 15 15
22. 2 m. yellow .. .. 10 10

**1920.** Stamps of Lithuania of 1919 surch. **SRODKOWA LITWA POCZTA,** new value and Arms of Poland and Lithuania. Perf.
4. 5. 2 m. on 15 s. violet .. 5·00 7·00
5. 4 m. on 10 s red .. .. 2·75 3·50
6. 4 m. on 20 s. blue .. 5·00 7·00
7. 4 m. on 30 s. orange .. 3·25 4·00
8. 6. 6 m. on 50 s. green .. 4·75 6·00
9. 6 m. on 60 s. red and violet 5·00 7·00
10. 6 m. on 75 s. red & yellow 5·00 7·00
11. 7. 10 m. on 1 a. red & grey 10·00 11·00
12. 10 m. on 3 a. red & brown £375 £475
13. 10 m. on 5 a. red and green £375 £450

**1920.** Imperf. or perf. Inscr. "LITWA SRODKOWA".
14. 3. 25 f. grey .. .. .. 10 15
15. – 1 m. orange .. .. 15 15
16. – 2 m. red .. .. .. 30 40
17. – 4 m. olive and yellow .. 40 60
18. – 6 m. grey and red .. 60 1·10
19. – 10 m. yellow and brown 90 1·60

DESIGNS: 1 m. Warrior. 2 m. Ostrabrama Gate, Vilnius. 4 m. St. Stanislaus Cathedral and Tower, Vilnius. 6 m. Rector's insignia. 10 m. Gen. Zeligowski.

**1921.** Fund for Polish Participation in Plebiscite for Upper Silesia. Surch **NA SLASK** and new value. Imperf or perf.
23. 1. 25 f.+2 m. red .. .. 40 60
24. 25 f.+2 m. green .. .. 40 60
25. 1 m.+2 m. blue .. .. 50 75
26. 1 m.+2 m. brown .. .. 50 75
27. 2 m.+2 m. violet .. .. 60 1·00
28. 2 m.+2 m. yellow .. .. 60 1·00

**1921.** Red Cross Fund. Nos. 16/17 surch with cross and value. Imperf or perf.
29 2 m.+1 m. red .. .. 40 65
30 4 m.+1 m. green and yellow 45 65

**1921.** White Cross Fund. As Nos. 16, 17 and 19, but with cross and value in white added. Imperf or perf.
31 2 m.+1 m. purple .. .. 20 25
32 4 m.+1 m. green and buff .. 20 25
33 10 m.+2 m. yellow & brown 20 25

13. St. Nicholas Cathedral.

14. St. Stanislaus Cathedral.

**1921.** Imperf. or perf.
34. 13. 1 m. yellow and slate .. 20 25
35. 14. 2 m. green and red .. 20 25
36. – 3 m. green .. .. .. 20 25
37. – 4 m. brown .. .. .. 20 30
38. – 5 m. brown .. .. .. 20 30
39. – 6 m. buff and green .. 20 30
40. – 10 m. buff and purple .. 35 45
41. – 20 m. buff and brown .. 40 50

DESIGNS—HORIZ. 4 m. Queen Jadwiga and King Wladislaw Jagiello. 6 m. Poczobut Observatory, Vilnius University. 10 m. Union of Lithuania and Poland, 1569. 20 m. Kosciuszko and Mickiewicz. VERT. 3 m. Arms (Eagle). 5 m. Arms (Shield).

21. Entry into Vilnius.

22. General Zeligowski.

**1921.** 1st Anniv of Entry of Gen. Zeligowski into Vilnius. Imperf or perf.
42 21 100 m. blue and bistre .. 1·75 1·40
43 22 150 m. green and brown 2·25 1·60

24. Arms.

**1922.** Opening of National Parliament. Inscr. "SEJM—WILNIE". Imperf. or perf.
44. – 10 m. brown .. .. 1·00 1·50
45. 24. 25 m. red and buff .. 1·00 1·50
46. – 50 m. blue .. .. 1·60 2·50
47. – 75 m. lilac .. .. 2·50 4·00

DESIGNS—HORIZ. 50 m. National Assembly, Vilnius. VERT. 10 m. Agriculture. 75 m. Industry.

### POSTAGE DUE STAMPS

D 9. Government Offices.

**1921.** Inscr. "DOPLATA". Imperf. or perf.
D23 D 9 50 f. red .. .. 40 35
D24 – 1 m. green .. .. 40 35
D25 – 2 m. purple .. .. 40 35
D26 – 3 m. purple .. .. 50 45
D27 – 5 m. purple .. .. 50 45
D28 – 20 m. red .. .. 70 70

DESIGNS—HORIZ. 2 m. Castle on Troki Island. VERT. 1 m. Castle Hill, Vilnius. 3 m. Ostrabrama Gate, Vilnius. 5 m. St. Stanislaus Cathedral. 20 m. (larger) St. Nicholas Cathedral.

## CHAD — Pt. 6; Pt. 12

Formerly a dependency of Ubangi-Shari. Became one of the separate colonies of Fr. Equatorial Africa in 1937. In 1958 became a republic within the French Community.

100 centimes = 1 franc.

**1922.** Stamps of Middle Congo, colours changed, optd **TCHAD.**
1 1 1 c. pink and violet .. 15 30
2 2 c. brown and pink .. 20 35
3 4 c. blue and violet .. 30 40
4 5 c. brown and green .. 45 60
5 10 c. green and turquoise 85 1·00
6 15 c. violet and pink .. 1·00 1·25
7 20 c. green and violet .. 2·75 3·00
8 2 25 c. brown and chocolate 5·25 5·25
9 30 c. red .. .. .. 55 70
10 35 c. blue and pink .. 1·25 1·40
11 40 c. brown and green .. 1·25 1·60
12 45 c. violet and green .. 1·25 1·60
13 50 c. blue and light blue 1·25 1·60
14 60 on 75 c. violet on pink 2·50 2·50
15 75 c. pink and violet .. 1·25 1·40
16 3 1 f. blue and pink .. 6·00 6·50
17 2 f. blue and violet .. 9·00 9·50
18 5 f. blue and brown .. 7·25 8·50

**1924.** Stamps of 1922 and similar stamps further optd **AFRIQUE EQUATORIALE FRANCAISE.**
19 1 1 c. pink and violet .. 15 30
20 2 c. brown and pink .. 15 30
21 4 c. blue and violet .. 15 30
22 5 c. brown and green .. 30 50
23 10 c. green and turquoise 35 55
24 10 c. red and grey .. 35 60
25 15 c. violet and red .. 40 55
26 20 c. green and violet .. 45 60
27 2 25 c. brown and chocolate 45 60
28 30 c. red .. .. .. 45 60
29 30 c. grey and blue .. 40 50
30 30 c. olive and green .. 60 70
31 35 c. blue and pink .. 45 60
32 40 c. brown and green .. 55 70
33 45 c. violet and green .. 45 60
34 50 c. blue and light blue 40 60
35 50 c. green and purple .. 60 70
36 60 on 75 c. violet on pink 45 60
37 65 c. brown and blue .. 1·10 1·25
38 75 c. pink and violet .. 40 50
39 75 c. blue and light blue 40 50
40 75 c. purple and brown .. 1·25 1·25
41 90 c. carmine and red .. 4·00 4·00
42 3 1 f. blue and pink .. 85 90
43 1 f. 10 green and blue .. 1·25 1·50
44 1 f. 25 brown and blue .. 4·00 4·50
45 1 f. 50 ultramarine & blue 4·00 4·50
46 1 f. 75 brown and mauve 27·00 27·00
47 2 f. blue and violet .. 1·50 1·50
48 3 f. mauve on pink .. 5·75 6·00
49 5 f. blue and brown .. 1·75 1·60

**1925.** Stamps of Middle Congo optd. **TCHAD** and **AFRIQUE EQUATORIALE FRANCAISE** and surch. also.
50. 3. 65 on 1 f. brown & green .. 85 90
51. 85 on 1 f. brown & green .. 90 90
52. 2. 90 on 75 c. red and pink .. 85 85
53. 3. 1 f. 25 on 1 f. blue & ultram. 45 60
54. 1 f. 50 on 1 f. blue & ultram 85 80
55. 3 f. on 5 f. brown and red 2·50 2·50
56. 10 f. on 5 f. green and red 6·00 6·00
57. 20 f. on 5 f. violet & orge. 9·50 9·50

**1931.** "Colonial Exhibition" key-types inscr. "TCHAD".
58. E. 40 c. green .. .. 2·50 2·75
59. F. 50 c. mauve .. .. 2·75 2·75
60. G. 90 c. red .. .. 2·50 2·50
61. H. 1 f. 50 blue .. .. 2·75 2·75

2. "Birth of the Republic".

3. Flag, Map and U.N. Emblem.

**1959.** 1st Anniv. of Republic.
62. 2. 15 f. multicoloured .. 45 35
63. – 25 f. lake and myrtle .. 50 25

DESIGN.: 25 f. Map and Birds.

**1960.** 10th African Technical Co-operation Commission. As T **62** of Cameroun.
64. 50 f. violet and purple .. 1·00 60

**1960.** Air. Olympic Games. No. 276 of French Equatorial Africa optd. with Olympic rings, **XVIIe OLYMPIADE 1960 REPUBLIQUE DU TCHAD** and surch. **250F** and bars.
65. 250 f. on 500 f. blue, black and green .. .. 9·25 9·25

**1961.** Admission into U.N.
66. 3. 15 f. multicoloured .. 45 20
67. 25 f. multicoloured .. 50 25
68. 85 f. multicoloured .. 1·60 80

4. Shari Bridge and Hippopotamus.

5. Red Bishops.

**1961.**
69. – 50 c. green and black .. 10 10
70. – 1 f. green and black .. 10 10
71. – 2 f. brown and black .. 10 10
72. – 3 f. orange and green .. 10 10
73. – 4 f. red and black .. 10 10
74. 4. 5 f. lemon and black .. 20 15
75. – 10 f. pink and black .. 20 20
76. – 15 f. violet and black .. 45 20
77. – 20 f. red and black .. 55 30
78. – 25 f. blue and black .. 60 30
79. – 30 f. blue and black .. 70 45
80. – 60 f. yellow and black .. 1·40 65
81. – 85 f. orange and black .. 1·60 95

DESIGNS (with animal silhouettes)—VERT. 50 c. Biltine and Dorcas gazelle. 1 f. Logone and elephant. 2 f. Batha and lion. 3 f. Salamat and buffalo. 4 f. Ouaddai and greater kudu. 10 f. Abtouyour and bullock. 15 f. Bessada and Derby's eland. 20 f. Tibesti and moufflon. 25 f. Tikem Rocks and hartebeest. 30 f. Kanem and cheetah. 60 f. Borkou and oryx. 85 f. Guelta D'Archei and addax.

**1961.** Air.
82. 5. 50 f. black, red and green 3·00 1·10
83. – 100 f. multicoloured .. 6·75 2·00
84. – 200 f. multicoloured .. 12·00 3·75
85. – 250 f. blue, orange & green 14·00 5·25
86. – 500 f. multicoloured .. 24·75 11·00

BIRDS: 100 f. Scarlet-chested Sunbird. 200 f. African Paradise Flycatcher. 250 f. Malachite Kingfisher. 500 f. Carmine Bee Eater.

**1962.** Air. "Air Afrique" Airline. As T **69** of Cameroun.
87. 25 f. blue, brown and black 60 25

**1962.** Malaria Eradication. As T **70** of Cameroun.
88. 25 f.+5 f. orange .. .. 75 75

**1962.** Sports. As T **12** of Central African Republic. Multicoloured.
89. 20 f. Relay-racing (horiz.) (postage) .. .. .. 45 30
90. 50 f. High-jumping (horiz.) 1·10 55
91. 100 f. Throwing the discus (air) .. .. .. 2·50 1·25

The 100 f. is 26×47 mm. in size.

**1962.** 1st Anniv. of Union of African and Malagasy States. As No. 328 of Cameroun.
92. 72. 30 f. deep blue .. .. 70 40

**1963.** Freedom from Hunger. As T **76** of Cameroun.
93. 25 f.+5 f. blue, brown and myrtle .. .. .. 80 80

6. Pres. Tombalbaye.

7. Carved Thread-weight.

**1963.**
94. **6.** 20 f. multicoloured .. 45 20
95. 85 f. multicoloured .. 1·10 55

**1963.** Air. African and Malagasy Posts and Telecommunications Union. As T **11** of Central African Republic.
96. 85 f. multicoloured .. 1·25 55

**1963.** Space Telecommunications. As Nos. 37/8 of Central African Republic.
97. 25 f. violet, emerald & green 50 35
98. 100 f. blue and pink .. 2·00 1·25

**1963.** Air. 1st Anniv. of "Air Afrique" and Inauguration of "DC–8" Service. As T **11** of Congo Republic.
99. 50 f. multicoloured .. .. 1·50 75

**1963.** Air. European–African Economic Convention. As T **24** of Central African Republic.
100. 50 f. multicoloured .. 1·00 60

**1963.** Sao Art.
101. **7.** 5 f. orange and turquoise 10 10
102. – 15 f. purple, slate & red .. 30 25
103. – 25 f. brown and blue .. 60 35
104. – 60 f. bronze and brown .. 1·40 60
105. – 80 f. bronze and brown .. 1·60 80

DESIGNS: 15 f. Ancestral mask. 25 f. Ancestral statuette. 60 f. Gazelle's-head pendant. 80 f. Pectoral.

**1963.** 15th Anniv. of Declaration of Human Rights. As Central African Republic T **26**.
106. 25 f. purple and green .. 65 35

**8.** Broussard Monoplane.

**1963.** Air.
107. **8.** 100 f. blue, green & brown 2·25 1·25

DESIGNS: 30 f. Canoe-building. 50 f. Carpet-weaving. 85 f. Blacksmith working iron.

**9.** Pottery.

**1964.** Sao Handicrafts.
108. **9.** 10 f. black, orge. & blue 30 20
109. – 30 f. red, black & yellow 55 30
110. – 50 f. black, red & green 1·00 45
111. – 85 f. black, yellow & pur. 1·25 65

**10.** Rameses II in War Chariot, Abu Simbel.

**1964.** Air. Nubian Monuments Preservation Fund.
112. **10.** 10 f. + 5 f. vio., grn. & red 60 35
113. 25 f. + 5 f. pur., grn. & red 95 50
114. 50 f. + 5 f. turq., grn. & red 1·90 1·40

**1964.** World Meteorological Day. As T **14** of Congo Republic.
115. 50 f. violet, blue and purple 1·00 50

**11.** Cotton.

**1964.** Multicoloured.
116. 20 f. Type **11** .. .. 95 50
117. 25 f. Flamboyant tree .. 1·10 55

**1964.** Air. 5th Anniv. of Equatorial African Heads of State Conf. As T **31** of Central African Republic.
118. 100 f. multicoloured .. 1·50 75

**12.** Globe, Chimneys and Ears of Wheat.

**1964.** Air. Europafrique.
119. **12.** 50 f. orge., pur. & brn. 1·00 55

**13.** Football.

**1964.** Air. Olympic Games, Tokyo.
120. **13.** 25 f. green, apple & brn. 75 45
121. – 50 f. brn., indigo & blue 1·00 55
122. – 100 f. blk., green & red 2·00 1·10
123. – 200 f. blk., bistre & red 4·25 2·10

DESIGNS—VERT. 50 f. Throwing the javelin. 100 f. High-jumping. HORIZ. 200 f. Running.

**1964.** Air. Pan-African and Malagasy Post. and Telecommunications Congress, Cairo As T **23** of Congo Republic.
124. 25 f. sepia, red and mauve 60 25

**1964.** French, African and Malagasy Co-operation. As T **547** of France.
125. 25 f. brown, blue and red 60 30

**14.** Pres. Kennedy. **15.** National Guard.

**1964.** Air. Pres. Kennedy Commem.
126. **14.** 100 f. multicoloured .. 1·75 1·10

**1964.** Chad Army. Multicoloured.
127. 20 f. Type **15** .. .. 50 20
128. 25 f. Standard-bearer and troops of Land Forces .. 55 25

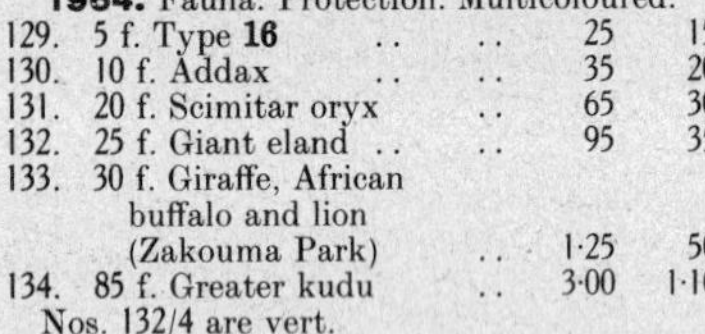

**16.** Barbary Sheep.

**1964.** Fauna. Protection. Multicoloured.
129. 5 f. Type **16** .. .. 25 15
130. 10 f. Addax .. .. 35 20
131. 20 f. Scimitar oryx .. 65 30
132. 25 f. Giant eland .. 95 35
133. 30 f. Giraffe, African buffalo and lion (Zakouma Park) .. 1·25 50
134. 85 f. Greater kudu .. 3·00 1·10

Nos. 132/4 are vert.

**17.** Perforator of Olsen's Telegraph Apparatus.

**1965.** I.T.U. Cent.
135. **17.** 30 f. brown, red & green 55 25
136. – 60 f. green, red & brown 1·00 45
137. – 100 f. green, brown & red 1·90 80

DESIGNS—VERT. 60 f. Milde's telephone. HORIZ. 100 f. Distributor of Baudot's telegraph apparatus.

**18.** Badge and Mobile Gendarmes.

**1965.** National Gendarmerie.
138. **18.** 25 f. multicoloured .. 60 35

**19.** I.C.Y. Emblem.

**1965.** Air. Int. Co-operation Year.
139. **19.** 100 f. multicoloured .. 1·25 70

**20.** Abraham Lincoln.

**1965.** Air. Death Cent. of Abraham Lincoln.
140. **20.** 100 f. multicoloured .. 1·75 75

**21.** Guitar. **22.** Sir Winston Churchill.

**1965.** Native Musical Instruments.
141. – 1 f. brn. & green (post.) 10 10
142. **21.** 2 f. brown, purple & red 10 10
143. – 3 f. lake, black & brown 20 15
144. – 15 f. green, oran. & red 50 25
145. – 60 f. green and lake .. 1·60 80
146. – 100 f. ultram., brn. & bl. (48½ × 27 mm.) (air) .. 1·90 1·25

DESIGNS—VERT. 1 f. Drum and seat. 3 f. Shoulder drum. 60 f. Harp. HORIZ. 15 f. Viol. 100 f. Xylophone.

**1965.** Air. Churchill Commem.
147. **22.** 50 f. black and green .. 1·00 50

**23.** Dr. Albert Schweitzer (philosopher and missionary) and "Appealing Hands".

**1966.** Air. Schweitzer Commem.
148. **23.** 100 f. multicoloured .. 1·90 95

**24.** Mask in Mortar. **26.** W.H.O. Building.

**1966.** World Festival of Negro Arts, Dakar.
149. **24.** 15 f. pur., bistre & blue 35 20
150. – 20 f. brown, red & green 50 25
151. – 60 f. purple, blue & red 1·40 55
152. – 80 f. grn., brn. & violet 2·10 85

DESIGNS—Sao Art: 20 f. Mask. 60 f. Mask (different). (All from J. Courtin's excavations at Bouta Kebira). 80 f. Armband (from I.N.T.S.H. excavations, Gawi).

**1966.** No. 94 surch.
153. **6.** 25 f. on 20 f. multicoloured 60 30

**1966.** Inaug. of W.H.O. Headquarters, Geneva.
154. **26.** 25 f. blue, yellow & red 45 20
155. 32 f. blue, yellow & grn. 50 25

**27.** Caduceus and Map of Africa.

**28.** Footballer. **29.** Youths, Flag and Arms.

**1966.** Central African Customs and Economic Union.
156. **27.** 30 f. multicoloured .. 60 30

**1966.** World Cup Football Championships.
157. **28.** 30 f. red, green and emerald .. .. 50 25
158. – 60 f. red, black and blue 1·25 50

DESIGN—VERT. 60 f. Footballer (different).

**1966.** Youth Movement.
159. **29.** 25 f. multicoloured .. 60 30

## INDEX

Countries can be quickly located by referring to the index at the end of this volume.

**30.** Columns. **31.** Skull of Lake Chad Man ("Tchadanthropus uxoris").

**1966.** 20th Anniv. of U.N.E.S.C.O.
160. **30.** 32 f. blue, vio. & red .. 65 30

**1966.** Air. Inaug. of "DC–8" Air Services. As T **54** of Central African Republic.
161. 30 f. grey, black and green 60 25

**1966.** Archaeological Excavation.
162. **31.** 30 f. slate, yellow & red 1·60 75

**32.** White-throated Bee Eater.

**1966.** Air. Birds. Multicoloured.
163. 50 f. Greater Blue-eared Glossy Starling .. 3·00 1·40
164. 100 f. Type **32** .. 4·50 2·40
165. 200 f. African Pigmy Kingfisher .. .. .. 8·00 2·50
166. 250 f. Red-throated Bee Eater .. .. .. 10·50 3·25
167. 500 f. Little Green Bee Eater .. .. .. 18·00 7·00

**33.** Battle-axe. **35.** Sportsmen and Dais on Map.

**34.** Congress Palace.

**1966.** Prehistoric Implements.
168. **33.** 25 f. brown, blue & red 35 25
169. – 30 f. black, brown & blue 45 25
170. – 85 f. brown, red and blue 1·50 60
171. – 100 f. brn., turq. & sepia 1·75 85

DESIGNS: 30 f. Arrowhead. 85 f. Harpoon. 100 f. Sandstone grindstone and pounder. From Tchad National Museum.

**1967.** Air.
173. **34.** 25 f. multicoloured .. 55 25

**1967.** Sports Day.
174. **35.** 25 f. multicoloured .. 60 35

**36.** "Colotis protomedia klug".

**39.** H.Q. Building. **37.** Lions Emblem.

**38.** Dagnaux's Breguet "19" Aircraft.

**1967.** Butterflies. Multicoloured.
175. 5 f. Type **36** .. .. 20 15
176. 10 f. "Charaxes jasius epijasius L" .. .. 35 20
177. 20 f. "Junonia cebrene trim" .. .. 1·00 50
178. 130 f. "Danaida petiverana H.D.". .. .. .. 3·25 1·40

**1967.** Air. 50th Anniv. of Lions Int.
179. **37.** 50 f. + 10 f. mult. .. 1·25 65

**1967.** Air. 1st Anniv. of Air Chad Airline.
180. **38.** 25 f. green, blue & brown 55 40
181. – 30 f. indigo, green & blue 75 40
182. – 50 f. brown, green & blue 1·25 75
183. – 100 f. red, blue & green 2·50 1·10
DESIGNS: 30 f. Latecoere "631" flying-boat. 50 f. Douglas "DC–3". 100 f. Piper Cherokee "6".

**1967.** Air. 5th Anniv. of U.A.M.P.T. As T **66** of Central African Republic.
184. 100 f. brown, bis. & mve. 1·25 75

**1967.** Opening of W.H.O. Regional Headquarters, Brazzaville.
185. **39.** 30 f. multicoloured .. 60 30

**40.** Scouts and Jamboree Emblem.

**1967.** World Scout Jamboree, Idaho. Multicoloured.
186. 25 f. Type **40** .. .. 45 20
187. 32 f. Scout and Jamboree emblem .. .. 65 25

**41.** Flour Mills.

**1967.** Economic Development.
188. **41.** 25 f. slate, brown & blue 45 20
189. – 30 f. blue, brown & green 55 30
DESIGN: 30 f. Land reclamation, Lake Bol.

**42.** Woman and Harpist. **43.** Emblem of Rotary International.

**1967.** Bailloud Mission in the Ennedi. Rock paintings.
190. – 2 f. chocolate, brn. & red (postage) .. .. 20 15
191. – 10 f. red, brn. and violet 45 25
192. **42.** 15 f. lake, brown & blue 55 25
193. – 20 f. red, brown & green 1·25 50
194. – 25 f. red, brown & blue 1·60 60
195. – 30 f. lake, brown & blue 1·00 50
196. – 50 f. lake, brown & green 1·90 80
197. – 100 f. lake, brown and green (air) .. .. 3·00 1·40
198. – 125 f. lake, brown & blue 4·25 2·10
DESIGNS: 2 f. Archers. 10 f. male and female costumes. 20 f. Funeral vigil. 25 f. "Dispute". 30 f. Giraffes. 50 f. Cameleer pursuing ostrich. (48×27 mm.) 100 f. Masked dancers. 125 f. Hunters and hare.

**1968.** 10th Anniv. of Rotary Club, Fort Lamy.
199. **43.** 50 f. multicoloured .. 95 45

**44.** Downhill Skiing.

**1968.** Air. Winter Olympic Games, Grenoble.
200. **44.** 30 f. brn., grn. & purple 95 35
201. – 100 f. blue, grn. & turq. 2·50 1·10
DESIGN—VERT. 100 f. Ski-jumping.

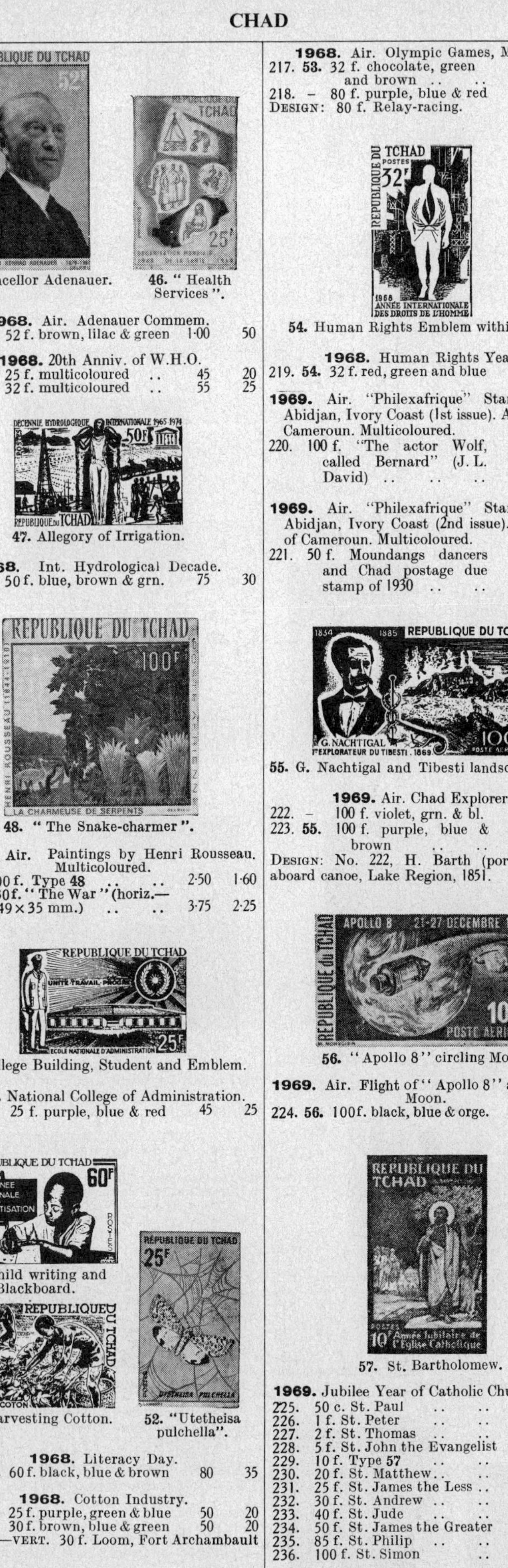

**45.** Chancellor Adenauer. **46.** "Health Services".

**1968.** Air. Adenauer Commem.
202. **45.** 52 f. brown, lilac & green 1·00 50

**1968.** 20th Anniv. of W.H.O.
204. **46.** 25 f. multicoloured .. 45 20
205. 32 f. multicoloured .. 55 25

**47.** Allegory of Irrigation.

**1968.** Int. Hydrological Decade.
206. **47.** 50 f. blue, brown & grn. 75 30

**48.** "The Snake-charmer".

**1968.** Air. Paintings by Henri Rousseau. Multicoloured.
207. 100 f. Type **48** .. .. 2·50 1·60
208. 130 f. "The War" (horiz.—49×35 mm.) .. .. 3·75 2·25

**49.** College Building, Student and Emblem.

**1968.** National College of Administration.
209. **49.** 25 f. purple, blue & red 45 25

**50.** Child writing and Blackboard.

**51.** Harvesting Cotton. **52.** "Utetheisa pulchella".

**1968.** Literacy Day.
210. **50.** 60 f. black, blue & brown 80 35

**1968.** Cotton Industry.
211. **51.** 25 f. purple, green & blue 50 20
212. – 30 f. brown, blue & green 50 20
DESIGN—VERT. 30 f. Loom, Fort Archambault Mill.

**1968.** Butterflies and Moths. Multicoloured.
213. 25 f. Type **52** .. .. 1·10 35
214. 30 f. "Ophideres materna" 1·40 35
215. 50 f. "Gynanisa maja" .. 2·75 70
216. 100 f. "Epiphora bauhiniae" .. .. 3·75 1·25

**53.** Hurdling.

**1968.** Air. Olympic Games, Mexico.
217. **53.** 32 f. chocolate, green and brown .. .. 80 50
218. – 80 f. purple, blue & red 1·75 75
DESIGN: 80 f. Relay-racing.

**54.** Human Rights Emblem within Man.

**1968.** Human Rights Year.
219. **54.** 32 f. red, green and blue 60 25

**1969.** Air. "Philexafrique" Stamp Exn., Abidjan, Ivory Coast (1st issue). As T **137** of Cameroun. Multicoloured.
220. 100 f. "The actor Wolf, called Bernard" (J. L. David) .. .. 2·75 2·75

**1969.** Air. "Philexafrique" Stamp Exn., Abidjan, Ivory Coast (2nd issue). As T **138** of Cameroun. Multicoloured.
221. 50 f. Moundangs dancers and Chad postage due stamp of 1930 .. .. 1·90 1·90

**55.** G. Nachtigal and Tibesti landscape, 1869.

**1969.** Air. Chad Explorers.
222. – 100 f. violet, grn. & bl. 1·75 75
223. **55.** 100 f. purple, blue & brown .. .. 1·75 75
DESIGN: No. 222, H. Barth (portrait) and aboard canoe, Lake Region, 1851.

**56.** "Apollo 8" circling Moon.

**1969.** Air. Flight of "Apollo 8" around the Moon.
224. **56.** 100 f. black, blue & orge. 1·75 75

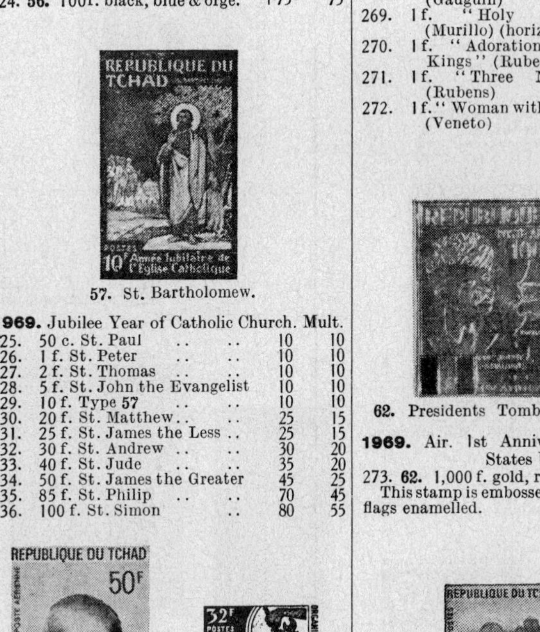

**57.** St. Bartholomew.

**1969.** Jubilee Year of Catholic Church. Mult.
225. 50 c. St. Paul .. .. 10 10
226. 1 f. St. Peter .. .. 10 10
227. 2 f. St. Thomas .. .. 10 10
228. 5 f. St. John the Evangelist 10 10
229. 10 f. Type **57** .. .. 10 10
230. 20 f. St. Matthew .. .. 25 15
231. 25 f. St. James the Less .. 25 15
232. 30 f. St. Andrew .. .. 30 20
233. 40 f. St. Jude .. .. 35 20
234. 50 f. St. James the Greater 45 25
235. 85 f. St. Philip .. .. 70 45
236. 100 f. St. Simon .. 80 55

**58.** Mahatma Gandhi. **59.** Motor Vehicles and I.L.O. Emblem.

**1969.** Air. "Apostles of Peace"
237. **58.** 50 f. brown and green .. 95 45
238. – 50 f. sepia and agate .. 95 45
239. – 50 f. brown and pink .. 95 45
240. – 50 f. brown and blue .. 95 45
DESIGNS: No. 238, President Kennedy. No. 239, Martin Luther King. No. 240, Robert F. Kennedy.

**1969.** 50th Anniv. of I.L.O.
242. **59.** 32 f. blue, pur. & grn. 60 30

**60.** Cipolla, Baran and Sambo (pair with cox). **61.** "African Woman" (Bezombes).

**1969.** "World Solidarity". Multicoloured.

(a) Gold Medal Winners, Mexico Olympics.
243. 1 f. Type **60** .. .. 25 25
244. 1 f. D. Beamon (long-jump) 25 25
245. 1 f. I. Becker (women's pentathlon) .. .. 25 25
246. 1 f. C. Besson (women's 400 metres) .. .. 25 25
247. 1 f. W. Davenport (110 metres hurdles) .. 25 25
248. 1 f. K. Dibiasi (diving) .. 25 25
249. 1 f. R. Fosbury (high-jump) .. .. 25 25
250. 1 f. M. Gamoudi (5000 metres) .. .. .. 25 25
251. 1 f. Great Britain (sailing) 25 25
252. 1 f. J. Guyon (cross-country riding) .. 25 25
253. 1 f. D. Hemery (200 metres hurdles) .. .. 25 25
254. 1 f. S. Kato (gymnastics) .. 25 25
255. 1 f. B. Klinger (small bore rifle-shooting) .. .. 25 25
256. 1 f. R. Matson (shot put) .. 25 25
257. 1 f. R. Matthes (100 metres backstroke) .. .. 25 25
258. 1 f. D. Meyer (women's 200 metres freestyle) .. 25 25
259. 1 f. Morelon and Trentin (tandem cycle) .. .. 25 25
260. 1 f. D. Rebillard (4000 m. cycle pursuit) .. .. 25 25
261. 1 f. T. Smith (200 metres) 25 25
262. 1 f. P. Trentin (1000 metres cycle) .. .. 25 25
263. 1 f. F. Vianelli (196 kilometre cycle race) .. 25 25
264. 1 f. West Germany (dressage) .. .. .. 25 25
265. 1 f. M. Wolke (welterweight boxing) .. .. .. 25 25
266. 1 f. Zimmermann and Esser (women's kayak pair) .. 25 25

(b) Paintings.
267. 1 f. Type **61** .. .. 25 25
268. 1 f. "Mother and Child" (Gauguin) .. .. 25 25
269. 1 f. "Holy Family" (Murillo) (horiz.) .. 25 25
270. 1 f. "Adoration of the Kings" (Rubens) .. 25 25
271. 1 f. "Three Negroes" (Rubens) .. .. 25 25
272. 1 f. "Woman with Flowers" (Veneto) .. .. 25 25

**62.** Presidents Tombalbaye and Mobutu.

**1969.** Air. 1st Anniv. of Central African States Union.
273. **62.** 1,000 f. gold, red & blue 20·00 20·00
This stamp is embossed in gold foil; colours of flags enamelled.

**63.** "Cochlospermum tinctorium".

**1969.** Flowers. Multicoloured.
274. 1 f. Type **63** .. .. 10 10
275. 4 f. "Parkia biglobosa" .. 20 15
276. 10 f. "Pancratium trianthum" 30 20
277. 15 f. "Ipomoea aquatica" 45 20

**1969.** Air. Birth Bicent. of Napoleon Bonaparte. Multicoloured. As T **144** of Cameroun.

278. 30 f. "Napoleon visiting the Hotel des Invalides" (Veron-Bellecourt) .. 95 50
279. 85 f. "The Battle of Wagram" (H. Vernet) .. 1·90 1·00
280. 130 f. "The Battle of Austerlitz" (Gerard) .. 3·50 1·90

64. Frozen Carcases.

**1969.** Frozen Meat Industry.

281. **64.** 25 f. red, green & orange 35 20
282. – 30 f. brown, slate & green 50 25

DESIGN: 30 f. Cattle and refrigerated abattoir, Farcha.

**1969.** 5th Anniv. of African Development Bank. As T **146** of Cameroun.

283. 30 f. brown, green and red 45 25

66. Astronaut and Lunar Module.

**1969.** Air. 1st Man on the Moon. Embossed on gold foil.

289. **66.** 1,000 f. gold .. .. 22·00 22·00

67. Nile Mouth Breeder. 68. President Tombalbaye.

**1969.** Fishes.

290. **67.** 2 f. purple, slate & green 15 10
291. – 3 f. slate, red and blue .. 20 15
292. – 5 f. blue, lemon & ochre 30 15
293. – 20 f. blue, green and red 95 40

FISHES: 3 f. Moonfish. 5 f. Puffer fish. 20 f. Tiger fish.

**1969.** 10th Anniv. of A.S.E.C.N.A. As T **150** of Cameroun.

294. 30 f. orange .. .. 55 30

**1970.** President Tombalbaye.

295. **68.** 25 f. multicoloured .. 45 20

69. "Village Life" (G. Narcisse).

**1970.** Air. African Paintings. Multicoloured.

296. 100 f. Type **69** .. .. 2·10 1·00
297. 250 f. "Market Woman" (I. N'Diaye) .. .. 4·00 1·60
298. 250 f. "Flower-seller" (I. N'Diaye) (vert.) .. 4·00 1·60

70. Lenin. 72. Osaka Print.

71. Class and Torchbearers.

**1970.** Birth Cent. of Lenin.

299. **70.** 150 f. blk., cream & gold 2·50 1·25

**1970.** New U.P.U. Headquarters Building, Berne. As T **156** of Cameroun.

300. 30 f. brn., violet & red .. 55 30

**1970.** Int. Education Year.

301. **71.** 100 f. multicoloured .. 1·50 80

**1970.** Air. World Fair "EXPO 70", Osaka, Japan.

302. **72.** 50 f. green, blue & red 45 30
303. – 100 f. blue, green & red 75 45
304. – 125 f. slate, brn. & red .. 1·00 55

DESIGNS: 100 f. Tower of the Sun. 125 f. Osaka print (different).

**1970.** Air. "Apollo" Moon Flights. Nos. 164/6 surch. with new value, and optd. with various inscriptions and diagrams concerning space flights.

305. **32.** 50 f. on 100 f. ("Apollo 11") .. .. .. 1·50 1·00
306. – 100 f. on 200 f. ("Apollo 12") .. .. .. 2·40 1·40
307. – 125 f. on 250 f. ("Apollo 13") .. .. .. 3·25 2·25

74. Meteorological Equipment and "Agriculture". 76. Ahmed Mangue (Minister of Education).

75. "DC 8-63" over Airport.

**1970.** World Meteorological Day.

308. **74.** 50 f. grey, grn. & orge. 75 30

**1970.** Air. "Air Afrique" DC-8 "Fort Lamy".

309. **75.** 30 f. multicoloured .. 75 35

**1970.** Ahmed Mangue (air crash victim). Commem.

310. **76.** 100 f. black, red and gold 1·10 50

77. Tanning.

**1970.** Trades and Handicrafts.

311. **77.** 1 f. bistre, brn. & blue 10 10
312. – 2 f. brn., blue & green 15 10
313. – 3 f. violet, brn & mauve 20 15
314. – 4 f. brn., bistre & green 25 15
315. – 5 f. brn., green and red 35 35

DESIGNS—VERT. 2 f. Dyeing. 4 f. Water-carrying. HORIZ. 3 f. Milling palm-nuts for oil. 5 f. Copper-founding.

78. U.N. Emblem and Dove. 79. "The Visitation" (Venetian School 15th cent.).

**1970.** 25th Anniv. of United Nations.

316. **78.** 32 f. multicoloured .. 60 35

**1970.** Air. Christmas. Multicoloured.

317. 20 f. Type **79** .. .. 50 30
318. 25 f. "The Nativity" (Venetian School, 15th cent.) .. .. 75 35
319. 30 f. "Virgin and Child" (Veneziano) .. .. 95 45

80. Map and O.C.A.M. Building.

**1971.** O.C.A.M. (Organization Commune Africaine et Malgache) Conference, Fort Lamy.

320. **80.** 30 f. multicoloured .. 60 30

81. Maritius "Post Office" 2d. of 1847.

**1971.** Air. "PHILEXOCAM" Stamp Exhib., Fort-Lamy.

321. **81.** 10 f. slate, brn. & turq. 30 20
322. – 20 f. brn., black & turq. 45 20
323. – 30 f. brn., black & red 55 30
324. – 60 f. black, brn. & pur. 80 50
325. – 80 f. slate, brn. and blue 1·25 70
326. – 100 f. brn., slate & blue 1·60 95

DESIGNS—20 f. Tuscany 3 lire of 1860. 30 f. France 1 f. of 1849. 30 f., 60 f. U.S.A. 10 c. of 1847. 80 f. Japan 5 sen of 1872. 100 f. Saxony 3 pf. of 1850.

82. Pres. Nasser. 83. "Racial Harmony" Tree.

**1971.** Air. 1st Death Anniv. of Gamal Abdel Nasser (Egypt).

328. **82.** 75 f. multicoloured .. 80 35

**1971.** Racial Equality Year.

329. **83.** 40 f. red, grn. and blue 75 30

**1971.** Air. Reconciliation with Central African Republic and Zaire. As T **106** of Central African Republic.

330. 100 f. multicoloured .. 1·50 75

84. Map and Dish Aerial.

**1971.** World Telecommunications Day.

331. **84.** 5 f. orange, red and blue (postage) .. .. 20 15
332. – 40 f. grn., brn. and pur. 55 25
333. – 50 f. black, brown & red 75 30
334. – 125 f. red, green & blue (air) .. .. .. 1·90 85

DESIGNS: 40 f. Map and communications tower. 50 f. Map and satellite. (49 × 27 mm.) 125 f. Map and telecommunications symbols. No. 288 commemorates Pan-African Telecommunications.

85. Scouts by Camp-fire.

**1971.** Air. World Scout Jamboree, Asagiri, Japan.

335. **85.** 250 f. multicoloured .. 3·75 1·90

86. Great Egret.

**1971.** Air.

336. **86.** 1,000 f. multicoloured .. 26·00 14·00

87. Ancient Marathon Race.

**1971.** Air. 75th Anniv. of Modern Olympic Games. Multicoloured.

337. 40 f. Type **87** .. .. 55 30
338. 45 f. Ancient stadium, Olympia .. .. 80 35
339. 75 f. Ancient wrestling .. 1·00 50
340. 130 f. Athens Stadium, 1896 Games .. .. 1·75 85

88. Sidney Bechet. 89. Gen. de Gaulle.

**1971.** Air. Famous American Black Musicians. Multicoloured.

341. 50 f. Type **88** .. .. 1·25 50
342. 75 f. Duke Ellington .. 1·60 75
343. 100 f. Louis Armstrong .. 2·50 1·25

**1971.** Air. 1st Death Anniv. of De Gaulle.

344. – 200 f. gold, bl. & light bl. 6·25 6·25
345. **89.** 200 f. gold, grn. & yell. 6·25 6·25

DESIGN: No. 344, Governor-General Felix Eboue.

**1971.** Air. 10th Anniv. of African and Malagasy Posts and Telecommunications Union. As T **184** of Cameroun. Mult.

347. 100 f. Headquarters building and Sao carved animal head .. .. .. 1·25 60

90. Children's Heads.

**1971.** 25th Anniv. of U.N.I.C.E.F.

348. **90.** 50 f. blue, grn. & purple 85 35

On the above stamp, "24e" has been obliterated and "25e" inserted in the commemorative inscription.

91. Gorane Nangara Dancers.

**1971.** Chad Dancers. Multicoloured.

349. 10 f. Type **91** .. .. 30 20
350. 15 f. Yondo initiates .. 45 25
351. 30 f. M'Boum (vert.) .. 80 35
352. 40 f. Sara Kaba (vert.) .. 1·25 55

93. Presidents Pompidou and Tombalbaye.

**1972.** Visit of French President.

354. **93.** 40 f. multicoloured .. 1·25 60

94. Bob-sleighing.

**1972.** Air. Winter Olympic Games, Sapporo, Japan.
355. **94.** 50 f. red and blue .. 70 40
356. – 100 f. green and purple 1·50 60
DESIGN: 100 f. Downhill skiing.

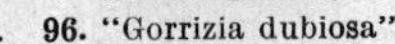
**95.** Human Heart. **96.** "Gorrizia dubiosa".

**1972.** World Heart Month.
357. **95.** 100 f. red, blue & violet 1·50 75

**1972.** Insects. Multicoloured.
358. 1 f. Type **96** .. .. 10 10
359. 2 f. "Argiope sector" .. 20 15
360. 3 f. "Nephila senegalense" 25 15
361. 4 f. "Oryctes boas" .. 35 25
362. 5 f. "Hemistigma albipunctata" .. 45 25
363. 25 f. "Dinothrombium tinctorium" .. .. 45 30
364. 30 f. "Bupreste sternocera H." .. .. .. 50 30
365. 40 f. "Hyperechia bomboides" .. .. 60 35
366. 50 f. "Chrysis" (Hymenoptere) .. .. .. 95 50
367. 100 f. "Tithoes confinis" (Longicore) .. .. 2·50 85
368. 130 f. "Galeodes araba" (Solifuge) .. .. 3·75 1·40

**1972.** Air. U.N.E.S.C.O. "Save Venice" Campaign. As T **191** of Cameroun. Mult.
369. 40 f. "Harbour Panorama" (detail Caffi) .. .. 95 50
370. 45 f. "Venice Panorama" (detail Caffi) (horiz.) .. 1·25 60
371. 140 f. "Grand Canal" (detail, Caffi) .. .. 3·00 1·40

97. Hurdling.

**1972.** Olympic Games, Munich. Mult.
372. 50 f. Type **97** .. .. 75 35
373. 130 f. Gymnastics .. .. 1·50 75
374. 150 f. Swimming .. .. 1·90 85

**98.** Alphonse Daudet and Scene from "Tartarin de Tarascon".

**1972.** Air. Int. Book Year.
376. **98.** 100 f. brn., red & purple 1·50 75

**100.** "Luna 16" and Moon Probe. **99.** Dromedary. **101.** Tobacco Production.

**1972.** Domestic Animals.
377. **99.** 25 f. brown and violet 45 20
378. – 30 f. blue and mauve .. 50 25
379. – 40 f. brown and green .. 70 30
380. – 45 f. brown and blue .. 85 35
DESIGNS: 30 f. Horse. 40 f. Saluki hound. 45 f. Goat.

**1972.** Air. Russian Moon Exploration.
381. **100.** 100 f. violet, brn. & blue 1·40 70
382. – 150 f. brn., blue and pur. 2·10 80
DESIGN—HORIZ. 150 f. "Lunokhod 1" Moon vehicle.

**1972.** Economic Development.
383. **101.** 40 f. grn., red & brown 50 25
384. – 50 f. brn., green & blue 75 35
DESIGN: 50 f. Ploughing with oxen.

102. Microscope, Cattle and Laboratory.

**1972.** Air. 20th Anniv. of Farcha Veterinary Laboratory.
385. **102.** 75 f. multicoloured .. 80 35

103. Massa Warrior.

**1972.** Chad Warriors. Multicoloured.
386. 15 f. Type **103** .. .. 55 25
387. 20 f. Moudang archer .. 70 35

**104.** King Faisal and Pres. Tombalbaye.

**1972.** Visit of King Faisal of Saudi Arabia. Multicoloured.
388. 100 f. Type **104** (postage) .. 1·90 95
389. 75 f. King Faisal and Kaaba, Mecca (air) .. .. 1·00 50

**105.** Gen. Gowon, Pres. Tombalbaye and Map.

**1972.** Visit of Gen. Gowon, Nigerian Head-of-State.
390. **105.** 70 f. multicoloured .. 75 30

**106.** "Madonna and Child" (G. Bellini).

**1972.** Air. Christmas. Paintings. Mult.
391. 40 f. Type **106** .. .. 45 25
392. 75 f. "Virgin and Child" (bas-relief, Da Santivo, Dall' Occhio) .. .. 80 45
393. 80 f. "Nativity" (B. Angelico) (horiz.) .. 1·25 65
394. 90 f. "Adoration of the Magi" (P. Perugino) .. 1·60 80

**HAVE YOU READ THE NOTES AT THE BEGINNING OF THIS CATALOGUE?**
These often provide answers to the enquiries we receive.

**107.** Commemorative Scroll.

**1972.** 50th Anniv. of U.S.S.R.
395. **107.** 150 f. multicoloured .. 1·50 55

108. High-jumping.

**1973.** 2nd African Games, Lagos. Mult.
396. 50 f. Type **108** .. .. 75 35
397. 125 f. Running .. .. 1·40 60
398. 200 f. Putting the shot .. 2·00 1·00

**109.** Copernicus and Planetary System Diagram.

**1973.** Air. 500th Birth Anniv. of Nicholas Copernicus.
400. **109.** 250 f. grey, brn. & mve. 4·00 1·90

**1973.** African Solidarity "Drought Relief" No. 377 surch. **SECHERESSE SOLIDARITE AFRICAINE** and value.
401. **99.** 100 f. on 25 f. brn. & vio. 1·60 90

**1973.** U.A.M.P.T. As Type **216** of Cameroun.
402. 100 f. green, red & brown 1·50 75

111. "Skylab" over Globe.

**1974.** Air. "Skylab" Exploits.
403. **111.** 100 f. brn., red & blue 1·25 55
404. – 150 f. turq., blue & brn. 1·90 80
DESIGN: 150 f. Close-up of "Skylab".

112. Chad Mother and Children.

**1974.** 1st Anniv. of Chad Red Cross.
405. **112.** 30 f. + 10 f. mult .. 60 60

113. Football Players.

**1974.** Air. World Cup Football Championships, West Germany.
406. **113.** 50 f. brown and red .. 50 30
407. – 125 f. green and red .. 1·40 60
408. – 150 f. red and green .. 1·90 95
DESIGNS: Nos. 407/8, Footballers in action similar to Type **113**.
No. 407 is vert.

**114.** Chad Family. **116.** Rotary Emblem.

**115.** U.P.U. Emblem and Mail Canoe.

**1974.** Air. World Population Year.
409. **114.** 250 f. brn., grn & blue 3·00 1·60

**1974.** Air. Cent. of U.P.U.
410. **115.** 30 f. brn., red and grn. 50 25
411. – 40 f. black and blue .. 1·50 1·00
412. – 100 f. blue, brn. & blk. 1·60 70
413. – 150 f. violet, green and turquoise .. .. 2·25 75
DESIGNS—U.P.U. Emblem and: 40 f. Electric train. 100 f. Jet airliner. 150 f. Satellite.

**1975.** 70th Anniv. of Rotary International.
414. **116.** 50 f. multicoloured .. 75 35

**117.** Heads of Women of Four Races.

**1975.** Air. International Women's Year.
415. **117.** 250 f. multicoloured .. 3·75 1·90

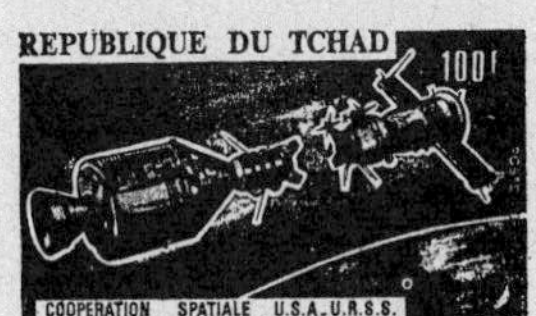
**118.** "Apollo" and "Soyuz" Spacecraft about to dock.

**1975.** Air. "Apollo-Soyuz" Test Project.
416. **118.** 100 f. brn., blue & grn. 1·10 50
417. – 130 f. brn., blue & green 1·40 75
DESIGN: 130 f. "Apollo" and "Soyuz" spacecraft docked.

**119.** "Craterostigma plantagineum".

**1975.** Flowers. Multicoloured.
418. 5 f. Type **119** .. .. 10 10
419. 10 f. "Tapinanthus globiferus" .. .. 20 15
420. 15 f. "Commelina forsalaei" (vert.) .. .. 30 15
421. 20 f. "Adenium obasum" 35 15
422. 25 f. "Hibiscus esulenus" 60 20
423. 30 f. "Hibiscus sabdariffa" 75 25
424. 40 f. "Kigelia africana" .. 1·10 30

120. Football.

**1975.** Air. Olympic Games, Montreal (1976).
425. **120.** 75 f. green and red .. 80 30
426. – 100 f. brown, blue & red 1·25 55
427. – 125 f. blue and brown 1·40 80
DESIGNS: 100 f. Throwing the discus. 125 f. Running.

**1975.** Air. Successful Rendezvous of "Apollo-Soyuz" Mission. Optd. **JONCTION 17 JUILLET 1975.**

428. **118.** 100 f. brn., bl. & grn... 1·10 70
429. – 130 f. brn., bl. & grn... 1·40 90

**122.** Stylized British and American Flags.

**1975.** Air. Bicent. of American Revolution.

430. **122.** 150 f. bl., red & brn. 1·90 95

**123.** "Adoration of the Shepherds" (Murillo).

**1975.** Air. Christmas. Religious Paintings. Multicoloured.

431. 40 f. Type **123** .. .. 55 35
432. 75 f. "Adoration of the Shepherds" (G. de la Tour) 1·00 55
433. 80 f. "Virgin of the Bible" (R. van der Weyden) (vert.) 1·25 60
434. 100 f. "Holy Family with the Lamb" (attrib. Raphael) (vert.) .. 1·90 95

**124.** Alexander Graham Bell and Satellite.

**1976.** Telephone Centenary.

435. **124.** 100 f. multicoloured .. 1·00 50
436. 125 f. multicoloured .. 1·50 75

**125.** U.S.S.R. (ice hockey).

**1976.** Winter Olympics. Medal-winners, Innsbruck. Multicoloured.

437. 60 f. Type **125** (postage).. 75 35
438. 90 f. Ski-jumping (K. Schnabl, Austria) 95 40
439. 250 f. Bobsleighing (West Germany) (air).. 2·25 75
440. 300 f. Speed-skating (J. E. Storholt, Norway) 2·75 1·10

These stamps were not issued without overprints.

**126.** Paul Revere (after Copley) and his Night Ride.

**1976.** Air. Bicent. of American Revolution.

442. 100 f. Type **126** .. .. 80 25
443. 125 f. Washington (after Stuart) and "Washington crossing the Delaware" (detail, Leutze).. .. 95 35
444. 150 f. Lafayette offering his services to America 1·25 45
445. 200 f. Rochambeau and detail "Siege of Yorktown" (Couder) .. 1·60 70
446. 250 f. Franklin (after Duplessis) and "Declaration of Independence" (detail, Trumball) .. .. 2·25 80

**127.** Hurdles.

**1976.** Olympic Games, Montreal. **Mult.**

448. 45 f. Type **127** (postage) .. 60 25
449. 100 f. Boxing (air) .. 95 35
450. 200 f. Pole vaulting .. 1·90 55
451. 300 f. Putting the shot .. 2·75 95

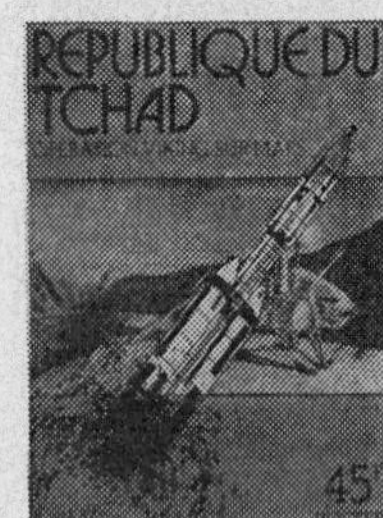


**128.** Launch of "Viking".

**1976.** "Viking" landing on Mars. Mult.

453. 45 f. Type **128** (postage).. 45 20
454. 90 f. Trajectory of flight.. 80 30
455. 100 f. Descent to Mars (air) 85 35
456. 200 f. "Viking" in flight 1·60 50
457. 250 f. "Viking" on landing approach .. .. 1·90 75

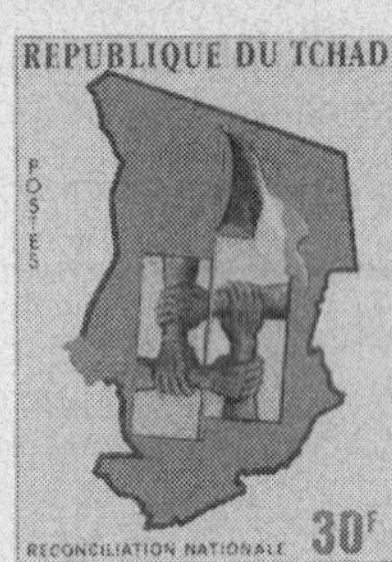


**129.** Flag and Clasped Hands on Map of Chad.

**1976.** National Reconciliation. Mult.

459. 30 f. Type **129** .. .. 35 25
460. 60 f. Type **129** .. .. 85 30
461. 120 f. Map, people and various occupations .. 1·60 70

**130.** Release of Political Prisoners.

**1976.** 1st Anniv. of April 1st Revolution. Multicoloured.

462. 30 f. Type **130** .. .. 25 20
463. 60 f. Officer-cadets on parade .. .. .. 50 30
464. 120 f. Type **130** .. .. 1·10 55

**131.** Concorde.

**1976.** Air. Concorde's First Commercial Flight.

465 **131** 250 f. blue, red & black 4·25 2·75

**1976.** Pyrograved Gourds.

466. **132.** 30 f. multicoloured .. 30 20
467. – 60 f. multicoloured .. 60 25
468. – 120 f. multicoloured .. 1·25 60

DESIGNS: 60 f., 120 f. Gourds with different decorations.

**1976.** Nobel Prizewinners. As T **189** of Central African Empire. Multicoloured.

469. 45 f. Robert Koch (Medicine, 1905) .. .. 95 35
470. 90 f. Anatole France (Literature, 1921) .. 1·25 60
471. 100 f. Albert Einstein (Physics, 1921) (air) .. 1·25 30
472. 200 f. Dag Hammarskjold (Peace, 1961) .. .. 1·90 50
473. 300 f. Dr. S. Tomonaga (Physics, 1965) .. .. 2·75 75

**133.** "The Nativity" (Hans Holbein).

**1976.** Air. Christmas. Multicoloured.

475. 30 f. "The Nativity" (Altdorfer) .. .. 30 20
476. 60 f. Type **133** .. .. 55 30
477. 120 f. "Adoration of the Shepherds" (Honthorst) (horiz.) .. .. .. 1·00 60
478. 150 f. "Adoration of the Magi" (David) (horiz.) 1·60 95

**134.** "Lesdiguieres Bridge".

**1976.** Air. Cent. of Impressionism. Paintings by Johan Bathold Jongkind. Mult.

479. 100 f. Type **134** .. 1·40 70
480. 120 f. "Warship" .. 2·50 90

**1977.** Zeppelin Flights. As T **190** of Central African Empire. Multicoloured.

481. 100 f. Friedrichshafen and German 50 pf. stamp, 1936 (postage) .. 1·25 50
482. 125 f. Polar scene and German 1 m. stamp, 1931 (air) .. .. 1·10 30
483. 150 f. Chicago store and German 4 m. stamp, 1933 .. .. .. 2·00 45
484. 175 f. New York, London and German 2 m. stamp, 1928 .. .. .. 2·50 55
485. 200 f. New York and U.S. $2·60 stamp, 1930 .. 2·75 85

**1977.** Air. 10th Anniv. of International French Language Council. As T **204** of Benin.

487. 100 f. multicoloured .. 85 50



**132.** Gourd and Ladle.



**135.** Simon Bolivar.

**1977.** Great Personalities. Multicoloured.

488. 150 f. Type **135** .. .. 1·25 50
489. 175 f. Joseph J. Roberts 1·50 50
490. 200 f. Queen Wilhelmina 1·75 60
491. 200 f. General de Gaulle.. 2·50 85
493. 250 f. Coronation of Queen Elizabeth II (horiz.) .. 2·50 90
492. 325 f. King Baudouin and Queen Fabiola .. .. 2·75 95

**137.** Lafayette and Arrival in America.

**1977.** Air. Bicentenary of American Independence. Multicoloured.

495. 100 f. Type **137** .. .. 1·10 50
496. 120 f. Abraham Lincoln .. 1·25 60
497. 150 f. F. J. Madison .. 1·75 75

**138.** Radio Aerial, Sound Waves and Map.

**1977.** Posts and Telecommunications Emblems.

498. – 30 f. black and yellow 35 20
499. **138.** 60 f. multicoloured .. 70 25
500. – 120 f. multicoloured .. 1·25 60

DESIGNS—HORIZ. (47 × 26 mm.). 30 f. Posthorn and initials "ONPT". VERT. (26 × 36 mm.). 120 f. Telecommunications skyline and initials "TIT".

**139.** Concorde.

**1977.** Air. "North Atlantic"—Concorde and Lindbergh Commemorations.

501. **139.** 100 f. blue, red and pale blue .. .. 75 45
502. – 120 f. brn., blue & grn. 85 50
503. – 150 f. violet, red & grn. 1·10 65
504. – 200 f. orge., pur. & brn. 1·60 85
505. – 300 f. blue, pur. & blk. 2·50 1·25

DESIGNS: 120 f. 150 f. 200 f. 300 f. Various portraits of Lindbergh with "Spirit of St. Louis" against different backgrounds.

**140.** "Mariner 10".

**1977.** Air. Space Research.

506. **140.** 100 f. bl., olive & grn. 80 50
507. – 200 f. brn., grn. & red 1·75 1·00
508. – 300 f. brn., grn. & bistre 2·50 1·25

DESIGNS: 200 f. "Luna 21". 300 f. "Viking".

**141.** Running.



**142.** "Back Pain".

**1977.** Air. Sports.

509. **141.** 30 f. brn., red & blue 30 20
510. – 60 f. brn., blue & orge. 55 30
511. – 120 f. multicoloured .. 1·00 50
512. – 125 f. mauve, vio. & grn. 1·25 60

DESIGNS: 60 f. Volleyball. 120 f. Football. 125 f. Basketball.

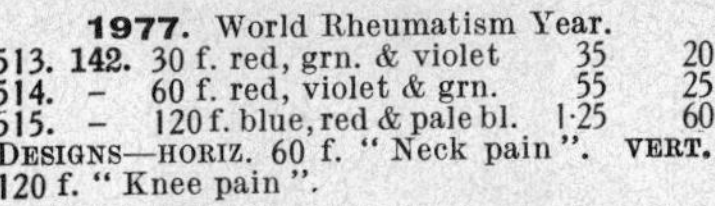

**1977.** World Rheumatism Year.

513. **142.** 30 f. red, grn. & violet 35 20
514. – 60 f. red, violet & grn. 55 25
515. – 120 f. blue, red & pale bl. 1·25 60

DESIGNS—HORIZ. 60 f. " Neck pain ". VERT. 120 f. " Knee pain ".

**1977.** Air. First Commercial Paris–New York Flight of Concorde. Optd **PARIS NEW-YORK 22.11.77**.

516 **139** 100 f. blue, red & lt blue 2·25 1·25

**144.** Saving a Goal.

**1977.** World Football Cup Championship Multicoloured.

517. 40 f. Type **144** .. .. 35 15
518. 60 f. Heading the ball .. 55 20
519. 100 f. Referee .. .. 95 30
520. 200 f. Foot kicking ball .. 1·90 60
521. 300 f. Pele (Brazilian player) .. .. .. 3·00 95

**145.** " Christ in the Manger ". (detail).

**1977.** Air. Christmas. Paintings by **Rubens.** Multicoloured.

523. 30 f. Type **145** .. .. 45 25
524. 60 f. " Virgin and Child with Two Donors " .. 75 35
525. 100 f. " The Adoration of the Shepherds " .. 1·25 60
526. 125 f. " The Adoration of the Magi " (detail) .. 1·60 80

**1978.** Coronation of Queen Elizabeth II. No. 493 optd. **ANNIVERSAIRE DU COURONNEMENT 1953-1978.**

527. 250 f. multicoloured .. 2·50 1·50

**147.** Antoine de Saint-Exupery

**1978.** Air. History of Aviation. Mult.

529. 40 f. Type **147** .. .. 50 20
530. 50 f. Wright Brothers and aircraft in flight .. .. 60 25
531. 80 f. Hugo Junkers .. 85 45
532. 100 f. Italo Balbo .. 1·10 55
533. 120 f. " Concorde " .. 1·25 75

**1978.** Air. "Philexafrique" Stamp Exhibition, Gabon (1st issue), and Int. Stamp Fair, Essen. As T **237** of Benin. Mult.

535. 100 f. Grey heron and Mecklenburg-Strelitz, ¼ sgr. stamp, 1864. .. 2·50 1·90
536. 100 f. Black rhinoceros and Chad 500 f. stamp, 1961 2·50 1·90

**148.** " Portrait ".

**150.** Head and Unhealthy and Healthy Villages.

**149.** " Helene Fourment ".

**1978.** 450th Death Anniv. of Albrecht Durer (artist). Multicoloured.

537. 60 f. Type **148** .. .. 50 15
538. 150 f. " Jacob Muffel " .. 1·40 30
539. 250 f. " Young Girl " .. 2·25 60
540. 350 f. " Oswolt Krel " .. 3·50 80

**1978.** 400th Birth Anniv. of Peter Paul Rubens (artist). Multicoloured.

541. 60 f. " Abraham and Melchisedek " (horiz.) 60 15
542. 120 f. Type **149** .. .. 1·10 25
543. 200 f. " David and the Elders of Israel " (horiz.) 1·90 60
544. 300 f. " Anne of Austria " 3·25 85

**1978.** National Health Day.

546. **150.** 60 f. multicoloured .. 60 35

**1978.** World Cup Football Championship Finalists. Nos. 517/21 optd. with teams and scores of past finals.

547. **144.** 40 f. multicoloured .. 35 20
548. – 60 f. multicoloured .. 50 30
549. – 100 f. multicoloured .. 85 50
550. – 200 f. multicoloured .. 1·90 95
551. – 300 f. multicoloured .. 3·00 1·50

OPTS: 40 f. **1962 BRESIL-TCHECOSLOVAQUIE, 3-1.** 60 f. **1966 GRAND BRETAGNE-ALLEMAGNE (RFA), 4-2.** 100 f. **1970 BRESIL-ITALIE, 4-1.** 200 f. **1974 ALLEMAGNE (RFA)-PAYS BAS, 2-1.** 300 f. **1978 ARGENTINE-PAYS BAS, 3-1.**

**152.** Camel Riders, Satellites and U.P.U. Emblem.

**1978.** " Philexafrique 2 " Exhibition, Libreville, Gabon. (2nd issue).

553. **152.** 60 f. red, mauve & blue 1·60 95
554. – 150 f. multicoloured .. 3·00 2·25

DESIGN: 150 f. Mother and child, native village and hibiscus.

**153.** Sand Gazelle.

**1979.** Endangered Animals. Multicoloured.

555. 40 f. Type **153** .. .. 45 15
556. 50 f. Addax .. .. 50 15
557. 60 f. Scimitar oryx .. 60 20
558. 100 f. Cheetah .. .. 1·00 40
559. 150 f. African ass .. 1·60 50
560. 300 f. Black rhinoceros .. 3·25 90

**154.** African Boy and Wall Painting.

**1979.** International Year of the Child Multicoloured.

561. 65 f. Type **154** .. .. 50 20
562. 75 f. Asian Girl .. .. 55 25
563. 100 f. European child and doves .. .. .. 80 30
564. 150 f. African boys and drawing of boats .. 1·25 50

**1979.** 10th Anniv. of "Apollo 11" Moon Landing. Nos. 453/7 optd. **ALUNISSAGE APOLLO XI JUILLET 1969.**

567. 45 f. Type **128** (postage) .. 35 25
568. 90 f. Trajectory of flight .. 80 35
569. 100 f. Descent on Mars (air) 75 50
570. 200 f. " Viking " in flight 1·50 85
571. 250 f. " Viking " on landing approach .. .. 1·90 1·10

**157.** Hurdles.

**1979.** Air. Olympic Games, Moscow 1980. Multicoloured.

573. 15 f. Type **157** .. .. 20 15
574. 30 f. Hockey .. .. 30 20
575. 250 f. Swimming .. .. 1·90 70
576. 350 f. Running .. .. 2·50 90

**158.** Reed Canoe and Austrian 10 k. stamp, 1910.

**1979.** Air. Death Centenary of Sir Rowland Hill. Multicoloured.

578 65 f. Type **158** .. .. 50 15
579 100 f. Sailing canoe and U.S. $1 stamp of 1894 .. 85 30
580 200 f. "Curacao" (paddle-steamer) and French 1 f. stamp of 1853 .. .. 1·75 60
581 300 f. "Calypso" (liner) and Holstein 1¼ s. stamp of 1864 .. .. .. 2·25 1·10

**159.** Slalom.

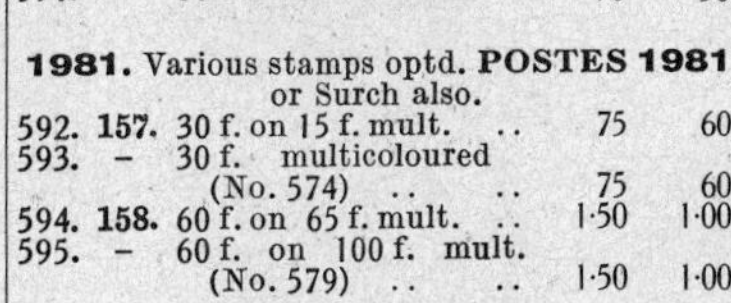


**160.** " Concorde " and Map of Africa.

**1979.** Winter Olympic Games, Lake **Placid** (1980). Multicoloured.

583. 20 f. Type **159** .. .. 20 15
584. 40 f. Biathlon .. .. 35 15
585. 60 f. Ski jump (horiz.) .. 40 15
586. 150 f. Slalom (different) .. 1·10 35
587. 350 f. Cross-country skiing (horiz.) .. .. .. 2·50 80
588. 500 f. Downhill skiing (horiz.) .. .. .. 3·75 1·25

**1980.** 20th Anniv. of African Air Safety Organization (ASECNA).

589. **160.** 15 f. multicoloured .. 30 10
590. 30 f. multicoloured .. 45 25
591. 60 f. multicoloured .. 90 50

**1981.** Various stamps optd. **POSTES 1981** or Surch also.

592. **157.** 30 f. on 15 f. mult. .. 75 60
593. – 30 f. multicoloured (No. 574) .. .. 75 60
594. **158.** 60 f. on 65 f. mult. .. 1·50 1·00
595. – 60 f. on 100 f. mult. (No. 579) .. .. 1·50 1·00

**162.** Footballer.

**1982.** World Cup Football Championship, Spain. Multicoloured.

596. 30 f. Hungary (postage) .. 25 15
597. 40 f. Type **162** .. .. 30 15
598. 50 f. Algeria .. .. 35 20
599. 60 f. Argentina .. .. 45 20
600. 80 f. Brazil (air) .. .. 55 20
601. 300 f. West Germany .. 2·25 70

DESIGNS: As T **162** but each value showing different team's footballer.

**163.** Lady Diana and her Brother (1967).

**1982.** 21st Birthday of Princess of Wales. Multicoloured.

603. 30 f. Lady Diana in christening robe (1961) (postage) .. .. 30 15
604. 40 f. Portrait of Lady Diana (1965) .. .. 35 15
605. 50 f. Type **163** .. .. 45 20
606. 60 f. Lady Diana and her pony (1975) .. .. 55 20
607. 80 f. Lady Diana in Switzerland (1977) (air) .. 60 20
608. 300 f. Lady Diana as nursery teacher (1980) .. 2·50 70

**164.** West German Scouts.

**1982.** 75th Anniv. of Scout Movement. Multicoloured.

610. 30 f. Type **164** (postage) .. 35 15
611. 40 f. Upper Volta scouts .. 35 15
612. 50 f. Mali scouts and African dancers .. 50 20
613. 60 f. Scottish scout, piper and dancer .. .. 60 20
614. 80 f. Kuwait scouts (air) .. 55 20
615. 300 f. Chad cub scout .. 2·25 70

**165.** Judo.

**1982.** Olympic Games, Los Angeles (1984.) (1st issue). Multicoloured.

617. 30 f. Gymnastics (horse exercise) (postage) .. 30 15
618. 40 f. Show jumping .. 30 15
619. 50 f. Type **165** .. .. 35 20
620. 60 f. High jumping .. 60 20
621. 80 f. Hurdling (air) .. 55 20
622. 300 f. Gymnastics (floor exercise) .. .. 2·25 70

See also Nos. 678/83 and 735/8.

**1982.** Birth of Prince William of **Wales.** Nos. 603/8 optd **21 JUIN 1982 WILLIAM ARTHUR PHILIP LOUIS PRINCE DE GALLES.**

624. 30 f. Type **163** (postage) .. 30 15
625. 40 f. Portrait of Lady Diana as a young girl .. 35 15
626. 50 f. Lady Diana and her brother .. .. 45 20
627. 60 f. Lady Diana with her pony .. .. 50 20
628. 80 f. Lady Diana in Switzerland (air) .. 60 20
629. 300 f. Lady Diana with children .. .. .. 2·50 70

**167.** Marco Tardelli (Italy) and Passarella (Argentine).

**1983.** World Cup Football Championship Results. Multicoloured.
631. 30 f. Type **167** (postage) .. 25 10
632. 40 f. Paolo Rossi (Italy) and Zico (Brazil) .. 30 15
633. 50 f. Pierre Littbarski (West Germany) and Platini (France) .. 35 20
634. 60 f. Gabriele Oriali (Italy) and Smolarek (Poland) .. 45 20
635. 70 f. Boniek (Poland) and Alain Giresse (France) (air) .. .. .. 55 20
636. 300 f. Bruno Conti (Italy) and Paul Breitner (West Germany) .. .. 2·25 70

**168.** Philidor and 19th-century European Rook.

**1982.** Chess Grand Masters. Multicoloured.
638 30 f. Type **168** (postage) .. 35 15
639 40 f. Paul Morphy and 19th-century Chinese knight .. .. .. 50 15
640 50 f. Howard Staunton and Lewis knight .. .. 60 25
641 60 f. Jean-Paul Capablanca and African knight .. 75 25
642 80 f. Boris Spassky and Staunton knight (air) .. 1·25 25
643 300 f. Anatoly Karpov and 19th-century Chinese knight .. .. .. 3·00 1·00

**169.** K. E. Tsiolkovski and "Soyuz".

**1983.** Exploitation of Space. Multicoloured.
645. 30 f. Type **169** (postage) .. 25 10
646. 40 f. R. H. Goddard and space telescope .. 30 15
647. 50 f. Korolev and ultra-violet telescope .. 35 20
648. 60 f. Von Braun and Space Shuttle .. .. 45 20
649. 80 f. Esnault Pelterie and "Ariane" rocket and "Symphonie" satellite (air) .. .. .. 55 25
650. 300 f. H. Oberth and construction of orbiting space station .. .. .. 2·25 70

**170.** Charles and Robert Balloon, 1783.

**1983.** Air. Balloons. Multicoloured.
652 100 f. Type **170** .. .. 95 50
653 200 f. Blanchard balloon, Berlin, 1788 .. .. 1·90 95
654 300 f. Charles Green balloon, London, 1837 (horiz) .. .. .. 2·50 1·75
655 400 f. Modern advertising airship (horiz) .. .. 3·25 1·75

**171.** Bobsleigh.

**1983.** Winter Olympic Games, Sarajevo. Multicoloured.
657. 30 f. Type **171** (postage) .. 25 10
658. 40 f. Speed skating .. 30 15
659. 50 f. Cross-country skiing 30 20
660. 60 f. Ice hockey .. .. 35 20
661. 80 f. Ski jump (air) .. 55 20
662. 300 f. Downhill skiing .. 2·25 70

**172.** Montgolfier Brothers and "Le Martial" Balloon, 1783.

**1983.** Bicentenary of Manned Flight. Multicoloured.
664. 25 f. Type **172** (postage) .. 20 15
665. 45 f. Pilatre de Rozier and first manned flight, 1783 35 20
666. 50 f. Jacques Garnerin and balloon (first parachute descent, 1797) .. .. 35 20
667. 60 f. J. P. Blanchard and balloon at Chelsea, 1784 45 30
668. 80 f. H. Giffard and steam-powered dirigible, 1852 (air) .. .. .. 75 40
669. 250 f. Zeppelin and airship "L 21", 1900 .. .. 2·10 1·25

**173.** Gottlieb Daimler, Karl Benz and Mercedes "Type S," 1927.

**1983.** Car Manufacturers. Multicoloured.
671. 25 f. Type **173** (postage) .. 30 10
672. 35 f. Friedrich von Martini and Torpedo Martini "Type GC 32", 1913 45 15
673. 50 f. Walter P. Chrysler and Chrysler "70", 1926 70 20
674. 60 f. Nicola Romeo and Alfa Romeo "6 C 1750 Grand Sport", 1929 .. 75 20
675. 80 f. Stewart Rolls, Henry Royce and "Phantom II Continental", 1934 (air) 95 20
676. 250 f. Lord Shrewsbury and Talbot-Lago "Record", 1948 .. .. .. 2·50 70

**174.** Kayak.

**1983.** Olympic Games, Los Angeles (2nd issue). Multicoloured.
678. 25 f. Type **174** (postage) .. 20 10
679. 45 f. Long jumping .. 30 15
680. 50 f. Boxing .. .. 35 15
681. 60 f. Discus-throwing .. 45 20
682. 80 f. Relay race (air) .. 60 20
683. 350 f. Horse jumping .. 2·50 70

**175.** Dove on Map.

**1983.** Peace and Reconciliation. Mult.
685. 50 f. Type **175** (postage) .. 35 15
686. 50 f. Foodstuffs on map .. 35 15
687. 50 f. President Habre .. 35 15
688. 60 f. As No. 687 .. .. 45 15
689. 80 f. Type **175** .. .. 65 25
690. 80 f. As No. 686 .. .. 65 25
691. 80 f. As No. 687 .. .. 65 25
692. 100 f. As No. 687 .. .. 75 25
693. 150 f. Type **175** (air) .. 1·00 30
694. 150 f. As No. 686 .. .. 1·00 30
695. 200 f. Type **175** .. .. 1·25 45
696. 200 f. As No. 686 .. .. 1·25 45

**1983.** 15th World Scout Jamboree, Canada. Nos. 610/15 optd. **XV WORLD JAMBOREE MONDIAL ALBERTA CANADA 1983.**
697. 30 f. multicoloured (postage) 25 15
698. 40 f. multicoloured .. 30 15
699. 50 f. multicoloured .. 35 20
700. 60 f. multicoloured .. 45 20
701. 80 f. multicoloured (air) .. 55 20
702. 300 f. multicoloured .. 2·25 70

**1983.** 60th Anniv of Int. Chess Federation. Nos. 638/43 optd **60e ANNIVERSAIRE FEDERATION MONDIAL D'ECHECS 1924–1984.**
704. 30 f. multicoloured (postage 50 20
705. 40 f. multicoloured .. 60 20
706. 50 f. multicoloured .. 60 25
707. 60 f. multicoloured .. 75 25
708. 80 f. multicoloured (air) .. 1·25 45
709. 300 f. multicoloured .. 3·75 1·25

**178.** Chad Martyrs.

**1984.** Celebrities. Multicoloured.
711. 50 f. Type **178** .. .. 35 15
712. 200 f. P. Harris and Rotary Headquarters, U.S.A. .. 1·50 35
713. 300 f. Alfred Nobel and will 2·50 60
714. 350 f. Raphael and "Virgin with the Infant and St. John the Baptist" .. 3·75 75
715. 400 f. Rembrandt and "The Holy Family" (air) 3·75 85
716. 500 f. Goethe and Scenes from "Faust" .. .. 4·25 1·00

**179.** Martyrs Memorial.

**1984.** Martyrs Memorial.
718. **179.** 50 f. mult. (postage) .. 35 15
719. 80 f. multicoloured .. 60 25
720. 120 f. multicoloured .. 85 25
721. 200 f. multicoloured (air) .. .. .. 1·60 50
722. 250 f. multicoloured .. 2·25 75

**180.** Durer and Painting.

**1984.** Celebrities and Events. Multicoloured.
723. 50 f. Type **180** (postage) .. 75 15
724. 200 f. Henri Dunant and battle scene .. .. 1·75 35
725. 300 f. Early telephone and satellite receiving station, Goonhilly Downs .. .. .. 2·25 60
726. 350 f. President Kennedy and first foot-print on Moon .. .. .. 2·75 75
727. 400 f. Infra-red satellite picture (Europe-Africa co-operation) (air) .. 2·50 75
728. 500 f. Prince and Princess of Wales .. .. .. 3·75 1·00

**181.** "Communications".

**1984.** World Communications Year.
730. **181.** 50 f. mult. (postage) .. 45 15
731. 60 f. multicoloured .. 50 35
732. 70 f. multicoloured .. 50 35
733. 125 f. multicoloured (air) .. .. .. 1·00 55
734. 250 f. multicoloured .. 1·90 1·10

**182.** Two-man Kayak.

**1984.** Air. Olympic Games, Los Angeles (3rd issue). Multicoloured.
735. 100 f. Type **182** .. .. 75 25
736. 200 f. Kayaks (close-up) .. 1·50 50
737. 300 f. One-man kayak .. 2·25 75
738. 400 f. Coxed fours .. .. 3·00 1·00

**183.** "Lady", 1879.

**1984.** Historic Transport. Multicoloured.
740. 50 f. Type **183** (postage) .. 50 40
741. 200 f. Sailing boat on Lake Chad .. .. .. 1·75 65
742. 300 f. Graf Zeppelin (airship) .. .. .. 3·00 1·25
743. 350 f. Six-wheel Renault automobile, 1930 .. 2·75 1·25
744. 400 f. Bloch "120" airplane (air) .. .. .. 2·50 1·50
745. 500 f. Douglas "DC 8" airplane .. .. .. 3·75 2·00

**184.** African with broken Manacles.

**185.** Pres. Hissein Habre.

**1984.** 2nd Anniv. of Entrance of Government Forces in N'Djamena.
747. **184.** 50 f. multicoloured .. 50 25

**1984.**
748. **185.** 125 f. black, blue and yellow .. .. 1·25 50

**186.** British East Indiaman.

**1984.** Transport. Multicoloured. (a) Ships.
749 90 f. Type **186** .. .. 95 45
750 125 f. "Vera Cruz" (steamer) .. .. 1·25 55
751 200 f. "Carlisle Castle" (sail merchantman) .. 2·25 75
752 300 f. "Britannia" (steamer) .. .. 2·75 1·25

(b) Locomotives.
753. 100 f. "Nord" 1885 .. 95 35
754. 150 f. "Columbia" 1888 .. 1·25 50
755. 250 f. "Rete Mediterranea", 1900 .. .. 2·25 75
756. 350 f. MAV "114" .. .. 2·75 1·25

**187.** Virgin and Child. **188.** Guitars.

**1984.** Christmas.

757. **187.** 50 f. brown and blue 45 15
758. 60 f. brown and orge. 50 20
759. 80 f. brown and green 65 25
760. 85 f. brown and purple 70 25
761. 100 f. brown and orge. 85 30
762. 135 f. brown and blue 1·25 45

**1985.** European Music Year. Multicoloured.

763. 20 f. Type **188** .. .. 20 10
764. 25 f. Harps .. .. .. 25 15
765. 30 f. Xylophones .. .. 30 15
766. 50 f. Drums .. .. 45 20
767. 70 f. As No. 766 .. .. 55 20
768. 80 f. As No. 764 .. .. 75 30
769. 100 f. Type **188** .. .. 90 45
770. 250 f. As No. 765 .. .. 2·25 85

**189.** "Chlorophyllum molybdites".

**1985.** Fungi. Multicoloured.

771. 25 f. Type **189** .. .. 55 30
772. 30 f. "Tulostoma volvulatum" .. .. .. 70 35
773. 50 f. "Lentinus tuberregium" .. .. .. 1·00 45
774. 70 f. As No. 773 .. .. 1·40 60
775. 80 f. "Podaxis pistillaris" 1·75 65
776. 100 f. Type **189** .. .. 2·50 1·00

**190.** Stylized Tree and Scout.

**1985.** Air "Philexafrique" Stamp Exhibition, Lome, Togo (1st issue). Multicoloured.

777. 200 f. Type **190** .. .. 1·90 1·50
778. 200 f. Fokker "27" airplane 1·90 1·50

See also Nos. 808/9.

**191.** Abraham Lincoln.

**1985.** Celebrities. Multicoloured.

779. 25 f. Type **191** (postage) .. 20 10
780. 45 f. Henri Dunant (founder of Red Cross) .. 45 15
781. 50 f. Gottlieb Daimler (automobile designer) .. 60 15
782. 60 f. Louis Bleriot (pilot) (air) .. .. .. 55 30
783. 80 f. Paul Harris (founder of Rotary International) 55 20
784. 350 f. Auguste Piccard (undersea explorer) .. 3·25 1·40

**192.** Figures within Geometric Pattern. **193.** Sun and Hands breaking through Darkness.

**1985.** International Youth Year. Mult.

786. 70 f. Type **192** .. .. 50 25
787. 200 f. Figures on ribbon around globe .. .. 1·50 75

**1985.** 3rd Anniv. of Entrance of Government Forces in N'Djamena. Multicoloured.

788. 70 f. Type **193** .. .. 55 25
789. 70 f. Claw attacking hand 55 25
790. 70 f. Pres. Hissein Habre (36 × 48 mm.) .. .. 25 20
791. 110 f. Type **193** .. .. 80 35
792. 110 f. As No. 789 .. .. 80 35
793. 110 f. As No. 790 .. .. 1·10 35

**194.** Saddle-bill Stork. **196.** Sitatunga.

**195.** Fokker Friendship, Farman M.F.11 and Emblem.

**1985.** Birth Bicentenary of John J. Audubon (ornithologist).

794. **194.** 70 f. black, blue and brown .. .. 1·40 85
795. – 110 f. olive, green and brown .. .. 2·00 1·25
796. – 150 f. blue, red and olive .. .. 3·00 1·90
797. – 200 f. deep blue, mauve and blue .. 3·50 2·10

Designs: 110 f. Ostrich. 150 f. Marabou stork. 200 f. Secretary bird.

**1985.** Air. 25th Anniv. of ASECNA (navigation agency). Multicoloured.

799. 70 f. Type **195** .. .. 50 30
800. 110 f. Fokker "F.27" "Friendship" and "Spirit of St. Louis" .. 75 50
801. 250 f. Fokker "F.27" "Friendship" and Vickers Vimy .. 1·90 1·25

**1985.** Mammals.

802. **196.** 50 f. brn., bl. & dp. brn. 55 35
803. – 70 f. brown, green and red .. .. .. 70 50
804. – 250 f. multicoloured .. 2·50 1·60

Designs—horiz. 70 f. Greater kudus. vert. 250 f. Bearded mouflons.

**197.** U.N. Emblem on Peace Dove and Girl with Flowers.

**1985.** 40th Anniv. of U.N.O. and 25th Anniv. of U.N. Membership.

806 **197** 200 f. blue, red and brown .. .. 1·50 1·00
807 – 300 f. blue, red and yellow .. .. 2·25 1·50

Design: 300 f. U.N. emblem as flower with peace doves forming stalk.

**198.** Girl with Posy, Youth Ceremony and I.Y.Y. Emblem.

**1985.** Air. "Philexafrique" Stamp Exhibition, Lome, Togo (2nd issue). Mult.

808 250 f. Type **198** (International Youth Year) .. 2·25 1·90
809 250 f. Computer terminal, liner, airplane, train, rocket and U.P.U. emblem .. .. 2·50 1·90

**199.** Hugo.

**1985.** Air. Death Centenary of Victor Hugo (writer).

810. **199.** 70 f. blue, sepia and brown .. .. 50 35
811. 110 f. brown, green and red .. .. 75 50
812. 250 f. black, red and orange .. .. 1·90 1·00
813. 300 f. purple, blue and red .. .. .. 2·25 1·25

**200.** Nativity. **201.** Pictures of Visit on Map.

**1985.** Air. Christmas.

814. **200.** 250 f. multicoloured .. 1·90 75

**1986.** Visit of President to Interior.

815. **201.** 100 f. yellow, black and green .. .. 95 50
816. 170 f. yellow, black and pink .. .. 1·90 75
817. 200 f. yellow, black and green .. .. 2·25 1·25

**1987.** Various stamps surch.

818 – 170 f. on 300 f. mult (725) (postage) .. 70 60
819 – 230 f. on 300 f. blue, red and yellow (807) .. 1·00 85
820 – 240 f. on 300 f. mult (742) .. .. 1·00 85
822 **175** 100 f. on 200 f. mult (air) .. .. 70 55
823 – 100 f. on 200 f. mult (696) .. .. 40 30
824 – 100 f. on 250 f. mult (669) .. .. 70 55
825 – 100 f. on 300 f. mult (643) .. .. 40 30
826 – 100 f. on 300 f. mult (662) .. .. 40 30
827 **179** 170 f. on 200 f. mult .. 70 60
828 **181** 170 f. on 250 f. mult .. 1·10 90
829 – 170 f. on 300 f. mult (601) .. .. 70 60
830 – 170 f. on 300 f. mult (622) .. .. 70 60
831 – 240 f. on 300 f. mult (636) .. .. 1·00 90

**203** Fada

**1987.** Liberation of Fada.

832 **203** 40 f. multicoloured ..

**204** Boy suffering from Trachoma

**1987.** Lions Club Anti-trachoma Campaign. Multicoloured.

835 30 f. Type **204** .. ..
837 100 f. Type **204** .. ..
838 120 f. Healthy boy and afflicted boys (horiz)
840 200 f. Doctor examining boy (horiz) .. ..

**205** 400 Metres Hurdles

**1988.** Air. Olympic Games, Seoul. Mult.

841 100 f. Type **205** .. .. 75 25
842 170 f. 5000 metres (horiz) .. 1·25 35
843 200 f. Long jump (horiz) .. 1·50 50
844 600 f. Triple jump .. 4·50 1·40

**206** Barbary Sheep

**1988.** Endangered Animals. Barbary Sheep. Multicoloured.

846 25 f. Type **206** .. .. 25 20
847 45 f. Mother and lamb .. 50 25
848 70 f. Two sheep .. .. 75 30
849 100 f. Two adults with lamb .. .. .. 1·00 50

**207** President and Crowd on Map **208** Boy posting Letter

**1989.** "Liberation".

850 **207** 20 f. multicoloured .. 25 15
851 25 f. multicoloured .. 25 15
852 40 f. multicoloured .. 35 20
853 100 f. multicoloured .. 1·00 30
854 170 f. multicoloured .. 1·60 50

**1989.** World Post Day.

855 **208** 100 f. multicoloured ..
856 120 f. multicoloured ..
857 170 f. violet .. ..
858 250 f. multicoloured ..

**209** N'Djamena Cathedral and Pope with Crucifix

**1990.** Visit of Pope John Paul II. Mult.

| | | | |
|---|---|---|---|
| 859 | 20 f. Type **209** .. .. | 25 | 10 |
| 860 | 80 f. Cathedral and Pope (different) .. .. | 70 | 35 |
| 861 | 100 f. Type **209** .. .. | 95 | 60 |
| 862 | 170 f. As No. 860 .. .. | 1·60 | 1·10 |

**210** Traditional Hairstyle

**1990.**

| | | | | |
|---|---|---|---|---|
| 863 | **210** | 100 f. multicoloured .. | 45 | 25 |
| 864 | | 120 f. multicoloured .. | 55 | 30 |
| 865 | | 170 f. multicoloured .. | 80 | 45 |
| 866 | | 250 f. multicoloured .. | 1·10 | 65 |

**215** Queues and Nurse vaccinating Child

**216** Torch, Hands with Broken Manacles and Ballot Box

**1991.** "Child Vaccination—Assured Future".

| | | | | |
|---|---|---|---|---|
| 880 | **215** | 30 f. multicoloured .. | 25 | 20 |
| 881 | | 100 f. multicoloured .. | 75 | 45 |
| 882 | | 170 f. multicoloured .. | 1·25 | 75 |
| 883 | | 180 f. multicoloured .. | 1·25 | 75 |
| 884 | | 200 f. multicoloured .. | 1·50 | 1·00 |

**1991.** Day of Freedom and Democracy.

| | | | | |
|---|---|---|---|---|
| 885 | **216** | 10 f. multicoloured .. | 10 | 10 |
| 886 | | 20 f. multicoloured .. | 20 | 15 |
| 887 | | 40 f. multicoloured .. | 30 | 20 |
| 888 | | 70 f. multicoloured .. | 50 | 30 |
| 889 | | 130 f. multicoloured .. | 95 | 60 |
| 890 | | 200 f. multicoloured .. | 1·50 | 80 |

**217** Mother and Child

**219** Mother and Child, Globe and Cereals

**218** Class

**1992.** 20th Anniv of Medecins sans Frontieres (medical relief organization).

| | | | | |
|---|---|---|---|---|
| 891 | **217** | 20 f. multicoloured .. | 20 | 10 |
| 892 | | 45 f. multicoloured .. | 30 | 20 |
| 893 | | 85 f. multicoloured .. | 70 | 35 |
| 894 | | 170 f. multicoloured .. | 1·25 | 70 |
| 895 | | 300 f. multicoloured .. | 2·25 | 1·10 |

**1992.** Literacy Campaign.

| | | | | |
|---|---|---|---|---|
| 896 | **218** | 25 f. multicoloured .. | 20 | 10 |
| 897 | | 40 f. multicoloured .. | 30 | 20 |
| 898 | | 70 f. multicoloured .. | 50 | 25 |
| 899 | | 100 f. multicoloured .. | 75 | 35 |
| 900 | | 180 f. multicoloured .. | 1·25 | 60 |
| 901 | | 200 f. multicoloured .. | 1·50 | 95 |

**1992.** International Nutrition Conference, Rome.

| | | | | |
|---|---|---|---|---|
| 902 | **219** | 10 f. multicoloured .. | 15 | 10 |
| 903 | | 60 f. multicoloured .. | 45 | 25 |
| 904 | | 120 f. multicoloured .. | 95 | 55 |
| 905 | | 500 f. multicoloured .. | 3·50 | 1·60 |

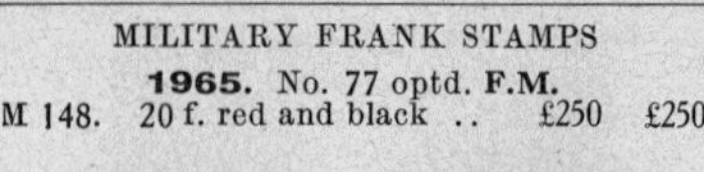

## MILITARY FRANK STAMPS

**1965.** No. 77 optd. **F.M.**

| | | | |
|---|---|---|---|
| M 148. | 20 f. red and black .. | £250 | £250 |

**M 24.** Soldier with Standard.

**M 92.** Shoulder Flash of 1st Regiment.

**1966.** No value indicated.

| | | | |
|---|---|---|---|
| M 149. **M 24.** | (—) multicoloured | 1·50 | 1·00 |

**1972.** No value indicated.

| | | | |
|---|---|---|---|
| M 353. **M 92.** | (—) multicoloured | 75 | 35 |

## OFFICIAL STAMPS

**O 23.** Flag and Map.

**1966.** Flag in blue, yellow and red.

| | | | |
|---|---|---|---|
| O 148. **O 23.** | 1 f. blue .. .. | 10 | 10 |
| O 149. | 2 f. grey .. .. | 10 | 10 |
| O 150. | 5 f. black .. .. | 15 | 10 |
| O 151. | 10 f. blue .. .. | 15 | 10 |
| O 152. | 25 f. orange .. .. | 25 | 15 |
| O 153. | 30 f. turquoise .. | 40 | 20 |
| O 154. | 40 f. red .. .. | 45 | 20 |
| O 155. | 50 f. purple .. .. | 55 | 25 |
| O 156. | 85 f. green .. .. | 85 | 45 |
| O 157. | 100 f. brown .. | 1·40 | 50 |
| O 158. | 200 f. red .. .. | 2·50 | 95 |

## POSTAGE DUE STAMPS

**1928.** Postage Due type of France optd **TCHAD A. E. F.**

| | | | |
|---|---|---|---|
| D 58. **D 11.** | 5 c. blue .. .. | 10 | 10 |
| D 59. | 10 c. brown .. .. | 15 | 15 |
| D 60. | 20 c. olive .. .. | 25 | 25 |
| D 61. | 25 c. red .. .. | 45 | 45 |
| D 62. | 30 c. red .. .. | 50 | 50 |
| D 63. | 45 c. green .. .. | 75 | 75 |
| D 64. | 50 c. purple .. .. | 1·10 | 1·10 |
| D 65. | 60 c. brown on cream | 1·25 | 1·25 |
| D 66. | 1 f. red on cream .. | 1·25 | 1·25 |
| D 67. | 2 f. red .. .. | 3·75 | 3·75 |
| D 68. | 3 f. violet .. .. | 2·25 | 2·25 |

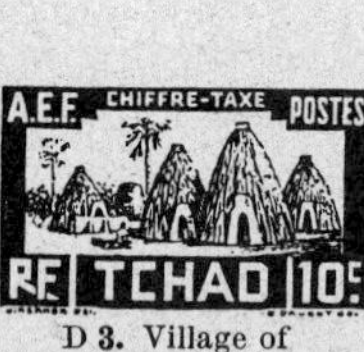

**D 3.** Village of Straw Huts.

**D 4.** Pirogue on Lake Chad.

**1930.**

| | | | |
|---|---|---|---|
| D 69. **D 3.** | 5 c. olive and blue .. | 25 | 25 |
| D 70. | 10 c. brown and red .. | 30 | 30 |
| D 71. | 20 c. brown and green | 55 | 55 |
| D 72. | 25 c. brown and blue | 70 | 70 |
| D 73. | 30 c. green and brown | 70 | 70 |
| D 74. | 45 c. olive and green | 1·00 | 1·00 |
| D 75. | 50 c. brn. and mauve | 1·25 | 1·25 |
| D 76. | 60 c. black and lilac .. | 2·25 | 2·25 |
| D 77. **D 4.** | 1 f. black and brown | 2·25 | 2·25 |
| D 78. | 2 f. brown and mauve | 4·25 | 4·25 |
| D 79. | 3 f. brown and red .. | 28·00 | 28·00 |

**D 6.** Gonoa Hippopotamus.

**1962.**

| | | | |
|---|---|---|---|
| D 89. | 50 c. bistre .. .. | 10 | 10 |
| D 90. | 50 c. brown .. .. | 10 | 10 |
| D 91. | 1 f. blue .. .. | 10 | 10 |
| D 92. | 1 f. green .. .. | 10 | 10 |
| D 93. | 2 f. red .. .. | 15 | 15 |
| D 94. | 2 f. red .. .. | 15 | 15 |
| D 95. | 5 f. myrtle .. .. | 30 | 30 |
| D 96. | 5 f. violet .. .. | 30 | 30 |
| D 97. | 10 f. brown .. .. | 75 | 75 |
| D 98. | 10 f. brown .. .. | 75 | 75 |
| D 99. | 25 f. purple .. .. | 1·75 | 1·75 |
| D 100. | 25 f. violet .. .. | 1·75 | 1·75 |

DESIGNS (rock-paintings): No. D 89, Type **D 6.** D 90, Gonoa kudu. D 91, Two Gonoa antelopes. D 92, Three Gonoa antelopes. D 93, Gonoa antelope. D 94, Tibestiram. D 95, Tibestiox. D 96, Oudingueur boar. D 97, Gonoa elephant. D 98, Gira-Gira rhinoceros. D 99, Bardai warrior. D 100, Gonoa masked archer. The two designs in each value are arranged in tetebeche pairs throughout the sheet.

**D 65.** Kanem Puppet.

**1969.** Native Puppets.

| | | | |
|---|---|---|---|
| D 284. **D 65.** | 1 f. brn., red & grn. | 10 | 10 |
| D 285. – | 2 f. brn., grn. & red | 10 | 10 |
| D 286. – | 5 f. green and brown | 10 | 10 |
| D 287. – | 10 f. brn., pur. & grn. | 20 | 20 |
| D 288. – | 25 f. brn., pur. & green | 45 | 25 |

DESIGNS: 2 f. Kotoko doll. 5 f. Copper doll. 10 f. Kotoko (diff.). 25 f. Guera doll.

## APPENDIX

The following stamps have either been issued in excess of postal needs or have not been available to the public in reasonable quantities at face value. Such stamps may later be given full listing if there is evidence of regular postal use.

**1970.**

"Apollo programme". Postage 40 f.; Air 15, 25 f.

Birth Bicent. of Napoleon. Air. 10, 25, 32 f.

World Cup Football Championships, Mexico. Air 5 f.

World Cup. Previous Winners. 1, 4 f., 5 f. × 2.

"Expo 70" World Fair, Osaka, Japan. Japanese Paintings. 50 c., 1, 2 f.

Christmas. Paintings. Postage 3, 25 f.; Air 32 f.

Past Olympic Venues. Postage 3, 8, 20 f.; Air 10, 35 f.

**1971.**

Space Exploration. 8, 10, 35 f.

Winter Olympic Games, Sapporo, Japan. Japanese Paintings. 50 c., 1, 2 f.

Kings and Queens of France. Postage 25 f. × 2, 30, 32, 35 f. 40 f. × 2, 50 f. × 4, 60 f.; Air 40, 50, 60, 70, 75, 80 f., 100 f. × 5, 150 f., 200 f. × 4.

150th Death Anniv. of Napoleon. Air. 10 f.

Famous Paintings. 1, 4, 5 f.

Past Olympic Venues. Postage 15, 20 f.; Air 25, 50 f.

Winter Olympic Games, Sapporo, Japan. Optd. on 1970 "Expo 70" issue 50 c., 1, 2 f.

Olympic Games Munich. World Cup Previous Winners issue (1970) optd. 1 f.

**1972.**

Moon Flight of "Apollo 15". Air 40, 80, 150, 250, 300, 500 f.

"Soyuz 11" Disaster. Air 30, 50, 100, 200, 300 400 f.

Pres. Tombalbaye. Postage 30, 40 f.; Air 70, 80 f.

Winter Olympic Games, Sapporo, Japan. Postage 25, 75, 150 f.; Air 130, 200 f.

13th World Scout Jamboree, Asagiri, Japan (1971). Postage 30, 70, 80 f.; Air 100, 200 f.

Medal Winners, Sapporo Winter Olympics. Postage 25, 75, 100, 130 f.; Air 150, 200 f.

Olympic Games, Munich. Postage 20, 40, 60 f.; Air 100, 120, 150 f.

African Animals. Air 20, 30, 100, 130, 150 f.

Medal Winners, Munich Olympics (1st series). Postage 10, 20, 40, 60 f.; Air 150, 250 f.

Medal Winners, Munich Olympics (2nd series). Gold frames, Postage 20, 30, 50 f.; Air 150, 250 f.

**1973.**

Locomotives. 10, 40, 50, 150, 200 f.

Domestic Animals (2nd issue). Postage 20, 30 f.; Air 100, 130, 150 f.

Horses. 20, 60, 100, 120 f.

Airplanes. Air. 5, 25, 70, 150, 200 f.

Christmas. Postage 30, 40, 55 f.; Air 60, 250 f.

Other issues exist which were prepared by various agencies, but it is uncertain whether these were placed on sale in Chad. They include further values in the "Kings and Queens of France" series.

All the stamps below are on gold foil.

**1982.**

World Cup Football Championship, Spain. Air 1500 f.

21st Birthday of Princess of Wales. Air 1500 f.

75th Anniv. of Scout Movement. Air 1500 f.

Olympic Games, Los Angeles, Air 1500 f.

Birth of Prince William of Wales. 21st Birthday of Princess of Wales stamp optd. Air 1500 f.

**1983.**

World Cup Football Championship Results. Air 1500 f.

Chess Grand Masters. Air 1500 f.

Exploitation of Space. Air 1500 f.

Winter Olympic Games, Sarajevo. Air 1500 f.

Bicentary of Manned Flight. Air 1500 f.

Olympic Games, Los Angeles. Air 1500 f.

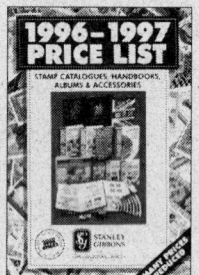

## CHILE Pt. 20

A republic on the W. coast of S. America.
1853. 100 centavos = 1 peso.
1960. 10 milesimos = 1 centesimo; 100 centesimos = 1 escudo.
1975. 100 centavos = 1 peso.

1. Columbus. 9. 10.

### 1853. Imperf.

| No. | Type | Description | Unused | Used |
|---|---|---|---|---|
| 29. | 1. | 1 c. yellow | 20·00 | 25·00 |
| 17. | | 5 c. brown | £100 | 11·00 |
| 37. | | 5 c. red | 23·00 | 6·50 |
| 32. | | 10 c. blue | 32·00 | 5·00 |
| 33. | | 20 c. green | 65·00 | 42·00 |

### 1867. Perf.

| No. | Type | Description | Unused | Used |
|---|---|---|---|---|
| 41. | 9. | 1 c. orange | 10·00 | 1·25 |
| 43. | | 2 c. black | 11·50 | 2·75 |
| 45. | | 5 c. red | 10·00 | 50 |
| 46. | | 10 c. blue | 10·00 | 75 |
| 48. | | 20 c. green | 22·00 | 2·00 |

### 1877. Roul.

| No. | Type | Description | Unused | Used |
|---|---|---|---|---|
| 49. | 10. | 1 c. slate | 2·00 | 75 |
| 50. | | 2 c. orange | 11·50 | 2·00 |
| 51. | | 5 c. lake | 11·50 | 50 |
| 52. | | 10 c. blue | 12·50 | 50 |
| 53. | | 20 c. green | 13·00 | 2·00 |

12. 15.

### 1878. Roul.

| No. | Type | Description | Unused | Used |
|---|---|---|---|---|
| 55. | 12. | 1 c. green | 1·00 | 15 |
| 57. | | 2 c. red | 1·00 | 15 |
| 58. | | 5 c. red | 3·00 | 25 |
| 59a. | | 5 c. blue | 1·50 | 50 |
| 60a. | | 10 c. orange | 2·00 | 10 |
| 61. | | 15 c. green | 2·50 | 15 |
| 62. | | 20 c. grey | 2·50 | 35 |
| 63. | | 25 c. brown | 2·50 | 15 |
| 64. | | 30 c. red | 5·00 | 1·25 |
| 65a. | | 50 c. violet | 2·50 | 1·00 |
| 66. | 15. | 1 p. black and brown | 13·50 | 2·00 |

16. 18.

### 1900. Roul.

| No. | Type | Description | Unused | Used |
|---|---|---|---|---|
| 82 | 16 | 1 c. green | 10 | 10 |
| 83 | | 2 c. red | 10 | 10 |
| 84a | | 5 c. blue | 4·00 | 25 |
| 85 | | 10 c. lilac | 4·75 | 35 |
| 79 | | 20 c. grey | 4·00 | 85 |
| 80 | | 30 c. brown | 4·50 | 85 |
| 81 | | 50 c. brown | 7·00 | 1·50 |

### 1900. Surch. 5.

| No. | Type | Description | Unused | Used |
|---|---|---|---|---|
| 86. | 12. | 5 c. on 30 c. red | 1·00 | 20 |

### 1901. Perf.

| No. | Type | Description | Unused | Used |
|---|---|---|---|---|
| 87. | 18. | 1 c. green | 25 | 15 |
| 88. | | 2 c. red | 35 | 15 |
| 89. | | 5 c. blue | 1·10 | 15 |
| 90. | | 10 c. black and red | 2·10 | 25 |
| 91. | | 30 c. black and violet | 6·50 | 95 |
| 92. | | 50 c. black and red | 8·25 | 3·75 |

### 1903. Surch. Diez CENTAVOS.

| No. | Type | Description | Unused | Used |
|---|---|---|---|---|
| 93. | 16. | 10 c. on 30 c. brown | 1·60 | 95 |

20. Huemul (mountain deer). 24. Pedro Valdivia.

### 1904. Animal supporting shield at left without mane and tail. Optd. CORREOS in frame.

| No. | Type | Description | Unused | Used |
|---|---|---|---|---|
| 94. | 20. | 2 c. brown | 25 | 15 |
| 95. | | 5 c. red | 40 | 15 |
| 96. | | 10 c. olive | 1·40 | 40 |

### 1904. As T 20, but animal with mane and tail optd. CORREOS in frame and the 1 p. also surch. CENTAVOS 3 3.

| No. | Type | Description | Unused | Used |
|---|---|---|---|---|
| 97 | 20 | 2 c. brown | 4·00 | |
| 98 | | 3 c. on 1 p. brown | 35 | 20 |
| 99 | | 5 c. red | 3·25 | |
| 100 | | 10 c. green | 16·50 | |

### 1904. Surch. CORREOS in frame and new value.

| No. | Type | Description | Unused | Used |
|---|---|---|---|---|
| 101. | 24. | 1 c. on 20 c. blue | 25 | 15 |
| 102. | | 3 c. on 5 c. red | 40·00 | 40·00 |
| 103. | | 12 c. on 5 c. red | 85 | 35 |

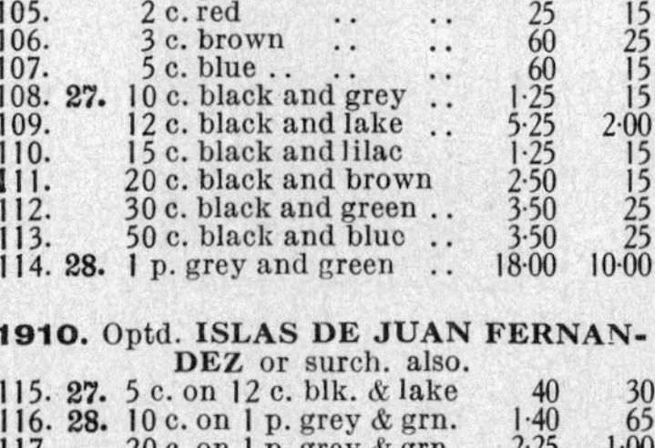

26. 27. 28. Christopher Columbus.

### 1905.

| No. | Type | Description | Unused | Used |
|---|---|---|---|---|
| 104. | 26. | 1 c. green | 25 | 15 |
| 105. | | 2 c. red | 25 | 15 |
| 106. | | 3 c. brown | 60 | 25 |
| 107. | | 5 c. blue | 60 | 15 |
| 108. | 27. | 10 c. black and grey | 1·25 | 15 |
| 109. | | 12 c. black and lake | 5·25 | 2·00 |
| 110. | | 15 c. black and lilac | 1·25 | 15 |
| 111. | | 20 c. black and brown | 2·50 | 15 |
| 112. | | 30 c. black and green | 3·50 | 25 |
| 113. | | 50 c. black and blue | 3·50 | 25 |
| 114. | 28. | 1 p. grey and green | 18·00 | 10·00 |

### 1910. Optd. ISLAS DE JUAN FERNANDEZ or surch. also.

| No. | Type | Description | Unused | Used |
|---|---|---|---|---|
| 115. | 27. | 5 c. on 12 c. blk. & lake | 40 | 30 |
| 116. | 28. | 10 c. on 1 p. grey & grn. | 1·40 | 65 |
| 117. | | 20 c. on 1 p. grey & grn. | 2·25 | 1·00 |
| 118. | | 1 p. grey and green | 4·25 | 2·40 |

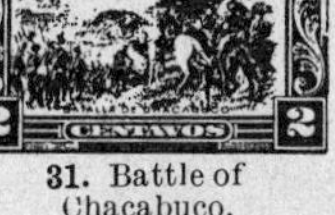

31. Battle of Chacabuco. 33. San Martin Monument.

### 1910. Centenary of Independence. Centres in black.

| No. | Type | Description | Unused | Used |
|---|---|---|---|---|
| 119. | – | 1 c. green | 25 | 15 |
| 120. | 31. | 2 c. lake | 25 | 15 |
| 121. | – | 3 c. brown | 1·00 | 65 |
| 122. | – | 5 c. blue | 35 | 10 |
| 123. | – | 10 c. brown | 1·25 | 25 |
| 124. | – | 12 c. red | 2·75 | 90 |
| 125. | – | 15 c. slate | 1·60 | 65 |
| 126. | – | 20 c. orange | 2·50 | 1·00 |
| 127. | – | 25 c. blue | 4·00 | 2·40 |
| 128. | – | 30 c. mauve | 2·75 | 1·40 |
| 129. | – | 50 c. olive | 6·75 | 3·50 |
| 130. | 33. | 1 p. yellow | 13·50 | 5·00 |
| 131. | – | 2 p. red | 13·50 | 3·75 |
| 132. | – | 5 p. green | 30·00 | 17·00 |
| 133. | – | 10 p. purple | 30·00 | 13·50 |

DESIGNS—HORIZ. 1 c. Oath of Independence. 3 c. Battle of Roble. 5 c. Battle of Maipu. 10 c. Fight between frigates "Lautaro" and "Esmeralda". 12 c. Capture of the "Maria Isabella". 15 c. First sortie of the liberating forces. 20 c. Abdication of O'Higgins. 25 c. First Chilean Congress. VERT. 30 c. O'Higgins Monument. 50 c. Carrera Monument. 2 p. General Blanco. 5 p. General Zenteno. 10 p. Admiral Cochrane.

46. Columbus. 47. Valdivia. 49. O'Higgins.

64. Admiral Cochrane. 50. Freire. 52. Prieto.

65. M. Rengifo. 57. A. Pinto.

### 1911. Inscr. "CHILE CORREOS".

| No. | Type | Description | Unused | Used |
|---|---|---|---|---|
| 135. | 46. | 1 c. green | 15 | 10 |
| 136. | 47. | 2 c. red | 15 | 10 |
| 150. | 46. | 2 c. red | 15 | 10 |
| 137. | – | 3 c. sepia | 50 | 35 |
| 151. | – | 4 c. sepia | 20 | 10 |
| 138. | 49. | 5 c. blue | 15 | 10 |
| 161. | 64. | 5 c. blue | 35 | 15 |
| 152. | – | 8 c. grey | 70 | 30 |
| 139. | 50. | 10 c. black and grey | 50 | 30 |
| 153. | 49. | 10 c. black and blue | 70 | 10 |
| 140. | – | 12 c. black and red | 85 | 30 |
| 154. | – | 14 c. black and red | 70 | 10 |
| 141. | 52. | 15 c. black and purple | 70 | 30 |
| 142. | – | 20 c. black and orange | 1·40 | 15 |
| 167. | – | 25 c. black and blue | 50 | 15 |
| 168. | – | 30 c. black and brown | 1·50 | 15 |
| 155. | 52. | 40 c. black and purple | 3·25 | 65 |
| 169. | 65. | 40 c. black and violet | 1·50 | 15 |
| 170. | – | 50 c. black and green | 1·50 | 15 |
| 156. | – | 60 c. black and blue | 8·50 | 1·60 |
| 171. | – | 80 c. black and sepia | 1·90 | 55 |
| 188. | 57. | 1 p. black and green | 70 | 10 |
| 189. | – | 2 p. black and red | 3·50 | 30 |
| 174. | – | 5 p. black and olive | 28·00 | 70 |
| 190a. | – | 10 p. black and orange | 5·50 | 1·00 |

PORTRAITS: 3 c., 4 c. Toro Z. 8 c. Freire. 12 c., 14 c. F. A. Pinto. 20 c. Bulnes. 25 c., 60 c. Montt. 30 c. Perez. 50 c. Errazuriz Z. 80 c. Admiral Latorre. 2 p. Santa Maria. 5 p. Balmaceda. 10 p. Errazuriz E.

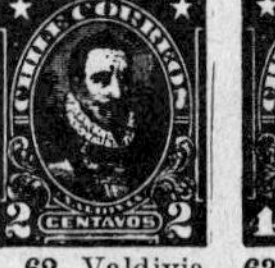

61. Columbus. 62. Valdivia. 63. Columbus.

### 1915. Larger Stars.

| No. | Type | Description | Unused | Used |
|---|---|---|---|---|
| 157 | 61 | 1 c. green | 20 | 10 |
| 158 | 62 | 2 c. red | 20 | 10 |
| 160 | 61 | 4 c. brown (small head) | 30 | 10 |
| 159 | 63 | 4 c. brown (large head) | 25 | 10 |

67. Chilean Congress Building. 67a. O'Higgins.

### 1923. Pan-American Conf.

| No. | Type | Description | Unused | Used |
|---|---|---|---|---|
| 176. | 67. | 2 c. red | 15 | 10 |
| 177. | | 4 c. brown | 15 | 10 |
| 178. | | 10 c. black and blue | 15 | 10 |
| 179. | | 20 c. black and orange | 40 | 15 |
| 180. | | 40 c. black and mauve | 70 | 20 |
| 181. | | 1 p. black and green | 85 | 35 |
| 182. | | 2 p. black and red | 3·00 | 40 |
| 183. | | 5 p. black and green | 11·00 | 2·75 |

### 1927. Air. Unissued stamp surch. Correo Aereo and value.

| No. | Type | Description | Unused | Used |
|---|---|---|---|---|
| 184. | 67a. | 40 c. on 10 c. bl. & brn. | £225 | 27·00 |
| 184a. | | 80 c. on 10 c. bl. & brn. | £225 | 42·00 |
| 184b. | | 1.20 p. on 10 c. blue and brown | £225 | 42·00 |
| 184c. | | 1.60 p. on 10 c. blue and brown | £225 | 42·00 |
| 184d. | | 2 p. on 10 c. bl. & brn. | £225 | 42·00 |

### 1928. Air. Optd. CORREO AEREO and bird or surch. also.

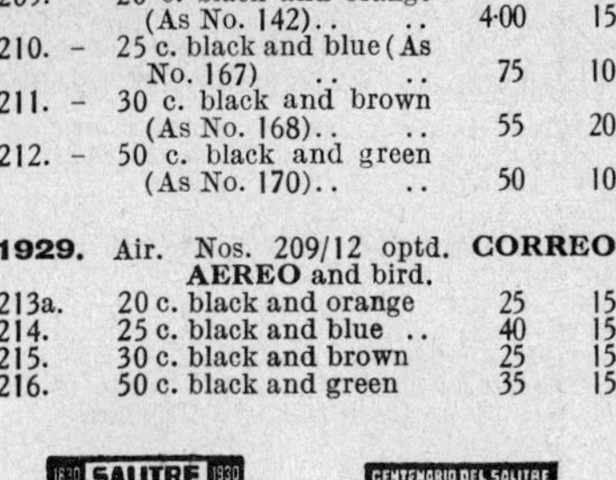

| No. | Type | Description | Unused | Used |
|---|---|---|---|---|
| 191. | – | 20 c. blk. & orge. (No. 142 | 35 | 15 |
| 199. | 65. | 40 c. black and violet | 40 | 20 |
| 200. | 57. | 1 p. black and green | 1·10 | 35 |
| 194. | – | 2 p. blk. & red (No. 189) | 1·60 | 25 |
| 201. | 64. | 3 p. on 5 c. blue | 45·00 | 30·00 |
| 195. | – | 5 p. blk. & ol. (No. 174) | 2·75 | 70 |
| 196. | 49. | 6 p. on 10 c. black & bl. | 65·00 | 30·00 |
| 198. | – | 10 p. black and orange (No. 190a) | 9·00 | 2·75 |

### 1928. As Types of 1911, but inscr. "CORREOS DE CHILE".

| No. | Type | Description | Unused | Used |
|---|---|---|---|---|
| 205. | 64. | 5 c. blue | 50 | 10 |
| 206. | | 5 c. green | 50 | 10 |
| 204. | 49. | 10 c. black and blue | 75 | 25 |
| 208. | 52. | 15 c. black and purple | 1·75 | 10 |
| 209. | – | 20 c. black and orange (As No. 142) | 4·00 | 15 |
| 210. | – | 25 c. black and blue (As No. 167) | 75 | 10 |
| 211. | – | 30 c. black and brown (As No. 168) | 55 | 20 |
| 212. | – | 50 c. black and green (As No. 170) | 50 | 10 |

### 1929. Air. Nos. 209/12 optd. CORREO AEREO and bird.

| No. | Type | Description | Unused | Used |
|---|---|---|---|---|
| 213a. | | 20 c. black and orange | 25 | 15 |
| 214. | | 25 c. black and blue | 40 | 15 |
| 215. | | 30 c. black and brown | 25 | 15 |
| 216. | | 50 c. black and green | 35 | 15 |

71. Winged Wheel. 72. Sower.

### 1930. Centenary of Nitrate Industry.

| No. | Type | Description | Unused | Used |
|---|---|---|---|---|
| 217. | 71. | 5 c. green | 35 | 15 |
| 218. | | 10 c. brown | 35 | 15 |
| 219. | | 15 c. violet | 35 | 15 |
| 220. | – | 25 c. slate (Girl harvester) | 1·40 | 15 |
| 221. | 72. | 70 c. blue | 3·25 | 1·00 |
| 222. | – | 1 p. green (24½ × 30 mm.) | 2·50 | 50 |

73. Andean Condor and Fokker Super Universal Airplane. 75. Ford 4AT Trimotor over Los Cerrillos Airport.

### 1931. Air. Inscr. "LINEA AEREA NACIONAL".

| No. | Type | Description | Unused | Used |
|---|---|---|---|---|
| 223. | 73. | 5 c. green | 40 | 25 |
| 224. | | 10 c. brown | 40 | 25 |
| 225. | | 20 c. red | 40 | 10 |
| 226a. | – | 50 c. sepia | 40 | 25 |
| 227. | 75. | 50 c. blue | 1·75 | 85 |
| 228. | – | 1 p. violet | 55 | 30 |
| 229. | – | 2 p. slate | 1·50 | 25 |
| 230. | 75. | 5 p. red | 3·50 | 60 |

DESIGN: 50 c. (No. 226a), 1 p., 2 p. Fokker Super Universal airplane.

76. O'Higgins. 79. Mariano Egana.

### 1931.

| No. | Type | Description | Unused | Used |
|---|---|---|---|---|
| 231. | 76. | 10 c. blue | 1·00 | 10 |
| 232. | – | 20 c. brown (Bulnes) | 85 | 10 |
| 233. | – | 30 c. mauve (Perez) | 1·40 | 10 |

### 1934. Cent. of Constitution of 1833.

| No. | Type | Description | Unused | Used |
|---|---|---|---|---|
| 234. | 79. | 30 c. mauve | 50 | 25 |
| 235. | – | 1 p. 20 blue | 90 | 25 |

PORTRAIT: 1 p. 20, Joaquin Tocornal (24½ × 29 mm).

83. Fokker Super Universal Aircraft over Globe. 87. Diego de Almagro.

### 1934. Air. As T 83.

| No. | Description | Unused | Used |
|---|---|---|---|
| 236 | 10 c. green | 15 | 10 |
| 237 | 15 c. green | 25 | 20 |
| 238 | 20 c. blue | 20 | 15 |
| 239 | 30 c. black | 20 | 15 |
| 239a | 40 c. blue | 20 | 15 |
| 240 | 50 c. brown | 20 | 15 |
| 241 | 60 c. black | 20 | 15 |
| 356a | 70 c. blue | 30 | 20 |
| 243 | 80 c. green | 20 | 15 |
| 244 | 1 p. grey | 20 | 15 |
| 245 | 2 p. blue | 20 | 15 |
| 360 | 3 p. brown | 25 | 15 |
| 361 | 4 p. brown | 25 | 15 |
| 248 | 5 p. red | 20 | 10 |
| 249 | 6 p. brown | 35 | 15 |
| 250 | 8 p. green | 30 | 10 |
| 251 | 10 p. purple | 35 | 15 |
| 252 | 20 p. olive | 35 | 15 |
| 253 | 30 p. grey | 35 | 10 |
| 254 | 40 p. violet | 70 | 40 |
| 255a | 50 p. purple | 85 | 40 |

DESIGNS—21 × 25 mm: 10, 15, 20 c. Fokker Super Universal over Santiago. 30, 40, 50 c. Junkers G.24 over landscape. 60 c. Condor in flight. 70 c. Airplane and star. 80 c. Condor and statue of Caupolican. 25 × 29 mm: 1, 2 p. Type 83. 3, 4, 5 p. Stinson Faucett F.19 seaplane in flight. 6, 8, 10 p. Northrop Alpha monoplane and rainbow. 20, 30 p. Stylized Dornier Wal flying boat and compass. 40, 50 p. Airplane riding a storm.

### 1936. 400th Anniv. of Discovery of Chile.

| No. | Type | Description | Unused | Used |
|---|---|---|---|---|
| 256. | – | 5 c. red | 35 | 15 |
| 257. | – | 10 c. violet | 15 | 10 |
| 258. | – | 20 c. mauve | 20 | 10 |
| 259. | – | 25 c. blue | 2·00 | 55 |
| 260. | – | 30 c. green | 20 | 10 |
| 261. | – | 40 c. black | 2·00 | 50 |
| 262. | – | 50 c. blue | 1·10 | 20 |
| 263. | – | 1 p. green | 1·25 | 35 |
| 264. | – | 1 p. 20 blue | 1·25 | 45 |
| 265. | 87. | 2 p. brown | 1·25 | 55 |
| 266. | – | 5 p. red | 3·50 | 1·40 |
| 267. | – | 10 p. purple | 7·75 | 4·75 |

DESIGNS: 5 c. Atacama desert. 10 c. Fishing boats. 20 c. Coquito palms. 25 c. Sheep. 30 c. Coal mines. 40 c. Lonquimay forests. 50 c. Lota coal port. 1 p. "Orduna" (liner), Valparaiso. 1 p. 20, Mt. Puntiaguda. 5 p. Cattle. 10 p. Shovelling nitrate.

88. Laja Waterfall. 90. "Calbuco" (fishingboat).

**1938.**

268 88 5 c. purple .. .. 15 10
269 – 10 c. red .. .. 15 10
269a – 15 c. red .. .. 15 10
270 – 20 c. blue .. .. 15 10
271 – 30 c. pink .. .. 15 10
272 – 40 c. green .. .. 15 10
273 – 50 c. violet .. .. 15 10
274 90 1 p. orange .. .. 15 10
275 – 1 p. 80 blue .. .. 60 20
338h – 2 p. red .. .. 15 10
278 – 5 p. green .. .. 35 10
338j – 10 p. purple .. .. 75 10

DESIGNS—As Type **88**: 10 c. Rural landscape. 15 c. Boldo tree. 20 c. Nitrate works. 30 c. Mineral spas. 40 c. Copper mine. 50 c. Petroleum tanks. As Type **90**: 1 p. 80, Osorno Volcano. 2 p. Freighter at Valparaiso. 5 p. Lake Villarrica. 10 p. Steam train.

**92.** "Abtao" (armed steamer) and Policarpo Toro.

**93.** Western Hemisphere.

**1940.** 50th Anniv. of Occupation of Easter Island and Local Hospital Fund.

279. **92.** 80 c.+2 p. 20 red & grn. 1·90 1·40
280. – 3 p. 60+6 p. 40 green and red .. .. 1·90 1·40

DESIGN: 3 p. 60, "Abtao" and E. Eyraud.

**1940.** 50th Anniv. of Pan-American Union.

281. **93.** 40 c. green .. .. 20 10

**1940.** Air. Surch. with winged device above new values.

282. **73.** 80 c. on 20 c. red .. 45 25
283. **75.** 1 p. 60 on 5 p. red .. 3·25 85
284. – 5 p. 10 on 2 p. slate (No. 229) .. .. 2·50 1·00

**96.** Fray Camilo Henriquez.

**97.** Founding of Santiago.

**1941.** 400th Anniv. of Santiago.

285. **96.** 10 c. red .. .. 30 15
286. – 40 c. green .. .. 40 10
287. – 1 p. 10 red .. .. 1·00 85
288. **97.** 1 p. 80 blue .. .. 1·00 50
289. – 3 p. 60 blue .. .. 3·25 4·00

PORTRAITS—As Type **96**: 40 c. P. Valdivia. 1 p. 10, B. V. MacKenna. 3 p. 60, D. B. Arana.

**98.** Potez 56 and Globe.



**99.** Sikorsky S-43 Amphibian and Galleon.

**1941.** Air. No. 304 is dated "1541 1941" and commemorates the 4th Cent. of Santiago.

290. – 10 c. olive .. .. 30 10
291. – 10 c. mauve .. .. 30 10
316. – 10 c. blue .. .. 20 10
292. **98.** 20 c. red .. .. 30 10
318. 20 c. green .. .. 20 10
294. 20 c. brown .. .. 20 10
295. – 30 c. violet .. .. 30 10
295a. – 30 c. olive .. .. 20 10
296. – 40 c. brown .. .. 30 10
297. – 40 c. blue .. .. 20 10
324. – 50 c. red .. .. 30 10
325. – 50 c. orange .. .. 30 10
299a. – 60 c. green .. .. 20 15
326. – 60 c. orange .. .. 30 10
300. – 70 c. red .. .. 60 20
301. – 80 c. blue .. .. 3·00 35
302. – 80 c. olive .. .. 20 15
303a. – 90 c. brown .. .. 30 10
304. **99.** 1 p. blue .. .. 60 20
304a. 1 p. green and blue .. 30 10
305. – 1 p. 60 violet .. .. 30 15
306. – 1 p. 80 violet .. .. 30 10
307. – 2 p. lake .. .. 85 25
308. – 2 p. brown .. .. 60 10
309. – 3 p. green .. .. 1·25 45
310a. – 3 p. violet and yellow 2·50 25
334. – 3 p. violet and orange 85 15
311. – 4 p. violet and brown 2·00 55
335. – 4 p. green .. .. 85 30
336a. – 5 p. brown .. .. 35 20
336. – 5 p. red .. .. 35 25
314. – 10 p. green and blue 9·50 4·00
337. – 10 p. blue .. .. 85 25

DESIGNS: (each incorporating a different type of airplane): 10 c. Steeple. 30 c. Flag. 40 c. Stars. 50 c. Mountains. 60 c. Tree. 70 c. Estuary. 80 c. Shore. 90 c. Sun rays. 1 p. 60, 1 p. 80, Wireless mast. 2 p. Compass. 3 p. Telegraph wires. 4 p. Rainbow. 5 p. Factory. 10 p. Snow-capped mountain.

See also Nos. 395 etc.

**101.** V. Letelier.

**102.** University of Chile.

**103.** Coat of arms and Aeroplane.

**1942.** Cent. of Santiago de Chile University.

339. **101.** 30 c. red (postage) .. 20 10
340. – 40 c. green .. .. 20 10
341. – 90 c. violet .. .. 1·50 70
342. **102.** 1 p. brown .. .. 1·00 40
343. – 1 p. 80 blue .. .. 2·50 1·40
344. **103.** 100 p. red (air) .. 30·00 20·00

DESIGNS—As Type **101**: 40 c. A. Bello. 90 c. M. Bulnes. 1 p. 80, M. Montt.

**104.** Manuel Bulnes.

**105.** Straits of Magellan.

**1944.** Cent. of Occupation of Magellan Straits.

345. **104.** 15 c. black .. .. 15 10
346. – 30 c. red .. .. 15 10
347. – 40 c. green .. .. 15 10
348. – 1 p. brown .. .. 85 25
349. **105.** 1 p. 80 blue .. .. 1·25 70

PORTRAITS: 30 c. J. W. Wilson. 40 c. D. D. Almeida. 1 p. Jose de los Santos Mardones.

DESIGN: 1 p. 80, Serpent and chalice symbol of Hygiene.

**106.** "Lamp of Life".

**1944.** International Red Cross.

350. **106.** 40 c. black, red & green 50 10
351. – 1 p. 80 red and blue .. 1·00 50

**107.** O'Higgins (after J. G. de Castro).

**108.** Battle of Rancagua (after Subercaseaux).

**1944.** Death Cent. of Bernardo O'Higgins.

367. **107.** 15 c. black and red .. 15 10
368. – 30 c. black and brown .. 25 10
369. – 40 c. black and green .. 25 10
370. **108.** 1 p. 80 black and blue .. 1·25 80

DESIGNS—As Type **108**: 30 c. Battle of the Maipu. 40 c. Abdication of O'Higgins.

**109.** Columbus Lighthouse Dominican Republic.

**110.** Andres Bello.

**1945.** 450th Anniv. of Discovery of America by Columbus.

371. **109.** 40 c. green .. .. 30 15

**1946.** 80th Death Anniv. of Andres Bello (educationist).

372. **110.** 40 c. green .. .. 15 10
373. 1 p. 80 blue .. .. 15 10

**111.** Antarctic Territory.

**113.** Miguel de Cervantes.

**112.** Eusebio Lillo and Ramon Carnicer.

**1947.**

374. **111.** 40 c. red .. .. 40 15
375. 2 p. 50 blue .. .. 1·00 30

**1947.** Cent. of National Anthem.

376. **112.** 40 c. green .. .. 15 10

**1947.** 400th Birth Anniv. of Cervantes.

377. **113.** 40 c. red .. .. 15 10

**114.** Arturo Prat and "Esmeralda" (sail corvette).

**1948.** Birth Cent. of Arturo Prat.

378. **114.** 40 c. blue .. .. 35 10

**115.** O'Higgins.

**119.** "Chiasognathus granti".

**1948.**

379. **115.** 60 c. black .. .. 10 10

**1948.** No. 272 surch. **VEINTE CTS.** and bar.

380. 20 c. on 40 c. green .. 10 10

**1948.** Cent. of Publication on Chilean Flora and Fauna. Botanical and zoological designs, as T **119**. inscr. "CENTENARIO DEL LIBRO DE GAY 1844–1944".

381 a/y. 60 c. bl. (postage) .. each 80 35
382 a/y. 2 p. 60 green .. each 1·50 45
383 a/y. 3 p. red (air) .. each 1·75 1·10

Each value in 25 different designs.

**120.** Airline Badge.

**121.** B. V. Mackenna.

**1949.** Air. 20th Anniv. of National Airline.

384. **120.** 2 p. blue .. .. 15 25

**1949.** Vicuna Mackenna Museum.

385. **121.** 60 c. blue (postage) .. 10 10
386. 3 p. red (air) .. .. 15 10

DESIGNS: 2 p. 60, Shield and book. 5 p. Shield, book and factory. 10 p. Wheel and column.

**122.** Wheel and Lamp.

**1949.** Centenary of School of Arts and Crafts, Santiago.

387. **122.** 60 c. mauve (postage) 15 10
388. – 2 p. 60 blue .. .. 30 20
389. – 5 p. green (air) .. 45 30
390. – 10 p. brown .. .. 75 40

**123.** Heinrich von Stephan.

**124.** Douglas DC-6B and Globe.

**1950.** 75th Anniv. of U.P.U.

391. **123.** 60 c. red (postage) .. 10 10
392. 2 p. 50 blue .. .. 45 20
393. **124.** 5 p. green (air) .. .. 30 20
394. 10 p. brown .. .. 60 35

**1950.** Air. As T **98/99**.

395 20 c. brown .. .. 15 10
396 40 c. violet .. .. 15 10
404c 60 c. blue .. .. 25 10
398 1 p. green .. .. 15 10
399 2 p. brown .. .. 15 10
404f 3 p. blue .. .. 15 10
401 4 p. orange .. .. 30 10
402 5 p. violet .. .. 15 10
403 10 p. green .. .. 20 10
480 20 p. brown .. .. 30 10
481 50 p. green .. .. 35 10
482 100 p. red .. .. 75 10
483 200 p. blue .. .. 80 10

DESIGNS (each including an aeroplane): 20 c. Mountains. 40 c. Coastline. 60 c. Fishing vessel. 1 p. Araucanian pine tree. 2 p. Chilean flag. 3 p. Dock crane. 4 p. River. 5 p. Industrial plant. 10 p. Landscape. 20 p. Aerial railway. 50 p. Mountainous coastline. 100 p. Antarctic map. 200 p. Rock "bridge" in sea.

**126.** Crossing the Andes (after V. Prades.)

**128.** Issabella the Catholic.

**1951.** Death Cent. of Gen. San Martin.

405. – 60 c. blue (postage) .. 10 10
406. **126.** 5 p. purple (air) .. 50 15

PORTRAIT (25×29 mm.): 60 c. San Martin.

**1951.** Air. No. 303a surch. **UN PESO.**

407. 1 p. on 90 c. brown .. 15 10

**1952.** 500th Birth Anniv. of Isabella the Catholic.

408. **128.** 60 c. blue (postage) .. 10 10
409. 10 p. red (air) .. .. 40 20

**1952.** Surch. **40 Ctvs.**

410. **115.** 40 c. on 60 c. black .. 10 10

**1952.** Air. No. 302 surch. **40 Centavos.**

411. 40 c. on 80 c. olive .. 15 10

**116.** M. de Toro y Zambrano.

**131.** Arms of Valdivia.

**132.** Old Spanish Watch-tower.

**1952.**

379b. **116.** 80 c. green .. .. 15 10
379c. – 1 p. turq. (O'Higgins) 10 10
446. – 2 p. lilac (Carrera) .. 10 10
447. – 3 p. blue (R. Freire) .. 10 10
448. – 5 p. sepia (M. Bulnes) 10 10
449. – 10 p. violet (F. A. Pinto) 10 10
450. – 50 p. red (M. Montt) .. 35 10

**1953.** 400th Anniv. of Valdivia.

414. **131.** 1 p. blue (postage) .. 15 10
415. – 2 p. violet .. .. 15 10
416. – 3 p. green .. .. 35 10
417. – 5 p. brown .. .. 45 10
418. **132.** 10 p. red (air) .. .. 90 20

DESIGNS—As Type **132**: 2 p. Ancient cannons, Corral Fort. 3 p. Valdivia from the river. 5 p. Street scene (after old engraving).

**133.** J. Toribio Medina. **134.** Stamp of 1853.

**1953.** Birth Cent. of Toribio Medina.
419. **133.** 1 p. brown .. .. 15 10
420. 2 p. 50 blue .. .. 25 10

**1953.** Chilean Stamp Cent.
421 **134.** 1 p. brown (postage) .. 15 10
422. 100 p. turquoise (air) .. 2·00 2·00

**135.** Map and Graph. **136.** Aircraft of 1929 and 1954.

**1953.** 12th National Census.
423. **135.** 1 p. green .. .. 10 10
424. 2 p. 50 blue .. .. 15 10
425. 3 p. brown .. .. 25 15
426. 4 p. red .. .. 35 15

**1954.** Air. 25th Anniv. of National Air Line.
427. **136.** 3 p. blue .. .. 10 10

**137.** Arms of Angol. **138.** I. Domeyko.

**1954.** 400th Anniv. of Angol City.
428. **137.** 2 p. red .. .. 10 15

**1954.** 150th Birth Anniv. of Domeyko (educationist and mineralogist).
429. **138.** 1 p. blue (postage) .. 15 10
430. 5 p. brown (air) .. 15 10

**139.** Early Locomotive. **140.** Arturo Prat.

**1954.** Cent. of Chilean Railways.
431. **139.** 1 p. red (postage) .. 15 15
432. 10 p. purple (air) .. 65 65

**1954.** 75th Anniv. of Naval Battle of Iquique.
433. **140.** 2 p. violet .. .. 15 10

**141.** Arms of Vina del Mar. **142.** Dr. A. del Rio.

**1955.** Int. Philatelic Exn., Valparaiso.
434. **141.** 1 p. blue .. .. 15 10
435. – 2 p. red .. .. .. 15 10
DESIGN: 2 p. Arms of Valparaiso.

**1955.** 14th Pan-American Sanitary Conf.
436. **142.** 2 p. blue .. .. 10 10

**143.** Christ of the Andes **144.** De Havilland Comet 1.

**1955.** Exchange of Visits between Argentine and Chilean Presidents.
437. **143.** 1 p. blue (postage) .. 15 10
438. 100 p. red (air) .. 1·90 75

**1955.** Air.
441a. **144.** 100 p. green .. .. 75 15
441b. – 200 p. blue .. .. 4·50 75
441c. – 500 p. red .. .. 6·00 75
AIRCRAFT: 200 p. Morane Saulnier Paris I. 500 p. Douglas DC-6B.

**145.** M. Rengifo. **147.** Bell Trooper Helicopter and Bridge.

**1955.** Death Centenary of Joaquin Prieto (President, 1833–41).
442. **145.** 3 p. blue .. .. 10 10
443. – 5 p. red (Egana) .. 10 10
444. – 50 p. purple (Portales) 1·40 25
For 15 p. in similar design see under Compulsory Tax Stamps.

**1956.** Air.
451. – 1 p. red .. .. .. 20 10
452. **147.** 2 p. sepia .. .. 20 10
455. – 5 p. violet .. .. 20 10
456. – 10 p. green .. .. 15 10
456a. – 20 p. blue .. .. 15 10
456b. – 50 p. red .. .. 20 10
DESIGNS: 1 p. De Havilland Venom FB.4. 5 p. Diesel locomotive and Douglas DC-6B. 10 p. Oil derricks and Douglas DC-6B. 20 p. De Havilland Venom FB.4 and Easter Island monolith. 50 p. Douglas DC-2 and control tower.
See also Nos. 524/7.

**148.** F. Santa Maria. **149.** Atomic Symbol and Cogwheels.

**1956.** 25th Anniv. of Santa Maria Technical University, Valparaiso.
457. **148.** 5 p. brown (postage) .. 15 10
458. **149.** 20 p. green (air) .. 25 15
459. – 100 p. violet .. .. 70 40
DESIGN—As Type **149**: 100 p. Aerial view of University.

**150.** Gabriela Mistral. **151.** Arms of Osorno.

**1958.** Gabriela Mistral (poetess, Nobel Prize Winner).
460. **150.** 10 p. brown (postage) .. 15 10
461. 100 p. green (air) .. 30 10

**1958.** 400th Anniv. of Osorno.
462 **151.** 10 p. red (postage) .. 15 10
463. – 50 p. green .. .. 35 10
464. – 100 p. blue (air) .. 65 25
PORTRAITS: 50 p. G. H. de Mendoza. 100 p. O'Higgins.

**152.** "La Araucana" (poem) and Antarctic Map. **153.** Arms of Santiago de Chile.

**1958.** Antarctic issue.
465. **152.** 10 p. blue (postage) .. 20 10
466. – 200 p. purple .. .. 3·25 1·25
467. **152.** 20 p. violet (air) .. 45 10
468. – 500 p. blue .. .. 5·50 1·75
DESIGN: 200 p., 500 p. Chilean map of 1588.

**1958.** National Philatelic Exn., Santiago.
469. **153.** 10 p. purple (postage) 15 10
470. 50 p. green (air) .. 25 10

**154.** **155.** Antarctic Territory.

**1958.** Centenary of Chilean Civil Servants' Savings Bank.
471. **154.** 10 p. blue (postage) 10 10
472. 50 p. brown (air) .. 25 10

**1958.** I.G.Y.
473. **155.** 40 p. red (postage) .. 40 10
474. 50 p. green (air) .. 50 15

**156.** Religious Emblems. **157.** Bridge, Valdivia.

**1959.** Air. Human Rights Day.
475. **156.** 50 p. red .. .. 65 1·00

**1959.** Cent. of German School, Valdivia and Philatelic Exn.
476. **157.** 40 p. green (postage) .. 20 10
477. – 20 p. red (air) .. .. 15 15
DESIGN—VERT. 20 p. A. C. Anwandter. (founder).

**158.** Expedition Map. **159.** D. Barros-Arana.

**1959.** 400th Anniv. of Juan Ladrillero's Expedition of 1557.
484. **158.** 10 p. violet (postage) .. 25 10
485. 50 p. green (air) .. 35 10

**1959.** 50th Death Anniv. of D. Barros-Arana (historian).
486. **159.** 40 p. blue (postage) .. 15 10
487. 100 p. lilac (air) .. 40 20

**160.** J. H. Dunant (founder).

**1959.** Red Cross Commem.
488. **160.** 20 p. lake & red (post) 20 10
489. 50 p. black & red (air) 25 10

**161.** F. A. Pinto. **162.** Choshuenco Volcano.

**1960.** (a) Portraits as T **161**.
490. – 5 m. turquoise .. 10 10
491. **161.** 1 c. red .. .. 10 10
493. – 5 c. blue .. .. 10 10

(b) Views as T **162**.
492. **162.** 2 c. blue .. .. 10 10
492a. 2 c. blue ($23\frac{1}{2} \times 18$ mm.) .. 10 10
494. – 10 c. green .. .. 20 10
495. – 20 c. blue .. .. 35 10
496. – 1 E. turquoise .. 40 15
DESIGNS—As Type **161**: 5 m. M. Bulnes. 5 c. M. Montt. As Type **162**: 10 c. R. Maule Valley. 20 c., 1 E. Inca Lake.

**163.** Martin 4-0-4 Airplane and Dock Crane.

**1960.** Air (Inland).
497. – 1 m. orange .. .. 10 10
498. – 2 m. green .. .. 10 10
499. **163.** 3 m. violet .. .. 10 10
500. – 4 m. olive .. .. 10 10
501. – 5 m. turquoise .. 10 10
502. – 1 c. blue .. .. 10 10
503. – 2 c. brown .. .. 25 10
504. – 5 c. green .. .. 1·60 15
505. – 10 c. red .. .. 45 10
506. – 20 c. blue .. .. 60 10
DESIGNS: Airplane over—1 m. Araucanian pine. 2 m. Chilean flag. 4 m. River. 5 m. Industrial plant. 1 c. Landscape. 2 c. Aerial railway. 5 c. Mountainous coastline. 10 c. Antarctic map. 20 c. Rock "bridge" in sea.

**164.** Refugee Family.

**1960.** World Refugee Year.
507. **164.** 1 c. green (postage) .. 35 10
508. 10 c. violet (air) .. 60 10

**165.** Arms of Chile. **166.** Rotary Emblem and Map.

**1960.** 150th Anniv. of 1st National Government. (1st issue).
509. **165.** 1 c. brn. & lake (post.) 15 10
510. 10 c. chest. & brn. (air) 20 10
See also Nos. 519/30.

**1960.** Air. Rotary International S. American Regional Conference, Santiago.
511. **166.** 10 c. blue .. .. 25 10

**167.** J. M. Carrera. **168.** "Population"

**1960.** 150th Anniv. of 1st National Government (2nd issue).

(a) Postage.
512 – 1 c. red and brown .. 15 10
513 – 5 c. turquoise & green 15 10
514 – 10 c. purple and brown 15 10
515 – 20 c. green and blue .. 15 10
516 – 50 c. red and brown .. 25 10
517 **167** 1 E. brown and green 1·00 40
DESIGNS—HORIZ. 1 c. Palace of Justice. 10 c. M. de Toro y Zambrano and M. de Rozas. 20 c. M. de Salas and Juan Egana. 50 c. M. Rodriguez and J. Mackenna. VERT. 5 c. Temple of the National Vow.

(b) Air.
518 – 2 c. violet and red .. 10 10
519 – 5 c. purple and blue .. 15 10
520 – 10 c. bistre and brown 15 10
521 – 20 c. violet and blue .. 25 10
522 – 50 c. blue and green .. 45 20
523 – 1 E. brown and red .. 1·00 40
DESIGNS—HORIZ. 2 c. Palace of Justice. 10 c. J. G. Martin and J. G. Argomedo. 20 c. J. A. Eyzaguirre and J. M. Infante. 50 c. Bishop J. I. Cienfuegos and Fray C. Henriquez. VERT. 5 c. Temple of the National Vow. 1 E. O'Higgins.

**1961.** Air (Foreign). As T **147** or **144** (10 c. and 50 c.), but values in new currency.
524 5 m. brown .. .. 15 10
525 1 c. blue .. .. 10 10
526 2 c. blue .. .. 10 10
527 5 c. red .. .. 10 10
528 10 c. blue .. .. 10 10
529 20 c. red .. .. 10 10
530 50 c. turquoise .. 10 10
DESIGNS: 5 m. Diesel locomotive and Douglas DC-6B. 1 c. Oil derricks and Douglas DC-6B. 2 c. De Havilland Venom FB.4 and monolith. 5 c. Douglas DC-2 and control tower. 10 c. De Havilland Comet 1. 20 c. Morane Saulnier Paris I. 50 c. Douglas DC-6B.

**1961.** National Census. 13th Population Census (5 c.); 2nd Housing Census (10 c.).
531. **168.** 5 c. green .. .. 40 10
532. – 10 c. violet (buildings) 40 10

**169.** Pedro de Valdivia. **170.** Congress Building.

**1961.** Earthquake Relief Fund. Inscr. "ESPANA A CHILE".
533. **169.** 5 c.+5 c. green & flesh (postage) .. 70 15
534. – 10 c.+10 c. violet & buff 70 15
535. – 10 c.+10 c. brown and salmon (air) .. 70 20
536. – 20 c.+20 c. lake & blue 70 20
PORTRAITS: No. 534, J. T. Medina. No. 535, A. de Ercilla. No. 536, Gabriela Mistral.

**1961.** 150th Anniv. of 1st National Congress.
537. **170.** 2 c. brown (postage) 40 10
538. 10 c. green (air) .. 70 70

**171.** Footballers and Globe.

**172.** Mother and Child.

**1962.** World Football Championships, Chile.
539. **171.** 2 c. blue (postage) .. 10 10
540. – 5 c. green .. 15 10
541. – 5 c. purple (air) .. 15 10
542. **171.** 10 c. lake .. .. 25 10
DESIGN—VERT. Nos. 540/1, Goalkeeper and stadium.

**1963.** Freedom from Hunger.
543. **172.** 3 c. purple (postage) 10 10
544. – 20 c. green (air) .. 15 10
DESIGN—HORIZ. 20 c. Mother holding out food bowl.

**173.** Centenary Emblem.

**174.** Fire Brigade Monument.

**1963.** Red Cross Cent.
545. **173.** 3 c. red & slate (post.) 10 10
546. – 20 c. red and grey (air) 15 10
DESIGN—HORIZ. 20 c. Centenary emblem and silhouette of aircraft.

**1963.** Centenary of Santiago Fire Brigade.
547. **174.** 3 c. violet (postage) .. 10 10
548. – 30 c. red (air) .. .. 30 15
DESIGN—HORIZ. (39×30 mm.): 30 c. Fire engine of 1863.

**175.** Band encircling Globe.

**176.** Enrique Molina.

**1964.** Air. "Alliance for Progress" and Pres. Kennedy Commem.
549. **175.** 4 c. blue .. .. 10 10

**1964.** Molina Commem. (founder of Concepcion University).
550. **176.** 4 c. bistre (postage) .. 10 10
551. 60 c. violet (air) .. 10 10

**1965.** Casanueva Commem. As T **176** but portrait of Mons. Carlos Casanueva, Rector of Catholic University.
552. 4 c. purple (postage) .. 10 10
553. 60 c. green (air) .. 10 10

**177.** Battle Scene. (after Subercasaux).

**1965.** Air. 150th Anniv. of Battle of Rancagua.
554. **177.** 5 c. brown and green 10 10

**178.** Monolith.

**179.** I.T.U. Emblem and Symbols.

**1965.** Easter Island Discoveries.
555. **178.** 6 c. purple .. .. 10 10
556. 10 c. mauve .. .. 15 10

**1965.** Air. Centenary of I.T.U.
557. **179.** 40 c. purple and red .. 15 10

**180.** Crusoe on Juan Fernandez.

**181.** Skier descending slope.

**1965.** Robinson Crusoe Commem.
558. **180.** 30 c. red .. .. 15 10

**1965.** World Skiing Championships.
559. **181.** 4 c. green (postage) .. 15 10
560. – 20 c. blue (air) .. .. 10 10
DESIGN—HORIZ. 20 c. Skier crossing slope.

**182.** Angelmo Harbour.

**183.** Aviators Monument.

**1965.** Air.
561. **182.** 40 c. brown .. .. 30 10
562. **183.** 1 E. red .. .. 20 10

**184.** Copihue (National Flower).

**185.** A. Bello.

**1965.**
563. **184.** 15 c. red and green .. 15 10
563a. 20 c. red and green .. 15 10

**1965.** Air. Death Cent. of Andres Bello (poet).
564. **185.** 10 c. red .. .. 10 10

**186.** Dr. L. Sazie.

**187.** Skiers.

**1966.** Death Cent. of Dr. L. Sazie.
565. **186.** 1 E. green .. .. 1·25 10

**1966.** Air. World Skiing Championships.
566. – 75 c. red and lilac .. 20 10
567. – 3 E. ultramarine & blue 40 10
568. **187.** 4 E. brown and blue .. 85 25
DESIGN—HORIZ. (38×25 mm.): 75 c. and 3 E. Skier in Slalom Race.

**188.** Ball and Basket.

**189.** J. Montt.

**1966.** Air. World Basketball Championships.
569. **188.** 13 c. red .. .. 15 10

**1966.**
570. **189.** 30 c. violet .. .. 10 10
571. – 50 c. brown (G. Riesco) 10 10

**190.** W. Wheelwright and Paddle-steamers "Chile" and "Peru".

**191.** "Learning".

**1966.** 125th Anniv. (1965) of Arrival of Paddle-steamers "Chile" and "Peru".
572. **190.** 10 c. ultram & bl. (post.) 20 10
573. 70 c. blue and green (air) 30 10

**1966.** Education Campaign.
574. **191.** 10 c. purple .. .. 10 10

**192.** I.C.Y. Emblem.

**193.** Chilean Flag and Ships.

**1966.** Int. Co-operation Year (1965).
575. **192.** 1 E. brn. & green (post) 1·75 10
576. 3 E. red and blue (air) 60 20

**1966.** Air. Antofagasta Cent.
577. **193.** 13 c. purple .. .. 10 10

**194.** Capt. Pardo and "Yelcho" (coastguard vessel).

**195.** Chilean Family.

**1967.** 50th Anniv. of Pardo's Rescue of Shackleton Expedition.
578. **194.** 20 c. turquoise (post) .. 30 10
579. – 40 c. blue (air) .. 30 15
DESIGN: 40 c. Capt. Pardo and Antarctic sectoral map.

**1967.** 8th Int. Family Planning Congress.
580. **195.** 10 c. black and purple (postage) .. .. 10 10
581. 80 c. black & blue (air) 20 10

**196.** R. Dario (poet).

**197.** Pine Forest.

**1967.** Air. Birth Centenary of Ruben Dario (Nicaraguan poet.)
582. **196.** 10 c. blue .. .. 15 10

**1967.** National Afforestation Campaign.
583. **197.** 10 c. green & bl. (post) 10 10
584. 75 c. green & brown (air) 20 10

**198.** Lions Emblem.

**199.** Chilean Flag.

**1967.** 50th Anniv. of Lions Int.
585. **198.** 20 c. blue & brn (post.) 15 10
586. 1 E. violet & yell (air) 15 10
587. 5 E. blue & yellow .. 95 25

**1967.** 150th Anniv. of National Flag.
588. **199.** 80 c. red & blue (post) 20 10
589. 50 c. red and blue (air) 15 10

**200.** I.T.Y. Emblem.

**201.** Cardinal Caro.

**1967.** Air. Int. Tourist Year.
590. **200.** 30 c. black and blue .. 10 10

**1967.** Birth Cent. of Cardinal Caro.
591. **201.** 20 c. lake (postage) .. 35 20
592. 40 c. violet (air) .. 40 15

**202.** San Martin and O'Higgins.

**203.** Farmer and Wife.

**1968.** 150th Anniv. of Battles of Chacabuco and Maipu.
593. **202.** 3 E. blue (postage) .. 10 10
594. 2 E. violet (air) .. 10 10

**1968.** Agrarian Reform.
595. **203.** 20 c. black, green and orange (postage) .. 15 10
596. 50 c. black, green and orange (air) .. .. 15 10

**204.** Juan I. Molina (scientist) and "Lamp of Learning".

**205.** Hand supporting Cogwheel.

**1968.** Molina Commem.
597. **204.** 2 E. purple (postage) .. 10 10
598. – 1 E. green (air) .. 10 10
DESIGN: 1 E. Molina and books.

**1968.** 4th Manufacturing Census.
599. **205.** 30 c. red .. .. 15 10

**206.** Map, Galleon and "Alonso de Erckla" (ferry).

**1968.** "Five Towns" Centenaries.
600. **206.** 30 c. blue (postage) .. 30 10
601. – 1 E. purple (air) .. 15 10
DESIGN—VERT. 1 E. Map of Chiloe Province.

**207.** Club Emblem.

**1968.** 40th Anniv. of Chilean Automobile Club.
602. **207.** 1 E. red (postage) .. 20 10
603. 5 E. blue (air) .. 15 15

**208.** Chilean Arms.

**1968.** Air. State Visit of Queen Elizabeth II.
604. **208.** 50 c. brown & green .. 15 10
605. – 3 E. brown and blue .. 15 10
606. – 5 E. purple and plum 25 15
DESIGN—HORIZ. 3 E. Royal arms of Great Britain. VERT. 5 E. St. Edward's Crown on map of South America.

**209.** Don Francisco Garcia Huidobro (founder)

**1968.** 225th Anniv. of Chilean Mint.
608. **209.** 2 E. blue & red (post.) 10 10
609. – 5 E. brown and green 20 10
610. – 50 c. pur. & yell. (air) 10 10
611. – 1 E. red and blue .. 15 15
DESIGNS: 50 c. First Chilean coin and press. 1 E. First Chilean stamp printed by the mint (1915). 5 E. Philip V. of Spain.

**210.** Satellite and Dish Aerial.

**1969.** Inaug. of "ENTEL-CHILE" Satellite Communications Ground Station, Longovilo (1st issue).

613. **210.** 30 c. blue (postage) .. 10 10
614. 2 E. purple (air) .. 20 10

See also Nos. 668/9.

**211.** Red Cross Symbols.

**1969.** 50th Anniv. of League of Red Cross Societies.

615. **211.** 2 E. red & violet (post.) 15 10
616. 5 E. red and black (air) 15 10

**212.** Rapel Dam.

**1969.** Rapel Hydro-Electric Project.

617. **212.** 40 c. green (postage) .. 10 10
618. 3 E. blue (air) .. 15 10

**213.** Rodriguez Memorial.

**1969.** 150th Death Anniv. of Col. Manuel Rodriguez.

619. **213.** 2 E. red (postage) .. 10 10
620. 30 c. brown (air) .. 10 10

**214.** Open Bible.

**1969.** 400th Anniv. of Spanish Translation of Bible.

621. **214.** 40 c. brown (postage) 10 10
622. 1 E. green (air) .. 15 10

**215.** Hemispheres and I.L.O. Emblem.

**1969.** 50th Anniv. of I.L.O.

623. **215.** 1 E. grn. & blk. (post.) 10 10
624. 2 E. purple & blk. (air) 10 10

**216.** Human Rights Emblem. **217.** "EXPO" Emblem.

**1969.** Human Rights Year (1968).

625. **216.** 4 E. red and blue (post.) 35 25
626. 4 E. red and brown (air) 45 25

**1969.** World Fair "EXPO 70", Osaka, Japan.

628. **217.** 3 E. blue (postage) .. 10 10
629. 5 E. red (air) .. .. 15 10

**218.** Mint, Santiago (18th cent.).

**1970.** Spanish Colonisation of Chile.

630. **218.** 2 E. purple .. .. 20 10
631. – 3 E. red .. .. 15 10
632. – 4 E. blue .. .. 15 10
633. – 5 E. brown .. .. 15 10
634. – 10 E. green .. .. 15 10

DESIGNS—HORIZ. 5 E. Cal y Canto Bridge. VERT. 3 E. Pedro de Valdivia. 4 E. Santo Domingo Church, Santiago. 10 E. Ambrosio O'Higgins.

**219.** Policarpo Toro and Map.

**1970.** 80th Anniv. of Seizure of Easter Island.

636. **219.** 5 E. violet (postage) .. 25 10
637. 50 c. turquoise (air) .. 35 10

**221.** Chilean Schooner and Arms. **222.** Paul Harris.

**1970.** 150th Anniv. of Capture of Valdivia by Lord Cochrane.

640. **221.** 40 c. lake (postage) .. 35 10
641. 2 E. blue (air) 65 10

**1970.** Birth Cent. of Paul Harris (founder of Rotary Int.).

642. **222.** 10 E. blue (postage) .. 30 20
643. 1 E. red (air) .. .. 30 15

**223.** Mahatma Gandhi. **225.** Education Year Emblem.

**1970.** Birth Centenary of Gandhi.

644. **223.** 40 c. green (postage) .. 2·50 20
645. 1 E. brown (air) .. 30 15

**1970.** Int. Education Year.

648. **225.** 2 E. red (postage) .. 10 10
649. 4 E. brown (air) .. 15 10

**226.** "Virgin and Child". **227.** Snake and Torch Emblem.

**1970.** O'Higgins National Shrine, Maipu.

650. **226.** 40 c. green (postage) .. 10 10
651. 1 E. blue (air) .. 15 15

**1970.** 10th Int. Cancer Congress, Houston, U.S.A.

652. **227.** 40 c. purple and blue (postage) .. .. 80 10
653. 2 E. brn. and olive (air) 50 10

**228.** Chilean Arms and Copper Symbol. **229.** Globe, Dove and Cogwheel.

**1970.** Copper Mines Nationalization

654. **228.** 40 c. red & brn. (postage) 15 10
655. 3 E. green & brown (air) 25 10

**1970.** 25th Anniv. of United Nations.

656. **229.** 3 E. violet and red (postage) .. .. 10 10
657. 5 E. green & lake (air) 20 10

**1970.** Nos. 613/14 surch.

658. **210.** 52 c. on 30 c. blue (postage) 30 10
659. 52 c. on 2 E. purple (air) 50 15

**231.** Freighter "Lago Maihue" and Ship's Wheel. **233.** Scout Badge.

**232.** Bernardo O'Higgins and Fleet.

**1971.** State Maritime Corporation.

660. **231.** 52 c. red (postage) 15 10
661. 5 E. brown (air) .. 25 10

**1971.** 150th Anniv. of Peruvian Liberation Expedition.

662. **232.** 5 E. grn. & blue (postage) 20 10
663. 1 E. pur. & blue (air) .. 25 10

**1971.** 60th Anniv. of Chilean Scouting Association.

664. **233.** 1 E. brn. & grn. (postage) 20 10
665. 5 c. grn. & lake (air) .. 20 10

**234.** Young People and U.N. Emblem.

**1971.** 1st Latin-American Meeting of U.N.I.C.E.F. Executive Council, Santiago (1969).

666. **234.** 52 c. brn. & blue (postage) 10 10
667. 2 E. grn. & blue (air) 15 10

**1971.** Longovilo Satellite Communications Ground Station (2nd issue). As T **210**, but with "LONGOVILO" added to centre inscr. and wording at foot of design changed to "PRIMERA ESTACION LATINOAMERICANA".

668. 40 c. green (postage) .. 30 10
669. 2 E. brown (air) .. 50 15

**235.** Diver with Harpoon-gun.

**1971.** 10th World Underwater Fishing Championships, Iquique.

670. **235.** 1 E. 15 myrtle and grn. 65 10
671. 2 E. 35 ultram. & blue 15 10

**239.** Magellan and Caravel.

**1971.** 450th Anniv. of Discovery of Magellan Straits.

676. **239.** 35 c. plum and blue .. 20 10

**240.** Dagoberto Godoy and Bristol Monoplane over Andes.

**1971.** 1st Trans-Andes Flight (1918). Commem.

677. **240.** 1 E. 15 green and blue 20 10

**241.** Statue of the Virgin, San Cristobal.

**1971.** 10th Postal Union of the Americas and Spain Congress, Santiago.

678 **241** 1 E. 15 blue .. .. 45 10
679 – 2 E. 35 blue and red .. 45 10
680 – 4 E. 35 red .. .. 45 10
681 – 9 E. 35 lilac .. .. 45 10
682 – 18 E. 35 mauve .. 60 10

DESIGNS—VERT. 4 E. 35, St. Francis's Church, Santiago. HORIZ. 2 E. 35, U.P.A.E. emblem. 9 E. 35, Central Post Office, Santiago. 18 E. 35, Corregidor Inn.

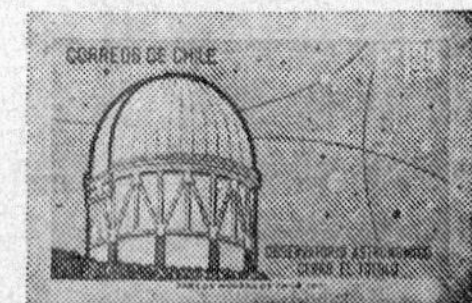


**242.** Cerro el Tololo Observatory.

**1972.** Inauguration of Astronomical Observatory, Cerro el Tololo.

683. **242.** 1 E. 95 bl. and new bl. 20 10

**243.** Boeing 707 over Tahiti.

**1972.** 1st Air Service Santiago-Easter Island-Tahiti.

684. **243.** 2 E. 35 purple & ochre 30 10

**244.** Alonso de Ercilla y Zuniga. **246.** Human Heart.

**245.** Antarctic Map and Dog-sledge.

**1972.** 400th Anniv. (1969) of "La Araucana" (epic poem by de Ercilla y Zungia).

685. **244.** 1 E. brown (postage) .. 15 10
686. 2 E. blue (air) .. .. 20 15

**1972.** 10th Anniv. of Antarctic Treaty.

687. **245.** 1 E. 15 black & blue .. 80 15
688. 3 E. 50 blue & green .. 55 10

**1972.** World Heart Month.

689. **246.** 1 E. 15 red and black .. 20 10

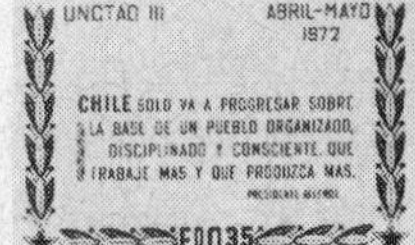


**247.** Text of Speech by Pres. Allende.

**1972.** 3rd United Nations Conf. on Trade and Development, Santiago.

690. **247.** 35 c. green & brown .. 15 15
691. – 1 E. 15 violet and blue 10 10
692. **247.** 4 E. violet and pink .. 30 20
693. – 6 E. blue and orange .. 20 10

DESIGNS: 1 E. 15, 6 E. Conference Hall Santiago.

**248.** Soldier and Crest.

**1972.** 150th Anniv. of O'Higgins Military Academy.
694. **248.** 1 E. 15 yellow & blue 15 10

**249.** Copper Miner. **250.** Barquentine "Esmeralda".

**1972.** Copper Mines Nationalization Law (1971).
695. **249.** 1 E. 15 blue and red .. 15 10
696. 5 E. black, blue & red 30 10

**1972.** 150th Anniv. of Arturo Prat Naval College.
697. **250.** 1 E. 15 purple .. 40 15

**251.** Observatory and Telescope. **252.** Dove with Letter.

**1972.** Inaug. of Cerro Calan Observatory.
698. **251.** 50 c. blue .. .. 20 10

**1972.** Int. Correspondence Week.
699. **252.** 1 E. 15 violet and mve. 15 10

**253.** Gen. Schneider, Flag and Quotation.

**1972.** 2nd Death Anniv. of General Rene Schneider.
700. **253.** 2 E. 30 multicoloured 30 20

**254.** Book and Students.

**1972.** International Book Year.
701. **254.** 50 c. black and red .. 15 10

**255.** Folklore and Handicrafts.

**1972.** Tourist Year of the Americas.
702. **255.** 1 E. 15 black and red 15 10
703. – 2 E. 65 purple and blue 30 10
704. – 3 E. 50 brown and red 15 10
DESIGNS—HORIZ. 2 E. 65, Natural produce. VERT. 3 E. 50, Stove and rug.

**256.** Carrera in Prison. **257.** Antarctic Map.

**1973.** 150th Death Anniv. of General J. M. Carrera.
705. **256.** 2 E. 30 blue .. .. 20 10

**1973.** 25th Anniv. of General Bernardo O'Higgins Antarctic Base.
706. **257.** 10 E. red and blue .. 35 15

**258.** Destroyer and Emblem. **259.** Telescope.

**1973.** 50 Years of Chilean Naval Aviation.
707. **258.** 20 E. blue and brown .. 30 10

**1973.** Inauguration of La Silla Astronomical Observatory.
708. **259.** 2 E. 30 black and blue 20 10

**260.** Interpol Emblem. **261.** Bunch of Grapes.

**1973.** 50th Anniv. of Interpol.
709 **260** 30 E. blue, blk & brn 1·40 20
710 – 50 E. black and red .. 1·40 25
DESIGN: 50 E. Fingerprint superimposed on Globe.

**1973.** Chilean Wine Exports. Multicoloured.
711 20 E. Type **261** .. .. 50 10
712 100 E. Inscribed Globe .. 1·00 20

**1974.** Centenary of World Meteorological Organization. No. 668 surch **"Centenario de la Organizacion Meteorologica Mundial IMO-W-MO 1973"** and value.
713 27 E.+3 E. on 40 c. green .. 15 10

**263.** U.P.U. Headquarters Building, Berne.

**1974.** U.P.U. Cent. Unissued stamp surch.
714. **263.** 500 E. on 45 c. green .. 85 20

**264.** Bernardo O'Higgins and Emblems.

**1974.** Chilean Armed Forces.
715. **264.** 30 E. yellow and red 20 10
716. – 30 E. lake and red .. 20 10
717. – 30 E. blue and light blue 20 10
718. – 30 E. blue and lilac .. 20 10
719. – 30 E. emerald and grn. 20 10
DESIGNS: No. 716, Soldiers with mortar. No. 717, Naval gunners. No. 718, Air-force pilot. No. 719, Mounted policeman.

**1974.** 500th Birth Anniv. (1973) of Copernicus. No. 683 surch. **"V Centenario del Nacimiento de Copernico 1473–1973"** and value.
720. **242.** 27 E.+3 E. on 1 E. 95 blue & new blue .. 30 10

**1974.** Vina del Mar. Cent. No. 496 surch. **"Centenario de la ciudad de Vina del Mar 1874-1974"** and value.
721. 27 E.+3 E. on 1 E. turquoise 15 10

**267.** Football and Globe. **269.** Police and Gloved Hand.

**1974.** World Cup Football Championships, West Germany.
722. **267.** 500 E. orange and red 20 10
723. – 1000 E. bl. & deep bl. 1·00 15
DESIGN—HORIZ. 1000 E. Football on stylized stadium.

**1974.** Various stamps surch.
724. **212.** 47 E.+3 E. on 40 c. grn. 15 10
725. **228.** 67 E.+3 E. on 40 c. red and brown .. 15 10
726. **214.** 97 E.+3 E. on 40 c. brn. 15 10
727. **223.** 100 E. on 40 c. green .. 20 10
728. – 300 E. on 50 c. brown (No. 571) .. .. 20 10

**1974.** Campaign for Prevention of Traffic Accidents.
729. **269.** 30 E. brown & green .. 25 10

**270.** Manutara and Part of Globe. **271.** Core of Globe.

**1974.** Inaugural LAN Flight to Tahiti, Fiji and Australia. Each green and brown.
730. 200 E. Type **270** .. .. 40 15
731. 200 E. Tahitian dancer and part of Globe .. .. 40 15
732. 200 E. Map of Fiji and part of Globe .. .. 40 15
733. 200 E. Eastern grey kangaroo and part of Globe 40 15

**1974.** Int. Symposium of Volcanology, Santiago de Chile.
734. **271.** 500 E. orge. & brown 60 10

**1974.** Inauguration of Votive Temple. No. 650 surch. **24 OCTOBRE 1974 INAUGURACION TEMPLO VOTIVO** and value.
735. **226.** 100 E. on 40 c. green .. 15 10

**273.** Map of Robinson Crusoe Island. **275.** F. Vidal Gormaz and Seal.

**274.** O'Higgins and Bolivar.

**1974.** 400th Anniv. of Discovery of Juan Fernandez Archipelago. Each brown and blue.
736. 200 E. Type **273** .. 60 20
737. 200 E. Chontas (hardwood palm-trees) .. .. 40 20
738. 200 E. Mountain goat .. 40 20
739. 200 E. Spiny lobster .. 40 20

**1974.** 150th Anniv. of Battles of Junin and Ayacucho.
740. **274.** 100 E. brown and buff 20 10

**1975.** Cent. of Naval Hydrographic Institute.
741. **275.** 100 E. blue & mauve 20 10

**1975.** Surch. **Revalorizada 1975** and value.
742. **228.** 70 c. on 40 c. red and brown .. .. 15 10

**277.** Dr. Schweitzer. **278.** Lighthouse.

**1975.** Birth Centenary of Dr. Albert Schweitzer (missionary).
743. **277.** 500 e. brown & yellow 35 10

**1975.** 50th Anniv. of Valparaiso Lifeboat Service. Each blue and green.
744 150 E. Type **278** .. .. 55 20
745 150 E. Wreck of "Teotopoulis" .. .. 55 20
746 150 E. "Cap Christiansen" (lifeboat) .. .. 55 20
747 150 E. Survivor in water .. 55 20

**279.** Sail/steam Corvette "Baquedano".

**1975.** 30th Anniv of Shipwreck of Sail Frigate "Lautaro".
749. **279.** 500 E. black and green 65 15
750. – 500 E. black and green 65 15
751. – 500 E. black and green 65 15
752. – 500 E. black and green 65 15
753. **279.** 800 E. black and brown 85 20
754. – 800 E. black and brown 85 20
755. – 800 E. black and brown 85 20
756. – 800 E. black and brown 85 20
757. **279.** 1000 E. black and blue 1·10 20
758. – 1000 E. black and blue 1·10 20
759. – 1000 E. black and blue 1·10 20
760. – 1000 E. black and blue 1·10 20
DESIGNS: Nos. 750, 754, 758, Sail frigate "Lautaro". Nos. 751, 755, 759, Cruiser "Chacabuco". Nos. 752, 756, 760, Cadet barquentine "Esmeralda".

**280.** " The Happy Mother " (A. Valenzuela.) **281.** Diego Portales (politician).

**1975.** International Women's Year. Chilean Paintings. Multicoloured.
761. 50 c. Type **280** .. .. 65 15
762. 50 c. " Girl " (F. J Mandiola) 65 15
763. 50 c. " Lucia Guzman " (P. L. Rencoret) .. 65 15
764. 50 c. " Unknown Woman " (Magdalena M. Mena) .. 65 15

**1975.** Inscr. "D. PORTALES".
765. **281.** 10 c. green .. .. 20 10
765a. 20 c. lilac .. .. 10 10
765b. 30 c. orange .. .. 10 10
766. 50 c. brown .. .. 15 10
767. 1 p. blue .. .. 15 10
767a. 1 p. 50 brown .. .. 15 10
767b. 2 p. black .. .. 15 10
767c. 2 p. 50 brown .. 15 10
767d. 3 p. 50 red .. .. 15 10
768. 5 p. mauve .. .. 15 15
For this design inscr "DIEGO PORTALES", see Nos. 901 etc.

**282.** Lord Cochrane and Fleet, 1820.

**1975.** Birth Bicent. of Lord Thomas Cochrane. Multicoloured.
769. 1 p. Type **282** .. .. 55 20
770. 1 p. Cochrane's capture of Valdivia, 1820 .. 55 20
771. 1 p. Capture of "Esmeralda", 1820 .. 55 20
772. 1 p. Cruiser "Cochrane", 1874 .. .. .. 55 20
773. 1 p. Destroyer "Cochrane" 1962 .. .. .. 55 20

**283.** Flags of Chile and Bolivia.

**1976.** 150th Anniv. of Bolivia's Independence.
774. **283.** 1 p. 50 multicoloured 1·40 10

**284.** Lake of the Incas.

**1976.** 6th General Assembly of Organization of American States.
775. **284.** 1 p. 50 multicoloured 1·40 10

**285.** George Washington. **286.** Minerva and Academy Emblem.

**1976.** Bicent. of American Revolution.
776. **285.** 5 p. multicoloured .. 1·50 15

**1976.** 50th Anniv. of Polytechnic Military Academy.
777. **286.** 2 p. 50 multicoloured 1·00 10

**287.** Indian Warrior.

**1976.** 3rd Anniv of Military Junta. Mult.
778 1 p. Type **287** .. .. 25 15
779 2 p. Andean condor with broken chain .. .. 25 15
780 3 p. Winged woman ("Rebirth of the Country") .. .. 25 15

**288.** Chilean Base, Antarctica.

**1977.** Presidential Visit to Antarctica.
781. **288.** 2 p. multicoloured .. 5·25 25

**289.** College Emblem and Cultivated Field. **290.** Statue of Justice.

**1977.** Centenary of Advanced Agricultural Education.
782. **289.** 2 p. multicoloured .. 1·40 15

**1977.** 150th Anniv. of Supreme Court.
783. **290.** 2 p. brown and slate .. 1·40 10

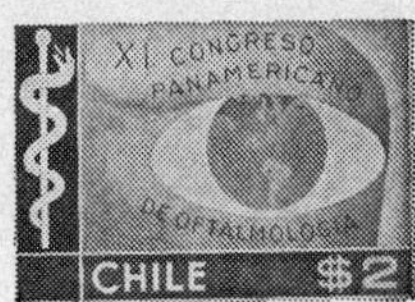


**291.** Globe within "Eye".

**1977.** 11th Pan-American Ophthalmological Congress.
784. **291.** 2 p. multicoloured .. 2·00 10

**292.** Police Emblem and Activities.

**1977.** 50th Anniv. of Chilean Police Force. Multicoloured.
785. 2 p. Type **292** .. .. 60 10
786. 2 p. Mounted carabinero (vert.) .. .. 25 10
787. 2 p. Policewoman with children (vert.) .. .. 25 10
788. 2 p. Torres del Paine and Osorno Volcano (vert.) 25 10

**293.** "Intelsat" Satellite and Globe.

**1977.** World Telecommunications Day.
789. **293.** 2 p. multicoloured .. 25 10

**294.** Front page, Press and Schooner.

**1977.** 150th Anniv. of Newspaper "El Mercurio de Valparaiso".
790. **294.** 2 p. multicoloured .. 20 15

**295.** St. Francis of Assisi. **296.** "Science and Technology".

**1977.** 750th Death Anniv. of St. Francis of Assisi.
791. **295.** 5 p. multicoloured .. 1·00 15

**1977.** Council for Science and Technology.
792. **296.** 4 p. multicoloured .. 40 15

**297.** Weaving (Mothers' Centres). **298.** Diego de Almagro (discoverer of Chile).

**1977.** 4th Anniv. of Government Junta. Welfare Facilities. Multicoloured.
793. 5 p. Type **297** .. .. 55 10
794. 5 p. Nurse with cripple (Care of the Disabled) .. 55 10
795. 10 p. Children dancing (Protection of Minors) (horiz.) 1·00 15
796. 10 p. Elderly man (Care for the Aged) (horiz.) .. 1·00 15

**1977.** Columbus Day.
797. **298.** 5 p. brown .. .. 45 10

**299.** Boy, Christmas Bell and Post Box.

**1977.** Christmas.
798. **299.** 2 p. 50 multicoloured .. 15 15

**300.** Freighter loading Timber.

**1978.** Timber Export. Multicoloured.
799. 10 p. Type **300** .. .. 1·00 25
800. 20 p. As T **300** but inscr. "CORREOS" and with ship flying Chilean flag 1·50 35

**301.** Papal Arms and Globe.

**1978.** World Peace Day.
801. **301.** 10 p. multicoloured .. 80 15

**302.** University.

**1978.** 50th Anniv. of Catholic University, Valparaiso.
802. **302.** 25 p. multicoloured .. 1·60 15

**303.** "Bernardo O'Higgins" (Gil de Castro). **304.** Chacabuco Victory Monument.

**1978.** Birth Bicent. of Bernardo O'Higgins. (1st issue).
803. **303.** 10 p. multicoloured .. 1·00 15
See also Nos. 804, 806/8 and 816.

**1978.** Birth Bicent. of Bernardo O'Higgins. (2nd issue), and 5th Anniv. of Military Junta.
804. **304.** 10 p. multicoloured .. 1·00 15

**305.** Teacher writing on Blackboard.

**1978.** 10th Anniv. and 9th Meeting of Inter-American Council for Education, Science and Culture.
805. **305.** 15 p. multicoloured .. 60 15

**306.** "The Last Moments at Rancagua" (Pedro Subercaseaux).

**1978.** Birth Bicent. of Bernardo O'Higgins. (3rd issue).
806. **306.** 30 p. multicoloured .. 2·00 65

**307.** "First National Naval Squadron" (Thomas Somerscales).

**1978.** Birth Bicent. of Bernardo O'Higgins. (4th issue).
807. **307.** 20 p. multicoloured .. 1·50 80

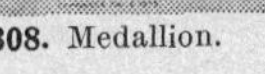

**308.** Medallion. **309.** Council Emblem.

**1978.** Birth Bicentenaries of O'Higgins (5th issue) and San Martin.
808 **308** 7 p. multicoloured .. 30 10

**1978.** 30th Anniv. of International Council of Military Sports.
809. **309.** 50 p. multicoloured .. 4·00 1·40

**310.** Three Kings. **311.** Bernardo and Rodulfo Philippi.

**1978.** Christmas. Multicoloured.
810. 3 p. Type **310** .. .. 65 15
811. 11 p. Virgin and Child .. 1·25 20

**1978.** The Philippi Brothers (scientists and travellers).
812. **311.** 3 p. 50 multicoloured 20 10

**1979.** No. 765 surch. **$3.50.**
813. **281.** 3 p. 50 on 10 c. green .. 15 10

**313.** Flowers, and Flags of Chile and the Salvation Army.

**1979.** 70th Anniv. of Salvation Army in Chile.
814. **313.** 10 p. multicoloured .. 55 25

**314.** Pope Paul VI.

**1979.** Pope Paul VI Commemoration.
815. **314.** 11 p. multicoloured .. 80 25

**315.** Battle of Maipu Monument.

**1979.** Birth Bicentenary of Bernardo O'Higgins (6th issue).
816. **315.** 8 p. 50 multicoloured 55 20

**316.** "Battle of Iquique". (Thomas Somerscales). **317.** Diego Portales.

**1979.** Naval Battle Centenaries. Mult.
817. 3 p. 50 Type **316** .. 65 25
818. 3 p. 50 "Battle of Punta Gruesa" (Alvaso Casanova Zenteno) .. .. 65 25
819. 3 p. 50 "Battle of Angamos" (Alvaso Casanova Zenteno) 65 25

**1979.**
820. **317.** 1 p. 50 brown .. 15 10
821. 2 p. grey .. .. 10 10
822. 3 p. 50 red .. .. 10 10
823. 4 p. 50 blue .. .. 20 10
824. 5 p. red .. .. 20 10
825. 6 p. green .. .. 20 10
826. 7 p. yellow .. .. 20 10
827. 10 p. blue .. .. 25 10
828. 12 p. orange .. .. 10 10

The 1 p. 50, 3 p. 50, 5 p. and 6 p. are inscribed "D PORTALES" and have the imprint "CAMONEDA CHILE". The 2 p., 4 p. 50, 7 p. and 10 p. are inscribed "DIEGO PORTALES" and have the imprint "CASA DE MONEDA DE CHILE".

**318.** Horse-drawn Ambulance.

**1979.** 75th Anniv. of Chilean Red Cross.
831. **318.** 25 p. multicoloured .. 2·75 60

**319.** Monument at Puntas Arenas. (Miodrag Zivkovic).

**1979.** Cent. of Yugoslav Immigration.
832. **319.** 10 p. multicoloured .. 45 15

**320.** Children in Playground (Kiochi Kayano Gomez).

**1979.** International Year of the Child. Mult.
833 9 p. 50 Type **320** .. .. 45 30
834 11 p. Running girl (Carmed Pizarro Toto) (vert) .. 55 35
835 12 p. Children dancing in circle (Ana Pizarro Munizaga) .. .. 1·00 50

**321.** Laveredo and Arms of Coyhaique.

**1979.** 50th Anniv. of Coyhaique.
836. **321.** 20 p. multicoloured .. 80 40

**322.** Exhibition Emblem and Posthorn.

**1979.** Third World Telecommunications Exhibition, Geneva.
837. **322.** 15 p. grey, blue & orge. 70 30

**323.** Canal

**1979.** 25th Anniv. of Puerto Williams, Navirino Island.
838. **323.** 3 p. 50 multicoloured 50 15

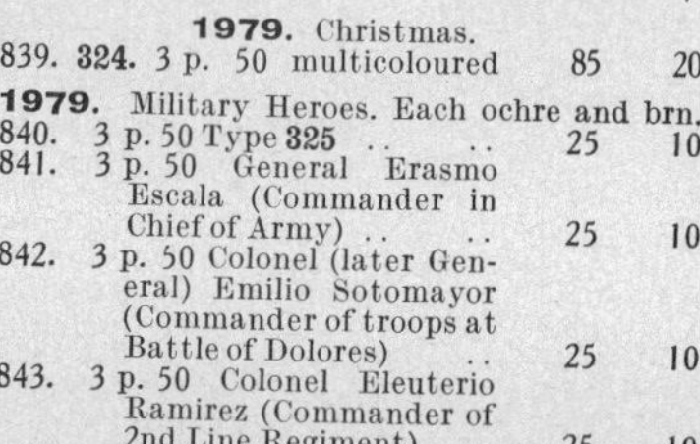


**324.** Chileans adoring child Jesus.

**325.** Rafael Sotomayor (Minister of War).

**1979.** Christmas.
839. **324.** 3 p. 50 multicoloured 85 20

**1979.** Military Heroes. Each ochre and brn.
840. 3 p. 50 Type **325** .. .. 25 10
841. 3 p. 50 General Erasmo Escala (Commander in Chief of Army) .. .. 25 10
842. 3 p. 50 Colonel (later General) Emilio Sotomayor (Commander of troops at Battle of Dolores) .. 25 10
843. 3 p. 50 Colonel Eleuterio Ramirez (Commander of 2nd Line Regiment) .. 25 10

**326.** Bell Model 205 Iroquois Rescue Helicopter at Tinguiririca Volcano.

**1980.** 50th Anniv of Chilean Air Force. Mult.
844 3 p. 50 Type **326** .. .. 40 15
845 3 p. 50 Consolidated Catalina Skua amphibian in Antarctic .. 40 15
846 3 p. 50 Northrop Tiger II jet fighter in Andes .. 40 15

**327.** Rotary Emblem and Globe.

**1980.** 75th Anniv. of Rotary International.
847. **327.** 10 p. multicoloured .. 50 25

**328.** " The Death of Bueras " (Pedro Leon Carmona).

**1980.** Cavalry Charge led by Colonel Santiago Bueras at Battle of Maipu, 1818.
848. **328.** 12 p. multicoloured .. 65 30

**329.** " Gen. Manuel Gaquedano " (after Pedro Subercaseaux).

**1980.** Cent. of Battle of Arica Head. Mult.
849. 3 p. 50 Type **329** .. .. 25 10
850. 3 p. 50 Gen Pedro Largos (43 × 26 mm.) .. .. 25 10
851. 3 p. 50 Col. Juan Jose San Martin(43 × 26 mm.) .. 25 10

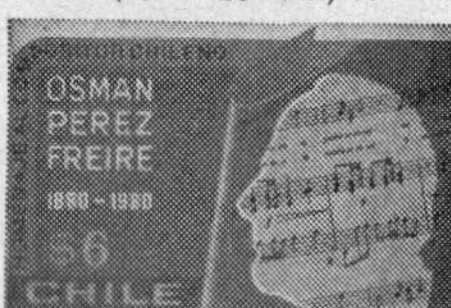


**330.** Freire and Bars of " Ay, Ay, Ay! ".

**1980.** Birth Centenary of Osman Perez Freire (composer).
852. **330.** 6 p. multicoloured .. 35 15

**331.** Mt. Gasherbrum II, Chileans flag and Ice-pick.

**1980.** Chilean Himalayan Expedition (1979).
853. **331.** 15 p. multicoloured .. 70 35

**332.** " St Vincent de Paul" (stained glass window, former Mother House).

**1980.** 125th Anniv of Sisters of Charity in Chile.
854 **332** 10 p. multicoloured .. 50 25

**333.** Andean Condor.

**1980.** 7th Anniv. of Military Government.
855. **333.** 3 p. 50 multicoloured 40 10

**334.** Mummy of Inca Child.

**1980.** 150th Anniv. of National History Museum. Multicoloured.
856. 5 p. Type **334** .. .. 30 15
857. 5 p. Claudio Gay (founder) (after Alejandro Laemlein) 30 15

**335.** "Pablo Burchard" (Pedro Lira).

**336.** Emblem and Buildings.

**1980.** Cent. of National Museum of Fine Arts.
858. **335.** 3 p. 50 multicoloured 20 10

**1980.** " Fisa '80 " International Fair, Santiago.
859. **336.** 3 p. 50 multicoloured 20 10

**337.** " Family and Angels " (Sara Hinojosa Orellana).

**338.** Infantryman.

**1980.** Christmas. Multicoloured.
860. 3 p. 50 Type **337** .. .. 85 10
861. 10 p. 50 " The Holy Family " (Catalina Imboden Fernandez) .. .. 1·10 20

**1980.** Army Uniforms of 1879 (1st series). Multicoloured.
862. 3 p. 50 Type **338** .. .. 30 15
863. 3 p. 50 Cavalry officer (parade uniform) .. 30 15
864. 3 p. 50 Artillery officer .. 30 15
865. 3 p. 50 Colonel of Engineers (parade uniform) .. 30 15
See also Nos. 887/90.

**339.** Congress Emblem.

**340.** Cattle.

**1980.** 23rd International Congress of Military Medicine and Pharmacy, Santiago.
866. **339.** 11 p. 50 multicoloured 55 30

**1981.** Eradication of Foot and Mouth Disease from Chile.
867. **340.** 9 p. 50 multicoloured 45 20

**341.** Robinson Crusoe Island.

**1981.** Tourism. Multicoloured.
868. 3 p. 50 Type **341** .. .. 25 15
869. 3 p. 50 Easter Island monoliths .. .. 25 15
870. 10 p. 50 Gentoo Penguins, Antarctica .. .. 1·75 50

**342.** " Javiera Carrera " (after D. M. Pizarro) and Flag.

**1981.** Birth Bicentenary of Javiera Carrera (creator of first national flag).
871. **342.** 3 p. 50 multicoloured 20 10

**343.** U.P.U. Emblem.

**1981.** Cent. of U.P.U. Membership.
872. **343.** 3 p. multicoloured .. 25 15

**344.** Unloading Cargo from Lockheed Hercules.

**1981.** 1st Anniv. of Lieutenant Marsh Antarctic Air Force Base.
873. **344.** 3 p. 50 multicoloured 50 15

**345.** I.T.U. and W.H.O. Emblems and Ribbons forming Caduceus.

**1981.** World Telecommunications Day.
874. **345.** 3 p. 50 multicoloured 20 15

**346.** Arturo Prat Antarctic Naval Base.

**1981.** 20th Anniv. of Antarctic Treaty.
875. **346.** 3 p. 50 multicoloured 75 20

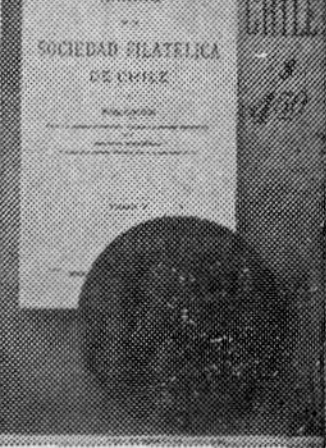


**347.** Capt. Jose Luis Araneda.

**348.** Philatelic Society Yearbook and Medal.

**1981.** Centenary of Battle of Sangrar.
876. **347.** 3 p. 50 multicoloured 25 15

**1981.** 92nd Anniv of Philatelic Society of Chile.
877 **348** 4 p. 50 multicoloured .. 25 15

**349.** " Exchange of Speeches between Minister Recabarren and Indian Chief Conuepan at the Nielol Hill " (Hector Robles Acuna).

**1981.** Centenary of Temuco City.
878. **349.** 4 p. 50 multicoloured 25 15

**350.** Exports (embroidery by J. L. Gutierrez).

**1981.** Exports.
879. **350.** 14 p. multicoloured .. 55 20

**351.** Moneda Palace (seat of Government).

**1981.** 8th Anniv. of Military Government.
880. **351.** 4 p. 50 multicoloured 25 15

**352.** St. Vincent de Paul.

**353.** Medallion by Rene Thenot, Quill and Law Code.

**1981.** 400th Birth Anniv. of St. Vincent de Paul (founder of Sisters of Charity).
881. **352.** 4 p. 50 multicoloured 25 15

**1981.** Birth Bicentenary of Andres Bello (statesman, lawyer, and founder of Chile University). Multicoloured.
882. 4 p. 50 Type **353** .. .. 25 15
883. 9 p. 50 Profile of Bello and three of his books .. 40 20
884. 11 p. 50 University of Chile arms and Nicanor Plaza's statue of Bello .. .. 45 20

**354.** Flag on Map of South America and Police Badge.

**1981.** Second South American Uniformed Police Congress, Santiago.
885. **354.** 4 p. 50 multicoloured 30 15

**355.** F.A.O. and U.N. Emblems.

**1981.** World Food Day.
886. **355.** 5 p. 50 multicoloured 30 15

**1981.** Army Uniforms of 1879 (2nd series). As T **338.** Multicoloured.
887. 5 p. 50 Infantryman .. 35 20
888. 5 p. 50 Military School cadet .. .. .. 35 20
889. 5 p. 50 Cavalryman .. 35 20
890. 5 p. 50 Artilleryman .. 35 20

**356.** Mother and Child.

**1981.** International Year of Disabled Persons.
891 **356** 5 p. 50 multicoloured .. 30 15

**357.** " Nativity " (Ruth Tatiana Aguero Eguili).

**1981.** Christmas. Multicoloured.
892. 5 p. 50 Type **357** .. .. 25 10
893. 11 p. 50 " The Three Kings " (Ignacio Jorge Manriquez Gonzalez) .. .. 55 20

**358.** Dario Salas.

**1981.** Birth Cent. of Dario Salas (educationist).
894. **358.** 5 p. 50 multicoloured 25 15

**359.** Main Buildings of University.

**1981.** 50th Anniv. of Federico Santa Maria Technical University, Valparaiso.
895. **359.** 5 p. 50 multicoloured 25 15

**360.** Fair Emblem.

**1982.** " Fida '82 " International Air Fair.
896. **360.** 4 p. 50 multicoloured 30 15

**361.** Cardinal Caro and Chilean Family.

**1982.** 1st Anniv of New Constitution. Mult.
897 4 p. 50 Type **361** .. .. 25 15
898 11 p. Diego Portales and national arms .. .. 45 20
899 30 p. Bernardo O'Higgins and national arms .. 1·25 40

**362.** Globe on Chilean Flag.

**363.** Pedro Montt (President, 1906–10).

**1982.** 12th Panamerican Institute of Geography and History General Assembly.
900. **362.** 4 p. 50 multicoloured 25 15

**1982.** As T **281** but inscr. "DIEGO PORTALES" and designs as T **363**.
901. **281.** 1 p. blue .. .. 10 10
902. – 1 p. blue .. .. 10 10
903. **281.** 1 p. 50 orange .. 10 10
904. 2 p. grey .. .. 10 10
905. – 2 p. lilac .. .. 10 10
906. **281.** 2 p. 50 yellow .. 10 10
907. **363.** 4 p. 50 mauve .. 30 10
908. – 5 p. red .. .. 10 10
909. **281.** 5 p. mauve .. .. 15 10
910. – 7 p. blue .. .. 25 10
911. – 10 p. black .. .. 15 10

DESIGNS: Nos. 902, 905, 908, 910, 911, Ramon Barros Luco (President, 1911–15).

**364.** Dassault Mirage IIIC Airplane and Chilean Air Force and American Air Forces Co-operation System Badges.

**1982.** American Air Forces Co-operation System.
916. **364.** 4 p. 50 multicoloured 50 15

**365.** Trawler and Map.

**367.** Capt. Ignacio Carrera Pinto.

**366.** Scout Emblems and Brownsea Island.

**1982.** Fisheries Exports.
917. **365.** 20 p. multicoloured .. 1·75 80

**1982.** 75th Anniv. of Boy Scout Movement and 125th Birth Anniv. of Lord Baden-Powell (founder). Multicoloured.
918. 4 p. 50 Type **366** .. .. 30 15
919. 4 p. 50 Lord Baden-Powell and Brownsea Island .. 30 15

**1982.** Centenary of Battle of Conception. Multicoloured.
920. 4 p. 50 Type **367** .. .. 25 20
921. 4 p. 50 Sub-lieutenant Arturo Perez Canto .. 25 20
922. 4 p. 50 Sub-lieutenant Julio Montt Salamanca 25 20
923. 4 p. 50 Sub-lieutenant Luis Cruz Martinez .. 25 20

**368.** Old Man at Window.

**1982.** World Assembly on Ageing, Vienna.
924. **368.** 4 p. 50 multicoloured 25 15

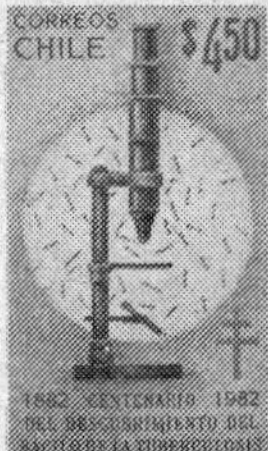


**369.** Microscope and Bacillus.

**1982.** Cent. of Discovery of Tubercle Bacillus.
925. **369.** 4 p. 50 multicoloured 30 15

**370.** National Flag and Flame of Freedom.

**1982.** 9th Anniv. of Military Government.
926. **370.** 4 p. 50 multicoloured 25 15

**1982.** Nos. 688/9 surch.
927. **245.** 1 p. on 3 e. 50 bl. & grn. 30 10
928. **246.** 2 p. on 1 e. 15 red & blk. 35 10

**372.** " Nativity " (Mariela Espinoza Fuentes).

**1982.** Christmas. Multicoloured.
929. 10 p. Type **372** .. .. 25 10
930. 25 p. "Adoration of the Shepherds" (Jared Jeria Abarca (vert.) .. .. 60 15

**373.** "Virgin Mary and Marcellus" (stained-glass window, Sacred Heart of Jesus Church, Barcelona).

**374.** "El Sur", Quill and Printing Press.

**1982.** Ninth World Union of Former Marist Alumni Congress.
931. **373.** 7 p. multicoloured .. 85 15

**1982.** Centenary of Concepcion's Newspaper "El Sur".
932. **374.** 7 p. multicoloured .. 25 15

**375.** "Steamship Copiapo" (W. Yorke).

**1982.** 110th Anniv. of South American Steamship Company.
933. **375.** 7 p. multicoloured .. 85 25

**376.** Club Badge, Radio Aerial, Dove and Globe.

**377.** Arms of Sovereign. Military Order.

**1982.** 60th Anniv. of Radio Club of Chile.
934. **376.** 7 p. multicoloured .. 25 10

**1983.** Postal Agreement with Sovereign Military Order of Malta. Multicoloured.
935. 25 p. Type **377** .. .. 65 40
936. 50 p. Arms of Chile .. 1·00 55

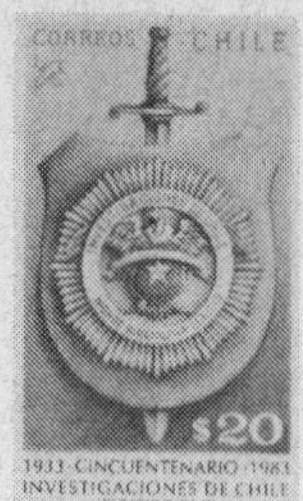


**378.** Badge.

**1983.** 50th Anniv. of Criminal Investigation Bureau.

937. **378.** 20 p. multicoloured .. 65 20

**379.** Cardinal Samore.

**1983.** Cardinal Antonio Samore Commem.

938. **379.** 30 p. multicoloured .. 80 25

**380.** Child watching Railway. **381.** Puoko Tangata (carved head from Easter Island).

**1983.** Cent of Valparaiso Incline Railway.

939 **380** 40 p. multicoloured .. 2·00 65

**1983.** Tourism. Multicoloured.

940 7 p. Type **381** .. .. 25 15

941 7 p. Ruins of Pucar de Quitor, San Pedro de Atacama .. .. 25 15

942 7 p. Rock painting, Rio Ibanez, Aisen .. .. 25 15

943 7 p. Diaguita pot .. 25 15

**382.** Winged Girl with Broken Chains.

**1983.** 10th Anniv of Military Government. Multicoloured.

944 7 p. Type **382** .. .. 25 15

945 7 p. Young couple with flag .. .. .. 25 15

946 10 p. Family with torch .. 30 15

947 40 p. National arms .. 1·40 40

**383.** General Francisco Morazan. **384.** Central Post Office, Santiago.

**1983.** Famous Hondurans. Multicoloured.

948. 7 p. Type **383** .. .. 20 10

949. 7 p. Sabio Jose Cecilio del Valle .. .. .. 20 10

**1983.** World Communications Year. Mult.

950. 7 p. Type **384** .. .. 55 10

951. 7 p. Space Shuttle "Challenger" .. .. 55 10

Nos. 950/1 were printed together in se-tenant pairs within the sheet forming a composite design.

**385.** "Holy Family" (Lucrecia Cardenas Gomez).

**1983.** Christmas.Children's Paintings. Mult.

952 10 p. "Nativity" (Hanny Chacon Scheel) .. 25 10

953 30 p. Type **385** .. .. 65 25

**386.** Presidential Coach, 1911. **387.** Juan Luis Sanfuentes.

**1984.** Railway Centenary. Multicoloured.

954. 9 p. Type **386** .. .. 60 35

955. 9 p. Service car and tender 60 35

956. 9 p. Type "80" locomotive, 1929 .. .. 60 35

Nos. 954/6 were printed together in se-tenant strips of three within the sheet, each strip forming a composite design.

**1984.** (a) Inscr. "CORREOS CHILE".

957. **387.** 5 p. red .. .. 10 10

958. 9 p. green .. .. 15 10

959. 10 p. grey .. .. 15 10

960. 15 p. blue .. .. 15 10

(b) Inscr. "D.S. No. 20 CHILE".

961 **387** 9 p. brown .. .. 15 10

962 15 p. blue .. .. 15 10

963 20 p. yellow .. .. 20 10

**388.** Piper Pillan Trainer and Flags.

**1984.** Third International Aeronautical Fair.

966. **388.** 9 p. multicoloured .. 60 10

**389.** Agriculture, Industry and Science.

**1984.** 20th Anniv. of Chilean Nuclear Energy Commission.

967. **389.** 9 p. multicoloured .. 25 10

**1984.** Nos. 944/5 surch.

968. 9 p. on 7 p. Type **382** .. 40 10

969. 9 p. on 7 p. Young couple with flag .. .. .. 40 10

**391.** Chilean Women's Antarctic Expedition.

**1984.** Chile's Antarctic Territories. Mult.

970. 15 p. Type **391** .. .. 90 50

971. 15 p. Villa Las Estrellas Antarctic settlement .. 50 30

972. 15 p. Scouts visiting Antarctic, 1983 .. .. 50 30

**392.** Parinacota Church (Tarapaca Region).

**1984.** 10th Anniv. of Regionalization. Mult.

973 9 p. Type **392** .. .. 25 20

974 9 p. El Tatio geyser (Antofagasta Region) .. 25 20

975 9 p. Copper miners (Atacama Region) .. 25 20

976 9 p. El Tololo observatory (Coquimbo Region) .. 25 20

977 9 p. Valparaiso harbour (Valparaiso Region) .. 55 20

978 9 p. Stone images (Easter Island Province) .. 25 20

979 9 p. St. Francis's Church (Santiago Metropolitan Region) .. .. 25 20

980 9 p. El Huique Hacienda (Libertador General Bernardo O'Higgins Region) .. .. 25 20

981 9 p. Hydro-electric dam and reservoir, Machicura (Maule Region) .. 25 20

982 9 p. Sta. Juana de Gaudalcazar Fort (Bio Bio Region) .. 25 20

983 9 p. Araucana woman (Araucania Region) .. 25 20

984 9 p. Church, Guar Island (Los Lagos Region) .. 25 20

985 9 p. South Highway (Aisen del General Carlos Ibanez del Campo Region) .. 25 20

986 9 p. Shepherd (Magallanes Region) .. .. 25 20

987 9 p. Villa Las Estrellas (Chile Antarctic Territories) .. .. 70 30

**393.** Pedro Sarmiento de Gamboa and Map.

**1984.** 400th Anniv of Spanish Settlements on Straits of Magellan.

988 **393** 100 p. multicoloured .. 1·75 80

**394.** Antonio Varas de la Barra (founder) and Coin.

**1984.** Centenary of State Savings Bank.

990. **394.** 35 p. multicoloured .. 50 20

**395.** Flame and Bernardo O'Higgins Monument.

**1984.** 11th Anniv. of Military Government.

991. **395.** 20 p. multicoloured .. 30 15

**396.** Clown.

**1984.** Centenary of Circus in Chile.

992 **396** 45 p. multicoloured .. 80 25

**397.** Blue Whale.

**1984.** Endangered Animals. Multicoloured.

993. 9 p. Type **397** .. .. 70 20

994. 9 p. Juan Fernandez fur seal .. .. .. 70 20

995. 9 p. Chilean guemal .. 70 20

996. 9 p. Long-tailed chinchilla 70 20

**398.** "Shepherds following Star" (Ruth M. Flores Rival).

**1984.** Christmas. Multicoloured.

997. 9 p. Type **398** .. .. 15 10

998. 40 p. "Bethlehem" (Vianka Pastrian Navea) .. 95 30

**399.** Satellite and Planetarium.

**1984.** Inauguration of Santiago University Planetarium.

999. **399.** 10 p. multicoloured .. 30 15

**400.** Andean Hog-nosed Skunk. **401.** Flags and Emblem.

**1985.** Flora and Fauna. Multicoloured.

1000. 10 p. Type **400** .. .. 60 25

1001. 10 p. "Leucocoryne purpurea" .. .. .. 60 25

1002. 10 p. Black-winged stilt 90 30

1003. 10 p. Marine otter .. 60 25

1004. 10 p. "Balbisia peduncularis" .. .. 60 25

1005. 10 p. Patagonian conure 90 30

1006. 10 p. Southern pudu .. 60 25

1007. 10 p. "Fuchsia magellanica" .. .. .. 60 25

1008. 10 p. Common diuca finch .. .. .. 90 30

1009. 10 p. Argentine grey fox 60 25

1010. 10 p. "Alstroemeria sierrae" .. .. 60 25

1011. 10 p. Ferruginous pygmy owl .. .. .. 90 30

**1985.** 25th Anniv. (1986) of American Air-forces Co-operation System.

1012. **401.** 45 p. multicoloured 1·50 1·00

**402.** Chile and Argentina Flags and Papal Arms.

**1985.** Chilean–Argentinian Peace Treaty.

1013. **402.** 20 p. multicoloured 45 25

**403.** Kentenich and Schoenstatt Sanctuary, La Florida.

**1985.** Birth Centenary of Father Jose Kentenich (founder of Schoenstatt Movement).

1014. **403.** 40 p. multicoloured 1·00 65

**404.** Landscape and Shrimp.

**1985.** Antarctic Territories and 25th Anniv of Antarctic Treaty. Multicoloured.

1015 15 p. Type **404** .. .. 50 30
1016 20 p. Seismological Station, O'Higgins Base .. 65 40
1017 35 p. Earth receiving station, Anvers Island 1·10 70

**405.** "Canis fulvipes".

**1985.** Endangered Animals. Multicoloured.

1018. 20 p. Type **405** .. .. 70 30
1019. 20 p. James's flamingo .. 1·25 40
1020. 20 p. Giant coot .. .. 1·25 40
1021. 20 p. Huidobria otter .. 70 30

**406.** Doves and "J".

**1985.** International Youth Year (1022) and 40th Anniv. of U.N.O. (1023). Multicoloured.

1022. 15 p. Type **406** .. .. 20 15
1023. 15 p. U.N. emblem .. 20 15

**407.** Farmer with Haycart. **408.** Carrera and Statue.

**1985.** Occupations. Each in brown.

1024. 10 p. Type **407** ... .. 10 15
1025. 10 p. Photographer with plate camera .. .. 10 15
1026. 10 p. Street entertainer .. 10 15
1027. 10 p. Basket maker .. 10 15

**1985.** Birth Bicentenary of Gen. Jose Miguel Carrera (Independence leader and first President).

1028. **408.** 40 p. multicoloured 75 30

**409.** "Holy Family". **411.** Escort of Light Infantry, 1818.

**410.** "Nativity" (Jennifer Gomez).

**1985.** Chilean Art.

1029. **409.** 10 p. brown & ochre 10 15

**1985.** Christmas. Multicoloured.

1030. 15 p. Type **410** .. .. 20 10
1031. 100 p. Man with donkey (Esteban Morales Medina) (vert.) .. .. 2·00 90

**1985.** 16th American Armies Conference. Multicoloured.

1032. 20 p. Type **411** .. .. 60 20
1033. 35 p. Officer of the Hussars of the Grand Guard, 1813 1·00 70

**412.** Moon, Earth and Comet.

**1985.** Appearance of Halley's Comet.

1034. **412.** 45 p. multicoloured 35 20

**413.** Living Trees and Flame. **414.** Saltpetre.

**1985.** Forest Fires Prevention. Multicoloured.

1036. 40 p. Type **413** .. .. 40 20
1037. 40 p. Burnt trees and flame 45 20

**1986.** Exports. Each brown and blue.

1038. 12 p. Type **414** .. .. 15 10
1039. 12 p. Iron .. .. .. 15 10
1040. 12 p. Copper .. .. 15 10
1041. 12 p. Molybdenum .. 15 10

**415.** Dungeness Point Lighthouse.

**1986.** Chilean Lighthouses. Multicoloured.

1042. 45 p. Type **415** .. .. 45 25
1043. 45 p. Evangelistas lighthouse in storm .. .. 45 25

**416.** St. Lucia Hill, Santiago.

**1986.** Death Centenary of Benjamin Vicuna Mackenna (Municipal Superintendent).

1044. **416.** 30 p. multicoloured 30 20

**417.** Diego Portales.

**1986.** Unissued stamp surch.

1045. **417.** 12 p. on 3 p. 50 mult. 15 10

**418.** National Stadium, Chile, 1962.

**1986.** World Cup Football Championship, Mexico. Multicoloured.

1046. 15 p. Type **418** .. .. 15 10
1047. 20 p. Azteca Stadium, Mexico, 1970 .. .. 20 15
1048. 35 p. Maracana Stadium, Brazil, 1950 .. .. 35 25
1049. 50 p. Wembley Stadium, England, 1966 .. .. 50 40

**419.** Birds flying above City.

**1986.** Environmental Protection. Mult.

1050. 20 p. Type **419** .. .. 20 10
1051. 20 p. Fish .. .. .. 20 10
1052. 20 p. Full litter bin in forest .. .. .. 20 10

**420.** "Santiaguillo" (caravel) and Flags. **421.** Emblem.

**1986.** 450th Anniv. of Valparaiso.

1053. **420.** 40 p. multicoloured 85 30

**1986.** 25th Anniv. of Inter-American Development Bank.

1054. **421.** 45 p. multicoloured 40 20

**422.** St. Rosa and Pelequen Sanctuary.

**1986.** 400th Birth Anniv. of St. Rosa of Lima.

1055. **422.** 15 p. multicoloured 15 10

**423.** Stone Head on Raraku Volcano.

**1986.** Easter Island. Multicoloured.

1056 60 p. Type **423** .. .. 1·00 50
1057 100 p. Tongariki ruins .. 1·60 85

**424.** Flags, Stamps in Album, Magnifying Glass and Tweezers.

**1986.** "Ameripex '86" International Stamp Exhibition, Chicago.

1059. **424.** 100 p. multicoloured 1·40 50

**425.** Schooner "Ancud".

**1986.** Naval Traditions. Multicoloured.

1060 35 p. Type **425** .. .. 80 45
1061 35 p. Brigantine "Aguila" 80 45
1062 35 p. Sail corvette "Esmeralda" .. .. 80 45
1063 35 p. Sail frigate "O'Higgins" .. .. 80 45

**426.** "Gate of Serenity".

**1986.** Paintings by Juan Gonzalez. Mult.

1064. 30 p. "Rushes and Chrysanthemums" .. 25 15
1065. 30 p. Type **426** .. .. 25 15

**427.** Swallow-tailed Terns.

**1986.** Antarctic Fauna. Sea Birds. Mult.

1066. 40 p. Type **427** .. .. 1·40 55
1067. 40 p. Blue-eyed cormorants 1·40 55
1068. 40 p. Emperor penguins .. 1·40 55
1069. 40 p. Great skuas .. .. 1·40 55

**428.** Pedro de Ona (poet).

**1986.** Chilean Literature. Multicoloured.

1070. 20 p. Type **428** .. .. 15 15
1071. 20 p. Vicente Huidobro .. 15 15

**429.** Major-General, 1878.

**1986.** Centenary of Military Academy. Multicoloured.

1072. 45 p. Type **429** .. .. 65 20
1073. 45 p. Major, 1950 .. 65 20

**430.** Diaguita Art.

**1986.** Indian Art. Multicoloured.

1074. 30 p. Type **430** .. .. 20 15
1075. 30 p. Mapuche art .. 20 15

**431.** "Nativity" (Begona Andrea Orrego Castro).

**1986.** Christmas. Multicoloured.

1076 15 p. Type **431** .. .. 15 10
1077 105 p. "Shrine and Mountains" (Andrea Maribel Riquelme Labarde) .. .. 1·60 80

432. Shepherds looking at Hill Town. 433. Emblem and Globe.

**1986.** Christmas.
1078. **432.** 12 p. multicoloured .. 20 10

**1986.** International Peace Year.
1079. **433.** 85 p. multicoloured 1·00 50

**1986.** No. 1029 surch.
1080. **409.** 12 p. on 10 p. brown and ochre .. .. 15 10

**1986.** Nos. 1024/7 surch.
1081. 12 p. on 10 p. Farmer with haycart .. .. 25 10
1082. 12 p. on 10 p. Photographer with plate camera .. .. 25 10
1083. 12 p. on 10 p. Street entertainer .. .. 25 10
1084. 12 p. on 10 p. Basket maker .. .. .. 25 10
1085. 15 p. on 10 p. Farmer with haycart .. .. 25 10
1086. 15 p. on 10 p. Photographer with plate camera .. .. 25 10
1087. 15 p. on 10 p. Street entertainer .. .. 25 10
1088. 15 p. on 10 p. Basket maker .. .. .. 25 10

436. Profiles and Flag.

**1986.** Women's Voluntary Organization.
1089. **436.** 15 p. multicoloured 15 10

437. Virgin of Carmelites. 439. "The Guitarist of Quinchamali".

438. Kitson Meyer Steam Locomotive.

**1986.** 60th Anniv. of Coronation of Virgin of the Carmelites.
1090. **437.** 25 p. multicoloured 40 15

**1987.** Railways.
1091. **438.** 95 p. multicoloured 2·50 1·00

**1987.** Folk Tales.
1092. **439.** 15 p. green .. .. 20 10
1093. – 15 p. blue .. .. 20 10
1094. – 15 p. brown .. .. 20 10
1095. – 15 p. mauve .. .. 20 10
DESIGNS: No. 1093, "El Caleuche". 1094, "El Pihuychen". 1095, "La Lola".

440. Rowing Boat and Storage Tanks.

**1987.** 40th Anniv. of Capt. Arturo Prat Antarctic Naval Base. Multicoloured.
1096 100 p. Type **440** .. .. 2·50 1·10
1097 100 p. Buildings and rowing boat at jetty .. 2·50 1·10
Nos. 1096/7 were printed together, se-tenant, forming a composite design.

441. Pope and "Christ the Redeemer" Statue.

**1987.** Visit of Pope John Paul II. Mult.
1098 20 p. Type **441** .. .. 10 10
1099 25 p. Votive Temple, Maipu .. .. 35 10
1100 90 p. "Cross of the Seas", Magellan Straits .. 1·10 50
1101 115 p. "Virgin of the Hill" statue, Santiago .. 1·60 80

442. Horse-riding Display. 443. Players and Ball.

**1987.** 60th Anniv. of Carabineers. Mult.
1103. 50 p. Type **442** .. .. 65 15
1104. 50 p. Sea rescue by Air Police .. .. .. 65 15

**1987.** World Youth Football Cup. Mult.
1105. 45 p. Type **443** .. .. 25 15
1106. 45 p. Player and Concepcion stadium .. 25 15
1107. 45 p. Player and Antofagasta stadium 25 15
1108. 45 p. Player and Valparaiso stadium .. 25 15

444. Battleship "Almirante Latorre".

**1987.** Naval Tradition. Multicoloured.
1110. 60 p. Type **444** .. .. 70 35
1111. 60 p. Cruiser "O'Higgins" 70 35

445. Portales and "El Vigia" Newspaper.

**1987.** 150th Death Anniv. of Diego Portales (statesman).
1112. **445.** 30 p. multicoloured 15 10

446. Works Projects.

**1987.** Centenary of Ministry of Works.
1113. **446.** 25 p. multicoloured 20 10

447. School Entrance.

**1987.** Centenary of Infantry School. Mult.
1114 50 p. Type **447** .. .. 25 10
1115 100 p. Soldiers and national flag .. .. 1·10 70

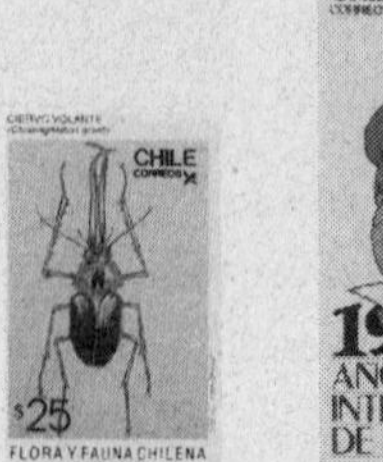


448. "Chiasognathus granti". 449. Family.

**1987.** Flora and Fauna. Multicoloured.
1116. 25 p. Type **448** .. .. 40 25
1117. 25 p. Sanderling .. .. 70 25
1118. 25 p. Peruvian guemal .. 40 25
1119. 25 p. Chilean palm .. 40 25
1120. 25 p. "Colias vauthieri" (butterfly) .. .. 50 25
1121. 25 p. Osprey .. .. 70 25
1122. 25 p. Commerson's dolphin .. .. 50 25
1123. 25 p. Mountain cypress 40 25
1124. 25 p. San Fernandez Island spiny lobster .. 40 25
1125. 25 p. Fernandez fire-crown .. .. .. 70 25
1126. 25 p. Vicuna .. .. 50 25
1127. 25 p. Arboreal fern .. 40 25
1128. 25 p. Spider-crab .. 45 25
1129. 25 p. Lesser rhea .. 70 25
1130. 25 p. Mountain viscacha 50 25
1131. 25 p. Giant cactus .. 40 25

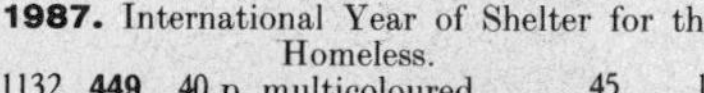

**1987.** International Year of Shelter for the Homeless.
1132. **449.** 40 p. multicoloured 45 10

450. Emblem. 452. "Holy Family" (Ximena Soledad Rosales Opazo).

451. Condell, Battle of Iquique and Statue.

**1987.** "fisa '87", 25th International Santiago Fair.
1133. **450.** 20 p. multicoloured 10 15

**1987.** Death Cent. of Admiral Carlos Condell.
1134. **451.** 50 p. multicoloured 80 60

**1987.** Christmas. Multicoloured.
1135. 30 p. Type **452** .. .. 35 10
1136. 100 p. "Star over Bethlehem" (Marcelo Bordones Meneses) .. 1·00 60

453. Casting. 454. "Nativity".

**1987.** "Cobre '87" International Copper Conference, Vina del Mar.
1137. **453.** 40 p. multicoloured 20 10

**1987.** Christmas. (a) Non-discount.
1139. **454.** 15 p. blue and orange 20 10

(b) Discount stamps. Additionally inscr. "D.S. No. 20".
1140. **454.** 15 p. blue and orange 20 10

455. Non-smokers inhaling Smoke. 457. Freire.

456. "Capitan Luis Alcazar" (supply ship) and Antarctic Landscape.

**1987.** Anti-smoking Campaign.
1141. **455.** 15 p. blue and orange 20 10

**1987.** 25th Anniv. of National Antarctic Research Commission.
1142. **456.** 45 p. multicoloured 90 30

**1987.** Birth Bicent. of General Ramon Freire Serrano (Director, 1823–27).
1143. **457.** 20 p. red and purple 25 20

458. Violin and Frutillar Church and Lake.

**1988.** 20th Music Weeks, Frutillar.
1144. **458.** 30 p. multicoloured 15 10

459. St. John with Boy (after C. Di Girolamo). 460. Bird, Da Vinci's Glider, Wright's Flyer I, Junkers Ju 52/3m, De Havilland Vampire and Grumman Tomcat.

**1988.** Death Cent. of St. John Bosco (founder of Salesian Brothers).
1145. **459.** 40 p. multicoloured 45 10

**1988.** "Fida '88" 5th International Air Fair.
1146. **460.** 60 p. blue and deep blue .. .. 75 25

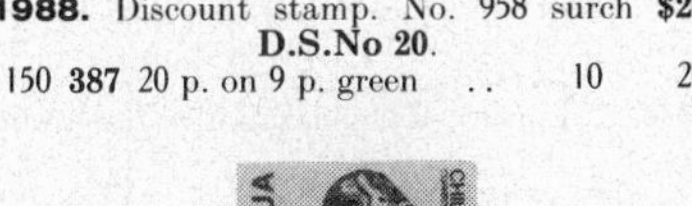


**461.** Shot Putting, Pole Vaulting and Javelin Throwing.

**1988.** Olympic Games, Seoul. Multicoloured.
1147 50 p. Type **461** .. .. 60 45
1148 100 p. Swimming, cycling and running .. .. 1·25 1·00

**1988.** Discount stamp. No. 958 surch **$20 D.S.No 20.**
1150 **387** 20 p. on 9 p. green .. 10 20

**463** Kava-Kava Head

**1988.** Easter Island.
(a) Inscr "CORREOS" only.
1151 **463** 20 p. black and pink 25 15
1152 – 20 p. black and pink 25 15
(b) Discount stamps. As T **463** but additionally inscr "D.S.No 20".
1153 **463** 20 p. black and yellow 25 15
1154 – 20 p. black and yellow 25 15
DESIGN: Nos. 1152, 1154, Tangata Manu bird-man (petroglyph).

**464** Medal, Scientist, Bull and Farm Workers

**1988.** 150th Anniv of National Agricultural Society.
1155 **464** 45 p. multicoloured .. 25 15

**465** Tending Accident Victim

**1988.** 125th Anniv of Red Cross.
1156 **465** 150 p. multicoloured .. 2·25 2·00

**466** Gipsy Moth, Boeing 767, Mirage 50 and Merino

**1988.** Birth Centenary of Commodore Arturo Merino Benitez (air pioneer).
1157 **466** 35 p. multicoloured .. 45 10

**467** Cadet Barquentine "Esmeralda"

**1988.** Naval Tradition. Multicoloured.
1158 50 p. Type **467** .. .. 75 45
1159 50 p. "Capt. Arturo Prat" (stained glass window, Valparaiso Naval Museum) .. .. 75 45

**468** Vatican City and University Arms

**1988.** Centenary of Pontifical Catholic University of Chile.
1160 **468** 40 p. multicoloured .. 45 10

**469** Esslingen Locomotive No. 3331

**1988.** Railway Anniversaries. Multicoloured.
1161 60 p. Type **469** (75th anniv of Arica–La Paz railway) .. .. 55 25
1162 60 p. North British locomotive No. 45 (cent of Antofagasta–Bolivia railway) .. .. 55 25

**470** Chemistry Student

**1988.** 175th Anniv of Jose Miguel Carrera National Institute.
1164 **470** 45 p. multicoloured .. 25 15

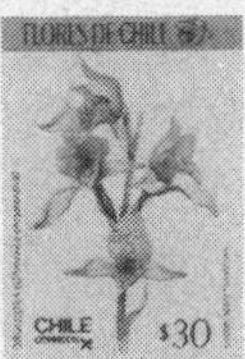


**471** "Chloraea chrysantha"

**1988.** Flowers. Multicoloured.
1165 30 p. Type **471** .. .. 20 10
1166 30 p. "Lapogeria rosea" 20 10
1167 30 p. "Nolana paradoxa" 20 10
1168 30 p. "Rhodophiala advena" .. .. 20 10
1169 30 p. "Schizanthus hookeri" .. .. 20 10
1170 30 p. "Acacia caven" .. 20 10
1171 30 p. "Cordia decanda" .. 20 10
1172 30 p. "Leontochir ovallei" 20 10
1173 30 p. "Alstroemeria pelegrina" .. .. 20 10
1174 30 p. "Copiapoa cinerea" 20 10
1175 30 p. "Salpiglossis sinuata" .. .. 20 10
1176 30 p. "Leucocoryne coquimbensis" .. 20 10
1177 30 p. "Eucryphia glutinosa" .. .. 20 10
1178 30 p. "Calandrinia longiscapa" .. .. 20 10
1179 30 p. "Desfontainia spinosa" .. .. 20 10
1180 30 p. "Sophora macrocarpa" .. .. 20 10

**472** Commander Policarpo Toro and "Angamos"

**1988.** Centenary of Incorporation of Easter Island into Chile. Multicoloured.
1181 50 p. Type **472** .. .. 55 20
1182 50 p. Map of Easter Island and globe .. .. 30 20
1183 100 p. Dancers .. .. 60 50
1184 100 p. Petroglyphs of bird-men .. .. 60 50

**473** Bleriot XI over Town

**1988.** 70th Anniv of First National Airmail Service.
1186 **473** 150 p. multicoloured .. 90 60

**474** Pottery

**1988.** 15th Anniv of Centre for Education of Women. Traditional Crafts. Multicoloured.
1187 25 p. Type **474** .. .. 10 10
1188 25 p. Embroidery .. 10 10

**475** Policeman and Brigade Members

**1988.** Schools' Security Brigade.
1189 **475** 45 p. multicoloured .. 20 10

**476** "Nativity" (Paulette Thiers)

**477** Cancelled 1881 2 c. Stamp

**1988.** Christmas. Multicoloured.
1190 35 p. Type **476** .. .. 15 10
1191 100 p. "Family going to church" (Jose M. Lamas) .. .. 45 35

**1988.** Centenary of Chile Philatelic Society.
1192 **477** 40 p. multicoloured .. 20 10

**478** Child in Manger

**479** Manuel Bulnes and Battle of Yungay, 1839

**1988.** Christmas.
(a) Non-discount.
1193 **478** 20 p. purple and yellow 10 10
(b) Discount stamps. As T **478** but additionally inscr "D.S. No. 20"
1194 **478** 20 p. purple and yellow 10 10

**1989.** Historic Heroes. Multicoloured.
1195 50 p. Type **479** .. .. 20 10
1196 50 p. Soldier and battle scene .. .. .. 20 10
1197 100 p. Roberto Simpson and Battle of Casma, 1839 .. .. .. 65 40
1198 100 p. Sailor and battle scene .. .. .. 65 40

**MORE DETAILED LISTS**
are given in the Stanley Gibbons Catalogues referred to in the country headings.
For lists of current volumes see Introduction.

**480** St. Ambrose's Church, Vallenar (bicentenary)

**483** Sister Teresa of the Andes

**1989.** Town Anniversaries. Multicoloured.
1199 30 p. Type **480** .. .. 10 10
1200 35 p. Craftsman, Combarbala (bicent) .. 15 10
1201 45 p. Laja Falls, Los Angeles (250th anniv) 20 10
See also No. 1306.

**1989.** Various stamps surcharged.
(a) Surch **$25** only
1202 25 p. on 15 p. green (1092) 10 10
1203 25 p. on 15 p. blue (1093) 10 10
1204 25 p. on 15 p. brown (1094) 10 10
1205 25 p. on 15 p. mauve (1095) .. .. .. 10 10
1206 25 p. on 20 p. black and pink (1151) .. .. 10 10
1207 25 p. on 20 p. black and pink (1152) .. .. 10 10
1208 25 p. on 20 p. black and yellow (1153) .. .. 10 10
1209 25 p. on 20 p. black and yellow (1154) .. .. 10 10
(b) Surch **D.S. No 20 $25**
1210 25 p. on 20 p. black and pink (1151) .. .. 10 10
1211 25 p. on 20 p. black and pink (1152) .. .. 10 10

**1989.** Beatifications. Multicoloured.
1212 40 p. Type **483** .. .. 20 10
1213 40 p. Laura Vicuna .. 20 10

**484** Christopher Columbus

**1989.** "Exfina '89" Stamp Exhibition, Santiago. Multicoloured.
1214 100 p. Type **484** .. .. 45 35
1215 100 p. "Nina", "Santa Maria" and "Pinta" .. 70 40

**485** Container Ship and Trawler

**1989.** 50th Anniv of Energy Production Corporation. Multicoloured.
1217 60 p. Type **485** .. .. 40 20
1218 60 p. Tree trunks on trailer and factory .. 25 15
1219 60 p. Telephone tower and pylon .. .. 25 15
1220 60 p. Coal trucks and colliery .. .. 25 15

**486** Town and Sketch

**1989.** Birth Cent of Gabriela Mistral (writer). Multicoloured.
1221 30 p. Type **486** .. .. 15 10
1222 30 p. Mistral with children 15 10
1223 30 p. Mistral writing .. 15 10
1224 30 p. Mistral receiving Nobel Prize .. .. 15 10

487 Grapes

**1989.** Exports.
(a) Inscribed as T487
1225 487 5 p. blue .. .. 15 10
1226 – 5 p. red and blue .. 15 10
1227 487 10 p. deep blue & blue 15 10
1228 – 10 p. red and blue .. 15 10
1229 487 25 p. blue and green 10 10
1230 – 25 p. red and green .. 10 10
1350 487 45 p. blue and mauve 15 10
1351 – 45 p. red and mauve 15 10

(b) Discount stamps. As T 487 but additionally inscr "D.S. No. 20"
1231 487 25 p. blue and yellow 10 10
1232 – 25 p. red and yellow 10 10
1352 487 45 p. blue and yellow 15 15
1353 – 45 p. red and yellow 15 15
DESIGNS: Nos. 1226, 1228, 1230, 1232, 1351, 1353, Apple.

488 Battle Scene, Soldiers and "Justice"

**1989.** 150th Anniv of Army Court of Justice.
1233 488 50 p. multicoloured .. 20 10

489 Monument

490 Victoria, Vina del Mar

**1989.** Frontier Guards' Martyrs' Monument.
1234 489 35 p. multicoloured .. 15 10

**1989.** Transport.
1235 490 30 p. black & orange 15 10
1236 – 35 p. black and blue 20 10
1237 – 40 p. black and green 20 10
1238 – 45 p. black and green 30 10
1239 – 50 p. black and red .. 30 10
1240 – 60 p. black and bistre 25 15
1241 – 100 p. black and green 45 35
DESIGNS—VERT. 35 p. Scow, Chiloe Archipelago. HORIZ. 40 p. Ox-cart, Cautin; 45 p. Raft ferry, Rio Palena; 50 p. Lighters, Gen. Carrera Lake; 60 p. Valparaiso incline railway; 100 p. Santiago funicular.
See also No. 1346.

491 Scientist and Chinstrap Penguins

**1989.** 25th Anniv of Chilean Antarctic Institute.
1245 491 150 p. multicoloured .. 1·75 80

492 Present Naval Engineers School and "Chacabuco" (first school)

**1989.** Cent of Naval Engineering. Mult.
1246 45 p. Type 492 .. .. 30 10
1247 45 p. Sailors in engine room .. .. .. 20 10
1248 45 p. Destroyer, Aerospatiale Dauphin 2 helicopter and submarine 40 10
1249 45 p. Launch of "Aquiles" (patrol boat) .. .. 30 10

493 Globes, Polar Bear and Gentoo Penguins

494 Atacamena Culture

**1989.** "World Stamp Expo '89" International Stamp Exhibition, Washington D.C.
1250 493 250 p. multicoloured 2·50 1·25

**1989.** America. Pre-Columbian Cultures. Multicoloured.
1252 30 p. Type 494 .. .. 15 10
1253 150 p. Selk'nam and Onas cultures .. .. 70 60

495 Balls

497 Vicuna, Lauca

496 "Rowing to Church" (Cristina Lopez)

**1989.** Christmas.
(a) As T 495.
1254 495 25 p. yellow and green 10 10
1255 – 25 p. yellow and green 10 10
(b) Discount stamps. Additionally inscr "D. S. No 20"
1256 495 25 p. red and green .. 10 10
1257 – 25 p. red and green .. 10 10
DESIGN: Nos. 1255, 1257, Bells.

**1989.** Christmas.
1258 496 100 p. multicoloured .. 60 40

**1990.** National Parks. Multicoloured.
1259 35 p. Type 497 .. .. 30 10
1260 35 p. Chilian flamingo, Salar de Surire .. 50 20
1261 35 p. Cactus , La Chimba 30 10
1262 35 p. Guanaco, Pan de Azucar .. .. 30 10
1263 35 p. Long-tailed meadow-lark, Fray Jorge .. 50 20
1264 35 p. Sooty tern, Rapa Nui .. .. .. 50 20
1265 35 p. Lesser grison, La Campana .. .. 30 10
1266 35 p. Torrent duck, Rio Clarillo .. .. 50 20
1267 35 p. Mountain cypress, Rio de los Cipreses .. 30 10
1268 35 p. Black-necked swan, Laguna de Torca .. 50 20
1269 35 p. Puma, Laguna del Laja .. .. .. 40 20
1270 35 p. Araucaria, Villarrica 30 10
1271 35 p. "Philesia magellanica", Vicente Perez Rosales .. .. 30 10
1272 35 p. "Nothofagus pumilio", Dos Lagunas 30 10
1273 35 p. Leopard seal, Laguna San Rafael .. 40 20
1274 35 p. Lesser rhea, Torres del Paine .. .. 50 20

498 Boot

**1990.** World Cup Football Championship, Italy. Multicoloured.
1275 50 p. Type 498 .. .. 20 10
1276 50 p. Hand .. .. 20 10
1277 50 p. Ball in net .. .. 20 10
1278 50 p. Player .. .. 20 10

499 Vickers Wibault Biplane I, 1927–37

**1990.** Chilean Airforce Airplanes. Mult.
1279 40 p. Type 499 .. .. 25 10
1280 40 p. Curtiss OIE Falcon, 1928–40 .. .. 25 10
1281 40 p. Pitts S-2A (Falcons aerobatic team, 1981–90) 25 10
1282 40 p. Extra 33 (Falcons aerobatic team, 1990) .. 25 10
No. 1282 is inscribed "EXTRA 300".

500 Inca

**1990.** 500th Anniv of Discovery of America by Columbus. Multicoloured.
1284 60 p. Type 500 .. .. 20 10
1285 60 p. Spanish officer .. 20 10

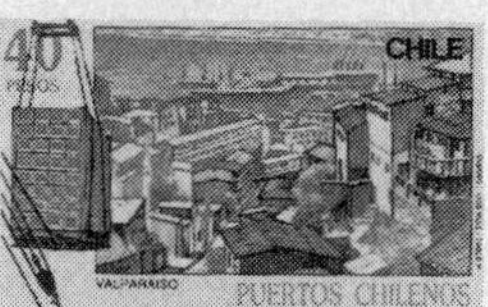

501 Valparaiso

**1990.** Ports. Multicoloured.
1286 40 p. Type 501 .. .. 15 10
1287 40 p. San Vicente .. 15 10

502 "Piloto Pardo" (Antarctic supply ship)

**1990.** Naval Tradition. Multicoloured.
1288 50 p. Type 502 .. .. 35 15
1289 50 p. "Yelcho" (survey ship) .. .. .. 35 15

503 "Sunrise in Chile"

**1990.** "Democracy in Chile". Multicoloured.
1290 20 p. Type 503 .. .. 10 10
1291 30 p. Dove ("Peace in Chile") .. .. 10 10
1292 60 p. "ChiLe" ("Rejoicing in Chile") .. .. 20 10
1293 100 p. Star ("Thus Chile pleases me") .. .. 35 25

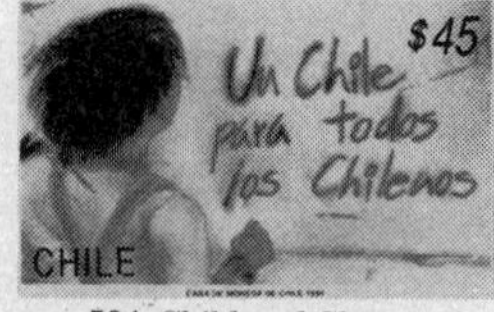

504 Child and Slogan

**1990.** "One Chile for All Chileans".
1295 504 45 p. multicoloured .. 15 10

505 Sir Rowland Hill

506 Flags

**1990.** 150th Anniv of the Penny Black.
1297 505 250 p. multicoloured 85 75

**1990.** Centenary of Organization of American States.
1299 506 150 p. multicoloured .. 50 40

507 Purplish Scallop and Diver with Net

**1990.** Fishing. Multicoloured.
1300 40 p. Type 507 .. .. 25 15
1301 40 p. Giant wedge clam and man with net .. 25 15
1302 40 p. Tunny and harpooner on "San Antonio" (fishing boat) 25 15
1303 40 p. Marine spider crab and fishing boat raising catch .. .. .. 25 15
1304 40 p. Cod and trawler .. 25 15
1305 40 p. Women baiting hooks .. .. .. 15 10

**1990.** Town Anniversaries. 250th Anniv of San Felipe. As T 480. Multicoloured.
1306 50 p. Curimon Convent .. 20 10

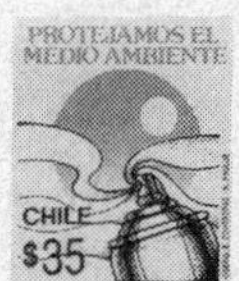

508 Aerosol

509 Salvador Allende

**1990.** Environmental Protection. Each red and black. (a) As T 508
1307 35 p. Type 508 .. .. 15 10
1308 35 p. Tree and tree stumps .. .. 15 10
1309 35 p. Factory chimneys emitting smoke .. 15 10
1310 35 p. Oil tanker polluting wildlife and sea .. 25 10
1311 35 p. Deer escaping from burning forest .. 15 10
(b) Discount stamps. Additionally inscr "D.S. No 20"
1312 35 p. Type 508 .. .. 15 10
1313 35 p. As No. 1308 .. 15 10
1314 35 p. As No. 1309 .. 15 10
1315 35 p. As No. 1310 .. 25 10
1316 35 p. As No. 1311 .. 15 10
See also Nos. 1421/30.

**1990.** Presidents.
1317 509 35 p. black and blue 15 10
1318 – 35 p. black and blue 15 10
1319 – 40 p. black and green 15 10
1320 – 45 p. black and green 15 10
1321 – 50 p. black and red .. 20 10
1322 – 60 p. black and red .. 20 10
1323 – 70 p. black and blue 25 15
1324 – 80 p. black and blue 30 20
1325 – 90 p. black and brown 30 20
1326 – 100 p. black & brown 35 25
DESIGNS: No. 1318, Eduardo Frei; 1319, Jorge Alessandri; 1320, Gabriel Gonzalez; 1321, Juan Antonio Rios; 1322, Pedro Aguirre Cerda; 1323, Juan E. Montero; 1324, Carlos Ibanez; 1325, Emiliano Figueroa; 1326, Arturo Alessandri.

510 Opening Ceremony

**1990.** Rodeo. Multicoloured.

1327 45 p. Type **510** .. .. 15 10
1328 45 p. Riders saluting crowd .. .. .. 15 10
1329 45 p. Rider reining in .. 15 10
1330 45 p. Two riders cornering steer .. .. .. 15 10

**511** Chilean Flamingoes

**1990.** America. The Natural World. Mult.

1331 30 p. Type **511** .. .. 60 20
1332 150 p. South American fur seals .. .. .. 50 40

**512** Chilean State Arms and Spanish Royal Arms

**1990.** State Visit by King Juan Carlos and Queen Sofia of Spain. Multicoloured.

1333 100 p. Type **512** .. .. 35 25
1334 100 p. Spanish and Chilean (at right) State Arms .. .. .. 35 25

**513** Construction Diagram of Viaduct

**1990.** Centenary of Malleco Viaduct. Mult.

1335 60 p. Type **513** .. .. 20 10
1336 60 p. Boy waving to train on completed viaduct 20 10

Nos. 1335/6 were printed together, se-tenant, forming a composite design.

**514** Great Skua, Whale and Supply Ship

**1990.** 50th Anniv of Chilean Antarctic Territory. Multicoloured.

1337 250 p. Type **514** .. .. 1·75 70
1338 250 p. Adelie penguins, Bell Model 206 jet helicopters and tents .. 2·00 80

**515** Children decorating Tree

**1990.** Christmas. (a) As T **515**.

1340 **515** 35 p. green & emerald 10 10

(b) Discount stamps. Additionally inscr "D.S. No 20".

1341 **515** 35 p. green and orange 10 10

**516** Santa Claus in Space (Carla Levill)

**1990.** Christmas. Children's drawings. Mult.

1342 35 p. Type **516** .. .. 10 10
1343 150 p. Television on sea bed (Jose M. Lamas) .. 50 35

**517** Assembly Hall

**1990.** National Congress. Multicoloured.

1344 100 p. Type **517** .. .. 30 25
1345 100 p. Painting above dais 30 25

**1991.** Discount stamp. As No. 1238 but colour changed and additionally inscr "D.S. No 20".

1346 45 p. black and yellow .. 20 10

**518** Casa Colorada

**1991.** 450th Anniv of Santiago. Multicoloured.

1347 100 p. Type **518** .. .. 30 25
1348 100 p. City landmarks .. 30 25

**519** Voisin "Boxkite"

**1991.** Aviation History. Multicoloured.

1354 150 p. Type **519** .. .. 60 45
1355 150 p. Royal Aircraft Factory S.E.5A .. 60 45
1356 150 p. Morane Saulnier MS 35 .. .. .. 60 45
1357 150 p. Consolidated PBY-5A/OA-10 Catalina amphibian .. .. 60 45

**520** Map, Player and Left Half of Ball

**1991.** America Cup Football Championship. Multicoloured.

1358 100 p. Type **520** .. .. 30 25
1359 100 p. Right half of ball and goalkeeper .. 30 25

Nos. 1358/9 were printed together, se-tenant, forming a composite design.

**521** Drill and Miner

**1991.** Coal Mining. Multicoloured.

1360 200 p. Type **521** .. .. 65 45
1361 200 p. Miners emptying truck .. .. .. 65 45

**522** Youths and Emblem

**525** Santiago Cathedral

**523** Dish and Hanging Ornaments

**1991.** Centenary of Scientific Society.

1362 **522** 45 p. black and green 15 10

**1991.** Traditional Crafts. Multicoloured.

1363 90 p. Type **523** .. .. 30 25
1364 90 p. Carvings and ceramics .. .. 30 25

**1991.** Various stamps surch.

1365 **463** 45 p. on 20 p. black and yellow .. 15 10
1366 – 45 p. on 20 p. black and yellow (1154) .. 15 10
1367 **487** 45 p. on 25 p. bl & yell 15 10
1368 – 45 p. on 25 p. red and yellow (1232) .. 15 10

**1991.** National Monuments.

1369 **525** 300 p. blk, pink & brn 1·00 70

**526** Dish Aerial and Transmission Masts

**1991.** World Telecommunications Day.

1370 **526** 90 p. multicoloured .. 30 25

**527** Pope Leo XIII and Factory Line

**528** Capt. L. Pardo and Sir Ernest Shackleton

**1991.** Cent of "Rerum Novarum" (papal encyclical on workers' rights).

1371 **527** 100 p. multicoloured .. 30 25

**1991.** Naval Tradition. 75th Anniv of Pardo's Rescue of Shackleton Expedition. Mult.

1372 50 p. Type **528** .. .. 15 10
1373 50 p. "Yelcho" (coast-guard vessel) .. .. 25 10
1374 50 p. Chilean sailor sighting stranded men on Elephant Island .. 15 10
1375 50 p. "Endurance" .. 15 10

**529** Flags and Globe

**531** "Maipo" (container ship)

**530** Building and Police Officers

**1991.** 21st General Assembly of Organization of American States, Santiago.

1377 **529** 70 p. multicoloured .. 20 15

**1991.** Opening of New Police School.

1378 **530** 50 p. multicoloured .. 15 10

**1991.** National Merchant Navy Day.

1379 **531** 45 p. black and red .. 20 10

**532** Opening Ceremony

**1991.** 11th Pan-American Games, Havana. Multicoloured.

1380 100 p. Type **532** .. .. 30 25
1381 100 p. Cycling, running and basketball competitors .. .. 30 25

**533** Carriage and Building

**1991.** Bicentenary of Los Andes.

1382 **533** 100 p. multicoloured .. 30 25

**534** Common Octopus

**536** "Woman in Red" (Pedro Reszka)

**535** Nitrate Processing and Jose Balmaceda (President, 1886–91)

**1991.** Marine Life. Multicoloured.

1383 50 p. Type **534** .. .. 30 15
1384 50 p. "Durvillaea antarctica" .. .. 30 15
1385 50 p. Halibut .. .. 30 15
1386 50 p. "Austromegabalanus psittacus" .. .. 30 15
1387 50 p. Barnacle rock shell ("Concholepas concholepas") .. 30 15
1388 50 p. Crab ("Cancer setosus") .. .. 30 15
1389 50 p. "Lessonia nigrescens" .. .. 30 15
1390 50 p. Sea-urchin .. .. 30 15
1391 50 p. Crab ("Homalaspis plana") .. .. 30 15
1392 50 p. "Porphyra columbina" .. .. 30 15
1393 50 p. Parrot fish .. .. 30 15
1394 50 p. "Chorus giganteus" .. 30 15
1395 50 p. Rock shrimp .. 30 15
1396 50 p. Peruvian anchovy .. 30 15
1397 50 p. "Gracilaria sp." .. 30 15
1398 50 p. "Pyura chilensis" .. 30 15

**1991.** Centenary of 1891 Revolution. Pre-Revolution Events. Multicoloured.

1399 100 p. Type **535** .. .. 30 25
1400 100 p. Education and Balmaceda .. .. 30 25

**1991.** Paintings. Multicoloured.

1401 50 p. Type **536** .. .. 15 10
1402 70 p. "The Traveller" (Camilo Mori) .. .. 20 15
1403 200 p. "Head of Child" (Benito Rebolledo) .. 65 45
1404 300 p. "Child in Fez" (A. Valenzuela Puelma) .. 1·00 70

**537** Map of South American Interests in Antarctica

**1991.** 30th Anniv of Antarctic Treaty. Mult.
1405 80 p. Type **537** .. .. 25 20
1406 80 p. Wildlife .. .. 90 45

**538** Globe in Envelope (Guillermo Suarez)

**1991.** International Letter Writing Week. Children's drawings. Multicoloured.
1407 45 p. Type **538** .. .. 15 10
1408 70 p. Human figures in envelope (Jorge Vargas) 20 15

**539** Amerindians watching Columbus's Fleet

**1991.** America. Voyages of Discovery. Mult.
1409 50 p. Type **539** .. .. 20 10
1410 150 p. Columbus's fleet and navigator .. 70 35

**540** Line Drawing of Neruda

**541** Boy and Stars

**1991.** 20th Anniv of Award of Nobel Prize for Literature to Pablo Neruda. Multicoloured, colour of cap given.
1411 **540** 45 p. blue .. .. 15 10
1412 45 p. red .. .. 15 10
Nos. 1411/12 were issued together, se-tenant, the backgrounds of the stamps forming a composite design of one of Neruda's manuscripts.

**1991.** Christmas. Multicoloured.
1414 45 p. Type **541** .. .. 15 10
1415 100 p. Girl and stars .. 30 25

**542** Postman making Delivery

**544** Houses and Figures

**1991.** Christmas. (a) As T **542**.
1416 **542** 45 p. mauve & violet 15 10
1417 – 45 p. mauve & violet 15 10
(b) Discount stamps. Additionally inscr "D.S. No 20" in left-hand margin
1418 **542** 45 p. mauve & violet 15 10
1419 – 45 p. mauve & violet 15 10
DESIGN: Nos. 1417, 1419, Starlit town.

**1992.** No. 1238 surch **$60**.
1420 60 p. on 45 p. black & grn 20 15

**1992.** Environmental Protection. As Nos. 1307/16 but values and colours changed.
(a) As T **508**, each yellow and green
1421 60 p. Type **508** .. .. 20 15
1422 60 p. As No. 1308 .. 20 15
1423 60 p. As No. 1309 .. 20 15
1424 60 p. As No. 1310 .. 20 15
1425 60 p. As No. 1311 .. 20 15

(b) Discount stamps. Additionally inscr "D.S. No 20". Each orange and green
1426 60 p. Type **508** .. .. 20 15
1427 60 p. As No. 1308 .. 20 15
1428 60 p. As No. 1309 .. 20 15
1429 60 p. As No. 1310 .. 20 15
1430 60 p. As No. 1311 .. 20 15

**1992.** 16th Population and Housing Census.
1431 **544** 60 p. blue, orge & blk 20 15

**545** Score and Mozart

**1992.** Death Bicentenary of Wolfgang Amadeus Mozart (composer). Multicoloured.
1432 60 p. Type **545** .. .. 20 15
1433 200 p. Mozart playing harpsichord .. .. 65 50

**546** Stylized Jet Fighter

**1992.** "Fidae '92" International Air and Space Fair.
1435 **546** 60 p. multicoloured .. 20 15

**547** Arms and Church, San Jose de Maipo

**1992.** 200th (60 p.) or 250th (others) Anniversaries of Cities. Multicoloured.
1436 80 p. Type **547** .. .. 25 20
1437 90 p. Pottery (Melipilla) 30 25
1438 100 p. Lircunlauta House (San Fernando) .. 35 25
1439 150 p. Fruits and woodsman (Cauquenes) .. 50 35
1440 250 p. Huilquilemu Cultural Villa (Talca) 85 60

**548** Chilean Pavilion

**1992.** "Expo '92" World's Fair, Seville. Mult.
1441 150 p. Type **548** .. .. 50 35
1442 200 p. Iceberg .. .. 65 50

**549** "Morula praecipua", Maculated Conch and Dragon's-head Cowrie

**1992.** Marine Flora and Fauna of Easter Island. Multicoloured.
1444 60 p. Type **549** .. .. 35 20
1445 60 p. "Codium pocockiae" 35 20
1446 60 p. Soldierfish ("Myripristis tiki") .. 35 20
1447 60 p. Seaweed .. .. 35 20
1448 60 p. Parrotfish ("Pseudolabrus fuentesi") .. .. 35 20
1449 60 p. Coral .. .. 35 20
1450 60 p. Spiny lobster .. 35 20
1451 60 p. Sea urchin .. .. 35 20

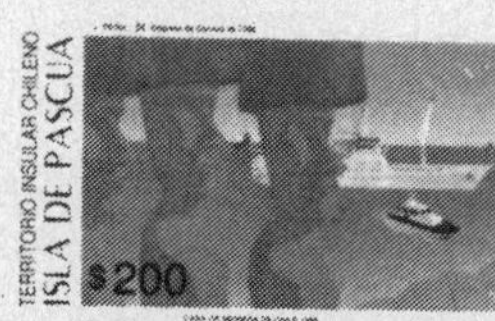

**550** Statues, Liner and Launch

**1992.** Easter Island Tourism. Multicoloured.
1452 200 p. Type **550** .. .. 85 50
1453 200 p. Airplane, dancers and hill-carving .. 85 50
Nos. 1452/3 were issued together, se-tenant, forming a composite design.

**551** Sun shining through Doorway and Handicapped People

**552** Flags and Emblem

**1992.** National Council for the Handicapped.
1454 **551** 60 p. multicoloured .. 20 15

**1992.** 50th Anniv of National Defence Staff.
1455 **552** 60 p. multicoloured .. 20 15

**553** Submarine Re-surfacing

**1992.** 75th Anniv of Chilean Submarine Fleet. Multicoloured.
1456 150 p. Type **553** .. .. 50 35
1457 250 p. Officer using periscope .. .. 85 60

**1992.** Discount stamp. As No. 1240 but additionally inscr "D/S No 20".
1458 60 p. black and bistre .. 20 15

**1992.** Nos. 1350/3 surch **$60**.
1459 **487** 60 p. on 45 p. blue and mauve .. .. 20 15
1460 – 60 p. on 45 p. red and mauve .. .. 20 15
1461 **487** 60 p. on 45 p. blue and yellow .. .. 20 15
1462 – 60 p. on 45 p. red and yellow .. .. 20 15

**1992.** Nos. 1416/19 surch **$60**.
1463 **542** 60 p. on 45 p. mauve and violet (1416) .. 20 15
1464 – 60 p. on 45 p. mauve and violet (1417) .. 20 15
1465 **542** 60 p. on 45 p. mauve and violet (1418) .. 20 15
1466 – 60 p. on 45 p. mauve and violet (1419) .. 20 15

**MINIMUM PRICE**

The minimum price quoted is 10p which represents a handling charge rather than a basis for valuing common stamps. For further notes about prices see introductory pages.

**556** Emperor Penguin

**1992.** The Emperor Penguin. Multicoloured.
1467 200 p. Type **556** .. .. 65 50
1468 250 p. Adult and chick .. 85 60

**557** Santiago Central Post Office

**1992.** National Monuments.
1470 **557** 200 p. multicoloured .. 65 50

**558** Columbus and Navigation Instruments

**1992.** America. 500th Anniv of Discovery of America by Columbus. Multicoloured.
1471 200 p. Type **558** .. .. 65 50
1472 250 p. Church, map of Americas and "Santa Maria" .. .. 85 60

**559** Presenter at Microphone

**560** O'Higgins, Flag and Monument

**1992.** 70th Anniv of Chilean Radio.
1473 **559** 250 p. multicoloured .. 85 60

**1992.** 150th Death Anniv of Bernardo O'Higgins.
1474 **560** 60 p. multicoloured .. 20 15

**561** Arrau as a Child

**1992.** Claudio Arrau (pianist). Multicoloured.
1475 150 p. Type **561** .. .. 50 35
1476 200 p. Arrau playing piano .. .. .. 65 50

**562** Statue

**563** Nativity

**1992.** 150th Anniv of University of Chile. Multicoloured.
1478 200 p. Type **562** . . . . 65 50
1479 200 p. Coat of arms, statues and clock . . 65 50
Nos. 1478/9 were issued together, se-tenant, forming a composite design.

**1992.** Christmas. (a) As T **563**
1480 **563** 60 p. brown and stone 20 15
1481 – 60 p. brown and stone 20 15
(b) Discount stamps. Additionally inscr "DS/20" in right-hand margin
1482 **563** 60 p. red and stone . . 20 15
1483 – 60 p. red and stone . . 20 15
DESIGN: Nos. 1481, 1483, Nativity (different).

**564** Dam

**1992.** 23rd Ministerial Meeting of Latin-American Energy Organization.
1484 **564** 70 p. black and yellow 25 20

**565** Hands and Stars

**1992.** National Human Rights Day.
1485 **565** 100 p. multicoloured . . 30 25

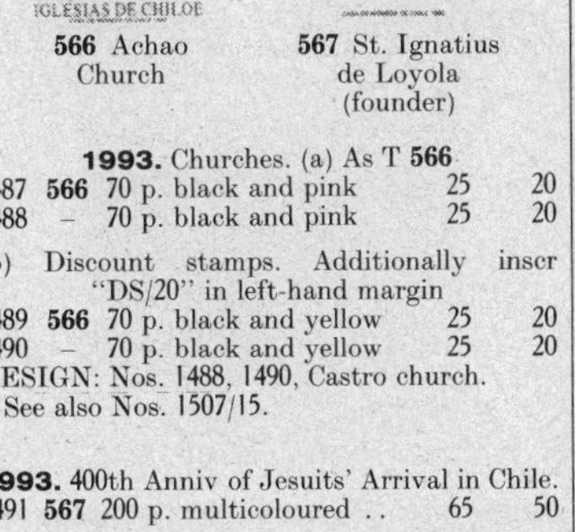


**566** Achao Church
**567** St. Ignatius de Loyola (founder)

**1993.** Churches. (a) As T **566**
1487 **566** 70 p. black and pink 25 20
1488 – 70 p. black and pink 25 20
(b) Discount stamps. Additionally inscr "DS/20" in left-hand margin
1489 **566** 70 p. black and yellow 25 20
1490 – 70 p. black and yellow 25 20
DESIGN: Nos. 1488, 1490, Castro church.
See also Nos. 1507/15.

**1993.** 400th Anniv of Jesuits' Arrival in Chile.
1491 **567** 200 p. multicoloured . . 65 50

**568** St. Teresa

**569** Finger-Puppets

**1993.** Canonization of St. Teresa of the Andes.
1493 **568** 300 p. multicoloured . . 1·00 70

**1993.** International Theatre Festival.
1494 **569** 250 p. multicoloured . . 80 60

**570** Satellite in Orbit

**1993.** 2nd Pan-American Space Conference.
1495 **570** 150 p. multicoloured . . 50 35

**571** Clotario Blest (Trade Union leader)

**572** Drawing of Huidobro by Picasso

**1993.** Labour Day.
1497 **571** 70 p. multicoloured . . 25 20

**1993.** Birth Centenary of Vicente Huidobro (poet). Each black, stone and red.
1498 100 p. Type **572** . . . . 30 25
1499 100 p. Drawing of Huidobro by Juan Gris 30 25

**573** Watterous, 1902

**1993.** Fire Engines (1st series). Multicoloured.
1500 100 p. Type **573** . . . . 30 25
1501 100 p. Merryweather, 1872 30 25
See also Nos. 1568/71.

**574** Douglas B-26 Invader

**1993.** Aviation and Space. Multicoloured.
1503 100 p. Type **574** . . . . 30 25
1504 100 p. Mirage M 50 Pantera . . . . 30 25
1505 100 p. Sanchez Besa biplane . . . . 30 25
1506 100 p. Bell- 47 D1 helicopter . . . . 30 25

**1993.** Churches. (a) As T **566**.
1507 10 p. black and green . . 10 10
1508 20 p. black and brown . . 10 10
1509 30 p. black and orange . . 10 10
1510 40 p. black and blue . . 10 10
1511 50 p. black and green . . 15 10
1512 80 p. black and buff . . 25 20
1513 90 p. black and green . . 25 20
1514 100 p. black and grey . . 30 25
(b) Discount stamp. Additionally inscr "DS/20" at left
1515 80 p. black and lilac . . 25 20
1516 90 p. black and red . . 25 20
1517 100 p. black and yellow . . 30 25
CHURCHES: 10 p. Chonchi; 20 p. Vilupulli; 30 p. Llau-Llao; 40 p. Dalcahue; 50 p. Tenaun; 80 p. Quinchao; 90 p. Quehui; 100 p. Nercon.

**575** Nortina

**577** Early Coin Production

**576** "Late Dawn" (Mario Carreno)

**1993.** Regional Variations of La Cueca (national dance). Multicoloured.
1525 70 p. Type **575** . . . . 20 15
1526 70 p. Central . . . . 20 15
1527 70 p. Chilota . . . . 20 15

**1993.** Santiago, Iberian-American City of Culture 1993. Paintings. Multicoloured.
1528 80 p. Type **576** . . . . 25 20
1529 90 p. "Summer" (Gracia Barrios) . . . . 25 20
1530 150 p. "Protection" (Roser Bru) (vert) . . 45 35
1531 200 p. "Tango, Valparaiso" (Nemesio Antunez) . . . . 60 45

**1993.** 250th Anniv of Chilean Mint.
1532 **577** 250 p. multicoloured . . 75 55

**578** Patagonian Conure

**579** Underground Train

**1993.** America. Endangered Animals. Mult.
1534 150 p. Type **578** . . . . 45 35
1535 200 p. Chilean guemal . . 60 45

**1993.** 25th Anniv of Chilean Metro.
1536 **579** 80 p. multicoloured . . 25 20

**580** "Ancud" (schooner) off Santa Ana Point

**1993.** 150th Anniv of Chilean Possession of Strait of Magellan.
1537 **580** 100 p. multicoloured . . 30 25

**581** Marines in Inflatable Assault Boats

**1993.** Naval Tradition. Multicoloured.
1538 80 p. Type **581** (175th anniv of Marines) . . 25 20
1539 80 p. Sailors making fast patrol boat (125th anniv of Alejandro Navarette Training School) . . 25 20
1540 80 p. "Esmeralda" (cadet barquentine) and cadets in traditional "un-loading the cannon" exercise (175th anniv of Arturo Prat Naval College) . . 25 20
1541 80 p. "Sailing of First Squadron" (175th anniv) (painting, Alvaro Casanova Zenteno) . . 25 20

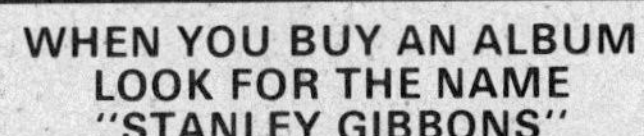

**582** Carved Figures

**1993.** Int Year of Indigenous Peoples.
1542 **582** 100 p. multicoloured . . 30 25

**583** Holy Family
**584** Adelie Penguins

**1993.** Christmas. (a) Sold at face value.
1543 **583** 70 p. lilac and stone 20 15
(b) Discount stamp. Additionally inscribed "DS/20" in right-hand margin
1544 **583** 70 p. blue and green 20 15

**1993.** Chilean Antarctic Territory. Mult.
1545 200 p. Type **584** . . . . 65 45
1546 250 p. Adelie penguin with young . . . . . . 75 55

**585** Plaza de Armas, Ancud

**1993.** City Anniversaries. Multicoloured.
1548 80 p. Type **585** (225th) . . 25 20
1549 80 p. Matriz church, Curico (250th) . . 25 20
1550 80 p. Corner Pillar House, Rancagua (250th) . . 25 20

**586** Hands

**1994.** International Year of the Family.
1551 **586** 100 p. multicoloured . . 30 25

**587** Violin

**1994.** 26th Music Weeks, Frutillar. Mult.
1552 150 p. Type **587** . . . . 45 35
1553 150 p. Cello . . . . 45 35
Nos. 1552/3 were issued together, se-tenant, forming a composite design.

**588** Sukhoi Su-30 Flanker

**1994.** "Fidae'94" International Air and Space Fair. Multicoloured.

1554 300 p. Type **588** .. .. 90 65
1555 300 p. Vought Sikorsky OS2U3 Kingfisher seaplane .. .. 90 65
1556 300 p. Lockheed F-117A Stealth .. .. 90 65
1557 300 p. Northrop F-5E Tiger III .. .. 90 65

**589** Ears of Grain

**1994.** 50th Anniv of Chile Agronomical Engineers' College.

1558 **589** 220 p. multicoloured .. 65 45

**1994.** Nos. 1092/5 surch **$80**.

1559 80 p. on 15 p. green .. 25 20
1560 80 p. on 15 p. blue .. 25 20
1561 80 p. on 15 p. brown .. 25 20
1562 80 p. on 15 p. mauve .. 25 20

**591** Skeletons buried under Cactus

**1994.** 75th Anniv of Concepcion University. Details of "Latin American Presence" (mural by Jorge Gonzalez Camarena). Mult.

1563 250 p. Type **591** .. .. 75 55
1564 250 p. Faces .. .. 75 55
1565 250 p. Building pyramid from spare parts .. 75 55
1566 250 p. Cablework in building .. .. 75 55

Nos. 1563/6 were issued together, se-tenant, forming a composite design.

**592** Gentoo Penguins and Harbour

**1994.** 30th Anniv of Chilean Antarctic Institute. Multicoloured.

1567 300 p. Type **592** .. .. 90 65
1568 300 p. Antarctic base .. 90 65

Nos. 1567/8 were issued together, se-tenant, forming a composite design.

**593** "Vanessa terpsichore"

**1994.** Butterflies. Multicoloured.

1569 100 p. Type **593** .. .. 30 25
1570 100 p. "Hypsochila wagenknechti" .. 30 25
1571 100 p. Polydamas swallowtail ("Battus polydamas") .. 30 25
1572 100 p. "Polythysana apollina" .. .. 30 25
1573 100 p. "Satyridae" .. 30 25
1574 100 p. "Tetraphloebia stellygera" .. .. 30 25
1575 100 p. "Eroessa chilensis" 30 25
1576 100 p. Cloudless sulphur ("Phoebis sennae") .. 30 25

**594** Merryweather Steam Fire Engine, 1869

**1994.** Fire Engines (2nd series). Mult.

1577 150 p. Type **594** .. .. 45 35
1578 150 p. Poniente steam fire engine, 1863 .. .. 45 35
1579 150 p. Mieusset steam fire engine, 1905 .. .. 45 35
1580 150 p. Merryweather motor fire engine, 1903 45 35

**595** Bust and Banner

**1994.** Centenary of Javiera Carrera School for Girls, Santiago.

1581 **595** 200 p. multicoloured .. 60 45

**596** Door Panels, Porvenir (centenary)

**1994.** Town Anniversaries. Multicoloured.

1582 90 p. Type **596** .. .. 25 20
1583 100 p. Railway station, Villa Alemana (cent) .. 30 25
1584 150 p. Church, Constitucion (bicentenary) .. 45 35
1585 200 p. Fountain and church, Linares (bicent) 60 45
1586 250 p. Steam locomotive and statue, Copiapo (250th) .. .. 75 55
1587 300 p. La Serena (450th) 90 65

**597** Painting by Carlos Maturana

**600** Fr. Hurtado

**599** First Chilean Mail Van

**1994.** 20th International Very Large Data Bases Conference, Santiago.

1588 **597** 100 p. multicoloured .. 30 25

**1994.** Nos. 1487/8 and 1544 surch **$80**.

1589 **566** 80 p. on 70 p. black and pink .. .. 25 20
1590 – 80 p. on 70 p. black and pink .. .. 25 20
1591 **583** 80 p. on 70 p. bl & grn 25 20

**1994.** America. Postal Transport. Mult.

1592 80 p. Type **599** .. .. 25 20
1593 220 p. De Havilland D.H.60G Gipsy Moth (first Chilean mail plane) .. .. .. 70 50

**1994.** Beatification of Fr. Alberto Hurtado.

1594 **600** 300 p. blue, grn & blk 95 70

**601** Madonna and Child

**603** "Almirante Williams" (destroyer)

**602** Star

**1994.** Christmas. (a) Sold at face value

1595 **601** 80 p. multicoloured .. 25 20

(b) Discount stamp. Additionally inscribed "DS/20" at foot

1596 **601** 80 p. multicoloured .. 25 20

**1995.** International Women's Day. Mult.

1597 90 p. Type **602** .. .. 30 25
1598 90 p. Moon and sun .. 30 25
1599 90 p. Dove .. .. 30 25
1600 90 p. Earth .. .. 30 25

**1995.** Naval Tradition.

1601 **603** 100 p. multicoloured .. 30 25

**604** Emblem

**605** Arms

**1995.** United Nations World Summit for Social Development, Copenhagen.

1602 **604** 150 p. multicoloured .. 50 35

**1995.** 150th Anniv of Conciliar Seminary of Ancud.

1603 **605** 200 p. multicoloured .. 65 45

**606** Stained Glass Window, Santiago Cathedral

**1995.** 400th Anniv of Augustinian Order in Chile.

1604 **606** 250 p. multicoloured .. 80 60

**607** Religious Mask, Limari

**1995.** Rock Paintings. Multicoloured.

1605 150 p. Type **607** .. .. 50 35
1606 150 p. Herdsmen and llamas, Taira .. .. 50 35
1607 150 p. Whale, Tal-tal .. 50 35
1608 150 p. Masks, Encanto Valley .. .. 50 35

## INDEX

Countries can be quickly located by referring to the index at the end of this volume.

**608** Camera and Director's Chair

**610** "Cheloderus childreni"

**609** Arms and Trains

**1995.** Centenary of Motion Pictures. Mult.

1609 100 p. Type **608** .. .. 30 25
1610 100 p. Advertising poster for "The Kid" .. 30 25
1611 100 p. Early cinema advertising poster .. 30 25
1612 100 p. Advertising poster for "Valparaiso Mi Amor" .. .. 30 25

**1995.** Bicentenary of Parral.

1613 **609** 200 p. multicoloured .. 65 45

**1995.** Flora and Fauna. Multicoloured.

1614 100 p. Type **610** .. .. 30 25
1615 100 p. "Eulychnia acida" (cactus) .. .. 30 25
1616 100 p. "Chiasognathus grantii" (stag beetle) .. 30 25
1617 100 p. "Browningia candelaris" (cactus) .. 30 25
1618 100 p. "Capiapoa dealbata" (cactus) .. 30 25
1619 100 p. "Acanthinodera cummingi" (beetle) .. 30 25
1620 100 p. "Neoporteria subgibbosa" (cactus) .. 30 25
1621 100 p. "Semiotus luteipennis" (beetle) .. 30 25

**611** Congress Emblem

**1995.** 2nd World Police Congress, Santiago.

1622 **611** 200 p. multicoloured .. 65 45

**612** "Tower of Babel V" (Mario Toral)

**1995.** 30th Anniv of Ministry of Housing and Town-planning.

1623 **612** 200 p. multicoloured .. 65 45

**613** Bello

**614** Open Book and Emblem

**1995.** 25th Anniv of Andres Bello Agreement (South American co-operation in education, science and culture).

1624 **613** 250 p. purple and black 80 60

**1995.** 50th Anniversaries. Multicoloured.

1625 100 p. Type **614** (U.N.E.S.C.O.) .. 30 25
1626 100 p. Globes and handshake (U.N.O.) .. 30 25
1627 100 p. Seedling in hand (F.A.O.) .. .. 30 25

Nos. 1625/7 were issued together, se-tenant, forming a composite design.

**615** Farming (M. Cruces)

**616** Ship and Cape Horn

**1995.** America. Environmental Protection. Children's Paintings. Multicoloured.

1628 100 p. Type **615** .. .. 30 25
1629 250 p. Forestry (E. Munoz) (horiz) .. 75 55

**1995.** 51st World Congress of Cape Horn Captains.

1630 **616** 250 p. multicoloured .. 75 55

**617** Crib and Inhabitants of North Chile

**618** Carlos Dittborn (trainer) and Arica Stadium

**1995.** Christmas. (a) Sold at face value.

1631 **617** 90 p. blue and violet 25 20
1632 – 90 p. blue and violet 25 20

(b) Discount stamps. Additionally inscr "DS/20".

1633 **617** 90 p. green and purple 25 20
1634 – 90 p. green and purple 25 20

DESIGNS: Nos. 1632, 1634, Crib and people of South Chile.

**1995.** Cent of Chile Football Federation. Mult.

1635 100 p. Type **618** .. .. 30 25
1636 100 p. Hugo Lepe (player) 30 25
1637 100 p. Eladio Rojas (player) .. .. 30 25
1638 100 p. Honorino Landa (player) .. .. 30 25

**619** Mistral

**1995.** 50th Anniv of Award of Nobel Prize for Literature to Gabriela Mistral.

1639 **619** 300 p. blue and black 90 65

**620** Penguins

**1995.** Chilean Antarctic Territory. The Macaroni Penguin. Multicoloured.

1640 100 p. Type **620** .. .. 30 25
1641 250 p. Penguins (different) 75 55

**621** Kiwi Fruit and Container Ship

**1995.** 60th Anniv of Chilean Exports Association. Fruit. Multicoloured.

1643 100 p. Type **621** .. .. 30 25
1644 100 p. Grapes and container ship .. 30 25
1645 100 p. Peaches and container ship .. 30 25
1646 100 p. Apples and container ship .. 30 25
1647 100 p. Soft fruit and airplane .. .. 30 25

**622** "Reunion" (Mario Toral)

**623** Oil Rig

**1995.** 50th Anniv of End of Second World War.

1648 **622** 200 p. multicoloured .. 60 45

**1995.** 50th Anniv of Discovery of Oil in Chile. Multicoloured.

1649 100 p. Type **623** .. .. 30 25
1650 100 p. Concon Refinery (grass in foreground) .. 30 25
1651 100 p. Concepcion Refinery .. .. 30 25
1652 100 p. Rig (different) .. 30 25

**624** Embraer EMB-145

**1996.** "FIDAE'96" International Air and Space Fair, Santiago. Aircraft. Mult.

1653 400 p. Type **624** .. .. 1·25 90
1654 400 p. Mirage M5M Elkan 1·25 90
1655 400 p. De Havilland D.H.C.6 Twin Otter .. 1·25 90
1656 400 p. Saab JAS-39 Gripen 1·25 90

**625** School

**1996.** 175th Anniv of Serena Boys' School.

1657 **625** 100 p. multicoloured .. 30 25

**626** Old Cordoba Rail Station, Seville

**1996.** "Espamer" and "Aviation and Space" Spanish and Latin American Stamp Exhibitions, Seville, Spain. Multicoloured.

1658 200 p. Type **626** .. .. 60 45
1659 200 p. Lope de Vega Theatre, Seville .. 60 45

**627** Extinguish Matches Properly

**629** "Weather Rose" (Ricardo Mesa)

**628** "Esmeralda" (cadet barquentine) in Dry-dock

**1996.** Safety Precautions. Multicoloured.

(a) Accidents in the Home.

1660 50 p. Type **627** .. .. 15 10
1661 50 p. Do not leave boiling water unattended .. 15 10
1662 50 p. Keep sharp objects away from children .. 15 10
1663 50 p. Protect electrical sockets .. .. 15 10
1664 50 p. Do not improvise electrical connections .. 15 10
1665 50 p. Do not play the television or radio too loud .. .. .. 15 10
1666 50 p. Check gas connections regularly .. 15 10
1667 50 p. Do not overload electrical circuits .. 15 10
1668 50 p. Keep inflammable materials away from fire .. .. .. 15 10
1669 50 p. Do not leave toys lying around on the floor .. .. .. 15 10

(b) Road Safety.

1670 50 p. Use crossings .. 15 10
1671 50 p. Obey the instructions of the traffic police .. .. 15 10
1672 50 p. Only cross on the green light .. 15 10
1673 50 p. Wait on the pavement for buses .. 15 10
1674 50 p. Do not cross the road between vehicles 15 10
1675 50 p. Do not travel on the step of buses .. 15 10
1676 50 p. Walk on the side of the road facing on-coming traffic .. 15 10
1677 50 p. Look out for drains 15 10
1678 50 p. Do not play ball in the road .. .. 15 10
1679 50 p. Bicyclists should obey the Highway Code 15 10

(c) Safety at School.

1680 50 p. Do not panic in emergencies .. .. 15 10
1681 50 p. Do not run around corners .. .. 15 10
1682 50 p. Do not play practical jokes .. 15 10
1683 50 p. Do not sit on banisters or railings .. 15 10
1684 50 p. Do not run on the stairs .. .. .. 15 10
1685 50 p. Do not drink while walking .. 15 10
1686 50 p. Do not swing on your chair .. 15 10
1687 50 p. Do not play with pointed or sharp objects 15 10
1688 50 p. Do not open doors sharply .. 15 10
1689 50 p. Go straight home after school and do not stop to talk to strangers 15 10

(d) Safety in the Workplace.

1690 50 p. Wear protective clothing .. .. 15 10
1691 50 p. Do not work with tools in bad condition 15 10
1692 50 p. Keep your attention on your work (man at lathe) .. .. .. 15 10
1693 50 p. Always use the proper tools .. .. 15 10
1694 50 p. Work carefully (man at filing cabinet) .. 15 10
1695 50 p. Do not leave objects on the stairs .. .. 15 10
1696 50 p. Do not carry so much that you cannot see where you are going 15 10
1697 50 p. Check ladders are safe .. .. .. 15 10
1698 50 p. Always keep the workplace clean and tidy .. .. .. 15 10
1699 50 p. Remove old nails first .. .. .. 15 10

(e) Enjoy Leisure Safely.

1700 50 p. Only swim in the permitted areas .. 15 10
1701 50 p. Do not put any part of the body out of the window of a moving vehicle .. .. 15 10
1702 50 p. Avoid excessive exposure to the sun .. 15 10
1703 50 p. Do not contaminate swimming water with detergents .. .. 15 10
1704 50 p. Do not throw litter 15 10
1705 50 p. Always put out fires before leaving them .. 15 10
1706 50 p. Do not play pranks in water .. .. 15 10
1707 50 p. Check safety precautions .. .. 15 10
1708 50 p. Do not fly kites near overhead electrical lines 15 10
1709 50 p. Do not run by the side of swimming pools 15 10

(f) Alcohol and Drugs Awareness.

1710 50 p. Do not drink and drive .. .. .. 15 10
1711 50 p. Do not drink if you are pregnant .. 15 10
1712 50 p. Do not give in to peer pressure .. .. 15 10
1713 50 p. Being under the influence of alcohol is irresponsible in the workplace .. .. 15 10
1714 50 p. Do not destroy your family through alcohol 15 10
1715 50 p. You do not need drugs to have a good time .. .. .. 15 10
1716 50 p. You do not need drugs to succeed .. 15 10
1717 50 p. You do not need drugs to entertain .. 15 10
1718 50 p. Do not abandon your friends and family for drugs .. .. 15 10
1719 50 p. Without drugs you are free and safe .. 15 10

**1996.** Centenary of Dry-dock No. 1, Talcahuano.

1720 **628** 200 p. multicoloured .. 60 45

**1996.** Modern Sculpture. Multicoloured.

1721 150 p. Type **629** .. .. 45 35
1722 150 p. "Friendship" (Francisca Cerda) .. 45 35
1723 200 p. "Memory" (Fernando Undurraga) (horiz) .. .. 45 35
1724 200 p. "Andean Airs" (Benito Rojo) (horiz) .. 45 35

**630** Addict and Syringe full of Pills

**1996.** International Day against Drug Abuse.

1725 **630** 250 p. multicoloured .. 75 55

**631** Boxing Glove

**1996.** Centenary of National Olympic Committee and Modern Olympic Games. Olympic Games, Atlanta. Multicoloured.

1726 450 p. Type **631** .. .. 1·40 1·00
1727 450 p. Running shoe .. 1·40 1·00
1728 450 p. Rollerblade .. 1·40 1·00
1729 450 p. Ball .. .. 1·40 1·00

## INDEX

Countries can be quickly located by referring to the index at the end of this volume.

**632** School

**1996.** 150th Anniv of San Fernando School.
1730 **632** 200 p. multicoloured .. 60 45

**633** Polluted Forest

**1996.** 4th International Congress on Earth Sciences. Multicoloured.
1731 200 p. Type **633** .. .. 60 45
1732 200 p. Industrial pollution 60 45
1733 200 p. Deforestation .. 60 45
1734 200 p. Map, camera and cracked earth .. .. 60 45
Nos. 1731/4 were issued together, se-tenant, forming a composite design.

**634** Crookesite and Open-cast Mine

**1996.** Mining. Multicoloured.
1735 150 p. Type **634** .. .. 45 35
1736 150 p. Lapis lazuli and pendant .. .. 45 35
1737 150 p. Bornite and calcium and crates .. 45 35
1738 150 p. Azurite and atacamite .. .. 45 35

**635** St. John Leonardi (founder)

**1996.** 50th Anniv of Order of Mother of God in Chile.
1739 **635** 200 p. multicoloured .. 60 45

## ACKNOWLEDGMENT OF RECEIPT STAMP

**1894.** Portrait of Columbus. Inscr. "A.R." Perf. or Imperf.
AR 77. 5 c. brown .. 1·00 1·00

## COMPULSORY TAX STAMPS

**T 100.** Arms of Talca. **T 224.** Chilean Arms.

**1942.** Talca Bicent.
T 338. **T 100.** 10 c. blue .. 10 10

**1955.** Pres. Prieto. Death Cent. As **T 145.**
T 445. 15 p. green .. .. 15 10
PORTRAIT: 15 p. Pres. Prieto.

**1970.** Postal Tax. No. 492 and 555 surch. E° 0, 10 **Art. 77 LEY 17272.**
T 638. **162a.** 10 c. on 2 c. blue.. 10 10
T 639. **178.** 10 c. on 6 c. purple 10 10

**1971.** Postal Modernisation.
T 646. **T 224.** 10 c. blue .. 15 10
T 647. 15 c. red .. 15 10

**1971.** Postal Modernisation. Nos. T 646/7 surch.
T 673 **T 224** 15 c. on 10 c. blue 10 10
T 674 20 c. on 15 c. red 10 10
T 675 50 c. on 15 c. red 10 10

## OFFICIAL STAMPS

**1928.** Stamps of 1911 inscr. "CHILE CORREOS" optd. **Servicio del ESTADO.**
O 190. **49.** 10 c. black and blue 3·75 1·00
O 191. – 20 c. (No. 142) .. 1·60 50
O 192. – 25 c. (No. 167) .. 4·25 50
O 193. – 50 c. (No. 170) .. 2·50 50
O 194. **57.** 1 p. black and green 2·75 70

**1930.** Stamps inscr. "CORREOS DE CHILE" optd. **Servicio del ESTADO.**
O 217. **49.** 10 c. (No. 204) .. 2·00 70
O 234. **76.** 10 c. blue .. .. 50 35
O 219. – 20 c. (No. 209) .. 50 25
O 235. – 20 c. brown (No. 232) 50 25
O 220. – 25 c. (No. 167) .. 50 25
O 221. – 50 c. (No. 168) .. 85 35

**1934.** Stamps inscr. "CORREOS DE CHILE" optd. **OFICIAL.**
O 236. **64.** 5 c. green (No. 206) 45 35
O 237. **76.** 10 c. blue .. .. 45 35
O 238. – 20 c. brown (No. 232) 7·25 35

**1939.** Optd. **Servicio del ESTADO**
O 279. – 50 c. violet (No. 273) 2·50 85
O 280. **90.** 1 p. orange .. .. 3·75 2·50

**1941.** Nos. 269/338j optd. **OFICIAL.**
O 281. – 10 c. red .. .. 1·40 1·00
O 282. – 15 c red .. .. 70 25
O 283. – 20 c. blue .. .. 2·00 75
O 284. – 30 c. red .. .. 45 25
O 285. – 40 c. green .. .. 45 25
O 286. – 50 c. violet .. .. 3·00 50
O 339. **90.** 1 p. orange .. .. 2·00 80
O 288. – 1 p. 80 blue .. .. 8·00 4·75
O 442. – 2 p. red .. .. 1·60 1·00
O 383. – 5 p. green .. .. 3·00 1·25
O 443. – 10 p. purple .. .. 8·00 4·25

**1953.** No. 379b optd. **OFICIAL.**
O 386. 1 p. turquoise .. .. 85 35

**1956.** Nos. 446/450 optd. **OFICIAL.**
O 451. 2 p. lilac .. .. 1·75 50
O 452. 3 p. blue .. .. 6·00 4·00
O 453. 5 p. sepia .. .. 1·50 40
O 454a. 10 p. violet .. .. 70 40
O 455. 50 p. red .. .. 5·00 1·40

**1958.** Optd. **OFICIAL.**
O 469. **152.** 10 p. blue .. .. £180 20·00

**1960.** No. 493 optd. **OFICIAL.**
O 507. 5 c. blue .. .. 2·50 1·00

## POSTAGE DUE STAMPS

**D 18.** **D 19.** **D 68.**

**1895.**
D 98. **D 18.** 1 c. red on yellow .. 45 40
D 99. 2 c. red on yellow .. 45 40
D 100. 4 c. red on yellow .. 45 40
D 101. 6 c. red on yellow .. 45 40
D 102. 8 c. red on yellow .. 45 40
D 103. 10 c. red on yellow .. 45 40
D 104. 20 c. red on yellow .. 45 40
D 93 40 c. red on yellow .. 1·00 90
D 94. 50 c. red on yellow .. 1·50 1·00
D 95. 60 c. red on yellow .. 2·50 1·50
D 96. 80 c. red on yellow .. 3·00 3·00
D 109. 100 c. red on yellow 17·00 11·50
D 97. 1 p. red on yellow .. 20·00 6·00

**1898.**
D 110. **D 19.** 1 c. red .. .. 35 20
D 111. 2 c. red .. .. 75 30
D 112. 4 c. red .. .. 35 20
D 113. 10 c. red .. .. 35 20
D 114. 20 c. red .. .. 35 20

**1924.**
D 184. **D 68.** 2 c. red and blue .. 60 40
D 185. 4 c. red and blue .. 60 40
D 186. 8 c. red and blue .. 60 40
D 187. 10 c. red and blue 60 40
D 188. 20 c. red and blue .. 60 40
D 189. 40 c. red and blue .. 60 40
D 190. 60 c. red and blue .. 60 40
D 191. 80 c. red and blue .. 60 40
D 192. 1 p. red and blue .. 85 45
D 193. 2 p. red and blue .. 1·75 1·75
D 194. 5 p. red and blue .. 1·75 1·00

## CHINA — Pt. 17

People's Republic in Eastern Asia, formerly an Empire.

### CHINESE CHARACTERS

| Simple | Formal | |
|---|---|---|
| 半 | 半 | = ½ |
| 一 | 壹 | = 1 |
| 二 | 貳 | = 2 |
| 三 | 叄 | = 3 |
| 四 | 肆 | = 4 |
| 五 | 伍 | = 5 |
| 六 | 陸 | = 6 |
| 七 | 柒 | = 7 |
| 八 | 捌 | = 8 |
| 九 | 玖 | = 9 |
| 十 | 拾 | = 10 |
| 百 | 佰 | = 100 |
| 千 | 仟 | = 1,000 |
| 萬 | 萬 | = 10,000 |

| | |
|---|---|
| 分 | = cent |
| 圓 | = dollar |

Examples:

| | |
|---|---|
| 十五 | = 15 |
| 五十 | = 50 |
| 叄佰圓 | = 300 dollars |
| 伍仟圓 | = 5,000 dollars |

### CHINESE EMPIRE

1878. 100 candarins = 1 tael.
1897. 100 cents = 1 dollar.

1. Dragon.  2.

**1878.**

| | | | | |
|---|---|---|---|---|
| 7 | 1. | 1 ca. green | 85·00 | 55·00 |
| 2 | | 3 ca. red | £100 | 25·00 |
| 3 | | 5 ca. orange | £150 | 38·00 |

**1885.**

| | | | | |
|---|---|---|---|---|
| 13a. | 2. | 1 ca. green | 5·50 | 6·00 |
| 14. | | 3 ca. mauve | 25·00 | 3·00 |
| 15. | | 5 ca. yellow | 38·00 | 5·00 |

4.  10.

**1894.** Dowager Empress's 60th Birthday.

| | | | | |
|---|---|---|---|---|
| 16. | 4. | 1 ca. orange | 7·50 | 5·00 |
| 17. | – | 2 ca. green | 7·50 | 7·50 |
| 18. | – | 3 ca. yellow | 7·50 | 2·50 |
| 19. | – | 4 ca. pink | 18·00 | 12·00 |
| 20. | 4. | 5 ca. orange | 45·00 | 32·00 |
| 21. | – | 6 ca. brown | 10·00 | 5·00 |
| 22. | 10. | 9 ca. green | 20·00 | 7·50 |
| 23. | | 12 ca. orange | 42·00 | 25·00 |
| 24. | – | 24 ca. red | 55·00 | 25·00 |

DESIGNS—VERT. (as Type 4): 2 ca. to 4 ca. and 6 ca Dragon. HORIZ. (as Type 10): 24 ca. Junks.

**1897.** Surch. in English and Chinese characters.

| | | | | |
|---|---|---|---|---|
| 78 | – | ½ c. on 3 ca. yell. (No. 18) | 2·00 | 2·00 |
| 34 | 2. | 1 c. on 1 ca. green | 10·00 | 11·00 |
| 79 | 4. | 1 c. on 1 ca. orange | 4·50 | 3·25 |
| 59 | – | 2 c. on 2 ca. grn. (No. 17) | 5·00 | 1·50 |
| 35 | 2. | 2 c. on 3 ca. mauve | 45·00 | 30·00 |
| 40 | – | 4 c. on 4 ca. pink (No. 19) | 6·50 | 3·50 |
| 36 | 2. | 5 c. on 5 ca. yellow | 35·00 | 18·00 |
| 41 | – | 5 c. on 5 ca. orge. (No. 20) | 7·50 | 3·50 |
| 42 | – | 8 c. on 6 ca. brn. (No. 21) | 7·50 | 3·00 |
| 43 | – | 10 c. on 6 ca. brn. (No. 21) | 32·00 | 35·00 |
| 63 | 10. | 10 c. on 9 ca. green | 30·00 | 18·00 |
| 64 | | 10 c. on 12 ca. orange | 40·00 | 30·00 |
| 46 | – | 30 c. on 24 ca. red (No. 24) | 50·00 | 30·00 |

17.  24.

30. Carp.  31. Bean Goose.

**1897.** Surch. in English and Chinese characters.

| | | | | |
|---|---|---|---|---|
| 88. | 17. | 1 c. on 3 c. red | 23·00 | 18·00 |
| 89. | | 2 c. on 3 c. red | 30·00 | 15·00 |
| 90. | | 4 c. on 3 c. red | £100 | 42·00 |
| 91. | | $1 on 3 c. red | £650 | £350 |
| 92. | | $5 on 3 c. red | £3250 | £2500 |

**1897.** Inscr. "IMPERIAL CHINESE POST".

| | | | | |
|---|---|---|---|---|
| 96. | 24. | ½ c. purple | 1·00 | 2·00 |
| 97. | | 1 c. yellow | 1·50 | 75 |
| 98. | | 2 c. orange | 1·50 | 30 |
| 99. | | 4 c. brown | 2·25 | 60 |
| 100. | | 5 c. red | 3·75 | 1·25 |
| 101. | | 10 c. green | 6·00 | 1·00 |
| 102. | 30. | 20 c. lake | 12·00 | 5·50 |
| 103. | | 30 c. red | 15·00 | 11·00 |
| 104. | | 50 c. green | 30·00 | 18·00 |
| 105. | 31. | $1 red | £110 | 95·00 |
| 106. | | $2 orange and yellow | £650 | £750 |
| 107. | | $5 green and red | £250 | £500 |

32. Dragon.  33. Carp.  34. Bean Goose.

**1898.** Inscr "CHINESE IMPERIAL POST".

| | | | | |
|---|---|---|---|---|
| 121 | 32 | ½ c. brown | 50 | 10 |
| 122 | | 1 c. buff | 50 | 10 |
| 123 | | 2 c. red | 75 | 15 |
| 151 | | 2 c. green | 1·25 | 10 |
| 152 | | 3 c. green | 1·25 | 10 |
| 124 | | 4 c. brown | 1·50 | 40 |
| 153a | | 4 c. red | 2·00 | 35 |
| 112 | | 5 c. pink | 5·00 | 90 |
| 126 | | 5 c. orange | 8·00 | 2·75 |
| 154 | | 5 c. mauve | 3·00 | 10 |
| 155 | | 7 c. red | 3·50 | 2·00 |
| 127 | | 10 c. green | 3·50 | 10 |
| 156 | | 10 c. blue | 3·75 | 10 |
| 157 | 33 | 16 c. green | 9·00 | 3·25 |
| 128 | | 20 c. purple | 4·50 | 50 |
| 115 | | 30 c. red | 7·50 | 2·00 |
| 130 | | 50 c. green | 13·00 | 1·75 |
| 131 | 34 | $1 red and orange | 40·00 | 4·50 |
| 132 | | $2 purple & yellow | 75·00 | 15·00 |
| 119 | | $5 green and orange | £140 | 30·00 |

36. Temple of Heaven.

**1909.** 1st Year of Reign of Emperor Hsuan T'ung.

| | | | | |
|---|---|---|---|---|
| 165. | 36. | 2 c. green and orange | 75 | 50 |
| 166. | | 3 c. blue and orange | 1·00 | 60 |
| 167. | | 7 c. purple and orange | 75 | 1·25 |

### POSTAGE DUE STAMPS

**1904.** Stamps of 1898 optd. POSTAGE DUE in English and Chinese characters.

| | | | | |
|---|---|---|---|---|
| D 137. | 32. | ½ c. brown | 2·25 | 2·50 |
| D 138. | | 1 c. buff | 2·50 | 1·00 |
| D 139a. | | 2 c. red | 4·25 | 1·50 |
| D 140. | | 4 c. brown | 4·25 | 2·00 |
| D 141. | | 5 c. red | 8·00 | 3·25 |
| D 142. | | 10 c. green | 14·00 | 2·25 |

D 37.

**1904.**

| | | | | |
|---|---|---|---|---|
| D143 | D 37 | ½ c. blue | 1·25 | 50 |
| D144 | | 1 c. blue | 3·00 | 45 |
| D168 | | 1 c. brown | 3·25 | 2·50 |
| D145 | | 2 c. blue | 3·00 | 50 |
| D169 | | 2 c. brown | 6·50 | 10·00 |
| D146 | | 4 c. blue | 3·25 | 60 |
| D170 | | 4 c. brown | £1000 | |
| D147 | | 5 c. blue | 3·75 | 1·00 |
| D171 | | 5 c. brown | £400 | £500 |
| D148 | | 10 c. blue | 4·00 | 1·40 |
| D149 | | 20 c. blue | 10·00 | 2·00 |
| D150 | | 30 c. blue | 12·00 | 3·50 |

### CHINESE REPUBLIC

1912. 100 cents = 1 dollar.
1948. 100 cents = 1 gold yuan.
1949. 100 cents = 1 silver yuan.

**1912.** Optd. vert. with four Chinese characters signifying "Republic of China".

| | | | | |
|---|---|---|---|---|
| 192 | 32. | ½ c. brown | 30 | 15 |
| 193 | | 1 c. buff | 40 | 10 |
| 194 | | 2 c. green | 75 | 15 |
| 221 | | 3 c. green | 80 | 10 |
| 196 | | 4 c. red | 1·50 | 25 |
| 197 | | 5 c. mauve | 2·25 | 25 |
| 198 | | 7 c. lake | 3·00 | 1·75 |
| 225 | | 10 c. blue | 2·50 | 10 |
| 200 | 33. | 16 c. olive | 5·50 | 2·50 |
| 201 | | 20 c. red | 6·50 | 75 |
| 202 | | 30 c. red | 7·50 | 1·00 |
| 203 | | 50 c. green | 13·00 | 1·00 |
| 204 | 34. | $1 red and salmon | 40·00 | 5·00 |
| 205 | | $2 red and yellow | 95·00 | 18·00 |
| 232 | | $5 green and salmon | £180 | £250 |

41. Dr. Sun Yat-sen.

**1912.** Revolution Commem.

| | | | | |
|---|---|---|---|---|
| 242. | 41. | 1 c. orange | 1·00 | 75 |
| 243. | | 2 c. green | 1·00 | 75 |
| 244. | | 3 c. blue | 1·00 | 20 |
| 245. | | 5 c. mauve | 1·00 | 65 |
| 246. | | 8 c. sepia | 1·50 | 1·25 |
| 247. | | 10 c. blue | 1·50 | 75 |
| 248. | | 16 c. olive | 6·00 | 6·00 |
| 249. | | 20 c. lake | 5·50 | 3·25 |
| 250. | | 50 c. green | 20·00 | 10·00 |
| 251. | | $1 red | 55·00 | 18·00 |
| 252. | | $2 brown | £190 | £120 |
| 253. | | $5 slate | 55·00 | 75·00 |

**1912.** As T 41 but portrait of Pres. Yuan Shih-kai, inscr. "Commemoration of the Republic".

| | | | |
|---|---|---|---|
| 254. | 1 c. orange | 1·00 | 75 |
| 255. | 2 c. green | 1·00 | 75 |
| 256. | 3 c. blue | 1·00 | 20 |
| 257. | 5 c. mauve | 1·00 | 75 |
| 258. | 8 c. sepia | 3·25 | 2·25 |
| 259. | 10 c. blue | 2·25 | 75 |
| 260. | 16 c. olive | 5·00 | 4·50 |
| 261. | 20 c. lake | 4·75 | 2·25 |
| 262. | 50 c. green | 14·00 | 8·50 |
| 263. | $1 red | 30·00 | 14·00 |
| 264. | $2 brown | 35·00 | 13·00 |
| 265. | $5 slate | £100 | 85·00 |

43. Junk.  44. Reaper.  45. Entrance Hall of Classics, Peking.

**1913.**

| | | | | |
|---|---|---|---|---|
| 287 | 43. | ½ c. sepia | 10 | 10 |
| 269 | | 1 c. orange | 25 | 10 |
| 289a | | 1½ c. purple | 50 | 60 |
| 270 | | 2 c. green | 75 | 10 |
| 313 | | 3 c. green | 75 | 10 |
| 292 | | 4 c. red | 1·10 | 10 |
| 314 | | 4 c. grey | 7·50 | 20 |
| 315 | | 4 c. olive | 1·00 | 10 |
| 293 | | 5 c. mauve | 1·00 | 10 |
| 294 | | 6 c. grey | 1·50 | 45 |
| 317 | | 6 c. red | 1·75 | 10 |
| 318 | | 6 c. brown | 15·00 | 2·00 |
| 319 | | 7 c. violet | 3·25 | 1·75 |
| 296 | | 8 c. orange | 3·25 | 20 |
| 321 | | 10 c. blue | 3·00 | 10 |
| 298 | 44. | 13 c. brown | 5·00 | 50 |
| 278 | | 15 c. brown | 6·50 | 4·00 |
| 323 | | 15 c. blue | 3·00 | 10 |
| 324 | | 16 c. olive | 3·00 | 15 |
| 325 | | 20 c. lake | 3·00 | 10 |
| 326 | | 30 c. purple | 3·00 | 10 |
| 282 | | 50 c. green | 7·50 | 1·00 |
| 304 | 45. | $1 black and yellow | 20·00 | 50 |
| 328 | | $1 sepia and brown | 11·00 | 30 |
| 305 | | $2 black and blue | 35·00 | 1·50 |
| 329 | | $2 brown and blue | 20·00 | 50 |
| 306 | 45. | $5 black and red | 75·00 | 18·00 |
| 330 | | $5 green and red | 45·00 | 3·75 |
| 307 | | $10 black and green | £200 | 80·00 |
| 331 | | $10 mauve and green | £110 | 18·00 |
| 308 | | $20 black and orange | £1400 | £1400 |
| 332 | | $20 blue and purple | £170 | 35·00 |

**1920.** Flood Relief Fund. Surch with new value in English and Chinese characters.

| | | | | |
|---|---|---|---|---|
| 349. | 43. | 1 c. on 2 c. green | 3·25 | 1·50 |
| 361. | | 2 c. on 3 c. green | 2·50 | 20 |
| 350. | | 3 c. on 4 c. red | 5·00 | 1·00 |
| 351. | | 5 c. on 6 c. grey | 6·75 | 4·50 |

47. Curtiss "Jenny" over Great Wall of China.

I  II

**1921.** Air. Tail fin of aeroplane as Type I.

| | | | | |
|---|---|---|---|---|
| 352. | 47. | 15 c. black and green | 12·00 | 10·00 |
| 353. | | 30 c. black and red | 12·00 | 10·00 |
| 354. | | 45 c. black and purple | 13·00 | 15·00 |
| 355. | | 60 c. black and blue | 16·00 | 17·00 |
| 356. | | 90 c. black and olive | 20·00 | 20·00 |

For similar stamps in this type but with tail fin as Type II, see Nos. 384a/8.

48. Yen Kung-cho, Pres. Hsu Shih-chang and Chin Yung-peng.  53. Temple of Heaven.

**1921.** 25th Anniv. of Chinese National Postal Service.

| | | | | |
|---|---|---|---|---|
| 357. | 48. | 1 c. orange | 2·50 | 50 |
| 358. | | 3 c. turquoise | 2·75 | 25 |
| 359. | | 6 c. grey | 4·00 | 2·25 |
| 360. | | 10 c. blue | 4·50 | 1·50 |

**1923.** Adoption of the Constitution.

| | | | | |
|---|---|---|---|---|
| 362. | 53. | 1 c. orange | 1·25 | 45 |
| 363. | | 3 c. turquoise | 1·25 | 30 |
| 364. | | 4 c. red | 2·75 | 1·25 |
| 365. | | 10 c. blue | 5·50 | 1·00 |

**1925.** Surch. in English and Chinese characters.

| | | | | |
|---|---|---|---|---|
| 366. | 43. | 1 c. on 2 c. green | 70 | 10 |
| 367. | | 1 c. on 3 c. green | 30 | 10 |
| 369. | | 1 c. on 4 c. olive | 85 | 10 |
| 370. | | 3 c. on 4 c. grey | 1·10 | 10 |

The figures in this surcharge are at the top and are smaller than for the 1920 provisionals.

55. Marshal Chang Tso-lin.  56. General Chiang Kai-shek.

**1928.** Assumption of Title of Marshal of the Army and Navy by Chang Tso-lin.

| | | | | |
|---|---|---|---|---|
| 372. | 55. | 1 c. orange | 1·00 | 1·00 |
| 373. | | 4 c. olive | 1·00 | 1·00 |
| 374. | | 10 c. blue | 4·50 | 3·50 |
| 375. | | $1 red | 30·00 | 35·00 |

**1929.** Unification of China under Gen. Chiang Kai-shek.

| | | | | |
|---|---|---|---|---|
| 376. | 56. | 1 c. orange | 2·00 | 30 |
| 377. | | 4 c. olive | 3·50 | 35 |
| 378. | | 10 c. blue | 7·50 | 1·25 |
| 379. | | $1 red | 75·00 | 30·00 |

57. Mausoleum at Nanking.  58. Dr. Sun Yat-sen.

**1929.** State Burial of Dr. Sun Yat-sen.

| | | | | |
|---|---|---|---|---|
| 380. | 57. | 1 c. orange | 1·00 | 50 |
| 381. | | 4 c. olive | 1·00 | 50 |
| 382. | | 10 c. blue | 5·00 | 1·00 |
| 383. | | $1 red | 42·00 | 22·00 |

**1929.** Air. As T 47, but tail fin of aeroplane as Type II.

| | | | | |
|---|---|---|---|---|
| 384a. | 47. | 15 c. black and green | 4·50 | 20 |
| 385. | | 30 c. black and red | 4·00 | 25 |
| 386. | | 45 c. black and purple | 4·50 | 4·25 |
| 387. | | 60 c. black and blue | 6·00 | 4·50 |
| 388. | | 90 c. black and olive | 9·50 | 9·00 |

**1931.**

389 58. 1 c. orange 30 15
396 2 c. olive 20 10
391 4 c. green 40 10
398 5 c. green 30 10
399 15 c. green 55 40
400 15 c. red 50 10
401 20 c. blue 75 15
402 25 c. blue 70 10
403a $1 sepia and brown 2·50 15
735 $1 violet 15 1·75
404a $2 brown and blue 5·00 35
736 $2 olive 15 3·00
405a $5 black and red 10·00 1·50
737 $20 green 1·10 50
738 $30 brown 15 55
739 $50 orange 45 55

59. "Nomads of the Desert" 60. General Teng K'eng.

**1932.** North-West China Scientific Expedition.

406. 59. 1 c. orange 17·00 19·00
407. 4 c. olive 17·00 19·00
408. 5 c. red 17·00 19·00
409. 10 c. blue 17·00 19·00

**1932.** Martyrs of the Revolution.

410 60 ½ c. brown 10 10
508 – 1 c. orange 10 10
509 – 2 c. blue 10 15
412 60 2½ c. purple 20 15
511 – 3 c. brown 10 10
512 60 4 c. lilac 10 20
513 – 5 c. orange 10 40
514 – 8 c. orange 10 10
515 – 10 c. purple 10 15
516 – 13 c. green 10 40
517 – 15 c. purple 30 45
417 – 17 c. green 30 15
418 – 20 c. red 45 10
519 – 20 c. blue 25 10
520 – 21 c. brown 15 15
521 – 25 c. purple 15 40
541 – 28 c. green 10 60
542 – 30 c. purple 20 25
543 – 40 c. orange 20 20
544 – 50 c. green 20 10

DESIGNS: 1 c., 25 c., 50 c. Ch'en Ying Shih. 2 c., 10 c., 17 c., 28 c. Shung Chiao-jen. 3 c., 5 c., 15 c., 30 c. Liao Chung k'ai. 8 c., 13 c., 21 c. Chu Chih-hsin. 20 c., 40 c. Gen. Huang Hsing.

61. Junkers F-13 over Great Wall.

**1932.** Air.

422 61 15 c. green 15 15
556 25 c. orange 10 45
557 30 c. red 10 40
558 45 c. purple 15 60
559 50 c. brown 10 45
560 60 c. blue 10 70
561 90 c. green 10 75
562 $1 green 15 45
563 $2 brown 15 40
564 $5 red 20 35

62. Tan Yen-kai. 63.

**1933.** Tan Yen-kai Memorial.

440. 62. 2 c. olive 1·25 85
441. 5 c. green 2·25 15
442. 25 c. blue 5·25 60
443. $1 red 38·00 20·00

**1936.** "New Life" Movement. Symbolic designs as T 63.

444. 63. 2 c. olive 1·00 20
445. 5 c. green 1·25 10
446. – 20 c. blue (various emblems) 3·25 30
447. – $1 red (Lighthouse) 20·00 6·00

66. "Postal Communications." 72. Dr. Sun Yat-sen.

**1936.** 40th Anniv. of Chinese National Postal Service.

448. 66. 2 c. orange 1·00 40
449. – 5 c. green 1·00 10
450. – 25 c. blue 2·50 20
451. – 100 c. red 16·00 6·00

DESIGNS: 5 c. The Bund, Shanghai. 25 c. G.P.O., Shanghai. 100 c. Ministry of Communications, Nanking.

**1936.** Surch. in figures and Chinese characters.

452. 44. 5 c. on 15 c. blue 1·00 10
453. 5 c. on 16 c. olive 2·00 25

**1937.** Surch in figures and Chinese characters.

454 58 1 on 4 c. green 35 10
455 – 8 on 40 c. orge (No. 543) 45 30
456 58 10 on 25 c. blue 35 10

**1938.**

462 72 2 c. green 10 10
464 3 c. red 10 10
489 5 c. green 10 10
492 8 c. green 10 10
469 10 c. green 10 10
470 15 c. red 75 1·00
471 16 c. brown 40 50
472 25 c. blue 75 75
494 30 c. red 35 25
495 50 c. blue 75 20
496 $1 sepia and brown 2·25 40
497 $2 brown and blue 2·00 40
475 $5 green and red 2·50 20
499 $10 violet and green 4·75 2·25
500 $20 blue and purple 8·50 4·25

For dollar values in single colours, see Nos. 666 etc.

For 15 c. brown see Japanese Occupation of China: IV Shanghai and Nanking No. 12.

74. Chinese and U.S. Flags and Map of China.

**1939.** 150th Anniv. of U.S. Constitution. Flags in red and blue.

501. 74. 5 c. green 40 15
502. 25 c. blue 60 60
503. 50 c. brown 1·25 1·40
504. $1 red 2·25 2·25

肆 暫
分 4 作
(76.)

**1940.** Surch as T 76.

576 72 3 c. on 5 c. green 1·00 1·50
582 4 c. on 5 c. green 75 20
619 7 c. on 8 c. green 1·00 1·10

77. Dr. Sun Yat-sen. 78. Industry.

**1941.**

583 77 ½ c. brown 10 15
584 1 c. orange 10 10
585 2 c. blue 15 15
586 5 c. green 10 15
587 8 c. orange 40 1·00
588 8 c. green 25 20
589 10 c. green 10 10
590 17 c. green 2·50 4·50
591 25 c. purple 20 30
592 30 c. red 20 25
593 50 c. blue 30 15
594 $1 black and brown 40 10
595 $2 black and blue 50 15
596 $5 black and red 80 35
597 $10 black and green 2·25 2·00
598 $20 black and purple 2·25 2·25

**1941.** Thrift Movement.

599. 78. 8 c. green 25 50
600. 21 c. brown 35 65
601. 28 c. olive 50 75
602. 33 c. red 75 85
603. 50 c. blue 85 95
604. $1 purple 1·00 1·10

中華民國創立
三十週年紀念
日十月十年十三
(79.)

伍 改
角 50 作
(81.)

82. Dr. Sun Yat-sen.

**1941.** 30th Anniv of Republic. Optd with T 79.

606 – 1 c. orange (No. 508) 75 1·00
607 72 2 c. green 75 1·00
608 60 4 c. lilac 75 1·00
609 72 8 c. green 75 1·00
610 10 c. green 75 1·00
611 16 c. brown 75 1·00
612 – 21 c. brown (No. 520) 75 1·00
613 – 28 c. green (No. 541) 75 1·00
614 72 30 c. red 75 1·00
615 $1 sepia and brown 85 1·00

**1942.** Provincial surcharges. Surch as T 81.

622 60 1 c. on ½ c. brown 50 1·25
624 77 1 c. on ½ c. brown 60 1·50
690a – 20 c. on 13 c. green (516) 1·00 5·00
691i 72 20 c. on 16 c. brown 1·00 5·00
693e – 20 c. on 17 c. green (417) 1·25 5·50
694f – 20 c. on 21 c. brown (520) 50 6·50
695e – 20 c. on 28 c. green (541) 50 7·50
625 72 40 c. on 50 c. blue 2·50 3·50
627 77 40 c. on 50 c. blue 3·50 5·00
626 – 40 c. on 50 c. green (544) 4·50 5·50
689a 50 c. on 16 c. brown 2·00 1·40

**1942.**

628 82. 10 c. green 10 1·00
629 16 c. olive 11·00 20·00
630 20 c. olive 10 1·00
631 25 c. purple 10 1·50
632 30 c. red 10 70
642 30 c. brown 20 7·50
633 40 c. brown 10 1·10
634 50 c. green 10 10
635 $1 red 75 10
636 $1 olive 10 10
637 $1·50 blue 10 40
638 $2 green 10 10
645 $2 blue 4·75 7·50
646 $2 purple 10 15
639 $3 yellow 10 10
640 $4 brown 20 20
641 $5 red 20 10
650 $6 violet 50 60
651 $10 brown 10 10
652 $20 blue 15 10
653 $50 green 4·50 15
654 $70 violet 4·75 35
655 $100 brown 50 45

**1942.** As T 72 but emblem at top redrawn with solid background. Perf., Imperf. or roul.

666 72. $4 blue 50 1·00
667 $5 grey 1·00 1·00
656 $10 brown 1·00 80
657 $20 green 1·00 50
658 $20 red 8·00 4·50
659 $30 purple 75 40
660 $40 red 75 50
661 $50 blue 1·25 1·00
662 $100 brown 4·25 3·00

附 國
加 內
已 平
付 信
(83.)

角 伍
(84.)

(T 83. Trans. "Surcharge for Domestic Postage Paid".)

**1942.** Surch. as T 83.

688e. 82. 16 c. olive 24·00 30·00

**1943.** No 688e surch as T 84.

701e 82 50 c. on 16 c. olive 4·00 4·00

89. Dr. Sun Yat-sen. 91. Savings Bank and Money Box.

90. War Refugees.

**1944.**

702. 89. 40 c. red 15 5·50
703. $2 brown 15 10
704. $3 red 10 10
705. $3 brown 50 45
706. $6 grey 15 25
707. $10 red 10 10
708. $20 pink 10 10
709. $50 brown 4·25 10
710. $70 violet 25 20

**1944.** War Refugees' Relief Fund. Various frames.

724. 90. $2+$2 on 50 c.+50 c. blue 85 1·75
725. $4+$4 on 8 c.+8 c. grn. 85 1·75
726. $5+$5 on 21 c.+21 c. brown 1·00 2·00
727. $6+$6 on 28 c.+28 c. olive 1·75 2·50
728. $10+$10 on 33 c.+33 c. red 2·25 2·75
729. $20+$20 on $1+$1 vio. 2·50 3·50

**1944.**

731. 91. $40 slate 20 60
732. $50 green 10 20
733. $100 brown 10 15
734. $200 green 25 15

92. Dr. Sun Yat-sen. 93.

**1944.** 50th Anniv. of Kuomintang.

740. 92. $2 green 1·00 2·00
741. $5 brown 1·25 2·50
742. $6 purple 2·00 2·40
743. $10 blue 2·75 4·75
744. $20 red 2·25 6·50

**1945.** 20th Death Anniv. of Dr. Sun Yat-sen.

746. 93. $2 green 75 1·50
747. $5 brown 75 1·50
748. $6 blue 1·00 2·00
749. $10 blue 1·50 1·40
750. $20 red 2·00 3·50
751. $30 buff 2·50 4·50

94. Dr. Sun Yat-sen. 96. Pres. Lin Sen.

95. Gen. Chiang Kai-shek.

**1945.**

758. 94. $2 green 25 60
759. $5 green 20 35
760. $10 blue 10 10
761. $20 red 10 10

**1945.** Equal Treaties with Great Britain and U.S.A., abolishing Foreign Concessions. Flags in national colours.

762. 95. $1 blue 60 1·25
763. $2 green 60 1·25
764. $5 olive 65 1·25
765. $6 brown 65 1·25
766. $10 red 2·75 5·00
767. $20 red 3·50 6·50

**1945.** In Memory of President Lin Sen.

768. 96. $1 black and blue 95 1·75
769. $2 black and green 95 1·50
770. $5 black and red 95 1·75
771. $6 black and violet 1·10 1·75
772. $10 black and brown 2·25 3·25
773. $20 black and olive 3·25 5·00

貳 暫
佰 售
圓 200.00
(97.)

壹 國
圓 幣
(98.)

貳 國
拾 幣
圓
(99.)

**1945.** Chinese National Currency (C.N.C.). Various issues surch. as T 97 (for Japanese controlled Government at Shanghai and Nanking) and further surch. as T 98.

774 72 10 c. on $20 on 3 c. red 10 1·50
775 – 15 c. on $30 on 2 c. blue (509) 10 1·50
776 77 25 c. on $50 on 1 c. orge 10 1·25
777 72 50 c. on $100 on 3 c. red 10 50
778 60 $1 on $200 on 1 c. orange (508) 10 15
779 72 $2 on $400 on 3 c. red 10 35
780 77 $5 on $1000 on 1 c. orge 10 10

**1945.** Kaifeng provisionals. C.N.C. surcharges. Stamps of Japanese Occupation of North China surch. as T 99.

781. 60. $10 on 20 c. lake (No. 166) 6·50 12·00
782. $20 on 40 c. orge. (No. 168) 8·50 15·00
783. $50 on 30 c. red (No. 167) 6·50 14·00

100. Pres. Chiang Kai-Shek. 101.

**1945.** Inaug. of Pres. Chiang Kai-shek. Flag in blue and red.

784. 100. $2 green 35 1·00
785. $4 blue 65 1·00
786. $5 olive 65 1·25
787. $6 brown 1·00 2·00
788. $10 grey 3·75 6·50
789. $20 red 4·00 6·50

**1945.** Victory. Flag in red.

790. **101.** $20 green and blue .. 10 15
791. $50 brown and blue .. 60 60
792. $100 blue .. 20 25
793. $300 red and blue .. 30 15

**102.** Dr. Sun Yat-sen. (**103.**)

**1945.**

794. **102.** $20 red .. .. .. 10 10
795. $30 blue .. .. .. 10 15
796. $40 orange .. .. .. 60 1·00
797. $50 green .. .. 1·00 25
798. $100 brown .. .. 15 10
799. $200 brown .. .. 15 10

**1945.** C.N.C. surcharges. Nos. 410, 412, 514, 516/17, 519/20 and 541 surch as T **103** (value tablet at top).

800 $3 on 2½ c. purple .. 10·00 16·00
801 $10 on 15 c. purple .. 10 15
802 $20 on 8 c. orange .. 10 10
803 $20 on 20 c. blue .. 30 10
804 $30 on ½ c. brown .. 10 1·00
805 $50 on 21 c. brown .. 15 10
812 $70 on 13 c. green .. 10 10
808 $100 on 28 c. green .. 15 10

(**104.**) (**108.**)

**1946.** Air. C.N.C. surcharges. Surch. as T **104**.

820. **61.** $23 on 30 c. red .. 10 1·00
821. $53 on 15 c. green .. 10 90
822. $73 on 25 c. orange .. 10 1·25
823. $100 on $2 brown .. 10 35
824. $200 on $5 red .. 10 15

**1946.** C.N.C. surcharges. Surch. as T **108** (octagonal value tablet at bottom).

898 – $10 on 1 c. orange (508) 10 55
903 77 $10 on 1 c. orange .. 30 1·10
896 72 $20 on 2 c. green .. 10 75
904 77 $20 on 2 c. blue .. 10 75
899 – $20 on 3 c. brown (511) 10 75
897 72 $20 on 3 c. red .. 10 70
879 – $20 on 8 c. orange (514) 10 1·10
869 72 $20 on 8 c. green .. 1·00 1·00
882 77 $20 on 8 c. orange .. 70 3·25
883 $20 on 8 c. green .. 10 60
900 60 $30 on 4 c. lilac .. 10 35
880 – $50 on 5 c. orange (513) 10 15
876 72 $50 on 5 c. green .. 20 10
884 77 $50 on 5 c. green .. 70 10

(**105.**) **107.** Dr. Sun Yat-sen.

**1946.** C.N.C. surcharges. Surch as T **105** (rectangular value tablet at bottom). (a) Box with chequered pattern.

831 72 $20 on 3 c. red .. 10 1·25
846 – $20 on 8 c. orange (514) 10 85
832 72 $50 on 3 c. red .. 10 45
833 $50 on 5 c. green .. 15 45
847 – $50 on 5 c. orange (513) 10 25
851 77 $50 on 5 c. green .. 60 1·10
854 82 $50 on $1 green .. 10 15
848 – $100 on 1 c. orge (508) 10 10
834 72 $100 on 3 c. red .. 10 10
842 $100 on 8 c. green .. 25 15
852 77 $100 on 8 c. green .. 45 20
860 58 $100 on $1 purple .. 50 10
868 107 $100 on $20 red .. 50 10
837 72 $200 on 10 c. green .. 10 10
861 58 $200 on $4 blue .. 50 10
855 82 $250 on $1.50 blue .. 40 1·75
862 58 $250 on $2 green .. 30 30
863 $250 on $5 red .. 40 10
838 72 $300 on 10 c. green .. 10 10
853 77 $300 on 10 c. green .. 10 75
839 72 $500 on 3 c. red .. 10 10
864 58 $500 on $20 green .. 15 10
865 $800 on $30 brown .. 10 2·50
830 $1000 on 2 c. green .. 1·00 10
856 82 $1000 on $2 green .. 50 25
857 $1000 on $2 blue .. 25 2·00
858 $1000 on $2 brown .. 30 25
866 94 $1000 on $2 green .. 10 2·00
859 82 $2000 on $5 red .. 50 50
867 94 $2000 on $5 green .. 15 30

(b) Box with diamond pattern.

978. **58.** $500 on $20 green .. 10 10
979. **107.** $1250 on $70 orange 10 2·50
980. **118.** $1800 on $350 buff .. 10 3·75
974. **82.** $2000 on $3 yellow .. 35 25
976. **89.** $2000 on $3 red .. 10 10
975. **82.** $3000 on $3 yellow .. 15 15
977. **89.** $3000 on $3 brown .. 15 80

**1946.**

885. **107.** $20 red .. .. 5·00 15
886. $30 blue .. .. 25 10
887. $50 violet .. .. 25 10
888. $70 orange .. .. 8·50 1·00
889. $100 red .. .. 10 10
890. $200 green .. .. 10 10
891. $500 green .. .. 25 15
892. $700 brown .. .. 15 1·50
893. $10000 purple .. .. 25 15
894. $3000 blue .. .. 30 10
895. $5000 red and green .. 75 10

**109.** Douglas DC-4 over Mausoleum of Dr. Sun Yat-sen. **110.** Pres. Chiang Kai-shek.

**1946.** Air.

905. **109.** $27 blue .. .. 10 75

**1946.** President's 60th Birthday.

906. **110.** $20 red .. .. 20 50
907. $30 green .. .. 25 70
908. $50 orange .. .. 25 60
909. $100 green .. .. 40 90
910. $200 yellow .. .. 50 80
911. $300 red .. .. 50 50

For stamps of this type, but additionally inscribed with four characters around head, see Taiwan Nos. 30/5, or North Eastern Provinces, Nos. 48/53.

**111.** National Assembly House, Nanking. **112.** Entrance to Dr. Sun Yat-sen Mausoleum.

**1946.** Opening of National Assembly, Nanking.

912. **111.** $20 green .. .. 10 30
913. $30 blue .. .. 20 40
914. $50 brown .. .. 30 40
915. $100 red .. .. 30 30

**1947.** 1st Anniv. of Return of Government to Nanking.

942. **112.** $100 green .. .. 10 25
943. $200 blue .. .. 20 25
944. $250 red .. .. 20 50
945. $350 brown .. .. 20 50
946. $400 purple .. .. 30 35

For stamps of this type but additionally inscribed with four characters above numeral of value, see Taiwan, Nos. 36/40, or North Eastern Provinces, Nos. 64/68.

**113.** Dr. Sun Yat-sen. **114.** Confucius. **115.** Confucius's Lecture School.

**116.** Tomb of Confucius. **118.** Dr. Sun Yat-sen and Plum Blossoms.

**1947.**

947. **113.** $500 olive .. .. 15 10
948. $1,000 red and green .. 20 10
949. $2,000 lake and blue .. 25 10
950. $5,000 black and orange 30 10

**1947.** Confucius Commem.

951. **114.** $500 red .. .. 25 40
952. **115.** $800 brown .. .. 10 65
953. **116.** $1,250 green .. .. 10 85
954. $1,800 blue .. .. 10 90

DESIGN—HORIZ. $1,800, Confucian Temple.

**1947.** (a) With noughts for cents.

955. **118.** $150 blue .. .. 10 10·00
956. $250 violet .. .. 15 3·50
957. $500 green .. .. 10 10
958. $1,000 red .. .. 10 10
959. $2,000 orange .. .. 10 10
960. $3,000 blue .. .. 10 10
961. $4,000 grey .. .. 10 20
962. $5,000 brown .. .. 15 10
963. $6,000 purple .. .. 10 20
964. $7,000 brown .. .. 10 20
965. $10,000 red and blue .. 25 10
966. $20,000 green and red 60 10
967. $50,000 blue and green 85 10
968. $100,000 green & orange 2·50 15
969. $200,000 blue & purple 2·50 15
970. $300,000 orange & brown 3·50 40
971. $500,000 brown & green 3·75 30

(b) Without noughts for cents.

1032. **118.** $20,000 red .. .. 30 30
1033. $30,000 brown .. 10 10
1034. $40,000 green .. 10 15
1035. $50,000 blue .. .. 10 10
1036. $100,000 olive .. 10 10
1037. $200,000 purple .. 15 10
1038. $300,000 green .. 1·75 50
1039. $500,000 mauve .. 10 10
1040. $1,000,000 red .. 10 10
1041. $2,000,000 orange .. 10 10
1042. $3,000,000 bistre .. 10 40
1043. $5,000,000 blue .. 4·00 55

**119.** Map of Taiwan and Chinese Flag. **122.** Postal Kiosk.

**1947.** Restoration of Taiwan (Formosa). (1st issue).

972. **119.** $500 red .. .. 15 75
973. $1,250 green .. .. 15 75

See also Nos. 1003/4.

**1947.** Progress of the Postal Service.

981. – $500 red .. .. 10 25
982. **122.** $1,000 violet .. .. 10 25
983. $1,250 green .. .. 15 45
984. – $1,800 blue .. .. 15 50

DESIGN: $500, $1,800, Mobile Post Office.

**123.** Air, Sea and Rail Transport. **124.** Postboy and Motor Van.

**1947.** 50th Anniv. of Directorate General of Posts.

985. **123.** $100 violet .. .. 10 75
986. **124.** $200 green .. .. 10 75
987. $300 lake .. .. 10 75
988. – $400 red .. .. 10 75
989. – $500 blue .. .. 10 75

DESIGN—As T **123**. $400, $500, Junk and airplane.

**126.** Book of the Constitution and National Assembly Building.

**1947.** Adoption of the Constitution.

990. **126.** $2,000 red .. .. 15 35
991. $3,000 blue .. .. 15 35
992. $5,000 green .. .. 20 40

**127.** Reproductions of 1947 and 1912 Stamps.

**1948.** Perf. or Imp. (a) Nanking Philatelic Exn.

1001. **127.** $5,000 red .. .. 30 1·75

(b) Shanghai Philatelic Exhibition.

1002. **127.** $5,000 green .. .. 25 1·50

**128.** Sun Yat-sen Memorial Hall.

**1948.** Restoration of Taiwan (Formosa) to Chinese Rule (2nd issue).

1003. **128.** $5,000 lilac .. .. 20 50
1004. $10,000 red .. .. 25 50

(**130.**) (**129.**)

(**133.**)

**1948.** "Re-valuation" surcharges.

(a) Surch. as T **130**.

1012. **118.** $4,000 on $100 red .. 20 12·00
1013. $5,000 on $100 red .. 15 10
1014. $8,000 on $800 brown 30 85

(b) Surch. as T **129**.

1005. **82.** $5,000 on $1 green .. 10 15
1007. $5,000 on $2 green .. 15 10
1008. **102.** $10,000 on $20 red .. 20 10
1018. **82.** $15,000 on 10 c. green 20 40
1015. $15,000 on 50 c. green 20 75
1019. $15,000 on $4 purple 20 70
1020. $15,000 on $6 blue .. 30 40
1009. $20,000 on 10 c. green 10 15
1010. $20,000 on 50 c. green 10 25
1011. $30,000 on 30 c. red 10 40
1016. $40,000 on 20 c. olive 20 75
1017. $60,000 on $4 brown 25 30

(c) Air. Surch. as T **133**.

1022. **61.** $10,000 on 30 c. red 10 30
1028. **109.** $10,000 on $27 blue 10 1·00
1023. **61.** $20,000 on 25 c. orange 10 30
1024. $30,000 on 90 c. olive 10 60
1025. $50,000 on 60 c. blue 10 60
1026. $50,000 on $1 green 10 50

On No. 1028 the Chinese characters read vertically.

**135.** Great Wall of China. **137.** "Hai Tien" (freighter) and "Eton" (steamer) of 1872.

**138.** "Kiang Ya" (freighter). (**138a.**)

**1948.** Tuberculosis Relief Fund. Cross in red. Perf. or Imperf.

1029. **135.** $5,000 + $2,000 violet 15 1·50
1030. $10,000 + $2,000 brown 15 1·50
1031. $15,000 + $2,000 grey 15 1·50

**1948.** 75th Anniv. of China Merchants' Steam Navigation Company.

1044. **137.** $20,000 blue .. .. 15 95
1045. $30,000 mauve .. 15 95
1046. **138.** $40,000 brown .. 20 1·00
1047. $60,000 red .. .. 20 1·00

**1948** C.N.C. surcharge. Surch. with T **138a**.

1048. **107.** $5,000 on $100 claret 6·50 30·00

(**139.**) (**140.**) (**141.**)

**1948.** Gold Yuan surcharges.

(a) Surch as T **139** or **140**.

1049 82 ½ c. on 30 c. brown 10 4·00
1050 118 ½ c. on $500 green .. 10 25
1051 107 1 c. on $20 red .. 10 2·00
1052 82 2 c. on $1.50 blue .. 10 2·00
1053 3 c. on $5 red .. 10 2·00
1054 4 c. on $1 red .. 10 2·00
1055 5 c. on 50 c. green .. 10 40

(b) Surch as T **141**.

1056 89 5 c. on $20 red .. 10 80
1057 102 5 c. on $30 blue .. 10 80
1058 72 10 c. on 2 c. green .. 20 1·00
1059 60 10 c. on 2½ c. purple 15 75
1061 82 10 c. on 25 c. brown 10 1·10
1062 89 10 c. on 40 c. red 10 1·00
1063 82 10 c. on $1 green .. 10 15
1065 89 10 c. on $2 brown .. 15 20
1066 82 10 c. on $20 blue .. 10 15
1067 89 10 c. on $20 red .. £110 £110
1068 94 10 c. on $20 red .. 10 60
1069 107 10 c. on $20 red .. 75 2·00
1070 102 10 c. on $30 blue .. 10 1·00
1071 89 10 c. on $70 violet .. 10 55
1072 118 10 c. on $7,000 brown 1·00 1·00
1073 10 c. on $20,000 red 15 3·00
1074 89 20 c. on $6 purple .. 10 25
1075 58 20 c. on $30 brown 15 2·50
1076 107 20 c. on $30 blue .. 50 2·50
1077 20 c. on $100 red .. 15 2·25
1079 60 50 c. on ½ c. brown 10 60
1081 82 50 c. on 20 c. green 15 50
1082 50 c. on 30 c. red .. 10 1·00
1083 50 c. on 40 c. brown 10 60
1084 89 50 c. on 40 c. red .. 10 75
1085a 82 50 c. on $4 purple .. 25 1·50
1086 50 c. on $20 blue .. 10 10
1087 94 50 c. on $20 red .. 40 1·00
1088 107 50 c. on $20 red .. 10 1·00
1089 82 50 c. on $70 lilac .. 30 30
1090a 118 50 c. on $6,000 purple 15 1·25
1091 82 $1 on 30 c. brown .. 10 20
1092 $1 on 40 c. brown .. 10 10

| No. | Type | Description | Unused | Used |
|---|---|---|---|---|
| 1093 | 82 | $1 on $1 red .. | 50 | 1·50 |
| 1094 | | $1 on $5 red .. | 60 | 35 |
| 1095 | 89 | $2 on $2 brown .. | 10 | 15 |
| 1096 | 102 | $2 on $20 red .. | 10 | 10 |
| 1097 | 107 | $2 on $100 red .. | 15 | 10 |
| 1098 | – | $5 on 17 c. green (417) .. .. | 75 | 75 |
| 1099 | 89 | $5 on $2 brown .. | 20 | 15 |
| 1100 | 118 | $5 on $3,000 blue .. | 10 | 1·25 |
| 1101 | – | $8 on 20 c. blue (519) | 50 | 50 |
| 1102 | 118 | $8 on $30,000 brown | 10 | 2·00 |
| 1103 | – | $10 on 40 c. orange (543) .. .. | 1·00 | 1·00 |
| 1104 | 89 | $10 on $2 brown .. | 20 | 10 |
| 1105 | | $20 on $2 brown .. | 25 | 15 |
| 1106 | 107 | $20 on $20 red .. | 3·50 | 2·25 |
| 1107 | 82 | $50 on 30 c. red .. | 20 | 20 |
| 1108 | 89 | $50 on $2 brown .. | 20 | 15 |
| 1109 | 107 | $80 on $20 red .. | 10 | 1·00 |
| 1110 | 82 | $100 on $1 green .. | 25 | 1·00 |
| 1111 | 89 | $100 on $2 brown .. | 35 | 20 |
| 1112 | 118 | $20,000 on $40,000 green .. .. | 3·50 | 4·50 |
| 1113 | | $50,000 on $20,000 red .. .. | 1·25 | 25 |
| 1114 | | $50,000 on $30,000 brown .. .. | 7·00 | 3·25 |
| 1115 | | $100,000 on $20,000 red .. .. | 3·00 | 2·25 |
| 1116 | | $100,000 on $30,000 brown .. .. | 1·75 | 10 |
| 1117 | | $200,000 on $40,000 green .. .. | 3·50 | 5·50 |
| 1118 | | $200,000 on $50,000 blue .. .. | 3·50 | 7·00 |

金圓貳佰圓 改作郵票 200.00

(142.)

143. Liner, Train and Airplane.

中華民國郵政 1.00 金圓壹圓

(144.)

145. Dr. Sun Yat-sen.

**1949.** Gold Yuan surcharges. Parcels Post stamps surch. as T **142**.

| No. | Type | Description | Unused | Used |
|---|---|---|---|---|
| 1119. | P **104.** | $200 on $3,000 orange | 50 | 40 |
| 1120. | | $500 on $5,000 blue | 70 | 25 |
| 1121. | | $1,000 on $10,000 vio. | 1·10 | 35 |

**1949.** Gold Yuan surcharges. Revenue stamps surch. (a) As T **144**.

| No. | Type | Description | Unused | Used |
|---|---|---|---|---|
| 1136 | **143.** | 50 c. on $20 brown .. | 10 | 45 |
| 1137 | | $1 on $15 orange .. | 10 | 5·50 |
| 1127 | | $2 on $50 blue .. | 10 | 1·00 |
| 1144 | | $3 on $50 blue .. | 10 | 50 |
| 1138 | | $5 on $500 brown .. | 10 | 20 |
| 1129 | | $10 on $30 mauve .. | 10 | 40 |
| 1140 | | $15 on $20 brown .. | 10 | 30 |
| 1141 | | $25 on $20 brown .. | 10 | 10 |
| 1145 | | $50 on $50 blue .. | 10 | 30 |
| 1147 | | $50 on $300 green .. | 10 | 60 |
| 1130 | | $80 on $50 blue .. | 10 | 85 |
| 1146 | | $100 on $50 blue .. | 30 | 40 |
| 1124 | | $200 on $50 blue .. | 50 | 65 |
| 1142 | | $200 on $500 brown | 30 | 40 |
| 1125 | | $300 on $50 blue .. | 70 | 75 |
| 1143 | | $500 on $15 orange .. | 1·00 | 3·00 |
| 1134 | | $500 on $30 mauve .. | 50 | 1·50 |
| 1135 | | $1,000 on $50 blue .. | 5·50 | 6·50 |
| 1148 | | $1,000 on $100 olive | 2·25 | 4·25 |
| 1126 | | $1,500 on $50 blue .. | 50 | 1·25 |
| 1151 | | $2,000 on $300 green | 30 | 75 |

(b) As T **144**. but with key pattern inverted at top and bottom.

| No. | Type | Description | Unused | Used |
|---|---|---|---|---|
| 1183. | **143.** | $50 on $10 green .. | 5·00 | 6·50 |
| 1184. | | $100 on $10 green .. | 1·00 | 3·25 |
| 1185. | | $500 on $10 green .. | 40 | 3·00 |
| 1186. | | $1,000 on $10 green | 40 | 3·25 |
| 1187. | | $5,000 on $20 brown | 15·00 | 7·50 |
| 1188. | | $10,000 on $20 brown | 5·00 | 3·00 |
| 1189. | | $50.000 on $20 brown | 7·50 | 4·50 |
| 1190. | | $100,000 on $20 brown | 7·50 | 4·00 |
| 1191. | | $500,000 on $20 brown | £170 | 70·00 |
| 1192. | | $2,000,000 on $20 brn. | £350 | £225 |
| 1193. | | $5,000.000 on $20 brn. | £475 | £300 |

**1949.**

| No. | Type | Description | Unused | Used |
|---|---|---|---|---|
| 1152. | **145.** | $1 orange .. .. | 10 | 20 |
| 1153. | | $10 green .. .. | 20 | 15 |
| 1154. | | $20 purple .. .. | 10 | 25 |
| 1155. | | $50 green .. .. | 10 | 15 |
| 1156. | | $100 brown .. .. | 10 | 10 |
| 1157. | | $200 red .. .. | 10 | 10 |
| 1158. | | $500 mauve .. .. | 10 | 10 |
| 1159. | | $800 red .. .. | 10 | 2·25 |
| 1160. | | $1,000 blue .. .. | 15 | 10 |
| 1168. | | $2,000 violet .. .. | 10 | 1·25 |
| 1169. | | $5,000 blue .. .. | 10 | 10 |
| 1177. | | $5,000 red .. .. | 25 | 35 |
| 1170. | | $10,000 brown .. | 10 | 10 |
| 1171. | | $20,000 green .. .. | 10 | 1·00 |
| 1179. | | $20,000 orange .. | 35 | 50 |
| 1172. | | $50,000 pink .. .. | 10 | 25 |
| 1180. | | $50,000 blue .. .. | 90 | 1·50 |
| 1173. | | $80,000 brown .. | 10 | 3·25 |
| 1174. | | $100,000 green .. | 20 | 10 |
| 1181. | | $200,000 blue .. .. | 1·25 | 1·75 |
| 1182. | | $500,000 purple .. | 1·25 | 1·25 |

For stamps of Type **145** in Silver Yuan currency see Nos. 1348/56.

146. Steam Locomotive.

147. Douglas DC-4.

148. Postman on Motor Cycle.

149. Mountains.

**1949.** No value indicated. Perf. or roul.

| No. | Type | Description | Unused | Used |
|---|---|---|---|---|
| 1211. | **146.** | Orange (Ord. postage) | 2·50 | 1·00 |
| 1212. | **147.** | Green (Air Mail) .. | 4·00 | 5·00 |
| 1213. | **148.** | Mauve (Express) .. | 4·00 | 6·00 |
| 1214. | **149.** | Red (Registration) .. | 4·00 | 6·00 |

Owing to the collapse of the Gold Yuan the above were sold at the rate for the day for the service indicated.

中華民國郵政 國內信函費

(154.)

中華郵政 銀員四分 4

(159.)

**1949.** Gold Yuan currency. Revenue stamps optd. as T **154**.

| No. | Type | Description | Unused | Used |
|---|---|---|---|---|
| 1232. | **143.** | $10 green (B) .. .. | 19·00 | 18·00 |
| 1233. | | $30 mauve (A) .. | 60·00 | 30·00 |
| 1234. | | $50 blue (C) .. .. | 18·00 | 18·00 |
| 1235. | | $100 olive (D) .. | 35·00 | 35·00 |
| 1236. | | $200 purple (A) .. | 8·00 | 5·50 |
| 1237. | | $500 green (A) .. | 8·00 | 5·50 |

Opt. translation: (A) Domestic Letter Fee. (B) Express Letter Fee. (C) Registered Letter Fee. (D) Air Mail Fee.

**1949.** Silver Yuan surcharges. Revenue stamps surch. as T **159**.

| No. | Type | Description | Unused | Used |
|---|---|---|---|---|
| 1312. | **143.** | 1 c. on $20 brown .. | 25·00 | 35·00 |
| 1284. | | 1 c. on $5,000 brown .. | 3·75 | 4·00 |
| 1285. | | 4 c. on $100 olive .. | 2·50 | 2·75 |
| 1286. | | 4 c. on $3,000 orange .. | 2·50 | 1·00 |
| 1313. | | 10 c. on $20 brown .. | 25·00 | 32·00 |
| 1287. | | 10 c. on $50 blue .. | 3·50 | 2·25 |
| 1288. | | 10 c. on $1,000 red .. | 3·75 | 2·50 |
| 1289. | | 20 c. on $1,000 red .. | 5·00 | 3·75 |
| 1290. | | 50 c. on $30 mauve .. | 4·50 | 4·00 |
| 1291. | | 50 c. on $50 blue .. | 9·00 | 1·75 |
| 1292. | | $1 on $50 blue .. | 6·50 | 4·50 |

On Nos. 1312 and 1313 the key pattern is inverted at top and bottom.

169. Whistling Swans over Globe.

170. Globe and Doves.

**1949.**

| No. | Type | Description | Unused | Used |
|---|---|---|---|---|
| 1344. | **169.** | $1 orange .. .. | 5·00 | 10·50 |
| 1345. | | $2 blue .. .. | 12·00 | 14·50 |
| 1346. | | $5 red .. .. | 20·00 | 21·00 |
| 1347. | | $10 green .. .. | 28·00 | 26·00 |

**1949.** Silver Yuan currency.

| No. | Type | Description | Unused | Used |
|---|---|---|---|---|
| 1348. | **145.** | 1 c. green .. .. | 10·00 | 8·00 |
| 1349. | | 2 c. orange .. .. | 3·25 | 10·00 |
| 1350. | | 4 c. green .. .. | 10 | 35 |
| 1351. | | 10 c. lilac .. .. | 10 | 10 |
| 1352. | | 16 c. red .. .. | 10 | 12·00 |
| 1353. | | 20 c. blue .. .. | 10 | 3·50 |
| 1354. | | 50 c. brown .. .. | 30 | 20·00 |
| 1355. | | 100 c. blue .. .. | £100 | £225 |
| 1356. | | 500 c. red .. .. | £180 | £250 |

**1949.** 75th Anniv. of U.P.U. Value optd. in black. Imperf.

| No. | Type | Description | Unused | Used |
|---|---|---|---|---|
| 1357. | **170.** | $1 orange .. .. | 3·50 | 7·50 |

171. Buddha's Tower, Peking.

172. Bronze Bull.

**1949.** Value optd. Roul.

| No. | Type | Description | Unused | Used |
|---|---|---|---|---|
| 1358. | **171.** | 15 c. green and brown | 4·50 | 6·50 |
| 1359. | **172.** | 40 c. red and green .. | 5·50 | 7·00 |

5 伍分

(173.)

15 壹角伍分

(174.)

**1949.** Silver Yuan surcharges.

(a) Chungking issue. Surch. as T **173**.

| No. | Type | Description | Unused | Used |
|---|---|---|---|---|
| 1360. | **145.** | 2½ c. on $50 green .. | 1·50 | 3·25 |
| 1361. | | 2½ c. on $50,000 blue | 2·50 | 3·25 |
| 1362. | | 5 c. on $1,000 blue .. | 2·50 | 3·00 |
| 1363. | | 5 c. on $20,000 orange | 50 | 1·25 |
| 1364. | | 5 c. on $200,000 blue | 3·00 | 3·00 |
| 1365. | | 5 c. on $500,000 purple | 3·00 | 3·00 |
| 1366. | | 10 c. on $5,000 red .. | 3·00 | 3·25 |
| 1367. | | 10 c. on $10,000 brown | 3·25 | 3·25 |
| 1368. | | 15 c. on $200 red .. | 3·75 | 14·00 |
| 1369. | | 25 c. on $100 brown | 7·50 | 20·00 |

(b) Canton issue. Surch. as T **174**.

| No. | Type | Description | Unused | Used |
|---|---|---|---|---|
| 1371 | **145.** | 1 c. on $100 brown .. | 3·00 | 6·50 |
| 1372 | | 2½ c. on $500 mauve | 5·00 | 7·50 |
| 1374 | | 15 c. on $10 green .. | 7·50 | 10·00 |
| 1375 | | 15 c. on $20 purple .. | 10·00 | 11·00 |

## EXPRESS DELIVERY STAMP

E 80.

**1941.** Perf.

| No. | Type | Description | Unused | Used |
|---|---|---|---|---|
| E616. | E **80.** | (No value) red & yell. | 20·00 | 15·00 |

This stamp was sold at $2 which included ordinary postage.

## MILITARY POST STAMPS

軍 郵

(M 85.)

M 93. Entrenched Soldiers.

**1942.** Optd. variously as Type M **85**.

| No. | Type | Description | Unused | Used |
|---|---|---|---|---|
| M 682. | **72.** | 8 c. olive .. .. | 4·00 | 7·00 |
| M 684. | **77.** | 8 c. green .. .. | 4·50 | 9·00 |
| M 676. | | 8 c. orange .. .. | £200 | |
| M 683. | **72.** | 16 c. olive .. .. | 14·00 | 18·00 |
| M 677. | **82.** | 16 c. olive .. .. | 5·00 | 9·50 |
| M 678. | | 50 c. green .. .. | 5·00 | 8·00 |
| M 679. | | $1 red .. .. | 4·00 | 7·50 |
| M 680. | | $1 olive .. .. | 4·25 | 7·50 |
| M 681. | | $2 green .. .. | 4·50 | 9·00 |
| M 687. | | $2 purple .. .. | 22·00 | 30·00 |

**1945.**

| No. | Type | Description | Unused | Used |
|---|---|---|---|---|
| M 745. | M **93.** | (No value) red .. | 1·00 | 10·00 |

## PARCELS POST STAMPS

P 90.

P 104.

P 112.

**1944.**

| No. | Type | Description | Unused | Used |
|---|---|---|---|---|
| P 711. | P **90.** | $500 green .. | — | 45 |
| P 712. | | $1,000 blue .. | — | 55 |
| P 713. | | $3,000 red .. | — | 60 |
| P 714. | | $5,000 brown .. | — | 13·00 |
| P 715. | | $10,000 purple .. | — | 20·00 |

**1946.**

| No. | Type | Description | Unused | Used |
|---|---|---|---|---|
| P 814. | P **104.** | $3,000 orange .. | — | 50 |
| P 815. | | $5,000 blue .. | — | 50 |
| P 816. | | $10,000 violet .. | — | 2·00 |
| P 817. | | $20,000 red .. | — | 3·75 |

**1947.** Type **P 112** and similar design.

| No. | Type | Description | Unused | Used |
|---|---|---|---|---|
| P 925. | | $1,000 yellow .. .. | — | 25 |
| P 926. | | $3,000 green .. .. | — | 25 |
| P 927. | | $5,000 red .. .. | — | 25 |
| P 928. | | $7,000 blue .. .. | — | 25 |
| P 929. | | $10,000 red .. .. | — | 25 |
| P 930. | | $30,000 olive .. | — | 1·00 |
| P 931. | | $50,000 black .. | — | 1·00 |
| P 932. | | $70,000 brown .. | — | 1·25 |
| P 933. | | $100,000 purple .. | — | 1·40 |
| P 934. | | $200,000 green .. | — | 1·50 |
| P 935. | | $300,000 pink .. .. | — | 1·60 |
| P 936. | | $500,000 plum .. | — | 1·60 |
| P 937. | | $3,000,000 blue .. | — | 2·00 |
| P 938. | | $5,000,000 lilac .. | — | 3·00 |
| P 939. | | $6,000,000 grey .. | — | 3·00 |
| P 940. | | $8,000,000 red .. | — | 3·25 |
| P 941. | | $10,000,000 olive .. | — | 4·00 |

金圓伍拾圓 50 金圓伍拾圓

(P 146.)

**1949.** Gold Yuan surcharges. 1947 issue surch. as Type **P 146**.

| No. | Type | Description | Unused | Used |
|---|---|---|---|---|
| P 1194. | | $10 on $3,000 green .. | — | 1·00 |
| P 1195. | | $20 on $5,000 red .. | — | 1·00 |
| P 1196. | | $50 on $10,000 red .. | — | 1·00 |
| P 1197. | | $100 on $3,000,000 blue | — | 1·40 |
| P 1198. | | $200 on $5,000,000 lilac | — | 1·75 |
| P 1199. | | $500 on $1,000 yellow | — | 2·00 |
| P 1200. | | $1,000 on $7,000 blue | — | 2·25 |

Parcels post stamps were not on sale in unused condition and those now on the market were probably stocks seized by the Communists.

## POSTAGE DUE STAMPS

中華民國

(D 41.)

D 46.

D 62.

**1912.** Chinese Empire stamps optd with vertical row of Chinese characters.

| No. | Type | Description | Unused | Used |
|---|---|---|---|---|
| D 207. | D **37.** | ½ c. blue .. .. | 60 | 40 |
| D 208. | | 1 c. brown .. .. | 75 | 35 |
| D 209. | | 2 c. brown .. .. | 1·10 | 50 |
| D 210. | | 4 c. blue .. .. | 2·75 | 1·10 |
| D 211. | | 5 c. blue .. .. | 75·00 | 85·00 |
| D 212. | | 5 c. brown .. .. | 4·00 | 1·50 |
| D 213. | | 10 c. blue .. .. | 6·00 | 2·50 |
| D 214. | | 20 c. blue .. .. | 6·00 | 6·50 |
| D 215. | | 30 c. blue .. .. | 10·00 | 10·00 |

**1912.** Optd. with Type D **41.**

| No. | Type | Description | Unused | Used |
|---|---|---|---|---|
| D 233. | D **37.** | ½ c. blue .. .. | 7·50 | 4·50 |
| D 234. | | ½ c. brown .. .. | 1·50 | 50 |
| D 235. | | 1 c. brown .. .. | 1·50 | 40 |
| D 236. | | 2 c. brown .. .. | 1·75 | 70 |
| D 237. | | 4 c. blue .. .. | 5·50 | 1·00 |
| D 238. | | 5 c. brown .. | 8·50 | 2·50 |
| D 239. | | 10 c. blue .. .. | 14·00 | 6·00 |
| D 240. | | 20 c. brown .. | 17·00 | 25·00 |
| D 241. | | 30 c. blue .. .. | 19·00 | 35·00 |

**1913.**

| No. | Type | Description | Unused | Used |
|---|---|---|---|---|
| D341 | D **46.** | ½ c. blue .. .. | 40 | 10 |
| D342 | | 1 c. blue .. .. | 50 | 10 |
| D343 | | 2 c. blue .. .. | 65 | 10 |
| D344 | | 4 c. blue .. .. | 85 | 30 |
| D345 | | 5 c. blue .. .. | 1·50 | 30 |
| D346 | | 10 c. blue .. .. | 3·50 | 60 |
| D347 | | 20 c. blue .. .. | 5·25 | 2·25 |
| D340 | | 30 c. blue .. .. | 9·00 | 6·50 |

**1932.**

| No. | Type | Description | Unused | Used |
|---|---|---|---|---|
| D432 | D **62.** | ½ c. orange .. .. | 10 | 10 |
| D433 | | 1 c. orange .. .. | 10 | 10 |
| D434 | | 2 c. orange .. .. | 15 | 15 |
| D435 | | 4 c. orange .. .. | 25 | 25 |
| D569 | | 5 c. orange .. | 10 | 30 |
| D570 | | 10 c. orange .. | 10 | 20 |
| D571 | | 20 c. orange .. | 15 | 20 |
| D572 | | 30 c. orange .. | 20 | 25 |
| D573 | | 50 c. orange .. | 20 | 20 |
| D574 | | $1 orange .. .. | 25 | 30 |
| D575 | | $2 orange .. .. | 40 | 40 |

暫作 欠資

(D 75.) ("Temporary-use Postage Due.")

**1940.** Optd. with Type D **75.**

| No. | Type | Description | Unused | Used |
|---|---|---|---|---|
| D 505. | **72.** | $1 brown and red .. | 2·75 | 7·50 |
| D 506. | | $2 brown and blue .. | 3·75 | 7·50 |

D 90.

D 94.

D 112.

**1944.**

| No. | Type | Description | Unused | Used |
|---|---|---|---|---|
| D 717. | D **90.** | 10 c. green .. .. | 10 | 1·00 |
| D 718. | | 20 c. blue .. .. | 10 | 1·25 |
| D 719. | | 40 c. red .. .. | 10 | 1·10 |
| D 720. | | 50 c. green .. .. | 10 | 1·10 |
| D 721. | | 60 c. blue .. .. | 15 | 2·00 |
| D 722. | | $1 red .. .. | 10 | 1·00 |
| D 723. | | $2 purple .. .. | 10 | 1·00 |

**1945.**

| No. | Type | Description | Unused | Used |
|---|---|---|---|---|
| D 752. | D **94.** | $2 red .. .. | 10 | 1·00 |
| D 753. | | $6 red .. .. | 10 | 1·00 |
| D 754. | | $8 red .. .. | 10 | 1·50 |
| D 755. | | $10 red .. .. | 10 | 1·00 |
| D 756. | | $20 red .. .. | 10 | 75 |
| D 757. | | $30 red .. .. | 10 | 50 |

**1947.**

| No. | Type | Description | Unused | Used |
|---|---|---|---|---|
| D 916. | D **112.** | $50 purple .. .. | 10 | 1·25 |
| D 917. | | $80 purple .. .. | 10 | 1·25 |
| D 918. | | $100 purple .. | 10 | 1·00 |
| D 919. | | $160 purple .. | 10 | 1·50 |
| D 920. | | $200 purple .. | 10 | 1·00 |
| D 921. | | $400 purple .. | 10 | 1·10 |
| D 922. | | $500 purple .. | 10 | 1·00 |
| D 923. | | $800 purple .. | 10 | 1·25 |
| D 924. | | $2,000 purple .. | 10 | 1·00 |

改作壹仟圓 1000.00

(D 127.)

改作欠資 金圓 壹分 1

(D 146.)

**1948.** Surch. as Type D 127.
D 993. D 94. $1,000 on $20 pur. 10 1·75
D 994. $2,000 on $30 pur. 10 1·50
D 995. $3,000 on $50 pur. 10 1·50
D 996. $4,000 on $100 pur. 10 1·75
D 997. $5,000 on $200 pur. 10 1·00
D 998. $10,000 on $300 pur. 10 40
D 999. $20,000 on $500 pur. 10 40
D 1000. $30,000 on $1,000 pur. 10 20

**1949.** Gold Yuan surcharges. Surch. as Type D 146.
D 1201. 102. 1 c. on $40 orange.. 10 7·50
D 1202. 2 c. on $40 orange.. 15 7·50
D 1203. 5 c. on $40 orange.. 10 6·00
D 1204. 10 c. on $40 orange 10 5·00
D 1205. 20 c. on $40 orange 20 5·00
D 1206. 50 c. on $40 orange 15 5·00
D 1207. $1 on $40 orange .. 15 4·00
D 1208. $2 on $40 orange .. 15 4·00
D 1209. $5 on $40 orange .. 20 4·00
D 1210. $10 on $40 orange.. 30 2·50

REGISTRATION STAMP

**1941.** Roul.
R 617. E 80. (No value) green & buff 18·00 14·00
This stamp was sold at $1·50 which included ordinary postage.

## CHINESE PROVINCES

### Manchuria

#### A. KIRIN AND HEILUNGKIANG

用貼黑吉限 (1.)

吉黑 貼用 (2.)

Stamps of China optd.

**1927.** Stamps of 1913 optd. with T 1.
1. 43. ½ c. sepia .. .. 25 25
2. 1 c. orange .. .. 60 10
3. 1½ c. purple .. .. 1·25 1·00
4. 2 c. green .. .. 1·00 45
5. 3 c. green .. .. 1·25 75
6. 4 c. olive .. .. 1·00 10
7. 5 c. mauve .. .. 1·25 30
8. 6 c. red .. .. 1·25 55
9. 7 c. violet .. .. 2·75 2·00
10. 8 c. orange .. .. 3·00 1·75
11. 10 c. blue .. .. 3·00 10
12. 44. 13 c. brown .. .. 4·25 3·50
13. 15 c. blue .. .. 4·00 1·50
14. 16 c. olive .. .. 4·50 3·25
15. 20 c. lake .. .. 4·25 2·25
16. 30 c. purple .. .. 6·00 2·75
17. 50 c. green .. .. 10·00 3·25
18. 45. $1 sepia and brown .. 24·00 5·00
19. $2 brown and blue .. 38·00 10·00
20. $5 green and red .. £140 £140

**1928.** Chang Tso-lin stamps optd. with T 2.
21. 55. 1 c. orange .. .. 1·00 1·00
22. 4 c. olive .. .. 1·50 1·00
23. 10 c. blue .. .. 3·75 3·25
24. $1 red .. .. 30·00 30·00

**1929.** Unification stamps optd. as T 2.
25. 56. 1 c. orange .. .. 1·00 1·25
26. 4 c. olive .. .. 1·75 1·75
27. 10 c. blue .. .. 10·00 4·50
28. $1 red .. .. 50·00 60·00

**1929.** Sun Yat-sen Memorial stamps optd. as T 2.
29. 57. 1 c. orange .. .. 1·00 1·00
30. 4 c. olive.. .. 1·00 1·00
31. 10 c. blue .. .. 7·00 3·00
32. $1 red .. .. 38·00 38·00

#### B. NORTH-EASTERN PROVINCES

Issues made by the Chinese Nationalist Government of Chiang Kai-shek.

1. Dr. Sun Yat-sen.

伍改 角作 用貼北東限 (2.)

**1946.** Surch. as T 2.
1. 1. 50 c. on $5 red .. .. 20 3·00
2. 50 c. on $10 green.. .. 20 3·00
3. $1 on $10 green .. .. 20 2·00
4. $2 on $20 purple .. .. 20 1·50
5. $4 on $50 brown .. .. 20 1·25

用貼北東限 (3.)

拾改 圓作 用貼北東限 (4.)

**1946.** Stamps of China optd with T 3 (="Limited for use in North East").
6 – 1 c. orange (508) .. 10 4·00
7 – 3 c. brown (511) .. 25 3·50
8 – 5 c. orange (513) .. 10 2·50
9 72 10 c. green .. .. 25 3·25
11 20 c. blue .. .. 20 3·50

**1946.** Stamps of China surch. as T 4 but larger.
14 – $5 on $50 on 21 c. sepia (No. 805) .. 35·00 55·00
15 – $10 on $100 on 28 c. olive (No. 808) .. 42·00 70·00
16 91 $20 on $200 green .. 38·00 55·00

5. Dr. Sun Yat-sen.

10⁰⁰ 拾圓 限東北貼用 (6.)

**1946.**
17. 5. 5 c. lake .. .. .. 10 2·50
18. 10 c. orange .. .. 10 2·50
19. 20 c. green .. .. 15 2·50
20. 25 c. brown .. .. 10 2·75
21. 50 c. orange .. .. 10 2·25
22. $1 blue .. .. 15 1·75
23. $2 purple .. .. 15 2·00
24. $2·50 blue .. .. 10 2·75
25. $3 brown .. .. 15 2·25
26. $4 brown .. .. 15 2·75
27. $5 green .. .. 10 2·25
28. $10 red .. .. 10 1·25
29. $20 olive .. .. 10 1·00
34. $22 black .. .. 48·00 65·00
35. $44 red .. .. 12·00 20·00
36. $50 violet .. .. 10 50
37. $65 green .. .. 50·00 75·00
38. $100 green .. .. 10 50
39. $109 green .. .. 55·00 75·00
40. $200 brown .. .. 10 1·00
41. $300 green .. .. 10 2·00
42. $500 red .. .. 10 50
43. $1,000 orange .. .. 10 20

**1946.** Nanking National Assembly stamps of China surch. as T 6.
44. 111. $2 on $20 green .. 20 2·50
45. $3 on $30 blue .. .. 25 2·50
46. $5 on $50 brown .. 25 2·50
47. $10 on $100 red .. 25 2·50

7. Pres. Chiang Kai-shek.

用貼北東限 壹佰圓 改作 100圓 (8.)

**1947.** President's 60th Birthday.
54. 7. $2 red .. .. .. 35 2·00
55. $3 green .. .. .. 60 2·00
56. $5 red .. .. .. 60 2·00
57. $10 green .. .. .. 60 2·00
58. $20 orange .. .. 70 2·00
59. $30 red .. .. .. 75 2·00

For other stamps as Types 7 and 9 but with different 3rd and 4th Chinese characters in positions shown by arrows, see China—Taiwan Types 4 and 5.

**1947.** Stamps of China surch. as T 8.
60. 107. $100 on $1,000 purple.. 60 3·25
61. $300 on $3,000 blue .. 60 3·25
62. 58. $500 on $30 brown .. 25 3·75
63. 107. $500 on $5,000 red & grn. 60 3·25

9. Entrance to Dr. Sun Yat-sen Mausoleum.

捌仟圓 改作 8000 (10.)

**1947.** 1st Anniv. of Return of Govt. to Nanking.
64. 9. $2 green .. .. .. 30 1·50
65. $4 blue .. .. .. 30 1·50
66. $6 red .. .. .. 30 1·50
67. $10 brown .. .. 30 1·50
68. $20 purple .. .. 30 1·50

**1948.** Surch. as T 10.
70. 5. $1,500 on 20 c. green .. 15 3·50
71. $3,000 on $1 blue .. 15 3·75
72. $4,000 on 25 c. brown .. 15 3·00
73. $8,000 on 50 c. orange .. 10 2·50
74. $10,000 on 10 c. orange.. 10 2·50
75. $50,000 on $109 green .. 25 2·75
76. $100,000 on $65 green .. 35 2·50
77. $500,000 on $22 black .. 50 2·75

No. 70 has five characters on the left side of the surcharge and No. 77 four characters.

MILITARY POST STAMPS

**1946.** Military Post stamp of China optd. as T 3 but larger.
M 13. M 93. (No value) red .. 2·00 14·00

郵軍 作暫 圓肆拾肆 (M 10.)

**1947.** Surch. with Type M 10.
M 69. 5. $44 on 50 c. orange .. 5·00 32·00

PARCELS POST STAMPS

P 11.

用貼北東限 伍拾萬圓 改作 (P 12.)

**1948.**
P 78. P 11. $500 red .. .. 25·00
P 79. $1,000 red .. .. 55·00
P 80. $3,000 olive.. .. 65·00
P 81. $5,000 blue .. .. 95·00
P 82. $10,000 green .. £100
P 83. $20,000 blue .. £120

**1948.** Parcels Post stamp of China surch. wtih Type P 12.
P 84. $500,000 on $5,000,000 lilac (No. P 938) .. — 90·00

Parcels Post stamps were not on sale unused.

POSTAGE DUE STAMPS

D 7.

拾改 圓作 (D 13.)

**1947.**
D 48. D 7. 10 c. blue .. .. 40 6·00
D 49. 20 c. blue .. .. 40 6·00
D 50. 50 c. blue .. .. 40 4·50
D 51. $1 blue .. .. 10 3·25
D 52. $2 blue .. .. 10 4·25
D 53. $5 blue .. .. 10 4·25

**1948.** Surch. as Type D 13.
D 85. D 7. $10 on 10 c. blue .. 10 7·00
D 86. $20 on 20 c. blue .. 10 7·00
D 87. $50 on 50 c. blue .. 10 7·00

### Sinkiang

(CHINESE TURKESTAN)

A province between Tibet and Mongolia. Issued distinguishing stamps because of its debased currency.

The following are all optd. on stamps of China.

限新省貼用 (1.)

用貼省新限 (3.)

**1915.** 1913 issue optd. with T 1.
47 43. ½ c. sepia.. .. .. 25 25
2 1 c. orange .. .. 75 10
49 1½ c. purple .. .. 1·50 1·75
3 2 c. green .. .. 1·00 45
4 3 c. green .. .. 1·00 10
5 4 c. red .. .. 1·00 45
52 4 c. grey .. .. 4·50 1·75
53 4 c. olive .. .. 2·50 75
6 5 c. mauve .. .. 1·00 40
7 6 c. grey .. .. 1·00 60
55 6 c. red .. .. 2·75 1·00
56 6 c. brown .. .. 15·00 14·00
8 7 c. violet .. .. 1·50 1·75
9 8 c. orange .. .. 2·25 1·25
10 10 c. blue .. .. 2·75 25
60 44. 13 c. brown .. .. 5·50 4·50
11 15 c. brown .. .. 3·00 2·50
61 15 c. blue .. .. 6·00 2·50
12 16 c. olive .. .. 3·25 2·50
63 20 c. lake.. .. .. 6·00 1·50
14 30 c. purple .. .. 5·50 2·50
65 50 c. green .. .. 10·00 3·50
34 45. $1 black and yellow .. 16·00 3·75
66 $1 sepia and brown .. 22·00 3·50
35 $2 black and blue .. 28·00 12·00
67 $2 brown and blue .. 26·00 8·50
36 $5 black and red .. 55·00 22·00
68 $5 green and red .. 50·00 17·00
37 $10 black and green .. £160 £150
69 $10 mauve and green .. £140 £120
38 $20 black and yellow .. £425 £425
70 $20 blue and purple .. £160 £140

**1921.** 25th Anniv. of Chinese Nat. Postal Service. Stamps optd. with T 3.
39. 48. 1 c. orange .. .. 1·25 1·50
40. 3 c. turquoise .. .. 1·25 1·50
41. 6 c. grey .. .. 2·75 2·50
42. 10 c. blue .. .. 32·00 32·00

新疆省 貼用 (4.)

**1923.** Adoption of the Constitution Stamps optd. with T 4.
43. 53. 1 c. orange .. .. 3·25 3·25
44. 3 c. turquoise .. .. 3·25 3·25
45. 4 c. red .. .. 3·25 3·25
46. 10 c. blue .. .. 4·75 4·25

新疆 貼用 (5.)

航空 (6.)

**1928.** Assumption of Title of Marshal of the Army and Navy by Chang Tso-lin. Optd. with T 5.
71. 55. 1 c. orange .. .. 1·25 1·25
72. 4 c. olive .. .. 2·00 2·25
73. 10 c. blue .. .. 5·00 5·00
74. $1 red .. .. 32·00 38·00

**1929.** Unification of China. Optd. as T 5.
75. 56. 1 c. orange .. .. 2·50 2·50
76. 4 c. olive.. .. .. 2·75 2·75
77. 10 c. blue .. .. 7·50 3·50
78. $1 red .. .. 55·00 50·00

**1929.** Sun Yat-sen State Burial. Optd. as T 5.
79. 57. 1 c. orange .. .. 1·25 1·25
80. 4 c. olive.. .. .. 2·25 2·25
81. 10 c. blue .. .. 5·50 3·25
82. $1 red .. .. 32·00 28·00

**1932.** Air. Handstamped on Sinkiang issues as T 6 ("By Air Mail").
83. 43. 5 c. mauve (No. 6) .. £225 £180
84. 10 c. blue (No. 10) .. £225 £150
85. 44. 15 c. blue (No. 61) .. £1500 £450
86. 30 c. purple (No. 14) .. £600 £600

**1932.** Dr. Sun Yat-sen stamps optd as T 3.
87 58 1 c. orange .. .. 1·00 2·25
95 2 c. olive .. .. 1·00 1·25
103 4 c. green .. .. 1·00 2·25
104 5 c. green .. .. 1·25 1·50
105 15 c. green .. .. 1·75 3·50
114 15 c. red .. .. 2·50 2·50
115 20 c. blue .. .. 2·00 75
98 25 c. blue .. .. 2·00 50
108 $1 sepia and brown .. 5·50 5·50
100 $2 brown and blue .. 13·00 13·00
101 $5 black and red .. 18·00 25·00

**1933.** Tan Yen-kai Memorial. Optd. as T 5.
117. 62. 2 c. olive .. .. 2·00 2·25
118. 5 c. green .. .. 2·50 1·25
119. 25 c. blue .. .. 6·50 3·50
120. $1 red .. .. 42·00 42·00

**1933.** Martyrs' issue optd. as T 3.
121 60. ½ c. sepia .. .. 10 1·00
122 – 1 c. orange .. .. 10 85
167 – 2 c. blue .. .. 20 2·25
123 60. 2½ c. mauve .. .. 20 1·75
124 – 3 c. brown .. .. 20 2·00
169 60. 4 c. lilac .. .. 30 2·50
125 – 8 c. orange .. .. 20 2·00
126 – 10 c. purple .. .. 20 2·00
171 – 13 c. green .. .. 35 3·25
172 – 15 c. purple .. .. 35 3·25
173 – 17 c. olive .. .. 40 3·25
137 – 20 c. lake .. .. 20 4·25
174 – 20 c. blue .. .. 40 3·00
175 – 21 c. sepia .. .. 35 3·50
185 – 25 c. purple .. .. 75 5·00
176 – 28 c. olive .. .. 45 3·25
130 – 30 c. red .. .. 25 3·25
131 – 40 c. orange .. .. 25 3·50
132 – 50 c. green .. .. 25 3·25

**1940.** Dr. Sun Yat-sen stamps optd as T 3.
139. 72. 2 c. olive .. .. 20 1·50
140. 3 c. red .. .. 25 2·25
141. 5 c. green .. .. 25 1·25
143. 8 c. olive .. .. 25 1·10
144. 10 c. green .. .. 25 1·25
145. 15 c. red .. .. 75 3·25
146. 16 c. olive .. .. 25 3·50
147. 25 c. blue .. .. 1·00 3·25
156. 30 c. red .. .. 75 2·75
158. 50 c. blue .. .. 1·00 3·00
160. $1 brown and red .. 1·25 5·00
161. $2 brown and blue .. 1·25 6·00
162. $5 green and red .. 1·50 7·50
163. $10 violet and green .. 1·50 7·50
164. $20 blue and red .. 2·50 11·00

用貼省新限 (8.)

用貼省新限 (9.)

**1942.** Air. Air stamps optd. with T 8 or larger.
187. 61. 15 c. green .. .. 2·50 7·00
197. 25 c. orange .. .. 2·50 10·00
198. 30 c. red .. .. 2·50 10·00
190. 45 c. purple .. .. 3·00 10·00
199. 50 c. brown .. .. 3·00 12·00
192. 60 c. blue .. .. 3·25 12·00
193. 90 c. olive .. .. 16·00 27·00
194. $1 green .. .. 4·25 13·00
200. $2 brown .. .. 18·00 24·00
201. $5 red .. .. 20·00 24·00

**1942.** Thrift stamps optd. as T 8.
221. 78. 8 c. green .. .. 3·25 10·00
215. 21 c. brown .. .. 2·50 10·00
216. 28 c. olive .. .. 2·50 10·00
223. 33 c. red .. .. 3·50 10·00
218. 50 c. blue .. .. 4·00 10·00
225. $1 purple .. .. 6·50 15·00

**1943.** Dr. Sun Yat-sen stamps optd. as T 3.
227. 82. 10 c. green .. .. 15 6·00
228. 20 c. olive .. .. 15 5·50
229. 25 c. purple .. .. 30 10·00
230. 30 c. red .. .. 15 6·50
231. 40 c. brown .. .. 15 6·00
232. 50 c. green .. .. 15 6·00
233. $1 red .. .. 35 5·50
234. $1 olive .. .. 25 5·00
235. $1.50 blue .. .. 25 8·00
236. $2 green .. .. 75 6·50
237. $3 yellow .. .. 35 6·50
238. $5 red .. .. 45 6·50

**1943.** Stamps optd. with T 9.
239. 72. 10 c. green .. .. 3·50 15·00
240. – 20 c. blue (No. 519) .. 3·50 14·00
241. 72. 50 c. blue .. .. 3·50 12·00

**1944.** Dr. Sun Yat-sen stamps optd. as T 3.

| No. | Type | Description | Unused | Used |
|---|---|---|---|---|
| 248 | **77.** | $4 blue .. .. .. | 80 | 10·00 |
| 249 | | $5 grey .. .. .. | 1·50 | 10·00 |
| 250 | | $10 brown .. .. | 1·50 | 10·00 |
| 251 | | $20 green .. .. | 1·00 | 10·00 |
| 243 | | $20 red .. .. .. | 2·75 | 13·00 |
| 253 | | $30 purple .. .. | 2·00 | 13·00 |
| 245 | | $40 red .. .. .. | 2·00 | 13·00 |
| 255 | | $50 blue .. .. | 3·00 | 14·00 |
| 247 | | $100 brown .. .. | 7·00 | 17·00 |

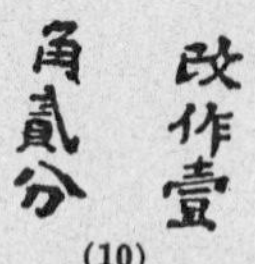

(10)

**1944.** Nos. 227 and 229 of Sinkiang surch. as T **10.**

| No. | Type | Description | Unused | Used |
|---|---|---|---|---|
| 257. | **82.** | 12 c. on 10 c. green .. | 5·00 | 20·00 |
| 258. | | 24 c. on 25 c. purple .. | 5·00 | 20·00 |

**1945.** Stamps optd. as T **3.**

| No. | Type | Description | Unused | Used |
|---|---|---|---|---|
| 259. | **89.** | 40 c. red .. .. | 35 | 16·00 |
| 260. | | $3 red .. .. .. | 35 | 14·00 |

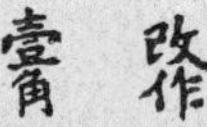

用貼疆新限

(11.)

**1949.** Silver Yuan surcharges. Sun Yat-sen issues of China surch. as T **11.**

| No. | Type | Description | Unused | Used |
|---|---|---|---|---|
| 261. | **107.** | 1 c. on $100 red (No. 889) .. .. | 4·50 | 11·00 |
| 262. | | 3 c. on $200 green (No. 890) .. .. | 4·50 | 14·00 |
| 263. | | 5 c. on $500 green (No. 891) .. .. | 5·50 | 10·00 |
| 264. | **136.** | 10 c. on $20,000 red (No. 1032) .. .. | 7·50 | 10·00 |
| 265. | | 50 c. on $4,000 grey (No. 961) .. .. | 20·00 | 20·00 |
| 266. | | $1 on $6,000 purple (No. 963) .. .. | 23·00 | 25·00 |

## Szechwan

A province of China. Issued distinguishing stamps because of its debased currency.

用貼川四限

(1.)

Stamps of China optd. with T 1.

**1933.** Issue of 1913.

| No. | Type | Description | Unused | Used |
|---|---|---|---|---|
| 1. | **43.** | 1 c. orange .. .. | 2·25 | 45 |
| 2. | | 5 c. mauve .. .. | 4·50 | 10 |
| 3. | **44.** | 50 c. green .. .. | 14·00 | 50 |

**1933.** Dr. Sun Yat Sen issue.

| No. | Type | Description | Unused | Used |
|---|---|---|---|---|
| 4. | **58.** | 2 c. olive .. .. | 1·00 | 50 |
| 5. | | 5 c. green .. .. | 1·00 | 10 |
| 6. | | 15 c. green .. .. | 2·50 | 2·75 |
| 7. | | 15 c. red .. .. | 5·00 | 7·50 |
| 8. | | 25 c. blue .. .. | 4·50 | 40 |
| 9. | | $1 sepia and brown .. | 14·00 | 2·75 |
| 10. | | $2 brown and blue .. | 30·00 | 3·75 |
| 11. | | $5 black and red .. | 60·00 | 12·00 |

**1933.** Martyrs issue (Nos. 410 etc.).

| No. | Type | Description | Unused | Used |
|---|---|---|---|---|
| 12. | **60.** | ½ c. sepia .. .. | 25 | 20 |
| 13. | – | 1 c. orange .. .. | 35 | 10 |
| 14. | **60.** | 2½ c. mauve .. .. | 85 | 50 |
| 15. | – | 3 c. brown .. .. | 1·00 | 55 |
| 16. | – | 8 c. orange .. .. | 1·25 | 75 |
| 17. | – | 10 c. purple .. .. | 1·50 | 15 |
| 18. | – | 13 c. green .. .. | 2·25 | 60 |
| 19. | – | 17 c. olive .. .. | 1·75 | 1·10 |
| 20. | – | 20 c. lake .. .. | 2·00 | 50 |
| 21. | – | 30 c. red .. .. | 2·75 | 45 |
| 22. | – | 40 c. orange .. .. | 11·00 | 85 |
| 23. | – | 50 c. green .. .. | 12·00 | 1·10 |

## Yunnan

A province of China which issued distinguishing stamps because of its debased currency.

貼 滇 用貼省滇限 用 省 用貼省滇限

(1.) (2.) (3.)

Stamps of China optd.

**1926.** Issue of 1913, optd. with T 1.

| No. | Type | Description | Unused | Used |
|---|---|---|---|---|
| 1. | **43.** | ½ c. sepia .. .. | 20 | 30 |
| 2. | | 1 c. orange .. .. | 1·00 | 10 |
| 3. | | 1½ c. purple .. .. | 1·25 | 1·25 |
| 4. | | 2 c. green .. .. | 1·50 | 40 |
| 5. | | 3 c. green .. .. | 1·75 | 40 |
| 6. | | 4 c. olive .. .. | 1·75 | 10 |
| 7. | | 5 c. mauve .. .. | 2·25 | 35 |
| 8. | | 6 c. red .. .. | 3·00 | 1·00 |
| 9. | | 7 c. violet .. .. | 4·50 | 2·50 |
| 10. | | 8 c. orange .. .. | 4·25 | 1·50 |
| 11. | | 10 c. blue .. .. | 3·75 | 10 |
| 12. | **44.** | 13 c. brown .. .. | 5·50 | 4·25 |
| 13. | | 15 c. blue .. .. | 5·00 | 1·50 |
| 14. | | 16 c. olive .. .. | 6·00 | 3·25 |
| 15. | | 20 c. lake .. .. | 5·50 | 1·75 |
| 16. | | 30 c. purple .. .. | 16·00 | 11·00 |
| 17. | | 50 c. green .. .. | 8·50 | 5·00 |
| 18. | **45.** | $1 sepia and brown .. | 22·00 | 8·50 |
| 19. | | $2 brown and blue .. | 45·00 | 14·00 |
| 20. | | $5 green and red .. | £140 | £150 |

**1929.** Unification of China. Optd. with T 2.

| No. | Type | Description | Unused | Used |
|---|---|---|---|---|
| 21. | **56.** | 1 c. orange .. .. | 1·50 | 1·50 |
| 22. | | 4 c. olive .. .. | 2·00 | 1·25 |
| 23. | | 10 c. blue .. .. | 7·50 | 2·00 |
| 24. | | $1 red .. .. .. | 65·00 | 55·00 |

**1929.** Sun Yat-sen State Burial. Optd. as T 2.

| No. | Type | Description | Unused | Used |
|---|---|---|---|---|
| 25. | **57.** | 1 c. orange .. .. | 1·50 | 1·50 |
| 26. | | 4 c. olive .. .. | 1·50 | 1·00 |
| 27. | | 10 c. blue .. .. | 5·50 | 1·50 |
| 28. | | $1 red .. .. .. | 40·00 | 40·00 |

**1932.** Dr. Sun Yat-sen stamps optd. with T 3.

| No. | Type | Description | Unused | Used |
|---|---|---|---|---|
| 29 | 58 | 1 c. orange .. .. | 75 | 75 |
| 30 | | 2 c. olive .. .. | 85 | 1·10 |
| 44 | | 4 c. green .. .. | 1·75 | 1·50 |
| 45 | | 5 c. green .. .. | 2·00 | 75 |
| 46 | | 15 c. green .. .. | 4·50 | 4·75 |
| 47 | | 15 c. red .. .. | 5·00 | 7·00 |
| 32 | | 20 c. blue .. .. | 2·50 | 85 |
| 48 | | 25 c. blue .. .. | 7·50 | 3·50 |
| 33 | | $1 sepia and brown .. | 17·00 | 16·00 |
| 34 | | $2 brown and blue .. | 35·00 | 30·00 |
| 35 | | $5 black and red .. | 85·00 | 85·00 |

**1933.** Tan Yen-kai Memorial. Optd. with T 2.

| No. | Type | Description | Unused | Used |
|---|---|---|---|---|
| 52. | **62.** | 2 c. olive .. .. | 1·75 | 2·25 |
| 53. | | 5 c. green .. .. | 2·00 | 1·00 |
| 54. | | 25 c. blue .. .. | 5·75 | 2·25 |
| 55. | | $1 red .. .. .. | 48·00 | 48·00 |

**1933.** Martyrs issue optd. as T 3.

| No. | Type | Description | Unused | Used |
|---|---|---|---|---|
| 56. | **60.** | ½ c. sepia .. .. | 65 | 1·00 |
| 57. | – | 1 c. orange .. .. | 1·25 | 20 |
| 58. | **60.** | 2½ c. mauve .. .. | 1·50 | 2·50 |
| 59. | – | 3 c. brown .. .. | 3·25 | 3·25 |
| 60. | – | 8 c. orange .. .. | 8·50 | 8·00 |
| 61. | – | 10 c. purple .. .. | 3·75 | 3·50 |
| 62. | – | 13 c. green .. .. | 3·75 | 3·75 |
| 63. | – | 17 c. olive .. .. | 3·75 | 3·75 |
| 64. | – | 20 c. lake .. .. | 4·00 | 2·00 |
| 65. | – | 30 c. red .. .. | 8·50 | 7·00 |
| 66. | – | 40 c. orange .. .. | 14·00 | 15·00 |
| 67. | – | 50 c. green .. .. | 16·00 | 7·50 |

## COMMUNIST CHINA

Issues were made by various Communist administrations from 1930 onward. These had limited local availability and are outside the scope of this catalogue. For details of such issues see Part 17.

In 1946 (North East China) and 1949 these local issues were consolidated into Regional People's Post stamps for those local administrations listed below.

### A. East China People's Post.

EC **105**. Methods of Transport.

**1949.** 7th Anniv of Shandong Communist Postal Administration.

| No. | Type | Description | Unused | Used |
|---|---|---|---|---|
| EC 322 | EC **105** | $1 green .. | 30 | 95 |
| EC 323 | | $2 green .. | 10 | 75 |
| EC 324 | | $3 red .. | 10 | 40 |
| EC 325 | | $5 brown .. | 10 | 30 |
| EC 326 | | $10 blue .. | 15 | 90 |
| EC 327 | | $13 violet .. | 10 | 70 |
| EC 328 | | $18 blue .. | 10 | 70 |
| EC 329 | | $21 red .. | 15 | 90 |
| EC 330 | | $30 green .. | 10 | 60 |
| EC 331 | | $50 red .. | 40 | 70 |
| EC 332 | | $100 green .. | 8·00 | 10·00 |

The $5 has an overprinted character obliterating a Japanese flag on the tower.

EC **106**. Train and Postal Runner.

EC **107**. Victorious Troops and Map of Battle.

**1949.** Dated " 1949.2.7.

| No. | Type | Description | Unused | Used |
|---|---|---|---|---|
| EC 333 | EC **106** | $1 green .. | 10 | 75 |
| EC 334 | | $2 green .. | 15 | 60 |
| EC 335 | | $3 red .. | 10 | 60 |
| EC 336 | | $5 brown .. | 10 | 50 |
| EC 337 | | $10 blue .. | 50 | 1·00 |
| EC 338 | | $13 violet .. | 10 | 80 |
| EC 339 | | $18 blue .. | 10 | 1·00 |
| EC 340 | | $21 red .. | 10 | 1·50 |
| EC 341 | | $30 green .. | 1·25 | 1·75 |
| EC 342 | | $50 red .. | 15 | 2·50 |
| EC 343 | | $100 green .. | 60 | 50 |

For stamps as Type EC **106**, but dated "1949", see Nos. EC 364/71.

**1949.** Victory in Huaihai Campaign.

| No. | Type | Description | Unused | Used |
|---|---|---|---|---|
| EC 344 | EC **107** | $1 green .. | 10 | 80 |
| EC 345 | | $2 green .. | 15 | 70 |
| EC 346 | | $3 red .. | 10 | 70 |
| EC 347 | | $5 brown .. | 10 | 40 |
| EC 348 | | $10 blue .. | 25 | 60 |
| EC 349 | | $13 violet .. | 10 | 80 |
| EC 350 | | $18 blue .. | 10 | 80 |
| EC 351 | | $21 red .. | 10 | 90 |
| EC 352 | | $30 green .. | 70 | 75 |
| EC 353 | | $50 red .. | 30 | 1·00 |
| EC 354 | | $100 green .. | 2·50 | 2·00 |

EC **108**. Maps of Shanghai and Nanjing.

**1949.** Liberation of Nanjing and Shanghai.

| No. | Type | Description | Unused | Used |
|---|---|---|---|---|
| EC 355 | EC **108** | $1 red .. | 10 | 1·25 |
| EC 356 | | $2 green .. | 10 | 1·00 |
| EC 357 | | $3 violet .. | 10 | 75 |
| EC 358 | | $5 brown .. | 10 | 50 |
| EC 359 | | $10 blue .. | 10 | 75 |
| EC 360 | | $30 green .. | 15 | 1·00 |
| EC 361 | | $50 red .. | 30 | 75 |
| EC 362 | | $100 green .. | 75 | 15 |
| EC 363 | | $500 orange .. | 2·00 | 75 |

**1949.** As Type EC **105** but dated "1949".

| No. | Type | Description | Unused | Used |
|---|---|---|---|---|
| EC 364 | | $10 blue .. .. | 10 | 20 |
| EC 365a | | $15 red .. .. | 10 | 20 |
| EC 366 | | $30 green .. .. | 10 | 10 |
| EC 367 | | $50 red .. .. | 10 | 10 |
| EC 368 | | $60 green .. .. | 10 | 1·50 |
| EC 369 | | $100 green .. .. | 3·50 | 75 |
| EC 370 | | $1,600 violet .. | 1·10 | 3·75 |
| EC 371 | | $2,000 purple .. | 1·10 | 3·50 |

EC **111**. Zhu De, Mao Tse-tung and Troops.

EC **112**. Mao Tse-tung.

**1949.** 22nd Anniv of Chinese People's Liberation Army.

| No. | Type | Description | Unused | Used |
|---|---|---|---|---|
| EC 378 | EC **111** | $70 orange .. | 10 | 10 |
| EC 379 | | $270 red .. | 10 | 15 |
| EC 380 | | $370 green .. | 10 | 40 |
| EC 381 | | $470 purple .. | 15 | 60 |
| EC 382 | | $570 blue .. | 10 | 45 |

For other values in this design with only three characters in bottom panel, see South West China Nos. SW9/19.

**1949.**

| No. | Type | Description | Unused | Used |
|---|---|---|---|---|
| EC 383 | EC **112** | $10 blue .. | 1·50 | 3·25 |
| EC 384 | | $15 red .. | 1·50 | 3·50 |
| EC 385 | | $70 brown .. | 10 | 35 |
| EC 386 | | $100 purple .. | 10 | 20 |
| EC 387 | | $150 orange .. | 10 | 30 |
| EC 388 | | $200 green .. | 10 | 10 |
| EC 389 | | $500 blue .. | 10 | 10 |
| EC 390 | | $1,000 red .. | 10 | 15 |
| EC 391 | | $2,000 green .. | 10 | 3·50 |

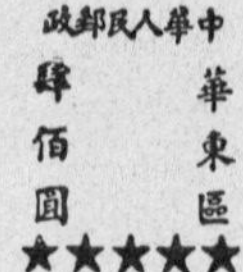

(EC **113**.)

("Chinese People's Postal Service East China Region").

**1949.** Stamps of Nationalist China surch. as Type EC **113**.

| No. | Type | Description | Unused | Used |
|---|---|---|---|---|
| EC392 | **145** | $400 on $200 red .. | 11·00 | 30 |
| EC393 | | $1,000 on $50 green | 25 | 25 |
| EC394 | | $1,200 on $100 brn | 10 | 1·75 |
| EC395 | | $1,600 on $20,000 grn | 10 | 2·25 |
| EC396 | | $2,000 on $1,000 blue | 10 | 15 |

PARCELS POST STAMPS

Stamps of Nationalist China surch.

紙印裹包 圓萬壹

政郵東華

$200 $500 $1,000

$2,000 $5,000 $10,000

(ECP **110**.)

**1949.** No. 1347 surch. as Type ECP **110**.

| No. | Type | Description | Unused | Used |
|---|---|---|---|---|
| ECP372 | **169** | $200 on $10 green | 11·00 | 8·00 |
| ECP373 | | $500 on $10 green | 12·00 | 3·75 |
| ECP374 | | $1,000 on $10 green | 13·00 | 7·00 |
| ECP375 | | $2,000 on $10 green | 20·00 | 13·00 |
| ECP376 | | $5,000 on $10 green | 32·00 | 21·00 |
| ECP377 | | $10,000 on $10 grn | 60·00 | 29·00 |

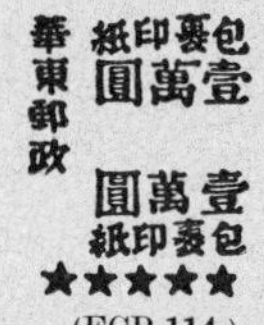

(ECP **114**.) (ECP **115**.)

**1949.** Nos. 1344/6 and unissued 10 c. surch as Type ECP **114**.

| No. | Type | Description | Unused | Used |
|---|---|---|---|---|
| ECP 397 | **169** | $5,000 on 10 c. blue | 22·00 | 19·00 |
| ECP 398 | | $10,000 on $1 orge | 40·00 | 30·00 |
| ECP 399 | | $20,000 on $2 blue | 75·00 | 65·00 |
| ECP 400 | | $50,000 on $5 red | £225 | 85·00 |

**1949.** Nos. P 711/2 and P 926/7 surch as Type ECP **115**.

| No. | Type | Description | Unused | Used |
|---|---|---|---|---|
| ECP 401 | P **90** | $5,000 on $500 green .. | 10 | 10·00 |
| ECP 402 | | $10,000 on $1,000 blue .. | 70·00 | 40·00 |
| ECP 403 | P **112** | $20,000 on $3,000 green | £110 | 75·00 |
| ECP 404 | | $50,000 on $5,000 red .. | 1·00 | 50·00 |

### B. North China People's Post.

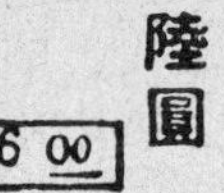

NC **68**.)

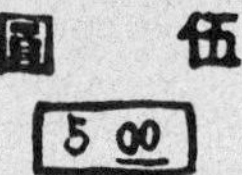

(NC **69**.)

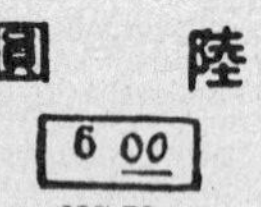

(NC **70**.)

**1949.** Surch "North China People's Postal Administration".

(a) Surch as Type NC **68**.

| No. | Type | Description | Unused | Used |
|---|---|---|---|---|
| NC 258 | | $5 on $500 orange .. | 17·00 | 15·00 |
| NC 259 | | $6 on $500 orange .. | 20·00 | 20·00 |
| NC 260 | | $12 on $200 red .. | 2·75 | 5·00 |

(b) Surch as Type NC **69**.

| No. | Type | Description | Unused | Used |
|---|---|---|---|---|
| NC 261 | | $3 on 2 (20 c.) brown .. | £180 | £120 |
| NC 262 | | $3 on 5 (50 c.) blue .. | 10·00 | 10·00 |
| NC 263 | | $5 on 2 (20 c.) brown .. | 12·00 | 10·00 |
| NC 264 | | $5 on 5 (50 c.) blue .. | £225 | £150 |

(c) Surch as Type NC **70**.

| No. | Type | Description | Unused | Used |
|---|---|---|---|---|
| NC 265 | | $1 on $60 red .. .. | 18·00 | 16·00 |
| NC 266 | | $5 on $80 purple .. | 14·00 | 12·00 |
| NC 267 | | $6 on $2 brown .. | 65·00 | 45·00 |
| NC 268 | | $6 on $40 brown .. | 15·00 | 10·00 |
| NC 269 | | $6 on $80 purple .. | £325 | £250 |

NC **71**. Infantry.

NC **72**. Industry.

**1948.** Imperf.

| No. | Type | Description | Unused | Used |
|---|---|---|---|---|
| NC 270 | NC **71** | 50 c. purple .. | 35 | 80 |
| NC 271 | | $1 blue .. | 4·50 | 7·00 |
| NC 272 | | $2 green .. | 60 | 1·50 |
| NC 273 | | $3 violet .. | 15 | 1·10 |
| NC 274 | | $5 brown .. | 50 | 1·25 |
| NC 275 | NC **72** | $6 purple .. | 30 | 1·00 |
| NC 276 | NC **71** | $10 green .. | 50 | 1·75 |
| NC 277 | | $12 red .. | 1·10 | 1·50 |

The 50 c. and $6 have value in Chinese characters only.

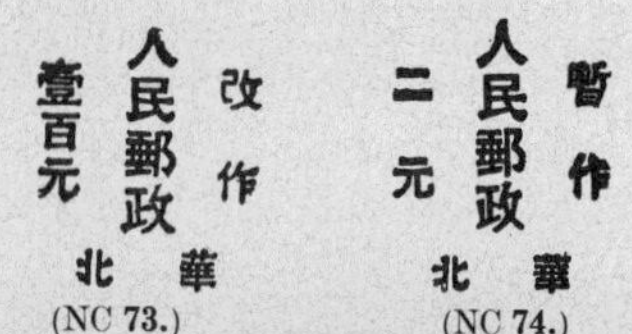

(NC **73**.) (NC **74**.)

("People's Postal Service North China.")

**1949.** Surch as Type NC **73**.

(a) On stamp of Nationalist China.

| | | | | |
|---|---|---|---|---|
| NC 278 | **107** | $100* on $100 red .. | 10·00 | 50 |

(b) On stamps of North Eastern Provinces.

| | | | | |
|---|---|---|---|---|
| NC 279 | **5** | 50 c. on 5 c. red .. | 40 | 3·50 |
| NC 280 | | $1 on 10 c. orange .. | 40 | 1·00 |
| NC 281 | | $2 on 20 c. green .. | 25·00 | 2·50 |
| NC 282 | | $3 on 50 c. orange .. | 20 | 3·00 |
| NC 283 | | $4 on $5 green .. | 3·25 | 2·75 |
| NC 284 | | $6 on $10 red .. | 50 | 1·00 |
| NC 285 | | $10 on $300 green .. | 2·25 | 2·50 |
| NC 286 | | $12 on $1 blue .. | 1·00 | 1·50 |
| NC 287 | | $18 on $3 brown .. | 1·50 | 1·00 |
| NC 288 | | $20* on 50 c. orange | 1·00 | 75 |
| NC 290 | | $20 on $20 green .. | 1·10 | 80 |
| NC 291 | | $30 on $2.50 blue .. | 1·50 | 1·50 |
| NC 292 | | $40 on 25 c. brown | 1·50 | 1·50 |
| NC 293 | | $50 on $109 green .. | 3·50 | 1·50 |
| NC 294 | | $80* on $1 blue .. | 6·00 | 1·00 |
| NC 295 | | $100 on $65 green .. | 7·00 | 1·75 |

**1949.** Surch as Type NC **74**.

(a) On stamps of Nationalist China.

| | | | | |
|---|---|---|---|---|
| NC 296 | **107** | $100* on $100 red | 22·00 | 6·00 |
| NC 297 | | $300* on $700 brn | 7·50 | 2·50 |
| NC 298 | **118** | $500* on $500 green | 5·00 | 1·00 |
| NC 299 | | $3,000* on $3,000 bl | 7·50 | 2·00 |

(b) On stamps of North Eastern Provinces.

| | | | | |
|---|---|---|---|---|
| NC 300a | **5** | $1* on 25 c. brown | 10 | 1·00 |
| NC 301 | | $2 on 20 c. green .. | 1·50 | 1·25 |
| NC 302 | | $3 on 50 c. orange | 15 | 1·00 |
| NC 303 | | $4 on $5 green .. | 1·50 | 1·75 |
| NC 305 | | $6 on $10 red .. | 1·50 | 1·00 |
| NC 306 | | $10* on $300 green | 8·50 | 2·25 |
| NC 307 | | $12 on $1 blue .. | 70 | 70 |
| NC 308 | | $20* on 50 c. orange | 8·00 | 1·50 |
| NC 309 | | $20* on $20 green | 4·00 | 60 |
| NC 310 | | $40* on 25 c. brown | 5·50 | 90 |
| NC 311 | | $50* on $109 green | 8·00 | 1·00 |
| NC 312 | | $80* on $1 blue .. | 5·00 | 1·00 |

*On these stamps the bottom character in the left-hand column of overprints is square in shape.

NC 75.

**1949.** Labour Day. Perf. or imperf.

| | | | | |
|---|---|---|---|---|
| NC 313 | NC **75** | $20 red .. | 1·50 | 1·75 |
| NC 314 | | $40 blue .. | 1·50 | 1·75 |
| NC 315 | | $60 brown .. | 1·50 | 2·25 |
| NC 316 | | $80 green .. | 1·75 | 2·25 |
| NC 317 | | $100 violet .. | 2·00 | 2·25 |

NC **79**. Mao Tse-tung. NC **80**.

**1949.** 28th Anniv of Chinese Communist Party. Perf. or imperf.

| | | | | |
|---|---|---|---|---|
| NC 327A | NC **79** | $10 red .. | 40 | 1·00 |
| NC 328A | NC **80** | $20 blue .. | 20 | 75 |
| NC 329A | NC **79** | $50 orange .. | 1·00 | 1·50 |
| NC 330A | NC **80** | $80 green .. | 20 | 75 |
| NC 331A | NC **79** | $100 violet .. | 1·25 | 1·50 |
| NC 332A | NC **80** | $120 green .. | 20 | 1·00 |
| NC 333A | NC **79** | $140 purple .. | 1·50 | 1·75 |

政郵民人
暫 拾 華
用 圓 北

(NC **81**.)

("People's Postal Service North China").

**1949.** Surch as Type NC **81**.

(a) On stamp of Nationalist China.

| | | | | |
|---|---|---|---|---|
| NC 334 | **118** | $10 on $7,000 brn | 10·00 | 5·00 |

(b) On stamps of North Eastern Provinces.

| | | | | |
|---|---|---|---|---|
| NC 336 | **5** | $10 on $10 red .. | 4·50 | 1·25 |
| NC 337 | | $30 on 20 c. green | 3·50 | 1·50 |
| NC 338 | | $50 on $44 red .. | 3·00 | 25 |
| NC 339 | | $100 on $3 brown | 6·00 | 1·50 |
| NC 341 | | $200 on $4 brown | 15·00 | 7·00 |

NC **83**. Gate of Heavenly Peace, Peking. NC **84**. Field Workers and Factory.

**1949**.

| | | | | |
|---|---|---|---|---|
| NC 349 | NC **83** | $50 orange .. | 1·25 | 5·50 |
| NC 350 | | $100 red .. | 10 | 30 |
| NC 351 | | $200 green .. | 75 | 35 |
| NC 352 | | $300 purple .. | 3·50 | 70 |
| NC 353 | | $400 blue .. | 3·50 | 70 |
| NC 354 | | $500 brown .. | 4·50 | 60 |
| NC 355 | | $700 violet .. | 2·00 | 1·50 |

**1949**.

| | | | | |
|---|---|---|---|---|
| NC 356 | NC **84** | $1,000 orange .. | 2·50 | 60 |
| NC 357 | | $3,000 blue .. | 10 | 90 |
| NC 358 | | $5,000 red .. | 10 | 10 |
| NC 359 | | $10,000 brown .. | 15 | 1·75 |

PARCELS POST STAMPS

Stamps of Nationalist China surch.

政郵民人
元百捌
北華

(NCP **76**.)

**1949.** Surch as Type NCP **76**.

| | | | | |
|---|---|---|---|---|
| NCP 318 | P **112** | $300 on $6,000,000 grey .. | — | 28·00 |
| NCP 319 | | $400 on $8,000,000 red | — | 28·00 |
| NCP 320 | | $500 on $10,000,000 green .. | — | 30·00 |
| NCP 321 | | $800 on $5,000,000 lilac .. | — | 30·00 |
| NCP 322 | | $1,000 on $3,000,000 blue .. | — | 35·00 |

NC **77**. Pagoda.

政郵民人
紙印褰包
元 六
北 華

(NCP **78**.)

**1949.** Money Order stamps. Type NC **77** surch as Type NCP **78**.

| | | | | |
|---|---|---|---|---|
| NCP 323 | | $6 on $5 red .. | 4·50 | 2·25 |
| NCP 324 | | $6 on $50 grey .. | 5·00 | 2·25 |
| NCP 325 | | $50 on $20 purple .. | 5·50 | 2·00 |
| NCP 326 | | $100 on $10 green .. | 8·50 | 4·25 |

NCP **82**. Railway Trains.

**1949**.

| | | | | |
|---|---|---|---|---|
| NCP 342 | NCP **82** | $500 red .. | 1·00 | 5·50 |
| NCP 343 | | $1,000 blue | 35·00 | 25·00 |
| NCP 344 | | $2,000 green | 35·00 | 25·00 |
| NCP 345 | | $5,000 green | 50·00 | 45·00 |
| NCP 346 | | $10,000 orange | £110 | 90·00 |
| NCP 347 | | $20,000 red .. | £200 | £180 |
| NCP 348 | | $50,000 purple | £425 | £350 |

## C. Port Arthur and Dairen

The Soviet Union obtained facilities in these two ports by treaty in 1945. The Chinese Communists retained the civil administration, but a separate postal authority was established.

(NE **6**.)

政郵寧遼
拾暫
壹
圓作
念記收接一四
節働勞一五

(NE **7**.)

七 七
念紀戰抗
拾 暫
伍
圓 作

(NE **8**.)

**1946.** Stamps of Japan handstamped "Liaoning Posts" and new value at Type NE **6**.

| | | | | |
|---|---|---|---|---|
| NE8 | | 20 c. on 3 s. green (No. 316) .. .. | 6·00 | 8·00 |
| NE9 | | $1 on 17 s. violet (No. 402) .. .. | 6·00 | 7·00 |
| NE11 | | $5 on 6 s. red (No. 242) | 7·00 | 12·00 |
| NE12 | | $5 on 6 s. orange (No. 319) .. | 6·50 | 7·00 |
| NE13 | | $15 on 40 s. purple (No. 406) .. .. | 32·00 | 30·00 |

**1946.** Transfer of Administration on 1 April and Labour Day. Stamps of Manchukuo handstamped as Type NE **7**.

| | | | | |
|---|---|---|---|---|
| NE 14 | **19** | $1 on 1 f. red .. | 5·00 | 5·00 |
| NE 15 | – | $5 on 4 f. green (No. 84) .. .. | 7·00 | 9·00 |
| NE 16 | **20** | $15 on 30 f. brown | 16·00 | 20·00 |

**1946.** 9th Anniv of Outbreak of War with Japan. Stamps of Manchukuo surch as Type NE **8**.

| | | | | |
|---|---|---|---|---|
| NE 17 | | $1 on 6 f. red (No. 86) | 4·50 | 7·50 |
| NE 18 | | $5 on 2 f. green (No. 82) .. .. .. | 15·00 | 20·00 |
| NE 19 | | $15 on 12 f. orange (No. 90) .. .. .. | 25·00 | 30·00 |

復光國民華中
念紀年週一
壹 暫
圓 作
五 一•八

(NE **9**.)

國民華中
念紀節十雙
壹 暫
圓 作

(NE **10**.)

**1946.** 1st Anniv of Japanese Surrender. Stamps of Manchukuo surch as Type NE **9**.

| | | | | |
|---|---|---|---|---|
| NE 20 | – | $1 on 12 f. orange (No. 90) .. .. | 8·00 | 9·00 |
| NE 21 | **19** | $5 on 1 f. red .. | 16·00 | 18·00 |
| NE 22 | **13** | $15 on 5 f. black .. | 32·00 | 30·00 |

**1946.** 35th Anniv of Chinese Revolution. Stamps of Manchukuo surch as Type NE **10**.

| | | | | |
|---|---|---|---|---|
| NE 23 | | $1 on 6 f. red (No. 86) | 7·00 | 8·00 |
| NE 24 | | $5 on 12 f. orge (No. 90) | 16·00 | 16·00 |
| NE 25 | | $15 on 2 f. grn (No. 82) | 32·00 | 32·00 |

國民華中
世逝迅魯
念紀年週十
五 暫
圓 作

(NE **11**.)

建聯蘇祝慶
十二第節軍
念紀年週九
五 暫
圓 作

(NE **12**.)

**1946.** 10th Death Anniv of Lu Xun (author). Stamps of Manchukuo surch as Type NE **11**.

| | | | | |
|---|---|---|---|---|
| NE 26 | **19** | $1 on 1 f. red .. | 18·00 | 15·00 |
| NE 27 | – | $5 on 6 f. red (No. 86) .. .. | 25·00 | 30·00 |
| NE 28 | – | $15 on 12 f. orange (No. 90) .. .. | 40·00 | 45·00 |

**1947.** 29th Anniv of Red Army. Stamps of Manchukuo surch as Type NE **12**.

| | | | | |
|---|---|---|---|---|
| NE 29 | – | $1 on 2 f. green (No. 82) | 20·00 | 20·00 |
| NE 30 | – | $5 on 6 f. red (No. 86) .. .. | 35·00 | 35·00 |
| NE 31 | **13** | $15 on 13 f. brown | £110 | £130 |

國 中
政郵東關
五暫
念 紀
圓作
節動勞一五

(NE **13**.)

政郵東關國中
貳 暫
拾
圓 作

(NE **14**.)

**1947.** Labour Day. Stamps of Manchukuo surch as Type NE **13**.

| | | | | |
|---|---|---|---|---|
| NE 32 | – | $1 on 2 f. green (No. 82) .. .. | 8·00 | 8·00 |
| NE 33 | – | $5 on 6 f. red (No. 86) .. .. | 20·00 | 20·00 |
| NE 34 | **20** | $15 on 30 f. brown | 40·00 | 45·00 |

**1947.** Stamps of Manchukuo surch. "Guandong Postal Service, China" and new value as Type NE **14**.

| | | | | |
|---|---|---|---|---|
| NE 35 | – | $5 on 2 f. green (No. 82) .. .. | 20·00 | 20·00 |
| NE 36 | – | $15 on 4 f. green (No. 84) .. | 30·00 | 20·00 |
| NE 37 | **20** | $20 on 30 f. brown | 38·00 | 38·00 |

(NE **15**.)

政郵東關
五 暫
拾
圓 作

(NE **16**.)

**1948.** 30th Anniv of Red Army. Surch as on Type NE **15**.

(a) On stamps of Manchukuo.

| | | | | |
|---|---|---|---|---|
| NE 39 | | $10 on 2 f. grn (No. 82) | 50·00 | 50·00 |
| NE 40 | | $20 on 6 f. red (No. 86) | 75·00 | 75·00 |

(b) On label (Type NE **15**) commemorating 2,600th Anniv of Japanese Empire.

| | | | | |
|---|---|---|---|---|
| NE 41 | | $100 on (no value) blue and brown .. .. | £275 | £275 |

**1948.** Stamps of Manchukuo surch. "Guangdong Postal Administration" and new value as Type NE **16**.

| | | | | |
|---|---|---|---|---|
| NE 42 | | $20 on 2 f. grn (No. 82) | £100 | £100 |
| NE 43 | | $50 on 4 f. grn (No. 84) | £200 | £180 |
| NE 44 | | $100 on 20 f. brown (No. 152) .. .. | £275 | £225 |

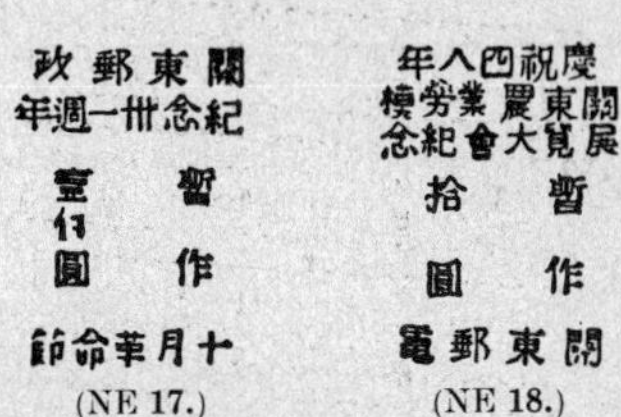


(NE **17**.) (NE **18**.)

**1948.** 31st Anniv. of Russian October Revolution. Stamps of Manchukuo surch as Type NE **17**.

| | | | | |
|---|---|---|---|---|
| NE 45 | **19** | $10 on 1 f. red .. | £120 | £120 |
| NE 46 | – | $50 on 2 f. green (No. 82) .. | £225 | £225 |
| NE 47 | – | $100 on 4 f. green (No. 84) .. .. | £325 | £325 |

**1948.** Guangdong Agricultural and Industrial Exhibition Stamps of Manchukuo surch as Type NE **18**.

| | | | | |
|---|---|---|---|---|
| NE 48 | | $10 on 2 f. grn (No. 82) | £180 | £150 |
| NE 49 | | $50 on 20 f. brown (No. 95) .. .. | £750 | £550 |

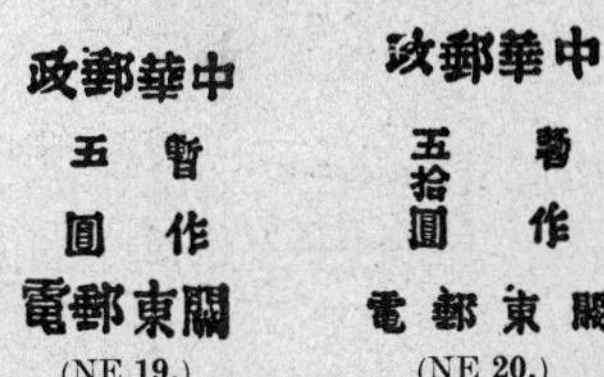


(NE **19**.) (NE **20**.)

**1948.** Stamps of Japan and Manchukuo surch "Chinese Postal Administration: Guangdong Posts and Telegraphs" and new values.

(a) No. 319 of Japan surch with Type NE **19**.

| | | | | |
|---|---|---|---|---|
| NE 50 | | $5 on 3 s. green .. | 32·00 | 20·00 |

(b) Stamps of Manchukuo surch as Type NE **19**.

| | | | | |
|---|---|---|---|---|
| NE 51 | | $10 on 1 f. red (No. 80) | 75·00 | 50·00 |
| NE 52 | | $50 on 2 f. grn (No. 82) | £200 | £130 |
| NE 53 | | $100 on 4 f. green (No. 84) .. .. .. | £300 | £225 |

(c) Stamps of Manchukuo surch as Type NE **20**.

| | | | | |
|---|---|---|---|---|
| NE 54 | | $10 on 2 f. grn (No. 82) | 85·00 | 50·00 |
| NE 55 | | $50 on 1 f. red (No. 80) | £100 | 70·00 |

NE **21**. Peasant and Artisan.

NE **23**. Dalian Port.

**1949**.

| | | | | |
|---|---|---|---|---|
| NE 56 | NE **21** | $5 green .. | 1·00 | 8·00 |
| NE 57 | – | $10 orange .. | 12·00 | 15·00 |
| NE 58 | NE **23** | $50 red .. | 10·00 | 12·00 |

DESIGN—VERT. $10, "Transport".

For designs as Type NE **23** but with different characters in bottom panel, see No. NE62.

NE 24. "Labour". NE 25. Mao Tse-tung.

**1949.** Labour Day.
NE 59 NE 24 $10 red .. .. 7·50 10·00

**1949.** 28th Anniv of Chinese Communist Party.
NE 61 NE 25 $50 red .. .. 18·00 22·00

**1949.** Bottom panel inscr. "Lushuan and Dalian Post and Telegraphic Administration".
NE 62 NE 23 $50 red .. .. 15·00 15·00

NE 27. Heroes' Monument, Dalian.

**1949.** 4th Anniv of Victory over Japan and Opening of Dalian Industrial Fair.
NE 63 NE 27 $10 red, blue and light blue .. 32·00 35·00
NE 64 $10 red, blue and green .. .. 8·00 11·00

暫作 柒圓 (NE 28.) 暫作 伍拾圓 (NE 29.) 暫作 伍佰圓 (NE 30.)

**1949.** Nos. NE 56/7 surch as Types NE 28/30.
NE 65 NE 28 $7 on $5 green 11·00 10·00
NE 66 NE 29 $50 on $5 green 38·00 35·00
NE 67 $100 on $10 orge £190 £190
NE 68 NE 30 $500 on $5 green £500
NE 70 $500 on $10 orge £325 £250

NE 31. Acclamation of Mao Tse-tung.

**1949.** Founding of Chinese People's Republic.
NE 71 NE 31 $35 red, yell & bl 11·00 14·00

NE 32. Stalin and Lenin.

**1949.** 32nd Anniv of Russian October Revolution.
NE 72 NE 32 $10 green .. 6·50 9·00

NE 33. Iosef Stalin. NE 34. Gate of Heavenly Peace, Peking.

**1949.** Stalin's 70th Birthday.
NE 73 NE 33 $20 purple .. 13·00 18·00
NE 74 $35 red .. .. 13·00 18·00

**1950.**
NE 75 NE 34 $10 blue .. 4·50 4·50
NE 76 $20 green .. 24·00 10·00
NE 77 $35 red .. .. 75 3·50
NE 78 $50 lilac .. 1·25 3·50
NE 79 $100 mauve .. 75 9·50

All Soviet forces were withdrawn by 26 May 1955 and the stamps of the Chinese People's Republic are now in use.

## D. North–East China People's Post.

NE 48. Mao Tse-tung. NE 49.

**1946.**
NE 133 NE 48 $1 violet .. 4·75 6·00
NE 134 NE 49 $2 red .. 1·00 2·75
NE 135 $5 orange .. 1·50 2·75
NE 136 $10 blue .. 1·00 2·75

NE 50. Map of China with Communist Lion, Japanese Wolf and Chiang Kai-shek. NE 51. Railwaymen.

**1946.** 10th Anniv of Seizure of Chiang Kai-shek at Xi'an.
NE 137 NE 50 $1 violet .. 25 3·50
NE 138 $2 orange .. 25 3·50
NE 139 $5 brown .. 2·50 5·50
NE 140 $10 green .. 6·50 8·00

**1947.** 24th Anniv of Massacre of Strikers at Zhengzhou Station.
NE 141 NE 51 $1 red .. 70 2·00
NE 142 $2 green .. 80 2·00
NE 143 $5 red .. 80 2·00
NE 144 $10 green .. 2·50 4·00

NE 52. Women Cheering.

東北 郵政 (NE 53.)

**1947.** Int. Women's Day.
NE 145 NE 52 $5 red .. 25 3·50
NE 146 $10 brown .. 25 3·50

**1947.** Optd with Type NE 53 ("North East Postal Service").
NE 147 NE 53 $5 red .. 3·25 4·50
NE 148 $10 brown .. 3·25 4·50

NE 54. Children's Troop-comforts Unit. NE 55. Peasant and Workman.

**1947.** Children's Day.
NE 149 NE 54 $5 red .. 1·50 3·50
NE 150 $10 green .. 1·50 3·75
NE 151 $30 orange .. 2·50 4·75

**1947.** Labour Day.
NE 152 NE 55 $10 red .. 50 2·50
NE 153 $30 blue .. 1·00 2·50
NE 154 $50 green .. 1·25 2·50

NE 56. "Freedom".

改作 伍拾圓 $50^{00}$ (NE 57.)

**1947.** 28th Anniv of Students' Rebellion, Peking University.
NE 155 NE 56 $10 green .. 1·50 3·25
NE 156 $30 brown .. 1·50 3·25
NE 157 $50 violet .. 1·50 3·25

**1947.** Surch as Type NE 57.
NE 158 NE 48 $50 on $1 vio 12·00 14·00
NE 159 NE 49 $50 on $2red 12·00 14·00
NE 160b NE 48 $100 on $1 vio 12·00 15·00
NE 161 NE 49 $100 on $2 red 12·00 15·00

NE 58. Youths with Banner.

**1947.** 22nd Anniv of Nanjing Road Incident, Shanghai.
NE 162 NE 58 $2 red & mauve 75 2·50
NE 163 $5 red & green 75 2·50
NE 164 $10 red & yell 1·00 2·50
NE 165 $20 red & vio 1·00 2·50
NE 166 $30 red & brn 1·75 3·00
NE 167 $50 red & blue 2·75 3·50
NE 168 $100 red & brn 3·75 5·00

NE 59. Mao Tse-tung.

**1947.** 26th Anniv of Chinese Communist Party.
NE 170 NE 59 $10 red .. 2·50 6·50
NE 171 $30 mauve .. 2·75 6·75
NE 172 $50 purple .. 5·00 7·00
NE 173 $100 red .. 7·50 9·00

NE 60. Hand grasping rifle. NE 61. Mountains and River.

**1947.** 10th Anniv of Outbreak of War with Japan.
NE 174 NE 60 $10 orange .. 2·50 5·50
NE 175 $30 green .. 2·50 5·50
NE 176 $50 blue .. 3·00 5·50
NE 177 $100 brown .. 3·50 5·50

**1947.** 2nd Anniv of Japanese Surrender.
NE 179 NE 61 $10 brown .. 4·75 8·00
NE 180 $30 green .. 4·75 8·00
NE 181 $50 green .. 2·50 8·00
NE 182 $100 brown .. 7·50 8·00

改作 拾圓 $10^{00}$ (NE 62.)

NE 63. Map of Manchuria.

**1947.** Surch as Type NE 62.
NE 183 NE 48 $5 on $1 violet 12·00 20·00
NE 184 NE 49 $10 on $2 red 12·00 20·00

**1947.** 16th Anniv of Japanese Attack on Manchuria.
NE 185 NE 63 $10 green .. 4·00 7·50
NE 186 $20 mauve .. 2·50 7·50
NE 187 $30 brown .. 1·00 7·50
NE 188 $50 red .. 7·00 7·50

NE 64. Mao Tse-tung. NE 65. Offices of N.E. Political Council.

**1947.**
NE 189 NE 64 $1 purple .. 1·50 6·00
NE 190 $5 green .. 2·00 6·00
NE 191 $10 green .. 7·00 12·00
NE 192 $15 violet .. 3·25 10·00
NE 193 $20 red .. 20 3·50
NE 194 $30 green .. 10 3·50
NE 195 $50 brown .. 9·50 13·00
NE 213 $50 green .. 50 3·00
NE 196 $90 blue .. 50 10·00
NE 197 $100 red .. 10 5·00
NE 215 $150 red .. 1·00 4·50
NE 214 $250 lilac .. 30 4·25
NE 228 $300 green .. 25·00 32·00
NE 198 $500 orange .. 6·00 6·50
NE 229 $1,000 yellow 40 2·50

For stamps as Type NE 64 but with "YUAN" in top right tablet, see Nos. NE 236/40.

**1947.** 35th Anniv of Chinese Republic.
NE 199 NE 65 $10 yellow .. 10·00 22·00
NE 200 $20 red .. 10·00 22·00
NE 201 $100 brown .. 38·00 35·00

NE 66. NE 67. Tomb of Gen. Li Zhaolin.

**1947.** 11th Anniv of Seizure of Chiang Kai-shek at Xi'an.
NE 202 NE 66 $30 red .. 2·00 10·00
NE 203 $90 blue .. 4·50 12·00
NE 204 $150 green .. 5·00 12·00

**1948.** 2nd Death Anniv of Gen. Li Zhaolin.
NE 205 NE 67 $30 green .. 7·00 12·00
NE 206 $150 lilac .. 9·00 12·00

NE 68. Flag and Globe. NE 69. Youth with Torch.

**1948.** Labour Day.
NE 207 NE 68 $50 red .. 2·25 10·00
NE 208 $150 green .. 1·00 12·00
NE 209 $250 violet .. 50 20·00

**1948.** Youth Day.
NE 210 NE 69 $50 green .. 5·00 10·00
NE 211 $150 brown .. 7·00 10·00
NE 212 $250 red .. 9·00 13·00

改作 壹佰圓 $100^{00}$ (NE 70.)

NE 71. Crane Operator.

**1948.** Surch as Type NE 70.
NE217a NE 64 $100 on $1 pur 15·00 18·00
NE218 $100 on $15 vio 12·00 15·00
NE219 $300 on $5 grn 15·00 20·00
NE220 $300 on $30 grn 5·00 12·00
NE221 $300 on $90 bl 5·00 12·00
NE230 NE 49 $500 on $2 red 4·50 7·50
NE222 NE 64 $500 on $50 grn 6·50 13·00
NE231 NE 49 $1,500 on $5 orange .. 4·50 7·50
NE 223 NE 64 $1,500 on $150 red .. 6·00 15·00
NE 232 NE 49 $2,500 on $10 bl 4·50 7·50
NE 224 NE 64 $2,500 on $300 green .. 5·50 15·00

**1948.** All-China Labour Conference.
NE 225 NE 71 $100 red & pink 25 2·50
NE 226 $300 brn & yell 2·00 4·50
NE 227 $500 blue & grn 75 2·50

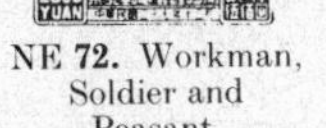
NE 72. Workman, Soldier and Peasant.

NE 74. "Production in Field and Industry".

**1948.** Liberation of the North East.
NE 233 NE 72 $500 red .. 3·00 5·50
NE 234 $1,500 green .. 4·50 7·50
NE 235 $2,500 brown .. 9·00 10·00

**1949.** As Type NE 64 but "YUAN" at top right.
NE 236 $300 green .. .. 1·00 3·50
NE 237 $500 orange .. 1·50 2·50
NE 238 $1,500 green .. 10 2·50
NE 239 $4,500 brown .. 10 2·75
NE 240 $6,500 blue .. .. 10 3·25

**1949.**
NE 241 NE 74 $5,000 blue .. 2·50 5·50
NE 242 $10,000 orange 10 4·00
NE 243 $50,000 green 10 5·00
NE 244 $100,000 violet 10 11·00

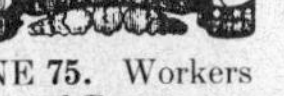
NE 75. Workers and Banners.

NE 76. Workers' Procession.

**1949.** Labour Day.
NE 245 NE 75 $1,000 red & bl 10 1·50
NE 246 $1,500 red & bl 10 1·50
NE 247 $4,500 red & brn 15 1·50
NE 248 $6,500 brn & grn 20 1·50
NE 249 $10,000 pur & bl 70 1·50

**1949.** 28th Anniv of Chinese Communist Party.
NE 250 NE 76 $1,500 red, violet & blue 10 1·50
NE 251 $4,500 red, brown & blue 20 1·50
NE 252 $6,500 red, pink and blue .. 80 1·50

NE 77. North-East Heroes, Monument.

NE 78. Factory.

**1949.** 4th Anniv of Japanese Surrender.
NE 253 NE 77 $1,500 red .. 20 1·50
NE 254 $4,500 green .. 75 1·50
NE 255 $6,500 blue .. 85 1·50

**REPRINTS.** The note above No. 1401 of China also refers here to Nos. NE 257/60, 261/3, 271/4, 286/89 and 312/4.

**1949.**
NE 256 NE 78 $1,500 red .. 20 1·75

**1949.** 1st Session of Chinese People's Political Conference. As T **181** of People's Republic but with additional inscr.
NE 257 $1,000 blue .. .. 3·00 5·00
NE 258 $1,500 red .. .. 3·00 5·00
NE 259 $3,000 green .. 3·00 5·00
NE 260 $4,500 purple .. 3·00 5·00

**1949.** World Federation of Trade Unions, Asiatic and Australasian Conference, Peking. As Type **182** of People's Republic but with additional inscr.
NE 261 $5,000 red .. .. 25·00 25·00
NE 262 $20,000 green .. 28·00 25·00
NE 263 $35,000 blue .. 42·00 35·00

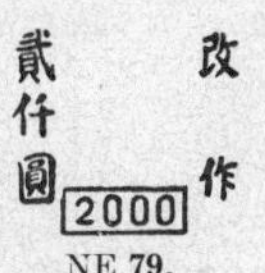
NE 79.

**1949.** Surch as Type NE 79.
NE 264 NE 64 $2,000 on $300 green .. 3·50 6·50
NE 265 $2,000 on $4,500 brown .. 28·00 28·00
NE 266 $2,500 on $1,500 green .. 20 5·00
NE 267 $2,500 on $6,500 blue .. 12·00 15·00
NE 268 NE 78 $5,000 on $1,500 red .. 30 2·50
NE 269 NE 64 $20,000 on $4,500 brown 10 3·50
NE 270 $35,000 on $300 green .. 10 3·50

**1950.** Chinese People's Political Conference As Type **183/4** of People's Republic but with additional inscr.
NE 271 $1,000 red .. .. 5·00 6·00
NE 272 $1,500 blue .. .. 5·00 6·00
NE 273 $5,000 purple .. 5·00 6·00
NE 274 $20,000 green .. 5·00 6·00

**1950.** As T **185** of People's Republic but with additional four-character inscr.
NE303 **185** $250 brown .. 10 5·00
NE275 $500 green .. 10 2·00
NE276 $1,000 orange .. 10 1·25
NE277 $1,000 mauve .. 10 2·00
NE306 $2,000 green .. 10 2·00
NE307 $2,500 yellow .. 10 2·00
NE300 $5,000 orange .. 60 90
NE309 $10,000 brown .. 15 2·00
NE310 $12,500 purple .. 20 6·00
NE283 $20,000 purple .. 20 2·00
NE301 $30,000 red .. 90 4·50
NE284 $35,000 blue .. 25 4·50
NE285 $50,000 green .. 1·75 4·50
NE302 $100,000 violet .. 30 4·50

**1950.** Foundation of People's Republic. Additional inscr. at left.
NE 286 **188** $5,000 red, yellow and green .. 10·00 11·00
NE 287 $10,000 red, yellow and brown .. 10·00 11·00
NE 288 $20,000 red, yellow and purple .. 13·00 14·00
NE 289 $30,000 red, yellow and blue .. 15·00 16·00

**1950.** Peace Campaign. Additional characters below olive branch.
NE 290 **191** $2,500 brown .. 4·00 5·50
NE 291 $5,000 green .. 4·50 4·50
NE 292 $20,000 blue .. 5·00 5·50

**1950.** 1st Anniv of People's Republic. Additional characters at left. Flag in red, yellow and brown.
NE 293 **193** $1,000 violet .. 5·50 8·00
NE 294 $2,500 brown .. 5·50 8·00
NE 295 $5,000 green (44 × 53 mm) .. 7·50 6·50
NE 296 $10,000 green .. 10·00 10·00
NE 297 $20,000 blue .. 13·00 13·00

**1950.** 1st All-China Postal Conference. Additional characters at left.
NE 298 **194** $2,500 brn & grn 3·50 4·75
NE 299 $5,000 grn & red 3·50 3·75

**1950.** Sino-Soviet Treaty. Additional characters in top right-hand coner.
NE 312 **195** $2,500 red .. 5·50 7·50
NE 313 $5,000 green .. 5·50 5·00
NE 314 $20,000 blue .. 8·00 10·00

PARCELS POST STAMPS

NEP 82.

**1951.** Type NEP 82.
NEP 315A $1,000,000 violet .. 25·00
NEP 316B $300,000 purple .. 65·00
NEP 317B $500,000 green .. £110
NEP 318B $1,000,000 red .. £200

## E. North-West China People's Post.

NW 25. Mao Tse-tung.

NW 26. Great Wall.

**1949.** Imperf.
NW 97 NW 25 $50 pink .. 1·75 3·25
NW 98 NW 26 $100 blue .. 10 50
NW 99 NW 25 $200 orange .. 2·50 3·75
NW 100 NW 26 $400 brown .. 1·75 2·00

## F. South-West China People's Post.

SW 3. Zhu De, Mao Tse-tung and Troops.

SW 4. Map of China with Flag in S.W.

**1949.**
SW 9 SW 3 $10 blue .. 3·50 3·50
SW 10 $20 purple .. 10 2·25
SW 11 $30 orange .. 10 1·00
SW 12 $50 green .. 35 75
SW 13 $100 red .. 10 60
SW 14 $200 blue .. 1·00 75
SW 15 $300 violet .. 3·00 1·25
SW 16 $500 grey .. 5·00 3·25
SW 17 $1,000 purple .. 7·50 6·00
SW 18 $2,000 green .. 12·00 15·00
SW 19 $5,000 orange .. 12·00 20·00
For other values in this design see East China, Nos. EC 378/82.

**1950.** Liberation of the South West.
SW 20 SW 4 $20 blue .. 15 1·00
SW 21 $30 green .. 1·50 2·25
SW 22 $50 red .. 20 1·25
SW 23 $100 brown .. 50 1·25

叁仟圓 改作
(SW 5.) ($3,000).

伍仟圓 ($5,000) 壹萬圓 ($10,000) 貳萬圓 ($20,000) 伍萬圓 ($50,000)

**1950.** Surch as Type SW 5 (characters in left-hand column of surcharge differ as indicated in illustrations and footnotes).
SW 24 SW 4 $60 on $30 green 10·00 12·00
SW 25 $150 on $30 green 10·00 10·00
SW 26 $300 on $20 blue 1·00 2·25
SW 27 $300 on $100 brn 12·00 6·00
SW 28 $1,500 on $100 brown .. 12·00 10·00
SW 29 $3,000 on $50 red 7·00 7·00
SW 30 $5,000 on $50 red 3·00 5·50
SW 31 $10,000 on $50 red 32·00 20·00
SW 32 $20,000 on $50 red 2·25 20·00
SW 33 $50,000 on $50 red 3·25 40·00
Nos. SW24 and SW26/7 have three characters in left-hand column, Nos. SW25 and SW28 have five.

## G. Chinese People's Republic.

1949. Yuans.
1955. 100 fen = 1 yuan.

**GUM or NO GUM.** Nos. 1401/1891 were issued without gum (except Nos. 1843/5 and 1850/7). From No. 1892 onwards all postage stamps were issued with gum, unless otherwise stated. From 1965 some issues seem to have no gum, though in fact they bear an adhesive substance.

**SERIAL MARKINGS.** Issues other than definitive issues are divided into two categories: "commemorative" and "special". Figures below the design of each stamp of such issues indicate: (a) serial number of the issue; (b) number of stamps in the issue; (c) number of stamps within the issue; and (d) year of issue (from No. 1557 on). Neither chronological order of issue nor sequence of value is always strictly followed. From No. 2343 these serial markings were omitted until No. 2433.

**REPRINTS** were later made in replacement of exhausted stocks by the Chinese Postal Administration for sale to stamp collectors and were not available for postal purposes. Nos. 1401/11, 1432/5, 1456/8, 1464/73, 1507/9, 1524/37, and 1543/52.
**Our prices are for originals. For notes describing the distinguishing features of the reprints, see Stanley Gibbons Part 17 (China) Catalogue.**

**For other values in the following types see North East China.**

181. Celebrations at Gate of Heavenly Peace, Peking.
182. Globe, Fist and Banner.

**1949.** Celebration of First Session of Chinese People's Political Conference.
1401. **181.** $30 blue .. .. 1·00 1·50
1402. $50 red .. .. 1·00 1·25
1403. $100 green .. .. 1·00 1·00
1404. $200 purple .. .. 1·00 1·25

**1949.** World Federation of Trade Unions. Asiatic and Australasian Congress, Peking.
1405. **182.** $100 red .. .. 2·00 2·25
1406. $300 green .. .. 2·00 1·25
1407. $500 blue .. .. 2·50 2·50

183. Conference Hall.

184. Mao Tse-tung.

**1950.** Chinese People's Political Conf.
1408. **183.** $50 red .. .. 1·50 2·00
1409. $100 blue .. .. 1·50 2·00
1410. **184.** $300 purple .. .. 1·50 2·00
1411. $500 green .. .. 1·50 1·75

185. Gate of Heavenly Peace, Peking.

**1950.**
1412. **185.** $200 green .. .. 2·50 30
1413. $300 lake .. .. 10 60
1414. $500 red .. .. 10 10
1415. $800 orange .. 27·00 10
1420a. $1,000 lilac .. .. 10 10
1417. $2,000 olive .. 2·50 10
1420b. $3,000 brown .. 10 25
1418. $5,000 pink .. .. 10 25
1419. $8,000 blue .. .. 10 3·25
1420c. $10,000 brown .. 10 15
See also Nos. 1481a/7 and 1493/8.

(186.)

187. Harvesters and Ox.

**1950.** Surch. as T **186.** Perf. or roul.
1427 **148.** $100 on (–) mauve .. 25 1·00
1428 **149.** $200 on (–) red .. 1·50 60
1429 **147.** $300 on (–) green .. 10 1·50
1424 **146.** $500 on (–) orange .. 10 15
1430 $800 on (–) orange .. 2·75 20
1426 $1,000 on (–) orange .. 10 10

**1950.** Unissued stamp of East China surch.
1431. **187.** $20,000 on $10,000 red .. .. £225 7·50

188. Mao Tse-tung, Flag and Parade.

**1950.** Foundation of People's Republic on 1 October 1949.
1432. **188.** $800 red, yellow & grn. 8·50 3·50
1433. $1,000 red, yell. & brn. 8·50 5·50
1434. $2,000 red, yell. & pur. 8·50 4·50
1435. $3,000 red, yell. & blue 9·00 4·00

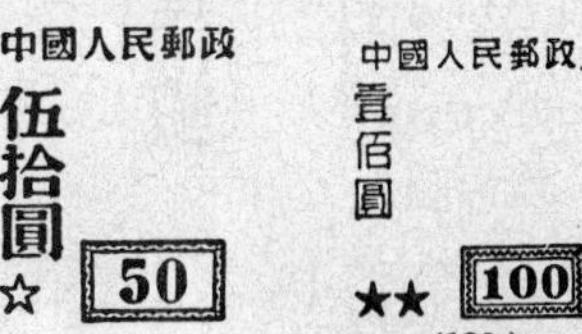

(189.) (190.)

**1950.** Stamps of North Eastern Provinces surch as T **189**.

| No. | Type | Description | Mint | Used |
|---|---|---|---|---|
| 1436 | 5 | $50 on 20 c. green | 3·25 | 3·50 |
| 1437 | | $50 on 25 c. brown | 2·00 | 2·75 |
| 1438 | | $50 on 50 c. orange | 10 | 15 |
| 1439 | | $100 on $2.50 blue | 10 | 20 |
| 1440 | | $100 on $3 brown | 2·50 | 2·75 |
| 1441 | | $100 on $4 brown | 2·50 | 2·50 |
| 1442 | | $100 on $5 green | 2·50 | 2·50 |
| 1443 | | $100 on $10 red | 50 | 2·00 |
| 1444 | | $400 on $20 green | 28·00 | 28·00 |
| 1445 | | $400 on $44 red | 20 | 1·50 |
| 1446 | | $400 on $65 green | 40·00 | 42·00 |
| 1447 | | $400 on $100 green | 6·00 | 3·50 |
| 1448 | | $400 on $200 brown | 28·00 | 11·00 |
| 1449 | | $400 on $300 green | 30·00 | 14·00 |

**1950.** Nos. 1344/7 and unissued values of Nationalist China (Whistling Swans) surch as T **190**.

| No. | Type | Description | Mint | Used |
|---|---|---|---|---|
| 1450 | 169 | $50 on 10 c. blue | 10 | 50 |
| 1451 | | $100 on 16 c. green | 10 | 35 |
| 1452 | | $100 on 50 c. green | 10 | 20 |
| 1453 | | $200 on $1 orange | 20 | 20 |
| 1453a | | $200 on $2 blue | 4·50 | 50 |
| 1454 | | $400 on $5 red | 30 | 30 |
| 1455 | | $400 on $10 green | 60 | 65 |
| 1455a | | $400 on $20 purple | 1·00 | 95 |

Nos. 1451/2 are imperf.

191. "Peace" (after Picasso).

192. Gate of Heavenly Peace, Peking.

**1950.** Peace Campaign (1st issue).

| No. | Type | Description | Mint | Used |
|---|---|---|---|---|
| 1456. | 191. | $400 brown | 3·75 | 3·00 |
| 1457. | | $800 green | 3·75 | 1·50 |
| 1458. | | $2,000 blue | 4·75 | 2·75 |

See also Nos. 1510/12 and 1590/2.

**1950.** Clouds redrawn.

| No. | Type | Description | Mint | Used |
|---|---|---|---|---|
| 1481a | 192. | $100 blue | 15 | 15 |
| 1482 | | $200 green | 3·50 | 40 |
| 1483 | | $300 lake | 10 | 75 |
| 1483a | | $400 green | 1·50 | 10 |
| 1484 | | $500 red | 10 | 10 |
| 1462 | | $800 orange | 2·75 | 10 |
| 1485a | | $1,000 violet | 15 | 25 |
| 1463 | | $2,000 olive | 1·00 | 20 |
| 1486a | | $3,000 brown | 10 | 75 |
| 1487 | | $5,000 pink | 10 | 35 |

193. Flag of People's Republic.

194. "Communications".

**1950.** 1st Anniv. of People's Republic. Flag in red, yellow and brown.

| No. | Type | Description | Mint | Used |
|---|---|---|---|---|
| 1464. | 193. | $100 violet | 5·00 | 2·75 |
| 1465. | | $400 brown | 5·00 | 2·50 |
| 1466. | | $800 green (44×53 mm) | 7·50 | 1·50 |
| 1467. | | $1,000 olive | 7·00 | 4·25 |
| 1468. | | $2,000 blue | 10·00 | 5·50 |

**1950.** 1st All-China Postal Conf.

| No. | Type | Description | Mint | Used |
|---|---|---|---|---|
| 1469. | 194. | $400 brown and green | 3·25 | 3·50 |
| 1470. | | $800 green and red | 3·25 | 1·50 |

195. Stalin greets Mao Tse-tung.

**1950.** Sino-Soviet Treaty.

| No. | Type | Description | Mint | Used |
|---|---|---|---|---|
| 1471. | 195. | $400 red | 5·00 | 3·50 |
| 1472. | | $800 green | 5·50 | 1·25 |
| 1473. | | $2,000 blue | 7·50 | 2·50 |

中國人民郵政
壹佰圓
★★ 100
(196.)

肆佰圓 中國人民郵政
400
(197.)

**1950.** Nos. EC364/5a, EC367 and EC370/1 of East China People's Post surch as T **196**.

| No. | Type | Description | Mint | Used |
|---|---|---|---|---|
| 1474. | | $50 on $10 blue | 10 | 40 |
| 1475. | | $100 on $15 red | 10 | 25 |
| 1476. | | $300 on $50 red | 10 | 25 |
| 1477. | | $400 on $1,600 purple | 60 | 1·25 |
| 1478. | | $400 on $2,000 lilac | 10 | 70 |

**1950.** Stamps of East China surch as T **197**.

| No. | Type | Description | Mint | Used |
|---|---|---|---|---|
| 1479 | EC 112 | $50 on $10 blue | 10 | 45 |
| 1480 | | $400 on $15 red | 10 | 35 |
| 1481 | | $400 on $2,000 grn | 50 | 50 |

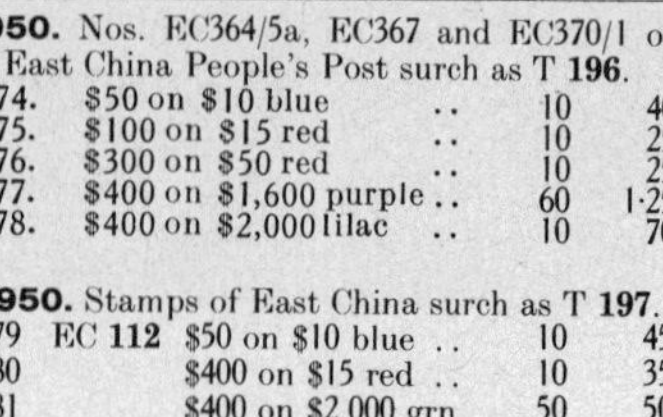

198. Temple of Heaven and Ilyushin Il-18.

**1951.** Air.

| No. | Type | Description | Mint | Used |
|---|---|---|---|---|
| 1488. | 198. | $1,000 red | 10 | 75 |
| 1489. | | $3,000 green | 10 | 50 |
| 1490. | | $5,000 orange | 15 | 50 |
| 1491. | | $10,000 green and pur. | 85 | 1·00 |
| 1492. | | $30,000 brn. and blue | 2·50 | 2·50 |

**1951.** Pink network background.

| No. | Type | Description | Mint | Used |
|---|---|---|---|---|
| 1493. | 185. | $10,000 brown | 25 | 5·00 |
| 1494. | | $20,000 olive | 50 | 50 |
| 1495. | | $30,000 green | 22·00 | 20·00 |
| 1496. | | $50,000 violet | 32·00 | 5·00 |
| 1497. | | $100,000 red | £1300 | 50·00 |
| 1498. | | $200,000 blue | £1800 | £150 |

中國人民郵政
貳拾伍圓
25
(200.)

201. Mao Tse-tung.

**1951.** Surch. as T **200**. Perf. or roul.

| No. | Type | Description | Mint | Used |
|---|---|---|---|---|
| 1503 | 148. | $5 on (–) mauve | 30 | 75 |
| 1500 | 147. | $10 on (–) green | 25 | 75 |
| 1501 | 149. | $15 on (–) red | 20 | 75 |
| 1506 | 146. | $25 on (–) orange | 10 | 75 |

**1951.** 30th Anniv. of Chinese Communist Party.

| No. | Type | Description | Mint | Used |
|---|---|---|---|---|
| 1507. | 201. | $400 brown | 2·25 | 1·75 |
| 1508. | | $500 green | 2·25 | 1·75 |
| 1509. | | $800 red | 2·00 | 1·00 |

202. Dove of Peace, after Picasso.

**1951.** Peace Campaign (2nd issue).

| No. | Type | Description | Mint | Used |
|---|---|---|---|---|
| 1510. | 202. | $400 brown | 3·75 | 3·25 |
| 1511. | | $800 green | 3·75 | 1·50 |
| 1512. | | $1,000 violet | 5·50 | 2·25 |

伍拾圓 中國人民郵政
★ 50 ★
(203.)

204. National Emblem.

**1951.** Money Order stamps as North China, Type NC **77**, surch with T **203** Perf or roul.

| No. | Type | Description | Mint | Used |
|---|---|---|---|---|
| 1513 | | $50 on $2 green | 25 | 2·00 |
| 1515 | | $50 on $5 orange | 15 | 70 |
| 1517 | | $50 on $50 grey | 10 | 15 |

**1951.** National Emblem Issue. Yellow network background.

| No. | Type | Description | Mint | Used |
|---|---|---|---|---|
| 1519 | 204 | $100 blue | 1·75 | 1·25 |
| 1520 | | $200 brown | 1·75 | 2·25 |
| 1521 | | $400 orange | 2·25 | 1·25 |
| 1522 | | $500 green | 2·75 | 1·25 |
| 1523 | | $800 red | 3·00 | 75 |

205. Lu Hsun.

**1951.** 15th Death Anniv of Lu Hsun (author).

| No. | Type | Description | Mint | Used |
|---|---|---|---|---|
| 1524. | 205. | $400 violet | 2·25 | 2·00 |
| 1525. | | $800 green | 3·25 | 1·00 |

**206. Rebels at Chintien.**

**1951.** Centenary of Taiping Rebellion.

| No. | Type | Description | Mint | Used |
|---|---|---|---|---|
| 1526. | 206. | $400 green | 3·25 | 3·25 |
| 1527. | | $800 red | 3·25 | 1·75 |
| 1528. | – | $800 orange | 3·25 | 1·75 |
| 1529. | – | $1,000 blue | 3·25 | 1·75 |

DESIGN: Nos. 1528/9, Coin and Documents of Taiping "Heavenly Kingdom of Great Peace".

**207. Peasants and Tractor.**

**1952.** Agrarian Reform.

| No. | Type | Description | Mint | Used |
|---|---|---|---|---|
| 1530. | 207. | $100 red | 2·25 | 2·25 |
| 1531. | | $200 blue | 2·25 | 2·25 |
| 1532. | | $400 brown | 2·25 | 2·00 |
| 1533. | | $800 green | 2·25 | 1·25 |

208. The Potala, Lhasa.

**209.** "Child Protection".

**1952.** Liberation of Tibet.

| No. | Type | Description | Mint | Used |
|---|---|---|---|---|
| 1534. | 208. | $400 red | 2·75 | 2·25 |
| 1535. | – | $800 green | 2·75 | 1·75 |
| 1536. | 208. | $800 red | 2·75 | 2·00 |
| 1537. | – | $1,000 violet | 2·75 | 1·75 |

DESIGN: Nos. 1535, 1537 Tibetan ploughing with yaks.

**1952.** Int. Child Protection Conf., Vienna.

| No. | Type | Description | Mint | Used |
|---|---|---|---|---|
| 1538. | 209. | $400 green | 10 | 10 |
| 1539. | | $800 blue | 10 | 10 |

210. Hammer and Sickle.

211. Gymnast.

**1952.** Labour Day. Dated "1952".

| No. | Type | Description | Mint | Used |
|---|---|---|---|---|
| 1540. | 210. | $800 red | 10 | 10 |
| 1541. | – | $800 green | 10 | 10 |
| 1542. | – | $800 brown | 10 | 10 |

DESIGNS: No. 1541, Hand and dove. No. 1542, Hammer, dove and ear of corn.

**1952.** Gymnastics by Radio. As T **211**.

| No. | Type | Description | Mint | Used |
|---|---|---|---|---|
| 1543. | | $400 red (14–17) | 50 | 75 |
| 1544. | | $400 deep blue (18–21) | 50 | 75 |
| 1545. | | $400 purple (22–25) | 50 | 75 |
| 1546. | | $400 green (26–29) | 50 | 75 |
| 1547. | | $400 red (30–33) | 50 | 75 |
| 1548. | | $400 blue (34–37) | 50 | 75 |
| 1549. | | $400 orange (38–41) | 50 | 75 |
| 1550. | | $400 violet (42–45) | 50 | 75 |
| 1551. | | $400 bistre (46–49) | 50 | 75 |
| 1552. | | $400 pale blue (50–53) | 50 | 75 |

DESIGNS: Various gymnastic exercises, the stamps in each colour being arranged in blocks of four throughout the sheet, each block showing four stages of the exercise depicted. Where two stages are the same, the stamps differ only in the serial number in brackets, in the right-hand corner of the bottom margin of the stamp. The serial numbers are shown above after the colours of the stamps.

Prices are for single stamps.

212. "A Winter Hunt" (A.D. 386–580).

**1952.** "Glorious Mother Country" (1st issue). Tun Huang Mural Paintings.

| No. | Type | Description | Mint | Used |
|---|---|---|---|---|
| 1553. | 212. | $800 sepia | 10 | 10 |
| 1554. | – | $800 brown | 10 | 10 |
| 1555. | – | $800 slate | 10 | 10 |
| 1556. | – | $800 purple | 10 | 10 |

PAINTINGS: No. 1554, "Benefactor" (A.D. 581–617). No. 1555, "Celestial Flight" (A.D. 618–906). No. 1556, "Tiger" (A.D. 618–906).

See also Nos. 1565/8, 1593/96, 1601/4 and 1628/31.

**213. Marco Polo Bridge, Lukouchiao.**

**1952.** 15th Anniv. of War with Japan.

| No. | Type | Description | Mint | Used |
|---|---|---|---|---|
| 1557. | 213. | $800 blue | 10 | 10 |
| 1558. | – | $800 green | 10 | 10 |
| 1559. | – | $800 plum | 10 | 10 |
| 1560. | – | $800 red | 10 | 10 |

DESIGNS (dated "1937–1952"): No. 1558, Victory at Pinghsingkwan. No. 1559, Departure of New Fourth Army from Central China. No. 1560, Mao Tse-tung and Chu Teh.

214. Airman, Sailor and Soldier.

217. Dove of Peace over Pacific Ocean.

216. Huai River Barrage.

**1952.** 25th Anniv. of People's Liberation Army.

| No. | Type | Description | Mint | Used |
|---|---|---|---|---|
| 1561. | 214. | $800 red | 10 | 10 |
| 1562. | – | $800 green | 10 | 10 |
| 1563. | – | $800 violet | 30 | 10 |
| 1564. | – | $800 brown | 10 | 10 |

DESIGNS—HORIZ. No. 1562, Soldier, tanks and guns. 1563, Sailor and destroyers. 1564, Pilot, Ilyushin Il-4 DB-3 bomber and Mikoyan Gurevich Mig-15 fighters.

**1952.** "Glorious Mother Country" (2nd issue).

| No. | Type | Description | Mint | Used |
|---|---|---|---|---|
| 1565 | 216 | $800 violet | 10 | 10 |
| 1566 | | $800 red | 20 | 10 |
| 1567 | | $800 purple | 10 | 10 |
| 1568 | | $800 green | 10 | 10 |

DESIGNS: No. 1566, Chungking–Chengtu railway viaduct. 1567, Oil refinery. 1568, Tractor, disc harrows and combine drill.

**1952.** Asia and Pacific Ocean Peace Conf.

| No. | Type | Description | Mint | Used |
|---|---|---|---|---|
| 1569 | 217 | $400 purple | 10 | 10 |
| 1570 | – | $800 orange | 10 | 10 |
| 1571 | 217 | $800 red | 10 | 10 |
| 1572 | – | $2,500 green | 10 | 10 |

DESIGNS–HORIZ Nos. 1570 and 1572, Doves and globe.

**218. Peasants collecting food for the Front.**

**DESIGNS—(dated "1950–1952"): HORIZ. No. 1573, Marching troops. No. 1575, Infantry attack. No. 1576, Meeting of Chinese and North Korean soldiers.**

**1952.** 2nd Anniv. of Chinese Volunteer Force in Korea.

| No. | Type | Description | Mint | Used |
|---|---|---|---|---|
| 1573 | – | $800 blue | 10 | 10 |
| 1574 | 218 | $800 red | 10 | 10 |
| 1575 | – | $800 violet | 10 | 10 |
| 1576 | – | $800 brown | 10 | 10 |

DESIGN: No. 1579, Woman harvesting grain.

**220. Textile Worker.**

**1953.** Int. Women's Day.
1578. **220.** $800 red .. .. 10 10
1579. – $800 green .. .. 10 10

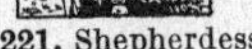
**221.** Shepherdess.

**222.** Karl Marx.

**1953.**
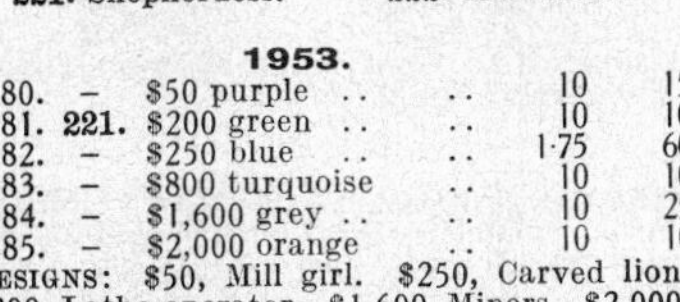
1580. – $50 purple .. .. 10 15
1581. **221.** $200 green .. .. 10 10
1582. – $250 blue .. .. 1·75 60
1583. – $800 turquoise .. 10 10
1584. – $1,600 grey .. .. 10 25
1585. – $2,000 orange .. 10 10
DESIGNS: $50, Mill girl. $250, Carved lion. $800, Lathe-operator. $1,600, Miners. $2,000, Old Palace, Peking.

**1953.** 135th Birth Anniv. of Karl Marx.
1586. **222.** $400 brown .. .. 10 15
1587. $800 green .. 10 15

**223.** Workers and Flags.

**224.** Dove of Peace.

**1953.** 7th National Labour Union Conf.
1588. **223.** $400 blue .. .. 10 15
1589. $800 red .. .. 10 15

**1953.** Peace Campaign (3rd issue).
1590. **224.** $250 green .. 10 10
1591. $400 brown .. .. 10 10
1592. $800 violet .. .. 15 10

**225.** Horseman and Steed (A.D. 386-580).

PAINTINGS: No. 1594, Court players (A.D 386-580). No. 1595, Battle scene (A.D. 581-617). No. 1596, Ox-drawn palanquin (A.D. 618-906).

**1953.** "Glorious Mother Country" (3rd issue).
1593. **225.** $800 green .. 10 10
1594. – $800 orange .. 10 10
1595. – $800 blue .. .. 10 10
1596. – $800 red .. .. 10 10

**226.** Mao Tse-tung and Stalin at Kremlin.

**1953.** 35th Anniv. of Russian Revolution.
1597. **226.** $800 green .. .. 10 10
1598. – $800 red .. .. 10 10
1599. – $800 blue .. .. 10 10
1600. – $800 brown .. .. 10 10
DESIGNS—HORIZ. No. 1598, Lenin addressing revolutionaries. VERT. No. 1599, Statue of Stalin. No. 1600, Stalin making speech.

**227.** Compass (300 B.C.).

**228.** Rabelais (writer).

**1953.** "Glorious Mother Country" (4th issue). Scientific instruments.
1601. **227.** $800 black .. .. 10 10
1602. – $800 green .. .. 10 10
1603. – $800 slate .. .. 10 10
1604. – $800 brown .. .. 10 10
DESIGNS: No. 1602, Seismoscope (A.D. 132). No. 1603, Drum cart for measuring distances (A.D. 300). No. 1604, Armillary sphere (A.D. 1437).

**1953.** Famous Men.
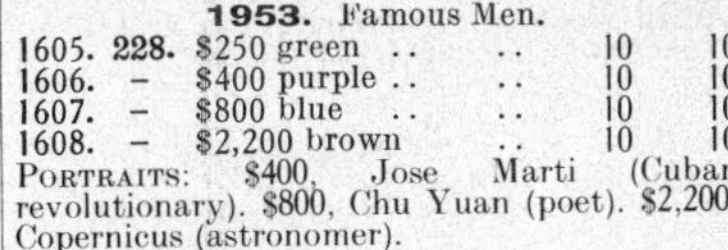
1605. **228.** $250 green .. .. 10 10
1606. – $400 purple .. .. 10 10
1607. – $800 blue .. .. 10 10
1608. – $2,200 brown .. 10 10
PORTRAITS: $400, Jose Marti (Cuban revolutionary). $800, Chu Yuan (poet). $2,200, Copernicus (astronomer).

**229.** Flax Mill, Harbin.

DESIGNS: No. 1610, Tangku Harbour. No. 1611, Tienshui-Lanchow Railway. No. 1612, Heavy machine works. No. 1613, Blast-furnace. No. 1614, Open-cast mines. No. 1615, North-East Electric power station. No. 1616, Geological survey team.

**1954.** Industrial Development.
1609. **229.** $100 brown .. .. 10 10
1610. – $200 green .. .. 10 10
1611. – $250 violet .. .. 10 10
1612. – $400 sepia .. .. 10 10
1613. – $800 purple .. .. 10 10
1614. – $800 blue .. .. 10 10
1615. – $2,000 red .. .. 10 10
1616. – $3,200 brown .. .. 10 10

**230.** Gate of Heavenly Peace, Peking.

**231.** Statue of Lenin and Stalin at Gorki.

**232.** Lenin Speaking.

**233.** Painted Pottery (c. 2000 B.C.).

**1954.**
1617. **230.** $50 red .. .. 10 10
1618. $100 blue .. .. 10 10
1619. $200 green .. .. 10 10
1620. $250 blue .. .. 10 10
1621. $400 green .. .. 10 10
1622. $800 orange .. .. 10 10
1623. $1,600 grey .. .. 10 10
1624. $2,000 olive .. .. 10 10

**1954.** 30th Death Anniv. of Lenin.
1625 **231** $400 green .. .. 35 15
1626 – $800 brown .. .. 25 15
1627 **232** $2,000 red .. .. 25 15
DESIGN: (25×37 mm.) $800, Lenin (full-face portrait).

**1954.** "Glorious Mother Country" (5th issue).
1628. **233.** $800 brown .. .. 10 10
1629. – $800 black .. .. 10 10
1630. – $800 turquoise .. 10 10
1631. – $800 lake .. .. 10 10
DESIGNS—As Type **233**: No. 1629, Musical stone (1200 B.C.). No. 1630, Bronze basin (816 B.C.). No. 1631, Lacquered wine cup and cosmetic tray (403–221 B.C.).

**234.** Heavy Rolling Mill.

**235.** Statue of Stalin.

**1954.** Anshan Steel Works.
1632. – $400 turquoise .. 20 10
1633. **234.** $800 purple .. .. 20 20
DESIGN: $400, Seamless steel-tubing mill.

**1954.** 1st Death Anniv. of Stalin.
1634. **235.** $400 black .. 20 10
1635. – $800 sepia .. .. 10 20
1636. – $2,000 red .. .. 25 20
DESIGNS—VERT. $800, Full-face portrait of Stalin (26×37 mm.). HORIZ. $2,000, Stalin and hydro-electric station (42½×25 mm.).

**236.** Exhibition Building.

**1954.** Russian Economic and Cultural Exn., Peking.
1637. **236.** $800 brown on yellow 4·25 1·25

**237.** The Universal Fixture.

**238.** Woman Worker.

**239.** Rejoicing Crowds.

**1954.** Workers' Inventions.
1638. **237.** $400 green .. .. 15 15
1639. – $800 red .. .. 15 10
DESIGN: $800, The reverse repeater.

**1954.** 1st Session of National Congress.
1640. **238.** $400 purple .. .. 10 10
1641. **239.** $800 red .. .. 10 10

**240.** "New Constitution".

**1954.** Constitution Commem.
1642. **240.** $400 brown on buff 10 15
1643. $800 red on yellow .. 10 15

**241.** Pylons.

**242.** Nurse and Red Cross Worker.

**1955.** Development of Overhead Transmission of Electricity.
1644 **241** $800 blue .. .. 40 20

**1955.** 50th Anniv. of Chinese Red Cross.
1645. **242.** 8 f. red and green .. 4·00 25

**243.** Miner.

**244.** Gate of Heavenly Peace, Peking.

**1955.**
1646 **243** ½ f. brown .. .. 75 10
1647 – 1 f. purple .. .. 75 10
1648 – 2 f. green .. .. 1·75 10
1648a – 2½ f. blue .. .. 1·00 10
1649 – 4 f. green .. .. 2·00 10
1650 – 8 f. red .. .. 5·00 10
1650b – 10 f. red .. .. 9·00 10
1651 – 20 f. blue .. .. 3·75 10
1652 – 50 f. grey .. .. 5·50 10
1653 **244** 1 y. red .. .. 70 10
1654 2 y. brown .. .. 1·00 10
1655 5 y. grey .. .. 2·00 10
1656 10 y. red .. .. 3·50 50
1657 20 y. violet .. .. 8·00 3·00
DESIGNS—As Type **243**: 1 f. Lathe operator. 2 f. Airman. 2½ f. Nurse. 4 f. Soldier. 8 f. Foundry worker. 10 f. Chemist. 20 f. Farm girl. 50 f. Sailor.

**246.** Workmen and Industrial Plant.

**247.** Chang-Heng (A.D. 78–139, astronomer).

**1955.** 5th Anniv. of Sino-Russian Treaty.
1658. – 8 f. brown .. .. 3·25 30
1659. **246.** 20 f. olive .. .. 4·25 30
DESIGN—HORIZ. (37×32 mm.): 8 f. Stalin and Mao Tse-tung.

**1955.** Scientists of Ancient China.
1660. **247.** 8 f. sepia on buff .. 75 10
1661. – 8 f. blue on buff .. 75 10
1662. – 8 f. black on buff .. 75 10
1663. – 8 f. purple on buff .. 75 10
PORTRAITS: No. 1661, Tsu Chung-chi (429-500 mathematician). No. 1662, Chang-Sui (683-727 astronomer). No. 1663, Li-Shih-chen (1518-1593 pharmacologist).

**248.** Foundry.

**249.** Lenin.

**1955.** Five Year Plan. Frames in black.
1664. **248.** 8 f. red and orange .. 25 10
1665. – 8 f. brown and yellow 25 10
1666. – 8 f. yellow and black 25 10
1667. – 8 f. violet and blue .. 25 10
1668. – 8 f. yellow and brown 25 10
1669. – 8 f. yellow and red .. 25 10
1670. – 8 f. grey and blue .. 25 10
1671. – 8 f. orange and black 25 10
1672. – 8 f. yellow and brown 25 10
1673. – 8 f. red and orange .. 30 10
1674. – 8 f. yellow and green 30 10
1675. – 8 f. red and yellow .. 35 10
1676. – 8 f. yellow and grey 30 15
1677. – 8 f. yellow and blue 35 10
1678. – 8 f. orange and blue 30 10
1679. – 8 f. yellow and brown 30 10
1680. – 8 f. red and brown .. 30 10
1681. – 8 f. yellow and brown 30 10
DESIGNS—No. 1665, Electricity pylons. No. 1666, Mining machinery. No. 1667, Oil tankers and derricks. No. 1668, Heavy machinery workshop. No. 1669, Factory guard and industrial plant. No. 1670, Textile machinery. No. 1671, Factory workers. No. 1672, Combine-harvester. No. 1673, Dairy herd and farm girl. No. 1674, Dam. No. 1675, Artists decorating pottery. No. 1676, Lorry. No. 1677, Freighter and wharf. No. 1678, Surveyors. No. 1679, Students. No. 1680, Man, woman and child. No. 1681, Workers' rest home.

**1955.** 85th Birth Anniv. of Lenin.
1682. **249.** 8 f. blue .. .. 2·50 15
1683. 20 f. lake .. .. 3·75 35

**250.** Engels.

**251.** Capture of Lu Ting Bridge.

**1955.** 60th Death Anniv. of Engels.
1684. **250.** 8 f. red .. .. 2·75 10
1685. 20 f. sepia .. .. 3·75 45

**1955.** 20th Anniv. of Long March by Communist Army.
1686. **251.** 8 f. red .. .. 3·25 15
1687. – 8 f. blue .. .. 3·75 45
DESIGN—VERT. (28 × 46 mm.): No. 1687, Crossing the Ta Hsueh Mountains.

**252.** Convoy of Lorries.

DESIGNS—VERT. (21 × 42 mm.): No. 1689, Suspension bridge: Tatu River. HORIZ. As Type **252**: No. 1690, Opening ceremony, Lhasa.

**1956.** Opening of Sikang-Tibet and Tsinghai-Tibet Highways.

| | | | | |
|---|---|---|---|---|
| 1688. | 252. | 4 f. blue | 25 | 10 |
| 1689. | – | 8 f. brown | 25 | 10 |
| 1690. | – | 8 f. red | 25 | 10 |

254. Summer Palace.

VIEWS: No. 1692 Peihai Park. No. 1693, Gate of Heavenly Peace. No. 1694, Temple of Heaven. No. 1695, Tai Ho Palace.

**1956.** Views of Peking.

| | | | | |
|---|---|---|---|---|
| 1691. | 254. | 4 f. red | 50 | 10 |
| 1692. | – | 4 f. green | 50 | 10 |
| 1693. | – | 8 f. red | 50 | 10 |
| 1694. | – | 8 f. blue | 50 | 10 |
| 1695. | – | 8 f. brown | 50 | 10 |

255. Salt Production.

DESIGNS—HORIZ. (Brick carvings of Tung Han Dynasty, A.D. 25–200): No. 1697, Residence. No. 1698, Hunting and farming. No. 1699, Carriage crossing bridge.

**1956.** Archaeological Discoveries at Chengtu.

| | | | | |
|---|---|---|---|---|
| 1696. | 255. | 4 f. green | 15 | 10 |
| 1697. | – | 4 f. black | 15 | 10 |
| 1698. | – | 8 f. sepia | 20 | 10 |
| 1699. | – | 8 f. sepia | 20 | 10 |

256.

257. Gate of Heavenly Peace, Peking.

**1956.** National Savings.

| | | | | |
|---|---|---|---|---|
| 1700. | 256. | 4 f. buff | 2·25 | 15 |
| 1701. | | 8 f. red | 2·75 | 10 |

**1956.** 8th National Communist Party Congress.

| | | | | |
|---|---|---|---|---|
| 1702. | 257. | 4 f. green | 1·75 | 15 |
| 1703. | | 8 f. red | 2·00 | 15 |
| 1704. | | 16 f. red | 3·25 | 15 |

258. Dr. Sun Yat-sen.

259. Putting the Shot.

**1956.** 90th Birth Anniv. of Dr. Sun Yat-sen.

| | | | | |
|---|---|---|---|---|
| 1705. | 258. | 4 f. brown | 3·25 | 20 |
| 1706. | | 8 f. blue | 3·00 | 45 |

**1957.** 1st Chinese Workers' Athletic Meeting, 1955. Inscr. "1955". Flower in red and green: inscr. in brown.

| | | | | |
|---|---|---|---|---|
| 1707. | 259. | 4 f. lake | 45 | 10 |
| 1708. | – | 4 f. purple (Weight-lifting) | 45 | 10 |
| 1709. | – | 8 f. grn. (Sprinting) | 55 | 10 |
| 1710. | – | 8 f. blue (Football) | 55 | 10 |
| 1711. | – | 8 f. brown (Cycling) | 55 | 10 |

260. Assembly Line.

**1957.** Lorry Production.

| | | | | |
|---|---|---|---|---|
| 1712. | – | 4 f. brown | 15 | 10 |
| 1713. | 260. | 8 f. blue | 25 | 10 |

DESIGN: 4 f. Changchun motor plant.

261. Nanchang Revolutionaries.

**1957.** 30th Anniv. of People's Liberation Army.

| | | | | |
|---|---|---|---|---|
| 1714. | 261. | 4 f. violet | 2·25 | 15 |
| 1715. | – | 4 f. green | 2·25 | 15 |
| 1716. | – | 8 f. brown | 2·25 | 10 |
| 1717. | – | 8 f. blue | 2·25 | 10 |

DESIGNS: No. 1715, Meeting of Red Armies at Chinkangshan. No. 1716, Liberation Army crossing the Yellow River. No. 1717, Liberation of Nanking.

262. Congress Emblem.

263. Yangtse River Bridge.

**1957.** 4th W.F.T.U. Congress, Leipzig.

| | | | | |
|---|---|---|---|---|
| 1718. | 262. | 8 f. brown | 2·00 | 10 |
| 1719. | | 22 f. blue | 1·75 | 15 |

**1957.** Opening of Yangtse River Bridge.

| | | | | |
|---|---|---|---|---|
| 1720. | 263. | 8 f. red | 25 | 10 |
| 1721. | – | 20 f. blue | 40 | 10 |

DESIGN: 20 f. Aerial view of bridge.

264. Fireworks over Kremlin.

265. Airport Scene.

**1957.** 40th Anniv. of Russian Revolution.

| | | | | |
|---|---|---|---|---|
| 1722. | 264. | 4 f. red | 2·25 | 10 |
| 1723. | – | 8 f. sepia | 2·25 | 10 |
| 1724. | – | 20 f. green | 2·50 | 10 |
| 1725. | – | 22 f. brown | 3·00 | 15 |
| 1726. | – | 32 f. blue | 3·25 | 30 |

DESIGNS: 8 f. Soviet emblem, globe and broken chains. 20 f. Dove of Peace and plant. 22 f. Hands supporting book bearing portraits of Marx and Lenin. 32 f. Electricity power pylon.

**1957.** Air.

| | | | | |
|---|---|---|---|---|
| 1727. | 265. | 16 f. blue | 2·50 | 10 |
| 1728. | – | 28 f. olive | 6·50 | 35 |
| 1729. | – | 35 f. black | 10·00 | 75 |
| 1730. | – | 52 f. blue | 10·00 | 50 |

DESIGNS—Lisunov Li-2 over—28 f. mountain highway. 35 f. railway tracks. 52 f. coaling station.

266. Yellow River Dam and Power Station.

267. Ploughing.

**1957.** Harnessing of the Yellow River.

| | | | | |
|---|---|---|---|---|
| 1731. | – | 4 f. orange | 1·75 | 10 |
| 1732. | 266. | 4 f. blue | 1·75 | 10 |
| 1733. | – | 8 f. lake | 2·50 | 40 |
| 1734. | – | 8 f. green | 2·00 | 10 |

DESIGNS: No. 1731, Map of Yellow River. No. 1733, Yellow River ferry. No. 1734, Aerial view of irrigation on Yellow River.

**1957.** Co-operative Agriculture. Mult.

| | | | |
|---|---|---|---|
| 1735. | 8 f. Farmer enrolling for farm | 20 | 10 |
| 1736. | 8 f. Type **267** | 20 | 10 |
| 1737. | 8 f. Tree-planting | 20 | 10 |
| 1738. | 8 f. Harvesting | 20 | 10 |

268. "Peaceful Construction".

269. High Peak Pagoda, Tenfeng.

**1958.** Completion of First Five Year Plan.

| | | | | |
|---|---|---|---|---|
| 1739. | 268. | 4 f. green | 20 | 10 |
| 1740. | – | 8 f. red | 20 | 10 |
| 1741. | – | 16 f. blue | 30 | 10 |

DESIGNS: 8 f. "Industry and Agriculture" (grapple and wheat-sheaves). 16 f. "Communications and Transport" (train on viaduct and ship).

**1958.** Ancient Chinese Pagodas.

| | | | | |
|---|---|---|---|---|
| 1742. | 269. | 8 f. brown | 50 | 10 |
| 1743. | – | 8 f. blue | 50 | 10 |
| 1744. | – | 8 f. brown | 50 | 10 |
| 1745. | – | 8 f. green | 50 | 10 |

DESIGNS: No. 1743, One Thousand League Pagoda, Tali. No. 1744, Buddha Pagoda, Yinghsien. No. 1745, Flying Rainbow Pagoda, Hungchao.

270. Trilobite of Hao Li Shan.

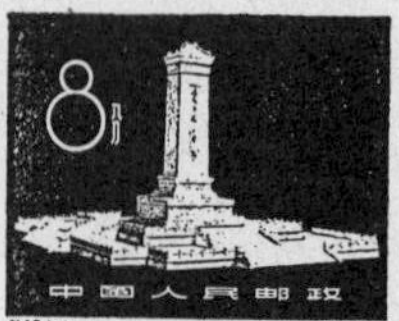

271.

**1958.** Chinese Fossils.

| | | | | |
|---|---|---|---|---|
| 1746. | 270. | 4 f. blue | 35 | 10 |
| 1747. | – | 8 f. sepia | 35 | 10 |
| 1748. | – | 16 f. green | 35 | 10 |

DESIGNS: 8 f. Dinosaur of Lufeng. 16 f. "Sinomegaceros pachyospeur" (deer).

**1958.** People's Heroes Monument, Peking. Unveiling.

| | | | | |
|---|---|---|---|---|
| 1749. | 271. | 8 f. red | 4·75 | 55 |

272. Karl Marx (after Zhukov).

273. Cogwheels of Industry.

**1958.** 140th Birth Anniv. of Karl Marx.

| | | | | |
|---|---|---|---|---|
| 1750. | 272. | 8 f. brown | 3·00 | 55 |
| 1751. | – | 22 f. myrtle | 3·00 | 45 |

DESIGN: 22 f. Marx addressing German workers' Educational Association, London.

**1958.** 8th All-China Trade Union Congress, Peking.

| | | | | |
|---|---|---|---|---|
| 1752. | 273. | 4 f. blue | 2·50 | 1·00 |
| 1753. | | 8 f. purple | 2·50 | 50 |

274. Federation Emblem.

275. Mother and Child.

**1958.** 4th Int. Democratic Women's Federation Congress, Vienna.

| | | | | |
|---|---|---|---|---|
| 1754. | 274. | 8 f. blue | 2·75 | 20 |
| 1755. | | 20 f. green | 2·75 | 55 |

**1958.** Chinese Children. Centre multicoloured. Inscriptions and values in green.

| | | | |
|---|---|---|---|
| 1756. | 8 f. Type **275** | 3·75 | 30 |
| 1757. | 8 f. Watering sunflowers | 3·75 | 30 |
| 1758. | 8 f. "Hide and seek" | 3·75 | 30 |
| 1759. | 8 f. Children sailing boat | 3·75 | 30 |

276. Kuan Han-ching (playwright).

277. Peking Planetarium.

**1958.** 700th Anniv. of Works of Kuan Han-ching.

| | | | | |
|---|---|---|---|---|
| 1760. | – | 4 f. green on cream | 3·00 | 75 |
| 1761. | 276. | 8 f. purple on cream | 3·25 | 30 |
| 1762. | – | 20 f. black on cream | 3·25 | 55 |

DESIGNS: Scenes from Han-ching's comedies: 4 f. "The Butterfly Dream". 20 f. "The Riverside Pavilion".

**1958.** Peking Planetarium.

| | | | | |
|---|---|---|---|---|
| 1763. | 277. | 8 f. green | 2·50 | 30 |
| 1764. | – | 20 f. blue | 4·00 | 15 |

DESIGN: 20 f. Planetarium in operation.

278. Marx and Engels.

279. Whistling Swan and Radio Pylon.

**1958.** 110th Anniv. of "Communist Manifesto".

| | | | | |
|---|---|---|---|---|
| 1765. | 278. | 4 f. purple | 3·00 | 1·00 |
| 1766. | – | 8 f. blue | 3·00 | 15 |

DESIGN: 8 f. Front cover of first German "Communist Manifesto".

**1958.** Organization of Socialist Countries' Postal Administrations Conference, Moscow.

| | | | | |
|---|---|---|---|---|
| 1767. | 279. | 4 f. blue | 5·50 | 65 |
| 1768. | | 8 f. green | 5·50 | 65 |

280. Peony and Doves.

281. Chang Heng's Weather-cock.

**1958.** Int. Disarmament Conf., Stockholm.

| | | | | |
|---|---|---|---|---|
| 1769. | 280. | 4 f. red | 5·50 | 1·00 |
| 1770. | – | 8 f. green | 5·50 | 1·00 |
| 1771. | – | 22 f. brown | 5·50 | 1·00 |

DESIGNS: 8 f. Olive branch. 22 f. Atomic symbol and factory plant.

**1958.** Chinese Meteorology.

| | | | | |
|---|---|---|---|---|
| 1772. | 281. | 8 f. black on yellow | 40 | 10 |
| 1773. | – | 8 f. black on blue | 40 | 10 |
| 1774. | – | 8 f. black on green | 40 | 10 |

DESIGNS: No. 1773, Meteorological balloon. No. 1774, Typhoon signal-tower.

282. Union Emblem within figure "5".

283. Chrysanthemum.

284. Telegraph Building, Peking.

**1958.** 5th Int. Students' Union Congress, Peking.

| | | | | |
|---|---|---|---|---|
| 1775. | 282. | 8 f. purple | 2·50 | 10 |
| 1776. | | 22 f. green | 3·25 | 40 |

**1958.** Flowers.

| | | | | |
|---|---|---|---|---|
| 1777. | – | 1½ f. mauve (Peony) | 1·50 | 10 |
| 1778. | – | 3 f. green (Lotus) | 6·50 | 15 |
| 1779. | 283. | 5 f. orange | 75 | 10 |

**1958.** Opening of Peking Telegraph Building.

| | | | | |
|---|---|---|---|---|
| 1780. | 284. | 4 f. olive | 50 | 10 |
| 1781. | | 8 f. red | 60 | 10 |

285. Exhibition Emblem and Symbols.

**1958.** National Exn. of Industry and Communications.

| | | | | |
|---|---|---|---|---|
| 1782. | 285. | 8 f. green | 2·50 | 15 |
| 1783. | – | 8 f. red | 2·50 | 15 |
| 1784. | – | 8 f. brown | 2·50 | 15 |

DESIGNS: No. 1783, Chinese dragon riding the waves. No. 1784, Horses in the sky.

**286.** Labourer on Reservoir Site. **287.** Sputnik and ancient Theodolite.

**1958.** Inaug. of Ming Tombs Reservoir.
1785. **286.** 4 f. brown .. .. 35 10
1786. – 8 f. blue .. .. 35 10
DESIGN: 8 f. Ming Tombs Reservoir.

**1958.** Russian Sputnik Commem.
1787. **287.** 4 f. red .. .. 1·40 10
1788. – 8 f. violet .. .. 1·40 10
1789. – 10 f. green .. .. 1·75 60
DESIGNS: 8 f. Third Russian sputnik encircling globe. 10 f. Three Russian sputniks encircling globe.

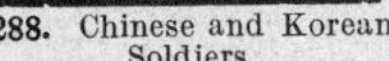

**288.** Chinese and Korean Soldiers. **289.** Forest Landscape.

**1958.** Return of Chinese People's Volunteers from Korea.
1790. **288.** 8 f. purple .. .. 35 10
1791. – 8 f. brown .. .. 35 10
1792. – 8 f. red .. .. 35 10
DESIGNS: No. 1791, Chinese soldier embracing Korean woman. No. 1792, Girl presenting bouquet to Chinese soldier.

**1958.** Afforestation Campaign.
1793. **289.** 8 f. green .. .. 75 10
1794. – 8 f. slate .. .. 75 10
1795. – 8 f. violet .. .. 75 10
1796. – 8 f. blue .. .. 75 10
DESIGNS—VERT. No. 1794, Forest patrol. HORIZ. No. 1795, Tree-felling by power-saw. No. 1796, Tree planting.

**290.** Atomic Reactor.

**1958.** Inaug. of China's First Atomic Reactor.
1797. **290.** 8 f. blue .. .. 2·50 15
1798. – 20 f. brown .. .. 3·50 95
DESIGN: 20 f. Cyclotron in action.

**291.** Children with Model Aircraft. **292.** Rooster.

**1958.** Aviation Sports.
1799. **291.** 4 f. red .. .. 25 10
1800. – 8 f. myrtle .. .. 25 10
1801. – 10 f. sepia .. .. 25 10
1802. – 20 f. slate .. .. 30 10
DESIGNS: 8 f. Gliders. 10 f. Parachutists. 20 f. Yakovlev Yak-18U trainers.

**1959.** Chinese Folk Paper-cuts.
1803. – 8 f. black on violet .. 2·75 15
1804. – 8 f. black on green .. 2·75 15
1805. **292.** 8 f. black on red .. 2·75 15
1806. – 8 f. black on blue .. 2·75 15
DESIGNS: No. 1803, Camel. No. 1804, Pomegranate. No. 1806, Actress on stage.

**293.** Mao Tse-tung and Steel Workers. **294.** Chinese Women.

**1959.** Steel Production Progress. Inscr. "1958".
1807. **293.** 4 f. red .. .. 2·50 15
1808. – 8 f. purple .. .. 2·50 15
1809. – 10 f. red .. .. 2·75 15
DESIGNS: 8 f. Battery of steel furnaces. 10 f. Steel "blowers" and workers.

**1959.** Int. Women's Day.
1810. **294.** 8 f. green on cream .. 25 10
1811. – 22 f. mauve on cream 30 10
DESIGN: 22 f. Russian and Chinese women.

**295.** Natural History Museum, Peking. **296.** Barley.

**1959.** Opening of Natural History Museum, Peking.
1812. **295.** 4 f. turquoise .. 25 10
1813. 8 f. sepia .. .. 25 10

**1959.** Successful Harvest.
1814. 8 f. red (T **296**) .. 25 10
1815. 8 f. red (Rice) .. 25 10
1816. 8 f. red (Cotton) .. 25 10
1817. 8 f. red (Soya beans, groundnuts and rape) .. .. 25 10

**297.** Workers with Marx-Lenin Banner. **298.** Airport Building.

**1959.** Labour Day. Inscr. "1889—1959".
1818. **297.** 4 f. blue .. .. 2·25 40
1819. – 8 f. red .. .. 3·25 25
1820. – 22 f. green .. .. 3·00 10
DESIGNS: 8 f. Hands clasping Red Flag. 22 f. "5.1" and workers.

**1959.** Inaug. of Peking Airport.
1821. **298.** 8 f. black on lilac .. 3·25 25
1822. – 10 f. black on green .. 4·00 10
DESIGN: 10 f. Ilyushin Il-14P at airport.

**299.** Students with Banners. **300.** F. Joliot-Curie (first President).

**1959.** 40th Anniv. of "May 4th" Students' Rising.
1823. **299.** 4 f. red, brown & olive 4·75 1·25
1824. – 8 f. red, brn. & bistre 5·75 70
DESIGN: 8 f. Workers with banners.

**1959.** 10th Anniv. of World Peace Council.
1825. **300.** 8 f. purple .. .. 2·25 30
1826. – 22 f. violet .. .. 3·00 20
DESIGN: 22 f. Silhouettes of European, Chinese and Negro.

**301.** Stamp Printing Works, Peking. **302.**

**1959.** Sino-Czech Co-operation in Postage Stamp Production.
1827. **301.** 8 f. myrtle .. .. 4·50 60

**1959.** World Table Tennis Championships, Dortmund.
1828. **302.** 4 f. blue and black .. 1·00 20
1829. 8 f. red and black .. 1·40 25

**303.** Moon Rocket. **304.** "Prologue".

**1959.** Launching of First Lunar Rocket.
1830. **303.** 8 f. red, blue & black 10·00 1·00

**1959.** 1st Anniv. of People's Communes.
1831. **304.** 8 f. red .. .. 30 10
1832. – 8 f. dull purple .. 30 10
1833. – 8 f. orange .. .. 30 10
1834. – 8 f. green .. .. 30 10
1835. – 8 f. blue .. .. 30 10
1836. – 8 f. olive .. .. 30 10
1837. – 8 f. blue .. .. 30 10
1838. – 8 f. mauve .. .. 30 10
1839. – 8 f. black .. .. 30 10
1840. – 8 f. green .. .. 30 10
1841. – 8 f. violet .. .. 30 10
1842. – 8 f. red .. .. 30 10

DESIGNS: No. 1832, Steel worker ("Rural Industries"). No. 1833, Farm girl ("Agriculture"). No. 1834, Salesgirl ("Trade"). No. 1835, Peasant ("Study"). No. 1836, Militiaman ("Militia"). No. 1837, Cook with tray of food ("Community Meals"). No. 1838, Child watering flowers ("Nursery"). No. 1839, Old man with pipe ("Old People's Homes"). No. 1840, Health worker ("Public Health"). No. 1841, Young flautist ("Recreation and Entertainment"). No. 1842, Star-shaped flower ("Epilogue").

**305.** Mao Tse-tung and Gate of Heavenly Peace, Peking. **306.** Republican Emblem.

**1959.** 10th Anniv. of People's Republic.
(a) 1st issue. Inscr. "1949–1959". With gum.
1843. **305.** 8 f. red and brown .. 6·00 1·50
1844. – 8 f. red and blue .. 5·00 1·50
1845. – 22 f. red and green .. 6·00 1·50
DESIGNS: No. 1844, Marx, Lenin and Kremlin. No. 1845, Dove of peace and globe.

(b) 2nd issue. Emblem in red and yellow; inscriptions in yellow; background colours given.
1846. **306.** 4 f. turquoise .. 2·25 75
1847. 8 f. lilac .. .. 2·75 25
1848. 10 f. blue .. .. 3·00 50
1849. 20 f. buff .. .. 3·25 85

**307.** Steel Plant.

DESIGNS: No. 1851, Coal-mine. No. 1852, Steelmill. No. 1853, Double-decked bridge. No. 1854, Combine-harvester. No. 1855, Dam construction. No. 1856, Textile mill. No. 1857, Chemical works.

(c) 3rd issue. Inscr. "1949–1959". Frames in purple; centre colours given. With gum.
1850. **307.** 8 f. red .. .. 35 10
1851. – 8 f. drab .. .. 35 10
1852. – 8 f. bistre .. .. 35 10
1853. – 8 f. blue .. .. 35 15
1854. – 8 f. salmon .. .. 35 10
1855. – 8 f. green .. .. 35 10
1856. – 8 f. turquoise .. 35 10
1857. – 8 f. lilac .. .. 35 10

**308.** Rejoicing Populace.

(d) 4th Issue. Multicoloured.
1858 8 f. Type **308** .. .. 1·25 25
1859 10 f. Rejoicing people and industrial plant (vert) 2·00 20
1860 20 f. Tree, banners and people carrying wheat and flowers (vert) .. 2·00 30

**309.** Mao Tse-tung proclaiming Republic.

(e) 5th issue.
1861. **309.** 20 f. lake .. .. 11·00 3·25

**310.** Boy Bugler ("Summer Camps"). **311.** Exhibition Emblem and Symbols of Communication.

**1959.** 10th Anniv of Chinese Youth Pioneers.
1862 – 4 f. yellow, red & blk 1·50 10
1863 **310** 4 f. red and blue .. 1·50 10
1864 – 8 f. red and brown .. 1·50 10
1865 – 8 f. red and blue .. 1·50 10
1866 – 8 f. red and green .. 1·50 10
1867 – 8 f. red and purple .. 1·50 10
DESIGNS: No. 1862, Pioneers' emblem. No. 1864, Schoolgirl with flowers and satchel ("Study"). No. 1865, Girl with rain gauge ("Science"). No. 1866, Boy with sapling ("Forestry"). No. 1867, Girl skater ("Athletic Sports").

**1959.** National Exn. of Industry and Communications, Peking. Inscr. "1949–1959".
1868. **311.** 4 f. blue .. .. 30 15
1869. – 8 f. red .. .. 30 15
DESIGN: 8 f. Exn. emblem and symbols of industry.

**312.** Cultural Palace of the Nationalities. **313.** "Statue of Sport".

**1959.** Inauguration of Cultural Palace of the Nationalities, Peking.
1870. **312.** 4 f. black and red .. 1·40 25
1871. 8 f. black and green .. 1·40 25

**1959.** 1st National Games, Peking. Mult.
1872 8 f. Type **313** .. 85 10
1873 8 f. Parachuting .. 85 10
1874 8 f. Pistol-shooting .. 85 10
1875 8 f. Diving .. 85 10
1876 8 f. Table tennis .. 85 10
1877 8 f. Weightlifting .. 85 10
1878 8 f. High jumping .. 85 10
1879 8 f. Rowing .. 85 10
1880 8 f. Running .. 85 10
1881 8 f. Basketball .. 85 10
1882 8 f. Fencing .. 85 10
1883 8 f. Motor cycling .. 85 10
1884 8 f. Gymnastics .. 85 10
1885 8 f. Cycling .. 85 10
1886 8 f. Horse-racing .. 85 10
1887 8 f. Football .. 85 10

**314.** Wheat (Main Pavilion).

DESIGNS: 8 f. Meteorological symbols (Meteorological Pavilion). 10 f. Cattle (Animal Husbandry Pavilion). 20 f. Fishes (Aquatic Products Pavilion).

**1960.** Opening of National Agricultural Exhibition Hall, Peking.
1888. **314.** 4 f. black, red & orge. 30 10
1889. – 8 f. black and blue .. 35 10
1890. – 10 f. black and brown 35 10
1891. – 20 f. black and turq. 45 10

**315.** Crossing the Chinsha River.

**1960.** 25th Anniv. of Conference during the Long March, Tsunyi, Kweichow.
1892. – 4 f. blue .. .. 5·50 60
1893. – 8 f. turquoise .. 5·50 1·75
1894. **315.** 10 f. green .. .. 7·00 2·00
DESIGNS: 4 f. Conference Hall, Tsunyi. 8 f. Mao Tse-tung and flags.

**316.** Clara Zetkin (founder.) **317.** Chinese and Soviet Workers.

**1960.** 50th Anniv. of Int. Women's Day. Frame and inscriptions black. Centre colours given.
1895. **316.** 4 f. blue, black & flesh 80 10
1896. – 8 f. multicoloured .. 80 10
1897. – 10 f. multicoloured .. 80 20
1898. – 22 f. multicoloured .. 1·10 30
DESIGNS: 8 f. Mother, child and dove. 10 f. Woman tractor-driver. 22 f. Women of three races.

**1960.** 10th Anniv. of Sino-Soviet Treaty.

1899. **317.** 4 f. brown .. .. 4·00 75
1900. – 8 f. black, yell. & red 4·00 1·00
1901. – 10 f. blue .. .. 5·00 2·50

DESIGNS: 8 f. Flowers and Sino-Soviet emblems. 10 f. Chinese and Soviet soldiers.

**318.** Flags of Hungary and China. **319.** Lenin speaking.

**1960.** 15th Anniv. of Hungarian Liberation.

1902. **318.** 8 f. multicoloured .. 3·75 1·50
1903. – 8 f. red, black & blue 3·75 1·50

DESIGN: No. 1903, Parliament Building, Budapest.

**1960.** 90th Birth Anniv. of Lenin.

1904. **319.** 4 f. lilac .. .. 3·25 40
1905. – 8 f. black and red .. 4·25 1·50
1906. – 20 f. brown .. .. 4·25 2·00

DESIGNS: 8 f. Lenin (portrait). 20 f. Lenin talking with Red Guards (after Vasilyev).

**320.** "Lunik 2". **321.** View of Prague.

**1960.** Lunar Rocket Flights.

1907. **320.** 8 f. red .. .. 2·00 25
1908. – 10 f. green (Lunik 3) 2·00 25

**1960.** 15th Anniv. of Liberation of Czechoslovakia.

1909. – 8 f. multicoloured .. 4·00 1·50
1910. **321.** 8 f. green .. .. 4·00 1·50

DESIGN—VERT. No. 1909, Child pioneers and flags of China and Czechoslovakia.

**SERIAL NUMBERS.** In this and many later multicoloured sets containing several stamps of the same denomination, the serial number is quoted in brackets to assist identification. This is the last figure in the bottom left corner of the stamp.

**322.** "Out-folded Operculum and Nostril Bouquet".

**1960.** Chinese Goldfish. Multicoloured.

1911. 4 f. (1) Type **322** .. 4·50 25
1912. 4 f. (2) "Black-back Dragon-eye" .. 4·50 25
1913. 4 f. (3) "Bubble-eye" .. 4·50 25
1914. 4 f. (4) "Red Tigerhead" 4·50 25
1915. 8 f. (5) "Pearl-scale" .. 5·50 25
1916. 8 f. (6) "Blue Dragon-eye" 5·50 90
1917. 8 f. (7) "Skyward-eye" .. 5·50 25
1918. 8 f. (8) "Red-cap" .. 5·50 1·00
1919. 8 f. (9) "Purple-cap" .. 10·00 3·00
1920. 8 f. (10) "Red-head" .. 10·00 3·00
1921. 8 f. (11) "Red and White Dragon-eye" .. 12·00 3·00
1922. 8 f. (12) "Red Dragon-eye" 15·00 3·00

**323.** Sow with Litter.

**1960.** Pig-breeding.

1923. **323.** 8 f. black and red .. 5·00 30
1924. – 8 f. black and green .. 5·00 30
1925. – 8 f. black and mauve 5·00 1·50
1926. – 8 f. black and olive .. 6·00 30
1927. – 8 f. black and orange 7·00 1·50

DESIGNS: No. 1924, Pig being inoculated. No. 1925, Group of pigs. No. 1926, Pig and feeding pens. No. 1927, Pig and crop-bales.

**HAVE YOU READ THE NOTES AT THE BEGINNING OF THIS CATALOGUE?**
These often provide answers to the enquiries we receive.

**324.** "Serving the Workers". **325.** N. Korean and Chinese Flags, and Flowers.

**1960.** 3rd National Literary and Art Workers' Congress, Peking. Inscr. "1960".

1928. **324.** 4 f. red, sepia & green 3·75 1·50
1929. – 8 f. red, bistre & turq. 3·75 1·50

DESIGN: 8 f. Inscribed stone seal.

**1960.** 15th Anniv. of Liberation of Korea.

1930. **325.** 8 f. red, yellow & green 5·75 2·25
1931. – 8 f. red, indigo & blue 5·75 2·75

DESIGN: No. 1931, "Flying Horse" of Korea.

**326.** Peking Railway Station.

**1960.** Opening of New Peking Railway Station.

1932. **326.** 8 f. multicoloured .. 6·50 2·00
1933. – 10 f. bl., cream & turq. 9·50 2·00

DESIGN: 10 f. Train arriving in station.

**327.** Chinese and N. Vietnamese Flags, and Children. **328.** Worker and Spray Fan.

**1960.** 15th Anniv. of N. Vietnam Republic.

1934. **327.** 8 f. red, yell. & black 1·75 75
1935. – 8 f. multicoloured .. 1·75 75

DESIGN—VERT. No. 1935, "Lake of the Returning Sword", Hanoi.

**1960.** Public Health Campaign.

1936. **328.** 8 f. black and orange 60 10
1937. – 8 f. green and blue .. 60 10
1938. – 8 f. brown and blue 60 10
1939. – 8 f. lake and brown .. 60 10
1940. – 8 f. blue and turquoise 60 10

DESIGNS: No. 1937, Spraying insecticide. No. 1938, Cleaning windows. No. 1939, Medical examination of child. No. 1940, "Tai Chi Chuan" (Chinese physical drill).

**329.** Façade of Great Hall.

**1960.** Completion of "Great Hall of the People". Multicoloured.

1941. 8 f. Type **329** .. .. 5·00 1·75
1942. 10 f. Interior of Great Hall 5·00 1·75

**330.** Dr. N. Bethune operating on Soldier. **331.** Friedrich Engels.

**1960.** 70th Birth Anniv of Dr. Norman Bethune (Canadian surgeon with 8th Route Army).

1943. **330.** 8 f. grey, blk. & red .. 1·50 25
1944. 8 f. brown .. .. 1·25 25

PORTRAIT. No. 1943 Dr. N. Bethune.

**1960.** 140th Birth Anniv. of Engels.

1945. – 8 f. brown .. .. 4·00 1·50
1946. **331.** 10 f. orange and blue 4·00 1·50

DESIGN: 8 f. Engels addressing Congress at The Hague.

**332.** Big "Ju-I". **333.** "Yue Jin".

**1960.** Chrysanthemums. Background colours given. Multicoloured.

1947. – 4 f. blue .. .. 2·50 10
1948. – 4 f. pink .. .. 2·50 10
1949. – 8 f. grey .. .. 2·50 10
1950. **332.** 8 f. blue .. .. 3·50 10
1951. – 8 f. green .. .. 3·50 10
1952. – 8 f. violet .. .. 3·50 10
1953. – 8 f. olive .. .. 2·50 10
1954. – 8 f. turquoise .. 2·50 10
1955. – 10 f. grey .. .. 3·25 10
1956. – 10 f. brown .. .. 3·25 10
1957. – 20 f. blue .. .. 3·75 75
1958. – 20 f. red .. .. 3·75 75
1959. – 22 f. brown .. .. 6·50 50
1960. – 22 f. red .. .. 7·50 1·25
1961. – 30 f. green .. .. 11·00 1·25
1962. – 30 f. mauve .. .. 13·00 2·75
1963. – 35 f. green .. .. 15·00 3·25
1964. – 52 f. purple .. .. 18·00 2·50

CHRYSANTHEMUMS: No. 1947, "Hwang Shih Pa". No. 1948, "Green Peony". No. 1949, "Er Chiao". No. 1951, "Ju-I" with Golden Hooks. No. 1952, "Golden Peony". No. 1953, "Generalissimo's Banner". No. 1954, "Willow Thread". No. 1955, "Cassia on Salver of Hibiscus". No. 1956, "Pearls on Jade Salver". No. 1957, "Red Gold Lion". No. 1958, "Milky White Jade". No. 1959, "Purple Jade with Fragrant Beads". No. 1960, "Cassia on Ice Salver". No. 1961, "Inky Black Lotus". No. 1962, "Jade Bamboo Shoot of Superior Class". No. 1963, "Smiling Face". No. 1964, "Swan Ballet".

**1960.** 1st Chinese-built Freighter. Launching. No gum.

1965. **333.** 8 f. blue .. .. 3·75 1·00

**334.** Pantheon, Paris. **336.** Chan Tien-yu.

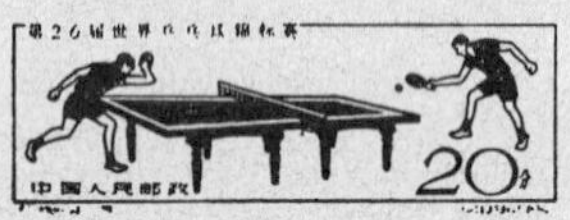

**335.** Table Tennis Match.

**1961.** 90th Anniv. of Paris Commune.

1966. **334.** 8 f. black and red .. 2·75 50
1967. – 8 f. sepia and red .. 2·75 50

DESIGN: No. 1967, Proclamation of Commune.

**1961.** 26th World Table Tennis Championships, Peking. Multicoloured.

1968 8 f. Championship emblem and jasmine .. .. 75 10
1969 10 f. Table tennis bat and ball and Temple of Heaven .. .. 75 10
1970 20 f. Type **335** .. .. 75 10
1971 22 f. Peking Workers' Gymnasium .. 75 10

**1961.** Birth Cent. of Chan Tien-yu (railway construction engineer).

1972. **336.** 8 f. black and sage .. 75 15
1973. – 10 f. brown and sepia 1·50 15

DESIGN: 10 f. Train on Peking–Changchow Railway.

**337.** Congress Building, Shanghai.

**1961.** 40th Anniv. of Chinese Communist Party. Flags, red; frames, gold.

1974. **337.** 4 f. purple .. .. 3·50 25
1975. – 8 f. green .. .. 3·75 25
1976. – 10 f. brown .. .. 3·75 1·25
1977. – 20 f. blue .. .. 4·75 1·25
1978. – 30 f. red .. .. 6·50 1·25

DESIGNS: 8 f. "August 1" Building, Nanchang. 10 f. Provisional Central Govt. Building, Juichin. 20 f. Pagoda Hill, Yenan. 30 f. Gate of Heavenly Peace, Peking.

**338.** Flags of China and Mongolia. **339.** "August 1" Building, Nanchang.

**1961.** 40th Anniv. of Mongolian People's Revolution.

1979 **338** 8 f. red, blue and yell 4·00 1·00
1980 – 10 f. orge, yell & grn 4·00 2·25

DESIGN: 10 f. Mongolian Government Building.

**1961.** Size 24 × 16½ mm. No gum.

1981 **339** 1 f. blue .. .. 4·25 10
1982 1½ f. red .. .. 5·00 10
1983 2 f. green .. .. 7·50 10
1984 A 3 f. violet .. .. 10·00 10
1985 4 f. green .. .. 1·50 10
1986 5 f. green .. .. 1·50 10
1987 B 8 f. green .. .. 1·25 10
1988 10 f. purple .. .. 1·25 10
1989 20 f. blue .. .. 65 10
1990 C 22 f. brown .. .. 65 10
1991 30 f. blue .. .. 65 10
1992 50 f. red .. .. 1·10 10

DESIGNS: A, Tree and Sha Chow Pa Building, Juichin. B, Yenan Pagoda. C, Gate of Heavenly Peace, Peking.

For redrawn, smaller, designs see Nos. 2010/21.

**340.** Military Museum.

**1961.** People's Revolutionary Military Museum.

1993. **340.** 8 f. brown, grn. & bl. 7·50 75
1994. 10 f. blk., grn. & brn. 7·50 50

DESIGN—VERT. 10 f. Dr. Sun Yat-sen.

**341.** Uprising at Wuhan.

**1961.** 50th Anniv. of Revolution of 1911.

1995. **341.** 8 f. black and grey .. 3·50 50
1996. – 10 f. black and brown 5·50 75

**342.** Donkey. **343.** Tibetans Rejoicing.

**1961.** Tang Dynasty Pottery (618–907 A.D.). Centres multicoloured. Background colours given.

1997. **342.** 4 f. blue .. .. 2·00 10
1998. – 8 f. green .. .. 2·00 10
1999. – 8 f. purple .. .. 2·00 10
2000. – 10 f. blue .. .. 2·25 35
2001. – 20 f. olive .. .. 2·25 60
2002. – 22 f. turquoise .. 2·75 1·25
2003. – 30 f. red .. .. 3·25 1·25
2004. – 50 f. slate .. .. 4·50 1·00

DESIGNS: No. 1998, Donkey. Nos. 1999/2002, Various horses. Nos. 2003/4, Various camels.

**1961.** "Rebirth of the Tibetan People".

2005. **343.** 4 f. brown and buff .. 1·75 10
2006. – 8 f. brown & turquoise 2·00 10
2007. – 10 f. brown & yellow 3·00 10
2008. – 20 f. brown and pink 6·50 1·00
2009. – 30 f. brown and blue 12·00 1·00

DESIGNS: 8 f. Sower. 10 f. Tibetan celebrating "bumper crop". 20 f. "Responsible Citizens". 30 f. Tibetan children.

**343a.** "August 1" Building, Nanchang. **344.** Lu Hsun (after Hsieh Chia-seng).

**1962.** Size $20\frac{1}{2} \times 16\frac{1}{2}$ mm. No gum.
2010 343a 1 f. blue 20 10
2011 2 f. green 20 10
2013 A 3 f. violet 20 10
2014 343a 3 f. brown 1·00 50
2015 A 4 f. green 20 10
2016 B 4 f. red 1·00 50
2017 C 8 f. green 50 10
2018 10 f. purple 20 10
2019 20 f. blue 40 10
2020 B 30 f. blue 75 10
2021 52 f. red 2·25 2·00
DESIGNS: A, Tree and Sha Chow Pa Building, Juichin. B, Gate of Heavenly Peace, Peking. C, Yenan Pagoda.

**1962.** 80th Birth Anniv. of Lu Hsun (writer).
2022. **344.** 8 f. black and red 40 10

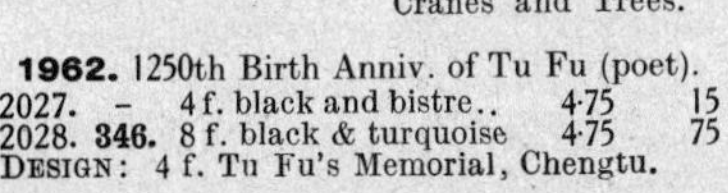

**345.** Anchi Bridge, Chaohsien.

**1962.** Ancient Chinese Bridges.
2023. **345.** 4 f. violet and lavender 40 10
2024. – 8 f. slate and green 65 10
2025. – 10 f. sepia and bistre 75 10
2026. – 20 f. blue & turquoise 85 10
BRIDGES: 8 f. Paotai, Soochow. 10 f. Chupu, Kuanhsien. 20 f. Chenyang, Sankiang.

**346.** Tu Fu. **347.** Manchurian Cranes and Trees.

**1962.** 1250th Birth Anniv. of Tu Fu (poet).
2027. – 4 f. black and bistre 4·75 15
2028. **346.** 8 f. black & turquoise 4·75 75
DESIGN: 4 f. Tu Fu's Memorial, Chengtu.

**1962.** "The Sacred Crane". Paintings by Chen Chi-fo. Multicoloured.
2029. 8 f. Type **347** 6·50 1·25
2030. 10 f. Two cranes in flight 6·50 1·50
2031. 20 f. Crane on rock 8·00 1·50

**348.** Cuban Soldier. **349.** Torch and Map.

**1962.** "Support for Cuba".
2032. **348.** 8 f. black and lake 10·00 1·00
2033. – 10 f. black and green 10·00 75
2034. – 22 f. black and blue 22·00 7·50
DESIGNS: 10 f. Sugar-cane planter. 22 f. Militiaman and woman.

**1961.** "Support for Algeria".
2035. **349.** 8 f. orange and brown 40 15
2036. – 22 f. brown & ochre 40 20
DESIGN: 22 f. Algerian patriots.

**350.** Mei Lan-fang (actor). **351.** Han "Flower Drum" Dance.

**1962.** "Stage Art of Mei Lan-fang". Multicoloured. Each showing Lan-fang in stage costume with items given below.
2037. 4 f. Type **350** 10·00 75
2038. 8 f. Drum 8·00 75
2039. 8 f. Fan 8·00 50
2040. 10 f. Swords 7·50 75
2041. 20 f. Bag 8·00 1·25
2042. 22 f. Ribbons 12·00 2·50
2043. 30 f. Loom 18·00 7·50
2044. 50 f. Long sleeves 18·00 5·50
Nos. 2042/4 are horiz.

**1962.** Chinese Folk Dances (1st issue). Multicoloured. No gum.
2045. 4 f. Type **351** 25 10
2046. 8 f. Mongolian "Ordos" 30 10
2047. 10 f. Chuang "Catching shrimp" 50 10
2048. 20 f. Tibetan "Fiddle" 75 20
2049. 30 f. Yi "Friend" 85 25
2050. 50 f. Uighur "Tambourine" 1·10 30
See also Nos. 2104/15.

**352.** Soldiers storming the Winter Palace, Petrograd.

**1962.** 45th Anniv. of Russian Revolution.
2051. – 8 f. brown and red 5·75 35
2052. **352.** 20 f. bronze and red 8·25 75
DESIGN—VERT. 8 f. Lenin leading soldiers.

**353.** Revolutionary Statue and Map. **354.** Tsai Lun (A.D. ?–121, inventor of paper making process).

**1962.** 50th Anniv. of Albanian Independence.
2053. **353.** 8 f. sepia and blue 75 30
2054. – 10 f. multicoloured 75 40
DESIGN: 10 f. Albanian flag and pioneer.

**1962.** Scientists of Ancient China. Multicoloured.
2055. 4 f. Type **354** 60 10
2056. 4 f. Paper-making 60 10
2057. 8 f. Sun Szu-miao (581–682, physician) 1·25 10
2058. 8 f. Preparing medical treatise 1·25 10
2059. 10 f. Shen Ko (1031–1095, geologist) 1·50 20
2060. 10 f. Making field notes 1·50 20
2061. 20 f. Ku Shou-chin (1231–1316, astronomer) 1·75 1·00
2062. 20 f. Astronomical equipment 1·75 1·00

**355.** Tank Monument, Havana.

DESIGNS—As Type **355**: No. 2064, Cuban revolutionaries. No. 2067, Cuban soldier. No. 2068, Castro and Cuban flag. LARGER ($48\frac{1}{2} \times 27$ mm.) No. 2065, Crowd in Havana (value on left). No. 2066, Crowd in Peking (value on right).

**1963.** 4th Anniv. of Cuban Revolution.
2063. **355.** 4 f. sepia and red 6·00 40
2064. – 4 f. black and green 6·00 40
2065. – 8 f. lake and brown 7·50 40
2066. – 8 f. lake and brown 7·50 40
2067. – 10 f. black and buff 10·00 2·50
2068. – 10 f. sepia, red & blue 10·00 5·50

**356.** Tibetan Clouded Yellow. **357.** Marx and Engels.

**1963.** Butterflies. Multicoloured. No gum.
2069 4 f. (1) Type **356** 2·00 15
2070 4 f. (2) Tritailed glory 2·00 15
2071 4 f. (3) Neumogeni jungle queen 2·00 15
2072 4 f. (4) Washan swordtail 2·00 15
2073 4 f. (5) Striped ringlet 2·00 10
2074 8 f. (6) Green dragontail 2·25 10
2075 8 f. (7) Dilunuleted peacock 2·25 10
2076 8 f. (8) Yamfly 2·25 10
2077 8 f. (9) Golden kaiser-i-hind 2·25 10
2078 8 f. (10) Mushaell hairstreak 2·25 10
2079 10 f. (11) Yellow orange-tip 2·75 15
2080 10 f. (12) Great jay 2·75 15
2081 10 f. (13) Striped punch 2·75 15
2082 10 f. (14) Beck butterfly 2·75 15
2083 10 f. (15) Omei skipper 2·75 15
2084 20 f. (16) Philippine birdwing 3·75 15
2085 20 f. (17) Keeled apollo 3·75 15
2086 22 f. (18) Blue-banded king crow 4·50 15
2087 30 f. (19) Solskyi copper 5·50 1·75
2088 50 f. (20) Clipper 7·50 1·25

**1963.** 145th Birth Anniv. of Karl Marx. No gum.
2089. – 8 f. blk., flesh & gold 2·50 75
2090. – 8 f. red and gold 2·50 75
2091. **357.** 8 f. brown and gold 2·50 75
DESIGNS: No. 2089, Marx. No. 2090, Slogan "Workers of the World Unite" over cover of 1st edition of "Communist Manifesto".

**358.** Child with Top. **359.** Giant Panda eating Apples.

**1963.** Children. Multicoloured, background colours given. No gum.
2092. **358.** 4 f. turquoise 20 10
2093. – 4 f. brown 20 10
2094. – 8 f. grey 20 10
2095. – 8 f. blue 20 10
2096. – 8 f. beige 20 10
2097. – 8 f. slate 20 10
2098. – 8 f. green 20 10
2099. – 8 f. grey 20 10
2100. – 10 f. green 45 10
2101. – 10 f. violet 45 10
2102. – 20 f. drab 1·10 10
2103. – 20 f. green 1·10 10
DESIGNS (each shows a child): No. 2093, Eating candied hawberries. No. 2094, As "traffic policeman". No. 2095, With toy windmill. No. 2096, Listening to caged cricket. No. 2097, With toy sword. No 2098, Embroidering. No. 2099, With umbrella. No. 2100, Playing with sand. No. 2101, Playing table tennis. No. 2102, Doing sums. No. 2103, Flying kite.

**1963.** Chinese Folk Dances (2nd issue). As T **351** but inscr. "(261) 1962" to "(266) 1962" in bottom right corner. Multicoloured. No gum.
2104. 4 f. Puyi "Weaving Cloth" 25 10
2105. 8 f. Kazakh 30 10
2106. 10 f. Olunchun 40 10
2107. 20 f. Kaochan "Labour" 50 10
2108. 30 f. Miao "Reed-pipe" 60 10
2109. 50 f. Korean "Fan" 70 10

**1963.** Chinese Folk Dances (3rd issue). As T **351** but inscr. "(279) 1963" to "(284) 1963" in bottom right corner. Multicoloured. No gum.
2110. 4 f. Yu "Wedding Ceremony" 25 10
2111. 8 f. Pai "Encircling Mountain Forest" 30 10
2112. 10 f. Yao "Long Drum" 40 10
2113. 20 f. Li "Third Day of Third Month" 50 10
2114. 30 f. Kava "Knife" 60 10
2115. 50 f. Tai "Peacock" 70 10

**1963.** Giant Panda. Perf. or imperf.
2116. **359.** 8 f. black and blue 11·00 60
2117. – 8 f. black and green 12·00 1·00
2118. – 10 f. black and drab 12·00 1·00
DESIGNS—As Type **278**. No. 2117, Giant panda eating bamboo shoots. HORIZ. (52 × 31 mm.): No. 2118, Two giant pandas.

**360.** Table Tennis Player. **361.** Snub-nosed Monkey.

**1963.** 27th World Table-Tennis Championships.
2119. **360.** 8 f. grey 4·50 20
2120. – 8 f. brown 4·50 30
DESIGN: No. 2120, Trophies won by Chinese team.

**1963.** Snub-nosed Monkeys. Mult.
2121. 8 f. Type **361** 3·50 35
2122. 10 f. Two monkeys 3·50 35
2123. 22 f. Two monkeys on branch of tree 4·50 1·25

**362.** Old Pines of Hwangshan.

**1963.** Hwangshan Landscapes. Multicoloured.
2124 4 f. (1) Mount of The Green Jade Screen 2·50 10
2125 4 f. (2) The Guest-welcoming Pines 2·50 10
2126 4 f. (3) Pines and rocks behind the lake 2·50 10
2127 4 f. (4) Terrace of Keeping Cool 2·50 10
2128 8 f. (5) Mount of the Heavenly Capital 3·50 10
2129 8 f. (6) Mount of Scissors 3·50 10
2130 8 f. (7) Forest of Ten Thousand Pines 3·50 10
2131 8 f. (8) The Flowering Bush in a Dream 3·50 10
2132 10 f. (9) Mount of the Lotus Flower 4·00 10
2133 10 f. (10) Cumulus Flood Wave of the Eastern Lake 4·00 10
2134 10 f. (11) Type **362** 4·00 10
2135 10 f. (12) Cumulus on the Eastern Lake 4·00 10
2136 20 f. (13) The Stalagmite Mountain Range 5·50 1·25
2137 22 f. (14) The Apes of the Stone watch the lake below 6·50 1·50
2138 30 f. (15) The Forest of Lions 14·00 7·50
2139 50 f. (16) The Fairy Isles of Peng Lai 15·00 2·75
The 4 f. and 8 f. values are vert.

**363.** Football. **364.** Clay Rooster and Goat.

**1963.** "GANEFO" Athletic Games, Jakarta.
2140. **363.** 8 f. red & blk. on lav. 3·25 40
2141. – 8 f. blue & blk. on buff 3·25 40
2142. – 8 f. brn. & blk. on blue 3·25 40
2143. – 8 f. pur. & blk. on mve. 3·25 40
2144. – 10 f. multicoloured 5·50 1·25
DESIGNS—As Type **282**: No. 2141, Throwing the discus. No. 2142, Diving. No. 2143, Gymnastics. HORIZ. ($48\frac{1}{2} \times 27\frac{1}{2}$ mm.). No. 2144, Athletes on parade.

**1963.** Chinese Folk Toys. Multicoloured. No gum.
2145. 4 f. (1) Type **364** 20 10
2146. 4 f. (4) Cloth camel 20 10
2147. 4 f. (7) Cloth tigers 20 10
2148. 8 f. (2) Clay ox and rider 20 10
2149. 8 f. (5) Cloth rabbit, wooden figure and clay cock 20 10
2150. 8 f. (8) Straw cock 20 10
2151. 10 f. (3) Cloth donkey and clay bird 20 10
2152. 10 f. (6) Clay lion 20 10
2153. 10 f. (9) Clay-paper tumble and cloth tiger 20 10

**365.** Vietnamese Family. **366.** Cuban and Chinese Flags.

**1963.** "Liberation of South Vietnam". Multicoloured.
2154. 8 f. Type **365** 1·75 25
2155. 8 f. Vietnamese with flag 1·75 35

**1964.** 5th Anniv of Cuban Revolution. Mult.
2156. 8 f. Type **366** 4·00 1·00
2157. 8 f. Boy waving flag 6·50 2·75

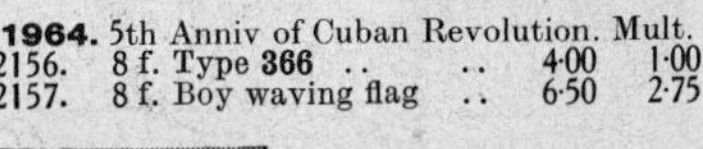

**367.** Woman driving Tractor. **368.** "Sino-African Friendship".

**1964.** "Women of the People's Commune". Multicoloured.

2158. 8 f. (1) Type **367** .. 20 10
2159. 8 f. (2) Harvesting .. 20 10
2160. 8 f. (3) Picking cotton .. 20 10
2161. 8 f. (4) Picking fruit .. 20 10
2162. 8 f. (5) Reading book .. 20 10
2163. 8 f. (6) Holding rifle .. 20 10

**1964.** African Freedom Day.

2164. **368.** 8 f. multicoloured .. 25 10
2165. – 8 f. brown and black 25 10
DESIGN: No. 2165, African beating drum.

DESIGN: No. 2167, Workers and banners.

**369.** Marx, Engels, Lenin and Stalin.

**1964.** Labour Day.

2166. **369.** 8 f. black, red & gold 10·00 3·50
2167. – 8 f. black, red & gold 5·00 2·00

**370.** History Museum.

**1964.** No gum.

2168 **370** 1 f. brown .. .. 10 10
2169 A 1½ f. purple .. .. 10 10
2170 B 2 f. green .. .. 10 10
2171 C 3 f. green .. .. 15 10
2172 **370** 4 f. blue .. .. 15 10
2172a A 5 f. purple .. .. 50 10
2173 B 8 f. red .. .. 20 10
2174 C 10 f. drab .. .. 25 10
2175 **370** 20 f. violet .. .. 35 10
2176 A 22 f. orange .. .. 40 10
2177 B 30 f. green .. .. 40 10
2177a C 50 f. blue .. .. 1·50 10
DESIGNS: A, Gate of Heavenly Peace. B, Great Hall of the People. C, Military Museum.

**371.** Date Orchard, Yenan.

**372.** Map of Vietnam and Flag.

**1964.** "Yenan—Shrine of the Chinese Revolution". Multicoloured.

2178 8 f. (1) Type **371** .. 3·75 20
2179 8 f. (2) Central Auditorium, Yang Chia Ling 75 20
2180 8 f. (3) Mao Tse-tung's Office and Residence at Date Orchard, Yenan 75 20
2181 8 f. (4) Auditorium, Wang Chia Ping .. .. 75 20
2182 8 f. (5) Border Region Assembly Hall .. 4·25 25
2183 52 f. (6) Pagoda Hill .. 3·25 2·00

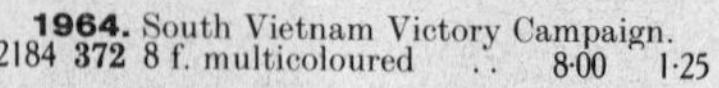

**1964.** South Vietnam Victory Campaign.

2184 **372** 8 f. multicoloured .. 8·00 1·25

**373.** "The Alchemist's Glowing Crucible" (peony).

**374.** "Chueh" (wine cup).

**1964.** Chinese Peonies. Multicoloured.

2185 4 f. (1) Type **373** .. 1·25 10
2186 4 f. (2) Night-shining Jade 1·25 10
2187 8 f. (3) Purple Kuo's Cap 1·25 10
2188 8 f. (4) Chao Pinks .. 1·25 10
2189 8 f. (5) Yao Yellows .. 1·25 10
2190 8 f. (6) Twin Beauties .. 1·25 10
2191 8 f. (7) Ice-veiled Rubies 1·25 10
2192 10 f. (8) Gold-sprinkled Chinese Ink .. 2·00 10
2193 10 f. (9) Cinnabar Jar .. 2·00 10
2194 10 f. (10) Lantien Jade .. 2·00 10
2195 10 f. (11) Imperial Robe Yellow .. .. 2·00 20
2196 10 f. (12) Hu Reds .. 2·00 20
2197 20 f. (13) Pea Green .. 3·75 75
2198 43 f. (14) Wei Purples .. 5·00 3·75
2199 52 f. (15) Intoxicated Celestial Peach .. 8·50 2·50

**1964.** Bronze Vessels of the Yin Dynasty (before 1050 B.C.).

2200 **374** 4 f. (1) blk, grn & yell 1·25 10
2201 – 4 f. (2) blk, grn & yell 1·25 10
2202 – 8 f. (3) blk, grn & yell 1·50 10
2203 – 8 f. (4) black, bl & grn 1·50 10
2204 – 10 f. (5) black & drab 1·75 10
2205 – 10 f. (6) blk, grn & yell 1·75 15
2206 – 20 f. (7) black & grey 2·75 1·00
2207 – 20 f. (8) blk, bl & yell 2·75 1·00
DESIGNS: No. 2201, "Ku" (beaker). 2202, "Kuang" (wine urn). 2203, "Chia" (wine cup). 2204, "Tsun" (wine vessel). 2205, "Yu" (wine urn). 2206, "Tsun" (wine vessel). 2207, "Ting" (ceremonial cauldron).

**375.** "Harvesting".

**376.** Marx, Engels and Trafalgar Square, London (vicinity of old St. Martin's Hall).

**1964.** Agricultural Students. Multicoloured.

2208 8 f. (1) Type **375** .. 45 10
2209 8 f. (2) "Sapling planting" 45 10
2210 8 f. (3) "Study" .. .. 45 10
2211 8 f. (4) "Scientific experiment" .. .. 45 10

**1964.** Cent. of "First International".

2212 **376** 8 f. red, brown & gold 15·00 4·50

**377.** Rejoicing people.

**378.** Oil Derrick.

**1964.** 15th Anniv of People's Republic. Mult.

2213 8 f. (1) Type **377** .. 3·00 75
2214 8 f. (2) Chinese flag .. 3·00 75
2215 8 f. (3) As T **377** in reverse 3·00 75
Nos. 2213/5 were issued in the form of a triptych, in sheets.

**1964.** Petroleum Industry. Multicoloured.

2216 4 f. Geological surveyors and van (horiz) .. 10·00 1·00
2217 8 f. Type **378** .. .. 5·50 20
2218 8 f. Oil-extraction equipment .. .. 5·50 20
2219 10 f. Refinery .. .. 8·50 25
2220 20 f. Railway petroleum trucks (horiz) .. .. 23·00 2·75

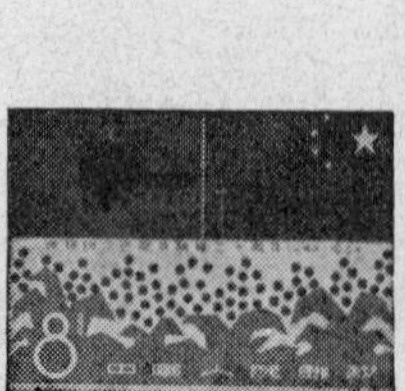

**379.** Albanian and Chinese Flags and Plants.

**380.** Dam under Construction.

**1964.** 20th Anniv of Liberation of Albania.

2221 **379** 8 f. multicoloured .. 5·00 65
2222 – 10 f. black, red & yell 7·50 4·75
DESIGN: 10 f. Enver Hoxha and Albanian arms.

**1964.** Hsinankiang Hydro-Electric Power Station. Multicoloured.

2223 4 f. Type **380** .. .. 13·00 75
2224 8 f. Installation of turbo-generator rotor 2·50 20
2225 8 f. Main dam .. .. 10·00 50
2226 20 f. Pylon .. .. 20·00 3·75

**381.** Fertilisers.

**1964.** Chemical Industry. Main design and inscr. in black; background colours given.

2227 **381** 8 f. (1) red .. .. 60 10
2228 – 8 f. (2) green .. .. 60 10
2229 – 8 f. (3) brown .. .. 60 10
2230 – 8 f. (4) mauve .. .. 60 10
2231 – 8 f. (5) blue .. .. 60 10
2232 – 8 f. (6) orange .. .. 60 10
2233 – 8 f. (7) violet .. .. 60 10
2234 – 8 f. (8) turquoise .. .. 60 10
DESIGNS: (2), Plastics. (3), Medicinal drugs. (4), Rubber. (5), Insecticides. (6), Acids. (7), Alkalis. (8), Synthetic fibres.

**382.** Mao Tse-tung standing in Room.

**1965.** 30th Anniv of Tsunyi Conf. Mult.

2235 8 f. (1) Type **382** .. 7·00 5·00
2236 8 f. (2) Mao Tse-tung .. 7·00 5·00
2237 8 f. (3) "Victory at Loushan Pass" .. 11·00 6·50
No. 2236 is vert (26½ × 36 mm).

**383.** Conference Hall.

**384.** Lenin.

**1965.** 10th Anniv of Bandung Conf. Mult.

2238 8 f. Type **383** .. .. 50 15
2239 8 f. Rejoicing Africans and Asians .. .. 50 15

**1965.** 95th Birth Anniv of Lenin.

2240 **384** 8 f. multicoloured .. 7·50 2·50

**385.** Table Tennis Player.

**386.** All China T.U. Federation Team scaling Mt. Minya Konka.

**1965.** World Table Tennis Championships, Peking.

2241 **385** 8 f. (1) multicoloured 20 10
2242 – 8 f. (2) multicoloured 20 10
2243 – 8 f. (3) multicoloured 20 10
2244 – 8 f. (4) multicoloured 20 10
DESIGNS: Nos. 2242/4 each show different views of table tennis players.

**1965.** Chinese Mountaineering Achievements. Each black, yellow and blue.

2245. 8 f. (1) Type **386** .. 1·75 50
2246. 8 f. (2) Men and women's mixed team on slopes of Muztagh Ata .. 1·75 50
2247. 8 f. (3) Climbers on Mt. Jolmo Lungma .. 1·75 50
2248. 8 f. (4) Women's team camping on Kongur Tiubie Tagh .. .. 1·75 50
2249. 8 f. (5) Climbers on Shishma Pangma .. .. 1·75 50

**387.** Marx and Lenin

**388.** Tseping.

**1965.** Organization of Socialist Countries' Postal Administrations Conference, Peking.

2250 **387** 8 f. multicoloured .. 7·50 2·50

**1965.** "Chingkang Mountains—Cradle of the Chinese Revolution". Multicoloured.

2251. 4 f. (1) Type **388** .. 3·50 10
2252. 8 f. (2) Sanwantsun .. 2·50 10
2253. 8 f. (3) Octagonal Building, Maoping .. .. 2·50 10
2254. 8 f. (4) River and bridge at Lungshih .. .. 2·50 20
2255. 8 f. (5) Tachingtsun .. 2·50 10
2256. 10 f. (6) Bridge at Lungyuankou .. .. 4·00 15
2257. 10 f. (7) Hwangyangchieh 4·00 15
2258. 52 f. (8) Chingkang peaks 11·00 2·50

**389.** Soldiers with Texts.

**1965.** People's Liberation Army. Mult.

2259. 8 f. (1) Type **389** .. 4·50 1·50
2260. 8 f. (2) Soldiers reading book .. .. .. 4·50 1·50
2261. 8 f. (3) Soldier with grenade-thrower .. .. 4·50 1·50
2262. 8 f. (4) Giving tuition in firing rifle .. .. 4·50 1·50
2263. 8 f. (5) Soldiers at rest .. 4·50 1·50
2264. 8 f. (6) Bayonet charge .. 4·50 1·50
2265. 8 f. (7) Soldier with banners 6·00 2·00
2266. 8 f. (8) Military band .. 4·50 1·50
Nos. 2263/6 are vert.

**390.** "Welcome to Peking".

**391.** Soldier firing Weapon.

**1965.** Chinese—Japanese Youth Meeting, Peking. Multicoloured.

2267. 4 f. (1) Type **390** .. 25 10
2268. 8 f. (2) Chinese and Japanese youths with linked arms .. .. 25 10
2269. 8 f. (3) Chinese and Japanese girls .. .. 25 10
2270. 10 f. (4) Musical entertainment .. .. 50 10
2271. 22 f. (5) Emblem of Meeting .. .. 75 10

**1965.** "Vietnamese People's Struggle".

2272. **391.** 8 f. (1) brown and red 50 20
2273. – 8 f. (2) olive and red .. 50 20
2274. – 8 f. (3) purple and red 50 20
2275. – 8 f. (4) black and red 50 20

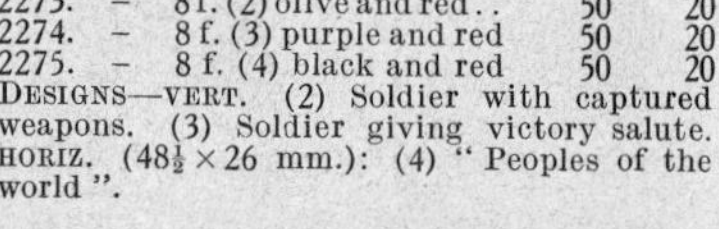

DESIGNS—VERT. (2) Soldier with captured weapons. (3) Soldier giving victory salute. HORIZ. (48½ × 26 mm.): (4) "Peoples of the world".

**392.** "Victory".

**393.** Football.

**1965.** 20th Anniv. of Victory over Japanese.

2276. – 8 f. (1) multicoloured 5·00 3·50
2277. – 8 f. (2) green and red 4·00 50
2278. **392.** 8 f. (3) sepia and red 4·00 50
2279. – 8 f. (4) green and red 4·00 50
DESIGNS—HORIZ. (50½ × 36 mm.): (1) Mao Tse-tung writing. As Type **392**—HORIZ. (2) Soldiers crossing Yellow River. (4) Recruits in cart.

**1965.** 2nd National Games. Multicoloured.
2280. 4 f. (1) Type **393** .. 2·25 10
2281. 4 f. (2) Archery .. .. 2·25 10
2282. 8 f. (3) Throwing the javelin .. .. .. 2·25 10
2283. 8 f. (4) Gymnastics .. 2·75 10
2284. 8 f. (5) Volleyball .. 2·25 10
2285. 10 f. (6) Opening ceremony .. .. 10·00 10
2286. 10 f. (7) Cycling .. .. 22·00 10
2287. 20 f. (8) Diving .. .. 13·00 25
2288. 22 f. (9) Hurdling .. 3·25 75
2289. 30 f. (10) Weightlifting .. 3·25 1·25
2290. 43 f. (11) Basketball .. 6·50 1·25
The 10 f. (6) is larger, 56 × 35½ mm.

**394.** Textile Workers.

**1965.** Women in Industry. Multicoloured.
2291. 8 f. (1) Type **394** .. 3·50 10
2292. 8 f. (2) Machine building 3·50 10
2293. 8 f. (3) Building construction .. .. .. 3·50 10
2294. 8 f. (4) Studying .. 3·50 10
2295. 8 f. (5) Militia guard .. 3·50 2·40

**395.** Children playing with ball.

**1966.** Children's Games. Multicoloured.
2296 4 f. (1) Type **395** .. 15 10
2297 4 f. (2) Racing .. .. 15 10
2298 8 f. (3) Tobogganing .. 15 10
2299 8 f. (4) Exercising .. 15 10
2300 8 f. (5) Swimming .. 15 10
2301 8 f. (6) Shooting .. .. 15 10
2302 10 f. (7) Jumping with rope .. .. .. 35 10
2303 52 f. (8) Playing table tennis .. .. .. 50 30

**396.** Mobile Transformer.

**1966.** New Industrial Machines.
2304. **396.** 4 f. (1) black & yellow 3·50 20
2305. – 8 f. (2) black and blue 3·50 20
2306. – 8 f. (3) black and pink 3·50 20
2307. – 8 f. (4) black & olive 3·50 20
2308. – 8 f. (5) black & purple 3·50 20
2309. – 10 f. (6) black and grey 5·00 70
2310. – 10 f. (7) black & turq. 5·00 70
2311. – 22 f. (8) black & lilac 6·00 2·25
DESIGNS—VERT. (2), Electron microscope. (4), Vertical boring and turning machine. (6), Hydraulic press. (8), Electron accelerator. HORIZ. (3), Lathe. (5), Gear-grinding machine. (7), Milling machine.

**397.** Women of Military and Other Services.

**1966.** Women in Public Service. Mult.
2312. 8 f. (1) Type **397** .. .. 20 10
2313. 8 f. (2) Train conductress 20 10
2314. 8 f. (3) Red Cross worker 20 10
2315. 8 f. (4) Kindergarten teacher .. .. .. 20 10
2316. 8 f. (5) Roadsweeper .. 20 10
2317. 8 f. (6) Hairdresser .. 20 10
2318. 8 f. (7) Bus conductress .. 20 10
2319. 8 f. (8) Travelling saleswoman .. .. .. 20 10
2320. 8 f. (9) Canteen worker .. 20 10
2321. 8 f. (10) Rural postwoman 20 10

**398.** "Thunderstorm" (sculpture).

**399.** Dr. Sun Yat-sen.

**1966.** Afro-Asian Writers' Meeting.
2322. **398.** 8 f. black and red .. 1·00 30
2323. – 22 f. gold, yellow & red 1·00 60
DESIGN: 22 f. Meeting emblem.

**1966.** Birth Cent. of Dr. Sun Yat-sen.
2324. **399.** 8 f. sepia and buff .. 10·00 3·25

**400.** Athletes with Mao Tse-tung's Portrait.

**1966.** "Cultural Revolution" Games. Multicoloured.
2325. 8 f. (1) Type **400** .. 4·50 2·10
2326. 8 f. (2) Athletes with linked arms hold Mao texts .. 4·50 2·10
2327. 8 f. (3) Two women athletes with Mao texts .. 4·50 1·50
2328. 8 f. (4) Athletes reading Mao texts .. .. 4·50 1·50
SIZES: No. 2326, As Type **400**, but vert. Nos. 2327/8, 36½ × 25 mm.

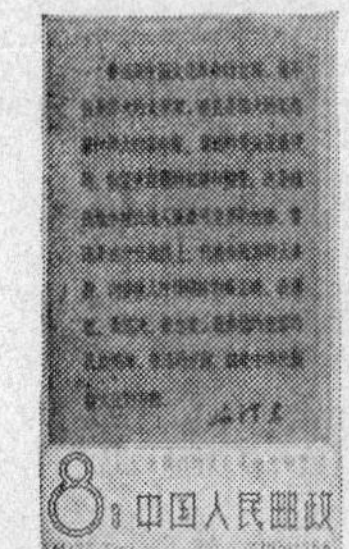
**401.** Mao's Appreciation of Lu Hsun (patriot and writer).
**402.** "Be Resolute ..." (Mao Tse-tung).

**1966.** 30th Death Anniv of Lu Hsun.
2329. **401.** 8 f. (1) black & orge. 9·00 2·50
2330. – 8 f. (2) blk., flesh & red 9·00 2·50
2331. – 8 f. (3) black & orge. 9·00 2·50
DESIGNS: (2) Lu Hsun. (3) Lu Hsun's manuscript.

**1967.** Heroic Oilwell Firefighters.
2332. **402.** 8 f. (1) gold, red & blk. 7·00 2·50
2333. – 8 f. (2) black and red 5·00 1·25
2334. – 8 f. (3) black and red 5·00 1·25
DESIGNS—HORIZ. (48 × 27 mm.): (2) Drilling Team No. 32111 fighting flames. VERT. (3) Smothering flames with tarpaulins.

**403.** Liu Ying-chun (military hero).

**1967.** Liu Ying-chun Commem. Mult.
2335 8 f. (1) Type **403** .. 6·00 1·50
2336 8 f. (2) Liu Ying-chun holding book of Mao texts .. .. .. 6·00 1·50
2337 8 f. (3) Liu Ying-chun holding horse's bridle 6·00 1·50
2338 8 f. (4) Liu Ying-chun looking at film slide 6·00 1·50
2339 8 f. (5) Liu Ying-chun lecturing .. .. 6·00 1·50
2340 8 f. (6) Liu Ying-chun making fatal attempt to stop bolting horse .. 6·00 1·50

**404.** Soldier, Nurse, Workers and Banners.

**1967.** 3rd Five-Year Plan. Multicoloured.
2341. 8 f. (1) Type **404** .. .. 11·00 2·25
2342. 8 f. (2) Armed woman, peasants and banners 11·00 2·25

**405.** Mao Tse-tung.

**406.** Mao Text (39 characters).

**1967.** "Thoughts of Mao Tse-tung" (1st issue). Similar designs showing Mao texts each gold and red. To assist identification of Nos. 2344/53 the total number of Chinese characters within the frames are given.

(a) Type **405.**
2343. 8 f. multicoloured .. 16·00 3·25

(b) As Type **406.** Red outer frames.
2344. 8 f. Type **406** .. .. 6·00 2·25
2345. 8 f. (50 characters) .. 6·00 2·25
2346. 8 f. (39—in six lines) .. 6·00 2·25
2347. 8 f. (53) .. .. .. 6·00 2·25
2348. 8 f. (46) .. .. .. 6·00 2·25

(c) As Type **406.** Gold outer frames.
2349. 8 f. (41) .. .. .. 6·00 2·25
2350. 8 f. (49) .. .. .. 6·00 2·25
2351. 8 f. (35) .. .. .. 6·00 2·25
2352. 8 f. (22) .. .. .. 6·00 2·25
2353. 8 f. (29) .. .. .. 6·00 2·25
See also No. 2405.

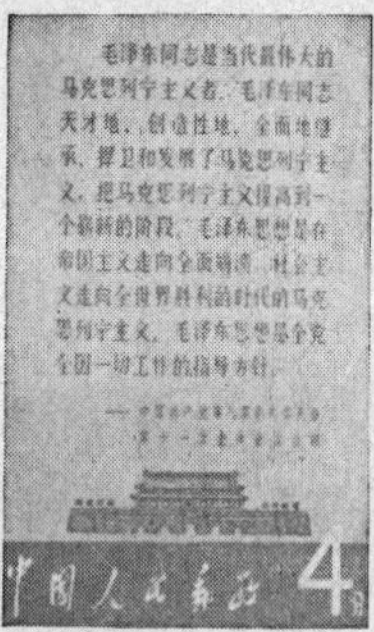
**407.** Text praising Mao.

**1967.** Labour Day.
2354. **407.** 4 f. multicoloured .. 8·00 3·25
2355. – 8 f. multicoloured .. 13·00 3·25
2356. – 8 f. multicoloured .. 8·50 3·25
2357. – 8 f. multicoloured .. 8·50 3·25
2358. – 8 f. multicoloured .. 14·00 3·75
DESIGNS (Mao Tse-tung and): No. 2355, Poem. No. 2356, Multi-racial crowd with texts. No. 2357, Red Guards. (36 × 50½ mm.): Mao with hand raised in greeting.
For stamps similar to No. 2358, see Nos. 2367/9.

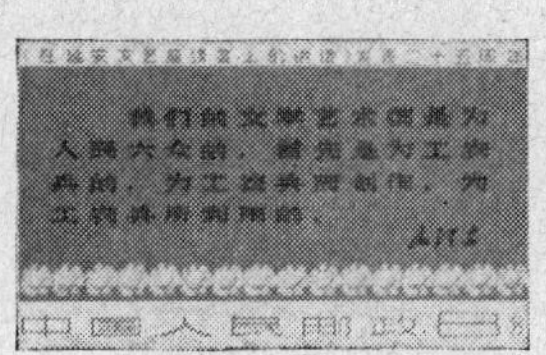
**408.** Mao Text.

**1967.** 25th Anniv. of Mao Tse-tung's "Talks on Literature and Art".
2359. **408.** 8 f. black, red & yellow 22·00 2·50
2360. – 8 f. black, red & yellow 22·00 2·50
2361. – 8 f. multicoloured .. 22·00 3·25
DESIGNS: No. 2360, As Type **408** but different text. (50 × 36½ mm.): No. 2361, Mao supporters in procession.

**409.** Mao Tse-tung.
**410.** Mao Tse-tung and Lin Piao.

**1967.** 46th Anniv. of Chinese Communist Party.
2362. **409.** 4 f. red .. .. 5·00 2·50
2363. 8 f. red .. .. 20·00 2·00
2364. 35 f. purple .. .. 17·00 10·00
2365. 43 f. red .. .. 18·00 10·00
2366. 52 f. red .. .. 20·00 1·25

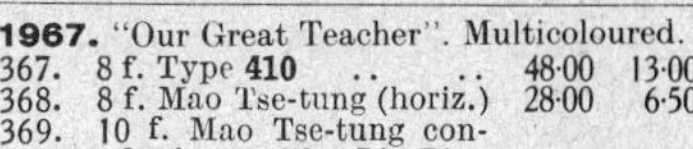
**1967.** "Our Great Teacher". Multicoloured.
2367. 8 f. Type **410** .. .. 48·00 13·00
2368. 8 f. Mao Tse-tung (horiz.) 28·00 6·50
2369. 10 f. Mao Tse-tung conferring with Lin Piao (horiz.) .. .. 50·00 12·00
For 8 f. stamp showing Mao with hand raised in greeting, see No. 2358.

**411.** Mao Tse-tung as "Sun".

**1967.** 18th Anniv. of People's Republic. Multicoloured.
2370. 8 f. Type **411** .. .. 12·00 4·50
2371. 8 f. Mao Tse-tung with representatives of Communist countries .. 8·00 3·50

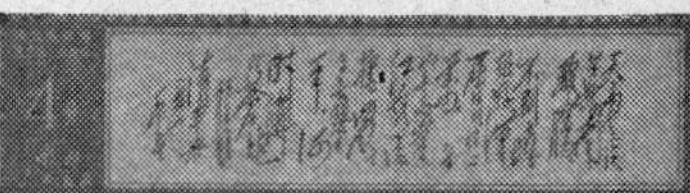
**412.** "Mount Liupan" (Illustration reduced. Actual size 81 × 20 mm)

**413.** "The Long March" (Illustration reduced. Actual size 81 × 20 mm)

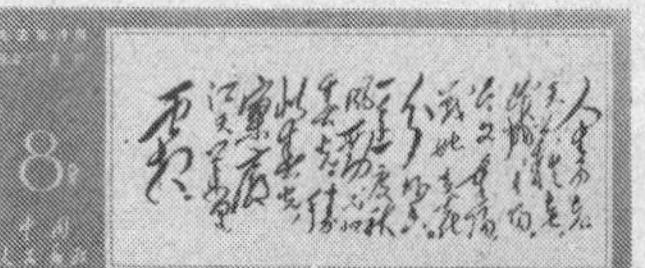
**414.** "Double Ninth" (Illustration reduced. Actual size 62 × 26 mm)

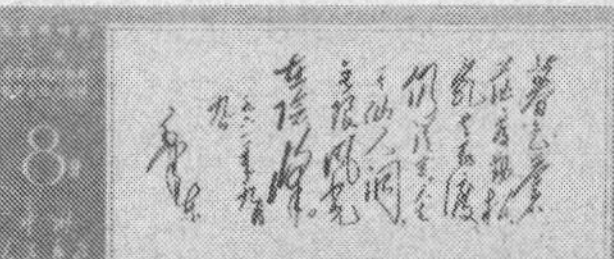
**415.** "Fairy Cave" (Illustration reduced. Actual size 62 × 26 mm)

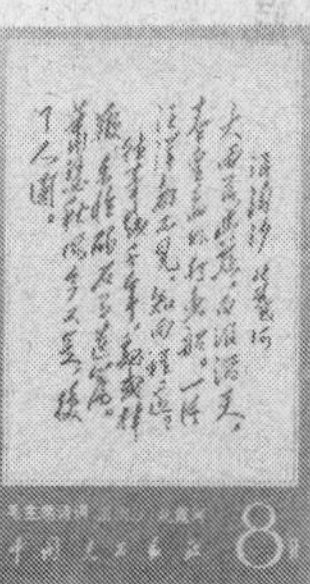
**416.** "Huichang" (Illustration reduced. Actual size 31 × 52 mm)

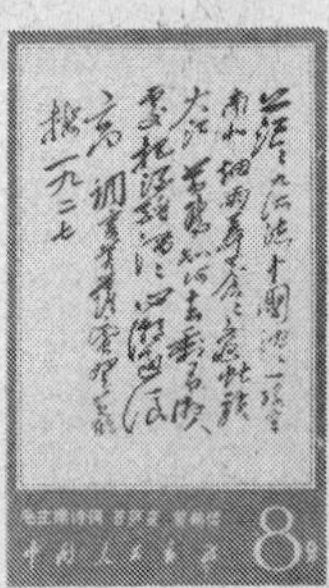
**417.** "Yellow Crane Pavilion" (Illustration reduced. Actual size 31 × 52 mm)

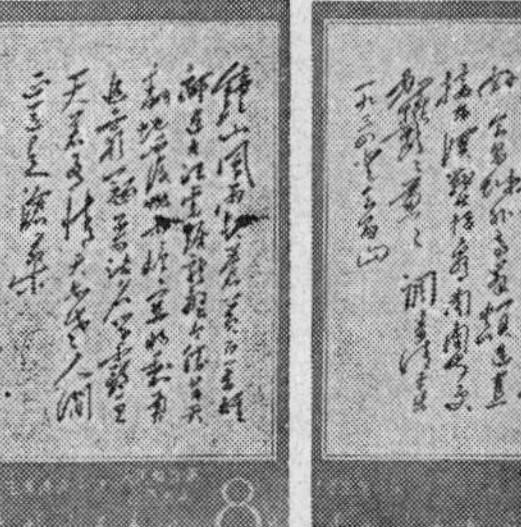
**418.** "Beidahe"
**419.** "Swimming"

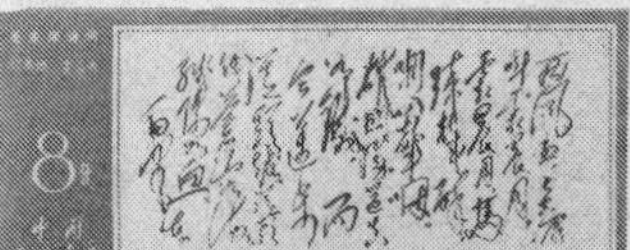
**420.** "Loushanguan Pass" (Illustration reduced. Actual size 62 × 26 mm)

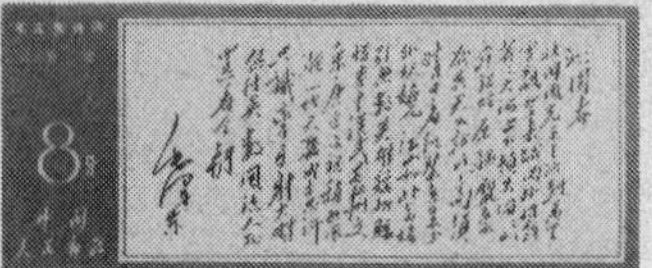

**421.** "Snow" (Illustration reduced. Actual Size 62 × 26 mm)

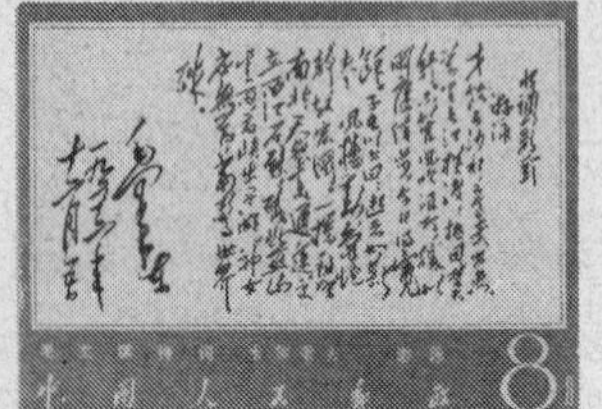

**422.** "Capture of Nanjing" (Illustration reduced. Actual size 54 × 40 mm)

**423.** Mao Writing Poems at Desk.

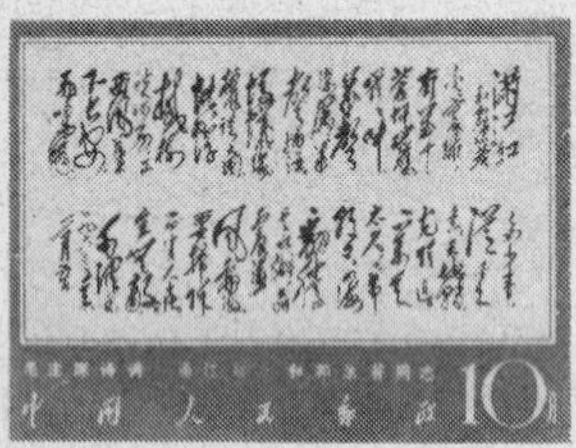

**424.** "Changsha"

**425.** "Reply to Guo Moro" (Illustration reduced. Actual size 54 × 40 mm)

**1967.** Poems of Mao Tse-tung.

2372 **412** 4 f. black, yell & red 10·00 3·50
2373 **413** 4 f. black, yell & red 15·00 3·50
2374 **414** 8 f. black, yell & red 15·00 2·75
2375 **415** 8 f. black, yell & red 15·00 2·75
2376 **416** 8 f. black, yell & red 40·00 2·75
2377 **417** 8 f. black, yell & red 25·00 5·00
2378 **418** 8 f. black, yell & red 60·00 5·00
2379 **419** 8 f. black, yell & red 14·00 5·00
2380 **420** 8 f. black, yell & red 16·00 4·50
2381 **421** 8 f. black, yell & red 14·00 5·00
2382 **422** 8 f. black, yell & red 16·00 2·75
2383 **423** 10 f. multicoloured .. 5·50 2·75
2384 **424** 10 f. black, yell & red 5·50 2·75
2385 **425** 10 f. black, yell & red 5·50 2·75

**426.** Epigram on Chairman Mao by Lin Piao.

**1967.** Fleet Expansionists' Congress.

2386 **426** 8 f. gold and red .. 11·00 3·50

**427.** Mao Tse-tung and Procession.

**1968.** "Revolutionary Literature and Art" (1st issue). Multicoloured designs showing scenes from People's Operas.

2387 8 f. Type **427** .. .. 6·00 2·25
2388 8 f. "Raid on the White Tiger Regiment" .. 6·00 2·25
2389 8 f. "Taking Tiger Mountain" .. .. 6·00 2·25
2390 8 f. "On the Docks" .. 6·00 2·25
2391 8 f. "Shachiapang" .. 6·00 2·25
2392 8 f. "The Red Lantern" (vert) .. .. .. 6·00 2·25

**428.** "Red Detachment of Women" (ballet).

**1968.** "Revolutionary Literature and Art" (2nd issue).

2393 8 f. Type **428** .. .. 8·50 3·00
2394 8 f. "The White-haired Girl" (ballet) .. .. 8·50 3·00
2395 8 f. Mao Tse-tung, Symphony Orchestra and Chorus (50 × 36 mm) .. .. .. 14·00 3·00

**429.** Mao Tse-tung ("Unite still more closely...").

**1968.** Mao's Anti-American Declaration.

2396 **429** 8 f. brown, gold & red 18·00 5·50

**430.** **431.**

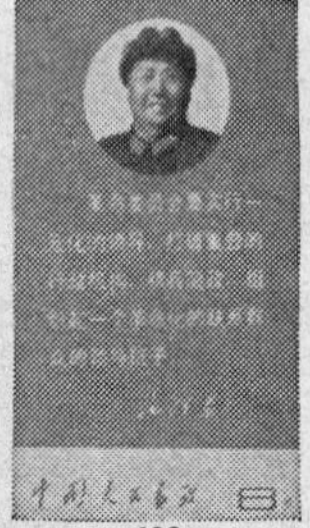

**432.** **433.**

**434.**

**1968.** "Directives of Mao Tse-tung".

2397. **430.** 8 f. brown, red & yell. 14·00 7·50
2398. **431.** 8 f. brown, red & yell. 14·00 7·50
2399. **432.** 8 f. brown, red & yell. 14·00 7·50
2400. **433.** 8 f. brown, red & yell. 14·00 7·50
2401. **434.** 8 f. brown, red & yell. 14·00 7·50

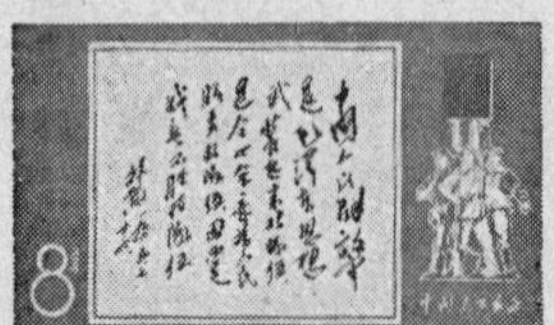

**435.** Inscription by Lin Piao, 26 July, 1965.

**1968.** 41st Anniv. of People's Liberation Army.

2402. **485.** 8 f. black, gold & red 4·25 1·25

**436.** "Chairman Mao goes to Anyuan" (Chiang Ching).

**1968.** Mao's Youth.

2403. **436.** 8 f. multicoloured .. 8·50 5·00

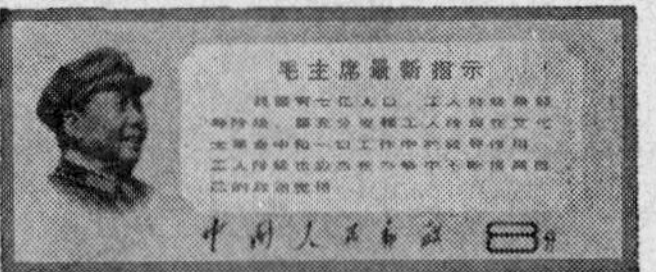


**438.** Mao Tse-tung and Text.

**1968.** "Thoughts of Mao Tse-tung" (2nd issue).

2405. **438.** 8 f. brown and red .. 12·00 4·50

**439.** Displaying "The Words of Mao Tse-tung".

**1968.** "The Words of Mao Tse-tung". No gum.

2406. **439.** 8 f. multicoloured .. 5·00 1·50

**440.** Yangtse Bridge.

**1968.** Completion of Yangtse Bridge, Nanking. Multicoloured. No gum.

2407. 4 f. Type **440** .. .. 1·50 1·25
2408. 8 f. Buses on bridge .. 4·50 3·00
2409. 8 f. View of end portals.. 1·75 40
2410. 10 f. Aerial view .. 1·75 1·25

Nos. 2408/9 are larger, size 49 × 27 mm.

**441.** Li Yu-ho singing "I am filled with Courage and Strength".

**1969.** Songs from "The Red Lantern" Opera. Multicoloured. No gum.

2411 8 f. Type **441** .. .. 5·50 3·25
2412 8 f. Li Ti-mei singing "Hatred in my Heart" 5·50 3·25

**442.** Communist Party Building, Shanghai. **443.** Rice Harvesters.

**1969.** No gum.

2413 **442** $1\frac{1}{2}$ f. red, brn & lilac 60 50
2414 – 8 f. brn, grn & cream 2·00 75
2415 – 8 f. red and purple .. 35 15
2416 – 8 f. brown and blue 1·00 40
2417 – 20 f. blue, pur & red 75 30
2418 – 50 f. brown and green 1·75 40

DESIGNS: "Historic Sites of the Revolution". Size 27 × 22 mm—No. 2414, Pagoda Hill, Yenan. No. 2415, Gate of Heavenly Peace, Peking. No. 2418, Mao Tse-tung's house, Yenan. Size as T **442**—No. 2416, People's Heroes Monument, Peking. No. 2417, Conference Hall, Tsunyi.

See also Nos. 2455/65.

**1969.** Agricultural Workers. Multicoloured. No gum.

2419. 4 f. Type **443** .. .. 2·25 1·25
2420. 8 f. Grain harvest .. 2·25 1·00
2421. 8 f. Study Group with "Thoughts of Mao" .. 12·00 4·25
2422. 10 f. Red Cross worker with mother and child .. 2·25 80

**444.** Snow Patrol. **445.** Farm Worker.

**1969.** Defence of Chen Pao Tao in the Ussuri River. Multicoloured. No gum.

2423. 8 f. Type **444** .. .. 2·50 2·25
2424. 8 f. Guards by river (horiz.) 2·50 2·25
2425. 8 f. Servicemen and Militia (horiz.) .. .. 2·50 2·25
2426. 35 f. As No. 2424 .. 2·75 2·75
2427. 43 f. Type **444** .. .. 3·25 2·75

**1969.** "The Chinese People" (woodcuts). No gum.

2428. **445.** 4 f. purple and orange 20 20
2429. – 8 f. purple and orange 30 25
2430. – 10 f. green and orange 20 20

DESIGNS: 8 f. Foundryman. 10 f. Soldier.

**446.** Chin Hsun-hua in Water. **447.** Tractor Driver.

**1970.** Heroic Death of Chin Hsun-hua in Kirin Border Floods. No gum.

2431. **446.** 8 f. black and red .. 3·25 3·00

**1970.** No gum.

2432 **447** 5 f. black, red &orge 60 15
2433 – 1 y. black and red .. 2·50 20

DESIGN—HORIZ. 1 y. Foundryman.

**448.** Cavalry Patrol. **449.** "Yang Tse-jung, Army Scout".

**1970.** 43rd Anniv of People's Liberation Army. No gum.

2434 **448** 8 f. multicoloured .. 2·75 1·75

**1970.** "Taking Tiger Mountain" (Revolutionary opera). Multicoloured. No gum.

2435 8 f. (1) Type **449** .. 1·50 1·00
2436 8 f. (2) "The patrol sets out" (horiz) .. .. 1·50 1·00
2437 8 f. (3) "Leaping through the forest" .. .. 1·50 1·00
2438 8 f. (4) "Li Yung-chi's farewell" (27 × 48 mm) 1·50 1·00
2439 8 f. (5) "Yang Tse-jung in disguise" (27 × 48 mm) 1·50 1·00
2440 8 f. (6) "Congratulating Yang Tse-jung" (horiz) 1·50 1·00

## MINIMUM PRICE

The minimum price quoted is 10p which represents a handling charge rather than a basis for valuing common stamps. For further notes about prices see introductory pages.

**450.** Soldiers in Snow.

**1970.** 2nd Anniv. of Defence of Chen Pao Tao. No gum.

| No. | Type | Description | Unused | Used |
|---|---|---|---|---|
| 2441a. | **450.** | 4 f. multicoloured .. | 60 | 20 |

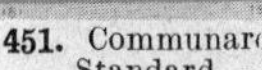

**451.** Communard Standard. **453.** Workers and Great Hall of the People, Peking.

**452.** Communist Party Building, Shanghai.

**1971.** Cent. of Paris Commune. Multicoloured. No gum.

| No. | Type | Description | Unused | Used |
|---|---|---|---|---|
| 2442. | **451.** | 4 f. multicoloured .. | 3·00 | 2·00 |
| 2443. | – | 8 f. brn., pink and red | 5·00 | 3·25 |
| 2444. | – | 10 f. red, brn. and pink | 3·00 | 1·25 |
| 2445. | – | 22 f. brn., red and pink | 8·50 | 1·25 |

DESIGNS—HORIZ. 8 f. Fighting in Paris, March 1871. 22 f. Communards in Place Vendome. VERT. 10 f. Commune proclaimed at the Hotel de Ville.

**1971.** 50th Anniv. of Chinese Communist Party. Multicoloured. No gum.

| No. | Description | Unused | Used |
|---|---|---|---|
| 2446. | 4 f. (12) Type **452** .. | 75 | 30 |
| 2447. | 4 f. (13) National Peasant Movement Inst., Canton | 75 | 30 |
| 2448. | 8 f. (14) Chingkang Mountains .. .. .. | 75 | 20 |
| 2449. | 8 f. (15) Conference Building, Tsunyi .. .. | 75 | 20 |
| 2450. | 8 f. (16) Pagoda Hill Yenan | 75 | 20 |
| 2452. | 8 f. (18) Workers and Industry .. .. .. | 75 | 40 |
| 2453. | 8 f. (19) Type **453** .. .. | 75 | 40 |
| 2454. | 8 f. (20) Workers and Agriculture .. .. | 75 | 40 |
| 2451. | 22 f. (17) Gate of Heavenly Peace, Peking .. | 2·50 | 1·50 |

SIZES: As Type **452**. Nos. 2447/2450 and 2451. As Type **453**. Nos. 2452/4.

**454.** National Peasant Movement Institute, Canton. **455.** Welcoming Bouquets.

**1971.** Revolutionary Sites. Multicoloured. No gum.

| No. | Description | Unused | Used |
|---|---|---|---|
| 2455. | 1 f. Communist Party Building, Shanghai (vert.) | 10 | 10 |
| 2456. | 2 f. Type **454** .. .. | 10 | 10 |
| 2457. | 3 f. Site of 1929 Congress, Kutien .. .. .. | 10 | 10 |
| 2458. | 4 f. Mao Tse-tung's house, Yenan .. .. .. | 15 | 10 |
| 2459. | 8 f. Gate of Heavenly Peace, Peking .. .. | 15 | 10 |
| 2460. | 10 f. Monument, Chingkang Mountains .. | 20 | 10 |
| 2461. | 20 f. River bridge, Yenan | 30 | 15 |
| 2462. | 22 f. Mao's birthplace, Shaoshan .. .. | 30 | 20 |
| 2463. | 35 f. Conference Building, Tsunyi .. .. .. | 35 | 20 |
| 2464. | 43 f. Start of the Long March, Chingkang Mountains .. .. | 50 | 35 |
| 2465. | 52 f. People's Palace, Peking .. .. .. | 75 | 25 |

**1971.** "Afro-Asian Friendship" Table Tennis Tournament, Peking. Multicoloured. No gum.

| No. | Description | Unused | Used |
|---|---|---|---|
| 2466. | 8 f. (22) Type **455** .. | 50 | 25 |
| 2467. | 8 f. (23) Group of players | 50 | 25 |
| 2468. | 8 f. (24) Asian and African players .. | 50 | 25 |
| 2469. | 43 f. (21) Tournament badge .. .. .. | 2·00 | 1·00 |

**456.** Enver Hoxha making speech. **457.** Conference Hall, Yenan.

**1971.** 30th Anniv. of Albanian Worker's Party. Multicoloured. No gum.

| No. | Description | Unused | Used |
|---|---|---|---|
| 2470. | 8 f. (25) Type **456** .. | 5·00 | 4·00 |
| 2471. | 8 f. (26) Party Headquarters | 1·00 | 50 |
| 2472. | 8 f. (27) Albanian flag, rifle and pick .. .. | 1·00 | 50 |
| 2473. | 52 f. (28) Soldier and Worker's Militia (horiz.) | 1·00 | 70 |

**1972.** 30th Anniv of Publication of "Yenan Forum's Discussions on Literature and Art". Multicoloured. No gum.

| No. | Description | Unused | Used |
|---|---|---|---|
| 2474 | 8 f. (33) Type **457** .. | 80 | 75 |
| 2475 | 8 f. (34) Army choir .. | 80 | 75 |
| 2476 | 8 f. (35) "Brother and Sister" .. | 80 | 75 |
| 2477 | 8 f. (36) "Open-air Theatre" .. | 80 | 75 |
| 2478 | 8 f. (37) "The Red Lantern" (opera) .. | 1·25 | 1·00 |
| 2479 | 8 f. (38) "Red Detachment of Women" (ballet) .. | 80 | 75 |

**458.** Ball Games.

**1972.** 10th Anniv. of Mao Tse-tungs's Edict on Physical Culture. Multicoloured. No gum.

| No. | Description | Unused | Used |
|---|---|---|---|
| 2480. | 8 f. (39) Type **458** .. | 60 | 30 |
| 2481. | 8 f. (40) Gymnastics .. | 60 | 30 |
| 2482. | 8 f. (41) Tug-of-War .. | 60 | 30 |
| 2483. | 8 f. (42) Rock-climbing .. | 60 | 30 |
| 2484. | 8 f. (43) High-diving .. | 60 | 30 |

Nos. 248/4 are size 26 × 36 mm.

**460.** Freighter "Fenglei".

**1972.** Chinese Merchant Shipping. Multicoloured. No gum.

| No. | Description | Unused | Used |
|---|---|---|---|
| 2485. | 8 f. (29) Type **460** .. | 1·50 | 1·00 |
| 2486. | 8 f. (30) Tanker "Taching No. 30" .. .. | 1·50 | 1·00 |
| 2487. | 8 f. (31) Cargo-liner "Chang Seng" .. | 1·50 | 1·00 |
| 2488. | 8 f. (32) Dredger "Hsien-feng" .. .. .. | 1·50 | 1·00 |

**461.** Championship Badge. **462.** Wang Chin-hsi, the "Iron Man".

**1972.** 1st Asian Table Tennis Championships, Peking. Multicoloured. No gum.

| No. | Description | Unused | Used |
|---|---|---|---|
| 2489. | 8 f. (45) Type **461** .. | 50 | 30 |
| 2490. | 8 f. (46) Welcoming crowd (horiz.) .. .. .. | 50 | 30 |
| 2491. | 8 f. (47) Game in progress (horiz.) .. .. .. | 50 | 30 |
| 2492. | 22 f. (48) Players from three countries .. | 1·75 | 1·00 |

**1972.** Wang Chin-hsi (workers' hero). Commem. No gum.

| No. | Type | Description | Unused | Used |
|---|---|---|---|---|
| 2493. | **462.** | 8 f. multicoloured .. | 1·00 | 60 |

**463.** Cliff-edge Construction. **464.** Giant Panda eating Bamboo Shoots.

**1972.** Construction of Red Flag Canal. Multicoloured.

| No. | Description | Unused | Used |
|---|---|---|---|
| 2494. | 8 f. (49) Type **463** .. | 40 | 20 |
| 2495. | 8 f. (50) "Youth" tunnel | 40 | 20 |
| 2496. | 8 f. (51) Taoguan bridge | 40 | 20 |
| 2497. | 8 f. (52) Cliff-edge canal | 40 | 20 |

**1973.** China's Giant Pandas. Various designs as T **464.**

| No. | Type | Description | Unused | Used |
|---|---|---|---|---|
| 2498. | **464.** | 4 f. (61) multicoloured | 2·25 | 1·75 |
| 2499. | – | 8 f. (59) mult. (horiz.) | 2·25 | 1·00 |
| 2500. | – | 8 f. (60) mult. (horiz.) | 2·25 | 1·00 |
| 2501. | – | 10 f. (58) multicoloured | 2·50 | 1·50 |
| 2502. | – | 20 f. (57) multicoloured | 9·00 | 2·25 |
| 2503. | – | 43 f. (62) multicoloured | 8·50 | 2·25 |

**465.** "New Power in the Mines" (Yang Shi-guang). **466.** Girl Dancer.

**1973.** Int. Working Women's Day. Mult.

| No. | Description | Unused | Used |
|---|---|---|---|
| 2504. | 8 f. (63) Type **465** .. | 70 | 30 |
| 2505. | 8 f. (64) "Woman Committee Member" (Tang Hsiaoming) .. | 70 | 30 |
| 2506. | 8 f. (65) "I am a Sea-gull" (Army telegraph line woman) (Pan Jia-jun) .. .. | 70 | 30 |

**1973.** Children's Day. Multicoloured.

| No. | Description | Unused | Used |
|---|---|---|---|
| 2507. | 8 f. (86) Type **466** .. | 15 | 20 |
| 2508. | 8 f. (87) Boy musician .. | 15 | 20 |
| 2509. | 8 f. (88) Boy with scarf .. | 15 | 20 |
| 2510. | 8 f. (89) Boy with tambourine | 15 | 20 |
| 2511. | 8 f. (90) Girl with drum .. | 15 | 20 |

**467.** Badge of Championships. **468.** " Hsi-erh ".

**1973.** Asian, African and Latin-American Table Tennis Invitation Championships. Mult.

| No. | Description | Unused | Used |
|---|---|---|---|
| 2512 | 8 f. (91) Type **467** .. | 25 | 20 |
| 2513 | 8 f. (92) Visitors .. | 25 | 20 |
| 2514 | 8 f. (93) Player .. | 25 | 20 |
| 2515 | 22 f. (94) Guest players .. | 80 | 60 |

**1973.** Revolutionary Ballet " The White-haired Girl ". Multicoloured.

| No. | Description | Unused | Used |
|---|---|---|---|
| 2516. | 8 f. (53) Type **468** .. | 1·00 | 50 |
| 2517. | 8 f. (54) Hsi-erh escapes from Huang (horiz.) .. | 1·00 | 50 |
| 2518. | 8 f. (55) Hsi-erh meets Ta-chun (horiz.) .. | 1·00 | 50 |
| 2519. | 8 f. (56) Hsi-erh becomes a soldier .. .. | 1·00 | 50 |

**469.** Fair Building.

**1973.** Chinese Exports Fair, Canton.

| No. | Type | Description | Unused | Used |
|---|---|---|---|---|
| 2520. | **469.** | 8 f. multicoloured .. | 75 | 75 |

**470.** Mao's Birthplace, Shaoshan.

**471.** Steam and Diesel Trains.

**1973.** No gum.

| No. | Type | Description | Unused | Used |
|---|---|---|---|---|
| 2521 | **470** | 1 f. green & pale grn | 10 | 10 |
| 2522 | – | 1½ f. red and yellow | 10 | 20 |
| 2523 | – | 2 f. blue and green .. | 10 | 10 |
| 2524 | – | 3 f. green and yellow | 10 | 10 |
| 2525 | – | 4 f. red and yellow .. | 10 | 10 |
| 2526 | – | 5 f. brown and yellow | 10 | 10 |
| 2527 | – | 8 f. purple and flesh | 10 | 10 |
| 2528 | – | 10 f. blue and flesh .. | 10 | 10 |
| 2529 | – | 20 f. red and buff .. | 20 | 10 |
| 2530 | – | 22 f. violet and yellow | 20 | 10 |
| 2531 | – | 35 f. purple & yellow | 30 | 15 |
| 2532 | – | 43 f. brown and buff | 35 | 25 |
| 2533 | – | 50 f. blue and mauve | 1·50 | 45 |
| 2534 | – | 52 f. brown & yellow | 1·00 | 25 |
| 2535 | **471** | 1 y. multicoloured .. | 2·75 | 25 |
| 2536 | – | 2 y. multicoloured .. | 2·25 | 40 |

DESIGNS. As Type **470**: 1½ f. National Peasant Movement Institute, Shanghai. 2 f. National Institute, Kwangcehow. 3 f. Headquarters Building, Nanching uprising. 4 f. Great Hall of the People, Peking. 5 f. Wen Chia Shih. 8 f. Gate of Heavenly Peace, Peking. 10 f. Chingkang Mountains. 20 f. Kutien Congress building. 22 f. Tsunyi Congress building. 35 f. Bridge, Yenan. 43 f. Hsi Pai Po. 50 f. "Fairy Gate", Lushan. 52 f. People's Heroes Monument, Peking. As Type **471**: 2 y. Trucks on mountain road.

**472.** " Phoenix " Pot. **473.** Dance Routine.

**1973.** Archaeological Treasures. Mult.

| No. | Description | Unused | Used |
|---|---|---|---|
| 2537. | 4 f. (66) Type **472** .. | 30 | 20 |
| 2538. | 4 f. (67) Silver pot .. | 30 | 20 |
| 2539. | 8 f. (68) Porcelain horse and groom .. .. | 30 | 10 |
| 2540. | 8 f. (69) Figure of woman | 30 | 10 |
| 2541. | 8 f. (70) Carved pedestals | 30 | 10 |
| 2542. | 8 f. (71) Bronze horse .. | 30 | 10 |
| 2543. | 8 f. (72) Gilded " frog " .. | 30 | 10 |
| 2544. | 8 f. (73) Lamp-holder figurine | 30 | 10 |
| 2545. | 10 f. (74) Tripod jar .. | 30 | 20 |
| 2546. | 10 f. (75) Bronze vessel .. | 30 | 20 |
| 2547. | 20 f. (76) Bronze wine vessel | 45 | 30 |
| 2548. | 52 f. (77) Tray with tripod | 90 | 55 |

**1974.** Popular Gymnastics. Multicoloured.

| No. | Description | Unused | Used |
|---|---|---|---|
| 2549. | 8 f. (1) Type **473** .. | 2·50 | 1·50 |
| 2550. | 8 f. (2) Rings exercise .. | 2·50 | 1·50 |
| 2551. | 8 f. (3) Dancing on beam | 2·50 | 1·50 |
| 2552. | 8 f. (4) Handstand on parallel bars .. .. .. | 2·50 | 1·50 |
| 2553. | 8 f. (5) Trapeze exercise .. | 2·50 | 1·50 |
| 2554. | 8 f. (6) Vaulting over horse | 2·50 | 1·50 |

**474.** Lion Dance. **475.** Man reading Book.

**1974.** Acrobatics. Multicoloured.

| No. | Description | Unused | Used |
|---|---|---|---|
| 2555. | 8 f. (1) Type **474** .. | 2·25 | 1·25 |
| 2556. | 8 f. (2) Handstand on chairs .. .. | 2·25 | 1·25 |
| 2557. | 8 f. (3) Diabolo team (horiz.) .. .. | 2·25 | 1·25 |
| 2558. | 8 f. Revolving jar (horiz.) .. .. | 2·25 | 1·25 |
| 2559. | 8 f. (5) Spinning plates .. | 2·25 | 1·25 |
| 2560. | 8 f. (6) Foot-juggling with parasol .. .. | 2·25 | 1·25 |

**1974.** Huhsien Paintings. Multicoloured.

| No. | Description | Unused | Used |
|---|---|---|---|
| 2561 | 8 f. (1) Type **475** .. | 80 | 60 |
| 2562 | 8 f. (2) Mineshaft (23 × 57 mm) .. .. | 80 | 60 |
| 2563 | 8 f. (3) Workers hoeing field (horiz) .. | 80 | 60 |
| 2564 | 8 f. (4) Workers eating (horiz) .. .. | 80 | 60 |
| 2565 | 8 f. (5) Wheatfield landscape (57 × 23 mm) .. | 80 | 60 |
| 2566 | 8 f. (6) Harvesting (horiz.) | 80 | 60 |

476. Postman.

**1974.** Cent. of U.P.U. Multicoloured.

2567. 8 f. (1) Type **476** .. .. 3·00 1·50
2568. 8 f. (2) People of five races 3·00 1·50
2569. 8 f. (3) Great Wall of China 3·00 1·50

477. Inoculating Children.

**1974.** Country Doctors. Multicoloured.

2570. 8 f. (1) Type **477** .. .. 50 30
2571. 8 f. (2) On country visit (vert.) .. .. .. 50 30
2572. 8 f. (3) Gathering herbs (vert.) .. .. .. 50 30
2573. 8 f. (4) Giving acupuncture 50 30

478. Wang Chin-hsi, "The Iron Man".

**1974.** Chairman Mao's Directives on Industrial and Agricultural Teaching. Multicoloured.

(a) "Learning Industry from Taching".

2574. 8 f. (1) Type **478** .. .. 90 75
2575. 8 f. (2) Pupils studying Mao's works .. .. 90 75
2576. 8 f. (3) Oil-workers sinking well .. .. .. 90 75
2577. 8 f. (4) Consultation with management .. .. 90 75
2578. 8 f. (5) Taching oilfield as development site .. 90 75

(b) "Learning Agriculture from Tachai".

2579. 8 f. (1) Tachai workers looking to future .. 90 75
2580. 8 f. (2) Construction workers .. .. .. 90 75
2581. 8 f. (3) Agricultural workers making field tests .. 90 75
2582. 8 f. (4) Trucks delivering grain to State granaries 90 75
2583. 8 f. (5) Workers going to fields .. .. .. 90 75

479. National Day Celebrations.

480. Steel Worker, Taching.

**1974.** 25th Anniv. of Chinese People's Republic. Multicoloured.

(a) National Day.

2584. 8 f. Type **479** .. .. 3·75 1·50

(b) Chairman Mao's Directives.

2585. 8 f. (1) Type **480** .. 35 25
2586. 8 f. (2) Agricultural worker, Tachai .. .. .. 35 25
2587. 8 f. (3) Coastal guard .. 35 25

481. Fair Building.

**1974.** Chinese Exports Fair Canton.

2588. **481.** 8 f. multicoloured .. 1·50 75

482. Revolutionary Monument, Permet. 483. Capital Stadium.

**1974.** 30th Anniv. of Albania's Liberation. Multicoloured

2589. 8 f. Type **482** .. 1·50 1·00
2590. 8 f. Albanian patriots .. 1·50 1·00

**1974.** Peking Buildings. No gum.

2591. **483.** 4 f. black and green 15 15
2592. – 8 f. black and blue .. 15 10

DESIGN: 8 f. Hotel Peking.

484. Water-cooled Turbine Generator.

**1974.** Industrial Production. Multicoloured.

2593 8 f. (78) Type **484** .. 1·25 80
2594 8 f. (79) Mechanical rice sprouts transplanter .. 1·50 80
2595 8 f. (80) Universal cylindrical grinding machine .. .. 1·25 80
2596 8 f. (81) Mobile rock drill (vert) .. .. .. 1·25 80

485. Congress Delegates.

**1975.** 4th National People's Congress, Peking. Multicoloured.

2597 8 f. (1) Type **485** .. 1·75 90
2598 8 f. (2) Flower-decked rostrum .. .. 1·75 90
2599 8 f. (3) Farmer, worker, soldier and steel mill .. 1·75 90

486. Teacher Studying.

**1975.** Country Women Teachers. Mult.

2600. 8 f. (1) Type **486** .. .. 1·75 75
2601. 8 f. (2) Teacher on rounds 1·75 75
2602. 8 f. (3) Open-air class .. 1·75 75
2603. 8 f. (4) Primary class aboard boat .. .. 1·75 75

487. Broadsword.

**1975.** "Wushu" (popular sport). Mult.

2604. 8 f. (1) Type **487** 75 60
2605. 8 f. (2) Sword exercises .. 75 60
2606. 8 f. (3) "Boxing" .. 75 60
2607. 8 f. (4) Leaping with spear .. .. .. 75 60
2608. 8 f. (5) Cudgel exercise .. 75 60
2609. 43 f. (6) Cudgel versus spears (60 × 30 mm.) .. 6·50 3·25

488. "Mass Revolutionary Criticism". 489. Parade of Athletes.

**1975.** Criticism of Confucius and Lin Piao. Multicoloured.

2610. 8 f. (1) Type **488** .. .. 2·00 60
2611. 8 f. (2) "Leaders of the production brigade" .. 2·00 60
2612. 8 f. (3) "The battle continues" (horiz.) 2·00 60
2613. 8 f. (4) "Liberated slave-pioneer critic" (horiz.) 2·00 60

**1975.** 3rd National Games, Peking. Mult.

2614. 8 f. (1) Type **489** .. .. 40 15
2615. 8 f. (2) Athletes studying (horiz.) .. .. 40 15
2616. 8 f. (3) Volleyball players (horiz.) .. .. 40 15
2617. 8 f. (4) Athlete, soldier, farmer and worker .. 40 15
2618. 8 f. (5) Various sports (horiz.) .. .. 40 15
2619. 8 f. (6) Ethnic types and horse racing (horiz.) .. 40 15
2620. 35 f. (7) Children and divers .. .. .. 2·25 1·00

490. Members of Expedition. 492. Children sticking Posters.

491. "Studying Together".

**1975.** Chinese Ascent of Mount Everest. Multicoloured.

2621. 8 f. (2) Type **490** .. .. 75 25
2622. 8 f. (3) Mountaineers with flag (horiz.) .. .. 75 25
2623. 43 f. (1) View of Mount Everest (horiz.) .. 1·25 50

**1975.** National Conference "Learning Agriculture from Tachai". Mult.

2624. 8 f. (1) Type **491** .. 1·25 75
2625. 8 f. (2) "Promote Hard Work" .. .. .. 1·25 75
2626. 8 f. (3) Chinese combine-harvester .. .. 1·25 75

**1975.** Children's Progress. Multicoloured.

2627. 8 f. (1) Girl and young boy 75 25
2628. 8 f. (2) Type **492** .. 75 25
2629. 8 f. (3) Studying .. .. 75 25
2630. 8 f. (4) Harvesting .. 75 25
2631. 52 f. (5) Tug-of-war .. 2·25 1·00

493. Ploughing Paddy Field.

**1975.** Mechanised Farming. Multicoloured.

2632. 8 f. (1) Type **493** .. 1·10 60
2633. 8 f. (2) Mechanical rice seedlings transplanter 1·10 60
2634. 8 f. (3) Irrigation pump 1·10 60
2635. 8 f. (4) Spraying cotton field .. .. .. 1·10 60
2636. 8 f. (5) Combine harvester 1·10 60

494. Bridge over Canal.

**1976.** Completion of 4th 5-Year Plan. Mult.

2637. 8 f. (1) Harvest scene .. 1·40 80
2638. 8 f. Type **494** .. .. 1·40 80
2639. 8 f. (3) Fertilizer plant .. 1·40 80
2640. 8 f. (4) Textile factory .. 1·40 80
2641. 8 f. (5) Iron foundry .. 1·40 80
2642. 8 f. (6) Steam coal train 1·40 80
2643. 8 f. (7) Hydro-electric power station .. 1·40 80
2644. 8 f. (8) Freighters in shipyard .. .. 1·40 80
2645. 8 f. (9) Oil industry .. 1·40 80
2646. 8 f. (10) Pipe-line and harbour .. .. 1·40 80
2647. 8 f. (11) Diesel train on viaduct .. .. 1·40 80
2648. 8 f. (12) Crystal formation (Scientific research) .. 1·40 80
2649. 8 f. (13) Classroom (rural education .. .. 1·40 80
2650. 8 f. (14) Workers' health centre .. .. .. 1·40 80
2651. 8 f. (15) Workers' tenements .. .. 1·40 80
2652. 8 f. (16) Department store .. .. .. 1·40 80

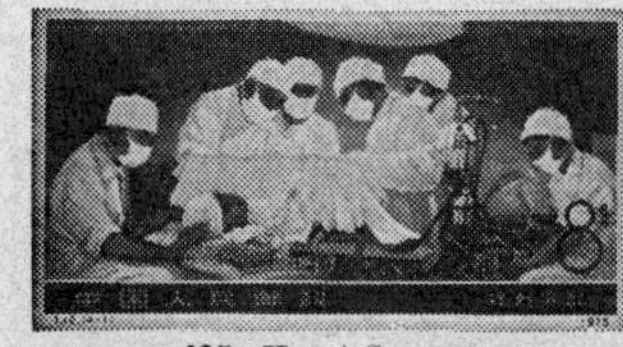

495. Heart Surgery.

**1976.** Medical Services' Achievements. Mult.

2653. 8 f. (1) Type **495** .. 50 25
2654. 8 f. (2) Restoration of tractor-driver's severed arm 50 25
2655. 8 f. (3) Exercise of fractured arm .. .. 50 25
2656. 8 f. (4) Cataract operation-patient threading needle 50 25

496. Students studying at "May 7" School.

**1976.** 10th Anniv. of Mao's "May 7 Directive". Multicoloured.

2657. 8 f. (1) Type **496** .. 1·10 70
2658. 8 f. (2) Students in agriculture.. .. .. 1·10 70
2659. 8 f. (3) Students in production team .. .. 1·10 70

497. Formation of Swimmers.

**1976.** 10th Anniv. of Chairman Mao's Swim in Yangtse River. Multicoloured.

2660. 8 f. (1) Type **497** .. 1·10 65
2661. 8 f. (2) Swimmers crossing Yangtse .. .. 1·10 65
2662. 8 f. (3) Swimmers in surf 1·10 65

Nos. 2661/2 are smaller, 35 × 27 mm.

498. Students with Rosettes.

**1976.** "Going to College". Multicoloured.

2663. 8 f. (1) Type **498** .. 1·10 70
2664. 8 f. (2) Study group .. 1·10 70
2665. 8 f. (3) On-site instructions 1·10 70
2666. 8 f. (3) Students operating computer .. 1·10 70
2667. 8 f. (5) Return of graduates from college .. 1·10 70

499. Electricity Lineswoman. 501. Peasant arranging Student's Headband.

500. Lu Hsun.

**1976.** Maintenance of Electric Power Lines. Multicoloured.
2668. 8 f. (1) Type **499** .. .. 1·10 60
2669. 8 f. (2) Linesman replacing insulator .. .. 1·10 60
2670. 8 f. (3) Linesman using hydraulic lift .. .. 1·10 60
2671. 8 f. (4) Technician inspecting transformer .. 1·10 60

**1976.** 95th Birth Anniv. of Lu Hsun (revolutionary leader).
2672. 8 f. (1) Type **500** .. 1·75 90
2673. 8 f. (2) Lu Hsun sick, writing in bed .. 1·75 90
2674. 8 f. (3) Lu Hsun, workers and soldiers .. .. 1·75 90

**1976.** Students and Country Life. Mult.
2675. 4 f. (1) Type **501** .. 75 20
2676. 8 f. (2) Student teaching farm woman (horiz.) .. 75 15
2677. 8 f. (3) Irrigation survey 75 15
2678. 8 f. (4) Agricultural student testing wheat (horiz.) .. .. 75 15
2679. 10 f. (5) Student feeding lamb .. .. .. 1·25 40
2680. 20 f. (6) Frontier guards (horiz.) .. .. 1·50 45

**502.** Mao Tse-tung's Birthplace.

**1976.** Shaoshan Revolutionary Sites. Mult.
2681. 4 f. (1) Type **502** .. .. 1·00 60
2682. 8 f. (2) School building .. 1·00 50
2683. 8 f. (3) Peasants' association building .. .. 1·00 50
2684. 10 f. (4) Railway station 1·00 60

**503.** Chou En-lai. **504.** Statue of Lui Hu-Lan.

**1977.** 1st Death Anniv. of Chou En-lai. Multicoloured.
2685. 8 f. (1) Type **503** .. 40 20
2686. 8 f. (2) Chou En-lai making report .. .. .. 40 20
2687. 8 f. (3) Chou meeting "Iron Man" – Wang Chin-hsi (horiz.) .. .. 40 20
2688. 8 f. (4) Chou with provincial representatives (horiz.) .. .. 40 20

**1977.** 30th Death Anniv. of Lin Hu-Lan (heroine and martyr). Multicoloured.
2689. 8 f. (1) Type **504** .. 1·75 1·25
2690. 8 f. (2) Text by Mao Tse-tung .. .. .. 1·75 1·25
2691. 8 f. (3) Lin Hu-Lan and people .. .. .. 1·75 1·25

**505.** Revolutionaries and Text.

**1977.** 30th Anniv. of 1947 Taiwan Rising. Multicoloured.
2692. 8 f. Type **505** .. .. 1·25 75
2693. 10 f. Three Taiwanese with banner .. .. .. 1·50 1·00

**506.** Weapon Maintenance.

**1977.** Chinese Militiawomen. Multicoloured.
2694. 8 f. (1) Type **506** .. 1·75 1·00
2695. 8 f. (2) On horseback .. 1·75 1·00
2696. 8 f. (3) Directing traffic in tunnel .. .. .. 1·75 1·00

**507.** Sheep Rearing. **508.** Cadre Members.

**1977.** Multicoloured.
2697. 1 f. Coal mining .. .. 10 10
2698. 1½ f. Type **507** .. .. 10 20
2699. 2 f. Exports .. .. 10 10
2700. 3 f. Forest and diesel-train .. .. .. 10 10
2701. 4 f. Hydro-electric power 10 10
2702. 5 f. Fishing .. .. 10 10
2703. 8 f. Agriculture .. .. 10 10
2704. 10 f. Radio tower and mail-vans .. .. 15 10
2705. 20 f. Steel production .. 20 10
2706. 30 f. Road transport .. 20 10
2707. 40 f. Textile manufacture 25 15
2708. 50 f. Tractor assembly .. 40 10
2709. 60 f. Oil-rigs and setting sun .. .. .. 45 15
2710. 70 f. Railway viaduct, Yangtse Gorge .. 55 35

**1977.** Promoting Tachai-type Developments. Multicoloured.
2711. 8 f. (1) Type **508** .. 65 25
2712. 8 f. (2) Modern cultivation .. .. .. 65 25
2713. 8 f. (3) Reading wall newspaper .. .. 65 25
2714. 8 f. (4) Reclaiming land for agriculture .. 65 25

**509.** Party Leader addressing Workers.

**1977.** "Taching-type" Industrial Conference. Multicoloured.
2715. 8 f. (1) Type **509** .. 65 25
2716. 8 f. (2) Drilling for oil in snowstorm .. .. 65 25
2717. 8 f. (3) Man with banner over mass formation of workers .. .. 65 25
2718. 8 f. (4) Smiling workers and industrial scene .. 65 25

**510.** Mongolians Rejoicing. **511.** Rumanian Flag.

**1977.** 30th Anniv. of Inner Mongolian Autonomous Region. Multicoloured.
2719. 8 f. Type **510** .. .. 35 15
2720. 10 f. Mongolian industrial scene and iron ore train .. .. 35 25
2721. 20 f. Mongolian pasture 85 35

**1977.** Cent. of Rumanian Independence. Multicoloured.
2722. 8 f. Type **511** .. .. 75 25
2723. 10 f. "The Battle of Smirdan" .. .. 1·25 75
2724. 20 f. Mihai Viteazu Memorial .. 1·50 75

**512.** Yenan and Floral Border.

**1977.** 35th Anniv. of Yenan Forum on Literature and Art. Multicoloured.
2725. 8 f. (1) Type **512** .. 45 25
2726. 8 f. (2) Hammer, sickle and gun .. .. 45 25

**513.** Chu Teh, National People's Congress Chairman. **514.** Soldier, Sailor and Airman under Banner of Mao Tse-tung.

**1977.** First Death Anniv. of Chu Teh.
2727. **513.** 8 f. (1) multicoloured 25 10
2728. – 8 f. (2) multicoloured 25 10
2729. – 8 f. (3) multicoloured 25 10
2730. – 8 f. (4) multicoloured 25 10

DESIGNS—VERT. No. 2728, Chu Teh during his last session of Congress. HORIZ. No. 2729, Chu Teh at his desk. No. 2730, Chu Teh on horseback as Commander of People's Liberation Army.

**1977.** People's Liberation Army Day. Mult.
2731. 8 f. (1) Type **514** .. 75 25
2732. 8 f. (2) Soldiers in Chingkang Mountains .. 75 25
2733. 8 f. (3) Guerrilla fighters returning to base .. 75 25
2734. 8 f. (4) Chinese forces crossing Yangtse River 75 25
2735. 8 f. (5) "The Steel Wall" (National Defence Forces) .. .. 75 25

**515.** Red Flags and Crowd.

**1977.** 11th National Communist Party Congress. Multicoloured.
2736. 8 f. (1) Type **515** .. 1·40 60
2737. 8 f. (2) Mao banner and procession .. .. 1·40 60
2738. 8 f. (3) Hammer and sickle banner and procession 1·40 60

**516.** Mao Tse-tung.

**1977.** 1st Death Anniv. of Mao Tse-tung. Multicoloured.
2739. 8 f. (1) Type **516** .. 30 15
2740. 8 f. (2) Mao as young man .. .. .. 30 15
2741. 8 f. (3) Making speech .. 30 15
2742. 8 f. (4) Mao broadcasting 30 15
2743. 8 f. (5) Mao with Chou En-lai and Chu Teh (horiz.) .. .. 30 15
2744. 8 f. (6) Reviewing the army .. .. .. 30 15

**517.** Mao Memorial Hall.

**1977.** Completion of Mao Memorial Hall, Peking. Multicoloured.
2745. 8 f. (1) Type **517** .. 1·50 75
2746. 8 f. (2) Commemoration text .. .. .. 1·50 75

**INDEX**
Countries can be quickly located by referring to the index at the end of this volume.

**518.** Tractors transporting Oil Rig.

**1978.** Development of Petroleum Industry. Multicoloured.
2747. 8 f. (1) Type **518** .. 35 10
2748. 8 f. (2) Clearing wax from oil well .. .. 35 10
2749. 8 f. (3) Laying pipe line .. 35 10
2750. 8 f. (4) Tung Fang Hung Oil Refinery, Peking .. 35 10
2751. 8 f. (5) Loading a tanker Taching .. .. 40 20
2752. 20 f. (6) Oil rig and drilling ship "Exploration" .. 75 35

**519.** Rifle Shooting from Sampan.

**1978.** "Army and People are One Family". Multicoloured.
2753. 8 f. (1) Type **519** .. 80 45
2754. 8 f. (2) Helping with rice harvest .. .. 80 45

**520.** Great Banner of Chairman Mao. **521.** "Learn from Comrade Lei Feng" (Inscription by Mao Tse-tung).

**1978.** 5th National People's Congress. Mult.
2755. 8 f. (1) Type **520** .. 50 25
2756. 8 f. (2) Constitution .. 50 25
2757. 8 f. (3) Emblems of modernization .. .. 50 25

**1978.** Lei Feng (Communist fighter) Commem.
2758. **521.** 8 f. (1) gold and red .. 65 35
2759. – 8 f. (2) gold and red .. 65 35
2760. – 8 f. (3) multicoloured 65 35

DESIGNS: No. 2759, Inscription by Chairman Hua. No. 2760, Lei Feng reading Mao's works.

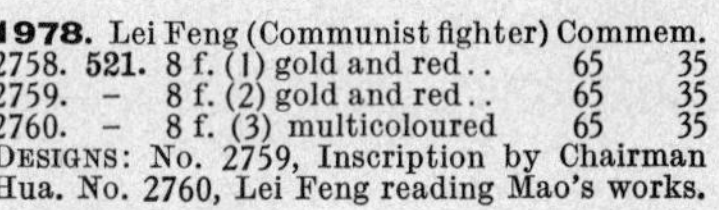

**522.** Hsiang Ching-yu (Women's Movement Pioneer). **523.** Conference Emblem and Tien on Men Gate, Peking.

**1978.** International Working Women's Day.
2761. **522.** 8 f. (1) blk., red & gold 45 25
2762. – 8 f. (2) blk., red & gold 45 25

DESIGN: No. 2762, Yang Kai-hui (communist fighter).

**1978.** National Science Conference. Mult.
2763. 8 f. (1) Type **523** .. 35 25
2764. 8 f. (2) Flags .. .. 35 25
2765. 8 f. (3) Emblem, flag and globe .. .. .. 35 25

**524.** Launching a Radio-sonde. **525.** Galloping Horse.

**1978.** Meteorological Services. Mult.
2766. 8 f. (1) Type **524** .. 30 10
2767. 8 f. (2) Radar station .. 30 10
2768. 8 f. (3) Weather forecasting with computers 30 10
2769. 8 f. (4) Commune group observing sky .. 30 10
2770. 8 f. (5) Cloud-dispersing rockets .. .. .. 30 10

**1978.** Galloping Horses.

2771. **525.** 4 f. (1) multicoloured .. 35 20
2772. – 8 f. (2) multicoloured 35 10
2773. – 8 f. (3) multicoloured 35 10
2774. – 10 f. (4) multicoloured 45 10
2775. – 20 f. (5) multicoloured 55 20
2776. – 30 f. (6) multicoloured 65 40
2777. – 40 f. (7) multicoloured (horiz.) .. .. 80 60
2778. – 50 f. (8) multicoloured (horiz.) .. .. 1·00 80
2779. – 60 f. (9) multicoloured (horiz.) .. .. 1·25 95
2780. – 70 f. (10) multicoloured (horiz.) .. 1·50 1·10

DESIGNS: No. 2772/80, various paintings of horses by Hsu Pei-hung.

**526.** Football.

**527.** Material Feeder.

**1978.** "Building up Strength for the Revolution". Multicoloured.

2782. 8 f. (2) Type **526** .. 15 10
2783. 8 f. (3) Swimming .. 15 10
2784. 8 f. (4) Gymnastics .. 15 10
2785. 8 f. (5) Running.. .. 15 10
2786. 20 f. (1) Group exercises 30 20

The 20 f. is larger, 48 × 27 mm.

**1978.** Chemical Industry Development. Fabric Production. Multicoloured.

2787. 8 f. (1) Type **527** .. 10 10
2788. 8 f. (2) Drawing-out threads 10 10
2789. 8 f. (3) Weaving.. .. 10 10
2790. 8 f. (4) Dyeing and printing .. .. .. .. 10 10
2791. 8 f. (5) Finished products 10 10

**528.** Conference Emblem.

**529.** Grassland Improvement, Mongolia.

**1978.** National Finance and Trade Conference. Multicoloured.

2792. 8 f. (1) Type **528** .. 40 20
2793. 8 f. (2) Inscription by Mao Tse-tung .. .. 40 20

**1978.** Progress in Animal Husbandry. Mult.

2794. 8 f. (1) Type **529** .. 55 25
2795. 8 f. (2) Sheep rearing by the Kazakhs .. .. 55 25
2796. 8 f. (3) Shearing sheep, Tibet .. .. .. 55 25

**530.** Automated loading of Burning Coke.

**1978.** Iron and Steel Industry. Mult.

2797. 8 f. (1) Type **530** .. 40 25
2798. 8 f. (2) Checking molten iron .. .. .. 40 25
2799. 8 f. (3) Pouring molten steel .. .. .. 40 25
2800. 8 f. (4) Steel-rolling mill 40 25
2801. 8 f. (5) Loading steel train 40 25

**531.** Soldier.

**532.** Cloth Toy Lion.

**1978.** Army Modernisation. Multicoloured.

2802. 8 f. (1) Type **531** .. 45 20
2803. 8 f. (2) Soldier firing missile 45 20
2804. 8 f. (3) Amphibious landing 45 20



**1978.** Arts and Crafts. Multicoloured.

2805. 4 f. (1) Type **532** .. 15 15
2806. 8 f. (2) Three-legged pot (vert.) .. .. .. 15 10
2807. 8 f. (3) Lacquerware rhinoceros .. .. .. 15 10
2808. 10 f. (4) Embroidered kitten (vert.) .. .. 20 15
2809. 20 f. (5) Basketware .. 25 20
2810. 30 f. (6) Cloissone pot (vert.) .. .. .. 35 30
2811. 40 f. (7) Lacquerware plate and swan .. .. 45 40
2812. 50 f. (8) Boxwood carving (vert.) .. .. .. 55 50
2813. 60 f. (9) Jade carving .. 65 40
2814. 70 f. (10) Ivory carving (vert.) .. .. .. 75 40

**533.** Worker, Peasant and Intellectual.

**534.** "Panax ginseng".

**1978.** Fourth National Women's Congress.

2816. **533.** 8 f. multicoloured .. 75 25

**1978.** Medicinal Plants. Multicoloured.

2817. 8 f. (1) Type **534** .. 35 15
2818. 8 f. (2) " Datura metel " 35 15
2819. 8 f. (3) " Belamcanda chinensis " .. .. 35 15
2820. 8 f. (4) " Platycodon grandiflorum " .. .. 35 15
2821. 55 f. (5) " Rhododendron dauricum " .. .. 90 50

**535.** Cogwheel, Grain, Rocket and Flag.

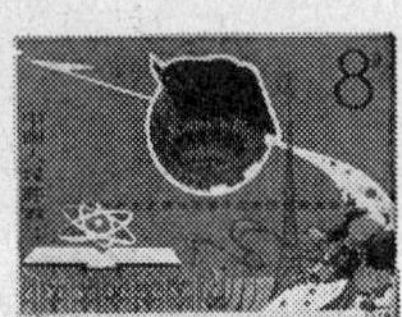

**536.** Emblem, Open Book and Flowers.

**1978.** 9th National Trades Union Congress.

2822. **535.** 8 f. multicoloured .. 85 40

**1978.** 10th National Congress of Communist Youth League.

2823. **536.** 8 f. multicoloured .. 85 40

**537.** Chinese and Japanese Children exchanging Gifts.

**538.** Hui, Han and Mongolian.

**1978.** Signing of Chinese–Japanese Treaty of Peace and Friendship.

2824. 8 f. Type **537** .. .. 30 15
2825. 55 f. Great Wall of China and Mt. Fuji .. .. 1·40 65

**1978.** 20th Anniv. of Ningsia Hui Autonomous Region. Multicoloured.

2826. 8 f. (1) Type **538** .. 30 15
2827. 8 f. (2) Coal loading machine, Holan colliery .. 30 15
2828. 10 f. (3) Irrigation and Chingtunghsia power station.. .. .. 30 20

**539.** Chinsha River Bridge, West Szechuan.

**540.** Transplanting Rice Seedlings by Machine.

**1978.** Highway Bridges. Multicoloured.

2829. 8 f. (1) Type **539** .. 35 10
2830. 8 f. (2) Hsinghong bridge, Wuhsi .. .. .. 35 10
2831. 8 f. (3) Chiuhsikou bridge, Fengdu .. .. 35 10
2832. 8 f. (4) Chinsha bridge .. 35 10
2833. 60 f. (5) Shangyeh bridge, Sanmen .. .. 80 70

**1978.** Water Country Modernisation. Mult.

2835. 8 f. (1) Type **540** .. 75 50
2836. 8 f. (2) Crop spraying .. 75 50
2837. 8 f. (3) Selecting seeds.. 75 50
2838. 8 f. (4) Canal-side village 75 50
2839. 8 f. (5) Delivering and storing grain .. .. 75 50

Nos. 2835/9 were issued together, se-tenant, forming a composite design.

**541.** Festivities.

**1978.** 20th Anniv. of Kwangsi Chuang Autonomous Region. Multicoloured.

2840. 8 f. (1) Type **541**.. .. 40 30
2841. 8 f. (2) Industrial complexes (vert.) .. .. 40 30
2842. 10 f. (3) River scene (vert.) 1·10 60

**542.** Tibetan Peasant reporting Mineralogical Discovery.

**543.** Golden Pheasants on Rock.

**1978.** Mining Development. Multicoloured.

2843. 4 f. Type **542** .. .. 25 20
2844. 8 f. Miners with pneumatic drill .. .. .. 25 10
2845. 10 f. Open-cast mining .. 25 15
2846. 20 f. Electric mine train 1·00 35

**1979.** Golden Pheasants. Multicoloured.

2847. 4 f. Type **543** .. .. 45 20
2848. 8 f. Golden Pheasant in flight .. .. .. 55 25
2849. 45 f. Golden Pheasant looking for food .. 2·25 1·10

**544.** Einstein.

**545.** Woman, Monster and Phoenix.

**1979.** Birth Centenary of Albert Einstein (physicist).

2850. **544.** 8 f. brn., gold & slate 95 35

**1979.** Silk Paintings from a Tomb of the Warring States Period (475—221 B.C.). Multicoloured.

2851. 8 f. Type **545** .. .. 40 20
2852. 60 f. Man riding dragon.. 2·25 75

**546.** Jing Shan.

**547.** Hammer and Sickle.

**1979.** Peking Scenes. Multicoloured.

2853. 1 y. Type **546** .. .. 50 10
2854. 2 y. Summer Palace .. 80 15
2855. 5 y. Beihai Park.. .. 1·90 30

**1979.** 90th Anniv. of International Labour Day.

2856. **547.** 8 f. multicoloured .. 60 25

**548.** Memorial Frieze.

**1979.** 60th Anniv. of May 4th Movement. Multicoloured.

2857. 8 f. (1) Type **548**.. .. 30 10
2858. 8 f. (2) Girl and symbols of progress .. .. 30 10

**549.** Children of Different Races.

**1979.** International Year of the Child. Multicoloured.

2859. 8 f. I.Y.C. emblem and children with balloons 65 25
2860. 60 f. Type **549** .. .. 3·75 2·00

**550.** Spring over Great Wall.

**1979** The Great Wall. Multicoloured.

2861. 8 f. (1) Type **550**.. .. 80 25
2862. 8 f. (2) Summer over Great Wall .. .. .. 80 25
2863. 8 f. (3) Autumn over Great Wall .. .. 80 25
2864. 60 f. (4) Winter over Great Wall .. .. 4·25 2·25

**551.** Roaring Tiger.

**1979.** Manchurian Tiger. Multicoloured. Designs showing paintings by Liu Jiyou.

2866. 4 f. Type **551** .. 20 20
2867. 8 f. Two young tigers .. 35 20
2868. 60 f. Tiger at rest .. 1·25 85

**552.** Mechanical Harvester.

**1979.** Trades of the People's Communes. Mult.

2869. 4 f. (1) Type **552** (Agriculture) .. .. 45 20
2870. 8 f. (2) Planting a sapling (Forestry) .. .. 50 15
2871. 8 f. (3) Herding ducks (Stock raising).. .. 50 15
2872. 8 f. (4) Basket weaving .. 50 15
2873. 10 f. (5) Fishermen with handcarts of fish (Fishing) .. .. .. 75 35

**554.** Games' Emblem, Running, Volleyball and Weight-lifting.

**1979.** Fourth National Games.

2875. **554.** 8 f. (1) multicoloured 10 10
2876. – 8 f. (2) multicoloured 10 10
2877. – 8 f. (3) blk., grn. & red 10 10
2878. – 8 f. (4) blk., red & grn. 10 10

DESIGNS: No. 2876, Football, badminton, high jumping and ice skating. No. 2877, Fencing, skiing, gymnastics and diving. No. 2878, Motor cycling, table tennis, basketball and archery.

**555.** National Flag and Mountains.

**556.** National Emblem.

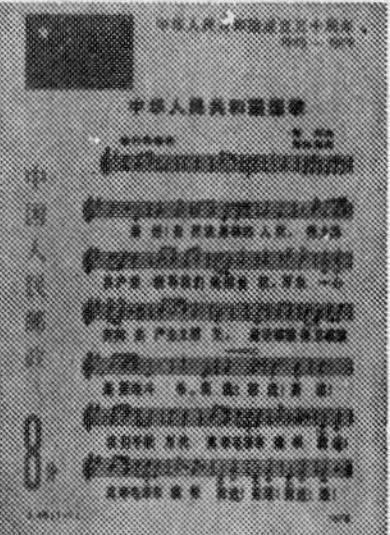

**557.** National Anthem.

**558.** Dancers and Drummer.

**559.** Tractor and Crop-spraying Antonov An-2.

**1979.** 30th Anniv. of People's Republic of China. Multicoloured.

2880 8 f. (1) National Flag and rainbow .. .. 90 40
2881 8 f. (2) Type **555** .. 90 40
2882 8 f. Type **556** .. 75 25
2884 8 f. Type **557** .. .. 1·00 60
2885 8 f. (1) Type **558** .. 15 15
2886 8 f. (2) Dancers and tambourine player .. 15 15
2887 8 f. (3) Dancers and banjo player .. .. .. 15 15
2888 8 f. (4) Dancers and drummer .. .. 15 15
2889 8 f. (1) Type **559** .. 35 15
2890 8 f. (2) Computer and cogwheels .. .. 35 15
2891 8 f. (3) Rocket, jet fighter and submarine .. 35 15
2892 8 f. (4) Atomic symbols .. 35 15

**560.** Exhibition Emblem.

**561.** Children with Model Airplanes.

**1979.** National Exhibition of Juniors' Scientific and Technological Works.

2893. **560.** 8 f. multicoloured .. 55 35

**1979.** Study of Science from Childhood. Multicoloured.

2894. 8 f. (1) Type **561** .. 20 10
2895. 8 f. (2) Girls with microscope and test tube .. 20 10
2896. 8 f. (3) Children with telescope .. .. .. 20 10
2897. 8 f. (4) Boy catching butterflies .. .. 20 10
2898. 8 f. (5) Girl noting weather readings .. .. 20 10
2899. 60 f. (6) Boys with model boat .. .. .. 75 30

**562.** Yu Shan.

**1979.** Taiwan Views. Multicoloured.

2901. 8 f. (1) Type **562** .. 25 10
2902. 8 f. (2) Sun Moon Lake .. 25 10
2903. 8 f. (3) Chikan Tower .. 25 10
2904. 8 f. (4) Suao-Hualien highway .. .. 25 10
2905. 55 f. (5) Tian Xiang Falls 1·25 60
2906. 60 f. (6) Moonlight over Banping Mountain .. 1·75 65

**563.** Symbols of Literature and Art.

**1979.** 4th National Congress of Literary and Art Workers. Multicoloured.

2907. 4 f. Type **563** .. .. 25 20
2908. 8 f. Seals, hammer, sickle, rifle, atomic symbol and flowers .. .. 35 20

**564.** Shaoshan-type Electric Locomotive.

**565.** " Chrysanthemum Petal ".

**1979.** Railway Construction. Multicoloured.

2909. 8 f. (1) Type **564** .. .. 70 20
2910. 8 f. (2) Modern railway viaduct .. .. .. 70 20
2911. 8 f. (3) Goods train crossing bridge .. .. 70 20

**1979.** Camellias of Yunnan. Multicoloured.

2912. 4 f. (1) Type **565** .. 20 20
2913. 8 f. (2) " Lion Head " .. 20 10
2914. 8 f. (3) Camellia " Chrysantha (Hu) Tuyama " 20 10
2915. 10 f. (4) " Small Osmanthus Leaf " .. .. 35 15
2916. 20 f. (5) " Baby Face " .. 45 20
2917. 30 f. (6) " Cornelian " .. 65 30
2918. 40 f. (7) Peony Camellia 75 35
2919. 50 f. (8) " Purple Gown " 95 40
2920. 60 f. (9) " Dwarf Rose " 1·00 30
2921. 70 f. (10) " Willow Leaf Spinel Pink " .. .. 1·75 35

**567.** Dr. Bethune attending Wounded Soldier.

**568.** Central Archives Hall.

**1979.** 40th Death Anniv. of Dr. Norman Bethune. Multicoloured.

2924. 8 f. Type **567** .. .. 25 10
2925. 70 f. Bethune Memorial, Mausoleum of Martyrs, Shijiazhuang .. .. 75 35

**1979.** International Archives Weeks. Mult.

2926. 8 f. (1) Type **568** .. 60 20
2927. 8 f. (2) Gold cabinet containing documents of Ming and Ching dynasties (vert.) .. .. 60 20
2928. 60 f. (3) Imperial Archives Main Hall .. .. 1·25 45

**569.** Waterfall Cave, Home of Monkey King.

**570.** Stalin.

**1979.** Scenes from " Pilgrimage to the West " (Chinese classical novel). Multicoloured.

2929. 8 f. (1) Type **569** .. 40 15
2930. 8 f. (2) Necha, son of Li, fighting Monkey .. 40 15
2931. 8 f. (3) Monkey in Mother Queen's peach orchard 40 15
2932. 8 f. (4) Monkey in alchemy furnace .. .. .. 40 15
2933. 10 f. (5) Monkey fighting White Bone Demon .. 45 15
2934. 20 f. (6) Monkey extinguishing fire with palm-leaf fan .. .. .. 75 25
2935. 60 f. (7) Monkey fighting Spider Demon in Cobweb Cave .. .. 2·75 1·50
2936. 70 f. (8) Monkey on scripture-seeking route to India .. .. .. 3·25 1·50

**1979.** Birth Centenary of Stalin.

2937. **570.** 8 f. (1) brown .. 55 25
2938. – 8 f. (2) black .. 55 25

DESIGN: No. 2038, Stalin appealing for unity against Germany.

**571.** Peony.

**572.** Meng Liang, " Hongyang Cave ".

**1980.** Paintings of Qi Baishi.

2939. **571.** 4 f. (1) multicoloured 15 15
2940. – 4 f. (2) multicoloured 15 15
2941. – 8 f. (3) multicoloured 15 10
2942. – 8 f. (4) blk., bl. & red 15 10
2943. – 8 f. (5) multicoloured 20 10
2944. – 8 f. (6) blk., grey & red 20 10
2945. – 8 f. (7) multicoloured 20 10
2946. – 8 f. (8) multicoloured 75 30
2947. – 10 f. (9) blk., yell. and red .. .. 35 15
2948. – 20 f. (10) grey, brn., & black .. .. 35 20
2949. – 30 f. (11) multicoloured 45 30
2950. – 40 f. (12) multicoloured 45 35
2951. – 50 f. (13) black, grey and red .. .. 60 40
2952. – 55 f. (14) multicoloured 60 45
2953. – 60 f. (15) black, grey and red .. .. 1·50 35
2954. – 70 f. (16) multicoloured 85 40

DESIGNS: No. 2940, Squirrels and grapes. No. 2941, Crabs and wine. No. 2942, Tadpoles in mountain spring. No. 2943, Chicks. No. 2944, Lotus. No. 2945, Red plum. No. 2946, Common Kingfisher. No. 2947, Bottle gourds. No. 2948, " The Voice of Autumn ". No. 2949, Wisteria. No. 2950, Chrysanthemums. No. 2951, Shrimps. No. 2952, Litchi. No. 2953, Cabbages and mushrooms. No. 2954, Peaches.

**1980.** Facial Makeup in Peking Operas. Multicoloured.

2956. 4 f. (1) Type **572** .. 35 15
2957. 4 f. (2) Li Kui, " Black Whirlwind " .. .. 35 15
2958. 8 f. (3) Huang Gai, " Meeting of Heroes " .. 40 10
2959. 8 f. (4) Monkey King, " Havoc in Heaven " 40 10
2960. 10 f. (5) Lu Zhishen, " Wild Boar Forest " 75 40
2961. 20 f. (6) Lian Po, " Reconciliation between the General and the Minister " .. .. .. 1·25 75
2962. 60 f. (7) Zhang Fei, " Reed Marsh " .. 2·25 1·25
2963. 70 f. (8) Dou Erdun, " Stealing the Emperor's Horse " .. .. 3·25 1·25

**573.** Chinese Olympic Committee Emblem.

**574.** Bear Macaque.

**1980.** Winter Olympic Games, Lake Placid. Multicoloured.

2964. 8 f. (1) Type **573** .. 20 10
2965. 8 f. (2) Speed skating .. 20 10
2966. 8 f. (3) Figure skating .. 20 10
2967. 60 f. (4) Skiing .. .. 1·00 30

**1980.** New Year. Year of the Monkey.

2968. **574.** 8 f. red, black & gold 22·00 10·00

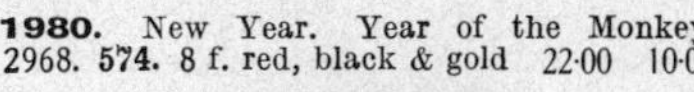

**575.** Klara Zetkin (journalist and politician).

**1980.** 70th Anniv. of International Working Women's Day.

2969. **575.** 8 f. blk., yell. & brn. 70 25

**576.** Orchard.

**1980.** Afforestation. Multicoloured.

2970. 4 f. Type **576** .. .. 15 15
2971. 8 f. Highway lined with trees .. .. .. 15 10
2972. 10 f. Aerial sowing .. 25 25
2973. 20 f. Factory amongst trees .. .. .. 75 35

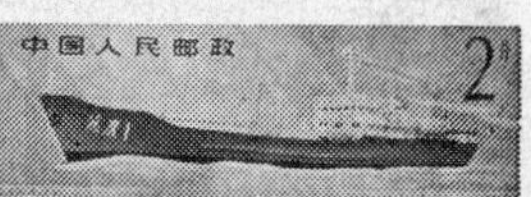

**577.** Apsaras (celestial beings).

**1980.** 2nd National Conference of Chinese Scientific and Technical Association.

2974. **577.** 8 f. multicoloured .. 80 25

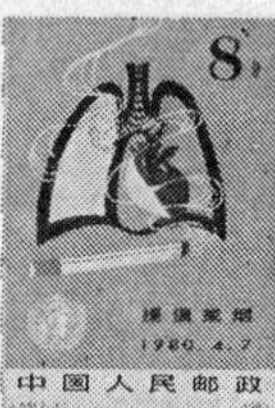

**578.** Freighter.

**1980.** Mail Transport. Multicoloured.

2975 2 f. Type **578** .. .. 85 75
2976 4 f. Mail bus .. .. 1·10 40
2977 8 f. Railway post office carriage .. .. 1·40 40
2978 10 f. Tupolev Tu-154 airplane .. .. 1·50 1·00

**579.** Cigarette damaging Heart and Lungs.

**1980.** Anti-Smoking Campaign. Multicoloured.

2979. 8 f. Type **579** .. .. 75 20
2980. 60 f. Face smoking and face holding flower in mouth, symbolising choice of smoking or health .. .. .. 2·25 85

**580.** Jian Zhen Memorial Hall, Yangzhou.

**1980.** Return of High Monk Jian Zhen's Statue. Multicoloured.

2981 8 f. (1) Type **580** .. 40 20
2982 8 f. (2) Statue of Jian Zhen (vert) .. .. 40 20
2983 60 f. (3) Junk in which Jian Zhen travelled to Japan .. .. .. 5·50 3·75

**581.** Lenin.

**582.** " Swallow Chick " Kite.

**1980.** 110th Birth Anniv. of Lenin.

2984. **581.** 8 f. brn., pink & grn. 85 35

**1980.** Kites. Multicoloured.

2985. 8 f. (1) Type **582** .. 40 20
2986. 8 f. (2) " Slender swallow " kite .. .. .. 40 20
2987. 8 f. (3) "Semi-slender swallow " kite .. .. 40 20
2988. 70 f. (4) " Dual swallows " kite .. .. .. 4·25 1·50

**583.** Hare running in Fright.

**1980.** Scenes from "Gu Dong" (Chinese fairy tale). Multicoloured.

2989 8 f. (1) Type **583** .. 20 20
2990 8 f. (2) Hare tells other animals "Gu Dong is coming" .. .. 20 20
2991 8 f. (3) Lion asks "What is Gu Dong?" .. .. 20 20
2992 8 f. (4) Animals discover sound of "Gu Dong" is made by falling papaya 20 20

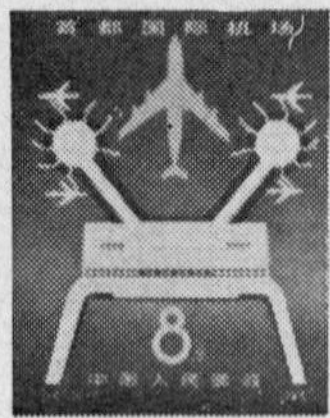

**584.** Plan of Terminal Building.

**585.** Sika Deer.

**1980.** Peking International Airport. Multicoloured.

2993. 8 f. Type **584** .. .. 35 15
2994. 10 f. Airplane and runway lights .. .. 75 25

**1980.** Sika Deer. Multicoloured.

2995. 4 f. Type **585** .. .. 35 25
2996. 8 f. Doe and fawn .. 35 25
2997. 60 f. Herd .. .. 2·25 1·10

**586.** " White Lotus ".

**1980.** Lotus Paintings by Yu Zhizhen. Multicoloured.

2998. 8 f. (1) Type **586** .. 35 25
2999. 8 f. (2) "Rose-tipped snow" .. .. 35 25
3000. 8 f. (3) "Buddha's Seat" 35 25
3001. 70 f. (4) "Variable Charming Face" .. .. 4·75 2·25

**587.** Returned Pearl Cave and Sword-cut Stone.

**1980.** Guilin Landscapes. Multicoloured.

3003. 8 f. (1) Type **587** .. 75 20
3004. 8 f. (2) Distant view of three mountains .. 75 20
3005. 8 f. (3) Nine-horse Fresco Hill .. .. .. 75 20
3006. 8 f. (4) Egrets around the aged banyan .. .. 75 20
3007. 8 f. (5) Western Hills at sunset (vert.) .. .. 75 20
3008. 8 f. (6) Moonlight on the Lijiang River (vert.) .. 75 20
3009. 60 f. (7) Springhead and ferry (vert.) .. .. 2·50 1·00
3010. 70 f. (8) Scenic path at Yangshuo (vert.) .. 2·50 1·00

**588.** Exhibition Gateway.

**589.** Burebista (founder-king) and Rumanian Flag.

**1980.** China Exhibition in United States. Multicoloured.

3011. 8 f. Type **588** .. .. 60 25
3012. 70 f. Great Wall and emblems of San Francisco, Chicago and New York 1·75 1·00

**1980.** 2050th Anniv. of Dacian State.

3013. **589.** 8 f. multicoloured .. 75 50

**590.** " Sea of Clouds " (Liu Haisu).

**1980.** U.N.E.S.C.O. Exhibition of Chinese Paintings and Drawings. Multicoloured.

3014. 8 f. (1) Type **590** .. 40 30
3015. 8 f. (2) "Black-naped Oriole and Magnolia" (Yu Feian) (vert.) .. 75 30
3016. 8 f. (3) "Tending Bactrian Camels" (Wu Zuoren .. .. .. 40 30

**591.** Quzi Tower in Spring.

**1980.** Liu Yuan (Tarrying Garden), Suzhou. Multicoloured.

3017. 8 f. (1) Type **591** .. 2·25 1·00
3018. 8 f. (2) Yuancui Pavilion in Summer .. .. 2·25 1·00
3019. 10 f. (3) Hanbi Shanfang in Autumn .. .. 2·25 1·00
3020. 60 f. (4) Guanyun Peak in Winter .. .. 7·50 2·50

**592.** Xu Guangqi.

**593.** Pistol Shooting.

**1980.** Scientists of Ancient China. Mult.

3021. 8 f. (1) Type **592** (agriculturalist and astronomer) 75 25
3022. 8 f. (2) Li Bing (hydraulic engineer) .. .. 75 25
3023. 8 f. (3) Jia Sixie (agronomist) .. .. .. 75 25
3024. 60 f. (4) Huang Daopo (textile expert) .. 3·75 2·25

**1980.** 1st Anniv. of Return to International Olympic Committe. Multicoloured.

3025. **593.** 4 f. (1) brown, yellow and mauve .. 20 10
3026. – 8 f. (2) brown, yellow and green .. 20 10
3027. – 8 f. (3) brown, yellow and blue .. .. 20 10
3028. – 10 f. (4) brown, yellow and orange .. 35 10
3029. – 60 f. (5) multicoloured 1·10 30

DESIGNS: No. 3026, Gymnastics. No. 3027, Diving. No. 3028, Volleyball. No. 3029, Archery.

**594.** White Flag Dolphin.

**595.** Cock.

**1980.** White Flag Dolphin. Mult.

3030. 8 f. Type **594** .. .. 20 20
3031. 60 f. Two dolphins .. 1·00 90

**1981.** New Year. Year of the Cock.

3032 **595** 8 f. multicoloured .. 1·25 80

**596.** Early Morning.

**1981.** Scenes of Xishuang Banna. Mult.

3033. 4 f. (1) Type **596** .. .. 35 10
3034. 4 f. (2) Mountain village of Dai nationality .. 35 10
3035. 8 f. (3) Rainbow over Lanchang River .. 35 15
3036. 8 f. (4) Ancient Temple (vert.) .. .. .. 35 15
3037. 8 f. (5) Moonlit night (vert.) 35 15
3038. 60 f. (6) Phoenix tree in bloom (vert.) .. .. 2·50 1·50

**597.** Flower Basket Lantern.

**1981.** Palace Lanterns. Multicoloured.

3039. 4 f. (1) Type **597** .. 25 15
3040. 8 f. (2) Dragons playing with a pearl .. .. 25 10
3041. 8 f. (3) Dragon and phoenix 25 10
3042. 8 f. (4) Treasure bowl .. 25 10
3043. 20 f. (5) Flower and birds 55 25
3044. 60 f. (6) Peony lantern painted with fishes .. 2·75 1·50

**598.** Crossing the River.

**1981.** Marking the Gunwale (Chinese fable). Multicoloured.

3045. 8 f. (1) Chinese text of story .. .. .. 10 10
3046. 8 f. (2) Type **598** .. 10 10
3047. 8 f. (3) The sword drops in the water .. .. 10 10
3048. 8 f. (4) Making mark on gunwale .. .. 10 10
3049. 8 f. (5) Diving into river to recover sword .. 10 10

**599.** Chinese Elm.

**600.** Vase with Two Tigers (Song Dynasty).

**1981.** Miniature Landscapes (dwarf trees). Multicoloured.

3050. 4 f. (1) Type **599** .. 25 15
3051. 8 f. (2) Juniper .. .. 35 10
3052. 8 f. (3) Maidenhair tree 35 10
3053. 10 f. (4) (Chinese Juniper (horiz.) .. .. 60 15
3054. 20 f. (5) Wild Kaki Persimmon (horiz.) .. 85 60
3055. 60 f. (6) Single-seed Juniper (horiz.) .. 2·50 1·00

**1981.** Ceramics from Cizhou Kilns. Mult.

3056. 4 f. (1) Type **600** .. 25 15
3057. 8 f. (2) Carved black glazed vase (Jin dynasty) (horiz.) 30 10
3058. 8 f. (3) Amphora with apricot blossoms (modern) 30 10
3059. 8 f. (4) Jar with two phoenixes (Yuan dynasty) (horiz.) .. .. 30 10
3060. 10 f. (5) Flat flask with dragon and phoenix (Yuan dynasty) (horiz.) .. .. 65 15
3061. 60 f. (6) Vessel with tiger-shapedhandles (modern) (horiz.) .. .. .. 1·50 55

**601.** Giant Panda "Stamp".

**1981.** People's Republic of China Stamp Exhibition, Japan. Multicoloured.

3062. 8 f. Type **601** .. .. 65 15
3063. 60 f. Cockerel and Junk " stamps " .. .. 1·25 75

**602.** Qinchuan Bull.

**603.** Inscription by Chou En-lai.

**1981.** Cattle. Multicoloured.

3064. 4 f. (1) Type **602** .. 25 15
3065. 8 f. (2) Binhu buffalo .. 25 10
3066. 8 f. (3) Yak .. .. 25 10
3067. 8 f. (4) Black and white dairy cattle .. .. 25 10
3068. 10 f. (5) Red pasture bull 35 20
3069. 55 f. (6) Simmental cross-breed bull .. .. 1·60 75

**1981.** " To Deliver Mail for Ten Thousand Li, Has Bearing on Arteries and Veins of the Country ".

3070. **603.** 8 f. multicoloured .. 20 15

**604.** I.T.U. and W.H.O. Emblems and Ribbons forming Caduceus.

**605.** Safety in Building Construction.

**1981.** World Telecommunications Day.

3071. **604.** 8 f. multicoloured .. 25 15

**1981.** National Safety Month. Multicoloured.

3072. 8 f. (1) Type **605** .. 20 10
3073. 8 f. (2) Mining safety .. 20 10
3074. 8 f. (3) Road safety .. 20 10
3075. 8 f. (4) Farming and forestry safety .. .. .. 20 10

**606.** Trunk Call Building.

**607.** St. Bride Vase (Men's singles).

**1981.**

3076. **606.** 8 f. brown .. .. 20 10

**1981.** Chinese Team's Victories at World Table Tennis Championships. Mult.

3077. 8 f. (3) Type **607** .. 10 15
3078. 8 f. (4) Iran Cup (Men's doubles) .. .. 10 15
3079. 8 f. (5) G. Geist Prize (Women's singles) .. 10 15
3080. 8 f. (6) W. J. Pope Trophy (Women's doubles) .. 10 15
3081. 8 f. (7) Heydusek Prize (Mixed doubles) .. 10 15
3082. 20 f. (1) Swathling Cup (Men's team) .. .. 20 15
3083. 20 f. (2) Marcel Corbillon Cup (Women's team) .. 20 15

**608.** Hammer and Sickle.

**609.** Five Veterans Peak.

**1981.** 60th Anniv. of Chinese Communist Party.

3084. **608.** 8 f. multicoloured .. 35 15

**1981.** Lushan Mountains. Multicoloured.

3085. 8 f. (1) Type **609** .. 30 15
3086. 8 f. (2) Hanpo Pass (horiz.) .. .. 30 15
3087. 8 f. (3) Yellow Dragon Pool and Waterfall .. 30 15
3088. 8 f. (4) Sunlit Peak (horiz.) .. .. 30 15
3089. 8 f. (5) Three-layer Spring .. .. .. 30 15
3090. 8 f. (6) Stone and pines (horiz.) .. .. 30 15
3091. 60 f. (7) Dragon Head Cliff .. .. .. 2·75 1·00

**610.** Silver Ear ("Tremella fuciformis").

**1981.** Edible Mushrooms. Multicoloured.

3092 4 f. (1) Type **610** .. 45 10
3093 8 f. (2) Veiled stinkhorn ("Dictyophora indusiata") .. .. 95 10
3094 8 f. (3) "Hericium erinaceus" .. .. 95 10
3095 8 f. (4) "Russula rubra" 95 10
3096 10 f. (5) Shii-take mushroom ("Lentinus edodes") .. .. 1·25 15
3097 70 f. (6) White button mushroom ("Agaricus bisporus") .. .. 2·75 1·00

611. Medal.

612. Huangguoshu Waterfall.

**1981.** Quality Month.

3098. 611. 8 f. (1) silver, black and red .. .. 20 10
3099. 8 f. (2) gold, brown and red .. .. 20 10

**1981.**

3100. – 1 f. green .. .. 10 10
3101. – 1½ f. red .. .. 10 10
3102. – 2 f. green .. .. 10 10
3103. 612. 3 f. brown .. .. 10 10
3118. – 3 f. deep brown, brown & light brown ..
3104. – 4 f. violet .. .. 10 10
3119. – 4 f. mauve & lilac .. 10 10
3105. – 5 f. brown .. .. 10 10
3106. – 8 f. blue .. .. 10 10
3107. – 10 f. purple .. .. 10 10
3121. – 10 f. brn. .. .. 20 10
3108. – 20 f. green .. .. 20 10
3122. – 20 f. blue .. .. 50 10
3109. – 30 f. brown .. .. 25 10
3110. – 40 f. black .. .. 25 10
3111. – 50 f. mauve .. .. 35 10
3112. – 70 f. black .. .. 50 10
3113. – 80 f. red .. .. 50 10
3114. – 1 y. lilac .. .. 60 10
3115. – 2 y. green .. .. 75 15
3116. – 5 y. blue .. .. 1·50 25

DESIGNS—VERT. 1 f. Xishuang Banna. 1½ f. Huashan Mountain. 2 f. Taishan Mountain. 4 f. Palm trees, Hainan. 5 f. Pagoda, Huqiu Hill, Suzhou. 8 f. Great Wall. 10 f. North-east Forest. HORIZ. 20 f. Herding sheep on Tianshan Mountain. 30 f. Sheep on grassland, Inner Mongolia. 40 f. Stone Forest. 50 f. Pagodas, Ban Pingshan Mountain, Taiwan. 70 f. Mt. Zhumulangma. 80 f. Seven Star Grotto, Guangdong. 1 y. Gorge, Yangtze River. 2 y. Guilin. 5 y. Mt. Huangshan.

613. Stone Forest in Autumn.

**1981.** Stone Forest. Multicoloured.

3125. 8 f. (1) Stone Forest in a mist .. .. .. 35 10
3126. 8 f. (2) Type 613 .. .. 35 10
3127. 8 f. (3) Pool in Stone Forest .. .. .. 35 10
3128. 10 f. (4) Dawn over Stone Forest (vert.) .. 40 10
3129. 70 f. (5) Stone Forest by starlight (vert.) .. 1·25 60

614. Lu Xun as Youth.

**1981.** Birth Cent. of Lu Xun (writer).

3130. 614. 8 f. blk., grn. & yell. 15 10
3131. – 20 f. black, brown & deep brown .. 35 15

DESIGN: 20 f. Lu Xun in later life.

615. Dr. Sun Yat-sen.

616. "Tree" symbolizing Co-ordination.

**1981.** 70th Anniv. of 1911 Revolution.

3132. 615. 8 f. (1) multicoloured 20 15
3133. – 8 f. (2) black, green and yellow .. 20 15
3134. – 8 f. (3) black, pink and yellow .. 20 15

DESIGNS: No. 3133, Grave of 72 Martyrs, Huang Hua Gate. No. 3134, Headquarters of Military Government of Hubei Province.

**1981.** Asian Conference of Parliamentarians on Population and Development. Mult.

3135. 8 f. Type 616 .. .. 15 10
3136. 70 f. Design symbolizing Enlightenment .. 55 30

617. Money Cowrie and Cowrie-shaped Bronze Coin.

618. Hands and Globe with I.Y.D.P. Emblem.

**1981.** Ancient Chinese Coins (1st series). Minted before 221 B.C. Multicoloured.

3137. 4 f. (1) Type 617 .. .. 25 15
3138. 4 f. (2) Shovel coin .. 25 15
3139. 8 f. (3) Shovel coin inscribed "Li" .. .. 25 10
3140. 8 f. (4) Shovel coin inscribed "An Yi Er Jin" 25 10
3141. 8 f. (5) Knife coin inscribed "Qi Fa Ha" .. .. 25 10
3142. 8 f. (6) Knife coin inscribed "Jie Mo Zhi Fa Hua" 25 10
3143. 60 f. (7) Knife coin inscribed "Cheng Bai" 1·25 50
3144. 70 f. (8) Circular coin with hole inscribed "Gong" 1·75 75

See also Nos. 3162/69.

**1981.** International Year of Disabled People.

3145. 618. 8 f. multicoloured .. 20 10

619. Daiyu.

620. Volleyball Player.

**1981.** The Twelve Beauties of Jinling from "A Dream of Red Mansions" by Cao Xueqin. Multicoloured. Designs showing paintings by Liu Danzhai.

3146. 4 f. (1) Type 619 .. 20 15
3147. 4 f. (2) Baochai chases butterfly .. .. 20 15
3148. 8 f. (3) Yuanchun visits parents .. .. 20 10
3149. 8 f. (4) Yingchun reading Buddhist sutras .. 20 10
3150. 8 f. (5) Tanchun forms poetry society .. 20 10
3151. 8 f. (6) Xichun painting .. 20 10
3152. 8 f. (7) Xiangyun picking up necklace .. .. 20 10
3153. 10 f. (8) Liwan lectures her son .. .. 35 10
3154. 20 f. (9) Xifeng hatches plot .. .. .. 45 25
3155. 30 f. (10) Sister Qiao escapes .. .. .. 55 25
3156. 40 f. (11) Keqing relaxing 65 35
3157. 80 f. (12) Miaoyu serves tea .. .. .. 2·25 1·00

**1981.** Victory of Chinese Women's Team in World Cup Volleyball Championships. Multicoloured.

3159. 8 f. Type 620 .. .. 15 10
3160. 20 f. Player holding Cup 60 20

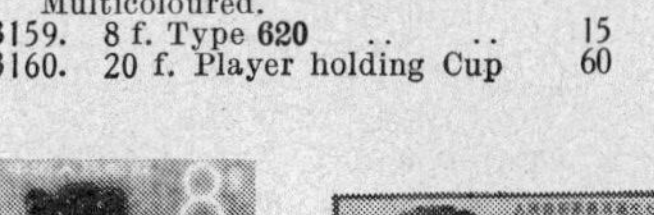

621. Dog.

622. Nie Er and Score of "March of the Volunteers".

**1982.** New Year. Year of the Dog.

3161 621 8 f. multicoloured .. 65 25

**1982.** Ancient Chinese Coins (2nd series). As T 617. Multicoloured.

3162. 4 f. (1) Guilian ("Monster Mask") .. .. 15 15
3163. 4 f. (2) Shu shovel coin .. 15 15
3164. 8 f. (3) Xia Zhuan shovel coin .. .. .. 15 10
3165. 8 f. (4) Han Dan shovel coin .. .. .. 15 10
3166. 8 f. (5) Pointed-head knife coin .. .. .. 15 10
3167. 8 f. (6) Ming knife coin .. 15 10
3168. 70 f. (7) Jin Hua knife coin .. .. .. 95 45
3169. 80 f. (8) Yi Liu Hua circular coin .. .. 1·75 65

**1982.** 70th Anniv. of Nie Er (composer).

3170. 622. 8 f. multicoloured .. 20 10

623. Children and dripping Water.

624. Dr. Robert Koch and Laboratory Equipment.

**1982.** International Drinking Water and Sanitation Decade.

3171. 623. 8 f. blue, orange and light blue .. .. 20 10

**1982.** Centenary of Discovery of Tubercle Bacillus.

3172. 624. 8 f. multicoloured .. 20 10

625. Building on Fire, Hoses and Fire Engine.

627. "Hemerocallis flava" and "H. fulva".

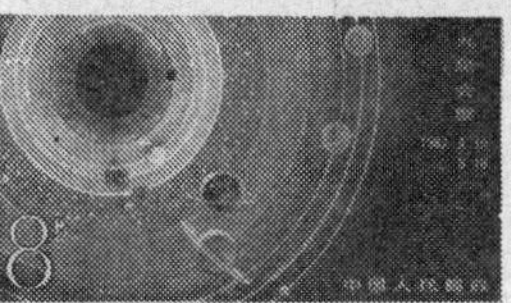

626. Solar System.

**1982.** Fire Control. Multicoloured.

3173. 8 f. (1) Type 625 .. 25 10
3174. 8 f. (2) Chemical fire extinguisher .. .. 25 10

**1982.** "Cluster of Nine Planets" (planetary conjunction).

3175. 626. 8 f. multicoloured .. 35 15

**1982.** Medicinal Plants. Multicoloured.

3176. 4 f. (1) Type 627. .. 10 10
3177. 8 f. (2) "Fritillaria unibracteata" .. .. 10 10
3178. 8 f. (3) "Aconitum carmichaeli" .. .. 10 10
3179. 10 f. (4) "Lilium brownii" 35 10
3180. 20 f. (5) "Arisaema consanguineum" .. .. 35 15
3181. 70 f. (6) "Paeonia lactiflora" .. .. .. 1·50 80

628. Soong Ching Ling addressing First Plenary Session.

**1982.** 1st Death Anniv. of Soong Ching Ling (former Head of State). Multicoloured.

3183. 8 f. Type 628 .. .. 20 10
3184. 20 f. Portrait of Soong Ching Ling .. .. 40 20

629. Sable.

**1982.** The Sable. Multicoloured.

3185. 8 f. Type 629 .. .. 25 20
3186. 80 f. Sable running .. 95 80

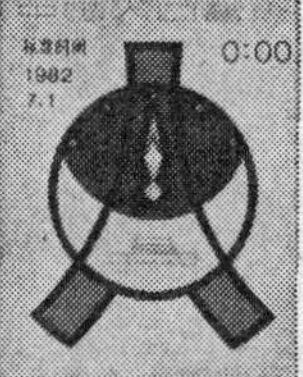

630. Census Emblem.

631. Text, Emblem and Globe.

**1982.** National Census.

3187. 630. 8 f. multicoloured .. 20 10

**1982.** Second U.N. Conference on the Exploration and Peaceful Uses of Outer Space, Vienna.

3188. 631. 8 f. multicoloured .. 20 10

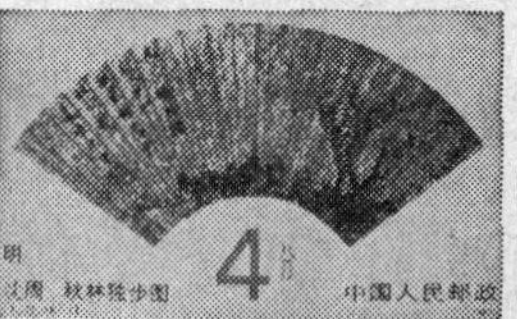

632. "Strolling Alone in Autumn Woods" (Shen Zhou).

**1982.** Fan Paintings of the Ming and Qing Dynasties. Multicoloured.

3189 4 f. (1) Type 632 .. 15 10
3190 8 f. (2) "Crow on withered Tree" (Tang Yin) .. 15 10
3191 8 f. (3) "Bamboos and Bramblings" (Zhou Zhimian) .. .. 15 10
3192 10 f. (4) "Writing Poem under Pine" (Chen Hongshou and Bai Han) .. .. .. 25 10
3193 20 f. (5) "Chrysanthemums" (Yun Shouping) 35 15
3194 70 f. (6) "Masked Hawfinch, Grape Myrtle and Chinese Parasol" (Wang Wu) .. 1·10 45

634. Society Emblem.

635. Orpiment.

**1982.** 60th Anniv. of Chinese Geological Society.

3196. 634. 8 f. gold, stone & blk. 20 10

**1982.** Minerals. Multicoloured.

3197 4 f. Type 635 .. .. 15 10
3198 8 f. Stibnite .. .. 20 10
3199 10 f. Cinnabar .. .. 25 10
3200 20 f. Wolframite .. 30 10

636. "12" Hammer and Sickle and Great Hall of the People.

637. Hoopoe.

**1982.** 12th National Communist Party Congress.

3201. 636. 8 f. multicoloured .. 20 10

**1982.** Birds. Multicoloured.

3202. 8 f. (1) Type 637 .. .. 35 15
3203. 8 f. (2) Barn swallow .. 35 15
3204. 8 f. (3) Black-naped oriole .. .. .. 35 15
3205. 20 f. (4) Great tit .. 1·00 50
3206. 70 f. (5) Great spotted woodpecker .. .. 2·75 1·25

638. "Plum Blossom" (Guan Shanyue).

**1982.** 10th Anniv. of Normalization of Diplomatic Relations with Japan. Mult.

| | | | |
|---|---|---|---|
| 3208. | 8 f. Type **638** .. .. | 10 | 10 |
| 3209. | 70 f. "Hibiscus" (Xiao Shufang) .. .. | 70 | 35 |

639. Globe, Profiles and Ear of Wheat.

640. Guo Moruo.

**1982.** World Food Day.

| | | | |
|---|---|---|---|
| 3210. **639.** | 8 f. multicoloured .. | 15 | 10 |

**1982.** 90th Birth Anniv. of Guo Moruo (writer). Multicoloured.

| | | | |
|---|---|---|---|
| 3211. | 8 f. type **640** .. .. | 10 | 10 |
| 3212. | 20 f. Guo Moruo writing | 20 | 10 |

641. Head of Bodhisattva.

642. Dr. D. S. Kotnis.

**1982.** Sculptures of Liao Dynasty. Mult.

| | | | |
|---|---|---|---|
| 3213. | 8 f. (1) Type **641.** .. | 25 | 10 |
| 3214. | 8 f. (2) Bust of Bodhisattva | 25 | 10 |
| 3215. | 8 f. (3) Boy on lotus flower | 25 | 10 |
| 3216. | 70 f. (4) Bodhisattva .. | 1·50 | 55 |

**1982.** 40th Death Anniv. of Dr. D. S. Kotnis

| | | | |
|---|---|---|---|
| 3218. **642.** | 8 f. green & black .. | 10 | 10 |
| 3219. – | 70 f. lilac & black .. | 65 | 35 |

DESIGN: Dr. Kotnis in army uniform.

643. Couple holding Flaming Torch.

644. Wine Container.

**1982.** 11th National Communist Youth League Congress.

| | | | |
|---|---|---|---|
| 3220. **643.** | 8 f. multicoloured .. | 20 | 10 |

**1982.** Bronzes of Western Zhou Dynasty. Multicoloured.

| | | | |
|---|---|---|---|
| 3221. | 4 f. (1) Type **644** .. | 25 | 10 |
| 3222. | 4 f. (2) Cooking vessel .. | 25 | 10 |
| 3223. | 8 f. (3) Food container .. | 25 | 10 |
| 3224. | 8 f. (4) Cooking vessel with ox head and dragon design .. | 25 | 10 |
| 3225. | 8 f. (5) Ram-shaped wine container .. .. | 25 | 10 |
| 3226. | 10 f. (6) Wine jar .. | 35 | 10 |
| 3227. | 20 f. (7) Food bowl .. | 70 | 20 |
| 3228. | 70 f. (8) Wine container | 2·00 | 85 |

645. "Pig" (Han Meilin).

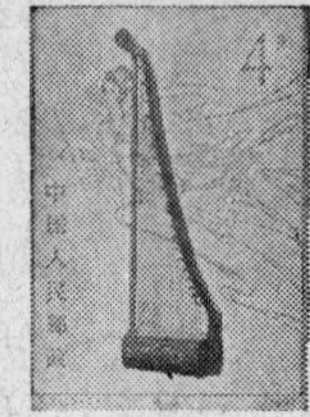

646. Harp.

**1983.** New Year. Year of the Pig.

| | | | |
|---|---|---|---|
| 3229. **645.** | 8 f. multicoloured .. | 85 | 50 |

**1983.** Stringed Musical Instruments.

| | | | |
|---|---|---|---|
| 3230. **646.** | 4 f (1) green & brown | 25 | 10 |
| 3231. – | 8 f (2) purple, green and brown .. .. | 25 | 10 |
| 3232. – | 8 f (3) multicoloured | 25 | 10 |
| 3233. – | 10 f (4) multicoloured | 35 | 10 |
| 3234. – | 70 f (5) multicoloured | 2·25 | 85 |

DESIGNS:—VERT. 8 f. (3231), Four string guitar. 10 f. Four string lute. 70 f. Three string lute. HORIZ. 8 f. (3232), Qin.

647. "February 7" Monument, Jiangan.

648. Zhang Gong attracted by Yingying's Beauty.

**1983.** 60th Anniv. of Peking-Hankow Railway Workers' Strike.

| | | | |
|---|---|---|---|
| 3235. **647.** | 8 f. (1) yell., blk. & grey | 25 | 20 |
| 3236. – | 8 f. (2) stone, brown & lilac .. .. | 25 | 20 |

DESIGN: No. 3236, "February 7" Memorial tower, Zhengzhou.

**1983.** Scenes from "The Western Chamber" (musical drama by Wang Shifu). Mult.

| | | | |
|---|---|---|---|
| 3237. | 8 f. (1) Type **648** .. | 85 | 25 |
| 3238. | 8 f. (2) Zhang Gong and Yingying listening to music .. .. .. | 85 | 25 |
| 3239. | 10 f. (3) Zhang Gong and Yingying's wedding .. | 1·10 | 35 |
| 3240. | 80 f. (4) Zhang Gong and Yingying parting at Chanting Pavilion .. | 4·75 | 1·75 |

649. Karl Marx.

650. Tomb, Mt. Qiaoshan, Huangling.

**1983.** Death Centenary of Karl Marx.

| | | | |
|---|---|---|---|
| 3242. **649.** | 8 f. grey and black .. | 10 | 10 |
| 3243. – | 20 f. lilac and black | 25 | 15 |

DESIGN: 20 f. "Marx making Speech" (Wen Guozhang).

**1983.** Tomb of the Yellow Emperor. Mult.

| | | | |
|---|---|---|---|
| 3244. | 8 f. Type **650** .. .. | 15 | 10 |
| 3245. | 10 f. Hall of Founder of Chinese Culture (horiz.) .. .. | 20 | 10 |
| 3246. | 20 f. Xuanyuan cypress | 35 | 15 |

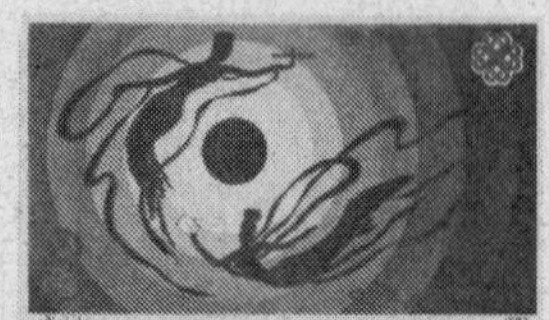

651. Messengers and Globe.

**1983.** World Communications Year.

| | | | |
|---|---|---|---|
| 3247. **651.** | 8 f. multicoloured .. | 25 | 15 |

652. Chinese Alligator.

**1983.** Chinese Alligator. Multicoloured.

| | | | |
|---|---|---|---|
| 3248. | 8 f. Type **652** .. .. | 20 | 10 |
| 3249. | 20 f. Alligator and hatching eggs .. .. | 65 | 25 |

653. "Scratching" (Wang Yani).

**1983.** Children's Paintings. Multicoloured.

| | | | |
|---|---|---|---|
| 3250. | 8 f. (1) type **653** .. .. | 15 | 10 |
| 3251. | 8 f. (2) "I Love the Great Wall" (Liu Zhong) .. | 15 | 10 |
| 3252. | 8 f. (3) "Kitten" (Tang Axi) .. .. | 15 | 10 |
| 3253. | 8 f. (4) "The Sun, Birds, Flowers and Me" (Bu Hua) .. .. .. | 15 | 10 |

654. Congress Hall.

**1983.** Sixth National People's Congress. Multicoloured.

| | | | |
|---|---|---|---|
| 3254. | 8 f. Type **654** .. .. | 25 | 10 |
| 3255. | 20 f. Score of National Anthem .. .. | 35 | 15 |

655. Terracotta Soldiers. 656. Sun Yujiao.

**1983.** Terracotta Figures from Qin Shi Huang's Tomb. Multicoloured.

| | | | |
|---|---|---|---|
| 3256. | 8 f. (1) Type **655** .. | 15 | 10 |
| 3257. | 8 f. (2) Heads figures .. | 15 | 10 |
| 3258. | 10 f. (3) Soldiers and horses .. .. .. | 35 | 10 |
| 3259. | 70 f. (4) Aerial view of excavation .. .. | 2·00 | 75 |

**1983.** Female Roles in Peking Opera. Mult.

| | | | |
|---|---|---|---|
| 3261. | 4 f. (1) Type **656** .. | 15 | 10 |
| 3262. | 8 f. (2) Chen Miaochang .. | 20 | 10 |
| 3263. | 8 f. (3) Bai Suzhen .. | 20 | 10 |
| 3264. | 8 f. (4) Sister Thirteen .. | 20 | 10 |
| 3265. | 10 f. (5) Qin Xianglian .. | 20 | 10 |
| 3266. | 20 f. (6) Yang Yuhuan .. | 40 | 15 |
| 3267. | 50 f. (7) Cui Yingying .. | 1·50 | 35 |
| 3268. | 80 f. (8) Mu Guiying .. | 2·75 | 65 |

657. Li Bai (poet).

**1983.** Poets and Philosophers of Ancient China. Paintings by Liu Lingcang. Mult.

| | | | |
|---|---|---|---|
| 3269. | 8 f. (1) Type **657** .. | 10 | 10 |
| 3270. | 8 f. (2) Du Fu (poet) .. | 10 | 10 |
| 3271. | 8 f. (Han Yu (philosopher) .. .. | 10 | 10 |
| 3272. | 70. f. (4) Liu Zongyuan (philosopher) .. .. | 1·90 | 75 |

658. Woman and Women working.

**1983.** Fifth National Women's Congress.

| | | | |
|---|---|---|---|
| 3273. **658.** | 8 f. multicoloured .. | 15 | 10 |

659. Games Emblem.

660. "One Child per Couple".

**1983.** Fifth National Games. Multicoloured.

| | | | |
|---|---|---|---|
| 3274. | 4 f. (1) Type **659** .. | 15 | 10 |
| 3275. | 8 f. (2) Gymnastics .. | 15 | 10 |
| 3276. | 8 f. (3) Badminton .. | 15 | 10 |
| 3277. | 8 f. (4) Diving .. .. | 15 | 10 |
| 3278. | 20 f. (5) High jump .. | 35 | 15 |
| 3279. | 70 f. (6) Windsurfing .. | 1·10 | 45 |

**1983.** Family Planning. Multicoloured.

| | | | |
|---|---|---|---|
| 3280. | 8 f. (1) Type **660** .. | 15 | 10 |
| 3281. | 8 f. (2) "Population, cultivated fields and grain" .. .. .. | 15 | 10 |

661. Hammer and Cogwheel as "10".

**1983.** Tenth National Trade Union Congress.

| | | | |
|---|---|---|---|
| 3282. **661.** | 8 f. multicoloured .. | 20 | 10 |

662. Mute Swan.

663. Liu Shaoqi.

**1983.** Swans. Multicoloured.

| | | | |
|---|---|---|---|
| 3283. | 8 f. (1) Type **662** .. | 15 | 10 |
| 3284. | 8 f. (2) Mute swans .. | 15 | 10 |
| 3285. | 10 f. Whistling swans .. | 20 | 15 |
| 3286. | 80 f. (4) Whooper swans in flight .. .. | 1·40 | 60 |

**1983.** 85th Birth Anniv. of Liu Shaoqi (former Head of State).

| | | | |
|---|---|---|---|
| 3287. **663.** | 8 f. (1) multicoloured | 10 | 10 |
| 3288. – | 8 f. (2) multicoloured | 10 | 10 |
| 3289. – | 8 f. (3) brown, blue & gold .. .. | 10 | 10 |
| 3290. – | 8 f. (4) brown, blue & gold .. .. | 10 | 10 |

DESIGNS: No. 3288, Liu reading a speech. 3289, Liu making a speech. 3290, Liu meeting model worker Shi Chuanxiang.

**664.** $100 National Emblem Stamp, 1951.
**665.** Mao Tse-tung in 1925.

**1983.** National Stamp Exhibition, Peking. Multicoloured.
3291 8 f. Type **664** .. .. 10 10
3292 20 f. North West China $1 Yanan Pagoda stamp of 1946 .. .. .. 25 15

**1983.** 90th Birth Anniv. of Mao Tse-tung.
3293. **665.** 8 f. (1) multicoloured 10 10
3294. – 8 f. (2) stone, brown and gold .. .. 10 10
3295. – 10 f. (3) grey, brown and gold .. .. 10 10
3296. – 20 f. (4) multicoloured 25 15
DESIGNS: No. 3294, Mao Tse-tung in Yanan, 1945. 3295, Mao Tse-tung inspecting Yellow River, 1952. 3296, Mao Tse-tung in library, 1961.

**666.** "Rat" (Zhan Tong).
**667.** Young Girl with Ball.

**1984.** New Year. Year of the Rat.
3297. **666.** 8 f. blk., yell & red .. 70 25

**1984.** Child Welfare. Multicoloured.
3298. 8 f.+2 f. Type **667** .. 20 15
3299. 8 f.+2 f. Young boy with toy panda .. .. 20 15

**668.** Women with Dog.

**1984.** Tang Dynasty Painting "Beauties wearing Flowers" by Zhou Fang. Mult.
3300 8 f. Type **668** .. .. 40 20
3301 10 f. Women and Manchurian crane .. 40 20
3302 70 f. Women, dog and Manchurian crane .. 2·00 1·00

**669.** "The Spring of Shanghai".
**670.** Ren Bishi.

**1984.** Chinese Roses. Multicoloured.
3304. 4 f. (1) Type **669** .. 10 10
3305. 8 f. (2) "Rosy Dawn of the Pujiang River" .. 10 10
3306. 8 f. (3) "Pearl" .. .. 10 10
3307. 10 f. (4) "Black Whirl-wind" .. .. 10 10
3308. 20 f. (5) "Yellow Flower in the Battlefield" .. 25 15
3309. 70 f. (6) "Blue Phoenix" 90 35

**1984.** 80th Birth Anniv. of Ren Bishi (member of Communist Party Secretariat) (1st issue).
3310. **670.** 8 f. brown, black and purple .. 15 10
See also Nos. 3361/3.

**671.** Japanese Crested Ibis.

**1984.** Japanese Crested Ibis. Multicoloured.
3311 8 f. (1) Type **671** .. 15 10
3312 8 f. (2) Ibis wading .. 15 10
3313 80 f. (3) Ibis perching .. 1·25 50

**672.** Red Cross Activities.

**1984.** 80th Anniv. of Chinese Red Cross Society.
3314. **672.** 8 f. multicoloured .. 15 10

**673.** Building Dam.

**1984.** Gezhou Dam Project. Multicoloured.
3315. 8 f. Type **673** .. .. 10 10
3316. 10 f. View of dam and lock gates (vert.) .. 10 10
3317. 20 f. Freighter in lock .. 25 15

**674.** Inverted Image Tower and Yilang Pavilion.

**1984.** Zhuo Zheng Garden, Suzhou. Mult.
3318. 8 f. (1) Type **674** .. 10 10
3319. 8 f. (2) Loquat Garden .. 10 10
3320. 10 f. (3) Water court of Xiao Cang Lang .. 10 10
3321. 70 f. (4) Yuanxiang Hall and Yiyu Study .. 75 45

**675.** Pistol Shooting.

**1984.** Olympic Games, Los Angeles. Multicoloured.
3322. 4 f. Type **675** .. .. 10 10
3323. 8 f. High jumping .. 10 10
3324. 8 f. Weightlifting .. 10 10
3325. 10 f. Gymnastics .. 10 10
3326. 20 f. Volleyball .. .. 25 15
3327. 80 f. Diving .. .. 85 50

**676.** Calligraphy.
**677.** Tianjin.

**1984.** Art Works by Wu Changshuo. Mult.
3329. 4 f. (1) Type **676** .. 10 10
3330. 4 f. (2) "Pair of Peaches" 10 10
3331. 8 f. (3) "Lotus" .. .. 10 10
3332. 8 f. (4) "Wisteria" .. 10 10
3333. 8 f. (5) "Peony" .. .. 10 10
3334. 10 f. (6) "Autumn Chrys-anthemum" .. .. 15 10
3335. 20 f. (7) "Plum Blossom" 40 20
3336. 70 f. (8) Seal and impres-sion .. .. .. 1·10 55

**1984.** Luanhe River-Tianjin Water Diversion Project. Multicoloured.
3337. 8 f. Type **677** .. .. 10 10
3338. 10 f. Locks and canal (horiz.) .. .. 10 10
3339. 20 f. Tunnel and sculp-ture .. .. .. 25 15

**678.** Chinese and Japanese Pagodas.

**1984.** Chinese-Japanese Youth Friendship Festival. Multicoloured.
3340. 8 f. Type **678** .. .. 10 10
3341. 20 f. Girls watering shrub 25 15
3342. 80 f. Young people dancing .. .. 1·00 40

**679.** Factory Worker.

**1984.** 35th Anniv. of People's Republic. Mult.
3343. 8 f. (1) Type **679** .. 10 10
3344. 8 f. (2) Girl and rainbow 10 10
3345. 8 f. (4) Girl and symbols of science .. .. 10 10
3346. 8 f. (5) Soldier .. .. 10 10
3347. 20 f. (3) Flag and Manchurian cranes (36×50 mm.) .. .. 40 15

**680.** Chen Jiageng.

**1984.** 110th Birth Anniv of Chen Jiageng (educationist and patriot). Multicoloured.
3348 8 f. Type **680** .. .. 15 10
3349 80 f. Jimei School .. 70 40

**681.** The Maiden's Study.

**1984.** Scenes from "Peony Pavilion" (drama) by Tang Xianzu. Paintings by Dai Dunbang. Multicoloured.
3350. 8 f. (1) Type **681** .. 15 10
3351. 8 f. (2) Du Liniang dreaming .. .. 15 10
3352. 20 f. (3) Du Liniang drawing self-portrait .. 35 15
3353. 70 f. (4) Du Liniang and Liu Mengmei married 1·10 50

**HAVE YOU READ THE NOTES AT THE BEGINNING OF THIS CATALOGUE?**
These often provide answers to the enquiries we receive.

**682.** Baoguo Temple.

**1984.** Landscapes of Mount Emei Shan. Multicoloured.
3355. 4 f. (1) Type **682** .. 10 10
3356. 8 f. (2) Leiyin Temple .. 10 10
3357. 8 f. (3) Hongchun Lawn 10 10
3358. 10 f. (4) Elephant Bath Pool .. .. .. 10 10
3359. 20 f. (5) Woyun Temple 40 15
3360. 80 f. (6) Shining Cloud Sea, Jinding .. .. 1·25 40

**683.** Ren Bishi.
**684.** Flowers in Chinese Vase.

**1984.** 80th Birth Anniv. of Ren Bishi (2nd issue).
3361. **683.** 8 f. brown and grey 10 10
3362. – 10 f. brown and grey 10 10
3363. – 20 f. black and brown 25 10
DESIGNS: 10 f. Ren Bishi reading speech at Communist Party Congress. 20 f. Ren Bishi saluting.

**1984.** Chinese Insurance Industry.
3364. **684.** 8 f. multicoloured .. 10 10

**685.** "Ox" (Yao Zhonghua).
**687.** Lotus of Good Luck.

**686.** "Zunyi Meeting" (Liu Xiangping).

**1985.** New Year. Year of the Ox.
3365. **685.** 8 f. multicoloured .. 10 10

**1985.** 50th Anniv. of Zunyi Meeting. Mult.
3366. 8 f. Type **686** .. .. 10 10
3367. 20 f. "Arrival of the Red Army in Northern Shaanxi" (Zhao Yu) .. 25 15

**1985.** Festival Lanterns. Multicoloured.
3368. 8 f. (1) Type **687** .. 20 10
3369. 8 f. (2) Auspicious dragon and phoenix .. .. 20 10
3370. 8 f. (3) A hundred flowers blossoming .. .. 20 10
3371. 70 f. (4) Prosperity and affluence .. .. 65 40

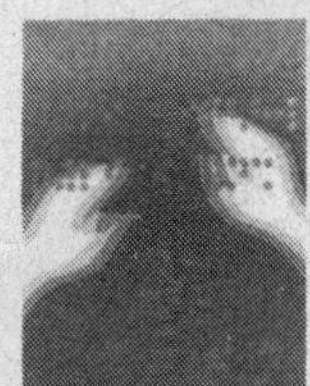

**688.** Stylized Dove and Women's Open Hands.
**689.** Hands reading Braille.

**1985.** United Nations Decade for Women.
3372. **688.** 20 f. multicoloured .. 25 10

**1985.** Welfare Fund for the Handicapped. Multicoloured.
3373. 8 f+2 f (1) Type **689** .. 15 15
3374. 8 f.+2 f. (2) Lips and sign language .. 15 15
3375. 8 f.+2 f. (3) Learning to use artificial limb .. 15 15
3376. 8 f.+2 f. (4) Stylized figure in wheelchair .. 15 15

**690.** "Green Calyx" Mei.

**691.** Headquarters.

**1985.** Mei Flowers. Multicoloured.
3377. 8 f. (1) Type **690** .. 10 10
3378. 8 f. (2) "Pendant" mei .. 10 10
3379. 8 f. (3) "Contorted dragon" mei .. .. 10 10
3380. 10 f. (4) "Cinnabar" mei 10 10
3381. 20 f. (5) "Versicolor" mei 25 10
3382. 80 f. (6) "Apricot" mei .. 75 50

**1985.** 60th Anniv. of All-China Trade Unions Federation.
3384. **691.** 8 f. multicoloured .. 10 10

**692.** Bird and Children.

**1985.** International Youth Year.
3385. **692.** 20 f. multicoloured .. 20 15

**693.** Giant Panda.

**694.** Xian Xinghai (bust, Cao Chongen).

**1985.** Giant Panda. Multicoloured.
3386. 8 f. Type **693** .. .. 10 10
3387 20 f. Giant panda (different) (horiz) .. 15 15
3388. 50 f. Giant panda (different) .. .. 35 30
3389. 80 f. Two giant pandas (horiz) .. .. .. 50 40

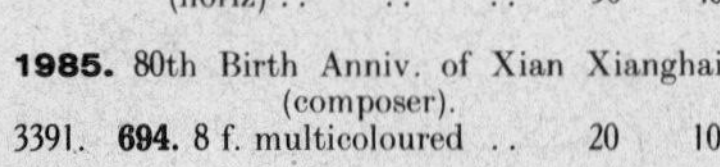

**1985.** 80th Birth Anniv. of Xian Xianghai (composer).
3391. **694.** 8 f. multicoloured .. 20 10

**695.** Agnes Smedley.

**696.** Zheng He (navigator).

**1985.** American Journalists in China.
3392. **695.** 8 f. brown, stone and ochre .. .. 10 10
3393. – 20 f. olive, grey and stone .. .. 20 10
3394. – 80 f. purple, lilac and cream .. .. 75 40
DESIGNS: 20 f. Anna Louise Strong. 80 f. Edgar Snow.

**1985.** 580th Anniv. of Zheng He's First Voyage to Western Seas. Multicoloured.
3395. 8 f. (1) Type **696** .. 10 10
3396. 8 f. (2) Zheng He on elephant .. .. 10 10
3397. 20 f. (3) Exchanging goods .. .. .. 20 10
3398. 80 f. (4) Bidding farewell 75 45

**697.** "Self-portrait".

**1985.** 90th Birth Anniv. of Xu Beihong (artist). Multicoloured.
3399. 8 f. Type **697** .. .. 10 10
3400. 20 f. Xu Beihong at work 20 15

**698.** Lin Zexu.

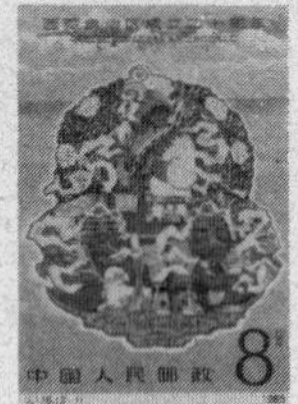

**699.** "Prosperity".

**1985.** Birth Bicentenary of Lin Zexu (statesman).
3401. **698.** 8 f. multicoloured .. 15 10
3402. – 80 f brown and black 75 40
DESIGN—55×23 mm. 80 f. "Burning opium at Humen" (relief).

**1985.** 20th Anniv. of Tibet Autonomous Region. Multicoloured.
3403. 8 f. Type **699** .. .. 10 10
3404. 10 f. "Celebration" .. 10 10
3405. 20 f. "Harvest .. .. 20 10

**700.** Chinese Army at Lugouqiao.

**1985.** 40th Anniv. of Victory over Japan.
3406. **700.** 8 f. blk., brn. & red 10 10
3407. – 80 f. blk., brn. & red 75 40
DESIGN: 80 f. Defending the Great Wall.

**701.** Cycling

**1985.** Second National Workers' Games, Peking. Multicoloured.
3408. 8 f. Type **701** .. .. 10 10
3409. 20 f. Hurdling .. .. 20 15

**702.** Gobi Oasis.

**703.** Athletes and Silhouette of Woman.

**1985.** 30th Anniv. of Xinjiang Uygur Autonomous Region. Multicoloured.
3410. 8 f. Type **702** .. .. 10 10
3411. 10 f. Oilfield and Lake Tianchi (54×26 mm.) 10 10
3412. 20 f. Tianshan pasture .. 20 15

**1985.** First National Youth Games, Zhengzhou.
3413. **703.** 8 f. multicoloured .. 10 10
3414. – 20 f. red, blue and black .. .. 20 10
DESIGN: 20 f. Basketball players and silhouette of man.

**704.** Forbidden City. (½-size illustration)

**1985.** 60th Anniv. of Imperial Palace Museum.
3415. **704.** 8 f. (1) multicoloured 10 10
3416. – 8 f. (2) multicoloured 10 10
3417. – 20 f. (3) multicoloured 20 10
3418. – 80 f. (4) multicoloured 70 30
DESIGNS: Nos. 3416/18, Different parts of Forbidden City.

**705.** Zou Taofen.

**706.** Memorial Pavilion.

**1985.** 90th Anniv. of Zou Taofen (journalist).
3419. **705.** 8 f. black, brn. & sil. 10 10
3420. – 20 f. blk., grn. & sil. 20 10
DESIGN: 20 f. Premier Chou En-lai's inscription in memory of Zou Taofen.

**1985.** 50th Anniv. of December 9th Movement.
3421 **706** 8 f. multicoloured .. 10 10

**707.** "Tiger".

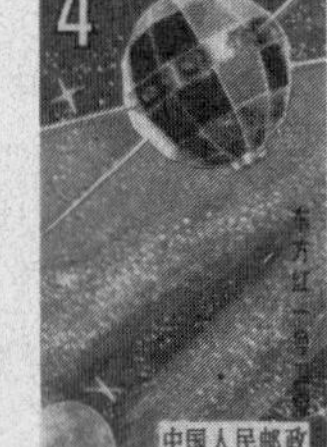

**708.** First Experimental Satellite.

**1986.** New Year. Year of the Tiger.
3422. **707.** 8 f. multicoloured .. 10 10

**1986.** Space Research. Multicoloured.
3423 4 f. (1) Type **708** .. 10 10
3424 8 f. (2) Mil-Mi8 helicopters recovering satellites .. 10 10
3425 8 f. (3) Underwater launched rocket .. 10 10
3426 10 f. (4) Rocket launched from land .. .. 15 10
3427 20 f. (5) Dish aerial .. 30 15
3428 70 f. (6) Satellite and diagram of orbit .. 60 45

**709.** Dong Biwu.

**710.** Lin Boqu.

**1986.** Birth Centenary of Dong Biwu (founder of Chinese Communist Party).
3429. **709.** 8 f. black and brown 10 10
3430. – 20 f. black and brown 20 10
DESIGN: 20 f. At meeting for ratification of U.N. Charter, Los Angeles, 1945.

**1986.** Birth Cent of Lin Boqu (politician).
3431 **710** 8 f. brown and black 10 10
3432 – 20 f. brown and black 20 10
DESIGN: 20 f. At Yanan.

**711.** He Long.

**1986.** 90th Birth Anniv of He Long (politician).
3433. **711.** 8 f. black and brown 10 10
3434. – 20 f. black and brown 20 10
DESIGN: 20 f. On horse.

**712.** Skin Tents, Inner Mongolia.

**713.** Comet and Earth.

**1986.** Traditional Houses.
3435 **712** 1 f. grn, brn & grey 10 10
3436 – 1½ f. brown, red & bl 10 10
3437 – 2 f. brown and bistre 10 10
3438 – 3 f. black and brown 10 10
3439 – 4 f. red and black .. 10 10
3439a – 5 f. black, grey & grn 10 10
3440 – 8 f. grey, red & black 10 10
3441 – 10 f. black & orange 15 10
3441b – 15 f. blk, grey & grn 15 10
3442 – 20 f. grey, grn & blk 20 10
3442b – 25 f. blk, grey & pink 25 15
3443 – 30 f. lilac, blue & brn 15 10
3444 – 40 f. brown, purple and stone .. 30 15
3445 – 50 f. bl, mve & dp bl 15 15
3445b – 80 f. black, grey & bl 70 25
3446 – 90 f. black and red 70 25
3447 – 1 y. brown and grey 35 20
3448 – 1 y. 10 bl, blk & brn 90 40
3448a – 1 y. 30 black, grey and red .. .. 45 20
3448b – 1 y. 60 blue & black 50 25
3448c – 2 y. blk, grey & brn 1·00 50
DESIGNS: 1½ f. Tibet. 2 f. North-East China. 3 f. Hunan. 4 f. Jiangsu. 5 f. Shandong. 8 f. Peking. 10 f. Yunnan. 15 f. Guangxi. 20 f. Shanghai. 25 f. Ningxia. 30 f. Anhui. 40 f. North Shaanxi. 50 f. Sichuan. 80 f. Shanxi. 90 f. Taiwan. 1 y. Fujian. 1 y. 10, Zhejiang. 1 y. 30, Qinghai. 1 y. 60, Guizhou. 2 y. Jiangxi.

**1986.** Appearance of Halley's Comet.
3449. **713.** 20 f. grey and blue .. 20 10

**714.** Cranes.

**1986.** Great White Crane. Multicoloured.
3450. 8 f. Type **714** .. .. 15 10
3451. 10 f. Crane flying (vert.) 25 20
3452. 70 f. Four cranes (vert.) 1·00 65

**715.** Li Weihan.

**1986.** 90th Birth Anniv. of Li Weihan (politician). Each green and black.
3454. 8 f. Type **715** .. .. 10 10
3455. 20 f. Li Weihan at work 20 10

**716.** Stylized People on Dove.

**1986.** International Peace Year.
3456. **716.** 8 f. multicoloured .. 10 10

**717.** Mao Dun.

**1986.** 90th Birth Anniv. of Mao Dun (writer). Each grey, black and brown.
3457. 8 f. Type **717** .. .. 10 10
3458. 20 f. Mao Dun and manuscript .. .. 20 10

**718.** Wang Jiaxiang.

**1986.** 80th Birth Anniv of Wang Jiaxiang (first People's Republic ambassador to U.S.S.R.). Multicoloured.
3459. 8 f. Type **718** .. .. 10 10
3460. 20 f. Wang Jiaxiang at Yan'an .. .. 20 10

**719.** Flowers on Desk.

**1986.** Teachers' Day.
3461. **719.** 8 f. multicoloured .. 10 10

**720.** "Magnolia sinensis".

**1986.** Magnolias. Multicoloured.
3462. 8 f. (1) Type **720** .. 10 10
3463. 8 f. (2) "Manglietia patungensis" .. .. 10 10
3464. 70 f. (3) "Alcimandra cathcartii" .. .. 60 30

**721.** Sun Yat-sen (120th birth anniv.)

**724.** Zhu De.

**1986.** 75th Anniv. of 1911 Revolution. Leaders. Multicoloured.
3466. 8 f. Type **721** .. .. 10 10
3467. 10 f. Huang Xing (70th death anniv.) .. .. 10 10
3468. 40 f. Zhang Taiyan (50th death anniv.) .. .. 30 15

**1986.** Birth Centenary of Marshal Zhu De.
3471 **724** 8 f. brown .. .. 10 10
3472 – 20 f. green .. .. 15 10
DESIGN: 20 f. Making speech, 1950.

**725.** Archery. **726.** "Rabbit".

**1986.** Sport in Ancient China. Each grey, black and red.
3473. 8 f. (1) Type **725** .. 10 10
3474. 8 f. (2) Weiqi (horiz.) .. 10 10
3475. 10 f. (3) Golf (horiz.) .. 10 10
3476. 50 f. (4) Football .. 40 20

**1987.** New Year. Year of the Rabbit.
3477. **726.** 8 f. multicoloured .. 10 10

**727.** Xu Xiake.

**728.** Steller's Sea Eagle.

**1987.** 400th Birth Anniv. of Xu Xiake (explorer). Multicoloured.
3478. 8 f. Type **727** .. .. 25 10
3479. 20 f. Recording observations in cave .. .. 45 10
3480. 40 f. Climbing mountain 85 15

**1987.** Birds of Prey. Multicoloured.
3481 8 f. (1) Black kite (horiz) 35 10
3482 8 f. (2) Type **728** .. 35 10
3483 10 f. (3) Himalayan griffon 35 10
3484 90 f. (4) Upland buzzard (horiz) .. .. 1·10 35

**729.** Hawk Kite.

**1987.** Kites. Multicoloured.
3485. 8 f. (1) Type **729** .. 10 10
3486. 8 f. (2) Centipede .. 10 10
3487. 30 f. (3) The Eight Diagrams .. .. 25 15
3488. 30 f. (4) Phoenix .. 25 15

**730.** Liao Zhongkai. **731.** "Eventful Years".

**1987.** 110th Birth Anniv. of Liao Zhongkai (politician). Multicoloured.
3489. 8 f. Type **730**. .. 10 10
3490. 20 f. Liao Zhongkai with wife .. .. 15 10

**1987.** 90th Birth Anniv. of Ye Jianying (revolutionary and co-founder of People's Army). Portraits. Multicoloured.
3491. 8 f. Type **731** .. .. 10 10
3492. 10 f. "Founder of the State" .. .. 10 10
3493. 30 f. "Everywhere Green Hills" .. .. 25 15

**732.** Worshipping Bodhisattvas (Northern Liang Dynasty).

**1987.** Dunhuang Cave Murals (1st series). Multicoloured.
3494. 8 f. Type **732** .. .. 15 10
3495. 10 f. Deer King Jataka (Northern Wei dynasty) .. .. 15 10
3496. 20 f. Heavenly musicians (Northern Wei dynasty) .. .. 25 10
3497. 40 f. Flying Devata (Northern Wei dynasty) .. .. 65 15
See also Nos. 3553/6, 3682/5, 3811/14, 3910/13 and 4131/4.

**733.** "Happy Holiday" (Yan Qinghu).

**734.** Town.

**1987.** Children's Day. Childrens' drawings. Multicoloured.
3499. 8 f. (1) Type **733** .. 10 10
3500. 8 f. (2) Children with doves and balloons (Liu Yuan) .. .. 10 10

**1987.** Improvements in Rural Areas. Multicoloured.
3501. 8 f. (1) Type **734** .. 10 10
3502. 8 f. (2) Fresh foods (horiz.) .. .. 10 10
3503. 10 f. (3) Feeding cattle (horiz.) .. 10 10
3504. 20 f. (4) Outdoor cinema 15 10

**735.** Emblem.

**736.** Globe.

**1987.** Postal Savings.
3505. **735.** 8 f. tur., yell. & red 10 10

**1987.** Centenary of Esperanto (invented language).
3506. **736.** 8 f. blue, blk. & grn. 10 10

**737.** Flag over Great Wall.

**1987.** 60th Anniv. of People's Liberation Army. Multicoloured.
3507 8 f. (1) Type **737** .. 10 10
3508 8 f. (2) Soldier and rocket launcher .. .. 10 10
3509 10 f. (3) Sailor and submarine .. .. 30 15
3510 30 f. (4) Pilot and jet fighters .. .. 25 15

**738.** Dove above Houses.

**1987.** International Year of Shelter for the Homeless.
3511. **738.** 8 f. multicoloured .. 10 10

**739.** Chinese Character.

**740.** Pan Gu inventing the Universe.

**1987.** China Art Festival, Peking.
3512. **739.** 8 f. black, red and gold .. .. 10 10

**1987.** Folk Tales. Multicoloured.
3513. 4 f. (1) Type **740** .. 10 10
3514. 8 f. (2) Nu Wa creating human being .. .. 10 10
3515. 8 f. (3) Yi shooting nine suns .. .. .. 10 10
3516. 10 f. (4) Chang'e flying to the moon .. .. 10 10
3517. 20 f. (5) Kua Fu chasing the sun .. .. 15 10
3518. 90 f. (6) Jing Wei filling the sea .. .. .. 70 35

**741.** Sun rising behind Party Flag.

**1987.** 13th National Communist Party Congress.
3519. **741.** 8 f. multicoloured .. 10 10

**742.** Yellow Crane Tower, Wuhan.

**743.** Pole Vaulting.

**1987.** Ancient Buildings. Multicoloured.
3520. 8 f. (1) Type **742** .. 10 10
3521. 8 f. (2) Yue Yang Tower 10 10
3522. 10 f. (3) Teng Wang Pavilion .. .. 25 10
3523. 90 f. (4) Peng Lai Pavilion .. .. 1·00 35

**1987.** 6th National Games, Guangdong Province. Multicoloured.
3525. 8 f. (1) Type **743** .. 10 10
3526. 8 f. (2) Women's softball 10 10
3527. 30 f. (3) Weightlifting .. 25 15
3528. 50 f. (4) Diving .. .. 40 20

**745.** Shi Jin practising Martial Arts.

**1987.** Literature. "Outlaws of the Marsh" (1st series). Multicoloured.
3530. 8 f. Type **745** .. .. 25 10
3531. 10 f. Sagacious Lu uprooting willow tree 45 10
3532. 30 f. Lin Chon sheltering in temple of mountain spirit .. .. 65 15
3533. 50 f. Song Jian helping Chao Gai to escape .. 75 20
See also Nos. 3614/17, 3778/81 and 3854/7.

**746.** Dragon. **747.** Cai Yuanpri.

**1988.** New Year. Year of the Dragon.
3535. **746.** 8 f. multicoloured .. 10 10

**1988.** 120th Birth Anniv of Cai Yuanpei (educationist). Multicoloured.
3536. 8 f. Type **747** .. .. 10 10
3537. 20 f. Cai Yuanpei seated in chair .. .. 15 10

**748.** Tao Zhu.

**1988.** 80th Birth Anniv. of Tao Zhu (Communist Party official). Multicoloured.
3538 8 f. Type **748** .. .. 10 10
3539 20 f. Tao Zhu (half-length portrait) .. .. 15 10

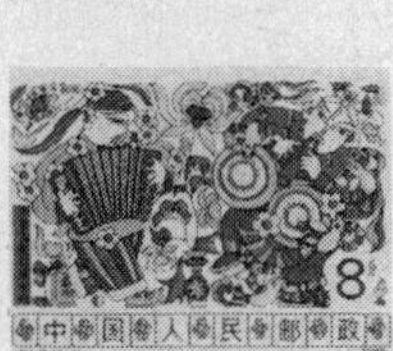

**749.** Harvest Festival. **750,** Flag and Rainbow.

**1988.** Flourishing Rural Areas of China. Multicoloured.
3540 8 f. Type **749** .. .. 10 10
3541 10 f. Couple with fish, flowers and chickens .. 10 10
3542 20 f. Couple making scientific study .. 15 10
3543 30 f. Happy family .. 20 10

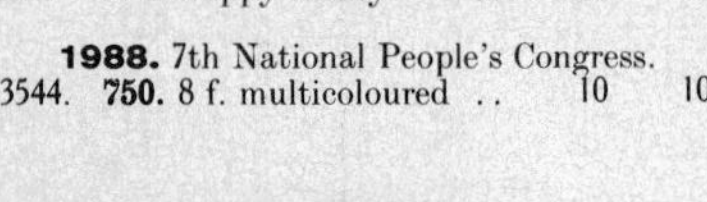

**1988.** 7th National People's Congress.
3544. **750.** 8 f. multicoloured .. 10 10

**751.** Wuzhi Mountain.

**1988.** Establishment of Hainan Province. Multicoloured.
3545. 8 f. Type **751** .. .. 10 10
3546. 10 f. Wanquan River .. 10 10
3547. 30 f. Beach .. 20 10
3548. 1 y. 10 Bay and deer .. 60 30

**752.** Li Siguang (geologist).

**1988.** Scientists (1st series). Multicoloured.
3549. 8 f. Type **752** .. .. 10 10
3550. 10 f. Zhu Kezhen (meteorologist) .. 10 10
3551. 20 f. Wu Youxun (physicist) .. .. 15 10
3552. 30 f. Hua Luogeng (mathematician) .. 20 10
See also Nos. 3702/5 and 3821/4.

**1988.** Dunhuang Cave Murals (2nd series). As T **732**. Multicoloured.
3553. 8 f. (1) Hunting (Western Wei dynasty) .. .. 10 10
3554. 8 f. (2) Fighting (Western Wei dynasty) .. .. 10 10
3555. 10 f. (3) Farming (Northern Zhou dynasty) .. .. 15 10
3556. 90 f. (4) Building pagoda (Northern Zhou dynasty) .. .. 50 20

**753.** Healthy Trees and Hand holding back polluted Soil.

**1988.** Environmental Protection. Mult.
3557. 8 f. (1) Type **753** .. 10 10
3558. 8 f. (2) Doves in clean air and hand holding back polluted air .. .. 10 10
3559. 8 f. (3) Fishes in clean water and hand holding back polluted water .. .. .. 10 10
3560. 8 f. (4) Peaceful landscape and hand holding back noise waves .. .. .. 10 10

**755.** Games Emblem.

**1988.** 11th Asian Games, Peking (1990) (1st issue). Multicoloured.
3562. 8 f. Type **755** .. .. 10 10
3563. 30 f. Games mascot .. 15 10
See also Nos. 3653/6 and 3695/3700.

**756.** Warrior, Longmen Grotto, Henan. **757.** Peony.

**1988.** Art of Chinese Grottoes.
3564 – 2 y. brown & lt brown 50 10
3565 **756** 5 y. black and brown 1·25 15
3566 – 10 y. brown and stone 2·00 35
3567 – 20 y. black and brown 4·75 1·50
DESIGNS: 2 y. Buddha, Yungang Grotto, Shanxi. 10 y. Bodhisattva, Maijishan Grotto, Gansu. 20 y. Woman with chickens, Dazu Grotto, Sichuan.

**1988.** 10th Anniv. of Chinese–Japanese Treaty of Peace and Friendship. Mult.
3568. 8 f. Type **757** .. .. 10 10
3569. 1 y. 60 Cherry blossom .. 60 30

**758.** Coal Wharf, Quinghuangdao.

**1988.** Achievements of Socialist Construction (1st series). Multicoloured.
3570. 8 f. Type **758** .. .. 30 15
3571. 10 f. Ethylene works, Shangdong .. .. 10 10
3572. 20 f. Baoshan steel works, Shanghai .. 10 10
3573. 30 f. Television centre, Peking .. .. .. 15 10
See also Nos. 3691/22, 3678/81 and 3759/62.

**759.** Taishan Temple.

**1988.** Mount Taishan Views. Multicoloured.
3574. 8 f. Type **759** .. .. 10 10
3575. 10 f. Ladder to Heaven 10 10
3576. 20 f. Daguang Park .. 10 10
3577. 90 f. Sun Watching Peak 25 15

**760.** Liao Chengzhi. **761.** Cycling.

**1988.** 80th Birth Anniv of Liao Chengzhi (Communist Party leader). Multicoloured.
3578 8 f. Type **760** .. .. 10 10
3579 20 f. Liao Chengzhi at work .. .. .. 10 10

**1988.** 1st National Peasant Games. Mult.
3580 8 f. Type **761** .. .. 10 10
3581 20 f. Wushu .. .. 10 10

**762.** Peng Dehuai.

**1988.** 90th Birth Anniv. of General Peng Dehuai. Multicoloured.
3582. 8 f. Type **762** .. .. 10 10
3583. 20 f. In uniform .. .. 10 10

**763** Battle against Lu Bu

**1988.** Literature. "Romance of the Three Kingdoms" by Luo Guanzhong (1st series). Multicoloured.
3584 8 f. (1) Heroes become sworn brothers (horiz) 15 10
3585 8 f. (2) Type **763** .. 15 10
3586 30 f. (3) Fengyi Pavilion (horiz) .. .. 35 15
3587 50 f. (4) Discussing heroes over wine .. .. 85 25
See also Nos. 3711/14, 3807/10 and 3944/7.

**764** People in Heart **765** Stag's Head

**1988.** International Volunteers' Day.
3589 **764** 20 f. multicoloured .. 10 10

**1988.** Pere David's Deer. Multicoloured.
3590 8 f. Type **765** .. .. 15 10
3591 40 f. Herd .. .. 40 10

**766** Da Yi Pin

**1988.** Orchids. Multicoloured.
3592 8 f. Type **766** .. .. 10 10
3593 10 f. Dragon .. .. 10 10
3594 20 f. Large phoenix tail .. 10 10
3595 50 f. Silver-edged black orchid .. .. .. 15 10

**767** Snake **768** Qu Quibai

**1989.** New Year. Year of the Snake.
3597 **767** 8 f. multicoloured .. 10 10

**1989.** 90th Birth Anniv of Qu Qiubai (writer). Multicoloured.
3598 8 f. Type **768** .. .. 10 10
3599 20 f. Qu Qiubai (half-length portrait) .. 10 10

**769** Pheasant

**1989.** Brown Eared-pheasant. Multicoloured.
3600 8 f. Type **769** .. .. 10 10
3601 50 f. Two pheasants .. 15 10

**770.** "Heaven" (top section)

**1989.** Silk Painting from Han Tomb, Mawangdui, Changsha. Multicoloured.
3602 8 f. Type **770** .. .. 25 10
3603 20 f. "Earth" (central section) .. .. 25 10
3604 30 f. "Underworld" (bottom section) .. 25 10

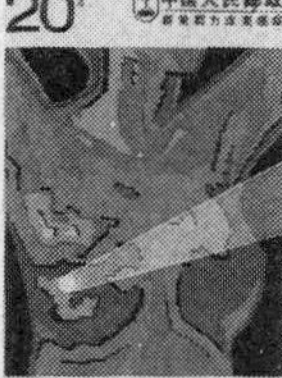

**771** Diagnosis by Thermography **773** Children

**772** Memorial Frieze

**1989.** Anti-cancer Campaign.
3606 **771** 8 f. grey, red & black 10 10
3607 – 20 f. multicoloured .. 10 10
DESIGN: 8 f. Crab and red crosses.

**1989.** 70th Anniv of May 4th Movement.
3608 **772** 8 f. multicoloured .. 10 10

**1989.** 40th International Children's Day. Children's paintings. Multicoloured.
3609 8 f. +4 f. (1) Type **773** .. 10 10
3610 8 f. +4 f. (2) Child and penguins .. .. 10 10
3611 8 f. +4 f. (3) Child flying on bird .. .. 10 10
3612 8 f. +4 f. (4) Boy and girl playing ball .. .. 10 10

**774** Globe, Doves and Lectern

**1989.** Cent of Interparliamentary Union.
3613 **774** 20 f. multicoloured .. 10 10

**1989.** Literature. "Outlaws of the Marsh" (2nd series). As T **745**. Multicoloured.
3614 8 f. Wu Song killing tiger on Jingyang Ridge .. 10 10
3615 10 f. Qin Ming riding through hail of arrows 10 10
3616 20 f. Hua Rong shooting wild goose .. .. 15 10
3617 1 y. 30 Li Kui fighting Zhang Shun on boat .. 60 30

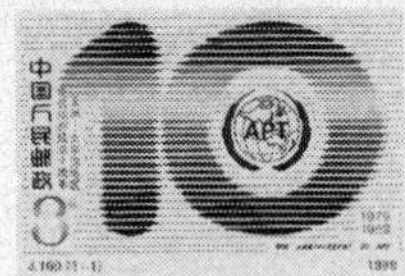

**775** Anniversary Emblem

**1989.** 10th Anniv of Asia–Pacific Telecommunity.
3618 **775** 8 f. multicoloured .. 10 10

**1989.** Achievements of Socialist Construction (2nd series). As T **758**. Multicoloured.
3619 8 f. International telecommunications building, Peking (vert) 10 10
3620 10 f. Xi Qu coal mine, Gu Jiao .. .. .. 10 10
3621 20 f. Long Yang Gorge hydro-electric power station, Qinghai .. 10 10
3622 30 f. Da Yao Shan tunnel on Guangzhou–Heng Yang railway .. .. 15 10

**776** Five Peaks of Mt. Huashan

**1989.** Mount Huashan. Multicoloured.
3623 8 f. Type **776** .. .. 10 10
3624 10 f. View from top of Mt. Huashan .. .. 10 10
3625 20 f. Thousand Foot Precipice .. .. 10 10
3626 90 f. Blue Dragon Ridge 40 20

**777** "Fable of the White Snake" (Stage design, Ye Qianyu)

**1989.** Contemporary Art. Multicoloured.
3627 8 f. Type **777** .. .. 10 10
3628 20 f. "Lijiang River in Fine Rain" (Li Keran) 15 10
3629 50 f. "Marching Together" (oxen) (Wu Zuoren) .. 25 10

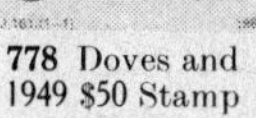

**778** Doves and 1949 $50 Stamp

**780** Ribbons and Gate of Heavenly Peace, Peking

**779** Lecturing in Temple of Apricot, Qufu

**1989.** 40th Anniv of Chinese People's Political Conference.
3630 **778** 8 f. red, blue & black 10 10

**1989.** 2540th Birth Anniv of Confucius (philosopher). Multicoloured.
3631 8 f. Type **779** .. .. 10 10
3632 1 y. 60 Confucius in ox-drawn cart .. 50 25

**1989.** 40th Anniv of People's Republic. Mult.
3634 8 f. Type **780** .. .. 10 10
3635 10 f. Flowers and ribbons 10 10
3636 20 f. Stars and ribbons .. 10 10
3637 40 f. Buildings and ribbons .. .. 15 10

**781** Woman using Camera

**1989.** 150th Anniv of Photography.
3640 **781** 8 f. multicoloured .. 10 10

**782** Li Dazhao

**1989.** Birth Cent of Li Dazhao (co-founder of Chinese Communist Party). Multicoloured.
3641 8 f. Type **782** .. .. 10 10
3642 20 f. Li Dazhao and script 10 10

**783** Diagram of Collider in Action

**1989.** Peking Electron-Positron Collider.
3643 **783** 8 f. multicoloured .. 10 10

**784** Rockets

**1989.** National Defence. Multicoloured.
3644 4 f. Type **784** .. .. 10 10
3645 8 f. Rocket on transporter 10 10
3646 10 f. Rocket launch (vert) 10 10
3647 20 f. Jettison of fuel tank 10 10

**785** Spring Morning, Su Causeway

**1989.** West Lake, Hangzhou. Multicoloured.
3648 8 f. Type **785** .. .. 10 10
3649 10 f. Crooked Courtyard 10 10
3650 30 f. Moon over Three Pools .. .. .. 15 10
3651 40 f. Snow on Broken Bridge .. .. 40 20

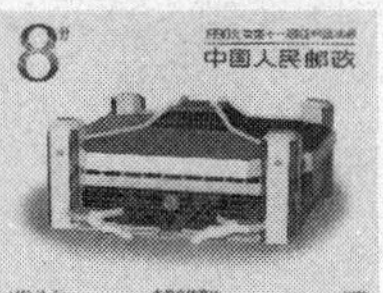

**786** Peking College Gymnasium

**787** Horse

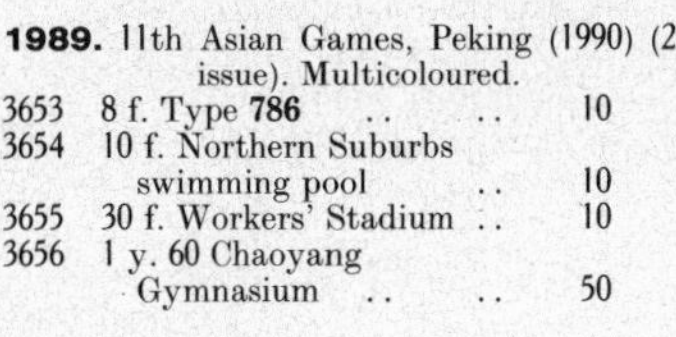

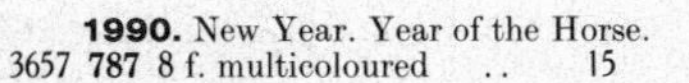

**1989.** 11th Asian Games, Peking (1990) (2nd issue). Multicoloured.
3653 8 f. Type **786** .. .. 10 10
3654 10 f. Northern Suburbs swimming pool .. 10 10
3655 30 f. Workers' Stadium .. 10 10
3656 1 y. 60 Chaoyang Gymnasium .. .. 50 25

**1990.** New Year. Year of the Horse.
3657 **787** 8 f. multicoloured .. 15 10

**788** Narcissi

**789** Bethune and Medical Team in Canada

**1990.** Narcissi. Multicoloured.
3658 8 f. Type **788** .. .. 10 10
3659 20 f. Natural group of narcissi .. .. 10 10
3660 30 f. Arrangement of narcissi .. .. 20 10
3661 1 y. 60 Arrangement (different) .. .. 75 35

**1990.** Birth Centenary of Norman Bethune (surgeon). Multicoloured.
3662 8 f. Type **789** .. .. 10 10
3663 1 y. 60 Bethune and medical team in China .. 50 20

**790** Emblem

**791** Birds flying above Trees

**1990.** 80th International Women's Day.
3664 **790** 20 f. red, green & black 10 10

**1990.** Tree Planting Day. Multicoloured.
3665 8 f. Type **791** .. .. 10 10
3666 10 f. Trees in city .. 10 10
3667 20 f. Great Wall and trees 10 10
3668 30 f. Forest and field of wheat .. .. .. 25 10

**792** Ban Po Plate

**793** Li Fuchun

**1990.** Pottery. Multicoloured.
3669 8 f. Type **792** .. .. 10 10
3670 20 f. Miao Di Gou dish .. 10 10
3671 30 f. Ma Jia Yao jar .. 15 10
3672 50 f. Ma Chang jar .. 25 15

**1990.** 90th Birth Anniv of Li Fuchun (politician). Multicoloured.
3673 8 f. Type **793** .. .. 10 10
3674 20 f. Li Fuchun (different) 10 10

**794** Charioteer

**795** Snow Leopard

**1990.** 10th Anniv of Discovery of Bronze Chariots in Emperor Qin Shi Huang's Tomb. Multicoloured.
3675 8 f. Type **794** .. .. 10 10
3676 50 f. Horse's head .. 25 10

**1990.** Achievements of Socialist Construction (3rd series). As T **758**. Multicoloured.
3678 8 f. Second automobile factory .. .. 10 10
3679 10 f. Yizheng chemical and fibre company .. 10 10
3680 20 f. Shengli oil field .. 10 10
3681 30 f. Qinshan nuclear power station .. 15 10

**1990.** Dunhuang Cave Murals (3rd series). Sui Dynasty. As T **732**. Multicoloured.
3682 8 f. Flying Devatas .. 10 10
3683 10 f. Worshipping Bodhisattva (vert) .. .. 10 10
3684 30 f. Saviour Avalokitesvara (vert) .. .. 15 10
3685 50 f. Indra .. .. 30 15

**1990.** The Snow Leopard. Multicoloured.
3686 8 f. Type **795** .. .. 10 10
3687 50 f. Leopard stalking .. 25 10

**796** West Fujian Communications Bureau (Red Posts) 4 p. Stamp

**1990.** 60th Anniv of Communist China Stamp Issues. Multicoloured.
3688 8 f. Type **796** .. .. 10 10
3689 20 f. Chinese Soviet Republic 1 c. stamp .. 10 10

**797** Zhang Wentian

**798** Emblem

**1990.** 90th Birth Anniv of Zhang Wentian (revolutionary).
3690 8 f. Type **797** .. .. 10 10
3691 20 f. Zhang Wentian and Zunyi Meeting venue .. 10 10

**1990.** International Literacy Year.
3692 **798** 20 f. multicoloured .. 10 10

**799** Great Wall, Film and Screen

**801** Athletics

**1990.** 85th Anniv of Chinese Films.
3693 **799** 20 f. multicoloured .. 10 10

**1990.** 11th Asian Games, Peking (3rd issue). Multicoloured.
3695 4 f. Type **801** .. .. 10 10
3696 8 f. Gymnastics .. .. 10 10
3697 10 f. Martial arts .. 10 10
3698 20 f. Volleyball .. .. 10 10
3699 30 f. Swimming .. .. 15 10
3700 1 y. 60 Shooting .. .. 50 25

**802** Zhang Yuzhe (astronomer)

**1990.** Scientists (2nd series). Multicoloured.
3702 8 f. Lin Qiaozhi (gynaecologist) .. .. 10 10
3703 10 f. Type **802** .. .. 10 10
3704 20 f. Hou Debang (chemist) .. .. 10 10
3705 30 f. Ding Ying (agronomist) .. .. 15 10

**803** Towering Temple

**1990.** Mount Hengshan, Hunan Province. Multicoloured.
3706 8 f. Type **803** .. .. 10 10
3707 10 f. Aerial view of mountain .. .. 10 10
3708 20 f. Trees and buildings on slopes .. .. 25 10
3709 50 f. Zhurong Peak .. 40 20

**1990.** Literature. "Romance of the Three Kingdoms" by Luo Guanzhong (2nd series). As T **763**. Multicoloured
3711 20 f. (1) Cao Cao leading night attack on Wuchao (horiz) .. 15 10
3712 20 f. (2) Liu Bei calling at Zhuge Liang's thatched cottage .. .. 15 10
3713 30 f. (3) General Zhao rescuing A Dou single-handedly (horiz) .. 25 15
3714 50 f. (4) Zhang Fei repulsing attackers at Changban Bridge .. 40 20

**805** Revellers listening to Music

**1990.** Painting "Han Xizai's Night Revels" by Gu Hongzhong. Multicoloured.
3715 50 f. (1) Type **805** .. 25 20
3716 50 f. (2) Drummer and dancers .. .. 25 20
3717 50 f. (3) Women attending man with fan and man and women in alcove .. 25 20
3718 50 f. (4) Women playing flutes and couple by painted screen .. 25 20
3719 50 f. (5) Young couple and women attending seated man .. .. 25 20
Nos. 3715/19 were printed together, se-tenant, each strip forming a composite design.

**806** Sheep

**808** Wreath on Wall and Last Verse of the "Internationale"

**807** Yuzui (dam at Dujiang)

**1991.** New Year. Year of the Sheep.
3720 **806** 20 f. multicoloured .. 15 10

**1991.** Dujiangyan Irrigation Project. Mult.
3721 20 f. Type **807** .. .. 10 10
3722 50 f. Feishayan (weir) .. 15 10
3723 80 f. Baopingkou (diversion of part of River Minjiang through new opening in Yulei Mountain) .. .. 40 20

**1991.** 120th Anniv of Paris Commune.
3724 **808** 20 f. multicoloured .. 10 10

**809** Apple **810** Saiga

**1991.** Family Planning. Multicoloured.
3725 20 f. Type **809** .. .. 10 10
3726 50 f. Child's and adult's hands within heart .. 25 10

**1991.** Horned Ruminants. Multicoloured.
3727 20 f. Type **810** .. .. 15 20
3728 20 f. Takin .. .. 15 10
3729 50 f. Argali .. .. 25 10
3730 2 y. Ibex .. .. 45 20

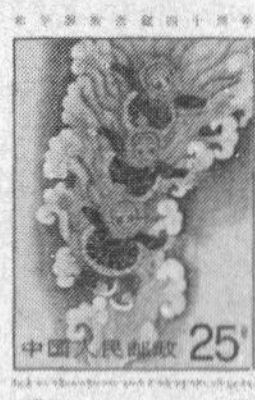

**811** Dancers **812** Map and Emperor Penguins

**1991.** 40th Anniv of Chinese Administration of Tibet. Multicoloured.
3731 25 f. Type **811** .. .. 10 10
3732 50 f. Rainbows over mountain road .. 15 10

**1991.** 30th Anniv of Implementation of Antarctic Treaty.
3734 **812** 20 f. multicoloured .. 10 10

**813** "Rhododendron delavayi"

**1991.** Rhododendrons. Multicoloured.
3735 10 f. Type **813** .. .. 10 10
3736 15 f. "Rhododendron molle" .. .. 10 10
3737 20 f. "Rhododendron simsii" .. .. 10 10
3738 20 f. "Rhododendron fictolacteum" .. .. 10 10
3739 50 f. "Rhododendron agglutinatum" (vert) .. 20 10
3740 80 f. "Rhododendron fortunei" (vert) .. 25 10
3741 90 f. "Rhododendron giganteum" (vert) .. 30 15
3742 1 y. 60 "Rhododendron rex" (vert) .. .. 55 25

**814** Pleasure Boat on Lake Nanhu (venue of first Party congress)

**1991.** 70th Anniv of Chinese Communist Party. Multicoloured.
3744 20 f. Type **814** .. .. 30 10
3745 50 f. Party emblem .. 15 10

**815** Statue, Xuxian

**1991.** 2200th Anniv of Peasant Uprising led by Chen Sheng and Wu Guang.
3746 **815** 20 f. black, brown and deep brown .. 10 10

**816** Hanging Temple

**1991.** Mount Hengshan, Shanxi Province. Multicoloured.
3747 20 f. Type **816** .. .. 10 10
3748 20 f. Snow-covered peak 10 10
3749 55 f. "Shrine of Hengshan" carved in rock face .. .. 25 10
3750 80 f. Temples in Flying Stone Grotto .. .. 40 20

**817** Mammoths and Man

**1991.** 13th International Union for Quaternary Research Conference, Peking.
3751 **817** 20 f. multicoloured .. 10 10

**818** Pine Valley

**1991.** Chengde Royal Summer Resort. Mult.
3752 15 f. Type **818** .. .. 10 10
3753 20 f. Pavilions around lake .. .. .. 10 10
3754 90 f. Maples and pavilions on islet .. .. 45 20

**819** Chen Yi **820** Clasped Hands forming Heart

**1991.** 90th Birth Anniv of Chen Yi (co-founder of People's Army).
3756 20 f. Type **819** .. .. 10 10
3757 50 f. Verse "The Green Pine" written by Chen Yi .. .. .. 10 10

**1991.** Flood Disaster Relief.
3758 **820** 80 f. multicoloured .. 25 10
The proceeds from the sale of No. 3758 were donated to the International Decade for Natural Disaster Reduction National Committee.

**1991.** Achievements of Socialist Construction (4th series). As T **758**. Multicoloured.
3759 20 f. Luoyang glassworks 10 10
3760 25 f. Urumchi chemical fertilizer works .. 10 10
3761 55 f. Shenyang–Dalian expressway .. .. 15 10
3762 80 f. Xichang satellite launching centre .. 25 10

**821** Xu Xilin **822** Wine Pot and Warming Bowl, Song Dynasty

**1991.** 80th Anniv of 1911 Revolution. Mult.
3763 20 f. (1) Type **821** .. 10 10
3764 20 f. (2) Qiu Jin .. .. 10 10
3765 20 f. (3) Song Jiaoren .. 10 10

**1991.** Jingdezhen China. Multicoloured.
3766 15 f. (1) Type **822** .. 10 10
3767 20 f. (2) Blue and white porcelain vase, Yuan dynasty .. .. 10 10
3768 20 f. (3) Covered jar with dragon design, Ming dynasty (horiz) .. 10 10
3769 25 f. (4) Vase with flower design, Qing dynasty .. 10 10
3770 50 f. (5) Modern plate with fish design .. .. 15 10
3771 2 y. (6) Modern octagonal bowl (horiz) .. .. 60 30

**823** Tao Xingzhi **824** Xu Xiangqian

**1991.** Birth Centenary of Tao Xingzhi (educationist). Each blue, grey and red.
3772 20 f. Type **823** .. .. 10 10
3773 50 f. Tao Xingzhi in traditional robes .. 10 10

**1991.** 90th Birth Anniv of Xu Xiangqian (revolutionary). Multicoloured.
3774 20 f. Type **824** .. .. 10 10
3775 50 f. In uniform .. .. 10 10

**825** Emblem **826** Monkey

**1991.** 1st Women's World Football Championship, Guangdong Province. Multicoloured.
3776 20 f. Type **825** .. .. 10 10
3777 50 f. Player .. .. 10 10

**1991.** Literature. Outlaws of the Marsh (3rd series). As T **745**. Multicoloured.
3778 20 f. (1) Dai Zong delivers forged letter from Liangshan Marsh .. 10 10
3779 25 f. (2) Yi Zhangqing captures Stumpy Tiger Wang .. .. 10 10
3780 25 f. (3) Mistress Gu rescues Xie brothers from Dengzhou jail .. 10 10
3781 90 f. (4) Sun Li gains entrance to Zhu family manor in guise of military magistrate .. 25 10

**1992.** New Year. Year of the Monkey. Paper-cut Designs.
3783 **826** 20 f. multicoloured .. 10 10
3784 – 50 f. black and red .. 15 10
DESIGN: 50 f. Magpies and plum blossom around Chinese character for monkey.

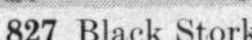
**827** Black Stork

**828** "Metasequoia glyptostroboides"

**1992.** Storks. Multicoloured.
3785 20 f. Type **827** .. .. 10 10
3786 1 y. 60 White stork .. 35 20

**1992.** Conifers. Multicoloured.
3787 20 f. Type **828** .. .. 10 10
3788 30 f. "Cathaya argyrophylla" .. .. 10 10
3789 50 f. "Taiwania flousiana" 10 10
3790 80 f. "Abies beshanzuensis" .. .. .. 20 10

**829** Red Sea Bream

**830** River Crossing at Yanan

**1992.** Offshore Breeding Projects. Mult.
3791 20 f. Type **829** .. .. 10 10
3792 25 f. Prawn .. .. 10 10
3793 50 f. Farrer's scallops .. 10 10
3794 80 f. "Laminaria japonica" (seaweed) .. 20 10

**1992.** 50th Anniv of Publication of Mao Tse-tung's Talks at the Yanan Forum on Literature and Art.
3795 **830** 20 f. black, orge & red 10 10

**831** Flower and Landscape on Globe

**1992.** World Environment Day. 20th Anniv of U. N. Environment Conference, Stockholm.
3796 **831** 20 f. multicoloured .. 10 10

**832** Seven-spotted Ladybird

**833** Basketball

**1992.** 19th International Entomology Congress, Peking. Insects. Multicoloured.
3797 20 f. Type **832** .. .. 10 10
3798 30 f. "Sympetrum croceolum" (dragonfly) .. 10 10
3799 50 f. "Chrysopa septempunctata" (lacewing) .. 10 10
3800 2 y. Praying mantis .. 45 25

**1992.** Olympic Games, Barcelona. Mult.
3801 20 f. Type **833** .. .. 10 10
3802 25 f. Gymnastics (horiz) 10 10
3803 50 f. Diving (horiz) .. 10 10
3804 80 f. Weightlifting .. 25 15

**834** Emblem

**835** Manchurian Cranes over Great Wall

**1992.** International Space Year.
3806 **834** 20 f. multicoloured .. 10 10

**1992.** Literature. "Romance of the Three Kingdoms" by Luo Guanzhong (3rd series). As T **763**. Multicoloured.
3807 20 f. Zhuge Liang urging Zhang Zhao to join fight against Cao Cao (horiz) .. .. 10 10
3808 30 f. Zhuge Liang's sarcastic goading of Sun Quan .. .. .. 10 10
3809 50 f. Jiang Gan stealing forged letter from Zhou Yu (horiz) .. .. 10 10
3810 1 y. 60 Zhuge Liang and Lu Su in straw-covered boat under arrow attack .. .. 35 20

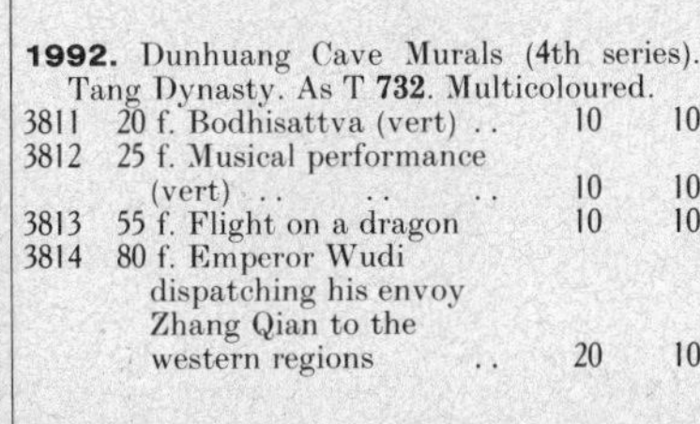

**1992.** Dunhuang Cave Murals (4th series). Tang Dynasty. As T **732**. Multicoloured.
3811 20 f. Bodhisattva (vert) .. 10 10
3812 25 f. Musical performance (vert) .. .. .. 10 10
3813 55 f. Flight on a dragon 10 10
3814 80 f. Emperor Wudi dispatching his envoy Zhang Qian to the western regions .. 20 10

**1992.** 20th Anniv of Normalization of Diplomatic Relations with Japan. Mult.
3816 20 f. Type **835** .. .. 10 10
3817 2 y. Japanese and Chinese girls and dove .. 45 25

**836** Statue of Mazu, Meizhou Islet

**837** Party Emblem

**1992.** Mazu, Sea Goddess.
3818 **836** 20 f. brown and blue 10 10

**1992.** 14th National Communist Party Congress.
3819 **837** 20 f. multicoloured .. 10 10

**838** Jiao Yulu

**839** Xiong Qinglai (mathematician) and Formula

**1992.** 70th Birth Anniv of Jiao Yulu (Party worker).
3820 **838** 20 f. multicoloured .. 10 10

**1992.** Scientists (3rd series). Multicoloured.
3821 20 f. Type **839** .. .. 10 10
3822 30 f. Tang Feifan (microbiologist) and medal .. 10 10
3823 50 f. Zhang Xiaoqian (doctor) and hospital scene .. .. 10 10
3824 1 y. Liang Sicheng (architect) and plan .. 20 10

**840** Luo Ronghuan in Officer's Uniform

**841** State Arms

**1992.** 90th Birth Anniv of Luo Ronghuan (army leader). Multicoloured.
3825 20 f. Type **840** .. .. 10 10
3826 50 f. Luo Ronghuan as young man .. .. 10 10

**1992.** 10th Anniv of Constitution.
3827 **841** 20 f. multicoloured .. 10 10

**842** Liu Bocheng in Officer's Uniform

**843** "Spring" (Zhou Baiqi)

**1992.** Birth Centenary of Liu Bocheng (army leader).
3828 **842** 20 f. multicoloured .. 10 10
3829 – 50 f. dp green & green 10 10
DESIGN—VERT. 50 f. Liu Bocheng as young man.

**1992.** Qingtian Stone Carvings. Multicoloured.
3830 10 f. Type **843** .. .. 10 10
3831 20 f. "Chinese Sorghum" (Lin Rukui) .. .. 10 10
3832 40 f. "Harvest" (Zhang Aiting) .. .. 10 10
3833 2 y. "Blooming Flowers and Full Moon" (Ni Dongfang) .. .. 45 25

**844** Cock

**845** Song Qing-ling

**1993.** New Year. Year of the Cock. Paper-cut designs by Cai Lanying.
3834 **844** 20 f. red and black .. 10 10
3835 – 50 f. white, red & blk 10 10
DESIGN: 50 f. Flowers around Chinese character for rooster.

**1993.** Birth Centenary of Song Qing-ling (Sun Yat-sen's wife). Multicoloured.
3836 20 f. Type **845** .. .. 10 10
3837 1 y. Song Qing-ling with children .. .. 20 10

**846** Bactrian Camel

**1993.** Bactrian Camel. Multicoloured.
3838 20 f. Type **846** .. .. 10 10
3839 1 y. 60 Adult with young 30 15

**847** Flag, Basket of Flowers and Streamers

**1993.** 8th National People's Congress, Peking.
3840 **847** 20 f. multicoloured .. 10 10

**848** Players

**849** Sportswomen

**1993.** Go.
3841 **848** 20 f. multicoloured .. 10 10
3842 – 1 y. 60 red, black and gold .. .. 30 15
DESIGN: 1 y. 60, "China Vogue" (black) and "linked stars" (white) formations on board.

**1993.** 1st East Asian Games, Shanghai. Mult.
3843 50 f. Type **849** .. .. 10 10
3844 50 f. Dong dong (mascot) 10 10
Nos. 3843/4 were printed together, se-tenant, forming a composite design of Shanghai Stadium.

**850** Li Jishen

**1993.** Revolutionaries (1st series). Each brown and black.
3845 20 f. Type **850** .. .. 10 10
3846 30 f. Zhang Lan (vert) .. 10 10
3847 50 f. Shan Junru (vert) .. 10 10
3848 1 y. Huang Yanpei .. 25 15
See also Nos. 3888/91.

**851** "Phyllostachys nigra"

**1993.** Bamboo. Multicoloured.
3849 20 f. Type **851** .. .. 10 10
3850 30 f. "Phyllostachys aureosulcata spectabilis" .. .. 10 10
3851 40 f. "Bambusa ventricosa" .. .. 10 10
3852 1 y. "Pseudosasa amabilis" .. .. 25 15

**1993.** Literature. Outlaws of the Marsh (4th series). As T **745**. Multicoloured.
3854 20 f. Yin Tianxi and gang capturing Chai Jin .. 10 10
3855 30 f. Shi Qian stealing Xu Ning's armour .. 10 10
3856 50 f. Xu Ning teaching use of barbed lance .. 10 10
3857 2 y. Shi Xiu saving Lu Junyi from execution 50 25

**852** Crater Lake in Winter

**1993.** Changbai Mountains. Multicoloured.
3858 20 f. Type **852** .. .. 10 10
3859 30 f. Mountain tundra in autumn .. .. 10 10
3860 50 f. Waterfall in summer 10 10
3861 1 y. Forest in spring .. 25 15

**HAVE YOU READ THE NOTES AT THE BEGINNING OF THIS CATALOGUE?**
These often provide answers to the enquiries we receive.

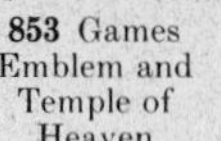

**853** Games Emblem and Temple of Heaven

**854** "Losana", Temple of Ancestors

**1993.** 7th National Games, Peking.
3862 **853** 20 f. multicoloured .. 10 10

**1993.** 1500th Anniv of Longmen Grottoes, Luoyang. Multicoloured.
3863 20 f. Type **854** .. .. 10 10
3864 30 f. "Sakyamuni", Middle Binyang Cave 10 10
3865 50 f. "King of Northern Heavens" standing on Yaksha .. .. 10 10
3866 1 y. "Bodhisattva", Guyang Cave .. .. 25 15

**855** Queen Bee and Workers on Comb

**1993.** The Honey Bee. Multicoloured.
3868 10 f. Type **855** .. .. 10 10
3869 15 f. Bee extracting nectar 10 10
3870 20 f. Two bees on blossom 10 10
3871 2 y. Two bees among flowers .. .. 45 25

**856** Bowl, New Stone Age

**1993.** Lacquer Work. Multicoloured.
3872 20 f. Type **856** .. .. 10 10
3873 30 f. Duck-shaped container (from Marquis Yi's tomb), Warring States Period .. .. 10 10
3874 50 f. Plate decorated with foliage (Zhang Cheng), Yuan Dynasty .. 10 10
3875 1 y. Chrysanthemum-shaped container, Qing Dynasty .. .. 20 10

**857** Mao Tse-tung in North Shaanxi

**1993.** Birth Centenary of Mao Tse-tung. Multicoloured.
3876 20 f. Type **857** .. .. 10 10
3877 1 y. Mao in library .. 20 10

**858** Fan Painting of Bamboo and Rock

**1993.** 300th Birth Anniv of Zheng Banqiao (artist). Multicoloured.
3879 10 f. Type **858** .. .. 10 10
3880 20 f. Orchids .. .. 10 10
3881 20 f. Orchids, bamboo and rock (scroll) (vert) .. 10 10
3882 30 f. Bamboo (scroll) (vert) .. .. .. 10 10
3883 50 f. Chrysanthemum in vase .. .. .. 10 10
3884 1 y. 60 Calligraphy on fan 20 10

**859** Yang Hucheng

**860** Dog (folk toy, Hebei)

**1993.** Birth Centenary of General Yang Hucheng.
3885 **859** 20 f. multicoloured .. 10 10

**1994.** New Year. Year of The Dog.
3886 **860** 20 f. multicoloured .. 10 10
3887 – 50 f. black, red & yell 10 10
DESIGN: 50 f. Dogs and flowers around Chinese character for dog.

**861** Ma Xulun

**1994.** Revolutionaries (2nd series). Each brown and black.
3888 20 f. Chen Qiyou (horiz) 10 10
3889 20 f. Chen Shutong .. 10 10
3890 50 f. Type **861** .. .. 10 10
3891 50 f. Xu Deheng (horiz) .. 10 10

**862** Great Siberian Sturgeon

**1994.** Sturgeons. Multicoloured.
3892 20 f. Type **862** .. .. 10 10
3893 40 f. Chinese sturgeon .. 10 10
3894 50 f. Chinese paddlefish .. 10 10
3895 1 y. Korean sturgeon .. 15 10

**863** Tree in Dunes

**864** Ming Dynasty Three-legged Round Teapot

**1994.** "Making the Desert Green". Mult.
3896 15 f. Type **863** .. .. 10 10
3897 20 f. Flower-covered dune 10 10
3898 40 f. Forest of poplars .. 10 10
3899 50 f. Oasis .. .. 10 10

**1994.** Yixing Unglazed Teapots. Mult.
3900 20 f. Type **864** .. .. 10 10
3901 30 f. Qing dynasty four-legged square teapot .. 10 10
3902 50 f. Qing dynasty patterned teapot .. 10 10
3903 1 y. Modern teapot .. 15 10

**865** Entrance Gate

**1994.** 70th Anniv of Huang-pu Military Academy.
3904 **865** 20 f. multicoloured .. 10 10

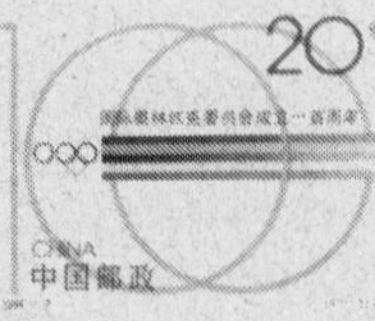


**866** "100" and Olympic Rings

**1994.** Cent of Int Olympic Committee.
3905 **866** 20 f. multicoloured .. 10 10

**867** Tao Yuanming (poet)

**1994.** Writers. Each black, brown and red.
3906 20 f. Type **867** .. .. 10 10
3907 30 f. Cao Zhi (poet) .. 10 10
3908 50 f. Sima Qian (historian) 10 10
3909 1 y. Qu Yuan (poet) .. 15 10

**1994.** Dunhuang Cave Murals (5th series). Tang Dynasty Frescoes in Mogao Caves. As T **732**. Multicoloured.
3910 10 f. Flying Devata .. 10 10
3911 20 f. Vimalakirti on dais 10 10
3912 50 f. Zhang Yichao's forces .. .. .. 10 10
3913 1 y. 60 Sorceresses .. 25 10

**868** Zhaojun

**1994.** Marriage of Zhaojun (from Han court) and Monarch of Xiongnu. Multicoloured.
3914 20 f. Type **868** .. .. 10 10
3915 50 f. Journey to Xiongnu 10 10

**869** Emblem

**870** Heaven's South Gate

**1994.** 6th Far East and South Pacific Games for the Disabled, Peking.
3917 **869** 20 f. multicoloured .. 10 10

**1994.** U.N.E.S.C.O. World Heritage Site. Wulingyuan. Multicoloured.
3918 20 f. Type **870** .. ..
3919 30 f. Shentangwan .. 10 10
3920 50 f. No. One Bridge (horiz) .. .. 10 10
3921 1 y. Writing Brush Peak (horiz) .. .. 15 10

**871** Jade Maiden Peak

**1994.** Mount Wuyi. Multicoloured.
3923 50 f. (1) Type **871** .. 10 10
3924 50 f. (2) Nine Turns Brook 10 10
3925 50 f. (3) Hanging Block .. 10 10
3926 50 f. (4) Elevated Meadow 10 10
Nos. 3923/6 were issued together, se-tenant, forming a composite design.

**872** Examining Scroll

**873** Whooping Crane

**1994.** Paintings by Fu Baoshi. Multicoloured.
3927 10 f. Waterfall and river 10 10
3928 20 f. Type **872** .. .. 10 10
3929 20 f. Tree .. .. 10 10
3930 40 f. Musicians .. .. 10 10
3931 50 f. Wooded landscape .. 10 10
3932 1 y. Scholars .. .. 15 10

**1994.** Cranes. Multicoloured.
3933 20 f. Type **873** .. .. 10 10
3934 2 y. Black-necked crane 30 15

**875** Sunlight striking Mountain

**1994.** Gorges of Yangtse River. Mult.
3936 10 f. (1) Type **875** .. 10 10
3937 20 f. (2) River steamer approaching bend in river with warning beacons .. .. 10 10
3938 20 f. (3) Small boat at fork in river .. .. 10 10
3939 30 f. (4) Mountain breaking through mist 10 10
3940 50 f. (5) Boats in gorge .. 10 10
3941 1 y. (6) Temple on cliffside 15 10

**1994.** Literature. "Romance of the Three Kingdoms" by Luo Guanzhong (4th series). As T **763**. Multicoloured.
3944 20 f. Composing poem with lance in hand (horiz) .. .. 10 10
3945 30 f. Liu Bei's wedding .. 10 10
3946 50 f. Ambush of Xiaoyaojin (horiz) .. 10 10
3947 1 y. Destruction of campsite .. .. 15 10

**877** Shenzhen

**1994.** Special Economic Zones. Mult.
3949 50 f. (1) Type **877** .. 10 10
3950 50 f. (2) Zhuhai .. .. 10 10
3951 50 f. (3) Shantou .. .. 10 10
3952 50 f. (4) Xiamen .. .. 10 10
3953 50 f. (5) Hainan .. .. 10 10

## MINIMUM PRICE

The minimum price quoted is 10p which represents a handling charge rather than a basis for valuing common stamps. For further notes about prices see introductory pages.

878 Dayan Pagoda, Cien Temple

879 Pig

**1994.** Pagodas. Each black, lt brown & brn.
3954 20 f. (1) Type **878** .. 10 10
3955 20 f. (2) Zhenguo Pagoda, Kaiyuan Temple .. 10 10
3956 50 f. (3) Liuhe Pagoda, Kaihua Temple .. 10 10
3957 2 y. (4) Youguo Temple .. 30 15

**1995.** New Year. Year of the Pig.
3959 **879** 20 f. multicoloured .. 10 10
3960 – 50 f. black and red .. 10 10
DESIGN: 50 f. Chinese character and pigs.

**880** Trees on Riverside

**1995.** Winter in Jilin. Multicoloured.
3961 20 f. Type **880** .. .. 10 10
3962 50 f. Trees on hillside (vert) .. .. .. 10 10

**881** Relief Map and Tropic of Cancer

**1995.** Mt. Dinghu. Multicoloured.
3963 15 f. (1) Type **881** .. 10 10
3964 20 f. (2) Ravine .. .. 10 10
3965 20 f. (3) Monastery on hillside and forest-covered slopes .. 10 10
3966 2 y. 30 (4) Pair of silver pheasants in forest .. 35 20

**882** Summit Emblem

**1995.** United Nations World Summit for Social Development, Copenhagen.
3967 **882** 20 f. multicoloured .. 10 10

**883** Snowy Owl

**1995.** Owls. Multicoloured.
3968 10 f. Eagle owl .. .. 10 10
3969 20 f. Long-eared owl .. 10 10
3970 50 f. Type **883** .. .. 10 10
3971 1 y. Eastern grass owls .. 15 10

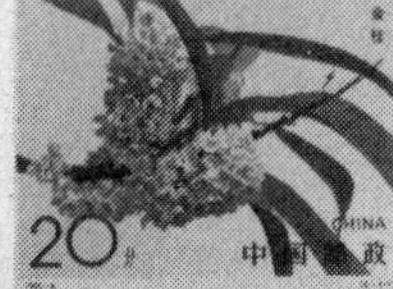

**884** "Osmanthus fragrans thunbergii"

**1995.** Sweet Osmanthus. Multicoloured.
3972 20 f. (1) Type **884** .. 10 10
3973 20 f. (2) "Osmanthus fragrans latifolius" .. 10 10
3974 50 f. (3) "Osmanthus fragrans aurantiacus" 10 10
3975 1 y. (4) "Osmanthus fragrans semperflorens" 15 10

**885** Player

**1995.** World Table Tennis Championships, Tianjin. Multicoloured.
3976 20 f. Type **885** .. .. 10 10
3977 50 f. Stadium .. .. 10 10

**886** Ladies and Courtiers

**1995.** "Spring Outing" by Zhang Xuan. Details of the painting. Multicoloured.
3979 50 f. (1) Type **886** .. 10 10
3980 50 f. (2) Courtiers on horseback .. .. 10 10
Nos. 3979/80 were issued together, se-tenant, forming a composite design.

**887** Shaanxi

**1995.** Shadow Play. Regional characters. Multicoloured.
3981 20 f. (1) Type **887** .. 10 10
3982 40 f. (2) Hebei .. .. 10 10
3983 50 f. (3) Shanxi .. .. 10 10
3984 50 f. (4) Sichuan .. .. 10 10

**888** Siyuan

**1995.** Motorway Interchanges, Peking. Mult.
3985 20 f. Type **888** .. .. 10 10
3986 30 f. Tianningsi .. .. 10 10
3987 50 f. Yuting .. .. 10 10
3988 1 y. Anhui .. .. 15 10

**890** Asian Elephants at River

**1995.** 20th Anniv of China–Thailand Diplomatic Relations. Multicoloured.
3990 1 y. (1) Type **890** .. 15 10
3991 1 y. (2) Asian elephants at river (face value at left) 15 10
Nos. 3990/1 were issued together, se-tenant, forming a composite design.

**891** Houses on Hillsides

**1995.** Lake Taihu. Multicoloured.
3992 20 f. (1) Type **891** .. 10 10
3993 20 f. (2) Waves lapping at lakeside in spring .. 10 10
3994 50 f. (3) Islets in summer 10 10
3995 50 f. (4) Trees in autumn colours .. .. 10 10
3996 230 f. (5) f. Snow-covered plum trees .. .. 35 20

**893** Yuchang Post

**1995.** Ancient Chinese Post Offices. Mult.
3999 20 f. Type **893** .. .. 10 10
4000 50 f. Jimingshan Post .. 10 10

**894** Temple Entrance

**1995.** 1500th Anniv of Shaolin Temple. Mult.
4001 20 f. Type **894** .. .. 10 10
4002 20 f. Pagoda Forest .. 10 10
4003 50 f. Martial arts practice (detail of fresco) .. 10 10
4004 100 f. Rescuers in battle (detail of fresco) .. 15 10

**895** New Stone Age Jar

**1995.** Tibetan Culture. Multicoloured.
4005 20 f. Type **895** .. .. 10 10
4006 30 f. Helmet .. .. 10 10
4007 50 f. Celestial chart .. 10 10
4008 100 f. Pearl and coral mandala .. 15 10

**896** Koalas in Eucalyptus Tree

**1995.** Australia–China Joint Issue. Endangered Species. Multicoloured.
4009 20 f. Type **896** .. .. 10 10
4010 2 y. 90 Giant pandas amongst bamboo .. 45 25

**897** Japanese Attack in North China, 7 July 1937

**1995.** 50th Anniv of End of Second World War and of War against Japan. Multicoloured.
4011 10 f. (1) Type **897** .. 10 10
4012 20 f. (2) Battle of Taier Village .. .. 10 10
4013 20 f. (3) Battle at Great Wall .. .. 10 10
4014 50 f. (4) Guerrillas .. 10 10
4015 50 f. (5) Forces at Mangyo 10 10
4016 60 f. (6) Airplane donated by overseas Chinese .. 10 10
4017 100 f. (7) Liberation of Taiwan .. .. 15 10
4018 100 f. (8) Crew on deck of battleship .. .. 15 10

**898** Woman's Profile and Flags (equality)

**899** Great Wall

**1995.** 4th World Conference on Women, Peking. Multicoloured.
4019 15 f. Type **898** .. .. 10 10
4020 20 f. Woman's profile and wheel of colours (development) .. 10 10
4021 50 f. Woman's profile and dove (peace) .. .. 10 10
4022 60 f. Dove and flower (friendship) .. .. 10 10

**1995.** The Great Wall of China.
4027 **899** 60 f. black and brown 10 10
4032 – 230 f. black and green 35 20
4035 – 290 f. black and blue 45 25
DESIGNS: 230, 290 f. Different parts of the wall.

**900** Peak Terrace

**1995.** The Jiuhua Mountains, Anhui. Mult.
4039 10 f. (1) Type **900** .. 10 10
4040 20 f. (2) Hall of Meditation (vert) .. 10 10
4041 20 f. (3) Temple of Bodhisattva .. 10 10
4042 50 f. (4) Zhiyuan .. 10 10
4043 50 f. (5) Great Rock (vert) 10 10
4044 290 f. (6) Phoenix pine .. 45 25

**901** Black and White Film

**1995.** Centenary of Motion Pictures. Mult.
4045 20 f. Type **901** .. .. 10 10
4046 50 f. Colour film .. .. 10 10

**902** Flag and New York Headquarters

**1995.** 50th Anniv of U.N.O. Multicoloured.
4047 20 f. Type **902** .. .. 10 10
4048 50 f. Anniversary emblem 10 10

**903** Blessing Spot

**1995.** Sanqing Mountain. Multicoloured.
4049 20 f. Type **903** .. .. 10 10
4050 20 f. Spring Goddess .. .. 10 10
4051 50 f. Music charm (vert) 10 10
4052 100 f. Supernatural python (vert) .. .. 15 10

**904** Old Temple

**1995.** The Song Mountains. Multicoloured.
4053 20 f. Type **904** .. .. 10 10
4054 50 f. Moon-rise .. .. 10 10
4055 60 f. Temple in snow .. 10 10
4056 1 y. Mountains .. .. 15 10

**905** Victoria Harbour

**1995.** Hong Kong. Multicoloured.
4057 20 f. Type **905** .. .. 10 10
4058 50 f. Central Plaza .. 10 10
4059 60 f. Hong Kong Cultural Centre .. .. 10 10
4060 290 f. Repulse Bay .. 45 25

**906** Sun Zi **907** Rat

**1995.** "Art of War" (book) by Sun Zi. Multicoloured.
4061 20 f. Type **906** .. .. 10 10
4062 20 f. Elaborating strategies .. .. 10 10
4063 30 f. Capturing Ying .. 10 10
4064 50 f. Battle at Ailing .. 10 10
4065 100 f. Conference at Huangchi .. .. 15 10

**1996.** New Year. Year of the Rat. Mult.
4066 20 f. Type **907** .. .. 10 10
4067 50 f. Pattern and Chinese character .. .. 10 10

**908** Speed Skating

**1996.** 3rd Asian Winter Games, Harbin. Mult.
4068 50 f. Type **908** .. .. 10 10
4069 50 f. Ice hockey .. .. 10 10
4070 50 f. Figure skating .. 10 10
4071 50 f. Skiing .. .. 10 10
Nos. 4068/71 were issued together, se-tenant, forming a composite design.

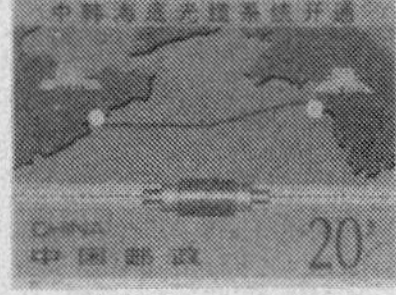

**909** Cable Route

**1996.** Inauguration of Korea–China Submarine Cable.
4072 **909** 20 f. multicoloured .. 10 10

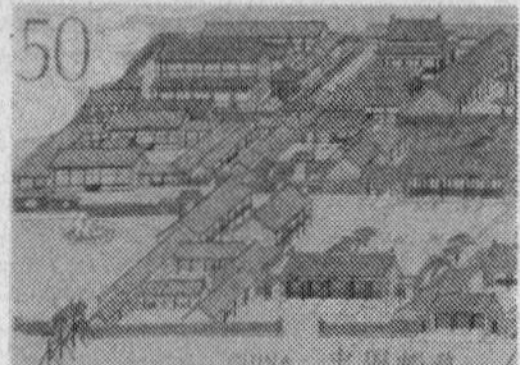

**910** Palace Complex

**1996.** Shenyang Imperial Palace. Mult.
4073 50 f. Type **910** .. .. 10 10
4074 50 f. Pagoda and buildings 10 10
Nos. 4073/4 were issued together, se-tenant, forming a composite design.

**911** Tianjin Posts Bureau

**1996.** Centenary of Chinese State Postal Service. Multicoloured.
4075 10 f. Type **911** .. .. 10 10
4076 20 f. Former Peking Postal Administration building .. .. 10 10
4077 50 f. Postal headquarters of Chinese Soviet Republic .. .. 10 10
4078 100 f. Present Peking postal complex .. 15 10

**912** Calligraphy

**1996.** Paintings by Huang Binhong. Mult.
4080 20 f. (1) Type **912** .. 10 10
4081 20 f. (2) Mountain landscape .. .. .. 10 10
4082 40 f. (3) Mountain in rain 10 10
4083 50 f. (4) View from Xiling 10 10
4084 50 f. (5) Landscape .. 10 10
4085 230 f. (6) Flowers .. 35 20

**913** F-8 (fighter)

**1996.** Chinese Aircraft. Multicoloured.
4086 20 f. (1) Type **913** .. 10 10
4087 50 f. (2) A-5 (ground attack plane) .. .. 10 10
4088 50 f. (3) Yun-7 (passenger plane) .. .. .. 10 10
4089 100 f. (4) Yun-12 (passenger plane) .. 15 10

**914** Green Scenery of Lijing River

**1996.** Bonsai Landscapes. Multicoloured.
4090 20 f. (1) Type **914** .. 10 10
4091 20 f. (2) Glistening Divine Peak .. .. .. 10 10
4092 50 f. (3) Melting snow fills the river .. .. 10 10
4093 50 f. (4) Eagle beak-shaped Rock .. 10 10
4094 100 f. (5) Most Uncommon Years .. .. 15 10
4095 100 f. (6) Peaks rising in Rosy Clouds .. 15 10

**915** Sago Cycad ("Cycas revoluta")

**1996.** Cycads. Multicoloured.
4096 20 f. Type **915** .. .. 10 10
4097 20 f. Panzhihua cycad ("Cycas panzhihuaensis") .. .. 10 10
4098 50 f. Nepal cycad .. 10 10
4099 230 f. Polytomous cycad 35 20

**916** Great Wall of China

**1996.** 25th Anniv of China–San Marino Diplomatic Relations. Multicoloured.
4100 100 f. Type **916** .. .. 15 10
4101 100 f. Walled rampart, San Marino .. .. 15 10
Nos. 4100/1 were issued together, se-tenant, forming a composite design.

**919** Paddy Agricultural Tool

**1996.** Hemudu Archaeological Site, Yuyao, Zhejiang. Multicoloured.
4104 20 f. Type **919** .. .. 10 10
4105 50 f. Building supports .. 10 10
4106 100 f. Oars .. .. 15 10
4107 230 f. Dish .. .. 35 20

**921** Children rejoicing **922** "The Discus Thrower" (Miron)

**1996.** Children. Multicoloured.
4109 20 f. Type **921** .. .. 10 10
4110 30 f. Girls pushing child in wheelchair in rain .. 10 10
4111 50 f. Expedition to Antarctic .. .. 10 10
4112 100 f. Planting tree .. 15 10

**1996.** Centenary of Modern Olympic Games.
4113 **922** 20 f. multicoloured .. 10 10

**923** "Land"

**1996.** Preserve Land. Designs showing Chinese characters. Multicoloured.
4114 20 f. Type **923** .. .. 10 10
4115 50 f. "Cultivation" .. 10 10

**924** Entrance

**1996.** Zhenwu Pavilion of Jinghua Terrace. Multicoloured.
4116 20 f. Type **924** .. .. 10 10
4117 50 f. Pagoda .. .. 10 10

**925** Red Flag Car

**1996.** Motor Vehicles. Multicoloured.
4118 20 f. Type **925** .. .. 10 10
4119 20 f. Two-door truck .. 10 10
4120 50 f. Four-door truck .. 10 10
4121 100 f. Four-wheel drive .. 10 10

**926** New Farm Cottages

**1996.** 20th Anniv of Tangshan Earthquake. Development of New City. Multicoloured.
4122 20 f. (1) Type **926** .. 10 10
4123 50 f. (2) Factory .. .. 10 10
4124 50 f. (3) Roundabout and city buildings .. .. 10 10
4125 100 f. (4) Bulk carrier coming into port .. 15 10

**927** Emblem, Globe and "30"

**1996.** 30th Int Geological Conf, Peking.
4126 **927** 20 f. multicoloured .. 10 10

**928** Tianchi Lake

**1996.** Tianshan Mountains, Xinjiang.
4127 **928** 20 f. (1) multicoloured 10 10
4128 – 50 f. (2) multicoloured 10 10
4129 – 50 f. (3) bl, mve & blk 10 10
4130 – 100 f. (4) mult .. 15 10
DESIGNS—VERT: No. 4128, Waterfalls; 4129, Snow-capped mountain peaks. HORIZ: No. 4130, Mountains and landscape.

**1996.** Dunhuang Cave Murals (6th series). As T **732**. Multicoloured.
4131 10 f. Mount Wutai (vert) 10 10
4132 20 f. King of Khotan (vert) .. .. .. 10 10
4133 50 f. Saviour Avalokitesvara .. 10 10
4134 100 f. Worshipping Bodhisattvas .. 15 10

**929** Tombs

**1996.** Emperors' Tombs, Western Xia. Mult.

| | | | |
|---|---|---|---|
| 4136 | 20 f. Type **929** .. .. | 10 | 10 |
| 4137 | 20 f. Divine Gate ornament .. .. | 10 | 10 |
| 4138 | 50 f. Stone base from Stele Pavilion .. .. | 10 | 10 |
| 4139 | 100 f. Piece of stele from Shouling Tomb .. | 15 | 10 |

**930** Datong–Qinhuangdao Line

**1996.** Railways. Multicoloured.

| | | | |
|---|---|---|---|
| 4140 | 15 f. Type **930** .. .. | 10 | 10 |
| 4141 | 20 f. Lanzhou–Xinjiang line .. .. .. | 10 | 10 |
| 4142 | 50 f. Peking–Kowloon line | 10 | 10 |
| 4143 | 100 f. Peking Western railway station .. | 15 | 10 |

**931** Shang Dynasty Tortoise Shell

**932** Ye Ting

**1996.** Ancient Archives. Multicoloured.

| | | | |
|---|---|---|---|
| 4144 | 20 f. Type **931** .. .. | 10 | 10 |
| 4145 | 20 f. Han dynasty wood slips .. .. .. | 10 | 10 |
| 4146 | 50 f. Ming dynasty iron scrolls .. .. .. | 10 | 10 |
| 4147 | 100 f. Qing dynasty books | 15 | 10 |

**1996.** Birth Cent of Ye Ting (revolutionary). Multicoloured.

| | | | |
|---|---|---|---|
| 4148 | 20 f. Type **932** .. .. | 10 | 10 |
| 4149 | 50 f. Ye Ting in uniform | 10 | 10 |

**933** Emblem

**1996.** 96th Interparliamentary Union Conference, Peking.

| | | | | |
|---|---|---|---|---|
| 4150 | **933** | 20 f. multicoloured .. | 10 | 10 |

**934** Transport and Telecommunications

**1996.** Pudong Area of Shanghai. Mult.

| | | | |
|---|---|---|---|
| 4151 | 10 f. (1) Type **934** .. | 10 | 10 |
| 4152 | 20 f. (2) Lujiazui finance and business area .. | 10 | 10 |
| 4153 | 20 f. (3) Jinqiao export centre .. .. .. | 10 | 10 |
| 4154 | 50 f. (4) Zhangjiang technology area .. | 10 | 10 |
| 4155 | 60 f. (5) Customs House, Waigaoqiao bonded area .. .. .. | 10 | 10 |
| 4156 | 100 f. (6) Apartment blocks .. .. .. | 15 | 10 |

MILITARY POST STAMPS

M 225.

M 892 Armed Forces

**1953.**

| | | | | |
|---|---|---|---|---|
| M1593 | **M 225** | $800 yellow, red and orange | 9·00 | 22·00 |
| M1594 | | $800 yellow, red and purple .. | £120 | |
| M1595 | | $800 yellow, red and blue .. | £18000 | |

Nos. M1593/5 were issued for the use of the Army, Air Force and Navy respectively.

**1995.**

| | | | | |
|---|---|---|---|---|
| M3998 | **M 892** | 20 f. multicoloured | 10 | 10 |

POSTAGE DUE STAMPS

D 192.

D 233.

**1950.**

| | | | | |
|---|---|---|---|---|
| D 1459. | **D 192.** | $100 blue .. | 10 | 85 |
| D 1460. | | $200 blue .. | 10 | 85 |
| D 1461. | | $500 blue .. | 10 | 1·00 |
| D 1462. | | $800 blue .. | 9·50 | 30 |
| D 1463. | | $1,000 blue .. | 10 | 50 |
| D 1464. | | $2,000 blue .. | 10 | 75 |
| D 1465. | | $5,000 blue .. | 10 | 80 |
| D 1466. | | $8,000 blue .. | 15 | 1·50 |
| D 1467. | | $10,000 blue .. | 15 | 2·50 |

**1954.**

| | | | | |
|---|---|---|---|---|
| D 1628. | **D 233.** | $100 red .. | 15 | 25 |
| D 1629. | | $200 red .. | 15 | 25 |
| D 1630. | | $500 red .. | 15 | 25 |
| D 1631. | | $800 red .. | 15 | 25 |
| D 1632. | | $1,600 red .. | 15 | 25 |

## CHINA—TAIWAN (FORMOSA)

### A. CHINESE PROVINCE.

The island of Taiwan was ceded by China to Japan in 1895 and was returned to China in 1945 after the defeat of Japan. From 1949 Taiwan was controlled by the remnants of the Nationalist Government under Chiang Kai-shek.

1945, 100 sen = 1 yen.
1947, 100 cents = 1 yuan (C.N.C.)

中華民國 臺灣省

(1. "Taiwan Province, Chinese Republic.")

**1945.** Optd as Type 1. (a) On stamps as Nos. J1/3 of Japanese Taiwan.

1. J 1. 3 s. red .. .. .. 75 4·50
2. 5 s. green .. .. .. 75 75
3. 10 s. blue .. .. .. 75 75
4. 30 s. blue .. .. .. 4·50 4·50
5. 40 s. purple .. .. .. 4·00 3·25
6. 50 s. brown .. .. .. 2·75 2·25
7. 1 y. green .. .. .. 3·00 2·25

(b) On stamps of Japan. Imperf.

8. 87. 5 y. olive (No. 424) .. 7·50 7·50
9. 88. 10 y. purple (No. 334) .. 12·00 12·00

限臺灣貼用 伍 錢 (2.)

3⁰⁰ 限臺灣省貼用 叁圓 (3.)

**1946.** Stamps of China surch as T 2 with two to four characters in lower line denoting value.

10 – 2 s. on 2 c. blue (No. 509) .. .. 10 1·25
11 – 5 s. on 5 c. orange (No. 513) .. .. 10 50
12 60 10 s. on 4 c. lilac .. 10 60
13 – 30 s. on 15 c. purple (No. 517) .. .. 10 75
19 107 50 s. on $20 red .. 10 1·00
16 58 65 s. on $20 green .. 20 1·00
15 – $1 on 20 c. blue (No. 519) .. .. 15 1·00
17 58 $1 on $30 brown .. 20 85
65 60 $2 on 2½ c. red .. 25 75
18 58 $2 on $50 orange .. 25 80
20 107 $3 on $100 red .. 10 75
77 102 $5 on $40 orange .. 25 90
78 107 $5 on $50 violet .. 40 45
79 $5 on $70 orange .. 10 1·00
80 $5 on $100 red .. 25 25
21 $5 on $200 green .. 10 60
67 82 $10 on $3 yellow .. 1·00 1·50
82 118 $10 on $150 blue .. 30 65
22 107 $10 on $500 green .. 10 40
66 72 $20 on 2 c. green .. 25 75
71 89 $20 on $3 red .. 1·00 1·00
83 118 $20 on $250 violet .. 25 50
23 107 $20 on $700 brown .. 20 50
68 82 $50 on 50 c. green .. 75 85
24 107 $50 on $1,000 red .. 85 60
72 89 $100 on $20 pink .. 25 25
73 94 $100 on $20 red .. £375 —
25 107 $100 on $3,000 blue .. 1·00 70
74 94 $200 on $10 blue .. 1·25 75
70 72 $500 on $30 purple .. 3·25 2·25
81 107 $600 on $100 red .. 4·75 1·25
69 82 $1,000 on $4 brown .. 2·50 2·50
85 118 $1,000 on $20,000 red .. 1·50 1·50
75 94 $5,000 on $10 blue .. 4·00 2·25
76 $10,000 on $20 red .. 5·00 1·75
84 118 $200,000 on $3,000 blue £200 14·00

**1946.** Opening of National Assembly, Nanking. Issue of China surch as Type 3.

26 111 70 s. on $20 green .. 1·00 2·25
27 $1 on $30 blue .. 1·00 2·25
28 $2 on $50 brown .. 1·00 2·25
29 $3 on $100 red .. 1·00 2·25

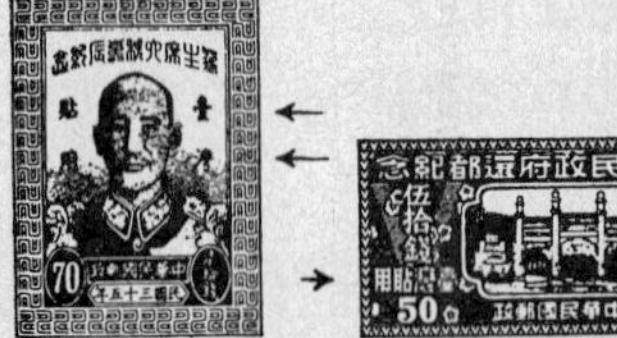

4. President Chiang Kai-shek. 5. Entrance to Dr. Sun Yat-sen Mausoleum.

**1947.** President's 60th Birthday.

30. 4. 70 s. red .. .. .. 1·00 2·00
31. $1 green .. .. .. 1·00 2·00
32. $2 red .. .. .. 1·00 2·00
33. $3 green .. .. .. 1·00 2·00
34. $7 orange .. .. .. 1·00 2·00
35. $10 red .. .. .. 1·00 2·00

**1947.** 1st Anniv of Return of Government to Nanking.

36 5 50 s. green .. .. 1·25 2·25
37 $3 blue .. .. .. 1·25 2·25
38 $7.50 red .. .. .. 1·25 2·25
39 $10 brown .. .. .. 1·25 2·25
40 $20 purple .. .. .. 1·25 2·25

For other stamps as Types 4 and 5, but with different 3rd and 4th Chinese characters in positions shown by arrows, see N.E. Provinces Types 7 and 9.

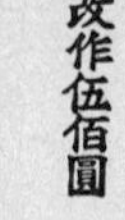

6. Sun Yat-sen and Palms. (7.)

**1947.**

41 169 $1 brown .. .. 25 1·50
42 $2 brown .. .. 35 1·25
43 $3 green .. .. 30 75
44 $5 orange .. .. 30 60
45 $9 blue .. .. 60 1·75
46 $10 red .. .. 25 75
47 $20 green .. .. 25 50
59 $25 green .. .. 35 35
48 $50 purple .. .. 35 35
49 $100 blue .. .. 35 35
50 $200 brown .. .. 35 35
60 $5,000 orange .. .. 2·50 85
61 $10,000 green .. .. 2·75 2·25
62 $20,000 brown .. .. 2·75 2·25
63 $30,000 blue .. .. 2·50 1·00
64 $40,000 brown .. .. 2·25 80

**1948.** "Re-valuation" surcharges. Surch. as T 7.

51. 6. $25 on $100 blue .. 85 1·75
52. $300 on $3 green .. 50 45
53. $500 on $7.50 orange .. 1·75 1·50
54. $1,000 on 30 c. grey .. 4·00 3·75
55. $1,000 on $3 green .. 1·00 35
56. $2,000 on $3 green .. 75 45
57. $3,000 on $3 green .. 3·00 1·75
58. $3,000 on $7.50 orange .. 38·00 2·25

**1949.** No value indicated. Stamps of China optd with five Chinese characters, similar to top line of T 2.

86.146. (–) Orange (Ord. postage) 1·00 20
87.147. (–) Green (Air Mail) .. 1·50 95
88.148. (–) Mauve (Express) .. 1·50 1·10
89.149. (–) Red (Registration) .. 1·50 1·10

### PARCELS POST STAMPS

**1948.** As Type P 112 of China with six Chinese characters in the sky above the lorry.

P 65. $100 green .. .. — 50
P 66. $300 red .. .. .. — 50
P 67. $500 olive .. .. — 50
P 68. $1,000 black .. .. — 50
P 69. $3,000 purple .. .. — 50

Parcels Post stamps were not on sale in unused condition.

### POSTAGE DUE STAMPS

(D 7.) (D 8.) (D 9.)

**1948.**

D 51. D 7. $1 blue .. .. 65 2·50
D 52. $3 blue .. .. 65 3·25
D 53. $5 blue .. .. 65 2·25
D 54. $10 blue .. .. 75 3·25
D 55. $20 blue .. .. 75 2·50

**1949.** "Re-valuation" surcharges. Surch. as Type D 8.

D 65. D 7. $50 on $1 blue .. 5·00 7·00
D 66. $100 on $3 blue .. 5·00 5·00
D 67. $300 on $5 blue .. 5·00 4·00
D 68. $500 on $10 blue .. 5·00 3·50

**1949.** Handstamped with Type D 9.

D 86. 6. $1,000 on $3 green (No. 55) .. .. 8·50 9·00
D 87. $3,000 on $3 green (No. 57) .. .. 13·00 14·00
D 88. $5,000 orange (No. 60) 27·00 30·00

### B. CHINESE NATIONALIST REPUBLIC.

1949 100 cents = 1 silver yuan (or New Taiwan Yuan).

Silver Yuan Surcharges.

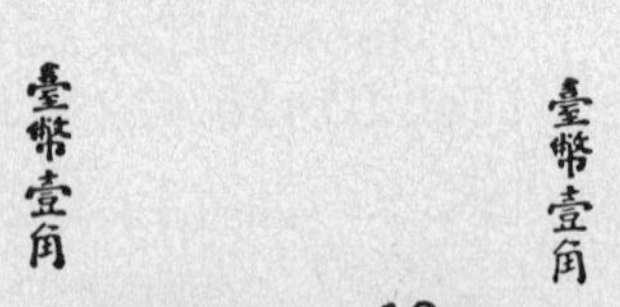

(8.) Small figures. (9.) Large figures.

**1949.** Stamps of Taiwan Province surch (a) With T 8.

90 6 10 c. on $50 purple .. 14·00 2·50

(b) As T 9 (figures at right).

91 6 2 c. on $30,000 blue .. 18·00 8·50
92 10 c. on $40,000 brown 32·00 6·50

(10.) (11.)

**1949.** Stamps of North Eastern Provinces (Manchuria), surch. as T 10.

93. 5. 2 c. on $44 red .. .. 10·00 5·00
95. 5 c. on $44 red .. .. 15·00 2·75
96. 10 c. on $44 red .. .. 18·00 1·50
97. 20 c. on $44 red .. .. 22·00 20
98. 30 c. on $44 red .. .. 28·00 6·00
99. 50 c. on $44 red .. .. 38·00 4·50

**1950.** Surch. as T 11 on stamp of China but with no indication of value.

100.169. $1 on (–) green .. .. 25·00 2·50
101. $2 on (–) green .. .. 60·00 6·50
102. $5 on (–) green .. .. £500 27·00
103. $10 on (–) green .. £900 45·00
104. $20 on (–) green .. £1900 £300

**1950.** Stamps of China surch.

(a) As T 8 (figure "5" at left).

105. 118. 5 c. on $200,000 purple 10·00 3·50

(b) As T 9 (figures at left).

106. 118. 3 c. on $30,000 brown .. 5·00 6·00
107. 3 c. on $40,000 green .. 7·50 7·50
108. 3 c. on $50,000 blue .. 5·50 5·50
108a. 10 c. on $4,000 grey .. 12·00 8·00
109. 10 c. on $6,000 purple .. 8·50 50
110. 10 c. on $20,000 red .. 5·00 3·50
110a. 10 c. on $2,000,000 orge. 6·00 3·50
110b. 20 c. on $500,000 mauve 15·00 7·50
110c. 20 c. on $1,000,000 red 28·00 6·50
110d. 30 c. on $3,000,000 bistre 35·00 10·00
110e. 50 c. on $5,000,000 blue 75·00 10·00

12. Koxinga.

**GUM.** All the following stamps to No. 616 were issued without gum except where otherwise stated.

**1950.** Rouletted. (a) Postage.

111. 12. 3 c. grey .. .. 1·00 1·00
112. 10 c. brown .. .. 1·00 10
113. 15 c. yellow .. .. 7·50 6·50
114. 20 c. green .. .. 1·00 10
115. 30 c. red .. .. 22·00 12·00
116. 40 c. orange .. .. 2·00 10
117. 50 c. brown .. .. 2·50 10
118. 80 c. red .. .. 7·50 2·50
119. $1 violet .. .. 6·50 10
120. $1.50 green .. .. 30·00 5·00
121. $1.60 blue .. .. 40·00 25
122. $2 mauve .. .. 8·00 25
123. $5 turquoise .. .. 45·00 2·50

(b) Air. With character at each side of head.

124. 12. 60 c. blue .. .. 10·00 6·00

13. Peasant and Ballot Box.

(14.) 15. Peasant and Scroll.

**1951.** Division of Country into Self-governing Districts. Perf. or imperf.

125. 13. 40 c. red .. .. 7·50 10
126. $1 blue .. .. 10·00 60
127. $1·60 purple .. .. 18·00 75
128. $2 brown .. .. 35·00 7·50

**1951.** Silver Yuan surcharges. As T 169 of China but without value, surch. as T 14.

129. $5 on (–) green .. 45·00 5·50
130. $10 on (–) green .. £225 4·00
131. $20 on (–) green .. £400 17·00
132. $50 on (–) green .. £450 60·00

**1952.** Land Tax Reduction. Perf. or imperf.

133. 15. 20 c. orange .. .. 5·00 25
134. 40 c. green .. .. 6·50 10
135. $1 brown .. .. 10·00 3·00
136. $1·40 blue .. .. 15·00 1·50
137. $2 grey .. .. 32·00 30·00
138. $5 red .. .. 40·00 1·50

16. President and Rejoicing crowds.

(17.)

**1952.** 2nd Anniv. of Re-election of Pres. Chiang Kai-shek. Flag in red and blue. Eight characters in scroll. Perf. or imperf.

139. 16. 40 c. red .. .. 5·00 10
140. $1 green .. .. 10·00 1·75
141. $1·60 orange .. .. 14·00 1·00
142. $2 blue .. .. 23·00 9·00
143. $5 purple .. .. 32·00 1·50

See also Nos. 151/6.

**1952.** Stamps of China surch. with T 17.

144. 145. 3 c. on 4 c. grn. (No. 1350) 1·75 2·50
145. 3 c. on 10 c. lilac (No. 1351) .. .. 3·50 3·75
146. 3 c. on 20 c. blue (No. 1353) .. .. 1·75 2·00
147. 3 c. on 50 c. brown (No. 1354) .. .. 5·00 7·50

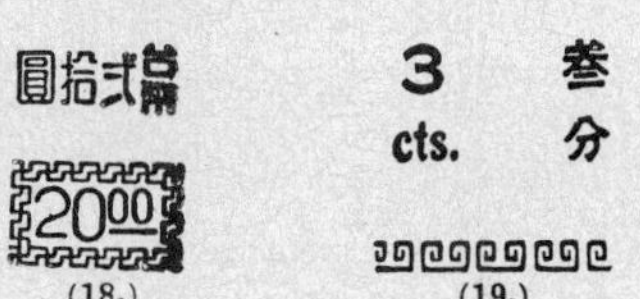

(18.) (19.)

**1953.** T 169 of China, but without value, surch. as T 18.

148. $10 on (–) green .. £120 5·50
149. $20 on (–) green .. £250 14·00
150. $50 on (–) green .. £800 £350

**1953.** 3rd Anniv. of Re-election of Pres. Chiang Kai-shek. As T 16 but eleven characters in scroll. Flag in red and blue. Perf. or imperf.

151. 10 c. orange .. .. 5·50 50
152. 20 c. green .. .. 5·50 40
153. 40 c. red .. .. 5·50 10
154. $1.40 blue .. .. 10·00 1·00
155. $2 sepia .. .. 20·00 1·75
156. $5 purple .. .. 42·00 8·00

**1953.** Surch. as T 19.

157. 12. 3 c. on $1 violet .. 85 1·00
158. 10 c. on 15 c. yellow .. 9·00 1·00
159. 10 c. on 30 c. red .. 2·25 50
160. 20 c. on $1 .60 blue .. 2·25 30

20. Doctor, Nurses and Patients.

21. Pres. Chiang Kai-shek.

**1953.** Establishment of Anti-tuberculosis Assn. Cross of Lorraine in red. On paper with coloured network.

161. 20. 40 c. brown on stone .. 7·50 10
162. $1.60 blue on turquoise 20·00 75
163. $2 green on yellow .. 25·00 50
164. $5 red on flesh .. .. 35·00 4·50

**1953.**

165. 21. 10 c. sepia .. .. 1·50 10
166. 20 c. purple .. .. 1·00 10
167. 40 c. green .. .. 1·00 10
168. 50 c. mauve .. .. 2·25 10
169. 80 c. brown .. .. 6·50 2·50
170. $1 olive .. .. 3·50 10
171. $1.40 blue .. .. 5·00 35
172. $1.60 red .. .. 6·00 10
173. $1.70 green .. .. 12·00 3·50
174. $2 brown .. .. 5·50 10
175. $3 blue .. .. £100 5·50
176. $4 turquoise .. .. 8·00 60
177. $5 red .. .. 5·50 20
178. $10 green .. .. 10·00 1·50
179. $20 lake .. .. 25·00 2·50

22. Silo Bridge over R. Cho-Shui-Chi.

23. Sapling, Tree and Plantation.

**1954.** Completion of Silo Bridge. Various frames.

180. 22. 40 c. red .. .. 8·00 20
181. – $1.60 blue .. .. 42·00 45
182. 22. $3.60 black .. .. 25·00 2·50
183. – $5 mauve .. .. 55·00 1·25

DESIGN: $1.60, $5, Silo Bridge.

**1954.** Afforestation Day.

184. 23. 40 c. blue .. .. 8·50 35
185. – $10 purple .. .. 42·00 3·25
186. – $20 red .. .. 25·00 70
187. – $50 blue .. .. 35·00 3·50

DESIGNS: $10, Tree plantation and houses. $20, Planting seedling. $50, Map of Taiwan and tree.

## INDEX

Countries can be quickly located by referring to the index at the end of this volume.

24. Runner.

25. Douglas DC-6 over City Gate, Taipeh.

**1954.** Youth Day.
188. 24. 40 c. blue 10·00 40
189. $5 red 38·00 5·00

**1954.** Air. 15th Anniv. of Air Force Day.
190. 25. $1 brown 10·00 45
191. – $1·60 black 6·00 10
192. – $5 blue 11·00 40
DESIGNS: $1.60, Republic F-84G Thunderjets over Chung Shang Bridge, Taipeh. $5, Doves over Chi Kan Lee (Fort Zeelandia) in Tainan City.

26. Refugees crossing Pontoon Bridge.

27. Junk and Bridge.

**1954.** Relief Fund for Chinese Refugees from North Vietnam.
193. 26. 40 c.+10 c. blue 13·00 1·50
194. $1·60+40 c. purple 42·00 12·00
195. $5+$1 red 75·00 55·00

**1954.** 2nd Anniv. of Overseas Chinese League.
196. 27. 40 c. red 12·00 10
197. $5 blue 7·50 1·75

28. "Chainbreaker".

(29.)

**1955.** Freedom Day.
198. 28. 40 c. green 3·00 10
199. – $1 olive 11·00 3·00
200. – $1.60 red 8·50 1·50
DESIGNS: $1, Soldier with torch and flag. $1.60, Torch and figures "1·23".

**1955.** Surch. as T 29.
201. 12. 3 c. on $1 violet 2·50 1·25
202. 20 c. on 40 c. orange 2·25 15

31. Pres. Chiang Kai-shek and Sun Yat-sen Memorial Building.

**1955.** 1st Anniv. of President Chiang Kai-shek's Second Re-election.
203. 31. 20 c. olive 2·50 10
204. 40 c. green 2·50 10
205. $2 red 6·50 40
206. $7 blue 11·00 65

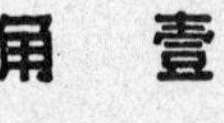

(32.)

33. Air Force Badge.

**1955.** Nos. 116/8, 120 and 124 surch. as T 32. Nos. 212/14 have additional floral ornament between two characters at top.
207. 12. 10 c. on 80 c. red 2·25 25
208. 10 c. on $1.50 green 2·75 50
212. 20 c. on 40 c. orange 3·50 10
213. 20 c. on 50 c. brown 4·00 10
214. 20 c. on 60 c. blue 5·50 1·25

**1955.** Armed Forces' Day.
209. 33. 40 c. blue 2·50 10
210. $2 red 12·00 1·00
211. $7 green 8·50 70

35. Flags of U.N. and Taiwan.

36. Pres. Chiang Kai-shek.

**1955.** 10th Anniv. of U.N.O.
215. 35. 40 c. blue 1·50 10
216. $2 red 4·75 40
217. $7 green 4·75 1·00

**1955.** President's 69th Birthday. With gum.
218. 36. 40 c. brown, blue & red 2·25 10
219. $2 blue, green and red 5·50 50
220. $7 green, brown & red 7·00 1·00

37. Sun Yat-sen's Birthplace.

角貳
0.20
(38.)

**1955.** 90th Birth Anniv. (1956) of Dr. Sun Yat-sen.
221. 37. 40 c. blue 2·00 10
222. $2 brown 3·50 50
223. $7 red 4·50 60

**1956.** Nos. 1025 and 1023 of China, surch. as T 38.
232. 148. 3 c. on (–) mauve 75 40
224. 146. 20 c. on (–) orange I 50 10
304. 20 c. on (–) orange II 25 10
In No. 232 the characters are smaller and there are leaves on either side of the "3".
(I) Surch. with Type 38. (II) The characters are below the figures.

39. Old and Modern Postal Transport.

40. Children at Play.

**1956.** 60th Anniv. of Postal Service.
225. 39. 40 c. red 75 10
226. $1 blue 1·25 40
227. $1.60 brown 2·00 25
228. $2 green 3·00 40

**1956.** Children's Day.
229. 40. 40 c. green 75 10
230. $1.60 blue 1·25 15
231. $2 red 2·25 40

42. Earliest and Latest Locomotives.

43. Pres. Chiang Kai-shek.

**1956.** 75th Anniv. of Chinese Railways.
233. 42. 40 c. red 2·00 10
234. $2 blue 3·25 15
235. $8 green 5·50 70

**1956.** 70th Birthday of President Chiang Kai-shek. Various portraits of President. With gum.
236. 43. 20 c. orange 1·00 10
237. – 40 c. red 1·00 10
238. – $1 blue 2·25 20
239. – $1.60 purple 2·75 10
240. – $2 brown 4·75 20
241. – $8 turquoise 12·00 50
SIZES—21½ × 30 mm.: 20 c., 40 c.; 26½ × 26½ mm.: $1, $1.60; 30 × 21½ mm.: $2, $8.

(44.) (45.) 46. Telecommunications Symbols.

**1956.** No. 1212 of China surch. with T 44.
242. 147. 3 c. on (–) green 50 15

**1956.** No. 1214 of China surch. with T 45.
243. 149. 10 c. on (–) red 50 15

**1956.** 75th Anniv. of Chinese Telegraph Service.
244. 46. 40 c. blue 35 10
245. $1.40 red 75 10
246. $1.60 green 1·00 10
247. $2 brown 2·50 20

47. Map of China.

**1957.** (a) Printed in one colour.
248. 47. 3 c. blue 10 10
249. 10 c. violet 65 15
250. 20 c. orange 55 10
251. 40 c. red 65 10
252. $1 brown 1·00 10
253. $1 60 green 1·50 15

(b) With frames in blue.
268. 47. 3 c. blue 10 10
269. 10 c. violet 35 10
270. 20 c. orange 45 10
271. 40 c. red 75 10
272. $1 brown 2·00 20
273. $1.60 green 2·00 10

48. Mencius with his Mother.

49. Chinese Scout Badges and Rosettes.

**1957.** Mothers' Teaching.
254. 48. 40 c. green 75 10
255. – $3 brown 1·40 35
DESIGN: $3, Marshal Yueh Fei with his mother.

**1957.** 50th Anniv. of Boy Scout Movement, Jubilee Jamboree and Birth Centenary of Lord Baden-Powell (Founder).
256. 49. 40 c. violet 30 10
257. $1 green 85 15
258. $1.60 blue 1·00 10

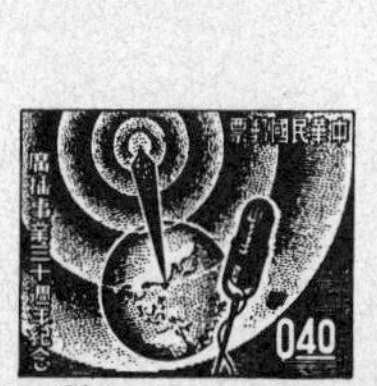
50. Globe, Radio Mast and Microphone.

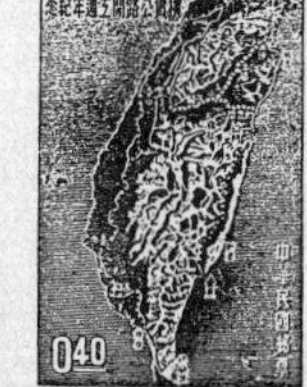
51. Highway Map of Taiwan.

**1957.** 30th Anniv. of Chinese Broadcasting Service.
259. 50. 40 c. salmon 20 10
260. 50 c. mauve 45 15
261. $3.50 blue 95 30

**1957.** 1st Anniv. of Taiwan Cross-Island Highway Project.
262. 51. 40 c. green 1·25 10
263. $1.40 blue 2·75 25
264. $2 sepia 3·25 25

52. Freighter "Hai Min" and River vessel "Kiang Foo".

53. "Batocera lineolata" (longhorn beetle).

**1957.** 85th Anniv of China Merchants' Steam Navigation Co.
265. 52. 40 c. blue 35 10
266. 80 c. red 75 25
267. $2.80 salmon 1·50 40

**1958.** Insects. Multicoloured. With gum.
274 10 c. Type 53 45 15
275 40 c. "Papilio maraho" (butterfly) 50 10
276 $1 Atlas moth 1·00 15
277 $1.40 "Erasmia pulchella" (moth) 1·50 25
278 $1.60 "Cheirotonus macleayi" (beetle) 1·75 15
279 $2 Great mormon (butterfly) 2·25 30

ORCHIDS—VERT. 40 c. "Laelia-cattleya" $1.40, "Cycnoches chlorochilon klotzsch". HORIZ. $3, "Dendrobium phalaenopsis".

54. "Phalaenopsis amabilis".

**1958.** Taiwan Orchids. Orchids in natural colours; backgrounds in colours given. With gum.
280. 54. 20 c. brown 1·00 10
281. – 40 c. violet 1·00 10
282. – $1.40 purple 2·00 20
283. – $3 blue 2·75 35

55. W.H.O. Emblem.

56. Presidential Mansion, Taipeh.

**1958.** 10th Anniv. of W.H.O.
284. 55. 40 c. blue 10 10
285. $1.60 red 20 15
286. $2 purple 40 20

**1958.**
290a 56 $5 green 6·50 10
290b $5.60 violet 6·50 30
290c $6 orange 6·50 10
290d $10 green 5·00 10
290e $20 red 7·00 10
289 $50 brown 40·00 1·00
290 $100 blue 48·00 1·75

58. Ploughman.

**1958.** 10th Anniv of Joint Commission on Chinese Rural Reconstruction.
291. 58. 20 c. green 45 10
292. 40 c. black 55 10
293. $1.40 purple 1·10 10
294. $3 blue 1·90 30

59. President Chiang Kai-shek Reviewing Troops.

**1958.** 72nd Birthday of President Chiang Kai-shek and National Day Review. With gum.
295 59 40 c. multicoloured 40 10

60. U.N.E.S.C.O. Headquarters, Paris.

61. Flame of Freedom encircling Globe.

**1958.** Inaug. of U.N.E.S.C.O. Headquarters.
296. 60. 20 c. blue 15 10
297. 40 c. green 25 10
298. $1.40 red 30 10
299. $3 purple 40 25

**1958.** 10th Anniv. of Declaration of Human Rights.
300. 61. 40 c. green 20 10
301. 60 c. sepia 20 10
302. $1 red 35 10
303. $3 blue 40 25

**1958.** No. 192 surch. 350.
305. – $3.50 on $5 blue 2·00 1·00

64. The Constitution.

65. Chu Kwang Tower, Quemoy.

**1958.** 10th Anniv. of Constitution.
306. 64. 40 c. green 25 10
307. 50 c. purple 35 10
308. $1.40 red 45 10
309. $3.50 blue 50 30

**1959.**
310. 65. 3 c. orange .. .. 10 10
311. 5 c. olive .. .. 50 10
312. 10 c. lilac .. .. 10 10
313. 20 c. blue .. .. 10 10
314. 40 c. brown .. .. 10 10
315. 50 c. turquoise .. .. 50 10
316. $1 red .. .. .. 50 10
317. $1.40 green .. .. 1·25 10
318. $2 myrtle .. .. 1·00 10
319. $2.80 mauve .. .. 3·25 60
320. $3 slate .. .. .. 1·75 10
See also Nos. 367/82g.

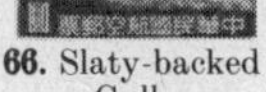
**66.** Slaty-backed Gull.

**67.** I.L.O. Emblem and Headquarters, Geneva.

**1959.** Air. With gum.
321. 66. $8 black, blue and green 2·50 25

**1959.** 40th Anniv. of I.L.O.
322. 67. 40 c. blue .. .. 20 10
323. $1.60 brown .. .. 25 10
324. $3 green .. .. 35 10
325. $5 red .. .. .. 40 25

**69.** Inscribed Rock on Mt. Tai-wu, Quemoy.

**68.** Scout Bugler.

**70.**

**1959.** 10th World Scout Jamboree. Manila.
326. 68. 40 c. red .. .. 30 10
327. 50 c. blue .. .. 70 15
328. $5 green .. .. 1·50 40

**1959.** Defence of Quemoy (Kinmen) and Matsu Islands, 1958.
329. 69. 40 c. brown .. .. 25 10
330. – $1.40 blue .. .. 65 15
331. – $2 green .. .. 1·40 25
332. 69. $3 blue .. .. 1·75 30
DESIGN—(41 × 23½ mm.): $1.40, $2, Map of Taiwan, Quemoy and Matsu Is.

**1959.** Int. Correspondence Week.
333. 70. 40 c. blue .. .. 25 10
334. $1 red .. .. 25 15
335. $2 sepia .. .. 25 10
336. $3.50 red .. .. 35 30

**71.** National Science Hall.

**72.** Confederation Emblem.

**1959.** Inaug. of Taiwan National Science Hall. With gum.
337. 71. 40 c. multicoloured .. 65 10
338. – $3 multicoloured (different view) .. 1·10 35

**1959.** 10th Anniv of International Confederation of Free Trade Unions.
339. 72. 40 c. green .. .. 20 10
340. $1.60 purple .. .. 35 10
341. $3 orange .. .. 55 20

**73.** Sun Yat-sen and Abraham Lincoln.

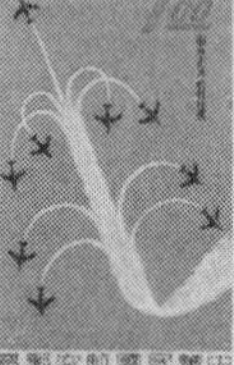
**74.** "Bomb Burst" by Thunder Tiger Aerobatic Squadron.

**1959.** 150th Birth Anniv. of Lincoln. With gum.
342. 73. 40 c. multicoloured .. 15 10
343. $3 multicoloured .. 35 25

**1960.** Air. Chinese Air Force Commem. With gum.
344 74 $1 multicoloured .. 3·50 30
345 – $2 multicoloured .. 2·50 15
346 – $5 multicoloured .. 4·50 50
DESIGNS—HORIZ. (Various aerobatics): $2, Loop. $5, Diamond formation flying over jet fighter.

**75.** Night Delivery.

**76.** "Uprooted Tree".

**1960.** Introduction of "Prompt Delivery" and "Postal Launch" Services.
347. 75. $1.40 purple .. .. 85 15
348. $1.60 blue "Yu-Khi" (postal launch) .. 85 20

**1960.** World Refugee Year. With gum.
349. 76. 40 c. green, brown & blk. 15 10
350 $3 green, orange & blk. 20 25

**77.** Cross-Island Highway.

**79.** Winged Tape-reel.

**1960.** Inaug. of Taiwan Cross-Island Highway.
351. 77. 40 c. green .. .. 40 10
352. – $1 blue .. .. .. 1·50 20
353. – $2 purple .. .. 1·00 15
354. 77. $3 brown .. .. 1·50 25
DESIGN—VERT. $1, $2, Tunnels on the Highway.

**1960.** Visit of Pres. Eisenhower. Nos. 331/2 optd. **WELCOME U.S. PRESIDENT DWIGHT D. EISENHOWER 1960** in English and Chinese.
355. – $2 green .. .. 1·25 1·00
356. 69. $3 blue .. .. .. 1·50 1·00

**1960.** Phonopost (tape-recordings) Service.
357 79 $2 red .. .. .. 65 20

**80.** "Flowers and Red-billed Blue Magpies" (after Hsiao Yung).

**81.** Youth Corps Flag and Summer Activities.

**1960.** Ancient Chinese Paintings from Palace Museum Collection. (1st series). With gum.
358. – $1 multicoloured .. 2·50 15
359. – $1.40 multicoloured .. 4·50 35
360. 80. $1.60 multicoloured .. 5·50 75
361. – $2 multicoloured .. 6·50 1·50
PAINTINGS—HORIZ. $1, "Two Riders" (after Wei Yen). $1.40, "Two Horses and Groom" (after Han Kan). $2, "A Pair of Green-winged Teals in a Rivulet" (after Monk Hui Ch'ung).
See also Nos. 451/4, 577/80 and 716/19.

**1960.** Youth Summer Activities.
362 81 50 c. green .. .. 35 10
363 – $3 brown .. .. 60 30
DESIGN—HORIZ. $3, Youth Corps Flag and other summer activities.

**82.** "Forest Cultivation".

**83.** Chu Kwang Tower, Quemoy.

**1960.** 5th World Forestry Congress, Seattle. Multicoloured. With gum.
364 $1 Type 82 .. .. 2·00 10
365 $2 "Forest Protection" (trees and sika deer) .. 2·75 65
366 $3 "Lumber Production" (cable railway) .. 3·50 30

**1960.** As T 65 but redrawn.
367 83 3 c. brown .. .. 10 10
382 10 c. green .. .. 1·25 15
368 40 c. violet .. .. 10 10
369 50 c. orange .. .. 25 10
370 60 c. purple .. .. 15 10
371 80 c. green .. .. 10 10
372 $1 green .. .. 1·75 10
373 $1.20 green .. .. 85 10
374 $1.50 blue .. .. 1·00 10
375 $2 red .. .. 75 10
376 $2.50 blue .. .. 75 15
377 $3 green .. .. 1·25 10
378 $3.20 brown .. .. 3·50 10
379 $3.60 blue .. .. 3·25 20
382f $4 green .. .. 4·50 15
380 $4.50 red .. .. 4·00 30

**84.** Diving.

**85.** Bronze Wine Vase (Shang Dynasty).

**1960.** Sports. With gum.
383. 84. 50 c. brown, yell. & blue 35 10
384. – 80 c. violet, yellow & pur. 35 10
385. – $2 multicoloured .. 1·00 10
386. – $2.50 black and orange 1·00 25
387. – $3 multicoloured .. 2·00 35
388. – $3.20 multicoloured .. 2·25 40
DESIGNS: 80 c. Discus-throwing. $2, Basketball. $2.50, Football. $3, Hurdling. $3.20, Sprinting.

**1961.** Ancient Chinese Art Treasures (1st series). With gum.
389 85 80 c. multicoloured .. 1·50 10
390 – $1 indigo, blue & red .. 3·25 20
391 – $1.20 blue, brown & yell 3·00 25
392 – $1.50 brown, blue & mve 3·50 70
393 – $2 brown, violet & green 3·75 40
394 – $2.50 black, lilac & blue 3·50 60
DESIGNS: $1, Bronze cauldron (Chou). $1.20, Porcelain vase (Sung). $1.50, Jade perforated tube (Chou). $2, Porcelain jug (Ming). $2.50, Jade flower vase (Ming).
See also Nos. 408/13 and 429/34.

**86.** Farmer and Mechanical Plough.

**87.** Mme. Chiang Kai-shek.

**1961.** Agricultural Census.
395. 86. 80 c. purple .. .. 35 10
396. $2 green .. .. 1·10 30
397. $3.20 red .. .. 1·90 25

**1961.** 10th Anniv (1960) of Chinese Women's Anti-Aggression League. With gum.
398. 87. 80 c. blk., red & turq. 65 10
399. $1 black, red & green .. 1·75 15
400. $2 black, red & brown .. 1·75 15
401. $3.20 blk., red & purple 3·00 1·10

**88.** Taiwan Lobster.

**89.** Jeme Tien-yao and Locomotive.

**1961.** Mail Order Service.
402. 88. $3 myrtle .. .. 1·25 20

**1961.** Birth Centenary of Jeme Tien-yao (railway engineer).
403. – 80 c. violet .. .. 75 10
404. 89. $2 black .. .. 1·75 35
DESIGN: 80 c. As Type 89 but locomotive heading right.

**90.** Pres. Chiang Kai-shek.

**91.** Convair 880 Jetliner ("The Mandarin Jet"), Biplane and Flag.

**1961.** 1st Anniv of Chiang Kai-shek's Third Term Inauguration. With gum.
405. – 80 c. multicoloured .. 1·00 10
406. 90. $2 multicoloured .. 3·75 70
DESIGN—HORIZ. 80 c. Map of China inscr. (in Chinese) "Recovery of the Mainland".

**1961.** 40th Anniv. of Chinese Civil Air Service. With gum.
407. 91. $10 multicoloured .. 2·50 30

**1961.** Ancient Chinese Art Treasures (2nd issue). As T 85. With gum.
408. 80 c. multicoloured .. 1·75 10
409. $1 blue, brown & bistre .. 3·50 20
410. $1.50 blue and salmon .. 3·50 75
411. $2 red, black and blue .. 5·00 25
412. $4 blue, sepia and red .. 5·00 45
413. $4.50 brn., sepia & blue .. 7·00 1·00
DESIGNS—VERT. 80 c. Palace perfumer (Ching). $1, Corn vase (Warring States). $2, Jade tankard (Sung). HORIZ. $1.50, Bronze bowl (Chou). $4, Porcelain bowl (Southern Sung). $4.50, Jade chimera (Han).

**92.** Sun Yat-sen and Chiang Kai-shek.

**93.** Lotus Lake.

**1961.** 50th National Day. With gum.
414 92 80 c. brown, blue & grey 1·00 10
415 – $5 multicoloured .. 3·00 1·00
DESIGN—HORIZ. $5, Map and flag.

**1961.** Taiwan Scenery. Multicoloured. With gum.
416. 80 c. Pitan (Green Lake) .. 2·25 10
417. $1 Type 93 .. .. 3·75 50
418. $2 Sun-Moon Lake .. 4·25 30
419. $3.20 Wulai Waterfall .. 5·50 75
The 80 c. and $3.20 are vertical.

**94.** Steel Furnace.

**95.** Atomic Reactor, National Tsing Hwa University.

**1961.** Taiwan Industries. Multicoloured. With gum.
420. 80 c. Oil refinery .. .. 1·50 10
421. $1.50 Type 94 .. .. 2·75 60
422. $2.50 Aluminium manufacture .. .. 3·50 55
423. $3.20 Fertiliser plant .. 4·50 50
The $3.20 is horiz.

**1961.** First Taiwan Atomic Reactor Inaug. Multicoloured. With gum.
424. 80 c. Type 95 .. .. 1·00 10
425. $2 Interior of reactor .. 3·00 1·00
426. $3.20 Reactor building (horiz.) .. .. 3·50 60

**96.** Telegraph Wires and Microwave Reflector Pylons.

**97.** Postal Segregating, Facing and Cancelling Machine.

**1961.** 80th Anniv. of Chinese Telecommunications. Multicoloured. With gum.
427 80 c. Type 96 .. .. 75 10
428 $3.20 Microwave parabolic antenna (horiz) .. 2·25 70

**1962.** Ancient Chinese Art Treasures (3rd issue). As T **85**. With gum.

429 80 c. brown, violet and red 2·25 10
430 $1 purple, brown and blue 1·50 15
431 $2.40 blue, brown and red 3·50 40
432 $3 multicoloured 6·50 1·50
433 $3.20 red, green and blue 8·50 15
434 $3.60 multicoloured 10·00 1·50

DESIGNS—VERT. 80 c. Jade topaz twin wine vessel (Chiang). $1, Bronze pouring vase (Warring States). $2.40, Porcelain vase (Ming). $3, Tsun bronze wine vase (Shang). $3.20, Porcelain jar (Ching). $3.60, Jade perforated disc (Han).

**1962.**

435. **97.** 80 c. purple 60 10

**98.** Mt. Yu Weather Station. **99.** Distribution of Milk and U.N. Emblem.

**1962.** World Meteorological Day.

436. **98.** 80 c. brown 50 10
437. – $1 blue 1·50 30
438. – $2 green 2·00 60

DESIGNS—HORIZ. $1, Route-map of Typhoon Pamela. VERT. $2, Weather balloon passing globe.

**1962.** 15th Anniv. of U.N.I.C.E.F.

439. **99.** 80 c. red 25 10
440. $3.20 green 1·50 45

**100.** Campaign Emblem. **101.** Yu Yu-jen (journalist).

**1962.** Malaria Eradication. With gum.

441 **100** 80 c. red, green & blue 15 10
442 $3.60 brown, green and deep brown 25 25

**1962.** "Elder Reporter" Yü Yu-jen Commem. With gum.

443. **101.** 80 c. sepia and pink 85 15

**102.** Koxinga.

**103.** Co-operative Emblem.

**1962.** Tercentenary of Koxinga's Recovery of Taiwan. With gum.

444. **102.** 80 c purple 1·50 10
445. $2 green 2·50 35

**1962.** 40th Int. Co-operative Day.

446. **103.** 80 c. brown 25 10
447. – $2 lilac 75 35

DESIGN: $2, Global handclasp.

**104.** U.N.E.S.C.O. Symbols.

**105.** Emperor T'ai Tsu (Ming Dynasty).

**1962.** U.N.E.S.C.O. Activities Commem.

448. **104.** 80 c. mauve 35 10
449. – $2 lake 1·25 35
450. – $3.20 green 1·25 25

DESIGNS—HORIZ. $2, U.N.E.S.C.O. emblem on open book. $3.20, Emblem linking hemispheres.

**1962.** Ancient Chinese Paintings from Palace Museum Collection (2nd series). Emperors. Multicoloured. With gum.

451. 80 c. T'ai Tsung (Tang) 12·00 10
452. $2 T'ai Tsu (Sung) 18·00 2·75
453. $3.20 Genghis Khan (Yuan) 22·00 2·25
454. $4 Type **105** 26·00 7·50

**106.** "Lions" Emblem and Activities. **107.** Pole-vaulting.

**1962.** 45th Anniv of Lions International. With gum.

455. **106.** 80 c. multicoloured 75 10
456. $3.60 multicoloured 1·75 50

**1962.** Sports. With gum.

457 **107** 80 c. brown, black & bl 50 10
458 $3.20 multicoloured 1·10 25

DESIGN—HORIZ. $3.20, Rifle shooting.

**108.** Young Farmers.

**109.** Liner.

**1962.** 10th Anniv. of Chinese 4-H Clubs.

459. **108.** 80 c. red 35 10
460. – $3.20 green 75 30

DESIGN: $3.20, 4-H Clubs emblem.

**1962.** 90th Anniv. of China Merchants' Steam Navigation Co. With gum.

461. **109.** 80 c. multicoloured 65 10
462. – $3.60 multicoloured 2·25 50

DESIGN—HORIZ. $3.60, Freighter "Hai Min" and Pacific route-map.

**110.** Harvesting.

**111.** Youth, Girl, Torch and Martyrs Monument, Huang Hua Kang.

**1963.** Freedom from Hunger. With gum.

463. **110.** $10 multicoloured 2·75 50

**1963.** 20th Youth Day.

464. **111.** 80 c. purple 20 10
465. $3.20 green 90 30

**112.** Barn Swallows and Pagoda.

**113.** Refugee in Tears.

**1963.** 1st Anniv of Asian-Oceanic Postal Union. With gum. Multicoloured.

466. 80 c. Type **112** 3·50 15
467. $2 Northern gannet 4·00 35
468. $6 Manchurian crane and pine tree (vert.) 8·50 2·75

**1963.** Refugees' Flight from Mainland.

469. **113.** 80 c. black 50 10
470. – $3.20 purple 1·00 25

DESIGN—HORIZ. $3.20, Refugees on march.

**114.** Convair 880 over Tropic of Cancer Monument, Kiai.

**115.** Red Cross Nurse and Emblem.

**1963.** Air. Multicoloured. With gum.

471. $2.50 Suspension Bridge, Pitan (horiz.) 3·25 10
472. $6 Type **114** 5·50 15
473. $10 Lion-head Mountain, Sinchu 8·50 1·00

**1963.** Red Cross Centenary. With gum.

474. **115.** 80 c. red and black 2·50 10
475. – $10 red, green & blue 7·00 1·60

DESIGN: $10, Globe and scroll.

**116.** Basketball.

**117.** Freedom Torch.

**1963.** 2nd Asian Basketball Championships, Taipeh.

476. **116.** 80 c. mauve 60 10
477. – $2 violet 1·25 40

DESIGN: $2, Hands reaching for inscribed ball.

**1963.** 15th Anniv. of Declaration of Human Rights.

478. **117.** 80 c. green 35 10
479. – $3.20 lake 85 20

DESIGN—HORIZ. $3.20, Human figures and scales of justice.

**118.** Country Scene.

**119.** Dr. Sun Yat-sen and his Book "Three Principles of the People".

**1963.** "Good-People, Good-Deeds" Campaign. Multicoloured. With gum.

480. 40 c. Type **118** 2·00 10
481. $4.50 Lighting candle 4·50 85

**1963.** 10th Anniv. of Land-to-Tillers Programme. With gum.

482. **119.** $5 multicoloured 5·00 75

**120.** Torch of Liberty.

**121.** Broadleaf Cactus.

**1964.** 10th Anniv. of Liberty Day.

483. **120.** 80 c. orange 25 10
484. – $3.20 blue 1·25 30

DESIGN—VERT. $3.20, Hands with broken manacles.

**1964.** Taiwan Cacti. Mult. With gum.

485. 80 c. Type **121** 75 10
486. $1 Crab cactus 4·25 40
487. $3.20 Nopalxochia 2·25 15
488. $5 Grizzly-Bear cactus 6·25 60

**122.** Wu Chih-hwei (politician).

**123.** Chu Kwang Tower, Quemoy.

**1964.** 99th Birth Anniv of Wu Chih-hwei (politician).

489 **122** 80 c. brown 80 10

**1964.**

490. **123.** 3 c. purple 10 10
491. 5 c. green 10 10
492. 10 c. olive 25 10
493. 20 c. turquoise 15 10
494. 40 c. red 15 10
495. 50 c. red 35 10
496. 80 c. orange 45 10
497. $1 violet 30 10
498. $1.50 purple 5·50 50
499. $2 mauve 60 10
500. $2.50 blue 75 10
501. $3 grey 1·10 10
502. $3.20 blue 1·00 10
504. $4 green 1·25 10

**124.** Nurse and Florence Nightingale.

**125.** Weir.

**1964.** Nurses Day.

506. – 80 c. violet 75 10
507. **124.** $4 red 1·50 25

DESIGN—HORIZ. 80 c. Nurses holding candle-light ceremony.

**1964.** Inaug. of Shihmen Reservoir. With gum. Multicoloured.

508. 80 c. Type **125** 1·75 10
509. $1 Irrigation channel 2·50 10
510. $3.20 Dam and powerhouse 5·50 10
511. $5 Main spillway 7·50 1·50

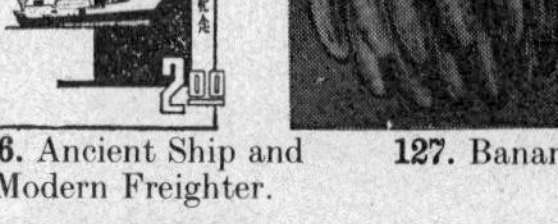

**126.** Ancient Ship and Modern Freighter. **127.** Bananas.

**1964.** Navigation Day.

512. **126.** $2 orange 35 10
513. $3.60 green 75 20

**1964.** Taiwan Fruits. Multicoloured. With gum.

514. 80 c. Type **127** 3·50 10
515. $1 Oranges 9·50 1·00
516. $3.20 Pineapples 14·00 35
517. $4 Water-melons 18·00 1·25

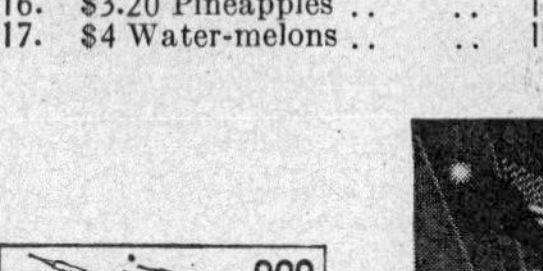

**128.** Lockheed Starfighters, "Tai Ho", "Tai Choa" and "Tai Tsung" (destroyers) and Artillery.

**129.** Globe and Flags of Formosa and U.S.A.

**1964.** Armed Forces Day.

518. **128.** 80 c. blue 65 10
519. $6 purple 2·10 30

**1964.** New York World's Fair (1st issue). With gum.

520. **129.** 80 c. multicoloured 75 10
521. – $5 multicoloured 2·00 50

DESIGN—HORIZ. $5, Taiwan Pavilion at Fair.

See also Nos. 550/1.

**130.** Cowman holding calf. **131.** Cycling.

**1964.** Animal Protection.

522. **130.** $2 purple 50 10
523. $4 blue 1·50 30

**1964.** Olympic Games, Tokyo.

524. **131.** 80 c. blue 50 10
525. – $1 red 1·25 10
526. – $3.20 green 2·00 10
527. – $10 violet 3·25 1·25

DESIGNS: $1, Runner breasting tape. $3.20, Gymnastics. $10, High jumping.

**132.** Hsu Kuang-chi (statesman).

**133.** Factory-bench ("Pharmaceutics").

**1964.** Famous Chinese.

528. **132.** 80 c. blue 85 10

See also Nos. 558/9, 586/7, 599, 606/9, 610, 738/40, 960 and 1072/7.

**1964.** Taiwan Industries. Multicoloured. With gum.

529. 40 c. Type **133** 1·50 10
530. $1.50 Loom ("Textiles") 2·50 1·00
531. $2 Refinery ("Chemicals") 4·25 10
532. $3.60 Cement-mixer ("Cement") 5·00 75

The $1.50 and $3.60 are horiz. designs.

**134.** Dr. Sun Yat-sen (founder).
**135.** Mrs. Eleanor Roosevelt and "Human Rights" Emblem.

**1964.** 70th Anniv. of Kuomintang.

533. **134.** 80 c. green .. .. 1·25 10
534. $3.60 purple .. .. 2·00 60

**1964.** 16th Anniv. of Declaration of Human Rights.

535. **135.** $10 brown and violet 75 30

**136.** Law Code and Scales of Justice.
**137.** Rotary Emblem and Mainspring.

**1965.** 20th Judicial Day.

536. **136.** 80 c. red .. .. 25 10
537. $3.20 green .. .. 50 20

**1965.** 60th Anniv. of Rotary Int.

538. **137.** $1.50 red .. .. 35 10
539. $2 green .. .. 50 10
540. $2.50 blue .. .. 65 25

**138.** "Double Carp". **139.** Mme. Chiang Kai-shek.

**1965.**

541. **138.** $5 violet .. .. 7·50 10
542. $5.60 blue .. .. 7·50 1·50
543. $6 brown .. .. 7·50 10
544. $10 mauve .. .. 9·50 10
545. $20 red .. .. 12·00 15
546. $50 green .. .. 25·00 50
547. $100 red .. .. 38·00 1·00

See also Nos. 695a/698a.

**1965.** 15th Anniv. of Chinese Women's Anti-Aggression League. With gum.

548. **139.** $2 multicoloured .. 8·00 15
549. $6 multicoloured .. 11·00 1·75

**140.** Unisphere and Taiwan Pavilion, N.Y. Fair.

**1965.** New York World's Fair (2nd issue). Multicoloured. With gum.

550. $2 Type **140** .. .. 3·25 10
551. $10 Peacock and various birds ("100 birds paying tribute to Queen Phoenix") .. .. 15·00 75

**141.** I.T.U. Emblem and Symbols.

**1965.** I.T.U. Cent. Multicoloured. With gum.

552. 80 c. Type **141** .. .. 50 10
553. $5 I.T.U. emblem and symbols (vert.) .. 1·25 30

**142.** Red Bream. **143.** I.C.Y. Emblem.

**1965.** Taiwan Fishes. Multicoloured. With gum.

554. 40 c. Type **142** .. .. 1·50 10
555. 80 c. White pomfret .. .. 2·50 10
556. $2 Skipjack tuna (vert.) .. 3·50 25
557. $4 Moonfish .. .. 6·00 35

**1965.** Famous Chinese. Portraits as T **132.**

558. $1 red (Confucius) .. 1·75 10
559. $3.60 blue (Mencius) .. 2·75 25

**1965.** Int. Co-operation Year. Multicoloured. With gum.

560. $2 Type **143** .. .. 2·50 10
561. $6 I.C.Y. emblem (horiz.) 2·50 65

**144.** Road Crossing. **145.** Dr. Sun Yat-sen.

**1965.** Road Safety.

562. **144.** $1 purple .. .. 75 10
563. $4 red .. .. .. 1·00 15

**1965.** Dr. Sun Yat-sen's Birth Cent. Multicoloured. With gum.

564. $1 Type **145** .. .. 2·00 10
565. $4 As T **145** but with portrait, etc., on right .. 3·75 20
566. $5 Dr. Sun Yat Sen and flags (horiz.) .. .. 6·00 70

**146.** Children with Firework.
**147.** Lien Po, "Marshal and Prime Minister Reconciled".

**1965.** Chinese Folklore. (1st Series). Multicoloured. With gum.

567. $1 Type **146** .. .. 3·25 10
568. $4.50 Dragon dance .. 3·75 60

See also Nos. 581/3 and 617.

**1966.** Painted Faces of Chinese Opera. With gum.

569. **147.** $1 multicoloured .. 9·00 15
570. – $3 multicoloured .. 10·00 35
571. – $4 multicoloured .. 18·00 75
572. – $6 multicoloured .. 20·00 3·25

FACES (role and opera): $3, Kuan Yu, "Reunion at Ku City". $4, Chang Fei, "Long Board Slope". $6, Buddha, "The Flower-scattering Angel".

**148.** Pigeon holding Postal Emblem.
**149.** "Fishing on a Snowy Day" (after artist of the "Five Dynasties").

**1966.** 70th Anniv. of Chinese Postal Services. Multicoloured. With gum.

573. $1 Type **148** .. .. 1·50 10
574. $2 Postman by Chu memorial stone (horiz.) .. 2·25 10
575. $3 Postal Museum (horiz.) 2·25 10
576. $4 "Postman climbing" 3·25 75

**1966.** Ancient Chinese Paintings from Palace Museum Collection (3rd series). With gum. Multicoloured.

577. $2.50 Type **149.** .. 2·25 10
578. $3.50 "Calves on the Plain" 4·75 10
579. $4.50 "Snowscape" .. 5·50 65
580. $5 "Magpies" (after Lin Ch'un) .. .. 7·50 75

Nos. 578/9 both after Sung artists.

**1966.** Chinese Folklore (2nd series). Designs as T **146.** With gum. Multicoloured.

581 $2.50 Dragon boat racing (horiz) .. .. 7·50 25
582 $4 "Lady Chang O Flying to the Moon" (horiz) .. 4·50 10
583 $6 Lion Dance .. .. 1·00 15

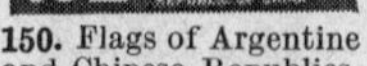

**150.** Flags of Argentine and Chinese Republics.
**151.** Lin Sen.

**1966.** 150th Anniv. of Argentine Republic's Independence. With gum.

584. **150.** $10 multicoloured .. 1·50 30

**1966.** Birth Cent. of Lin Sen (statesman).

585. **151.** $1 sepia .. .. 75 10

**1966.** Famous Chinese. Portraits as T **132.**

586. $2.50 sepia .. .. 2·00 10
587. $3.50 red .. .. .. 2·75 15

PORTRAITS: $2.50, General Yueh Fei. $3.50, Wen Tien-hsiang (statesman).

**153.** Bean Geese. **154.** Pres. Chiang Kai-shek.

**1966.**

588. **153.** $3.50 brown .. .. 1·00 25
589. $4 red .. .. .. 65 10
590. $4.50 green .. .. 1·50 15
591. $5 purple .. .. 75 10
592. $5.50 green .. .. 1·25 20
593. $6 blue .. .. 5·00 1·75
594. $6.50 violet .. .. 1·75 30
595. $7 black .. .. 1·25 10
596. $8 red .. .. .. 1·75 10

**1966.** President Chiang Kai-shek's re-election for 4th Term. With gum. Multicoloured.

597. $1 Type **154** .. .. 90 10
598. $5 President in Uniform .. 1·90 30

**1966.** Famous Chinese. Portrait as T **132.**

599 $1 blue (Tsai Yuan-Pei, scholar) .. .. 85 10

**155.** Various means of Transport.
**156.** Boeing 727-100 over Chilin Pavilion, Grand Hotel, Taipeh.

**1967.** Development of Taiwan Communications. Multicoloured. With gum.

600 $1 Mobile postman and microwave station (vert) 75 10
601 $5 Type **155** .. .. 1·50 15

**1967.** Air. Multicoloured. With gum.

602 $5 Type **156** .. .. 2·00 10
603 $8 Boeing 727-100 over Palace Museum, Taipeh 2·25 20

**157.** Pres. Chiang Kai-shek.
**158.** "God of Happiness" (wood carving).

**1967.** Chiang Kai-shek's 4th Presidential Term. With gum.

604. **157.** $1 multicoloured .. 2·00 10
605. $4 multicoloured .. 2·50 20

**1967.** Famous Chinese. Poets. Portraits As T **132.**

606. $1 black (Chu Yuan) .. 1·00 10
607. $2 brown (Li Po) .. 1·75 20
608. $2.50 (Tu Fu) .. .. 2·25 20
609. $3 olive (Po Chu-i) .. 2·75 20

**1967.** Famous Chinese. Portrait as T **132.**

610. $1 black (Chiu Ching, female revolutionary) .. 75 10

**1967.** Chinese Handicrafts. Multicoloured. With gum.

611. $1 Type **158** .. .. 1·50 10
612. $2.50 Vase and dish .. 2·00 10
613. $3 Chinese dolls .. 3·00 10
614. $5 Palace lanterns .. 4·75 35

**159.** "WACL" on World Map.
**160.** Muller's Barbet.

**1967.** 1st World Anti-Communist League Conf., Taipei.

615. **159.** $1 red .. .. .. 20 10
616. $5 blue .. .. .. 40 15

**GUM.** From No. 617 all stamps were issued with gum unless otherwise stated.

**1967.** Chinese Folklore (3rd series). Stilts Pastime. As T **146**

617. $4.50 multicoloured .. 75 15

DESIGN: "The Fisherman and the Woodcutter" (Chinese play on stilts).

**1967.** Taiwan Birds. Multicoloured.

618. $1 Type **160** .. .. 2·25 15
619. $2 Maroon Oriole (horiz.) .. 4·75 20
620. $2.50 White-bellied Wedge-tailed Green Pigeon (horiz.) 5·50 65
621. $3 Formosan Blue Magpie (horiz.) .. .. 6·50 40
622. $5 Crested Serpent Eagle 7·00 75
623. $8 Mikado Pheasant (horiz.) 7·50 75

**161.** Chung Hsing Pagoda.
**162.** Flags and China Park, Manila.

**1967.** Int. Tourist Year. Multicoloured

624. $1 Type **161** .. .. 1·25 10
625. $2.50 Yeh Liu National Park (coastal scene) (horiz.) .. 3·25 25
626. $4 Statue of Buddha (horiz.) 3·50 20
627. $5 National Palace Museum, Taipei (horiz.) .. 4·50 30

**1967.** China-Philippines Friendship.

628. **162.** $1 multicoloured .. 20 10
629. $5 multicoloured .. 75 15

**163.** Chungshan Building, Yangmingshan.
**164.** Taroko Gorge.

**1968.**

630. **163.** 5 c. brown .. .. 10 10
631. 10 c. green .. .. 15 15
632. 50 c. purple .. .. 10 10
633. $1 red .. .. .. 15 10
634. $1.50 green .. .. 2·25 20
635. $2 purple .. .. 45 10
636. $2.50 blue .. .. 50 10
637. $3 blue .. .. 60 10

For redrawn design see Nos. 791/8.

**1968.** 17th Pacific Area Travel Association Conference, Taipei. Multicoloured.

638 $5 Type **164** .. .. 1·25 30
689 $8 Chungshan Building, Yangmingshan .. 75 15

**165.** Harvesting Sugar-cane.
**166.** Vice-Pres. Cheng.

**1968.** Sugar-cane Technologists Congress, Taiwan.

640. **165.** $1 multicoloured .. 75 10
641. $4 multicoloured .. 1·75 25

**1968.** 3rd Death Anniv. of Vice-Pres. Chen Cheng.

642. **166.** $1 multicoloured .. 50 10

**167.** Bean Geese. **168.** Jade Cabbage (Ching Dynasty).

**1968.** 90th Anniv. of Chinese Postage Stamps.
643 **167** $1 red .. .. .. 65 15

**1968.** Chinese Art Treasures, National Palace Museum (1st series). Multicoloured.
645. $1 Type **168** .. .. 75 10
646. $1.50 Jade battle-axe (Warring States period) 2·25 35
647. $2 Lung-ch'uan porcelain flower bowl (Sung dynasty) 2·50 10
648. $2.50 Yung Cheng enamelled vase (Ching dynasty) .. 2·75 35
649. $4 Agate "fingered" flower-holder (Ching dynasty) 3·00 35
650. $5 Sacrificial vessel (Western Chou) .. .. 3·50 45
The $2 and $4 are horiz.
See also Nos. 682/7 and 732/7.

**169.** W.H.O. Emblem on "20". **170.** Sun, Planets and "Rainfall".

**1968.** 20th Anniv of W.H.O.
651. **169.** $1 green .. .. 20 10
652. $5 red .. .. 40 20

**1968.** Int. Hydrological Decade.
653. **170.** $1 green and orange .. 20 10
654. $4 blue and orange .. 30 10

**171.** "A City of Cathay" (section of hand-scroll painting).

**1968.** "A City of Cathay" (Scroll, Palace Museum) (1st series).
655. **171.** $1 (1) multicoloured .. 50 10
656. – $1 (2) multicoloured .. 50 10
657. – $1 (3) multicoloured .. 50 10
658. – $1 (4) multicoloured .. 50 10
659. – $1 (5) multicoloured .. 50 10
660. – $5 multicoloured .. 7·50 1·00
661. – $8 multicoloured .. 8·00 1·50
DESIGNS—As Type **171**: Nos. 655/9 together show panorama of the city ending with the palace. LARGER (61 × 32 mm.). $5, City wall and gate. $8, Great bridge.
The five $1 stamps were issued together se-tenant in horiz. strips, representing the last 11 feet of the 37 foot scroll, which is viewed from right to left as it is unrolled.
The stamps may be identified by the numbers given in brackets which correspond to the numbers in the bottom right-hand corners of the stamps.
See also Nos. 699/703.

**172.** Map and Radio "Waves". **173.** Human Rights Emblem.

**1968.** 40th Anniv. of Chinese Broadcasting Service.
662. **172.** $1 grey, ultram & blue 20 10
663. – $4 red and blue .. 40 10
DESIGN—VERT. $4, Stereo broadcast "waves".

**1968.** Human Rights Year.
664. **173.** $1 multicoloured .. 15 10
665. $5 multicoloured .. 25 10

**174.** Harvesting Rice. **175.** Throwing the Javelin.

**1968.** Rural Reconstruction.
666. **174.** $1 brown, ochre & yell. 15 10
667. $5 bronze, grn. & lemon. 40 30

**1968.** Olympic Games, Mexico. Multicoloured.
668. $1 Type **175** .. .. 25 10
669. $2.50 Weightlifting .. 35 10
670. $5 Pole-vaulting (horiz.) .. 45 10
671. $8 Hurdling (horiz) .. 60 20

**176.** President Chiang Kai-shek and Main Gate, Whampoa Military Academy.

**1968.** "President Chiang Kai-shek's Meritorious Services". Multicoloured.
672. $1 Type **176** .. .. 30 10
673. $2 Reviewing Northern Expedition Forces .. 80 20
674. $2.50 Suppression of bandits .. .. .. 2·25 30
675. $3.50 Marco Polo Bridge and Victory Parade, Nanking, 1945 .. .. 85 25
676. $4 Chinese Constitution .. 1·00 25
677. $5 National flag .. .. 1·25 30
Each stamp bears the portrait of President Chiang Kai-shek as in Type **176**.

**177.** Cockerel. **178.** National Flag.

**1968.** New Year Greetings. "Year of the Cock".
678. **177.** $1 multicoloured .. 14·00 10
679. $4.50 multicoloured .. 16·00 3·25

**1968.** 20th Anniv. of Chinese Constitution.
680. **178.** $1 multicoloured .. 40 10
681. $5 multicoloured .. 65 15

**1969.** Chinese Art Treasures, National Palace Museum (2nd series). Multicoloured as T **168**.
682 $1 Jade buckle (Ching dynasty) (horiz) .. 60 10
683 $1.50 Jade vase (Sung dynasty) .. .. 1·25 15
684 $2 Cloisonne enamel teapot (Ching dynasty) (horiz) 75 10
685 $2.50 Bronze sacrificial vessel (Kuei) (horiz) .. 1·10 20
686 $4 Hsuan-te "heavenly ball" vase (Ming dynasty) .. .. 1·50 20
687 $5 "Gourd" vase (Ching dynasty) .. .. 2·00 30

**179.** Servicemen and Savings Emblem. **180.** Ti (flute).

**1969.** 10th Anniv of Forces' Savings Services.
688. **179.** $1 purple .. .. 15 10
689. $4 blue .. .. 45 15

**1969.** Chinese Musical Instruments. Mult.
690 $1 Type **180** .. .. 75 10
691 $2.50 Sheng (pipes) .. 1·25 15
692 $4 P'i-p'a (lute) .. 1·75 30
693 $5 Cheng (zither) .. 1·75 15

**181.** Chungshan Building, Yangmingshan **182.** "Double Carp".

**1969.** 10th Kuomintang Congress.
694. **181.** $1 multicoloured .. 35 10

**1969.**
695ab **182** $10 blue .. .. 1·75 10
695c $14 red .. .. 1·50 10
696ab $20 brown .. .. 2·25 10
697ab $50 green .. .. 5·50 10
698ab $100 red .. .. 6·50 10
Type **182** is a redrawn version of Type **138**.

**1969.** "A City of Cathay" (scroll). (2nd series). As T **171**. Multicoloured.
699. $1 "Musicians" .. .. 20 10
700. $1 "Bridal chair" .. 20 10
701. $2.50 Emigrants with ox-car 55 60
702. $5 "Scroll gallery" .. 2·75 45
703. $8 "Roadside cafe" .. 4·75 60
Nos. 699/70 form a composite picture of a bridal procession.

**184.** I.L.O. Emblem. **185.** "Food and Clothing".

**1969.** 50th Anniv. of I.L.O.
704. **184.** $1 blue .. .. 25 10
705 $8 red .. .. 40 20

**1969.** "Model Citizen's Life" Movement.
706. **185.** $1 red .. .. .. 10 10
707. – $2.50 blue .. .. 35 15
708. – $4 green .. .. 35 15
DESIGNS: $2.50, "Housekeeping and Road Safety". $4, "Schooling and Recreation".

**186.** Bean Geese over Mountains. **187.** Children and Symbols of Learning.

**1969.** Air. Multicoloured.
709. $2.50 Type **186** .. 2·75 60
710. $5 Bean geese over sea .. 2·50 25
711. $8 Bean geese over land .. 2·75 25
No. 711 is horiz.

**1969.** 1st Anniv. of Nine-Year Free Education System.
712. **187.** $1 red .. .. .. 15 10
713. – $2.50 green .. .. 25 15
714. – $4 blue .. .. 35 15
715. **187.** $5 brown .. .. 40 20
DESIGNS—VERT. $2.50 and $4, Children and school.

**188.** "Flowers and Ring-necked Pheasants", Ming dynasty (Lu Chih). **189.** "Charles Mallerin" Rose.

**1969.** Ancient Chinese Paintings from Palace Museum Collection (4th series). Birds and Flowers. Multicoloured.
716. $1 Type **188** .. .. 1·25 10
717. $2.50 "Bamboos and Ring-necked Pheasants" Sung dynasty (artist unknown) .. .. 2·25 15
718. $5 "Flowers and Birds" Sung dynasty (artist unknown) .. .. 5·00 40
719. $8 "Two Manchurian Cranes and Flowers" Ching dynasty (G. Castiglione) .. .. 5·00 60

**1969.** Roses. Multicoloured.
720. $1 Type **189** .. .. 1·10 10
721. $2.50 "Golden Sceptre" 1·60 20
722. $5 "Peace" .. .. 2·25 30
723. $8 "Josephine Bruce" .. 3·25 25

**190.** Launching Missile. **191.** A.P.U. Emblem.

**1969.** 30th Air Defence Day.
724 **190** $1 purple .. .. 50 10

**1969.** 5th Asian Parliamentarians' Union General Assembly, Taipeh.
725. **191.** $1 red .. .. .. 20 10
726. $5 green .. .. 35 15

**192.** Pekingese Dogs. **193.** Satellite and Earth Station.

**1969.** New Year Greetings. "Year of the Dog".
727. **192.** 50 c. multicoloured .. 2·50 10
728. $4.50 multicoloured .. 4·00 65

**1969.** Inaug. of Satellite Earth Station, Yangmingshan.
729. **193.** $1 multicoloured .. 50 10
730. $5 multicoloured .. 75 20
731. $8 multicoloured .. 1·75 30

**1970.** Chinese Art Treasures, National Palace Museum (3rd series). Multicoloured as T **168**.
732 $1 Lacquer vase (Ching dynasty) .. .. 75 10
733 $1.50 Agate grinding-stone (Ching dynasty) (horiz) 1·50 15
734 $2 Jade carving (Ching dynasty) (horiz) .. 1·50 10
735 $2.50 "Shepherd and Ram" jade carving (Han dynasty) (horiz) .. 1·75 15
736 $4 Porcelain jar (Ching dynasty) .. .. 1·75 15
737 $5 "Bull" porcelain urn (Northern Sung dynasty) 2·00 35

**1970.** Famous Chinese. Portraits as T **132**.
738. $1 red .. .. .. 1·00 10
739. $2.50 green .. .. 2·75 15
740. $4 blue .. .. 1·00 20
PORTRAITS: $1, Hsuan Chuang (traveller). $2.50, Hua To (physician). $4, Chu Hsi (philosopher).

**194.** Taiwan Pavilion and EXPO Emblem. **195.** Chungshan Building, Yangmingshan.

**1970.** World Fair "EXPO 70", Osaka, Japan. Multicoloured.
741. $5 Type **194** .. .. 60 15
742. $8 Pavilion encircled by national flags .. .. 1·00 25

**1970.**
743. **195.** $1 red .. .. .. 30 20
For redrawn design see No 1039.

**196.** Rain-cloud, Palm and Recording apparatus. **197.** Martyrs' Shrine.

**1970.** World Meteorological Day. Mult.
744. $1 Type **196** .. .. 30 10
745. $8 "Nimbus 3" satellite (horiz.) .. .. .. 70 25

**1970.** Revolutionary Martyrs' Shrine. Mult.
746. $1 Type **197** .. .. 45 10
747. $8 Shrine gateway .. 85 25

**198.** General Yueh Fei ("Loyalty").

**1970.** Chinese Opera. "The Virtues". Multicoloured.

748. $1 Type **198** .. .. 1·75 10
749. $2.50 Emperor Shun tortured by stepmother ("Filial Piety") .. 2·50 20
750. $5 Chin Liang-yu "The Lady General" ("Chastity") .. .. 2·75 20
751. $8 Kuan Yu and groom ("Fidelity") .. .. 3·75 30

**199.** Three Horses at Play.

**1970.** "One Hundred Horses" (handscroll by Lang Shi-ning (G. Castiglione)). Multicoloured.

752. $1 (1) Horses on plain .. 10 10
753. $1 (2) Horses on plain (different) .. .. 10 10
754. $1 (3) Horses playing .. 10 10
755. $1 (4) Horses on river bank 10 10
756. $1 (5) Horses crossing river 10 10
757. $5 Type **199** .. .. 2·75 45
758. $8 Groom roping horses .. 3·75 20

**SERIAL NUMBERS** are indicated to aid identification of the above and certain other sets. For key to Chinese numerals see table at the beginning of CHINA.

**200.** Old Lai-tsu dropping Buckets.

**201.** Chiang Kai-shek's Moon Message.

**1970.** Chinese Folk-tales. (1st series). Mult.

759. 10 c. Type **200** .. .. 10 10
760. 10 c. Yien-tsu disguised as a deer .. .. 10 10
761. 10 c. Hwang Hsiang with fan .. .. .. 10 10
762. 10 c. Wang Shiang fishing 10 10
763. 10 c. Chu Hsiu-chang reunited with mother .. 10 10
764. 50 c. Emperor Wen tasting mother's medicine .. 20 10
765. $1 Lu Chi dropping oranges 30 15
766. $1 Yang Hsiang fighting tiger .. .. .. 30 15

See also Nos. 817/24, 1000/7, 1064/7, 1210/13 and 1312/15.

**1970.** 1st Man on the Moon. Multicoloured.

767. $1 Type **201** .. .. 35 10
768. $5 "Apollo 11" astronauts (horiz.) .. .. 65 15
769. $8 "First step on the Moon" .. .. .. 1·25 30

**202.** Productivity Symbol.

**203.** Flags of Taiwan and United Nations.

**1970.** Asian Productivity Year.

770. **202.** $1 multicoloured .. 35 10
771. $5 multicoloured .. 65 15

**1970.** 25th Anniv. of United Nations.

772. **203.** $5 multicoloured .. 95 25

**204.** Postal Zone Map.

**205.** "Cultural Activities" (10th month).

**1970.** Postal Zone Numbers Campaign. Multicoloured.

773. $1 Type **204** .. .. 60 10
774. $2.50 Postal Zone emblem (horiz.) .. .. 70 15

**1970.** "Occupations of the Twelve Months" Hanging Scrolls. Multicoloured.

(a) "Winter".

775 $1 Type **205** .. .. 2·50 10
776 $2.50 "School Buildings" (11th month) .. .. 3·50 75
777 $5 "Games in the Snow" (12th month) .. .. 6·00 50

(b) "Spring".

778 $1 "Lantern Festival" (1st month) .. .. .. 2·00 10
779 $2.50 "Apricots in Blossom" (2nd month) .. 2·50 70
780 $5 "Purification Ceremony" (3rd month) .. 2·75 35

(c) "Summer".

781 $1 "Summer Shower" (4th month) .. .. .. 2·00 10
782 $2.50 "Dragon boat Festival" (5th month) .. 2·75 70
783 $5 "Lotus Pond" (6th month) .. .. .. 2·75 35

(d) "Autumn".

784 $1 "Weaver Festival" (7th month) .. .. .. 2·50 10
785 $2.50 "Moon Festival" (8th month) .. .. .. 3·25 75
786 $5 "Chrysanthemum Blossom" (9th month) .. 4·50 35

The month numbers are given by the Chinese characters in brackets, which follow the face value on the stamps.

**206.** "Planned Family".

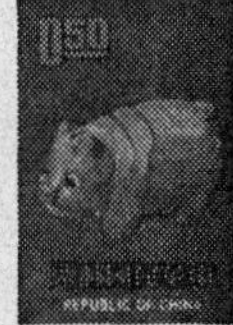

**207.** Toy Pig.

**1970.** Family Planning. Multicoloured.

787. $1 Type **206** .. .. 35 10
788. $4 "Family excursion" (vert.) .. .. .. 75 15

**1970.** New Year Greetings. "Year of the Boar".

789. **207.** 50 c. multicoloured .. 1·75 10
790. $4.50 multicoloured .. 3·00 60

**208.** Chungshan Building, Yangmingshan.

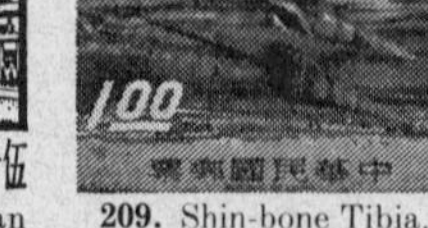

**209.** Shin-bone Tibia.

**1971.**

791. **208.** 5 c. brown .. .. 15 10
792. 10 c. green .. .. 15 10
793. 50 c. red .. .. 25 10
794. $1 red .. .. .. 25 10
795. $1.50 blue .. .. 75 10
796. $2 purple .. .. 1·75 10
797. $2.50 green .. .. 2·25 10
798. $3 blue .. .. 2·25 10

Type **208** is a redrawn version of Type **163**.

**1971.** Taiwan Shells. Multicoloured.

799 $1 Type **209** .. .. 1·00 10
800 $2.50 Kuroda's lyria .. 1·10 20
801 $5 "Conus stupa kuroda" 1·50 30
802 $8 Rumphius's slit shell .. 3·00 15

**210.** Savings Book and Certificate.

**211.** Chinese greeting African Farmer.

**1971.** National Savings Campaign. Mult.

803. $1 Type **210** .. .. 35 10
804. $4 Hand dropping coin in savings bank .. .. 55 20

**1971.** 10th Anniv. of Sino-African Technical Co-operation Committee. Multicoloured.

805. $1 Type **211** .. .. 25 10
806. $8 Rice-growing (horiz.) .. 50 25

**212.** Red and White Flying Squirrel.

**213.** Pitcher delivering ball.

**1971.** Taiwan Animals. Multicoloured.

807. $1 Taiwan macaque (vert.) 55 10
808. $2 Type **212** .. .. 1·00 40
809. $3 Chinese pangolin .. 1·50 50
810 $5 Sika deer .. .. 1·75 55

**1971.** World Little League Baseball Championships, Taiwan. Multicoloured.

811. $1 Type **213** .. .. 15 10
812. $2.50 Players at base (horiz.) 20 15
813. $4 Striker and catcher .. 35 15

(214.)

**215.** 60th Anniv Emblem and Flag.

**1971.** Tainan Giants' Victory in World Little League Baseball Championships. Optd with T **214**.

814. **163.** $1 red .. .. .. 15 10
815. $2.50 blue .. .. 30 20
816. $3 blue .. .. 25 20

**1971.** Chinese Folk-tales (2nd series). As T **200**. Multicoloured.

817. 10 c. Yu Hsun and elephant 10 10
818. 10 c. Tsai Hsun with mulberries .. .. .. 10 10
819. 10 c. Tseng Sun with firewood .. .. .. 10 10
820. 10 c. Kiang Keh and bandits 10 10
821. 10 c. Tsu Lu with sack of rice .. .. .. 10 10
822. 50 c. Meng Chung gathering bamboo shoots .. .. 25 10
823. $1 Tung Yung and wife .. 75 20
824. $1 Tzu Chien shivering with cold .. .. .. 75 20

**1971.** 60th National Day. Multicoloured.

825. $1 Type **215** .. .. 30 10
826. $2.50 National anthem, map and flag .. .. 40 10
827. $5 Pres. Chiang Kai-shek, constitution and flag .. 55 30
828. $8 Dr. Sun Yat-sen, "Three Principles" and flag .. 65 30

**216.** A.O.P.U. Emblem.

**217.** "White Frost Hawk".

**1971.** Asian-Oceanic Postal Union Executive Committee Session, Taipeh.

829. **216.** $2.50 multicoloured .. 35 30
830. $5 multicoloured .. 35 15

**1971.** "Ten Prized Dogs" (paintings on silk by Lang Shih-ning (G. Castiglione)). Multicoloured.

831. $1 Type **217** .. .. 75 10
832. $1 "Black Dog with Snow-white Claws" .. .. 2·50 10
833. $2 "Star-glancing Wolf" 1·25 10
834. $2 "Yellow Leopard" .. 3·50 10
835. $2.50 "Golden-winged Face" 1·50 85
836. $2.50 "Flying Magpie" .. 7·50 85
837. $5 "Young Black Dragon" 2·75 75
838. $5 "Heavenly Lion" .. 7·50 75
839. $8 "Young Grey Dragon" 3·00 65
840. $8 "Mottle-coated Tiger" 8·50 65

**218/221.** Squirrels.

**1971.** New Year Greetings. "Year of the Rat".

841. **218.** 50 c. multicoloured .. 20 10
842. **219.** 50 c. multicoloured .. 20 10
843. **220.** 50 c. multicoloured .. 20 10
844. **221.** 50 c. multicoloured .. 20 10
845. **218.** $4.50 multicoloured .. 75 40
846. **219.** $4.50 multicoloured .. 75 40
847. **220.** $4.50 multicoloured .. 75 40
848. **221.** $4.50 multicoloured .. 75 40

**222.** Flags of Taiwan and Jordan.

**1971.** 50th Anniv. of Hashemite Kingdom of Jordan.

849. **222.** $5 multicoloured .. 50 15

**223.** Freighter "Hai King".

**1971.** Centenary of China Merchants Steam Navigation Company. Multicoloured.

850. **223.** $4 blue, red & green .. 60 40
851. – $7 multicoloured .. 80 25

DESIGN—VERT. $7, Liner on Pacific.

**224.** Downhill Skiing.

**1972.** Winter Olympic Games, Sapporo, Japan.

852. **224.** $1 blk., yell. and blue 15 10
853. – $5 black, orge. & grn. 45 15
854. – $8 blk., red & grey .. 50 20

DESIGNS: $5, Cross-country skiing, $8, Giant slalom.

**225.** Yung Cheng Vase.

**226.** Doves.

**1972.** Chinese Porcelain. (1st series). Ch'ing Dynasty. Multicoloured.

855. $1 Type **225** .. .. 60 10
856. $2 Kang Hsi jar .. 1·10 25
857. $2.50 Yung Cheng jug .. 1·25 30
858. $5 Chien Lung vase .. 1·50 20
859. $8 Chien Lung jar .. 2·25 25

See also Nos. 914/18, 927/31 and 977/81.

**1972.** 10th Anniv. of Asian-Oceanic Postal Union.

860. **226.** $1 black and blue .. 50 10
861. $5 black and violet .. 75 25

227. " Dignity with Self-Reliance " (Pres. Chiang Kai-shek).

229. First Day Covers.

228. Mounted Messengers.

**1972.**

862 **227** 5 c. brown and yellow 15 10
863 10 c. blue and orange 10 10
863b 20 c. purple and green 20 10
864 50 c. mauve & purple 20 10
865 $1 red and blue .. 10 10
866 $1.50 yellow and blue 20 10
867 $2 violet, pur & orge 20 10
868 $2.50 green and red .. 50 10
869 $3 red and green .. 35 10

**1972.** "The Emperor's Procession" (Ming dynasty handscrolls). Multicoloured.

(a) First issue.

870. $1 (1) Pagoda and crowds 10 10
871. $1 (2) Seven carriages .. 10 10
872. $1 (3) Emperor's coach .. 10 10
873. $1 (4) Horsemen with flags 10 10
874. $1 (5) Horsemen and Emperor 10 10
875. $2.50 Type **228** .. .. 2·50 25
876. $5 Guards .. .. .. 2·50 25
877. $8 Imperial sedan chair .. 2·50 20

(b) Second issue.

878. $1 (1) Three ceremonial barges .. .. .. 10 10
879. $1 (2) Sedan chairs .. 10 10
880. $1 (3) Two ceremonial barges 10 10
881. $1 (4) Horsemen and mounted orchestra .. 10 10
882. $1 (5) Two carriages .. 10 10
883. $2.50 City gate .. .. 2·50 25
884. $5 Mounted orchestra .. 2·50 25
885. $8 Ceremonial barge .. 5·00 30

Nos. 870/4 are numbered from right to left and Nos. 878/82 are numbered from left to right. They were each issued together, se-tenant, forming composite designs showing the departure of the procession from the palace and its return.

Nos. 875/7 and 883/5 show enlarged details from the scrolls.

See also Nos. 937/50 and 1040/7.

**1972.** Philately Day.

886. **229.** $1 blue .. .. 15 10
887. – $2.50 green .. .. 15 15
888. – $8 red .. .. .. 40 15

DESIGNS—VERT. $2.50, Magnifying glass and stamps. HORIZ. $8, Magnifying glass, perforation-gauge and tweezers.

(230.) 231. Emperor Yao.

**1972.** Taiwan's Victories in Senior and Little World Baseball Leagues. Nos. 865/7 and 869 optd. with T **230**.

889. **227.** $1 red and blue .. 15 10
890. $1.50 yellow & blue .. 25 20
891. $2 violet, pur. & orge. 25 15
892. $3 red and green .. 25 20

**1972.** Chinese Cultural Heroes.

893. **231.** $3.50 blue .. .. 35 30
894. – $4 red .. .. .. 35 10
895. – $4.50 violet .. .. 40 20
896. – $5 green .. .. 40 10
897. – $5.50 purple .. .. 1·10 35
898. – $6 orange .. .. 1·10 30
899. – $7 brown .. .. 1·25 10
900. – $8 blue .. .. 1·25 15

DESIGNS: $4, Emperor Shun. $4.50, Yu the Great. $5, King T'ang. $5.50, King Weng. $6, King Wu. $7, Chou Kung. $8, Confucius.

232. Mountaineering.

233. Microwave Systems and Electronic Sorting Machine.

**1972.** 20th Anniv. of China Youth Corps. Multicoloured.

902. $1 Type **232** .. .. 25 10
903. $2.50 Winter sport .. 35 10
904. $4 Diving .. .. .. 45 15
905. $8 Parachuting .. .. 75 25

**1972.** Improvement of Communications.

906. **233.** $1 red .. .. .. 20 10
907. – $2.50 blue .. .. 40 20
908. – $5 purple .. .. 75 30

DESIGNS—HORIZ. $2.50, Boeing 727 airliner and container ship. $5, Diesel railcar and motorway.

234. " Eyes " and J.C.I. Emblem.

235. Cow and Calf.

**1972.** 27th World Congress of Junior Chamber International, Taipeh.

909. **234.** $1 multicoloured .. 15 10
910. $5 multicoloured .. 30 20
911. $8 multicoloured .. 30 30

**1972.** New Year Greetings. "Year of the Ox".

912. **235.** 50 c. black and red .. 2·00 10
913. $4.50 brn., red & yell. 2·75 50

**1973.** Chinese Porcelain (2nd series). Ming Dynasty. As T **225**. Multicoloured.

914. $1 Fu vase .. .. 1·00 10
915. $2 Floral vase .. .. 1·50 10
916. $2.50 Ku vase .. .. 1·75 20
917. $5 Hu flask .. .. 2·00 30
918. $8 Garlic-head vase .. 3·25 30

236. " Kicking the Shuttlecock ".

237. Bamboo Sampan.

**1973.** Chinese Folklore (1st series). Mult.

919. $1 Type **236** .. .. 30 10
920. $4 "The fisherman and the Oyster-fairy" (horiz.) 75 15
921. $5 "Lady in a Boat (horiz.) 75 15
922. $8 "The Old Man and the Lady" .. .. .. 1·00 35

See also Nos. 982/3 and 1037/8.

**1973.** Taiwan Handicrafts (1st series). Mult.

923. $1 Type **237** .. .. 45 10
924. $2.50 Marble vase (vert.) 65 10
925. $5 Glass plate .. .. 70 15
926. $8 Aborigine Doll (vert.).. 75 25

See also Nos. 988/91.

**1973.** Chinese Porcelain (3rd series). Ming Dynasty. Horiz. designs as T **225**. Mult.

927. $1 Dragon stem-bowl .. 60 10
928. $2 Dragon pot .. .. 85 10
929. $2.50 Covered jar with lotus decor .. .. 1·50 10
930. $5 Covered jar showing horses .. .. 1·50 15
931. $8 " Immortals " bowl .. 1·75 15

238. Contractors' Equipment.

239. Pres. Chiang Kai-shek and Flag.

**1973.** 12th Convention of Int. Federation of Asian and Western Pacific Contractors' Association.

932. **238.** $1 multicoloured .. 15 10
933. – $5 blue and black .. 35 15

DESIGN—HORIZ. $5, Bulldozer.

**1973.** Inauguration of Pres. Chiang Kai-shek's 5th Term of Office.

934. **239.** $1 multicoloured .. 30 10
935. $4 multicoloured .. 45 15

240. Lin Tse-hsu (statesman).

**1973.** Lin Tse-hsu Commemoration.

936. **240.** $1 purple .. .. 25 10

**1973.** "Spring Morning in the Han Palace" (Ming dynasty handscroll). As T **228**. Mult.

(a) First issue.

937 $1 (1) Palace gate .. 10 10
938 $1 (2) Feeding green pea-fowl .. .. .. 40 10
939 $1 (3) Emperor's wife .. 10 10
940 $1 (4) Ladies and pear tree 10 10
941 $1 (5) Music pavilion .. 10 10
942 $5 Giant rock (vert) 3·00 50
943 $8 Lady musicians (vert) 3·50 20

(b) Second issue.

944 $1 (6) Game with flowers 10 10
945 $1 (7) Leisure room .. 10 10
946 $1 (8) Ladies with teapots 10 10
947 $1 (9) Artist at work .. 10 10
948 $1 (10) Palace wall and guards .. .. .. 10 10
949 $5 Playing game at table (vert) .. .. 3·00 50
950 $8 Swatting insect (vert) 3·50 20

Nos. 937/41 and 944/8 are numbered from right to left and were each issued together, se-tenant. When the two strips are placed side by side, they form a composite design showing the complete handscroll.

Nos. 942/3 and 949/50 show enlarged details from the scroll.

241. " Bamboo " (Hsiang Te-hsin).

**1973.** Ancient Chinese Fan Paintings. (1st series). Multicoloured.

951. $1 Type **241** .. .. 70 10
952. $2.50 " Flowers " (Sun K'O-Hung) .. .. 1·25 10
953. $5 "Landscape" (Ch'iu Ying) 1·50 20
954. $8 " Seated Figure and Tree " (Shen Chou) .. 1·75 20

See also Nos. 1052/5.

243. Emblem of World Series.

245. Interpol Emblem.

**1973.** Little League World Baseball Series. Taiwan Victory in Twin Championships.

955. **243.** $1 blue, red and yellow 50 10
956. $4 blue, green & yell. 75 15

**1973.** 50th Anniv. of International Criminal Police Organization (Interpol).

957. **245.** $1 blue and orange .. 20 10
958. $5 green and orange .. 40 15
959. $8 purple and orange 55 25

**1973.** Famous Chinese. Portrait as T **132.**

960. $1 violet (Ch'iu Feng-chia (poet)) .. .. .. 55 10

246. Dam and Power Station.

**1973.** Opening of Tsengwen Reservoir. Multicoloured.

961. $1 Upper section of reservoir .. .. .. 10 10
962. $1 Middle section of reservoir .. .. .. 10 10
963. $1 Lower section of reservoir .. .. .. 10 10
964. $5 Type **246** (30 × 22 mm.) 75 25
965. $8 Spillway (50 × 22 mm.) 95 15

The $1 values together show complete map of reservoir (each 38 × 26 mm.).

247. " Snow-dotted Eagle ".

**1973.** Paintings of Horses. Multicoloured.

966. 50 c. Type **247** .. .. 10 10
967. $1 " Comfortable Ride " .. 10 10
968. $1 " Red Flower Eagle " .. 10 10
969. $1 " Cloud-running Steed " 10 10
970. $1 " Sky-running Steed " 10 10
971. $2.50 " Red Jade Steed " 2·50 25
972. $5 " Thunder-clap Steed " 4·00 25
973. $8 " Arabian Champion " 5·00 20

248. Tiger.

249. Road Tunnel Taroko Gorge.

**1973.** New Year Greetings. " Year of the Tiger ".

975. **248.** 50 c. multicoloured .. 60 10
976. $4.50 multicoloured .. 1·40 30

**1974.** Chinese Porcelain (4th series). Sung Dynasty. As T **225.** Multicoloured.

977. $1 Ko vase .. .. .. 60 10
978. $2 Kuan vase (horiz.) .. 60 10
979 $2.50 Ju bowl (horiz.) .. 85 20
980. $5 Kuan incense burner (horiz.) .. .. .. 95 20
981. $8 Chun incense burner (horiz.) .. .. .. 1·10 20

**1974.** Chinese Folklore (2nd series). As T **236.** Multicoloured.

982. $1 Balancing pot .. .. 35 10
983. $8 Magicians (horiz.) .. 75 20

**1974.** Taiwan Scenery (1st series). Mult.

984. $1 T **249** .. .. 45 10
985. $2.50 Luce Chapel, Tungai University .. .. 55 10
986. $5 Tzu En Pagoda, Sun Moon Lake .. .. 75 15
987. $8 Goddess of Mercy Statue, Keelung .. 95 15

See also Nos. 992/5.

**1974.** Taiwan Handicrafts (2nd series). As T **237.** Multicoloured.

988. $1 " Fighting Cocks " (brass) 25 10
989. $2.50 " Fruits " (jade) .. 35 15
990. $5 " Fisherman " (wood-carving) (vert.) .. .. 45 15
991. $8 " Bouquet of Flowers " (plastic) vert.) .. .. 65 15

**1974.** Taiwan Scenery (2nd series). As T **249** but all horiz. Multicoloured.

992. $1 Dr. Sun Yat-Sen Memorial Hall, Taipeh .. .. 35 10
993. $2.50 Reaching-Moon Tower, Cheng Ching Lake .. 45 10
994. $5 Seashore, Lanyu .. 60 15
995. $8 Inter-island bridge, Penghu .. .. .. 85 15

250. Pres. Chiang Kai-shek.

251. Long-distance Runner.

**1974.** 50th Anniv. of Chinese Military Academy.

996 **250** $1 mauve .. .. 25 10
997 – $14 blue .. .. 75 30

DESIGN—VERT. $14, Cadets on parade.

**1974.** 80th Anniv. of Int. Olympic Committee.

998. **251.** $1 blue, black & red .. 15 10
999. – $8 multicoloured .. 45 15

DESIGN: $8, Female relay runner.

**1974.** Chinese Folk tales (3rd series). As T **200.** Multicoloured.

1000. 50 c. Wen Yen-po retrieving ball .. .. .. 10 10
1001. 50 c. T'i Ying pleading for mercy .. .. .. 10 10
1002. 50 c. Wang Ch'i in battle 10 10
1003. 50 c. Wang Hua returning gold .. .. .. 10 10
1004. $1 Pu Shih offering sheep to the emperor .. 10 10
1005. $1 Szu Ma Kuang saving playmate from water-jar 10 10
1006. $1 Tung Yu at study .. 10 10
1007. $1 K'ung Yung selecting the smallest pear .. 10 10

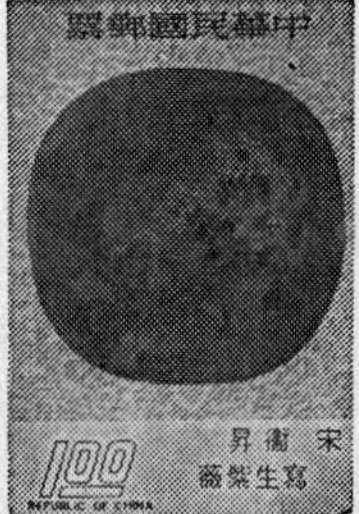

252. " Crape Myrtle " (Wei Sheng).

**1974.** Ancient Chinese Moon-shaped Fan-paintings (1st series). Multicoloured.

1008. $1 Type **252** .. .. 75 10
1009. $2.50 "White Cabbage and Insects" (Hsu Ti) 85 20
1010. $5 "Hibiscus and Rock" (Li Ti) .. .. .. 1·25 20
1011. $8 "Pomegranates and Narcissus Fly-catcher" (Wu Ping) .. 2·50 40

See also Nos. 1068/71 and 1115/1118.

**253.** " The Battle of Marco Polo Bridge ". **254.** Chrysanthemum.

**1974.** Armed Forces' Day.

1012. **253.** $1 multicoloured .. 35 10

**1974.** Chrysanthemums.

1014. **254.** $1 multicoloured .. 35 10
1015. – $2.50 multicoloured 75 20
1016. – $5 multicoloured .. 1·00 20
1017. – $8 multicoloured .. 1·25 15

DESIGNS: Nos. 1015/17, various chrysanthemums.

**255.** Chinese Pavilion. **256.** Steel Mill, Kaohsiung.

**1974.** "Expo 74" World Fair, Spokane, Washington. Multicoloured.

1018. $1 Type **255** .. .. 15 10
1019. $8 Fairground map .. 35 15

**1974.** Major Construction Projects (1st series). Chinese inscr. in single-line characters, figures of value solid.* Multicoloured.

1020. 50 c. Type **256** .. .. 10 10
1021. $1 Taiwan North link railway .. .. 15 10
1022. $2 Petrochemical works, Kaohsiung .. .. 15 10
1023. $2.50 TRA trunk line electrification .. .. 25 10
1024. $3 Taichung harbour (horiz.) .. .. 20 10
1025. $3.50 Taoyuan international airport (horiz.) 20 10
1026. $4 Taiwan North-south motorway (horiz.) .. 20 10
1027. $4.50 Giant shipyard, Kaohsiung (horiz.) .. 35 25
1028. $5 Su-ao port (horiz.) .. 35 10

*The first series can also be distinguished by the Chinese and English inscr. at the foot being in different colours; in the second and third series only one colour is used.

See also Nos. 1122a/1122i and 1145/1153.

**257.** White Button Mushrooms. **258.** Baseball Strikers.

**1974.** Edible Fungi. Multicoloured.

1029 $1 Type **257** .. .. 95 10
1030 $2.50 Oyster fungus .. 1·25 20
1031 $5 Veiled stinkhorn .. 1·60 30
1032 $8 Golden mushroom .. 1·60 20

**1974.** Taiwan Triple Championship Victories in World Little League Baseball Series, U.S.A. Multicoloured.

1033. $1 Type **258** .. .. 15 10
1034. $8 Player and banners .. 35 15

**259.** Chinese Hare.

**1974.** New Year Greetings. " Year of the Hare ".

1035. **259.** 50 c. multicoloured .. 25 10
1036. $4.50 multicoloured 75 25

**1975.** Chinese Folklore (3rd series). As T **236.** Multicoloured.

1037. $4 Acrobat .. .. 45 15
1038. $5 Jugglers with diabolo 55 20

**260.** Chungshan Building, Yangmingshan. **261.** Sun Yat-Sen Memorial Hall, Taipeh.

**1975.**

1039. **260.** $1 red .. .. 25 15

Type **260** is a redrawn version of Type **195.**

**1975.** " New Year Festivals " (handscroll by Ting Kuan-p'eng). As T **228.** Mult.

1040. $1 (1) Greetings .. .. 10 10
1041. $1 (2) Entertainer .. 10 10
1042. $1 (3) Crowd and musicians 10 10
1043. $1 (4) Picnic .. .. 10 10
1044. $1 (5) Puppet show .. 10 10
1045. $2.50 New Year greetings 2·25 20
1046. $5 Children buying fireworks 3·25 25
1047. $8 Entertainer with monkey and dog .. 4·00 35

Nos. 1040/4 were issued together, se-tenant, forming a composite design.

**1975.** 50th Death Anniv. of Dr. Sun Yat-sen.

1048. $1 Type **261** .. .. 15 10
1049. $4 Sun Yat-Sen's hand-writing .. .. 25 15
1050. $5 Bronze statue of Sun Yat-Sen (vert.) .. 35 15
1051. $8 Sun Yat-Sen Memorial Hall, St. John's University, U.S.A. .. .. 50 15

**1975.** Ancient Chinese Fan Paintings (2nd series). As T **241.** Multicoloured.

1052. $1 " Landscape " (Li Liu-fang) .. .. 75 10
1053. $2.50 " Landscape " (Wen Cheng-ming) .. 75 20
1054. $5 " Landscape " (Chou Ch'en) .. .. 1·00 20
1055. $8 " Landscape " (T'ang Yin) .. .. 1·25 15

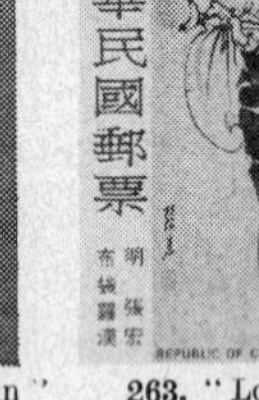

**262.** " Yuan-chin " Coin (Chou dynasty). **263.** " Lohan, the Cloth-bag Monk " (Chang Hung).

**1975.** Ancient Chinese Coins. (1st series). Multicoloured.

1056. $1 Type **262** .. .. 40 10
1057. $4 " Pan-liang " coin (Chin dynasty) .. 75 15
1058. $5 " Five chu " coin (Han dynasty) .. .. 85 15
1059. $8 " Five chu " coin (Liang dynasty) .. 1·00 10

See also Nos. 1111/14 and 1184/7.

**1975.** Ancient Chinese Figure Paintings. Multicoloured.

1060. $2 Type **263** .. .. 65 10
1061. $4 " Lao-tzu on buffalo " (Chao Pu-chih) .. 1·50 15
1062. $5 " Shih-te " (Wang-wen) .. .. 2·00 15
1063. $8 " Splashed-ink Immortal " (Liang K'ai) .. 2·00 15

**1975.** Chinese Folk-tales (4th series). As T **200.** Multicoloured.

1064. $1 Chu-Yin reading by light of fireflies .. 15 10
1065. $2 Hua Mu-lan going to battle disguised as a man 25 10
1066. $2 Ling Kou Chien living a humble life .. 25 10
1067. $5 Chou Ch'u defeating the tiger .. .. 75 25

**1975. Ancient Chinese Moon-shaped Fan Paintings (2nd series). As T 252. Mult.**

1068. $1 " Cherry-apple blossoms " (Lin Ch'un) .. .. 60 10
1069. $2 " Spring blossoms and a colourful butterfly " (Ma K'uei) .. .. 75 10
1070. $5 " Monkeys and deer " (I Yuan-chi) .. .. 95 20
1071. $8 " Tree sparrows among bamboo " (anon.) .. 2·50 40

**1975.** Famous Chinese. Martyrs of War against Japan. Portraits as T **132.**

1072 $2 red (Gen. Chang Tzu-chung) .. .. 25 10
1073 $2 brown (Maj.-Gen. Kao Chih-hang) .. 25 10
1074 $2 green (Capt. Sha Shih-chiun) .. .. 25 10
1075 $5 brown (Maj-Gen. Hsieh Chin-yuan) .. 40 15
1076 $5 blue (Lt. Yen Hai-wen) 40 15
1077 $5 blue (Lt.-Gen. Tai An-lan) .. .. 40 15

**264.** " Lotus Pond with Willows ".

**1975.** Madame Chiang Kai-Shek's Landscape Paintings (1st series). Multicoloured.

1078. $2 Type **264** .. .. 1·00 10
1079. $5 " Sun breaks through Mountain Clouds " .. 1·50 30
1080. $8 " A Pair of Pine Trees " 2·75 40
1081. $10 " Fishing and Farming " 3·50 55

See also Nos. 1139/1142 and 1727/30.

**265.** Rectangular Cauldron. **266.** Dragon, Nine-Dragon Wall, Peihai.

**1975.** Ancient Bronzes (1st series). Mult.

1082. $2 Type **265** .. .. 40 10
1083. $5 Cauldron with " Phoenix " handles (horiz.) .. 60 15
1084. $8 Flat jar (horiz.) .. 85 25
1085. $10 Wine vessel .. .. 1·00 30

See also Nos. 1119/1122.

**1975.** New Year Greetings. " Year of the Dragon ".

1086. **266.** $1 multicoloured .. 35 10
1087. $5 multicoloured .. 75 20

**267.** Techi Dam. **268.** Biathlon.

**1975.** Completion of Techi Reservoir. Mult.

1088. $2 Type **267** .. .. 20 10
1089. $10 Dam and reservoir .. 45 30

**1976.** Winter Olympic Games, Innsbruck. Multicoloured.

1090 $2 Type **268** .. .. 20 10
1091 $5 Luge .. .. .. 30 15
1092 $8 Skiing .. .. 40 15

**269.** " Chin ".

**1976.** Chinese Musical Instruments (1st series). Multicoloured.

1093 $2 Type **269** .. .. 40 10
1094 $5 "Se" (string instrument) .. .. 60 10
1095 $8 "Standing Kong-ho" (harp) .. .. 70 15
1096 $10 "Sleeping Kong-ho" (harp) .. .. 85 20

See also Nos. 1156/9.

**270.** Postman collecting Mail.

**1976.** 80th Anniv. of Chinese Postal Service. Multicoloured.

1097. $2 Type **270** .. .. 20 10
1098. $5 Mail-sorting systems (vert.) .. .. 30 15
1099. $8 Mail transport (vert.) 50 15
1100. $10 Traditional and modern post deliveries 70 20

**MINIMUM PRICE**

The minimum price quoted is 10p which represents a handling charge rather than a basis for valuing common stamps. For further notes about prices see introductory pages.

**271.** Pres. Chiang Kai-shek.

**1976.** 1st Death Anniv. of President Chiang Kai-shek. Multicoloured.

1102. $2 Type **271** .. .. 20 10
1103. $2 People paying homage (horiz.) .. .. 20 10
1104. $2 Lying-in-state (horiz.) 20 10
1105. $2 Start of funeral procession (horiz.) .. 20 10
1106. $5 Roadside obeisance (horiz.) .. .. 30 15
1107. $8 Altar, Tzuhu Guest-house (horiz.) .. 40 20
1108. $10 Tzuhu Guest-house (horiz.) .. .. 60 25

**272.** Chinese and U.S. Flags. **273.** " Kung Shou Pu" Coin (Shang/Chou Dynasties).

**1976.** Bicent. of American Revolution.

1109. **272.** $2 multicoloured .. 15 10
1110. $10 multicoloured .. 35 25

**1976.** Ancient Chinese Coins (2nd series). Multicoloured.

1111. $2 Type **273** .. .. 40 10
1112. $5 " Chien Tsu Pu " coin (Chao Kingdom) .. 50 15
1113. $8 " Yuan Tsu Pu " coin (Tsin Kingdom) .. 75 20
1114. $10 " Fang Tsu Pu " coin (Chin/Han Dynasties) 95 25

**1976.** Ancient Chinese Moon-shaped Fan-paintings (3rd series). As T **252.** Mult.

1115. $2 "Hibiscus" (Li Tung) 40 10
1116. $5 "Lilies" (Lin Chun) .. 75 15
1117. $8 "Two Sika Deer, Mushrooms and Pine" (Mou Chung-fu) .. 1·25 30
1118. $10 "Wild Flowers and Japanese Quail" (Li An-chung) .. .. 2·50 45

**1976.** Ancient Bronzes (2nd series). As T **265.** Multicoloured.

1119. $2 Square cauldron .. 45 10
1120. $5 Round cauldron .. 70 10
1121. $8 Wine vessel .. .. 85 15
1122. $10 Wine vessel with legs 1·00 20

No. 1119 is similar to Type **265,** but has four characters at left only.

**1976.** Major Construction Projects (2nd series). Designs as Nos. 1020/8, but Chinese inscr. in double-lined characters. Figures of value solid. Multicoloured.

1122a. $1 As No. 1021 .. .. 25 10
1122b. $2 As No. 1023 .. .. 25 10
1122c. $3 As No. 1024 .. .. 15 10
1122d. $4 As No. 1026 .. .. 20 10
1122e. $5 As Type **256** .. .. 25 10
1122f. $6 As No. 1025 .. .. 35 10
1122g. $7 As No. 1027 .. .. 35 10
1122h. $8 As No. 1022 .. .. 40 15
1122i. $9 As No. 1028 .. .. 40 20

See also Nos. 1145/53.

**274.** Chiang Kai-shek and Mother.

**1976.** 90th Birth Anniv. of President Chiang Kai-shek. Multicoloured.

1123. $2 Type **274** .. .. 30 10
1124. $5 Chiang Kai-shek .. 30 15
1125. $10 Chiang Kai-shek and Dr. Sun Yat-sen in railway carriage (horiz.) 70 25

**275.** Chinese and KMT Flags.

**1976.** 11th Kuomintang National Congress. Multicoloured.

1126 $2 Type **275** .. .. 15 10
1127 $10 President Chiang Kai-shek and Dr. Sun Yat-sen .. .. .. 35 25

**276.** Brazen Serpent. **277.** "Bird and Plum Blossom" (Ch'en Hung-shou).

**1976.** New Year Greetings. "Year of the Snake".

1129. **276.** $1 multicoloured .. 35 10
1130. $5 multicoloured .. 65 10

**1977.** Ancient Chinese Paintings. "Three Friends of Winter".

1131. $2 Type **277** .. .. 1·00 10
1132. $8 "Wintry Days" (Yang Wei-chen) .. 2·25 25
1133. $10 "Rock and Bamboo" (Hsia Ch'ang) .. .. 2·50 20

**278.** Black-naped Orioles.

**1977.** Taiwan Birds. Multicoloured.

1134. $2 Type **278** .. .. 95 10
1135. $8 Common Kingfisher .. 1·90 50
1136. $10 Pheasant-tailed Jacana 3·25 50

**279.** Emblems of Industry and Commerce.

**1977.** Industry and Commerce Census.

1137. **279.** $2 multicoloured .. 15 10
1138. $10 multicoloured .. 55 20

**280.** "Green Mountains rising into Clouds".

**1977.** Madame Chiang Kai-shek's Landscape Paintings (2nd series). Multicoloured.

1139. $2 Type **280** .. .. 65 10
1140. $5 "Boat amidst Spring's Beauty" .. .. 85 20
1141. $8 "Scholar beside the Rivulet" .. .. 1·25 15
1142. $10 "Green Water rising to meet the Bridge" .. 1·60 30

**281.** W.A.C.L. Emblem. **282.** Steel Mill, Kaohsiung.

**1977.** 10th World Anti-Communist League Conference.

1143. **281.** $2 multicoloured .. 15 10
1144. $10 multicoloured .. 40 15

**1977.** Major Construction Projects (3rd series). Designs as Nos. 1122a/i, but redrawn with double lined figures of value as in T **282.** Multicoloured.

1145 $1 Taiwan North link railway .. .. 25 10
1146 $2 TRA trunk line electrification .. .. 25 10
1147 $3 Taichung harbour (horiz) .. .. 20 10
1148 $4 Taiwan north-south highway (horiz) .. 25 10
1149 $5 Type **282** .. .. 35 10
1150 $6 Taoyuan international airport (horiz) .. 35 10
1151 $7 Giant shipyard, Kaohsiung (horiz) .. .. 40 10
1152 $8 Petrochemical works, Kaohsiung .. .. 50 10
1153 $9 Su-ao port (horiz) .. 60 10

**283.** "Blood Donation".

**1977.** Blood Donation Movement.

1154. **283.** $2 red, black & yellow 20 10
1155. – $10 red and black .. 40 15

DESIGN—VERT. $10, "Blood Transfusion".

**284.** San-hsien. **285.** "Idea leuconoe".

**1977.** Chinese Musical Instruments (2nd series). Multicoloured.

1156 $2 Type **284** .. .. 40 10
1157 $5 Tung-hsiao (wind instrument) .. .. 70 10
1158 $8 Yang-chin (xylophone) 80 12
1159 $10 Pai-hsiao (pipes) .. 90 15

**1977.** Taiwan Butterflies. Multicoloured.

1160 $2 Type **285** .. .. 50 10
1161 $4 Great orange-tip .. 75 20
1162 $6 "Stichophthalma howqua" .. .. 85 25
1163 $10 "Atrophaneura horishanus" .. .. 1·50 15

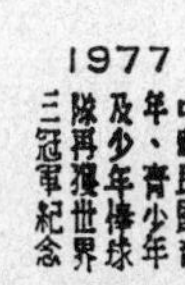

**286.** "National Palace Museum". (**287.**)

**1977.** Children's Drawings. Multicoloured.

1164. $1 Type **286** .. .. 10 10
1165. $2 "Festival of Sea Goddess" 15 10
1166. $4 "Boats on Lan-yu" .. 20 10
1167. $5 "Temple" (vert.) .. 25 10

**1977.** Triple Championships of the 1977 Little League World Baseball Series. Nos. 1146 and 1152 optd. with Type **287.**

1168. $2 multicoloured .. 20 10
1169. $8 multicoloured .. 35 15

**288.** Plate. **289.** Lions Club Emblem.

**1977.** Ancient Chinese Carved Lacquer Ware (1st series). Multicoloured.

1170. $2 Type **288** .. .. 60 10
1171. $5 Bowl .. .. 85 10
1172. $8 Box .. .. 85 10
1173. $10 Three-tiered box .. 1·00 15

See also Nos. 1206/1209.

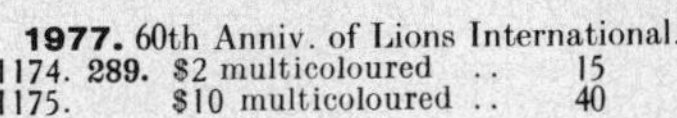

**1977.** 60th Anniv. of Lions International.

1174. **289.** $2 multicoloured .. 15 10
1175. $10 multicoloured .. 40 15

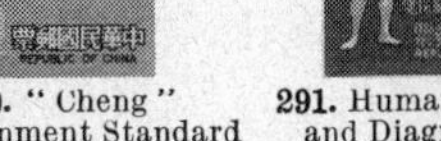

**290.** "Cheng" Government Standard Mark. **291.** Human Figure and Diagram of Heart.

**1977.** Standardization Movement.

1176. **290.** $2 multicoloured .. 15 10
1177. $10 multicoloured .. 40 15

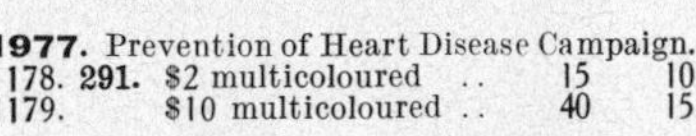

**1977.** Prevention of Heart Disease Campaign.

1178. **291.** $2 multicoloured .. 15 10
1179. $10 multicoloured .. 40 15

**292.** White Horse. **293.** First Page of Constitution.

**1977.** New Year Greetings. "Year of the Horse". Multicoloured.

1180. $1 Type **292** .. .. 50 10
1181 $5 Two horses (horiz.) .. 1·75 15

**1977.** 30th Anniv. of Constitution. Mult.

1182. $2 Type **293** .. .. 15 10
1183. $10 President Chiang accepting constitution 40 20

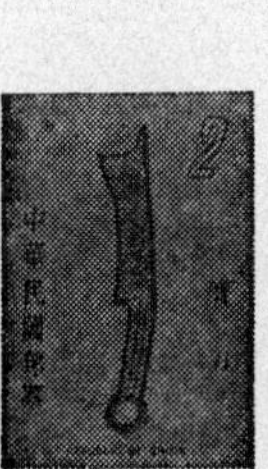

**294.** "Three-character" Knife (Chi State). **295.** 1878 "Dragon" Stamp.

**1978.** Ancient Chinese Coins (3rd series). Multicoloured.

1184. $2 Type **294** .. .. 40 10
1185. $5 Longer sharp-headed knife (Yen State) .. 75 10
1186. $8 Sharp-headed knife (Yet State) .. .. 85 15
1187. $10 Chao or Ming knife 1·10 20

**1978.** Cent. of Chinese Postage Stamp. Mult.

1188. $2 Type **295** .. .. 25 10
1189 $5 "Dr. Sun Yat-sen" stamp, 1941 .. .. 30 10
1190. $10 "Chiang Kai-shek" stamp 1958. .. .. 50 20

**296.** Dr. Sun Yat-sen Memorial Hall.

**1978.** "Rocpex" Taipeh 1978 Philatelic Exhibition. Multicoloured.

1192. $2 Type **296** .. .. 15 10
1193. $10 "Dragon" and 1977 "New Year" stamps 50 20

**297.** Chiang Kai-shek as a Young Man. **298.** Section through Nuclear Reactor.

**1978.** 3rd Death Anniv. of Pres. Chiang Kai-shek. Multicoloured.

1194. $2 Type **297** .. .. 20 10
1195. $5 Chiang on horseback (horiz.) .. .. 35 10
1196. $8 Chiang making speech (horiz.) .. .. 45 15
1197. $10 Reviewing armed forces .. .. .. 60 20

**1978.** Nuclear Power Plant.

1198. **298.** $10 multicoloured .. 40 15

**299.** Letter by Wang Hsi-chih **300.** Human Figure in Polluted Environment.

**1978.** Chinese Calligraphy. Multicoloured.

1199. $2 Type **299** .. .. 75 10
1200. $4 Eulogy of Ni K'uan by Chu Sui-liang .. .. 1·25 15
1201. $6 Inscription on poem "Lake Tai" by Wen Cheng-ming .. .. 1·50 25
1202. $8 Autobiography by Huai-su .. .. 2·50 30
1203. $10 Poem by Ch'ang Piao 5·00 40

**1978.** Cancer Prevention.

1204. **300.** $2 green, yell. & red 15 10
1205. $10 blue, green and deep blue .. .. 30 15

**1978.** Ancient Chinese Carved Lacquer Ware (2nd series). As T **288.** Multicoloured.

1206. $2 Square box .. .. 50 10
1207. $5 Box on legs .. .. 85 10
1208. $8 Round box .. .. 1·25 15
1209. $10 Vase (vert.) .. .. 1·50 20

**1978.** Chinese Folk-tales (5th series). As T **200.** Multicoloured.

1210. $1 Tsu Ti brandishing sword .. .. .. 10 10
1211. $2 Pan Ch'ao throwing down pen .. .. 25 10
1212. $2 Tien Tan's "Fire Bull Battle" .. .. 35 10
1213. $5 Liang Hung-yu as army drummer .. 45 10

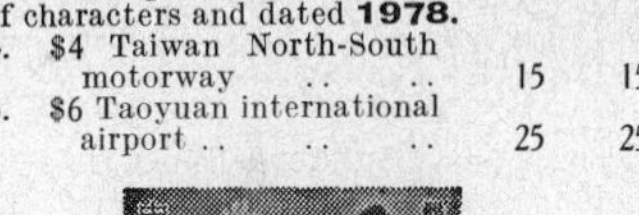

**1978.** Triple Championships of the Little League World Baseball Series. Nos. 1148 and 1150 optd. as T **287,** but with four lines of characters and dated **1978.**

1214. $4 Taiwan North-South motorway .. .. 15 15
1215. $6 Taoyuan international airport .. .. .. 25 25

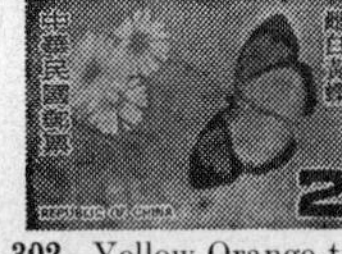

**302.** Yellow Orange-tip.

**1978.** Taiwan Butterflies. Multicoloured.

1216 $2 Type **302** .. .. 50 10
1217 $4 Two-brand crow .. 95 10
1218 $6 Common map butterfly 1·00 15
1219 $10 "Atrophaneura polyeuctes" .. 1·00 25

**303.** Jamboree Badge, Camp and Scout Salute. **304.** Tropical Tomatoes.

**1978.** Taiwanese Boy Scouts' 5th Jamboree.

1220. **303.** $2 multicoloured .. 30 10
1221. $10 multicoloured .. 45 20

**1978.** Asian Vegetable Research and Development Centre. Multicoloured.

1222. $2 Type **304** .. .. 35 10
1223. $10 Tropical tomatoes (diff.) .. .. .. 85 25

305. Aerial View of Bridge.

306. National Flag.

**1978.** Opening of the Sino-Saudi Bridge. Multicoloured.

| | | | |
|---|---|---|---|
| 1224. | $2 Type **305** | 35 | 10 |
| 1225. | $6 Close-up of bridge | 70 | 15 |

**1978.**

| | | | |
|---|---|---|---|
| 1226. **306.** | $1 red and blue | 15 | 10 |
| 1377. | $1 red and blue | 15 | 10 |
| 1378. | $1·50 red, bl. & yell. | 30 | 10 |
| 1227. | $2 red and blue | 15 | 10 |
| 1379. | $2 red, blue & yellow | 15 | 10 |
| 1297. | $3 red, blue & green | 30 | 10 |
| 1380. | $3 red and blue | 20 | 10 |
| 1298. | $4 red, blue & brown | 35 | 15 |
| 1381. | $4 red, blue and light blue | 20 | 10 |
| 1228. | $5 red, blue & green | 20 | 10 |
| 1382. | $5 red, blue & brown | 20 | 10 |
| 1229. | $6 red, blue & orange | 30 | 10 |
| 1300. | $7 red, blue & brown | 35 | 10 |
| 1384. | $7 red, blue & green | 35 | 10 |
| 1230. | $8 red, blue & green | 35 | 10 |
| 1385. | $8 red, bl. & deep red | 30 | 10 |
| 1386. | $9 red, blue & green | 40 | 10 |
| 1231. | $10 red, bl. & light bl. | 55 | 15 |
| 1387. | $10 red, blue & violet | 35 | 10 |
| 1302. | $12 red, blue & mauve | 50 | 25 |
| 1389. | $14 red, blue & green | 75 | 10 |

The $1 values differ in the face value, which is printed in colour on No. 1226, whilst on No. 1377 it is white.

Nos. 1377/8, 1379, 1380, 1381, 1382 and the $6 to $14 values are as Type **306** but have solid background panel to face value and inscr.

307. " Imitation of the Three Sheep by Emperor Hsuan-tsung of the Ming Dynasty " (Emperor Kao-tsung).

308. Boeing 747-100 and Control Building.

**1978.** New Year Greetings. " Year of the Sheep ".

| | | | |
|---|---|---|---|
| 1232. **307.** | $1 multicoloured | 35 | 10 |
| 1233. | $5 multicoloured | 65 | 15 |

**1978.** Completion of Taoyuan International Airport. Multicoloured.

| | | | |
|---|---|---|---|
| 1234. | $2 Type **308** | 25 | 10 |
| 1235. | $10 Passenger terminal building (horiz.) | 40 | 25 |

309. Oracle Bones and Inscription (Yin Dynasty).

**1979.** Origin and Development of Chinese Characters. Multicoloured.

| | | | |
|---|---|---|---|
| 1236. | $2 Type **309** | 50 | 10 |
| 1237. | $5 " Leh-chi " cauldron and inscription (Spring and Autumn period) | 85 | 15 |
| 1238. | $8 Engraved seal and seal-style characters (Western Han dynasty) | 1·10 | 25 |
| 1239. | $10 Square plain-style characters inscribed on stone (Eastern Han dynasty) | 2·00 | 45 |

310. Chihkan Tower, Tainan.

**1979.** Tourism. Multicoloured.

| | | | |
|---|---|---|---|
| 1240. | $2 Type **310** | 25 | 10 |
| 1241. | $5 Confucius Temple, Tainan | 25 | 15 |
| 1242. | $8 Koxinga Shrine, Tainan | 40 | 25 |
| 1243. | $10 Eternal Castle, Tainan | 75 | 30 |

311/314. " Children Playing Games on a Winter Day ".
(Illustration reduced. Overall size 72 × 102 mm.)

**1979.** Sung Dynasty Painting.

| | | | |
|---|---|---|---|
| 1244. **311.** | $5 multicoloured | 1·00 | 25 |
| 1245. **312.** | $5 multicoloured | 1·00 | 25 |
| 1246. **313.** | $5 multicoloured | 1·00 | 25 |
| 1247. **314.** | $5 multicoloured | 1·00 | 25 |

Nos. 1244/7 were printed together, se-tenant, forming the composite design illustrated.

315. Lu Hao-tung (revolutionary).

316. White Jade Brush Washer (Ming dynasty).

**1979.** Famous Chinese.

| | | | |
|---|---|---|---|
| 1249. **315.** | $2 blue | 25 | 10 |

**1979.** Ancient Chinese Jade (1st series). Multicoloured.

| | | | |
|---|---|---|---|
| 1250. | $2 Yellow jade brush holder embossed with clouds and dragons (Sung dynasty) (vert.) | 35 | 10 |
| 1251. | $5 Type **316** | 75 | 15 |
| 1252. | $8 Dark green jade brush washer carved with clouds and dragons (Ch'ing dynasty) | 85 | 20 |
| 1253. | $10 Bluish jade washer in shape of lotus (Ch'ing dynasty) | 1·40 | 25 |

See also Nos. 1291/4.

317. Plum Blossom.

318. Houses.

**1979.**

| | | | | |
|---|---|---|---|---|
| 1254a | **317** | $10 blue | 40 | 10 |
| 1255a | | $20 brown | 80 | 10 |
| 1255ba | | $40 red | 1·60 | 10 |
| 1256a | | $50 green | 2·00 | 10 |
| 1257 | | $100 red | 3·50 | 10 |
| 1257b | | $300 red and violet | 20·00 | 2·00 |
| 1257c | | $500 red and brown | 32·00 | 4·00 |

Nos. 1257ba/ca are size 25 × 32½ mm.

**1979.** Environmental Protection. Mult.

| | | | |
|---|---|---|---|
| 1258. | $2 Type **318** | 25 | 10 |
| 1259. | $10 Rural scene (horiz.) | 65 | 25 |

319. Savings Bank Counter.

**1979.** 60th Anniv. of Postal Savings Bank. Multicoloured.

| | | | |
|---|---|---|---|
| 1260. | $2 Type **319** | 20 | 10 |
| 1261. | $5 Savings bank queue | 25 | 15 |
| 1262. | $8 Computer and savings book (horiz.) | 35 | 20 |
| 1263. | $10 Money box and " tree " emblem (horiz.) | 40 | 25 |

320. Steere's Liocichla.

**1979.** Birds. Multicoloured.

| | | | |
|---|---|---|---|
| 1264. | $2 Swinhoe's pheasant | 95 | 10 |
| 1265. | $8 Type **320** | 2·10 | 40 |
| 1266. | $10 Formosan yuhina | 2·50 | 60 |

321. Sir Rowland Hill.

322. Jar with Rope Pattern.

**1979.** Death Cent. of Sir Rowland Hill.

| | | | |
|---|---|---|---|
| 1267. **321.** | $10 multicoloured | 60 | 25 |

**1979.** Ancient Chinese Pottery. Multicoloured.

| | | | |
|---|---|---|---|
| 1268. | $2 Type **322** (Shang dynasty) | 25 | 10 |
| 1269. | $5 Two handled jar (Shang dynasty) | 75 | 15 |
| 1270. | $8 Red jar with " ears " (Han dynasty) | 1·40 | 20 |
| 1271. | $10 Green glazed jar (Han dynasty) | 1·50 | 25 |

323. Children and I.Y.C. Emblem.

324. " Trees on a Winter Plain " (Li Ch'eng).

**1979.** International Year of the Child.

| | | | |
|---|---|---|---|
| 1272. **323.** | $2 multicoloured | 15 | 10 |
| 1273. | $10 multicoloured | 35 | 25 |

**1979.** Ancient Chinese Paintings. Mult.

| | | | |
|---|---|---|---|
| 1274. | $2 Type **324** (Sung dynasty) | 35 | 10 |
| 1275. | $5 " Bamboo " (Wen T'ung, Sung dynasty) | 90 | 15 |
| 1276. | $8 " Old Tree, Bamboo and Rock " (Chao Meng-fu, Yuan dynasty) | 1·25 | 20 |
| 1277. | $10 " Twin Pines " (Li K'an, Yuan dynasty) | 1·60 | 25 |

325. Taiwan Macaque.

326. Competition Emblem and Symbols of Ten Trades.

**1979.** New Year Greetings. " Year of the Monkey ".

| | | | |
|---|---|---|---|
| 1278. **325.** | $1 multicoloured | 75 | 10 |
| 1279. | $6 multicoloured | 1·50 | 25 |

**1979.** Tenth National Vocational Training Competition, Taichung.

| | | | |
|---|---|---|---|
| 1280. **326.** | $2 multicoloured | 10 | 10 |
| 1281. | $10 multicoloured | 30 | 25 |

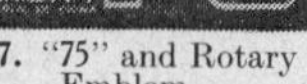
327. "75" and Rotary Emblem.

328. Tunnel of Nine Turns.

**1980.** 75th Anniv. of Rotary International. Multicoloured.

| | | | |
|---|---|---|---|
| 1282. | $2 Type **327** | 25 | 10 |
| 1283. | $12 Anniversary emblem and symbols of Rotary's services (vert.) | 40 | 25 |

**1980.** Tourism. Scenic spots on the East-West Cross-Island Highway. Multicoloured.

| | | | |
|---|---|---|---|
| 1284. | $2 Type **328** | 25 | 10 |
| 1285. | $8 Mt. Hohuan (horiz.) | 40 | 15 |
| 1286. | $12 Bridge, Tien Hsiang | 85 | 30 |

329. Shih Chien-ju (hero of revolution).

330. Chung-cheng Memorial Hall.

**1980.** Famous Chinese.

| | | | |
|---|---|---|---|
| 1287. **329.** | $2 brown | 15 | 10 |

**1980.** 5th Death Anniv. of Chiang Kai-shek. Multicoloured.

| | | | |
|---|---|---|---|
| 1288. | $2 Type **330** | 10 | 10 |
| 1289. | $8 Quotation of Chiang Kai-shek | 30 | 15 |
| 1290. | $12 Bronze statue of Chiang Kai-shek | 40 | 30 |

**1980.** Ancient Chinese Jade (2nd series). As T **316**. Multicoloured.

| | | | |
|---|---|---|---|
| 1291. | $2 Kuang (cup) decorated with dragons (Sung dynasty) (vert.) | 75 | 10 |
| 1292. | $5 Dark green jade melon-shaped brush washer (Ming dynasty) | 1·25 | 15 |
| 1293. | $8 Bluish jade Po Monk's alms bowl (Ch'ing dynasty) | 1·50 | 20 |
| 1294. | $10 Yellow jade brush washer (Ch'ing dynasty) | 1·60 | 25 |

331. Tzu-Ch'iang Squadron over Presidential Mansion.

**1980.** Air. Multicoloured.

| | | | |
|---|---|---|---|
| 1303 | $5 Type **331** | 35 | 10 |
| 1304 | $7 Boeing 747 airliner and insignia of CAL (state airline) | 75 | 20 |
| 1305 | $12 National Flag and Boeing 747 | 90 | 30 |

332. " Wasted Resources ".

333. Military Official.

**1980.** Energy Conservation.

| | | | |
|---|---|---|---|
| 1306. **332.** | $2 multicoloured | 15 | 10 |
| 1307. | $12 multicoloured | 40 | 30 |

**1980.** T'ang Dynasty Tri coloured Pottery. Multicoloured.

| | | | |
|---|---|---|---|
| 1308. | $2 Type **333** | 60 | 10 |
| 1309. | $5 Chickens | 1·00 | 10 |
| 1310. | $8 Horse | 1·40 | 20 |
| 1311. | $10 Camel | 1·25 | 25 |

**1980.** Chinese Folk-tails (6th series). As T **200**. Multicoloured.

| | | | |
|---|---|---|---|
| 1312. | $1 Grinding mortar into a needle | 15 | 10 |
| 1313. | $2 Returning lost articles | 25 | 10 |
| 1314. | $2 Wen Tien-hsiang in prison | 45 | 10 |
| 1315. | $5 Sending coal to poor during snow | 50 | 15 |

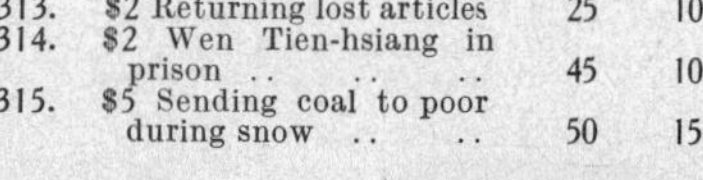

334. TRA Trunk Line Electrification.

335. Money Boxes within Ancient Chinese Coin.

**1980.** Completion of Ten Major Construction Projects. Multicoloured.

1316. $2 Type **334** .. .. 15 10
1317. $2 Taichung Harbour .. 15 10
1318. $2 Chiang Kai-shek International Airport .. 15 10
1319. $2 Integrated steel mill 15 10
1320. $2 Sun Yat-sen National Freeway .. .. 15 10
1321. $2 Nuclear power plant 15 10
1322. $2 Petrochemical industrial zone in south .. 15 10
1323. $2 Su-ao Harbour .. 15 10
1324. $2 Kaohsiung Shipyard 40 10
1325. $2 Taiwan North Link Railway .. .. 15 10

**1980.** 10th National Savings Day. Mult.

1327. $2 Type **335** .. .. 20 10
1328. $12 Hand placing coin in money box .. .. 45 25

**336/339.** Landscape.
(Illustration reduced. Overall size 72 × 102 mm.)

**1980.** Painting by Ch'iu Ying.

1329. **336.** $5 multicoloured .. 30 20
1330. **337.** $5 multicoloured .. 30 20
1331. **338.** $5 multicoloured .. 30 20
1332. **339.** $5 multicoloured .. 30 20

Nos. 1329/32 were printed together, se-tenant, forming the composite design illustrated.

**340.** Cock. **341.** Heads, Flag and Census Form.

**1980.** New Year Greetings. "Year of the Cock".

1334. **340.** $1 multicoloured .. 40 10
1335. $6 multicoloured .. 1·60 25

See also No. 2047.

**1980.** Population and Housing Census. Multicoloured.

1337. $2 Type **341** .. .. 15 10
1338. $12 Flag and buildings (horiz.) .. .. .. 40 30

**342.** Central Weather Bureau.

**1981.** Completion of Meteorological Satellite Ground Station, Taipei. Multicoloured.

1339. $2 "TIROS-N" weather satellite (vert.) .. 15 10
1340. $10 Type **342** .. .. 40 30

**343.** "Happiness".

**344.** "Wealth".

**345.** "Longevity".

**346.** "Joy".

**1981.** New Year Calligraphy.

1341. **343.** $5 gold, red and black 25 25
1342. **344.** $5 gold, red and black 25 25
1343. **345.** $5 gold, red and black 25 25
1344. **346.** $5 gold, red and black 25 25

**347.** Candle and Siamese Twins.

**1981.** International Year for Disabled Persons.

1345. **347.** $2 multicoloured .. 10 10
1346. $10 multicoloured .. 40 30

**348.** Mt. Ali.

**1981.** Tourism. Multicoloured.

1347. $2 Type **348** .. .. 25 10
1348. $7 Oluanpi .. .. 40 15
1349. $12 Sun Moon Lake .. 85 25

**349.** "Children on River Bank".

**1981.** Children's Day. Children's Drawings. Multicoloured.

1350 $1 Type **349** .. .. 10 10
1351 $2 "Cable-cars" .. .. 10 10
1352 $5 "Lobsters" .. .. 20 10
1353 $7 "Village" .. .. 20 15

**350.** Main Gate Chiang Kai-shek Memorial Hall.

**1981.** 6th Death Anniv. of Chiang Kai-shek.

1712. **350.** 10 c. red .. .. 10 10
1354. 20 c. violet .. .. 10 10
1714. 30 c. green .. .. 10 10
1355. 40 c. red .. .. 10 10
1356. 50 c. brown .. .. 10 10
1717. 60 c. blue .. .. 10 10

**351.** Brush Washer (Hsuan-te ware). **352.** Electric and First Steam Locomotives.

**1981.** Ancient Chinese Enamelware (1st series). Ming Dynasty Cloisonne Enamelware. Multicoloured.

1357. $2 Type **351** .. .. 35 10
1358. $5 Ritual vessel with ring handles (Chiang-ta'i ware) (vert.) .. .. 65 10
1359. $8 Plate decorated with dragons (Wan-li ware) 75 10
1360. $10 Vase (vert.) .. .. 1·00 25

See also Nos. 1438/41, 1472/5 and 1542/5.

**1981.** Centenary of Railway. Mult.

1361. $2 Type **352** .. .. 25 10
1362. $14 Side views of steam and electric locomotives (horiz.) .. .. .. 75 40

**353.** "Liagore rubromaculata".

**1981.** Crabs. Multicoloured.

1363. $2 Type **353** .. .. 25 10
1364. $5 "Ranina ranina" (vert.) .. .. 40 10
1365. $8 "Platymaia wyvillethomsoni" .. .. 55 15
1366. $14 "Lambrus nummifera" (vert.) .. .. .. 85 35

**354.** Bureau Emblem. **355.** The Cowherd.

**1981.** 40th Anniv. of Central Weather Bureau.

1367. **354.** $2 multicoloured .. 15 10
1368. $14 multicoloured 55 35

**1981.** Fairy Tales. "The Cowherd and the Weaving Maid". Multicoloured.

1369. $2 Type **355** .. .. 60 10
1370. $4 The cowherd watching the weaving maid through rushes .. .. .. 75 10
1371. $8 The cowherd and the weaving maid on opposite sides of Heavenly River .. .. .. 1·25 15
1372. $14 The cowherd and the weaving maid meeting on bridge of magpies .. 2·50 35

**356.** Laser Display.

**1981.** Lasography Exhibition. Designs showing different laser displays.

1373. **356.** $2 multicoloured .. 15 10
1374. – $5 multicoloured .. 25 10
1375. – $8 multicoloured .. 35 15
1376. – $14 multicoloured .. 1·00 40

**357.** Goalkeeper catching Ball. **359.** Chinese Republic Anniv. Emblem and "Stamps".

**358.** Officers watching Battle from Mound.

**1981.** Athletics Day. Multicoloured.

1390. $5 Women soccer players 15 10
1391. $5 Type **357** .. .. 15 10

**1981.** 70th Anniv. of Founding of Chinese Republic. Multicoloured.

1392. $2 Type **358** .. 15 10
1393. $2 Officer clenching fist and soldiers awaiting battle .. .. .. 15 10
1394. $2 Officer on horseback saluting .. .. 15 10
1395. $2 Attacking buildings .. 15 10
1396. $3 Attacking fortifications 30 10
1397. $3 Dockside scene .. 30 10
1398. $8 Chiang Kai-shek .. 45 10
1399. $14 Sun Yat-sen .. .. 75 15

**1981.** "Rocpex Taipei '81" International Stamp Exhibition.

1401. **359.** $2 multicoloured .. 10 10
1402. $14 multicoloured .. 35 35

**360.** Detail of Scroll.

**1981.** Sung Dynasty painting "One Hundred Young Boys". Designs showing details of Scroll.

1403. **360.** $2 (1) multicoloured 25 25
1404. – $2 (2) multicoloured 25 25
1405. – $2 (3) multicoloured 25 25
1406. – $2 (4) multicoloured 25 25
1407. – $2 (5) multicoloured 25 25
1408. – $2 (6) multicoloured 25 25
1409. – $2 (7) multicoloured 25 25
1410. – $2 (8) multicoloured 25 25
1411. – $2 (9) multicoloured 25 25
1412. – $2 (10) multicoloured 25 25

See note below No. 661 on identification of designs.

Nos. 1403/12 were printed together in se-tenant blocks of ten (5 × 2) within the sheet, each strip of five forming a composite design.

**361.** Dog. **362.** Information-using Services and Emblem.

**1981.** New Year Greetings. "Year of the Dog".

1413. **361.** $1 multicoloured .. 1·25 10
1414. $14 multicoloured .. 2·50 25

See also No. 2048.

**1981.** Information Week.

1416. **362.** $2 multicoloured .. 15 10

**363.** Telephones of 1881 and 1981. **364.** Arrangement in Basket.

**1981.** Centenary of Chinese Telecommunications Service. Multicoloured.

1417. $2 Map and hand holding telephone handset (vert.) 15 10
1418. $3 Type **363** .. .. 25 10
1419. $8 Submarine cable map 35 10
1420. $18 Computer and telecommunication units (vert.) .. .. .. 50 20

**1982.** Chinese Flower Arrangements. Mult.

1421. $2 Type **364** .. .. 25 10
1422. $3 Arrangement in jug .. 40 10
1423. $8 Arrangement in vase 75 10
1424. $18 Arrangement in holder .. .. .. 1·25 20

**365.** Kuan Yu leaves for Cheng City.

**1982.** Scenes from "The Ku Cheng Reunion" (opera). Multicoloured.
1425. $2 Type **365** .. .. 75 10
1426. $3 Chang Fei refuses to open city gates .. 85 10
1427. $4 Chang Fei apologises to Kuan Yu .. .. 1·25 10
1428. $18 Liu Pei, Kuan Yu and Chang Fei are reunited .. .. 2·50 30

**366.** Dr. Robert Koch and Tubercle Bacillus. **367.** Chang Shih-liang (revolutionary).

**1982.** Centenary of Discovery of Tubercle Bacillus.
1429. **366.** $2 multicoloured .. 15 10

**1982.** Famous Chinese.
1430. **367.** $2 red .. .. 15 10

**368.** " Martyrs' Shrine ". **369.** Tooth and Child holding Toothbrush and Mug.

**1982.** Children's Day. Designs showing children's paintings.
1431. $2 Type **368** .. .. 25 10
1432. $3 " House Yard " .. 30 10
1433. $5 " Cattle Herd " .. 40 10
1434. $8 " A Sacrificial Ceremony for a Plentiful Year " .. .. .. 65 10

**1982.** Dental Health. Multicoloured.
1435. $2 Type **369** .. .. 20 10
1436. $3 Methods of cleaning teeth .. .. .. 35 10
1437. $10 Dental check-up .. 1·00 10

**1982.** Ancient Chinese Enamelware (2nd series). As T **351**. Multicoloured.
1438. $2 Champleve cup and plate (Ch'ien-lung ware) .. .. .. 35 10
1439. $5 Cloisonné duck container (Ch'ien-lung ware) (vert.) .. .. 85 10
1440. $8 Painted incense burner (K'ang-hsi period) .. .. .. 1·50 10
1441. $12 Cloisonné Tibetan lama milk-tea pot (Ch'ien-lung ware) (vert.) .. .. .. 1·75 15

**370.** " Spring Dawn " (Meng Hao-jan).

**1982.** Chinese Classical Poetry (1st series). Tang Dynasty Poems. Multicoloured.
1442. $2 Type **370** .. .. 1·50 10
1443. $3 " On Looking for a Hermit and not Finding Him " (Chia Tao) 3·00 10
1444. $5 " Summer Dying " (Liu Yu-hsi) .. 4·25 10
1445. $18 " Looking at the Snow Drifts on South Mountains " (Tsu Yung) 6·50 55
See also Nos. 1476/9, 1524/7, 1594/7, 1866/9, 1910/13 and 2074/7.

**371.** Softball.

**1982.** Fifth World Women's Softball Championship, Taipeh.
1446. **371.** $2 multicoloured .. 25 10
1447. $18 multicoloured .. 60 20

**372.** Scouts on Rope Bridge. and Lord Baden-Powell.

**1982.** 75th Anniv. of Boy Scout Movement and 125th Birth Anniv. of Lord Baden-Powell. Multicoloured.
1448. $2 Type **372** .. .. 15 10
1449. $18 Emblem, scouts making frame and camp .. .. .. 65 15

**373.** Tweezers holding Stamp. **374.** Carved Lion.

**1982.** Philately Day. Multicoloured.
1450. $2 Type **373** .. .. 25 10
1451. $18 Examining stamp album with magnifying glass .. .. .. 65 20

**1982.** Tsu Shih Temple, Sanhsia. Mult.
1452. $2 Type **374** .. .. 25 10
1453. $3 Lion brackets (horiz.) 35 10
1454. $5 Carved sub-lintels in passageway .. .. 55 10
1455. $18 Temple roofs (horiz.) 1·40 20

**1982.** Chinese Folk-tales (7th series). Stories from "36 Examples of Filial Piety" by Wu Yen-huan. As T **200**. Multicoloured.
1456 $1 Shao K'ang supporting his mother .. .. 20 10
1457 $2 Hsun Kuan leading soldier reinforcements to her father .. .. 35 10
1458 $3 Ku Yen-wu refusing to serve Ch'ing dynasty .. 45 10
1459 $5 Ting Ch'un-liang caring for his paralysed father 75 10

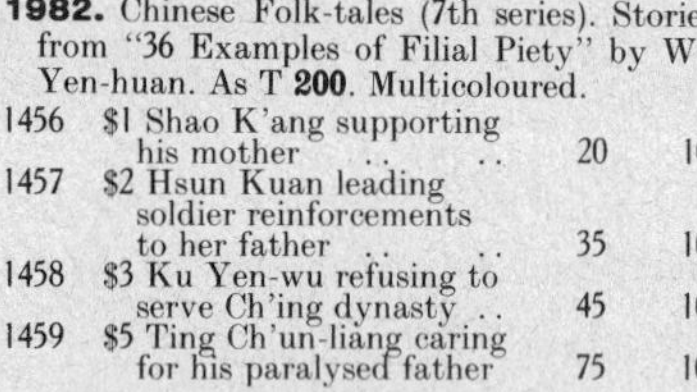

**375.** Riding Horses.

**1982.** 30th Anniv. of China Youth Corps. Multicoloured.
1460. $2 Type **375** .. .. 10 10
1461. $3 Flag and water sport 15 10
1462. $18 Mountaineering (vert.) .. .. .. 40 20

**376.** Lohan with Boy Attendant and Monkey. **378.** Pig.

**1982.** Lohan (Buddhist Saint) Scroll Paintings by Liu Sung-nien. Multicoloured.
1463. $2 Type **376** .. .. 1·25 10
1464. $3 Monk presenting seated Lohan with scroll .. .. .. 1·75 10
1465. $18 Tribal king paying homage to seated Lohan .. .. .. 4·25 40

**1982.** New Year. "Year of the Pig".
1468. **378.** $1 multicoloured .. 1·25 10
1469. $10 multicoloured .. 2·25 25
See also No. 2049.

**1983.** Ancient Chinese Enamelware (3rd series). Ch'ing Dynasty Enamelware. As T **351**. Multicoloured.
1472. $2 Square basin with rounded corners .. 30 10
1473. $3 Vase decorated with landscape panels (vert.) .. .. .. 85 10
1474. $4 Blue teapot with flower pattern .. 1·50 10
1475. $18 Cloisonné elephant with vase on back (vert.) .. .. .. 1·75 20

**379.** " Wan-hsi-sha " (Yen Shu). **380.** Hsin-hsien Concealed Fall, Wawa Valley.

**1983.** Chinese Classical Poetry (2nd series) Sung Dynasty Lyrical Poems. Multicoloured.
1476. $2 Type **379** .. .. 2·25 10
1477. $3 " Ch'ing-yu-an " (Ho Chu) .. .. .. 3·00 10
1478. $5 " Su-mu-che " (Fan Chung-yen) .. .. 4·25 10
1479. $11 " Hsing-hsiang-tzu " (Ch'ao Pu-chih) .. 7·00 25

**1983.** Landscapes. Multicoloured.
1480. $2 Type **380** .. .. 1·00 10
1481. $3 University Pond, Chitou Forest .. .. 1·25 10
1482. $18 Mount Jade (horiz.) .. 1·50 20

**381.** Matteo Ricci and Astrolabe.

**1983.** 400th Anniv. of Matteo Ricci's (missionary) Arrival in China. Mult.
1483. $2 Type **381** .. .. 25 10
1484. $18 Matteo Ricci and Great Wall .. .. 85 20

**382.** Wu Ching-heng. (Chairman of development committee). **383.** Hsu Hsien meets Pai Su-chen.

**1983.** 70th Anniv. of Mandarin Phonetic Symbols. Multicoloured.
1485. $2 Type **382** .. .. 25 10
1486. $18 Children studying symbols .. .. 75 25

**1983.** Fairy Tales. "Lady White Snake". Multicoloured.
1487. $2 Type **383** .. .. 50 10
1488. $3 Pai Su-chen steals Tree of Life .. .. 65 10
1489. $3 Confrontation with Fahai at Chin Shan Temple .. .. 2·25 10
1490. $18 Pai Su-chen is imprisoned beneath Thunder Peak Pagoda 3·50 30

**384.** Pot with Cord Pattern. **385.** Communication Emblems circling Globe.

**1983.** Ancient Chinese Bamboo Carvings. Multicoloured.
1491. $2 Type **384** .. .. 40 10
1492. $3 Vase with Tao-t'ien motif .. .. .. 75 10
1493. $4 Carved mountain scene with figures .. 75 10
1494. $18 Brush-holder with relief showing ladies .. 2·25 20

**1983.** World Communications Year. Mult.
1495. $2 Type **385** .. .. 15 10
1496. $18 W.C.Y. emblem .. 60 20

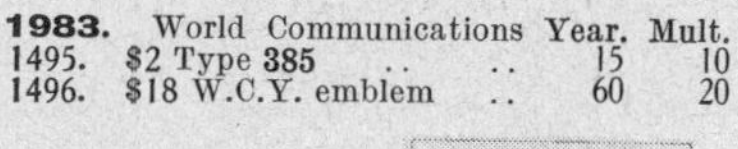

**386.** "Epinephelus tauvina". **387.** T.V. Screen, Antenna and Radio Waves.

**1983.** Protection of Fishery Resources. Mult.
1497. $2 Type **386** .. .. 25 10
1498. $18 " Saurida undosquamis " 75 20

**1983.** Journalists' Day.
1499. **387.** $2 multicoloured .. 15 10

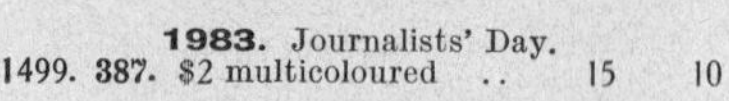

**388.** Yurt. **389.** Brown Shrike.

**1983.** Mongolian and Tibetan Scenes.
1500. $2 Type **388** .. .. 25 10
1501. $3 Potala Palace .. 45 10
1502. $5 Sheep on prairie .. 55 10
1503. $11 Camel caravan .. 75 20

**1983.** 2nd East Asian Bird Protection Conference. Multicoloured.
1504. $2 Type **389** .. .. 1·00 10
1505. $18 Grey-faced buzzard-eagle .. .. .. 1·75 40

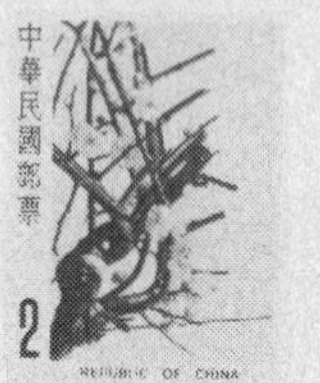

**390.** Pink Plum Blossom. **391.** Congress Emblem.

**1983.** Plum Blossom. Multicoloured.
1506. $2 Type **390** .. .. 15 10
1507. $3 Red plum blossom .. 20 10
1508. $5 Plum blossom and pagoda .. .. .. 45 15
1509. $11 White plum blossom 75 15

**1983.** 38th Jaycees International World Congress. Multicoloured.
1510. $2 Type **391** .. .. 15 10
1511. $18 Emblems and globe .. 55 20

**392.** World Map as Heart. **393.** Rat.

**1983.** Eighth Asian-Pacific Cardiology Congress. Multicoloured.
1512. $2 Type **392** .. .. 10 10
1513. $18 Heart and electrocardiogram .. .. 60 20

**1983.** New Year. "Year of the Rat".
1514. **393.** $1 multicoloured .. 1·50 10
1515. $10 multicoloured .. 3·25 20
See also No. 2038.

**394.** Mother and Child reading and Chin Ting Prize.

**1983.** National Reading Week. Mult.
1517. $2 Type **394** .. .. 10 10
1518. $18 Chin Ting prize (for outstanding publications) books and father and son reading (vert.) 60 20

**395.** Boeing 737 over Chiang Kai-shek Airport.

**396.** Soldiers with Flags.

**1984.** Air. 37th Anniv. of Civil Aeronautics Administration. Multicoloured
1519 $7 Type **395** .. .. 35 15
1520 $11 Boeing 747 over Chung-cheng Memorial Hall (horiz) .. .. 50 15
1521 $18 Boeing 737 over Sun Yat-sen Memorial Hall (horiz) .. .. 65 20

**1984.** World Freedom Day. Multicoloured.
1522 $2 Type **396** .. .. 15 10
1523 $18 Globe and people of the world .. .. 50 20

**397.** " Hsiao-liang-chou " (Kuan Yun-shih).

**1984.** Chinese Classical Poetry (3rd series). Yuan Dynasty Lyric Poems. Multicoloured.
1524. $2 Type **397** .. .. 3·00 20
1525. $3 "A Lady holds a fine fan of silk", "Tien-ching-sha", (Po P'u) .. 4·50 25
1526. $5 "Picnic under banana leaves "Ch'ing-chiang-yin", (Chang Ko-chiu) 5·00 25
1527. $18 "Plum blossoms in the snowbound wilderness "Tien-ching-sha" (Shang Cheng-shu) .. 9·00 75

**398.** Forest Scene.

**400.** Lin Chueh-min (revolutionary).

**1984.** Forest Resources. Multicoloured.
1528. $2 Type **398** .. .. 20 10
1529. $2 Reservoir and dam .. 20 10
1530. $2 Camp in forest .. 20 10
1531. $2 Wooded slopes .. 20 10
Nos. 1528/31 were printed together se-tenant, forming a composite design.

**1984.** Famous Chinese.
1536. **400.** $2 green .. .. 15 10

**401.** Agency Emblem and Broadcasting Equipment.

**402.** "Five Auspicious Tokens".

**1984.** 60th Anniv. of Central News Agency. Multicoloured.
1537. $2 Type **401** .. .. 10 10
1538. $10 Agency emblem and satellite communications .. .. .. 35 15

**1984.** 85th Birth Anniv. of Chang Ta-chien (artist). Multicoloured.
1539. $2 Type **402** .. .. 1·00 10
1540. $5 "The God of Longevity" .. .. 1·50 15
1541. $18 "Lotus Blossoms in Ink Splash" .. .. 3·50 40

**1984.** Ancient Chinese Enamelware (4th series). Ch'ing Dynasty Enamelware. As T **351**. Multicoloured.
1542. $2 Lidded cup and teapot on tray .. .. 20 10
1543. $3 Cloisonne wine vessel on phoenix (vert.) .. 50 10
1544. $4 Yellow teapot with pink and blue chrysanthemum decoration .. 75 15
1545. $18 Cloisonné candleholder on bird .. 1·50 40

**403.** Boeing 747 circling Globe.

**1984.** Inauguration of China Airlines Global Service. Multicoloured.
1546 $2 Type **403** .. .. 15 10
1547 $7 Globe and Boeing 747 50 20
1548 $11 Boeing 747 over New York .. .. 75 30
1549 $18 Boeing 747 over Netherlands .. .. 1·25 55

**404.** Judo.

**1984.** Olympic Games, Los Angeles. Mult.
1550. $2 Type **404** .. .. 10 10
1551. $5 Archery (vert.) .. 25 15
1552. $18 Swimming .. .. 95 60

**405.** "Ming Comfort" (Container Ship).

**406.** "Gentiana arisanensis".

**1984.** 30th Navigation Day. Mult.
1553. $2 Type **405** .. .. 75 10
1554. $18 "Prosperity" (tanker) 1·50 65

**1984.** Alpine Plants. Multicoloured.
1555. $2 Type **406** .. .. 30 10
1556. $3 "Epilobium nankotaizanense" .. 45 10
1557. $5 "Adenophora uehatae" 65 15
1558. $18 "Aconitum fukutomei" 2·00 25

**407.** Scholars listening to Music.

**408.** Volleyball Players.

**1984.** Sung Dynasty Painting "The Eighteen Scholars". Multicoloured.
1559. $2 Type **407** .. .. 2·00 10
1560. $3 Scholars playing chess 4·00 10
1561. $5 Scholars writing .. 2·50 15
1562. $18 Scholars painting .. 10·00 65

**1984.** Athletics Day. Multicoloured.
1563. $5 Type **408** .. .. 25 15
1564. $5 Volleyball player .. 25 15
Nos. 1563/4 were printed together, se-tenant, forming a composite design.

**409.** Union Emblem.

**410.** 1965 Confucius $1 Stamp.

**1984.** 20th Anniv. of Asian-Pacific Parliamentarians' Union.
1565. **409.** $10 multicoloured .. 50 25

**1984.** New Postal Museum Building, Taipeh. Multicoloured.
1566. $2 Type **410** .. .. 10 10
1567. $5 1933 Sun Yat-sen 5 c. stamp .. .. .. 25 15
1568. $18 New Postal Museum building .. .. 95 65

**411.** Flag and Emblem.

**412.** Commission Services.

**1984.** Grand Alliance for China's Reunification Convention.
1570. **411.** $2 multicoloured .. 20 10

**1984.** 30th Anniv. of Vocational Assistance Commission for Retired Servicemen.
1571. **412.** $2 multicoloured .. 20 10

**413.** Pine Tree.

**414.** Ox.

**1984.** Pine, Bamboo and Plum (1st series). Multicoloured.
1572. $2 Type **413** .. .. 10 10
1573. $8 Bamboo .. .. 40 20
1574. $10 Plum blossom .. 50 20
See also Nos. 1633/5, 1783/5 and 1845/7.

**1984.** New Year Greetings. "Year of the Ox".
1575. **414.** $1 multicoloured .. 75 10
1576. $10 multicoloured .. 1·75 20
See also No. 2039.

**415.** Legal Code Book and Scales.

**416.** Ku-kang Lake and Pagoda, Quemoy.

**1985.** Judicial Day.
1578. **415.** $5 multicoloured .. 25 15

**1985.** Scenery of Quemoy and Matsu. Multicoloured.
1579 $2 Type **416** .. .. 15 10
1580 $5 Kuang-hai stone, Quemoy .. .. 45 15
1581 $8 Sheng-li reservoir, Matsu .. .. .. 1·50 20
1582 $10 Tung-chu lighthouse, Matsu .. .. .. 1·50 20

**417.** Sir Robert Hart and 1878 3 c. Stamp.

**418.** Lo Fu-hsing.

**1985.** 150th Anniv. of Sir Robert Hart (founder of Chinese Postal Service).
1583. **417.** $2 multicoloured .. 25 10

**1985.** Birth Cent. of Lo Fu-hsing (patriot).
1584. **418.** $2 multicoloured .. 20 10

**419.** Tsou Jung.

**421.** Lily.

**420.** Main Gate, Chung-cheng Memorial Hall.

**1985.** 80th Death Anniv. of Tsou Jung (revolutionary).
1585. **419.** $3 green .. .. 20 10

**1985.** 10th Death Anniv. of President Chiang Kai-shek. Multicoloured.
1586. $2 Type **420** .. .. 10 10
1587. $8 Tzuhu, President Chiang's temporary resting place .. .. 50 20
1588. $10 President Chiang Kai-shek (vert.) .. 65 20

**1985.** Mothers' Day. Multicoloured.
1589. $2 Type **421** .. .. 15 10
1590. $2 Carnation .. .. 15 10

**422.** View of Tunnel.

**423.** Girl Guide saluting.

**1985.** 1st Anniv. of Kaohsiung Cross-harbour Tunnel.
1591. **422.** $5 multicoloured .. 35 15

**1985.** 75th Anniv. of Girl Guide Movement.
1592. **423.** $2 multicoloured .. 10 10
1593. $18 multicoloured .. 80 25

**424.** "Buxom is the Peach Tree . . .".

**1985.** Chinese Classical Poetry (4th series). Poems from "Book of Odes", edited by Confucius. Multicoloured.
1594. $2 Type **424** .. .. 50 10
1595. $5 "Thick grows that tarragon . . ." .. .. 1·75 15
1596. $8 "Thick grow the rush leaves . . ." .. .. 2·25 20
1597. $10 ". . . The snowflakes fly" .. .. .. 3·00 20

**425.** Wax Jambo.

**1985.** Fruit. Multicoloured.
1598. $2 Type **425** 50 10
1599. $3 Guavas 75 10
1600. $5 Carambolas 1·25 15
1601. $8 Lychees 2·00 20

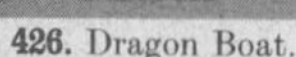
**426.** Dragon Boat.

**427.** Lady of Rank, T'ang Dynasty.

**1985.** Ch'ing Dynasty Ivory Carvings. Mult.
1602. $2 Type **426** 65 10
1603. $3 Carved landscape 75 10
1604. $5 Melon-shaped water container 1·25 15
1605. $18 Brush-holder (vert.) 1·50 35

**1985.** 4th Asian Costume Conference. Chinese Costumes (1st series). Multicoloured.
1606. $2 Type **427** 75 10
1607. $5 Palace woman, Sung dynasty 1·10 10
1608. $8 Lady of rank, Yuan dynasty 2·25 20
1609. $11 Lady of rank, Ming dynasty 2·50 25
See also Nos. 1687/90, 1767/70, 1833/6, 1906/9 and 1973/6.

**428.** Bird feeding Chicks.

**1985.** Social Welfare.
1610. **428.** $2 multicoloured 15 10

**429.** North Gate, Taipeh.

**430.** Oak Tree.

**1985.** Historic Buildings (1st series). Mult.
1611. $2 Type **429** 15 10
1612. $5 San Domingo fort, Tamsui 35 15
1613. $8 Lung Shan Temple, Lukang 45 20
1614. $10 Confucius Temple, Changhua 75 20
See also Nos. 1700/3.

**1985.** Bonsai. Multicoloured.
1615. $2 Type **430** 20 10
1616. $5 Five-leaf pine 35 15
1617. $8 Lohan pine 45 20
1618. $18 Banyan 1·00 25

**431.** World Trade Centre and Sports Goods Logo.

**432.** Flag, Map and Scenes of Peace.

**1985.** Trade Shows. Multicoloured.
1619. $2 Type **431** 10 10
1620. $2 Toys and gifts logo (blue and red) 10 10
1621. $2 Electronics logo (blue) 10 10
1622. $2 Machinery logo (black and orange) 10 10
Nos. 1619/22 were printed together, se-tenant, forming a composite design depicting Taipeh World Trade Centre.

**1985.** 40th Anniv. of Return of Taiwan to China. Multicoloured.
1623. $2 Type **432** 25 10
1624. $18 Chiang Kai-shek and triumphal arch 1·00 25

**433.** Emblem.

**434.** Sun Yat-sen.

**1985.** Seventh Asian Federation for the Mentally Retarded Conference, Taipeh.
1625. **433.** $2 multicoloured 15 10
1626. $11 multicoloured 65 25

**1985.** 120th Birth Anniv. of Sun Yat-sen.
1627. **434.** $2 multicoloured 10 10
1628. $18 multicoloured 95 25

**435.** Tiger.

**436.** Emblem.

**1985.** New Year Greetings. "Year of the Tiger".
1629. **435.** $1 multicoloured 50 10
1630. $10 multicoloured 2·00 20
See also No. 2040.

**1985.** 50th Anniv. of Postal Simple Life Insurance.
1632. **436.** $2 multicoloured 20 10

**437.** Pine Tree.

**1986.** Pine, Bamboo and Plum (2nd series). Multicoloured.
1633. $1 Type **437** 25 10
1634. $11 Bamboo 65 20
1635. $18 Plum blossom 1·10 25

**438.** Detail of Scroll.

**1986.** Painting "Hermit Anglers on a Mountain Stream" by T'ang Yin. Designs showing details of the scroll. Multicoloured.
1636. $2 (1) Type **438** 10 10
1637. $2 (2) Pavilions on bank 10 10
1638. $2 (3) Anglers in boats near waterfall 10 10
1639. $2 (4) Pavilions on stilts 10 10
1640. $2 (5) Anglers in boat near island 10 10
Nos. 1636/40 were printed together, forming a composite design.
See note below No. 661 on identification of designs in se-tenant strips.

**439.** Gladioli in Vase.

**440.** Loading and unloading Mail Plane.

**1986.** Flower Arrangements (1st series). Multicoloured.
1641. $2 Type **439** 10 10
1642. $5 Roses in double wicker holders 35 10
1643. $8 Roses and fern in pot on stand 65 10
1644. $10 Various flowers in large and small pots 80 10
See also Nos. 1741/4.

**1986.** 90th Anniv of Post Office. Mult.
1645 $2 Type **440** 15 10
1646 $5 Postman on motor-cycle (vert) 30 10
1647 $8 Customer at cash dispenser and clerk at savings bank computer terminal (vert) 45 10
1648 $10 Electronic sorting machine and envelopes circling globe 65 15

**441.** Chen Tien-hva (revolutionary writer).

**442.** Mountain shrouded in Mist.

**1986.** Famous Chinese.
1650. **441.** $2 violet 10 10

**1986.** Yushan National Park. Multicoloured.
1651. $2 Type **442** 25 10
1652. $5 People on mountain top 65 10
1653. $8 Snow covered mountain peak 95 10
1654. $10 Forest on mountain side 1·25 15

**443.** Hydro-electric Power Station.

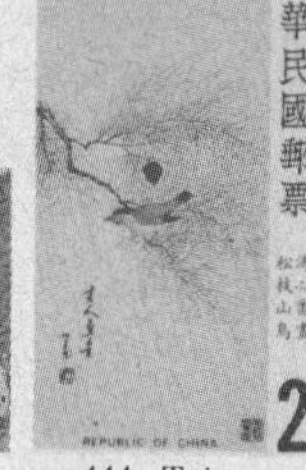
**444.** Taiwan Firecrest in Tree.

**1986.** Power Stations. Multicoloured.
1655. $2 Type **443** 20 10
1656. $8 Thermo-electric power station 45 10
1657. $10 Nuclear power station 55 15

**1986.** Paintings by P'u Hsin-yu. Mult.
1658. $2 Type **444** 1·00 10
1659. $8 Landscape 2·25 10
1660. $10 Woman in garden 2·75 15

**445.** Emblems.

**446.** Green-winged Macaw.

**1986.** 25th Anniv. of Asian Productivity Organization and 30th Anniv. of China Productivity Centre.
1661. **445.** $2 multicoloured 15 10
1662. $11 multicoloured 75 20

**1986.** Protection of Intellectual Property.
1663. **446.** $2 multicoloured 45 10

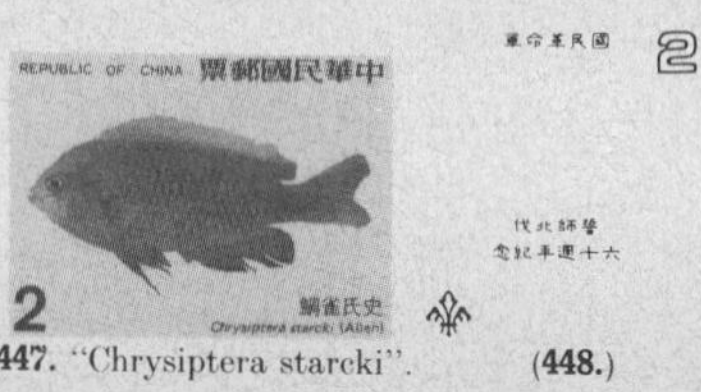
**447.** "*Chrysiptera starcki*". (**448.**)

**1986.** Coral Reef Fishes. Multicoloured.
1664. $2 Type **447** 15 10
1665. $2 "Chelmon rostratus" 15 10
1666. $2 "Chaetodon xanthurus" 15 10
1667. $2 "Chaetodon quadrimaculatus" 15 10
1668. $2 "Chaetodon meyeri" 15 10
1669. $2 "Genicanthus semifasciatus" (female) 15 10
1670. $2 "Genicanthus semifasciatus" (male) 15 10
1671. $2 "Pomacanthus annularis" 15 10
1672. $2 "Lienardella fasciata" 15 10
1673. $2 "Balistapus undulatus" 15 10

**1986.** 60th Anniv of Chiang Kai-shek's Northward Expedition. Nos. 1229 and 1386 surch as T **448**.
1674. **306.** $2 on $6 red, blue and orange 15 15
1675. $8 on $9 red, blue and green 35 25

**449.** Tzu Mu Bridge.

**450.** Yingtai and Shanpo going to School.

**1986.** Road Bridges. Multicoloured.
1676 $2 Type **449** 35 10
1677 $5 Chang Hung bridge over Hsiu-ku-luan-chi 55 10
1678 $8 Kuan Fu bridge over Hsintien River 95 10
1679 $10 Kuan Tu bridge over Tanshui River 1·50 15

**1986.** Folk Tales. "Love between Liang Shanpo and Chu Yingtai". Multicoloured.
1680. $5 Type **450** 30 10
1681. $5 Classmates 30 10
1682. $5 Yingtai and Shanpo by lake 30 10
1683. $5 Yingtai telling Shanpo she is to be married 30 10
1684. $5 Ascending to heaven as butterflies 30 10

**451.** Children playing by Lake and Rainbow.

**452.** Lady of Warring States Period.

**1986.** Cleanliness and Courtesy. Mult.
1685 $2 Type **451** 15 10
1686 $8 Children helping others in street 35 10

**1986.** Chinese Costumes (2nd series). Mult.
1687 $2 Lady of rank, Shang dynasty 90 10
1688 $5 Type **452** 1·90 10
1689 $8 Empress's assembly dress, later Han dynasty 2·50 10
1690 $10 Beribboned dress of lady of rank, Wei and Tsin dynasties 3·75 25

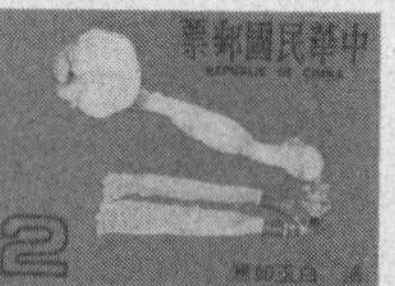
**453.** White Jade Ju-i Sceptre with Fish Decoration.

**1986.** Ch'ing Dynasty Ju-i (1st series). Mult.
1691. $2 Type **453** 25 10
1692. $3 Coral ju-i sceptre with fungus motif 60 10
1693. $4 Redwood ju-i sceptre inlaid with precious stones 50 10
1694. $18 Gold-painted ju-i sceptre with three abundances (fruit) 2·00 25
See also Nos 1735/8.

**454.** Chiang Kai-shek and Books.

**1986.** Birth Centenary of Chiang Kai-shek. Multicoloured.
1695. $2 Type **454** .. .. 20 10
1696. $5 Chiang Kai-shek, flag, map and crowd .. 40 10
1697. $8 Chiang Kai-shek, emblem and youths .. 50 10
1698. $10 Chiang Kai-shek, flags on globe and clasped hands .. 65 15

**455.** Erh-sha-wan Gun Emplacement, Keelung. **456.** Hare.

**1986.** Historic Buildings (2nd series). Mult.
1700 $2 Chin-kuang-fu house, Pei-pu .. .. 20 10
1701 $5 Type **455** .. .. 60 10
1702 $8 Hsi T'ai fort .. .. 65 10
1703 $10 Matsu Temple, Peng-hu .. .. 75 15

**1986.** New Year Greetings. "Year of the Hare".
1704. **456.** $1 multicoloured .. 25 10
1705. $10 multicoloured .. 1·75 15
See also No. 2041.

**457.** Shrubs on Rock Formation. **458.** Glove Puppet.

**1987.** Kenting National Park. Multicoloured.
1707. $2 Type **457** .. .. 25 10
1708. $5 Rocky outcrop .. 60 10
1709. $8 Sandy bay .. 85 10
1710. $10 Rocky bays .. .. 1·25 15

**1987.** Puppets. Multicoloured.
1721 $2 Type **458** .. .. 60 10
1722 $5 String puppet .. 1·25 10
1723 $18 Shadow show puppet 1·75 25

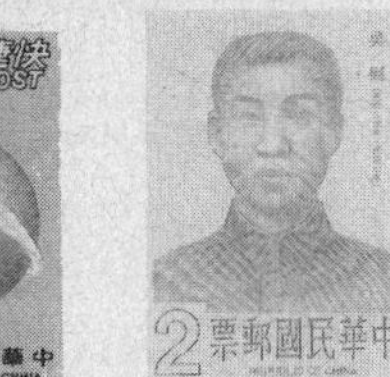

**459.** Envelope, Parcel and Globe. **460.** Wu Yueh (revolutionary).

**1987.** Speedpost Service.
1724. **459.** $2 multicoloured .. 15 10
1725. $18 multicoloured .. 75 25

**1987.** Famous Chinese.
1726. **460.** $2 red and pink .. 50 10

**461.** "Singing Creek with Bamboo Orchestra".

**1987.** Madame Chiang Kai-shek's Landscape Paintings (3rd series). Each black, stone and red.
1727. $2 Type **461** .. .. 40 10
1728. $5 "Mountains draped in Clouds" .. .. 1·00 10
1729. $5 "Vista of Tranquility" 1·25 10
1730. $10 "Mountains after a Snowfall" .. .. 1·50 15

**462.** Bodhisattva Head, Northern Wei Dynasty. **463.** View of Dam.

**1987.** Ancient Chinese Stone Carvings. Multicoloured.
1731. $5 Type **462** .. .. 25 10
1732. $5 Standing Buddha, Northern Ch'i dynasty 25 10
1733. $5 Bodhisattva head, T'ang dynasty .. 25 10
1734. $5 Seated Buddha, T'ang dynasty .. 25 10

**1987.** Ch'ing Dynasty Ju-i (2nd series). As T **453**. Multicoloured.
1735. $2 Silver ju-i sceptre with fungus decoration of pearls and precious stones .. .. .. 60 10
1736. $3 Gold ju-i sceptre with Eight Treasures decoration of pearls and precious stones .. 60 10
1737. $4 Gilt ju-i sceptre inlaid with precious stones and kingfisher feather 75 10
1738. $18 Gilt ju-i sceptre with wirework and inlaid with malachite .. 3·25 25

**1987.** Feitsui Reservoir Inauguration. Multicoloured.
1739. $2 Type **463** .. .. 15 10
1740. $18 View of reservoir .. 95 25

**1987.** Flower Arrangements (2nd series). As T **439**. Multicoloured.
1741. $2 Roses and pine twig in holder .. .. .. 15 10
1742. $5 Flowers in pot .. 30 10
1743. $8 Tasselled pendant hanging from bamboo in vase .. .. .. 65 10
1744. $10 Pine in flask .. 75 15

**464.** Emblem. **465.** Soldiers firing from behind Barricades.

**1987.** 70th Lions Clubs International Convention, Taipeh.
1745. **464.** $2 multicoloured .. 15 10
1746. $18 multicoloured .. 75 25

**1987.** 50th Anniv of Start of Sino-Japanese War. Multicoloured.
1747. $1 Type **465** .. .. 10 10
1748. $2 Chiang Kai-shek making speech from balcony .. .. 15 10
1749. $5 Crowd throwing money onto flag .. 30 10
1750. $6 Columns of soldiers and tanks on mountain road .. 40 10
1751. $8 General giving written message to Chiang Kai-shek .. 50 10
1752. $18 Pres. and Madame Chiang Kai-shek at front of crowd .. 85 25

**466.** Airplane flying to Left. **467.** Wang Yun-wu.

**1987.** Air. Multicoloured.
1753. $9 Type **466** .. .. 35 15
1754. $14 Airplane .. .. 55 20
1755. $18 Airplane flying to right .. .. .. 70 25

**1987.** Birth Centenary (1988) of Wang Yun-wu (lexicographer).
1756. **467.** $2 black .. .. 15 10

**468** Trees on Islands and Fisherman

**1987.** Painting "After Chao Po-su's 'Red Cliff'" by Wen Cheng-ming. Designs showing details of the scroll. Multicoloured.
1757 $3 (1) Type **468** .. 20 10
1758 $3 (2) Tree and three figures on island .. 20 10
1759 $3 (3) House in walled enclosure on island .. 20 10
1760 $3 (4) Figures in doorway of building and horse in stable .. .. 20 10
1761 $3 (5) Cliffs and sea .. 20 10
1762 $3 (6) Islets, trees and figures on shore .. 20 10
1763 $3 (7) Trees among cliffs 20 10
1764 $3 (8) People in sampan 20 10
1765 $3 (9) Building surrounded by trees and cliffs .. .. 20 10
1766 $3 (10) Cliffs, trees and waterfall .. .. 20 10
Nos. 1757/66 were printed together, se-tenant, forming a composite design.
See note below No. 661 on identification of designs in se-tenant strips.

**469** Han Lady of Rank, Early Ch'ing Dynasty **470** Ta Chen Tian, Confucius Temple, Taichung

**1987.** Chinese Costumes (3rd series). Mult.
1767 $1.50 Type **469** .. 50 10
1768 $3 Manchu bannerman's wife, Ch'ing dynasty 60 10
1769 $7.50 Woman's Manchu-style Ch'i-p'ao, early Republic period .. 1·75 10
1770 $18 Jacket and skirt, early Republic period 4·25 35

**1987.** International Confucianism and the Modern World Symposium, Taipeh. Mult.
1771 $3 Type **470** .. .. 20 10
1772 $18 Confucius and fresco 80 25

**471** Dragon **472** Flag and Emblem as "40"

**1987.** New Year Greetings. "Year of the Dragon".
1773 **471** $1.50 multicoloured .. 50 10
1774 $12 multicoloured .. 2·00 20
See also No. 2042.

**1987.** 40th Anniv of Constitution. Mult.
1776 $3 Type **472** .. .. 10 10
1777 $16 "40" in national colours and emblem .. 75 25

**473** Sphygmomanometer **474** Plum

**1988.** National Health. Prevent Hypertension Campaign.
1778 **473** $3 multicoloured .. 20 10

**1988.** Flowers (1st series). Multicoloured.
1779 $3 Type **474** .. .. 40 10
1780 $7.50 Apricot .. .. 1·25 10
1781 $12 Peach .. .. 2·00 20
See also Nos. 1798/1800, 1809/11 and 1829/31.

**475** Pine Tree **476** Modelled Dough Figurines

**1988.** Pine, Bamboo and Plum (3rd series). Multicoloured.
1783 $1.50 Type **475** .. .. 25 10
1784 $7.50 Bamboo .. .. 45 10
1785 $16 Plum blossom .. 85 25

**1988.** Traditional Handicrafts. Multicoloured.
1786 $3 Type **476** .. .. 35 10
1787 $7.50 Blown sugar fish .. 1·00 10
1788 $16 Sugar painting .. 1·75 25

**477** Hsu Hsi-lin (revolutionary) **478** Bio-technology

**1988.** Famous Chinese.
1789 **477** $3 brown .. .. 25 10

**1988.** Science and Technology. Multicoloured.
1790 $1.50 Type **478** .. .. 15 10
1791 $3 Surveyors at oil field (energy) .. .. 20 10
1792 $7 Syringe piercing letter "B" (hepatitis control) 25 10
1793 $7.50 Mechanised production line (automation) .. .. 30 10
1794 $10 Satellite and computer terminal (information) .. .. 40 15
1795 $12 Laser (electro-optics) 50 20
1796 $16 Laboratory worker (materials) .. .. 65 25
1797 $16.50 Tin of fruit and technician (food technology) .. .. 65 25

**1988.** Flowers (2nd series). As T **474**. Mult.
1798 $3 Tree peony .. .. 40 10
1799 $7.50 Pomegranate .. 1·25 10
1800 $12 East Indian lotus .. 2·00 20

**479** Policemen on Point Duty and Motor Cycle

**1988.** Police Day. Multicoloured.
1802 $3 Type **479** .. .. 40 10
1803 $12 Communications operator and fire-fighters .. .. 75 20

**480** Butler's Pigmy Frog

**1988.** Amphibians. Multicoloured.

| | | | |
|---|---|---|---|
| 1804 | $1.50 Type **480** .. .. | 50 | 10 |
| 1805 | $3 Taipeh striped slender frog .. .. .. | 60 | 10 |
| 1806 | $7.50 "Microhyla inornata" .. .. | 2·25 | 10 |
| 1807 | $16 Tree frog .. .. | 4·50 | 35 |

**481** "60" on Map

**1988.** 60th Anniv of Broadcasting Corporation of China.

| | | | |
|---|---|---|---|
| 1808 | **481** $3 multicoloured .. | 20 | 10 |

**1988.** Flowers (3rd series). As T **474**. Mult.

| | | | |
|---|---|---|---|
| 1809 | $3 Garden balsam .. | 40 | 10 |
| 1810 | $7.50 Sweet osmanthus .. | 1·25 | 10 |
| 1811 | $12 Chrysanthemum .. | 2·00 | 20 |

**482** Chiang Kai-shek and Soldiers

**1988.** 30th Anniv of Kinmen Bombardment. Multicoloured.

| | | | |
|---|---|---|---|
| 1813 | $1.50 Type **482** .. .. | 25 | 10 |
| 1814 | $3 Chiang Kai-shek and soldier reporters .. | 25 | 10 |
| 1815 | $7.50 Soldiers firing howitzer .. .. | 65 | 10 |
| 1816 | $12 Tank battle .. | 75 | 20 |

**483** Basketball Player

**1988.** Sports Day. Multicoloured.

| | | | |
|---|---|---|---|
| 1817 | $5 Type **483** .. .. | 20 | 10 |
| 1818 | $5 Two basketball players | 20 | 10 |
| 1819 | $5 Baseball hitter .. | 20 | 10 |
| 1820 | $5 Baseball catcher .. | 20 | 10 |

**484** Crater

**1988.** Yangmingshan National Park. Mult.

| | | | |
|---|---|---|---|
| 1821 | $1.50 Type **484** .. .. | 50 | 10 |
| 1822 | $3 Lake .. .. | 75 | 10 |
| 1823 | $7.50 Mountains .. .. | 2·00 | 10 |
| 1824 | $16 Lake and mountains | 2·50 | 25 |

**485/8** "Lofty Mount Lu"

**1988.** Painting by Shen Chou.

| | | | | |
|---|---|---|---|---|
| 1825 | **485** | $5 multicoloured .. | 20 | 10 |
| 1826 | **486** | $5 multicoloured .. | 20 | 10 |
| 1827 | **487** | $5 multicoloured .. | 20 | 10 |
| 1828 | **488** | $5 multicoloured .. | 20 | 10 |

Nos. 1825/8 were printed together, se-tenant, forming the composite design illustrated.

**1988.** Flowers (4th series). As T **474**. Mult.

| | | | |
|---|---|---|---|
| 1829 | $3 Cotton rose hibiscus .. | 65 | 10 |
| 1830 | $7.50 Camellia .. .. | 1·75 | 10 |
| 1831 | $12 Narcissus .. .. | 2·25 | 20 |

**1988.** Chinese Costumes (4th series). As T **469**. Multicoloured.

| | | | |
|---|---|---|---|
| 1833 | $2 Nobleman with tall hat, Shang dynasty .. | 65 | 10 |
| 1834 | $3 Ruler with topknot, Warring States period | 75 | 10 |
| 1835 | $7.50 Male official with writing brush in hair, Wei-chin dynasty .. | 95 | 10 |
| 1836 | $12 Male court official with hanging brush on hat, late Northern dynasties .. .. | 1·75 | 20 |

**489** Snake

**490** Tai Ch'uan-hsien

**1988.** New Year Greetings. "Year of the Snake".

| | | | | |
|---|---|---|---|---|
| 1837 | **489** | $2 multicoloured .. | 1·25 | 10 |
| 1838 | | $13 multicoloured .. | 2·25 | 20 |

See also No. 2043.

**1989.** Birth Centenary (1990) of Tai Ch'uan-hsien (Civil Service reformer).

| | | | | |
|---|---|---|---|---|
| 1840 | **490** | $3 black .. .. | 35 | 10 |

**491** Pres. Chiang Ching-kuo

**1989.** 1st Death Anniv. of President Chiang Ching-Kuo. Multicoloured.

| | | | |
|---|---|---|---|
| 1841 | $3 Type **491** .. .. | 15 | 10 |
| 1842 | $6 Chiang Ching-kuo, political rally and voters .. .. .. | 35 | 10 |
| 1843 | $7.50 Chiang Ching-kuo at docks .. .. .. | 75 | 15 |
| 1844 | $16 Chiang Ching-kuo with children .. .. | 85 | 25 |

**492** Pine Tree

**1989.** Pine, Bamboo and Plum (4th series). Multicoloured.

| | | | |
|---|---|---|---|
| 1845 | $3 Type **492** .. .. | 10 | 10 |
| 1846 | $16.50 Bamboo .. .. | 65 | 25 |
| 1847 | $21 Plum blossom .. | 80 | 30 |

**493** Ni Ying-tien

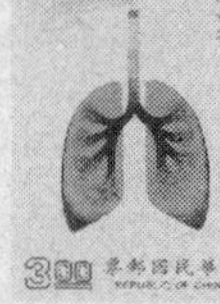

**494** Lungs smoking

**1989.** 79th Death Anniv of Ni Ying-tien (revolutionary).

| | | | | |
|---|---|---|---|---|
| 1848 | **493** | $3 black .. .. | 20 | 10 |

**1989.** Anti-smoking Campaign.

| | | | | |
|---|---|---|---|---|
| 1849 | **494** | $3 multicoloured .. | 20 | 10 |

**495** Mu Tou Yu Lighthouse

**496** Distribution of Industrial Goods

**1989.** Lighthouses. White panel at foot. Mult.

| | | | |
|---|---|---|---|
| 1850 | 75 c. Type **495** .. .. | 10 | 10 |
| 1851 | $2 Lu Tao lighthouse .. | 10 | 10 |
| 1852 | $2.25 Pen Chia Yu lighthouse .. .. .. | 15 | 10 |
| 1853 | $3 Pitou Chiao lighthouse | 15 | 10 |
| 1854 | $4.50 Tungyin Tao lighthouse .. .. .. | 25 | 10 |
| 1855 | $6 Chilai Pi lighthouse .. | 35 | 25 |
| 1856 | $7 Fukwei Chiao lighthouse .. .. .. | 45 | 30 |
| 1857 | $7.50 Hua Yu lighthouse | 45 | 30 |
| 1858 | $9 Oluan Pi lighthouse .. | 50 | 25 |
| 1859 | $10 Kaohsiung lighthouse | 60 | 40 |
| 1860 | $10.50 Yuweng Tao lighthouse .. .. .. | 60 | 30 |
| 1861 | $12 Tungchu Tao lighthouse .. .. | 70 | 50 |
| 1862 | $13 Yeh Liu lighthouse .. | 75 | 35 |
| 1863 | $15 Tungchi Yu lighthouse .. .. .. | 90 | 70 |
| 1864 | $16.50 Chimei Yu lighthouse .. .. .. | 95 | 65 |

For designs with blue panel at foot, see Nos. 2003/15.

**1989.** National Wealth Survey.

| | | | | |
|---|---|---|---|---|
| 1865 | **496** | $3 multicoloured | 30 | 10 |

**497** "I once tended nine Fields of Orchids"

**1989.** Chinese Classical Poetry (5th series). Poems from "Ch'u Ts'u". Multicoloured.

| | | | |
|---|---|---|---|
| 1866 | $3 Type **497** .. .. | 25 | 10 |
| 1867 | $7.50 "No grief is greater than parting" .. | 65 | 10 |
| 1868 | $12 "...living remote and neglected" .. .. | 2·00 | 20 |
| 1869 | $16 "The horse will not gallop into servitude" | 2·50 | 25 |

**498** Underground Train

**1989.** Completion of Taipeh Underground Section of Western Railway Line. Mult.

| | | | |
|---|---|---|---|
| 1870 | $3 Type **498** .. .. | 30 | 10 |
| 1871 | $16 Train leaving tunnel | 1·25 | 25 |

**499** Blue Triangle

**1989.** Butterflies (1st series). Multicoloured.

| | | | |
|---|---|---|---|
| 1872 | $2 Type **499** .. .. | 25 | 15 |
| 1873 | $3 Great mormon .. | 45 | 15 |
| 1874 | $7.50 Chequered swallow-tail .. .. .. | 75 | 20 |
| 1875 | $9 Common rose .. | 1·00 | 20 |

See also Nos. 1902/5.

**500** Pumpkin Teapot

**501** Fan Chung-yen

**1989.** Teapots (1st series). Multicoloured.

| | | | |
|---|---|---|---|
| 1876 | $2 Type **500** .. .. | 50 | 10 |
| 1877 | $3 Clay teapot .. .. | 75 | 10 |
| 1878 | $12 "Chopped wood" teapot .. .. | 1·25 | 25 |
| 1879 | $16 Clay pear teapot .. | 1·50 | 30 |

See also Nos. 1946/50.

**1989.** Birth Millenary of Fan Chung-yen (civil service reformer).

| | | | | |
|---|---|---|---|---|
| 1880 | **501** | $12 multicoloured .. | 1·00 | 25 |

**502** Trees and Right Side of Mountain

**1989.** Painting "Autumn Colours on the Ch'iao and Hua Mountains" by Ch'iao Meng-fu. Designs showing details of the scroll. Multicoloured.

| | | | |
|---|---|---|---|
| 1881 | $7.50 (1) Type **502** .. | 75 | 15 |
| 1882 | $7.50 (2) Left side of mountain and trees .. | 75 | 15 |
| 1883 | $7.50 (3) Trees and house | 75 | 15 |
| 1884 | $7.50 (4) Mountain, trees and house .. | 75 | 15 |

Nos. 1872/5 were printed together, se-tenant, forming a composite design.

**503** Insured Groups and Family

**504** Liwu River Gorge

**1989.** Social Welfare.

| | | | | |
|---|---|---|---|---|
| 1885 | **503** | $3 multicoloured .. | 25 | 10 |

**1989.** Taroko National Park. Multicoloured.
1886 $2 Type **504** .. .. 15 10
1887 $3 North Peak of Chilai, Taroko Mountain .. 25 10
1888 $12 Waterfalls .. .. 90 25
1889 $16 Chingshui Cliff .. 1·10 30

**505** Horse

**506** Yu Lu

**1989.** New Year Greetings. "Year of the Horse".
1890 **505** $2 multicoloured .. 25 10
1891 $13 multicoloured .. 1·25 25
See also No. 2044.

**1990.** Door Gods. Multicoloured.
1893 $3 Type **506** .. .. 1·00 20
1894 $3 Shen Shu .. .. 1·00 20
1895 $7.50 Wei-ch'ih Ching-te (facing right) .. .. 2·00 40
1896 $7.50 Ch'in Shu-pao (facing left) .. .. 2·00 40

**507** Lishan

**508** Crystal containing Emblem and Industrial Symbols

**1990.** Tourism. Multicoloured.
1897 $2 Type **507** .. .. 15 10
1898 $18 Fir tree at Tayuling (vert) .. .. .. 1·25 25

**1990.** 40th Anniv of National Insurance.
1899 **508** $3 multicoloured .. 35 10

**509** Harbour and Tanks

**1990.** Yung-An Hsiang Liquefied Natural Gas Terminal. Multicoloured.
1900 $3 Type **509** .. .. 25 10
1901 $16 Gas tanker and map showing pipeline route (vert) .. .. .. 1·25 25

**510** African Monarch

**511** Court Official, Northern Wei Period to T'ang Dynasty

**1990.** Butterflies (2nd series). Multicoloured.
1902 $2 Orange tiger .. .. 25 10
1903 $3 Type **510** .. .. 30 10
1904 $7.50 "Pieris canidia" .. 65 20
1905 $9 Peacock .. .. 80 25

**1990.** Chinese Costumes (5th series). Mult.
1906 $2 Type **511** .. .. 30 10
1907 $3 Civil official in winged hat and green robe, Three Kingdoms period to Ming dynasty .. 40 10
1908 $7.50 Royal guard in bamboo hat, Yuan dynasty .. .. 85 15
1909 $12 Highest grade civil official in robe decorated with crane bird, Ming dynasty .. 1·10 40

**512** "Spring Song at Midnight"

**1990.** Chinese Classical Poetry (6th series). Multicoloured.
1910 $3 Type **512** .. .. 30 10
1911 $7.50 Couple on river bank ("Summer Song at Midnight") .. 75 15
1912 $12 Girl washing clothes in river ("Autumn Song at Midnight") .. 1·00 20
1913 $16 Snow-bound river scene ("Winter Song at Midnight") .. .. 1·25 25

**513** Japanese Black Pine

**514** Bamboo-shaped Glass Snuff Bottle

**1990.** Bonsai. Multicoloured.
1914 $3 Type **513** .. .. 30 10
1915 $6.50 "Ehretia microphylla" .. .. 50 10
1916 $12 "Buxus harlandii" .. 80 20
1917 $16 "Celtis sinensis" .. 1·00 25

**1990.** Snuff Bottles. Multicoloured.
1918 $3 Type **514** .. .. 25 10
1919 $6 Glass bottle with peony design .. .. 50 10
1920 $9 Melon-shaped amber bottle .. .. 75 15
1921 $16 White jade bottle .. 1·10 25

**515** Taiwan Firecrest

**516** Running

**1990.** Birds. Multicoloured.
1922 $2 Type **515** .. .. 20 10
1923 $3 Formosan barwing .. 25 10
1924 $7.50 White-eared sibia .. 60 10
1925 $16 Formosan yellow tit 1·10 25

**1990.** Sports. Multicoloured.
1926 $2 Type **516** .. .. 15 10
1927 $3 Long jumping .. 25 10
1928 $7 Pole vaulting .. 50 10
1929 $16 Hurdling .. .. 1·25 25

**517** Curtiss Tomahawk II Fighters and Air Crews

**1990.** 50th Anniv of Arrival of "Flying Tigers" American Volunteer Group.
1930 **517** $3 multicoloured .. 25 10

**INDEX**
Countries can be quickly located by referring to the index at the end of this volume.

**518** Cats

**1990.** Children's Drawings. Multicoloured.
1931 $2 Type **518** .. .. 15 10
1932 $3 Common peafowl .. 25 10
1933 $7.50 Chickens .. 60 15
1934 $12 Cattle market .. 1·00 20

**519** National Theatre

**520** Cowrie Shells

**1990.** Cultural Buildings in Chiang Kai-shek Memorial Park, Taipeh.
1935 **519** $3 orange, dp bl & bl 25 10
1936 – $12 mauve, vio & lilac 1·00 20
DESIGN: $12 National Concert Hall.

**1990.** Ancient Coins. "Shell" Money. Mult.
1937 $2 Type **520** .. .. 15 10
1938 $3 Oyster shell .. .. 25 10
1939 $6.50 Bone .. .. 50 10
1940 $7.50 Bronze .. .. 60 15
1941 $9 Jade .. .. .. 80 20

**521** Sheep

**522** Hu Shih

**1990.** New Year Greetings. "Year of the Sheep".
1942 **521** $2 multicoloured .. 25 10
1943 $13 multicoloured .. 1·00 20
See also No. 2045.

**1990.** Birth Centenary of Hu Shih (written Chinese reformer).
1945 **522** $3 violet .. 25 10

**523** Teapot with Dragon Spout and Handle

**524** Happiness

**1991.** Teapots (2nd series). Multicoloured.
1946 $2 Blue and white teapot with phoenix design .. 15 10
1947 $3 Type **523** .. .. 25 10
1948 $9 Teapot with floral design on lid and landscape on body .. 55 15
1949 $12 Rectangular teapot with passion flower design .. .. .. 75 20
1950 $16 Brown rectangular teapot with floral decoration .. .. 90 25

**1991.** Greetings Stamps. Gods of Prosperity. Multicoloured.
1951 $3 Type **524** .. .. 25 10
1952 $3 Wealth .. .. 25 10
1953 $7.50 Longevity .. 65 15
1954 $7.50 Joy .. .. 65 15

**525** "Petasites formosanus"

**526** Hsiung Cheng-chi (revolutionary)

**1991.** Plants (1st series). Multicoloured.
1955 $2 Type **525** .. .. 15 10
1956 $3 "Heloniopsis acutifolia" .. .. .. 25 10
1957 $7.50 "Disporum shimadai" .. .. 65 15
1958 $9 "Viola nagasawai" .. 75 15
See also Nos. 1969/72, 1995/8 and 2026/9.

**1991.** Famous Chinese.
1959 **526** $3 blue .. .. 25 10

**527** Agriculture

**528** Bamboo Hobby-horse

**1991.** 80th Anniv (1992) of Founding of Chinese Republic. Multicoloured.
1960 $3 Type **527** .. .. 25 10
1961 $7.50 Industry .. .. 65 10
1962 $12 Dancer and leisure equipment .. .. 1·00 20
1963 $16 Transport and communications .. 1·25 30

**1991.** Children's Games (1st series). Mult.
1964 $3 Type **528** .. .. 25 10
1965 $3 Woven-grass grasshoppers .. .. 25 10
1966 $3 Spinning tops .. 25 10
1967 $3 Windmills .. .. 25 10
See also Nos. 2056/9, 2120/3 and 2184/7.

**1991.** Plants (2nd series). As T **525**. Mult.
1969 $2 "Gaultheria itoana" .. 15 10
1970 $3 "Lysionotus montanus" .. .. 25 10
1971 $7.50 "Leontopodium microphyllum" .. 65 15
1972 $9 "Gentiana flavomaculata" .. .. 75 15

**529** Male Official's Summer Court Dress

**530** Heart, Pedestrian Crossing and Hand

**1991.** Chinese Costumes (6th series). Ch'ing Dynasty. Multicoloured.
1973 $2 Male official's winter court dress with dragon design .. .. 20 10
1974 $3 Type **529** .. .. 30 10
1975 $7.50 Male official's winter overcoat .. .. 65 15
1976 $12 Everyday skull-cap, jacket and travelling robe .. .. .. 1·00 20

**1991.** Road Safety. Multicoloured.
1977 $3 Type **530** .. .. 30 10
1978 $7.50 Hand, road and broken bottle ("Don't Drink and Drive") .. 65 15

**531** Ch'ing Dynasty Cloisonne Lion

**532** Strawberries

**1991.** No value expressed. Multicoloured.
1979 (-) Type **531** .. .. 40 15
1980 (-) Cloisonne lioness .. 1·10 25
Nos. 1979/80 were sold at the prevailing rates for domestic ordinary and domestic prompt delivery letters.

**1991.** Fruits. Multicoloured.
1981 $3 Type **532** .. .. 30 10
1982 $7.50 Grapes .. .. 65 15
1983 $9 Mango .. .. 80 20
1984 $16 Sugar apple .. 1·10 25

533 Formosan Whistling Thrush

**1991.** River Birds. Multicoloured.

| | | | |
|---|---|---|---|
| 1985 | $5 Type **533** .. .. | 40 | 10 |
| 1986 | $5 Brown dipper .. | 40 | 10 |
| 1987 | $5 Mandarins .. .. | 40 | 10 |
| 1988 | $5 Black-crowned night herons .. .. | 40 | 10 |
| 1989 | $5 Little egrets .. .. | 40 | 10 |
| 1990 | $5 Plumbeous redstarts .. | 40 | 10 |
| 1991 | $5 Little forktail .. | 40 | 10 |
| 1992 | $5 Grey wagtail .. .. | 40 | 10 |
| 1993 | $5 Common kingfishers .. | 40 | 10 |
| 1994 | $5 Pied wagtails .. | 40 | 10 |

Nos. 1985/94 were printed together, se-tenant, forming a composite design.

**1991.** Plants (3rd series). As T **525**. Mult.

| | | | |
|---|---|---|---|
| 1995 | $3.50 "Rosa transmorrisonensis" .. | 30 | 10 |
| 1996 | $5 "Impatiens devolii" .. | 50 | 10 |
| 1997 | $9 "Impatiens uniflora" | 80 | 20 |
| 1998 | $12 "Impatiens tayemonii" .. .. | 1·00 | 20 |

534 Rock Climbing

**1991.** International Camping and Caravanning Federation Rally, Fulung Beach. Mult.

| | | | |
|---|---|---|---|
| 1999 | $2 Type **534** .. .. | 15 | 10 |
| 2000 | $3 Fishing .. .. | 25 | 10 |
| 2001 | $7.50 Bird-watching .. | 65 | 15 |
| 2002 | $10 Boys with pail wading in water .. .. | 90 | 20 |

**1991.** Lighthouses. As Nos. 1851/3 and 1855/64 but with blue panel at foot.

| | | | |
|---|---|---|---|
| 2003 | 50 c. As No. 1863 .. | 10 | 10 |
| 2004 | $1 As No. 1851 .. .. | 10 | 10 |
| 2005 | $3.50 As No. 1855 .. | 20 | 10 |
| 2006 | $5 As No. 1856 .. .. | 25 | 10 |
| 2007 | $7 As No. 1853 .. .. | 35 | 10 |
| 2008 | $9 As No. 1858 .. .. | 45 | 15 |
| 2009 | $10 As No. 1859 .. .. | 50 | 10 |
| 2010 | $12 As No. 1861 .. .. | 60 | 15 |
| 2011 | $13 As No. 1852 .. .. | 65 | 15 |
| 2012 | $19 As No. 1857 .. .. | 95 | 20 |
| 2013 | $20 As No. 1862 .. .. | 1·00 | 20 |
| 2014 | $26 As No. 1860 .. .. | 1·25 | 25 |
| 2015 | $28 As No. 1864 .. .. | 1·40 | 30 |

535 Peacock

536 Monkey

**1991.** "Peacocks" by Giuseppe Castiglione. Designs showing details of painting. Mult.

| | | | |
|---|---|---|---|
| 2020 | $5 Type **535** .. .. | 30 | 10 |
| 2021 | $20 Peacock displaying tail .. .. .. | 1·75 | 35 |

**1991.** New Year Greetings. "Year of the Monkey".

| | | | |
|---|---|---|---|
| 2023 | **536** $3.50 multicoloured .. | 25 | 10 |
| 2024 | $13 multicoloured .. | 1·25 | 25 |

See also No. 2046.

**1991.** Plants (4th series). As T **525**. Mult.

| | | | |
|---|---|---|---|
| 2026 | $3.50 "Kalanchoe garambiensis" .. | 30 | 10 |
| 2027 | $5 "Pieris taiwanensis" .. | 50 | 10 |
| 2028 | $9 "Pleione formosana" | 80 | 20 |
| 2029 | $12 "Elaeagnus oldhamii" | 1·00 | 20 |

537 Scrolls

538 Peace in the Wake of Firecrackers

**1992.** International Book Fair, Taipeh. Mult.

| | | | |
|---|---|---|---|
| 2030 | $3.50 Type **537** .. .. | 30 | 10 |
| 2031 | $5 Folded-leaves book .. | 40 | 10 |
| 2032 | $9 Butterfly-bound books | 75 | 15 |
| 2033 | $15 Sewn books .. .. | 1·10 | 25 |

**1992.** Greetings Stamps. Nienhwas (paintings conveying wishes for the coming year). Multicoloured.

| | | | |
|---|---|---|---|
| 2034 | $5 Type **538** .. .. | 40 | 10 |
| 2035 | $5 Elephant with riders (Good fortune and satisfaction) .. .. | 40 | 10 |
| 2036 | $12 Children and five "birds" (Five blessings upon the house) .. | 90 | 20 |
| 2037 | $12 Children angling for large fish (Abundance for every year) .. | 90 | 20 |

**1992.** Signs of Chinese Zodiac. As previous designs but with additional symbol in top left-hand corner.

| | | | | |
|---|---|---|---|---|
| 2038 | **393** | $5 multicoloured .. | 35 | 10 |
| 2039 | **414** | $5 multicoloured .. | 35 | 10 |
| 2040 | **435** | $5 multicoloured .. | 35 | 10 |
| 2041 | **456** | $5 multicoloured .. | 35 | 10 |
| 2042 | **471** | $5 multicoloured .. | 35 | 10 |
| 2043 | **489** | $5 multicoloured .. | 35 | 10 |
| 2044 | **505** | $5 multicoloured .. | 35 | 10 |
| 2045 | **521** | $5 multicoloured .. | 35 | 10 |
| 2046 | **536** | $5 multicoloured .. | 35 | 10 |
| 2047 | **340** | $5 multicoloured .. | 35 | 10 |
| 2048 | **361** | $5 multicoloured .. | 35 | 10 |
| 2049 | **378** | $5 multicoloured .. | 35 | 10 |

Nos. 2038/49 were issued together in se-tenant blocks of 12 stamps within the sheet. The stamps are listed in order from right to left of the block.

539 Taiwan Red Cypress ("Chamaecyparis formosensis")

541 Mother and Son (Spring)

**1992.** Forest Resources. Conifers. Mult.

| | | | |
|---|---|---|---|
| 2051 | $5 Type **539** .. .. | 40 | 10 |
| 2052 | $5 Taiwan cypress ("Chamaecyparis taiwanensis") .. .. | 40 | 10 |
| 2053 | $5 Taiwan incense cedar ("Calocedrus formosana") .. .. | 40 | 10 |
| 2054 | $5 Ranta fir ("Cunninghamia konishii") .. | 40 | 10 |
| 2055 | $5 Taiwania ("Taiwania cryptomerioides") .. | 40 | 10 |

Nos. 2051/5 were printed together, se-tenant, forming a composite design.

**1992.** Children's Games (2nd series). As T **528**. Multicoloured.

| | | | |
|---|---|---|---|
| 2056 | $5 Walking on tin cans .. | 40 | 10 |
| 2057 | $5 Chopstick guns .. | 40 | 10 |
| 2058 | $5 Rolling hoops .. | 40 | 10 |
| 2059 | $5 Grass fighting .. | 40 | 10 |

**1992.** Parent–Child Relationships. Mult.

| | | | |
|---|---|---|---|
| 2062 | $3.50 Type **541** .. .. | 25 | 10 |
| 2063 | $5 Mother carrying child on back (summer) .. | 35 | 10 |
| 2064 | $9 Mother and child pushing toy rabbits (autumn) .. .. | 65 | 15 |
| 2065 | $10 Mother feeding child (winter) .. .. | 75 | 15 |

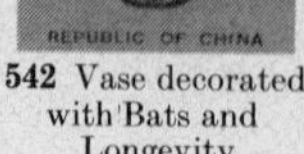

542 Vase decorated with Bats and Longevity Characters

543 Lion and Stone Pavilion

**1992.** Glassware decorated with Enamel. Multicoloured.

| | | | |
|---|---|---|---|
| 2066 | $3.50 Type **542** .. .. | 30 | 10 |
| 2067 | $5 Gourd-shaped vase decorated with landscape and children at play .. .. .. | 40 | 10 |
| 2068 | $7 Vase with peony decoration .. .. | 75 | 15 |
| 2069 | $17 Vase showing mother teaching child to read | 1·25 | 25 |

**1992.** Stone Lions from Lugouqiao Bridge.

| | | | | |
|---|---|---|---|---|
| 2070 | **543** | $5 blue and brown .. | 30 | 10 |
| 2071 | – | $5 green and violet .. | 30 | 10 |
| 2072 | – | $12 orange and green | 80 | 20 |
| 2073 | – | $12 violet and black | 80 | 20 |

DESIGNS: No. 2071, Bridge and lioness with cub; 2070, Bridge parapet and lion; 2073, Bridge parapet and lioness with two cubs.

544 "People make Friends and are tied to Each Other as Roots to a Plant"

**1992.** Chinese Classical Poetry. Multicoloured.

| | | | |
|---|---|---|---|
| 2074 | $3.50 Type **544** .. .. | 25 | 10 |
| 2075 | $5 Couple at window ("Conjugal love will last forever") .. .. | 30 | 10 |
| 2076 | $9 Couple in garden ("Man takes pains to uphold virtue / Till one's hair turns forever grey") .. .. | 65 | 15 |
| 2077 | $15 "Tartar horses lean toward the north wind" | 1·10 | 25 |

545 Drummer and Crowd

546 "Two Birds perched on a Red Camellia Branch"

**1992.** Temple Fair. Multicoloured.

| | | | |
|---|---|---|---|
| 2078 | $5 Type **545** .. .. | 35 | 10 |
| 2079 | $5 Man with basket dancing .. .. | 35 | 10 |
| 2080 | $5 Musicians .. .. | 35 | 10 |
| 2081 | $5 Man pushing cart .. | 35 | 10 |
| 2082 | $5 Women and children | 35 | 10 |

Nos. 2078/82 were printed together, se-tenant, forming a composite design.

**1992.** Ming Dynasty Silk Tapestries. Mult.

| | | | |
|---|---|---|---|
| 2083 | $5 Type **546** .. .. | 30 | 10 |
| 2084 | $12 "Two Birds playing on a Peach Branch" .. | 1·00 | 20 |

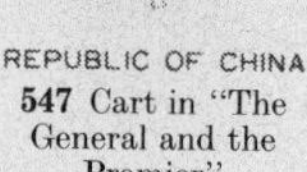

547 Cart in "The General and the Premier"

548 Steam Locomotive and Train

**1992.** Chinese Opera Props. Multicoloured.

| | | | |
|---|---|---|---|
| 2086 | $3.50 Type **547** .. .. | 30 | 10 |
| 2087 | $5 Ship in "The Lucky Pearl" .. .. | 40 | 10 |
| 2088 | $9 Horse in "Chao-chun serves as an Envoy" .. | 60 | 15 |
| 2089 | $12 Sedan chair in "Escort to the Wedding" .. | 75 | 15 |

**1992.** Alishan Mountain Railway. Mult.

| | | | |
|---|---|---|---|
| 2090 | $5 Type **548** .. .. | 40 | 10 |
| 2091 | $15 Diesel locomotive and train .. .. .. | 1·00 | 20 |

549 Chinese River Otter

550 Cock

**1992.** Mammals. Multicoloured.

| | | | |
|---|---|---|---|
| 2092 | $5 Type **549** .. .. | 35 | 10 |
| 2093 | $5 Formosan flying fox .. | 35 | 10 |
| 2094 | $5 Formosan clouded leopard .. .. | 35 | 10 |
| 2095 | $5 Formosan black bear | 35 | 10 |

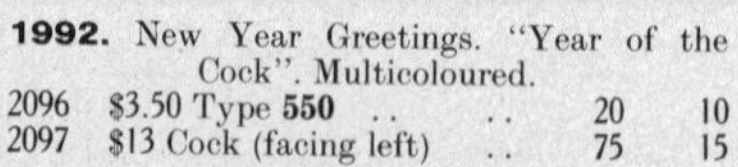

**1992.** New Year Greetings. "Year of the Cock". Multicoloured.

| | | | |
|---|---|---|---|
| 2096 | $3.50 Type **550** .. .. | 20 | 10 |
| 2097 | $13 Cock (facing left) .. | 75 | 15 |

552 Schall and Astronomical Instruments

**1992.** 400th Birth Anniv of Johann Adam Schall von Bell (missionary astronomer).

| | | | |
|---|---|---|---|
| 2100 | **552** $5 multicoloured .. | 25 | 10 |

553 Satisfaction for Every Year

**1993.** Greetings Stamps. Nienhwas (paintings conveying wishes for the coming year). Multicoloured.

| | | | |
|---|---|---|---|
| 2101 | $5 Type **553** .. .. | 25 | 10 |
| 2102 | $5 Birds and flowers (Joy) | 25 | 10 |
| 2103 | $12 Butterfly and flowers (Happiness and longevity) .. .. | 65 | 15 |
| 2104 | $12 Flowers in vase (Wealth and peace) .. | 65 | 15 |

554 Applying Enamel and Glass Decoration to Temple Roof

**1992.** International Traditional Crafts Exhibition, Taipeh. Multicoloured.

2105 $3.50 Type **554** .. .. 20 10
2106 $5 Ceremonial lantern .. 25 10
2107 $9 Pottery jars .. .. 50 10
2108 $15 Oil-paper umbrella .. 85 20

**555** Pan Gu creating Universe

**1993.** The Creation. Multicoloured.

2109 $3.50 Type **555** .. .. 20 10
2110 $5 Pan Gu creating animals (horiz) .. 25 10
2111 $9 Nu Wa creating human beings (horiz) .. 50 10
2112 $19 Nu Wa mending the sky with smelted stone 1·00 20

**556** Mandarins **557** Water Lily

**1993.** Lucky Animals (1st series).

2113 **556** $3.50 multicoloured .. 20 10
2114 – $5 multicoloured .. 25 10
2115 – $10 red and black .. 55 15
2116 – $15 multicoloured .. 85 20

DESIGNS: $5, Chinese unicorn. $10, Deer. $15, Crane.

See also Nos. 2151/4.

**1993.** Water Plants. Multicoloured.

2117 $5 Type **557** .. .. 25 10
2118 $9 Taiwan cow lily .. 50 10
2119 $12 Water hyacinth .. 65 15

**1993.** Children's Games (3rd series). As T **528**. Multicoloured.

2120 $5 Tossing sandbags .. 25 10
2121 $5 Bamboo dragonflies .. 25 10
2122 $5 Skipping .. .. 25 10
2123 $5 Duel of strength with rope passed round waists .. .. .. 25 10

**560** Ching-Kang-Chang Plateau (source)

**1993.** Yangtze River. Multicoloured.

2127 $3.50 Type **560** .. .. 20 10
2128 $3.50 Turn in river (Chinsha River) .. 20 10
2129 $5 Roaring Tiger Gorge (white water in narrow ravine) .. .. 25 10
2130 $5 Chutang Gorge (calm water in wide gorge) .. 25 10
2131 $9 Dragon Gate, Pawu and Titsui Gorges .. 50 10

**561** Noise Pollution and Music

**1993.** Environmental Protection. Children's Drawings. Multicoloured.

2132 $5 Type **561** .. .. 25 10
2133 $17 Family looking out over green fields (vert) 90 20

**562** Cup with Tou-Ts'ai Figures

**1993.** Ch'eng-hua Porcelain Cups of Ming Dynasty. Multicoloured.

2134 $3.50 Type **562** .. .. 20 10
2135 $5 Chicken decoration .. 25 10
2136 $7 Flowers and fruits of four seasons decoration 40 10
2137 $9 Dragon decoration .. 50 10

**563** Graphic Design **564** Child on Father's Shoulders

**1993.** 32nd International Vocational Training Competition, Taipeh. Multicoloured.

2138 $3.50 Type **563** .. .. 20 10
2139 $5 Computer technology 25 10
2140 $9 Carpentry .. .. 50 10
2141 $12 Welding .. .. 65 15

**1993.** Parent–Child Relationships. Mult.

2142 $3.50 Type **564** .. .. 20 10
2143 $5 Father playing flute to child .. .. 25 10
2144 $9 Child reading to father 50 10
2145 $10 Father pointing at bird .. .. .. 55 15

**566** Persimmons **567** Gymnastics

**1993.** Fruits. Multicoloured.

2147 $5 Type **566** .. .. 25 10
2148 $5 Peaches .. .. 25 10
2149 $12 Loquats .. .. 65 15
2150 $12 Papayas .. .. 65 15

**1993.** Lucky Animals (2nd series). As T **556**. Multicoloured.

2151 $1 Blue dragon (representing Spring, wood and the East) .. 10 10
2152 $2.50 White tiger (Autumn, metal and the West) .. .. 15 10
2153 $9 Linnet (Summer, fire and the South) .. 45 15
2154 $19 Black tortoise (Winter, water and the North) .. .. 95 20

**1993.** Taiwan Area Games, Taoyuan. Mult.

2155 $5 Type **567** .. .. 25 10
2156 $5 Taekwondo .. .. 25 10

**568** Stone Lion, New Park, Taipeh **569** Chick

**1993.** Stone Lions. Multicoloured.

2157 $3.50 Type **568** .. .. 15 10
2158 $5 Hsinchu City Council building .. .. 25 10
2159 $9 Temple, Hsinchu City 45 10
2160 $12 Fort Providentia, Tainan .. .. 60 15

**1993.** Mikado Pheasant. Multicoloured.

2161 $5 Type **569** .. .. 25 10
2162 $5 Mother and chicks .. 25 10
2163 $5 Immature male and female .. .. 25 10
2164 $5 Adults .. .. 25 10

Nos. 2161/4 were issued together, se-tenant, forming a composite design.

**570** Dog **571** Scientist and Vegetables

**1993.** New Year Greetings. "Year of the Dog". Multicoloured.

2165 $3.50 Type **570** .. .. 15 10
2166 $13 Dog (facing left) .. 65 15

**1993.** 20th Anniv of Asian Vegetable Research and Development Centre. Multicoloured.

2168 $5 Type **571** .. .. 25 10
2169 $13 Scientists and fields of crops .. .. .. 65 15

**573** Courtroom **574** Cutting Bamboo

**1994.** Inauguration of Taiwan Constitutional Court.

2171 **573** $5 multicoloured .. 25 10

**1994.** Traditional Paper Making. Mult.

2172 $3.50 Type **574** .. .. 15 10
2173 $3.50 Cooking bamboo .. 15 10
2174 $5 Moulding bamboo pulp in wooden panels .. 25 10
2175 $5 Stacking wet paper for pressing .. .. 25 10
2176 $12 Drying paper .. 60 15

**575** "Clivia miniata" **576** Wind Lion Lord

**1994.** Flowers. Multicoloured.

2177 $5 Type **575** .. .. 25 10
2178 $12 "Cymbidium sinense" 60 15
2179 $19 "Primula malacoides" 95 20

**1994.** Kinmen Wind Lion Lords.

2180 **576** $5 multicoloured .. 25 10
2181 – $9 multicoloured .. 45 10
2182 – $12 multicoloured .. 60 15
2183 – $17 multicoloured .. 85 20

DESIGNS: $9 to $17 Different Lion Lord statues.

**577** Sailing Paper Boats **578** Playing Chess

**1994.** Children's Games (4th series). Mult.

2184 $5 Type **577** .. .. 25 10
2185 $5 Fighting with water-guns .. .. 25 10
2186 $5 Throwing paper plane 25 10
2187 $5 Human train .. .. 25 10

**1994.** Rural Pastimes. Multicoloured.

2189 $5 Type **578** .. .. 25 10
2190 $10 Playing the flute .. 50 10
2191 $12 Telling stories .. 60 15
2192 $19 Drinking tea .. 95 20

**579** Tiger Bittern and Chicks **580** Book with Hand on Cover

**1994.** Parent–Child Relationships. Birds with their Young. Multicoloured.

2193 $5 Type **579** .. .. 25 10
2194 $7 Little tern (horiz) .. 35 10
2195 $10 Common noddy (horiz) 50 10
2196 $12 Muller's barbet .. 60 15

**1994.** Protection of Intellectual Property Rights. Multicoloured.

2197 $5 Type **580** .. .. 25 10
2198 $15 Head with locked computer disk as brain 75 15

**581** Caring for the Young **582** Anniversary Emblem and Olympic Rings

**1994.** International Rotary Clubs Convention, Taipeh. "Towards an Harmonious Society". Multicoloured.

2199 $5 Type **581** .. .. 25 10
2200 $17 Caring for the aged .. 85 20

**1994.** Centenary of International Olympic Committee. Multicoloured.

2201 $5 Type **582** .. .. 25 10
2202 $15 Running, high jumping and weight-lifting .. .. .. 75 15

**583** Summit of Dah-pa Mountain **584** Chien Mu

**1994.** Shei-pa National Park. Multicoloured.

2203 $5 Type **583** .. .. 25 10
2204 $7 Shei-san Valley .. 35 10
2205 $10 Holy Ridge .. .. 50 10
2206 $17 Shiah-tsuei Pool .. 85 20

**1994.** Birth Centenary of Chien Mu (academic).

2207 **584** $5 multicoloured .. 25 10

**585** Window

**1994.** International Year of the Family. Mult.

2208 $5 Type **585** .. .. 25 10
2209 $15 Globe and house .. 70 25

**586** Sueirenjy making Flame **587** Lin Yutang

**1994.** Invention Myths. Multicoloured.

2210 $5 Type **586** .. .. 25 10
2211 $10 Fushijy drawing Pa-kua characters .. 50 10
2212 $12 Shennungjy making pitchfork .. .. 60 20
2213 $15 Tsangjier inventing pictorial characters .. 70 25

**1994.** Birth Centenary of Dr. Lin Yutang (essayist and lexicographer).

2214 **587** $5 multicoloured .. 25 10

**588** Cheng Ho's Ship

**589** Dr. Sun Yat-sen

**1994.** World Trade Week. Multicoloured.

2215 $5 Type **588** .. .. 25 10

2216 $17 Cheng Ho and route map .. .. .. 85 20

**1994.** Centenary of Kuomintang Party. Mult.

2217 $5 Type **589** .. .. 25 10

2218 $19 Modern developments and voter placing slip in ballot box .. .. 95 20

**590** Pig

**591** Yen Chia-kan

**1994.** New Year Greetings. "Year of the Pig". Multicoloured.

2219 $3.50 Type **590** .. .. 15 10

2220 $13 Pig (facing left) .. 60 15

**1994.** 1st Death Anniv of Yen Chia-kan (President, 1974–78). Multicoloured.

2222 $5 Type **591** .. .. 25 10

2223 $15 Visiting farmers .. 70 15

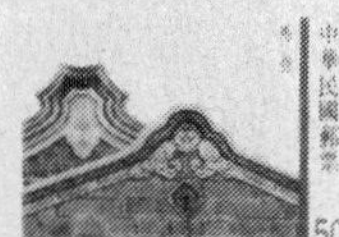
**592** Horse's Back

**593** Begonia

**1995.** Traditional Architecture. Roof Styles. Multicoloured.

2224 $5 Type **592** .. .. 25 10

2225 $5 Swallow's tail .. .. 25 10

2226 $12 Talisman (stove and bowl) .. .. 55 15

2227 $19 Cylinder-shaped brick 90 20

**1995.** Chinese Engravings. Flowers. Mult.

2228 $3.50 Type **593** .. .. 15 10

2229 $5 Rose .. .. .. 25 10

2230 $19 Flower .. .. 90 20

2231 $26 Climbing rose .. 1·25 25

**594** Rotating Wheel of Pipes

**595** Courtiers

**1995.** Irrigation Techniques from "Tian Gong Kai Wu" (encyclopaedia) by Sung Yin-shing. Multicoloured.

2232 $3.50 Type **594** .. .. 15 10

2233 $3.50 Donkey turning wheel to raise water .. 15 10

2234 $5 Pedal-driven device to raise water .. 25 10

2235 $12 Man turning wheel to raise water .. .. 55 15

2236 $13 Well .. .. .. 60 15

**1995.** "Beauties on an Outing" by Lee Gong-lin. Details of the painting. Mult.

2237 $9 Type **595** .. .. 45 10

2238 $9 Courtier and beauty with child .. .. 45 10

2239 $9 Courtier with two beauties .. .. 45 10

2240 $9 Courtier .. .. 45 10

Nos. 2237/40 were issued together, se-tenant, forming a composite design.

**596** Emblem and Landscape

**597** Chinese Showy Lily

**1995.** Inauguration of National Health Insurance Plan.

2242 **596** $12 multicoloured .. 55 15

**1995.** Flowers. Multicoloured.

2243 $5 Type **597** .. .. 25 10

2244 $12 Blood lily .. .. 55 15

2245 $19 Hyacinth .. .. 90 20

**598** Opening Lines

**1995.** Chinese Calligraphy. "Cold Food Observance" (poem) by Su Shih.

2246 **598** $5 (1) multicoloured 25 10

2247 – $5 (2) multicoloured 25 10

2248 – $5 (3) multicoloured 25 10

2249 – $5 (4) multicoloured 25 10

Nos. 2246/9 were issued together, se-tenant, forming a composite design; the stamps are numbered in Chinese numerals to the right of the face value, from right to left.

**599** Red Peony

**600** Hand, Birds and Cracked Symbol

**1995.** Peonies. Paintings by Tsou I-kuei. Self-adhesive. Imperf.

2250 $5 Type **599** .. .. 25 10

2251 $5 Pink peony .. .. 25 10

**1995.** Anti-drugs Campaign. Multicoloured.

2252 $5 Type **600** .. .. 25 10

2253 $12 Arm and syringe forming cross .. .. 55 15

**601** Old Hospital Building

**1995.** Centenary of National Taiwan University Hospital, Taipeh. Multicoloured.

2254 $5 Type **601** .. .. 25 10

2255 $19 New building .. 90 20

**602** Chichi Bay

**1995.** Tourism. East Coast National Scenic Area. Multicoloured.

2256 $5 Type **602** .. 25 10

2257 $5 Shihyuesan (rocky promontory) .. 25 10

2258 $12 Hsiaoyehlieu (eroded rocks) .. .. .. 55 15

2259 $15 Changhong Bridge .. 70 15

**603** Mating

**604** Bird feeding on Branch

**1995.** The Taiwan Salmon Trout. Mult.

2260 $5 Type **603** .. .. 25 10

2261 $7 Female digging redd .. 35 10

2262 $10 Fry hatching .. 50 10

2263 $17 Fry swimming .. 80 20

**1995.** Chinese Engravings. Birds. Mult.

2264 $2.50 Type **604** .. .. 10 10

2265 $7 Bird on branch of peach tree .. .. 35 10

2266 $13 Bird preening .. 60 15

2267 $28 Yellow bird .. .. 1·40 30

**605** "Tubastraea aurea"

**606** Pasteur

**1995.** Marine Life. Multicoloured.

2268 $3.50 Type **605** .. .. 15 10

2269 $3.50 "Chromodoris elizabethina" .. .. 15 10

2270 $5 "Spirobranchus giganteus corniculatus" 25 10

2271 $17 "Himerometra magnipinna" .. .. 80 20

**1995.** Death Cent of Louis Pasteur (chemist).

2272 **606** $17 multicoloured .. 80 20

**607** Porcelain Vase

**608** Soldiers

**1995.** 70th Anniv of National Palace Museum. Multicoloured.

2273 $3.50 "Strange Peaks and Myriad Trees" (painting) (horiz) .. 15 10

2274 $3.50 Type **607** .. .. 15 10

2275 $5 X Fu-K'uei Ting bronze three-fronted vessel .. .. .. 25 10

2276 $26 "The Fragrance of Flowers" (quatrain) (horiz) .. .. 1·25 25

**1995.** 50th Anniv of End of Sino-Japanese War. Multicoloured.

2277 $5 Type **608** .. .. 25 10

2278 $19 Taiwan flag, map and city .. .. .. 90 20

**609** Common Green Turtle ("Chelonia mydas")

**610** Scientists in Crop Field

**1995.** Year of the Sea Turtle. Multicoloured.

2280 $5 Type **609** .. .. 25 10

2281 $5 Loggerhead turtle ("Caretta caretta") .. 25 10

2282 $5 Olive ridley turtle ("Lepidochelys olivacea") .. .. 25 10

2283 $5 Hawksbill turtle ("Eretmochelys imbricata") .. .. 25 10

**1995.** Centenary of Taiwan Agricultural Research Institute. Multicoloured.

2284 $5 Type **610** .. .. 25 10

2285 $28 Scientists in greenhouse .. .. 1·40 30

**611** Rat

**612** Escorting Bride to Ceremony

**1996.** New Year Greetings. "Year of the Rat". Multicoloured.

2286 $3.50 Type **611** .. .. 15 10

2287 $13 Rat (different) .. 60 15

**1996.** Traditional Wedding Ceremonies. Multicoloured.

2289 $5 Type **612** .. .. 25 10

2290 $12 Honouring Heaven, Earth and ancestors .. 55 15

2291 $19 Nuptial chamber .. 90 20

**613** Sharon Fruit

**618** "Bougainvillea spectabilis"

**614/17** "Scenic Dwelling at Chu-Ch'u"

**1996.** Chinese Engravings of Fruit by Hu Chen-yan.

2292 **613** $9 multicoloured .. 40 10

2293 – $12 multicoloured .. 55 15

2294 – $15 multicoloured .. 70 15

2295 – $17 multicoloured .. 75 15

DESIGNS: $12 to $17, Different fruits.

**1996.** Painting by Wang Meng.

2296 **614** $5 multicoloured .. 25 10

2297 **615** $5 multicoloured .. 25 10

2298 **616** $5 multicoloured .. 25 10

2299 **617** $5 multicoloured .. 25 10

Nos. 2296/9 were issued together, se-tenant, forming the composite design illustrated.

**1996.** Flowering Vines. Multicoloured.

2300 $5 Type **618** .. .. 25 10

2301 $12 Wisteria .. .. 55 15

2302 $19 Wood rose .. .. 85 20

**619** Postboxes

**620** Lecture and University

**1996.** Centenary of Chinese State Postal Service. Multicoloured.

2303 $5 Type **619** .. .. 25 10

2304 $9 Weighing equipment 40 10

2305 $12 Postal transport .. 55 15

2306 $13 Modern technology .. 60 15

**1996.** Centenary of National Chiao Tung University.

2308 **620** $19 multicoloured .. 85 20

621 Chimei Giant Lion

**1996.** Tourism. Penghu National Scenic Area. Multicoloured.

| | | | |
|---|---|---|---|
| 2309 | $5 Type **621** .. .. | 25 | 10 |
| 2310 | $5 Chipei beach .. .. | 25 | 10 |
| 2311 | $12 Tungpan Yu .. | 55 | 15 |
| 2312 | $17 Tingkou Yu .. .. | 75 | 15 |

622 Hand holding Family (charity)

**1996.** 30th Anniv of Tzu-Chi Foundation (Buddhist relief organization). Mult.

| | | | |
|---|---|---|---|
| 2313 | $5 Type **622** .. .. | 25 | 10 |
| 2314 | $19 Hospital patient in tulip petal (medicine) | 85 | 20 |

623 With National Flag

**1996.** Inauguration of First Directly-elected President. Designs showing President Lee Teng-Hui and Vice-President Lien Chan. Multicoloured.

| | | | |
|---|---|---|---|
| 2315 | $3.50 Type **623** .. .. | 15 | 10 |
| 2316 | $5 Outside Presidential Office building | 25 | 10 |
| 2317 | $13 Asia-Pacific Operations Hub project | 60 | 15 |
| 2318 | $15 Meeting public at celebrations .. .. | 70 | 15 |

624 Monument

**1996.** South China Sea Archipelago. Pratas and Itu Aba Islands. Multicoloured.

| | | | |
|---|---|---|---|
| 2320 | $5 Type **624** .. .. | 25 | 10 |
| 2321 | $12 Monument (different) | 55 | 15 |

625 Modern Gymnast and Cyclist

626 Feeding Silkworms

**1996.** Centenary of Modern Olympic Games. Multicoloured.

| | | | |
|---|---|---|---|
| 2323 | $5 Type **625** .. .. | 25 | 10 |
| 2324 | $15 Ancient Greek athletes .. .. | 70 | 15 |

**1996.** Silk Production Techniques from "Tian Gong Kai Wu" (encyclopaedia) by Sung Yin-shing. Multicoloured.

| | | | |
|---|---|---|---|
| 2325 | $5 Type **626** .. .. | 25 | 10 |
| 2326 | $5 Picking out cocoons .. | 25 | 10 |
| 2327 | $7 Degumming raw silk | 30 | 10 |
| 2328 | $10 Reeling raw silk .. | 45 | 10 |
| 2329 | $13 Weaving silk .. | 60 | 15 |

628 Bamboo

629 Tou-kung Bracket

**1996.** Chinese Engravings. Plants. Mult.

| | | | |
|---|---|---|---|
| 2330 | $1 Type **628** .. .. | 10 | 10 |
| 2331 | $10 Orchid .. .. | 45 | 10 |
| 2332 | $20 Plum tree .. .. | 90 | 20 |

**1996.** Traditional Architecture. Roof Supports. Multicoloured.

| | | | |
|---|---|---|---|
| 2333 | $5 Type **629** .. .. | 25 | 10 |
| 2334 | $5 Chiue-ti bracket .. | 25 | 10 |
| 2335 | $10 Bu-tong beam .. | 45 | 10 |
| 2336 | $12 Dye-tou structure .. | 55 | 15 |

630 "Princess Iron Fan" (1941)

**1996.** Chinese Film Production. Mult.

| | | | |
|---|---|---|---|
| 2337 | $3.50 Type **630** .. | 15 | 10 |
| 2338 | $3.50 "Chin Shan Bi Xie" (1957) .. .. | 15 | 10 |
| 2339 | $5 "Oyster Girl" (1964) .. | 25 | 10 |
| 2340 | $19 "City of Sadness" (1989) .. .. | 85 | 20 |

631 Children dancing

**1996.** Winning Entries in Children's Stamp Design Competition. Multicoloured.

| | | | |
|---|---|---|---|
| 2341 | $5 Type **631** .. .. | 25 | 10 |
| 2342 | $5 Children playing in park .. .. | 25 | 10 |
| 2343 | $5 Black and white spotted cat .. | 25 | 10 |
| 2344 | $5 Ship .. .. | 25 | 10 |
| 2345 | $5 Children showering .. | 25 | 10 |
| 2346 | $5 Chinese gods and crowd .. .. | 25 | 10 |
| 2347 | $5 Pair of peacocks .. | 25 | 10 |
| 2348 | $5 Flying horse and rainbow .. .. | 25 | 10 |
| 2349 | $5 Elephant .. .. | 25 | 10 |
| 2350 | $5 Man and striped animals .. .. | 25 | 10 |
| 2351 | $5 Painting paper lampshades .. | 25 | 10 |
| 2352 | $5 Flock of geese .. | 25 | 10 |
| 2353 | $5 Children joining hands in garden .. .. | 25 | 10 |
| 2354 | $5 Archer .. .. | 25 | 10 |
| 2355 | $5 Children on ostrich's back .. .. | 25 | 10 |
| 2356 | $5 New Year celebrations | 25 | 10 |
| 2357 | $5 Butterflies on bamboo plant .. .. | 25 | 10 |
| 2358 | $5 Goatherd .. .. | 25 | 10 |
| 2359 | $5 Waterlilies on pond .. | 25 | 10 |
| 2360 | $5 Cats eating fish .. | 25 | 10 |

## POSTAGE DUE STAMPS

臺幣貳角 資欠 20
(D 12.)

捌角 臺幣 資欠 80 80
(D 15.)

**1950.** Surch. as Type D **12**.

| | | | | |
|---|---|---|---|---|
| D 105. | **6.** | 4 c. on $100 blue .. | 10·00 | 7·50 |
| D 106. | | 10 c. on $100 blue .. | 16·00 | 4·50 |
| D 107. | | 20 c. on $100 blue .. | 10·00 | 8·00 |
| D 108. | | 40 c. on $100 blue .. | 28·00 | 18·00 |
| D 109. | | $1 on $100 blue .. | 22·00 | 28·00 |

**1951.** No. 524 of China surch. as Type D **15**.

| | | | |
|---|---|---|---|
| D 133. | 40 c. on 40 c. orange .. | 13·00 | 13·00 |
| D 134. | 80 c. on 40 c. orange .. | 12·00 | 12·00 |

中華民國郵政
欠資台幣肆角

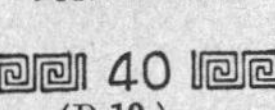
(D 19.)

(D 43.)

**1953.** Revenue stamps as T **143** of China surch. as Type D **19**.

| | | | |
|---|---|---|---|
| D 151. | 10 c. on $50 blue .. | 12·00 | 12·00 |
| D 152. | 20 c. on $100 olive .. | 12·00 | 7·50 |
| D 153. | 40 c. on $20 brown .. | 12·00 | 2·50 |
| D 154. | 80 c. on $500 green .. | 15·00 | 4·50 |
| D 155. | 100 c. on $30 mauve .. | 30·00 | 16·00 |

**1956.**

| | | | | |
|---|---|---|---|---|
| D 236. | D **43.** | 20 c. red and blue | 40 | 50 |
| D 237. | | 40 c. green and buff | 45 | 50 |
| D 238. | | 80 c. brown and grey | 75 | 75 |
| D 239. | | $1 blue and mauve | 1·25 | 75 |

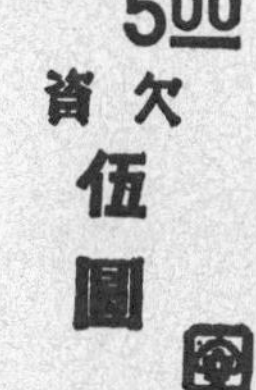

(D 97.)

D 152.

**1961.** Surch. with Type D **97**.

| | | | | |
|---|---|---|---|---|
| D 429. | **56.** | $5 on $20 red .. | 2·25 | 2·25 |

**1964.** Surch. as Type D **97**.

| | | | | |
|---|---|---|---|---|
| D 490. | **83.** | 10 c. on 80 c. green .. | 20 | 30 |
| D 491. | | 20 c. on $3·60 blue .. | 30 | 40 |
| D 492. | | 40 c. on $4·50 red .. | 40 | 35 |

**1966.**

| | | | | |
|---|---|---|---|---|
| D588 | D **152.** | 10 c. brown and lilac | 10 | 25 |
| D589 | | 20 c. blue and yellow | 15 | 25 |
| D590 | | 50 c. ultram. & blue | 1·00 | 40 |
| D591 | | $1 violet and flesh | 25 | 15 |
| D592 | | $2 green and blue | 25 | 15 |
| D593 | | $5 red and buff | 40 | 20 |
| D594a | | $10 purple & mauve | 6·50 | 1·00 |

D 399.

**1984.**

| | | | | |
|---|---|---|---|---|
| D1532a | D **399** | $1 red and blue | 10 | 10 |
| D1533a | | $2 yellow & blue | 10 | 10 |
| D1534 | | $3 green &mav | 10 | 10 |
| D1535a | | $5 blue & yellow | 20 | 15 |
| D1536 | | $5.50 mav & bl | 20 | 15 |
| D1537 | | $7.50 yell & vio | 30 | 25 |
| D1538b | | $10 yell & red | 25 | 20 |
| D1539 | | $20 blue & green | 75 | 65 |

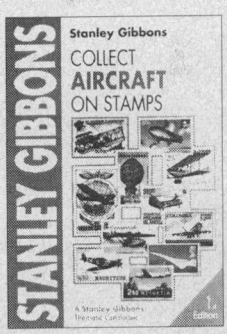

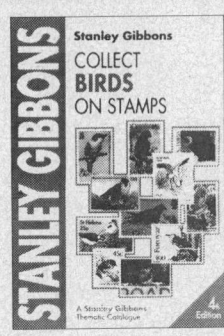

## CILICIA Pt. 16

A district in Asia Minor, occupied and temporarily controlled by the French between 1919 and 20 October 1921. The territory was then returned to Turkey.

40 paras = 1 piastre

**1919.** Various issues of Turkey optd **CILICIE**.

A. On No. 726 (surch Printed Matter stamp optd with Star and Crescent).
31 **15** 5 pa. on 10 pa. green .. 75 55

B. On 1901 issue optd with Star and Crescent.
2 **21** 1 pi. blue (No. 543) .. 45 40
33 1 pi. blue (No. 631) .. 80 70

C. On 1909 issue optd with Star and Crescent (No. 7 also optd as T **24**).
4 **28** 20 pa. red (No. 572) .. 50 45
35 20 pa. red (No. 643) .. 45 45
7 1 pi. blue (No. 649) .. £550 £225
8 1 pi. blue (No. 645) .. 3·75 2·25

D. On 1913 issue.
36 **30** 20 pa. pink .. .. 45 45

E. On Pictorial issue of 1914.
37 **32** 2 pa. purple .. .. 35 35
11 – 4 pa. brown (No. 500) .. 55 55
12 – 6 pa. blue (No. 502) .. 3·25 2·25
13 – 1¾ pi. brn & grey (No. 507) 95 90

F. On Postal Anniv issue of 1916.
14 **60** 5 pa. green .. .. 50·00 18·00
15 20 pa. blue .. .. 85 55
40 1 pi. black and violet .. 45 45
17 5 pi. black and brown .. 95 1·10

G. On Pictorial issues of 1916 and 1917.
18 **73** 10 pa. green .. .. 70 70
19 **76** 50 pa. blue .. .. 2·50 90
41 **69** 5 pi. on 2 pa. blue (No. 914) 55 55
21 **63** 25 pi. red on buff .. 1·00 80
22 **64** 50 pi. red .. .. 75 55
23 50 pi. blue .. .. 8·50 8·00

H. On Armistice issue of 1919 optd with T **81** of Turkey.
24 **76** 50 pa. blue .. .. 3·25 1·50
25 **77** 2 pi. blue and brown .. 70 65
26 **78** 5 pi. brown and blue .. 4·25 1·50

**1919.** Various issues of Turkey optd **Cilicie**.

A. On No. 726 (surch Printed Matter stamp optd with Star and Crescent).
46 **15** 5 pa. on 10 pa. green .. 55 55

B. On 1901 issue optd with Star and Crescent.
47 **21** 1 pi. blue (No. 543) .. 25 25
48 1 pi. blue (No. 631) .. 70 70
49 1 pi. blue (No. 669) .. 30·00 15·00

C. On 1908 issue optd with T **24** and Star and Crescent.
50 **25** 20 pa. red .. .. 3·25 1·60

D. On 1909 issue optd with Star and Crescent (No. 52 also optd as T **24**).
52a **28** 20 pa. red (No. 643) .. 55·00 21·00
52 20 pa. red (No. 647) .. 55 55

E. On 1913 issue.
53 **30** 5 pa. bistre .. .. 1·10 1·00
54 20 pa. pink .. .. 60 60

F. On Pictorial issue of 1914.
55 **32** 2 pa. purple .. .. 45 45
56 – 4 pa. brown (No. 500) .. 45 45

G. On Postal Anniv issue of 1916.
57 **60** 20 pa. blue .. .. 50 50
58 1 pi. black and violet .. 55 55
59 5 pi. black and brown .. 55 55

H. On Pictorial issues of 1916 and 1917.
60 **72** 5 pa. orange .. .. 1·10 1·10
61 **75** 1 pi. blue .. .. 80 65
62 **69** 5 pi. on 2 pa. bl (No. 914) 3·00 2·50
63 **64** 50 pi. green on yellow .. 18·00 10·00

**1919.** Various issues of Turkey optd **T.E.O. Cilicie**.

A. On No. 726 (surch Printed Matter stamp optd with Star and Crescent).
69 **15** 5 pa. on 10 pa. green .. 25 25

B. On 1892 issue optd with Star and Crescent and Arabic surch.
70 **15** 10 pa. on 20 pa. red (No. 630) .. .. .. 25 25

C. On 1909 issue optd with Star and Crescent.
71 **28** 20 pa. red (No. 572) .. 55 55
72 20 pa. red (No. 643) .. 55 55

D. On 1909 issue optd with Tougra and surch in Turkish.
73 **28** 5 pa. on 2 pa. grn (No. 938) 25 25

E. On Pictorial stamp of 1914.
74 – 1 pi. blue (No. 505) .. 35 25

F. On Postal Anniv issue of 1916.
75 **60** 5 pa. green .. .. 80·00 42·00
76 20 pa. blue .. .. 45 45
77 1 pi. black and violet .. 35 25

G. On Postal Anniv issue of 1916 optd with Star and Crescent.
78 **60** 10 pa. red (No. 654) .. 30 25

H. On Pictorial issues of 1916 and 1917.
79 **72** 5 pa. orange .. .. 25 25
80 **73** 10 pa. green .. .. 25 25
81 **74** 20 pa. red .. .. 25 25
82 **77** 2 pi. blue and brown .. 35 25
83 **78** 5 pi. brown and blue .. 40 25
84 **69** 5 pi. on 2 pa. blue .. 2·50 2·50
85 **63** 25 pi. red on buff .. 2·50 2·50
86 **64** 50 pi. green on yellow .. 40·00 28·00

I. On Charity stamp of 1917.
87 **65** 10 pa. purple .. .. 45 25

**1920.** "Mouchon" key-type of French Levant surch. **T.E.O. 20 PARAS.**
88. B. 20 pa. on 10 c. red .. 40 25

7.

**1920.** Surch. **OCCUPATION MILITAIRE Francaise CILICIE** and value.
89. **7.** 70 pa. on 5 pa. red .. 30 40
90 3½ pi. on 5 pa. red .. 30 40

**1920.** Stamps of France surch. **O.M.F. Cilicie** and new value.
100 **11** 5 pa. on 2 c. red .. 15 15
101 **18** 10 pa. on 5 c. green .. 20 20
102 20 pa. on 10 c. red .. 20 20
103 1 pi. on 25 c. blue .. 20 20
104 **15** 2 pi. on 15 c. green .. 30 30
105 **13** 5 pi. on 40 c. red & blue 40 40
106 10 pi. on 50 c. brn. & lav. 50 55
107 50 pi. on 1 f. red & green 85 85
108 100 pi. on 5 f. blue & yell. 6·50 7·00

**1920.** Stamps of France surch. **O.M.F. Cilicie SAND. EST** and new value.
109. **11.** 5 pa. on 2 c. red .. 1·75
110. **18.** 10 pa. on 5 c. green .. 1·75
111. 20 pa. on 10 c. red .. 1·10
112. 1 pi. on 25 c. blue .. 1·10
113. **15.** 2 pi. on 15 c. green .. 3·25
114. **13.** 5 pi. on 40 c. red and blue 32·00
115. 20 pi. on 1 f. red & green 40·00

**1921.** Air. Nos. 104/5 optd **POSTE PAR AVION** in frame.
116 **15** 2 pi. on 15 c. green .. £2500 £2500
117 **13** 5 pi. on 40 c. red and blue £2500 £2500

POSTAGE DUE STAMPS

**1919.** Postage Due stamps of Turkey optd **CILICIE**.
D42 D **49** 5 pa. brown .. .. 70 70
D43 D **50** 20 pa. red .. .. 70 70
D29 D **51** 1 pi. blue .. .. 2·25 2·00
D45 D **52** 2 pi. blue .. .. 1·40 1·40

**1919.** Postage Due stamps of Turkey optd **Cilicie**.
D64 D **49** 5 pa. brown .. .. 80 80
D65 D **50** 20 pa. red .. .. 80 80
D66 D **51** 1 pi. blue .. .. 2·50 2·00
D67 D **52** 2 pi. blue .. .. 2·25 1·75

**1921.** Postage Due Stamps of France surch. **O.M.F. Cilicie** and value.
D 118. D **11.** 1 pi. on 10 c. brown 2·25 2·25
D 119. 2 pi. on 20 c. olive 2·25 2·25
D 120. 3 pi. on 30 c. red .. 2·25 2·25
D 121. 4 pi. on 50 c. purple 2·25 2·25

## COCHIN-CHINA Pt. 6

A former French colony in the extreme S. of Indo-China, subsequently incorporated into French Indo-China.

100 centimes = 1 franc

**1886.** Stamps of French Colonies surch.
1. J. 5 on 25 c. brn. on yellow .. £120 85·00
2. 5 on 2 c. brown on yellow 8·00 7·75
3. 5 on 25 c. brn. on yellow .. 8·75 8·75
4. 5 on 25 c. black on red .. 26·00 23·00

Nos. 1 and 4 are surcharged with numeral only; Nos. 2 and 3 are additionally optd **C. CH.**

## COLOMBIA Pt. 20

A republic in the N.W. of South America. Formerly part of the Spanish Empire, Colombia became independent in 1819. The constituent states became the Granadine Confederation in 1858. The name was changed to the United States of New Granada in 1861, and the name Colombia was adopted later the same year.

100 centavos = 1 peso.

**Prices.** For the early issues prices in the used column are for postmarked copies, pen-cancellations are generally worth less.

1. 3.

**1859.** Imperf.
1 **1** 2½ green .. .. .. 70·00 80·00
2 5 c. blue .. .. .. 70·00 70·00
8 5 c. slate .. .. .. 55·00 45·00
9 10 c. yellow .. .. .. 45·00 40·00
5 20 c. blue .. .. .. 70·00 48·00
6 1 p. red .. .. .. 48·00 80·00

**1861.** Imperf.
11 **3** 2½ c. black .. .. £1000 £400
12 5 c. yellow .. .. £160 £120
13 10 c. blue .. .. .. £650 £120
14 20 c. red .. .. .. £350 £150
15 1 p. red .. .. .. £800 £250

4. 5. 6.

**1862.** Imperf.
16. **4.** 10 c. blue .. .. .. £140 70·00
17. 20 c. red .. .. .. — £500
18. 50 c. green .. .. £100 85·00
19. 1 p. lilac .. .. .. £350 £225

**1862.** Imperf.
21 **5** 5 c. orange .. .. 55·00 42·00
24 10 c. blue .. .. 90·00 13·50
23 20 c. red .. .. £130 35·00
25 50 c. green .. .. £150 £110

**1863.** Imperf.
26 **6** 5 c. orange .. .. 42·00 32·00
27 10 c. blue .. .. 32·00 13·50
28 20 c. red .. .. 65·00 32·00
29 50 c. green .. .. 55·00 32·00
30 1 p. mauve .. .. £275 £110

7. 8. 9.

**1865.** Imperf.
31 **7** 1 c. red .. .. .. 8·00 8·00
32 **8** 2½ c. black on lilac .. 20·00 13·50
33 **9** 5 c. orange .. .. 35·00 17·00
34 10 c. violet .. .. 40·00 6·00
35 20 c. blue .. .. 45·00 13·50
37 50 c. green .. .. 60·00 32·00
38 1 p. red .. .. .. 70·00 13·50

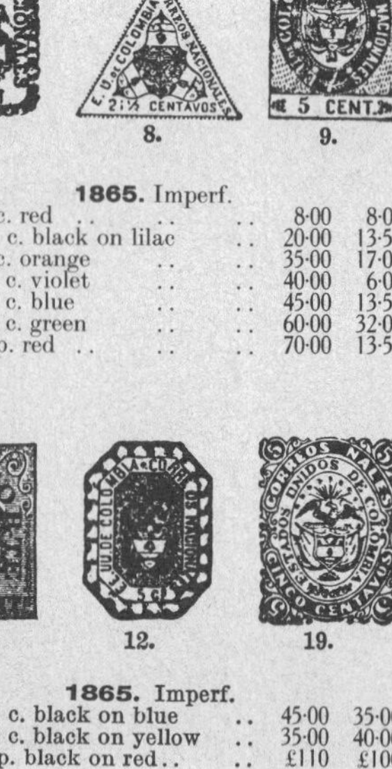
10. 12. 19.

**1865.** Imperf.
39. **10.** 25 c. black on blue .. 45·00 35·00
40. 50 c. black on yellow .. 35·00 40·00
41. 1 p. black on red .. £110 £100

**1866.** Imperf. Various Arms Designs.
44 **12** 5 c. orange .. .. 42·00 25·00
45 – 10 c. lilac .. .. 13·00 6·00
46 – 20 c. blue .. .. 27·00 15·00
47 – 50 c. green .. .. 10·50 10·50
48 – 1 p. red .. .. 60·00 20·00
49 – 5 p. black on green .. — £130
50 – 10 p. black on red .. £275 £120

**1868.** Arms (various frames) inscr. "ESTADOS UNIDOS DE COLOMBIA". Imperf.
51. **19.** 5 c. yellow .. .. 60·00 42·00
52. 10 c. lilac .. .. 1·25 70
54. 20 c. blue .. .. 1·25 45
55. 50 c. green .. .. 1·25 85
57. 1 p. red .. .. 3·00 1·25

24. 25.

26 27.

28. 30.

**1869.** Imperf.
58. **24.** 2½ c. black on violet .. 3·50 1·40

**1870.** Imperf.
59a **25** 1 c. green .. .. 3·00 2·10
60 1 c. red .. .. 2·10 2·10
61 **26** 2 c. brown .. .. 45 45
62 **27** 5 c. orange .. .. 55 35
65a **28** 10 c mauve .. .. 55 25
67 25 c. black on blue .. 6·50 6·00
87 25 c. green .. .. 15·00 15·00

**1870.** Different frames. Imperf.
69 **30** 5 p. black on green .. 5·00 4·25
71 10 p. black on red .. 5·50 3·25
See also Nos. 118/19.

32. Andean Condor. 33. 35.

**1876.** Imperf.
84 **32** 5 c. violet .. .. 7·50 1·00
85 **33** 10 c. brown .. .. 90 25
86 – 20 c. blue .. .. 1·10 35
DESIGN: 20 c. As Type **33** but with different frame.

**1881.** Imperf.
93. **35.** 1 c. green .. .. 2·75 1·75
99. 2 c. red .. .. 80 65
100. 5 c. blue .. .. 1·75 45
101. 10 c. purple .. .. 1·25 85
97. 20 c. black .. .. 1·40 55

39. 40.

**1881.** Imperf.
102. **39.** 1 c. black on green .. 1·25 1·25
103. 2 c. black on rose .. 1·25 1·25
104. 5 c. black on lilac .. 1·75 75

**1883.** Inscr. "CORREOS NACIONALES DE LOS E.E. U.U. DE COLOMBIA".
106a **40** 1 c. yellow on green .. 35 35
107 2 c. red on pink .. 45 45
109 5 c. blue on blue .. 45 25
111 10 c. orange on yellow 25 25
112 20 c. mauve on lilac .. 35 35
113 50 c. brown on buff .. 90 90
114 1 p. red on blue .. 3·00 55
115 5 p. brown on yellow .. 2·50 2·25
116 10 p. black on red .. 5·50 6·50

**1886.** Perf.
118. **30.** 5 p. brown .. .. 1·25 1·00
119. 10 p. black on lilac .. 1·25 1·00

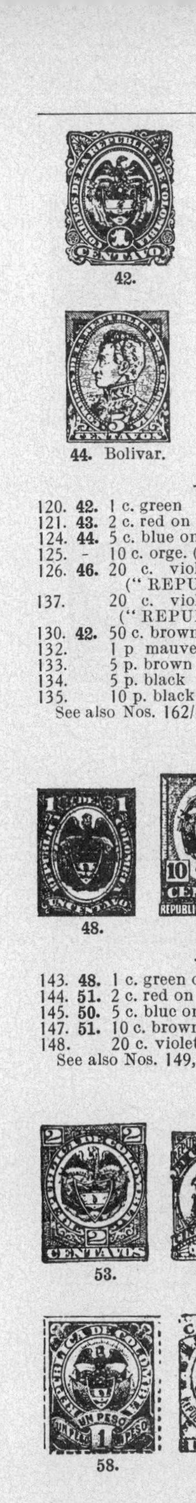

42. 43. Gen. Sucre.

44. Bolivar. 46. Gen. Narino.

**1886.**

| No. | Type | Description | Unused | Used |
|---|---|---|---|---|
| 120. | 42. | 1 c. green | 1·75 | 60 |
| 121. | 43. | 2 c. red on pink | 75 | 75 |
| 124. | 44. | 5 c. blue on blue | 2·10 | 15 |
| 125. | – | 10 c. orge. (Pres. Nunez) | 1·40 | 25 |
| 126. | 46. | 20 c. violet on lilac ("REPULICA") | 90 | 35 |
| 137. | | 20 c. violet on lilac ("REPUBLICA") | 1·10 | 50 |
| 130. | 42. | 50 c. brown on buff | 40 | 45 |
| 132. | | 1 p mauve | 2·10 | 1·00 |
| 133. | | 5 p. brown | 8·50 | 5·00 |
| 134. | | 5 p. black | 10·00 | 7·50 |
| 135. | | 10 p. black on pink | 16·00 | 4·25 |

See also Nos. 162/4a.

48. 51. 50.

**1890.**

| No. | Type | Description | Unused | Used |
|---|---|---|---|---|
| 143. | 48. | 1 c. green on green | 2·50 | 85 |
| 144. | 51. | 2 c. red on pink | 70 | 50 |
| 145. | 50. | 5 c. blue on blue | 55 | 20 |
| 147. | 51. | 10 c. brown on yellow | 55 | 20 |
| 148. | | 20 c. violet | 1·60 | 1·60 |

See also Nos. 149, etc.

53. 54. 55.

58. 61. 75.

**1892.**

| No. | Type | Description | Unused | Used |
|---|---|---|---|---|
| 149b | 48 | 1 c. red on yellow | 15 | 10 |
| 150 | 53 | 2 c. red on rose | 9·00 | 9·00 |
| 151a | | 2 c. green | 15 | 10 |
| 152a | 50 | 5 c. black on brown | 6·50 | 20 |
| 153 | 54 | 5 c. brown on brown | 20 | 20 |
| 155 | 51 | 10 c. brown on red | 20 | 20 |
| 156 | 55 | 20 c. brown on blue | 20 | 20 |
| 159 | 42 | 50 c. violet on lilac | 35 | 20 |
| 161 | 58 | 1 p. blue on green | 85 | 20 |
| 162 | 42 | 5 p. red on pink | 9·00 | 1·25 |
| 164 | | 10 p. blue | 7·50 | 1·25 |

**1898.**

| No. | Type | Description | Unused | Used |
|---|---|---|---|---|
| 171. | 61. | 1 c. red on yellow | 25 | 25 |
| 172. | | 5 c. brown on brown | 25 | 25 |
| 173. | | 10 c. brown on red | 3·25 | 1·25 |
| 174. | | 50 c. blue on lilac | 1·00 | 75 |

For stamps showing map of Panama and inscr. "COLOMBIA" see Panama Nos. 5/18.

For provisionals issued at Cartagena during the Civil War, 1899–1902, see list in Stanley Gibbons Stamp Catalogue **Part 20** (South America).

**1902.** Arms in various frames. Imperf. or perf.

| No. | Type | Description | Unused | Used |
|---|---|---|---|---|
| 259. | 75. | ½ c. brown | 85 | 85 |
| 260. | | 1 c. green | 2·50 | 2·10 |
| 192. | | 2 c. black on red | 15 | 15 |
| 261. | | 2 c. blue | 60 | 35 |
| 193. | | 4 c. red on green | 15 | 15 |
| 194. | | 4 c. blue on green | 20 | 20 |
| 195. | | 5 c. green on green | 15 | 15 |
| 196. | | 5 c. blue on blue | 10 | 10 |
| 262. | | 5 c. red | 60 | 60 |
| 197. | | 10 c. black on pink | 15 | 15 |
| 263. | | 10 c. mauve | 85 | 25 |
| 198. | | 20 c. brown on brown | 15 | 15 |
| 199. | | 20 c. blue on brown | 20 | 20 |
| 200. | | 50 c. green on red | 45 | 45 |
| 201. | | 50 c. blue on red | 1·50 | 1·50 |
| 202. | | 1 p. purple on brown | 25 | 25 |

82. 85. River Magdalena.

**1903.** Imperf. or perf.

| No. | Type | Description | Unused | Used |
|---|---|---|---|---|
| 203. | 82. | 5 p. green on blue | 9·00 | 4·25 |
| 204. | | 10 p. green on green | 9·00 | 9·00 |
| 205. | | 50 p. orange on red | 45·00 | 42·00 |
| 206. | | 100 p. blue on red | 38·00 | 35·00 |

Nos. 205/6 are larger (31 × 38 mm.).

**1902.** Imperf. or perf.

| No. | Type | Description | Unused | Used |
|---|---|---|---|---|
| 212. | 85. | 2 c. green | 80 | 80 |
| 213. | | 2 c. blue | 80 | 80 |
| 214. | | 2 c. red | 10·00 | 10·00 |
| 215. | – | 10 c. red | 50 | 50 |
| 216. | – | 10 c. pink | 50 | 50 |
| 219. | – | 10 c. orange | 8·00 | 8·00 |
| 242. | – | 10 c. blue on brown | 1·75 | 1·75 |
| 243. | – | 10 c. blue on green | 5·00 | 4·25 |
| 247. | – | 10 c. blue on red | 2·50 | 2·50 |
| 245. | – | 10 c. blue on lilac | 13·00 | 13·00 |
| 220. | – | 20 c. violet | 40 | 40 |
| 221. | – | 20 c. blue | 3·25 | 3·25 |
| 224. | – | 20 c. red | 12·00 | 12·00 |

DESIGNS: 10 c. Iron Quay, Savanilla, with eagle above. 20 c. Hill of La Popa.

88. Gunboat "Cartagena". 89. Bolivar.

90. General Pinzon. 91. 92.

**1903.** Imperf. or perf.

| No. | Type | Description | Unused | Used |
|---|---|---|---|---|
| 225. | 88. | 5 c. blue | 2·10 | 2·10 |
| 226. | | 5 c. brown | 3·25 | 3·25 |
| 227. | 89. | 50 c. green | 5·00 | 5·00 |
| 228. | | 50 c. brown | 4·25 | 4·25 |
| 230. | | 50 c. orange | 4·25 | 4·25 |
| 231. | | 50 c. red | 3·25 | 3·25 |
| 233. | 90. | 1 p. brown | 90 | 65 |
| 234. | | 1 p. red | 90 | 90 |
| 235. | | 1 p. blue | 3·50 | 3·25 |
| 237. | 91. | 5 p. brown | 6·00 | 6·00 |
| 238. | | 5 p. purple | 3·75 | 3·75 |
| 239. | | 5 p. green | 6·00 | 6·00 |
| 240. | 92. | 10 p. green | 6·50 | 6·00 |
| 241. | | 10 p. purple | 14·00 | 14·00 |

93. 96.

97. 98. President Marroquin.

**1902.**

| No. | Type | Description | Unused | Used |
|---|---|---|---|---|
| 248. | 93. | 1 c. green on yellow | 20 | 20 |
| 249. | | 2 c. red on pink | 20 | 20 |
| 250. | | 5 c. blue | 20 | 20 |
| 251. | | 10 c. brown on yellow | 20 | 20 |
| 252. | | 20 c. mauve on pink | 10 | 10 |
| 253. | | 50 c. red on green | 1·00 | 1·25 |
| 254. | | 1 p. black on yellow | 3·25 | 2·50 |
| 255. | | 5 p. blue on blue | 20·00 | 15·00 |
| 256. | | 10 p. brown on pink | 14·00 | 11·00 |

**1904.**

| No. | Type | Description | Unused | Used |
|---|---|---|---|---|
| 270. | 96. | ½ c. yellow | 55 | 10 |
| 274. | | 1 c. green | 40 | 10 |
| 278. | | 2 c. red | 40 | 10 |
| 281. | | 5 c. blue | 1·00 | 10 |
| 283. | | 10 c. violet | 45 | 20 |
| 284. | | 20 c. black | 75 | 15 |
| 286. | 97. | 1 p. brown | 13·00 | 1·60 |
| 287. | 98. | 5 p. black and red | 38·00 | 30·00 |
| 288. | | 10 p. black and blue | 42·00 | 32·00 |

102. Camilo Torres. 104. Narino Demanding Liberation of Slaves.

**1910.** Cent. of Independence.

| No. | Type | Description | Unused | Used |
|---|---|---|---|---|
| 345. | 102. | ½ c. black and purple | 35 | 20 |
| 346. | – | 1 c. green | 35 | 10 |
| 347. | – | 2 c. red | 35 | 10 |
| 348. | – | 5 c. blue | 1·00 | 25 |
| 349. | – | 10 c. purple | 6·50 | 5·00 |
| 350. | – | 20 c. brown | 12·00 | 7·50 |
| 351. | 104. | 1 p. purple | 75·00 | 22·00 |
| 352. | – | 10 p. lake | £300 | £200 |

DESIGNS—As Type **102**: 1 c. P. Salavarrieta. 2 c. Narino. 5 c. Bolivar. 10 c. Caldas. 20 c. Santander. As Type **104**: 10 p. Bolivar resigning.

110. C. Torres. 113. Arms. 111. Boyaca Monument.

123. La Sabana Station. 112. Cartagena.

**1917.** Portraits as T **110**.

| No. | Type | Description | Unused | Used |
|---|---|---|---|---|
| 357. | 110. | ½ c. yellow (Caldas) | 10 | 15 |
| 358. | | 1 c. green (Torres) | 10 | 10 |
| 393. | 113. | 1½ c. brown | 45 | 45 |
| 359. | 110. | 2 c. red (Narino) | 10 | 10 |
| 380. | 113. | 3 c. red on yellow | 20 | 10 |
| 394. | | 3 c. blue | 20 | 15 |
| 360. | 110. | 4 c. purple (Santander) | 45 | 10 |
| 395. | | 4 c. blue (Santander) | 20 | 10 |
| 361. | | 5 c. blue (Bolivar) | 2·50 | 20 |
| 396. | | 5 c. red (Bolivar) | 2·50 | 15 |
| 397. | 113. | 8 c. blue | 20 | 15 |
| 362. | 110. | 10 c. grey (Cordoba) | 2·50 | 20 |
| 398. | | 10 c. blue (Cordoba) | 6·50 | 35 |
| 363. | 111. | 20 c. red | 1·40 | 25 |
| 399 | 113. | 30 c. bistre (Caldas) | 7·00 | 25 |
| 400. | 123. | 40 c. brown | 11·00 | 55 |
| 364. | 112. | 50 c. red | 1·60 | 25 |
| 606. | | 50 c. red (San Pedro Alejandrino) | 8·25 | 3·75 |
| 365a. | 110. | 1 p. blue (Sucre) | 10·00 | 40 |
| 366. | | 2 p. orange (Cuervo) | 12·00 | 25 |
| 367. | | 5 p. grey (Ricaurte) | 35·00 | 10·00 |
| 401. | | 5 p. violet (Ricaurte) | 3·50 | 35 |
| 368. | 113. | 10 p. brown | 35·00 | 8·50 |
| 402. | | 10 p. green | 5·00 | 90 |

For similar 40 c. see No. 541.

**1918.** Surch. **Especie Provisional** and value.

| No. | Type | Description | Unused | Used |
|---|---|---|---|---|
| 374. | 96. | 0.00½ c. on 20 c. black | 70 | 10 |
| 376. | | 0·03 c. on 10 c. violet | 1·40 | 35 |

115. 124.

**1918.**

| No. | Type | Description | Unused | Used |
|---|---|---|---|---|
| 378. | 115. | 3 c. red | 75 | 10 |

**1918.** Air. No. 359 optd **1er Servicio Postal Aereo 6-18-19.**

| No. | Type | Description | Unused | Used |
|---|---|---|---|---|
| 379 | | 2 c. red | £2500 | £1600 |

**1920.** As T **75**, **96** and **113**, but with "PROVISIONAL" added in label across design.

| No. | Type | Description | Unused | Used |
|---|---|---|---|---|
| 381. | 96. | ½ c. yellow | 1·10 | 20 |
| 382. | | 1 c. green | 55 | 10 |
| 383. | | 2 c. red | 55 | 20 |
| 384. | 113. | 3 c. green | 40 | 20 |
| 385. | 96. | 5 c. blue | 90 | 25 |
| 386. | | 10 c. violet | 5·00 | 1·25 |
| 387. | | 10 c. blue | 8·50 | 4·00 |
| 388. | | 20 c. green | 6·00 | 3·25 |
| 389. | 75. | 50 c. red | 7·50 | 2·50 |

**1921.** No. 360 surch **PROVICIONAL $ 003.**

| No. | Type | Description | Unused | Used |
|---|---|---|---|---|
| 390 | | $0.03 on 4 c. purple | 65 | 20 |

**1921.** No. 360 surch **PROVISIONAL $0.03.**

| No. | Type | Description | Unused | Used |
|---|---|---|---|---|
| 392 | | $0.03 on 4 c. purple | 2·75 | 75 |

**1924.**

| No. | Type | Description | Unused | Used |
|---|---|---|---|---|
| 403. | 124. | 1 c. red | 75 | 25 |
| 404. | | 3 c. blue | 65 | 25 |

**1925.** Large fiscal stamps surch. **CORREOS 1 CENTAVO** or optd. **CORREOS PROVISIONAL.**

| No. | Type | Description | Unused | Used |
|---|---|---|---|---|
| 405. | | 1 c. on 3 c. brown | 55 | 10 |
| 406. | | 4 c. purple | 55 | 25 |

127. 129. Death of Bolivar (after P. A. Quijano).

**1926.**

| No. | Type | Description | Unused | Used |
|---|---|---|---|---|
| 410 | 127 | 1 c. green | 40 | 10 |
| 411 | | 4 c. blue | 40 | 10 |

**1930.** Death Cent. of Bolivar.

| No. | Type | Description | Unused | Used |
|---|---|---|---|---|
| 412. | 129. | 4 c. black and blue | 25 | 10 |

132. 133. Galleon.

**1932.** Air. Optd. **CORREO AEREO.**

| No. | Type | Description | Unused | Used |
|---|---|---|---|---|
| 413 | 132 | 5 c. yellow | 3·25 | 3·25 |
| 414 | | 10 c. purple | 80 | 25 |
| 415 | | 15 c. green | 1·40 | 1·40 |
| 416 | | 20 c. red | 80 | 45 |
| 417 | | 30 c. blue | 80 | 25 |
| 418 | | 40 c. lilac | 1·60 | 55 |
| 419 | | 50 c. olive | 3·50 | 2·50 |
| 420 | | 60 c. brown | 3·50 | 2·50 |
| 421 | | 80 c. green | 10·00 | 8·50 |
| 422 | 133 | 1 p. blue | 8·50 | 5·00 |
| 423 | | 2 p. red | 26·00 | 19·00 |
| 424 | | 3 p. mauve | 55·00 | 50·00 |
| 425 | | 5 p. olive | 75·00 | 65·00 |

These and similar stamps without the "CORREO AEREO" overprint were issues of a private air company and are not listed in this catalogue.

**1932.** Nos. 395 and 399 surch.

| No. | Type | Description | Unused | Used |
|---|---|---|---|---|
| 427. | | 1 c. on 4 c. blue | 20 | 10 |
| 428. | | 20 c. on 30 c. bistre | 7·00 | 20 |

138. Coffee Plantation. 137. Oil Wells.

140. Gold Mining. 141. Columbus.

**1932.** 1 c. is vert., 8 c. is horiz.

| No. | Type | Description | Unused | Used |
|---|---|---|---|---|
| 429. | – | 1 c. green (Emeralds) | 85 | 10 |
| 430. | 137. | 2 c. red (Oil) | 85 | 10 |
| 431. | 138. | 5 c. brown (Coffee) | 85 | 10 |
| 432. | – | 8 c. blue (Platinum) | 7·50 | 25 |
| 485. | 140. | 10 c. yellow (Gold) | 6·50 | 10 |
| 486. | 141. | 20 c. blue | 21·00 | 60 |

142. Coffee. 143. Gold.

**1932.** Air.

| No. | Type | Description | Unused | Used |
|---|---|---|---|---|
| 435 | 142 | 5 c. brown and orange | 45 | 20 |
| 436 | – | 10 c. black and red | 85 | 20 |
| 437 | – | 15 c. violet and green | 40 | 15 |
| 438 | – | 15 c. violet and red | 5·00 | 15 |
| 439 | – | 20 c. green and red | 85 | 10 |
| 440 | – | 20 c. olive and green | 4·00 | 25 |
| 441 | 142 | 30 c. brown and blue | 3·25 | 10 |
| 442 | – | 40 c. bistre and violet | 1·60 | 10 |
| 443 | – | 50 c. brown and green | 13·00 | 1·25 |
| 444 | – | 60 c. violet and brown | 2·50 | 25 |
| 445 | 142 | 80 c. brown and green | 15·00 | 65 |
| 446 | 143 | 1 p. bistre and blue | 13·00 | 70 |
| 447 | | 2 p. bister and red | 14·00 | 1·90 |
| 448 | – | 3 p. green and violet | 21·00 | 7·00 |
| 449 | – | 5 p. green and olive | 50·00 | 19·00 |

DESIGNS—As Type **142**: 10 c., 50 c. Cattle. 15 c., 60 c. Oil Wells. 20 c., 40 c. Bananas. As Type **143**: 3 p., 5 p. Emeralds.

144. Pedro de Heredia. 148. Coffee Plantation.

147. Oil Wells. 151. Allegory of 1935 Olympiad.

**1934.** 4th Cent. of Cartagena.

| No. | Type | Description | Unused | Used |
|---|---|---|---|---|
| 451. | 144. | 1 c. green | 1·50 | 55 |
| 452. | | 5 c. brown | 2·50 | 55 |
| 453. | | 8 c. blue | 1·50 | 55 |

**1934.** Air. 4th Cent. of Cartagena. Surch. **CARTAGENA 1533-1933** and value.

454 – 10 c. on 50 c. brown and green (No. 443) 3·50 3·50
455 142 15 c. on 80 c. brown and green .. 3·50 3·50
456 143 20 c. on 1 p. bistre and blue .. .. 5·50 6·00
457 30 c. on 2 p. bistre and red .. .. 6·00 6·00

**1934.**

458. 147. 2 c. red .. .. 10 10
459. 148. 5 c. brown .. .. 3·50 10
460. – 10 c. orange .. .. 17·00 10
DESIGN: 10 c. Gold miner facing left.

**1935.** 3rd National Olympiad. Inscr. "III OLIMPIADA BARRANQUILLA 1935".

461. – 2 c. orange and green .. 75 25
462. – 4 c. green .. .. 75 25
463. 151. 5 c. yellow and brown .. 75 20
464. – 7 c. red .. .. 1·75 1·50
465. – 8 c. mauve and black .. 1·75 1·50
466. – 10 c. blue and brown .. 1·75 1·10
467. – 12 c. blue .. .. 1·75 1·90
468. – 15 c. red and blue .. 4·25 3·00
469. – 18 c. yellow and purple 5·00 5·00
470. – 20 c. green and violet .. 5·00 3·25
471. – 24 c. blue and green .. 6·00 4·25
472. – 50 c. orange and blue .. 6·00 3·75
473. – 1 p. blue and olive .. 60·00 38·00
474. – 2 p. blue and green .. £100 70·00
475. – 5 p. blue and violet .. £300 £250
476. – 10 p. blue and black .. £650 £400
DESIGNS—VERT. 2 c. Footballers. 4 c. Discus thrower. 1 p. G.P.O. 2 p. "Flag of the Race" Monument. 5 p. Arms. 10 p. Andean condor. HORIZ. 7 c. Runners. 8 c. Tennis player. 10 c. Hurdler. 12 c. Pier. 15 c. Athlete. 18 c. Baseball. 20 c. Seashore. 24 c. Swimmer. 50 c. Aerial view of Barranquilla.

152. Nurse and Patients.

**1935.** Obligatory Tax. Red Cross.

477. 152. 5 c. red and green .. 1·75 45

**1935.** Surch. **12 CENTAVOS.**

478. 12 c. on 1 p. blue (No. 365a) 4·25 1·25

154. Simon Bolivar. 155. Tequendama Falls.

**1937.**

487. 154. 1 c. green .. .. 10 10
488. 155. 10 c. red .. .. 10 10
489. 12 c. blue .. .. 3·75 1·25

156. Footballer. 157. Discus Thrower.

**1937.** 4th National Olympiad.

490. 156. 3 c. green .. .. 80 55
491. 157. 10 c. red .. .. 3·25 1·60
492. – 1 p. black .. .. 30·00 24·00
DESIGN: 1 p. Runner (20½ × 27 mm.).

159. Exhibition Palace. 161. Mother and Child.

**1937.** Barranquilla Industrial Exn.

493 159 5 c. purple .. .. 1·60 25
494 – 15 c. blue .. .. 6·00 3·25
495 – 50 c. brown .. .. 17·00 6·00
DESIGNS—HORIZ. 15 c. Stadium. VERT. 50 c. "Flag of the Race" Monument.

**1937.** Obligatory Tax. Red Cross.

509. 161. 5 c. red .. .. 1·40 55

**1937.** Surch. in figures and words.

510. 156. 1 c. on 3 c. green .. 60 55
511. 155. 2 c. on 12 c. blue .. 30 30
512. – 5 c. on 8 c. (No. 432) .. 35 25
513. – 5 c. on 8 c. bl. (No. 397) 35 25
514. 155. 10 c. on 12 c. blue .. 4·25 85

164. Entrance to Church of the Rosary. 166. "Bochica" (Indian god).

**1938.** 400th Anniv of Bogota.

515. – 1 c. green .. .. 15 15
516. 164. 2 c. red .. .. 15 10
517. – 5 c. black .. .. 20 10
518. – 10 c. brown .. .. 40 25
519. 166. 15 c. blue .. .. 3·25 90
520. – 20 c. mauve .. .. 3·25 90
521. – 1 p. brown .. .. 30·00 25·00
DESIGNS—VERT. 1 c. "Calle del Arco" ("Street of the Arch") Old Bogota. 5 c. Bogota Arms. 10 c. G. J. de Quesada. HORIZ. (larger): 20 c. Convent of S. Domingo. 1 p. First Mass on Site of Bogota.

168. Proposed P.O., Bogota.

**1939.** Obligatory Tax. P.O. Rebuilding Fund.

522. 168. ¼ c. blue .. .. 10 10
564. ¼ c. purple .. .. 10 10
523. ½ c. red .. .. .. 10 10
524. 1 c. violet .. .. 10 10
567. 1 c. orange .. .. 10 10
525. 2 c. green .. .. 25 10
526. 20 c. brown .. .. 3·25 30

**1939.** Air. Surch. **5 cts.** or **15 cts.** and bar.

527. 5 c. on 20 c. (No. 439) 25 20
528. 5 c. on 40 c. (No. 442) 25 20
530. 15 c. on 30 c. (No. 441) 60 15
531. 15 c. on 40 c. (No. 442) 1·10 25

171. Bolivar. 172. Coffee Plantation. 173. Arms of Colombia.

174. Columbus. 175. Caldas. 176. La Sabana Station.

**1939.**

533. 171. 1 c. green .. .. 10 10
535. 172. 5 c. brown .. .. 10 10
536. 5 c. blue .. .. 10 10
538. 173. 15 c. blue .. .. 1·40 10
539. 174. 20 c. black .. .. 17·00 30
540. 175. 30 c. olive .. .. 5·50 40
541. 176. 40 c. brown .. .. 18·00 3·25
For similar 40 c. see No. 400.

178. Proposed new P.O., Bogota.

**1940.** Obligatory Tax. P.O. Rebuilding Fund.

542. 178. ¼ c. blue .. .. 10 10
543. ½ c. red .. .. 10 10
544. 1 c. violet .. .. 10 10
545. 2 c. green .. .. 15 10
546. 20 c. brown .. .. 1·60 25

179. "Arms and the Law". 180. Bridge at Boyaca.

**1940.** Death Cent. of Gen. Santander.

547. – 1 c. olive .. .. 20 20
548. 179. 2 c. red .. .. 25 15
549. – 5 c. brown .. .. 25 20
550. – 8 c. red .. .. 90 40
551. – 10 c. yellow .. .. 45 40
552. – 15 c. blue .. .. 1·10 55
553. – 20 c. green .. .. 1·40 60
554. 180. 50 c. violet .. .. 2·50 2·10
555. – 1 p. red .. .. 11·00 10·00
556. – 2 p. orange .. .. 35·00 32·00
DESIGNS—VERT. 1 c. Gen. Santander. 5 c. Medallion of Santander by David. 8 c. Santander's statue, Cucuta. 15 c. Church at Rosario. HORIZ. 10 c. Santander's birthplace, Rosario. 20 c. Battlefield at Paya. 1 p. Death of Santander. 2 p. Victorious Army at Zamora.

181, Tobacco Plant. 182. Santander. 183. Garcia Rovira.

184. General Sucre. 185. "Protection".

**1940.**

557. 181. 8 c. green and red .. 45 30
558. 182. 15 c. blue .. .. 80 25
559. 183. 20 c. grey .. .. 4·00 25
560. – 40 c. brown (Galan) .. 2·50 40
561. 184. 1 p. black .. .. 11·00 1·25
562. 1 p. violet .. .. 2·50 70

**1940.** Obligatory Tax. Red Cross Fund.

563. 185. 5 c. red .. .. 25 15

186. Pre-Colombian Monument. 187. Proclamation of Independence.

**1941.** Air.

568. 186. 5 c. grey .. .. 25 10
691. 5 c. yellow .. .. 20 10
742. 5 c. blue .. .. 35 15
747. 5 c. red .. .. 35 15
569. – 10 c. orange .. .. 25 10
692. – 10 c. red .. .. 20 10
743. – 10 c. blue .. .. 35 20
570. 15 c. red .. .. 25 10
693. – 15 c. blue .. .. 20 10
571. – 20 c. green .. .. 40 10
694. – 20 c. violet .. .. 20 10
745. – 20 c. blue .. .. 45 25
749. – 20 c. red .. .. 45 25
572. 186. 30 c. blue .. .. 40 10
695. 30 c. green .. .. 35 10
750. 30 c. red .. .. 75 10
573. – 40 c. purple .. .. 1·60 10
696. – 40 c. grey .. .. 55 10
574. – 50 c. green .. .. 1·60 10
697. – 50 c. red .. .. 65 10
575. – 60 c. purple .. .. 1·60 10
698. – 60 c. olive .. .. 85 10
576. 186. 80 c. olive .. .. 4·00 35
699. 80 c. brown .. .. 1·25 10
577. 187. 1 p. black and blue .. 4·00 20
700. 1 p. brown and olive .. 3·00 35
578. – 2 p. black and red .. 8·00 1·25
701. – 2 p. blue and green .. 3·75 55
579. 187. 3 p. black and violet .. 14·00 4·00
702. 3 p. black and red .. 7·00 3·50
580. – 5 p. black and green .. 35·00 17·00
703. – 5 p. green and sepia .. 20·00 8·50
DESIGNS: As Type **186**: 10 c., 40 c. "El Dorado" Monument. 15 c., 50 c. Spanish Fort, Cartagena. 20 c., 60 c. Street in Old Bogota. As Type **187**: 2 p., 5 p. National Library, Bogota.

188. Arms of Palmira. 189. Home of Jorge Isaacs (author).

**1942.** 8th National Agricultural Exn., Palmira.

581. 188. 30 c. red .. .. 5·00 70

**1942.** Honouring J. Isaacs.

582. 189. 50 c. green .. .. 3·25 35

190. Peace Conference Delegates.

**1942.** 40th Anniv. of Wisconsin Peace Treaty ending Civil War.

583. 190. 10 c. orange .. .. 3·25 45

**1943.** Surch. **$0.0½ MEDIO CENTAVO**

584. 168. ½ c. on 1 c. violet .. 10 10
585. ½ c. on 2 c. green .. 10 10
586. ½ c. on 20 c. brown .. 20 20

**1944.** Surch. **5 Centavos.**

587. – 5 c. on 10 c. orge. (No. 460) 20 15

193. National Shrine. 194. San Pedro, Alejandrino.

**1944.**

592. 193. 30 c. olive .. .. 2·10 1·25
593. 194. 50 c. red .. .. 2·10 1·25

**1944.** Surch. with new values in figures and words.

594. 172. 1 c. on 5 c. brn. (No. 535) 15 15
595. 2 c. on 5 c. brn. (No. 535) 15 15

195. Banner. 199. Manuel Murillo Toro.

196. Viceroy Solis Building.

**1944.** 75th Anniv. of General Benefit Institution of Cundinamarca.

596. 195. 2 c. blue and yellow .. 10 10
597. – 5 c. blue and yellow .. 10 10
598. – 20 c. black and green 95 75
599. – 40 c. black and red .. 4·25 3·25
600. 196. 1 p. black and red .. 8·50 6·50
DESIGNS: As T **195**: 5 c. Arms of the Institution. 20 c. Manuel Murillo Toro. As T **196**: 40 c. St. Juan de Dios Maternity Hospital.

**1944.**

602. 199. 5 c. olive .. .. 35 20

201. Proposed P.O., Bogota. (202. Stalin, Roosevelt and Churchill.)

**1945.** Obligatory Tax. P.O. Rebuilding Fund.

609 201 ¼ c. blue .. .. 10 10
610 ¼ c. brown .. .. 10 10
611 ½ c. red .. .. 10 10
612 ½ c. mauve .. .. 10 10
613 1 c. violet .. .. 10 10
614 1 c. orange .. .. 10 10
615 1 c. green .. .. 10 10
616 2 c. green .. .. 10 10
617a 20 c. brown .. .. 80 10

**1945.** Victory. Optd. with T **202.**

618. 172. 5 c. brown .. .. 25 15

203. Clock Tower, Cartagena. 204. Fort San Sebastian Cartagena.

**1945.**

621 203 50 c. green .. .. 2·50 80

**1945.** Air.

622 204 5 c. grey .. .. 20 10
623 – 10 c. orange .. .. 20 10
624 – 15 c. red .. .. 20 10
625 204 20 c. green .. .. 25 10
626 – 30 c. blue .. .. 35 10
627 – 40 c. red .. .. 55 10
628 204 50 c. green .. .. 70 15
629 – 60 c. purple .. .. 3·25 80
630 – 80 c. grey .. .. 5·00 55
631 – 1 p. blue .. .. 5·00 55
632 – 2 p. red .. .. 7·50 2·40
DESIGNS—As Type **204**: 10 c., 30 c., 60 c. Tequendama Falls. 15 c., 40 c., 80 c. Santa Marta. HORIZ. (larger) 1 p., 2 p. Capitol, Bogota.

207. Sierra Nevada de Santa Maria.

**1945.** 25th Anniv of 1st Air Mail Service in America.
633. **207.** 20 c. green .. .. 1·25 60
634. – 30 c. blue .. .. 1·25 60
635. – 50 c. red .. .. 1·25 60
DESIGNS: 30 c. Junkers F-13 seaplane "Tolima". 50 c. San Sebastian Fortress, Cartagena.

**1946.** Surch. **1** above **UN CENTAVO.**
636. **138.** 1 c. on 5 c. brown .. 15 15

**209.** Gen. Sucre. **211.** Map of South America. **212.** Bogota Observatory.

**1946.**
638. **209.** 1 c. blue and brown .. 20 10
639. 2 c. red and violet .. 20 10
640. 5 c. blue and olive .. 20 10
641. 9 c. red and green .. 45 35
642. 10 c. orange and blue .. 35 25
643. 20 c. orange and black 45 25
644. 30 c. green and red .. 45 25
645. 40 c. red and green .. 45 25
646. 50 c. violet and purple 45 25
The 5 c. to 50 c. are larger (23½ × 32 mm.).

**1946.** Obligatory Tax. Red Cross Fund. Optd. with red cross.
647. **172.** 5 c. brown (No. 535) .. 25 20

**1946.**
648. **211.** 15 c. blue .. .. 25 10

**1946.**
649. **212.** 5 c. brown .. .. 10 10
650. 5 c. blue .. .. 10 10

**213.** Andres Bello. **214.** Joaquin de Cayzedo y Cuero.

**1946.** 80th Death Anniv. of Andres Bello (poet and teacher).
651. **213.** 3 c. brown (postage) .. 25 15
652. 10 c. orange .. .. 40 10
653. 15 c. black .. .. 55 10
654. 5 c. blue (air) .. 25 15

**1946.**
655. **214.** 2 p. turquoise .. .. 5·00 45
656. 2 p. green .. .. 65 20

**215.** Proposed New P.O., Bogota. **217.** Coffee Plant.

**1946.** Obligatory Tax. P.O. Rebuilding Fund.
657. **215.** 3 c. blue .. .. 15 10

**1946.** 5th Central American and Caribbean Games, Barranquilla. As No. 621 optd. **V JUEGOS C. A. Y DEL C. 1946.**
658. – 50 c. red .. .. 2·50 1·60

**1947.**
659. **217.** 5 c. multicoloured .. 35 10

**218.** "Masdevallia Nicterina". **220.** Antonio Narino.

**1947.** Colombian Orchids. Multicoloured.
660. 1 c. Type **218** .. .. 10 10
661. 2 c. "Miltonia Vexillaria" 10 10
662. 5 c. "Cattleya Dowiana Aurea" .. .. 45 20
663. 5 c. "Cattleya Chocoensis" 45 20
664. 5 c. "Odontoglossum Crispum" .. .. 45 20
665. 10 c. "Cattleya Labiata Trianae" .. .. 65 15

**1947.** Obligatory Tax. Optd. **SOBRETASA** in fancy letters.
666. **183.** 20 c. grey (No. 559) .. 4·25 1·75
676. **141.** 20 c. blue (No. 486) .. 25·00 17·00

**1947.** 4th Pan-American Press Conf., Bogota.
667. **220.** 5 c. blue on blue (post.) 25 15
668. – 10 c. brown on blue .. 35 15
669. – 5 c. blue on blue (air) 20 10
670. – 10 c. red on blue .. 35 20
PORTRAITS: No. 668, A. Urdaneta y Urdaneta. No. 669, F. J. de Caldas. No. 670, M. del Socorro Rodriguez.

**222.** Arms of Colombia and Cross. **223.** J. C. Mutis and J. J. Triana.

**224.** M. A. Caro and R. J. Cuervo.

**1947.** Obligatory Tax. Red Cross Fund.
671. **222.** 5 c. lake .. .. 20 10
704. 5 c. red .. .. 20 10

**1947.**
673 **223** 25 c. green .. .. 35 15
675 **224** 3 p. purple .. .. 45 10

**225.** Bogota Cathedral.

DESIGNS—No. 678, National Capitol. No. 679, Foreign Office. No. 680, Chancellery. No. 681, Raphael Court, Capitol.

**1948.** 9th Pan-American Congress, Bogota. Inscr. as in T **225.**
677. **225.** 5 c. brown (postage) .. 15 10
678. – 10 c. orange .. 25 20
679. – 15 c. blue .. .. 25 20
680. – 5 c. brown (air) .. 15 10
681. – 15 c. blue .. .. 35 25

**1948.** Obligatory Tax. Savings Bank stamps surch. **COLOMBIA SOBRETASA 1 CENTAVO.** various designs.
682. 1 c. on 5 c. brown .. 10 10
683. 1 c. on 10 c. violet .. 10 10
684. 1 c. on 25 c. red .. 10 10
685. 1 c. on 50 c. blue .. 10 10

**1948.** Optd. C(= "CORREOS"). No gum.
686. **168.** 1 c. orange .. .. 10 10

**1948.** Optd. **CORREOS.**
687. **201.** 1 c. olive .. .. 10 10
688. 2 c. green .. .. 10 10
689. 20 c. brown .. .. 20 10

**232.** Simon Bolivar. **234.** Carlos Martinez Silva.

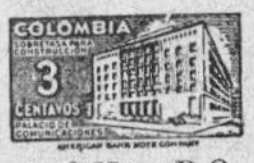

**233.** Proposed New P.O., Bogota.

**1948.**
690. **232.** 15 c. green .. .. 35 15

**1948.** Obligatory Tax. P.O. Rebuilding Fund.
705 **233.** 1 c. red .. .. 10 10
706. 2 c. green .. .. 10 10
707. 3 c. blue .. .. 10 10
708. 5 c. grey .. .. 10 10
709. 10 c. violet .. .. 20 10
See also Nos. 756 and 758/62.

**1949.**
710. **234.** 40 c. red .. .. 35 10

**235.** Julio Garavito Armero. **236.** Dr. Juan de Dios Carrasquilla.

**1949.** J. G. Armero (mathematician).
711. **235.** 4 c. green .. .. 25 15

**1949.** 75th Anniv. of National Agricultural Society.
712. **236.** 5 c. bistre .. .. 20 10

**237.** Arms of Colombia. **238.** Allegory of Justice.

**1949.** New Constitution.
713. **237.** 15 c. blue (postage) .. 20 10
714. **238.** 5 c. green (air) .. 15 10
715. – 10 c. orange .. .. 15 10
DESIGN: 10 c. Allegory of Constitution.

**239.** Tree and Congress Emblem. **240.** F. J. Cisneros.

**1949.** 1st Forestry Congress, Bogota.
716. **239.** 5 c. olive .. .. 20 10

**1949.** 50th Death Anniv. of Francisco Javier Cisneros (engineer).
717. **240.** 50 c. blue and brown .. 1·00 50
718. 50 c. violet and green .. 1·00 50
719. 50 c. yellow and purple 1·00 50

**241.** Mother and Child.

**1950.** Red Cross Fund. Surch. with new value and date as in T **241.**
720. **241.** 5 on 2 c. multicoloured 80 35

**1950.** Obligatory Tax. Optd. **SOBRETASA.**
721. **172.** 5 c. blue .. .. 15 10

**243.** " Masdevallia Chimaera ". **244.** Santo Domingo Post Office.

**1950.** 75th Anniv. of U.P.U.
722. **243.** 1 c. brown .. .. 30 10
723. – 2 c. violet .. .. 30 10
724. – 3 c. mauve .. .. 10 10
725. – 4 c. green .. .. 20 10
726. – 5 c. orange .. .. 35 10
727. – 11 c. red .. .. 1·60 75
728. **244.** 18 c. blue .. .. 80 40
DESIGNS—VERT. 3 c. "Cattleya labiata trianae". 4 c. "Masdevallia nicterina". 5 c. "Cattleya dowiana aurea". HORIZ. 2 c. "Odontoglossum crispum". 11 c. "Miltonia vexillaria".

**245.** Antonio Baraya (patriot). **246.** Farm.

**1950.**
729. **245.** 2 c. red .. .. 10 10

**1950.**
730. **246.** 5 c. red and buff .. 30 15
731. 5 c. green and turquoise 30 15
732. 5 c. blue and light blue 30 15

**247.** Arms of Bogota. **248.** Map and Badge.

**1950.**
733. **247.** 5 p. green .. .. 1·60 10
734. – 10 p. orange (Arms of Colombia) .. .. 2·40 15

**1951.** 60th Anniv. of Colombian Society of Engineers.
735. **248.** 20 c. red, yellow & bl. 35 15

**249.** Arms of Colombia and Cross. **250.** Fray Bartolome de Las Casas.

**1951.** Obligatory Tax. Red Cross Fund.
736. **249.** 5 c. red .. .. 20 15
737. **250.** 5 c. red .. .. 20 15
738. 5 c. green and red .. 20 10

**251.** D. G. Valencia. **254.** Dr. Nicolas Osorio.

**1951.** 8th Death Anniv. of D. G. Valencia (poet and orator).
739. **251.** 25 c. black .. .. 40 10

**1951.** Surch **1 centavo.**
740 **233** 1 c. on 3 c. blue .. 10 10

**1951.** Nationalization of Barranca Oilfields. Optd. **REVERSION CONCESION MARES 25 Agosto 1951.**
741. **147.** 2 c. red .. .. 10 10

**1952.** Colombian Doctors.
751 **254** 1 c. blue .. .. 10 10
752 – 1 c. blue (P. Martinez) 10 10
753 – 1 c. bl (E. Uriocoechea) 10 10
754 – 1 c. blue (Jose M. Lombana) .. 10 10

**255.** Proposed New P.O. Bogota. **256.** Manizales Cathedral. **258.** Queen Isabella and Columbus Monument.

**1952.**
755. **255.** 5 c. blue .. .. 15 10
756. **233.** 20 c. brown .. .. 8·00 10
757. **201.** 25 c. grey .. .. 12·00 1·60
758. **233.** 25 c. green .. .. 20 10
759. – 50 c. orange .. 25·00 14·00
760. – 1 p. red .. .. 55 25
761. – 2 p. purple .. 27·00 2·50
762. – 2 p. violet .. .. 65 10
DESIGN: 50 c. to 2 p. Similar to T **233** but larger, 24½ × 19 mm.
Owing to a shortage of postage stamps the above obligatory tax types were issued for ordinary postal use.

**1952.** Obligatory Tax. No. 759 surch.
763. 8 c. on 50 c. orange 15 10

**1952.** Centenary of Manizales.
764. **256.** 23 c. black and blue 25 15

**1952.** 1st Latin-American Congress of Iron Specialists. Surch. **1952 1º CONFERENCIA SIDERURGICA LATINO-AMERICANA** and new value
765. **223.** 15 c. on 25 c. green (postage) .. .. 30 20
766. **186.** 70 c. on 80 c. red (air) 75 25

**1953.** 500th Birth Anniv. of Isabella the Catholic.
767. **258.** 23 c. black and blue .. 35 35

**1953.** Air. Optd. **CORREO AEREO** or surch. also
768. **233.** 5 c. on 8 c. blue .. 15 10
769. 15 c. on 20 c. brown .. 25 10
770. 15 c. on 25 c green .. 65 10
771. 25 c. green .. .. 30 10

**1953.** Air. Optd. **AEREO.**
772. **155.** 10 c. red .. .. 15 10

**EXTRA RAPIDO.** Stamps bearing this overprint or inscription were used to prepay the additional cost of air carriage of inland mail handled by the National Postal Service from 1953 to 1964. Subsequently remaining stocks of these stamps were used for other classes of correspondence. Since the 1920's regular air service for inland and foreign mail has been provided by the Air Postal Service, a separate undertaking which is administered by the Avianca airline and for which the regular air stamps are used.

**1953.** Air. No. 727 surch. **CORREO EXTRA RAPIDO 5 5.**
773. 5 c. on 11 c. red .. .. 20 10

262.

**1953.** Air. Fiscal stamps optd. as in **262** or surch. also.

774. **262.** 1 c. on 2 c. green .. 10 10
775. 50 c. red .. .. 10 10

263.

**1953.** Air. Real Estate Tax stamps optd. as in **263.**

776. **263.** 5 c. red .. .. 15 10
777. 20 c. brown .. .. 20 10

**1953.** Surch.

778. – 40 c. on 1 p. red (No. 760) .. .. .. 45 10
779. **214.** 50 c. on 2 p. green .. 45 10

266. Don M. Ancizar.

267.

**1953.** Colombian Chorographical Commission Cent. Portraits inscr. as in T **266.**

780. **266.** 14 c. red and black .. 40 30
781. – 23 c. blue and black .. 35 20
782. – 30 c. sepia and black .. 35 15
783. – 1 p. green and black .. 15 10

PORTRAITS: 23 c. J. J. Triana. 30 c. M. Ponce de Leon. 1 p A. Codazzi.

**1953.** 2nd National Philatelic Exn., Bogota. Real Estate Tax stamps surch. as in T **267.**

784. **267.** 5 c. on 5 p. mult. (post.) 35 15
785. – 15 c. on 10 p. multicoloured (air) .. .. 40 25

DESIGN: 15 c. Map of Colombia.

**1953.** Air. Optd. **CORREO EXTRA-RAPIDO** or surch. also.

786. **238.** 2 c. on 8 c. blue .. 10 10
787. 10 c. violet .. .. 15 10

269. Fountain, Tunja.

271. Map of Colombia.

270. Pastelillo Fort, Cartagena.

**1954.** Air.

788. – 5 c. purple .. .. 30 10
789. – 10 c. black .. .. 20 10
790. – 15 c. red .. .. 20 10
791. – 15 c. vermilion .. 20 10
792. – 20 c. brown .. .. 30 10
793. – 25 c. blue .. .. 30 10
794. – 25 c. purple .. .. 30 10
795. – 30 c. brown .. .. 15 10
796. – 40 c. blue .. .. 25 10
797. – 50 c. purple .. .. 25 10
798. **269.** 60 c. sepia .. .. 35 10
799. – 80 c. lake .. .. 25 20
800. – 1 p. black and blue .. 1·40 20
801. **270.** 2 p. black and green .. 3·25 25
802. – 3 p. black and red .. 5·00 55
803. – 5 p. green and brown 7·00 1·40
804. **271.** 10 p. olive and red .. 8·50 3·50

DESIGNS. As Type **269**—VERT. 5 c., 30 c. Galeras volcano, Pasto. 15 c. red, 50 c. Bolivar Monument, Boyaca. 15 c. vermilion, 25 c. (2) Sanctuary of the Rocks, Narino. 20 c., 80 c. Nevado del Ruiz Mts., Manizales. 40 c. J. Isaacs Monument, Cali. HORIZ. 10 c. San Diego Monastery, Bogota. As Type **270**—HORIZ. 1 p. Girardot Stadium, Medellin. 3 p. Santo Domingo Gateway and University, Popayan. As Type **271**—HORIZ. 5 p. Sanctuary of the Rocks, Narino.

**1954.** Surch.

805. **266.** 5 c. on 14 c. red & blk. 30 15
806. **256.** 5 c. on 23 c. blk. & blue 30 15

272. Condor carrying Shield.

273.

**1954.** Air.

807. **272.** 5 c. purple .. .. 50 20

**1954.** 400th Anniv. of Franciscan Community in Colombia.

808. **273.** 5 c. brown, grn. & sep. 25 15

**1954.** Obligatory Tax. Red Cross Fund. No. 807 optd. with cross and bar in red.

809. **272.** 5 c. purple .. .. 1·60 40

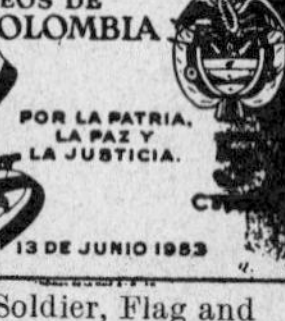

275. Soldier, Flag and Arms of Republic.



276.

**1954.** National Army Commem.

810. **275.** 5 c. blue (postage) .. 20 10
811. 15 c. red (air) .. 30 10

**1954.** 7th National Athletic Games, Cali. Inscr. "VII JUEGOS ATLETICOS", etc.

812. – 5 c. blue (postage) .. 15 10
813. **276.** 10 c. red .. .. 25 10
814. – 15 c. brown (air) .. 25 15
815. **276.** 20 c. green .. .. 60 35

DESIGN: 5 c., 15 c. Badge of the Games.

277.



278. Saint's Convent and Cell, Cartagena.

**1954.** 50th Anniv. of Colombian Academy of History.

816. **277.** 5 c. green and blue .. 20 10

**1954.** Death Tercent. of San Pedro Claver.

817. **278.** 5 c. green (postage) .. 15 10
819. – 15 c. brown (air) .. 30 10

DESIGN: 15 c. San Pedro Claver Church, Cartagena.

279. Mercury.

280. Archbishop Mosquera.

**1954.** 1st Int. Fair, Bogota.

821. **279.** 5 c. orange (postage) 25 10
822. 15 c. blue (air) .. 25 10
823. 50 c. red ("EXTRA RAPIDO") .. 30 10

**1954.** Air. Death Centenary of Archbishop Mosquera.

824. **280.** 2 c. green .. .. 10 10

281. Virgin of Chiquinquira.

**1954.** Air.

825. **281.** 5 c. mult. (brown frame) 10 10
826. 5 c. mult. (violet frame) 10 10

282. Tapestry presented by Queen Margaret of Austria.

**1954.** Tercentenary of Senior College of Our Lady of the Rosary, Bogota.

827. **282.** 5 c. black and orange (postage) .. .. 25 15
828. – 10 c. blue .. .. 25 15
829. – 15 c. brown .. .. 35 15
830. – 20 c. brown and black 60 25
832. **282.** 15 c. black & red (air) 35 15
833. – 20 c. blue .. .. 55 15
834. – 25 c. brown .. .. 55 15
835. – 50 c. red and black .. 85 30

DESIGNS—VERT. Nos. 828, 833, Friar Cristobal de Torres (founder). HORIZ. Nos. 829, 834, Cloisters and statue. Nos. 830, 835, Chapel and coat of arms.

283. Paz de Rio Steel Works.

284. J. Marti.

**1954.** Inaug. of Paz del Rio Steel Plant.

837. **283.** 5 c. blk. & bl. (post.) 15 10
838. 20 c. black & grn. (air) 70 45

**1955.** Birth Centenary of Marti (Cuban revolutionary).

839 **284** 5 c. red (postage) .. 15 10
840 – 15 c. green (air) .. 25 10

285. Badge, Flags and Korean Landscape.

**1955.** Colombian Forces in Korea.

841. **285.** 10 c. purple (postage) 25 10
842. 20 c. green (air) .. 25 15

286. Merchant Marine Emblem.

287. M. Fidel Suarez.

**1955.** Greater Colombia Merchant Marine Commem. Inscr. as in T **286.**

843. **286.** 15 c. green (postage) .. 20 10
844. – 20 c. violet .. .. 55 15
846. **286.** 25 c. black (air) .. 35 10
847. – 50 c. green .. .. 75 15

DESIGN—HORIZ. 20, 50 c. "City of Manizales" (freighter) and skyscrapers.

**1955.** Air. Birth Centenary of Marco Fidel Suarez (President, 1918–21).

849. **287.** 10 c. blue .. .. 15 10

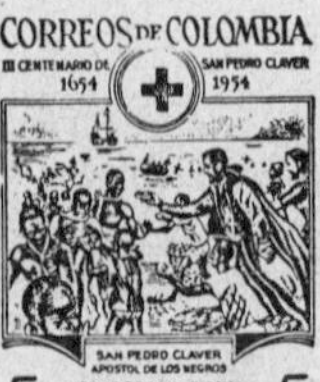


288. San Pedro Claver feeding Slaves.

**1955.** Obligatory Tax. Red Cross Fund and 300th Anniv. of San Pedro Claver.

850. **288.** 5 c. purple and red .. 25 10

289. Hotel Tequendama and San Diego Church.

**1955.**

851. **289.** 5 c. blue and pale blue (postage) .. .. 15 10
852. 15 c. lake and pink (air) 25 10

290. Bolivar's Country House.

**1955.** 50th Anniv. of Rotary Int.

853. **290.** 5 c. blue (postage) .. 15 10
854. 15 c. red (air) .. 25 10

291. Belalcazar, De Quesada and Balboa.

292. J. E. Caro.

**1955.** 7th Postal Union Congress of the Americas and Spain. Inscr. as in T **291.**

855. **291.** 2 c. brn. & grn. (post.) 10 10
856. – 5 c. brown and blue .. 15 10
857. – 23 c. black and blue .. 1·25 30
859. – 15 c. black and red (air) 15 10
860. – 20 c. black and brown 25 10
862. – 2 c. black and brown ("EXTRA RAPIDO") 10 10
863. – 5 c. sepia and yellow .. 15 10
864. – 1 p. brown and slate .. 12·00 5·50
865. – 2 p. black and violet .. 7·50 6·50

DESIGNS—HORIZ. 2 c. (No. 855), Type **291.** 2 c. (No. 862), Atahualpa, Tisquesuza, Montezuma. 5 c. (No. 856), San Martin, Bolivar and Washington. 5 c. (No. 863), King Ferdinand, Queen Isabella and coat of arms. 15 c. O'Higgins, Santander and Sucre. 20 c. Marti, Hidalgo and Petion. 23 c. Colombus, "Santa Maria", "Pinta" and "Nina". 1 p. Artigas, Lopez and Murillo. 2 p. Calderon, Baron de Rio Branco and De La Mar.

**1955.** Death Cent of Jose Eusebio Caro (poet).

866. **292.** 5 c. brown (postage) .. 10 10
867. 15 c. green (air) .. 25 10

293. Salamanca University.

294. Gold Mining, Narino.

**1955.** Air. 700th Anniv. of Salamanca University.

868. **293.** 20 c. brown .. .. 15 10

**1956.** Regional Industries. Inscr. "DEPARTAMENTO", "PROVIDENCIA" (No. 874), "INTENDENCIA" (2 p. to 5 p.) or "COMISARIA" (10 p.).

869. – 2 c. green and red .. 10 10
870. – 3 c. black and purple .. 10 10
871. – 3 c. brown and blue .. 10 10
872. – 3 c. violet and green .. 10 10
873. – 4 c. black and green .. 25 10
874. – 5 c. black and blue .. 20 10
875. – 5 c. slate and red .. 30 10
876. – 5 c. olive and brown .. 30 10
877. – 5 c. brown and olive .. 25 10
878. – 5 c. brown and blue .. 30 10
879. – 10 c. black and yellow 25 10
880. – 10 c. brown and green 20 10
881. – 10 c. brown and blue .. 20 10
882. – 15 c. black and blue .. 25 10
883. – 20 c. blue and brown .. 30 10
884. – 23 c. red and blue .. 35 15
885. – 25 c. black and olive .. 35 15
886. **294.** 30 c. brown and blue .. 30 10
887. – 40 c. brown and purple 10 10
888. – 50 c. black and green .. 25 10
889. – 60 c. green and sepia .. 25 10
890. – 1 p. slate and purple .. 90 10
891. – 2 p. brown and green .. 1·90 25
892. – 3 p. black and red .. 1·75 35
893. – 5 p. blue and brown .. 4·00 25
894. – 10 p. green and brown 9·50 3·00

DESIGNS—As Type **294**. HORIZ. 2 c. Barranquilla naval workshops, Atlantico. 4 c. Fishing, Cartagena Port, Bolivar. 5 c. (No. 875) View of Port, San Andres. 5 c. (No. 876) Cocoa, Cauca. 5 c. (No. 877) Prize cattle, Cordoba. 23 c. Rice harvesting, Huila. 25 c. Bananas, Magdalena. 40 c. Tobacco, Santander. 50 c. Oil wells of Catatumbo, Norte de Santander. 60 c. Cotton harvesting, Tolima. VERT. 3 c. (3), Allegory of Industry, Antioquia. 5 c. (No. 874) Map of San Andres Archipelago. 5 c. (No. 878) Steel plant, Boyaca. 10 c. (3), Coffee, Caldas. 15 c. Cathedral at Sal Salinas de Zipaquira, Cundinamarca. 20 c. Platinum and map, Choco. LARGER (37½×27 mm.)—HORIZ. 1 p. Sugar factory, Valle del Cauca. 2 p. Cattle fording river, Meta. 3 p. Statue and River Amazon, Leticia. 5 p. Landscape, La Guajira. VERT. 10 p. Rubber tapping, Vaupes.

**295.** Henri Dunant and S. Samper Brush.

**1956.** Obligatory Tax. Red Cross Fund.
895. **295.** 5 c. brown .. .. 20 10

**1956.** Air. No. 783 optd. **EXTRA-RAPIDO**.
896. 1 p. green and black .. 25 10

**297.** Columbus and Lighthouse.

**1956.** Columbus Memorial Lighthouse.
897. **297.** 3 c. black (postage) .. 15 10
898. 15 c. blue (air) .. 20 10
899. 3 c. green ("EXTRA RAPIDO") .. 15 10

**298.** Altar of St. Elisabeth and Sarcophagus of Jimenez de Quesada, Primada Basilica, Bogota.

**299.** St. Ignatius of Loyola.

**1956.** 700th Anniv. of St. Elisabeth of Hungary.
900. **298.** 5 c. purple (postage) .. 15 10
901. 15 c. brown (air) .. 30 15

**1956.** 400th Death Anniv. of St. Ignatius of Loyola.
902. **299.** 5 c. blue (postage) .. 15 10
903. 5 c. brown (air) .. 20 10

**300.** Javier Pereira. **302.** Dairy Farm.

**1956.** Pereira Commem.
904. **300.** 5 c. blue (postage) .. 10 10
905. 20 c. red (air) .. 10 10

**1957.** Air. No. 874 optd. **EXTRA-RAPIDO.**
906. 5 c. black and blue 20 10

**1957.** Air. As No. 580 (colours changed) optd. **EXTRA-RAPIDO.**
907. 5 p. black and buff .. 6·00 3·75

**1957.** 25th Anniv. of Agricultural Credit Bank.
908. **302.** 1 c. olive (postage) .. 10 10
909. – 2 c. brown .. .. 10 10
910. – 5 c. blue .. .. 15 10
911. **302.** 5 c. orange (air) .. 15 10
912. – 10 c. green .. .. 25 20
913. – 15 c. black .. .. 25 10
914. – 20 c. red .. .. 40 30
915. – 5 c. brown ("EXTRA RAPIDO") .. 15 10

DESIGNS: 2 c., 10 c. Farm tractor. 5 c. (No. 910), 15 c. Emblem of agricultural prosperity. 5 c. (No. 915), Livestock. 20 c. Livestock.

**303.** Racing Cyclist.

**1957.** Air. 7th Round Colombia Cycle Race.
916. **303.** 2 c. brown .. 15 15
917. 5 c. blue .. .. 25 25

**304.** Arms and Gen. Rayes (founder).

**305.** Father J. M. Delgado.

**1957.** 50th Anniv. of Military Cadet School.
918. **304.** 5 c. blue (postage) .. 15 10
919. – 10 c. orange .. .. 20 10
921. **304.** 15 c. red (air) .. .. 20 10
922. – 20 c. brown .. .. 30 10

DESIGN: 10 c., 20 c. Arms and Military Cadet School.

**1957.** Father Delgado Commemoration.
923. **305.** 2 c. lake (postage) .. 10 10
924. 10 c. blue (air) .. 15 10

**306.** St. Vincent de Paul with Children.

**308.** Fencer.

**307.** Signatories to Bogota Postal Convention of 1838, and U.P.U. Monument, Berne.

**1957.** Centenary of Colombian Order of St. Vincent de Paul.
925. **306.** 1 c. green (postage) .. 10 10
926. 5 c. red (air) .. .. 15 10

**1957.** 14th U.P.U. Congress, Ottawa and Int. Correspondence Week.
927. **307.** 5 c. green (postage) .. 15 10
928. 10 c. grey .. .. 15 10
929. 15 c. brown (air) .. 20 10
930. 25 c. blue .. .. 20 10

**1957.** 3rd S. American Fencing Championships.
931. **308.** 4 c. purple (postage) .. 20 10
932. 20 c. brown (air) .. 35 10

**309.** Discovery of Hypsometry by F. J. de Caldas.

**310.** Nurses with Patient, and Ambulance.

**1958.** Int. Geophysical Year.
933. **309.** 10 c. black (postage) 30 10
934. 25 c. green (air) .. 45 10
935. 1 p. violet ("EXTRA RAPIDO") .. 15 10

**1958.** Obligatory Tax. Red Cross Fund.
936. **310.** 5 c. red & black .. 15 10

**1958.** Nos. 882 and 884 surch.
937. 5 c. on 15 c. black & blue 10 10
938. 5 c. on 23 c. red and blue 25 20

**1958.** Air. No. 888 optd. **AEREO.**
939. 50 c. black and green 20 10

**313.** Father R. Al manza and San Diego Church, Bogota.

**315.** Msr. Carrasquilla and Rosario College, Bogota.

**1958.** Father Almanza Commem.
940. **313.** 10 c. lilac (postage) .. 10 10
941. 25 c. grey (air) .. 30 10
942. 10 c. green ("EXTRA RAPIDO") .. 10 10

**1958.** Nos. 780/2 surch. **CINCO** (5 c.) or **VEINTE** (20 c.).
943. **266.** 5 c. on 14 c. red & blk. 15 10
944. – 5 c. on 30 c. sepia & blk. 10 10
945. – 20 c. on 23 c. bl. & blk. 25 15

**1959.** Birth Cent of Msr. R. M. Carrasquilla.
946. **315.** 10 c. brown (postage) 15 10
947. 25 c. red (air) .. 20 10
948. 1 p. blue .. .. 60 20

**1959.** Surch. **20. c.** and ornament.
949. **258.** 20 c. on 23 c. blk. & bl. 25 15

**1959.** As No. 826 but with "**CORREO EXTRA RAPIDO**" obliterated.
950. **281.** 5 c. multicoloured .. 10 10

**1959.** No. 794 surch.
951. 10 c. on 25 c. purple .. 15 10

**318.** Luz Marina Zuluaga ("Miss Universe 1959").

**320.** J. E. Gaitan (political leader).

**1959.** "Miss Universe 1959" Commem.
952. **318.** 10 c. mult. (postage) .. 10 10
953. 1 p. 20 mult. (air) .. 65 45
954. 5 p. mult. ("EXTRA RAPIDO") .. 25·00 24·00

**1959.** No. 873 surch.
955. 2 c. on 4 c. black and green 10 10

**1959.** J. E. Gaitan Commem. Nos. 956 and 958 are surch. on T **320.**
956. **320.** 10 c. on 3 c. grey .. 15 10
957. 30 c. purple .. .. 25 15
958. 2 p. on 1 p. black ("EXTRA RAPIDO") 60 25

**1959.** Air. Surch.
960. **269.** 50 c. on 60 c. sepia .. 5·00 30

**323.** Capitol, Bogota. **324.** Santander.

**1959.**
961. **323.** 2 c. brn. & blue (post.) 10 10
962. 3 c. violet and black .. 10 10
963. **324.** 5 c. brown and yellow 15 10
964. – 5 c. ultramarine & blue 15 10
965. – 10 c. black and red .. 15 10
966. **324.** 10 c. black and green .. 15 10
967. – 35 c. black & grey (air) 1·75 10

PORTRAIT (as Type **324**): Nos. 964/5, 967, Bolivar.

**1959.** Air. Unification of Airmail Rates. Optd. **UNIFICADO** within outline of aeroplane.
968. **299.** 5 c. brown .. .. 15 10
969. **302.** 5 c. orange .. .. 35 35
970. **306.** 5 c. red .. .. 20 20
971. **155.** 10 c. red (No. 772) .. 10 10
972. – 10 c. black (No. 789) .. 20 10
973. **304.** 15 c. red .. .. 30 10
974. – 20 c. brown (No. 792) 20 10
975. – 20 c. brown (No. 922) 20 10
976. **308.** 20 c. brown .. .. 25 15
977. – 25 c. blue (No. 793) .. 25 10
978. – 25 c. purple (No. 794) 25 10
979. **313.** 25 c. grey .. .. 25 10
980. **315.** 25 c. red .. .. 30 10
981. – 30 c. brown (No. 795) 20 10
982. **269.** 50 c. on 60 c. sepia (No. 960) .. .. 15 10
983. **315.** 1 p. blue .. .. 35 10
984. **318.** 1 p. 20 multicoloured 45 35
985. **270.** 2 p. black and green .. 2·10 20
986. – 3 p. blk. & red (No. 802) 7·00 45
987. – 5 p. grn. & brn. (No. 803) 7·50 45
988. **271.** 10 p. olive and red .. 9·50 1·60

INDEX
Countries can be quickly located by referring to the index at the end of this volume.

**326.** Colombian 2½c. stamp of 1859 and Postman with Mule.

**328.** 2 c. Air Stamp of 1918, Junkers F-13 "Colombia" and Lockheed Constellation.

**1959.** Colombian Stamp Cent. Inscr. "1859 1959".
989. **326.** 5 c. grn. & orge. (post.) 20 15
990. – 10 c. blue and lake .. 25 15
991. **326.** 15 c. green and red .. 35 10
992. – 25 c. brown and blue 35 15
993. – 25 c. red & brown (air) 40 20
994. – 50 c. blue and red .. 55 20
995. – 1 p. 20 brown & green 2·10 1·25
996. – 10 c. lilac and bistre ("EXTRA-RAPIDO") 20 10

DESIGNS—VERT. Colombian stamps of 1859 (except No. 993): No. 990, 5 c. and river steamer. No. 992, 10 c. and railway train. No. 993, Postal decree of 1859 and Pres. M. Ospina. No. 996, 10 c. and map of Colombia. HORIZ. No. 994, 20 c. and Junkers F-13 seaplane "Colombia". No. 995, 1 p. and Lockheed Constellation airliner over valley.

**1959.** Air. 40th Anniv of Colombian "AVIANCA" Air Mail Services.
998. **328.** 35 c. red, black & blue 15 10
999. – 60 c. black and green 25 15

DESIGN: 60 c. As Type **328** but without Colombian 2 c. stamp.

**329.** Eldorado Airport, Bogota.

**331.** A. von Humboldt (after J. K. Stieler).

**1960.** Air.
1002. **329.** 35 c. orange and black 45 20
1003. 60 c. red and grey .. 35 35
1004. 1 p. blue and grey ("EXTRA RAPIDO") 1·00 45

**1960.** Death Centenary of Alexander von Humboldt (naturalist). Animals.
1005. – 5 c. brn. & turq. (post.) .. .. 10 10
1006. **331.** 10 c. sepia and red .. 10 10
1007. – 20 c. purple & yellow 20 10
1008. – 35 c. brown (air) .. 45 10
1009. – 1 p. 30 brown and red 1·25 90
1010. – 1 p. 45 lemon & blue 75 45

DESIGNS—VERT. 5 c. Two-toed sloth. 20 c. Long-haired spider monkey. HORIZ. 35 c. Giant anteater. 1 p. 30, Nine-banded armadillo. 1 p. 45, Parrot fish.

**332.** "Anthurium andreanum".

**333.** Refugee Family.

**1960.** Colombian Flowers.
1011. **332.** 5 c. mult. (postage) .. 20 10
1012. A. 20 c. yell., grn. & sep. 10 10
1013. B. 5 c. mult. (air) .. 10 10
1014. 5 c. multicoloured .. 10 10
1015. A. 10 c. yell., grn. & blue 10 10
1016. C. 20 c. multicoloured 10 10
1017. D. 25 c. multicoloured .. 35 10
1018. C. 35 c. multicoloured .. 25 10
1019. B. 60 c. multicoloured .. 35 20
1020. **332.** 60 c. multicoloured .. 35 10
1021. 1 p. 45, multicoloured 90 35
1022. C. 5 c. mult. ("EXTRA RAPIDO") .. 10 10
1023. D. 10 c. multicoloured .. 10 10
1024. **332.** 1 p. multicoloured .. 90 55
1025. A. 1 p. yellow, green & sepia .. .. 90 55
1026. B. 1 p. multicoloured .. 90 55
1027. C. 1 p. multicoloured .. 90 55
1028. D. 1 p. multicoloured .. 90 55
1029. C. 2 p. multicoloured .. 1·60 80

FLOWERS: A, "Espelitia grandiflora". B, "Passiflora mollissima". C, Odontoglossum luteo purpureum". D, "Stanhopea tigrina".

**1960.** Air. World Refugee Year.
1030a **333** 60 c. grey and green 15 15

334. Lincoln Statue, Washington.

335. "House of the Flower Vase".

**1960.** 150th Birth Anniv. of Abraham Lincoln.
1032. **334.** 20 c. blk. & mve. (post.) 15 10
1033. 40 c. black & brn. (air) 45 25
1034. 60 c. black and red .. 25 10

**1960.** 150th Anniv. of Independence.
1035. – 5 c. brn. & grn. (post.) 10 10
1036. **335.** 20 c. purple & brown 15 10
1037. – 20 c. yellow, blue and mauve .. .. 10 15
1038. – 5 c. multicoloured (air) 15 10
1039. – 5 c. sepia and violet .. 15 10
1040. – 35 c. multicoloured .. 20 10
1041. – 60 c. green and brown 40 10
1042. – 1 p. green and red .. 35 20
1043. – 1 p. 20 indigo & blue 35 20
1044. – 1 p. 30 black & orange 35 20
1045. – 1 p. 45 multicoloured 65 55
1046. – 1 p. 65 brown & green 45 35

DESIGNS—VERT. No. 1035, Cartagena coins of 1811–13. No. 1038, Arms of Cartagena. No. 1037, Arms of Mompos. No. 1043, Statue of A. Galan. HORIZ. No. 1039, J. Camacho, J. T. Lozano and J. M. Pey. Nos. 1040, 1045, Colombian Flag. No. 1041, A. Rosillo, A. Villavicencio and J. Caicedo. No. 1042, B. Alvares and J. Gutierrez. No. 1044, Front page of "La Bagatela" (newspaper). No. 1046, A. Santos, J. A. Gomez and L. Mejia.

336. St. Luisa de Marillac and Sanctuary.

337. St. Isidro Labrador (after G. Vasquez).

**1960.** Obligatory Tax. Red Cross Fund.
1048. **336.** 5 c. red and brown .. 20 10
1049. – 5 c. red and blue .. 20 10

DESIGN: No. 1049, H. Dunant and battle scene.

**1960.** St. Isidro Labrador Commem. (1st issue).
1050. **337.** 10 c. mult. (postage) .. 10 10
1051. – 20 c. multicoloured .. 15 10
1052. **337.** 35 c. multicoloured (air) 20 10

DESIGN: 20 c. "The Nativity" (after Vasquez).
See also Nos. 1126/8.

338. U.N. Headquarters, New York.

339. Highway Map of Northern Colombia.

**1960.** U.N. Day.
1054. **338.** 20 c. red and black .. 15 10

**1961.** 8th Pan-American Highway Congress.
1056. **339.** 20 c. brn. & blue (post.) 30 25
1057. 10 c. pur. & grn. (air) .. 30 25
1058. 20 c. red and blue .. 30 25
1059. 30 c. black and green .. 30 25
1060. 10 c. blue and green ("EXTRA RAPIDO") 30 25

340. Alfonso Lopez (statesman).

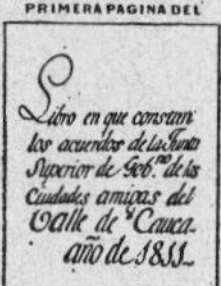


341. Text from Resolution of Confederated Cities.

345. Arms of Barranquilla.

342. Arms and View of Cucuta.

**1961.** 75th Birth Anniv of Alfonso Lopez (President 1934–38 and 1941–45).
1061. **340.** 10 c. brn. & red (post.) 15 10
1062. 20 c. brown and violet 15 10
1063. 35 c. brn. & blue (air) 35 10
1064. 10 c. brown and green ("EXTRA RAPIDO") 15 10

**1961.** 50th Anniv. of Valle del Cauca.
1066. – 10 c. multicoloured (postage) .. .. 10 10
1067. **341.** 20 c. brown and black 15 10
1068. – 35 c. brn. & olive (air) 30 10
1069. – 35 c. brown and green 30 10
1070. – 1 p. 30 sepia & purple 35 15
1071. – 1 p. 45 green & brown 35 15
1072. – 10 c. brown and olive ("EXTRA RAPIDO") 15 10

DESIGNS—HORIZ. 10 c. (No. 1066), La Ermita Church, bridge and arms of Cali. 35 c. (No. 1068), St. Francis' Church, Cali. 1 p. 30, Conservatoire. 1 p. 45, Agricultural College, Palmira. VERT. 10 c. (No. 1072), Aerial view of Cali. 35 c. (No. 1069), University emblem.

**1961.** 50th Anniv. of North Santander.
1073. – 20 c. multicoloured (post.) 15 10
1074. **342.** 20 c. multicoloured .. 15 10
1075. – 35 c. grn. & bistre (air) 45 10
1076. – 10 c. purple & green ("EXTRA RAPIDO") 15 10

DESIGNS—HORIZ. No. 1073, Arms of Ocana and Pamplona. No. 1075, Panoramic view of Cucuta. VERT. No. 1076, Villa del Rosario, Cucuta.

**1961.** Air. Optd **Aereo** (1077) or **AEREO** (others) and airplane or surch also.
1077. **332.** 5 c. multicoloured .. 10 10
1078. – 5 c. brown & turquoise (No. 1005) .. .. 10 10
1079. – 10 c. on 20 c. purple & yellow (No. 1007) 10 10

**1961.** Atlantico Tourist Issue.
1080. 10 c. multicoloured (post.) 10 10
1081. 20 c. red, blue and yellow 15 10
1082. 20 c. multicoloured 15 10
1083. 35 c. sepia and red (air) .. 45 10
1084. 35 c. red, yellow and green 35 10
1085. 35 c. blue and gold .. 45 10
1086. 1 p. 45 brown and green .. 45 20
1088. 10 c. yellow and brown ("EXTRA RAPIDO") 15 10

DESIGNS—VERT. No. 1080, Arms of Popayan. No. 1081, Type **345**. No. 1082, Arms of Bucaramanga. No. 1083, Courtyard of Tourist Hotel. No. 1087, Holy Week procession, Popayan. HORIZ. No. 1084, View of San Gill. No. 1085, Barranquilla Port. No. 1086, View of Velez.

346. Nurse M. de la Cruz.

347. Boxing.

**1961.** Red Cross Fund. Cross in red.
1090. **346.** 5 c. brown .. .. 15 10
1091. 5 c. purple .. .. 15 10

**1961.** 4th Bolivarian Games. Inscr. as in T **347**. Multicoloured.
1092. 20 c. Type **347** (postage) 20 10
1093. 20 c. Basketball .. .. 10 10
1094. 20 c. Running .. .. 10 10
1095. 25 c. Football .. .. 20 10
1096. 35 c. Diving (air) .. .. 25 10
1097. 35 c. Tennis .. .. 25 10
1098. 1 p. 45 Baseball .. .. 35 15
1099. 10 c. Statue and flags ("EXTRA RAPIDO") 10 10
1100. 10 c. Runner with Olympic torch ("EXTRA RAPIDO") .. 10 10

348. "S.E.M." Emblem and Mosquito.

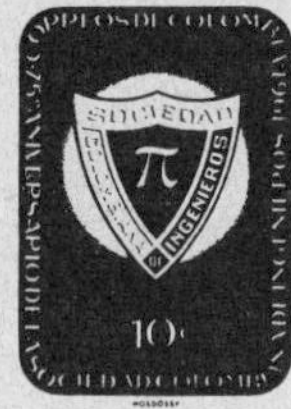


349. Society Emblem.

**1962.** Malaria Eradication.
1102. **348.** 20 c. red & ochre (post.) 15 15
1103 – 50 c. blue and ochre .. 15 15
1104 **348.** 40 c. red & yell. (air) 15 15
1105. – 1 p. 45 blue and grey 40 40
1106. – 1 p. blue and green ("EXTRA RAPIDO") 2·75 2·75

DESIGN: 50 c., 1 p., 1 p. 45, Campaign emblem and mosquito.

**1962.** 6th National Engineers' Congress, 1961 and 75th Anniv. of Colombian Society of Engineers.
1107. **349.** 10 c. multicoloured .. (postage) .. .. 20 20
1108. – 5 c. red and blue (air) 10 10
1109. – 10 c. brown and green 15 15
1110. – 15 c. brown & purple 25 15
1111. **349.** 2 p. multicoloured ("EXTRA RAPIDO") 1·60 90

DESIGNS: No. 1108, A. Ramos and Engineering Faculty, Cauca University, Popayan. No. 1109, M. Triana, A. Arroyo and Monserrate cable and funicular railways. No. 1110, D. Sanchez and first Society H.Q., Bogota.

350. O.E.A. Emblem.

351. Mother Voting and Statue of Policarpa Salavarrieta.

**1962.** 70th Anniv. of Organization of American States (O.E.A.). Flags mult. Background colours given.
1112. **350.** 25 c. red & blk. (post.) 15 10
1114. 35 c. blue & black (air) 15 10

**1962.** Women's Franchise.
1115. **351.** 5 c. black, grey and brown (postage) .. 10 10
1116. 10 c. blk., grey & blue 15 10
1117. 5 c. black, grey and pink (air) .. .. 10 10
1118. 35 c. black, grey & buff 25 10
1119. 45 c. blk., grey & grn. 25 10
1120. 45 c. blk., grey & mve. 25 10

353. Scouts in Camp.

354. St. Isidro Labrador (after G. Vasquez).

**1962.** 30th Anniv. of Colombian Boy Scouts and 25th Anniv. of Colombian Girl Scouts. As T **353** but without "EXTRA RAPIDO".
1121. **353.** 10 c. brn. & turq. (post.) 10 10
1122. 15 c. brn. & red (air) 25 10
1123. – 40 c. lake and red .. 15 10
1124. – 1 p. blue and Salmon 30 15
1125. **353** 1 p. violet & yellow ("EXTRA RAPIDO") 3·50 3·25

DESIGN: 40 c., 1 p. Girl Scouts.

**1962.** St. Isidro Labrador Commem. (2nd issue).
1126. **354.** 10 c. multicoloured .. 10 10
1127. – 10 c. mult. (air—"EXTRA RAPIDO") 10 10
1128. **354.** 2 p. multicoloured .. 2·50 1·50

DESIGN: 10 c. (No. 1127), "The Nativity" (after G. Vasquez).

355. Railway Map.

356. Posthorn.

**1962.** Completion of Colombia Atlantic Railway.
1129. **355.** 10 c. red, green and olive (postage) .. 10 15
1130. – 5 c. myrtle & sepia (air) 10 10
1131. **355.** 10 c. red, turq. & bistre 10 10
1132. – 1 p. brown & purple .. 1·50 10
1133. – 5 p. brn., blue & green ("EXTRA RAPIDO") 3·75 1·10

DESIGNS—HORIZ. 5 c. 1854 and 1961 locomotives. 1 p., 5 p. Pres. A. Parra and R. Magdalena railway bridge.

**1962.** 50th Anniv. of Postal Union of the Americas and Spain.
1134. **356.** 20 c. gold & blue (post.) 15 10
1135. – 50 c. gold and grey-green (air) .. .. 30 10
1136. **356.** 60 c. gold and purple 20 10

DESIGN: 50 c. Posthorn, dove and map.

357. Virgin of the Mountain, Bogota.

358. Centenary Emblem.

**1963.** Ecumenical Council, Vatican City.
1137. **357.** 60 c. multicoloured (postage) .. .. 20 10
1138. – 60 c. red, yellow and gold (air) .. .. 10 10

DESIGN: No. 1138, Pope John XXIII.

**1963.** Obligatory Tax. Red Cross Cent.
1139. **358.** 5 c. red and bistre .. 10 10

359. Hurdling and Flags.

**1963.** Air. South American Athletic Championships, Cali.
1140. **359.** 20 c. multicoloured .. 15 10
1141. 80 c. multicoloured .. 15 10

360. Bolivar Monument.

361. Tennis Player.

363. Veracruz Church.

362. Pres. Kennedy and Alliance Emblem.

**1963.** Air. Centenary of Pereira.
1142. **360.** 1 p. 90 brown and blue 10 10

**1963.** Air. 30th South American Tennis Championships, Medellin.
1143. **361.** 55 c. multicoloured .. 25 10

**1963.** Air. "Alliance for Progress".
1144. **362.** 10 c. multicoloured .. 10 10

**1964.** Air. National Pantheon, Veracruz Church. Multicoloured.
1145. 1 p. Type **363**. .. .. 25 10
1146. 2 p. "The Crucifixion" .. 35 20

**364.** Cartagena. **365.** Eleanor Roosevelt.

**1964.** Air. Cartagena Commemoration.
1147. **364.** 3 p. multicoloured .. 80 55

**1964.** Air. 15th Anniv. of Declaration of Human Rights.
1148. **365.** 20 c. brown and olive 10 10

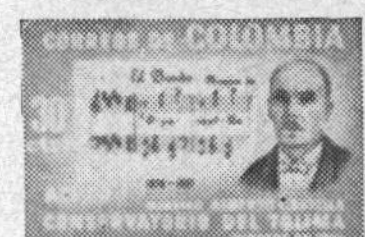


**366.** A. Castilla (composer and founder) and Music.

**1964.** Air. Tolima Conservatoire Commem.
1149. **366.** 30 c. turq. and bistre 20 10

**367.** Manuel Mejia and Coffee Growers' Flag Emblem. **368.** Nurse with Patient.

**1965.** Manuel Mejia Commem.
1150. **367.** 25 c. sepia & red (post.) 10 10
1151. – 45 c. sepia & brown (air) 15 10
1152. – 5 p. black and green .. 1·60 30
1153. – 10 p. black and blue .. 2·10 25
DESIGNS: 45 c. Gathering coffee-beans 5 p. Mule transport. 10 p. Freighter "Manuel Mejia" at Buenaventura Port. Each design includes a portrait of M. Mejia, director of the National Coffee Growers' Association.

**1965.** Obligatory Tax. Red Cross Fund.
1154. **368.** 5 c. blue and red .. 10 10

**369.** I.T.U. Emblem and "Waves". **370.** Orchid ("Cattleya trianae").

**1965.** Air. Centenary of I.T.U.
1155. **369.** 80 c. indigo, red & blue 15 10

**1965.** Air. 5th Philatelic Exn., Bogota.
1156. **370.** 20 c. multicoloured .. 20 10

**371.** Satellites, Telegraph Pole and Map.

**1965.** Air. Cent of Colombian Telegraphs. Multicoloured.
1157. 60 c. Type **371** .. .. 15 10
1158. 60 c. Statue of Pres. Murrilo Toro, Bogota (vert.) .. 15 10

**372.** Junkers F-13 Seaplane "Colombia" (1920).

**1965.** Air "History of Colombian Aviation". Multicoloured.
1159 5 c. Type **372** .. .. 10 10
1160 10 c. Dornier Wal Do-J (1924) .. .. 10 10
1161 20 c. Dornier Do-B Merkur seaplane (1926) 20 10
1162 50 c. Ford 5-AT Trimotor (1932) .. .. 20 10
1163 60 c. De Havilland Gipsy Moth (1930) .. .. 30 10
1164 1 p. Douglas DC-4 (1947) 35 10
1165 1 p. 40 Douglas DC-3 (1944) .. .. 20 15
1166 2 p. 80 Lockheed Constellation (1951) .. 45 30
1167 3 p. Boeing 720 B jet liner (1961) .. .. 65 55
See also No. E1168.

**373.** Badge, and Car on Mountain Road.

**1966.** Air. 25th Anniv. (1965) of Colombian Automobile Club.
1168. **373.** 20 c. multicoloured .. 10 10

**374.** J. Arboleda (writer). **375.** Red Cross and Children as Nurse and Patient.

**1966.** Julio Arboleda Commem.
1169. **374.** 5 c. multicoloured .. 10 10

**1966.** Obligatory Tax. Red Cross Fund.
1170. **375.** 5 c. + 5 c. mult. .. 10 10

**376.** 16th-century Galleon.

**1966.** History of Maritime Mail. Mult.
1171 5 c. Type **376** .. .. 15 10
1172 15 c. Riohacha brigantine (1850) .. .. 25 10
1173 20 c. Uraba Schooner .. 25 10
1174 40 c. Steamer and barge, Magdalena, 1900 .. 45 10
1175 50 c. Modern freighter .. 1·10 35

**377.** Hogfish.

**1966.** Fishes. Multicoloured.
1176 80 c. Type **377** (postage) 25 10
1177 10 p. Electric ray .. 3·75 3·25
1178 2 p. Flying fish (air) .. 15 20
1179 2 p. 80 Angel fish .. 45 30
1180 20 p. Spanish mackerel .. 7·00 5·50

**378.** Arms of Colombia, Venezuela and Chile. **379.** C. Torres (patriot).

**1966.** Visits of Chilean and Venezuelan Presidents.
1181. **378.** 40 c. mult. (postage) 10 10
1182. 1 p. multicoloured (air) 25 10
1183. 1 p. 40 multicoloured 25 10

**1967.** Famous Colombians.
1184. **379.** 25 c. vio. & yell. (post.) 10 10
1185. – 60 c. purple & yellow 10 10
1186. – 1 p. green and yellow 35 10
1187. – 80 c. blue & yell. (air) 15 10
1188. – 1 p. 70 black & yellow 30 10
PORTRAITS: 60 c. J. T. Lozano (naturalist). 80 c. Father F. R. Mejia (scholar). 1 p. F. A. Zea (writer). 1 p. 70, J. J. Casas (diplomat).

**380.** Map of Signatory Countries.

**1967.** "Declaration of Bogota".
1189 **380** 40 c. mult. (postage) 15 10
1190 60 c. multicoloured .. 15 10
1191 3 p. multicoloured (air) 30 15

**381.** "Monochaetum" and Bee.

**1967.** National Orchid Congress and Tropical Flora and Fauna Exn., Medellin. Mult.
1192 25 c. Type **381** (postage) 10 10
1193 2 p. "Passiflora vitifolia" and butterfly .. .. 45 35
1194 1 p. "Cattleya dowiana" (vert) (air) .. .. 15 10
1195 1 p. 20 "Masdevallia coccinea" (vert) .. 10 10
1196 5 p. "Catasetum macrocarpum" and bee .. 55 10

**382.** Nurse's Cap. **383.** Lions Emblem.

**1967.** Obligatory Tax. Red Cross Fund.
1198. **382.** 5 c. red and blue .. 10 10

**1967.** 50th Anniv. of Lions Int.
1199. **383.** 10 p. mult. (postage) 1·40 35
1200. 25 c. multicoloured (air) 15 10

**384.** "Caesarean Operation, 1844" (from painting by Grau). **385.** S.E.N.A. Emblem.

**1967.** Air. 6th Colombian Surgeons' Congress, Bogota and Cent. of National University.
1201 **384** 80 c. multicoloured .. 15 10

**1967.** 10th Anniv. of National Apprenticeship Service.
1202. **385.** 5 p. black, gold and green (postage) .. 1·25 20
1203. 2 p. black, gold and red (air) .. .. 20 10

**386.** Calima Diadem. **387.** Radio Antenna.

**1967.** Administrative Council of U.P.U. Consultative Commission of Postal Studies. Main design and lower inscr. in brown and gold.
1204. **386.** 1 p. 60 purple (post.) 15 10
1205. – 3 p. blue .. .. 35 10
1206. – 30 c. red (air) .. 20 10
1207. – 5 p. red .. .. 90 20
1208. – 20 p. violet .. .. 7·00 4·25
DESIGNS (Colombian archaeological treasures) VERT. 30 c. Chief's head-dress. 5 p. Cauca breastplate. 20 p. Quimbaya jug. HORIZ. 3 p. Tolima anthropomorphic figure and postal "pigeon on globe" emblem.

**1968.** "21 Years of National Telecommunications Services". Inscr. "1947-1968".
1210. **387.** 50 c. mult. (postage) 15 10
1211. – 1 p. multicoloured .. 30 10
1212. – 50 c. mult. (air) .. 15 10
1213. – 1 p. yell., grey & blue 30 10
DESIGNS: No. 1211, Communications network. No. 1212, Diagram. No. 1213, Satellite.

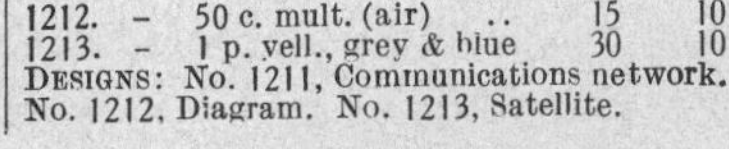

**388.** The Eucharist. **389.** "St. Augustine" (Vasquez).

**1968.** 39th Int. Eucharistic Congress, Bogota. (1st issue).
1214. **388.** 60 c. multicoloured (postage) .. .. 15 10
1215. 80 c. multicoloured (air) 15 10
1216. 3 p. multicoloured .. 35 10

**1968.** 39th International Eucharistic Congress, Bogota (2nd Issue). Multicoloured.
1217. 25 c. Type **389** (postage) 10 10
1218. 60 c. "Gathering Manna" (Vasquez) .. 10 10
1219. 1 p. "Betrothal of the Virgin and St. Joseph" (B. de Figueroa) .. 10 10
1220. 5 p. "La Lechuga" (Jesuit Statuette) .. 25 20
1221. 10 p. "Pope Paul VI" (painting by Franciscan Missionary Mothers) .. 55 10
1222. 80 c. "The Last Supper" (Vasquez) (air) .. 15 10
1223. 1 p. "St. Francis Xavier's Sermon" (Vasquez) .. .. 25 10
1224. 2 p. "Elijah's Dream" (Vasquez) .. .. 10 10
1225. 3 p. As No. 1220 .. .. 25 10
1226. 20 p. As No. 1221 .. 3·25 90
No. 1222 is horiz.

**390.** Pope Paul VI. **391.** University Arms.

**1968.** Pope Paul's Visit to Colombia. Multicoloured.
1228. 25 c. Type **390** (postage) 15 10
1229. 80 c. Reception podium (air) .. .. .. 15 10
1230. 1 p. 20 Pope Paul giving Blessing .. .. 10 10
1231. 1 p. 80 Cathedral, Bogota 10 15
No. 1229 is horiz.

**1968.** Cent. of National University.
1232. **391.** 80 c. mult. (postage) 10 10
1233. – 20 c. red, green and yellow (air) .. 10 10
DESIGN: 20 c. Mathematical symbols.

**392.** Antioquia 2½ c. Stamp of 1858. **393.** Institute Emblem & Split Leaf.

**1968** Cent. of 1st Antioquia Stamps.
1234. **392.** 30 c. blue and green 10 10

**1969.** 25th Anniv (1967) of Inter-American Agricultural Sciences Institute.
1236. **393.** 20 c. multicoloured (postage) .. .. 10 10
1237. 1 p. multicoloured (air) 15 10

**394.** Pen and Microscope.

**1969.** Air. 20th Anniv. of University of the Andes.
1238. **394.** 5 p. multicoloured .. 45 10

**395.** Von Humboldt and Andes (Quindio Region).

**1969.** Air. Birth Bicentenary of Alexander von Humboldt (naturalist).
1239. **395.** 1 p. green and brown 15 10

COLOMBIA
5¢
CRUZ ROJA

**396.** Junkers F-13 Seaplane and Map. **397.** Red Cross.

**1969.** Air. 50th Anniv. of 1st Colombian Airmail Flight. Multicoloured.
1240 1 p. Type **396** .. .. 25 15
1241 1 p. 50 Boeing 720-B and globe .. .. .. 30 10
See also Nos. 1249/50.

**1969.** Obligatory Tax. Colombian Red Cross.
1243. **397.** 5 c. red and violet .. 10 10

**398.** "The Battle of Boyaca" (J. M. Espinosa).

**1969.** 150th Anniv. of Independence. Mult.
1244. 20 c. Type **398** (postage) 15 10
1245. 30 c. "Liberation Army crossing Pisba Pass" (F. A. Caro) .. .. 15 10
1246. 2 p. 30 "Entry into Santa Fe" (I. Castillo-Cervantes) (air) .. .. .. 20 20

**399.** Institute Emblem. **400.** Cranial Diagram.

**1969.** Air. 20th Anniv. of Colombian Social Security Institute.
1247. **399.** 20 c. green and black 10 10

**1969.** Air. 13th Latin-American Neurological Congress, Bogota.
1248. **400.** 70 c. multicoloured 20 10

**401.** Junkers F-13 Seaplane and Puerto Colombia. **402.** Child posting Christmas Card.

**1969.** Air. 50th Anniv. of "Avianca" Airline. Multicoloured.
1249 2 p. Type **401** .. .. 40 10
1250 3 p. 50 Boeing 720-B and globe .. .. .. 35 25

**1969.** Air. Christmas. Multicoloured.
1252. 60 c. Type **402** .. .. 15 10
1253. 1 p. Type **402** .. .. 15 10
1254. 1 p. 50 Child with Christmas presents .. .. 45 10

**403.** "Poverty". **405.** National Sports Institute Emblem.

**404.** Dish Aerial and Ancient Head.

**1970.** Colombian Social Welfare Institute and 10th Anniv. of Children's Rights Law.
1255. **403.** 30 c. multicoloured .. 10 10

**1970.** Air. Opening of Satellite Earth Station, Choconta.
1256. **404.** 1 p. black, red & grn. 40 10

**1970.** Air. 9th National Games, Ibague (1st issue).
1257. **405.** 1 p. 50 blk., yell. & grn. 25 15
1258. – 2 p. 30 multicoloured 15 20
DESIGN: 2 p. 30, Dove and rings (Games emblem).
See No. 1265.

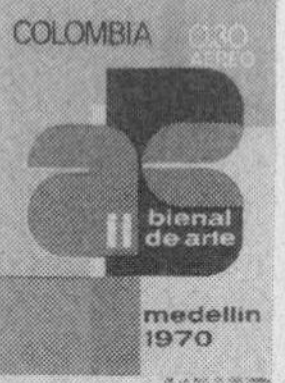

**406.** Exhibition Emblem. **407.** Dr. E. Santos (founder and Buildings.

**1970.** Air. 2nd Fine Arts Biennial, Medellin
1259. **406.** 30 c. multicoloured .. 10 10

**1970.** Air. 30th Anniv. (1969) of Territorial Credit Institute.
1260. **407.** 1 p. blk., yell. & grn. 15 10

**408.** U.N. Emblem, Scales and Dove. **409.** Hands protecting Child.

**1970.** Air. 25th Anniv. of United Nations.
1261. **408.** 1 p. 50 yellow, blue and ultramarine .. 20 10

**1970.** Obligatory Tax. Colombian Red Cross.
1262. **409.** 5 c. red and blue .. 10 10

**410.** Theatrical Mask.

**1970.** Latin-American University Theatre Festival, Manizales.
1263. **410.** 30 c. brown, orange & black .. .. 10 10

**411.** Postal Emblem, Letter and Stamps.

**1970.** Philatelic Week.
1264. **411.** 2 p. multicoloured .. 30 10

**412.** Discus-thrower and Ibague Arms. **413.** "St. Teresa" (B. de Figueroa).

**1970.** 9th National Games, Ibague (2nd issue).
1265. **412.** 80 c. brn., grn. & yell. 20 10

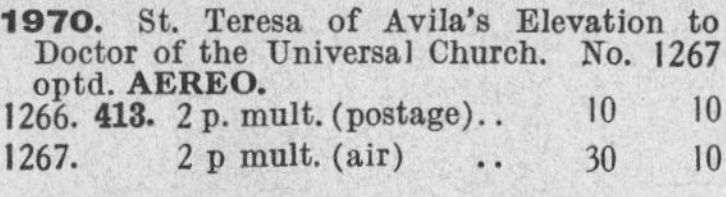

**1970.** St. Teresa of Avila's Elevation to Doctor of the Universal Church. No. 1267 optd. **AEREO.**
1266. **413.** 2 p. mult. (postage) .. 10 10
1267. 2 p. mult. (air) .. 30 10

**414.** Int. Philatelic Federation Emblem. **415.** Chicha Maya Dance.

**1970.** Air. "EXFILCA 70" Stamp Exhibition, Caracas, Venezuela.
1268. **414.** 10 p. multicoloured .. 1·50 20

**1970.** Folklore Dances and Costumes. Mult.
1269. 1 p. Type **415** (postage) .. 35 10
1270. 1 p. 10 Currulao dance .. 35 10
1271. 60 c. Napanga Costume (air) .. .. .. 20 15
1272. 1 p. Joropo dance .. 20 10
1273. 1 p. 30 Guabina dance .. 30 10
1274. 1 p. 30 Bambuco dance .. 20 10
1275. 1 p. 30 Cumbia dance .. 20 10

**416.** Stylised Athlete. **417.** G. Alzate Avendano.

**1971.** Air. 6th Pan-American Games. Cali. (1st issue).
1277. **416.** 1 p. 50 multicoloured 35 45
1278. – 2 p. orange green and black .. 35 40
DESIGN: 2 p. Games Emblem.

**1971.** Air. 10th Anniv. of Gilberto Alzate Avendano (politician).
1279. **417.** 1 p. multicoloured .. 15 25

**418.** Priest's House, Guacari.

**1971.** 400th Anniv. of Guacari (town).
1280. **418.** 1 p. multicoloured .. 25 10

**419.** Commemorative Medal.

**1971.** Air. Cent. of Bank of Bogota.
1281. **419.** 1 p. gold, brn & grn. 40 20

**420.** Sports Centre. **421.** Weightlifting.

**1971.** Air. 6th Pan-American Games (2nd issue) and "EXFICALI 71" Stamp Exhibition, Cali. Multicoloured.
1282. 1 p. 30 Type **420** (yellow emblem) .. .. 40 30
1283. 1 p. 30 Football .. .. 40 30
1284. 1 p. 30 Wrestling .. 40 30
1285. 1 p. 30 Cycling .. 40 30
1286. 1 p. 30 Volleyball .. 40 30
1287. 1 p. 30 Diving .. 40 30
1288. 1 p. 30 Fencing .. 40 30
1289. 1 p. 30 Type **420** (green emblem) .. .. 40 30
1290. 1 p. 30 Sailing .. 40 30
1291. 1 p. 30 Show-jumping .. 40 30
1292. 1 p. 30 Athletics .. 40 30
1293. 1 p. 30 Rowing .. 40 30
1294. 1 p. 30 Cali emblem .. 40 30
1295. 1 p. 30 Netball .. 40 30

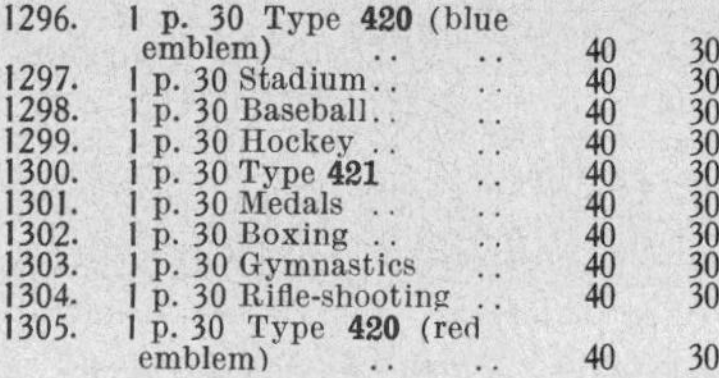

1296. 1 p. 30 Type **420** (blue emblem) .. .. 40 30
1297. 1 p. 30 Stadium .. .. 40 30
1298. 1 p. 30 Baseball .. .. 40 30
1299. 1 p. 30 Hockey .. .. 40 30
1300. 1 p. 30 Type **421** .. 40 30
1301. 1 p. 30 Medals .. .. 40 30
1302. 1 p. 30 Boxing .. .. 40 30
1303. 1 p. 30 Gymnastics .. 40 30
1304. 1 p. 30 Rifle-shooting .. 40 30
1305. 1 p. 30 Type **420** (red emblem) .. .. 40 30

**422.** "Bolivar at Congress". (after S. Martinez-Delgado).

**1971.** 150th Anniv. of Great Colombia Constituent Assembly, Rosario del Cucuta.
1306. **422.** 80 c. multicoloured .. 15 10

**423.** "Battle of Carabobo" (M. Tovar y Tovar).

**1971.** Air. 150th Anniv. of Battle of Carabobo.
1307. **423.** 1 p. 50 multicoloured 15 15

COLOMBIA $0.60

**424.** C.I.M.E. Emblem. **425.** I.C.E.T.E.X. Symbol.

**1972.** 20th Anniv. of Inter-Governmental Committee on European Migration.
1308. **424.** 60 c. black and grey 25 10

**1972.** 20th Anniv. of Institute of Educational Credit and Technical Training Abroad.
1309. **425.** 1 p. 10 brn. and grn. 20 10

**426.** Rev. Mother Francisca del Castillo. **427.** Soldier and Frigate "Almirante Padilla".

**1972.** 300th Birth Anniv. of Reverend Mother Francisca J. del Castillo.
1310. **426.** 1 p. 20 multicoloured 20 10

**1972.** 20th Anniv. of Colombian Troops' Participation in Korean War.
1311. **427.** 1 p. 20 multicoloured 75 15

**428.** Hat and Ceramics. **429.** "Maxillaria triloris" (orchid).

**1972.** Colombian Crafts and Products. Multicoloured.

| | | | |
|---|---|---|---|
| 1312. | 1 p. 10 Type **428** (postage) | 30 | 10 |
| 1313. | 50 c. Woman in shawl (air) | 30 | 10 |
| 1314. | 1 p. Male doll .. .. | 20 | 10 |
| 1315. | 3 p. Female doll .. .. | 20 | 25 |

**1972.** National, Stamp Exn., and 7th World Orchid-growers Congress, Medellin Conference. Multicoloured.

| | | | |
|---|---|---|---|
| 1316. | 20 p. Type **429** (postage) | 5·00 | 25 |
| 1317. | 1 p. 30 "Mormodes rolfeanum" (orchid) (horiz.) (air) .. .. | 15 | 10 |

**430.** Uncut Emeralds and Pendant. **432.** Congo Dance.

**431.** Pres. Narino's House.

**1972.** Colombian Emeralds.
1318. **430.** 1 p. 10 multicoloured 30 10

**1972.** 400th Anniv. of Leyva (town).
1319. **431.** 1 p. 10 multicoloured 30 10

**1972.** Air Barranquilla Int. Carnival.
1320. **432.** 1 p. 30 multicoloured 10 10

**433.** Island Scene. **435.** "Pres. Laureano Gomez" (R. Cubillos).

**1972.** 150th Anniv. of Annexation of San Andres and Providencia Islands.
1321. **433.** 60 c. multicoloured .. 20 10

**1972.** Air. No. 1142 surch.
1322. **360.** 1 p. 30 on 1 p. 90 brown and blue .. 20 15

**1972.** Air. Pres. Gomez Commem.
1323. **435.** 1 p. 30 multicoloured 20 10

**436.** Postal Administration Emblem. **437.** Colombian Family.

**1972.** National Postal Administration.
1324. **436.** 1 p. 10 green .. 15 10

**1972.** "Social Front for the People" Campaign.
1325. **437.** 60 c. orange .. 10 10

**438.** Pres. Guillermo Valencia. **439.** Benito Juarez.

**1972.** Air. Pres. Valencia Commem.
1326. **438.** 1 p. 30 multicoloured 25 10

**1972.** Air. Death Centenary of Benito Juarez (Mexican statesman).
1327. **439.** 1 p. 50 multicoloured 20 10



**440.** "La Rebeca" Monument. **441.** "350" and Arms of Bucaramanga.

**1972.** Air. "La Rebeca" Monument, Centenary Park, Bogota.

| | | | | |
|---|---|---|---|---|
| 1328. | **440.** | 80 c. multicoloured .. | 25 | 30 |
| 1329. | | 1 p. multicoloured .. | 20 | 10 |

**1972.** Air. 350th Anniv of Bucaramanga (city).
1330. **441.** 5 p. multicoloured .. 30 10

**442.** University Buildings. **443.** League Emblems.

**1973.** Air 350th Anniv. of Javeriana University.

| | | | | |
|---|---|---|---|---|
| 1331. | **442.** | 1 p. 30 brown & grn. | 25 | 10 |
| 1332. | | 1 p. 50 brown & bl. | 25 | 10 |

**1973.** 40th Anniv. of Colombian Radio Amateurs League.
1333. **443.** 60 c. red, new blue and blue .. .. 15 10

**444.** Tamalameque Vessel. **445.** "Battle of Maracaibo" (M. F. Rincon).

**1973.** Inauguration of Museum of Pre-Colombian Antiques, Bogota. Multicoloured.

| | | | |
|---|---|---|---|
| 1334. | 60 c. Type **444** (postage) | 25 | 10 |
| 1335. | 1 p. Tairona axe-head .. | 45 | 10 |
| 1336. | 1 p. 10 Muisca jug | 30 | 10 |
| 1337. | 1 p. As No. 1335 (air) .. | 40 | 35 |
| 1338. | 1 p. 30 Sinu vessel .. | 20 | 10 |
| 1339. | 1 p. 70 Quimbaya vessel | 25 | 20 |
| 1340. | 3 p. 50 Tumaco figurine | 50 | 30 |

**1973.** Air. 150th Anniv. of Naval Battle of Maracaibo.
1341. **445.** 10 p. multicoloured 2·75 30

**446.** Banknote Emblem.

**1973.** Air. 50th Anniv. of Republican Bank.
1342. **446.** 2 p. multicoloured .. 25 10

**1973.** Air. No. 1306 optd. **AEREO.**
1343. **422.** 80 c. multicoloured .. 15 10

**448.** "Pres. Ospina" (after C. Leudo) **449.** Arms of Toro.

**1973.** Air. 50th Anniv. of Ministry of Communications.
1344. **448.** 1 p. 50 multicoloured 20 10

**1973.** Air. 400th Anniv. of Toro.
1345. **449.** 1 p. multicoloured .. 15 10

**450.** Bolivar at Bombona.

**1973.** Air. 150th Anniv. of Battle of Bombona.
1346. **450.** 1 p. 30 multicoloured 20 10

**451.** "General Narino" (after J. M. Espinosa). **452.** Young Child.

**1973.** 150th Death Anniv. of General Antonio Narino.
1347. **451.** 60 c. multicoloured .. 15 10

**1973.** Child Welfare Campaign.
1348. **452.** 1 p. 10 multicoloured 20 10

**453.** Fiscal Emblem.

**1974.** 50th Anniv. of Republic's General Comptrollership.
1349. **453.** 80 c. black, brn. & bl. 15 10

**454.** Copernicus. **455.** Andes Communications and Map.

**1974.** Air. 500th Birth Anniv. of Copernicus.
1350. **454.** 2 p. multicoloured .. 20 15

**1974.** Air. Meeting of Communications Ministers, Andean Group, Cali.
1351. **455.** 2 p. multicoloured .. 10 15

**456.** Laura Montoya and Cross. **457.** Television Set with Inravision Emblem.

**1974.** Birth Centenary of Revd. Mother Laura Montoya. (missionary).
1352. **456.** 1 p. multicoloured .. 15 10

**1974.** Air. 20th Anniv. of Inravision (National Institute of Radio and Television).
1353. **457.** 1 p. 30 black, brown and orange .. 20 10

**458.** Athlete.

**1974.** Tenth National Games, Pereira.
1354. **458.** 2 p. brown, red & yell. 20 10

**459.** Rivera and Statue.

**1974.** 50th Anniv. of Novel "La Voragine".
1355. **459.** 10 p. multicoloured 35 15

**460.** Aquatic Emblem.

**1974.** Air. 2nd World Swimming Championships, Cali. (1975).
1356. **460.** 4 p. 50 bl., turq. & blk. 30 15

**461.** Condor Emblem.

**1974.** Air. Cent. of Bank of Colombia.
1357. **461.** 1 p. 50 multicoloured 20 10

**462.** Tailplane.

**1974.** Air.
1358. **462.** 20 c. brown .. .. 10 10

**463.** U.P.U. "Letter".

**1974.** Air. Cent. of Universal Postal Union. (1st issue).
1359. **463.** 20 p. red, bl. & blk. 1·10 30
See also Nos. 1363/6.

**464.** General Jose Maria Cordoba. **465.** "Progress and Expansion".

**1974.** Air. 150th Anniv. of Battles of Junin and Ayacucho.
1360. **464.** 1 p. 30 multicoloured 20 10

**1974.** Cent. of Colombian Insurance Company.

| | | | | |
|---|---|---|---|---|
| 1361. | **465.** | 1 p. 10 mult. (post) .. | 20 | 10 |
| 1362. | | 3 p. mult. (air) .. | 35 | 10 |

**466.** White-tailed Trogon and U.P.U. "Letter". **467.** La Quiebra Tunnel.

**1974.** Air. Cent. of U.P.U. (2nd issue). Colombian Birds. Multicoloured.

| | | | |
|---|---|---|---|
| 1363. | 1 p. Type **466** .. .. | 15 | 10 |
| 1364. | 1 p. 30 Red-billed Toucan (horiz.) .. .. | 20 | 15 |
| 1365. | 2 p. Andean Cock of the Rock (horiz.) .. | 25 | 15 |
| 1366. | 2 p. 50 Scarlet Macaw .. | 30 | 25 |

Nos. 1364/6 also depict the U.P.U. "letter".

**1974.** Cent. of Antioquia Railway.
1367. **467.** 1 p. 10 multicoloured 30 10

**468.** Boy with Ball.

**1974.** Christmas. Multicoloured.
1368. 80 c. Type **468** .. .. 10 10
1369. 1 p. Girl with racquet .. 10 15

**469.** " Protect the Trees ".

**1975.** Air. Colombian Ecology. Mult.
1370. 1 p. Type **469** .. .. 20 10
1371. 6 p. " Protect the Amazon" 20 15

**470.** " Wood No. 1 " (R. Roncancio).

**1975.** Air. Colombian Art. Multicoloured.
1372. 2 p. Type **470** .. .. 1·00 30
1373. 3 p. " The Market " (M. Diaz Vargas) .. .. 1·00 30
1374. 4 p. " Child with Thorn " (G. Vazquez) .. .. 15 10
1375. 5 p. " The Annunciation " (Santaferena School) .. 45 30
Nos. 1373/5 are vert.

**471.** Gold Cat.

**1975.** Pre-Colombian Archaeological Discoveries. Sinu Culture. Multicoloured.
1376. 80 c. Type **471** (postage) 20 10
1377. 1 p. 10 Gold necklace .. 20 10
1378. 2 p. Nose Pendant (air) .. 40 10
1379. 10 p. " Alligator " staff ornament .. .. 2·10 35

**472.** Marconi and "Elettra" (steam yacht).

**473.** Santa Marta Cathedral.

**1975.** Birth Cent. of Guglielmo Marconi (radio pioneer).
1380. **472.** 3 p. multicoloured .. 50 10

**1975.** 450th Anniv. of Santa Marta. Mult.
1381. 80 c. Type **473** (postage) 10 10
1382. 2 p. " El Rodadero " (sea-front), Santa Marta (horiz.) (air) .. .. 20 10

**474.** Maria de J. Paramo (educationalist).

**475.** Pres. Nunez.

**1975.** International Women's Year.
1383. **474.** 4 p. multicoloured .. 25 10

**1975.** 150th Birth Anniv. of President Rafael Nunez.
1384. **475.** 1 p. 10 multicoloured 15 10

**476.** Arms of Medellin.

**479.** Sugar Cane.

**1975.** 300th Anniv. of Medellin.
1385. **476.** 1 p. multicoloured .. 25 10
See also Nos. 1386, 1388, 1394, 1404, 1419, 1434, 1481/3, 1672/4, 1678/9, 1752, 1758, 1859 and 1876.

**1976.** Centenary of Reconstruction of Cucuta City. As T **476**.
1386. 1 p. 50 multicoloured .. 30 10

**1976.** Surch.
1387. **471.** 1 p. 20 on 80 c. mult. 15 10

**1976.** Arms of Cartagena. As T **476**.
1388. 1 p. 50 multicoloured .. 20 10

**1976.** 4th Cane Sugar Export and Production Congress, Cali.
1389. **479.** 5 p. green and black 45 10


**480.** Bogota.

**1976.** Air. Habitat. U.N. Conference on Human Settlements. Multicoloured.
1390. 10 p. Type **480** .. .. 1·10 35
1391. 10 p. Barranquilla .. 1·10 35
1392. 10 p. Cali .. .. 1·10 35
1393. 10 p. Medellin .. .. 1·10 35

**1976.** Arms of Ibague. As T **476**.
1394. 1 p. 20 multicoloured .. 15 10


**481.** University Emblem and " 90 ".


**482.** M. Samper.

**1976.** Air. 90th Anniv. of Colombia University.
1395. **481.** 5 p. multicoloured .. 20 10

**1976.** Air. 150th Birth Anniv. of Miguel Samper (statesman and writer).
1396. **482.** 2 p. multicoloured .. 20 10


**483.** Early Telephone.


**484.** " Callicore sp."

**1976.** Air. Telephone Cent.
1397. **483.** 3 p. multicoloured .. 20 10

**1976.** Colombian Fauna and Flora. Mult.
1398 3 p. Type **484** .. .. 75 10
1399 5 p. "Morpho sp." (butterfly) .. .. 1·25 20
1400 20 p. Black anthurium (plant) .. .. 1·10 25

**485.** Purace Indians, Cauca.

**486.** Rotary Emblem.

**1976.**
1401. **485.** 1 p. 50 multicoloured 10 10

**1976.** 50th Anniv. of Colombian Rotary Club.
1402. **486.** 1 p. multicoloured .. 10 10

**487.** Boeing 747 Jumbo Jet.

**1976.** Air. Inauguration of Avianca Jumbo Jet Service.
1403. **487.** 2 p. multicoloured .. 15 10

**1976.** 535th Anniv. of Tunja City Arms. As T **476**.
1404. 1 p. 20 multicoloured .. 15 10

**488.** " The Signing of Declaration of Independence " (left-hand detail of painting, Trumbull).


**489.** Police Handler and Dog.

**1976.** Bicent. of American Revolution. Mult.
1405. **488.** 30 p. " Signing the 1·75 1·10
1406. – 30 p. Declaration of 1·75 1·10
1407. – 30 p. Independence " 1·75 1·10
DESIGNS: Nos. 1406/7 show different portions of the painting.

**1976.** National Police.
1408. **489.** 1 p. 50 multicoloured 25 10

**490.** Franciscan Convent.

**1976.** Air. 150th Anniv. of Panama Congress.
1409. **490.** 6 p. multicoloured .. 20 20

**1977.** Surch.
1411. **475.** 2 p. on 1 p. 10 mult. (postage) .. .. 25 10
1412. – 2 p. on 1 p. 20 mult. (No. 1404) .. .. 20 10
1413. **489.** 2 p. on 1 p. 50 mult. .. 20 10
1414. **487.** 3 p. on 2 p. mult. (air) 15 10

**494.** Coffee Plant and Beans.

**495.** Coffee Grower with mule.

**1977.** Air. Coffee Production.
1416. **494.** 3 p. multicoloured .. 15 10
1416a. 3 p. 50, multicoloured 20 10

**1977.** Air. 50th Anniv. of National Federation of Coffee Growers.
1417. **495.** 10 p. multicoloured 20 15

**496.** Beethoven and Score of Ninth Symphony.

**1977.** Air. 150th Anniv. of Beethoven.
1418. **496.** 8 p. multicoloured .. 25 15

**1977.** Arms of Popayan. As T **476**.
1419. 5 p. multicoloured .. 30 15

**497.** Mother feeding Baby.

**498.** Wattled Jacana and " Eichhornia crassipes ".

**1977.** Nutrition Campaign.
1420 **497** 2 p. multicoloured .. 15 10
1420a 2 p. 50 multicoloured 80 10

**1977.** Colombian Birds and Plants. Mult.
1421. 10 p. Type **498** (postage) 1·75 40
1422. 20 p. Plum-throated cotinga and "Pyrostegia venusta" .. .. 2·25 50
1423. 5 p. Crimson-mantled woodpecker and "Meriania" (air) .. 1·00 30
1424. 5 p. Purple gallinule and "Nymphaea" .. .. 1·00 30
1425. 10 p. Pampadour cotinga and "Cochlospermum orinocense" .. .. 1·40 35
1426. 10 p. Northern royal flycatcher and "Jacaranda copaia" .. 1·40 35

**499.** Games Emblem.


**500.** " La Cayetana " (E. Grau).

**1977.** Air. 13th Central American and Caribbean Games, Medellin (1978).
1427. **499.** 6 p. multicoloured .. 25 10

**1977.** Air 20th Anniv. of Female Suffrage. Multicoloured.
1428. 8 p. Type **500** .. .. 20 20
1429. 8 p. " Nayade " (Beatriz Gonzalez) .. .. 20 20

**501.** " Judge Francisco Antonio Moreno y Escandon " (J. Gutierrez).

**502.** " Fidel Cano " (Francisco Cano).

**1977.** Air. Bicentenary of National Library. Multicoloured.
1430. 20 p. Type **501** .. .. 55 10
1431. 25 p. " Viceroy Manuel de Guiror " (unknown artist) .. .. 55 20

**1977.** 90th Anniv of "El Espectador" Magazine by Fidel Cano.
1432. **502.** 4 p. multicoloured .. 20 10

**503.** Abacus and Alphabet.

**1977.** Popular Education.
1433. **503.** 3 p. multicoloured .. 15 10

**1977.** Arms of Barranquilla. As T **476**.
1434. 5 p. multicoloured .. 30 15

**504.** Dr. F. L. Acosta. **505.** Cauca University Arms.

**1977.** Air. Birth Cent. of Dr. Federico Lleras Acosta (veterinary surgeon).
1435. **504.** 5 p. multicoloured .. 30 10

**1977.** Air. 150th Anniv. of Cauca University.
1436. **505.** 5 p. multicoloured .. 25 10

**506.** " Cudecom " Building, Bogota. **508.** " Cattleya triannae ".

**1977.** Air. 90th Anniv. of Society of Colombian Engineers.
1437. **506.** 1 p. 50 multicoloured 10 10

**1977.** Air. No. 1364 surch. **$2.00.**
1438. 2 p. on 1 p. 30 mult. .. 85 25

**1978.**
1439. **508.** 2 p. 50 multicoloured 25 10
1439a. 3 p. multicoloured .. 25 10

**509.** Tayronan Lost City. **510.** " Creator of Energy " (A. Betancourt).

**1978.** Air.
1440. **509.** 3 p. 50 multicoloured 35 10

**1978.** Air. 150th Anniv. of Antioquia University Law School.
1441. **510.** 4 p. multicoloured .. 20 10

**511.** Column of the Slaves. **512.** " Catalina ".

**1978.** Air. 150th Anniv. of Ocana Convention.
1442. **511.** 2 p. 50 multicoloured 15 10

**1978.** Air. 150th Anniv. of Cartagena University.
1443. **512.** 4 p. multicoloured .. 20 10

**513.** Running.

**1978.** 13th Central American and Caribbean Games. Medellin. Multicoloured.
1444. 10 p. Type **513** .. .. 35 25
1445. 10 p. Basketball .. 35 25
1446. 10 p. Baseball .. .. 35 25
1447. 10 p. Boxing .. .. 35 25
1448. 10 p. Cycling .. .. 35 25
1449. 10 p. Fencing .. .. 35 25
1450. 10 p. Football .. .. 35 25
1451. 10 p. Gymnastics .. 35 25
1452. 10 p. Judo .. .. 35 25
1453. 10 p. Weightlifting .. 35 25
1454. 10 p. Wrestling .. .. 35 25
1455. 10 p. Swimming .. .. 35 25
1456. 10 p. Tennis .. .. 35 25
1457. 10 p. Shooting .. .. 35 25
1458. 10 p. Volleyball .. .. 35 25
1459. 10 p. Water polo .. 35 25

**514.** " Sigma 2 " (A. Herran). **515.** Human Figure from Gold Pendant.

**1978.** Cent. of Bogota Chamber of Commerce.
1460. **514.** 8 p. multicoloured .. 20 20

**1978.** Air. Tolima Culture.
1461. **515.** 3 p. 50 multicoloured 20 20

**516.** " Apotheosis of the Spanish Language " (Left-hand detail of mural, L. A. Acuna). **517.** Presidential Guard.

**1978.** Air. Millenary of Castilian Language. Multicoloured.
1462. 11 p. Type **516** .. .. 55 50
1463. 11 p. Central detail .. 55 50
1464. 11 p. Right-hand detail .. 55 50
Nos. 1462/4 were issued together, **se-tenant,** forming a composite design.

**1978.** Air. 50th Anniv. of Presidential Guard Battalion.
1465. **517.** 9 p. multicoloured .. 25 25

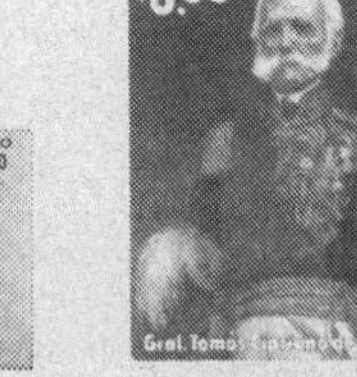


**518.** Human Figure. **519.** General Tomas Cipriano de Mosquera.

**1978.** Air. Muisca Culture.
1466. **518.** 3 p. 50 multicoloured 20 10

**1978.** Death Centenary of General Tomas Cipriano de Mosquera (statesman).
1467. **519.** 6 p. multicoloured .. 20 20

**520.** El Camarin de Carmen, Bogota. **521.** Gold Owl Ornament.

**1978.** Air. " Espamer '78 " Stamp Exhibition Bogota.
1468. **520.** 30 p. multicoloured .. 1·75 20

**1978.** Air. Calima Culture.
1470. **521.** 3 p. 50 multicoloured 20 10
1470a. 4 p. multicoloured .. 25 10

**522.** " Virgin and Child " (Gregorio Vasquez). **523.** Church and Bullring.

**1978.** Air. Christmas.
1471. **522.** 2 p. 50 multicoloured 10 10

**1978.** Air. Manizales Fair.
1472. **523.** 7 p. multicoloured .. 25 15

**524.** Frog in beaten gold. **525.** Children playing Hopscotch.

**1979.** Air. Quimbaya Culture.
1473. **524.** 4 p. multicoloured .. 15 10

**1979.** Air. International Year of the Child. Multicoloured.
1474 8 p. Type **525** .. .. 30 10
1475 12 p. Child in sou'wester and oilskins .. .. 20 20
1476 12 p. Child at blackboard (horiz) .. .. 20 20

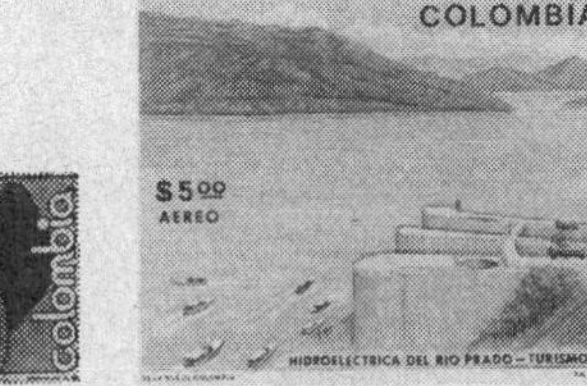


**526.** Anthurium. **527.** Rio Prado Hydro-electric Barrage.

**1979.** Anthurium Flowers from Narino. Multicoloured, background colours given.
1477. **526.** 3 p. light green .. 25 10
1478. 3 p. red .. .. 25 10
1479. 3 p. green .. .. 25 10
1480. 3 p. blue .. .. 25 10

**1979.** Arms. Designs as T **476**. Multicoloured.
1481 4 p. Sogamoso .. .. 45 10
1482 10 p. Socorro .. .. 20 15
1483 10 p. Santa Cruz y San Gil de la Nueva Baeza .. 20 15

**1979.** Air. Tourism. Multicoloured.
1484. 5 p. Type **527** .. .. 35 10
1485. 7 p. River Amazon .. 1·00 30
1486. 8 p. Tomb, San Agustin Archaeological Park .. 25 20
1487. 14 p. San Fernando Fort, Cartagena .. .. 45 35

**528.** " Jimenez de Quesada " (after C. Leudo).

**1979.** Air. 400th Death Anniv. of Gonzalo Jimenez de Quesada (conquistador).
1488. **528.** 20 p. multicoloured 1·60 65

**529.** Hill and First Stamps of Great Britain and Colombia.

**1979.** Air. Death Cent. of Sir Rowland Hill.
1489. **529.** 15 p. multicoloured 25 25

**530.** " Uribe " (after Acevedo Bernal).

**1979.** 65th Death Anniv. of General Rafael Uribe Uribe (statesman).
1490. **530.** 8 p. multicoloured .. 30 15

**531.** " Village " (Leonor Alarcon).

**1979.** 20th Anniv. of Community Works Boards.
1491. **531.** 15 p. multicoloured 85 30

**532.** Three Kings and Soldiers.

**1979.** Air. Christmas. Multicoloured.
1492. 3 p. Type **532** .. .. 75 40
1493. 3 p. Nativity .. .. 75 40
1494. 3 p. Shepherds .. .. 75 40

**533.** River Magdalena Bridge and Avianca Emblem. **534.** Gold Nose Pendant.

**1979.** Air. 350th Anniv. of Barranquilla and 60th Anniv. of Avianca National Airline.
1495. **533.** 15 p. multicoloured 25 15

**1980.** Air. Tairona Culture.
1496. **534.** 5 p. multicoloured .. 25 10

**535.** " Boy playing Flute " (Judith Leyster). **536.** Antonio Jose de Sucre.

**1980.** Air. 2nd International Music Competition, Ibague.
1497. **535.** 6 p. multicoloured .. 30 10

**1980.** Air. 150th Death Anniv. of General Antonio Jose de Sucre.
1498. **536.** 12 p. multicoloured 20 15

**537.** " The Watchman " (Edgar Negret).

**1980.** Air. Modern Sculpture.
1499. **537.** 25 p. multicoloured .. 1·40 1·25

**538.** Television Screen.

**1980.** Inauguration of Colour Television in Colombia.
1500. **538.** 5 p. multicoloured .. 25 10

539. Bullfighting Poster (H. Courttin).  540. " Learn to Write ".

**1980.** Tourism. Festival of Cali.
1501. **539.** 5 p. multicoloured .. 35 15

**1980.** The Alphabet.
1502. **540.** 4 p. blk., brn. and grn. 25 10
1503. – 4 p. multicoloured .. 25 10
1504. – 4 p. brown, black and light brown .. 25 10
1505. – 4 p. multicoloured .. 35 10
1506. – 4 p. brn., blk. and grn. 25 10
1507. – 4 p. black & turquoise 25 10
1508. – 4 p. black and green 25 10
1509. – 4 p. mauve, blk. & grn. 35 10
1510. – 4 p. black and blue .. 25 10
1511. – 4 p. black and green 25 10
1512. – 4 p. grn., blk. and brn. 25 10
1513. – 4 p. multicoloured .. 25 10
1514. – 4 p. brn., blk. and grn. 25 10
1515. – 4 p. multicoloured .. 25 10
1516. – 4 p. yell., blk. and grn. 25 10
1517. – 4 p. blk., brn. & yell. 25 10
1518. – 4 p. brn., blk. & turq. 25 10
1519. – 4 p. brn., blk. and grn. 25 10
1520. – 4 p. brn., blk. and grn. 25 10
1521. – 4 p. yell., blk. & turq. 25 10
1522. – 4 p. grn., blk. & blue 35 10
1523. – 4 p. brn., blk. and grn. 25 10
1524. – 4 p. green, black and light green .. 25 10
1525. – 4 p. multicoloured .. 25 10
1526. – 4 p. multicoloured .. 25 10
1527. – 4 p. brn., blk. and grn. 25 10
1528. – 4 p. multicoloured .. 35 10
1529. – 4 p. multicoloured .. 25 10
1530. – 4 p. brn., blk. and grn. 25 10
1531. – 4 p. brown and black 25 10

DESIGNS: No. 1503, " a " Eagle. No. 1504, " b " Buffalo. No. 1505, " c " Andean Condor. No. 1506, " ch " Chimpanzee. No. 1507, " d " Dolphin. No. 1508, " e " Elephant. No. 1509, " f " Greater Flamingo. No. 1510, " g " Seagull. No. 1511, " h " Hippopotamus. No. 1512, " i " Iguana. No. 1513, " j " Giraffe. No. 1514, " k " Koala. No. 1515, " l " Lion. No. 1516, " ll " Llama. No. 1517, " m " Blackbird. No. 1518, " n " Otter. No. 1519, " ñ " Gnu. No. 1520, " o " Bear. No. 1521, " p " Pelican. No. 1522, " q " Resplendent Quetzal. No. 1523, " r " Rhinoceros. No. 1524, " s " Grasshopper. No. 1525, " t " Tortoise. No. 1526, " u " Magpie. No. 1527, " v " Viper. No. 1528, " w " Wagon with animals. No. 1529, " x " Fox playing xylophone. No. 1530, " y " Yak. No. 1531, " z " Fox.

541. " Miraculous Virgin " (statue, Real del Sarte).

**1980.** Air. 150th Anniv. of Apparition of Holy Virgin to Sister Catalina Labouri Gontard in Paris.
1532. **541.** 12 p. multicoloured 45 15

542. " Country Scene, San Gil " (painting, Luis Roncancio).

**1980.** Air. Agriculture.
1533. **542.** 12 p. multicoloured .. 1·50 30

**543.** Villavicencio Song Festival.

**1980.** Tourism. Festivals. Multicoloured.
1534. 5 p. Type **543** .. .. 30 15
1535. 9 p. Vallenato festival .. 15 15

**544.** Gustavo Uribe Ramirez and " Samanea saman ".

**1980.** 12th Death Anniv. of Gustavo Uribe Ramirez (ecologist).
1536. **544.** 10 p. multicoloured 35 15

**545.** Narino Palace.

**1980.** Narino Palace (Presidential residence).
1537. **545.** 5 p. multicoloured .. 30 10

**546.** Monument to First Pioneers, Armenia.

**1980.** City of Armenia.
1538. **546.** 5 p. multicoloured .. 30 10

547. Olaya Herrera (after Miguel Diaz Varges).  549. Athlete with Torch.

548. " Simple Simon ".

**1980.** Air. Birth Centenary of Dr. Enrique Olaya Herrera (President, 1930-34).
1539. **547.** 20 p. multicoloured 45 25

**1980.** Air. Christmas. Illustrations to stories by Rafael Pombo. Multicoloured.
1540. 4 p. Type **548** .. .. 25 15
1541. 4 p. " The Cat's Seven Lives " .. .. .. 25 15
1542. 4 p. " The Walking Tadpole " .. .. .. 25 15

**1980.** 11th National Games, Neiva.
1543. **549.** 5 p. multicoloured .. 20 10

550. Golfers.  551. Crab pierced by Sword.

**1980.** Air. 28th World Cup Golf, Cajica.
1544. **550.** 30 p. multicoloured 2·10 1·50

**1980.** 20th Anniv of Colombian Anti-cancer League.
1545 **551** 10 p. multicoloured .. 35 20

552. " Justice " and University Emblem.

**1980.** 50th Anniv. of Refounding of Pontifical Xavier University Law Faculty.
1546. **552.** 20 p. multicoloured 25 30

553. " Bolivar's Last Moments " (Marcos Leon Marino).

**1980.** 150th Death Anniv. of Simon Bolivar. Multicoloured.
1547. 25 p. Type **553** (postage) 45 35
1548. 6 p. Bolivar and his last proclamation (air) .. 25 25

**554.** St. Pedro Claver.  **555.** Statue of Bird, San Agustin.

**1981.** Air. 400th Birth Anniv. of St. Pedro Claver.
1549. **554.** 15 p. multicoloured 20 30

**1981.** Air. Archaeological Discoveries. Mult.
1550. 7 p. Type **555** .. .. 30 15
1551. 7 p. Hypogeum (funeral chamber), Tierradentro 30 15
1552. 7 p. Hypogeum, Tierradentro (different) .. 30 15
1553. 7 p. Statue of man, San Augustin .. .. 30 15

556. " Square Abstract " (Omar Rayo).

**1981.** Air. 4th Biennial Arts Exhibition, Medellin. Multicoloured.
1554. 20 p. Type **556** .. .. 30 20
1555. 25 p. " Flowers " (Alejandro Obregon) .. 40 30
1556. 50 p. " Child with Hobby Horse " (Fernando Botero) .. .. 1·50 1·25

557. Diver.

**1981.** Air. 8th South American Swimming Championships, Medellin.
1557. **557.** 15 p. multicoloured .. 25 30

558. Santamaria Bull Ring.

**1981.** Air. 50th Anniv. of Santamaria Bull Ring, Bogota.
1558. **558.** 30 p. multicoloured 1·50 80

559. Mariano Ospina Perez (after Delio Ramirez).

**1981.** Presidents of Colombia (1st series). Multicoloured.
1559. 5 p. Type **559** .. .. 25 10
1560. 5 p. Eduardo Santos (after Ines Acevedo) .. .. 25 10
1561. 5 p. Miguel Abadia Mendez (after Gomez Compuzano 25 10
1562. 5 p. Jose Vicente Concha (after Acevedo Bernal) 25 10
1563. 5 p. Carlos E. Restrepo .. 25 10
1564. 5 p. Rafael Reyes (after Acevedo Bernal) .. 25 10
1565. 5 p. Santiago Perez .. 25 10
1566. 5 p. Manuel Murillo Toro (after Moreno Otero) .. 25 10
1567. 5 p. Jose Hilario Lopez .. 25 10
1568. 5 p. Jose Maria Obando .. 25 10

See also Nos. 1569/78, 1579/88, 1599/1608, 1615/24 and 1634/43.

**1981.** Presidents of Colombia (2nd series). Multicoloured.
1569. 7 p. Type **559** .. .. 2·75 35
1570. 7 p. As No. 1560 .. .. 2·75 35
1571. 7 p. As No. 1561 .. .. 2·75 35
1572. 7 p. As No. 1562 .. .. 2·75 35
1573. 7 p. As No. 1563 .. .. 2·75 35
1574. 7 p. As No. 1564 .. .. 2·75 35
1575. 7 p. As No. 1565 .. .. 2·75 35
1576. 7 p. As No. 1566 .. .. 2·75 35
1577. 7 p. As No. 1567 .. .. 2·75 35
1578. 7 p. As No. 1568 .. .. 2·75 35

**1981.** Presidents of Colombia (3rd series). As T **559.** Multicoloured.
1579. 7 p. Pedro Alcantara Herran 2·10 20
1580. 7 p. Mariano Ospina Rodriguez (after Coriolando Leudo) .. .. 2·10 20
1581. 7 p. Tomas Cipriano de Mosquera .. .. 2·10 20
1582. 7 p. Santos Gutierrez .. 2·10 20
1583. 7 p. Aquileo Parra (after Constancio Franco) .. 2·10 20
1584. 7 p. Rafael Nunez .. 2·10 20
1585. 7 p. Marco Fidel Suarez (after Jesus Maria Duque) 2·10 20
1586. 7 p. Pedro Nel Ospina (after Coriolano Leudo) 2·10 20
1587. 7 p. Enrique Olaya Herrera (after M. Diaz Vargas) 2·10 20
1588. 7 p. Alfonso Lopez Pumarejo (after Luis F. Uscategui) 2·10 20

560. Crossed-legged Figure.

**1981.** Air. Quimbaya Culture. Multicoloured.
1589. 9 p. Type **560** .. .. 40 15
1590. 9 p. Seated figure .. 40 15
1591. 9 p. Printing block and print .. .. .. 40 15
1592. 9 p. Clay pot .. .. 40 15

**561.** Fruit.

**1981.** Air. Fruit. Designs showing Fruit.
1593. **561.** 25 p. multicoloured .. 2·10 1·40
1594. – 25 p. multicoloured .. 2·10 1·40
1595. – 25 p. multicoloured .. 2·10 1·40
1596. – 25 p. multicoloured .. 2·10 1·40
1597. – 25 p. multicoloured .. 2·10 1·40
1598. – 25 p. multicoloured .. 2·10 1·40

Nos. 1593/8 were issued together in se-tenant blocks of six forming a composite design.

**1981.** Presidents of Colombia (4th series). As T **559.** Multicoloured.
1599. 7 p. Manuel Maria Mallarino .. .. .. 1·00 15
1600. 7 p. Santos Acosta .. 1·00 15

1601. 7 p. Eustorgio Salgar .. 1·00 15
1602. 7 p. Julian Trujillo .. 1·00 15
1603. 7 p. Francisco Javier Zaldua (after Francisco Valles) 1·00 15
1604. 7 p. Jose Eusebio Otalora (after Ricardo Moros).. 1·00 15
1605. 7 p. Miguel Antonio Caro 1·00 15
1606. 7 p. Manuel A. Sanclemente (after Epifanio Garay) 1·00 15
1607. 7 p. Laureano Gomez (after Jose Bascones).. 1·00 15
1608. 7 p. Guillermo Leon Valencia (after Luis Angel Rengifo) 1·00 15

562. " Comunero tearing down Edict " (Manuela Beltran).

**1981.** Air. Bicent of Comuneros Uprising.
1609. **562.** 20 p. multicoloured 25 30

563. Jose Maria Villa and West Bridge.
564. Restrepo (after R. Acevedo Bernal).

**1981.** West Bridge, Santa Fe de Antioquia.
1610. **563.** 60 p. multicoloured 65 10

**1981.** Air. Birth Centenary of Jose Manuel Restrepo (historian).
1611. **564.** 35 p. multicoloured 35 15

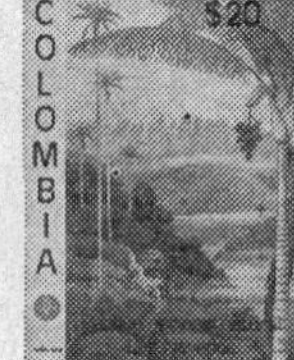


565. Anniversary Emblem.
566. Los Nevados National Park.

**1981.** 50th Anniv of Caja Agraria (peasants' bank).
1612. **565.** 15 p. multicoloured 15 10

**1981.** Los Nevados National Park.
1613. **566.** 20 p. multicoloured.. 20 10

567. Andres Bello.
568. Squatting Figure.

**1981.** Birth Cent. of Andres Bello (poet).
1614. **567.** 18 p. multicoloured 20 15

**1981.** Presidents of Colombia (5th series). As T **559.** Multicoloured.
1615. 7 p. Bartolome Calvo (after Miguel Diaz Vargas) .. 60 15
1616. 7 p. Sergio Camargo .. 60 15
1617. 7 p. Jose Maria Rojas Garrido.. .. .. 60 15
1618. 7 p. J. M. Campo Serrano (after H. L. Brown) .. 60 15
1619. 7 p. Eliseo Payan (after R. Moros Urbina) .. 60 15
1620. 7 p. Carlos Holguin (after Coriolano Leudo) .. 60 15
1621. 7 p. Jose Manuel Marroquin (after Rafael Tavera).. 60 15
1622. 7 p. Ramon Gonzalez Valencia (after Jose Maria Vidal) .. 60 15
1623. 7 p. Jorge Holguin (after M. Salas Yepes) .. 60 15
1624. 7 p. Ruben Piedrahita Arango.. .. .. 60 15

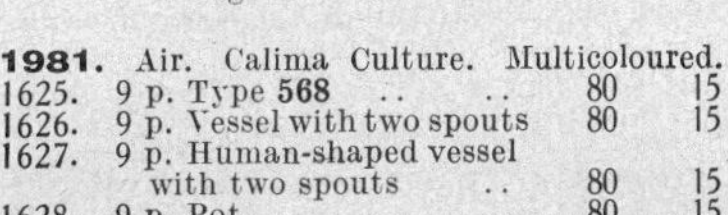
**1981.** Air. Calima Culture. Multicoloured.
1625. 9 p. Type **568** .. .. 80 15
1626. 9 p. Vessel with two spouts 80 15
1627. 9 p. Human-shaped vessel with two spouts .. 80 15
1628. 9 p. Pot .. .. .. 80 15

569. 1 c. Stamp of 1881.

**1981.** Air. Cent. of Admission to U.P.U.
1629. **569.** 30 p. green and pink 30 20

570. Girl with Water Jug.

**1981.** Colombian Solidarity.
1631. **570.** 30 p. brn., blk. & orge. 70 30
1632. – 30 p. brn., blk. & orge. 70 30
1633. – 30 p. brn., blk. & orge. 70 30
DESIGNS: No. 1632, Baby with basket. No. 1633, Boy sitting on wheelbarrow.

**1982.** Presidents of Colombia (6th series). As T **559.** Multicoloured.
1634. 7 p. Simon Bolivar .. 50 15
1635. 7 p. Francisco de Paula Santander .. .. 50 15
1636. 7 p. Joaquin Mosquera (after C. Franco) .. 50 15
1637. 7 p. Domingo Caicedo .. 50 15
1638. 7 p. Jose Ignacio de Marquez (after C. Franco) .. 50 15
1639. 7 p. Juan de Dios Aranzazu 50 15
1640. 7 p. Jose de Obaldia (after Jesus M. Duque) .. 50 15
1641. 7 p. Guillermo Quintero Calderon (after Silvano Cuellar) .. .. 50 15
1642. 7 p. Carlos Lozano y Lozano (after Helio Ramierz) .. .. 50 15
1643. 7 p. Roberto Urdaneta Arbelaez (after Jose Bascones Agneto) .. 50 15

571. Solano Bay, Choco.

**1982.** Air. Tourism. Multicoloured.
1644. 20 p. Type **571** .. .. 25 30
1645. 20 p. Tota Lake, Boyaca 25 30
1646. 20 p. Corrales, Boyaca .. 25 30

573. Gun Club Emblem.

**1982.** Air. Cent. of Bogota Gun Club.
1648. **573.** 20 p. multicoloured 25 15

574. Flower arrangement in Basket.

575. Zoomorphic Figure (crocodile).
576. Capitalization Certificate.

**1982.** Country Flowers. Designs showing flower arrangements. Multicoloured.
1649. 7 p. Type **574** .. .. 75 15
1650. 7 p. Pink arrangement in basket .. .. .. 75 15
1651. 7 p. Red roses in pot .. 75 15
1652. 7 p. Lilac and white arrangement in basket .. 75 15
1653. 7 p. Orange and yellow arrangement in basket 75 15
1654. 7 p. Mixed arrangement in vase .. .. .. 75 15
1655. 7 p. Pink roses in vase .. 75 15
1656. 7 p. Daisies in pot .. 75 15
1657. 7 p. Bouquet of yellow roses .. .. .. 75 15
1658. 7 p. Pink and yellow arrangement .. .. 75 15

**1982.** Air. Tairona Culture.
1659 **575** 25 p. gold, blk & brn 90 35
1660 – 25 p. gold, blk & mve 90 35
1661 – 25 p. gold, blk & grn 90 35
1662 – 25 p. gold, blk & mve 90 35
1663 – 25 p. gold, black & bl 90 35
1664 – 25 p. gold, blk & red 90 35
DESIGNS—VERT. No. 1660, Anthropomorphic figure with crest; 1661, Anthropomorphic figure with two crests; 1662, Anthropozoomorphic figure; 1663, Anthropozoomorphic figure with elaborate headdress; 1664, Pectoral.

**1982.** 50th Anniv. of Central Mortgage Bank.
1665. **576.** 9 p. green and black 35 20

577. State Governor's Palace, Pereira.

**1982.** Air. Pereira City.
1666. **577.** 35 p. multicoloured.. 35 20

578. Biplane and Badge.

**1982.** Air. American Air Force Co-operation.
1667. **578.** 18 p. multicoloured.. 25 15

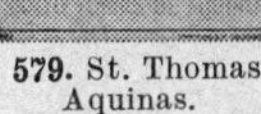

579. St. Thomas Aquinas.
580. St. Theresa of Avila (after Zurbaran).

**1982.** St. Thomas Aquinas Commemoration.
1668. **579.** 5 p. multicoloured .. 15 10

**1982.** 400th Death Anniv. of St. Theresa of Avila.
1669. **580.** 5 p. multicoloured .. 15 10

581. St. Francis of Assisi (after Zurbaran).
583. Gabriel Garcia Marquez.

582. Magdalena River.

**1982.** 800th Birth Anniv. of St. Francis of Assisi.
1670. **581.** 5 p. multicoloured .. 15 10

**1982.** Air. Tourism.
1671. **582.** 30 p. multicoloured.. 2·50 70

**1982.** Town Arms. As T **476.** Multicoloured.
1672. 10 p. Buga .. .. 25 10
1673. 16 p. Rionegro .. .. 45 15
1674. 23 p. Honda .. .. 25 20

**1982.** Award of Nobel Prize for Literature to Gabriel Garcia Marquez.
1675. **583.** 7 p. grey and green (postage) .. .. 25 15
1676. 25 p. grey & bl. (air) 20 10
1677. 30 p. grey and brown 25 10

**1983.** Town Arms. As T **476.** Multicoloured.
1678. 10 p. San Juan de Pasto 30 15
1679. 20 p. Santa Fe de Bogota 25 10

584. " Liberty Fort " (drawing in National Archives).

**1983.** Air. San Andres Archipelago.
1680. **584.** 25 p. multicoloured.. 25 10

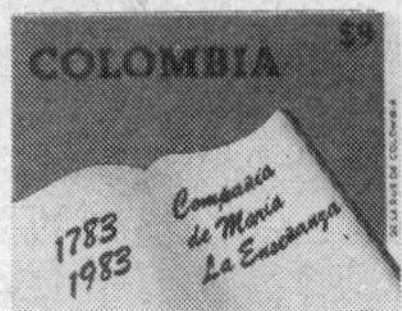


585. Open Book.

**1983.** Bicentenary of First Girls' School, Santa Fe de Bogota.
1681. **585.** 9 p. grey, blk. & gold 25 15

586. Sunset.

**1983.** Air. Las Gaviotas Ecological Centre.
1682. **586.** 12 p. multicoloured.. 15 10

587. Self-portrait.
588. Radio Bands.

**1983.** Death Centenary of Jose Maria Espinosa (artist).
1683. **587.** 9 p. multicoloured .. 20 10

**1983.** Air. 50th Anniv. of Radio Amateurs League.
1684. **588.** 12 p. multicoloured 35 20

589. " Dona Rangel de Cuellas donating Territory " (Marcos L. Marino).
590. Bolivar.

**1983.** 250th Anniv. of Cucuta.
1685. **589.** 9 p. multicoloured .. 30 15

**1983.** Birth Bicent. of Simon Bolivar.
1686. **590.** 9 p. multicoloured (postage) .. .. 25 10
1687. – 30 p. yellow, blue and red (air) .. 35 25
1688. – 100 p. multicoloured 1·25 85

DESIGNS—HORIZ. 30 p. Bolivar as national flag. VERT. 100 p. Bolivar and flag.

**591.** Porfirio Barba Jacob (after Frank Linas).

**592.** " Passiflora laurifolia ".

**1983.** Birth Cent. of Porfirio Barba Jacob.
1689. **591.** 9 p. brown & black 20 10

**1983.** Bicentenary of Royal Botanical Expedition from Spain to South America. Mult.
1690 9 p. Type **592** (postage) .. 20 10
1691 9 p. "Cinchona lanceifolia" .. .. .. 20 10
1692 60 p. "Cinchona cordifolia" .. .. .. 65 15
1693 12 p. "Cinchona ovalifolia" (air) .. .. 30 15
1694 12 p. "Begonia guaduensis" .. .. .. 30 15
1695 40 p. "Begonia urticae" 1·10 80

**593.** Plaza de la Aduana.

**1983.** Air. 450th Anniv. of Cartagena. Mult.
1696. 12 p. Type **593** .. .. 30 15
1697. 35 p. Cartagena buildings and monuments .. 45 20

**594.** " Dawn in the Andes " (Alejandro Obregon).

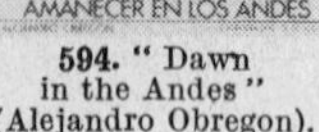

**595.** Scout Badge.

**1983.**
1698. **594.** 20 p. mult. (postage) 1·25 45
1699. 30 p. mult. (air) .. 2·25 65

**1983.** Air. 75th Anniv. of Boy Scout Movement.
1700. **595.** 12 p. multicoloured 20 15

**596.** Santander.

**597.** Coffee.

**1984.** Francisco de Paula Santander (President of New Granada, 1832–37).
1701. **596.** 12 p. green .. .. 25 15
1702. 12 p. blue .. .. 25 15
1703. 12 p. red .. .. 25 15

**1984.** Air. Exports.
1704. **597.** 14 p. purple & green 10 10

**598.** Admiral Jose Prudencio Padilla.

**1984.** Anniversaries. Multicoloured.
1705 10 p. Type **598** (birth bicentenary) .. .. 50 15
1706 18 p. Luis A. Calvo (composer, birth cent) 35 15
1707 20 p. Diego Fallon (writer, 150th birth anniv) .. 35 15
1708 20 p. Candelario Obeso (writer, death cent) .. 60 20
1709 22 p. Luis Eduardo Lopez de Mesa (writer, birth centenary) .. .. 45 15

**599.** Rainbow over Countryside.

**600.** Stylised Globe on Stand.

**1984.** Marandua, City of the Future.
1710 **599** 15 p. mult (post) .. 30 15
1711 30 p. mult (air) .. 20 20

**1984.** Air. 45th Congress of Americanists, Bogota.
1712 **600** 45 p. multicoloured .. 30 30

**601.** Nativity and Children playing.

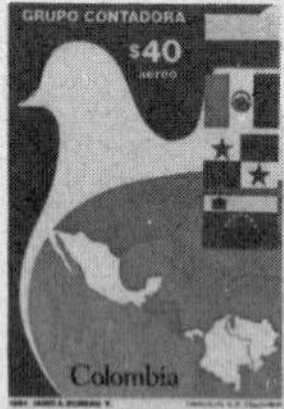

**602.** Maria Concepcion Loperena.

**1984.** Christmas.
1713 **601** 12 p. mult (post) .. 25 10
1714 14 p. mult (air) .. 30 10

**1985.** 150th Birth Anniv of Maria Concepcion Loperena (Independence heroine).
1715 **602** 12 p. multicoloured .. 35 25

603 Dove, Map and Members' Flags


604 Mejia and Farman F.40 Type Biplane

**1985.** Air. Contadora Group.
1716 **603** 40 p. multicoloured .. 40 25

**1985.** Birth Centenary of Gonzalo Mejia (airport architect).
1717 **604** 12 p. multicoloured .. 20 10

605 "Married Couple" (Pedro nel Gomez)

**1985.**
1718 **605** 37 p. mult (postage).. 25 10
1719 40 p. mult (air) .. 40 25

**606** Capybara

**607** Straight-billed Woodcreepers

**1985.** Fauna. Multicoloured.
(a) Mammals.
1720 12 p. Type **606** (postage) 15 10
1721 15 p. Ocelot .. .. 35 25
1722 15 p. Spectacled bear .. 35 25
1723 20 p. Mountain tapir .. 35 25

(b) Birds.
1724 14 p. Lineated woodpeckers (air) .. .. 1·25 45
1725 20 p. Type **607** .. .. 1·50 50
1726 50 p. Coppery-bellied pufflegs .. .. 2·50 1·40
1727 55 p. Blue-crowned motmots .. .. 2·75 1·60

**608** Scenery and Gardel

**609** "Gloria" (cadet ship), "Caldas" (frigate) and Naval Officer

**1985.** 50th Death Anniv of Carlos Gardel (singer).
1728 **608** 15 p. multicoloured .. 20 10

**1985.** Air. 50th Anniv of Almirante Padilla Naval College.
1729 **609** 20 p. multicoloured .. 75 35

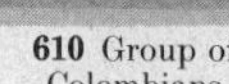

**610** Group of Colombians

**611** Alphabet Tree

**1985.** Air. National Census.
1730 **610** 20 p. multicoloured .. 35 25

**1985.** National Education Year.
1731 **611** 15 p. multicoloured .. 30 15

**612** Boy Playing Flute to Toys

**613** Pumarejo

**1985.** Christmas. Multicoloured.
1732 15 p. Type **612** (postage) 25 15
1733 20 p. Girl looking at dressed tree (air) .. 30 20

**1986.** Air. Birth Centenary of Alfonso Lopez Pumarejo (President, 1934–38 and 1942–45).
1734 **613** 24 p. multicoloured .. 30 15

**614** Cyclists and Countryside

**615** Carranza (after Carlos Dupuy)

**1986.** Air. "Coffee and Cycling, Pride of Colombia".
1735 **614** 60 p. multicoloured .. 45 25

**1986.** Eduardo Carranza (poet) Commem.
1736 **615** 18 p. multicoloured .. 20 15

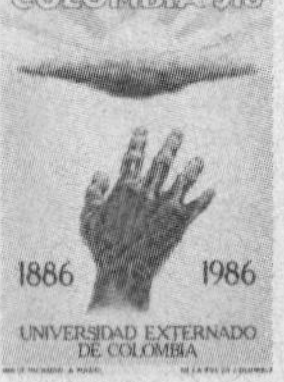

**616** Hand reaching for Sun

**617** Northern Pudu

**1986.** Centenary of External University.
1737 **616** 18 p. multicoloured .. 30 20

**1986.** Air.
1738 **617** 50 p. multicoloured .. 60 35

**618** Ricaurte and Birth Place, Leiva

**1986.** Birth Bicentenary of Gen. Antonio Ricaurte (Independence hero).
1739 **618** 18 p. multicoloured .. 20 15

**619** Pope and Arms

**620** Couple and Satellite

**1986.** Air. Visit of Pope John Paul II (1st issue).
1740 **619** 24 p. multicoloured .. 35 20
See also Nos. 1745/6.

**1986.** Air. World Communications Day.
1741 **620** 50 p. multicoloured .. 60 35

**621** Silva and Illustration of "Nocturne"

**622** Girl and Doves

**1986.** 90th Death Anniv. of Jose Asuncion Silva (poet).
1742 **621** 18 p. multicoloured .. 20 15

**1986.** Air. International Peace Year.
1743 **622** 55 p. multicoloured .. 65 40

**623** Martinez

**624** Pope and Medellin Cathedral

**1986.** 10th Death Anniv. of Fernando Gomez Martinez (politician and founder of "El Colombiano" newspaper).
1744 **623** 24 p. multicoloured .. 30 20

**1986.** Air. Visit of Pope John Paul II (2nd issue). Multicoloured.
1745 55 p. Type **624** .. .. 50 45
1746 60 p. Pope giving blessing in Bogota .. .. 50 45

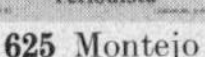

**625** Montejo

**626** Computer Portrait of Bach

**1986.** Air. Birth Centenary of Enrique Santos Montejo (journalist and editor of "El Tiempo").
1748 **625** 25 p. multicoloured .. 30 20

**1986.** Air. Composers' Birth Anniversaries (1985). Multicoloured.
1749 70 p. Type **626** (300th anniv) .. .. 65 60
1750 100 p. "The Permanency of Baroque" (300th annivs of Handel and Bach and 400th anniv of H. Schutz) .. .. 75 55

**627** De La Salle (founder) and National Colours

**1986.** Air. Centenary of Brothers of Christian Schools in Colombia.
1751 **627** 25 p. multicoloured .. 30 15

**628** Convent of Mercy

**1986.** 450th Anniv. of Santiago de Cali.
1752 20 p. Arms (as T **476**) .. 15 10
1753 25 p. Type **628** .. .. 15 10

**629** Piece of Coal and National Colours

**630** Castro Silva

**1986.** Air. Completion of El Cerrejon Coal Complex.
1754 **629** 55 p. multicoloured .. 40 40

**1986.** Birth Centenary (1985) of Jose Vincente Castro Silva. (Principal of Senior College of the Rosary).
1755 **630** 20 p. multicoloured .. 25 15

**631** "The Five Signatories" (detail, R. Vasquez).

**1986.** Air. Centenary of Constitution.
1756 **631** 25 p. multicoloured .. 30 20

**1986.** Arms of Antioquia. As T **476**.
1758 55 p. multicoloured .. 20 10

**632** Garcia Lorca

**1986.** Air. 50th Death Anniv of Federico Garcia Lorca (poet).
1759 **632** 60 p. multicoloured .. 35 25

**633** Symbolic Prism

**634** Maya

**1986.** Centenary of Fine Art Faculty and 50th Anniv. of Architecture Faculty at National University.
1760 **633** 40 p. multicoloured .. 20 30

**1986.** 6th Death Anniv of Rafael Maya (poet and critic).
1761 **634** 25 p. multicoloured .. 30 20

**635** Andean Condor

**636** "Thanks! Friends of the World"

**1986.**
1762 **635** 20 p. blue .. .. 50 10
1763 25 p. blue .. .. 50 10

**1986.** Air. Thanks for Help after Devastation of Armero by Volcanic Eruption, 1985.
1767 **636** 50 p. multicoloured .. 60 35

**637** Mestiza Virgin (from crib at Pasto)

**638** Left-hand Side of Mural

**1986.** Air. Christmas.
1768 **637** 25 p. multicoloured .. 30 15

**1987.** Air. 450th Anniv of Popayan City. "The Apotheosis of Popayan" by Ephram Martinez Zambrano. Multicoloured.
1769 100 p. Type **638** .. .. 1·40 75
1770 100 p. Right-hand side of mural .. .. .. 1·40 75
Nos. 1769/70 were printed together, se-tenant, forming a composite design.

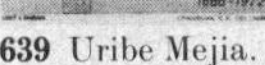

**639** Uribe Mejia.

**640** "Conversion of St. Augustine of Hippo".

**1987.** Birth Centenary (1986) of Pedro Uribe Mejia (coffee industry pioneer).
1771 **639** 25 p. multicoloured .. 30 15

**1987.** Air. 1600th Anniv of Conversion of St. Augustine.
1772 **640** 30 p. multicoloured .. 10 10

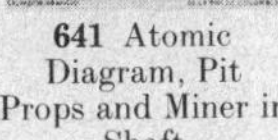

**641** Atomic Diagram, Pit Props and Miner in Shaft

**642** St. Barbara's Church

**1987.** Air. Centenary of National Mines Faculty of National University, Medellin.
1773 **641** 25 p. multicoloured .. 10 10

**1987.** 450th Anniv of Mompox City.
1774 **642** 500 p. multicoloured .. 2·50 2·50

**643** Hawk-headed Parrot

**644** White Horse

**1987.** Fauna.
1775 **643** 30 p. green (postage) 1·25 20
1776 – 30 p. purple .. .. 45 20
1777 – 30 p. red (air) .. 1·25 20
1778 – 35 p. brown .. .. 15 20
DESIGNS—HORIZ. No. 1776, Boutu. 1778, South American red-lined turtle. VERT. No. 1777, Greater flamingo.
See also Nos. 1807/9, 1815/17, 1823/6 and 1855/8.

**1987.** Air. Pure-bred Horses. Multicoloured.
1779 60 p. Type **644** .. .. 45 35
1780 70 p. Black horse .. 45 35

**645** Mastheads, Fidel Cano (founder), Luis Cano, Luis Gabriel Cano Isaza and Alfonso Cano Isaza (editors)

**1987.** Air. Centenary of "El Espectador" (newspaper).
1781 **645** 60 p. multicoloured .. 25 15

**646** Isaacs and Scene from "Maria"

**1987.** 150th Birth Anniv of Jorge Isaacs (writer).
1782 **646** 70 p. multicoloured .. 25 10

**648** Muti and Illustration of "Condor"

**1987.** 33rd Death Anniv of Aurelio Martinez Mutis (poet).
1785 **648** 90 p. multicoloured .. 2·00 75

**649** Houses forming House

**650** Family and Dish Aerial

**1987.** Air. International Year of Shelter for the Homeless.
1786 **649** 60 p. multicoloured .. 65 35

**1987.** Social Security and Communications.
1787 **650** 35 p. multicoloured .. 30 20

**651** Flags

**652** Nativity Scene in Globe

**1987.** Air. 1st Meeting of Eight Latin-American Presidents of Contadora and Lima Groups, Acapulco, Mexico.
1788 **651** 80 p. multicoloured .. 55 55

**1987.** Air. Christmas.
1789 **652** 30 p. multicoloured .. 30 15

**653** Houses, Telephone Wires and Dials

**1987.** Air. Rural Telephone Network.
1790 **653** 70 p. multicoloured .. 35 10

**654** Mountain Sanctuaries

**655** Flower (Life)

**1988.** Air. 450th Anniv of Bogota (1st issue).
1791 **654** 70 p. multicoloured 25 70
See also Nos. 1803/4.

**1988.** 40th Anniv of Declaration of Human Rights (1st issue).
1792 **655** 30 p. green .. .. 10 10
1793 – 35 p. red .. .. 10 10
1794 – 40 p. lilac .. .. 15 10
1795 – 40 p. blue .. .. 10 10
DESIGNS—VERT. No. 1793, Road (Freedom of choice). HORIZ. 1794, Circle of children (Freedom of association); 1795, Couple on bench (Communication).
See also Nos. 1840/1.

657 Mask

**1988.** Air. Gold Museum, Bogota. Mult.
1796 70 p. Type **657** .. .. 30 30
1797 80 p. Votive figure .. 60 30
1798 90 p. Human figure .. 85 65

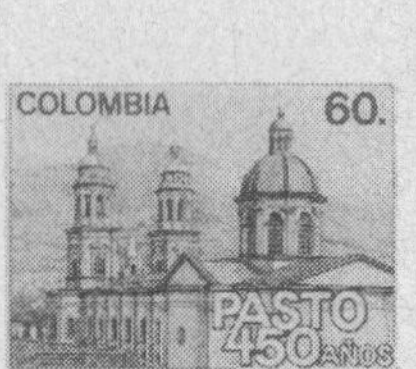

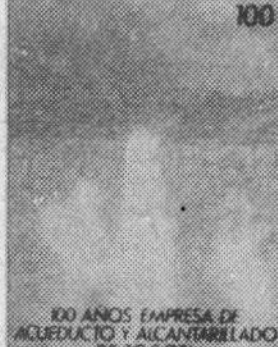

658 Pasto Cathedral
659 Waterfall

**1988.** 450th Anniv of Pasto.
1799 **658** 60 p. multicoloured .. 40 20

**1988.** Centenary of Bogota Water Supply and Sewerage Organization.
1800 **659** 100 p. multicoloured .. 35 10

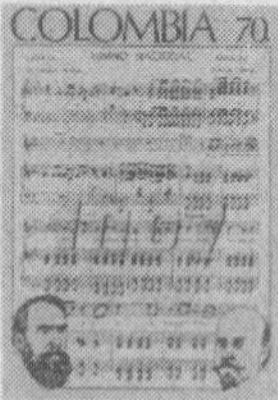

660 Score and Composers
661 M. Currea de Aya

**1988.** Centenary (1987) of National Anthem by Rafael Nunez and Oreste Sindici.
1801 **660** 70 p. multicoloured .. 25 25

**1988.** Birth Centenary of Maria Currea de Aya (women's rights pioneer).
1802 **661** 80 p. multicoloured .. 25 10

662 Modern Bogota
664 College

**1988.** Air. 450th Anniv of Bogota (2nd issue). Multicoloured.
1803 80 p. Type **662** .. .. 55 30
1804 90 p. Street in old Bogota (horiz) .. .. 60 30

**1988.** Fauna. As T **643**.
1807 35 p. brown .. .. 25 15
1808 35 p. green .. .. 25 15
1809 40 p. orange .. .. 25 15
DESIGNS—HORIZ. No. 1807, Crab-eating racoon; 1808, Caribbean monk seal; 1809, Giant otter.

**1988.** Centenary of Return of Society of Jesus to St. Bartholomew's Senior College.
1810 **664** 120 p. multicoloured .. 35 20

665 Eduardo Santos
666 Mother and Children

**1988.** Personalities. Multicoloured.
1811 80 p. Type **665** (birth centenary) (postage) .. 45 25
1812 90 p. Jorge Alvarez Lleras (astronomer) .. .. 45 25
1813 80 p. Zipa Tisquesusa (16th-century Indian chief) (air) .. .. 45 25

**1988.** Air. Christmas.
1814 **666** 40 p. multicoloured .. 15 10

**1988.** Fauna. As T **643**.
1815 40 p. grey (postage) .. 15 10
1816 45 p. violet .. .. 50 10
1817 45 p. blue (air) .. .. 50 10
DESIGNS—HORIZ. No. 1815, American manatee; 1816, Masked trogon. VERT. No. 1817, Blue-bellied curassow.

667 Andres Bello College

**1988.**
1818 **667** 115 p. multicoloured .. 35 20

668 Building and Nieto Caballero
669 Gomez

**1989.** Air. Birth Centenary of Agustin Nieto Caballero (educationalist).
1819 **668** 100 p. multicoloured .. 30 15

**1989.** Air. Birth Centenary of Laureano Gomez (President, 1950–53).
1820 **669** 45 p. multicoloured .. 15 10

670 Map

**1989.** Air. International Coffee Organization.
1821 **670** 110 p. multicoloured .. 30 15

671 Modern Flats, Recreation Area and Hands holding Brick

**1989.** Air. 12th Habitat U.N. Conference on Human Settlements, Cartagena.
1822 **671** 100 p. multicoloured .. 20 10

**1989.** Fauna. As T **643**.
1823 40 p. brown (postage) .. 10 10
1824 45 p. black .. .. 50 10
1825 55 p. brown .. .. 15 10
1826 45 p. blue (air) .. .. 10 10
DESIGNS—HORIZ. No. 1823, White-tailed deer; 1824, Harpy eagle; 1826, Brown discus. VERT. 1825, False anole.

672 Emblem

**1989.** 25th Anniv of Adpostal (postal administration).
1827 **672** 45 p. multicoloured .. 10 10

673 Hands
675 "Simon Bolivar" (Pedro Jose Figueroa)

**1989.** Air. Bicentenary of French Revolution.
1828 **673** 100 p. multicoloured .. 20 10

**1989.** 170th Anniv of Liberation Campaign. Multicoloured.
1830 40 p. Type **675** .. .. 10 10
1831 40 p. "Santander" (Figueroa) .. .. 10 10
1832 45 p. "Bolivar and Santander during the Campaign for the Plains" (J. M. Zamora) (46 × 37 mm) .. .. 10 10
1833 45 p. "From Boyaca to Santa Fe" (left-hand detail) (Francisco de P. Alvarez) (29 × 36 mm) 10 10
1834 45 p. Right-hand detail (29 × 36 mm) .. .. 10 10
1835 45 p. Mounted officer and foot soldiers (left-hand detail) (31 × 51 mm) .. 35 10
1836 45 p. Mounted officer (centre detail) (33 × 51 mm) .. .. .. 35 10
1837 45 p. Mounted soldiers with flag (right-hand detail) (31 × 51 mm) .. 35 35
Nos. 1833/4 and 1835/7 (showing details of triptych by A. de Santa Maria) were each issued together, se-tenant, each forming a composite design.

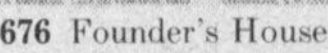
676 Founder's House
677 Healthy Children and Shadowy Figures

**1989.** 450th Anniv of Tunja.
1839 **676** 45 p. multicoloured .. 10 10

**1989.** Human Rights (2nd issue). As T **655**.
1840 45 p. brown (postage) .. 10 10
1841 55 p. green (air) .. 15 10
DESIGNS—HORIZ. 45 p. Musicians (Culture). VERT. 55 p. Family.

**1989.** Air. Anti-drugs Campaign.
1842 **677** 115 p. multicoloured .. 25 15

678 Gold Ornaments of Quimbaya, Calima and Tolima
679 Quimbaya Museum

**1989.** Air. America. Pre-Columbian Crafts. Multicoloured.
1843 115 p. Type **678** .. .. 25 15
1844 130 p. Indian making pot and Sinu ceramic figure (horiz) .. .. .. 25 15

**1989.** Centenary of Armenia City.
1845 **679** 135 p. multicoloured .. 25 15

680 Mantilla

**1989.** Air. 45th Death Anniv of Joaquin Quijano Mantilla (chronicler).
1846 **680** 170 p. multicoloured .. 75 20

681 Boeing 767 and Globe
682 "The Fathers of the Fatherland leaving Congress" (R. Acevedo Bernal)

**1989.** Air.
1847 **681** 130 p. multicoloured .. 45 15

**1989.** Air. 170th Anniv of Creation of First Republic of Colombia (1851) and 168th Anniv of its Constitution (others). Multicoloured.
1848 130 p. Type **682** .. .. 55 15
1849 130 p. "Church of the Rosary, Cucuta" (Carmelo Fernandez) .. 55 15
1850 130 p. Republic's arms .. 55 15
1851 130 p. "Bolivar at Congress of Angostura" (46 × 36 mm) (Tito Salas) .. .. .. 55 15

683 Nativity (Barro-Raquira clay figures)
684 "Plaza de la Aduana" (H. Lemaitre)

**1989.** Air. Christmas.
1852 **683** 55 p. multicoloured .. 40 10

**1990.** Air. Presidential Summit, Cartagena.
1853 **684** 130 p. multicoloured .. 60 40

685 Headphones on Marble Head
687 "Espeletia hartwegiana"

686 Cuervo Borda and National Museum

**1990.** Air. 50th Anniv of Colombia National Radio.
1854 **685** 150 p. multicoloured .. 30 15

**1990.** Fauna. As T **643**.
1855 50 p. grey .. .. 10 10
1856 50 p. purple .. .. 10 10
1857 60 p. brown .. .. 15 10
1858 60 p. brown .. .. 50 10
DESIGNS: No. 1855, Grey fox; 1856, Common poison-arrow frog; 1857, Pygmy marmoset; 1858, Sun-bittern.

**1990.** Air. Velez City Arms. As T **476**.
1859 60 p. multicoloured .. 15 10

**1990.** Air. Birth Cent (1989) of Teresa Cuervo Borda (artist).
1860 **686** 60 p. muticoloured .. 15 10

**1990.** Multicoloured.
1861 60 p. Type **687** .. .. 15 10
1862 60 p. "Ceiba pentandra" (horiz) .. .. 15 10
1863 70 p. "Ceroxylon quindiuense" .. .. 15 10
1864 70 p. "Tibouchina lepidota" .. .. .. 15 10

**688** Theatrical Masks

**689** Statue, Bogota

**1990.** Air. 2nd Iberian-American Theatre Festival, Bogota.
1865 **688** 150 p. gold, brn & orge 60 15

**1990.** 150th Death Anniv of Francisco de Paula Santander (President of New Granada, 1832–37). Multicoloured.
1866 50 p. Type **689** (postage) 40 10
1867 60 p. Gateway of National Pantheon (air) .. 40 10
1868 60 p. "General Santander with the Constitution" (Jose Maria Espinosa) 40 10
1869 70 p. Santander, organizer of public education (after F. S. Guitierrez) 40 10
1870 70 p. "The Postal Carrier" (Jose Maria del Castillo) (horiz) .. .. 40 10

**690** Postmen

**1990.** Air. 150th Anniv of the Penny Black.
1872 **690** 150 p. multicoloured .. 30 15

**691** Cadet, Arms and School

**693** Graph

**692** Cable

**1990.** 50th Anniv of General Santander Police Cadets School.
1873 **691** 60 p. multicoloured .. 15 10

**1990.** Air. Trans-Caribbean Submarine Fibre Optic Cable.
1874 **692** 150 p. multicoloured .. 60 15

**1990.** Air. 50th Anniv of IFI.
1875 **693** 60 p. multicoloured .. 15 10

**1990.** Arms of Cartago. As T **476**.
1876 50 p. multicoloured .. 35 10

**695** Map

**696** Women on Beach

**1990.** Air. 10th Anniv of Organization of American States.
1878 **695** 130 p. multicoloured .. 55 15

**1990.** La Guajira.
1879 **696** 60 p. multicoloured .. 15 10

**697** Indian wearing Gold Ornaments

**698** St. John Bosco (founder) and Boys

**1990.** Air. 50th Anniv of Gold Museum, Bogota.
1880 **697** 170 p. multicoloured .. 35 20

**1990.** Centenary of Salesian Brothers in Colombia.
1881 **698** 60 p. multicoloured .. 15 10

**699** Brown Pelican, Roseate Spoonbills and Dolphins

**1990.** Air. America. Natural World. Mult.
1882 150 p. Type **699** .. .. 80 30
1883 170 p. Land animals and Salvin's curassows .. 95 35

**700** Christ Child

**701** Monastery

**1990.** Air. Christmas.
1884 **700** 70 p. multicoloured .. 15 10

**1990.** Air. Monastery of Nostra Senhora de las Lajas, Ipiales.
1885 **701** 70 p. multicoloured .. 15 10

**702** Titles and Abstract

**703** Christ of the Miracles, Buga Church

**1991.** Air. Bicentenary of "La Prensa".
1886 **702** 170 p. multicoloured .. 30 15

**1991.**
1887 **703** 70 p. multicoloured .. 15 10

**704** "Anaea syene"

**705** Humpback Whale leaping from Water

**1991.** Butterflies. Multicoloured.
1888 70 p. Type **704** (postage) 15 10
1889 70 p. "Callithea philotima" (horiz) .. 15 10
1890 80 p. "Thecla coronata" 15 10
1891 80 p. "Agrias amydon" (horiz) (air) .. .. 15 10
1892 170 p. "Morpho rhetenor" (horiz) .. .. 30 15
1893 190 p. "Heliconius longarenus ernestus" (horiz) .. .. 35 20

**1991.** Air. Marine Mammals. Multicoloured.
1894 80 p. Type **705** .. .. 15 10
1895 170 p. Humpback whale diving .. .. .. 60 15
1896 190 p. Amazon dolphins (horiz) .. .. 65 20

**706** National Colours

**1991.** New Constitution.
1897 **706** 70 p. multicoloured .. 15 10
See also No. 1914.

**707** Dario Echandia Olaya (after Delio Ramirez)

**708** Girardot (after Jose Maria Espinosa)

**1991.** 2nd Death Anniv of Dario Echandia Olaya.
1898 **707** 80 p. multicoloured .. 15 10

**1991.** Birth Bicentenary of Colonel Atanasio Girardot.
1899 **708** 70 p. multicoloured .. 15 10

**709** Galan

**710** Stone Statue of God, San Agustin

**1991.** 2nd Death Anniv of Luis Carlos Galan Sarmiento (politician).
1900 **709** 80 p. multicoloured .. 15 10

**1991.** Pre-Columbian Art. Multicoloured.
1901 80 p. Type **710** (postage) 15 10
1902 90 p. Burial vessel, Tierradentro .. .. 15 10
1903 90 p. Statue, San Agustin (air) .. .. .. 15 10
1904 210 p. Gold flying fish, San Agustin (horiz) .. 40 20

## INDEX

Countries can be quickly located by referring to the index at the end of this volume.

**711** Sailfish

**1991.**
1905 **711** 830 p. multicoloured .. 2·50 1·00

**712** Cloisters of St. Augustine's, Tunja

**1991.** Architecture. Multicoloured.
1906 80 p. Type **712** (postage) 15 10
1907 90 p. Bridge, Chia .. 15 10
1908 90 p. Roadside chapel, Pamplona (vert) (air) 15 10
1909 190 p. Church of the Conception, Santa Fe de Bogota (vert) .. 60 20

**713** "Santa Maria"

**714** Lleras Camargo (after Rafael Salas)

**1991.** Air. America. Voyages of Discovery. Multicoloured.
1910 90 p. Type **713** .. .. 25 15
1911 190 p. Amerindians and approaching ship .. 55 25

**1991.** 1st Death Anniv of Alberto Lleras Camargo (President, 1945–46 and 1958–62).
1912 **714** 80 p. multicoloured .. 15 10

**715** Police Officers, Transport, Emblem and Flag

**1991.** Centenary of Police.
1913 **715** 80 p. multicoloured .. 30 10

**1991.** Air. New Constitution (2nd issue). As No. 1897 but new value and additionally inscr "SANTAFE DE BOGOTA, D.C. Julio 4 de 1991".
1914 90 p. multicoloured .. 15 10

**716** Member Nations' Flags

**717** First Government Building, Sogamoso

**1991.** Air. 5th Group of Rio Presidential Summit, Cartagena.
1915 **716** 190 p. multicoloured .. 30 15

**1991.**
1916 **717** 80 p. multicoloured .. 10 10

718 "Adoration of the Kings" (Baltazar de Figueroa)

719 D. Turbay Quintero

**1991.** Air. Christmas.
1917 **718** 90 p. multicoloured .. 15 10

**1992.** Diana Turbay Quintero (journalist) Commemoration.
1918 **719** 80 p. multicoloured .. 10 10

720 Hand holding Posy of Flowers

721 Cut Flowers

**1992.** Air. 8th U.N. Conference on Trade and Development Session, Cartagena.
1919 **720** 210 p. multicoloured .. 35 20

**1992.** Air. Exports.
1920 90 p. Type **721** .. .. 15 10
1921 210 p. Fruits and nuts (horiz) .. .. 35 20

722 Statue of General Santander, Barranquilla (R. Verlet)

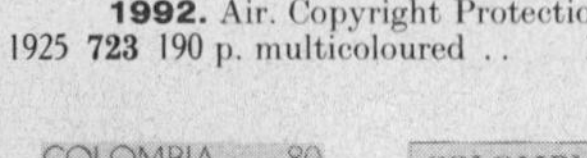

723 Music, Book and Paint Brush

**1992.** Birth Bicentenary of General Francisco de Paula Santander. Multicoloured.
1922 80 p. Type **722** (postage) 10 10
1923 190 p. Francisco de Paula Santander (after Sergio Trujillo Magnenat) (air) 30 15

**1992.** Air. Copyright Protection.
1925 **723** 190 p. multicoloured .. 30 15

725 Lievano Aguirre

726 Enrique Low Murtra (1st anniv)

**1992.** 10th Death Anniv of Indalecio Lievano Aguirre (ambassador to United Nations).
1928 **725** 80 p. multicoloured .. 10 10

**1992.** Death Anniversaries of Justice Ministers. Multicoloured.
1929 100 p. Type **726** .. .. 15 10
1930 110 p. Rodrigo Lara Bonilla (8th anniv) .. 20 10

## MINIMUM PRICE

The minimum price quoted is 10p which represents a handling charge rather than a basis for valuing common stamps. For further notes about prices see introductory pages.

727 Town Arms and Rings

**1992.** 14th National Games, Barranquilla.
1931 **727** 110 p. multicoloured .. 20 10

728 Landscape

729 Athlete and Olympic Rings

**1992.** Air. 2nd U.N. Conference on Environment and Development, Rio de Janeiro. Paintings by Roberto Palomino. Mult.
1932 230 p. Type **728** .. .. 35 20
1933 230 p. Birds in trees .. 35 20

**1992.** Air. Olympic Games, Barcelona.
1934 **729** 110 p. multicoloured .. 20 10

730 "Discovery of America by C. Columbus" (Dali)

**1992.** Air. America. Multicoloured.
1935 230 p. Type **730** .. .. 50 20
1936 260 p. "America Magic, Myth and Legend" (Al. Vivero) .. .. 40 20

731 American Crocodile

**1992.** Endangered Animals. Multicoloured.
1937 100 p. Type **731** .. .. 15 10
1938 100 p. Andean condor (vert) .. .. .. 15 10

732 Maria Lopez de Escobar (founder)

734 Map of the Americas

733 Avianca Colombia McDonnell Douglas MD-83

**1992.** 50th Anniv of House of Mother and Child.
1939 **732** 100 p. mult (postage) 15 10
1940 110 p. mult (air) .. 20 10

**1992.** Air.
1941 **733** 110 p. multicoloured .. 20 10

**1992.** Meeting of First Ladies of the Americas and the Caribbean, Cartagena.
1942 **734** 100 p. multicoloured .. 15 10

735 "Zenaida" (Ana Mercedes Hoyos)

**1992.** 500th Anniv of Discovery of America by Columbus. Paintings.
1943 **735** 100 p. mult (postage) 15 10
1944 – 110 p. multicoloured 20 10
1946 – 110 p. mult (air) .. 20 10
1947 – 230 p. multicoloured 35 20
1948 – 260 p. green and violet 40 20
DESIGNS: 110 p. (1944), "Study for 1/500" (Beatriz Gonzalez); 110 p. (1946), "Blue Eagle" (Alejandro Obregon); 230 p. "Cantileo" (Luis Luna); 260 p. "Maize" (Antonio Caro).

736 Recycling

**1992.**
1949 **736** 100 p. multicoloured .. 15 10

737 Front Curtain

**1992.** Air. Columbus Theatre.
1950 **737** 230 p. multicoloured .. 35 20

739 "Nativity" (Carlos Alfonso Mendez)

**1992.** Christmas. Children's Drawings. Mult.
1952 100 p. Type **739** (postage) 15 10
1953 110 p. Kings approaching stable (Catalina del Valle) (air) .. .. 20 10

740 G. Lara

748 Footballers

742 Campaign Emblem

**1992.** Air. 10th Death Anniv of Gloria Lara (ambassador to the United Nations).
1954 **740** 230 p. multicoloured .. 40 20

**1993.** Lions Club International Amblyopia Prevention Campaign.
1956 **742** 100 p. multicoloured .. 15 10

**1993.** Air. America Cup Football Championship, Ecuador.
1962 **748** 220 p. multicoloured .. 35 20

749 Prisoners

**1993.** Bicentenary of French Declaration of Human Rights. Multicoloured.
1963 150 p. Type **749** (postage) 25 15
1964 150 p. The elderly .. 25 15
1965 200 p. The infirm .. 35 20
1966 200 p. Children .. .. 35 20
1968 220 p. Women (air) .. 35 20
1969 220 p. The poor .. .. 35 20
1970 460 p. Environmental protection .. .. 1·00 40
1971 520 p. Immigrants .. 1·10 45

750 Amerindian (Jose Luis Correal)

752 Green-winged Macaw

751 Emblem and Flags

**1993.** Air. International Year of Indigenous Peoples.
1972 **750** 460 p. multicoloured .. 70 35

**1993.** Air. World Cup Football Championship, U.S.A. (1994) (1st issue).
1973 **751** 220 p. multicoloured .. 35 20
See also Nos. 2006/9.

**1993.** The Amazon. Multicoloured.
1974 150 p. Type **752** (postage) 20 10
1975 150 p. Anaconda .. 20 10
1976 220 p. Water-lilies (air) .. 35 20
1977 220 p. Ipecacuanha flower 35 20

753 Cotton-headed Tamarin

755 Nativity

754 Alberto Pumarejo (politician)

**1993.** Air. America. Endangered Animals. Multicoloured.
1979 220 p. Type **753** .. .. 35 20
1980 220 p. Purple gallinule .. 35 20
1981 460 p. Andean cock of the rock .. .. .. 70 35
1982 520 p. American manatee 80 40

**1993.** Famous Colombians. Multicoloured.
1983 150 p. Type **754** .. .. 20 10
1984 150 p. Lorencita Villegas de Santos (First Lady, 1938–42) .. .. 20 10
1985 150 p. Meliton Rodriguez (photographer) .. 20 10
1986 150 p. Tomas Carrasquilla (writer) .. .. 20 10

**1993.** Christmas. Multicoloured.
1987 200 p. Type **755** .. .. 30 15
1988 220 p. Shepherd (air) .. 35 20

**756** San Andres y Providencia

**1993.** Tourism. Multicoloured.
1989 220 p. Type **756** .. .. 35 20
1990 220 p. Cocuy National Park .. .. .. 35 20
1991 220 p. La Cocha Lake .. 35 20
1992 220 p. Waterfall, La Macarena mountains .. 35 20
1993 460 p. Chicamocha (vert) 70 35
1994 460 p. Sierra Nevada de Santa Marta (vert) .. 70 35
1995 520 p. Embalse de Penol (vert) .. .. .. 80 40
See also No. E1996.

**757** Museum Entrance

**759** Yellow-eared Conure

**1993.** 170th Anniv of National Museum.
1997 **757** 150 p. multicoloured .. 20 10

**1994.** Birds. Multicoloured.
1999 180 p. Type **759** (postage) 25 15
2000 240 p. Bogota rail .. 35 20
2001 270 p. Toucan barbets (horiz) (air) .. .. 40 20
2002 560 p. Cinnamon teals (horiz) .. .. 85 45

**760** Emblem

**1994.** Air. International Decade for Natural Disaster Reduction. National Disaster Prevention System.
2003 **760** 630 p. blue, yell & red 95 50

**762** Escriva de Balaguer

**1994.** Air. Beatification of Josemaria Escriva de Balaguer (founder of Opus Dei).
2005 **762** 560 p. multicoloured .. 85 45

**763** Trophy and Player and Emblem on Flag

**1994.** World Cup Football Championship, U.S.A. (2nd issue). Multicoloured.
2006 180 p. Type **763** (postage) 25 15
2008 270 p. Match scene, trophy and emblem (air) .. .. .. 40 20
2009 560 p. Trophy, emblem, ball and national colours (vert) .. .. 85 45

**764** Flagpoles **765** "Self-portrait"

**1994.** Air. 4th Latin American Presidential Summit, Cartagena.
2011 **764** 630 p. multicoloured .. 95 50
See also No. E2010.

**1994.** Birth Centenary of Ricardo Rendon (painter).
2012 **765** 240 p. black .. .. 30 15

**766** Biplane and William Knox Martin

**1994.** Air. 75th Anniv of First Airmail Flight.
2013 **766** 270 p. multicoloured .. 35 20

**767** Emblem

**1994.** 40th Anniv of Radio and Television Network.
2014 **767** 180 p. multicoloured .. 25 15

**768** Numbers, Graphs and Pie Chart

**770** Horse and Bicycle

**1994.** 1993 Census.
2015 **768** 240 p. multicoloured .. 30 15

**1994.** Air. America. Postal Transport. Mult.
2017 **770** 270 p. multicoloured .. 35 20
See also No. E2018.

**771** Founders and Pi Symbol

**1994.** Centenary of Colombian Society of Engineers.
2019 **771** 180 p. multicoloured .. 25 15

**772** Building and Scales

**1994.** Air. 80th Anniv of National Institute of Legal Medicine and Forensic Sciences.
2020 **772** 560 p. multicoloured .. 75 40

**773** Three Wise Men

**1994.** Air. Christmas.
2021 **773** 270 p. multicoloured 35 20
See also No. E2022.

**774** 1921 SCADTA 30 c. Stamp

**775** Common Iguana

**1995.** Air. 75th Anniv (1994) of Sociedad Colombo-Alemana de Transportes Aereos (SCADTA) (private air company contracted to carry mail).
2023 **774** 330 p. pink, brn & blk 45 25

**1995.** Air. Flora and Fauna. Multicoloured.
2024 650 p. Type **775** .. .. 85 45
2025 650 p. Iguana facing left 85 45
2026 750 p. Forest (left detail) 1·00 50
2027 750 p. Forest (right detail) 1·00 50
Stamps of the same value were issued together in se-tenant pairs, each pair forming a composite design.

**776** 1920 10 c. Stamp

**1995.** Air. 75th Anniv of Compania Colombiana de Navagacion Aerea (private air company contracted to carry mail).
2028 **776** 330 p. multicoloured .. 45 25

**778** Jose Miguel Pey

**1995.** Colombian Patriots. Multicoloured.
2030 270 p. Type **778** (revolutionary) .. 35 20
2031 270 p. Jorge Tadeo Lozana (zoologist and revolutionary) .. 35 20
2032 270 p. Antonio Narino (journalist and politician) .. .. 35 20
2033 270 p. Camilo Torres (lawyer and revolutionary) .. 35 20
2034 270 p. Jose Fernandez Madrid (doctor and revolutionary) .. 35 20
2035 270 p. Jose Maria del Castillo y Rada (lawyer) .. .. 35 20
2036 270 p. Custodio Garcia Rovira (revolutionary) 35 20
2037 270 p. Antonio Villavicencio (revolutionary) .. 35 20
2038 270 p. Liborio Mejia (lawyer and historian) 35 20
2039 270 p. Rafael Urdaneta (diplomat) .. .. 35 20
2040 270 p. Juan Garcia del Rio (writer and politician) 35 20
2041 270 p. Gen. Jose Maria Melo .. .. 35 20
2042 270 p. Gen. Tomas Herrera .. .. 35 20
2043 270 p. Froilan Largacha (acting President, Feb–June 1863) .. 35 20
2044 270 p. Salvador Camacho Roldan (writer) .. 35 20
2045 270 p. Gen. Ezequiel Hurtado (acting President, Apr–Aug 1884) .. .. .. 35 20
2046 270 p. Dario Echandia Olaya (lawyer) .. 35 20
2047 270 p. Alberto Lleras Camargo (President, 1945–46) .. .. 35 20
2048 270 p. Gen. Gustavo Rojas Pinilla (President, 1953–57) .. .. 35 20
2049 270 p. Carlos Lleras Restrepo (President, 1966–70) .. .. 35 20

**779** Farmers on Hillside

**1995.** Air. 50th Anniv of F.A.O.
2050 **779** 750 p. multicoloured .. 1·00 50

**780** Bello **781** Fireman

**1995.** Air. 25th Anniv of Andres Bello (scholar and writer) Agreement on Intellectual Co-operation.
2051 **780** 650 p. multicoloured .. 85 45

**1995.** Air. Centenary of Fire Brigade of Bogota.
2052 **781** 330 p. multicoloured .. 45 25

**MORE DETAILED LISTS**
are given in the Stanley Gibbons Catalogues referred to in the country headings.
For lists of current volumes see Introduction.

782 Emblem

783 Anniversary Emblem

**1995.** Air. 50th Anniv of National Chamber of Commerce.
2053 **782** 330 p. multicoloured .. 45 25

**1995.** Air. 50th Anniv. of U.N.O.
2054 **783** 750 p. multicoloured .. 45 25

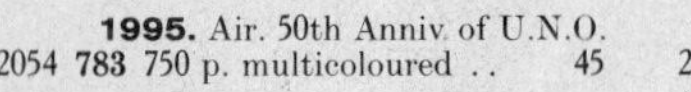

784 Emblem

786 Obando (after Efrain Martinez)

**1995.** Air. 1st Pacific Ocean Games, Cali.
2055 **784** 750 p. multicoloured .. 1·00 50

**1995.** Birth Bicentenary of General Jose Maria Obando.
2057 **786** 220 p. multicoloured .. 25 15

787 San Filipe de Barajas Castle

**1995.** Air. 11th Non-aligned Countries' Conference, Cartagena de Indias.
2058 **787** 650 p. multicoloured .. 80 40

788 Estela Lopez Pomareda in "Maria", Charlie Chaplin and Jackie Coogan

**1995.** Air. Centenary of Motion Pictures.
2059 **788** 330 p. black and brown 40 20

789 Harvesting Poppies for Opium

790 Anniversary Emblem

**1995.** Air. World Campaign against Drug Trafficking. Multicoloured.
2060 330 p. Type **789** .. .. 40 20
2061 330 p. Manacled hands (horiz) .. .. 40 20

**1995.** Air. 25th Anniv of Andean Development Corporation.
2062 **790** 650 p. multicoloured .. 80 40

792 Madre-Monte

**1995.** Air. Myths and Legends. Multicoloured.
2065 750 p. Type **792** .. .. 90 45
2066 750 p. La Llorana .. 90 45
2067 750 p. El Mohan (river spirit) .. .. .. 90 45
2068 750 p. Alligator man .. 90 45

Nos. 2065/8 were issued together, se-tenant, in sheetlets in which the background colour gradually changes down the sheet; each design therefore occurs in four slightly different colours.

793 Holy Family

**1995.** Christmas. Stained Glass Windows from Chapel of the Apostles, Bogota School. Multicoloured.
2069 220 p. Type **793** (postage) 25 15
2070 330 p. Nativity (air) .. 40 20

794 Asuncion Silva

**1996.** Air. Death Centenary of Jose Asuncion Silva (poet).
2071 **794** 400 p. multicoloured .. 50 25

795 Painting by Luz Maria Tobon Mesa

796 Salavarrieta (after Jose Maria Espinosa)

**1996.** Air. Providence Island.
2072 **795** 800 p. multicoloured .. 1·00 50

**1996.** Air. Birth Bicentenary of Policarpa Salavarrieta.
2073 **796** 900 p. multicoloured .. 1·10 55

797 De Greiff (Ricardo Rendon)

**1996.** 1st Death Anniv of Leon De Greiff (poet).
2074 **797** 400 p. black .. .. 50 25

PRIVATE AIR COMPANIES

The "LANSA" and Avianca Companies operated inland and foreign air mail services on behalf of the Government and issued the following stamps. Later only the Avianca Company performed this service and the regular air stamps were used on the mail without overprints.

**Similar issues were also made by Compania Colombiana de Navegacion Aerea during 1920. These are very rare and will be found listed in the Stanley Gibbons Stamp Catalogue, Part 20 (South America).**

A. "LANSA" (Lineas Aereas Nacionales Sociedad Anonima).

**1.** Wing.

**1950.** Air.
1. **1.** 5 c. yellow .. .. .. 15 10
2. 10 c. red .. .. .. 25 15
3. 15 c. blue .. .. .. 25 10
4. 20 c. green .. .. .. 40 25
5. 30 c. purple .. .. 1·25 1·25
6. 60 c. brown .. .. 1·50 1·75

With background network colours in brackets.
7 **1** 1 p. grey (buff) .. .. 6·00 7·50
8 2 p. blue (green) .. .. 8·50 9·50
9 5 p. red (red) .. .. 29·00 29·00

The 1 p. was also issued without the network.

**1950.** Air. Nos. 691/7 and 700/3 optd **L.**
10. 5 c. yellow .. .. .. 15 10
11. 10 c. red .. .. .. 15 10
12. 15 c. blue .. .. .. 15 10
13. 20 c. violet .. .. 15 10
14. 30 c. green .. .. .. 15 15
15. 40 c. grey .. .. .. 3·50 15
16. 50 c. red .. .. .. 55 15
17. 1 p. purple and green .. 4·25 1·75
18. 2 p. blue and green .. 8·50 3·25
19. 3 p. black and red .. .. 8·50 9·50
20. 5 p. turquoise & sepia .. 28·00 28·00

**1951.** As Nos. 696/703 but colours changed and optd **L.**
21. 40 c. orange .. .. .. 90 55
22. 50 c. blue .. .. .. 90 55
23. 60 c. grey .. .. .. 90 45
24. 80 c. red .. .. .. 75 45
25. 1 p. red and vermilion .. 3·75 3·75
26. 2 p. blue and red .. .. 4·50 4·50
27. 3 p. green and brown .. 8·25 7·25
28. 5 p. grey and yellow .. 21·00 23·00

B. Avianca Company.

**1950.** Air. Nos. 691/703 optd. **A.**
1 5 c. yellow .. .. .. 10 10
2 10 c. red .. .. .. 15 10
3 15 c. blue .. .. .. 10 10
4 20 c. violet .. .. 20 10
5 30 c. green .. .. .. 15 10
6 40 c. grey .. .. 45 10
7 50 c. red .. .. .. 25 10
8 60 c. olive .. .. .. 75 15
9 80 c. brown .. .. 1·40 15
10 1 p. purple and green .. 1·60 15
11 2 p. blue and green .. 5·00 1·60
12 3 p. black and red .. .. 8·50 7·50
13 5 p. turquoise and sepia .. 25·00 22·00

**1951.** Air. As Nos. 696/703 but colours changed and optd **A**.
14. 40 c. orange .. .. 4·50 25
15. 50 c. blue .. .. .. 6·25 25
16. 60 c. grey .. .. .. 1·75 15
17. 80 c. red .. .. .. 60 15
18. 1 p. red and vermilion .. 2·10 15
19. 1 p. brown and green .. 2·25 35
20. 2 p. blue and red .. .. 2·10 35
21. 3 p. green and brown .. 4·50 90
22. 5 p. grey and yellow .. 8·25 90

The 60 c. also comes with the A in the centre.

**All values except the 2 p. and 3 p. exist without the overprint.**

ACKNOWLEDGMENT OF RECEIPT STAMPS

AR **60**.

AR **100**.

**1894.**
AR 169. AR **60.** 5 c. red .. 2·50 2·10

**1902.** Similar to Type AR **60**. Imperf. or perf.
AR 265. 5 c. blue .. .. 12·00 12·00
AR 211. 10 c. blue on blue .. 90 90

**1903.** No. 197 optd. **Habilitado Medellin A R.**
AR 258. **75.** 10 c. black on pink 13·00

**1904.** No. 262 optd. **A R.**
AR 266. **75.** 5 c. red .. .. 21·00 21·00

**1904.**
AR 290. AR **100.** 5 c. blue .. 7·50 3·50

AR **106.** A. Gomez.

AR **117.** Map of Colombia.

**1910.**
AR 354. AR **106.** 5 c. grn. & orge. 6·00 15·00

**1917.** Inscr. "AR".
AR 371. **123.** 4 c. brown .. 7·50 6·50
AR 372. AR **117.** 5 c. brown .. 5·00 4·00

OFFICIAL STAMPS

**1937.** Optd. **OFICIAL.**
O 496. – 1 c. green (No. 429) 10 10
O 497. **137.** 2 c. red (No. 430) .. 20 20
O 498. – 5 c. brown (No. 431) 10 10
O 499. – 10 c. orge. (No. 485) 25 20
O 500. **156.** 12 c. blue .. .. 90 25
O 501. **141.** 20 c. blue .. .. 1·40 65
O 502. **110.** 30 c. bistre .. .. 2·10 65
O 503. **123.** 40 c. brown .. 13·00 8·50
O 504. **112.** 50 c. red .. .. 1·75 80
O 505. **110.** 1 p. blue .. .. 14·00 6·00
O 506. 2 p. orange .. .. 15·00 6·00
O 507. 5 p. grey .. .. 50·00 50·00
O 508. **57.** 10 p. brown .. £110 £110

REGISTRATION STAMPS

R **12.**

R **32.**

**1865.** Imperf.
R 42. R **12.** 5 c. black .. .. 90·00 45·00

**1865.** Type similar to R **12**, but letter "R" in star. Imperf.
R 43. 5 c. black .. .. £100 50·00

**1870.** Imperf.
R 73. R **32.** 5 c. black .. .. 2·50 2·50

**1870.** Type similar to R 32 but with "R" in centre and inscr "REJISTRO". Imperf.
R 74. 5 c. black .. .. 1·10 90

**1881.** **Eagle and arms in oval frame, inscr. "RECOMENDADA" at foot. Imperf. or pin-perf.**
R 105. 10 c. lilac .. .. 30·00 30·00

R **42.**

R **48.**

**1883.** Perf.
R 117. R **42.** 10 c. red on orge... 80 1·00

**1899.**
R 141. R **48.** 10 c. red .. .. 5·00 3·50
R 166. 10 c. brown .. 1·40 75

R **85.**

**1902.** Imperf. or perf.
R 264. R **85.** 10 c. purple .. 4·00 4·00
R 207. 20 c. red on blue .. 80 80
R 208. 20 c. blue on blue .. 1·25 1·25

R **94.**

**1902.** Perf.
R 257 R **94.** 10 c. purple .. 19·00 19·00

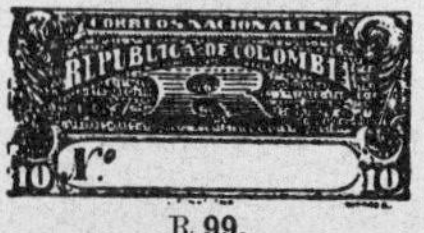

R **99.**

**1904.**
R 289. R **99.** 10 c. purple .. 13·00 35

R 105. Execution of 24th Feb., 1810.

**1910.**

R 353. R 105. 10 c. blk. & red .. 20·00 50·00

R 114. Puerto Colombia.

**1917.**

R 369. R 114. 4 c. blue & green 35 3·25
R 370. – 10 c. blue .. 7·50 25
DESIGN: 10 c. Tequendama Falls.

R 127.

**1925.**

R 409. R 127. (10 c.) blue .. 9·50 1·75

**1932.** Air. Air stamps of 1932 optd. **R.**

R 426. 132. 20 c. red .. .. 6·00 4·25
R 450. – 20 c. grn. & red (439) 6·00 75

SPECIAL DELIVERY STAMPS

E 118. Express Messenger.

**1917.**

E 373. E 118. 5 c. green .. 5·00 4·25

E 310.

**1958.** Air.

E 936. E 310. 25 c. red & blue.. 25 15

**1959.** Air. Unification of Air Mail Rates. Optd. **UNIFICADO** within outline of aeroplane.

E 989. E 310. 25 c. red & blue.. 45 10

E 361. Boeing 720B on Back of "Express" Letter.

**1963.** Air.

E 1143. E 361. 50 c. blk. & red 20 10

**1966.** Air. "History of Colombian Aviation" As T 372. Inscr. "EXPRESO". Mult.

E1168 80 c. Boeing 727 jet liner (1966) .. .. 10 15

E 647 Numeral

**1987.**

E1783 E 647 25 p. green & red 25 15
E1784 30 p. green & red 25 15

E 663 "Istiaophorus americanus"

**1988.** No Value expressed.

E1805 E 663 (A) blue .. 2·25 1·10
E1806 (B) blue .. 75 10

E 724 Isidor's Eagle

E 738 Postman climbing out of Envelope

**1992.** No value expressed. Multicoloured.

E1926 B (200 p.) Type E 724 30 15
E1927 A (950 p.) Spectacled bear .. .. .. 2·50 75

**1992.** World Post Day. No value expressed.

E1951 E 738 B (200 p.) mult .. 35 20

E 741 "Three Musicians"

**1993.** Fernando Botero (painter) Commemoration. No value expressed.

E1955 E 741 B multicoloured .. 35 20

E 743 Parading "Virgin of the Sorrows"

**1993.** Popayan Holy Week. No value expressed.

E1957 E 743 B multicoloured .. 35 20

E 744 Mother and Child

E 745 Mother House, Pasto

**1993.** 90th Anniv of Pan-American Health Organization. No value expressed.

E1958 E 744 B multicoloured .. 35 20

**1993.** Centenary of Franciscan Convent of Mary Immaculate. No value expressed.

E1959 E 745 B multicoloured .. 35 20

E 746 Stamps, Magnifying Glass and Tweezers

E 747 Cano

**1993.** 18th National Stamp Exhibition. No value expressed.

E1960 E 746 B multicoloured .. 35 20

**1993.** 7th Death Anniv of Guillermo Cano (newspaper editor).

E1961 E 747 250 p. mult .. 40 20

**1993.** Tourism. As T 756. Multicoloured.

E1996 250 p. Otun Lake (vert) 35 20

E 758 Marie Poussepin (founder)

E 761 Biplane

**1994.** Order of Sisters of the Presentation.

E1998 E 758 300 p. mult .. 45 25

**1994.** 75th Anniv of Airforce.

E2004 E 761 300 p. mult .. 45 25

**1994.** 4th Latin American Presidential Summit, Cartagena. As T 764. Multicoloured.

E2010 300 p. Setting sun over harbour walls .. 45 25

E 769 Emblem

**1994.** International Year of The Family.

E2016 E 769 300 p. mult .. 40 20

**1994.** American Postal Transport. As T 770. Multicoloured.

E2018 300 p. Men carrying "stamps" depicting van, ship and aircraft 40 20

**1994.** Christmas. As T 773. Multicoloured.

E2022 300 p. Nativity .. 40 20

E 777 Championship Advertising Poster and Gold Ornament

**1995.** B.M.X. World Championship, Melgar.

E2029 E 777 400 p. mult .. 55 30

E 785 Bicycle

**1995.** World Cycling Championships, Bogota and Boyaca.

E2056 E 785 400 p. mult .. 50 25

E 791 Hands protecting Lake and Fish

**1995.** America. Environmental Protection. Multicoloured.

E2063 400 p. Type E 791 .. 50 25
E2064 400 p. Hands protecting tree .. .. .. 50 25

TOO LATE STAMPS

L 47.

L 59.

**1888.** Perf.

L 136. L 47. 2½ c. blk. on lilac.. 4·00 1·50

**1892.** Perf.

L 167. L 59. 2½ c. blue on red .. 4·00 3·25

L 86.

L 107.

**1902.** Imperf. or perf.

L 209. L 86. 5 c. violet on red.. 45 45

**1914.** Perf.

L 355. L 107. 2 c. brown .. 8·50 6·00
L 356. 5 c. green .. 8·50 6·00

## COMORO ISLANDS Pt. 6; Pt. 12

An archipelago N.W. of Madagascar comprising Anjouan, Great Comoro, Mayotte and Moheli. A French colony from 1891. Mayotte became an Overseas Department of France in December 1974, the remaining islands forming the Independent State of Comoro.

100 centimes = 1 franc

1. Anjouan Bay.

2. Native Woman.

6. Mutsamudu Village.

**1950.**

1. 1. 10 c. blue (postage) .. 15 25
2. 50 c. green .. .. 15 25
3. 1 f. brown.. .. .. 15 25
4. 2. 2 f. green .. .. .. 40 30
5. – 5 f. violet .. .. .. 45 40
6. 6 f. purple.. .. .. 55 50
7. – 7 f. red .. .. .. 55 50
8. – 10 f. green .. .. .. 65 60
9. – 11 f. blue .. .. .. 70 70
10. – 15 f. brown .. .. 1·10 95
11. – 20 f. lake .. .. .. 1·50 1·40
12. – 40 f. indigo and blue .. 19·00 12·50
13. 6. 50 f. lake and green (air).. 2·25 1·25
14. – 100 f. brown and red .. 3·00 2·50
15. – 200 f. lake, grn. & violet.. 14·50 8·50

DESIGNS (as Type 1)—HORIZ. 7 f., 10 f., 11 f. Mosque at Moroni. 40 f. Coelacanth. VERT. 15 f., 20 f. Ouani Mosque, Anjouan. (As Type 6)—HORIZ. 100 f. Natives and Mosque de Vendredi. 200 f. Ouani Mosque, Anjouan (different).

**1952.** Military Medal Cent. As T 48 of Cameroun.

16. 15 f. blue, yellow and green 26·00 32·00

**1954.** Air. 10th Anniv. of Liberation As T. 52 of Cameroun.

17. 15 f. red and brown .. 19·00 20·00

9. Village Pump.

**1956.** Economic and Social Development Fund.

18. 9. 9 f. violet .. .. 1·00 1·00

10. "Human Rights".

**1958.** 10th Anniv. of Declaration of Human Rights.

19 10 20 f. green and blue .. 8·00 8·25

**1959.** Tropical Flora. As T 56 of French Equatorial Africa. Multicoloured.

20 10 f. "Colvillea" (horiz) .. 3·50 2·75

11. Radio Station, Dzaoudzi.

**1960.** Inaug. of Comoro Broadcasting Service.

21. 11. 20 f. grn., violet & red .. 1·25 90
22. – 25 f. green, brown & blue 1·40 1·00

DESIGN: 25 f. Radio mast and map.

12. Bull-mouth Helmet.

12a. Giant Clam.

**1962.** Multicoloured. (a) Postage. Sea Shells.

23 50 c. Type 12 .. .. 1·10 90
24 1 f. Common harp .. .. 1·10 90
25 2 f. Ramose murex .. 2·25 1·60
26 5 f. Giant green turban .. 2·75 2·50
27 20 f. Scorpion conch .. 8·50 7·50
28 25 f. Trumpet triton .. 12·00 9·50

(b) Air. Marine plants.

29 100 f. Type 12a .. .. 8·50 8·00
30 500 f. Stoney coral .. 26·00 18·00

**1962.** Malaria Eradication. As T 70 of Cameroun.

31. 25 f.+5 f. red .. .. 2·75 2·75

**1962.** Air. 1st Trans-Atlantic T.V. Satellite Link. As Type F 23 of Andorra.

32. 25 f. mauve, purple & violet 4·50 2·50

14. Emblem in Hands and Globe.

14a. Centenary Emblem.

**1963.** Freedom from Hunger.

33 14 20 f. green and brown .. 3·75 3·25

**1963.** Red Cross Cent.

34. 14a. 50 f. red, grey and green .. .. 6·50 5·00

15. Globe and Scales of Justice.

**1963.** 15th Anniv. of Declaration of Human Rights.

35. 15. 15 f. green and red .. 6·50 5·50

16. Tobacco Pouch.

17. Pirogue.

**1963.** Handicrafts. (a) Postage as T 17.

36. 16. 3 f. ochre, red & green.. 60 60
37. – 4 f. myrtle, purple & orge. 75 75
38. – 10 f. brown grn. & chest. 1·40 1·40

(b) Air. Size 27 × 48 mm.

39. – 65 f. red, brown & green 3·50 2·50
40. – 200 f. pink, red & turq... 7·00 4·00

DESIGNS: 4 f. Perfume-burner. 10 f. Lamp bracket. 65 f. Baskets. 200 f. Filigree pendant.

**1964.** "PHILATEC 1964" Int. Stamp Exn., Paris. As T 528 of France.

41. 50 f. red, green and blue .. 3·50 3·25

**1964.** Native Craft. Multicoloured.

42. 15 f. Type 17 (postage) .. 1·75 1·75
43. 30 f. Boutre felucca.. .. 3·75 3·75
44. 50 f. Mayotte pirogue (air) 3·00 1·40
45. 85 f. Schooner .. .. 4·25 2·40

Nos. 44/5 are larger, 27 × 48½ mm.

18. Boxing (Ancient bronze plaque).

19. Medal.

**1964.** Air. Olympic Games, Tokyo.

46. 18. 100 f. grn., brown & choc. 6·00 6·00

**1964.** Air. Star of Grand Comoro.

47. 19. 500 f. multicoloured .. 15·00 11·50

20. "Syncom" Communications Satellite, Telegraph Poles and Morse Key.

21. Hammer-head Shark.

22. Lake Sale.

**1965.** Air. Centenary of I.T.U.

48 20 50 f. blue, green and grey 15·00 13·00

**1965.** Marine Life.

49. – 1 f. green, orange & violet 65 45
50. 21. 12 f. black, blue and red 1·40 90
51. – 20 f. red and green .. 1·90 1·25
52. – 25 f. brown, red and green 3·25 1·90

DESIGNS—VERT. 1 f. Spiny lobster. 25 f. Grouper. HORIZ. 20 f. Scaly turtle.

**1966.** Air. Launching of 1st French Satellite. As Nos. 1696/7 of France.

53 25 f. lilac, blue and violet .. 3·25 3·25
54 30 f. lilac, violet and blue .. 4·50 4·50

**1966.** Air. Launching of Satellite "D1". As T 569 of France.

55. 30 f. purple, green & orange 2·75 2·25

**1966.** Comoro Views. Multicoloured.

56. 15 f. Type 22 (postage) .. 75 55
57. 25 f. Itsandra Hotel, Moroni 1·00 65
58. 50 f. The Battery, Dzaoudzi (air) .. .. .. 3·00 2·25
59. 200 f. Ksar Fort, Mutsamudu (vert.) .. .. .. 6·50 3·75

Nos. 58/9 are larger, 48 × 27 mm. and 27 × 48 mm. respectively.

23. Anjouan Sunbird.

24. Nurse tending Child.

**1967.** Birds. Multicoloured.

60. 2 f. Type 23 (postage) .. 3·50 2·00
61. 10 f. Malachite kingfisher .. 5·25 2·75
62. 15 f. Mascarene fody .. 7·50 4·00
63. 30 f. Courol .. .. 17·00 9·00
64. 75 f. Madagascar paradise flycatcher (air) .. .. 11·50 6·25
65. 100 f. Blue-cheeked bee eater .. .. .. 17·00 9·00

Nos. 64/5 are vert. and also larger 27 × 48 mm.

**1967.** Comoro Red Cross.

66. 24. 25 f.+5 f. purple, red and green .. .. 1·75 1·75

25. Slalom Skiing.

26. Bouquet, Sun and W.H.O. Emblem.

**1968.** Air. Winter Olympic Games, Grenoble.

67. 25. 70 f. brown, blue & green 3·75 2·50

**1968.** 20th Anniv of W.H.O.

68 26 40 f. red, violet and green 1·50 1·25

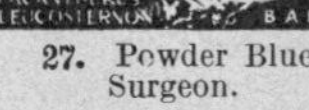

27. Powder Blue Surgeon.

28. Human Rights Emblem.

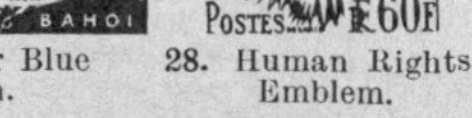

**1968.** Fishes.

69. 27. 20 f. blue, yellow and red (postage) .. .. 2·40 2·40
70. – 25 f. blue, orge. & turq. 3·00 3·00
71. – 50 f. ochre, blue & purple (air) .. .. .. 5·00 2·75
72. – 90 f. ochre, grn. & emer. 7·00 3·75

DESIGNS: 25 f. Imperial Angelfish. LARGER 48 × 27 mm. 50 f. Moorish Idol. 90 f. Yellow-banded sweetlips.

**1968.** Human Rights Year.

73. 28. 60 f. green, brown & orge. 2·75 2·75

29. Swimming.

**1968.** Air. Olympic Games, Mexico.

74. 29. 65 f. multicoloured .. 3·25 2·25

30. Prayer Mat and Worshipper.

**1969.** Msoila Prayer Mats.

75. 30. 20 f. red, green and violet 75 50
76. – 30 f. green, violet and red 1·00 75
77. – 45 f. violet, red and green 2·00 1·50

DESIGNS: As Type 30, but worshipper stooping (30 f.) or kneeling upright (45 f.).

31. Vanilla Flower.

**1969.** Flowers. Multicoloured.

78. 10 f. Type 31 (postage) .. 1·00 75
79. 15 f. Ylang-ylang blossom 1·00 75
80. 50 f. "Heliconia" (air) .. 3·25 2·25
81. 85 f. Tuberose .. .. 4·00 2·75
82. 200 f. Orchid .. .. 7·50 4·50

Nos. 80/2 are vert., size 27 × 49 mm.

32. Concorde in Flight.

**1969.** Air. 1st Flight of Concorde.

83 32 100 f. purple and brown 13·00 10·00

33. I.L.O. Building, Geneva.

**1969.** 50th Anniv. of I.L.O.

84. 33. 5 f. grey, green & orange 75 50

34. Poinsettia.

35. "EXPO" Panorama.

**1970.** Flowers.

85. 34. 25 f. multicoloured .. 2·00 1·00

**1970.** New U.P.U. Headquarters Building, Berne. As T 156 of Cameroun.

86. 65 f. brown, green and violet 3·00 2·25

**1970.** Air. World Fair "EXPO 70", Osaka, Japan. Multicoloured.

87. 60 f. Type 35 .. .. 2·50 1·50
88. 90 f. Geisha and map of Japan .. .. .. 3·00 1·50

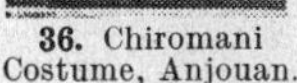
**36.** Chiromani Costume, Anjouan.

**37.** Mosque de Vendredi, Moroni.

**1970.** Comoro Costumes. Multicoloured.
89. 20 f. Type **36** .. .. 1·00 75
90. 25 f. Bouiboui, Great Comoro 1·50 75

**1970.**
91. **37.** 5 f. turq., green and red 50 50
92. 10 f. violet, green & purple 75 75
93. 40 f. brn., green and red 1·50 1·00

**38.** Great Egret.

**1971.** Birds. Multicoloured.
94. 5 f. Type **38** .. .. .. 1·10 90
95. 10 f. Comoro olive pigeon .. 1·25 90
96. 15 f. Green heron .. .. 1·60 1·25
97. 25 f. Comoro blue pigeon .. 2·75 1·50
98. 35 f. Humblot's flycatcher 4·25 2·75
99. 40 f. Allen's gallinule .. 6·75 3·25

**39.** Sunset, Moutsamoudou (Anjouan).

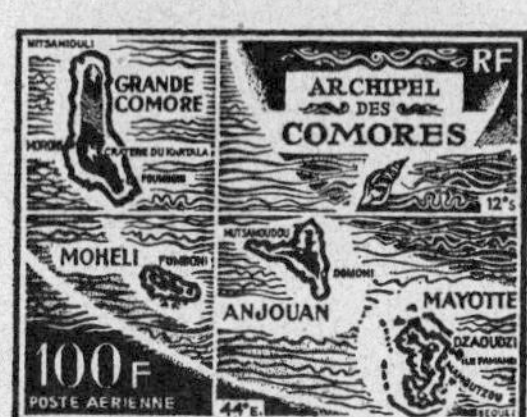

**40.** Map of Comoro Archipelago.

**1971.** Air. Comoro Landscapes. Mult.
100. **39.** 15 f. multicoloured .. 50 25
101. 20 f. multicoloured .. 75 50
102. – 65 f. multicoloured .. 2·00 1·00
103. – 85 f. multicoloured .. 2·50 1·50
104. **40.** 100 f. brn., grn. & blue 6·00 3·50
DESIGNS—(As Type **39**). 20 f. Sada village (Mayotte). 65 f. Ruined palace, Iconi (Great Comoro). 85 f. Off-shore islands, Moumatchoua (Moheli).
See also Nos. 124/8, 132/6, 157/60 and 168/71.

**41.** " Pyrostegia venusta ".

**1971.** Tropical Plants. Multicoloured.
105. 1 f. Type **41** (postage) .. 50 50
106. 3 f. " Allamanda cathartica " (horiz.) .. .. 75 50
107. 20 f. " Plumeria rubra " .. 2·50 1·50
108. 60 f. " Hibiscus schizopetalous " (air) .. .. 2·25 2·00
109. 85 f. " Acalypha sanderii " 5·00 3·00
The 60 and 85 f. are 27 × 48 mm.

**42.** Lithograph Cone.

**1971.** Sea Shells. Mudlticoloured.
110 5 f. Type **42** .. .. 55 50
111 10 f. Lettered cone .. 85 60
112 20 f. Princely cone .. 1·40 1·10
113 35 f. Polished nerite .. 2·75 1·10
114 60 f. Serpent's-head cowrie 4·50 1·60

**1971.** 1st Death Anniv. of Charles de Gaulle. Designs as Nos. 1937 and 1940 of France.
115. 20 f. black and purple .. 2·00 1·50
116. 35 f. black and purple .. 2·50 2·00

**44.** Mural, Airport Lounge.

**1972.** Air. Inaug. of New Airport, Moroni.
117. **44.** 65 f. multicoloured .. 1·00 50
118. – 85 f. multicoloured .. 1·50 50
119. – 100 f. green, brn & blue 2·50 1·50
DESIGNS: 85 f. Mural similar to T **44**. 100 f. Airport buildings.

**45.** Eiffel Tower, Paris, and Telecommunications Centre, Moroni.

**1972.** Air. Inauguration of Paris–Moroni Radio-Telephone Link.
120 **45** 35 f. red, purple & blue 1·00 50
121 – 75 f. red, violet and blue 1·50 50
DESIGN: 75 f. Telephone conversation.

**46.** Underwater Spear-fishing.

**1972.** Air. Aquatic Sports.
122 **46** 70 f. red, green and blue 4·25 3·00

**47.** Pasteur, Crucibles and Microscope.

**1972.** 150th Birth Anniv. of Louis Pasteur.
123. **47.** 65 f. blue, brn. & orge. 3·50 2·25

**1972.** Air. Anjouan Landscapes. (a) As T **39**. Multicoloured.
124. 20 f. Fortress wall, Cape Sima 50 25
125. 35 f. Bambao Palace .. 75 50
126. 40 f. Palace, Domoni .. 1·00 50
127. 60 f. Gomajou Island .. 2·00 1·00

(b). As T **40**.
128. – 100 f. grn., blue & brn. 4·50 3·00
DESIGN: 100 f. Map of Anjouan.

**48.** Pres. Said Mohamed Cheikh.

**50.** Bank.

**1973.** Air. Said Mohamed Cheikh, President of Comoro Council, Commem.
129. **48.** 20 f. multicoloured .. 75 50
130. 35 f. multicoloured .. 1·00 75

**1973.** Air. Int. Coelacanth Study Expedition. No. 72 surch. **Mission Internationale pour l'etude du Coelacanthe** and value.
131. 120 f. on 90 f. brn., grn. & emerald .. .. .. 6·00 4·00

**1973.** Great Comoro Landscapes. (a) **Postage.** As T **39**. Multicoloured.
132. 10 f. Goulaivoini .. .. 75 25
133. 20 f. Mitsamiouli .. 1·00 50
134. 35 f. Foumbouni .. .. 1·50 1·00
135. 50 f. Moroni .. .. 2·00 1·50

(b) Air. As Type **40**.
136. – 135 f. pur., grn. & violet 6·00 3·50
DESIGN—VERT. 135 f. Map of Great Comoro.

**1973.** Moroni Buildings. Multicoloured.
137. 5 f. Type **50** .. .. 50 50
138. 15 f. Post Office .. .. 75 75
139. 20 f. Prefecture .. .. 1·00 1·00

**51.** Volcanic Eruption.

**1973.** Air. Karthala Volcanic Eruption (Sept. 1972).
140. **51.** 120 f. multicoloured .. 5·50 3·75

**52.** Dr. G. A. Hansen.

**54.** Zaouiyat Chaduli Mosque.

**53.** Pablo Picasso (artist).

**1973.** Air. Centenary of Hansen's Identification of Leprosy Bacillus.
141. **52.** 100 f. grn., pur. & blue 3·50 2·00

**1973.** Air. 500th Birth Anniv of Nicolas Copernicus. As T **52**.
142 150 f. purple, blue and ultramarine .. .. 4·50 3·00
DESIGN: 150 f. Copernicus and Solar System.

**1973.** Air. Picasso Commem.
143. **53.** 200 f. multicoloured .. 7·00 4·50

**1973.** Mosques. Multicoloured.
145. 20 f. Type **54** .. .. 1·00 1·00
146. 35 f. Salimata Hamissi Mosque (horiz.) .. .. 2·00 1·00

**55.** Star and Ribbon.

**56.** Said Omar Ben Soumeth (Grand Mufti of the Comoros).

**1974.** Air. Order of the Star of Anjouan.
147. **55.** 500 f. gold, blue & brown 9·00 7·50

**1974.** Air. Multicoloured.
148. 135 f. Type **56** .. .. 2·75 1·00
149. 200 f. Ben Soumeth seated (vert.) .. .. .. 3·75 2·50

## INDEX

Countries can be quickly located by referring to the index at the end of this volume.

**57.** Doorway of Mausoleum.

**58.** Wooden Combs.

**1974.** Mausoleum of Shaikh Said Mohamed.
150. **57.** 35 f. brn., blk. & grn... 1·25 1·00
151. – 50 f. brn., blk. & grn... 2·00 1·00
DESIGN: 50 f. Mausoleum.

**1974.** Comoro Handicrafts (1st series). Mult.
152. 15 f. Type **58** .. .. 75 50
153. 20 f. Three-legged table .. 1·00 50
154. 35 f. Koran lectern (horiz.) 1·50 1·00
155. 75 f. Sugar-cane press (horiz.) 3·00 1·75
See also Nos. 164/7.

**59.** Mother and Child.

**1974.** Comoros Red Cross Fund.
156. **59.** 35 f. + 10 f. brn. & red .. 1·00 1·00

**1974.** Air. Mayotte Landscapes. (a) As T **39**. Multicoloured.
157. 20 f. Moya beach .. .. 50 25
158. 35 f. Chiconi .. .. 75 25
159. 90 f. Mamutzu harbour .. 2·25 1·50

(b). As T **40**.
160. 120 f. green and blue .. 5·00 2·75
DESIGN:—VERT. 120 f. Map of Mayotte.

**60.** U.P.U. Emblem and Globe.

**1974.** Centenary of Universal Postal Union.
161. **60.** 30 f. red, brown & green 1·25 1·25

**61.** Boeing 707 taking off.

**1975.** Inauguration of Direct Moroni-Hahaya-Paris Air Service.
162. **61.** 135 f. blue, green and red 5·00 3·50

**62.** Rotary Emblem, Moroni Clubhouse and Map.

**1975.** Air. 70th Anniv. of Rotary International and 10th Anniv. of Moroni Rotary Club.
163. **62.** 250 f. multicoloured .. 7·00 5·00

**63.** Bracelet.

**1975.** Comoro Handicrafts (2nd series).
164. **63.** 20 f. brown and purple 75 50
165. – 35 f. brown and green .. 1·00 75
166. – 120 f. brown and blue .. 3·50 2·50
167. – 135 f. brown and red .. 5·00 3·00
DESIGNS: 35 f. Diadem. 120 f. Sabre. 125 f. Dagger.

**1975.** Moheli Landscapes (a) Postage As T **39**. Multicoloured.
168. 30 f. Mohani Village .. 1·25 75
169. 50 f. Djoezi Village .. 1·75 1·00
170. 55 f. Chirazian tombs .. 2·50 1·50

(b) Air. As T **40**.
171. 230 f. grn., blue & brown .. 7·00 4·50
DESIGN: 230 f. Map of Moheli.

64. Coelacanth and Skin-diver.

**1975.** Coelacanth Expedition.
172. **64.** 50 f. bistre, blue & brn. 3·75 2·50

65. Tambourine-player.

**1976.** Folklore Dances. Multicoloured.
173. 100 f. Type **65** .. .. 22·00 22·00
174. 150 f. Dancers with tambourines .. .. 22·00 22·00

66. Athlete and Athens 1896 Motifs.

**1976.** Olympic Games – Munich (1972) and Montreal (1976). Multicoloured.
175. 20 f. Type **66** (postage) .. 15 10
176. 25 f. Running .. .. 15 10
177. 40 f. Athlete and Paris 1900 motif .. .. 25 15
178. 75 f. High-jumping .. 45 20
179. 100 f. Exercises and World's Fair, St. Louis 1904 motif (air) .. 55 35
180. 500 f. Gymnast on bars .. 3·25 1·40

67. Government House, Flag and Map.

**1976.** 1st Anniv. of Independence. Mult.
182. **67.** 30 f. multicoloured .. 25 15
183. 50 f. multicoloured .. 35 20

68. Agricultural Scene and U.N. Stamp.

**1976.** 25th Anniv. of U.N. Postal Services. Multicoloured.
184 15 f. Type **68** (postage) .. 10 10
185 30 f. Surgery scene and U.N. W.H.O. stamp .. 20 10
186 50 f. Village scene and U.N.I.C.E.F. stamp .. 75 40
187 75 f. Telecommunications satellite and U.N. I.T.U. stamp .. .. 45 20
188 200 f. Concorde, airship "Graf Zeppelin" and U.N. I.C.A.O. stamp (air) .. .. 2·50 85
189 400 f. Lufthansa jet airliner and U.N. U.P.U. stamp 3·00 1·40

69. Copernicus, and Rocket on Launch-pad. 70. U.N. Headquarters, New York and Flags.

**1976.** "Success of Operation Viking", and Bicent. of American Revolution. Mult.
191. 5 f. Type **69** (postage) .. 10 10
192. 10 f. Einstein, Sagan and Young (horiz.) .. 10 10
193. 25 f. "Viking" orbiting Mars 15 10
194. 35 f. Vikings' discovery of America (horiz.) .. 30 15
195. 100 f. U.S. flag and Mars landing .. .. 65 30
196. 500 f. First colour photograph of Martian terrain (horiz.) (air) .. .. 3·00 1·25

**1976.** 1st Anniv. of Comoro Islands Admission to United Nations.
198. **70.** 40 f. multicoloured .. 30 20
199. 50 f. multicoloured .. 40 25

71. President Lincoln and Bombardment of Fort Sumter.

**1976.** Bicent. of American Revolution. Showing various battle scenes of American Civil War. Multicoloured.
200. 10 f. Type **71** (postage) .. 10 10
201. 30 f. General Beauregard and Bull Run (vert.) .. 20 10
202. 50 f. General Johnston and Antietam .. .. 30 15
203. 100 f. General Meade and Gettysburg (air) .. 55 30
204. 200 f. General Sherman and Chattanooga (vert.) .. 1·10 45
205. 400 f. General Pickett and Appomattox .. .. 2·25 90

72. Andean Condor. 74. Giffard's Dirigible, 1851 and French Locomotive, 1837.

73. Wolf.

**1976.** "Endangered Animals" (1st series). Multicoloured.
207. 15 f. Type **72** (postage) .. 1·75 55
208. 20 f. Tiger cat (horiz.) .. 25 15
209. 35 f. Leopard .. .. 30 15
210. 40 f. White rhinoceros (horiz.) .. .. 35 15
211. 75 f. Mountain nyala .. 60 15
212. 400 f. Orang-utan (horiz.) (air) .. .. 3·00 1·25

**1977.** "Endangered Animals" (2nd series). Multicoloured.
214. 10 f. Type **73** (postage) .. 10 10
215. 30 f. Aye-aye .. .. 20 10
216. 40 f. Banded duiker .. 25 15
217. 50 f. Giant tortoise .. 30 15
218. 200 f. Ocelot (air) .. .. 1·40 55
219. 400 f. Galapagos penguin .. 7·00 3·00

**1977.** History of Communications. **Airships** and Railways. Multicoloured.
221 20 f. Type **74** (postage) .. 20 10
222 25 f. Santos-Dumont's airship "Ballon No. 6" (1906) and Brazilian steam locomotive (19th century) .. .. 45 15
223 50 f. Russian airship "Astra" (1914) and Trans-Siberian Express (1905) .. .. 55 20
224 75 f. British airship R-34 (1919) and "Southern Belle" pullman express (1910–1925) .. .. 70 35
225 200 f. U.S. Navy airship "Los Angeles" (1930) and "Pacific" locomotive (1930) (air) .. .. 2·40 60
226 500 f. German airship "Hindenburg", 1933, and "Rheingold Express", 1933 .. .. .. 4·50 1·60

75. Koch, Morgan, Fleming, Muller and Waksman (medicine).

**1977.** Nobel Prize Winners. Multicoloured.
228 30 f. Type **75** (postage) .. 20 10
229 40 f. Michelson, Bragg, Raman and Zernike (physics) .. .. 20 15
230 50 f. Tagore, Yeats, Russell and Hemingway (literature) .. .. 30 15
231 100 f. Rontgen, Becquerel, Planck, Lawrence and Einstein (physics) .. 55 25
232 200 f. Ramsey and Marie Curie (chemistry), Banting and Hench (medicine) and Perrin (physics) (air) .. .. 1·40 45
233 400 f. Dunant, Briand, Schweitzer and Martin Luther King (peace) .. 2·50 90

The 200 f. wrongly attributes the chemistry prize to all those depicted and gives the date 1913 instead of 1911 for Marie Curie. On the 50 and 100 f. names are wrongly spelt.

76. "Clara, Ruben's Daughter".

**1977.** 400th Birth Anniv. of Peter Paul Rubens (1st issue). Multicoloured.
235. 20 f. Type **76** (postage) .. 10 10
236. 25 f. "Suzanne Fourment" 15 10
237. 50 f. "Venus in front of Mirror" .. .. 30 15
238. 75 f. "Ceres" .. .. 45 25
239. 200 f. "Young Girl with Blond Hair" (air) .. 1·40 95
240. 500 f. "Helene Fourment in Wedding Dress" .. 3·00 1·25
See also Nos. 407/10.

77. Queen Elizabeth II, Westminster Abbey and Guards.

**1977.** Air. Silver Jubilee of Queen Elizabeth II.
242. **77.** 500 f. multicoloured .. 3·00 1·40

79. Swordfish.

**1977.** Fish. Multicoloured.
256. 30 f. Type **79** (postage) .. 20 10
257. 40 f. Gaterin .. .. 30 15
258. 50 f. Scorpion fish .. 35 15
259. 100 f. "Chaetodon lunula" 60 25
260. 200 f. Amphiprion (air) .. 1·40 40
261. 400 f. Tetrodon .. .. 2·75 1·00

80. Jupiter Lander.

**1977.** Space Research. Multicoloured.
263. 30 f. Type **80** (postage) .. 20 10
264. 50 f. Uranus probe (vert.) 35 15
265. 75 f. Venus probe .. 45 20
266. 100 f. Space shuttle (vert.) 55 25
267. 200 f. "Viking 3" (air) .. 1·25 45
268. 400 f. "Apollo-Soyuz" link (vert.) .. .. 2·40 90

**1977.** Air. First Paris–New York Commercial Flight of "Concorde". No. 188 optd **Paris–New-York–22 nov. 1977.**
270 200 f. multicoloured .. 2·75 2·00

82. Allen's Gallinule.

**1978.** Birds. Multicoloured.
271. 15 f. Type **82** (postage) .. 45 25
272. 20 f. Blue-cheeked bee eater .. .. .. 65 35
273. 35 f. Malachite kingfisher 80 45
274. 40 f. Madagascar paradise flycatcher .. .. 90 55
275. 75 f. Anjouan sunbird .. 1·40 80
276. 400 f. Great egret (air) .. 6·25 3·75

83. Greek Ball Game and Modern Match.

**1978.** World Cup Football Championship, Argentina. Multicoloured.
278. 30 f. Type **83** (postage) .. 20 10
279. 50 f. Breton football .. 25 15
280. 75 f. 14th-century London game .. .. .. 45 25
281. 100 f. 18th-century Italian game .. .. 55 25
282. 200 f. 19th-century English game (air) .. .. 1·10 45
283. 400 f. English cup-tie, 1891 2·25 85

84. "Oswolt Krel".

**1978.** 450th Death Anniv of Albrecht Durer (artist) (1st issue). Multicoloured.
286. 20 f. Type **84** (postage) .. 10 10
287. 25 f. "Elspeth Tucher" 15 10
288. 50 f. "Hieronymus Holzshuher" .. .. 35 15
289. 75 f. "Young Girl" .. 50 25
290. 200 f. "Emperor Maximilian I" (air) .. 1·10 45
291. 500 f. "Young Girl" (detail) 2·75 1·10
See also Nos. 411/15.

85. Bach.

**1978.** Composers. Multicoloured.
293. 30 f. Type **85** (postage) .. 20 10
294. 40 f. Mozart .. .. 25 15
295. 50 f. Berlioz .. .. 35 15
296. 100 f. Verdi .. .. 55 25
297. 200 f. Tchaikovsky (air) .. 1·10 45
298. 400 f. Gershwin .. .. 2·25 85

Following a revolution on 13 May 1978, it was announced that sets showing Butterflies or commemorating the 25th Anniversary of the Coronation of Queen Elizabeth II, 10th World Telecommunications Day and Aviation History had not been placed on sale in the islands and were not valid for postage there.

**86.** Rowland Hill, Locomotive and Saxony 3 pf. Stamp, 1860.

**1978.** Death Centenary of Sir Rowland Hill. Multicoloured.

300. 20 f. Type **86** (postage) .. 80 50
301. 30 f. Penny-farthing and Netherlands 5 c. stamp, 1852 .. .. .. 20 10
302. 40 f. Early letter-box and 2 d. blue.. .. .. 25 15
303. 75 f. Pony Express and U.S. stamp, 1847 .. 45 20
304. 200 f. Airship and French 20 c. stamp, 1863 (air).. 1·50 65
305. 400 f. Postman and Basel 2½ r. stamp, 1845 .. 2·00 85

**87.** Interpreting Meteorological Satellite Photographs.

**1978.** European Space Agency. Multicoloured.

307 10 f. Type **87** (postage) .. 10 10
308 25 f. Writing weather forecast .. .. .. 15 10
309 35 f. Aiding wrecked ship 45 15
310 50 f. Telecommunications as teaching aid .. 35 15
311 100 f. Boeing 727 landing (air) .. .. .. 75 40
312 500 f. Space shuttle .. 2·75 1·10

**1978.** Argentina's Victory in World Cup Football Championship. Nos. 278/284 optd. **REP. FED. ISLAMIQUE DES COMORES, 1 ARGENTINE, 2 HOLLANDE, 3 BRESIL.**

314 **83** 30 f. multicoloured (postage) .. .. 20 10
315 – 50 f. multicoloured .. 35 15
316 – 75 f. multicoloured .. 45 20
317 – 100 f. multicoloured .. 50 25
318 – 200 f. multicoloured (air) 1·00 45
319 – 400 f. multicoloured .. 2·00 85

**89.** Philidor, Anderssen and Steinitz.

**1979.** Chess Grand Masters. Multicoloured.

321 40 f. Type **89** (postage) .. 20 10
322 100 f. Venetian players and pieces .. .. 45 20
323 500 f. Alekhine, Spassky and Fischer (air) .. 2·25 1·10

**90.** Galileo and " Voyager 1 ".

**1979.** Exploration of the Solar System. Mult.

324. 20 f. Type **90** (postage).. 10 10
325. 30 f. Kepler and " Voyager 2 " .. .. 15 10
326. 40 f. Copernicus and " Voyager 1 " .. .. 20 10
327. 100 f. Huygens and " Voyager 2 ".. .. 45 20
328. 200 f. Herschel and "Voyager 2" (air) .. 90 35
329. 400 f. Leverrier and " Voyager 2 ".. .. .. 1·90 80

**91.** Kayak.

**1979.** Olympic Games, Moscow (1980). Multicoloured.

330. 10 f. Type **91** (postage) .. 10 10
331. 25 f. Swimming .. .. 15 10
332. 35 f. Archery .. .. 20 10
333. 50 f. Pole vault .. .. 25 15
334. 75 f. Long jump .. .. 35 20
335. 500 f. High jump (air) .. 2·25 1·00

**92.** " Charaxes defulvata."

**1979.** Fauna. Multicoloured.

336. 30 f. Type **92** .. .. 50 15
337. 50 f. Courol .. .. 1·25 60
338. 75 f. Blue-cheeked bee eater .. .. .. 1·75 90

**1979.** Optd. or surch. **REPUBLIC FEDERALE ISLAMIQUE DES COMORES.**

(a) Birds, Nos. 271/275.

339. 15 f. Type **82** .. .. 40 40
340. 30 f on 35 f. Malachite kingfisher .. .. 70 70
341. 50 f. on 20 f. Blue-cheeked bee eater .. .. 1·10 1·10
342. 50 f. on 40 f. Madagascar paradise flycatcher .. 1·25 1·25
343. 200 f. on 75 f. Anjouan sunbird .. .. .. 3·25 3·25

(b) World Cup, Nos. 278/282.

344. 1 f. on 100 f. Italian game (postage) .. .. 10 10
345. 2 f. on 75 f. London game 10 10
346. 3 f on 30 f. Type **83** .. 10 10
347. 50 f. Breton football .. 35 35
348. 200 f. English game (air) .. 1·10 1·10

**1979.** Nos. 293/7 surch. or optd. **Republique Federale Islamique des Comores.**

349. – 5 f. on 100 f. Verdi (post.) 10 10
350. **85.** 30 f. J. S. Bach .. 25 25
351. – 40 f. Mozart .. .. 25 25
352. – 50 f. Berlioz .. .. 40 40
353. 50 f. on 200 f. Tchaikovsky (air) .. .. .. 40 40

**94.** State Coach.

**1979.** 25th Anniv. of Coronation of Queen Elizabeth II. Multicoloured.

354. 5 f. on 25 f. Type **94** (postage) .. .. .. 10 10
355. 10 f. Drum Major .. 15 15
356. 50 f. on 40 f. Queen carrying orb and sceptre .. 40 40
357. 100 f. St. Edward's Crown 80 80
358. 50 f. on 200 f. Herald reading Proclamation (air).. 35 35

Nos. 354/8 were only valid for postage overprinted as in Type **94**.

**95.** " Papilio dardanus-cenea stoll".

**1979.** Butterflies. Multicoloured.

359. 5 f. on 20 f. Type **95** .. 10 10
360. 15 f. " Papilio dardanus "–brown .. .. .. 15 15
361. 30 f. " Chrysiridia croesus " 40 30
362. 50 f. " Precis octavia " .. 80 70
363. 75 f. " Bunaea alcinoe ".. 1·25 1·00

Nos. 359/63 were only valid for postage overprinted as in Type **95**.

**96.** Otto Lilienthal and Glider.

**1979.** History of Aviation. Multicoloured.

364. 30 f. Type **96** (postage) .. 30 30
365. 50 f. Wright Brothers .. 50 50
366. 50 f. on 75 f. Louis Bleriot 50 50
367. 100 f. Claude Dornier .. 1·00 1·00
368. 200 f. Charles Lindbergh (air) .. .. .. 1·25 1·25

Nos. 364/8 were only valid for postage overprinted as in Type **96**.

**97.** Tobogganing.

**98.** Lychees.

**1979.** International Year of the Child. (1st issue). Multicoloured.

369. 20 f. Astronauts (postage) 10 10
370. 30 f. Type **97** .. .. 15 10
371. 40 f. Painting .. .. 20 10
372. 100 f. Locomotives .. 1·25 60
373. 200 f. Football (air) .. 90 35
374. 400 f. Canoeing .. .. 1·90 80

See also Nos. 389/90.

**1979.** Fruit. Multicoloured.

375. 60 f. Type **98** .. .. 40 15
376. 70 f. Papaws .. .. 45 20
377. 100 f. Avocado pears .. 55 30
378. 125 f. Bananas .. .. 65 35

**101.** Rotary Emblem and Village Scene.

**1979.** Air. Rotary International.

388. **101.** 400 f. multicoloured .. 3·00 1·40

**102.** Mother and Child on Boat.

**103.** Basketball.

**1979.** Air. International Year of the Child (2nd issue). Multicoloured.

389. 200 f.+30 f. Type **102** .. 1·40 1·40
390. 250 f. Mother and baby .. 1·40 70

**1979.** Indian Ocean Olympic Games.

391. **103.** 200 f. multicoloured .. 95 65



**1979.** Various stamps optd. **REPUBLIQUE FEDERALE ISLAMIQUE DES COMORES:**

(a) Air. Apollo–Soyuz Experiment (Appendix).

392. 100 f. Presidents Brezhnev and Ford with astronauts .. .. 45 45
393. 200 f. Space link-up .. 90 90

(b) Bicentenary of American Revolution (Appendix).

394. 25 f. Fremont, Kit Carson and dancing Indian .. 15 15
395. 35 f. D. Boone, Buffalo Bill and wagon train .. 20 20
396. 35 f. H. Wells, W. Fargo and stagecoach ambush 40 40

(c) Winter Olympic Games, Innsbruck (Appendix).

397. 35 f. Speed skating .. 20 20

(d) Telephone Centenary (Appendix).

398. 75 f. Philip Reis .. .. 40 40

(e) Air. Olympic Games, Munich and Montreal.

399. 100 f. mult. (No. 179) (air) 45 45

(f) U.N. Postal Services.

400. 75 f. mult. (No. 187) .. 40 40

(g) Endangered Animals.

401. 35 f. mult. (No. 209) .. 30 20
402. 40 f. mult. (No. 210) .. 40 25

(h) Nobel Prize Winners.

403. 100 f. mult. (No. 231) .. 55 55

(i) Rubens.

404. 25 f. mult (No. 236) .. 15 15

(j) Durer.

405. 25 f. mult. (No. 287) .. 15 15
406. 75 f. mult. (No. 289) .. 40 40

**105.** " Profile Head of Old Man ".

**1979.** 400th Birth Anniv. of Peter Paul Rubens (artist) (2nd issue). Multicoloured.

407. 25 f. Type **105** .. .. 15 15
408. 35 f. " Young Girl with Flag " .. .. .. 20 20
409. 50 f. " Isabelle d'Este, Margave of Mantua " .. 35 35
410. 75 f. " Philip IV, King of Spain " .. .. .. 40 40

**106.** " Portrait of Young Girl ".

**1979.** 450th Death Anniv. of Albrecht Durer (artist) (2nd issue). Multicoloured.

411. 20 f. " Self-portrait " .. 15 15
412. 30 f. " Young Man " .. 20 20
413. 40 f. Type **106** .. .. 25 25
414. 100 f. " Jerome " (air) .. 45 45
415. 200 f. " Jacob Muffel " .. 90 90

**107.** Satellite and Receiving Station.

**1979.** 10th World Telecommunications Day. Multicoloured.

416. 75 f. Satellites (postage) .. 40 40
417. 100 f. Two satellites .. 45 45
418. 200 f. Type **107** .. .. 90 90

108. Pirogue.

**1980.** Handicrafts. Multicoloured.

| | | | |
|---|---|---|---|
| 419. | 60 f. Type **108** .. .. | 45 | 15 |
| 420. | 100 f. Anjouan Puppet .. | 45 | 25 |

109. Sultan Said Ali.

**1980.** Sultans. Multicoloured.

| | | | |
|---|---|---|---|
| 421. | 40 f. Type **109** .. .. | 20 | 15 |
| 422. | 60 f. Sultan Ahmed .. | 30 | 15 |

110. Dimadjou Dispensary.

**1980.** Air. 75th Anniv. of Rotary International and 15th Anniv. of Moroni Rotary Club (100 f.).

| | | | |
|---|---|---|---|
| 423 | 100 f. Type **110** .. .. | 55 | 35 |
| 424 | 260 f. Concorde airplane .. | 2·25 | 1·10 |

111. Sherlock Holmes and Sir Arthur Conan Doyle.

**1980.** 50th Death Anniv. of Sir Arthur Conan Doyle (writer).

| | | | | |
|---|---|---|---|---|
| 425. | **111.** | 200 f. multicoloured .. | 90 | 70 |

112. Grand Mosque and Holy Ka'aba, Mecca.

**1980.** 1350th Anniv. of Occupation of Mecca by Mohammed.

| | | | | |
|---|---|---|---|---|
| 426. | **112.** | 75 f. multicoloured .. | 35 | 25 |

113. Dome of the Rock.

**1980.** Year of the Holy City, Jerusalem.

| | | | | |
|---|---|---|---|---|
| 427. | **113.** | 60 f. multicoloured .. | 30 | 20 |

114. Kepler, Copernicus.

**1980.** 50th Anniv. of Discovery of Pluto.

| | | | | |
|---|---|---|---|---|
| 428. | **114.** | 400 f. vio., red & mve. | 1·90 | 1·40 |

115. Avicenna.

**1980.** Birth Millenary of Avicenna (physician and philosopher).

| | | | | |
|---|---|---|---|---|
| 429. | **115.** | 60 f. multicoloured .. | 30 | 25 |

116. Mermoz, Dabry, Gimie and Seaplane "Comte da la Vaulx".

**1980.** 50th Anniv. of First South Atlantic Flight.

| | | | | |
|---|---|---|---|---|
| 430. | **116.** | 200 f. multicoloured .. | 1·25 | 80 |

**1981.** Various stamps surch.

| | | | |
|---|---|---|---|
| 431. | 15 f. on 200 f. multicoloured (postage) (No. 425) | 10 | 10 |
| 432. | 20 f. on 75 f. multicoloured (No. 426) .. | 15 | 15 |
| 433. | 40 f. on 125 f. multicoloured (No. 378) .. | 25 | 25 |
| 434. | 60 f. on 75 f. multicoloured (No. 388) .. | 1·50 | 75 |
| 435. | 30 f. on 200 f. multicoloured (air) (No. 430) .. | 30 | 30 |

118. Team posing with Shield.

**1981.** World Cup Football Championships, Spain (1982). Multicoloured.

| | | | |
|---|---|---|---|
| 436. | 60 f. Footballers coming on Field (vert.) .. .. | 30 | 15 |
| 437. | 75 f. Type **118** .. .. | 35 | 20 |
| 438. | 90 f. Captains shaking hands | 40 | 20 |
| 439. | 100 f. Tackle .. .. | 45 | 25 |
| 440. | 150 f. Players hugging after goal (vert.) .. .. | 70 | 30 |

119. "Bowls and Pot".

**1981.** Birth Centenary of Pablo Picasso. Multicoloured.

| | | | |
|---|---|---|---|
| 442. | 40 f. "Dove and Rainbow" | 20 | 10 |
| 443. | 70 f. "Still-life on Chest of Drawers" .. | 30 | 15 |
| 444. | 150 f. "Studio with Plaster Head" .. | 70 | 35 |
| 445. | 250 f. Type **119** .. | 1·10 | 55 |
| 446. | 500 f. "Red Tablecloth" .. | 2·25 | 1·10 |

120. "Apollo" Launch.

**1981.** Conquest of Space. Multicoloured.

| | | | |
|---|---|---|---|
| 447. | 50 f. Type **120** .. .. | 25 | 15 |
| 448. | 75 f. Space Shuttle launch | 35 | 20 |
| 449. | 100 f. Space Shuttle releasing fuel tank .. | 45 | 30 |
| 450. | 450 f. Space Shuttle in orbit | 2·10 | 1·10 |

121. Buckingham Palace.

**1981.** British Royal Wedding. Multicoloured.

| | | | |
|---|---|---|---|
| 452. | 125 f. Type **121** .. .. | 55 | 25 |
| 453. | 200 f. Highgrove House .. | 95 | 45 |
| 454. | 450 f. Caernarvon Castle | 2·00 | 1·00 |

**1981.** Design as Type O **99** but inscr. "POSTES 1981".

| | | | |
|---|---|---|---|
| 456. | 5 f. grn., blk. & brn. .. | 10 | 10 |
| 457. | 15 f. grn., blk. & yell. .. | 10 | 10 |
| 458. | 25 f. grn., blk. & red .. | 15 | 10 |
| 459. | 35 f. grn., blk. & lt. grn. | 20 | 10 |
| 460. | 75 f. grn., blk. & blue .. | 35 | 20 |

**1981.** Various stamps surch.

| | | | | |
|---|---|---|---|---|
| 461. | **114.** | 5 f. on 400 f violet, red and mauve (postage) | 10 | 10 |
| 462. | – | 20 f. on 90 f. mult. (No. 438) .. .. | 10 | 10 |
| 463. | – | 45 f. on 100 f. mult. (No. 377) .. .. | 20 | 10 |
| 464. | – | 45 f. on 100 f. mult. (No. 420) .. .. | 20 | 10 |
| 465. | – | 10 f. on 70 f. mult. (No. 443) (air) .. | 10 | 10 |
| 466. | **110.** | 10 f. on 100 f. mult. .. | 10 | 10 |
| 467. | **102.** | 50 f. on 200 f. + 30 f. mult. | 25 | 15 |
| 468. | – | 50 f. on 260 f. mult. (No. 424) .. .. | 60 | 30 |

123. Mercedes, 1914.

**1981.** 75th Anniv. of French Grand Prix Motor Race. Multicoloured.

| | | | |
|---|---|---|---|
| 469. | 20 f. Type **123** .. .. | 10 | 10 |
| 470. | 50 f. Delage, 1925 .. .. | 25 | 15 |
| 471. | 75 f. Rudi Caracciola .. | 35 | 20 |
| 472. | 90 f. Stirling Moss .. .. | 40 | 20 |
| 473. | 150 f. Maserati, 1957 .. | 65 | 30 |

124. Scouts preparing to Sail.

**1981.** 75th Anniv of Boy Scout Movement. Multicoloured.

| | | | |
|---|---|---|---|
| 475 | 50 f. Type **124** .. .. | 25 | 15 |
| 476 | 75 f. Paddling pirogue .. | 60 | 20 |
| 477 | 250 f. Sailing felucca .. | 1·60 | 55 |
| 478 | 350 f. Scouts looking out to sea from boat .. .. | 1·75 | 85 |

**HAVE YOU READ THE NOTES AT THE BEGINNING OF THIS CATALOGUE?**
These often provide answers to the enquiries we receive.

125. Goethe.

**1982.** 150th Death Anniv. of Goethe (poet).

| | | | | |
|---|---|---|---|---|
| 480. | **125.** | 75 f. multicoloured .. | 35 | 20 |
| 481. | | 350 f. multicoloured .. | 1·75 | 85 |

126. Princess of Wales.

**1982.** 21st Birthday of Princess of Wales.

| | | | | |
|---|---|---|---|---|
| 482. | **126.** | 200 f. multicoloured .. | 95 | 45 |
| 483. | – | 300 f. multicoloured .. | 1·40 | 70 |

DESIGN: 300 f. Different portrait of Princess.

**1982.** Birth of Prince William of Wales. Nos. 452/4 optd. **NAISSANCE ROYALE 1982.**

| | | | |
|---|---|---|---|
| 485. | 125 f. Type **121** .. .. | 55 | 25 |
| 486. | 200 f. Highgrove House .. | 95 | 45 |
| 487. | 450 f. Caernarvon Castle .. | 2·00 | 1·00 |

**1982.** World Cup Football Championship Winners. Nos. 436/40 optd.

| | | | |
|---|---|---|---|
| 489. | 60 f. Type **117** .. .. | 30 | 15 |
| 490. | 75 f. Team posing with shield (horiz.) .. | 35 | 20 |
| 491. | 90 f. Captains shaking hands (horiz.) .. .. | 40 | 20 |
| 492. | 100 f. Tackle (horiz.) .. | 45 | 25 |
| 493. | 150 f. Players hugging after goal .. .. | 70 | 30 |

OVERPRINTS: 60 f., 150 f. **ITALIE - ALLEMAGNE (R.F.A.) 3 - 1.** 75 f., 90 f., 100 f. **ITALIE 3 ALLEMAGNE (R.F.A.) 1.**

129. Boy playing Trumpet.

**1982.** Norman Rockwell Paintings. Mult.

| | | | |
|---|---|---|---|
| 495. | 60 f. Type **129** .. .. | 30 | 15 |
| 496. | 75 f. Sleeping porter .. | 1·25 | 85 |
| 497. | 100 f. Couple listening to early radio .. .. | 45 | 25 |
| 498. | 150 f. Children playing Leapfrog .. .. | 70 | 30 |
| 499. | 200 f. Tramp cooking sausages .. .. | 95 | 45 |
| 500. | 300 f. Boy talking to clown | 1·40 | 70 |

130. Sultan Said Mohamed Sidi.

**1982.** Sultans. Multicoloured.

| | | | |
|---|---|---|---|
| 501. | 30 f. Type **130** .. .. | 15 | 10 |
| 502. | 60 f. Sultan Ahmed Abdallah | 30 | 15 |
| 503. | 75 f. Sultan Salim (horiz.) | 35 | 20 |
| 504. | 300 f. Sultans Said Mohamed Sidi and Ahmed Abdallah (horiz.) .. .. | 1·40 | 70 |

**131.** Montgolfier Brothers' Balloon, 1783.

**1983.** Air. Bicent of Manned Flight. Mult.

505 100 f. Type **131** .. .. 35 35
506 200 f. Vincenzo Lunardi's balloon over London, 1784 .. .. .. 70 65
507 300 f. Blanchard and Jeffries crossing the Channel, 1785 .. .. 1·00 1·00
508 400 f. Henri Giffard's steam-powered dirigible airship, 1852 (horiz) .. 1·40 1·25

**132.** Type "470" Yacht.

**1983.** Air. Pre-Olympic Year. Multicoloured.

510. 150 f. Type **132** .. .. 70 55
511. 200 f. "Flying Dutchman" 85 70
512. 300 f. Type "470" (different) .. .. 1·10 1·10
513. 400 f. "Finn" class yachts 1·75 1·40

**133.** Lake Ziani.

**1983.** Landscapes. Multicoloured.

515. 60 f. Type **133** .. .. 25 20
516. 100 f. Sunset .. .. 35 35
517. 175 f. Chiromani (vert.) .. 65 60
518. 360 f. Itsandra beach .. 1·40 1·25
519. 400 f. Anjouan .. .. 1·40 1·25

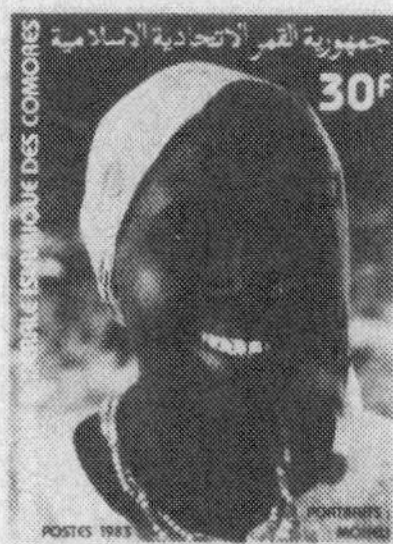

**134.** Moheli.

**1983.** Portraits. Multicoloured.

520. 30 f. Type **134** .. .. 15 10
521. 35 f. " Mask of Beauty " .. 20 15
522. 50 f. Mayotte .. .. 20 15

**135.** Pure-bred Arab.

**1983.** Horses. Multicoloured.

523. 75 f. Type **135** .. .. 30 25
524. 100 f. Anglo-Arab .. 35 35
525. 125 f. Lipizzan .. .. 45 40
526. 150 f. Tennessee .. .. 55 50
527. 200 f. Appaloosa .. .. 70 65
528. 300 f. Pure-bred English .. 1·00 1·00
529. 400 f. Clydesdale .. .. 1·40 1·25
530. 500 f. Andalusian .. 1·75 1·50

**136.** " Double Portrait ". **137.** Symbols of Development.

**1983.** 500th Birth Anniv. of Raphael. Mult.

531. 100 f. Type **136** .. .. 35 35
532. 200 f. Fresco detail .. 70 65
533. 300 f. " St. George and the Dragon " .. .. 1·00 1·00
534. 400 f. " Balthazar Castiglione " .. .. .. 1·40 1·25

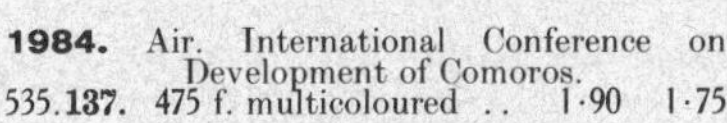

**1984.** Air. International Conference on Development of Comoros.

535.**137.** 475 f. multicoloured .. 1·90 1·75

**138.** Basketball.

**1984.** Air. Olympic Games, Los Angeles. Multicoloured.

536. 60 f. Type **138** .. .. 25 20
537. 100 f. Basketball (different) 45 35
538. 165 f. Basketball (different) 75 55
539. 175 f. Baseball (horiz.) .. 75 55
540. 200 f. Baseball (different) (horiz.) .. .. .. 75 55

**139.** "William Fawcett".

**1984.** Transport. Multicoloured. (a) Ships.

542. 100 f. Type **139** .. .. 70 60
543. 150 f. "Lightning" .. 90 70
544. 200 f. "Rapido" .. .. 1·10 80
545. 350 f. "Sindia" .. .. 2·25 1·75

(b) Automobiles.

546. 100 f. De Dion Bouton and Trepardoux, 1885 .. 45 35
547. 150 f. Benz "Victoria", 1893 .. .. .. 55 45
548. 200 f. Colombia electric, 1901 .. .. .. 75 55
549. 350 f. Fiat, 1902 .. .. 1·25 1·10

**140.** Barn Swallows.

**1985.** Air. Birth Bicentenary of John J. Audubon (ornithologist). Multicoloured.

550 100 f. Type **140** .. .. 1·10 90
551 125 f. Northern oriole .. 1·25 1·10
552 150 f. Red-shouldered hawk (horiz) .. .. .. 1·60 1·25
553 500 f. Red-breasted sapsucker (horiz) .. .. 6·00 4·50

**142.** Harbours.

**1985.** Air. "Philexafrique" Stamp Exhibition, Lome, Togo (1st issue). Multicoloured.

555. 200 f. Type **142** .. .. 1·50 85
556. 200 f. Scouts walking along road. .. .. .. 70 60

See also Nos. 576/7.

**143.** Victor Hugo (novelist, death centenary).

**1985.** Anniversaries. Multicoloured.

557. 100 f. Type **143** .. .. 35 30
558. 200 f. Jules Verne (novelist) (80th death anniv.) 70 60
559. 300 f. Mark Twain (150th birth anniv.) .. 1·75 1·25
560. 450 f. Queen Elizabeth, the Queen Mother (85th birth anniv.) (vert.) .. 1·60 1·40
561. 500 f. Statue of Liberty (centenary) (vert.) .. 1·75 1·60

The 200 f. and 300 f. also commemorate International Youth Year.

**144.** Map and Flag on Sun.

**1985.** Air. 10th Anniv. of Independence.

562. **144.** 10 f. multicoloured .. 10 10
563. 15 f. multicoloured .. 10 10
564. 125 f. multicoloured .. 50 40
565. 300 f. multicoloured .. 1·25 1·10

**145.** Arthritic Spider Conch.

**1985.** Shells. Multicoloured.

566 75 f. Type **145** .. .. 45 35
567 125 f. Silver conch .. 65 45
568 200 f. Costate tun .. 1·10 85
569 300 f. Elephant's snout .. 1·60 1·25
570 450 f. Orange spider conch 2·25 1·60

**146.** U.N. Emblem and Map of Islands.

**1985.** 10th Anniv. of Membership of U.N.O.

571. **146.** 5 f. multicoloured .. 10 10
572. 30 f multicoloured .. 15 10
573. 75 f. multicoloured .. 35 30
574. 125 f. multicoloured .. 50 40
575. 400 f. multicoloured .. 1·75 1·50

**147.** Runners ("Youth").

**1985.** Air. "Philexafrique" Stamp Exhibition, Lome, Togo (2nd issue). Mult.

576. 250 f. Type **147** .. .. 1·00 90
577. 250 f. Earth mover and road construction ("Development") .. 1·00 90

**148.** Globe, Galleon, Wright Type A Biplane and Rocket Capsule.

**1985.** 20th Anniv. of Moroni Rotary Club.

578. **148.** 25 f. multicoloured .. 20 15
579. 75 f. multicoloured .. 65 55
580. 125 f. multicoloured .. 1·10 75
581. 500 f. multicoloured .. 3·50 3·00

**149.** "Astraeus hygrometricus".

**1985.** Fungi. Multicoloured.

582. 75 f. "Boletus edulis" .. 80 45
583. 125 f. "Sarcoscypha coccinea" .. .. 1·00 60
584. 200 f. "Hypholoma fasciculare" .. .. 1·60 1·10
585. 350 f. Type **149** .. .. 3·00 1·75
586. 500 f. "Armillariella mellea" .. .. .. 4·00 2·75

**150.** Sikorsky S-43 Amphibian.

**1985.** Air. 50th Anniv of Union des Transports Aeriennes. Multicoloured.

587 25 f. Type **150** .. .. 10 10
588 75 f. Douglas DC-9 airplane and camel .. .. 45 30
589 100 f. Douglas DC-4, DC-6, Nord 2501 Noratlas and De Havilland Heron 2 aircraft .. .. 55 35
590 125 f. Maintenance .. 60 40
591 1000 f. Emblem and Latecoere 28, Sikorsky S-43, Douglas DC-10 and Boeing 747-200 aircraft (35 × 47 mm) .. .. 5·00 3·75

**151.** Edmond Halley, Comet and "Giotto" Space Probe.

**1986.** Air. Appearance of Halley's Comet. Multicoloured.

593. 125 f. Type **151** .. .. 50 40
594. 150 f. Giacobini-Zinner comet, 1959. .. .. 65 55
595. 225 f. J. F. Encke and Encke comet, 1961 .. 85 75
596. 300 f. Computer enhanced picture of Bradfield comet, 1980 .. .. 1·25 1·10
597. 450 f. Halley's comet and "Planet A" space probe 1·75 1·50

**152.** Footballers.

**1986.** Air. World Cup Football Championship, Mexico. Designs showing footballers.

598. **152.** 125 f. multicoloured .. 50 40
599. – 210 f. multicoloured .. 80 70
600. – 500 f. multicoloured .. 2·10 1·90
601. – 600 f. multicoloured .. 2·40 2·25

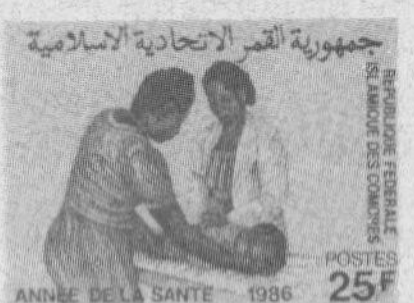


**153.** Doctor examining Child.

**1986.** World Health Year. Multicoloured.

602. 25 f. Type **153** .. .. 10 10
603. 100 f. Doctor weighing child .. .. .. 45 35
604. 200 f. Nurse innoculating baby .. .. .. 80 70

**154.** Ndzoumara (wind instrument).

**155.** Server.

**1986.** Musical Instruments. Multicoloured.

605. 75 f. Type **154** .. .. 30 25
606. 125 f. Ndzedze (string instrument) .. .. 50 40
607. 210 f. Gaboussi (string instrument) .. .. 80 70
608. 500 f. Ngoma (drums) .. 2·00 1·75

**1987.** Air. Tennis as 1988 Olympic Games Discipline. Multicoloured.

609. 150 f. Type **155** .. .. 60 50
610. 250 f. Player preparing shot .. .. .. 1·00 90
611. 500 f. Player being lobbed 2·00 1·75
612. 600 f. Players each side of net .. .. .. 2·40 2·25

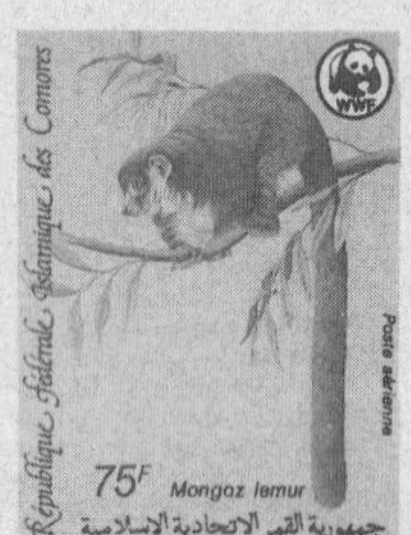


**156.** On Tree Branch.

**1987.** Air. Endangered Animals. Mongoose-Lemur. Multicoloured.

613. 75 f. Type **156** .. .. 30 25
614. 100 f. Head of mongoose-lemur with ruff .. .. 40 30
615. 125 f. Mongoose-lemur on rock .. .. .. 50 40
616. 150 f. Head of mongoose-lemur without ruff .. 60 50

**157.** Women working in Field.

**1987.** Woman and Development. Mult.

617. 75 f. Type **157** .. .. 30 25
618. 125 f. Woman picking musk seeds (vert.) .. 50 40
619. 1000 f. Woman making basket .. .. .. 3·75 3·50

**158.** Men's Downhill.

**1987.** Air. Winter Olympic Games, Calgary (1988). Multicoloured.

620. 150 f. Type **158** .. .. 60 50
621. 225 f. Ski jumping .. 90 80
622. 500 f. Women's slalom .. 2·00 1·75
623. 600 f. Men's luge .. .. 2·40 2·25

**159** Didier Daurat, Raymond Vanier and "Air Bleu"

**1987.** Air. Aviation. Multicoloured.

624 200 f. Type **159** .. .. 85 70
625 300 f. Letord 4 Lorraine and route map (1st regular airmail service, Paris–Le Mans–St. Nazaire, 1918) .. .. 1·40 1·10
626 500 f. Morane Saulnier Type H and route map (1st airmail flight, Villacoublay–Pauillac, 1913) .. .. .. 2·10 1·90
627 1000 f. Henri Pequet flying Humber-Sommer biplane (1st aerophilately exn, Allahabad) (36 × 49 mm) 4·50 4·00

**160** Ice Skating

**1988.** Multicoloured.

(a) Winter Olympic Games, Calgary.

628 75 f. Type **160** (postage) .. 30 25
629 125 f. Speed skating .. 50 40
630 350 f. Two-man bobsleigh 1·40 1·25
631 400 f. Biathlon (air) .. 1·50 1·25

(b) Olympic Games, Seoul.

633 100 f. Relay (postage) .. 40 30
634 150 f. Showjumping .. 60 50
635 500 f. Pole-vaulting .. 1·90 1·75
636 600 f. Football (air) .. 2·25 2·00

**161** Kiwanis International Emblem and Hand supporting Figures

**1988.** Child Health Campaigns. Multicoloured.

638 75 f. Type **161** .. .. 30 25
639 125 f. Kiwanis emblem, wheelchair and crutch .. 50 40
640 210 f. Kiwanis emblem and man with children (country inscr in black) 80 70
641 210 f. As No. 640 but country inscr in white .. 80 70
642 425 f. As No. 639 .. 1·60 1·40
643 425 f. As No. 639 but with Lions International emblem .. .. 1·60 1·40
644 500 f. Type **161** .. 1·90 1·75
645 500 f. As Type **161** but with Rotary emblem .. 1·90 1·75

**162** Throwing the Discus

**163** Columbus and "Santa Maria"

**1988.** Olympic Games, Barcelona (1992) (1st issue). Multicoloured.

646 75 f. Type **162** (postage) .. 30 25
647 100 f. Rowing (horiz) .. 40 30
648 125 f. Cycling (horiz) .. 50 40
649 150 f. Wrestling (horiz) .. 60 50
650 375 f. Basketball (air) .. 1·40 1·25
651 600 f. Tennis .. .. 2·25 2·00

See also Nos. 709/14.

**1988.** 500th Anniv (1992) of Discovery of America by Columbus. Multicoloured.

653 75 f. Type **163** (postage) .. 45 30
654 125 f. Martin Alonzo Pinzon and "Pinta" .. 75 50
655 150 f. Vicente Yanez Pinzon and "Nina" .. 90 60
656 250 f. Search for gold .. 95 85
657 375 f. Wreck of "Santa Maria" (air) .. .. 2·00 1·50
658 450 f. Preparation for fourth voyage .. .. 2·50 2·00

**1988.** Nos. 641, 643 and 645 (125 and 400 f. with colours changed) surch.

660 75 f. on 210 f. mult .. 30 25
661 125 f. on 425 f. mult .. 50 40
662 200 f. on 425 f. mult .. 75 65
663 300 f. on 500 f. mult .. 1·25 1·00
664 400 f. on 500 f. mult .. 1·50 1·25

**1988.** Olympic Games Medal Winners for Tennis. Nos. 609/12 optd.

665 150 f. Optd **Medalle d'or Seoul Miloslav Mecir (Tchec.)** .. .. 60 50
666 250 f. Optd **Medaille d'argent Seoul Tim Mayotte (U.S.A)** .. 95 85
667 500 f. Optd **Medaille d'or Seoul Steffi Graf (R.F.A.)** .. .. 1·90 1·75
668 600 f. Optd **Medaille d'argent Seoul Gabriela Sabatini (Argentine)** 2·25 2·00

**166** Alberto Santos-Dumont and "14 bis"

**1988.** Air. Aviation Pioneers.

669 **166** 100 f. purple .. .. 40 30
670 – 150 f. mauve .. .. 65 50
671 – 200 f. black .. .. 80 65
672 – 300 f. brown .. .. 1·25 1·00
673 – 500 f. blue .. .. 2·00 1·75
674 – 800 f. green .. .. 3·25 3·00

DESIGNS: 150 f. Wright Type A and Orville and Wilbur Wright; 200 f. Louis Bleriot and Bleriot XI; 300 f. Farman Voisin No. 1 bis and Henri Farman; 500 f. Gabriel and Charles Voisin and Voisin "Boxkite"; 800 f. Roland Garros and Morane Saulnier Type I.

**167** Galileo Galilei

**168** Yury Gagarin (cosmonaut) and Daughters

**1988.** Appearance of Halley's Comet. Mult.

675 200 f. + 10 f. Type **167** .. 80 70
676 200 f. + 10 f. Nicolas Copernicus .. .. 80 70
677 200 f. + 10 f. Johannes Kepler .. .. .. 80 70
678 200 f. + 10 f. Edmond Halley .. .. .. 80 70
679 200 f. + 10 f. Japanese "Planet A" space probe 80 70
680 200 f. + 10 f. American "Ice" space probe .. 80 70
681 200 f. + 10 f. "Planet A" space probe (different) 80 70
682 200 f. + 10 f. Russian "Vega" space probe .. 80 70

**1988.** Personalities. Multicoloured.

684 150 f. Type **168** (20th death anniv) (postage) .. 60 50
685 300 f. Henri Dunant (founder of Red Cross) (125th anniv of Red Cross Movement) .. 1·25 1·00
686 400 f. Roger Clemens (baseball player) .. .. 1·50 1·25
687 500 f. Gary Kasparov (chess player) (air) .. 1·90 1·75
688 600 f. Paul Harris (founder of Rotary International) (birth centenary) .. 2·25 2·00

**169** Alain Prost (racing driver) and Formula 1 Racing Car

**1988.** Cars, Trains and Yachts. Multicoloured.

690 75 f. Type **169** (postage) .. 30 25
691 125 f. George Stephenson (railway engineer), "Rocket" and "Borsig de 1935" (diesel locomotive) .. .. 50 40
692 500 f. Ettore Bugatti (motor manufacturer) and Aravis "Type 57" .. 1·90 1·75
693 600 f. Rudolph Diesel (engineer) and "V 200 BB" type locomotive .. 2·25 2·00
694 750 f. Dennis Conner and "Stars and Stripes" (America's Cup contender) .. .. 3·50 3·00
695 1000 f. Michael Fay and "New Zealand" (America's Cup contender) .. .. .. 4·50 4·00

**170** "Papilio nireus aristophontes" (female)

**1989.** Scouts, Butterflies and Birds. Mult.

697 50 f. Type **170** (postage) .. 20 10
698 75 f. "Papilio nireus aristophontes" (male) .. 30 15
699 150 f. "Charaxes fulvescens separanus" .. .. 60 40
700 375 f. Bronze mannikin .. 2·75 1·50
701 450 f. "Charaxes castor comoranus" (air) .. 1·75 1·25
702 500 f. Madagascar white eye .. .. .. 3·75 2·25

**171** Aussat "K3" and N. Uphoff (individual dressage)

**1989.** Satellites and Olympic Games Medal Winners for Equestrian Events. Mult.

704 75 f. Type **171** (postage) .. 30 15
705 150 f. "Brasil sat" and P. Durand (individual show jumping) .. .. 60 40
706 375 f. "ECS 4" and J. Martinek (modern pentathlon) .. .. 1·50 1·00
707 600 f. "Olympus 1" and M. Todd (cross-country) (air) .. .. .. 2·40 1·60

**172** Running

**1989.** Olympic Games, Barcelona (1992) (2nd issue). Multicoloured.

709 75 f. Type **172** (postage) .. 30 15
710 150 f. Football .. .. 60 40
711 300 f. Tennis .. .. 1·25 90
712 375 f. Baseball .. .. 1·50 1·00
713 500 f. Gymnastics (air) .. 2·00 1·50
714 600 f. Table tennis .. 2·40 1·60

**173** Dr. Joseph-Ignace Guillotin and Guillotine

**1989.** Bicent of French Revolution. Mult.

716 75 f. Type **173** (postage) .. 30 15
717 150 f. Soldiers with cannon (Battle of Valmy) and Gen. Kellermann .. 60 40
718 375 f. Jean Cottereau (Chouan) and Vendeens 1·50 90
719 600 f. Invasion of Les Tuileries (air) .. .. 2·40 1·60

**1989.** Various stamps surch.

721 25 f. on 250 f. mult (No. 656) .. .. .. 10 10
722 150 f. on 200 f. mult (No. 532) .. .. .. 60 40
723 150 f. on 200 f. mult (No. 558) .. .. .. 60 40
724 150 f. on 200 f. mult (No. 604) .. .. .. 60 40
725 5 f. on 250 f. multicoloured (No. 390) (air) .. .. 10 10
726 25 f. on 250 f. mult (No. 610) .. .. .. 10 10
727 50 f. on 250 f. mult (No. 576) .. .. .. 20 10
728 50 f. on 250 f. mult (No. 577) .. .. .. 20 10
729 150 f. on 200 f. mult (No. 511) .. .. .. 85 50
730 150 f. on 200 f. mult (No. 555) .. .. .. 85 50
731 150 f. on 200 f. mult (No. 556) .. .. .. 60 40
732 150 f. on 200 f. black (No. 671) .. .. .. 90 60

**175** Airport Pavilion

**1990.**

733 **175** 5 f. orange, brn & red 10 10
734 – 10 f. orange, brn & bl 10 10
735 – 25 f. orange, brn & grn 10 10
736 – 50 f. black and red .. 20 10
737 – 75 f. black and blue .. 35 10
738 – 150 f. black and green 70 35

DESIGNS: 50 to 150 f. Federal Assembly.

**176** Player challenging Goalkeeper

**1990.** Air. World Cup Football Championship, Italy (1st issue). Multicoloured.

739 75 f. Type **176** .. .. 35 10
740 150 f. Player heading ball 70 35
741 500 f. Overhead kick .. 2·40 1·25
742 1000 f. Player evading tackle .. .. .. 4·75 2·25

See also Nos. 743/8.

**177** Brazilian Player

**1990.** World Cup Football Championship, Italy (2nd issue). Multicoloured.

743 50 f. Type **177** (postage) .. 20 10
744 75 f. English player .. 35 10
745 100 f. West German player 50 25
746 150 f. Belgian player .. 70 35
747 375 f. Italian player (air) .. 1·75 85
748 600 f. Argentinian player 2·75 1·25

**178** U.S. Space Telescope

**1990.** Multicoloured.

750 75 f. Type **178** (postage) .. 35 10
751 150 f. Pope John Paul II and Mikhail Gorbachev, 1989 .. .. .. 70 35
752 200 f. Kevin Mitchell (San Francisco Giants baseball player) .. 1·00 50
753 250 f. De Gaulle and Adenauer, 1962 .. 1·25 60
754 300 f. "Titan 2002" space probe .. .. 1·40 70
755 375 f. "TGV-Atlantique" express train and Concorde airplane .. 2·00 1·00
756 450 f. Gary Kasparov (World chess champion) and Anderssen v Steinitz chess match (air) .. 2·10 1·00
757 500 f. Paul Harris (founder of Rotary International) and symbols of health, hunger and humanity .. 2·40 1·25

**179** Edi Reinalter (skiing, 1948)

**180** Dish Aerial, Moroni Volo-volo

**1990.** Winter Olympics, Albertville (1992). Medal Winners at previous Games. Mult.

759 75 f. Type **179** (postage) .. 35 10
760 100 f. Canada (ice hockey, 1924) .. .. .. 50 25
761 375 f. Baroness Gratia Schimmelpenninck van der Oye (skiing, 1936) (air) .. .. .. 1·75 85
762 600 f. Hasu Haikki (ski jumping, 1948) .. 2·75 1·25

**1991.**

764 **180** 75 f. multicoloured .. 35 10
765 150 f. multicoloured .. 70 35
766 225 f. multicoloured .. 1·10 55
767 300 f. multicoloured .. 1·40 70
768 500 f. multicoloured .. 2·40 1·25

**181** Emblem and Leaves

**1991.** Indian Ocean Commission Conference.

769 **181** 75 f. multicoloured .. 35 10
770 150 f. multicoloured .. 70 35
771 225 f. multicoloured .. 1·10 55

**182** De Gaulle and Battle of Koufra, 1941

**183** Emblem and Stylized View of Exhibition

**1991.** 50th Anniv of World War II. Mult.

772 125 f. Type **182** (postage) 60 30
773 150 f. Errol Flynn in "Adventures in Burma" 70 35
774 300 f. Henry Fonda in "The Longest Day" .. 1·40 70
775 375 f. De Gaulle and Battle of Britain, 1940 .. 2·00 1·00
776 450 f. Humphrey Bogart in "Sahara" .. .. 2·40 1·25
777 500 f. De Gaulle and Battle of Monte Cassino, 1944 2·40 1·25

**1991.** "Telecom '91" International Telecommunications Exhibition, Geneva. Mult.

779 75 f. Type **183** .. .. 35 10
780 150 f. Emblem (horiz) .. 70 25

**184** Weather Space Station "Columbus"

**1991.** Anniversaries and Events. Mult.

781 100 f. Type **184** (postage) 45 15
782 150 f. Gandhi (43rd death anniv) .. .. .. 70 25
783 250 f. Henri Dunant (founder of Red Cross) (90th anniv of award of Nobel Peace Prize) .. 1·10 40
784 300 f. Wolfgang Amadeus Mozart (composer, death bicentenary) .. .. 1·40 55
785 375 f. Brandenburg Gate (bicent and second anniv of fall of Berlin Wall) 1·75 70
786 400 f. Konrad Adenauer (German Chancellor) signing new constitution (25th death anniv) .. 1·75 70
787 450 f. Elvis Presley (entertainer, 14th death anniv) (air) .. .. 2·10 80
788 500 f. Ferdinand von Zeppelin (airship pioneer, 75th death anniv) .. .. .. 2·75 1·50

**185** Cep

**1992.** Fungi and Shells. Multicoloured.

789 75 f. Type **185** (postage) .. 60 15
790 125 f. Textile cone .. 80 35
791 150 f. Puff-ball .. .. 1·50 55
792 150 f. Bull-mouth helmet (shell) .. .. .. 1·00 40
793 500 f. Map cowrie (air) .. 3·25 1·50
794 600 f. Scarlet elf cups .. 6·50 4·50

**186** Ham (chimpanzee) on "Mercury" flight, 1960

**1992.** Space Research. Multicoloured.

796 75 f. Type **186** (postage) .. 35 10
797 125 f. "Mars Observer" space probe .. .. 60 20
798 150 f. Felix (cat) and "Veronique" rocket, 1963 70 25
799 150 f. "Mars Rover" and "Marsokod" space vehicles .. .. 70 25
800 500f. "Phobos" project (air) .. .. .. 2·25 90
801 600 f. Laika (dog) and "Sputnik 2" flight, 1957 2·75 1·10

**187** "Endeavour" (space shuttle), Capt. James Cook and H.M.S. "Endeavour"

**1992.** Space and Nautical Exploration. Multicoloured.

803 75 f. Type **187** (postage) .. 35 10
804 100 f. "Cariane" space microphone, Sir Francis Drake and "Golden Hind" .. .. 45 15
805 150 f. Infra-red astronomical observation device, John Smith and "Susan Constant" .. 70 25
806 225 f. Space probe "B", Robert F. Scott and "Discovery" .. .. 1·00 40
807 375 f. "Magellan" (Venus space probe), Ferdinand Magellan and ship (air) 1·75 70
808 500 f. "Newton" (satellite), Vasco da Gama and "Sao Gabriel" .. 2·25 90

188 Map 189 Footballers

**1993.** 30th Anniv of Organization of African Unity.

| | | | | |
|---|---|---|---|---|
| 810 | 188 | 25 f. multicoloured .. | 10 | 10 |
| 811 | | 50 f. multicoloured .. | 20 | 10 |
| 812 | | 75 f. multicoloured .. | 35 | 10 |
| 813 | | 150 f. multicoloured .. | 70 | 25 |

**1993.** World Cup Football Championship, U.S.A. (1994).

| | | | | |
|---|---|---|---|---|
| 814 | 189 | 25 f. multicoloured .. | 10 | 10 |
| 815 | | 75 f. multicoloured .. | 35 | 10 |
| 816 | | 100 f. multicoloured .. | 45 | 15 |
| 817 | | 150 f. multicoloured .. | 70 | 25 |

190 I.T.U. Emblem

**1993.** World Telecommunications Day. "Telecommunications and Human Development".

| | | | | |
|---|---|---|---|---|
| 818 | 190 | 50 f. multicoloured .. | 20 | 10 |
| 819 | | 75 f. multicoloured .. | 35 | 10 |
| 820 | | 100 f. multicoloured .. | 45 | 15 |
| 821 | | 150 f. multicoloured .. | 70 | 25 |

191 Edaphosaurus

**1994.** Prehistoric Animals. Multicoloured.

| | | | |
|---|---|---|---|
| 822 | 75 f. Type **191** .. | 25 | 10 |
| 823 | 75 f. Moschops .. | 25 | 10 |
| 824 | 75 f. Kentrosaurus .. | 25 | 10 |
| 825 | 75 f. Compsognathus .. | 25 | 10 |
| 826 | 75 f. Sauroctonus .. | 25 | 10 |
| 827 | 75 f. Ornitholestes .. | 25 | 10 |
| 828 | 75 f. Styracosaurus .. | 25 | 10 |
| 829 | 75 f. Acanthopholis .. | 25 | 10 |
| 830 | 150 f. Edmontonia .. | 50 | 20 |
| 831 | 150 f. Struthiomimus .. | 50 | 20 |
| 832 | 150 f. Diatryma .. | 50 | 20 |
| 833 | 150 f. Uintatherium .. | 50 | 20 |
| 834 | 450 f. Dromiceiomimus .. | 1·60 | 60 |
| 835 | 450 f. Iguanodon .. | 1·60 | 60 |
| 836 | 525 f. Synthetoceras .. | 1·90 | 75 |
| 837 | 525 f. Euryapteryx .. | 1·90 | 75 |

192 "Hibiscus syriacus"

**1994.** Plants. Multicoloured.

| | | | |
|---|---|---|---|
| 839 | 75 f. Type **192** .. .. | 25 | 10 |
| 840 | 75 f. Cashew nut .. .. | 25 | 10 |
| 841 | 75 f. Butter mushroom .. | 40 | 15 |
| 842 | 150 f. "Pyrostegia venusta" (flower) .. | 50 | 20 |
| 843 | 150 f. Manioc (root) .. | 50 | 20 |
| 844 | 150 f. "Lycogala epidendron" (fungus) .. | 80 | 35 |
| 845 | 525 f. "Allamanda cathartica" (flower) .. | 1·90 | 75 |
| 846 | 525 f. Cacao (nut) .. | 1·90 | 75 |
| 847 | 525 f. "Clathrus ruber" (fungus) .. .. | 3·00 | 1·50 |

193 Purple-tip ("Colotis zoe")

**1994.** Insects. Multicoloured.

| | | | |
|---|---|---|---|
| 848 | 75 f. Type **193** .. .. | 25 | 10 |
| 849 | 75 f. "Charaxes comoranus" (butterfly) | 25 | 10 |
| 850 | 75 f. "Hypurgus ova" (beetle) .. .. | 25 | 10 |
| 851 | 150 f. Death's-head hawk moth ("Acherontia atropos") .. .. | 50 | 20 |
| 852 | 150 f. "Verdant hawk moth ("Euchloron megaera") | 50 | 20 |
| 853 | 150 f. "Onthophagus catta" (beetle) .. .. | 50 | 20 |
| 854 | 450 f. African monarch ("Danaus chrysippus") (butterfly) .. .. | 1·60 | 60 |
| 855 | 450 f. "Papilio phorbanta" (butterfly) .. .. | 1·60 | 60 |
| 856 | 450 f. "Echinosoma bolivari" (beetle) .. | 1·60 | 60 |

OFFICIAL STAMPS

O **99**. Comoro Flag.

**1979.**

| | | | | |
|---|---|---|---|---|
| O379 | O **99** | 5 f. green, black and azure .. | 10 | 10 |
| O380 | | 10 f. green, black and grey .. | 10 | 10 |
| O381 | | 20 f. green, black and stone .. | 10 | 10 |
| O382 | | 30 f. grn, blk & bl | 20 | 10 |
| O383 | | 40 f. grn, blk & yell | 25 | 15 |
| O384 | | 60 f. green, black and pale green | 30 | 25 |
| O384a | | 75 f. green, black and light green | 25 | 15 |
| O385 | | 100 f. green, black and yellow .. | 50 | 35 |
| O386 | – | 100 f. mult .. | 45 | 35 |
| O386a | – | 125 f. mult .. | 50 | 55 |
| O387 | – | 400 f. mult .. | 1·90 | 1·25 |

DESIGNS: 100 (No. O386), 125, 400 f. President Cheikh.

POSTAGE DUE STAMPS

D **9**. Mosque in Anjouan. D **10**. Coelacanth.

**1950.**

| | | | | |
|---|---|---|---|---|
| D 16. | D **9**. | 50 c. green .. .. | 15 | 60 |
| D 17. | | 1 f. brown .. .. | 15 | 60 |

**1954.**

| | | | | |
|---|---|---|---|---|
| D 18. | D **10**. | 5 f. sepia and green .. | 50 | 75 |
| D 19. | | 10 f. violet and brown | 65 | 70 |
| D 20. | | 20 f. indigo and blue | 1·10 | 1·25 |

D **78**. Pineapple.

**1977.** Multicoloured.

| | | | |
|---|---|---|---|
| D244 | 1 f. Hibiscus (horiz) .. | 10 | 10 |
| D245 | 2 f. Type D **78** .. .. | 10 | 10 |
| D246 | 5 f. White butterfly (horiz) .. .. | 10 | 10 |
| D247 | 10 f. Chameleon (horiz) | 10 | 10 |
| D248 | 15 f. Banana flower (horiz) .. .. | 10 | 10 |
| D249 | 20 f. Orchid (horiz) .. | 10 | 10 |
| D250 | 30 f. "Allamanda cathartica" (horiz) .. | 20 | 10 |
| D251 | 40 f. Cashew nuts .. | 25 | 15 |
| D252 | 50 f. Custard apple .. | 25 | 15 |
| D253 | 100 f. Breadfruit (horiz) | 45 | 25 |
| D254 | 200 f. Vanilla (horiz) .. | 90 | 45 |
| D255 | 500 f. Ylang-ylang flower (horiz) .. | 2·25 | 1·10 |

## APPENDIX

The following stamps have either been issued in excess of postal needs or have not been available to the public in reasonable quantities at face value. Such stamps may later be given full listing if there is evidence of regular postal use.

**1975.**

Various stamps optd. **ETAT COMORIEN** or surch. also.

Birds issue (No. 60). 10 f. on 2 f.

Fishes issue (No. 71). Air 50 f.

Birds issue (No. 99). 40 f.

Comoro Landscapes issue (Nos. 102/4). Air 75 f. on 65 f., 100 f. on 85 f., 100 f.

Tropical Plants issue (Nos. 105/9). Postage 5 f. on 1 f., 5 f. on 3 f.; Air 75 f. on 60 f., 100 f. on 85 f.

Seashells issue (No. 114). 75 f. on 60 f.

Aquatic Sports issue (No. 122). Air 75 f. on 70 f.

Anjouan Landscapes issue (Nos. 126/8). Air 40 f., 75 f. on 60 f., 100 f.

Said Mohamed Cheikh issue (Nos. 129/30). Air 20 f., 35 f.

Great Comoro Landscapes issue (Nos. 134 and 136). Postage 35 f.; Air 200 f. on 135 f.

Moroni Buildings issue (No. 139). 20 f.

Karthala Volcano issue (No. 140). Air 200 f. on 120 f.

Hansen issue (No. 141). Air 100 f.

Copernicus issue (No. 142). Air 400 f. on 150 f.

Picasso issue (No. 143). Air 200 f.

Mosques issue (Nos. 145/6). 15 f. on 20 f., 25 f. on 35 f.

Star of Anjouan issue (No. 147). 500 f.

Said Omar Ben Soumeth issue (Nos. 148/9). Air 100 f. on 135 f., 200 f.

Shaikh Said Mohamed issue (No. 150). 30 f. on 35 f.

Handicrafts issue (Nos. 153/5). 20 f., 30 f. on 35 f., 75 f.

Mayotte Landscapes issue (Nos. 157/60). Air 10 f. on 20 f., 30 f. on 35 f., 100 f. on 90 f., 200 f. on 120 f.

U.P.U. Centenary issue (No. 161). 500 f. on 30 f.

Air Service issue (No. 162). Air 100 f. on 135 f.

Rotary issue (No. 163). Air 400 f. on 250 f.

Handicrafts issue (Nos. 164/7). 15 f. on 20 f., 30 f. on 35 f., 100 f. on 120 f., 200 f. on 135 f.

Moheli Landscapes issue (Nos. 168/71). Postage 30 f., 50 f., 50 f. on 55 f.; Air 200 f. on 230 f.

Coelacanth issue (No. 172). 50 f.

Folk-dances issue (Nos. 173/4). 100 f., 100 f. on 150 f.

Apollo-Soyuz Space Test Project. Postage 10, 30, 50 f.; Air 100, 200, 400 f. Embossed on gold foil. Air 1500 f.

**1976.**

Bicentenary of American Revolution. Postage 15, 25, 35, 40, 75 f.; Air 500 f. Embossed on gold foil: Air 1000 f.

Winter Olympic Games, Innsbruck. Postage 5, 30, 35, 50 f.; Air 200, 400 f. Embossed on gold foil; Air 1000 f.

Children's Stories. Postage 15, 30, 35, 40, 50 f.; Air 400 f.

Telephone Centenary. Postage 10, 25, 75 f.; Air 100, 200, 500 f.

Bicentenary of American Revolution. (Early Settler and Viking Space Rocket). Embossed on gold foil; Air 1500 f.

Bicentenary of American Revolution. (J. F. Kennedy and Apollo). Embossed on gold foil; Air 1500 f.

**1978.**

World Cup Football Championship, Argentina. Embossed on gold foil. Air 1000 f.

Death Centenary of Sir Rowland Hill. Embossed on gold foil; Air 1500 f.

Argentina's World Cup Victory. Optd. on World Cup issue. Air 1000 f.

**1979.**

International Year of the Child. Embossed on gold foil. Air 1500 f.

**1988.**

Rotary International. Embossed on gold foil. Air 1500 f.

**1989.**

Scouts, Butterflies and Birds. Embossed on gold foil. Air 1500 f.

Satellites and Olympic Winners. Embossed on gold foil. Air 1500 f.

Bicentenary of French Revolution. Embossed on gold foil. Air 1500 f.

**1990.**

World Cup Football Championship. Embossed on gold foil. Air 1500 f.

Winter Olympic Games, Albertville (1992). Embossed on gold foil. Air 1500 f.

**1991.**

Birth Centenary of Charles De Gaulle (1990). Embossed on gold foil. Air 1500 f.

**1992.**

Olympic Games, Barcelona. Boxing. Embossed on gold foil. Air 1500 f.

## CONFEDERATE STATES OF AMERICA Pt. 22

Stamps issued by the seceding states in the American Civil War.

1. Jefferson Davis.

2. T. Jefferson.

**1861.** Imperf.
1. 1. 5 c. green .. .. .. £100 70·00
3. 2. 10 c. blue .. .. .. £130 95·00

3. Jackson.

4. Jefferson Davis.

**1862.** Imperf.
4. 3. 2 c. green .. .. .. £300 £400
5. 1. 5 c. blue .. .. .. 65·00 55·00
6. 2. 10 c. red .. .. .. £600 £300

**1862.** Imperf.
7 4 5 c. blue .. .. .. .. 6·00 11·00

5. Jackson.

6. Jefferson Davis.

9. Washington.

**1863.** Imperf. or perf. (10 c.)
9 5 2 c. red .. .. .. 30·00 £170
10 6 10 c. blue (TEN CENTS) £425 £300
13 10 c. blue (10 CENTS) .. 6·00 9·00
14 9 20 c. green .. .. 25·00 £225

## CONGO (Kinshasa) Pt. 14

This Belgian colony in Central Africa became independent in 1960. There were separate issues for the province of Katanga (q.v.).

In 1971 the country was renamed ZAIRE REPUBLIC and later issues will be found under that heading.

1967. 100 sengi = 1 (li)kuta; 100 (ma) kuta = 1 zaire.

**1960.** Various stamps of Belgian Congo optd. **CONGO** or surch. also. (a) Flowers issue of 1952. Multicoloured.
360. 10 c. "Dissotis" .. .. 10 10
361. 10 c. on 15 c. "Protea" .. 10 10
362. 20 c. "Vellozia" .. .. 10 10
363. 40 c. "Ipomoea" .. .. 10 10
364. 50 c. on 60 c. "Euphorbia" 10 10
365. 50 c. on 75 c. "Ochna" .. 10 10
366. 1 f. "Hibiscus" .. .. 10 10
367. 1 f. 50 "Schizoglossum" .. 10 10
368. 2 f. "Ansellia" .. .. 10 10
369. 3 f. "Costus" .. .. 20 10
370. 4 f. "Nymphaea" .. .. 20 20
371. 5 f. "Thunbergia" .. .. 20 10
372. 6 f. 50 "Thonningia" .. 30 10
373. 8 f. "Gloriosa" .. .. 40 20
374. 10 f. "Silene" .. .. 60 20
375. 20 f. "Aristolochia" .. 1·25 50
376. 50 f. "Eulophia" .. .. 7·00 3·25
377. 100 f. "Cryptosepalum" .. 12·00 5·50

(b) Wild animals issue of 1959.
378. 10 c. brown, sepia & blue 10 10
379. 20 c. blue and red .. .. 10 10
380. 40 c. brown and blue .. 10 10
381. 50 c. multicoloured .. 10 10
382. 1 f. black, green & brown 10 10
383. 1 f. 50 black and yellow .. 15 10
384. 2 f. black, brown and red 20 10
385. 3 f. 50 on 3 f. black, purple and slate .. .. 25 10
386. 5 f. brown, green and sepia 35 15
387. 6 f. 50 brown, yellow and blue .. .. .. 45 15
388. 8 f. bistre, violet & brown 55 30
389. 10 f. multicoloured .. 70 35

(c) Madonna.
390. 102. 50 c. brn., ochre & chest. 50 50

(d) African Technical Co-operation Commission. Inscr. in French or Flemish.
391. 103. 3 f. 50 on 3 f. salmon and slate .. .. .. 40 40

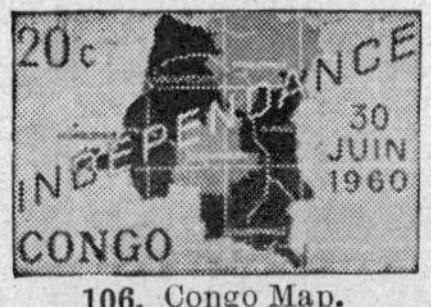

106. Congo Map.

**1960.** Independence Commem.
392. 106. 20 c. bistre .. .. 10 10
393. 50 c. red .. .. 10 10
394. 1 f. green .. .. 10 10
395. 1 f. 50 brown .. .. 10 10
396. 2 f. mauve .. .. 10 10
397. 3 f. 50 violet .. .. 10 10
398. 5 f. blue .. .. .. 15 10
399. 6 f. 50 black .. .. 20 10
400. 10 f. orange .. .. 30 20
401. 20 f. blue .. .. 50 30

107. Congo Flag and People breaking Chain.

109. Pres. Kasavubu.

**1961.** 2nd Anniv. of Congo Independence Agreement. Flag in yellow and blue.
402. 107. 2 f. violet .. .. 10 10
403. 3 f. 50 red .. .. 10 10
404. 6 f. 50 brown .. .. 20 10
405. 10 f. green .. .. 25 15
406. 20 f. mauve .. .. 45 30

**1961.** Coquilhatville Conf. Optd. **CONFERENCE COQUILHATVILLE AVRIL -MAI-1961.**
407. 106. 20 c. bistre .. .. 60 60
408. 50 c. red .. .. 60 60
409. 1 f. green .. .. 60 60
410. 1 f. 50 brown .. .. 60 60
411. 2 f. mauve .. .. 60 60
412. 3 f. 50 violet .. .. 60 60
413. 5 f. blue .. .. 60 60
414. 6 f. 50 black .. .. 60 60
415. 10 f. orange .. .. 60 60
416. 20 f. blue .. .. 60 60

**1961.** 1st Anniv. of Independence. Inscr. as in T 109. Portraits and inscriptions in sepia.
417. 109. 10 c. yellow .. .. 10 10
418. 20 c. red .. .. 10 10
419. 40 c. turquoise .. .. 10 10
420. 50 c. salmon .. .. 10 10
421. 1 f. lilac .. .. 10 10
422. 1 f. 50 brown .. .. 10 10
423. 2 f. green .. .. 10 10
424. – 3 f. 50 mauve .. .. 15 10
425. – 5 f. grey .. .. 1·75 15
426. – 6 f. 50 blue .. .. 30 10
427. – 8 f. olive .. .. 35 10
428. – 10 f. blue .. .. 75 10
429. – 20 f. orange .. .. 75 15
430. – 50 f. blue .. .. 1·40 30
431. – 100 f. green .. .. 2·50 50

DESIGNS—HORIZ. 3 f. 50 to 8 f. Pres. Kasavubu and map of Congo Republic. VERT. 10 f. to 100 f. Pres. Kasavubu in full uniform and outline map.

**1961.** Re-opening of Parliament. Optd. **REOUVERTURE du PARLEMENT, JUILLET 1961.**
432. 109. 10 c. yellow .. .. 10 10
433. 20 c. red .. .. 10 10
434. 40 c. turquoise .. 10 10
435. 50 c. salmon .. .. 30 20
436. 1 f. lilac .. .. 30 20
437. 1 f. 50 brown .. .. 80 70
438. 2 f. green .. .. 80 70
439. – 5 f. grey (No. 425) .. 80 70
440. – 10 f. violet (No. 428) 80 85

111. Dag Hammarskjold.

112. Campaign Emblem.

**1962.** Dag Hammarskjold Commemoration.
441. 111. 10 c. brown and grey .. 10 10
442. 20 c. blue and grey .. 10 10
443. 30 c. bistre and grey .. 10 10
444. 40 c. blue and grey .. 10 10
445. 50 c. red and grey .. 10 10
446. 3 f. olive and grey .. 2·50 1·60
447. 6 f. 50 violet and grey .. 70 50
448. 8 f. brown and grey .. 80 60

**1962.** Malaria Eradication.
449. 112. 1 f. 50 brn., blk. & yell. 10 10
450. 2 f. turq., brown & green 30 15
451. 6 f. 50 lake, black & blue 15 10

**1962.** Reorganization of Aboula Ministry. Optd. **"Paix Travail, Austerite . . . , C. ADOULA 11 juillet 1962.**
452. 111. 10 c. brown and grey .. 10 10
453. 20 c. blue and grey .. 10 10
454. 30 c. bistre and grey .. 10 10
455. 40 c. blue and grey .. 10 10
456. 50 c. red and grey .. 1·25 50
457. 3 f. olive and grey .. 15 10
458. 6 f. 50 violet and grey .. 20 10
459. 8 f. brown and grey .. 30 15

114.

**1963.** 1st Participation in U.P.U. Congress.
460. 114. 2 f. violet .. .. 1·40 1·00
461. 4 f. red .. .. .. 10 10
462. 7 f. blue .. .. 20 10
463. 20 f. green .. .. 30 15

115. Emblem, Bears and Tractor.

116. Whale-headed Stork.

**1963.** Freedom from Hunger.
464. 115. 5 f. + 2 f. violet & mauve 15 10
465. 9 f. + 4 f. green & yellow 30 20
466. 12 f. + 6 f. violet & blue 35 25
467. 20 f. + 10 f. green & red 1·75 1·60

**1963.** Protected Birds.
468. – 10 c. multicoloured .. 10 10
469. – 20 c. blue, black and red 10 10
470. – 30 c. black, brn. & grn. 10 10
471. – 40 c. black, oran. & grey 10 10
472. 116. 1 f. blk., green & brown 20 15
473. – 2 f. blue, brown and red 5·00 1·25
474. – 3 f. black, pink & green 40 20
475. – 4 f. blue, green and red 40 20
476. – 5 f. black, red and blue 60 20
477. – 6 f. black, bistre & violet 5·00 1·25
478. – 7 f. indigo, blue & turq. 85 20
479. – 8 f. blue, yellow & orge. 1·00 20
480. – 10 f. black, red and blue 1·00 20
481. – 20 f. black, red & yellow 1·75 30

BIRDS—VERT. 10 c. Eastern white pelicans. 30 c. African open-bill stork. 2 f. Marabou stork. 4 f. Congo peafowl. 6 f. Secretary bird. 8 f. Sacred ibis. HORIZ. 20 c. Crested guineafowl. 40 c. Abdim's stork. 3 f. Greater flamingoes. 5 f. Hartlaub's duck. 7 f. Blackcasqued hornbill. 10 f. South African crowned cranes. 20 f. Saddle-bill stork.

117. Strophanthus ("S. sarmentosus").

118. "Reconciliation".

**1963.** Red Cross Cent. Cross in red.
482. 117. 10 c. green and violet .. 10 10
483. A. 20 c. blue and red .. 10 10
484. 117. 30 c. red and green .. 10 10
485. A. 40 c. violet and blue .. 10 10
486. 117. 5 f. lake and olive .. 10 10
487. A 7 f. purple and orange .. 10 10
488. B. 9 f. olive .. .. 15 10
489 20 f. violet .. .. 1·25 70

DESIGNS—VERT: A, "Cinchona ledgeriana". HORIZ: B, Red Cross nurse.

**1963.** "National Reconciliation".
490. 118. 4 f. multicoloured .. 90 30
491. 5 f. multicoloured .. 10 10
492. 9 f. multicoloured .. 15 10
493. 12 f. multicoloured .. 20 10

119. Kabambare Sewer, Leopoldville.

DESIGNS: A, Tractor, bridge, etc. B, Construction of Ituri Road.

**1963.** European Economic Community Aid.
494. 119. 20 c. multicoloured .. 10 10
495. A. 30 c. multicoloured .. 10 10
496. B. 50 c. multicoloured .. 10 10
497. 119. 3 f. multicoloured .. 90 35
498. A. 5 f. multicoloured .. 15 10
499. B. 9 f. multicoloured .. 15 10
500. A. 12 f. multicoloured .. 15 10

120. N'Djili Airport, Leopoldville.

DESIGN: 5 f., 7f. 50f. Mailplane and control tower.

**1963.** "Air Congo" Commemoration.
501. 120. 2 f. multicoloured .. 10 10
502. – 5 f. multicoloured .. 10 10
503. 120. 6 f. multicoloured .. 90 40
504. – 7 f. multicoloured .. 10 10
505. 120. 30 f. multicoloured .. 25 15
506. – 50 f. multicoloured .. 40 25

**1963.** 15th Anniv. of Declaration of Human Rights. Optd. **10 DECEMBRE 1948 10 DECEMBRE 1963 15e anniversaire DROITS DE L'HOMME.**
507. 114. 2 f. violet .. .. 10 10
508. 4 f. red .. .. 10 10
509. 7 f. blue .. .. 20 20
510. 20 f. green .. .. 20 20

122. Student in Laboratory.

**1964.** 10th Anniv. of Lovanium University. Multicoloured.
511. 50 c. Type 122 .. .. 10 10
512. 1 f. 50 University buildings 10 10
513. 8 f. Atomic and nuclear reactor symbols .. 1·75 1·60
514. 25 f. University arms and buildings .. .. 20 15
515. 30 f. Type 122 .. .. 20 20
516. 60 f. As 1 f. 50 .. .. 40 30
517. 75 f. As 8 f. .. .. 50 50
518. 100 f. As 25 f. .. .. 70 60

**1964.** Various stamps surch. over coloured metallic panels.

(a) Stamps of Belgian Congo surch. **REPUBLIQUE DU CONGO** and value.
519. – 1 f. on 20 c. (No. 340) .. 10 10
520. – 2 f. on 1 f. 50 (No. 306) 1·75 1·25
521. – 5 f. on 6 f. 50 (No. 348) 30 20
522. – 8 f. on 6 f. 50 (No. 311) 35 25

(b) Stamps of Congo (Kinshasa) surch.
523. – 1 f. on 20 c. (No. 379) .. 10 10
524. – 1 f. on 6 f. 50 (No. 372) 10 10
525. – 2 f. on 1 f. 50 (No. 367) 10 10
530. 109. 3 f. on 20 c. .. .. 25 20
531. 4 f. on 40 c. .. .. 25 20
526. – 5 f. on 6 f. 50 (No. 387) 30 20
528. 106. 6 f. on 6 f. 50 .. .. 30 20
529. 7 f. on 20 c. .. .. 40 25

125. Pole-vaulting.

DESIGNS — VERT. 7 f., 20 f. Throwing the javelin. HORIZ. 8 f., 100 f. Hurdling.

**1964.** Olympic Games, Tokyo.
532. 125. 5 f. sepia, grey and red 10 10
533. – 7 f. violet, red and green 80 40
534. – 8 f. brown, yellow & blue 10 10
535. 125. 10 f. purple, blue & pur. 10 10
536. – 20 f. brn., green & orge. 20 10
537. – 100 f. brn., mauve & grn. 80 20

**OCCUPATION OF STANLEYVILLE**

During the occupation of Stanleyville from 5th August to 24th November, 1964, stocks of a number of contemporary issues were overprinted **REPUBLIQUE POPULAIRE** and issued by the rebel authorities.

126. National Palace.

**1964.** National Palace, Leopoldville.
538. 126. 50 c. mauve and blue .. 10 10
539. 1 f. blue and purple .. 10 10
540. 2 f. brown and violet .. 10 10
541. 3 f. green and brown .. 10 10
542. 4 f. orange and blue .. 10 10
543. 5 f. violet and green .. 10 10
544. 6 f. brown and orange .. 10 10
545. 7 f. olive and brown .. 10 10
546. 8 f. red and blue .. 2·00 35
547. 9 f. violet and red .. 10 10
548. 10 f. brown and green .. 10 10
549. 20 f. blue and brown .. 10 10
550. 30 f. red and green .. 15 10
551. 40 f. blue and purple .. 25 10
552. 50 f. brown and green .. 35 10
553. 100 f. black and orange 65 15

**127.** Pres. Kennedy. **128.** Rocket and Unisphere.

**1964.** Pres. Kennedy Commem.
554. **127.** 5 f. blue and black .. 10 10
555. 6 f. purple and black .. 10 10
556. 9 f. brown and black .. 10 10
557. 30 f. violet and black .. 30 10
558. 40 f. green and black .. 2·00 60
559. 60 f. brown and black .. 50 25

**1965.** New York World's Fair.
560. **128.** 50 c. purple and black 10 10
561. 1 f. 50 blue and violet 10 10
562. 2 f. brown and green .. 10 10
563. 10 f. green and red .. 70 40
564. 18 f. blue and brown .. 10 10
565. 27 f. red and green .. 25 10
566. 40 f. grey and red .. 40 15

**129.** Football.

**1965.** 1st African Games, Leopoldville.
567. – 5 f. black, brown & blue 10 10
568. **129.** 6 f. red, black & blue .. 10 10
569. – 15 f. black, green & orge. 10 10
570. – 24 f. black, grn. & mve. 20 10
571. **129.** 40 f. blue, blk. & turq. 1·25 45
572. – 60 f. purple, black & bl. 45 15
SPORTS—VERT. 5 f., 24 f. Basketball. 15 f., 60 f. Volleyball.

**130.** Telecommunications Satellites.

**1965.** Cent. of I.T.U. Multicoloured.
573. 6 f. Type **130** .. .. 10 10
574. 9 f. Telecommunications satellites (different view) 10 10
575. 12 f. Type **130** .. .. 10 10
576. 15 f. As 9 f. .. .. 10 10
577. 18 f. Type **130** .. .. 1·00 30
578. 20 f. As 9 f. .. .. 15 10
579. 30 f. Type **130** .. .. 25 10
580. 40 f. As 9 f. .. .. 30 10

**131.** Parachutist and troops landing.

**1965.** 5th Anniv. of Independence.
581. **131.** 5 f. brown and blue .. 10 10
582. 6 f. brown and orange 10 10
583. 7 f. brown and green .. 45 20
584. 9 f. brown and mauve .. 10 10
585. 18 f. brown and yellow 15 10

**132.** Matadi Port.

**1965.** Int. Co-operation Year.
586. **132.** 6 f. blue, black & yellow 10 10
587. – 8 f. brown, blk. & blue 10 10
588. – 9 f. turq., black & brown 10 10
589. **132.** 12 f. mauve, black & grey 80 30
590. – 25 f. olive, black & red 20 10
591. – 60 f. grey, black & yell. 40 10
DESIGNS: 8 f., 25 f. Katanga mines. 9 f., 60 f. Tshopo Barrage, Stanleyville.

**133.** Medical Care.

**1965.** Congolese Army.
592. **133.** 2 f. blue and red 10 10
593. 5 f. brown, red and pink 10 10
594. – 6 f. brown and blue .. 10 10
595. – 7 f. green and yellow .. 10 10
596. – 9 f. brown and green .. 10 10
597. – 10 f. brown and green 40 40
598. – 18 f. violet and red 15 10
599. – 19 f. brown & turq. .. 60 40
600. – 20 f. brown and blue .. 15 10
601. – 24 f. multicoloured .. 20 15
602. – 30 f. multicoloured .. 25 10
DESIGNS—HORIZ. 6 f., 9 f. Feeding child. 7 f., 18 f. Bridge-building. VERT. 10 f., 20 f. Building construction. 19 f. Telegraph line maintenance. 24 f., 30 f. Soldier and flag.

**1966.** World Meteorological Day. Nos. 590/1 optd. **6e Journee Meteorologique Mondiale / 23.3.66** (on coloured metallic panel) and W.M.O. Emblem.
603. – 25 f. olive, black and red 75 45
604. – 60 f. grey, black & yellow 75 50

**135.** Carved Stool and Head.

**1966.** World Festival of Negro Arts, Dakar.
605. **135.** 10 f. black, red and grey 10 10
606. – 12 f. black, green & blue 10 10
607. – 15 f. black, blue & pur. 15 15
608. – 53 f. black, red and blue 1·10 90
DESIGNS—VERT. 12 f. Statuettes. 53 f. Statuettes of women. HORIZ. 15 f. Woman's head and carved goat.

**136.** Pres. Mobutu and Fish Workers.

**1966.** Pres. Mobutu Commem.
609. **136.** 2 f. brown and blue .. 10 10
610. – 4 f. brown and red .. 10 10
611. – 6 f. brown and olive .. 65 60
612. – 8 f. brown and turquoise 10 10
613. – 10 f. brown and lake .. 10 10
614. – 12 f. brown and violet .. 10 10
615. – 15 f. brown and green .. 10 10
616. – 24 f. brown and mauve 20 15
DESIGNS (Pres. Mobutu and): 4 f. Harvesting pyrethrum. 6 f. Building construction. 8 f. Winnowing maize. 10 f. Cotton-picking. 12 f. Harvesting fruit. 15 f. Picking coffee-beans. 24 f. Harvesting pineapples.

**1966.** Inaug. of W.H.O. Headquarters, Geneva. Nos. 550/3 optd. **O.M.S. Geneve 1966** and WHO Emblem.
618. **126.** 30 f. red and green 70 70
619. 40 f. blue and purple .. 70 70
620. 50 f. brown and green .. 75 75
621. 100 f. black and orange 75 75

**139.** Footballer.

**1966.** World Cup Football Championships.
622. **139.** 10 f. green, violet & brn. 10 10
623. – 30 f. grn., violet & purple 25 20
624. – 50 f. brown, blue & grn 85 80
625. – 60 f. gold, sepia & green 45 40
DESIGNS: 30 f. Two footballers. 50 f. Three footballers. 60 f. Jules Rimet Cup and football.

**1966.** World Cup Football Championships Final. Nos. 622/5 optd. **FINALE. ANGLETERRE—ALLEMAGNE 4 - 2.**
626. **139.** 10 f. green, violet & brn. 15 15
627. – 30 f. green, violet & pur. 50 45
628. – 50 f. brown, blue & grn. 75 60
629. – 60 f. gold, sepia & green 90 75

**1967.** 4th African Unity Organization (O.U.A.) Conf., Kinshasa. Nos. 538/43 surch. **4e Sommet OUA KINSHASA du 11 au 14-9-67** and value.
631. **126.** 1 k. on 2 f. .. .. 10 10
632. 3 k. on 5 f. .. .. 10 10
633. 5 k. on 4 f. .. .. 20 15
634. 6 k. 60 on 1 f. .. 25 20
635. 9 k. 60 on 50 c. .. 40 25
636. 9 k. 80 on 3 f. .. 50 40

**1967.** New Constitution. Nos. 609/10 and 592 surch. **1967 NOUVELLE CONSTITUTION** with coloured metallic panel obliterating old value.
639. **136.** 4 k. on 2 f. .. .. 20 15
640. **133.** 5 k. on 2 f. .. .. 20 15
641. – 21 k. on 4 f. .. .. 90 70

**1967.** 1st Congolese Games, Kinshasa. Nos. 567 and 569 surch. **1ers Jeux Congolais 25/6 au 2/7/67 Kinshasa** and value.
642. 1 k. on 5 f. .. .. 10 10
643. 9·6 k. on 15 f. .. .. 50 50

**1967.** 1st Flight by Air Congo BAC "One-Eleven". No. 504 surch. **1er VOL BAC ONE ELEVEN 14/5/67** and value.
644. 9.6 k. on 7 f. .. .. 70 20

**1968.** World Children's Day (8.10.67). Nos. 586 and 588 surch. **JOURNEE MONDIALE DE L'ENFANCE 8-10-67** and new value.
645. **132.** 1 k. on 6 f. .. .. 10 10
646. 9 k. on 9 f. .. .. 50 50

**1968.** Int. Tourist Year (1967). Nos. 538, 541 and 544 surch. **Annee Internationale du Tourisme 24-10-67** and new value.
647. **126.** 5 k. on 50 c. .. .. 20 20
648. 10 k. on 6 f. .. .. 40 40
649. 15 k. on 3 f. .. .. 60 60

**1968.** (a) No. 540 surch.
650. **126.** 1 k. on 2 f. .. .. 10 10

(b) Surch. (coloured panel obliterating old value, and new value surch. on panel. Panel colour given first, followed by colour of new value).

(i) Nos. 538 and 542.
651. **126.** 2 k. on 50 c. (Bronze and Black) .. .. 10 10
652. 2 k. on 50 c. (Blue and White) .. .. 10 10
653. 9.6 k. on 4 f. (Black and White) .. .. 50 45

(ii) No. 609.
654. **136.** 10 k. on 2 f. (Black & White) .. .. 45 10

**152.** Leaping Leopard.

**1968.**
655. **152.** 2 k. black on green .. 15 10
656. 9.6 k. black on red .. 65 15

**1968.** As Nos. 609, etc., but with colours changed and surch. in new value.
657. **136.** 15 s. on 2 f. brown & blue 10 10
658. – 1 k. on 6 f. brn. & chestnut 10 10
659. – 3 k. on 10 f. brn. & grn. 10 10
660. – 5 k. on 12 f. brn. & oran. 20 15
661. – 20 k. on 15 f. brn. & grn. 70 50
662. – 50 k. on 24 f. brn. & pur. 1·90 1·25

**154.** Human Rights Emblem.

**1968.** Human Rights Year.
663. **154.** 2 k. green and blue .. 10 10
664. 9.6 k. red and green .. 40 25
665. 10 k. brown and lilac 40 25
666. 40 k. violet and brown 1·50 1·10

**1969.** 4th O.C.A.M. (Organization Commune Africaine et Malgache) Summit Meeting, Kinshasa. Nos. 663/6 with colours changed optd. **4 EME SOMMET OCAM 27-1-1969 KINSHASA** and emblem.
667. **154.** 2 k. brown and green .. 10 10
668. 9.60 k. green and pink .. 40 25
669. 10 k. blue and grey .. 40 25
670. 40 k. violet and blue .. 1·50 1·10

**156.** Map of Africa and "Cotton".

**1969.** Int. Fair, Kinshasa. (1st Issue).
671. **156.** 2 k. multicoloured .. 10 10
672. – 6 k. multicoloured .. 30 30
673. – 9.6 k. multicoloured .. 40 20
674. – 9.8 k. multicoloured .. 40 35
675. – 11.6 k. multicoloured .. 50 50
DESIGNS: Map of Africa and: 6 k. "Copper". 9.6 k. "Coffee". 9.8 k. "Diamonds". 11.6 k. "Palm-oil".

**157.** Fair Entrance.

**1969.** Inaug of Int. Fair, Kinshasa (2nd issue).
676. **157.** 2 k. purple and gold .. 10 10
677. – 3 k. blue and gold .. 10 10
678. – 10 k. green and gold .. 40 40
679. – 25 k. red and gold .. 1·00 85
DESIGNS: 3 k. "Gecomin" (mining company) pavilion. 10 k. Administration building. 25 k. African Unity Organization pavilion.

**158.** Congo Arms. **159.** Pres. Mobutu.

**1969.**
680. **158.** 10 s. red and black .. 10 10
681. 15 s. blue and black .. 10 10
682. 30 s. green and black .. 10 10
683. 60 s. purple and black 10 10
684. 90 s. bistre and black .. 10 10
685. **159.** 1 k. multicoloured .. 10 10
686. 2 k. multicoloured .. 10 10
687. 3 k. multicoloured .. 15 10
688. 5 k. multicoloured .. 15 15
689. 6 k. multicoloured .. 20 15
690. 9.6 k. multicoloured .. 30 25
691. 10 k. multicoloured .. 40 30
692. 20 k. multicoloured .. 80 60
693. 50 k. multicoloured .. 2·00 1·75
694. 100 k. multicoloured .. 4·00 3·50

**160.** "The Well-sinker" (O. Bonnevalle).

**1969.** 50th Anniv. of Int. Labour Organization. Paintings. Multicoloured.
695. 3 k. Type **160** .. .. 15 15
696. 4 k. "Cocoa Production" (J. van Noten) .. .. 20 15
697. 8 k. "The Harbour" (C. Meunier) .. .. 55 25
698. 10 k. "The Poulterer" (H. Evenepoel) .. 45 35
699. 15 k. "Industry" (C. Meunier) .. .. 85 50
No. 697 is vert., size 29 × 42 mm.

**162.** Pres. Mobutu, Map and Flag.

**1970.** 10th Anniv. of Independence.
701. **162.** 10 s. multicoloured .. 10 10
702. 90 s. multicoloured .. 10 10
703. 1 k. multicoloured .. 10 10
704. 2 k. multicoloured .. 10 10
705. 7 k. multicoloured .. 25 15
706. 10 k. multicoloured .. 40 25
707. 20 k. multicoloured .. 80 50

**1970.** Surch. (a) National Palace series.
708. **126.** 10 s. on 1 f. .. .. 10 10
709. 20 s. on 2 f. .. .. 10 10
710. 30 s. on 3 f. .. .. 10 10
711. 40 s. on 4 f. .. .. 10 10
712. 60 s. on 7 f. .. .. 80 75
713. 90 s. on 9 f. .. .. 80 75
714. 1 k. on 6 f. .. .. 15 10
715. 3 k. on 30 f. .. .. 80 75
716. 4 k. on 40 f. .. .. 15 10
717. 5 k. on 50 f. .. .. 2·00 1·90
718. 10 k. on 100 f. .. .. 90 75

(b) Congolese Army series.
719. 90 s. on 9 f. (No. 596) 15 10
720. 1 k. on 7 f. (No. 595) .. 15 10
721. 2 k. on 24 f. (No. 601) 15 10

(c) Pres. Mobutu series.
722. **136.** 20 s. on 2 f. .. .. 15 10
723. – 40 s. on 4 f. (No. 610) .. 15 10
724. – 1 k. on 12 f. (No. 614) 80 70
725. – 2 k. on 24 f. (No. 616) 15 10

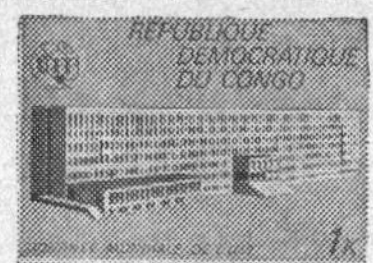


164. I.T.U. Headquarters, Geneva.

**1970.** United Nations Commemorations.
726. 164. 1 k. olive, grn. & pink .. 10 10
727. – 2 k. grey, grn. & orge. .. 10 10
728. – 6 k. 60 red, pink & blue 25 25
729. 164. 9 k. 60 multicoloured .. 30 30
730. – 9 k. 80 sepia, brn. & bl. 35 35
731. – 10 k. sepia, brn. & lilac 35 35
732. – 11 k. sepia, brn. & pink 40 40

DESIGNS AND EVENTS: 1 k., 9 k. 60, (I.T.U. World Day). 2 k., 6 k. 60, New U.P.U. Headquarters, Berne (Inauguration). 9 k. 80, 10 k., 11 k. U.N. Headquarters, New York (25th anniversary).

165. Pres. Mobutu and Independence Arch.

**1970.** 5th Anniv. of "New Regime".
733. 165. 2 k. multicoloured .. 10 10
734. 10 k. multicoloured .. 45 35
735. 20 k. multicoloured .. 85 80

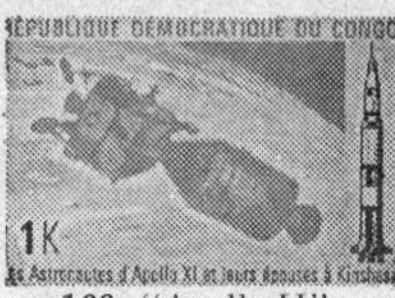


166. "Apollo 11".

**1970.** Visit of "Apollo 11" Astronauts to Kinshasa.
736. 166. 1 k. bl., blk. & red .. 10 10
737. – 2 k. violet, blk. & red .. 10 10
738. – 7 k. blk., orge. & red .. 25 25
739. – 10 k. blk., pink & red .. 35 35
740. – 30 k. blk., grn. & red .. 1·00 1·00

DESIGNS: 2 k. Astronauts on Moon. 7 k. Pres. Mobutu decorating wives. 10 k. Pres. Mobutu with astronauts. 30 k. Astronauts after splashdown.

167. "Metopodontus savagei".

**1971.** Insects. Multicoloured.
741. 10 s. Type 167 .. .. 10 10
742. 50 s. "Cicindela regalis" .. 10 10
743. 90 s. "Magacephala catenulata" .. .. 10 10
744. 1 k. "Stephanorrhina guttata" .. .. .. 10 10
745. 2 k. "Pupuricenus congoanus" .. .. 10 10
746. 3 k. "Sagra tristis" .. 20 15
747. 5 k. "Steraspis subcalida" 70 50
748. 10 k. "Mecosaspis explanata" .. .. 95 75
749. 30 k. "Goliathus meleagris" 2·25 2·00
750. 40 k. "Sternotomis virescens" 3·25 3·00

168. "Colotis protomedia".

**1971.** Butterflies and Moths. Multicoloured.
751. 10 s. Type 168 .. .. 10 10
752. 20 s. "Rhodophitus simplex" 10 10
753. 70 s. "Euphaedra overlaeti" 10 10
754. 1 k. "Argema bouvieri" .. 10 10
755. 3 k. "Cymothoe reginae-elisabethae" .. 20 15
756. 5 k. "Miniodes maculifera" 55 35
757. 10 k. "Salamis temora" .. 75 55
758. 15 k. "Eronia leda" .. 1·50 1·00
759. 25 k. "Cymothoe sangaris" 2·10 1·50
760. 40 k. "Euchloron megaera" 3·25 2·75

169. "Four Races" around Globe.

170. Pres. Mobutu and Obelisk.

**1971.** Racial Equality Year.
761. 169. 1 k. multicoloured .. 10 10
762. 4 k. multicoloured .. 15 15
763. 5 k. multicoloured .. 20 20
764. 10 k. multicoloured .. 40 40

**1971.** 4th Anniv. of Popular Revolutionary Movement (M.P.R.).
765. 170. 4 k. multicoloured .. 15 15

171. "Hypericum bequaertii".

**1971.** Tropical Plants. Multicoloured.
766. 1 k. Type 171 .. .. 10 10
767. 4 k. "Dissotis brazzae" .. 20 20
768. 20 k. "Begonia wollasti" 95 95
769. 25 k. "Cassia alata" .. 1·25 1·25

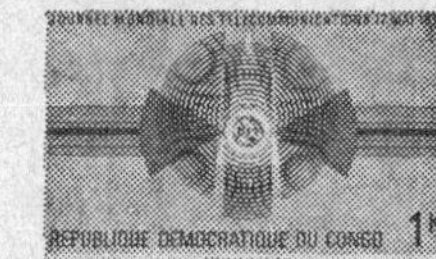


172. I.T.U. Emblem (International Telecommunications Day).

**1971.** "Telecommunications and Space". Multicoloured.
770. 1 k. Type 172 .. .. 10 10
771. 3 k. Dish aerial (Satellite Earth Station, Kinshasa) 15 15
772. 6 k. Map of Pan-African telecommunications network .. .. 30 30

173. Savanna Monkey.

**1971.** Congo Monkeys. Multicoloured.
773 10 s. Type 173 .. .. 15 10
774 20 s. Moustached monkey (vert) .. .. 15 10
775 70 s. De Brazza's monkey 20 10
776 1 k. Yellow baboon .. 20 15
777 3 k. Pygmy chimpanzee (vert) .. .. .. 35 30
778 5 k. Black mangabey (vert) 80 75
779 10 k. Owl-faced monkey .. 1·50 1·40
780 15 k. Diana monkey .. 2·50 2·00
781 25 k. Western black-and-white colobus (vert) .. 4·25 3·50
782 40 k. L'Hoest's monkey (vert) .. .. .. 5·50 5·00

174. Hotel Inter-Continental.

**1971.** Opening of Hotel Inter-Continental, Kinshasa.
783. 174. 2 k. multicoloured .. 10 10
784. 12 k. multicoloured .. 50 50

175. "Reader".

**1971.** Literacy Campaign. Multicoloured.
785. 50 s. Type 175 .. .. 10 10
786. 2 k. 50 Open book and abacus .. .. .. 20 10
787. 7 k. Symbolic alphabet .. 45 35

For later issues see **ZAIRE REPUBLIC**.

## CONGO (Brazzaville) Pt. 6; Pt. 12

Formerly Middle Congo. An independent republic within the French Community.

1. "Birth of the Republic".

**1959.** 1st Anniv of Republic.
1 1 25 f. multicoloured .. 35 15

**1960.** 10th Anniv. of African Technical Co-operation Commission. As T 62 of Cameroun.
2. 50 f. lake and green .. 60 55

**1960.** Air. Olympic Games. No. 276 of French Equatorial Africa optd. with Olympic rings, **XVIIe OLYMPIADE 1960 REPUBLIQUE DU CONGO** and surch. **250 F.** and bars.
3. 250 f. on 500 f. blue, black and green .. .. 6·00 6·00

2. Pres. Youlou.

3. U.N. Emblem, Map and Flag.

**1960.**
4. 2. 15 f. green, red & turquoise 25 15
5. 85 f. blue and red .. 1·00 50

**1961.** Admission into U.N.O.
6. 3. 5 f. multicoloured .. .. 15 10
7. 20 f. multicoloured .. 25 20
8. 100 f. multicoloured .. 1·25 90

4. "Thesium tencio".

**1961.** Air.
9. – 100 f. purple, yell. & green 1·75 1·00
10. – 200 f. yell., turq. & brown 3·00 1·50
11. 4. 500 f. yell., myrtle & brn. 8·00 3·50

FLOWERS: 100 f. "Helicrysum mechowiam". 200 f. "Cogniauxia podolaena".

**1961.** Air. Foundation of "Air Afrique" Airline. As T 69 of Cameroun.
12. 50 f. purple, myrtle & green 60 45

6. "Elegatis bipinnulatus".

7. Brazzaville Market.

**1961.** Tropical Fish.
13. 6. 50 c. multicoloured .. 10 10
14. – 1 f. brown and green .. 10 10
15. – 2 f. brown and blue .. 10 10
15a.– 2 f. red, brown and green 20 10
16. 6. 3 f. green, orange and blue 20 15
17 – 5 f. sepia, brown and green 30 15
18. – 10 f. brown and turquoise 55 25
18a.– 15 f. purple, green & violet 80 45

FISH: 1 f., 2 f. (No. 15) "Chauliodus sloanei". 2 f. (No. 15a), "Lycoteuthis diadema". 5 f. "Argyropelecus gigas". 10 f. "Caulolepis longidens". 15 f. "Melanocetus johnsoni".

**1962.**
19. 7. 20 f. red, green and black 30 15

**1962.** Malaria Eradication. As T 70 of Cameroun.
20. 25 f. + 5 f. brown .. .. 55 55

8. "Yang-tse" (freighter) loading Timber, Pointe Noire.

**1962.** Air. International Fair, Pointe Noire.
21. 8. 50 f. multicoloured .. 1·00 50

**1962.** Sports. As T 12 of Central African Republic.
22. 20 f. sepia, red & blk. (post.) 30 25
23. 50 f. sepia, red and black .. 65 50
24. 100 f. sepia, red & black (air) 1·50 1·00

DESIGNS—HORIZ. 20 f. Boxing. 50 f. Running. VERT. (26 × 47 mm.): 100 f. Basketball.

**1962.** Union of African and Malagasy States. 1st Anniv. As No. 328 of Cameroun.
25. 72. 30 f. violet .. .. 55 50

**1962.** Freedom from Hunger. As T 76 of Cameroun.
26. 25 f. + 5 f. turquoise, brown and blue .. .. .. 55 55

9. Town Hall, Brazzaville and Pres. Youlou.

**1963.** Air.
27. 9. 100 f. multicoloured .. 60·00 60·00

9a. "Costus spectabilis" (K. Schum).



10. King Makoko's Gold Chain.

**1963.** Air. Flowers. Mult.
28. 100 f. Type 9a .. .. 1·75 1·10
29. 250 f. "Acanthus montanus T. anders" .. .. 3·75 1·90

**1963.** Air African and Malagasy Posts and Telecommunications Union. As T 18 of Central African Republic.
30. 85 f. red, buff and violet .. 1·25 75

**1963.** Space Telecommunications. As Nos. 37/8 of Central African Republic.
31. 25 f. blue, orange and green 45 30
32. 100 f. violet, brown & blue 1·25 1·10

**1963.** Folklore and Tourism.
33. 10. 10 f. bistre and black .. 25 30
34. – 15 f. multicoloured .. 30 25

DESIGN: 15 f. Kebekebe mask.

See also Nos. 45/6 and 62/4.

11. Airline Emblem.

**1963.** Air. 1st Anniv of "Air Afrique", and Inaug of DC-8 Service.
35. 11. 50 f. multicoloured .. 60 45

12. Liberty Square, Brazzaville.

**1963.** Air.
36. **12.** 25 f. multicoloured .. 30 35
See also No. 56.

**1963.** Air. European–African Economic Convention. As T **24** of Central African Republic.
37. 50 f. multicoloured .. 70 50

**1963.** 15th Anniv. of Declaration of Human Rights. As T **26** of Central African Republic.
38. 25 f. blue, turq. and brown 45 30

**13.** Statue of Hathor, Abu Simbel. **14.** Barograph.

**1964.** Air. Nubian Monuments.
39. **13.** 10 f.+5 f. violet & brown 35 20
40. 25 f.+5 f. brn. & turq. 45 40
41. 50 f.+5 f. turq. & brown 1·10 90

**1964.** World Meteorological Day.
42. **14.** 50 f. brown, blue & green 70 65

**15.** Machinist. **16.** Emblem and Implements of Manual Labour.

**1964.** " Technical Instruction ".
43. **15.** 20 f. brn., mauve & turq. 35 25

**1964.** Manual Labour Rehabilitation.
44. **16.** 80 f. green, red and sepia 85 45

**17.** Diaboua Ballet. **19.** Wood Carving.

**18.** Tree-felling.

**1964.** Folklore and Tourism. Multicoloured.
45. 30 f. Type **17** .. .. 60 30
46. 60 f. Kebekebe dance (vert.) 90 65

**1964.** Air.
47 **18** 100 f. brown, red & green 1·25 70

**1964.** Congo Sculpture.
48. **19.** 50 f. sepia and red .. 65 45

**20.** Students in Classroom. **21.** Sun, Ears of Wheat, and Globe within Cogwheel.

**1964.** Development of Education.
49. **20.** 25 f. red, purple & blue .. 40 30

**1964** Air. 5th Anniv. of Equatorial African Heads of State Conference. As T **31** of Central African Republic.
50. 100 f. multicoloured .. 1·25 65

**1964.** Air. Europafrique.
51. **21.** 50 f. yellow, blue & red .. 70 50

**22.** Stadium, Olympic Flame and Throwing the Hammer.

**1964.** Air. Olympic Games, Tokyo. Sport and flame orange.
52. **22.** 25 f. violet and brown .. 35 25
53. – 50 f. purple and olive .. 60 40
54. – 100 f. green and brown .. 1·25 85
55. – 200 f. olive and red .. 2·50 75
DESIGNS—Stadium, Olympic Flame and: VERT. 50 f. Weightlifting. 100 f. Volley-ball. HORIZ. 200 f. High-jumping.

**1964.** 1st Anniv. of Revolution and National Festival. As T **12** but inscr. "1er ANNIVERSAIRE DE LA REVOLUTION FETE NATIONALE 15 AOUT 1964".
56. 20 f. multicoloured .. .. 30 20

**23.** Posthorns, Envelope and Radio Mast.

**1964.** Air. Pan-African and Malagasy Posts and Telecommunications Congress, Cairo.
57. **23.** 25 f. sepia and red .. 35 25

**1964.** French, African and Malagasy Co-operation. As T **547** of France.
58. 25 f. brown, green and red 45 35

**24.** Dove, Envelope and Radio Mast.

**1965.** Establishment of Posts and Telecommunications Office, Brazzaville.
59. **24.** 25 f. multicoloured .. 35 25

**25.** Town Hall, Brazzaville and Arms.

**1965.** Air.
60. **25.** 100 f. multicoloured .. 1·10 55

**26.** " Europafrique ".

**1965.** Air. Europafrique.
61. **26.** 50 f. multicoloured .. 60 40

**27.** African Elephant. **29.** Pres. Massamba-Debat.

**28.** Cadran de Breguet's Telegraph and " Telstar ".

**1965.** Folklore and Tourism.
62. – 15 f. purple, grn. & blue 35 25
63. **27.** 20 f. black, blue & green 40 30
64. – 85 f. multicoloured .. 1·60 1·10
DESIGNS—VERT. 15 f. Bushbuck. 85 f. Dancer on stilts.

**1965.** Air. Centenary of I.T.U.
65. **28.** 100 f. brown and blue .. 1·75 80

**1965.** Portrait in sepia.
66. **29.** 20 f. yellow, grn. & brn. 25 15
66a. 25 f. green, turq. & brn. 35 20
66b. 30 f. orange, turq. & brn 40 20

**30.** Sir Winston Churchill. **31.** Pope John XXIII.

**1965.** Air. Famous Men.
67. – 25 f. on 50 f. sepia & red 45 45
68. **30.** 50 f. sepia and green .. 90 90
69. – 80 f. sepia and blue .. 1·10 1·10
70. – 100 f. sepia and yellow .. 1·75 1·75
PORTRAITS: 25 f. Lumumba. 80 f. Pres. Boganda. 100 f. Pres. Kennedy.

**1965.** Air. Pope John Commem.
71. **31.** 100 f. multicoloured .. 1·25 90

**32.** Athletes and Map of Africa. **33.** Natives hauling Log.

**1965.** 1st African Games, Brazzaville. Inscr. "PREMIERS JEUX AFRICAINS". Multicoloured.
72. 25 f. Type **32** .. .. 40 30
73. 40 f. Football .. .. 55 40
74. 50 f. Handball .. .. 60 40
75. 85 f. Running .. .. 1·00 65
76. 100 f. Cycling .. .. 1·40 85
Nos. 73/6 are larger 34½ × 34½ mm.

**1965.** Air. National Unity.
77. **33.** 50 f. brown and green .. 60 40

**34.** "World Co-operation".

**1965.** Air. Int. Co-operation Year.
78. **34.** 50 f. multicoloured .. 90 55

**35.** Arms of Congo. **37.** Trench-digging.

**36.** Lincoln.

**1965.**
79. **35.** 20 f. multicoloured .. 30 15

**1965.** Air. Death Cent. of Abraham Lincoln.
80. **36.** 90 f. multicoloured .. 90 50

**1966.** Village Co-operative.
81. **37.** 25 f. multicoloured .. 30 20

**1966.** National Youth Day. As T **37** but showing Youth display.
82. 30 f. multicoloured .. 40 30

**38.** De Gaulle and Flaming Torch.

**1966.** Air. 22nd Anniv. of Brazzaville Conf.
83. **38.** 500 f. brown, red & green 21·00 17·00

**39.** Weaving. **40.** People and Clocks.

**41.** W.H.O. Building. **42.** Satellite " D1 " and Brazzaville Tracking Station.

**1966.** World Festival of Negro Arts, Dakar. Multicoloured.
84. 30 f. Type **39** .. .. 45 25
85. 85 f. Musical Instrument (horiz.) .. .. .. 1·10 65
86. 90 f. Mask .. .. 1·40 85

**1966.** Establishment of Shorter Working Day.
87. **40.** 70 f. multicoloured .. 80 40

**1966.** Inaug. of W.H.O. Headquarters, Geneva.
88. **41.** 50 f. violet, yellow & blue 65 40

**1966.** Air. Launching of Satellite " D1 ".
89. **42.** 150 f. black, red & green 1·75 80

**43.** St. Pierre Claver Church. **44.** Volleyball.

**45.** Jules Rimet Cup and Globe. **46.** Corn, Atomic Emblem and Map.

**1966.**
90. **43.** 70 f. multicoloured .. 80 40

**1966.** Sports.
91. **44.** 1 f. brown, bistre & blue 10 10
92. – 2 f. brown, green & blue 15 10
93. – 3 f. brown, lake and green 15 15
94. – 5 f. brown, blue & green 20 15
95. – 10 f. violet, turq. & green 25 20
96. – 15 f. brown, violet & lake 35 30
DESIGNS—VERT. 2 f. Basketball. 5 f. Sportsmen. 10 f. Athlete. 15 f. Football. HORIZ. 3 f. Handball.

**1966.** World Cup Football Championships, England.
97. **45.** 30 f. multicoloured .. 45 30

**1966.** Air. Europafrique.
98. **46.** 50 f. multicoloured .. 55 35

**47.** Pres. Massamba-Debat and Presidential Palace, Brazzaville.

**1966.** Air. 3rd Anniv. of Congolese Revolution. Multicoloured.
99. 25 f. Type **47** .. .. 30 15
100. 30 f. Robespierre and Bastille, Paris .. .. 35 20
101. 50 f. Lenin and Winter Palace, St. Petersburg 55 30

**1966.** Air. Inauguration of DC-8F Air Services. As T **54** of Central African Republic.
103 30 f. yellow, black & violet 60 25

**48.** Dr. Albert Schweitzer.

**1966.** Air. Schweitzer Commem.
104. **48.** 100 f. multicoloured .. 1·50 85

**49.** View of School.

**1966.** Inauguration of Savorgnan de Brazza High School.
105. **49.** 30 f. multicoloured .. 35 20

**50.** Pointe-Noire Railway Station. **51.** Silhouette of Congolese, and U.N.E.S.C.O. Emblem.

**1966.**
106. **50.** 60 f. red, brown & green 1·25 75

**1966.** 20th Anniv. of U.N.E.S.C.O.
107. **51.** 90 f. blue, brown & green .. .. 1·10 80

**52.** Balumbu Mask. **53.** Cancer "The Crab", Microscope and Pagoda.

**1966.** Congolese Masks.
108. **52.** 5 f. sepia and red .. 20 15
109. – 10 f. brown and blue .. 25 15
110. – 15 f. blue, sepia & brn. 25 25
111. – 20 f. multicoloured .. 35 25
MASKS: 10 f. Kuyu. 15 f. Bakwele. 20 f. Bateke.

**1966.** Air. 9th Int. Cancer Congress, Tokyo.
112. **53.** 100 f. multicoloured 1·25 80

**54.** Sociable Weaver. **55.** Medal, Ribbon and Map.

**1967.** Air. Birds. Multicoloured.
113. 50 f. Type **54** .. .. 4·00 1·25
114. 75 f. European bee eater .. 4·50 1·75
115. 100 f. Lilac-breasted roller 7·00 2·00
116. 150 f. Regal sunbird .. 8·00 3·25
117. 200 f. South African crowned crane .. .. 10·00 3·75
118. 250 f. Secretary bird .. 11·00 4·75
119. 300 f. Knysna turaco .. 16·00 6·25

**1967.** "Companion of the Revolution" Order.
120. **55.** 20 f. multicoloured .. 30 25

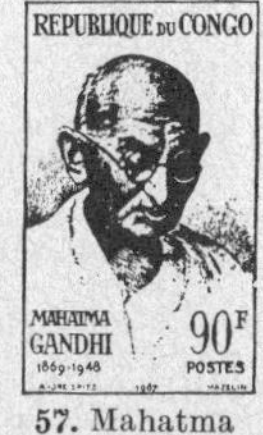

**56.** Learning the Alphabet (Educational Campaign). **57.** Mahatma Gandhi.

**1967.** Education and Sugar Production Campaigns. Multicoloured.
121. 25 f. Type **56** .. .. 35 30
122. 45 f. Cutting sugar-cane .. 50 30

**1967.** Gandhi Commem.
123. **57.** 90 f. black and blue .. 1·25 55

**58.** Prisoner's Hands in Chains. **59.** Ndumba, Lady of Fashion.

**1967.** Air. African Liberation Day.
124. **58.** 500 f. multicoloured .. 5·50 2·50

**1967.** Congolese Dolls. Multicoloured.
125. 5 f. Type **59** .. .. 15 15
126. 10 f. Fruit seller .. 25 20
127. 25 f. Girl pounding saka-saka 30 20
128. 30 f. Mother and child .. 35 25

**60.** Congo Scenery. **61.** "Europafrique".

**1967.** Int. Tourist Year.
129. **60.** 50 f. red, orge. and grn. 65 40

**1967.** Europafrique.
130. **61.** 50 f. multicoloured .. 55 30

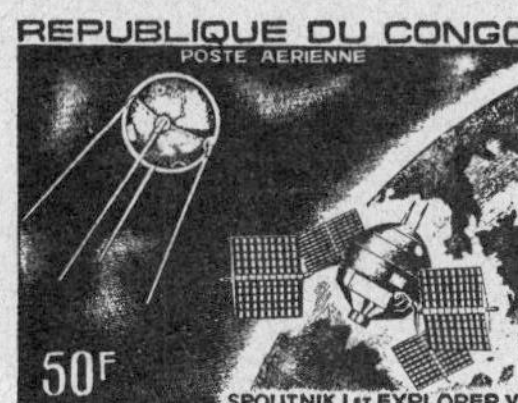

**62.** "Sputnik 1" and "Explorer 6".

**1967.** Air. Space Exploration.
131. **62.** 50 f. blue, violet & brn. 55 30
132. – 75 f. lake and slate .. 75 40
133. – 100 f. blue, red & turq. 1·10 65
134. – 200 f. red, blue & lake .. 2·25 1·50
DESIGNS: 75 f. "Ranger 6" and "Lunik 2". 100 f. "Mars 1" and "Mariner 4". 200 f. "Gemini" and "Vostok".

**63.** Brazzaville Arms.

**1967.** 4th Anniv. of Congo Revolution.
135. **63.** 30 f. multicoloured .. 40 20

**1967.** Air. 5th Anniv. of African and Malagasy Posts and Telecommunications Union. As T **66** of Central African Republic.
136. 100 f. green, red and brown 1·10 65

**64.** Jamboree Emblem, Scouts and Tents.

**1967.** Air. World Scout Jamboree, Idaho.
137. **64.** 50 f. blue, brn. & chestnut 55 30
138. – 70 f. red, green and blue 80 40
DESIGN: 70 f. Saluting hand, Jamboree camp and emblem.

**65.** Sikorsky S-43 Amphibian and Map.

**1967.** Air. 30th Anniv. of Aeromaritime Airmail Link.
139. **65.** 30 f. multicoloured .. 40 25

**66.** Dove, Human Figures and U.N. Emblem. **67.** Young Congolese.

**1967.** U.N. Day and Campaign in Support of U.N.
140. **66.** 90 f. multicoloured .. 1·25 65

**1967.** 21st Anniv. of U.N.I.C.E.F.
141. **67.** 90 f. black, bl. & brn. 1·25 65

**68.** Albert Luthuli (winner of Nobel Peace Prize) and Dove. **70.** Arms of Pointe Noire.

**69.** Global Dance.

**1968.** Luthuli Commem.
142. **68.** 30 f. brown and green .. 35 30

**1968.** Air. "Friendship of the Peoples".
143. **69.** 70 f. brown, green & blue 75 40

**1968.**
144. **70.** 10 f. multicoloured .. 35 30

**71.** "Old Man and His Grandson" (Ghirlandaio).

**1968.** Air. Paintings. Multicoloured.
145. 30 f. Type **71** .. .. 45 30
146. 100 f. "The Horatian Oath" (J.-L. David) .. .. 1·25 65
147. 200 f. "The Negress with Peonies" (Bazille) .. 2·75 1·60
The 100 f. and 200 f. are horiz. designs.
See also Nos. 209/13.

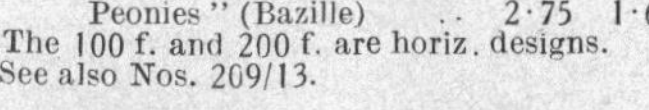

**72.** "Mother and Child". **73.** Train crossing Mayombe Viaduct.

**1968.** Mothers' Festival.
148. **72.** 15 f. black blue & lake 30 25

**1968.**
149. **73.** 45 f. lake, blue & green 1·25 40

**74.** Beribboned Rope.

**1968.** Air. 5th Anniv. of Europafrique.
150. **74.** 50 f. multicoloured .. 55 25

**75.** Daimler, 1889.

**1968.** Veteran Motor Cars. Multicoloured.
151. 5 f. Type **75** (postage) .. 20 15
152. 20 f. Berliet, 1897 .. 35 20
153. 60 f. Peugeot, 1898 .. 70 40
154. 80 f. Renault, 1900 .. 1·00 55
155. 85 f. Fiat, 1902 .. .. 1·40 70
156. 150 f. Ford, 1915 (air) .. 2·10 1·40
157. 200 f. Citroen .. .. 2·75 1·50

**1968.** Inauguration of Petroleum Refinery, Port Gentil, Gaboon. As T **80** of Central African Republic.
158. 30 f. multicoloured .. 60 25

**76.** Dr. Martin Luther King. **78.** Robert Kennedy.

**77.** "The Barricade" (Delacroix).

**1968.** Air. Martin Luther King Commem.
159. **76.** 50 f. black, green & emerald .. .. 60 30

**1968.** Air. 5th Anniv. of Revolution Paintings. Multicoloured.
160. 25 f. Type **77** .. .. 35 15
161. 30 f. " Destruction of the Bastille " (H. Robert) .. 40 20

**1968.** Air. Robert Kennedy Commem.
162. **78.** 50 f. black, green & red 55 30

**79.** "Tree of Life" and W.H.O. Emblem.

**1968.** 20th Anniv. of W.H.O.
163. **79.** 25 f. red, purple & grn. 30 15

**80.** Start of Race.

**1968.** Air. Olympic Games, Mexico.
164. **80.** 5 f. brown, blue & green 10 10
165. – 20 f. green, brn. & blue 30 15
166. – 60 f. brown, green & red 60 35
167. – 85 f. brown, red & slate 90 50
DESIGNS—VERT. 20 f. Football; 60 f. Boxing HORIZ. 85 f. High-jumping.

**1968.** Air. " Philexafrique " Stamp Exn. Abidjan (1969) (1st issue). As T **86** of Central African Republic.
168. 100 f. multicoloured .. 1·60 1·10
DESIGN: 100 f. " G. de Gueidan writing " (N. de Largilliere).

**1969.** Air. " Philexafrique " Stamp Exn., Abidjan, Ivory Coast (2nd issue). As Type **138** of Cameroun.
169. 50 f. green, brn. & mauve 1·40 1·00
DESIGN: 50 f. Pointe-Noire harbour, lumbering and Middle Congo stamp of 1933.

**1969.** Air. Birth Bicent. of Napoleon Bonaparte. As T **144** of Cameroun. Mult.
170. 25 f. Battle of Rivoli (C. Vernet) .. .. .. 55 30
171. 50 f. " Battle of Marengo " (Pahou) .. .. .. 80 50
172. 75 f. " Battle of Friedland " (H. Vernet) .. .. 1·40 55
173. 100 f. " Battle of Jena " (Thevenin) .. .. 2·00 85

**81.** " Che " Guevara.

**1969.** Air. Ernesto " Che " Guevara (Latin-American revolutionary) Commem.
174. **81.** 90 f. brown, orge. & lake 80 40

**82.** Doll and Toys.

**1969.** Air. Int. Toy Fair, Nuremberg.
175. **82.** 100 f. slate, mve. & oran. 1·75 60

**HAVE YOU READ THE NOTES AT THE BEGINNING OF THIS CATALOGUE?**
These often provide answers to the enquiries we receive.

**83.** Beribboned Bar.

**1969.** Air. Europafrique.
176. **83.** 50 f. vio., blk. & turq. 45 25

**1969.** 5th Anniv. of African Development Bank. As T **146** of Cameroun.
177. 25 f. brown, red & green .. 25 15
178. 30 f. brown, green & blue 30 15

**85.** Modern Bicycle.

**1969.** Cycles and Motor-cycles.
180. **85.** 50 f. pur., orge. & brn. 55 30
181. – 75 f. black, lake & orge. 80 35
182. – 80 f. green, blue & pur. 85 45
183. – 85 f. green, slate & brn. 95 55
184. – 100 f. multicoloured .. 1·40 65
185. – 150 f. brown, red & blk. 1·75 80
186. – 200 f. purple, deep green and green .. .. 2·75 1·40
187. – 300 f. green, pur. & blk. 4·00 1·90
DESIGNS: 75 f. " Hirondelle " cycle. 80 f. Folding cycle. 85 f. " Peugeot " cycle. 100 f. " Excelsior Manxman " motor-cycle. 150 f. " Norton " motor-cycle 200 f. " Brough Superior " motor-cycle. 300 f. " Matchless and N.I.G –J.A.P.S. " motor-cycle.

**86.** Train entering Mbamba Tunnel.

**1969.** African Int. Tourist Year. Mult.
188. 40 f. Type **86** .. .. 1·90 40
189. 60 f. Train crossing the Mayombe (horiz.) .. 2·25 50

**87.** Mortar Tanks.

**1969.** Loutete Cement Works.
190. **87.** 10 f. slate, brown & lake 10 10
191. – 15 f. violet, blue & brn. 25 15
192. – 25 f. blue, brown & red 30 25
193. – 30 f. blue, violet and ultramarine .. .. 35 25
DESIGNS—VERT. 15 f. Mixing tower. 25 f. Cableway. HORIZ. 30 f. General view of works.

**1969.** 10th Anniv. of A.S.E.C.N.A. As T **150** of Cameroun.
195. 100 f. brown .. .. 2·00 75

**88.** Harvesting Pineapples.

**1969.** 50th Anniv. of I.L.O.
196. **88.** 25 f. brown, grn. & blue 30 20
197. – 30 f. slate, purple & red 35 20
DESIGN: 30 f. Operating lathe.

**89.** Textile Plant.

**1970.** " SOTEXCO " Textile Plant, Kinsoundi.
198. **89.** 15 f. black, violet & grn. 20 15
199. – 20 f. green, red & purple 25 15
200. – 25 f. brn., bl. & new bl. 30 15
201. – 30 f. brown, red & slate 35 15
DESIGNS: 20 f. Spinning machines. 25 f. Printing textiles. 30 f. Checking finished cloth.

**90.** Linzolo Church.

**91.** Artist at work.

**92.** Diosso Gorges.

**1970.** Buildings.
202. **90.** 25 f. grn., brown & blue 35 15
203. – 90 f. brn., green & blue 80 35
DESIGN: HORIZ. 90 f. Cosmos Hotel, Brazzaville.

**1970.** Air. " Art and Culture ".
204. **91.** 100 f. brn., plum & grn. 1·00 50
205. – 150 f. plum, lake & grn. 1·60 75
206. – 200 f. brn., choc. & ochre 2·25 1·50
DESIGNS: 150 f. Lesson in wood-carving. 200 f. Potter at wheel.

**1970.** Tourism.
207. **92.** 70 f. pur., brn. & green 65 35
208. – 90 f. pur., green & brn. 85 45
DESIGN: 90 f. Foulakari Falls.

**1970.** Air. Paintings. As T **71.** Multicoloured.
209. 150 f. " Child with Cherries " (J. Russell) .. .. 1·90 1·00
210. 200 f. " Erasmus " (Holbein the younger) .. .. 2·75 1·25
211. 250 f. " Silence " (Bernadino Luini) .. .. 3·00 1·50
212. 300 f. " Scenes from the Scio Massacre " (Delacroix) 4·00 1·90
213. 500 f. " Capture of Constantinople " (Delacroix) .. 6·00 2·75

**93.** Aurichalcite.

**94.** " Volvaria esculenta ".

**1970.** Air. Minerals. Multicoloured.
214. 100 f. Type **93** .. .. 1·00 50
215. 150 f. Dioptase .. .. 1·50 70

**1970.** Mushrooms. Multicoloured.
216. 5 f. Type **94** .. .. 50 20
217. 10 f. " Termitomyces entolomoides " .. .. 55 25
218. 15 f. " Termitomyces microcarpus " .. .. 85 35
219. 25 f. " Termitomyces aurantiacus " .. .. 1·10 45
220. 30 f. " Termitomyces mammiformis " .. .. 1·40 55
221. 50 f. " Tremella fuciformis " 3·25 1·25

**95.** Laying Cable.

**96.** Mother feeding Child.

**1970.** Laying of Coaxial Cable, Brazzaville. Pointe-Noire.
222. **95.** 25 f. buff, brown & blue 1·40 25
223. – 30 f. brown and green .. 1·60 35
DESIGN: 30 f. Diesel locomotive and cable-laying gang.

**1970.** New U.P.U. Headquarters Building, Berne. As T **156** of Cameroun.
224. 30 f. purple, slate and plum 45 25

**1970.** Mothers' Day. Multicoloured.
225. 85 f. Type **96** .. .. 75 40
226. 90 f. Mother suckling baby 85 45

**97.** U.N. Emblem and Trygve Lie.

**98.** Lenin in Cap.

**1970.** 25th Anniv. of United Nations.
227. **97.** 100 f. blue, indigo & lake 1·10 70
228. – 100 f. lilac, red and lake 1·10 70
229. – 100 f. grn., turq. & lake 1·10 70
DESIGNS—VERT. No. 228, as Type **97**, but with portrait of Dag Hammarskjold. HORIZ. No. 229, as Type **97**, but with portrait of U Thant and arrangement reversed.

**1970.** Air. Birth Cent. of Lenin.
231. **98.** 45 f. brown, yell. & grn. 40 20
232. – 75 f. brown, red & blue 65 30
DESIGN: 75 f. Lenin seated (after Vassiliev).

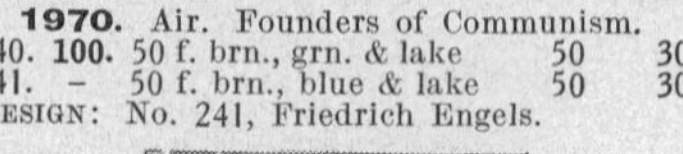

**99.** " Brillantaisia vogeliana ".

**100.** Karl Marx.

**1970.** " Flora and Fauna ". Multicoloured.
(a) Flowers. Horiz. designs.
233. 1 f. Type **99** .. .. 10 10
234. 2 f. " Plectranthus decurrens " .. .. 10 10
235. 3 f. " Myrianthemum mirabile " .. .. 10 10
236. 5 f. " Connarus griffonianus " .. .. 15 10
(b) Insects. Vert. designs.
237. 10 f. " Sternotomis variabilis " .. .. 30 20
238. 15 f. " Chelorrhina polyphemus " .. .. 45 20
239. 20 f. " Metopodontus savagei " .. .. 55 30

**1970.** Air. Founders of Communism.
240. **100.** 50 f. brn., grn. & lake 50 30
241. – 50 f. brn., blue & lake 50 30
DESIGN: No. 241, Friedrich Engels.

**101.** Kentrosarus.

**1970.** Prehistoric Creatures. Multicoloured.
242. 15 f. Type **101** .. .. 30 25
243. 20 f. Dinotherium .. 30 25
244. 60 f. Brachiosaurus .. 75 40
245. 80 f. Arsinoitherium .. 1·10 55
Nos. 243/4 are vert.

**102.** " Mikado 141 " Steam Engine (1932).

**1970.** Locomotives of Congo Railways. (1st series).
246. **102.** 40 f. black, grn. & pur. 1·75 1·10
247. – 60 f. black, green & blue 2·00 1·25
248. – 75 f. black, red & blue 3·00 1·75
249. – 85 f. red, green & orge. 4·25 2·50
DESIGNS: 60 f. Type 130+032 Steam loco (1947). 75 f. Alsthom BB 1100 engine (1962). 85 f. C.E.M. C.A.F.L. " BB BB 302 " diesel (1969).
See also Nos. 371/4.

**103.** Lilienthal's Glider, 1891.

**1970.** Air. History of Flight and Space Travel.
250. **103.** 45 f. brown, blue & red 60 25
251. – 50 f. green & brown .. 60 25
252. – 70 f. brown, lake & blue 70 35
253. – 90 f. brown, olive & blue 1·10 50
DESIGNS: 50 f. Lindbergh's " Spirit of St. Louis ", 1927. 70 f. " Sputnik I ". 90 f. First man on the Moon, 1969.

104. " Wise Man".

**1970.** Air. Christmas. Stained-glass Windows, Brazzaville Cathedral. Multicoloured.
254. 100 f. Type **104** .. .. 90 45
255. 150 f. " Shepherd " .. 1·60 70
256. 250 f. " Angels " .. .. 2·50 1·40

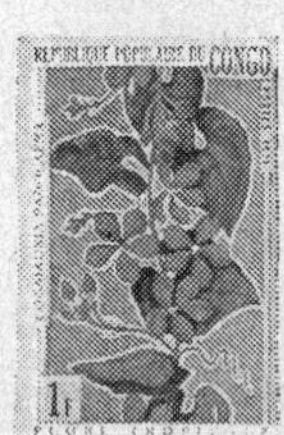

**105.** "Cogniauxia padolaena". **106.** Marilyn Monroe.

**1971.** Tropical Flowers. Multicoloured.
258. 1 f. Type **105** .. .. 10 10
259. 2 f. "Celosia cristata" .. 10 10
260. 5 f. "Plumeria acutifolia" 10 10
261. 10 f. "Bauhinia variegata" 20 15
262. 15 f. "Euphorbia pulcherrima" 35 25
263. 20 f. "Thunbergia grandiflora" .. .. 45 25
See also D 264/9.

**1971.** Air. Great Names of the Cinema.
270. **106.** 100 f. brn., blue & grn. 80 35
271. – 150 f. mve., blue & pur. 1·25 50
272. – 200 f. brown and blue 1·75 75
273. – 250 f. plum, blue & grn. 2·00 90
PORTRAITS: 150 f. Martine Carol 200 f. Eric K. von Stroheim. 250 f. Sergei Eisenstein.

**107.** "Carrying the Cross" (Veronese).

**1971.** Air. Easter. Religious Paintings. Multicoloured.
274. 100 f. Type **107** .. .. 95 55
275. 150 f. "Christ on the Cross" (Burgundian School c. 1500) (vert.) .. .. 1·60 65
276. 200 f. "Descent from the Cross" (Van der Weyden) 1·90 90
277. 250 f. "The Entombment" (Flemish School c.1500) (vert.) .. .. 2·75 1·10
278. 500 f. "The Resurrection" (Memling) (vert.) .. 5·00 2·00

**108.** Telecommunications Map.

**1971.** Air. Pan-African Telecommunications Network.
279. **108.** 70 f. multicoloured .. 60 30
280. 85 f. multicoloured .. 70 35
281. 90 f. multicoloured .. 1·10 45

**109.** Global Emblem.

**1971.** Air. World Telecommunications Day.
282. **109.** 65 f. multicoloured .. 55 25

**110.** Green Night Adder. **111.** Afro-Japanese Allegory.

**1971.** Reptiles. Multicoloured.
283. 5 f. Type **110** .. .. 15 10
284. 10 f. African egg-eating snake (horiz.) .. .. 15 10
285. 15 f. Flap-necked chameleon 25 15
286. 20 f. Nile crocodile (horiz.) 30 20
287. 25 f. Rock python (horiz.) 40 30
288. 30 f. Gaboon viper 50 35
289. 40 f. Brown house snake (horiz.) .. .. .. 55 40
290. 45 f. Jameson's mamba .. 75 45

**1971.** Air. "Philatokyo 1971". Stamp Exhib., Tokyo.
291. **111.** 75 f. black, mve. & violet 65 35
292. – 150 f. brn., red & pur. 1·25 65
DESIGN: 150 f. "Tree of Life", Japanese girl and African in mask.

**112.** " Pseudimbrasia deyrollei ".

**1971.** Caterpillars. Multicoloured.
293. 10 f. Type **112** .. .. 35 25
294. 15 f. " Bunaca alcinoe " (vert.) .. .. .. 35 25
295. 20 f. " Epiphora vacuna ploetzi " .. .. 45 35
296. 25 f. " Imbrasia eblis " .. 60 45
297. 30 f. " Imbrasia dione " (vert.) .. .. 85 60
298. 40 f. " Holocera angulata " 1·50 80

**113.** Japanese Scout. **114.** Olympic Torch.

**1971.** World Scout Jamboree, Asagiri, Japan (1st issue). On foil.
299. **113.** 90 f. silver (postage).. 1·25 85
300. – 90 f. silver .. .. 1·25 85
301. – 90 f. silver .. .. 1·25 85
302. – 90 f. silver .. .. 1·25 85
303. – 1,000 f. gold (air) .. 10·00
DESIGNS—VERT. No. 300, French Scout. No. 301, Congolese Scout. No. 302, Lord Baden-Powell. HORIZ. No. 303, Scouts and Lord Baden-Powell.
See also Nos. 306/9.

**1971.** Air. Olympic Games, Munich.
304. **114.** 150 f. red, grn. & pur. 1·40 70
305. – 350 f. violet, grn. & brn. 3·25 1·60
DESIGN-HORIZ. 350 f. Sporting cameos within Olympic rings.

**115.** Scout Badge, Dragon and Congolese Wood-carving.

**1971.** Air. World Scout Jamboree, Asagiri, Japan (2nd issue).
306. **115.** 85 f. pur., brn. & green 65 30
307. – 90 f. brn., violet & lake 70 35
308. – 100 f. grn., lake & brn. 90 45
309. – 250 f. brn., red & grn. 1·90 95
DESIGNS—HORIZ. 250 f. Congolese mask, geisha and scout badge. VERT. 90 f. African and Japanese mask. 100 f. Japanese woman and African.

**116.** Running.

**1971.** Air. 75th Anniv. of Modern Olympic Games.
310. **116.** 75 f. brn., blue & lake 60 30
311. – 85 f. brn., blue & red 65 30
312. – 90 f. brown & violet.. 75 40
313. – 100 f. brown and blue 85 45
314. – 150 f. brn., red & grn. 1·50 75
DESIGNS: 85 f. Hurdling. 90 f. Various events. 100 f. Wrestling. 150 f. Boxing.

**117.** " Cymothae sangaris ".

**1971.** Butterflies. Multicoloured.
315 30 f. Type **117** .. .. 65 35
316 40 f. "Papilio dardanus" (vert) .. .. 80 55
317 75 f. "Iolaus timon" .. 1·75 75
318 90 f. "Papilio phorcas" (vert) .. .. 2·00 1·00
319 100 f. "Euchloron megaera" .. .. 2·50 2·00

**118.** African and European Workers.

**1971.** Racial Equality Year.
320. **118.** 50 f. multicoloured .. 55 30

**119.** De Gaulle and Congo 1966 Brazzaville Conference Stamp.

**1971.** Air. 1st Death Anniv. of General De Gaulle.
321. **119.** 500 f. brn., grn. & red 8·00 8·00
322. – 1000 f. red & grn. on gold 16·00
323. – 1000 f. red & grn. on gold 16·00
DESIGNS—VERT. (29×38 mm.). No. 322, Tribute by Pres. Ngouabi. No. 323, De Gaulle and Cross of Lorraine.

**1971.** Air. 10th Anniv. of African and Malagasy Posts and Telecommunications Union. Similar to T **184** of Cameroun. Mult.
324. 100 f. U.A.M.P.T. H.Q. and Congolese woman .. 1·00 45

**1971.** Inaug. of Brazzaville-Pointe Noire Cable Link. Surch. **REPUBLIQUE POPULAIRE DU CONGO INAUGURATION DE LA LIAISON COXIALE 18-11-71** and new value.
325. **95.** 30 f. on 25 f. buff, brown and blue .. .. 90 30
326. – 40 f. on 30 f. brown and green (No. 223) .. 1·10 30

**121.** Congo Republic Flag and Allegory of Revolution.

**1971.** Air. 8th Anniv. of Revolution.
327. **121.** 100 f. multicoloured .. 80 40

**122.** Congolese with Flag.

**1971.** Air. 2nd Anniv. of Congolese Workers' Party, and Adoption of New National Flag. Multicoloured.
328. 30 f. Type **122** .. .. 25 10
329. 40 f. National flag .. .. 35 20

**123.** Map and Emblems. **124.** Lion.

**1971.** " Work-Democracy-Peace ".
330. **123.** 30 f. multicoloured .. 25 20
331. 40 f. multicoloured .. 30 15
332. 100 f. multicoloured 75 40

**1972.** Wild Animals.
333. **124.** 1 f. brn., bl. and grn... 10 10
334. – 2 f. brn., grn. and red 10 10
335. – 3 f. brn., red and lake 15 10
336. – 4 f. brn., blue and vio. 15 10
337. – 5 f. brn., green and red 20 15
338. – 20 f. brn., bl. and orge. 40 30
339. – 30 f. grn., emer. & brn. 50 30
340. – 40 f. blk., grn. and blue 70 45
DESIGNS—HORIZ. 2 f. African elephants. 3 f. Leopard. 4 f. Hippopotamus. 20 f. Potto. 30 f. De Brazza's monkey. VERT. 5 f. Gorilla. 40 f. Pygmy chimpanzee.

**125.** Book Year Emblem. **126.** Team Captain with Cup.

**1972.** Air. Int. Book Year.
341. **125.** 50 f. grn., yellow & red 40 25

**1973.** Air. Congolese Victory in Africa Football Cup. Multicoloured.
342. 100 f. Type **126** .. .. 95 50
343. 100 f. Congolese team (horiz.) 95 50

**127.** Girl with Bird. **128.** Miles Davis.

**1973.** Air. U.N. Environmental Conservation Conf., Stockholm.
344. **127.** 85 f. grn., blue & orge. 65 40

**1973.** Air. Famous Negro Musicians.
345. **128.** 125 f. multicoloured 80 40
346. – 140 f. red, lilac & mauve 90 45
347. – 160 f. grn., emer. & orge. 1·10 55
348. – 175 f. pur., red & blue 1·40 60
DESIGNS: 140 f. Ella Fitzgerald. 160 f. Count Basie. 175 f. John Coltrane.

**129.** Hurdling.

**1973.** Air. Olympic Games, Munich (1972).
349. **129.** 100 f. violet & mauve 90 50
350. – 150 f. violet and green 1·40 65
351. – 250 f. red and blue .. 2·50 1·40
DESIGNS-VERT. 150 f. Pole-vaulting. HORIZ. 250 f. Wrestling.

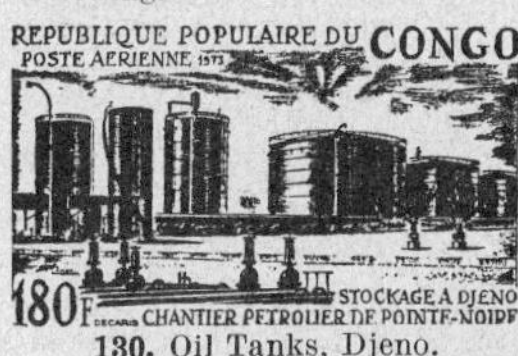


**130.** Oil Tanks, Djeno.

**1973.** Air. Oil Installations, Pointe Noire.
352. **130.** 180 f. indigo, red & blue 1·90 80
353. – 230 f. black, red & blue 2·20 1·00
354. – 240 f. purple, blue & red 2·50 1·10
355. – 260 f. black, red and blue 3·75 1·50
DESIGNS—VERT. 230 f. Oil-well head. 240 f. Drill in operation. HORIZ. 260 f. Off-shore oil-rig.

**131.** Lunar Module and Astronaut on Moon.

**1973.** Air. Moon Flight of " Apollo 17 ".
356. **131.** 250 f. multicoloured 2·75 1·75

**132.** " Telecommunications ".

**1973.** Air. World Telecommunications Day.
357. **132.** 120 f. multicoloured .. 1·00 65

**133.** Copernicus and Solar System.

**1973.** Air. 500th Birth Anniv. of Copernicus (astronomer).
358. **133.** 50 f. grn., bl. & light bl. 45 35

**134.** Rocket and African Scenes.

**1973.** Air. Centenary of World Meteorological Organization.
359. **134.** 50 f. multicoloured .. 75 35

**135.** W.H.O. Emblem. **137.** General View of Brewery.

**136.** " Study of a White Horse ".

**1973.** 25th Anniv. of World Health Organization. Multicoloured.
360. 40 f. Type **135** .. .. 35 20
361. 50 f. Design similar to T **135** (horiz.) .. .. .. 45 25

**1973.** Air. Paintings by Delacroix. Mult.
362. 150 f. Type **136** .. .. 1·40 1·25
363. 250 f. " Sleeping Lion " .. 2·75 1·75
364. 300 f. " Tiger and Lion " .. 3·25 2·00
See also Nos. 384/6 and 437/40.

**1973.** Congo Brewers Assn. Views of Kronenbourg Brewery.
365. **137.** 30 f. blue, red & bright bl. 25 20
366. – 40 f. grey, orge. & red 30 20
367. – 75 f. blue, red & black 55 30
368. – 85 f. multicoloured .. 75 40
369. – 100 f. multicoloured 90 55
370. – 250 f. green, brn. & red 1·90 95
DESIGNS: 40 f. Laboratory. 75 f. Regulating vats. 85 f. Control console. 100 f. Bottling plant. 250 f. Capping bottles.

**1973.** Locomotives of Congo Railways (2nd series). As T **102**. Multicoloured.
371. 30 f. Golwe steam locomotive c. 1935 .. .. 1·50 75
372. 40 f. Diesel-electric locomotive, 1935 .. .. 1·90 1·00
373. 75 f. Whitcomb diesel-electric locomotive, 1946 3·00 1·75
374. 85 f. CC/200 diesel-electric locomotive, 1973 .. 3·50 2·00

**138.** Stamp Map, Album, Dancer and Oil Rig. **139.** President Marien Ngouabi.

**1973.** Air. Int. Stamp Exhib., Brazzaville and 10th Anniv. of Revolution.
375. **138.** 30 f. grey, lilac and brn. 55 20
376. – 40 f. red, brn. & purple 30 25
377. **138.** 100 f. blue, brn. & pur. 1·75 85
378. – 100 f. lilac, pur. & red 80 60
DESIGNS: 40 f., 100 f. Map, album and Globes.

**1973.** Air.
379. **139.** 30 f. multicoloured .. 25 10
380. 40 f. multicoloured .. 30 15
381. 75 f. multicoloured .. 60 30

**1973.** Pan-African Drought Relief. No. 236 surch. **SECHERESSE SOLIDARITE AFRICAINE** and value.
382. 100 f. on 5 f. multicoloured 90 50

**1973.** 12th Anniv. of African and Malagasy Posts and Telecommunications Union. As T **216** of Cameroun.
383. 100 f. violet, blue & purple 80 50

**1973.** Air. Europafrique. As T **136**. Mult.
384. 100 f. " Wild Dog " .. 1·50 75
385. 100 f. " Lion and Leopard " 1·50 75
386. 100 f. " Adam and Eve in Paradise " .. .. 1·50 75
Nos. 384/6 are details taken from J. Brueghel's " Earth and Paradise ".

**141.** " Apollo " and " Soyuz " Spacecraft.

**1973.** Air. International Co-operation in Space.
387. **141.** 40 f. brn., red & blue .. 30 25
388. – 80 f. blue, red & green 55 40
DESIGN: 80 f. Spacecraft docked.

**142.** U.P.U. Monument and Satellite.

**1973.** Air. U.P.U. Day.
389. **142.** 80 f. blue & ultramarine 60 35

**1973.** Air. " Skylab " Space Laboratory. As T **141**.
390. 30 f. grn., brn. & blue .. 30 15
391. 40 f. grn., red & orange .. 35 25
DESIGNS: 30 f. Astronauts walking outside " Skylab ". 40 f. " Skylab " and " Apollo " spacecraft docked.

**143.** Hive and Bees.

**1973.** " Labour and Economy ".
392. **143.** 30 f. grn., blue & red 25 20
393. 40 f. green, blue & grn. 25 20

**144.** Congo Family and Emblems.

**1973.** 10th Anniv. of World Food Programme.
394. **144.** 30 f. brown and red .. 25 15
395. – 40 f. orge., green & blue 30 25
396. – 100 f. brn., grn. & orge. 75 45
DESIGNS—HORIZ. 40 f. Ears of corn and emblems. VERT. 100 f. Ear of corn, granary and emblems.

**145.** Goalkeeper. **146.** Runners.

**1973.** Air. World Football Cup Championships, West Germany (1974). (1st issue).
397. **145.** 40 f. grn., deep brown and brown .. .. 35 25
398. – 100 f. grn., red & violet 85 45
DESIGN: 100 f. Foward.
See also Nos. 403 and 408.

**1973.** Air. 2nd African Games, Lagos, Nigeria.
399. **146.** 40 f. red, green & brn. 35 25
400. 100 f. grn., red & brn. 85 45

**147.** Pres. John F. Kennedy. **148.** Map and Flag.

**1973.** Air. 10th Death Anniv. of President Kennedy.
401. **147.** 150 f. black, gold & bl. 1·10 70

**1973.** Air. 4th Anniv. of Congo Worker's Party.
402. **148.** 40 f. multicoloured .. 30 20

**149.** Players seen through Goalkeeper's Legs.

**1974.** Air. World Cup Football Championships, West Germany (2nd issue).
403. **149.** 250 f. grn., red & brn. 1·90 1·40

**150.** Globe, Flags and Names of Dead Astronauts.

**1974.** Air. Conquest of Space.
404. **150.** 30 f. brn., bl. & red .. 25 15
405. – 40 f. multicoloured .. 35 25
406. – 100 f. brn., bl. & red .. 85 55
DESIGNS: 40 f. Gagarin and Shepard. 100 f. Leonov in space, and Armstrong on Moon.

**151.** A. Cabral. **152.** Spacecraft docking.

**1974.** 1st Death Anniv. of Cabral (Guinea-Bissau guerilla leader).
407. **151.** 100 f. purple, red & bl. 70 45

**1974.** Air. West Germany's Victory in World Cup Football Championships. As T **149**.
408. 250 f. brn., pink & blue .. 1·90 1·40
DESIGN: Footballers within Ball.

**1974.** Air. Soviet-American Space Co-operation.
409. **152.** 200 f. bl., violet & red 1·40 90
410. – 300 f. blue, brn. & red 2·00 1·25
DESIGN—HORIZ. 300 f. Spacecraft on segments of globe.

**153.** "Sound and Vision".

**1974.** Air. Centenary of U.P.U.
411. **153.** 500 f. black and red .. 3·50 2·25

**154.** Felix Eboue and Cross of Lorraine.

**1974.** 30th Death Anniv. of Eboue ("Free French" Leader).
412. **154.** 30 f. multicoloured .. 25 10
413. 40 f. multicoloured .. 25 20

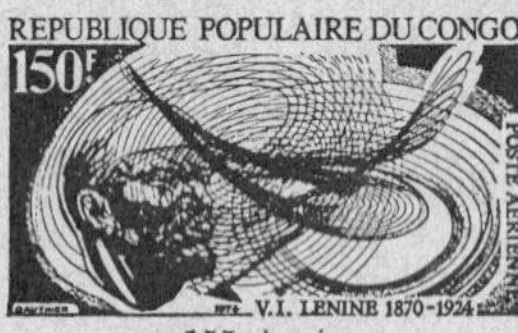


**155.** Lenin.

**1974.** Air. 30th Death Anniv. of Lenin.
414. **155.** 150 f. orge., red & grn. 1·00 65

**1974.** Birth Cent. of Churchill. As T **154**. Multicoloured.
415. 200 f. Churchill and Order of the Garter .. .. 1·50 1·00

**1974.** Birth Cent. of Guglielmo Marconi (radio pioneer). As T **154**. Multicoloured.
416. 200 f. Marconi and early apparatus .. .. 1·40 85

**1974.** Air. Centenary of Berne Convention. No. 411 surch **9 OCTOBRE 1974 300F**.
417. **153.** 300 f. on 500 f. blk. & red 2·25 1·40

**157.** Pineapple.

**1974.** Congolese Fruits. Multicoloured.
418. 30 f. Type **157** .. .. 35 25
419. 30 f. Bananas .. .. 35 25
420. 30 f. Safous .. .. 35 25
421. 40 f. Avocado pears .. 35 25
422. 40 f. Mangoes .. .. 35 25
423. 40 f. Papaya .. .. 35 25
424. 40 f. Oranges .. .. 35 25

**158.** Gen. Charles De Gaulle.

**1974.** 30th Anniv. of Brazzaville Conference.
425. **158.** 100 f. brown and green 1·40 90

**1974.** 10th Anniv. of Central African Customs and Economic Union. As Nos. 734/5 of Cameroun.
426. 40 f. mult. (postage) .. 35 20
427. 100 f. multicoloured (air) .. 65 45

**159.** George Stephenson (railway pioneer) and Early and Modern Locomotives. (Illustration reduced. Actual size 77 × 23 mm.)

**1974.** 150th Anniv. (1975) of Public Railways.
428. **159.** 75 f. olive and green 1·00 60

160. Irish Setter.

**1974.** Dogs. Multicoloured.
429. 30 f. Type **160** .. .. 30 25
430. 40 f. Borzoi .. .. 35 25
431. 75 f. Pointer .. .. 70 35
432. 100 f. Great Dane .. 90 45

**1974.** Cats. As T **160**. Multicoloured.
433. 30 f. Havana chestnut .. 30 25
434. 40 f. Red Persian .. .. 35 25
435. 75 f. British blue .. .. 70 35
436. 100 f. Serval .. .. 1·00 50

**1974.** Air. Impressionist Paintings. As T **136**. Multicoloured.
437. 30 f. " The Argenteuil Regatta " (Monet) .. 35 25
438. 40 f. " Seated Dancer " (Degas) (vert.) .. .. 45 30
439. 50 f. " Girl on Swing " (Renoir) (vert.) .. .. 65 45
440. 75 f. " Girl in Straw Hat " (Renoir) (vert.) .. 80 55

161. National Fair.

**1974.** Air. National Fair, Brazzaville.
441. **161.** 30 f. multicoloured .. 30 25

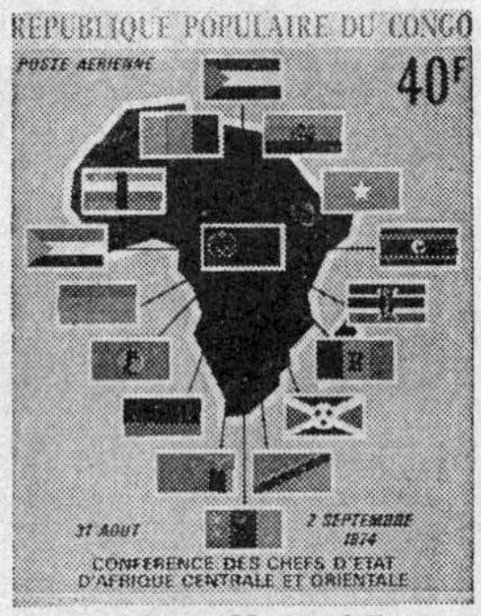

162. African Map and Flags.

**1974.** Air. African Heads-of-State Conference, Brazzaville.
442. **162.** 40 f. multicoloured .. 35 25

163. Flags and Dove.

**1974.** 5th Anniv. of Congo Labour Party.
443. **163.** 30 f. red, yellow & green 25 15
444. – 40 f. brown, red & yellow 30 25
DESIGN: 40 f. Hands holding flowers and hammer.

164. U Thant and U.N. Headquarters Building.

**1975.** 1st Death Anniv. of U Thant (U.N. Secretary-General).
445. **164.** 50 f. multicoloured .. 40 25

**1975.** 1st Death Anniv. of Paul G. Hoffman (U.N. Programme for Under developed Countries administrator). As T **164**. Multicoloured.
446. 50 f. Hoffman and U.N. "Laurel Wreath" (vert.) 35 25

166. Workers and Development.

**1975.** National Economic Development.
447. **166.** 40 f. multicoloured .. 30 25

167. Mao Tse-tung and Map of China.

**1975.** 25th Anniv. (1974) of Chinese People's Republic.
448. **167.** 75 f. red, mauve & bl. 55 35

168. Women with Hoe.

**1975.** 10th Anniv. of Revolutionary Union of Congolese Women.
449. **168.** 40 f. multicoloured .. 30 20

169. Paris–Brussels Line, 1890. (Illustration reduced, actual size 80×25 mm.)

**1975.** Air. Railway History. Multicoloured.
450. 50 f. Type **169** .. .. 85 50
451. 75 f. Santa Fe Line, 1880 .. 1·40 60

170. " Five Weeks in a Balloon ".

**1975.** Air. 70th Anniv. of Jules Verne (novelist). Multicoloured.
452. 40 f. Type **170** .. .. 50 40
453. 50 f. " Around the World in 80 Days " .. .. 1·00 50

171. Line-up of Team.

**1975.** Victory of Cara Football Team in Africa Cup. Multicoloured.
454. 30 f. Type **171** .. .. 30 25
455. 40 f. Receiving trophy (vert.) 35 25

172. 1935 Citroen and Notre Dame Cathedral, Paris.

**1975.** Veteran Cars. Multicoloured.
456. 30 f. Type **172** .. .. 30 20
457. 40 f. 1911 Alfa Romeo and St. Peter's, Rome .. 35 20
458. 50 f. 1926 Rolls Royce and Houses of Parliament, London .. .. .. 40 30
459. 75 f. 1893 C. F. Duryea and Manhattan skyline, New York .. .. .. 70 35

173. " Soyuz " Spacecraft.

**1975.** Air. " Apollo-Soyuz " Space Test Project.
460. **173.** 95 f. blk., red & crimson 55 35
461. – 100 f. blk., vio. & blue 65 40
DESIGNS: 100 f. " Apollo " Spacecraft.

174. Tipoye Carriage.

**1975.** Traditional Congo Transport. Mult.
462 30 f. Type **174** .. .. 30 20
463 40 f. Pirogue .. .. 65 30

175. " Raising the Flag ".

**1975.** 2nd Anniv. of Institutions of Popular Tasks.
464. **175.** 30 f. multicoloured .. 25 20

**1975.** 3rd Anniv. of Congolese National Conference. As T **175**. Multicoloured.
465. 40 f. Conference Hall .. 35 25

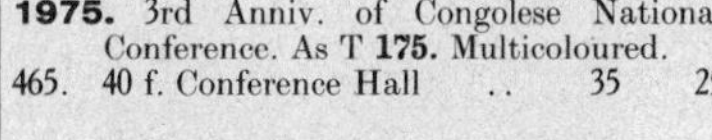

177. Fishing with Wooden Baskets.

**1975.** Traditional Fishing. Multicoloured.
466. 30 f. Type **177** .. .. 30 20
467. 40 f. Fishing with line (vert.) 65 30
468. 60 f. Fishing with spear (vert.) .. .. .. 45 25
469. 90 f. Fishing with net .. 1·40 80

178. Chopping Firewood.

179. " Esanga ".

**1975.** Domestic Chores. Multicoloured.
470. 30 f. Type **178** .. .. 25 15
471. 30 f. Pounding meal .. 25 15
472. 40 f. Preparing manioc (horiz.) .. .. .. 40 20

**1975.** Traditional Musical Instruments. Multicoloured.
473. 30 f. Type **179** .. .. 30 20
474. 40 f. " Kalakwa " .. .. 40 25
475. 60 f. " Likembe " .. .. 55 30
476. 75 f. " Ngongui " .. .. 70 40

180. "Dzeke" Money Cowrie.

**1975.** Ancient Congolese Money.
477 **180** 30 f. ochre, brn & red 40 25
478 – 30 f. ochre, vio & brn 30 20
478a **180** 35 f. orange & brown 45 30
478b – 35 f. red, bistre and violet .. .. 35 25
479 – 40 f. brown and blue 45 25
480 – 50 f. blue and brown 45 25
481 – 60 f. brown and green 55 30
482 – 85 f. green and red .. 70 35
DESIGNS: 30, 35 (478b) f. "Okengo" iron money. 40 f. Gallic coin (60 BC). 50 f. Roman coin (37 BC). 60 f. Danubian coin (2nd century BC). 85 f. Greek coin (4th century BC).

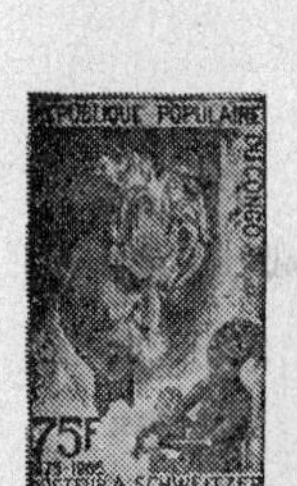

181. Dr. Schweitzer.

183. Boxing.

182. "Moschops".

**1975.** Birth Cent. of Dr. Albert Schweitzer.
483. **181.** 75 f. grn., mve. & brn. 75 40

**1975.** Prehistoric Animals. Multicoloured.
484. 55 f. Type **182** .. .. 45 25
485. 75 f. " Tyrannosaurus " .. 60 30
486. 95 f. " Cryptocleidus " .. 80 40
487. 100 f. " Stegosauras " .. 85 45

**1975.** Air. Olympic Games, Montreal (1976). Multicoloured.
488. 40 f. Type **183** .. .. 30 25
489. 50 f. Basketball .. .. 35 25
490. 85 f. Cycling (horiz.) .. 55 35
491. 95 f. High jumping (horiz.) 60 35
492. 100 f. Throwing the javelin (horiz.) .. .. .. 65 40
493. 150 f. Running (horiz.) .. 80 65

184. Alexander Fleming (biochemist). (20th Death Anniv.).

**1975.** Celebrities.
494. **184.** 60 f. black, green & red 90 30
495. – 95 f. black, blue & red 1·25 50
496. – 95 f. green, red & lilac 80 40
DESIGNS: No. 495, Clement Ader (aviation pioneer) (50th death anniv.). No. 496, Andre Marie Ampere (physicist) (birth bicent.).

185. U.N. Emblem with Laurel Wreaths.

**1975.** 30th Anniv. of U.N.O.
497 **185** 95 f. blue, red and green 80 40

**186.** Map of Africa and Sportsmen.

**1975.** Air. 10th Anniv. of 1st African Games, Brazzaville.

| | | | | |
|---|---|---|---|---|
| 498. | **186.** | 30 f. multicoloured .. | 30 | 25 |

**187.** Chained Women and Broken Link.

**1975.** International Women's Year. Mult.

| | | | |
|---|---|---|---|
| 499 | 35 f. Type **187** .. .. | 35 | 15 |
| 500 | 60 f. Global handclasp .. | 45 | 30 |

**188.** Pres. Ngouabi and Crowd with Flags.

**1975.** 6th Anniv. of Congolese Workers Party. Multicoloured.

| | | | |
|---|---|---|---|
| 501. | 30 f. Type **188** (postage).. | 25 | 20 |
| 502. | 35 f. "Echo"–P.C.T. "man" with roll of newsprint and radio waves | 30 | 20 |
| 503. | 60 f. Party members with Flag (air) .. .. | 35 | 25 |

SIZES: 35 f. 36 × 27 mm. 60 f. 26 × 38 mm.

**189.** River Steamer "Alphonse Fondere"

**1976.** Air. Old-time Ships. Multicoloured.

| | | | |
|---|---|---|---|
| 504 | 5 f. Type **189** .. .. | 20 | 20 |
| 505 | 10 f. Paddle-steamer "Hamburg", 1839 | 30 | 20 |
| 506 | 15 f. Paddle-steamer "Gomer", 1831 .. | 30 | 20 |
| 507 | 20 f. Paddle-steamer "Great Eastern", 1858 | 30 | 20 |
| 508 | 30 f. Type **189** .. .. | 45 | 20 |
| 509 | 40 f. Paddle-steamer "Hamburg", 1839 .. | 55 | 45 |
| 510 | 50 f. Paddle-steamer "Gomer", 1831 .. | 60 | 45 |
| 511 | 60 f. Paddle-steamer "Great Eastern", 1858 .. | 80 | 60 |
| 512 | 95 f. River steamer "J.M. White II" 1878 .. | 1·25 | 90 |

**190.** " The Peasant Family " (L. le Nain).

**1976.** Air. Europafrique. Paintings. Mult.

| | | | |
|---|---|---|---|
| 513. | 60 f. Type **190** .. .. | 30 | 15 |
| 514. | 80 f. " Boy with spinning Top " (Chardin) .. | 35 | 25 |
| 515. | 95 f. " Venus and Aeneas " (Poussin) .. | 40 | 30 |
| 516. | 100 f. " The Sabines " (David) .. .. .. | 45 | 35 |

**191.** Alexander Graham Bell and Early Telephone.

**1976.** Telephone Centenary.

| | | | | |
|---|---|---|---|---|
| 517 | **191** | 35 f. brown, light brown and yellow (postage) | 30 | 25 |
| 518 | | 60 f. red, mauve and pink (air) .. .. | 40 | 25 |

**192.** Fruit Market.

**1976.** Market Scenes. Multicoloured.

| | | | |
|---|---|---|---|
| 519. | 35 f. Type **192** .. .. | 25 | 20 |
| 520. | 60 f. Laying out produce .. | 40 | 25 |

**193.** Congolese Woman. **194.** Pole-vaulting.

**1976.** Congolese Women's Hair-styles.

| | | | | |
|---|---|---|---|---|
| 521. | **193.** | 35 f. multicoloured .. | 30 | 25 |
| 522. | – | 60 f. multicoloured .. | 45 | 25 |
| 523. | – | 95 f. multicoloured .. | 70 | 35 |
| 524. | – | 100 f. multicoloured .. | 75 | 40 |

DESIGNS: 60 f. to 100 f. Various Congolese Women's hair-styles.

**1976.** 1st Central African Games, Yaounde. Multicoloured.

| | | | |
|---|---|---|---|
| 525. | 60 f. Type **194** (postage).. | 45 | 30 |
| 526. | 95 f. Long-jumping .. | 75 | 45 |
| 527. | 150 f. Running (air) .. | 1·00 | 60 |
| 528. | 200 f. Throwing the discus | 1·50 | 90 |

**195.** Kob. **196.** Saddle-bill Storks.

**1976.** Congolese Fauna. Multicoloured.

| | | | |
|---|---|---|---|
| 529. | 5 f. Type **195** .. .. | 10 | 10 |
| 530. | 10 f. African buffaloes .. | 15 | 10 |
| 531. | 15 f. Hippopotami .. | 15 | 15 |
| 532. | 20 f. Warthog .. .. | 35 | 25 |
| 533. | 25 f. African elephants .. | 40 | 30 |

**1976.** Birds. Multicoloured.

| | | | |
|---|---|---|---|
| 534. | 5 f. Type **196** .. .. | 35 | 30 |
| 535. | 10 f. Shining-blue Kingfisher (37 × 37 mm.) .. | 65 | 35 |
| 536. | 20 f. Crowned Cranes (37 × 37 mm.) .. .. .. | 2·00 | 90 |

**197.** O.A.U. Building on Map. **198.** Cycling.

**1976.** Air. 13th Anniv. of O.U.A.

| | | | | |
|---|---|---|---|---|
| 537. | **197.** | 60 f. multicoloured .. | 35 | 25 |

**1976.** Central African Games, Libreville. Multicoloured.

| | | | |
|---|---|---|---|
| 538. | 35 f. Type **198** .. .. | 25 | 15 |
| 539. | 60 f. Handball .. .. | 35 | 25 |
| 540. | 80 f. Running .. .. | 55 | 30 |
| 541. | 95 f. Football .. .. | 50 | 35 |

**199.** " Nymphaea micrantha ".

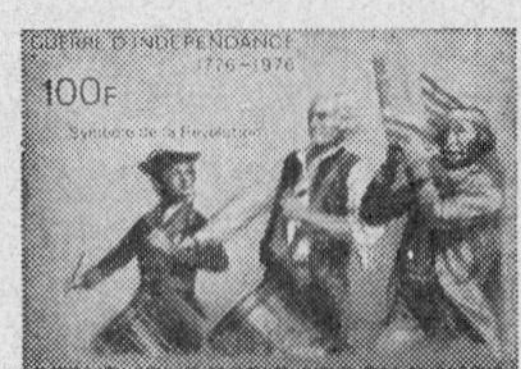


**200.** Pioneers' Emblem.

**1976.** Tropical Flowers. Multicoloured.

| | | | |
|---|---|---|---|
| 542. | 5 f. Type **199** .. .. | 10 | 10 |
| 543. | 10 f. " Heliotrope " .. | 10 | 10 |
| 544. | 15 f. " Strelitzia reginae " | 20 | 10 |

**1976.** National Pioneers Movement.

| | | | | |
|---|---|---|---|---|
| 545. | **200.** | 35 f. multicoloured .. | 20 | 20 |

**201.** "Spirit of 76" (detail, A. M. Willard).

**1976.** Bicent. of American Revolution. Mult.

| | | | |
|---|---|---|---|
| 546. | 100 f. Type **201** .. .. | 55 | 25 |
| 547. | 125 f. Destruction of George III's statue .. | 65 | 35 |
| 548. | 150 f. Gunners-Battle of Princeton .. | 90 | 40 |
| 549. | 175 f. Wartime generals.. | 1·25 | 50 |
| 550. | 200 f. Surrender of Gen. Burgoyne, Saratoga .. | 1·40 | 60 |

**202.** Pirogue Race.

**1977.** Pirogue Racing. Multicoloured.

| | | | |
|---|---|---|---|
| 552. | 35 f. Type **202** .. .. | 50 | 30 |
| 553. | 60 f. Race in progress .. | 75 | 45 |

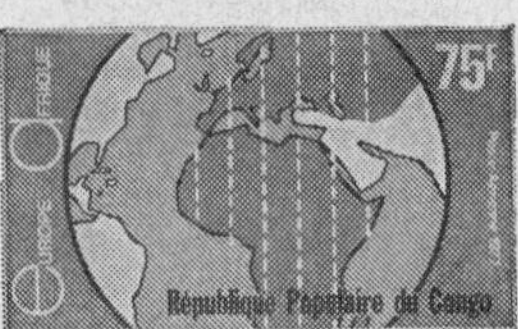


**203.** "Lilan goua ".

**1977.** Freshwater Fishes. Multicoloured.

| | | | |
|---|---|---|---|
| 554. | 10 f. Type **203** .. .. | 10 | 10 |
| 555. | 15 f. " Liko ko " .. .. | 10 | 10 |
| 556. | 25 f. " Liyan ga " .. | 15 | 10 |
| 557. | 35 f. " Mbessi " .. .. | 25 | 15 |
| 558. | 60 f. " Mongandza " .. | 35 | 30 |

**204.** Map of Europe and Africa.

**1977.** Air. Europafrique.

| | | | | |
|---|---|---|---|---|
| 559. | **204.** | 75 f. multicoloured .. | 45 | 35 |

**205.** Headdress.

**1977.** Traditional Headdresses. Mult.

| | | | |
|---|---|---|---|
| 560. | 35 f. Type **205** (postage).. | 30 | 20 |
| 561. | 60 f. Headdress with tail.. | 35 | 25 |
| 562. | 250 f. Two headdresses (air) | 1·40 | 95 |
| 563. | 300 f. Headdresses with beads .. .. .. | 1·75 | 1·10 |

**206.** Wrestling.

**1977.** Bondjo Wrestling.

| | | | | |
|---|---|---|---|---|
| 564. | – | 25 f. multicoloured .. | 20 | 10 |
| 565. | **206.** | 40 f. multicoloured .. | 25 | 15 |
| 566. | – | 50 f. multicoloured .. | 35 | 25 |

DESIGNS—VERT. 25 f., 50 f. Different wrestling scenes.

**207.** "Schwaben", 1911.

**1977.** History of the Zeppelin. Mult.

| | | | |
|---|---|---|---|
| 567 | 40 f. Type **207** .. .. | 25 | 20 |
| 568 | 60 f. "Viktoria Luise", 1913 | 35 | 30 |
| 569 | 100 f. "Bodensee" .. | 55 | 30 |
| 570 | 200 f. "Graf Zeppelin" .. | 1·25 | 45 |
| 571 | 300 f. "Graf Zeppelin II" | 1·75 | 60 |

**208.** Rising Sun of " Revolution ". **209.** " Flow of Trade ".

**1977.** 14th Anniv. of Revolution.

| | | | | |
|---|---|---|---|---|
| 573. | **208.** | 40 f. multicoloured .. | 25 | 25 |

**1977.** Air. G.A.T.T. Trade Convention, Lome.

| | | | | |
|---|---|---|---|---|
| 574. | **209.** | 60 f. black and red .. | 45 | 25 |

**210.** Hugo and Scene from " Hunchback of Notre Dame ".

**1977.** 175th Birth Anniv. of Victor Hugo.

| | | | | |
|---|---|---|---|---|
| 575. | **210.** | 35 f. brn., red and blue | 25 | 15 |
| 576. | – | 60 f. grn., drab and blue | 35 | 25 |
| 577. | – | 100 f. brn., blue & red | 70 | 45 |

DESIGNS: 60 f. Scene from " Les Miserables ". 100 f. Scene from " The Toilers of the Sea ".

**211.** Newton and Constellations.

**1977.** Air. 250th Death Anniv. of Isaac Newton.

| | | | | |
|---|---|---|---|---|
| 578. | **211.** | 140 f. mauve, green and brown .. .. | 1·00 | 65 |

**212.** Mao Tse-tung.

**1977.** 1st Death Anniv. of Mao Tse-tung.

| | | | | |
|---|---|---|---|---|
| 579. | **212.** | 400 f. gold and red .. | 2·25 | 1·75 |

213. Rubens.

**1977.** 400th Birth Anniv. of Peter Paul Rubens.

580. 213. 600 f. gold and blue .. 4·00 3·00

214. Child leading Blind Person.

**1977.** Fight Against Blindness.

581. 214. 35 f. multicoloured .. 30 25

215. Paul Kamba and Records.

**1977.** Paul Kamba (musician) Commem.

582. 215. 100 f. multicoloured .. 55 40

216. Trajan Vuia and his Vuia No. 1.

**1977.** Aviation History. Multicoloured.

583 60 f. Type 216 .. .. 35 20
584 75 f. Bleriot and Bleriot XI over Channel .. .. 40 20
585 100 f. Roland Garros and Morane Saulnier Type I 55 30
586 200 f. Lindbergh and "Spirit of St. Louis" .. 1·10 45
587 300 f. Tupolev Tu-144 .. 1·75 65

217. General de Gaulle.

**1977.** Historic Personalities, and Silver Jubilee of Queen Elizabeth II. Mult.

589. 200 f. Type 217 .. .. 1·10 45
590. 200 f. King Baudouin of Belgium .. .. 1·25 45
591. 250 f. Queen and Prince Philip in open car .. 1·50 65
592. 300 f. Queen Elizabeth .. 1·75 70

218. Ambete Statue.

219. " The Apostle Simon ".

**1978.** Congolese Sculpture.

594. 218. 35 f. lake, brn. & grn. 30 25
595. – 85 f. brn., grn. & lake 55 35

DESIGN: 85 f. Babembe statue.

**1978.** 400th Birth Anniv. of Peter Paul Rubens (2nd issue). Multicoloured

596. 60 f. Type 219 .. .. 35 20
597. 140 f. " The Duke of Lerma " .. .. 75 35
598. 200 f. " Madonna and Saints " .. .. .. 1·10 50
599. 300 f. " The Artist and his Wife " .. .. 1·75 65

220. Pres. Ngouabi making Speech.

**1978.** 1st Death Anniv. of President Marien Ngouabi.

601. 220. 35 f. blk., yell. & red 15 15
602. – 60 f. multicoloured .. 30 20
603. – 100 f. blk., yell. & red 45 35

DESIGNS—HORIZ. 60 f. Pres. Ngouabi at his desk. VERT. 100 f. Portrait of Pres. Ngouabi.

221. Ferenc Puskas (Hungary).

**1978.** World Cup Football Championship, Argentina. Famous Players. Multicoloured.

604. 60 f. Type 221 .. .. 35 20
605. 75 f. Giacinto Facchetti (Italy) .. .. .. 40 20
606. 100 f. Bobby Moore (England) 55 25
607. 200 f. Raymond Kopa (France) .. .. 1·10 50
608. 300 f. Pele (Brazil) .. 1·75 65

222. Pearl S. Buck (Literature, 1938).

**1978.** Nobel Prize Winners. Multicoloured.

610. 60 f. Type 222 .. .. 40 25
611. 75 f. Fridtjof Nansen and camp scene (Peace) .. 40 20
612. 100 f. Henri Bergson and " Elan Vita " (Literature) 55 30
613. 200 f. Alexander Fleming and penicillin (Medicine) 1·50 60
614. 300 f. Gerhart Hauptmann and hands with book (Literature) .. .. 1·75 65

223. Purple Heron.

224. Okapi.

**1978.** Air. Birds. Multicoloured.

616. 65 f. Mallard .. .. 2·00 95
617. 75 f. Type 223 .. .. 2·00 1·10
618. 150 f. Great reed warbler .. 4·00 1·50
619. 240 f. Hoopoe .. .. 5·25 2·40

**1978.** Endangered Animals. Multicoloured.

620. 35 f. Type 224 .. .. 25 20
621. 60 f. African buffalo (horiz.) .. .. .. 45 30
622. 85 f. Black rhinoceros (horiz.) .. .. .. 60 40
623. 150 f. Chimpanzee .. .. 1·00 50
624. 200 f. Hippopotamus (horiz.) .. .. .. 1·50 65
625. 300 f. Kob .. .. .. 2·40 1·00

225. Clenched Fist, Emblem and Crowd.

**1978.** 11th World Youth and Students Festival, Havana, Cuba.

626. 225. 35 f. multicoloured .. 30 25

226. Pyramids, Egypt.

**1978.** The Seven Wonders of the Ancient World. Multicoloured.

627. 35 f. Type 226 .. .. 20 15
628. 50 f. Hanging Gardens of Babylon (vert.) .. .. 25 20
629. 60 f. Statue of Zeus, Olympia (vert.) .. .. .. 35 20
630. 95 f. Colossos of Rhodes (vert.) .. .. .. 50 25
631. 125 f. Mausoleum, Halicarnassus (vert.) .. 60 30
632. 150 f. Temple of Artemis, Ephesus .. .. .. 75 40
633. 200 f. Pharos, Alexandria (vert.) .. .. .. 1·25 55
634. 300 f. Map showing sites of the Seven Wonders .. 1·75 65

**1978.** 25th Anniv. of Coronation of Queen Elizabeth II. Nos. 591/2 optd. **ANNIVERSAIRE DU COURONNEMENT 1953-1978.**

635. 250 f. Queen Elizabeth and Prince Philip in open car 1·40 85
636. 300 f. Queen Elizabeth II 1·75 1·40

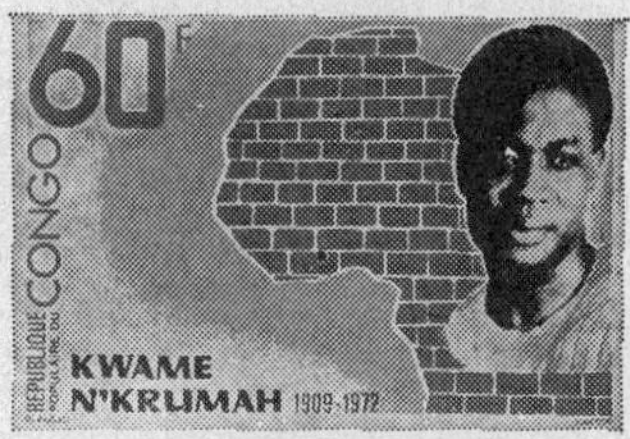

228. Kwame Nkrumah and Map of Africa.

**1978.** Kwame Nkrumah (Ghanaian statesman) Commemoration.

638. 228. 60 f. multicoloured .. 35 20

229. Hunting Wild Pigs.

**1978.** Multicoloured.

639. 35 f. Type 229 .. .. 25 20
640. 50 f. Smoking fish .. 35 30
641. 60 f. Hunter with kill (vert.) 35 20
642. 140 f. Woman hoeing (vert.) 80 40

**1978.** Air. " Philexafrique " Stamp Exn., Libreville, Gabon (1st issue) and International Stamp Fair, Essen, West Germany. As T 237 of Benin. Multicoloured.

643. 100 f. Peregrine Falcon and Wurttemberg 1851 1 k. stamp .. .. 1·25 80
644. 100 f. Leopard and Congo 1978 240 f. stamp .. 1·25 80

See also Nos. 668/9.

230. Basket Weaving.

232. Satellites, Antennae and Map of Africa.

231. " Kalchreut ".

**1978.** Occupations. Multicoloured.

645. 85 f. Type 230 .. .. 50 25
646. 90 f. Wood sculpture .. 50 25

**1978.** 450th Death Anniv. of Albrecht Durer (artist). Multicoloured.

647. 65 f. Type 231 .. .. 35 20
648. 150 f. " Elspeth Tucher " 75 35
649. 250 f. " Grasses " .. 1·40 60
650. 350 f. " Self-portrait " .. 1·90 90

**1978.** Air. Pan African Telecommunications.

651. 232. 100 f. red, green & orge. 65 35

**1978.** World Cup Football Championship Winners. Nos. 604/8 optd. with names of past winners.

652. 221. 60 f. multicoloured .. 35 25
653. – 75 f. multicoloured .. 40 30
654. – 100 f. multicoloured .. 55 35
655. – 200 f. multicoloured .. 1·10 60
656. – 300 f. multicoloured .. 1·60 1·00

OPTS: 60 f. **1962 "VAINQUEUR BRESIL".** 75 f. **1966 "VAINQUEUR GRANDE BRETAGNE".** 100 f. **1970 "VAINQUEUR BRESIL".** 200 f. **1974 "VAINQUEUR ALLEMAGNE (RFA)".** 300 f. **1978 "VAINQUEUR ARGENTINE".**

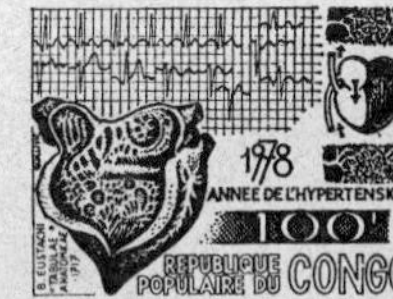

234. Diseased Heart, Blood Pressure Graph and Circulation Diagram.

**1978.** World Hypertension Year.

658. 234. 100 f. brn., red & turq. 55 35

235. Road to the Sun.

**1978.** 9th Anniv. of Congolese Workers' Party.

659. 235. 60 f. multicoloured .. 30 15

236. Captain Cook and Native Feast.

237. Pres. Ngouabi.

**1979.** Death Bicentenary of Captain James Cook. Multicoloured.

660 65 f. Type **236** 35 20

661 150 f. Easter Island Monuments 75 35

662 250 f. Hawaiian canoes 2·00 70

663 350 f. H.M.S. "Resolution" and H.M.S. "Adventure" at anchor 2·75 1·10

**1979.** 2nd Anniv. of Assassination of President Ngouabi.

664. **237.** 35 f. multicoloured 20 15

665. 60 f. multicoloured 35 20

**238.** I.Y.C. Emblem and Child.

**1979.** International Year of the Child.

666. **238.** 45 f. multicoloured 25 20

667. 75 f. multicoloured 30 15

**239.** "Solanum torvum" and Earthenware Jars.

**1979.** "Philexafrique" Stamp Exhibition, Libreville, Gabon (2nd issue).

668. **239.** 60 f. multicoloured 55 45

669. – 150 f. orge., brn. & grn. 2·00 1·25

DESIGN: 150 f. U.P.U. emblem, Concorde airplane, postal runner and locomotive.

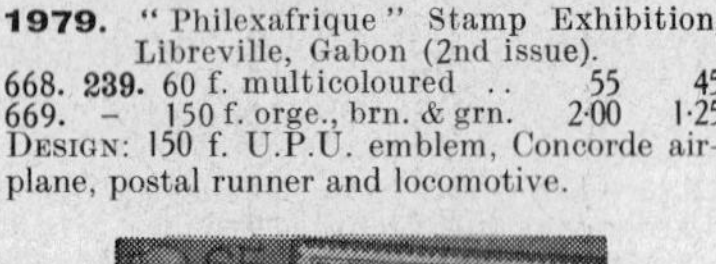

**240.** Rowland Hill, Diesel Locomotive and German 5 m. Stamp, 1900.

**1979.** Death Centenary of Sir Rowland Hill. Multicoloured.

670. 65 f. Type **240** 60 10

671. 100 f. Steam Locomotive and French "War Orphans" stamp of 1917 80 15

672. 200 f. Diesel Locomotive and U.S. Columbus stamp of 1893 1·75 30

673. 300 f. Steam Locomotive and England–Australia "First Aerial Post" vignette 3·00 90

**241.** Pres. Salvador Allende.

**1979.** Salvador Allende (former President of Chile). Commemoration.

675. **241.** 100 f. multicoloured 50 25

**242.** "The Teller of Legends".

**1979.** African Folk Tales as Part of Children's Education.

676. **242.** 45 f. multicoloured 30 20

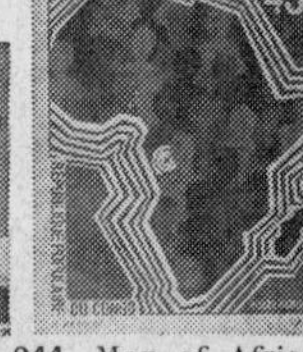


**243.** Handball Players. **244.** Map of Africa filled with Heads.

**1979.** Marien Ngouabi Handball Cup. Multicoloured.

677. 45 f. Type **243** 30 20

678. 75 f. Handball Players 40 25

679. 250 f. Cup on map of Africa, player and Marien Ngouabi 1·40 70

No. 679 is vert., 22 × 37 mm.

**1979.** Air. 5th Pan-African Youth Conference, Brazzaville.

680. **244.** 45 f. multicoloured 30 20

681. 75 f. multicoloured 45 30

**246.** Congo Map and Flag.

**1979.** 16th Anniv. of Revolution.

683. **246.** 50 f. multicoloured 25 15

**247.** Abala Peasant Woman.

**1979.** Air.

684. **247.** 150 f. multicoloured 90 60

**249.** Bach and Musical Instruments.

**1979.** Personalities. Multicoloured.

686. 200 f. Type **249** 1·00 50

687. 200 f. Albert Einstein and astronauts on the Moon 1·00 50

**250.** Yoro.

**1979.** Yoro Fishing Port. Multicoloured.

688. 45 f. Type **250** 30 20

689. 75 f. Yoro at night 40 25

**251.** Moukoukoulou Dam and Power Station.

**1979.** Moukoukoulou Hydro-Electric Power Station.

690. **251.** 20 f. multicoloured 15 10

691. 45 f. multicoloured 30 20

**1979.** Air. 10th Anniv. of "Apollo 11" Moon Landing. Optd. **ALUNISSAGE APOLLO XI JUILLET 1969.**

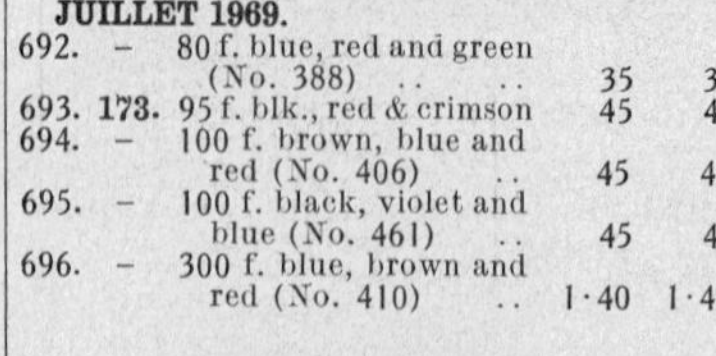

692. – 80 f. blue, red and green (No. 388) 35 35

693. **173.** 95 f. blk., red & crimson 45 45

694. – 100 f. brown, blue and red (No. 406) 45 45

695. – 100 f. black, violet and blue (No. 461) 45 45

696. – 300 f. blue, brown and red (No. 410) 1·40 1·40

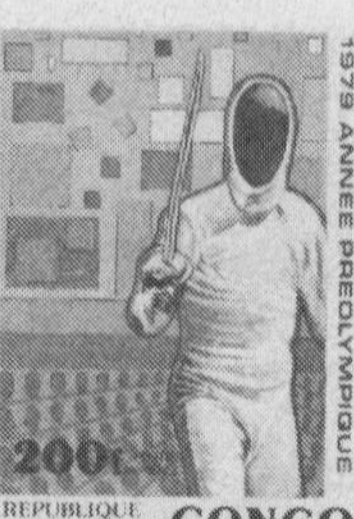


**253.** Fencer.

**1979.** Air. Pre-Olympic Year (1st issue) Multicoloured.

697. 65 f. Runner, map of Africa and Olympic rings (horiz.) 30 20

698. 100 f. Boxer (horiz.) 50 25

699. 200 f. Type **253** 95 40

700. 300 f. Footballer (horiz.) 1·40 65

701. 500 f. Olympic emblem 2·25 1·10

See also Nos. 716/9.

**254.** ASECNA Emblem and Douglas DC-10.

**1979.** 20th Anniv. of ASECNA (African Air Safety Organization).

702. **254.** 100 f. multicoloured 70 45

**255.** Party Emblem Workers and Flowers.  **256.** Cross-country Skiing.

**1979.** 10th Anniv. of Congolese Workers' Party.

703. **255.** 45 f. multicoloured 25 15

**1979.** Air. Winter Olympic Games, Lake Placid (1980). Multicoloured.

704. 40 f. Type **256** 20 15

705. 60 f. Slalom 30 20

706. 200 f. Ski-jump 95 40

707. 350 f. Downhill skiing (horiz.) 1·60 80

708. 500 f. Skier (vert. 31 × 46 mm.) 2·25 1·10

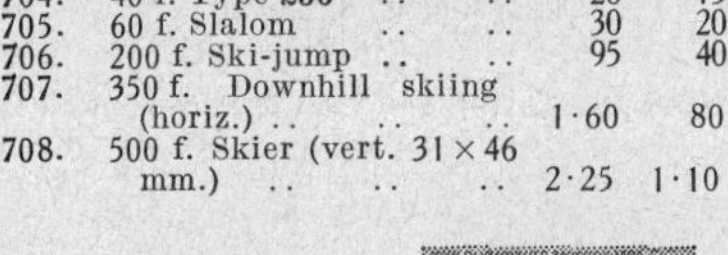

**257.** Emblem and Globe.  **259.** Long jump.

**1980.** 15th Anniv. of National Posts and Telecommunications Office.

709. **257.** 45 f. multicoloured 25 15

710. 95 f. multicoloured 45 25

**1980.** Air. Winter Olympic Games Medal Winners. Nos. 704/8 optd. with names of winners.

711. 40 f. Cross-country skiing 20 15

712. 60 f. Slalom 30 20

713. 200 f. Ski jump 95 45

714. 350 f. Downhill skiing 1·60 1·00

715. 500 f. Skier 2·25 1·40

OVERPRINTS: 40 f. **VAINQUEUR ZIMIATOV U.R.S.S.** 60 f. **VAINQUEUR MOSER-PROELL Autriche.** 200 f. **VAINQUEUR TOMANEN Finlande.** 350 f. **VAINQUEUR STOCK AUTRICHE.** 500 f. **VAINQUEURS STENMARK-WENZEL.**

**1980.** Air. Olympic Games, Moscow.

716. **259.** 75 f. multicoloured 30 10

717. – 150 f. multicoloured (horiz.) 70 25

718. – 250 f. multicoloured 1·10 45

719. – 350 f. multicoloured 1·60 60

Nos. 717/19 show different views of the long jump.

**260.** Pope John Paul II.

**1980.** Papal Visit.

721. **260.** 100 f. multicoloured 45 30

**261.** Rotary Emblem.

**1980.** 75th Anniv. of Rotary International.

722. **261.** 150 f. multicoloured 70 45

**262.** Glass Works.

**1980.** Pointe-Noire Glass Works. Mult.

723. 30 f. Type **262** 15 10

724. 35 f. Glass works (different) 20 10

**263.** Claude Chappe and Semaphore Tower.

**1980.** Claude Chappe Commemoration.

725. **263.** 200 f. multicoloured 90 70

**264.** Real Madrid Stadium.

**1980.** Air. World Cup Football Championship, Spain (1982). Multicoloured.

726. 60 f. Type **264** 30 15

727. 75 f. Real Zaragoza 35 15

728. 100 f. Atletico de Madrid 45 20

729. 150 f. Valencia C.F. 70 30

730. 175 f. R.C.D. Espanol 80 35

**265.** Floating Quay.

**1980.** Port of Mossaka. Multicoloured.

732. 45 f. Type **265** 25 15

733. 90 f. Aerial view of port 40 20

**266.** "Crucifixion".

**1980.** Air. Paintings by Rembrandt. Mult.

734. 65 f. "Adoration of the Shepherd's (detail) (horiz.) 30 10

735. 100 f. "Entombment" (horiz.) 45 25

736. 200 f. "Christ at Emmaus" (horiz.) 90 40

737. 300 f. "Annunciation" 1·40 60

738. 500 f. Type **266** 2·25 80

**267.** Jacques Offenbach (composer).

**1980.** Air. Death Anniversaries. Mult.
739. 100 f. Albert Camus (writer) (20th anniv.) .. .. 45 35
740. Type 267 (centenary) .. 70 50

268. " Papilio dardanus ".

**1980.** Butterflies. Multicoloured.
741 5 f. Type 268 .. .. 10 10
742 15 f. "Kallima aethiops" .. 10 10
743 20 f. "Papilio demodocus" 15 10
744 60 f. "Euphaedra" .. 55 40
745 90 f. "Hypolimnas misippus" .. .. 75 50

269. Hospital.

**1980.** " 31 July " Hospital.
747. 269. 45 f. multicoloured .. 25 20

270. Man presenting Human Rights Charter.

**1980.** 32nd Anniv. of Human Rights Convention. Multicoloured.
748. 350 f. Type 270 .. .. 1·60 1·10
749. 500 f. Man breaking chains 2·25 1·50

271. Raffia Dancing Skirts.

**1980.** Air. Traditional Dancing Costumes. Multicoloured.
750. 250 f. Type 271 .. .. 1·10 70
751. 300 f. Tam-tam dancers (vert.) .. .. .. 1·40 1·00
752. 350 f. Masks .. .. 1·60 1·10

272. Clenched Fists, Flag and Dove. 273. Coffee and Cocoa Trees on Map of Congo.

**1980.** 17th Anniv. of Revolution. Mult.
753. 75 f. Citizens and State emblem (36×23 mm.) .. 35 25
754. 95 f. Type 272 .. .. 45 30
755. 150 f. Dove carrying state emblem (36×23 mm.) .. 70 45

**1980.** Coffee and Cocoa Day. Multicoloured.
756. 45 f. Type 273 .. .. 25 20
757. 95 f. Coffee and cocoa beans 45 35

274. Cut Logs. 275. President Neto.

**1980.** Forest Exploitation. Multicoloured.
758. 70 f. Type 274 .. .. 35 25
759. 75 f. Lorry with logs .. 35 25

**1980.** 1st Death Anniv. of President Neto.
760. 275. 100 f. multicoloured .. 45 30

276. Olive-bellied Sunbird.

**1980.** Birds. Multicoloured.
761. 45 f. Type 276 .. .. 1·25 50
762. 75 f. Red-crowned Bishop 1·75 65
763. 90 f. Moorhen .. .. 2·00 75
764. 150 f. African Pied Wagtail 3·25 1·50
765. 200 f. Yellow-mantled Whydah (vert.) .. 4·00 1·75
766. 250 f. " Geai-bleu " (vert.) 2·10 85

277. Conference Emblem.

**1980.** World Tourism Conference, Manila.
768. 277. 100 f. multicoloured .. 25 15

278. Child Writing.

**1980.** Return to School.
769. 278. 50 f. multicoloured .. 25 15

279. The First House.

**1980.** Brazzaville Centenary.
770. 279. 45 f. ochre, grey, & brn. 25 15
771. – 65 f. lt. brn., brn. & orge. 30 20
772. – 75 f. multicoloured .. 35 25
773. – 150 f. multicoloured .. 70 45
774. – 200 f. multicoloured .. 90 70

DESIGNS: 65 f. First native village. 75 f. The old Town Hall. 150 f. Brazzaville from the Bacongo Promontory, 1912. 200 f. Meeting between Savorgnan de Brazza (explorer) and Makoko (local chieftain).

280. Cataracts.

**1980.** The River Congo. Multicoloured.
775. 80 f. Type 280 .. .. 40 25
776. 150 f. Bridge at Djoue .. 70 35

**1980.** Air. Olympic Medal Winners. Nos. 716/19 optd.
777 75 f. **DOMBROWSKI (RDA)** .. .. 35 25
778 150 f. **SANEIEV (URSS)** 70 45
779 250 f. **SIMEONI (IT)** .. 1·10 80
780 350 f. **THOMPSON (GB)** 1·60 1·10

282. Stadium and Sportsmen.

**1980.** Revolutionary Stadium. Heroes of Congolese Sport.
782. 282. 60 f. multicoloured .. 30 20

283. New Railway Bridge.

**1980.** Realignment of Railway.
783. 283. 75 f. multicoloured .. 45 25

284. Mangoes.

**1980.** Loudima Fruit Station. Multicoloured.
784. 10 f. Type 284 .. .. 10 10
785. 25 f. Oranges .. .. 15 10
786. 40 f. Lemons .. .. 20 10
787. 85 f. Mandarins .. .. 40 20

**1980.** 5th Anniv. of African Posts and Telecommunications Union. As T 269 of Benin.
788. 100 f. multicoloured .. 45 35

285. Microwave Communication.

**1980.** Communications. Multicoloured.
789. 75 f. Moungouni Earth Station (36×36 mm.) .. 35 25
790. 150 f. Type 285 .. .. 70 45

286. Presentation of Marien Ngouabi Handball Cup.

**1981.** African Handball Champions. Mult.
791. 100 f. Type 286 .. .. 45 30
792. 150 f. Team members .. 70 45

287. Pres. Sassou-Nguesso.

**1981.** President Sassou-Nguesso.
793. 287. 45 f. multicoloured .. 20 15
794. 75 f. multicoloured .. 40 25
795. 100 f. multicoloured .. 45 30

288. Space Shuttle.

**1981.** Conquest of Space. Multicoloured.
796 100 f. "Luna 17" .. .. 45 25
797 150 f. Type 288 .. .. 70 35
798 200 f. Satellite and space shuttle .. .. .. 90 45
799 300 f. Space shuttle approaching landing strip .. .. .. 1·40 70

289. Head and Dove. 290. Twin Palm Tree.

**1981.** Anti-Apartheid Campaign.
801. 289. 100 f. blue .. .. 45 30

**1981.** The Twin Palm Tree of Louingui.
802. 290. 75 f. multicoloured .. 35 25

291. Bird approaching Snare.

**1981.** Traditional Snares and Traps. Mult.
803. 5 f. Type 291 .. .. 10 10
804. 10 f. Bird in snare (vert.) 10 10
805. 15 f. Rodent approaching snare .. .. .. 10 10
806. 20 f. Rodent in snare .. 10 10
807. 30 f. Sprung trap .. .. 15 10
808. 35 f. Deer approaching trap 20 10

292. Human Figure and Caduceus.

**1981.** World Telecommunications Day.
809. 292. 120 f. multicoloured .. 55 35

293. Sleeping Sickness and Malaria Victim.

**1981.** Campaign against Transmissible Diseases. Multicoloured.
810. 40 f. + 5 f. Doctor, nurse, patients and mosquito .. 25 20
811. 65 f. + 10 f. Type 293 .. 45 20

294. Collecting Rubber.

**1981.** Rubber Extraction. Multicoloured.
812. 50 f. Tapping rubber tree 20 15
813. 70 f. Type 294 .. .. 40 30

295. Helping a Disabled Person.

**1981.** International Year of Disabled People.
814. 295. 45 f. blue, purple & red 20 15
815. – 75 f. + 5 f. multicoloured 40 30

DESIGN: 75 f. Disabled people superimposed on globe.

296. " The Studio ".

**1981.** Air. Birth Centenary of Pablo Picasso. Multicoloured.

816. 100 f. Type **296** .. .. 40 30

817. 150 f. "Landscape Land and Sea" .. 70 40

818. 200 f. "The Studio at Cannes" .. 90 50

819. 300 f. "Still-life with Water Melon" .. 1·40 85

820. 500 f. "Large Still-life" .. 2·25 1·40

**297.** King Maloango and Mausoleum.

**1981.** Mausoleum of King Maloango. Mult.

821. 75 f. Mausoleum .. .. 35 20

822. 150 f. Type **297** .. .. 70 45

**298.** Prince Charles, Lady Diana Spencer and Coach.

**1981.** Wedding of Prince of Wales. Mult.

823. 100 f. Type **298** .. 85 30

824. 200 f. Couple and Landau 1·40 25

825. 300 f. Couple and horses .. 1·75 85

**299.** Preparing Food. **300.** Bird carrying Letter.

**1981.** World Food Day.

827. **299.** 150 f. multicoloured .. 1·25 45

**1981.** Universal Postal Union Day.

828. **300.** 90 f. blue, red & grey .. 40 25

**301.** Guardsman. **302.** Spraying Cassava.

**1981.** Royal Guard.

829 **301** 45 f. multicoloured .. 25 15

**1981.** Campaign for the Control of Cassava Beetle.

830. **302.** 75 f. multicoloured .. 35 20

**303.** Bandaging a Patient. **304.** Brazza's Tree.

**1981.** Red Cross. Multicoloured.

831. 10 f. Type **303** .. .. 10 10

832. 35 f. Inoculating a young girl .. .. 20 10

833. 60 f. Nurse and villagers .. 30 15

**1981.** Tree of Brazza.

834. **304.** 45 f. multicoloured .. 25 15

835. 75 f. multicoloured .. 35 20

**305.** Fetish. **306.** Bangou Caves.

**1981.** Fetishes.

836. **305.** 15 f. multicoloured .. 10 10

837. – 25 f. multicoloured .. 15 10

838. – 45 f. multicoloured .. 20 15

839. – 50 f. multicoloured .. 25 15

840. – 60 f. multicoloured .. 25 20

DESIGNS: 25 f. to 60 f. Different fetishes.

**1981.** Bangou Caves.

841. **306.** 20 f. multicoloured .. 10 10

842. 25 f. multicoloured .. 15 10

**307.** "Congolese Coiffure"

**1982.** Ivory Sculptures by R. Engongodzo. Multicoloured.

843. 25 f. Type **307** .. .. 15 10

844. 35 f. "Congo Coiffure" (different) .. .. 20 10

845. 100 f. "King Makoko, his Queen and Counsellor" (horiz.) .. .. .. 45 25

**308.** "Inter-City 125" Train.

**1982.** Birth Bicentenary (1981) of George Stephenson (railway engineer). Multicoloured.

846. 100 f. Type **308** .. .. 55 30

847. 150 f. Sinkansen train .. 90 45

848. 200 f. Advanced Passenger Train .. .. 1·25 60

849. 300 f. TGV 001 .. .. 1·90 90

**309.** Scout with Binoculars.

**1982.** 75th Anniv. of Boy Scout Movement. Multicoloured.

850. 100 f. Type **309** .. .. 45 25

851. 150 f. Scout reading map .. 70 35

852. 200 f. Scout talking to village woman .. .. 90 45

853. 300 f. Scouts on rope bridge 1·40 70

**310.** Franklin D. Roosevelt.

**1982.** Anniversaries. Multicoloured.

855. 150 f. Type **310** (birth cent) 70 35

856. 250 f. George Washington on horseback (250th birth anniv.) .. .. 1·25 60

857. 350 f. Johann von Goethe (writer) (150th death anniv.) .. .. .. 1·60 80

**311.** Princess of Wales and Candles.

**1982.** 21st Birthday of Princess of Wales. Multicoloured.

858. 200 f. Type **311** .. .. 90 45

859. 300 f. Princess and "21" 1·40 70

**312.** Road Building.

**1982.** Five Year Plan. Multicoloured.

861. 60 f. Type **312** .. .. 25 20

862. 100 f. Telecommunications 45 25

863. 125 f. Operating theatre equipment .. .. 60 30

864. 150 f. Hydro-electric project 70 55

**313.** Dish Antenna.

**1982.** I.T.U. Delegates' Conference, Nairobi.

865. **313.** 300 f. multicoloured .. 1·40 70

**314.** Mosque, Medina.

**1982.** Air. 1350th Death Anniv. of Mohammed.

866. **314.** 400 f. multicoloured .. 1·75 90

**315.** W.H.O. Regional Office.

**1982.** World Health Organization Regional Office, Brazzaville.

867. **315.** 125 f. multicoloured .. 60 30

**316.** Mother feeding Baby.

**1982.** Health Campaign.

868. **316.** 100 f. multicoloured .. 45 25

**1982.** Birth of Prince William of Wales. Nos. 823/25 optd. **NAISSANCE ROYALE 1982.**

869. 100 f. multicoloured .. 45 25

870. 200 f. multicoloured .. 90 45

871. 300 f. multicoloured .. 1·40 70

**318.** Dr. Robert Koch and Bacillus.

**1982.** Centenary of Discovery of Tubercle Bacillus.

873. **318.** 250 f. multicoloured .. 1·25 60

**1982.** World Cup Football Championship Results. Nos. 724/28 optd.

874. 60 f. "EQUIPE QUATRIEME FRANCE" .. 25 20

875. 75 f. "EQUIPE TROISIEME/POLOGNE" .. 35 20

876. 100 f. "EQUIPE SECONDE ALLEMAGNE (RFA)" 45 25

877. 150 f. "EQUIPE VAINQUEUR/ITALIE" .. 70 35

878. 175 f. "ITALIE-ALLEMAGNE (RFA) 3 1" .. 80 40

**320.** Pres. Sassou-Ngeusso and Prize.

**1982.** Award of 1980 Simba Prize to Pres. Sassou-Nguesso.

880. **320.** 100 f. multicoloured .. 45 25

**321.** Turtle.

**1982.** Turtles.

881. **321.** 30 f. multicoloured .. 15 10

882. – 45 f. multicoloured .. 20 15

883. – 55 f. multicoloured .. 25 15

DESIGNS: 45, 55 f Different turtles.

**322.** Amelia Earhart and "Friendship".

**1982.** 50th Anniv. of Amelia Earhart's Transatlantic Flight.

884. **322.** 150 f. light brown, green and brown .. 1·00 45

**323.** "La Malafoutier". **324.** Grey Parrots nesting in Hole in Tree.

**1982.**

885. **323.** 100 f. multicoloured .. 45 25

**1982.** Bird's Nests. Multicoloured.

886. 40 f. Type **324** .. .. 90 20

887. 75 f. Palm tree and nest .. 1·00 20

888. 100 f. Nest hanging from branch .. .. .. 1·10 25

**325.** Map of Network.

**1982.** Hertzian Wave Network.

889. **325.** 45 f. multicoloured .. 20 15
890. 60 f. multicoloured .. 25 20
891. 95 f. multicoloured .. 45 25

**326.** Council Headquarters, Brussels.

**1983.** 30th Anniv. of Customs Co-operation Council.

892. **326.** 100 f. multicoloured .. 45 25

**327.** Marien N'Gouabi Mausoleum.

**1983.**

893. **327.** 60 f. multicoloured .. 25 20
894. 80 f. multicoloured .. 35 20

**328.** Raffia Weaving.

**1983.**

895. **328.** 150 f. multicoloured .. 70 35

**329.** Chess Pieces.

**1983. Chess Pieces Carved by R. Engongonzo. Multicoloured.**

896. 40 f. Type **329** .. .. 20 10
897. 60 f. Close-up of white pawn, king, queen and bishop 25 20
898. 95 f. Close-up of black rook, bishop, queen and king 45 25

**330.** Blacksmiths.

**1983.**

899. **330.** 45 f. multicoloured .. 20 15

**331.** Study for "The Transfiguration".

**1983.** Easter. 500th Birth Anniv. of Raphael. Multicoloured.

900. 200 f. Type **331** .. .. 90 45
901. 300 f. "Deposition from the Cross" (horiz.) .. 1·40 70
902. 400 f. "Christ in his Glory" 1·75 90

**332.** Comb. **333.** "Pila ovata".

**1983.** Traditional Combs. Multicoloured.

903. 30 f. Type **332** .. .. 15 10
904. 70 f. Comb (different) .. 25 25
905. 85 f. Three combs .. .. 30 30

**1983.** Shells. Multicoloured.

906 35 f. Type **333** .. .. 25 20
907 65 f. True achatina .. 50 35

**334.** Windsurfing.

**1983.** Air. Pre-Olympic Year.

908 **334** 100 f. multicoloured .. 40 40
909 – 200 f. multicoloured (horiz) .. .. 80 80
910 – 300 f. multicoloured .. 1·40 1·40
911 – 400 f. multicoloured .. 1·75 1·75

DESIGNS: 200 to 400 f. Various windsurfing scenes.

**335.** Montgolfier Balloon, 1783. **336.** Hands holding Gun and Pick.

**1983.** Air. Bicent of Manned Flight. Mult.

913 100 f. Type **335** .. .. 45 40
914 200 f. Montgolfier balloon "Le Flesselles", 1784 .. 90 80
915 300 f. Auguste Piccard's stratosphere balloon "F.N.R.S.", 1931 .. 1·40 1·25
916 400 f. Modern hot-air balloon .. .. 1·75 1·50

**1983.** 20th Anniv. of Revolution.

918. **336.** 60 f. multicoloured .. 25 20
919. 100 f. multicoloured .. 35 35

**337.** Mgr. A. Carrie and Church of the Sacred Heart, Loango.

**1983.** Centenary of Evangelism. Mult.

920. 150 f. Type **337** .. .. 55 50
921. 250 f. Mgr. Augouard and St. Joseph's Church, Linzolo .. .. .. 85 80

**338.** Thunbergia. **339.** "Virgin and Child with St. John".

**1984.** Flowers. Multicoloured.

922. 5 f. Type **338** .. .. 10 10
923. 15 f. Bougainvillaea (horiz.) 10 10
924. 20 f. Anthurium .. .. 15 10
925. 45 f. Allamanda (horiz.) .. 30 25
926. 75 f. Hibiscus .. .. 45 40

**1984.** Air. Christmas. Paintings by Botticelli. Multicoloured.

927. 150 f. Type **339** .. .. 85 55
928. 350 f. "Virgin and Child" (St. Barnabas) .. .. 2·00 1·75
929. 500 f. "Virgin and Child" 2·75 2·50

**340.** "Vase of Flowers" (Manet).

**1984.** Air. Paintings. Multicoloured.

930. 100 f. Type **340** .. .. 55 50
931. 200 f. "The Small Holy Family" (Raphael) .. 1·10 85
932. 300 f. "La Belle Jardiniere" (detail) (Raphael) 1·75 1·40
933. 400 f. "The Virgin of Lorette" (Raphael) .. 2·25 2·00
934. 500 f. "Richard Wagner" (Giuseppe Tivoli) .. 2·75 2·50

**341.** Peace Dove.

**1984.** 34th Anniv. of World Peace Council.

935. **341.** 50 f. multicoloured .. 30 25
936. 100 f. multicoloured .. 55 50

**342.** Judo. **343.** Mushroom Cloud.

**1984.** Air. Olympic Games, Los Angeles. Multicoloured.

937. 45 f. Type **342** .. .. 30 25
938. 75 f. Judo (different) (horiz.) 45 40
939. 150 f. Wrestling (horiz.) .. 85 55
940. 175 f. Fencing (horiz.) .. 1·10 85
941. 350 f. Fencing (different) (horiz.) .. .. 2·00 1·75

**1984.** Campaign against Weapons of Mass Destruction.

943. **343.** 200 f. black, brown and orange .. .. 1·10 85

**344.** Rice.

**1984.** Agriculture. Multicoloured.

944 10 f. Type **344** .. .. 10 10
945. 15 f. Pineapples .. .. 10 10
946. 60 f. Manioc (vert.) .. 35 30
947. 100 f. Palms (vert.) .. 55 50

**345.** Congress Palace.

**1984.** Chinese-Congolese Co-operation.

948. **345.** 60 f. multicoloured .. 35 30
949. 100 f. multicoloured .. 55 50

**346.** Loulombo Station.

**1984.** 50th Anniv. of Congo Railways. Mult.

950. 10 f. Type **346** .. .. 10 10
951. 25 f. Chinese workers' camp at Les Bandas .. 30 15
952. 125 f. "50" forming bridge and tunnel .. .. 1·25 55
953. 200 f. Headquarters building .. .. .. 1·90 85

**347.** "C C 203" Diesel.

**1984.** Transport. Multicoloured.

(a) Locomotives

954 100 f. Type **347** .. .. 55 50
955 150 f. "BB 103" diesel .. 85 55
956 300 f. "BB-BB301" diesel 1·75 1·40
957 500 f. "BB420" diesel "L'Eclair" .. .. 2·75 2·50

(b) Ships

958 100 f. Pusher tug .. .. 80 55
959 150 f. Pusher tug (different) .. .. 1·25 65
960 300 f. Buoying boat .. 2·50 1·75
961 500 f. "Saint" (freighter) .. 3·75 3·25

**348.** Giant Ground Pangolin.

**1984.** Animals. Multicoloured.

962. 30 f. Type **348** .. .. 25 15
963. 70 f. Bat .. .. 50 35
964. 85 f. African civet .. .. 65 45

Nos. 962/4 are inscribed "1983".

**349.** Fish in Basket. **350.** Polio Victims and Hand.

**1984.** World Fisheries Year. Multicoloured.

965. 5 f. Type **349** .. .. 10 10
966. 20 f. Casting nets .. .. 20 10
967. 25 f. Fishes .. .. 15 10
968. 40 f. Men pulling nets in .. 25 20
969. 55 f. Boat, net and fishes 35 30

**1984.** Anti-Polio Campaign. Multicoloured.

970. 250 f. Type **350** .. .. 1·40 1·10
971. 300 f. Polio victims within target .. .. .. 1·75 1·40

## INDEX

Countries can be quickly located by referring to the index at the end of this volume.

**351.** M'bamou Palace Hotel, Brazzaville.

**352.** S. van den Berg, Windsurfing.

**1984.**

972. **351.** 60 f. multicoloured .. 35 30
973. 100 f. multicoloured .. 55 50

**1984.** Air. Olympic Games Yachting Gold Medal Winners. Multicoloured.

974. 100 f. Type **352** .. .. 75 70
975. 150 f. U.S.A., "Soling" class (horiz.) .. .. .. 1·10 85
976. 200 f. Spain, "470" class (horiz.) .. .. .. 1·50 1·25
977. 500 f. U.S.A., "Flying Dutchman" class .. 3·75 3·25

**353.** Floating Logs.

**1984.** Floating Logs on River Congo. Multicoloured.

978. 60 f. Type **353** .. .. 50 25
979. 100 f. Logs and boat on river .. .. .. 75 50

**354.** "The Holy Family".

**355.** "Zonocerus variegatus".

**1985.** Air. Christmas. Multicoloured.

980. 100 f. Type **354** .. .. 35 30
981. 200 f. "Virgin and Child" (G. Bellini) (horiz.) .. 70 60
982. 400 f. "Virgin and Child with Angels" (Cimabue) 1·40 1·25

**1985.**

983. **355.** 125 f. multicoloured .. 60 40

**357.** Black-headed Grosbeaks.

**1985.** Air. Birth Bicentenary of John J. Audubon (ornithologist). Multicoloured.

985. 100 f. Type **357** .. .. 1·25 1·00
986. 150 f. Scarlet ibis .. .. 2·00 1·10
987. 200 f. Red-tailed hawk (horiz.) .. .. .. 2·50 1·50
988. 350 f. Labrador duck .. 5·25 3·00

**358.** Funeral Procession.

**1985.** Burial of Teke Chief.

989. **358.** 225 f. multicoloured .. 80 70

**359.** Mother weighing Child.

**1985.** "Philexafrique" Stamp Exhibition, Lome, Togo (1st issue). Multicoloured.

990. 200 f. Type **359** .. .. 70 60
991. 200 f. Boy writing and man ploughing field .. .. 70 60

See also Nos. 1004/5.

**360.** "Trichoscypha acuminata".

**361.** Brazzaville Lions Club Pennant.

**1985.** Fruits. Multicoloured.

992. 5 f. Type **360** .. .. 10 10
993. 10 f. "Aframomum africanum" .. .. .. 10 10
994. 125 f. "Gambeya lacuurtiana" .. .. .. 45 40
995. 150 f. "Landolphia jumelei" .. .. .. 50 40

**1985.** 30th Anniv. of Lions Club.

996. **361.** 250 f. multicoloured .. 85 75

**362.** Moscow Kremlin, Soldier and Battlefield.

**1985.** 40th Anniv. of End of World War II.

997. **362.** 60 f. multicoloured .. 20 15

**363.** Doves forming Heart.

**1985.** Air. 25th Anniv. of United Nations Membership.

998. **363.** 190 f. multicoloured .. 70 60

**365.** Girl Guide with Yellow-bellied Wattle-eye (International Youth Year).

**1985.** Anniversaries and Events. Mult.

999. 150 f. Type **365** .. .. 1·75 85
1000. 250 f. Jacob Grimm (folklorist) and scene from "Snow White and the Seven Dwarfs" (birth bicentenary. International Youth Year) .. .. 85 75
1001. 350 f. Johann Sebastian Bach (composer) and organ (300th birth anniv. European Music Year) .. .. .. 1·25 1·10
1002. 450 f. Queen Elizabeth, the Queen Mother (85th birthday) (vert.) 1·60 1·25
1003. 500 f. Statue of Liberty (centenary) (vert.) .. 1·75 1·50

**366.** Construction Equipment within Heads and Building.

**1985.** "Philexafrique" Stamp Exhibition, Lome, Togo (2nd issue). Multicoloured.

1004. 250 f. Type **366** .. .. 85 75
1005. 250 f. Loading mail at airport .. .. .. 1·25 90

**367.** Emblem and Rainbow.

**368.** "Coprinus".

**1985.** Air. 40th Anniv. of U.N.O.

1006. **367.** 180 f. multicoloured 65 55

**1985.** Fungi. Multicoloured.

1007. 100 f. Type **368** .. .. 80 40
1008. 150 f. "Cortinarius" .. 1·10 55
1009. 200 f. "Armillariella mellea" .. .. 1·40 80
1010. 300 f. "Dictyophora" .. 2·50 1·25
1011. 400 f. "Crucibulum vulgare" .. .. 3·10 1·50

**369.** "Virgin and Child" (Gerard David).

**1985.** Air. Christmas. Multicoloured.

1012. 100 f. Type **369** .. .. 35 30
1013. 200 f. "Adoration of the Magi" (Hieronymus Bosch) .. .. 70 60
1014. 400 f. "Virgin and Child" (Anthony Van Dyck) (horiz.) .. .. 1·40 1·10

**370.** Edmond Halley and Computer Picture of Comet.

**1986.** Air. Appearance of Halley's Comet. Multicoloured.

1015. 125 f. Type **370** .. .. 50 40
1016. 150 f. West's Comet, 1976 (vert.) .. .. .. 65 55
1017. 225 f. Ikeya-Seki Comet, 1965 (vert.) .. .. 1·00 90
1018. 300 f. "Giotto" space probe and comet trajectory .. .. 1·25 1·10
1019. 350 f. Comet and "Vega" space probe .. .. 1·50 1·25

**371.** President planting Sapling.

**372.** Boys and Hoops with Handles.

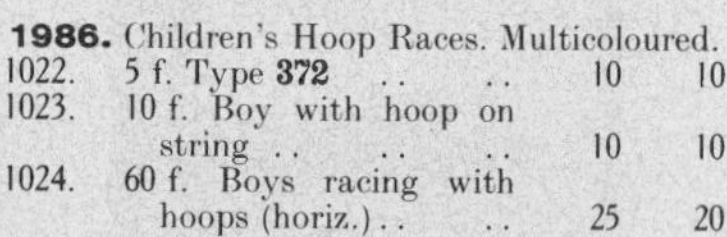

**1986.** National Tree Day. Multicoloured.

1020. 60 f. Type **371** .. .. 25 20
1021. 200 f. Map, tree and production of oxygen and carbon dioxide .. 85 75

**1986.** Children's Hoop Races. Multicoloured.

1022. 5 f. Type **372** .. .. 10 10
1023. 10 f. Boy with hoop on string .. .. .. 10 10
1024. 60 f. Boys racing with hoops (horiz.) .. .. 25 20

**373.** Cosmos-Frantel Hotel.

**1986.** Air.

1026. **373.** 250 f. multicoloured 1·10 95

**375.** Emptying Rubbish into Dustbin.

**376.** Woman carrying Basket on Head.

**1986.** World Environment Day. Mult.

1030. 60 f. Type **375** .. .. 25 20
1031. 125 f. Woman dumping rubbish in street .. 45 35

**1986.** Traditional Methods of Carrying Goods. Multicoloured.

1032. 5 f. Type **376** .. .. 10 10
1033. 10 f. Woman carrying basket at back held by rope from head .. 10 10
1034. 60 f. Man carrying wood on shoulder .. .. 25 20

**377.** Footballers.

**1986.** Air. World Cup Football Championship, Mexico.

1035. **377.** 150 f. multicoloured 65 55
1036. – 250 f. multicoloured 1·00 90
1037. – 440 f. multicoloured 1·75 1·50
1038. – 600 f. multicoloured 2·50 2·25

DESIGNS: 250 f to 600 f. Various football scenes.

**378.** Sisters tending Patients.

**379.** Programme Emblem.

**1986.** Centenary of Sisters of St. Joseph of Cluny Mission.
1039. **378.** 230 f. multicoloured 1·00 90

**1986.** International Communications Development Programme.
1040. **379.** 40 f. multicoloured .. 15 10
1041. 60 f. multicoloured .. 25 20
1042. 100 f. multicoloured 45 35

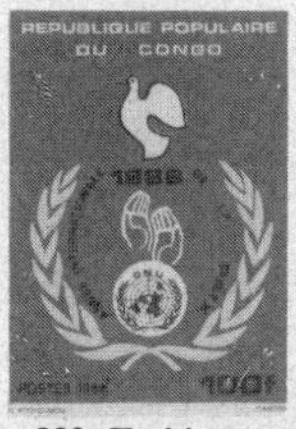


**380.** Emblem.

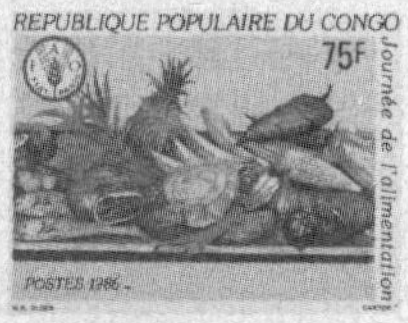


**381.** Foodstuffs.

**1986.** International Peace Year.
1043. **380.** 100 f. blue, green and light green .. 45 35

**1986.** World Food Day. Multicoloured.
1044. 75 f. Type **381** .. .. 30 20
1045. 120 f. Woman spoon-feeding child .. .. 50 40

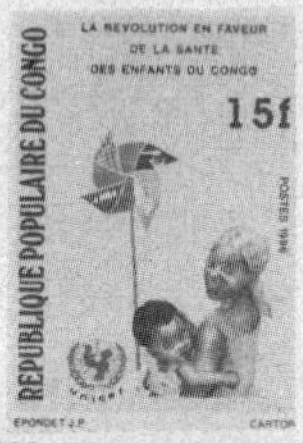


**382.** Woman holding Child and Windmill with Medical Symbols.

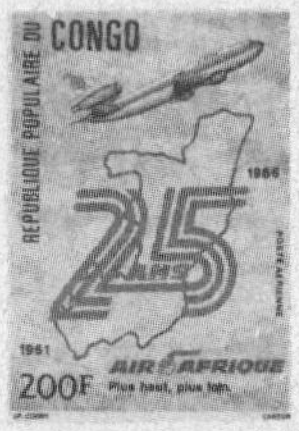


**383.** Douglas DC-10 and "25" on Map.

**1986.** U.N.I.C.E.F. Child Survival Campaign. Multicoloured.
1046. 15 f. Type **382** .. .. 10 10
1047. 30 f. Children (horiz.) .. 15 10
1048. 70 f. Woman and child .. 30 20

**1986.** Air. 25th Anniv. of Air Afrique.
1049. **383.** 200 f. multicoloured 1·40 90

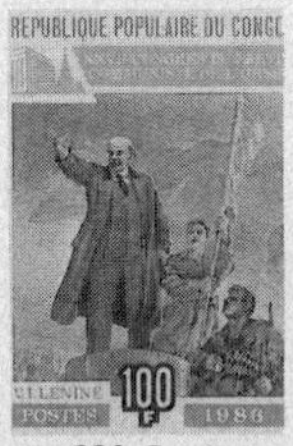


**384.** Lenin.

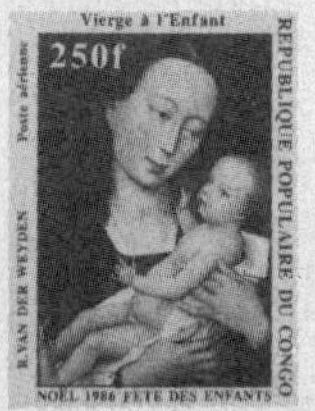


**386.** "Virgin and Child".

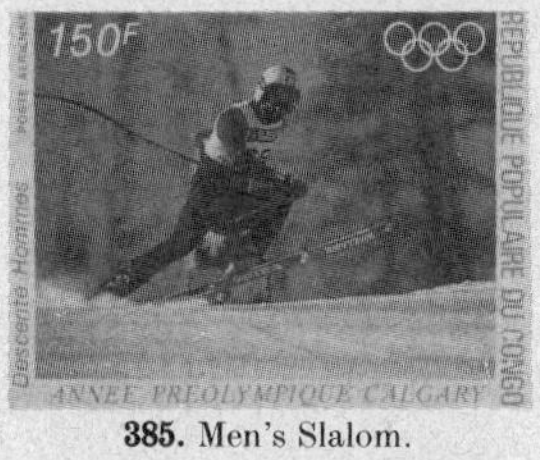


**385.** Men's Slalom.

**1986.** 27th U.S.S.R. Communist Party Congress.
1050. **384.** 100 f. multicoloured 40 30

**1986.** Air. Winter Olympics Games, Calgary (1988). Multicoloured.
1051. 150 f. Type **385** .. .. 65 55
1052. 250 f. Four-man bobsleigh (vert.) .. .. .. 1·10 95
1053. 440 f. Ladies cross-country skiing (vert.) 1·75 1·50
1054. 600 f. Ski-jumping .. 2·50 2·25

**1986.** Air. Christmas. Paintings by Rogier van der Weyden. Multicoloured.
1055. 250 f. Type **386** .. .. 1·10 95
1056. 440 f. "Nativity" .. 1·50 1·25
1057. 500 f. "Virgin of the Pink" .. .. .. 2·25 1·90

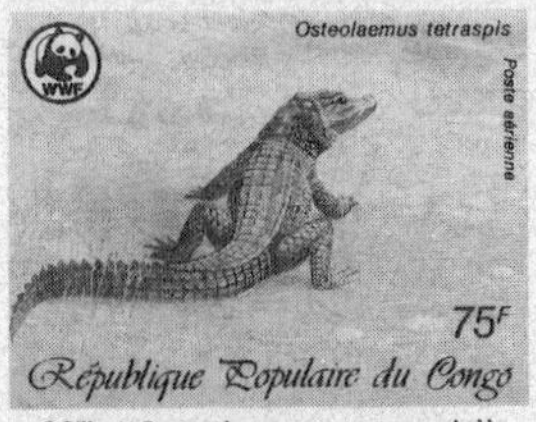


**387.** "Osteolaemus tetraspis".

**1987.** Air. Crocodiles. Multicoloured.
1058. 75 f. Type **387** .. .. 30 20
1059. 100 f. "Crocodylus cataphractus" .. .. 40 30
1060. 125 f. "Osteolaemus tetraspis" (different) .. 50 40
1061. 150 f. "Crocodylus cataphractus" (different) .. 60 50

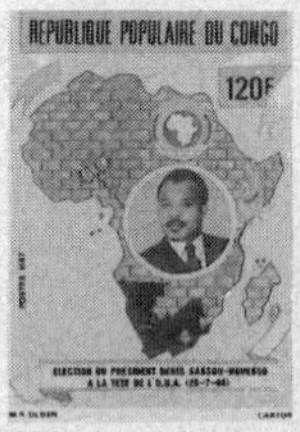


**388.** Pres. Sassou-Nguesso and Map.

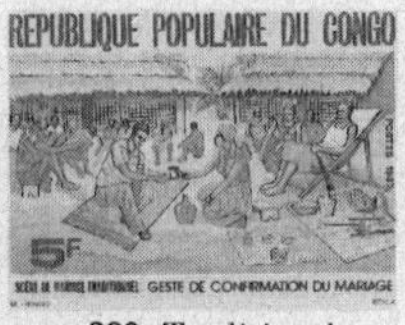


**389.** Traditional Marriage Ceremony.

**1987.** Election of Pres. Sassou-Nguesso as Chairman of Organization of African Unity.
1062. **388.** 30 f. multicoloured .. 15 10
1063. 45 f. multicoloured .. 20 15
1064. 75 f. multicoloured .. 30 20
1065. 120 f. multicoloured 50 40

**1987.**
1066. **389.** 5 f. multicoloured .. 10 10
1067. 15 f. multicoloured .. 10 10
1068. 20 f. multicoloured .. 10 10

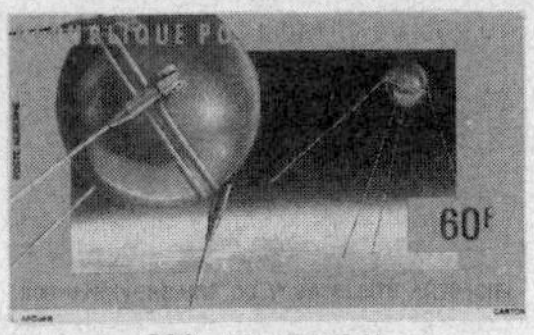


**390.** "Sputnik".

**1987.** Air. 30th Anniv. of First Artificial Space Satellite.
1069. **390.** 60 f. multicoloured .. 25 15
1070. 240 f. multicoloured 1·00 90

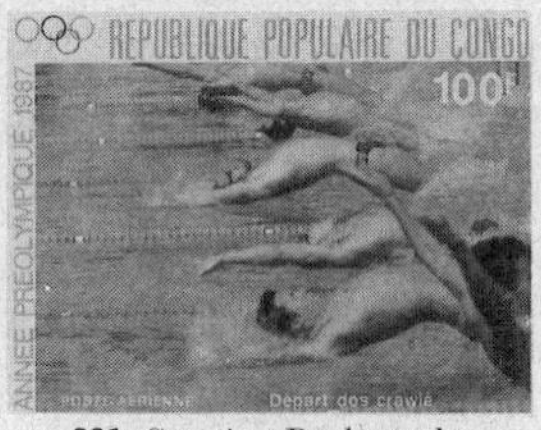


**391.** Starting Back-stroke Race.

**1987.** Air. Olympic Games, Seoul (1988) (1st issue). Swimming. Multicoloured.
1071. 100 f. Type **391** .. .. 40 30
1072. 200 f. Freestyle .. .. 80 70
1073. 300 f. Breast-stroke .. 1·25 1·00
1074. 400 f. Butterfly .. .. 1·60 1·40
See also Nos. 1121/4.

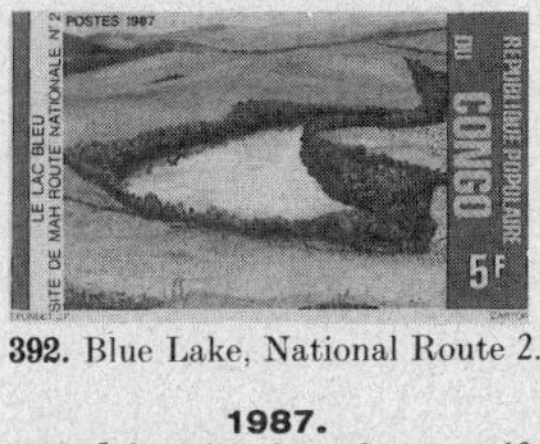


**392.** Blue Lake, National Route 2.

**1987.**
1076. **392.** 5 f. multicoloured .. 10 10
1077. 15 f. multicoloured .. 10 10
1078. 75 f. multicoloured .. 30 20
1079. 120 f. multicoloured 50 40

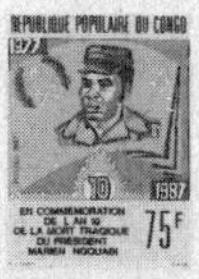


**393.** Flags and Pres. Ngouabi.

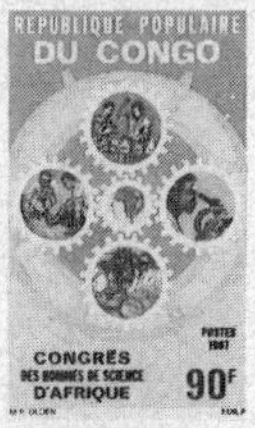


**395.** Emblem.

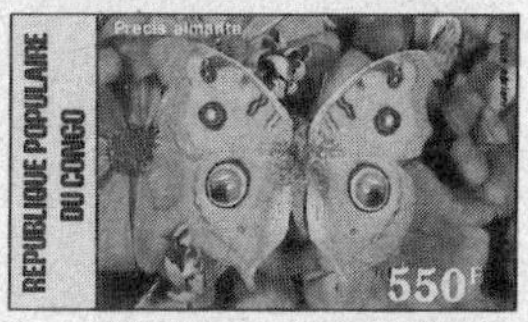


**394.** "Precis almanta".

**1987.** 10th Death Anniv. of President Marien Ngouabi.
1080. **393.** 75 f. multicoloured .. 30 20
1081. 120 f. multicoloured 50 40

**1987.** Butterflies. Multicoloured.
1082. 75 f. "Precis epicleli" .. 40 25
1083. 120 f. "Deilephila nerii" 65 45
1084. 450 f. "Euryphene senegalensis" .. .. 2·25 1·90
1085. 550 f. Type **394** .. .. 2·75 2·40

**1987.** African Men of Science Congress.
1086. **395.** 15 f. multicoloured .. 10 10
1087. 90 f. multicoloured .. 40 30
1088. 230 f. multicoloured 95 85

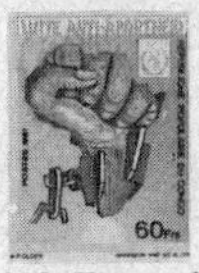

**396.** Fist and Broken Manacle.

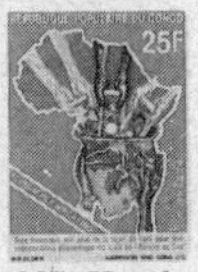


**397.** Hands putting Money into Pot within Map.

**1987.** Anti-Apartheid Campaign. Mult.
1089. 60 f. Type **396** .. .. 25 15
1090. 240 f. Chain forming outline of map, Nelson Mandela and bars (26 × 38 mm) .. .. 1·00 90

**1987.** African Fund.
1091. **397.** 25 f. multicoloured .. 10 10
1092. 50 f. multicoloured .. 20 15
1093. 70 f. multicoloured .. 30 20

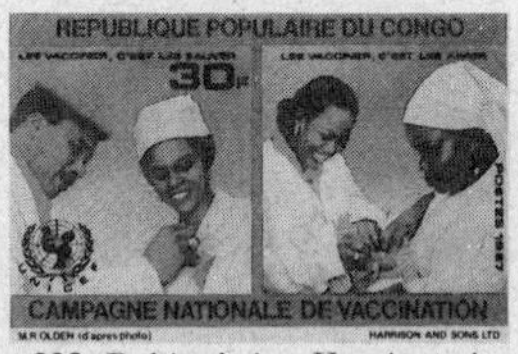


**398.** Babies being Vaccinated.

**1987.** National Vaccination Campaign. Mult.
1094. 30 f. Type **398** (postage) 15 10
1095. 34 f. Doctor vaccinating child (vert.) .. .. 20 15
1096. 500 f. Queue waiting for vaccination (air) .. 2·00 1·90

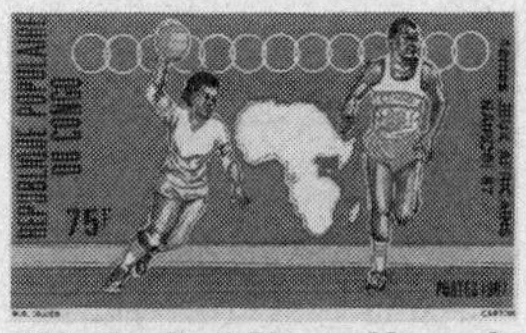


**399.** Handball Player, Map and Runner.

**1987.** 4th African Games, Nairobi.
1097. **399.** 75 f. multicoloured .. 30 20
1098. 120 f. multicoloured 50 40

**HAVE YOU READ THE NOTES AT THE BEGINNING OF THIS CATALOGUE?**
These often provide answers to the enquiries we receive.

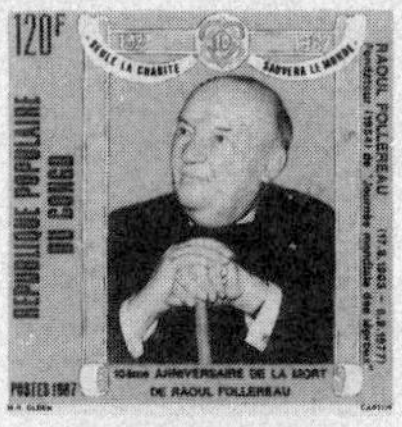


**400.** Follereau.

**1987.** 10th Death Anniv. of Raoul Follereau (leprosy pioneer).
1099. **400.** 120 f. multicoloured 50 40

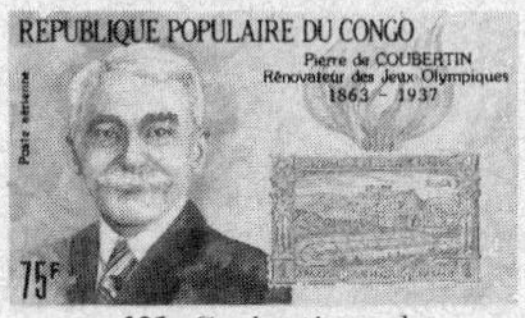


**401.** Coubertin and Greece 1896 1 d. Stamp.

**1987.** Air. 50th Death Anniv. of Pierre de Coubertin (founder of modern Olympic games). Multicoloured.
1100. 75 f. Type **401** .. .. 30 20
1101. 120 f. Runners and France 1924 10 c. stamp .. .. .. 50 40
1102. 350 f. Congo 1964 100 f. stamp and hurdler .. 1·50 1·25
1103. 600 f. High jumper and Congo 1968 85 f. stamp 2·40 2·25

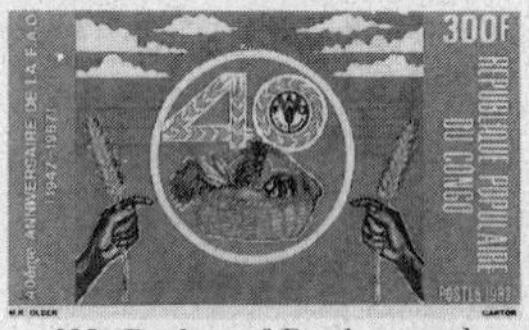


**402.** Basket of Produce and Hands holding Ears of Wheat.

**1987.** 40th Anniv. of F.A.O.
1104. **402.** 300 f. multicoloured 1·25 1·00

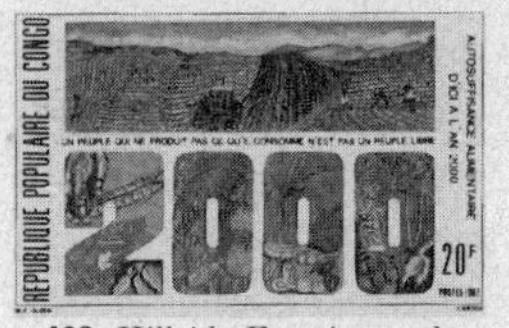


**403.** Hillside Farming and Produce within "2000".

**1987.** "Food Self-sufficiency by Year 2000".
1105. **403.** 20 f. multicoloured .. 10 10
1106. 55 f. multicoloured .. 25 20
1107. 100 f. multicoloured 40 30

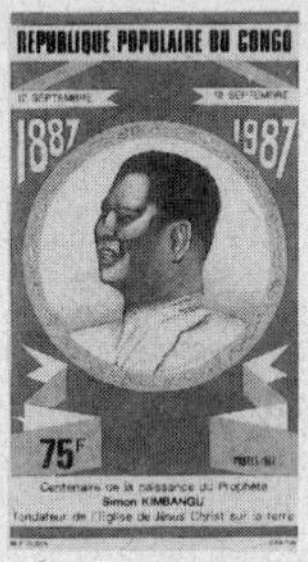


**404.** Simon Kimbangu.

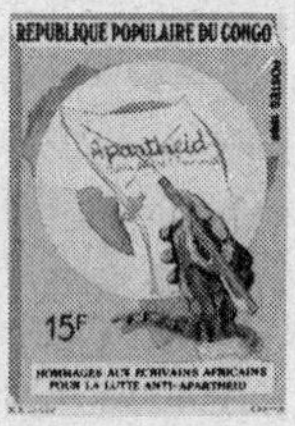


**406.** Writer crossing through "Apartheid".

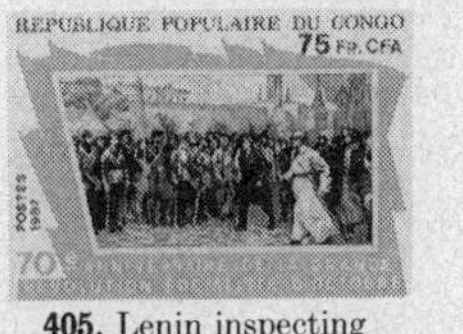


**405.** Lenin inspecting Parade in Red Square.

**1987.** Birth Centenary of Simon Kimbangu (founder of Church of Jesus Christ on Earth). Multicoloured.
1108 75 f. Type **404** .. .. 30 20
1109 120 f. Kimbangu feeding grey parrot .. .. 1·50 80
1110 240 f. Kimbanguiste Temple, Nkamba (horiz) .. .. 1·00 90

**1988.** 70th Anniv. of Russian Revolution.
1112. **405.** 75 f. multicoloured .. 30 20
1113. 120 f. multicoloured 45 35

**1988.** African Anti-apartheid Writers.
1114. **406.** 15 f. multicoloured .. 10 10
1115. 60 f. multicoloured .. 25 15
1116. 75 f. multicoloured .. 30 20

**407.** Schweitzer and Hospital.

**1988.** Air. 75th Anniv. of Arrival at Lambarene of Dr. Albert Schweitzer (missionary).
1117. **407.** 240 f. multicoloured 1·00 90

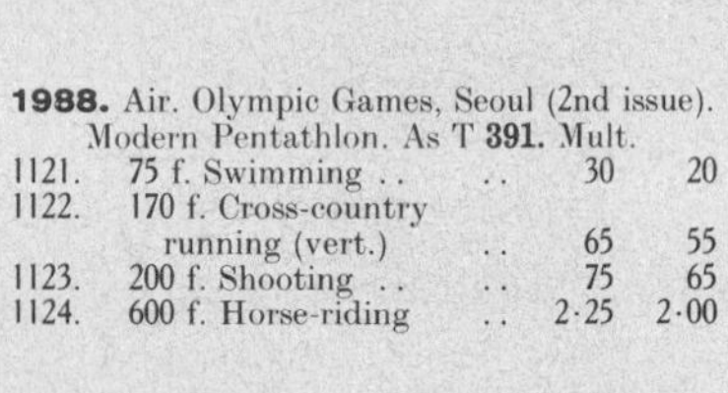

**408.** Samuel Morse. **409.** Banknote and Field within "10".

**1988.** 150th Anniv. of Morse Telegraph. Mult.
1118. 90 f. Type **408** .. .. 35 25
1119. 120 f. Morse and telegraph equipment .. 45 35

**1988.** 10th Anniv. of International Agricultural Development Fund.
1120. **409.** 240 f. multicoloured 90 80

**1988.** Air. Olympic Games, Seoul (2nd issue). Modern Pentathlon. As T **391.** Mult.
1121. 75 f. Swimming .. .. 30 20
1122. 170 f. Cross-country running (vert.) .. 65 55
1123. 200 f. Shooting .. .. 75 65
1124. 600 f. Horse-riding .. 2·25 2·00

**411.** Eucalyptus Plantation, Brazzaville. **412.** Hands holding Gun and Pick.

**1988.** Anti-desertification Campaign. Mult.
1126. 5 f. Type **411** .. .. 10 10
1127. 10 f. Stop sign and man chopping down tree .. 10 10

**1988.** 25th Anniv. of Revolution. Mult.
1128. 75 f. Type **412** .. .. 30 20
1129. 75 f. People tending crops .. .. .. 30 20
1130. 120 f. Pres. Sassou-Nguesso holding aubergine .. .. 45 35

**413.** Yoro Fishing Village.

**1988.**
1131. 35 f. Type **413** .. .. 20 10
1132. 40 f. Place de la Liberte 20 10

**414** People on Map and Jet Fighters attacking Virus

**1988.** 1st International Day against A.I.D.S.
1133 **414** 60 f. multicoloured .. 30 10
1134 – 75 f. multicoloured .. 30 20
1135 – 180 f. black, red & bl 70 60
DESIGNS: 75 f. Virus consisting of healthy and infected people; 180 f. Globe and laurel branches.

**415** Pres. Sassou-Nguesso addressing Crowd

**1989.** 10th Anniv of 5 February Movement. Multicoloured.
1136 75 f. Type **415** .. .. 30 20
1137 120 f. Pres. Sassou-Nguesso and symbols of progress .. .. 45 35

**416** Emblems

**1989.** 40th Anniv of Declaration of Human Rights.
1138 **416** 120 f. multicoloured 45 35
1139 350 f. multicoloured 1·40 1·10

**417** Bari

**1989.** Air. World Cup Football Championship, Italy (1990) (1st issue). Multicoloured.
1140 75 f. Type **417** .. .. 30 20
1141 120 f. Rome .. .. 45 35
1142 500 f. Florence .. .. 1·90 1·60
1143 550 f. Naples .. .. 2·10 1·90
See also Nos. 1174/7.

**418** "Storming of the Bastille" (detail, J.P. Houel)

**1989.** Air. "Philexfrance 89" International Stamp Exhibition. Multicoloured.
1144 300 f. Type **418** (bicent of French revolution) .. 1·25 1·00
1145 400 f. "Eiffel Tower" (G. Seurat) (centenary of Eiffel Tower (1986)) .. 1·50 1·25

**419** Astronaut and Landing Module

**1989.** Air. 20th Anniv of First Manned Landing on Moon. Multicoloured.
1146 400 f. Type **419** .. .. 1·50 1·25
1147 400 f. Astronaut on lunar surface .. .. 1·50 1·25

**420** Marien Ngouabi

**1989.** 50th Birth Anniv (1988) of Marien Ngouabi (President, 1969–77).
1148 **420** 240 f. blk, yell &mve 1·00 90

**421** Henri Dunant (founder), Volunteer with Child and Anniversary Emblem **422** Emblem on Dove

**1989.** 125th Anniv (1988) of Red Cross.
1149 75 f. Type **421** (postage) 30 20
1150 120 f. Emblem, Dunant and Congolese Red Cross station (air) .. 45 35

**1989.** 25th Anniv of Organization of African Unity.
1151 **422** 120 f. multicoloured .. 45 35

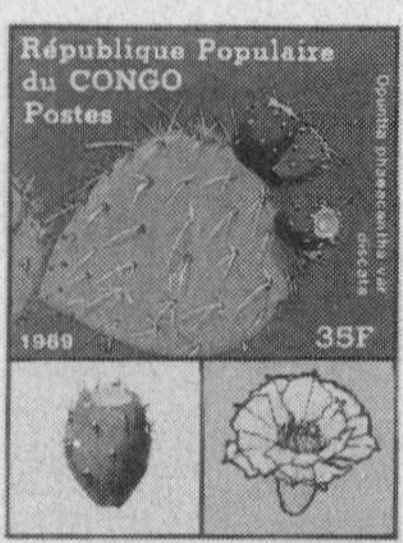


**423** "Opuntia phaeacantha"

**1989.** Cacti. Multicoloured.
1152 35 f. Type **423** .. .. 15 10
1153 40 f. "Opuntia ficus-indica" .. .. 15 10
1154 60 f. "Opuntia erinacea" (horiz) .. .. 25 15
1155 75 f. "Opuntia rufida" .. 30 20
1156 120 f. "Opuntia leptocaulis" (horiz) .. 50 40

**424** Banknote, Coins and Woman

**1989.** 25th Anniv of African Development Bank.
1158 **424** 75 f. multicoloured .. 30 20
1159 120 f. multicoloured .. 50 40

**425** Ice Dancing

**1989.** Winter Olympic Games, Albertville (1992) (1st issue). Multicoloured.
1160 75 f. Type **425** .. .. 30 20
1161 80 f. Cross-country skiing 30 20
1162 100 f. Speed skating .. 40 30
1163 120 f. Luge .. .. 50 40
1164 200 f. Slalom .. .. 80 70
1165 240 f. Ice hockey .. 1·00 90
1166 400 f. Ski jumping .. 1·60 1·40
See also No. 1245/6.

**426** Doctor examining Patient **427** Emblem and People with raised Fists

**1989.** 40th Anniv of W.H.O. Multicoloured.
1168 60 f. Type **426** .. .. 25 15
1169 75 f. Blood donation (vert) .. .. .. 30 20

**1989.** 20th Anniv of Congolese Workers' Party.
1170 **427** 75 f. multicoloured .. 30 20
1171 120 f. multicoloured .. 50 40

**1990.** Local Health Campaigns. Nos. 1168/9 optd **NOTRE PLANETE, NOTRE SANTE PENSER GLOBALEMENT AGIR LOCALEMENT.**
1172 60 f. multicoloured .. 25 15
1173 75 f. multicoloured .. 30 20

**429** Footballers **430** Family supporting Open Book

**1990.** Air. World Cup Football Championship, Italy (2nd issue). Designs showing footballers.
1174 **429** 120 f. multicoloured .. 50 40
1175 – 240 f. multicoloured .. 1·00 90
1176 – 500 f. multicoloured .. 2·00 1·75
1177 – 600 f. multicoloured .. 2·40 2·10

**1990.** International Literacy Year.
1178 **430** 75 f. black, yellow & bl 30 20

**431** Ramblas, Barcelona

**1990.** Olympic Games, Barcelona (1992) (1st issue). Multicoloured.
1179 100 f. Type **431** (postage) .. 40 30
1180 150 f. Yachting (horiz) .. 80 60
1181 200 f. Yachting (different) (horiz) .. .. 95 80
1182 240 f. Market stalls, Barcelona (horiz) .. 1·00 90
1183 350 f. Harbour, Barcelona (horiz) (air) .. .. 1·75 1·50
1184 500 f. Monument, Barcelona .. .. 2·00 1·75
See also Nos. 1322/7.

**432** Turtle Dove **433** Mondo Mask

**1990.** Birds. Multicoloured.
1186 25 f. Type **432** .. .. 35 30
1187 50 f. Dartford warbler (vert) .. .. .. 65 40
1188 70 f. Common kestrel (vert) .. .. .. 1·10 70
1189 150 f. Grey parrot (vert) 2·00 1·60

**1990.** Dance Masks. Multicoloured.
1190 120 f. Type **433** .. .. 50 40
1191 360 f. Bapunu mask .. 1·50 1·25
1192 400 f. Kwele mask .. 1·60 1·40

**434** Necklace **435** Sunflower

**1990.** Traditional Royal Necklaces. Mult.
1193 75 f. Type **434** .. .. 30 20
1194 100 f. Money cowrie necklace .. .. 55 35

**1990.** Flowers. Multicoloured.
1195 30 f. Type **435** .. .. 15 10
1196 45 f. "Cassia alata" (horiz) 20 10
1197 75 f. Opium poppy .. 30 20
1198 90 f. "Acalypha sanderil" 35 25

**436** Hot-air Balloon dropping Envelopes on Africa **437** The Blusher

**1991.** Air. 10th Anniv of Pan-African Postal Union. Multicoloured.
1199 60 f. Type **436** .. .. 40 20
1200 120 f. Envelopes on map of Africa .. .. 60 30

**1991.** Fungi. Multicoloured.
1201 30 f. Type **437** .. .. 25 10
1202 45 f. "Catathelasma imperiale" .. .. 35 15
1203 75 f. Caesar's mushroom 55 25
1204 90 f. Royal boletus .. 65 30
1205 120 f. Deer mushroom .. 1·00 45
1206 150 f. "Boletus chrysenteron" .. .. .. 1·10 50
1207 200 f. Horse mushroom .. 1·60 70

**438** "Dr-16", Finland

**1991.** Trains. Multicoloured.
1209 60 f. Type **438** .. .. 30 15
1210 75 f. "T.G.V." express, France .. .. 35 20
1211 120 f. "S 350", Italy .. 60 30
1212 200 f. "DE 24000", Turkey 1·00 50
1213 250 f. "DE 1024", Germany .. .. 1·25 65

**439** Canoe, Palm Tree and Setting Sun **440** Congolese Woman

**1991.** International African Tourism Year. Multicoloured.
1215 75 f. Type **439** .. .. 55 20
1216 120 f. Zebra and map of Africa .. .. 60 30

**1991.**
1217 **440** 15 f. blue .. .. 10 10
1218 30 f. green .. .. 15 10
1219 60 f. yellow .. .. 30 15
1220 75 f. mauve .. .. 35 20
1221 120 f. brown .. .. 60 30

**441** Christopher Columbus (after Sebastian del Pombo) **442** "Kalanchoe pinnata"

**1991.** 500th Anniv (1992) of Discovery of America by Columbus. Multicoloured.
1222 20 f. Type **441** .. .. 10 10
1223 35 f. Christopher Columbus .. .. .. 15 10
1224 40 f. Christopher Columbus (different) .. 20 10
1225 55 f. "Santa Maria" .. 45 20
1226 75 f. "Nina" .. .. 70 30
1227 150 f. "Pinta" .. .. 1·25 30
1228 200 f. Arms and signature of Columbus .. .. 1·00 50

**1991.** Medicinal Plants. Multicoloured.
1229 15 f. "Ocimum viride" (horiz) .. .. 10 10
1230 20 f. Type **442** .. .. 10 10
1231 30 f. "Euphorbia hirta" (horiz) .. .. 15 10
1232 60 f. "Catharantheus roseus" .. .. 30 15
1233 75 f. "Bidens pilosa" .. 35 20
1234 100 f. "Brillantasia patula" .. .. 50 25
1235 120 f. "Cassia occidentalis" .. .. .. 60 30

**INDEX**
Countries can be quickly located by referring to the index at the end of this volume.

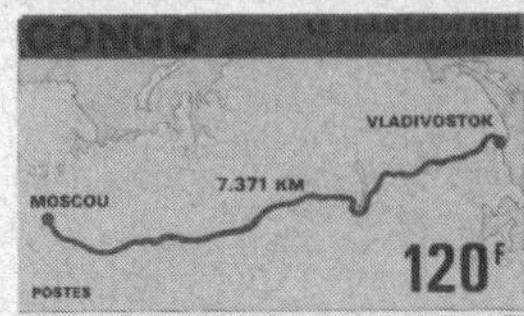

**443** Route Map

**1991.** Cent of Trans-Siberian Railway. Mult.
1236 120 f. Type **443** .. .. 60 30
1237 240 f. Steam train .. 1·00 50

**444** Honey fungus

**1991.** Scouts, Butterflies and Fungi. Mult.
1238 35 f. "Euphaedra eusemoides" (butterfly) (post) 15 10
1239 40 f. Type **444** .. .. 40 15
1240 75 f. "Palla decius" (butterfly) .. .. 35 20
1241 80 f. "Kallima ansorgei" (butterfly) .. .. 40 20
1242 500 f. "Cortinarius speciocissimus" (fungus) (air) .. 3·75 1·75
1243 600 f. "Graphium illyris" (butterfly) .. .. 2·75 1·40

**445** Ice Hockey

**1991.** Air. Winter Olympic Games, Albertville (1992) (2nd issue). Multicoloured.
1245 120 f. Type **445** .. .. 60 30
1246 300 f. Speed skating .. 1·40 70

**446** "Telecom 91"

**1991.** "Telecom 91" World Telecommunications Exhibition, Geneva. Multicoloured.
1248 75 f. Type **446** .. .. 35 20
1249 120 f. Stylised view of exhibition (vert) .. 60 30

**447** Beetle and Peanuts **448** Woman drinking at Waterfall

**1991.** Harmful Insects. Multicoloured.
1250 75 f. Type **447** .. .. 35 20
1251 120 f. Stag beetle (horiz) 60 30
1252 200 f. Beetle and coffee 1·00 50
1253 300 f. Goliath beetle .. 1·40 70

**1991.** "Water is Life".
1254 **448** 75 f. multicoloured .. 35 20

**449** Pintail **450** Breaking Chain and Hand holding Dove

**1991.** Wild Ducks. Multicoloured.
1255 75 f. Type **449** .. .. 35 20
1256 120 f. Eider (vert) .. 60 30
1257 200 f. Common shoveler (vert) .. .. .. 1·00 50
1258 240 f. Mallard .. .. 1·10 55

**1991.** 30th Anniv of Amnesty International. Multicoloured.
1259 40 f. Candle, barbed wire and sun .. .. 20 10
1260 75 f. Type **450** .. .. 35 20
1261 80 f. Boy holding human rights banner and soldiers threatening boy (horiz) .. .. 40 20

**451** 1891 5 c. on 1 c. "Commerce" stamp

**1991.** Centenary of Congolese Stamps.
1262 **451** 75 f. green and brown 35 20
1263 – 120 f. deep brown, green and brown .. 60 30
1264 – 240 f. multicoloured .. 1·10 55
1265 – 500 f. multicoloured .. 2·40 1·25
DESIGNS: 120 f. 1900 1 c. "Leopard in ambush" stamp; 240 f. 1959 25 f. "Birth of the Republic" stamp; 500 f. "Commerce", "Leopard" and "Republic" stamps.

**452** Ferrari "512 S"

**1991.** Cars and Space. Multicoloured.
1266 35 f. Type **452** (postage) 15 10
1267 40 f. Vincenzo Lancia and Lancia "Stratos" .. 20 10
1268 75 f. Airship "Graf Zeppelin", Maybach "Type 12" car and Wilhelm Maybach .. 45 25
1269 80 f. Mars space probe .. 40 20
1270 500 f. "Magellan" space probe over Venus (air) 2·40 1·25
1271 600 f. "Ulysses" space probe photographing sun spot .. .. 2·75 1·40

**453** Small Blue

**1991.** Butterflies. Multicoloured.
1273 75 f. Type **453** .. .. 35 20
1274 120 f. Charaxes .. .. 60 30
1275 240 f. Leaf butterfly (vert) 1·10 55
1276 300 f. Butterfly on orange (vert) .. .. .. 1·40 70

**454** General De Gaulle

**1991.** De Gaulle and Africa. Multicoloured.
1277 75 f. Type **454** .. .. .. 35 20
1278 120 f. De Gaulle, soldiers and Free French flag (vert) .. .. .. 60 30
1279 240 f. De Gaulle making speech, Brazzaville 1940 1·10 55

**455** Bo Jackson (American footballer)

**1991.** Celebrities and International Organizations. Multicoloured.
1280 100 f. Type **455** .. .. 50 25
1281 150 f. Nick Faldo (golfer) 70 35
1282 200 f. Rickey Henderson and Barry Bonds (baseball players) .. 1·00 50
1283 240 f. Gary Kasparov (World chess champion) 1·10 55
1284 300 f. Starving child and Lions International and Rotary International emblems .. 1·40 70
1285 350 f. Wolfgang Amadeus Mozart (composer) .. 1·60 80
1286 400 f. De Gaulle and Churchill visiting the Eastern Front, 1944 .. 1·90 95
1287 500 f. Henry Dunant (founder of Red Cross) 2·50 1·25

**456** Painting

**1991.** Paintings. Multicoloured.
1289 75 f. Type **456** .. .. 35 20
1290 120 f. Couple in silhouette (vert) .. .. .. 60 30

**457** Diana Monkey

**1991.** Primates. Multicoloured.
1291 30 f. Type **457** .. .. 15 10
1292 45 f. Chimpanzee .. 20 10
1293 60 f. Gelada (vert) .. 30 15
1294 75 f. Hamadryas baboon (vert) .. .. .. 35 20
1295 90 f. Pigtail macaque (vert) .. .. .. 40 20
1296 120 f. Gorilla (vert) .. 60 30
1297 240 f. Mandrill (vert) .. 1·10 55

**458** "Sputnik 2" and Laika (space dog)

**1992.** Celebrities, Anniversaries and Events. Multicoloured.
1299 50 f. Type **458** (35th anniv of space flight) (postage) 20 10
1300 75 f. Martin Luther King (Nobel Peace Prize winner, 1964) and Gandhi .. 35 20
1301 120 f. Meteosat "MOP-2" and "ERS-1" satellites, globe and stern trawler ("Europe-Africa") .. 60 30
1302 300 f. Konrad Adenauer (German statesman, 25th death anniv) and crowd before Brandenburg Gate (3rd anniv of opening of Berlin Wall 1·40 70
1303 240 f. "Graf Zeppelin", Ferdinand von Zeppelin (75th death anniv) and Maybach Zeppelin motor car (air) .. 1·40 70
1304 500 f. Pope and globe (Papal visit to Africa) 2·40 1·25

**459** Juan de la Cosa and Map

**460** Secretary Bird

**1992.** "Genova 92" International Thematic Stamp Exhibition. Multicoloured.
1306 75 f. Type **459** .. .. 35 20
1307 95 f. Martin Alonso Pinzon and astrolabe .. 45 25
1308 120 f. Alonso de Ojeda and hourglass .. .. 55 30
1309 200 f. Vicente Yanez Pinzon and sun clock .. 90 45
1310 250 f. Bartholomew Columbus and quadrant 1·10 55

**1992.** Birds. Multicoloured.
1312 60 f. Type **460** .. .. 30 15
1313 75 f. Saddle-bill stork .. 35 20
1314 120 f. Wattled crane .. 55 30
1315 200 f. Black-headed heron 90 45
1316 250 f. Greater flamingo .. 1·10 55

**461** Lion

**462** "Madonna of the Grand Duke" (Raphael)

**1992.** Big Cats. Multicoloured.
1318 45 f. Type **461** .. .. 50 25
1319 60 f. Tiger .. .. 70 35
1320 75 f. Lynx .. .. 85 40
1321 95 f. Caracal .. 1·10 55
1322 250 f. Ocelot .. 2·75 1·40

**1992.** Christmas. Multicoloured.
1324 95 f. Type **462** .. .. 45 25
1325 200 f. "Madonna of the Book" (Sandro Botticelli) .. 95 50
1326 250 f. "Carondelet Madonna" (Fra Bartolommeo) .. 1·25 65

No. 1325 is wrongly inscribed "Boticelli" and No. 1326 "Bartolomeo".

**463** Baseball and Towers of Church of the Holy Family

**464** N. Mishkutienok and A. Dmitriev (Unified Team)

**1992.** Olympic Games, Barcelona (2nd issue). Multicoloured.
1328 75 f. Type **463** (postage) 35 20
1329 100 f. Running and "The Muses" (Eusebio Arnau) 50 25
1330 150 f. Hurdling and painted dome (Miguel Barcelo) of Market Theatre .. 70 35
1331 200 f. High jumping and Sant Pau hospital .. 95 50
1332 400 f. Putting the shot and "Miss Barcelona" (Joan Miro) (air) .. 1·90 85
1333 500 f. Table tennis and "Don Juan of Austria" (galley .. .. 2·40 1·25

**1992.** Winter Olympic Games Gold Medal Winners. Multicoloured.
1335 150 f. Type **464** (pairs figure skating) (postage) 70 35
1336 200 f. Austrian team (four-man bobsleighing) 95 50
1337 500 f. Gunda Niemann (Germany, women's speed skating) (air) .. 2·40 1·25
1338 600 f. Bjorn Daehlie (Norway, 50 km cross-country skiing) .. 2·75 1·40

No. 1338 is wrongly inscribed "Blorn Daehlle".

**465** African Red-tailed Buzzard

**467** Topi

**466** Overhead Volley

**1993.** Birds of Prey. Multicoloured.
1340 45 f. Type **465** .. .. 20 10
1341 75 f. Ruppell's griffon .. 35 20
1342 120 f. Verreaux's eagle .. 55 30

**1993.** World Cup Football Championship U.S.A. (1994).
1343 **466** 75 f. multicoloured .. 35 20
1344 – 95 f. multicoloured .. 45 25
1345 – 120 f. multicoloured .. 55 30
1346 – 200 f. multicoloured .. 95 50
1347 – 250 f. multicoloured .. 1·25 65

DESIGNS: 95 f. to 250 f. Different footballing scenes.

**1993.** Animals. Multicoloured.
1349 60 f. Type **467** .. .. 30 15
1350 75 f. Grant's gazelle .. 35 20
1351 95 f. Quagga .. .. 45 25
1352 120 f. Leopard .. .. 55 30
1353 200 f. African buffalo .. 95 50
1354 250 f. Hippopotamus .. 1·25 65
1355 300 f. Hooded vulture .. 1·40 70
1356 350 f. Lioness and cub .. 1·60 80

Nos. 1349/56 were issued together, se-tenant, forming a composite design.

**468** Jars from Liloko

**1993.** Traditional Pottery. Multicoloured.
1357 45 f. Type **468** .. .. 20 10
1358 75 f. Jug from Mbeya .. 35 20
1359 120 f. Jar from Mbeya .. 60 30

**470** Show Jumping

**1993.** Summer Olympic Games, Atlanta (1996) and Winter Olympic Games, Lillehammer, Norway (1994). Multicoloured.
1366 50 f. Type **470** (postage) 25 15
1367 75 f. Cycling .. .. 35 20
1368 120 f. Yachting .. .. 60 30
1369 240 f. Fencing .. .. 1·10 55
1370 300 f. Hurdling (air) .. 1·40 70
1371 400 f. Figure skating .. 1·90 95
1372 500 f. Basketball .. 2·40 1·25
1373 600 f. Ice hockey .. 3·00 1·50

**471** "Hibiscus schizopetalus"

**1993.** Wild Flowers. Multicoloured.
1375 75 f. Type **471** .. .. 35 20
1376 95 f. "Pentas lanceolata" 45 25
1377 120 f. "Ricinus communis" .. .. 60 30
1378 200 f. "Delonix regia" .. 95 50
1379 250 f. "Stapelia gigantea" 1·25 65

OFFICIAL STAMPS

O **68**. Arms.

**1968.**
O 142. O **68**. 1 f. multicoloured .. 10 10
O 143. 2 f. multicoloured .. 10 10
O 144. 5 f. multicoloured .. 10 10
O 145. 10 f. multicoloured .. 20 15
O 146. 25 f. multicoloured .. 20 10
O 147. 30 f. multicoloured .. 20 10
O 148. 50 f. multicoloured .. 60 30
O 149. 85 f. multicoloured 1·25 65
O 150. 100 f. multicoloured 1·50 75
O 151. 200 f. multicoloured 1·90 1·60

POSTAGE DUE STAMPS

D **7**. Letter-carrier.

**1961.** Transport designs.
D 19. D **7**. 50 c. bistre, red & blue 10 10
D 20. – 50 c. bistre, pur. & bl. 10 10
D 21. – 1 f. brn., red and grn. 10 10
D 22. – 1 f. green, red & lake 10 10
D 23. – 2 f. brn., grn. & blue 10 15
D 24. – 2 f. brn., grn. & blue 10 15
D 25. – 5 f. sepia and violet .. 15 15
D 26. – 5 f. sepia and violet .. 15 15
D 27. – 10 f. brn., blue & grn. 60 40
D 28. – 10 f. brown and green 60 40
D 29. – 25 f. brn., blue & turq. 60 60
D 30. – 25 f. black and blue .. 60 60

DESIGNS: D20, Holste Broussard monoplane. D21, Hammock-bearers. D22, "Land Rover" car. D23, Pirogue. D24, River steamer of 1932. D25, Cyclist. D26, Motor lorry. D27, Steam locomotive. D28, Diesel locomotive. D29, Seaplane of 1935. D30, Boeing 707 airliner.

**1971.** Tropical Flowers. Similar to T **105**, but inscr. "Timbre-Taxe". Multicoloured.
D 264. 1 f. Stylised bouquet .. 10 10
D 265. 2 f. "Phaeomeria magnifica" 10 10
D 266. 5 f. "Millettia laurentii" 10 10
D 267. 10 f. "Polianthes tuberosa" 15 15
D 268. 15 f. "Pyrostegia venusta" 20 20
D 269. 20 f. "Hibiscus rosa sinensis" .. 25 25

D **374**. Passion Flower.

**1986.** Flowers and Fruit. Mult.
D1027. 5 f. Type D **374** .. 10 10
D1028. 10 f. Canna lily .. 10 10
D1029. 15 f. Pineapple .. 10 10

## APPENDIX

The following stamps have either been issued in excess of postal needs or have not been availble to the public in reasonable quantities at face value. Such stamps may later be given full listing if there is evidence of regular postal use.

All embossed on gold foil.

**1991.**

Scout and Butterfly. Air 1500 f.

Winter Olympic Games, Albertville (1992). Air 1500 f.

**1992.**

Olympic Games, Barcelona. Air 1500 f.

## COSTA RICA Pt. 15

A Republic of Central America. Independent since 1821.

1863. 8 reales = 1 peso.
1881. 100 centavos = 1 peso.
1901. 100 centimos = 1 colon.

1. 8. General P. Fernandez. 14. Pres. Soto.

**1863.**
1. 1. ½ r. blue .. 50 35
3. 2 r. red .. 55 85
4. 4 r. green .. 6·00 6·00
5. 1 p. orange .. 12·00 12·00

**1881.** Surch.
6. 1. 1 c. on ½ r. blue .. 1·10 4·50
8. 2 c. on ½ r. blue .. 90 2·10
9. 5 c. on ½ r. blue .. 2·75 7·25

**1882.** Surch. **U.P.U.** and value.
10. 1. 5 c. on ½ r. blue .. 30·00 30·00
11. 10 c. on 2 r. red .. 30·00 30·00
12. 20 c. on 4 r. green .. 90·00 90·00

**1883.**
13. 8. 1 c. green .. 40 25
14. 2 c. red .. 40 30
15. 5 c. violet .. 7·25 25
16. 10 c. orange .. 21·00 2·75
17. 40 c. blue .. 45 55

**1887.**
18. 14. 5 c. violet .. 3·25 25
19. 10 c. orange .. 90 50

**1887.** Fiscal stamps similar to Types 8 and 14 optd. **CORREOS.**
20. 1 c. red .. 1·50 65
21. 5 c. brown .. 1·50 45

17. Pres. Soto. 19.

**1889.** Various frames.
22. 17. 1 c. brown .. 25 25
23. 2 c. green .. 20 20
24. 5 c. orange .. 40 25
25. 10 c. lake .. 20 20
26. 20 c. green .. 20 20
27. 50 c. red .. 45 80
28. 1 p. blue .. 65 1·25
29. 2 p. violet .. 6·00 7·00
30. 5 p. olive .. 15·00 18·00
31. 10 p. black .. 38·00 35·00

**1892.** Various frames.
32. 19. 1 c. blue .. 20 20
33. 2 c. orange .. 20 20
34a. 5 c. mauve .. 20 20
35. 10 c. green .. 50 25
36. 20 c. red .. 6·00 25
37. 50 c. blue .. 3·00 2·00
38. 1 p. green on yellow .. 55 80
39. 2 p. red on grey .. 1·50 50
40. 5 p. blue on blue .. 1·25 50
41a. 10 p. brown on buff .. 4·25 2·40

29. Juan Santamaria. 31. Puerto Limon.

**1901.** Various designs dated "1900".
42. 29. 1 c. black and green .. 40 10
43. – 2 c. black and red .. 25 15
52. – 4 c. black and purple .. 1·90 75
44. 31. 5 c. black and blue .. 35 15
53. – 6 c. black and olive .. 4·50 2·40
45. – 10 c. black and brown .. 1·00 15
46. – 20 c. black and lake .. 2·75 15
54. – 25 c. brown and lilac .. 8·75 20
47. – 50 c. blue and red .. 2·40 70
48. – 1 col. black and olive .. 27·00 1·75
49. – 2 col. black and red .. 6·50 1·75
50. – 5 col. black and brown .. 17·00 1·75
51. – 10 col. red and green .. 13·50 1·40

DESIGNS—VERT. 2 c. Juan Mora F. 4 c. Jose M. Canas. 6 c. Julian Volio. 10 c. Braulio (wrongly inscr. "BRANLIO") Carrillo. 25 c. Eusebio Figueroa. 50 c. Jose M. Castro. 1 col. Puente de Birris. 2 col. Juan Rafael Mora. 5 col. Jesus Jimenez. HORIZ. 20 c. National Theatre. 10 col. Arms.

**1905.** No. 46 surch. **UN CENTIMO** in ornamental frame.
55. 1 c. on 20 c. black & lake 50 50

43. Juan Santamaria. 44. Juan Mora.

**1907.** Dated "1907".
57. 43. 1 c. blue and brown .. 50 20
58. 44. 2 c. black and green .. 45 20
69. – 4 c. blue and red .. 3·00 65
60. – 5 c. blue and orange .. 35 20
71. – 10 c. black and blue .. 4·25 10
72. – 20 c. black and olive .. 4·75 2·40
63. – 25 c. slate and lavender .. 1·10 35
74. – 50 c. blue and red .. 17·00 4·25
75. – 1 col. black and brown .. 8·25 4·25
76. – 2 col. green and red .. 42·00 16·00

PORTRAITS: 4 c. Jose M. Canas. 5 c. Mauro Fernandez. 10 c. Braulio Carrillo. 20 c. Julian Volio. 25 c. Eusebio Figueroa. 50 c. Jose M. Castro. 1 col. Jesus Jimenez. 2 col. Juan Rafael Mora.

53. Juan Santamaria. 54. Julian Volio.

**1910.** Various frames.
77. 53. 1 c. brown .. 10 10
78. – 2 c. green (Juan Mora F.) 20 10
79. – 4 c. red (Jose M. Canas) .. 20 10
80. – 5 c. orange (Mauro Fernandez) .. 20 10
81. – 10 c. blue (B. Carrillo) .. 10 10
82. 54. 20 c. olive .. 20 10
83. – 25 c. purple (Eusebio Figueroa) .. 4·25 50
84. – 1 col. brown (Jesus Jimenez) .. 40 25

**1911.** Optd. **1911** between stars.
85. 29. 1 c. black and green .. 50 35
86. 43. 1 c. blue and brown .. 35 35
88. 44. 2 c. black and green .. 35 35

**1911.** Optd. **Habilitado 1911.**
93. 4 c. black & purple (No. 52) 1·00 10
90. 5 c. blue & orange (No. 60) 1·00 10
91. 10 c. black & blue (No. 71) 3·00 2·75

59. Liner "Antilles". 62.

**1911.** Surch. **Correos Un centimo** or **Correos 5 centimos.**
94. 59. 1 c. on 10 c. blue .. 30 15
96. 1 c. on 25 c. violet .. 30 15
97. 1 c. on 50 c. brown .. 55 45
98. 1 c. on 1 col. brown .. 55 45
99. 1 c. on 5 col. red .. 90 65
100. 1 c. on 10 col. brown .. 1·10 95
101. 5 c. on 5 c. orange .. 55 20

**1912.** Surch. **Correos Dos centimos 2.**
102. 62. 2 c. on 5 c. brown .. 1·75 1·25
109. 2 c. on 10 c. blue .. 40·00 48·00
104. 2 c. on 50 c. red .. 25 30
105. 2 c. on 1 col. brown .. 40 40
112. 2 c. on 2 col. red .. 30 30
107. 2 c. on 5 col. green .. 40 40
108. 2 c. on 10 col purple .. 50 40

67. Plantation and Administration Building.

**1921.** Cent. of Coffee Cultivation.
115. 67. 5 c. black and blue .. 1·00 85

68. Simon Bolivar. 69.

**1921.**
116. 68. 15 c. violet .. .. 25 15

**1921.** Centenary of Independence of Central America.
117. 69. 5 c. violet .. .. 25 35

70. Juan Mora and Julio Acosta.

**1921.** Cent. of Independence.
118. 70. 2 c. black and orange .. 50 50
119. 3 c. black and green .. 50 50
120. 6 c. black and red .. 65 55
121. 15 c. black and blue .. 1·75 1·75
122. 30 c. black and brown 2·75 2·75

**1922.** Coffee Publicity. Nos. 77/81 and 116. Optd. with a sack inscr. "CAFE DE COSTA RICA".
123. 53. 1 c. brown .. .. 10 10
124. 54. 2 c. green .. .. 15 10
125. 4 c. red .. .. 15 15
126. 5 c. orange .. .. 15 15
127. 10 c. blue .. .. 30 25
128. 68. 15 c. violet .. .. 75 70

**1922.** Optd. **CORREOS 1922.**
129. 69. 5 c. violet .. .. 40 25

**1922.** Surch. with red cross and **5 c.**
130. 54. 5 c.+5 c. orge. (No. 80) 50 25

**1923.** Optd. **COMPRE UD. CAFE DE COSTA RICA** in circular frame.
131. 54. 5 c. orange (No. 80) .. 25 15

77. Jesus Jimenez (statesman). 81. Coffee-growing.

80. National Monument.

**1923.** Birth Centenary of J. Jimenez.
132. 77. 2 c. brown .. .. 15 15
133. 4 c. green .. .. 15 15
134. 5 c. blue .. .. 35 15
135. 20 c. red .. .. 20 20
136. 1 col. violet .. .. 35 35

**1923.**
137. 80. 1 c. purple .. .. 10 10
138. 81. 2 c. yellow .. .. 20 15
139. – 4 c. green .. .. 40 35
140. – 5 c. blue .. .. 70 10
141. – 5 c. green .. .. 20 10
142. – 10 c. brown .. .. 85 15
143. – 10 c. red .. .. 25 10
144. – 12 c. red .. .. 5·50 1·75
145. – 20 c. blue .. .. 3·00 60
146. – 40 c. orange .. .. 2·75 90
147. – 1 col. olive .. .. 75 40

All the above are inscr. "U.P.U. 1923." except the 10 c. and 12 c. which are inscr. "1921 EN COMMEMORACION DEL PRIMER CONGRESO POSTAL", etc.

DESIGNS—HORIZ. 5 c. P.O., San Jose. 10 c. Columbus and Isabella I. 12 c. "Santa Maria". 20 c. Columbus at Cariari. 40 c. Map of Costa Rica. VERT. 4 c. Banana-growing. 1 col M. Gutierrez.

85. Don R. A. Maldonado y Velasco. 86. Map of Guanacaste.

**1924.**
148. 85. 2 c. green .. .. 15 10

For 3 c. green see No. 211 and for other portraits as T 85 see Nos. 308/12.

**1924.** Centenary of Province of Nicoya (Guanacaste).
149. 86. 1 c. red .. .. 35 20
150. 2 c. purple .. .. 35 20
151. 5 c. green .. .. 35 20
152. 10 c. orange .. .. 1·25 50
153. – 15 c. blue .. .. 40 45
154. – 20 c. grey .. .. 65 45
155. – 25 c. brown .. .. 90 75

DESIGN: 15 c., 20 c. 25 c. Church at Nicoya.

88. Discus Thrower. 93. Arms and Curtiss "Jenny".

**1925.** Inscr. "JUEGOS OLIMPICOS". Imperf. or perf.
156. 88. 5 c. green .. .. 2·00 2·40
157. – 10 c. red .. .. 2·00 2·40
158. – 20 c. blue .. .. 4·00 3·50

DESIGNS—VERT. 10 c. Trophy. HORIZ. 20 c. Parthenon.

**1926.** Surch. with values in ornamental designs.
159. 3 c. on 5 c. (No. 140) .. 20 15
160. 6 c. on 10 c. (No. 142) .. 35 25
161. 30 c. on 40 c. (No. 146) 50 40
162. 45 c. on 1 col. (No. 147) 55 50

**1926.** Surch. with value between bars.
163. 10 on 12 c. red (No. 144) 1·75 45

**1926.** Air.
164. 93. 20 c. blue .. .. 1·25 40

DESIGNS: 3 c. St. Louis College, Cartago. 6 c. Chapui Asylum, San Jose. 45 c. Ruins of Ujarras.

94. Heredia Normal School.

**1926.** Dated "1926".
165. – 3 c. blue .. .. 15 15
166. – 6 c. brown .. .. 25 20
167. 94. 30 c. orange .. .. 35 25
168. – 45 c. violet .. .. 90 50

**1928.** Lindbergh Good Will Tour of Central America. Surch. with aeroplane, **LINDBERGH ENERO 1928** and new value.
169. 10 c. on 12 c. red (No. 144) 9·50 7·50

**1928.** Surcharged with new value.
170. 68. 5 c. on 15 c. violet .. 15 10

**1929.** Surch. **CORREOS** and value.
171. 62. 5 c. on 2 col. red .. 20 20
173. 13 c. on 40 c. green .. 30 20

98. Post Office. 103. Juan Rafael Mora.

**1930.** Types of 1923 reduced in size and dated "1929" as T 98.
174. – 1 c. purple (as No. 137) 10 10
175. 98. 5 c. green .. .. 10 10
176. – 10 c. red (as No. 143) 35 10

**1930.** Air. No. O178 surch **CORREO 1930 AEREO**, Bleriot XI airplane and new value.
177. O 95. 8 c. on 1 col. .. .. 50 40
178. 20 c. on 1 col. .. 70 50
179. 40 c. on 1 col. .. 1·40 1·00
180. 1 col. on 1 col. .. 2·00 1·40

**1930.** Air. Optd. **CORREO AEREO** or surch. also.
182. 62. 5 c. on 10 c. brown .. 20 10
181. – 10 c. red (No. 143) .. 45 15
183. 62. 20 c. on 50 c. blue .. 20 15
184. 40 c. on 50 c. blue .. 40 15
185. 1 col. orange .. 1·50 20

**1931.**
186. 103. 13 c. red .. .. 25 15

**1931.** Air. Fiscal stamps (Arms design) inscr. "TIMBRE 1929" (or "1930", 3 col.), surch. **Habilitado 1931 Correo Aereo** and new value.
190. 2 col. on 2 col. green .. 16·00 16·00
191. 3 col. on 5 col. brown .. 16·00 16·00
192. 5 col. on 10 col. black .. 16·00 16·00

**1932.** Air. Telegraph stamp optd. with wings inscr. **CORREO CR AEREO.**
193. 62. 40 c. green .. .. 2·50 35

106.

**1932.** 1st National Philatelic Exn.

| | | | | |
|---|---|---|---|---|
| 194. | **106.** | 3 c. orange | 15 | 15 |
| 195. | | 5 c. green | 25 | 25 |
| 196. | | 10 c. red | 25 | 25 |
| 197. | | 20 c. blue | 35 | 35 |

See also Nos. 231/4.

107. Ryan Brougham over La Sabana Airport, San Jose.

**1934.** Air.

| | | | | |
|---|---|---|---|---|
| 198 | **107** | 5 c. green | 15 | 10 |
| 507 | | 5 c. deep blue | 10 | 10 |
| 508 | | 5 c. pale blue | 10 | 10 |
| 199 | | 10 c. red | 15 | 10 |
| 509 | | 10 c. green | 10 | 10 |
| 510 | | 10 c. turquoise | 10 | 10 |
| 200 | | 15 c. brown | 30 | 10 |
| 511 | | 15 c. red | 10 | 10 |
| 201 | | 20 c. blue | 45 | 10 |
| 202 | | 25 c. orange | 55 | 15 |
| 512 | | 35 c. violet | 35 | 10 |
| 203 | | 40 c. brown | 55 | 10 |
| 204 | | 50 c. black | 40 | 15 |
| 205 | | 60 c. yellow | 75 | 25 |
| 206 | | 75 c. violet | 1·10 | 40 |
| 207 | – | 1 col. red | 85 | 10 |
| 208 | – | 2 col. blue | 90 | 35 |
| 209 | – | 5 col. black | 2·40 | 2·40 |
| 210 | – | 10 col. brown | 4·00 | 4·00 |

DESIGN: 1, 2, 5, 10 col. Allegory of the Air Mail.

**1934.**

| | | | | |
|---|---|---|---|---|
| 211. | 85. | 3 c. green | 10 | 10 |

109. Nurse at Altar. 111. Our Lady of the Angels.

**1935.** Costa Rican Red Cross Jubilee.

| | | | | |
|---|---|---|---|---|
| 212. | **109.** | 10 c. red | 35 | 15 |

**1935.** 300th Anniv. of Apparition of Our Lady of the Angels.

| | | | | |
|---|---|---|---|---|
| 213. | – | 5 c. green | 15 | 10 |
| 214. | **111.** | 10 c. red | 35 | 15 |
| 215. | – | 30 c. orange | 50 | 25 |
| 216. | – | 45 c. violet | 65 | 40 |
| 217. | **111.** | 50 c. black | 1·10 | 45 |

DESIGNS: 5 c., 30 c. Aerial view of Cartago. 45 c. Allegory of the Apparition.

112. Cocos Island.

**1936.**

| | | | | |
|---|---|---|---|---|
| 218. | **112.** | 4 c. brown | 25 | 10 |
| 219. | | 8 c. violet | 30 | 15 |
| 220. | | 25 c. orange | 35 | 15 |
| 221. | | 35 c. brown | 50 | 15 |
| 222. | | 40 c. brown | 40 | 25 |
| 223. | | 50 c. yellow | 40 | 35 |
| 224. | | 2 col. green | 4·75 | 3·75 |
| 225. | | 5 col. green | 12·00 | 7·25 |

113. Cocos Is. and Fleet of Columbus.

**1936.**

| | | | | |
|---|---|---|---|---|
| 226. | **113.** | 5 c. green | 55 | 15 |
| 227. | | 10 c. red | 70 | 15 |

114. Airplane over Mt. Poas.

**1937.** Air. 1st Annual Fair.

| | | | | |
|---|---|---|---|---|
| 228. | **114.** | 1 c. black | 10 | 10 |
| 229. | | 2 c. brown | 10 | 10 |
| 230. | | 3 c. violet | 10 | 10 |

**1937.** 2nd National Philatelic Exn. As T **106**, but inscr. " DICIEMBRE 1937 ".

| | | | | |
|---|---|---|---|---|
| 231. | **106.** | 2 c. purple | 15 | 15 |
| 232. | | 3 c. black | 15 | 15 |
| 233. | | 5 c. green | 15 | 15 |
| 234. | | 10 c. orange | 15 | 15 |

115. Tunny.

116. Native and Donkey carrying Bananas.

DESIGN — As Type **116**: 10 c. Coffee Gathering.

117. Puntarenas.

**1937.** National Exn., San Jose. 1st issue.

| | | | | |
|---|---|---|---|---|
| 235. | **115.** | 2 c. black (postage) | 20 | 15 |
| 236. | **116.** | 5 c. green | 25 | 15 |
| 237. | – | 10 c. red | 35 | 20 |
| 238. | **117.** | 2 c. black (air) | 10 | 10 |
| 239. | | 5 c. green | 10 | 10 |
| 240. | | 20 c. blue | 30 | 25 |
| 241. | | 1 col. 40 brown | 1·75 | 1·75 |

118. Purple Guaria Orchid " Carrleya skinneri ".

119. National Bank.

DESIGN—As Type **118**: 3 c. Cocoa-bean.

**1938.** National Exn., San Jose. 2nd Issue.

| | | | | |
|---|---|---|---|---|
| 242. | **118.** | 1 c. violet & grn. (post) | 15 | 10 |
| 243. | | 3 c. brown | 15 | 10 |
| 244. | **119.** | 1 c. violet (air) | 10 | 10 |
| 245. | | 3 c. red | 10 | 10 |
| 246. | | 10 c. red | 15 | 10 |
| 247. | | 75 c. brown | 90 | 90 |

**1938.** No. 145 optd. **1938.**

| | | | | |
|---|---|---|---|---|
| 248. | | 20 c. blue | 35 | 15 |

121. La Sabana Airport.

**1940.** Air. Opening of San Jose Airport.

| | | | | |
|---|---|---|---|---|
| 249. | **121.** | 5 c. green | 10 | 10 |
| 250. | | 10 c. red | 15 | 10 |
| 251. | | 25 c. blue | 15 | 15 |
| 252. | | 35 c. brown | 30 | 30 |
| 253. | | 60 c. orange | 45 | 45 |
| 254. | | 85 c. violet | 60 | 50 |
| 255. | | 2 col. 35 green | 3·25 | 3·25 |

**1940.** No. 168 variously surch. **15 CENTIMOS** in ornamental frame.

| | | | | |
|---|---|---|---|---|
| 256. | – | 15 c. on 45 c. violet | 25 | 20 |

There are five distinct varieties of this surcharge.

**1940.** Pan-American Health Day. Unissued stamps prepared for the 8th Pan-American Child Welfare Congress optd. **DIA PAN-AMERICANO DE LA SALUD 2 DICIEMBRE 1940** and bars.

(a) Postage. Allegorical design.

| | | | | |
|---|---|---|---|---|
| 261. | | 5 c. green | 20 | 10 |
| 262. | | 10 c. red | 25 | 15 |
| 263. | | 20 c. blue | 50 | 20 |
| 264. | | 40 c. brown | 85 | 70 |
| 265. | | 55 c. orange | 1·40 | 60 |

(b) Air. View of Duran Sanatorium.

| | | | | |
|---|---|---|---|---|
| 266. | | 10 c. red | 15 | 10 |
| 267. | | 15 c. violet | 15 | 15 |
| 268. | | 25 c. blue | 30 | 25 |
| 269. | | 35 c. brown | 45 | 45 |
| 270. | | 60 c. green | 35 | 35 |
| 271. | | 75 c. olive | 75 | 85 |
| 272. | | 1 col. 35 orange | 3·25 | 3·25 |
| 273. | | 5 col. brown | 14·00 | 14·00 |
| 274. | | 10 col. mauve | 27·00 | 27·00 |

**1940.** Air. Pan-American Aviation Day. Surch. **AERO Aviacion Panamericana Dic. 17 1940** and value.

| | | | | |
|---|---|---|---|---|
| 275. | | 15 c. on 50 c. yellow | 50 | 50 |
| 276. | | 30 c. on 50 c. yellow | 50 | 50 |

**1941.** Surch. **15 CENTIMOS 15** and ornamental rule.

| | | | | |
|---|---|---|---|---|
| 277. | **112.** | 15 c. on 25 c. orange | 25 | 20 |
| 278. | | 15 c. on 35 c. brown | 25 | 20 |
| 279. | | 15 c. on 40 c. brown | 25 | 20 |
| 280. | | 15 c. on 2 col. green | 25 | 20 |
| 281. | | 15 c. on 5 col. green | 40 | 35 |

131. Stadium and Flag.

132. Football Match.

**1941.** Central American and Caribbean Football Championship.

| | | | | |
|---|---|---|---|---|
| 282. | **131.** | 5 c. green (postage) | 45 | 25 |
| 283. | | 10 c. orange | 40 | 25 |
| 284. | | 15 c. red | 55 | 35 |
| 285. | | 25 c. blue | 60 | 35 |
| 286. | | 40 c. brown | 1·90 | 75 |
| 287. | | 50 c. violet | 2·40 | 90 |
| 288. | | 75 c. orange | 4·75 | 1·90 |
| 289. | | 1 col. red | 7·75 | 3·75 |
| 290. | **132.** | 15 c. red (air) | 45 | 15 |
| 291. | | 30 c. blue | 50 | 25 |
| 292. | | 40 c. brown | 50 | 40 |
| 293. | | 50 c. violet | 65 | 45 |
| 294. | | 60 c. green | 85 | 50 |
| 295. | | 75 c. yellow | 1·40 | 75 |
| 296. | | 1 col. mauve | 2·40 | 2·40 |
| 297. | | 1 col. 40 red | 5·00 | 5·00 |
| 298. | | 2 col. green | 9·50 | 9·50 |
| 299. | | 5 col. black | 21·00 | 21·00 |

**1941.** Air. Costa Rica–Panama Boundary Treaty. Optd. **MAYO 1941 TRATADO LIMITROFE COSTA RICA-PANAMA** or surch. also.

| | | | | |
|---|---|---|---|---|
| 300. | **107.** | 5 c. on 20 c. blue | 20 | 15 |
| 301. | | 15 c. on 20 c. blue | 25 | 20 |
| 302. | | 40 c. on 75 c. violet | 40 | 25 |
| 303. | – | 65 c. on 1 col. red (No. 207) | 40 | 30 |
| 304. | – | 1 col. 40 on 2 col. blue (No. 208) | 1·90 | 1·90 |
| 305. | – | 5 col. black (No. 209) | 6·50 | 6·50 |
| 306. | – | 10 col. brown (No. 210) | 7·50 | 7·50 |

**1941.** As Type **85** but with new portraits.

| | | | | |
|---|---|---|---|---|
| 308. | – | 3 c. orange | 10 | 10 |
| 309. | – | 3 c. purple | 10 | 10 |
| 310. | – | 3 c. red | 10 | 10 |
| 310a. | – | 3 c. blue | 10 | 10 |
| 311. | – | 5 c. violet | 10 | 10 |
| 312. | – | 5 c. black | 10 | 10 |

PORTRAITS: 3 c. (Nos. 308/10) C. G. Viquez. 3 c. (No. 310a) Mgr. B. A. Thiel. 5 c. J. J. Rodriguez.

136. New Decree and Restored University.

**1941.** Restoration of National University.

| | | | | |
|---|---|---|---|---|
| 313. | – | 5 c. green (postage) | 25 | 10 |
| 314. | **136.** | 10 c. orange | 30 | 10 |
| 315. | – | 15 c. red | 40 | 10 |
| 316. | **136.** | 25 c. blue | 60 | 25 |
| 317. | – | 50 c. brown | 1·50 | 75 |
| 318. | **136.** | 15 c. red (air) | 25 | 15 |
| 319. | – | 30 c. blue | 40 | 15 |
| 320. | **136.** | 40 c. orange | 45 | 35 |
| 321. | – | 60 c. blue | 55 | 50 |
| 322. | **136.** | 1 col. violet | 2·00 | 1·60 |
| 323. | – | 2 col. black | 5·00 | 3·75 |
| 324. | **136.** | 5 col. purple | 16·00 | 13·00 |

DESIGN—(Nos. 313, 315, 317, 319, 321 and 323): The original Decree and University.

**1941.** Surch.

| | | | | |
|---|---|---|---|---|
| 325. | | 5 c. on 6 c. brn. (No. 166) | 15 | 15 |
| 326. | | 15 c. on 20 c. blue (No. 248) | 25 | 15 |

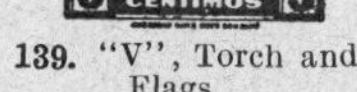

139. "V", Torch and Flags.

140. Francisco Morazan.

**1942.** War Effort.

| | | | | |
|---|---|---|---|---|
| 327. | **139.** | 5 c. red | 20 | 10 |
| 328. | | 5 c. orange | 20 | 10 |
| 329. | | 5 c. green | 20 | 10 |
| 330. | | 5 c. blue | 20 | 10 |
| 331. | | 5 c. violet | 20 | 10 |

**1942.** Portraits and dates.

| | | | | |
|---|---|---|---|---|
| 332. | A. | 1 c. lilac (postage) | 10 | 10 |
| 333. | B. | 2 c. black | 10 | 10 |
| 334. | C. | 3 c. blue | 10 | 10 |
| 335. | D. | 5 c. turquoise | 10 | 10 |
| 336. | | 5 c. green | 10 | 10 |
| 337. | **140.** | 15 c. red | 10 | 10 |
| 338. | E. | 25 c. blue | 20 | 15 |
| 339. | F. | 50 c. violet | 1·25 | 50 |
| 340. | G. | 1 col. black | 2·00 | 1·00 |
| 341. | H. | 2 col. orange | 2·40 | 1·25 |
| 341a. | I. | 5 c. brown (air) | 10 | 10 |
| 342. | A. | 10 c. red | 10 | 10 |
| 342a. | | 10 c. olive | 10 | 10 |
| 342b. | J. | 15 c. violet | 10 | 10 |
| 343. | K. | 25 c. blue | 15 | 10 |
| 344. | L. | 30 c. brown | 15 | 10 |
| 345. | D. | 40 c. blue | 25 | 10 |
| 346. | | 40 c. red | 25 | 15 |
| 347. | **140.** | 45 c. purple | 35 | 25 |
| 348. | M. | 45 c. black | 20 | 15 |
| 349. | E. | 50 c. green | 90 | 20 |
| 350. | | 50 c. orange | 20 | 20 |
| 351. | N. | 55 c. purple | 25 | 20 |
| 352. | F. | 60 c. blue | 45 | 15 |
| 353. | | 60 c. green | 20 | 15 |
| 354. | G. | 65 c. red | 45 | 25 |
| 355. | | 65 c. blue | 25 | 20 |
| 356. | O. | 75 c. green | 40 | 25 |
| 357. | H. | 85 c. orange | 55 | 35 |
| 358. | | 85 c. violet | 65 | 45 |
| 359. | P. | 1 col. black | 65 | 30 |
| 360. | | 1 col. red | 50 | 20 |
| 361. | Q. | 1 col. 5 sepia | 60 | 40 |
| 362. | R. | 1 col. 15 brown | 90 | 85 |
| 363. | | 1 col. 15 green | 1·25 | 85 |
| 364. | B. | 1 col. 40 violet | 1·40 | 1·25 |
| 365. | | 1 col. 40 yellow | 85 | 75 |
| 366. | C. | 2 col. black | 2·10 | 85 |
| 367. | | 2 col. olive | 65 | 35 |

PORTRAITS: A, J. Mora Fernandez. B, B. Carranza. C, T. Guardia. D, M. Aguilar. E, J. M. Alfaro. F, F. M. Oreamuno. G, J. M. Castro. H, J. R. Mora. I, S. Lara. J, C. Duran. K, A. Esquivel. L, V. Herrera. M, J. R. de Gallegos. N, P. Fernandez. O, B. Soto. P, J. M. Montealegre. Q, B. Carrillo. R, J. Jimenez.

**1943.** Air. Optd. **Legislacion Social 15 Setiembre 1943.**

| | | | | |
|---|---|---|---|---|
| 368. | | 5 col. black (No. 209) | 3·25 | 2·75 |
| 369. | | 10 col. brown (No. 210) | 5·75 | 4·50 |

142. San Ramon.

143. Allegory of Flight.

**1944.** Centenary of San Ramon.

| | | | | |
|---|---|---|---|---|
| 370. | **142.** | 5 c. green (postage) | 10 | 10 |
| 371. | | 10 c. orange | 15 | 10 |
| 372. | | 15 c. red | 20 | 10 |
| 373. | | 40 c. grey | 55 | 50 |
| 374. | | 50 c. blue | 90 | 45 |

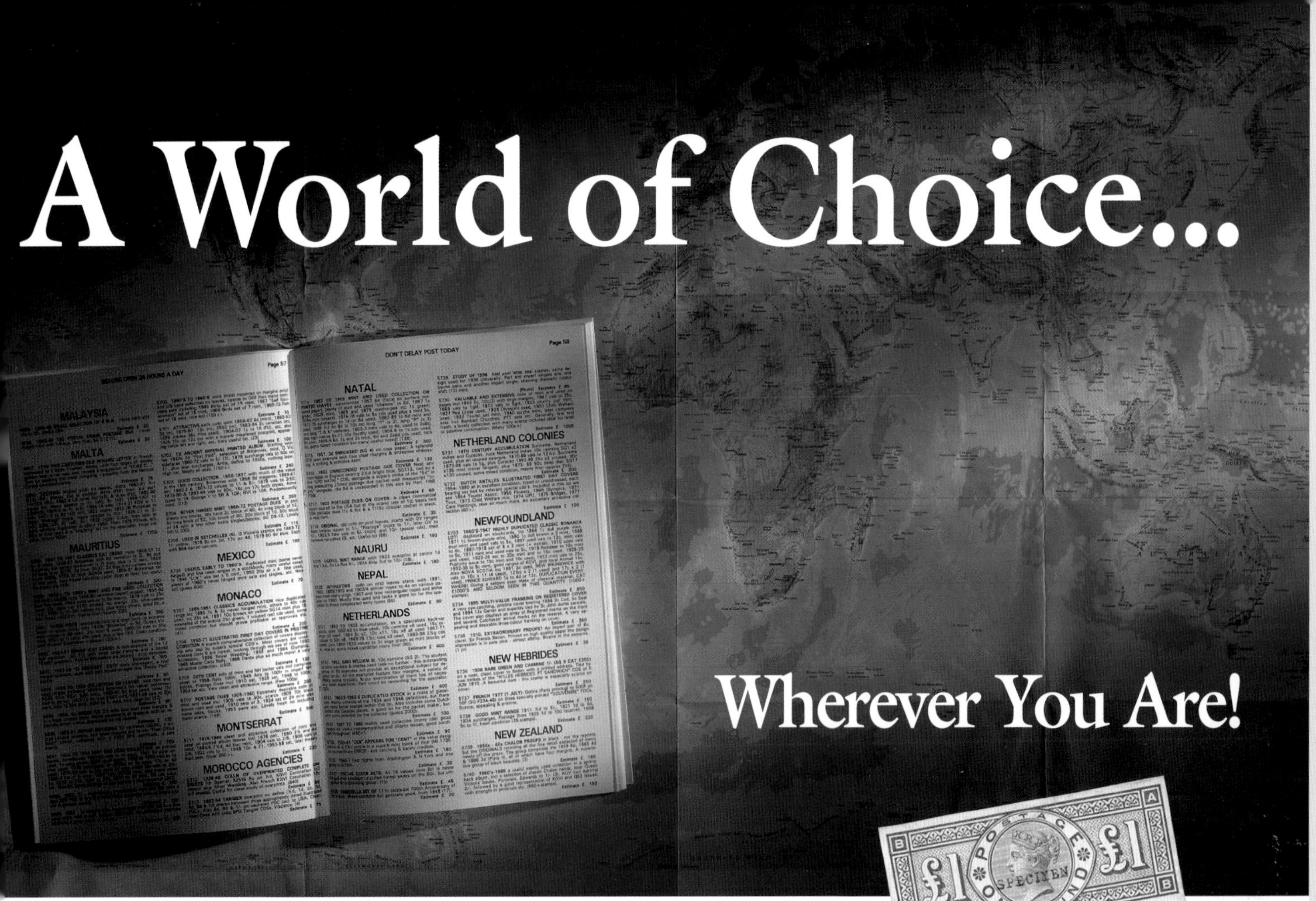

# A World of Choice...

## Wherever You Are!

**SELLERS? We're major buyers of stamps**

*The*
**WORLD'S LARGEST**
**MAIL-BID**
**AUCTION COMPANY**

*"We are in our 21st year and still determined to make your stamp buying a true pleasure."*

### Buy in Comfort from your Home, Office, Aircraft or Train

Snatch a minute to buy from the World's largest monthly source of interesting and unusual lots - it just couldn't be easier, safer or more enjoyable.

### The Ultimate Source of World Stamps

Our monthly auction catalogue has been designed to fit into your pocket, ensure you carry it with you wherever you go. You never quite know when you may decide to participate in one of the great stamp auctions, in England!

### It's SIMPLE to Bid

- Enter the lot number(s) and your bid price(s)
- Fill in your name and address
- Select your payment option
- Post or fax the bid form

### It's SAFE to Bid

- Money-back guarantees
- Accurate descriptions by world experts
- All lots fully insured in transit

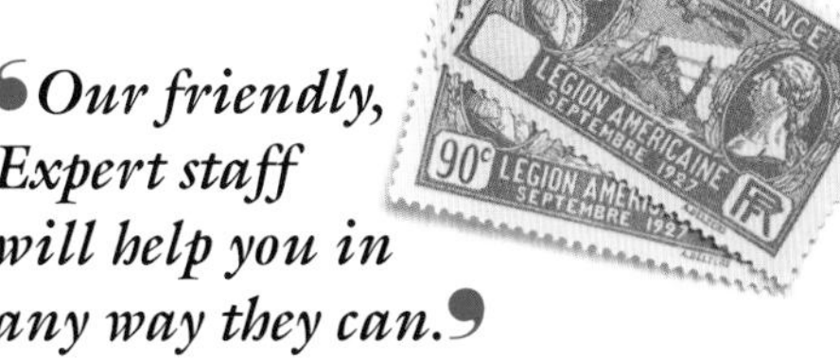

*"Our friendly, Expert staff will help you in any way they can."*

## IF YOU NEED IT WE HAVE IT!

From delightful topical stamp collections to serious specialist studies. From multi-volume world collections to cigarette cards. From huge boxes with hidden gems to silk flags dropped over Java during World War II.

From rare single stamps and postal history to complete traders' stocks - **we offer you more, month in, month out, than anyone else in the world.**

AFFIX
POSTAGE
HERE

**Sandafayre Limited**
**Knutsford**
**Cheshire**
**UK**
**WA16 8XN**

SELLERS? We're major buyers of stamps

# Why buy from Postal Auctions?

Even the richest and most enthusiastic collector would find it impossible to attend a mere fraction of the stamp auctions that take place throughout the world.

Thousands of overseas buyers choose us *(in fact most of our clients live outside the UK)* because we offer the widest choice of material from all over the world at the most competetive estimates.

**The World's Largest Postal Bid Catalogue**
Every month, your Sandafayre catalogue contains thousands of different lots with suggested bid prices from £30 to £30,000

## It's Safe and Fun with More to Explore

Your time is valuable. Can you really afford to wade through piles of catalogues from small auction houses, trying to understand the abbreviated descriptions? *(You may also find the complicated rules or crazy pricing are a hassle too).* Month in and month out our catalogue offers more than any other mail sale in the world with detailed descriptions, accurate 'estimate' levels together with money-back guarantees.

- Overseas buying made easy
- No credit card charges *(great for quick, free currency conversion)*
- Every lot carries a total refund guarantee
- We've never missed a monthly sale in 15 years

## The largest and most diverse range of stamps to choose from

★All the World ★Great Britain ★Commonwealth and Foreign Country Collections ★Early and Modern ★Single Stamps and Covers ★Accumulations ★Albums ★Mixed Lots ★Cinderellas and Revenues ★Postcards and Cigarette Cards ★Classics ★Postal History

**SANDAFAYRE**
The World's Largest Postal Auction Company

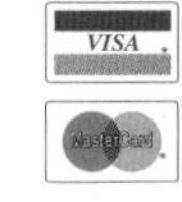


SANDAFAYRE SGW, KNUTSFORD, CHESHIRE, UK WA16 8XN. TEL: 01144 1565 653214 FAX: 01144 1565 651637
INTERNET SITE: http://www.sandafayre.com

## YOUR NEXT CATALOGUE ABSOLUTELY FREE!

Access us on the INTERNET

*Simply complete this card, send it to us, and you'll receive the next edition of our Postal Bid Catalogue free of charge.*

Name

Address

Country

Area of special interest

*Also send one free catalogue to my friend*

Name

Address

Country

*SEND TO: SANDAFAYRE, SGW, KNUTSFORD, UK WA16 8XN.*

375.143. 10 c. orange (air) 15 10
376. 15 c. red 20 15
377. 40 c. blue 35 25
378. 45 c. red 40 35
379. 60 c. green 30 25
380. 1 col. brown 65 50
381. 1 col. 40 grey 3·75 3·00
382. 5 col. violet 9·50 9·00
383. 10 col. black 27·00 24·00

**1944.** Ratification of Costa Rica and Panama Boundary Treaty. Optd. **La entrevista ....1944.**

384.139. 5 c. orange 10 10
385. 5 c. green 10 10
386. 5 c. blue 10 10
387. 5 c. violet 10 10

**1944.** Air. No. 207 optd. **1944.**

388. 1 col. red 45 40

**1945.** Air. Official Air stamps of 1934 optd. **1945,** in oblong network frame.

389.107. 5 c. green 40 35
390. 10 c. red 40 35
391. 15 c. brown 40 35
392. 20 c. blue 40 40
393. 25 c. orange 40 40
394. 40 c. brown 40 40
395. 50 c. black 40 40
396. 60 c. yellow 55 40
397. 75 c. violet 45 40
398. – 1 col. red (No. O 220) 45 40
399. – 2 col. blue (No. O 221) 3·00 2·75
400. – 5 col. black (No. O 222) 3·75 3·25
401. – 10 col. brown (No. O 223) 5·50 5·00

**1945.** Air stamps. Telegraph stamps as Type **62** optd. **CORREO AEREO 1945** and bar.

402. 62. 40 c. green 30 15
403. 50 c. blue 40 15
404. 1 col. orange 40 25

**148.** Mauro Fernandez. **149.** Coffee Gathering.

**1945.** Birth Cent. of Fernandez.

405.148. 20 c. green 15 10

**1945.**

406.149. 5 c. black and green 10 10
407. 10 c. black and orange 15 10
408. 20 c. black and red 20 15

**150.** Florence Nightingale and Nurse Cavell.

**1945.** Air. 60th Anniv. of National Red Cross Society.

409.150. 1 col. black 50 35

**1946.** Air. Central American and Caribbean Football Championship. As Type **132**, but inscribed "FEBRERO 1946"

410.132. 25 c. green 45 40
411. 30 c. orange 45 40
412. 55 c. blue 55 40

**1946.** Surch. **15 15.**

413.148. 15 c. on 20 c. green 15 10

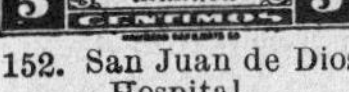

**152.** San Juan de Dios, Hospital. **153.** Ascension Esquivel.

**1946.** Air. Cent. San Juan de Dios Hospital.

414.152. 5 c. black and green 10 10
415. 10 c. black and brown 10 10
416. 15 c. black and red 10 10
417. 25 c. black and blue 15 15
418. 30 c. black and orange 25 20
419. 40 c. black and olive 15 15
420. 50 c. black and violet 25 25
421. 60 c. black and green 50 45
422. 75 c. black and brown 40 35
423. 1 col. black and blue 50 25
424. 2 col. black and brown 55 60
425. 3 col. black and purple 1·40 1·40
426. 5 col. black and yellow 1·75 1·75

**1947.** Air. Former Presidents.

427. – 2 col. black and blue 65 50
428.153. 3 col. black and red 1·00 65
429. – 5 col. black and green 1·50 1·00
430. – 10 col. black & orange 3·00 1·90

PORTRAITS: 2 col. Rafael Iglesias. 5 col. Cleto Gonzalez Viquez. 10 col. Ricardo Jimenez.

**1947.** No. O 228 optd. **CORREOS 1947.**

431. 57. 5 c. green 30 10

**1947.** Air. Nos. 410/2 surch. **Habilitado para ₡0.15 Decreto No. 16 de 28 abril de 1947.**

432.132. 15 c. on 25 c. green 55 45
433. 15 c. on 30 c. orange 55 45
434. 15 c. on 55 c. blue 55 45

**156.** Columbus at Cariari. **158.** Franklin D. Roosevelt.

**1947.** Air.

435.156. 25 c. black and green 50 10
436. 30 c. black and blue 50 10
437. 40 c. black and orange 65 15
438. 45 c. black and violet 90 25
439. 50 c. black and red 1·00 20
440. 65 c. black and brown 2·50 75

**1947.** Air. Stamps of 1942 surch **C 0.15.**

441. E. 15 c. on 50 c. orange 15 15
442. F. 15 c. on 60 c. green 15 15
443. O. 15 c. on 75 c. green 15 15
444. P. 15 c. on 1 col. red 20 20
445. Q. 15 c. on 1 col. 5 sepia 15 15

**1947.**

446.158. 5 c. green (postage) 10 10
447. 10 c. red 10 10
448. 15 c. blue 15 15
449. 25 c. orange 15 15
450. 30 c. red 35 25
451. 15 c. green (air) 10 10
452. 30 c. red 15 10
453. 45 c. brown 25 25
454. 65 c. orange 25 25
455. 75 c. blue 35 25
456. 1 col. green 50 45
457. 2 col. black 75 60
458. 5 col. red 1·50 1·50

**159.** Miguel de Cervantes Saavedra. **160.** Steam Locomotive.

**1947.** 400th Birth Anniv. of Cervantes.

459.159. 30 c. blue 20 10
460. 55 c. red 35 25

**1947.** Air. 50th Anniv. of Pacific Electric Railway.

461.160. 35 c. black and green 2·50 90

**161.** National Theatre. **162.** Rafael Iglesias.

**1948.** Air. 50th Anniv. of National Theatre.

462.161. 15 c. black and blue 15 10
463. 20 c. black and red 15 15
464.162. 35 c. black and green 25 20
465.161. 45 c. black and violet 35 25
466. 50 c. black and red 35 25
467. 75 c. black and purple 45 45
468. 1 col. black and green 85 60
469. 2 col. black and lake 1·25 90
470.162. 5 col. black and yellow 2·10 2·00
471. 10 col. black and blue 4·75 3·00

**1948.** Air. Surch. **HABILITADO PARA ₡ 0.35.**

472.156. 35 c. on 40 c. black and orange 45 30

**1949.** Air. 125th Anniv. of Annexation of Guanacaste. Nos. 361, 409, 363 and 365 variously surch. **1824-1949 125 Aniversario de la Anexion Guanacaste** and value.

473. Q. 35 c. on 1 col. 5 sepia 15 15
474.150. 50 c. on 1 col. black 25 15
475. R. 55 c. on 1 col. 15 green 45 35
476. B. 55 c. on 1 col. 40 yellow 45 35

**165.** Globe and Dove.

**1950.** Air. 75th Anniv. of U.P.U.

477.165. 15 c. red 15 10
478. 25 c. blue 15 10
479. 1 col. green 35 15

**166.** Battle of El Tejar, Cartago. **167.** Capture of Limon.

**1950.** Air. Inscr. "GUERRA DE LIBERACION NACIONAL 1948".

480. 166. 15 c. black and red 15 10
481. 167. 20 c. black and green 20 15
482. – 25 c. black and blue 25 15
483. – 35 c. black and brown 25 15
484. – 55 c. black and violet 55 25
485. – 75 c. black and orange 55 35
486. – 80 c. black and grey 55 50
487. – 1 col. black and orange 75 55

DESIGNS—VERT. 80 c, 1 col. Dr. C. L. Valverde. HORIZ. 25 c. La Lucha Ranch. 35 c. Trench of San Isidro Battalion. 55 c., 75 c. Observation post.

**169.** Bull. **170.** Queen Isabella and Caravels.

**1950.** Air. National Agriculture and Industries Fair. Centres in black.

488.169. 1 c. green 10 10
489. A. 2 c. blue 10 10
490. B. 3 c. brown 10 10
491. C. 5 c. blue 10 10
492.169. 10 c. green 10 10
493. A. 30 c. violet 20 10
494. D. 45 c. orange 25 15
495. C. 50 c. grey 35 10
496. B. 65 c. blue 45 25
497. D. 80 c. red 45 30
498.169. 2 col. orange 1·25 1·00
499. A. 3 col. blue 2·75 2·40
500. C. 5 col. red 4·00 3·75
501. D. 10 col. red 4·00 3·75

DESIGNS—VERT. A, Fishing. B, Pineapple. C, Bananas. D, Coffee.

**1952.** Air. 500th Anniv. of Isabella the Catholic.

502.170. 15 c. red 25 10
503. 20 c. orange 30 15
504. 25 c. blue 50 10
505. 55 c. green 95 45
506. 2 col. violet 2·40 90

**1953.** Air. Surch.

513.158. 15 c. on 30 c. red 15 10
514. 15 c. on 45 c. brown 15 10
515. 15 c. on 65 c. orange 15 10

**1953.** Air. Surch. **HABILITADO PARA CINCO CENTIMOS 1953.**

515a.155. 5 c. on 30 c. blk. & blue 1·25 1·00
516. 5 c. on 40 c. blk. & orge. 15 10
517. 5 c. on 45 c. blk. & vio. 15 10
518. 5 c. on 65 c. blk. & brn. 35 30

**173.**

**1953.** Fiscal stamps surch. as in T **173.**

519.173. 5 c. on 10 c. green 10 10

**174.** "Vegetable Oil". **(175).**

**1954.** Air. National Industries. Horiz. designs as T **174.** Centres in black.

520. 5 c. red (T 174) 10 10
520a. 5 c. blue (as No. 520) 15 10
521. 10 c. indigo (Pottery) 10 10
521a. 10 c. blue (Pottery) 15 10
522. 15 c. green (Sugar) 10 10
522a. 15 c. yellow (Sugar) 15 10
523. 20 c. violet (Soap) 10 10
524. 25 c. lake (Timber) 10 10
525. 30 c. lilac (Matches) 30 20
526. 35 c. purple (Textiles) 15 10
527. 40 c. black (Leather) 25 15
528. 45 c. green (Tobacco) 50 25
529. 50 c. purple (Confectionery) 35 10
530. 55 c. yellow (Canning) 25 10
531. 60 c. brown (General Industries) 60 35
532. 65 c. red (Metals) 45 50
533. 75 c. violet (Pharmaceutics) 65 45
533a. 75 c. red (as No. 533) 25 15
533b. 80 c. violet (as No. 533) 45 40
534. 1 col. turq. (Paper) 35 20
535. 2 col. mauve (Rubber) 55 55
536. 3 col. green (Aircraft) 90 55
537. 5 col. black (Marble) 1·40 45
538. 10 col. yellow (Beer) 4·00 3·00

**1955.** Fiscal stamps optd. for postal use as in T **175.**

539.175. 5 c. on 2 c. green 10 10
540. 15 c. on 2 c. green 15 10

**176.** Rotary Emblem over Central America. **177.** Map of Costa Rica.

**1956.** Air. 50th Anniv. Rotary International.

542.176. 10 c. green 10 10
543. – 25 c. blue 15 10
544. – 40 c. brown 35 25
545. – 45 c. red 25 20
546. – 60 c. purple 25 20
547. – 2 col. orange 45 45

DESIGNS: 25 c. Emblem, hand and boy. 40 c., 2 col. Emblem and hospital. 45 c. Emblem, leaves and C. America. 60 c. Emblem and lighthouse.

**1957.** Air. Centenary of War of 1856–67.

548.177. 5 c. blue 10 10
549. – 10 c. green 10 10
550. – 15 c. orange 10 10
551. – 20 c. brown 15 10
552. – 25 c. blue 15 10
553. – 30 c. violet 20 15
554. – 35 c. red 20 15
555. – 40 c. black 20 15
556. – 45 c. red 25 15
557. – 50 c. blue 25 15
558. – 55 c. ochre 40 15
559. – 60 c. red 30 25
560. – 65 c. red 35 25
561. – 70 c. yellow 45 30
562. – 75 c. green 40 25
563. – 80 c. sepia 45 35
564. – 1 col. black 50 35

DESIGNS: 10 c. Map of Guanacaste. 15 c. Wartime inn. 20 c. Santa Rosa house. 25 c. Gen. D. J. M. Quiros. 30 c. Old Presidential Palace. 35 c. Minister D. J. B. Calvo. 40 c. Dr. Luis Molina. 45 c. Gen. D. J. J. Mora. 50 c. Gen. D. J. M. Canas. 55 c. Juan Santamaria Monument. 60 c. National Monument. 65 c. A. Vallerriestra. 70 c. Pres. R. Castilla Marquesado of Peru. 75 c. San Carlos Fortress. 80 c. Vice-President D. F. M. Oreamuno of Costa Rica. 1 col. Pres. D. J. R. Mora of Costa Rica.

**1958.** Obligatory Tax. Juvenile Delinquents' Fund. Nos. 489 and 521a surch. **SELLO DE NAVIDAD PRO-CIUDAD DE LOS NINOS 5 5.**

565. A. 5 c. on 2 c. black & blue 10 10
566. – 5 c. on 10 c. black & blue 25 10

**179.** Pres. Gonzalez Viquez. **180.** Pres. R. J. Oreamuno and Electric Train.

**1959.** Air. Birth Centenaries of Presidents Gonzalez (1958) and Oreamuno (1959).
567.179. 5 c. blue and pink .. 10 10
568. – 10 c. slate and red .. 10 10
569. – 15 c. black and slate .. 10 10
570. – 20 c. brown and red .. 10 10
571. – 35 c. blue and purple .. 15 15
572. – 55 c. violet and brown 25 20
573. – 80 c. blue .. .. 40 35
574.180. 1 col. lake and orange 1·60 40
575. – 2 col. lake and black .. 60 45
DESIGNS—As Type 179: 10 c. Pres. Oreamuno. As Type 180: Pres. Gonzalez and: 15 c. Highway bridge. 55 c. Water pipe-line. 80 c. National Library. Pres. Oreamuno and: 20 c. Puntarenas Quay. 35 c. Post Office, San Jose. 2 col. Both presidents and open book inscr. "PROBIDAD" ("Honesty").

181. Father Flanagan. 182. Goal Attack.

**1959.** Obligatory Tax. Christmas. Inscr. "SELLO DE NAVIDAD".
576.181. 5 c. green .. .. 20 10
577. – 5 c. mauve .. .. 20 10
578. – 5 c. olive .. .. 20 10
579. – 5 c. black .. .. 20 10
PAINTINGS: No. 577, "Girl with braids" (after Modigliani). No. 578, "Boy with a clubfoot" (after Ribera). No. 579, "The boy blowing on charcoal" (after "El Greco").

**1960.** Air. 3rd Pan-American Football Games.
580.182. 10 c. blue .. .. 10 10
581. – 25 c. blue .. .. 15 10
582. – 35 c. red .. .. 15 15
583. – 50 c. brown .. .. 20 15
584. – 85 c. turquoise .. .. 40 50
585. – 5 col. purple .. .. 1·25 1·25
DESIGNS: 25 c. Player heading ball. 35 c. Defender tackling forward. 50 c. Referee bouncing ball. 85 c. Goalkeeper seizing ball. 5 col. Player kicking high ball.

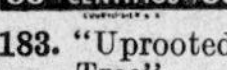

183. "Uprooted Tree". 184. Prof. J. A. Facio.

**1960.** Air. World Refugee Year.
586.183. 35 c. blue and yellow .. 20 15
587. 85 c. black and rose .. 40 35

**1960.** Birth Cent. of Professor Justo A. Facio.
588. 184. 10 c. red .. .. 10 10

185. "O E A" and Banner.

**1960.** Air. 6th and 7th Chancellors' Reunion Conference, Organization of American States, San Jose. As T 99. Multicoloured.
589. 25 c. Type 185 .. .. 15 10
590. 35 c. "OEA" within oval chains .. .. 35 30
591. 55 c. Clasped hands and chains .. .. 50 40
592. 5 col. Flags in form of flying bird .. .. 1·90 1·75
593. 10 col. "OEA" on map of Costa Rica, and flags .. 3·00 2·40

186. St. Louise de Marillac, Sister of Charity & Children. 187. Father Peralta.

**1960.** Air. 300th Death Anniv. of St. Vincent de Paul.
594. 186. 10 c. green .. .. 10 10
595. – 25 c. lake .. .. 10 10
596. – 50 c. blue .. .. 25 15
597. – 1 col. bistre .. .. 40 35
598. – 5 col. sepia .. .. 1·25 95
DESIGNS—HORIZ. St. Vincent de Paul, and: 25 c. Two-storey building. 1 col. Modern building. 50 c. As Type 186, but scene shows Sister at bedside. VERT. 5 col. Stained-glass window picturing St. Vincent de Paul with children.

**1960.** Obligatory Tax. Christmas. Inscr. "SELLO DE NAVIDAD".
599. 187. 5 c. brown .. .. 35 10
600. – 5 c. orange .. .. 35 10
601. – 5 c. red .. .. 35 10
602. – 5 c. blue .. .. 35 10
DESIGNS: No. 600, "Girl" (after Renoir). No. 601, "The Drinkers" (after Velasquez). No. 602, "Children Singing" (sculpture, after Zuniga).

188. Running.

**1960.** Air. Olympics Game, Rome. Centres and inscriptions in black.
603. 1 c. yellow (T 188) .. 10 10
604. 2 c. blue (Diving) .. 10 10
605. 3 c. red (Cycling) .. .. 10 10
606. 4 c. yellow (Weightlifting) 10 10
607. 5 c. green (Tennis) .. 10 10
608. 10 c. red (Boxing) .. 10 10
609. 25 c. turquoise (Football) 10 10
610. 85 c. mauve (Basketball) .. 55 45
611. 1 col. grey (Baseball) .. 65 55
612. 10 col. lavender (Pistol-shooting) .. .. 5·50 4·50

**1961.** Air. 15th World Amateur Baseball Championships. No. 533a optd. **XV Campeonato Mundial de Beisbol de Aficionados** or surch. in figs. also.
613. 25 c. on 75 c. black and red 20 10
614. 75 c. black and red .. 55 25

190. M. Aguilar. 191. Prof. M. Obregon. 192. Granary (F.A.O.).

**1961.** Air. First Continental Lawyers' Conference.
615. 190. 10 c. blue .. .. 10 10
616. – 10 c. purple .. .. 10 10
617. – 25 c. violet .. .. 15 10
618. – 25 c. sepia .. .. 15 10
PORTRAITS: No. 616, A. Brenes. No. 617, A. Gutierrez. No. 618, V. Herrera.
See also Nos. 628/31.

**1961.** Air. Birth Centenary of Obregon.
619. 191. 10 c. turquoise .. 10 10

**1961.** Air. United Nations Commem.
620. 192. 10 c. green .. .. 10 10
621. – 20 c. orange .. .. 15 15
622. – 25 c. slate .. .. 20 15
623. – 30 c. blue .. .. 20 15
624. – 35 c. red .. .. 50 25
625. – 45 c. violet .. .. 35 20
626. – 85 c. blue .. .. 40 30
627. – 10 col. black .. .. 3·00 2·40
DESIGNS: 20 c. "Medical Care" (W.H.O.). 25 c. Globe and workers (I.L.O.). 30 c. Globe and communications satellite "Correo 1B" (I.T.U.). 35 c. Compass and rocket (W.M.O.). 45 c. "The Thinker" (statue) and open book (U.N.E.S.C.O.). 85 c. Douglas DC-6 airliner and globe (I.C.A.O.). 10 col. "Spiderman" on girder (International Bank).

**1961.** Air. 9th Central American Medical Congress. As T 190 but inscr. "NOVENO CONGRESO MEDICO", etc.
628. 10 c. violet .. .. 10 10
629. 10 c. turquoise .. .. 10 10
630. 25 c. sepia .. .. 15 10
631. 25. c. purple .. .. 15 10
PORTRAITS: No. 628, Dr. E. J. Roman. No. 629, Dr. J. M. S. Alfaro. No. 630, Dr. A. S. Llorente. No. 631, Dr. J. J. U. Giralt.

**1961.** Air. Children's City Christmas Issue. No. 522 surch. **SELLO DE NAVIDAD PRO-CIUDAD DE LOS NINOS** and value.
632. 5 c. on 15 c. black & green 15 10

**1962.** Air. Surch. in figures.
633. 10 c. on 15 c. black & green (No. 522) .. .. 10 10
634. 25 c. on 15 c. black & green (No. 522) .. .. 10 10
635. 35 c. on 50 c. blk. & purple (No. 529) .. .. 20 15
636. 85 c. on 80 c. blue (No. 573) 55 45

**1962.** Air. 2nd Central American Philatelic Convention. Optd. **11 CONVENCION FILATELICA CENTROAMERICANA SETIEMBRE 1962.**
637. 30 c. blue (No. 623) .. 45 35
638. 2 col. lake & black (No. 575) 85 65

**1962.** Air. No. 522 surch.
639. 10 c. on 15 c. blk. & green 10 10

**1962.** Air. Fiscal stamps as T 175 optd. **CORREO AEREO** and surch. with new value for postal use.
640. 25 c. on 2 c. green .. 10 10
641. 35 c. on 2 c. green .. 15 10
642. 45 c. on 2 c. green .. 25 20
643. 85 c. on 2 c. green .. 45 35

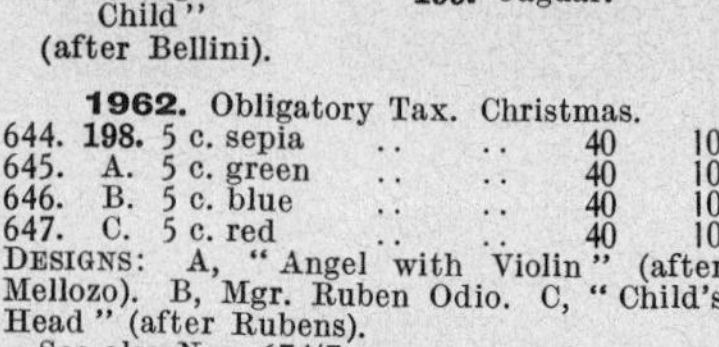

198. "Virgin and Child" (after Bellini). 199. Jaguar.

**1962.** Obligatory Tax. Christmas.
644. 198. 5 c. sepia .. .. 40 10
645. A. 5 c. green .. .. 40 10
646. B. 5 c. blue .. .. 40 10
647. C. 5 c. red .. .. 40 10
DESIGNS: A, "Angel with Violin" (after Mellozo). B, Mgr. Ruben Odio. C, "Child's Head" (after Rubens).
See also Nos. 674/7.

**1963.** Air.
648. – 5 c. brown and olive .. 10 10
649. – 10 c. blue and orange .. 10 10
650. 199. 25 c. yellow and blue .. 20 10
651. – 30 c. brown and green 35 30
652. – 35 c. brown and bistre 65 30
653. – 40 c. blue and green .. 70 45
654. – 85 c. black and green .. 1·10 70
655. – 5 col. brown and green 5·75 4·75
ANIMALS (As Type 199): 5 c. Paca. 10 c. Bairds tapir. 30 c. Ocelot. 35 c. White-tailed deer. 40 c. American manatee. 85 c. White-throated capuchin. 5 col. White-lipped peccary.

200. Arms and Campaign Emblem. 202. Anglo-Costa Rican Bank.

**1963.** Air. Malaria Eradication.
656. 200. 25 c. red .. .. 10 10
657. 35 c. brown .. .. 15 15
658. 45 c. blue .. .. 25 20
659. 85 c. green .. .. 45 35
660. 1 col. blue .. .. 55 45

**1963.** Obligatory Tax Fund for Children's Village. Nos. 644/7 surch. **1963 10 CENTIMOS.**
661. 198. 10 c. on 5 c. sepia .. 15 15
662. A. 10 c. on 5 c. green .. 15 15
663. B. 10 c. on 5 c. blue .. 15 15
664. C. 10 c. on 5 c. red .. 15 15

**1963.** Anglo-Costa Rican Bank Centenary.
665. 202. 10 c. blue .. .. 10 10

203. ½ real Stamp of 1863 and Sail Merchantman "William le Lacheur".

**1963.** Air. Stamp Cent.
666. 203. 25 c. blue and purple .. 30 10
667. – 2 col. orange and grey 1·25 85
668. – 3 col. green and ochre 2·00 1·50
669. – 10 col. brown and green 7·50 4·00
DESIGNS: 2 col. 2 reales stamp of 1863 and Postmaster-General R. B. Carrillo. 3 col. 4 reales stamp of 1863, and mounted postman and pack-mule of 1839. 10 col. 1 peso stamp of 1863 and mule-drawn mail-car.

**1963.** Unissued animal designs as T 199. Surch.
670. 10 c. on 1 c. brown & green 15 10
671. 25 c. on 2 c. sepia & brown 20 10
672. 35 c. on 3 c. brown & myrtle 25 15
673. 85 c. on 4 c. brown and lake 55 25
ANIMALS: 1 c. Tamandua. 2 c. Grey fox. 3 c. Nine-banded armadillo. 4 c. Giant anteater.

**1963.** Obligatory Tax. Christmas. As Nos. 644/7 but inscr. "1963" and new colours.
674. 198. 5 c. blue .. .. 20 10
675. A. 5 c. red .. .. 20 10
676. B. 5 c. black .. .. 20 10
677. C. 5 c. sepia .. .. 20 10

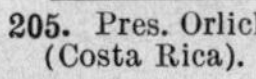

205. Pres. Orlich (Costa Rica). 206. Puma (clay statuette).

**1963.** Air. Presidential Reunion, San Jose. Portraits in sepia.
678. 205. 25 c. purple .. .. 10 10
679. – 30 c. mauve .. .. 15 10
680. – 35 c. ochre .. .. 15 15
681. – 85 c. blue .. .. 40 25
682. – 1 col. brown .. .. 40 30
683. – 3 col. green .. .. 1·00 65
684. – 5 col. slate .. .. 1·40 1·00
PRESIDENTS: 30 c. Rivera (Salvador). 35 c. Ydigoras (Guatemala). 85 c. Villeda (Honduras). 1 col. Somoza (Nicaragua). 3 col. Chiari (Panama). 5 col. Kennedy (U.S.A.).

**1963.** Air. Archaeological Discoveries.
685. 206. 5 c. turquoise and green 10 10
686. – 10 c. turquoise and light yellow .. 10 10
687. – 25 c. sepia and red .. 10 10
688. – 30 c. turquoise & buff 10 10
689. – 35 c. green and salmon 15 10
690. – 45 c. brown and blue .. 15 10
691. – 50 c. brown and blue .. 15 10
692. – 55 c. brown and green 20 10
693. – 75 c. brown and buff .. 20 15
694. – 85 c. brown & yellow .. 55 35
695. – 90 c. brown and yellow 45 35
696. – 1 col. brown and blue 40 25
697. – 2 col. turq. and yellow 70 45
698. – 3 col. brown and green 1·25 80
699. – 5 col. brown & yellow 1·25 75
700. – 10 col. myrtle & mauve 2·00 1·90
DESIGNS—HORIZ. 10 c. Ceremonial stool. 1 col. Twin beakers. 2 col. Alligator. VERT. 25 c. Man (statuette). 30 c. Dancer. 35 c. Vase. 45 c. Deity. 50 c Frog. 55 c. "Eagle" bell. 75 c. Multi-limbed deity. 85 c. Kneeling effigy. 90 c. "Bird" jug. 3 col. Twin-tailed lizard. 5 col. Child. 10 col. Stone effigy of woman.

207. Flags. 210. Mgr. R. Odio and Children.

**1964.** Air. "Centro America".
701. 207. 30 c. multicoloured .. 35 25

**1964.** Air. Surch.
702. – 5 c. on 30 c. (No. 688) 10 10
703. 207. 15 c. on 30 c. .. .. 10 10
704. – 15 c. on 85 c. (No. 694) 10 10
See Nos. 745/9.

**1964.** Paris Postal Conf. No. 695 surch. **C 0.15 CONFERENCIA POSTAL DE PARIS-1864.**
705. 15 c. on 90 c. brn. & yellow 10 10

**1964.** Obligatory Tax. Christmas. Inscr. "SELLO DE NAVIDAD" etc.
706. 210. 5 c. brown .. .. 15 10
707. A. 5 c. blue .. .. 15 10
708. B. 5 c. purple .. .. 15 10
709. C. 5 c. green .. .. 15 10
DESIGNS: A, Teacher and child. B, Children at play. C, Children in class.

211. A. Gonzalez F. 213. Handfuls of grain.

**1965.** Air. 50th Anniv. of National Bank.
710. 211. 35 c. green .. .. 10 10

**1965.** Air. 75th Anniv. of Chapui Hospital. No. 697 surch. **75. ANIVERSARIO ASILO CHAPUI 1890-1965.**
711. 2 col. turquoise and yellow 60 45

**1965.** Air. Freedom from Hunger.
712. – 15 c. blk., grey & brn. 10 10
713. 213. 35 c. black and buff .. 15 10
714. – 50 c. green and blue .. 20 15
715. – 1 col. silver, blk. & grn. 35 20
DESIGNS—HORIZ. 15 c. Map and grain silo. 1 col. Douglas DC-8 airliner over map. VERT. 50 c. Children and population graph.

214. National Children's Hospital. 215. L. Briceno B.

**1965.** Christmas Charity. Obligatory Tax. Inscr. "SELLO DE NAVIDAD", etc.
716. 214. 5 c. green .. .. 15 10
717. A. 5 c. brown .. .. 15 10
718. B. 5 c. red .. .. 15 10
719. C. 5 c. blue .. .. 15 10
DESIGNS—As Type 214: A, Father Casiano. B, Poinsettia. DIAMOND: C, Father Christmas with children.

**1965.** Air. Incorporation of Nicoya District.

720. **215.** 5 c. slate, black & brn. 10 10
721. – 10 c. slate and blue .. 10 10
722. – 15 c. slate and bistre .. 10 10
723. – 35 c. slate and blue .. 10 10
724. – 50 c. violet and grey .. 15 10
725. – 1 col. slate and ochre .. 40 25

DESIGNS: 10 c. Nicoya Church. 15 c. Incorporation scroll. 35 c. Map of Guanacaste Province. 50 c. Provincial dance. 1 col. Guanacaste map and produce.

**216.** Running.

**217.** Pres. John F. Kennedy and " Mercury " Space Capsule encircling Globe.

**1965.** Air. Olympic Games (1964). Mult.

726. 5 c. Type **216** .. .. 10 10
727. 10 c. Cycling .. .. 10 10
728. 40 c. Judo .. .. 15 10
729. 65 c. Handball .. .. 25 15
730. 80 c. Football .. .. 35 20
731. 1 col. Olympic torches .. 45 25

**1965.** Air. 2nd Death Anniv. of Pres. Kennedy. Multicoloured.

732. 45 c. Type **217** .. .. 15 15
733. 55 c. Kennedy in San Jose Cathedral .. .. 25 15
734. 85 c. President with son .. 35 25
735. 1 col. Facade of White House, Washington .. 35 30

Nos. 733/5 are vert.

**218.** Fire Engine.

**219.** Angel.

**1966.** Air. Cent. of Fire Brigade.

736. **218.** 5 c. red and black .. 10 10
737. – 10 c. red and yellow .. 10 10
738. – 15 c. black and red .. 10 10
739. – 35 c. yellow and black 40 10
740. – 50 c. red and blue .. 75 10

DESIGNS—VERT. 10 c. Fire engine of 1866. 15 c. Firemen with hoses. 35 c. Brigade badge. 50 c. Emblem of Central American Fire Brigades Confederation.

**1966.** Obligatory Tax. Christmas. Inscr. " SELLO DE NAVIDAD ", etc.

741. **219.** 5 c. blue .. .. 15 10
742. – 5 c. red (Trinkets) .. 15 10
743. – 5 c. green (Church) .. 15 10
744. – 5 c. brown (Reindeer) 15 10

**1966.** Air (a) Surch.

745 – 15 c. on 30 c. (No. 688) 10 10
746 – 15 c. on 45 c. (No. 690) 10 10
747 – 35 c. on 75 c. (No. 693) 15 10
748 – 35 c. on 55 c. (No. 733) 15 10
749 – 50 c. on 85 c. (No. 734) 25 15

(b) Revenue stamps (as **T 175**) surch.

750. – 15 c. on 5 c. blue .. 10 10
751. – 35 c. on 10 c. red .. 15 10
752. – 50 c. on 20 c. red .. 25 15

**221.** Central Bank, San Jose.

**222.** Telecommunications Building, San Pedro.

**1967.** Obligatory Tax. Social Plan for Postal Workers.

753. – 10 c. blue (postage) .. 10 10

DESIGN as Type **221** (34 × 26 mm.): 10 c. Post Office, San Jose.

**1967.** Air. 50th Anniv. of Central Bank.

754. **221.** 5 c. green .. .. 10 10
755. 15 c. brown .. .. 10 10
756. 35 c. red .. .. 15 10

**1967.** Air. Costa Rican Electrical Industry

757. – 5 c. black .. .. 10 10
758. **222.** 10 c. mauve .. .. 10 10
759. – 15 c. orange .. .. 10 10
760. – 25 c. blue .. .. 10 10
761. – 35 c. green .. .. 15 10
762. – 50 c. brown .. .. 25 15

DESIGNS—VERT. 5 c. Electric pylons. 15 c. Central Telephone Exchange, San Jose. HORIZ. 25 c. La Garita Dam. 35 c. Rio Macho Reservoir. 50 c. Cachi Dam.

**223.** " Chondrorhyncha aromatica ".

**224.** O.E.A. Emblem and Split Leaf.

**1967.** Air. University Library. Orchids. Multicoloured.

763. 5 c. Type **223** .. .. 10 10
764. 10 c. " Miltonia endresii " 10 10
765. 15 c. " Stanhopea cirrhata " 10 10
766. 25 c. " Trichopilia suavis " 15 10
767. 35 c. " Odontoglossum schlieperianum " .. 20 15
768. 50 c. " Cattleya skinneri " 25 15
769. 1 col. " Cattleya dowiana " 45 35
770. 2 col. " Odontoglossum chiriquense " .. .. 1·00 40

**1967.** Air. 25th Anniv. of Inter-American Institute of Agricultural Science.

771. **224.** 50 c. ultramarine & blue .. .. 15 10

**225.** Madonna and Child

**226.** LACSA Emblem.

**1967.** Obligatory Tax. Christmas.

772. **225.** 5 c. green .. .. 10 10
773. 5 c. mauve .. .. 10 10
774. 5 c. blue .. .. 10 10
775. 5 c. turquoise .. .. 10 10

**1967.** Air. 20th Anniv. (1966) of Lineas Aereas Costaricenses (L.A.C.S.A. – Costa Rica Airlines). Multicoloured.

776. 40 c. Type **226** .. .. 10 10
777. 45 c. L.A.C.S.A. emblem and jetliner .. .. 15 10
778. 50 c. Wheel and emblem .. 15 15

The 45 c. is a horiz. design.

**227.** Church of Solitude.

**228.** Scouts in Camp.

**1967.** Air. Churches and Cathedrals (1st series).

779. **227.** 5 c. green .. .. 10 10
780. – 10 c. blue .. .. 10 10
781. – 15 c. purple .. .. 10 10
782. – 25 c. ochre .. .. 10 10
783. – 30 c. brown .. .. 10 10
784. – 35 c. blue .. .. 10 10
785. – 40 c. orange .. .. 10 10
786. – 45 c. green .. .. 10 10
787. – 50 c. olive .. .. 15 10
788. – 55 c. brown .. .. 15 10
789. – 65 c. mauve .. .. 15 15
790. – 75 c. sepia .. .. 20 15
791. – 80 c. yellow .. .. 25 20
792. – 85 c. purple .. .. 1·10 20
793. – 90 c. green .. .. 1·10 25
794. – 1 col. slate .. .. 25 25
795. – 2 col. green .. .. 75 90
796. – 3 col. orange .. .. 2·10 1·25
797. – 5 col. blue .. .. 2·00 1·50
798. – 10 col. red .. .. 2·50 2·00

DESIGNS: 10 c. Santo Domingo **Basilica**, Heredia. 15 c. Tilaran Cathedral. 25 c. Alajuela Cathedral. 30 c. Church of Mercy. 35 c. Our Lady of the Angels Basilica. 40 c. San Rafael Church, Heredia. 45 c. Ruins, Ujarras. 50 c. Ruins of Parish Church, Cartago. 55 c. San Jose Cathedral. 65 c. Parish Church, Puntarenas. 75 c. Orosi Church. 80 c. Cathedral of San Isidro the General. 85 c. San Ramon Church. 90 c. Church of the Forsaken. 1 col. Coronado Church. 2 col. Church of St. Teresita. 3 col. Parish Church, Heredia. 5 col. Carmelite Church. 10 col. Limon Cathedral.

See also Nos. 918/33.

**1968.** Air. Golden Jubilee (1966) of Scout Movement in Costa Rica. Multicoloured.

799. 15 c. Scout on traffic control 10 10
800. 25 c. Scouts tending camp-fire .. .. 15 10
801. 35 c. Scout badge and flags 20 15
802. 50 c. Type **228** .. .. 25 15
803. 65 c. First scout troop on parade (1916) .. .. 35 20

The 15 c., 25 c. and 35 c. are vert. designs.

**229.** " Madonna and Child ".

**230.** Running.

**1968.** Christmas Charity. Obligatory Tax.

805. **229.** 5 c. black .. .. 10 10
806. 5 c. purple .. .. 10 10
807. 5 c. brown .. .. 10 10
808. 5 c. red .. .. 10 10

**1969.** Air. Olympic Games, Mexico. Mult.

809. 30 c. Type **230** .. .. 10 10
810. 40 c. Woman breasting tape 15 10
811. 55 c. Boxing .. .. 25 15
812. 65 c. Cycling .. .. 30 15
813. 75 c. Weightlifting .. 30 15
814. 1 col. High-diving .. 35 25
815. 3 col. Rifle-shooting .. 90 55

**231.** Exhibition Emblem.

**232.** Arms of San Jose.

**1969.** Air. " Costa Rica 69 " Philatelic Exn.

816. **231.** 35 c. multicoloured .. 10 10
817. 40 c. multicoloured .. 15 10
818. 50 c. multicoloured .. 15 10
819. 2 col. multicoloured .. 1·10 40

**1969.** Coats of Arms. Multicoloured.

820. 15 c. Type **232** .. .. 10 10
821. 35 c. Cartago .. .. 10 10
822. 50 c. Heredia .. .. 15 10
823. 55 c. Alajuela .. .. 15 15
824. 65 c. Guanacaste .. .. 25 15
825. 1 col. Puntarenas .. 60 15
826. 2 col. Limon .. .. 70 35

**233.** I.L.O. Emblem.

**234.** Map on Football.

**1969.** Air. 50th Anniv. of I.L.O.

827. **233.** 35 c. turquoise & black 15 10
828. 50 c. red and black .. 20 10

**1969.** Air. 4th CONCACAF Football Championships. Multicoloured.

829. 65 c. Type **234** .. .. 20 15
830. 75 c. Goal mouth melee .. 20 15
831. 85 c. Players with ball .. 25 15
832. 1 col. Two players with ball 30 20

**235.** Madonna and Child.

**236.** Stylised Crab.

**1969.** Christmas. Charity. Obligatory Tax.

833. **235.** 5 c. turquoise .. .. 10 10
834. 5 c. lake .. .. 10 10
835. 5 c. blue .. .. 10 10
836. 5 c. orange .. .. 10 10

**1970.** Air. 10th Inter-American Cancer Congress, San Jose.

837. **236.** 10 c. black and mauve 10 10
838. 15 c. black and yellow 10 10
839. 50 c. black and orange 15 10
840. 1 col. 10 black & green 30 15

**238.** Costa Rican stamps and Magnifier.

**239.** Japanese Vase and Flowers.

**1970.** Air. " Costa Rica 70 " Philatelic Exhibition.

843. **238.** 1 col. red and blue .. 40 15
844. 2 col. mauve and blue 70 40

**1970.** Air. Expo 70. Multicoloured.

845. 10 c. Type **239** .. .. 10 10
846. 15 c. Ornamental cart .. 10 10
847. 35 c. Sun tower .. .. 15 10
848. 40 c. Tea-ceremony .. 15 10
849. 45 c. Coffee-picking .. 15 10
850. 55 c. Earth from the Moon 15 10

The 15 c., 35 c. and 40 c. are horiz.

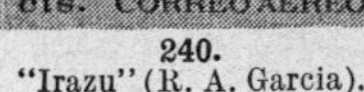

**240.** "Irazu" (R. A. Garcia).

**241.** "Holy Child".

**1970.** Air. Costa Rican Paintings. Mult.

851. 25 c. Type **240** .. .. 30 10
852. 45 c. "Escazu Valley" (M. Bertheau) .. .. 30 10
853. 80 c. "Estuary Landscape" (T. Quiros) .. 65 15
854. 1 col. "The Other Face" (C. Valverde) .. .. 45 15
855. 2 col. 50 "Madonna" (L. Daell) .. .. 1·25 60

The 2 col. 50 is vert.

**1970.** Christmas Charity. Obligatory Tax.

856. **241.** 5 c. mauve .. .. 10 10
857. 5 c. brown .. .. 10 10
858. 5 c. olive .. .. 10 10
859. 5 c. violet .. .. 10 10

**242.** Costa Rican Arms of 21 October 1964.

**243.** National Theatre, San Jose.

**1971.** Air. Various Costa Rican Coats of Arms (with dates). Multicoloured.

860. 5 c. Type **242** .. .. 10 10
861. 10 c. 27 November 1906 .. 10 10
862. 15 c. 29 September 1848 .. 10 10
863. 25 c. 21 April 1840 .. 10 10
864. 35 c. 22 November 1824 .. 10 10
865. 50 c. 2 November 1824 .. 10 10
866. 1 col. 6 March 1824 .. 15 10
867. 2 col. 10 May 1823 .. 60 20

**1971.** Air. O.E.A. General Assembly. San Jose.

868. **243.** 2 col. purple .. .. 35 25

**244.** J. M. Delgado and M. J. Arce (Salvador).

**1971.** Air. 150th Anniv. of Central-American Independence. Multicoloured.

869. 5 c. Type **244** .. .. 10 10
870. 10 c. M. Larreinaga and M. A. de la Cerda (Nicaragua) 10 10
871. 15 c. J. C. del Valle and D. de Herrera (Honduras) 10 10
872. 35 c. P. Alvarado and F. del Castillo (Costa Rica) 10 10
873. 50 c. A. Larrazabal and P. Molina (Guatemala) .. 10 10
874. 1 col. O.D.E.C.A. flag (vert.) 15 10
875. 2 col. O.D.E.C.A. emblem (vert.) .. .. .. 35 25

O.D.E.C.A. = Organization of Central American States.

**245.** Cradle on "PAX".

**246.** Federation Emblem.

**1971.** Christmas Charity. Obligatory Tax.

876. **245.** 10 c. orange .. .. 10 10
877. 10 c. brown .. .. 10 10
878. 10 c. green .. .. 10 10
879. 10 c. blue .. .. 10 10

**1971.** Air. 50th Anniv. of Costa Rican Football Federation.

880. **246.** 50 c. multicoloured .. 10 10
881. 60 c. multicoloured .. 10 10

**247.** " Children of the World ".

**248.** Guanacaste Tree.

**1972.** Air. 25th Anniv. of U.N.I.C.E.F.

882. **247.** 50 c. multicoloured .. 10 10
883. 1 col. 10 multicoloured 20 15

**1972.** Air. Bicent. of Liberia City. Mult.

884. 20 c. Type **248** .. .. 10 10
885. 40 c. Hermitage, Liberia .. 10 10
886. 55 c. Mayan petroglyphs .. 10 10
887. 60 c. Clay head (vert.) .. 15 10

**250.** Farmer's Family and Farm. **251.** Inter-American Stamp Exhibitions.

**1972.** Air. 30th Anniv. of OEA Institute of Agricultural Sciences (IICA).

892. **250.** 20 c. multicoloured .. 10 10
893. – 45 c. multicoloured .. 10 10
894. – 50 c. yell., grn. & blk. 10 10
895. – 10 col. multicoloured 1·10 60

DESIGNS—HORIZ. 45 c. Cattle. VERT. 50 c. Tree-planting. 10 col. Agricultural worker and map.

**1972.** Air. "Exfilbra 72" Stamp Exhib.

896. **251.** 50 c. brown and orange 10 10
897. 2 col. violet and blue.. 35 25

**252.** Madonna and Child. **253.** First Book printed in Costa Rica.

**1972.** Christmas Charity. Obligatory Tax.

898. **252.** 10 c. red .. .. 10 10
899. 10 c. lilac .. .. 10 10
900. 10 c. blue .. .. 10 10
901. 10 c. green .. .. 10 10

**1972.** Air. Int. Book Year. Mult.

902. 20 c. Type **253** .. .. 10 10
903. 50 c. National Library, San Jose (horiz.) .. .. 10 10
904. 75 c. Type **253** .. .. 15 10
905. 5 col. As 50 c. .. .. 60 45

**254.** View near Irazu. **255.** Madonna and Child.

**1972.** Air. American Tourist Year. Mult.

906. 5 c. Type **254** .. .. 10 10
907. 15 c. Entrance to Culebra Bay .. .. 10 10
908. 20 c. Type **254** .. .. 10 10
909. 25 c. As 15 c. .. .. 10 10
910. 40 c. Manuel Antonio Beach 10 10
911. 45 c. Costa Rican Tourist Institute emblem .. 10 10
912. 50 c. Lindora Lake .. 10 10
913. 60 c. Post Office Building, San Jose (vert.).. .. 15 10
914. 80 c. As 40 c. .. .. 15 15
915. 90 c. As 45 c. .. .. 15 15
916. 1 col. As 50 c. .. .. 15 15
917. 2 col. As 60 c. .. .. 35 25

**1973.** Air. Churches and Cathedrals. (2nd series). As Nos. 779/94 but colours changed.

918. **227.** 5 c. grey .. .. 10 10
919. – 10 c. green .. .. 10 10
920. – 15 c. orange .. .. 10 10
921. – 25 c. brown .. .. 10 10
922. – 30 c. purple .. .. 10 10
923. – 35 c. violet .. .. 15 10
924. – 40 c. green .. .. 15 10
925. – 45 c. brown .. .. 15 10
926. – 50 c. red .. .. 10 10
927. – 55 c. blue .. .. 10 10
928. – 65 c. black .. .. 15 10
929. – 75 c. red .. .. 15 10
930. – 80 c. green .. .. 15 10
931. – 85 c. lilac .. .. 15 15
932. – 90 c. red .. .. 15 15
933. – 1 col. blue .. .. 15 15

**1973.** Obligatory Tax. Christmas Charity.

934. **255.** 10 c. red .. .. 10 10
935. 10 c. purple .. .. 10 10
936. 10 c. black .. .. 10 10
937. 10 c. brown .. .. 10 10

**256.** Flame Emblem. **257.** O.E.A. Emblem.

**1973.** Air. 25th Anniv. of Declaration of Human Rights.

938. **256.** 50 c. red and blue .. 10 10

**1973.** Air. 25th Anniv. of O.E.A. (Organization of American States).

939. **257.** 20 c. red and blue .. 10 10

**258.** J. Vargas Calvo. **260.** Telephone Centre, San Pedro.

**1974.** Air. Costa Rican Composers. Mult.

940. 20 c. Type **258** .. .. 10 10
941. 20 c. Alejandro Monestel.. 10 10
942. 20 c. Julio Mata .. .. 10 10
943. 60 c. Julio Fonseca .. 15 10
944. 2 col. Rafael Chaves .. 35 25
945. 5 col. Manuel Gutierrez .. 85 70

**1974.** Air. Fiscal stamps as Type **175** (but without surcharge) optd. **HABILITADO PARA CORREO AEREO.**

946. 50 c. brown .. .. 10 10
947. 1 col. violet .. .. 15 10
948. 2 col. orange .. .. 35 20
949. 5 col. green .. .. 85 70

**1974.** Air. 25th Anniv. of Costa Rican Electrical Institute. Multicoloured.

950. 50 c. Type **260** .. .. 10 10
951. 65 c. Control Room, Rio Macho (horiz.) .. .. 15 10
952. 85 c. Powerhouse, Rio Macho 15 15
953. 1 col. 25 Cachi Dam, Rio Macho (horiz.) .. .. 20 15
954. 2 col. Institute H.Q. Building 35 20

**261.** "Exfilmex" Emblem. **262.** Couple on Map.

**1974.** Air. "Exfilmex" Stamp Exhibition, Mexico City.

955. **261.** 65 c. green .. .. 15 10
956. 3 col. pink .. .. 50 35

**1974.** Air. 25th Anniv. of 4-S Clubs.

957. **262.** 20 c. emerald & green 10 10
958. – 50 c. multicoloured .. 10 10

DESIGN. 50 c. Young agricultural workers

**263.** Brenes Mesen. **264.** Child's and Adult's Hands.

**1974.** Air. Birth Centenary of Roberto Brenes Mesen (educator).

959. **263.** 20 c. black and brown 10 10
960. – 85 c. black and red .. 15 15
961. – 5 col. brown and black 85 70

DESIGNS-VERT. 85 c. Brenes Mesen's "Poems of Love and Death". HORIZ. 5 col. Brenes Mesen's hands.

**1974.** Air. 50th Anniv. of Costa Rican Insurance Institute.

962. – 20 c. multicoloured .. 10 10
963. – 50 c. multicoloured .. 10 10
964. **264.** 65 c. multicoloured .. 10 15
965. – 85 c. multicoloured .. 15 15
966. – 1 col. 25 black & gold.. 20 15
967. – 2 col. multicoloured .. 35 20
968. – 2 col. 50 multicoloured 45 35
969. – 20 col. multicoloured .. 2·50 2·40

DESIGNS—HORIZ. 20 c. R. Jimenez Oreamuno and T. Soley Guell (founders). 50 c. Spade ("Harvest Insurance"). VERT. 85 c. Paper boat within hand ("Marine Insurance"). 1 col. 25 Institute emblem. 2 col. Arm in brace ("Workers' Rehabilitation"). 2 col. 50 Hand holding spanner ("Risks at Work"). 20 col. House in protective hands ("Fire Insurance").

**265.** W.P.Y. Emblem. **266.** "Boys eating Cakes" (Murillo).

**1974.** Air. World Population Year.

970. **265.** 2 col. red and blue .. 35 20

**1974.** Obligatory Tax. Christmas.

971. **266.** 10 c. red .. .. 10 10
972. – 10 c. purple .. .. 10 10
973. – 10 c. black .. .. 10 10
974. – 10 c. blue .. .. 10 10

DESIGNS: No. 972, "The Beautiful Gardener" (Raphael). No. 973, "Maternity" (J. R. Bonilla). No. 974, "The Prayer" (J. Reynolds).

**267.** F. Oscar J. Pinto (football pioneer). **268.** "Mormodes buccinator".

**1974.** Air. First Central American Olympic Games, Guatemala (1973). Each grey and blue.

975. 20 c. Type **267** .. .. 10 10
976. 50 c. D. A. Montes de Oca (shooting champion) .. 10 10
977. 1 col. Eduardo Garnier (promoter of athletics).. 15 10

**1975.** Air. First Central American Orchids Exhibition. Multicoloured.

978. 25 c. Type **268** .. .. 10 10
979. 25 c. "Gongora claviodora" 10 10
980. 25 c. "Masdevallia ephippium" .. .. 10 10
981. 25 c. "Encyclia spondiadum" 10 10
982. 65 c. "Lycaste skinneri alba" .. .. 40 10
983. 65 c. "Peristeria elata" .. 40 10
984. 65 c. "Miltonia roezelii" .. 40 10
985. 65 c. "Brassavola digbyana" 40 10
986. 80 c. "Epidendrum mirabile" .. .. 50 15
987. 80 c. "Barkeria lindleyana" 50 15
988. 80 c. "Cattleya skinneri" 50 15
989. 80 c. "Sobralia macrantha splendens" .. .. 50 15
990. 1 col. 40 "Lycaste cruenta" .. .. 65 15
991. 1 col. 40 "Oncidium obryzatum" .. .. 65 15
992. 1 col. 40 "Gongora armeniaca" .. .. 65 15
993. 1 col. 40 "Sievekingia suavis" .. .. 65 15
994. 1 col. 75 "Hexisea imbricata" .. .. 65 20
995. 2 col. 15 "Warcewiczella discolor" .. .. 65 20
996. 2 col. 50 "Oncidium kramerianum".. .. 90 35
997. 3 col. 25 "Cattleya dowiana" .. .. 1·25 40

**269.** Emblem of Costa Rica Radio Club.

**1975.** Air. 16th Convention of Radio Amateurs Federation of Central America and Panama, San Jose.

998. **269.** 1 col. purple & black 15 10
999. – 1 col. 10 red and blue 20 15
1000. – 2 col. blue and black 35 20

DESIGNS—VERT. 1 col. 10, Federation emblem within "V" of Flags. HORIZ. 2 col. Federation emblem.

**270.** Nicoyan Beach.

**1975.** Air. 150th Anniv. of Annexation of Nicoya. Multicoloured.

1001. 25 c. Type **270** .. .. 10 10
1002. 75 c. Cattle-drive .. 15 15
1003. 1 col. Colonial church .. 15 15
1004. 3 col. Savannah riders (vert.) .. .. 50 40

**271.** 3 c. Philatelic Exhibition Stamp of 1932.

**1975.** Air. 6th National Philatelic Exhibition, San Jose.

1005. **271.** 2 col. 20 orange & blk. 40 35
1006. – 2 col. 20 green & blk. 40 35
1007. – 2 col. 20 red & black 40 35
1008. – 2 col. 20 blue & black 40 35

DESIGNS: Stamps of 1932. No. 1006, 5 c. stamp No. 1007, 10 c. stamp. No. 1008, 20 c. stamp.

**272.** I.W.Y. Emblem. **273.** U.N. Emblem.

**1975.** Air. International Women's Year.

1009. **272.** 40 c. red and blue .. 10 10
1010. 1 col. 25 blue & black 20 15

**1975.** Air. 30th Anniv. of United Nations.

1011. **273.** 10 c. blue and black.. 10 10
1012. – 60 c. multicoloured .. 10 10
1013. – 1 col. 20 multicoloured 20 15

DESIGNS—HORIZ. 60 c. General Assembly. VERT. 1 col. 20, U.N. Headquarters, New York.

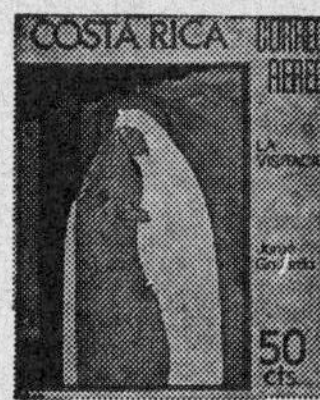

**274.** "The Visitation". **275.** "Children with Tortoise" (F. Amighetti).

**1975.** Air. "The Christmas Tradition". Paintings by Jorge Gallardo. Mult.

1014. 50 c. Type **274** .. .. 10 10
1015. 1 col. "The Nativity and the Comet" .. .. 15 10
1016. 5 col. "St. Joseph in his workshop" .. .. 60 45

**1975.** Obligatory Tax. Christmas. Children's Village. Multicoloured.

1017. **275.** 10 c. brown .. .. 10 10
1018. – 10 c. purple .. .. 10 10
1019. – 10 c. grey .. .. 10 10
1020. – 10 c. blue .. .. 10 10

DESIGNS: No. 1018, "The Virgin of the Carnation" (Da Vinci). No. 1019, "Happy Dreams" (child in bed—Sonia Romero). No. 1020, "Child with Pigeon" (Picasso).

**276.** Schoolboy and Flags. **277.** Prof. A. M. Brenes Mora.

**1976.** Air. 20th Anniv. of "20–30" Youth Clubs in Costa Rica.

1021. **276.** 1 col. multicoloured 15 10

**1976.** Birth Centenary (1970) of Professor A. M. Brenes Mora (botanist).

1022. **277.** 1 col. violet (postage) 15 15
1023. – 5 c. multicoloured (air) 10 10
1024. – 30 c. multicoloured .. 10 10
1025. – 55 c. multicoloured .. 10 10
1026. – 2 col. multicoloured .. 35 20
1027. – 10 col. multicoloured 1·10 85

DESIGNS: 5 c. "Quercus breneseii". 30 c. "Maxillaria albertii". 55 c. "Calathea brenesii". 2 col. "Brenesia costaricensis". 10 col. "Philodendron brenesii".

No. 1023 is wrongly inscribed "brenessi".

**278.** Open Book as "Flower". **281.** Early and Modern Telephones.

**280.** Mounted Postman with Pack Mule.

**1976.** Air. Costa Rican Literature. Mult.

1028. 15 c. Type **278** .. .. 10 10
1029. 1 col. 10 Reader with "TV eye" .. .. 15 15
1030. 5 col. Book and flag (horiz.) .. .. 55 45

**1976.** Cent. (1974) of U.P.U.
1032. **280.** 20 c. black and yellow 10 10
1033. – 50 c. multicoloured .. 10 10
1034. – 65 c. multicoloured .. 15 10
1035. – 85 c. multicoloured .. 15 15
1036. – 2 col. black and blue 35 25
DESIGNS—HORIZ. 50 c. 5 c. U.P.U. stamp of 1882. 65 c. 10 c. U.P.U. stamp of 1882. 85 c. 20 c. U.P.U. stamp of 1882. VERT. 2 col. U.P.U. Monument, Berne.

**1976.** Telephone Centenary.
1037. **281.** 1 col. 60 black & blue 25 20
1038. – 2 col. blk., brn. & grn. 35 20
1039. – 5 col. black & yellow 55 45
DESIGNS: 2 col. Costa Rica's first telephone. 5 col. Alexander Graham Bell.

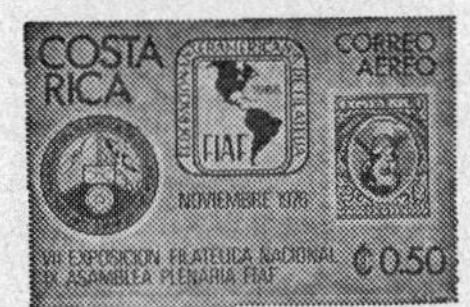

**282.** Emblems and Costa Rica 2 c. Stamp of 1901 with centre inverted.

**1976.** Air. 7th National Philatelic Exhibition.
1040. **282.** 50 c. multicoloured .. 10 10
1041. 1 col. multicoloured .. 15 10
1042. 2 col. multicoloured .. 35 20

**283.** Emblem of Comptroller General. **284.** "Girl in Wide-brimmed Hat" (Renoir).

**1976.** Air. 25th Anniv. of Comptroller General.
1044. **283.** 35 c. blue and black .. 10 10
1045. – 2 col. blk., brn. & blue 35 20
DESIGN—VERT. 2 col. Amadeo Quiros Blanco (1st Comptroller).

**1976.** Obligatory Tax. Christmas.
1046. **284.** 10 c. lake .. .. 10 10
1047. – 10 c. purple .. .. 10 10
1048. – 10 c. slate .. .. 10 10
1049. – 10 c. blue .. .. 10 10
DESIGNS: No 1047, "Virgin and Child" (Hans Memling). No. 1048, "Meditation" (Floria Pinto de Herrero). No. 1049, "Gaston de Mezerville" (Lolita Zeller de Peralta).

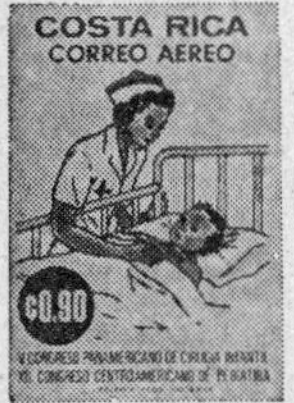

**285.** Nurse tending Child. **286.** "L.A.C.S.A." encircling Globe.

**1976.** Air. 5th Pan-American Children's Surgery Congress. Multicoloured.
1050. 90 c. Type **285** .. .. 15 15
1051. 1 col. 10 National Children's Hospital (horiz.) .. 20 15

**1976.** Air. 30th Anniv. of L.A.C.S.A. Airline. Multicoloured.
1052. 1 col. Type **286** .. .. 20 10
1053. 1 col. 20 Route-map of L.A.C.S.A. service .. 25 15
1054. 3 col. L.A.C.S.A. emblem and Costa Rican flag .. 65 45

**287.** Boston Tea Party.

**1976.** Air. Bicentenary of American Revolution. Multicoloured.
1055. 2 col. 20 Type **287** .. 70 25
1056. 5 col. Declaration of Independence .. .. 55 45
1057. 10 col. Ringing the Independence Bell (vert.) .. 1·10 85

**288.** Boruca Textile. **289.** "Tree of Guanacaste".

**1977.** Air. National Handicrafts Project. Multicoloured.
1058. 75 c. Type **288** .. .. 15 10
1059. 1 col. 50 Decorative handicraft in wood .. 25 15

**1977.** Air. 50th Anniv. of Rotary Club, San Jose.
1060. **289.** 40 c. grn., blue & yell. 10 10
1061. – 50 c. blk., blue & yell. 10 10
1062. – 60 c. blk., blue & yell. 10 10
1063. – 3 col. multicoloured .. 50 40
1064. – 10 col. black, blue and yellow .. .. 1·25 85
DESIGNS—VERT. 50 c. Felipe J. Alvarado (founder). 10 col. Paul Harris, founder of Rotary International. HORIZ. 60 c. Dr. Blanco Cervantes Hospital. 3 col. Map of Costa Rica.

**290.** Juana Pereira. **291.** Alonso de Anguciana de Gamboa.

**1977.** Air. 50th Anniv. of Coronation of Our Lady of the Angels (Patron Saint of Costa Rica).
1065. 50 c. Type **290** .. .. 10 10
1066. 1 col. First church of Our Lady of the Angels (horiz.) .. .. 15 10
1067. 1 col. 10 Our Lady of the Angels .. .. 20 15
1068. 1 col. 25 Our Lady's crown .. .. 25 15

**1977.** Air. 400th Anniv. of Foundation of Esparza.
1069. **291.** 35 c. pur., mve. & blk. 10 10
1070. – 75 c. brn., red & blk. 15 10
1071. – 1 col. deep blue, blue and black .. .. 15 10
1072. – 2 col. green and black 35 25
DESIGNS: 75 c. Church of Esparza. 1 col. Our Lady of Candelaria, Patron Saint of Esparza. 2 col. Diego de Artieda y Chirino.

**292.** Child. **293.** Institute Emblem.

**1977.** Air. 20 Years of "CARE" in Costa Rica. Multicoloured.
1073. 80 c. Type **292** .. .. 15 10
1074. 1 col. Soya beans (horiz.) 15 10

**1977.** Air. 25th Anniv. of Hispanic Cultural Institute of Costa Rica. Multicoloured.
1075. 50 c. Type **293** .. .. 10 10
1076. 1 col. 40 First map of the Americas, 1540. (40 × 30 mm.) .. .. 25 20

**294.** "Our Lady of Mercy Church" (R. Ulloa). **295.** Health Ministry on Map.

**1977.** Air. Mystical Paintings. Multicoloured.
1077. 50 c. Type **294** .. .. 10 10
1078. 1 col. "Christ" (F. Pinto de Herrero) .. .. 15 10
1079. 5 col. "St. Francis and the Birds" (L. Gonzalez de Saenz) .. .. 55 45

**1977.** Air. 50th Anniv. of Health Ministry.
1080. **295.** 1 col. 40 multicoloured 25 20

**296.** "Child's Head" (Rubens). **297.** Weaving.

**1977.** Obligatory Tax. Christmas.
1081. **296.** 10 c. red .. .. 10 10
1082. – 10 c. blue .. .. 10 10
1083. – 10 c. green .. .. 10 10
1084. – 10 c. purple .. .. 10 10
DESIGNS: No. 1082, "Tenderness" (Cristina Fournier). No. 1083, "Abstraction" (Amparo Cruz). No. 1084, "Mariano Goya" (Francisco de Goya).

**1978.** Air. 21st Congress of Confederation of Latin American Tourist Organizations. Multicoloured.
1085. 50 c. Type **297** .. .. 10 10
1086. 1 col. Picnic .. .. 15 15
1087. 2 col. Beach scene .. 35 20
1088. 5 col. Fruit market .. 55 45
1089. 10 col. Lake scene .. 1·25 85

**298.** Reader with Book. **299.** Jose de San Martin.

**1978.** National Literacy Campaign.
1090. **298.** 50 c. blue, blk. & orge. 10 10

**1978.** Air. Birth Bicent. of Jose de San Martin.
1091. **299.** 5 col. multicoloured 60 40

**300.** Globe. **301.** "XXX".

**1978.** Air. 50th Anniv. of Panamerican Institute of Geography and History.
1092. **300.** 5 col. blue, gold and light blue .. .. 50 60

**1978.** Air. 30th Anniv. of Central American University Confederation.
1093. **301.** 80 c. blue .. .. 15 10

**302.** Emblems.

**1978.** Air. 6th Interamerican Philatelic Exn., Buenos Aires.
1094. **302.** 2 col. turq., gold & blk. 35 25

**1978.** Air. 50th Anniv. of 1st PanAm Flight in Costa Rica. Nos. 994/6 optd. **"50 Aniversario del primer vuelo de PAN AM en Costa Rica 1928-1978".**
1095. 1 col. 75 "Hexisea imbricata" .. .. 25 20
1096. 2 col. 15 "Warcewiczella discolor" .. .. 35 25
1097. 2 col. 50 "Oncidium kramerianum" .. 40 30

**1978.** Air. 50th Anniv. of Lindbergh's Visit to Costa Rica. Nos. 994/6 optd. **"50 Aniversario de la visita de Lindbergh a Costa Rica 1928-1978".**
1098. 1 col. 75 "Hexisea imbricata" .. .. 30 20
1099. 2 col. 15 "Warcewiczella discolor" .. .. 35 25
1100. 2 col. 50 "Oncidium kramerianum" .. 40 30

**1978.** Air. Carlos Maria Ulloa Hospital. Cent. Nos. 964 and 968 surch. **"Centenario del Asilo Carlos Maria Ulloa 1878-1978".**
1101. 50 c. on 65 c. multicoloured 10 10
1102. 2 col. on 2 col. 50 mult. 35 25

**306.** Star over Map of Costa Rica. **308.** "Christmas Winds" (L. F. Chacon).

**1978.** Air. Christmas.
1103. **306.** 50 c. blue and black .. 10 10
1104. 1 col. mauve & black 15 15
1105. 5 col. red and black .. 55 55

**1978.** Air. Nos. 982/5 and 995/6 surch.
1106. 50 c. on 65 c. "Lycaste skinneri alba" .. 10 10
1107. 50 c. on 65 c. "Peristeria elata" .. .. 10 10
1108. 50 c. on 65 c. "Miltonia roezelii" .. .. 10 10
1109. 50 c. on 65 c. "Brassavola digbyana" .. .. 10 10
1110. 1 col. 20 on 2 col. 15 "Warcewiczella discolor" .. .. 20 15
1111. 2 col. on 2 col. 50 "Onicidium kramerianum" 35 25

**1978.** Obligatory Tax. Christmas. Children's Village.
1112. **308.** 10 c. slate .. .. 10 10
1113. 10 c. red .. .. 10 10
1114. – 10 c. mauve .. .. 10 10
1115. – 10 c. blue .. .. 10 10
DESIGN: Nos. 1114/15, "Girl playing with Kite" (sculpture by Nester Zeledon.)

**309.** "The Flying Men" Chorotega Ritual. **310.** Domingo Rivas.

**1978.** Air. 500th Anniv. of Gonzalo Fernandez de Oviedo (first chronicler of Spanish Indies).
1116. **309.** 85 c. multicoloured .. 15 10
1117. – 1 col. 20 blue & black 20 15
1118. – 10 col. multicoloured 1·25 75
DESIGNS—HORIZ. 1 col. 20, Oviedo giving his "History of Indies" to Duke of Calabria. VERT. 10 col. Lord of Oviedo's coat of arms.

**1978.** Air. Cent. of San Jose Cathedral.
1119. **310.** 1 col. blue and black 15 15
1120. – 20 col. multicoloured 2·10 2·00
DESIGN: 20 col. San Jose Cathedral.

**311.** Cocos Island.

**1979.** Air. Presidential Visit to Cocos Island. Multicoloured.
1121. 90 c. Type **311** .. .. 15 10
1122. 2 col. 10 Cocos Island (different) .. .. 35 25
1123. 3 col. Cocos Island (different) .. .. 50 35
1124. 5 col. Moon over Cocos Island (vert.) .. .. 55 60
1125. 10 col. Commemorative plaque and people with flag (vert.) .. .. 1·00 75

**312.** Shrimp.

**1979.** Air. Conservation of Marine Fauna. Multicoloured.
1127. 60 c. Type **312** .. .. 10 10
1128. 85 c. Red snapper .. 15 10
1129. 1 col. 80 Hake .. .. 30 20
1130. 3 col. Lobster .. .. 50 35
1131. 10 col. Yellowfin tuna .. 1·10 75

**313.** Hungry Nestlings (Song Thrushes).

**1979.** Air. International Year of the Child.
1132. **313.** 1 col. multicoloured .. 45 10
1133. 2 col. multicoloured .. 60 20
1134. 20 col. multicoloured 5·50 1·90

315. Microwave Transmitters.

**1979.** Air. 30th Anniv. of Costa Rican Electricity Institute. Multicoloured.
1136 1 col. Arenal Dam .. .. 20 15
1137 5 col. Type **315** .. .. 60 65

**316.** Sir Rowland Hill and Penny Black.

**1979.** Air. Death Cent. of Sir Rowland Hill.
1138. – 5 col. mauve and blue .. .. 55 45
1139. **316.** 10 col. blue and black 90 65
DESIGN: 5 col. Sir Rowland Hill and first Costa Rican stamp.

**317.** "Waiting" (Hernan Gonzalez). **318.** "Danaus plexippus".

**1979.** Air. National Sculpture Competition. Multicoloured.
1140. 60 c. Type **317** .. .. 10 10
1141. 1 col. "The Heroes of Misery" (Juan Ramon Bonilla) .. .. .. 20 15
1142. 2 col. 10 "Bullocks" (Victor M. Bermudez) (horiz.) .. 30 25
1143. 5 col. "Chlorite Head" (Juan Rafael Chacon) .. 65 65
1144. 20 col. "Motherhood" (Francisco Zuniga) .. 2·50 2·10

**1979.** Air. Butterflies. Multicoloured.
1145. 60 c. Type **318** .. .. 15 10
1146. 1 col. "Phoebis philea" .. 35 15
1147. 1 col. 80 "Rothschildia sp." 45 35
1148. 2 col. 10 "Prepona omphale" 50 35
1149. 2 col. 60 "Marpesia marcella" 70 55
1150. 4 col. 05 "Morpho cypris" 95 75

**319.** "Green House" (M. Murillo). **320.** Jose Joaquin Rodriguez Zeledon.

**1979.** Air. 30th Anniv. of SOS Children's Villages. Children's Paintings. Multicoloured.
1151. 2 col. 50 Type **319** .. .. 45 30
1152. 5 col. "Four houses" (L. Varela) .. .. .. 60 65
1153. 5 col. 50 "Blue house" (M. Perez) .. .. .. 65 70

**1979.** Air. Costa Rican Presidents (1st series).
1154. **320.** 10 c. blue .. .. 10 10
1155. – 60 c. purple .. .. 10 10
1156. – 85 c. red .. .. 15 10
1157. – 1 col. orange .. .. 20 10
1158. – 2 col. brown .. .. 35 25
DESIGNS: 60 c. Rafael Iglesias Castro. 85 c. Ascension Esquivel Ibarra; 1 col. Cleto Gonzalez Viquez. 2 col. Ricardo Jimenez Oreamuno.
See also Nos. 1180/4 and 1256/60.

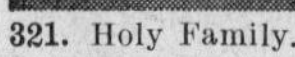

321. Holy Family. 322. Boy leaning on Tree.

**1979.** Air. Christmas.
1159. **321.** 1 col. multicoloured 20 15
1160. 1 col. 60 multicoloured 30 20

**1979.** Obligatory Tax. Christmas. Children's Village.
1161. **322.** 10 c. blue .. .. 10 10
1162. 10 c. orange .. .. 10 10
1163. 10 c. mauve .. .. 10 10
1164. 10 c. green .. .. 10 10

**323.** Tree. **324.** " Anatomy Lesson " (Rembrandt).

**1980.** Air. Reafforestation.
1165. **323.** 1 col. brn., blue & grn. 20 15
1166. 3 col. 40 brown, olive and green .. .. 35 45

**1980.** Air. 50th anniv. of Legal Medical Teaching in Costa Rica.
1167. **324.** 10 col. multicoloured 90 90

325. Rotary Anniversary Emblem. 326. Puerto Limon.

**1980.** 75th Anniv. of Rotary International.
1168. **325.** 2 col. 10 green, yellow and black .. .. 35 25
1169. 5 col. multicoloured 50 40

**1980.** Air. 14th International Symposium on Remote Sensing of the Environment. Multicoloured.
1170. 2 col. 10 Type **326** .. .. 35 25
1171. 5 col. Gulf of Nicoya, Guanacaste .. .. 50 40

**327.** Football. **328.** Poas Volcano.

**1980.** Air. Olympic Games, Moscow. Mult.
1172. 1 col. Type **327** .. .. 20 15
1173. 3 col. Cycling .. .. 30 40
1174. 4 col. 05 Baseball .. 40 30
1175. 20 col. Swimming .. 1·50 2·00

**1980.** Air. 10th Anniv. of National Parks Service.
1176. 1 col. Type **328** .. .. 20 15
1177. 2 col. 50 Beach at Cahuita 45 30

**329.** Jose Maria Zeledon Brenes (lyric writer). **330.** Exhibition Emblem.

**1980.** Air. National Anthem. Multicoloured.
1178. 1 col. Type **329** .. .. 20 15
1179. 10 col. Manuel Maria Gutierrez (composer) .. 90 90

**1980.** Air. Costa Rican Presidents (2nd series). As T **320**.
1180. 1 col. red .. .. 20 15
1181. 1 col. 60 turquoise .. 30 20
1182. 1 col. 80 brown .. .. 30 20
1183. 2 col. 10 green .. .. 35 25
1184. 3 col. lilac .. .. 55 40
DESIGNS: 1 col. Alfredo Gonzalez. 1 col. 60, Federico Tinoco. 1 col. 80, Francisco Aguilar. 2 col. 10, Julio Acosta. 3 col. Leon Cortes.

**1980.** Air. Eighth National Stamp Exhibition.
1185. **330.** 5 col. multicoloured 90 65
1186. 20 col. multicoloured 2·40 2·00

331. Fruit. 332. "Giant Poro" (Jorge Carvajal).

**1980.** Air. Costa Rican Produce. Mult.
1187. 10 c. Type **331** .. .. 10 10
1188. 60 c. Chocolate .. .. 10 10
1189. 1 col. Coffee .. .. 20 15
1190. 2 col. 10 Bananas .. .. 35 25
1191. 3 col. 40 Flowers .. .. 35 45
1192. 5 col. Cane Sugar .. .. 60 15

**1980.** Air. Paintings. Multicoloured.
1193. 1 col. Type **332** .. .. 20 15
1194. 2 col. 10 "Secret Look" (Rolando Cubero) .. 35 25
1195. 2 col. 45 "Consuelo" (Fernando Carballo) (31 × 32 mm.) .. .. 45 30
1196. 3 col. "Volcano" (Lola Fernandez) .. .. .. 30 40
1197. 4 col. 05 "Hearing Mass" (Francisco Amighetti) .. 40 30

**333.** " Madonna and Child " (Raphael). **334.** Boy on Swing.

**1980.** Air. Christmas. Multicoloured.
1198. 1 col. Type **333** .. .. 20 15
1199. 10 col. " Madonna, Jesus and St. John" (Raphael) 90 90

**1980.** Obligatory Tax. Christmas. Children's Village.
1200. **334.** 10 c. red .. .. 10 10
1201. 10 c. yellow .. .. 10 10
1202. 10 c. blue .. .. 10 10
1203. 10 c. green .. .. 10 10

**335.** New Harbour, Caldera. **336.** Harpy Eagle.

**1980.** Air. "Paying your Taxes Means Progress". Multicoloured.
1204. 1 col. Type **335** .. .. 20 15
1205. 1 col. 30 Juan Santamaria International Airport (horiz.) .. .. .. 30 15
1206. 2 col. 10 River Frio railway bridge .. .. .. 2·50 90
1207. 2 col. 60 Highway to Colon City .. .. .. 45 35
1208. 5 col. Regional postal centre, Huetar .. .. 50 40

**1980.** Air. Fauna. Multicoloured.
1209. 2 col. 10 Type **336** .. .. 1·50 60
1210. 2 col. 50 Scarlet macaw .. 1·60 80
1211. 3 col. Puma .. .. 55 40
1212. 5 col. 50 Black-handed spider monkey .. 1·00 1·75

**337.** Monge and Magazine "Repertorio Americano".

**1980.** Air. Birth Centenary of Joaquin Garcia Monge.
1213. **337.** 1 col. 60 blue, yellow and red .. .. 30 20
1214. 3 col. blue, pale blue and red .. .. 30 40

HAVE YOU READ THE NOTES AT THE BEGINNING OF THIS CATALOGUE?
These often provide answers to the enquiries we receive.

**338.** Arms of Aserri. **339.** Rodrigo Facio Brenes (rector)

**1981.** Air. Cornea Bank.
1215. **338.** 1 col. multicoloured 20 15
1216. 1 col. 80 multicoloured 30 25
1217. 5 col. blue .. .. 50 40
DESIGNS: 1 col. 80, Eye. 5 col. Abelardo Rojas (founder).

**1981.** Air. 40th Anniv. of University of Costa Rica and 20th Anniv. of Medical School.
1218. – 5 c. multicoloured .. 10 10
1219. – 10 c. multicoloured .. 10 10
1220. – 50 c. multicoloured .. 10 10
1221. – 1 col. 30 multicoloured .. .. 10 10
1222. – 3 col. 40 multicoloured .. .. 25 20
1223. **399.** 4 col. 05 green, blue and dark blue .. 30 20
DESIGNS: HORIZ. 5 c. Medical-surgical clinic. 10 c. Physiology lesson. 50 c. Medical School and Dr. Antonia Pena Chavarria (first Dean). 1 col. 30, School of Music and Fine Arts. 3 col. 40, Carlos Monge Alfaro Library.

**340.** Donkey-drawn Mail Van 1857.

**1981.** Air. 150th Birth Anniv. of Heinrich von Stephan (founder of U.P.U.).
1224. – 1 col. pale blue, green and blue .. .. 20 15
1225. **340.** 2 col. 10 yellow, red and brown .. 2·50 1·50
1226. – 10 col. grey, mauve and green .. .. 1·75 1·25
DESIGNS: 1 col. Mail carried by mule, 1839. 10 col. Carrying mail to Sarapiqui, 1858.

**341.** I.T.U. and W.H.O. Emblems and Ribbons forming Caduceus. **342.** Sts. Peter and Paul.

**1981.** Air. World Telecommunications Day.
1227. **341.** 5 col. blue and black 50 40
1228. 25 col. multicoloured 2·40 1·75

**1981.** Air. Centenary of Consecration of Bernardo August Thiel as Bishop of San Jose. Multicoloured.
1229. 1 col. Type **342** .. .. 10 10
1230. 1 col. St. Vincent de Paul 10 10
1231. 1 col. Death of St. Joseph 10 10
1232. 1 col. Archangel St. Michael 10 10
1233. 1 col. Holy Family .. 10 10
1234. 1 col. Bishop Thiel .. 15 10

**343.** Juan Santamaria (national hero). **344.** Potter.

**1981.** Air. Homage to the Province of Alajuela. Multicoloured.
1235. 1 col. Type **343** (150th birth anniv.) .. .. 10 10
1236. 2 col. 45 Alajuela Cathedral 20 15

**1981.** Air. Banco Popular and the Development of the Community. Multicoloured.
1237. 15 c. Type **344** .. .. 10 10
1238. 1 col. 60 Building construction .. .. 15 10
1239. 1 col. 80 Farming .. 15 10
1240. 2 col. 50 Fishermen .. 20 15
1241. 3 col. Nurse and patient 25 15
1242. 5 col. Rural Guard .. 45 30

345. Leon Fernandez Bonilla (founder).

346. Disabled Person in Wheelchair holding Scales of Justice.

**1981.** Air. National Archives. Multicoloured.

| No. | Type | Description | | |
|---|---|---|---|---|
| 1243. | | 1 col. 40 Type **345** .. | 15 | 10 |
| 1244. | | 2 col. Arms of National Archives .. .. | 15 | 15 |
| 1245. | | 3 col. University of Santo Tomas (horiz.) .. .. | 25 | 15 |
| 1246. | | 3 col. 50 Model of new archives' building (horiz.) | 30 | 25 |

**1981.** Air. International Year of Disabled People.

| No. | Type | Description | | |
|---|---|---|---|---|
| 1247. | – | 1 col. multicoloured .. | 10 | 10 |
| 1248. | **346.** | 2 col. 60 deep orge., orge. and black .. | 25 | 25 |
| 1249. | – | 10 col. multicoloured | 60 | 40 |

DESIGNS—VERT. 1 col. Steps and disabled person in wheelchair. HORIZ. 10 col. Healthy person helping disabled towards the sun.

347. F.A.O. Emblem.

348. Boy in Pedal-car.

**1981.** Air. World Food Day.

| No. | Type | Description | | |
|---|---|---|---|---|
| 1250. | **347.** | 5 col. multicoloured | 45 | 30 |
| 1251. | | 10 col. multicoloured | 60 | 55 |

**1981.** Obligatory Tax. Christmas. Children's Village.

| No. | Type | Description | | |
|---|---|---|---|---|
| 1252. | **348.** | 10 c. red .. .. | 10 | 10 |
| 1253. | | 10 c. orange .. .. | 10 | 10 |
| 1254. | | 10 c. blue .. .. | 10 | 10 |
| 1255. | | 10 c. green .. .. | 10 | 10 |

**1981.** Air. Costa Rican Presidents (3rd series) As T **320.**

| No. | Description | | |
|---|---|---|---|
| 1256. | 1 col. red .. .. .. | 10 | 10 |
| 1257. | 2 col. orange .. .. | 15 | 15 |
| 1258. | 3 col. green .. .. | 25 | 15 |
| 1259. | 5 col. blue .. .. | 20 | 30 |
| 1260. | 10 col. blue .. .. | 45 | 55 |

DESIGNS: 1 col. Rafael Angel Calderon Guardia. 2 col. Teodoro Picado Milchalski. 3 col. Jose Figueres Ferrer. 5 col. Otilio Ulate Blanco. 10 col. Mario Echandi Jimenez.

349. Arms of Bar Association.

**1982.** Air. Centenary of Bar Association.

| No. | Type | Description | | |
|---|---|---|---|---|
| 1261. | **349.** | 1 col. blue & black .. | 10 | 10 |
| 1262. | – | 2 col. multicoloured .. | 15 | 10 |
| 1263. | – | 20 col. green & black | 90 | 45 |

DESIGNS—VERT. 2 col. Eusebio Figueroa (first president of Association). HORIZ. 20 col. Bar Association building.

350. Housing.

**1982.** Air. Costa-Rican Progress. Mult.

| No. | Description | | |
|---|---|---|---|
| 1264. | 95 c. Type **350** .. .. | 10 | 10 |
| 1265. | 1 col. 15 Farmers' fairs .. | 10 | 10 |
| 1266. | 1 col. 45 Grade and high schools .. .. .. | 15 | 10 |
| 1267. | 1 col. 65 National plan for drinking water .. .. | 15 | 10 |
| 1268. | 1 col. 80 Rural health .. | 15 | 10 |
| 1269. | 2 col. 10 Playgrounds .. | 20 | 10 |
| 1270. | 2 col. 35 National Theatre Square .. .. .. | 20 | 10 |
| 1271. | 2 col. 60 Dish aerial (International and national telephone system) .. | 20 | 15 |
| 1272. | 3 col. Electric railway to Atlantic coast .. .. | 2·00 | 75 |
| 1273. | 4 col. 05 Irrigation at Guanacaste .. .. | 35 | 15 |

351. Fountain, Central Park.

352. Saint's Stone.

**1982.** Air. Bicentenary of Alajuela. Mult.

| No. | Description | | |
|---|---|---|---|
| 1274. | 5 col. Type **351** .. .. | 20 | 20 |
| 1275. | 10 col. Juan Santamaria Historical and Cultural Museum (horiz.) .. | 40 | 10 |
| 1276. | 15 col. Christ of Esquipulas Church .. .. .. | 60 | 20 |
| 1277. | 20 col. Mgr. Estevan Lorenzo de Tristan .. | 80 | 45 |
| 1278. | 25 col. Padre Juan Manuel Lopez del Corral .. | 1·00 | 60 |

**1982.** Air. 50th Anniv. of Perez Zeledon County. Multicoloured.

| No. | Description | | |
|---|---|---|---|
| 1279. | 10 c. Type **352** .. .. | 10 | 10 |
| 1280. | 50 c. Monument to Mothers | 10 | 10 |
| 1281. | 1 col. Pedro Perez Zeledon | 10 | 10 |
| 1282. | 1 col. 25 San Isidro Labrador Church .. .. | 10 | 10 |
| 1283. | 3 col. 50 Municipal building (horiz.) .. .. .. | 30 | 15 |
| 1284. | 4 col. 25 County arms .. | 35 | 15 |

**1982.** Air. Nos. 1070 and 1207 surch.

| No. | Description | | |
|---|---|---|---|
| 1285. | 3 col. on 75 c. red & black | 25 | 15 |
| 1286. | 5 col. on 2 col. 60, mult... | 45 | 20 |

**1982.** Air. 9th National Stamp Exhibition. Nos. 1005/8 surch. and optd. **IX EXPOSICION FILATELICA—1982.**

| No. | Type | Description | | |
|---|---|---|---|---|
| 1287. | **271.** | 8 col. 40 on 2 col. 20 orange and black .. | 35 | 35 |
| 1288. | – | 8 col. 40 on 2 col. 20 green and black .. | 35 | 35 |
| 1289. | – | 8 col. 40 on 2 col. 20 red and black .. | 35 | 35 |
| 1290. | – | 8 col. 40 on 2 col. 20 blue and black .. | 35 | 35 |
| 1291. | **271.** | 9 col. 70 on 2 col. 20 orange and black .. | 45 | 45 |
| 1292. | – | 9 col. 70 on 2 col. 20 green and black .. | 45 | 45 |
| 1293. | – | 9 col. 70 on 2 col. 20 red and black .. | 45 | 45 |
| 1294. | – | 9 col. 70 on 2 col. 20 blue and black .. | 45 | 45 |

355. Dr Robert Koch and Cross of Lorraine.

356. Student at Lathe.

**1982.** Air. Centenary of Discovery of Tubercle Bacillus.

| No. | Type | Description | | |
|---|---|---|---|---|
| 1295. | – | 1 col. 50 red and black .. | 15 | 10 |
| 1296. | **355.** | 3 col. grey and black | 25 | 15 |
| 1297. | – | 3 col. 30 mult. .. | 30 | 15 |

DESIGNS: 1 col. 50 Koch and anti-T.B. Campaign emblem. 3 col. 30 Koch and Ministry of Public Health Building, San Jose.

**1982.** Obligatory Tax. Christmas. Children's Village.

| No. | Type | Description | | |
|---|---|---|---|---|
| 1298. | **356.** | 10 c. red .. .. | 10 | 10 |
| 1299. | | 10 c. grey .. .. | 10 | 10 |
| 1300. | | 10 c. violet .. .. | 10 | 10 |
| 1301. | | 10 c. blue .. .. | 10 | 10 |

357. Blood Donors Association Emblem.

358. Migration Committee Emblem.

**1982.** Air. 7th Pan-American Blood Donors Congress. Multicoloured.

| No. | Type | Description | | |
|---|---|---|---|---|
| 1302. | **357.** | 30 col. multicoloured | 90 | 75 |
| 1303. | – | 50 col. red, bl. & blk. | 1·50 | 75 |

DESIGN: 50 col. Congress emblem.

**1982.** Air. 30th Anniv. of Intergovernmental Migration Committee.

| No. | Type | Description | | |
|---|---|---|---|---|
| 1304. | **358.** | 8 col. 40 lt. blue, blue and black .. .. | 35 | 20 |
| 1305. | – | 9 col. 70 blue & black | 45 | 20 |
| 1306. | – | 11 col. 70 mult. .. | 55 | 25 |
| 1307. | – | 13 col. 05 blue, black and grey .. | 55 | 30 |

DESIGNS—HORIZ. 11 col. 70 Emblem and handshake. 13 col. 05 Emblem within double-headed arrow. VERT. 9 col. 70 Emblem.

359. "St. Francis" (El Greco).

360. Pope John Paul II.

**1983.** Air. 800th Birth Anniv. (1982) of St. Francis of Assisi.

| No. | Type | Description | | |
|---|---|---|---|---|
| 1308. | **359.** | 4 col. 80 brn, blk & bl. | 20 | 10 |
| 1309. | – | 7 col. 40 brn, blk. & grey | 30 | 10 |

DESIGN: 7 col. 40 Portrait of Francis by unknown artist.

**1983.** Air. Papal Visit.

| No. | Type | Description | | |
|---|---|---|---|---|
| 1310. | **360.** | 5 col. brn., yell. & bl. | 25 | 10 |
| 1311. | | 10 col. brn., grn. & bl. | 50 | 20 |
| 1312. | | 15 col. brn., mve. & bl. | 1·00 | 30 |

361. W.C.Y. Emblem.

362. Egg.

**1983.** World Communications Year.

| No. | Type | Description | | |
|---|---|---|---|---|
| 1313. | **361.** | 10 c. multicoloured .. | 10 | 10 |
| 1314. | | 50 c. multicoloured .. | 10 | 10 |
| 1315. | | 10 col. multicoloured | 50 | 20 |

**1983.** First World Conference on Human Rights, Alajuela (1982).

| No. | Type | Description | | |
|---|---|---|---|---|
| 1316. | **362.** | 20 col. grey & black .. | 1·00 | 40 |

363. U.P.U. Monument, Berne, and 1883 2 c. Stamp.

**1983.** Centenary of U.P.U. Membership.

| No. | Type | Description | | |
|---|---|---|---|---|
| 1317. | **363.** | 3 col. yell., red & blk. | 45 | 10 |
| 1318. | – | 10 col. yell., bl. & blk. | 90 | 20 |

DESIGN: 10 col. Central Post Office, San Jose, and 1883 40 c. stamp.

364. "Alliance Building, San Jose" (Cristina Fournier).

365. Bolivar (after Francisco Zuniga).

**1983.** Centenary of French Alliance (French language-teaching association).

| No. | Type | Description | | |
|---|---|---|---|---|
| 1319. | **364.** | 12 col. multicoloured | 55 | 25 |

**1983.** Air. Birth Bicent. of Simon Bolivar.

| No. | Type | Description | | |
|---|---|---|---|---|
| 1320. | **365.** | 10 col. multicoloured | 50 | 20 |

**1983.** Nos. 1308/9 surch.

| No. | Description | | |
|---|---|---|---|
| 1321. | 10 c. on 4 col. 80 brown, black and blue .. | 10 | 10 |
| 1321a. | 50 c. on 4 col. 80 brown, black and blue .. | 10 | 10 |
| 1322. | 1 col. 50 on 7 col. 40 brn., black and grey .. | 15 | 10 |
| 1323. | 3 col. on 7 col. 40 brown, black and grey .. | 20 | 10 |

367. Repairing Wheelchair.

368. Three Kings.

**1983.** Obligatory Tax. Christmas. Children's Village.

| No. | Type | Description | | |
|---|---|---|---|---|
| 1324. | **367.** | 10 c. red .. .. | 10 | 10 |
| 1325. | | 10 c. orange .. .. | 10 | 10 |
| 1326. | | 10 c. blue .. .. | 10 | 10 |
| 1327. | | 10 c. green .. .. | 10 | 10 |

**1983.** Christmas. Multicoloured.

| No. | Description | | |
|---|---|---|---|
| 1328. | 1 col. 50 Type **368** .. | 15 | 10 |
| 1329. | 1 col. 50 Holy Family and Shepherds .. .. | 15 | 10 |
| 1330. | 1 col. 50 People bearing gifts | 15 | 10 |

Nos. 1328/30 were printed together, se-tenant, forming a composite design.

369. Fisherman.

370. Resplendent Quetzal.

**1983.** Fisheries Development.

| No. | Type | Description | | |
|---|---|---|---|---|
| 1331. | **369.** | 8 col. 50 mult. .. | 40 | 15 |

**1984.** Birds. Multicoloured.

| No. | Description | | |
|---|---|---|---|
| 1332. | 10 c. Type **370** .. .. | 25 | 15 |
| 1333. | 50 c. Red-legged Honey-creeper (horiz.) .. | 25 | 20 |
| 1334. | 1 col. Clay-coloured Thrush (horiz.) .. .. .. | 50 | 25 |
| 1335. | 1 col. 50 Blue-crowned Motmot .. .. | 60 | 25 |
| 1336. | 3 col. Green Violetear .. | 95 | 35 |
| 1337. | 10 col. Blue and White Swallow (horiz.) .. | 2·40 | 55 |

371. Jose Joaquin Mora.

**1984.** 1856 Campaign Heroes. Multicoloured.

| No. | Description | | |
|---|---|---|---|
| 1339. | 50 c. Type **371** .. .. | 10 | 10 |
| 1340. | 1 col. 50 Pancha Carrasco | 10 | 10 |
| 1341. | 3 col. Juan Santamaria (horiz.) .. .. .. | 10 | 10 |
| 1342. | 8 col. 50 Juan Rafael Mora Porras .. .. .. | 35 | 30 |

372. Jesus Bonilla Chavarria.

373. Necklace Bead.

**1984.** Musicians.

| No. | Type | Description | | |
|---|---|---|---|---|
| 1343. | **372.** | 3 col 50 vio. & blk... | 15 | 10 |
| 1344. | – | 5 col red and black .. | 20 | 15 |
| 1345. | – | 12 col. green & blk. | 15 | 10 |
| 1346. | – | 13 col. yellow & blk. | 20 | 10 |

DESIGNS: 5 col. Benjamin Gutierrez. 12 col. Pilar Jimenez. 13 col. Jose Daniel Zuniga.

**1984.** Jade Museum Artifacts. Multicoloured.

| No. | Description | | |
|---|---|---|---|
| 1347. | 4 col. Type **373** .. .. | 15 | 10 |
| 1348. | 7 col. Seated figure .. | 25 | 20 |
| 1349. | 10 col. Ceramic dish (horiz.) .. .. .. | 35 | 30 |

374. Basketball Players.

375. Street Scene.

**1984.** Olympic Games, Los Angeles. Mult.

| No. | Description | | |
|---|---|---|---|
| 1350. | 1 col. Type **374** .. .. | 10 | 10 |
| 1351. | 8 col. Swimming .. .. | 10 | 10 |
| 1352. | 11 col. Cycling .. .. | 15 | 10 |
| 1353. | 14 col. Running .. .. | 20 | 10 |
| 1354. | 20 col. Boxing .. .. | 25 | 10 |
| 1355. | 30 col. Football .. .. | 35 | 10 |

**1984.** Cent. of Public Street Lighting.

| No. | Type | Description | | |
|---|---|---|---|---|
| 1356. | **375.** | 6 col. multicoloured | 20 | 15 |

**376.** Emblem and National Independence Monument.

**1984.** 10th National Philatelic Exhibition. Multicoloured.

1357. 10 col. Type **376** .. 35 30
1358. 10 col. Emblem and Juan Mora Fernandez statue 35 30

**377.** National Coat of Arms.

**378.** Child on Tricycle

**1984.**

1360. **377.** 100 col. blue .. .. 2·40 1·90
1361. 100 col. yellow .. 2·40 1·90

**1984.** Obligatory Tax. Christmas. Children's Village.

1362. **378.** 10 c. violet .. .. 10 10

**379.** "Sistine Virgin" (detail, Raphael).

**380.** Cyclists.

**1984.** Christmas. Multicoloured.

1363. 3 col. Type **379** .. .. 10 10
1364. 3 col. "Sistine Virgin" (detail) (different) .. 10 10

**1984.** 20th Costa Rica Cycle Race.

1365. **380.** 6 col. multicoloured 15 15

**381.** Emblem and 1968 Scouting Jubilee Stamp

**1985.** International Youth Year.

1366. **381.** 11 col. multicoloured 25 20

**382.** Workers' Monument (Francisco Zuniga)

**383.** U.N. Emblem and 1935 Red Cross Jubilee Stamp

**1985.** "National Values".

1367. **382.** 6 col. mve. and blk. 15 15
1368. – 11 col. yellow, black and blue .. 25 20
1369. – 13 col. multicoloured 35 30
1370. – 30 col. multicoloured 70 70

DESIGNS—As T **382.** 11 col. First printing press (Freedom of speech). 13 col. Dove, flag and globe (Neutrality). 65 × 35 mm—30 col. Nos. 1367/9.

**1985.** Cent. of Costa Rican Red Cross.

1371. **383.** 3 col. red, brown and black .. .. 10 10
1372. – 5 col. black, red and grey .. .. 15 10

DESIGN: 5 col. U.N. Emblem and 1946 Red Cross Society stamp.

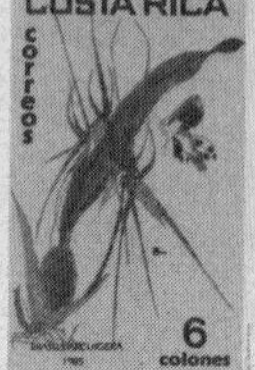


**384.** Hands holding "S".

**385.** "Brassia arcuigera".

**1985.** 50th Anniv. of Saprissa Football Club.

1373. **384.** 3 col. mauve & grn. 10 10
1374. – 3 col. black & mve. 10 10
1375. – 6 col. mauve, brown and green .. .. 15 15

DESIGNS: As T **384**—Hands holding football. 34 × 26 mm—6 col. Ricardo Saprissa and Saprissa Stadium.

**1985.** Orchids. Multicoloured.

1376. 6 col. Type **385** .. .. 10 10
1377. 6 col. "Encyclia peraltensis" .. .. 10 10
1378. 6 col. "Maxillaria especie" .. .. 10 10
1379. 13 col. "Oncidium turialbae" .. .. 30 25
1380. 13 col. "Trichopilia marginata" .. .. 30 25
1381. 13 col. "Stanhopea ecornuta" .. .. 30 25

**386.** 1940 25 c. Stamp and Hand holding Tweezers.

**387.** Hands reaching out to Child.

**1985.** 11th National Stamp Exhibition.

1382. **386.** 20 col. blue, ultramarine and pink .. 50 45

**1985.** Obligatory Tax. Christmas. Children's Village.

1383. **387.** 10 c. brown .. .. 10 10

**388.** Children looking at Star.

**1985.** Christmas.

1384. **388.** 3 col. multicoloured 10 10

**390.** Costa Rica Lyceum.

**391.** Land and Cattle College Project.

**1986.** Centenary of Free Compulsory Education.

1390 **390** 3 col. brown and light brown .. 10 10
1391 30 col. brn. & pink 60 20

DESIGN: 30 col. Mauro Fernandez Acuna (education Minister).

**1986.** 27th Annual Inter-American Development Bank Assembly, San Jose. Multicoloured.

1392. 10 col. Type **391** .. 20 15
1393. 10 col. Bank emblem .. 20 15
1394. 10 col. Cape Blanco fisherman .. .. 20 15

**392.** Francisco J. Orlich Bolmarcich.

**393.** Pique (mascot).

**1986.** Former Presidents of Costa Rica.

1395. **392.** 3 col. green .. .. 10 10
1396. – 3 col. green .. .. 10 10
1397. – 3 col. green .. .. 10 10
1398. – 3 col. green .. .. 10 10
1399. – 3 col. green .. .. 10 10
1400. – 6 col. brown .. .. 15 10
1401. – 6 col. brown .. .. 15 10
1402. – 6 col. brown .. .. 15 10
1403. – 6 col. brown .. .. 15 10
1404. – 6 col. brown .. .. 15 10
1405. – 10 col. orange .. 20 15
1406. – 10 col. orange .. 20 15
1407. – 10 col. orange .. 20 15
1408. – 10 col. orange .. 20 15
1409. – 10 col. orange .. 20 15
1410. – 11 col. grey .. .. 20 15
1411. – 11 col. grey .. .. 20 15
1412. – 11 col. grey .. .. 20 15
1413. – 11 col. grey .. .. 20 15
1414. – 11 col. grey .. .. 20 15
1415. – 13 col. brown .. 25 20
1416. – 13 col. brown .. 25 20
1417. – 13 col. brown .. 25 20
1418. – 13 col. brown .. 25 20
1419. – 13 col. brown .. 25 20

DESIGNS: Nos. 1395, 1400, 1405, 1410, 1415, Type **392.** 1396, 1401, 1406, 1411, 1416, Jose Joaquin Trejos Fernandez. 1397, 1402, 1407, 1412, 1417, Daniel Oduber Quiros. 1398, 1403, 1408, 1413, 1418, Rodrigo Carazo Odio. 1399, 1404, 1409, 1414, 1419, Luis Alberto Monge Alvarez.

**1986.** World Cup Football Championship, Mexico.

1420. **393.** 1 col. multicoloured 10 10
1421. – 1 col. multicoloured 10 10
1422. – 4 col. multicoloured 10 10
1423. – 6 col. purple, brown and black .. .. 15 10
1424. – 11 col. purple, red and black .. .. 20 15

DESIGNS:—VERT. No. 1420, 1422, Type **393.** HORIZ. No. 1421, 1423, Footballs and players. 1424, Footballs and players (different).

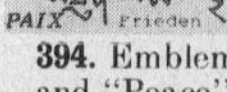

**394.** Emblem and "Peace".

**395.** Gold Artefact.

**1986.** International Peace Year. Each bearing the Year emblem and "Peace" in various languages (first language given in brackets).

1425. **394.** 5 col. blue and brown (Hoa Binh) .. 10 10
1426. – 5 col. blue and brown (Vrede) .. .. 10 10
1427. – 5 col. blue and brown (Pace) .. .. 10 10

**1986.** Exhibits in Gold Museum. Mult.

1428. 6 col. Type **395** .. .. 15 10
1429. 6 col. Figure with three-lobed base .. .. 15 10
1430. 6 col. Frog .. .. 15 10
1431. 6 col. Centipede .. .. 15 10
1432. 6 col. Two monkeys in sun .. .. .. 15 10
1433. 13 col. Figure with dragon-head arms .. 25 10
1434. 13 col. Two monkeys .. 25 10
1435. 13 col. Animal-shaped figure .. .. .. 25 10
1436. 13 col. Sun with ball pendant .. .. 25 10
1437. 13 col. Figure within frame .. .. .. 25 10

**396.** Child.

**397.** Fork-lift Truck and Airplane (Osvaldo Andres Gonzalez Vega).

**1986.** Obligatory Tax. Christmas. Children's Village.

1438. **396.** 10 c. brown .. .. 10 10

**1986.** Air. 40th Anniv. of LACSA (national airline). Children's Drawings. Multicoloured.

1439. 1 col. Airplane flying over house and van (Adriana Elias Hidalgo) .. .. 10 10
1440. 7 col. Type **397** .. .. 15 15
1441. 16 col. Airplane, letters and photographs (David Valverde Rodiguez) .. .. 30 25

**398.** Lattice-winged Bat.

**399.** Extracting Snake's Venom (detail of mural, Francisco Amighetti).

**1986.** Flora and Fauna. Bats and Frogs. Multicoloured.

1442. 2 col. Type **398** .. .. 10 10
1443. 3 col. Common long-tongued bat .. .. 10 10
1444. 4 col. White bat .. .. 10 10
1445. 5 col. Group of white bats .. .. 10 10
1446. 6 col. "Agalychnis callidryas" (frog) .. .. 15 10
1447. 10 col. "Dendrobates pumilio" (frog) .. 20 15
1448. 11 col. "Hyla ebraccata" (frog) .. .. 20 15
1449. 20 col. "Phyllobates lugubris" (frog) .. 40 35

**1987.** National Science and Technology Day.

1451. **399.** 8 col. multicoloured 20 15

**400.** Statuette.

**401.** Arms of San Jose Province.

**1987.** Centenary of National Museum. Pre-Colombian Art. Multicoloured.

1452. 8 col. Type **400** .. .. 20 15
1453. 8 col. Jug in form of human figure .. .. 20 15
1454. 8 col. Vase in form of human figure .. .. 20 15
1455. 8 col. Stone jar .. .. 20 15
1456. 8 col. Pot with human-type legs and arms .. 20 15
1457. 15 col. Bowl (horiz.) .. 30 25
1458. 15 col. Carving of animal defeating human (horiz.) .. .. 30 25
1459. 15 col. Flask (horiz.) .. 30 25

**1987.** 250th Anniv. of San Jose.

1460. **401.** 20 col. multicoloured 30 25
1461. – 20 col. red, black and blue .. .. 30 25
1462. – 20 col. red, black and blue .. .. 30 25

DESIGNS: Nos. 1461, Donkey cart in cobbled street. 1462, View down street.

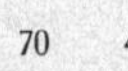

**402.** 16th-century Map of Audiencia, Guatemala.

**1987.** Columbus Day.
1463. **402.** 30 col. brown and yellow .. .. 70 40

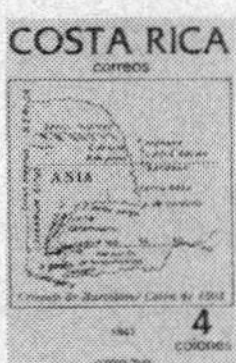

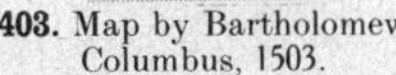

**403.** Map by Bartholomew Columbus, 1503. **404.** Cross and Doves.

**1987.** 500th Anniv (1992) of Discovery of America by Columbus (1st issue). Each brown and yellow.
1464. 4 col. Type **403** .. .. 10 10
1465. 4 col. 16th-century map of Costa Rica .. .. 10 10
See also Nos. 1480, 1496, 1521 and 1538/40.

**1987.** Obligatory Tax. Christmas. Children's Village.
1466. **404.** 10 c. blue and brown 10 10

**405.** "Village Scene" (Fausto Pacheco). **406.** Pres. Arias and National Flag.

**1987.** International Year of Shelter for the Homeless.
1467. **405.** 1 col. multicoloured 10 10

**1987.** Award of Nobel Peace Prize to Pres. Oscar Arias Sanchez.
1468. **406.** 10 col. multicoloured 15 15

**407.** Green Turtle. **408.** Anniversary Emblem.

**1988.** 17th Annual General Assembly of International Union for Nature Conservation. Multicoloured.
1469 5 col. Type **407** .. .. 10 10
1470 5 col. Golden toad on leaf 10 10
1471 5 col. Emperor (butterfly) 15 10

**1988.** 125th Anniv. of Red Cross.
1472. **408.** 30 col. red and blue 45 40

**409.** Man with Pen and Radio (Adult Education). **410.** Symbols of Bank Activities.

**1988.** Costa Rica–Liechtenstein Cultural Co-operation.
1473 **409** 18 col. red, brn & grn 30 25
1474 – 20 col. multicoloured 30 25
DESIGN: 20 col. Headphones on books (radio broadcasts).

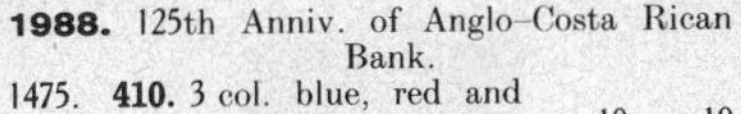

**1988.** 125th Anniv. of Anglo–Costa Rican Bank.
1475. **410.** 3 col. blue, red and yellow .. .. 10 10

**411.** Games Emblem. **412.** Roman Macava and Curtiss Robin.

**1988.** Olympic Games, Seoul. Multicoloured.
1476. 25 col. Type **411** .. 40 35
1477. 25 col. Games mascot .. 40 35

**1988.** Airmail Pioneers.
1478. **412.** 10 col. multicoloured 25 15

**413** School Courtyard **414** Amerindian Necklace

**1988.** Centenary of Girls' High School.
1479 **413** 10 col. brown & yell 15 10

**1988.** 500th Anniv (1992) of Discovery of America by Columbus (2nd issue).
1480 **414** 4 col. multicoloured .. 10 10

**415** Dengo and College **416** Former Observation Tower

**1988.** Birth Centenary of Omar Dengo (Director of Heredia Teachers' College).
1481 **415** 10 col. brn, grey & bl 15 10

**1988.** Centenary of National Meteorological Institute.
1482 **416** 2 col. multicoloured .. 10 10

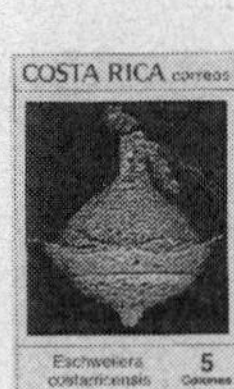

**417** "Eschweilera costarricensis" **418** Map of France and Costa Rican National Monument

**1989.** Flowers. Multicoloured.
1483 5 col. Type **417** .. .. 10 10
1484 10 col. "Heliconia wagneriana" .. .. .. 15 10
1485 15 col. "Heliconia lophocarpa" .. .. 20 15
1486 20 col. "Aechmea magdalenae" .. .. 30 25
1487 25 col. "Psammisia ramiflora" .. .. 35 30
1488 30 col. Passion flower .. 45 40

**1989.** Bicentenary of French Revolution.
1489 **418** 30 col. blk, bl & red 45 40

**MORE DETAILED LISTS**
are given in the Stanley Gibbons Catalogues referred to in the country headings.
For lists of current volumes see Introduction.

**419** Sugar Mill **420** Corn Grinder

**1989.** 151st Anniv of Grecia County.
1490 **419** 10 col. multicoloured 15 10

**1989.** America. Pre-Columbian Artefacts. Multicoloured.
1491 50 col. Type **420** .. 75 20
1492 100 col. Granite sphere, 1500 A.D. .. .. 1·50 40

**422** Orchid **423** Dr. Henri Pittier (first Director)

**1989.** "100 Years of Democracy" Presidents' Summit.
1493 **422** 10 col. multicoloured 15 10

**1989.** Centenary of National Geographical Institute.
1494 **423** 18 col. multicoloured 20 15

**424** Teacher and Children **425** Pre-Columbian Gold Frog and Spanish Coin

**1989.** Obligatory Tax. Christmas. Children's Village.
1495 **424** 1 col. blue, green & blk 10 10

**1989.** 500th Anniv (1992) of Discovery of America by Columbus (3rd issue).
1496 **425** 4 col. multicoloured .. 10 10

**426** "Exporting Coffee" (painting in theatre by Jose Villa) **427** Football in Cube

**1990.** Centenary of National Theatre.
1497 **426** 5 col. multicoloured .. 10 10

**1990.** World Cup Football Championship, Italy.
1498 **427** 5 col. multicoloured .. 10 10

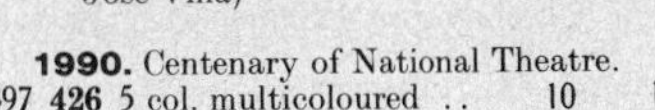

**428** "50 U"

**1990.** 50th Anniv of University of Costa Rica.
1499 **428** 18 col. multicoloured 15 10

**429** "Education Democracy Peace" **431** Painting by Juan Ramirez

**1990.** Patriotic Symbols.
1500 **429** 100 col. blue and black 90 30
1501 – 200 col. multicoloured 1·90 65
1502 – 500 col. multicoloured 4·75 1·60
DESIGNS: 200 col. Map of Costa Rica in national colours; 500 col. State arms.

**1991.** Air. No. 1491 optd **LEY 7097 CORREO AEREO**.
1503 **420** 50 col. multicoloured 45 15

**1990.** Costa Rican Coffee.
1504 **431** 50 col. multicoloured 45 15

**432** Penny Black **433** Heredia Hospital

**1990.** 150th Anniv of the Penny Black.
1505 **432** 50 col. black and blue 45 15

**1990.** Hospital Centenaries.
1506 **433** 50 col. bl, orge & grn 45 15
1507 – 100 col. orge, bl & grn 90 30
DESIGN: 100 col. National Psychiatric Hospital.

**434** Yellow-bark Tree ("Tabebuia ochracea") **436** "Banana Picker" (Alleardo Villa, Ceiling of Grand Staircase)

**1990.** America. The Natural World. Mult.
1508 18 col. Scarlet macaw ("Ara macao") .. 15 10
1509 18 col. Buffon's macaw ("Ara ambigua") .. 15 10
1510 24 col. Carao tree ("Cassia grandis") .. .. 20 10
1511 24 col. Type **434** .. 20 10

**1990.** Obligatory Tax. Children's Village. No. 1490 optd **LEY 7157 PRO-CIUDAD DE LOS NINOS 1990**.
1512 **419** 10 col. multicoloured 10 10

**1991.** Air. Paintings in National Theatre.
1516 **436** 30 col. multicoloured 30 10

**437** Costa Rica and Panama Flags and Seals **439** Route of First Voyage on Stone Globe

**1991.** 50th Anniv of Costa Rica–Panama Boundary Treaty.
1517 **437** 10 col. multicoloured 10 10
1518 – 10 col. black and blue 10 10
1519 – 10 col. blue, brn & blk 10 10
DESIGNS: No. 1518, Presidents meeting; 1519, Map.

**1991.** Air. "Exfilcori '91" National Stamp Exhibition. No. 1501 optd **Aereo EXFILCORI '91**.
1520 200 col. multicoloured .. 1·75 60

**1991.** 500th Anniv (1992) of Discovery of America by Columbus (4th issue).
1521 **439** 4 col. red, black & blue 10 10

**1991.** Air. Centenary of Basketball. No. 1474 optd **CENTENARIO DEL BALONCESTO CORREO AEREO.**
1522 20 col. multicoloured .. 20 10

**1991.** Nos. 1482 and 1342 surch.
1523 **416** 1 col. on 2 col. mult .. 10 10
1524 – 3 col. on 8 col. 50 mult 10 10

**443** Dr. Rafael Angel Calderon Guardia Hospital

**444** Child praying

**1991.** Air. 50th Anniv of Social Security Administration.
1525 **443** 15 col. multicoloured 15 10

**1991.** Obligatory Tax. Christmas. Children's Village.
1526 **444** 10 col. blue .. .. 10 10

**445** "La Poesia" (Vespaciano Bignami)

**446** Benito Serrano Jimenez

**1992.** Air. Paintings in National Theatre.
1527 **445** 35 col. multicoloured 30 10

**1992.** Former Presidents of Supreme Court of Justice. Multicoloured.
1528 5 col. Type **446** .. .. 10 10
1529 5 col. Luis Davila Solera 10 10
1530 5 col. Fernando Baudrit Solera .. .. .. 10 10
1531 5 col. Alejandro Alvarado Garcia .. .. 10 10

**447** Oxcart

**448** Dr. Solon Nunez Frutos (public health pioneer)

**1992.** 25th Anniv of National Directorate of Community Development.
1532 **447** 15 col. multicoloured 15 10

**1992.**
1533 **448** 15 col. black and red 15 10

**449** Total Solar Eclipse

**450** Crops

**1992.** International Space Year. Mult.
1534 45 col. Type **449** .. 40 15
1535 45 col. Post office building and total eclipse .. 40 15
1536 45 col. Partial eclipse .. 40 15

**1992.** 50th Anniv of Inter-American Institute for Agricultural Co-operation.
1537 **450** 35 col. multicoloured 30 10

**451** "Nina" **452** Waterfall

**1992.** Air. 500th Anniv of Discovery of America by Columbus (5th issue). Mult.
1538 45 col. Type **451** .. 40 15
1539 45 col. "Santa Maria" .. 40 15
1540 45 col. "Pinta" .. .. 40 15

**1992.** 450th Anniv of Discovery of Coco Island. Multicoloured.
1541 2 col. Type **452** .. .. 10 10
1542 15 col. View of cliffs from sea .. .. .. 15 10

**453** Drilling

**454** American Chameleon

**1992.** Obligatory Tax. Christmas. Children's Village.
1543 **453** 10 col. red .. .. 10 10

**1992.** America. Coco Island Fauna. Mult.
1544 15 col. Type **454** .. 15 10
1545 35 col. Cocos finch .. 30 10

**1992.** Centenary of Limon. No. 1500 optd **CENTENARIO DE LIMON.**
1546 **429** 100 col. blue and black 90 30

**456** "Allegory of the Fine Arts" (detail, R. Fontana)

**457** Emblem

**1993.** Paintings in National Theatre.
1547 **456** 20 col. multicoloured 20 10

**1993.** Air. International Arts Festival.
1548 **457** 45 col. multicoloured 40 15

**1993.** No. 1494 surch.
1549 **423** 5 col. on 18 col. mult 10 10

**459** Common Dolphin

**460** Emblem

**1993.** Dolphins. Multicoloured.
1550 10 col. Type **459** .. 10 10
1551 20 col. Striped dolphins .. 20 10

**1993.** 40th Anniv of Civil Service Statute.
1552 **460** 5 col. multicoloured .. 10 10

**461** Anniversary Emblem

**462** Communication Zone

**1993.** 50th Anniv of Chamber of Industry.
1553 **461** 45 col. multicoloured 35 15

**1993.** 25th Anniv of University of Costa Rica School of Communication and Sciences.
1554 **462** 20 col. black, red & bl 15 10

**463** "Passiflora vitifolia"

**1993.** Tropical Rainforest Flora. Mult.
1555 2 col. Type **463** .. .. 10 10
1556 35 col. "Gurania megistantha" .. .. 25 10

**464** Campaigners

**465** Association Emblem

**1993.** 50th Anniv of Guaranteed Social Rights.
1557 **464** 20 col. multicoloured 15 10

**1993.** 15th International Customs Officers' Associations Congress.
1558 **465** 45 col. multicoloured 35 15

**466** Carpentry

**467** Dish Aerial

**1993.** Obligatory Tax. Christmas. Children's Village.
1559 **466** 10 col. multicoloured 10 10

**1993.** Air. 30th Anniv of Costa Rican Electrical Institute's Responsibility for Development of Telecommunications.
1560 **467** 45 col. multicoloured 35 15

**468** Prof. Castro

**469** Assembly Hall

**1993.** Birth Centenary of Miguel Angel Castro Carazo (founder of Commercial School).
1561 **468** 20 col. red and blue .. 15 10

**1993.** 150th Anniv of Costa Rica University Faculty of Law.
1562 **469** 20 col. multicoloured 15 10

**470** "The Dancer" (Adriatico Froli)

**471** Mural (Luis Feron)

**1994.** National Theatre.
1563 **470** 20 col. multicoloured 15 10

**1994.** Air. 150th Anniv of Ministry of Government and Police.
1564 **471** 45 col. multicoloured 35 15

**472** Flamingo Tongue

**473** Hands forming Shelter

**1994.** Marine Animals. Multicoloured.
1565 5 col. Type **472** .. .. 10 10
1566 10 col. "Ophioderma rubicundum" .. .. 10 10
1567 15 col. Blackbar soldier-fish .. .. .. 10 10
1568 20 col. "Holocanthus passer" .. .. 15 10
1569 35 col. Creole fish .. 25 10
1570 45 col. "Tubastraea coccinea" .. .. 35 15
1571 50 col. "Acanthaster planci" .. .. 40 15
1572 55 col. "Ocypode sp." .. 45 15
1573 70 col. Speckled balloon-fish .. .. .. 55 20

**1994.** Air. International Year of the Family.
1575 **473** 45 col. multicoloured 35 15

**474** Child

**1994.** Obligatory Tax. Christmas. Children's Village.
1576 **474** 11 col. green and lilac 10 10

**475** Courier

**1994.** America. Postal Transport. Details of an illustration from "Album de Figueroa". Each orange, light orange and blue.
1577 20 col. Type **475** .. 15 10
1578 20 col. Rear of pack ox .. 15 10
Nos. 1577/8 were issued together in se-tenant pairs with intervening label, each strip forming a composite design.

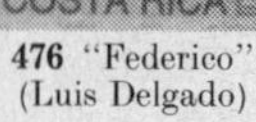

**476** "Federico" (Luis Delgado)

**477** Antonio Jose de Sucre (President of Bolivia, 1826–28)

**1995.** 90th Anniv of Rotary International.
1579 **476** 20 col. multicoloured 15 10

**1995.** Anniversaries. Multicoloured.
1580 10 col. Type **477** (birth bicentenary) .. .. 15 10
1581 30 col. Jose Marti (poet and Cuban revolutionary) (death centenary) 20 10

478 "Rider" (sculpture, Nestor Varela)

480 "The Boy and the Cloud" (Francisco Amighetti)

**1995.** 50th Anniv of Guanacaste Institute.
1582 **478** 50 col. grn, blk & gold 35 15

**1995.** No. 1561 surch **5**.
1583 **468** 5 col. on 20 col. red and blue .. .. 10 10

**1995.** 50th Anniv of U.N.O.
1584 **480** 5 col. multicoloured .. 10 10

481 Woman holding Baby

482 "January"

**1995.** Obligatory Tax. Christmas. Children's Village.
1585 **481** 12 col. multicoloured 10 10

**1995.** 13th National Stamp Exn. Seasonal paintings by Lola Fernandez. Mult.
1587 50 col. Type **482** .. 35 15
1588 50 col. "November" .. 35 15

483 Jabiru

**1995.** America. Environmental Protection. Multicoloured. Rouletted.
1589 30 col. Type **483** .. 20 10
1590 40 col. Coastline .. .. 25 10
1591 40 col. Woodland and lake 25 10
1592 50 col. Leaf-cutting ant .. 35 15

484 Steam Locomotive

**1996.** Postcards from Limon. Multicoloured.
1594 30 col. Type **484** .. 15 10
1595 30 col. Freighter at quay 15 10
1596 30 col. View of Port Moin 15 10
1597 30 col. "Fruitsellers" (Diego Villalobos) .. 15 10
1598 30 col. "Calypso" (Jorge Esquivel) .. .. 15 10

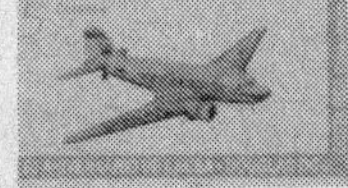
485 Douglas DC-3

**1996.** Air. 50th Anniv of LACSA (national airline). Multicoloured.
1599 5 col. Type **485** .. .. 10 10
1600 10 col. Curtiss C-46 Commando .. .. 10 10
1601 20 col. Beechcraft .. 10 10
1602 30 col. Douglas DC-6B .. 15 10
1603 35 col. B.A.C. One Eleven 20 10
1604 40 col. Convair CV 440 Metropolitan .. .. 25 10
1605 45 col. Lockheed L.188 Electra .. .. 25 10
1606 50 col. Boeing 727-200 .. 30 10
1607 55 col. Douglas DC-8 .. 30 10
1608 60 col. Airbus Industrie A320 .. .. .. 35 15

486 Mosque, Synagogue and Christian Church

**1996.** 3000th Anniv of Jerusalem.
1609 **486** 30 col. multicoloured 15 10

487 Maria del Milagro Paris and Francisco Rivas

**1996.** Olympic Games, Atlanta. Costa Rican Swimmers. Multicoloured.
1610 5 col. Type **487** .. .. 10 10
1611 5 col. Sylvia Poll and Federico Yglesias .. 10 10
1612 5 col. Claudia Poll and Alfredo Cruz .. .. 10 10
Nos. 1610/12 were issued together, se-tenant, forming a composite design of a swimming pool.

EXPRESS DELIVERY STAMPS

E 237. New U.P.U. Headquarters Building and Emblem.

**1970.** Air. New U.P.U. Headquarters Building.
E841 **E 237** 35 c. multicoloured 15 10
E842 60 c. multicoloured 20 10
In Type **E 237** "**ENTREGA INMEDIATA**" is in the form of a perforated tab.
No. E842 has the same main design, but the tab is inscr "**EXPRES**".

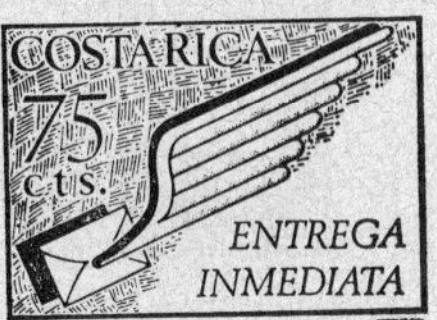
E 249. Winged Letter.

**1972.**
E 888. **E 249.** 75 c. brn. & red .. 15 15
E 889. 75 c. grn. & red .. 15 15
E 890. 75 c. mve. & red .. 15 15
E 891. 1 col. 50 bl. & red 45 25

E 279. Concorde.

**1976.**
E 1031. **E 279.** 1 col. mult. .. 25 15
E 1135. – 2 col. red, black, buff & mve. .. 50 30
E 1136. – 2 col. red, black, bl. & lt. bl. .. 50 30
E 1137. – 4 col. mult. .. 55 25
Nos. E 1135/7 is as Type **E 279**, but inscribed "**EXPRESS**".

OFFICIAL STAMPS

Various issues optd. **OFICIAL** except where otherwise stated.

**1883.** Stamps of 1883.
O 35. **8.** 1 c. green .. .. 45 45
O 36. 2 c. red .. .. 40 40
O 22. 5 c. violet .. .. 2·75 2·75
O 37. 10 c. orange .. .. 3·50 3·50
O 38. 40 c. blue .. .. 2·50 2·10

**1887.** Stamps of 1887.
O 39. **14.** 5 c. violet .. .. 1·60 1·60
O 40. 10 c. orange .. .. 40 40

**1889.** Stamps of 1889.
O 41. **17.** 1 c. brown .. .. 25 20
O 42. 2 c. blue .. .. 25 20
O 43. 5 c. orange .. .. 25 20
O 44. 10 c. lake .. .. 25 20
O 45. 20 c. green .. .. 25 20
O 46. 50 c. red .. .. 60 60

**1892.** Stamps of 1892.
O 47. **19.** 1 c. blue .. .. 25 20
O 48. 2 c. orange .. .. 25 20
O 49. 5 c. mauve .. .. 25 20
O 50. 10 c. green .. .. 60 60
O 51. 20 c. red .. .. 25 20
O 52. 50 c. blue .. .. 60 50

**1901.** Stamps of 1901 (Nos. 42/48).
O 53. 1 c. black and green .. 35 35
O 54. 2 c. black and red .. 35 35
O 61. 4 c. black and purple .. 1·25 1·25
O 55. 5 c. black and blue .. 35 35
O 62. 6 c. black and olive .. 1·25 1·25
O 56. 10 c. black and brown .. 60 60
O 57. 20 black and lake .. 80 80
O 63. 25 c. brown and lilac .. 5·25 3·25
O 58. 50 c. blue and red .. 1·75 1·75
O 59. 1 col. black and olive .. 32·00 22·00

**1903.** Stamp of 1901 optd. **PROVISORIO OFICIAL.**
O 60. – 2 c. blk. & red (No. 43) 2·00 2·00

**1908.** Stamps of 1907 (Nos. 57/76).
O 77. 1 c. blue and brown .. 10 10
O 78. 2 c. black and green .. 10 10
O 79. 4 c. blue and red .. 10 10
O 80. 5 c. blue and orange .. 15 15
O 81. 10 c. black and blue .. 85 85
O 82. 25 c. slate and lavender 15 15
O 83. 50 c. blue and red .. 25 25
O 84. 1 col. black and brown 45 45

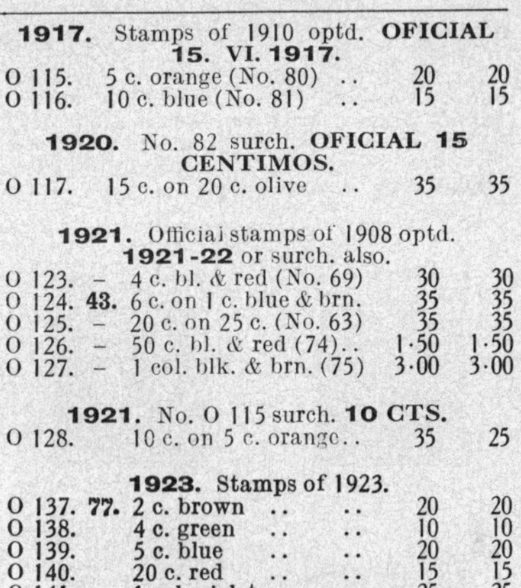
**1917.** Stamps of 1910 optd. **OFICIAL 15. VI. 1917.**
O 115. 5 c. orange (No. 80) .. 20 20
O 116. 10 c. blue (No. 81) .. 15 15

**1920.** No. 82 surch. **OFICIAL 15 CENTIMOS.**
O 117. 15 c. on 20 c. olive .. 35 35

**1921.** Official stamps of 1908 optd. **1921-22** or surch. also.
O 123. – 4 c. bl. & red (No. 69) 30 30
O 124. **43.** 6 c. on 1 c. blue & brn. 35 35
O 125. – 20 c. on 25 c. (No. 63) 35 35
O 126. – 50 c. bl. & red (74) .. 1·50 1·50
O 127. – 1 col. blk. & brn. (75) 3·00 3·00

**1921.** No. O 115 surch. **10 CTS.**
O 128. 10 c. on 5 c. orange .. 35 25

**1923.** Stamps of 1923.
O 137. **77.** 2 c. brown .. .. 20 20
O 138. 4 c. green .. .. 10 10
O 139. 5 c. blue .. .. 20 20
O 140. 20 c. red .. .. 15 15
O 141. 1 col. violet .. 25 25

O 95.

**1926.**
O 169. **O 95.** 2 c. black and blue .. 10 10
O 231. 2 c. black and lilac .. 10 10
O 170. 3 c. black and red .. 10 10
O 232. 3 c. black and brown 10 10
O 171. 4 c. black and blue .. 10 10
O 233. 4 c. black and red .. 10 10
O 172. 5 c. black and green 10 10
O 173. 6 c. black and yellow 10 10
O 235. 8 c. black and brown 10 10
O 174. 10 c. black and red .. 10 10
O 175. 20 c. black and green 10 10
O 237. 20 c. black and blue 10 10
O 176. 30 c. black and orange 10 10
O 238. 40 c. black and orange 15 15
O 177. 45 c. black and brown 15 15
O 239. 55 c. black and lilac 25 25
O 178. 1 col. black and lilac 20 20
O 240. 1 col. black and brown 20 20
O 241. 2 col. black and blue 40 40
O 242. 5 col. black & yellow 1·50 1·50
O 243. 10 col. blue and black 9·50 9·50

**1934.** Air. Air stamps of 1934.
O 211. **107.** 5 c. green .. .. 25 25
O 212. 10 c. red .. .. 25 25
O 213. 15 c. brown .. .. 40 40
O 214. 20 c. blue .. .. 60 60
O 215. 25 c. orange .. 60 60
O 216. 40 c. brown .. 70 70
O 217. 50 c. black .. 70 70
O 218. 60 c. yellow .. .. 80 80
O 219. 75 c. violet .. .. 80 80
O 220. – 1 col. red .. .. 1·25 1·25
O 221. – 2 col. blue .. .. 3·50 3·50
O 222. – 5 col. black .. .. 6·50 6·50
O 223. – 10 col. brown .. 7·50 7·50

**1936.** Stamps of 1936.
O 228. **113.** 5 c. green .. .. 20 10
O 229. – 10 c. red .. .. 20 10

POSTAGE DUE STAMPS

D 42.

D 64.

**1903.**
D 55. **D 42.** 5 c. blue .. .. 4·50 90
D 56. 10 c. brown .. .. 4·50 70
D 57. 15 c. green .. .. 1·90 1·60
D 58. 20 c. red .. .. 2·10 1·60
D 59. 25 c. blue .. .. 2·75 1·60
D 60. 30 c. brown .. .. 4·25 2·50
D 61. 40 c. olive .. .. 4·25 2·50
D 62. 50 c. red .. .. 4·25 2·10

**1915.**
D 115. **D 64.** 2 c. orange .. 10 10
D 116. 4 c. blue .. .. 10 10
D 117. 8 c. green .. .. 35 35
D 118. 10 c. violet .. .. 15 15
D 119. 20 c. brown .. 15 15

## CRETE — Pt. 3

Former Turkish island in the E. Mediterranean under the joint protection of Gt. Britain, France, Italy and Russia from 1898 to 1908, when the island was united to Greece. This was recognised by Turkey in 1913. Greek stamps now used.

100 lepta = 1 drachma.

1. Hermes. 2. Hera.

3. Prince George of Greece.

4. Talos.

**1900.**

1. **1.** 1 l. brown .. .. .. 75 10
12. 1 l. yellow .. .. .. 75 60
2. **2.** 5 l. green .. .. .. 70 15
3. **3.** 10 l. red .. .. .. 95 10
4. **2.** 20 l. red .. .. .. 2·75 50
13. 20 l. orange .. .. .. 1·90 60
15. **3.** 25 l. blue .. .. .. 5·00 60
14. **1.** 50 l. blue .. .. .. 5·25 4·25
16. 50 l. lilac .. .. .. 15·00 9·50
17. **4.** 1 d. violet .. .. .. 15·00 11·50
18. – 2 d. brown .. .. .. 4·00 3·50
19. – 5 d. black and green .. 4·00 3·50

DESIGNS (as Type **4**): 2 d. Minos. 5 d. St. George and Dragon.

**ΠΡΟΣΩΡΙΝΟΝ**
(7.)

**1900.** Optd. as T **7.**

5. **3.** 25 l. blue .. .. .. 1·25 30
6. **1.** 50 l. lilac .. .. .. 1·25 60
7. **4.** 1 d. violet .. .. .. 3·50 1·40
8. – 2 d. brown (No. 18) .. 7·75 5·50
9. – 5 d. black & grn. (No. 19) 27·00 23·00

**1904.** Surch. **5** twice.

20. **2.** 5 on 20 l. orange .. 1·90 75

10. Rhea.

12. Prince George of Greece.

16. Europa and Jupiter.

DESIGNS (As Type **10**): 5 l. Britomartis. 20 l. Miletus. 25 l. Triton. 50 l. Ariadne. (As Type **16**): 3 d. Minos Ruins. (44 × 28½ mm.): 5 d. Mt. Ida.

**1905.**

21. **10.** 2 l. lilac .. .. .. 80 25
22. – 5 l. green .. .. .. 3·00 25
23. **12.** 10 l. red .. .. .. 3·00 35
24. – 20 l. green .. .. .. 3·00 70
25. – 25 l. blue .. .. .. 3·00 75
26. – 50 l. brown .. .. .. 3·00 1·60
27. **16.** 1 d. sepia and red .. 25·00 21·00
28. – 3 d. black and orange .. 19·00 14·50
29. – 5 d. black and olive .. 9·50 9·50

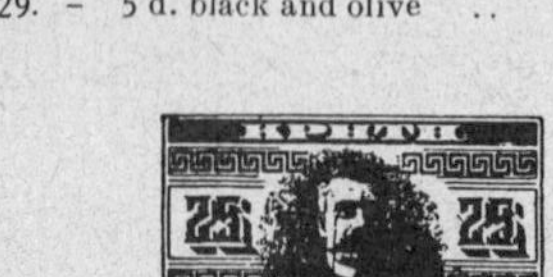

19. High Commissioner A. T. A. Zaimis.

**1907.** Various designs.

30. **19.** 25 l. black and blue .. 13·50 40
31. – 1 d. black and green .. 4·00 3·50

DESIGN—HORIZ. (larger). 1 d. Landing of Prince George of Greece at Suda.

21. Hermes.

**ΕΛΛΑΣ**
(22.)

**1908.** Optd. **HELLAS** as T **22** in various sizes and styles.

32. **1.** 1 l. brown .. .. .. 40 10
33. **10.** 2 l. lilac .. .. .. 45 10
34. – 5 l. green (No. 22) .. 50 15
35. **3.** 10 l. red .. .. .. 70 15
36. **21.** 10 l. red .. .. .. 1·90 50
37. – 20 l. green (No. 24) .. 1·25 55
38. **19.** 25 l. black and blue .. 3·50 70
63. – 25 l. blue (No. 25) .. 1·25 40
39. – 50 l. brown (No. 26) .. 3·50 1·25
40. **16.** 1 d. sepia and red .. 27·00 26·00
52. – 1 d. blk. & grn. (No. 31) 3·25 1·75
41. – 2 d. brown (No. 18) .. 3·00 3·00
42. – 3 d. blk. & or. (No. 28) 16·00 13·50
43. – 5 d. blk. & olive (No. 29) 16·00 13·50

**1909.** Optd. with T **7** and **22** or surcharged with new value also.

44. **1.** 1 l. yellow (No. 12) .. 55 55
45. D **8.** 1 l. red (No. D 10) .. 60 55
46. 2 on 20 l. red (No. D 73) 60 55
47. 2 on 20 l. red (No. D 13) 60 55
48. **2.** 5 on 20 l. red (No. 4) .. 55·00 45·00
49. 5 on 20 l. orange (No. 13) 75 55

OFFICIAL STAMPS

O 21.

**1908.**

O 32. O **21.** 10 l. red .. .. 7·75 75
O 33. 30 l. blue .. .. 19·00 75

In the 30 l. the central figures are in an oval frame.

**1908.** Optd. with T **22.**

O 68. O **21.** 10 l. red .. .. 1·25 75
O 69. 30 l. blue .. .. 1·25 75

POSTAGE DUE STAMPS

D 8.

**1901.**

D 10. D **8.** 1 l. red .. .. 25 15
D 11. 5 l. red .. .. 40 15
D 12. 10 l. red .. .. 75 40
D 13. 20 l. red .. .. 95 70
D 14. 40 l. red .. .. 7·75 7·00
D 15. 50 l. red .. .. 7·75 7·00
D 16. 1 d. red .. .. 7·75 7·00
D 17. 2 d. red .. .. 7·75 7·25

**1901.** Surch. "1 drachma" in Greek characters.

D 18. D **8.** 1 d. on 1 d. red .. 5·50 5·50

**1908.** Optd. with T **22.**

D 70. D **8.** 1 l. red .. .. 35 25
D 71. 5 l. red .. .. 80 35
D 72. 10 l. red .. .. 55 55
D 73. 20 l. red .. .. 1·75 95
D 74. 40 l. red .. .. 5·75 2·75
D 75. 50 l. red .. .. 6·50 4·00
D 76. 1 d. red .. .. 13·50 13·00
D 51. 1 d. on 1 d. red (No. D 18) .. .. 4·75 4·75
D 77. 2 d. red .. .. 13·50 13·50

**REVOLUTIONARY ASSEMBLY, 1905.**

In March, a revolt in favour of union with Greece began, organised by Venizelos with Headquarters at Theriso, South of Canea. The revolt collapsed in November, 1905.

R 1.

R 2. Crete enslaved.

**1905.** Imperf.

R 1. R **1.** 5 l. green and red .. 5·75 4·00
R 2. 10 l. red and green .. 5·75 4·00
R 3. 20 l. red and blue .. 5·75 4·00
R 4. 50 l. violet and green 5·75 4·00
R 5. 1 d. blue and red .. 5·75 4·00

**1905.**

R 6. R **2.** 5 l. orange .. .. 40 40
R 7. 10 l. grey .. .. 40 40
R 8. 20 l. mauve .. .. 40 40
R 9. 50 l. blue .. .. 40 40
R 10. – 1 d. violet and red .. 2·75 2·75
R 11. – 2 d. brown and green .. 3·25 3·25

DESIGN: 1 d., 2 d. King George of Greece.

## CROATIA — Pt. 3

Part of Hungary until 1918 when it became part of Yugoslavia. In 1941 it was proclaimed an independent state but in 1945 it became a constituent republic of the Federal People's Republic of Yugoslavia.

In 1991 Croatia became independent.

April 1941. 100 paras = dinar.
Sept 1941. 100 banicas = 1 kuna.
1991. 100 paras = 1 dinar.
1994. 100 lipa = 1 kuna.

NEZAVISNA
DRŽAVA
HRVATSKA
IIIIII
(1.)

(2.)

**1941.** Stamps of Yugoslavia optd. as T **1** ("Independent Croat State").

1. **99.** 50 p. orange .. .. 1·75 2·25
2. 1 d. green .. .. 1·75 2·25
3. 1 d. 50 red .. .. 1·75 1·00
4. 2 d. mauve .. .. 1·50 1·50
5. 3 d. brown .. .. 3·25 4·50
6. 4 d. blue .. .. 3·25 5·00
7. 5 d. blue .. .. 4·25 5·75
8. 5 d. 50 violet .. .. 4·50 6·00

**1941.** Stamps of Yugoslavia optd. as T **2.**

9. **99.** 25 p. black .. .. 20 30
10. 50 p. orange .. .. 20 30
11. 1 d. green .. .. 20 30
12. 1 d. 50 red .. .. 20 30
13. 2 d. mauve .. .. 20 60
14. 3 d. brown .. .. 20 90
15. 4 d. blue .. .. 25 1·00
16. 5 d. blue .. .. 40 1·00
17. 5 d. 50 violet .. .. 40 1·25
18. 6 d. blue .. .. 1·00 1·75
19. 8 d. brown .. .. 1·75 2·00
20. 12 d. violet .. .. 1·50 3·00
21. 16 d. purple .. .. 2·25 2·75
22. 20 d. blue .. .. 2·50 3·75
23. 30 d. pink .. .. 3·75 5·25

(3.)

10.
IV.
1941
NEZAVISNA
DRŽAVA
HRVATSKA
(4.)

**1941.** Stamps of Yugoslavia surch. as T **3.**

24. **99.** 1 d. on 3 d. brown .. 15 25
25. 2 d. on 4 d. blue .. 15 25

**1941.** Founding of Croatian Army. Nos. 414/26 of Yugoslavia optd. with T **4.**

25a. **99.** 25 p. black
25b. 50 p. orange
25c. 1 d. green
25d. 1 d. 50 red
25e. 2 d. mauve
25f. 3 d. brown
25g. 4 d. blue
25h. 5 d. blue
25i. 5 d. 50 violet
25j. 6 d. blue
25k. 8 d. brown
25l. 12 d. violet
25m. 16 d. purple
25n. 20 d. blue
25o. 30 d. pink
Set of 15 .. .. £160 £275

Sold at double face value.

**1941.** Stamps of Yugoslavia optd. as T **2** but without shield.

26. **109.** 1 d. 50+1 d. 50 black .. 7·75 12·50
27. – 4 d.+3 d. brn. (No. 457) 7·75 12·50

**1941.** Postage Due stamps of Yugoslavia optd. **NEZAVISNA DRZAVA HRVATSKA** and **FRANCO.**

28. D **56.** 50 p. violet .. .. 10 20
29. 2 d. blue .. .. 20 40
30. 5 d. orange .. .. 20 40
31. 10 d. brown .. .. 25 55

7. Mt. Ozalj.

8. Banjaluka.

**1941.**

32. **7.** 25 b. red .. .. 10 10
33. – 50 b. green .. .. 10 10
34. – 75 b. olive .. .. 10 10
35. – 1 k. green .. .. 10 10
36. – 1 k. 50 green .. .. 10 10
37. – 2 k. red .. .. 10 10
38. – 3 k. red .. .. 10 10
39. – 4 k. blue .. .. 10 10
40. – 5 k. black .. .. 50 40
41. – 5 k. blue .. .. 10 10
42. – 6 k. olive .. .. 10 10
43. – 7 k. orange .. .. 10 10
44. – 8 k. brown .. .. 10 10
45. – 10 k. violet .. .. 20 10
46. – 12 k. brown .. .. 25 20
47. – 20 k. brown .. .. 20 10
48. – 30 k. brown .. .. 25 15
49. – 50 k. green .. .. 75 20
50. **8.** 100 k. violet .. .. 1·10 1·25

DESIGNS: 50 b. Waterfall at Jajce. 75 b. Varazdin. 1 k. Mt. Velebit. 1 k. 50, Zelenjak. 2 k. Zagreb Cathedral. 3 k. Church at Osijek. 4 k. River Drina. 5 k. (No. 40), Konjic Bridge. 5 k. (No. 41), Modern building at Zemun. 6 k. Dubrovnik. 7 k. R. Save in Slavonia. 8 k. Mosque at Sarajevo. 10 k. Lake Plitvice. 12 k. Klis Fortress near Split. 20 k. Hvar. 30 k. Harvesting in Syrmia. 50 k. Senj.

9. Croat (Sinj) Costume.

10. Emblems of Germany, Croatia and Italy.

**1941.** Red Cross.

51. **9.** 1 k. 50+1 k. 50 blue .. 15 30
52. – 2 k.+2 k. brown .. 20 40
53. – 5 k.+4 k. red .. 35 95

COSTUMES: 2 k. Travnik. 4 k. Turopolje.

**1941.** Eastern Front Volunteer Fund.

54. **10.** 4 k.+2 k. blue .. .. 75 2·25

11.

(12.)

**1942.** Aviation Fund. Designs showing glider in flight as T **11.**

55. **11.** 2 k.+2 k. brown .. .. 15 30
56. – 2 k. 50 b.+2 k. 50 b. green 25 50
57. – 3 k.+3 k. red .. .. 30 55
58. – 4 k.+4 k. blue .. .. 45 85

The 2 k. and 3 k. are vert.

**1942.** 1st Anniv. of Croat Independence. Optd with T **12.**

59. 2 k. brown (as No. 37) .. 10 20
60. 5 k. red (as No. 40) .. 10 30
61. 10 k. green (as No. 45) .. 25 50

**1942.** Banjaluka Philatelic Exn. Inscr. "F.I." in top right corner.

62. **8.** 100 k. violet .. .. 1·60 2·75

**1942.** Surch. **O 25. Kn.** and bar.

63. 0·25 k. on 2 k. red (No. 37) 10 20

14. Trumpeters.

15. Sestine (Croatia).

**1942.** National Relief Fund.

64. **14.** 3 k.+1 k. red .. .. 30 50
65. – 4 k.+2 k. brown .. .. 30 65
66. – 5 k.+5 k. blue .. .. 30 75

DESIGNS—HORIZ. 4 k. Procession beneath triumphal archways. VERT. 5 k. Mother and child.

**1942.** Red Cross Fund. Peasant girls in provincial costumes.

67. **15.** 1 k. 50+50 b. brown .. 40 65
68. – 3 k.+1 k. violet .. 40 65
69. – 4 k.+2 k. blue .. .. 40 90
70. – 10 k.+5 k. bistre .. 80 1·25
71. **15.** 13 k.+6 k. red .. 1·75 3·25

COSTUMES: 3 k. Slavonia. 4 k. Bosnia. 10 k. Dalmatia.

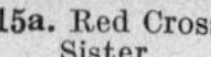

15a. Red Cross Sister.

16. M. Gubec.

**1942.** Charity Tax. Red Cross Fund. Cross in red.

71a. **15a.** 1 k. green .. .. 15 25

**1942.** Croat ("USTASCHA") Youth Fund.

72. **16.** 3 k.+6 k. red .. .. 15 25
73. – 4 k.+7 k. brown .. 15 25

PORTRAIT: 4 k. A. Starcevic.

**17.**

**19.** Arms of Zagreb.

**1943.** Labour Front. Vert. designs showing workers as T **17.**

| No. | Type | Description | Unused | Used |
|---|---|---|---|---|
| 74. | **17.** | 2 k. + 1 k. brown & olive | 80 | 2·00 |
| 75. | – | 3 k. + 3 k. brn. & purple | 80 | 2·00 |
| 76. | – | 7 k. + 4 k. brown & grey | 80 | 2·10 |

**1943.** Zagreb. 7th Cent.

| No. | Type | Description | Unused | Used |
|---|---|---|---|---|
| 77. | **19.** | 3 k. 50 (+ 6 k. 50) blue | 40 | 1·75 |

**1943.** Pictorial designs as T **8,** but with views surrounded by frame line.

| No. | Type | Description | Unused | Used |
|---|---|---|---|---|
| 78. | | 3 k. 50 brown .. .. | 25 | 25 |
| 79. | | 12 k. 50 black .. .. | 25 | 30 |

DESIGNS: 3 k. 50, Trakoscan Castle, 12 k. 50, Veliki Tabor.

**21.** A. Pavelic.

**22.** Krsto Frankopan.

**1943.** Croat ("Ustascha") Youth Fund.

| No. | Type | Description | Unused | Used |
|---|---|---|---|---|
| 80. | **21.** | 5 k. + 3 k. red .. .. | 15 | 25 |
| 81. | | 7 k. + 5 k. green .. | 15 | 25 |

**1943.** Famous Croats.

| No. | Type | Description | Unused | Used |
|---|---|---|---|---|
| 82. | – | 1 k. blue .. .. .. | 10 | 15 |
| 83. | **22.** | 2 k. olive .. .. | 10 | 15 |
| 84. | – | 3 k. 50 red .. .. | 10 | 20 |

PORTRAITS: 1 k. Katarina Zrinska. 3 k. 50, Peter Zrinski.

**23.** Croat Sailor.

**1943.** Croat Legion. Relief Fund.

| No. | Type | Description | Unused | Used |
|---|---|---|---|---|
| 85. | **23.** | 1 k.+50 b. green .. | 10 | 15 |
| 86. | – | 2 k.+1 k. red .. | 10 | 15 |
| 87. | – | 3 k. 50+1 k. 50 blue .. | 10 | 15 |
| 88. | – | 9 k.+4 k. 50 brown .. | 10 | 20 |

DESIGNS: 2 k. Pilot and Heinkel He bomber. 3 k. 50, Infantrymen. 9 k. Mechanized column.

**24.** St. Mary's Church and Cistercian Monastery, 1650.

**1943.** Philatelic Exhibition, Zagreb.

| No. | Type | Description | Unused | Used |
|---|---|---|---|---|
| 89. | **24.** | 18 k.+9 k. blue.. .. | 60 | 1·75 |

**1943.** Return of Sibenik to Croatia. Optd. **HRVATSKO MORE/8, IX./1943.**

| No. | Type | Description | Unused | Used |
|---|---|---|---|---|
| 90. | **24.** | 18 k.+9 k. blue.. .. | 3·75 | 3·75 |

**26.** Nurse and Patient.

**26a.**

**1943.** Red Cross Fund.

| No. | Type | Description | Unused | Used |
|---|---|---|---|---|
| 91. | – | 1 k.+50 b. blue .. | 10 | 20 |
| 92. | – | 2 k.+1 k. red .. | 10 | 20 |
| 93. | – | 3 k. 50+1 k. 50 blue .. | 10 | 20 |
| 94. | **26.** | 8 k.+3 k. brown .. | 10 | 20 |
| 95. | | 9 k.+4 k. green .. | 10 | 25 |
| 96. | – | 10 k.+ 5 k. violet .. | 15 | 30 |
| 97. | **26.** | 12 k.+6 k. blue .. | 20 | 40 |
| 98. | – | 12 k. 50+6 k. brown .. | 25 | 55 |
| 99. | **26.** | 18 k.+8 k. orange .. | 35 | 75 |
| 100. | | 32 k.+12 k. grey .. | 70 | 1·25 |

DESIGN: 1 k., 2 k., 3 k. 50, 10 k., 12 k. 50, Mother and children.

**1943.** Charity Tax. Red Cross Fund. Cross in red.

| No. | Type | Description | Unused | Used |
|---|---|---|---|---|
| 100a. | **26a.** | 2 k. blue .. .. | 15 | 15 |

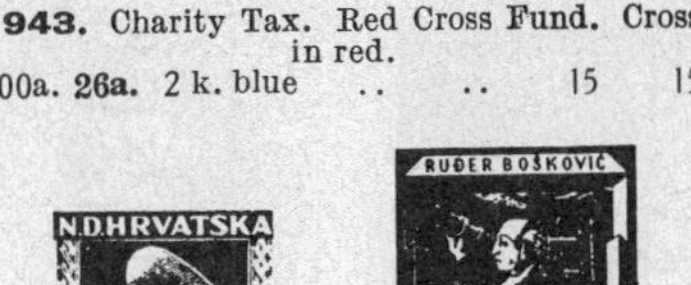

**27.** A. Pavelic.

**28.** Ruder Boskovic.

**1943.**

| No. | Type | Description | Unused | Used |
|---|---|---|---|---|
| 101. | **27.** | 25 b. red .. .. | 10 | 10 |
| 105. | | 50 b. blue .. .. | 10 | 10 |
| 102. | | 75 b. green .. .. | 10 | 10 |
| 106. | | 1 k. green .. .. | 10 | 10 |
| 107. | | 1 k. 50 violet .. .. | 10 | 10 |
| 108. | | 2 k. red .. .. | 10 | 10 |
| 109. | | 3 k. red .. .. | 10 | 10 |
| 110. | | 3 k. 50 blue .. .. | 10 | 10 |
| 111. | | 4 k. purple .. .. | 10 | 10 |
| 103. | | 5 k. blue .. .. | 10 | 10 |
| 112. | | 8 k. brown .. .. | 10 | 10 |
| 113. | | 9 k. red .. .. | 10 | 10 |
| 114. | | 10 k. purple .. .. | 10 | 15 |
| 115. | | 12 k. brown .. .. | 10 | 15 |
| 116. | | 12 k. 50 black .. .. | 10 | 10 |
| 117. | | 18 k. brown .. .. | 10 | 15 |
| 104. | | 32 k. brown .. .. | 10 | 15 |
| 118. | | 50 k. green .. .. | 10 | 20 |
| 119. | | 70 k. orange .. .. | 15 | 30 |
| 120. | | 100 k. violet .. .. | 30 | 55 |

The design of the 25 b., 75 b., 5 k., and 32 k. is 20½ × 26 mm., the rest are 22 × 28 mm.

**1943.** R. Boskovic (astronomer). Commem.

| No. | Type | Description | Unused | Used |
|---|---|---|---|---|
| 121. | **28.** | 3 k. 50 red .. .. | 15 | 20 |
| 122. | | 12 k. 50 purple .. | 20 | 30 |

**29.** Posthorn. **30.** St. Sebastian.

**1944.** Postal and Railway Employees' Relief Fund.

| No. | Type | Description | Unused | Used |
|---|---|---|---|---|
| 123. | **29.** | 7 k.+3 k. 50 brn., red & bis. | 10 | 15 |
| 124. | – | 16 k.+8 k. blue .. | 10 | 20 |
| 125. | – | 24 k.+12 k. red .. | 15 | 25 |
| 126. | – | 32 k.+16 k. blk. & red | 25 | 40 |

DESIGNS—VERT. 16 k. Dove, aeroplane and globe. 24 k. Mercury. HORIZ. 32 k. Winged wheel.

**1944.** War Invalids' Relief Fund.

| No. | Type | Description | Unused | Used |
|---|---|---|---|---|
| 127. | **30.** | 7 k.+3 k. 50 clar. & red | 15 | 25 |
| 128. | – | 16 k.+8 k. green .. | 20 | 35 |
| 129. | – | 24 k.+12 k. yellow, brown and red .. | 20 | 35 |
| 130. | – | 32 k.+16 k. blue .. | 20 | 55 |

DESIGNS—HORIZ. 16 k. Blind man and cripple. 32 k. Death of Peter Svacic, 1094. VERT. 24 k. Mediaeval statuette.

**31.** The Legion in Action. **32.** Jure-Ritter Francetic.

**1944.** Croat Youth Fund. No. 134 perf. others imperf.

| No. | Type | Description | Unused | Used |
|---|---|---|---|---|
| 131. | **31.** | 3 k. 50 + 1 k. 50 brown | 10 | 10 |
| 132. | – | 12 k. 50 + 6 k. 50 blue.. | 10 | 10 |
| 134. | **32.** | 12 k. 50 + 287 k. 50 black | 1·90 | 12·50 |
| 133. | | 18 k. + 9 k. brown .. | 10 | 10 |

DESIGN: No. 132, Sentries on the Drina.

**33.**

**1944.** Labour Front. Inscr. "D.R.S.".

| No. | Type | Description | Unused | Used |
|---|---|---|---|---|
| 135. | **33.** | 3 k. 50+1 k. red .. | 10 | 10 |
| 136. | – | 12 k. 50+6 k. brown .. | 10 | 15 |
| 137. | – | 18 k.+9 k. blue .. | 10 | 15 |
| 138. | – | 32 k.+16 k. green .. | 10 | 15 |

DESIGNS: 12 k. 50, Digging. 18 k. Instruction. 32 k. " On Parade ".

**34.** Bombed Home.

**35.** War Victim.

**1944.** Charity Tax. War Victims.

| No. | Type | Description | Unused | Used |
|---|---|---|---|---|
| 138b. | **34.** | 1 k. green .. .. | 10 | 10 |
| 138c. | **35.** | 2 k. red .. .. | 10 | 10 |
| 138d. | | 5 k. green .. .. | 10 | 10 |
| 138e. | | 10 k. blue .. .. | 10 | 15 |
| 138f. | | 20 k. brown .. .. | 20 | 35 |

**36.**

**37.** Storm Division Soldiers.

**1944.** Red Cross. Cross in red.

| No. | Type | Description | Unused | Used |
|---|---|---|---|---|
| 139. | **36.** | 2 k.+1 k. green .. | 10 | 10 |
| 140. | | 3 k. 50+1 k. 50 red .. | 10 | 15 |
| 141. | | 12 k. 50+6 k. blue .. | 10 | 15 |

**1945.** Creation of Croatian Storm Division.

| No. | Type | Description | Unused | Used |
|---|---|---|---|---|
| 142. | **37.** | 50 k.+50 k. red and grey | 35·00 | 55·00 |
| 143. | – | 70 k.+70 k. sepia & grey | 35·00 | 55·00 |
| 144. | – | 100 k.+100 k. bl. & grey | 35·00 | 55·00 |

DESIGNS: 70 k. Storm Division soldiers in action. 100 k. Division emblem.

**38.**

**39.**

**1945.** Postal Employees' Fund.

| No. | Type | Description | Unused | Used |
|---|---|---|---|---|
| 145. | **38.** | 3 k. 50+1 k. 50 grey .. | 10 | 10 |
| 146. | – | 12 k. 50+6 k. purple .. | 10 | 15 |
| 147. | – | 24 k.+12 k. green .. | 10 | 15 |
| 148. | – | 50 k.+25 k. purple .. | 15 | 25 |

DESIGNS: 12 k. 50, Telegraph linesman. 24 k. Telephone switchboard. 50 k. The postman calls.

**1945.**

| No. | Type | Description | Unused | Used |
|---|---|---|---|---|
| 149. | **39.** | 3 k. 50 brown .. | 15 | 75 |

**40** Interior of Zagreb Cathedral

**41** Statue of the Virgin and Shrine

**1991.** Obligatory Tax. Workers' Fund. Mass for Croatia. Perf or imperf.

| No. | Type | Description | Unused | Used |
|---|---|---|---|---|
| 150 | **40** | 1 d. 20 gold and black .. | 10 | 10 |

**1991.** Obligatory Tax. Workers' Fund. 700th Anniv of Shrine of the Virgin, Trsat. Perf or imperf.

| No. | Type | Description | Unused | Used |
|---|---|---|---|---|
| 151 | **41** | 1 d. 70 multicoloured .. | 10 | 10 |

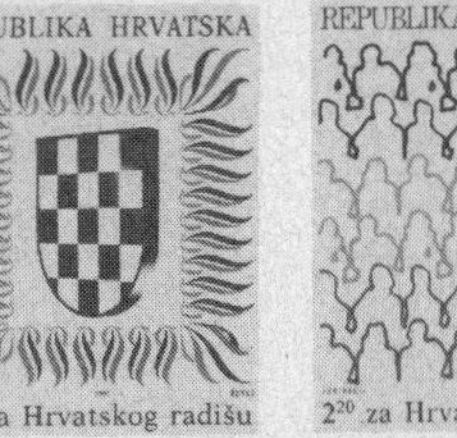

**42** Croatian Arms **43** Members of Parliament

**1991.** Obligatory Tax. Workers' Fund. Rally in Ban Jelacic Square, Zagreb. Perf or imperf.

| No. | Type | Description | Unused | Used |
|---|---|---|---|---|
| 152 | **42** | 2 d. 20 multicoloured .. | 10 | 10 |

See also No. 170.

**1991.** Obligatory Tax. Workers' Fund. First Multi-party Session of Croatian Parliament, 30 May 1990. Perf or imperf.

| No. | Type | Description | Unused | Used |
|---|---|---|---|---|
| 153 | **43** | 2 d. 20 multicoloured .. | 10 | 10 |

**44** Sud Aviation Caravelle over Zagreb Cathedral and Port of Dubrovnik

**45** Anti-tuberculosis Emblem

**1991.** Air.

| No. | Type | Description | Unused | Used |
|---|---|---|---|---|
| 154 | **44** | 1 d. blue, black and red | 10 | 10 |
| 155 | – | 2 d. multicoloured .. | 20 | 20 |
| 156 | – | 3 d. multicoloured .. | 30 | 30 |

DESGINS: 2 d. Bell tower and ruins of Diocletian's Palace, Split; 3 d. Airliner over Zagreb Cathedral and Pula amphitheatre.

**1991.** Obligatory Tax. Anti-tuberculosis Week.

| No. | Type | Description | Unused | Used |
|---|---|---|---|---|
| 157 | **45** | 2 d. 20 red and blue .. | 20 | 20 |

**46** Ban Jelacic Statue

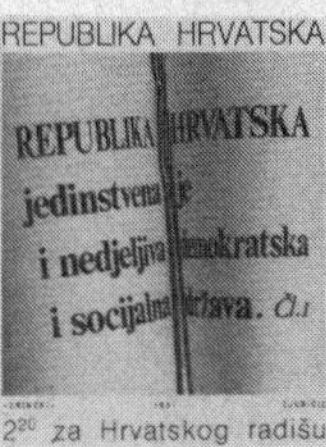

**48** First Article of Constitution in Croatian

**1991.** Obligatory Tax. Workers' Fund. Re-erection of Ban Josip Jelacic Equestrian Statue, Zagreb. Perf or imperf.

| No. | Type | Description | Unused | Used |
|---|---|---|---|---|
| 158 | **46** | 2 d. 20 multicoloured .. | 20 | 20 |

**1991.** No. 150 surch $4^{00}$ **HPT** and posthorn.

| No. | Type | Description | Unused | Used |
|---|---|---|---|---|
| 159 | **40** | 4 d. on 1 d. 20 gold & blk | 35 | 35 |

**1991.** Obligatory Tax. Workers' Fund. 1st Anniv of New Constitution. Multicoloured. Perf or imperf.

| No. | Type | Description | Unused | Used |
|---|---|---|---|---|
| 160 | | 2 d. 20 Type **48** .. .. | 20 | 20 |
| 161 | | 2 d. 20 Text in English .. | 20 | 20 |
| 162 | | 2 d. 20 Text in French .. | 20 | 20 |
| 163 | | 2 d. 20 Text in German .. | 20 | 20 |
| 164 | | 2 d. 20 Text in Russian .. | 20 | 20 |
| 165 | | 2 d. 20 Text in Spanish .. | 20 | 20 |

**49** Book of Croatian Independence

**50** 17th-century Crib Figures, Kosljun Monastery, Krk

**1991.** Recognition of Independence.

| No. | Type | Description | Unused | Used |
|---|---|---|---|---|
| 166 | **49** | 30 d. multicoloured .. | 2·75 | 2·75 |

**1991.** Christmas.

| No. | Type | Description | Unused | Used |
|---|---|---|---|---|
| 167 | **50** | 4 d. multicoloured .. | 35 | 35 |

**51** "VUKOVAR" and Barbed Wire

**52** Ban Josip Jelacic

**1992.** Obligatory Tax. Vukovar Refugees' Fund.

| No. | Type | Description | Unused | Used |
|---|---|---|---|---|
| 168 | **51** | 2 d. 20 brown and black | 10 | 10 |

**1992.** No.151 surch $20^{00}$ **HPT** and posthorn.

| No. | Type | Description | Unused | Used |
|---|---|---|---|---|
| 169 | **41** | 20 d. on 1 d. 70 mult .. | 20 | 20 |

**1992.** As No. 152, but redrawn with new value and "HPT" emblem replacing obligatory tax inscr at foot.

| No. | Type | Description | Unused | Used |
|---|---|---|---|---|
| 170 | **42** | 10 d. multicoloured .. | 10 | 10 |

**1992.** Obligatory Tax. Famous Croatians. Multicoloured.

| No. | Type | Description | Unused | Used |
|---|---|---|---|---|
| 171 | | 4 d.+2 d. Type **52** .. | 10 | 10 |
| 172 | | 4 d.+2 d. Dr. Ante Starcevic .. .. .. | 10 | 10 |
| 173 | | 7 d.+3 d. Stjepan Radic .. | 10 | 10 |

53 Olympic Rings

54 Osijek Cathedral on Paper Dart

**1992.** Winter Olympic Games, Albertville.
174 **53** 30 d. multicoloured .. 25 25

**1992.** Air.
175 **54** 4 d. multicoloured .. 10 10

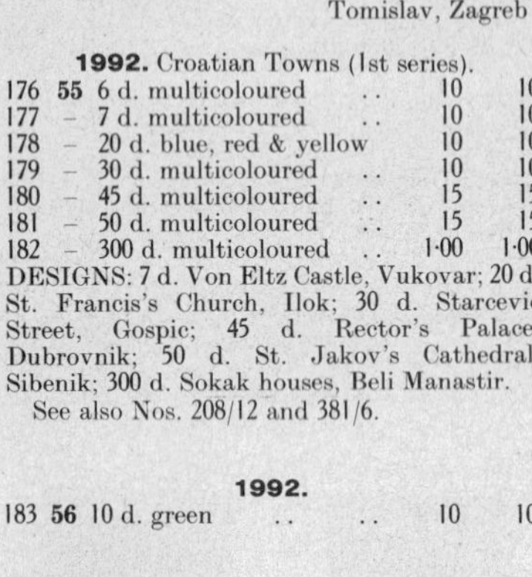

55 Knin

56 Statue of King Tomislav, Zagreb

**1992.** Croatian Towns (1st series).
176 **55** 6 d. multicoloured .. 10 10
177 – 7 d. multicoloured .. 10 10
178 – 20 d. blue, red & yellow 10 10
179 – 30 d. multicoloured .. 10 10
180 – 45 d. multicoloured .. 15 15
181 – 50 d. multicoloured .. 15 15
182 – 300 d. multicoloured .. 1·00 1·00
DESIGNS: 7 d. Von Eltz Castle, Vukovar; 20 d. St. Francis's Church, Ilok; 30 d. Starcevic Street, Gospic; 45 d. Rector's Palace, Dubrovnik; 50 d. St. Jakov's Cathedral, Sibenik; 300 d. Sokak houses, Beli Manastir.
See also Nos. 208/12 and 381/6.

**1992.**
183 **56** 10 d. green .. .. 10 10

57 Red Cross Emblems on Globe

58 Map of Croatia on Red Cross

**1992.** Obligatory Tax. Red Cross Week.
184 **57** 3 d. red and black .. 10 10

**1992.** Obligatory Tax. Solidarity Week.
185 **58** 3 d. red and black .. 10 10

59 Central Railway Station, Zagreb

**1992.** Centenary of Zagreb Central Railway Station.
186 **59** 30 d. multicoloured .. 10 10

60 Society Imprint

61 Bishop Josip Strossmayer and Academy Building

**1992.** 150th Anniv of Matica Hrvatska (Croatian language society).
187 **60** 20 d. gold and red .. 10 10

**1992.** 125th Anniv of Croatian Academy of Sciences and Arts.
188 **61** 30 d. multicoloured .. 10 10

62 Olympic Rings on Computer Pattern

**1992.** Olympic Games, Barcelona. Mult.
189 40 d. Type **62** .. .. 10 10
190 105 d. Rings and symbolic sports .. .. .. 20 20

63 Bluebell

64 Blue Rock Thrush

**1992.** Flowers. Multicoloured.
191 30 d. Type **63** .. .. 10 10
192 85 d. Degenia (vert) .. 15 15

**1992.** Environmental Protection. Mult.
193 40 d. Type **64** .. .. 10 10
194 75 d. Red-spot snake .. 15 15

65 15th-century Carrack, Dubrovnik

66 "Madonna of Bistrica"

**1992.** Europa. 500th Anniv of Discovery of America by Columbus (1st issue).
195 **65** 30 d. multicoloured .. 25 25
196 – 75 d. black and red .. 15 15
DESIGN: 75 d. "Indian Horseman" (bronze statue by Ivan Mestrovic).
See also Nos. 198/9.

**1992.** Obligatory Tax. Fund for National Shrine to Madonna of Bistrica.
197 **66** 5 d. gold and blue .. 10 10

**1992.** Europa. 500th Anniv of Discovery of America by Columbus (2nd issue). As Nos. 195/6, but new face values and with additional C.E.P.T. posthorns emblem.
198 **65** 60 d. multicoloured .. 30 30
199 – 130 d. black, red and gold (as No. 196) .. 60 60

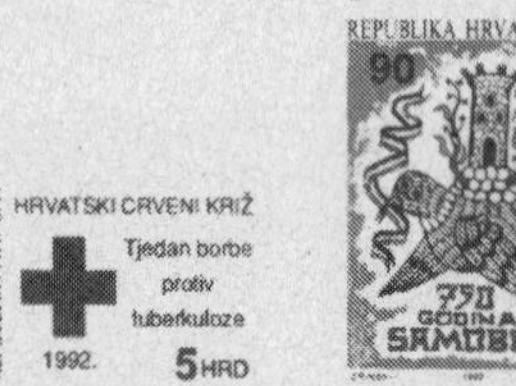

67 Red Cross

69 Dove and Coat of Arms

68 "25"

**1992.** Obligatory Tax. Anti-tuberculosis Week.
200 **67** 5 d. red and black .. 10 10

**1992.** Croatian Language Anniversaries. Mult.
201 40 d. Type **68** (25th anniv of Croatian Language Declaration) .. .. 15 15
202 130 d. "100" (centenary of "Croatian Orthography" by Dr. I. Broz) .. 50 50

**1992.** 750th Anniv of Grant of Royal City Charter to Samobor.
203 **69** 90 d. multicoloured .. 25 25

70 Remains of Altar Screen from Uzdolje Church

71 St. George and the Dragon

**1992.** 1100th Anniv of Duke Mucimir's Donation (judgement in ecclesiastical dispute).
204 **70** 60 d. multicoloured .. 20 20

**1992.** Obligatory Tax. Croatian Anti-cancer League.
205 **71** 15 d. multicoloured .. 10 10

72 Seal of King Bela IV

**1992.** 750th Anniv of Zagreb's Charter from King Bela IV.
206 **72** 180 d. multicoloured .. 45 45

73 "Croatian Christmas" (Ljubo Babic)

**1992.** Christmas.
207 **73** 80 d. multicoloured .. 20 20

74 Former Town Hall, Vinkovci

75 Blaz Lorkovic

**1992.** Croatian Towns (2nd series). Mult.
208 100 d. Type **74** .. .. 10 10
209 200 d. Castle, Pazin (vert) 10 10
210 500 d. Jelacic Square, Slavonski Brod .. 10 10
211 1000 d. Town Hall, Jelacic Square, Varazdin .. 20 20
212 2000 d. Zorin cultural centre, Karlovac .. 45 45
215 5000 d. St. Donat's Church and St. Stosija's Cathedral belltower, Zadar (vert) .. .. 1·10 1·10
217 10000 d. Pirovo peninsula and Franciscan Monastery, Vis .. 2·10 2·10

**1992.** Death Centenary of Blaz Lorkovic (political economist).
218 **75** 250 d. multicoloured .. 35 35

76 Coiled National Colours

77 Vucic

**1992.** 150th Anniv of "Kolo" Literary Magazine.
219 **76** 300 d. multicoloured .. 45 45

**1992.** 400th Birth Anniv of Ivan Bunic-Vucic (poet).
220 **77** 350 d. multicoloured .. 50 50

78 Ljudevit Gaj Square, Krapina

**1993.** 800th Anniv of Krapina.
221 **78** 300 d. multicoloured .. 30 30

79 Tesla

**1993.** 50th Death Anniv of Nikola Tesla (physicist).
222 **79** 250 d. multicoloured .. 35 35

80 "Self-portrait"

**1993.** Death Centenary of Ferdo Quiquerez (painter).
223 **80** 100 d. multicoloured .. 15 15

81 Red Deer

**1993.** Croatian Fauna. Multicoloured.
224 500 d. Type **81** .. .. 60 60
225 550 d. White-tailed sea eagle .. .. .. 60 60

82 "Self-portrait"

**1993.** Birth Centenary of Zlatko Sulentic (painter).
226 **82** 350 d. multicoloured .. 35 35

83 Kursalon, Lipik

**1993.** Centenary of Lipik Spa.
227 **83** 400 d. multicoloured .. 35 35

84 Kovacic (statue, Vojin Bakic)

**1993.** 50th Death Anniv of Ivan Goran Kovacic (writer).
228 **84** 200 d. multicoloured .. 15 15

**85** Minceta Fortress, Dubrovnik

**1993.** 59th P.E.N. Literary Congress, Dubrovnik.
229 **85** 800 d. multicoloured .. 60 60

**86** Ivan Kakaljevic (writer)

**87** Mask and Split Theatre

**1993.** 150th Anniv of First Speech in Croatian Language made to Croatian Parliament.
230 **86** 500 d. multicoloured .. 35 35

**1993.** Centenary of Split Theatre.
231 **87** 600 d. multicoloured .. 40 40

**88** Boy and Ruined House

**89** Pag in 16th Century

**1993.** Obligatory Tax. Red Cross Week.
232 **88** 80 d. black and red .. 10 10

**1993.** 550th Anniv of Refoundation of Pag.
233 **89** 800 d. multicoloured .. 50 50

**90** Dove

**91** Girl at Window

**1993.** 1st Anniv of Croatia's Membership of United Nations.
234 **90** 500 d. multicoloured .. 30 30

**1993.** Obligatory Tax. Solidarity Week.
235 **91** 100 d. black and red .. 10 10

**92** "In the Cafe" (I. Dulcic)

**1993.** Europa. Contemporary Art. Mult.
236 700 d. Type **92** .. .. 40 40
237 1000 d. "The Waiting Room" (M. Stancic) .. 60 60
238 1100 d. "Two Figures" (L. Ivancic) .. .. 65 65

**93** "Homodukt" (Milivoj Bijelic)

**1993.** Croatia's Participation in 45th Art Biennial, Venice. Multicoloured.
239 250 d. Type **93** .. .. 10 10
240 600 d. "Snails" (Ivo Dekovic) .. .. 30 30
241 1000 d. "Esa carta de mi flor" (Zeljko Kipke) .. 50 50

**94** Symbolic Running Track

**1993.** 12th Mediterranean Games, Roussillon (Languedoc), France.
242 **94** 700 d. multicoloured .. 35 35

**95** "Slavonian Oaks"

**1993.** 150th Birth Anniv of Adolf Waldinger (painter).
243 **95** 300 d. multicoloured .. 15 15

**96** Battle of Krbava, 1493

**1993.** Anniversaries of Famous Battles. 16th-century engravings.
244 800 d. Type **96** .. .. 40 40
245 1300 d. Battle of Sisak, 1593 .. .. .. 60 60

**97** "Miroslav Krleza" (Marija Ujevic)

**1993.** Birth Centenary of Miroslav Krleza (writer).
246 **97** 400 d. multicoloured .. 20 20

**98** Cardinal Stepinac

**99** Croatian Postman

**1993.** Obligatory Tax. Cardinal Stepinac Foundation.
247 **98** 150 d. black, mve & gold 10 10

**1993.** 1st Anniv of Croatia's Membership of Universal Postal Union.
248 **99** 1800 d. multicoloured .. 70 70

**100** Paljetak

**1993.** Birth Centenary of Vlaho Paljetak (singer-songwriter).
249 **100** 500 d. multicoloured .. 10 10

**101** Peter Zrinski and Krsto Frankopan

**1993.** Obligatory Tax. Zrinski-Frankopan Foundation.
250 **101** 200 d. blue and grey .. 10 10

**102** "Freedom of Croatia" (central motif of 1918 stamp)

**1993.** Stamp Day.
251 **102** 600 d. multicoloured .. 10 10

**103** Red Cross

**1993.** Obligatory Tax. Anti-tuberculosis Week.
252 **103** 300 d. green, blk & red 10 10

**104** Antonio Magini's Map of Istria, 1620

**105** Smiciklas

**1993.** 50th Anniv of Incorporation of Istria, Rijeka and Zadar into Croatia.
253 **104** 2200 d. multicoloured .. 45 45

**1993.** 150th Birth Anniv of Tadija Smiciklas (historian).
254 **105** 800 d. black, gold & red 20 20

**1993.** Obligatory Tax. Croatian Anti-cancer League.
255 **71** 400 d. multicoloured .. 10 10

**106** Allegory of Birth of Croatian History on Shores of the Adriatic

**1993.** Centenary of National Archaeological Museum, Split.
256 **106** 1000 d. multicoloured .. 20 20

**107** Girl In Heart

**108** Croatian and French Flags and Soldiers

**1993.** Obligatory Tax.
257 **107** 400 d. red, blue & black 10 10

**1993.** 50th Anniv of Uprising of 13th Pioneer Battalion, Villefranche-de-Rouergue, France.
258 **108** 3000 d. multicoloured .. 65 65

**109** Tomic

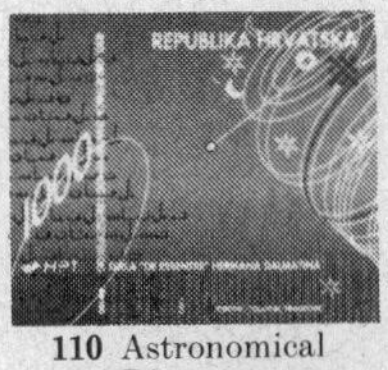

**110** Astronomical Diagram

**1993.** 150th Birth Anniv of Josip Eugen Tomic (writer).
259 **109** 900 d. brown, grn & red 20 20

**1993.** 850th Anniv of Publication of "De Essentiis" by Herman Dalmatin.
260 **110** 1000 d. multicoloured .. 20 20

**111** Christmas on the Battlefield

**112** Skiers

**1993.** Christmas. Multicoloured.
261 1000 d. Type **111** .. .. 20 20
262 4000 d. "Nativity" (fresco, St. Mary's Church, Dvigrad) .. .. 85 85

**1993.** Cent of Competitive Skiing in Croatia.
263 **112** 1000 d. multicoloured .. 20 20

**113** Decorations and Badge

**1993.** 125th Anniv of Croatian Militia.
264 **113** 1100 d. multicoloured .. 25 25

**114** Printing Press

**1994.** 500th Anniv of Printing of First Croatian Book (a Glagolitic missal), Senj.
265 **114** 2200 d. brown and red 50 50

115 Skier

**1994.** Winter Olympic Games, Lillehammer, Norway.
266 **115** 4000 d. multicoloured . . 85 85

116 Iguanodon

117 Masthead

**1994.** Croatian Dinosaur Fossils from West Istria. Multicoloured.
267 2400 d. Type **116** . . . . 50 50
268 4000 d. Iguanodon, skeleton and map . . 85 85
Nos. 267/8 were issued together, se-tenant, forming a composite design.

**1994.** 150th Anniv of "Zora Dalmatinska" (literary periodical).
269 **117** 800 d. multicoloured . . 15 15

118 University, Emperor Leopold I's Seal and Vice-chancellor's Chain

119 Wolf

**1994.** 325th Anniv of Croatian University, Zagreb.
270 **118** 2200 d. multicoloured . . 50 50

**1994.** Planet Earth Day.
271 **119** 3800 d. multicoloured . . 80 80

120 Safety Signs and Worker wearing Protective Clothing

121 Globe and Map

**1994.** 75th Anniv of I.L.O. and 50th Anniv of Philadelphia Declaration (social charter).
272 **120** 1000 d. multicoloured . . 20 20

**1994.** Obligatory Tax. Red Cross Week.
273 **121** 500 d. blk, stone & red 10 10

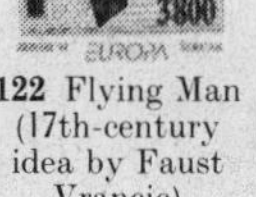

122 Flying Man (17th-century idea by Faust Vrancic)

123 Red Cross

**1994.** Europa. Inventions. Multicoloured.
274 3800 d. Type **122** . . . . 80 80
275 4000 d. Quill and pencil writing surname (technical pencil by Slavoljub Penkala, 1906) (34 × 28 mm) . . . . 85 85

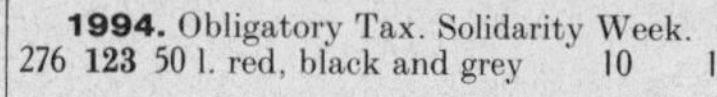
**1994.** Obligatory Tax. Solidarity Week.
276 **123** 50 l. red, black and grey 10 10

124 Croatian Iris

125 Petrovic

**1994.** Flowers. Multicoloured.
277 2 k. 40 Type **124** . . . . 55 55
278 4 k. Meadow saffron . . 90 90

**1994.** 1st Death Anniv of Drazen Petrovic (basketball player).
279 **125** 1 k. multicoloured . . 20 20

126 Plitvice Lakes

**1994.** 150th Anniv of Tourism in Croatia. Multicoloured.
280 80 l. Type **126** . . . . 20 20
281 1 k. River Krka . . . . 20 20
282 1 k. 10 Kornati Islands . . 25 25
283 2 k. 20 Kopacki Trscak ornithological reserve . . 50 50
284 2 k. 40 Opatija Riviera . . 55 55
285 3 k. 80 Brijuni Islands . . 85 85
286 4 k. Trakoscan Castle, Zagorje . . . . 90 90

127 Baranovic at Keyboard

128 Ornament from Ludbreg Shrine

**1994.** Musical Anniversaries.
287 **127** 1 k. multicoloured . . 20 20
288 – 2 k. 20 silver, blk & red 50 50
289 – 2 k. 40 multicoloured 55 55
DESIGNS—VERT: 1 k. Type **127** (birth centenary of Kresimir Baranovic (composer and conductor/director of Croatian National Theatre Opera, Zagreb, 1915–40)); 2 k. 20, Vatroslav Lisinski (composer, 175th birth anniv). HORIZ: 2 k. 40, Score and harp player (350th anniv of Pauline song-book).

**1994.** Obligatory Tax.
290 **128** 50 l. multicoloured . . 10 10

129 Men dressed in Croatian and American Colours

130 Mother and Children

**1994.** Centenary of Croatian Brotherhood in U.S.A.
291 **129** 2 k. 20 multicoloured . . 50 50

**1994.** Obligatory Tax. Spastic Children's Week.
292 **130** 50 l. multicoloured . . 10 10

131 Family

132 St. George and the Dragon

**1994.** International Year of the Family.
293 **131** 80 l. multicoloured . . 20 20

**1994.** Obligatory Tax. Croatian Anti-Cancer League.
294 **132** 50 l. multicoloured . . 10 10

133 Pope John Paul II and his Arms

134 Franjo Bucar (Committee member, 1920–46)

**1994.** Papal Visit.
295 **133** 1 k. multicoloured . . 20 20

**1994.** Centenary of International Olympic Committee.
296 **134** 1 k. multicoloured . . 20 20

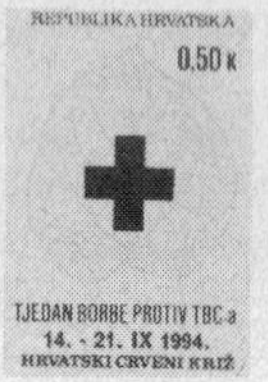

135 Red Cross on Leaf

136 The Little Prince (book character)

**1994.** Obligatory Tax. Anti-tuberculosis Week.
297 **135** 50 l. red, green & black 10 10

**1994.** 50th Death Anniv of Antoine de Saint-Exupery (writer).
298 **136** 3 k. 80 multicoloured . . 85 85

137 "Resurrection" (lunette, Gati, Omis)

**1994.** 13th International Convention on Christian Archaeology, Split and Porec.
299 **137** 4 k. multicoloured . . 90 90

138 "Still Life with Fruits and Basket" (Marino Tartaglia)

**1994.** Paintings. Multicoloured.
300 2 k. 40 Type **138** . . . . 55 55
301 3 k. 80 "In the Park" (Milan Steiner) . . 85 85
302 4 k. "Self-portrait" (Vilko Gecan) . . . . . . 90 90

**MINIMUM PRICE**

The minimum price quoted is 10p which represents a handling charge rather than a basis for valuing common stamps. For further notes about prices see introductory pages.

139 Plan of Fortress

**1994.** Obligatory Tax. 750th Anniv of Slavonski Brod.
303 **139** 50 l. yellow, black & red 10 10

140 I.O.C. Centenary Emblem and Flame

**1994.** Obligatory Tax. National Olympic Committee. Designs incorporating either the National Olympic Committee emblem or the International Olympic Committee centenary emblem.
304 50 l. Type **140** . . . . 10 10
305 50 l. As T **140** but with National Olympic Committee emblem . . 10 10
306 50 l. Tennis and national emblem (vert) . . . . 10 10
307 50 l. Football and centenary emblem (vert) 10 10
308 50 l. As No. 306 but with centenary emblem (vert) 10 10
309 50 l. As No. 307 but with national emblem (vert) 10 10
310 50 l. Basketball and centenary emblem (vert) 10 10
311 50 l. Handball and national emblem (vert) . . . . 10 10
312 50 l. As No. 310 but with national emblem (vert) 10 10
313 50 l. As No. 311 but with centenary emblem (vert) 10 10
314 50 l. Kayaks and national emblem (vert) . . . . 10 10
315 50 l. Water polo and centenary emblem (vert) 10 10
316 50 l. As No. 314 but with centenary emblem (vert) 10 10
317 50 l. As No. 315 but with national emblem (vert) 10 10
318 50 l. Running and centenary emblem (vert) 10 10
319 50 l. Gymnastics and national emblem (vert) 10 10
320 50 l. As No. 318 but with national emblem (vert) 10 10
321 50 l. As No. 319 but with centenary emblem (vert) 10 10

141 Cover of "Gazophylacium"

142 St. Mark's Church and Gas Lamp

**1994.** 400th Birth Anniv of Ivan Belostenec (lexicographer).
322 **141** 2 k. 20 multicoloured . . 55 55

**1994.** 900th Annivs of Zagreb (323/5) and Zagreb Bishopric (326). Multicoloured.
323 1 k. Type **142** . . . . 25 25
324 1 k. Street scene from early film, Maxi Cat (cartoon character) and left side of Zagreb Exchange . . 25 25
325 1 k. Right side of Zagreb Exchange, S. Penkala's biplane and Cibona building . . . . 25 25
326 4 k. 15th-century bishop's crosier and 17th-century view of Zagreb by Valvasor . . . . 25 25
Nos. 323/6 were issued together, se-tenant, forming a composite design.

**143** "Epiphany" (relief, Vrhovac Church)

**1994.** Christmas.
328 **143** 1 k. multicoloured .. 25 25

**144** "The Moving of the Holy House" (Giovanni Battista Tiepolo)

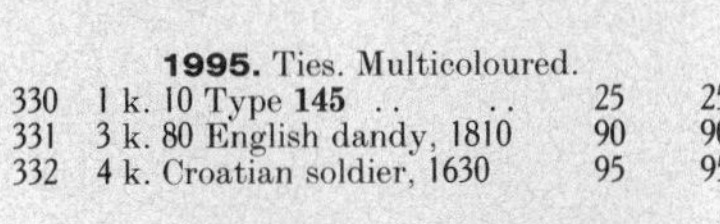

**145** Modern Tie

**1994.** 700th Anniv of St. Mary's Sanctuary, Loreto.
329 **144** 4 k. multicoloured .. 95 95

**1995.** Ties. Multicoloured.
330 1 k. 10 Type **145** .. .. 25 25
331 3 k. 80 English dandy, 1810 90 90
332 4 k. Croatian soldier, 1630 95 95

**146** St. Catherine's Church and Monastery, Zagreb, and Jesuit

**1995.** Monasteries. Multicoloured.
334 1 k. Type **146** (350th anniv) 25 25
335 2 k. 40 St Paul's Monastery, Visovac, and Franciscan monk (550th anniv) .. .. .. 60 60

**147** Istrian Short-haired Hunting Dog

**1995.** Dogs. Multicoloured.
336 2 k. 20 Type **147** .. .. 55 55
337 2 k. 40 Posavinian hunting dog .. .. .. 60 60
338 3 k. 80 Istrian wire-haired hunting dog .. .. 90 90

**148** Rowing

**1995.** Obligatory Tax. National Olympic Committee. Multicoloured.
339 50 l. Type **148** .. .. 10 10
340 50 l. Petanque .. .. 10 10
341 50 l. Monument to Drazen Petrovic, Olympic Park, Lausanne .. .. 10 10
342 50 l. Tennis .. .. 10 10
343 50 l. Basketball .. .. 10 10

**149** Emperor Diocletian's Palace

**1995.** 1700th Anniv of Split. Multicoloured.
344 1 k. Type **149** .. .. 10 10
345 2 k. 20 "Split Harbour" (Emanuel Vidovic) .. 55 55
346 4 k. View of city and bust of Marko Marulic (Ivan Mestrovic) .. .. 95 95

**150** Player

**151** Woman's Head

**1995.** World Handball Championship, Iceland.
348 **150** 4 k. multicoloured .. 95 95

**1995.** Obligatory Tax. Red Cross Week.
349 **151** 50 l. black and red .. 10 10

**152** Storm Clouds and Clear Sky

**1995.** Europa. Peace and Freedom. Mult.
350 2 k. 40 Type **152** .. .. 60 60
351 4 k. Angel (detail of sculpture, Francesco Robba) .. .. 95 95

**153** Shadow behind Cross

**1995.** 150th Anniv of July Riots (352) and 50th Anniv of Croatian Surrender at Bleiburg (353). Multicoloured.
352 1 k. 10 Type **153** .. 25 25
353 3 k. 80 Sunrise behind cross 90 90

**154** Arms and Hand holding Rose

**155** Hands

**1995.** Independence Day.
354 **154** 1 k. 10 multicoloured .. 25 25

**1995.** Obligatory Tax. Red Cross.
355 **155** 50 l. multicoloured .. 10 10

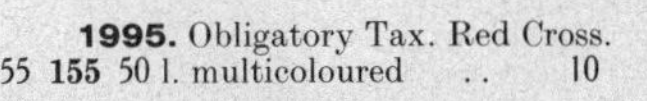

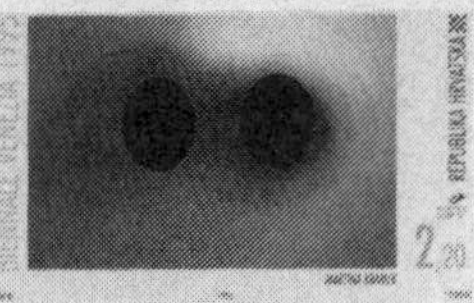

**156** "Installation" (detail) (Martina Kramer)

**1995.** 46th Venice Biennale. Work by Croatian artists. Multicoloured.
356 2 k. 20 Type **156** .. .. 55 55
357 2 k. 40 "Paracelsus Paraduchamps" (Mirk Zrinscak) (vert) .. 60 60
358 4 k. "Shadows/136" (Goran Petercol) .. .. 95 95

**157** "St. Antony" (detail of polyptych, Ljubo Babic)

**1995.** 800th Birth Anniv of St. Antony of Padua.
359 **157** 1 k. multicoloured .. 25 25

**158** Loggerhead Turtle

**1995.** Animals. Multicoloured.
360 2 k. 40 Type **158** .. .. 60 60
361 4 k. Bottle-nosed dolphin 95 95

**159** Osijek Cathedral

**160** "Croatian Pieta"

**1995.** Obligatory Tax.
362 **159** 65 l. multicoloured .. 15 15

**1995.** Obligatory Tax. "Holy Mother of Freedom" War Memorial.
363 **160** 65 l. on 50 l. black, red and blue .. .. 15 15
364 – 65 l. blue and yellow .. 15 15
DESIGN: 65 l. Projected memorial church.
No. 363 was not issued without surcharge.

**161** Town and Fortress

**1995.** Liberation of Knin.
365 **161** 1 k. 30 multicoloured .. 30 30

**162** Electric Power Plant

**1995.** Centenary of Jaruga Hydro-electric Power Station, River Krka.
366 **162** 3 k. 60 multicoloured .. 85 85

**163** Postman

**1995.** Stamp Day.
367 **163** 1 k. 30 multicoloured .. 30 30

**165** Suppe and "The Fair Galatea" (statue)

**1995.** Death Centenary of Franz von Suppe (composer).
369 **165** 6 k. 50 multicoloured .. 1·50 1·50

**166** Arms, Fortress and Knights

**167** Ivo Tijardovic

**1995.** 400th Anniv of Habsburg Capture of Petrinja.
370 **166** 2 k. 20 multicoloured .. 50 50

**1995.** Composers' Anniversaries. Mult.
371 1 k. 20 Type **167** (birth centenary) .. .. 30 30
372 1 k. 40 Lovro von Matacic (10th death) .. .. 30 30
373 6 k. 50 Jakov Gotovac (birth centenary) .. 1·50 1·50

**168** Herman Bolle (architect, 150th birth)

**1995.** Anniversaries. Multicoloured.
374 1 k. 30 Type **168** .. .. 30 30
375 2 k. 40 Izidor Krsnjavi (artist and art administrator, 150th birth) .. .. .. 55 55
376 3 k. 60 Gala curtain by Vlaho Bukovac (cent of National Theatre) .. 85 85

**169** Children in Nest

**170** Left-hand Detail of Curtain

**1995.** Obligatory Tax.
377 **169** 65 l. multicoloured .. 15 15

**1995.** Obligatory Tax. Centenary of National Theatre, Zagreb. Details of gala curtain by Vlaho Bukovac. Multicoloured.
378 65 l. Type **170** .. .. 15 15
379 65 l. Central detail .. 15 15
380 65 l. Right-hand detail .. 15 15
Nos. 378/80 were issued together, se-tenant, forming a composite design.

171 Zagrebacka Street, Bjelovar

172 "50"

**1995.** Croatian Towns (3rd series). Mult.
381 1 k. Type **171** .. .. 25 25
382 1 k. 30 St. Peter and St. Paul's Cathedral, Osijek (vert) .. .. .. 30 30
383 1 k. 40 Castle, Cakovec (vert) .. .. .. 30 30
384 2 k. 20 Rovinj .. 50 50
385 2 k. 40 Korcula .. .. 55 55
386 3 k. 60 Town Hall, Zupanja 85 85

**1996.** 50th Anniversaries. Multicoloured.
395 3 k. 60 Type **172** (U.N.O.) 85 85
396 3 k. 60 "5" and "FAO" within biscuit forming "50" (F.A.O.) .. .. 85 85

173 Spiro Brusina (zoologist)

174 Birds flying through Sky

**1995.** Anniversaries. Multicoloured.
397 1 k. Type **173** (150th birth) 25 25
398 2 k. 20 Bogoslav Sulek (philologist, death cent) 50 50
399 6 k. 50 Faust Vrancic's "Dictionary of Five European Languages" (400th anniv of publication) .. .. 1·50 1·50

**1995.** Obligatory Tax. Anti-drugs Campaign.
400 **174** 65 l. multicoloured .. 15 15

175 Breast Screening

176 Hands reading Braille

**1995.** Obligatory Tax. Breast Screening Campaign.
401 **175** 65 l. multicoloured .. 15 15

**1995.** Centenary of Institute for Blind Children, Zagreb.
402 **176** 1 k. 20 multicoloured .. 30 30

177 Animals under Christmas Tree

**1995.** Christmas.
403 **177** 1 k. 30 multicoloured .. 30 30

178 Polo, Animals in Boat and Court of Kublai Khan

**1995.** 700th Anniv of Marco Polo's Return from China.
404 **178** 3 k. 60 multicoloured .. 85 85

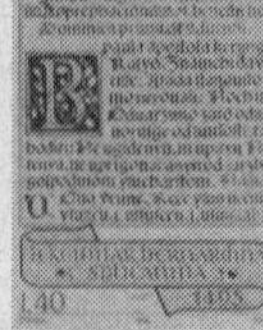

179 Hrvatska Kostajnica

180 Lectionary of Bernardin of Split, 1495 (first printed book using Cakavian dialect)

**1995.** Liberated Towns. Multicoloured.
405 20 l. Type **179** .. .. 10 10
406 30 l. Slunj .. .. 10 10
407 50 l. Gracac .. .. 10 10
410 1 k. 20 Drnis (vert) .. 30 30
414 6 k. 50 Glina .. .. 1·50 1·50
418 10 k. Obrovac (vert) .. 2·25 2·25

**1995.** Incunabula. Multicoloured.
420 1 k. 40 Type **180** .. .. 30 30
421 3 k. 60 "Spovid Opcena" (manual for confessors), 1496 (first book printed in Croatia) .. .. 85 85

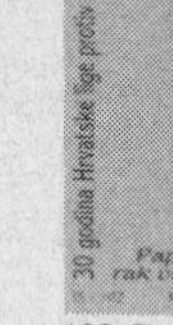

181 Crucifix

182 Breast Cancer Campaign

**1996.** Events and Anniversaries. Mult.
422 1 k. 30 St. Marko Krizevcanin (detail of mosaic (Ante Starcevic), St. Marko's Church, Zagreb) (canonization) 30 30
423 1 k. 30 Type **181** (700th anniv of veneration of miraculous crucifix, St. Guido's Church, Rijeka) 30 30
424 1 k. 30 Ivan Merz (teacher and Catholic youth worker, birth centenary) 30 30

**1996.** Obligatory Tax. 30th Anniv of Anti-Cancer League.
425 **182** 65 l. multicoloured .. 15 15

183 Eugen Kvaternik (125th anniv of Rakovica Uprising)

184 Madonna and Child and Church

**1996.** Anniversaries. Muticoloured.
426 1 k. 20 Type **183** .. .. 30 30
427 1 k. 40 Ante Starcevic (politician, death centenary) (vert) .. 30 30
428 2 k. 20 Stjepan Radic (founder of Neutral Peasant Party) (125th birth anniv and 75th anniv of Peasant Republic constitution) (vert) .. .. .. 50 50
429 3 k. 60 Collage (75th anniv of Labin Republic) (vert) 85 85

**1996.** Obligatory Tax. St. Mary of Bistrica Sanctuary.
430 **184** 65 l. multicoloured .. 15 15

185 Julije Domac (founder) and Culture

**1996.** Centenary of Pharmacology Institute, University of Zagreb.
431 **185** 6 k. 50 multicoloured .. 1·50 1·50

186 Score

187 Cvijeta Zuzoric (beauty)

**1996.** Music Anniversaries. Multicoloured.
432 2 k. 20 Type **186** (400th birth anniv of Vinko Jelic, composer) .. 50 50
433 2 k. 20 "O" over musical bars (150th anniv of "Love and Malice" (first Croatian opera) by Vatroslav Lisinski) .. 50 50
434 2 k. 20 Josip Slavenski (composer, birth cent) .. 50 50
435 2 k. 20 "Lijepa nasa domovino" (birth bicent of Antun Mihanovic and 175th birth anniv of Josip Runjanin (composers of National Anthem)) .. .. 50 50

**1996.** Europa. Famous Women. Mult.
436 2 k. 20 Type **187** .. .. 50 50
437 3 k. 60 Ivana Brlic-Mazuranic (writer) .. 85 85

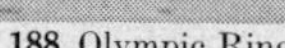

188 Olympic Rings

189 Nikola Subic Zrinski of Sziget (Ban of Croatia)

**1996.** Obligatory Tax. National Olympic Committee.
438 **188** 65 l. multicoloured .. 15 15

**1996.** 16th and 17th-century Members of Zrinski and Frankopan Families. Mult.
439 1 k. 30 Type **189** .. .. 30 30
440 1 k. 40 Nikola Zrinski (Ban (vice-roy) of Croatia) .. 30 30
441 2 k. 20 Petar Zrinski (Ban of Croatia) .. .. 50 50
442 2 k. 40 Katarina Zrinski (wife of Petar) .. .. 55 55
443 3 k. 60 Fran Krsto Frankopan (writer and revolutionary) .. .. 85 85

190 Child outside House

191 Soldier carrying Child

**1996.** Obligatory Tax. Red Cross Fund.
445 **190** 65 l. black and red .. 15 15

**1996.** 5th Anniv of National Guard.
446 **191** 1 k. 30 multicoloured .. 30 30

192 Istrian Bluebell

193 Child with Red Cross Parcel

**1996.** Flowers. Multicoloured.
447 2 k. 40 Type **192** .. .. 55 55
448 3 k. 60 Dubrovnik corn-flower .. .. .. 85 85

**1996.** Obligatory Tax. Solidarity Week.
449 **193** 65 l. black and red .. 15 15

194 Football

**1996.** European Football Championship, England.
450 **194** 2 k. 20 black and red .. 50 50

195 Konscak's Map of California

196 Children sitting outside House

**1996.** 250th Anniv of Father Ferdinand Konscak's Expedition to Lower California.
451 **195** 2 k. 40 multicoloured .. 55 55

**1996.** Obligatory Tax. Children's Rights.
452 **196** 65 l. multicoloured .. 15 15

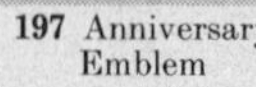

197 Anniversary Emblem

198 Man holding Dumb-bell and Falcon

**1996.** Obligatory Tax. 800th Anniv of Osijek.
453 **197** 65 l. blue, orge & grey 15 15

**1996.** 150th Birth Anniv of Josip Fon (founder of Croatian Falcon gymnastics society).
454 **198** 1 k. 40 multicoloured .. 30 30

199 Olympic Colours and Rings

200 Cathedral

**1996.** Olympic Games, Atlanta, and Centenary of Modern Olympics.
455 **199** 3 k. 60 multicoloured .. 85 85

**1996.** Obligatory Tax. Dakovo Cathedral.
456 **200** 65 l. multicoloured .. 15 15

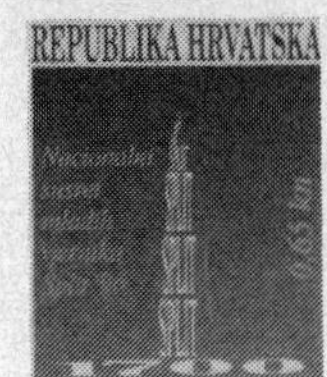

**201** "Church Tower"

**202** Crucifix

**1996.** Obligatory Tax. 1700th Anniv of Split.

457 **201** 65 l. ultramarine & blue 15 15

**1996.** Obligatory Tax. Vukovar.

458 **202** 65 l. multicoloured .. 15 15

**203** Lighted Candle, Shell and Lilies

**204** Tweezers holding Stamp

**1996.** Obligatory Tax. Anti-drugs Campaign.

459 **203** 65 l. multicoloured .. 15 15

**1996.** Stamp Day. 5th Anniv of Issue of First Postage Stamp by Independent Croatia.

460 **204** 1 k. 30 multicoloured .. 30 30

OFFICIAL STAMPS

O **11.**

O **12.**

**1942.**

O 55. O **11.** 25 b. red .. .. 10 10
O 56. 50 b. grey .. .. 10 10
O 57. 75 b. green .. .. 10 10
O 58. 1 k. brown .. .. 10 10
O 59. 2 k. blue .. .. 10 10
O 60. 3 k. red .. .. 10 10
O 61. 3 k. 50 red .. .. 10 10
O 62. 4 k. purple .. .. 10 10
O 63. 5 k. blue .. .. 10 15
O 64. 6 k. violet .. .. 10 10
O 65. 10 k. green .. .. 10 10
O 66. 12 k. red .. .. 10 10
O 67. 12 k. 50 orange .. 10 10
O 68. 20 k. blue .. .. 10 10
O 69. O **12.** 30 k. grey and brown 10 10
O 70. 40 k. grey and violet 10 15
O 71. 50 k. grey and red .. 25 30
O 72. 100 k. salmon & black 25 30

POSTAGE DUE STAMPS

**1941.** Nos. D 259/63 of Yugoslavia optd. **NEZAVISNA/DRZAVA/HRVATSKA** in three lines above a chequered shield.

D 26. D **10.** 50 p. violet .. .. 15 25
D 27. 1 d. red .. .. 15 25
D 28. 2 d. blue .. .. 6·00 9·25
D 29. 5 d. orange .. .. 35 70
D 30. 10 d. brown .. 2·75 4·50

D **9.**

D **15.**

**1941.**

D 51. D **9.** 50 b. red .. .. 10 15
D 52. 1 k. red .. .. 10 15
D 53. 2 k. red .. .. 15 30
D 54. 5 k. red .. .. 25 50
D 55. 10 k. red .. .. 35 60

**1942.**

D 67. D **15.** 50 b. olive and blue 10 15
D 68. 1 k. olive and blue .. 10 15
D 69. 2 k. olive and blue .. 15 25
D 76. 4 k. olive and blue .. 10 15
D 70. 5 k. olive and blue .. 15 25
D 78. 6 k. olive and blue .. 10 20
D 79. 10 k. blue and indigo 15 25
D 80. 15 k. blue and indigo 15 25
D 72. 20 k. blue and indigo 45 80

## CUBA Pt. 15

An island in the W. Indies, ceded by Spain to the United States in 1898. A republic under U.S. protection until 1901 when the island became independent. The issues to 1871, except Nos. 13, 14, 19, 20/7, 32, 44 and 48, were for Puerto Rico also.

1855. 8 reales Plata Fuerte (strong silver reales) = 1 peso.
1866. 100 centimos = 1 escudo.
1871. 100 centimos = 1 peseta.
1881. 100 milesimas = 100 centavos = 1 peso.
1898. 100 cents = $1 U.S.A.
1899. 100 centavos = 1 peso.

### SPANISH COLONY

1. 5.

**1855.** Imperf.
6 1 ½ r. green .. .. 5·00 50
9 ½ r. blue .. .. 2·50 50
10 1 r. green .. .. 2·40 50
11a 2 r. red .. .. .. 9·25 2·75

Nos. 10/11 optd **HABILITADO POR LA NACION** were issues of Philippines (Nos. 44/5).

**1855.** No. 11a surch **Y ¼**.
12 1 Y¼ on 2 r. red .. .. £160 55·00

**1862.** Imperf.
13 5 ¼ r. black on buff .. 9·50 11·50

6. 7.

**1864.** Imperf.
14 6 ¼ r. black on buff .. 11·50 16·00
15 ½ r. green .. .. 3·00 50
16 ½ r. green on pink .. 9·00 1·50
17 1 r. blue on brown .. 2·50 55
18b 2 r. red .. .. .. 15·00 4·50

**1866.** Dated "1866". Imperf.
19 7 5 c. mauve .. .. 21·00 27·00
20 10 c. blue .. .. 2·75 60
21 20 c. green .. .. 1·25 60
22 40 c. pink .. .. 7·00 5·50

**1866.** No. 14 optd **66**. Imperf.
23 6 ¼ r. black on buff .. 42·00 55·00

**1867.** Dated "1867". Perf.
24 7 5 c. mauve .. .. 32·00 15·00
25 10 c. blue .. .. 16·00 60
26 20 c. green .. .. 11·00 60
27 40 c. pink .. .. 11·00 12·00

9. 11.

**1868.** Dated "1868".
28 9 5 c. lilac .. .. 11·00 9·00
29 10 c. blue .. .. 2·50 1·00
30 20 c. green .. .. 4·50 2·25
31 40 c. pink .. .. 11·00 5·25

**1868.** Nos. 28/31 optd **HABILITADO POR LA NACION**.
36 9 5 c. lilac .. .. 42·00 27·00
37 10 c. blue .. .. 42·00 27·00
38 20 c. green .. .. 42·00 27·00
39 40 c. pink .. .. 42·00 27·00

**1869.** Dated "1869".
32 9 5 c. pink .. .. 17·00 8·50
33 10 c. brown .. .. 2·50 1·25
34 20 c. orange .. .. 4·00 1·90
35 40 c. lilac .. .. 24·00 8·00

**1869.** Nos. 32/5 optd **HABILITADO POR LA NACION**.
40 9 5 c. pink .. .. 95·00 32·00
41 10 c. brown .. .. 40·00 25·00
42 20 c. orange .. .. 35·00 25·00
43 40 c. lilac .. .. 50·00 25·00

**1870.**
44 11 5 c. blue .. .. £120 55·00
45 10 c. green .. .. 1·50 50
46 20 c. brown .. .. 1·50 50
47 40 c. pink .. .. £120 28·00

12. 13.

**1871.** Dated "1871".
48 12 12 c. lilac .. .. 10·00 8·00
49 25 c. blue .. .. 1·60 60
50 50 c. green .. .. 1·60 60
51 1 p. brown .. .. 23·00 5·50

**1873.**
52 13 12½ c. green .. .. 16·00 9·00
53 25 c. grey .. .. 1·50 50
54 50 c. brown .. .. 85 50
55 1 p. brown .. .. £200 28·00

**1874.** Dated "1874".
56 12 12½ c. brown .. .. 6·50 6·00
57 25 c. blue .. .. 45 40
58 50 c. lilac .. .. 55 40
59 1 p. red .. .. £100 50·00

14. 15.

**1875.**
60 14 12½ c. mauve .. .. 60 85
61 25 c. blue .. .. 30 15
62 50 c. green .. .. 30 15
63 1 p. brown .. .. 6·00 3·25

**1876.** Inscr "ULTRAMAR 1876".
64 15 12½ c. green .. .. 1·40 1·50
65a 25 c. lilac .. .. 45 25
66 50 c. blue .. .. 45 25
67 1 p. black .. .. 5·75 2·75

**1877.** Inscr "CUBA 1877".
68 15 10 c. green .. .. 17·00
69 12½ c. lilac .. .. 4·50 3·00
70 25 c. green .. .. 30 10
71 50 c. black .. .. 30 10
72 1 p. brown .. .. 22·00 8·75

**1878.** Inscr "CUBA 1878".
73 15 5 c. blue .. .. 25 20
74 10 c. black .. .. 45·00
75a 12½ c. bistre .. .. 2·40 1·75
76a 25 c. green .. .. 15 10
77 50 c. green .. .. 15 10
78 1 p. red .. .. 6·00 3·75

**1879.** Inscr "CUBA 1879".
79 15 5 c. black .. .. 35 25
80 10 c. orange .. .. 70·00 30·00
81 12½ c. pink .. .. 35 25
82 25 c. blue .. .. 35 25
83 50 c. grey .. .. 35 25
84 1 p. bistre .. .. 11·00 7·25

**1880.** "Alfonso XII" key-type inscr "CUBA 1880".
85 X 5 c. green .. .. 25 10
86 10 c. red .. .. 50·00
87 12½ c. lilac .. .. 25 10
88 25 c. lilac .. .. 25 10
89 50 c. brown .. .. 25 10
90 1 p. brown .. .. 3·00 1·90

**1881.** "Alfonso XII" key-type inscr "CUBA 1881".
91 X 1 c. green .. .. 25 10
92 2 c. pink .. .. 26·00
93a 2½ c. bistre .. .. 50 10
94 5 c. lilac .. .. 25 10
95 10 c. brown .. .. 25 10
96 20 c. brown .. .. 3·25 3·25

**1882.** "Alfonso XII" key-type inscr "CUBA".
97 X 1 c. green .. .. 35 15
98 2 c. pink .. .. 1·40 15
118 2½ c. brown .. .. 20 10
119 2½ c. mauve .. .. 65 45
100 5 c. lilac .. .. 1·40 20
123 5 c. grey .. .. 1·75 25
101 10 c. brown .. .. 30 10
126 10 c. blue .. .. 85 55
121 20 c. brown .. .. 11·00 1·90
122 20 c. lilac .. .. 11·00 2·75

**1883.** 1882 issue optd or surch with fancy pattern.
103 X 5 c. lilac .. .. 1·50 80
106 5 on 5 c. lilac .. .. 1·00 65
104 10 c. brown .. .. 4·00 3·75
107 10 on 10 c. brown .. 1·60 1·00
105 20 c. brown .. .. 65·00 29·00
111 20 on 20 c. brown .. 16·00 11·50

The surcharges exist in four different patterns.

**1890.** "Baby" key-type inscr "ISLA DE CUBA".
135 Y 1 c. brown .. .. 8·75 5·50
147 1 c. grey .. .. 5·00 2·75
159 1 c. blue .. .. 2·10 30
169 1 c. purple .. .. 65 20
136 2 c. blue .. .. 4·75 1·75
148 2 c. brown .. .. 95 35
160 2 c. pink .. .. 21·00 4·25
170 2 c. red .. .. 5·50 15
137 2½ c. green .. .. 6·50 3·50
149 2½ c. orange .. .. 29·00 8·00
161 2½ c. mauve .. .. 1·90 20
171 2½ c. pink .. .. 40 15
138 5 c. grey .. .. 50 55
150 5 c. green .. .. 60 35
172 5 c. blue .. .. 30 15
139 10 c. brown .. .. 1·90 70
151 10 c. pink .. .. 1·25 35
173 10 c. green .. .. 1·50 15
140 20 c. purple .. .. 50 45
152 20 c. blue .. .. 6·50 6·50
162 20 c. brown .. .. 16·00 8·50
174 20 c. lilac .. .. 9·50 4·25
175 40 c. brown .. .. 19·00 10·00
176 80 c. brown .. .. 32·00 15·00

**1898.** "Curly Head" key-type inscr "CUBA 1898 y 99".
183 Z 1 m. brown .. .. 20 15
184 2 m. brown .. .. 20 15
185 3 m. brown .. .. 20 15
186 4 m. brown .. .. 2·50 1·25
187 5 m. brown .. .. 15 15
188 1 c. purple .. .. 15 15
189 2 c. green .. .. 15 15
190 3 c. brown .. .. 15 15
191 4 c. orange .. .. 6·00 2·00
192 5 c. pink .. .. 55 15
193 6 c. blue .. .. 20 15
194 8 c. brown .. .. 50 20
195 10 c. red .. .. 65 20
196 15 c. grey .. .. 2·50 20
197 20 c. purple .. .. 30 10
198 40 c. mauve .. .. 1·60 15
199 60 c. black .. .. 1·75 15
200 80 c. brown .. .. 8·00 6·00
201 1 p. green .. .. 8·00 6·00
202 2 p. blue .. .. 16·00 6·00

### OFFICIAL STAMPS

**1860.** As Nos. O50/3 of Spain but without full points after "OFICIAL" and "ONZAS" or "LIBRA". Imperf.
O12 ½ o. black on yellow .. — 30·00
O13 1 o. black on pink .. — 30·00
O14 4 o. black on green .. — £170
O15 1 l. black on blue .. — £350

The face values of Nos. O12/15 are expressed in onzas (ounces) or libra (pound), referring to the maximum weight for which each value could prepay postage.

### PRINTED MATTER STAMPS

All Printed Matter stamps are key-types inscribed "CUBA IMPRESOS".

**1888.** "Alfonso XII".
P 129. X. ½ m. black .. .. 15 10
P 130. 1 m. black .. .. 15 10
P 131. 2 m. black .. .. 15 10
P 132. 3 m. black .. .. 70 40
P 133. 4 m. black .. .. 1·10 70
P 134. 8 m. black .. .. 5·50 2·40

**1890.** "Baby".
P 141. Y. ½ m. brown .. .. 45 35
P 142. 1 m. brown .. .. 45 35
P 143. 2 m. brown .. .. 75 50
P 144. 3 m. brown .. .. 75 50
P 145. 4 m. brown .. .. 6·25 3·50
P 146. 8 m. brown .. .. 6·25 3·50

**1892.** "Baby".
P153 Y ½ m. lilac .. .. 10 10
P154 1 m. lilac .. .. 10 10
P155 2 m. lilac .. .. 20 10
P156 3 m. lilac .. .. 1·50 50
P157 4 m. lilac .. .. 3·50 3·00
P158 8 m. lilac .. .. 6·00 4·25

**1894.** "Baby".
P 163. Y. ½ m. pink .. .. 15 10
P 164. 1 m. pink .. .. 40 10
P 165. 2 m. pink .. .. 40 10
P 166. 3 m. pink .. .. 1·40 60
P 167. 4 m. pink .. .. 2·50 70
P 168. 8 m. pink .. .. 5·25 3·00

**1896.** "Baby".
P177 Y ½ m. green .. .. 15 10
P178 1 m. green .. .. 15 10
P179 2 m. green .. .. 15 10
P180 3 m. green .. .. 1·50 50
P181 4 m. green .. .. 3·50 3·00
P182 8 m. green .. .. 6·00 4·25

### UNITED STATES ADMINISTRATION

**1899.** Stamps of United States of 1894 surch. **CUBA** and value.
246. 1 c. on 1 c. green (No. 283) 2·50 45
247. 2 c. on 2 c. red (No. 270 C) 2·50 30
248. 2½ c. on 2 c. red (No. 270 C) 2·00 40
249. 3 c. on 3 c. violet (No. 271) 5·50 90
250. 5 c. on 5 c. blue (No. 286) 6·00 70
251. 10 c. on 10 c. brn. (No. 289) 14·00 5·50

**29.** Statue of Columbus.

Designs: 2 c. Palms. 3 c. Statue of "La India" (Woman). 5 c. Liner "Umbria" (Commerce). 10 c. Ploughing Sugar Plantation.

**1899.**
307. **29.** 1 c. green .. .. 1·10 10
308. – 2 c. red .. .. .. 1·10 10
303. – 3 c. purple .. .. 2·00 15
304. – 5 c. blue .. .. .. 3·00 45
310. – 10 c. brown .. .. 2·25 35

### POSTAGE DUE STAMPS

**1899.** Postage Due stamps of United States of 1894 surch. **CUBA** and value.
D 253. D **87.** 1 c. on 1 c. red .. 18·00 3·00
D 254. 2 c. on 2 c. red .. 18·00 2·75
D 255. 5 c. on 5 c. red .. 18·00 2·50
D 256. 10 c. on 10 c. red .. 16·00 1·00

### SPECIAL DELIVERY STAMP

**1899.** No. E283 of United States surch **CUBA. 10 c. de Peso.**
E252 E **46** 10 c. on 10 c. blue .. 90·00 70·00

### INDEPENDENT REPUBLIC

**1902.** Surch. **UN CENTAVO HABILITADO OCTUBRE 1902** and figure **1.**
306. – 1 c. on 3 c. pur. (No. 303) 1·75 40

**36.** Major-General Antonio Maceo. **37.** B. Maso.

**1907.**
311. **36.** 50 c. black and slate .. 1·10 40
318. 50 c. black and violet .. 1·10 40

**1910.**
312. **37.** 1 c. violet and green .. 55 15
320. 1 c. green .. .. 85 10
313. – 2 c. green and red .. 1·10 10
321. – 2 c. red .. .. 85 10
314. – 3 c. blue and violet .. 55 20
315. – 5 c. green and blue .. 10·00 75
322. – 5 c. blue .. .. 2·00 10
316. – 8 c. violet and olive .. 55 20
323. – 8 c. black and olive .. 2·00 35
317. – 10 c. blue and sepia .. 4·50 25
319. – 1 p. black and slate .. 6·50 3·00
324. – 1 p. black .. .. 4·00 1·10

Portraits: 2 c. M. Gomez. 3 c. J. Sanguily. 5 c. I. Agramonte. 8 c. C. Garcia. 10 c. Mayia. 1 p. C. Roloff.

**40.** Map of W. Indies. **43.** Gertrudis Gomez de Avellaneda.

**1914.**
325. **40.** 1 c. green .. .. 40 15
326. 2 c. red .. .. 40 15
328. 3 c. violet .. .. 2·00 25
329. 5 c. blue .. .. 2·25 15
330. 8 c. olive .. .. 2·25 65
331. 10 c. brown .. .. 3·75 70
332. 10 c. olive .. .. 3·25 70
333. 50 c. orange .. .. 28·00 9·00
334. $1 slate .. .. .. 40·00 17·00

**1914.** Birth Centenary of Gertrudis Gomez de Avellaneda (poetess).
335. **43.** 5 c. blue .. .. 8·00 3·00

44. Jose Marti.

47.

**1917.**

336 44 1 c. green .. 65 10
337 – 2 c. red (Gomez) .. 65 10
338 – 3 c. violet (La Luz) .. 65 10
339 – 5 c. blue (Garcia) .. 65 10
349a – 8 c. brown (Agramonte) 2·75 20
341 – 10 c. brown (Palma) .. 1·60 10
342 – 20 c. green (Saco) .. 5·00 45
343 – 50 c. red (Maceo) .. 8·00 45
344 – 1 p. black (Cespedes) .. 8·00 45

**1927.** 25th Anniv. of Republic.
352. **47.** 25 c. violet .. .. 8·50 3·25

48. PN 9 Flying Boat over Havana Harbour.

**1927.** Air.
353. **48.** 5 c. blue .. .. 3·25 1·40

49. T. Estrada Palma.

**1928.** 6th Pan-American Conf. As T **49.**
354. 1 c. green .. .. .. 25 15
355. 2 c. red .. .. .. 25 15
356. 5 c. blue .. .. .. 55 25
357. 8 c. brown .. .. 2·00 1·00
358. 10 c. brown .. .. 55 45
359. 13 c. orange .. .. 1·10 50
360. 20 c. olive .. .. 1·40 60
361. 30 c. purple .. .. 3·50 75
362. 50 c. red .. .. .. 4·50 1·75
363. 1 p. black .. .. 9·00 5·00

DESIGNS: 2 c. Gen. G. Machado. 5 c. El Morro, Havana. 8 c. Railway Station, Havana. 10 c. President's Palace. 13 c. Tobacco plantation. 20 c. Treasury Secretariat. 30 c. Sugar Mill. 50 c. Havana Cathedral. 1 p. Galician Immigrants' Centre, Havana.

**1928.** Air. Lindbergh Commem. Optd. **LINDBERGH FEBRERO 1928.**
364. **48.** 5 c. red .. .. 4·00 1·60

51. The Capitol, Havana.

52. Hurdler.

**1929.** Inaug. of Capitol.
365. **51.** 1 c. green .. .. 25 20
366. 2 c. red .. .. .. 30 35
367. 5 c. blue .. .. 40 30
368. 10 c. brown .. .. 75 35
369. 20 c. purple .. .. 3·25 1·40

**1930.** 2nd Central American Games, Havana.
370. **52.** 1 c. green .. .. 55 35
371. 2 c. red .. .. .. 55 40
372. 5 c. blue .. .. 85 40
373. 10 c. brown .. .. 1·40 85
374. 20 c. purple .. .. 9·00 3·00

**1930.** Air. Surch. **CORREO AEREO NACIONAL 10 C.**
375. **47.** 10 c. on 25 c. violet .. 2·75 1·10

54. Fokker Super Trimotor over Beach.

**1931.** Air.
376 54 5 c. green .. .. 20 10
377 8 c. red .. .. 2·25 60
378 10 c. blue .. .. 25 10
379 15 c. red .. .. 60 25
380 20 c. brown .. .. 65 10
381 30 c. purple .. .. 1·10 25
382 40 c. orange .. .. 2·75 45
383 50 c. green .. .. 3·00 50
384 1 p. black .. .. 5·75 1·75

55. Ford "Tin Goose" over Forest.

**1931.** Air.
385. **55.** 5 c. purple .. .. 20 10
386. 10 c. black .. .. 25 10
387. 20 c. red .. .. 1·25 35
388. 20 c. pink .. .. 2·25 70
389. 50 c. blue .. .. 3·75 1·00
390. 50 c. turquoise .. .. 2·75 90

56. Mangos of Baragua.

57. Battle of Mal Tiempo.

**1933.** 35th Anniv. of War of Independence.
391. **56.** 3 c. brown .. .. 80 20
392. **57.** 5 c. blue .. .. 60 30
393. – 10 c. green .. .. 1·60 30
394. – 13 c. red .. .. 1·90 90
395. – 20 c. black .. .. 4·00 3·25

DESIGNS—HORIZ. 10 c. Battle of Coliseo. 13 c. Maceo, Gomez and Zayas. VERT. 20 c. Campaign Monument.

**1933.** Establishment of Revolutionary Govt. Stamps of 1917 optd. **GOBIERNO REVOLUCIONARIO 4-9-1933** or surch. also.
396. **44.** 1 c. green .. .. 85 30
397. – 2 c. on 3 c. vio. (No. 338) 85 30

59. Dr. Carlos J. Finlay.

61. Map of Caribbean.

**1934.** 101st Birth Anniv. of C. J. Finlay ("yellow-fever" researcher).
398. **59.** 2 c. red .. .. 1·10 35
399. 5 c. blue .. .. 2·00 45

**1935.** Air. Havana-Miami "Air Train". Surch. **PRIMER TREN AEREO INTERNACIONAL. 1935 O'Meara y du Pont+10 cts.** Imperf. or perf.
400. **54.** 10 c.+10 c. red .. 4·25 4·25

**1936.** Free Port of Matanzas. Inscr. as in T **61.** Perf. or imperf. (same prices).
401. – 1 c. green (postage) .. 20 15
402. **61.** 2 c. red .. .. 30 15
403. – 4 c. purple .. .. 1·25 20
404. – 5 c. blue .. .. 1·25 20
405. – 8 c. brown .. .. 1·40 55
406. – 10 c. green .. .. 1·40 55
407. – 20 c. brown .. .. 2·75 2·25
408. – 50 c. slate .. .. 7·00 3·25
409. – 5 c. violet (air) .. 40 20
410. – 10 c. orange .. .. 1·00 30
411. – 20 c. green .. .. 2·75 80
412. – 50 c. black .. .. 7·00 2·00

DESIGNS—POSTAGE: 2 c. Matanzas Bay and Free Zone. 4 c. "Rex" (liner) in Mantanzas Bay. 5 c. Ships in the Free Zone. 8 c. Bellamar Caves. 10 c. Yumuri Valley. 20 c. Yumuri River. 50 c. Sailing ship and steamer. AIR: 5 c. Aerial panorama. 10 c. Airship "Macon" over Concord Bridge. 20 c. Airplane "Cuatro Vientos" over Matanzas. 50 c. San Severino Fortress.

63. President J. M. Gomez.

64. Gen. J. M. Gomez Monument.

**1936.** Inauguration of Gomez Monument.
413. **63.** 1 c. green .. .. 1·60 45
414. **64.** 2 c. red .. .. 2·10 65

65. "Peace and Labour".

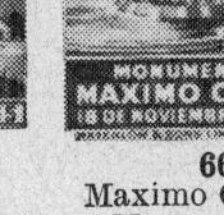

66. Maximo Gomez Monument.

**1936.** Inaug. of Maximo Gomez Monument.
415. **65.** 1 c. green (postage) .. 30 15
416. **66.** 2 c. red .. .. .. 30 15
417. – 4 c. purple .. .. 55 15
418. – 5 c. blue .. .. 2·75 70
419. – 8 c. olive .. .. 4·00 1·10
420. – 5 c. violet (air) .. .. 2·25 1·40
421. – 10 c. brown .. .. 4·00 2·00

DESIGNS—VERT. 4 c. Flaming torch. 8 c. Dove of Peace. HORIZ. 5 c. (No. 418) Army of Liberation. 5 c. (No. 420) Lightning. 10 c. "Flying Wing".

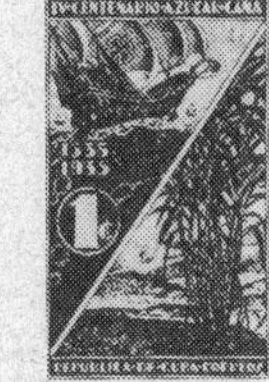

68. Caravel and Sugar Cane.

DESIGNS (each with caravel in upper triangle). HORIZ. 2 c. Early sugar mill. 5 c. Modern sugar mill.

**1937.** 400th Anniv. of Cane Sugar Industry.
422. – 1 c. green .. .. 1·10 45
423. – 2 c. red .. .. 80 20
424. **68.** 5 c. blue .. .. 1·10 45

69. Mountain View (Bolivia).

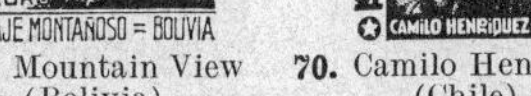

70. Camilo Henriquez (Chile).

**1937.** American Writers and Artists Assn.

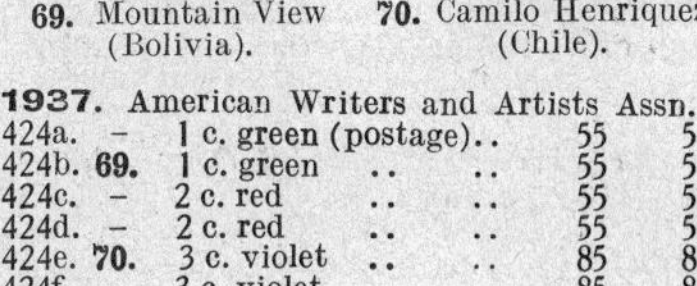

424a. – 1 c. green (postage) .. 55 55
424b. **69.** 1 c. green .. .. 55 55
424c. – 2 c. red .. .. 55 55
424d. – 2 c. red .. .. 55 55
424e. **70.** 3 c. violet .. .. 85 85
424f. – 3 c. violet .. .. 85 85
424g. – 4 c. brown .. .. 85 85
424h. – 4 c. brown .. .. 1·75 1·75
424i. – 5 c. blue .. .. 1·10 1·10
424j. – 5 c. blue .. .. 1·10 1·10
424k. – 8 c. green .. .. 3·25 3·25
424l. – 8 c. green .. .. 1·40 1·40
424m. – 10 c. brown .. .. 1·75 1·75
424n. – 10 c. brown .. .. 1·75 1·75
424o. – 25 c. lilac .. .. 28·00 18·00
424p. – 5 c. red (air) .. .. 3·75 3·25
424q. – 5 c. red .. .. 3·75 3·25
424r. – 10 c. blue .. .. 3·75 3·25
424s. – 10 c. blue .. .. 3·75 3·25
424t. – 20 c. green .. .. 6·00 5·50
424u. – 20 c. green .. .. 6·00 5·50

DESIGNS—VERT. No. 424a, Arms of the Republic (Argentina). No. 424c, Arms (Brazil). No. 424f, Gen. F. de Paula Santander (Colombia). No. 424g, Autograph of Jose Marti (Cuba). No. 424j, Juan Montalvo (Ecuador). No. 424k, Abraham Lincoln (U.S.A.). No. 424l, Quetzal and scroll (Guatemala). No. 424m, Arms (Haiti). No. 424n, Francisco Morazan (Honduras). No. 424r, Inca gate, Cuzco (Peru). No. 424s, Atlacatl (Indian warrior) (El Salvador). No. 424t, Simon Bolivar (Venezuela). No. 424u, Jose Rodo (Uruguay). HORIZ. No. 424d, River scene (Canada). No. 424h, National Monument (Costa Rica). No. 424i, Columbus Lighthouse (Dominican Republic). No. 424o, Ships of Columbus. No. 424p, Arch (Panama). No. 424q, Carlos Lopez (Paraguay).

**1937.** Cuban Railway Cent. Surch. **1837 1937 PRIMER CENTENARIO FERROCARRIL EN CUBA** and value either side of an early engine and coach.
425. **47.** 10 c. on 25 c. violet .. 4·50 1·00

**1938.** Air. 25th Anniv. of D. Rosillo's Overseas Flight from Key West to Havana. Optd. **1913 1938 ROSILLO Key West-Habana.**
426. **48.** 5 c. orange .. .. 3·75 1·75

74. Pierre and Marie Curie.

75. Allegory of Child Care.

**1938.** Int. Anti-Cancer Fund. 40th Anniv. of Discovery of Radium.
427. **74.** 2 c.+1 c. red .. .. 2·50 95
428. 5 c.+1 c. blue .. .. 2·50 95

**1938.** Obligatory Tax. Anti-T.B. Fund.
429. **75.** 1 c. green .. .. 20 10

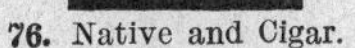

76. Native and Cigar.

80. Calixto Garcia.

**1939.** Havana Tobacco Industry.
430. **76.** 1 c. green .. .. 20 10
431. – 2 c. red .. .. 45 10
432. – 5 c. blue .. .. 1·00 15

DESIGNS: 2 c. Cigar, globe and wreath of leaves. 5 c. Tobacco plant and box of cigars.

**1939.** Air. Experimental Rocket Post. Optd. **EXPERIMENTO DEL/COHETE/ Postal/ANO DE 1939.**
433. **55.** 10 c. green .. .. 35·00 5·50

**1939.** Birth Cent. of Gen. Calixto Garcia. Perf. or imperf.
434. **80.** 2 c. red .. .. .. 55 20
435. – 5 c. blue .. .. 1·10 45

DESIGN: 5 c. Garcia on horseback.

82. Nurse and Child.

83. Gonzalo de Quesada and Union Flags.

84. Rotarian Symbol, Flag and Tobacco Plant.

**1939.** Obligatory Tax. Anti-T.B.
436. **82.** 1 c. red .. .. .. 20 10

**1940.** 50th Anniv. of Pan-American Union.
437. **83.** 2 c. red .. .. 1·10 55

**1940.** Rotary Int. Convention.
438. **84.** 2 c. red .. .. 1·75 80

85. Lions, Emblem, Flag and Palms.

86. Dr. Gutierrez.

**1940.** Lions Int. Convention. Havana.
439. **85.** 2 c. red .. .. .. 1·75 80

**1940.** Centenary of Publication of First Cuban Medical Review.
440. **86.** 2 c. red .. .. 85 55
441. 5 c. blue .. .. 1·40 55

87. Sir Rowland Hill and G.B. 1d. of 1840 and Cuba Issues of 1855 and 1899.

**1940.** Air. Centenary of 1st Adhesive Postage Stamps.
443. **87.** 10 c. brown .. .. 4·50 2·50

88. "Health" protecting Children.

89. Heredia and Niagara Falls.

**1940.** Obligatory Tax. Children's Hospital and Anti-T.B. Funds.
445. **88.** 1 c. blue .. .. 20 10

**1940.** Air. Death Centenary of J. M. Heredia y Campuzaono (poet).
446. – 5 c. green .. .. 2·25 1·10
447. **89.** 10 c. grey .. .. 2·75 1·40

DESIGN: 5 c. Heredia and palms.

90. General Moncada and Sword.

91. Moncada riding into Battle.

**1941.** Birth Centenary of H. Moncada.
448. **90.** 3 c. brown .. .. 1·00 50
449. **91.** 5 c. blue .. .. 1·00 50

**92.** Mother and Child.

**95.** " Labour, Wealth of America".

**1941.** Obligatory Tax. Anti-T.B.
450. **92.** 1 c. brown .. .. 20 10

**1942.** American Democracy. Imperf or perf.
451. – 1 c. green .. .. 25 10
452. – 3 c. brown .. .. 35 15
453. **95.** 5 c. blue .. .. 55 20
454. – 10 c. mauve .. .. 1·40 65
455. – 13 c. red .. .. 2·00 85
DESIGNS: 1 c. Western Hemisphere. 3 c. Cuban Arms and portraits of Maceo, Bolivar, Juarez and Lincoln. 10 c. Tree of Fraternity, Havana. 13 c. Statue of Liberty.

**98.** Gen. Ignacio Agramonte Loynaz.

**99.** Rescue of Sanguily.

**1942.** Birth Cent. of Gen. I. A. Loynaz.
456. **98.** 3 c. brown .. .. 75 40
457. **99.** 5 c. blue .. .. 1·50 55

**100.** " Victory ".

**102.** " Unmask Fifth Columnists ".

**1942.** Obligatory Tax. Red Cross Fund.
458. **100.** ½ c. orange .. .. 20 10
459. ½ c. grey .. .. 20 10

**1942.** Obligatory Tax. Anti-T.B. Fund. Optd. **1942.**
460. **92.** 1 c. red .. .. 20 10

**1943.** Anti-Fifth Column.
461. **102.** 1 c. green .. .. 25 15
462 – 3 c. red .. .. .. 45 15
463. – 5 c. blue .. .. 45 20
464. – 10 c. brown .. .. 1·75 70
465. – 13 c. purple .. .. 2·25 1·10
DESIGNS—HORIZ. (45×25 mm.) 5 c. Woman in snake's coils (" The Fifth Column is like the Serpent – destroy it "). 10 c. Men demolishing column with battering-ram (" Fulfil your patriotic duty by destroying the Fifth Column "). As Type **102.** 13 c. Woman with monster " Don't be afraid of the Fifth Column. Attack it ". VERT. Girl with finger to lips " Be Careful! The Fifth Column is spying on you ".

**105.** Eloy Alfaro, Flags of Ecuador and Cuba and Scroll of Independence.

**1943.** Birth Centenary of E. Alfaro (former President of Ecuador).
466. **105.** 3 c. green .. .. 1·25 55

**106.** " The Long Road to Retirement ".

**107.** " Health " Protecting Child.

**1943.** Postal Employees' Retirement Fund.
467. **106.** 1 c. green .. .. 65 35
470. 3 c. red .. .. 55 35
471. 5 c. blue .. .. 90 35

**1943.** Obligatory Tax. Anti-Tuberculosis.
473. **107.** 1 c. brown .. .. 20 10

**108.** Columbus.

**109.** Discovery of Tobacco.

**1944.** 450th Anniv. of Discovery of America.
474. **108.** 1 c. green (postage) .. 20 15
475. – 3 c. brown .. .. 30 15
476. – 5 c. blue .. .. 40 20
477. **109.** 10 c. violet .. .. 2·25 65
478. – 13 c. red .. .. 5·50 1·25
479. – 5 c. olive (air) .. .. 75 35
480. – 10 c. grey .. .. 1·75 65
DESIGNS—VERT. 3 c. Bartolome de las Casas. 5 c. (No. 476), Statue of Columbus. HORIZ. 5 c. (No. 479) Mountains of Gibara. 10 c. (No. 480), Columbus Light-house. 13 c. Columbus at Pinar del Rio.

**110.** Carlos Roloff.

**111.** American Continents and Brazilian " Bull's Eyes " stamps.

**1944.** Birth Cent. of Major-Gen. Roloff.
481. **110.** 3 c. violet .. .. 95 30

**1944.** Cent. of 1st American Postage stamps.
482. **111.** 3 c. brown .. .. 1·75 55

**112.** Society Seal.

**113.** Governor Las Casas and Bishop Penalver.

**1945.** 150th Anniv. of Economic Society of Friends of Havana.
483. **112.** 1 c. green .. .. 35 15
484. **113.** 2 c. red .. .. 65 30

**115.** Old Age Pensioners.

**1945.** Postal Employees' Retirement Fund.
485. **115.** 1 c. green .. .. 20 10
487. 2 c. red .. .. 40 15
489. 5 c. blue .. .. 75 30

**116.** Valdes.

**1946.** Death Centenary of Gabriel de la Concepcion Valdes (poet).
491. **116.** 2 c. red .. .. 85 45

**117.** Manuel Marquez Sterling.

**118.** Red Cross and Globe.

**1946.** Founding of "Manuel Marquez Sterling" Professional School of Journalism.
492. **117.** 2 c. red .. .. 85 45

**1946.** 80th Anniv. of Int. Red Cross.
493. **118.** 2 c. red .. .. 90 45

**119.** Prize Cattle and Dairymaid.

**120.** Franklin D. Roosevelt.

**1947.** National Cattle Show.
494. **119.** 2 c. red .. .. .. 1·10 35

**1947.** 2nd Death Anniv. of Pres. Roosevelt.
495. **120.** 2 c. red .. .. 1·25 35

**121.** Antonio Oms and Pensioners.

**1947.** Postal Employees' Retirement Fund.
496. **121.** 1 c. green .. .. 15 15
497. 2 c. red .. .. 25 15
498. 5 c. blue .. .. 75 30

**122.** Marta Abreu.

**1947.** Birth Cent. of M. Abreu (philanthropist).
499 **122** 1 c. green .. .. 30 15
500 – 2 c. red .. .. 45 20
501 – 5 c. blue .. .. 65 30
502 – 10 c. violet .. .. 1·40 65
DESIGNS: 2 c. Allegory of Charity. 5 c. Monument. 10 c. Allegory of Patriotism.

**123.** Dr. G. A. Hansen and Isle of Pines.

**1948.** Int. Leprosy Relief Congress, Havana.
503. **123.** 2 c. red .. .. .. 90 40

**124.** Council of War.

**1948.** Air. 50th Anniv. of War of Independence.
504. **124.** 8 c. black and yellow 1·90 85

**125.** Woman and Child.

**126.** Death of Marti.

**1948.** Postal Employees' Retirement Fund.
506. **125.** 1 c. green .. .. 30 15
507. 2 c. red .. .. 30 15
508. 5 c. blue .. .. 75 30

**1948.** 50th Death Anniv. of Jose Marti.
509. **126.** 2 c. red .. .. 35 20
510. – 5 c. blue .. .. 1·10 35
DESIGN: 5 c. Marti disembarking at Playitas

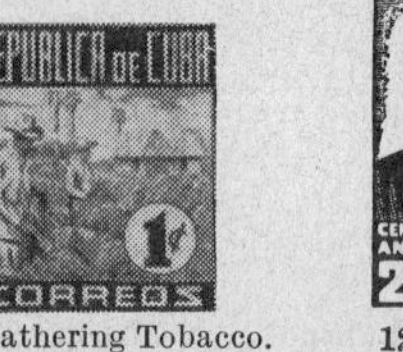

**127.** Gathering Tobacco.

**129.** Antonio Maceo.

**1948.** Havana Tobacco Industry.
511. **127.** 1 c. green .. .. 15 10
512. – 2 c. red .. .. .. 20 10
513. – 5 c. blue .. .. 35 15
DESIGNS: 2 c. Girl with box of cigars and flag. 5 c. Cigar and shield.
This set comes again redrawn with smaller designs of 21×25 mm.

**1948.** Birth Cent. of Gen. Maceo.
514. – 1 c. green .. .. 10 10
515. **129.** 2 c. red .. .. .. 15 10
516. – 5 c. blue .. .. 25 15
517. – 8 c. brown and black .. 35 30
518. – 10 c. green and brown .. 45 20
519. – 20 c. blue and red .. 1·75 75
520. – 50 c. blue and red .. 3·00 2·00
521. – 1 p. violet and black .. 6·00 2·75
DESIGNS—VERT. 1 c. Equestrian statue of Maceo. 5 c. Mausoleum at El Cacahual. HORIZ. 8 c. Maceo and raised swords. 10 c. Maceo leading charge. 20 c. Maceo at Peralejo. 50 c. Declaration at Baragua. 1 p. Death of Maceo at San Pedro.

**131.** Symbol of Medicine.

**132.** Morro Castle and Lighthouse.

**1948.** 1st Pan-American Pharmaceutical Congress.
522. **131.** 2 c. red .. .. .. 95 40

**1949.** Cent. of El Morro Lighthouse.
523. **132.** 2 c. red .. .. 95 40

**133.** Jagua Castle.

**1949.** Cent. of Newspaper "Hoja Economica" and Bicentenary of Jagua Fortress.
524. **133.** 1 c. green .. .. 40 20
525. 2 c. red .. .. 65 35

**134.** M. Sanguily.

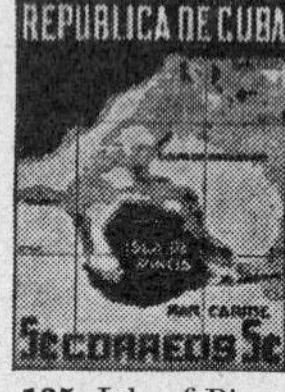

**135.** Isle of Pines.

**1949.** Birth Centenary of Manuel Sanguilly y Garritte (poet).
526. **134.** 2 c. red .. .. 35 20
527. 5 c. blue .. .. 90 35

**1949.** 20th Anniv. of Return of Isle of Pines to Cuba.
528. **135.** 5 c. blue .. .. 95 35

**136.** Ismael Cespedes.

**137.** Woman and Child.

**1949.** Postal Employees' Retirement Fund.
529. **136.** 1 c. green .. .. 25 15
530. 2 c. red .. .. 25 15
531. 5 c. blue .. .. 75 30

**1949.** Obligatory Tax. Anti-Tuberculosis.
532. **137.** 1 c. blue .. .. 25 10
547. 1 c. red .. .. 25 10
No. 547 is dated " 1950 ".

**138.** Enrique Collazo.

**139.** E. J. Varona.

**1950.** Birth Cent. of Gen. Collazo.
533. **138.** 2 c. red .. .. 30 15
534. 5 c. blue .. .. 90 35

**1950.** Birth Cent. of Varona (writer).
535. **139.** 2 c. red . . . . 35 20
536. 5 c. blue . . . . 90 35

**1950.** National Bank Opening. No. 512 optd. **BANCO NACIONAL DE CUBA INAUGURACION 27 ABRIL 1950.**
540. – 2 c. red . . . . 90 35

**1950.** 75th Anniv. of U.P.U. Optd. **U.P.U. 1874 1949.**
541. **127.** 1 c. green . . . . 35 15
542. – 2 c. pink (As No. 512) . . 40 25
543. – 5 c. blue (As No. 513) . . 95 35

**142.** Balanzategui, Pausa and Railway Crash. **143.** F. Figueredo.

**1950.** Postal Employees' Retirement Fund.
544. **142.** 1 c. green . . . . 80 35
545. 2 c. red . . . . 80 35
546. 5 c. blue . . . . 1·75 65

**1951.** Postal Employees' Retirement Fund.
548. **143.** 1 c. green . . . . 55 20
549. 2 c. red . . . . 55 20
550. 5 c. blue . . . . 90 35

**144.** Foundation Stone. **145.** Narciso Lopez.

**1951.** Obligatory Tax. P.O. Rebuilding Fund.
551. **144.** 1 c. violet . . . . 25 10

**1951.** Centenary of Cuban Flag.
552. – 1 c. red, bl. & grn. (post.) 30 15
553. **145.** 2 c. black and red . . 50 25
554. – 5 c. red and blue . . 1·10 50
555. – 10 c. red, blue & violet 2·00 70
556. – 5 c. red, bl. & olive (air) 1·10 45
557. – 8 c. red, blue & brown . . 1·75 65
558. – 25 c. red, blue and black 2·25 1·10

DESIGNS—VERT. 1 c. Miguel Teurbe Tolon. 5 c. (No. 554) Emilia Teurbe Tolon. 8 c. Raising the flag. 10 c. Flag. 25 c. Flag and El Morro lighthouse. HORIZ. 5 c. (No. 556) Lopez landing at Cardenas.

**147.** Clara Maass, Newark Memorial and Las Animas, Havana, Hospitals.

**1951.** 50th Death Anniv. of Clara Maass (nurse).
559. **147.** 2 c. red . . . . 1·00 40

**148.** Capablanca (after E. Valderrama). **149.** Chessboard showing end of Capablanca v. Lasker.

**1951.** 30th Anniv of Jose Capablanca's Victory in World Chess Championship.
562. **148.** 1 c. orge. & grn. (post.) 1·75 45
563. – 2 c. brown and red . . 2·25 85
564. E **150.** 5 c. blue and black . . 5·50 1·75
565. **149.** 5 c. yell. & grn. (air) 2·75 85
566. – 8 c. purple and blue . . 4·00 1·10
567. **148.** 25 c. sep. & brn. . . 7·00 1·90

DESIGN—VERT. 2 c., 8 c. Capablanca playing chess.

**151.** Dr. A. Guiteras Holmes. **152.** Morrillo Fortress.

**1951.** 16th Death Anniv. of Dr. A. Guiteras Holmes in skirmish at Morrillo.
568. **151.** 1 c. green (postage) . . 45 15
569. – 2 c. red . . . . 65 30
570. **152.** 5 c. blue . . . . 1·40 50
571. **151.** 5 c. mauve (air) . . 1·60 1·10
572. – 8 c. green . . . . 2·25 1·60
573. **152.** 25 c. black . . . . 4·00 2·75

DESIGN—HORIZ. 2 c., 8 c. Guiteras framing social laws.

**153.** Mother and Child. **154.** Christmas Emblems.

**1951.** Obligatory Tax. Anti-tuberculosis.
575. **153.** 1 c. brown . . . . 20 10
576. 1 c. red . . . . 20 10
577. 1 c. green . . . . 20 10
578. 1 c. blue . . . . 20 10

**1951.** Christmas Greetings.
579. **154.** 1 c. red and green . . 2·00 55
580. 2 c. green and red . . 2·50 65

**155.** Jose Maceo. **156.** General Post Office. **157.** Isabella the Catholic.

**1952.** Birth Cent. of Gen. Maceo.
581. **155.** 2 c. brown . . . . 50 15
582. 5 c. blue . . . . 90 35

**1952.** Obligatory Tax. P.O. Rebuilding Fund.
583. **156.** 1 c. blue . . . . 20 10
584. 1 c. red . . . . 55 15

**1952.** 5th Birth Cent. of Isabella the Catholic.
585. **157.** 2 c. red (postage) . . 2·75 75
586. 25 c. purple (air) . . 4·75 1·25

**1952.** As No. 549 surch. with new value.

(a) Postage.
588. **143.** 10 c. on 2 c. brown . . 1·25 40

(b) Air. Optd. **AEREO** in addition.
589. **143.** 5 c. on 2 c. brown . . 45 20
590. 8 c. on 2 c. brown . . 65 20
591. 10 c. on 2 c. brown . . 1·10 20
592. 25 c. on 2 c. brown . . 1·10 45
593. 50 c. on 2 c. brown . . 3·75 1·40
594. 1 p. on 2 c. brown . . 5·50 2·75

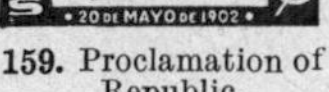

**159.** Proclamation of Republic. **160.** Statue, Havana University.

**1952.** 50th Anniv. of Republic.
595. **159.** 1 c. blk. & grn. (postage) 20 15
596. – 2 c. black and red . . 30 15
597. – 5 c. black and blue . . 40 15
598. – 8 c. black and brown 55 15
599. – 20 c. black and olive . . 1·40 50
600. – 50 c. black and orange 2·75 90
601. – 5 c. green & violet (air) 55 25
602. **160.** 8 c. green and red . . 55 35
603. – 10 c. green and blue . . 1·40 55
604. – 25 c. green and purple 1·75 85

DESIGNS—HORIZ.—POSTAGE: 2 c. Estrada Palma and Estevez Romero. 5 c. Barnet, Finlay, Guiteras and Nunez. 8 c. The Capitol. 20 c. Map showing central highway. 50 c. Sugar factory. AIR: 5 c. Rural school. 10 c. Presidential Palace. 25 c. Banknote.

**162.** Seaplane and Route of Flight. **164.** Coffee Beans.

**1952.** Air. 39th Anniv. of Florida-Cuba flight by A. Parla.
605. **162.** 8 c. black . . . . 1·25 30
606. – 25 c. blue . . . . 2·75 85

DESIGN—HORIZ. 25 c. Agustin Parla Orduna and Curtiss A-1 seaplane.

**1952.** Bicent. of Coffee Cultivation.
608. **164.** 1 c. green . . . . 35 15
609. – 2 c. red . . . . 55 30
610. – 5 c. green and blue . . 95 35

DESIGNS: 2 c. Plantation worker and map. 5 c. Coffee plantation.

**HAVE YOU READ THE NOTES AT THE BEGINNING OF THIS CATALOGUE?**
These often provide answers to the enquiries we receive.

**165.** Col. C. Hernandez.

**1952.** Postal Employees' Retirement Fund.
611. **165.** 1 c. green (postage) . . 20 15
612. 2 c. red . . . . 40 15
613. 5 c. blue . . . . 40 15
614. 8 c. black . . . . 1·00 35
615. 10 c. red . . . . 1·10 40
616. 20 c. brown . . . . 4·00 2·75
617. 5 c. orange (air) . . 25 10
618. 8 c. green . . . . 45 10
619. 10 c. brown . . . . 50 15
620. 15 c. green . . . . 55 20
621. 20 c. turquoise . . 55 30
622. 25 c. red . . . . 85 40
623. 30 c. violet . . . . 1·75 40
624. 45 c. mauve . . . . 1·90 1·40
625. 50 c. blue . . . . 1·60 85
626. 1 p. yellow . . . . 5·00 2·50

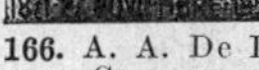

**166.** A. A. De La Campa. **167.** Statue, Havana University.

**168.** Dominguez, Estebanez and Capdevila (defence lawyers).

**1952.** 81st Anniv. of Execution of Eight Rebel Medical Students.
627. **166.** 1 c. black and green (post.) 15 10
628. – 2 c. black and red . . 30 15
629. – 3 c. black and violet . . 35 15
630. – 5 c. black and blue . . 35 15
631. – 8 c. black and sepia . . 65 35
632. – 10 c. black and brown 75 30
633. – 13 c. black and purple 1·90 45
634. – 20 c. black and olive . . 2·25 65
635. **167.** 5 c. blue and indigo (air) 85 35
636. **168.** 25 c. green and orange 2·25 80

PORTRAITS: 2 c. C. A. de la Torre. 3 c. A. Bermudez. 5 c. E. G. Toledo. 8 c. A. Laborde. 10 c. J. De M. Medina. 13 c. P. Rodriguez. 20 c. C. Verdugo.

**169.** Child's Face. **170.** Christmas Tree.

**1952.** Obligatory Tax. Anti-Tuberculosis.
637. **169.** 1 c. orange . . . . 25 10
638. 1 c. red . . . . 25 10
639. 1 c. green . . . . 25 10
640. 1 c. blue . . . . 25 10

**1952.** Christmas.
641. **170.** 1 c. red and green . . 2·75 1·75
642. 3 c. green and violet . . 2·75 1·75

**171.** Marti's Birthplace. **172.** Dr. Rafael Montoro.

**1953.** Birth Cent. of Jose Marti.
643. **171.** 1 c. brn. & grn. (post.) 15 10
644. – 1 c. brown and green 15 10
645. – 3 c. brown and violet 25 15
646. – 3 c. brown and violet 25 15
647. – 5 c. brown and blue . . 35 15
648. – 5 c. brown and blue . . 35 15
649. – 10 c. black and brown 90 30
650. – 10 c. black and brown 75 30
651. – 13 c. brown and green 1·60 55
652. – 13 c. brown and green 1·60 55
653. – 5 c. black & red (air) 25 15
654. – 5 c. black and red 25 15
655. – 8 c. black and green 30 15
656. – 8 c. black and green 30 15
657. – 10 c. red and blue . . 40 15
658. – 10 c. blue and red . . 40 15
659. – 15 c. black and violet 50 25
660. – 15 c. black and violet 50 25
661. – 25 c. red and brown . . 1·75 60
662. – 25 c. red and brown . . 1·75 60
663. – 50 c. blue and yellow 2·75 1·00

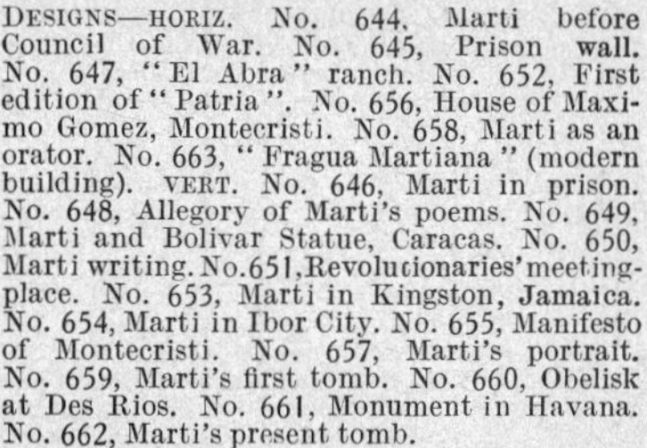

DESIGNS—HORIZ. No. 644, Marti before Council of War. No. 645, Prison wall. No. 647, "El Abra" ranch. No. 652, First edition of "Patria". No. 656, House of Maximo Gomez, Montecristi. No. 658, Marti as an orator. No. 663, "Fragua Martiana" (modern building). VERT. No. 646, Marti in prison. No. 648, Allegory of Marti's poems. No. 649, Marti and Bolivar Statue, Caracas. No. 650, Marti writing. No. 651, Revolutionaries' meeting-place. No. 653, Marti in Kingston, Jamaica. No. 654, Marti in Ibor City. No. 655, Manifesto of Montecristi. No. 657, Marti's portrait. No. 659, Marti's first tomb. No. 660, Obelisk at Des Rios. No. 661, Monument in Havana. No. 662, Marti's present tomb.

**1953.** Birth Cent. of Montoro (statesman).
664. **172.** 3 c. purple . . . . 1·00 45

**173.** Dr. F. Carrera Justiz. **174.** Lockheed Constellation.

**1953.**
665. **173.** 3 c. red . . . . 1·00 45

**1953.** Air.
666. **174.** 8 c. brown . . . . 55 25
667. 15 c. red . . . . 1·10 60
668. – 2 p. brown and green 11·00 4·50
670. – 2 p. myrtle and blue . . 11·00 4·50
669. – 5 p. brown and blue . . 22·00 7·50
671. – 5 p. myrtle and red . . 19·00 9·50

DESIGN: Nos. 668/71, Constellation facing right.

**1953.** No. 512 surch.
672. 3 c. on 2 c. red . . . . 55 30

**176.** Congress Building. **177.**

**1953.** 1st Int. Accountancy Congress, Havana.
673. **176.** 3 c. blue (postage) . . 70 35
674. – 8 c. red (air) . . . . 1·60 55
675. – 25 c. green . . . . 2·50 85

DESIGNS: 8 c. Congress building and "Cuba". 25 c. Aerial view of building and airplane.

**1953.** Obligatory Tax. Anti-T.B.
676. **177.** 1 c. red . . . . 20 10

**178.** M. Coyula Llaguno. **179.** Postal Employees' Retirement Association Flag.

**1954.** Postal Employees' Retirement Fund. Inscr. "1953".
677. **178.** 1 c. green (postage) . . 30 10
678. – 3 c. red . . . . 30 10
679. **179.** 5 c. blue . . . . 55 15
680. – 8 c. red . . . . 1·10 45
681. – 10 c. sepia . . . . 2·25 65
682. – 5 c. blue (air) . . . . 55 25
683. – 8 c. purple . . . . 65 25
684. – 10 c. orange . . . . 1·00 25
685. **179.** 1 p. grey . . . . 3·50 2·00

PORTRAITS—VERT. Nos. 678, 680, F. L. C. Hensell. Nos. 681, 683, A. G. Rojas. No. 684, G. H. Saez. HORIZ. No. 682, M. C. Llaguno.

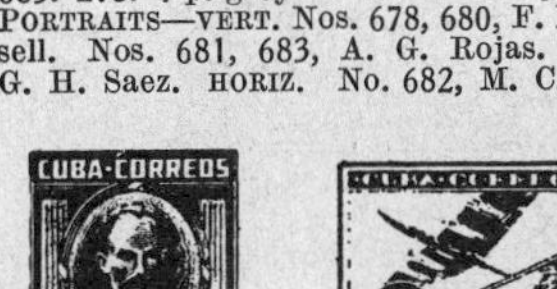

**180.** Jose Marti. **181.** Hauling Sugar.

**1954.** Portraits. Roul. (No. 1180a/b) or perf. (others).
686 **180** 1 c. green . . . . 15 10
990 1 c. red . . . . 35 15
1680 1 c. blue . . . . 10 10
687 – 2 c. red (Gomez) . . 10 10
991 – 2 c. olive (Gomez) . . 45 15
1681 – 2 c. green (Gomez) . . 15 10
688 – 3 c. violet (de la Luz Caballero) . . 10 10
1180a – 3 c. orange (Caballero) 25 15
689 – 4 c. mauve (Aldama) 10 10
690 – 5 c. blue (Garcia) . . 10 10
691 – 8 c. lake (Agramonte) 15 10
692 – 10 c. sepia (Palma) . . 20 10
693 – 13 c. red (Finlay) . . 30 10
1180b – 13 c. brown (Finlay) 95 25
694 – 14 c. grey (Sanchez) . . 55 15
695 – 20 c. olive (Saco) . . 1·40 35
1682 – 20 c. violet (Saco) . . 1·40 20
696 – 50 c. ochre (Maceo) . . 2·00 40
697 – 1 p. orange (Cespedes) 3·00 40

**1954.** Air. Sugar Industry.

| No. | Type | Description | | |
|---|---|---|---|---|
| 698. | – | 5 c. green | 35 | 10 |
| 699. | – | 8 c. brown | 85 | 35 |
| 700. | 181. | 10 c. green | 85 | 35 |
| 701. | – | 15 c. brown | 2·25 | 10 |
| 702. | – | 20 c. blue | 1·00 | 15 |
| 703. | – | 25 c. red | 65 | 30 |
| 704a. | – | 30 c. purple | 1·90 | 75 |
| 705. | – | 40 c. blue | 3·25 | 65 |
| 706. | – | 45 c. violet | 3·00 | 65 |
| 707. | – | 50 c. blue | 3·00 | 65 |
| 708. | – | 1 p. blue | 7·25 | 1·25 |

DESIGNS—VERT. 5 c. Sugar cane. 1 p. A. Reinoso. HORIZ. 8 c. Sugar harvesting. 15 c. Train load of sugar cane. 20 c. Modern sugar factory. 25 c. Evaporators. 30 c. Stacking sugar in sacks. 40 c. Loading sugar on ship. 45 c. Oxen hauling cane. 50 c. Primitive sugar factory.

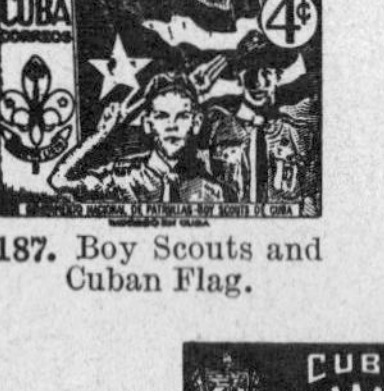


**182.** Jose M. Rodriguez.

**183.** View of Sanatorium.

**1954.** Birth Cent. of Rodriguez.

| No. | Type | Description | | |
|---|---|---|---|---|
| 709. | 182. | 2 c. sepia and lake | 45 | 25 |
| 710. | – | 5 c. sepia and blue | 90 | 45 |

DESIGN: 5 c. Rodrigues on horseback.

**1954.** General Batista Sanatorium.

| No. | Type | Description | | |
|---|---|---|---|---|
| 711. | 183. | 3 c. blue (postage) | 90 | 40 |
| 712. | | 9 c. green (air) | 1·75 | 65 |



**184.**



**185.** Father Christmas.



**186.** Maria Luisa Dolz.

**1954.** Obligatory Tax. Anti-T.B.

| No. | Type | Description | | |
|---|---|---|---|---|
| 713. | 184. | 1 c. red | 20 | 10 |
| 714. | | 1 c. green | 20 | 10 |
| 715. | | 1 c. blue | 20 | 10 |
| 716. | | 1 c. violet | 20 | 10 |

**1954.** Christmas Greetings.

| No. | Type | Description | | |
|---|---|---|---|---|
| 717. | 185. | 2 c. green and red | 3·00 | 1·40 |
| 718. | | 4 c. red and green | 3·00 | 1·40 |

**1954.** Birth Cent. of Maria Dolz (educationist).

| No. | Type | Description | | |
|---|---|---|---|---|
| 719. | 186. | 4 c. blue (postage) | 95 | 35 |
| 720. | | 12 c. mauve (air) | 1·75 | 75 |



**187.** Boy Scouts and Cuban Flag.



**189.** Major-Gen. F. Carrillo.

**188.** P. P. Harris and Rotary Emblem.

**1954.** 3rd National Scout Camp.

| No. | Type | Description | | |
|---|---|---|---|---|
| 721. | 187. | 4 c. green | 95 | 40 |

**1954.** 50th Anniv. of Rotary Int.

| No. | Type | Description | | |
|---|---|---|---|---|
| 722. | 188. | 4 c. blue (postage) | 95 | 55 |
| 723. | | 12 c. red (air) | 1·75 | 65 |

**1955.** Birth Centenary of Carrillo.

| No. | Type | Description | | |
|---|---|---|---|---|
| 724. | 189. | 2 c. blue and red | 45 | 20 |
| 725. | – | 5 c. sepia and blue | 75 | 35 |

DESIGN: 5 c. Half-length portrait.

**190.** 1855 Stamp and "La Volanta".

**1955.** Cent. of First Cuban Postage Stamps and 50th Anniv. of First Republican Stamps.

| No. | Type | Description | | |
|---|---|---|---|---|
| 726. | – | 2 c. blue & pur. (post.) | 35 | 10 |
| 727. | 190. | 4 c. green and buff | 55 | 35 |
| 728. | – | 10 c. red and blue | 3·00 | 65 |
| 729. | – | 14 c. orange and green | 3·25 | 1·40 |
| 730. | – | 8 c. green & blue (air) | 55 | 20 |
| 731. | – | 12 c. red and green | 65 | 20 |
| 732. | – | 24 c. blue and red | 1·90 | 55 |
| 733. | – | 30 c. brown & orange | 1·75 | 85 |

DESIGNS (a) With 1855 stamp: 2 c. Old Square and Convent of St. Francis. 10 c. Havana in 19th century. 14 c. Captain-General's residence and Plaza de Armas. (b) With 1855 and 1905 stamps: 8 c. Palace of Fine Arts. 12 c. Plaza de la Fraternidad. 24 c. Aerial view of Havana. 30 c. Plaza de la Republica.

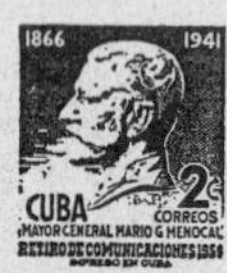


**191.** Maj.-Gen. Menocal.

**192.** Mariel Bay.

**1955.** Postal Employees' Retirement Fund.

| No. | Type | Description | | |
|---|---|---|---|---|
| 734. | 191. | 2 c. green (postage) | 45 | 10 |
| 735. | – | 4 c. mauve | 55 | 25 |
| 736. | – | 10 c. blue | 95 | 35 |
| 737. | – | 14 c. grey | 2·25 | 85 |
| 738. | 192. | 8 c. green and red (air) | 55 | 25 |
| 739. | – | 12 c. blue and brown | 1·10 | 55 |
| 740. | – | 1 p. ochre and green | 3·00 | 1·75 |

DESIGNS—As Type **191**: HORIZ. 4 c. Gen. E. Nunez. 14 c. Dr. A. de Bustamante. VERT. 10 c. J. Gomez. As Type **192**: HORIZ. 12 c. Varadero Beach. 1 p. Vinales Valley.

**193.** Cuban Academy.

**194.** Route of 1914 Flight.

**1955.** Air. Cent. of Tampa, Florida.

| No. | Type | Description | | |
|---|---|---|---|---|
| 741. | 193. | 12 c. brown and red | 1·60 | 65 |

**1955.** Air. 35th Death Anniv. of Crocier (aviator).

| No. | Type | Description | | |
|---|---|---|---|---|
| 742. | 194. | 12 c. green and red | 85 | 35 |
| 743. | – | 30 c. mauve and green | 1·60 | 65 |

DESIGN: 30 c. Crocier in aircraft cockpit.

**195.**

**196.** Wright Flyer I.

**1955.** Obligatory Tax. Anti-T.B.

| No. | Type | Description | | |
|---|---|---|---|---|
| 744. | 195. | 1 c. orange | 30 | 15 |
| 745. | | 1 c. yellow | 30 | 15 |
| 746. | | 1 c. blue | 30 | 15 |
| 747. | | 1 c. mauve | 30 | 15 |

**1955.** Air. Int. Philatelic Exn., Havana.

| No. | Type | Description | | |
|---|---|---|---|---|
| 748. | 196. | 8 c. black, red and blue | 1·25 | 55 |
| 749. | – | 12 c. black, green & red | 1·40 | 55 |
| 750. | – | 24 c. blk., violet & red | 1·60 | 85 |
| 751. | – | 30 c. blk., blue & orge. | 3·50 | 1·90 |
| 752. | – | 50 c. blk. olive & orge. | 5·50 | 2·25 |

DESIGNS: 12 c. Lindbergh's airplane "Spirit of St. Louis". 24 c. Airship "Graf Zeppelin". 30 c. Lockheed Super Constellation airplane. 50 c. Convair Delta Dagger airplane.

**197.** Turkey.

**198.** Expedition Disembarking.

**1955.** Christmas Greetings.

| No. | Type | Description | | |
|---|---|---|---|---|
| 754. | 197. | 2 c. green and red | 3·00 | 1·40 |
| 755. | | 4 c. lake and green | 3·00 | 1·40 |

**1955.** Birth Cent. of General Nunez.

| No. | Type | Description | | |
|---|---|---|---|---|
| 756. | – | 4 c. lake (postage) | 90 | 35 |
| 757. | – | 8 c. blue and red (air) | 1·50 | 45 |
| 758. | 198. | 12 c. green and brown | 1·75 | 65 |

DESIGNS—VERT. ($22\frac{1}{2} \times 32\frac{1}{2}$ mm.): 4 c. Portrait of Nunez. HORIZ. As Type **198**: 8 c. "Three Friends" (tug).

**199.** Bishop P. A. Morell de Santa Cruz.

**200.** J. del Casal.

**1956.** Bicent. of Cuban Postal Service.

| No. | Type | Description | | |
|---|---|---|---|---|
| 759. | – | 4 c. blue & brn. (post.) | 90 | 40 |
| 760. | 199. | 12 c. green & brn. (air) | 1·60 | 40 |

PORTRAIT: 4 c. F. C. de la Vega.

**1956.** Postal Employees' Retirement Fund.

| No. | Type | Description | | |
|---|---|---|---|---|
| 761. | 200. | 2 c. blk. & green (post.) | 20 | 15 |
| 762. | – | 4 c. black and mauve | 55 | 20 |
| 763. | – | 10 c. black and blue | 90 | 35 |
| 764. | – | 14 c. black and violet | 1·90 | 75 |
| 765. | – | 8 c. black & brown (air) | 55 | 30 |
| 766. | – | 12 c. black and ochre | 85 | 35 |
| 767. | – | 30 c. black and blue | 1·60 | 55 |

PORTRAITS: 4 c. Luisa Perez de Zambrana. 8 c. Gen. J. Sanguily. 10 c. J. Clemente Zenea. 12 c. Gen. J. M. Aguirre. 14 c. J. J. Palma. 30 c. Col. E. Fonts Sterling.

**201.** Victor Munoz.

**202.** Mother and Baby.

**1956.** Munoz Commem.

| No. | Type | Description | | |
|---|---|---|---|---|
| 768. | 201. | 4 c. brown and green | 90 | 40 |

**1956.** Air. Mothers' Day.

| No. | Type | Description | | |
|---|---|---|---|---|
| 769. | 202. | 12 c. blue and red | 1·75 | 40 |

**203.** Aerial View of Temple.

**204.** Gundlach's Hawk.

**1956.** Masonic Grand Lodge of Cuba Temple, Havana.

| No. | Type | Description | | |
|---|---|---|---|---|
| 770. | – | 4 c. blue (postage) | 95 | 40 |
| 771. | 203. | 12 c. green (air) | 1·75 | 45 |

DESIGN: 4 c. Ground level view of Temple.

**1956.** Air. Birds.

| No. | Type | Description | | |
|---|---|---|---|---|
| 772. | – | 8 c. blue | 1·40 | 65 |
| 773. | – | 12 c. grey | 9·00 | 1·25 |
| 783. | – | 12 c. green | 3·25 | 75 |
| 774. | 204. | 14 c. olive | 2·10 | 65 |
| 775. | – | 19 c. brown | 2·10 | 75 |
| 776. | – | 24 c. mauve | 2·10 | 75 |
| 777. | – | 29 c. green | 3·00 | 80 |
| 778. | – | 30 c. brown | 3·25 | 80 |
| 779. | – | 50 c. slate | 6·00 | 1·10 |
| 780. | – | 1 p. red | 13·00 | 2·75 |
| 784. | – | 1 p. blue | 6·50 | 3·50 |
| 781. | – | 2 p. purple | 22·00 | 4·25 |
| 785. | – | 2 p. red | 19·00 | 8·00 |
| 782. | – | 5 p. red | 55·00 | 10·00 |
| 786. | – | 5 p. purple | 42·00 | 19·00 |

DESIGNS—HORIZ. 8 c. Wood Duck. 12 c. (2) Plain Pigeon. 29 c. Goosander. 30 c. Bobwhite. 2 p. (2) Northern Jacana. VERT. 19 c. Herring Gull. 24 c. American White Pelican. 50 c. Great Blue Heron. 1 p. (2) Common Caracara. 5 p. (2) Ivory-billed Woodpecker.

**205.** H. de Blanck.

**207.** Church of Our Lady of Charity.

**1956.** Air. Birth Centenary of H. De Blanck (composer).

| No. | Type | Description | | |
|---|---|---|---|---|
| 787. | 205. | 12 c. blue | 1·60 | 45 |

**1956.** Air. Inaug. of Philatelic Club of Cuba Building. No. 776 but colour changed and surch. **"Inauguracion Edificio Club Filatelico de la Republica de Cuba Julio 13 de 1956"** and value.

| No. | Type | Description | | |
|---|---|---|---|---|
| 788. | – | 8 c. on 24 c. orange | 1·75 | 80 |

**1956.** Inscr. "NTRA. SRA. DE LA CARIDAD", etc.

| No. | Type | Description | | |
|---|---|---|---|---|
| 789. | – | 4 c. blue & yellow (post.) | 95 | 40 |
| 790. | 207. | 12 c. grn. and red (air) | 1·90 | 55 |

DESIGN: 4 c. Our Lady of Charity over landscape.

**208.**

**209.**

**1956.** Air. 250th Birth Anniv. of Benjamin Franklin.

| No. | Type | Description | | |
|---|---|---|---|---|
| 792. | 208. | 12 c. brown | 1·75 | 40 |

**1956.** "Grito de Yara" (War of Independence). Commem.

| No. | Type | Description | | |
|---|---|---|---|---|
| 793. | 209. | 4 c. sepia and green | 95 | 35 |

**(210.)** **211.**

**1956.** Air. 12th Inter-American Press Assn. Meeting. As No. 781 but colour changed and surch with T **210.**

| No. | Type | Description | | |
|---|---|---|---|---|
| 794. | – | 12 c. on 2 p. grey | 1·75 | 80 |

**1956.** Obligatory Tax. Anti-T.B.

| No. | Type | Description | | |
|---|---|---|---|---|
| 795. | 211. | 1 c. red | 20 | 10 |
| 796. | | 1 c. green | 20 | 10 |
| 797. | | 1 c. blue | 20 | 10 |
| 798. | | 1 c. brown | 20 | 10 |

**212.**

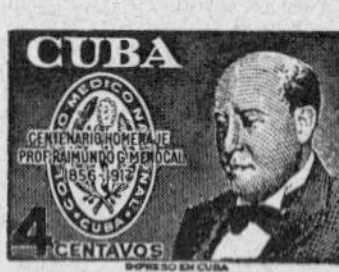


**213.** Prof. R. G. Menocal.

**1956.** Christmas Greetings.

| No. | Type | Description | | |
|---|---|---|---|---|
| 799. | 212. | 2 c. red and green | 3·00 | 1·40 |
| 800. | | 4 c. green and red | 3·00 | 1·40 |

**1956.** Birth Cent. of Prof. R. G. Menocal.

| No. | Type | Description | | |
|---|---|---|---|---|
| 801. | 213. | 4 c. brown | 90 | 35 |

**214a.** Martin M. Delgado.

**215.** Scouts around Camp Fire.

**1957.** Birth Cent. of Delgado (patriot).

| No. | Type | Description | | |
|---|---|---|---|---|
| 802. | 214a. | 4 c. green | 90 | 40 |

**1957.** Birth Cent. of Lord Baden-Powell.

| No. | Type | Description | | |
|---|---|---|---|---|
| 803. | 215. | 4 c. green & red (post.) | 1·10 | 45 |
| 804. | – | 12 c. slate (air) | 1·75 | 85 |

DESIGN—VERT. 12 c. Lord Baden-Powell.

**216.** "The Art Critics" (Melero).

**217.** Hanabanilla Falls.

**1957.** Postal Employees' Retirement Fund.

| No. | Type | Description | | |
|---|---|---|---|---|
| 805. | – | 2 c. olive & brn. (post.) | 35 | 15 |
| 806. | 216. | 4 c. red and brown | 65 | 25 |
| 807. | – | 10 c. olive and brown | 95 | 35 |
| 808. | – | 14 c. blue and brown | 1·10 | 40 |
| 809. | 217. | 8 c. blue and red (air) | 40 | 15 |
| 810. | – | 12 c. green and red | 1·60 | 30 |
| 811. | – | 30 c. olive and violet | 1·75 | 50 |

DESIGNS—HORIZ. As Type **216** (Paintings): 2 c. "The Blind" (Vega). 10 c. "Carriage in the Storm" (Menocal). 14 c. "The Convalescent" (Romanach). As Type **217**: 12 c. Sierra de Cubitas. 30 c. Puerto Boniato.

**218.** Posthorn Emblem of Cuban Philatelic Society.

**219.** Juan F. Steegers.

**1957.** Stamp Day. Cuban Philatelic Exn.

| No. | Type | Description | | |
|---|---|---|---|---|
| 812. | 218. | 4 c. blue, brown and red (postage) | 90 | 35 |
| 813. | – | 12 c. brown, yellow and green (air) | 1·40 | 50 |

DESIGN: 12 c. Philatelic Society Building, Havana.

**1957.** Birth Centenary of Steegers (finger-print pioneer).

| No. | Type | Description | | |
|---|---|---|---|---|
| 814. | 219. | 4 c. blue (postage) | 90 | 35 |
| 815. | – | 12 c. brown (air) | 1·40 | 45 |

DESIGN: 12 c. Thumbprint.

**220.** Baseball Player. **221.** Nurse Victoria Bru Sanchez.

**1957.** Air. Youth Recreation. Centres in brown.
816. **220.** 8 c. green on green .. 85 30
817. – 12 c. lilac on lavender 1·10 55
818. – 24 c. blue on blue .. 1·75 85
819. – 30 c. flesh on orange 2·25 1·40
DESIGNS—12 c. Ballet dancer. 24 c. Diver. 30 c. Boxers.

**1957.** Nurse Victoria Bru Sanchez Commem.
820. **221.** 4 c. blue .. .. 90 35

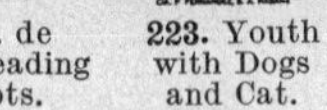

**222.** J. de Aguero leading Patriots. **223.** Youth with Dogs and Cat. **224.** Col. R. Manduley del Rio (patriot).

**1957.** Joaquin de Aguero (patriot) Commem.
821. **222.** 4 c. green (postage) .. 90 35
822. – 12 c. blue (portrait) (air) 1·40 50

**1957.** 50th Anniv. of Band of Charity (for prevention of cruelty to animals).
823. **223.** 4 c. green (postage) .. 90 55
824. – 12 c. brown (air) .. 1·40 40
DESIGN: 12 c. Jeanette Ryder (founder).

**1957.** Col. R. Manduley del Rio. Commem.
825. **224.** 4 c. green .. .. 2·25 1·40

**225.** J. M. Heredia y Girard. **226.** Palace of Justice, Havana.

**1957.** Air. J. M. Heredia y Girard (poet). Commem.
826. **225.** 8 c. violet .. .. 95 35

**1957.** Inaug. of Palace of Justice.
827. **226.** 4 c. grey (postage) .. 90 35
828. 12 c. green (air) .. 1·40 40

**227.** Army Leaders of 1856. **228.** J. R. Gregg.

**1957.** Cent. of Cuban Army of Liberation.
829. **227.** 4 c. brown and green .. 65 35
830. 4 c. brown and blue .. 65 35
831. 4 c. brown and pink .. 65 35
832. 4 c. brown and yellow 65 35
833. 4 c. brown and lilac .. 65 35

**1957.** Air. J. R. Gregg (shorthand pioneer) Commem.
834. **228.** 12 c. green .. .. 1·40 40

**229.** Cuba's First Publication, 1723. **230.** Jose Marti Public Library.

**1957.** "Jose Marti" Public Library. Inscr. "BIBLIOTECA NACIONAL".
835. **229.** 4 c. slate (postage) .. 90 35
836. – 8 c. blue (air) .. 40 20
837. **230.** 12 c. sepia .. .. 1·25 40
DESIGN—VERT. As Type **230**: 8 c. D. F. Caneda, first Director.

**231.** U.N. Emblem and Map of Cuba. **232.** Fokker Trimotor "General New" and Map.

**1957.** Air. U.N. Day.
838. **231.** 8 c. brown and green .. 65 30
839. 12 c. green and red .. 1·25 35
840. 30 c. mauve and blue .. 2·50 80

**1957.** Air. 30th Anniv. of Inaug. of Air Mail Services between Havana and Key West, Florida.
841. **232.** 12 c. blue and purple .. 1·75 45

**233.** **235.** Courtyard.

**1957.** Obligatory Tax. Anti-Tuberculosis.
842. **233.** 1 c. red .. .. 30 10
843. 1 c. green .. .. 30 10
844. 1 c. blue .. .. 30 10
845. 1 c. grey .. .. 30 10

**1957.** Centenary of 1st Cuban Teachers' Training College.
846. **235.** 4 c. brn. & grn. (post.) 90 35
847. – 12 c. buff and blue (air) 95 35
848. – 30 c. sepia and red .. 1·60 45
DESIGNS—VERT. 12 c. School facade. HORIZ. 30 c. General view of school.

**236.** Street Scene, Trinidad. **237.** Christmas Crib.

**1957.** Postal Employees' Retirement Fund.
849. **236.** 2 c. brn. & blue (post.) 20 10
850. – 4 c. green and brown 45 15
851. – 10 c. sepia and red .. 70 30
852. – 14 c. green and red .. 1·10 25
853. – 8 c. black and red (air) 45 20
854. – 12 c. black and brown 95 35
855. – 30 c. brown and grey .. 1·75 45
DESIGNS—VERT. 4 c. Sentry-box on old wall of Havana. 10 c. Calle Padre Pico (street), Santiago de Cuba. 12 c. Sancti Spiritus Church. 14 c. Church and street scene, Camaguey. HORIZ. 8 c. "El Viso" Fort, El Caney. 30 c. Concordia Bridge, Matanzas.

**1957.** Christmas. Multicoloured centres.
856. **237.** 2 c. sepia .. .. 2·25 1·10
857. 4 c. black .. .. 2·25 1·10

**239.** Dayton Hedges and Textile Factories. **240.** Dr. F. D. Roldan.

**1958.** Dayton Hedges (founder of Cuban Textile Industry) Commem.
858. **239.** 4 c. blue (postage) .. 1·40 65
859. 8 c. green (air) .. 1·40 65

**1958.** Dr. Francisco D. Roldan (physiotherapy pioneer) Commem.
861. **240.** 4 c. green .. .. 95 35

**241.** "Diario de la Marina" Building.

**1958.** 125th Anniv. of "Diario de la Marina" Newspaper.
862. – 4 c. olive (postage) .. 95 35
863. **241.** 29 c. black (air) .. 1·75 85
PORTRAIT—VERT. 4 c. J. I. Rivero y Alonso (journalist).

**242.** Map of Cuba showing Postal Routes of 1756. **243.** Gen. J. M. Gomez.

**1958.** Stamp Day and National Philatelic Exn. Havana. Inscr. as in T **242**.
864. **242.** 4 c. myrtle, buff and blue (postage) .. 95 40
865. – 29 c. indigo, buff and blue (air) .. .. 1·90 85
DESIGN: 29 c. Ocean map showing sea-post routes of 1765.

**1958.** Birth Cent. of Gen. J. M. Gomez.
866. **243.** 4 c. blue (postage) .. 90 35
867. – 12 c. myrtle (air) .. 1·25 50
DESIGN: 12 c. Gomez at Arroyo Blanco.

**244.** Dr. T. Romay Chacon. **245.** Dr. C. de la Torre.

**246.** Painted Polymita.

**1958.** Famous Cubans. Portraits as T **244**.
(a) Doctors. With emblem of medicine.
868. 2 c. brown and green .. 45 15
869. 4 c. black and green .. 45 15
870. 10 c. red and green .. 45 15
871. 14 c. blue and green .. 65 15
(b) Lawyers. With emblem of law.
872. 2 c. sepia and red .. 50 15
873. 4 c. black and red .. 50 15
874. 10 c. green and red .. 50 15
875. 14 c. blue and red .. 55 20
(c) Composers. With lyre emblem of music.
876. 2 c. brown and blue .. 40 15
877. 4 c. purple and blue .. 40 15
878. 10 c. green and blue .. 55 15
879. 14 c. red and blue .. 60 15
PORTRAITS—Doctors: 2 c. Type **244**. 4 c. A. A. Aballi. 10 c. F. G. del Valle. 14 c. V. A. de Castro. Lawyers: 2 c. J. M. G. Montes. 4 c. J. A. G. Lanuza. 10 c. J. B. H. Barreiro. 14 c. P. G. Llorente. Composers: 2 c. N. R. Espadero. 4 c. I. Cervantes. 10 c. J. White. 14 c. B. de Salas.

**1958.** Birth Cent. of De la Torre (archaeologist).
880. **245.** 4 c. blue (postage) .. 95 35
881. **246.** 8 c. red, yell. & blk. (air) 2·25 85
882. – 12 c. sepia on green .. 3·25 1·40
883. – 30 c. green on pink .. 5·00 2·00
DESIGNS—As Type **246**: 12 c. "Megalocnus rodens". 30 c. "Perisphinctes spinatus" (ammonite).

**247.** Felipe Poey (naturalist). **248.** "Papilio caiguanabus" (butterfly).

**1958.** Poey Commem. Designs as T **247/8** inscr. "1799-FELIPE POEY-1891".
884. – 2 c. black and lavender (postage) .. .. 40 15
885. **247.** 4 c. sepia .. .. 95 35
886. **248.** 8 c. multicoloured (air) 1·75 35
887. – 12 c. orge., blk. & grn. 2·00 45
888. – 14 c. yellow, black, orange and purple .. 2·50 45
889. – 19 c. multicoloured .. 3·25 55
890. – 24 c. multicoloured .. 3·25 1·00
891. – 29 c. blue, brn. & blk. 5·50 2·25
892. – 30 c. brn., grn. & blk. 8·50 3·25
DESIGNS—VERT. 2 c. Cover of Poey's book. 12 c. "Teria gundlachia". 14 c. "Teria ebriola". 19 c. "Nathalis felicia" (all butterflies). HORIZ. 24 c. Jacome. 29 c. Anil. 30 c. Diana (all fishes).

**249.** Theodore Roosevelt. **250.** National Tuberculosis Hospital.

**1958.** Birth Cent. of Roosevelt.
893. **249.** 4 c. green (postage) .. 95 35
894. – 12 c. sepia (air) .. 1·40 50
DESIGN—HORIZ. 12 c. Roosevelt leading Rough Riders at San Juan 1898.

**1958.** Obligatory Tax. Anti-T.B.
895. **250.** 1 c. brown .. .. 20 10
896. 1 c. green .. .. 20 10
897. 1 c. red .. .. 20 10
898. 1 c. grey .. .. 20 10

**251.** U.N.E.S.C.O. Headquarters, Paris. **252.** "Cattleyopsis lindenii" (orchid).

**1958.** Air. Inauguration of U.N.E.S.C.O. Headquarters.
899. **251.** 12 c. green .. .. 1·25 45
900. – 30 c. blue .. .. 1·60 65
DESIGN: 30 c. Facade composed of letters "UNESCO" and map of Cuba.

**1958.** Christmas. Orchids. Multicoloured.
901. 2 c. Type **252** .. .. 2·50 1·10
902. 4 c. "Oncidium guibertianum" .. .. .. 2·50 1·10

**253.** "The Revolutionary". **254.** Gen. A. F. Crombet.

**1959.** Liberation Day.
903. **253.** 2 c. black and red .. 65 25

**1959.** Gen. Crombet Commem.
904. **254.** 4 c. myrtle .. .. 90 35

**255.** Postal Notice of 1765. **256.** Hand Supporting Sugar Factory.

**1959.** Air. Stamp Day and National Philatelic Exn., Havana.
905. **255.** 12 c. sepia and blue .. 1·10 35
906. – 30 c. blue and sepia .. 1·40 65
DESIGN: 30 c. Administrative postal book of St. Cristobal, Havana, 1765.

**1959.** Agricultural Reform.
907. **256.** 2 c.+1 c. blue and red (postage) .. .. 65 20
908. – 12 c.+3 c. green & red (air) .. .. .. 1·40 45
DESIGN (42 × 30 mm.): 12 c. Farm workers and factory plant.

**257.** Red Cross Nurse.

**1959.** "For Charity".
909. **257.** 2 c.+1 c. red .. .. 35 25

**259.** Teresa Garcia Montes (founder). **260.** Pres. C. M. de Cespedes.

**1959.** Air. American Society of Travel Agents Convention, Havana. No. 780 (colour changed) surch. **CONVENCION ASTA OCTUBRE 17 1919 12 c.** and bar.

910. 12 c. on 1 p. green .. 1·90 1·00

**1959.** Musical Arts Society Festival, Havana.

911. **259.** 4 c. brown (postage) .. 90 35
912. – 12 c. green (air) .. 1·40 55

DESIGN—HORIZ. 12 c. Society Headquarters, Havana.

**1959.** Cuban Presidents.

913. 2 c. slate (Type **260**) .. 35 15
914. 2 c. green (Betancourt) .. 35 15
915. 2 c. violet (Calvar) .. 35 15
916. 2 c. brown (Maso) .. 35 15
917. 4 c. red (Spotorno) .. 65 20
918. 4 c. brown (Palma) .. 65 20
919. 4 c. blk. (F. J. de Cespedes) 65 20
920. 4 c. violet (Garcia) .. 65 20

**261.** Rebel Attack at Moncada Barracks. **264.** Pres. T. Estrada Palma Monument.

**1960.** 1st Anniv. of Cuban Revolution.

921. **261.** 1 c. green, red and blue (postage) .. .. 15 10
922. – 2 c. green, sepia & blue 90 15
923. – 10 c. green, red & blue 1·40 55
924. – 12 c. green, pur. & blue 1·90 65
925. – 8 c. green, red and blue (air) .. .. 1·40 40
926. – 12 c. grn., pur. & brn. 1·40 35
927. – 29 c. red, blk. & grn. 1·75 70

DESIGNS: 2 c. Rebels disembarking from "Granma". 8 c. Battle of Santa Clara. 10 c. Battle of the Uvero. 12 c. postage, "The Invasion" (Rebel and map of Cuba). 12 c. air, Rebel Army entering Havana. 29 c. Passing on propaganda ("Clandestine activities in the towns").

**1960.** Surch. **HABILITADO PARA** and value (No. 932 without **PARA**).

928 **256** 2 c. on 2 c.+1 c. blue and red (postage) .. 90 20
929 – 2 c. on 4 c. mauve (No. 689) .. .. 65 35
930 – 2 c. on 5 c. blue (690) 65 35
931 – 2 c. on 13 c. red (693) 65 35
932 – 10 c. on 20 c. olive (342) 1·10 45
933 – 12 c. on 12 c.+3 c. grn & red (908) (air) 1·40 55

**1960.** Surch in figures.

934. – 1 c. on 4 c. (No. 869) (postage) .. .. 40 15
935. – 1 c. on 4 c. (No. 873) .. 40 15
936. – 1 c. on 4 c. (No. 877) .. 40 15
937. **245.** 1 c. on 4 c. blue .. 40 15
938. 1 c. on 4 c. (No. 902) .. 45 25
939. **254.** 1 c. on 4 c. myrtle .. 40 15
940. **260.** 1 c. on 4 c. brown .. 40 15
941. – 2 c. on 14 c. (No. 694) 80 15
942. **54.** 12 c. on 40 c. orge. (air) 1·40 50
943. – 12 c. on 45 c. (No. 706) 1·40 50

**1960.** Postal Employees' Retirement Fund.

944. **264.** 1 c. brn. & blue (post.) 15 10
945. – 2 c. green and red .. 35 10
946. – 10 c. brown and red .. 65 25
947. – 12 c. green and violet 1·10 45
948. – 8 c. grey and red (air) 55 15
949. – 12 c. blue and red .. 1·40 35
950. – 30 c. violet and red .. 1·75 50

MONUMENTS—VERT. 2 c. "Mambi Victorioso", 8 c. Marti. 10 c. Marta Abreu. 12 c. postage. Agramonte. 12 c. air, Heroes of Cacarajicara. HORIZ. 30 c. Dr. C. de la Torriente.

(265.)

**267.** C. Cienfuegos and View of Escolar. **266.** Pistol-shooting.

**1960.** Air. Stamp Day and National Philatelic Exn., Havana. Nos. 772/3 in new colours optd. with T **265.**

951. 8 c. yellow .. .. 55 35
952. 12 c. red .. .. 1·50 50

**1960.** Olympic Games.

954. – 1 c. violet (Sailing) (postage) .. .. 45 20
955. **266.** 2 c. orange .. .. 1·00 35
956. – 8 c. blue (Boxing) (air) 85 30
957. – 12 c. red (Running) .. 1·40 55

**1960.** 1st Death Anniv. of Cienfuegos (revolutionary leader). Centre multicoloured.

959. **267.** 2 c. sepia .. .. 1·00 15

**268.** Air Stamp of 1930, Ford "Tin Goose" Airplane and "Sputnik".

**1960.** Air. 80th Anniv. of National Airmail Service. Centre multicoloured.

960. **268.** 8 c. violet .. .. 3·25 1·40

**270.** Ipomoea.

**271.** Tobacco Plant and Bars of "Christmas Hymn".

**1960.** Christmas. Inscr. "NAVIDAD 1960–61".

(a) T **270.**

961. 1 c. multicoloured .. 55 55
962. 2 c. multicoloured .. 75 75
963. 10 c. multicoloured .. 1·50 1·50

(b) As T **271.**

964a/d. 1 c. multicoloured .. 1·75 1·40
965a/d. 2 c. multicoloured .. 2·75 2·50
966a/d. 10 c. multicoloured .. 5·00 4·75

DESIGNS: As **T271** (same for each value) a, Type **271.** b, Mariposa. c, Lignum-vitae. d, Coffee plant.

Prices are for single stamps.

**272.**

DESIGNS — HORIZ. 2 c. Graph and symbols. 6 c. Cogwheels. 12 c. Workers holding lever. 30 c. Maps. VERT. 8 c. Hand holding machete. 50 c. Upraised hand.

**1960.** Sub-Industrialized Countries Conf.

967. **272.** 1 c. black, yellow and red (postage) .. 15 10
968. – 2 c. multicoloured .. 15 10
969. – 6 c. red, black & cream 1·10 40
970. – 8 c. multicoloured (air) 40 15
971. – 12 c. multicoloured .. 1·10 15
972. – 30 c. red and grey .. 1·40 50
973. – 50 c. multicoloured .. 1·75 60

**273.** J. Menendez. **274.** Jose Marti and "Declaration of Havana".

**1961.** Jesus Menendez Commem.

974. **273.** 2 c. sepia and green .. 85 25

**1961.** Air. Declaration of Havana.

975. **274.** 8 c. red, black & yellow 75 65
976. 12 c. violet, blk. & buff 1·25 1·00
977. 30 c. brown, blk. & blue 3·00 2·75

The above were issued with part of background text of the declaration in English, French and Spanish. Prices the same for each language.

**275.** U.N. Emblem within Dove of Peace.

**1961.** 15th Anniv. of U.N.O.

979. **275.** 2 c. brn & grn. (post.) 25 10
980. 10 c. green and purple 1·00 45
982. 8 c. red & yellow (air) 45 20
983. 12 c. blue and orange .. 1·10 40

**276.** 10 c. Revolutionary Label of 1874 and "CUBA MAMBISA" "Postmark".

**1961.** Stamp Day. Inscr. "24 DE ABRIL DIA DEL SELLO".

985. **276.** 1 c. red, green & black 15 10
986. – 2 c. orge., slate & black 30 15
987. – 10 c. turq., red & black 1·25 45

DESIGNS: 2 c., 50 c. stamp of 1907 and "CUBA REPUBLICANA" "postmark". 10 c., 2 c. stamp of 1959 and "CUBA REVOLUCIONARIA" "postmark".

**1961.** May Day. Optd. **PRIMERO DE MAYO 1961 ESTAMOS VENCIENDO** in red.

988. **273.** 2 c. sepia and green .. 1·00 20

**278.**

**1961.** "For Peace and Socialism".

989. **278.** 2 c. multicoloured .. 1·00 20

No. 989 is lightly printed on back with pattern of wavy lines and multiple inscr. "CORREOS CUBA" in buff.

**1961.** Air. Surch. **HABILITADO PARA 8 cts.**

992. **174.** 8 c. on 15 c. red .. 50 30
993. **54.** 8 c. on 20 c. brown .. 50 30

**1961.** 1st Official Philatelic Exn. No. 987 optd. **primera exposicion filatelica oficial oct. 7-17, 1961.**

994. 10 c. turq., red and black 1·00 35

The 2, 10 and 12 c. show the letters "U", "B" and "A" on the book forming the word "CUBA".

**281.** Book and Lamp.

**1961.** Education Year.

995. **281.** 1 c. red, black & green 10 10
996. 2 c. red, black & blue 15 10
997. 10 c. red, black & violet 60 20
998. 12 c. red., black & orge. 1·10 45

**282.** "Polymita sulfurosa flammulata"

**283.** "Polymita picta fulminata"

**1961.** Christmas. Inscr "NAVIDAD 1961-62". Multicoloured.

(a) Various designs as T **282.**

999. 1 c. Type **282** .. .. 30 15
1000. 2 c. Cuban Grassquit (vert.) .. .. 1·25 35
1001. 10 c. "Othreis toddi" (horiz.) .. .. 1·75 70

(b) Various designs as T **283.**

1002a/d. 1 c. Snails (horiz.) .. 30 15
1003a/d. 2 c. Birds (vert.) .. 1·25 35
1004a/d. 10 c. Butterflies (horiz.) 1·75 70

DESIGNS: No. 1002a, Type **283.** 1002b, "Polymita p. nigrofasciata". 1002c, "Polymita p. fuscolimbata". 1002d, "Polymita p. roseolimbata". 1003a, Cuban macaw. 1003b, Cuban trogon. 1003c, Bee hummingbird. 1003d, Ivory-billed woodpecker. 1004a, "Uranidia boisduvalii". 1004b, "Phoebis avellaneda". 1004c, "Phaloe cubana". 1004d, "Papoilio gundlacchianus".

Prices are for single stamps.

**284.** Castro Emblem. **285.** Hand with Machete.

**1962.** 3rd Anniv. of Cuban Revolution. Emblem in yellow, red, grey and blue. Colours of background and inscriptions given.

1005. **284.** 1 c. green & pink (post.) 45 25
1006. 2 c. black and orange 95 30
1007. 8 c. brn. & blue (air) 45 20
1008. 12 c. ochre and green 1·10 35
1009. 30 c. violet and yellow 1·40 1·10

**1962.** Air. 1st Anniv. of Socialist Republic's First Sugar Harvest.

1010. **285.** 8 c. sepia and red .. 50 15
1011. 12 c. black and lilac .. 1·10 40

**286.** Armed Peasant and Tractor.

**1962.** National Militia.

1012. **286.** 1 c. black and green .. 20 10
1013. – 2 c. black and blue .. 35 20
1014. – 10 c. black and orange 1·10 35

DESIGNS: 2 c. Armed worker and welder. 10 c. Armed woman and sewing-machinist.

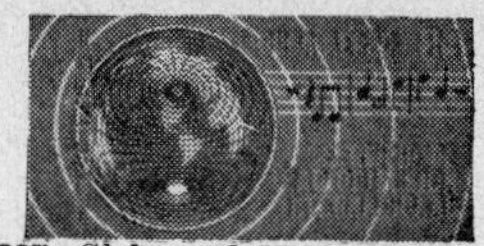

**287.** Globe and Music Emblem.

**1962.** Air. Int. Radio Service. Inscr. and aerial yellow; musical notation black; lines on globe brown, background colours given.

1015. **287.** 8 c. grey .. .. 55 20
1016. 12 c. blue .. .. 1·10 35
1017. 30 c. green .. .. 1·60 85
1018. 1 p. lilac .. .. 3·25 2·25

**288.** Soldiers, Aircraft and Burning Ship.

**1962.** 1st Anniv. of "Playa Giron" (Sea Invasion Attempt of Cuban Exiles).

1019. **288.** 2 c. multicoloured .. 20 10
1020. 3 c. multicoloured .. 20 10
1021. 10 c. multicoloured .. 1·25 50

**289.** Arrival of First Mail from the Indies.

**1962.** Stamp Day.

1022. **289.** 10 c. black & red on cream .. .. 2·50 60

**290.** Clenched Fist Salute.

**1962.** Labour Day.

1023. **290.** 2 c. black on buff .. 20 10
1024. 3 c. black on red .. 35 20
1025. 10 c. black on blue .. 1·10 45

**291.** Wrestling.

**1962.** National Sports Institute (I.N.D.E.R.) Commem. As T **291**. On cream paper.
1026a/e. 1 c. brown and red .. 20 10
1027a/e. 2 c. red and green .. 20 15
1028a/e. 3 c. blue and red .. 75 15
1029a/e. 9 c. purple and blue .. 40 15
1030a/e. 10 c. orange and purple 45 20
1031a/e. 13 c. black and red .. 50 30
DESIGNS: No. 1026a, Type **291**. 1026b, Weight-lifting. 1026c, Gymnastics. 1026d, Judo. 1026e, Throwing the discus. 1027a, Archery. 1027b, Roller skating. 1027c, Show jumping. 1027d, Ninepin bowling. 1027e, Cycling. 1028a, Rowing (coxed four). 1028b, Speed boat. 1028c, Swimming. 1028d, Kayak 1028e, Yachting. 1029a, Football. 1029b, Tennis. 1029c, Baseball. 1029d, Basketball. 1029e, Volleyball. 1030a, Underwater fishing. 1030b, Shooting. 1030c, Model airplane flying. 1030d, Water polo. 1030e, Boxing. 1031a, Pelota. 1031b, Sports stadium. 1031c, Jai alai. 1031d, Chess. 1031e, Fencing.
Prices are for single stamps.

**292.** A. Santamaria and Soldiers. **293.** Dove and Festival Emblem.

**1962.** 9th Anniv. of "Rebel Day".
1032. **292.** 2 c. lake and blue .. 35 25
1033. – 3 c. blue and lake .. 65 35
DESIGN: 3 c. Santamaria and children.

**1962.** World Youth Festival, Helsinki.
1034. **293.** 2 c. multicoloured .. 45 20
1035. – 3 c. multicoloured .. 65 30
DESIGN: 3 c. As Type **293** but with "clasped hands" instead of dove.

**294.** Czech 5 k. "Praga 1962" stamp of 1961.

**1962.** Air. Int. Stamp Exn., Prague.
1037. **294.** 31 c. multicoloured .. 1·75 75

DESIGNS: Rings and: 2 c. Tennis rackets. 3 c. Baseball bats. 13 c. Rapiers and mask.

**295.** Rings and Boxing Gloves.

**1962.** 9th Central American and Caribbean Games, Jamaica.
1039. **295.** 1 c. ochre and red .. 10 10
1040. – 2 c. ochre and blue .. 15 10
1041. – 3 c. ochre and purple 15 10
1042. – 13 c. ochre and green 1·00 55

DESIGN — VERT. 13 c. Mother and child, and Globe.

**296.** "Cuban Women".

**1962.** 1st Cuban Women's Federation National Congress.
1043. **296.** 9 c. red, green & black 45 20
1044. – 13 c. black, blue & grn. 1·25 50

**297.** Running.

**1962.** 1st Latin-American University Games. Multicoloured.
1045. 1 c. Type **297** .. .. 20 10
1046. 2 c. Baseball .. .. 20 10
1047. 3 c. Netball .. .. 45 20
1048. 13 c. Globe .. .. 1·10 45

**298.** Microscope and Parasites.

**1962.** Malaria Eradication. Mult.
1049. 1 c. Type **298** .. .. 30 20
1050. 2 c. Mosquito and pool .. 30 20
1051. 3 c. Cinchona plant and formulae .. .. 95 30

**299.** "Epicrates angulifer B." (snake).

**300.** Cuban Night Lizard.

**1962.** Christmas. Inscr. "NAVIDAD 1962–63". Multicoloured.
(a) Various designs as T**299**.
1052. 2 c. Type **299** .. .. 35 15
1053. 3 c. "Cubispa turquino" (vert.) .. .. .. 50 45
1054. 10 c. Jamacian long-tonged bat .. .. 2·00 1·00
(b) Various designs as T**300**.
1055a/d. 2 c. Reptiles .. .. 35 15
1056a/d. 3 c. Insects (vert.) .. 50 45
1057a/d. 10 c. Mammals .. .. 2·00 1·00
DESIGNS: No. 1055a, Type **300**. 1055b, Knight anole. 1055c, Wright's ground boa. 1055d, Cuban ground iguana. 1056a, "Chrysis superba". 1056b, "Essosthutha roberto". 1056c, "Hortensia conciliata". 1056d, "Lachnopus argus". 1057a, Desmarest's hutia. 1057b, Prehensile-tailed hutia. 1057c, Cuban solenodon. 1057d, Desmarest's hutia (white race).
Prices are for single stamps.

**301.** Titov and "Vostok 2".

**1963.** Cosmic Flights (1st issue).
1058. – 1 c. blue, lake & yellow 20 10
1059. **301.** 2 c. grn., pur. & yellow 35 20
1060. – 3 c. violet, red & yell. 35 20
DESIGNS: 1 c. Gagarin and "Vostok 1". 3 c. Nikolaev, Popovich and "Vostoks 3 and 4".
See also Nos. 1133/4.

DESIGNS: 13 c. Rodriguez. C. Servia, Machado and Westbrook. 30 c. J. Echeverria and M. Mora.

**302.** Attackers.

**1963.** 6th Anniv. of Attack on Presidential Palace.
1061. **302.** 9 c. black and red .. 55 15
1062. – 13 c. purple and blue 65 35
1063. – 30 c. green and red .. 1·60 65

**303.** Baseball.

**1963.** 4th Pan-American Games, Sao Paulo.
1064. **303.** 1 c. green .. .. 45 20
1065. – 13 c. red (Boxing) .. 1·40 40

**304.** "Mask" Letter Box.

**1963.** Stamp Day.
1066. **304.** 3 c. black and brown 45 20
1067. – 10 c. black and violet 1·10 45
DESIGN: 10 c. 19th-century Post Office, Cathedral Place, Havana.

**305.** Revolutionaries and Statue. **306.** Child.

**1963.** Labour Day. Multicoloured.
1068. 3 c. Type **305** .. .. 30 10
1069. 13 c. Celebrating Labour Day .. .. .. 1·00 45

**1963.** Children's Week.
1070. **306.** 3 c. brown and blue .. 30 15
1071. 30 c. red and blue .. 1·40 65

**307.** Ritual Effigy. **308.** "Breaking chains of old regime".

**1963.** 60th Anniv. of Montane Anthropological Museum.
1072. **307.** 2 c. brown & salmon 45 15
1073. – 3 c. purple and blue .. 45 15
1074. – 9 c. grey and red .. 75 40
DESIGNS—HORIZ. 3 c. Carved chair. VERT. 9 c. Statutette.

**1963.** 10th Anniv. of "Rebel Day".
1075. **308.** 1 c. black and pink .. 15 10
1076. – 2 c. purple & pale blue 15 10
1077. – 3 c. sepia and lilac .. 15 10
1078. – 7 c. purple and green 15 10
1079. – 9 c. purple and yellow 40 20
1080. – 10 c. green and ochre 1·00 35
1081. – 13 c. blue and buff .. 1·40 60
DESIGNS: 2 c. Palace attack. 3 c. "The Insurrection". 7 c. "Strike of April 9th" (defence of radio station). 9 c. "Triumph of the Revolution" (upraised flag and weapons). 10 c. "Agrarian Reform and Nationalization" (artisan and peasant). 13 c. "Victory of Giron" (soliders in battle).

**309.** Star Apple. **310.** "Roof and Window".

**1963.** Cuban Fruits. Multicoloured.
1082. 1 c. Type **309** .. .. 15 10
1083. 2 c. Chiromoya .. .. 15 10
1084. 3 c. Cashew nut .. .. 20 15
1085. 10 c. Custard apple .. 95 35
1086. 13 c. Mango .. .. 1·40 1·00

**1963.** 7th Int. Architects Union Congress, Havana.
1087. 3 c. multicoloured .. 25 10
1088. 3 c. multicoloured .. 25 10
1089. 3 c. black, blue and bistre 25 10
1090. 3 c. multicoloured .. 25 10
1091. 13 c. multicoloured .. 90 45
1092. 13 c. multicoloured .. 90 45
1093. 13 c. red, olive and black 90 45
1094. 13 c. multicoloured .. 90 45
DESIGNS—VERT. No. 1087, Type **310**. Nos. 1090/2, Symbols of building construction as Type **310**. HORIZ. Nos. 1089/90 and 1093, Sketches of urban buildings. No. 1094, as Type **310** (girders and outline of house).

**311.** Hemingway and Scene from "The Old Man and the Sea".

**1963.** Ernest Hemingway Commemoration.
1095. **311.** 3 c. brown and blue .. 20 10
1096. – 9 c. turq. and mauve 45 20
1097. – 13 c. black and green 1·25 55
DESIGNS—Hemingway and: 9 c. Scene from "For Whom the Bell Tolls". 13 c. Residence at San Francisco de Paula, near Havana.

DESIGNS—VERT. (32 × 42½ mm.): 3 c. "The Rape of the Mulattos" (after C. Enriquez). 9 c. Greek amphora. 13 c. "Dilecta Mea" (bust, after J. A. Houdon).

**312.** "Zapateo" (dance) after V. P. de Landaluze.

**1964.** 50th Anniv. of National Museum.
1098. **312.** 2 c. multicoloured .. 15 10
1099. – 3 c. multicoloured .. 40 15
1100. – 9 c. multicoloured .. 55 30
1101. – 13 c. black and violet 1·10 55

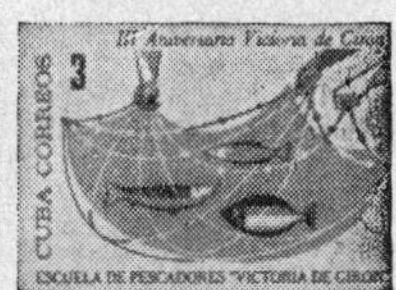


**313.** B. J. Borrell (revolutionary). **314.** Fish in Net.

**1964.** 5th Anniv. of Revolution.
1102. **313.** 2 c. black, orge. & grn. 20 10
1103. – 3 c. black, orge. & red 30 15
1104. – 10 c. black, orge. & pur. 55 25
1105. – 13 c. black, orge. & bl. 1·10 50
PORTRAITS: 3 c. M. Salado. 10 c. O. Lucero. 13 c. S. Gonzalez (revolutionaries).

**1964.** 3rd Anniv. of Giron Victory.
1106. **314.** 3 c. multicoloured .. 20 10
1107. – 10 c. blk., grey & bistre 40 25
1108. – 13 c. slate, blk. & orge. 1·10 45
DESIGNS—HORIZ. 10 c. Victory Monument. VERT. 13 c. Fallen eagle.

**315.** V. M. Pera (1st Director of Military Posts, 1868-71).

**1964.** Stamp Day.
1109. **315.** 3 c. blue and brown .. 25 15
1110. – 13 c. green and lilac .. 90 45
DESIGN: 13 c. Cuba's first (10 c.) military stamp.

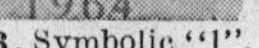

**316.** Symbolic "1". **317.** Chinese Monument, Havana.

**1964.** Labour Day.
1111. **316.** 3 c. multicoloured .. 20 15
1112. – 13 c. multicoloured .. 85 45
DESIGN: 13 c. As Type **316** but different symbols within "1".

**1964.** Cuban-Chinese Friendship.
1113. **317.** 1 c. multicoloured .. 15 10
1114. – 2 c. red, olive & black 25 10
1115. – 3 c. multicoloured .. 40 15
DESIGNS—HORIZ. 2 c. Cuban and Chinese. VERT. 3 c. Flags of Cuba and China.

DESIGNS: 30 c. H. von Stephan (founder of U.P.U.). 50 c. U.P.U. Monument, Berne.

**318.** Globe.

**1964.** U.P.U. Congress, Vienna.
1116. **318.** 13 c. brn., grn. & red 55 20
1117. – 30 c. black, bistre & red 1·10 45
1118. – 50 c. black, blue & red 2·25 75

**319.** Fish.

**1964.** Popular Savings Movement. Mult.
1119. 1 c. Type **319** .. .. 25 10
1120. 2 c. Cow .. .. 25 10
1121. 13 c. Poultry .. .. 1·25 45

320. " Rio Jibacoa ".

**1964.** Cuban Merchant Fleet. Multicoloured.
1122. 1 c. Type **320** .. .. 20 10
1123. 2 c. " Camilo Cienfuegos " 30 10
1124. 3 c. " Sierra Maestra " .. 40 10
1125. 9 c. " Bahia de Siguanea " 95 40
1126. 10 c. " Oriente " .. .. 2·50 75

321. Vietnamese Fighter. 322. Raul Gomez Garcia and Poem.

**1964.** " Unification of Vietnam " Campaign. Multicoloured.
1127. 2 c. Type **321** .. .. 15 10
1128. 3 c. Vietnamese shaking hands across map .. 20 15
1129. 10 c. Hand and mechanical ploughing .. .. 45 20
1130. 13 c. Vietnamese, Cuban and flags .. .. 1·10 45

**1964.** 11th Anniv. of "Rebel Day".
1131. **322** 3 c. black, red & ochre 20 10
1132. – 13 c. multicoloured .. 90 40
DESIGN: 13 c. Inscr. " LA HISTORIA ME ABSOLVERA " (Castro's book).

**1964.** Cosmic Flights (2nd issue). As T **301**.
1133. 9 c. yellow, violet and red 75 40
1134. 13 c. yellow, red & green 1·40 55
DESIGNS: 9 c. " Vostok-5 " and Bykovksy. 13 c. " Vostok-6 " and Tereshkova.

323. Start of Race.

**1964.** Olympic Games, Tokyo.
1135. – 1 c. yellow, blue & pur. 20 10
1136. – 2 c. multicoloured .. 20 10
1137. – 3 c. brown, blk. & red 20 10
1138. **323.** 7 c. violet, blue & orge. 40 15
1139. – 10 c. yellow, pur. & bl. 85 40
1140. – 13 c. multicoloured .. 1·50 65
DESIGNS—VERT. 1 c. Gymnastics. 2 c. Rowing. 3 c. Boxing. HORIZ. 10 c. Fencing. 13 c. Games symbols.

325. Satellite and Globe.

326. Rocket and part of Globe.

**1964.** Cuban Postal Rocket Experiment. 25th Anniv. Various rockets and satellites.
(a) Horiz. designs as T **325**.
1141. **325.** 1 c. multicoloured .. 15 10
1142. – 2 c. multicoloured .. 35 15
1143. – 3 c. multicoloured .. 45 25
1144. – 9 c. multicoloured .. 1·25 45
1145. – 13 c. multicoloured .. 1·75 1·00
(b) Horiz. designs as T **326**.
1146. – 1 c. multicoloured .. 15 10
1147. – 2 c. multicoloured .. 35 15
1148. – 3 c. multicoloured .. 45 25
1149. – 9 c. multicoloured .. 1·25 45
1150. – 13 c. multicoloured .. 1·75 1·00
(c) Larger 44 × 28 mm.
1151. – 50 c. green and black 2·50 1·60
DESIGN: 50 c. Cuban Rocket Post. 10 c. Stamp of 1939.

Nos. 1141 and 1146, 1142 and 1147, 1143 and 1148, 1144 and 1149, 1145 and 1150 were printed together in five sheets of 25, each comprising four stamps as Type **325** plus five se-tenant stamp-size labels inscribed overall "1939 COHETE POSTAL CUBANO 25 ANIVERSARIO 1964" forming a centre cross and four blocks of four different stamps as Type **326** in each corner. The four-stamp design incorporates different subjects, which together form a composite design around a globe. Prices are for single stamps.

**1964.** 1st Three-Manned Space Flight. As No. 1151 but colours changed. Optd. **VOSJOD-1 octubre 12 1964 PRIMERA TRIPULACION DEL ESPACIO** and large rocket.
1153. 50 c. green and brown .. 2·75 1·10

328. Lenin addressing Meeting. 329. Leopard.

**1964.** 40th Death Anniv of Lenin.
1154. **328.** 3 c. black and orange 20 10
1155. – 13 c. red and violet .. 45 25
1156. – 30 c. black and blue .. 1·00 55
DESIGNS—HORIZ. 13 c. Lenin mausoleum. VERT. 30 c. Lenin and hammer and sickle emblem.

**1964.** Havana Zoo Animals. Multicoloured.
1157. 1 c. Type **329** .. .. 10 10
1158. 2 c. Indian elephant (vert.) .. .. .. 10 10
1159. 3 c. Red deer (vert.) .. 15 10
1160. 4 c. Eastern grey kangaroo .. .. .. 20 10
1161. 5 c. Lions .. .. 25 10
1162. 6 c. Eland .. .. 25 10
1163. 7 c. Common zebra .. 25 15
1164. 8 c. Striped hyena .. 45 15
1165. 9 c. Tiger .. .. 45 15
1166. 10 c. Guanaco .. .. 50 15
1167. 13 c. Chimpanzees .. 50 15
1168. 20 c. Collared Peccary .. 70 20
1169. 30 c. Common racoon (vert.) .. .. 1·00 50
1170. 40 c. Hippopotamus .. 2·10 85
1171. 50 c. Brazilian tapir .. 2·75 1·10
1172. 60 c. Dromedary (vert.) 3·00 1·50
1173. 70 c. American Bison .. 3·00 1·50
1174. 80 c. Asiatic black bear (vert.) .. .. 3·75 1·90
1175. 90 c. Water buffalo .. 3·75 2·40
1176. 1 p. Roe deer at Zoo Entrance .. .. 4·75 2·40

330. Jose Marti.

**1964.** "Liberators of Independence". Multicoloured. Each showing portraits and campaigning scenes.
1177. 1 c. Type **330** .. .. 15 10
1178. 2 c. A. Maceo .. .. 20 15
1179. 3 c. M. Gomez .. .. 45 25
1180. 13 c. C. Garcia .. .. 1·00 55

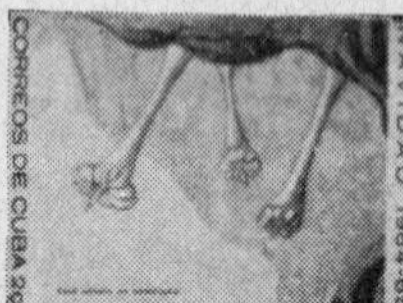

331. Dwarf Cup Coral.

332. Small Flower Coral.

**1964.** Christmas. Inscr. "NAVIDAD 1964–65". Multicoloured.
(a) As T **331**.
1181. 2 c. Type **331** .. .. 35 25
1182. 3 c. Sea anemone .. 65 35
1183. 10 c. Stone lily .. .. 1·00 65
(b) As T **332**.
1184a/d. 2 c. Coral .. .. 35 25
1185a/d. 3 c. Jellyfish .. .. 65 35
1186a/d. 10 c. Sea stars and urchins .. .. 1·00 65
DESIGNS: No. 1184a, Type **332**. 1184b, Elkhorn coral. 1184c, Dense moosehorn coral. 1184d, Yellow brain coral. 1185a, Portuguese man-of-war. 1185b, Moon jellyfish. 1185c, Thimble jellyfish. 1185d, Upside-down jellyfish. 1186a, Big-spined sea-urchin. 1186b, Edible sea urchin. 1186c, Caribbean brittle star. 1186d, Reticulated sea star.

Prices are for single stamps.

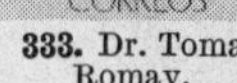

333. Dr. Tomas Romay. 334. Map of Latin America and Part of Declaration.

**1964.** Birth Bicentenary of Dr. Tomas Romay (scientist).
1187. **333.** 1 c. black and bistre .. 20 10
1188. – 2 c. sepia and brown .. 20 10
1189. – 3 c. brown and bistre .. 30 15
1190. – 10 c. black and bistre .. 1·00 40
DESIGNS—VERT. 2 c. First vaccination against smallpox. HORIZ. 3 c. Dr. Romay and extract from his treatise on the vaccine. 10 c. Dr. Romay's statue.

**1964.** 2nd Declaration of Havana. Mult.
1191. 3 c. Type **334** .. .. 45 30
1192. 13 c. Map of Cuba and native receiving revolutionary message .. 1·75 90

The two stamps have the declaration superimposed in tiny print across each horiz. row of five stamps, thus requiring strips of five to show the complete declaration.

335. " Maritime Post " (diorama).

**1965.** Inaug. of Cuban Postal Museum. Mult.
1193. 13 c. Type **335** .. .. 2·50 65
1194. 30 c. " Insurgent Post" (diorama) .. .. 1·90 1·00

336. "Sondero" (schooner).

**1965.** Cuban Fishing Fleet. Multicoloured. Fishing crafts.
1196. 1 c. Type **336** .. .. 15 10
1197. 2 c. " Omicron " .. .. 25 10
1198. 3 c. " Victoria " .. .. 35 15
1199. 9 c. " Cardenas " .. .. 55 25
1200. 10 c. " Sigma " .. .. 2·10 50
1201. 13 c. " Lambda " .. .. 3·25 80

337. Lydia Doce.

**1965.** Int. Women's Day. Multicoloured.
1202. 3 c. Type **337** .. .. 55 25
1203. 13 c. Clara Zetkin .. .. 85 45

338. Jose Antonio Echeverria University City.

**1965.** " Technical Revolution ". Inscr. " REVOLUCION TECNICA ".
1204. **338.** 3 c. blk., brn. & chest. 25 15
1205. – 13 c. multicoloured .. 1·10 45
DESIGN: 13 c. Scientific symbols.

339. Leonov.

**1965.** "Voskhod 2", Space flight.
1206. **339.** 30 c. brown and blue 1·40 55
1207. – 50 c. blue and magenta 2·75 1·10
DESIGN: 50 c. Beliaiev, Leonov and "Voskhod 2".

340. "Figure" (after E. Rodrigues). 341. Lincoln Statue, Washington.

**1965.** National Museum Treasures. **Mult.**
1208. 2 c. Type **340** (27 × 42 mm.) 30 10
1209. 3 c. " Landscape with sunflowers " (V. Manuel) (31 × 42 mm.) .. .. 30 15
1210. 10 c. " Abstract " (W. Lam) (42 × 31 mm.) .. .. 80 30
1211. 13 c. " Children " (E. Ponce) (39 × 33½ mm.) .. 1·40 55

**1965.** Death Cent. of Abraham Lincoln.
1212. – 1 c. brown, grey & yell. 10 10
1213. – 2 c. ultramarine & blue 25 10
1214. **341.** 3 c. black, red and blue 55 30
1215. – 13 c. black, orge. & blue 1·10 50
DESIGNS—HORIZ. 1 c. Cabin at Hodgenville, Kentucky (Lincoln's birthplace). 2 c. Lincoln Monument, Washington. VERT. 13 c. Abraham Lincoln.

342. 18th-century Mail Ship and Old Postmarks (bicent of Maritime Mail).

**1965.** Stamp Day.
1216. **342.** 3 c. bistre and red .. 1·50 20
1217. – 13 c. red, black & blue 1·40 45
DESIGN: 13 c. Cuban. 10 c. "Air Train" stamp of 1935 and glider train over Capitol, Havana.

343. Sun and Earth's Magnetic Pole.

**1965.** Int. Quiet Sun Year. Multicoloured.
1218. 1 c. Type **343** .. .. 20 10
1219. 2 c. I.Q.S.Y. emblem (vert.) 20 10
1220. 3 c. Earth's magnetic fields 35 10
1221. 6 c. Solar rays .. .. 40 15
1222. 30 c. Effect of solar rays on various atmospheric layers .. .. .. 1·40 40
1223. 50 c. Effect of solar rays on satellite orbits .. 1·90 95

Nos. 1221/3 are larger, 47 × 20 mm. or 20 × 47 mm. (30 c.).

344. Telecommunications Station.

**1965.** Cent. of I.T.U. Multicoloured.
1225. 1 c. Type **344** .. .. 15 10
1226. 2 c. Satellite (vert.) .. 15 10
1227. 3 c. "Telstar" .. .. 20 10
1228. 10 c. "Telstar" and receiving station (vert.) .. 65 20
1229. 30 c. I.T.U. emblem .. 1·75 65

**345.** Festival Emblem and Flags.

**1965.** World Youth and Students Festival. Multicoloured.

1230. 13 c. Type **345** .. .. 75 35
1231. 30 c. Soldiers of three races and flags .. .. 1·60 45

**346.** M. Perez (pioneer balloonist), Balloon and Satellite.

**1965.** Matias Perez Commem.

1232. **346.** 3 c. black and red .. 1·10 85
1233. – 13 c. black and blue .. 1·40 85

DESIGN: 13 c. As Type **346**, but with rockets in place of satellite.

**347.** Rose (Europe).

**1965.** Flowers of the World. Multicoloured.

1234. 1 c. Type **347** .. .. 15 10
1235. 2 c. Chrysanthemum (Asia) 15 10
1236. 3 c. Strelitzia (Africa) .. 20 10
1237. 4 c. Dahlia (N. America) .. 20 10
1238. 5 c. Orchid (S. America) .. 55 15
1239. 13 c. "Grevillea banksii" (Oceania) .. .. 1·75 75
1240. 30 c. "Brunfelsia nitida" (Cuba) .. .. 2·25 1·40

**348.** Swimming.

**1965.** First National Games.

1241. **348.** 1 c. multicoloured .. 15 10
1242. – 2 c. multicoloured .. 20 10
1243. – 3 c. black, red & grey 45 20
1244. – 30 c. black, red & grey 1·50 55

SPORTS: 2 c. Basketball. 3 c. Gymnastics. 30 c. Hurdling.

**349.** Anti-tank gun.

**1965.** Museum of the Revolution. Mult.

1245. 1 c. Type **349** .. .. 10 10
1246. 2 c. Tank .. .. 10 10
1247. 3 c. Bazooka .. .. 20 10
1248. 10 c. Rebel Uniform .. 55 20
1249. 13 c. Launch "Granma" and compass .. 1·60 40

**350.** C. J. Finlay. **351.** "Anetia numidia" (butterfly).

**1965.** 50th Death Anniv. of Carlos J. Finlay (malaria researcher).

1250. – 1 c. blk., grn. & blue 10 10
1251. – 2 c. brown, ochre & blk. 15 10
1252. **350.** 3 c. brown and black 15 10
1253. – 7 c. black and lilac .. 20 10
1254. – 9 c. bronze and black 40 20
1255. – 10 c. black and blue .. 85 25
1256. – 13 c. multicoloured .. 1·25 55

DESIGNS—HORIZ. 1 c. Finlay's signature. VERT. 2 c. Yellow fever mosquito. 7 c. Finlay's microscope. 9 c. Dr. C. Delgado. 10 c. Finlay's monument. 13 c. Finlay demonstrating his theories, after painting by Valderrama.

**1965.** Cuban Butterflies. Multicoloured.

1257. 2 c. Type **351** .. .. 20 10
1258. 2 c. "Carathis gortynoides" 20 10
1259. 2 c. "Hymenitis cubana" 20 10
1260. 2 c. "Eubaphe heros" .. 20 10
1261. 2 c. "Dismorphia cubana" 20 10
1262. 3 c. "Siderone nemesis" .. 30 15
1263. 3 c. "Syntomidopsis variegata" .. .. .. 30 15
1264. 3 c. "Ctenuchidia virgo" 30 15
1265. 3 c. "Lycorea ceres" .. 30 15
1266. 3 c. "Eubaphe disparilis" 30 15
1267. 13 c. "Anetia cubana" .. 1·50 55
1268. 13 c. "Prepona antimache" 1·50 55
1269. 13 c. "Sylepta regnalis" 1·50 55
1270. 13 c. "Chlosyne perezi" 1·50 55
1271. 13 c. "Anaea clytemnestra" .. .. 1·50 55

**352.** 20 c. Coin of 1962.

**1965.** 50th Anniv. of Cuban Coinage. Mult.

1273. 1 c. Type **352** .. .. 10 10
1274. 2 c. 1 p. coin of 1934 .. 10 10
1275. 3 c. 40 c. coin of 1962 .. 15 15
1276. 8 c. 1 p. coin of 1915 .. 30 15
1277. 10 c. 1 p. coin of 1953 .. 75 35
1278. 13 c. 20 p. coin of 1915 1·10 40

**353.** Oranges.

**1965.** Tropical Fruits. Multicoloured.

1279. 1 c. Type **353** .. .. 10 10
1280. 2 c. Custard-apples .. 10 10
1281. 3 c. Papayas .. .. 15 15
1282. 4 c. Bananas .. .. 20 10
1283. 10 c. Avocado pears .. 30 15
1284. 13 c. Pineapples .. 55 50
1285. 20 c. Guavas .. .. 1·40 50
1286. 50 c. Mameys .. .. 2·75 85

**354.** Northern oriole. **355.** Painted bunting.

**1965.** Christmas. Vert. designs showing bird life.

(a) As T **354.** Multicoloured.

1287. 3 c. Type **354** .. .. 2·50 1·60
1288. 5 c. Scarlet tanager .. 3·00 2·00
1289. 13 c. Indigo bunting .. 6·75 3·75

(b) As T **355.**

1290a/d. 3 c. multicoloured .. 2·50 1·60
1291a/d. 5 c. multicoloured .. 3·00 2·00
1292a/d. 13 c. multicoloured .. 6·75 3·75

DESIGNS: No. 1290a, Type **355.** 1290b, American redstart. 1290c, Blackburnian warbler. 1290d, Rose-breasted grosbeak. 1291a, Yellow-throated warbler. 1291b, Blue-winged warbler. 1291c, Prothonotary warbler. 1291d, Hooded warbler. 1292a, Blue-winged teal. 1292b, Wood duck. 1292c, Common shoveler. 1292d, Black-crowned night heron.

Prices are for single stamps.

**356.** Hurdling.

**1965.** 7th Anniv. of Int. Athletics, Havana. Multicoloured.

1293. 1 c. Type **356** .. .. 15 10
1294. 2 c. Throwing the discus 15 10
1295. 3 c. Putting the shot .. 35 10
1296. 7 c. Throwing the javelin 35 20
1297. 9 c. High-jumping .. 45 25
1298. 10 c. Throwing the hammer 95 40
1299. 13 c. Running .. .. 1·25 60

**357.** Shark-sucker.

**1965.** National Aquarium. Multicoloured.

1300. 1 c. Type **357** .. .. 15 10
1301. 2 c. Bonito .. .. 15 10
1302. 3 c. Sergeant Major .. 30 10
1303. 4 c. Sailfish .. .. 35 10
1304. 5 c. Nassau grouper .. 35 10
1305. 10 c. Muttonfish .. 45 25
1306. 13 c. Yellowtail snapper 1·40 70
1307. 30 c. Atlantic squirrelfish 2·25 95

**358.** A. Voisin, Cuban and French Flags.

**1965.** 1st Death Anniv. of Prof. Andre Voisin (scientist).

1308. **358.** 3 c. multicoloured .. 40 20
1309. – 13 c. multicoloured .. 1·10 40

DESIGN: 13 c. Similar to Type **358** but with microscope and plant in place of cattle.

**359.** Skoda Omnibus.

**1965.** Cuban Transport. Multicoloured.

1310 1 c. Type **359** .. .. 10 10
1311 2 c. Ikarus omnibus .. 10 10
1312 3 c. Leyland omnibus .. 15 10
1313 4 c. "Tem-4" diesel locomotive .. .. 1·40 30
1314 7 c. "BB.69,000" diesel locomotive .. .. 1·40 30
1315 10 c. Tug "R.D.A." .. 1·00 25
1316 13 c. Freighter "13 de Marzo" .. .. 1·60 45
1317 20 c. Ilyushin Il-18 airliner 1·75 65

**360.** Infantry Column.

**1966.** 7th Anniv. of Revolution. Mult.

1318. 1 c. Type **360** .. .. 20 10
1319. 2 c. Soldier and tank .. 20 10
1320. 3 c. Sailor and torpedo-boat .. .. .. 45 10
1321. 10 c. MiG-21 jet fighter .. 1·00 30
1322. 13 c. Rocket missile .. 1·25 45

SIZES—As Type **360**: 2 c., 3 c. HORIZ. 38½ × 23½ mm.): 10 c., 13 c.

**361.** Conference Emblem.

**1966.** Tricontinental Conf., Havana.

1323. **361.** 2 c. multicoloured .. 15 10
1324. – 3 c. multicoloured .. 20 10
1325. – 13 c. multicoloured .. 95 40

DESIGNS: 3 c., 13 c. As Type **361** but re-arranged.

**362.** Guardalabarca Beach.

**1966.** Tourism. Multicoloured.

1326. 1 c. Type **362** .. .. 10 10
1327. 2 c. La Gran Piedra (mountain resort) .. 15 10
1328. 3 c. Guama, Las Villas (country scene) .. 35 15
1329. 13 c. Waterfall, Soroa (vert.) .. .. .. 1·40 40

**363.** Congress Emblem and "Treating Patient" (old engraving).

**1966.** Medical and Stomachal Congresses, Havana. Multicoloured.

1330. 3 c. Type **363** .. .. 25 10
1331. 13 c. Congress emblem and children receiving treatment .. .. .. 1·10 40

**364.** Afro-Cuban Doll.

**1966.** Cuban Handicrafts. Multicoloured.

1332 1 c. Type **364** .. .. 10 10
1333 2 c. Sombreros .. .. 10 10
1334 3 c. Vase .. .. 10 10
1335 7 c. Gourd lampshades .. 15 10
1336 9 c. Rare-wood lampstand 35 15
1337 10 c. "Horn" shark (horiz) 55 25
1338 13 c. Painted polymita shell necklace and earrings (horiz) .. 1·10 45

**365.** "Chelsea College" (after Canaletto).

**1966.** National Museum Exhibits. Inscr. "1966". Multicoloured.

1339. 1 c. Ming Dynasty vase (vert.) .. .. .. 10 10
1340. 2 c. Type **365** .. .. 40 10
1341. 3 c. "Portrait of a Young Girl" (after Goya) (vert.) .. .. .. 35 20
1342. 13 c. Portrait of Fayum (vert.) .. .. .. 1·40 45

**366.** Cosmonauts in Training. **367.** Tank in Battle.

**1966.** 5th Anniv. of 1st Manned Space Flight. Multicoloured.

1343. 1 c. Tsiolkovsky and diagram .. .. 10 10
1344. 2 c. Type **366** .. .. 10 10
1345. 3 c. Gagarin, rocket and globe .. .. .. 20 10
1346. 7 c. Nikolaev and Popovich .. .. .. 35 10
1347. 9 c. Tereshkova and Bykovsky .. .. 45 20
1348. 10 c. Komarov, Feoktistov and Yegorov .. 55 25
1349. 13 c. Leonov in space .. 1·10 45

Nos. 1343, 1345 and 1347/9 are horiz.

**1966.** 5th Anniv. of Giron Victory.
1350. **367.** 2 c. blk., grn. & bistre 10 10
1351. – 3 c. black, blue & red 40 10
1352. – 9 c. blk., brown & grey 20 10
1353. – 10 c. blk., blue & green 70 15
1354. – 13 c. black, brn. & blue 1·40 50
DESIGNS: 3 c. "Houston" (freighter) sinking. 9 c. Disabled tank and poster-hoarding. 10 c. Young soldier. 13 c. Operations map.

**368.** Interior of Postal Museum (1st Anniv.).

**1966.** Stamp Day.
1355. **368.** 3 c. green and red .. 45 10
1356. – 13 c. brown, blk. & red 1·40 45
DESIGN: 13 c. Stamp collector and Cuban 2 c. stamp of 1959.

**369.** Bouquet and Anvil. **370.** W.H.O. Building.

**1966.** Labour Day. Multicoloured.
1357. 2 c. Type **369** .. .. 15 10
1358. 3 c. Bouquet and Machete 15 10
1359. 10 c. Bouquet and Hammer 45 20
1360. 13 c. Bouquet and parts of globe and cogwheel .. 1·10 60

**1966.** Inaug. of W.H.O. Headquarters, Geneva.
1361. **370.** 2 c. blk., grn. & yellow 15 10
1362. – 3 c. blk., blue & yell. 35 10
1363. – 13 c. blk., yell. & blue 1·10 45
DESIGNS (W.H.O. Building on): 3 c. Flag. 13 c. Emblem.

**371.** Athletics. **372.** Makarenko Pedagogical Institute.

**1966.** 10th Central American and Caribbean Games.
1364. **371.** 1 c. sepia and green 10 10
1365. – 2 c. sepia and orange 10 10
1366. – 3 c. brown and yellow 10 10
1367. – 7 c. blue and mauve 15 10
1368. – 9 c. black and blue .. 30 15
1369. – 10 c. black and brown 55 15
1370. – 13 c. blue and red .. 1·25 40
DESIGNS—HORIZ. 2 c. Rifle-shooting. VERT. 3 c. Baseball. 7 c. Volleyball. 9 c. Football. 10 c. Boxing. 13 c. Basketball.

**1966.** Educational Development.
1371. **372.** 1 c. black and green .. 10 10
1372. – 2 c. blk., ochre & yell. 10 10
1373. – 3 c. black, ultram. & bl. 15 10
1374. – 10 c. black, brn. & grn. 35 20
1375. – 13 c. multicoloured .. 95 40
DESIGNS: 2 c. Alphabetisation Museum. 3 c. Lamp (5th anniv. of National Alphabetisation Campaign). 10 c. Open-air class. 13 c. "Farmers' and Workers' Education".

**373.** "Agrarian Reform".

**1966.** Air. "Conquests of the Revolution". Multicoloured.
1376. 1 c. Type **373** .. .. 15 10
1377. 2 c. "Industrialisation" .. 15 10
1378. 3 c. "Urban Reform" .. 20 10
1379. 7 c. "Eradication of Unemployment" .. 20 10
1380. 9 c. "Education" .. 40 15
1381. 10 c. "Public Health" .. 85 15
1382. 13 c. Paragraph from Castro's book, "La Historia me Absolvera" 1·10 30

**374.** Workers with Flag.

**1966.** 12th Revolutionary Workers' Union Congress, Havana.
1383. **374.** 3 c. multicoloured .. 55 20

**375.** Flamed Cuban Liguus. **377.** Arms of Pinar del Rio.

**376.** Pigeon and Breeding Pen.

**1966.** Cuban Shells. Multicoloured.
1384 1 c. Type **375** .. .. 20 10
1385 2 c. Measled cowrie .. 25 15
1386 3 c. West Indian fighting conch .. .. .. 35 15
1387 7 c. Rough American scallops .. .. 40 20
1388 9 c. Crenate liguus .. 50 20
1389 10 c. Atlantic trumpet triton .. .. .. 80 30
1390 13 c. Archer's Cuban liguus .. .. .. 1·90 55

**1966.** Pigeon-breeding. Multicoloured.
1391. 1 c. Type **376** .. .. 20 10
1392. 2 c. Pigeon and time-clock 20 10
1393. 3 c. Pigeon and pigeon-loft 20 15
1394. 7 c. Pigeon and breeder tending pigeon-loft .. 35 20
1395. 9 c. Pigeon and pigeon-yard 35 25
1396. 10 c. Pigeon and breeder placing message in capsule 1·10 35
1397. 13 c. Pigeons in flight over map of Cuba (44½ × 28 mm.) .. .. .. 1·75 60

**1966.** National and Provincial Arms. Mult.
1398. 1 c. Type **377** .. .. 10 10
1399. 2 c. Arms of Havana .. 10 10
1400. 3 c. Arms of Matanzas .. 15 10
1401. 4 c. Arms of Las Villas .. 20 10
1402. 5 c. Arms of Camaguey .. 30 15
1403. 9 c. Arms of Oriente .. 45 30
1404. 13 c. National Arms (26 × 44 mm.) .. .. 1·00 40

**378.** "Queen" and Simultaneous Games.

**1966.** 17th Chess Olympiad, Havana.
1405. – 1 c. black and green .. 10 10
1406. – 2 c. black and blue 10 10
1407. – 3 c. black and red .. 20 10
1408. – 9 c. black and ochre .. 35 20
1409. **378.** 10 c. black & mauve 85 30
1410. – 13 c. blk., bl. & turq. 1·10 65
DESIGNS—VERT. 1 c. "Pawn". 2 c. "Rook". 3 c. "Knight". 9 c. "Bishop". HORIZ. 13 c. Olympiad Emblem and "King".

**380.** Lenin Hospital.

**1966.** Cuban–Soviet Friendship. Mult.
1412 2 c. Type **380** .. .. 15 10
1413 3 c. World map and "Havana" (tanker) .. 40 10
1414 10 c. Cuban and Soviet technicians .. .. 60 20
1415 13 c. Cuban fruit-pickers and Soviet tractor technicians .. .. 1·10 55

**381.** A. Roldan and Music of "Fiesta Negra".

**1966.** Song Festival.
1416. **381.** 1 c. brn., blk. & grn. 10 10
1417. – 2 c. brn., blk. & mve. 10 10
1418. – 3 c. brown, black & bl. 15 10
1419. – 7 c. brown, blk. & vio. 30 10
1420. – 9 c. brown, blk. & yell. 30 20
1421. – 10 c. brn., blk. & orge. 1·10 30
1422. – 13 c. brown, blk. & bl. 1·60 60
CUBAN COMPOSERS AND WORKS: 2 c. E. S. de Fuentes and "Tu" (habanera, Cuban dance). 3 c. M. Simons and "El Manisero". 7 c. J. Anckermann and "El arroyo que murmura". 9 c. A. G. Caturla and "Pastoral Lullaby". 10 c. E. Grenet and "Ay Mama Ines". 13 c. E. Lecuona and "La Comparsa" (dance).

**382.** Bacteriological Warfare. **383.** A. L. Fernandez ("Nico") and Beach Landing.

**1966.** "Genocide in Viet-Nam". Mult.
1423. 2 c. Type **382** .. .. 10 10
1424. 3 c. Gas warfare .. .. 20 10
1425. 13 c. "Conventional" bombing .. .. 1·10 45

**1966.** 10th Anniv. of 1956 Revolutionary Successes. Portrait in black and brown.
1426. **383.** 1 c. brown and green 10 10
1427. – 2 c. brown and purple 10 10
1428. – 3 c. brown and purple 15 10
1429. – 7 c. brown and blue .. 20 15
1430. – 9 c. brown & turquoise 35 15
1431. – 10 c. brown and olive 1·25 35
1432. – 13 c. brown & orange 1·10 55
HEROES AND SCENES: 2 c. C. Gonzalez and beach landing. 3 c. J. Tey and street fighting. 7 c. T. Aloma and street fighting. 9 c. O. Parellada and street fighting. 10 c. J. M. Marquez and beach landing. 13 c. F. Pais and trial scene.

**384.** Globe and Recreational Activities.

**1966.** Int. Leisure Time and Recreation Seminar. Multicoloured.
1433. 3 c. Type **384** .. .. 15 10
1434. 9 c. Clock, eye and world map .. .. .. 85 20
1435. 13 c. Seminar poster .. 1·10 45

**385.** Arrow and Telecommunications Symbols.

**1966.** 1st National Telecommunications Forum. Multicoloured.
1436. 3 c. Type **385** .. .. 20 10
1437. 10 c. Target and satellites 85 20
1438. 13 c. Shell and satellites (28½ × 36 mm.) 1·25 45

**386.** "Cypripedium eurilochus". **387.** "Cattleya speciosissima".

**1966.** Christmas. Vert. designs showing orchids. Multicoloured.

(a) As T **386**.
1440. 1 c. Type **386** .. .. 30 15
1441. 3 c. "Cypripedium hookerae volunteanum .. 45 25
1442. 13 c. "Cypripedium stonei" .. .. 1·75 95

(b) As T **387**.
1443a/d. 1 c. multicoloured .. 30 15
1444a/d. 3 c. multicoloured .. 45 25
1445a/d. 13 c. multicoloured .. 1·75 95
DESIGNS: No. 1443a, Type **387**. 1443b, "Cattleya mendelli". 1443c, "Cattleya trianae". 1443d, "Cattleya labiata". 1444a, "Cypripedium morganiae". 1444b, "Cattleya" "Countess of Derby". 1444c, "Cattleya gigas". 1444d, "Cypripedium stonei". 1445a, "Cattleya mendelli" "Countess of Montrose". 1445b, "Oncidium macranthum". 1445c, "Cattleya aurea". 1445d, "Laelia anceps".
Prices are for single stamps.

**388.** Flag and Hands ("1959—Liberation").

**1967.** 8th Anniv. of Revolution. Mult.
1446. 3 c. Type **388** .. .. 15 10
1447. 3 c. Clenched fist ("1960—Agrarian Reform") .. 15 10
1448. 3 c. Hands holding pencil ("1961—Education") .. 15 10
1449. 3 c. Hand protecting plant ("1965—Agriculture") 15 10
1450. 13 c. Head of Rodin's statue, "The Thinker", and arrows ("1962—Planning") .. .. 90 35
1451. 13 c. Hands moving lever ("1963—Organization") 90 35
1452. 13 c. Hand holding plant within cogwheel ("1964—Economy") .. .. 90 35
1453. 13 c. Hand holding rifle-butt, and part of globe ("1966—Solidarity") .. 90 35
Nos. 1450/3 are vert.

**389.** "Spring" (after J. Arche).

**1967.** National Museum Exhibits. Paintings (1st series). Multicoloured.
1454. 1 c. "Coffee-pot" (A. A. Leon) .. .. 20 10
1455. 2 c. "Peasants" (E. Abela) 30 10
1456. 3 c. Type **389** .. .. 45 15
1457. 13 c. "Still Life" (Amelia Pelaez) .. .. 1·25 65
1458. 30 c. "Landscape" (G. Escalante) .. .. 3·50 1·25
The 1, 2 and 13 c. are vert.
See also Nos. 1648/54, 1785/91, 1871/7, 1900/6, 2005/11, 2048/54, 2104/9, 2180/5, 2260/5, 2346/51, 2430/5, 2530/5, 2620/5, 2685/90, 2816/21, 3218/23 and 3229/34.

**390.** Menelao Mora, Jose A. Echeverria and Attack on Presidential Palace.

**1967.** National Events of 13 March 1957.
1459. **390.** 3 c. green and black .. 15 10
1460. – 13 c. brown and black 1·50 50
1461. – 30 c. blue and black .. 1·40 55
DESIGNS (36½ × 24½ mm.): 13 c. Calixto Sanchez and "Corynthia" landing. 30 c. Dionisio San Roman and Cienfuegos revolt.

**391.** "Homo habilis".

**1967.** "Prehistoric Man". Multicoloured.

| | | | |
|---|---|---|---|
| 1462. | 1 c. Type **391** .. .. | 10 | 10 |
| 1463. | 2 c. "Australopithecus" | 15 | 10 |
| 1464. | 3 c. "Pithecanthropus erectus" .. .. | 15 | 10 |
| 1465. | 4 c. Peking man.. | 20 | 15 |
| 1466. | 5 c. Neanderthal man .. | 30 | 20 |
| 1467. | 13 c. Cro-Magnon man carving ivory tusk .. | 1·00 | 45 |
| 1468. | 20 c. Cro-Magnon man painting on wall of cave | 2·00 | 65 |

392. Victoria.

**1967.** Stamp Day. Carriages. Multicoloured.

| | | | |
|---|---|---|---|
| 1469. | 3 c. Type **392** .. .. | 20 | 15 |
| 1470. | 9 c. Volanta .. .. | 95 | 30 |
| 1471. | 13 c. Quitrin .. .. | 1·40 | 55 |

393. Cuban Pavilion.

**1967.** "Expo 67" Montreal.

| | | | | |
|---|---|---|---|---|
| 1472. | **393.** | 1 c. multicoloured .. | 20 | 10 |
| 1473. | – | 2 c. multicoloured .. | 20 | 10 |
| 1474. | – | 3 c. multicoloured .. | 25 | 10 |
| 1475. | – | 13 c. multicoloured.. | 1·25 | 55 |
| 1476. | – | 20 c. multicoloured.. | 1·50 | 60 |

DESIGNS: 2 c. Bathysphere, satellite and met. balloon ("Man as Explorer"). 3 c. Ancient rock-drawing and tablet ("Man as Creator"). 13 c. Tractor, ear of wheat and electronic console ("Man as Producer"). 20 c. Olympic athletes ("Man in the Community").

394. "Eugenia malaccencis". 395. "Giselle".

**1967.** 150th Anniv. of Cuban Botanical Gardens. Multicoloured.

| | | | |
|---|---|---|---|
| 1477. | 1 c. Type **394** .. .. | 10 | 10 |
| 1478. | 2 c. "Jacaranda filicifolia" | 10 | 10 |
| 1479. | 3 c. "Coroupita guianensis" | 20 | 10 |
| 1480. | 4 c. "Spathodea campanulata" .. .. | 20 | 10 |
| 1481. | 5 c. "Cassia fistula" .. | 25 | 15 |
| 1482. | 13 c. "Plumieria alba" .. | 1·10 | 55 |
| 1483. | 20 c. "Erythrina poeppigiana" .. .. | 1·75 | 65 |

**1967.** Int. Ballet Festival, Havana. Mult.

| | | | |
|---|---|---|---|
| 1484. | 1 c. Type **395** .. .. | 20 | 10 |
| 1485. | 2 c. "Swan Lake" .. | 20 | 10 |
| 1486. | 3 c. "Don Quixote" .. | 25 | 10 |
| 1487. | 4 c. "Calaucan" .. | 50 | 15 |
| 1488. | 13 c. "Swan Lake" (different) .. .. | 1·40 | 50 |
| 1489. | 20 c. "Nutcracker" .. | 2·00 | 85 |

396. Baseball.

**1967.** 5th Pan-American Games, Winnipeg. Multicoloured.

| | | | |
|---|---|---|---|
| 1490. | 1 c. Type **396** .. .. | 10 | 10 |
| 1491. | 2 c. Swimming .. .. | 10 | 10 |
| 1492. | 3 c. Basketball (vert.) .. | 15 | 10 |
| 1493. | 4 c. Gymnastics (vert.) .. | 20 | 10 |
| 1494. | 5 c. Water-polo (vert.) .. | 30 | 15 |
| 1495. | 13 c. Weight-lifting .. | 1·10 | 35 |
| 1496. | 20 c. Hurling the javelin | 1·75 | 65 |

397. L. A. Turcios Lima, Map and OLAS Emblem. 399. Common Octopus.

398. "Portrait of Sonny Rollins" (Alan Davie).

**1967.** 1st Conf. of Latin-American Solidarity Organization (OLAS), Havana.

| | | | |
|---|---|---|---|
| 1497. | 13 c. black, red and blue | 95 | 40 |
| 1498. | 13 c. black, red and brown | 95 | 40 |
| 1499. | 13 c. black, red and lilac | 95 | 40 |
| 1500. | 13 c. black, red and green | 95 | 40 |

DESIGNS: No. 1497, Type **397**. No. 1498, Fabricio Ojidia. No. 1499, L. de La Puente Uceda. No. 1500, Camilo Torres. Martyrs of Guatemala, Venezuela, Peru and Colombia respectively. Each with map and OLAS emblem.

**1967.** "Contemporary Art" (Havana Exn. from the Paris "Salon de Mayo"). Various designs showing modern paintings. Sizes given in millimetres. Multicoloured.

| | | | |
|---|---|---|---|
| 1501. | 1 c. Type **398** .. .. | 10 | 10 |
| 1502. | 1 c. "Twelve Selenites" (F. Labisse) (39 × 41) .. | 10 | 10 |
| 1503. | 1 c. "Night of the Drinker" (F. Hundertwasser) (53 × 41) .. .. | 10 | 10 |
| 1504. | 1 c. "Figure" (Mariano) (48 × 41) .. .. | 10 | 10 |
| 1505. | 1 c. "All-Souls" (W. Lam) (45 × 41) .. .. | 10 | 10 |
| 1506. | 2 c. "Darkness and Cracks" (A. Tapies) (37 × 54) .. | 15 | 10 |
| 1507. | 2 c. "Bathers" (G. Singier) (37 × 54) .. .. | 15 | 10 |
| 1508. | 2 c. "Torso of a Muse" (J. Arp) (37 × 46) .. | 15 | 10 |
| 1509. | 2 c. "Figure" (M. W. Svanberg) (57 × 54) .. | 15 | 10 |
| 1510. | 2 c. "Oppenheimer's Information" (Erro) (37 × 41) .. .. | 15 | 10 |
| 1511. | 3 c. "Where Cardinals are Born" (Max Ernst) (37 × 52) .. .. | 35 | 15 |
| 1512. | 3 c. "Havana Landscape" (Portocarrero) (37 × 41) | 35 | 15 |
| 1513. | 3 c. "EG 12" (V. Vasarely) (37 × 42) .. .. | 35 | 15 |
| 1514. | 3 c. "Frisco" (A. Calder) (37 × 50) .. .. | 35 | 15 |
| 1515. | 3 c. "The Man with the Pipe" (Picasso) (37 × 52) | 35 | 15 |
| 1516. | 4 c. "Abstract Composition" (S. Poliakoff) (36 × 50) | 40 | 15 |
| 1517. | 4 c. "Painting" (Bram van Velde) (36 × 68) .. | 40 | 15 |
| 1518. | 4 c. "Sower of Fires" (detail, Matta) (36 × 47) | 40 | 15 |
| 1519. | 4 c. "The Art of Living" (R. Magritte) (36 × 50) | 40 | 15 |
| 1520. | 4 c. "Poem" (J. Miro) (36 × 56) .. .. | 40 | 15 |
| 1521. | 13 c. "Young Tigers" (J. Messagier) (50 × 33) .. | 95 | 45 |
| 1522. | 13 c. "Painting" (Vieira da Silva) (50 × 36) .. | 95 | 45 |
| 1523. | 13 c. "Live Cobra" (P. Alechinsky) (50 × 35) .. | 95 | 45 |
| 1524. | 13 c. "Stalingrad" (detail, A. Jorn) (50 × 46) .. | 95 | 45 |
| 1525. | 30 c. "Warriors" (E. Pignon) (55 × 32) .. | 4·00 | 1·75 |

**1967.** World Underwater Fishing Championships. Multicoloured.

| | | | |
|---|---|---|---|
| 1527. | 1 c. Green Moray eel .. | 10 | 10 |
| 1528. | 2 c. Type **399** .. | 10 | 10 |
| 1529. | 3 c. Great barracuda .. | 10 | 10 |
| 1530. | 4 c. Bull shark .. | 25 | 10 |
| 1531. | 5 c. Spotted Jewfish .. | 55 | 20 |
| 1532. | 13 c. Ray .. .. | 1·00 | 55 |
| 1533. | 20 c. Green turtle .. | 2·25 | 65 |

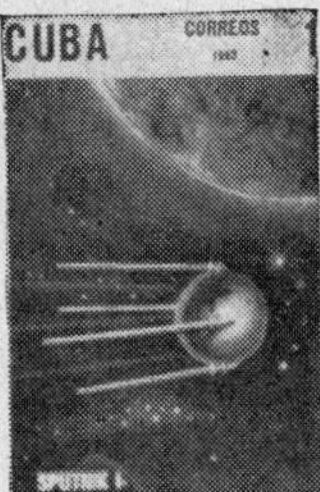

400. "Sputnik 1".

**1967.** Soviet Space Achievements. Mult.

| | | | |
|---|---|---|---|
| 1534. | 1 c. Type **400** .. .. | 10 | 10 |
| 1535. | 2 c. "Lunik 3" .. .. | 10 | 10 |
| 1536. | 3 c. "Venusik" .. .. | 15 | 10 |
| 1537. | 4 c. "Cosmos" .. .. | 20 | 10 |
| 1538. | 5 c. "Mars 1" .. .. | 30 | 15 |
| 1539. | 9 c. "Electron 1, 2" .. | 40 | 20 |
| 1540. | 10 c. "Luna 9" .. .. | 55 | 35 |
| 1541. | 13 c. "Luna 10" .. .. | 1·25 | 50 |

401. "Storming the Winter Palace" (from painting by Sokolov, Skalia and Miasnikova).

**1967.** 50th Anniv. of October Revolution. Multicoloured. Designs showing paintings. Sizes given in millimetres.

| | | | |
|---|---|---|---|
| 1543. | 1 c. Type **401** .. .. | 10 | 10 |
| 1544. | 2 c. "Lenin addressing 2nd Soviet Congress" (Serov) (48 × 36) .. | 10 | 10 |
| 1545. | 3 c. "Lenin in the year 1919" (Nalbandian) (35 × 37) .. | 20 | 10 |
| 1546. | 4 c. "Lenin explaining the GOELRO Map" (Schmatko) (48 × 36) .. | 20 | 15 |
| 1547. | 5 c. "Dawn of the Five-Year Plan" construction work (Romas) (50 × 36) | 85 | 25 |
| 1548. | 13 c. "Kusnetzkroi steel Furnace No. 1" (Kotov) (36 × 51) .. .. | 1·10 | 40 |
| 1549. | 30 c. "Victory Jubilation" (Krivonogov) (50 × 36) | 1·60 | 65 |

402. Royal Force Castle, Havana.

**1967.** Historic Cuban Buildings. Multicoloured. Sizes given in millimetres.

| | | | |
|---|---|---|---|
| 1550. | 1 c. Type **402** .. .. | 10 | 10 |
| 1551. | 2 c. Iznaga Tower, Trinidad (26½ × 47½) .. | 15 | 10 |
| 1552. | 3 c. Castle of Our Lady of the Angels, Cienfuegos (41½ × 29) .. .. | 20 | 10 |
| 1553. | 4 c. Church of St. Francis of Paula, Havana (41½ × 29) .. .. | 20 | 10 |
| 1554. | 13 c. Convent of St. Francis, Havana (39 × 13) .. | 1·10 | 45 |
| 1555. | 30 c. Morro Castle, Santiago de Cuba (43 × 26) .. | 1·75 | 75 |

403. Ostrich. 404. Golden Pheasant.

**1967.** Christmas. Vert. designs showing birds of Havana Zoo. Multicoloured.

(a) As T **403**.

| | | | |
|---|---|---|---|
| 1556. | 1 c. Type **403** .. .. | 65 | 15 |
| 1557. | 3 c. Hyacinth macaw .. | 1·25 | 30 |
| 1558. | 13 c. Greater flamingoes | 3·00 | 1·00 |

(b) As T **404**.

| | | | |
|---|---|---|---|
| 1559a/d. | 1 c. multicoloured .. | 65 | 15 |
| 1560a/d. | 3 c. multicoloured .. | 1·25 | 30 |
| 1561a/d. | 13 c. multicoloured .. | 3·00 | 1·00 |

DESIGNS: No. 1559a, Type **404**. 1559b, White stork. 1559c, Crowned crane. 1559d, Emu. 1560a, Grey parrot. 1560b, Chattering lory. 1560c, Keel-billed toucan. 1560d, Sulphur-creasted cockatoo. 1561a, American white pelican. 1561b, Egyptian goose. 1561c, Mandarin. 1561d, Black swan.

Prices are for single stamps.

405. "Che" Guevara

**1968.** Major Ernesto "Che" Guevara Commem.

| | | | | |
|---|---|---|---|---|
| 1562. | **405.** | 13 c. black and red .. | 1·60 | 40 |

406. Man and Tree ("Problems of Artistic Creation, Scientific and Technical Work").

**1968.** Cultural Congress, Havana. Mult.

| | | | |
|---|---|---|---|
| 1563. | 3 c. Chainbreaker cradling flame ("Culture and Independence") .. | 10 | 10 |
| 1564. | 3 c. Hand with spanner and rifle ("Integral Formation of Man") .. | 10 | 10 |
| 1565. | 13 c. Demographic emblems ("Intellectual Responsibility") .. .. | 85 | 30 |
| 1566. | 13 c. Hand with communications emblems ("Culture and Mass-Communications Media") .. | 90 | 35 |
| 1567. | 30 c. Type **406** .. .. | 1·25 | 65 |

The 3 and 13 c. values are all vert.

407. Canaries. 408. "The Village Postman" (after J. Harris).

**1968.** Canary-breeding.

| | | | | |
|---|---|---|---|---|
| 1568. | **407.** | 1 c. multicoloured .. | 10 | 10 |
| 1569. | – | 2 c. multicoloured .. | 10 | 10 |
| 1570. | – | 3 c. multicoloured .. | 10 | 10 |
| 1571. | – | 4 c. multicoloured .. | 15 | 10 |
| 1572. | – | 5 c. multicoloured .. | 30 | 15 |
| 1573. | – | 13 c. multicoloured.. | 1·40 | 55 |
| 1574. | – | 20 c. multicoloured.. | 1·60 | 65 |

DESIGNS: Canaries and breeding cycle—mating, eggs, incubation and rearing young.

**1968.** Stamp Day. Multicoloured.

| | | | |
|---|---|---|---|
| 1575. | 13 c. Type **408** .. .. | 1·10 | 35 |
| 1576. | 30 c. "The Philatelist" (after G. Sciltian) .. | 1·60 | 50 |

409. Nurse tending Child ("Anti-Polio Campaign"). 410. "Children".

**1968.** 20th Anniv. of W.H.O.

| | | | | |
|---|---|---|---|---|
| 1577. | **409.** | 13 c. black, red & olive | 1·10 | 40 |
| 1578. | – | 30 c. blk., blue & olive | 1·40 | 55 |

DESIGN: 30 c. Two doctors ("Hospital Services").

**1968.** Int. Children's Day.

| | | | | |
|---|---|---|---|---|
| 1579. | **410.** | 3 c. multicoloured .. | 55 | 20 |

411. "Cuatro Vientos" and Route Map.

**1968.** 35th Anniv. of Seville—Camaguey Flight by Barberan and Collar. Multicoloured.

| | | | |
|---|---|---|---|
| 1580. | 13 c. Type **411** .. .. | 1·40 | 30 |
| 1581. | 30 c. Captain M. Barberan and Lieut. J. Collar | 1·40 | 40 |

412. "Canned Fish".

**1968.** Cuban Food Products. Multicoloured.
1582. 1 c. Type **412** .. .. 10 10
1583. 2 c. "Milk Products" .. 15 10
1584. 3 c. "Poultry and Eggs" 25 20
1585. 13 c. "Cuban Rum" .. 1·40 35
1586. 20 c. "Canned Shell-fish" 1·60 50

**413.** Siboney Farmhouse. **414.** Committee Members and Emblem.

**1968.** 15th Anniv. of Attack on Moncada Barracks. Multicoloured.
1587. 3 c. Type **413** .. .. 10 10
1588. 13 c. Map of Santiago de Cuba and assault route 1·00 40
1589. 30 c. Students and school buildings (on site of Moncada Barracks) .. 1·60 55

**1968.** 8th Anniv. of Revolutionary Defence Committee.
1590. **414.** 3 c. multicoloured .. 55 15

**415.** Che Guevara and Rifleman.

**1968.** Day of the Guerrillas.
1591. **415.** 1 c. black, grn. & gold 10 10
1592. – 3 c. black, brn. & gold 10 10
1593. – 9 c. multicoloured .. 30 10
1594. – 10 c. blk., grn. & gold 60 15
1595. – 13 c. blk., pink & gold 1·10 45
DESIGNS—"Che" Guevara and: 3 c. Machine-gunners. 9 c. Riflemen. 10 c. Soldiers cheering. 13 c. Map of Caribbean and South America.

**416.** C. M. de Cespedes and Broken Wheel.

**1968.** Cent. of Cuban War of Independence. Multicoloured.
1596. 1 c. Type **416** .. .. 10 10
1597. 1 c. E. Betances and horsemen .. .. 10 10
1598. 1 c. I. Agramonte and monument .. .. 10 10
1599. 1 c. A. Maceo and "The Protest" .. 10 10
1600. 1 c. J. Marti & patriots 10 10
1601. 3 c. M. Gomez and "Invasion" .. .. 10 10
1602. 3 c. J. A. Mella and declaration .. .. 10 10
1603. 3 c. A. Guiteras and monument .. .. 10 10
1604. 3 c. A Santamaria and riflemen .. .. 10 10
1605. 3 c. F. Pais & graffiti .. 10 10
1606. 9 c. J. Echeverria and students .. .. 50 15
1607. 13 c. C. Cienfuegos and rebels .. .. .. 1·25 45
1608. 30 c. "Che" Guevara and Castro addressing meeting .. .. 1·50 70

**418.** Parade of Athletes, Olympic Flag and Flame.

**1968.** Olympic Games, Mexico. Multicoloured.
1610. 1 c. Type **418** .. .. 10 10
1611. 2 c. Basketball (vert.) .. 10 10
1612. 3 c. Throwing the hammer (vert.) .. .. 10 10
1613. 4 c. Boxing .. .. 15 10
1614. 5 c. Water-polo .. .. 20 10
1615. 13 c. Pistol-shooting .. 1·10 40
1616. 30 c. Calendar-stone ($32\frac{1}{2} \times 50$ mm.) .. 1·60 55

**419.** Crop-spraying.

**1968.** Civil Activities of Cuban Armed Forces. Multicoloured.
1618. 3 c. Type **419** .. .. 10 10
1619. 9 c. "Che Guevara" Brigade .. .. 30 10
1620. 10 c. Road-building Brigade .. .. 45 20
1621. 13 c. Agricultural Brigade 1·00 50

**420.** "Manrique de Lara's Family" (J.-B. Vermay).

**1968.** 150th Anniv. of San Alejandro Painting School. Multicoloured. Sizes given in millimetres.
1622. 1 c. Type **420** .. .. 10 10
1623. 2 c. "Seascape" (L. Romanach) ($48 \times 37$) .. 15 10
1624. 3 c. "Wild Cane" (A. Rodriguez) ($40 \times 48$) .. 15 10
1625. 4 c. "Self-portrait" (M. Melero) ($40 \times 50$) .. 15 15
1626. 5 c. "The Lottery List" (J. J. Tejada) ($48 \times 37$) 45 30
1627. 13 c. "Portrait of Nina" (A. Menocal) ($40 \times 50$) 1·25 50
1628. 30 c. "Landscape" (E. S. Chartrand) ($54 \times 37$) .. 1·90 75

**421.** Cuban Flag and Rifles. **423.** Mariana Grajales, Rose and Statue.

**422.** Gutierrez and Sanchez.

**1969.** 10th Anniv. of "The Triumph of the Rebellion".
1630. **421.** 13 c. multicoloured .. 1·10 40

**1969.** Cent. of Villaclarenos Patriots Rebellion.
1631. **422.** 3 c. multicoloured .. 55 20

**1969.** Cuban Women's Day.
1632. **423.** 3 c. multicoloured .. 55 20

**424.** Cuban Pioneers.

**1969.** Cuban Pioneers and Young Communist Unions. Multicoloured.
1633. 3 c. Type **424** .. .. 20 15
1634. 13 c. Young Communists 1·00 50

**425.** Guaimaro Assembly.

**1969.** Cent. of Guaimaro Assembly.
1635. **425.** 3 c. brown and sepia 55 20

**426.** "The Postman" (J. C. Cazin).

**1969.** Cuban Stamp Day. Multicoloured.
1636. 13 c. Type **426** .. .. 1·10 45
1637. 30 c. "Portrait of a Young Man" (George Romney) ($36 \times 44$ mm.) .. .. 1·75 65

**427.** Agrarian Law, Headquarters, Eviction of Family, and Tractor.

**1969.** 10th Anniv. of Agrarian Reform.
1638. **427.** 13 c. multicoloured .. 1·10 45

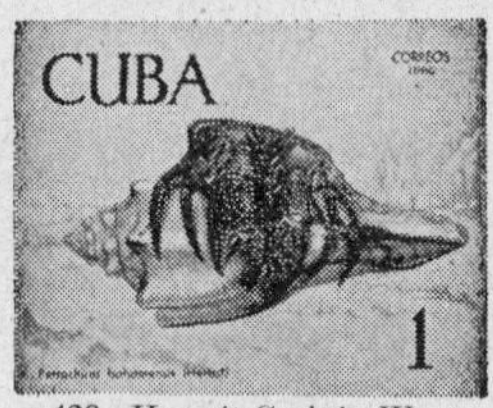


**428.** Hermit Crab in West Indian Chank.

**1969.** Crustaceans. Multicoloured.
1639. 1 c. Type **428** .. .. 15 10
1640. 2 c. Spiny shrimp .. 15 10
1641. 3 c. Spiny lobster .. 15 10
1642. 4 c. Blue crab .. .. 15 15
1643. 5 c. Land crab .. .. 30 15
1644. 13 c. Freshwater prawn 1·40 40
1645. 30 c. Pebble crab .. 2·50 60

**429.** Factory and Peasants.

**1969.** 50th Anniv. of I.L.O. Mult.
1646. 3 c. Type **429** .. .. 20 15
1647. 13 c. Worker breaking chain 1·10 45

**430.** "Flowers" (R. Milian).

**1969.** National Museum Paintings (2nd series). Multicoloured.
1648. 1 c. Type **430** .. .. 10 10
1649. 2 c. "The Annunciation" (A. Eiriz) .. .. 10 10
1650. 3 c. "Factory" (M. Pogolotti) .. .. 15 10
1651. 4 c. "Territorial Waters" (L. M. Pedro) .. .. 20 10
1652. 5 c. "Miss Sarah Gale" (John Hoppner) .. 20 10
1653. 13 c. "Two Women wearing Mantillas" (I. Zuloaga) .. .. 1·10 45
1654. 30 c. "Virgin and Child" (F. Zurbaran) .. .. 1·60 55
SIZES—HORIZ. 2 c. As No. 1648. VERT. 3 c. As No. 1648. 4 c. $40 \times 44$ mm.; 5 c. and 30 c. $40 \times 46$ mm.; 13 c. $38 \times 42$ mm.

**431.** Television Cameras and Emblem.

**1969.** Cuban Radiodiffusion Institute. Mult.
1655. 3 c. Type **431** .. .. 20 15
1656. 13 c. Broadcasting tower and "Globe" .. 1·10 50
1657. 1 p. TV Reception diagram 2·50 1·10

**432.** Spotted Cardinal.

**1969.** Cuban Pisciculture. Multicoloured.
1658. 1 c. Type **432** .. .. 10 10
1659. 2 c. Spanish hogfish .. 10 10
1660. 3 c. Yellowtail damsel fish .. .. .. 20 10
1661. 4 c. Royal gramma .. 20 10
1662. 5 c. Blue chromis .. 25 15
1663. 13 c. Squirrel fish .. 1·40 45
1664. 30 c. Portuguese man-of-war fish (vert.) .. 1·90 75

**433.** "Cuban Film Library".

**1969.** 10th Anniv. of Cuban Cinema Industry. Multicoloured.
1665. 1 c. Type **433** .. .. 10 10
1666. 3 c. "Documentaries" .. 15 10
1667. 13 c. "Cartoons" .. 1·10 50
1668. 30 c. "Full-length Features" .. .. 1·75 60

**434.** "Napoleon in Milan". (A. Appiani (the Elder)).

**1969.** Paintings in Napoleonic Museum, Havana. Multicoloured.
1669. 1 c. Type **434** .. .. 10 10
1670. 2 c. "Hortensia de Beauharnais" (F. Gerard) .. 15 10
1671. 3 c. "Napoleon-First Consul" (J. B. Regnault) 15 10
1672. 4 c. "Elisa Bonaparte" (R. Lefevre) .. 20 10
1673. 5 c. "Napoleon planning the Coronation" (J. G. Vibert) .. .. 35 25
1674. 13 c. "Corporal of Cuirassiers" (J. Meissonier) .. 1·60 55
1675. 30 c. "Napoleon Bonaparte" (R. Lefevre) .. 2·00 65
SIZES—VERT. 2 c. $42\frac{1}{2} \times 55$ mm.; 3 c. $46 \times 56\frac{1}{2}$ mm.; 4 c., 13 c., $44 \times 63$ mm.; 30 c. $45\frac{1}{2} \times 60$ mm. HORIZ. 5 c. $64 \times 47$ mm.

**435.** Baseball Players.

**1969.** Cuba's Victory in World Amateur Baseball Championships, Dominican Republic.
1676. **435.** 13 c multicoloured .. 1·10 50

**436.** Von Humboldt, Book and Surinam Eel.

**1969.** Birth Bicentenary of Alexander von Humboldt. Multicoloured.

1677. 3 c. Type **436** .. .. 10 10
1678. 13 c. Night monkey .. 1·50 75
1679. 30 c. Andean condors .. 2·25 65

**437.** Ancient Egyptians in Combat.

**1969.** World Fencing Championships, Havana. Multicoloured.

1683. 1 c. Type **437** .. .. 10 10
1684. 2 c. Roman Gladiators .. 10 10
1685. 3 c. Norman and Viking .. 10 10
1686. 4 c. Medieval tournament 15 10
1687. 5 c. French musketeers .. 20 10
1688. 13 c. Japanese samurai .. 1·10 35
1689. 30 c. Mounted Cubans, War of Independence .. 1·60 60

**438.** Militiaman. **439.** Major Cienfuegos and Wreath on Sea.

**1969.** 10th Anniv. of National Revolutionary Militias.

1691. **438.** 3 c. multicoloured .. 55 20

**1969.** 10th Anniv. of Disappearance of Major Camilo Cienfuego.

1692. **439.** 13 c. multicoloured .. 1·10 50

**440.** Strawberries and Grapes.

**1969.** Agriculture and Livestock Projects. Multicoloured.

1693. 1 c. Type **440** .. .. 10 10
1694. 1 c. Onion and asparagus 10 10
1695. 1 c. Rice .. .. 10 10
1696. 1 c. Bananas .. .. 10 10
1697. 3 c. Pineapple .. .. 20 10
1698. 3 c. Tobacco plant .. 20 10
1699. 3 c. Citrus fruits .. 20 10
1700. 3 c. Coffee .. .. 20 10
1701. 3 c. Rabbits .. .. 20 10
1702. 10 c. Pigs .. .. 25 10
1703. 13 c. Sugar-cane .. 1·40 55
1704. 30 c. Bull .. .. 1·75 65

Nos. 1697/1702 are vert.

**441.** Stadium and Map of Cuba (2nd National Games).

**1969.** Sporting Events of 1969. Multicoloured.

1705 1 c. Type **441** .. .. 10 10
1706 2 c. Throwing the discus (9th Anniv Games) .. 10 10
1707 3 c. Running (Barrientos commemoration) (vert) 10 10
1708 10 c. Basketball (2nd Olympic Trial Games) (vert) .. .. .. 20 10
1709 13 c. Cycling (6th Cycle Race) (vert) .. .. 1·25 55
1710 30 c. Chessmen and Globe (7th Capablanca Int. Chess Tournament, Havana) (vert) .. 1·75 85

**442.** "Plumbago capensis". **443.** "Petrea volubilis".

**1969.** Christmas. Vert designs showing flowers. (a) As T **442**. Multicoloured.

1711. 1 c. Type **442** .. .. 25 10
1712. 3 c. "Turnera ulmifolia" 55 20
1713. 13 c. "Delonix regia" .. 1·25 75

(b) As T **443**.

1714a/d. 1 c. multicoloured .. 25 10
1715a/d. 3 c. multicoloured .. 55 20
1716a/d. 13 c. multicoloured .. 1·25 75

DESIGNS: No. 1714a, Type **443**. 1714b, "Clitoria ternatea". 1714c, "Duranta repens". 1714d, "Ruellia tuberosa". 1715a, "Thevetia peruviana". 1715b, "Hibiscus elatus". 1715c, "Allamanda cathartica". 1715d, "Cosmos sulphureus". 1716a, "Nerium oleander (wrongly inscr. "Neriun")". 1716b, "Cordia sebestena". 1716c, "Lochnera rosea". 1716d, "Jatropha integerrima".

Prices are for single stamps.

**444.** River Snake.

**1969.** Swamp Fauna. Multicoloured.

1717. 1 c. Type **444** .. .. 10 10
1718. 2 c. Banana Frog .. 10 10
1719. 3 c. Manjuari (fish) .. 10 10
1720. 4 c. Dwarf hutia (vert.) 15 20
1721. 5 c. Alligator .. .. 15 10
1722. 13 c. Cuban Amazon (vert.) 2·50 40
1723. 30 c. Red-winged Blackbird (vert.) .. .. 3·25 65

**445.** "Jibacoa Beach" (J. Hernandez). **446.** Yamagua.

**1970.** Tourism. Multicoloured.

1724. 1 c. Type **445** .. .. 10 10
1725. 3 c. "Trinidad City" .. 10 10
1726. 13 c. Santiago de Cuba .. 1·25 55
1727. 30 c. Vinales Valley .. 1·75 65

**1970.** Medicinal Plants. Multicoloured.

1728. 1 c. Type **446** .. .. 10 10
1729. 3 c. Albahaca Morada .. 10 10
1730. 10 c. Curbana .. .. 25 10
1731. 13 c. Romerillo .. .. 1·25 55
1732. 30 c. Marilope .. .. 1·60 65
1733. 50 c. Aguedita .. .. 2·25 80

**447.** Weightlifting.

**1970.** 11th Central American and Caribbean Games. Multicoloured.

1734. 1 c. Type **447** .. .. 10 10
1735. 3 c. Boxing .. .. 10 10
1736. 10 c. Gymnastics .. 15 10
1737. 13 c. Athletics .. .. 1·10 40
1738. 30 c. Fencing .. .. 1·60 60

**448.** "Enjoyment of Life".

**1970.** "EXPO 70" World Fair, Osaka, Japan. Multicoloured.

1740. 1 c. Type **448** .. .. 10 10
1741. 2 c. "Uses of nature" .. 10 10
1742. 3 c. "Better Living Standards" .. .. 20 10
1743. 13 c. "International Co-operation" .. 1·25 35
1744. 30 c. Cuban Pavilion 1·75 55

Nos. 1741 and 1743 are vert.

**449.** Oval Pictograph, Ambrosio Cave.

**1970.** 30th Anniv. of Cuban Spelaeological Society.

1745. **449.** 1 c. red and brown .. 10 10
1746. – 2 c. black and brown 10 10
1747. – 3 c. red and brown .. 10 10
1748. – 4 c. black and brown 10 10
1749. – 5 c. blackish brown, red and brown .. 15 10
1750. – 13 c. blackish brown and brown .. 1·10 50
1751. – 30 c. red and brown 1·75 55

DESIGNS—HORIZ. (42 × 32½ mm.): 2 c. Cave 1, Punta del Este, Isle of Pines. 5 c. As 2 c. (different). 30 c. Stylised fish, Cave 2, Punta del Este. VERT. 3 c. Stylised mask, Pichardo Cave, Sierra de Cubitas. 4 c. Conical complex, Ambrosio Cave, Varadero. 13 c. Human face, Garcia Robiou Cave, Catalina de Guines.

**450.** J. D. Blino, Balloon and Spacecraft.

**1970.** Aviation Pioneers. Multicoloured.

1752. 3 c. Type **450** .. .. 40 10
1753. 13 c. A. Theodore, balloon and satellite .. .. 1·60 45

**451.** "Lenin in Kazan" (O. Vishniakov).

**1970.** Birth Cent. of Lenin. Paintings. Mult.

1754. 1 c. Type **451** .. .. 10 10
1755. 2 c. "Lenin's Youth" (Prager) .. .. 10 10
1756. 3 c. "The 2nd Socialist Party Congress" (Vinogradov) 10 10
1757. 4 c. "The First Manifesto" (Golubkov) .. .. 15 10
1758. 5 c. "The First Day of Soviet Power" (Babasiuk) 15 10
1759. 13 c. "Lenin in the Smolny Institute" (Sokolov) .. 1·10 45
1760. 30 c. "Autumn in Gorky" (Varlamov) .. .. 1·40 55

SIZES: 4 c., 5 c. As Type **451**: 2 c., 3 c., 13 c., 30 c. 70 × 34 mm.

**452.** "The Letter" (J. Archer)

**1970.** Cuban Stamp Day. Paintings. Mult.

1762. 13 c. Type **452** .. 1·10 45
1763. 30 c. "Portrait of a Cadet" (anonymous) (35 × 49 mm.) 1·40 55

**453.** Da Vinci's Anatomical Drawing, Earth and Moon.

**1970.** World Telecommunications Day.

1764. **453.** 30 c. multicoloured .. 1·40 55

**454.** Vietnamese Fisherman.

**1970.** 80th Birthday of Ho Chi Minh (North Vietnamese leader). Multicoloured.

1765. 1 c. Type **454** .. .. 10 10
1766. 3 c. Cultivating rice-fields 20 10
1767. 3 c. Two Vietnamese children .. .. 20 10
1768. 3 c. Children entering air-raid shelter .. .. 20 10
1769. 3 c. Camouflaged machine-shop .. .. .. 25 10
1770. 3 c. Rice harvest .. 25 10
1771. 13 c. Pres. Ho Chi Minh 1·10 50

SIZES: Nos. 1766/7 33 × 44½ mm. Nos. 1768, 1770, 33½ × 46 mm. No. 1769, 35 × 42 mm. No. 1771, 34½ × 39½ mm.

**455.** Tobacco Plantation and "Eden" Cigar band.

**1970.** "Cuban Cigar Industry". Mult.

1772. 3 c. Type **455** .. .. 10 10
1773. 13 c. 19th century cigar factory and "El Mambi" band .. .. .. 95 50
1774. 30 c. Packing cigars (19th-century) and "Gran Pena" band .. .. 1·50 70

**456.** Cane crushing Machinery.

**1970.** Cuban Sugar Harvest Target. "Over 10 Million Tons". Multicoloured.

1775. 1 c. Type **456** .. .. 10 10
1776. 2 c. Sowing and crop-spraying .. .. 10 10
1777. 3 c. Cutting sugar-cane .. 10 10
1778. 10 c. Ox-cart and diesel locomotive .. .. 1·50 30
1779. 13 c. Modern cane cutting machine .. .. 1·00 20
1780. 30 c. Cane-cutters and Globe (vert.) .. .. 1·40 50
1781. 1 p. Sugar Warehouse .. 2·75 1·25

**457.** P. Figueredo and National Anthem (original version).

**1970.** Death Cent. of Pedro Figueredo (composer of National Anthem). Mult.

1782. 3 c. Type **457** .. .. 20 10
1783. 20 c. 1898 version of anthem .. .. .. 1·10 40

**458.** Cuban Girl, Flag and Federation Badge.

**1970.** 10th Anniv. of Cuban Women's Federation.

1784. **458.** 3 c. multicoloured .. 50 35

**459.** "Peasant Militia" (S. C. Moreno).

**1970.** National Museum Paintings (3rd series). Multicoloured.

1785. 1 c. Type **459** .. .. 10 10
1786. 2 c. "Washerwoman" (A. Fernandez) .. .. 10 10
1787. 3 c. "Puerta del Sol, Madrid" (L.P. Alcazar) 10 10
1788. 4 c. "Fishermen's Wives" (J. Sorolla) .. .. 10 10
1789. 5 c. "Portrait of a Lady" (T. de Keyser) .. 15 10
1790. 13 c. "Mrs. Edward Foster" (Lawrence).. 95 45
1791. 30 c. "Tropical Gipsy" (V. M. Garcia) .. 1·40 65

SIZES—HORIZ. 2 c., 3 c. 46×42 mm. SQUARE. 4 c. 41×41 mm. VERT. 5 c., 13 c., 30 c. 39×46 mm.

**460.** Crowd in Jose Marti Square, Havana. (Illustration reduced. Actual size 75 × 26 mm.)

**1970.** 10th Anniv. of Havana Declaration.

1792. **460.** 3 c. blue, red & black 15 10

**461.** C. D. R. Emblem.

**1970.** 10th Anniv. of Revolution Defence Committees.

1793. **461.** 3 c. multicoloured .. 40 15

**462.** Laboratory, Emblem and Microscope.

**1970.** 39th A.T.A.C. (Sugar Technicians Assn.) Conference.

1794. **462.** 30 c. multicoloured .. 1·50 50

**463.** Helmet Guineafowl.

**1970.** Wildlife. Multicoloured.

1795. 1 c. Type **463** .. .. 50 15
1796. 2 c. Black-billed whistling duck .. .. 55 15
1797. 3 c. Ring-necked pheasant 70 15
1798. 4 c. Mourning dove .. 80 15
1799. 5 c. Bobwhite .. .. 85 20
1800. 13 c. Wild boar .. .. 1·50 70
1801. 30 c. White-tailed deer .. 2·50 1·00

**464.** "Black Magic Parade" (M. Puente).

**1970.** Afro-Cuban Folklore Paintings. Mult.

1802. 1 c. Type **464** .. .. 10 10
1803. 3 c. "Zapateo Hat Dance" (V. L. Landaluze) .. 10 10
1804. 10 c. "Los Hoyos Conga Dance" (D. Ravenet) 50 40
1805. 13 c. "Climax of the Rumba" (E. Abela).. 1·25 55

SIZES—HORIZ. 10 c. 45×44 mm. VERT. 3 c., 13 c. 37×49 mm.

**465.** Common Zebra on Road Crossing.

**1970.** Road Safety Week. Multicoloured.

1806. 3 c. Type **465** .. .. 35 15
1807. 9 c. Prudence the Bear on point duty .. .. 55 15

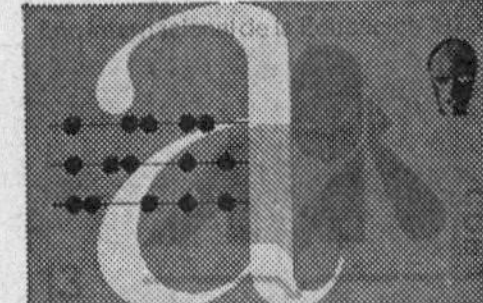

**466.** Letter 'a' and Abacus.

**1970.** International Education Year. Mult.

1808. 13 c. Type **466** .. .. 1·10 20
1809. 30 c. Microscope and cow 1·40 45

**467.** Cuban Blackbird. **468.** Cuban Pygmy Owl.

**1970.** Christmas. Vert. designs showing birds.

(a) As T **467**. Multicoloured.

1810. 1 c. Type **467** .. .. 75 20
1811. 3 c. Oriente warbler .. 1·75 35
1812. 13 c. Zapata sparrow .. 3·25 90

(b) As T **468**.

1813a/d. 1 c. multicoloured .. 75 20
1814a/d. 3 c. multicoloured .. 1·75 35
1815a/d. 13 c. multicoloured .. 3·25 90

DESIGNS: No. 1813a, Type **468**. 1813b, Cuban tody. 1813c, Cuban green woodpecker. 1813d, Zapata wren. 1814a, Cuban solitaire. 1814b, Blue-grey gnatcatcher. 1814c, Cuban vireo. 1814d, Yellow-headed warbler. 1815a, Hook-billed kite. 1815b, Gundlach's hawk. 1815c, Blue-headed quail dove. 1815d, Cuban conure. Prices are for single stamps.

**469.** School Badge and Cadet Colour-party.

**1970.** "Camilo Cienfuegos" Military School.

1816. **469.** 3 c. multicoloured.. 40 20

**470.** "Reporter" with Pen.

**1971.** 7th Journalists International Organization Congress, Havana.

1817. **470.** 13 c. multicoloured.. 95 35

**471.** Lockheed 8A Sirius.

**1971.** 35th Anniv. of Camaguey-Seville Flight by Menendez Pelaez. Multicoloured.

1818. 13 c. Type **471** .. .. 1·40 20
1819. 30 c. Lieut. Menendez Pelaez and map .. 1·75 50

---

## INDEX

Countries can be quickly located by referring to the index at the end of this volume.

---

**472.** Meteorological Class. **473.** Games Emblem.

**1971.** World Meteorological Day. Multicoloured.

1820. 1 c. Type **472** .. .. 10 10
1821. 3 c. Hurricane map (40×36 mm.).. .. 10 10
1822. 8 c. Meteorological equipment .. .. 55 20
1823. 30 c. Weather radar systems (horiz.) .. 2·50 80

**1971.** 6th Pan-American Games, Cali, Colombia. Multicoloured.

1824. 1 c. Type **473** .. .. 10 10
1825. 2 c. Athletics .. .. 10 10
1826. 3 c. Rifle-shooting (horiz.) 10 10
1827. 4 c. Gymnastics .. .. 10 10
1828. 5 c. Boxing .. .. 10 10
1829. 13 c. Water-polo (horiz.) 1·10 25
1830. 30 c. Baseball (horiz.) .. 1·50 40

**474.** Paris Porcelain, 19th-century. **475.** Mother and Child.

**1971.** Porcelain and Mosaics in Metropolitan Museum, Havana. Mult.

1831. 1 c. Type **474** .. .. 10 10
1832. 3 c. Mexican pottery bowl, 17th-century .. 10 10
1833. 10 c. 19th-century Paris porcelain (similar to T **474**) .. .. 20 10
1834. 13 c. "Colosseum" Italian mosaic, 19th-century 1·10 20
1835. 20 c. 17th-century Mexican pottery dish (similar to 3 c.) .. .. 1·10 45
1836. 30 c. "St. Peter's Square" (Italian mosaic 19th-cent.) .. .. 1·40 50

SIZES—VERT. 3 c. 46×54 mm. 10 c. as Type **474**. 20 c. 43×49 mm. HORIZ. 13 c., 30 c. 50×33 mm.

**1971.** 10th Anniv. of Cuban Infant Centres.

1837. **475.** 3 c. multicoloured .. 35 10

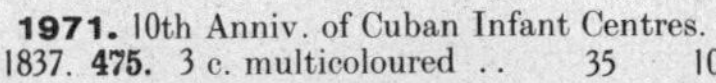

**476.** Cosmonaut in Training.

**1971.** 10th Anniv. of First Manned Space Flight. Multicoloured.

1838. 1 c. Type **476** .. .. 10 10
1839. 2 c. Speedometer test .. 10 10
1840. 3 c. Medical examination 10 10
1841. 4 c. Acceleration tower.. 10 10
1842. 5 c. Pressurisation test.. 10 10
1843. 13 c. Cosmonaut in gravity chamber .. .. 1·00 25
1844. 30 c. Crew in flight simulator .. .. .. 1·25 55

**477.** Cuban and Burning Ship.

**1971.** 10th Anniv. of Giron Victory.

1846. **477.** 13 c. multicoloured.. 1·50 40

**478.** Sailing Packet "Windsor Castle" attacked by French Privateer Brig "Jeune Richard" (1807).

**1971.** Stamp Day. Multicoloured.

1847. 13 c. Type **478** .. .. 1·75 60
1848. 30 c. Mail steamer "Orinoco", 1851 .. 2·50 80

**479.** Transmitter and Hemispheres.

**1971.** 10th Anniv. of Cuban Int. Broadcasting Services.

1849. **479.** 3 c. multicoloured .. 20 10
1850. 50 c. multicoloured .. 2·10 60

**480.** "Cattleya skinnerii". **482.** Larvae and Pupae.

**481.** Loynaz del Castillo and "Invasion Hymn".

**1971.** Tropical Orchids (1st series). Mult.

1851. 1 c. Type **480** .. .. 10 10
1852. 2 c. "Vanda hibrida" .. 10 10
1853. 3 c. "Cypripedium callossum" .. .. 10 10
1854. 4 c. "Cypripedium glaucophyllum" .. 10 10
1855. 5 c. "Vanda tricolor" .. 10 10
1856. 13 c. "Cypripedium mowgh" .. .. 1·25 30
1857. 30 c. "Cypripedium solum" 1·90 55

See also Nos. 1908/14 and 2012/18.

**1971.** Birth Cent. of Enrique Loynaz del Castillo (composer).

1858. **481.** 3 c. multicoloured .. 40 20

**1971.** Apiculture. Multicoloured.

1859. 1 c. Type **482** .. .. 15 10
1860. 3 c. Working bee .. 15 10
1861. 9 c. Drone .. .. 30 10
1862. 13 c. Defending the hive 1·60 25
1863. 30 c. Queen bee .. .. 2·25 55

**483.** "The Ship" (Lydia Rivera).

**1971.** Exhibition of Children's Drawings, Havana. Multicoloured.

1864. 1 c. Type **483** .. .. 10 10
1865. 3 c. "Little Train" (Yuri Ruiz) .. .. .. 25 15
1866. 9 c. "Sugar-cane Cutter" (Horacio Carracedo) .. 10 10
1867. 10 c. "Return of Cuban Fisherman" (Angela Munoz and Lazaro Hernandez) .. .. 25 15
1868. 13 c. "The Zoo" (Victoria Castillo) .. .. 85 25
1869. 20 c. "House and Garden" (Elsa Garcia) 1·40 45
1870. 30 c. "Landscape" (Orestes Rodriguez) (vert.) 1·60 65

SIZES: 9 c. 13 c. 45×35 mm. 10 c. 45×38 mm. 20 c. 47×42 mm. 30 c. 39×49 mm.

**1971.** National Museum Paintings (4th series). As T **459**. Multicoloured.

1871. 1 c. "St. Catherine of Alexandria" (Zurbaran) .. 10 10
1872. 2 c. "The Cart" (F. Americo) (horiz.) .. 10 10
1873. 3 c. "St. Christopher and the Child" (J. Bassano) 10 10
1874. 4 c. "Little Devil" (R. Portocarrero) .. .. 10 10
1875. 5 c. "Portrait of a Lady" (N. Maes) .. .. 10 10
1876. 13 c. "Phoenix" (R. Martinez) .. .. 1·00 30
1877. 30 c. "Sir William Pitt" (Gainsborough) .. 1·40 50

SIZES: 1 c., 3 c. 30×56 mm. 2 c. 48×37 mm. 4 c., 5 c. 37×49 mm. 13 c., 30 c. 39×49 mm.

**485.** Macabi.

**1971.** Sport Fishing. Multicoloured.

1878. 1 c. Type **485** .. .. 10 10
1879. 2 c. Great amberjack .. 10 10
1880. 3 c. Large-mouth black bass .. .. .. 10 10
1881. 4 c. Dorado .. .. 10 10
1882. 5 c. Tarpon .. .. 15 10
1883. 13 c. Waho .. .. 85 30
1884. 30 c. Swordfish .. .. 1·50 50

**486.** Ball within "C".

**1971.** World Amateur Baseball Championships. Multicoloured.

1885. 3 c. Type **486** .. .. 15 10
1886. 1 p. Hand holding globe within "C" .. .. 2·75 1·10

**487.** "Dr. F. Valdes Dominguez" (artist unknown).

**1971.** Centenary of Medical Students' Execution. Multicoloured.

1887. 3 c. Type **487** .. .. 20 10
1888. 13 c. "Students Execution" (M. Mesa) .. 90 30
1889. 30 c. "Captain Federico Capdevila" (unknown artist) .. .. .. 1·40 40

The 13 c. is horiz. and larger, 62×47 mm.

**488.** American Kestrel.

**1971.** Death Cent. of Ramon de la Sagra (naturalist). Cuban Birds. Multicoloured.

1890. 1 c. Type **488** .. .. 40 10
1891. 2 c. Cuban Pygmy Owl .. 40 10
1892. 3 c. Cuban Trogon .. 60 10
1893. 4 c. Great Lizard Cuckoo 70 15
1894. 5 c. Fernandina's Flicker 80 20
1895. 13 c. Stripe-headed Tanager (horiz.) .. 1·60 40
1896. 30 c. Red-legged Thrush (horiz.) .. 3·00 80
1897. 50 c. Cuban Emerald and Ruby-throated Hummingbirds (horiz. 56 × 30 mm.) .. .. 5·75 1·25

**489.** Baseball Player and Global Emblem.

**1971.** Cuba's Victory in World Amateur Baseball.

1898. **489.** 13 c. multicoloured .. 85 45

**490.** "Children of the World".

**1971.** 25th Anniv. of U.N.I.C.E.F.

1899. **490.** 13 c. multicoloured .. 1·10 45

**1972.** National Museum Paintings (5th series). As T **459**. Multicoloured.

1900. 1 c. "The Reception of Ambassadors" (V. Carpaccio) .. .. .. 10 10
1901. 2 c. "Senora Malpica" (G. Collazo) .. .. 10 10
1902. 3 c. "La Chorrera Fortress" (E. Chartrand) .. 10 10
1903. 4 c. "Creole Landscape" (C. Enriquez) .. .. 10 10
1904. 5 c. "Sir William Lemon" (G. Romney) .. .. 10 10
1905. 13 c. "La Tajona Beach" (H. Cleenewek) .. 1·10 30
1906. 30 c. "Valencia Beach" (J. Sorolla y Bastida) .. 2·00 70

SIZES: 1 c., 3 c. 51×33 mm. 2 c. 28×53 mm. 4 c., 5 c. 36×44 mm. 13 c., 30 c. 43×34 mm.

**492.** "Capitol" Stamp of 1929. (now Natural History Museum).

**1972.** 10th Anniv. of Academy of Sciences.

1907. **492.** 13 c. purple & yellow 95 40

**1972.** Tropical Orchids (2nd series). As T **480**. Multicoloured.

1908. 1 c. "Brasso Cattleya sindorossiana" .. 10 10
1909. 2 c. "Cypripedium doraeus" 10 10
1910. 3 c. "Cypripedium exul" 10 10
1911. 4 c. "Cypripedium rosy-dawn" .. .. .. 10 10
1912. 5 c. "Cypripedium champolliom" .. .. 10 10
1913. 13 c. "Cypripedium bucolique" .. .. .. 1·10 55
1914. 30 c. "Cypripedium sullanum" .. .. .. 1·40 65

**493.** "Eduardo Agramonte" (F. Martinez).

**1972.** Death Centenary of Dr. E. Agramonte (surgeon and patriot).

1915. **493.** 3 c. multicoloured .. 30 15

**494.** Human Heart and Thorax. **496.** "Vincente Mora Pera" (Postmaster General, War of Independence) (R. Loy).

**495.** "Sputnik 1".

**1972.** World Health Day.

1916. **494.** 13 c. multicoloured .. 95 40

**1972.** "History of Space". Multicoloured.

1917. 1 c. Type **495** .. .. 10 10
1918. 2 c. "Vostok 1" .. 10 10
1919. 3 c. Valentina Tereshkova in capsule .. .. 10 10
1920. 4 c. A. Leonov in space 10 10
1921. 5 c. "Lunokhod 1" moon Vehicle .. .. 10 10
1922. 13 c. Linking of "Soyuz" Capsules .. .. 95 35
1923. 30 c. Dobrovolsky, Volkov & Pataiev, victims of "Soyuz 11" disaster .. 1·10 45

**1972.** Stamp Day. Multicoloured.

1924. 13 c. Type **496** .. .. 85 40
1925. 30 c. Mambi Mail cover of 1897 (48 × 39 mm.) .. 1·40 45

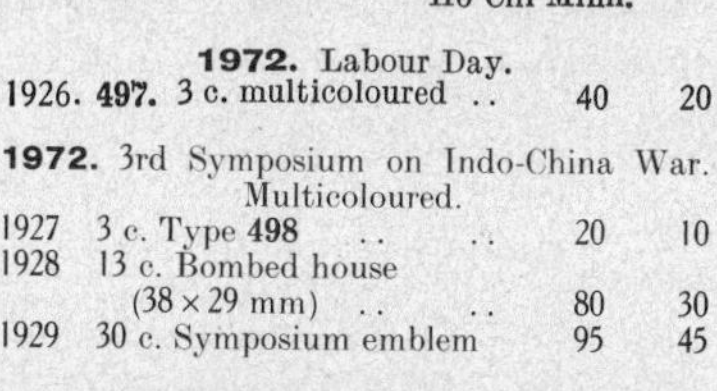

**497.** Cuban Workers. **498.** Jose Marti and Ho Chi Minh.

**1972.** Labour Day.

1926. **497.** 3 c. multicoloured .. 40 20

**1972.** 3rd Symposium on Indo-China War. Multicoloured.

1927 3 c. Type **498** .. .. 20 10
1928 13 c. Bombed house (38×29 mm) .. .. 80 30
1929 30 c. Symposium emblem 95 45

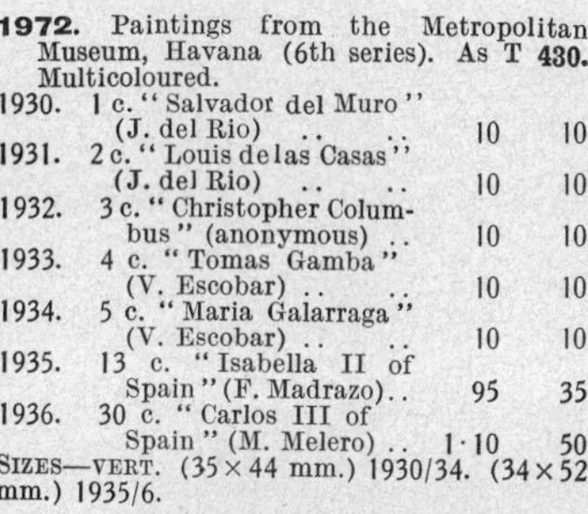

**1972.** Paintings from the Metropolitan Museum, Havana (6th series). As T **430**. Multicoloured.

1930. 1 c. "Salvador del Muro" (J. del Rio) .. .. 10 10
1931. 2 c. "Louis de las Casas" (J. del Rio) .. .. 10 10
1932. 3 c. "Christopher Columbus" (anonymous) .. 10 10
1933. 4 c. "Tomas Gamba" (V. Escobar) .. .. 10 10
1934. 5 c. "Maria Galarraga" (V. Escobar) .. .. 10 10
1935. 13 c. "Isabella II of Spain" (F. Madrazo) .. 95 35
1936. 30 c. "Carlos III of Spain" (M. Melero) .. 1·10 50

SIZES—VERT. (35×44 mm.) 1930/34. (34×52 mm.) 1935/6.

**500.** Children in Boat.

**1972.** Children's Song Competition.

1937. **500.** 3 c. multicoloured .. 50 20

**501.** Ilyushin Il-18, Map and Flags.

**1972.** Air. 1st Anniv. of Havana-Santiago de Chile Air Service.

1938. **501.** 25 c. multicoloured .. 1·40 55

**502.** Tarpan.

**1972.** Thoroughbred Horses. Multicoloured.

1939. 1 c. Type **502** .. .. 10 10
1940. 2 c. Kertag .. .. 10 10
1941. 3 c. Creole .. .. 10 10
1942. 4 c. Andalusian .. .. 10 10
1943. 5 c. Arab .. .. 10 10
1944. 13 c. Quarter-horse .. 1·25 50
1945. 30 c. Pursang .. .. 1·60 75

**503.** Frank Pais.

**1972.** 15th Death Anniv. of Frank Pais.

1946. **503.** 13 c. multicoloured .. 85 40

**504.** Athlete and Emblem.

**1972.** Olympic Games, Munich.

1947. **504.** 1 c. orange & brown 10 10
1948. – 2 c. pur., blue & orge. 10 10
1949. – 3 c. grn., yell. & blk. 10 10
1950. – 4 c. blue, yell. & brn. 10 10
1951. – 5 c. red, black & yell. 10 10
1952. – 13 c. lilac, grn. & blue 85 35
1953. – 30 c. blue, red & grn. 1·10 50

DESIGNS—HORIZ. 2 c. "M" and boxing. 3 c. "U" and weightlifting. 4 c. "N" and fencing. 5 c. "I" and rifle-shooting. 13 c. "C" and running. 30 c. "H" and basketball.

**505.** "Landscape with Tree-trunks" (D. Ramos).

**1972.** Int. Hydrological Decade. Mult.

1955. 1 c. Type **505** .. .. 10 10
1956. 3 c. "Cyclone" (T. Lorenzo) .. .. 15 10
1957. 8 c. "Vineyards" (D. Ramos) .. .. 35 10
1958. 30 c. "Forest and Stream" (A. R. Morey) (vert.) .. 1·10 45

**506.** "Papilio thoas oviedo".

**1972.** Butterflies from the Gundlach Collection. Multicoloured.

1959. 1 c. Type **506** .. .. 10 10
1960. 2 c. "Papilio devilliers" 15 10
1961. 3 c. "Papilio polixenes polixenes" .. .. 15 10
1962. 4 c. "Papilio androgeus epidaurus" .. .. 15 10
1963. 5 c. "Papilio cayguanabus" 25 10
1964. 13 c. "Papilio andraemon hernandezi" .. .. 2·50 60
1965. 30 c. "Papilio celadon" 3·25 80

**507.** "In La Mancha" (A. Fernandez).

**1972.** 425th Birth Anniv. of Cervantes. Paintings by A. Fernandez. Mult.

1966. 3 c. Type **507** .. .. 10 10
1967. 13 c. " Battle with the Wine Skins " (horiz.) .. 1·00 35
1968. 30 c. " Don Quixote of La Mancha" .. .. 1·10 40

**508.** E. " Che" Guevara and Map of Bolivia.

**1972.** 5th Anniv. of Guerrillas' Day. Mult.

1970. 3 c. Type **508** .. .. 10 10
1971. 13 c. T. " Tania " Bunke and map of Bolivia .. 1·00 35
1972. 30 c. G. " Inti " Peredo and map of Bolivia .. 1·10 40

**509.** " Abwe " (shakers).

**1972.** Traditional Musical Instruments. Mult.

1973. 3 c. Type **509** .. .. 10 10
1974. 13 c. "Bonko enchemiya" (drum) .. .. 1·00 35
1975. 30 c. " Iya " (drum) .. 1·10 40

**510.** Cuban 2 c. Stamp of 1951.

**1972.** National Philatelic Exhib., Matanzas. Multicoloured.

1976. 13 c. Type **510** .. .. 1·10 35
1977. 30 c. Cuban 25 c. airmail stamp of 1951 .. 1·40 45

**511.** Viking Longship.

**1972.** Maritime History. Ships Through the Ages. Multicoloured.

1978 1 c. Type **511** .. .. 15 10
1979 2 c. Caravel (vert) .. 15 10
1980 3 c. Galley .. .. 15 10
1981 4 c. Galleon (vert) .. 20 10
1982 5 c. Clipper .. .. 20 10
1983 13 c. Steam packet .. 1·50 55
1984 30 c. Atomic ice-breaker "Lenin" and Adelie penguins (55 × 29 mm) 4·25 90

**512.** Lion of St. Mark.

**1972.** U.N.E.S.C.O. "Save Venice" Campaign. Multicoloured.

1985. 3 c. Type **512** .. .. 10 10
1986. 13 c. Bridge of Sighs (vert.) 85 35
1987. 30 c. St. Mark's Cathedral 1·10 65

**513.** Baseball Coach (poster).

**516.** " Gertrude G. de Avellaneda " (A. Esquivel).

**515.** Bronze Medal, Woman's 100 metres.

**1972.** "Cuba, World Amateur Baseball Champions of 1972".

1988. **513.** 3 c. violet and orange 35 10

**1972.** Sports events of 1972.

1989. – 1 c. multicoloured .. 10 10
1990. – 2 c. multicoloured .. 10 10
1991. **513.** 3 c. blk., orge. & grn. 10 10
1992. – 4 c. red, black & blue 10 10
1993. – 5 c. orge., bl. & light bl. 10 10
1994. – 13 c. multicoloured .. 85 45
1995. – 30 c. violet, blk. & blue 1·10 65

DESIGNS AND EVENTS: 1 c. Various sports (10th National Schoolchildren's Games). 2 c. Pole vaulting (Barrientos Memorial Athletics. 3. c. As Type **513**, but inscription changed to read " XI serie nacional de beisbol aficionado " and colours changed (11th National Amateur Baseball Series). 4. c. Wrestling (Cerro Pelado International Wrestling Championships). 5 c. Foil (Central American and Caribbean Fencing Tournament). 13 c. Boxing (Giraldo Cordova Boxing Tournament). 30 c. Fishes (Ernest Hemingway National Marlin Fishing Contest).

**1972.** Cuban Successes in Olympic Games, Munich. Multicoloured.

1996. 1 c. Type **515** .. .. 10 10
1997. 2 c. Bronze (women's 4 × 100 m. relay) .. .. 10 10
1998. 3 c. Gold (boxing, 54 kg.) 10 10
1999. 4 c. Silver (boxing, 81 kg.) 10 10
2000. 5 c. Bronze (boxing, 51 kg.) 10 10
2001. 13 c. Gold (boxing, 67 kg.) 85 45
2002. 30 c. Gold (boxing, 81 kg.) and Silver Cup (boxing Teofilo Stevenons) .. 1·10 65

**1973.** Death Centenary of Gertrude Gomez de Avellaneda (poetess).

2004. **516.** 13 c. multicoloured .. 95 40

**1973.** National Museum Paintings (6th series). As T **459**. Multicoloured.

2005. 1 c. " Bathers in the Lagoon " (C. Enriquez) (vert.) .. .. .. 10 10
2006. 2 c. " Still Life " (W. C. Heda) (vert.) .. .. 10 10
2007. 3 c. " Scene of Gallantry " (V. de Landaluse) (vert.) 10 10
2008. 4 c. " Return at Evening " (C. Troyon) (vert.) .. 10 10
2009. 5 c. " Elizabetta Mascagni" (F. X. Fabre) (vert.) .. 10 10
2010. 13 c. " The Picador " (E. de Lucas Padilla) (horiz.) 85 45
2011. 30 c. " In the Garden " (J. A. Morell) (vert.) .. 1·10 65

**1973.** Tropical Orchids (3rd series). As Type **480**. Multicoloured.

2012. 1 c. " Dendrobium " (hybrid) 10 10
2013. 2 c. " Cypripedium exul. O' Brien " .. .. 10 10
2014. 3 c. " Vanda miss. Joaquin " 10 10
2015. 4 c. " Phalaenopsis schilleriana Reichb " .. 10 10
2016. 5 c. " Vanda gilbert tribulet" 10 10
2017. 13 c. " Dendrobium " (hybrid) (different) .. 85 45
2018. 30 c. " Arachnis catherine" 1·10 65

**518.** Medical Examination.

**520.** " Soyuz " Rocket on Launch-pad.

**519.** Children and Vaccine.

**1973.** 25th Anniv. of W.H.O.

2019. **518.** 10 c. multicoloured .. 55 25

**1973.** Freedom from Polio Campaign.

2020. **519.** 3 c. multicoloured .. 35 20

**HAVE YOU READ THE NOTES AT THE BEGINNING OF THIS CATALOGUE?**
These often provide answers to the enquiries we receive.

**1973.** Cosmonautics Day. Russian Space Exploration. Multicoloured.

2021 1 c. Type **520** .. .. 10 10
2022 2 c. "Luna 1" in moon orbit (horiz) .. .. 10 10
2023 3 c. "Luna 16" leaving moon .. .. 10 10
2024 4 c. "Venus 7" probe (horiz) .. .. 10 10
2025 5 c. "Molniya 1" communications satellite .. 10 10
2026 13 c. "Mars 3" probe (horiz) .. .. 85 55
2027 30 c. Research ship "Kosmonavt Yury Gargarin" (horiz) .. 2·50 65

**521.** Santiago de Cuba Postmark, 1839.

**1973.** Stamp Day. Multicoloured.

2028. 13 c. Type **521** .. .. 95 35
2029. 30 c. " Havana " postmark, 1760 .. .. 1·10 40

**522.** " Ignacio Agramonte " (A. Espinosa).

**1973.** Death Centenary of Maj.-Gen. Ignacio Agramonte.

2030. **522.** 13 c. multicoloured .. 75 35

**523.** Copernicus' Birthplace and Instruments.

**1973.** 500th Birth Anniv. of Copernicus. Mult.

2031. 3 c. Type **523** .. .. 10 10
2032. 13 c. Copernicus and " spaceship " .. .. 75 35
2033. 30 c. " De Revolutionibus Orbium Celestium " and Frombork Tower .. 1·40 45

**524.** Emblem of Basic Schools.

**1973.** Educational Development.

2035. **524.** 13 c. multicoloured .. 75 20

**525.** Jersey Breed.

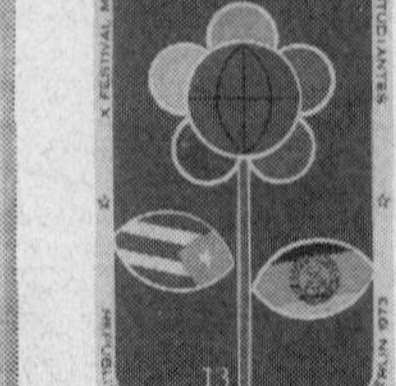

**526.** Festival Emblem.

**1973.** Cattle Breeds. Multicoloured.

2036. 1 c. Type **525** .. .. 10 10
2037. 2 c. Charolais .. .. 10 10
2038. 3 c. Creole .. .. 10 10
2039. 4 c. Swiss .. .. 10 10
2040. 5 c. Holstein .. .. 10 10
2041. 13 c. St. Gertrude's .. 85 20
2042. 30 c. Brahman Cebu .. 1·40 40

**1973.** 10th World Youth and Students Festival, East Berlin.

2043. **526.** 13 c. multicoloured .. 75 20

**527.** Siboney Farmhouse.

**529.** " Amalia de Sajonia " (J. K. Rossler).

**528.** Midshipman and Destroyer.

**1973.** 20th Anniv. of Revolution. Mult.

2044. 3 c. Type **527** .. .. 20 15
2045. 13 c. Moncada Barracks 75 25
2046. 30 c. Revolution Square, Havana .. .. 1·10 40

**1973.** 10th Anniv. of Revolutionary Navy.

2047. **528.** 3 c. multicoloured .. 60 20

**1973.** National Museum Paintings (7th series). Multicoloured.

2048. 1 c. Type **529** .. .. 10 10
2049. 2 c. " Interior " (M. Vicens) (horiz.) .. .. 10 10
2050. 3 c. " Margaret of Austria " (J. Pantoja de la Cruz) 10 10
2051. 4 c. " Syndic of the City Hall " (anon.) .. .. 10 10
2052. 5 c. " View of Santiago de Cuba " (J. H. Giro) (horiz.) 10 10
2053. 13 c. " The Catalan " (J. J. Tejada) .. .. 85 35
2054. 30 c. " Guayo Alley " (J. J. Tejada) .. .. 1·10 40

**530.** "Spring".

**1973.** Cent. of World Meteorological Organization. Paintings by J. Madrazo. Mult.

2055. 8 c. Type **530** .. .. 30 10
2056. 8 c. " Summer " .. .. 30 10
2057. 8 c. " Autumn " .. .. 30 10
2058. 8 c. " Winter " .. .. 30 10

**531.** Weightlifting.

**532.** "Erythrina standleyana".

**1973.** 27th Pan-American World Weightlifting Championships, Havana. Designs showing various stages of weightlifting exercise.

2059. **531.** 1 c. multicoloured .. 10 10
2060. – 2 c. multicoloured .. 10 10
2061. – 3 c. multicoloured .. 10 10
2062. – 4 c. multicoloured .. 10 10
2063. – 5 c. multicoloured .. 10 10
2064. – 13 c. multicoloured .. 85 35
2065. – 30 c. multicoloured .. 1·40 50

**1973.** Wild Flowers (1st series). Mult.

2066. 1 c. Type **532** .. .. 10 10
2067. 2 c. " Lantana camara " 10 10
2068. 3 c. " Canavalia maritima " 10 10
2069. 4 c. " Dichromena colorata " 10 10
2070. 5 c. " Borrichia arborescens " .. .. 10 10
2071. 13 c. " Anguria pedata " 85 45
2072. 30 c. " Cordia sebestena " 1·40 65

See also Nos. 2152/6.

**533.** Congress Emblem.

**1973.** 8th World Trade Union Congress, Varna, Bulgaria.

2073. **533.** 13 c. multicoloured .. 70 25

**534.** Ballet Dancers. **535.** True Fasciate Liguus.

**1973.** 25th Anniv. of Cuban National Ballet.
2074. **534.** 13 c. bright blue, blue and gold 70 25

**1973.** Shells. Multicoloured.
2075 1 c. Type **535** 10 10
2076 2 c. Guitart's liguus 10 10
2077 3 c. Wharton's Cuban liguus 10 10
2078 4 c. Angela's Cuban liguus 15 10
2079 5 c. Yellow-banded liguus 15 10
2080 13 c. "Liguus blainianus" 1·50 50
2081 30 c. Ribbon liguus 1·90 60

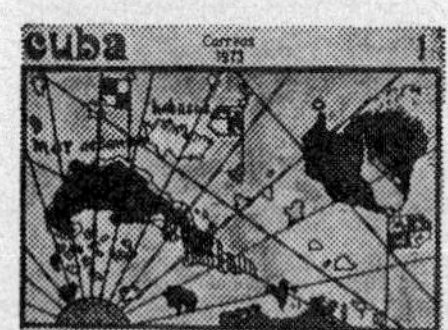

**536.** Juan de la Cosa's Map, 1502.

**1973.** Maps of Cuba. Multicoloured.
2082. 1 c. Type **536** 10 10
2083. 3 c. Ortelius's map, 1572 10 10
2084. 13 c. Bellini's map, 1762 80 20
2085. 40 c. Cartographic survey map, 1973 1·10 50

**537.** 1 c. Stamp of 1960 (No. 921).

**1974.** 15th Anniv. of Revolution. Revolution stamps of 1960. Multicoloured.
2086. 1 c. Type **537** 10 10
2087. 3 c. 2 c. stamp 20 10
2088. 13 c. 8 c. air stamp 1·40 40
2089. 40 c. 12 c. air stamp 1·10 55

**538.** "Head of a Woman" (F. Ponce de Leon).

**1974.** Paintings in Camaguey Museum. Multicoloured.
2090. 1 c. Type **538** 10 10
2091. 3 c. "Mexican Children" (J. Arche) 10 10
2092. 8 c. "Portrait of a Young Woman" (A. Menocal) 20 10
2093. 10 c. "Mulatto Woman with Coconut" (L. Romanach) 55 20
2094. 13 c. "Head of Old Man" (J. Arburu) 85 30

**539.** A. Cabral. **540.** "Lenin" (after J. V. Kosmin).

**1974.** 1st Death Anniv. of Amilcar Cabral (Guinea-Bissau guerilla leader).
2095. **539.** 13 c. multicoloured 70 20

**1974.** 50th Anniv. of Lenin's Death.
2096. **540.** 30 c. multicoloured 1·10 45

**541.** Games Emblem. **542.** "C. M. de Cespedes" (after F. Martinez).

**1974.** 12th Central American and Caribbean Games, Santo Domingo. Multicoloured.
2097. 1 c. Type **541** 10 10
2098. 2 c. Throwing the javelin 10 10
2199. 3 c. Boxing 10 10
2100. 4 c. Baseball player (horiz.) 10 10
2101. 13 c. Handball player (horiz.) 75 15
2102. 30 c. Volleyball (horiz.) 1·10 40

**1974.** Carlos M. de Cespedes (patriot). Death Centenary.
2103. **542.** 13 c. multicoloured 70 15

**543.** "Portrait of a Man" (J. B. Vermay). **544.** "Comecon" Headquarters Building, Moscow.

**1974.** National Museum Paintings (8th series). Multicoloured.
2104. 1 c. Type **543** 10 10
2105. 2 c. "Nodriza" (C. A. Van Loo) 10 10
2106. 3 c. "Cattle by a River" (R. Morey) 10 10
2107. 4 c. "Village Landscape" (R. Morey) 10 10
2108. 13 c. "Faun and Bacchus" (Rubens) 65 20
2109. 30 c. "Playing Patience" (R. Madrazo) 1·10 45
Nos. 2106/7 are horiz. designs, size 46 × 32 mm.

**1974.** 25th Anniv. of Council for Mutual Economic Aid.
2110. **544.** 30 c. multicoloured 1·00 45

**545.** Jose Marti and Lenin.

**1974.** Visit of Leonid Brezhnev (General Secretary of Soviet Communist Party). Mult.
2111. 13 c. Type **545** 65 25
2112. 30 c. Brezhnev with Castro 1·00 45

**546.** "Martian Crater".

**1974.** Cosmonautics Day. Science Fiction paintings by Sokolov. Multicoloured.
2113. 1 c. Type **546** 10 10
2114. 2 c. "Fiery Labyrinth" 10 10
2115. 3 c. "Amber Wave" 10 10
2116. 4 c. "Space Navigators" 15 10
2117. 13 c. "Planet in the Nebula" 85 20
2118. 30 c. "The World of the Two Suns" 1·40 40
See also Nos. 2196/201.

**547.** Cuban Letter of 1874.

**1974.** Cent. of U.P.U.
2119. **547.** 30 c. multicoloured 1·00 45



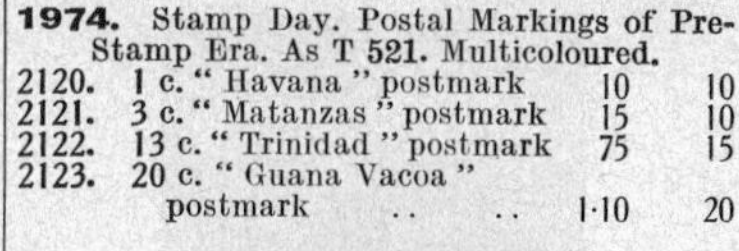

**1974.** Stamp Day. Postal Markings of Pre-Stamp Era. As T **521**. Multicoloured.
2120. 1 c. "Havana" postmark 10 10
2121. 3 c. "Matanzas" postmark 15 10
2122. 13 c. "Trinidad" postmark 75 15
2123. 20 c. "Guana Vacoa" postmark 1·10 20

**548.** Congress Emblem.

**1974.** 18th Sports' Congress of "Friendly Armies".
2124. **548.** 3 c. multicoloured 40 10

**549.** "Eumaeus atala atala" (butterfly).

**1974.** 175th Birth Anniv. of Felipe Poey (naturalist). Multicoloured.
2125. 1 c. Type **549** 20 10
2126. 2 c. "Pineria terebra" (shell) 10 10
2127. 3 c. "Chaetodon sedenterius" (fish) 10 10
2128. 4 c. "Eurema dina dina" (butterfly) 50 10
2129. 13 c. "Hemitrochus fusco-labiata" (shell) 1·75 35
2130. 30 c. "Eupomacentrus partitus" (fish) 1·90 45

**550.** A. Mompo and 'Cello.

**1974.** 50th Anniv. of Havana Philharmonic Orchestra. Leading Personalities. Mult.
2132. 1 c. Type **550** 10 10
2133. 3 c. C. P. Sentenat and piano 10 10
2134. 5 c. P. Mercado and trumpet 10 10
2135. 10 c. P. Sanjuan and emblem 55 15
2136. 13 c. R. Ondina and flute 75 20

**551.** "Heliconia humilis". **552.** Boxers and Global Emblem.

**1974.** Garden Flowers. Multicoloured.
2137. 1 c. Type **551** 10 10
2138. 2 c. "Anthurium andraeanum" 10 10
2139. 3 c. "Canna generalis" 10 10
2140. 4 c. "Alpinia purpurata" 20 10
2141. 13 c. "Gladiolus grandiflorus" 1·10 10
2142. 30 c. "Amomum capitatum" 2·75 45

**1974.** World Amateur Boxing Championships.
2143. **552.** 1 c. multicoloured 15 10
2144. – 3 c. multicoloured 20 10
2145. – 13 c. multicoloured 75 20
DESIGNS: 3 c., 13 c. Stages of Boxing matches similar to Type **552**.

**553.** Mauritius Dodo. **555.** "Suriana maritima".

**554.** Salvador Allende.

**1974.** Extinct Birds. Multicoloured.
2146. 1 c. Type **553** 40 10
2147. 3 c. Cuban macaw 40 10
2148. 8 c. Passenger pigeon 85 20
2149. 10 c. Moa 2·75 40
2150. 13 c. Great auk 3·50 55

**1974.** 1st Death Anniv. of Pres. Allende of Chile.
2151. **554.** 13 c. multicoloured 65 30

**1974.** Wild Flowers. (2nd series). Mult.
2152. 1 c. Type **555** 10 10
2153. 3 c. "Cassia ligustrina" 10 10
2154. 8 c. "Flaveria linearis" 20 15
2155. 10 c. "Stachytarpheta jamaicensis" 1·10 20
2156. 13 c. "Bacopa monnieri" 2·00 60

**556.** Flying Model Airplane. **557.** Indians playing Ball.

**1974.** 10th Anniv. of Civil Aeronautical Institute. Multicoloured.
2157 1 c. Type **556** 10 10
2158 3 c. Parachutist 10 10
2159 8 c. Glider in flight (horiz) 20 10
2160 10 c. Antonov An-2 biplane spraying crops (horiz) 60 20
2161 13 c. Ilyushin Il-62M in flight (horiz) 1·00 20

**1974.** History of Baseball in Cuba. Mult.
2162. 1 c. Type **557** 10 10
2163. 3 c. Players of 1874 (First official game) 10 10
2164. 8 c. Emilio Sabourin 15 10
2165. 10 c. Modern players 45 10
2166. 13 c. Latin-American Stadium, Havana 85 20
Nos. 2165/6 are horiz. size, 44 × 27 mm.

**558.** Stamp, Cachet and Horseman.

**1974.** Cent. of "Mambi" Revolutionary Stamp.
2167. **558.** 13 c. multicoloured 65 20

**559.** Comecon Headquarters Building, Moscow and Emblem.

**1974.** 16th Socialist Countries' Customs Conference.
2168. **559.** 30 c. blue and gold 1·00 35

**560.** Maj. C. Cienfuegos (revolutionary).

**1974.** 15th Anniv. of Camilo Cienfuegos. Disappearance.
2169. **560.** 3 c. multicoloured 35 10

561. Miner's Helmet.

**1974.** 8th World Mining Congress.
2170. **561.** 13 c. multicoloured .. 65 20

562. Oil Refinery.

**1974.** 15th Anniv. of Cuban Petroleum Institute.
2171. **562.** 3 c. multicoloured .. 35 10

563. Earth Station.

**1974.** Inauguration of "Inter-Sputnik" Satellite Earth Station. Multicoloured.
2172 3 c. Type **563** .. .. 10 10
2173. 13 c. Satellite and aerial .. 55 10
2174. 1 p. Satellite and flags .. 1·50 65

564. Emblems and Magnifying Glass.

**1974.** 10th Anniv. of Cuban Philatelic Federation.
2175. **564.** 30 c. multicoloured .. 1·10 40

566. F. Joliot-Curie (1st president) (Picasso).

**1974.** 25th Anniv. of World Peace Congress.
2177. **566.** 30 c. multicoloured .. 1·10 40

567. R. M. Villena.

**1974.** 75th Birth Anniv. of Ruben Martinez Villena (revolutionary).
2178. **567.** 3 c. red and yellow .. 30 10

569. " The Word " (M. Pogolotti).

**1975.** National Museum Paintings (9th series). Multicoloured.
2180. 1 c. Type **569** .. .. 10 10
2181. 2 c. " The Silk-Cotton Tree " (H. Cleenewerk) 10 10
2182. 3 c. " Landscape " (G. Collazo) 10 10
2183. 5 c. " Still Life " (F. Peralta) 15 10
2184. 13 c. " Maria Wilson " (F. Martinez) (vert.) .. 70 20
2185. 30 c. " The Couple " (M. Fortunay) .. .. 1·10 40

570. Bouquet and Woman's Head.

**1975.** International Woman's Year.
2186. **570.** 13 c. multicoloured .. 65 20

571. Bonito and Fishing-boat.

**1975.** Cuban Fishing Industry. Mult.
2187. 1 c. Type **571** .. .. 15 10
2188. 2 c. Tunny .. .. 15 10
2189. 3 c. Grouper .. .. 15 10
2190. 8 c. Hake .. .. 30 15
2191. 13 c. Prawn .. .. 70 50
2192. 30 c. Lobster .. .. 1·90 50

572. Nickel.

**1975.** Cuban Minerals. Multicoloured.
2193. 3 c. Type **572** .. .. 10 10
2194. 13 c. Copper .. .. 65 15
2195. 30 c. Chromium .. .. 85 45

**1975.** Cosmonautics Day. Science Fiction paintings as T **546**. Multicoloured.
2196. 1 c. " Cosmodrome " .. 10 10
2197. 2 c. " Exploration craft " (vert.) .. .. 10 10
2198. 3 c. " Earth eclipsing the Sun " 10 10
2199. 5 c. " On the Threshold " 15 10
2200. 13 c. " Astronauts on Mars " 70 15
2201. 30 c. " Astronauts' view of Earth " .. .. 1·10 35

573. Letter and " Correos " Postmark.

**1975.** Stamp Day. Multicoloured.
2202. 3 c. Type **573** .. .. 10 10
2203. 13 c. Letter and steamship postmark .. 65 15
2204. 30 c. Letter and " N.A. " postmark .. .. 1·00 30

574. Hoisting Red Flag over Reichstag, Berlin.

**1975.** 30th Anniv. of "Victory over Fascism".
2205. **574.** 30 c. multicoloured .. 1·00 30

575. Sevres Vase.

**1975.** National Museum Treasures. Mult.
2206. 1 c. Type **575** .. .. 10 10
2207. 2 c. Meissen " Shepherdess and Dancers " .. 10 10
2208. 3 c. Chinese Porcelain Dish—" Lady with Parasol " (horiz.) .. .. 10 10
2209. 5 c. Chinese Bamboo Screen—" The Phoenix " .. 15 10
2210. 13 c. " Allegory of Music " (F. Boucher) .. 75 15
2211. 30 c. " Portrait of a Lady " (L. Toque) .. .. 85 30

576. Coloured Balls and Globe " Man ".

**1975.** International Children's Day.
2213. **576.** 3 c. multicoloured .. 20 10

577. Cuban Vireo.

**1975.** Birds (1st series). Multicoloured.
2214. 1 c. Type **577** .. .. 25 10
2215. 2 c. Bare-legged owl .. 25 10
2216. 3 c. Cuban conure .. 25 10
2217. 5 c. Blue-headed quail dove .. .. .. 50 10
2218. 13 c. Hook-billed kite .. 2·00 30
2219. 30 c. Zapata rail .. 3·00 55
See also Nos. 2301/6.

578. View of Centre.

**1975.** 10th Anniv. of National Scientific Investigation Centre.
2220. **578.** 13 c. multicoloured .. 65 15

579. Commission Emblem and Drainage Equipment.

**1975.** International Commission on Irrigation and Drainage.
2221. **579.** 13 c. multicoloured .. 65 15

580. " Cedrea mexicana ".

581. Women cultivating Young Plants.

**1975.** Reafforestation. Multicoloured.
2222 1 c. Type **580** .. .. 10 10
2223 3 c. "Swietonia mahagoni" .. .. 15 10
2224 5 c. "Calophyllum brasiliense" .. .. 15 10
2225 13 c. "Hibiscus tiliaceus" 55 15
2226 30 c. "Pinus caribaea" .. 90 35

**1975.** 15th Anniv. of Cuban Women's Federation.
2227. **581.** 3 c. multicoloured .. 25 10

582. Conference Emblem and Broken Chains.

583. Baseball.

**1975.** International Conference on the Independence of Puerto Rico.
2228. **582.** 13 c. multicoloured .. 50 15

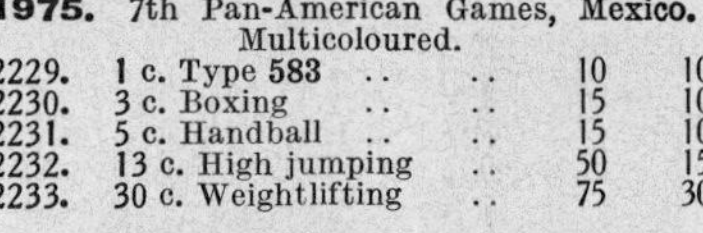

**1975.** 7th Pan-American Games, Mexico. Multicoloured.
2229. 1 c. Type **583** .. .. 10 10
2230. 3 c. Boxing .. .. 15 10
2231. 5 c. Handball .. .. 15 10
2232. 13 c. High jumping .. 50 15
2233. 30 c. Weightlifting .. 75 30

584. Emblem and Crowd.

**1975.** 15th Anniv. of Revolutionary Defence Committees.
2235. **584.** 3 c. multicoloured .. 20 10

585. Institute Emblem.

**1975.** 15th Anniv. of Cuban "Friendship Amongst the Peoples" Institute.
2236. **585.** 3 c. multicoloured .. 15 10

586. Silver 1 Peso Coin, 1913.

**1975.** 15th Anniv. of Nationalization of Bank of Cuba. Multicoloured.
2237. 13 c. Type **586** .. .. 45 15
2238. 13 c. 1 peso banknote, 1934 45 15
2239. 13 c. 1 peso banknote, 1946 45 15
2240. 13 c. 1 peso banknote, 1964 45 15
2241. 13 c. 1 peso banknote, 1973 45 15

587. " La Junta ", Cuba's first locomotive, 1837.

**1975.** "Evolution of Railways". Mult.
2242. 1 c. Type **587** .. .. 10 10
2243. 3 c. Steam locomotive "M.M. Prieto", 1910 .. 15 10
2244. 5 c. Soviet "TEM-4" diesel locomotive .. 15 10
2245. 13 c. Hungarian "DVM-9" diesel locomotive .. 1·10 20
2246. 30 c. Soviet "M-62K" diesel locomotive .. 1·25 35

588. Bobbins and Flag.

**1975.** Textile Industry.
2247. **588.** 13 c. multicoloured .. 55 15

589. Sheep and Diagram.

**1975.** Development of Veterinary Medicine. Animals and Disease Cycles. Mult.
2248 1 c. Type **589** .. .. 10 10
2249 2 c. Dog .. .. 10 10
2250 3 c. Cockerel .. .. 10 10
2251 5 c. Horse .. .. 10 10
2252 13 c. Pig .. .. 65 15
2253 30 c. Ox .. .. 1·10 30

**590.** Manuel Ascunce Domenech.  **592.** Communists with Flags inside Figure " 1 ".

**591.** " Irrigation ".

**1975.** Manuel Domenech Educational Detachment.
2254. **590.** 3 c. multicoloured .. 20 10

**1975.** Agriculture and Water-supply.
2255. **591.** 13 c. multicoloured .. 65 15

**1976.** 1st Cuban Communist Party Congress. Multicoloured.
2256. 3 c. Type **592** .. .. 10 10
2257. 13 c. Workers with banner (horiz.) .. .. .. 60 15
2258. 30 c. Jose Marti and Cuban leaders (horiz.) .. 75 30

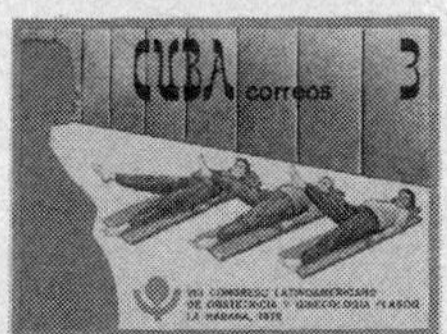


**593.** Pre-natal Exercises.

**1976.** 8th Latin-American Obstetrics and Gynaecology Congress, Havana.
2259. **593.** 3 c. multicoloured .. 25 10

**594.** " Seated Woman " (V. Manuel).  **595.** Conference Emblem and Building.

**1976.** National Museum Paintings (10th series). Mult.
2260. 1 c. Type **594** .. .. 10 10
2261. 2 c. " Garden " (S. Rusinol) (horiz.) .. .. .. 10 10
2262. 3 c. " Guadalquivir River " (M. Barron y Carrillo) (horiz.) .. .. .. 30 10
2263. 5 c. " Self-portrait " (Jan Steen) .. .. .. 10 10
2264. 13 c. " Portrait of Woman " (L. M. van Loo) .. 55 15
2265. 30 c. " La Chula " (J. A. Morell) (27 × 44 mm.) .. 65 30

**1976.** Socialist Communications Ministers' Conference, Havana.
2266. **595.** 13 c. multicoloured .. 65 15

**596.** American Foxhound.

**1976.** Hunting Dogs. Multicoloured.
2267. 1 c. Type **596** .. .. 10 10
2268. 2 c. Labrador retriever .. 10 10
2269. 3 c. Borzoi .. .. 10 10
2270. 5 c. Irish setter .. .. 10 10
2271. 13 c. Pointer .. .. 75 15
2272. 30 c. Cocker Spaniel .. 1·00 30

**597.** Flags, Arms and Anthem.

**1976.** Socialist Constitution, 1976.
2273. **597.** 13 c. multicoloured .. 65 20

**598.** Ruy Lopez Segura.

**1976.** History of Chess. Multicoloured.
2274. 1 c. Type **598** .. .. 10 10
2275. 2 c. Francois Philidor .. 10 10
2276. 3 c. Wilhelm Steinitz .. 10 10
2277. 13 c. Emanuel Lasker .. 65 15
2278. 30 c. Jose Raul Capablanca 70 30

**599.** Radio Aerial and Map.

**1976.** 15th Anniv. of Cuban International Broadcasting Services.
2279. **599.** 50 c. multicoloured .. 1·00 50

**600.** Section of Human Eye and Microscope Slide.  **601.** Children in Creche.

**1976.** World Health Day.
2280. **600.** 30 c. multicoloured .. 75 30

**1976.** 15th Anniv. of Infant Welfare Centres.
2281. **601.** 3 c. multicoloured .. 25 10

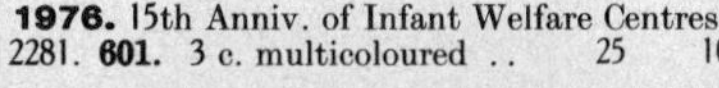

**602.** Y. Gagarin in Space-suit.

**1976.** 15th Anniv. of First Manned Space Flight. Multicoloured.
2282. 1 c. Type **602** .. .. 10 10
2283. 2 c. V. Tereshkova and rockets .. .. 10 10
2284. 3 c. Cosmonaut on " space walk " (vert.) .. .. 10 10
2285. 5 c. Spacecraft and Moon (vert.) .. .. .. 15 10
2286. 13 c. Spacecraft in man-oeuvre (vert.) .. .. 55 20
2287. 30 c. Space link .. .. 70 30

**603.** Cuban Machine-gunner.

**1976.** 15th Anniv of Giron Victory. Mult.
2288 3 c. Type **603** .. .. 10 10
2289 13 c. Cuban pilot and Lockheed F-80 Shooting Star fighter attacking ship .. .. .. 70 15
2290 30 c. Cuban soldier wielding rifle (vert) .. 85 35

**604.** Heads of Farmers.

**1976.** 15th Anniv. of Nat. Assn. of Small Farmers (ANAP).
2291. **604.** 3 c. multicoloured .. 20 10

**605.** Volleyball.

**1976.** Olympic Games, Montreal. Mult.
2292. 1 c. Type **605** .. .. 10 10
2293. 2 c. Basketball .. .. 10 10
2294. 3 c. Long-jumping .. 10 10
2295. 4 c. Boxing .. .. 10 10
2296. 5 c. Weightlifting .. 10 10
2297. 13 c. Judo .. .. 45 15
2298. 30 c. Swimming .. .. 75 35

**606.** Modern Secondary School.

**1976.** Rural Secondary Schools.
2300. **606.** 3 c. black and red .. 20 10

**607.** Oriente Warbler.

**1976.** Birds (2nd series). Multicoloured.
2301. 1 c. Type **607** .. .. 35 10
2302. 2 c. Cuban Pygmy Owl 35 10
2303. 3 c. Fernandina's Flicker 35 10
2304. 5 c. Cuban Tody .. 70 15
2305. 13 c. Gundlach's Hawk 1·40 20
2306. 30 c. Cuban Trogon .. 3·00 60

**608.** Medical Treatment.  **609.** " El Inglesito ".

**1976.** "Expo", Havana. Soviet Science and Technology. Multicoloured.
2307 1 c. Type **608** .. .. 10 10
2308 3 c. Child and deer ("Environmental Protection") .. .. .. 10 10
2309 10 c. Cosmonauts on launch pad ("Cosmos Investigation") .. 25 10
2310 30 c. Tupolev Tu-144 airplane ("Soviet Transport") (horiz) .. 1·25 35

**1976.** Death Cent. of Henry M. Reeve (patriot).
2311. **609.** 13 c. multicoloured .. 35 15

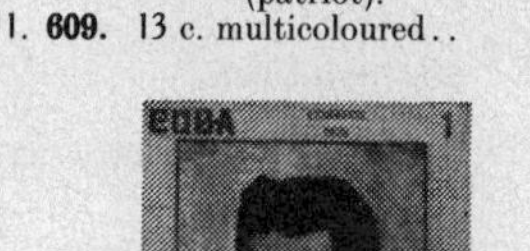

**610.** " G. Collazo " (J. Dabour).

**1976.** Cuban Paintings. Multicoloured.
2312. 1 c. Type **610** .. .. 10 10
2313. 2 c. " The Art Lovers " (G. Collazo) (horiz.) .. 10 10
2314. 3 c. " The Patio " (G. Collazo) .. .. 10 10
2315. 5 c. " Cocotero " (G. Collazo) .. .. 10 10
2316. 13 c. " New York Studio " (G. Collazo) (horiz.) .. 25 15
2317. 30 c. " Emelinz Collazo " (G. Collazo) (horiz.) .. 85 35

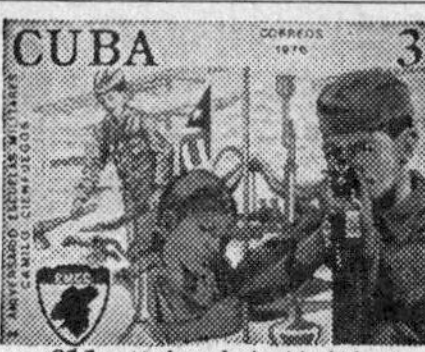

**611.** School Activities.

**1976.** 10th Anniv. of "Cambilo Cienfuegos" Military School.
2318. **611.** 3 c. multicoloured .. 15 10

**612.** "Imias" (freighter).

**1976.** Development of Cuban Merchant Marine. Multicoloured.
2319 1 c. Type **612** .. .. 25 10
2320 2 c. "Comandante Camilo Cienfuegos" (freighter) 25 10
2321 3 c. "Comandante Pinares" (cargo liner) 25 10
2322 5 c. "Vietnam Heroico" (cargo liner) .. .. 40 10
2323 13 c. "Presidente Allende" (ore carrier) .. .. 1·10 35
2324 30 c. "XIII Congreso" (bulk carrier) .. .. 2·25 60

**613.** Emblem and Part of Cine Film.

**1976.** 8th International Cinematographic Festival of Socialist Countries, Havana.
2325. **613.** 3 c. multicoloured .. 15 10

**614.** Scene from " Apollo ".

**1976.** 5th International Ballet Festival, Havana. Multicoloured.
2326. 1 c. Type **614** .. .. 10 10
2327. 2 c. " The River and the Forest " (vert.) .. 10 10
2328. 3 c. " Giselle " .. .. 10 10
2329. 5 c. " Oedipus Rex " (vert.) 15 10
2330. 13 c. " Carmen " (vert.) 45 10
2331. 30 c. " Vital Song " (vert.) 85 30

**615.** Soldier and Sportsmen.

**1976.** 3rd Military Games.
2332. **615.** 3 c. multicoloured .. 15 10

**616.** "Granma".

**1976.** 20th Anniv. of "Granma" Landings.
2333. **616.** 1 c. multicoloured .. 10 10
2334. – 3 c. multicoloured .. 10 10
2335. – 13 c. multicoloured .. 45 10
2336. – 30 c. multicoloured .. 75 35
DESIGNS: 3 c. to 30 c. Different scenes showing guerrillas.

**618.** Volleyball.

**1976.** Cuban Victories in Montreal Olympic Games. Multicoloured.

2338. 1 c. Type **618** .. .. 10 10
2339. 2 c. Hurdling .. .. 10 10
2340. 3 c. Running .. .. 10 10
2341. 8 c. Boxing .. .. 15 10
2342. 13 c. Winning race .. 35 15
2343. 30 c. Judo .. .. 70 35

**619.** "Golden Cross Inn" (S. Scott).

**1977.** National Museum Paintings (11th series). Multicoloured.

2345. 1 c. Type **619** .. .. 10 10
2346. 3 c. " Portrait of a Man " (J. Verspronck) (vert.) 10 10
2347. 5 c. " Venetian Landscape " (F. Guardi) .. 20 10
2348. 10 c. " Valley Corner " (H. Cleenewerck) (vert.) 15 10
2349. 13 c. " F. Xaviera Paula " (anon.) (vert.) .. 35 15
2350. 30 c. " F. de Medici " (C. Allori) (vert.) .. 70 35

The vertical designs are slightly larger, 27×43 mm.

**620.** Motor Bus.

**1977.** Rural Transport.

2351. **620.** 3 c. multicoloured .. 15 10

**621.** Map of Cuba.

**1977.** Constitution of Popular Government.

2352. **621.** 13 c. multicoloured .. 35 15

**622.** Cuban Green Woodpecker.

**1977.** Cuban Birds. Multicoloured.

2353. 1 c. Type **622** .. .. 45 15
2354. 4 c. Cuban Grassquit .. 55 15
2355. 10 c. Cuban Blackbird .. 1·10 20
2356. 13 c. Zapata Wren .. 1·50 20
2357. 30 c. Bee Hummingbird 3·00 50

**623.** Mechanical Scoop and Emblem.

**1977.** Air. 6th Latin-American and Caribbean Sugar Exporters Meeting, Havana.

2358. **623.** 13 c. multicoloured .. 40 15

**624.** "Cichlasoma meeki".

**1977.** Fish in Lenin Park Aquarium, Havana. Multicoloured.

2359. 1 c. Type **624** .. .. 10 10
2360. 3 c. " Barbus tetrazona " 10 10
2361. 5 c. " Cyprinus carpio " 10 10
2362. 10 c. " Betta splendens " 15 10
2363. 13 c. " Pterophyllum scalare " (vert.) .. 50 15
2364. 30 c. " Hemigrammus caudovittatus " .. 95 30

**625.** " Sputnik 1 " and East German Stamp.

**1977.** 20th Anniv. of 1st Artificial Satellite. Multicoloured.

2365. 1 c. Type **625** .. .. 10 10
2366. 3 c. " Luna 16 " and Hungarian stamp .. 10 10
2367. 5 c. " Cosmos " and North Korean stamp .. 10 10
2368. 10 c. " Sputnik 3 " and Polish stamp .. .. 20 10
2369. 13 c. Earth, Moon and Yugoslav stamp .. 50 15
2370. 30 c. Earth, Moon and Cuban stamp .. .. 85 30

**626.** Antonio Maria Romeu.

**1977.** Cuban Musicians. Multicoloured.

2372. 3 c. Type **626** (postage) 15 10
2373. 13 c. Jorge Ankerman (air) .. .. .. 45 15

**627.** " Hibiscus rosa sinensis ".

**1977.** Birth Cent. of Dr. Juan Tomas Roig (botanist). Cuban Flowers. Multicoloured.

2374. 1 c. Type **627** (postage) .. 10 10
2375. 2 c. " Nerium oleander " 10 10
2376. 5 c. " Allamanda cathartica " .. .. 10 10
2377. 10 c. " Pelargonium zonale " .. .. 20 10
2378. 13 c. " Caesalpinia pulcherrima " (air.) .. 30 10
2379. 30 c. " Catharanthus roseus " .. .. 65 30

**628.** Horse-drawn Fire Engine.

**1977.** Fire Prevention Week. Multicoloured.

2381. 1 c. Type **628** .. .. 10 10
2382. 2 c. Horse-drawn fire engine (different) .. 10 10
2383. 6 c. Early motor fire pump 10 10
2384. 10 c. Modern motor fire pump .. .. .. 15 10
2385. 13 c. Turntable-ladder .. 30 15
2386. 30 c. Heavy rescue vehicle 85 30

**629.** 20th Anniversary Medal.

**1977.** National Decorations.

2387. **629.** 1 c. multicoloured (postage) .. .. 10 10
2388. – 3 c. multicoloured .. 15 10
2389. – 13 c. multicoloured (air) 35 10
2390. – 30 c. multicoloured .. 65 30

DESIGNS: 3 c. to 30 c. Various medals and ribbons.

**630.** " Portrait of Mary ".

**631.** Boxing.

**1977.** Painting by Jorge Arche. Mult.

2391. 1 c. Type **630** (postage) .. 10 10
2392. 3 c. " Jose Marti " .. 10 10
2393. 5 c. " Portrait of Aristides " 10 10
2394. 10 c. " Bathers " (horiz.) 25 10
2395. 13 c. " My Wife and I " (air) .. .. .. 30 10
2396. 30 c. " The Game of Dominoes " (horiz.) .. 65 30

**1977.** Military Spartakiad. Multicoloured.

2398. 1 c. Type **631** (postage) .. 10 10
2399. 3 c. Volleyball .. .. 10 10
2400. 5 c. Parachuting .. .. 10 10
2401. 10 c. Running .. .. 20 10
2402. 13 c. Grenade-throwing (air) .. .. .. 30 10
2403. 30 c. Rifle-shooting (horiz.) 65 30

**632.** Che Guevara.

**1977.** Air. 10th Anniv. of Guerrilla Heroes Day.

2404. **632.** 13 c. multicoloured .. 40 10

**633.** Curtiss A-1 Seaplane and Parla Stamp of 1952.

**1977.** 50th Anniv of Cuban Air Mail. Mult.

2405 1 c. Type **633** (postage) .. 10 10
2406 2 c. Ford 5-AT trimotor airplane and Havana–Key West cachet .. 10 10
2407 5 c. Flying boat "American Clipper" and first flight cachet 15 10
2408 10 c. Douglas DC-4 and Havana–Madrid cachet 25 15
2409 13 c. Lockheed Super Constellation and Havana–Mexico cachet (air) .. 45 15
2410 30 c. Ilyushin Il-18 and Havana–Prague cachet 80 40

**634.** Cruiser " Aurora ".

**1977.** 60th Anniv. of Russian Revolution.

2411. **634.** 3 c. blk., red & gold 20 10
2412. – 13 c. blk., red & gold 25 15
2413. – 30 c. gold, red & blk. 75 30

DESIGNS: 13 c. Lenin and flags. 30 c. Hammer and sickle with scenes of technology.

**636.** Cat.

**1977.** Felines in Havana Zoo. Multicoloured.

2415. 1 c. Type **636** (postage) 10 10
2416. 2 c. Leopard (black race) 10 10
2417. 8 c. Puma .. .. 15 10
2418. 10 c. Leopard .. .. 60 15
2419. 13 c. Tiger (air) .. .. 70 15
2420. 30 c. Lion .. .. 1·00 40

**637.** Cienfuegos Uprising.

**1977.** 20th Anniv. of Martyrs of the Revolution. Multicoloured.

2421. 3 c. Type **637** (postage) .. 10 10
2422. 20 c. Attack on the Presidential Palace .. 30 15
2423. 13 c. Landing from the " Corynthia " (air) .. 45 10

**638.** Clinic, Havana.

**1977.** 75th Anniv. of Pan-American Health Organization.

2424. **638.** 13 c. multicoloured .. 10 10

**639.** Map of Cuba and Units of Measurement.

**1977.** International System of Measurement.

2425. **639.** 3 c. multicoloured .. 10 10

**640.** University Building and Coat of Arms.

**1978.** 250th Anniv. of Havana University. Multicoloured.

2426. 3 c. Type **640** (postage) .. 10 10
2427. 13 c. University building and crossed sabres (air) 30 10
2428. 30 c. Student crowd and statue .. .. .. 50 30

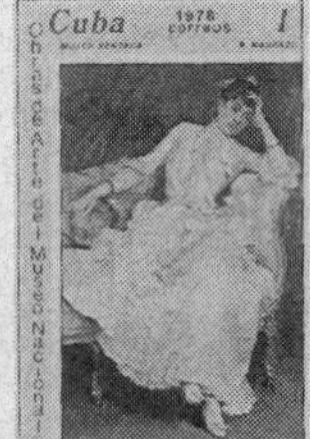


**641.** " Jose Marti " (A. Menocal).

**642.** " Seated Woman " (R. Madrazo).

**1978.** Air. 125th Anniv. of Jose Marti (patriot).

2429. **641.** 13 c. multicoloured .. 30 10

**1978.** National Museum Paintings (12th series). Multicoloured.

2430. 1 c. Type **642** (postage) .. 10 10
2431. 4 c. " Girl " (J. Sorolla) 10 10
2432. 6 c. " Landscape with Figures " (J. Pilliment) (horiz.) .. .. .. 10 10
2433. 10 c. " The Cow " (E. Abela) (horiz.) .. 25 10
2434. 13 c. " El Guadalquivir " (M. Barron) (horiz.) (air) .. .. .. 50 10
2435. 30 c. " H. E. Ridley " (J. J. Masqueries) .. 50 25

**643.** Patrol Boat, Frontier Guard and Dog.

**1978.** 15th Anniv. of Frontier Troops.

2436. **643.** 13 c. multicoloured .. 70 15

**644.** Cuban Solitaire.

**1978.** Cuban Birds. Multicoloured.

2437. 1 c. Type **644** (postage) 50 10
2438. 4 c. Cuban gnatcatcher 50 15
2439. 10 c. Oriente warbler .. 1·40 20
2440. 13 c. Zapata sparrow (air) .. .. .. 1·75 35
2441. 30 c. Cuban macaw and ivory-billed woodpecker (vert.) .. .. 2·50 65

**645.** " Antonio Maceo " (A. Melero). **646.** " Intercosmos " Satellite.

**1978.** Air. Cent. of Baragua Protest.

2442. **645.** 13 c. multicoloured .. 30 10

**1978.** Cosmonautics Day. Multicoloured.

2443. 1 c. Type **646** (postage) .. 10 10
2444. 2 c. " Luna 24 " (horiz.) 10 10
2445. 5 c. " Venus 9 " .. .. 15 10
2446. 10 c. " Cosmos " (horiz.) 15 10
2447. 13 c. " Venus 10 " (horiz.) (air) .. .. .. 30 10
2448. 30 c. " Lunokhod 2 " (36 × 46 mm.) .. 55 30

**647.** Smiling Worker and Emblem. **649.** " Melocactus guitarti ".

**648.** Parliament Building, Budapest and 1919 Hungarian Stamp.

**1978.** 9th World Federation of Trade Unions Congress, Prague.

2449. **647.** 30 c. red and black .. 45 25

**1978.** Air. " Socifilex " Stamp Exhibition, Budapest.

2450. **648.** 30 c. multicoloured .. 55 30

**1978.** Cactus Flowers. Multicoloured.

2451. 1 c. Type **649** (postage) .. 10 10
2452. 4 c. " Leptocereus wrightii " 10 10
2453. 6 c. " Opuntia militaris " 10 10
2454. 10 c. " Cylindropuntia hystrix " .. .. 20 10
2455. 13 c " Rhodocactus cubensis " (air) .. .. 30 15
2456. 30 c. " Harrisia taetra " 55 30

**650.** Satellite and Globe.

**1978.** Air. World Telecommunications Day.

2457. **650.** 30 c. multicoloured .. 55 30

**651.** Africans and O.A.U. Emblem.

**1978.** Air. 15th Anniv. of Organization of African Unity.

2458. **651.** 30 c. multicoloured .. 50 30

**653.** " Barbus arulios ".

**1978.** Fish in the Lenin Park Aquarium. Multicoloured.

2460. 1 c. Type **653** (postage) .. 10 10
2461. 4 c. " Hiphessobrycon flammeus " .. .. 10 10
2462. 6 c. " Poecilia reticulata " 10 10
2463. 10 c. " Colisa lalia " .. 20 10
2464. 13 c. " Carassius auratua auratus " (vert.) (air) 25 15
2465. 30 c. " Symphysodon aequifasciata axelrodi " 55 30

**654.** Basketball. **655.** Moncada Fortress.

**1978.** 13th Central American and Caribbean Games. Multicoloured.

2466. 1 c. Type **654** (postage) .. 10 10
2467. 3 c. Boxing .. .. 10 10
2468. 5 c. Weightlifting .. 10 10
2469. 10 c. Fencing (horiz.) .. 25 10
2470. 13 c. Volleyball (air) .. 30 15
2471. 30 c. Running .. .. 55 30

**1978.** 25th Anniv. of Attack on Moncada Fortress. Multicoloured.

2472. 3 c. Type **655** (postage) .. 10 10
2473. 13 c. Soldiers with rifles (air) .. .. .. 25 10
2474. 30 c. Dove and flags .. 50 25

**656.** Prague.

**1978.** 11th World Youth and Students' Festival, Havana. Multicoloured.

2475. 3 c. Type **656** (postage) .. 10 10
2476. 3 c. Budapest .. .. 10 10
2477. 3 c. Berlin .. .. 10 10
2478. 3 c. Bucharest .. .. 10 10
2479. 3 c. Warsaw .. .. 10 10
2480. 13 c. Moscow (air) .. 25 15
2481. 13 c. Vienna .. .. 25 15
2482. 13 c. Helsinki .. .. 25 15
2483. 13 c. Sofia .. .. 25 15
2484. 13 c. Berlin .. .. 25 15
2485. 30 c. Havana (46 × 36 mm.) 55 25

**657.** Marching Soldiers with Flag.

**1978.** 5th Anniv. of Young Workers Army.

2486. **657.** 3 c. multicoloured .. 10 10

**658.** "Pargo".

**1978.** Fishing Fleet. Multicoloured.

2487 1 c. Type **658** (postage) .. 15 10
2488 2 c. Fish-processing ship 15 10
2489 5 c. Shrimp fishing boat 15 10
2490 10 c. Stern trawler .. 35 15
2491 13 c. "Mar Carbide" (air) 60 20
2492 30 c. Refrigeration and processing ship .. 1·10 40

**660.** " The White Coat " (Pelaez del Casal).

**1978.** Painting by Amelia Pelaez del Casal Multicoloured.

2494. 1 c. Type **660** (postage) .. 10 10
2495. 3 c. " Still Life with Flowers " .. .. 10 10
2496. 6 c. " Women " .. .. 10 10
2497. 10 c. " Fish " .. .. 20 10
2498. 13 c. " Flowering Almond " (air) .. .. .. 25 10
2499. 30 c. " Still Life in Blue " 55 25

**661.** Letters, Satellite and Globe. **663.** Hand.

**1978.** Air. 20th Anniv. of Organization for Communication Co-operation between Socialist Countries.

2501. **661.** 30 c. multicoloured .. 50 30

**1978.** Air. International Anti-Apartheid Year.

2503. **663.** 13 c. blk., flesh & mve. 1·10 1·10

**664.** White Rhinoceros.

**1978.** Animals in Havana Zoo. Multicoloured.

2504. 1 c. Type **664** (postage) 10 10
2505. 4 c. Okapi (vert.) .. 15 10
2506. 6 c. Mandrill .. .. 15 10
2507. 10 c. Giraffe (vert.) .. 30 15
2508. 13 c. Cheetah (air) .. 40 20
2509. 30 c. African elephant (vert.) .. .. .. 85 40

**665.** " Grand Pas de Quatre ".

**1978.** 30th Anniv. of National Ballet Company. Multicoloured.

2510. 3 c. Type **665** (postage) .. 10 10
2511. 13 c. " Giselle " (air) .. 25 15
2512. 30 c. " Genesis " .. 55 30

**666.** Hibiscus. **668.** Fidel Castro and Soldier.

**667.** Julius and Ethel Rosenberg.

**1978.** Pacific Flowers.

2513. **666.** 1 c. mult. (postage) 10 10
2514. – 4 c. multicoloured .. 10 10
2515. – 6 c. multicoloured .. 10 10
2516. – 10 c. multicoloured .. 20 10
2517. – 13 c. mult. (air) .. 30 15
2518. – 30 c. multicoloured .. 55 30

DESIGNS: 4 c. to 30 c. Different flowers.

**1978.** Air. 25th Death Anniv. of Julius and Ethel Rosenberg (American Communists).

2519. **667.** 13 c. multicoloured .. 25 10

**1979.** 20th Anniv. of Revolution. Mult.

2520. 3 c. Type **668** .. .. 10 10
2521. 13 c. Symbols of industry 30 15
2522. 1 p. Flag, flame and globe 1·75 95

**669.** Julio Mella.

**1979.** 50th Death Anniv. of J. A. Mella.

2523. **669.** 13 c. multicoloured .. 20 10

**670.** Blue-headed Quail Dove.

**1979.** Doves and Pigeons. Multicoloured.

2524. 1 c. Type **670** .. .. 40 10
2525. 3 c. Key West Quail Dove 45 10
2526. 7 c. Grey-faced Quail Dove 45 10
2527. 8 c. Ruddy Quail Dove .. 55 10
2528. 13 c. White-crowned Pigeon 1·00 20
2529. 30 c. Plain Pigeon .. 2·10 60

**671.** " Genre Scene " (D. Teniers).

**1979.** National Museum Paintings (13th series). Multicoloured.

2530. 1 c. Type **671** .. 10 10
2531. 3 c. "Arrival of Spanish Troops" (J. Meissonier) 10 10
2532. 6 c. "A Joyful Gathering" (Sir David Wilkie) .. 10 10
2533. 10 c. "Capea" (E. de Lucas Padilla) .. 15 10
2534. 13 c. "Teatime" (R. Madrazo) (vert.) .. .. 20 15
2535. 30 c. "Peasant in front of a Tavern" (Adriaen van Ostade) .. .. 50 25

672. " Nymphaea capensis ". 673. " 20 " Flag and Film Frames.

**1979.** Aquatic Flowers. Multicoloured.
2536. 3 c. Type **672** .. .. 10 10
2537. 10 c. " Nymphaea ampla " 15 10
2538. 13 c. " Nymphaea coerulea " 25 15
2539. 30 c. " Nymphaea rubra " 55 25

**1979.** 20th Anniv. of Cuban Cinema.
2540. **673.** 3 c. multicoloured .. 10 10

674. Rocket Launch.

**1979.** Cosmonautics Day. Multicoloured.
2541. 1 c. Type **674** .. .. 10 10
2542. 4 c. "Soyuz" .. .. 10 10
2543. 6 c. "Salyut" .. .. 10 10
2544. 10 c. "Soyuz" and "Salyut" link-up .. 15 10
2545. 13 c. "Soyuz" and "Salyut" .. .. 25 10
2546. 30 c. Parachute and capsule .. .. .. 50 30

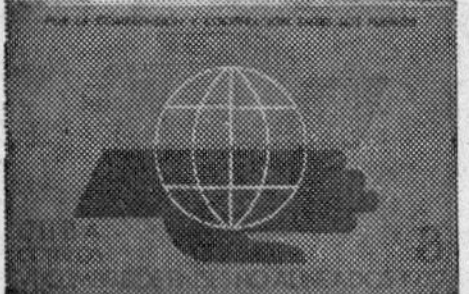

675. Hands and Globe.

**1979.** 6th Non-Aligned Countries Summit Conference. Multicoloured.
2548. 3 c. Type **675** .. .. 10 10
2549. 13 c. "6" ("Against Colonialism") .. .. 20 10
2550. 30 c. Joined coin and globe ("A New Economic Order") .. 50 30

676. Cuna Indian Tapestry, Panama.

**1979.** 20th Anniv. of "House of the Americas" Museum.
2551. **676.** 13 c. multicoloured .. 20 10

677. Farmer holding Title Deed.

**1979.** 20th Anniv. of Agrarian Reform.
2552. **677.** 3 c. multicoloured .. 10 10

679. " Eulepidotis rectimargo".

**1979.** Cuban Nocturnal Butterflies. **Mult.**
2554. 1 c. Type **679** .. .. 10 10
2555. 4 c. " Othreis materna " 10 10
2556. 6 c. " Noropsis hieroglphica " 15 10
2557. 10 c. " Heterochroma sp " 15 10
2558. 13 c. " Melanchroia regnatrix " .. .. 40 20
2559. 30 c. " Attera gemmata " 1·00 40

680. Children's Heads.

**1979.** Air. International Year of the **Child.**
2560 **680** 13 c. multicoloured .. 20 10

681. " Avenue du Maine, Paris".

**1979.** 10th Death Anniv. of Victor Manuel Garcia (painter). Multicoloured.
2561. 1 c. Type **681** .. .. 10 10
2562. 3 c. " Portrait of Enmita " 10 10
2563. 6 c. " Rio San Juan, Matanzas " .. .. 10 10
2564. 10 c. " Landscape with Woman carrying Hay " 10 10
2565. 13 c. " Still-life with Vase " 20 10
2566. 30 c. " Street by Night " 45 30

682. Clenched Fists, Dove and Bombs.

**1979.** 30th Anniv. of World Peace Council.
2568. **682.** 30 c. multicoloured .. 55 25

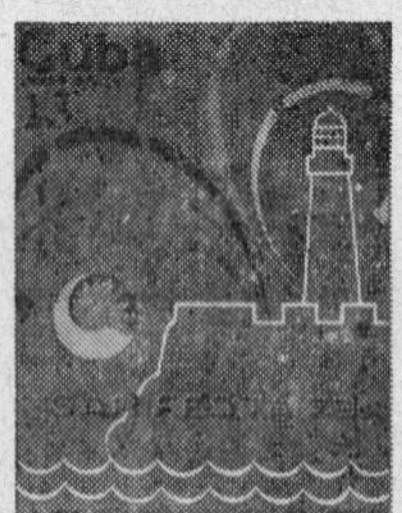

683. Lighthouse and Fireworks.

**1979.** Air. " Carifesta 79 " Festival, Havana.
2569. **683.** 13 c. multicoloured .. 20 10

684. Wrestling.

**1979.** Pre-Olympics, Moscow 1980. Mult.
2570. 1 c. Type **684** .. .. 10 10
2571. 4 c. Boxing .. .. 10 10
2572. 6 c. Volleyball .. .. 10 10
2573. 10 c. Rifle-shooting .. 10 10
2574. 13 c. Weightlifting .. 20 10
2575. 30 c. High jump .. 55 25

685. " Rosa eglanteria ". 686. Council Emblem.

**1979.** Roses. Multicoloured.
2576. 1 c. Type **685** .. .. 10 10
2577. 2 c. " Rosa centifolia anemonoides " .. 10 10
2578. 3 c. " Rosa indica vulgaris " 10 10
2579. 5 c. " Rosa eglanteria var. punicea " .. .. 10 10
2580. 10 c. " Rosa sulfurea " .. 10 10
2581. 13 c. " Rosa muscosa alba " 20 10
2582. 20 c. " Rosa gallica purpurea velutina, Parva " 35 20

**1979.** 30th Anniv. of Council of Mutual Economic Aid.
2583. **686.** 13 c. multicoloured .. 20 15

687. Games Emblem and Activities.

**1979.** Air. " Universiada 79 " 10th World University Games, Mexico City.
2584. **687.** 13 c. grn., gold & turq. 25 15

688. Conventions Palace.

**1979.** Air. 6th Non-Aligned Countries Summit Conference, Havana.
2585. **688.** 50 c. multicoloured .. 80 60

689. Sir Rowland Hill and Casket containing Freedom of the City of London.

**1979.** Air. Death Centenary of Sir Rowland Hill.
2586. **689.** 30 c. multicoloured .. 55 20

690. Ford 5-AT Trimotor.

**1979.** 50th Anniv of Cuban Airlines. Mult.
2587 1 c. Type **690** .. .. 10 10
2588 2 c. Sikorsky S-38 flying boat .. .. 10 10
2589 3 c. Douglas DC-3 .. 15 10
2590 4 c. Ilyushin Il-18 .. 15 10
2591 13 c. Yakovlev Yak-40 .. 40 15
2592 40 c. Ilyushin Il-62M .. 90 50

691. Rumanian " New Constitution " Stamp of 1948.

**1979.** Air. " Socfilex 79 " Stamp **Exhibition,** Bucharest.
2593. **691.** 30 c. multicoloured .. 50 30

692. Camilo Cienfuegos.

**1979.** 20th Anniv. of Disappearance of Camilo Cienfuegos (revolutionary).
2594. **692.** 3 c. multicoloured .. 15 10

693. Alvaro Reinoso and Sugar **Cane.**

**1979.** 15th Anniv. of Sugar Cane Institute and 150th Birth Anniv. of Alvaro Reinoso.
2595. **693.** 13 c. multicoloured .. 30 15

694. Chimpanzees.

**1979.** Young Zoo Animals. Multicoloured.
2596. 1 c. Type **694** .. .. 10 10
2597. 2 c. Leopards .. .. 10 10
2598. 3 c. Fallow deer .. .. 10 10
2599. 4 c. Lions .. .. 10 10
2600. 5 c. Brown bears .. 10 10
2601. 13 c. Eurasian red squirrels .. .. .. 30 15
2602. 30 c. Giant pandas .. 60 30
2603. 50 c. Tigers .. .. 1·10 55

695. Ground Receiving Station.

**1979.** Air. 50th Anniv. of International Radio Consultative Committee.
2604. **695.** 30 c. multicoloured .. 50 20

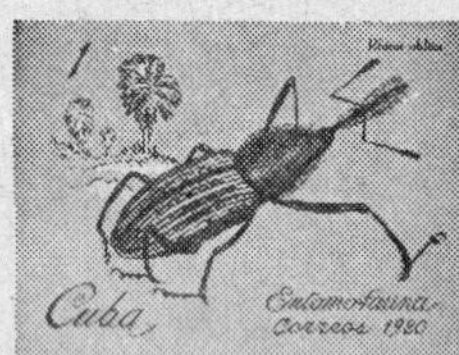


696. " Rhina oblita ".

**1980.** Insects. Multicoloured.
2605. 1 c. Type **696** .. .. 10 10
2606. 5 c. " Odontocera josemartii " (vert.) .. 10 10
2607. 6 c. " Pinthocoelium columbinum " .. .. 10 10
2608. 10 c. " Calosoma splendida " (vert.) .. 20 10
2609. 13 c. " Homophileurus cubanus " (vert.) .. 40 15
2610. 30 c. " Heterops dimidiata " (vert.) .. .. .. 80 45

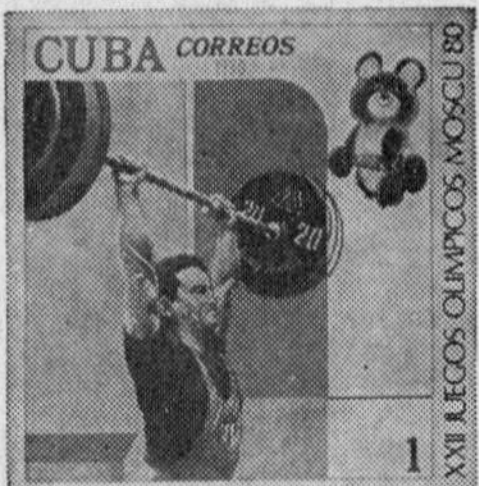


697. Weightlifting.

**1980.** Olympic Games, Moscow. **Multicoloured.**
2611. 1 c. Type **697** .. .. 10 10
2612. 2 c. Shooting .. .. 10 10
2613. 5 c. Javelin .. .. 10 10
2614. 6 c. Wrestling .. .. 10 10
2615. 8 c. Judo .. .. 15 10
2616. 10 c. Running .. 15 10
2617. 13 c. Boxing .. .. 25 10
2618. 30 c. Volleyball .. .. 60 35

**698.** " Oak Trees " (Henry Joseph Harpignies).

**1980.** National Museum Paintings (14th series). Multicoloured.

2620. 1 c. Type **698** .. .. 10 10
2621. 4 c. " Family Reunion " (Willem van Mieris) (horiz.) .. .. 10 10
2622. 6 c. " Poultry " (Melchior de Hondecoeter) .. 10 10
2623. 9 c. " Innocence " (Williams A. Bouguereau) .. 15 10
2624. 13 c. " Venetian Scene II " (Michele Marieschi) (horiz.) .. .. 25 10
2625. 30 c. " Spanish Country-women " (Joaquin Dominguez Bequer) .. 55 35

**700.** Intercosmos Emblem.

**1980.** Intercosmos Programme. Mult.

2627. 1 c. Type **700** .. .. 10 10
2628. 4 c. Satellite and globe (Physics) .. .. 10 10
2629. 6 c. Satellite and dish aerial (Communications) .. .. .. 10 10
2630. 10 c. Satellite, grid lines and map (Meteorology) .. .. .. 15 10
2631. 13 c. Staff of Aesculapius, rocket and satellites (Biology and Medicine) 25 10
2632. 30 c. Surveying Satellite 50 35

**701.** Cuban Stamps of 1855 and 1959. (Illustration reduced. Actual size: 68 × 27 mm.)

**1980.** 125th Anniv. of Cuban Stamps.

2633. **701.** 30 c. blue, red and bright blue .. 55 30

**702.** "Bletia purpurea".

**1980.** Orchids. Multicoloured.

2634. 1 c. Type **702** .. .. 10 10
2635. 4 c. " Oncidium leiboldii " 10 10
2636. 6 c. " Epidendrum cochieatum " .. .. 10 10
2637. 10 c. " Cattleyopsis lindenii " .. .. 15 10
2638. 13 c. " Encyclia fucata " 20 15
2639. 30 c. " Encyclia phoenicea " 60 35

**703.** Bottle-nosed Dolphin.

**1980.** Marine Mammals. Multicoloured.

2640. 1 c. Type **703** .. .. 10 10
2641. 3 c. Humpback whale (vert.) 10 10
2642. 13 c. Cuvier's beaked whale 30 15
2643. 30 c. Caribbean monk seal 70 35

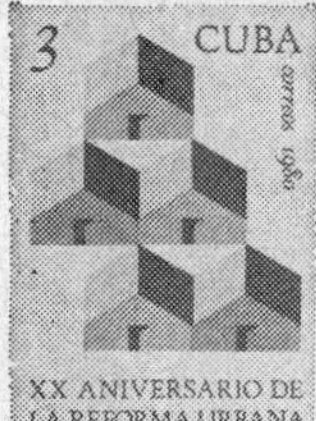


**704.** Houses. **705.** Pitcher.

**1980.** " Moncada " Programme. Mult.

2644. 3 c. Type **704** .. .. 10 10
2645. 13 c. Refinery .. .. 20 10

ANNIVERSARIES: 3 c. Urban Reform (20th Anniv.). 13 c. Foreign industry (20th Anniv.).

**1980.** Copper Handicrafts. Multicoloured.

2646. 3 c. Type **705** .. .. 10 10
2647. 13 c. Wine container (38 × 26 mm.) .. .. 20 15
2648. 30 c. Two handled pitcher 50 30

**706.** Emblem, Flag and Roses. **708.** Flags.

**1980.** 20th Anniv. of Cuban Women's Federation.

2649. **706.** 3 c. multicoloured .. 10 10

**1980.** 20th Anniv. of 1st Havana Declaration.

2651. **708.** 13 c. multicoloured .. 20 15

**709.** Building Galleon "Nuesta Sra. de Atocha", 1620.

**1980.** Cuban Shipbuilding. Multicoloured

2652 1 c. Type **709** .. .. 15 10
2653 3 c. Building ship of the line "El Rayo", 1749 .. 15 10
2654 7 c. Building ship of the line "Santisima Trinidad", 1769 .. 15 10
2655 10 c. "Santisima Trinidad" at sea, 1805 (vert) .. .. 35 10
2656 13 c. Building steamships "Colon" and "Congreso", 1851 .. 75 15
2657 30 c. Cardenas and Chullima shipyards .. 1·25 45

**710.** Arnaldo Tamayo.

**1980.** Air. First Cuban-Soviet Space Flight.

2658. **710.** 13 c. multicoloured .. 30 15
2659. 30 c. multicoloured .. 55 30

**711.** U.N. General Assembly. **712.** Child being Fed.

**1980.** 20th Anniv. of Fidel Castro's First Speech at the United Nations.

2660. **711.** 13 c. multicoloured .. 20 10

**1980.** 20th Anniv. of Revolution's Defence Committees.

2661. **712.** 3 c. multicoloured .. 15 10

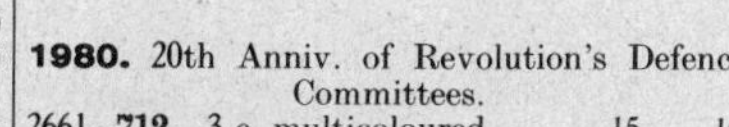

**714.** Inspection Locomotive.

**1980.** Early Locomotives. Multicoloured.

2663. 1 c. Type **714** .. .. 10 10
2664. 2 c. Inspection locomotive, Chaparra Sugar Company .. .. 10 10
2665. 7 c. Steam storage locomotive .. .. .. 15 10
2666. 10 c. 2–4–2 locomotive .. 20 10
2667. 13 c. 2–4–0 locomotive .. 35 10
2668. 30 c. Oil combustion locomotive, 1909 .. 90 30

**715.** "Roncali" Lighthouse, San Antonio.

**1980.** Lighthouses (1st series). Multicoloured.

2669. 3 c. Type **715** .. .. 10 10
2670. 13 c. Jagua, Cienfuegos .. 20 15
2671. 30 c. Punta Maisi, Guantanamo .. .. 55 20

See also Nos. 2746/8, 2859/61 and 2920/2.

**716.** Bronze Medal.

**1980.** Cuban Olympic Medal Winners. Multicoloured.

2672. 13 c. Type **716** .. .. 20 15
2673. 30 c. Silver medal .. 45 20
2674. 50 c. Gold medal .. 85 50

**717.** " Pancratium arenicolum ". **719.** Congress Emblem.

**1980.** Forest Flowers. Multicoloured.

2675. 1 c. Type **717** .. .. 10 10
2676. 4 c. " Urechites lutea " 10 10
2677. 6 c. " Solanum elaegnifolium " .. .. 10 10
2678. 10 c. " Hamelia patens " 15 10
2679. 13 c. " Morinda royoc " 20 10
2680. 30 c. " Centrosema virginianum " .. 55 25

**1980.** Second Communist Party Congress. Multicoloured.

2682. 3 c. Type **719** .. .. 10 10
2683. 13 c. Dish aerial and factories (Industry) .. 20 10
2684. 30 c. Gymnast, reader and elderly man resting (Recreation) .. 45 20

**720.** "Lady Mayo" (Anton van Dyck).

**1981.** National Museum Paintings (15th series). Multicoloured.

2685. 1 c. Type **720** .. .. 10 10
2686. 6 c. " La Hilandera " (Giovanni B. Piazzeta) 10 10
2687. 10 c. " Daniel Collyer " (Francis Cotes) .. 15 10
2688. 13 c. " Gardens of Palma de Mallorca " (Santiago Rusinol) (horiz.) .. 20 15
2689. 20 c. " Landscape with Road and Houses " (Frederick W. Watts) (horiz.) .. .. .. 30 15
2690. 50 c. " Landscape with Sheep " (Jean F. Millet) (horiz.) .. .. .. 90 50

**721.** Shortfin Mako Shark.

**1981.** Fishes. Multicoloured.

2691. 1 c. Type **721** .. .. 10 10
2692. 3 c. Moonfish .. .. 10 10
2693. 10 c. Sailfish .. .. 15 10
2694. 13 c. "Mola mola" (vert.) 75 15
2695. 30 c. Dolphin fish .. 50 20
2696. 50 c. White Merlin .. 80 50

**722.** Saving Ball.

**1981.** World Cup Football Championships, Spain (1982). (1st issue). Multicoloured.

2697. 1 c. Diving for ball (horiz.) .. .. 10 10
2698. 2 c. Passing ball (horiz.) 10 10
2699. 3 c. Running with ball (horiz.) .. .. 10 10
2700. 10 c. Type **722** .. .. 15 10
2701. 13 c. Heading ball .. 20 10
2702. 50 c. Tackle (horiz.) .. 90 50

See also Nos. 2775/81.

**723.** Mother, Child, Boots and Toy Train. **724.** Jules Verne, Konstantin Tsiolkovsky and Sergei Korolev.

**1981.** 20th Anniv. of Kindergartens.

2704. **723.** 3 c. multicoloured .. 20 10

**1981.** 20th Anniv of First Man in Space. Multicoloured.

2705 1 c. Type **724** .. .. 10 10
2706 2 c. Yury Gagarin (first man in space) (horiz) 10 10
2707 3 c. Valentina Tereshkova (first woman in space) (horiz) .. .. 10 10
2708 5 c. Aleksandr Leonov (first space walker) (horiz) .. .. 10 10
2709 13 c. Crew of "Voskhod 1" (horiz) .. .. 20 10
2710 30 c. Ryumen and Popov (horiz) .. .. 50 30
2711 50 c. Tamayo and Romanenko (crew of Soviet–Cuban flight) .. 90 40

**725.** Jet Fighters and Rocket.

**1981.** 20th Anniv. of Defeat of Invasion Attempt by Cuban Exiles. Multicoloured.

| | | | |
|---|---|---|---|
| 2712. | 3 c. Type **725** (Defence and Air Force Day) .. | 10 | 10 |
| 2713. | 13 c. Hand waving machine-pistol (Victory at Giron) .. | 20 | 15 |
| 2714. | 30 c. Book and flags (Proclamation of Revolution's socialist character) (horiz.) .. | 45 | 30 |

**726.** Reynold Garcia Garcia (leader of attack), Barracks and Children.

**1981.** 25th Anniv. of Attack on Goicuria Barracks.

| | | | |
|---|---|---|---|
| 2715. **726.** | 3 c. multicoloured .. | 15 | 10 |

**727.** Tractor and Women planting Crops.

**1981.** 20th Anniv. of National Association of Small Farmers.

| | | | |
|---|---|---|---|
| 2716. **727.** | 3 c. multicoloured .. | 15 | 10 |

**729.** Canelo.

**1981.** Fighting Cocks. Multicoloured.

| | | | |
|---|---|---|---|
| 2718. | 1 c. Type **729** .. .. | 10 | 10 |
| 2719. | 3 c. Cenizo (horiz.) .. | 10 | 10 |
| 2720. | 7 c. Blanco .. .. | 15 | 10 |
| 2721. | 13 c. Pinto .. .. | 15 | 10 |
| 2722. | 30 c. Giro (horiz.) .. | 50 | 30 |
| 2723. | 50 c. Jabao .. .. | 95 | 50 |

**730.** Anniversary Emblem.

**733.** 'House in the Country" (Maria Cardidad de la O).

**732.** Tram.

**1981.** 20th Anniv. of Ministry of the Interior.

| | | | |
|---|---|---|---|
| 2724. **730.** | 13 c. multicoloured .. | 15 | 10 |

**1981.** Horse-drawn Vehicles. Multicoloured.

| | | | |
|---|---|---|---|
| 2726. | 1 c. Type **732** .. .. | 10 | 10 |
| 2727. | 4 c. Village bus .. .. | 10 | 10 |
| 2728. | 9 c. Brake .. .. | 15 | 10 |
| 2729. | 13 c. Landau .. .. | 15 | 10 |
| 2730. | 30 c. Phaeton .. .. | 50 | 30 |
| 2731. | 50 c. Hearse .. .. | 95 | 50 |

**1981.** International Year of Disabled People.

| | | | |
|---|---|---|---|
| 2732. **733.** | 30 c. multicoloured .. | 55 | 30 |

**734.** Sandinista Guerrilla and Map of Nicaragua.

**1981.** 20th Anniv. of Sandinista National Liberation Front.

| | | | |
|---|---|---|---|
| 2733. **734.** | 13 c. multicoloured .. | 20 | 15 |

**735.** Gymnasts.

**1981.** 20th Anniv. of State Organizations. Multicoloured.

| | | | |
|---|---|---|---|
| 2734. | 3 c. Type **735** (National Sports and Physical Recreation Institute) | 10 | 10 |
| 2735. | 13 c. "RHC", radio waves and map (Radio Havana) .. .. | 15 | 10 |
| 2736. | 30 c. Arrows ("Mincex" Foreign Trade Ministry) | 55 | 30 |

**736.** Carlos J. Finlay, Mosquito and Theory.

**1981.** Cent. of Biological Vectors Theory.

| | | | |
|---|---|---|---|
| 2737. **736.** | 13 c. multicoloured .. | 20 | 15 |

**737.** Arms of Non-aligned Countries, Manacled Hands and Hands releasing Dove.

**1981.** 20th Anniv. of Non-aligned Countries Movement.

| | | | |
|---|---|---|---|
| 2738. **737.** | 50 c. multicoloured .. | 90 | 50 |

**738.** White Horse.

**1981.** Horses. Multicoloured.

| | | | |
|---|---|---|---|
| 2739. | 1 c. Type **738** .. .. | 10 | 10 |
| 2740. | 3 c. Brown horse .. | 10 | 10 |
| 2741. | 8 c. Bucking white horse | 15 | 10 |
| 2742. | 13 c. Horse being broken-in .. .. .. | 15 | 10 |
| 2743. | 30 c. Black horse .. | 55 | 30 |
| 2744. | 50 c. Herd of horses (horiz.) .. .. | 90 | 45 |

**1981.** Lighthouses (2nd series). As T **715**. Multicoloured.

| | | | |
|---|---|---|---|
| 2746. | 3 c. Piedras del Norte .. | 10 | 10 |
| 2747. | 13 c. Punta Lucrecia .. | 20 | 10 |
| 2748. | 40 c. Guano del Este .. | 85 | 40 |

**740.** "Flor de Cuba Sugar Mill".

**1981.** 80th Anniv. of Jose Marti National Library. Lithographs by Eduardo Laplante. Multicoloured.

| | | | |
|---|---|---|---|
| 2749. | 3 c. Type **740** .. .. | 10 | 10 |
| 2750. | 13 c. "El Progreso Sugar Mill" .. .. .. | 15 | 10 |
| 2751. | 30 c. "Santa Teresa Sugar Mill" .. .. | 50 | 30 |

**741.** Pablo Picasso and Cuban Stamp.

**1981.** Birth Cent. of Pablo Picasso (artist).

| | | | |
|---|---|---|---|
| 2752. **741.** | 30 c. multicoloured .. | 55 | 35 |

**743.** "Napoleon in Coronation Regalia" (Anon.).

**1981.** 20th Anniv. of Napoleonic Museum. Multicoloured.

| | | | |
|---|---|---|---|
| 2754. | 1 c. Type **743** .. .. | 10 | 10 |
| 2755. | 3 c. "Napoleon with Landscape" (J. H. Vernet) (horiz.) .. | 10 | 10 |
| 2756. | 10 c. "Bonaparte in Egypt" (Eduard Detaille) .. | 15 | 10 |
| 2757. | 13 c. "Napoleon on Horseback" (Hippolyte Bellange) (horiz.). .. | 15 | 10 |
| 2758. | 30 c. "Napoleon in Normandy" (Bellange) (horiz.) .. .. | 50 | 30 |
| 2759. | 50 c. "Death of Napoleon" (Anon.) .. | 90 | 45 |

**744.** Revolutionaries.

**745.** Cuban Emerald.

**1981.** 25th Anniversaries. Multicoloured.

| | | | |
|---|---|---|---|
| 2760 | 3 c. Type **744** (30th November insurrection) | 10 | 10 |
| 2761 | 20 c. Soldier (Revolutionary Armed Forces) .. | 20 | 10 |
| 2762 | 1 p. Launch "Granma" (disembarkation of revolutionary forces) .. | 2·25 | 1·00 |

**1981.** Fauna.

| | | | |
|---|---|---|---|
| 2763. **745.** | 1 c. blue .. .. | 50 | 10 |
| 2764. – | 2 c. green .. .. | 75 | 15 |
| 2765. – | 5 c. brown .. .. | 15 | 15 |
| 2766. – | 20 c. red .. .. | 50 | 15 |
| 2767. – | 35 c. lilac .. .. | 90 | 20 |
| 2768. – | 40 c. grey .. .. | 70 | 35 |

DESIGNS: 2 c. Cuban Conure. 5 c. Desmarest's hutia. 20 c. Cuban solenodon. 35 c. American Manatee. 40 c. Crocodile.

**746.** Ortiz (after Jorge Arche y Silva).

**747.** Conrado Benitez.

**1981.** Birth Centenary of Fernando Ortiz (folklorist). Multicoloured.

| | | | |
|---|---|---|---|
| 2769. | 3 c. Type **746** .. .. | 10 | 10 |
| 2770. | 10 c. Idol (pendant) .. | 15 | 10 |
| 2771. | 30 c. Arara drum .. | 55 | 25 |
| 2772. | 50 c. Thunder god (Chango carving) .. .. | 90 | 45 |

**1981.** 20th Anniv. of Literacy Campaign. Multicoloured.

| | | | |
|---|---|---|---|
| 2773. | 5 c. Type **747** .. .. | 15 | 10 |
| 2774. | 5 c. Manuel Ascunce .. | 15 | 10 |

**748.** Goalkeeper.

**749.** Lazaro Pena (trade union delegate).

**1982.** World Cup Football Championship, Spain (2nd issue). Multicoloured.

| | | | |
|---|---|---|---|
| 2775. | 1 c. Type **748** .. .. | 10 | 10 |
| 2776. | 2 c. Footballers .. .. | 10 | 10 |
| 2777. | 5 c. Heading ball .. | 10 | 10 |
| 2778. | 10 c. Kicking ball .. | 15 | 10 |
| 2779. | 20 c. Running for ball (horiz.) .. .. | 35 | 15 |
| 2780. | 40 c. Tackle (horiz.) .. | 60 | 40 |
| 2781. | 50 c. Shooting for goal .. | 85 | 60 |

**1982.** Tenth World Trade Unions' Congress, Havana.

| | | | |
|---|---|---|---|
| 2783. **749.** | 30 c. multicoloured .. | 50 | 30 |

**750.** "Euptoieta hegesia hegesia".

**1982.** Butterflies. Multicoloured.

| | | | |
|---|---|---|---|
| 2784. | 1 c. Type **750** .. .. | 10 | 10 |
| 2785. | 4 c. "Metamorpha stelenes insularis" .. .. | 10 | 10 |
| 2786. | 5 c. "Helicantus charithanius ramsdeni" .. | 10 | 10 |
| 2787. | 20 c. "Phoebis avellaneda" | 75 | 25 |
| 2788. | 30 c. "Hamadryas ferox diasia" .. .. | 1·25 | 45 |
| 2789. | 50 c. "Marpesia eleuchea eleuchea" .. .. | 2·10 | 75 |

**751.** Lobster.

**1982.** Exports.

| | | | |
|---|---|---|---|
| 2790. – | 3 c. green .. .. | 10 | 10 |
| 2791. **751.** | 4 c. red .. .. | 30 | 10 |
| 2792. – | 6 c. blue .. .. | 15 | 10 |
| 2793. – | 7 c. orange .. .. | 15 | 10 |
| 2794. – | 8 c. lilac .. .. | 15 | 10 |
| 2795. – | 9 c. grey .. .. | 15 | 10 |
| 2796. – | 10 c. lilac .. .. | 20 | 10 |
| 2797. – | 30 c. brown .. .. | 30 | 15 |
| 2798. – | 50 c. red .. .. | 85 | 25 |
| 2799. – | 1 p. brown .. .. | 1·60 | 80 |

DESIGNS–HORIZ. 3 c. Sugar. 6 c. Tinned fruit. 7 c. Agricultural machinery. 8 c. Nickel. VERT. 9 c. Rum. 10 c. Coffee. 30 c. Citrus fruit. 50 c. Cigars. 1 p. Cement.

**752.** "Greenland" (cottage tulip).

**1982.** Tulips. Multicoloured.

| No. | Description | Unused | Used |
|---|---|---|---|
| 2800. | 1 c. Type **752** .. .. | 10 | 10 |
| 2801. | 3 c. "Mariette" (Lily-flowered tulip) .. | 10 | 10 |
| 2802. | 8 c. "Ringo" (triumph) | 15 | 10 |
| 2803. | 20 c. "Black Tulip" (Darwin) .. .. | 35 | 15 |
| 2804. | 30 c. "Jewel of Spring" (Darwin hybrid) .. | 55 | 25 |
| 2805. | 50 c. "Orange Parrot" (parrot tulip) .. .. | 90 | 30 |

**753.** Youth Activities.

**1982.** 20th Anniv. of Communist Youth Union.

| No. | Description | Unused | Used |
|---|---|---|---|
| 2806. **753.** | 5 c. multicoloured .. | 15 | 10 |

**754.** " Mars " Satellite.

**1982.** Cosmonautics Day. Second United Nations Conference on Exploration and Peaceful Uses of Outer Space. Mult.

| No. | Description | Unused | Used |
|---|---|---|---|
| 2807. | 1 c. Type **754** .. .. | 10 | 10 |
| 2808. | 3 c. "Venera" satellite .. | 10 | 10 |
| 2809. | 6 c. "Salyut-Soyuz" link-up .. .. .. | 10 | 10 |
| 2810. | 20 c. "Lunochod" moon vehicle .. .. .. | 15 | 10 |
| 2811. | 30 c. "Venera" with heatshield .. .. | 50 | 20 |
| 2812. | 50 c. "Kosmos" satellite | 85 | 40 |

**755.** Letter from British Postal Agency, Havana, to Vera Cruz.

**1982.** Stamp Day. Multicoloured.

| No. | Description | Unused | Used |
|---|---|---|---|
| 2813. | 20 c. Type **755** .. .. | 35 | 15 |
| 2814. | 30 c. Letter from French postal agency, Havana, to Tampico, Mexico .. .. .. | 50 | 20 |

**756.** Map of Cuba and Wave Pattern.

**757.** " Portrait of Young Woman" (Jean Greuze).

**1982.** 20th Anniv. of Cuban Broadcasting and Television Institute.

| No. | Description | Unused | Used |
|---|---|---|---|
| 2815. **756.** | 30 c. multicoloured .. | 50 | 20 |

**1982.** National Museum Paintings (16th series). Multicoloured.

| No. | Description | Unused | Used |
|---|---|---|---|
| 2816. | 1 c. Type **757** .. .. | 10 | 10 |
| 2817. | 3 c. "Procession in Brittany" (Jules Breton) (46 × 36 mm.) .. .. | 10 | 10 |
| 2818. | 9 c. "Landscape" (Jean Piliment) (horiz.) .. | 40 | 10 |
| 2819. | 20 c. "Towards Evening" (William Bourgueran) | 30 | 15 |
| 2820. | 30 c. "Tiger" (Delacroix) (horiz.) .. .. | 50 | 20 |
| 2821. | 40 c. "The Chair" (Wilfredo Lam) .. | 60 | 30 |

**759.** Hurdling and 1930 Sports Stamp.

**1982.** "Deporfilex '82" Stamp and Coin Exhibition, Havana.

| No. | Description | Unused | Used |
|---|---|---|---|
| 2823. **759.** | 20 c. multicoloured .. | 40 | 20 |

**760.** Tortoise.

**1982.** Reptiles. Multicoloured.

| No. | Description | Unused | Used |
|---|---|---|---|
| 2824. | 1 c. Type **760** .. .. | 10 | 10 |
| 2825. | 2 c. Snake .. .. | 10 | 10 |
| 2826. | 3 c. Cuban crocodile .. | 10 | 10 |
| 2827. | 20 c. Iguana .. .. | 35 | 15 |
| 2828. | 30 c. Lizard .. .. | 50 | 20 |
| 2829. | 50 c. Snake .. .. | 85 | 40 |

**761.** Georgi Dimitrov. **763.** Baseball.

**762.** Dr. Robert Koch and Bacillus.

**1982.** Birth Centenary of Georgi Dimitrov (Bulgarian statesman).

| No. | Description | Unused | Used |
|---|---|---|---|
| 2830. **761.** | 30 c. multicoloured .. | 55 | 20 |

**1982.** Centenary of Discovery of Tubercle Bacillus.

| No. | Description | Unused | Used |
|---|---|---|---|
| 2831. **762.** | 20 c. multicoloured .. | 40 | 20 |

**1982.** 14th Central American and Caribbean Games, Havana. Multicoloured.

| No. | Description | Unused | Used |
|---|---|---|---|
| 2832. | 1 c. Type **763** .. .. | 10 | 10 |
| 2833. | 2 c. Boxing .. .. | 10 | 10 |
| 2834. | 10 c. Water polo .. .. | 15 | 10 |
| 2835. | 20 c. Javelin .. .. | 35 | 20 |
| 2836. | 35 c. Weightlifting .. | 85 | 30 |
| 2837. | 50 c. Volleyball .. .. | 80 | 35 |

**764.** "Eichornia crassipes".

**1982.** 20th Anniv. of Hydraulic Development Plan. Multicoloured.

| No. | Description | Unused | Used |
|---|---|---|---|
| 2838. | 5 c. Type **764** .. .. | 15 | 10 |
| 2839. | 20 c. " Nymphaea alba " | 35 | 15 |

**766.** Hand holding Gun.

**1982.** Namibia Day.

| No. | Description | Unused | Used |
|---|---|---|---|
| 2841. **766.** | 50 c. multicoloured .. | 80 | 35 |

**767.** Goal. **768.** "Devil" (V.P. Landaluse).

**1982.** World Cup Football Championship Finalists. Multicoloured.

| No. | Description | Unused | Used |
|---|---|---|---|
| 2842. | 5 c. Type **767** .. .. | 15 | 10 |
| 2843. | 20 c. Heading ball .. | 35 | 20 |
| 2844. | 30 c. Tackle .. .. | 50 | 25 |
| 2845. | 50 c. Saving goal .. | 85 | 45 |

**1982.** 20th Anniv. of National Folk Ensemble. Multicoloured.

| No. | Description | Unused | Used |
|---|---|---|---|
| 2846. | 20 c. Type **768** .. .. | 40 | 20 |
| 2847. | 30 c. "Epiphany festival" (V.P. Landaluze) (horiz.) | 55 | 30 |

**769.** Prehistoric Owl.

**1982.** Prehistoric Animals. Multicoloured.

| No. | Description | Unused | Used |
|---|---|---|---|
| 2848. | 1 c. Type **769** .. .. | 45 | 20 |
| 2849. | 5 c. "Crocodylus rhombifer" (horiz.) .. | 10 | 10 |
| 2850. | 7 c. Prehistoric eagle .. | 2·00 | 30 |
| 2851. | 20 c. "Geocapromys colombianus" (horiz.) | 40 | 15 |
| 2852. | 35 c. "Megalocnus rodens" .. .. | 75 | 35 |
| 2853. | 50 c. "Nesophontes micrus" (horiz.) .. | 85 | 45 |

**770.** Che Guevara.

**1982.** 15th Death Anniv. of Che Guevara (guerrilla fighter).

| No. | Description | Unused | Used |
|---|---|---|---|
| 2854. **770.** | 20 c. multicoloured .. | 40 | 20 |

**771.** Christopher Columbus, "Santa Maria" and Map of Cuba.

**1982.** 490th Anniv. of Discovery of America by Columbus. Multicoloured.

| No. | Description | Unused | Used |
|---|---|---|---|
| 2855 | 5 c. Type **771** .. .. | 75 | 20 |
| 2856 | 20 c. "Santa Maria" (vert) | 85 | 30 |
| 2857 | 35 c. Caravel "Pinta" (vert) .. .. .. | 1·40 | 65 |
| 2858 | 50 c. Caravel "Nina" (vert) .. .. .. | 1·75 | 80 |

**1982.** Lighthouses (3rd series). As T **715**. Multicoloured.

| No. | Description | Unused | Used |
|---|---|---|---|
| 2859. | 5 c. Cayo Jutias .. .. | 15 | 10 |
| 2860. | 20 c. Cayo Paredon Grande | 40 | 15 |
| 2861. | 30 c. Morro, Santiago de Cuba .. .. .. | 55 | 30 |

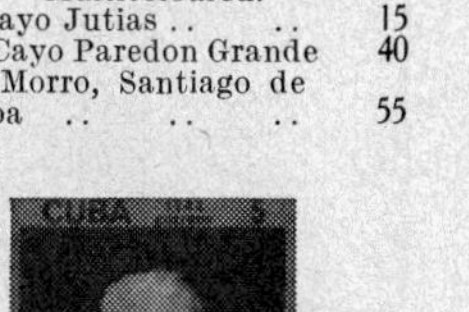

**772.** George Washington (anonymous painting).

**1982.** 250th Birth Anniv. of George Washington. Multicoloured.

| No. | Description | Unused | Used |
|---|---|---|---|
| 2862. | 5 c. Type **772** .. | 15 | 10 |
| 2863. | 20 c. Portrait of Washington by Daniel Huntington .. .. .. | 40 | 15 |

**774.** Steam Train and Boating Lake.

**1982.** 10th Anniv. of Lenin Park, Havana.

| No. | Description | Unused | Used |
|---|---|---|---|
| 2865. **774.** | 5 c. multicoloured .. | 15 | 10 |

**775.** Capablanca as Child and Chess King.

**1982.** 40th Death Anniv of Jose Capablanca (chess player). Multicoloured.

| No. | Description | Unused | Used |
|---|---|---|---|
| 2866 | 5 c. Type **775** .. .. | 15 | 10 |
| 2867 | 20 c. Capablanca and rook | 40 | 15 |
| 2868 | 30 c. Capablanca and knight .. .. | 55 | 30 |
| 2869 | 50 c. Capablanca and queen .. .. .. | 85 | 45 |

**776.** Lenin, Marx, Russian Arms and Kremlin Tower.

**1982.** 60th Anniv. of U.S.S.R.

| No. | Description | Unused | Used |
|---|---|---|---|
| 2870. **776.** | 30 c. multicoloured .. | 55 | 30 |

**777.** Methods of Communications.

**1983.** World Communications Year (1st issue).

| No. | Description | Unused | Used |
|---|---|---|---|
| 2871. **777.** | 20 c. multicoloured .. | 40 | 15 |

See also Nos 2929/33.

**778.** Birthplace and Birth Centenary Stamp.

**1983.** 130th Birth Anniv. of Jose Marti (writer).

2872. **778.** 5 c. multicoloured .. 15 10

**779.** Throwing the Javelin. **780.** Che Guevara and Radio Waves.

**1983.** Olympic Games, Los Angeles (1984). Multicoloured.

2873. 1 c. Type **779** .. .. 10 10
2874. 5 c. Volleyball .. .. 15 10
2875. 6 c. Basketball .. .. 15 10
2876. 20 c. Weightlifting .. 40 15
2877. 30 c. Wrestling .. .. 55 30
2878. 50 c. Boxing .. .. 85 45

**1983.** 25th Anniv. of Radio Rebelde.

2880. **780.** 20 c. multicoloured .. 40 15

**781.** Karl Marx.

**1983.** Death Centenary of Karl Marx.

2881. **781.** 30 c. multicoloured .. 55 30

**782.** Charles's Hydrogen Balloon. **783.** "Vostok 1".

**1983.** Bicent of Manned Flight. Mult.

2882 1 c. Type **782** .. .. 10 10
2883 3 c. Montgolfier balloon 10 10
2884 5 c. Montgolfier balloon "Le Gustave" .. 15 10
2885 7 c. Eugene Godard's quintuple "acrobatic" balloon .. .. 20 10
2886 30 c. Montgolfier unmanned balloon .. 1·10 55
2887 50 c. Charles Green's balloon "Royal Vauxhall" 1·10 55

**1983.** Cosmonautics Day. Multicoloured.

2889 1 c. Type **783** .. .. 10 10
2890 4 c. French "D1" satellite 10 10
2891 5 c. "Mars 2" .. .. 15 10
2892 20 c. "Soyuz" .. .. 40 15
2893 30 c. Meteorological satellite .. .. 55 30
2894 50 c. Intercosmos programme .. .. 85 45

**784.** Letter sent by First International Airmail Service.

**1983.** Stamp Day. Multicoloured.

2895. 20 c. Type **784** .. .. 40 15
2896. 30 c. Letter sent by first Atlantic airmail service 55 30

**786.** Jose Rafael de las Heras.

**1983.** Birth Bicentenary of Simon Bolivar. Multicoloured.

2898. 5 c. Type **786** .. .. 15 10
2899. 20 c. Simon Bolivar .. 40 15

**787.** J. L. Tasende, Abel Santamaria and B. L. Santa Coloma.

**1983.** 30th Anniv. of Attack on Moncada Fortress. Multicoloured.

2900. 5 c. Jose Marti and fortress (horiz.) .. 15 10
2901. 20 c. Type **787** .. .. 40 15
2902. 30 c. Symbol of Castro's book "History Will Absolve Me" .. .. 55 30

**789.** Weightlifting.

**1983.** Ninth Pan-American Games, Caracas. Multicoloured.

2904. 1 c. Type **789** .. .. 10 10
2905. 2 c. Volleyball .. .. 10 10
2906. 3 c. Baseball .. .. 10 10
2907. 20 c. High jump .. .. 40 15
2908. 30 c. Basketball .. .. 55 30
2909. 40 c. Boxing .. .. 85 45

**790.** "Harbour" (Claude Vernet).

**1983.** Centenary of French Alliance (French language-teaching association).

2910. **790.** 30 c. multicoloured .. 1·25 45

**791.** Salvador Allende and burning Presidential Palace.

**1983.** 10th Death Anniv. of Salvador Allende (President of Chile).

2911. **791.** 20 c. multicoloured .. 40 15

**792.** Regional Peasants Committee.

**1983.** 25th Anniv. of Peasants in Arms Congress.

2912. **792.** 5 c. multicoloured .. 10 10

**793.** "Portrait of a Young Man".

**1983.** 500th Birth Anniv. of Raphael. Mult.

2913. 1 c. "Girl with Veil" .. 10 10
2914. 2 c. "The Cardinal" .. 10 10
2915. 5 c. "Francesco m. della Rovere" .. .. 10 10
2916. 20 c. Type **793** .. .. 40 15
2917. 30 c. "Magdalena Doni" 55 30
2918. 50 c. "La Fornarina" .. 85 45

**794.** Quality Seal and Exports.

**1983.** State Quality Seal.

2919. **794.** 5 c. multicoloured .. 15 10

**1983.** Lighthouses (4th series). As T **715**. Multicoloured.

2920. 5 c. Carapachibey, Isle of Youth .. .. .. 10 10
2921. 20 c. Cadiz Bay .. .. 40 15
2922. 30 c. Punta Gobernadora 55 30

**795.** Hawksbill Turtle

**1983.** Turtles. Multicoloured.

2923. 1 c. Type **795** .. .. 10 10
2924. 2 c. "Lepidochelys kempi" 10 10
2925. 5 c. "Chrysemys decussata" .. .. .. 10 10
2926. 20 c. Loggerhead turtle 40 15
2927. 30 c. Green turtle .. 55 30
2928. 50 c. "Dermochelys coriacea" .. .. .. 85 45

**796.** Bell's Gallow Frame and Modern Telephones.

**1983.** World Communications Year (2nd issue). Multicoloured.

2929. 1 c. Type **796** .. .. 10 10
2930. 5 c. Telegram and air-mail envelopes and U.P.U. emblem .. 10 10
2931. 10 c. Satellite and antenna .. .. 25 10
2932. 20 c. Telecommunications satellite and dish aerial .. .. .. 40 15
2933. 30 c. Television and Radio Commemorative plaque and tower block .. .. .. 55 30

**MORE DETAILED LISTS**
are given in the Stanley Gibbons Catalogues referred to in the country headings.
For lists of current volumes see Introduction.

**797.** Cuban Stamps of 1933 and 1965.

**1983.** 150th Birth Anniv. of Carlos J. Finlay (malaria researcher).

2934. **797.** 20 c. multicoloured .. 50 15

**798.** "Jatropha angustifolia". **799.** Tobacco Flowers.

**1983.** Flora and Fauna. Multicoloured.

(a) Flowers.

2935. 5 c. Type **798** .. .. 10 10
2936. 5 c. "Cochlospermum vitifolium" .. .. 10 10
2937. 5 c. "Tabebuia lepidota" 10 10
2938. 5 c. "Kalmiella ericoides" 10 10
2939. 5 c. "Jatropha integerrima" .. .. .. 10 10
2940. 5 c. "Melocactus actinacanthus" .. .. 10 10
2941. 5 c. "Cordia sebestana" 10 10
2942. 5 c. "Tabernaemontana apoda" .. .. 10 10
2943. 5 c. "Lantana camera" 10 10
2944. 5 c. "Cordia gerascanthus" 10 10
2945. 5 c. "Opuntia dillenii" .. 10 10
2946. 5 c. "Euphorbia podocarpifolia" .. .. 10 10
2947. 5 c. "Dinema cubincola" 10 10
2948. 5 c. "Guaiacum officinale" 10 10
2949. 5 c. "Magnolia cubensis" 10 10

(b) Birds.

2950. 5 c. Bee Hummingbird .. 60 15
2951. 5 c. Northern Mockingbird 60 15
2952. 5 c. Cuban Tody .. 60 15
2953. 5 c. Cuban Amazon .. 60 15
2954. 5 c. Zapata Wren .. 60 15
2955. 5 c. Brown Pelican .. 60 15
2956. 5 c. West Indian Red-bellied Woodpecker .. 60 15
2957. 5 c. Red-legged Thrush 60 15
2958. 5 c. Cuban Conure .. 60 15
2959. 5 c. Eastern Meadowlark 60 15
2960. 5 c. Cuban Grassquit .. 60 15
2961. 5 c. White-tailed Tropic Bird .. .. .. 60 15
2962. 5 c. Cuban Solitaire .. 60 15
2963. 5 c. Great Lizard Cuckoo 60 15
2964. 5 c. Cuban Gnatcatcher 60 15

**1983.** Flowers.

2966. **799.** 60 c. green .. .. 1·00 55
2967. – 70 c. red .. .. 1·10 65
2968. – 80 c. blue .. .. 1·25 75
2969. – 90 c. violet .. .. 1·40 85

DESIGNS: 70 c. Lily. 80 c. Mariposa. 90 c. Orchid.

**800.** Flag and Plan of El Jigue Battlefield.

**1983.** 25th Anniv. of Revolution (1st issue). Multicoloured.

2970. 5 c. Type **800** .. .. 10 10
2971. 20 c. Flag and railway tracks at Santa Clara 75 35

**801.** Flag and Revolutionaries.

**1983.** 25th Anniv. of Revolution (2nd issue). Multicoloured.

2972. 20 c. Type **801** .. .. 35 15
2973. 20 c. "25" and star .. 35 15
2974. 20 c. Workers and Cuban Communist Party emblem .. .. 35 15

**802.** Lazaro Gonzalez, CTC Emblem and 15th Congress Flag.

**1984.** 45th Anniv. of Revolutionary Workers' Union.

2975. **802.** 5 c. multicoloured .. 10 10

**803.** " Ixias balice balice ".

**1984.** Butterflies. Multicoloured.

2976. 1 c. Type **803** .. .. 10 10
2977. 2 c. " Phoebis avellaneda avellaneda " .. .. 10 10
2978. 3 c. " Anthocaris sara sara " .. .. 10 10
2979. 5 c. " Victorina superba superba " .. .. 20 10
2980. 20 c. " Heliconius cydno cydnides " .. .. 70 10
2981. 30 c. " Parides gundlachianus calzadillae " .. 1·25 45
2982. 50 c. " Catagramma sorana sorana " .. .. 2·00 70

**804.** Clocktower and Russian Stamps of 1924–25.

**1984.** 60th Death Anniv. of Lenin.

2983. **804.** 30 c. multicoloured .. 50 25

**805.** Risso's Dolphin.

**1984.** Whales and Dolphins. Multicoloured.

2984. 1 c. Type **805** .. .. 10 10
2985. 2 c. Common dolphin .. 10 10
2986. 5 c. Sperm whale (horiz.) 10 10
2987. 6 c. Spotted dolphin .. 10 10
2988. 10 c. False killer whale (horiz.) .. .. 35 15
2989. 30 c. Bottle-nosed dolphin .. .. 75 30
2990. 50 c. Humpback whale (horiz.) .. .. 1·25 55

**806.** Sandino and Crowd holding Banner.

**1984.** 50th Death Anniv. of Augusto C. Sandino.

2991. **806.** 20 c. multicoloured .. 35 15

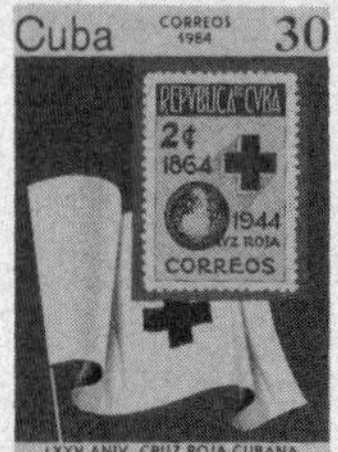


**807.** Red Cross Flag and Stamp of 1946.

**1984.** 75th Anniv. of Cuban Red Cross.

2992. **807.** 30 c. multicoloured .. 80 70

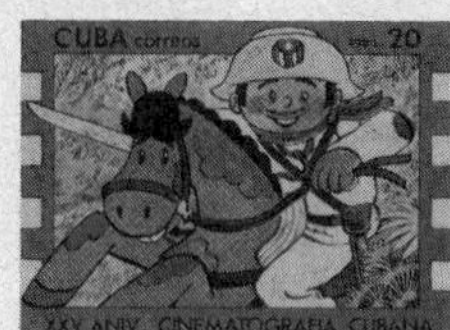


**808.** Scene from Cartoon Film.

**1984.** 25th Anniv. of Cuban Cinema.

2993. **808.** 20 c. multicoloured .. 55 50

**809.** "Brownea grandiceps".

**1984.** Caribbean Flowers. Multicoloured.

2994. 1 c. Type **809** .. .. 10 10
2995. 2 c. "Couroupita guianensis" .. .. 10 10
2996. 5 c. "Triplaris surinamensis" .. .. 15 10
2997. 20 c. "Amherstia nobilis" 55 50
2998. 30 c. "Plumieria alba" .. 80 70
2999. 50 c. "Delonix regia" .. 1·40 1·25

**810.** "Electron 1".

**1984.** Cosmonautics Day. Multicoloured.

3000. 2 c. Type **810** .. .. 10 10
3001. 3 c. "Electron 2" .. 10 10
3002. 5 c. "Intercosmos 1" .. 15 10
3003. 10 c. "Mars 5" .. .. 30 15
3004. 30 c. "Soyuz 1" .. .. 80 70
3005. 50 c. Soviet-Bulgarian space flight, 1979 .. 1·40 1·25

**811.** Mexican Mail Runner.

**1984.** Stamp Day. Multicoloured.

3007. 20 c. Type **811** .. .. 55 50
3008. 30 c. Egyptian boatman 80 70

Nos. 3007/8 show details of mural by R. R. Radillo in Havana Stamp Museum.

See also Nos. 3097/8, 3170/1, 3336/7 and 3619/20.

## MINIMUM PRICE

The minimum price quoted is 10p which represents a handling charge rather than a basis for valuing common stamps. For further notes about prices see introductory pages.

**813.** Basketball.

**1984.** Pre-Olympics.

3010. **813.** 20 c. multicoloured .. 55 50

**814.** Pink Roses.

**816.** Saver and Pile of Coins.

**815.** Workers in Field.

**1984.** Mothers' Day. Multicoloured.

3011. 20 c. Type **814** .. .. 55 50
3012. 20 c. Red roses .. .. 55 50

**1984.** 25th Anniv. of Land Reform Act.

3013. **815.** 5 c. multicoloured .. 15 10

**1984.** 1st Anniv. of People's Saving Bank.

3014. **816.** 5 c. multicoloured .. 15 10

**817.** Locomotive.

**1984.** Locomotives. Multicoloured.

3015. 1 c. Type **817** .. .. 10 10
3016. 4 c. Locomotive No. 73 15 10
3017. 5 c. Locomotive (diff.) .. 20 10
3018. 10 c. Locomotive (diff.) 35 15
3019. 30 c. Locomotive No. 350 90 70
3020. 50 c. Locomotive No. 495 1·60 1·25

**819.** Baron de Coubertin and Runner with Olympic Flame.

**1984.** 90th Anniv. of International Olympic Committee.

3022. **819.** 30 c. multicoloured .. 80 70

**820.** Baby with Toy Dog.

**1984.** Children's Day.

3023. **820.** 5 c. multicoloured .. 15 10

**821.** Wrestling.

**822.** Emilio Roig de Leuchsenring.

**1984.** Olympic Games, Los Angeles. Mult.

3024 1 c. Type **821** .. .. 10 10
3025 3 c. Throwing the discus 10 10
3026 5 c. Volleyball .. .. 15 10
3027 20 c. Boxing .. .. 55 50
3028 30 c. Basketball .. .. 80 70
3029 50 c. Weightlifting .. 1·40 1·25

**1984.** 20th Death Anniv of Emilio Roig de Leuchsenring.

3031 **822** 5 c. multicoloured .. 15 10

**824.** Cow in Pasture.

**1984.** Cattle. Multicoloured.

3033. 2 c. Type **824** .. .. 10 10
3034. 3 c. Cuban Carib .. 10 10
3035. 5 c. Charolaise (vert.) .. 10 10
3036. 30 c. Cuban Cebu (vert.) 45 40
3037. 50 c. White-udder cow .. 75 70

**825.** Men's Volleyball.

**1984.** Friendship Tournament. Mult.

3038. 3 c. Type **825** .. .. 10 10
3039. 5 c. Women's volleyball 10 10
3040. 8 c. Water polo .. .. 15 10
3041. 30 c. Boxing .. .. 45 40

**826.** Polymita.

**1984.** Cuban Wildlife. Multicoloured.

3042. 1 c. Type **826** .. .. 10 10
3043. 2 c. Cuban solenodon .. 10 10
3044. 3 c. "Alsophis cantherigerus" (snake) .. 10 10
3045. 4 c. "Osteopilus septentrionalis" (frog) 10 10
3046. 5 c. Bee hummingbirds 45 15
3047. 10 c. Bushy-tailed hutia 30 15
3048. 30 c. Cuban tody .. 2·00 65
3049. 50 c. Peach-faced lovebird 3·00 85

**827.** King Ferdinand and Queen Isabella.

**1984.** "Espamer '85" International Stamp Exhibition, Havana. Multicoloured.

3050. 5 c. Type **827** .. .. 10 10
3051. 20 c. Columbus departing from Palos de Moguer 1·00 45
3052. 30 c. "Santa Maria", "Pinta" and "Nina" .. 1·40 65
3053. 50 c. Columbus arriving in America .. .. 75 70

**829.** Flag and Soldier.

**1984.** 25th Anniv. of National Militia.
3055. **829.** 5 c. multicoloured .. 10 10

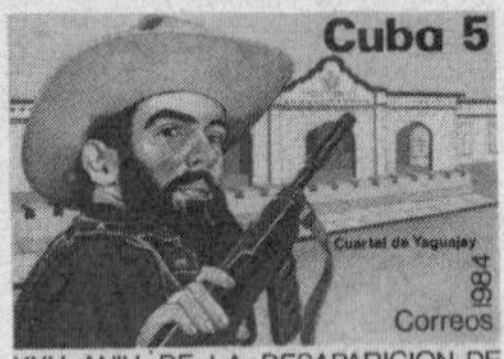


**830.** Camilo Cienfuegos.

**1984.** 25th Anniv. of Disappearance of Camilo Cienfuegos (revolutionary).
3056. **830.** 5 c. multicoloured .. 10 10

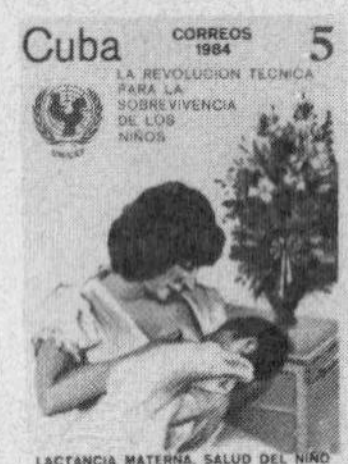


**831.** Mother breast-feeding Baby.

**1984.** Infant Survival Campaign.
3057. **831.** 5 c. multicoloured .. 10 10

**832.** Morgan, 1909.

**1984.** Cars. Multicoloured.
3058. 1 c. Type **832** .. .. 10 10
3059. 2 c. Austin, 1922 .. 10 10
3060. 5 c. Dion-Bouton, 1903 .. 10 10
3061. 20 c. "T" Ford, 1908 .. 30 25
3062. 30 c. Karl Benz, 1885 .. 45 40
3063. 50 c. Karl Benz, 1910 .. 75 70

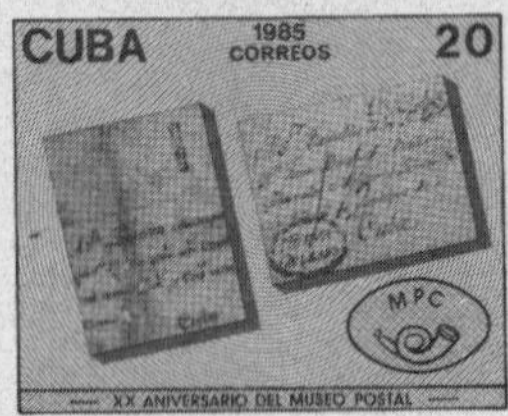


**833.** 18th-century Letters and Museum Emblem.

**1985.** 20th Anniv. of Cuban Postal Museum.
3064. **833.** 20 c. multicoloured .. 30 25

**834.** Celia Sanchez (after E. Escobedo).

**1985.** 5th Death Anniv. of Celia Sanchez (revolutionary).
3065. **834.** 5 c. multicoloured .. 10 10

**835.** Pigeon.

**1985.** "Porto-1985" International Pigeon Exhibition, Oporto, Portugal.
3066. **835.** 20 c. multicoloured .. 30 25

**836.** Chile (1962).

**1985.** World Cup Football Championship, Mexico (1986) (1st issue) Multicoloured.
3067. 1 c. Type **836** .. .. 10 10
3068. 2 c. England (1966) .. 10 10
3069. 3 c. Mexico (1970) .. 10 10
3070. 4 c. West Germany (1974) 10 10
3071. 5 c. Argentina (1978) .. 10 10
3072. 30 c. Spain (1982) .. 45 40
3073. 50 c. Sweden (1958) .. 75 70
See also Nos. 3135/40.

**837.** Pteranodon.

**1985.** Baconao Valley National Park. Prehistoric Animals (1st series). Multicoloured.
3075. 1 c. Type **837** .. .. 10 10
3076. 2 c. Brontosaurus .. 10 10
3077. 4 c. Iguanodontus .. 10 10
3078. 5 c. Estegosaurus .. 10 10
3079. 8 c. Monoclonius .. 15 10
3080. 30 c. Corythosaurus .. 45 40
3081. 50 c. Tyrannosaurus .. 75 70
See also Nos. 3264/9.

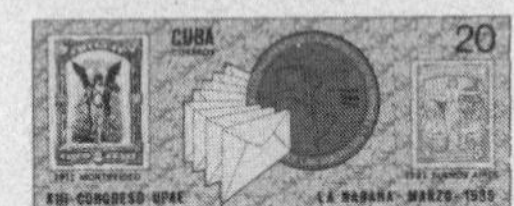


**838.** Uruguay 1911 and Argentina 1921 Congress Stamps and Emblem. (½-size illustration)

**1985.** 13th Postal Union of the Americas and Spain Congress, Havana.
3082. **838.** 20 c. multicoloured .. 65 25

**839.** Indians playing Football.

**1985.** "Espamer '85" International Stamp Exhibition, Havana, Multicoloured.
3083. 1 c. Type **839** .. .. 10 10
3084. 2 c. Indian sitting by fire 10 10
3085. 5 c. Fishing with nets and spears .. .. 20 10
3086. 20 c. Making pottery .. 30 25
3087. 30 c. Hunting with spears .. .. .. 45 40
3088. 50 c. Decorating canoe and paddle .. .. 1·90 1·10

**840.** Spaceship circling Moon.

**1985.** Cosmonautics Day. Multicoloured.
3090. 2 c. Type **840** .. .. 10 10
3091. 3 c. Spaceships .. .. 10 10
3092. 10 c. Cosmonauts meeting in space .. .. 15 15
3093. 13 c. Cosmonauts soldering in space .. .. 20 15
3094. 20 c. "Vostok II" and Earth .. .. .. 30 25
3095. 50 c. "Lunayod I" crossing moon crater 75 70

**841.** Lenin's Tomb. **842.** Peonies.

**1985.** 12th World Youth and Students' Festival, Moscow.
3096. **841.** 30 c. multicoloured .. 45 40

**1985.** Stamp Day. As T **811.** Multicoloured.
3097. 20 c. Roman soldier and chariot .. .. .. 30 25
3098. 30 c. Medieval nobleman and monks .. .. 45 40

**1985.** Mothers' Day. Multicoloured.
3099. 1 c. Type **842** .. .. 10 10
3100. 4 c. Carnations .. .. 10 10
3101. 5 c. Dahlias .. .. 10 10
3102. 13 c. Roses .. .. 20 15
3103. 20 c. Roses (different) .. 30 25
3104. 50 c. Tulips .. .. 75 70

**843.** Guiteras and Aponte.

**1985.** 50th Death Anniv. of Antonio Guiteras and Carlos Aponte (revolutionaries).
3105. **843.** 5 c. multicoloured .. 10 10

**844.** Star, "40" and Soldier with Flag.

**1985.** 40th Anniv. of End of Second World War.
3106. **844.** 5 c. multicoloured .. 10 10
3107. – 20 c. multicoloured .. 30 25
3108. – 30 c. red yellow and violet .. .. 45 40
Designs: 20 c. "40" and Soviet Memorial, Berlin-Treptow. 30 c. Dove within '40'.

**846.** Daimler, 1885.

**1985.** Centenary of the Motor Cycle. Multicoloured.
3110. 2 c. Type **846** .. .. 10 10
3111. 5 c. Kayser tricycle, 1910 10 10
3112. 10 c. Fanomovil, 1925 .. 15 15
3113. 30 c. Mars "A 20", 1926 55 50
3114. 50 c. Simson "BSW", 1936 .. .. .. 90 85

**847.** La Plata and Hermanos Ameijeiras Hospitals.

**1985.** Development of Health Care since the Revolution.
3115. **847.** 5 c. multicoloured .. 10 10

**848.** Flowers and Soldier with Gun.

**1985.** 25th Anniv. of Federation of Cuban Women.
3116. **848.** 5 c. multicoloured .. 10 10

**849.** Athletes and Emblem.

**1985.** World University Games, Kobe, Japan.
3117. **849.** 50 c. multicoloured .. 90 85

**850.** Crowd, Flags and Statue.

**1985.** 25th Anniv. of First Havana Declaration.
3118. **850.** 5 c. multicoloured .. 10 10

**852.** Emblem in "25".

**1985.** 25th Anniv. of Committees for Defence of the Revolution.
3120. **852.** 5 c. multicoloured .. 10 10

**853.** "Centropyge argi".

**1985.** Fishes. Multicoloured.
3121. 1 c. Type **853** .. .. 10 10
3122. 3 c. "Holacanthus tricolor" .. .. 10 10
3123. 5 c. "Chaetodon capistratus" .. .. 10 10
3124. 10 c. "Chaetodon sedentarius" .. .. 15 15
3125. 20 c. "Chaetodon ocellatus" .. .. 35 30
3126. 50 c. "Holacanthus ciliaris" .. .. 90 85

**854.** Cuban and Party Flags and Central Committee Building.

**856.** U.N. Building, New York, and Emblem.

**1985.** 20th Anniv. of Cuban Communist Party and Third Party Congress.

3127. **854.** 5 c. multicoloured .. 10 10

**1985.** 40th Anniv. of U.N.O.

3129. **856.** 20 c. multicoloured .. 35 30

**857.** Old Square and Arms.

**1985.** U.N.E.S.C.O. World Heritage. Old Havana. Multicoloured.

3130. 2 c. Type **857** .. .. 10 10
3131. 5 c. Real Fuerza Castle 10 10
3132. 20 c. Havana Cathedral 35 30
3133. 30 c. Captain General's Palace .. .. .. 55 50
3134. 50 c. El Templete .. 90 85

**858.** Footballers.

**860.** Ministry Emblem.

**859.** Red Flags and Emblem.

**1986.** World Cup Football Championship, Mexico (2nd issue).

3135. **858.** 1 c. multicoloured .. 10 10
3136. – 4 c. multicoloured .. 10 10
3137. – 5 c. multicoloured .. 10 10
3138. – 10 c. multicoloured .. 15 10
3139. – 30 c. multicoloured .. 55 45
3140. – 50 c. multicoloured .. 90 85

DESIGNS: 4 c. to 50 c. Various footballing scenes.

**1986.** 3rd Cuban Communist Party Congress, Havana. Multicoloured.

3142. 5 c. Type **859** .. .. 10 10
3143. 20 c. Red and national flags .. .. .. 35 30

**1986.** 25th Anniv. of Ministry of Interior Trade.

3144. **860.** 5 c. multicoloured .. 10 10

**861.** People practising Sports.

**862.** "Tecomaria capensis".

**1986.** 25th Anniv. of National Sports Institute.

3145. **861.** 5 c. multicoloured .. 10 10

**1986.** Exotic Flowers. Multicoloured.

3146. 1 c. Type **862** .. .. 10 10
3147. 3 c. "Michelia champaca" .. .. 10 10
3148. 5 c. "Thunbergia grandiflora" .. .. 10 10
3149. 8 c. "Dendrobium phalaenopsis" .. 15 10
3150. 30 c. "Allamanda violacea" .. .. 55 50
3151. 50 c. "Rhodocactus bleo" 90 85

**863.** Gundlach and Red-winged Blackbird.

**1986.** 90th Death Anniv. of Juan C. Gundlach (ornithologist). Multicoloured.

3152. 1 c. Type **863** .. .. 35 10
3153. 3 c. Olive-capped warbler 35 10
3154. 7 c. La Sagra's flycatcher 65 25
3155. 9 c. Yellow warbler .. 85 30
3156. 30 c. Grey-faced quail dove .. .. .. 3·50 1·40
3157. 50 c. Common flicker .. 5·25 2·25

**864.** Pioneers and "25". **865.** Gomez and Statue.

**1986.** 25th Anniv. of Jose Marti Pioneers.

3158. **864.** 5 c. multicoloured .. 10 10

**1986.** 150th Birth Anniv. of Maximo Gomez.

3159. **865.** 20 c. multicoloured .. 35 30

**866.** Nursery Nurse with Children.

**867.** "Vostok" and Korolev (designer).

**1986.** 25th Anniv. of Children's Day Care Centres.

3160. **866.** 5 c. multicoloured .. 10 10

**1986.** 25th Anniv. of First Man in Space. Multicoloured.

3161. 1 c. Type **867** .. .. 10 10
3162. 2 c. Yuri Gargarin (first man in space) and "Vostok" .. .. 10 10
3163. 5 c. Valentina Tereshkova (first woman in space) and "Vostok" .. .. 10 10
3164. 20 c. "Salyut" space station .. .. 30 25
3165. 30 c. Capsule descending with parachute .. 35 30
3166. 50 c. "Soyuz" rocket on launch pad .. .. 90 85

**868.** National Flag and 1981 Stamp.

**869.** Reels as National Flag and Globe and Tape forming "25".

**1986.** 25th Anniv. of Socialist State (1959) and Victory at Giron. Multicoloured.

3168. 5 c. Type **868** .. .. 10 10
3169. 20 c. Flags and arms .. 30 25

**1986.** Stamp Day. As T **811** showing details of mural by R. R. Radillo in Havana Stamp Museum. Multicoloured.

3170. 20 c. Early mail coach .. 30 25
3171. 30 c. Express rider .. 35 30

**1986.** 25th Anniv. of Radio Havana Cuba.

3172. **869.** 5 c. multicoloured .. 10 10

**870.** "Stourbridge Lion", U.S.A., 1829.

**1986.** "Expo '86" World's Fair, Vancouver. Railway Locomotives. Multicoloured.

3173. 1 c. Type **870** .. .. 10 10
3174. 4 c. "Rocket", England, 1829 .. .. .. 10 10
3175. 5 c. First Russian locomotive, 1845 .. 10 10
3176. 8 c. Seguin's locomotive, France, 1830 .. .. 15 10
3177. 30 c. First Canadian locomotive, 1836 .. .. 40 30
3178. 50 c. Urban locomotive, Belgian Grand Central Railway, 1872 .. .. 1·25 85

**871.** Hand holding Machete and Farmer ploughing and driving Tractor.

**1986.** 25th Anniv. of National Association of Small Farmers.

3180. **871.** 5 c. multicoloured .. 10 10

**872.** Dove and Arms on Coin.

**1986.** International Peace Year.

3181. **872.** 30 c. multicoloured .. 35 30

**873.** Emblem.

**1986.** 25th Anniv. of Ministry of the Interior.

3182. **873.** 5 c. multicoloured .. 10 10

**874.** King.

**1986.** 18th Death Anniv. of Martin Luther King (human rights campaigner).

3183. **874.** 20 c. multicoloured .. 30 25

**875.** Bonifacio Byrne.

**1986.** 50th Death Anniv. of Bonifacio Byrne (poet).

3184. **875.** 5 c. multicoloured .. 10 10

**876.** Dove, Pen Nib and Paint Brush.

**877.** Sandino and Pres. Ortega of Nicaragua.

**1986.** 25th Anniv. of National Union of Cuban Writers and Artists.

3185. **876.** 5 c. multicoloured .. 10 10

**1986.** 25th Anniv. of Sandinista Movement of Nicaragua.

3186. **877.** 20 c. multicoloured .. 30 25

**878.** Tanker, Tupolev Tu-154 and Lorry.

**1986.** 25th Anniv. of Ministry of Transport.

3187. **878.** 5 c. multicoloured .. 30 15

**879.** Sportsmen and Emblem.

**882.** "Cattleya hardyana".

**881.** Map.

**1986.** 5th Central American and Caribbean University Games, Havana.

3188. **879.** 20 c. multicoloured .. 35 30

**1986.** 25th Anniv. of Non-Aligned Countries Movement.

3190. **881.** 50 c. multicoloured .. 80 75

**1986.** Orchids. Multicoloured.

3191. 1 c. Type **882** .. .. 10 10
3192. 4 c. "Brassolaelio-cattleya" "Horizon Flight" .. .. 10 10
3193. 5 c. "Phalaenopsis" "Margit Moses" .. 10 10
3194. 10 c. "Laeliocattleya" "Prism Palette" .. 15 15
3195. 30 c. "Phalaenopsis violacea" .. .. 50 45
3196. 50 c. "Disa uniflora" .. 80 75

**883.** Mayan House and Jade Statue (Belize).

**1986.** Latin American History. Pre-Columbian Culture (1st series). Multicoloured.

3197. 1 c. Type **883** .. .. 10 10
3198. 1 c. Inca vessel and Gateway of the Sun, Tiahuanacu (Bolivia) 10 10
3199. 1 c. Spain 1930 1 p. stamp of Columbus and 500th anniv. of Columbus's discovery of America emblem .. 10 10
3200. 1 c. Diaguitan duck-shaped pitcher and ruins, Pucara de Quitor (Chile) .. .. 10 10
3201. 1 c. Archaeological park, San Augustin and Quimbayan statuette (Columbia) .. .. 10 10
3202. 5 c. Moler memorial and Chorotega decorated earthenware statue (Costa Rica) .. .. 10 10
3203. 5 c. Tabaco idol and typical aboriginal houses (Cuba) .. .. 10 10
3204. 5 c. Spain 1930 40 c. stamp of Martin Pinzon and anniversary emblem .. 10 10
3205. 5 c. Typical houses and animal shaped seat (Dominica) .. .. 10 10
3206. 5 c. Tolita statue and Ingapirca fort (Ecuador) .. .. 10 10

3207. 10 c. Maya vase and Tikal temple (Guatemala) .. .. 15 15
3208. 10 c. Copan ruins and Maya idol (Honduras) 15 15
3209. 10 c. Spain 1930 30 c. stamp of Vincent Pinzon and anniversary emblem .. 15 15
3210. 10 c. Chichen-Itza temple and Zapoteca urn (Mexico) .. .. 15 15
3211. 10 c. Punta de Zapote idols and Ometepe ceramic (Nicaragua) .. 15 15
3212. 20 c. Tonosi ceramic and Barrile monolithic sculptures (Panama) .. 35 30
3213. 20 c. Machu Picchu ruin and Inca figure (Peru) 35 30
3214. 20 c. Spain 1930 10 p. stamp of Columbus and Pinzon brothers and anniversary emblem .. .. 35 30
3215. 20 c. Typical aboriginal dwellings and triangular stone carving (Puerto Rico) 35 30
3216. 20 c. Santa Ana female figure and Santo Domingo cave (Venezuela) .. .. 35 30

See also Nos. 3276/95, 3371/90, 3458/77, 3563/82, 3666/85 and 3769/88.

**884.** Medal and Soldier with Rifle.

**1986.** 50th Anniv. of Formation of International Brigades in Spain.
3217. **884.** 30 c. multicoloured .. 50 45

**885.** "Two Children" (Gutierrez de la Vega).

**1986.** National Museum Paintings (17th series). Multicoloured.
3218. 2 c. Type **885** .. .. 10 10
3219. 4 c. "Sed" (Jean-Gorges Vibert) (horiz.) .. 10 10
3220. 6 c. "Virgin and Child" (Niccolo Abbate) .. 10 10
3221. 10 c. "Bullfight" (Eugenio de Lucas Velazquez) (horiz.) .. 15 15
3222. 30 c. "The Five Senses" (Anon) (horiz.) .. 50 45
3223. 50 c. "Meeting at Thomops Castle" (Jean Louis Ernest) (horiz.) .. .. 80 75

**886.** People and "Granma".

**1986.** 30th Annivs. of "Granma" Landings (5 c.) and Revolutionary Armed Forces (20 c.). Multicoloured.
3224. 5 c. Type **886** .. .. 10 10
3225. 20 c. Soldier, rifle and flag .. .. .. 35 30

## MORE DETAILED LISTS
are given in the Stanley Gibbons Catalogues referred to in the country headings.
For lists of current volumes see Introduction.

**887.** Scholars and Che Guevara.

**1986.** 25th Anniv. of Scholarship Programme.
3226. **887.** 5 c. multicoloured .. 10 10

**888.** Man learning to write and Sanmarti. **890.** "Gitana" (Joaquin Sorolla).

**889.** Map and Revolutionaries.

**1986.** 25th Anniv. of Literacy Campaign.
3227. **888.** 5 c. multicoloured .. 10 10

**1987.** 30th Anniv. of Attack on La Plata Garrison.
3228. **889.** 5 c. multicoloured .. 10 10

**1987.** National Museum Paintings (18th series). Multicoloured.
3229. 3 c. Type **890** .. .. 10 10
3230. 5 c. "Sir Walter Scott" (Sir John W. Gordon) 10 10
3231. 10 c. "Farm Meadows" (Alfred de Breanski) (horiz.) .. .. 15 15
3232. 20 c. "Still Life" (Isaac van Duynen) (horiz.) 35 30
3233. 30 c. "Landscape with Figures" (Francesco Zuccarelli) (horiz.) .. 50 45
3234. 40 c. "Waffle Seller" (Ignacio Zuloaga) .. 65 60

**891.** Palace, Delivery Van and Echeverria.

**1987.** 30th Anniv. of Attack on Presidential Palace.
3235. **891.** 5 c. multicoloured .. 10 10

**892.** Lazarus Ludwig Zamenhof (inventor) and Russia 1927 14 k. Stamp.

**1987.** Centenary of Esperanto (invented languague).
3236. **892.** 30 c. multicoloured .. 50 45

**894.** Badge and Slogan.

**1987.** 25th Anniv. and 5th Congress of Youth Communist League.
3238. **894.** 5 c. multicoloured .. 10 10

**895.** "Intercosmos I" Satellite. **897.** Dahlias.

**896.** Cover with Postal Fiscal Stamp, 1890.

**1987.** Cosmonautics Day. 20th Anniv. of Intercosmos Programme. Multicoloured.
3239. 3 c. Type **895** .. .. 10 10
3240. 5 c. "Intercosmos II" .. 10 10
3241. 10 c. "TD" .. .. 15 15
3242. 20 c. "Cosmos 93" .. 35 30
3243. 30 c. "Molniya" .. .. 50 45
3244. 50 c. "Vostok 3" .. 80 75

**1987.** Stamp Day. Multicoloured.
3246. 30 c. Type **896** .. .. 50 45
3247. 50 c. Cover with bisect, 1869 .. .. .. 80 75

**1987.** Mothers' Day. Multicoloured.
3248. 3 c. Type **897** .. .. 10 10
3249. 5 c. Roses .. .. 10 10
3250. 10 c. Roses in basket .. 15 15
3251. 13 c. Decorative dahlias 25 20
3252. 30 c. Cactus dahlias .. 50 45
3253. 50 c. Roses (different) .. 80 75

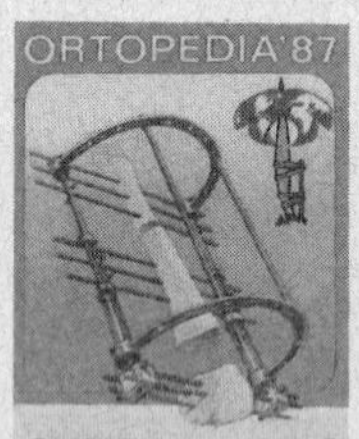

**898.** Fractured Femur Immobilised in Frame. **899.** Emblem.

**1987.** "Orthopedia '87" Portuguese and Spanish Speaking Countries' Orthopedists Meeting, Havana.
3254. **898.** 5 c. multicoloured .. 10 10

**1987.** 25th Anniv. of Cuban Broadcasting and Television Institute.
3255. **899.** 5 c. multicoloured .. 10 10

**900.** Battle Monument, Sierra Maestra Mountains.

**1987.** 30th Anniv. of Battle of El Uvero.
3256. **900.** 5 c. multicoloured .. 10 10

**901.** Messenger with Pack Llamas and 1868 Stamp (Bolivia).

**1987.** "Capex '87" International Stamp Exhibition, Toronto. 19th-century Mail Carriers as depicted on cigarette cards. Multicoloured.
3257. 3 c. Type **901** .. .. 10 10
3258. 5 c. Postman and motor car and 1900 stamp (France) .. .. 10 10
3259. 10 c. Messenger on elephant and 1883 stamp (Siam) .. .. 15 15
3260. 20 c. Messenger on camel and 1879 stamp (Egypt) .. .. 35 30
3261. 30 c. Mail troika and stamp (Russia) .. 50 45
3262. 50 c. Messenger on horseback and stamp (Indo-China) .. .. 80 75

**902.** Model of Prehistoric Animal.

**1987.** Prehistoric Valley, Baconao National Park (2nd series). Designs showing various exhibits.
3264. **902.** 3 c. multicoloured .. 10 10
3265. – 5 c. multicoloured .. 10 10
3266. – 10 c. multicoloured .. 15 15
3267. – 20 c. multicoloured .. 35 30
3268. – 35 c. multicoloured .. 55 50
3269. – 40 c. multicoloured .. 65 60

**903.** Pais and Rafael Maria Mendive Popular University Buildings.

**1987.** 30th Death Anniv. of Frank Pais (teacher and student leader).
3270. **903.** 5 c. multicoloured .. 10 10

**904.** Flags and Sportsmen.

**1987.** 10th Pan-American Games, Indianapolis.
3271. **904.** 50 c. multicoloured .. 80 75

**905.** Memorial.

**1987.** 30th Anniv. of Cienfuegos Uprising.
3272. **905.** 5 c. multicoloured .. 10 10

**908.** Coins and 1968 Independence War Centenary 30 c. Stamp.

**1987.** 20th Anniv. of Heroic Guerilla Fighters Day.
3275. **908.** 50 c. multicoloured .. 80 75

**909.** Tehuelche Man and Red-crowned Ant-tanager (Argentina).

**1987.** Latin American History (2nd series). Multicoloured.

3276. 1 c. Type **909** . . . . 20 10
3277. 1 c. Cuvier's toucan and Tibirica man (Brazil) 20 10
3278. 1 c. Spain 1930 5 c. stamp of La Rabida Monastery and 500th anniv. of Columbus's discovery of America emblem . . . . 10 10
3279. 1 c. Andean condor and Lautaro man (Chile) . . 20 10
3280. 1 c. Calarca man and hoatzin (Colombia) . . 20 10
3281. 5 c. Cuban trogon and Hatuey man (Cuba) . . 45 10
3282. 5 c. Scaly-breasted ground dove and Enriquillo man (Dominican Republic) 45 10
3283. 5 c. Spain 1930 30 c. stamp of departure from Palos and anniversary emblem . . 10 10
3284. 5 c. Toucan barbet and Ruminahui man (Ecuador) . . . . 45 10
3285. 5 c. Resplendent quetzal and Tecum Uman man (Guatemala) . . . . 45 10
3286. 10 c. Anacaona woman and limpkin (Haiti) . . 75 10
3287. 10 c. Lempira man and slaty flower-piercer (Honduras) . . . . 75 10
3288. 10 c. Spain 1930 10 p. Columbus stamp and anniversary emblem . . 15 10
3289. 10 c. Northern royal fly-catcher and Cuauhtemoc woman (Mexico) . . . . 75 10
3290. 10 c. Painted redstart and Nicarao man (Nicaragua) . . 75 10
3291. 20 c. Andean cock of the rock and Atahualpa man (Peru) . . . . 1·25 30
3292. 20 c. Atlactl man and red-tailed hawk (El Salvador) . . . . 1·25 30
3293. 20 c. Spain 1930 10 p. stamp of arrival in America and anniversary emblem . . 35 30
3294. 20 c. Abayuba man and red-breasted plant-cutter (Uruguay) . . 1·25 30
3295. 20 c. Guaycaypuro man and blue and yellow macaw (Venezuela) . . 1·25 30

**910.** 1950 2 c. Train Stamp.

**1987.** 150th Anniv. of Cuban Railway. Designs showing Cuban stamps.

3296. **910.** 3 c. red, brn. & blk. 10 10
3297. – 5 c. multicoloured . . 10 10
3298. – 10 c. multicoloured . . 15 15
3299. – 20 c. multicoloured . . 35 30
3300. – 35 c. multicoloured . . 55 50
3301. – 40 c. multicoloured . . 65 60

DESIGNS: 5 c. 1965 7 c. "BB. 69,000" diesel locomotive stamp. 10 c. 1975 1 c. La Junta stamp. 20 c. 1975 3 c. locomotive stamp. 35 c. 1980 10 c. locomotive stamp. 40 c. 1980 13 c. locomotive stamp.

**911.** Satellites and Russia 1927 14 k. Stamp.

**1987.** 70th Anniv. of Russian Revolution.

3303. **911.** 30 c. multicoloured . . 50 45

**912.** "Landscape" (Domingo Ramos).

**1988.** 170th Anniv. of San Alejandro Arts School, Havana. Multicoloured.

3304. 1 c. Type **912** . . . . 10 10
3305. 2 c. "Portrait of Rodriguez Morey" (Eugenio Gonzalez Olivera) . . . . 10 10
3306. 3 c. "Landscape with Malangas and Palm Trees" (Valentin Sanz Carta) . . . . . . 10 10
3307. 5 c. "Ox-carts" (Eduardo Morales) . . . . 10 10
3308. 10 c. "Portrait of Elena Herrera" (Armando Menocal) (vert.) . . 15 15
3309. 30 c. "The Rape of Dejanira" (Miguel Melero) (vert.) . . 45 40
3310. 50 c. "The Card Player" (Leopoldo Romanach) 75 70

**913.** "Boletus satanas".

**915.** Mario Munoz Santiago Monument, de Cuba.

**914.** Radio Operator, Satellite and Caribe Ground Station.

**1988.** Poisonous Mushrooms. Multicoloured.

3311. 1 c. Type **913** . . . . 10 10
3312. 2 c. "Amanita citrina" . . 10 10
3313. 3 c. "Tylopilus felleus" 10 10
3314. 5 c. "Paxillus involutus" . . 20 10
3315. 10 c. "Inocybe patouillardii" . . . . 40 15
3316. 30 c. "Amanita muscaria" . . . . 1·00 40
3317. 50 c. "Hypholoma fasciculare" . . . . 1·60 70

**1988.** 30th Anniv. of Radio Rebelde.

3318. **914.** 5 c. multicoloured . . 10 10

**1988.** 30th Anniv. of Mario Munoz Third Front.

3319. **915.** 5 c. multicoloured . . 10 10

**916.** Frank Pais Memorial and Eternal Flame.

**917.** Red Roses.

**1988.** 30th Anniv. of Frank Pais Second Eastern Front.

3320. **916.** 5 c. multicoloured . . 10 10

**1988.** Mothers' Day. Multicoloured.

3321. 1 c. Type **917** . . . . 10 10
3322. 2 c. Pale pink roses . . 10 10
3323. 3 c. Daisies . . . . 10 10
3324. 5 c. Dahlias . . . . 10 10
3325. 13 c. White roses . . 15 15
3326. 35 c. Carnations . . . . 50 45
3327. 40 c. Pink roses . . . . 60 55

**918.** "Gorizont" Satellite.

**1988.** Cosmonautics Day. Multicoloured.

3328. 2 c. Type **918** . . . . 10 10
3329. 3 c. "Mir"–"Kvant" link 10 10
3330. 4 c. "Signo 3" . . . . 10 10
3331. 5 c. Mars space probe . . 10 10
3332. 10 c. "Phobos" . . . . 15 15
3333. 30 c. "Vega" space probe 45 40
3334. 50 c. Space craft . . 75 70

**1988.** Stamp Day. As T **811**. Details of mural by R. R. Radillo in Havana Stamp Museum. Multicoloured.

3336. 30 c. Telegraphist and mail coach . . . . 45 40
3337. 50 c. Carrier pigeon . . 75 70

**919.** Storage Tanks, Products, Sugar Cane and Laboratory Equipment.

**1988.** 25th Anniv. of ICIDCA (Cuban Institute for Research on Sugarcane Byproducts).

3338. **919.** 5 c. multicoloured . . 10 10

**920.** Havana–Madrid, 1948.

**1988.** Cubana Airlines Transatlantic Flights. Multicoloured.

3339. 2 c. Type **920** . . . . 10 10
3340. 4 c. Havana–Prague, 1961 . . . . . . 10 10
3341. 5 c. Havana–Berlin, 1972 10 10
3342. 10 c. Havana–Luanda, 1975 . . . . . . 20 15
3343. 30 c. Havana–Paris, 1983 55 40
3344. 50 c. Havana–Moscow, 1987 . . . . . . 95 70

**922.** Steam Train. ($\frac{1}{2}$-size illustration).

**1988.** Postal Union of the Americas and Spain Colloquium on "America" Postage Stamps, Havana.

3346. **922.** 20 c. multicoloured . . 30 25

**923.** "Megasoma elephas".

**1988.** Beetles. Multicoloured.

3347. 1 c. Type **923** . . . . 10 10
3348. 3 c. "Platycoelia flavoscutellata" (vert.) . . 10 10
3349. 4 c. "Plusiotis argenteola" . . . . 10 10
3350. 5 c. "Hetersoternus oberthuri" . . . . 10 10
3351. 10 c. "Odontotaenius zodiacus" . . . . 25 15
3352. 35 c. "Chrysophora chrysochlora" (vert.) 70 55
3353. 40 c. "Phanaeus leander" 85 75

**924.** Chess Pieces.

**1988.** Birth Centenary of Jose Capablanca (chess master). Multicoloured.

3354 30 c. Type **924** . . . . 45 40
3355 40 c. Juan Corzo, Capablanca and flags (1901 Cuban Championship) (horiz) . . . . 60 55
3356 50 c. Emanuel Lasker and Capablanca (1921 World Championship) (horiz) 75 70
3357 1 p. Checkmate in 1921 game with Lasker . . 1·50 1·25
3358 3 p. "J. R. Capablanca" (E. Valderrama) . . 4·00 3·50
3359 5 p. Chess pieces, flag, globe and Capablanca 6·00 5·50

**925.** Sun and Fortress.

**1988.** 35th Anniv. of Assault on Moncada Fortress.

3361. **925.** 5 c. red, yell. & blk. 10 10

**927.** Camilo Cienfuegos and Che Guevara and Map.

**1988.** 30th Anniv. of Rebel Invasion Columns.

3363. **927.** 5 c. multicoloured . . 10 10

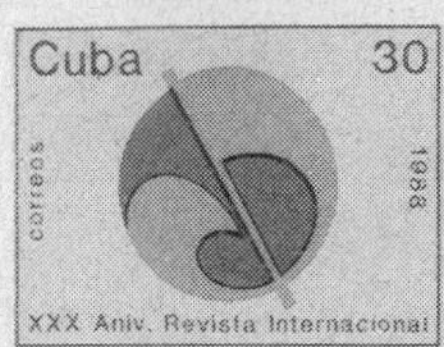

**928.** Emblem.

**1988.** 30th Anniv. of "Revista Internacional" (magazine).

3364. **928.** 30 c. multicoloured . . 45 40

**929** Early English Steam Locomotive

**1988.** Railway Development. Multicoloured.

3365 20 c. Type **929** . . . . 30 25
3366 30 c. Early French steam locomotive . . . . 50 45
3367 50 c. "La Junta" (Cuba's first locomotive, 1837) 80 75
3368 1 p. Electric tram . . 1·60 1·25
3369 2 p. Diesel locomotive . . 3·25 2·75
3370 5 p. Diesel railcar . . 8·00 7·50

**930** Arms and Jose de San Martin (Argentina)

**1988.** Latin-American History (3rd series). Multicoloured.

| | | | |
|---|---|---|---|
| 3371 | 1 c. Type **930** .. .. | 10 | 10 |
| 3372 | 1 c. Arms and M. A. Padilla (Bolivia) .. | 10 | 10 |
| 3373 | 1 c. 1944 10 c. Discovery of America stamp .. | 10 | 10 |
| 3374 | 1 c. Arms and A. de Silva Xavier, "Tiradentes" (Brazil) .. .. | 10 | 10 |
| 3375 | 1 c. Arms and Bernardo O'Higgins (Chile) .. | 10 | 10 |
| 3376 | 5 c. A. Narino and arms (Colombia) .. .. | 10 | 10 |
| 3377 | 5 c. Arms and Jose Marti (Cuba) .. .. | 10 | 10 |
| 3378 | 5 c. 1944 13 c. Discovery of America stamp .. | 10 | 10 |
| 3379 | 5 c. Arms and Juan Pablo Duarte (Dominican Republic) .. .. | 10 | 10 |
| 3380 | 5 c. Arms and Antonio Jose de Sucre (Ecuador) | 10 | 10 |
| 3381 | 10 c. Manuel Jose Arce and arms (El Salvador) | 15 | 10 |
| 3382 | 10 c. Arms and Jean Jacques Dessalines (Haiti) .. .. | 15 | 10 |
| 3383 | 10 c. 1944 5 c. Discovery of America airmail stamp | 15 | 10 |
| 3384 | 10 c. Miguel Hidalgo and arms (Mexico) .. | 15 | 10 |
| 3385 | 10 c. Arms and J. Dolores Estrada (Nicaragua) .. | 15 | 10 |
| 3386 | 20 c. Jose E. Diaz and arms (Paraguay) .. | 30 | 25 |
| 3387 | 20 c. Arms and Francisco Bolognesi (Peru) .. | 30 | 25 |
| 3388 | 20 c. 1944 10 c. Discovery of America airmail stamp .. .. .. | 30 | 25 |
| 3389 | 20 c. Arms and Jose Gervasio Artigas (Uruguay) .. .. | 30 | 25 |
| 3390 | 20 c. Simon Bolivar and arms (Venezuela) .. | 30 | 25 |

**931** Maces and Governor's Palace

**1988.** 20th Anniv of Havana Museum.

| | | | | |
|---|---|---|---|---|
| 3391 | **931** | 5 c. multicoloured .. | 10 | 10 |

**932** Ballerinas and Mute Swan

**1988.** 40th Anniv of National Ballet (3392) and 150th Anniv of Grand Theatre, Havana (3393). Multicoloured.

| | | | |
|---|---|---|---|
| 3392 | 5 c. Type **932** .. .. | 30 | 10 |
| 3393 | 5 c. Theatre, 1838 and 1988 | 10 | 10 |

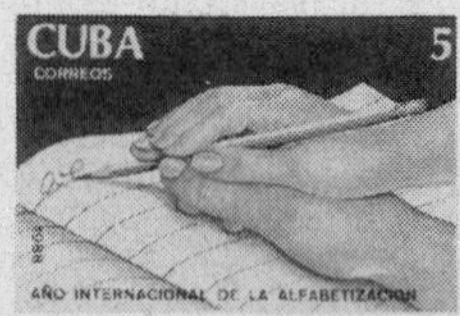

**933** Practising Letters

**1988.** International Literacy Year.

| | | | | |
|---|---|---|---|---|
| 3394 | **933** | 5 c. multicoloured .. | 10 | 10 |

**934** Emblem

**1988.** 40th Anniv of Declaration of Human Rights.

| | | | | |
|---|---|---|---|---|
| 3395 | **934** | 30 c. multicoloured .. | 50 | 45 |

**935** Ernesto Che Guevara Plaza

**1988.** 30th Anniv of Battle of Santa Clara.

| | | | | |
|---|---|---|---|---|
| 3396 | **935** | 30 c. multicoloured .. | 50 | 45 |

**936** National Flag forming "30"

**1989.** 30th Anniv of Revolution.

| | | | | |
|---|---|---|---|---|
| 3397 | **936** | 5 c. multicoloured .. | 10 | 10 |
| 3398 | | 20 c. multicoloured .. | 30 | 25 |
| 3399 | | 30 c. gold, blue & red | 50 | 45 |
| 3400 | | 50 c. gold, blue & red | 80 | 75 |

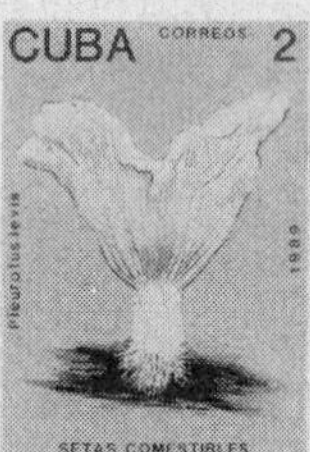

**937** "Pleurotus levis"

**1989.** Edible Mushrooms. Multicoloured.

| | | | |
|---|---|---|---|
| 3401 | 2 c. Type **937** .. .. | 10 | 10 |
| 3402 | 3 c. "Pleurotus florid-anus" .. .. .. | 10 | 10 |
| 3403 | 5 c. "Amanita caesarea" | 15 | 10 |
| 3404 | 10 c. "Lentinus cubensis" (horiz) .. .. | 35 | 10 |
| 3405 | 40 c. "Pleurotus ostre-atus" (red) .. .. | 1·25 | 60 |
| 3406 | 50 c. "Pleurotus ostre-atus" (brown) .. | 1·40 | 75 |

**939** 1982 30 c. Cuban Stamp

**1989.** 50th Anniv of Revolutionary Workers' Union.

| | | | | |
|---|---|---|---|---|
| 3408 | **939** | 5 c. multicoloured .. | 10 | 10 |

**940** "Metamorpho dido"

**1989.** Butterflies. Multicoloured.

| | | | |
|---|---|---|---|
| 3409 | 1 c. Type **940** .. .. | 10 | 10 |
| 3410 | 3 c. "Callithea saphhira" | 10 | 10 |
| 3411 | 5 c. "Papilio zagreus" .. | 10 | 10 |
| 3412 | 10 c. "Mynes sestia" .. | 20 | 15 |
| 3413 | 30 c. "Papilio dardanus" | 80 | 55 |
| 3414 | 50 c. "Catagranma sorana" .. .. | 1·40 | 90 |

**941** Footballer

**942** "30" and Arms

**1989.** World Cup Football Championship, Italy (1990).

| | | | | |
|---|---|---|---|---|
| 3415 | **941** | 1 c. multicoloured .. | 10 | 10 |
| 3416 | – | 3 c. multicoloured .. | 10 | 10 |
| 3417 | – | 5 c. multicoloured .. | 10 | 10 |
| 3418 | – | 10 c. multicoloured .. | 15 | 10 |
| 3419 | – | 30 c. multicoloured .. | 50 | 45 |
| 3420 | – | 50 c. multicoloured .. | 80 | 75 |

DESIGNS: 3 to 50 c. Various footballers.

**1989.** 30th Anniv of National Revolutionary Police.

| | | | | |
|---|---|---|---|---|
| 3422 | **942** | 5 c. multicoloured .. | 10 | 10 |

**943** "Zodiac" Rocket and 1934 Australian Cover

**1989.** Cosmonautics Day. Rocket Post (1st series). Multicoloured.

| | | | |
|---|---|---|---|
| 3423 | 1 c. Type **943** .. .. | 10 | 10 |
| 3424 | 3 c. Rocket and cover from India to Poland, 1934 .. .. .. | 10 | 10 |
| 3425 | 5 c. Rocket and 1934 English cover .. .. | 10 | 10 |
| 3426 | 10 c. "Icarus" rocket and 1935 Dutch cover .. | 15 | 10 |
| 3427 | 40 c. "La Douce France" rocket and 1935 French cover .. .. .. | 65 | 60 |
| 3428 | 50 c. Rocket and 1939 Cuban cover .. .. | 80 | 75 |

See also Nos. 3516/21.

**1989.** Stamp Day. As T **811**. Details of mural by R. R. Radillo in Havana Stamp Museum. Multicoloured.

| | | | |
|---|---|---|---|
| 3429 | 30 c. Mail coach .. .. | 50 | 45 |
| 3430 | 50 c. 18th-century sailing packet .. .. | 1·25 | 80 |

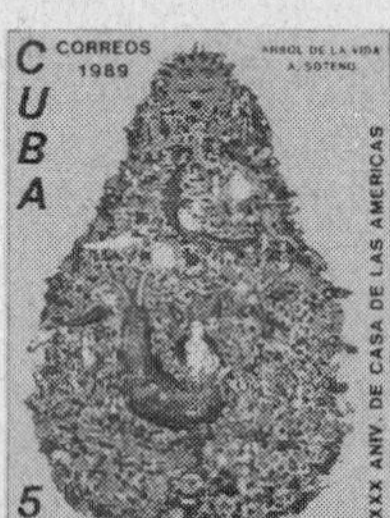

**944** "Tree of Life" (A. Soteno)

**1989.** 30th Anniv of "House of the Americas" Museum, Havana.

| | | | | |
|---|---|---|---|---|
| 3431 | **944** | 5 c. multicoloured .. | 10 | 10 |

**946** Coded Envelope

**1989.** Post Codes.

| | | | | |
|---|---|---|---|---|
| 3433 | **946** | 5 c. multicoloured .. | 10 | 10 |

**947** Tobacco Flowers

**948** Signing Decree

**1989.** Mothers' Day. Perfumes and Flowers. Multicoloured.

| | | | |
|---|---|---|---|
| 3434 | 1 c. Type **947** .. .. | 10 | 10 |
| 3435 | 3 c. Violets .. .. | 10 | 10 |
| 3436 | 5 c. Mariposa .. .. | 10 | 10 |
| 3437 | 13 c. Roses .. .. | 20 | 15 |
| 3438 | 30 c. Jasmine .. .. | 50 | 45 |
| 3439 | 50 c. Orange-flower .. | 80 | 75 |

**1989.** 30th Anniv of Agrarian Reform Law.

| | | | | |
|---|---|---|---|---|
| 3440 | **948** | 5 c. multicoloured .. | 10 | 10 |

**949** "40" and Headquarters Building, Moscow

**1989.** 40th Anniv of Council for Mutual Economic Aid.

| | | | | |
|---|---|---|---|---|
| 3441 | **949** | 30 c. multicoloured .. | 50 | 45 |

**950** Tower of Juche Idea, Pyongyang

**1989.** 13th World Youth and Students' Festival, Pyongyang.

| | | | | |
|---|---|---|---|---|
| 3442 | **950** | 30 c. multicoloured .. | 50 | 45 |

**952** Toco Toucan

**1989.** "Brasiliana '89" Stamp Exhibition, Rio de Janeiro. Birds. Multicoloured.

| | | | |
|---|---|---|---|
| 3444 | 1 c. Type **952** .. .. | 15 | 10 |
| 3445 | 3 c. Chestnut-bellied heron .. .. .. | 15 | 10 |
| 3446 | 5 c. Scarlet ibis .. .. | 25 | 10 |
| 3447 | 10 c. White-winged trumpeter .. .. | 40 | 15 |
| 3448 | 35 c. Harpy eagle .. | 1·50 | 70 |
| 3449 | 50 c. Amazonian umbrellabird .. .. | 2·00 | 1·10 |

**953** "El Fenix"(galleon)

**1989.** Cuban Sailing Ships. Multicoloured.

| | | | |
|---|---|---|---|
| 3450 | 1 c. Type **953** .. .. | 10 | 10 |
| 3451 | 3 c. "Triunfo" (ship of the line) .. .. .. | 10 | 10 |
| 3452 | 5 c. "El Rayo" (ship of the line) .. .. | 10 | 10 |
| 3453 | 10 c. "San Carlos" (ship of the line) .. .. | 25 | 10 |
| 3454 | 30 c. "San Jose" (ship of the line) .. .. | 85 | 50 |
| 3455 | 50 c. "San Genaro" (ship of the line) .. .. | 1·40 | 85 |

**954** Carved Stone and Men in Dugout Canoe

**1989.** America. Pre-Columbian Cultures. Multicoloured.
3456 5 c. Type **954** .. .. 10 10
3457 20 c. Cave painters .. 30 25

**955** Domingo F. Sarmiento and "Govenia utriculata" (Argentina)

**1989.** Latin American History (4th series). Multicoloured.
3458 1 c. Type **955** .. .. 10 10
3459 1 c. Machado de Assis and "Laelia grandis" (Brazil) .. .. 10 10
3460 1 c. El Salvador 1892 1 p. Columbus stamp .. 10 10
3461 1 c. Jorge Isaacs and "Cattleya trianae" (Colombia) .. .. 10 10
3462 1 c. Alejo Carpentier and "Cochleanthes discolor" (Cuba) .. .. 10 10
3463 5 c. "Oxalis adenophylla" and Pablo Neruda (Chile) .. .. 10 10
3464 5 c. Pedro H. Urena and "Epidendrum fragrans" (Dominican Republic) 10 10
3465 5 c. El Salvador 1893 2 p. City of Isabela stamp 10 10
3466 5 c. Juan Montalvo and "Miltonia vexillaria" (Ecuador) .. .. 10 10
3467 5 c. "Odontoglossum rossii" and Miguel A. Asturias (Guatemala) 10 10
3468 10 c. "Laelia anceps" and Jose C. del Valle (Honduras) .. .. 15 10
3469 10 c. "Laelia ancepes alba" and Alfonso Reyes (Mexico) .. 15 10
3470 10 c. El Salvador 1893 5 p. Columbus Statue stamp 15 10
3471 10 c. "Brassavola acaulis" and Ruben Dario (Nicaragua) .. .. 15 10
3472 10 c. Belisario Porras and "Pescatorea cerina" (Panama) .. .. 15 10
3473 20 c. Ricardo Palma and "Coryanthes leucocorys" (Peru) .. .. 30 25
3474 20 c. Eugenio Maria de Hostos and "Guzmania berteroniana" (Puerto Rico) .. .. .. 30 25
3475 20 c. El Salvador 1893 10 p. Departure from Palos stamp .. .. 30 25
3476 20 c. "Cypella herbertii" and Jose E. Rodo (Uruguay) .. .. 30 25
3477 20 c. "Cattleya mossiae" and Romulo Gallegos (Venezuela) .. .. 30 25

**956** Cienfuegos and Flag

**1989.** 30th Anniv of Disappearance of Camilo Cienfuegos (revolutionary).
3478 **956** 5 c. multicoloured .. 10 10

## INDEX

Countries can be quickly located by referring to the index at the end of this volume.

**957** Church Tower

**1989.** 475th Anniv of Trinidad City.
3479 **957** 5 c. multicoloured .. 10 10

**958** "Outskirts of Niza" (E. Boudin)

**1989.** Paintings in National Museum. Mult.
3480 1 c. "Family Scene" (Antoine Faivre) .. 10 10
3481 2 c. "Flowers" (Emile J. H. Vernet) .. .. 10 10
3482 5 c. "Judgement of Paris" (Charles Le Brun) .. 10 10
3483 20 c. Type **958** .. .. 35 20
3484 30 c. "Portrait of Sarah Bernhardt" (G. J. V. Clairin) (36 × 46 mm) .. 40 35
3485 50 c. "Fishermen in Harbour" (C. J. Vernet) .. 90 60

**959** Archery

**1989.** 11th Pan-American Games, Havana (1st issue). Multicoloured.
3486 5 c. Type **959** .. .. 10 10
3487 5 c. Shooting .. .. 10 10
3488 5 c. Fencing .. .. 10 10
3489 5 c. Cycling .. .. 10 10
3490 5 c. Water polo .. .. 10 10
3491 20 c. Lawn tennis (vert) 25 20
3492 30 c. Swimming (vert) .. 40 35
3493 35 c. Diving (vert) .. 45 40
3494 40 c. Hockey .. .. 55 50
3495 50 c. Basketball (vert) .. 65 60
See also Nos. 3584/93 and 3621/30.

**960** Front Page

**1989.** Centenary of "Golden Age" (children's magazine compiled by Jose Marti).
3496 **960** 5 c. blue, black & red 10 10

**961** "Almendares" (paddle-steamer)

**1990.** 25th Anniv of Postal Museum. Mult.
3497 5 c. Type **961** .. .. 15 10
3498 30 c. Mail train .. .. 40 35

**962** Cave Painters

**1990.** 50th Anniv of Speleological Society.
3499 **962** 30 c. multicoloured .. 40 35

**963** Player No. 11 and Colosseum

**964** Baseball

**1990.** World Cup Football Championship, Italy. Multicoloured.
3500 5 c. Type **963** .. .. 10 10
3501 5 c. Player No. 10 .. 10 10
3502 5 c. Player No. 8 .. 10 10
3503 10 c. Goalkeeper .. 15 10
3504 30 c. Player No. 11 and arch .. .. .. 40 35
3505 50 c. Player .. .. 65 60

**1990.** Olympic Games, Barcelona (1992) (1st issue). Multicoloured.
3507 1 c. Type **964** .. .. 10 10
3508 4 c. Running .. .. 10 10
3509 5 c. Basketball .. .. 10 10
3510 10 c. Volleyball .. .. 15 10
3511 30 c. Wrestling (horiz) .. 40 35
3512 50 c. Boxing .. .. 65 60
See also Nos. 3604/9 and 3692/7.

**965** Tower of Babel, Dove and Globe

**1990.** 75th Esperanto Congress, Havana.
3514 **965** 30 c. multicoloured .. 40 35

**1990.** Cosmonautics Day. Rocket Post (2nd series). As T **943**. Multicoloured.
3516 1 c. 1932 Austrian Cover and "U12" rocket .. 10 10
3517 2 c. 1933 German cover, rocket and liner .. 10 10
3518 3 c. 1934 Netherlands cover, "NRB" rocket and windmill .. .. 10 10
3519 10 c. 1935 Belgian cover and rocket .. .. 15 10
3520 30 c. 1935 Yugoslavian cover and "JUG1" rocket .. .. .. 40 35
3521 50 c. 1936 U.S.A. cover and rocket .. .. 65 60

**1990.** Stamp Day. As T **811**. Showing details of mural by R. R. Radillo in Havana Stamp Museum. Multicoloured.
3522 30 c. Train leaving station 40 35
3523 50 c. De Havilland Comet 1 airplane .. 65 60

**967** Flag and Globe

**1990.** Centenary of Labour Day.
3524 **967** 5 c. multicoloured .. 10 10

**969** Hill and Penny Black

**1990.** 150th Anniv of the Penny Black. Mult.
3526 2 c. Type **969** .. .. 10 10
3527 3 c. Twopenny blue .. 10 10
3528 5 c. G.B. 1855 4d. stamp 10 10
3529 10 c. G.B. 1847 1s. embossed stamp .. 15 10
3530 30 c. G.B. paid hand-stamp .. .. .. 40 35
3531 50 c. Twopenny blues on cover to Malta .. 65 60

**970** Celia Sanchez (after O. Yanes)

**1990.** 70th Birth Anniv of Celia Sanchez Manduley (revolutionary).
3532 **970** 5 c. multicoloured .. 10 10

**971** Flags and Ho Chi Minh

**1990.** Birth Centenary of Ho Chi Minh (Vietnamese leader).
3533 **971** 50 c. multicoloured .. 65 60

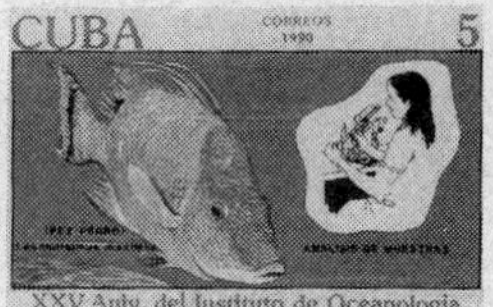


**972** Hogfish and Sample Analysis

**1990.** 25th Anniv of Oceanology Institute. Multicoloured.
3534 5 c. Type **972** .. .. 10 10
3535 30 c. "Arrecife coralino" and research vessel .. 60 35
3536 50 c. Lobster and diver collecting samples .. 65 60

**973** "Banara minutiflora"

**974** Windsurfing

**1990.** 5th Latin American Botanical Congress. Multicoloured.
3537 3 c. Type **973** .. .. 10 10
3538 5 c. "Oplonia nannophylla" .. .. .. 10 10
3539 10 c. "Jacquinia brunnescens" .. .. .. 15 10
3540 30 c. "Rondeletia brachycarpa" .. .. .. 40 35
3541 50 c. "Rondeletia odorata" .. .. 65 60

**1990.** Tourist Sports. Multicoloured.
3542 5 c. Type **974** .. .. 15 10
3543 10 c. Underwater fishing (horiz) .. .. .. 15 10
3544 30 c. Sea fishing (horiz) .. 40 35
3545 40 c. Shooting .. .. 55 50

**975** "The Flute of Pan" (detail)

**1990.** Paintings by A. G. Menocal in National Museum. Multicoloured.

3546 5 c. Type **975** .. .. 10 10
3547 20 c. "Shepherd" .. .. 25 20
3548 50 c. "Ganymede" .. .. 65 60
3549 1 p. "Venus Anadiomena" 1·50 1·10

**976** Great Crested Grebe

**1990.** "New Zealand 90" International Stamp Exhibition, Auckland. Birds. Multicoloured.

3551 2 c. Type **976** .. .. 10 10
3552 3 c. Weka rail .. .. 10 10
3553 5 c. Kea .. .. .. 10 10
3554 10 c. Bush wren .. .. 25 15
3555 30 c. Grey butcher bird .. 75 55
3556 50 c. Tui .. .. .. 1·25 1·00

**977** Lighthouse

**1990.** 8th U.N.O. Congress on Crime Prevention and Treatment of Delinquents.

3558 **977** 50 c. red, blue & silver 65 60

**978** Caravel and Shoreline

**1990.** America. The Natural World. Mult.

3559 5 c. Type **978** .. .. 15 10
3560 20 c. Christopher Columbus and native village .. .. 25 20

**979** Cameraman

**1990.** 40th Anniv of Cuban Television.

3561 **979** 5 c. multicoloured .. 10 10

**980** Station and Steam Locomotive

**1990.** 30th Anniv of Nationalization of Railways.

3562 **980** 50 c. multicoloured .. 65 60

**981** Flag and Couple (Argentina)

**1990.** Latin-American History (5th series). Multicoloured.

3563 1 c. Type **981** .. .. 10 10
3564 1 c. Flag and couple (Bolivia) .. .. 10 10
3565 1 c. Argentina 1892 5 c. Discovery of America stamp .. .. .. 10 10
3566 1 c. Flag and couple (Colombia) .. .. 10 10
3567 1 c. Flag and couple (Costa Rica) .. .. 10 10
3568 5 c. Flag and couple (Cuba) .. .. 10 10
3569 5 c. Flag and couple (Chile) .. .. 10 10
3570 5 c. Dominican Republic 1900 ½ c. Columbus stamp .. .. .. 10 10
3571 5 c. Flag and couple (Ecuador) .. .. 10 10
3572 5 c. Flag and couple (El Salvador) .. .. 10 10
3573 10 c. Flag and couple (Guatemala) .. .. 15 10
3574 10 c. Flag and couple (Mexico) .. .. 15 10
3575 10 c. Puerto Rico 1893 3 c. Discovery of America stamp .. .. .. 25 10
3576 10 c. Flag and couple (Nicaragua) .. .. 15 10
3577 10 c. Flag and couple (Panama) .. .. 15 10
3578 20 c. Flag and couple (Paraguay) .. .. 30 20
3579 20 c. Flag and couple (Peru) .. .. .. 30 20
3580 20 c. El Salvador 1894 10 p. Columbus stamp 30 20
3581 20 c. Flag and couple (Puerto Rico) .. .. 30 20
3582 20 c. Flag and couple (Venezuela) .. .. 30 20

**982** Player **983** Boxing

**1990.** 11th World Pelota Championship.

3583 **982** 30 c. multicoloured .. 45 30

**1990.** 11th Pan-American Games, Havana (1991) (2nd issue). As T **959**. Multicoloured.

3584 5 c. Kayaking .. .. 10 10
3585 5 c. Rowing .. .. 10 10
3586 5 c. Yachting .. .. 15 10
3587 5 c. Judo .. .. 10 10
3588 5 c. Show jumping .. 10 10
3589 10 c. Table tennis .. 15 10
3590 20 c. Gymnastics (vert) .. 30 20
3591 30 c. Baseball (vert) .. 45 30
3592 35 c. Basketball (vert) .. 55 30
3593 50 c. Football (vert) .. 80 45

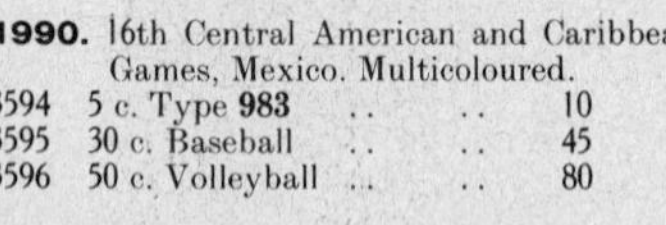

**1990.** 16th Central American and Caribbean Games, Mexico. Multicoloured.

3594 5 c. Type **983** .. .. 10 10
3595 30 c. Baseball .. .. 45 30
3596 50 c. Volleyball .. .. 80 45

**984** "Chioides marmorosa" **986** Long Jumping

**985** Guerra Aguiar and 1966 3 c. Stamp

**1991.** Butterflies. Multicoloured.

3597 2 c. Type **984** .. .. 10 10
3598 3 c. "Composia fidelissima" .. .. 10 10
3599 5 c. "Danaus plexippus" .. 10 10
3600 10 c. "Hypolimnas misippus" .. .. 15 10
3601 30 c. "Hypna iphigenia" .. 45 30
3602 50 c. "Hemiargus ammon" .. .. 80 45

**1991.** 1st Death Anniv of Jose Guerra Aguiar (founder of Cuban Postal Museum).

3603 **985** 5 c. multicoloured .. 10 10

**1991.** Olympic Games, Barcelona (1992) (2nd issue). Multicoloured.

3604 1 c. Type **986** .. .. 10 10
3605 2 c. Throwing the javelin 10 10
3606 3 c. Hockey .. .. 10 10
3607 5 c. Weightlifting .. 10 10
3608 40 c. Cycling .. .. 60 35
3609 50 c. Gymnastics .. 80 45

**987** Yury Gagarin and "Vostok" **988** Statue and Flag

**1991.** 30th Anniv of First Man in Space. Mult.

3611 5 c. Type **987** .. .. 10 10
3612 10 c. "Soyuz" and Y. Romanenko .. .. 15 10
3613 10 c. "Salyut" space station and A. Tamayo 15 10
3614 30 c. "Mir" space station (left half) .. .. 45 30
3615 30 c. "Mir" space station (right half) .. .. 45 30
3616 50 c. Launch of "Buran" space shuttle .. .. 80 45

Nos. 3612/13 and 3614/15 respectively were issued together, se-tenant, forming composite designs.

**1991.** 30th Anniversaries. Multicoloured.

3617 5 c. Type **988** (proclamation of Socialism) .. 10 10
3618 50 c. Playa Giron (invasion attempt by Cuban exiles) .. .. .. 1·25 55

**1991.** Stamp Day. Designs as T **811** showing details of mural by R. R. Radillo in Havana Stamp Museum. Multicoloured.

3619 30 c. Rocket (vert) .. 45 30
3620 50 c. Dish aerial .. 80 45

**1991.** 11th Pan-American Games, Havana (3rd series). As T **959**. Multicoloured.

3621 5 c. Volleyball (vert) .. 10 10
3622 5 c. Synchronized swimming (vert) .. .. 10 10
3623 5 c. Weightlifting (vert) 10 10
3624 5 c. Baseball (vert) .. 10 10
3625 5 c. Gymnastics (vert) .. 10 10
3626 10 c. Ten-pin bowling .. 15 10
3627 20 c. Boxing (vert) .. 30 20
3628 30 c. Running .. .. 45 30
3629 35 c. Wrestling .. .. 55 30
3630 50 c. Judo .. .. 80 45

**989** Simon Bolivar and Map

**1991.** 165th Anniv of Panama Congress.

3631 **989** 50 c. multicoloured .. 80 45

**990** Dirigible Balloon Design and Jean-Baptiste Meusnier

**1991.** "Espamer '91" Iberia–Latin America Stamp Exhibition, Buenos Aires. Airships. Multicoloured.

3632 5 c. Type **990** .. .. 10 10
3633 10 c. First steam-powered dirigible airship and Henri Giffard .. .. 20 10
3634 20 c. Paul Haenlein and first airship with gas-powered motor .. 35 20
3635 30 c. "Deutschland" (first airship with petrol motor) and Karl Wolfert .. .. 55 30
3636 50 c. David Schwarz and first rigid aluminium airship .. .. 95 45
3637 1 p. Ferdinand von Zeppelin and airship "Graf Zeppelin" .. 1·75 90

No. 3637 is inscr "Hindenberg".

**992** Cayo Largo

**1991.** Tourism. Multicoloured.

3645 20 c. Type **992** .. .. 40 20
3646 20 c. Varadero .. .. 40 20
3647 30 c. San Carlos de la Cabana Fortress (horiz) 45 30
3648 30 c. Castillo de los Tres Reyes del Morro (horiz) 45 30

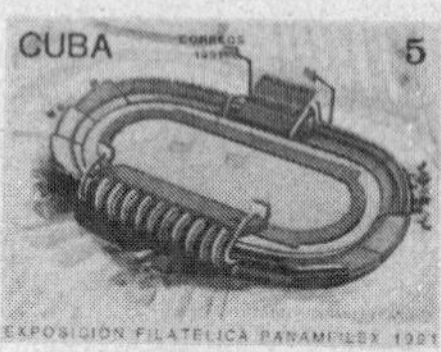


**993** Stadium

**1991.** "Panamfilex 1991" Pan-American Stamp Exhibition. Multicoloured.

3649 5 c. Type **993** .. .. 10 10
3650 20 c. Baragua swimming-pool complex .. .. 30 20
3651 30 c. Ramon Fonst hall .. 45 30
3652 50 c. Reynaldo Paseiro cycle-track .. .. 80 45

**994** "Kataoka Dengoemon Takafusa" (Utagawa Kuniyoshi)

**1991.** "Phila Nippon '91" International Stamp Exhibition, Tokyo. Multicoloured.

3654 5 c. Type **994** .. .. 10 10
3655 10 c. "Night Walk" (Hosoda Eishi) .. 15 10
3656 20 c. "Courtesans" (Torii Kiyonaga) .. .. 30 15
3657 30 c. "Conversation" (Kitagawa Utamaro) .. 45 25
3658 50 c. "Inari-bashi Bridge" (Ando Hiroshige) .. 1·25 55
3659 1 p. "On the Terrace" (Torii Kiyonaga) .. 1·50 90

996 Statue of Jose Marti

**1991.** 4th Cuban Communist Party Congress.
3661 996 5 c. multicolouredl . . 10 10
3662 – 50 c. black, blue & red . . 80 45
DESIGN: 50 c. Party emblem.

997 Christopher Columbus and Pinzon Brothers

**1991.** America. Voyages of Discovery. Mult.
3663 5 c. Type **997** . . . . 10 10
3664 20 c. "Santa Maria", "Nina" and "Pinta" . . 60 20

998 Marti (after F. Martinez)

**1991.** Centenary of Publication of "The Simple Verses" by Jose Marti.
3665 998 50 c. multicoloured . . 80 45

999 Julian Aguirre and Charango (Argentina)

**1991.** Latin-American History (6th series). Music. Multicoloured.
3666 1 c. Type **999** . . . . 10 10
3667 1 c. Eduardo Caba and antara (pipes) (Bolivia) 10 10
3668 1 c. Chile 1853 10 c. stamp 10 10
3669 1 c. Heitor Villalobos and trumpet with gourd resonator (Brazil) . . 10 10
3670 1 c. Guillermo Uribe-Holguin and cununo macho (drum) (Colombia) . . . . 10 10
3671 5 c. Claves (sticks) and Miguel Failde (Cuba) . . 10 10
3672 5 c. Enrique Soro and Araucanian kultrum (Chile) . . . . 10 10
3673 5 c. Chile 1903 10 c. on 30 c. stamp . . . . 10 10
3674 5 c. Rondador (xylophone) and Segundo L. Moreno (Ecuador) . . 10 10
3675 5 c. Marimba and Ricardo Castillo (Guatemala) . . 10 10
3676 10 c. Vihuela and Carlos Chavez (Mexico) . . 15 10
3677 10 c. Luis A. Delgadillo and maracas (Nicaragua) . . . . 15 10
3678 10 c. Chile 1906 2 c. stamp 15 10
3679 10 c. Alfredo de Saint-Malo and mejorana (Panama) . . . . 15 10
3680 10 c. Jose Asuncion Flores and harp (Paraguay) . . 15 10
3681 20 c. Daniel Alomia and quena (flute) (Peru) . . 30 15
3682 20 c. Cuatro (guitar) and Juan Morell y Campos (Puerto Rico) . . . . 30 15
3683 20 c. Chile 1905 10 c. stamp . . . . . . 30 15
3684 20 c. Eduardo Fabini and tamboril (drums) (Uruguay) . . . . 30 15
3685 20 c. Cuatro (guitar) and Juan V. Lecuna (Venezuela) . . . . 30 15

1000 Mascot

**1991.** 1st Jose Marti Pioneers Congress.
3686 1000 5 p. multicoloured . . 10 10

1001 Toussaint L'Ouverture (revolutionary leader)

**1991.** Bicentenary of Haitian Revolution.
3687 1001 50 c. multicoloured . . 80 45

1002 "35", Stars and Soldier

**1991.** 35th Anniversaries. Multicoloured.
3688 5 c. Type **1002** (Revolutionary Armed Forces) 10 10
3689 50 c. Launch "Granma" (disembarkation of revolutionary forces) (vert) . . . . . . 1·25 60

1003 Agramonte (after F. Martinez)

**1991.** 150th Birth Anniv of Ignacio Agramonte (poet).
3690 1003 5 c. multicoloured . . 10 10

1005 Table Tennis and Plan of Montjuic Complex

**1992.** Olympic Games, Barcelona (3rd issue). Multicoloured.
3692 3 c. Type **1005** . . . . 10 10
3693 5 c. Handball and Vall d'Hebron complex . . 10 10
3694 10 c. Shooting and Badalona complex . . 15 10
3695 20 c. Long jumping and Montjuic complex (vert) 35 20
3696 35 c. Judo and Diagonal complex . . . . 60 35
3697 50 c. Fencing and Montjuic complex . . 85 50

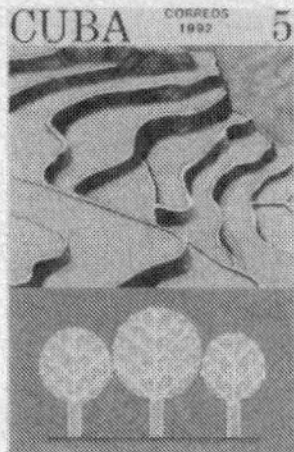


1006 Flooded Terraces and Dead Trees

**1992.** Environmental Protection. Mult.
3699 5 c. Type **1006** . . . . 10 10
3700 20 c. Whale and dead fish in polluted sea . . 35 20
3701 35 c. Satellite picture of ozone levels over Antarctica and gas mask in polluted air . . 60 35
3702 40 c. Rainbows, globe, doves and nuclear explosion . . . . 70 40

1007 "Holacanthus isabelita"

**1992.** Fishes. Multicoloured.
3703 5 c. Type **1007** . . . . 10 10
3704 10 c. Jackknife . . . . 15 10
3705 20 c. "Acanthurus coeruleus" . . . . 35 20
3706 30 c. Sergeant-major . . 50 30
3707 50 c. Yellow damselfish . . 85 50

1008 Boxer

**1992.** Dogs. Multicoloured.
3708 5 c. Type **1008** . . . . 10 10
3709 10 c. Great dane . . 15 10
3710 20 c. German shepherd . . 35 20
3711 30 c. Short-haired, long-haired and wire-haired dachshunds . . . . 50 30
3712 35 c. Dobermann . . 60 35
3713 40 c. Fox terrier . . . . 70 40
3714 50 c. Poodle . . . . 85 50

1009 Badge

**1992.** 30th Anniv and Sixth Congress of Youth Communist League.
3716 1009 5 c. multicoloured . . 10 10

1010 Jose Marti

**1992.** Cent of Cuban Revolutionary Party.
3717 1010 5 c. multicoloured . . 10 10
3718 50 c. multicoloured 85 50

1011 Columbus Sighting Land

**1992.** America. 500th Anniv of Discovery of America by Columbus. Multicoloured.
3719 5 c. Type **1011** . . . . 15 10
3720 20 c. Columbus landing at San Salvador . . . . 55 20

1012 Alhambra, Sierra Nevada

**1992.** "Granada 92" International Philatelic Exhibition. Designs showing views of the Alhambra. Multicoloured.
3721 5 c. Type **1012** . . . . 10 10
3722 10 c. Sunset . . . . 15 10
3723 20 c. Doorway and arches 35 20
3724 30 c. Courtyard of the Lions . . . . . . 50 30
3725 35 c. Bedroom . . . . 60 35
3726 50 c. View of Albaicin from balcony . . . . 85 50

1013 Facade and Plate

**1992.** 50th Anniv of La Bodeguita del Medio (restaurant).
3727 1013 50 c. multicoloured . . 85 50

1014 "Cattleya hibrida"

**1992.** 40th Anniv of Soroa Orchid Garden. Multicoloured.
3728 3 c. Type **1014** . . . . 10 10
3729 5 c. "Phalaenopsis sp." . . 10 10
3730 10 c. "Cattleyopsis lindenii" . . . . 15 10
3731 30 c. "Bletia purpurea" . . 50 30
3732 35 c. "Oncidium luridum" 60 35
3733 40 c. "Vanda hibrida" . . 70 40

1015 Hummingbird

**1992.** The Bee Hummingbird. Multicoloured.
3734 5 c. Type **1015** . . . . 10 10
3735 10 c. Perched on twig . . 15 10
3736 20 c. Perched on twig with flowers . . . . 35 20
3737 30 c. Hovering over flower 50 30

**1016** Guardalavaca Beach

**1992.** Tourism. Multicoloured.

| | | | |
|---|---|---|---|
| 3738 | 10 c. Type **1016** | 20 | 10 |
| 3739 | 20 c. Hotel Bucanero | 45 | 25 |
| 3740 | 30 c. View of Havana | 70 | 35 |
| 3741 | 50 c. Varadero beach | 1·10 | 65 |

**1017** Eligio Sardinas

**1992.** "Olymphilex '92" International Olympic Stamps Exhibition, Barcelona. Designs showing Cuban sportsmen. Mult.

| | | | |
|---|---|---|---|
| 3742 | 5 c. Type **1017** | 10 | 10 |
| 3743 | 35 c. Ramon Fonst (fencer) | 60 | 35 |
| 3744 | 40 c. Sergio "Pipian" Martinez (cyclist) | 70 | 40 |
| 3745 | 50 c. Martin Dihigo (baseball player) | 85 | 50 |

**1019** Alvarez Cabral

**1992.** "Genova '92" International Thematic Stamp Exhibition. Explorers and their ships. Multicoloured.

| | | | |
|---|---|---|---|
| 3747 | 5 c. Type **1019** | 10 | 10 |
| 3748 | 10 c. Alonso Pinzon | 20 | 10 |
| 3749 | 20 c. Alonso de Ojeda | 45 | 25 |
| 3750 | 30 c. Amerigo Vespucci | 65 | 35 |
| 3751 | 35 c. Henry the Navigator | 75 | 40 |
| 3752 | 40 c. Bartolomeu Dias | 90 | 45 |

**1020** High Jumping

**1992.** 6th World Athletics Cup, Havana. Mult.

| | | | |
|---|---|---|---|
| 3754 | 5 c. Type **1020** | 10 | 10 |
| 3755 | 20 c. Throwing the javelin | 35 | 20 |
| 3756 | 30 c. Throwing the hammer | 50 | 30 |
| 3757 | 40 c. Long jumping (vert) | 70 | 40 |
| 3758 | 50 c. Hurdling (vert) | 85 | 50 |

**1021** Men's High Jump (Gold) and Women's Discus (Gold)

**1992.** Cuban Olympic Games Medal Winners. Multicoloured.

| | | | |
|---|---|---|---|
| 3760 | 5 c. Type **1021** | 10 | 10 |
| 3761 | 5 c. Men's 4×400 m relay (silver) and men's discus (bronze) | 10 | 10 |
| 3762 | 5 c. Men's 4×100 m relay and women's high jump and 800 m (bronze) | 10 | 10 |
| 3763 | 20 c. Baseball (gold) | 35 | 20 |
| 3764 | 20 c. Boxing (7 gold and 2 silver) | 35 | 20 |
| 3765 | 20 c. Women's volleyball (gold) | 35 | 20 |
| 3766 | 50 c. Men's judo (bronze) and women's judo (gold, silver and 2 bronze) | 85 | 50 |
| 3767 | 50 c. Greco-roman (gold and 2 bronze) and freestyle (gold and bronze) wrestling | 85 | 50 |
| 3768 | 50 c. Fencing (silver, bronze) and weight-lifting (silver) | 85 | 50 |

**1022** Christopher Columbus and Queen Isabella the Catholic

**1992.** Latin-American History (7th series). Multicoloured.

| | | | |
|---|---|---|---|
| 3769 | 1 c. Type **1022** | 10 | 10 |
| 3770 | 1 c. Columbus at Rabida Monastery | 10 | 10 |
| 3771 | 1 c. Columbus presenting plans to King Ferdinand and Queen Isabella | 10 | 10 |
| 3772 | 1 c. Columbus before Salamanca Council | 10 | 10 |
| 3773 | 1 c. Departure from Palos | 10 | 10 |
| 3774 | 5 c. Fleet stopping off at Canary Islands | 10 | 10 |
| 3775 | 5 c. Columbus reassuring crew | 10 | 10 |
| 3776 | 5 c. Sighting of land | 10 | 10 |
| 3777 | 5 c. Columbus landing | 10 | 10 |
| 3778 | 5 c. Columbus's encounter with Amerindians | 10 | 10 |
| 3779 | 10 c. "Santa Maria" grounded off Hispaniola | 15 | 10 |
| 3780 | 10 c. Arrival of "Nina" at Palos | 15 | 10 |
| 3781 | 10 c. Columbus's procession through Barcelona | 15 | 10 |
| 3782 | 10 c. Columbus before King and Queen | 15 | 10 |
| 3783 | 10 c. Departure from Cadiz on second voyage | 15 | 10 |
| 3784 | 20 c. King and Queen welcoming Columbus | 35 | 20 |
| 3785 | 20 c. Fleet leaving on third voyage | 35 | 20 |
| 3786 | 20 c. Columbus's deportation in chains from Hispaniola | 35 | 20 |
| 3787 | 20 c. Fleet embarking on fourth voyage | 35 | 20 |
| 3788 | 20 c. Death of Columbus at Valladolid | 35 | 20 |

**1023** Chacon

**1024** Sanctuary of Our Lady of Charity, Cobre

**1992.** Birth Centenary of Jose Maria Chacon y Calvo (historian).

| | | | |
|---|---|---|---|
| 3789 | **1023** 30 c. multicoloured | 50 | 30 |

**1992.** Churches. Multicoloured.

| | | | |
|---|---|---|---|
| 3790 | 5 c. Type **1024** | 10 | 10 |
| 3791 | 20 c. St. Mary's Church, Rosario | 35 | 20 |
| 3792 | 30 c. Church of the Holy Spirit, Havana | 50 | 30 |
| 3793 | 50 c. Guardian of the Holy Angel Church, Pena Pobre, Havana | 85 | 50 |

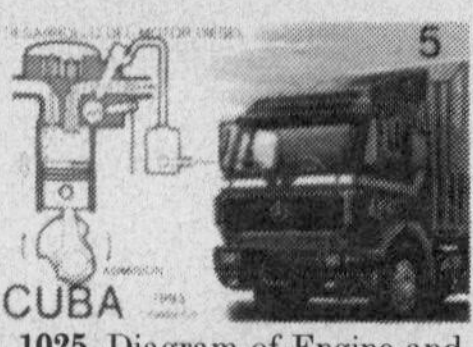


**1025** Diagram of Engine and Truck

**1993.** Development of Diesel Engine. Each showing an engine at a different stage of cycle. Multicoloured.

| | | | |
|---|---|---|---|
| 3794 | 5 c. Type **1025** | 10 | 10 |
| 3795 | 10 c. Motor car | 15 | 10 |
| 3796 | 30 c. Tug | 50 | 30 |
| 3797 | 40 c. Locomotive | 70 | 40 |
| 3798 | 50 c. Tractor | 85 | 50 |

**1026** Player

**1993.** Davis Cup Men's Team Tennis Championship. Designs showing tennis players. Multicoloured.

| | | | |
|---|---|---|---|
| 3800 | 5 c. Type **1026** | 10 | 10 |
| 3801 | 20 c. Double-handed back-hand | 35 | 20 |
| 3802 | 30 c. Serve | 55 | 30 |
| 3803 | 35 c. Stretched forehand (horiz) | 60 | 35 |
| 3804 | 40 c. Returning drop shot (horiz) | 70 | 40 |

**1027** Pedro Emilio Roux

**1993.** Scientists. Multicoloured.

| | | | |
|---|---|---|---|
| 3806 | 3 c. Type **1027** (bacteriologist) | 10 | 10 |
| 3807 | 5 c. Carlos Finlay (biologist) | 10 | 10 |
| 3808 | 10 c. Ivan Petrovich Pavlov (physiologist) | 20 | 10 |
| 3809 | 20 c. Louis Pasteur (chemist) | 35 | 20 |
| 3810 | 30 c. Santiago Ramon y Cajal (histologist) | 55 | 30 |
| 3811 | 35 c. Sigmund Freud (psychiatrist) | 60 | 35 |
| 3812 | 40 c. Wilhelm Roentgen (physicist) | 70 | 40 |
| 3813 | 50 c. Joseph Lister (surgeon) | 90 | 50 |

**1028** Bicycle Design by Leonardo da Vinci

**1993.** Bicycles. Multicoloured.

| | | | |
|---|---|---|---|
| 3815 | 3 c. Type **1028** | 10 | 10 |
| 3816 | 5 c. Draisiana hobby-horse | 10 | 10 |
| 3817 | 10 c. Michaux boneshaker | 20 | 10 |
| 3818 | 20 c. Starley penny-farthing | 35 | 20 |
| 3819 | 30 c. Lawson "Safety" bicycle | 55 | 30 |
| 3820 | 35 c. Modern bicycle | 60 | 35 |

**1029** "Valencian Fishwives"

**1993.** Paintings by Joaquin Sorolla in the National Museum. Multicoloured.

| | | | |
|---|---|---|---|
| 3821 | 3 c. "Child eating Melon" (vert) | 10 | 10 |
| 3822 | 5 c. Type **1029** | 10 | 10 |
| 3823 | 10 c. "Regatta" | 20 | 10 |
| 3824 | 20 c. "Peasant Girl" | 35 | 20 |
| 3825 | 40 c. "Summertime" | 70 | 40 |
| 3826 | 50 c. "By the Sea" | 90 | 50 |

**1030** "Four Winds" and Statue of Barberan and Collar

**1993.** 60th Anniv of Seville (Spain)–Camaguey (Cuba) Flight by Mariano Barberan and Joaquin Collar.

| | | | |
|---|---|---|---|
| 3827 | **1030** 30 c. multicoloured | 40 | 20 |

**1031** Northern Jacana

**1993.** "Brasiliana '93" International Stamp Exn, Rio de Janeiro. Water Birds. Mult.

| | | | |
|---|---|---|---|
| 3828 | 3 c. Type **1031** | 10 | 10 |
| 3829 | 5 c. Great blue heron (27×44 mm) | 10 | 10 |
| 3830 | 10 c. Black-necked stilt | 20 | 10 |
| 3831 | 20 c. Black-crowned night heron | 35 | 20 |
| 3832 | 30 c. Sandhill crane (27×44 mm) | 55 | 30 |
| 3833 | 50 c. Limpkin | 90 | 50 |

**1032** Fidel Castro and Text

**1993.** Anniversaries. Multicoloured.

| | | | |
|---|---|---|---|
| 3834 | 5 c. Type **1032** (40th anniv of publication of "History Will Absolve Me") | 10 | 10 |
| 3835 | 5 c. Jose Marti (140th birth anniv) and Rafael M. Mendive (vert) | 10 | 10 |
| 3836 | 5 c. Carlos M. de Cespedes and broken wheel (125th anniv of Yara Proclamation) | 10 | 10 |
| 3837 | 5 c. Moncada Barracks (40th anniv of attack on barracks) | 10 | 10 |

**1033** "Sedum allantoides"

**1034** Devillier's Swallowtail

**1993.** Cienfuegos Botanical Garden. Mult.

| | | | |
|---|---|---|---|
| 3838 | 3 c. Type **1033** | 10 | 10 |
| 3839 | 5 c. "Heliconia caribaea" | 10 | 10 |
| 3840 | 10 c. "Anthurium andraeanum" | 20 | 10 |
| 3841 | 20 c. "Pseudobombax ellipticum" | 35 | 20 |
| 3842 | 35 c. "Ixora coccinea" | 60 | 35 |
| 3843 | 50 c. "Callistemon specious" | 90 | 50 |

**1993.** "Bangkok 1993" International Stamp Exhibition. Butterflies. Multicoloured.

| | | | |
|---|---|---|---|
| 3844 | 3 c. Type **1034** | 10 | 10 |
| 3845 | 5 c. Giant brimstone | 10 | 10 |
| 3846 | 20 c. Great southern white | 25 | 15 |
| 3847 | 30 c. Buckeye | 35 | 20 |
| 3848 | 35 c. White peacock | 45 | 25 |
| 3849 | 50 c. African monarch | 60 | 35 |

**1035** Greater Flamingo

**1036** Simon Bolivar

**1993.** America. Endangered Animals. Mult.
3850 5 c. Type **1035** .. .. 10 10
3851 50 c. Roseate spoonbill .. 60 35

**1993.** Latin-American Integration. Mult.
3852 50 c. Type **1036** .. .. 60 35
3853 50 c. Jose Marti .. .. 60 35
3854 50 c. Benito Juarez .. 60 35
3855 50 c. Che Guevara .. 60 35
Nos. 3852/5 were issued together, se-tenant, forming a composite design.

**1037** Swimming

**1993.** 17th Central American and Caribbean Games, Ponce, Puerto Rico. Mult.
3856 5 c. Type **1037** .. .. 10 10
3857 10 c. Pole vaulting .. 10 10
3858 20 c. Boxing .. .. 25 15
3859 35 c. Gymnastics (parallel bars) (vert) .. .. 45 25
3860 50 c. Baseball (vert) .. 60 35

**1038** Grajales

**1039** Tchaikovsky

**1993.** Death Centenary of Mariana Grajales.
3862 **1038** 5 c. multicoloured .. 10 10

**1993.** Death Centenary of Pyotr Tchaikovsky (composer). Multicoloured.
3863 5 c. Type **1039** .. .. 10 10
3864 20 c. Ballerina in "Swan Lake" .. .. .. 25 15
3865 30 c. Statue of Tchaikovsky .. .. 35 20
3866 50 c. Tchaikovsky Museum (horiz) .. 60 35

**1040** Flag, Dove and Broken Chains

**1041** Players Challenging for Ball

**1994.** 35th Anniv of Revolution.
3867 **1040** 5 c. multicoloured .. 10 10

**1994.** World Cup Football Championship, U.S.A.
3868 **1041** 5 c. multicoloured .. 10 10
3869 – 20 c. multicoloured 25 15
3870 – 30 c. multicoloured 35 20
3871 – 35 c. multicoloured 45 25
3872 – 40 c. multicoloured 50 30
3873 – 50 c. multicoloured 60 35
DESIGNS: 20 c. to 50 c. Various footballing scenes.

**1042** Blue Persian

**1994.** Cats. Multicoloured.
3875 5 c. Type **1042** .. .. 10 10
3876 10 c. Havana .. .. 10 10
3877 20 c. Maine coon .. 25 15
3878 30 c. British blue shorthair .. .. 35 20
3879 35 c. Black and white bicolour Persian .. 45 25
3880 50 c. Golden Persian .. 60 35

**1043** Sage

**1994.** Medicinal Plants. Multicoloured.
3882 5 c. Type **1043** .. .. 10 10
3883 10 c. Aloe .. .. 10 10
3884 20 c. Sunflower .. .. 25 15
3885 30 c. False chamomile .. 35 20
3886 40 c. Pot marigold .. 50 30
3887 50 c. Large-leaved lime .. 60 35

**1044** London Public Transport, 1860

**1994.** Carriages. Multicoloured.
3888 5 c. Type **1044** .. .. 10 10
3889 10 c. Coach of King Fernando VII and Maria Luisa of Spain .. 10 10
3890 30 c. French Louis XV style coach .. .. 35 20
3891 35 c. Queen Isabel II of Spain's gala-day coach 45 25
3892 40 c. Empress Catherine II of Russia's summer carriage .. .. 50 30
3893 50 c. Havana cab (68 × 27 mm) .. .. 60 35

**1045** Caribbean Edible Oyster

**1994.** Aquaculture. Multicoloured.
3894 5 c. Type **1045** .. .. 10 10
3895 20 c. "Cardisoma guanhumi" (crab) .. 25 15
3896 30 c. Tilapia .. .. 35 20
3897 35 c. "Hippospongia lachne" (sponge) .. 45 25
3898 40 c. "Panulirus argus" (crustacean) .. .. 50 30
3899 50 c. Mirror carp .. 60 35

**1046** Ancient Greek Athletes and Olympic Flag

**1994.** Centenary of International Olympic Committee Multicoloured.
3900 5 c. Type **1046** .. .. 10 10
3901 30 c. Olympic flag and world map in Olympic colours .. .. 35 20
3902 50 c. Olympic flag and flame .. .. .. 60 35

**1047** Michael Faraday (discoverer of electricity)

**1994.** Scientists. Multicoloured.
3903 5 c. Type **1047** .. .. 10 10
3904 10 c. Marie Sklodowska-Curie (co-discoverer of radium) .. .. 10 10
3905 20 c. Pierre Curie (co-discoverer of radium) .. .. 25 15
3906 30 c. Albert Einstein (formulated Theory of Relativity) .. .. 35 20
3907 40 c. Max Planck (physicist) .. .. 50 30
3908 50 c. Otto Hahn (chemist) 60 35

**1048** "Opuntia dillenii"

**1994.** Cacti. Multicoloured.
3909 5 c. Type **1048** .. .. 10 10
3910 10 c. "Opuntia millspaughii" (vert) .. 10 10
3911 30 c. "Leptocereus santamarinae" .. 35 20
3912 35 c. "Pereskia marcanoi" 45 25
3913 40 c. "Dendrocereus nudiflorus" (vert) .. 50 30
3914 50 c. "Pilocereus robinii" 60 35

**1050** Rough Collies

**1994.** Dogs. Multicoloured.
3916 5 c. Type **1050** .. .. 10 10
3917 20 c. American cocker spaniels .. .. 25 15
3918 30 c. Dalmatians .. 35 20
3919 40 c. Afghan hounds .. 50 30
3920 50 c. English cocker spaniels .. .. 60 35

**1051** "Carpilius corallinus" (crab)

**1994.** Cayo Largo. Multicoloured.
3921 15 c. Type **1051** .. .. 20 10
3922 65 c. Shore and Cayman Islands ground iguana (vert) .. .. .. 80 45
3923 75 c. House and brown pelican .. .. 95 55
3924 1 p. Fence and common green turtle .. .. 1·25 75

**HAVE YOU READ THE NOTES AT THE BEGINNING OF THIS CATALOGUE?**
These often provide answers to the enquiries we receive.

**1052** Cienfuegos

**1994.** 35th Anniv of Disappearance of Camilo Cienfuegos (revolutionary).
3925 **1052** 15 c. multicoloured .. 20 10

**1053** Grouper

**1994.** Caribbean Animals. Multicoloured.
3926 10 c. Type **1053** .. .. 15 10
3927 15 c. Spotted duck-billed ray (vert) .. .. 20 10
3928 15 c. Indo-Pacific sailfish 20 10
3929 15 c. Greater flamingoes (vert) .. .. .. 20 10
3930 65 c. Bottle-nosed dolphin 85 50
3931 65 c. Brown pelican (vert) 85 50

**1054** Douglas DC-3

**1994.** 50th Anniv of I.C.A.O.
3932 **1054** 65 c. multicoloured .. 85 50

**1055** Bronze Statues of Deer

**1994.** 55th Anniv of Havana Zoo. Mult.
3933 15 c. Type **1055** .. .. 20 10
3934 65 c. Green-winged macaw 85 50
3935 75 c. Goldfinch .. .. 95 55

**1056** Boy with Stockbook

**1994.** 30th Anniv of Cuban Philatelic Federation.
3936 **1056** 15 c. multicoloured .. 20 10

**1057** Anole

**1994.** Reptiles. Multicoloured.
3937 15 c. Type **1057** .. .. 20 10
3938 65 c. Dwarf gecko .. 85 50
3939 75 c. Curly-tailed lizard 95 55
3940 85 c. Dwarf gecko (different) .. .. 1·10 65
3941 90 c. Anole .. .. 1·10 65
3942 1 p. Dwarf gecko (different) .. .. 1·25 75

1058 Cover and Spanish Mail Packet (18-century sea mail)

1059 Cover of "Postal History of Cuba" by Jose Guerra Aguiar

**1994.** America. Postal Transport. Mult.
3943 15 c. Type **1058** .. .. 20 10
3944 65 c. Cover and messenger on horseback (19th-century rebel post) (horiz) .. .. 85 50

**1995.** 30th Anniv of Postal Museum.
3945 **1059** 15 c. multicoloured .. 20 10

1060 Jose Marti and Flag

**1995.** Centenary of War of Independence.
3946 **1060** 15 c. multicoloured .. 20 10

1061 Boxing

1063 1855 Cuba and Puerto Rico ½ r. Stamp

1062 Siboney Cow

**1995.** 12th Pan-American Games, Mar del Plata, Argentina. Multicoloured.
3947 10 c. Type **1061** .. .. 15 10
3948 15 c. Weightlifting .. 20 10
3949 65 c. Volleyball .. 85 50
3950 75 c. Wrestling (horiz) .. 95 55
3951 85 c. Baseball (horiz) .. 1·10 65
3952 90 c. High jumping (horiz) 1·10 65

**1995.** 50th Anniv of F.A.O.
3953 **1062** 75 c. multicoloured .. 95 55

**1995.** Postal Anniversaries.
3954 **1063** 15 c. blue and black 20 10
3955 – 65 c. multicoloured 85 50
DESIGNS: 15 c. Type **1063** (140th anniv of first Cuban postage stamp); 65 c. Colonial-style letterbox and letter (140th anniv of domestic postal service).

1064 Queen Angel Fish

**1995.** 35th Anniv of National Aquarium. Mult.
3956 10 c. Type **1064** .. .. 15 10
3957 15 c. Vaca .. .. 20 10
3958 65 c. Porkfish .. .. 85 50
3959 75 c. Hawkfish .. .. 95 55
3960 85 c. Angel fish .. .. 1·10 65
3961 90 c. Surgeon fish .. 1·10 65

1065 Portrait of Marti and Death Scene

**1995.** Death Centenary of Jose Marti (revolutionary). Multicoloured.
3962 15 c. Type **1065** .. .. 20 10
3963 65 c. Marti and Maximo Gomez in boat .. 85 50
3964 75 c. Marti and Montecristi Declaration 95 55
3965 85 c. Marti, Antonio Maceo and Gomez .. 1·10 65
3966 90 c. Mausoleum and casket (vert) .. .. 1·10 65

1066 Maceo

**1995.** Centenary of Battle of Peralejo and 150th Birth Anniv of Antonio Maceo (revolutionary).
3967 **1066** 15 c. multicoloured .. 20 10

1067 Gulf Fritillary

**1995.** Butterflies. Multicoloured.
3968 10 c. Type **1067** .. .. 15 10
3969 15 c. "Eunica tatila" .. 20 10
3970 65 c. "Melete salacia" .. 85 50
3971 75 c. Cuban clearwing .. 95 55
3972 85 c. Palmira sulphur .. 1·10 65
3973 90 c. Cloudless sulphur .. 1·10 65

1068 Supermarine Spitfire (Great Britain)

**1995.** Second World War Combat Planes. Multicoloured.
3974 10 c. Type **1068** .. .. 15 10
3975 15 c. Ilyushin Il-2 (Russia) 20 10
3976 65 c. Curtiss P-40 (United States) .. .. 85 50
3977 75 c. Messerschmitt ME-109 (Germany) .. 95 55
3978 85 c. Morane Saulnier 406 (France) .. .. 1·10 65

1069 Lecuona

1070 Horse in Stable

**1995.** Birth Centenary of Ernesto Lecuona (composer).
3979 **1069** 15 c. multicoloured .. 20 10

**1995.** "Singapore'95" International Stamp Exhibition. Arab Horses. Multicoloured.
3980 10 c. Type **1070** .. .. 15 10
3981 15 c. Two greys (horiz) .. 20 10
3982 65 c. Tethered horse .. 85 50
3983 75 c. Horse in field .. 95 55
3984 85 c. Mare and foal .. 1·10 65
3985 90 c. Grey galloping in field .. .. 1·10 65

1072 Wrestling

**1995.** Olympic Games, Atlanta (1996) (1st issue). Multicoloured.
3987 10 c. Type **1072** .. .. 15 10
3988 15 c. Weightlifting .. 20 10
3989 65 c. Volleyball .. .. 85 50
3990 75 c. Running .. .. 95 55
3991 85 c. Baseball .. .. 1·10 65
3992 90 c. Judo .. .. 1·10 65
See also Nos. 4044/8.

1073 Acana Factory

**1995.** 400th Anniv of Sugar Production in Cuba. Paintings by Eduardo Laplante. Multicoloured.
3994 15 c. Type **1073** .. .. 20 10
3995 65 c. Manaca factory .. 85 50

1074 Flag and Anniversary Emblem

**1995.** 50th Anniv of U.N.O.
3996 **1074** 65 c. multicoloured .. 85 50

1075 Lion

1076 St. Clare of Assisi's Convent

**1995.** Animals from Havana Zoological Gardens. Multicoloured.
3997 10 c. Type **1075** .. .. 15 10
3998 15 c. Grevy's zebra (horiz) 20 10
3999 65 c. Orang-utan .. 85 50
4000 75 c. Indian elephant (horiz) .. .. 95 55
4001 85 c. Eurasian red squirrel (horiz) .. .. 1·10 65
4002 90 c. Common racoon (horiz) .. .. 1·10 65

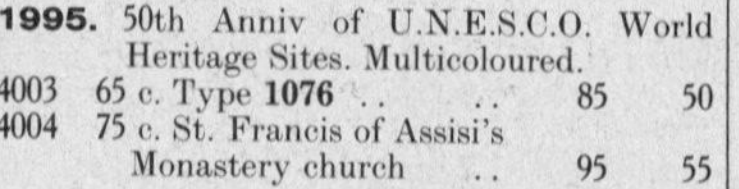

**1995.** 50th Anniv of U.N.E.S.C.O. World Heritage Sites. Multicoloured.
4003 65 c. Type **1076** .. .. 85 50
4004 75 c. St. Francis of Assisi's Monastery church .. 95 55

1077 "Bletia patula"

1078 Greta Garbo

**1995.** Orchids. Multicoloured.
4005 40 c. Type **1077** .. .. 50 30
4006 45 c. "Galeandra beyrichii" .. .. 60 35
4007 50 c. "Vanilla dilloniana" 65 35
4008 65 c. "Macradenia lutescens" .. .. 85 50
4009 75 c. "Oncidium luridum" 95 55
4010 85 c. "Ionopsis utricularioides" .. 1·10 65

**1995.** Centenary of Motion Pictures. Designs showing film stars (except 4015). Mult.
4011 15 c. Type **1078** .. .. 20 10
4012 15 c. Marlene Dietrich .. 20 10
4013 15 c. Marilyn Monroe .. 20 10
4014 15 c. Charlie Chaplin .. 20 10
4015 15 c. Lumiere brothers (inventors of cine camera) .. .. 20 10
4016 15 c. Vittorio de Sica .. 20 10
4017 15 c. Humphrey Bogart 20 10
4018 15 c. Rita Montaner .. 20 10
4019 15 c. Cantinflas .. .. 20 10

1080 West Indian Red-bellied Woodpecker

**1995.** America. Environmental Protection. Multicoloured.
4021 15 c. Type **1080** .. .. 20 10
4022 65 c. Cuban tody .. 80 45

1081 Alfonso Goulet and Francisco Crombet Ballon

**1995.** Death Centenaries of Generals killed during War of Independence. Mult.
4023 15 c. Type **1081** .. .. 20 10
4024 15 c. Jesus Calvar, Jose Guillermo Moncada and Tomas Jordan .. 20 10
4025 15 c. Francisco Borrero and Francisco Inchaustegui .. .. 20 10
Nos. 4023/5 were issued together, se-tenant, forming a composite design of the national flag behind the portraits.

1082 Puerto Rican Tern and Aerial View

1083 Carlos de Cespedes

**1995.** Coco Key. Multicoloured.
4026 10 c. Type **1082** .. .. 10 10
4027 15 c. White ibis and beach 20 10
4028 45 c. Stripe-headed tanager and villas .. 55 30
4029 50 c. Red-legged thrush and apartments .. 60 35
4030 65 c. Northern mocking-bird and villas around pool .. .. 80 45
4031 75 c. Greater flamingo and couple in pool .. 95 55

**1996.** Independence Fighters.
4032 **1083** 15 c. green .. .. 20 10
4033 – 65 c. blue .. .. 80 45
4034 – 75 c. red .. .. 95 55
4035 – 1 p. 05 mauve .. 1·25 75
4036 – 2 p. 05 brown .. 2·50 1·50
4037 – 3 p. brown .. .. 3·75 2·25
DESIGNS: 65 c. Jose Marti; 75 c. Antonio Maceo; 1 p. 05, Ignacio Agramonte; 2 p. 05, Maximo Gomez; 3 p. Calixto Garcia.

1084 Leonardo da Vinci

**1996.** Scientists. Multicoloured.
4038 10 c. Type **1084** .. .. 10 10
4039 15 c. Mikhail Lomonosov (aerodromic machines) 20 10
4040 65 c. James Watt (steam engine) .. .. 80 45
4041 75 c. Guglielmo Marconi (first radio transmitter) 95 55
4042 85 c. Charles Darwin (theory of evolution) .. 1·10 65

1085 Che Guevara and Emblem

**1996.** 30th Anniv of Organization of Solidarity of Peoples of Africa, Asia and Latin America.
4043 **1085** 65 c. multicoloured .. 80 45

1086 Athletics

**1996.** Olympic Games, Atlanta (2nd issue). Multicoloured.
4044 10 c. Type **1086** .. .. 10 10
4045 15 c. Weightlifting .. 20 10
4046 65 c. Judo .. .. 80 45
4047 75 c. Wrestling (horiz) .. 95 55
4048 85 c. Boxing (horiz) .. 1·10 65

1087 Cierva C.4 Autogyro

**1996.** "Espamer" Spanish–Latin American and "Aviation and Space" Stamp Exhibitions, Seville, Spain. Multicoloured.
4050 15 c. Type **1087** .. .. 20 10
4051 65 c. 352-L airplane .. 80 45
4052 75 c. C-201 Alcotan airplane .. .. 95 55
4053 85 c. CASA C-212 Aviocar 1·10 65

1088 Belted Kingfisher

**1996.** Death Centenary of Juan Gundlach (ornithologist). Birds. Multicoloured.
4054 10 c. Type **1088** .. .. 10 10
4055 15 c. American redstart .. 20 10
4056 65 c. Yellowthroat .. 80 45
4057 75 c. Painted bunting .. 95 55
4058 85 c. Cedar waxwing .. 1·10 65

## INDEX

Countries can be quickly located by referring to the index at the end of this volume.

1089 Yury Gagarin (cosmonaut)

1090 National Flag and Hand holding Gun

**1996.** 35th Anniv of First Man in Space. Multicoloured.
4060 15 c. Type **1089** .. .. 20 10
4061 65 c. Globes and "Vostok I" (spaceship) (horiz) .. 80 45

**1996.** 35th Anniversaries. Multicoloured.
4062 15 c. Type **1090** (victory at Giron) .. .. 20 10
4063 65 c. Flags and "35" (Declaration of Socialist character of the Revolution) .. .. 80 45

1091 "Bahama"

**1996.** "CAPEX'96" International Stamp Exhibition, Toronto, Canada. 18th-century Ships of the Line built in Cuban Yards. Multicoloured.
4064 10 c. Type **1091** .. .. 10 10
4065 15 c. "Santissima Trinidad" .. .. 20 10
4066 65 c. "Principe de Asturias" .. .. 80 45
4067 75 c. "San Pedro de Alcantara" .. .. 95 55
4068 85 c. "Santa Ana" .. 1·10 65

1092 Cuban Tody

**1996.** Caribbean Animals. Multicoloured.
4070 10 c. Type **1092** .. .. 10 10
4071 15 c. Purple-throated carib ("Eulampis jugularis") .. .. 20 10
4072 15 c. Wood duck ("Aix sponsa") .. .. 20 10
4073 15 c. Common butterfly fish .. .. 20 10
4074 65 c. "Papilio cresphontes" (butterfly) 80 45
4075 65 c. Indigo vaca ("Hypoplectrus indigo") .. .. 80 45

1093 Charging into Battle and Maceo

**1996.** Death Cent of General Jose Maceo.
4076 **1093** 15 c. multicoloured 20 10

### EXPRESS MAIL STAMPS

E 34.

**1900.** As Type E **34**, but inscr. "immediata".
E 306. E **34.** 10 c. orange .. 32·00 8·50

**1902.** Inscribed "inmediata".
E 307. E **34.** 10 c. orange .. 2·00 1·00

E **39.** J. B. Zayas.

**1910.**
E 320. E **39.** 10 c. blue and orange 4·00 1·40

E **41.** Bleriot XI and Morro Castle.

**1914.**
E352 E **41** 10 c. blue .. .. 6·00 1·40

E **62.** Mercury.

**1936.** Free Port of Matanzas. Inscr. as T **61** Perf. or imperf. (same prices).
E 409. E **62.** 10 c. purple (Express) 3·50 3·50
E 413. – 15 c. blue (Air express) 8·50 2·00
DESIGN: 15 c. Maya Lighthouse.

E **67.** "Triumph of the Revolution".

**1936.** Maximo Gomez Monument.
E 422. E **67.** 10 c. orange .. 3·75 2·75

E **71.** Temple of Quetzalcoatl (Mexico).

**1937.** American Writers and Artists Assn.
E 424v. E **71.** 10 c. orange .. 3·75 2·75
E 424w. – 10 c. orange .. 3·75 2·75
DESIGN: No. 424w, Ruben Dario (Nicaragua).

E **114.**

**1945.**
E 485. E **114.** 10 c. brown .. 2·25 40

E **146.** Government House, Cardenas. E **150.** Capablanca Club, Havana.

**1951.** Centenary of Cuban Flag.
E 559. E **146.** 10 c. red, bl. & orge. 2·75 95

**1951.** 30th Anniv of Jose Capablanca's Victory in World Chess Championship.
E568 E **150** 10 c. purple & green 5·50 2·25

**1952.** As No. 549 surch. **10 c. E. ESPECIAL.**
E 595. **143.** 10 c. on 2 c. brown .. 1·25 40

E **161.** National Anthem and Arms.

E **176.** Roseate Tern.

**1952.** 50th Anniv of Republic.
E605 E **161** 10 c. blue & orange 2·75 1·10

**1952.** Postal Employees' Retirement Fund. Inscr. "ENTREGA ESPECIAL".
E 627. **165.** 10 c. olive .. .. 1·75 85

**1953.**
E 673. E **176.** 10 c. blue .. .. 5·50 1·50

**1954.** Postal Employees' Retirement Fund Portrait of G. H. Saez as No. 684, inscr. "ENTREGA ESPECIAL".
E 686. 10 c. olive .. .. 1·90 95

**1955.** Postal Employees' Retirement Fund. Vert. portrait (F. Varela) as T **191**, inscr. "ENTREGA ESPECIAL".
E 741. 10 c. lake .. .. 2·00 95

**1956.** Postal Employees' Retirement Fund. Vert. portrait (J. J. Milanes) as T **200**, inscr. "ENTREGA ESPECIAL".
E 768. 10 c. black and red .. 1·90 95

**1957.** Postal Employees' Retirement Fund. As T **216** but inscr. "ENTREGA ESPECIAL".
E 812. 10 c. turquoise & brown 1·75 85
PAINTING: 10 c. "Yesterday" (Cabrera).

**1957.** Postal Employees' Retirement Fund. As T **236** but inscr. "ENTREGA ESPECIAL".
E 856. 10 c. violet and brown .. 1·75 85
DESIGN—HORIZ. 10 c. Statue of Gen. A. Maceo, Independence Park, Pinar del Rio.

E **238.** Motor-cyclist in Havana.

**1958.**
E 858. E **238.** 10 c. blue .. .. 1·40 65
E 954. 10 c. violet .. 1·40 65
E 955. 10 c. orange .. 1·40 65
E 859. 20 c. green .. 1·40 65

**1958.** Poey Commem. As Nos. 890/2 but inscr. "ENTREGA ESPECIAL"
E 893. 10 c. multicoloured 5·50 2·75
E 894. 20 c. red, blue and black 8·50 5·50
DESIGNS—HORIZ. Fish: 10 c. Rabiche. 20 c. Guajacon.

**1960.** Surch. **HABILITADO ENTREGA ESPECIAL 10 c.**
E 961. **55.** 10 c. on 20 c. pink .. 1·10 35
E 962. 10 c. on 50 c. turq... 1·10 35

**1962.** Stamp Day. As T **289** but inscr. "ENTREGA ESPECIAL".
E 1023. 10 c. brn. & bl. on yell. 5·50 1·25
DESIGN: 10 c. 18th-century sailing packet.

E **991** West Indian Red-bellied Woodpecker

**1991.** Birds. Multicoloured.
E3638 45 c. Type E **991** .. 80 45
E3639 50 c. Cuban solitaire .. 80 45
E3640 2 p. Cuban trogon .. 3·00 2·00
E3641 4 p. Cuban grassquit .. 6·00 4·00
E3642 5 p. Ivory-billed woodpecker .. .. 7·00 5·00
E3643 10 p. Cuban amazon (horiz) .. .. 15·00 10·00
E3644 16 p. 45 Bee hummingbird (horiz) .. .. 25·00 20·00

### POSTAGE DUE STAMPS

D **42**

**1914.**
D 335. D **42.** 1 c. red .. .. 1·25 65
D 337. 2 c. red .. .. 1·25 65
D 340. 5 c. red .. .. 2·75 1·10

## CUNDINAMARCA Pt. 20

One of the states of the Granadine Confederation.

A Department of Colombia from 1886, now uses Colombian stamps.

100 centavos = 1 peso.

1. 2.

**1870.** Imperf.

| | | | | |
|---|---|---|---|---|
| 1. | 1. | 5 c. blue | 2·75 | 2·75 |
| 2. | 2. | 10 c. red | 10·00 | 10·00 |

3. 4.

**1877.** Imperf.

| | | | | |
|---|---|---|---|---|
| 5. | 3. | 10 c. red | 1·25 | 1·25 |
| 6. | 4. | 20c. green | 2·25 | 2·25 |
| 7. | – | 50 c. mauve | 3·00 | 3·00 |
| 8a. | – | 1 p. brown | 5·00 | 5·00 |

The 50 c. and 1 p. are in larger Arms designs.

11. 13.

**1884.** Imperf.

| | | | | |
|---|---|---|---|---|
| 14. | 11. | 5 c. blue | 50 | 60 |

**1885.** Imperf.

| | | | | |
|---|---|---|---|---|
| 17. | 13. | 5 c. blue | 30 | 30 |
| 18. | | 10 c. red | 1·50 | 1·50 |
| 19. | | 10 c. red on lilac | 90 | 90 |
| 20. | | 20 c. green | 1·25 | 1·25 |
| 21. | | 50 c. mauve | 1·75 | 1·75 |
| 22. | | 1 p. brown | 2·00 | 2·00 |

14. 15.

**1904.** Imperf. or perf. Various frames.

| | | | | |
|---|---|---|---|---|
| 23. | 14. | 1 c. orange | 15 | 15 |
| 24. | | 2 c. blue | 15 | 15 |
| 35. | | 2 c. grey | 45 | 45 |
| 25. | 15. | 3 c. red | 20 | 20 |
| 26. | | 5 c. green | 20 | 20 |
| 27. | | 10 c. brown | 20 | 20 |
| 28. | | 15 c. pink | 25 | 25 |
| 29. | | 20 c. blue on green | 20 | 20 |
| 32. | | 20 c. blue | 40 | 40 |
| 42. | | 40 c. blue | 30 | 30 |
| 30. | | 50 c. mauve | 25 | 25 |
| 31. | | 1 p. green | 25 | 25 |

The illustrations show the main type. The frames and position of the arms in Type **15** differ for each value.

REGISTRATION STAMP

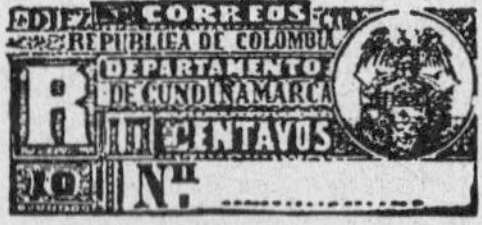


R 17.

**1904.** Imperf. or perf.

| | | | | |
|---|---|---|---|---|
| R 46. | R 17. | 10 c. brown | 75 | 75 |

## CURACAO Pt. 4

A Netherlands colony consisting of two groups of islands in the Caribbean Sea, N. of Venezuela. Later part of Netherlands Antilles.

100 cents = 1 gulden.

1.

2.

4.

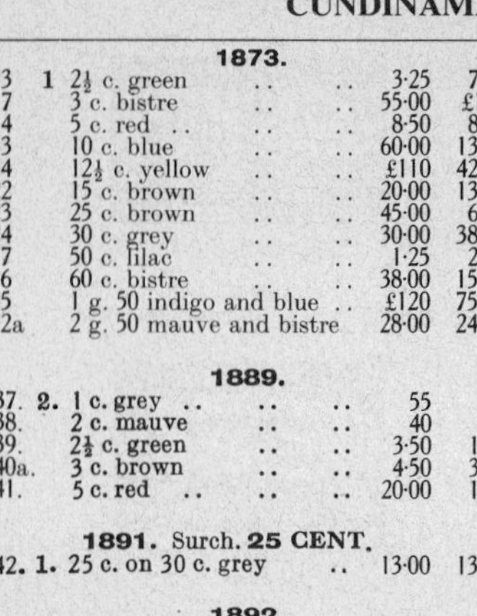

**1873.**

| | | | | |
|---|---|---|---|---|
| 13 | 1 | 2½ c. green | 3·25 | 7·00 |
| 7 | | 3 c. bistre | 55·00 | £120 |
| 14 | | 5 c. red | 8·50 | 8·50 |
| 33 | | 10 c. blue | 60·00 | 13·00 |
| 34 | | 12½ c. yellow | £110 | 42·00 |
| 22 | | 15 c. brown | 20·00 | 13·00 |
| 23 | | 25 c. brown | 45·00 | 6·00 |
| 24 | | 30 c. grey | 30·00 | 38·00 |
| 17 | | 50 c. lilac | 1·25 | 2·25 |
| 26 | | 60 c. bistre | 38·00 | 15·00 |
| 35 | | 1 g. 50 indigo and blue | £120 | 75·00 |
| 12a | | 2 g. 50 mauve and bistre | 28·00 | 24·00 |

**1889.**

| | | | | |
|---|---|---|---|---|
| 37. | 2. | 1 c. grey | 55 | 75 |
| 38. | | 2 c. mauve | 40 | 95 |
| 39. | | 2½ c. green | 3·50 | 1·50 |
| 40a. | | 3 c. brown | 4·50 | 3·75 |
| 41. | | 5 c. red | 20·00 | 1·00 |

**1891.** Surch. **25 CENT.**

| | | | | |
|---|---|---|---|---|
| 42. | 1. | 25 c. on 30 c. grey | 13·00 | 13·00 |

**1892.**

| | | | | |
|---|---|---|---|---|
| 43. | 4. | 10 c. blue | 85 | 85 |
| 44. | | 12½ c. green | 24·00 | 5·00 |
| 45. | | 15 c. red | 2·00 | 2·25 |
| 46. | | 25 c. brown | 90·00 | 4·50 |
| 47. | | 30 c. grey | 2·00 | 6·50 |

**1895.** Surch. **2½ CENT.**

| | | | | |
|---|---|---|---|---|
| 48. | 1. | 2½ c. on 10 c. blue | 10·00 | 6·00 |
| 50. | | 2½ c. on 30 c. grey | £120 | 4·00 |

**1899.** 1898 stamps of Netherlands surch. **CURACAO** and value

| | | | | |
|---|---|---|---|---|
| 51. | 12. | 12½ c. on 12½ c. blue | 23·00 | 6·00 |
| 52. | | 25 c. on 25 c. blue & red | 85 | 85 |
| 53. | 13. | 1 g. 50 on 2½ g. lilac | 13·00 | 19·00 |

9.

10.

11.

(Shaded background).

**1903.**

| | | | | |
|---|---|---|---|---|
| 54. | 9. | 1 c. olive | 1·00 | 50 |
| 55a. | | 2 c. brown | 11·00 | 2·75 |
| 56. | | 2½ c. green | 3·25 | 25 |
| 57. | | 3 c. orange | 6·50 | 4·00 |
| 58. | | 5 c. red | 5·50 | 25 |
| 59. | | 7½ c. grey | 26·00 | 4·50 |
| 60. | 10. | 10 c. slate | 10·00 | 2·50 |
| 61. | | 12½ c. blue | 1·00 | 20 |
| 62. | | 15 c. brown | 13·00 | 9·00 |
| 63. | | 22½ c. olive and brown | 13·00 | 7·00 |
| 64. | | 25 c. violet | 13·00 | 1·75 |
| 65. | | 30 c. brown | 32·00 | 12·00 |
| 66. | | 50 c. brown | 26·00 | 7·50 |
| 67. | 11. | 1½ g. brown | 35·00 | 25·00 |
| 68. | | 2½ g. blue | 35·00 | 25·00 |

12.

13.

14.

(Unshaded background).

**1915.**

| | | | | |
|---|---|---|---|---|
| 69 | 12 | ½ c. lilac | 40 | 70 |
| 70 | | 1 c. olive | 20 | 15 |
| 71 | | 1½ c. blue | 15 | 10 |
| 72 | | 2 c. brown | 1·25 | 1·10 |
| 73 | | 2½ c. green | 1·00 | 15 |
| 74 | | 3 c. yellow | 1·25 | 1·25 |
| 75 | | 3 c. green | 2·00 | 2·00 |
| 76 | | 5 c. red | 1·40 | 10 |
| 77 | | 5 c. green | 2·50 | 2·00 |
| 78 | | 5 c. mauve | 1·10 | 15 |
| 79c | | 7½c. bistre | 1·10 | 15 |
| 80 | 13 | 10 c. red | 13·00 | 2·50 |
| 81 | 12 | 10 c. lilac | 3·50 | 3·75 |
| 82 | | 10 c. red | 4·50 | 1·25 |
| 83 | 13 | 12½ c. blue | 1·50 | 45 |
| 84 | | 12½ c. red | 1·40 | 1·50 |
| 85 | | 15 c. olive | 40 | 65 |
| 86 | | 15 c. blue | 2·75 | 2·25 |
| 87 | | 20 c. blue | 6·00 | 2·50 |
| 88 | | 20 c. olive | 1·60 | 2·25 |
| 89 | | 22½ c. orange | 1·25 | 2·25 |
| 90 | | 25 c. mauve | 2·75 | 85 |
| 91 | | 30 c. slate | 2·75 | 65 |
| 92 | | 35 c. slate and orange | 2·75 | 3·50 |
| 93a | 14 | 50 c. green | 2·25 | 20 |
| 94 | | 1½ g. violet | 11·00 | 11·00 |
| 95 | | 2½ g. red | 20·00 | 20·00 |

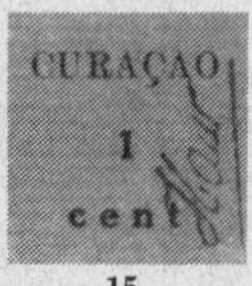


15.

**1918.**

| | | | | |
|---|---|---|---|---|
| 96 | 15 | 1 c. black on buff | 7·00 | 3·50 |

**1919.** Surch. **5 CENT.**

| | | | | |
|---|---|---|---|---|
| 97. | 13. | 5 c. on 12½ c. blue | 3·50 | 2·00 |

17. Queen Wilhelmina. 20.

**1923.** Queen's Silver Jubilee.

| | | | | |
|---|---|---|---|---|
| 98 | 17 | 5 c. green | 55 | 1·75 |
| 99 | | 7½ c. green | 1·10 | 1·40 |
| 100 | | 10 c. red | 1·10 | 1·75 |
| 101 | | 20 c. grey | 1·75 | 2·75 |
| 102 | | 1 g. purple | 30·00 | 17·00 |
| 103 | | 2 g. 50 black | 60·00 | £180 |
| 104 | | 5 g. brown | 80·00 | £200 |

**1927.** Unissued Marine Insurance stamps, as Type M **22** of Netherlands, inscr. "CURACAO", surch. **FRANKEERZEGEL** and value.

| | | | | |
|---|---|---|---|---|
| 105. | | 3 c. on 15 c. green | 20 | 35 |
| 106. | | 10 c. on 60 c. red | 20 | 30 |
| 107. | | 12½ c. on 75 c. brown | 25 | 30 |
| 108. | | 15 c. on 1 g. 50 blue | 3·00 | 2·50 |
| 109. | | 25 c. on 2 g. 25 brown | 7·00 | 6·50 |
| 110. | | 30 c. on 4½ g. black | 13·00 | 12·00 |
| 111. | | 50 c. on 7½ g. red | 7·50 | 7·50 |

**1928.**

| | | | | |
|---|---|---|---|---|
| 112. | 20. | 6 c. orange | 1·40 | 25 |
| 113. | | 7½ c. orange | 55 | 50 |
| 114. | | 10 c. red | 1·40 | 45 |
| 115. | | 12½ c. brown | 1·40 | 1·25 |
| 116. | | 15 c. blue | 1·40 | 35 |
| 117. | | 20 c. blue | 5·50 | 65 |
| 118. | | 21 c. green | 8·50 | 11·00 |
| 119. | | 25 c. purple | 3·25 | 1·60 |
| 120. | | 27½ c. black | 11·00 | 14·00 |
| 121. | | 30 c. green | 5·50 | 65 |
| 122. | | 35 c. black | 1·75 | 2·25 |

**1929.** Air. Surch. **LUCHTPOST** and value.

| | | | | |
|---|---|---|---|---|
| 123. | 13. | 50 c. on 12½ c. red | 11·00 | 12·00 |
| 124. | | 1 g. on 20 c. blue | 11·00 | 12·00 |
| 125. | | 2 g. on 15 c. olive | 38·00 | 45·00 |

**1929.** Surch. **6ct.** and bars.

| | | | | |
|---|---|---|---|---|
| 126. | 20. | 6 c. on 7½ c. orange | 1·10 | 85 |

23.

24a.

**1931.** Air.

| | | | | |
|---|---|---|---|---|
| 126a. | 23. | 10 c. green | 15 | 10 |
| 126b. | | 15 c. slate | 25 | 15 |
| 127. | | 20 c. red | 75 | 15 |
| 127a. | | 25 c. olive | 45 | 40 |
| 127b. | | 30 c. yellow | 30 | 20 |
| 128. | | 35 c. blue | 75 | 70 |
| 129. | | 40 c. green | 55 | 20 |
| 130. | | 45 c. orange | 2·00 | 2·00 |
| 130a. | | 50 c. red | 40 | 55 |
| 131. | | 60 c. purple | 55 | 25 |
| 132. | | 70 c. black | 6·00 | 2·00 |
| 133. | | 1 g. 40 brown | 3·75 | 5·00 |
| 134. | | 2 g. 80 bistre | 4·25 | 5·50 |

**1931.** Surch.

| | | | | |
|---|---|---|---|---|
| 134a. | 12. | 1½ on 2½ c. green | 3·00 | 3·00 |
| 135. | | 2½ on 3 c. green | 1·00 | 1·00 |

**1933.** 400th Birth Anniv. of William I of Orange.

| | | | | |
|---|---|---|---|---|
| 136. | 24a. | 6 c. orange | 1·25 | 1·00 |

25. Frederik Hendrik.

26. "Johannes van Walbeeck".

**1934.** 300th Anniv. of Dutch Colonization. Inscr. "1634 1934".

| | | | | |
|---|---|---|---|---|
| 137. | – | 1 c. black | 1·00 | 1·50 |
| 138. | – | 1½ c. mauve | 75 | 30 |
| 139. | – | 2 c. orange | 1·00 | 1·50 |
| 140. | 25. | 2½ c. green | 85 | 1·50 |
| 141. | | 5 c. brown | 85 | 95 |
| 142. | | 6 c. blue | 75 | 25 |
| 143. | – | 10 c. red | 2·25 | 85 |
| 144. | – | 12½ c. brown | 6·00 | 5·50 |
| 145. | – | 15 c. blue | 1·75 | 90 |
| 146. | 26. | 20 c. black | 3·50 | 2·25 |
| 147. | | 21 c. brown | 12·00 | 17·00 |
| 148. | | 25 c. green | 11·00 | 11·00 |
| 149. | – | 27½ c. purple | 14·00 | 18·00 |
| 150. | – | 30 c. red | 11·00 | 4·25 |
| 151. | – | 50 c. yellow | 11·00 | 7·50 |
| 152. | – | 1 g. 50 blue | 50·00 | 60·00 |
| 153. | – | 2 g. 50 green | 60·00 | 55·00 |

PORTRAITS: 1 c. to 2 c. Willem Usselinx. 10 c. to 15 c. Jacob Binckes. 27½ c. to 50 c. Cornelis Evertsen, the younger. 1 g. 50, 2 g. 50, Louis Brion.

**1934.** Air. Surch. **10 CT.**

| | | | | |
|---|---|---|---|---|
| 154. | 23. | 10 c. on 20 c. red | 20·00 | 17·00 |

27.

28. Queen Wilhelmina.

**1936.**

| | | | | |
|---|---|---|---|---|
| 155. | 27. | 1 c. brown | 20 | 15 |
| 156. | | 1½ c. blue | 20 | 10 |
| 157. | | 2 c. orange | 25 | 25 |
| 158. | | 2½ c. green | 20 | 20 |
| 159. | | 5 c. red | 20 | 10 |

**1936.**

| | | | | |
|---|---|---|---|---|
| 160. | 28. | 6 c. purple | 50 | 10 |
| 161. | | 10 c. red | 1·00 | 15 |
| 162. | | 12½ c. green | 1·50 | 70 |
| 163. | | 15 c. blue | 1·10 | 35 |
| 164. | | 20 c. orange | 1·10 | 55 |
| 165. | | 21 c. black | 2·25 | 2·50 |
| 166. | | 25 c. red | 1·50 | 80 |
| 167. | | 27½ c. brown | 2·50 | 2·75 |
| 168. | | 30 c. bistre | 60 | 15 |
| 169. | | 50 c. green | 3·00 | 20 |
| 170. | | 1 g. 50 brown | 22·00 | 15·00 |
| 171a. | | 2 g. 50 red | 12·00 | 7·50 |

29. Queen Wilhelmina.

30. Dutch Flags and Arms.

**1938.** 40th Anniv. of Coronation.

| | | | | |
|---|---|---|---|---|
| 172. | 29. | 1½ c. violet | 15 | 20 |
| 173. | | 6 c. red | 70 | 65 |
| 174. | | 15 c. blue | 1·25 | 95 |

**1941.** Air. Prince Bernhard Fund to equip Dutch Forces. Centres in red, blue and orange.

| | | | | |
|---|---|---|---|---|
| 175. | 30. | 10 c. + 10 c. red | 2·75 | 3·25 |
| 176. | | 15 c. + 25 c. blue | 14·00 | 14·00 |
| 177. | | 20 c. + 25 c. brown | 14·00 | 18·00 |
| 178. | | 25 c. + 25 c. violet | 14·00 | 18·00 |
| 179. | | 30 c. + 50 c. orange | 14·00 | 18·00 |
| 180. | | 35 c. + 50 c. green | 14·00 | 18·00 |
| 181. | | 40 c. + 50 c. brown | 14·00 | 18·00 |
| 182. | | 50 c. + 1 g. blue | 14·00 | 18·00 |

31. Queen Wilhelmina.

33. Aruba.

**1941.**

| | | | | |
|---|---|---|---|---|
| 248 | 31 | 6 c. violet | 1·40 | 2·00 |
| 184a | | 10 c. red | 1·00 | 85 |
| 185 | | 12½ c. green | 1·50 | 55 |
| 251 | | 15 c. blue | 1·40 | 2·00 |
| 187 | | 20 c. orange | 30 | 45 |
| 188 | | 21 c. grey | 1·40 | 1·60 |
| 254 | | 25 c. red | 20 | 15 |
| 255 | | 27½ c. brown | 1·40 | 1·40 |
| 256 | | 30 c. bistre | 1·75 | 75 |
| 257 | | 50 c. green | 2·00 | 15 |
| 192 | | 50 c. green | 10·00 | 20 |
| 193 | | 1½ g. brown | 12·00 | 90 |
| 194 | | 2½ g. purple | 11·00 | 1·00 |

Nos. 192/4 are larger, 21 × 26 mm.

See also Nos. 258/61.

**1942.**

| | | | | |
|---|---|---|---|---|
| 195. | – | 1 c. brown and violet | 10 | 10 |
| 196. | – | 1½ c. green and blue | 15 | 15 |
| 197. | – | 2 c. brown and black | 40 | 35 |
| 198. | – | 2½ c. yellow and green | 20 | 20 |
| 199. | 33. | 5 c. black and red | 85 | 15 |
| 200. | – | 6 c. blue and purple | 60 | 65 |

DESIGNS—HORIZ. 1 c. Bonaire. 2 c. Saba. 2½ c. St. Maarten. 6 c. Curacao. VERT. 1½ c. St. Eustatius.

34. Queen Wilhelmina and Douglas DC-2 over Atlantic Ocean.

35. Dutch Royal Family.

**1942.** Air.

| | | | | |
|---|---|---|---|---|
| 201 | 34 | 10 c. blue and green | 15 | 10 |
| 202 | – | 15 c. green and red | 20 | 15 |
| 203 | – | 20 c. green and brown | 25 | 15 |
| 204 | – | 25 c. brown and blue | 15 | 20 |
| 205 | – | 30 c. violet and red | 30 | 30 |
| 206 | 34 | 35 c. green and violet | 45 | 30 |
| 207 | – | 40 c. brown and green | 55 | 40 |
| 208 | – | 45 c. black and red | 35 | 20 |
| 209 | – | 50 c. black and violet | 75 | 15 |

210 – 60 c. blue and brown 75 60
211 34 70 c. blue and brown 1·00 60
212 – 1 g. 40 green and blue 4·50 1·25
213 – 2 g. 80 blue & ultram 6·50 2·50
214 – 5 g. green and purple 12·00 11·00
215 – 10 g. brown and green 17·00 17·00

DESIGNS: 15, 40 c., 1 g. 40, Fokker airplane "Zilvermeeuw" over coast. 20, 45 c., 2 g. 80, Map of Netherlands West Indies. 25, 50 c., 5 g. Side view of Douglas DC-2 airplane. 30, 60 c., 10 g. Front view of Douglas DC-2 airplane.

**1943.** Birth of Princess Margriet.
216. 35. 1½ c. orange 10 10
217. 2½ c. red 15 10
218. 6 c. black 70 55
219. 10 c. blue 70 80

**1943.** Air. Dutch Prisoners of War Relief Fund. Nos. 212/15 surch **Voor Krijgsgevangenen** and new value.
220 – 40 c.+50 c. on 1 g. 40 green and blue 3·75 4·50
221 – 45 c.+50 c. on 2 g. 80 blue and ultramarine 3·50 4·25
222 – 50 c.+75 c. on 5 g. green and purple 3·50 4·25
223 – 60 c.+100 c. on 10 g. brown and green 3·50 4·50

**37.** Princess Juliana. **38.** Map of Netherlands.

**1944.** Air. Red Cross Fund. Cross in red; frame in red and blue.
224. 37. 10 c.+10 c. brown 1·50 1·75
225. 15 c.+25 c. green 1·40 1·75
226. 20 c.+25 c. black 1·40 1·75
227. 25 c.+25 c. grey 1·40 1·75
228. 30 c.+50 c. purple 1·40 1·75
229. 35 c.+50 c. brown 1·40 1·75
230. 40 c.+50 c. green 1·40 1·75
231. 50 c.+100 c. violet 1·50 2·00

**1946.** Air. Netherlands Relief Fund. Value in black.
232. 38. 10 c.+10 c. orge. & grey 1·00 1·25
233. 15 c.+25 c. grey and red 1·25 1·25
234. 20 c.+25 c. orge. & grn. 1·25 1·25
235. 25 c.+25 c. grey & violet 1·25 1·25
236. 30 c.+50 c. buff & green 1·25 1·50
237. 35 c.+50 c. orge. & red 1·25 1·50
238. 40 c.+75 c. buff & blue 1·25 1·75
239. 50 c.+100 c. buff & vio. 1·25 1·75

**1946.** Air. National Relief Fund. As T 38 but showing map of Netherlands Indies and inscr. "CURACAO HELPT ONZEOOST". Value in black.
240. 10 c.+10 c. buff & violet 1·00 1·25
241. 15 c.+25 c. buff & blue 1·25 1·25
242. 20 c.+25 c. orge. & red 1·25 1·25
243. 25 c.+25 c. buff & grn. 1·25 1·25
244. 30 c.+50 c. grey & violet 1·25 1·50
245. 35 c.+50 c. orge. & grn. 1·25 1·50
246. 40 c.+75 c. grey & red 1·25 1·75
247. 50 c.+100 c. orge. & grey 1·25 1·75

**1947.** Size 25×31½ mm.
258. 31. 1½ g. brown 90 55
259. 2½ g. purple 23·00 5·00
260. 5 g. olive 95·00 £130
261. 10 g. orange £120 £190

**40.** Aeroplane and Posthorn. **41.** Douglas DC-2 and Waves.

**1947.** Air.
262. 40. 6 c. black 20 10
263. 10 c. red 20 15
264. 12½ c. purple 35 15
265. 15 c. blue 35 20
266. 20 c. green 50 25
267. 25 c. orange 50 15
268. 30 c. violet 75 30
269. 35 c. red 80 50
270. 40 c. green 75 50
271. 45 c. violet 90 75
272. 50 c. red 90 15
273. 60 c. blue 1·10 50
274. 70 c. brown 2·50 1·25
275. 41. 1 g. 50 black 1·40 50
276. 2 g. 50 red 12·00 2·75
277. 5 g. green 22·00 6·00
278. 7 g. 50 blue 70·00 65·00
279. 10 g. violet 50·00 12·00
280. 15 g. red 90·00 80·00
281. 25 g. brown 80·00 65·00

**1947.** Netherlands Indies Social Welfare Fund. Surch **NIWIN** and value.
282 28 1½ c.+2½ c. on 6 c. pur 80 80
283 2½ c.+5 c. on 10 c. red 80 80
284 5 c.+7½ c. on 15 c. blue 80 80

**1948.** Portrait of Queen Wilhelmina as T 81 of Netherlands Indies.
285. 6 c. purple 1·00 1·25
286. 10 c. red 1·00 1·60
287. 12½ c. green 1·00 80
288. 15 c. blue 1·00 1·25
289. 20 c. orange 1·00 1·75
290. 21 c. black 1·00 1·75
291. 25 c. mauve 35 10
292. 27½ c. brown 18·00 17·00
293. 30 c. olive 15·00 80
294. 50 c. green 15·00 25
295. 1 g. 50 c. brown 24·00 4·50
No. 295 is larger, 21½×28½ mm.

**45.** Queen Wilhelmina.

**1948.** Queen Wilhelmina's Golden Jubilee.
296. 45. 6 c. orange 50 50
297. 12½ c. blue 50 50

**46.** Queen Juliana. **47.**

**1948.** Accession of Queen Juliana.
298. 46. 6 c. red 45 45
299. 12½ c. green 45 45

**1948.** Child Welfare Fund. Inscr. "VOOR HET KIND".
300. 47. 6 c.+10 c. brown 2·25 1·50
301. – 10 c.+15 c. red 2·25 1·50
302. – 12½ c.+20 c. green 2·25 1·60
303. 47. 15 c.+25 c. blue 2·25 1·75
304. – 20 c.+30 c. brown 2·25 1·75
305. – 25 c.+35 c. violet 2·25 2·00

DESIGNS: 10, 20 c. Native boy in straw hat. 12½, 25 c. Curly-haired girl.

POSTAGE DUE STAMPS

For stamps as Nos. D42/61 and D96/105 in other colours see Postage Due stamps of Netherlands Indies and Surinam.

D 3.

D 5.

**1889.**
D 42. D 3. 2½ c. black and green 1·60 2·25
D 43. 5 c. black and green 1·00 1·00
D 44. 10 c. black and green 20·00 17·00
D 45. 12½ c. black and green £275 £140
D 46. 15 c. black and green 14·00 11·00
D 47. 20 c. black and green 5·50 5·50
D 48. 25 c. black and green £130 £110
D 49. 30 c. black and green 7·00 5·50
D 50. 40 c. black and green 7·00 5·50
D 51. 50 c. black and green 26·00 25·00

**1892.**
D 52. D 5. 2½ c. black and green 20 15
D 53. 5 c. black and green 45 30
D 54. 10 c. black and green 1·00 25
D 55. 12½ c. black and green 1·10 40
D 56. 15 c. black and green 1·75 70
D 57. 20 c. black and green 2·25 1·00
D 58. 25 c. black and green 85 55
D 59. 30 c. black and green 18·00 10·00
D 60. 40 c. black and green 18·00 11·00
D 61. 50 c. black and green 22·00 11·00

**1915.**
D 96. D 5. 2½ c. green 50 50
D 97. 5 c. green 50 50
D 98. 10 c. green 45 45
D 99. 12½ c. green 55 55
D 100. 15 c. green 1·00 1·25
D 101. 20 c. green 50 1·00
D 102. 25 c. green 20 10
D 103. 30 c. green 2·00 2·25
D 104. 40 c. green 2·00 2·25
D 105. 50 c. green 1·60 1·90

For later issues see **NETHERLANDS ANTILLES.**

## MINIMUM PRICE

The minimum price quoted is 10p which represents a handling charge rather than a basis for valuing common stamps. For further notes about prices see introductory pages.

## CYRENAICA Pt. 8

Part of the former Italian colony of Libya, N. Africa. Allied Occupation, 1942-49. Independent Administration, 1949-52. Then part of independent Libya.

Stamps optd **BENGASI** formerly listed here will be found under Italian P.Os. in the Turkish Empire, Nos. 169/70.

100 centesimi = 1 lira.

Stamps of Italy optd. **CIRENAICA.**

**1923.** Tercent of Propagation of the Faith.
1. 66. 20 c. orange and green 2·00 6·00
2. 30 c. orange and red 2·00 6·00
3. 50 c. orange and violet 2·00 6·00
4. 1 l. orange and blue 2·00 6·00

**1923.** Fascist March on Rome stamps.
5. 77. 10 c. green 1·40 6·00
6. 30 c. violet 1·40 6·00
7. 50 c. red 1·40 6·00
8. 74. 1 l. blue 1·40 6·00
9. 2 l. brown 1·40 6·00
10. 75. 5 l. black and blue 1·40 7·50

**1924.** Manzoni stamps (Nos. 155/60).
11 77 10 c. black and purple 75 12·00
12 – 15 c. black and green 75 12·00
13 – 30 c. black 75 12·00
14 – 50 c. black and brown 75 12·00
15 – 1 l. black and blue 18·00 90·00
16 – 5 l. black and purple £250 £1000

**1925.** Holy Year stamps.
17. – 20 c.+10 c. brown & grn. 1·00 4·25
18. 81. 30 c.+15 c. brn. & choc. 1·00 4·25
19. – 50 c.+25 c. brn. & violet 1·00 4·25
20. – 60 c.+30 c. brown & red 1·00 4·25
21. – 1 l.+50 c. purple & blue 1·00 4·25
22. – 5 l.+2 l. 50 purple & red 1·00 4·25

**1925.** Royal Jubilee stamps.
23. 82. 60 c. red 25 2·75
24. 1 l. blue 35 2·75
24a. 1 l. 25 blue 60 8·50

**1926.** St. Francis of Assisi stamps.
25. 83. 20 c. green 1·00 4·25
26. – 40 c. violet 1·00 4·25
27. – 60 c. red 1·00 4·25
28. – 1 l. 25 blue 1·00 4·25
29. – 5 l.+2 l. 50 olive (as No. 196) 2·00 5·50

**6.**

**8.**

**1926.** Colonial Propaganda.
30. 6. 5 c.+5 c. brown 20 2·25
31. 10 c.+5 c. olive 20 2·25
32. 20 c.+5 c. green 20 2·25
33. 40 c.+5 c. red 20 2·25
34. 60 c.+5 c. orange 20 2·25
35. 1 l.+5 c. blue 20 2·25

**1927.** First National Defence stamps of Italy optd **CIRENAICA.**
36. 89. 40+20 c. black & brown 1·00 4·25
37. – 60+30 c. brown and red 1·00 4·25
38. – 1 l. 25+60 c. black & blue 1·00 4·25
39. – 5 l.+2 l. 50 black & green 1·50 6·50

**1927.** Volta Centenary stamps of Italy optd **Cirenaica.**
40. 90. 20 c. violet 3·00 10·00
41. 50 c. orange 3·00 7·00
42. 1 l. 25 blue 4·00 10·00

**1928.** 45th Anniv. of Italian-African Society.
43. 8. 20 c.+5 c. green 75 4·00
44. 30 c.+5 c. red 75 4·00
45. 50 c.+10 c. violet 75 4·00
46. 1 l. 25+20 c. blue 75 4·00

Stamps of Italy optd. **CIRENAICA.** Colours changed in some instances.

**1929.** Second National Defence stamps.
47 89 30 c.+10 c. black & red 1·40 4·75
48 – 50 c.+20 c. grey & lilac 1·40 4·75
49 – 1 l. 25+50 c. blue & brn 1·75 6·00
50 – 5 l.+2 l. black & green 1·75 6·00

**1929.** Montecassino stamps (No. 57 optd **Cirenaica**).
51 104 20 c. green 1·75 4·25
52 – 25 c. red 1·75 4·25
53 – 50 c.+10 c. red 1·75 8·50
54 – 75 c.+15 c. brown 1·75 8·50
55 104 1 l. 25+25 c. purple 3·25 8·50
56 – 5 l.+1 l. blue 3·25 8·50
57 – 10 l.+2 l. brown 3·25 10·00

**1930.** Marriage of Prince Humbert and Princess Marie Jose stamps.
58 109 20 c. green 40 1·90
59 50 c.+10 c. red 35 2·50
60 1 l. 25+25 c. red 35 6·00

**1930.** Ferrucci stamps (optd. **Cirenaica**).
61. 114. 20 c. violet 50 1·60
62. – 25 c. green 50 1·60
63. – 50 c. black 50 1·60
64. – 1 l. 25 blue 50 1·60
65. – 5 l.+2 l. red 1·75 2·75

**1930.** Third National Defence stamps.
66 89 30 c.+10 c. turq & grn 5·00 15·00
67 – 50 c.+10 c. purple & grn 5·00 15·00
68 – 1 l. 25+30 c. lt brn & brn 5·00 20·00
69 – 5 l.+1 l. 50 green & blue 14·00 50·00

**13.**

**17.** Columns of Leptis.

**1930.** 25th Anniv. (1929) of Italian Colonial Agricultural Institute.
70 13 50 c.+20 c. brown 1·00 5·00
71 1 l. 25+20 c. blue 1·00 5·00
72 1 l. 75+20 c. green 1·00 5·00
73 2 l. 55+50 c. violet 1·75 7·00
74 5 l.+1 l. red 1·75 10·00

**1930.** Virgil Bimillenary stamps optd **CIRENAICA.**
75. 118. 15 c. violet 40 1·40
76. – 20 c. brown 40 1·40
77. – 25 c. green 40 1·40
78. – 30 c. brown 40 1·40
79. – 50 c. purple 40 1·40
80. – 75 c. red 40 1·40
81. – 1 l. 25 blue 40 1·40
82. – 5 l.+1 l. 50 purple 2·00 10·00
83. – 10 l.+2 l. 50 brown 2·00 10·00

**1931.** St. Anthony of Padua stamps optd **Cirenaica** (75 c., 5 l.) or **CIRENAICA** (others).
84 121 20 c. brown 55 2·50
85 – 25 c. green 55 2·50
86 – 30 c. brown 55 2·50
87 – 50 c. purple 55 1·40
88 – 75 c. grey (as No. 308) 55 2·50
89 – 1 l. 25 blue 55 4·00
90 – 5 l.+2 l. 50 brown (as No. 310) 2·00 18·00

**1932.** Air stamps of Tripolitania optd. **Cirenaica.**
91. 18. 50 c. red 30 10
92. 60 c. orange 1·60 8·50
93. 80 c. purple 1·60 8·50

**1932.** Air stamps of Tripolitania of 1931 optd. **CIRENAICA** and bars.
94. 18. 50 c. red 50 20
95. 80 c. purple 2·00 11·00

**1932.** Air.
96. – 50 c. violet 1·25 10
97. – 75 c. red 2·00 5·00
98. – 80 c. blue 2·00 5·00
99. 17. 1 l. black 50 10
100. 2 l. green 85 2·50
101. 5 l. red 1·40 5·50

DESIGN—VERT. 50 c. to 80 c. Arab on Camel.

**18.** "Graf Zeppelin".

DESIGNS: 5 l., 12 l. "Graf Zeppelin" and Roman galley. 10 l., 20 l. "Graf Zeppelin" and giant archer.

**1933.** Air. "Graf Zeppelin". Inscr. "CROCIERA ZEPPELIN".
102. 18. 3 l. brown 5·00 35·00
103. – 5 l. violet 5·00 35·00
104. – 10 l. green 5·00 55·00
105. – 12 l. blue 5·00 85·00
106. 18. 15 l. red 5·00 70·00
107. – 20 l. black 5·00 £100

**19.** Air Squadron.

**1933.** Air. Balbo Transatlantic Mass Formation Flight by Savoia Marchetti S-55X Flying Boats.
108 19 19 l. 75 blue and green 10·00 £225
109 44 l. 75 blue and red 10·00 £225

**1934.** Air. Rome–Buenos Aires Flight. T 17 (new colours) optd with Savoia Marchetti S-71 Airplane and **1934-XII PRIMO VOLO DIRETTO ROMA = BUENOS-AYRES TRIMOTORE "LOMBARDI-MAZZOTTI"** or surch also.
110 17 2 l. on 5 l. brown 1·50 28·00
111 3 l. on 5 l. green 1·50 28·00
112 5 l. brown 1·50 28·00
113 10 l. on 5 l. pink 1·50 28·00

**21.** Arab Horseman.

**1934.** 2nd Internationl Colonial Exn, Naples.
114 21 5 c. brn & grn (postage) 1·50 7·50
115 10 c. black and brown .. 1·50 7·50
116 20 c. blue and red .. 1·50 7·50
117 50 c. brown and violet 1·50 7·50
118 60 c. blue and brown .. 1·50 7·50
119 1 l. 25 green and blue .. 1·50 7·50

120 – 25 c. orange & blue (air) 1·50 7·50
121 – 50 c. blue and green .. 1·50 7·50
122 – 75 c. orange and brown 1·50 7·50
123 – 80 c. green and brown .. 1·50 7·50
124 – 1 l. green and red .. 1·50 7·50
125 – 2 l. brown and blue .. 1·50 7·50

DESIGNS: 25 to 75 c. Arrival of Caproni Ca 101 mail plane. 80 c. to 2 l. Caproni Ca 101 mail plane and Venus of Cyrene.

22.

**1934.** Air. Rome–Mogadiscio Flight.
126 22 25 c. + 10 c. green .. 2·00 5·00
127 50 c. + 10 c. brown .. 2·00 5·00
128 75 c. + 15 c. red .. 2·00 5·00
129 80 c. + 15 c. black .. 2·00 5·00
130 1 l. + 20 c. brown .. 2·00 5·00
131 2 l. + 20 c. blue .. 2·00 5·00
132 3 l. + 25 c. violet .. 16·00 40·00
133 5 l. + 25 c. orange .. 16·00 40·00
134 10 l. + 30 c. purple .. 16·00 40·00
135 25 l. + 2 l. green .. 16·00 40·00

OFFICIAL AIR STAMP

**1934.** Optd **SERVIZIO DI STATO** and Crown.
O136 22 25 l. + 2 l. red .. £1400 £850

For stamps of British Occupation see Volume 3.

## CZECHOSLOVAK ARMY IN SIBERIA Pt. 5

During the War of 1914–18 many Czech and Slovak soldiers in the Austro-Hungarian armies surrendered to the Russian Army. After the war many of these formed an army in Siberia and fought the Bolshevists. They issued stamps for their own postal service and these were also sold to the public on the Siberian Railway.

100 kopeks = 1 rouble.

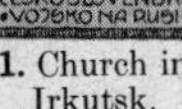
1. Church in Irkutsk.

3. Sentry.

**1919.** Imperf.
1. 1. 25 k. red .. .. .. 8·75 12·50
2. – 50 k green .. .. 8·75 12·50
3. 3. 1 r. red .. .. .. 20·00 25·00

DESIGN: 50 k. Armoured train "Orlik".

**1920.** Perf.
4. 1. 25 k. red .. .. .. 8·25 8·25
5. – 50 k. green .. .. 8·25 8·25
6. 3. 1 r. brown .. .. 19·00 19·00

DESIGN: 50 k. Armoured train "Orlik".

4. Lion of Bohemia.

**1919.**
7. 4. (25 k) red and blue .. 1·25

**1920.** No. 7 optd. **1920**.
8. 4. (25 k.) red and blue .. 6·75

**1920.** No. 8 surch.
9. 4. 2 (k.) red and blue .. 18·00
10. 3 (k.) red and blue .. 18·00
11. 5 (k.) red and blue .. 18·00
12. 10 (k.) red and blue .. 18·00
13. 15 (k.) red and blue .. 18·00
14. 25 (k.) red and blue .. 18·00
15. 35 (k.) red and blue .. 18·00
16. 50 (k.) red and blue .. 18·00
17. 1 r. red and blue .. 18·00

## CZECHOSLOVAKIA Pt. 5

Formed in 1918 by the Czechs of Bohemia and Moravia and the Slovaks of northern Hungary (both part of Austro-Hungarian Empire). Occupied by Germany in 1939 (see note after No. 393c); independence restored 1945.

On 31 December 1992 the Czech and Slovak Federative Republic was dissolved, the two constituent republics becoming independent as the Czech Republic and Slovakia.

100 haleru = 1 koruna.

1.

2. Hradcany, Prague.

**1918.** Roul.
1. 1. 10 h. blue .. .. .. 12·50 14·00
2. 20 h. red .. .. .. 12·50 14·00

**1918.** (a) Imperf.
4. 2. 3 h. mauve .. .. 10 10
9. 30 h. olive .. .. .. 25 10
10. 40 h. orange .. .. 25 10
12. 100 h. brown .. .. 75 10
14. 400 h. violet .. .. 1·50 10

(b) Imperf. or perf.
5. 5 h. green .. .. .. 10 10
6. 10 h. red .. .. .. 10 10
7. 20 h. green .. .. 15 10
8. 25 h. blue .. .. .. 15 10
13. 200 h. blue .. .. 1·25 10

3.

**1919.** Imperf or perf.
3 3 1 h. brown .. .. 10 10
38 5 h. green .. .. 15 10
39 10 h. green .. .. 20 10
40 15 h. red .. .. .. 15 10
41 20 h. red .. .. .. 20 10
28 25 h. purple .. .. 20 10
49 30 h. mauve .. .. 15 10
11 50 h. purple .. .. 25 10
30 50 h. blue .. .. 25 10
50 60 h. orange .. .. 25 10
32 75 h. green .. .. 1·00 10
33 80 h. green .. .. 1·50 15
34 120 h. black .. .. 1·25 10
35 300 h. green .. .. 5·00 15
36 500 h. brown .. .. 2·50 15
37 1000 h. purple .. .. 12·50 50

6.

7.

**1919.** 1st Anniv of Independence and Czechoslovak Legion Commemoration.
61 6 15 h. green .. .. 10 10
62 25 h. brown .. .. 10 10
63 50 h. blue .. .. 10 10
64 7 75 h. grey .. .. 10 10
65 100 h. brown .. .. 10 10
66 120 h. violet on yellow .. 10 10

**1919.** Charity. Stamps of Austria optd. **POSTA CESKOSLOVENSKA 1919.**

A. Postage stamp issue of 1916.
67 49 3 h. violet .. .. 15 10
68 5 h. green .. .. 15 10
69 6 h. orange .. .. 40 50
70 10 h. purple .. .. 50 65
71 12 h. blue .. .. 50 50
72 60 15 h. red .. .. 15 15
73 20 h. green .. .. 15 15
75 25 h. blue .. .. 20 15
76 30 h. violet .. .. 20 15
77 51 40 h. green .. .. 20 20
78 50 h. green .. .. 20 15
79 60 h. blue .. .. 25 25
80 80 h. brown .. .. 20 20
81 90 h. purple .. .. 45 45
82 1 k. red on yellow .. 30 30
83aa 52 2 k. blue .. .. 1·50 1·25
85aa 3 k. red .. .. 6·25 5·00
87a 4 k. green .. .. 12·50 6·25
89a 10 k. violet .. .. £250 £300

B. Air stamps of 1918 optd. **FLUGPOST** or surch. also.
91. 52. 1 k. 50 on 2 k. mauve .. £170 £150
92. 2 k. 50 on 3 k. yellow .. £200 £170
93. 4 k. grey .. .. .. £650 £600

C. Newspaper stamp of 1908. Imperf.
94. N 43. 10 h. red .. .. £1600 £1400

D. Newspaper stamps of 1916. Imperf.
95. N 53. 2 h. brown .. .. 10 10
96. 4 h. green .. .. 25 25
97. 6 h. blue .. .. 25 25
98. 10 h. orange .. .. 3·75 3·75
99. 30 h. red .. .. 1·50 1·25

E. Express Newspaper stamps of 1916.
100. N 54. 2 h. red on yellow .. 30·00 30·00
101. 5 h. green on yellow £1200 £1000

F. Express Newspaper stamps of 1917.
102. N 61. 2 h. red on yellow .. 10 15
103. 5 h. green on yellow 10 10

G. Postage Due stamps of 1908.
104. D 44. 2 h. red .. .. £3000 £2500
105. 4 h. red .. .. 25·00 25·00
106. 6 h. red .. .. 12·50 7·50
108. 14 h. red .. .. 75·00 75·00
109. 25 h. red .. .. 50·00 50·00
110. 30 h. red .. .. £425 £425
111. 50 h. red .. .. £1000 £1000

H. Postage Due stamps of 1916.
112. D 55. 5 h. red .. .. 10 15
113. 10 h. red .. .. 15 20
114. 15 h. red .. .. 15 20
115. 20 h. red .. .. 2·00 2·00
116. 25 h. red .. .. 1·25 1·25
117. 30 h. red .. .. 45 45
118. 40 h. red .. .. 1·25 1·25
119. 50 h. red .. .. £450 £375
120. D 56. 1 k. blue .. .. 12·50 12·50
121. 5 k. blue .. .. 50·00 50·00
122. 10 k. blue .. .. £350 £300

I. Postage Due stamps of 1916 (optd. **PORTO** or surch. **15** also).
123. 36. 1 h. black .. .. 25·00 20·00
124. – 15 h. on 2 h. violet .. £150 £130

J. Postage Due stamps of 1917 (surch. **PORTO** and value).
125. 50. 10 h. on 24 h. blue .. 85·00 £100
126. 15 h. on 36 h. violet .. 50 50
127. 20 h. on 54 h. orange .. 90·00 £100
128. 50 h. on 42 h. brown .. 60 65

**1919.** Various stamps of Hungary optd. **POSTA CESKOSLOVENSKA 1919.**

A. Postage stamp issue of 1900 ("Turul" type).
129. 7. 1 f. grey .. .. .. £1600 £1200
130. 2 f. yellow .. .. 4·25 3·75
131. 3 f. orange .. .. 65·00 65·00
132. 6 f. olive .. .. .. 5·00 5·00
133. 50 f. lake on blue .. 60 55
134. 60 f. green on red .. 60·00 25·00
135. 70 f. brown on green .. £1800 £1500

B. Postage stamp issue of 1916 ("Harvester" and "Parliament" types).
136 18 2 f. brown (No. 245) .. 10 10
137 3 f. red .. .. 10 10
138 5 f. green .. .. 10 10
139 6 f. blue .. .. 50 50
140 10 f. red (No. 250) .. 1·00 1·50
141 10 f. red (No. 243) .. £400 £325
142 15 f. purple (No. 251) .. 20 15
143 15 f. purple (No. 244) .. £170 £180
144 20 f. brown .. .. 8·50 7·50
145 25 f. blue .. .. 60 50
146 35 f. brown .. .. 8·75 8·75
147 40 f. green .. .. 2·00 1·60
148 19 50 f. purple .. .. 75 65
149 75 f. green .. .. 65 50
150 80 f. green .. .. 1·25 1·00
151 1 k. red .. .. 1·50 1·25
152 2 k. brown .. .. 8·75 8·75
153 3 k. grey and violet .. 50·00 55·00
154 5 k. lt brown & brown .. £120 £110
155 10 k. mauve and brown .. £1300 £1200

C. Postage stamp issue of 1918 ("Charles" and "Zita" types).
156 27 10 f. red .. .. 15 15
157 20 f. brown .. .. 25 20
158 25 f. blue .. .. 1·50 1·00
159 28 40 f. green .. .. 2·50 2·00
160 50 f. purple .. .. 55·00 75·00

D. War Charity stamps of 1916.
161 20 10 + 2 f. red .. .. 40 50
162 – 15 + 2 f. lilac (No. 265) .. 55 75
163 22 40 + 2 f. red .. .. 5·00 4·50

E. Postage stamps of 1919 ("Harvester" type inscr. "MAGYAR POSTA").
164. 30. 10 f. red (No. 305) .. 8·75 7·50
165. 20 f. brown .. .. £3750 £3750

F. Newspaper stamp of 1900.
166 N 9 2 f. orange (No. N136) 10 10

G. Express Letter stamp of 1916.
167. E 18. 2 f. olive & red (No. E 245) 10 10

H. Postage Due stamps of 1903 with figures in black.
170. D 9. 1 f. green (No. D 170) £1000 £650
173. 2 f. green .. .. £500 £450
174. 5 f. green .. .. £900 £750
168. 12 f green .. .. £3250 £2750
172. 50 f. green .. .. £325 £250

I. Postage Due Stamps of 1915 with figures in red.
176. D 9. 1 f. green (No. D 190) £200 £180
177. 2 f. green .. .. 70 50
178. 5 f. green .. .. 15·00 13·00
179. 6 f. green .. .. 1·50 1·50
180. 10 f. green .. .. 40 40
181. 12 f. green .. .. 2·00 2·00
182. 15 f. green .. .. 8·50 5·50
183. 20 f. green .. .. 75 1·00
184. 30 f. green .. .. 50·00 50·00

9. President Masaryk.

10.

11. Allegories of Republic.

12. Hussite.

13.

**1920.**
185. 9. 125 h. blue .. .. 45 20
186. 500 h. black .. .. 2·50 2·50
187. 1,000 h. brown .. .. 5·00 5·00

**1920.**
188. 10. 5 h. blue .. .. 10 10
189. 5 h. violet .. .. 10 10
190. 10 h. green .. .. 10 10
191. 10 h. olive .. .. 10 10
192. 15 h. brown .. .. 10 10
196. 11. 20 h. red .. .. 10 10
193b. 10. 20 h. orange .. .. 10 10
197. 11. 25 h. brown .. .. 10 10
194a. 10. 25 h. green .. .. 15 10
198. 11. 30 h. purple .. .. 10 10
195. 10. 30 h. purple .. .. 1·75 10
199. 11. 40 h. brown .. .. 15 10
200. 50 h. red .. .. 15 10
201. 50 h. green .. .. 15 10
202. 60 h. blue .. .. 15 10
203. 12. 80 h. violet .. .. 20 25
204. 90 h. sepia .. .. 40 70
205. 13. 100 h. green .. .. 30 10
206. 11. 100 h. brown .. .. 30 10
227. 13. 100 h. red on yellow .. 2·00 10
207. 11. 150 h. red .. .. 2·25 70
208. 185 h. orange .. .. 85 20
209. 13. 200 h. purple .. .. 60 10
228. 200 h. blue on yellow .. 7·50 10
210. 11. 250 h. green .. .. 2·25 40
211. 13. 300 h. red .. .. 1·50 10
229. 300 h. purple on yellow 6·00 15
212. 400 h. brown .. .. 4·50 50
213. 500 h. green .. .. 6·25 50
214. 600 h. purple .. .. 7·50 50

**1920.** Air. Surch with airplane and value. Imperf or perf.
215 2 14 k. on 200 h. bl (No. 13) 22·00 25·00
216 3 24 k. on 500 h. brown (No. 36) .. .. 50·00 50·00
220 28 k. on 1000 h. purple (No. 37) .. .. 45·00 45·00

**1920.** Red Cross Fund. Surch. with new value, etc.
221. 2. 40 h. + 20 h. yellow .. 1·00 1·00
222. 3. 60 h. + 20 h. green .. 1·00 1·00
223. 9. 125 h. + 25 h. blue .. 2·50 2·50

**1922.** Surch with airplane and value.
224. 13. 50 on 100 h. green .. 1·90 1·75
225. 100 on 200 h. purple .. 5·00 3·75
226. 250 on 400 h. brown .. 7·50 7·50

18. President Masaryk, after portrait by M. Savatimsky.

20.

23a.

**1923.** 5th Anniv. of Republic.
230. 18. 50 h. (+50 h.) green .. 1·00 75
231. 100 h. (+100 h.) red .. 1·25 1·00
232. 200 h. (+200 h.) blue .. 6·00 6·25
233. 300 h. (+300 h.) brown 9·00 7·00

**1925.**
234 20. 40 h. orange .. .. 1·00 15
235 50 h. green .. .. 1·75 10
236 60 h. purple .. .. 2·40 10
237 18. 1 k. red .. .. 90 10
238 2 k. blue .. .. 3·50 25
245 3 k. brown .. .. 4·50 15
240 5 k. green .. .. 1·50 25

The 1, 2 and 3 k. (which with the 5 k. differ slightly in design from the haleru values) come in various sizes, differing in some cases in the details of the designs.

**1925.** Int. Olympic Congress. Optd. **CONGRES OLYMP. INTERNAT. PRAHA 1925.**
246 18 50 h. (+50 h.) green .. 5·00 10·00
247 100 h. (+100 h.) red .. 10·00 15·00
248 200 h. (+200 h.) blue .. 70·00 £100

**1926.** 8th All-Sokol Display, Prague. Optd **VIII. SLET VSESOKOLSKY PRAHA 1926.**
249. 18. 50 h. (+50 h.) green .. 6·00 6·50
250. 100 h. (+100 h.) red .. 6·00 6·50
251. 200 h. (+200 h.) blue .. 25·00 25·00
252. 300 h. (+300 h.) brown 45·00 55·00

**1926.**
254b. 23a. 50 h. green .. .. 15 10
254c. 60 h. purple .. .. 50 10
254d. 1 k. red .. .. 25 10

25. Karluv Tyn Castle. 26. Strahov. 27. Pernstyn Castle.

28. Orava Castle. 30. Hradcany, Prague.

**1926.** Perf or imperf. × perf.
267 25 20 h. red .. .. 25 10
268 27 30 h. green .. .. 15 10
258 28 40 h. brown .. .. 40 10
259 25 1 k. 20 purple .. .. 50 40
270 26 1 k. 20 purple .. .. 25 10
271 25 1 k. 50 red .. .. 25 10
272 27 2 k. green .. .. 30 10
263 30 2 k. blue .. .. 90 10
273 25 2 k. 50 blue .. .. 4·00 25
273a – 2 k. 50 blue .. .. 35 10
273b 28 3 k. brown .. .. 50 10
264a 30 3 k. red .. .. 1·75 10
276 – 4 k. purple .. .. 6·00 1·00
277 – 5 k. green .. .. 6·50 60
DESIGNS—As T 25/28. 2 k. 50 (No. 273a), Statue of St. Wenceslas, Prague. As T 30. 4, 5 k. Upper Tatra.

32. Hradek Castle. 33. Pres. Masaryk.

**1928.** 10th Anniv. of Independence.
278. 32. 30 h. black .. .. 10 10
279. – 40 h. brown .. .. 10 15
280. – 50 h. green .. .. 15 10
281. – 60 h. red .. .. 15 20
282. – 1 k. red .. .. 25 15
283. – 1 k. 20 purple .. .. 45 80
284. – 2 k. blue .. .. 50 75
285. – 2 k. 50 blue .. .. 1·60 2·50
286. 33. 3 k. sepia .. .. 1·25 1·40
287. – 5 k. violet .. .. 1·60 2·50
DESIGNS—HORIZ. 40 h. Town Hall, Levoca. 50 h. Telephone Exchange, Prague. 60 h. Village of Jasina. 1 k. Hluboka Castle 1 k. 20, Pilgrim's House, Velehrad. 2 k. 50, The Grand Tatra. VERT. 2 k. Brno Cathedral. 5 k. Town Hall, Prague.

34. National Arms. 35. St. Wenceslas on Horseback.

**1929.** Perf. or imperf. × perf.
287a. 34. 5 h. blue .. .. 10 10
287b. 10 h. brown .. .. 10 10
288. 20 h. red .. .. 10 10
289. 25 h. green .. .. 10 10
290. 30 h. purple .. .. 10 10
291a. 40 h. brown .. .. 10 10

**1929.** Death Millenary of St. Wenceslas.
293. 35. 50 h. green .. .. 15 10
294. – 60 h. violet .. .. 35 10
295. – 2 k. blue .. .. 90 50
296. – 3 k. brown .. .. 95 25
297. – 5 k. purple .. .. 4·75 2·75
DESIGNS: 2 k. Foundation of St. Vitus's Church. 3 k., 5 k. Martyrdom of St. Wenceslas.

36. Brno Cathedral.

**1929.**
298. 36. 3 k. brown .. .. 1·60 10
299. – 4 k. blue .. .. 3·75 50
300. – 5 k. green .. .. 4·50 25
301. – 10 k. violet .. .. 8·00 2·75
DESIGNS: 4 k. Tatra Mountains. 5 k. Town Hall, Prague. 10 k. St. Nicholas Church, Prague.

38. 39.

**1930.**
302a. 38. 50 h. green .. .. 15 10
303. 60 h. purple .. .. 50 10
304. 1 k. red .. .. 20 10
See also No. 373.

**1930.** 80th Birthday of President Masaryk.
305. 39. 2 k. green .. .. 70 40
306. 3 k. red .. .. 1·25 40
307. 5 k. blue .. .. 4·00 2·50
308. 10 k. black .. .. 7·50 5·00

40. Fokker F.IXD. 41. Smolik S.19.

**1930.** Air.
394. 40. 30 h. violet .. .. 10 15
309. 50 h. green .. .. 10 15
310. 1 k. red .. .. 20 30
311. 41. 2 k. green .. .. 50 70
312. 3 k. purple .. .. 1·00 1·00
313. – 4 k. blue .. .. 75 1·00
314. – 5 k. brown .. .. 1·60 2·25
315. – 10 k. blue .. .. 3·75 5·00
316a. – 20 k. violet .. .. 4·75 4·50
DESIGNS—As Type 41: 4, 5 k. Smolik S.19 with tree in foreground. 10, 20 k. Fokker F.IXD over Prague.

43. Krumlov. 44. Dr. Miroslav Tyrs.

**1932.** Views.
317. – 3 k. 50 pur. (Krivoklat) 1·25 90
318. – 4 k. blue (Orlik) .. 1·75 50
319. 43. 5 k. green .. .. 3·00 50

**1932.** Birth Centenary of Dr. Tyrs, founder of the "Sokol" Movement.
320. 44. 50 h. green .. .. 30 10
321. 1 k. red .. .. 50 10
322. – 2 k. blue .. .. 6·00 40
323. – 3 k. brown .. .. 11·00 45
On the 2 k. and 3 k. the portrait faces left.

46. Dr. M. Tyrs. 47. Church and Episcopal Palace, Nitra.

**1933.**
324. 46. 60 h. violet .. .. 10 10

**1933.** 1100th Anniv of Foundation of 1st Christian Church at Nitra.
325. 47. 50 h. green .. .. 30 10
326. – 1 k. red (Church gateway) .. .. 3·50 25

49. Frederick Smetana. 50. Consecrating Colours at Kiev.

**1934.** 50th Death Anniv. of Smetana.
327. 49. 50 h. green .. .. 15 10

**1934.** 20th Anniv. of Czechoslovak Foreign Legions.
328. 50. 50 h. green .. .. 25 10
329. – 1 k. red .. .. 30 10
330. – 2 k. blue .. .. 1·75 30
331. – 3 k. brown .. .. 3·00 30
DESIGNS—HORIZ. 1 k. French battalion enrolling at Bayonne. VERT. 2 k. Standard of the Russian Legion. 3 k. French, Russian and Serbian legionaries.

52. Antonin Dvorak. 53. "Where is my Fatherland?".

**1934.** 30th Death Anniv. of Dvorak.
332. 52. 50 h. green .. .. 20 10

**1934.** Cent. of Czech National Anthem.
333. 53. 1 k. purple .. .. 30 15
334. 2 k. blue .. .. 90 40

54 Autograph portraits of Pres. Masaryk. 55

**1935.** 85th Birthday of President Masaryk.
335. 54. 50 h. green .. .. 20 10
336. 1 k. red .. .. 35 10
337. 55. 2 k. blue .. .. 90 40
338. 3 k. brown .. .. 1·75 40
See also No. 374.

56. Czech Monument, Arras. 57. Gen. M. R. Stefanik.

**1935.** 20th Anniv. of Battle of Arras.
339. 56. 1 k. red .. .. 35 10
340. 2 k. blue .. .. 90 40

**1935.** 16th Death Anniv. of Gen. Stefanik.
341. 57. 50 h. green .. .. 10 10

58. St Cyril and St. Methodius. 59. J. A. Komensky (Comenius).

60. Dr. Edward Benes. 60a. Gen. M. R. Stefanik. 61. Pres. Masaryk.

**1935.** Prague Catholic Congress.
342. 58. 50 h. green .. .. 20 10
343. 1 k. red .. .. 30 10
344. 2 k. blue .. .. 95 40

**1935.**
345 59 40 h. blue .. .. 10 10
346 60 50 h. green .. .. 10 10
390 60a 50 h. green .. .. 10 10
347 60 h. violet .. .. 10 10
391 60 h. blue .. .. 9·00 14·00
348 61 1 k. purple .. .. 10 10
395 1 k. purple .. .. 15 10
No. 390 differs from No. 341 in having an ornament in place of the word "HALERU".
No. 348 has "1 Kc" in value tablets, No. 395 "1 K".

62. Symbolic of Infancy. 63. K. H. Macha.

**1936.** Child Welfare.
349. – 50 h.+50 h. green .. 30 40
350. 62. 1 k.+50 h. red .. 50 65
351. – 2 k.+50 h. blue .. 1·25 1·90
DESIGN: 50 h., 2 k. Grandfather, mother and child from centre of Type 62 (enlarged).

**1936.** Death Cent. of Macha (poet).
352. 63. 50 h. green .. .. 10 10
353. 1 k. red .. .. 25 10

64. Banska Bystrica. 65. Podebrady.

**1936.**
354. – 1 k. 20 purple .. .. 10 10
355. 64. 1 k. 50 red .. .. 10 10
355a. – 1 k. 60 olive .. .. 10 10
356. – 2 k. green .. .. 10 10
357. – 2 k. 50 blue .. .. 15 10
358. – 3 k. brown .. .. 20 10
359. – 3 k. 50 violet .. .. 70 40
360. 65. 4 k. violet .. .. 25 10
361. – 5 k. green .. .. 30 10
362. – 10 k. blue .. .. 70 40
DESIGNS—As Type 64: 1 k. 20, Palanok Castle. 1 k. 60, St. Barbara's Church, Kutna Hora. 2 k. Zvikov (Klingden Berg) Castle. 2 k. 50, Strecno Castle. 3 k. Hruba Skala Castle (Cesky Raj). 3 k. 50, Slavkov Castle. 5 k. Town Hall, Olomouc (23½ × 29½ mm). As Type 65: 10 k. Bratislava and Danube.

66. President Benes.

**1937.**
363. 66. 50 h. green .. .. 10 10

67. Mother and Child. 68. "Lullaby".

**1937.** Child Welfare.
364. 67. 50 h.+50 h. green .. 35 40
365. 1 k.+50 h. red .. .. 50 75
366. 68. 2 k.+1 k. blue .. .. 90 1·60

69. Czech Legionaries. 70. Prague.

**1937.** 20th Anniv. of Battle of Zborov.
367. 69. 50 h. green .. .. 15 10
368. 1 k. red .. .. 20 10

**1937.** 16th Anniv of Founding of Little Entente.
369. 70. 2 k. green .. .. 50 15
370. 2 k. 50 blue .. .. 70 50

71. J. E. Purkyne. 73. Peregrine Falcon.

**1937.** 150th Birth Anniv. of J. E. Purkyne (physiologist).
371. 71. 50 h. green .. .. 10 10
372. 1 k. red .. .. 20 10

**1937.** Mourning for Pres. Masaryk. As T 38 and 55, but panels of T 55 dated "14.IX.1937".
373. 38. 50 h. black .. .. 10 10
374. 55. 2 k. black .. .. 30 15

**1937.** Labour Congress, Prague. Optd **B.I.T. 1937**.
375 66 50 h. green .. .. 20 25
376 64 1 k. 50 red .. .. 20 25
377 – 2 k. green (No. 356) 35 55

**1938.** 10th Int. Sokol Display, Prague.
378. 73. 50 h. green .. .. 1·25 20
379. 1 k. red .. .. 1·25 20

74. Pres. Masaryk and Slovak Girl. 75. Czech Legionaries at Bachmac.

**1938.** Child Welfare and Birthday of Late President Masaryk.

| | | | | |
|---|---|---|---|---|
| 380. | 74. | 50 h.+50 h green | 25 | 50 |
| 381. | | 1 k.+50 h red | 40 | 65 |

**1938.** 20th Anniv. of Battles in Russia, Italy and France. Inscr. "1918 1938".

| | | | | |
|---|---|---|---|---|
| 382. | 75. | 50 h. green | 15 | 10 |
| 383. | – | 50 h. green | 15 | 10 |
| 384. | – | 50 h. green | 15 | 10 |

DESIGNS: Czech Legionaries at Doss Alto (No. 383) and at Vouziers (No. 384).

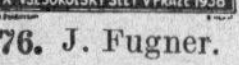
**76.** J. Fugner.

**77.** Armament Factories, Pilsen.

**1938.** 10th Sokol Summer Games.

| | | | | |
|---|---|---|---|---|
| 385. | 76. | 50 h. green | 10 | 10 |
| 386. | | 1 k. red | 10 | 10 |
| 387. | | 2 k. blue | 15 | 10 |

**1938.** Provincial Economic Council Meeting, Pilsen.

| | | | | |
|---|---|---|---|---|
| 388. | 77. | 50 h. green | 10 | 10 |

**78.** St. Elizabeth's Cathedral, Kosice.

**79.** "Peace".

**1938.** Kosice Cultural Exhibition.

| | | | | |
|---|---|---|---|---|
| 389. | 78. | 50 h. green | 10 | 10 |

**1938.** 20th Anniv. of Czech Republic.

| | | | | |
|---|---|---|---|---|
| 392. | 79. | 2 k. blue | 20 | 15 |
| 393. | | 3 k. brown | 40 | 15 |

**1939.** Inaug of Slovak Parliament. No 362 surcharged **Otvorenie slovenskeho snemu 18.1.1939** and **300 h.** between bars.

| | | | | |
|---|---|---|---|---|
| 393b. | | 300 h. on 10 k. blue | 75 | 90 |

No. 393b was only issued in Slovakia but was withdrawn prior to the establishment of the Slovak state. The used price is for cancelled to order stamps.

**80.** Jasina.

**1939.** Inaug. of Carpatho-Ukrainian Parliament.

| | | | | |
|---|---|---|---|---|
| 393c | 80 | 3 k. blue | 10·00 | 30·00 |

The used price is for cancelled-to-order.

From mid-1939 until 1945, Czechoslovakia was divided into the German Protectorate of Bohemia and Moravia and the independent state of Slovakia. Both these countries issued their own stamps. Germany had already occupied Sudetenland where a number of unauthorised local issues were made at Asch, Karlsbad, Konstantinsbad, Hiklasdorf, Reichenberg-Maffersdorf and Rumburg. Hungary occupied Carpatho-Ukraine and the stamps of Hungary were used there. In 1945, upon liberation, stamps of Czechoslovakia were once again issued.

**81.** Clasped Hands. **82.** Arms and Soldier.

**1945.** Kosice Issue. Imperf.

| | | | | |
|---|---|---|---|---|
| 396 | 81 | 1 k. 50 purple | 1·90 | 1·90 |
| 397 | 82 | 2 k. red | 15 | 15 |
| 398 | | 5 k. green | 1·50 | 1·50 |
| 399 | | 6 k. blue | 40 | 40 |
| 400 | 81 | 9 k. red | 40 | 40 |
| 401 | | 13 k. brown | 75 | 75 |
| 402 | | 20 k. blue | 1·75 | 1·75 |

83 Arms and Linden Leaf

84 Linden Leaf and Buds

85 Linden Leaf and Flower

**1945.** Bratislava Issue. Imperf.

| | | | | |
|---|---|---|---|---|
| 403. | 83. | 50 h. green | 10 | 10 |
| 404. | | 1 k. purple | 10 | 10 |
| 405. | | 1 k. 50 red | 10 | 10 |
| 406. | | 2 k. blue | 10 | 10 |
| 407. | | 2 k. 40 red | 35 | 20 |
| 408. | | 3 k. brown | 10 | 10 |
| 409. | | 4 k. green | 15 | 10 |
| 410. | | 6 k. violet | 15 | 10 |
| 411. | | 10 k. brown | 35 | 20 |

**1945.** Prague Issue.

| | | | | |
|---|---|---|---|---|
| 412 | 84 | 10 (h.) black | 10 | 10 |
| 413 | | 30 (h.) brown | 10 | 10 |
| 414 | | 50 (h.) green | 10 | 10 |
| 415 | | 60 (h.) blue | 10 | 10 |
| 416 | 85 | 60 (h.) blue | 10 | 10 |
| 417 | | 80 (h.) red | 10 | 10 |
| 418 | | 120 (h.) red | 10 | 10 |
| 419 | | 300 (h.) purple | 10 | 10 |
| 420 | | 500 (h.) green | 10 | 10 |

**86.** Pres. Masaryk. **87.** Staff Capt. Ridky.

**1945.** Moscow Issue. Perf.

| | | | | |
|---|---|---|---|---|
| 421. | 86. | 5 h. violet | 10 | 10 |
| 422. | | 10 h. yellow | 10 | 10 |
| 423. | | 20 h. brown | 10 | 10 |
| 424. | | 50 h. green | 10 | 10 |
| 425. | | 1 k. red | 10 | 10 |
| 426. | | 2 k. blue | 10 | 10 |

**1945.** War Heroes.

| | | | | |
|---|---|---|---|---|
| 427. | 87. | 5 h. grey | 10 | 10 |
| 428. | – | 10 h. brown | 10 | 10 |
| 429. | – | 20 h. red | 10 | 10 |
| 430. | – | 25 h. red | 10 | 10 |
| 431. | – | 30 h. violet | 20 | 10 |
| 432. | – | 40 h. brown | 10 | 10 |
| 433. | – | 50 h. green | 10 | 10 |
| 434. | – | 60 h. violet | 20 | 15 |
| 435. | 87. | 1 k. red | 10 | 10 |
| 436. | – | 1 k. 50 red | 10 | 10 |
| 437. | – | 2 k. blue | 10 | 10 |
| 438. | – | 2 k. 50 violet | 10 | 10 |
| 439. | – | 3 k. brown | 10 | 10 |
| 440. | – | 4 k. mauve | 10 | 10 |
| 441. | – | 5 k. green | 20 | 10 |
| 442. | – | 10 k. blue | 40 | 10 |

PORTRAITS: 10 h., 1 k. 50, Dr. Novak. 20 h., 2 k. Capt. O. Jaros. 25 h., 2 k. 50, Staff Capt. Zimprich. 30 h., 3 k. Lt. J. Kral. 40 h., 4 k. J. Gabcik (parachutist). 50 h., 5 k. Staff Capt. Vasatko. 60 h., 10 k. Fr. Adamek.

**88.** Allied Flags.

**89.** Russian Soldier and Slovak Partisan.

**1945.** 1st Anniv of Slovak Rising.

| | | | | |
|---|---|---|---|---|
| 443. | 88. | 1 k. 50 red | 10 | 10 |
| 444. | – | 2 k. blue | 10 | 10 |
| 445. | 89. | 4 k. brown | 20 | 20 |
| 446. | – | 4 k. 50 violet | 20 | 20 |
| 447. | – | 5 k. green | 30 | 35 |

DESIGNS—VERT. 2 k. Banska Bystrica. HORIZ. 4 k. 50, Sklabina. 5 k. Strecno and partisan.

**90.** Pres. Masaryk.

**91.** Pres. Benes. **92.**

**1945.**

| | | | | |
|---|---|---|---|---|
| 452. | – | 30 h. purple | 10 | 10 |
| 448. | 90. | 50 h. brown | 10 | 10 |
| 453. | 91. | 60 h. blue | 15 | 10 |
| 449. | – | 80 h. green | 10 | 10 |
| 454. | – | 1 k. orange | 10 | 10 |
| 455. | 90. | 1 k. 20 red | 15 | 10 |
| 456. | | 1 k. 20 mauve | 10 | 10 |
| 450. | 91. | 1 k. 60 green | 15 | 10 |
| 457. | – | 2 k. 40 red | 15 | 10 |
| 458. | 91. | 3 k. purple | 20 | 10 |
| 459. | 90. | 4 k. blue | 15 | 10 |
| 460. | | 5 k. green | 20 | 10 |
| 461. | 91. | 7 k. black | 25 | 10 |
| 462. | – | 10 k. blue | 55 | 10 |
| 451. | 90. | 15 k. purple | 50 | 10 |
| 462a. | – | 20 k. brown | 85 | 10 |

PORTRAIT: 30 h., 80 h., 1 k., 2 k. 40, 10 k. 20 k. Gen. M. R. Stefanik.

**1945.** Students' World Congress, Prague.

| | | | | |
|---|---|---|---|---|
| 463. | 92. | 1 k. 50+1 k. 50 red | 10 | 10 |
| 464. | | 2 k. 50+2 k. 50 blue | 20 | 20 |

**93.** J. S. Kozina Monument.

**94.** St. George and Dragon.

**1945.** Execution of Jan Stadky Kozina, 1695.

| | | | | |
|---|---|---|---|---|
| 465. | 93. | 2 k. 40 red | 15 | 10 |
| 466. | | 4 k. blue | 20 | 20 |

**1946.** Victory.

| | | | | |
|---|---|---|---|---|
| 467. | 94. | 2 k. 40+2 k. 60 red | 10 | 15 |
| 468. | | 4 k.+6 k. blue | 15 | 15 |

**94a.** Lockheed Constellation over Charles Bridge, Prague.

**1946.** Air. First Prague–New York Flight.

| | | | | |
|---|---|---|---|---|
| 468b | 94a | 24 k. blue on buff | 75 | 75 |

**95.** Capt. F. Novak and Westland Lysander.

**96.** Lockheed Constellation over Bratislava.

**1946.** Air.

| | | | | |
|---|---|---|---|---|
| 469. | 95. | 1 k. 50 red | 15 | 10 |
| 470. | | 5 k. 50 blue | 45 | 15 |
| 471. | | 9 k. purple | 75 | 15 |
| 472. | 96. | 10 k. green | 65 | 35 |
| 473. | 95. | 16 k. violet | 75 | 45 |
| 474. | 96. | 20 k. blue | 1·00 | 75 |
| 475. | 94a. | 24 k. red | 1·25 | 75 |
| 476. | | 50 k. blue | 2·10 | 1·40 |

**97.** K. H. Borovsky.

**98.** Brno.

**1946.** 90th Death Anniv. of Borovsky (Independence advocate).

| | | | | |
|---|---|---|---|---|
| 477. | 97. | 1 k. 20 h. grey | 15 | 15 |

**1946.**

| | | | | |
|---|---|---|---|---|
| 478. | 98. | 2 k. 40 red | 35 | 15 |
| 479. | – | 7 k. 40 violet (Hodonin) (horiz.) | 20 | 10 |

**100.** Emigrants.

**101.** President Benes.

**1946.** Repatriation Fund.

| | | | | |
|---|---|---|---|---|
| 480. | – | 1 k. 60+1 k. 40 brown | 50 | 50 |
| 481. | 100. | 2 k. 40+2 k. 60 red | 25 | 25 |
| 482. | – | 4 k.+4 k. blue | 40 | 40 |

DESIGNS: 1 k. 60, Emigrants' departure. 4 k. Emigrants' return.

**1946.** Independence Day.

| | | | | |
|---|---|---|---|---|
| 483 | 101 | 60 h. blue | 10 | 10 |
| 484 | | 1 k. 60 green | 10 | 10 |
| 485 | | 3 k. purple | 10 | 10 |
| 486 | | 8 k. purple | 20 | 10 |

**102.** Flag and Symbols of Transport, Industry, Agriculture and Learning.

**103.** St. Adalbert.

**1947.** "Two Year Plan".

| | | | | |
|---|---|---|---|---|
| 487. | 102. | 1 k. 20 green | 10 | 10 |
| 488. | | 2 k. 40 red | 10 | 10 |
| 489. | | 4 k. blue | 50 | 20 |

**1947.** 950th Death Anniv of St. Adalbert (Bishop of Prague).

| | | | | |
|---|---|---|---|---|
| 490. | 103. | 1 k. 60 black | 45 | 35 |
| 491. | | 2 k. 40 red | 65 | 50 |
| 492. | | 5 k. green | 75 | 40 |

**104.** "Grief".

**105.** Rekindling Flame of Remembrance.

**1947.** 5th Anniv. of Destruction of Lidice.

| | | | | |
|---|---|---|---|---|
| 493. | 104. | 1 k. 20 black | 30 | 25 |
| 494. | | 1 k. 60 black | 40 | 40 |
| 495. | 105. | 2 k. 40 mauve | 50 | 45 |

**106.** Congress Emblem. **107.** Pres. Masaryk.

**1947.** Youth Festival.

| | | | | |
|---|---|---|---|---|
| 496. | 106. | 1 k. 20 purple | 40 | 25 |
| 497. | | 4 k. grey | 40 | 15 |

**1947.** 10th Death Anniv. of Pres Masaryk.

| | | | | |
|---|---|---|---|---|
| 498. | 107. | 1 k. 20 black on buff | 15 | 15 |
| 499. | | 4 k. blue on cream | 25 | 25 |

**108.** Stefan Moyses.

**109.** "Freedom".

**1947.** 150th Birth Anniv. of Stefan Moyses (Slavonic Society Organizer).

| | | | | |
|---|---|---|---|---|
| 500. | 108. | 1 k. 20 purple | 15 | 15 |
| 501. | | 4 k. blue | 25 | 25 |

**1947.** 30th Anniv. of Russian Revolution.

| | | | | |
|---|---|---|---|---|
| 502. | 109. | 2 k. 40 red | 25 | 20 |
| 503. | | 4 k. blue | 40 | 20 |

**110.** Pres. Benes. **111.** "Athletes paying Homage to Republic".

**115.** Dr. J. Vanicek.

**1948.**

| | | | | |
|---|---|---|---|---|
| 504. | 110. | 1 k. 50 brown | 10 | 10 |
| 505. | | 2 k. purple | 10 | 10 |
| 506. | | 5 k. blue | 15 | 10 |

The 2 k. and 5 k. are larger, 19×23 mm.

**1948.** 11th Sokol Congress, Prague. (a) 1st issue.

| | | | | |
|---|---|---|---|---|
| 507. | 111. | 1 k. 50 brown | 10 | 10 |
| 508. | | 3 k. red | 15 | 10 |
| 509. | | 5 k. blue | 40 | 10 |

(b) 2nd issue. Inscr. "XI. VSESOKOLSKY SLET V PRAZE 1948".

| | | | | |
|---|---|---|---|---|
| 515 | 115 | 1 k. green | 10 | 10 |
| 516 | – | 1 k. 50 brown | 15 | 10 |
| 517 | – | 2 k. blue | 15 | 10 |
| 518 | 115 | 3 k. purple | 25 | 10 |

PORTRAIT: 1 k. 50, 2 k. Dr. J. Scheiner.

**112.** Charles IV.

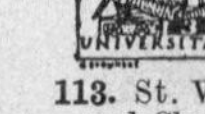
**113.** St. Wenceslas and Charles IV.

**1948.** 600th Anniv. of Charles IV University, Prague.

| | | | | |
|---|---|---|---|---|
| 510 | 112 | 1 k. 50 brown on buff | 10 | 10 |
| 511 | 113 | 2 k. brown on buff | 15 | 10 |
| 512 | | 3 k. red on buff | 15 | 10 |
| 513 | 112 | 5 k. blue on buff | 20 | 15 |

**114.** Insurgents.

**117.** Fr. Palacky and Dr. F. L. Rieger.

**1948.** Cent. of Abolition of Serfdom.

| | | | | |
|---|---|---|---|---|
| 514. | 114. | 1 k. 50 black | 10 | 10 |

**1948.** Centenary of Constituent Assembly at Kromeriz.

| | | | | |
|---|---|---|---|---|
| 519 | 117 | 1 k. 50 violet on buff | 10 | 10 |
| 520 | | 3 k. purple on buff | 15 | 10 |

**118.** J. M. Hurban.

**119.** President Benes.

**1948.** Centenary of Slovak Insurrection.
521. 118. 1 k. 50 brown .. .. 10 10
522. – 3 k. red (L. Stur) .. 10 10
523. – 5 k. blue (M. Hodza) .. 25 15

**1948.** Death of President Benes.
524 119 8 k. black .. .. 15 10

120. "Independence". 121. President Gottwald.

**1948.** 30th Anniv. of Independence.
525. 120. 1 k. 50 blue .. .. 10 10
526. 3 k. red .. .. 15 15

**1948.**
772 121 15 h. green .. .. 40 10
773 20 h. brown .. .. 50 10
526a 1 k. green .. .. 10 10
774 1 k. lilac .. .. 1·25 10
527 1 k. 50 brown 10 10
528b 3 k. red .. .. 15 10
775 3 k. black .. .. 85 10
529 5 k. blue .. .. 25 10
530 20 k. violet (23 × 30 mm) 60 10
See also No. 538.

122. Czech and Russian Workers. 123. Girl and Birds.

**1948.** 5th Anniv. of Russian Alliance.
531. 122. 3 k. red .. .. 15 10

**1948.** Child Welfare.
532. – 1 k. 50+1 k. purple .. 30 10
533. – 2 k.+1 k. blue .. 15 10
534. 123. 3 k.+1 k. red .. 25 10
DESIGNS: 1 k. 50, Boy and birds. 2 k. Mother and child.

124. V. I. Lenin. 125. Pres. Gottwald Addressing Rally.

**1949.** 25th Death Anniv. of Lenin.
535. 124. 1 k. 50 purple .. 25 15
536. 5 k. blue .. .. 25 20

**1949.** 1st Anniv. of Gottwald Government.
537. 125. 3 k. brown .. .. 10 10

**1949.** As T 121 (23 × 30 mm) but inscr "UNOR 1948".
538 121 10 k. green .. .. 40 15

126. P. O. Hviezdoslav. 127. Mail Coach and Steam Train.

**1949.** Poets.
539. 126. 50 h. purple .. .. 10 10
540 – 80 h. red .. .. 10 10
541. – 1 k. green .. .. 10 10
542. – 2 k. blue .. .. 30 10
543. – 4 k. purple .. .. 30 10
544. – 8 k. black .. .. 45 10
PORTRAITS: 80 h. V. Vancura. 1 k. J. Sverma. 2 k. J. Fucik. 4 k. J. Wolker. 8 k. A. Jirasek.

**1949.** 75th Anniv. of U.P.U.
545. 127. 3 k. red .. .. 2·40 1·75
546. – 5 k. blue .. .. 65 65
547. – 13 k. green .. .. 2·00 55
DESIGNS: 5 k. Mounted postman and mail van. 13 k. Sailing ship and Douglas DC-2 airliner.

128. Girl Agricultural Worker. 130. Industrial Worker.

**1949.** 9th Meeting of Czechoslovak Communist Party.
548. 128. 1 k. 50 green .. .. 45 45
549. – 3 k. red .. .. 25 25
550. 130. 5 k. blue .. .. 45 45
DESIGN—HORIZ. 3 k. Workers and flag.

131. F. Smetana and National Theatre, Prague. 132. A. S. Pushkin.

**1949.** 125th Birth Anniv. of Smetana (composer).
551. 131. 1 k. 50 green .. .. 15 10
552. 5 k. blue .. .. 60 20

**1949.** 150th Birth Anniv. of A. S. Pushkin (poet).
553. 132. 2 k. green .. .. 20 20

133. F. Chopin and Warsaw Conservatoire. 134. Globe and Ribbon.

**1949.** Death Cent. of Chopin (composer).
554. 133. 3 k. red .. .. 50 20
555. 8 k. purple .. .. 50 40

**1949.** 50th Sample Fair, Prague.
556. 134. 1 k. 50 purple .. 25 25
557. 5 k. blue .. .. 75 75

135. Zvolen Castle.

**1949.**
558. 135. 10 k. lake .. .. 60 15

**1949.** Air. Nos. 469/76 surch.
559. 95. 1 k. on 1 k. 50 red .. 15 10
560. 3 k. on 5 k. 50 blue .. 25 10
561. 6 k. on 9 k. purple .. 45 10
562. 7 k. 50 on 16 k. violet .. 55 20
563. 96. 8 k. on 10 k. green .. 55 50
564. 12 k. 50 on 20 k. blue .. 75 40
565. 94a. 15 k. on 24 k. red .. 2·25 70
566. 30 k. on 50 k. blue .. 1·50 70

137. Mediaeval Miners. 138. Modern Miner.

**1949.** 700th Anniv of Czechoslovak Mining Industry and 150th Anniv of Miners' Laws.
567. 137. 1 k. 50 violet .. .. 50 40
568. 138. 3 k. red .. .. 5·25 1·75
569. – 5 k. blue .. .. 4·00 1·60
DESIGN—HORIZ. 5 k. Miner with cutting machine.

139. Carpenters. 140. Dove and Buildings.

**1949.** 2nd T.U.C., Prague. Inscr. "1949".
570. 139. 1 k. green .. .. 2·25 1·00
571. – 2 k. pur. (Mechanic) .. 1·50 50

**1949.** Red Cross Fund. Inscr. "CS CERVENY KRIZ".
572 140 1 k. 50 h.+50 h. red .. 3·00 1·75
573 – 3 k.+1 k. red .. .. 3·00 1·75
DESIGN—VERT. 3 k. Dove and globe.

141. Mother and Child. 142. Joseph Stalin.

**1949.** Child Welfare Fund. Inscr. "DETEM 1949".
574. 141. 1 k. 50+50 h. grey .. 3·00 1·50
575. – 3 k.+1 k. red .. .. 4·50 1·75
DESIGN: 3 k. Father and child.

**1949.** 70th Birth Anniv of Joseph Stalin.
576 142 1 k. 50 green on buff .. 80 50
577 – 3 k. purple on buff .. 3·25 1·50
PORTRAIT: 3 k. Stalin facing left.

143. Skier. 144. Efficiency Badge.

**1950.** Tatra Cup Ski Championship.
578. 143. 1 k. 50 blue .. .. 2·00 80
579. 144. 3 k. red and buff .. 2·00 1·25
580. 143. 5 k. blue .. .. 2·75 1·50

145. V. Mayakovsky. 146. Soviet Tank Driver and Hradcany, Prague.

**1950.** 20th Death Anniv. of Mayakovsky (poet).
581. 145. 1 k. 50 purple .. 1·60 70
582. 3 k. red .. .. 1·60 70

**1950.** 5th Anniv. of Republic (1st issue).
583. 146. 1 k. 50 green .. .. 25 20
584. – 2 k. purple .. .. 80 50
585. – 3 k. red .. .. 20 10
586. – 5 k. blue .. .. 45 15
DESIGNS: 2 k. "Hero of Labour" medal. 3 k. Workers and Town Hall. 5 k. "The Kosice Programme" (part of text).

147. Factory and Workers. 148. S. K. Neumann.

**1950.** 5th Anniv. of Republic (2nd issue).
587 147. 1 k. 50 green .. .. 1·50 90
588. – 2 k. brown .. .. 1·50 75
589. – 3 k. red .. .. 90 40
590. – 5 k. blue .. .. 90 40
DESIGNS: 2 k. Crane and Tatra Mts. 3 k. Labourer and tractor. 5 k. Three workers.

**1950.** 75th Birth Anniv of S. K. Neumann (writer).
591. 148. 1 k. 50 blue .. .. 25 10
592. 3 k. purple .. .. 90 75

149. Bozena Nemcova. 150. "Liberation of Colonial Nations".

**1950.** 130th Birth Anniv of Bozena Nemcova (authoress).
593. 149. 1 k. 50 blue .. .. 1·00 75
594. 7 k. purple .. .. 25 20

**1950.** 2nd Int. Students' World Congress, Prague. Inscr. "II KONGRES MSS".
595. 150. 1 k. 50 green .. .. 15 10
596. – 2 k. purple .. .. 1·25 50
597. – 3 k. red .. .. 20 15
598. – 5 k. blue .. .. 40 35
DESIGNS—HORIZ. 2 k. Woman, globe and dove ("Fight for Peace"). 3 k. Group of students ("Democratisation of Education"). 5 k. Students and banner ("International Students, Solidarity").

151. Miner, Soldier and Farmer. 152. Z. Fibich.

**1950.** Army Day.
599. 151. 1 k. 50 blue .. .. 75 70
600. – 3 k. red .. .. 25 20
DESIGN: 3 k. Czechoslovak and Russian soldiers.

**1950.** Birth Cent. of Fibich (composer).
601. 152. 3 k. red .. .. 90 50
602. 8 k. green .. .. 25 15

153. "Communications". 154. J. G. Tajovsky.

**1950.** 1st Anniv of League of Postal, Telephone and Telegraph Employees.
603. 153. 1 k. 50 brown .. 20 10
604. 3 k. red .. .. 75 30

**1950.** 10th Death Anniv of J. Gregor Tajovsky (writer).
605. 154. 1 k. 50 brown .. 75 40
606. 5 k. blue .. .. 75 55

155. Reconstruction of Prague.

**1950.** Philatelic Exhibition, Prague.
607. 155. 1 k. 50 blue .. .. 35 15
608. 3 k. red .. .. 60 45

156. Czech and Russian Workers. 157. Dove (after Picasso).

**1950.** Czechoslovak-Soviet Friendship.
609. 156. 1 k. 50 brown .. .. 35 25
610. 5 k. blue .. .. 65 45

**1951.** Czechoslovak Peace Congress.
611. 157. 2 k. blue .. .. 4·75 2·75
612. 3 k. red .. .. 3·00 1·50

158. Julius Fucik. 159. Mechanical Hammer.

**1951.** Peace Propaganda.
613. 158. 1 k. 50 grey .. .. 50 30
614. 5 k. blue .. .. 1·75 1·00

**1951.** Five Year Plan (heavy industry).
615. 159. 1 k. 50 black .. .. 10 10
616. – 3 k. brown .. .. 15 10
617. 159. 4 k. blue .. .. 65 45
DESIGN—HORIZ. 3 k. Installing machinery.

160. Industrial Workers. 161. Karlovy Vary.

**1951.** International Women's Day.
618. 160. 1 k. 50 olive .. .. 25 10
619. – 3 k. red .. .. 1·40 55
620. – 5 k. blue .. .. 50 10
DESIGNS: 3 k. Woman driving tractor. 5 k. Korean woman and group.

**1951.** Air. Spas.

621. 161. 6 k. green .. .. 2·50 75
622. – 10 k. purple .. .. 2·25 95
623. – 15 k. blue .. .. 5·00 1·50
624. – 20 k. brown .. .. 6·75 1·60

DESIGNS—Ilyushin Il-12 airplane over: 10 k. Piestany. 15 k. Marianske Lazne. 20 k. Silac.

**162.** Miners. **163.** Ploughing.

**1951.** Mining Industry.

625 162 1 k. 50 black .. .. 75 20
626 3 k. purple .. .. 10 10

**1951.** Agriculture.

627. 163. 1 k. 50 brown .. .. 50 50
628. – 2 k. green (Woman and cows) .. .. 1·75 60

**164.** Tatra Mountains. **165.** Partisan and Soviet Soldier.

**1951.** Recreation Centres. Inscr. "ROH".

629. 164. 1 k. 50 green .. .. 20 10
630. – 2 k. brown .. .. 1·00 50
631. – 3 k. red .. .. 25 10

DESIGNS: 2 k. Beskydy Mts. 3 k. Krkonose Mts.

**1951.** 30th Anniv. of Czechoslovak Communist Party. Inscr. "30 LET" etc.

635 – 1 k. 50 grey .. .. 75 25
632 – 2 k. brown .. .. 25 10
633 165 3 k. red .. .. 30 10
636 – 5 k. blue .. .. 2·00 1·00
634 – 8 k. black .. .. 75 30

DESIGNS—HORIZ. 1 k. 50, 5 k. Gottwald and Stalin. 8 k. Marx, Engels, Lenin and Stalin. VERT. 2 k. Factory militiaman.

**167.** Dvorak. **168.** Gymnast.

**1951.** Prague Musical Festival.

637. 167. 1 k. brown .. .. 25 10
638. – 1 k. 50 grey (Smetana) 1·00 50
639. 167. 2 k. brown .. .. 1·00 65
640. – 3 k. purple (Smetana) 25 15

**1951.** 9th Sokol Congress.

641 168 1 k. green .. .. 60 20
642 – 1 k. 50 brown (Women discus thrower) .. 55 25
643 – 3 k. red (Footballers) 1·25 25
644 – 5 k. blue (Skier) .. 2·50 1·00

**1951.** 10th Death Anniv. of Bohumir Smeral. As T **154**, but portrait of Smeral.

645 1 k. 50 grey .. .. 45 30
646 3 k. purple .. .. 45 15

**170.** Scene from "Fall of Berlin".

**172.** A. Jirasek. **173.** "Fables and Fates" (M. Ales).

**1951.** Int. Film Festival, Karlovy Vary. Inscr. "SE SOVETSKYM FILMEM", etc.

647. 170. 80 h. red .. .. 35 20
648. – 1 k. 50 grey .. .. 35 20
649. 170. 4 k. blue .. .. 1·25 90

DESIGN: 1 k. 50, Scene from "The Great Citizen".

**1951.** 30th Death Anniv. of J. Hybes (politician). As T **154**, but portrait of Hybes.

650. 1 k. 50 brown .. .. 10 10
651. 2 k. red .. .. 90 40

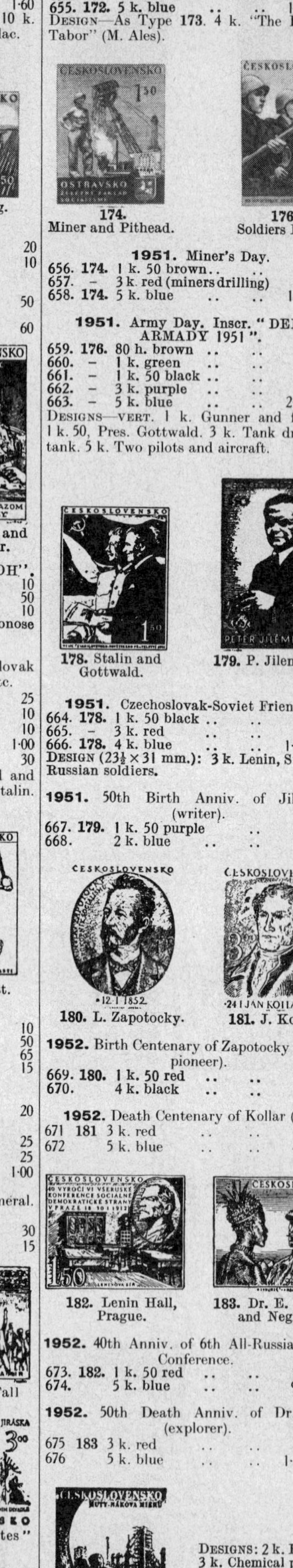

**1951.** Birth Cent. of Jirasek (author).

652. 172. 1 k. 50 black .. .. 40 10
653. 173. 3 k. red .. .. 40 10
654. – 4 k. black .. .. 40 10
655. 172. 5 k. blue .. .. 1·50 85

DESIGN—As Type **173**. 4 k. "The Region of Tabor" (M. Ales).

**174.** Miner and Pithead. **176.** Soldiers Parading.

**1951.** Miner's Day.

656. 174. 1 k. 50 brown .. .. 15 10
657. – 3 k. red (miners drilling) 15 10
658. 174. 5 k. blue .. .. 1·00 85

**1951.** Army Day. Inscr. "DEN CS ARMADY 1951".

659. 176. 80 h. brown .. .. 25 15
660. – 1 k. green .. .. 25 25
661. – 1 k. 50 black .. .. 40 25
662. – 3 k. purple .. .. 45 25
663. – 5 k. blue .. .. 2·00 95

DESIGNS—VERT. 1 k. Gunner and field-gun. 1 k. 50, Pres. Gottwald. 3 k. Tank driver and tank. 5 k. Two pilots and aircraft.

**178.** Stalin and Gottwald. **179.** P. Jilemnicky.

**1951.** Czechoslovak-Soviet Friendship.

664. 178. 1 k. 50 black .. .. 10 10
665. – 3 k. red .. .. 15 10
666. 178. 4 k. blue .. .. 1·00 50

DESIGN (23½ × 31 mm.): 3 k. Lenin, Stalin and Russian soldiers.

**1951.** 50th Birth Anniv. of Jilemnicky (writer).

667. 179. 1 k. 50 purple .. 20 15
668. 2 k. blue .. .. 70 40

**180.** L. Zapotocky. **181.** J. Kollar.

**1952.** Birth Centenary of Zapotocky (socialist pioneer).

669. 180. 1 k. 50 red .. .. 10 15
670. 4 k. black .. .. 50 40

**1952.** Death Centenary of Kollar (poet).

671 181 3 k. red .. .. 10 10
672 5 k. blue .. .. 45 45

**182.** Lenin Hall, Prague. **183.** Dr. E. Holub and Negro.

**1952.** 40th Anniv. of 6th All-Russian Party Conference.

673. 182. 1 k. 50 red .. .. 10 20
674. 5 k. blue .. .. 90 35

**1952.** 50th Death Anniv. of Dr. Holub (explorer).

675 183 3 k. red .. .. 40 25
676 5 k. blue .. .. 1·75 1·10

DESIGNS: 2 k. Foundry. 3 k. Chemical plant.

**184.** Electric Welding.

**1952.** Industrial Development.

677. 184. 1 k. 50 black .. .. 25 10
678. – 2 k. brown .. .. 1·25 50
679. – 3 k. red .. .. 15 10

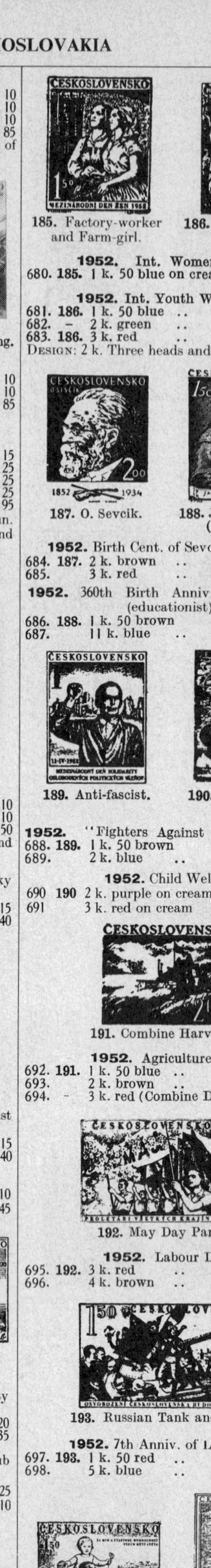

**185.** Factory-worker and Farm-girl. **186.** Young Workers.

**1952.** Int. Women's Day.

680. 185. 1 k. 50 blue on cream 1·00 40

**1952.** Int. Youth Week.

681. 186. 1 k. 50 blue .. .. 10 10
682. – 2 k. green .. .. 15 10
683. 186. 3 k. red .. .. 1·25 60

DESIGN: 2 k. Three heads and globe.

**187.** O. Sevcik. **188.** J. A. Komensky (Comenius).

**1952.** Birth Cent. of Sevcik (musician).

684. 187. 2 k. brown .. .. 65 45
685. 3 k. red .. .. 15 15

**1952.** 360th Birth Anniv. of Komensky (educationist).

686. 188. 1 k. 50 brown .. 1·00 50
687. 11 k. blue .. .. 25 10

**189.** Anti-fascist. **190.** Woman and Children.

**1952.** "Fighters Against Fascism" Day.

688. 189. 1 k. 50 brown .. 10 10
689. 2 k. blue .. .. 70 50

**1952.** Child Welfare.

690 190 2 k. purple on cream .. 95 10
691 3 k. red on cream .. 15 75

**191.** Combine Harvester.

**1952.** Agriculture Day.

692. 191. 1 k. 50 blue .. .. 90 75
693. 2 k. brown .. .. 25 20
694. – 3 k. red (Combine Drill) 25 20

**192.** May Day Parade.

**1952.** Labour Day.

695. 192. 3 k. red .. .. 35 35
696. 4 k. brown .. .. 1·10 85

**193.** Russian Tank and Crowd.

**1952.** 7th Anniv. of Liberation.

697. 193. 1 k. 50 red .. .. 60 50
698. 5 k. blue .. .. 1·75 1·25

**194.** Boy Pioneer and Children. **195.** J. V. Myslbek.

**1952.** International Children's Day.

699 194 1 k. 50 brown .. 10 10
700 2 k. green .. .. 1·25 60
701 – 3 k. red (Pioneers and teacher) .. .. 15 10

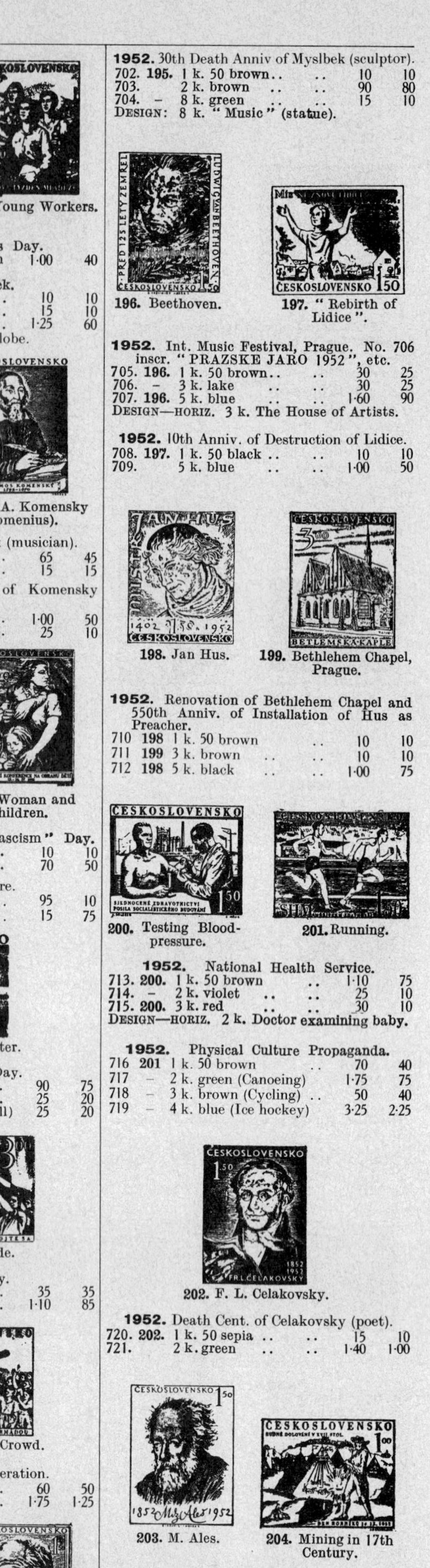

**1952.** 30th Death Anniv of Myslbek (sculptor).

702. 195. 1 k. 50 brown .. .. 10 10
703. 2 k. brown .. .. 90 80
704. – 8 k. green .. .. 15 10

DESIGN: 8 k. "Music" (statue).

**196.** Beethoven. **197.** "Rebirth of Lidice".

**1952.** Int. Music Festival, Prague. No. 706 inscr. "PRAZSKE JARO 1952", etc.

705. 196. 1 k. 50 brown .. .. 30 25
706. – 3 k. lake .. .. 30 25
707. 196. 5 k. blue .. .. 1·60 90

DESIGN—HORIZ. 3 k. The House of Artists.

**1952.** 10th Anniv. of Destruction of Lidice.

708. 197. 1 k. 50 black .. .. 10 10
709. 5 k. blue .. .. 1·00 50

**198.** Jan Hus. **199.** Bethlehem Chapel, Prague.

**1952.** Renovation of Bethlehem Chapel and 550th Anniv. of Installation of Hus as Preacher.

710 198 1 k. 50 brown .. 10 10
711 199 3 k. brown .. .. 10 10
712 198 5 k. black .. .. 1·00 75

**200.** Testing Blood-pressure. **201.** Running.

**1952.** National Health Service.

713. 200. 1 k. 50 brown .. 1·10 75
714. – 2 k. violet .. .. 25 10
715. 200. 3 k. red .. .. 30 10

DESIGN—HORIZ. 2 k. Doctor examining baby.

**1952.** Physical Culture Propaganda.

716 201 1 k. 50 brown .. 70 40
717 – 2 k. green (Canoeing) 1·75 75
718 – 3 k. brown (Cycling) .. 50 40
719 – 4 k. blue (Ice hockey) 3·25 2·25

**202.** F. L. Celakovsky.

**1952.** Death Cent. of Celakovsky (poet).

720. 202. 1 k. 50 sepia .. .. 15 10
721. 2 k. green .. .. 1·40 1·00

**203.** M. Ales. **204.** Mining in 17th Century.

**1952.** Birth Centenary of Mikulas Ales (painter) (1st issue).

722 203 1 k. 50 green .. .. 40 25
723 6 k. brown .. .. 2·00 1·50

See also Nos. 737/8.

**1952.** Miner's Day.

724 204 1 k. brown .. .. 1·25 90
725 – 1 k. 50 blue .. .. 10 10
726 – 2 k. black .. .. 10 10
727 – 3 k. brown .. .. 10 10

DESIGNS: 1 k. 50, Mining machinery. 2 k. Petr Bezruc Mine, Ostrava. 3 k. Mechanical excavator.

**205.** Jan Zizka. **206.** "Fraternization" (after Pokorny).

**1952.** Army Day.
728 205 1 k. 50 red .. .. 15 10
729 206 2 k. brown .. .. 15 10
730 – 3 k. red .. .. 15 10
731 205 4 k. black .. .. 1·50 60
DESIGNS: 3 k. Soldiers marching with flag.

**207.** R. Danube, Bratislava. **208.** Lenin, Stalin and Revolutionaries.

**1952.** National Philatelic Exn., Bratislava.
732 207 1 k. 50 brown .. .. 30 10

**1952.** 35th Anniv. of Russian Revolution.
733 208 2 k. brown .. .. 1·10 75
734 3 k. red .. .. 10 10

**209.** Nurses and Red Cross Flag. **211.** Flags.

**210.** Matej Louda z Chlumu (Hussite Warrior).

**1952.** 1st Czechoslovak Red Cross Conf.
735. 209. 2 k. brown .. .. 1·00 50
736. 3 k. red .. .. 15 10

**1952.** Birth Centenary of Mikulas Ales (2nd issue).
737 210 2 k. brown .. .. 20 10
738 – 3 k. black .. .. 50 10
DESIGN: 3 k. "Trutnov" (warrior fighting dragon).

**1952.** Peace Congress, Vienna.
739. 211. 3 k. red .. .. 20 10
740. 4 k. blue .. .. 1·00 65

**212.** " Dove of Peace " (after Picasso). **213.** Smetana Museum, Prague.

**1953.** 2nd Czechoslovak Peace Congress, Prague.
741. 212. 1 k. 50 sepia .. .. 10 10
742. – 4 k. blue .. .. 50 30
DESIGN: 4 k. Workman, woman and child (after Lev Haas).

**1953.** 75th Birth Anniv. of Prof. Z. Nejedly (museum founder).
743. 213. 1 k. 50 brown .. .. 10 10
744. – 4 k. black .. .. 1·00 60
DESIGN: 4 k. Jirasek Museum, Prague.

**214.** Marching Soldiers. **215.** M. Kukucin.

**1953.** 5th Anniv. of Communist Govt.
745. 214. 1 k. 50 blue .. .. 15 10
746. – 3 k. red .. .. 15 10
747. – 8 k. brown .. .. 1·60 75
DESIGNS—VERT. 3 k. Pres. Gottwald addressing meeting. HORIZ. 8 k. Stalin, Gottwald and crowd with banners.

**1953.** Czech Writers and Poets.
748. 215. 1 k. grey .. .. 10 10
749. – 1 k. 50 brown .. .. 10 10
750. – 2 k. lake .. .. 10 10
751. – 3 k. brown .. .. 50 35
752. – 5 k. blue .. .. 1·25 70
PORTRAITS—VERT. 1 k. 50, J. Vrchlicky. 2 k. E. J. Erben. 3 k. V. M. Kramerius. 5 k. J. Dobrovsky.

**216.** Torch and Open Book. **217.** Woman Revolutionary.

**1953.** 10th Death Anniv. of Vaclavek (writer).
753. 216. 1 k. brown .. .. 1·00 50
754. – 3 k. brown (Vaclavek) 15 10

**1953.** Int. Women's Day.
755. – 1 k. 50 blue .. .. 15 10
756. 217. 2 k. red .. .. 90 45
DESIGN—VERT. 1 k. 50, Mother and baby.

**218.** Stalin. **219.** Pres. Gottwald.

**1953.** Death of Stalin.
757. 218. 1 k. 50 black .. .. 30 15

**1953.** Death of President Gottwald.
758. 219. 1 k. 50 black .. .. 20 10
759. 3 k. black .. .. 20 10

**220.** Pecka, Zapotocky and Hybes. **221.** Cyclists.

**1953.** 75th Anniv. of 1st Czech Social Democratic Party Congress.
760. 220. 2 k. brown .. .. 20 10

**1953.** 6th Int. Cycle Race.
761. 221. 3 k. blue .. .. 50 25

**222.** 1890 May Day Medal.

**223.** Marching Crowds.

**1953.** Labour Day.
762. 222. 1 k. brown .. .. 1·60 75
763. – 1 k. 50 blue .. .. 10 10
764. 223. 3 k. red .. .. 20 10
765. – 8 k. green .. .. 25 15
DESIGNS—As Type 222: 1 k. 50, Lenin and Stalin. 8 k. Marx and Engels.

**224.** Hydro-electric Barrage. **225.** Seed-drills.

**1953.**
766. 224. 1 k. 50 green .. .. 90 40
767. – 2 k. blue .. .. 15 10
768. – 3 k. brown .. .. 15 10
DESIGNS—VERT. 2 k. Welder and blast furnaces, Kuncice. HORIZ. 3 k. Gottwald Foundry, Kuncice.

**1953.**
769. 225. 1 k. 50 brown .. .. 20 10
770. – 7 k. green (Combine-harvester) .. .. 1·25 85

**226.** President Zapotocky. **229.**

**1953.**
776 226 30 h. blue .. .. 50 10
780 229 30 h. blue .. .. 25 10
777 226 60 h. red .. .. 25 10
781 229 60 h. pink .. .. 55 10

**227.** J. Slavik. **228.** L. Janacek.

**1953.** Prague Music Festival. (a) 120th Death Anniv. of Slavik (violinist).
778. 227. 75 h. blue .. .. 50 15

(b) 25th Death Anniv. of Janacek (composer).
779. 228. 1 k. 60 brown .. .. 1·00 10

**230.** Charles Bridge, Prague.

**1953.**
782a 230 5 k. grey .. .. 2·75 10

**231.** J. Fucik. **232.** Book, Carnation and Laurels.

**1953.** 10th Death Anniv of Julius Fucik (writer).
783 231 40 h. black .. .. 20 10
784 232 60 h. mauve .. .. 45 25

**233.** Miner and Banner. **234.** Volleyball.

**1953.** Miner's Day.
785 233 30 h. black .. .. 20 10
786 – 60 h. purple .. .. 1·10 50
DESIGN: 60 h. Miners and colliery shafthead.

**1953.** Sports.
787 234 30 h. red .. .. 2·00 1·50
788 – 40 h. purple .. .. 3·75 90
789 – 60 h. purple .. .. 3·75 90
DESIGNS—HORIZ. 40 h. Motor cycling. VERT. 60 h. Throwing the javelin.

**235.** Hussite Warrior. **236.** " Friendship " (after T. Bartfay).

**1953.** Army Day.
790. 235. 30 h. sepia .. .. 25 10
791. – 60 h. red .. .. 30 10
792. – 1 k. red .. .. 85 80
DESIGNS: 60 h. Soldier presenting arms. 1 k. Czechoslovak Red Army soldiers.

**1953.** Czechoslovak-Korean Friendship.
793. 236. 30 h. sepia .. .. 2·25 1·25

**237.** Hradcany, Prague and Kremlin, Moscow.

**1953.** Czechoslovak-Soviet Friendship: Inscr. " MESIC CESKOSLOVENSKO-SOVETSKEHO ", etc.
794 237 30 h. black .. .. 1·00 65
795 – 60 h. brown .. .. 1·25 85
796 – 1 k. 20 blue .. .. 3·25 2·00
DESIGNS: 60 h. Lomonosov University, Moscow. 1 k. 20, "Stalingrad" tug, Lenin Ship-Canal.

**238.** Ema Destinnova (Opera singer). **239.** National Theatre, Prague.

**1953.** 70th Anniv. of National Theatre, Prague.
797. 238. 30 h. black .. .. 1·00 90
798. 239. 60 h. brown .. .. 25 10
799. – 2 k. sepia .. .. 2·50 1·25
PORTRAIT—As Type 238: 2 k. E. Vojan (actor).

**240.** J. Manes (painter). **241.** Vaclav Hollar (etcher).

**1953.**
800. 240. 60 h. lake .. .. 25 10
801. 1 k. 20 blue .. .. 1·10 90

**1953.** Inscr. " 1607 1677 ".
802 241 30 h. black .. .. 25 10
803 1 k. 20 black .. .. 95 50
PORTRAIT: 1 k. 20, Hollar and engraving tools.

**242.** Leo Tolstoy. **243.** Steam Locomotive.

**1953.** 125th Birth Anniv of Tolstoy (writer).
804 242 60 h. green .. .. 15 10
805 1 k. brown .. .. 1·40 45

**1953.**
806 243 60 h. blue and brown 50 25
807 – 1 k. blue and brown .. 2·00 1·00
DESIGN: 1 k. Ilyushin Il-12 (30th anniv of Czech airmail services).

**244.** Lenin (after J. Lauda).

**245.** Lenin Museum, Prague.

**1954.** 30th Death Anniv. of Lenin.
808. 244. 30 h. sepia .. .. 45 10
809. 245. 1 k. 40 brown .. .. 1·40 90

**246.** Gottwald Speaking. **247.** Gottwald Mausoleum, Prague.

**248.** Gottwald and Stalin (after relief by O. Spaniel).

**1954.** 25th Anniv. of 5th Czechoslovak Communist Party Congress. Inscr. "1929 1954".
810. 246. 60 h. brown .. .. 25 10
811. – 2 k. 40 lake .. .. 3·25 1·25
DESIGN: 2 k. 40, Revolutionary and flag.

**1954.** 1st Anniv. of Deaths of Stalin and Gottwald.
812. 247. 30 h. sepia .. .. 25 10
813. 248. 60 h. blue .. .. 30 10
814. – 1 k. 20 h. lake .. .. 1·40 1·00
DESIGN—HORIZ. As Type 247: 1 k. 20 h. Lenin-Stalin Mausoleum, Moscow.

**249.** Girl and Sheaf of Corn. **250.** Athletics.

**1954.**

815 – 15 h. green .. .. 20 10
816 – 20 h. lilac .. .. 25 10
817 – 40 h. brown .. .. 35 10
818 – 45 h. blue .. .. 10 10
819 – 50 h. green .. .. 25 10
820 – 75 h. blue .. .. 25 10
821 – 80 h. brown .. .. 25 10
822 249 1 k. green .. .. 50 10
823 – 1 k. 20 blue .. .. 25 10
824 – 1 k. 60 black .. .. 90 10
825 – 2 k. brown .. .. 1·10 10
826 – 2 k. 40 blue .. .. 1·25 10
827 – 3 k. red .. .. 1·10 10

DESIGNS: 15 h. Labourer. 20 h. Nurse. 40 h. Postwoman. 45 h. Foundry worker. 50 h. Soldier. 75 h. Metal worker. 80 h. Mill girl. 1 k. 20, Scientist. 1 k. 60, Miner. 2 k. Doctor and baby. 2 k. 40 Engine-driver. 3 k. Chemist.

**1954.** Sports.

828. 250. 30 h. sepia .. .. 2·00 60
829. – 80 h. green .. .. 6·75 3·25
830. – 1 k. blue .. .. 1·25 40

DESIGNS—HORIZ. 80 h. Hiking. VERT. 1 k. Girl diving.

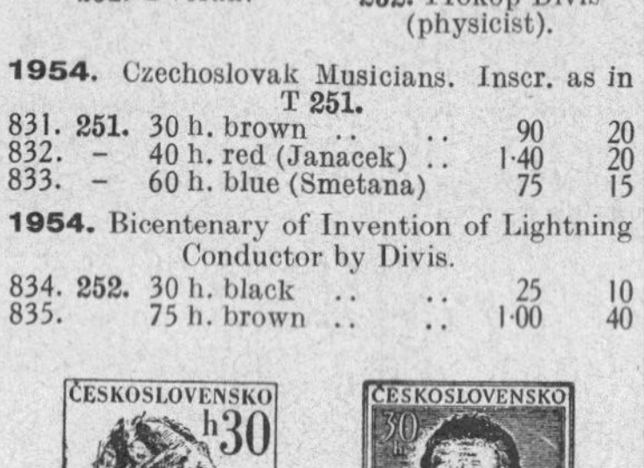

251. Dvorak. 252. Prokop Divis (physicist).

**1954.** Czechoslovak Musicians. Inscr. as in T 251.

831. 251. 30 h. brown .. .. 90 20
832. – 40 h. red (Janacek) .. 1·40 20
833. – 60 h. blue (Smetana) 75 15

**1954.** Bicentenary of Invention of Lightning Conductor by Divis.

834. 252. 30 h. black .. .. 25 10
835. 75 h. brown .. .. 1·00 40

253. Partisan. 254. A. P. Chekhov.

**1954.** 10th Anniv. of Slovak National Uprising. Inscr. "1944–29. 8–1954".

836. 253. 30 h. red .. .. 20 10
837. – 1 k. 20 blue (Woman partisan) .. .. 90 85

**1954.** 50th Death Anniv. of Chekhov (playwright).

838. 254. 30 h. green .. .. 20 10
839. 45 h. brown .. .. 1·00 40

255. Soldiers in Battle.

256. Farm Workers in Cornfield.

**1954.** Army Day. 2 k. inscr. "ARMADY 1954".

840. 255. 60 h. green .. .. 20 10
841. – 2 k. brown .. .. 1·10 1·00

DESIGN: 2 k. Soldier carrying girl.

**1954.** Czechoslovak-Russian Friendship.

842. 256. 30 h. brown .. .. 15 10
843. – 60 h. blue .. .. 25 10
844. – 2 k. salmon .. .. 1·50 1·10

DESIGNS: 60 h. Factory workers and machinery. 2 k. Group of girl folk dancers.

257. J. Neruda.

258. Ceske Budejovice.

**1954.** Czechoslovak Poets.

845. 257. 30 h. blue .. .. 90 15
846. – 60 h. red .. .. 1·25 50
847. – 1 k. 60 h. purple .. 40 15

PORTRAITS—VERT. 60 h. J. Jesensky. 1 k. 60 h. J. Wolker.

**1954.** Czechoslovak Architecture. Horiz. views. Background in buff.

848. – 30 h. black (Telc) .. 80 10
849. – 60 h. brown (Levoca) .. 40 10
850. 258. 3 k. blue .. .. 2·00 1·40

259. President Zapotocky.

260. "Spirit of the Games".

**1954.** 70th Birthday of Zapotocky.

851. 259. 30 h. sepia .. .. 45 10
852. 60 h. blue .. .. 20 10

See also Nos. 1006/7.

**1955.** 1st National Spartacist Games (1st issue). Inscr. as in T 260.

853. 260. 30 h. red .. .. 2·25 30
854. – 45 h. blk. & blue (Skier) 3·00 25

See also Nos. 880/2.

261. University Building.

DESIGN: 75 h. Comenius Medal (after O. Spaniel).

**1955.** 35th Anniv. of Comenius University, Bratislava. Inscr. as in T 261.

855. 261. 60 h. green .. .. 25 10
856. – 75 h. brown .. .. 90 50

262. Cesky Krumlov.

**1955.** Air.

857. 262. 80 h. green .. .. 1·60 30
858. – 1 k. 55 sepia .. .. 1·60 25
859. – 2 k. 35 blue .. .. 1·60 20
860. – 2 k. 75 purple .. 3·00 40
861. – 10 k. blue .. .. 5·50 1·50

DESIGNS: 1 k. 55, Olomouc. 2 k. 35, Banska Bystrica. 2 k. 75, Bratislava. 10 k. Prague.

263. Skoda Motor Car.

264. Russian Tank-driver.

**1955.** Czechoslovak Industries.

862. 263. 45 h. green .. .. 70 45
863. – 60 h. blue .. .. 15 10
864. – 75 h. black .. .. 25 10

DESIGNS: 60 h. Shuttleless jet loom. 75 h. Skoda Machine-tool.

**1955.** 10th Anniv. of Liberation. Inscr. as in T 264.

865 – 30 h. blue .. .. 25 10
866 264 35 h. brown .. .. 1·00 50
867 – 60 h. red .. .. 25 10
868 – 60 h. black .. .. 25 10

DESIGNS—VERT. 30 h. Girl and Russian soldier. No. 867, Children and Russian soldier. HORIZ. No. 868, Stalin Monument, Prague.

265. Agricultural Workers.

266. "Music and Spring".

**1955.** 3rd Trades' Union Congress. Inscr. as in T 265.

869. – 30 h. blue .. .. 15 10
870. 265. 45 h. green .. .. 65 45

DESIGN: 30 h. Foundry worker.

**1955.** International Music Festival, Prague. Inscr. as in T 266.

871. 266. 30 h. indigo and blue .. 35 10
872. – 1 k. blue and pink .. 1·25 75

DESIGN: 1 k. "Music" playing a lyre.

267. A. S. Popov (60th anniv of radio discoveries).

268. Folk Dancers.

**1955.** Cultural Anniversaries. Vert portraits as T 267.

873 – 20 h. brown .. .. 25 10
874 – 30 h. black .. .. 25 10
875 – 40 h. green .. .. 75 10
876 – 60 h. black .. .. 40 10
877 267 75 h. purple .. .. 90 50
878 – 1 k. 40 black on yellow 50 20
879 – 1 k. 60 blue .. .. 50 15

PORTRAITS: 20 h. Jakub Arbes (writer). 30 h. Jan Stursa (sculptor). 40 h. Elena Marothy-Soltesova (writer). 60 h. Josef V. Sladek (poet). 1 k. 40 Jan Holly (poet). 1 k. 60 Pavel J. Safarik (philologist).

**1955.** 1st National Spartacist Games (2nd issue). Inscr. as in T 268.

880. – 20 h. blue .. .. 75 40
881. 268. 60 h. green .. .. 25 10
882. – 1 k. 60 red .. .. 80 20

DESIGNS: 20 h. Girl athlete. 1 k. 60, Male athlete.

269. "Friendship".

270. Ocova Woman, Slovakia.

**1955.** 5th World Youth Festival, Warsaw.

883. 269. 60 h. blue .. .. 25 10

**1955.** National Costumes (1st series).

884. 270. 60 h. sepia, rose & red 11·00 7·00
885. – 75 h. sep., orge. & lake 6·50 3·75
886. – 1 k. 60 sepia, blue and orange .. .. 11·00 6·50
887. – 2 k. sepia, yell. & red 14·00 7·00

DESIGNS: 75 h. Detva man, Slovakia. 1 k. 60, Chodsko man, Bohemia. 2 k. Hana woman, Moravia.

See also Nos. 952/5 and 1008/11.

271. Swallowtail.

**1955.** Animals and Insects. Horiz. designs as T 271.

888. – 20 h. black & blue (Carp) .. .. 70 15
889. – 30 h. brown and red (Stag beetle) .. 70 10
890. – 35 h. brown and buff (Grey Partridge) .. 1·50 20
891. 271. 1 k. 40 blk. & yell. .. 5·25 2·50
892. – 1 k. 50 black and green (Brown hare) 70 20

272. Tabor.

273. Motor Cyclists and Trophy.

**1955.** Towns of Southern Bohemia.

893 272 30 h. purple .. .. 20 10
894 – 45 h. red .. .. 75 65
895 – 60 h. green .. .. 20 10

TOWNS: 45 h. Prachatice. 60 h. Jindrichuv Hradec.

**1955.** 30th Int. Motor Cycle Six-Day Trial.

896 273 60 h. purple .. .. 3·00 50

274. Soldier and Family.

275. Hans Andersen.

**1955.** Army Day. Inscr. as in T 274.

897. 274. 30 h. brown .. .. 25 10
898. – 60 h. grn. (Tank attack 2·40 2·00

**1955.** Famous Writers. Vert. portraits.

899. 275. 30 h. red .. .. 15 10
900. – 40 h. blue (Schiller) .. 1·60 75
901. – 60 h. pur. (Mickiewicz) 25 10
902. – 75 h. blk. (Walt Whitman) .. .. 50 10

276 Railway Viaduct

**1955.** Building Progress. Insc. "STAVBA SOCIALISMU".

903. 276. 20 h. green .. .. 25 20
904. – 30 h. brown .. .. 25 10
905. – 60 h. blue .. .. 25 10
906. – 1 k. 60 h. red .. 40 10

DESIGNS: 30 h. Train crossing viaduct. 60 k. Train approaching tunnel. 1 k. 60, Housing project, Ostrava.

277. "Electricity".

278. Karlovy Vary.

**1956.** Five Year Plan. Inscr. "1956–1960".

907. 277. 5 h. brown .. .. 20 10
908. – 10 h. black .. .. 20 10
909. – 25 h. red .. .. 20 10
910. – 30 h. green .. .. 20 10
911. – 60 h. blue .. .. 30 10

DESIGNS—HORIZ. 10 h. "Mining". 25 h. "Building". 30 h. "Agriculture". 60 h. "Industry".

**1956.** Czechoslovak Spas (1st series).

912. 278. 30 h. green .. .. 1·40 25
913. – 45 h. brown .. .. 1·10 40
914. – 75 h. purple .. .. 7·00 4·25
915. – 1 k. 20 blue .. .. 65 15

SPAS: 45 h. Marianske Lazne. 75 h. Piestany. 1 k. 20, Vysne Ruzbachy, Tatra Mountains.

279. Jewellery.

280. "We serve our People" (after J. Cumpelik).

**1956.** Czechoslovak Products.

916. 279. 30 h. green .. .. 25 10
917. – 45 h. blue (Glassware) 5·00 2·50
918. – 60 h. purple (Ceramics) 75 10
919. – 75 h. black (Textiles) .. 25 10

**1956.** Defence Exn.

920. 280. 30 h. brown .. .. 35 10
921. – 60 h. red .. .. 35 10
922. – 1 k. blue .. .. 5·75 3·50

DESIGNS: 60 h. Liberation Monument, Berlin. 1 k. "Tank Soldier with Standard" (after T. Schor).

281. Cyclists.

282. Discus Thrower, Hurdler and Runner.

**1956.** Sports Events of 1956.
923. **281.** 30 h. green and blue .. 2·50 20
924. – 45 h. blue and red .. 1·25 20
925. – 60 h. blue and buff .. 1·90 25
926. **282.** 75 h. brown and yellow 1·10 20
927. – 80 h. purple & lavender 1·10 15
928. **282.** 1 k. 20 green & orange 75 25
DESIGNS—As Type **281**. VERT: 30 h. T **281** (9th International Cycle Race). 45 h. Basketball players (5th European Women's Basketball Championship, Prague). HORIZ: 60 h. Horsemen jumping (Pardubice Steeplechase). 80 h. Runners (International Marathon, Kosice). T **282**: 75 h., 1 k. 20 (16th Olympic Games, Melbourne).

**283.** Mozart. **284.**

**1956.** Bicentenary of Birth of Mozart and Prague Music Festival. Centres in black.
929. **283.** 30 h. yellow .. .. 80 35
930. – 45 h. green .. .. 17·00 11·00
931. – 60 h. purple .. .. 60 10
932. – 1 k. salmon .. .. 1·40 20
933. – 1 k. 40 blue .. .. 3·50 70
934. – 1 k. 60 lemon .. 80 15
DESIGNS: 45 h. J. Myslivecek. 60 h. J. Benda. 1 k. "Bertramka" (Mozart's villa). 1 k. 40, Mr. and Mrs. Dushek. 1 k. 60, Nostic Theatre.

**1956.** 1st National Meeting of Home Guard.
935. **284.** 60 h. blue .. .. 75 15

**285.** J. K. Tyl. **286.** Naval Guard.

**1956.** Czech Writers (1st issue).
936. – 20 h. purple (Stur) .. 60 10
937. – 30 h. blue (Sramek) .. 40 10
938. **285.** 60 h. black .. .. 30 10
939. – 1 k. 40 pur. (Borovsky) 5·00 2·50
See also Nos. 956/9.

**1956.** Frontier Guards' Day.
940. **286.** 30 h. blue .. .. 90 35
941. – 60 h. green .. .. 15 10
DESIGN: 60 h. Military guard and watchdog.

**287.** Picking Grapes. **288.** "Kladno", 1855.

**1956.** National Products.
942. **287.** 30 h. lake .. .. 25 10
943. – 35 h. green .. .. 30 20
944. – 80 h. blue .. .. 60 15
945. – 95 h. brown .. .. 1·75 1·40
DESIGNS—VERT. 35 h. Picking hops. HORIZ. 80 h. Fishing. 95 h. Logging.

**1956.** European Freight Services Timetable Conference. Designs showing railway engines.
946 – 10 h. brown .. .. 1·25 10
947 **288** 30 h. black .. .. 70 10
948 – 40 h. green .. .. 3·25 20
949 – 45 h. purple .. .. 18·00 11·00
950 – 60 h. blue .. .. 70 10
951 – 1 k. blue .. .. 1·25 20
DESIGNS—VERT. 10 h. "Zbraslav", 1846. HORIZ. 40 h. Class "534.0", 1945. 45 h. Class "556.0", 1952. 60 h. Class "477.0", 1955. 1 k. Electric locomotive "E499.0", 1954.

**1956.** National Costumes (2nd series). As T **270**.
952. 30 h. sepia, red and blue .. 2·50 80
953. 1 k. 20 sepia, blue and red 1·90 15
954. 1 k. 40 brown, yell. & red 5·25 2·00
955. 1 k. 60 sepia, green & red 2·50 40
DESIGNS: 30 h. Slovacko woman. 1 k. 20, Blata woman. 1 k. 40, Cicmany woman, 1 k. 60, Novohradsko woman.

**1957.** Czech Writers (2nd issue). As T **285**. On buff paper.
956. 15 h. brown (Olbracht) .. 25 10
957. 20 h. green (Toman) .. 25 10
958. 30 h. sepia (Salda) .. 25 10
959. 1 k. 60 blue (Vansova) .. 40 10

**289.** Forestry Academy, Banska Stiavnica. **290.** Girl Harvester.

**1957.** Towns and Monuments Anniversaries.
960 – 30 h. blue .. .. 20 10
961 **289** 30 h. purple .. .. 20 10
962 – 60 h. red .. .. 40 10
963 – 60 h. brown .. .. 40 10
964 – 60 h. green .. .. 40 10
965 – 1 k. 25 black .. .. 2·75 2·00
DESIGNS: No. 960, Kolin. No. 962, Uherske Hradiste. No. 963, Charles Bridge, Prague. No. 964, Karlstejn Castle. No. 965, Moravska Trebova.

**1957.** 3rd Collective Farming Agricultural Congress, Prague.
966. **290.** 30 h. turquoise .. 55 10

**291.** Komensky's Mausoleum. **292.** J. A. Komensky (Comenius).

**1957.** 300th Anniv. of Publication of Komensky's "Opera Didactica Omnia".
967 **291** 30 h. brown .. .. 45 15
968 – 40 h green .. .. 45 15
969 **292** 60 h. brown .. .. 1·50 80
970 – 1 k. red .. .. 60 10
DESIGNS: As Type **291**. 40 h. Komensky at work. 1 k. Illustration from "Opera Didactica Omnia".

**293.** Racing Cyclists. **294.** J. B. Foerster.

**1957.** Sports Events of 1957.
971. **293.** 30 h. purple and blue .. 30 10
972. 60 h. green and bistre 1·75 1·50
973. – 60 h. violet and brown 30 10
974. – 60 h. purple and brown 30 10
975. – 60 h. black and green .. 30 10
976. – 60 h. black and blue .. 90 10
DESIGNS—HORIZ. Nos. 971/2 (10th Int. Cycle Race). 973, Rescue squad (Mountain Rescue Service). 975, Archer (World Archery Championships, Prague). VERT. 974, Boxers (European Boxing Championships, Prague). 976, Motor Cyclists (32nd Int. Motor Cycle Six-Day Trial).

**1957.** Int. Music Festival Jubilee. Musicians.
977. – 60 h. violet (Stamic) .. 25 10
978. – 60 h. black (Laub) .. 25 10
979. – 60 h. blue (Ondricek) 25 10
980. **294.** 60 h. sepia .. .. 25 10
981. – 60 h. brown (Novak) 95 10
982. – 60 h. turquoise (Suk) .. 25 10

**295.** J. Bozek (founder). **296.** Young Collector Blowing Posthorn.

**1957.** 250th Anniv. of Polytechnic Engineering Schools, Prague.
983 **295** 30 h. black .. .. 15 10
984 – 60 h. brown .. .. 30 10
985 – 1 k. purple .. .. 30 15
986 – 1 k. 40 violet .. .. 45 15
DESIGNS—VERT. 60 h. F. J. Gerstner. 1 k. R. Skuhersky. HORIZ. 1 k. 40, Polytechnic Engineering Schools Building, Prague.

**1957.** Junior Philatelic Exn., Pardubice.
987. **296.** 30 h. orange and green 50 10
988. – 60 h. blue and brown .. 2·00 90
DESIGN: 60 h. Girl sending letter by pigeon.

**297.** "Rose of Friendship and Peace". **298.** Karel Klic and Printing Press.

**1957.** 15th Anniv. of Destruction of Lidice.
989. – 30 h. black .. .. 35 10
990. **297.** 60 h. red and black .. 55 25
DESIGN: 30 h. Veiled woman.

**1957.** Czech Inventors.
991. **298.** 30 h. black .. .. 15 10
992. – 60 h. blue .. .. 25 10
DESIGN: 60 h. Joseph Ressel and propeller.

**299.** Chamois. **300.** Marycka Magdonova.

**1957.** Tatra National Park.
993. **299.** 20 h. black and green 65 50
994. – 30 h. brown and blue 65 10
995. – 40 h. blue and brown 1·10 10
996. – 60 h. green and yellow 50 10
997. – 1 k. 25 black and ochre 1·25 1·50
DESIGNS—VERT. 30 h. Brown bear. HORIZ. 40 h. Gentian. 60 h. Edelweiss. 1 k. 25 (49 × 29 mm.), Tatra Mountains.

**1957.** 90th Birthday of Petr Bezruc (poet).
998 **300** 60 h. black and red .. 45 10

**301.** Worker with Banner. **303.** Television Tower and Aerials.

**302.** Tupolev Tu-104A and Paris–Prague–Moscow Route.

**1957.** 4th World T.U.C., Leipzig.
999. **301.** 75 h. red .. .. 45 15

**1957.** Air. Opening of Czechoslovak Airlines.
1000. **302.** 75 h. blue and red .. 90 10
1001. – 2 k. 35 blue and yellow 1·10 20
DESIGN: 2 k. 35, "Prague–Cairo–Beirut–Damascus".

**1957.** Television Development.
1002. **303.** 40 h. blue and red .. 20 10
1003. – 60 h. brown and green 25 10
DESIGN: 60 h. Family watching television.

**304.** Youth, Globe and Lenin.

**1957.** 40th Anniv. of Russian Revolution.
1004 **304** 30 h. red .. .. 20 10
1005 – 60 h. blue .. .. 25 10
DESIGN: 60 h. Lenin, refinery and Russian emblem.

**1957.** Death of President Zapotocky. As T **259** but dated "19 XII 1884–13 XI 1957".
1006. 30 h. black .. .. 10 10
1007. 60 h. black .. .. 20 10

**1957.** National Costumes (3rd series). As T **270**.
1008. 45 h. sepia, red and blue 3·25 1·40
1009. 75 h. sepia, red and green 2·25 90
1010. 1 k. 25 sepia, red & yellow 3·25 75
1011. 1 k. 95 sepia, blue and red 3·75 2·50
DESIGNS—VERT. 45 h. Pilsen woman. 75 h. Slovacko man. 1 k. 25, Hana woman. 1 k. 95, Tesin woman.

**305.** Artificial Satellite ("Sputnik 2"). **306.** Figure Skating (European Championships, Bratislava).

**1957.** Int. Geophysical Year. Design showing globe and dated "1957–1958".
1012 – 30 h. brown .. .. 1·75 45
1013 – 45 h. brown and blue 30 25
1014 **305** 75 h. red and blue .. 2·25 65
DESIGNS—HORIZ. 30 h. Radio-telescope and observatory. VERT. 45 h. Lomnicky Stit meteorological station.

**1958.** Sports Events of 1958.
1015 **306** 30 h. purple .. .. 1·40 25
1016 – 40 h. blue .. .. 30 20
1017 – 60 h. brown .. .. 30 10
1018 – 80 h. violet .. .. 1·90 80
1019 – 1 k. 60 green .. 50 15
EVENTS: 40 h. Canoeing (World Canoeing Championships, Prague). 60 h. Volleyball (European Volleyball Championships, Prague). 80 h. Parachuting (4th World Parachute-jumping Championship, Bratislava). 1 k. 60, Football (World Cup Football Championship, Stockholm).

DESIGN—HORIZ. 60 h. Bethlehem Chapel, Prague.

**307.** Litomysl Castle (birthplace of Nejedly).

**1958.** 80th Birthday of Nejedly (musician).
1020. **307.** 30 h. green .. .. 20 10
1021. – 60 h. brown .. .. 20 10

DESIGNS—VERT. 30 h. Giant mine-excavator. HORIZ. 1 k. 60, Combine-harvester.

**308.** Soldiers guarding Shrine of "Victorious February".

**1958.** 10th Anniv. of Communist Govt.
1022. – 30 h. blue and yellow 30 10
1023. **308.** 60 h. brown and red 30 10
1024. – 1 k. 60 green & orange 45 10

**309.** Jewellery. **310.** George of Podebrady and his Seal.

**1958.** Brussels Int. Exhibition. Inscr. "Bruxelles 1958".
1025 **309** 30 h. red and blue .. 20 10
1026 – 45 h. red and lilac .. 45 10
1027 – 60 h. violet and green 20 10
1028 – 75 h. blue and orange 1·40 75
1029 – 1 k. 20 green and red 45 10
1030 – 1 k. 95 brown and blue 70 15
DESIGNS—VERT. 45 h. Toy dolls. 60 h. Draperies. 75 h. Kaplan turbine. 1 k. 20, Glassware. HORIZ. ($48\frac{1}{2} \times 29\frac{1}{2}$ mm.), 1 k. 95, Czech pavilion.

**1958.** National Exhibition of Archive Documents. Inscr. as in T **310**.

1031. **310.** 30 h. red .. .. 30 10
1032. – 60 h. violet .. .. 25 10

DESIGN: 60 h. Prague, 1628 (from engraving).

**311.** Hammer and Sickle.  **312.** "Towards the Stars" (after sculpture by G. Postnikov).

**1958.** 11th Czech Communist Party Congress and 15th Anniv. of Czech-Soviet Friendship Treaty. 45 h. inscr. as in T **311** and 60 h. inscr. "15. VYROCI UZAVRENI".

1033. **311.** 30 h. red .. .. 20 10
1034. – 45 h. green .. .. 20 10
1035. – 60 h. blue .. .. 20 10

DESIGNS: 45 h. Map of Czechoslovakia, with hammer and sickle. 60 h. Atomic reactor, Rez (near Prague).

**1958.** Cultural and Political Events. 45 h. inscr. "IV. KONGRES MEZINARODNI", etc., and 60 h. inscr. "I. SVETOVA ODBOROVA", etc.

1036. **312** 30 h. red .. .. 65 40
1037. – 45 h. purple .. .. 20 20
1038. – 60 h. blue .. .. 20 10

DESIGNS—VERT. 45 h. Three women of different races and globe (4th Int. Democratic Women's Federation Congress, Vienna). HORIZ. 60 h. Boy and girl with globes (1st World T.U. Conference of Working Youth, Prague). Type **312** represents the Society for the Dissemination of Cultural and Political Knowledge.

**313.** Pres. Novotny. **314.** Telephone Operator.

**1958.**

1039. **313.** 30 h. violet .. .. 20 10
1039a. 30 h. purple .. .. 2·50 1·00
1040. 60 h. red .. .. 20 10

**1958.** Communist Postal Conference. Prague. Inscr. as in T **314**.

1041. **314.** 30 h. sepia and brown 25 10
1042. – 45 h. black and green 25 20

DESIGN: 45 h. Aerial mast.

**315.** Karlovy Vary (600th Anniv.).

SPAS: 40 h. Podebrady. 60 h. Marianske Lazne (150th Anniv.). 80 h. Luhacovice. 1 k. 20, Strbske Pleso. 1 k. 60, Trencianske.

**1958.** Czech Spas (2nd series).

1043. **315.** 30 h. lake .. .. 10 10
1044. – 40 h. brown .. .. 10 10
1045. – 60 h. green .. .. 15 10
1046. – 80 h. sepia .. .. 25 10
1047. – 1 k. 20 blue .. .. 40 15
1048. – 1 k. 60 violet .. .. 1·00 90

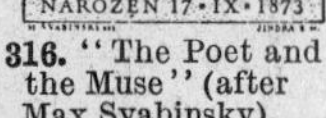

**316.** "The Poet and the Muse" (after Max Svabinsky). **317.** S. Cech.

**1958.** 85th Birthday of Dr. Max Svabinsky (artist).

1049 **316** 1 k. 60 black .. .. 3·00 1·25

**1958.** Writers' Anniversaries.

1050 – 30 h. red (Julius Fucik) .. .. 25 10
1051 – 45 h. violet (Gustav K. Zechenter) .. 1·25 50
1052 – 60 h. blue (Karel Capek) .. .. 15 10
1053 **317** 1 k. 40 black .. 50 15

**318.** Children's Hospital, Brno. **319.** Parasol Mushroom.

**1958.** National Stamp Exn., Brno. Inscr. as in T **318.**

1054. **318.** 30 h. violet .. .. 20 10
1055. – 60 h. red .. .. 20 10
1056. – 1 k. sepia .. .. 45 10
1057. – 1 k. 60 myrtle .. 1·75 1·75

DESIGNS: 60 h. New Town Hall, Brno. 1 k. St. Thomas's Church, Red Army Square. 1 k. 60 (50 × 28½ mm.), Brno view.

**1958.** Mushrooms.

1058. **319.** 30 h. buff, green & brn. 45 15
1059. – 40 h. buff, red & brown 50 15
1060. – 60 h. red, buff and black 65 20
1061. – 1 k. 40 red, grn. & brn. 80 25
1062. – 1 k. 60 red, grn. & blk. 8·25 1·75

DESIGNS—VERT. 40 h. Cep. 60 h. Red cap. 1 k. 40, Fly agaric. 1 k. 60, Boot-lace fungus.

**320.** Children sailing. **321.** Bozek's Steam Car of 1815.

**1958.** Inaug. of U.N.E.S.C.O. Headquarters Building, Paris. Inscr. "ZE SOUTEZE PRO UNESCO".

1063. **320.** 30 h. red, yell. & blue 20 10
1064. – 45 h. red and blue .. 25 10
1065. – 60 h. blue, yell. & brn. 20 10

DESIGNS: 45 h. Mother, child and bird. 60 h. Child skier.

**1958.** Czech Motor Industry Commem.

1066 **321** 30 h. violet and yellow 70 10
1067 – 45 h. brown and green 50 10
1068 – 60 h. green and orange 70 10
1069 – 80 h. red and green .. 50 10
1070 – 1 k. brown and green 50 10
1071 – 1 k. 25 green & yellow 2·25 75

DESIGNS: 45 h. "President" car of 1897. 60 h. Skoda "450" car. 80 h. Tatra "603" car. 1 k. Skoda "706" motor coach. 1 k. 25, Tatra "III" and Praga "VS 3" motor trucks in Tibet.

**322.** Garlanded Woman ("Republic") with First Czech Stamp. **323.** Ice Hockey Goalkeeper.

**1958.** 40th Anniv. of 1st Czech Postage Stamps.

1072. **322.** 60 h. blue .. .. 25 10

**1959.** Sports Events of 1959.

1073. – 20 h. brown and grey 30 10
1074. – 30 h. brown & orange 30 10
1075. **323.** 60 h. blue and green 30 10
1076. – 1 k. lake and yellow 30 10
1077. – 1 k. 60 violet and blue 45 10
1078. – 2 k. brown and blue 1·60 1·40

DESIGNS: 20 h. Ice hockey player (50th anniv of Czech Ice Hockey Association). 30 h. Throwing the javelin. 60 h. (Type **323**) World Ice Hockey Championships, 1959. 1 k. Hurdling. 1 k. 60, Rowing. 2 k. High jumping.

**324.** U.A.C. Emblem. **325.** "Equal Rights".

**1959.** 4th National Unified Agricultural Co-operatives Congress, Prague.

1079. **324.** 30 h. lake and blue .. 15 10
1080. – 60 h. blue and yellow 30 10

DESIGN: 60 h. Artisan shaking hand with farmer.

**1959.** 10th Anniv of Declaration of Human Rights.

1081. **325.** 60 h. green .. .. 15 10
1082. – 1 k. sepia .. .. 25 10
1083. – 2 k. blue .. .. 1·10 50

DESIGNS: 1 k. "World Freedom" (girl with Dove of Peace). 2 k. "Freedom for Colonial Peoples" (native woman with child).

**326.** Girl with Doll. **327.** F. Joliot-Curie (scientist).

**1959.** 10th Anniv. of Young Pioneers' Movement.

1084. **326.** 30 h. blue & yellow .. 30 10
1085. – 40 h. black and blue .. 30 20
1086. – 60 h. black and purple 30 10
1087. – 80 h. brown and green 30 20

DESIGNS: 40 h. Boy hiker. 60 h. Young radio technician. 80 h. Girl planting tree.

**1959.** 10th Anniv. of Peace Movement.

1088. **327.** 60 h. purple .. .. 1·60 25

**328.** Man in outer space and Moon Rocket. **329.** Pilsen Town Hall.

**1959.** 2nd Czech Political and Cultural Knowledge Congress, Prague.

1089. **328.** 30 h. blue .. .. 1·25 25

**1959.** Skoda Works Cent. and National Stamp Exn., Pilsen. Inscr. "PLZEN 1959".

1090. **329.** 30 h. brown .. .. 15 10
1091. – 60 h. violet and green 15 10
1092. – 1 k. blue .. .. 25 15
1093. – 1 k. 60 black & yellow 1·25 1·10

DESIGNS: 60 h. Part of steam turbine. 1 k. St. Bartholomew's Church, Pilsen. 1 k. 60, Part of SR-1200 lathe.

**330.** Congress Emblem and Industrial Plant.

**1959.** 4th Trades Union Congress, Prague.

1094. **330.** 30 h. red and yellow .. 20 10
1095. – 60 h. olive and blue .. 20 10

DESIGN: 60 h. Dam.

**331.** Zvolen Castle. **332.** F. Benda (composer).

**1959.** Slovak Stamp Exhibition, Zvolen.

1096. **331.** 60 h. olive and yellow 50 10

**1959.** Cultural Anniversaries.

1097 **332** 15 h. blue .. .. 20 10
1098 – 30 h. red .. .. 20 10
1099 – 40 h. green .. .. 25 10
1100 – 60 h. brown .. .. 25 10
1101 – 60 h. black .. .. 45 15
1102 – 80 h. violet .. .. 25 10
1103 – 1 k. brown .. .. 25 10
1104 – 3 k. brown .. .. 1·25 75

PORTRAITS: 30 h. Vaclav Klicpera (dramatist). 40 h. Aurel Stodola (engineer). 60 h. (1100) Karel V. Rais (writer). 60 h. (1101) Haydn (composer). 80 h. Antonin Slavicek (painter). 1 k. Petr Bezruc (poet). 3 k. Charles Darwin (naturalist).

**333.** "Z" Pavilion.

DESIGNS: 30 h. View of Fair. 60 h. Fair emblem and world map.

**1959.** Int. Fair, Brno. Inscr. "BRNO 6-20. IX. 1959".

1105. – 30 h. purple & yellow .. 15 10
1106. – 60 h. blue .. .. 15 10
1107. **333.** 1 k. 60 blue & yellow 40 10

**334.** Revolutionary (after A. Holly).

**1959.** 15th Anniv. of Slovak National Uprising and 40th Anniv. of Republic. Inscr. "1944 29.8.1959".

1108. **334.** 30 h. black & mauve 15 10
1109. – 60 h. red .. .. 20 10
1110. – 1 k. 60 blue & yell. 40 10

DESIGNS—VERT. 60 h. Revolutionary with upraised rifle (after sculpture "Forward" by L. Snopka). HORIZ. 1 k. 60, Factory, sun and linden leaves.

**335.** Moon Rocket. **336.** Lynx.

**1959.** Landing of Russian Rocket on Moon.

1111. **335.** 60 h. red and blue .. 1·40 25

**1959.** 10th Anniv. of Tatra National Park. Inscr. "1949 TATRANSKY NARODNY PARK 1959".

1112. – 30 h. black and grey 65 10
1113. – 40 h. brown & turq. 65 10
1114. **336.** 60 h. red & yell. .. 1·40 10
1115. – 1 k. brn. & blue .. 1·90 75
1116. – 1 k. 60 brown .. 1·40 10

DESIGNS—HORIZ. 30 h. Alpine marmots. 40 h. European bison. 1 k Wolf. 1 k. 60, Red deer.

**337.** Stamp Printing Works, Peking.

**1959.** 10th Anniv. of Chinese People's Republic.

1117. **337.** 30 h. red and green .. 35 10

**338.** Bleriot XI Monoplanes at First Czech Aviation School.

**1959.** Air. 50th Anniv. of 1st Flight by Jan Kaspar.

1118. **338.** 1 k. black and yellow 20 10
1119. – 1 k. 80 black & blue 1·00 10

DESIGN: 1 k. 80, Jan Kaspar and Bleriot XI in flight.

339. Great Spotted Woodpecker.

BIRDS: 30 h. Blue tit. 40 h. European nuthatch. 60 h. Golden oriole. 80 h. Goldfinch. 1 k. Bullfinch. 1 k. 20, Common kingfisher.

**1959.** Birds.
1120. **339.** 20 h. multicoloured.. 1·60 25
1121. – 30 h. multicoloured.. 1·60 25
1122. – 40 h. multicoloured.. 5·25 1·40
1123. – 60 h. multicoloured.. 1·60 25
1124. – 80 h. multicoloured.. 1·60 25
1125. – 1 k. red, blue & black 1·60 25
1126. – 1 k. 20 brn., blue & blk. 3·50 65

340. Tesla and Electrical Apparatus. 341. Exercises.

**1959.** Radio Inventors.
1127. **340.** 25 h. black and red.. 1·25 25
1128. – 30 h. black and brown 15 10
1129. – 35 h. black and lilac.. 20 10
1130. – 60 h. black and blue.. 30 10
1131. – 1 k. black and green.. 20 10
1132. – 2 k. black and bistre 90 70
INVENTORS (each with sketch of invention): 30 h. Aleksandr Popov. 35 h. Edouard Branly. 60 h. Guglielmo Marconi. 1 k. Heinrich Hertz. 2 k. Edwin Armstrong.

**1960.** 2nd National Spartacist Games (1st issue). Inscr. as in T **341.**
1133 **341** 30 h. brown and red 1·00 10
1134 – 60 h. blue & light blue 50 15
1135 – 1 k. 60 brown & bistre 55 25
DESIGNS: 60 h. Skiing. 1 k. 60, Basketball.
See also Nos. 1160/2.

342. Freighter "Lidice".

**1960.** Czech Ships.
1136. – 30 h. green and red.. 80 15
1137. – 60 h. lake & turquoise 35 10
1138. – 1 k. violet and yellow 80 20
1139. **342.** 1 k. 20 purple & green 1·90 1·50
SHIPS: 30 h. Dredger "Praha Liben". 60 h. Tug "Kharito Latjev". 1 k. River boat "Komarno".

DESIGN: 1 k. 80, Skating pair.
See also Nos. 1163/5.

343. Ice Hockey.

**1960.** Winter Olympic Games. Inscr. as in T **343.**
1140. **343.** 60 h. sepia and blue 40 25
1141. – 1 k. 80 black & green 4·00 2·50

344. Trencin Castle. 345. Lenin. 346. Soldier and Child.

**1960.** Czechoslovak Castles.
1142 5 h. blue (Type 344) .. 15 10
1143 10 h. black (Bezdez) .. 15 10
1144 20 h. orange (Kost) .. 25 10
1145 30 h. green (Pernstejn) 25 10
1146 40 h. brn (Kremnica) 25 10
1146a 50 h. black (Krivoklat) 25 10
1147 60 h. red (Karestejn) .. 40 10
1148 1 k. purple (Smolenice) 30 10
1149 1 k. 60 blue (Kokorin) 60 10

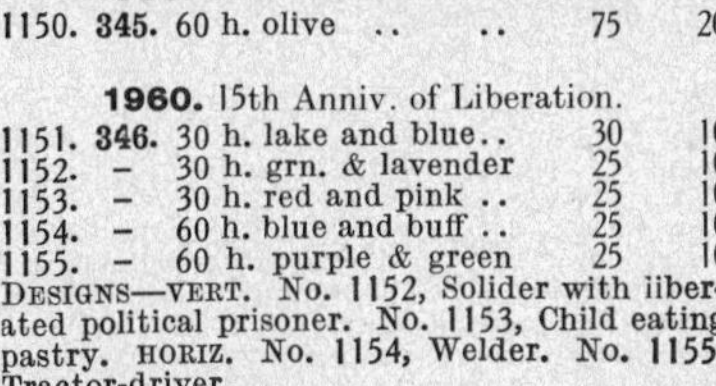

**1960.** 90th Birth Anniv. of Lenin.
1150. **345.** 60 h. olive .. .. 75 20

**1960.** 15th Anniv. of Liberation.
1151. **346.** 30 h. lake and blue.. 30 10
1152. – 30 h. grn. & lavender 25 10
1153. – 30 h. red and pink .. 25 10
1154. – 60 h. blue and buff .. 25 10
1155. – 60 h. purple & green 25 10
DESIGNS—VERT. No. 1152, Solider with liberated political prisoner. No. 1153, Child eating pastry. HORIZ. No. 1154, Welder. No. 1155, Tractor-driver.

DESIGN: 60 h. Country woman and child.

347. Smelter.

**1960.** Parliamentary Elections.
1156. **347.** 30 h. red and grey .. 15 10
1157. – 60 h. green and blue 20 10

348. Red Cross Woman with Dove.

**1960.** 3rd Czechoslovak Red Cross Congress.
1158. **348.** 30 h. red and blue .. 20 10

349. Fire-prevention Team with Hose.

**1960.** 2nd Firemen's Union Congress.
1159. **349.** 60 h. blue and pink.. 30 10

**1960.** 2nd National Spartacist Games (2nd issue). As T **341.**
1160. 30 h. red and green .. 45 10
1161. 60 h. black and pink.. 45 10
1162. 1 k. blue and orange.. 65 15
DESIGNS: 30 h. Ball exercises. 60 h. Stick exercises. 1 k. Girls with hoops.

**1960.** Olympic Games, Rome. As Type **343.**
1163. 1 k. black and orange.. 50 20
1164. 1 k. 80 black and red .. 1·25 25
1165. 2 k. black and blue .. 2·50 80
DESIGNS: 1 k. Sprinting. 1 k. 80, Gymnastics. 2 k. Rowing.

350. Czech 10 k. Stamp of 1936.

**1960.** National Philatelic Exn., Bratislava (1st issue).
1166. – 60 h. black and yellow 45 15
1167. **350.** 1 k. black and blue.. 80 15
DESIGN: 60 h. Hand of philatelist holding stamp Type **350.**
See also Nos. 1183/4.

351. Stalin Mine, Ostrava-Hermanice. 352. V. Cornelius of Vsehra (historian).

**1960.** 3rd Five Year Plan (1st issue).
1168. **351.** 10 h. black and green 20 10
1169. – 20 h. lake and blue .. 20 10
1170. – 30 h. blue and red .. 20 10
1171. – 40 h. green and lilac.. 20 10
1172. – 60 h. blue and yellow 20 10
DESIGNS: 20 h. Hodonin Power Station. 30 h. Klement Gottwald Iron Works, Kuncice. 40 h. Excavator. 60 h. Naphtha refinery.
See also Nos. 1198/1200.

**1960.** Cultural Anniversaries.
1173. **352.** 10 h. black .. .. 20 10
1174. – 20 h. brown .. .. 30 10
1175. – 30 h. red .. .. 40 10
1176. – 40 h. green .. .. 45 10
1177. – 60 h. violet .. .. 50 10
PORTRAITS: 20 h. K. M. Capek Chod (writer). 30 h. Hana Kvapilova (actress). 40 h. Oskar Nedbal (composer). 60 h. Otakar Ostricil (composer).

353. Zlin Trener 6 flying upside-down.

**1960.** 1st World Aviation Aerobatic Championships, Bratislava.
1178. **353.** 60 h. violet and blue 60 15

354. "New Constitution". 355. Worker with "Rude Pravo".

**1960.** Proclamation of New Constitution.
1179. **354.** 30 h. blue and red .. 20 10

**1960.** Czechoslovak Press Day (30 h.) and 40th Anniv. of Newspaper "Rude Pravo".
1180. – 30 h. blue & orange 10 10
1181. **355.** 60 h. black and red .. 20 10
DESIGN—HORIZ. (inscr. "DEN TISKU"): 30 h. Steel-workers with newspaper.

356. Globes.

**1960.** 15th Anniv. of W.F.T.U.
1182. **356.** 30 h. blue and bistre 25 10

357. Mail Coach and Ilyushin Il-18B.

**1960.** Air. National Philatelic Exn., Bratislava (2nd issue).
1183. **357.** 1 k. 60 blue and grey 3·00 1·25
1184. – 2 k. 80 green & cream 4·50 1·60
DESIGN: 2 k. 80, MIL Mi-4 helicopter over Bratislava.

358. Mallard. 359. "Doronicum clusii tausch".

**1960.** Water Birds.
1185 – 25 h. black and blue 60 10
1186 – 30 h. black and green 1·90 10
1187 – 40 h. black and blue 90 15
1188 – 60 h. black and pink 1·40 10
1189 – 1 k. black and yellow 1·90 15
1190 **358** 1 k. 60 black and lilac 5·50 1·60
BIRDS—VERT. 25 h. Black-crowned night heron. 30 h. Great crested grebe. 40 h. Lapwing. 60 h. Grey heron. HORIZ. 1 k. Greylag goose.

**1960.** Flowers. Inscr. in black.
1191. **359.** 20 h. yell., orge. & grn. 30 10
1192. – 30 h. red and green.. 50 15
1193. – 40 h. yellow and green 50 10
1194. – 60 h. pink and green 55 10
1195. – 1 k. blue, violet & grn. 85 20
1196. – 2 k. yell., grn. & pur. 2·50 1·00
FLOWERS: 30 h. "Cyclamen europaeum L". 40 h. "Primula auricula L". 60 h. "Sempervivum mont L". 1 k. "Gentiana clusii perr, et song". 2 k. "Pulsatilla slavica reuss".

360. A. Mucha (painter and stamp designer). 361. Automatic Machinery.

**1960.** Stamp Day and Birth Cent of Mucha.
1197 **360** 60 h. blue .. .. 60 10

**1961.** 3rd Five Year Plan (2nd issue).
1198. **361.** 20 h. blue .. .. 10 10
1199. – 30 h. red .. .. 15 10
1200. – 60 h. green .. .. 15 10
DESIGNS: 30 h. Turbo-generator and control desk. 60 h. Excavator.

362. Motor Cyclists (Int. Grand Prix, Brno). 363. Exhibition Emblem.

**1961.** Sports Events of 1961.
1201. **362.** 30 h. blue and mauve 20 10
1202. – 30 h. red and blue .. 20 10
1203. – 40 h. black and red.. 45 10
1204. – 60 h. purple and blue 45 10
1205. – 1 k. blue and yellow 45 10
1206. – 1 k. 20 green & salmon 45 15
1207. – 1 k. 60 brown and red 2·00 1·25
DESIGNS—VERT. 30 h. (No. 1202), Athletes with banners (40th anniv of Czech Physical Culture). 60 h. Figure skating (World Figure Skating Championships, Prague). 1 k. Rugger (35th anniv of rugby football in Czechoslovakia). 1 k. 20, Football (60th anniv of football in Czechoslovakia). 1 k. 60, Running (65th anniv of Bechovice–Prague Marathon Race). HORIZ. 40 h. Rowing (European Rowing Championships, Prague).

**1961.** "PRAGA 1962" Int. Stamp Exn. (1st issue).
1208. **363.** 2 k. red and blue .. 1·90 10
See also Nos. 1250/6, 1267/70, 1297/1300 and 1311/15.

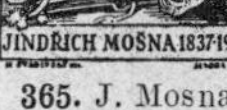

364. "Sputnik 3". 365. J. Mosna.

**1961.** Space Research (1st series).
1209 – 20 h. red and violet .. 50 10
1210 **364** 30 h. blue and buff .. 50 10
1211 – 40 h. red and green .. 45 15
1212 – 60 h. violet and yellow 30 10
1213 – 1 k. 60 blue and green 50 10
1214 – 2 k. purple and blue 2·10 1·25
DESIGNS—VERT. 20 h. Launching cosmic rocket. 40 h. Venus rocket. HORIZ. 60 h. "Lunik 1". 1 k. 60, "Lunik 3" and Moon. 2 k. Cosmonaut. (similar to T **366**).
See also Nos. 1285/90 and 1349/54.

**1961.** Cultural Annniversaries.
1215 **365** 60 h. green .. .. 25 10
1216 – 60 h. black .. .. 30 10
1217 – 60 h. blue .. .. 30 10
1218 – 60 h. red .. .. 25 10
1219 – 60 h. brown .. .. 25 10
PORTRAITS: No. 1216, J. Uprka (painter). 1217, P. O. Hviezdoslav (poet). 1218, A. Mrstik (writer). 1219, J. Hora (poet).

366. Man in Space.

**1961.** World's 1st Manned Space Flight.
1220 **366.** 60 h. red & turquoise 50 10
1221. – 3 k. blue and yellow 2·25 65

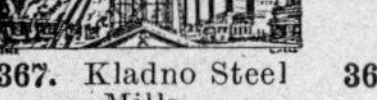


367. Kladno Steel Mills. 368. "Instrumental Music".

**1961.**

1222. 367. 3 k. red .. .. 90 10

**1961.** 150th Anniv. of Prague Conservatoire.

1223. 368. 30 h. sepia .. .. 30 15
1224. – 30 h. red .. .. 35 15
1225. – 60 h. blue .. .. 30 15

DESIGNS: No. 1224, Dancer. No. 1225, Girl playing lyre.

369. "People's House" (Lenin Museum), Prague. 370. Manasek Doll.

**1961.** 40th Anniv. of Czech Communist Party.

1226. 369. 30 h. brown .. .. 20 10
1227. – 30 h. blue .. .. 20 10
1228. – 30 h. violet .. .. 20 10
1229. – 60 h. red .. .. 20 10
1230. – 60 h. myrtle .. .. 20 10
1231. – 60 h. red .. .. 20 10

DESIGNS—HORIZ. No. 1227, Gottwald's Museum, Prague. VERT. No. 1228, Workers in Wenceslas Square, Prague. No. 1229, Worker, star and factory plant. No. 1230, Woman wielding hammer and sickle. No. 1231, May Day procession, Wenceslas Square.

**1961.** Czech Puppets.

1232. 370. 30 h. red and yellow .. 20 10
1233. – 40 h. sepia & turquoise 20 10
1234. – 60 h. blue & salmon .. 20 10
1235. – 1 k. green and blue .. 20 10
1236. – 1 k. 60 red and blue .. 1·25 40

PUPPETS: 40 h. "Dr. Faustus and Caspar". 60 h. "Spejbl and Hurvinek". 1 k. Scene from "Difficulties with the Moon" (Askenazy). 1 k. 60, "Jasanek" of Brno.

371. Gagarin waving Flags. 372. Woman's Head and Map of Africa.

**1961.** Yury Gagarin's (first man in space) Visit to Prague.

1237. 371. 60 h. black and red .. 25 10
1238. – 1 k. 80 black and blue 40 15

DESIGN: 1 k. 80, Yury Gagarin in space helmet, rocket and dove.

**1961.** Czecho-African Friendship.

1239. 372. 60 h. red and blue .. 25 10

373. Map of Europe and Fair Emblem. 374. Clover and Cow.

**1961.** Int. Trade Fair, Brno. Inscr. "M.V.B. 1961".

1240. 373. 30 h. blue and green .. 15 10
1241. – 60 h. green & salmon 25 10
1242. – 1 k. brown and blue .. 25 10

DESIGNS—VERT. 60 h. Horizontal drill. HORIZ. 1 k. Scientific discussion group.

**1961.** Agricultural Produce.

1243. – 20 h. purple and blue 15 10
1244. 374. 30 h. ochre and purple 15 10
1245. – 40 h. orange & brown 15 10
1246. – 60 h. bistre and green 20 10
1247. – 1 k. 40 brn. & choc... 40 10
1248. – 2 k. blue and purple 1·40 55

DESIGNS: 20 h. Sugar beet; cup and saucer. 40 h. Wheat and bread. 60 h. Hops and beer. 1 k. 40, Maize and cattle. 2 k. Potatoes and factory.

375. Prague. 376. Orlik Dam.

**1961.** 26th Session of Red Cross Societies League Governors' Council, Prague.

1249. 375. 60 h. violet and red .. 85 10

**1961.** "Praga 1962" Int. Stamp Exn. (2nd and 3rd issues).

1250. 376. 20 h. black and blue 65 15
1251. – 30 h. blue and red .. 20 10
1252. – 40 h. blue and green 65 15
1253. – 60 h. slate and bistre 65 15
1267. – 1 k. purple and green 65 50
1254. – 1 k. 20 myrtle & pink 85 50
1268. – 1 k. 60 brown & violet 1·10 70
1269. – 2 k. black and orange 1·50 1·25
1255. – 3 k. blue and yellow 2·00 50
1256. – 4 k. violet and orange 2·50 1·25
1270. – 5 k. multicoloured .. 24·00 22·00

DESIGNS—As Type 376: 30 h. Prague. 40 h. Hluboka Castle from lake. 60 h. Karlovy Vary. 1 k. Pilsen. 1 k. 20, North Bohemian landscape. 1 k. 60, High Tatras. 2 k. Ironworks, Ostrava-Kuncice. 3 k. Brno. 4 k. Bratislava. (50 × 29 mm.): 5 k. Prague and flags.

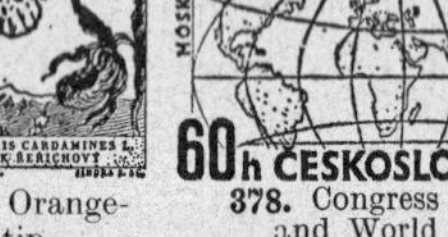


377. Orange-tip. 378. Congress Emblem and World Map.

**1961.** Butterflies and Moths. Multicoloured.

1257 15 h. Type 377 .. .. 50 10
1258 20 h. Southern festoon .. 70 10
1259 30 h. Apollo .. 1·00 15
1260 40 h. Swallowtail .. 1·00 25
1261 60 h. Peacock .. 1·25 25
1262 80 h. Camberwell beauty 1·50 30
1263 1 k. Clifden's nonpareil 1·50 30
1264 1 k. 60 Red admiral .. 1·75 40
1265 2 k. Brimstone .. .. 4·50 2·00

**1961.** 5th W.F.T.U. Congress, Moscow.

1266. 378. 60 h. blue and red .. 35 10

379. Racing Cyclists (Berlin-Prague-Warsaw Cycle Race). 380. K. Kovarovic (composer, centenary of birth).

**1962.** Sports Events of 1962.

1271 379 30 h. black and blue 25 10
1272 – 40 h. black and yellow 20 10
1273 – 60 h. grey and blue .. 30 10
1274 – 1 k. black and pink .. 30 10
1275 – 1 k. 20 black & green 30 10
1276 – 1 k. 60 black & green 1·40 70

DESIGNS: 40 h. Gymnastics (15th World Gymnastics Championships, Prague). 60 h. Figure Skating (World Figure Skating Championships, Prague). 1 k. Bowling (World Bowling Championships, Bratislava). 1 k. 20, Football (World Cup Football Championship, Chile). 1 k. 60 Throwing the discus (7th European Athletic Championships, Belgrade).

See also No. 1306.

**1962.** Cultural Celebrities and Anniversaries.

1277. 380. 10 h. brown .. .. 10 10
1278. – 20 h. blue .. .. 10 10
1279. – 30 h. brown .. .. 10 10
1280. – 40 h. purple .. .. 15 10
1281. – 60 h. black .. .. 15 10
1282. – 1 k. 60 myrtle .. 40 10
1283. – 1 k. 80 blue .. .. 50 10

DESIGNS—As Type 380: 20 h. F. Skroup (composer). 30 h. Bozena Nemcova (writer). 60 h. Rod of Aesculapius and Prague Castle (Czech Medical Association Cent.). 1 k. 60, L. Celakovsky (founder, Czech Botanical Society). HORIZ. (41 × 22½ mm.): 40 h. F. Zaviska and K. Petr. 1 k. 80, M. Valouch and J. Hronec. (These two commemorate Czech Mathematics and Physics Union Cent.)

381. Miner holding Lamp. 382. "Man Conquers Space".

**1962.** 30th Anniv. of Miners' Strike, Most.

1284. 381. 60 h. blue and red .. 25 10

**1962.** Space Research (2nd series).

1285. 382. 30 h. red and blue .. 25 10
1286. – 40 h. blue and orange 25 10
1287. – 60 h. blue and pink .. 25 10
1288. – 80 h. purple and green 60 10
1289. – 1 k. blue and yellow 25 20
1290. – 1 k. 60 green & yellow 2·00 75

DESIGNS—VERT. 40 h. Launching of Soviet rocket. 1 k. Automatic station on Moon. HORIZ. 60 h. "Vostok-II". 80 h. Multi-stage automatic rocket. 1 k. 60, Television satellite station.

383. Indian and African Elephants. 384. Dove and Nest.

**1962.** Animals of Prague Zoos.

1291. – 20 h. black & turq. 30 10
1292. – 30 h. black and violet 30 10
1293. – 60 h. black and yellow 30 10
1294. 383. 1 k. black and green 50 10
1295. – 1 k. 40 blk. & mauve 50 20
1296. – 1 k. 60 black & brown 2·00 80

ANIMALS—VERT. 20 h. Polar bear. 30 h. Chimpanzee. 60 h. Bactrian camel. HORIZ. 1 k. 40, Leopard. 1 k. 60, Wild horses.

**1962.** Air. "Praga 1962" International Stamp Exhibition (4th issue).

1297 384 80 h. multicoloured .. 50 25
1298 – 1 k. 40 red, blue & blk 2·50 2·50
1299 – 2 k. 80 multicoloured 4·00 3·50
1300 – 4 k. 20 multicoloured 5·50 5·00

DESIGNS: 1 k. 40, Dove. 2 k. 80, Flower and bird. 4 k. 20, Plant and bird. All designs feature "Praga 62" emblem. The 80 h. and 2 k. 80 are inscr in Slovakian and the others in Czech.

385. Girl of Lidice. 386. Klary's Fountain Teplice.

**1962.** 20th Anniv. of Destruction of Lidice and Lezaky.

1301. 385. 30 h. black and red .. 30 10
1302. – 60 h. black and blue .. 30 10

DESIGN: 60 h. Flowers and Lezaky ruins.

**1962.** 1200th Anniv of Discovery of Teplice Springs.

1303 386 60 h. green and yellow 35 10

387. Campaign Emblem. 388. Swimmer with Rifle.

**1962.** Malaria Eradication.

1304. 387. 60 h. red and black .. 15 10
1305. – 3 k. blue and yellow .. 1·25 75

DESIGN: 3 k. Campaign emblem and dove (different).

**1962.** Czechoslovakia's Participation in World Cup Football Championship Final, Chile. As No. 1275 but inscr. "CSSR VE FINALE" and new value.

1306 1 k. 60 green and yellow .. 1·10 15

**1962.** 2nd Military Spartacist Games. Inscr. as in T 388.

1307. 388. 30 h. myrtle and blue 15 10
1308. – 40 h. violet and yellow 20 10
1309. – 60 h. brown and green 25 10
1310. – 1 k. blue and red .. 30 10

DESIGNS: 40 h. Soldier mounting obstacle. 60 h. Footballer. 1 k. Relay Race.

389. "Sun" and Field (Socialized Agriculture). 390. Swallow, "Praga 62" and Congress Emblems.

**1962.** "Praga 1962" Int. Stamp Exn. (5th issue).

1311. 389. 30 h. multicoloured .. 3·25 1·25
1312. – 60 h. multicoloured .. 80 10
1313. – 80 h. multicoloured .. 4·00 2·00
1314. – 1 k. multicoloured .. 4·00 3·00
1315. – 1 k. 40 multicoloured 4·00 3·50

DESIGNS—VERT. 60 h. Astronaut in "spaceship". 1 k. 40, Children playing under "tree". HORIZ. 80 h. Boy with flute, and peace doves. 1 k. Workers of three races. All have "Praga 62" emblem.

**1962.** F.I.P. Day (Federation Internationale de Philatelie).

1316. 390. 1 k. 60 multicoloured 5·50 4·75

391. Zinkovy Sanatorium and Sailing Dinghy. 392. Cruiser "Aurora".

**1962.** Czech Workers' Social Facilities.

1317. – 30 h. black and blue 20 10
1318. 391. 60 h. sepia and ochre 30 10

DESIGN—HORIZ. 30 h. Children in day nursery, and factory.

**1962.** 45th Anniv. of Russian Revolution.

1319. 392. 30 h. sepia and blue 25 10
1320. 60 h. black and pink 40 10

393. Astronaut and Worker.

**1962.** 40th Anniv. of U.S.S.R.

1321. 393. 30 h. red and blue .. 20 10
1322. – 60 h. black and pink 25 10

DESIGN—VERT. 60 h. Lenin.

394. Crane ("Building Construction").

**1962.** 12th Czech Communist Party Congress, Prague..
1323 **394** 30 h. red and yellow 25 10
1324 – 40 h. blue and yellow 25 10
1325 – 60 h. black and pink 25 10
DESIGNS—VERT. 40 h. Produce ("Agriculture"). HORIZ. 60 h. Factory plants ("Industry").

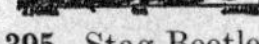

**395.** Stag Beetle. **396.** Table Tennis (World Championships, Prague).

**1962.** Beetles. Multicoloured.
1326 20 h. Caterpillar-hunter (horiz) .. .. 35 15
1327 30 h. Cardinal beetle (horiz) .. .. 35 10
1328 60 h. Type **395** .. .. 35 15
1329 1 k. Great dung beetle (horiz) .. .. 1·00 25
1330 1 k. 60 Alpine longhorn beetle .. .. .. 1·40 25
1331 2 k. Blue ground beetle .. 3·25 1·60

**1963.** Sports Events of 1963.
1332. **396.** 30 h. black and green 25 10
1333. – 60 h. black & orange 25 10
1334. – 80 h. black and blue.. 25 10
1335. – 1 k. black and violet 30 10
1336. – 1 k. 20 black & brown 30 15
1337. – 1 k. 60 black and red 65 15
DESIGNS: 60 h. Cycling (80th Anniv. of Czech Cycling). 80 h. Ski-ing (1st Czech Winter Games). 1 k. Motor-cycle dirt track racing (15th Anniv. of "Golden Helmet" Race, Pardubice). 1 k. 20, Weightlifting (World Championships, Prague). 1 k. 60, Hurdling (1st Czech Summer Games).

**397.** Industrial Plant. **398.** Guild Emblem.

**1963.** 15th Anniv. of "Victorious February" and 5th T.U. Congress.
1338. **397.** 30h. red and blue .. 15 10
1339. – 60 h. red and black.. 15 10
1340. – 60 h. black and red.. 15 10
DESIGNS—VERT. No. 1339, Sun and campfire. HORIZ. No. 1340, Industrial plant and annual "stepping stones".

**1963.** Cultural Anniversaries.
1341. **398.** 20 h. black and blue 10 10
1342. – 30 h. red .. .. 10 10
1343. – 30 h. red and blue .. 10 10
1344. – 60 h. black .. .. 15 10
1345. – 60 h. purple and blue 15 10
1346. – 60 h. myrtle.. .. 15 10
1347. – 1 k. 60 brown .. 50 15
DESIGNS—VERT. No. 1341 (Artist's Guild cent). 1342, E. Urx (journalist). 1343, J. Janosik (national hero). 1344, J. Palkovic (author). 1346, Woman with book, and children (cent of Slovak Cultural Society, Slovenska Matice). 1347, M. Svabinsky (artist; after self-portrait). HORIZ. 1345, Allegorical figure and National Theatre, Prague (80th anniv).

**399.** Young People. **400.** TV Cameras and Receiver.

**1963.** 4th Czech Youth Federation Congress, Prague.
1348. **399.** 30 h. blue and red .. 25 10

**1963.** Space Research (3rd series). As T **364** but inscr "1963" at foot.
1349. 30 h. purple, red & yellow 15 10
1350. 50 h. blue and turquoise 25 10
1351. 60 h. turquoise & yellow 25 10
1352. 1 k. black and brown .. 55 15
1353. 1 k. 60 sepia and green.. 40 15
1354. 2 k. violet and yellow .. 2·25 75
DESIGNS—HORIZ. 30 h. Rocket circling Sun. 50 h. Rockets and Sputniks leaving Earth. 60 h. Spacecraft and Moon. 1 k. "Mars 1" rocket and Mars. 1 k. 60, Rocket heading for Jupiter. 2 k. Spacecraft returning from Saturn.

**1963.** 10th Anniv. of Czech Television Service. Inscr. as in T **400.**
1355. **400.** 40 h. blue and orange 20 10
1356. – 60 h. red and blue .. 20 10
DESIGN—VERT. 60 h. TV transmitting aerial.

**401.** Broadcasting Studio and Receiver. **402.** Ancient Ring and Moravian Settlements Map.

**1963.** 40th Anniv. of Czech Radio Service. Inscr. as in T **401.**
1357. **401.** 30 h. purple and blue 15 10
1358. – 1 k. purple & turquoise 25 10
DESIGN—VERT. 1 k. Aerial mast, globe and doves.

**1963.** 1100th Anniv. of Moravian Empire.
1359. **402.** 30 h. black and green 20 10
1360. – 1 k. 60 black & yellow 40 10
DESIGN: 1 k. 60, Ancient silver plate showing falconer with hawk.

**403.** Tupolev Tu-104A. **404.** Singer.

**1963.** 40th Anniv. of Czech Airlines.
1361. **403.** 80 h. violet and blue 40 10
1362. – 1 k. 80 blue and green 75 15
DESIGN: 1 k. 80, Ilyushin Il-18B.

**1963.** 60th Anniv of Moravian Teachers' Singing Club.
1363 **404** 30 h. red .. .. 35 10

**405.** Nurse and Child. **406.** Wheatears and Kromeriz Castle.

**1963.** Centenary of Red Cross.
1364. **405.** 30 h. blue and red .. 40 10

**1963.** Nat. Agricultural Exn.
1365. **406.** 30 h. green and yellow 40 10

**407.** Honey Bee, Honeycomb and Congress Emblem.

**1963.** 19th Int. Bee-keepers' Congress ("Apimondia '63").
1366. **407.** 1 k. brown and yellow 60 10

**408.** "Vostok 5" and Bykovsky. **409.** "Modern Fashion".

**1963.** 2nd "Team" Manned Space Flights.
1367 **408** 80 h. pink and blue .. 35 10
1368 – 2 k. 80 blue & purple 1·90 25
DESIGN: 2 k. 80, "Vostok 6" and Valentina Tereshkova.

**1963.** Liberec Consumer Goods Fair.
1369. **409.** 30 h. black & mauve 40 10

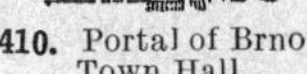

**410.** Portal of Brno Town Hall. **411.** Cave and Stalagmites.

**1963.** Brno International Fair.
1370. **410.** 30h. purple & blue .. 20 10
1371. – 60 h. blue and salmon 25 10
DESIGN: 60 h. Tower of Brno Town Hall.

**1963.** Czech Scenery. (a) Moravia.
1372 **411** 30 h. brown and blue 30 10
1373 – 80 h. brown and pink 45 10

(b) Slovakia.
1374 – 30 h. blue and green 35 10
1375 – 60 h. blue, grn & yell 30 10
DESIGNS: No. 1373, Macocha Chasm. No. **1374,** Pool, Hornad Valley. No. 1375, Waterfall, Great Hawk Gorge.

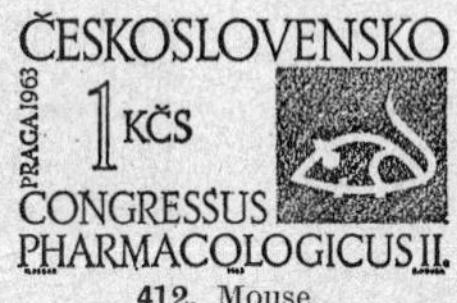

**412.** Mouse.

**1963.** 2nd International Pharmacological Congress, Prague.
1376. **412.** 1 k. red and black .. 40 10

**413.** Blast Furnace. **414.** "Aid for Farmers Abroad".

**1963.** 30th Int. Foundry Congress, Prague.
1377. **413.** 60h. black and blue.. 25 10

**1963.** Freedom from Hunger.
1378. **414.** 1 k. 60 sepia .. .. 55 15

**415.** Dolls. **416.** Canoeing.

**1963.** U.N.E.S.C.O. Folk Art. Multicoloured.
1379. 60 h. Type **415** .. .. 35 15
1380. 80 h. Rooster .. .. 40 20
1381. 1 k. Vase of flowers 55 30
1382. 1 k. 20 Detail of glass-painting "Janosik and his Men" .. .. 55 20
1383. 1 k. 60 Stag .. .. 55 20
1384. 2 k. Horseman .. .. 2·50 1·25

**1963.** Olympic Games, Tokyo, 1964, and 50th Anniv. of Czech Canoeing. (30 h.).
1385. **416.** 30 h. blue & green .. 30 10
1386. – 40 h. brown and blue 30 10
1387. – 60 h. lake and yellow 25 10
1388. – 80 h. violet and red.. 30 15
1389. – 1 k. blue and red .. 30 15
1390. – 1 k. 60 ultram. & blue 2·25 1·00
DESIGNS: 40 h. Volleyball. 60 h Wrestling. 80 h. Basketball. 1 k. Boxing. 1 k. 60, Gymnastics.

**417.** Linden Tree. **418.** "Human Reason and Technology."

**1963.** 20th Anniv of Czech–Soviet Treaty of Friendship.
1391 **417** 30 h. brown and blue 15 10
1392 – 60 h. red and green .. 15 10
DESIGN: 60 h. Hammer and sickle, and star.

**1963.** Technical and Scientific Knowledge Society Congress.
1393. **418.** 60 h. violet .. .. 40 10

**419.** Chamois. **420.** Figure Skating.

**1963.** Mountain Animals.
1394. **419.** 30 h. multicoloured.. 90 25
1395. – 40 h. multicoloured.. 90 40
1396. – 60 h. sepia, yell. & grn. 1·10 30
1397. – 1 k. 20 multicoloured 1·10 25
1398. – 1 k. 60 multicoloured 1·50 40
1399. – 2 k. brn., orge. & grn. 4·25 2·00
ANIMALS: 40 h. Ibex. 60 h. Mouflon. 1 k. 20, Roe deer. 1 k. 60, Fallow deer. 2 k. Red deer.

**1964.** Sports Events of 1964.
1400. **420.** 30 h. violet and yellow 25 10
1401. – 80 h. blue and orange 25 10
1402. – 1 k. brown and lilac.. 75 15
DESIGNS—VERT. 30 h. Type **420** (Czech Students Games). 1 k. Handball (World Handball Championships). HORIZ. 80 h. Cross-country skiing (Students' Games).

**421.** Ice Hockey. **423.** Magura Hotel, Zdiar, High Tatra.

**422.** Belanske Tatra Mountains, Skiers and Tree.

**1964.** Winter Olympic Games, Innsbruck.
1403. **421.** 1 k. purple and turq. 1·25 40
1404. – 1 k. 80 green & lav... 1·10 60
1405. – 2 k. blue and green... 2·75 2·00
DESIGNS—VERT. 1 k. 80, Tobogganing. HORIZ. 2 k. Ski jumping.

**1964.** Tourist Issue.
1406. **422.** 30 h. purple and blue 20 10
1407. – 60 h. blue and red .. 30 10
1408. – 1 k. brown and olive 50 10
1409. – 1 k. 80 green & orange 90 25
DESIGNS: 60 h. Telc (Moravia) and motor-camp. 1 k. Spis Castle (Slovakia) and angler. 1 k. 80, Cesky Krumlov (Bohemia) and sailing dinghies. Each design includes a tree.

**1964.** Trade Union Recreation Hotels.
1410. **423.** 60 h. green and yellow 20 10
1411. – 80 h. blue and pink.. 20 10
DESIGN: 80 h. "Slovak Insurrection" Hotel, Lower Tatra.

**424.** Statuary (after Michelangelo).

**1964.** U.N.E.S.C.O. Cultural Anniversaries.
1412. **424.** 40 h. black and green 20 10
1413. – 60 h. black and red.. 20 10
1414. – 1 k. black and blue.. 40 10
1415. – 1 k. 60 black & yellow 40 10
DESIGNS—HORIZ. 40 h. Type **424** (400th death anniv of Michelangelo). 60 h. Bottom, "Midsummer Night's Dream" (400th birth anniv of Shakespeare). 1 k. 60 King George of Podebrady (500th anniv of his mediation in Europe). VERT. 1 k. Galileo Galilei (400th birth anniv).

**425.** Yury Gagarin.

**1964.** "Space Exploration". On cream paper.
1416. **425.** 30 h. blue and black .. 50 25
1417. – 60 h. red and green .. 25 10
1418. – 80 h. violet and lake 50 20
1419. – 1 k. violet and blue .. 75 25
1420. – 1 k. 20 bronze and red 50 25
1421. – 1 k. 40 turq. and black 1·25 75
1422. – 1 k. 60 turq. & violet 4·00 1·90
1423. – 2 k. red and blue .. 75 30
ASTRONAUTS—HORIZ. 60 h. Titov. 80 h. Glenn. 1 k. 20, Popovich and Nikolaev. VERT. 1 k. Carpenter. 1 k. 40, Schirra. 1 k. 60, Cooper. 2 k. Tereshkova and Bykovsky.

**426.** Campanula. **427.** Miner of 1764.

**1964.** Wild Flowers.
1424. **426.** 60 h. pur., orge. & grn. 1·60 20
1425. – 80 h. multicoloured .. 1·60 20
1426. – 1 k. blue, pink & grn. 1·60 40
1427. – 1 k. 20 multicoloured 80 25
1428. – 1 k. 60 violet & green 1·00 40
1429. – 2 k. red, turq. & violet 5·50 1·90
FLOWERS: 80 h. Musk thistle. 1 k. Chicory. 1 k. 20, Yellow iris. 1 k. 60, Marsh gentian. 2 k. Common poppy.

**1964.** Czech Anniversaries.
1430. – 30 h. black and yellow 25 10
1431. – 60 h. red and blue .. 50 10
1432. **427.** 60 h. sepia and green 25 10
DESIGNS—HORIZ. (30½ × 22½ mm.): 30 h. Silesian coat of arms (stylised) (150th Anniv. of Silesian Museum, Opava). (41½ × 23 mm.): 60 h. (No. 1431), Skoda ASC-16 fire engine (Centenary of Voluntary Fire Brigades). 60 h. (No. 1432) (Bicentenary of Banska Stiavnica Mining School).

**428.** Cine-film "Flower".

**429.** Hradcany, Prague and Black-headed Gulls.

**1964.** 14th Int. Film Festival, Karlovy Vary.
1433. **428.** 60 h. black, blue & red 1·50 15

**1964.** 4th Czech Red Cross Congress, Prague.
1434. **429.** 60 h. violet and red .. 75 10

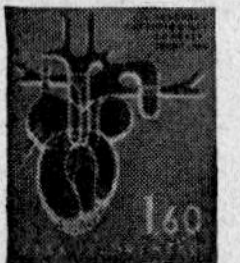
**430.** Human Heart.

**431.** Slovak Girl and Workers.

**1964.** 4th European Cardiological Congress, Prague.
1435. **430.** 1 k. 60 red and blue .. 90 10

**1964.** 20th Anniv. of Slovak Rising and Dukla Battles.
1436. **431.** 30 h. red and brown .. 15 10
1437. – 60 h. blue and red .. 15 10
1438. – 60 h. sepia and red .. 15 10
DESIGNS: No. 1437, Armed Slovaks. No. 1438, Soldiers in battle at Dukla Pass.

**432.** Hradcany, Prague.

**433.** Cycling.

**1964.** Millenary of Prague.
1439 **432** 60 h. brown & mauve 50 10

**1964.** Olympic Games, Tokyo. Multicoloured.
1440 60 h. Type **433** .. .. 40 15
1441 80 h. Throwing the discus and pole vaulting (vert) 50 25
1442 1 k. Football (vert) .. 50 25
1443 1 k. 20 Rowing (vert) .. 65 40
1444 1 k. 60 Swimming .. 75 55
1445 2 k. 80 Weightlifting .. 4·50 2·50

**434.** Redstart.

**435.** Brno Engineering Works (150th Anniv.).

**1964.** Birds. Multicoloured.
1446. 30 h. Type **434** .. .. 55 10
1447. 60 h. Green woodpecker 1·00 10
1448. 80 h. Hawfinch .. .. 1·75 20
1449. 1 k. Black woodpecker .. 1·75 40
1450. 1 k. 20 European robin .. 1·10 50
1451. 1 k. 60 Common roller .. 3·75 90

**1964.** Czech Engineering.
1452. **435.** 30 h. brown .. .. 10 10
1453. – 60 h. green and salmon 25 10
DESIGN: 60 h. Diesel-electric shunter.

**436.** "Dancing Girl".

**437.** Mountain Rescue Service (10th Anniv.).

**1965.** 3rd National Spartacist Games.
1454. **436.** 30 h. red and blue .. 15 10
See also Nos. 1489/92.

**1965.** Sports Events of 1965.
1455. **437.** 60 h. violet and blue 20 10
1456. – 60 h. lake and orange 20 10
1457. – 60 h. green and red .. 20 10
1458. – 60 h. green and yellow 20 10
SPORTS: No. 1456, Exercising with hoop (1st World Artistic Gymnastics Championships, Prague). No. 1457, Cycling (World Indoor Cycling Championships, Prague). No. 1458, Hurdling (Czech University Championships, Brno).

**438.** Domazlice. **439.** Exploration of Mars.

**1965.** 700th Annivs. of Six Czech Towns, and 20th Anniv. of Terezin Concentration Camp (No. 1465).
1459. **438.** 30 h. violet and yellow 20 10
1460. – 30 h. violet and blue 20 10
1461. – 30 h. blue and olive .. 20 10
1462. – 30 h. sepia and olive 20 10
1463. – 30 h. green and buff 20 10
1464. – 30 h. slate and drab 20 10
1465. – 30 h. red and black .. 20 10
TOWNS: No. 1460, Beroun. No. 1461, Zatec. No. 1462, Policka. No. 1463, Lipnik and Becvou. No. 1464, Frydek-Mistek. No. 1465, Terezin concentration camp.

**1965.** Int. Quiet Sun Years and Space Research.
1466. – 20 h. purple and red 30 10
1467. – 30 h. yellow and red 30 10
1468. – 60 h. blue and yellow 30 10
1469. – 1 k. violet & turquoise 65 10
1470. – 1 k. 40 slate and salmon 65 20
1471. **439.** 1 k. 60 black and pink 65 20
1472. – 2 k. blue & turquoise 2·00 1·25
DESIGNS—HORIZ. 20 h. Maximum sun-spot activity. 30 h. Minimum sun-spot activity ("Quiet Sun"). 60 h. Moon exploration. 1 k. 40, Artificial satellite and space station. 2 k. Soviet "Kosmos" and U.S. "Tiros" satellites. VERT. 1 k. Space-ships rendezvous.

**440.** Horse Jumping (Amsterdam, 1928).

DESIGNS (each with city feature): 30 h. Throwing the discus (Paris, 1900). 60 h. Marathon (Helsinki, 1952). 1 k. Weightlifting (Los Angeles, 1932). 1 k. 40, Gymnastics (Berlin, 1936). 1 k. 60, Rowing (Rome, 1960). 2 k. Gymnastics (Tokyo, 1964).

**1965.** Czechoslovakia's Olympic Victories.
1473. **440.** 20 h. brown and gold 20 10
1474. – 30 h. violet and green 20 10
1475. – 60 h. blue and gold .. 20 10
1476. – 1 k. brown and gold 40 20
1477. – 1 k. 40 green and gold 90 65
1478. – 1 k. 60 black and gold 90 65
1479. – 2 k. red and gold .. 90 25

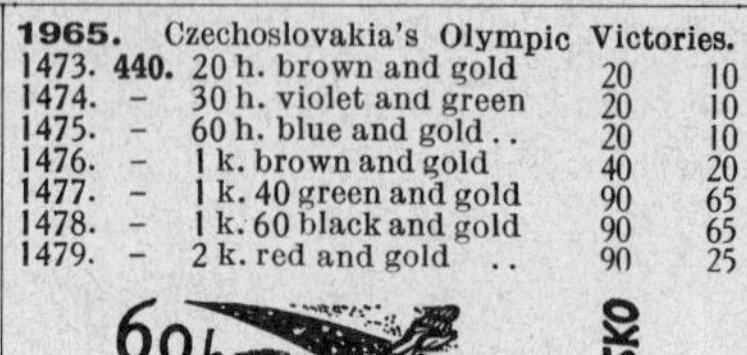

**441.** Leonov in Space.

**1965.** Space Achievements.
1480. **441.** 60 h. purple and blue 25 20
1481. – 60 h. blue and mauve 25 20
1482. – 3 k. purple and blue 1·50 1·25
1483. – 3 k. blue and mauve 1·50 1·25
DESIGNS: No. 1481, Grissom, Young and "Gemini 3". No. 1482, Leonov leaving spaceship "Voskhod 2". No. 1483, "Gemini 3" on launching pad at Cape Kennedy.

**442.** Soldier.

**1965.** 20th Anniv of Liberation. Inscr. "20 LET CSSR".
1484. **442.** 30 h. olive, blk. & red 20 10
1485. – 30 h. violet, blue & red 20 10
1486. – 60 h. black, red & blue 25 10
1487. – 1 k. violet, brn. & orge. 50 15
1488. – 1 k. 60 multicoloured 75 40
DESIGNS: 30 h. (No. 1485), Workers. 60 h. Mechanic. 1 k. Building worker. 1 k. 60, Peasant.

**443.** Children's Exercises.

**444.** Slovak "Kopov".

**1965.** 3rd National Spartacist Games.
1489 **443** 30 h. blue and red .. 15 10
1490 – 60 h. brown and blue 20 10
1491 – 1 k. blue and yellow 35 10
1492 – 1 k. 60 red and brown 40 25
DESIGNS: 60 h. Young gymnasts. 1 k. Women's exercises. 1 k. 60, Start of race.

**1965.** Canine Events.
1493. **444.** 30 h. black and red .. 40 10
1494. – 40 h. black & yellow 40 10
1495. – 60 h. black and red .. 50 10
1496. – 1 k. black and red .. 90 15
1497. – 1 k. 60 black & yellow 60 25
1498. – 2 k. black and orange 2·00 1·00
DOGS: 30 h. Type **444.** 1 k. Poodle (Int. Dogbreeders' Congress, Prague). 40 h. German sheepdog. 60 h. Czech "fousek" (retriever), (both World Dog Exn., Brno). 1 k. 60, Czech terrier. 2 k. Afghan hound (both Plenary Session of F.C.I.—Int. Federation of Cynology, Prague).

**445.** U.N. Emblem.

**1965.** U.N. Commem. and Int. Co-operation Year.
1499. **445.** 60 h. brown & yellow 20 10
1500. – 1 k. blue and turquoise 40 10
1501. – 1 k. 60 red and gold .. 40 35
DESIGNS: 60 h. T **445.** (The inscr. reads "Twentieth Anniversary of the signing of the U.N. Charter"). 1 k. U.N. Headquarters ("20th Anniv. of U.N."). 1 k. 60, I.C.Y. emblem.

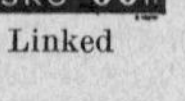
**446.** "SOF" and Linked Rings.

**447.** Women of Three Races.

**1965.** 20th Anniv. of World Federation of Trade Unions.
1502. **446.** 60 h. red and blue .. 40 10

**1965.** 20th Anniv. of Int. Democratic Women's Federation.
1503. **447.** 60 h. blue .. .. 40 10

**448.** Children's House.

**449.** Marx and Lenin.

**1965.** Prague Castle (1st series). Inscr. "PRAHA HRAD".
1504. **448.** 30 h. green .. .. 20 10
1505. – 60 h. sepia .. .. 25 10
DESIGN—VERT. 60 h. Mathias Gate.
See also Nos. 1572/3, 1656/7, 1740/1, 1827/8, 1892/3, 1959/60, 2037/8, 2103/4, 2163/4, 2253/4, 2305/6, 2337/8, 2404/5, 2466/7, 2543/4, 2599/2600, 2637/8, 2685/6, 2739/40, 2803/4, 2834/5, 2878/9, 2950/1, 2977/8 and 3026/7.

**1965.** 6th Organization of Socialist Countries' Postal Ministers Conference, Peking.
1506. **449.** 60 h. red and gold .. 20 10

**450.** Jan Hus. **452.** "Fourfold Aid".

**1965.** Various Anniversaries and Events (1st issue).
1507. **450.** 60 h. black and red .. 20 10
1508. – 60 h. blue & red 20 10
1509. – 60 h. lilac and gold .. 20 10
1510. – 1 k. blue and orange 25 10
DESIGNS—VERT. No. 1507, T **450** (reformer, 550th death anniv.). No. 1508, G. J. Mendel (publication cent. in Brno of his study of heredity). HORIZ. (30½ × 23 mm.): No. 1509, Jewellery emblems ("Jablonec 65" Jewellery Exn.). No. 1510, Early telegraph and telecommunications satellite (I.T.U. cent.).

**1965.** Various Anniversaries and Events (2nd issue).
1512. 30 h. black and green .. 15 10
1513. 30 h. black and brown .. 15 10
1514. 60 h. black and red .. 20 10
1515. 60 h. brown on cream .. 20 10
1516. 1 k. black and orange .. 20 10
DESIGNS—As Type **450**: HORIZ. No. 1512, L. Stur (nationalist; 150th birth anniv.). No. 1513, J. Navratil (painter; death cent.). VERT. No. 1514, B. Martinu (composer: 75th birth anniv.). LARGER—VERT. (23½ × 30½ mm.): No. 1515, Allegoric figure (Academia Istropolitana, Bratislava. 500th anniv.). HORIZ. (30 × 22½ mm.): No. 1516, Emblem (IUPAC Macromolecular Symposium, Prague.)

**1965.** Flood Relief.
1517. **452.** 30 h. blue .. .. 15 10
1518. – 2 k. black and olive .. 70 30
DESIGN—HORIZ. 2 k. Rescue by boat.

**453.** Dotterel

**454.** Levoca.

**1965.** Mountain Birds. Multicoloured.
1519. 30 h. Type **453** .. .. 80 10
1520. 60 h. Wallcreeper (vert.) 80 10
1521. 1 k. 20 Redpoll .. .. 1·25 30
1522. 1 k. 40 Golden Eagle (vert.) .. .. 1·75 25
1523. 1 k. 60 Ring Ousel 1·25 40
1524. 2 k. Nutcracker (vert.) .. 3·50 1·50

**1965.** Czech Towns. (1) Size 23 × 19 mm.
1525. **454.** 5 h. black and yellow 10 10
1526. – 10 h. blue and bistre 15 10
1527. – 20 h. sepia and blue .. 10 10
1528. – 30 h. blue and green .. 15 10
1529. – 40 h. sepia and blue .. 15 10
1530. – 50 h. black and buff .. 20 10
1531. – 60 h. red and blue .. 25 10
1532. – 1 k. violet and green 35 10

(b) Size 30½ × 23½ mm.
1533. – 1 k. 20 olive and blue 30 10
1534. – 1 k. 60 blue and yellow 50 10
1535. – 2 k. bronze and green 65 10
1536. – 3 k. purple & yellow .. 80 10
1537. – 5 k. black and pink .. 1·25 10
TOWNS: 10 h. Jindrichuv Hradec. 20 h. Nitra. 30 h. Kosice. 40 h. Hradec Kralove. 50 h. Telc. 60 h. Ostrava. 1 k. Olomouc. 1 k. 20, Ceske Budejovice. 1 k. 60, Cheb. 2 k. Brno. 3 k. Bratislava. 5 k. Prague.

455. Coltsfoot. 457. "Music".

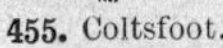

456. Panorama of "Stamps".

**1965.** Medicinal Plants. Multicoloured.
1538 30 h. Type **455** .. .. 25 10
1539 60 h. Meadow saffron .. 45 15
1540 80 h. Common poppy .. 50 15
1541 1 k. Foxglove .. .. 60 20
1542 1 k. 20 Arnica .. .. 1·40 30
1543 1 k. 60 Cornflower .. 80 40
1544 2 k. Dog rose .. .. 4·00 1·75

**1965.** Stamp Day.
1545. **456.** 1 k. red and green .. 3·75 3·50

**1966.** 70th Anniv. of Czech Philharmonic Orchestra.
1546. **457.** 30 h. black and gold .. 50 20

458. Pair Dancing. 459. S. Sucharda (sculptor).

**1966.** Sports Events of 1966.
(a) European Figure Skating Championships, Bratislava.
1547. **458.** 30 h. red and pink .. 15 10
1548. – 60 h. emerald & green 20 10
1549. – 1 k. 60 brown & yellow 40 10
1550. – 2 k. blue and turquoise 2·10 50
DESIGNS: 60 h. Male skater leaping. 1 k. 60, Female skater leaping. 2 k. Pair-skaters taking bows.

(b) World Volleyball Championships, Prague.
1551. – 60 h. red and buff .. 20 10
1552. – 1 k. violet and blue .. 25 10
DESIGNS—VERT. 60 h. Player leaping to ball. 1 k. Player falling.

**1966.** Cultural Anniversaries.
1553. **459.** 30 h. green .. .. 10 10
1554. – 30 h. blue .. .. 10 10
1555. – 60 h. red .. .. 20 10
1556. – 60 h. brown .. .. 20 10
PORTRAITS: No. 1553, Type **459** (birth centenary). 1554, Ignac J. Pesina (veterinary surgeon, birth bicentenary). 1555, Romain Rolland (writer, birth centenary). 1556, Donatello (sculptor, 500th death anniv).

460. "Ajax", 1841. 462. Trout.

**1966.** Czech Locomotives.
1557. **460.** 20 h. sepia on cream 35 10
1558. – 30 h. violet on cream 35 10
1559. – 60 h. plum on cream 35 10
1560. – 1 k. ultram. on cream 60 15
1561. – 1 k. 60 blue on cream 80 15
1562. – 2 k. lake on cream .. 3·50 1·40
LOCOMOTIVES: 30 h "Karlstejn", 1865. 60 h. "423.0" type, 1946. 1 k. "498.0" type, 1946. 1 k. 60, "E699.0" (electric) type, 1964. 2 k. "T669.0" (diesel-electric) type, 1964.

**1966.** World Angling Championships, Svit. Multicoloured.
1564. 30 h. Type **462** .. .. 30 10
1565. 60 h. Perch .. .. 45 10
1566. 1 k. Carp .. .. 60 15
1567. 1 k. 20 Pike .. .. 60 20
1568. 1 k. 40 Grayling .. .. 90 30
1569. 1 k. 60 Eel .. .. 3·25 1·25
Nos. 1565/9 are horiz.

463. "Solidarity of Mankind". 465. Belvedere Palace.

464. W.H.O. Building.

**1966.** 20th Anniv. of U.N.E.S.C.O.
1570. **463.** 60 h. black and yellow 25 10

**1966.** Inaug. of W.H.O. Headquarters, Geneva.
1571. **464.** 1 k. ultram. and blue 45 10

**1966.** Prague Castle (2nd series).
1572. **465.** 30 h. blue .. .. 20 10
1573. – 60 h. black and yellow 40 15
DESIGN: 60 h. "Wood triptych, "Virgin and Child" (St. George's Church).
See also Nos. 1656/7 and 1740/1.

467. Scarce Swallowtail.

**1966.** Butterflies and Moths. Multicoloured.
1575 30 h. Type **467** .. .. 40 10
1576 60 h. Moorland clouded yellow .. .. 70 10
1577 80 h. Lesser purple emperor .. .. 70 15
1578 1 k. Apollo .. .. 70 25
1579 1 k. 20 Scarlet tiger moth 1·50 35
1580 2 k. Cream-spot tiger moth .. .. 3·75 1·90

468. Flags.

**1966.** 13th Czechoslovakian Communist Party Congress.
1581. **468.** 30 h. red and blue .. 15 10
1582. – 60 h. red and blue .. 15 10
1583. – 1 k. 60 red and blue .. 40 10
DESIGNS: 60 h. Hammer and sickle. 1 k. 60, Girl.

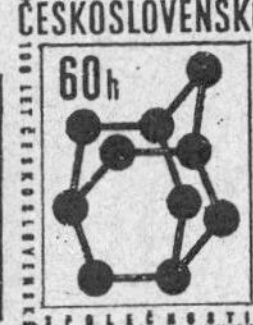

469. Indian Village. 470. Atomic Symbol.

**1966.** "North American Indians". Cent of Naprstek's Ethnographic Museum, Prague.
1584. **469.** 20 h. blue and orange 20 10
1585. – 30 h. black & brown .. 20 10
1586. – 40 h. sepia and blue .. 20 10
1587. – 60 h. green & yellow 25 10
1588. – 1 k. purple & green .. 35 10
1589. – 1 k. 20 blue & mauve 50 20
1590. – 1 k. 40 multicoloured 2·00 90
DESIGNS—VERT. 30 h. Tomahawk. 40 h. Haida totem poles. 60 h. Katchina, "good spirit" of Hopi tribe. 1 k. 20, Dakote calumet (pipe of peace). 1 k. 40, Dakota Indian chief. HORIZ. 1 k. Hunting American bison.

**1966.** Cent. of Czech Chemical Society.
1591. **470.** 60 h. black and blue .. 30 10

471. "Guernica", after Picasso.

**1966.** 30th Anniv. of Int. Brigade's War Service in Spain.
1592. **471.** 60 h. black and blue 1·60 1·60

472. Pantheon Bratislava. 473. Fair Emblem.

**1966.** Cultural Anniversaries.
1593 472 30 h. lilac .. .. 15 10
1594 – 60 h. blue .. .. 20 10
1595 – 60 h. green .. .. 20 10
1596 – 60 h. brown .. .. 20 10
DESIGNS: Type **472** (21st anniv of liberation of Bratislava). 1594, L. Stur (Slovak leader) and Devin Castle. 1595, Nachod (700th anniv). 1596, Arms, globe, books and view of Olomouc (400th anniv of State Science Library).

**1966.** Brno Int. Fair.
1597. **473.** 60 h. black and red .. 25 10

474. "Atomic Age". 475. Olympic Coin.

**1966.** Jachymov (source of pitch-blende).
1598 474 60 h. black and red .. 30 10

**1966.** 70th Anniv. of Olympic Committee.
1599. **475.** 60 h. black and gold .. 20 10
1600. – 1 k. blue and red .. 80 25
DESIGN: 1 k. Olympic flame and rings.

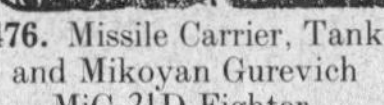

476. Missile Carrier, Tank and Mikoyan Gurevich MiG-21D Fighter. 477. Moravian Silver Thaler (reverse and obverse).

**1966.** Military Manoeuvres.
1601. **476.** 60 h. black and yellow 35 10

**1966.** Brno Stamp Exn.
1602. **477.** 30 h. black and red .. 30 10
1603. – 60 h. black & orange 30 10
1604. – 1 k. 60 black and green 80 25
DESIGNS—HORIZ. 60 h. "Mercury". 1 k. 60, Brno buildings and crest.

479. First Space Rendezvous.

**1966.** Space Research.
1606. **479.** 20 h. violet and green 20 10
1607. – 30 h. green & orange 20 10
1608. – 60 h. blue & mauve 20 10
1609. – 80 h. purple and blue 20 10
1610. – 1 k. black and violet 20 20
1611. – 1 k. 20 red and blue .. 1·90 50
DESIGNS: 30 h. Satellite and "back" of Moon. 60 h. "Mariner 4" and first pictures of Mars. 80 h. Satellite making "soft" landing on Moon. 1 k. Satellite, laser beam and binary code. 1 k. 20, "Telstar", Earth and tracking station.

480. Eurasian badger.

**1966.** Game Animals. Multicoloured.
1612. 30 h. Type **480** .. .. 20 10
1613. 40 h. Red deer (vert.) .. 25 10
1614. 60 h. Lynx .. .. 30 10
1615. 80 h. Brown hare .. 40 20
1616. 1 k. Red fox .. .. 50 30
1617. 1 k. 20 Brown bear (vert.) 50 40
1618. 2 k. Wild boar .. .. 2·75 1·25

481. "Spring" (V. Hollar).

**1966.** Art (1st series).
1619. **481.** 1 k. black .. .. 7·00 6·50
1620. – 1 k. multicoloured .. 3·00 2·50
1621. – 1 k. multicoloured .. 3·50 3·00
1622. – 1 k. multicoloured .. 3·00 2·50
1623. – 1 k. multicoloured .. 35·00 27·00
PAINTINGS: No. 1620, "Mrs. F. Wussin" (J. Kupecky). No. 1621, "Snowy Owl" (K. Purkyne). No. 1622, "Bouquet" (V. Spale). No. 1623, "Recruit" (L. Fulla).
See also Nos. 1669, 1699/1703, 1747, 1753, 1756, 1790/4, 1835/8, 1861/5, 1914/18, 1999/2003, 2067/71, 2134/9, 2194/8, 2256/60, 2313/16, 2375/9, 2495/9, 2549/53, 2601/5, 2655/9, 2702/6, 2757/61, 2810/14, 2858/62, 2904/8, 2954/6, 3000/2, 3044/7, 3077/81 and 3107/9.

482. "Carrier Pigeon".

**1966.** Stamp Day.
1624. **482.** 1 k. blue and yellow 50 50

483. "Youth" (5th Czech Youth Federation Congress). 484. Distressed Family.

**1967.** Czech Congresses.
1625. **483.** 30 h. red and blue .. 15 10
1626. – 30 h. red and yellow .. 15 10
DESIGN: No. 1626, Rose and T.U. emblem (6th Trade Union Congress).

**1967.** "Peace for Viet-Nam".
1627. **484.** 60 h. black and salmon 25 10

485. Jihlava.

**1967.** Int. Tourist Year.
1628. **485.** 30 h. purple .. .. 15 10
1629. – 40 h. red .. .. 15 10
1630. – 1 k. 20 blue .. .. 45 20
1631. – 1 k. 60 black .. 1·60 50
DESIGNS—As Type **485**: 40 h. Brno (76×30 mm.): 1 k. 20, Bratislava. 1 k. 60, Prague.

486. Black-tailed Godwit. 488. Gothic Art (after painting by Theodoric).

487. Sun and Satellite.

**1967.** Water Birds. Multicoloured.
1632. 30 h. Type **486** .. .. 35 10
1633. 40 h. Common shoveler (horiz.) .. .. 45 15
1634. 60 h. Purple heron .. 45 10
1635. 80 h. Penduline tit .. 95 30
1636. 1 k. Avocet .. .. 95 30
1637. 1 k. 40 Black stork .. 2·00 50
1638. 1 k. 60 Tufted duck (horiz.) .. .. 4·75 1·75

**1967.** Space Research.
1639. **487.** 30 h. red and yellow . . 15 10
1640. – 40 h. blue and grey . . 15 10
1941. – 60 h. green and violet 25 10
1642. – 1 k. blue and mauve 25 10
1643. – 1 k. 20 black and blue 40 20
1644. – 1 k. 60 lake and grey 1·75 35
DESIGNS: 40 h. Space vehicles in orbit. 60 h. " Man on the Moon " and orientation systems. 1 k. " Exploration of the planets ". 1 k. 20, Lunar satellites. 1 k. 60, Lunar observatory and landscape.

**1967.** World Fair, Montreal. Multicoloured.
1645. 30 h. Type **488** . . . . 15 10
1646. 40 h. Jena Codex-ancient manuscript, " Burning of John Hus " . . 15 10
1647. 60 h. Lead crystal glass . . 20 15
1648. 80 h. " The Shepherdess and the Chimney Sweep " (Andersen's Fairy Tales), after painting by J. Trnka 30 15
1649. 1 k. Atomic diagram ("Technical Progress") 35 30
1650. 1 k. 20 Dolls by P. Rada ("Ceramics") . . . . 1·25 40

**489.** Bicycle Wheels and Dove.

**1967.** Sports Events of 1967.
1652. **489.** 60 h. black and red . . 20 10
1653. – 60 h. black & turquoise 20 10
1654. – 60 h. black and blue 20 10
1655. – 1 k. 60 black and violet 1·50 60
DESIGNS—HORIZ. Type **489** (20th Warsaw–Berlin–Prague Cycle Race). No. 1654, Canoeist in kayak (5th World Canoeing Championships). VERT. No. 1653, Basketball players (World Women's Basketball Championships). No. 1655, Canoeist (10th World Water-slalom Championships).

**1967.** Prague Castle (3rd series). As Type **465.**
1656. 30 h. lake . . . . 20 10
1657. 60 h. slate . . . . 45 15
DESIGNS: 30 h. " Golden Street ". 60 h. St. Wenceslas' Hall.

**490.** " PRAZSKE 1967 ". **491.** Synagogue Curtain (detail).

**1967.** Prague Music Festival.
1659. **490.** 60 h. violet and green 25 10

**1967.** Jewish Culture.
1660. **491.** 30 h. red and blue . . 20 10
1661. – 60 h. black & green . . 25 10
1662. – 1 k. blue and mauve 35 10
1663. – 1 k. 20 lake & brown 50 15
1664. – 1 k. 40 black & yellow 50 15
1665. – 1 k. 60 green & yellow 6·00 3·25
DESIGNS: 60 h. Printers' imprint (1530). 1 k. Mikulov jug. (1801). 1 k. 20, "Old-New" Synagogue, Prague (1268). 1 k. 40, Jewish memorial candelabra. Pinkas Synagogue (1536) (The memorial is for Czech victims of Nazi persecution). 1 k. 60, David Gans' tombstone (1613).

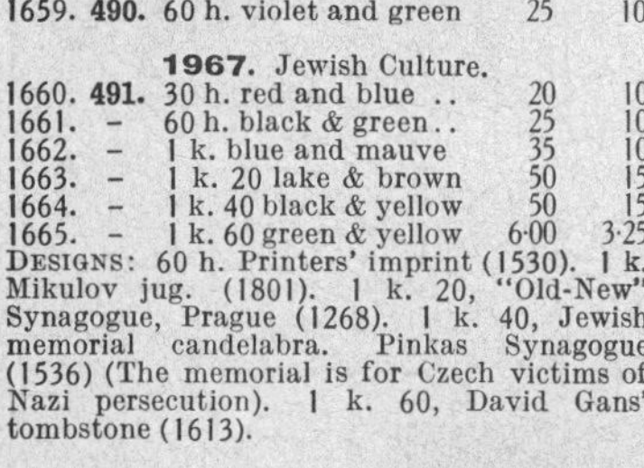

**492.** Lidice Rose. **493.** "Architecture".

**1967.** 25th Anniv. of Destruction of Lidice.
1666. **492.** 30 h. black and red . . 20 10

**1967.** 9th Int. Architects' Union Congress, Prague.
1667. **493.** 1 k. black and gold . . 40 15

**494.** Petr Bezruc.

**1967.** Birth Cent. of Petr Bezruc (poet).
1668. **494.** 60 h. black and red . . 25 10

**1967.** Publicity for "Praga 68" Stamp Exn. As Type **481.** Multicoloured.
1669. 2 k. "Henri Rousseau" (self-portrait) . . . . 2·00 1·25

**495.** Skalica.

**1967.** Czech Towns.
1670. **495.** 30 h. blue . . . . 15 10
1671. – 30 h. lake (Presov) . . 15 10
1672. – 30 h. green (Pribram) 15 10

**496.** Thermal Fountain and Colonnade, Karlovy Vary.

**1967.** Postal Employees' Games.
1673. **496.** 30 h. violet and gold 25 10

**497.** Ondrejov Observatory and Universe. **498.** "Miltonia spectabilis".

**1967.** 13th Int. Astronomic Union Congress, Prague.
1674. **497.** 60 h. silver, blue & pur. 1·40 25

**1967.** Botanical Garden Flowers. Mult.
1675 20 h. Type **498** . . . . 25 10
1676 30 h. Cup and saucer plant . . . . 25 10
1677 40 h. "Lycaste deppei" . . 25 15
1678 60 h. "Glottiphyllum davisii" . . . . 40 10
1679 1 k. Painter's palette . . 60 20
1680 1 k. 20 "Rhodocactus bleo" . . . . 60 35
1681 1 k. 40 "Dendrobium phalaenopsis" . . 2·00 65

**499.** Eurasian Red Squirrel. **500.** Military Vehicles.

**1967.** Fauna of Tatra National Park.
1682. **499.** 30 h. blk., orge. & yell. 35 10
1683. – 60 h. black and buff . . 35 10
1684. – 1 k. black and blue . . 40 15
1685. – 1 k. 20 blk., yell. & grn. 60 15
1686. – 1 k. 40 blk., yell. & pink 85 20
1687. – 1 k. 60 blk., orge. & yell. 3·00 1·25
DESIGNS: 60 h. Wild cat. 1 k. Stoat 1 k. 20, Hazel dormouse. 1 k. 40, West european hedgehog. 1 k. 60, Pine marten.

**1967.** Army Day.
1688. **500.** 30 h. green . . . . 35 10

**501.** Prague Castle (" PRAGA 62 ").

**1967.** Air. " PRAGA 1968 " Int. Stamp Exn. (1st issue).
1689. **501.** 30 h. multicoloured . . 15 10
1690. – 60 h. multicoloured . . 25 10
1691. – 1 k. multicoloured . . 25 15
1692. – 1 k. 40 multicoloured 40 20
1693. – 1 k. 60 multicoloured 40 30
1694. – 2 k. multicoloured . . 65 25
1695. – 5 k. multicoloured . . 3·50 3·50
DESIGNS (Sites of previous Int. Stamp Exns.): 60 h. Selimiye Mosque, Edirne (" ISTANBUL 1963 "). 1 k. Notre Dame, Paris (" PHILATEC 1964 "). 1 k. 40, Belvedere Palace, Vienna (" WIPA 1965 "). 1 k. 60, Capitol, Washington (" SIPEX 1965 "). 2 k. Amsterdam (" AMPHILEX 1967 "). (40×55 mm.) 5 k. Prague (" PRAGA 1968 ").
See also Nos. 1718/20, 1743/8, 1749/54, and 1756.

**502.** Cruiser " Aurora ". **503.** Pres. Novotny.

**1967.** 50th Anniv. of October Revolution.
1696. **502.** 30 h. red and black . . 10 10
1697. – 60 h. red and black . . 15 10
1698. – 1 k. red and black . . 15 10
DESIGNS—VERT. 60 h. Hammer and sickle emblems. 1 k. " Reaching hands ".

**1967.** Art (2nd series). As T **481.** Mult.
1699. 60 h. " Conjurer with Cards " (F. Tichy) . . 25 25
1700. 80 h. " Don Quixote " (C. Majernik) . . . . 25 25
1701. 1 k. " Promenade in the Park " (N. Grund) . . 55 55
1702. 1 k. 20 " Self-Portrait " (P. J. Brandl) . . . . 55 55
1703. 1 k. 60 " Epitaph to Jan of Jeren " (Czech master) 4·25 4·25
All in National Gallery, Prague.

**1967.**
1704. **503.** 2 k. green . . . . 1·25 10
1705. 3 k. brown . . . . 1·75 10

**504.** Letov L-13 Glider.

**1967.** Czech Aircraft. Multicoloured.
1706 30 h. Type **504** . . . . 15 10
1707 60 h. Letov L-40 Meta-Sokol . . . . 20 10
1708 80 h. Letov L-200 Morava 20 10
1709 1 k. Letov Z-37 Cmelak crop-sprayer . . . . 45 15
1710 1 k. 60 Zlin Z-526 Trener Master . . . . 55 20
1711 2 k. Aero L-29 Delfin jet trainer . . . . 2·25 65

**505.** Czech Stamps of 1920.

**1967.** Stamp Day.
1712. **505.** 1 k. lake and silver . . 1·50 1·40

**506.** "CESKOSLOVENSKO 1918-1968".

**1968.** 50th Anniv. of Republic. (1st issue).
1713. **506.** 30 h. red, blue & ult. 55 15
See Nos. 1780/1.

**507.** Skater and Stadium.

**1968.** Winter Olympic Games, Grenoble.
1714. **507.** 60 h. blk., yell. & ochre 15 10
1715. – 1 k. brown, bistre & bl. 30 10
1716. – 1 k. 60 blk., grn. & lilac 55 15
1717. – 2 k. blk., blue & yell. 1·50 60
DESIGNS: 1 k. Bobsleigh run. 1 k. 60, Ski jump. 2 k. Ice hockey.

**508.** Charles Bridge, Prague, and Charles's Hydrogen Balloon. **509.** Industrial Scene and Red Sun.

**1968.** Air. "PRAGA 1968" International Stamp Exhibition (2nd issue). Multicoloured.
1718 60 h. Type **508** . . . . 40 15
1719 1 k. Royal Summer-house, Belvedere, and William Henson's "Aerial Steam Carriage" . . . . 65 25
1720 2 k. Prague Castle and airship . . . . 1·25 65

**1968.** 20th Anniv. of "Victorious February".
1721. **509.** 30 h. red and blue . . 10 10
1722. – 60 h. red and blue . . 15 10
DESIGN: 60 h. Workers and banner.

**510.** Battle Plan. **511.** Human Rights Emblem.

**1968.** 25th Anniv. of Sokolovo Battles.
1723. **510.** 30 h. red, blue & green 35 10

**1968.** Human Rights Year.
1724. **511.** 1 k. red . . . . 75 35

**512.** Liptovsky Mikulas (town) and Janko Kral (writer).

**1968.** Various Commems.
1725. **512.** 30 h. green . . 25 10
1726. – 30 h. blue and orange 25 10
1727. – 30 h. red and gold . . 25 10
1728. – 30 h. purple . . . . 25 10
1729. – 1 k. multicoloured . . 40 10
DESIGNS—VERT. No. 1726, Allegorical figure of woman (150th anniv. of Prague National Museum). No. 1727, Girl's head (cent. of Prague National Theatre). No. 1728, Karl Marx (150th anniv. of birth). No. 1729, Diagrammatic skull (20th anniv. of W.H.O.).

**513.** " Radio " (45th anniv.).

**1968.** Czech Radio and Television Annivs.
1730. **513.** 30 h. black, red & blue 15 10
1731. – 30 h. black, red & blue 15 10
DESIGN: No. 1731, " Television " (15th anniv.).

**514.** Athlete and Statuettes. **515.** Pres. Svoboda.

**1968.** Olympic Games, Mexico. Multicoloured.
1732. 30 h. Type **514** . . . . 15 10
1733. 40 h. Runner and seated figure (Quetzalcoatl) . . 20 10
1734. 60 h. Netball and ornaments 25 10
1735. 1 k. Altar and Olympic emblems . . . . 35 15
1736. 1 k. 60 Football and ornaments . . . . 50 20
1737. 2 k. Prague Castle and key 2·50 70

**1968.**
1738. **515.** 30 h. blue . . . . 10 10
1738a. 50 h. green . . . . 10 10
1739. 60 h. red . . . . 20 10
1739a. 1 k. red . . . . 25 10

**1968.** Prague Castle (4th series). As Type **465.**
1740. 30 h. multicoloured . . 25 10
1741. 60 h. black, grn. & red . . 25 10
DESIGN: 30 h. " Bretislav I " (from tomb in St. Vitus' Cathedral). 60 h. Knocker on door of St. Wenceslas' Chapel.

516. "Business" (sculpture by O. Gutfreund).

**1968.** "PRAGA 1968" Int. Stamp Exn. (3rd Issue). Multicoloured.
1743. 30 h. Type **516** .. .. 20 10
1744. 40 h. Broadcasting building, Prague .. .. .. 20 10
1745. 60 h. Parliament Building 20 15
1746. 1 k. 40 "Prague" (Gobelin tapestry by Jan Bauch) 80 25
1747. 2 k. "The Cabaret Artiste" (painting by F. Kupka) (size 40 × 50 mm.) .. 2·25 2·25
1748. 3 k. Presidential standard 80 45

**1969.** "PRAGA 1968" Int. Stamp Exn. (4th issue).
1749. 30 h. green, yell. & grey 20 10
1750. 60 h. violet, gold & green 20 10
1751. 1 k. indigo, pink and blue 30 15
1752. 1 k. 60 multicoloured .. 55 25
1753. 2 k. multicoloured .. 1·50 1·50
1754. 3 k. blk., blue, pink & yell. 1·60 40
DESIGNS—As Type **516**: 30 h. St. George's Basilica, Prague Castle. 60 h. Renaissance fountain. 1 k. Dvorak's Museum. 1 k. 60, "Three Violins" insignia (18th-cent. house). 3 k. Prague emblem of 1475. As Type **481**: 2 k. "Josefina" (painting by Josef Manes, National Gallery, Prague).

**1968.** "PRAGA 1968" (6th issue—F.I.P. Day) As T **481**.
1756 5 k. multicoloured .. 4·00 3·25
DESIGN: 5 k. "Madonna of the Rosary" (detail from painting by Albrecht Durer in National Gallery, Prague).

518. Horse-drawn Coach on Rails (140th Anniv. of Ceske Budejovice-Linz Railway).

519. Symbolic "S".

**1968.** Railway Anniversaries.
1757 **518** 60 h. multicoloured .. 25 15
1758 – 1 k. multicoloured .. 80 25
DESIGNS: 1 k. Early steam locomotive "Johann Adolf" and modern electric locomotive (centenary of Ceske Budejovice–Pilsen Railway).

**1968.** 6th Int. Slavonic Congress, Prague.
1759. **519.** 30 h. red and blue .. 50 10

520. Adrspach Rocks and "Hypophylloceras bizonatum" (ammonite).

**1968.** 23rd Int. Geological Congress, Prague.
1760. **520.** 30 h. black & yellow 20 10
1761. – 60 h. black and mauve 20 10
1762. – 80 h. blk., pink & lav. 30 10
1763. – 1 k. black and blue.. 40 10
1764. – 1 k. 60 black & yellow 2·00 70
DESIGNS: 60 h. Basalt columns and fossilised frog. 80 h. Bohemian "Paradise" and agate. 1 k. Tatra landscape and "Chlamys gigas" shell. 1 k. 60, Barrandien (Bohemia) and limestone.

521. M. J. Hurban and Standard-bearer.

**1968.** 120th Anniv. of Slovak Insurrection and 25th Anniv. of Slovak National Council.
1765. **521.** 30 h. blue .. .. 15 10
1766. – 60 h. red .. .. 15 10
DESIGN: 60 h. Partisans (120th anniv of Slovak Insurrection).

522. "Man and Child" (Jiri Beutler, aged 10). 523. Banska Bystrica.

**1968.** Munich Agreement. Drawings by children in Terezin concentration camp. Multicoloured.
1767. 30 h. Type **522** .. 15 10
1768. 60 h. "Butterflies" (Kitty Brunnerova, aged 11) 20 10
1769. 1 k. "The Window" (Jiri Schlessinger, aged 10) .. .. 30 10
The 1 k. is larger (40 × 22 mm).

**1968.** Arms of Czech Regional Capitals (1st series). Multicoloured.
1770. 60 h. Type **523** .. 20 10
1771. 60 h. Bratislava.. .. 20 10
1772. 60 h. Brno .. .. 20 10
1773. 60 h. Ceske Budejovice 20 10
1774. 60 h. Hradec Kralove .. 20 10
1775. 60 h. Kosice .. .. 20 10
1776. 60 h. Ostrava .. .. 20 10
1777. 60 h. Pilsen .. .. 20 10
1778. 60 h. Usti nad Labem 20 10
1779. 1 k. Prague (vert.) .. 1·00 15
See also Nos. 1855/60, 1951/6, 2106/8 and 2214/15.

524. National Flag. 525. Ernest Hemingway.

**1968.** 50th Anniv of Republic (2nd issue).
1780 **524** 30 h. deep blue & blue 20 10
1781 – 60 h. multicoloured .. 20 10
DESIGN: 60 h. Prague and Bratislava within outline "map".

**1968.** U.N.E.S.C.O. "Cultural Personalities of the 20th century in Caricature" (1st series).
1783. **525.** 20 h. black and red.. 15 10
1784. – 30 h. multicoloured.. 15 10
1785. – 40 h. red, black & lilac 15 10
1786. – 60 h. blk., grn. & blue 15 10
1787. – 1 k. blk., brn. & yell. 50 10
1788. – 1 k. 20 black, violet and red .. .. 55 20
1789. – 1 k.40 blk., brn. & orge. 2·00 60
PERSONALITIES: 30 h. Karel Capek (dramatist); 40 h. George Bernard Shaw; 60 h. Maxim Gorky; 1 k. Picasso; 1 k. 20, Taikan Yokoyama (painter); 1 k. 40, Charlie Chaplin.
See also Nos. 1829/34.

**1968.** Art (3rd series). As T **481**. Paintings in National Gallery, Prague. Multicoloured.
1790. 60 h. "Cleopatra II" (J. Zrzavy). .. 50 40
1791. 80 h. "The Black Lake" (J. Preisler) .. .. 50 50
1792. 1 k. 20, "Giovanni Francisci as a Volunteer" (P. Bohun) .. .. 1·50 70
1793. 1 k. 60, "Princess Hyacinth" (A. Mucha) .. 1·00 70
1794. 3 k. "Madonna and Child" (altar detail, Master Paul of Levoca) .. 5·00 4·50

526. "Cinder Boy". 528. Red Crosses forming Cross.

527. 5 h. and 10 h. Stamps of 1918.

**1968.** Slovak Fairy Tales. Mult.
1795. 30 h. Type **526** .. .. 15 10
1796. 60 h. "The Proud Lady" 25 10
1797. 80 h. "The Knight who ruled the World" .. 30 10
1798. 1 k. "Good Day, Little Bench" .. .. 40 15
1799. 1 k. 20 "The Enchanted Castle" .. .. 45 15
1800. 1 k. 80 "The Miraculous Hunter" .. .. 2·10 55

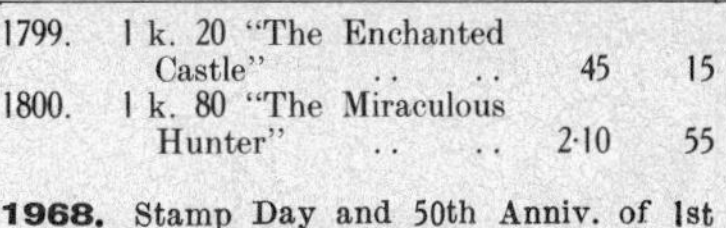

**1968.** Stamp Day and 50th Anniv. of 1st Czech Stamps.
1801. **527.** 1 k. gold and blue .. 80 80

**1969.** 50th Anniv of Czech Red Cross and League of Red Cross Societies.
1802. **528.** 60 h. red, gold & sepia 25 10
1803. – 1 k. red, blue & black 45 15
DESIGN: 1 k. Red Cross symbols within heart-shaped "dove".

529. I.L.O. Emblem. 530. Wheel-lock Pistol, *circa* 1580.

**1969.** 50th Anniv. of Int. Labour Organization.
1804. **529.** 1 k. black and grey.. 25 10

**1969.** Early Pistols. Multicoloured.
1805. 30 h. Type **530** .. .. 15 10
1806. 40 h. Italian horse-pistol, c. 1600.. .. .. 20 10
1807. 60 h. Kubik wheel-lock carbine, c. 1720 .. 20 10
1808. 1 k. Flint-lock pistol, c. 1760 .. .. 30 10
1809. 1 k. 40 Lebeda duelling pistols, c. 1830 .. 50 15
1810. 1 k. 60 Derringer pistols, c. 1865.. .. .. 1·75 35

531. University Emblem and Symbols (50th Anniv. of Brno University).

**1969.** Anniversaries.
1811. **531.** 60 h. blk., blue & gold 20 10
1812. – 60 h. blue .. .. 20 10
1813. – 60 h. multicoloured.. 20 10
1814. – 60 h. black and red.. 20 10
1815. – 60 h. red, silver & blue 20 10
1816. – 60 h. black and gold.. 20 10
DESIGNS and ANNIVERSARIES:—No. 1812, Bratislava Castle, open book and head of woman (50th Anniv. Comenius University, Bratislava); No. 1813, Harp and symbolic eagle (50th Anniv. Brno Conservatoire); No. 1814, Theatrical allegory (50th Anniv. Slovak National Theatre (1970); No. 1815, Arms and floral emblems (Slovak Republican Council. 50th Anniv.). No. 1816, Grammar school and allegories of Learning (Zniev Grammar School. Cent.).

532. Veteran Cars of 1900-05.

**1969.** Motor Vehicles. Multicoloured.
1817. 30 h. Type **532** .. .. 40 10
1818. 1 k. 60 Veteran Cars of 1907 .. .. .. 70 15
1819. 1 k. 80 Prague Buses of 1907 and 1967 .. .. 1·75 70

533. "Peace" (after L. Guderna).

**1969.** 20th Anniv. of Peace Movement.
1820. **533.** 1 k. 60 multicoloured 45 30

534. Engraving by H. Goltzius.

**1969.** Horses. Works of Art.
1821. **534.** 30 h. sepia on cream 25 10
1822. – 80 h. purple on cream 25 10
1823. – 1 k. 60 slate on cream 45 15
1824. – 1 k. 80 black on cream 45 25
1825. – 2 k. 40 mult. on cream 2·50 70
DESIGNS—HORIZ. 80 h. Engraving by M. Merian. VERT. 1 k. 60, Engraving by V. Hollar. 1 k. 80, Engraving by A. Durer. 2 k. 40, Painting by J. E. Ridinger.

535. Dr. M. R. Stefanik as Civilian and Soldier.

**1969.** 50th Death Anniv. of General Stefanik.
1826. **535.** 60 h. red .. .. 40 10

536. "St. Wenceslas" (mural detail, Master of Litomerice, 1511).

**1969.** Prague Castle (5th series). Mult.
1827. 3 k. Type **536** .. .. 2·25 1·40
1828. 3 k. Coronation Banner of the Czech Estates, 1723 2·25 1·40
See also Nos. 1892/3, 1959/60, 2037/8, 2103/4, 2163/4, 2253/4, 2305/6, 2337/8, 2404/5, 2466/7, 2543/4, 2599/600 and 2637/8.

**1969.** U.N.E.S.C.O. "Cultural Personalities of the 20th Century in Caricature" (2nd series). Designs as Type **525**.
1829. 30 h. black, red and blue 10 10
1830. 40 h. black, violet & blue 15 10
1831. 60 h. black, red & yellow 15 10
1832. 1 k. multicoloured .. 30 10
1833. 1 k. 80 black, blue & orge. 40 10
1834. 2 k. black, yellow & green 2·00 65
DESIGNS: 30 h. P. O. Hviezdoslav (poet). 40 h. G. K. Chesterton (writer). 60 h. V. Mayakovsky (poet). 1 k. Henri Matisse (painter). 1 k. 80, A. Hrdlicka (anthropologist). 2 k. Franz Kafka (novelist).

537. "Music". 538. Astronaut, Moon and Aerial View of Manhattan.

**1969.** "Woman and Art". Paintings by Alfons Mucha. Multicoloured.
1835 30 h. Type **537** .. .. 25 10
1836 60 h. "Painting" .. 30 10
1837 1 k. "Dance" .. .. 50 10
1838 2 k. 40 "Ruby and Amethyst" (40 × 51 mm) 2·50 1·25

**1969.** Air. 1st Man on the Moon. Mult.
1839 60 h. Type **538** .. .. 20 10
1840 3 k. "Eagle" module and aerial view of J. F. Kennedy Airport, New York .. .. .. 2·00 1·00

539. Soldier and Civilians.

**1969.** 25th Anniv. of Slovak Rising and Battle of Dukla.
1841. **539.** 30 h. blue and red on cream .. .. 15 10
1842. – 30 h. green and red on cream .. .. 15 10
DESIGN: No. 1842, General Svoboda and partisans.

**540.** Ganek.
(Illustration reduced. Actual size 71 × 33½ mm.).

**1969.** 20th Anniv. of Tatra National Park.

| No. | Type | Description | Unused | Used |
|---|---|---|---|---|
| 1843. | 540 | 60 h. purple .. .. .. | 15 | 10 |
| 1844. | – | 60 h. blue .. .. .. | 15 | 10 |
| 1845. | – | 60 h. green .. .. .. | 15 | 10 |
| 1846. | – | 1 k. 60 multicoloured | 2·50 | 50 |
| 1847. | – | 1 k. 60 multicoloured | 50 | 15 |
| 1848. | – | 1 k. 60 multicoloured | 50 | 15 |

DESIGNS: No. 1844, Mala Valley. 1845, Bielovodska Valley. (SMALLER 40 × 23 mm): 1846, Velka Valley and gentian. 1847, Mountain stream, Mala Valley and gentian. 1848, Krivan Peak and autumn crocus.

**541.** Bronze Belt Fittings (8th–9th century).

**1969.** Archaeological Discoveries in Bohemia and Slovakia. Multicoloured.

| No. | Description | Unused | Used |
|---|---|---|---|
| 1849. | 20 h. Type **541** .. .. | 15 | 10 |
| 1850. | 30 h. Decoration showing masks (6th-8th century) | 15 | 10 |
| 1851. | 1 k. Gold Ear-rings (8th-9th century) .. .. | 25 | 10 |
| 1852. | 1 k. 80 Metal Crucifix (obverse and reverse) (9th century) .. .. | 50 | 20 |
| 1853. | 2 k. Gilt ornament with figure (9th century) | 2·25 | 45 |

**542.** "Focal Point"—Tokyo.

**1969.** 16th U.P.U. Congress, Tokyo.

| No. | Type | Description | Unused | Used |
|---|---|---|---|---|
| 1854. | 542. | 3 k. 20 multicoloured | 1·90 | 1·00 |

**1969.** Arms of Czech Regional Capitals (2nd series). As T **523.** Multicoloured.

| No. | Description | Unused | Used |
|---|---|---|---|
| 1855. | 50 h. Bardejov .. .. | 20 | 10 |
| 1856. | 50 h. Hranice .. .. | 20 | 10 |
| 1857. | 50 h. Kezmarok .. .. | 20 | 10 |
| 1858. | 50 h. Krnov .. .. | 20 | 10 |
| 1859. | 50 h. Litomerice .. .. | 20 | 10 |
| 1860. | 50 h. Manetin .. .. | 20 | 10 |

**1969.** Art (4th series). As T **481.** Multicoloured.

| No. | Description | Unused | Used |
|---|---|---|---|
| 1861. | 60 h. "Great Requiem" (F. Muzika) .. .. | 70 | 45 |
| 1862. | 1 k. "Resurrection" (Master of Trebon) .. | 70 | 45 |
| 1863. | 1 k. 60 "Crucifixion" (V. Hloznik) .. | 70 | 45 |
| 1864. | 1 k. 80 "Girl with Doll" (J. Bencur) .. | 70 | 65 |
| 1865. | 2 k. 20 "St. Jerome" (Master Theodoric) .. | 2·75 | 2·50 |

**543.** Emblem and "Stamps".

**1969.** Stamp Day.

| No. | Type | Description | Unused | Used |
|---|---|---|---|---|
| 1866. | 543. | 1 k. pur., gold & blue | 80 | 80 |

**544.** Ski Jumping.

**1970.** World Skiing Championships, High Tatras. Multicoloured.

| No. | Description | Unused | Used |
|---|---|---|---|
| 1867 | 50 h. Type **544** .. .. | 20 | 10 |
| 1868 | 60 h. Cross-country skiing | 20 | 10 |
| 1869 | 1 k. Ski jumper "taking off" .. .. | 20 | 10 |
| 1870 | 1 k. 60 Woman skier .. | 1·40 | 30 |

**545.** J. A. Comenius (300th Death Anniv.). **546.** Bells.

**1970.** U.N.E.S.C.O. Anniversaries of World Figures.

| No. | Type | Description | Unused | Used |
|---|---|---|---|---|
| 1871. | 545. | 40 h. black .. .. | 15 | 10 |
| 1872. | – | 40 h. grey .. .. | 25 | 10 |
| 1873. | – | 40 h. brown .. .. | 25 | 10 |
| 1874. | – | 40 h. red .. .. | 15 | 10 |
| 1875. | – | 40 h. red .. .. | 15 | 10 |
| 1876. | – | 40 h. brown .. .. | 15 | 10 |

DESIGNS: No. 1872, Ludwig van Beethoven (composer, birth bicent). 1873, Josef Manes (artist, 150th birth anniv). 1874, Lenin (birth cent). 1875, Friedrich Engels (150th birth anniv). 1876, Maximilian Hell (astronomer, 250th birth anniv).

**1970.** World Fair, Osaka, Japan. "Expo 70". Multicoloured.

| No. | Description | Unused | Used |
|---|---|---|---|
| 1877. | 50 h. Type **546** .. .. | 15 | 10 |
| 1878. | 80 h. Heavy Machinery .. | 25 | 10 |
| 1879. | 1 k. Beehives (folk sculpture) .. .. | 25 | 15 |
| 1880. | 1 k. 60 "Angels and Saints" (17th-century icon) .. .. | 50 | 40 |
| 1881. | 2 k. "Orlik Castle, 1787" (F. K. Wolf) .. .. | 55 | 40 |
| 1882. | 3 k. "Fujiyama" (Hokusai) | 3·25 | 1·00 |

Nos. 1880/2 are larger, 51 × 37 mm.

**547.** Town Hall, Kosice. **549.** Lenin.

**548.** "Autumn, 1955".

**1970.** 25th Anniv. of Kosice Reforms.

| No. | Type | Description | Unused | Used |
|---|---|---|---|---|
| 1883. | 547. | 60 h. blue, gold & red | 35 | 10 |

**1970.** Paintings by Joseph Lada. Mult.

| No. | Description | Unused | Used |
|---|---|---|---|
| 1884. | 60 h. Type **548** .. .. | 20 | 10 |
| 1885. | 1 k. "The Magic Horse" | 40 | 10 |
| 1886. | 1 k. 80 "The Water Demon" | 45 | 15 |
| 1887. | 2 k. 40 "Children in Winter, 1943" .. | 2·10 | 60 |

Nos. 1885/6 are vert.

**1970.** Birth Centenary of Lenin.

| No. | Type | Description | Unused | Used |
|---|---|---|---|---|
| 1888. | 549. | 30 h. red and gold .. | 10 | 10 |
| 1889. | – | 60 h. black and gold | 15 | 10 |

DESIGN: 60 h. Lenin (bareheaded).

**550.** Prague Panorama and Hand giving "V" Sign.

**1970.** 25th Anniv of Prague Rising and Liberation of Czechoslovakia.

| No. | Type | Description | Unused | Used |
|---|---|---|---|---|
| 1890 | 550 | 30 h. purple, gold & bl | 20 | 10 |
| 1891 | – | 30 h. green, gold & red | 20 | 10 |

DESIGN: No. 1891, Soviet tank entering Prague.

**1970.** Prague Castle. Art Treasures (6th series). As Type **536.** Multicoloured.

| No. | Description | Unused | Used |
|---|---|---|---|
| 1892. | 3 k. "Hermes and Athena" (painting by B. Spranger) | 1·60 | 1·60 |
| 1893. | 3 k. "St. Vitus" (bust) .. | 1·60 | 1·60 |

**551.** Compass and "World Capitals".

**1970.** 25th Anniv. of United Nations.

| No. | Type | Description | Unused | Used |
|---|---|---|---|---|
| 1894. | 551. | 1 k. multicoloured .. | 35 | 25 |

**552.** Thirty Years War Cannon and "Baron Munchausen".

**1970.** Historic Artillery. Multicoloured.

| No. | Description | Unused | Used |
|---|---|---|---|
| 1895. | 30 h. Type **552** .. | 15 | 10 |
| 1896. | 60 h. Hussite bombard and St. Barbara .. .. | 15 | 10 |
| 1897. | 1 k. 20 Austro-Prussian War field-gun and Hradec Kralove .. | 45 | 10 |
| 1898. | 1 k. 80 Howitzer (1911) and Verne's "Colombiad" .. .. | 50 | 25 |
| 1899. | 2 k. 40 Mountain-gun (1915) and "Good Soldier Schweik" .. | 2·00 | 55 |

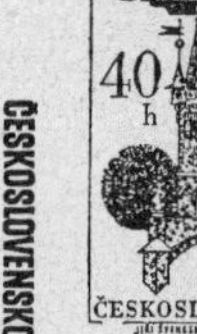


**553.** "Rude Pravo". **554.** "Golden Sun", Bridge-tower, Prague.

**1970.** 50th Anniv. of "Rude Pravo" (newspaper).

| No. | Type | Description | Unused | Used |
|---|---|---|---|---|
| 1900. | 553. | 60 h. red, drab & blk. | 15 | 10 |

**1970.** Ancient Buildings and House-signs from Prague. Brno and Bratislava. Mult.

| No. | Description | Unused | Used |
|---|---|---|---|
| 1901. | 40 h. Type **554** .. | 15 | 10 |
| 1902. | 60 h. "Blue Lion" and Town Hall tower, Brno | 25 | 10 |
| 1903. | 1 k. Gothic bolt and Town Hall tower, Bratislava | 25 | 10 |
| 1904. | 1 k. 40 Coat of arms and Michael Gate, Bratislava | 2·10 | 40 |
| 1905. | 1 k. 60 "Moravian Eagle" and Town Hall gate, Brno .. .. | 40 | 20 |
| 1906. | 1 k. 80 "Black Sun", "Green Frog" and bridge-tower, Prague .. | 60 | 20 |

**555.** World Cup Emblem and Flags.

**1970.** World Cup Football Championships, Mexico. Multicoloured.

| No. | Description | Unused | Used |
|---|---|---|---|
| 1907. | 20 h. Type **555** .. .. | 10 | 10 |
| 1908. | 40 h. Two players and badges of Germany and Uruguay .. .. | 15 | 10 |
| 1909. | 60 h. Two players and badges of England and Czechoslovakia .. | 20 | 10 |
| 1910. | 1 k. Three players and badges of Rumania and Czechoslovakia .. | 30 | 10 |
| 1911. | 1 k. 20 Three players and badges of Brazil and Italy .. .. | 50 | 10 |
| 1912. | 1 k. 80 Two players and badges of Brazil and Czechoslovakia .. | 2·00 | 40 |

**556.** "S.S.M." and Flags. **557.** Dish Aerial.

**1970.** 1st Congress of Czechoslovak Socialist Youth Federation.

| No. | Type | Description | Unused | Used |
|---|---|---|---|---|
| 1913 | 556 | 30 h. multicoloured .. | 40 | 10 |

**1970.** Art (5th series). As T **481.** Mult.

| No. | Description | Unused | Used |
|---|---|---|---|
| 1914. | 1 k. "Mother and Child" (M. Galanda) .. .. | 25 | 25 |
| 1915. | 1 k. 20, "The Bridesmaid" (K. Svolinsky) .. | 50 | 50 |
| 1916. | 1 k. 40 "Walk by Night" (F. Hudecek) .. .. | 50 | 50 |
| 1917. | 1 k. 80 "Banska Bystrica Market" (detail, D. Skutecky) .. .. | 65 | 65 |
| 1918. | 2 k. 40 "Adoration of the Kings" (Vysehrad Codex) | 2·75 | 2·75 |

**1970.** "Intercosmos". Space Research Programme. Multicoloured.

| No. | Description | Unused | Used |
|---|---|---|---|
| 1919. | 20 h. Type **557** .. .. | 10 | 10 |
| 1920. | 40 h. Experimental satellite | 15 | 10 |
| 1921. | 60 h. Meteorological satellite | 20 | 10 |
| 1922. | 1 k. Astronaut ("medical research") .. .. | 25 | 10 |
| 1923. | 1 k. 20 Solar research .. | 30 | 10 |
| 1924. | 1 k. 60 Rocket on Launch-pad .. .. .. | 1·50 | 45 |

**558.** "Adam and Eve with Archangel Michael" (16th-century).

**1970.** Slovak Icons. Multicoloured.

| No. | Description | Unused | Used |
|---|---|---|---|
| 1925. | 60 h. Type **558** .. | 20 | 20 |
| 1926. | 1 k. "Mandylon" (16th-century) (horiz.) .. | 30 | 30 |
| 1927. | 2 k. "St. George slaying the Dragon" (18th-century) (horiz.) .. | 50 | 50 |
| 1928. | 2 k. 80 "St. Michael the Archangel" (18th-century) .. .. .. | 2·25 | 2·25 |

**559.** Czech 5 h. Stamps of 1920.

**1970.** Stamp Day.

| No. | Type | Description | Unused | Used |
|---|---|---|---|---|
| 1929. | 559. | 1 k. red, black & green | 70 | 70 |

**560.** "Songs from the Walls" (frontispiece, K. Stika). **561.** Saris Church.

**1971.** Czechoslovak Graphic Art (1st series).

| No. | Type | Description | Unused | Used |
|---|---|---|---|---|
| 1930. | 560. | 40 h. brown .. .. | 15 | 10 |
| 1931. | – | 50 h. multicoloured .. | 20 | 10 |
| 1932. | – | 60 h. grey .. .. | 20 | 10 |
| 1933. | – | 1 k. grey .. .. | 25 | 10 |
| 1934. | – | 1 k. 60 black & cream | 45 | 10 |
| 1935. | – | 2 k. multicoloured .. | 2·00 | 60 |

DESIGNS: 50 h. "The Fruit Trader" (C. Bouda). 60 h. "Moon searching for Lilies-of-the-valley" (J. Zrzavy). 1 k. "At the End of the Town" (K. Sokol). 1 k. 60, "Summer" (V. Hollar). 2 k. "Shepherd and Gamekeeper. Orava Castle" (P. Bohun).

See also Nos. 2026/30, 2079/82, 2147/50 and 2202/5.

**1971.** Regional Buildings.

| No. | Type | Description | Unused | Used |
|---|---|---|---|---|
| 1936 | – | 50 h. multicoloured | 10 | 10 |
| 1936a | – | 1 k. black, red & bl | 20 | 10 |
| 1937 | 561 | 1 k. 60 blk, vio & grn | 50 | 10 |
| 1938 | – | 2 k. multicoloured .. | 60 | 10 |
| 1939 | – | 2 k. 40 multicoloured | 60 | 10 |
| 1940 | – | 3 k. multicoloured .. | 80 | 10 |
| 1941 | – | 3 k. 60 multicoloured | 1·00 | 10 |
| 1942 | – | 5 k. multicoloured .. | 1·25 | 10 |
| 1943 | – | 5 k. 40 multicoloured | 1·25 | 10 |
| 1944 | – | 6 k. multicoloured .. | 1·75 | 10 |
| 1945 | – | 9 k. multicoloured .. | 2·50 | 10 |
| 1946 | – | 10 k. multicoloured | 2·40 | 10 |
| 1947 | – | 14 k. multicoloured | 3·25 | 10 |
| 1948 | – | 20 k. multicoloured | 5·00 | 50 |

DESIGNS—HORIZ. 50 h., 3 k. 60, Church, Chrudimsko. 2 k. 40, House, Jicinsko. 5 k. 40 Southern Bohemia baroque house, Posumavi. 10 k. Wooden houses, Liptov. 14 k. House and belfry, Valassko. 20 k. Decorated house, Cicmany. (22 × 19 mm). 3 k. Half-timbered house, Melnicko. 6 k. Cottages, Orava. 9 k. Cottage, Turnovsko. VERT. (19 × 22 mm). 1 k. Ornamental roofs, Horacko. 2 k. Bell-tower, Hornsek. 5 k. Watch-tower, Nachodsko.

**562.** "The Paris Commune" (allegory).

**1971.** U.N.E.S.C.O. World Annivs. Mult.
1949. 1 k. Type **562** .. .. 30 15
1950. 1 k. "World Fight against Racial Discrimination" (allegory) .. .. 30 15

**1971.** Arms of Czech Regional Capitals (3rd series). As Type **523**. Multicoloured.
1951. 60 h. Ceska Trebova .. 20 10
1952. 60 h. Karlovy Vary .. 20 10
1953. 60 h. Levoca .. .. 20 10
1954. 60 h. Trutnov .. .. 20 10
1955. 60 h. Uhersky Brod .. 20 10
1956. 60 h. Zilina .. .. 20 10

**563.** Chorister. **564.** Lenin.

**1971.** 50th Annivs. Multicoloured.
1957. 30 h. Type **563** (Slovak Teachers' Choir) .. 15 10
1958. 30 h. Edelweiss, ice-pick and mountain (Slovak Alpine Organisation) (19 × 48 mm.) .. .. 15 10

**1971.** Prague Castle (7th series). Art Treasures. As Type **536**. Multicoloured.
1959 3 k. brown, buff and black 1·75 1·75
1960 3 k. multicoloured .. 1·75 1·75
DESIGNS: No. 1959, "Music" (16th-century wall painting). No. 1960, Head of 16th-century crozier.

**1971.** 50th Anniv. of Czech Communist Party.
1961. 30 h. Type **564** .. .. 10 10
1962. 40 h. Hammer and sickle emblems .. .. 10 10
1963. 60 h. Clenched fists .. 15 10
1964. 1 k. Emblem on pinnacle 20 10

**565.** "50" Star Emblem.

**1971.** 14th Czech Communist Party Congress. Multicoloured.
1965. 30 h. Type **565** .. .. 10 10
1966 60 h. Clenched fist, worker and emblems (vert.) .. 15 10

**566.** Ring-necked Pheasant.

**1971.** World Hunting Exhib., Budapest. Multicoloured.
1967. 20 h. Type **566** .. .. 45 10
1968. 60 h. Trout .. .. 15 10
1969. 80 h. Mouflon .. .. 20 10
1970. 1 k. Chamois .. .. 20 10
1971. 2 k. Red deer .. .. 45 15
1972. 2 k. 60 Wild boar .. 2·10 45

**567.** Motorway Junction (diagram). **568.** Diesel Locomotives.

**1971.** World Road Congress.
1973. **567.** 1 k. multicoloured .. 25 10

**1971.** Centenary of Prague C.K.D. Locomotive Works.
1974. **568.** 30 h. blk., red & blue 20 10

**569.** Gymnasts.

**1971.** 50th Anniv. of Proletarian Physical Federation.
1975. **569.** 30 h. multicoloured .. 15 10

**570.** "Procession" (from "The Miraculous Bamboo Shoot" by K. Segawa).

**1971.** Biennial Exhibition of Book Illustrations for Children, Bratislava. Mult.
1976. 60 h. "Princess" (Chinese Folk Tales, E. Bednarova) (vert.) .. .. 20 10
1977. 1 k. "Tiger" (Animal Fairy Tales, Hanak) (vert.) .. .. .. 20 10
1978. 1 k. 60 Type **570** .. .. 50 20

**571.** Coltsfoot and Canisters.

**1971.** Int. Pharmaceutical Congress, Prague. Medicinal Plants and Historic Pharmaceutical Utensils. Multicoloured.
1979 30 h. Type **571** .. .. 10 10
1980 60 h. Dog rose and glass jars .. .. 15 10
1981 1 k. Yellow pheasant's-eye and hand scales .. 25 10
1982 1 k. 20 Common valerian, pestle and mortar .. 40 15
1983 1 k. 80 Chicory and crucibles .. .. 60 15
1984 2 k. 40 Henbane and grinder .. .. 2·10 55

**573.** "Co-operation in Space".

**1971.** "Intersputnik" Day.
1997. **573.** 1 k. 20 multicoloured 35 10

**574.** "The Krompachy Revolt". (J. Nemcik). (Actual size 76 × 29 mm.)

**1971.** 50th Anniv. of The Krompachy Revolt.
1998. **574.** 60 h. multicoloured .. 35 10

**1971.** Art (6th issue). As Type **481**. Mult.
1999. 1 k. "Waiting" (I. Weiner-Kral) .. 15 10
2000. 1 k. 20 "The Resurrection" (unknown 14th century artist) .. .. .. 40 40
2001. 1 k. 40 "Woman with Jug" (M. Bazovsky) .. 50 50
2002. 1 k. 80 "Woman in National Costume" (J. Manes) .. .. 65 65
2003. 2 k. 40 "Festival of the Rosary" (Durer) .. 3·25 3·25

**575.** Wooden Dolls and Birds. **576.** Ancient Greek Runners.

**1971.** 25th Anniv. of U.N.I.C.E.F. Czech and Slovak Folk Art. Multicoloured.
2004. 60 h. Type **575** (frame and U.N.I.C.E.F. emblem in bl.) 15 10
2005. 60 h. Type **575** (frame and and U.N.I.C.E.F. emblem in black) .. .. 3·00 1·50
2006. 80 h. Decorated handle 20 10
2007. 1 k. Horse and rider .. 30 15
2008. 1 k. 60 Shepherd .. 45 20
2009. 2 k. Easter eggs and rattle 65 25
2010. 3 k. Folk hero .. .. 3·25 75

**1971.** 75th Anniv. of Czechoslovak Olympic Committee and 1972 Games at Sapporo and Munich. Multicoloured.
2011. 30 h. Type **576** .. 10 10
2012. 40 h. High Jumper .. 10 10
2013. 1 k. 60 Skiers .. .. 50 10
2014. 2 k. 60 Discus-throwers, ancient and modern .. 1·75 70

**577.** Posthorns.

**1971.** Stamp Day.
2015. **577.** 1 k. multicoloured .. 35 15

**578.** Figure Skating.

**1972.** Winter Olympic Games, Sapporo, Japan. Multicoloured.
2016 40 h. Type **578** .. .. 10 10
2017 50 h. Skiing .. .. 15 10
2018 1 k. Ice hockey .. .. 50 10
2019 1 k. 60 Bobsleighing .. 1·50 40

**579.** Sentry. **580.** Book Year Emblem.

**1972.** 30th Annivs.
2020. – 30 h. black & brown 10 10
2021. – 30 h. blk., red & yell. 10 10
2022. **579.** 60 h. multicoloured .. 20 10
2023. – 60 h. blk., red & yell. 20 10
ANNIVERSARIES: No. 2020, Child and barbed wire (Terezin Concentration Camp). No. 2021, Widow and buildings (Destruction of Lezaky). No. 2022, Type **579** (Czechoslovak Unit in Russian Army). No. 2023, Hand and ruined building (Destruction of Lidice).

**1972.** Int. Book Year.
2024. **580.** 1 k. black and red .. 30 10

**581.** Steam and Electric Locomotives. **582.** Cycling.

**1972.** Cent. of Kosice-Bohumin Railway.
2025. **581.** 30 h. multicoloured 30 10

**1972.** Czechoslovak Graphic Art (2nd series). As Type **560** Multicoloured.
2026. 40 h. "Pasture" (V. Sedlacek) 10 10
2027. 50 h. "Dressage" (F. Tichy) 15 10
2028. 60 h. "Otakar Kubin" (V. Fiala) .. .. 20 15
2029. 1 k. "The Three Kings" (E. Zmetak) .. .. 30 25
2030. 1 k. 60 "Toilet" (L. Fulla) 1·75 1·75

**1972.** Olympic Games, Munich. Mult.
2031. 50 h. Type **582** .. .. 15 10
2032. 1 k. 60 Diving .. .. 40 10
2033. 1 k. 80 Kayak-canoeing 45 20
2034. 2 k. Gymnastics .. .. 1·75 50

**583.** Players in Tackle. **585.** Frantisek Bilek (sculptor, birth centenary).

**1972.** World and European Ice Hockey Championships, Prague. Multicoloured.
2035 60 h. Type **583** .. .. 30 10
2036 1 k. Attacking goal .. 50 10

**1972.** Prague Castle (8th series). Roof Decorations. As T **536**. Multicoloured.
2037 3 k. Bohemian Lion emblem (roof boss), Royal Palace .. .. 1·50 75
2038 3 k. "Adam and Eve" (bracket), St. Vitus Cathedral .. .. 2·75 2·50

**1972.** Czech Victory in Ice Hockey Championships. Nos. 2035/6 optd **CSSR MAJSTROM SVETA** ("Czechoslovakia World Champions").
2039 **583** 60 h. multicoloured .. 5·00 5·00
2040 – 1 k. multicoloured .. 5·00 5·00

**1972.** Cultural Anniversaries.
2041. **585.** 40 h. multicoloured .. 15 10
2042. – 40 h. multicoloured .. 15 10
2043. – 40 h. grn., yell. & blue 15 10
2044. – 40 h. multicoloured .. 15 10
2045. – 40 h. vio., blue & grn. 15 10
2046. – 40 h. grn., brn. & orge. 15 10
DESIGNS: No. 2042, Antonin Hudecek (painter, birth cent.). No. 2043, Janko Kral (poet, 150th birth anniv.). No. 2044, Ludmila Podjavorinska (writer, birth cent.). No. 2045, Andrej Sladkovic (painter, death cent.). No. 2046, Jan Preisler (painter, birth cent.).

**586.** Workers with Banners. **587.** Wire Coil and Cockerel.

**1972.** 8th Trade Union Congress, Prague.
2047. **586.** 30 h. violet, red & yell. 15 10

**1972.** Slovak Wireworking. Multicoloured.
2048. 20 h. Type **587** .. .. 10 10
2049. 60 h. Aeroplane and rosette .. .. .. 15 10
2050. 80 h. Dragon and gilded ornament .. .. 20 10
2051. 1 k. Steam locomotive and pendant .. .. 25 15
2052. 2 k. 60 Owl and tray .. 1·75 60

**588.** "Jiskra" (freighter).

**1972.** Czechoslovak Ocean-going Ships. Mult.
2053 50 h. Type **588** .. .. 25 10
2054 60 h. "Mir" (freighter) .. 35 10
2055 80 h. "Republika" (freighter) .. .. 40 10
2056 1 k. "Kosice" (tanker) .. 45 10
2057 1 k. 60 "Dukla" (freighter) 75 20
2058 2 k. "Kladno" (freighter) 2·75 60
Nos. 2056/8 are size 49 × 30 mm.

**589.** "Hussar" (ceramic tile).

**1972.** "Horsemanship". Ceramics and Glass. Multicoloured.
2059. 30 h. Type **589** .. .. 10 10
2060. 60 h. "Turkish Janissary" (enamel on glass) .. 15 10
2061. 80 h. "St. Martin" (painting on glass) .. .. 25 10
2062. 1 k. 60 "St. George" (enamel on glass) .. 50 10
2063. 1 k. 80 "Nobleman's Guard, Bohemia" (enamel on glass) .. .. .. 60 15
2064. 2 k. 20 "Cavalryman, c. 1800" (ceramic tile) .. 2·25 50

**590.** Revolutionary and Red Flag.

**1972.** 55th Anniv. of Russian October Revolution and 50th Anniv. of U.S.S.R.
2065. **590.** 30 h. multicoloured .. 15 10
2066. – 60 h. red and gold .. 15 10
DESIGN: 60 h. Soviet star emblem.

**1972.** Art (7th issue). As T **481.**

2067. 1 k. multicoloured .. 70 55
2068. 1 k. 20 multicoloured .. 75 60
2069. 1 k. 40 brown and cream 1·00 75
2070. 1 k. 80 multicoloured .. 1·25 1·10
2071. 2 k. 40 multicoloured .. 3·25 2·75

DESIGN: 1 k. " Nosegay " (M. Svabinsky). 1 k. 20, " St. Ladislav fighting a Nomad " (14th century painter). 1 k. 40, "Lady with Fur Cap" (V. Hollar). 1 k. 80, " Midsummer Night's Dream " (J. Liesler). 2 k. 40, " Self-portrait " (P. Picasso).

591. Warbler feeding young Cuckoo.

**1972.** Songbirds. Multicoloured.

2072. 60 h. Type **591** .. .. 50 15
2073. 80 h. European Cuckoo .. 65 15
2074. 1 k. Magpie .. .. 65 15
2075. 1 k. 60 Bullfinch .. .. 90 25
2076. 2 k. Goldfinch .. .. 1·90 60
2077. 3 k. Song thrush .. .. 9·75 1·75

SIZES: 1 k. 60, 2 k., 3 k. 30 × 23 mm.

592. "Thoughts into Letters".

**1972.** Stamp Day.

2078. **592.** 1 k. black, gold & pur. 45 45

**1973.** Czechoslovak Graphic Art (3rd series). As Type **560.** Multicoloured.

2079. 30 h. "Flowers in the Window" (J. Grus) .. 10 10
2080. 60 h. "Quest for Happiness" (J. Balaz) .. .. 15 10
2081. 1 k. 60 "Balloon" (K. Lhotak) 45 20
2082. 1 k. 80 "Woman with Viola" (R. Wiesner) .. 1·60 35

593. "Tennis Player".

594. Red Star and Factory Buildings.

**1973.** Sports Events. Multicoloured.

2083 30 h. Type **593** .. .. 30 10
2084 60 h. Figure skating .. 15 10
2085 1 k. Spartakaid emblem 30 10

EVENTS: 30 h. 80th anniv of lawn tennis in Czechoslovakia. 60 h. World Figure Skating Championships, Bratislava. 1 k. 3rd Warsaw Pact Armies Summer Spartakiad.

**1973.** 25th Anniv. of "Victorious February" and People's Militia (60 h.).

2086. **594.** 30 h. multicoloured .. 10 10
2087. – 60 h. blue, red & gold 15 10

DESIGN: 60 h. Militiaman and banners.

595. Jan Nalepka and Antonin Sochar.

**1973.** Czechoslovak Martyrs during World War II.

2088. **595.** 30 h. black, red and gold on cream .. 10 10
2089. – 40 h. black, red and green on cream .. 15 10
2090. – 60 h. black, red and gold on cream .. 15 10
2091. – 80 h. black, red and green on cream .. 15 10
2092. – 1 k. black, pink and green on cream .. 20 10
2093. – 1 k. 60 black, red and silver on cream .. 1·25 40

DESIGNS: 40 h. Evzen Rosicky and Mirko Nespor. 60 h. Vlado Clementis and Karol Smidke. 80 h. Jan Osoha and Josef Molak. 1 k. Marie Kuderikova and Jozka Jaburkova. 1 k. 60, Vaclav Sinkule and Eduard Urx.

596. Russian " Venera " Space-probe.

**1973.** Cosmonautics' Day. Multicoloured.

2094 20 h. Type **596** .. .. 10 10
2095 30 h. "Cosmos" satellite 10 10
2096 40 h. "Lunokhod" on Moon .. .. .. 10 10
2097 3 k. American astronauts Grissom, White and Chaffee .. .. 1·50 1·40
2098 3 k. 60 Russian cosmonaut Komarov, and crew of "Soyuz II" .. .. 1·60 1·50
2099 5 k. Death of Yuri Gagarin (first cosmonaut) .. .. .. 5·00 4·50

Nos. 2094/6 are size 40 × 23mm.

597. Radio Aerial and Receiver.

598. Czechoslovak Arms.

**1973.** Telecommunications Annivs. Mult.

2100 30 h. Type **597** .. .. 10 10
2101 30 h. T.V. colour chart .. 10 10
2102 30 h. Map and telephone 10 10

ANNIVERSARIES: No. 2100, 50th anniv of Czech broadcasting. 2101, 20th anniv of Czechoslovak television service. 2102, 20th anniv of nation-wide telephone system.

**1973.** Prague Castle (9th series). As Type **536.** Multicoloured.

2103 3 k. Gold seal of Charles IV .. .. .. 3·00 2·75
2104 3 k. Rook showing Imperial Legate (from "The Game and Playe of Chesse" by William Caxton) .. .. 1·00 75

**1973.** 25th Anniv. of May 9th Constitution.

2105. **598.** 60 h. multicoloured 20 10

**1973.** Arms of Czech Regional Capitals (4th series). As T **523.**

2106. 60 h. multicoloured (Mikulov) .. .. 15 10
2107. 60 h. multicoloured (Smolenice) .. .. 15 10
2108. 60 h. black and gold (Zlutice) .. .. 15 10

599. "Learning."

600. Tulip.

**1973.** 400th Anniv. of Olomouc University.

2109. **599.** 30 h. multicoloured .. 10 10

**1973.** Olomouc Flower Show. Multicoloured.

2110. 60 h. Type **600** .. .. 80 60
2111. 1 k. Rose .. .. .. 50 40
2112. 1 k. 60 Anthurium .. 45 15
2113. 1 k. 80 Iris .. .. 50 20
2114. 2 k. Chrysanthemum .. 2·75 2·75
2115. 3 k. 60 Boat orchid .. 1·50 30

Nos. 2112/13 and 2115 are smaller, size 23 × 50 mm.

601. Irish Setter.

**1973.** 50th Anniv of Czechoslovak Hunting Organization. Hunting Dogs. Multicoloured.

2116. 20 h. Type **601** .. .. 10 10
2117. 30 h. Czech whisker .. 10 10
2118. 40 h. Bavarian mountain bloodhound .. .. 10 10
2119. 60 h. German pointer .. 15 10
2120. 1 k. Golden cocker spaniel 20 10
2121. 1 k. 60 Dachshund .. 1·75 40

602. "St. John the Baptist" (M. Svabinsky).

603. Congress Emblem.

**1973.** Birth Centenary of Max Svabinsky (artist and designer).

2122. **602.** 20 h. black and green 10 10
2123. – 60 h. black and yellow 20 10
2124. – 80 h. black .. .. 25 25
2125. – 1 k. green .. .. 25 25
2126. – 2 k. 60 multicoloured 2·25 2·25

DESIGNS: 60 h. " August Noon ". 80 h. " Marriage of True Minds ". 1 k. " Paradise Sonata I ". 2 k. 60, " The Last Judgement " (stained glass window).

**1973.** 8th World Trade Union Congress, Varna, Bulgaria.

2127 **603** 1 k. multicoloured .. 15 10

604. Tupolev Tu-104A over Bitov Castle.

**1973.** 50th Anniv of Czechoslovak Airlines. Multicoloured.

2128 30 h. Type **604** .. .. 10 10
2129 60 h. Ilyushin Il-62 and Bezdez Castle .. .. 15 10
2130 1 k. 40 Tupolev Tu-134A and Orava Castle .. 40 10
2131 1 k. 90 Ilyushin Il-18 and Veveri Castle .. .. 55 20
2132 2 k. 40 Ilyushin Il-14P and Pernstejn Castle .. 3·75 80
2133 3 k. 60 Tupolev Tu-154 and Trencin Castle .. 70 30

**1973.** Art (8th series). As Type **481.**

2134. 1 k. multicoloured .. 2·50 2·50
2135. 1 k. 20 multicoloured .. 2·50 2·50
2136. 1 k. 80 black and buff .. 65 65
2137. 2 k. multicoloured .. 75 75
2138. 2 k. 40 multicoloured .. 90 90
2139. 3 k. 60 multicoloured .. 1·00 1·00

DESIGNS: 1 k. " Boy from Martinique " (A. Pelc). 1 k. 20, " Fortitude " (M. Benka). 1 k. 80 Self-portrait (Rembrandt). 2 k. " Pierrot " (B. Kubista). 2 k. 40, " Ilona Kubinyiova " (P. Bohun). 3 k. 60, Madonna and Child " (unknown artist, c. 1350).

605. Mounted Postman.

**1973.** Stamp Day.

2140. **605.** 1 k. multicoloured .. 25 15

606. "CSSR 1969-1974".



607. Bedrich Smetana (composer) (150th birth anniv.).

**1974.** 5th Anniv. of Federal Constitution.

2141. **606.** 30 h. red, blue and gold 10 10

**1974.** Celebrities' Birth Anniversaries.

2142. **607.** 60 h. multicoloured .. 20 10
2143. – 60 h. multicoloured .. 20 10
2144. – 60 h. brn., blue & red 20 10

DESIGNS AND ANNIVERSARIES: No. 2143, Josef Suk (composer, birth anniv.). No. 2144, Pablo Neruda (Chilean poet, 70th birth Anniv.).

608. Council Building, Moscow.

610. Oskar Benes and Vaclav Prochazka.

609. Exhibition Allegory.

**1974.** 25th Anniv. of Communist Bloc Council of Mutual Economic Assistance.

2145. **608.** 1 k. violet, red & gold 20 10

**1974.** "BRNO 74" National Stamp Exhibition (1st issue).

2146. **609.** 3 k. 60 multicoloured 75 25

**1974.** Czechoslovak Graphic Art (4th series). As T **560.** Inscr. " 1974 ". Multicoloured.

2147. 60 h. " Tulips " (J. Broz) 20 10
2148. 1 k. " Structures " (O. Dubay) .. .. 30 15
2149. 1 k. 60 " Golden Sun-Glowing Day " (A. Zabransky) .. .. 55 20
2150. 1 k. 80 "Artificial Flowers" (F. Gross) .. .. 1·40 35

**1974.** Czechoslovak Partisan Heroes. Multicoloured.

2151. 30 h. Type **610** .. .. 10 10
2152. 40 h. Milos Uher and Anton Sedlacek .. 10 10
2153. 60 h. Jan Hajecek and Marie Sedlackova .. 15 10
2154. 80 h. Jan Sverma and Albin Grznar .. .. 20 10
2155. 1 k. Jaroslav Neliba and Alois Hovorka .. .. 30 10
2156. 1 k. 60 Ladislav Exnar and Ludovit Kukorelli .. 1·50 30

611. "Water-Source of Energy".

**1974.** International Hydrological Decade. Multicoloured.

2157. 60 h. Type **611** .. .. 60 50
2158. 1 k. "Water for Agriculture" 60 50
2159. 1 k. 20 "Study of the Oceans" 60 50
2160. 1 k. 60 Decade emblem .. 65 50
2161. 2 k. "Keeping water pure" 2·40 2·40

612. " Telecommunications ".

613. Sousaphone.

**1974.** Inauguration of Czechoslovak Satellite Telecommunications Earth Station.

2162. **612.** 30 h. multicoloured .. 25 10

**1974.** Prague Castle (10th series). As Type **536.** Multicoloured.

2163 3 k. "Golden Cockerel", 17th-century enamel locket .. .. .. 1·90 1·90
2164 3 k. Bohemian glass monstrance, 1840 .. 1·90 1·90

**1974.** Musical Instruments. Multicoloured.

2165 20 h. Type **613** .. .. 15 10
2166 30 h. Bagpipes .. .. 15 10
2167 40 h. Benka violin .. 20 10
2168 1 k. Sauer pyramid piano 30 15
2169 1 k. 60 Hulinsky tenor quinton .. .. 1·25 40

**614.** Child and Flowers (book illustration). **615.** "Stamp Collectors".

**1974.** 25th International Children's Day.
2170. **614.** 60 h. multicoloured .. 15 10

**1974.** "BRNO 74" National Stamp Exhibition (2nd issue). Multicoloured.
2171. 30 h. Type **615** .. .. 10 10
2172. 6 k. "Rocket Post" .. 2·40 1·10

**616.** Slovak Partisan. **617.** "Hero and Leander".

**1974.** Czechoslovak Anniversaries. Mult.
2173 30 h. Type **616** .. .. 10 10
2174 30 h. Folk-dancer .. 10 10
2175 30 h. Actress holding masks .. .. .. 10 10

EVENTS: No. 2173, 30th anniv of Slovak Uprising. 2174, 25th anniv of Slovak SLUK Folk Song and Dance Ensemble. 2175, 25th anniv of Bratislava Academy of Music and Dramatic Arts.

**1974.** Bratislava Tapestries, "Hero and Leander" (1st series). Multicoloured.
2176. 2 k. Type **617** .. .. 1·40 1·40
2177. 2 k. 40 "Leander Swimming across the Hellespont" 1·75 1·75

See also Nos. 2227/8 and 2281/2.

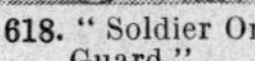

**618.** "Soldier On Guard". **620.** Posthorn and Old Town Bridge Tower, Prague.

**619.** U.P.U. Emblem and Postilion.

**1974.** Old Shooting Targets. Multicoloured.
2178. 30 h. Type **618** .. 15 10
2179. 60 h. "Pierrot and Owl", 1828 .. 20 15
2180. 1 k. "Diana awarding Marksman's Crown", 1832 .. 30 15
2181. 1 k. 60 "Still Life with Guitar", 1839 .. 45 45
2182. 2 k. 40 "Stag", 1834 50 50
2183. 3 k. "Turk and Giraffe", 1831 .. 3·50 3·50

**1974.** Cent of Universal Postal Union. Mult.
2184 30 h. Type **619** .. .. 10 10
2185 40 h. Early mail coach .. 10 10
2186 60 h. Early railway carriage .. .. 25 10
2187 80 h. Modern mobile post office .. .. .. 25 10
2188 1 k. Ilyushin Il-14 mail plane .. .. 60 10
2189 1 k. 60 Dish aerial, earth station .. .. 1·40 40

**1974.** Czechoslovak Postal Services.
2190 **620** 20 h. multicoloured .. 10 10
2191 – 30 h. red, blue & brn 10 10
2192 – 40 h. multicoloured .. 15 10
2193 – 60 h. orange, yell & bl 20 10

DESIGNS: 30 h. P.T.T. emblem within letter. 40 h. Postilion. 60 h. P.T.T. emblem on dove's wing.

See also No. 2900.

**1974.** Art (9th series). As Type **481**. Multicoloured.
2194. 1 k. "Self-portrait" (L. Kuba) .. .. 75 75
2195. 1 k. 20, "Frantisek Ondricek" (V. Brozik) .. 75 75
2196. 1 k. 60, "Pitcher with Flowers" (O. Khubin) 75 75
2197. 1 k. 80, "Woman with Pitcher" (J. Alexy) .. 75 75
2198. 2 k. 40, "Bacchanalia" (K. Skreta) .. .. 3·25 3·25

**621.** Stylised Posthorn.

**1974.** Stamp Day.
2199. **621.** 1 k. multicoloured 25 15

**622.** Winged Emblem.

**1975.** Coil Stamps.
2200. **622.** 30 h. blue .. .. 10 10
2201. 60 h. red .. .. 15 15

**1975.** Czechoslovak Graphic Art (5th series). Engraved Hunting Scenes. As T **560**.
2202 60 h. brown & cream .. 25 10
2203 1 k. brown and cream .. 35 20
2204 1 k. 60 brown & green .. 50 25
2205 1 k. 80 brown & lt brown 1·50 50

DESIGNS: 60 h. "Still Life with Hare" (V. Hollar). 1 k. "The Lion and the Mouse" (V. Hollar). 1 k. 60, "Deer Hunt" (detail, P. Galle). 1 k. 80, "Grand Hunt" (detail, J.Callot).

**623.** "Woman". **624.** Village Family.

**1975.** International Women's Year.
2206. **623.** 30 h. multicoloured .. 15 10

**1975.** 30th Anniv. of Razing of 14 Villages. Multicoloured.
2207. 60 h. Type **624** .. .. 20 10
2208. 1 k. Women and flames .. 25 10
2209. 1 k. 20 Villagers and flowers 35 15

**625.** "Little Queens" (Moravia).

**1975.** Czechoslovak Folk Customs. Mult.
2210 60 h. Type **625** .. .. 75 75
2211 1 k. Shrovetide parade, Slovakia .. .. 75 75
2212 1 k. 40 "Maid Dorothea" (play) .. .. .. 75 75
2213 2 k. "Morena" effigy, Slovakia .. .. 1·50 1·50

**1975.** Arms of Czech Regional Capitals (5th series). As T **523**.
2214. 60 h. black, gold and red 15 10
2215. 60 h. multicoloured .. 15 10

ARMS: No. 2214, Nymburk. No. 2215, Znojmo.

**626.** Partisans at Barricade. (Actual size 70×34 mm.)

**1975.** Czechoslovak Anniversaries.
2216. **626.** 1 k. multicoloured .. 20 15
2217. – 1 k. sepia and cream 20 15
2218. – 1 k. multicoloured .. 20 15

DESIGNS and ANNIVERSARIES: No. 2216, Type **626** (30th anniv. of Czech Rising). No. 2217, Liberation celebrations (30th anniv. of Liberation by Soviet Army). No. 2218, Czech-Soviet fraternity (5th anniv. of Czech-Soviet Treaty).

**627.** Youth Exercises.

**1975.** National Spartacist Games.
2219. **627.** 30 h. pur., bl. & pink 10 10
2220. – 60 h. red, lilac & yell. 15 10
2221. – 1 k. vio., red and yell. 25 15

DESIGNS: 60 h. Children's exercises; 1 k. Adult exercises.

**628.** "Datrioides microlepis" and Sea Horse.

**1975.** Aquarium Fishes. Multicoloured.
2222. 60 h. Type **628** .. .. 15 10
2223. 1 k. Siamese fighting fish and freshwater angel fish .. .. 30 10
2224. 1 k. 20 Goldfish .. .. 50 15
2225. 1 k. 60 Clown fish and butterfly fish .. .. 60 20
2226. 2 k. Korean angel fish, purple moon angel fish and tang .. .. 2·75 55

**1975.** Bratislava Tapestries. "Hero and Leander" (2nd series). As T **617**. Mult.
2227 3 k. "Leander's Arrival" 1·00 90
2228 3 k. 60 "Hermione" .. 2·75 2·75

**629.** "Pelicans" (N. Charushin). **630.** "CZ-150" Motor Cycle (1951).

**1975.** Biennial Exhibition of Book Illustrations for Children, Bratislava. Mult.
2229. 20 h. Type **629** .. .. 10 10
2230. 30 h. "Sleeping Hero" (L. Schwarz) .. .. 10 10
2231. 40 h. "Horseman" (V. Munteau) .. .. 15 10
2232. 60 h. "Peacock" (K. Ensikat) .. .. 20 10
2233. 80 h. "The Stone King" (R. Dubravec) .. .. 70 20

**1975.** Czechoslovak Motor Cycles. Mult.
2234 20 h. Type **630** .. .. 15 10
2235 40 h. "Jawa 250", 1945 .. 20 10
2236 60 h. "Jawa 175", 1935 .. 25 10
2237 1 k. Janatka "ITAR", 1921 .. .. 30 15
2238 1 k. 20 Michi "Orion", 1903 .. .. 50 20
2239 1 k. 80 Laurin and Klement, 1898 .. 1·90 45

**631.** "Solar Radiation". **632.** President Gustav Husak.

**1975.** Co-operation in Space Research.
2240. **631.** 30 h. violet, yell. & red 15 10
2241. – 60 h. red, lilac & yell. 20 10
2242. – 1 k. pur., yell. & blue 30 10
2243. – 2 k. multicoloured .. 70 15
2244. – 5 k. multicoloured .. 3·25 3·25

DESIGNS—HORIZ. 60 h. "Auroa Borealis". 1 k. Cosmic radiation measurement. 2 k. Copernicus and solar radiation. VERT. (40×50 mm). 5 k. "Apollo-soyuz" space link.

**1975.**
2245. **632.** 30 h. blue .. .. 10 10
2246. 60 h. red .. .. 20 10

**633.** Oil Refinery.

**1975.** 30th Anniv. of Liberation. Mult.
2247. 30 h. Type **633** .. .. 15 10
2248. 60 h. Atomic power complex .. .. 15 10
2249. 1 k. Underground Railway, Prague .. .. 25 10
2250. 1 k. 20 Laying oil pipelines .. .. .. 40 15
2251. 1 k. 40 Combine-harvesters and granary 35 20
2252. 1 k. 60 Building construction .. .. 1·40 40

**1975.** Prague Castle. Art Treasures. (11th series). As T **536**. Multicoloured.
2253 3 k. Late 9th-century gold earring .. .. 75 75
2254 3 k. 60 Leather Bohemian Crown case, 1347 .. 2·40 2·40

**1975.** Art (10th series). As T **481**.
2256. 1 k. red, brown and black 75 50
2257. 1 k. 40 multicoloured .. 75 50
2258. 1 k. 80 multicoloured .. 75 50
2259. 2 k. 40 multicoloured .. 1·50 1·50
2260. 3 k. 40 multicoloured .. 2·25 2·25

PAINTINGS—VERT. 1 k. "May" (Z. Sklenar). 1 k. 40, "Girl in National Costume" (E. Nevan). 2 k. 40, "Fire" (J. Capek). 3 k. 40, "Prague, 1828" (V. Morstadt). HORIZ: 1 k. 80, "Liberation of Prague" (A. Cermakova).

**635.** Posthorn Motif.

**1975.** Stamp Day.
2261. **635.** 1 k. multicoloured .. 30 15

**636.** Frantisek Halas (poet).

**1975.** Celebrities' Anniversaries.
2262. **636.** 60 h. multicoloured .. 15 10
2263. – 60 h. multicoloured .. 15 10
2264. – 60 h. multicoloured .. 30 10
2265. – 60 h. blue, red & yell. 15 10
2266. – 60 h. multicoloured .. 15 10

DESIGNS AND ANNIVERSARIES—HORIZ. No. 2262, Type **636** (75th birth anniv). 2266, Ivan Krasko (poet, birth cent). VERT. No. 2263, Wilhelm Pieck (German statesman, birth cent). 2264, Frantisek Lexa (Egyptologist, birth cent). 2265, Jindrich Jindrich (ethnographer, birth cent).

**637.** Ski Jumping.

**1976.** Winter Olympics Games, Innsbruck. Multicoloured.
2267 1 k. Type **637** .. .. 20 10
2268 1 k. 40 Figure skating .. 30 15
2269 1 k. 60 Ice hockey .. 1·50 35

**638.** Throwing the Javelin.

**1976.** Olympic Games, Montreal. Mult.
2270. 2 k. Type **638** .. .. 40 25
2271. 3 k. Relay-racing .. 65 35
2272. 3 k. 60 Putting the Shot 2·75 70

**639.** Table Tennis Player.

**1976.** European Table Tennis Championships, Prague and 50th Anniv of Organized Table Tennis in Czechoslovakia.
2273 **639** 1 k. multicoloured .. 40 20

**640.** Star Emblem and Workers. **641.** Microphone and Musical Instruments.

**1976.** 15th Czechoslovak Communist Party Congress, Prague. Multicoloured.
2274. 30 h. Type **640** .. .. 10 10
2275. 60 h. Furnace and monolith 15 10

**1976.** Cultural Events and Anniversaries.
2276. **641.** 20 h. multicoloured .. 10 10
2277. – 20 h. multicoloured .. 10 10
2278. – 20 h. multicoloured .. 10 10
2279. – 30 h. multicoloured .. 10 10
2280. – 30 h. violet, red & blue 10 10
DESIGNS—HORIZ. No. 2276, Type **641** (50th anniv of Czechoslovak Radio Symphony Orchestra). 2278, Stage revellers (30th anniv of Nova Scena Theatre, Bratislava). 2279, Folk dancers, Wallachia (International Folk Song and Dance Festival, Straznice). VERT. No. 2277, Ballerina, violin and mask (30th anniv of Prague Academy of Music and Dramatic Art). 2280, Film "profile" (20th Film Festival, Karlovy Vary).

**1976.** Bratislava Tapestries. "Hero and Leander" (3rd series). As T **617**. Mult.
2281. 3 k. " Hero with Leander's body " .. .. .. 2·50 1·50
2282. 3 k. 60 " Eros grieving " 1·25 90

**642.** Hammer, Sickle and Red Flags.

**1976.** 55th Anniv. of Czechoslovak Communist Party.
2283. **642.** 30 h. blue, gold and red 15 10
2284. – 60 h. multicoloured .. 20 10
DESIGN: 60 h. Hammer and Sickle on flag.

**643.** Manes Hall, Czechoslovakia Artists' Union.

**1976.** Air. "PRAGA 78" International Stamp Exhibition (1st issue). Prague Architecture. Multicoloured.
2286 60 h. Type **643** .. .. 40 10
2287 1 k. 60 Congress Hall, Julius Fucik Park .. 45 15
2288 2 k. Powder Tower, Old Town (vert) .. .. 80 20
2289 2 k. 40 Charles Bridge and Old Bridge Tower .. 60 20
2290 4 k. Old Town Square and Town Hall (vert) .. 1·00 35
2291 6 k. Prague Castle and St. Vitus Cathedral (vert) 4·50 1·00
See also 2313/16, 2326/30, 2339/42, 2349/52, 2358/62, 2389/93, 2407/12, 2413/17 and 2420/3.

**644.** " Warship " (Frans Huys). **645.** " UNESCO " Plant.

**1976.** Ship Engravings.
2292. **644** 40 h. blk., cream & drab 25 10
2293. – 60 h. blk., cream & grey 25 10
2294. – 1 k. blk., cream & grn. 50 10
2295. – 2 k. blk., cream & blue 1·75 70
DESIGNS: 60 h. " Dutch Merchantman " (V. Hollar). 1 k. " Ship at Anchor " (N. Zeeman). 2 k. " Galleon under Full Sail " (F. Chereau).

**1976.** 30th Anniv. of U.N.E.S.C.O.
2296. **645.** 2 k. multicoloured .. 90 50

**647.** Merino Ram. **648.** " Stop Smoking ".

**1976.** "Bountiful Earth" Agricultural Exhibition, Ceske Budejovice. Multicoloured.
2298. 30 h. Type **647** .. .. 15 10
2299. 40 h. Berna-Hana Cow .. 15 10
2300. 1 k. 60 Kladruby stallion 45 15

**1976.** WHO Campaign against Smoking.
2301. **648.** 2 k. multicoloured .. 1·25 45

**649.** Postal Code Emblem. **650.** " Guernica 1937 " (I. Weiner-Kral).

**1976.** Coil Stamps. Postal Code Campaign.
2302 **649** 30 h. green .. .. 10 10
2303 – 60 h. red .. .. 15 10
DESIGN: 60 h. Postal map.

**1976.** 40th Anniv of International Brigades in Spanish Civil War.
2304 **650** 5 k. multicoloured .. 1·40 50

**1976.** Prague Castle. Art Treasures (12th series). As T **536**. Multicoloured.
2305 3 k. "Prague Castle, 1572" (F. Hoogenberghe) .. 2·50 2·50
2306 3 k. 60 "Satyrs" (relief from summer-house balustrade) .. .. 90 90

**651.** Common Zebra with foal.

**1976.** Dvurkralove Wildlife Park. Mult.
2307. 10 h. Type **651** .. .. 15 10
2308. 20 h. African elephant, calf and cattle egret (vert.) .. .. .. 1·00 15
2309. 30 h. Cheetah .. .. 20 10
2310. 40 h. Giraffe and calf (vert.) .. .. .. 20 10
2311. 60 h. Black rhinoceros .. 25 10
2312. 3 k. Bongo with offspring (vert.) .. .. 2·25 70

**1976.** "PRAGA 1978" International Stamp Exhibition (2nd series). Art (11th series). As T **481**. Multicoloured.
2313 1 k. "Flowers in Vase" (P. Matejka) .. .. 1·00 70
2314 1 k. 40 "Oleander Blossoms" (C. Bouda) 1·25 1·00
2315 2 k. "Flowers in Vase" (J. Brueghel) .. .. 2·25 1·60
2316 3 k. 60 "Tulips and Narcissi" (J. R. Bys) .. 1·10 65

**652.** Postilion, Postal Emblem and Satellite.

**1976.** Stamp Day.
2317. **652.** 1 k. blue, mauve & gold 25 10

**653.** Ice Hockey. **654.** Arms of Vranov.

**1977.** 6th Winter Spartakiad of Warsaw Pact Armies. Multicoloured.
2318 60 h. Type **653** .. .. 25 10
2319 1 k. Rifle shooting (Biathlon) .. .. 30 10
2320 1 k. 60 Ski jumping .. 2·00 60
2321 2 k. Slalom .. .. 55 20

**1977.** Coats of Arms of Czechoslovak Towns (1st series). Multicoloured.
2322. 60 h. Type **654** .. .. 20 10
2323. 60 h. Kralupy and Vltavou 20 10
2324. 60 h. Jicin .. .. 20 10
2325. 60 h. Valasske Mezirici .. 20 10
See also Nos. 2511/14, 2612/15, 2720/3, 2765/7, 2819/21 and 3017/20.

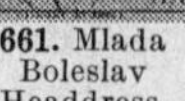

**655.** Window, Michna Palace. **656.** Children Crossing Road.

**1977.** " PRAGA 78 " International Stamp Exhibition (3rd issue). Historic Prague Windows. Multicoloured.
2326. 20 h. Type **655** .. .. 10 10
2327. 30 h. Michna Palace (different) .. .. .. 10 10
2328. 40 h. Thun Palace .. 10 10
2329. 60 h. Archbishop's Palace 15 10
2330. 5 k. Church of St. Nicholas .. .. 3·25 75

**1977.** 25th Anniv of Police Aides Corps.
2331 **656** 60 h. multicoloured .. 25 10

**657.** Cyclists at Warsaw (starting point). **658.** Congress Emblem.

**1977.** 30th Anniv. of Peace Cycle Race. Mult.
2332 30 h. Type **657** .. .. 15 10
2333 60 h. Cyclists at Berlin .. 20 10
2334 1 k. Cyclists at Prague (finishing point) .. 1·50 30
2335 1 k. 40 Cyclists and modern buildings .. 50 15

**1977.** Ninth Trade Unions Congress.
2336. **658.** 30 h. gold, red and carmine .. .. 10 10

**1977.** Prague Castle (13th series). As T **536**.
2337 3 k. multicoloured .. 1·25 1·25
2338 3 k. 60 green, gold & black 1·75 1·75
DESIGNS: 3 k. Onyx cup, 1350 (St. Vitus Cathedral). 3 k. 60, Bronze horse, 1619 (A. de Vries).

**659.** French Postal Rider, 19th-century. **660.** Coffee Pots.

**1977.** "PRAGA 78" International Stamp Exhibition (4th issue). Multicoloured.
2339 60 h. Type **659** .. .. 15 10
2340 1 k. Austrian postal rider, 1838 .. .. .. 25 10
2341 2 k. Austrian postal rider, c. 1770 .. .. 50 20
2342 3 k. 60 German postal rider, 1700 .. .. 3·00 90

**1977.** Czechoslovak Porcelain.
2343. **660.** 20 h. multicoloured .. 10 10
2344. – 30 h. multicoloured .. 10 10
2345. – 40 h. multicoloured .. 15 10
2346. – 60 h. multicoloured .. 20 10
2347. – 1 k. blue, grn. & violet 25 10
2348. – 3 k. blue, gold and red 2·25 75
DESIGNS: 30 h. Vase. 40 h. Amphora. 60 h. Jug, beaker, cup and saucer. 1 k. Plate and candlestick. 3 k. Coffee pot, cup and saucer.

**661.** Mlada Boleslav Headdress. **662.** V. Bombova's Illustrations of " Janko Gondashik and the Golden Lady ".

**1977.** " PRAGA 78 " International Stamp Exhibition (5th issue). Regional Headdresses. Multicoloured.
2349. 1 k. Type **661** .. .. 75 75
2350. 1 k. 60 Vazek .. 3·50 3·50
2351. 3 k. 60 Zavadka .. 75 75
2352. 5 k. Belkovice .. 1·25 1·25

**1977.** 6th Biennial Exhibition of Children's Book Illustrators. Bratislava. Multicoloured.
2353. 40 h. Type **662** .. .. 10 10
2354. 60 h. " Tales of Amur " (G. Pavlishin) .. .. 15 10
2355. 1 k. " Almgist et Wiksel " (U. Lofgren) .. .. 25 10
2356. 2 k. " Alice in Wonderland " and " Through the Looking Glass " (Nicole Claveloux) .. 75 25
2357. 3 k. " Eventyr " (J. Trnka) 3·00 65

**663.** Airships LZ-5 and "Graf Zeppelin". **664.** U.N.E.S.C.O. Emblem, Violin and Doves.

**1977.** Air. "PRAGA 1978" Int Stamp Exn (6th issue). Early Aviation. Mult.
2358 60 h. Type **663** .. .. 15 10
2359 1 k. Clement Ader's monoplane "Eole", Etrich Holubice and Dunne D-8 .. .. 30 10
2360 1 k. 60 Jeffries and Blanchard balloon, 1785 .. 40 15
2361 2 k. Lilienthal biplane glider, 1896 .. .. 50 20
2362 4 k. 40 Jan Kaspar's Bleriot XI over Prague 3·50 90

**1977.** Congress of U.N.E.S.C.O. International Music Council.
2363 **664** 60 h. multicoloured .. 15 10





**665.** " Peace ". **666.** Yury Gagarin.

**1977.** European Co-operation for Peace. Multicoloured.

2364. 60 h. Type **665** .. .. 15 10
2365. 1 k. 60 " Co-operation " 40 20
2366. 2 k. 40 " Social Progress " 1·25 40

**1977.** Space Research. Multicoloured.

2367 20 h. S. P. Koroliov (space technician, launch of first satellite) .. .. 10 10
2368 30 h. Type **666** (first man in space) .. .. 10 10
2369 40 h. Aleksei Leonov (first space walker) .. .. 10 10
2370 1 k. Neil Armstrong (first man on the moon) .. 25 10
2371 1 k. 60 "Salyut" and "Skylab" space stations 1·40 35

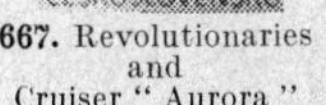


**667.** Revolutionaries and Cruiser " Aurora "

**668.** " Wisdom ".

**1977.** 60th Anniv. of Russian Revolution, and 55th Anniv. of U.S.S.R. Mult.

2372. 30 h. Type **667** .. .. 15 10
2373. 30 h. Russian woman, Kremlin, rocket and U.S.S.R. arms .. .. 15 10

**1977.** 25th Anniv. of Czechoslovak Academy of Science.

2374. **668.** 3 k. multicoloured .. 70 25

**1977.** Art (12th series). As Type **481.**

2375. 2 k. multicoloured .. 75 75
2376. 2 k. 40 multicoloured .. 3·25 3·25
2377. 2 k. 60 stone and black .. 2·50 2·50
2378. 3 k. multicoloured .. 1·00 1·00
2379. 5 k. multicoloured .. 1·00 1·00

DESIGNS: 2 k. " Fear " (J. Mudroch). 2 k. 40, " Portrait of Jan Francis " (P. M. Bohun). 2 k. 60, " Self Portrait " (V. Hollar). 3 k. " Portrait of a Girl " (L. Cranach). 5 k. " Cleopatra " (Rubens).

**669.** " Bratislava, 1574 " (G. Hoefnagel).

**1977.** Historic Bratislava (1st series). Mult.

2380. 3 k. Type **669** .. .. 2·25 2·25
2381. 3 k. 60 Bratislava Arms, 1436 .. .. 75 65

See also Nos. 2402/3, 2500/1, 2545/6, 2582/3, 2642/3, 2698/9, 2736/7, 2793/4, 2842/3, 2898/9, 2952/3, 2997/8 and 3034/5.

**670.** Posthorn and Stamps.

**1977.** Stamp Day.

2382. **670.** 1 k. multicoloured .. 20 10

**671.** Z. Nejedly (historian).

**674.** Modern Coins.

**672.** Civilians greeting Armed Guards.

**1978.** Cultural Anniversaries. Multicoloured.

2383. 30 h. Type **671** (birth cent.) 10 10
2384. 40 h. Karl Marx (160th birth anniv.) .. .. 10 10

**1978.** 30th Annivs of "Victorious February" and National Front. Multicoloured.

2385 1 k. Type **672** .. .. 20 10
2386 1 k. Intellectual, peasant woman and steel worker .. .. 20 10

**1978.** Soviet-Czechoslovak Space Flight. No. 2368 optd **SPOLECNY LET SSSR*CSSR.**

2387 30 h. red .. .. .. 20 20
2388 3 k. 60 blue .. .. 5·00 5·00

**1978.** 650th Anniv of Kremnica Mint and "PRAGA 1978" International Stamp Exhibition (7th issue). Multicoloured.

2389 20 h. Type **674** .. .. 10 10
2390 40 h. Culture medal, 1972 (Jan Kulich) .. .. 10 10
2391 1 k. 40 Charles University Medal, 1948 (O. Spaniel) 3·25 40
2392 3 k. Ferdinand I medal, 1563 (L. Richter) .. 75 45
2393 5 k. Gold florin of Charles Robert, 1335 .. .. 1·25 60

**675.** Tyre Marks and Ball.

**676.** Hands supporting Globe.

**1978.** Road Safety.

2394. **675.** 60 h. multicoloured .. 20 10

**1978.** 9th World Federation of Trade Unions Congress, Prague.

2395. **676.** 1 k. multicoloured .. 20 10

**677.** Putting the Shot.

**1978.** Sports.

2396 – 30 h. multicoloured .. 15 10
2397 **677** 40 h. multicoloured .. 15 10
2398 – 60 h. multicoloured .. 80 20
2399 – 1 k. multicoloured .. 40 10
2400 – 2 k. yellow, blue & red 60 25
2401 – 3 k. 60 multicoloured 2·40 75

DESIGNS AND EVENTS—HORIZ. 70th anniv of bandy hockey: 30 h. Three hockey players, World Ice Hockey Championships: 60 h. Tackle in front of goal. 2 k. Goalmouth scrimmage. VERT. European Athletics Championships, Prague: 1 k. Pole vault; 3 k. 60, Running.

**1978.** Historic Bratislava (2nd series). As T **669.**

2402 3 k. green, violet and red 1·40 1·40
2403 3 k. 60 multicoloured .. 2·40 2·40

DESIGNS: 3 k. "Bratislava" (Orest Dubay). 3 k. 60, "Fishpond Square, Bratislava" (Imro Weiner-Kral).

**1978.** Prague Castle (14th series). As T **536.**

2404. 3 k. yellow, black & green 80 80
2405. 3 k. 60 multicoloured .. 2·75 2·25

DESIGNS: 3 k. Memorial to King Premysl Otakar II, St. Vitus Cathedral. 3 k. 60, Portrait of King Charles IV (Jan Ocka).

**678.** Ministry of Posts, Prague.

**1978.** 14th COMECON Meeting, Prague.

2406. **678.** 60 h. multicoloured .. 15 10

**679.** Palacky Bridge.

**1978.** " PRAGA 78 " International Stamp Exhibition (8th issue). Prague Bridges. Multicoloured.

2407. 20 h. Type **679** .. .. 10 10
2408. 40 h. Railway bridge .. 35 10
2409. 1 k. Bridge of 1st May .. 25 10
2410. 2 k. Manes Bridge .. 45 20
2411. 3 k. Svatopluk Cech Bridge 55 40
2412. 5 k. 40 Charles Bridge .. 4·50 1·25

**680.** St. Peter and other Apostles.

**681.** Dancers.

**1978.** "PRAGA 78" International Stamp Exhibition (9th issue). Prague Town Hall Astronomical Clock. Multicoloured.

2413 40 h. Type **680** .. .. 15 10
2414 1 k. Astronomical clock face .. .. .. 20 15
2415 2 k. Centre of Manes's calendar .. .. 35 20
2416 3 k. "September" (grape harvest) .. .. 3·25 1·10
2417 3 k. 60 "Libra" (sign of the Zodiac) .. .. 1·25 25

**1978.** 25th Vychodna Folklore Festival.

2419. **681.** 30 h. multicoloured .. 10 10

**682.** Gottwald Bridge.

**1978.** "PRAGA 78" International Stamp Exhibition (10th issue). Modern Prague. Mult.

2420 60 h. Type **682** .. .. 40 10
2421 1 k. Powder Gate Tower and Kotva department store .. .. .. 25 10
2422 2 k. Ministry of Posts .. 50 20
2423 6 k. Prague Castle and flats .. .. .. 3·50 1·40

**685.** Fair Buildings.

**686.** " Postal Newspaper Service " (25th Anniv.).

**1978.** 20th International Engineering Fair, Brno.

2426. **685.** 30 h. multicoloured .. 10 10

**1978.** Press, Broadcasting and Television Days.

2427 **686** 30 h. green, bl & orge 10 10
2428 – 30 h. multicoloured .. 10 10
2429 – 30 h. multicoloured .. 10 10

DESIGNS: No. 2428, Microphone, newspapers, camera and Ministry of Information and Broadcasting. 2429, Television screen and Television Centre, Prague (25th anniv of Czechoslovak television).

**687.** Horses falling at Fence.

**1978.** Pardubice Steeplechase. Multicoloured.

2430. 10 h. Type **687** .. .. 10 10
2431. 20 h. Sulky racing .. 10 10
2432. 30 h. Racing horses .. 15 10
2433. 40 h. Passing the winning post .. .. .. 15 10
2434. 1 k. 60 Jumping a fence .. 40 20
2435. 4 k. 40 Jockey leading a winning horse .. .. 3·00 1·10

**688.** Woman holding Arms of Czechoslovakia.

**1978.** 60th Anniv. of Independence.

2436. **688.** 60 h. multicoloured .. 15 10

**689.** " Still Life with Flowers " (J. Bohdan).

**690.** Violinist and Bass Player (J. Konyves).

**1978.** 30th Anniv of Slovak National Gallery, Bratislava. Multicoloured.

2437. 2 k. 40 Type **689** .. 75 60
2438. 3 k. " Dream in a Shepherd's Hut " (L. Fulla) (horiz.) .. .. 75 75
2439. 3 k. 60 " Apostle with Censer " (detail, Master of the Spis Chapter) .. 3·00 3·00

**1978.** Slovak Ceramics.

2440 **690** 20 h. multicoloured .. 10 10
2441 – 30 h. blue and violet 10 10
2442 – 40 h. multicoloured .. 10 10
2443 – 1 k. multicoloured .. 25 10
2444 – 1 k. 60 multicoloured 2·25 30

DESIGNS: 30 h. Horseman (J. Franko). 40 h. Man in kilt (M. Polasko). 1 k. Three girl singers (I. Bizmayer). 1 k. 60, Miner with axe (F. Kostka).

**691.** Alfons Mucha and design for 1918 Hradcany Stamp.

**1978.** Stamp Day.

2445. **691.** 1 k. multicoloured .. 20 15

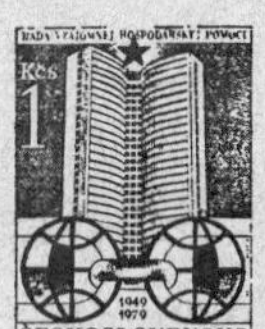


**692.** Council Building, Moscow.

**1979.** Anniversaries.

2446. – 30 h. brn., grn. & orge. 10 10
2447. – 60 h. multicoloured .. 15 10
2448. **692.** 1 k. multicoloured .. 20 10

DESIGNS—HORIZ. 30 h. Girl's head and ears of wheat (30th anniv. of Unified Agricultural Co-operatives). 60 h. Czechoslovakians and doves (10th anniv. of Czechoslovak Federation). VERT. 1 k. Type **692.** (30th anniv. of Council of Economic Mutual Aid).

**693.** " Soyuz 28 ".

**1979.** 1st Anniv. of Russian-Czech Space Flight. Multicoloured.
2449 30 h. Type **693** .. .. 15 10
2450 60 h. A. Gubarev and V. Remek (vert) .. .. 15 10
2451 1 k. 60 J. Romanenko and G. Grechko .. .. 45 25
2452 2 k. "Salyut 6" space laboratory .. .. 2·50 50
2453 4 k. "Soyuz 28" touch down (vert) .. .. 90 50

**694.** " Campanula alpina ".

**695.** Stylized Satellite.

**1979.** 25th Anniv. of Mountain Rescue Service. Multicoloured.
2455 10 h. Type **694** .. 10 10
2456 20 h. "Crocus scepusiensis" .. 10 10
2457 30 h. "Dianthus glacialis" 10 10
2458 40 h. Alpine hawkweed 15 10
2459a 3 k. "Delphinium oxysepalum" .. 1·75 80

**1979.** Anniversaries.
2460. **695.** 10 h. multicoloured.. 10 10
2461. – 20 h. multicoloured.. 10 10
2462. – 20 h. blue, orange and light blue .. .. 10 10
2463. – 30 h. blue, gold & red 10 10
2464. – 30 h. red, blue & blk. 10 10
2465. – 60 h. multicoloured.. 20 10

DESIGNS AND EVENTS—HORIZ. No. 2460, Type **695** 30th anniv of Telecommunications Research. 46 × 19 mm: (No. 2461), Artist and model (30th anniv of Academy of Fine Arts, Bratislava). 2462, Student and technological equipment (40th anniv of Slovak Technical University, Bratislava). 2463, Musical instruments and Bratislava Castle (50th anniv of Radio Symphony Orchestra, Bratislava). 2464, Pioneer's scarf and I.Y.C. emblem (30th anniv of Young Pioneer Organization and International Year of the Child). 2465, Adult and child with doves (30th anniv of Peace Movement).

**1979.** Prague Castle (15th series). As T **536**. Multicoloured.
2466 3 k. Burial crown of King Premysl Otakar II .. 2·25 2·25
2467 3 k. 60 Portrait of Miss B. Reitmayer (Karel Purkyne) .. .. 1·00 1·00

**696.** Arms of Vlachovo Brezi.

**697.** Healthy and Polluted Forests.

**1979.** Animals in Heraldry. Multicoloured.
2468 30 h. Type **696** .. .. 10 10
2469 60 h. Jesenik (bear and eagle) .. .. .. 15 10
2470 1 k. 20 Vysoke Myto (St. George and the dragon) 30 10
2471 1 k. 80 Martin (St. Martin on horseback) .. 1·75 50
2472 2 k. Zebrak (half bear, half lion) .. .. 40 15

**1979.** Man and the Biosphere. Mult.
2473. 60 h. Type **697** .. .. 15 15
2474. 1 k. 80 Clear and polluted water .. .. .. 45 35
2475. 3 k. 60 Healthy and polluted urban environment .. .. .. 3·25 1·00
2476. 4 k. Healthy and polluted pasture .. .. 90 40

**698.** Numeral and Printed Circuit.

**699.** Industrial Complex.

**1979.** Coil Stamps.
2477. – 50 h. red .. .. 20 10
2478. **698.** 1 k. brown .. .. 25 10
2478a. – 2 k. green .. .. 50 20
2478b. – 3 k. purple .. .. 80 30

DESIGNS: Numeral and — 50 h. Dish aerial. 2 k. Airplane. 3 k. Punched tape.

**1979.** 35th Anniv of Slovak Uprising.
2479 **699** 30 h. multicoloured .. 10 10

**700.** Illustration by Janos Kass.

**1979.** International Year of the Child and Biennial Exhibition of Children's Book Illustrations, Bratislava. Designs showing illustrations by artists named. Multicoloured.
2480 20 h. Type **700** .. .. 10 10
2481 40 h. Rumen Skorcev .. 15 10
2482 60 h. Karel Svolinsky .. 15 10
2483 1 k. Otto S. Svend .. 30 10
2484 3 k. Tatyana Mavrina .. 2·10 55

**701.** Modern Bicycles.

**1979.** Historic Bicycles. Multicoloured.
2485 20 h. Type **701** .. .. 15 10
2486 40 h. Bicycles, 1910 .. 15 10
2487 60 h. "Ordinary" and tricycle, 1886 .. .. 15 10
2488 2 k. "Bone-shakers", 1870 50 20
2489 3 k. 60 Drais cycles, 1820 2·75 75

**702.** Bracket Clock (Jan Kraus).

**1979.** Historic Clocks. Multicoloured.
2490. 40 h. Type **702** .. .. 10 10
2491. 60 h. Rococo clock .. 15 10
2492. 80 h. Classicist clock .. 2·00 35
2493. 1 k. Rococo porcelain clock (J. Kandler) .. .. 25 10
2494. 2 k. Urn-shaped clock (Dufaud) .. .. 55 20

**1979.** Art (13th series). As T **481**.
2495. 1 k. 60 multicoloured .. 45 35
2496. 2 k. multicoloured .. 55 45
2497. 3 k. multicoloured .. 80 70
2498. 3 k. 60 multicoloured .. 4·75 4·75
2499. 5 k. yellow and black .. 1·25 1·25

DESIGNS: 1 k. 60, " Sunday by the River " (Alois Moravec). 2 k. " Self-portrait " (Gustav Mally). 3 k. " Self-portrait " (Ilja Jefimovic Repin). 3 k. 60, " Horseback Rider " (Jan Bauch). 5 k. " Village Dancers " (Albrecht Durer).

**1979.** Historic Bratislava (3rd issue). As T **669**. Multicoloured.
2500 3 k. "Bratislava, 1787" (L. Janscha) .. .. 1·00 1·00
2501 3 k. 60 "Bratislava, 1815" (after stone engraving by Wolf) .. .. 2·50 2·50

**703.** Postmarks, Charles Bridge and Prague Castle.

**1979.** Stamp Day.
2502. **703.** 1 k. multicoloured .. 25 10

**MORE DETAILED LISTS**
are given in the Stanley Gibbons Catalogues referred to in the country headings.
For lists of current volumes see Introduction.

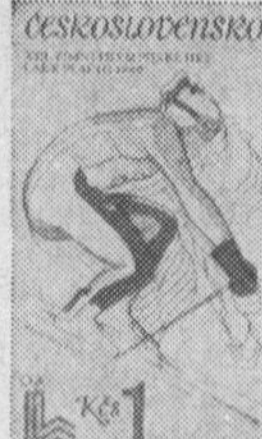


**704.** Skiing.

**1980.** Winter Olympic Games, Lake Placid.
2503. **704.** 1 k. multicoloured .. 25 10
2504. – 2 k. red, pink & blue 1·75 40
2505. – 3 k. multicoloured .. 70 50

DESIGNS: 2 k. Ice skating. 3 k. Four-man bobsleigh.

**705.** Basketball.

**1980.** Olympic Games, Moscow. Multicoloured.
2506. 40 h. Type **705** .. .. 15 10
2507. 1 k. Swimming .. .. 25 10
2508. 2 k. Hurdles .. .. 2·25 45
2509. 3 k. 60 Fencing .. .. 75 35

**706.** Marathon.

**1980.** 50th International Peace Marathon, Kosice.
2510. **706.** 50 h. multicoloured.. 15 10

**1980.** Arms of Czech Towns (2nd series). As T **654**.
2511 50 h. blue, black and gold 15 10
2512 50 h. black and silver .. 15 10
2513 50 h. multicoloured .. 15 10
2514 50 h. gold, black and blue 15 10

DESIGNS: No. 2511, Bystrice nad Pernstejnem. 2512, Kunstat. 2513, Rozmital pod Tremsinem. 2514, Zlata Idka.

**707.** Bratislava Opera House and Bakovazena as King Lear.

**708.** Tragic Mask.

**1980.** 60th Anniv of Slovak National Theatre, Bratislava.
2515 **707** 1 k. blue, yell & orge 20 10

**1980.** 50th Anniv of Theatrical Review "Jiraskuv Hronov".
2516 **708** 50 h. multicoloured .. 15 10

**709.** Mouse in Space.

**710.** Police Parade Banner.

**1980.** "Intercosmos" Space Programme.
2517 **709** 50 h. blue, black & red 15 10
2518 – 1 k. multicoloured .. 30 10
2519 – 1 k. 60 vio, blk & red 3·25 60
2520 – 4 k. multicoloured .. 1·00 35
2521 – 5 k. blue, black & pur 1·50 45

DESIGNS—VERT. 1 k. Weather map and satellite. 1 k. 60, " Inter-sputnik " T.V. transmission. 4 k. Survey satellite and camera. HORIZ. 5 k. Czech-built satellite station. 10 k. " Intercosmos " emblem.

**1980.** 35th Anniv. of National Police Corps.
2523. **710.** 50 h. gold, red & blue 15 10

**711.** Lenin. **712.** Flag, Flowers and Prague Buildings.

**1980.** 110th Birth Anniv. of Lenin and 160th Birth Anniv. of Engels.
2524. **711.** 1 k. brown, red & grey 20 10
2525. – 1 k. blue and brown.. 20 10

DESIGN: No. 2525, Engels.

**1980.** Anniversaries. Multicoloured.
2526. 50 h. Type **712** .. .. 15 10
2527. 1 k. Child writing " Mir " (peace) .. .. .. 25 10
2528. 1 k. Czech and Soviet arms 25 10
2529. 1 k. Flowers, flags and dove 25 10

ANNIVERSARIES: No. 2526, 35th anniv of May uprising. 2527, 35th anniv of Liberation. 2528, 10th anniv of Czech–Soviet Treaty. 2529, 25th anniv of Warsaw Pact.

**713.** Gymnast.

**1980.** National Spartakiad.
2530. – 50 h. black, red & blue 10 10
2531. **713.** 1 k. multicoloured .. 25 10

DESIGN: HORIZ.—50 h. Opening parade of athletes.

**715.** " Gerbera jamesonii ".

**716.** " Chod Girl ".

**1980.** Olomuc and Bratislava Flower Shows. Multicoloured.
2533 50 h. Type **715** .. .. 15 15
2534 1 k. "Aechmea fasciata" 2·25 50
2535 2 k. Bird of paradise flower .. .. .. 40 30
2536 4 k. Slipper orchid .. 85 60

**1980.** Graphic Cut-outs by Cornelia Nemeckova.
2537 **716** 50 h. multicoloured .. 15 10
2238 – 1 k. mauve, brn & red 25 10
2539 – 2 k. multicoloured .. 45 20
2540 – 4 k. multicoloured .. 3·50 90
2541 – 5 k. blue, mve & lt bl 1·10 50

DESIGNS: 1 k. "Punch with his dog". 2 k. "Dandy cat with Posy". 4 k. Lion and Moon ("Evening Contemplation"). 5 k. Dancer and piper ("Wallacchian Dance").

**717.** Map of Czechoslovakia and Family.

**718.** Heads.

**1980.** National Census.
2542. **717.** 1 k. multicoloured .. 20 10

**1980.** Prague Castle (16th series). As T **536**. Multicoloured.
2543. 3 k. Gateway of Old Palace 2·25 2·25
2544. 4 k. Armorial lion .. 1·40 1·40

**1980.** Historic Bratislava (4th issue). As T **669**. Multicoloured.
2545. 3 k. " View across the Danube " (J. Eder) .. 2·25 2·25
2546. 4 k. " The Old Royal Bridge " (J. A. Lantz) 1·40 1·40

**1980.** 10th Anniv. of Socialist Youth Federation.
2547. **718.** 50 h. blue, orge. & red 15 10

**1980.** Paintings (14th series). As T **481**.
2549. 1 k. buff, blue and brown 1·75 1·75
2550. 2 k. multicoloured .. 2·75 2·75
2551. 3 k. red, brown and green 60 60
2552. 4 k. multicoloured .. 1·00 1·00
2553. 5 k. green, buff and black 1·25 1·25

DESIGNS—VERT. 1 k. "Pavel Jozef Safarik" (Jozef B. Klemens). 2 k. "Peasant Revolt" (mosaic, A. Podzemma). 3 k. Bust of Saint from Lucivna Church. 5 k. "Labour" (sculpture Jan Stursa). HORIZ. 4 k. "Waste Heaps" (Jan Zrzavy).

719. Carrier Pigeon.

**1980.** Stamp Day.
2554. **719.** 1 k. black, red & blue 25 10

720. Five Year Plan Emblem. 721. Invalid and Half-bare Tree.

**1981.** 7th Five Year Plan.
2555 **720** 50 h. multicoloured .. 15 10

**1981.** International Year of Disabled Persons.
2556 **721** 1 k. multicoloured .. 25 10

722. Landau, 1800. 723. Jan Sverma (partisan).

**1981.** Historic Coaches in Postal Museum.
2557. **722.** 50 h. yell., blk. & red 20 10
2558. – 1 k. yell., blk. & grn. 30 10
2559. – 3 k. 60 pale blue, black and blue .. 4·00 75
2560. – 5 k. stone, blk. & red 1·25 55
2561. – 7 k. yell., blk. & blue 1·75 75
DESIGNS: 1 k. Mail coach, c. 1830–40. 3 k. 60, Postal sleigh, 1840. 5 k. Mail coach and four horses, 1860. 7 k. Coupe carriage, 1840.

**1981.** Celebrities' Anniversaries. Multicoloured.
2562. 50 h. Type **723** (80th birth anniv.) .. .. .. 20 10
2563. 50 h. Mikulas Schneider-Trnavsky (composer) (birth cent.) .. .. 30 10
2564. 50 h. Juraj Hronec (mathematician) (birth cent.) .. 20 10
2565. 50 h. Josef Hlavka (architect) (150th birth anniv.) 20 10
2566. 1 k. Dimitri Shostakovich (composer) (75th birth anniv.) .. .. 50 15
2567. 1 k. George Bernard Shaw (dramatist) (125th birth anniv.) .. .. 50 15
2568. 1 k. Bernardo Bolzano (philosopher) (birth bicent.) .. .. 1·75 40
2569. 1 k. Wolfgang Amadeus Mozart (composer) (225th birth anniv.) .. 1·00 30

725. Party Member with Flag.

**1981.** 60th Anniv. of Czechoslovak Communist Party. Multicoloured.
2571 50 h. Type **725** .. .. 10 15
2572 1 k. Symbols of progress and hands holding flag 25 15
2573 4 k. Party member holding flag bearing symbols of industry (vert.) .. 75 45

726. Hammer and Sickle.

**1981.** 16th Czechoslovak Communist Party Congress. Multicoloured.
2574 50 h. Type **726** .. .. 10 10
2575 1 k. "XVI" and Prague buildings .. .. 20 10

## MINIMUM PRICE

The minimum price quoted is 10p which represents a handling charge rather than a basis for valuing common stamps. For further notes about prices see introductory pages.

727. Fallow-plough. 728. Man, Woman and Dove.

**1981.** 90th Anniv. of Agricultural Museum.
2577. **727.** 1 k. multicoloured .. 20 10

**1981.** Elections to Representative Assemblies.
2578 **728** 50 h. red, stone & blue 15 10

729. " Uran " (Tatra Mountains) and " Rudy Rijen " (Bohemia).

**1981.** Achievements of Socialist Construction (1st series). Multicoloured.
2579 80 h. Type **729** (Trade Union recreational facilities .. .. 25 10
2580 1 k. Prague–Brno–Bratislava expressway 30 15
2581 2 k. Jaslovske Bohunice nuclear plant .. .. 50 20
See also Nos. 2644/6, 2695/7, 2753/5 and 2800/2.

**1981.** Historic Bratislava (5th issue). As T **669**. Multicoloured.
2582 3 k. "Bratislava, 1760" (G. B. Probst) .. .. 2·75 2·75
2583 4 k. "Grassalkovichov Palace, 1815" (C. Bschor) .. .. 70 70

731. Puppets. 732. Map.

**1981.** 30th National Festival of Amateur Puppetry Ensembles, Chrudim.
2585. **731.** 2 k. multicoloured .. 40 20

**1981.** National Defence. Multicoloured.
2586. 40 h. Type **732** (Defence of borders) .. .. 10 10
2587. 50 h. Emblem of Civil Defence Organization (30th Anniv.) (vert.) .. 15 10
2588. 1 k. Emblem of Svazarm (Organization for Co-operation with Army, 30th anniv. 28 × 23 mm) 20 10

733. Edelweiss, Climbers and Lenin. 734. Illustration by Albin Brunovsky.

**1981.** 25th International Youth Climb of Rysy Peaks.
2589. **733.** 3 k. 60 multicoloured 80 35

**1981.** Biennial Exhibition of Book Illustrations for Children, Bratislava. Mult.
2590. 50 h. Type **734** .. .. 15 10
2591. 1 k. Adolf Born .. .. 30 10
2592. 2 k. Vive Tolli .. .. 60 30
2593. 4 k. Etienne Delessert .. 90 55
2594. 10 k. Suekichi Akaba .. 4·00 1·60

735. Gorilla Family.

**1981.** 50th Anniv. of Prague Zoo. Mult.
2595 50 h. Type **735** .. .. 30 10
2596 1 k. Lion family .. .. 35 15
2597 7 k. Przewalski's horses 3·50 1·25

736. Skeletal Hand removing Cigarette.

**1981.** Anti-smoking Campaign.
2598. **736.** 4 k. multicoloured .. 2·00 80

**1981.** Prague Castle (17th series). As T **536**. Multicoloured.
2599. 3 k. Fragment of Pernstejn terracotta from Lobkovic Palace (16th century) .. 70 70
2600. 4 k. St. Vitus' Cathedral (19th century engraving by J. Sembera and G. Dobler) .. .. 2·75 2·75

**1981.** Art (15th series). As T **481**.
2601. 1 k. multicoloured .. 4·50 4·50
2602. 2 k. brown .. .. 60 60
2603. 3 k. multicoloured .. 80 80
2604. 4 k. multicoloured .. 1·25 1·25
2605. 5 k. multicoloured .. 1·50 1·50
DESIGNS: 1 k. " View of Prague from Petrin Hill " (V. Hollar). 2 k. " Czech Academy of Arts and Sciences Medallion " (Otakar Spaniel). 3 k. South Bohemian embroidery (Zdenek Sklenar). 4 k. " Peonies " (A. M. Gerasimov). 5 k. " Figure of a Woman Standing " (Picasso).

737. Eduard Karel (engraver).

**1981.** Stamp Day.
2606. **737.** 1 k. yell., red and blue 20 15

738. Lenin. 739. Player kicking Ball.

**1982.** 70th Anniv. of 6th Russian Workers' Party Congress, Prague.
2607. **738.** 2 k. red, gold and blue 55 25

**1982.** World Cup Football Championship, Spain. Multicoloured.
2609. 1 k. Type **739** .. .. 20 15
2610. 3 k. 60 Heading ball .. 70 40
2611. 4 k. Saving goal .. 2·75 65

740. Hrob. 741. Conference Emblem.

**1982.** Arms of Czech Towns (3rd series). Multicoloured.
2612. 50 h. Type **740** .. .. 15 10
2613. 50 h. Mlada Boleslav .. 15 10
2614. 50 h. Nove Mesto and Metuji .. .. 15 10
2615. 50 h. Trencin .. .. 15 10
See also Nos. 2720/3, 2765/7, 2819/21 and 3017/20.

**1982.** Tenth World Federation of Trade Unions Congress, Havana.
2616. **741.** 1 k. multicoloured .. 25 10

742. Workers and Mine.

**1982.** 50th Anniversary of Great Strike at Most (coalminers' and general strike).
2617. **742.** 1 k. multicoloured .. 25 10

743. Locomotives of 1922 and 1982.

**1982.** 60th Anniv. of International Railways Union.
2618. **743.** 6 k. multicoloured .. 1·50 80

744. Worker with Flag. 745. Georgi Dimitrov.

**1982.** Tenth Trade Unions Congress, Prague.
2619. **744.** 1 k. multicoloured .. 25 15

**1982.** Birth Centenary of Georgi Dimitrov (Bulgarian statesman).
2620. **745.** 50 h. multicoloured 15 10

747. "Euterpe" (Crispin de Passe). 749. Child's Head, Rose and Barbed Wire (Lidice).

**1982.** Engravings with a Music Theme.
2622. **747.** 40 h. black, gold and brown .. .. 15 10
2623. – 50 h. blk., gold and red 20 10
2624. – 1 k. blk., gold and brn. 30 15
2625. – 2 k. blk., gold and bl. 50 25
2626. – 3 k. blk., gold and grn. 2·25 75
DESIGNS: 50 h. " The Sanguine Man " (Jacob de Gheyn). 1 k. " The Crossing of the Red Sea " (Adriaen Collaert). 2 k. " Wandering Musicians " (Rembrandt). 3 k. " Beggar with Viol " (Jacques Callot).

**1982.** 40th Anniv. of Destruction of Lidice and Lezaky. Multicoloured.
2628 1 k. Type **749** .. .. 25 15
2629 1 k. Hands and barbed wire (Lezaky) .. .. 25 15

750. Memorial and Statue of Jan Zizka.

**1982.** 50th Anniv. of National Memorial, Prague.
2630. **750.** 1 k. multicoloured .. 25 10

752. Krivoklat Castle.

**1982.** Castles. Multicoloured.
2632. 50 h. Type **752** .. .. 20 10
2633. 1 k. Interior and sculptures at Krivoklat Castle .. .. .. 35 15
2634. 2 k. Nitra Castle .. 65 30
2635. 3 k. Archaeological finds from Nitra Castle .. 1·00 45

**1982.** Prague Castle (18th series). As T **536**. Multicoloured.
2637. 3 k. brown and green .. 3·00 1·00
2638. 4 k. multicoloured .. 1·60 1·25
DESIGNS: 3 k. "St. George" (statue by George and Martin of Kluz, 1372). 4 k. Tomb of Prince Vratislav I, Basilica of St. George.

753. Ferry "Kamzik" in Bratislava Harbour.

**1982.** Danube Commission. Multicoloured.
2639. 3 k. Type **753** .. .. 1·25 55
2640. 3 k. 60 "TR 100" tug at Budapest .. .. 1·50 70

**1982.** Historic Bratislava (6th issue). As T **669**. Multicoloured.
2642. 3 k. black and red .. 2·40 75
2643. 4 k. multicoloured .. 1·10 1·10
DESIGNS: 3 k. "View of Bratislava with Steamer". 4 k. "View of Bratislavia with Bridge".

**754.** Agriculture. **755.** "Scientific Research".

**1982.** Achievements of Socialist Construction (2nd series). Multicoloured.

2644. 20 h. Type **754** .. .. 10 10
2645. 1 k. Industry .. .. 35 10
2646. 3 k. Science and technology .. .. .. 90 40

See also Nos. 2695/7, 2753/5 and 2800/2.

**1982.** 30th Anniv. of Academy of Sciences.

2647. **755.** 6 k. multicoloured .. 1·50 70

**756.** Couple with Flowers and Silhouette of Rider.

**1982.** 65th Anniv of October Revolution and 60th Anniv of U.S.S.R. Multicoloured.

2648. 50 h. Type **756**. .. .. 15 10
2649. 1 k. Cosmonauts and industrial complex .. 30 20

**757.** "Jaroslav Hasek" (writer) (Jose Malejovsky). **759.** President Husak.

**758.** Jaroslav Goldschmied (engraver) and Engraving Tools.

**1982.** Sculptures. Multicoloured.

2650. 1 k. Type **757** .. .. 30 10
2651. 2 k. "Jan Zrzavy" (patriot) (Jan Simota) .. 55 20
2652. 4 k. 40 "Leos Janacek" (composer) (Milos Axman) .. .. 1·10 50
2653. 6 k. "Martin Kukucin" (patriot) (Jan Kulich) 1·50 70
2654. 7 k. "Peaceful Work" (detail) (Rudolf Pribis) 4·00 1·50

**1982.** Art (16th series). As T 481. Mult.

2655. 1 k. "Revolution in Spain" (Josef Sima) .. 1·60 30
2656. 2 k. "Woman drying Herself" (Rudolf Kremlicka) .. .. 3·00 1·40
2657. 3 k. "The Girl Bride" (Dezider Milly) .. 1·50 1·00
2658. 4 k. "Oil Field Workers" (Jan Zelibsky) .. 1·50 1·60
2659. 5 k. "The Birds Lament" (Emil Filla) .. .. 1·75 1·75

**1983.** Stamp Day.

2660. **758.** 1 k. multicoloured .. 30 15

**1983.** 70th Birthday of President Husak.

2661 **759** 50 h. blue .. .. 15 10

See also No. 2911.

**760.** Jaroslav Hasek (writer). **761.** Armed Workers.

**1983.** Celebrities' Anniversaries.

2662. **760.** 50 h. green, bl. & red 15 10
2663. – 1 k. brown, bl. & red 30 10
2664. – 2 k. multicoloured .. 50 20
2665. – 5 k. black, bl. & red 1·50 55

Designs: Type **760** (birth centenary). 1 k. Julius Fucik (journalist), 80th birth and 40th death annivs.) 2 k. Martin Luther (church reformist) (500th birth anniv.). 5 k. Johannes Brahms (composer) (150th birth anniv.).

**1983.** Anniversaries. Multicoloured.

2666. 50 h. Type **761** (35th anniv. of "Victorious February") .. .. 15 10
2667. 1 k. Family and agriculture and industrial landscapes (35th anniversary of National Front) .. .. .. 25 15

**762.** Radio Waves and Broadcasting Emblem. **763.** Ski Flyer.

**1983.** Communications. Multicoloured.

2668 40 h. Type **762** (60th anniv of Czech broadcasting) .. .. 15 10
2669 1 k. Television emblem (30th anniv of Czech television) .. .. 25 10
2670 2 k. W.C.Y. emblem and "1983" (World Communications Year) (40 × 23 mm) .. .. 60 25
2671 3 k. 60 Envelopes, Aero A-10 aircraft and mail vans (60th anniv of airmail and 75th anniv of mail transport by motor vehicles) (49 × 19 mm) .. .. 1·40 60

**1983.** Seventh World Ski Flying Championships, Harrachov.

2672. **763.** 1 k. multicoloured .. 25 10

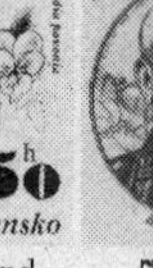


**765.** Emperor Moth and "Viola sudetica". **766.** Ivan Stepanovich Kbnev.

**1983.** Nature Protection. Multicoloured.

2674 50 h. Type **765** .. .. 25 15
2675 1 k. Water lilies and edible frogs .. .. 50 25
2676 2 k. Red crossbill and cones .. .. .. 2·00 75
2677 3 k. 60 Grey herons .. 2·50 85
2678 5 k. Lynx and "Gentiana asclepiadea" .. .. 1·90 70
2679 7 k. Red deer .. .. 5·00 2·00

**1983.** Soviet Army Commanders. Mult.

2680. 50 h. Type **766** .. .. 15 10
2681. 1 k. Andrei Ivanovich Yeremenko .. .. 25 15
2682. 2 k. Rodion Yakovlevich Malinovsky .. .. 55 30

**767.** Dove. **768.** "Rudolf II" (Adrian de Vries).

**1983.** World Peace and Life Congress, Prague.

2683. **767.** 2 k. multicoloured .. 55 55

**1983.** Prague Castle (19th series).

2685. **768.** 4 k. multicoloured .. 1·40 90
2686. – 5 k. orge, blk. & red 90 90

Design: 5 k. Kinetic relief with timepiece by Rudolf Svoboda.

**769.** Mounted Messenger (Oleg K. Zotov).

**1983.** Ninth Biennial Exhibition of Book Illustration for Children.

2687. **769.** 50 h. multicoloured 15 10
2688. – 1 k. multicoloured .. 30 10
2689. – 4 k. multicoloured .. 1·10 45
2690. – 7 k. red and black .. 2·00 90

Designs: 1 k. Boy looking from window at birds in tree (Zbigniew Rychlicki). 4 k. "Hansel and Gretel" (Lisbeth Zwerger). 7 k. Three young negroes (Antonio P. Domingues).

**770.** Ilyushin Il-62 and Globe.

**1983.** World Communications Year and 60th Anniv. of Czechoslovak Airlines.

2692 **770** 50 h. red, pur & pink 15 10
2693 – 1 k. pur, red & pink 30 10
2694 – 4 k. pur, red & pink 2·50 1·25

Designs—vert. 1 k. Ilyushin Il-62 and envelope. horiz. 4 k. Ilyushin Il-62 and Aero A-14 biplane.

**1983.** Achievements of Socialist Construction (3rd series). As T **754**.

2695. 50 h. Surveyor .. .. 15 10
2696. 1 k. Refinery .. .. 30 10
2697. 3 k. Hospital and operating theatre .. .. 75 45

**1983.** Historic Bratislava (7th series). As T **669**.

2698. 3 k. green, red and black 2·00 70
2699. 4 k. multicoloured .. 1·75 70

Designs: 3 k. Sculptures by Viktor Tilgner. 4 k. "Mirbachov Palace" (Julius Schubert).

**771.** National Theatre, Prague. **772.** "Soldier with Sword and Shield" (Hendrik Goltzius).

**1983.** Czechoslovak Theatre Year.

2700. **771.** 50 h. brown .. .. 15 10
2701. – 2 k. green .. .. 60 20

Design: 2 k. National Theatre and Tyl Theatre, Prague.

**1983.** Art (17th series), showing works from the National Theatre, Prague. As Type **481**.

2702. 1 k. multicoloured .. 1·75 1·75
2703. 2 k. multicoloured .. 4·00 2·25
2704. 3 k. yellow, black and blue 1·10 1·10
2705. 4 k. multicoloured .. 1·40 1·75
2706. 5 k. multicoloured .. 1·50 2·50

Designs: 1 k. "Zalov" (lunette detail by Mikolas Ales). 2 k. "Genius" (stage curtain detail, Vojtech Hynais). 3 k. "Music" and "Lyrics" (ceiling drawings, Frantisek Zenisek). 4 k. "Prague" (detail from President's box, Vaclav Brozik.) 5 k. "Hradcany Castle (detail from President's box, Julius Marak).

**1983.** Period Costume from Old Engravings. Multicoloured.

2707. 40 h. Type **772** .. .. 15 10
2708. 50 h. "Warrior with Sword and Lance" (Jacob de Gheyn) .. 15 10
2709. 1 k. "Lady with Muff" (Jacques Callot) .. 30 10
2710. 4 k. "Lady with Flower" (Vaclav Hollar) .. 1·10 40
2711. 5 k. "Gentleman with Cane" (Antoine Watteau) .. .. 3·50 80

**773.** Karel Seizinger (stamp engraver).

**1983.** Stamp Day.

2712. **773.** 1 k. multicoloured .. 25 15

**INDEX**

Countries can be quickly located by referring to the index at the end of this volume.

**774.** National Flag, with Bratislava and Prague Castles. **775.** Council Emblem.

**1984.** 15th Anniv. of Czechoslovak Federation.

2713. **774.** 50 h. multicoloured 20 10

**1984.** 35th Anniv. of Council for Mutual Economic Aid.

2714. **775.** 1 k. multicoloured .. 20 10

**776.** Cross-country Skiing.

**1984.** Winter Olympic Games, Sarajevo. Multicoloured.

2715. 2 k. Type **776** .. .. 45 25
2716. 3 k. Ice hockey .. .. 65 35
2717. 5 k. Biathlon .. .. 1·40 60

**777.** Olympic Flag, Ancient Greek Athletes and Olympic Flame.

**1984.** 90th Anniv. of International Olympic Committee.

2719. **777.** 7 k. multicoloured .. 1·60 60

**1984.** Arms of Czech Towns (4th series). As T **740**. Multicoloured.

2720. 50 h. Turnov .. .. 20 10
2721. 50 h. Kutna Hora .. 20 10
2722. 1 k. Milevsko .. .. 30 10
2723. 1 k. Martin .. .. 30 10

**778.** "Soyuz" and Dish Aerials. **779.** Vendellin Opatrny.

**1984.** "Interkosmos" International Space Flights. Multicoloured.

2724. 50 h. Type **778** .. .. 20 10
2725. 1 k. "Salyut"–"Soyuz" complex .. .. 35 15
2726. 2 k. Cross-section of orbital station .. 50 25
2727. 4 k. "Salyut" taking pictures of Earth's surface .. .. .. 1·00 60
2728. 5 k. "Soyuz" returning to Earth .. .. 1·25 70

**1984.** Anti-fascist Heroes.

2729. **779.** 50 h. blk., red & bl. 20 10
2730. – 1 k. blk., red & bl. .. 30 15
2731. – 2 k. blk., red & bl. .. 55 25
2732. – 4 k. blk., red & bl. .. 1·10 40

Designs: 1 k. Ladislav Novomesky. 2 k. Rudolf Jasiok. 4 k. Jan Nalepka.

**780.** Musical Instruments **781.** Telecommunications Building.

**1984.** Music Year.

2733. **780.** 50 h. light brown, gold and brown .. 20 10
2734. – 1 k. multicoloured .. 30 15

Design: 1 k. Organ pipes.

**1984.** Central Telecommunications Building, Bratislava.

2735. **781.** 2 k. multicoloured .. 60 25

**1984.** Historic Bratislava (8th series). As T **669**. Multicoloured.

2736. 3 k. Arms of Vintners' Guild .. .. .. 1·50 80
2737. 4 k. Painting of 1827 Shooting Festival .. 1·50 80

**1984.** Prague Castle (20th series). As T **768.** Multicoloured.

2739. 3 k. Weather cock, St. Vitus Cathedral.. .. 80 80
2740. 4 k. King David playing psaltery (initial from Roudnice Book of Psalms) .. .. .. 1·25 1·25

**783.** Jack of Spades (16th century).

**784.** Family and Industrial Complex.

**1984.** Playing Cards. Multicoloured.

2741. 50 h. Type **783** .. .. 25 10
2742. 1 k. Queen of Spades (17th century) .. .. .. 40 10
2743. 2 k. Nine of Hearts (18th century) .. .. .. 60 30
2744. 3 k. Jack of Clubs (18th century) .. .. .. 1·00 50
2745. 5 k. King of Hearts (19th century) .. .. .. 1·60 80

**1984.** 40th Anniv. of Slovak Uprising.

2746. **784.** 50 h. multicoloured 20 10

**785.** Soldiers with Banner.

**1984.** 40th Anniv. of Battle of Dukla Pass.

2747. **785.** 2 k. multicoloured .. 45 20

**786.** High Jumping.

**1984.** Olympic Games, Los Angeles. Mult.

2748. 1 k. Type **786** .. .. 30 15
2749. 2 k. Cycling .. .. 60 30
2750. 3 k. Rowing .. .. 80 60
2751. 5 k. Weightlifting .. .. 1·50 75

**1984.** Achievements of Socialist Construction (4th series). As T **754**. Multicoloured.

2753 1 k. Telephone handset and letters (Communications) .. 50 10
2754 2 k. Containers on railway trucks and river barge (Transport) .. .. 60 30
2755 3 k. Map of Transgas pipeline .. .. 80 45

**1984.** Art (18th series). As T **481**. Multicoloured.

2757. 1 k. "Milevsky River" (Karel Stehlik) .. .. 1·50 70
2758. 2 k. "Under the Trees" (Viktor Barvitius) .. 1·50 70
2759. 3 k. "Landscape with Flowers" (Zolo Palugyay) 1·50 70
2760. 4 k. Illustration of king from Vysehrad Codex .. 1·50 70
2761. 5 k. "Kokorin" (Antonin Manes) .. .. .. 1·50 70

**787.** Dove and Head of Girl.

**788.** Zapotocky.

**1984.** 45th Anniv. of International Students Day.

2762. **787.** 1 k. multicoloured .. 20 15

**1984.** Birth Centenary of Antonin Zapotocky (politician).

2763. **788.** 50 h. multicoloured 20 10

**789.** Bohumil Heinz (engraver) and Hands engraving.

**1984.** Stamp Day.

2764. **789.** 1 k. multicoloured .. 20 15

**1985.** Arms of Czech Towns (5th series). As T **740**. Multicoloured.

2765. 50 h. Kamyk nad Vltavou .. .. 20 10
2766. 50 h. Havirov .. .. 20 10
2767. 50 h. Trnava .. .. 20 10

**790.** "Art and Pleasure" (Jan Simota).

**792.** Helmet, Mail Shirt and Crossbow.

**791.** View of Trnava.

**1985.** Centenary of Prague University of Applied Arts.

2768. **790.** 3 k. multicoloured .. 65 35

**1985.** 350th Anniv. of Trnava University.

2769. **791.** 2 k. multicoloured .. 35 25

**1985.** Exhibits from Military Museum. Multicoloured.

2770 50 h. Type **792** .. .. 15 10
2771 1 k. Cross and star of Za vitezstvi order .. 30 15
2772 2 k. Avia B-534 airplane and "Soyuz 28" (horiz) 1·00 45

**795.** State Arms and Crowd.

**796.** State Arms and Soldiers with National Flag.

**1985.** 40th Anniv. of Kosice Reforms.

2775. **795.** 4 k. multicoloured .. 70 35

**1985.** 40th Anniv. of National Security Forces.

2776. **796.** 50 h. multicoloured 20 10

**798.** Emblem and Ice Hockey Players.

**1985.** World and European Ice Hockey Championships, Prague.

2778. **798.** 1 k. multicoloured .. 25 15

**799.** Pieces on Chessboard.

**1985.** 80th Anniv. of Czechoslovak Chess Organization.

2779. **799.** 6 k. multicoloured .. 2·40 80

**800.** Freedom Fighters and Prague.

**1985.** Anniversaries. Multicoloured.

2780. 1 k. Type **800** (40th anniv. of May uprising) .. .. 30 15
2781. 1 k. Workers shaking hands, flags and industrial motifs (15th anniv. of Czecho-slovak–Soviet Treaty) 30 15
2782. 1 k. Girl giving flowers to soldier, Prague Castle and tank (40th anniv. of liberation) .. .. 30 15
2783. 1 k. Soldiers and industrial motifs (30th anniv. of Warsaw Pact) .. .. .. 30 15

**1985.** Czechoslovak Victory in Ice Hockey Championships. No. 2778 optd. **CSSR MISTREM SVETA.**

2784. **798.** 1 k. multicoloured .. 5·50 5·50

**802.** Tennis.

**803.** Study for "Fire" and "Republic" (Josef Capek).

**1985.** National Spartakiad. Multicoloured.

2785. 50 h. Type **802** .. .. 20 10
2786. 1 k. Gymnasts performing with ribbons (48 × 19 mm.) .. .. 30 15

**1985.** Anti-fascist Artists. Multicoloured.

2787. 50 h. Type **803** .. .. 15 10
2788. 2 k. "Geneva Conference on Disarmament" and "Prophecy of Three Parrots" (Frantisek Bidlo) .. .. .. 45 25
2789. 4 k. "Unknown Conscript" and "The almost peaceful Dove" (Antonin Pelc) .. 65 40

**805.** Moscow Buildings and Young People holding Doves.

**1985.** 12th World Youth and Students' Festival, Moscow.

2791. **805.** 1 k. multicoloured .. 25 15

**806.** Figures on Globe.

**807.** Rocking Horse (Kveta Pacovska).

**1985.** 40th Anniv. of World Federation of Trade Unions.

2792. **806.** 50 h. multicoloured 10 10

**1985.** Historic Bratislava (9th series). As T **669**.

2793 3 k. light brown, green and brown .. .. 70 70
2794 4 k. black, green and red 1·00 1·00

Designs: 3 k. Tapestry (Elena Holeczyova). 4 k. Pottery.

**1985.** 10th Biennial Exhibition of Book Illustrations for Children, Bratislava. Mult.

2795 1 k. Type **807** .. .. 20 10
2796 2 k. Elves (Gennady Spirin) .. .. 35 15
2797 3 k. Girl, butterfly and flowers (Kaarina Kaila) 60 40
2798 4 k. Boy shaking hands with hedgehog (Erick Ingraham) .. .. 70 45

**1985.** Achievements of Socialist Construction (5th series). As T **754**. Multicoloured.

2800. 50 h. Mechanical excavator .. .. 10 10
2801. 1 k. Train and map of Prague underground railway .. .. 40 20
2802. 2 k. Modern textile spinning equipment .. 45 30

**808.** Gateway to First Courtyard.

**809.** Jug (4th century).

**1985.** Prague Castle (21st series).

2803 **808** 2 k. black, blue & red 50 50
2804 – 3 k. multicoloured .. 80 60

Design: 3 k. East side of Castle.

**1985.** Centenary of Prague Arts and Crafts Museum. Glassware. Multicoloured.

2805. 50 h. Type **809** .. .. 10 10
2806. 1 k. Venetian glass container (16th century).. 20 10
2807. 2 k. Bohemian glass with hunting scene (18th century) .. .. 40 25
2808. 4 k. Bohemian vase (18th century) .. .. 75 40
2809. 6 k. Bohemian vase (c. 1900) .. .. 1·40 75

**1985.** Art (19th series). As T **481**. Mult.

2810 1 k. "Young Woman in Blue Dress" (Josef Ginovsky) .. .. 1·75 90
2811 2 k. "Lenin on Charles Bridge" (Martin Sladky) .. .. 1·75 90
2812 3 k. "Avenue of Poplars" (Vaclav Rabas) .. 1·75 90
2813 4 k. "Beheading of St. Dorothea" (Hans Baldung Grien) .. 1·75 90
2814 5 k. "Jasper Schade van Westrum" (Frans Hals) 1·75 90

**810.** Bohdan Roule (engraver) and Engraving Plate.

**1985.** Stamp Day.

2815. **810.** 1 k. multicoloured .. 50 15

**811.** Peace Dove and Olive Twig.

**1986.** International Peace Year. Mult.

2816. **811.** 1 k. multicoloured .. 25 15

**812.** Victory Statue Prague.

**813.** Zlin Z-50LS Airplane, Locomotive "Kladno" and Rock Drawing of Chariot.

**1986.** 90th Anniv of Czech Philharmonic Orchestra.
2817. **812.** 1 k. black, brown and violet .. .. 25 15

**1986.** "Expo '86" International Transport and Communications Exhibition, Vancouver.
2818. **813.** 4 k. multicoloured .. 1·25 35

**1986.** Arms of Czech Towns (6th series). As T **740** Multicoloured.
2819. 50 h. Vodnany .. .. 15 10
2820. 50 h. Zamberk .. .. 15 10
2821. 50 h. Myjava .. .. 15 10

**814.** Banner, Industry and Hammer and Sickle.

**1986.** 17th Communist Party Congress, Prague. Multicoloured.
2822. 50 h. Type **814** .. .. 10 10
2823. 1 k. Buildings, hammer and sickle and star .. 20 10

**815.** Couple, Banner and Star.

**1986.** 65th Anniv. of Czechoslovakian Communist Party. Multicoloured.
2824. 50 h. Type **815** .. .. 10 10
2825. 1 k. Workers, banner and hammer and sickle .. 20 10

**816.** Map and Stylized Man.

**817.** Emblem and Crest on Film.

**1986.** National Front Election Programme.
2826. **816.** 50 h. multicoloured 10 10

**1986.** 25th International Film Festival, Karlovy Vary.
2827 **817** 1 k. multicoloured .. 25 10

**818.** Musical Instruments.

**819.** Ilyushin Il-86 and Airspeed Envoy II.

**1986.** 40th Anniv of Prague Spring Music Festival.
2828 **818** 1 k. multicoloured .. 25 10

**1986.** 50th Anniv of Prague–Moscow Air Service.
2829 **819** 50 h. multicoloured .. 25 10

**820.** Sports Pictograms.

**1986.** 90th Anniv. of Czechoslovak Olympic Committee.
2830. **820.** 2 k. multicoloured .. 40 20

**821.** Map and Goalkeeper.

**1986.** World Cup Football Championship, Mexico.
2831. **821.** 4 k. multicoloured .. 75 45

**822.** Globe, Net and Ball.

**1986.** Women's World Volleyball Championship, Prague.
2832. **822.** 1 k. multicoloured .. 30 15

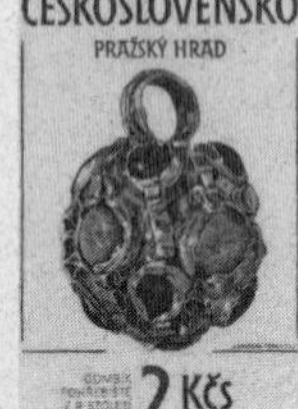
**824.** Funeral Pendant.

**825.** Wooden Cock, Slovakia.

**1986.** Prague Castle (22nd series).
2834. **824.** 2 k. multicoloured .. 55 45
2835. – 3 k. orge, brn. & bl. 65 55
DESIGN: 3 k. "Allegory of Blossoms" (sculpture, Jaroslav Horejc).

**1986.** 40th Anniv. of U.N.I.C.E.F. Toys. Multicoloured.
2836 10 h. Type **825** .. .. 10 10
2837 20 h. Wooden soldier on hobby horse, Bohemia 10 10
2838 1 k. Rag doll, Slovakia .. 15 10
2839 2 k. Doll .. .. .. 40 15
2840 3 k. Mechanical bus .. 55 20

**826.** Registration Label and Mail Coach.

**1986.** Centenary of Registration Label.
2841. **826.** 4 k. multicoloured .. 65 35

**1986.** Historic Bratislava (10th series). As T **669.**
2842. 3 k. black, red and blue 50 50
2843. 4 k. black, red and green 65 65
DESIGNS: 3 k. Sigismund Gate, Bratislava Castle. 4 k. "St. Margaret with a Lamb" (relief from Castle).

**827.** Eagle Owl.

**1986.** Owls. Multicoloured.
2844. 50 h. Type **827** .. .. 35 10
2845. 2 k. Long-eared owl .. 90 35
2846. 3 k. Tawny owl .. .. 1·25 45
2847. 4 k. Barn owl .. .. 1·60 60
2848. 5 k. Short-eared owl .. 3·00 70

**829.** Type "Kt8" Articulated Tram and 1920s' Prague Tram.

**1986.** Rail Vehicles. Multicoloured.
2850 50 h. Type **829** .. .. 15 10
2851 1 k. Series "E 458.1" electic shunting engine and 1882–1913 steam locomotives .. .. 25 15
2852 3 k. Series "T 466.2" diesel and steam locomotive 70 40
2853 5 k. Series "M 152.0" railcar and 1930–35 railbus .. .. 1·50 1·00

**830.** "The Circus Rider" (Jan Bauch).

**1986.** Circus and Variety Acts on Paintings. Multicoloured.
2854. 1 k. Type **830** .. .. 35 35
2855. 2 k. "The Ventriloquist" (Frantisek Tichy) .. 70 70
2856. 3 k. "In the Circus" (Vincent Hloznik) .. 80 80
2857. 6 k. "Clown" (Karel Svolinsky) .. .. 1·90 1·90

**1986.** Art (20th series). As T **481.** Mult.
2858 1 k. "The Czech Lion, May 1918" (Vratislav H. Brunner) .. .. 40 40
2859 2 k. "Boy with Mandolin" (Jozef Sturdik) .. 70 70
2860 3 k. "The Metra Building" (Frantisek Gross) 80 80
2861 4 k. "Maria Maximiliana of Sternberk" (Karel Skreta) .. .. 1·10 1·10
2862 5 k. "Adam and Eve" (Lucas Cranach) .. 1·75 1·75

**831.** Brunner and Stamps of 1920.

**1986.** Stamp Day. Birth Centenary of Vratislav Hugo Brunner (stamp designer).
2863 **831** 1 k. multicoloured .. 25 15

**832.** Bicyclists.

**1987.** World Cross-country Cycling Championships, Mlada Boleslav.
2864 **832** 6 k. multicoloured .. 90 50

**833.** Pins and Ball.

**834.** Gold Stars of Heroes of C.S.S.R. and of Socialist Labour.

**1987.** 50th Anniv of Czechoslovakian Bowling Federation.
2865 **833** 2 k. multicoloured .. 40 20

**1987.** State Orders and Medals.
2866. **834.** 50 h. red, blk. & gold 10 10
2867. – 2 k. multicoloured .. 30 20
2868. – 3 k. multicoloured .. 50 35
2869. – 4 k. multicoloured .. 65 50
2870. – 5 k. multicoloured .. 80 50
DESIGNS: 2 k. Order of Klement Gottwald. 3 k. Order of the Republic. 4 k. Order of Victorious February. 5 k. Order of Labour.

**835.** Poplar Admiral.

**1987.** Butterflies and Moths. Multicoloured.
2871 1 k. Type **835** .. .. 25 10
2872 2 k. Eyed hawk moth .. 55 25
2873 3 k. Large tiger moth .. 95 40
2874 4 k. Viennese emperor moth .. .. .. 1·25 50

**836.** Emblem.

**1987.** Nuclear Power Industry.
2875. **836.** 5 k. multicoloured .. 75 45

**837.** Emblem.

**839.** Stained Glass Window, St. Vitus's Cathedral (Frantisek Sequens).

**1987.** 11th Trades Union Congress, Prague.
2876. **837.** 1 k. multicoloured .. 15 10

**1987.** Prague Castle (23rd series). Mult.
2878. 2 k. Type **839** .. .. 40 35
2879. 3 k. Arms (mural), New Land Rolls Hall, Old Royal Palace .. .. 70 50
See also Nos. 2950/1 and 2977/8.

**840.** Telephone, 1894.

**1987.** "Praga 88" Int. Stamp Exhibition (1st issue). Technical Monuments. Mult.
2880 3 k. Type **840** .. .. 70 35
2881 3 k. Mail Van, 1924 .. 70 35
2882 4 k. Tank locomotive "Archduke Charles", 1907 .. .. .. 95 35
2883 4 k. Prague tram, 1900 .. 95 35
2884 5 k. Steam roller, 1936 .. 1·10 60
See also Nos. 2900, 2923/6, 2929/32 2934/7 and 2940/3.

**841.** "When the Fighting Ended" (Pavel Simon).

**843.** Chickens in Kitchen (Asun Balzola).

**842.** Prague Town Hall Clock and Theory of Functions Diagram.

**1987.** 45th Anniv. of Destruction of Lidice and Lezaky. Multicoloured.
2885. 1 k. Type **841** .. .. 15 10
2886. 1 k. "The End of the Game" (Ludmila Jirincova) .. .. 15 10

**1987.** 125th Anniv. of Union of Czech Mathematicians and Physicists. Multicoloured.
2887. 50 h. Type **842** .. .. 10 10
2888. 50 h. J. M. Petzval, C. Strouhal and V. Iarnik 10 10
2889. 50 h. Trajectory of Brownian motion and earth fold diagram .. 10 10

**1987.** 11th Biennial Exhibition of Book Illustrations for Children, Bratislava. Designs showing illustrations by artists named. Multicoloured.

2890 50 h. Type **843** .. .. 40 15
2891 1 k. Cranes with egg at railway points (Frederic Clement) .. .. 30 10
2892 2 k. Birds on nest (Elzbieta Gaudasinska) 40 25
2893 4 k. Couple looking over rooftops (Marija Lucija Stupica) .. .. 70 40

**844.** Barbed Wire, Flames and Menorah.

**845.** "OSS" and Communications Equipment.

**1987.** 40th Anniv of Terezin Memorial.
2895 **844** 50 h. multicoloured .. 10 10

**1987.** 30th Anniv. of Organization of Socialist Countries' Postal Administrations.
2896. **845.** 4 k. multicoloured .. 65 35

**846.** Purkyne and Microtome.

**1987.** Birth Bicentenary of Jan Evangelista Purkyne (physiologist)
2897 **846** 7 k. multicoloured .. 1·10 65

**1987.** Historic Bratislava (11th series). As T **669**.
2898. 3 k. buff, black and blue 50 50
2899. 4 k. black and brown .. 75 75
DESIGNS: 3 k. Detail of projecting window by Vyzdoby. 4 k. "View of Bratislava" (engraving, Hans Mayer).

**848.** Postilion.

**849.** Symbols of Industry, Lenin and Red Flag.

**1987.** "Praga '88" International Stamp Exhibition (2nd issue).
2900. **848.** 1 k. multicoloured .. 20 10

**1987.** 70th Anniv. of Russian Revolution (2901) and 65th Anniv. of USSR (2902). Multicoloured.
2901. 50 h. Type **849** .. 10 10
2902. 50 h. Hammer and sickle 10 10

**1987.** Art (21st series). As T **481**.
2904 1 k. multicoloured .. 25 25
2905 2 k. multicoloured .. 60 60
2906 3 k. multicoloured .. 80 80
2907 4 k. black, blue and red 1·00 1·00
2908 5 k. multicoloured .. 1·40 1·40
DESIGNS: 1 k. "Enclosure of Dreams" (Kamil Lhotak); 2 k. "Tulips" (Ester Simerova-Martincekova); 3 k. "Bohemian Landscape" (triptych, Josef Lada); 4 k. "Accordion Player" (Josef Capek); 5 k. "Self-portrait" (Jiri Trnka).

**850.** Obrovsky and Detail of 1919 Stamp.

**1987.** Stamp Day. 105th Birth Anniv. of Jakub Obrovsky (designer).
2909. **850.** 1 k. multicoloured .. 15 10

**851.** "Czechoslovakia", Linden Tree and Arms.

**1988.** 70th Anniv. of Czechoslovakia.
2910. **851.** 1 k. multicoloured .. 15 10

**1988.** 75th Birthday of President Husak.
2911 **759** 1 k. brown and red .. 15 10

**852.** Ski Jumping and Ice Hockey.

**1988.** Olympic Games, Calgary and Seoul. Multicoloured.
2912. 50 h. Type **852** .. .. 10 10
2913. 1 k. Basketball and football .. .. 15 10
2914. 6 k. Throwing the discus and weightlifting .. 75 40

**853.** Red Flags and Klement Gottwald Monument, Pecky.

**1988.** 40th Annivs. of "Victorious February" (2915) and National Front (2916). Mult.
2915. 50 h. Type **853** .. .. 10 10
2916. 50 h. Couple and detail of "Czech Constitution, 1961" (Vincent Hloznik) .. .. 10 10

**854.** Laurin and Klement Car, 1914.

**1988.** Historic Motor Cars. Multicoloured.
2918. 50 h. Type **854** .. .. 10 10
2919. 1 k. Tatra "NW" type B, 1902 .. .. 15 10
2920. 2 k. Tatra "NW" type E, 1905 .. .. 30 15
2921. 3 k. Tatra "12 Normandie", 1929 .. 45 20
2922. 4 k. "Meteor", 1899 .. 60 35

**855.** Praga Post Office and Velka Javorina T.V. Transmitter.

**1988.** "Praga '88" International Stamp Exhibition (3rd issue) and 70th Anniv of Postal Museum. Multicoloured.
2923 50 h. Type **855** .. .. 10 10
2924 1 k. Mlada Boleslav telecommunications centre and Carmelite Street post office, Prague .. 30 10
2925 2 k. Prague 1 and Bratislava 56 post offices .. 40 20
2926 4 k. Malta Square, Prague, and Prachatice post offices .. .. 80 40

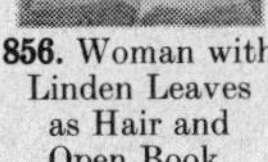


**856.** Woman with Linden Leaves as Hair and Open Book.

**857.** Strahov Monastery.

**1988.** 125th Anniv. of Slovak Cultural Society.
2928. **856.** 50 h. multicoloured 10 10

**1988.** "Praga '88" International Stamp Exhibition (4th issue). National Literature Memorial, Strahov Monastery. Mult.
2929. 1 k. Type **857** .. .. 15 10
2930. 2 k. Open book and celestial globe .. 35 15
2931. 5 k. Illuminated initial "B", scrolls and decorative binding .. 80 45
2932. 7 k. Astrological signs, Strahov, illuminated book and globe .. 1·25 95

**858.** Waldstein Garden Fountain.

**1988.** "Praga '88" International Stamp Exhibition (5th issue). Prague Fountains.
2934 **858** 1 k. black, lilac & blue 15 10
2935 – 2 k. multicoloured .. 35 15
2936 – 3 k. black, orge & lilac 55 25
2937 – 4 k. black, orge & grn 65 40
DESIGNS: 2 k. Old Town Square. 3 k. Charles University. 4 k. Courtyard, Prague Castle.

**860.** Trade Unions Central Recreation Centre.

**1988.** "Praga '88" Int. Stamp Exhibition (6th issue). Present-day Prague. Multicoloured.
2941 50 h. Type **860** .. .. 10 10
2942 1 k. Koospol foreign trade company .. .. 20 10
2943 2 k. Motol teaching hospital .. .. 35 15
2944 4 k. Palace of Culture .. 65 40

**1988.** Prague Castle (24th series). As T **839**. Multicoloured.
2950 2 k. 17th-century pottery jug .. .. .. 30 30
2951 3 k. "St. Catherine" (Paolo Veronese) .. 45 45

**1988.** Historic Bratislava (12th series). As T **669**. Multicoloured.
2952. 3 k. Hlavne Square (detail of print by R. Alt-Sandman) .. 40 40
2953. 4 k. Ferdinand House .. 50 50

**1988.** Art (22nd series). As T **481**.
2954 2 k. multicoloured .. 40 40
2955 6 k. brown, black & blue 1·00 1·00
2956 7 k. multicoloured .. 1·40 1·40
DESIGNS: 2 k. "Field Workers carrying Sacks" (Martin Benka); 6 k. "Woman watching Bird" (Vojtech Preissig); 7 k. "Leopard attacking Horseman" (Eugene Delacroix).

**865** Benda and Drawings

**1988.** Stamp Day. 106th Birth Anniv of Jaroslav Benda (stamp designer).
2957 **865** 1 k. multicoloured .. 15 10

**866** Emblem **867** Globe and Truck

**1989.** 20th Anniv of Czechoslovak Federal Socialist Republic.
2958 **866** 50 h. multicoloured .. 10 10

**1989.** Paris–Dakar Rally. Multicoloured.
2959 50 h. Type **867** .. .. 10 10
2960 1 k. Globe and view of desert on truck side .. 15 10
2961 2 k. Globe and truck (different) .. .. 30 15
2962 4 k. Route map, turban and truck .. .. 50 30

**868** Taras G. Shevchenko

**870** Dove and Pioneers

**869** 'Republika" (freighter)

**1989.** Birth Anniversaries.
2963 **868** 50 h. multicoloured .. 10 10
2964 – 50 h. multicoloured .. 10 10
2965 – 50 h. brown and green 10 10
2966 – 50 h. brown and green 10 10
2967 – 50 h. black, brown and deep brown .. 10 10
2968 – 50 h. multicoloured .. 10 10
DESIGNS: No. 2963, Type **868** (Ukrainian poet and painter, 175th anniv); 2964, Modest Petrovich Musorgsky (composer, 150th anniv); 2965, Jan Botto (poet, 160th anniv); 2966, Jawaharlal Nehru (Indian statesman, cent); 2967, Jean Cocteau (writer and painter, centenary); 2968, Charlie Chaplin (actor, centenary).

**1989.** Shipping.
2969 **869** 50 h. grey, red & blue 10 10
2970 – 1 k. multicoloured .. 15 10
2971 – 2 k. multicoloured .. 30 15
2972 – 3 k. grey, red & blue 50 20
2973 – 4 k. multicoloured .. 65 40
2974 – 5 k. multicoloured .. 75 45
DESIGNS: 1 k. "Pionyr" (trawler); 2 k. "Brno" (tanker); 3 k. "Trinec" (container ship); 4 k. "Orlik" (container ship); 5 k. "Vltava" (tanker) and communications equipment.

**1989.** 40th Anniv of Young Pioneer Organization.
2975 **870** 50 h. multicoloured .. 10 10

**1989.** Prague Castle (25th series). As T **839**.
2977 2 k. brown, yellow & red 20 20
2978 3 k. multicoloured .. 35 35
DESIGNS: 2 k. King Kard of Bohemia (relief by Alexandra Colin from Archduke Ferdinand I's mausoleum); 3 k. "Self-portrait" (V. V. Reiner).

**872** White-tailed Sea Eagle

**1989.** Endangered Species.
2980 **872** 1 k. multicoloured .. 40 15

**873** Fire-bellied Toads

**1989.** Endangered Amphibians. Mult.
2981 2 k. Type **873** .. .. 30 15
2982 3 k. Yellow-bellied toad 45 20
2983 4 k. Alpine newts .. 60 35
2984 5 k. Carpathian newts .. 70 40

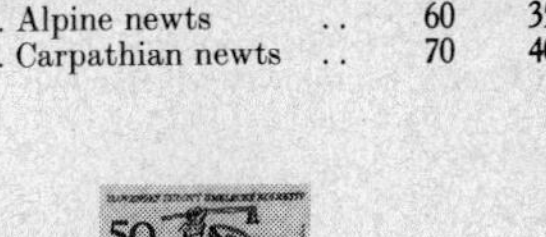

**874** Dancers

**1989.** 40th Anniv of Slovak Folk Art Collective.
2985 **874** 50 h. multicoloured .. 10 10

875 Horsemen and Mountains

**1989.** 45th Anniv of Slovak Rising.
2986 **875** 1 k. multicoloured .. 15 10

876 "Going Fishing" (Hannu Taina)

877 "Nolanea verna"

**1989.** 12th Biennial Exhibition of Book Illustrations for Children. Multicoloured.
2987 50 h. Type **876** .. .. 10 10
2988 1 k. "Donkey Rider" (Aleksandur Aleksov) 15 10
2989 2 k. "Animal Dreams" (Jurgen Spohn Zapadny) .. .. 30 15
2990 4 k. "Scarecrow" (Robert Brun) .. .. .. 55 35

**1989.** Poisonous Fungi.
2992 **877** 50 h. brown, deep brown and green .. 10 10
2993 – 1 k. multicoloured .. 25 10
2994 – 2 k. green and brown 45 20
2995 – 3 k. brown, yell & red 70 30
2996 – 5 k. multicoloured .. 1·00 55
DESIGNS: 1 k. Death cap; 2 k. Destroying angel; 3 k. "Cortinarius orellanus"; 5 k. "Galerina marginata".

**1989.** Historic Bratislava (13th series). As T **669**.
2997 3 k. multicoloured .. 30 30
2998 4 k. black, red and green 45 45
DESIGNS: 3 k. Devin Fortress and flower; 4 k. Devin Fortress and pitcher.

878 Jan Opletal (Nazi victim)

**1989.** 50th Anniv of International Students Day.
2999 **878** 1 k. multicoloured .. 15 10

**1989.** Art (24th series). As T **481**. Mult.
3000 2 k. "Nirvana" (Anton Jasusch) .. .. 25 25
3001 4 k. "Dusk in the Town" (Jakub Schikaneder) (horiz) .. .. 50 50
3002 5 k. "Bakers" (Pravoslav Kotik) (horiz) .. 60 60

879 Peregrine Falcon Stamp, Pens and Bouda

**1989.** Stamp Day. 5th Death Anniv of Cyril Bouda (stamp designer).
3003 **879** 1 k. brown, yell & red 40 15

880 Practising Alphabet

881 Tomas Masaryk (first President)

**1990.** International Literacy Year.
3004 **880** 1 k. multicoloured .. 15 10

**1990.** Birth Anniversaries. Multicoloured.
3005 50 h. Type **881** (140th anniv) .. .. 10 10
3006 50 h. Karel Capek (writer, centenary) .. .. 10 10
3007 1 k. Vladimir Ilyich Lenin (120th anniv) .. .. 15 10
3008 2 k. Emile Zola (novelist, 150th anniv) .. .. 30 15
3009 3 k. Jaroslav Heyrovsky (chemist, centenary) .. 35 20
3010 10 k. Bohuslav Martinu (composer, centenary) 1·25 85

882 Pres. Vaclav Havel

883 Players

**1990.**
3011 **882** 50 h. ultram, bl & red 10 10

**1990.** Men's World Handball Championship.
3012 **883** 50 h. multicoloured .. 10 10

884 Snapdragon

885 Pope John Paul II

**1990.** Flowers. Multicoloured.
3013 50 h. Type **884** .. .. 10 10
3014 1 k. "Zinnia elegans" .. 15 10
3015 3 k. Tiger flower .. 35 20
3016 5 k. Madonna lily .. 60 50

**1990.** Arms of Czech Towns (7th series). As T **740**. Multicoloured.
3017 50 h. Bytca .. .. 10 10
3018 50 h. Podebrady .. 10 10
3019 50 h. Sobeslav .. .. 10 10
3020 50 h. Prostejov .. .. 10 10

**1990.** Papal Visit.
3021 **885** 1 k. brown, yell & red 15 10

886 Woman holding Flags

888 Footballers

**1990.** 45th Anniv of Liberation.
3022 **886** 1 k. multicoloured .. 15 10

**1990.** World Cup Football Championship, Italy.
3024 **888** 1 k. multicoloured .. 15 10

889 Victory Signs

**1990.** Free General Election.
3025 **889** 1 k. multicoloured .. 15 10

**1990.** Prague Castle (26th series). As T **824**.
3026 2 k. multicoloured .. 20 20
3027 3 k. green, dp green & red 35 35
DESIGNS: 2 k. Jewelled glove (from reliquary of St. George); 3 k. Seal of King Premsyl Otakar II of Bohemia.

890 Map of Europe and Branch

**1990.** 15th Anniv of European Security and Co-operation Conference, Helsinki.
3028 **890** 7 k. multicoloured .. 80 50

891 Milada Horakova

**1990.** 40th Anniv of Execution of Milada Horakova.
3029 **891** 1 k. multicoloured .. 15 10

892 Poodles

**1990.** "Inter Canis" Dog Show, Brno. Mult.
3030 50 h. Type **892** .. .. 10 10
3031 1 k. Afghan hound, Irish wolfhound and grey-hound .. .. .. 15 10
3032 4 k. Czech terrier, blood-hound and Hanoverian bearhound .. .. 50 35
3033 7 k. Cavalier King Charles, cocker and American cocker spaniels .. .. 80 60

**1990.** Historic Bratislava (14th series). As T **669**. Multicoloured.
3034 3 k. black and red .. 35 35
3035 4 k. multicoloured .. 50 50
DESIGNS: 3 k. Coin; 4 k. "M. R. Stefanik" (J. Mudroch).

893 Horses jumping

**1990.** Cent of Pardubice Steeplechase. Mult.
3036 50 h. Type **893** .. .. 10 10
3037 4 k. Horses galloping .. 45 35

894 Alpine Marmot

**1990.** Mammals. Multicoloured.
3038 50 h. Type **894** .. .. 10 10
3039 1 k. European wild cat .. 10 10
3040 4 k. Eurasian beaver .. 40 35
3041 5 k. Common long-eared bat .. .. .. 50 40

895 European Flag

896 Snow-covered Church

**1990.** Helsinki Pact Civic Gathering, Prague.
3042 **895** 3 k. blue, yell & gold 30 20

**1990.** Christmas.
3043 **896** 50 h. multicoloured .. 10 10

**1990.** Art (25th series). As T **481**. Mult.
3044 2 k. multicoloured .. 20 20
3045 3 k. black, brown & blue 30 30
3046 4 k. multicoloured .. 40 40
3047 5 k. multicoloured .. 50 50
DESIGNS—HORIZ. 2 k. "Krucemburk" (Jan Zrzavy). VERT. 3 k. "St. Agnes" (detail of sculpture, Josef Vaclav Myslbek); 4 k. "Slovene in his Homeland" (detail, Alfons Mucha); 5 k. "St. John the Baptist" (detail of sculpture, Auguste Rodin).

897 Karel Svolinsky (stamp designer) and "Czechoslovakia"

**1990.** Stamp Day.
3048 **897** 1 k. purple, lilac & bl 10 10

898 Judo Throw

899 Svojsik

**1991.** European Judo Championships, Prague.
3049 **898** 1 k. multicoloured .. 10 10

**1991.** 80th Anniv of Czechoslovak Scout Movement and 115th Birth Anniv of A. B. Svojsik (founder).
3050 **899** 3 k. multicoloured .. 30 20

900 Jan Hus preaching

901 Alois Senefelder

**1991.** Anniversaries.
3051 **900** 50 h. brn, stone & red 10 10
3052 – 1 k. multicoloured .. 10 10
3053 – 5 k. multicoloured .. 50 40
DESIGNS AND EVENTS: 50 h. Type **900** (600th anniv of Bethlehem Chapel, Prague). 40×23 mm: 1 k. Estates Theatre, Prague (re-opening) and Mozart (death bicent). 49×20 mm: 5 k. Paddle-steamer "Bohemia" (150th anniv of boat excursions in Bohemia).

**1991.** Birth Anniversaries.
3054 **901** 1 k. green, brn & red 10 10
3055 – 1 k. black, grn & red 10 10
3056 – 1 k. blue, mve & red 10 10
3057 – 1 k. violet, blue & red 10 10
3058 – 1 k. brown, orge & red 10 10
DESIGNS: No. 3054, Type **901** (inventor of lithography, 220th anniv); 3055, Andrej Kmet (naturalist, 150th anniv); 3056, Jan Masaryk (politician, 105th anniv); 3057, Jaroslav Seifert (composer, 90th anniv); 3058, Antonin Dvorak (composer, 150th anniv).

902 "Magion II" Satellite and Earth

903 Exhibition Pavilion, 1891

**1991.** Europa. Europe in Space.
3059 **902** 6 k. blue, black & red 60 45

**1991.** Cent of International Exn., Prague.
3060 **903** 1 k. blue, grey & mve 10 10

**HAVE YOU READ THE NOTES AT THE BEGINNING OF THIS CATALOGUE?**
These often provide answers to the enquiries we receive.

**904** Chinstrap Penguins, Map and Flag

**1991.** 30th Anniv of Antarctic Treaty.
3061 **904** 8 k. multicoloured .. 75 55

**905** Blatna Castle **906** Jan Palach

**1991.** Castles. Multicoloured.
3062 50 h. Type **905** .. .. 10 10
3063 1 k. Bouzov .. .. 10 10
3064 3 k. Kezmarok .. .. 30 20

**1991** Jan Palach Scholarship.
3065 **906** 4 k. black .. .. 30 25

**907** Rip **908** "The Frog King" (Binette Schroeder)

**1991.** Beauty Spots.
3066 **907** 4 k. red, blue & yellow 30 25
3067 – 4 k. purple, grn & blk 30 25
DESIGN: No. 3067, Krivan.

**1991.** 13th Biennial Exhibition of Book Illustrations for Children. Multicoloured.
3068 1 k. Type **908** .. .. 10 10
3069 2 k. "Pinocchio" (Stasys Eidrigevicius) .. .. 20 15

**909** Hlinka **910** "Prague Jesus Child" (Maria-Victoria Church)

**1991.** 53rd Death Anniv of Father Andrej Hlinka (Slovak nationalist).
3070 **909** 10 k. black .. 1·00 75

**1991.** Prague and Bratislava. Multicoloured.
3071 3 k. Type **910** .. .. 25 25
3072 3 k. St. Elisabeth's Church, Bratislava .. 25 25

**911** "Gagea bohemica" **912** Boys in Costume

**1991.** Nature Protection. Flowers. Mult.
3073 1 k. Type **911** .. .. 10 10
3074 2 k. "Aster alpinus" .. 20 15
3075 5 k. "Fritillaria meleagris" .. .. 50 40
3076 11 k. "Daphne cneorum" 1·00 75

**1991.** Art (26th series). As T **481**. Mult.
3077 2 k. "Family at Home" (Max Ernst) .. .. 20 20
3078 3 k. "Milenci" (Auguste Renoir) .. .. 30 30
3079 4 k. "Christ" (El Greco) 40 40
3080 5 k. "Coincidence" (Ladislav Guderna) .. 50 50
3081 7 k. "Two Japanese Women" (Utamaro) .. 70 70

**1991.** Christmas.
3082 **912** 50 h. multicoloured .. 10 10

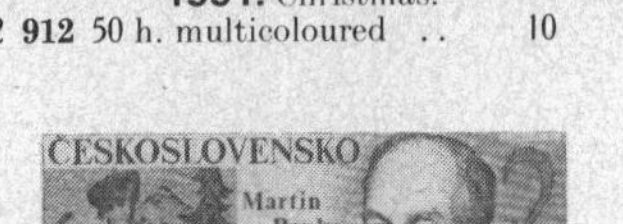

**913** Martin Benka (stamp designer) and Slovakian 1939 Stamp

**1991.** Stamp Day.
3083 **913** 2 k. red, black & orge 20 15

**914** Biathlon **916** Player

**1992.** Winter Olympic Games, Albertville.
3084 **914** 1 k. multicoloured .. 10 10

**1992.** World Ice Hockey Championship, Prague and Bratislava.
3086 **916** 3 k. multicoloured .. 25 20

**917** Traffic Lights

**1992.** Road Safety Campaign.
3087 **917** 2 k. multicoloured .. 20 15

**918** Tower, Seville Cathedral

**1992.** "Expo '92" World's Fair, Seville.
3088 **918** 4 k. multicoloured .. 30 25

**919** Amerindian, "Santa Maria" and Columbus

**1992.** Europa. 500th Anniv of Discovery of America by Columbus.
3089 **919** 22 k. multicoloured .. 1·50 1·10

**920** J. Kubis and J. Gabcik

**1992.** Free Czechoslovak Forces in World War II. Multicoloured.
3090 1 k. Type **920** (50th anniv of assassination of Reinhard Heydrich) .. 10 10
3091 2 k. Spitfires (air battles over England, 1939–45) 20 15
3092 3 k. Barbed wire and soldier (Tobruk, 1941) 25 20
3093 6 k. Soldiers (Dunkirk, 1944–45) .. .. 50 40

**921** Tennis Player **922** Nurse's Hats and Red Cross

**1992.** Olympic Games, Barcelona.
3094 **921** 2 k. multicoloured .. 20 15

**1992.** Red Cross.
3095 **922** 2 k. multicoloured .. 20 15

**923** Player **924** Crawling Cockchafer

**1992.** European Junior Table Tennis Championships, Topolcany.
3096 **923** 1 k. multicoloured .. 10 10

**1992.** Beetles. Multicoloured.
3097 1 k. Type **924** .. .. 10 10
3098 2 k. "Ergates faber" .. 20 15
3099 3 k. "Meloe violaceus" .. 25 20
3100 4 k. "Dytiscus latissimus" 30 25

**925** Troja Castle **926** Double Head and Posthorns

**1992.**
3101 **925** 6 k. multicoloured .. 50 40
3102 – 7 k. black and lilac .. 60 45
3103 – 8 k. multicoloured .. 70 55
DESIGNS—VERT. 7 k. "St. Martin" (sculpture, G. R. Donner), Bratislava Cathedral. HORIZ. 8 k. Lednice Castle.

**1992.** Post Bank.
3104 **926** 20 k. multicoloured .. 1·50 1·00

**927** Anton Bernolak and Georgius Fandly

**1992.** Bicentenary of Slovak Education Ass.
3105 **927** 5 k. multicoloured .. 40 30

**928** Cesky Krumlov **929** Organ

**1992.**
3106 **928** 3 k. brown and red .. 25 20

**1992.** Art (27th series). As T **481**.
3107 6 k. black and brown .. 50 40
3108 7 k. multicoloured .. 60 45
3109 8 k. multicoloured .. 70 55
DESIGNS—VERT. 6 k. "The Old Raftsman" (Koloman Sokol); 8 k. "Abandonned" (Toyen). HORIZ. 7 k. "Still Life with Grapes" (Georges Braque).

**1992.** Christmas.
3110 **929** 2 k. multicoloured .. 20 15

**930** Jindra Schmidt (engraver)

**1992.** Stamp Day.
3111 **930** 2 k. multicoloured .. 20 15

NEWSPAPER STAMPS

N 4. N **67.** Dove. N **94.** Messenger.

**1918.** Imperf.
N 24. N **4.** 2 h. green .. .. 10 10
N 25. 5 h. green .. .. 10 10
N 26. 6 h. red .. .. 20 20
N 27. 10 h. lilac .. .. 10 10
N 28. 20 h. blue .. .. 10 10
N 29. 30 h. brown .. .. 15 10
N 30. 50 h. orange .. 15 10
N 31. 100 h. brown .. 50 10

**1925.** Surch. with new value and stars.
N 249. N **4.** 5 on 2 h. green .. 50 50
N 250. 5 on 6 h. red .. 20 75

**1926.** Newspaper Express stamps optd **NOVINY** or surch also.
N 251. E **4.** 5 h. on 2 h. purple on yellow .. .. 10 10
N 253. 5 h. green on yellow 20 20
N 254. 10 h. brown on yellow 10 15

**1934.** Optd. **O.T.**
N 332. N **4.** 10 h. lilac .. .. 10 10
N 333. 20 h. blue .. .. 10 10
N 334. 30 h. brown .. 15 15

**1937.** Imperf.
N 364. N **67.** 2 h. brown .. .. 10 10
N 365. 5 h. blue .. .. 10 10
N 366. 7 h. orange .. 10 10
N 367. 9 h. green .. .. 10 10
N 368. 10 h. lake .. .. 10 10
N 369. 12 h. blue .. .. 10 10
N 370. 20 h. green .. 10 10
N 371. 50 h. brown .. 10 10
N 372. 1 k. olive .. .. 10 10

**1946.** Imperf.
N 467. N **94.** 5 h. blue .. .. 10 10
N 468. 10 h. red .. .. 10 10
N 469. 15 h. green .. 10 10
N 470. 20 h. green .. 10 10
N 471. 25 h. purple .. 15 15
N 472. 30 h. brown .. 10 10
N 473. 40 h. red .. .. 10 10
N 474. 50 h. brown .. 10 10
N 475. 1 k. grey .. .. 10 10
N 476. 5 k. blue .. .. 15 15

EXPRESS NEWSPAPER STAMPS

E **4.**

**1918.** Imperf. On yellow or white paper.
E 24. E **4.** 2 h. purple .. .. 10 10
E 25. 5 h. green .. .. 10 10
E 26. 10 h. brown .. .. 50 50

OFFICIAL STAMPS

O **92.** O **103.**

**1945.**
O 463. O **92.** 50 h. green .. 10 10
O 464. 1 k. blue .. .. 10 10
O 465. 1 k. 20 purple .. 15 15
O 466. 1 k. 50 red .. .. 10 10
O 467. 2 k. 50 blue .. 15 15
O 468. 5 k. purple .. 25 25
O 469. 8 k. red .. .. 40 40

**1947.**
O 490. O **103.** 60 h. red .. .. 10 10
O 491. 80 h. olive .. 10 10
O 492. 1 k. blue .. .. 10 10
O 493. 1 k. 20 purple .. 10 10
O 494. 2 k. 40 red .. .. 10 10
O 495. 4 k. blue .. .. 15 15
O 496. 5 k. purple .. 15 15
O 497. 7 k. 40 violet .. 25 25

PERSONAL DELIVERY STAMPS

P **66.**

**1937.** For Prepayment. "V" in each corner.
P 363. P **66.** 50 h. blue .. .. 20 45

**1937.** For Payment on Delivery. "D" in each corner.
P 364. P **66.** 50 h. red .. .. 20 45

P 95.

**1946.**
P 469. P 95. 2 k. blue .. .. 20 20

POSTAGE DUE STAMPS

D 4.

**1919.** Imperf.
D 24. D 4. 5 h. olive .. .. 10 10
D 25. 10 h. olive .. .. 10 10
D 26. 15 h. olive .. .. 10 10
D 27. 20 h. olive .. .. 15 10
D 28. 25 h. olive .. .. 20 15
D 29. 30 h. olive .. .. 40 10
D 30. 40 h. olive .. .. 40 25
D 31. 50 h. olive .. .. 40 10
D 32. 100 h. brown .. 1·50 15
D 33. 250 h. orange .. 5·50 1·00
D 34. 400 h. red .. .. 7·00 1·00
D 35. 500 h. green .. 3·00 20
D 36. 1000 h. violet .. 4·00 40
D 37. 2000 h. blue .. 15·00 90

**1922** Postage Stamps surch **DOPLATIT** and new value. Imperf or perf.
D 229 2 10 on 3 h. mauve .. 10 10
D 224a 20 on 3 h. mauve .. 10 10
D 230 30 on 3 h. mauve .. 10 10
D 257 3 30 on 15 h. red .. 35 15
D 231 2 40 on 3 h. mauve .. 10 10
D 258 3 40 on 15 h. red .. 30 15
D 225 50 on 75 h. green .. 25 20
D 262 60 on 50 h. purple .. 3·00 1·25
D 263 60 on 50 h. blue .. 3·25 1·50
D 232 60 on 75 h. green .. 40 10
D 226 60 on 80 h. green .. 20 10
D 227 100 on 80 h. green .. 30 10
D 233 100 on 120 h. black 70 10
D 264 2 100 on 400 h. violet 40 10
D 265 3 100 on 1000 h. purple 85 25
D 228 2 200 on 400 h. violet 50 15

**1924.** Postage Due stamp surch.
D 249. D 4. 10 on 5 h. olive .. 10 10
D 250. 20 on 5 h. olive .. 10 10
D 251. 30 on 15 h. olive 10 10
D 252. 40 on 15 h. olive 15 10
D 253. 50 on 250 h. orange 70 10
D 234. 50 on 400 h. red .. 50 10
D 254. 60 on 250 h. orange 1·00 20
D 235. 60 on 400 h. red .. 1·75 45
D 255. 100 on 250 h. orange 1·25 15
D 236. 100 on 400 h. red .. 1·25 20
D 256. 200 on 500 h. green 3·00 1·75

**1926.** Postage stamps optd. **DOPLATIT** or surch. also.
D 266. 13. 30 on 100 h. green .. 10 10
D 279. 11. 40 on 185 h. orange 10 10
D 267. 13. 40 on 200 h. purple 15 10
D 268. 40 on 300 h. red .. 1·00 25
D 280. 11. 50 on 20 h. red .. 15 10
D 281. 50 on 150 h. red .. 20 10
D 269. 13. 50 on 500 h. green .. 50 10
D 282. 11. 60 on 25 h. brown .. 20 20
D 283. 60 on 185 h. orange 15 10
D 270. 13. 60 on 400 h. brown.. 40 10
D 278. 11. 100 h. brown .. 35 10
D 284. 100 on 25 h. brown 30 10
D 271. 13. 100 on 600 h. purple 2·00 25

D 34.

D 94.

**1928.**
D 285. D34. 5 h. red .. .. 10 10
D 286. 10 h. red .. .. 10 10
D 287. 20 h. red .. .. 10 10
D 288. 30 h. red .. .. 10 10
D 289. 40 h. red .. .. 10 10
D 290. 50 h. red .. .. 10 10
D 291. 60 h. red .. .. 10 10
D 292. 1 k. blue .. .. 15 10
D 293. 2 k. blue .. .. 30 10
D 294. 5 k. blue .. .. 60 10
D 295. 10 k. blue .. .. 1·25 10
D 296. 20 k. blue .. .. 2·50 10

**1946.**
D 467. D 94. 10 h. blue .. .. 10 10
D 468. 20 h. blue .. .. 10 10
D 469. 50 h. blue .. .. 15 10
D 470. 1 k. red .. .. 30 10
D 471. 1 k. 20 red .. .. 35 10
D 472. 1 k. 50 red .. .. 40 10
D 473. 1 k. 60 red .. .. 45 10
D 474. 2 k. red .. .. 55 10
D 475. 2 k. 40 red .. .. 60 10
D 476. 3 k. red .. .. 75 10
D 477. 5 k. red .. .. 1·40 10
D 478. 6 k. red .. .. 1·75 10

D 257.

D 258.

**1954.**
D 845 D 257 5 h. green .. 10 10
D 846 10 h. green .. 10 10
D 860 30 h. green .. 10 10
D 861 50 h. green .. 15 10
D 849 60 h. green .. 15 10
D 850 95 h. green .. 35 10
D 863 D 258 1 k. violet .. 25 10
D 864 1 k. 20 violet .. 30 10
D 865 1 k. 50 violet .. 45 10
D 854 1 k. 60 violet .. 40 10
D 855 2 k. violet .. 75 10
D 866 3 k. violet .. 75 20
D 867 5 k. violet .. 1·25 30

D 572. Stylized Plant.

**1971.**
D 1985. – 10 h. pink and blue 10 10
D 1986. – 20 h. blue & purple 10 10
D 1987. – 30 h. pink & green 10 10
D 1988. – 60 h. green & pur. 15 10
D 1989. – 80 h. blue & orange 20 10
D 1990. – 1 k. green & red .. 25 10
D 1991. – 1 k. 20 orange & grn. 30 10
D 1992. – 2 k. red and blue .. 55 10
D 1993. – 3 k. yellow & black 85 10
D 1994. – 4 k. blue & brown 1·10 15
D 1995. D572. 5 k. 40 lilac and red 1·40 20
D 1996. – 6 k. yellow and red 1·60 25
DESIGNS: Various stylized plants as Type D 572.

## CZECH REPUBLIC Pt. 5

Formerly part of Czechoslovakia, a federation dissolved on 31 December 1992 when the constituent republics became separate states.

100 haleru = 1 koruna

1 State Arms

**1993.**
1 1 3 k. multicoloured .. 15 10

2 Skater's Boots and Tulip

3 Pres. Vaclav Havel

**1993.** Ice Skating Championships, Prague.
2 2 2 k. multicoloured .. 10 10

**1993.**
3 3 2 k. purple, blue & mauve 10 10
3a 3 k. 60 violet, mauve & bl 20 15

4 St. John and Charles Bridge, Prague

**1993.** 600th Death Anniv of St. John of Nepomuk (patron saint of Bohemia).
4 4 8 k. multicoloured .. 60 50

5 "Hladovy Svaty I" (Mikulas Medek)

**1993.** Europa. Contemporary Art.
5 5 14 k. multicoloured .. 1·40 1·40

6 Church of Sacred Heart, Prague

**1993.**
6 6 5 k. multicoloured .. 40 40
See also No. 45.

7 Brevnov Monastery

**1993.** U.N.E.S.C.O. World Heritage Site. Millenary of Brevnov Monastery, Prague.
7 7 4 k. multicoloured .. 30 15

8 Weightlifter

9 Town Hall Tower and Cathedral of St. Peter and St. Paul

**1993.** Junior Weightlifting Championships, Cheb.
8 8 6 k. multicoloured .. 40 25

**1993.** 750th Anniv of Brno.
9 9 8 k. multicoloured .. 60 35

10 Sts. Cyril and Methodius

12 Ceske Budejovice

**1993.** 1130th Anniv of Arrival of Sts. Cyril and Methodius in Moravia.
10 10 8 k. multicoloured .. 60 35

**1993.** Towns.
12 12 1 k. brown and red .. 10 10
13 – 2 k. red and blue .. 10 10
14 – 3 k. blue and red .. 15 10
15 – 3 k. blue and red .. 15 10
16 – 5 k. green and brown .. 25 20
17 – 6 k. green and yellow .. 25 20
18 – 7 k. brown and green .. 30 20
20 – 8 k. violet and yellow .. 40 30
21 – 10 k. green and red .. 55 35
23 – 20 k. red and blue .. 1·10 70
26 – 50 k. brown and green .. 2·50 1·60
DESIGNS—VERT: 2 k. Usti nad Labem; 3 k. (15) Brno; 5 k. Pilsen; 6 k. Slanyi; 7 k. Antonin Dvorak Theatre, Ostrava; 8 k. Olomouc; 10 k. Hradec Kralove; 20 k. Prague; 50 k. Opava. HORIZ: 3 k. (14) Cesky Krumlov (U.N.E.S.C.O. World Heritage Site).

13 Rower

14 August Sedlacek (historian, 150th anniv)

**1993.** World Rowing Championships, Racice.
27 13 3 k. multicoloured .. 15 10

**1993.** Birth Anniversaries.
28 14 2 k. buff, blue and green 10 10
29 – 3 k. buff, blue and violet 15 10
DESIGN: 3 k. Eduard Cech (mathematician, centenary).

15 Pedunculate Oak

17 St. Nicholas

16 "Composition" (Joan Miro)

**1993.** Trees. Multicoloured.
30 5 k. Type **15** .. .. 25 10
31 7 k. Hornbeam .. .. 35 25
32 9 k. Scots pine .. .. 50 35

**1993.** Art (1st series). Multicoloured.
33 11 k. Type **16** .. .. 75 75
34 14 k. "Green Corn Field with Cypress" (Vincent van Gogh) .. .. 95 95
See also Nos. 62/4, 116/18 and 140/2.

**1993.** Christmas.
35 17 2 k. multicoloured .. 10 10

18 "Strahov Madonna"

**1993.** Christmas.
36 18 9 k. multicoloured .. 60 60

19 "Family" (C. Littasy-Rollier)

20 Kubelik

**1994.** International Year of the Family.
37 19 2 k. multicoloured .. 10 10

**1994.** 54th Death Anniv of Jan Kublik (composer and violinist).
38 20 3 k. yellow and black .. 15 10

21 Voltaire (writer, 300th anniv)

**1994.** Birth Anniversaries.
39 **21** 2 k. purple, grey & mve 10 10
40 – 6 k. black, blue and green 30 20
DESIGN: 6 k. Georg Agricola (mineralogist, 500th anniv).

**22** Athletes **23** Marco Polo and Fantasy Animal

**1994.** Winter Olympic Games, Lillehammer, Norway.
41 **22** 5 k. multicoloured .. 25 20

**1994.** Europa. Discoveries. Marco Polo's Journeys to the Orient. Multicoloured.
42 14 k. Type **23** .. .. 75 75
43 14 k. Marco Polo and woman on fantasy animals .. .. .. 75 75

**24** Benes **26** Crayon Figures

**25** Cubist Flats by Josef Chochol, Prague

**1994.** 110th Birth Anniv of Edvard Benes (President of Czechoslovakia 1935–38 and 1945–48).
44 **24** 5 k. violet and purple .. 25 20

**1994.** U.N.E.S.C.O. World Heritage Sites. Multicoloured.
45 8 k. Market place, Telc .. 40 40
46 9 k. Type **25** .. .. 50 50
No. 45 is similar to Type **6**.

**1994.** For Children.
47 **26** 2 k. multicoloured .. 10 10

**27** "Stegosaurus ungulatus"

**1994.** Prehistoric Animals. Multicoloured.
48 2 k. Type **27** .. .. 10 10
49 3 k. "Apatosaurus excelsus" 15 10
50 5 k. "Tarbosaurus bataar" (vert) .. .. .. 25 10

**28** Statue of Liberty holding Football **29** Flag of Prague Section

**1994.** World Cup Football Championship, U.S.A.
51 **28** 8 k. multicoloured .. 35 35

**1994.** 12th Sokol (sports organization) Congress, Prague.
52 **29** 2 k. multicoloured .. 10 10

**30** Olympic Flag and Flame **31** Stylized Carrier Pigeons

**1994.** Cent of Int Olympic Committee.
53 **30** 7 k. multicoloured .. 30 20

**1994.** 120th Anniv of Universal Postal Union.
54 **31** 11 k. multicoloured .. 50 50

**32** Stonechat **33** NW, 1900

**1994.** Birds. Multicoloured.
55 3 k. Type **32** .. .. 15 10
56 5 k. Common rosefinch .. 25 10
57 14 k. Bluethroat .. 65 45

**1994.** Racing Cars. Multicoloured.
58 2 k. Type **33** .. .. 10 10
59 3 k. L & K, 1908 .. .. 15 10
60 9 k. Praga, 1912 .. .. 40 30

**34** Angel **35** Emblem

**1994.** Christmas.
61 **34** 2 k. multicoloured .. 10 10

**1994.** Art (2nd series). As T **16**.
62 7 k. black and buff .. 30 30
63 10 k. multicoloured .. 45 45
64 14 k. multicoloured .. 60 60
DESIGNS—VERT: 7 k. "The Old Man and the Woman" (Lucas van Leyden); 10 k. "Moulin Rouge" (Henri de Toulouse-Lautrec); 14 k. "Madonna of St. Vitus".

**1995.** 20th Anniv of World Tourism Organization.
65 **35** 8 k. blue and red .. 40 30

**36** E.U. and Czech Republic Flags **37** Engraver's Transposition of 1918 Czechoslovakia 2 h. Newspaper Stamp

**1995.** Association Agreement with European Union.
66 **36** 8 k. multicoloured .. 40 30

**1995.** Czech Stamp Production.
67 **37** 3 k. blue, grey and red .. 15 10

**38** Johannes Marcus Marci **39** Jiri Voskovec (actor and dramatist)

**1995.** Birth Anniversaries.
68 **38** 2 k. sepia, stone & brown 10 10
69 – 5 k. multicoloured .. 25 20
70 – 7 k. purple, grey & mve 35 25
DESIGNS: 2 k. Type **38** (academic, 400th anniv); 5 k. Ferdinand Peroutka (journalist and dramatist, centenary); 7 k. Premysl Pitter (founder of Youth Care Centre, centenary).

**1995.** 90th Birth Anniversaries of Members of the Liberated Theatre, Prague. Caricatures from posters by Adolf Hoffmeister.
71 **39** 3 k. black, yellow & orge 15 10
72 – 3 k. black, yellow & green 15 10
73 – 3 k. black, yellow & blue 15 10
DESIGNS: No. 72, Jan Werich (dramatist and actor); 73, Jaroslav Jezek (composer) (anniv 1996).

**40** Church and Buildings **41** Buff-tailed Bumble Bee

**1995.** Townscapes.
75 **40** 40 h. brown and pink .. 10 10
76 – 60 h. brown and stone .. 10 10
DESIGN: 60 h. Buildings, church and archway.

**1995.** European Nature Conservation Year. Endangered Insects. Multicoloured.
84 3 k. Type **41** .. .. 15 10
85 5 k. Praying mantis .. 25 20
86 6 k. Banded agrion .. 30 20

**42** Sandstone Arch, Labske Piskovce

**1995.** Rock Formations. Multicoloured.
87 8 k. Stone Organ (basalt columns), Central Bohemia .. .. 40 40
88 9 k. Type **42** .. .. 45 45

**43** Rose and Women's Profiles

**1995.** Europa. Peace and Freedom. Mult.
89 9 k. Type **43** .. .. 45 30
90 14 k. Butterfly, girl and profiles of ageing woman 70 50

**44** Cat

**1995.** For Children.
91 **44** 3 k. 60 multicoloured .. 20 15

**45** Train leaving Chocen Tunnel

**1995.** 150th Anniv of Olomouc–Prague Railway.
92 **45** 3 k. black, brown & blue 15 10
93 – 9 k. 60 black, brn & red 45 30
DESIGN: 9 k. 60, Crowd welcoming arrival of first train at Prague.

**46** Wrestlers **47** Violinist and Washerwoman (Vladimir Rencin)

**1995.** World Greco-Roman Wrestling Championship, Prague.
94 **46** 3 k. brown, stone and red 15 10

**1995.** Cartoons. Cartoons by named artists. Multicoloured.
95 3 k. Type **47** .. .. 15 10
96 3 k. 60 Angel and naked man (Vladimir Jiranek) 20 15
97 5 k. Champagne cork flying through ringmaster's hoop (Jiri Sliva) .. 25 20

**49** Houses around smiling Sun **50** Gothic Window

**1995.** 25th Anniv of SOS Children's Villages.
99 **49** 3 k. multicoloured .. 15 10

**1995.** Architectural Styles.
101 **50** 2 k. 40 red and green .. 10 10
102 – 3 k. green and blue .. 15 10
103 – 3 k. 60 violet and green 20 15
104 – 4 k. blue and red .. 20 15
107 – 9 k. 60 blue and mauve 45 30
109 – 14 k. green and mauve 70 50
DESIGNS: 3 k. Secession window; 3 k. 60, Roman window; 4 k. Classicist doorway; 9 k. 60, Renaissance doorway; 14 k. Baroque doorway.

**51** Rontgen and X-Ray Tube

**1995.** Centenary of Discovery of X-Rays by Wilhelm Rontgen.
113 **51** 6 k. buff, black & violet 30 20

**52** Emblem

**1995.** 50th Anniv of U.N.O.
114 **52** 14 k. multicoloured .. 70 50

**53** Christmas Tree **55** Stamp Design by Jaroslav Benda

**54** Allegory of Music

**1995.** Christmas.
115 **53** 3 k. multicoloured .. 15 10

**1995.** Art (3rd series). As T **16**.
116 6 k. black, blue and buff . . 30 30
117 9 k. multicoloured . . 45 45
118 14 k. multicoloured . . 70 70
DESIGNS: 6 k. "Parisienne" (Ludek Marold); 9 k. "Bouquet" (J. K. Hirschely); 14 k. "Portrait of the Sculptor Josef Malinsky" (Antonin Machek).

**1996.** Cent of Czech Philharmonic Orchestra.
119 **54** 3 k. 60 multicoloured . . 20 15

**1996.** Tradition of Czech Stamp Production.
120 **55** 3 k. 60 multicoloured . . 20 15

**56** Mencikova and Chessmen

**1996.** 90th Birth Anniv of Vera Mencikova (chess champion).
121 **56** 6 k. black, buff and red 30 20

**57** Woman with Bowl of Easter Eggs

**58** Sudek and Camera

**1996.** Easter.
122 **57** 3 k. multicoloured . . 15 10

**1996.** Birth Centenary of Josef Sudek (photographer).
123 **58** 9 k. 60 buff, black & grey 45 30

**59** Jiri Guth-Jarkovsky (first President of National Olympic Committee) and Stadium

**62** Ema Destinnova (singer)

**60** Jan (John the Blind)

**1996.** Centenary of Modern Olympic Games.
124 **59** 9 k. 60 multicoloured . . 45 30

**1996.** Bohemian Kings of the Luxembourg Dynasty.
125 **60** 14 k. blue, grey & purple 65 65
126 – 14 k. green, grey & pur 65 65
127 – 14 k. green, grey & pur 65 65
128 – 14 k. blue, grey & purple 65 65
DESIGNS: No. 126, Karel (Charles IV, Holy Roman Emperor); 127, Vaclav IV; 128, Sigismund.

**1996.** Europa. Famous Women.
130 **62** 8 k. lilac, black & mauve 35 25

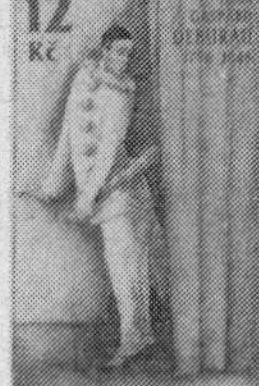

**63** Entering Stage as Pierrot

**64** Throwing the Javelin

**1996.** Birth Bicentenary of Jean Gasparde Deburau (mime actor).
131 **63** 12 k. multicoloured . . 55 40

**1996.** Olympic Games, Atlanta.
132 **64** 3 k. multicoloured . . 15 10

**65** Boy and Girl on Cat

**66** St. John of Nepomuk's Church, Zelena Hora

**1996.** For Children.
133 **65** 3 k. multicoloured . . 15 10

**1996.** Tourist Sites. Multicoloured.
134 8 k. Type **66** (U.N.E.S.C.O. World Heritage Site) . . 35 35
135 9 k. Prague Loretto . . 40 40

**67** Boy playing Flute and Flowers forming Butterfly

**1996.** 50th Anniv of U.N.I.C.E.F.
136 **67** 3 k. multicoloured . . 15 10

**68** Black Horse

**1996.** Kladruby Horses. Multicoloured.
137 3 k. Type **68** . . . . 15 10
138 3 k. White horse . . . . 15 10

**1996.** Art (4th series). As T **16**. Mult.
140 9 k. "Eden" (Josef Vachal) 40 40
141 11 k. "Breakfast with Egg" (Georg Flegel) (vert) . . 50 50
142 20 k. "Baroque Chair" (Endre Nemes) (vert) . . 95 95

**70** Brahe

**1996.** 450th Birth Anniv of Tycho Brahe (astronomer).
143 **70** 5 k. multicoloured . . 25 20

**71** Letov S-1

**72** Nativity

**1996.** Biplanes. Multicoloured.
144 7 k. Type **71** . . . . 30 20
145 8 k. Aero A-11 . . . . 35 25
146 10 k. Avia BH-21 . . . . 45 30

**1996.** Christmas.
147 **72** 3 k. multicoloured . . 15 10

## DAHOMEY Pt. 6; Pt. 12

A French colony on the W. Coast of Africa, incorporated in French West Africa in 1944. In 1958 it became an autonomous republic within the French Community, and in 1960 was proclaimed fully independent.

The area used the issues of French West Africa from 1944 until 1960.

100 centimes = 1 franc.

**1899.** "Tablet" key-type inscr "DAHOMEY ET DEPENDANCES".

| | | | | |
|---|---|---|---|---|
| 1 | D | 1 c. black and red on blue | 45 | 40 |
| 2 | | 2 c. brown & blue on buff | 50 | 55 |
| 3 | | 4 c. brown & blue on grey | 85 | 85 |
| 4 | | 5 c. green and red | 1·75 | 1·60 |
| 5 | | 10 c. red and blue | 2·25 | 1·25 |
| 6 | | 15 c. grey and red | 1·60 | 90 |
| 7 | | 20 c. red & blue on green | 6·00 | 6·00 |
| 8 | | 25 c. black & red on pink | 5·75 | 4·00 |
| 9 | | 25 c. blue and red | 5·75 | 6·50 |
| 10 | | 30 c. brown & bl on drab | 9·00 | 8·50 |
| 11 | | 40 c. red & blue on yellow | 7·00 | 6·25 |
| 12 | | 50 c. brown & red on blue | 8·50 | 8·25 |
| 13 | | 50 c. brown & blue on bl | 19·00 | 10·50 |
| 14 | | 75 c. brown & red on orge | 55·00 | 30·00 |
| 15 | | 1 f. green and red | 28·00 | 16·00 |
| 16 | | 2 f. violet and red on pink | 70·00 | 45·00 |
| 17 | | 5 f. mauve & blue on blue | 90·00 | 65·00 |

**1906.** "Faidherbe", "Palms" and "Balay" key-types inscr "DAHOMEY".

| | | | | |
|---|---|---|---|---|
| 18 | I | 1 c. grey and red | 50 | 50 |
| 19 | | 2 c. brown and red | 50 | 50 |
| 20 | | 4 c. brown & red on blue | 1·00 | 70 |
| 21 | | 5 c. green and red | 3·75 | 85 |
| 22 | | 10 c. pink and blue | 9·25 | 1·10 |
| 23 | J | 20 c. black & red on blue | 5·75 | 5·00 |
| 24 | | 25 c. blue and red | 5·75 | 4·75 |
| 25 | | 30 c. brown & red on pink | 7·00 | 5·50 |
| 26 | | 35 c. black & red on yell | 38·00 | 5·75 |
| 27 | | 45 c. brown & red on grn | 8·00 | 7·00 |
| 28 | | 50 c. violet and red | 7·50 | 7·50 |
| 29 | | 75 c. green & red on orge | 9·00 | 9·00 |
| 30 | K | 1 f. black and red on blue | 11·50 | 9·25 |
| 31 | | 2 f. blue and red on pink | 75·00 | 70·00 |
| 32 | | 5 f. red & blue on yellow | 65·00 | 55·00 |

**1912.** Surch in figures.

| | | | | |
|---|---|---|---|---|
| 33 | D | 05 on 2 c. brown and blue on buff | 35 | 45 |
| 34 | | 05 on 4 c. brown and blue on grey | 50 | 65 |
| 35 | | 05 on 15 c. grey and red | 45 | 65 |
| 36 | | 05 on 20 c. red and blue on green | 50 | 65 |
| 37 | | 05 on 25 c. blue and red | 50 | 70 |
| 38 | | 05 on 30 c. brown and blue on drab | 50 | 65 |
| 39 | | 10 on 40 c. red and blue on yellow | 50 | 60 |
| 40 | | 10 on 50 c. brown and blue on blue | 55 | 85 |
| 40a | | 10 on 50 c. brown and red on blue | £675 | £750 |
| 41 | | 10 on 75 c. brown and red on orange | 3·00 | 3·75 |

**6.** Native Climbing Palm.

**11.** Rene Caillie.

**1913.**

| | | | | |
|---|---|---|---|---|
| 42 | 6 | 1 c. black and violet | 10 | 15 |
| 43 | | 2 c. pink and brown | 10 | 15 |
| 44 | | 4 c. brown and black | 10 | 15 |
| 45 | | 5 c. green and light green | 20 | 20 |
| 60 | | 5 c. violet and purple | 15 | 15 |
| 46 | | 10 c. pink and red | 45 | 40 |
| 61 | | 10 c. green and lt green | 20 | 30 |
| 75 | | 10 c. green and red | 10 | 10 |
| 47 | | 15 c. purple and brown | 20 | 25 |
| 48 | | 20 c. brown and grey | 20 | 30 |
| 76 | | 20 c. green | 15 | 25 |
| 77 | | 20 c. black and mauve | 15 | 25 |
| 49 | | 25 c. blue & ultramarine | 75 | 95 |
| 62 | | 25 c. orange and purple | 40 | 40 |
| 50 | | 30 c. violet and brown | 1·00 | 1·25 |
| 63 | | 30 c. carmine and red | 75 | 1·25 |
| 78 | | 30 c. violet and yellow | 15 | 30 |
| 79 | | 30 c. green and olive | 50 | 60 |
| 51 | | 35 c. black and brown | 35 | 50 |
| 80 | | 35 c. green and turquoise | 50 | 60 |
| 52 | | 40 c. orange and black | 20 | 30 |
| 53 | | 45 c. blue and grey | 20 | 35 |
| 54 | | 50 c. brown & chocolate | 2·50 | 3·00 |
| 64 | | 50 c. blue & ultramarine | 35 | 60 |
| 81 | | 50 c. blue and red | 25 | 20 |
| 82 | | 55 c. brown and green | 40 | 55 |
| 83 | | 60 c. violet on pink | 15 | 30 |
| 84 | | 65 c. green and brown | 25 | 40 |
| 55 | | 75 c. violet and blue | 35 | 35 |
| 85 | 6 | 80 c. blue and brown | 30 | 45 |
| 86 | | 85 c. pink and blue | 40 | 75 |
| 87 | | 90 c. red and carmine | 45 | 60 |
| 87a | | 90 c. red and brown | 55 | 65 |
| 56 | | 1 f. black and green | 50 | 50 |
| 88 | | 1 f. light blue and blue | 45 | 55 |
| 89 | | 1 f. red and brown | 50 | 65 |
| 90 | | 1 f. red and light red | 55 | 70 |
| 91 | | 1 f. 10 brown and violet | 1·25 | 1·50 |
| 92 | | 1 f. 25 brown and blue | 9·00 | 9·00 |
| 93 | | 1 f. 50 light blue and blue | 45 | 65 |
| 94 | | 1 f. 75 orange and brown | 1·60 | 1·75 |
| 94a | | 1 f. 75 ultramarine & blue | 40 | 60 |
| 57 | | 2 f. brown and yellow | 60 | 65 |
| 95 | | 3 f. mauve on pink | 1·25 | 1·25 |
| 58 | | 5 f. blue and violet | 85 | 1·10 |

**1915.** Surch 5c and red cross.

| | | | | |
|---|---|---|---|---|
| 59 | 6 | 10 c.+5 c. pink and red | 30 | 60 |

**1922.** Surch in figures and bars.

| | | | | |
|---|---|---|---|---|
| 65 | 6 | 25 c. on 2 f. brown & yell | 40 | 50 |
| 66 | | 60 on 75 c. violet on pink | 40 | 50 |
| 67 | | 65 on 15 c. purple & brown | 65 | 95 |
| 68 | | 85 on 15 c. purple & brown | 65 | 95 |
| 69 | | 90 c. on 75 c. red and carmine | 70 | 1·10 |
| 70 | | 1 f. 25 on 1 f. lt blue & bl | 60 | 75 |
| 71 | | 1 f. 50 on 1 f. lt blue & bl | 60 | 70 |
| 72 | | 3 f. on 5 f. red and green | 5·50 | 4·75 |
| 73 | | 10 f. on 5 f. brown & blue | 4·00 | 4·75 |
| 74 | | 20 f. on 5 f. green and red | 4·75 | 5·00 |

**1931.** "Colonial Exn." key-types inscr. "DAHOMEY".

| | | | | |
|---|---|---|---|---|
| 96. | E. | 40 c. green | 2·75 | 3·00 |
| 97. | F. | 50 c. mauve | 2·75 | 3·00 |
| 98. | G. | 90 c. red | 2·75 | 3·00 |
| 99. | H. | 1 f. 50 blue | 2·75 | 3·00 |

**1937.** Paris Int. Exn. As Nos. 110/15 of Cameroun.

| | | | | |
|---|---|---|---|---|
| 100. | | 20 c. violet | 35 | 70 |
| 101. | | 30 c. green | 35 | 80 |
| 102. | | 40 c. red | 35 | 85 |
| 103. | | 50 c. brown | 35 | 70 |
| 104. | | 90 c. red | 35 | 70 |
| 105. | | 1 f. 50 blue | 35 | 80 |

**1938.** Int. Anti-Cancer Fund. As T 19 of Cameroun.

| | | | | |
|---|---|---|---|---|
| 106. | | 1 f. 75+50 c. blue | 3·50 | 6·00 |

**1939.** Death Cent. of R. Caillie (explorer).

| | | | | |
|---|---|---|---|---|
| 107. | 11. | 90 c. orange | 50 | 75 |
| 108. | | 2 f. violet | 50 | 95 |
| 109. | | 2 f. 25 blue | 60 | 1·00 |

**1939.** New York World's Fair. As T 20 of Cameroun.

| | | | | |
|---|---|---|---|---|
| 110. | | 1 f. 25 red | 50 | 55 |
| 111. | | 2 f. 25 blue | 50 | 55 |

**1939.** 150th Anniv. of French Revolution. As T 25 of Cameroun.

| | | | | |
|---|---|---|---|---|
| 112. | | 45 c.+25 c. green | 3·75 | 4·50 |
| 113. | | 70 c.+30 c. brown | 3·75 | 4·50 |
| 114. | | 90 c.+35 c. orange | 4·00 | 4·50 |
| 115. | | 1 f. 25+1 f. red | 3·75 | 4·50 |
| 116. | | 2 f. 25+2 f. blue | 3·75 | 4·50 |

**12.** African Landscape.

**13.** Native Poling Canoe.

**1940.** Air.

| | | | | |
|---|---|---|---|---|
| 117. | 12. | 1 f. 90 blue | 20 | 30 |
| 118. | | 2 f. 90 red | 25 | 40 |
| 119. | | 4 f. 50 green | 40 | 55 |
| 120. | | 4 f. 90 olive | 40 | 60 |
| 121. | | 6 f. 90 orange | 50 | 90 |

**1941.**

| | | | | |
|---|---|---|---|---|
| 122. | 13. | 2 c. red | 15 | 25 |
| 123. | | 3 c. blue | 15 | 25 |
| 124. | | 5 c. violet | 35 | 40 |
| 125. | | 10 c. green | 15 | 30 |
| 126. | | 15 c. black | 10 | 25 |
| 127. | – | 20 c. brown | 15 | 25 |
| 128. | – | 30 c. violet | 15 | 30 |
| 129. | – | 40 c. red | 35 | 50 |
| 130. | – | 50 c. green | 35 | 50 |
| 131. | – | 60 c. black | 25 | 35 |
| 132. | – | 70 c. mauve | 45 | 60 |
| 133. | – | 80 c. black | 40 | 55 |
| 134. | – | 1 f. violet | 30 | 45 |
| 135. | – | 1 f. 30 violet | 50 | 60 |
| 136. | – | 1 f. 40 green | 60 | 70 |
| 137. | – | 1 f. 50 red | 50 | 70 |
| 138. | – | 2 f. orange | 55 | 90 |
| 139. | – | 2 f. 50 blue | 55 | 70 |
| 140. | – | 3 f. red | 50 | 80 |
| 141. | – | 5 f. green | 50 | 60 |
| 142. | – | 10 f. brown | 1·00 | 1·25 |
| 143. | – | 20 f. black | 1·40 | 1·60 |

DESIGNS—HORIZ. 20 c. to 70 c. Village on piles. VERT. 80 c. to 2 f. Sailing pirogue on Lake Nokoue. 2 f. 50 to 20 f. Dahomey warrior.

**1941.** National Defence Fund. Surch **SECOURS NATIONAL** and value.

| | | | | |
|---|---|---|---|---|
| 143a | 6 | +1 f. on 50 c. bl & red | 2·00 | 2·50 |
| 143b | | +2 f. on 80 c. bl & brn | 2·75 | 2·75 |
| 143c | | +2 f. on 1 f. 50 light blue and blue | 3·50 | 3·75 |
| 143d | | +3 f. on 2 f. brown and yellow | 3·50 | 3·75 |

**14b.** Village on Piles and Marshal Petain.

**1942.** Marshal Petain Issue.

| | | | | |
|---|---|---|---|---|
| 143e. | 14b. | 1 f. green | 10 | 45 |
| 143f. | | 2 f. 50 blue | 10 | 45 |

**14c.** Maternity Hospital, Dakar.

**1942.** Air. Colonial Child Welfare Fund.

| | | | | |
|---|---|---|---|---|
| 143g. | 14c. | 1 f. 50+3 f. 50 green | 20 | 50 |
| 143h. | – | 2 f.+6 f. brown | 20 | 45 |
| 143i. | – | 3 f.+9 f. red | 20 | 50 |

DESIGNS: 2 f. Dispensary, Mopti. (48½×27 mm.). 3 f. "Child welfare".

**14d.** "Vocation".

**14e.** Camel Caravan.

**1942.** Air. "Imperial Fortnight".

| | | | | |
|---|---|---|---|---|
| 143j. | 14d. | 1 f. 20+1 f. 80 bl. & red | 20 | 50 |

**1942.** Air.

| | | | | |
|---|---|---|---|---|
| 143k. | 14e. | 50 f. blue and green | 1·25 | 2·00 |

**15.** Ganvie Village.

**1960.**

| | | | | |
|---|---|---|---|---|
| 144. | 15. | 25 f. brown, red and blue (postage) | 45 | 25 |
| 145. | – | 100 f. brown, ochre and blue (air) | 2·00 | 60 |
| 146. | – | 500 f. red, bistre & green | 8·50 | 2·50 |

DESIGNS: 100 f. Somba fort. 500 f. Royal Court, Abomey.

**1960.** 10th Anniv. of African Technical Co-operation Commission. As T 62 of Cameroun.

| | | | | |
|---|---|---|---|---|
| 147. | | 5 f. blue and purple | 50 | 30 |

**16.** Conseil de l'Entente Emblem.

**17.** Prime Minister Maga.

**18.** Weaver.

**1960.** 1st Anniv. of Conseil de l'Entente.

| | | | | |
|---|---|---|---|---|
| 148. | 16. | 25 f. multicoloured | 60 | 40 |

**1960.** Independence Proclamation.

| | | | | |
|---|---|---|---|---|
| 149. | 17. | 85 f. purple and sepia | 90 | 55 |

**1961.** Artisans.

| | | | | |
|---|---|---|---|---|
| 150. | 18. | 1 f. purple and orange | 10 | 10 |
| 151. | – | 2 f. chocolate and brown | 10 | 10 |
| 152. | – | 3 f. orange and green | 10 | 10 |
| 153. | – | 4 f. lake and bistre | 15 | 15 |
| 154. | 18. | 6 f. red and lilac | 15 | 15 |
| 155. | – | 10 f. myrtle and blue | 25 | 20 |
| 156. | – | 15 f. violet and purple | 35 | 25 |
| 157. | – | 20 f. turquoise and blue | 45 | 30 |

DESIGNS—VERT. 2 f., 10 f. Wood-carver. HORIZ. 3 f., 15 f. Fisherman casting net. 4 f., 20 f. Potter.

**1961.** 1st Anniv. of Independence. No. 149 surch. **100 F** and **President de la Republique.**

| | | | | |
|---|---|---|---|---|
| 158. | 17. | 100 f. on 85 f. purple & sepia | 1·50 | 1·50 |

**20.** Doves and U.N. Emblem.

**22.** Wrecked Car and Fort.

**1961.** 1st Anniv. of Admission into U.N.O.

| | | | | |
|---|---|---|---|---|
| 159. | 20. | 5 f. multicoloured (postage) | 25 | 20 |
| 160. | | 60 f. multicoloured | 75 | 60 |
| 161. | | 200 f. multicoloured (air) | 2·50 | 1·90 |

**1961.** Abidjan Games. Optd. **JEUX SPORTIFS D'ABIDJAN 24 AU 31 DECEMBRE 1961.**

| | | | | |
|---|---|---|---|---|
| 162. | 15. | 25 f. brown, red and blue | 45 | 30 |

**1962.** Air. Foundation of "Air Afrique" Airline As T 69 of Cameroun

| | | | | |
|---|---|---|---|---|
| 163. | | 25 f. blue, brown & black | 45 | 35 |

**1962.** Malaria Eradication. As T 70 of Cameroun.

| | | | | |
|---|---|---|---|---|
| 164. | | 25 f.+5 f. brown | 45 | 45 |

**1962.** 1st Anniv. of Portuguese Evacuation from Fort Ouidah.

| | | | | |
|---|---|---|---|---|
| 165. | 22. | 30 f. multicoloured | 45 | 25 |
| 166. | | 60 f. multicoloured | 70 | 40 |

**1962.** 1st Anniv. of Union of African and Malagasy States. As No. 328 of Cameroun.

| | | | | |
|---|---|---|---|---|
| 167. | 72. | 30 f. multicoloured | 50 | 35 |

**23.** Map, Nurses and Patients.

**1962.** Red Cross.

| | | | | |
|---|---|---|---|---|
| 168. | 23. | 5 f. red, blue & purple | 15 | 15 |
| 169. | | 20 f. red, blue & green | 30 | 25 |
| 170. | | 25 f. red, blue & sepia | 40 | 30 |
| 171. | | 30 f. red, blue & brown | 45 | 40 |

**24.** Peuhl Herd-boy.

**25.** Boxing.

**1963.** Dahomey Tribes.

| | | | | |
|---|---|---|---|---|
| 172. | A. | 2 f. violet and blue | 10 | 10 |
| 173. | B. | 3 f. black and blue | 10 | 10 |
| 174. | 24. | 5 f. grn., brn. & blk. | 15 | 10 |
| 175. | C. | 15 f. brn., chest. & turq. | 25 | 15 |
| 176. | D. | 20 f. black, red & green | 40 | 20 |
| 177. | E. | 25 f. turq., brn. and blue | 40 | 15 |
| 178. | D. | 30 f. brn., mauve & red | 45 | 30 |
| 179. | E. | 40 f. blue, brn. & green | 55 | 25 |
| 180. | C. | 50 f. brn., black & grn. | 65 | 30 |
| 181. | 24. | 60 f. orge., red & purple | 70 | 45 |
| 182. | B. | 65 f. brown and red | 90 | 50 |
| 183. | A. | 85 f. brown and blue | 1·50 | 75 |

DESIGNS—VERT. A, Ganvie girl in pirogue. B, Bariba chief of Nikki. C, Ouidah witch-doctor and python. D, Nessoukoue witch-doctors of Abomey. HORIZ. E, Dahomey girl.

**1963.** Freedom from Hunger. As T 76 of Cameroun.

| | | | | |
|---|---|---|---|---|
| 184. | | 25 f.+5 f. lake, brn. & olive | 50 | 50 |

**1963.** Dakar Games.

| | | | | |
|---|---|---|---|---|
| 185. | 25. | 50 c. black and green | 10 | 10 |
| 186. | – | 1 f. black, bistre & brn. | 10 | 10 |
| 187. | – | 2 f. brn., blue & bronze | 10 | 10 |
| 188. | – | 5 f. black, red & brown | 15 | 10 |
| 189. | 25. | 15 f. purple and violet | 25 | 20 |
| 190. | – | 20 f. black, green & red | 40 | 30 |

DESIGNS—HORIZ. 1 f., 20 f. Football. VERT. 2 f., 5 f. Running.

27. U.A.M. Palace.

**1963.** Air. Meeting of Heads of State of African and Malagasy Union.
191. **27.** 250 f. multicoloured .. 3·00 1·75

28. Presidential Palace, Cotonou.

**1963.** 3rd Anniv. of Independence.
192. **28.** 25 f. multicoloured .. 35 25

**1963.** Air. African and Malagasy Posts and Telecommunications Union. As T **18** of Central African Republic.
193. 25 f. red, buff, brown & blue 40 25

29. Boeing 707 Airliner.

**1963.** Air.
194. **29.** 100 f. bistre, grn. & vio. 1·75 60
195. – 200 f. violet, brn. & grn. 3·00 1·60
196. – 300 f. pur., grn and blue 4·25 2·25
197. – 500 f. pur., brn. & blue 7·75 3·25
DESIGNS: 200 f. Aerial views of Boeing 707. 300 f. Cotonou Airport. 500 f. Boeing 707 in flight.

30. Toussaint L'Ouverture. 31. Flame on U.N. Emblem.

**1963.** 150th Death Anniv. of Toussaint L'Ouverture (Haitian statesman).
198. **30.** 25 f. multicoloured .. 35 20
199. 30 f. multicoloured .. 40 25
200. 100 f. multicoloured .. 1·10 65

**1963.** 15th Anniv. of Declaration of Human Rights. Multicoloured. Background colours given.
201. **31.** 4 f. blue .. .. 10 10
202. 6 f. brown .. .. 15 15
203. 25 f. green .. .. 35 25

32. Sacred Boat of Isis, Philae.

**1964.** Air. Nubian Monuments Preservation.
204. **32.** 25 f. brown and violet 80 50

33. Somba Dance (Taneka Coco).

DANCES—HORIZ. 3 f. Nago (Pobe-Ketou). 15 f. Nago (Ouidah). 30 f. Nessou houessi (Abomey). VERT. 10 f. Baton (Paysbariba). 25 f. Sakpatassi (Abomey).

**1964.** Native Dances.
205. **33.** 2 f. black, red and green 10 10
206. – 3 f. red, green and blue 10 10
207. – 10 f. black, red & violet 20 15
208. – 15 f. sepia, lake & green 25 15
209. – 25 f. blue, brn. and orge. 40 25
210. – 30 f. red, orange & brn. 45 30

34. Running.

**1964.** Olympic Games, Tokyo.
211. **34.** 60 f. green and brown .. 65 50
212. – 85 f. purple and blue .. 1·25 75
DESIGN: 85 f. Cycling.

**1964.** French, African and Malagasy Co-operation. As T **547** of France.
213. 25 f. brown, violet & orge. 40 25

35. Mother and Child. 36. Satellite and Sun.

**1964.** 18th Anniv. of U.N.I.C.E.F.
214. **35.** 20 f. black, green & red 35 25
215. – 25 f. black, blue & red .. 40 25
DESIGN: 25 f. Mother and child (different).

**1964.** Int. Quiet Sun Year.
216. **36.** 25 f. green and yellow .. 45 20
217. – 100 f. yellow and purple 1·25 65
DESIGN: 100 f. Another satellite and Sun.

37. "Weather".

**1965.** Air. World Meteorological Day.
218. **37.** 50 f. multicoloured .. 65 45

38. Rug Pattern.

**1965.** Abomey Rug-weaving. Mult.
219. 20 f. Bull, tree, etc. (vert.) 30 25
220. 25 f. Witch-doctor, etc. (vert.) 45 30
221. 50 f. Type **38** .. .. 70 35
222. 85 f. Ship, tree, etc. .. 1·25 70

39. Baudot's Telegraph and Ader's Telephone. 40. Sir Winston Churchill.

**1965.** Cent. of I.T.U.
223. **39.** 100 f. blk., purple & orge. 1·40 1·00

**1965.** Air. Churchill Commem.
224. **40.** 100 f. multicoloured .. 1·40 1·10

41. Heads of Three Races within I.C.Y. Emblem.

**1965.** Air. Int. Co-operation Year.
225. **41.** 25 f. lake, green & violet 35 20
226. 85 f. lake, green & blue 80 55

42. Lincoln.

**1965.** Air. Death Cent of Abraham Lincoln.
227 **42** 100 f. multicoloured .. 1·25 95

43. Cotonou Port.

**1965.** Inaug of Cotonou Port. Multicoloured.
228. 25 f. Type **43** .. .. 45 25
229. 100 f. Cotonou Port .. 1·60 85

The two stamps joined together form a complete design and were issued se-tenant in the sheets.

44. Spanish Mackerel. 45. Independence Monument.

**1965.** Fishes.
230. **44.** 10 f. blk., turq. and blue 25 20
231. – 25 f. orge., grey & blue 35 30
232. – 30 f. blue and turquoise 65 35
233. – 50 f. grey, orge. & blue 80 55
FISHES: 25 f. Sea bream. 30 f. Sailfish. 50 f. Tripletail.

**1965.** 2nd Annniv. of 28th October Revolution.
234. **45.** 25 f. red, grey and black 35 20
235. 30 f. red, blue and black 40 25

**1965.** No. 177 surch. **1 f.**
236. 1 f. on 25 f. turq., brn. & bl. 15 10

47. Arms and Pres. Kennedy.

**1965.** Air. 2nd Death Anniv. of Pres. Kennedy.
237. **47.** 100 f. brown and green 1·50 1·00

48. Dr. Schweitzer and Hospital Scene.

**1966.** Air. Schweitzer Commem.
238. **48.** 100 f. multicoloured .. 1·50 90

49. Porto-Novo Cathedral. 50. Beads, Bangles and Anklets.

**1966.** Dahomey Cathedrals.
239. **49.** 30 f. purple, blue & green 30 20
240. – 50 f. brown, blue & pur. 50 30
241. – 70 f. purple, blue & grn. 80 50
DESIGNS—VERT. 50 f. Ouidah Church (old Pro-Cathedral). HORIZ. 70 f. Cotonou Cathedral.

**1966.** World Festival of Negro Arts, Dakar.
242. **50.** 15 f. purple and black .. 25 15
243. – 30 f. red, purple & blue 35 25
244. – 50 f. blue and brown .. 60 40
245. – 70 f. lake and black .. 1·10 65
DESIGNS: 30 f. Building construction. 50 f. Craftsman. 70 f. Religious carvings.

**1966.** 5th Anniv. of France-Dahomey Treaty. Nos. 228/9 surch. **ACCORD DE COOPERATION FRANCE – DAHOMEY 5e Anniversaire - 24 Avril 1966.**
246. **43.** 15 f. on 25 f. mult. .. 35 25
247. – 15 f. on 100 f. mult. .. 35 25

52. W.H.O. Building and Emblem.

**1966.** Inaug. of W.H.O. Headquarters, Geneva.
248. **52.** 30 f. multicoloured (post.) 40 30
249. – 100 f. multicoloured (air) 1·40 1·00
DESIGN (48×27 mm.): 100 f. W.H.O. building (different view) and emblem.

53. African Pygmy Goose. 54. Industrial Emblems.

**1966.** Air. Birds. Multicoloured.
250. 50 f. Type **53** .. .. 4·50 2·25
251. 100 f. Fiery-breasted bush shrike .. .. 8·00 1·75
252. 500 f. Iris glossy starling .. 26·00 12·50
See also Nos. 271/2.

**1966.** Air. "Europafrique".
253. **54.** 100 f. multicoloured .. 1·50 85

55. Pope Paul and St. Peter's.

**1966.** Air. Pope Paul's Visit to U.N.
254. **55.** 50 f. red, brown & green 55 35
255. – 70 f. red, green and blue 85 45
256. – 100 f. purple and blue 1·25 85
DESIGNS—HORIZ. 70 f. Pope Paul and New York. VERT. (36×48 mm.). 100 f. Pope Paul and U.N. General Assembly.

**1966.** Air. Inaug of DC-8F Air Services. As T **54** of Central African Republic.
258 30 f. grey, black and purple 50 30

56. Scout signalling with flags.

**1966.** Scouting.
259. **56.** 5 f. red, ochre and brown 10 10
260. – 10 f. mauve, grn. & blk. 15 10
261. – 30 f. orange, red & violet 35 25
262. – 50 f. brown, grn. & blue 70 40
DESIGNS—VERT. 10 f. Tent-pole and banners. 30 f. Scouts, camp-fire and map. HORIZ. 50 f. Constructing bridge.

57. Scientific Emblem.

**1966.** Air. 20th Anniv. of U.N.E.S.C.O.
264. **57.** 30 f. plum, blue & purple 35 25
265. – 45 f. lake and green .. 50 40
266. – 100 f. blue, lake & black 1·25 80
DESIGNS—VERT. 45 f. Cultural Emblem. HORIZ. 100 f. Educational emblem.

58. "The Nativity" (15th-cent. Beaune Tapestry). 59. Broad-billed Roller.

**1966.** Air. Christmas. Multicoloured.
268. 50 f. Type **58** .. .. 2·25 1·60
269. 100 f. "The Adoration of the Shepherds" (after Jose Ribera) .. .. 3·25 2·50
270. 200 f. "Madonna and Child" (after A. Baldovinetti) .. 6·50 4·00
See also Nos. 311/14, 348/51, 384/7 and 423/6.

**1967.** Air. Birds. Multicoloured.
271. 200 f. Type **59** .. .. 9·50 3·75
272. 250 f. African Emerald cuckoo .. .. .. 12·50 5·25

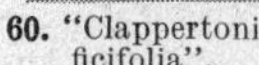

**60.** "Clappertonia ficifolia". **62.** Bird bearing Lions Emblem.

**1967.** Flowers. Multicoloured.
273. 1 f. Type **60** .. .. 10 10
274. 3 f. "Hewittia sublobata" 15 10
275. 5 f. "Clitoria ternatea" .. 20 15
276. 10 f. "Nymphaea micrantha" .. .. .. 35 15
277. 5 f. "Commelina forskalaei" .. .. .. 35 25
278. 30 f. "Eremomastax speciosa" .. .. 75 35

**1967.** Nos. 182/3 surch.
279. 30 f. on 65 f. brown & red 40 30
280. 30 f. on 85 f. brown & blue 40 30

**1967.** 50th Anniv. of Lions Int.
281. **62.** 100 f. blue, grn. & vio. 1·50 80

**63.** "Ingres" (self-portrait).

**1967.** Air. Death Cent. of Ingres (painter). Multicoloured.
282. 100 f. Type **63** .. .. 2·10 1·25
283. 100 f. "Oedipus and the Sphinx" (after Ingres) 2·10 1·25
See also Nos. 388/90, 429/30, 431/2 and 486/7.

**64.** "Suzanne" (barque).

**1967.** Air. French Sailing ships. Mult.
284. 30 f. Type **64** .. .. 55 35
285. 45 f. "Esmeralda" (schooner) (vert.) .. 90 55
286. 80 f. "Marie Alice" (schooner) (vert.) .. 1·75 75
287. 100 f. "Antonin" (barque) 2·10 1·10

**1967.** Air. 50th Birth Anniv. of Pres. Kennedy. Nos. 227 and 237 surch. **29 MAI 1967 50e Anniversaire de la naissance de John F. Kennedy.**
288. **42.** 125 f. on 100 f. mult... 1·75 90
289. **47.** 125 f. on 100 f. brown and green .. .. 1·75 90

**66.** "Man in the City" Pavilion.

**1967.** World Fair, Montreal.
290. **66.** 30 f. brn. & grn. (post.) 40 20
291. – 70 f. red and green .. 90 50
292. – 100 f. blue & brown (air) 1·10 65
DESIGNS—HORIZ. 70 f. "New Africa" pavilions. VERT. (27×48 mm.). 100 f. "Man Examines the Universe".

**67.** Dr. Konrad Adenauer (from painting by O. Kokoschka). **68.** "Economic Association".

**1967.** Air. Dr. Adenauer Commem.
294. **67.** 70 f. multicoloured .. 1·10 90

**1967.** Europafrique.
296. **68.** 30 f. multicoloured .. 35 25
297. – 45 f. multicoloured .. 50 25

**69.** Scouts Climbing.

**1967.** World Scout Jamboree, Idaho.
298. **69.** 30 f. ind., brn. & bl. (post.) 35 15
299. – 70 f. purple, green & blue 90 55
300. – 100 f. pur., grn. & bl. (air) 1·10 65
DESIGNS—HORIZ. 70 f. Scouts with canoe. VERT. (27×48 mm.). 100 f. Jamboree emblem, rope and map.

**1967.** Air. Riccione Stamp Exn. No. 270 surch. **RICCIONE 12 - 29 Aout 1967** and value.
302. 150 f. on 200 f. mult. .. 2·10 1·50

**71.** Rhone at Grenoble.

**1967.** Winter Olympic Games, Grenoble.
303. **71.** 30 f. blue, brn. & grn... 40 25
304. – 45 f. blue, grn. & brn... 60 40
305. – 100 f. purple, grn. & bl. 1·40 90
DESIGNS—VERT. 45 f. View of Grenoble. HORIZ. 100 f. Rhone Bridge, Grenoble, and Pierre de Coubertin.

**1967.** Air. 5th Anniv. of U.A.M.P.T. As T **123** of Cameroun.
307. 100 f. green, red & purple 1·10 90

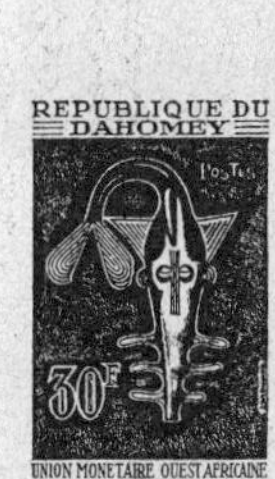

**72.** Currency Tokens. **73.** Pres. de Gaulle.

**1967.** 5th Anniv. of West African Monetary Union.
308. **72.** 30 f. black, red & green 40 30

**1967.** Air. "Homage to General de Gaulle". President Soglo of Dahomey's visit to Paris.
309. **73.** 100 f. multicoloured .. 2·10 1·40

**74.** "The Adoration" (Master of St. Sebastian).

**1967.** Air. Christmas. Religious paintings. Multicoloured.
311. 30 f. "Virgin and Child" (M. Grunewald) (vert.).. 40 35
312. 50 f. Type **74** .. .. 80 45
313. 100 f. "The Adoration of the Magi" (Ulrich Apt the Elder) (vert.) .. 1·40 90
314. 200 f. "The Annunciation" (M. Grunewald) (vert.).. 3·00 1·40

**75.** Venus de Milo and "Mariner 5". **76.** African Buffalo. **77.** W.H.O. Emblem.

**1968.** Air. "Exploration of the Planet Venus". Multicoloured.
315. 70 f. Type **75** .. .. 1·00 55
316. 70 f. Venus de Milo and "Venus 4" .. .. 1·00 55

**1968.** Fauna (1st series). Multicoloured.
318. 15 f. Type **76** .. .. 25 15
319. 30 f. Lion .. .. 45 25
320. 45 f. Kob .. .. 80 40
321. 70 f. Crocodile .. .. 1·25 45
322. 100 f. Hippopotamus .. 2·25 1·10
See also Nos. 353/7.

**1968.** 20th Anniv. of W.H.O.
323. **77.** 30 f. brn., blue & ultram. 40 30
324. 70 f. multicoloured .. 95 55

**78.** Gutenberg Memorial, Strasbourg. **79.** Dr. Martin Luther King.

**1968.** Air. 500th Death Anniv. of Johann Gutenberg.
325. **78.** 45 f. green and orange.. 60 35
326. – 100 f. deep blue & blue 1·40 85
DESIGNS: 100 f. Gutenberg statue Mainz, and printing-press.

**1968.** Air. Martin Luther King Commem.
328. – 30 f. blk., brn. and yell. 50 30
329. – 55 f. multicoloured .. 80 45
330. **79.** 100 f. multicoloured .. 1·25 80
DESIGNS: 55 f. Dr. King receiving Nobel Peace Prize. LARGER (25×46 mm.). 30 f. Inscription "We must meet hate with creative love" (also in French and German).

**80.** Schuman.

**1968.** Air. 5th Anniv. of Europafrique.
332. **80.** 30 f. multicoloured .. 40 25
333. – 45 f. pur., olive & orge. 55 35
334. – 70 f. multicoloured .. 90 40
DESIGNS: 45 f. De Gasperi. 70 f. Dr. Adenauer.

**81.** "Battle of Montebello" (Philippoteaux).

**1968.** Air. Red Cross. Designs showing paintings. Multicoloured.
335. 30 f. Type **81** .. .. 50 35
336. 45 f. "2nd Zouaves at Magenta" (Riballier) .. 65 45
337. 70 f. "Battle of Magenta" (Charpentier) .. .. 1·25 80
338. 100 f. "Battle of Solferino" (Charpentier) .. 1·75 1·00

**82.** Mail Van.

**1968.** Air. Rural Mail Service. Multicoloured.
339. 30 f. Type **82** .. .. 35 25
340. 45 f. Rural Post Office and mail van .. .. 45 30
341. 55 f. Collecting mail at river-side .. .. 60 35
342. 70 f. Loading mail on train 1·90 80

**83.** Aztec Stadium.

**1968.** Air. Olympic Games, Mexico.
343. **83.** 30 f. green and purple.. 40 25
344. – 45 f. lake and blue .. 65 35
345. – 70 f. brown and green.. 1·00 55
346. – 150 f. brown and red .. 1·90 1·10
DESIGNS—VERT. 45 f. "Pelota-player" (Aztec figure); 70 f. "Uxpanapan wrestler" (Aztec figure). HORIZ. 150 f. Olympic Stadium.

**1968.** Air. Christmas Paintings by Foujita. Multicoloured as T **74.**
348. 30 f. "The Nativity" .. 55 40
349. 70 f. "The Visitation".. 1·10 55
350. 100 f. "Virgin and Child" 1·40 95
351. 200 f. "Baptism of Christ" 2·75 1·90
No. 348 is horiz.

**1968.** Air. "Philexafrique" Stamp Exn., Abidjan (Ivory Coast, 1969). As T **137** of Cameroun. Multicoloured.
352. 100 f. "Diderot" (L. M. Vanloo).. .. .. 1·75 1·75

**84.** Warthog.

**1969.** Fauna (2nd series). Multicoloured.
353. 5 f. Type **84** .. .. 15 10
354. 30 f. Leopard .. .. 50 25
355. 60 f. Spotted hyena .. 1·00 45
356. 75 f. Olive baboon.. .. 1·40 55
357. 90 f. Hartebeest .. 2·00 90

**1969.** Air. "Philexafrique" Stamp Exn., Abidjan, Ivory Coast (2nd issue). As T **138** of Cameroun.
358. 50 f. violet, sepia and blue 1·10 1·10
DESIGN: 50 f. Cotonou harbour and stamp of 1941.

**85.** Heads and Globe.

**1969.** 50th Anniv. of I.L.O.
359. **85.** 30 f. multicoloured .. 40 25
360. 70 f. multicoloured .. 95 55

**86.** "The Virgin of the Scales" (C. da Sesto —Da Vinci School).

**1969.** Air. Leonardo da Vinci Commem. Multicoloured.
361. 100 f. Type **86** .. .. 1·40 75
362. 100 f. "The Virgin of the Rocks" (Da Vinci) .. 1·40 75

**87.** "General Bonaparte" (J. L. David).

**1969.** Air. Birth Bicent. of Napoleon Bonaparte. Multicoloured.
363. 30 f. Type **87** .. .. 1·10 1·00
364. 60 f. "Napoleon I in 1809" (Lefevre) .. .. 2·00 1·25
365. 75 f. "Napoleon at the Battle of Eylau" (Gros) (horiz.).. .. .. 2·50 1·75
366. 200 f. "General Bonaparte at Arcola" (Gros) .. 5·50 3·25

**88.** Arms of Dahomey.

**1969.**
367. **88.** 5 f. multicoloured (post.) 15 15
368. 30 f. multicoloured .. 45 30
369. 50 f. multicoloured (air) 45 25

89. " Apollo 8 " over Moon.

**1969.** Air. Moon flight of " Apollo 8 ". Embossed on gold foil.
370. **89.** 1,000 f. gold .. .. 15·00

**1969.** Air. 1st Man on the Moon (1st issue). Nos. 315/6 surch. **ALUNISSAGE APOLLO XI JUILLET 1969** with " Apollo 11 " and value.
371. **75.** 125 f. on 70 f. (No. 315) 1·75 1·40
372. – 125 f. on 70 f. (No. 316) 1·75 1·40

91. Bank Emblem and Cornucopia.

93. Dahomey Rotary Emblem.

92. Kenaf Plant and Mill, Bohicon.

**1969.** 5th Anniv. of African Development Bank.
373. **91.** 30 f. multicoloured .. 50 40

**1969.** " Europafrique ". Multicoloured.
374. 30 f. Type **92** (postage) .. 40 25
375. 45 f. Cotton plant & Mill, Parakou .. .. 50 30
376. 100 f. Coconut and Palm-oil Plant, Cotonou (air) .. 1·10 70

**1969.** Air. Rotary International Organization.
378 **93** 50 f. multicoloured .. 65 40

**1969.** Air. No. 250 Surch.
379. **53.** 10 f. on 50 f. mult. .. 1·25 30

95. Sakpata Dance.

96. F. D. Roosevelt.

**1969.** Dahomey Dances. Multicoloured.
380. 10 f. Type **95** (postage) .. 30 25
381. 30 f. Guelede dance .. 40 30
382. 45 f. Sato dance .. .. 50 35
383. 70 f. Teke dance (air) .. 80 45

**1969.** Air. Christmas. Paintings. Multicoloured. As T **58.**
384. 30 f. " The Annunciation " (Van der Stockt) .. 40 30
385. 45 f. " The Nativity " (15th-cent. Swabian School) 60 40
386. 110 f. " Virgin and Child " (Masters of the Gold Brocade) .. .. 1·60 1·00
387. 200 f. " The Adoration of the Magi " (Antwerp School, c. 1530) .. .. 2·50 1·90

**1969.** Air. Old Masters. Multicoloured. As T **63.**
388. 100 f. " The Painter's Studio " (G. Courbet) .. .. 1·40 90
389. 100 f. " Self-portrait with Gold Chain " (Rembrandt) 1·40 90
390. 150 f. " Hendrickje Stoffels " (Rembrandt) .. .. 2·10 1·25

**1970.** Air. 25th Death Anniv. of Franklin D. Roosevelt.
391. **96.** 100 f. blk, grn. & bl. .. 1·25 55

97. Rocket and Men on Moon.

98. " U.N. in "War and Peace ".

**1970.** Air. 1st Man on Moon (2nd issue).
392. **97.** 30 f. multicoloured .. 40 25
The 50, 70, 110 f. values were only issued in miniature sheet form.

**1970.** 25th Anniv. of U.N.
394. **98.** 30 f. indigo, blue & red 40 25
395. 40 f. green, blue & brown 50 30

99. Walt Whitman and African Village.

**1970.** Air. 150th Birth. Anniv. of Walt Whitman (American poet).
396. **99.** 100 f. brown, blue & grn. 1·25 50

**1970.** Air. Space Flight of " Apollo 13 ". No. 392 surch. **40 f.** and **APOLLO 13 SOLIDARITE SPATIALE INTERNATIONALE.**
397. **97.** 40 f. on 30 f. mult. .. 75 75

101. Footballers and Globe.

**1970.** Air. World Cup Football Championships, Mexico. Multicoloured.
398. 40 f. Type **101** .. .. 50 40
399. 50 f. Goalkeeper saving goal 60 45
400. 200 f. Player kicking ball .. 2·50 1·10

**1970.** 10th Anniv. (1969) of Aerial Navigation Security Agency for Africa and Madagascar (A.S.E.C.N.A.). As T **150** of Cameroun.
401. 40 f. red and purple .. 60 25

103. Mt. Fuji and " EXPO " Emblem.

104. "La Justice" and "La Concorde" (French warships).

**1970.** World Fair " EXPO 70 ", Osaka, Japan. Multicoloured.
402. 5 f. Type **103** (postage) .. 15 10
403. 70 f. Dahomey Pavilion (air) .. .. 70 45
404. 120 f. Mt. Fuji and temple 1·25 65

**1970.** 300th Anniv. of Ardres Embassy to Louis XIV of France.
405. **104.** 40 f. brn., blue & green 85 35
406. – 50 f. red, brown & green 60 35
407. – 70 f. brown, slate & bistre 90 50
408. – 200 f. brown, blue & red 2·50 1·10
DESIGNS: 50 f. Matheo Lopes. 70 f. King Alkemy of Ardres. 200 f. Louis XIV of France.

**1970.** Air. Brazil's Victory in World Cup Football Championships. No. 400 surch. **BRESIL-ITALIE 4-1** and value.
409. 100 f. on 200 f. multicoloured 1·40 70

106. Mercury.

107. Order of Independence.

**1970.** Air. Europafrique.
410. **106.** 40 f. multicoloured .. 50 35
411. 70 f. multicoloured .. 80 45

**1970.** 10th Anniv. of Independence.
412. **107.** 30 f. multicoloured .. 25 15
413. 40 f. multicoloured .. 40 20

108. Bariba Horseman.

109. Beethoven.

**1970.** Bariba Horsemen. Multicoloured.
414. 1 f. Type **108.** .. .. 10 10
415. 2 f. Two horsemen .. 10 10
416. 10 f. Horseman facing left 25 20
417. 40 f. Type **108** .. .. 50 30
418. 50 f. As 2 f. .. .. 70 35
419. 70 f. as 10 f. .. .. 95 60

**1970.** Air. Birth Bicentenary of Beethoven.
420. **109.** 90 f. violet and blue .. 90 40
421. 110 f. brown and green 1·00 55

110. Emblems of Learning.

111. " The Annunciation ".

**1970.** Air. Laying of Foundation Stone, Calavi University.
422. **110.** 100 f. multicoloured .. 1·00 50

**1970.** Air. Christmas. Miniatures of the Rhenish School c.1340. Multicoloured.
423. 40 f. Type **111** .. .. 40 25
424. 70 f. " The Nativity " .. 70 45
425. 110 f. " The Adoration of the Magi " .. .. 1·60 90
426. 200 f. " The Presentation in the Temple " .. 2·50 1·60

112. De Gaulle and Arc de Triomphe.

**1971.** Air. 1st Death Anniv. of Gen. Charles de Gaulle. Multicoloured.
427. 40 f. Type **112** .. .. 55 45
428. 500 f. De Gaulle and Notre Dame, Paris .. .. 5·00 2·50

**1971.** Air. 250th Death Anniv. of Watteau. Paintings. As T **63.** Multicoloured.
429. 100 f. " The Dandy " .. 1·75 1·10
430. 100 f. " Girl with Lute " .. 1·75 1·10

**1971.** Air. 500th Birth Anniv. of Durer. As T **63.** Multicoloured.
431. 100 f. Self-portrait, 1498 .. 1·40 90
432. 200 f. Self-portrait, 1500 .. 2·75 1·60

113. Hands supporting Heart.

114. " The Twins " (wood-carving) and Lottery Ticket.

**1971.** Racial Equality Year.
433. **113.** 40 f. red, brn. & green 40 25
434. – 100 f. red, blue & green 95 50
DESIGN—HORIZ. 100 f. " Heart " on Globe.

**1971.** 4th Anniv. of National Lottery.
435. **114.** 35 f. multicoloured .. 35 15
436. 40 f. multicoloured .. 40 25

115. Kepler, Earth and Planets.

**1971.** Air. 400th Birth Anniv. of Johannes Kepler (astronomer).
437. **115.** 40 f. blk., pur. and blue 55 40
438. – 200 f. green, red & blue 2·25 1·25
DESIGN: 200 f. Kepler, globe, satellite and rocket.

116. Boeing 747 Airliner linking Europe and Africa.

**1971.** Air. Europafrique.
439. **116.** 50 f. orge., blue & black 75 45
440. – 100 f. multicoloured .. 1·75 70
DESIGN: 100 f. "General Mangin" (liner) and maps of Europe and Africa.

117. Cockerel and Drum (King Ganyehoussou).

**1971.** Emblems of Dahomey Kings. Mult.
441. 25 f. Leg, saw and hatchet (Agoliagbo) .. 25 15
442. 35 f. Type **117** .. 40 25
443. 40 f. Fish and egg (Behanzin) (vert.) .. 40 25
444. 100 f. Cow, tree and birds (Guezo) (vert.) .. 1·00 45
445. 135 f. Fish and hoe (Ouegbadja) .. .. 1·40 80
446. 140 f. Lion and sickle (Glele) 1·60 90

**1971.** Air. 10th Anniv. of U.A.M.P.T. As T **184** of Cameroun. Multicoloured.
447. 100 f. U.A.M.P.T H.Q., Brazzaville and Arms of Dahomey .. .. 1·00 50

119. " Adoration of the Shepherds " (Master of the Hausbuch).

**1971.** Air. Christmas. Paintings. Mult.
448. 40 f. Type **119** .. .. 60 35
449. 70 f. " Adoration of the Magi " (Holbein) .. 95 45
450. 100 f. " Flight into Egypt " (Van Dyck) (horiz.) .. 1·25 60
451. 200 f. " Birth of Christ " (Durer) (horiz.) .. .. 2·50 1·40

120. "Prince Balthazar" (Velazquez).

**1971.** Air. 25th Anniv. of U.N.I.C.E.F. Paintings of Children. Multicoloured.

452. 40 f. Type **120** .. .. 65 40
453. 100 f. "The Maids of Honour" (detail, Velazquez) .. .. 1·40 65

**1972.** No. 395. Surch. in figures.

454. **98.** 35 f. on 40 f. grn., bl. & brown .. .. 40 25

**122.** Cross-country Skiing. **123.** Scout taking Oath.

**1972.** Winter Olympic Games, Sapporo, Japan.

455. **122.** 35 f. purple, brown and green (postage) .. 50 30
456. – 150 f. purple, blue and brown (air) .. .. 1·75 90

DESIGN: 150 f. Ski-jumping.

**1972.** Air. Int. Scout Seminar, Cotonou. Multicoloured.

457. 35 f. Type **123** .. .. 25 20
458. 40 f. Scout playing "xylophone" .. .. 40 25
459. 100 f. Scouts working on the land (26 × 47 mm.) .. 1·00 55

124. Friedrich Naumann and Institute Building.

**1972.** Air. Laying of Foundation Stone for National Workers Education Institute. Multicoloured.

461. 100 f. Type **124** .. .. 90 50
462. 250 f. Pres. Heuss of West Germany and Institute .. .. 25 1·10

125. Stork with Serpent.

**1972.** Air. U.N.E.S.C.O. "Save Venice" Campaign. Mosaics in St. Mark's Basilica. Multicoloured.

463. 35 f. Type **125** .. .. 55 35
464. 40 f. Cockerels carrying fox .. .. .. 65 45
465. 65 f. Noah releasing dove .. 1·10 80

126. Exhibition Emblem and Dancers.

**1972.** Air. 12th International Philatelic Exhib., Naples.

466. **126.** 100 f. multicoloured .. 95 50

127. Running.

129. Brahms, and Clara Schumann at Piano.

128. Louis Bleriot and Bleriot XI.

**1972.** Air. Olympic Games. Munich.

467. **127.** 20 f. brn., grn. & blue 30 20
468. – 85 f. brn., blue & green 85 45
469. – 150 f. brn., blue & grn. 1·75 80

DESIGNS: 85 f. High-jumping. 150 f. Putting the shot.

**1972.** Air. Birth Centenary of Louis Bleriot (pioneer airman).

471. **128.** 100 f. blue, violet & red .. .. .. 1·75 90

**1972.** 75th Death Anniv. of Johannes Brahms (composer).

472. – 30 f. blk., brn. & violet 40 25
473. **129** 65 f. blk., violet & lake 70 45

DESIGN—VERT. Brahms and opening bars of "Soir d'Ete".

130. "The Hare and the Tortoise".

**1972.** Fables of Jean de La Fontaine.

474. **130.** 10 f. grey, blue & lake 25 15
475. – 35 f. blue, lake & purple 40 25
476. – 40 f. indigo, blue & pur. 55 35

DESIGNS—VERT. 35 f. "The Fox and the Stork". HORIZ. 40 f. "The Cat, the Weasel and the Little Rabbit".

131. "Adam" (Cranach).

**1972.** Air. 500th Birth Anniv. of Lucas Cranach (painter). Multicoloured.

477. 150 f. Type **131** .. .. 1·75 1·00
478. 200 f. "Eve" (Cranach) .. 2·50 1·40

132. Africans and 500 f. Coin.

**1972.** 10th Anniv. of West African Monetary Union.

479. **132.** 40 f. brown, grey & yell. 65 20

133. "Pauline Borghese" (Canova).

**1972.** Air. 150th Death Anniv. of Antonio Canova.

480. **133.** 250 f. multicoloured .. 2·75 1·40

**1972.** Air. Olympic Medal Winners. Nos. 467/9 optd. as listed below.

481. **127.** 20 f. brn., blue & grn. 30 20
482. – 85 f. brn., blue & green 85 40
483. – 150 f. brn., blue & grn. 1·75 85

OVERPRINTS: 20 f. **5,000 M.-10,000 M. VIREN 2 MEDAILLES D'OR.** 85 f. **HAUTEUR DAMES MEYFARTH MEDAILLE D'OR.** 150 f. **POIDS KOMAR MEDAILLE D'OR.**

135. Pasteur and Apparatus.

**1972.** Air. 150th Birth Anniv. of Louis Pasteur (scientist).

485. **135.** 100 f. pur., violet & grn. 1·00 50

**1972.** Air. Paintings by G. de la Tour. As T **63.** Multicoloured.

486. 35 f. "Hurdy-gurdy Player (vert.) .. .. .. 40 30
487. 150 f. "The New-born Child" .. .. .. 1·75 1·10

136. "The Annunciation" (School of Agnolo Gaddi).

**1972.** Air. Christmas. Religious Paintings. Multicoloured.

488. 35 f. Type **136** .. .. 35 20
489. 125 f. "The Nativity" (Simone dei Crocifissi) .. 1·00 50
490. 140 f. "The Adoration of the Shepherds" (P. di Giovanni) .. .. 1·50 80
491. 250 f. "Adoration of the Magi" (Giotto) .. .. 2·25 1·25

137. Dr. Hansen, Microscope and Bacillus. 139. Arms of Dahomey.

138. Statue and Basilica, Lisieux.

**1973.** Centenary of Identification of Leprosy Bacillus by Hansen.

492. **137.** 35 f. brown, pur. & blue 30 25
493. – 85 f. brn., orge. & grn. 65 50

DESIGN: 85 f. Dr. Gerhard Armauer Hansen.

**1973.** Air. Birth Cent. of St. Theresa of Lisieux. Multicoloured.

494. 40 f. Type **138** .. .. 45 30
495. 100 f. St. Theresa of Lisieux (vert.) .. .. .. 1·20 65

**1973.**

496. **139.** 5 f. multicoloured .. 10 10
497. 35 f. multicoloured .. 25 15
498. 40 f. multicoloured .. 30 15

140. Scouts in Pirogue.

**1973.** Air. 24th World Scouting Congress, Nairobi, Kenya.

499. **140.** 15 f. pur., grn. & blue 35 15
500. – 20 f. blue and brown .. 25 20
501. – 40 f. blue, grn. & brn. 40 25

DESIGNS—VERT. 20 f. Lord Baden-Powell. HORIZ. 40 f. Bridge-building.

141. Interpol Badge and "Communications". 142. "Education in Nutrition".

**1973.** 50th Anniv. of Int. Criminal Police Organization (Interpol).

503. – 35 f. brn., grn. & red .. 30 20
504. **141.** 50 f. grn., brown & red 45 30

DESIGN—HORIZ. 35 f. Interpol emblem and web.

**1973.** 25th Anniv. of World Health Organization. Multicoloured.

505. 35 f. Type **142** .. .. 30 20
506. 100 f. Pre-natal examination 80 45

**1973.** Pan-African Drought Relief. No. 321 surch. **SECHERESSE SOLIDARITE AFRICAINE** and value.

507. 100 f. on 70 f. multicoloured 1·00 55

144. Copernicus, "Venera" and "Mariner" Probes and Plane of Solar System.

**1973.** Air. 500th Birth Anniv. of Copernicus.

508. **144.** 65 f. blk., purple & yell. 85 45
509. – 125 f. grn., blue & pur. 1·40 70

DESIGN-VERT. 125 f. Copernicus.

**1973.** U.A.M.P.T. As Type **216** of Cameroun.

510. 100 f. violet, red & black 80 40

**1973.** Air. African Fortnight, Brussels. As Type **217** of Cameroun.

511. 100 f. black, green & blue 70 40

145. Grouper.

**1973.** Fishes.

512. **145.** 5 f. steel and blue .. 15 15
513. – 15 f. black and blue .. 25 15
514. – 35 f. light brown, brown and green .. .. 55 30

DESIGNS: 15 f. Sickle Fish. 35 f. Sea Bream.

148. W.M.O. Emblem and World Weather Map.

**1973.** Air. Cent. of I.M.O./W.M.O.

515. **148.** 100 f. brown and green 95 10

149. "Europafrique".

**1973.** Air. Europafrique.

516. **149.** 35 f. blue, grn. & yell. 35 20
517. – 40 f. brn., ultram. & bl. 40 25

DESIGN: 40 f. Europafrique, plant and cogwheels.

150. President John F. Kennedy. 152. Chameleon.

151. Footballers.

**1973.** Air. 10th Death Anniv. of President Kennedy.
518. **150.** 200 f. grn., violet & grn. 1·90 1·40

**1973.** Air. World Football Championship Cup.
520. **151.** 35 f. grn., brn. & bistre 35 20
521. – 40 f. brown, blue and orange .. .. 40 25
522. – 100 f. grn., brn. & blue 65 45
DESIGNS: 40 f., 100 f. Football scenes similar to Type **151**.

**1973.** 1st Anniv. of 26th October Revolution. Multicoloured.
523. 35 f. Type **152** .. .. 35 20
524. 40 f. Arms of Dahomey (vert.) .. .. .. 35 25

153. "The Annunciation" (Dirk Bouts).

155. "The Elephant, the Chicken and the Dog".

**1973.** Air. Christmas. Multicoloured.
525 35 f. Type **153** .. .. 40 30
526 100 f. "The Nativity" (Giotto) .. .. 70 50
527 150 f. "The Adoration of the Magi" (Botticelli) .. 1·40 80
528 200 f. "The Adoration of the Shepherds" (Bassano) (horiz) .. 1·75 1·25

**1974.** Air. "Skylab". No. 515 surch. **OPERATION SKYLAB 1973-1974** and value.
529. **148.** 200 f. on 100 f. brn. & grn. 1·50 95

**1974.** Dahomey Folk Tales. Multicoloured.
530. 5 f. Type **155** .. .. 15 10
531. 10 f. "The Sparrowhawk and the Dog" .. .. 20 10
532. 25 f. "The Windy Tree" (horiz.) .. .. 30 20
533. 40 f. "The Eagle, the Snake and the Chicken" (horiz.) 40 20

156. Snow Crystal and Skiers.

**1974.** Air. 50th Anniv. of Winter Olympic Games.
534. **156.** 100 f. blue, brn. and vio. 95 65

157. Alsatian.

**1974.** Breeds of Dogs. Multicoloured.
535. 40 f. Type **157** .. .. 35 25
536. 50 f. Boxer .. .. 40 25
537. 100 f. Saluki .. .. 80 50

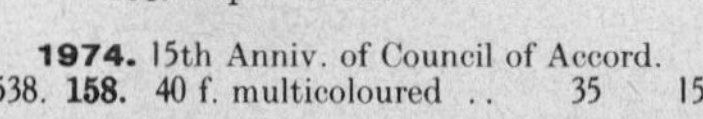
158. Map of Member Countries.

**1974.** 15th Anniv. of Council of Accord.
538. **158.** 40 f. multicoloured .. 35 15

159. Lenin (50th Death Anniv.).

160. 18th-century Persian Bishop.

**1974.** Air. Celebrities' Anniversaries.
539. **159.** 50 f. purple and red .. 50 30
540. – 125 f. brn. & green .. 1·10 65
541. – 150 f. blue & purple .. 1·60 1·10
DESIGNS AND ANNIVERSARIES: 125 f. Marie Curie (40th death anniv.). 150 f. Sir Winston Churchill (Birth Cent.).

**1974.** Air. 21st Chess Olympiad, Nice. Mult.
542 50 f. Type **160** .. .. 55 35
543 200 f. 19th-century Siamese queen .. .. .. 1·75 1·10

161. Beethoven and opening bars of the "Moonlight" Sonata.

162. Earth seen through Astronaut's Legs.

**1974.** Air. Famous Composers.
544. **161.** 150 f. red and black .. 1·25 80
545. – 150 f. red and black .. 1·25 80
DESIGN: No. 545, Chopin.

**1974.** Air. 5th Anniv. of 1st Manned Moon Landing.
546. **162.** 150 f. brn., blue & red 1·40 85

Sets commemorating the World Cup, U.P.U. Centenary, Treaty of Berne, Space Exploration and West Germany's World Cup Victory appeared in 1974. Their status is uncertain.

**1974.** Air. 11th Pan-Arab Scout Jamboree, Batroun, Lebanon. Nos. 499/500 surch. **XIe JAMBOREE PANARABE DE BATROUN—LIBAN** and value.
547. **140.** 100 f. on 15 f. purple, green and blue .. 65 45
548. – 140 f. on 20 f. bl. & brn. 1·25 65

**1974.** Air. West Germany's Victory in World Cup Football Championships. Nos. 521/2 surch. **R F A 2 HOLLANDE 1** and value.
549. 100 f. on 40 f. brown, blue and orange .. .. 65 45
550. 150 f. on 100 f. grn., brn. & bl. 1·00 80

165. U.P.U. Emblem and Globe.

**1974.** Air. Cent. of U.P.U.
551. **165.** 35 f. violet and red .. 35 30
552. – 65 f. blue and red .. 1·25 60
553. – 125 f. grn., bl. & lt. bl. 2·00 75
554. – 200 f. blue, yell. & brn. 1·75 1·25
DESIGNS: 65 f. Concorde in flight over African village. 125 f. French mobile post office, circa 1860. 200 f. Drummer and mail van.

166. "Lion of Belfort".

**1974.** Air. 70th Death Anniv. of F. Bartholdi (sculptor).
555. **166.** 100 f. brown .. .. 1·25 65

**1974.** Air. 30th Death Anniv. of Philippe de Champaigne (painter). As T **153**. Mult.
556. 250 f. "Young Girl with Falcon" .. .. .. 2·25 1·40

167. Locomotive, 1911.

**1974.** Steam Locomotives.
557. **167.** 35 f. multicoloured .. 55 25
558. – 40 f. grey, blk. & red .. 65 30
559. – 100 f. multicoloured .. 1·50 65
560. – 200 f. multicoloured .. 2·50 1·10
DESIGNS: 40 f. Goods locomotive, 1877. 100 f. "Crampton" locomotive, 1849. 200 f. "Stephenson" locomotive, 1846.

168. Rhamphorhynchus.

**1974.** Air. Prehistoric Animals. Multicoloured.
561. 35 f. Type **168** .. .. 35 20
562. 150 f. Stegosaurus .. 1·00 70
563. 200 f. Tyrannosaurus .. 1·50 95

169. Globe, Notes and Savings Bank.

**1974.** World Savings Day.
564. **169.** 35 f. brn., myrtle & grn. 35 25

170. Europafrique Emblem on Globe.

**1974.** Air. Europafrique.
565. **170.** 250 f. multicoloured .. 1·90 1·40

**1974.** Air. Christmas. Paintings by Old Masters. As Type **153**. Multicoloured.
566. 35 f. "The Annunciation" (Schongauer) .. .. 30 20
567. 40 f. "The Nativity" (Schongauer) .. .. 35 25
568. 100 f. "The Virgin of the Rose Bush" (Schongauer) 80 45
569. 250 f. "The Virgin, Infant Jesus and St. John the Baptist" (Botticelli) .. 2·25 1·40

171. "Apollo" and "Soyuz" Spacecraft.

**1975.** Air. "Apollo-Soyuz" Space Link. Mult.
570. 35 f. Type **171** .. .. 35 25
571. 200 f. Rocket launch and flags of Russia and U.S.A. 1·60 90
572. 500 f. "Apollo" and "Soyuz" docked together 3·50 2·25

172. Dompago Dance, Hissi.

173. Flags on Map of Africa.

**1975.** Dahomey Dances and Folklore. Mult.
573. 10 f. Type **172** .. .. 20 15
574. 25 f. Fetish dance, Vaudou-Tchinan .. .. .. 30 15
575. 40 f. Bamboo dance, Agbehoun 40 30
576. 100 f. Somba dance, Sandoua (horiz.) .. .. .. 75 50

**1975.** "Close Co-operation with Nigeria". Multicoloured.
577. 65 f. Type **173** .. .. 40 30
578. 100 f. Arrows linking maps of Dahomey and Nigeria (horiz.) .. .. .. 65 40

174. Community Emblem and Pylons.

**1975.** Benin Electricity Community. Mult.
579. 40 f. Type **174** .. .. 35 25
580. 150 f. Emblem and pylon (vert.) .. .. .. 1·10 65
C.E.B. = "Communate Electrique du Benin".

175. Head of Ceres.

**1975.** Air. "Arphila 75" International Stamp Exhibition, Paris.
581. **175.** 100 f. pur., ind. & blue 90 55

176. Rays of Light and Map.

178. Dr. Schweitzer.

**1975.** "New Dahomey Society".
582. **176.** 35 f. multicoloured .. 30 20

**1975.** Air. "Apollo-Soyuz" Space Link. Project. Nos. 570/1 surch. **RENCONTRE APOLLO-SOYOUZ 17 Juil. 1975** and value.
583. **171.** 100 f. on 35 f. mult... 65 45
584. – 300 f. on 200 f. mult... 2·00 1·10

**1975.** Birth Cent. of Dr. Albert Schweitzer.
585. **178.** 200 f. olive, brown and green .. .. 1·75 90

179. "The Holy Family" (Michelangelo).

180. Woman and I.W.Y. Emblem.

**1975.** Air. Europafrique.
586. 179. 300 f. multicoloured .. 1·90 1·25

**1975.** International Women's Year.
587. 180. 50 f. blue and violet .. 35 25
588. – 150 f. orge., brn. & grn. 1·10 65
DESIGN: 150 f. I.W.Y. emblem within ring of bangles.

181. Continental Infantry. 183. "Allamanda cathartica".

182. Diving.

**1975.** Air. Bicent. of American Revolution.
589. 181. 75 f. lilac red & green 55 35
590. – 135 f. brn., pur. & bl... 95 70
591. – 300 f. brn. red & bl... 2·00 1·40
592. – 500 f. brn. red & grn. 3·50 1·75
DESIGNS: 135 f. "Spirit of 76". 300 f. Artillery battery. 500 f. Cavalry.

**1975.** Air. Olympic Games, Montreal.
593. 182. 40 f. brn., bl. and vio. 35 25
594. – 250 f. brn., grn. & red 1·60 1·10
DESIGN: 250 f. Football.

**1975.** Flowers. Multicoloured.
595. 10 f. Type **183** .. .. 15 10
596. 35 f. "Ixora coccinea" .. 30 15
597. 45 f. "Hibiscus rosa-sinensis" 45 30
598. 60 f. "Phaemeria magnifica" 55 40

184. "The Nativity" (Van Leyden).

**1975.** Air. Christmas. Multicoloured.
599. 40 f. Type **184** .. .. 35 25
600. 85 f. "Adoration of the Magi" (Rubens) (vert.) 55 45
601. 140 f. "Adoration of the Shepherds" (Le Brun) 1·00 65
602. 300 f. "The Virgin of the Blue Diadem" (Raphael) (vert.) .. .. .. 2·00 1·50

For later issues see **BENIN**.

PARCEL POST STAMPS

**1967.** Surch. **COLIS POSTAUX** and value.
P 271. 18. 5 f. on 1 f. (postage).. 10 10
P 272. – 10 f. on 2 f. (No. 151).. 25 25
P 273. 18. 20 f. on 6 f. .. .. 30 30
P 274. – 25 f. on 3 f. (No. 152).. 40 40
P 275. – 30 f. on 4 f. (No. 153).. 45 45
P 276. – 50 f. on 10 f. (No. 155) 70 70
P 277. – 100 f. on 20 f. (No. 157) 1·50 1·50
P 278. – 200 f. on 200 f. (No. 195) (air) .. 3·00 2·25
P 279. 29. 300 f. on 100 f. 3·50 3·00
P 280. – 500 f. on 300 f. (No. 196) 6·50 4·50
P 281. – 1000 f. on 500 f. (No. 197) 14·00 11·00
P 282. – 5000 f. on 100 f. (No. 145) .. .. 55·00 55·00

POSTAGE DUE STAMPS

**1906.** "Natives" key-type inscr "DAHOMEY" in blue (10, 30 c.) or red (others).
D 33. L. 5 c. green .. .. 90 1·25
D 34. 10 c. red .. .. 1·60 2·25
D 35. 15 c. blue on blue .. 3·00 3·50
D 36. 20 c. black on yellow 1·75 3·25
D 37. 30 c. red on cream 1·75 4·00
D 38. 50 c. violet .. 7·00 13·00
D 39. 60 c. black on buff 6·00 8·75
D 40. 1 f. black on pink .. 21·00 24·00

**1914.** "Figure" key-type inscr. "DAHOMEY".
D 59. M. 5 c. green .. .. 10 20
D 60. 10 c. red .. .. 15 25
D 61. 15 c. grey .. .. 15 40
D 62. 20 c. brown .. .. 35 55
D 63. 30 c. blue .. .. 45 60
D 64. 50 c. black .. .. 70 90
D 65. 60 c. orange .. .. 75 1·25
D 66. 1 f. violet .. .. 80 1·25

**1927.** Surch. in figures.
D 96. M. 2 f. on 1 f. mauve .. 2·00 3·25
D 97. 3 f. on 1 f. brown .. 1·75 3·00

D 14. Native Head. D 26. Panther attacking African.

**1941.**
D 143. D 14. 5 c. black .. .. 10 25
D 144. 10 c. red .. .. 10 25
D 145. 15 c. blue .. .. 10 25
D 146. 20 c. green .. .. 15 30
D 147. 30 c. orange .. .. 25 40
D 148. 50 c. brown .. .. 45 65
D 149. 60 c. green .. .. 55 75
D 150. 1 f. red .. .. 50 80
D 151. 2 f. yellow .. .. 60 95
D 152. 3 f. purple .. .. 60 1·25

**1963.**
D 191. D 26. 1 f. red and green .. 10 10
D 192. 2 f. green & brown 10 10
D 193. 5 f. blue and orange 10 10
D 194. 10 f. black and purple 25 25
D 195. 20 f. orange & blue 30 30

D 72. Pirogue.

**1967.**
D 308. D 72. 1 f. plum, bl. & brn. 10 10
D 309. A. 1 f. brn., bl. & plum 10 10
D 310. B. 3 f. grn., orge. & brn. 10 10
D 311. C. 3 f. brn., orge. & grn. 10 10
D 312. D. 5 f. pur., blue & brn. 15 15
D 313. E. 5 f. brn., blue & pur. 25 20
D 314. F. 10 f. grn., vio. & brn. 30 30
D 315. G. 10 f. brn., grn. & vio. 30 30
D 316. H. 30 f. vio., red & bl. 50 50
D 317. I. 30 f. bl., red & vio. 50 50
DESIGNS: A, Heliograph. B, Old morse receiver. C, Postman on cycle. D, Old telephone. E, Modern railcar. F, Citroen "2-CV" mail van. G, Radio station. H, Douglas DC-8-10/50CF airliner. I, "Early Bird" satellite.

## DANISH WEST INDIES Pt. 11

A group of islands in the West Indies formerly belonging to Denmark and purchased in 1917 by the United States, whose stamps they now use. Now known as the United States Virgin Islands.

1855. 100 cents = 1 dollar.
1905. 100 bit = 1 franc.

1. 2. 5.

**1855.** Imperf.
4. 1. 3 c. red .. .. .. 29·00 48·00

**1872.** Perf.
6. 1. 3 c. red .. .. .. 70·00 £120
7. 4 c. blue .. .. .. £150 £300

**1873.**
31 2. 1 c. red and green .. 8·75 14·50
32 3 c. red and blue .. 7·25 9·75
33 4 c. blue and brown .. 7·75 7·75
19 5 c. brown and green .. 19·00 12·00
21 7 c. yellow and purple .. 22·00 80·00
25 10 c. brown and blue .. 19·00 19·00
27 12 c. green and purple .. 30·00 £120
28 14 c. green and lilac .. £475 £750
29 50 c. lilac .. .. £100 £190

**1887.** Handstamped **1 CENT.**
37 2 1 c. on 7 c. yellow & purple 60·00 £150

**1895.** Surch **10 CENTS 1895.**
38 2 10 c. on 50 c. lilac .. 24·00 60·00

**1900.**
39. 5. 1 c. green .. .. 2·25 2·25
40. 2 c. red .. .. 5·75 19·00
41. 5 c. blue .. .. 9·50 19·00
42. 8 c. brown .. .. 19·00 38·00

**1902.** Surch **2** (or **8**) **CENTS 1902.**
43 2 2 c. on 3 c. red and blue .. 6·00 19·00
47 8 c. on 10 c. brown & blue 7·25 7·25

**1905.** Surch. **5 BIT 1905.**
48. 2. 5 b. on 4 c. blue & brown 12·00 32·00
49. 5. 5 b. on 5 c. blue .. 10·00 29·00
50. 5 b. on 8 c. brown .. 10·00 29·00

10. King Christian IX. 11. Charlotte Amalie Harbour and Training ship "Ingolf".

**1905.**
51. 10. 5 b. green .. .. 3·50 3·00
52. 10 b. red .. .. 3·50 3·00
53. 20 b. blue and green 7·75 6·00
54. 25 b. blue .. .. 7·75 7·75
55. 40 b. grey and red 7·75 6·00
56. 50 b. grey and yellow 7·75 8·75
57. 11. 1 f. blue and green 16·00 30·00
58. 2 f. brown and red 23·00 42·00
59. 5 f. brown and yellow 50·00 £190

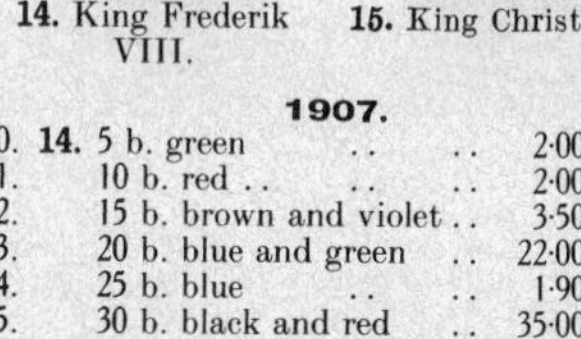

14. King Frederik VIII. 15. King Christian X.

**1907.**
60. 14. 5 b. green .. .. 2·00 1·50
61. 10 b. red .. .. 2·00 1·50
62. 15 b. brown and violet .. 3·50 3·50
63. 20 b. blue and green .. 22·00 19·00
64. 25 b. blue .. .. 1·90 1·90
65. 30 b. black and red .. 35·00 35·00
66. 40 b. grey and red .. 5·00 5·75
67. 50 b. brown and yellow 5·00 8·75

**1915.**
68. 15. 5 b. green .. .. 3·75 3·50
69. 10 b. red .. .. 3·75 38·00
70. 15 b. brown and lilac 3·75 40·00
71. 20 b. blue and green 3·75 40·00
72. 25 b. blue .. .. 3·75 9·50
73. 30 b. black and red 3·75 48·00
74. 40 b. grey and red 3·75 48·00
75. 50 b. brown and yellow .. 3·75 48·00

POSTAGE DUE STAMPS

D 6. D 12.

**1902.**
D 43. D 6. 1 c. blue .. .. 3·75 10·50
D 44. 4 c. blue .. .. 7·25 14·50
D 45. 6 c. blue .. .. 14·50 40·00
D 46. 10 c. blue .. .. 9·75 38·00

**1905.**
D 60. D 12. 5 b. grey and red .. 3·75 4·75
D 61. 20 b. grey and red .. 4·75 12·00
D 62. 30 b. grey and red .. 4·75 12·00
D 63. 50 b. grey and red .. 4·00 24·00

## DANZIG Pt. 7

A Baltic seaport, from 1920-1939 (with the surrounding district) a free state under the protection of the League of Nations. Later incorporated in Germany. Now part of Poland.

1920. 100 pfennige = 1 mark.
1923. 100 pfennige = 1 Danzig gulden.

Stamps of Germany inscr. "DEUTSCHES REICH" optd. or surch.

**1920.** Optd. **Danzig** horiz.
1. 10. 5 pf. green .. .. 20 30
2. 10 pf. red .. .. 30 30
3. 24. 15 pf. brown .. .. 25 35
4. 10. 20 pf. blue .. .. 20 20
5. 30 pf. black and orange on buff .. .. 25 25
6. 40 pf. red .. .. 25 20
7. 50 pf. black and purple on buff .. .. 35 20
8. 12. 1 m. red .. .. 50 75
9. 1 m. 25 green .. .. 50 75
10. 1 m. 50 brown .. .. 90 1·10
11. 13. 2 m. blue .. .. 1·75 5·00
12. 2 m. 50 red .. .. 1·60 3·25
13. 14. 3 m. black .. .. 7·00 11·00
14. 10. 4 m. red and black .. 5·00 7·50
15a. 15. 5 m. red and black .. 2·00 3·00

**1920.** Surch. **Danzig** horiz. and large figures of value.
16. 10. 5 on 30 pf. black and orange on buff .. 10 20
17. 10 on 20 pf. blue .. 10 15
18. 25 on 30 pf. black and orange on buff .. 10 20
19. 60 on 30 pf. black and orange on buff .. 65 80
20. 80 on 30 pf. black and orange on buff .. 65 80

**1920.** Optd **Danzig** diagonally and bar.
21 24 2 pf. grey .. .. £110 £225
22 2½ pf. grey .. .. £160 £275
23 10 3 pf. brown .. .. 7·00 15·00
24 5 pf. green .. .. 30 35
25 24 7½ pf. orange .. .. 30·00 60·00
26 10 10 pf. red .. .. 3·00 5·75
27 24 15 pf. violet .. .. 50 65
28 10 20 pf. blue .. .. 65 60
29 25 pf. blk & red on yell 50 65
30 30 pf. blk & orge on buff 45·00 90·00
31 40 pf. black and red .. 1·25 2·25
32 50 pf. blk & pur on buff £140 £300
32a 60 pf. mauve .. .. £1400 £3500
33 75 pf. black and green 50 65
34 80 pf. blk & red on pink 2·00 4·75
34a 12 1 m. red .. .. £600 £1500

**1920.** Optd. **DANZIG three times in semi-circle.**
34b. 13. 2 m. blue .. .. £700 £1600

**1920.** No. 5 of Danzig surch **MARK 1 MARK** and Types of Germany with burelage added surch with new value and **DANZIG** (36/37), **Danzig** (38, 40f) or **DANZIG** and flag (40e).
35 10 1 m. on 30 pf. black and orange on buff 65 1·60
36 1¼ m. on 3 pf. brown .. 65 1·60
37 24 2 m. on 35 pf. brown .. 80 2·00
38 3 m. on 7½ pf. orange 80 2·00
40e 5 m. on 2 pf. grey 1·00 1·75
40f 10 m. on 7½ pf. orange 1·00 1·75

**1920.** Air. No. 6 of Danzig surch with airplane or wings and value.
41. 10. 40 on 40 pf. red .. .. 1·25 3·00
42. 60 on 40 pf. red .. .. 1·25 3·00
43. 1 m. on 40 pf. red .. 1·25 3·00

13. Hanse Kogge.

**1921.** Constitution of 1920.
44 13 5 pf. purple and brown .. 25 30
45 10 pf. violet and orange 25 30
46 25 pf. red and green .. 50 70
55 40 pf. red .. .. 70 1·25
48 80 pf. blue .. .. 30 60
49 – 1 m. grey and red 1·40 2·00
50 – 2 m. green and blue .. 6·00 7·00
51 – 3 m. green and black .. 1·50 2·00
52 – 5 m. red and grey .. 1·50 2·00
53 – 10 m. brown and green .. 3·00 6·00
The mark values are as Type **13**, but larger.

15. Sabaltnig PIII over Danzig. 16.

**1921.** Air.
57. 15. 40 pf. green .. .. 20 50
58. 60 pf. purple .. .. 20 50
59. 1 m. red .. .. 20 50
60. 2 m. brown .. .. 20 50
116. 16. 5 m. violet .. .. 30 65
117. 10 m. green .. .. 30 65
118. 20 m. brown .. .. 30 65
119. 15. 25 m. blue .. .. 30 65
120. 16. 50 m. orange .. .. 30 65
121. 100 m. red .. .. 30 65
122. 250 m. brown .. .. 30 65
123. 500 m. red .. .. 30 65
Nos. 120 to 123 are similar to Type **16**, but larger.

**1921.** No. 33 of Danzig surch. **60** and bars.
63 10 60 on 75 pf. black & green 50 1·25

18. 19.

**1921.**
64. 18. 5 pf. orange .. .. 25 25
65. 10 pf. brown .. .. 15 10
66. 15 pf. green .. .. 15 15
67. 20 pf. grey .. .. 15 15
68. 25 pf. green .. .. 15 15
69. 30 pf. red and blue .. 20 25
70. 40 pf. red and green .. 15 15
71. 50 pf. red and green .. 15 10
72. 60 pf. red .. .. 25 20
73. 75 pf. purple .. .. 15 10
74. 80 pf. red and black .. 20 50
75. 80 pf. green .. .. 15 20
76. 1 m. red and orange .. 10 25

| No. | Type | Description | Unused | Used |
|---|---|---|---|---|
| 77. | 18. | 1.20 m. blue | 75 | 1·00 |
| 78. | | 1.25 m. red and purple | 15 | 15 |
| 79. | | 1.50 m. grey | 15 | 15 |
| 80. | | 2 m. red and grey | 3·00 | 4·00 |
| 81. | | 2 m. red | 15 | 10 |
| 82. | | 2.40 m. red and brown | 1·00 | 1·75 |
| 83a. | | 3 m. red and purple | 8·75 | 12·00 |
| 84. | | 3 m. red | 15 | 15 |
| 106. | | 4 m. blue | 15 | 35 |
| 86. | | 5 m. green | 10 | 15 |
| 87. | | 6 m. red | 10 | 25 |
| 88. | | 8 m. blue | 30 | 85 |
| 89. | | 10 m. orange | 10 | 25 |
| 90. | | 20 m. brown | 10 | 25 |
| 110. | | 40 m. blue | 10 | 25 |
| 111. | | 80 m. red | 10 | 25 |

**1921.** Rouletted.

| No. | Type | Description | Unused | Used |
|---|---|---|---|---|
| 91. | 19. | 5 m. green, black and red | 1·10 | 2·25 |
| 91a. | | 9 m. orange and red | 2·75 | 8·00 |
| 92. | | 10 m. blue, black and red | 1·10 | 2·25 |
| 93. | | 20 m. black and red | 1·10 | 2·25 |

20. 21.

**1921.** Tuberculosis Week.

| No. | Type | Description | Unused | Used |
|---|---|---|---|---|
| 93a. | 20. | 30 pf. (+30 pf.) grn. & orge | 60 | 50 |
| 93b. | | 60 pf. (+60 pf.) red & yell. | 1·25 | 1·25 |
| 93c. | | 1.20 m. (+1.20 m.) bl. & orge. (25×29½ mm.) | 2·00 | 2·25 |

**1922.**

| No. | Type | Description | Unused | Used |
|---|---|---|---|---|
| 94a. | 21. | 50 m. red and gold | 90 | 3·25 |
| 95. | | 100 m. red and green | 2·25 | 4·75 |

**1922.** Surch. in figures.

| No. | Type | Description | Unused | Used |
|---|---|---|---|---|
| 96. | 18. | 6 on 3 m. red | 15 | 40 |
| 97. | | 8 on 4 m. blue | 20 | 60 |
| 98. | | 20 on 8 m. blue | 20 | 50 |

25. 26.

**1923.**

| No. | Type | Description | Unused | Used |
|---|---|---|---|---|
| 99 | 25 | 50 m. red and blue | 15 | 35 |
| 136 | | 50 m. blue | 15 | 35 |
| 100 | | 100 m. red and green | 15 | 35 |
| 137 | | 100 m. green | 15 | 35 |
| 101 | | 150 m. red and purple | 15 | 35 |
| 138 | | 200 m. orange | 15 | 35 |
| 102 | 26 | 250 m. red and purple | 20 | 35 |
| 103 | | 500 m. red and grey | 15 | 35 |
| 104 | | 1000 m. pink and brown | 15 | 35 |
| 105 | | 5000 m. pink and silver | 1·00 | 5·00 |
| 139 | | 10000 m. red and orange | 25 | 50 |
| 140 | | 20000 m. red and blue | 35 | 85 |
| 141 | | 50000 m. red and green | 30 | 65 |

28.

**1923.** Poor People's Fund.

| No. | Type | Description | Unused | Used |
|---|---|---|---|---|
| 123b | 28 | 50+20 m. red | 15 | 60 |
| 123c | | 100+30 m. purple | 15 | 60 |

29. 35. Etrich/Rumpler Taube.

**1923.**

| No. | Type | Description | Unused | Used |
|---|---|---|---|---|
| 124 | 29 | 250 m. red and purple | 15 | 25 |
| 125 | | 300 m. red and green | 15 | 35 |
| 126 | | 500 m. red and grey | 15 | 25 |
| 127 | | 1000 m. brown | 15 | 30 |
| 128 | | 1000 m. red and brown | 15 | 30 |
| 129 | | 3000 m. red and violet | 15 | 30 |
| 130 | | 5000 m. pink | 15 | 30 |
| 131 | | 20000 m. blue | 15 | 30 |
| 132 | | 50000 m. green | 15 | 30 |
| 133 | | 100000 m. blue | 15 | 30 |
| 134 | | 250000 m. purple | 15 | 30 |
| 135 | | 500000 m. grey | 15 | 30 |

**1923.** Surch **100000** and bar.

| No. | Type | Description | Unused | Used |
|---|---|---|---|---|
| 157 | 26 | 100000 on 20000 m. red and blue | 75 | 5·50 |

**1923.** Surch with figure of value and **Tausend** (T) or **Million** or **Millionen** (M).

| No. | Type | Description | Unused | Used |
|---|---|---|---|---|
| 142 | 25 | 40 T. on 200 m. orange | 60 | 2·10 |
| 143 | | 100 T. on 200 m. orange | 60 | 2·10 |
| 144 | | 250 T. on 200 m. orange | 6·00 | 14·00 |
| 145 | | 400 T. on 100 m. green | 30 | 60 |
| 146 | 29 | 500 T. on 50000 m. green | 30 | 60 |
| 147 | | 1 M. on 10000 m. orange | 3·00 | 7·00 |
| 148 | | 1 M. on 10000 m. red | 15 | 35 |
| 149 | 29 | 2 M. on 10000 m. red | 15 | 35 |
| 150 | | 3 M. on 10000 m. red | 15 | 35 |
| 151 | | 5 M. on 10000 m. red | 15 | 35 |
| 152 | | 10 M. on 10000 m. lav | 25 | 45 |
| 158 | 26 | 10 M. on 1000000 m. orge | 30 | 30 |
| 153 | 29 | 20 M. on 10000 m. lav | 25 | 45 |
| 154 | | 25 M. on 10000 m. lav | 20 | 45 |
| 155 | | 40 M. on 10000 m. lav | 20 | 45 |
| 156 | | 50 M. on 10000 m. lav | 20 | 45 |
| 159 | | 100 M. on 10000 m. lav | 20 | 45 |
| 160 | | 300 M. on 10000 m. lav | 20 | 45 |
| 161 | | 500 M. on 10000 m. lav | 20 | 45 |

**1923.** Air.

| No. | Type | Description | Unused | Used |
|---|---|---|---|---|
| 162. | 35. | 250,000 m. red | 30 | 1·40 |
| 163. | | 500,000 m. red | 30 | 1·40 |

**1923.** Surch. in **Millionen.**

| No. | Type | Description | Unused | Used |
|---|---|---|---|---|
| 164. | 35. | 2 M. on 100,000 m. red | 30 | 1·40 |
| 165. | | 5 M. on 50,000 m. red | 30 | 1·40 |

**1923.** Surch with new currency, **Pfennige** or **Gulden**.

| No. | Type | Description | Unused | Used |
|---|---|---|---|---|
| 166 | 25 | 5 pf. on 50 m. red | 50 | 40 |
| 167 | | 10 pf. on 50 m. red | 50 | 40 |
| 168 | | 20 pf. on 100 m. red | 50 | 50 |
| 169 | | 25 pf. on 50 m. red | 4·25 | 12·00 |
| 170 | | 30 pf. on 50 m. red | 3·00 | 2·00 |
| 171 | | 40 pf. on 100 m. red | 2·50 | 2·25 |
| 172 | | 50 pf. on 100 m. red | 2·75 | 3·00 |
| 173 | | 75 pf. on 100 m. red | 8·00 | 17·00 |
| 174 | 26 | 1 g. on 1000000 m. red | 5·00 | 6·00 |
| 175 | | 2 g. on 1000000 m. red | 13·00 | 20·00 |
| 176 | | 3 g. on 1000000 m. red | 32·00 | 70·00 |
| 177 | | 5 g. on 1000000 m. red | 38·00 | 80·00 |

39. 40. Etrich/Rumpler Taube.

**1924.**

| No. | Type | Description | Unused | Used |
|---|---|---|---|---|
| 177b | 39 | 3 pf. brown | 1·25 | 1·00 |
| 268 | | 5 pf. orange | 60 | 1·40 |
| 178e | | 7 pf. green | 1·40 | 2·25 |
| 178f | | 8 pf. green | 2·25 | 5·75 |
| 270 | | 10 pf. green | 75 | 1·40 |
| 180 | | 15 pf. grey | 3·50 | 50 |
| 180a | | 15 pf. red | 2·75 | 30 |
| 181 | | 20 pf. red & carmine | 10·00 | 40 |
| 182 | | 20 pf. grey | 1·10 | 1·60 |
| 183 | | 25 pf. red and grey | 14·00 | 2·25 |
| 272 | | 25 pf. red | 3·50 | 5·50 |
| 185 | | 30 pf. red and green | 10·00 | 60 |
| 186 | | 30 pf. purple | 1·25 | 4·50 |
| 186a | | 35 pf. blue | 2·00 | 1·00 |
| 187 | | 40 pf. blue and indigo | 8·00 | 75 |
| 188 | | 40 pf. red and brown | 8·50 | 17·00 |
| 189 | | 40 pf. blue | 1·25 | 2·25 |
| 274 | | 50 pf. red and blue | 3·25 | 9·50 |
| 190b | | 55 pf. red and purple | 5·00 | 12·00 |
| 191 | | 60 pf. red and green | 8·50 | 17·00 |
| 192 | | 70 pf. red and green | 2·50 | 5·00 |
| 193a | | 75 pf. red and purple | 4·00 | 6·00 |
| 194 | | 80 pf. red and brown | 3·00 | 10·00 |

**1924.** Air.

| No. | Type | Description | Unused | Used |
|---|---|---|---|---|
| 195 | 40 | 10 pf. red | 22·00 | 3·50 |
| 196 | | 20 pf. mauve | 1·25 | 1·25 |
| 197 | | 40 pf. brown | 3·00 | 1·75 |
| 198 | | 1 g. green | 3·00 | 1·75 |
| 199 | | 2½ g. purple (22×40 mm) | 19·00 | 40·00 |

42. Oliva. 44. Fountain of Neptune.

**1924.**

| No. | Type | Description | Unused | Used |
|---|---|---|---|---|
| 200. | 42. | 1 g. black and green | 24·00 | 40·00 |
| 275. | | 1 g. black and orange | 5·00 | 10·00 |
| 201. | – | 2 g. black and purple | 55·00 | £110 |
| 206. | – | 2 g. black and red | 3·00 | 5·00 |
| 202. | – | 3 g. black and blue | 3·75 | 6·75 |
| 203. | – | 5 g. black and lake | 5·75 | 9·00 |
| 204. | – | 10 g. black and brown | 30·00 | 90·00 |

DESIGNS—HORIZ. 2 g. Krantor and River Mottlau. 3 g. Zoppot. VERT. 5 g. St. Mary's Church. 10 g. Town Hall and Langemarkt.

**1929.** Int. Philatelic Exn. Various frames.

| No. | Type | Description | Unused | Used |
|---|---|---|---|---|
| 207. | 44. | 10 pf. (+10 pf.) black and green | 2·25 | 3·25 |
| 208. | | 15 pf. (+15 pf.) blk. & red | 2·25 | 3·25 |
| 209. | | 25 pf. (+25 pf.) blk. & bl. | 8·00 | 6·00 |

**1930.** 10th Anniv. of Constitution of Free City of Danzig. Optd. **1920 15. November 1930.**

| No. | Type | Description | Unused | Used |
|---|---|---|---|---|
| 210 | 39 | 5 pf. orange | 2·00 | 3·00 |
| 211 | | 10 pf. green | 3·00 | 3·50 |
| 212 | | 15 pf. red | 4·00 | 10·00 |
| 213 | | 20 pf. red and carmine | 2·25 | 5·00 |
| 214 | | 25 pf. red and grey | 5·00 | 10·00 |
| 215 | | 30 pf. red and green | 10·00 | 25·00 |
| 216 | | 35 pf. blue | 40·00 | 80·00 |
| 217 | | 40 pf. blue and indigo | 10·00 | 27·00 |
| 218 | | 50 pf. red and blue | 40·00 | 70·00 |
| 219 | – | 75 pf. red and purple | 40·00 | 70·00 |
| 220 | 42 | 1 g. black and orange | 40·00 | 70·00 |

**1932.** Danzig Int. Air Post Exn. ("Luposta"). Nos. 200/4 surch. **Luftpost-Ausstellung 1932** and value.

| No. | Type | Description | Unused | Used |
|---|---|---|---|---|
| 221. | 42. | 10 pf. + 10 pf. on 1 g. black and green | 10·00 | 22·00 |
| 222. | – | 15 pf. + 15 pf. on 2 g. black and purple | 10·00 | 22·00 |
| 223. | – | 20 pf. + 20 pf. on 3 g. black and blue | 10·00 | 22·00 |
| 224. | – | 25 pf. + 25 pf. on 5 g. black and lake | 10·00 | 22·00 |
| 225. | – | 30 pf. + 30 pf. on 10 g. black and brown | 10·00 | 22·00 |

**1934.** "Winter Relief Work" Charity. Surch. **5 W.H.W.** in gothic characters.

| No. | Type | Description | Unused | Used |
|---|---|---|---|---|
| 226. | 39. | 5 pf.+5 pf. orange | 10·00 | 22·00 |
| 227. | | 10 pf.+5 pf. green | 28·00 | 55·00 |
| 228. | | 15 pf.+5 pf. red | 20·00 | 40·00 |

**1934.** Surch.

| No. | Type | Description | Unused | Used |
|---|---|---|---|---|
| 229. | 39. | 6 pf. on 7 pf. green | 90 | 1·40 |
| 230a. | | 8 pf. on 7 pf. green | 1·40 | 2·00 |
| 231. | | 30 pf. on 35 pf. blue | 12·00 | 18·00 |

50. Junkers F-13. 51.

**1935.** Air.

| No. | Type | Description | Unused | Used |
|---|---|---|---|---|
| 233. | 50. | 10 pf. red | 1·40 | 80 |
| 234. | | 15 pf. yellow | 1·25 | 1·40 |
| 235. | | 25 pf. green | 1·40 | 1·60 |
| 236. | | 50 pf. blue | 8·75 | 9·50 |
| 237. | 51. | 1 g. purple | 6·00 | 13·00 |

52. Stockturm, 1346. 54. Brosen War Memorial.

**1935.** Winter Relief Fund.

| No. | Type | Description | Unused | Used |
|---|---|---|---|---|
| 238. | 52. | 5 pf.+5 pf. orange | 60 | 1·40 |
| 239. | – | 10 pf.+5 pf. green | 1·00 | 2·00 |
| 240. | – | 15 pf.+10 pf. red | 1·40 | 4·50 |

DESIGNS—HORIZ. 10 pf. Lege Tor. VERT. 15 pf. Georgshalle, 1487.

**1936.** 125th Anniv. of Brosen. Inscr. "125 JAHRE OSTEEBAD BROSEN".

| No. | Type | Description | Unused | Used |
|---|---|---|---|---|
| 241. | – | 10 pf. green | 60 | 1·25 |
| 242. | – | 25 pf. red | 90 | 2·25 |
| 243. | 54. | 40 pf. blue | 2·00 | 4·50 |

DESIGNS—HORIZ. 10 pf. Brosen Beach. 25 pf. Zoppot end of Brosen Beach.

55. Frauentor and Observatory. 56. D(anziger) L(uftschutz) B(und). 57a. Danziger Dorf, Magdeburg.

**1936.** Winter Relief Fund.

| No. | Type | Description | Unused | Used |
|---|---|---|---|---|
| 244. | – | 10 pf.+5 pf. blue | 2·00 | 5·00 |
| 245. | 55. | 15 pf.+5 pf. green | 2·25 | 5·50 |
| 246. | – | 25 pf.+10 pf. red | 3·00 | 6·50 |
| 247. | – | 40 pf.+20 pf. brn. & red | 4·50 | 11·00 |
| 248. | – | 50 pf.+20 pf. blue | 6·00 | 16·00 |

DESIGNS—VERT. 10 pf. Milchkannenturm, 25 pf. Krantor. HORIZ. 40 pf. Langgartertor. 50 pf. Hohestor.

**1937.** Air. Defence League.

| No. | Type | Description | Unused | Used |
|---|---|---|---|---|
| 249. | 56. | 10 pf. blue | 65 | 1·60 |
| 250. | | 15 pf. purple | 1·60 | 2·50 |

**1937.** Foundation of Danzig Community, Magdeburg.

| No. | Type | Description | Unused | Used |
|---|---|---|---|---|
| 253. | 57a. | 25 pf. (+25 pf.) red | 2·25 | 6·00 |
| 254. | – | 40 pf. (+40 pf.) red and blue | 2·25 | 6·00 |

DESIGN—HORIZ. 40 pf. Village and Arms of Danzig and Magdeburg.

58. Madonna and Child. 59. Schopenhauer.

**1937.** Winter Relief Fund. Statues.

| No. | Type | Description | Unused | Used |
|---|---|---|---|---|
| 255 | 58 | 5 pf.+5 pf. violet | 2·00 | 5·00 |
| 256 | – | 10 pf.+5 pf. brown | 2·50 | 6·00 |
| 257 | – | 15 pf.+5 pf. orange & bl | 3·00 | 7·00 |
| 258 | – | 25 pf.+10 pf. green & bl | 4·00 | 8·50 |
| 259 | – | 40 pf.+25 pf. blue & red | 7·50 | 16·00 |

DESIGNS: 10 pf. Mercury. 15 pf. The "Golden Knight". 25 pf. Fountain of Neptune. 40 pf. St. George and Dragon.

**1938.** 150th Birth Anniv of Schopenhauer (philosopher). Portraits inscr as in T **59.**

| No. | Type | Description | Unused | Used |
|---|---|---|---|---|
| 260. | – | 15 pf. blue (as old man) | 1·40 | 2·40 |
| 261. | – | 25 pf. brown (as youth) | 3·50 | 6·50 |
| 262. | 59. | 40 pf. red | 1·50 | 3·75 |

60. Yacht "Peter von Danzig" (1936). 61. Teutonic Knights.

**1938.** Winter Relief Fund. Ships.

| No. | Type | Description | Unused | Used |
|---|---|---|---|---|
| 276 | 60 | 5 pf.+5 pf. green | 1·25 | 2·50 |
| 277 | – | 10 pf.+5 pf. brown | 1·50 | 3·00 |
| 278 | – | 15 pf.+10 pf. olive | 1·50 | 3·75 |
| 279 | – | 25 pf.+10 pf. blue | 2·50 | 5·00 |
| 280 | – | 40 pf.+15 pf. purple | 3·00 | 7·00 |

DESIGNS: 10 pf. Dredger "Fu Shing". 15 pf. Liner "Columbus". 25 pf. Liner "Hansestadt Danzig". 40 pf. Sailing ship "Peter von Danzig" (1472).

**1939.** 125th Anniv of Prussian Annexation. Historical designs.

| No. | Type | Description | Unused | Used |
|---|---|---|---|---|
| 281. | 61. | 5 pf. green | 85 | 2·25 |
| 282. | – | 10 pf. brown | 90 | 2·75 |
| 283. | – | 15 pf. blue | 1·25 | 3·25 |
| 284. | – | 25 pf. purple | 1·50 | 4·00 |

DESIGNS: 10 pf. Danzig-Swedish treaty of neutrality, 1630. 15 pf. Danzig united to Prussia, 2.1.1814. 25 pf. Stephen Batori's defeat at Weichselmunde, 1577.

62. Gregor Mendel.

**1939.** Anti-Cancer Campaign.

| No. | Type | Description | Unused | Used |
|---|---|---|---|---|
| 285. | 62. | 10 pf. brown | 45 | 90 |
| 286. | – | 15 pf. black (Koch) | 50 | 1·10 |
| 287. | – | 25 pf. green (Rontgen) | 85 | 2·00 |

## OFFICIAL STAMPS

**1921.** Stamps of Danzig optd. **D M.**

| No. | Type | Description | Unused | Used |
|---|---|---|---|---|
| O 94. | 18. | 5 f. orange | 30 | 30 |
| O 95. | | 10 pf. brown | 20 | 15 |
| O 96. | | 15 pf. green | 20 | 20 |
| O 97. | | 20 pf. grey | 20 | 20 |
| O 98. | | 25 pf. green | 20 | 20 |
| O 99. | | 30 pf. red and blue | 60 | 50 |
| O100. | | 40 pf. red and green | 25 | 25 |
| O101. | | 50 pf. red and green | 20 | 20 |
| O102. | | 60 pf. red | 20 | 20 |
| O103. | | 75 f. purple | 15 | 25 |
| O104. | | 80 pf. red and black | 1·25 | 1·50 |
| O105. | | 80 pf. green | 20 | 30 |
| O106. | | 1 m. orange | 20 | 20 |
| O107. | | 1 m. 20 blue | 1·25 | 1·50 |
| O108. | | 1 m. 25 red and purple | 20 | 35 |
| O109. | | 1 m. 50 grey | 15 | 30 |
| O110. | | 2 m. red and grey | 16·00 | 15·00 |
| O111. | | 2 m. red | 20 | 30 |
| O112. | | 2 m. 40 red and brown | 1·10 | 2·50 |
| O113. | | 3 m. red and purple | 9·00 | 14·00 |
| O114. | | 3 m. red | 15 | 30 |
| O122. | | 4 m. blue | 15 | 40 |
| O116. | | 5 m. green | 15 | 20 |
| O117. | | 6 m. red | 15 | 20 |
| O121. | | 6 on 3 m. red (No. 96) | 15 | 55 |
| O118. | | 10 m. orange | 15 | 30 |
| O119. | | 20 m. brown | 15 | 25 |

**1922.** Stamps of Danzig optd **D. M.**

| No. | Type | Description | Unused | Used |
|---|---|---|---|---|
| O120 | 19 | 5 m. green, black and red (No. 91) | 2·75 | 7·00 |
| O126 | 25 | 50 m. red and blue | 15 | 40 |
| O142 | | 50 m. blue | 15 | 30 |
| O127 | | 100 m. red and green | 15 | 40 |
| O143 | | 100 m. green | 15 | 30 |
| O144 | | 200 m. orange | 15 | 30 |
| O145 | 29 | 300 m. red and green | 15 | 30 |
| O146 | | 500 m. red and grey | 15 | 30 |
| O147 | | 1000m. red and brown | 15 | 30 |

**1924.** Optd. **Dienst-marke.**
O 195. **39.** 5 pf. orange .. .. 1·75 1·50
O 196. 10 pf. green .. .. 1·75 1·50
O 197. 15 pf. grey .. .. 1·75 1·50
O 198. 15 pf. red .. .. 20·00 8·75
O 199. 20 pf. red and carmine 1·90 1·25
O 200. 25 pf. red and black .. 17·00 24·00
O 201. 30 pf. red and green .. 2·75 2·00
O 202. 35 f. blue .. .. 40·00 45·00
O 203. 40 pf. blue and indigo 6·00 7·00
O 204. 50 pf. red and blue .. 16·00 27·00
O 205. 75 pf. red and purple 35·00 90·00

POSTAGE DUE STAMPS

D 20. D 39.

**1921.** Value in "pfennig" (figures only).
D 94. D **20.** 10 pf. purple .. 20 35
D 95. 20 pf. purple .. 20 35
D 96. 40 pf. purple .. 20 35
D 97. 60 pf. purple .. 20 35
D 98. 75 pf. purple .. 20 35
D 99. 80 pf. purple .. 20 35
D 112. 100 pf. purple .. 40 55
D 100. 120 pf. purple .. 20 35
D 101. 200 pf. purple .. 70 1·00
D 102. 240 pf. purple .. 20 1·00
D 114. 300 pf. purple .. 40 55
D 115. 400 pf. purple .. 40 55
D 116. 500 pf. purple .. 40 55
D 117. 800 pf. purple .. 55 1·00

Value in "marks" ("M" after figure).
D 118. D **20.** 10 m. purple .. 40 55
D 119. 20 m. purple .. 40 55
D 120. 50 m. purple .. 40 55
D 121. 100 m. purple .. 40 85
D 122. 500 m. purple .. 40 85

**1923.** Surch with figures and bar.
D162 D **20** 1000 on 100 m. pur £120 £300
D163 5000 on 50 m. purple 20 45
D164 10000 on 20 m. pur 20 45
D165 50000 on 20 m. pur 20 45
D166 100000 on 20 m. pur 70 1·40

**1924.**
D 178. D **39.** 5 pf. blue and black .. 70 65
D 179. 10 pf. blue and black 55 45
D 180. 15 pf. blue and black 1·25 1·10
D 181. 20 pf. blue and black 1·40 1·75
D 182. 30 pf. blue and black 9·00 1·75
D 183. 40 pf. blue and black 2·25 3·00
D 184. 50 pf. blue and black 2·25 2·25
D 185. 60 pf. blue and black 15·00 24·00
D 186. 100 pf. blue and black 20·00 11·00
D 187. 3 g. blue and red .. 8·00 60·00

**1932.** Surch. in figures over bar.
D 226. D **39.** 5 on 40 pf. blue & blk. 2·00 8·00
D 227. 10 on 60 pf. blue and black .. .. 32·00 8·00
D 228. 20 on 100 pf. blue and black .. .. 2·10 6·50

## DEDEAGATZ Pt. 6

Former French Post Office, closed in Aug. 1914. Dedeagatz was part of Turkey to 1913, then a Bulgarian town.

25 centimes = 1 piastre.

**1893.** Stamps of France optd. **Dedeagh** or surch. also in figures and words.
59 **10** 5 c. green .. .. 6·00 6·50
60 10 c. black on lilac .. 11·50 10·00
62a 15 c. blue .. .. 16·00 10·00
63 1 pi. on 25 c. black on red 15·00 13·00
64 2 pi. on 50 c. red .. 35·00 25·00
65 4 pi. on 1 f. olive .. 40·00 32·00
66 8 pi. on 2 f. brn. on blue 60·00 48·00

**1902.** "Blanc", "Mouchon" and "Merson" key-types inscr. "DEDEAGH". Some surch. in figures and words.
67a A 5 c. green .. .. 55 60
68 B 10 c. red .. .. 60 70
70 15 c. orange .. .. 85 90
71 1 pi. on 25 c. blue .. 1·00 1·00
72 C 2 pi. on 50 c. brown & lav. 2·75 3·50
73 4 pi. on 1 f. red and green 8·00 6·25
74 8 pi. on 2 f. lilac & yellow 11·50 11·50

## DENMARK Pt. 11

A kingdom in N. Europe, on a peninsula between the Baltic and the North Sea.

1851. 96 rigsbank skilling = 1 rigsdaler.
1875. 100 ore = 1 krone.

1. 2. 4.

**1851.** Imperf.
3 **1.** 2 R.B.S. blue .. .. £2250 £850
4 **2.** 4 R.B.S. brown .. .. £400 26·00

**1854.** Dotted background. Brown burelage. Imperf.
8 **4** 2 sk. blue .. .. 48·00 45·00
9b 4 sk. orange .. .. £250 9·50
12 8 sk. green .. .. £275 55·00
13 16 sk. lilac .. .. £375 £140

5. 7. 8.

**1858.** Background of wavy lines. Brown burelage. Imperf.
15 **5** 4 sk. brown .. .. 48·00 6·75
18 8 sk. green .. .. £500 70·00

**1863.** Brown burelage. Roul.
19 **5** 4 sk. brown .. .. 70·00 12·00
21 **4** 16 sk. mauve .. .. £1200 £450

**1864.** Perf.
22 **7** 2 sk. blue .. .. 45·00 29·00
25 3 sk. mauve .. .. 60·00 55·00
28 4 sk. red .. .. 29·00 6·75
29 8 sk. bistre .. .. £225 90·00
30a 16 sk. green .. .. £300 80·00

**1870.** Value in "skilling".
39 **8** 2 sk. blue and grey .. 38·00 20·00
42 3 sk. purple and grey .. 60·00 48·00
44 4 sk. red and grey .. 29·00 5·50
46 8 sk. brown and grey .. £120 48·00
48 16 sk. green and grey .. £160 £100
37 48 sk. lilac and brown .. £300 £180

**1875.** As T **8**, but value in "ore".
80 **8** 3 ore grey and blue .. 2·00 2·00
81 4 ore blue and grey .. 3·00 10
56 5 ore blue and red .. 20·00 50·00
82 8 ore red and grey .. 3·00 10
83 12 ore purple and grey .. 3·00 2·25
84 16 ore brown and grey .. 10·50 2·40
72 20 ore grey and red .. 55·00 20·00
85 25 ore green and grey .. 4·75 2·40
86 50 ore purple and brown 17·00 9·75
87 100 ore orange and grey .. 14·50 7·25

10. 14. King Christian IX. 15.

**1882.**
96. **10.** 1 ore orange .. .. 40 40
97. 5 ore green .. .. 1·50 10
98. 10 ore red .. .. 1·75 10
99. 15 ore mauve .. .. 7·25 45
100. 20 ore blue .. .. 8·75 2·00
101. 24 ore brown .. .. 4·00 2·00

**1904.** No. 82 and 101 surch.
102 **8** 4 ore on 8 ore red & grey 1·50 2·25
103 **10** 15 ore on 24 ore brown 2·40 2·40

**1904.**
117 **14** 5 ore green .. .. 2·00 10
104 10 ore red .. .. 1·50 10
105 20 ore blue .. .. 7·25 1·00
106 25 ore brown .. .. 10·50 2·00
107 50 ore lilac .. .. 29·00 40·00
108 100 ore brown .. .. 7·25 28·00

**1905.** Solid background.
173 **15** 1 ore orange .. .. 35 20
174 2 ore red .. .. 1·40 10
175 3 ore grey .. .. 2·75 10
176 4 ore blue .. .. 2·75 10
177 5 ore brown .. .. 70 10
178 5 ore green .. .. 90 10
179 7 ore green .. .. 2·00 10
180 7 ore violet .. .. 6·75 2·25
181 8 ore grey .. .. 2·75 1·50
114 10 ore pink .. .. 3·00 10
182 10 ore green .. .. 60 10
183 10 ore brown .. .. 95 10
184 12 ore lilac .. .. 8·75 3·25
115 15 ore mauve .. .. 7·75 55
116 20 ore blue .. .. 17·00 45

For stamps with lined background but without hearts, see Nos. 265/76j.

17. King Frederik VIII. 20. G.P.O. Copenhagen.

**1907.**
121 **17** 5 ore green .. .. 1·00 10
122 10 ore red .. .. 1·50 10
124 20 ore blue .. .. 7·25 50
125 25 ore brown .. .. 12·00 35
127 35 ore orange .. .. 2·50 2·50
128 50 ore purple .. .. 14·50 2·40
130 100 ore brown .. .. 45·00 1·75

**1912.** (a) Nos. 84 and 72 surch **35 ORE.**
131 **8** 35 ore on 16 ore brown and grey .. .. 7·75 24·00
132 35 ore on 20 ore grey and red .. .. .. 14·50 38·00

(b) No. O98 surch **35 ORE FRIMAERKE.**
133 O **9** 35 ore on 32 ore green 12·00 45·00

**1912.**
134. **20.** 5 k. red .. .. £160 75·00

21. King Christian X. 22.

**1913.**
135 **21** 5 ore green .. .. 90 10
136 7 ore orange .. .. 1·75 25
137 8 ore grey .. .. 4·00 2·75
138 10 ore red .. .. 1·25 10
139 12 ore grey .. .. 4·00 4·75
141a 15 ore mauve .. .. 1·10 10
142 20 ore blue .. .. 4·50 10
143 20 ore brown .. .. 60 10
144 20 ore red .. .. 1·00 10
145 25 ore brown .. .. 4·75 15
146 25 ore black and brown 32·00 2·50
147 25 ore red .. .. 2·00 20
148 25 ore green .. .. 2·00 20
149 27 ore black and red .. 14·50 26·00
150 30 ore black and green 12·00 90
151 30 ore orange .. .. 1·40 30
152 30 ore blue .. .. 1·00 20
153 35 ore yellow .. .. 9·75 1·50
154 35 ore black and yellow 3·50 3·00
155 40 ore black and violet 7·75 2·00
156 40 ore blue .. .. 2·40 50
157 40 ore yellow .. .. 1·00 60
158 50 ore purple .. .. 20·00 1·75
159 50 ore black and purple 32·00 70
160a 50 ore grey .. .. 4·75 10
161 60 ore blue and brown 2·00 2·40
162 60 ore blue .. .. 4·75 35
163 70 ore green and brown 12·00 1·50
164 80 ore green .. .. 20·00 6·75
165 90 ore red and brown 7·75 2·00
166 **22** 1 k. brown .. .. 40·00 40
167 **21** 1 k. blue and brown 24·00 1·50
168 **22** 2 k. black .. .. 45·00 3·00
169 **21** 2 k. purple and grey .. 29·00 7·75
170 **22** 5 k. violet .. .. 7·75 5·50
171 **21** 5 k. brown and mauve 3·50 3·50
172 10 k. green and red .. £160 24·00

**1915.** (a) No. O94 surch **DANMARK 80 ORE POSTFRIM.**
186 O **9** 80 ore on 8 ore red .. 20·00 65·00

(b) No. 83 surch **80 ORE.**
187 **8** 80 ore on 12 ore purple and grey .. .. 14·50 48·00

**1918.** Newspaper stamps surch **POSTFRIM. ORE 27 ORE DANMARK.**
197 N **18** 27 ore on 1 ore green 2·00 7·25
198 27 ore on 5 ore blue 3·75 14·50
199 27 ore on 7 ore red 2·00 4·75
200 27 ore on 8 ore green 2·50 7·25
201 27 ore on 10 ore lilac 2·25 5·75
202 27 ore on 20 ore green 2·50 6·75
203 27 ore on 29 ore orge 2·00 4·75
204 27 ore on 38 ore orge 14·50 48·00
205 27 ore on 41 ore brn 4·75 24·00
194 27 ore on 68 ore brn 3·75 17·00
206 27 ore on 1 k. purple and green .. 1·50 4·75
195 27 ore on 5 k. green and pink .. 3·00 9·75
196 27 ore on 10 k. blue and stone .. 3·75 14·50

**1919.** No. 135 surch **2 ORE.**
207 **21** 2 ore on 5 ore green .. £800 £350

27. Castle of Kronborg, Elsinore. 29. Roskilde Cathedral.

**1920.** Recovery of Northern Schleswig.
208. **27.** 10 ore red .. .. 2·40 20
209. 10 ore green .. .. 3·50 20
210. – 20 ore slate .. .. 2·00 15
211. **29.** 40 ore brown .. .. 6·75 2·40
212. 40 ore blue .. .. 22·00 3·50

DESIGN—HORIZ. 20 ore Sonderborg Castle.

**1921.** Nos. 136 and 139 surch **8 8.**
217 **21** 8 on 7 ore orange .. 1·25 2·00
213 8 on 12 ore green .. 1·25 5·00

**1921.** Red Cross. Nos. 209/10 surch with figure of value between red crosses.
214 **27** 10 ore + 5 ore green .. 7·75 17·00
215 – 20 ore + 10 ore grey .. 7·75 24·00

**1921.** No. 175 surch **8.**
216 **15** 8 on 3 ore grey .. 1·25 2·00

33. Christian IV. 34. Christian X. 35.

**1924.** 300th Anniv of Danish Post. A. Head facing to left. B. Head facing to right.

| | | | A | | B | |
|---|---|---|---|---|---|---|
| 218 | **33** | 10 ore green | 3·00 | 2·40 | 3·00 | 2·40 |
| 221 | **34** | 10 ore green | 3·00 | 2·40 | 3·00 | 2·40 |
| 219 | **33** | 15 ore mauve | 3·00 | 2·40 | 3·00 | 2·40 |
| 222 | **34** | 15 ore mauve | 3·00 | 2·40 | 3·00 | 2·40 |
| 220 | **33** | 20 ore brown | 3·00 | 2·40 | 3·00 | 2·40 |
| 223 | **34** | 20 ore brown | 3·00 | 2·40 | 3·00 | 2·40 |

**1925.** Air.
224. **35.** 10 ore green .. .. 15·00 19·00
225. 15 ore lilac .. .. 32·00 35·00
226. 25 ore red .. .. 24·00 28·00
227. 50 ore grey .. .. 75·00 £100
228. 1 k. brown .. .. 70·00 80·00

**1926.** Surch **20 20.**
229 **21** 20 on 30 ore orange .. 2·75 5·75
230 20 on 40 ore blue .. 3·75 7·75

38. 39. 40. Caravel.

**1926.** 75th Anniv. of First Danish stamps.
231. **38.** 10 ore olive .. .. 75 10
232. **39.** 20 ore red .. .. 1·00 10
233. 30 ore blue .. .. 3·50 50

**1926.** Various stamps surch.
234 **15** 7 on 8 ore grey .. 75 2·50
235 **21** 7 on 20 ore red .. 45 50
236 7 on 27 ore black & red 2·50 5·00
237 12 on 15 ore lilac .. 1·50 3·00

**1926.** Official stamps surch. **DANMARK 7 ORE POSTFRIM.**
238. O **9.** 7 ore on 1 ore orange .. 2·25 4·75
239. 7 ore on 3 ore grey .. 3·75 12·00
240. 7 ore on 4 ore blue .. 2·00 4·75
241. 7 ore on 5 ore green .. 35·00 60·00
242. 7 ore on 10 ore green .. 2·00 5·00
243. 7 ore on 15 ore lilac .. 2·00 5·00
244. 7 ore on 20 ore blue .. 7·75 24·00

**1927.** Solid background.
246 **40** 15 ore red .. .. 4·75 10
247 20 ore grey .. .. 6·50 50
248 25 ore blue .. .. 55 10
249 30 ore yellow .. .. 50 10
250 35 ore red .. .. 13·00 35
251 40 ore green .. .. 11·00 10

For stamps with lined background see Nos. 277b, etc.

41. 42. King Christian X. 43. Numeral.

**1929.** Danish Cancer Research Fund.
252. **41.** 10 ore (+5 ore) green .. 2·40 3·25
253. 15 ore (+5 ore) red .. 3·50 5·75
254. 25 ore (+5 ore) blue .. 14·50 19·00

**1930.** 60th Birthday of King Christian X.
255 **42** 5 ore green .. .. 1·50 10
256 7 ore violet .. .. 4·75 2·00
257 8 ore grey .. .. 14·50 14·50
258 10 ore brown .. .. 3·00 10
259 15 ore red .. .. 5·75 10
260 20 ore grey .. .. 14·50 3·00
261 25 ore blue .. .. 4·75 30
262 30 ore yellow .. .. 5·75 1·25
263 35 ore red .. .. 7·25 2·00
264 40 ore green .. .. 5·75 75

**1933.** Lined background.
265 **43** 1 ore green .. .. 10 10
266 2 ore red .. .. 10 10
267 4 ore blue .. .. 30 10
268 5 ore green .. .. 80 10
268c 5 ore purple .. .. 15 10
268d 5 ore orange .. .. 10 10
268e 6 ore orange .. .. 30 10
269 7 ore violet .. .. 1·50 15
269a 7 ore green .. .. 1·50 30
269b 7 ore brown .. .. 30 10
270 8 ore grey .. .. 50 10
270a 8 ore green .. .. 30 10
271 10 ore orange .. .. 6·00 10
271b 10 ore brown .. .. 3·75 10
271c 10 ore violet .. .. 30 10
271d 10 ore green .. .. 10 10
272 12 ore green .. .. 25 10
272a 15 ore green .. .. 20 10
272c 20 ore blue .. .. 10 10
272e 25 ore green .. .. 30 10
272f 25 ore blue .. .. 10 10
273 30 ore green .. .. 15 10
273a 30 ore orange .. .. 10 10
273c 40 ore orange .. .. 25 10
273d 40 ore purple .. .. 10 10
274 50 ore brown .. .. 10 10
274d 60 ore green .. .. 1·00 20

| No. | Type | Description | | |
|---|---|---|---|---|
| 274e | 43 | 60 ore grey | 70 | 70 |
| 275 | | 70 ore red | 70 | 10 |
| 275a | | 70 ore green | 20 | 10 |
| 275d | | 80 ore green | 30 | 10 |
| 275e | | 80 ore brown | 30 | 30 |
| 276 | | 100 ore green | 45 | 10 |
| 276a | | 100 ore blue | 20 | 10 |
| 276b | | 125 ore brown | 25 | 10 |
| 276c | | 150 ore green | 40 | 20 |
| 276d | | 200 ore green | 40 | 10 |
| 276e | | 230 ore green | 70 | 25 |
| 276f | | 250 ore green | 70 | 20 |
| 276g | | 270 ore green | 70 | 15 |
| 276h | | 300 ore green | 60 | 15 |
| 276i | | 325 ore green | 65 | 15 |
| 276j | | 350 ore green | 70 | 15 |

**45.** King Christian X.  **47.** Fokker FVIIa over Copenhagen.  **49.** Hans Andersen.

**1933.** Type **40** with lined background.

| No. | Type | Description | | |
|---|---|---|---|---|
| 277b | 40 | 15 ore red | 2·75 | 10 |
| 277de | | 15 ore green | 7·00 | 30 |
| 278a | | 20 ore grey | 4·00 | 10 |
| 278b | | 20 ore red | 65 | 10 |
| 279 | | 25 ore blue | 50·00 | 8·50 |
| 279b | | 25 ore brown | 80 | 10 |
| 280a | | 30 ore orange | 65 | 10 |
| 280b | | 30 ore blue | 1·25 | 10 |
| 281 | | 35 ore violet | 65 | 15 |
| 282 | | 40 ore green | 3·00 | 10 |
| 282b | | 40 ore blue | 1·10 | 10 |
| 283 | 45 | 50 ore grey | 90 | 10 |
| 283a | | 60 ore green | 1·60 | 10 |
| 283b | | 75 ore blue | 60 | 15 |
| 284 | | 1 k. brown | 2·75 | 10 |
| 284a | | 2 k. red | 3·75 | 55 |
| 284b | | 5 k. violet | 5·75 | 1·75 |

**1934.** Nos. 279 and 280a surch.

| No. | Type | Description | | |
|---|---|---|---|---|
| 285 | 40 | 4 on 25 ore blue | 50 | 20 |
| 286 | | 10 on 30 ore orange | 3·25 | 1·75 |

**1934.** Air.

| No. | Type | Description | | |
|---|---|---|---|---|
| 287. | 47. | 10 ore orange | 60 | 90 |
| 288. | | 15 ore red | 2·50 | 3·00 |
| 289. | | 20 ore green | 3·00 | 4·00 |
| 290. | | 50 ore green | 3·00 | 4·00 |
| 291. | | 1 k. brown | 11·00 | 13·00 |

**1935.** Cent of Hans Andersen's Fairy Tales.

| No. | Type | Description | | |
|---|---|---|---|---|
| 292. | – | 5 ore green | 4·00 | 10 |
| 293. | 49. | 7 ore violet | 1·50 | 2·00 |
| 294. | – | 10 ore orange | 3·50 | 10 |
| 295. | 49. | 15 ore red | 7·75 | 10 |
| 296. | | 20 ore grey | 7·75 | 75 |
| 297. | | 30 ore blue | 1·50 | 20 |

DESIGNS: 5 ore " The Ugly Duckling ". 10 ore " The Little Mermaid ".

**51.** St. Nicholas's Church, Copenhagen.  **52.** Hans Tausen.

**53.** Ribe Cathedral.  **54.** Dybbol Mill.

**1936.** 400th Anniv. of Reformation.

| No. | Type | Description | | |
|---|---|---|---|---|
| 298. | 51. | 5 ore green | 1·00 | 10 |
| 299. | | 7 ore mauve | 1·10 | 1·10 |
| 300. | 52. | 10 ore brown | 1·10 | 10 |
| 301. | | 15 ore red | 2·00 | 10 |
| 302. | 53. | 30 ore blue | 7·75 | 50 |

**1937.** H. P. Hanssen (North Schleswig patriot) Memorial Fund.

| No. | Type | Description | | |
|---|---|---|---|---|
| 303. | 54. | 5 ore + 5 ore green | 60 | 85 |
| 304. | | 10 ore + 5 ore brown | 2·00 | 4·50 |
| 305. | | 15 ore + 5 ore red | 2·00 | 4·50 |

**56.** King Christian X.

**1937.** Silver Jubilee of King Christian X.

| No. | Type | Description | | |
|---|---|---|---|---|
| 306. | – | 5 ore green | 1·50 | 15 |
| 307. | 56. | 10 ore brown | 1·00 | 10 |
| 308. | – | 15 ore red | 1·00 | 10 |
| 309. | 56. | 30 ore blue | 12·00 | 1·75 |

DESIGNS—HORIZ: 5 ore Marselisborg Castle and "Rita" (King's yacht). 15 ore Amalienborg Castle.

**1937.** Copenhagen Philatelic Club's 50th Anniversary Stamp Exhibition. No. 271b optd **K.P.K. 17.-26. SEPT. 19 37** (= "Kobenhavns Philatelist Klub").

| No. | Type | Description | | |
|---|---|---|---|---|
| 310 | 43 | 10 ore brown | 85 | 1·25 |

**58.** Emancipation Monument.  **59.** B. Thorvaldsen.  **61.** Queen Alexandrine.

**1938.** 150th Anniv. of Abolition of Villeinage.

| No. | Type | Description | | |
|---|---|---|---|---|
| 311. | 58. | 15 ore red | 50 | 10 |

**1938.** Centenary of Return of Sculptor Thorvaldsen to Denmark.

| No. | Type | Description | | |
|---|---|---|---|---|
| 312. | 59. | 5 ore purple | 20 | 10 |
| 313. | – | 10 ore violet | 30 | 10 |
| 314. | 59. | 30 ore blue | 95 | 35 |

DESIGN: 10 ore Statue of Jason.

**1939.** Red Cross Charity. Cross in red.

| No. | Type | Description | | |
|---|---|---|---|---|
| 314a | 61 | 5 ore + 3 ore purple | 20 | 25 |
| 315 | | 10 ore + 5 ore violet | 20 | 20 |
| 316 | | 15 ore + 5 ore red | 30 | 40 |

**1940.** Stamps of 1933 (lined background) surch.

| No. | Type | Description | | |
|---|---|---|---|---|
| 317 | 43 | 6 on 7 ore green | 30 | 20 |
| 318 | | 6 on 8 ore grey | 20 | 20 |
| 319a | 40 | 15 on 40 ore green | 90 | 90 |
| 320 | | 20 on 15 ore red | 1·10 | 10 |
| 321 | | 40 on 30 ore blue | 1·00 | 20 |

**65.** Queen Ingrid (when Princess) and Princess Margrethe.  **66.** Bering's Ship "Sv. Pyotr".

**1941.** Child Welfare.

| No. | Type | Description | | |
|---|---|---|---|---|
| 322. | 65. | 10 ore + 5 ore violet | 20 | 20 |
| 323. | | 20 ore + 5 ore red | 30 | 20 |

**1941.** Death Bicent. of Vitus Bering (explorer).

| No. | Type | Description | | |
|---|---|---|---|---|
| 324. | 66. | 10 ore violet | 45 | 10 |
| 325. | | 20 ore brown | 1·00 | 10 |
| 326. | | 40 ore blue | 65 | 30 |

**67.** King Christian X.  **68.** Round Tower of Trinity Church.

**1942.**

| No. | Type | Description | | |
|---|---|---|---|---|
| 327. | 67. | 10 ore violet | 20 | 10 |
| 328. | | 15 ore green | 40 | 10 |
| 329. | | 20 ore red | 40 | 10 |
| 330. | | 25 ore brown | 60 | 15 |
| 331. | | 30 ore orange | 60 | 10 |
| 332. | | 35 ore purple | 60 | 15 |
| 333. | | 40 ore blue | 60 | 10 |
| 333a. | | 45 ore olive | 60 | 20 |
| 334. | | 50 ore grey | 80 | 10 |
| 335. | | 60 ore green | 70 | 10 |
| 335a. | | 75 ore blue | 80 | 10 |

**1942.** Tercent. of the Round Tower.

| No. | Type | Description | | |
|---|---|---|---|---|
| 336. | 68. | 10 ore violet | 15 | 10 |

**69.** Focke-Wulf Condor.  **70.** Osterlars Church.

**1943.** 25th Anniv of D.D.L. Danish Airlines.

| No. | Type | Description | | |
|---|---|---|---|---|
| 337 | 69 | 20 ore red | 15 | 10 |

**1944.** Red Cross. No. 336 surch **5** and red cross.

| No. | Type | Description | | |
|---|---|---|---|---|
| 338 | 68 | 10 ore + 5 ore violet | 15 | 10 |

**1944.** Danish Churches.

| No. | Type | Description | | |
|---|---|---|---|---|
| 339. | – | 10 ore violet | 10 | 10 |
| 340. | 70. | 15 ore green | 15 | 20 |
| 341. | – | 20 ore red | 10 | 10 |

DESIGNS: 10 ore Ejby Church. 20 ore Hvidbjerg Church.

**71.** Ole Romer.  **72.** King Christian X.  **73.** Arms

**1944.** Birth Tercent. of Romer (astronomer).

| No. | Type | Description | | |
|---|---|---|---|---|
| 342. | 71. | 20 ore brown | 15 | 10 |

**1945.** King Christian's 75th Birthday.

| No. | Type | Description | | |
|---|---|---|---|---|
| 343. | 72. | 10 ore mauve | 15 | 10 |
| 344. | | 20 ore red | 20 | 10 |
| 345. | | 40 ore blue | 40 | 15 |

**1946.**

| No. | Type | Description | | |
|---|---|---|---|---|
| 346 | 73 | 1 k. brown | 80 | 10 |
| 346a | | 1 k. 10 purple | 3·00 | 75 |
| 346b | | 1 k. 20 grey | 2·00 | 10 |
| 346c | | 1 k. 20 blue | 1·00 | 15 |
| 346d | | 1 k. 25 orange | 2·00 | 10 |
| 346e | | 1 k. 30 green | 3·50 | 1·10 |
| 346f | | 1 k. 50 purple | 70 | 10 |
| 346g | | 2 k. red | 55 | 10 |
| 347 | | 2 k. 20 orange | 1·50 | 10 |
| 347a | | 2 k. 50 orange | 1·00 | 10 |
| 347b | | 2 k. 80 grey | 1·25 | 10 |
| 347c | | 2 k. 80 green | 70 | 45 |
| 347d | | 2 k. 80 green | 60 | 10 |
| 347e | | 2 k. 90 purple | 3·00 | 10 |
| 347f | | 3 k. green | 60 | 10 |
| 347g | | 3 k. 10 purple | 5·00 | 10 |
| 347h | | 3 k. 30 red | 80 | 35 |
| 347i | | 3 k. 50 purple | 1·25 | 10 |
| 347j | | 3 k. 50 blue | 1·50 | 1·40 |
| 347k | | 4 k. grey | 80 | 10 |
| 347l | | 4 k. 10 brown | 5·00 | 10 |
| 347m | | 4 k. 30 brown | 1·50 | 1·75 |
| 347n | | 4 k. 30 green | 2·25 | 1·90 |
| 347o | | 4 k. 50 brown | 3·25 | 10 |
| 347p | | 4 k. 60 grey | 1·50 | 1·50 |
| 347q | | 4 k. 70 purple | 2·00 | 2·00 |
| 348 | | 5 k. blue | 1·00 | 10 |
| 348a | | 5 k. 50 blue | 1·50 | 35 |
| 348b | | 6 k. black | 1·25 | 10 |
| 348c | | 6 k. 50 green | 1·40 | 30 |
| 348d | | 6 k. 60 green | 1·40 | 1·25 |
| 348e | | 7 k. mauve | 1·40 | 10 |
| 348f | | 7 k. 10 purple | 1·50 | 60 |
| 348g | | 7 k. 30 green | 1·50 | 1·50 |
| 348h | | 7 k. 70 purple | 1·50 | 95 |
| 348i | | 8 k. orange | 1·60 | 10 |
| 348j | | 9 k. brown | 1·75 | 10 |
| 348k | | 10 k. yellow | 2·00 | 10 |
| 348l | | 11 k. brown | 2·25 | 2·25 |
| 348m | | 12 k. brown | 3·00 | 30 |
| 348n | | 14 k. brown | 3·00 | 35 |
| 348o | | 16 k. red | 3·50 | 30 |
| 348p | | 17 k. red | 4·50 | 50 |
| 348q | | 18 k. brown | 4·75 | 45 |
| 348s | | 20 k. blue | 4·00 | 25 |
| 348t | | 22 k. red | 4·50 | 85 |
| 348u | | 23 k. green | 4·75 | 1·00 |
| 348v | | 24 k. green | 4·75 | 40 |
| 348w | | 25 k. green | 4·75 | 10 |
| 348x | | 26 k. green | 4·75 | 50 |
| 348z | | 50 k. red | 9·75 | 1·25 |

**74.** Tycho Brahe.  **75.** Symbols of Freedom.

**1946.** 400th Birth Anniv. of Tycho Brahe (astronomer).

| No. | Type | Description | | |
|---|---|---|---|---|
| 349. | 74. | 20 ore red | 20 | 10 |

**1947.** Liberation Fund.

| No. | Type | Description | | |
|---|---|---|---|---|
| 350. | 75. | 15 ore + 5 ore green | 15 | 30 |
| 351. | – | 20 ore + 5 ore red (Bombed railways) | 60 | 60 |
| 352. | – | 40 ore + 5 ore blue (Flag) | 60 | 80 |

**77.** Steam Train.  **79.** I.C. Jacobsen.

**1947.** Cent. of Danish Railways.

| No. | Type | Description | | |
|---|---|---|---|---|
| 353. | – | 15 ore green | 35 | 15 |
| 354. | 77. | 20 ore red | 45 | 10 |
| 355. | – | 40 ore blue | 1·75 | 90 |

DESIGNS—HORIZ: 15 ore First Danish locomotive "Odin". 40 ore Electric train "Lyntog" and train ferry "Fyn".

**1947.** 60th Death Anniv of Jacobsen and Centenary of Carlsberg Foundation for Promotion of Scientific Research.

| No. | Type | Description | | |
|---|---|---|---|---|
| 356 | 79 | 20 ore red | 15 | 10 |

**80.** King Frederick IX.  **81.** " The Constituent Assembly of the Kingdom " after Constantin Hansen.

**1948.**

| No. | Type | Description | | |
|---|---|---|---|---|
| 357a | 80 | 15 ore green | 75 | 10 |
| 358 | | 15 ore violet | 80 | 10 |
| 359a | | 20 ore red | 80 | 10 |
| 360 | | 20 ore brown | 40 | 10 |
| 361 | 80 | 25 ore brown | 1·10 | 10 |
| 362 | | 25 ore red | 2·40 | 10 |
| 362a | | 25 ore blue | 1·25 | 15 |
| 362b | | 25 ore violet | 30 | 10 |
| 363 | | 30 ore orange | 9·00 | 15 |
| 363b | | 30 ore red | 45 | 10 |
| 364 | | 35 ore green | 70 | 10 |
| 365 | | 40 ore blue | 3·25 | 30 |
| 366 | | 40 ore grey | 70 | 10 |
| 367 | | 45 ore bistre | 1·10 | 10 |
| 368 | | 50 ore grey | 1·10 | 10 |
| 369 | | 50 ore blue | 2·00 | 10 |
| 369a | | 50 ore green | 50 | 10 |
| 370 | | 55 ore brown | 16·00 | 1·00 |
| 371a | | 60 ore blue | 65 | 10 |
| 371b | | 65 ore grey | 65 | 15 |
| 372 | | 70 ore green | 1·60 | 10 |
| 373 | | 75 ore purple | 70 | 10 |
| 373a | | 80 ore orange | 80 | 10 |
| 373b | | 90 ore bistre | 2·00 | 10 |
| 373c | | 95 ore orange | 90 | 25 |

**1949.** Centenary of Danish Constitution.

| No. | Type | Description | | |
|---|---|---|---|---|
| 374. | 81. | 20 ore brown | 15 | 10 |

**82.** Globe.  **83.** Kalundborg Transmitter.

**1949.** 75th Anniv. of U.P.U.

| No. | Type | Description | | |
|---|---|---|---|---|
| 375. | 82. | 40 ore blue | 30 | 25 |

**1950.** 25th Anniv. of State Broadcasting.

| No. | Type | Description | | |
|---|---|---|---|---|
| 376. | 83. | 20 ore brown | 20 | 10 |

**84.** Princess Anne-Marie.  **85.** "Fredericus Quartus" (warship).  **86.** H. C. Oersted (after C. A. Jensen).

**1950.** National Children's Welfare Assn.

| No. | Type | Description | | |
|---|---|---|---|---|
| 377 | 84 | 25 ore + 5 ore red | 30 | 40 |

**1951.** 250th Anniv of Naval Officers' College.

| No. | Type | Description | | |
|---|---|---|---|---|
| 378 | 85 | 25 ore red | 55 | 10 |
| 379 | | 50 ore blue | 2·75 | 55 |

**1951.** Death Cent. of Oersted (physicist).

| No. | Type | Description | | |
|---|---|---|---|---|
| 380. | 86. | 50 ore blue | 95 | 35 |

**87.** Mail Coach.  **88.** Hospital ship " Jutlandia ".

**1951.** Danish Stamp Cent.

| No. | Type | Description | | |
|---|---|---|---|---|
| 381. | 87. | 15 ore violet | 40 | 10 |
| 382. | | 25 ore red | 40 | 10 |

**1951.** Danish Red Cross Fund.

| No. | Type | Description | | |
|---|---|---|---|---|
| 383. | 88. | 25 ore + 5 ore red | 60 | 80 |

**89.** "Life-Saving" (relief, H. Solomon).  **91.** Memorial Stone, Skamlingsbanken.  **92.** Runic Stone at Jelling.

**1952.** Cent. of Danish Life-Saving Service.

| No. | Type | Description | | |
|---|---|---|---|---|
| 384. | 89. | 25 ore red | 30 | 10 |

**1953.** Netherlands Flood Relief Fund. Surch. **NL + 10.**

| No. | Type | Description | | |
|---|---|---|---|---|
| 385. | 80. | 30 ore + 10 ore red | 65 | 85 |

**1953.** Danish Border Union Fund.

| No. | Type | Description | | |
|---|---|---|---|---|
| 386. | 91. | 30 ore + 5 ore red | 95 | 90 |

**1953.** 1,000 years of Danish Kingdom. Inscr. " KONGERIGE I 1000 AR ". (a) 1st series.

| No. | Type | Description | | |
|---|---|---|---|---|
| 387. | 92. | 10 ore green | 10 | 10 |
| 388. | – | 15 ore lilac | 10 | 10 |
| 389. | – | 20 ore brown | 10 | 10 |
| 390. | – | 30 ore red | 20 | 10 |
| 391. | – | 60 ore blue | 30 | 10 |

DESIGNS: 15 ore Vikings' camp Trelleborg. 20 ore Kalundborg Church. 30 ore Nyborg Castle. 60 ore Goose Tower, Vordinborg.

(b) 2nd series.

| No. | Type | Description | | |
|---|---|---|---|---|
| 392. | – | 10 ore green | 10 | 10 |
| 393. | – | 15 ore lilac | 10 | 10 |
| 394. | – | 20 ore brown | 10 | 10 |
| 395. | – | 30 ore red | 20 | 10 |
| 396. | – | 60 ore blue | 50 | 10 |

DESIGNS: 10 ore Spottrup Castle. 15 ore Hammershus Castle. 20 ore Copenhagen Stock Exchange. 30 ore King Frederik V statue. 60 ore Soldier's Statue (H. V. Bissen).

**93.** Telegraph Table, 1854. **94.** Head of Statue of King Frederik V at Amalienborg.

**1954.** Telecommunications Centenary.
397 93 30 ore brown .. .. 30 10

**1954.** Bicent. of Royal Academy of Fine Arts.
398. **94.** 30 ore red .. .. 30 10

**1955.** Liberty Fund. Nos. 350/1 surch.
399. **75.** 20+5 on 15 ore+5 ore green .. .. .. 60 70
400. – 30+5 on 20 ore+5 ore red .. .. .. 60 70

**1955.** Nos. 268e, 269b, 359a and 362 surch.
401. **43.** 5 ore on 6 ore orange .. 15 10
402. 5 ore on 7 ore brown .. 15 10
403. **80.** 30 ore on 20 ore red .. 30 10
404. 30 ore on 25 ore red .. 55 10

**98.** S. Kierkegaard (philosopher). **99.** Ellehammer's Aircraft.

**1955.** Death Cent. of Kierkegaard.
405. **98.** 30 ore red .. .. 30 10

**1956.** 50th Anniv. of 1st Flight by J. C. H. Ellehammer.
406. **99.** 30 ore red .. .. 30 10

**100.** Whooper Swans. **102.** National Museum.

**1956.** Northern Countries' Day.
407.**100.** 30 ore red .. .. 3·25 10
408. 60 ore blue .. .. 2·25 40

**1957.** Danish Red Cross Hungarian Relief Fund. No. 373c surch **Ungarns- hjaelpen 30 + 5.**
409 **80** 30 ore+5 ore on 95 ore orange .. .. 30 45

**1957.** 150th Anniv. of National Museum.
410. **102.** 30 ore red .. .. 60 10
411. – 60 ore blue .. .. 80 40
DESIGN: 50 ore "Sun-God's Chariot" (bronze age model).

**103.** Harvester. **105.** King Frederik IX. **106.** Margrethe Schanne in "La Sylphide".

**1958.** Centenary of Danish Royal Veterinary and Agricultural College.
412. **103.** 30 ore red .. .. 15 10

**1959.** Greenland Fund. No. 363b surch **Gronlands fonden + 10.**
413 **80** 30 ore+10 ore red .. 55 70
The Greenland Fund was devoted to the relatives of the crew and passengers of the "Hans Hedtoft", the Greenland vessel lost at sea on 30 January 1959.

**1959.** 60th Birthday of King Frederik IX.
414. **105.** 30 ore red .. .. 20 10
415. 35 ore purple .. .. 25 15
416. 60 ore blue .. .. 25 15

**1959.** Danish Ballet and Music Festival, 1959.
417. **106.** 35 ore purple .. .. 30 10
See also Nos. 445 and 467.

**107.** **109.** Sowing Machine.

**1959.** Centenary of Red Cross.
418. **107.** 30 ore+5 ore red .. 30 35
419. 60 ore+5 ore red & bl. 60 75

**1960.** World Refugee Year. Surch **30 Verdensflygtninge- aret 1959-60** and uprooted tree.
420 **80** 30 ore on 15 ore violet .. 10 10

**1960.** 1st Danish Food Fair.
421. **109.** 12 ore green .. .. 10 10
422. – 30 ore red .. .. 15 10
423. – 60 ore blue .. .. 30 15
DESIGNS: 30 ore Combine-harvester. 60 ore Plough.

**110.** King Frederik and Queen Ingrid. **111.** Ancient Bascule Light.

**1960.** Royal Silver Wedding.
424. **110.** 30 ore red .. .. 40 10
425. 60 ore blue .. .. 65 50

**1960.** 400th Anniv. of Danish Lighthouse Service.
426. **111.** 30 ore red .. .. 30 10

**112.** N. Finsen. **113.** Mother and Child.

**1960.** Birth Cent. of Niels R. Finsen (physician).
427. **112.** 30 ore red .. .. 20 10

**1960.** W.H.O. 10th European Regional Committee Meeting.
428. **113.** 60 ore blue .. .. 50 20

**113a.** Conference Emblem. **114.** Queen Ingrid.

**1960.** Europa.
429 **113a** 60 ore blue .. .. 65 50

**1960.** 25th Year of Queen Ingrid's Service in Girl Guides.
430. **114.** 30 ore+10 ore red .. 60 75

**115.** Douglas DC-8. **116.** Coastal Scene.

**1961.** 10th Anniv. of Scandinavian Airlines System (SAS).
431. **115.** 60 ore blue .. .. 40 10

**1961.** 50th Anniv. of Society for Preservation of Danish National Amenities.
432. **116.** 30 ore red .. .. 20 10

**117.** King Frederik IX. **118.** Borkop Watermill. **119.** African Mother and Child.

**1961.**
433. **117.** 20 ore brown .. .. 30 10
434. 25 ore brown .. .. 20 10
435. 30 ore red .. .. 45 10
436. 35 ore green .. .. 70 30
437. 35 ore red .. .. 20 10
438. 40 ore grey .. .. 80 10
438a. 40 ore brown .. .. 20 10
439. 50 ore turquoise .. .. 40 10
439a. 50 ore red .. .. 60 10
439b. 50 ore brown .. .. 50 10
440. 60 ore blue .. .. 70 10
440a. 60 ore red .. .. 55 10
441. 70 ore green .. .. 90 15
442. 80 ore orange .. .. 1·00 10
442a. 80 ore blue .. .. 1·40 10
442b. 80 ore green .. .. 50 10
443. 90 ore olive .. .. 2·75 10
443a. 90 ore blue .. .. 70 10
444. 95 ore purple .. .. 80 60

**1962.** Danish Ballet and Music Festival, 1962. As T **106** but inscr. " 15–31 MAJ ".
445. 60 ore blue.. .. .. 20 10

**1962.** "Dansk Fredning" (Preservation of Danish Natural Amenities and Ancient Monuments) and Centenary of Abolition of Mill Monopolies.
446 118 10 ore brown .. .. 10 10

**1962.** Aid for Under-developed Countries.
447. **119.** 30 ore+10 ore red .. 60 55

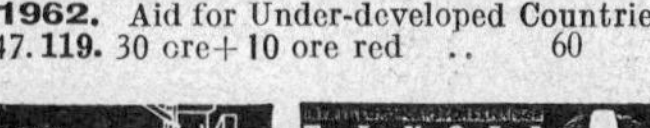

**120.** "Selandia". **121.** "Tivoli".

**1962.** 50th Anniv of Freighter "Selandia".
448 **120** 60 ore blue .. .. 1·75 1·25

**1962.** 150th Birth Anniv. of George Carstensen (founder of Tivoli Pleasure Gardens, Copenhagen).
449. **121.** 35 ore purple .. .. 20 10

**122.** Cliffs, Island of Mon. **123.** Wheat.

**1962.** " Dansk Fredning" (Preservation of Danish Natural Amenities and Ancient Monuments).
450. **122.** 20 ore brown .. .. 10 10

**1963.** Freedom from Hunger.
451. **123.** 35 ore red .. .. 10 10

**124.** Rail and Sea Symbols. **125.** 19th-century Mail Transport.

**1963.** Opening of Denmark-Germany Railway (" Bird-flight Line ").
452. **124.** 15 ore green .. .. 20 10

**1963.** Cent. of Paris Postal Conference.
453. **125.** 60 ore blue .. .. 25 20

**126.** Hands. **127.** Prof. Niels Bohr.

**1963.** Danish Cripples Foundation Fund.
454. **126.** 35 ore+10 ore red .. 50 70

**1963.** 50th Anniv. of Bohr's Atomic Theory.
455. **127.** 35 ore red .. .. 15 10
456. 60 ore blue .. .. 30 10

**128.** Ancient Bridge, Immervad. **129.** "Going to School" (child's slate).

**1964.** Danish Border Union Fund.
457. **128.** 35 ore+10 ore red .. 35 45

**1964.** 150th Anniv of Institution of Primary Schools.
458 **129** 35 ore brown .. .. 15 10

**130.** Princesses Margrethe, Benedikte and Anne-Marie. **131.** " Exploration of the Sea".

**1964.** Danish Red Cross Fund.
459. **130.** 35 ore+10 ore red .. 40 50
460. 60 ore+10 ore blue & red 50 70

**1964.** Int. Council for the Exploration of the Sea Conference, Copenhagen.
461. **131.** 60 ore blue .. .. 30 10

**132.** Danish Stamp "Watermarks, Perforations and Varieties". **133.** Landscape, R. Karup.

**1964.** 25th Anniv of Stamp Day.
462 **132** 35 ore pink .. .. 10 10

**1964.** "Dansk Fredning" (Preservation of Danish Natural Amenities and Ancient Monuments).
463. **133.** 25 ore brown .. .. 10 10

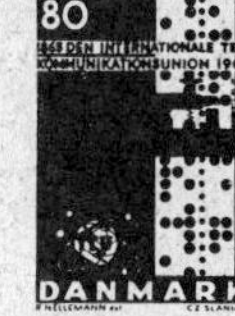

**134.** Office Equipment. **135.** Morse Key, Teleprinter Tape and I.T.U. Emblem.

**1965.** Centenary of 1st Commercial School.
464. **134.** 15 ore green .. .. 10 10

**1965.** Centenary of I.T.U.
465. **135.** 80 ore blue .. .. 30 10

**136.** C. Nielsen. **137.** Child in Meadow. **138.** Bogo Windmill.

**1965.** Birth Cent of Carl Nielsen (composer).
466 **136** 50 ore red .. .. 20 10

**1965.** Danish Ballet and Music Festival, 1965. As T **106** but inscr. " 15–31 MAJ ".
467. 50 ore red .. .. 20 10

**1965.** Child Welfare.
468. **137.** 50 ore+10 ore red .. 30 40

**1965.** " Dansk Fredning" (Preservation of Danish Natural Amenities and Ancient Monuments).
469. **138.** 40 ore brown .. .. 15 10

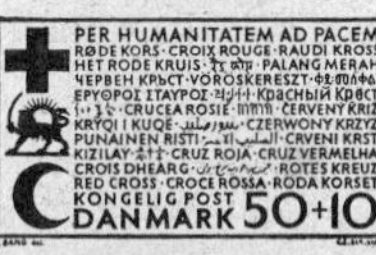

**139.** Titles of International Red Cross Organizations. **140.** Heathland.

**1966.** Danish Red Cross Fund.
470. **139.** 50 ore+10 ore red .. 25 35
471. 80 ore+10 ore bl. & red 40 55

**1966.** Centenary of Danish Heath Society.
472. **140.** 25 ore green .. .. 10 10

**141.** C. Kold. **142.** Almshouses, Copenhagen.

**143.** Trees at Bregentved. **144.** G. Jensen. **145.** Fund Emblem.

**1966.** 150th Birth Anniv. of Christen Kold (educationist).
473. **141.** 50 ore red .. .. 10 10

**1966.** " Dansk Fredning" (Preservation of Danish Natural Amenities and Ancient Monuments).
474. **142.** 50 ore red .. .. 10 10
475. **143.** 80 ore blue .. .. 60 10

**1966.** Birth Cent. of Georg Jensen (silversmith).
476. **144.** 80 ore blue .. .. 60 10

**1966.** " Refugee 66 " Fund.
477. **145.** 40 ore+10 ore brown 35 50
478. 50 ore+10 ore red .. 35 50
479. 80 ore+10 ore blue.. 95 1·00

**146.** Barrow in Jutland. **147.** Musical Instruments.

**1966.** " Dansk Fredning " (Preservation of Danish Natural Amenities and Ancient Monuments).
480. **146.** 1 k. 50 green.. .. 40 10

**1967.** Cent. of Royal Danish Academy of Music.
481. **147.** 50 ore red .. .. 15 10

**148.** Cogwheels. **149.** Old City and Windmill.

**1967.** European Free Trade Assn.
482. **148.** 80 ore blue .. .. 35 10

**1967.** 800th Anniv. of Copenhagen.
483. **149.** 25 ore green .. .. 20 15
484. – 40 ore brown .. .. 20 10
485. – 50 ore brown .. .. 20 10
486. – 80 ore blue .. .. 55 20
DESIGNS: 40 ore Old bank and ship's masts. 50 ore Church steeple and burgher's house. 80 ore Building construction.

**150.** Princess Margrethe and Prince Henri de Monpezat. **151.** H. C. Sonne.

**1967.** Royal Wedding.
487. **150.** 50 ore red .. .. 15 10

**1967.** 150th Anniv. of Hans Sonne (founder of Danish Co-operative Movement).
488. **151.** 60 ore red .. .. 10 10

**152.** "Rose". **153.** Porpoise and Cross-anchor.

**1967.** The Salvation Army.
489. **152.** 60 ore+10 ore red .. 30 35

**1967.** Centenary of Danish Seamen's Church in Foreign Ports.
490. **153.** 90 ore blue .. .. 30 20

**154.** Esbjerg Harbour. **155.** Koldinghus Castle.

**1968.** Centenary of Esbjerg Harbour Construction Act.
491. **154.** 30 ore green .. .. 15 10

**1968.** 700th Anniv. of Koldinghus Castle.
492. **155.** 60 ore red .. .. 15 10

**156.** "The Children in the Round Tower" (Greenlandic legend). **157.** Shipbuilding.

**1968.** Greenlandic Child Welfare.
493. **156.** 60 ore+10 ore red .. 35 50

**1968.** Danish Industries.
494. **157.** 30 ore green .. .. 15 10
495. – 50 ore brown .. .. 15 10
496. – 60 ore red .. .. 15 10
497. – 90 ore blue .. .. 25 30
INDUSTRIES: 50 ore Chemicals. 60 ore Electric power. 90 ore Engineering.

**158.** "The Sower". **159.** Viking Ships (from old Swedish coin).

**1969.** Bicentenary of Danish Royal Agricultural Society.
498. **158.** 30 ore green .. .. 10 10

**1969.** 50th Anniv. of Northern Countries' Union.
499. **159.** 60 ore red .. .. 50 10
500. 90 ore blue .. .. 1·10 1·10

**160.** King Frederik IX. **161.** Colonnade.

**1969.** King Frederik's 70th Birthday.
501. **160.** 50 ore brown .. .. 15 10
502. 60 ore red .. .. 15 10

**1969.** Europa.
503. **161.** 90 ore blue .. .. 60 60

**162.** Kronborg Castle. **163.** Fall of Danish Flag.

**1969.** 50th Anniv. of "Danes Living Abroad" Association.
504. **162.** 50 ore brown .. .. 10 10

**1969.** 750th Anniv. of "Danish Flag Falling from Heaven".
505. **163.** 60 ore red, blue & black 15 10

**164.** M. A. Nexo. **165.** Niels Stensen (geologist).

**1969.** Birth Centenary of Martin Andersen Nexo (poet).
506 **164** 80 ore green .. .. 15 10

**1969.** 300th Anniv. of Stensen's "On Solid Bodies".
507. **165.** 1 k. sepia .. .. 15 10

**166.** "Abstract". **167.** Symbolic "P".

**1969.** "Non-figurative" stamp.
508. **166.** 60 ore red, rose and blue 10 10

**1969.** Birth Centenary of Valdemar Poulsen (inventor).
509. **167.** 30 ore green .. .. 10 10

**168.** Princess Margrethe, Prince Henri and Prince Frederik (baby). **169.** "Postgiro".

**1969.** Danish Red Cross.
510 **168** 50 ore+10 ore brown and red .. .. 35 50
511 60 ore+10 ore brown and red .. .. 35 50

**1970.** 50th Anniv. of Danish Postal Giro Service.
512. **169.** 60 ore red and orange 10 10

**170.** School Safety Patrol. **171.** Child appealing for Help.

**1970.** Road Safety.
513. **170.** 50 ore brown .. .. 20 10

**1970.** 25th Anniv. of Save the Children Fund.
514. **171.** 60 ore+10 ore red .. 30 45

**172.** Candle in Window. **173.** Red Deer in Park.

**1970.** 25th Anniv. of Liberation.
515. **172.** 50 ore black, yell. & blue 10 10

**1970.** 300th Anniv. of Jaegersborg Deer Park.
516. **173.** 60 ore brown, red and green .. .. .. 10 10

**174.** Ship's Figurehead, ("Elephanten"). **175.** "The Reunion".

**1970.** 300th Anniv. of "Royal Majesty's Model Chamber" (Danish Naval Museum).
517. **174.** 30 ore multicoloured .. 10 10

**1970.** 50th Anniv. of North Schleswig's Reunion with Denmark.
518. **175.** 60 ore violet, yellow and olive .. .. 10 10

**176.** Electromagnetic Apparatus.

**1970.** 150th Anniv. of Oersted's Discovery of Electromagnetism.
519. **176.** 80 ore green .. .. 20 10

**177.** Bronze-age Ship (from engraving on razor).

**1970.** Danish Shipping.
520. **177.** 30 ore purple and brn. 20 10
521. – 50 ore brn. and purple 20 10
522. – 60 ore brown and green 25 10
523. – 90 ore blue and green 60 65
DESIGNS: 50 ore Viking shipbuilders (Bayeux Tapestry). 60 ore "Emanuel" (schooner). 90 ore "A. P. Moller" (tanker).

**178.** Strands of Rope. **179.** B. Thorvaldsen from self-portrait.

**1970.** 25th Anniv. of United Nations.
524. **178.** 90 ore red, green & blue 75 75

**1970.** Birth Bicentenary of Bertel Thorvaldsen (sculptor).
525. **179.** 2 k. blue .. .. 35 40

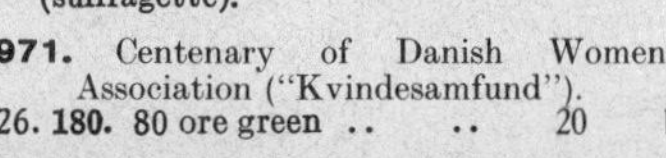
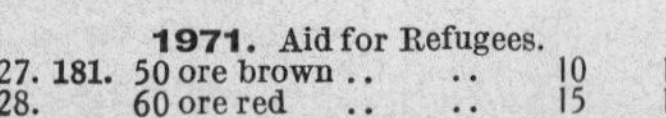
**180.** Mathilde Fibiger (suffragette). **181.** Refugees.

**1971.** Centenary of Danish Women's Association ("Kvindesamfund").
526. **180.** 80 ore green .. .. 20 10

**1971.** Aid for Refugees.
527. **181.** 50 ore brown .. .. 10 10
528. 60 ore red .. .. 15 10

**182.** Danish Child. **183.** Hans Egede.

**1971.** National Children's Welfare Association.
529. **182.** 60 ore+10 ore red .. 30 45

**1971.** 25th Anniv. of Hans Egede's Arrival in Greenland.
530. **183.** 1 k. brown .. .. 45 10

**184.** Swimming. **185.** Georg Brandes.

**1971.** Sports.
531 **184** 30 ore green and blue 15 20
532 – 50 ore dp brown & brn 15 10
533 – 60 ore yellow, bl & grey 20 10
534 – 90 ore violet, grn & bl 35 50
DESIGNS: 50 ore Hurdling. 60 ore Football. 90 ore Yachting.

**1971.** Centenary of First Lectures by Georg Brandes (writer).
535. **185.** 90 ore blue .. .. 20 15

**186.** Beet Harvester.

**1972.** Cent. of Danish Sugar Production.
536. **186.** 80 ore green .. .. 20 10

**187.** Meteorological Symbols.

**1972.** Cent of Danish Meteorological Office.
537 **187** 1 k. 20 brown, bl & pur 35 45

**188.** King Frederik IX. **189.** "N. F. S. Grundtvig" (pencil sketch, P. Skovgaard).

**1972.** King Frederik IX–In Memoriam
538. **188.** 60 ore red .. .. 10 10

**1972.** Death Centenary of N. F. S. Grundtvig (poet and clergyman).
539 **189** 1 k. brown .. .. 20 20

**190.** Early Locomotive, Ship and Passengers. **191.** Rebild Hills.

**1972.** 125th Anniv. of Danish State Railways.
540. **190.** 70 ore red .. .. 40 10

**1972.** Nature Protection.
541. **191** 1 k. grn., brn. & blue .. 30 10

**192.** Marsh Marigold. **193.** "The Tinker" (from Holberg's satire).

**1972.** Centenary of "Vanforehjemmet" (Home for the Disabled).
542 **192** 70 ore + 10 ore yellow and blue .. .. 35 50

**1972.** 250th Anniv of Theatre in Denmark and of Holberg's Comedies.
543 **193** 70 ore red .. .. 15 10

**194.** W.H.O. Building, Copenhagen. **195.** Little Belt Bridge.

**1972.** Inauguration of World Health Organization Building, Copenhagen.
544 **194** 2 k. black, blue and red 40 50

**1972.** Danish Construction Projects.
545. **195.** 40 ore green .. .. 15 20
546. – 60 ore brown .. .. 20 15
547. – 70 ore red .. .. 20 10
548. – 90 ore green .. .. 30 30
DESIGNS: 60 ore Hanstholm port. 70 ore Limfjord Tunnel. 90 ore Knudshoved port.

**196.** House, Aeroskobing. **197.** Johannes Jensen.

**1972.** Danish Architecture.
549 **196** 40 ore black, brn & red 15 15
550 – 60 ore blue, grn & brn 15 15
551 – 70 ore brn, red & verm 20 10
552 – 1 k. 20 green, brown and deep brown .. 50 65
DESIGNS—28 × 21 mm: 60 ore Farmhouse, East Bornholm. 37 × 21 mm: 1 k. 20, Farmhouse, Hvide Sande. 21 × 37 mm: 70 ore House, Christanshavn.

**1973.** Birth Cent. of Johannes Jensen (writer).
553. **197.** 90 ore green .. .. 15 10

**198.** Cogwheels and Guardrails. **199.** P. C. Abildgaard (founder).

**1973.** Cent. of 1st Danish Factory Act.
554. **198.** 50 ore brown .. .. 10 10

**1973.** Bicentenary of Royal Veterinary College, Christianshavn.
555. **199.** 1 k. blue .. .. 20 15

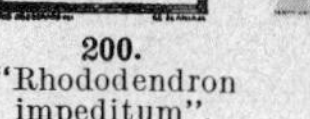

**200.** "Rhododendron impeditum". **201.** Nordic House, Reykjavik.

**1973.** Cent of Jutland Horticultural Society.
556 **200** 60 ore violet, grn & brn 30 10
557 – 70 ore pink, grn & red 30 10
DESIGN: 70 ore "Queen of Denmark" rose.

**1973.** Nordic Countries' Postal Co-operation.
558. **201.** 70 ore multicoloured 30 10
559. 1 k. multicoloured .. 80 65

## MINIMUM PRICE

The minimum price quoted is 10p which represents a handling charge rather than a basis for valuing common stamps. For further notes about prices see introductory pages.

**202.** Stella Nova and Sextant. **203.** "St. Mark the Evangelist" (Book of Dalby).

**1973.** 400th Anniv of Tycho Brahe's "De Nove Stella" (book on astronomy).
560 **202** 2 k. blue .. .. 30 15

**1973.** 300th Anniv. of Royal Library.
561. **203.** 1 k. 20 multicoloured .. 40 55

**204.** Heimaey Eruption. **205.** "Devil and Scandalmongers" (Fanefjord Church).

**1973.** Aid for Victims of Heimaey Eruption, Iceland.
562. **204.** 70 ore + 20 ore red & bl. 50 50

**1973.** Church Frescoes. Each red, turquoise and yellow on cream.
563 70 ore Type **205** .. .. 1·10 30
564 70 ore "Queen Esther and King Xerxes" (Tirsted Church) .. 1·10 30
565 70 ore "The Harvest Miracle" (Jetsmark Church) 1·40 30
566 70 ore "The Crowning with Thorns" (Biersted Church) .. .. 1·10 30
567 70 ore "Creation of Eve" (Fanefjord Church) .. 1·10 30

**206.** Drop of Blood and Donors. **207.** Queen Margrethe.

**1974.** Blood Donors Campaign.
568. **206.** 90 ore red and violet .. 20 10

**1974.**
569. **207.** 60 ore brown .. .. 30 20
570. 60 ore orange .. .. 30 10
571. 70 ore red .. .. 30 10
572. 70 ore brown .. .. 30 10
573. 80 ore green .. .. 40 20
574. 80 ore brown .. .. 45 15
575. 90 ore purple .. .. 40 15
576. 90 ore red .. .. 1·40 10
577. 90 ore olive .. .. 50 15
577a. 90 ore grey .. .. 1·40 1·50
578. 100 ore blue .. .. 40 10
579. 100 ore grey .. .. 40 15
580. 100 ore red .. .. 30 10
580a. 100 ore brown .. 40 10
580b. 110 ore orange .. 50 20
580c. 110 ore brown .. 40 15
581. 120 ore grey .. .. 60 10
581b. 120 ore red .. .. 30 10
582. 130 ore blue .. .. 1·00 90
582a. 130 ore red .. .. 30 10
582b. 130 ore brown .. 60 25
582c. 140 ore orange .. 80 90
582d. 150 ore blue .. .. 70 60
582e. 150 ore red .. .. 70 35
582f. 160 ore blue .. .. 70 60
582g. 160 ore red .. .. 60 10
582h. 180 ore green .. .. 45 15
582i. 180 ore blue .. .. 70 80
582j. 200 ore blue .. .. 60 60
582k. 210 ore grey .. .. 1·00 1·00
582l. 230 ore green .. .. 80 15
582m. 250 ore green .. .. 1·00 40

**208.** Theatre Facade. **209.** Hverringe.

**1974.** Centenary of Tivoli Pantomime Theatre, Copenhagen.
583. **208.** 100 ore blue .. .. 30 10

**1974.** Provincial Series.
584. **209.** 50 ore multicoloured 30 25
585. – 60 ore green, deep green and mauve .. 20 35

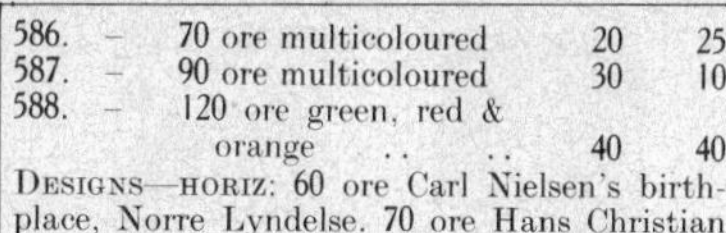

586. – 70 ore multicoloured 20 25
587. – 90 ore multicoloured 30 10
588. – 120 ore green, red & orange .. .. 40 40
DESIGNS—HORIZ: 60 ore Carl Nielsen's birthplace, Norre Lyndelse. 70 ore Hans Christian Andersen's birthplace, Odense. 1 k. 20, Hindsholm. VERT: 90 ore Hesselagergaard.

**210.** Orienteering. **211.** "Iris spuria".

**1974.** World Orienteering Championships.
589. **210.** 70 ore brown and blue 50 50
590. – 80 ore blue and brown 20 15
DESIGN: 80 ore Compass.

**1974.** Cent. of Botanical Gardens, Copenhagen.
591. **211.** 90 ore bl., grn. & brn. 15 10
592. – 120 ore red, green and blue .. .. 40 35
DESIGN: 120 ore "Dactylorhiza purpurella" (orchid).

**212.** Mail-carriers of 1624 and 1780. **213.** Pigeon with Letter.

**1974.** 350th Anniv of Danish Post Office.
593 **212** 70 ore bistre and purple 30 30
594 – 90 ore green and purple 40 10
DESIGN: 90 ore Johan Colding's postal balloon (1808), H.M.S. "Edgar" and H.M.S. "Dictator".

**1974.** Cent. of U.P.U.
595. **213.** 120 ore blue .. .. 30 15

**215.** Radio Equipment of 1925. **216.** Queen Margrethe and IWY Emblem.

**1975.** 50th Anniv of Danish Broadcasting.
597 **215** 90 ore pink .. .. 30 10

**1975.** International Women's Year.
598. **216.** 90 ore + 20 ore red .. 50 70

**217.** Floral Decorated Plate. **218.** Moravian Brethren Church Christiansfeld.

**1975.** Danish Porcelain.
599. **217.** 50 ore green .. .. 20 10
600. – 90 ore red .. .. 40 10
601. – 130 ore blue .. .. 65 80
DESIGNS: 90 ore Floral decorated tureen. 130 ore Floral decorated vase and tea-caddy.

**1975.** European Architectural Heritage Year.
602 **218** 70 ore brown .. .. 20 30
603 – 120 ore green .. .. 45 40
604 – 150 ore blue .. .. 30 10
DESIGNS—HORIZ: 120 ore Farmhouse, Lejre. VERT: 150 ore Anna Queenstraede (street), Helsingor.

**219.** "Numskull Jack" (V. Pedersen). **220.** Watchman's Square, Aabenraa.

**1975.** 170th Birth Anniv. of Hans Christian Andersen.
605. **219.** 70 ore grey & brown 50 60
606. – 90 ore brown and red 60 10
607. – 130 ore brown & blue 1·00 1·00
DESIGNS: 90 ore Hans Andersen (from photograph by G. E. Hansen). 130 ore "The Marshking's Daughter" (L. Frolich).

**1975.** Provincial series. South Jutland.
608 **220** 70 ore multicoloured .. 25 35
609 – 90 ore brown, red & bl 25 10
610 – 100 ore multicoloured 25 15
611 – 120 ore blue, blk & grn 40 30
DESIGNS—VERT. 90 ore, Haderslev Cathedral. HORIZ. 100 ore, Mogeltonder Polder. 120 ore, Estuary of Vidaaen at Hojer floodgates.

**221.** Common Kingfisher.

**1975.** Danish Endangered Animals.
612. **221.** 50 ore blue .. .. 70 30
613. – 70 ore brown .. .. 50 30
614. – 90 ore brown .. .. 50 10
615. – 130 ore blue .. .. 1·10 80
616. – 200 ore black .. .. 60 10
DESIGNS: 70 ore West European hedgehog. 90 ore Cats. 130 ore Avocets. 200 ore European otter.

The 90 ore also commemorates the centenary of the Danish Society for the Prevention of Cruelty to Animals.

**222.** Viking Longship.

**1976.** Bicent. of American Revolution.
618. **222.** 70 ore + 20 ore brown 80 80
619. – 90 ore + 20 ore red .. 80 80
620. – 100 ore + 20 ore green 80 80
621. – 130 ore + 20 ore blue 80 80
DESIGNS: 90 ore Freighter "Thingvalla". 100 ore Liner "Frederik VIII". 130 ore Cadet full-rigged ship "Danmark".

**223.** "Humanity". **224.** Old Copenhagen.

**1976.** Centenary of Danish Red Cross.
622. **223.** 100 ore + 20 ore black and red .. .. 50 40
623. 130 ore + 20 ore black, red and blue .. 60 50

**1976.** Provincial Series. Copenhagen.
624 **224** 60 ore multicoloured .. 30 35
625 – 80 ore multicoloured .. 30 25
626 – 100 ore red & vermilion 50 10
627 – 130 ore green, deep brown and brown .. 1·00 95
DESIGNS—VERT: 80 ore View from the Round Tower. 100 ore Interior of the Central Railway Station. HORIZ: 130 ore Harbour buildings.

**225.** Handicapped Person in Wheel-chair. **226.** Mail Coach Driver (detail from "A String of Horses outside an Inn" (O. Bache)).

**1976.** Danish Foundation for the Disabled.
628. **225.** 100 ore + 20 ore black and red .. .. 50 50

**1976.** "Hafnia 76" Stamp Exhibition.
629 **226** 130 ore multicoloured 60 80

**227.** Prof. Emil Hansen.

**228.** Moulding Glass.

**1976.** Cent. of Carlsberg Foundation.
631. **227.** 100 ore red .. .. 20 10

**1976.** Danish Glass Industry.
632 **228** 60 ore green .. .. 10 25
633 – 80 ore brown .. .. 10 10
634 – 130 ore blue .. .. 75 75
635 – 150 ore red .. .. 20 10
DESIGNS: 80 ore Removing glass from pipe. 130 ore Cutting glass. 150 ore Blowing glass.

**229.** Five Water Lilies.

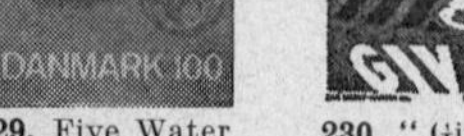

**230.** " Give Way ".

**1977.** Northern Countries Co-operation in Nature Conservation and Environment Protection.
636. **229.** 100 ore multicoloured 20 10
637. 130 ore multicoloured 1·10 1·00

**1977.** Road Safety.
638. **230.** 100 ore brown .. 30 10

**231.** Mother and Child.


**232.** Allinge.

**1977.** 25th Anniv. of Danish Society for the Mentally Handicapped.
639. **231.** 100 ore + 20 ore green, blue and brown .. 60 55

**1977.** Europa.
640. **232.** 1 k. brown .. .. 30 10
641. – 1 k. 30 blue .. .. 2·75 2·25
DESIGN: 1 k. 30, Farm near Ringsted.

**233.** Kongeaen.

**234.** Hammers and Horseshoes.

**1977.** Provincial Series. South Jutland.
642 **233** 60 ore green and blue 1·00 90
643 – 90 ore multicoloured .. 55 20
644 – 150 ore multicoloured 55 20
645 – 200 ore grn, pur & emer 55 25
DESIGNS: 90 ore Skallingen. 150 ore Torskind. 200 ore Jelling.

**1977.** Danish Crafts.
646. **234.** 80 ore brown .. .. 20 15
647. – 1 k. red .. .. 20 10
648. – 1 k. 30 blue .. .. 45 35
DESIGNS: 1 k. Chisel, square and plane. 1 k. 30, Trowel, ceiling brush and folding rule.

**235.** Globe Flower.

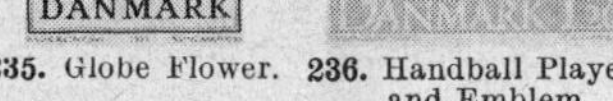

**236.** Handball Player and Emblem.

**1977.** Endangered Flora.
649. **235.** 1 k. grn., yell. & brn. 30 10
650. – 1 k. 50 grn., ol. & brn. 60 70
DESIGN: 1 k. 50, "Cnidium dubium".

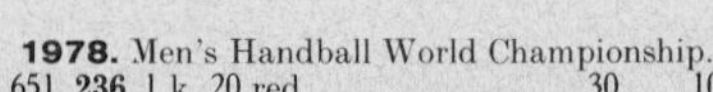

**1978.** Men's Handball World Championship.
651 **236** 1 k. 20 red .. .. 30 10

**237.** Christian IV on Horseback.

**238.** Jens Bang's House, Aalborg.

**1978.** Centenary of National History Museum, Frederiksborg.
652. **237.** 1 k. 20 brown.. .. 20 10
653. – 1 k. 80 black .. .. 30 20
DESIGN: 1 k. 80, North-west aspect of Frederiksborg Castle.

**1978.** Europa.
654. **238.** 1 k. 20 brown.. .. 20 10
655. – 1 k. 50 blue and dp. blue 95 60
DESIGN: 1 k. 50, Plan and front elevation of Frederiksborg Castle, Copenhagen.

**239.** Kongenshus Memorial Park.

**240.** Boats in Harbour.

**1978.** Provincial Series. Central Jutland.
656. **239.** 70 ore. multicoloured 20 30
657. – 1 k. 20 multicoloured 20 10
658. – 1 k. 50 multicoloured 60 60
659. – 1 k. 80 blue,brn.&grn. 35 40
DESIGNS: 1 k. 20, Post office, Aarhus Old Town. 1 k. 50, Lignite fields, Soby. 1 k. 80, Church wall, Stadil Church.

**1978.** Fishing Industry.
660. **240.** 70 ore. green .. .. 25 30
661. – 1 k. brown .. .. 25 20
662. – 1 k. 80 black .. .. 35 20
663. – 2 k. 50 brown .. .. 50 30
DESIGNS: 1 k. Eel traps. 1 k. 80, Fishing boats on the slipway. 2 k. 50, Drying ground.

**241.** Campaign Emblem.

**1978.** 50th Anniv. of Danish Cancer Campaign.
664. **241** 120 ore. + 20 ore. red.. 30 40

**242.** Common Morel.

**243.** Early and Modern Telephones.

**1978.** Mushrooms.
665 **242** 1 k. brown .. .. 75 50
666 – 1 k. 20 red .. .. 75 15
DESIGN: 1 k. 20, Satan's mushroom.

**1979.** Cent. of Danish Telephone System.
667. **243.** 1 k. 20 red .. .. 20 10

**244.** Child.

**245.** University Seal.

**1979.** International Year of the Child.
668. **244.** 1 k. 20 + 20 ore red and brown .. .. 30 45

**1979.** 500th Anniv of Copenhagen University.
669 **245** 1 k. 30 red .. .. 20 10
670 – 1 k. 60 black .. .. 30 40
DESIGN: 1 k. 60, Pentagram representing the five faculties.

**246.** Letter Mail Cariole.

**247.** Pendant.

**1979.** Europa.
671. **246.** 1 k. 30 red .. .. 70 10
672. – 1 k. 60 blue .. .. 90 80
DESIGN: 1 k. 60, Morse key and sounder.

**1979.** Viking "Gripping Beast" Decorations.
673. **247.** 1 k. 10 brown .. 15 10
674. – 2 k. green .. .. 25 15
DESIGN: 2 k. Key.

**248.** Mols Bjerge.

**249.** Silhouette of Oehlenschlager.

**1979.** Provincial Series. North Jutland.
675. **248.** 80 ore green, ultram. and brown .. .. 20 30
676. – 90 ore multicoloured.. 1·00 90
677. – 200 ore grn., orge. & red 30 10
678. – 280 ore slate, sepia & brn. 50 65
DESIGNS: 90 ore Orslev Kloster. 200 ore Trans. 280 ore Bovbjerg.

**1979.** Birth Bicentenary of Adam Oehlenschlager (poet).
679. **249.** 1 k. 30 red .. .. 15 10

**250.** Music, Violin and Dancers (birth cent. of Jacob Gade (composer)).

**251.** Royal Mail Guards' Office, Copenhagen (drawing, Peter Klaestrup).

**1979.** Anniversaries.
680. **250.** 1 k. 10 brown.. .. 20 15
681. – 1 k. 60 blue .. .. 30 35
DESIGN: 1 k. 60, Dancer at bar (death centenary of August Bournonville (ballet master)).

**1980.** Bicent. of National Postal Service.
682. **251.** 1 k. 30 red .. .. 15 10

**252.** Stylised Wheelchair.

**253.** Karen Blixen (writer).

**1980.** 25th Anniv. of Foundation for the Disabled.
683. **252.** 130 ore + 20 ore red .. 20 35

**1980.** Europa.
684. **253.** 1 k. 30 red .. .. 20 10
685. – 1 k. 60 blue .. .. 40 50
DESIGN: 1 k. 60, August Krogh (physiologist).

**254.** Symbols of Employment, Health and Education.

**255.** Lindholme Hoje.

**1980.** U.N. Decade for Women World Conference.
686. **254.** 1 k. 60 blue .. .. 30 20

**1980.** Provincial Series. Jutland North of Limfjorden. Multicoloured.
687 80 ore Type **255** .. .. 20 30
688 110 ore Skagen lighthouse (vert) .. .. .. 30 20
689 200 ore Borglum .. .. 30 15
690 280 ore Fishing boats at Vorupor .. .. 95 85

**256.** Silver Pitcher, c. 1641.

**1980.** Nordic Countries Postal Co-operation.
691 **256** 1 k. 30 black and red 30 10
692 – 1 k. 80 blue & dp blue 70 80
DESIGN: 1 k. 80, Bishop's bowl.

**257.** Earliest Danish Coin, Hedeby (c. 800).

**1980.** Coins from the Royal Collection.
693 **257** 1 k. 30 red and brown 30 10
694 – 1 k. 40 olive and green 65 80
695 – 1 k. 80 blue and grey 65 80
DESIGNS: 1 k. 40, Silver coin of Valdemar the Great and Bishop Absalon (1152–82). 1 k. 80, Christian VII gold current ducat (1781).

**258.** Lace Pattern.

**259.** Children Playing in Yard.

**1980.** Lace Patterns. Various designs showing lace.
696. **258.** 1 k. 10 brown.. .. 30 30
697. – 1 k. 30 red .. .. 30 10
698. – 2 k. green .. .. 40 15

**1981.** National Children's Welfare Association.
699. **259.** 1 k. 60 + 20 ore red .. 45 60

**260.** Original Houses, 1631.

**261.** Tilting at a Barrel (Shrovetide custom).

**1981.** 350th Anniv. of Nyboder (Naval Barracks), Copenhagen.
700. **260.** 1 k. 30 red and yellow 50 50
701. – 1 k. 60 red and yellow 40 10
DESIGN: 1 k. 60, 18th-century terraced houses.

**1981.** Europa.
702. **261.** 1 k. 60 red .. .. 30 10
703. – 2 k. blue .. .. 45 40
DESIGN: 2 k. Midsummer bonfire.

**262.** Soro.

**263.** Rigensgade District, Copenhagen.

**1981.** Provincial Series. Zealand and Surrounding Islands.
704 **262** 100 ore blue & brown 30 30
705 – 150 ore black and green 40 40
706 – 160 ore brown & green 40 10
707 – 200 ore multicoloured 50 60
708 – 230 ore blue and brown 60 40
DESIGNS: 150 ore N. F. S. Grundtvig's childhood home, Udby. 160 ore Kaj Munk's childhood home, Opager. 200 ore Gronsund. 230 ore Bornholm.

**1981.** European Urban Renaissance Year.
709. **263.** 1 k. 60 red .. .. 40 10

**264.** Decaying Tree.

**265.** Ellehammer at Lindholm, 1906.

**1981.** International Year for Disabled Persons.
710. **264.** 2 k. + 20 ore blue .. 65 65

**1981.** History of Aviation.
711 **265** 1 k. green and black .. 40 40
712 – 1 k. 30 brown & dp brn 45 50
713 – 1 k. 60 vermilion & red 40 10
714 – 2 k. 30 blue & dp blue 60 30
DESIGNS: 1 k. 30, A. T. Botved's Fokker biplane "R-1" (Copenhagen–Tokyo, 1926). 1 k. 60, Hojriis Hillig's Bellanca Special "Liberty" (U.S.A.–Denmark, 1931). 2 k. 30, Douglas DC-7C "Seven Seas" (first Polar flight, 1957).

**266.** Queen Margrethe II.

**267.** Revenue Cutter "Argus".

**1982.**

| | | | | |
|---|---|---|---|---|
| 715 | 266 | 1 k. 60 red .. .. | 40 | 10 |
| 716 | | 1 k. 60 green .. | 1·50 | 1·50 |
| 717 | | 1 k. 80 brown .. | 50 | 15 |
| 718 | | 2 k. red .. .. | 40 | 10 |
| 719 | | 2 k. 20 green .. | 85 | 85 |
| 720 | | 2 k. 30 violet .. | 60 | 60 |
| 721 | | 2 k. 50 red .. .. | 50 | 10 |
| 722 | | 2 k. 70 blue .. .. | 70 | 30 |
| 723 | | 2 k. 70 red .. .. | 65 | 10 |
| 724 | | 2 k. 80 red .. .. | 60 | 10 |
| 725 | | 3 k. violet .. .. | 70 | 15 |
| 726 | | 3 k. red .. .. | 60 | 10 |
| 727 | | 3 k. 20 violet .. | 60 | 40 |
| 727a | | 3 k. 20 red .. .. | 65 | 10 |
| 728 | | 3 k. 30 black .. | 1·00 | 30 |
| 729 | | 3 k. 40 green .. | 1·00 | 70 |
| 730 | | 3 k. 50 blue .. .. | 85 | 20 |
| 730a | | 3 k. 50 purple .. | 90 | 30 |
| 730b | | 3 k. 50 red .. .. | 70 | 10 |
| 731 | | 3 k. 70 blue .. .. | 90 | 20 |
| 732 | | 3 k. 75 green .. | 1·00 | 75 |
| 733 | | 3 k. 80 blue .. .. | 70 | 40 |
| 734 | | 3 k. 80 purple .. | 70 | 20 |
| 735 | | 4 k. 10 blue .. .. | 80 | 20 |
| 736 | | 4 k. 20 violet .. | 85 | 80 |
| 737 | | 4 k. 40 blue .. .. | 90 | 20 |
| 738 | | 4 k. 50 purple .. | 90 | 90 |
| 739 | | 4 k. 75 blue .. .. | 95 | 20 |

**1982.** 350th Anniv. Customs Service.
740. **267.** 1 k. 60 red .. .. .. 60 10

**268.** Skater.

**269.** Villein (Abolition of adscription, 1788).

**1982.** World Figure Skating Championships, Copenhagen.
741. **268.** 2 k. blue .. .. .. 70 25

**1982.** Europa.
742. **269.** 2 k. brown .. .. .. 60 10
743. – 2 k. 70 blue .. .. .. 65 60
DESIGN: 2 k. 70, Procession of women (Enfranchisement of women, 1915).

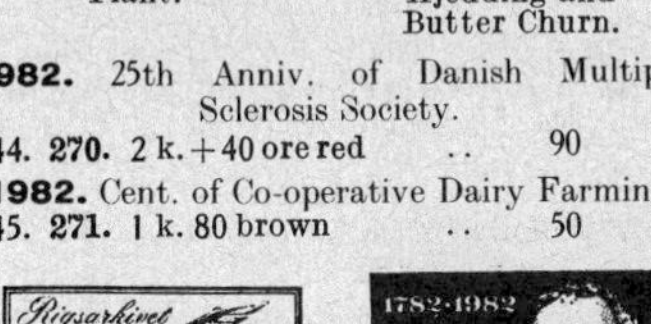

**270.** Distorted Plant.

**271.** Dairy Farm at Hjedding and Butter Churn.

**1982.** 25th Anniv. of Danish Multiple Sclerosis Society.
744. **270.** 2 k.+40 ore red .. 90 90

**1982.** Cent. of Co-operative Dairy Farming.
745. **271.** 1 k. 80 brown .. 50 15

**272.** Hand holding Quill Pen.

**273.** Blicher (after J. V. Gertner).

**1982.** 400th Anniv. of Record Office.
746. **272.** 2 k. 70 green .. .. 70 30

**1982.** Birth Bicentenary of Steen Steensen Blicher (poet).
747. **273.** 2 k. red .. .. .. 35 10

**274.** Odense Printing Press, 1482.

**275.** Petersen and the Number Men.

**1982.** 500th Anniv. of Printing in Denmark.
748. **274.** 1 k. 80 brown .. 45 45

**1982.** Birth Centenary of Robert Storm Petersen (cartoonist).
749. **275.** 1 k. 50 red and blue .. 40 40
750. – 2 k. green and red .. 45 15
DESIGN—HORIZ: 2 k. Peter and Ping with dog.

**276.** Library Seal.

**1982.** 500th Anniv. University Library.
751. **276.** 2 k. 70 brown and black 40 20

**277.** "Interglobal Communications".

**278.** Nurse tending Patient.

**1983.** World Communications Year.
752. **277.** 2 k. orge, red & blue .. 30 15

**1983.** Red Cross.
753. **278.** 2 k.+40 ore bl. & red 80 1·00

**279.** Clown and Girl with Balloon.

**280.** Lene Koppen.

**1983.** 400th Anniv. of Dyrehavsbakken Amusement Park.
754. **279.** 2 k. multicoloured .. 35 15

**1983.** World Badminton Championships.
755. **280.** 2 k. 70 blue .. .. 60 20

**281.** Burin and Engraving of 1 ore Numeral Stamp

**282.** Egeskov Castle.

**1983.** 50th Anniv of Danish Recess-printed Stamps.
756 281 2 k. 50 red .. .. 40 10

**1983.** Nordic Countries Postal Co-operation. "Visit the North".
757. **282.** 2 k. 50 dp. brn. & brn. 45 10
758. – 3 k. 50 dp. blue & blue 65 35
DESIGN: 3 k. 50, Troldkirken long barrow, North Jutland.

**283.** Kildeskovshallen Recreation Centre, Copenhagen.

**284.** Weights and Measures.

**1983.** Europa.
759 283 2 k. 50 red and brown 60 10
760 – 3 k. 50 dp blue & blue 1·25 40
DESIGN: 3 k. 50, Sallingsund Bridge.

**1983.** 300th Anniv. of Weights and Measures Ordinance.
761. **284.** 2 k. 50 red .. .. 60 10

**285.** Title Page of Law.

**286.** Crashed Car and Hand with Eye (Police).

**1983.** 300th Anniv of King Christian V's Danish Law (code of laws for Norway).
762 285 5 k. dp brown & brown 1·25 50

**1983.** Life-saving Services.
763. **286.** 1 k. brown .. .. 45 30
764. – 2 k. 50 red .. .. 85 30
765. – 3 k. 50 blue .. .. 1·10 55
DESIGNS: 2 k. 50 Ladder, stretcher and fire-hose (ambulance and fire services). 3 k. 50 Lifebelt and lifeboat (sea-rescue services).

**287.** Family Group.

**288** Grundtvig (after Constantin Hansen).

**1983.** The Elderly in Society.
766. **287.** 2 k. green .. .. 55 50
767. – 2 k. 50 red .. .. 60 15
DESIGN: 2 k. 50 Elderly people in train.

**1983.** Birth Bicentenary of Nicolai Frederik Severin Grundtvig (writer).
768. **288.** 2 k. 50 brown .. .. 50 15

**289.** Perspective Painting.

**1983.** Birth Bicentenary of Christoffer Wilhelm Eckersberg (painter).
769 289 2 k. 50 red .. .. 50 10

**290.** Spade and Sapling.

**291.** Billiards.

**1984.** Plant a Tree Campaign.
770. **290.** 2 k. 70 yellow, red & green .. .. 55 10

**1984.** World Billiards Championships.
771. **291.** 3 k. 70 green .. .. 1·00 30

**292.** Athletes.

**293.** Compass Rose.

**1984.** Olympic Games, Los Angeles.
772. **292.** 2 k. 70+40 ore. mult. 1·00 1·00

**1984.** Bicentenary of Hydrographic Department (2 k. 30) and 300th Anniv of Pilotage Service (2 k. 70).
773. **293.** 2 k. 30 green .. .. 60 60
774. – 2 k. 70 red .. .. 65 15
DESIGN: 2 k. 70 Pilot boat.

**294.** Parliament Emblem.

**295.** Girl Guides.

**1984.** 2nd Direct Elections to European Parliament.
775. **294.** 2 k. 70 yell. & bl. .. 1·00 15

**1984.** Scout Movement.
776. **295.** 2 k. 70 multicoloured 65 15

**296.** Bridge.

**297.** Anchor (memorial to Danish Sailors).

**1984.** Europa. 25th Anniv. of European Post and Telecommunications Conference.
777. **296.** 2 k. 70 red .. .. 1·00 15
778. 3 k. 70 blue .. .. 1·40 1·10

**1984.** 40th Anniv. of Normandy Invasion.
779. **297.** 2 k. 70 purple .. .. 50 15

**298.** Prince Henrik.

**299.** Old Danish Inn.

**1984.** 50th Birthday of Prince Henrik.
780. **298.** 2 k. 70 brown .. .. 50 10

**1984.**
781. **299.** 3 k. multicoloured .. 60 70

**300.** Shoal of Fish (research).

**1984.** Danish Fisheries and Shipping.
782 **300** 2 k. 30 blue and green 1·00 1·00
783 – 2 k. 70 blue and red .. 75 15
784 – 3 k. 30 blue and violet 1·00 1·00
785 – 3 k. 70 blue & ultram 1·10 1·00
DESIGNS: 2 k. 70, Ships (sea transport). 3 k. 30, "Bettina" (deep sea fishing boat). 3 k. 70, Deck of trawler "Jonna Tornby".

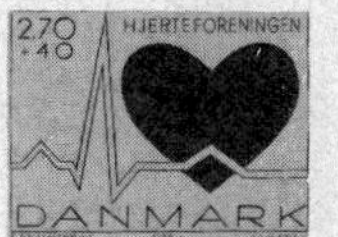

**301.** Heart and Cardiograph.

**302.** Bird with Letter.

**1984.** Heart Foundation.
786. **301.** 2 k. 70+40 ore red .. 80 1·00

**1984.**
787. **302.** 1 k. multicoloured .. 20 10

**303.** "Holberg meeting Officer and Dandy" (Wilhelm Marstrand).

**304.** Woman and Sabbath Candles.

**1984.** 300th Birth Anniv of Ludvig Holberg (historian and playwright).
788 **303** 2 k. 70 blk, stone & red 45 10

**1984.** 300th Anniv. of Jewish Community.
789. **304.** 3 k. 70 multicoloured .. 1·00 70

**305.** "Ymer sucking Milk from the Cow Odhumble" (Nicolai Abildgaard).

**1984.** Paintings. Multicoloured.
790 5 k. "Carnival in Rome" (Christoffer Wilhelm Eckersberg) (horiz) .. 2·00 2·00
791 10 k. Type **305** .. .. 3·25 3·25

**306.** Gothersgade Reformed Church, Copenhagen.

**1985.** 300th Anniv. of French and German Reformed Church in Denmark.
792. **306.** 2 k. 80 red .. .. 55 10

**307.** Flags and Border.

**1985.** 30th Anniv. of Copenhagen–Bonn Declarations.
793. **307.** 2 k. 80 multicoloured 75 15

**308.** Flag, Girl and Boy.

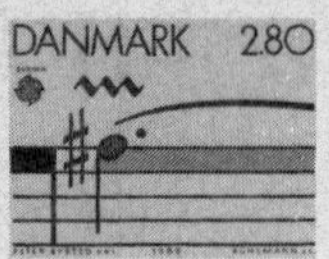

**310.** Music Score.

**1985.** International Youth Year.
794. **308.** 3 k. 80 multicoloured 90 45

**1985.** Europa. Music Year.
796 **310** 2 k. 80 yell, red & verm 90 25
797 – 3 k. 80 black, bl & grn 1·40 70
DESIGN: 3 k. 80, Music score (different).

**311.** Flames and Houses.

**312.** Queen Ingrid and "Chrysanthemum frutescens" "Sofieri".

**1985.** 40th Anniv of Liberation.
798 **311** 2 k. 80+50 ore mult .. 1·00 1·10
The surtax was for the benefit of Resistance veterans.

**1985.** 50th Anniv. of Queen Ingrid's Arrival in Denmark.
799. **312.** 2 k. 80 multicoloured 70 15

**313.** Faro Bridges.

**314.** St. Canute and Lund Cathedral.

**1985.** Inauguration of Faro Bridges.
800. **313.** 2 k. 80 multicoloured 70 10

**1985.** 900th Anniv. of Saint Canute's Deed of Gift to Lund.
801. **314.** 2 k. 80 black and red 60 15
802. – 3 k. black and red .. 1·00 1·25
DESIGN: 3 k. Saint Canute and Helsingborg.

**315.** Gymnastics.

**316.** Woman Cyclist.

**1985.** Sports. Multicoloured.
803. 2 k. 80 Type **315** .. .. 70 15
804. 3 k. 80 Canoeing .. .. 90 60
805. 6 k. Cycling .. .. 1·40 1·00

**1985.** United Nations Women's Decade.
806. **316.** 3 k. 80 multicoloured 80 60

**317.** Kronborg Castle.

**318.** Dove and U.N. Emblem.

**1985.** 400th Anniv. of Kronborg Castle, Elsinore.
807. **317.** 2 k. 80 multicoloured 55 10

**1985.** 40th Anniv. of U.N.O.
808. **318.** 3 k. 80 multicoloured 1·00 60

**319.** Niels and Margrethe Bohr.

**320.** Tapestry (detail) by Caroline Ebbesen.

**1985.** Birth Centenary of Niels Bohr (nuclear physicist).
809. **319.** 2 k. 80 multicoloured. 1·25 1·25

**1985.** 25th Anniv. of National Society for Welfare of the Mentally Ill.
810. **320.** 2 k. 80+40 ore mult. 1·00 1·25

**321.** "D" in Sign Language.

**322.** Stern of Boat.

**1985.** 50th Anniv. of Danish Association of the Deaf.
811. **321.** 2 k. 80 brown & blk. 1·00 30

**1985.**
812. **322.** 2 k. 80 multicoloured 80 30

**323.** "Head".

**1985.**
813. **323.** 3 k. 80 multicoloured 2·00 2·00

**324.** Leaves and Barbed Wire.

**1986.** 25th Anniv. of Amnesty International.
814. **324.** 2 k. 80 multicoloured 75 10

**325.** Girl with Bird.

**326.** Reichhardt as Papageno in "The Magic Flute".

**1986.**
815. **325.** 2 k. 80 multicoloured 1·00 90

**1986.** 1st Death Anniv of Poul Reichhardt (actor).
816 **326** 2 k. 80+50 ore mult .. 1·00 1·00

**328.** Hands reading Braille.

**329.** Bands of Colour.

**1986.** 75th Anniv. of Danish Society for the Blind.
818. **328.** 2 k. 80+50 ore red, brown and black .. 1·25 1·25

**1986.** 50th Anniv. of Danish Arthritis Association.
819. **329.** 2 k. 80+50 ore mult. 1·10 1·10

**330.** Changing the Guard at Barracks.

**1986.** Bicentenary of Royal Danish Life Guards Barracks, Rosenborg.
820. **330.** 2 k. 80 multicoloured 70 15

**331.** Academy and Arms.

**332.** Hands reaching out.

**1986.** 400th Anniv. of Soro Academy.
821. **331.** 2 k. 80 multicoloured 75 15

**1986.** International Peace Year.
822. **332.** 3 k. 80 multicoloured 85 40

**333.** Prince Frederik.

**334.** Station.

**1986.** 18th Birthday of Crown Prince Frederik.
823. **333.** 2 k. 80 black and red 70 15

**1986.** Inauguration of Hoje Tastrup Railway Station.
824. **334.** 2 k. 80 blk, bl. & red 1·00 20

**335.** Aalborg.

**336.** Raven.

**1986.** Nordic Countries Postal Co-operation. Twinned Towns.
825. **335.** 2 k. 80 black .. .. 90 15
826. – 3 k. 80 blue and red .. 1·00 45
DESIGN: 3 k. 80, Thisted.

**1986.** Birds. Multicoloured.
827 2 k. 80 Type **336** .. .. 1·40 75
828 2 k. 80 Common starling ("Sturnus vulgaris") .. 1·40 75
829 2 k. 80 Mute swan ("Cygnus olor") .. 1·40 75
830 2 k. 80 Lapwing ("Vanellus vanellus") .. .. 1·40 75
831 2 k. 80 Sky lark ("Alauda arvensis") .. .. 1·40 75

**337.** Post Box, Wires and Telephone.

**338.** Sports Pictograms.

**1986.** 19th International Postal Telegraph and Telephone Congress, Copenhagen.
832. **337.** 2 k. 80 multicoloured 75 15

**1986.** 125th Anniv. of Danish Rifle, Gymnastics and Sports Clubs.
833. **338.** 2 k. 80 multicoloured 80 15

**339.** Roadsweeper.

**341.** Man fleeing.

**1986.** Europa.
834. **339.** 2 k. 80 red .. .. 1·25 15
835. – 3 k. 80 blue .. .. 1·50 70
DESIGN: 3 k. 80, Refuse truck.

**1986.** Aid for Refugees.
837. **341.** 2 k. 80 blue, brown and black .. .. 75 10

**342.** Cupid.

**343.** Lutheran Communion Service in Thorslunde Church.

**1986.** Bicentenary of First Performance of "The Whims of Cupid and the Ballet Master" by V. Galeotti and J. Lolle.
838. **342.** 3 k. 80 multicoloured 1·10 60

**1986.** 450th Anniv. of Reformation.
839. **343.** 6 k. 50 multicoloured 1·50 1·00

**344.** Graph of Danish Economic Growth and Unemployment Rate.

**345.** Abstract.

**1986.** 25th Anniv. of Organization of Economic Co-operation and Development.
840. **344.** 3 k. 80 multicoloured 1·25 1·00

**1987.**
841. **345.** 2 k. 80 multicoloured 75 10

**346.** Price Label through Magnifying Glass.

**347.** Fresco.

**1987.** 40th Anniv. of Danish Consumer Council.
842. **346.** 2 k. 80 black and red 75 10

**1987.** Ribe Cathedral. Multicoloured.
843. 3 k. Type **347** .. .. 60 40
844. 3 k. 80 Stained glass window (detail) .. .. 90 75
845. 6 k. 50 Mosaic (detail) .. 1·25 1·10

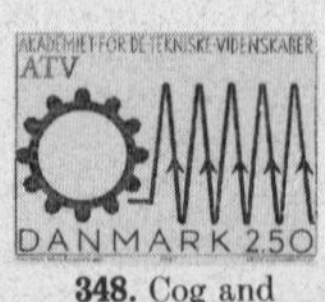

**348.** Cog and Oscillating Waves.

**349.** Gentofte Central Library.

**1987.** 50th Anniv. of Danish Academy of Technical Sciences.
846. **348.** 2 k. 50 black and red 80 60

**1987.** Europa. Architecture.
847. **349.** 2 k. 80 red .. .. 75 10
848. – 3 k. 80 blue .. .. 1·25 85
DESIGN—HORIZ. 3 k. 80, Hoje Tastrup Senior School.

**350.** Ball and Ribbons. **351.** Pigs.

**1987.** 8th Gymnaestrada (World Gymnastics Show), Herning.
849. **350.** 2 k. 80 multicoloured 60 10

**1987.** Centenary of First Co-operative Bacon Factory, Horsens.
850. **351.** 3 k. 80 multicoloured 1·00 80

**352.** 1912 5 k. Stamp and Mail Wagon.

**1987.** "Hafnia 87" International Stamp Exhibition, Copenhagen.
851. **352.** 280 ore multicoloured 1·00 1·00

**353.** Single Scull. **354.** Abstract.

**1987.** World Rowing Championships, Bagsvaerd Lake.
853 **353** 3 k. 80 indigo and blue 85 60

**1987.**
854. **354.** 2 k. 80 multicoloured 60 10

**355.** Waves.

**1987.** 25th Anniv. of Danish Epileptics Association.
855. **355.** 2 k. 80+50 ore blue, red and green .. 90 1·00

**356.** Rask. **357.** Association Badge.

**1987.** Birth Bicentenary of Rasmus Kristjan Rask (philologist).
856 **356** 2 k. 80 red and brown 60 10

**1987.** 125th Anniv. of Clerical Association for Home Mission in Denmark.
857. **357.** 3 k. brown .. .. 60 15

**358.** Lions supporting Monogram.

**1988.** 400th Anniv. of Accession of King Christian IV.
858. **358.** 3 k. gold and blue .. 60 10
859. – 4 k. 10 multicoloured 80 50
DESIGN: 4 k. 10, Portrait of Christian IV by P. Isaacsz.

**359.** Worm and Artefacts. **360.** St. Canute's Church.

**1988.** 400th Birth Anniv. of Ole Worm (antiquarian).
860. **359.** 7 k. 10 brown .. 1·60 1·50

**1988.** Millenary of Odense.
861 **360** 3 k. brown, black & grn 60 10

**361.** African Mother and Child. **362.** Sirens, Workers and Emblem.

**1988.** Danish Church Aid.
862. **361.** 3 k.+50 ore mult. .. 75 1·00

**1988.** 50th Anniv. of Civil Defence Administration.
863. **362.** 2 k. 70 blue & orange 65 30

**363.** Blood Circulation of Heart. **364.** Postwoman on Bicycle.

**1988.** 40th Anniv. of W.H.O.
864. **363.** 4 k. 10 red, blue and black .. .. 90 65

**1988.** Europa. Transport and Communications. Multicoloured.
865. 3 k. Type **364** .. .. 60 10
866. 4 k. 10 Mobile telephone .. 1·25 50

**365.** "King Christian VII riding past Liberty Monument" (C. W. Eckersberg). **366.** "Men of Industry" (detail, P. S. Kroyer).

**1988.** Bicentenary of Abolition of Villeinage.
867. **365.** 3 k. 20 multicoloured 80 80

**1988.** 150th Anniv. of Federation of Danish Industries.
868. **366.** 3 k. multicoloured .. 60 30

**367.** Speedway Riders. **368.** Glass Mosaic (Niels Winkel).

**1988.** World Speedway Championships.
869. **367.** 4 k. 10 multicoloured 90 50

**1988.** Centenary of Danish Metalworkers' Union.
870. **368.** 3 k. multicoloured .. 60 20

**369.** College.

**1988.** Bicentenary of Tonder Teacher Training College.
871 **369** 3 k. brown .. .. 60 10

**370.** "Tribute to Leon Degand" (Robert Jacobsen).

**1988.** Franco-Danish Cultural Co-operation.
872 **370** 4 k. 10 red and black .. 1·50 1·50

**371.** Emblem. **372** Lumby Windmill

**1988.** 5th Anniv. of National Council for the Unmarried Mother and Her Child.
873. **371.** 3 k.+50 ore red .. 80 80

**1988.** Mills.
874 **372** 3 k. black, red & orge 60 10
875 – 7 k. 10 black, ultramarine and blue .. 1·50 1·00
DESIGN: 7 k. 10, Veistrup water mill.

**373** "Bathing Boys 1902" (Peter Hansen)

**1988.** Paintings. Multicoloured.
876 4 k. 10 Type **373** .. .. 1·25 1·25
877 10 k. "Hill at Overkoerby. Winter 1917" (Fritz Syberg) .. .. 2·50 2·50

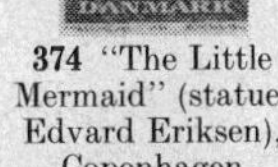

**374** "The Little Mermaid" (statue, Edvard Eriksen), Copenhagen **375** Army Members in Public House

**1989.** Cent of Danish Tourist Association.
878 **374** 3 k. 20 green .. .. 65 20

**1989.** 102nd Anniv of Salvation Army in Denmark.
879 **375** 3 k. 20+50 ore mult .. 90 90

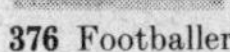

**376** Footballer **377** Emblem

**1989.** Cent of Danish Football Association.
880 **376** 3 k. 20 red, blk & lt red 70 10

**1989.** 40th Anniv of N.A.T.O.
881 **377** 4 k. 40 bl, cobalt & gold 90 60

**378** "Valby Woman" **379** Parliament Flag

**1989.** Nordic Countries' Postal Co-operation. Traditional Costumes. Engravings by Christoffer Wilhelm Eckersberg. Mult.
882 3 k. 20 Type **378** .. .. 70 20
883 4 k. 40 "Pork Butcher" .. 1·00 50

**1989.** 3rd Direct Elections to European Parliament.
884 **379** 3 k. blue and yellow .. 70 70

**380** Lego Bricks **381** Tractor, 1917

**1989.** Europa. Children's Toys. Multicoloured.
885 3 k. 20 Type **380** .. .. 70 20
886 4 k. 40 Wooden guardsmen by Kay Bojesen .. 1·25 50

**1989.** Cent of Danish Agricultural Museum.
887 **381** 3 k. 20 red .. 70 10

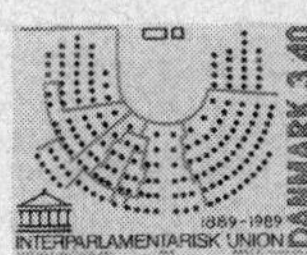


**382** Diagram of Folketing (Parliament) Chamber

**1989.** Cent of Interparliamentary Union.
888 **382** 3 k. 40 red and black .. 1·25 1·25

**383** Chart and Boat Identity Number

**1989.** Centenary of Danish Fishery and Marine Research Institute.
889 **383** 3 k. 20 multicoloured .. 70 20

**384** "Ingemann" (after J. V. Gertner) **385** Scene from "They Caught the Ferry" (50th anniv of Danish Government Film Office)

**1989.** Birth Bicentenary of Bernhard Severin Ingemann (poet).
890 **384** 7 k. 70 green .. .. 1·60 1·00

**1989.** Danish Film Industry.
891 **385** 3 k. blue, black & orge 60 50
892 – 3 k. 20, pink, black and orange .. .. 70 20
893 – 4 k. 40, brown, black and orange .. 90 40
DESIGNS: 3 k. 20, Scene from "The Golden Smile" (birth cent of Bodil Ipsen, actress); 4 k. 40, Carl Th. Dreyer (director, birth cent).

**386** Stamps **387** "Part of Northern Citadel Bridge" (Christen Kobke)

**1989.** 50th Stamp Day.

894 **386** 3 k. 20 salmon, orange and brown .. 65 20

**1989.** Paintings. Multicoloured.

895 4 k. 40 Type **387** .. .. 1·10 1·10
896 10 k. "A Little Girl, Elise Kobke, with Cup" (Constantin Hansen) 2·25 2·25

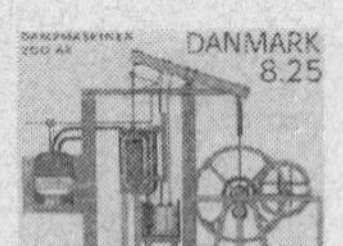


**388** Silver Coffee Pot (Axel Johannes Kroyer, 1726) **389** Andrew Mitchell's Steam Engine

**1990.** Centenary of Museum of Decorative Art, Copenhagen.

897 **388** 3 k. 50 black and blue 70 10

**1990.** Bicentenary of Denmark's First Steam Engine.

898 **389** 8 k. 25 brown .. 1·60 1·25

**390** Queen Margrethe II **391** Royal Monogram over Door of Haderslev Post Office

**1990.**

910 **390** 3 k. 50 red .. .. 70 10
911 3 k. 75 green .. 75 30
912 3 k. 75 red .. .. 75 10
913 4 k. brown .. .. 85 10
914 4 k. 50 violet .. 90 30
915 4 k. 75 blue .. .. 1·00 35
916 4 k. 75 violet .. 95 30
917 5 k. blue .. .. 1·00 35
917a 5 k. 25 black .. 1·10 65
918 5 k. 50 green .. 1·40 50

**1990.** Europa. Post Office Buildings.

930 **391** 3 k. 50 yell, red & blk 70 10
931 – 4 k. 75 multicoloured 95 55
DESIGN: 4 k. 75, Odense Post Office.

**392** Main Guardhouse, Rigging Crane and Ships (after C. O. Willars)

**1990.** 300th Anniv of Nyholm.

932 **392** 4 k. 75 black .. .. 1·00 55

**393** Covered Ice Dish

**394** Marsh Mallow

**1990.** Bicentenary of Flora Danica Banquet Service. Multicoloured.

933 3 k. 50 Type **393** .. .. 80 80
934 3 k. 50 Sauce boat .. 80 80
935 3 k. 50 Lidded ice pot .. 80 80
936 3 k. 50 Serving dish .. 80 80

**1990.** Endangered Flowers. Multicoloured.

937 3 k. 25 Type **394** .. .. 80 70
938 3 k. 50 Red helleborine .. 90 10
939 3 k. 75 Purple orchis .. 1·00 1·00
940 4 k. 75 Lady's slipper .. 1·00 60

**395** Insulin Crystals **396** Gjellerup Church

**1990.** 50th Anniv of Danish Diabetes Association.

941 **395** 3 k. 50+50 ore mult .. 1·50 1·50

**1990.** Jutland Churches. Each brown.

942 3 k. 50 Type **396** .. .. 70 10
943 4 k. 75 Veng Church .. 95 60
944 8 k. 25 Bredsten Church (vert) .. .. .. 1·75 1·25

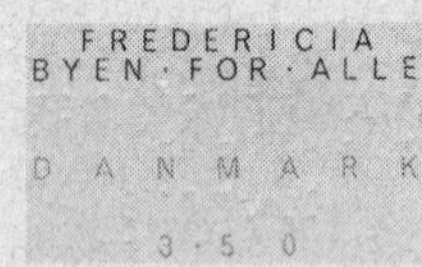


**397** Slogan and Braille

**1990.** Fredericia: "Town for Everybody" (access for the handicapped project).

945 **397** 3 k. 50 red and black .. 70 10

**398** "Tordenskiold and Karlsten's Commandant" (Otto Bache) **399** Bicycle (Bicycle stealing)

**1990.** 300th Birth Anniv of Admiral Tordenskiold (Peter Wessel).

946 **398** 3 k. 50 multicoloured .. 70 10

**1990.** Campaigns.

947 **399** 3 k. 25 multicoloured 60 60
948 – 3 k. 50 black, bl & mve 70 10
DESIGN: 3 k. 50, Glass and car (Drunken driving).

**400** "IC 3" Electric Passenger Train, 1990

**1991.** Railway Locomotives.

949 **400** 3 k. 25 blue, red & grn 60 60
950 – 3 k. 50 black and red 70 10
951 – 3 k. 75 brown & dp brn 80 80
952 – 4 k. 75 black and red 1·00 50
DESIGNS: 3 k. 50, Class "A" steam locomotive, 1882; 3 k. 75, Class "MY" diesel locomotive, 1954; 4 k. 75, Class "P" steam locomotive, 1907.

**401** Satellite Picture of Denmark's Water Temperatures **402** First Page of 1280s Manuscript

**1991.** Europa. Europe in Space. Mult.

953 3 k. 50 Type **401** .. .. 70 10
954 4 k. 75 Denmark's land temperatures .. .. 1·00 50

**1991.** 750th Anniv of Jutland Law.

955 **402** 8 k. 25 multicoloured .. 1·75 1·50

**403** Fano

**404** Child using Emergency Helpline

**1991.** Nordic Countries' Postal Co-operation. Tourism. Multicoloured.

956 3 k. 50 Type **403** .. .. 70 10
957 4 k. 75 Christianso .. 1·00 60

**1991.** 15th Anniv of Living Conditions of Children (child welfare organization).

958 **404** 3 k. 50+50 ore blue .. 90 90

**405** Stoneware Vessels (Christian Poulsen) **406** Man cleaning up after Dog

**1991.** Danish Design. Multicoloured.

959 3 k. 25 Type **405** .. .. 60 60
960 3 k. 50 Chair, 1949 (Hans Wegner) (vert) .. .. 70 10
961 4 k. 75 Silver cutlery, 1938 (Kay Bojesen) (vert) .. 1·00 60
962 8 k. 25 "PH5" lamp, 1958 (Poul Henningsen) .. 1·75 1·40

**1991.** "Keep Denmark Clean".

963 **406** 3 k. 50 red .. .. 70 10
964 – 4 k. 75 blue .. .. 95 55
DESIGN: 4 k. 75, Woman putting litter into bin.

**407** Nordic Advertising Congress 1947 (Arne Ungermann)

**1991.** Posters. Multicoloured.

965 3 k. 50 Type **407** .. .. 70 10
966 4 k. 50 Poster Exhibition, Copenhagen Zoo, 1907 (Valdemar Andersen) .. 90 90
967 4 k. 75 D.D.L. (Danish Airlines, 1945) (Ib Andersen) .. .. 95 55
968 12 k. Casino's "The Sinner", 1925 (Sven Brasch) .. .. 2·50 2·50

**408** "Lady at Her Toilet" (Harald Giersing) **409** Skarpsalling Earthenware Bowl

**1991.** Paintings. Multicoloured.

969 4 k. 75 Type **408** .. .. 95 55
970 14 k. "Road through Wood" (Edvard Weie) 2·75 2·40

**1992.** Re-opening of National Museum, Copenhagen. Exhibits from Prehistoric Denmark Collection.

971 **409** 3 k. 50 brown and lilac 70 10
972 – 4 k. 50 green and blue 90 90
973 – 4 k. 75 black & brown 95 95
974 – 8 k. 25 purple & green 1·60 1·25
DESIGNS: 4 k. 50, Grevensvaenge bronze figure of dancer; 4 k. 75, Bottom plate of Gundestrup Cauldron; 8 k. 25, Hindsgavl flint knife.

**410** Aspects of Engineering **412** Potato Plant

**1992.** Cent of Danish Society of Chemical, Civil, Electrical and Mechanical Engineers.

975 **410** 3 k. 50 red .. .. 70 10

**1992.** Europa. 500th Anniv of Discovery of America by Columbus.

977 **412** 3 k. 50 green & brown 70 10
978 – 4 k. 75 green & yellow 95 55
DESIGN: 4 k. 75, Head of maize.

**413** Royal Couple in 1992 and in Official Wedding Photograph

**1992.** Silver Wedding of Queen Margrethe and Prince Henrik.

979 **413** 3 k. 75 multicoloured .. 75 10

**414** Hare and Cars

**1992.** Environmental Protection. Mult.

980 3 k. 75 Type **414** .. .. 75 10
981 5 k. Fishes and sea pollution .. .. .. 1·00 60
982 8 k. 75 Felled trees and saplings (vert) .. .. 1·75 1·25

**415** Celebrating Crowd **416** Danish Pavilion

**1992.** Denmark, European Football Champion.

983 **415** 3 k. 75 multicoloured .. 75 10

**1992.** "Expo '92" World's Fair, Seville.

984 **416** 3 k. 75 blue .. 75 10

**417** "Word" **418** "A Hug"

**1992.** 50th Anniv of Danish Dyslexia Association.

985 **417** 3 k. 75+50 ore mult .. 85 85

**1992.** Danish Cartoon Characters.

986 **418** 3 k. 50 pur, red & gold 70 70
987 – 3 k. 75 violet and red 75 10
988 – 4 k. 75 black and red 95 95
989 – 5 k. blue and red .. 1·00 60
DESIGNS: 3 k. 75, "Love Letter"; 4 k. 75, "Domestic Triangle"; 5 k. "The Poet and his Little Wife".

419 Abstract

420 "Jacob's Fight with the Angel" (bible illustration by Bodil Kaalund)

**1992.** European Single Market.
990 **419** 3 k. 75 blue and yellow 75 10

**1992.** Publication of New Danish Bible.
991 **420** 3 k. 75 multicoloured .. 75 10

DANMARK 5.00

421 "Landscape from Vejby, 1843" (Johan Thomas Lundbye)

**1992.** Paintings. Multicoloured.
992 5 k. Type **421** .. .. 1·25 60
993 10 k. "Motif from Halleby Brook, 1847" (Peter Christian Skovgaard) .. 2·00 1·50

422 Funen Guldgubber

423 Small Tortoiseshell

**1993.** Danish Treasure Trove. Guldgubber (anthropomorphic gold foil figures). Mult.
994 3 k. 75 Type **422** .. .. 75 10
995 5 k. Bornholm guldgubber (vert) .. .. .. 1·00 60

**1993.** Butterflies. Multicoloured.
996 3 k. 75 Type **423** .. .. 75 10
997 5 k. Large blue .. .. 1·00 60
998 8 k. 75 Marsh fritillary .. 1·75 1·25
999 12 k. Red admiral .. 2·40 2·40

424 Untitled Painting (Troels Worsel)

**1993.** Europa. Contemporary Art. Mult.
1000 3 k. 75 Type **424** .. .. 75 10
1001 5 k. "The 7 Corners of the Earth" (Stig Brogger) (vert) .. .. .. 1·25 60

425 "Pierrot" (Thor Bogelund, 1947)

DANMARK 3.75

426 "Danmark"

**1993.** Nordic Countries' Postal Co-operation. Tourism. Publicity posters for Tivoli Gardens, Copenhagen. Multicoloured.
1002 3 k. 75 Type **425** .. 75 10
1003 5 k. Child holding balloons (Wilhelm Freddie, 1987) (vert) .. 1·25 60

**1993.** Training Ships. Multicoloured.
1004 3 k. 75 Type **426** .. 75 10
1005 4 k. 75 "Jens Krogh" (25 × 30 mm) .. .. 95 95
1006 5 k. "Georg Stage" .. 1·00 60
1007 9 k. 50 "Marilyn Anne" (36 × 26 mm) .. .. 2·25 1·90

427 Map

428 Prow of Viking Ship

**1993.** Inauguration of Denmark–Russia Submarine Cable and 500th Anniv of Friendship Treaty.
1008 **427** 5 k. green .. .. 1·00 60

**1993.** Children's Stamp Design Competition.
1009 **428** 3 k. 75 multicoloured 75 10

429 Emblem

430 "If you want a Letter...Write one Yourself"

**1993.** 75th Anniv of Social Work of Young Men's Christian Association.
1010 **429** 3 k. 75 + 50 ore. green, red and black 85 85

**1993.** Letter-writing Campaign.
1011 **430** 5 k. ultram, bl & blk 1·00 60

431 Silver Brooch and Chain, North Falster

**1993.** Traditional Jewellery. Multicoloured.
1012 3 k. 50 Type **431** .. 70 70
1013 3 k. 75 Gilt-silver brooch with owner's monogram, Amager .. 75 10
1014 5 k. Silver buttons and brooches, Laeso .. 1·25 10
1015 8 k. 75 Silver buttons, Romo .. .. .. 2·00 1·00

432 "Assemblage" (Vilhelm Lundstrom)

433 Duck

**1993.** Paintings. Multicoloured.
1016 5 k. Type **432** .. .. 1·25 1·00
1017 15 k. "Composition" (Franciska Clausen) .. 3·50 2·40

**1994.** Save Water and Energy Campaign.
1018 **433** 3 k. 75 multicoloured 75 10
1019 – 5 k. green, red & blk 1·00 60
DESIGN: 5 k. Spade (in Danish "spar" = save) and "CO2".

434 Marselisborg Castle, Aarhus

**1994.** Royal Residences.
1020 **434** 3 k. 50 deep brown, green and brown .. 70 70
1021 – 3 k. 75 multicoloured 80 10
1022 – 5 k. green, deep brown and brown .. 1·25 10
1023 – 8 k. 75 deep brown, green and brown .. 2·00 1·00
DESIGNS: 3 k. 75, Amalienborg Castle, Copenhagen; 5 k. Fredensborg Castle, North Zealand; 8 k. 75, Graasten Castle, South Jutland.

435 "Danmark" and Wegener's Weather Balloon, Danmarkshavn

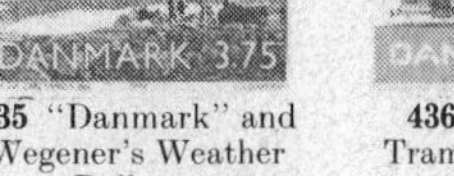


436 Engelhardt Tram, Copenhagen

**1994.** Europa. Discoveries. "Danmark" Expedition to North-east Greenland, 1906–08.
1024 **435** 3 k. 75 purple .. 80 10
1025 – 5 k. black .. .. 1·25 10
DESIGN: 5k. Johan Peter Koch and theodolite.

**1994.** Trams. Multicoloured.
1026 3 k. 75 Type **436** .. 80 10
1027 4 k. 75 Tram car, Aarhus 1·25 60
1028 5 k. Tram, Odense (vert) 1·25 60
1029 12 k. Horse-drawn tram, Copenhagen (37 × 21 mm) .. .. 2·75 2·75

437 Prince Henrik

438 Kite

**1994.** Danish Red Cross Fund. 60th Birthday of Prince Henrik, the Prince Consort.
1030 **437** 3 k. 75 + 50 ore mult .. 90 90

**1994.** Children's Stamp Design Competition.
1031 **438** 3 k. 75 multicoloured 80 10

439 Emblem

440 House Sparrows

**1994.** 75th Anniv of I.L.O.
1032 **439** 5 k. multicoloured .. 1·25 60

**1994.** Protected Animals. Multicoloured.
1033 3 k. 75 Type **440** .. 80 10
1034 4 k. 75 Badger .. .. 1·25 1·00
1035 5 k. Red squirrel (vert) 1·25 60
1036 9 k. 50 Pair of black grouse .. .. 2·40 2·00
1037 12 k. Black grass snake (36 × 26 mm) .. .. 3·00 2·50

441 Teacher

**1994.** 150th Anniv of Folk High Schools.
1038 **441** 3 k. 75 multicoloured 80 10

442 Study for "Italian Woman with Sleeping Child" (Wilhelm Marstrand)

**1994.** Paintings. Multicoloured.
1039 5 k. Type **442** .. .. 1·25 60
1040 15 k. "Interior from Amaliegade with the Artist's Brothers" (Wilhelm Bendz) .. 3·50 1·75

443 The Red Building (architect's drawing, Hack Kampmann)

444 Anniversary Emblem

**1995.** 800th Anniv of Aarhus Cathedral School.
1041 **443** 3 k. 75 multicoloured 1·10 10

**1995.** 50th Anniv of United Nations Organization. U.N. World Summit for Social Development, Copenhagen.
1042 **444** 5 k. multicoloured .. 1·50 65

445 Avernako

446 Field-Marshal Montgomery and Copenhagen Town Hall

**1995.** Danish Islands. Each brown, blue and red.
1043 3 k. 75 Type **445** .. 85 10
1044 4 k. 75 Fejo .. .. 1·10 1·10
1045 5 k. Fur .. .. .. 1·10 65
1046 9 k. 50 Endelave .. 2·25 2·25

**1995.** Europa. Peace and Freedom. Mult.
1047 3 k. 75 Type **446** .. 85 10
1048 5 k. White coaches (repatriation of Danes from German concentration camps) (horiz) 1·10 65
1049 8 k. 75 Dropping of supplies from Allied aircraft (horiz) .. 2·00 1·00
1050 12 k. Boatload of Jews escaping to Sweden (horiz) .. .. 3·00 1·75

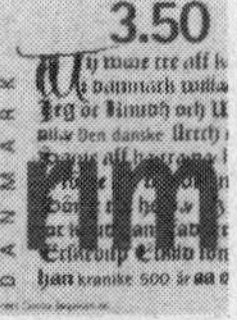


447 Detail of Page

448 Stage

**1995.** 500th Anniv of "The Rhymed Chronicle" by Friar Niels (first book printed in Danish).
1051 **447** 3 k. 50 multicoloured 80 80

**1995.** Nordic Countries' Postal Co-operation. Music Festivals. Multicoloured.
1052 3 k. 75 Type **448** (25th anniv of Roskilde Festival) .. .. 80 10
1053 5 k. Violinist (21st anniv of Tonder Festival) (20 × 38 mm) .. .. 1·10 65

449 Broken Feather

**1995.** 50th Anniv of National Society of Polio and Accident Victims.

| No. | Type | Description | Unused | Used |
|---|---|---|---|---|
| 1054 | 449 | 3 k. 75+50 ore red | 1·00 | 1·00 |

450 "Midsummer Eve" (Jens Sondergaard)

**1995.** Paintings. Multicoloured.

| No. | Type | Description | Unused | Used |
|---|---|---|---|---|
| 1055 | | 10 k. Type **450** | 2·40 | 1·25 |
| 1056 | | 15 k. "Landscape at Gudhjem" (Niels Lergaard) | 3·50 | 2·00 |

451 Sextant

453 The Round Tower

452 TEKNO Model Vehicles

**1995.** 450th Birth Anniv of Tycho Brahe (astronomer). Multicoloured.

| No. | Type | Description | Unused | Used |
|---|---|---|---|---|
| 1057 | | 3 k. 75 Uraniborg (Palace Observatory) | 1·10 | 10 |
| 1058 | | 5 k. 50 Type **451** | 1·60 | 75 |

**1995.** Danish Toys. Multicoloured.

| No. | Type | Description | Unused | Used |
|---|---|---|---|---|
| 1059 | | 3 k. 75 Type **452** | 1·10 | 10 |
| 1060 | | 5 k. Edna (celluloid doll), Kirstine (china doll) and Holstebro teddy bear | 1·10 | 65 |
| 1061 | | 8 k. 75 Wittroch and Petersen tin trains | 2·25 | 1·50 |
| 1062 | | 12 k. Glud & Marstrand horse-drawn fire engine and carriage | 3·00 | 2·75 |

**1996.** Copenhagen, European Cultural Capital. Multicoloured.

| No. | Type | Description | Unused | Used |
|---|---|---|---|---|
| 1063 | | 3 k. 75 Type **453** | 85 | 10 |
| 1064 | | 5 k. Christiansborg | 1·10 | 65 |
| 1065 | | 8 k. 75 Dome of Marble Church as hot-air balloon | 2·00 | 1·50 |
| 1066 | | 12 k. "The Little Mermaid" on stage | 2·75 | 2·75 |

454 Disabled Basketball Player

455 Businessmen

**1996.** Sport. Multicoloured.

| No. | Type | Description | Unused | Used |
|---|---|---|---|---|
| 1067 | | 3 k. 75 Type **454** | 80 | 10 |
| 1068 | | 4 k. 75 Swimming | 1·00 | 1·00 |
| 1069 | | 5 k. Yachting | 1·10 | 65 |
| 1070 | | 9 k. 50 Cycling | 2·00 | 2·00 |

**1996.** Centenary of Danish Employers' Confederation.

| No. | Type | Description | Unused | Used |
|---|---|---|---|---|
| 1071 | 455 | 3 k. 75 multicoloured | 80 | 10 |

456 Asta Nielsen (actress)

457 Roskilde Fjord Boat

**1996.** Europa. Famous Women.

| No. | Type | Description | Unused | Used |
|---|---|---|---|---|
| 1072 | – | 3 k. 75 brn & dp brn | 80 | 10 |
| 1073 | 456 | 5 k. grey and blue | 1·10 | 65 |

DESIGN: 3 k. 75, Karin Blixen (writer).

**1996.** Wooden Sailing Boats.

| No. | Type | Description | Unused | Used |
|---|---|---|---|---|
| 1074 | 457 | 3 k. 50 brn, bl & red | 75 | 75 |
| 1075 | – | 3 k. 75 lilac, grn & red | 80 | 10 |
| 1076 | – | 12 k. 25 blk, brn & red | 2·50 | 2·50 |

DESIGNS—As T **457**: 12 k. 25, South Funen Archipelago smack. 20×38 mm: 3 k. 75, Limfjorden skiff.

458 Fornaes

459 Ribbons forming Hearts within Star

**1996.** Lighthouses. Multicoloured.

| No. | Type | Description | Unused | Used |
|---|---|---|---|---|
| 1077 | | 3 k. 75 Type **458** | 80 | 10 |
| 1078 | | 5 k. Blavandshuk | 1·10 | 65 |
| 1079 | | 5 k. 25 Bovbjerg | 1·10 | 65 |
| 1080 | | 8 k. 75 Mon | 1·90 | 1·40 |

**1996.** AIDS Foundation.

| No. | Type | Description | Unused | Used |
|---|---|---|---|---|
| 1081 | 459 | 3 k. 75+50 ore red and black | 90 | 90 |

460 Vase

**1996.** 150th Birth Anniv of Thorvald Bindesboll (ceramic artist). Multicoloured.

| No. | Type | Description | Unused | Used |
|---|---|---|---|---|
| 1082 | | 3 k. 75 Type **460** | 80 | 10 |
| 1083 | | 4 k. Portfolio cover | 85 | 85 |

## MILITARY FRANK STAMPS

**1917.** Nos. 135 and 138 optd **S F** (= "Soldater Frimaerke").

| No. | Type | Description | Unused | Used |
|---|---|---|---|---|
| M188 | 21 | 5 ore green | 12·00 | 22·00 |
| M189 | | 10 ore red | 11·00 | 16·00 |

## NEWSPAPER STAMPS

N 18.

**1901.**

| No. | Type | Description | Unused | Used |
|---|---|---|---|---|
| N185 | N 18 | 1 ore green | 6·00 | 2·00 |
| N186 | | 5 ore blue | 14·50 | 9·75 |
| N133 | | 7 ore red | 6·00 | 2·00 |
| N188 | | 8 ore green | 13·00 | 1·00 |
| N189 | | 10 ore lilac | 13·00 | 2·00 |
| N135 | | 20 ore green | 12·00 | 90 |
| N191 | | 29 ore orange | 24·00 | 2·00 |
| N136 | | 38 ore orange | 17·00 | 1·00 |
| N193 | | 41 ore brown | 27·00 | 1·50 |
| N137 | | 68 ore brown | 40·00 | 17·00 |
| N138 | | 1 k. purple & green | 12·50 | 2·00 |
| N139 | | 5 k. green and pink | 90·00 | 17·00 |
| N140 | | 10 k. blue and stone | £100 | 16·00 |

## OFFICIAL STAMPS

O 9.

**1871.** Value in "skilling".

| No. | Type | Description | Unused | Used |
|---|---|---|---|---|
| O51a | O 9 | 2 sk. blue | 70·00 | 50·00 |
| O52 | | 4 sk. red | 35·00 | 7·75 |
| O53 | | 16 sk. green | £250 | £140 |

**1875.** Value in "ore".

| No. | Type | Description | Unused | Used |
|---|---|---|---|---|
| O185 | O 9 | 1 ore orange | 1·00 | 1·50 |
| O100 | | 3 ore lilac | 70 | 60 |
| O186 | | 3 ore grey | 2·40 | 24·00 |
| O101 | | 4 ore blue | 1·60 | 1·50 |
| O188 | | 5 ore green | 1·10 | 20 |
| O189 | | 5 ore brown | 2·40 | 12·00 |
| O 94 | | 8 ore red | 4·75 | 1·00 |
| O104 | | 10 ore red | 1·25 | 85 |
| O191 | | 10 ore green | 1·00 | 1·25 |
| O192 | | 15 ore lilac | 7·75 | 20·00 |
| O193 | | 20 ore blue | 8·75 | 5·00 |
| O 98 | | 32 ore green | 17·00 | 17·00 |

## PARCEL POST STAMPS

**1919.** Various types optd **POSTFAERGE**.

| No. | Type | Description | Unused | Used |
|---|---|---|---|---|
| P208 | 21 | 10 ore red | 23·00 | 40·00 |
| P209 | 15 | 10 ore green | 8·75 | 9·75 |
| P210 | | 10 ore brown | 7·75 | 5·00 |
| P211 | 21 | 15 ore lilac | 12·00 | 20·00 |
| P212 | | 30 ore orange | 8·75 | 14·50 |
| P213 | | 30 ore blue | 3·00 | 3·00 |
| P214 | | 50 ore black & purple | £200 | £200 |
| P215a | | 50 ore grey | 20·00 | 8·75 |
| P216 | 22 | 1 k. brown | 90·00 | £120 |
| P217 | 21 | 1 k. blue and brown | 40·00 | 12·50 |
| P218 | | 5 k. brown & mauve | 1·50 | 1·25 |
| P219 | | 10 k. green and red | 48·00 | 60·00 |

**1927.** Stamps of 1927 (solid background) optd **POSTFAERGE**.

| No. | Type | Description | Unused | Used |
|---|---|---|---|---|
| P252 | 40 | 15 ore red | 15·00 | 8·00 |
| P253 | | 30 ore yellow | 14·00 | 9·00 |
| P254 | | 40 ore green | 20·00 | 8·50 |

**1936.** Stamps of 1933 (lined background) optd **POSTFAERGE**.

| No. | Type | Description | Unused | Used |
|---|---|---|---|---|
| P491 | 43 | 5 ore purple | 20 | 20 |
| P299 | | 10 ore orange | 15·00 | 15·00 |
| P300 | | 10 ore brown | 1·00 | 1·00 |
| P301 | | 10 ore violet | 30 | 20 |
| P302 | | 10 ore green | 30 | 20 |
| P303a | 40 | 15 ore red | 65 | 85 |
| P304 | | 30 ore blue | 4·00 | 3·00 |
| P305 | | 30 ore orange | 50 | 50 |
| P306 | | 40 ore green | 4·50 | 4·50 |
| P307 | | 40 ore blue | 60 | 70 |
| P308 | 45 | 50 ore grey | 1·25 | 1·00 |
| P309 | | 1 k. brown | 1·00 | 70 |

**1945.** Stamps of 1942 optd **POSTFAERGE**.

| No. | Type | Description | Unused | Used |
|---|---|---|---|---|
| P346 | 67 | 30 ore orange | 1·50 | 1·00 |
| P347 | | 40 ore blue | 1·00 | 60 |
| P348 | | 50 ore grey | 1·00 | 75 |

**1949.** Stamps of 1946 and 1948 optd **POSTFAERGE**.

| No. | Type | Description | Unused | Used |
|---|---|---|---|---|
| P376 | 80 | 30 ore orange | 2·40 | 1·00 |
| P377 | | 30 ore red | 1·00 | 1·00 |
| P378 | | 40 ore blue | 2·00 | 1·00 |
| P379 | | 40 ore grey | 1·00 | 1·00 |
| P380 | | 50 ore grey | 10·50 | 2·25 |
| P381 | | 50 ore green | 1·00 | 1·00 |
| P382 | | 70 ore green | 1·00 | 1·00 |
| P383 | 73 | 1 k. brown | 1·00 | 85 |
| P384 | | 1 k. 25 orange | 3·75 | 5·00 |
| P495 | | 2 k. red | 1·00 | 1·00 |
| P496 | | 5 k. blue | 2·40 | 2·40 |

**1967.** Optd **POSTFAERGE**.

| No. | Type | Description | Unused | Used |
|---|---|---|---|---|
| P488 | 117 | 40 ore brown | 60 | 65 |
| P492 | | 50 ore brown | 50 | 50 |
| P489 | | 80 ore blue | 80 | 60 |
| P493 | | 90 ore blue | 1·00 | 1·00 |

**1975.** Overprinted **POSTFAERGE**.

| No. | Type | Description | Unused | Used |
|---|---|---|---|---|
| P597 | 207 | 100 ore blue | 65 | 65 |

## POSTAGE DUE STAMPS

**1921.** Stamps of 1905 and 1913 optd **PORTO**.

| No. | Type | Description | Unused | Used |
|---|---|---|---|---|
| D214 | 15 | 1 ore orange | 1·25 | 1·50 |
| D215 | 21 | 5 ore green | 3·50 | 1·50 |
| D216 | | 7 ore orange | 2·00 | 1·50 |
| D217 | | 10 ore red | 12·00 | 6·00 |
| D218 | | 20 ore blue | 7·25 | 4·00 |
| D219 | | 25 ore black and brown | 14·50 | 2·00 |
| D220 | | 50 ore black & purple | 6·00 | 2·50 |

D 32.

**1921.** Solid background.

| No. | Type | Description | Unused | Used |
|---|---|---|---|---|
| D 221. | D 32. | 1 ore orange | 35 | 45 |
| D 222. | | 4 ore blue | 1·60 | 1·60 |
| D 223. | | 5 ore brown | 1·50 | 60 |
| D 224. | | 5 ore green | 75 | 35 |
| D 225. | | 7 ore green | 9·75 | 12·00 |
| D 226. | | 7 ore violet | 18·00 | 18·00 |
| D 227. | | 10 ore green | 1·50 | 35 |
| D 228. | | 10 ore brown | 85 | 30 |
| D 229. | | 20 ore blue | 1·00 | 50 |
| D 230. | | 20 ore grey | 1·25 | 70 |
| D 231. | | 25 ore red | 2·00 | 80 |
| D 232. | | 25 ore lilac | 1·75 | 1·00 |
| D 233. | | 25 ore blue | 3·50 | 2·00 |
| D 234. | | 1 k. blue | 40·00 | 5·00 |
| D 235. | | 1 k. blue and brown | 7·00 | 2·75 |
| D 236. | | 5 k. violet | 14·50 | 5·00 |

For stamps with lined background see Nos. D285/97.

**1921.** Military Frank stamp optd. **PORTO.**

| No. | Type | Description | Unused | Used |
|---|---|---|---|---|
| D 237. | 21. | 10 ore red (No. M 189) | 7·50 | 5·00 |

**1934.** Lined background.

| No. | Type | Description | Unused | Used |
|---|---|---|---|---|
| D285 | D 32 | 1 ore green | 10 | 10 |
| D286 | | 2 ore red | 10 | 10 |
| D287 | | 5 ore green | 10 | 10 |
| D288 | | 6 ore green | 40 | 20 |
| D289 | | 8 ore mauve | 1·60 | 1·60 |
| D290 | | 10 ore orange | 10 | 10 |
| D291 | | 12 ore blue | 30 | 20 |
| D292 | | 15 ore violet | 40 | 10 |
| D293 | | 20 ore grey | 30 | 10 |
| D294 | | 25 ore blue | 40 | 10 |
| D295 | | 30 ore green | 40 | 10 |
| D296 | | 40 ore purple | 50 | 15 |
| D297 | | 1 k. brown | 70 | 10 |

**1934.** Surch **PORTO 15**.

| No. | Type | Description | Unused | Used |
|---|---|---|---|---|
| D298 | 15 | 15 on 12 ore lilac | 2·00 | 2·00 |

## SPECIAL FEE STAMPS

**1923.** No. D227 optd **GEBYR GEBYR**.

| No. | Type | Description | Unused | Used |
|---|---|---|---|---|
| S218 | D 32 | 10 ore green | 8·00 | 2·00 |

S 36.

**1926.** Solid background.

| No. | Type | Description | Unused | Used |
|---|---|---|---|---|
| S229 | S 36 | 10 ore green | 3·75 | 70 |
| S230 | | 10 ore brown | 3·25 | 60 |

**1934.** Lined background.

| No. | Type | Description | Unused | Used |
|---|---|---|---|---|
| S285 | S 36 | 5 ore green | 15 | 10 |
| S286 | | 10 ore orange | 15 | 10 |

## DIEGO-SUAREZ Pt. 6

A port in N. Madagascar. A separate colony till 1896, when it was incorporated with Madagascar.

100 centimes = 1 franc.

**1890.** Stamps of French Colonies (Type J Commerce), surch. **15** sideways.

| No. | Type | Description | | |
|---|---|---|---|---|
| 1. | J. | 15 on 1 c. black on blue | £160 | 55·00 |
| 2. | | 15 on 5 c. green | £425 | 55·00 |
| 3. | | 15 on 10 c. black on lilac | £170 | 48·00 |
| 4. | | 15 on 20 c. red on green | £425 | 55·00 |
| 5. | | 15 on 25 c. black on red | 75·00 | 17·00 |

2.

3.

**1890.** Various designs.

| No. | Type | Description | | |
|---|---|---|---|---|
| 6. | 2. | 1 c. black | £325 | 70·00 |
| 7. | | 5 c. black | £300 | 60·00 |
| 8. | | 15 c. black | 65·00 | 28·00 |
| 9. | | 25 c. black | 85·00 | 35·00 |

**1891.**

| No. | Type | Description | | |
|---|---|---|---|---|
| 10. | 3. | 5 c. black | £110 | 60·00 |

**1891.** Stamps of French Colonies. (Type J Commerce) surch. **1891. DIEGO-SUAREZ 5 c.**

| No. | Type | Description | | |
|---|---|---|---|---|
| 13. | J. | **5 c. on 10 c. black on lilac** | £140 | 70·00 |
| 14. | | **5 c. on 20 c. red on green** | £120 | 50·00 |

**1892.** Stamps of French Colonies (Type J Commerce) optd **DIEGO-SUAREZ.**

| No. | Type | Description | | |
|---|---|---|---|---|
| 15 | J | 1 c. black on blue | 17·00 | 9·50 |
| 16 | | 2 c. brown on buff | 17·00 | 9·50 |
| 17 | | 4 c. brown on grey | 28·00 | 18·00 |
| 18 | | 5 c. green on green | 70·00 | 50·00 |
| 19 | | 10 c. black on lilac | 20·00 | 17·00 |
| 20 | | 15 c. blue on blue | 15·00 | 10·00 |
| 21 | | 20 c. red on green | 20·00 | 15·00 |
| 22 | | 25 c. black on pink | 14·50 | 9·25 |
| 23 | | 30 c. brown on drab | £800 | £575 |
| 24 | | 35 c. black on orange | £800 | £575 |
| 25 | | 75 c. red on pink | 42·00 | 24·00 |
| 26 | | 1 f. green | 42·00 | 30·00 |

**1892.** "Tablet" key-type inscr "DIEGO-SUAREZ ET DEPENDANCES".

| No. | Type | Description | | |
|---|---|---|---|---|
| 38 | D | 1 c. black on blue | 1·25 | 1·40 |
| 39 | | 2 c. brown on buff | 1·40 | 1·25 |
| 40 | | 4 c. brown on grey | 1·10 | 1·25 |
| 41 | | 5 c. green on green | 2·00 | 2·25 |
| 42 | | 10 c. black on lilac | 4·75 | 2·75 |
| 43 | | 15 c. blue | 5·00 | 4·75 |
| 44 | | 20 c. red on green | 11·50 | 7·00 |
| 45 | | 25 c. black on pink | 9·00 | 5·75 |
| 46 | | 30 c. brown on drab | 10·50 | 8·25 |
| 47 | | 40 c. red on yellow | 12·50 | 9·50 |
| 48 | | 50 c. red on pink | 27·00 | 10·00 |
| 49 | | 75 c. brown on yellow | 28·00 | 20·00 |
| 50 | | 1 f. green | 45·00 | 28·00 |

**1894.** "Tablet" key-type inscr "DIEGO-SUAREZ".

| No. | Type | Description | | |
|---|---|---|---|---|
| 51 | D | 1 c. black on blue | 70 | 75 |
| 52 | | 2 c. brown on buff | 1·50 | 1·10 |
| 53 | | 4 c. brown on grey | 1·40 | 1·25 |
| 54 | | 5 c. green on green | 3·00 | 2·25 |
| 55 | | 10 c. black on lilac | 4·00 | 2·75 |
| 56 | | 15 c. blue | 4·50 | 2·50 |
| 57 | | 20 c. red on green | 9·00 | 6·25 |
| 58 | | 25 c. black on pink | 3·75 | 2·50 |
| 59 | | 30 c. brown on drab | 6·50 | 3·00 |
| 60 | | 40 c. red on yellow | 6·25 | 3·00 |
| 61 | | 50 c. red on pink | 7·75 | 5·75 |
| 62 | | 75 c. brown on yellow | 4·00 | 3·25 |
| 63 | | 1 f. green | 9·00 | 10·50 |

### POSTAGE DUE STAMPS

D 4.

**1891.**

| No. | Type | Description | | |
|---|---|---|---|---|
| D 11. | D 4. | 5 c. violet | 50·00 | 20·00 |
| D 12. | | 50 c. black on yellow | 50·00 | 25·00 |

**1892.** Postage Due stamps of French Colonies overprinted **DIEGO-SUAREZ.**

| No. | Type | Description | | |
|---|---|---|---|---|
| D 27. | D 4. | 1 c. black | 85·00 | 42·00 |
| D 28. | | 2 c. black | 85·00 | 40·00 |
| D 29. | | 3 c. black | 85·00 | 40·00 |
| D 30. | | 4 c. black | 85·00 | 45·00 |
| D 31. | | 5 c. black | 85·00 | 45·00 |
| D 32. | | 10 c. black | 23·00 | 19·00 |
| D 33. | | 15 c. black | 22·00 | 17·00 |
| D 34. | | 20 c. black | £150 | 90·00 |
| D 35. | | 30 c. black | 75·00 | 45·00 |
| D 36. | | 60 c. black | £800 | £550 |
| D 37. | | 1 f. brown | £1300 | £800 |

## DJIBOUTI Pt. 6

A port in French Somaliland S. of the Red Sea, later capital of French Territory of the Afars and the Issas.

100 centimes = 1 franc.

**1893.** "Tablet" key-type stamp of Obock optd **DJ.**

| No. | Type | Description | | |
|---|---|---|---|---|
| 83 | D | 5 c. green & red on grn | 95·00 | 90·00 |

**1894.** Same type surch in figures and **DJIBOUTI.**

| No. | Type | Description | | |
|---|---|---|---|---|
| 85 | D | 25 on 2 c. brown and blue on buff | £225 | £150 |
| 86 | | 50 on 1 c. black and red on blue | £250 | £180 |

**1894.** Triangular stamp of Obock optd. **DJIBOUTI** or surch. **1** also.

| No. | Type | Description | | |
|---|---|---|---|---|
| 87. | 5. | 1 f. on 5 f. red | £475 | £325 |
| 88. | | 5 f. red | £1100 | £850 |

12. Djibouti. (The apparent perforation is part of the design.).

13. "Pingouin" (French gunboat).

14. Crossing Desert.

**1894.** Imperf.

| No. | Type | Description | | |
|---|---|---|---|---|
| 89 | 12 | 1 c. red and black | 60 | 60 |
| 90 | | 2 c. black and red | 70 | 70 |
| 91 | | 4 c. blue and brown | 2·50 | 2·00 |
| 92 | | 5 c. red and green | 2·00 | 2·00 |
| 93 | | 5 c. green | 2·00 | 2·00 |
| 94 | – | 10 c. green and brown | 2·00 | 2·00 |
| 95 | – | 15 c. green and lilac | 3·00 | 2·50 |
| 96 | – | 25 c. blue and red | 3·50 | 3·50 |
| 97 | – | 30 c. red and brown | 3·50 | 3·50 |
| 98 | – | 40 c. blue and yellow | 35·00 | 32·00 |
| 99 | – | 50 c. red and blue | 12·00 | 5·00 |
| 100 | – | 75 c. orange and mauve | 20·00 | 20·00 |
| 101 | – | 1 f. black and olive | 13·50 | 5·50 |
| 102 | – | 2 f. red and brown | 60·00 | 55·00 |
| 103 | 13 | 5 f. blue and red | £150 | 95·00 |
| 104 | 14 | 25 f. blue and red | £700 | £700 |
| 105 | | 50 f. red and blue | £525 | £525 |

DESIGNS— As Type **12**: 10 to 75 c. Different views of Djibouti. 1, 2 f. Port of Djibouti.

**1899.** As Last, surch.

| No. | Type | Description | | |
|---|---|---|---|---|
| 108 | – | 0·05 on 75 c. orge. & mve. | 40·00 | 25·00 |
| 109 | – | 0.10 on 1 f. blk. & olive | 55·00 | 45·00 |
| 106 | 12 | 0.40 on 4 c. blue & brown | £2250 | 7·00 |
| 110 | – | 0.40 on 2 f. red & brown | £400 | £300 |
| 111 | 13 | 0.75 on 5 f. blue and red | £375 | £300 |

**1902.** Rectangular stamp of Obock surch **0.05.**

| No. | Type | Description | | |
|---|---|---|---|---|
| 107 | 6 | 0.05 on 75 c. lilac & orange | £1000 | £750 |

**1902.** Triangular stamps of Obock surch.

| No. | Type | Description | | |
|---|---|---|---|---|
| 112 | 7 | 5 c. on 25 f. blue and brown | 38·00 | 38·00 |
| 113 | | 10 c. on 50 f. grn & red | 50·00 | 38·00 |

**1902.** Nos. 98/9 surch.

| No. | Type | Description | | |
|---|---|---|---|---|
| 114. | | 5 c. on 40 c. blue and yellow | 2·00 | 2·00 |
| 115. | | 10 c. on 50 c. red and blue | 16·00 | 18·00 |

**1902.** Stamps of Obock surch. **DJIBOUTI** and value.

| No. | Type | Description | | |
|---|---|---|---|---|
| 120. | 6. | 5 c. on 30 c. yell. & grn. | 6·00 | 6·50 |
| 116. | | 10 c. on 25 c. black & blue | 5·00 | 5·00 |
| 118. | 7. | 10 c. on 2 f. orange & lilac | 38·00 | 30·00 |
| 119. | | 10 c. on 10 f. lake and red | 22·00 | 17·00 |

For later issues see **FRENCH SOMALI COAST, FRENCH TERRITORY OF THE AFARS AND ISSAS** and **DJIBOUTI REPUBLIC.**

## DJIBOUTI REPUBLIC Pt. 12

Formerly French Territory of the Afars and the Issas.

112. Map and Flag.

115. Head Rest.

**1977.** Independence. Multicoloured.

| No. | Type | Description | | |
|---|---|---|---|---|
| 685. | | 45 f. Type **112** | 90 | 55 |
| 686. | | 65 f. Map of Djibouti (horiz.) | 1·40 | 65 |

**1977.** Various stamps of the French Territory of the Afars and the Issas optd **REPUBLIQUE DE DJIBOUTI** or surch also. (a) Sea Shells

| No. | Type | Description | | |
|---|---|---|---|---|
| 687 | 81 | 1 f. on 4 f. mult | 20 | 20 |
| 688 | – | 2 f. on 5 f. brown, mauve & violet (629) | 20 | 20 |
| 689 | – | 20 f. brown & grn (633) | 55 | 55 |
| 690 | – | 30 f. brown, purple and green (634) | 65 | 65 |
| 691 | – | 40 f. brown & grn (635) | 90 | 90 |
| 692 | – | 45 f. brown, green and blue (636) | 1·00 | 1·00 |
| 693 | – | 60 f. black & brn (638) | 1·40 | 1·40 |
| 694 | – | 70 f. brown, blue and black (639) | 1·90 | 1·90 |
| | | (b) Flora and Fauna | | |
| 695 | 103 | 5 f. on 20 f. mult | 20 | 20 |
| 696 | 106 | 45 f. multicoloured | 90 | 90 |
| 697 | – | 50 f. mult (675) | 1·40 | 1·40 |
| 698 | 107 | 70 f. multicoloured | 1·60 | 1·60 |
| 699 | – | 100 f. mult (653) | 2·50 | 2·50 |
| 700 | – | 150 f. mult (676) | 3·00 | 3·00 |
| 701 | – | 300 f. mult (654) | 7·50 | 7·50 |
| | | (c) Buildings | | |
| 702 | 99 | 8 f. grey, red and blue (postage) | 30 | 30 |
| 703 | 109 | 500 f. mult (air) | 9·75 | 8·25 |
| | | (d) Celebrities | | |
| 704 | 111 | 55 f. red, grey and green (air) | 1·40 | 1·10 |
| 705 | – | 75 f. red, brown and green (682) | 1·60 | 1·60 |
| 706 | 104 | 200 f. blue, green and orange (postage) | 3·75 | 3·75 |
| | | (e) Sport | | |
| 707 | 108 | 200 f. multicoloured | 4·50 | 4·50 |

**1977.** Local Art. Multicoloured.

| No. | Type | Description | | |
|---|---|---|---|---|
| 708. | | 10 f. Type **115** | 20 | 10 |
| 709. | | 20 f. Water cask (vert.) | 45 | 15 |
| 710. | | 25 f. Washing jar (vert.) | 65 | 20 |

116. Ostrich.

117. "Glossodoris".

**1977.** Birds. Multicoloured.

| No. | Type | Description | | |
|---|---|---|---|---|
| 711. | | 90 f. Type **116** | 2·75 | 1·00 |
| 712. | | 100 f. Vitelline Masked Weaver | 3·75 | 1·75 |

**1977.** Sea Life. Multicoloured.

| No. | Type | Description | | |
|---|---|---|---|---|
| 713. | | 45 f. Type **117** | 1·00 | 90 |
| 714. | | 70 f. Turtle | 1·10 | 45 |
| 715. | | 80 f. "Priacanthus hamrur" | 1·40 | 55 |

118. Map, Dove and U.N. Emblem.

**1977.** Air. Admission to the United Nations.

| No. | Type | Description | | |
|---|---|---|---|---|
| 716. | 118. | 300 f. multicoloured | 4·50 | 2·75 |

### MINIMUM PRICE

The minimum price quoted is 10p which represents a handling charge rather than a basis for valuing common stamps. For further notes about prices see introductory pages.

119. Crabs "Uca lactea".

**1977.** Fauna. Multicoloured.

| No. | Type | Description | | |
|---|---|---|---|---|
| 717. | | 15 f. Type **119** | 45 | 15 |
| 718. | | 50 f. Klipspringer | 1·25 | 40 |
| 719. | | 150 f. "Coryphaena hippurus" | 3·00 | 1·40 |

120. President Hassan Gouled Aptidon and Flag.

**1978.**

| No. | Type | Description | | |
|---|---|---|---|---|
| 720. | 120. | 65 f. multicoloured | 90 | 45 |

121. Marcel Brochet MB 101.

**1978.** Air. Djibouti Aero Club. Multicoloured.

| No. | Type | Description | | |
|---|---|---|---|---|
| 721 | | 60 f. Type **121** | 95 | 60 |
| 722 | | 85 f. De Havilland Tiger Moth | 1·25 | 80 |
| 723 | | 200 f. Morane Saulnier Rallye Commodore | 2·75 | 1·60 |

122. "Charaxes hansali".

123. "Head of an Old Man".

**1978.** Butterflies. Multicoloured.

| No. | Type | Description | | |
|---|---|---|---|---|
| 724. | | 5 f. Type **122** | 10 | 10 |
| 725. | | 20 f. "Colias electo" | 55 | 20 |
| 726. | | 25 f. "Acraea chilo" | 80 | 40 |
| 727. | | 150 f. "Junonia hierta" | 3·00 | 1·50 |

**1978.** Air. 400th Birth Anniv. of Rubens. Multicoloured.

| No. | Type | Description | | |
|---|---|---|---|---|
| 728. | | 50 f. Type **123** | 85 | 35 |
| 729. | | 500 f. "The Hippopotamus Hunt" (detail) | 8·00 | 3·25 |

124. Necklace.

125. Player with Cup.

**1978.** Native Handicrafts. Multicoloured.

| No. | Type | Description | | |
|---|---|---|---|---|
| 730. | | 45 f. Type **124** | 85 | 40 |
| 731. | | 55 f. Necklace | 1·10 | 45 |

**1978.** Air. World Cup Football Championship, Argentina. Multicoloured.
732. 100 f. Type **125** .. .. 1·40 45
733. 300 f. World Cup, footballer and map of Argentina .. 4·25 1·25

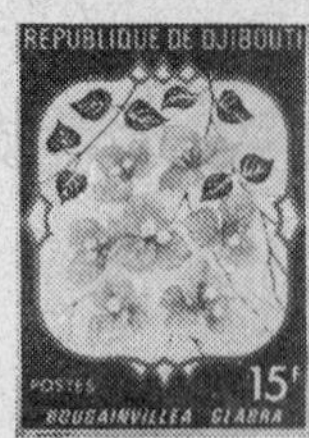
**126.** "Bougainvillea glabra".

**1978.** Flowers. Multicoloured.
734. 15 f. Type **126** .. .. 40 10
735. 35 f. "Hibiscus schizopetalus" .. .. 70 20
736. 250 f. "Caesalpinia pulcherrima" .. .. 4·50 85

**1978.** Air. Argentina's Victory in World Cup Football Championship. Nos. 722/3 surch. with **ARGENTINE CHAMPION 1978.**
737. 100 f. Type **125** .. 1·60 45
738. 300 f. World Cup, footballer and map of Argentina .. 4·50 1·50

**128.** "The Hare" (Albrecht Durer).

**1978.** Air. Paintings. Multicoloured.
739. 100 f. "Tahitian Women" (Paul Gauguin) (horiz.) 1·90 55
740. 250 f. Type **128** .. .. 4·75 1·90

**129.** Knobbed Triton.

**1978.** Sea Shells. Multicoloured.
741 10 f. Type **129** .. .. 75 35
742 80 f. Trumpet triton .. 2·50 90

**130.** "Chelmon rostratus". **131.** Dove and U.P.U. Emblem.

**1978.** Fishes. Multicoloured.
743. 8 f. Type **130** .. .. 30 10
744. 30 f. "Zebrasoma flavescens" .. .. 65 15
745. 40 f. "Gaterin chaetodonoides" .. .. 1·10 20

**1978.** Air. "Philexafrique" Exhibition, Libreville, Gabon (1st issue) and Int. Stamp Fair, Essen, W. Germany. As T **262** of Niger. Multicoloured.
746. 90 f. Jay and Brunswick 1852 3 sgr. stamp 1·90 1·40
747. 90 f. Caracal and Djibouti 1977 optd. 300 f. stamp 1·90 1·40

**1978.** Air. Cent. of Paris U.P.U. Congress.
748. **131.** 200 f. green, brown & turquoise .. .. 2·75 1·40

**132.** Alsthom "BB 1201" Locomotive.

**1979.** Djibouti-Addis Ababa Railway. Multicoloured.
749. 40 f. Type **132** .. .. 80 30
750. 55 f. Locomotive "231" .. 90 30
751. 60 f. Locomotive "130" .. 1·25 30
752. 75 f. Locomotive "CC 2001" 1·60 35

**133.** Children learning to Count.

**1979.** International Year of the Child. Multicoloured.
753. 20 f. Type **133** .. .. 35 10
754. 200 f. Mother and child .. 3·00 1·25

**134.** De Havilland Twin Otter over Crater.

**1979.** Ardoukoba Volcano. Multicoloured.
755 30 f. Sud Aviation Alouette II helicopter over crater 65 40
756 90 f. Type **134** .. .. 1·90 70

**135.** Sir Rowland Hill and 300 f. Stamp, 1977.

**1979.** Death Centenary of Sir Rowland Hill. Multicoloured.
757. 25 f. Type **135** .. .. 35 10
758. 100 f. Letters with 1894 50 f. and 1977 45 f. stamps 1·50 45
759. 150 f. Loading mail on ship 2·25 80

**136.** Junkers Ju 52/3m and Dewoitine D-338 Trimotor.

**1979.** Air. 75th Anniv of Powered Flight. Multicoloured.
760 140 f. Type **136** .. .. 2·25 95
761 250 f. Potez 63-11 bomber and Supermarine Spitfire MK VII .. .. 3·25 1·90
762 500 f. Concorde and Sikorsky S-40 flying boat "American Clipper" .. 7·25 3·25

**137.** Djibouti, Local Woman and Namaqua Dove.

**1979.** "Philexafrique 2" Exhibition, Gabon (2nd issue). Multicoloured.
763 55 f. Type **137** .. .. 1·90 1·10
764 80 f. U.P.U. emblem, map, Douglas DC-8-60 "Super Sixty", diesel train and postal runner .. .. 2·00 1·25

**138.** "Opuntia".

**1979.** Flowers. Multicoloured.
765. 2 f. Type **138** .. .. 10 10
766. 8 f. "Solanacea" (horiz.) 20 10
767. 15 f. "Trichodesma" (horiz.) .. .. 35 10
768. 45 f. "Acacia etbaica" (horiz.) .. .. 65 15
769. 50 f. "Thunbergia alata" 90 15

**139.** "The Washerwoman".

**1979.** Air. Death Centenary of Honore Daumier (painter).
770. **139.** 500 f. multicoloured .. 8·25 2·75

**140.** Basketball. **141.** Bull-mouth Helmet.

**1979.** Pre-Olympic Year. Multicoloured.
771. 70 f. Type **140** .. .. 1·10 30
772. 120 f. Running .. .. 1·60 55
773. 200 f. Football .. .. 2·75 85

**1979.** Shells. Multicoloured.
774 10 f. Type **141** .. .. 20 15
775 40 f. Arthritic spider conch 1·00 20
776 300 f. Ventral harp .. 5·50 1·60

**142.** Winter Sports Equipment and Mosque.

**1980.** Air. Winter Olympic Games, Lake Placid.
777. **142.** 150 f. multicoloured .. 2·25 65

**143.** Lions Club Banner and Steam Locomotive.

**1980.** Djibouti Clubs. Multicoloured.
778 90 f. Rotary Club banner and Morane Saulnier MS 892 (75th anniv of Rotary International) .. 1·75 70
779 100 f. Type **143** .. .. 1·60 65

**144.** "Colotis danae". **147.** Basketball.

**145.** Boeing 737.

**1980.** Butterflies. Multicoloured.
780. 5 f. Type **144** .. .. 20 20
781. 55 f. "Danaus chrysippus" .. .. 1·00 65

**1980.** Air. Foundation of "Air Djibouti".
782. **145.** 400 f. multicoloured .. 6·00 2·25

**1980.** Air. Winter Olympic Games. No. **777** surch. with names of Medal Winners.
783. **142.** 80 f. on 150 f. .. .. 1·10 45
784. 200 f. on 150 f. .. 2·75 1·25
OVERPRINTS: 80 f., **A.M. MOSER-PROEL AUTRICHE DESCENT DAMES MEDAILLE D'OR.** 200 f., **HEIDEN USA 5 MEDAILLES D'OR PATINAGE DE VITESSE.**

**1980.** Olympic Games, Moscow. Multicoloured.
785. 60 f. Type **147** .. .. 90 20
786. 120 f. Football .. .. 1·60 45
787. 250 f. Running .. .. 3·00 1·00

**148.** "Apollo XI" Moon Landing.

**1980.** Air. Conquest of Space. Multicoloured.
788. 200 f. Type **148** .. .. 2·75 65
789. 300 f. "Apollo–Soyuz" link-up .. .. .. 4·50 1·00

**149.** Samisch v Romanovsky Game, Moscow, 1925.

**1980.** Founding of International Chess Federation, 1924. Multicoloured.
790 20 f. Type **149** .. .. 70 15
791 75 f. "Royal Chess Party" (15th-century Italian book illustration) .. 1·90 40

**150.** Satellite and Earth Station.

**1980.** Air. Inauguration of Satellite Earth Station.
792. **150.** 500 f. multicoloured .. 7·25 1·90

151. Sieve Cowrie.

**1980.** Shells. Multicoloured.

| | | | |
|---|---|---|---|
| 793 | 15 f. Type **151** .. .. | 50 | 20 |
| 794 | 85 f. Chambered nautilus | 1·90 | 65 |

152. Sir Alexander Fleming and Penicillin.

**1980.** Anniversaries. Multicoloured.

| | | | |
|---|---|---|---|
| 795. | 20 f. Type **152** .. .. | 50 | 20 |
| 796. | 130 f. Jules Verne and space capsules.. .. .. | 2·25 | 65 |

ANNIVERSARIES: 20 f. Discovery of penicillin, 25th anniv. 130 f. Jules Verne, 75th death anniv.

153. " Graf Zeppelin " and Sphinx.

**1980.** Air. 80th Anniv. of First Zeppelin Flight. Multicoloured.

| | | | |
|---|---|---|---|
| 797. | 100 f. Type **153** .. .. | 2·00 | 60 |
| 798. | 150 f. Ferdinand von Zeppelin .. .. | 2·50 | 90 |

154. Capt. Cook and H.M.S. "Endeavour".

**1980.** Death Bicentenary (1979) of Captain James Cook. Multicoloured.

| | | | |
|---|---|---|---|
| 799. | 55 f. Type **154** .. .. | 90 | 75 |
| 800. | 90 f. Cook's ships and map of voyages .. .. | 1·60 | 1·00 |

155. " Voyager " and Saturn.

**1980.** Air. Space Exploration.

| | | | |
|---|---|---|---|
| 801. **155** | 250 f. multicoloured .. | 4·00 | 1·10 |

156. Saving a Goal.

**1981.** Air. World Cup Football Eliminators. Multicoloured.

| | | | |
|---|---|---|---|
| 802. | 80 f. Type **156** .. .. | 1·10 | 35 |
| 803. | 200 f. Tackle .. .. | 2·75 | 80 |

**INDEX**

Countries can be quickly located by referring to the index at the end of this volume.

157. Transport.

158. Yury Gagarin and "Vostok 1".

**1981.** Air European-African Economic Convention.

| | | | |
|---|---|---|---|
| 804. **157.** | 100 f. multicoloured .. | 2·75 | 1·40 |

**1981.** Air. Space Anniversaries and Events. Multicoloured.

| | | | |
|---|---|---|---|
| 805. | 75 f. Type **158** (20th anniv. of first man in space) .. | 1·10 | 35 |
| 806. | 120 f. " Viking " exploration of Mars (horiz.) .. | 1·60 | 50 |
| 807. | 150 f. Alan Shepard and " Freedom 7 " (20th anniv. of first American in space).. .. .. | 2·25 | 65 |

159. " Arusetta asfur ".

**1981.** Djibouti Tropical Aquarium. Mult.

| | | | |
|---|---|---|---|
| 808. | 25 f. Type **159** .. .. | 45 | 10 |
| 809. | 55 f. " Zanclus canescens " | 95 | 20 |
| 810. | 70 f. " Gnathanodon speciosus " .. .. | 1·10 | 45 |

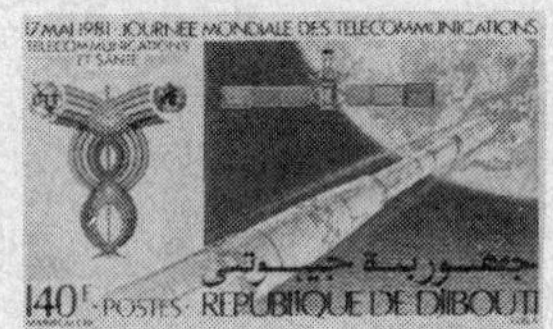

160. Caduceus, Satellite and Rocket.

**1981.** World Telecommunications Day.

| | | | |
|---|---|---|---|
| 811. **160** | 140 f. multicoloured .. | 1·90 | 55 |

161. German " 231 " and American " RC4 " Locomotives.

**1981.** Locomotives. Multicoloured.

| | | | |
|---|---|---|---|
| 812. | 40 f. Type **161** .. .. | 65 | 25 |
| 813. | 55 f. George Stephenson, " Rocket " and Djibouti locomotive .. .. | 90 | 30 |
| 814. | 65 f. French and Japanese high speed trains .. | 1·10 | 30 |

162. Antenna on Globe and Morse Key.

**1981.** Djibouti Amateur Radio Club.

| | | | |
|---|---|---|---|
| 815. **162** | 250 f. multicoloured. .. | 3·50 | 1·10 |

163. Prince Charles and Lady Diana Spencer.

**1981.** Royal Wedding. Multicoloured.

| | | | |
|---|---|---|---|
| 816. | 180 f. Type **163** .. .. | 2·75 | 85 |
| 817. | 200 f. Prince Charles and Lady Diana in wedding dress .. .. .. | 3·00 | 1·10 |

164. Admiral Nelson and H.M.S. "Victory".

**1981.** Admiral Nelson Commemoration. Mult.

| | | | |
|---|---|---|---|
| 818 | 100 f. Type **164** .. .. | 1·40 | 1·00 |
| 819 | 175 f. Nelson and stern view of H.M.S. "Victory" .. .. | 2·50 | 1·50 |

165. Tree Hyrax and Scout tending Camp-fire.

**1981.** 28th World Scouting Congress, Dakar, and Fourth Panafrican Scouting Conference. Abidjan. Multicoloured.

| | | | |
|---|---|---|---|
| 820. | 60 f. Type **165** .. .. | 1·25 | 40 |
| 821. | 105 f. Scouts saluting, map reading and greater kudu .. .. .. | 1·60 | 50 |

166. " Football Players " (Picasso).

**1981.** Air. Paintings. Multicoloured.

| | | | |
|---|---|---|---|
| 822. | 300 f. Type **166** .. .. | 5·00 | 1·40 |
| 823. | 400 f. " Portrait of a Man in a Turban " (Rembrandt) .. .. | 5·50 | 1·90 |

167. Launch. 168. 19th-century Chinese Pawn and Knight.

**1981.** Air. Space Shuttle. Multicoloured.

| | | | |
|---|---|---|---|
| 824. | 90 f. Type **167** .. .. | 1·40 | 45 |
| 825. | 120 f. Space Shuttle landing .. .. .. | 1·75 | 65 |

**1981.** Chess Pieces. Multicoloured.

| | | | |
|---|---|---|---|
| 826 | 50 f. 13th-century Swedish pawn and queen (horiz) | 1·10 | 35 |
| 827 | 130 f. Type **168** .. .. | 2·25 | 80 |

169. Aerial View.

**1981.** Inauguration of Djibouti Sheraton Hotel.

| | | | |
|---|---|---|---|
| 828. **169.** | 75 f. multicoloured .. | 1·10 | 40 |

**1981.** Second Flight of Space Shuttle " Columbia ". Nos. 824/5 optd.

| | | | |
|---|---|---|---|
| 829. | 90 f. Type **167** .. .. | 1·40 | 55 |
| 830. | 120 f. Space Shuttle landing .. .. .. | 1·75 | 85 |

OPTS: 90 f. **COLUMBIA 2eme VOL SPATIAL 12 NOVEMBRE 1981.** 120 f. **" JOE ENGLE et RICHARD TRULY/2eme VOL SPATIAL - 12 Nov. 1981 ".**

171. " Clitoria ternatea ".

**1981.** Flowers. Multicoloured.

| | | | |
|---|---|---|---|
| 831. | 10 f. Type **171** .. .. | 20 | 10 |
| 832. | 30 f. " Acacia mellifera" (horiz.) .. .. .. | 45 | 15 |
| 833. | 35 f. " Punica granatum " (horiz.) .. .. .. | 70 | 20 |
| 834. | 45 f. Malvacee .. .. | 85 | 20 |

**1981.** World Chess Championship, Merano (1st issue). Nos. 826/7 optd.

| | | | |
|---|---|---|---|
| 835 | 50 f. multicoloured .. | 95 | 35 |
| 836 | 130 f. multicoloured .. | 2·25 | 80 |

OPTS: 50 f. **Octobre-Novembre 1981 ANATOLI KARPOV VICTOR KORTCHNOI MERANO (ITALIE).** 130 f. **ANATOLI KARPOV Champion du Monde 1981.**

See also Nos. 843/4.

173. Saving Goal.

**1982.** Air. World Cup Football Championship, Spain. Multicoloured.

| | | | |
|---|---|---|---|
| 837. | 110 f. Type **173** .. .. | 1·60 | 55 |
| 838. | 220 f. Footballers.. .. | 3·25 | 1·10 |

174. John H. Glenn. 175. Dr. Robert Koch, Bacillus and Microscope.

**1982.** Air. Space Anniversaries. Mult.

| | | | |
|---|---|---|---|
| 839. | 40 f. " Luna 9 " (15th anniv. of first unmanned moon landing) .. .. | 55 | 20 |
| 840. | 60 f. Type **174** (20th anniv. of flight).. .. .. | 90 | 35 |
| 841. | 180 f. " Viking 1 " (5th anniv. of first Mars landing) (horiz.) .. | 2·40 | 85 |

**1982.** Centenary of Robert Koch's Discovery of Tubercle Bacillus.

| | | | |
|---|---|---|---|
| 842. **175.** | 305 f. multicoloured .. | 4·75 | 1·60 |

**176.** 14th-century German Bishop and 18th-century Marie de Medici Bishop.

**177.** Princess of Wales.

**1982.** World Chess Championship, Merano (2nd issue). Multicoloured.

843 125 f. Type **176** .. .. 2·50 75
844 175 f. Late 19th-century queen and pawn from Nuremberg .. .. 3·00 95

**1982.** Air. 21st Birthday of Princess of Wales Multicoloured.

845. 120 f. Type **177** .. .. 1·60 85
846. 180 f. Princess of Wales (different) .. .. 2·50 1·00

**178.** I.Y.C. Stamp, Collector, Greater Flamingoes and Emblems.

**1982.** " Philexfrance " International Stamp Exhibition, Paris. Multicoloured.

847. 80 f. Type **178** .. .. 2·50 1·25
848. 140 f. Rowland Hill stamp Exhibition Centre and U.P.U. emblem .. 2·25 95

**179.** Microwave Antenna.

**180.** Mosque, Medina.

**1982.** World Telecommunications Day.

849. **179.** 150 f. multicoloured .. 2·25 90

**1982.** Air. 1350th Death Anniv. of Mohammed.

850. **180.** 500 f. multicoloured .. 6·75 2·50

**181.** Lord Baden-Powell.

**1982.** Air. 125th Birth Anniv. of Lord Baden-Powell. Multicoloured.

851. 95 f. Type **181** .. .. 1·25 55
852. 200 f. Saluting Scout and camp .. .. .. 2·75 1·10

**182.** Bus and Jeep.

**1982.** Transport. Multicoloured.

853 20 f. Type **182** .. .. 35 15
854 25 f. Ferry and dhow .. .. 50 25
855 55 f. Boeing 727-100 airliner and locomotive .. 1·75 70

**1982.** Air. World Cup Football Championship winners. Nos. 837/8 optd.

856. 110 f. Type **173** .. .. 1·60 65
857. 220 f. Footballers .. .. 3·00 1·40

OPTS: 110 f. **ITALIE RFA 3-1 POLOGNE FRANCE 3-2.** 220 f. **ITALIE RFA 3-1 2 RFA 3 POLOGNE.**

**1982.** Air. Birth of Prince William of Wales. Nos. 845/6 optd.

858. 120 f. Type **177** .. .. 1·60 85
859. 180 f. Princess of Wales (different) .. .. 2·50 1·10

OPTS: 120 f. **21 JUIN 1982 WILLIAM ARTHUR PHILIPPE LOUIS PRINCE DES GALLES.** 180 f. **21ST JUNE 1982 WILLIAM ARTHUR PHILIP LOUIS PRINCE OF WALES.**

**185.** Satellite, Dish Aerial and Conference.

**1982.** Air. Second U.N. Conference on the Exploration and Peaceful Uses of Outer Space, Vienna.

860. **185.** 350 f. multicoloured .. 5·00 1·60

**186.** Franklin D. Roosevelt.

**187.** Red Sea Cowrie.

**1982.** Air. 250th Birth Anniv. of George Washington and Birth Centenary of Franklin D. Roosevelt. Multicoloured.

861. 115 f. Type **186** .. .. 1·60 55
862. 250 f. George Washington 3·25 1·10

**1982.** Shells. Multicoloured.

863 10 f. Type **187** .. .. 25 15
864 15 f. Sumatran cone .. 40 20
865 25 f. Lovely cowrie .. 55 25
866 30 f. Engraved cone .. 75 40
867 70 f. Heavy bonnet .. 1·75 75
868 150 f. Burnt cowrie .. 3·50 1·25

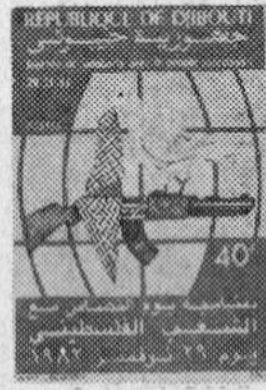


**188.** Dove perched on Gun.

**189.** Montgolfier's Balloon, 1783.

**1982.** Palestinian Solidarity Day.

869. **188.** 40 f. multicoloured .. 55 25

**1983.** Air. Bicentenary of Manned Flight. Multicoloured.

870 35 f. Type **189** .. .. 60 25
871 45 f. Henri Giffard's balloon "Le Grand Ballon Captif", 1878 .. 90 45
872 120 f. Balloon "Double Eagle II", 1978 .. 2·25 1·10

**190.** Volleyball.

**192.** Martin Luther King.

**191.** Bloch 220 Gascogne.

**1983.** Air. Olympic Games, Los Angeles (1984). Multicoloured.

873. 75 f. Type **190** .. .. 1·10 45
874. 125 f. Wind-surfing .. 2·00 1·00

**1983.** Air. 50th Anniv of Air France. Mult.

875 25 f. Type **191** .. .. 40 25
876 100 f. Douglas DC-4 .. 1·40 1·00
877 175 f. Boeing 747-200 .. 2·50 1·25

**1983.** Flowers. As Type **171.** Multicoloured.

878. 5 f. Ipomoea .. .. 10 10
879. 50 f. Moringa (horiz.) .. 85 35
880. 55 f. Cotton flower .. 1·00 40

**1983.** Air. Celebrities. Multicoloured.

881. 180 f. Type **192** (15th death anniv.) .. .. .. 2·25 90
882. 250 f. Alfred Nobel (150th birth anniv.) .. .. 3·25 1·40

**193.** W.C.Y. Emblem.

**194.** Yacht and Rotary Club Emblem.

**1983.** World Communications Year.

883. **193.** 500 f. multicoloured .. 6·75 2·75

**1983.** Air. International Club Meetings. Multicoloured.

884. 90 f. Type **194** .. .. 1·75 1·25
885. 150 f. Minaret and Lions Club emblem .. .. 2·00 90

**195.** Renault, 1904.

**1983.** Air. Early Motor Cars. Multicoloured.

886. 60 f. Type **195** .. .. 1·25 40
887. 80 f. Mercedes Knight, 1910 (vert.) .. .. 1·90 50
888. 100 f. Lorraine-Dietrich, 1912 .. .. .. 2·25 80

**197.** " Vostok VI ".

**1983.** Air. Conquest of Space. Multicoloured.

890. 120 f. Type **197** .. .. 1·60 65
891. 200 f. " Explorer I " .. 2·75 1·10

**198.** Development Projects.

**1983.** Donors Conference.

892. **198.** 75 f. multicoloured .. 1·10 55

**199.** Red Sea Marginella.

**1983.** Shells. Multicoloured.

893 15 f. Type **199** .. .. 40 15
894 30 f. Jickeli's cone .. 85 25
895 55 f. MacAndrew's cowrie 1·40 60
896 80 f. Cuvier's cone .. 1·90 75
897 100 f. Tapestry turban .. 2·10 1·00

**200.** " Colotis chrysonome ".

**1984.** Butterflies.

898. 5 f. Type **200** .. .. 10 10
899. 20 f. " Colias erate " .. 25 20
900. 30 f. " Junonia orithyia " 45 30
901. 75 f. " Acraea doubledayi " 1·40 90
902. 110 f. " Byblia ilithya " .. 1·75 1·40

**201.** Speed Skating.

**1984.** Air. Winter Olympic Games, Sarajevo. Multicoloured.

903. 70 f. Type **201** .. .. 1·10 40
904. 130 f. Ice dancing .. .. 1·90 70

**203.** Microlight.

**1984.** Air. Microlight Aircraft. Multicoloured.

906 65 f. Type **203** .. .. 1·00 80
907 85 f. Powered hang-glider "Jules" .. .. 1·25 1·00
908 100 f. Microlight (different) 1·50 1·25

**1984.** Air. Winter Olympic Games Medal Winners. Nos. 903/4 optd.

909. 70 f. **1000 METRES HOMMES/ OR: BOUCHER (CANADA)/ARGENT: KHLEBNIKOV (URSS)/ BRONZE: ENGELSTADT (NORV.)** 1·10 55
910. 130 f. **"DANSE/OR TORVILL-DEAN (G.B.)/ARGENT: BESTEMIANOVA-BUKIN (URSS)/ BRONZE: KLIMOVA-PONOMARENKO (URSS)"** .. .. .. 1·90 85

**205.** "Marguerite Matisse with Cat".

**1984.** Air. 30th Death Anniv. of Matisse and Birth Centenary of Modigliani. Multicoloured.

911. 150 f. Type **205** .. .. 2·50 90
912. 200 f. "Mario Varvogli" (Modigliani) .. .. 3·50 1·40

**206.** Randa.

**1984.** Landscapes. Multicoloured.

913. 2 f. Type **206** .. .. 10 10
914. 8 f. Ali Sabieh .. .. 10 10
915. 10 f. Lake Assal .. .. 15 10
916. 15 f. Tadjoura .. .. 20 10
917. 40 f. Alaili Dada (vert.) .. 55 20
918. 45 f. Lake Abbe .. .. 60 25
919. 55 f. Obock .. .. 1·50 85
920. 125 f. Presidential Palace 3·00 1·60

**207.** Marathon.

**1984.** Air. Olympic Games, Los Angeles. Multicoloured.

921. 50 f. Type **207** .. .. 65 30
922. 60 f. High jump .. .. 85 35
923. 80 f. Swimming .. .. 1·10 45

**208.** Battle of Solferino.

**1984.** Air. 125th Anniv. of Battle of Solferino. and 120th Anniv. of Red Cross.

924. **208.** 300 f. multicoloured .. 4·50 1·60

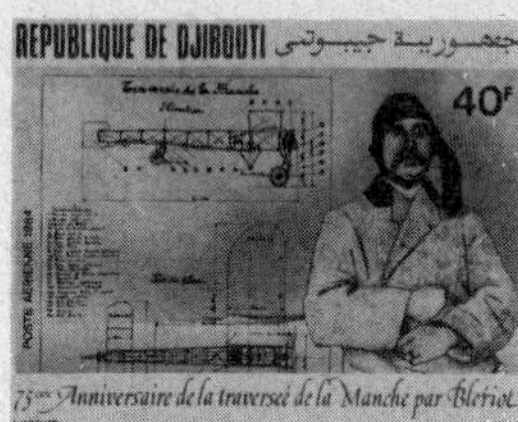

**209.** Bleriot and Diagram of Bleriot XI.

**1984.** Air. 75th Anniv of Louis Bleriot's Cross-Channel Flight. Multicoloured.

925 40 f. Type **209** .. .. 65 50
926 75 f. Bleriot and Bleriot XI and Britten Norman Islander aircraft .. 1·10 90
927 90 f. Bleriot and Boeing 727 airliner .. .. .. 1·25 1·10

**210.** Marathon.

**212.** Men on Moon, Telescope and Planets.

**211.** U.S.A. Attack-pumper Fire Engine.

**1984.** Membership of International Olympic Committee.

928. **210.** 45 f. multicoloured .. 65 30

**1984.** Fire Fighting. Multicoloured.

929 25 f. Type **211** .. .. 70 20
930 95 f. French P.P.M. rescue crane .. .. .. 2·10 65
931 100 f. Canadair CL-215 fire-fighting amphibian 2·25 1·25

**1984.** Air. 375th Anniv. of Galileo's Telescope. Multicoloured.

932. 120 f. Type **212** .. .. 1·60 65
933. 180 f. Galileo, telescope and planets .. .. .. 2·50 1·00

**213.** Football Teams (Europa Cup).

**1984.** Air. European Football Championship and Olympic Games, Los Angeles. Multicoloured.

934. 80 f. Type **213** .. .. 1·25 55
935. 80 f. Football teams (Olympic Games) .. 1·25 55

**214.** Motor Carriage, 1886.

**1984.** 150th Birth Anniv. of Gottlieb Daimler (automobile designer). Multicoloured.

936. 35 f. Type **214** .. .. 55 20
937. 65 f. Cannstatt-Daimler cabriolet, 1896 .. .. 1·00 35
938. 90 f. Daimler "Phoenix", 1900 .. .. .. 1·50 55

**215.** Pierre Curie.

**1985.** Pierre and Marie Curie (physicists). Multicoloured.

939. 150 f. Type **215** (150th birth anniv.) .. .. .. 2·25 85
940. 150 f. Marie Curie (50th death anniv.) .. .. 2·25 85

**216.** White-throated Bee Eater.

**1985.** Birth Bicentenary of John J. Audubon. Multicoloured

941. 5 f. Type **216** .. .. 25 15
942. 15 f. Chestnut-bellied sand-grouse .. .. .. 1·10 45
943. 20 f. Yellow-breasted barbet .. .. .. 1·25 50
944. 25 f. Common roller .. 1·50 55

**217.** Dr. Hansen, Bacilli, Lepers and Lions Emblem.

**218.** Globe and Pictograms.

**1985.** Air. International Organizations. Mult.

946. 50 f. Type **217** (World Leprosy Day) .. .. 80 40
947. 60 f. Rotary International emblem and pieces on chessboard .. .. 1·40 65

**1985.** International Youth Year.

948. **218.** 10 f. multicoloured .. 15 10
949. 30 f. multicoloured .. 40 20
950. 40 f. multicoloured .. 55 35

**219.** Locomotive No. 29, Addis Ababa–Djibouti Railway.

**1985.** Railway Locomotives. Multicoloured.

951. 55 f. Type **219** .. .. 85 40
952. 75 f. "Der Adler" (150th anniv. of German railways) .. .. .. 1·10 55

**220.** Planting Sapling.

**221.** Victo Hugo (novelist).

**1985.** Foundation of Djibouti Scouting Association. Multicoloured.

953. 35 f. Type **220** .. .. 65 30
954. 65 f. Childcare .. .. 1·40 45

**1985.** Writers. Multicoloured.

955. 80 f. Type **221** .. .. 1·10 50
956. 100 f. Arthur Rimbaud (poet) .. .. .. 1·40 60

**222.** Dish Aerials, Off-shore Oil Rigs and Building.

**1985.** Air. "Philexafrique" Stamp Exhibition, Lome (1st issue) Multicoloured.

957. 80 f. Type **222** .. .. 1·75 1·25
958. 80 f. Carpenter, girl at microscope and man at visual display unit .. 1·60 1·10

See also Nos. 969/70.

**1985.** Shells. As T **199**. Multicoloured.

959 10 f. Twin-blotch cowrie .. 25 15
960 15 f. Thrush cowrie .. 35 20
961 30 f. Vice-Admiral cowrie 95 25
962 40 f. Giraffe cone .. .. 1·10 55
963 55 f. Terebra cone .. 1·75 75

**223.** Team Winners on Rostrum.

**224.** Launch of "Ariane".

**1985.** First Marathon World Cup, Hiroshima. Multicoloured.

964. 75 f. Type **223** .. .. 1·00 45
965. 100 f. Finishing line and officials .. .. .. 1·50 65

**1985.** Air. Telecommunications Development. Multicoloured.

966. 50 f. International Transmission Centre .. .. 65 30
967. 90 f. Type **224** .. .. 1·25 50
968. 120 f. "Arabsat" satellite .. 1·60 65

**225.** Windsurfing and Tennis.

**1985.** Air. "Philexafrique" Stamp Exhibition, Lome, Togo (2nd issue). Mult.

969 100 f. Type **225** .. .. 1·75 1·10
970 100 f. Construction of Tadjoura road .. .. 1·60 1·10

**226.** Edmond Halley, Bayeux Tapestry and Comet.

**1986.** Appearance of Halley's Comet. Multicoloured.

971. 85 f. Type **226** .. .. 1·10 45
972. 90 f. Solar system, comet trajectory and space probes "Giotto" and "Vega 1" .. .. 1·40 55

**227.** Footballers.

**1986.** Air. World Cup Football Championship, Mexico. Multicoloured.

973. 75 f. Type **227** .. .. 1·00 45
974. 100 f. Players and stadium 1·40 65

**228.** Runners on Shore.

**1986.** "ISERST" Solar Energy Project. Multicoloured.

975. 50 f. Type **228** .. .. 65 30
976. 150 f. "ISERST" building 2·00 85

**229.** "Santa Maria".

**1986.** Historic Ships of Columbus, 1492. Multicoloured.

977. 60 f. Type **229** .. .. 1·25 90
978. 90 f. "Nina" and "Pinta" 2·00 1·60

**230.** Statue of Liberty, Eiffel Tower and French and U.S. Flags.

**1986.** Air. Centenary of Statue of Liberty.

979. **230.** 250 f. multicoloured .. 3·25 1·40

231. "Elagatis bipinnulatus".

**1986.** Red Sea Fish. Multicoloured.
980. 20 f. Type **231** . . . . 35 15
981. 25 f. "Valamugil seheli" . . 40 15
982. 55 f. "Lutjanus rivulatus" 95 35

232. People's Palace.

**1986.** Public Buildings. Multicoloured.
983. 105 f. Type **232** . . . . 1·40 55
984. 115 f. Ministry of the Interior, Posts and Telecommunications . . 1·60 65

233. Transmission Building and Keyboard.

**1986.** Inauguration of Sea-Me-We Submarine Communications Cable.
985. **233.** 100 f. multicoloured . . 1·40 65

**1986.** Air. World Cup Football Championship Winners. Nos. 973/4 optd. Multicoloured.
987. 75 f. **FRANCE–BELGIQUE 4–2** . . . . . . 1·00 65
988. 100 f. **3–2 ARGENTINA -RFA** . . . . . . 1·40 90

235. African Bishop, Knight and Queen.

**1986.** Air. World Chess Championship, London and Leningrad. Multicoloured.
989 80 f. Type **235** . . . . 1·40 65
990 120 f. African rook, pawn and king . . . . 2·25 1·00

**1986.** 5th Anniv. of Inauguration of Djibouti Sheraton Hotel. No. 828 surch. **5e ANNIVERSAIRE**
991. **169.** 55 f. on 75 f. mult. . . 90 55

237. Gagarin and Space Capsule.

**1986.** Air. 25th Anniv. of First Man in Space and 20th Anniv. of "Gemini 8"–"Agena" Link-up. Multicoloured.
992. 150 f. Type **237** . . . . 2·25 65
993. 200 f. "Gemini 8" and "Agena" craft over Earth . . . . . . 3·00 1·00

238. Amiot 370.

**1987.** Air. Flight Anniversaries and Events. Multicoloured.
994. 55 f. Type **238** (45th anniv. of first Istres–Djibouti flight) . . . . . . 90 60
995. 80 f. "Spirit of St Louis" and Charles Lindbergh (60th anniv. of first solo flight across North Atlantic) . . . . . . 1·10 95
996. 120 f. Dick Rutan, Jeana Yeager and "Voyager" (first non-stop flight around the world) . . 1·75 1·25

239. Louis Pasteur and Vaccination Session.

**1987.** Centenary of Pasteur Institute. National Vaccination Campaign in Djibouti.
997. **239.** 220 f. multicoloured . . 3·25 1·10

241. "Macrolepiota imbricata". 242. Hare.

**1987.** Fungi. Multicoloured.
999. 35 f. Type **241** . . . . 1·25 65
1000. 50 f. "Lentinus squarrosulus" . . . . 2·00 95
1001. 95 f. "Terfezia boudieri" . . 3·50 1·50

**1987.** Wild Animals. Multicoloured.
1002. 5 f. Type **242** . . . . 10 10
1003. 30 f. Young dromedary with mother . . . . 45 20
1004. 140 f. Cheetah . . . . 2·25 80

243. President Hassan Gouled Aptidon, Map, Flag and Crest.

**1987.** Air. 10th Anniv. of Independence.
1005. **243.** 250 f. multicoloured 3·25 1·40

244. Pierre de Coubertin (founder of modern Games) and Athlete lighting Flame.

**1987.** Olympic Games, Calgary and Seoul (1st issue) (1988). Multicoloured.
1006. 85 f. Type **244** . . . . 1·10 45
1007. 135 f. Ski-jumper . . . . 1·60 65
1008. 140 f. Runners and spectators . . . . 1·90 80
See also No. 1021.

245. "Telstar" Satellite.

**1987.** Air. Telecommunications Anniversaries. Multicoloured.
1009. 190 f. Type **245** (25th anniv.) . . . . . . 2·50 90
1010. 250 f. Samuel Morse and morse key (150th anniv. of morse telegraph) . . . . 3·25 1·40

246. Djibouti Creek and Quay, 1887.

**1987.** Air. Centenary of Djibouti City.
1011. **246.** 100 f. agate and stone 1·50 1·00
1012. – 150 f. multicoloured 2·25 80
DESIGN: 150 f. Aerial view of Djibouti, 1987.

247. Comb. 249. Anniversary Emblem.

**1988.** Traditional Djibouti Art. Mult.
1014. 30 f. Type **247** . . . . 45 20
1015. 70 f. Water pitcher . . . . 95 45

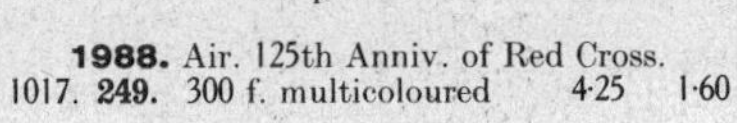

**1988.** Air. 125th Anniv. of Red Cross.
1017. **249.** 300 f. multicoloured 4·25 1·60

250. Rabat and Footballers.

**1988.** 16th African Nations Cup Football Championship, Morocco.
1018. **250.** 55 f. multicoloured . . 85 35

251. Ski Jumping. 252. Doctor examining Child.

**1988.** Winter Olympic Games, Calgary.
1019. **251.** 45 f. multicoloured . . 65 30

**1988.** U.N.I.C.E.F. "Universal Vaccinations by 1990" Campaign.
1020. **252.** 125 f. multicoloured 1·75 65

253. Runners and Stadium.

**1988.** Air. Olympic Games, Seoul (2nd issue).
1021. **253.** 105 f. multicoloured 1·40 55

**1988.** Air. Paris–Djibouti–St. Denis (Reunion) Roland Garros Air Race. No. 994 surch. **PARIS-DJIBOUTI-ST DENIS LA REUNION RALLYE ROLAND GARROS 70 F.**
1022. **238.** 70 f. on 55 f. mult. . . 1·25 65

255 Animals at Water Trough

**1988.** Anti-drought Campaign.
1023 **255** 50 f. multicoloured . . 85 35

256 Djibouti Post Offices of 1890 and 1977

**1988.** Air. World Post Day.
1024 **256** 1000 f. multicoloured 13·50 4·00

257 Combine Harvester, Tractor and Ploughman with Camel

**1988.** 10th Anniv of International Agricultural Development Fund.
1025 **257** 135 f. multicoloured 1·75 65

258 De Havilland Tiger Moth, 1948, and Socata Tobago, 1988

**1988.** 40th Anniv of Michel Lafoux Air Club.
1026 **258** 145 f. multicoloured . . 2·00 95

**1988.** 1st Djibouti Olympic Medal Winner. No. 1021 optd **AHMED SALAH 1re MEDAILLE OLYMPIQUE**.
1027 **253** 105 f. multicoloured . . 1·40 90

260 "Lobophyllia costata"

**1989.** Underwater Animals. Multicoloured.
1028 90 f. Type **260** . . . . 1·40 35
1029 160 f. Giant spider conch 3·25 1·40

261 "Colotis protomedia"

**1989.**
1030 **261** 70 f. multicoloured . . 90 60

**1989.** Nos. 849 and 913 surch **70f.**
1031 **206** 70 f. on 2 f. mult . . 95 45
1032 **179** 70 f. on 150 f. mult . . 95 45

263 Dancers

264 Pale-bellied Francolin

**1989.** Folklore. Multicoloured.
1033 30 f. Type **263** .. .. 40 20
1034 70 f. Dancers with parasol 1·00 45

**1989.**
1035 **264** 35 f. multicoloured .. 65 20

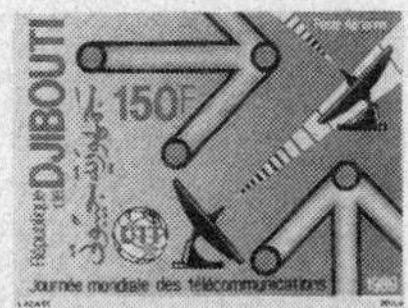

**265** Arrows and Dish Aerials

**1989.** Air. World Telecommunications Day.
1036 **265** 150 f. multicoloured .. 1·90 65

**266** "Calotropis procera"

**1989.**
1037 **266** 25 f. multicoloured .. 35 15

**267** Emblem, Declaration and People

**1989.** Air. "Philexfrance 89" International Stamp Exhibition, Paris, and Bicentenary of Declaration of Rights of Man.
1038 **267** 120 f. multicoloured .. 1·60 65

**268** Emblem and State Arms

**270** Child going to School

**269** Collecting Salt

**1989.** Cent of Interparliamentary Union.
1039 **268** 70 f. multicoloured .. 95 35

**1989.** Air. Lake Assal.
1040 **269** 300 f. multicoloured .. 4·00 1·10

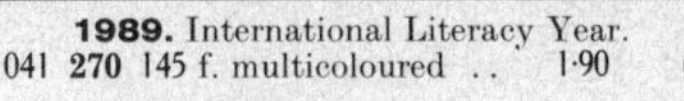

**1989.** International Literacy Year.
1041 **270** 145 f. multicoloured .. 1·90 65

**271** Tourka Maddw Cave Painting

**1989.**
1042 **271** 5 f. multicoloured .. 10 10

**272** Traditional Ornaments

**1989.**
1043 **272** 55 f. multicoloured .. 80 35

**1990.** Nos. 914 and 916/17 surch.
1044 30 f. on 8 f. multicoloured 40 15
1045 50 f. on 40 f. mult .. 65 30
1046 120 f. on 15 f. mult .. 1·60 45

**274** Water-storage Drums and Arid Landscape

**1990.** Anti-drought Campaign.
1047 **274** 120 f. multicoloured .. 1·60 55

**275** Basketry

**1990.** Traditional Crafts. Multicoloured.
1048 30 f. Type **275** .. .. 40 20
1049 70 f. Jewellery (vert) .. 95 35

**276** "Commiphora sp."

**277** Footballers

**1990.**
1050 **276** 30 f. multicoloured .. 45 30

**1990.** World Cup Football Championship, Italy.
1051 **277** 100 f. multicoloured .. 1·40 55

**278** Athlete

**279** Queue of Patients

**1990.** Djibouti 20 km Race.
1052 **278** 55 f. multicoloured .. 80 35

**1990.** Vaccination Campaign.
1053 **279** 300 f. multicoloured .. 3·25 1·40

**280** De Gaulle

**281** Technology in Developed Countries

**1990.** Birth Centenary of Charles de Gaulle (French statesman).
1054 **280** 200 f. multicoloured .. 2·50 1·25

**1990.** United Nations Conference on Less Developed Countries.
1055 **281** 45 f. multicoloured .. 60 35

**282** Mammoth and Fossilized Remains

**283** Hamadryas Baboon

**1990.**
1056 **282** 90 f. multicoloured .. 1·40 65

**1990.**
1057 **283** 50 f. multicoloured .. 65 35

**284** Emblem and Map

**285** "Acropora"

**1991.** African Tourism Year.
1058 **284** 115 f. multicoloured .. 1·50 85

**1991.** Corals. Multicoloured.
1059 40 f. Type **285** .. .. 55 35
1060 45 f. "Seriatopora hytrise" 65 35

**286** Pink-backed Pelican

**1991.** Birds. Multicoloured.
1061 10 f. Type **286** .. .. 15 10
1062 15 f. Western reef heron 35 20
1063 20 f. Goliath heron (horiz) 40 25
1064 25 f. White spoonbill (horiz) .. .. 45 30

**287** Osprey

**1991.**
1065 **287** 200 f. multicoloured .. 3·00 1·40

**288** Traditional Game

**1991.**
1066 **288** 250 f. multicoloured .. 3·25 1·40

**289** Diesel Locomotive

**1991.** Djibouti–Ethiopia Railway (1st issue).
1067 **289** 85 f. multicoloured .. 1·10 55
See also No. 1076.

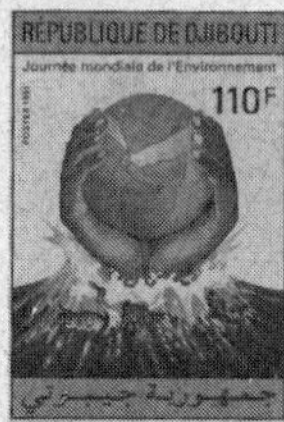

**290** Hands holding Earth above Polluted Sea

**1991.** World Environment Day.
1068 **290** 110 f. multicoloured .. 1·50 55

**291** Windsurfers and Islets

**1991.** "Philexafrique" Stamp Exhibition.
1069 **291** 120 f. multicoloured .. 90 45

**292** Handball

**293** Harvesting Crops

**1991.** Olympic Games, Barcelona (1992) (1st issue).
1070 **292** 175 f. multicoloured .. 1·40 70
See also No. 1079.

**1991.** World Food Day.
1071 **293** 105 f. multicoloured .. 80 40

**294** Route-map, Woman using Telephone and Cable-laying Ship

**1991.** Inauguration of Marseilles–Djibouti–Singapore Submarine Cable.
1072 **294** 130 f. multicoloured .. 1·00 50

**295** Columbus and Ships

**1991.** 500th Anniv (1992) of Discovery of America by Columbus (1st issue).
1073 **295** 145 f. multicoloured .. 1·10 55
See also No. 1080.

**296** Rimbaud, Ship and Serpent

**1991.** Death Centenary of Arthur Rimbaud (poet). Multicoloured.
1074 90 f. Type **296** .. .. 70 35
1075 150 f. Rimbaud, camel train and map .. 1·10 55

**297** Camel Driver and Train

**1992.** Djibouti–Ethiopia Railway (2nd issue).
1076 **297** 70 f. multicoloured .. 55 25

**298** Boys Playing Game

**1992.** Traditional Games.
1078 **298** 100 f. multicoloured .. 80 40

**299** Athlete and Globe

**301** Crushing Grain

**300** Caravel crossing Atlantic

**1992.** Olympic Games, Barcelona (2nd issue).
1079 **299** 80 f. multicoloured .. 60 30

**1992.** 500th Anniv of Discovery of America by Columbus (2nd issue).
1080 **300** 125 f. multicoloured .. 95 45

**1992.** Traditional Methods of Preparing Food. Multicoloured.
1081 30 f. Type **301** .. .. 25 10
1082 70 f. Winnowing .. .. 55 25

**302** Players, Map of Africa and Final Result

**303** "Ariane" Rocket and Satellite

**1992.** 18th African Nations Cup Football Championship, Senegal.
1083 **302** 15 f. multicoloured .. 10 10

**1992.** International Space Year. Mult.
1084 120 f. Type **303** .. .. 90 45
1085 135 f. Satellite and astronaut (horiz) .. 1·00 50

**304** Salt's Dik-dik

**1992.**
1086 **304** 5 f. multicoloured .. 10 10

**305** Loggerhead Turtle

**1992.**
1087 **305** 200 f. multicoloured .. 1·50 75

**306** Nomadic Girl

**1993.** Traditional Costumes. Multicoloured.
1088 70 f. Type **306** .. .. 55 25
1089 120 f. Nomadic girl with headband .. .. 90 45

**307** White-eyed Gull

**1993.**
1090 **307** 300 f. multicoloured .. 2·25 1·10

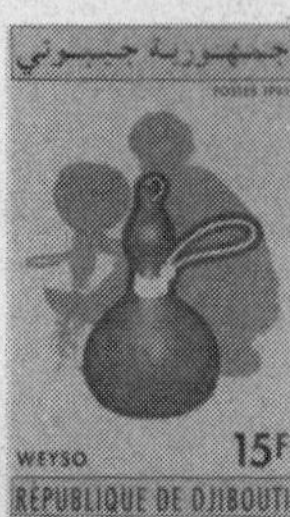

**314** Water Jar

**315** Pipes

**1993.** Utensils. Multicoloured.
1099 15 f. Type **314** .. .. 10 10
1100 20 f. Hangol (agricultural tool) .. .. .. 15 10
1101 25 f. Comb .. .. 20 10
1102 30 f. Water-skin .. .. 25 10

**1993.** Musical Instruments. Multicoloured.
1103 5 f. Type **315** .. .. 10 10
1104 10 f. Hand-held drum and lines of women .. 10 10

**317** Runners and Route Map

**318** Mother with Children

**1994.** Djibouti 20 Kilometre Race.
1106 **317** 50 f. multicoloured .. 40 20

**1994.** U.N.I.C.E.F. Breastfeeding Campaign. Multicoloured.
1107 40 f. Type **318** .. .. 30 15
1108 45 f. Woman breast-feeding baby .. .. 35 15

**319** Stadium

**1994.** Hassan Gouled Aptidon Stadium.
1109 **319** 70 f. multicoloured .. 55 25

POSTAGE DUE STAMPS

D **248.** Milking bowl.

**1988.** Traditional Djibouti Art.
D1016. D **248.** 60 f. mult. .. 90 65

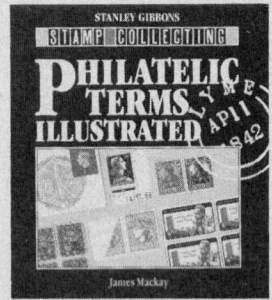

# DODECANESE ISLANDS Pt. 8

## ITALIAN OCCUPATION

A group of islands off the coast of Asia Minor occupied by Italy in May 1912 and ceded to her by Turkey in 1920. The islands concerned are now known as Kalimnos, Kasos, Kos, Khalki, Leros, Lipsoi, Nisiros, Patmos, Tilos (Piskopi), Rhodes (Rodos), Karpathos, Simi and Astipalaia. Castelrosso came under the same administration in 1921.

In 1944 the Dodecanese Islands were occupied by British forces (see BRITISH OCCUPATION OF ITALIAN COLONIES in volume 3). In 1947 they were transferred to Greek administration, since when Greek stamps have been used.

100 centesimi = 1 lira.

**1912.** Stamps of Italy optd **EGEO**.

| | | | | |
|---|---|---|---|---|
| 1 | **39** | 25 c. blue | 8·75 | 9·50 |
| 2 | – | 50 c. violet | 8·75 | 9·50 |

**1912.** Stamps of Italy optd, or surch also, for the individual islands (all in capitals on Nos. 6 and 10, in upper and lower case on others).

| | | | A Calimno | |
|---|---|---|---|---|
| 3 | **31** | 2 c. brown | 2·00 | 2·50 |
| 4 | **37** | 5 c. green | 35 | 2·50 |
| 5 | | 10 c. red | 15 | 2·50 |
| 6 | **41** | 15 c. grey | 15·00 | 7·50 |
| 7 | **37** | 15 c. grey | 90 | 19·00 |
| 8 | **41** | 20 c. on 15 c. grey | 4·25 | 7·50 |
| 10 | | 20 c. orange | 90 | 19·00 |
| 11 | **39** | 25 c. blue | 1·10 | 2·50 |
| 12 | | 40 c. brown | 15 | 2·50 |
| 13 | | 50 c. violet | 15 | 2·50 |

| | | | B Caso | | C Cos | |
|---|---|---|---|---|---|---|
| 3 | **31** | 2 c. | 2·00 | 2·50 | 2·00 | 2·50 |
| 4 | **37** | 5 c. | 35 | 2·50 | 15·00 | 2·50 |
| 5 | | 10 c. | 15 | 2·50 | 15 | 2·50 |
| 6 | **41** | 15 c. | 15·00 | 7·50 | 15·00 | 7·50 |
| 7 | **37** | 15 c. | 90 | 19·00 | 90 | 19·00 |
| 8 | **41** | 20/15 c. | 30 | 7·50 | 4·25 | 7·50 |
| 10 | | 20 c. | 70 | 19·00 | 70 | 19·00 |
| 11 | **39** | 25 c. | 15 | 2·50 | 10·00 | 5·00 |
| 12 | | 40 c. | 15 | 2·50 | 15 | 2·50 |
| 13 | | 50 c. | 15 | 2·50 | 15 | 2·50 |

| | | | D Karki | | E Leros | |
|---|---|---|---|---|---|---|
| 3 | **31** | 2 c. | 2·00 | 2·50 | 2·00 | 2·50 |
| 4 | **37** | 5 c. | 15 | 2·50 | 40 | 2·50 |
| 5 | | 10 c. | 15 | 2·50 | 20 | 2·50 |
| 6 | **41** | 15 c. | 15·00 | 7·50 | 15·00 | 7·50 |
| 7 | **37** | 15 c. | 1·60 | 19·00 | 90 | 19·00 |
| 8 | **41** | 20/15 c. | 40 | 7·50 | 4·25 | 7·50 |
| 10 | | 20 c. | 90 | 19·00 | 40·00 | 19·00 |
| 11 | **39** | 25 c. | 15 | 2·50 | 15·00 | 5·00 |
| 12 | | 40 c. | 15 | 2·50 | 15 | 2·50 |
| 13 | | 50 c. | 15 | 2·50 | 15 | 2·50 |

| | | | F Lipso | | G Nisiros | |
|---|---|---|---|---|---|---|
| 3 | **31** | 2 c. | 2·00 | 2·50 | 2·00 | 2·50 |
| 4 | **37** | 5 c. | 15 | 2·50 | 15 | 2·50 |
| 5 | | 10 c. | 15 | 2·50 | 15 | 2·50 |
| 6 | **41** | 15 c. | 15·00 | 7·50 | 15·00 | 7·50 |
| 7 | **37** | 15 c. | 1·25 | 19·00 | 6·00 | 19·00 |
| 8 | **41** | 20/15 c. | 35 | 7·50 | 35 | 7·50 |
| 10 | | 20 c. | 90 | 19·00 | 28·00 | 19·00 |
| 11 | **39** | 25 c. | 15 | 2·50 | 15 | 2·50 |
| 12 | | 40 c. | 15 | 2·50 | 15 | 2·50 |
| 13 | | 50 c. | 15 | 2·50 | 15 | 2·50 |

| | | | H Patmos | | I Piscopi | |
|---|---|---|---|---|---|---|
| 3 | **31** | 2 c. | 2·00 | 2·50 | 2·00 | 2·50 |
| 4 | **37** | 5 c. | 15 | 2·50 | 15 | 2·50 |
| 5 | | 10 c. | 15 | 2·50 | 15 | 2·50 |
| 6 | **41** | 15 c. | 15·00 | 7·50 | 15·00 | 7·50 |
| 7 | **37** | 15 c. | 90 | 19·00 | 2·75 | 19·00 |
| 8 | **41** | 20/15 c. | 4·25 | 7·50 | 35 | 7·50 |
| 10 | | 20 c. | 40·00 | 19·00 | 13·00 | 19·00 |
| 11 | **39** | 25 c. | 15 | 2·50 | 15 | 2·50 |
| 12 | | 40 c. | 15 | 2·50 | 15 | 2·50 |
| 13 | | 50 c. | 15 | 2·50 | 15 | 2·50 |

| | | | J Rodi | | K Scarpanto | |
|---|---|---|---|---|---|---|
| 3 | **31** | 2 c. | 15 | 1·50 | 2·00 | 2·50 |
| 4 | **37** | 5 c. | 15 | 95 | 15 | 2·50 |
| 5 | | 10 c. | 15 | 95 | 15 | 2·50 |
| 6 | **41** | 15 c. | 15·00 | 7·50 | 15·00 | 7·50 |
| 7 | **37** | 15 c. | 48·00 | 19·00 | 2·75 | 19·00 |
| 8 | **41** | 20/15 c. | 35·00 | 50·00 | 35 | 7·50 |
| 10 | | 20 c. | 1·50 | 2·75 | 13·00 | 19·00 |
| 11 | **39** | 25 c. | 15 | 1·50 | 1·50 | 2·50 |
| 12 | | 40 c. | 15 | 1·60 | 15 | 2·50 |
| 13 | | 50 c. | 15 | 1·60 | 15 | 2·50 |

| | | | L Simi | | M Stampalia | |
|---|---|---|---|---|---|---|
| 3 | **31** | 2 c. | 2·00 | 2·50 | 2·00 | 2·50 |
| 4 | **37** | 5 c. | 4·00 | 2·50 | 15 | 2·50 |
| 5 | | 10 c. | 15 | 2·50 | 15 | 2·50 |
| 6 | **41** | 15 c. | 15·00 | 7·50 | 15·00 | 7·50 |
| 7 | **37** | 15 c. | 42·00 | 19·00 | 2·75 | 19·00 |
| 8 | **41** | 20/15 c. | 4·25 | 7·50 | 35 | 7·50 |
| 10 | | 20 c. | 16·00 | 19·00 | 13·00 | 19·00 |
| 11 | **39** | 25 c. | 35 | 2·50 | 15 | 2·50 |
| 12 | | 40 c. | 15 | 2·50 | 15 | 2·50 |
| 13 | | 50 c. | 15 | 2·50 | 15 | 2·50 |

**1916.** Optd. **Rodi.**

| | | | | |
|---|---|---|---|---|
| 14. | **33.** | 20 c. orange | 60 | 1·50 |
| 15. | **39.** | 85 c. brown | 9·00 | 15·00 |
| 16. | **34.** | 1 l. brown & green | 60 | |

1. Rhodian Windmill.

2. Knight kneeling before the Holy City.

**1929.** King of Italy's Visit.

| | | | | |
|---|---|---|---|---|
| 17 | **1** | 5 c. purple | 15 | 15 |
| 18 | – | 10 c. brown | 20 | 15 |
| 19 | – | 20 c. red | 20 | 15 |
| 20 | – | 25 c. green | 20 | 15 |
| 21 | **2** | 30 c. blue | 20 | 15 |
| 22 | – | 50 c. brown | 20 | 15 |
| 23 | – | 1 l. 25 blue | 20 | 15 |
| 24 | **2** | 5 l. purple | 15 | 15 |
| 25 | | 10 l. green | 20 | 15 |

DESIGNS—As Type **1**: 10 c. Galley of Knights of St. John. 20 c., 25 c. Knight defending Christianity. 50 c., 1 l. 25, Knight's tomb.

**1930.** 21st Hydrological Congress. Nos. 17/25 optd **XXI Congresso Idrologico**.

| | | | |
|---|---|---|---|
| 26 | 5 c. purple | 1·50 | 4·00 |
| 27 | 10 c. brown | 1·50 | 3·50 |
| 28 | 20 c. red | 2·00 | 3·50 |
| 29 | 25 c. green | 2·50 | 3·75 |
| 30 | 30 c. blue | 1·50 | 4·00 |
| 31 | 50 c. brown | £190 | 22·00 |
| 32 | 1 l. 25 blue | £125 | 32·00 |
| 33 | 5 l. purple | 35·00 | 85·00 |
| 34 | 10 l. green | 35·00 | 85·00 |

**1930.** Ferrucci issue of Italy (colours changed) optd for each individual island, in capitals. A. CALINO; B. CASO; C. COO; D. CALCHI; E. LERO; F. LISSO; G. NISIRO; H. PATMO; I. PISCOPI; J. RODI; K. SCARPANTO; L. SIMI; M. STAMPALIA.

| | | | | |
|---|---|---|---|---|
| 35 | **114** | 20 c. violet | 50 | 1·25 |
| 36 | – | 25 c. green | 50 | 1·25 |
| 37 | – | 50 c. black | 50 | 1·25 |
| 38 | – | 1 l. 25 blue | 50 | 1·25 |
| 39 | – | 5 l. + 2 l. red | 4·50 | 12·00 |

Same prices for each of the 13 islands.

**1930.** Air. Ferrucci air stamps of Italy (colours changed) optd **ISOLE ITALIANE DELL'EGEO**.

| | | | | |
|---|---|---|---|---|
| 40 | **117** | 50 c. purple | 4·50 | 7·50 |
| 41 | | 1 l. blue | 4·50 | 7·50 |
| 42 | | 5 l. + 2 l. red | 12·00 | 24·00 |

**1930.** Virgil stamps of Italy optd **ISOLE ITALIANE DELL'EGEO**.

| | | | | |
|---|---|---|---|---|
| 43. | – | 15 c. violet (postage) | 45 | 2·25 |
| 44. | – | 20 c. brown | 45 | 2·25 |
| 45. | – | 25 c. green | 45 | 2·25 |
| 46. | – | 30 c. brown | 45 | 2·25 |
| 47. | – | 50 c. purple | 45 | 2·25 |
| 48. | – | 75 c. red | 45 | 2·25 |
| 49. | – | 1 l. 25 blue | 45 | 2·25 |
| 50. | – | 5 l + 1 l. 50 purple | 3·00 | 6·00 |
| 51. | – | 10 l. + 2 l. 50 brown | 3·00 | 6·00 |
| 52. | **119.** | 50 c. green (air) | 1·50 | 3·75 |
| 53. | | 1 l. red | 1·50 | 3·75 |
| 54. | | 7 l. 70 + 1 l. 30 brown | 2·50 | 6·00 |
| 55. | | 9 l. + 2 l. grey | 2·50 | 6·00 |

**1931.** Italian Eucharistic Congress. Nos. 17/25 optd **1931 CONGRESSO EUCARISTICO ITALIANO.**

| | | | |
|---|---|---|---|
| 56. | 5 c. red | 1·50 | 1·50 |
| 57. | 10 c. brown | 1·50 | 1·50 |
| 58. | 20 c. red | 75 | 1·50 |
| 59. | 25 c. green | 1·50 | 1·50 |
| 60. | 30 c. blue | 1·50 | 1·50 |
| 61. | 50 c. brown | 35·00 | 18·00 |
| 62. | 1 l. 25 blue | 25·00 | 40·00 |

**1932.** St. Antony of Padua stamps of Italy optd **ISOLE ITALIANE DELL'EGEO**.

| | | | | |
|---|---|---|---|---|
| 63. | **121.** | 20 c. purple | 10·00 | 15·00 |
| 64. | – | 25 c. green | 10·00 | 15·00 |
| 65. | – | 30 c. brown | 10·00 | 15·00 |
| 66. | – | 50 c. purple | 10·00 | 15·00 |
| 67. | – | 75 c. red | 10·00 | 15·00 |
| 68. | – | 1 l. 25 blue | 10·00 | 15·00 |
| 69. | – | 5 l. + 2 l. 50 orange | 10·00 | 30·00 |

**1932.** Dante stamps of Italy optd **ISOLE ITALIANE DELL'EGEO**.

| | | | | |
|---|---|---|---|---|
| 70. | – | 10 c. green (postage) | 50 | 1·25 |
| 71. | – | 15 c. violet | 50 | 1·25 |
| 72. | – | 20 c. brown | 50 | 1·25 |
| 73. | – | 25 c. green | 50 | 1·00 |
| 74. | – | 30 c. red | 50 | 1·25 |
| 75. | – | 50 c. purple | 50 | 75 |
| 76. | – | 75 c. red | 75 | 1·50 |
| 77. | – | 1 l. 25 blue | 75 | 1·50 |
| 78. | – | 1 l. 75 sepia | 1·25 | 2·75 |
| 79. | – | 2 l. 75 red | 1·25 | 2·75 |
| 80. | – | 5 l. + 2 l. violet | 1·75 | 3·75 |
| 81. | **124.** | 10 l. + 2 l. 50 brown | 2·00 | 5·00 |
| 82. | **125.** | 50 c. red (air) | 1·50 | 2·00 |
| 83. | – | 1 l. green | 1·50 | 2·00 |
| 84. | – | 3 l. purple | 1·50 | 2·00 |
| 85. | – | 5 l. red | 1·50 | 2·00 |
| 86. | **125.** | 7 l. 70 + 2 l. sepia | 1·75 | 3·00 |
| 87. | – | 10 l. + 2 l. 50 blue | 1·75 | 3·00 |
| 88. | **127.** | 100 l. olive and blue | 18·00 | 25·00 |

No. 88 is inscribed instead of optd.

**1932.** Garibaldi issue of Italy (colours changed) optd for each individual island in capital letters.
A. CALINO; B. CASO; C. COO; D. CARCHI; E. LERO; F. LIBO; G. NISIRO; H. PATMO; I. PISCOPI; J. RODI; K. SCARPANTO; L. SIMI; M. STAMPALIA.

| | | | | |
|---|---|---|---|---|
| 89. | – | 10 c. sepia | 3·25 | 5·50 |
| 90. | **128.** | 20 c. brown | 3·25 | 5·50 |
| 91. | – | 25 c. green | 3·25 | 5·50 |
| 92. | **128.** | 30 c. black | 3·25 | 5·50 |
| 93. | – | 50 c. lilac | 3·25 | 5·50 |
| 94. | – | 75 c. red | 3·25 | 5·50 |
| 95. | – | 1 l. 25 blue | 3·25 | 5·50 |
| 96. | – | 1 l. 75 + 25 c. sepia | 3·25 | 5·50 |
| 97. | – | 2 l. 55 + 50 c. red | 3·25 | 5·50 |
| 98. | – | 5 l. + 1 l. violet | 3·25 | 5·50 |

**Same price for each of the 13 islands.**

**1932.** Air. Garibaldi air stamps of Italy optd **ISOLE ITALIANE DELL'EGEO**.

| | | | | |
|---|---|---|---|---|
| 99. | **130.** | 50 c. green | 19·00 | 35·00 |
| 100. | – | 80 c. red | 19·00 | 35·00 |
| 101. | **130.** | 1 l. + 25 c. blue | 19·00 | 35·00 |
| 102. | – | 2 l. + 50 c. brown | 19·00 | 35·00 |
| 103. | – | 5 l. + 1 l. black | 19·00 | 35·00 |

8.

**1932.** 20th Anniv of Italian Occupation of Dodecanese Islands.

| | | | | |
|---|---|---|---|---|
| 106. | **8.** | 5 c. red, black and green | 3·00 | 6·50 |
| 107. | | 10 c. red, black and blue | 3·00 | 6·50 |
| 108. | | 20 c. red, black and yellow | 3·00 | 6·50 |
| 109. | | 25 c. red, black and violet | 3·00 | 6·50 |
| 110. | | 30 c. red, black and red | 3·00 | 6·50 |
| 111. | – | 50 c. red, black and blue | 3·00 | 6·50 |
| 112. | – | 1 l. 25 red, purple & blue | 3·00 | 6·50 |
| 113 | – | 5 l. red and blue | 10·00 | 14·00 |
| 114. | – | 10 l. red, green and blue | 20·00 | 38·00 |
| 115. | – | 25 l. red, brown and blue | £250 | £400 |

DESIGN—VERT 50 c. to 25 l. Arms on map of Rhodes.

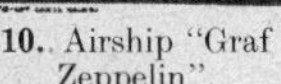

10. Airship "Graf Zeppelin".

11. Wing from Arms of Francesco Sans.

**1933.** Air. "Graf Zeppelin".

| | | | | |
|---|---|---|---|---|
| 116 | **10** | 3 l. brown | 24·00 | 60·00 |
| 117 | | 5 l. purple | 20·00 | 60·00 |
| 118 | | 10 l. green | 20·00 | £120 |
| 119 | | 12 l. blue | 20·00 | £120 |
| 120 | | 15 l. red | 20·00 | £120 |
| 121 | | 20 l. black | 20·00 | £120 |

**1933.** Air. Balbo Mass Formation Flight issue of Italy optd **ISOLE ITALIANE DELL'EGEO**.

| | | | | |
|---|---|---|---|---|
| 122. | **135.** | 5 l. 25 + 19 l. 75 red, green and blue | 20·00 | 30·00 |
| 123. | **136.** | 5 l. 25 + 44 l. 75 red, green and blue | 20·00 | 35·00 |

**1934.** Air.

| | | | | |
|---|---|---|---|---|
| 124 | **11** | 50 c. black and yellow | 50 | 50 |
| 125 | | 80 c. black and red | 1·50 | 1·75 |
| 126 | | 1 l. black and green | 1·00 | 85 |
| 127 | | 5 l. black and mauve | 3·75 | 4·00 |

**1934.** World Football Championship stamps of Italy (some colours changed) optd **ISOLE ITALIANE DELL'EGEO**.

| | | | | |
|---|---|---|---|---|
| 128. | **142.** | 20 c. red (postage) | 18·00 | 18·00 |
| 129. | – | 25 c. green | 18·00 | 18·00 |
| 130. | – | 50 c. violet | 20·00 | 12·00 |
| 131. | – | 1 l. 25 blue | 20·00 | 25·00 |
| 132. | – | 5 l. + 2 l. 50 blue | 20·00 | 60·00 |
| 133. | – | 50 c. brown (air) | 7·50 | 12·00 |
| 134. | – | 75 c. red | 7·50 | 12·00 |
| 135. | – | 5 l. + 2 l. 50 orange | 11·00 | 18·00 |
| 136. | – | 10 l. + 5 l. green | 11·00 | 18·00 |

**1934.** Military Medal Centenary stamps of Italy (some colours changed) optd **ISOLE ITALIANE DELL'EGEO**.

| | | | | |
|---|---|---|---|---|
| 157. | **146.** | 10 c. grey (postage) | 16·00 | 35·00 |
| 158. | – | 15 c. brown | 16·00 | 35·00 |
| 159. | – | 20 c. orange | 16·00 | 35·00 |
| 160. | – | 25 c. green | 16·00 | 35·00 |
| 161. | – | 30 c. red | 16·00 | 35·00 |
| 162. | – | 50 c. green | 16·00 | 35·00 |
| 163. | – | 75 c. red | 16·00 | 35·00 |
| 164. | – | 1 l. 25 blue | 16·00 | 35·00 |
| 165. | – | 1 l. 75 + 1 l. violet | 12·00 | 35·00 |
| 166. | – | 2 l. 55 + 2 l. red | 12·00 | 35·00 |
| 167. | – | 2 l. 75 + 2 l. brown | 12·00 | 35·00 |
| 168. | – | 25 c. green (air) | 23·00 | 42·00 |
| 169. | – | 50 c. grey | 23·00 | 42·00 |
| 170. | – | 75 c. red | 23·00 | 42·00 |
| 171. | – | 80 c. brown | 23·00 | 42·00 |
| 172. | – | 1 l. + 50 c. green | 14·00 | 42·00 |
| 173. | – | 2 l. + 1 l. blue | 14·00 | 42·00 |
| 174. | – | 3 l. + 2 l. violet | 14·00 | 42·00 |

16.

19. Dante House, Rhodes.

**1935.** Holy Year.

| | | | | |
|---|---|---|---|---|
| 177. | **16.** | 5 c. orange | 3·75 | 7·00 |
| 178. | | 10 c. brown | 3·75 | 7·00 |
| 179. | | 20 c. red | 3·75 | 7·00 |
| 180. | | 25 c. green | 3·75 | 7·00 |
| 181. | | 30 c. purple | 3·75 | 7·00 |
| 182. | | 50 c. brown | 3·75 | 7·00 |
| 183. | | 1 l. 25 blue | 3·75 | 7·00 |

**1938.** Augustus the Great stamps of Italy (colours changed) optd **ISOLE ITALIANE DELL'EGEO**.

| | | | | |
|---|---|---|---|---|
| 186. | **163.** | 10 c. brown (postage) | 75 | 90 |
| 187. | – | 15 c. violet | 75 | 90 |
| 188. | – | 20 c. brown | 75 | 90 |
| 189. | – | 25 c. green | 75 | 90 |
| 190. | – | 30 c. purple | 75 | 90 |
| 191. | – | 50 c. green | 75 | 90 |
| 192. | – | 75 c. red | 75 | 90 |
| 193. | – | 1 l. 25 blue | 75 | 90 |
| 194. | – | 1 l. 75 + 1 l. orange | 3·25 | 3·75 |
| 195. | – | 2 l. 55 + 2 l. brown | 4·75 | 6·75 |
| 196. | – | 25 c. violet (air) | 1·50 | 1·75 |
| 197. | – | 50 c. green | 1·50 | 1·75 |
| 198. | – | 80 c. blue | 1·50 | 1·75 |
| 199. | – | 1 l. + 1 l. purple | 2·50 | 4·75 |
| 200. | **164.** | 5 l. + 1 l. red | 3·50 | 6·00 |

**1938.** Giotto stamps of Italy optd **ITALIANE ISOLE DELL'EGEO**.

| | | | |
|---|---|---|---|
| 201 | 1 l. 25 blue (No. 527) | 3·00 | 3·00 |
| 202 | 2 l. 75 + 2 l. brown (530) | 4·00 | 9·00 |

**1940.** Colonial Exhibition. Inscr. as in **T 19.**

| | | | | |
|---|---|---|---|---|
| 203. | – | 5 c. brown (postage) | 10 | 40 |
| 204. | – | 10 c. orange | 10 | 40 |
| 205. | **19.** | 25 c. green | 50 | 75 |
| 206. | – | 50 c. violet | 50 | 75 |
| 207. | – | 75 c. red | 50 | 75 |
| 208. | **19.** | 1 l. 25 blue | 50 | 75 |
| 209. | – | 2 l. + 75 c. red | 50 | 75 |

DESIGN—VERT. 5 c., 50 c. Roman Wolf statue, 10 c., 75 c., 2 l. Crown and Maltese Cross.

| | | | |
|---|---|---|---|
| 210. | 50 c. brown (air) | 1·00 | 1·50 |
| 211. | 1 l. violet | 1·00 | 1·50 |
| 212. | 2 l. + 75 c. blue | 1·00 | 3·00 |
| 213. | 5 l. + 2 l. 50 brown | 1·00 | 3·00 |

DESIGNS—HORIZ: Savoia Marchetti S.M.75 airplane over: 50 c., 2 l. statues, Rhodes Harbour; 1, 5 l. Government House, Rhodes.

**1943.** Aegean Relief Fund. Nos. 17/25 surch **PRO ASSISTENZA EGEO** and value.

| | | | | |
|---|---|---|---|---|
| 214 | **1** | 5 c. + 5 c. purple | 25 | 1·00 |
| 215 | – | 10 c. + 10 c. brown | 25 | 1·00 |
| 216 | – | 20 c. + 20 c. red | 25 | 1·00 |
| 217 | – | 25 c. + 25 c. green | 25 | 1·00 |
| 218 | **2** | 30 c. + 30 c. blue | 1·00 | 1·00 |
| 219 | – | 50 c. + 50 c. brown | 2·00 | 3·00 |
| 220 | – | 1 l. 25 + 1 l. 25 blue | 3·00 | 5·00 |
| 221 | **2** | 5 l. + 5 l. purple | 35·00 | 30·00 |

**1944.** War Victims' Relief. Nos. 17/20 and 22/23 surch **PRO SINISTRATI DI GUERRA**, value and stag symbol.

| | | | | |
|---|---|---|---|---|
| 224 | **1** | 5 c. + 3 l. purple | 1·00 | 2·50 |
| 225 | – | 10 c. + 3 l. brown | 1·00 | 2·50 |
| 226 | – | 20 c. + 3 l. red | 1·00 | 2·50 |
| 227 | – | 25 c. + 3 l. green | 1·00 | 2·50 |
| 228 | – | 50 c. + 3 l. brown | 1·00 | 2·50 |
| 229 | – | 1 l. 25 + 5 l. blue | 18·00 | 20·00 |

**1944.** Air. War Victims Relief. Surch. **PRO SINISTRATI DI GUERRA** and value.

| | | | | |
|---|---|---|---|---|
| 232. | **11.** | 50 c. + 2 l. blk. & yellow | 3·50 | 3·75 |
| 233. | | 80 c. + 2 l. black and red | 4·50 | 4·75 |
| 234. | | 1 l. + 2 l. black & green | 5·50 | 6·00 |
| 235. | | 5 l. + 2 l. black & mauve | 23·00 | 38·00 |

**1945.** Red Cross Fund. Nos. 24/5 surch **FEBBRAIO 1945 + 10** and Cross.

| | | | |
|---|---|---|---|
| 236 | + 10 l. on 5 l. purple | 4·25 | 7·00 |
| 237 | + 10 l. on 10 l. green | 4·25 | 7·00 |

## EXPRESS STAMPS

**1932.** Air. Garibaldi Air Express stamps of Italy optd **ISOLE ITALIANE DELL'EGEO**.

| | | | | |
|---|---|---|---|---|
| E104 | **E 3** | 2 l. 25 + 1 l. red & bl | 16·00 | 35·00 |
| E105 | | 4 l. 50 + 1 l. 50 grey and yellow | 16·00 | 35·00 |

**1934.** Air. As Nos. E442/3 of Italy, but colours changed, optd **ISOLE ITALIANE DELL'EGEO**.

| | | | |
|---|---|---|---|
| E175 | 2 l. + 1 l. 25 blue | 14·00 | 42·00 |
| E176 | 4 l. 50 + 2 l. green | 14·00 | 42·00 |

E 17.

**1935.**

| | | | | |
|---|---|---|---|---|
| E 184. | **E 17.** | 1 l. 25 green | 2·75 | 4·75 |
| E 185. | | 2 l. 50 orange | 2·75 | 4·75 |

**1943.** Aegean Relief Fund. Surch **PRO ASSISTENZA EGEO** and value.
E 222. E 17. 1 l. 25+1 l. 25 green 7·50 12·00
E 223. 2 l. 50+2 l. 50 orge. 10·00 17·00

**1944.** Nos. 19/20 surch **ESPRESSO** and value.
E230 1 l. 25 on 25 c. green .. 50 75
E231 2 l. 50 on 50 c. red .. 50 75

PARCEL POST STAMPS

P 12.

**1934.**
P 137. P 12. 5 c. orange .. 65 50
P 138. 10 c. red .. .. 65 50
P 139. 20 c. green .. 65 50
P 140. 25 c. violet .. 65 50
P 141. 50 c. blue .. 65 50
P 142. 60 c. black .. 65 50
P 143. – 1 l. orange .. 65 50
P 144. – 2 l. red .. .. 65 50
P 145. – 3 l. green .. .. 65 50
P 146. – 4 l. violet .. .. 65 50
P 147. – 10 l. blue .. .. 65 50
DESIGN: 1 l. to 10 l. Left half: Stag as in Type E 17; Right half: Castle.

POSTAGE DUE STAMPS

D 14. Badge of the Knights of St. John.

D 15. Immortelle.

**1934.**
D 148. D 14. 5 c. orange .. 40 50
D 149. 10 c. red .. .. 40 50
D 150. 20 c. green .. 40 50
D 151. 30 c. violet .. 40 50
D 152. 40 c. blue .. 40 50
D 153. D 15. 50 c. orange .. 40 50
D 154. 60 c. red .. .. 40 50
D 155. 1 l. green .. .. 40 50
D 156. 2 l. violet .. .. 40 50

## DOMINICAN REPUBLIC Pt. 15

The Eastern portion of the island of San Domingo in the W. Indies finally became independent of Spain in 1865.

1865. 8 reales = 1 peso.
1880. 100 centavos = 1 peso.
1883. 100 centimos = 1 franco.
1885. 100 centavos = 1 peso.

1. 3.

**1865.** Imperf.
1. 1. ½ r. black on red .. .. £225 £200
3. ½ r. black on green .. £350 £350
2. 1 r. black on green .. £600 £550
4. 1 r. black on yellow .. £1100 £950

**1865.** Imperf.
5. 3. ½ r. black on buff .. £125 £100
7. ½ r. black on red .. 40·00 40·00
12. ½ r. black on grey .. £120 £120
18. ½ r. black and blue on red 50·00 30·00
19. ½ r. black on yellow .. 25·00 25·00
20. 1 r. black on green .. 50·00 50·00
9. 1 r. black on blue .. 35·00 35·00
15. 1 r. black on flesh .. £100 £100
21. 1 r. black on lilac .. £200 £200

4. 5. 15.

**1879.** Perf.
22. 4. ½ r. violet .. .. .. 1·50 1·50
24. 1 r. red .. .. .. 1·50 1·50

**1880.** Rouletted.
35. 5. 1 c. green .. .. .. 60 60
36. 2 c. red .. .. .. 60 60
28. 5 c. blue .. .. .. 85 70
38. 10 c. pink .. .. .. 60 60
39. 20 c. bistre .. .. .. 70 70
40. 25 c. mauve .. .. 1·25 1·00
32. 50 c. orange .. .. 1·50 1·10
33. 75 c. blue .. .. .. 3·25 3·25
34. 1 p. gold .. .. .. 4·00 4·00

**1883.** Surch.
44. 5. 5 c. on 1 c. green .. .. 1·10 1·00
73. 10 c. on 2 c. red .. .. 2·00 2·00
46. 25 c. on 5 c. blue .. .. 4·00 3·50
47. 50 c. on 10 c. pink .. 12·00 6·00
58. 1 f. on 20 c. bistre .. 7·00 7·00
51. 1 f. 25 on 25 c. mauve .. 11·00 11·00
52. 2 f. 50 c. on 50 c. orange .. 14·00 14·00
53. 3 f. 75 c. on 75 c. blue .. 16·00 16·00
64. 5 f. on 1 p. gold .. .. 50·00 50·00

**1885.** Figures in lower corner only.
77. 15. 1 c. green .. .. .. 30 15
78. 2 c. red .. .. .. 30 15
79. 5 c. blue .. .. .. 50 20
80. 10 c. orange .. .. 80 30
81. 20 c. brown .. .. 85 50
82. 50 c. violet .. .. 4·50 3·00
83. 1 p. red .. .. .. 10·00 10·00
84. 2 p. brown .. .. 12·00 10·00

**1895.** As T 15 but figures in four corners.
85. 1 c. green .. .. .. 60 30
86. 2 c. red .. .. .. 60 30
87. 5 c. blue .. .. .. 70 30
88. 10 c. orange .. .. 75 30

18. Voyage of Mendez from Jamaica to S. Domingo.

19. Sarcophagus of Columbus.

**1899.** Columbus Mausoleum Fund.
98. 19. ½ c. black .. .. .. 1·00 1·00
99. – ½ c. black .. .. .. 1·00 1·00
89. 18. 1 c. purple .. .. 4·50 3·50
90. 1 c. green .. .. .. 1·00 40
91. – 2 c. red .. .. .. 50 50
92. 19. 5 c. blue .. .. .. 75 55
93. – 10 c. orange .. .. 2·00 1·00
94. – 20 c. brown .. .. 4·00 4·00
95. – 50 c. green .. .. 4·00 4·00
96. – 1 p. black on blue .. 12·00 10·00
97. – 2 p. brown on cream .. 25·00 25·00
DESIGNS—As Type **18**: ½ c. (No. 99), 1 p. Columbus at Salamanca Assembly. 2 c. Enriquillo's rebellion. 20 c. Toscanelli replying to Columbus. 50 c. Las Casas defending Indians. As Type **19**: 10 c. Hispaniola guarding remains of Columbus. 2 p. Columbus Mausoleum, Santo Domingo Cathedral.

20. Island of Hispaniola.

21.

**1900.**
100. 20. ½ c. blue .. .. .. 45 40
101. ¼ c. red .. .. .. 45 40
102. 1 c. olive .. .. .. 45 35
103. 2 c. green .. .. .. 45 35
104. 5 c. brown .. .. .. 45 35
105. 10 c. orange .. .. 35 35
106. 20 c. purple .. .. 1·50 1·50
107. 50 c. black .. .. 1·40 1·25
108. 1 p. brown .. .. 1·40 1·25

**1901.**
109. 21. ½ c. lilac and red .. .. 25 25
110. 1 c. lilac and olive .. 35 20
111. 2 c. lilac and green .. 35 20
112. 5 c. lilac and brown .. 35 25
113. 10 c. lilac and orange .. 75 30
114. 20 c. lilac and brown .. 1·50 80
115. 50 c. lilac and black .. 4·50 2·50
116. 1 p. lilac and brown .. 9·50 7·00

24. Sanchez.

25. Fortress of Santo Domingo.

**1902.** 400th Anniv. of Santo Domingo.
125. 24. 1 c. blk. & grn. .. 25 25
126. 2 c. blk. & red (Duarte) 25 25
127. 5 c. blk. & blue (Duarte) 25 25
128. 10 c. blk. & or. (Sanchez) 25 25
129. 12 c. blk. & violet (Mella) 25 25
130. 20 c. black & red (Mella) 25 25
131. 25. 50 c. black and brown .. 50 1·00

**1904.** Surch. with new value.
132. 21. 2 c. on 50 c. lilac & black 5·50 4·25
133. 2 c. on 1 p. lilac & brown 7·50 4·50
134. 5 c. on 50 c. lilac & black 2·00 1·60
135. 5 c. on 1 p. lilac and brown 3·00 2·40
136. 10 c. on 50 c. lilac & black 4·75 4·00
137. 10 c. on 1 p. lilac & brown 4·75 4·00

**1904.** Official stamps optd. **16 de Agosto 1904** or surch. with figure **1** also.
138. O 23. 1 c. on 20 c. blk. & yell 3·25 2·75
139. 2 c. black and red .. 5·00 3·00
140. 5 c. black and blue .. 3·00 2·25
141. 10 c. black and green 4·75 3·25

**1904.** Postage Due stamps optd. **REPUBLICA DOMINICANA CENTAVOS CORREOS** or surch. with figure **1** also.
142. D 22. 1 c. on 2 c. sepia .. 1·75 85
143. 1 c. on 4 c. sepia .. 70 50
145. 2 c. sepia .. .. 70 35

**1905.** Surch. **1905**, and new value.
146. 15. 2 c. on 20 c. brown .. 5·00 4·00
147. 5 c. on 20 c. brown .. 2·25 1·40
148. 10 c. on 20 c. brown .. 5·00 4·00

**1905.**
149. 21. ½ c. orange and black .. 1·00 55
150. 1 c. blue and black .. 1·25 50
151. 2 c. mauve and black .. 1·25 40
152. 5 c. red and black .. 1·50 70
153. 10 c. green and black .. 2·75 1·40
154. 20 c. olive and black .. 8·50 4·75
155. 50 c. brown and black .. 27·00 15·00
156. 1 p. grey and black .. £150 £150

**1906.** Postage Due stamps surch. **REPUBLICA DOMINICANA** and new value.
157. D 22. 1 c. on 4 c. sepia .. 70 40
158. 1 c. on 10 c. sepia .. 85 40
159. 2 c. on 5 c. sepia .. 85 40

**1907.**
168. 21. ½ c. black and green .. 55 15
169. 1 c. black and red .. 55 15
170. 2 c. black and brown .. 55 15
171. 5 c. black and blue .. 60 20
164. 10 c. black and purple .. 85 35
165. 20 c. black and olive .. 4·75 2·40
166. 50 c. black and brown .. 4·75 4·00
167. 1 p. black and violet .. 12·00 6·50

**1911.** No. O 178 optd. **HABILITADO. 1911.**
182. O 23. 2 c. black and red .. 1·00 50

34.

35. Jaun Pablo Duarte.

**1911.**
183. 34. ½ c. black and orange .. 25 15
184. 1 c. black and green .. 25 10
185. 2 c. black and red .. 25 10
186. 5 c. black and blue .. 50 15
187. 10 c. black and purple .. 1·00 40
188. 20 c. black and olive .. 5·50 3·25
189. 50 c. black and brown .. 2·40 2·00
190. 1 p. black and violet .. 4·00 2·40
For stamps in other colours see Nos. 235/8 and for stamps in similar type see No. 240/6.

**1914.** Birth Cent. of Duarte. Background in red, white and blue.
195. 35. ½ c. black and orange .. 45 35
196. 1 c. black and green .. 45 35
197. 2 c. black and red .. 45 35
198. 5 c. black and grey .. 55 40
199. 10 c. black and mauve .. 85 50
200. 20 c. black and olive .. 2·00 1·40
201. 50 c. black and brown .. 2·75 2·40
202. 1 p. black and lilac .. 4·00 3·00

**1915.** Nos. O 177/181 optd. **Habilitado 1915** or surch. **MEDIO CENTAVO** also.
203. O 23. ½ c. on 20 c. blk. & yell. 50 35
204. 1 c. black and green .. 70 25
205. 2 c. black and red .. 70 35
206. 5 c. black and blue .. 85 35
207. 10 c. black and green .. 2·00 1·60
208. 20 c. black and yellow .. 6·50 5·50

**1915.** Optd. **1915.**
209. 34. ½ c. black and mauve .. 55 15
210. 1 c. black and brown .. 55 10
211. 2 c. black and olive .. 2·00 25
212. 5 c. black and red .. 2·00 25
214. 10 c. black and blue .. 2·00 35
215. 20 c. black and red .. 5·50 1·25
216. 50 c. black and green .. 6·00 2·75
217. 1 p. black and orange .. 12·00 5·50

**1916.** Optd. **1916.**
218. 34. ½ c. black and mauve .. 70 10
219. 1 c. black and green .. 1·40 10

**1917.** Optd. **1917.**
220. 34. ½ c. black and mauve .. 1·00 25
221. 1 c. black and green .. 1·00 10
222. 2 c. black and olive .. 85 10
223. 5 c. black and red .. 7·50 70

**1919.** Optd. **1919.**
224. 34. 2 c. black and olive .. 4·00 10

**1920.** Optd. **1920.**
225. 34. ½ c. black and mauve .. 45 20
226. 1 c. black and green .. 45 10
227. 2 c. black and olive .. 45 10
228. 5 c. black and red .. 4·75 45
229. 10 c. black and blue .. 2·75 20
230. 20 c. black and red .. 4·75 45
231. 50 c. black and green .. 40·00 10·00

**1921.** Optd. **1921.**
233. 34. 1 c. black and green .. 1·25 25
234. 2 c. black and olive .. 2·40 30

**1922.**
235. 34. ½ c. black and red .. 25 10
236. 1 c. green .. .. 70 10
237. 2 c. red .. .. 1·00 10
238. 5 c. blue .. .. 2·00 25

41.

43. Exhibition Pavilion.

**1924.** Straight top to shield.
240. 41. 1 c. green .. .. 40 10
241. 2 c. red .. .. 55 10
242. 5 c. blue .. .. 55 10
243. 10 c. black and blue .. 6·50 1·40
245. 50 c. black and green .. 35·00 2·00
246. 1 p. black and orange .. 12·00 8·50

**1927.** National and West Indian Exn. Santiago.
248. 43. 2 c. red .. .. .. 70 45
249. 5 c. blue .. .. .. 85 45

45. Air Mail Routes.

**1928.** Air.
256. 45. 10 c. deep blue .. .. 5·75 3·00
280. 10 c. pale blue .. .. 1·90 75
271. 10 c. yellow .. .. 4·00 3·00
272. 15 c. red .. .. 7·75 4·00
281. 15 c. turquoise .. .. 4·00 1·10
273. 20 c. green .. .. 3·75 60
282. 20 c. brown .. .. 4·50 55
274. 30 c. violet .. .. 7·75 4·50
283. 30 c. brown .. .. 7·25 1·75

46. Ruins of Fortress of Columbus.

47. Horacio Vasquez.

**1928.**
258. 46. ½ c. red .. .. 45 25
259. 1 c. green .. .. 40 10
260. 2 c. red .. .. 40 10
261. 5 c. blue .. .. 1·00 25
262. 10 c. blue .. .. 1·00 25
263. 20 c. red .. .. 1·50 40
264. 50 c. green .. .. 8·50 4·75
265. 1 p. yellow .. .. 15·00 10·00

**1929.** Frontier Agreement with Haiti.
266. 47. ½ c. red .. .. 40 20
267. 1 c. green .. .. 40 15
268. 2 c. red .. .. 45 15
269. 5 c. blue .. .. 85 25
270. 10 c. blue .. .. 3·00 55

48. Jesuit Convent of San Ignacio de Loyola.

49. After the Hurricane.

**1930.**
275. 48. ½ c. brown .. .. 50 40
276. 1 c. green .. .. 45 10
277. 2 c. red .. .. 45 10
278. 5 c. blue .. .. 1·25 35
279. 10 c. blue .. .. 2·40 85

**1930.** Hurricane Relief.
284. – 1 c. green and red .. 15 35
285. – 2 c. red .. .. .. 20 25
286. 49. 5 c. blue and red .. 35 50
287. 10 c. yellow and red .. 40 70
DESIGN: 1 c., 2 c. Riverside.

**1931.** Air. Hurricane Relief. Surch with airplane, **HABILITADO PARA CORREO AEREO** and premium. Imperf or perf.
288. 49. 5 c.+5 c. blue and red 6·50 6·50
289. 5 c.+5 c. black and red 15·00 15·00
290. 10 c.+10 c. yellow & red 5·00 6·50
291. 10 c.+10 c. black & red 15·00 15·00

## MINIMUM PRICE

The minimum price quoted is 10p which represents a handling charge rather than a basis for valuing common stamps. For further notes about prices see introductory pages.

**52.** Cathedral of Santo Domingo.

**1931.**
294. **52.** 1 c. green .. .. 50 15
295. 2 c. red .. .. .. 50 15
296. 3 c. purple .. .. 55 10
297. 7 c. blue .. .. 1·40 20
298. 8 c. brown .. .. 2·40 70
299. 10 c. blue .. .. 3·00 85

**53.** Old Sun Dial, 1754.

**1931.** Air.
300. **53.** 10 c. red .. .. 5·00 60
301. 10 c. blue .. .. 2·00 55
302. 10 c. green .. .. 8·00 2·75
303. 15 c. mauve .. .. 3·75 55
304. 20 c. blue .. .. 7·25 1·60
306. 30 c. green .. .. 3·25 40
307. 50 c. brown .. .. 8·00 80
308. 1 p. orange .. .. 13·00 2·75

**54.** Fort Ozama.

**1932.**
309. **54.** 1 c. green .. .. 50 40
310. 1 c. green .. .. 25 10
311. 3 c. violet .. .. 35 10
No. 310 is inscribed "CORREOS".

**1932.** Red Cross stamps inscr. "CRUZ ROJA DOMINICANA", with cross in red and optd. **HABILITADO Dic. 20-1932 En. 5-1933 CORREOS** or surch. also.
312. 1 c. green .. .. 20 15
313. 3 c. on 2 c. violet .. 30 15
314. 5 c. blue .. .. 70 60
315. 7 c. on 10 c. blue .. 1·10 85

**56.** F. A. de Merino. **57.** Cathedral of Santo Domingo.

**1933.** Birth Cent. of F. A. de Merino.
316. – ½ c. violet .. .. 25 15
317. **56.** 1 c. green .. .. 25 15
318. – 2 c. red .. .. .. 70 55
319. **56.** 3 c. violet .. .. 35 15
320. – 5 c. blue .. .. 45 20
321. – 7 c. blue .. .. 90 35
322. – 8 c. green .. .. 1·25 70
323. **56.** 10 c. orange .. .. 1·00 25
324. – 20 c. red .. .. 2·25 1·40
325. **57.** 50 c. olive .. .. 9·00 5·50
326. 1 p. sepia .. .. 22·00 13·00
DESIGNS—VERT. ½ c., 5 c., 8 c. Merino's Tomb. 2 c., 7 c., 20 c. Merino in uniform.

**1933.** Portraits as T **56.**
327. 1 c. black and green .. 50 25
328. 3 c. black and violet .. 55 15
329. 7 c. black and blue .. 1·60 55
DESIGNS: 1 c., 7 c. Pres. Trujillo in uniform. 3 c. Pres. Trujillo in evening dress.

**1933.** Air. Optd. **CORREO AEREO INTERNO.**
330. **52.** 2 c. red .. .. .. 40 30

**60.** Fokker Super Universal over Fort Ozama.

**1933.** Air.
331. **60.** 10 c. blue .. .. 3·50 50

**61.** San Rafael Suspension Bridge.

**1934.**
332. **61.** ½ c. mauve .. .. 55 25
333. 1 c. green .. .. 80 15
334. 3 c. violet .. .. 1·25 10

**62.** Trujillo Bridge.

**1934.** (a) Postage. As T **62** but without airplane and inscr "CORREOS".
335. – ½ c. brown .. .. 50 15
336. – 1 c. green .. .. 80 10
337. – 3 c. violet .. .. 1·00 10
(b) Air.
338. **62.** 10 c. blue .. .. 3·25 50

**64.** National Palace.

**1935.** For obligatory use on mail addressed to the President.
346. **64.** 25 c. orange .. .. 2·00 15

**1935.** Opening of Ramfis Bridge. As T **62** but view of Ramfis Suspension Bridge.
347. 1 c. green .. .. 45 10
348. 3 c. brown .. .. 45 10
349. 5 c. purple .. .. 1·00 50
350. 10 c. pink .. .. 2·00 1·00

**66.** Airplane and Carrier Pigeon.

**1935.** Air.
351. **66.** 10 c. light blue and blue 2·50 45

**67.** President Trujillo.

**1935.** Frontier Agreement.
352. **67.** 3 c. brown and yellow .. 30 15
353. – 5 c. brown and orange .. 35 10
354. – 7 c. brown and blue .. 55 10
355. – 10 c. brown and purple 85 10
RECTANGULAR DESIGNS: Portrait as Type **67.** Red, white and blue ribbons in side panels on 7 c. or diagonally across 5 c. and 10 c.

**69.** Post Office, Santiago de los Caballeros.

**1936.**
356. **69.** ½ c. violet .. .. 30 20
357. 1 c. green .. .. 30 10

**70.**

**1936.** Air.
358. **70.** 10 c. blue .. .. 2·75 45

**71.** George Washington Avenue, Ciudad Trujillo.

**1936.** Dedication of George Washington Ave.
359. **71.** ½ c. brown .. .. 35 25
360. 2 c. brown and red .. 60 20
361. 3 c. brown and yellow 60 15
362. 7 c. brown and blue .. 85 50

**72.** Gen. A. Duverge. **74.** "Flight".

**1936.** National Archives and Library Fund. Inscr. "PRO ARCHIVO Y BIBLIOTECA NACIONALES".
363. – ½ c. lilac .. .. 25 15
364. – 1 c. green .. .. 20 10
365. – 2 c. red .. .. .. 20 10
366. – 3 c. violet .. .. 25 10
367. – 5 c. blue .. .. 40 25
368. **72.** 7 c. blue .. .. 70 50
369. – 10 c. orange .. .. 85 30
370. – 20 c. olive .. .. 3·25 1·90
371. – 25 c. purple .. .. 3·25 2·00
372. – 30 c. red .. .. 5·00 2·75
373. – 50 c. brown .. .. 6·00 2·75
374. – 1 p. black .. .. 15·00 12·00
375. – 2 p. brown .. .. 40·00 35·00
DESIGNS—As Type **72**: ½ c. J. N. de Caceres 1 c. Gen. G. Luperon. 2 c. E. Tejera. 3 c. Pres. Trujillo. 5 c. Jose Reyes. 10 c. Felix M. Del Monte. 25 c. F. J. Peynado. 30 c. Salome Urena. 50 c. Gen. Jose Ma. Cabral. 1 p. Manuel Js. Galvan. 2 p. Gaston F. Deligne. TRIANGULAR: 20 c. National Library.

**1936.** Air.
376. **74.** 10 c. blue .. .. 2·10 35

**75.** Obelisk in Ciudad Trujillo.

**1937.** 1st Anniv. of Naming of Ciudad Trujillo (formerly Santo Domingo).
377. **75.** 1 c. green .. .. 20 10
378. 3 c. violet .. .. 40 10
379. 7 c. blue .. .. 1·25 60

**76.** Discus Thrower and National Flag. **77.** "Peace, Labour and Progress".

**1937.** 1st National Olympic Games, Ciudad Trujillo. Flag blue, white and red.
380. **76.** 1 c. green .. .. 6·50 70
381. 3 c. violet .. .. 8·50 50
382. 7 c. blue .. .. 15·00 2·75

**1937.** 8th Year of Trujillo Presidency.
383. **77.** 3 c. violet .. .. 35 10

**78.** San Pedro de Macoris Airport.

**1937.** Air.
384. **78.** 10 c. green .. .. 1·25 10

**INDEX**
Countries can be quickly located by referring to the index at the end of this volume.

**79.** Fleet of Columbus.

**1937.** Air. Pan-American Goodwill **Flight.**
385. **79.** 10 c. red .. .. 3·75 1·25
386. A. 15 c. violet .. .. 1·75 70
387. B. 20 c. blue .. .. 1·75 70
388. A. 25 c. purple .. .. 2·50 85
389. B. 30 c. green .. .. 2·25 70
390. A. 50 c. brown .. .. 4·25 1·00
391. B. 75 c. olive .. .. 11·00 11·00
392. **79.** 1 p. red .. .. 12·00 2·75
Designs: A, Junkers F-13 aircraft in Goodwill Flight. B, Junkers F-13 aircraft over Columbus Lighthouse.

**83.** Father Billini. **84.** Globe and Torch of Liberty.

**1938.** Birth Cent. of Father Billini.
396. **83.** ½ c. orange .. .. 15 10
397. 5 c. violet .. .. 45 15

**1938.** 150th Anniv. of U.S. Constitution.
398. **84.** 1 c. green .. .. 30 10
399. 3 c. violet .. .. 45 10
400. 10 c. orange .. .. 85 20

**85.** Bastion, Trinitarian Oath and National Flag.

**1938.** Cent. of Trinitarian Rebellion.
401. **85.** 1 c. green .. .. 40 20
402. 3 c. violet .. .. 50 15
403. 10 c. orange .. .. 1·00 45

**86.** Martin M-130 Flying Boat over Obelisk. **87.** Arms of University.

**1938.** Air.
404. **86.** 10 c. green .. .. 1·40 15

**1938.** 400th Anniv. of S. Domingo University.
405. **87.** ½ c. orange .. .. 25 15
406. 1 c. green .. .. 35 10
407. 3 c. violet .. .. 40 10
408. 7 c. blue .. .. 85 40

**89.** N.Y. Fair Symbol, Lighthouse, Flag and Cornucopia.

**1939.** New York World's Fair. (a) **Postage.** Flag in blue, white and red.
418. **89.** ½ c. orange .. .. 35 15
419. 1 c. green .. .. 40 15
420. 3 c. violet .. .. 40 15
421. 10 c. yellow .. .. 1·25 45
(b) Air. Flag, etc, replaced by airplane.
422 – 10 c. green .. .. 1·50 55

**90.** Jose Trujillo V. **91.**

**1939.** 4th Death Anniv. of Jose Trujillo Valdez. Black borders.

| | | | | |
|---|---|---|---|---|
| 423. | 90. | ½ c. grey | 25 | 15 |
| 424. | | 1 c. green | 35 | 10 |
| 425. | | 3 c. brown | 40 | 10 |
| 426 | | 7 c. blue | 85 | 50 |
| 427. | | 10 c. violet | 1·50 | 40 |

**1939.** Air.

| | | | | |
|---|---|---|---|---|
| 428. | 91. | 10 c. green | 1·40 | 20 |

**92.** Western Hemisphere and Union Flags. **93.** Sir Rowland Hill.

**1940.** 50th Anniv. of Pan-American Union. Flags in national colours.

| | | | | |
|---|---|---|---|---|
| 429. | 92. | 1 c. green | 25 | 10 |
| 430. | | 2 c. red | 35 | 15 |
| 431. | | 3 c. violet | 55 | 10 |
| 432. | | 10 c. orange | 1·10 | 20 |
| 433. | | 1 p. brown | 15·00 | 10·00 |

**1940.** Cent. of 1st Adhesive Postage Stamps.

| | | | | |
|---|---|---|---|---|
| 434. | 93. | 3 c. mauve | 6·50 | 40 |
| 435. | | 7 c. blue | 12·00 | 1·50 |

**94.** Julia Molina de Trujillo.

**1940.** Mothers' Day.

| | | | | |
|---|---|---|---|---|
| 436. | 94. | 1 c. green | 30 | 10 |
| 437. | | 2 c. red | 40 | 10 |
| 438. | | 3 c. orange | 50 | 10 |
| 439. | | 7 c. blue | 1·25 | 45 |

**95.** Central America and Arms of Dominican Republic.

**1940.** 2nd Caribbean Conf., Trujillo City.

| | | | | |
|---|---|---|---|---|
| 440. | 95. | 3 c. red | 40 | 10 |
| 441. | | 7 c. blue | 85 | 15 |
| 442. | | 1 p. green | 8·50 | 4·25 |

**96.** Lighthouse, Aeroplane and Caravels.

**1940.** Air. Discovery of America and Columbus Memorial Lighthouse. Inscr. "PRO FARO DE COLON".

| | | | | |
|---|---|---|---|---|
| 443. | 96. | 10 c. blue | 1·00 | 50 |
| 444. | – | 15 c. brown | 80 | 70 |
| 445. | – | 20 c. red | 80 | 70 |
| 446. | – | 25 c. mauve | 80 | 35 |
| 447. | – | 50 c. green | 3·25 | 1·60 |

**DESIGNS:** 15 c. Columbus and lighthouse. 20 c. Lighthouse. 25 c. Columbus. 50 c. Caravel and wings.

**99.** Marion Military Hospital. **100.** Post Office, San Cristobal.

**1940.**

| | | | | |
|---|---|---|---|---|
| 457. | 99. | ½ c. brown | 25 | 20 |

**1941.** Air.

| | | | | |
|---|---|---|---|---|
| 458. | 100. | 10 c. mauve | 65 | 15 |

**101.** Trujillo Fortress.

DESIGN—VERT. 2c., 10 c. Statue of Columbus, Ciudad Trujillo.

**1941.**

| | | | | |
|---|---|---|---|---|
| 460. | 101. | 1 c. green | 15 | 10 |
| 461. | – | 2 c. red | 15 | 10 |
| 462. | – | 10 c. brown | 55 | 10 |

**103.** Sanchez, Duarte, Mella and Trujillo.

**1941.** Trujillo-Hull Treaty.

| | | | | |
|---|---|---|---|---|
| 463. | 103. | 3 c. mauve | 25 | 10 |
| 464. | | 4 c. red | 30 | 10 |
| 465. | | 13 c. blue | 70 | 20 |
| 466. | | 15 c. brown | 2·00 | 85 |
| 467. | | 17 c. blue | 2·00 | 90 |
| 468. | | 1 p. orange | 7·50 | 3·25 |
| 469. | | 2 p. grey | 15·00 | 7·50 |

**104.** Bastion of 27 February.

**1941.**

| | | | | |
|---|---|---|---|---|
| 470. | 104. | 5 c. blue | 55 | 20 |

**105.** Rural School, Torch of Knowledge and Pres. Trujillo.

**1941.** Popular Education Campaign.

| | | | | |
|---|---|---|---|---|
| 471. | 105. | ½ c. brown | 20 | 10 |
| 472. | | 1 c. green | 25 | 10 |

**106.** Globe and Winged Envelope.

**1941.** Air.

| | | | | |
|---|---|---|---|---|
| 473. | 106. | 10 c. brown | 55 | 10 |
| 474. | | 75 c. orange | 3·25 | 2·00 |

**107.** National Reserve Bank.

**1942.**

| | | | | |
|---|---|---|---|---|
| 475. | 107. | 5 c. brown | 40 | 10 |
| 476. | | 17 c. blue | 1·00 | 40 |

**108.** Symbolic of Communications. **109.** Our Lady of Highest Grace.

**1942.** 8th Anniv. of Postal and Telegraph Services Day.

| | | | | |
|---|---|---|---|---|
| 477. | 108. | 3 c. multicoloured | 4·75 | 1·00 |
| 478. | | 15 c. multicoloured | 9·25 | 4·50 |

**1942.** 20th Anniv. of Our Lady of Highest Grace.

| | | | | |
|---|---|---|---|---|
| 479. | 109. | ½ c. grey | 85 | 10 |
| 480. | | 1 c. green | 1·60 | 10 |
| 481. | | 3 c. mauve | 7·50 | 10 |
| 482. | | 5 c. purple | 2·40 | 10 |
| 483. | | 10 c. red | 6·50 | 25 |
| 484. | | 15 c. blue | 7·50 | 35 |

**111.** Banana Tree. **112.** Cows.

**1942.**

| | | | | |
|---|---|---|---|---|
| 494. | 111. | 3 c. green and brown | 45 | 10 |
| 495. | | 4 c. black and red | 50 | 20 |
| 496. | 112. | 5 c. brown and blue | 45 | 10 |
| 497. | | 15 c. green and purple | 85 | 35 |

**113.** Party Emblems and Votes.

**1943.** Re-election of Gen. Trujillo to Presidency.

| | | | | |
|---|---|---|---|---|
| 498. | 113. | 3 c. orange | 40 | 10 |
| 499. | | 4 c. red | 50 | 15 |
| 500. | | 13 c. purple | 1·10 | 20 |
| 501. | | 1p. blue | 5·00 | 1·90 |

**114.** Trujillo Market.

**1943.**

| | | | | |
|---|---|---|---|---|
| 502. | 114. | 2 c. brown | 15 | 10 |

**115.** Douglas DC-3.

**1943.** Air.

| | | | | |
|---|---|---|---|---|
| 503. | 115. | 10 c. mauve | 50 | 10 |
| 504. | | 20 c. blue | 55 | 15 |
| 505. | | 25 c. olive | 6·75 | 2·75 |

**116.** Bastion of 27 February. **117.** Monument and Dates.

**1944.** Centenary of Independence. (a) Postage. Flag in blue and red.

| | | | | |
|---|---|---|---|---|
| 506. | 116. | ½ c. ochre | 10 | 10 |
| 507. | | 1 c. green | 10 | 10 |
| 508. | | 2 c. red | 15 | 10 |
| 509. | | 3 c. purple | 15 | 10 |
| 510. | | 5 c. orange | 20 | 10 |
| 511. | | 7 c. blue | 25 | 10 |
| 512. | | 10 c. brown | 40 | 30 |
| 513. | | 20 c. olive | 70 | 45 |
| 514. | | 50 c. blue | 2·00 | 1·40 |

(b) Air. Flag in grey, blue and red.

| | | | | |
|---|---|---|---|---|
| 515. | 117. | 10 c. multicoloured | 40 | 10 |
| 516. | | 20 c. multicoloured | 50 | 15 |
| 517. | | 1 p. multicoloured | 2·40 | 1·60 |

**118.** Dr. Martos Sanatorium. **119.** Nurse and Battlefield.

**1944.** Tuberculosis Relief Fund.

| | | | | |
|---|---|---|---|---|
| 518. | 118. | 1 c. blue and red | 15 | 10 |

**1944.** 80th Anniv. of International Red Cross.

| | | | | |
|---|---|---|---|---|
| 519. | 119. | 1 c. green, red and yellow | 15 | 10 |
| 520. | | 2 c. brown, red and yellow | 35 | 10 |
| 521. | | 3 c. blue, red and yellow | 35 | 10 |
| 522. | | 10 c. red and yellow | 70 | 15 |

**120.** Communications Building, Ciudad Trujillo.

**1944.** Air.

| | | | | |
|---|---|---|---|---|
| 523. | 120. | 9 c. blue and green | 25 | 10 |
| 524. | | 13 c. red and brown | 35 | 10 |
| 525. | | 25 c. red and orange | 50 | 10 |
| 526. | | 30 c. blue and black | 1·10 | 80 |

**121.** Municipal Building, San Cristobal. **122.** Emblem of Communications.

**1945.** Centenary of 1st Constitution of Dominican Republic.

| | | | | |
|---|---|---|---|---|
| 527. | 121. | ½ c. blue | 10 | 10 |
| 528. | | 1 c. green | 10 | 10 |
| 529. | | 2 c. orange | 10 | 10 |
| 530. | | 3 c. brown | 15 | 10 |
| 531. | | 10 c. blue | 45 | 15 |

**1945.** Centres in blue and red.

| | | | | |
|---|---|---|---|---|
| 532 | 122. | 3 c. orange (postage) | 15 | 10 |
| 533. | | 20 c. green | 80 | 20 |
| 534. | | 50 c. blue | 1·60 | 60 |
| 535. | | 7 c. green (air) | 20 | 25 |
| 536. | | 12 c. orange | 25 | 15 |
| 537. | | 13 c. blue | 30 | 15 |
| 538. | | 25 c. brown | 60 | 20 |

**124.** Flags and National Anthem. **125.** Law Courts, Ciudad Trujillo.

**1946.** Air. National Anthem.

| | | | | |
|---|---|---|---|---|
| 540. | 124. | 10 c. red | 45 | 40 |
| 541. | | 15 c. blue | 1·00 | 70 |
| 542. | | 20 c. brown | 1·25 | 70 |
| 543. | | 35 c. orange | 1·40 | 70 |
| 544. | – | 1 p. green | 13·00 | 10·00 |

**DESIGN:** 1 p. As Type **124**, but horiz.

**1946.**

| | | | | |
|---|---|---|---|---|
| 545. | 125. | 3 c. brown and buff | 20 | 10 |

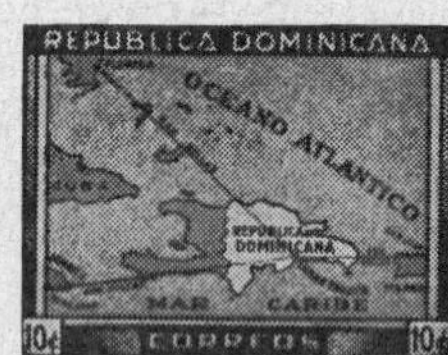

**126.** Caribbean Air Routes.

**1946.** 450th Anniv. of Santo Domingo.

| | | | | |
|---|---|---|---|---|
| 546. | 126. | 10 c. multicoloured (post.) | 40 | 15 |
| 547. | | 10 c. multicoloured (air) | 35 | 15 |
| 548. | | 13 c. multicoloured | 55 | 15 |

**127.** Jimenoa Waterfall. **128.** Nurse and Child

**1947.** Centres multicoloured, frame colours given.

| | | | | |
|---|---|---|---|---|
| 549. | 127. | 1 c. green (postage) | 15 | 10 |
| 550. | | 2 c. red | 15 | 10 |
| 551. | | 3 c. blue | 15 | 10 |
| 552. | | 13 c. purple | 45 | 25 |
| 553. | | 20 c. brown | 1·00 | 25 |
| 554. | | 50 c. yellow | 1·90 | 1·00 |
| 555. | | 18 c. blue (air) | 50 | 50 |
| 556. | | 23 c. red | 70 | 55 |
| 557. | | 50 c. violet | 1·00 | 45 |
| 558. | | 75 c. brown | 1·40 | 1·00 |

**1947.** Obligatory Tax. Tuberculosis Relief Fund.

| | | | | |
|---|---|---|---|---|
| 559. | 128. | 1 c. blue and red | 15 | 10 |

**129.** State Building, Ciudad Trujillo.

**1948.**

| | | | | |
|---|---|---|---|---|
| 560. | 129. | 1 c. green (postage) | 10 | 10 |
| 561. | | 3 c. blue | 15 | 10 |
| 562. | | 37 c. brown (air) | 1·00 | 70 |
| 563. | | 1 p. orange | 2·75 | 1·60 |

130. Ruins of San Francisco Church, Ciudad Trujillo. 131. El Santo Socorro Sanatorium.

**1949.**
564. 130. 1 c. green (postage) .. 10 10
565. 3 c. blue .. .. 15 10
566. 7 c. olive (air) .. .. 15 10
567. 10 c. brown .. .. 15 10
568. 15 c. red .. .. 50 25
569. 20 c. green .. .. 70 45

**1949.** Tuberculosis Relief Fund.
570. 131. 1 c. blue and red .. 15 10

132. General Pedro Santana. 133. Monument.

**1949.** Cent. of Battle of Las Carreras.
571. 132. 3 c. blue (postage) .. 15 10
572. 133. 10 c. red (air) .. .. 25 10

134. Bird and Globe. 136. Hotel Jimani.

135. Youth Holding Banner. 138. Ruins of Church and Hospital of St. Nicholas of Bari.

**1949.** 75th Anniv. of U.P.U.
573. 134. 1 c. brown and green .. 15 10
574. 2 c. brown and yellow 15 10
575. 5 c. brown and blue .. 20 10
576. 7 c. brown and blue .. 45 15

**1950.** Tuberculosis Relief Fund.
584. 135. 1 c. blue and red .. 20 10

**1950.** Various Hotels.
585. 136. ½ c. brown (postage).. 10 10
586. – 1 c. green (Hamaca) .. 10 10
587. – 2 c. orange (Hamaca) .. 10 10
588. – 5 c. blue (Montana) .. 20 10
589. – 15 c. orge. (San Cristobal) 45 10
590. – 20 c. lilac (Maguana) .. 85 15
591. 136. $1 yellow and brown .. 3·25 1·40
592. – 12 c. bl. (Montana) (air) 25 10
593. – 37 c. red (San Cristobal) 1·90 1·50

**1950.** 13th Pan-American Sanitary Congress. Insc. as T 138.
595. 138. 2 c. brown & grn. (post.) 20 10
596. – 5 c. brown and blue .. 25 10
597. – 12 c. orange & brn. (air) 55 10
DESIGNS—VERT. 5 c. Medical school. 12 c. Map and aeroplane.

139. 148. 148a.

" Suffer Little Children to Come Unto Me ".

148b. 140. Isabella the Catholic.

**1950.** Child Welfare.
(a) Child at left with light hair.
598. 139. 1 c. pale light blue .. 25 10
(b) Child at left with dark hair.
599. 139. 1 c. pale light blue .. 85 15
(c) Child at left with dark hair.
626. 148. 1 c. blue .. .. 20 10
(d) Child at left with light hair.
627. 148a. 1 c. blue .. .. 15 10
(e) Dark hair, smaller figures and square value tablet.
628. 148b. 1 c. blue .. .. 15 10
There are two versions of No. 628, differing in size. See also Nos. 835 and 907.

**1951.** 500th Birth Anniv. of Isabella the Catholic.
600. 140. 5 c. brown and blue .. 25 10

141. Santiago Tuberculosis Sanatorium.

**1952.** Tuberculosis Relief Fund.
601. 141. 1 c. blue and red .. 15 10

142. Dr. S. B. Gautier Hospital.

**1952.**
602. 142. 1 c. green (postage) .. 10 10
603. 2 c. red .. .. 15 10
604. 5 c. blue .. .. 25 10
605. 23 c. blue (air) .. 55 55
606. 29 c. red .. .. 1·40 1·00

143. Columbus Lighthouse and Flags. 144.

**1953.** 460th Anniv. of Columbus's Discovery of Santo Domingo. (a) Postage.
607. 143. 2 c. green .. .. 15 10
608. 5 c. blue .. .. 20 10
609. 10 c. red .. .. 35 20
(b) Air. Similar design inscr. " S./S.A.S./XMY " etc.
610. 12 c. brown .. .. 35 15
611. 14 c. blue .. .. 35 20
612. 20 c. sepia .. .. 65 40
613. 23 c. purple .. .. 70 45
614. 25 c. blue .. .. 70 45
615. 29 c. green .. .. 90 45
616. 1 p. brown .. .. 3·25 2·00
DESIGN: Nos. 610/16, Douglas DC-6 airplane over Columbus Lighthouse.

**1953.** Anti-Cancer Fund. No. 619 has "1 c" larger with line through "c" and no stop. No. 620 is as 619 but with smaller "c".
618. 144. 1 c. red.. .. .. 20 10
619. 1 c. red.. .. .. 35 10
620. 1 c. red.. .. .. 15 10
See also Nos. 1029/30, 1066/7, 1171a, 1196a, 1237a, 1270a and 1338a.

145. T.B. Children's Dispensary.

**1953.** Obligatory Tax. Tuberculosis Relief Fund.
621. 145. 1 c. blue and red .. 15 10
There are two versions of this design.

146. Treasury.

149. Jose Marti.

150. Monument to Trujillo Peace. 147. Rio Haina Sugar Factory.

**1953.**
622. 146. ½ c. brown .. .. 10 10
623. 2 c. blue .. .. 10 10
624. 147. 5 c. brn. and blue .. 15 10
625. 146. 15 c. orange .. .. 50 15

**1953.** Birth Cent. of Marti (Cuban revolutionary).
629. 149. 10 c. sepia and blue .. 30 15

**1954.**
630. 150. 2 c. green .. .. 10 10
631. 7 c. blue .. .. 15 10
632. 20 c. orange .. .. 55 10
There are two versions of No. 631.

151. 152. Rotary Emblem.

**1954.** Air. Marian Year.
633. 151. 8 c. purple .. .. 15 10
634. 11 c. blue .. .. 25 10
635. 33 c. orange .. .. 70 45

**1955.** 50th Anniv. of Rotary International.
636. 152. 7 c. blue (postage) .. 30 10
637. 11 c. red (air).. .. 25 15

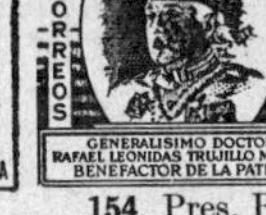

153. 154. Pres. R. Trujillo. 156. Angelita Trujillo.

**1955.** Obligatory Tax. Tuberculosis Relief Fund.
638. 153. 1 c. black, red & yellow 15 10

**1955.** 25th Year of Trujillo Era.
639. 154. 2 c. red (postage) .. 10 10
640. – 4 c. green .. .. 15 10
641. – 7 c. blue .. .. 15 10
642. – 10 c. brown .. .. 35 15
643. – 11 c. red, yell. & bl. (air) 30 10
644. – 25 c. purple .. .. 45 25
645. – 33 c. brown .. .. 70 40
DESIGNS: 4 c. Pres. R. Trujillo in civilian clothes. 7 c. Equestrian statue. 10 c. Allegory of Prosperity. 11 c. National flags. 25 c. Gen. Hector B in evening clothes. 33 c. Gen. Hector B in uniform.

**1955.** Child Welfare.
654. 156. 1 c. violet .. .. 15 10

157. Angelita Trujillo. 158. Gen. R. Trujillo.

**1955.** Peace and Brotherhood Fair, Ciudad Trujillo.
656. 158. 7 c. purple (postage) .. 25 10
657. 10 c. green .. .. 35 15
655. 157. 10 c. blue and ultram. 35 15
658. 158. 11 c. red (air) .. .. 25 10

159. " B.C.G. " = " Bacillus " Calmette-Guerin. 160. Punta Caucedo Airport.

**1956.** Obligatory Tax, Tuberculosis Relief Fund.
659. 159. 1 c. multicoloured .. 15 10

**1956.** 3rd Caribbean Region Aerial Navigation Conf.
660. 160. 1 c. brown (postage).. 10 10
661. 2 c. orange .. .. 20 10
662. 11 c. blue (air) .. 35 10

161. Cedar Tree. 162. Fanny Blankers-Koen and Dutch Flag.

**1956.** Re-afforestation. Inscr. "REPOBLACION FORESTAL".
664. 161. 5 c. green, brown and red (postage) .. 20 10
665. – 6 c. green and purple.. 25 10
666. – 13 c. grn. & orge. (air) 35 10
DESIGNS: 6 c. Pine tree. 13 c. Mahogany tree.

**1957.** Olympic Games (1st issue). Famous Athletes. Flags in national colours.
667. 162. 1 c. multicoloured (postage) .. .. 10 10
668. – 2 c. sepia, purple & blue 10 10
669. – 3 c. purple and red .. 15 15
670. – 5 c. orge., pur. & blue 25 15
671. – 7 c. green and purple.. 35 25
673. – 11 c. blue and red (air) 20 20
674. – 16 c. red and green .. 30 30
675. – 17 c. black and purple 40 40
DESIGNS—(each with national flag of athlete): 2 c. Jesse Owens. 3 c. Kee Chung Sohn. 5 c. Lord Burghley. 7 c. Bob Mathias. 11 c. Paavo Nurmi. 16 c. Ugo Frigerio. 17 c. Mildred Didrickson.
See also Nos. 689/96, 713/21, 748/56 and 784/91.

163. Horse's Head and Globe. 165.

**1957.** 2nd Int. Livestock Fair, Ciudad Trujillo.
677. 163. 7 c. blue, brown & red 25 10

**1957.** Hungarian Refugees Fund. Nos. 667/75 surch. with red cross in circle surrounded by **ASISTENCIA REFUGIADOS HUNGAROS 1957** and **+2c.**
678. 162. 1 c.+2 c. (postage) .. 10 10
679. – 2 c.+2 c. .. .. 10 10
680. – 3 c.+2 c. .. .. 10 10
681. – 5 c.+2 c. .. .. 15 15
682. – 7 c.+2 c. .. .. 25 25
684. – 11 c.+2 c. (air) .. 40 40
685. – 16 c.+2 c. .. .. 40 40
686. – 17 c.+2 c. .. .. 1·50 1·50

**1957.** Obligatory Tax. Tuberculosis Relief Fund.
688. 165. 1 c. multicoloured .. 15 10

166. Chris Brasher and Union Jack (steeplechase).

**1957.** Olympic Games (2nd issue). Winning Athletes. Inscr. " MELBOURNE 1956 ". Flags in national colours.
689. – 1 c brown & blue (post.) 10 10
690. – 2 c. red and blue .. 10 10
691. – 3 c. blue .. .. 10 10
692. – 5 c. olive and blue .. 15 10
693. – 7 c. red and blue .. 25 15
694. – 11 c. grn. & blue (air) 20 20
695. 166. 16 c. purple and blue 25 25
696. – 17 c. sepia and green 30 30
DESIGNS—(each with national flag of athlete): 1 c. Lars Hall (Sweden; pentathlon). 2 c. Betty Cuthbert (Australia; 100 and 200 metres). 3 c. Egil Danielson (Norway; javelin-throwing). 5 c. Alain Mimoum (France; marathon). 7 c. Norman Read (New Zealand; 50 km. walk). 11 c. Robert Morrow (U.S.A.; 100 and 200 metres). 17 c. A. Ferreira da Silva (Brazil; hop, step and jump).

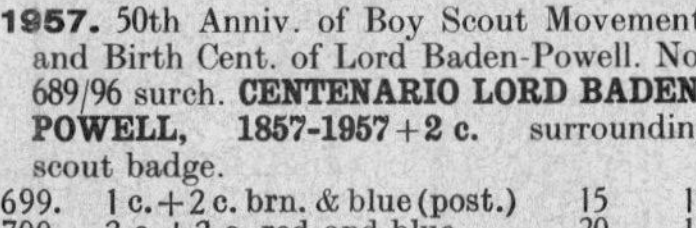

**1957.** 50th Anniv. of Boy Scout Movement, and Birth Cent. of Lord Baden-Powell. Nos 689/96 surch. **CENTENARIO LORD BADEN-POWELL, 1857-1957+2 c.** surrounding scout badge.

699. 1 c.+2 c. brn. & blue (post.) 15 15
700. 2 c.+2 c. red and blue .. 20 15
701. 3 c.+2 c. blue .. .. 25 25
702. 5 c.+2 c. olive and blue .. 35 25
703. 7 c.+2 c. red and blue .. 40 30
704. 11 c.+2 c. grn. & blue (air) 40 35
705. 16 c.+2 c. purple and blue 50 50
706. 17 c.+2 c. sepia and green 55 55

168. Mahogany Flower.

**1957.**

709. **168.** 2 c. red and green .. 10 10
710. 4 c. red and mauve .. 10 10
711. 7 c. green and blue .. 25 10
712. 25 c. orange and brown 55 25

169. Gerald Ouellette and Canadian Flag (rifle-shooting).

**1957.** Olympic Games (3rd issue). More winning athletes. Flags in national colours.

713. **169.** 1 c. brown (postage) .. 10 10
714. – 2 c. sepia .. .. 10 10
715. – 3 c. violet .. .. 10 10
716. – 5 c. orange .. .. 15 15
717. – 7 c. slate .. .. 20 20
719. – 11 c. blue (air) .. 20 15
720. – 16 c. red .. .. 30 30
721. – 17 c. purple .. .. 35 35

DESIGNS—(each with national flag of athlete): 2 c. Ron Delaney (Ireland; 1500 metres). 3 c. Tenley Albright (U.S.A.; figure-skating). 5 c. J. Capilla (Mexico; high-diving). 7 c. Ercole Baldini (Italy; cycle-racing). 11 c. Hans Winkler (Germany; horse-jumping). 16 c. Alfred Oerter (U.S.A.; discus-throwing). 17 c. Shirley Strickland (Australia; 80 metres hurdles). The designs of Nos. 714, 716 and 720 are arranged with the long side of the triangular format uppermost.

170.

171. Cervantes, Open Book, Marker and Globe.

**1958.** Tuberculosis Relief Fund.

723. **170.** 1 c. red and claret .. 10 10

See also No. 763.

**1958.** 4th Latin-American Book Fair.

724. **171.** 4 c. green .. .. 10 10
725. 7 c. mauve .. .. 15 10
726. 10 c. bistre .. .. 25 10

**1958.** U.N. Relief and Works Agency for Palestine Refugees. Nos. 713/21 surch.

A. For Jewish Refugees. Star of David and **REFUGIADOS**.

727. 1 c.+2 c. brown (postage) 15 15
728. 2 c.+2 c. brown .. 20 20
729. 3 c.+2 c. violet .. 20 20
730. 5 c.+2 c. orange .. 25 25
731. 7 c.+2 c. blue .. 35 35
732. 11 c.+2 c. blue (air) 25 25
733. 16 c.+2 c. red .. 35 35
734. 17 c.+2 c. purple .. 40 40

B. For Arab Refugees. Red Crescent and **REFUGIADOS**

735. 1 c.+2 c. brown (postage) 15 15
736. 2 c.+2 c. brown .. 20 20
737. 3 c.+2 c. violet .. 20 20
738. 5 c.+2 c. orange .. 25 25
739. 7 c.+2 c. blue .. 35 35
740. 11 c.+2 c. blue (air) 25 25
741. 16 c.+2 c. red .. 35 35
742. 17 c.+2 c. purple .. 40 40

**HAVE YOU READ THE NOTES AT THE BEGINNING OF THIS CATALOGUE?**

These often provide answers to the enquiries we receive.

172. Gen. R. Trujillo and Arms of Republic.

173. "Rhadames" (freighter).

**1958.** 25th Anniv. of Gen Trujillo's designation as "Benefactor of the Country".

743. **172.** 2 c. mauve and yellow 10 10
744. 4 c. green and yellow .. 10 10
745. 7 c. sepia and yellow .. 15 10

**1958.** Merchant Marine Day.

747. **173.** 7 c. blue .. .. 75 20

175.

174. Gillian Sheen and Union Jack (fencing).

176. Dominican Republic Pavilion.

**1958.** Olympic Games (4th issue). More winning athletes. Flags in national colours.

748. **174.** 1 c. slate, blue and red (postage) .. .. 10 10
749. – 2 c. brown and blue .. 10 10
750. – 3 c. multicoloured .. 15 15
751. – 5 c. multicoloured .. 20 20
752. – 7 c. multicoloured .. 25 25
754. – 11 c. sepia, olive and blue (air) .. 25 25
755. – 16 c. blue, orge. & grn. 30 30
756. – 17 c. blue, yell. and red 75 40

DESIGNS (each with national flag of athlete)—VERT. 2 c. Milton Campbell (U.S.A., decathlon). HORIZ. 3 c. Shozo Sasahara (Japan, feather-weight wrestling). 5 c. Madeleine Berthod (Switzerland, skiing). 7 c. Murray Rose (Australia, 400 m. and 1,500 m. freestyle). 11 c. Charles Jenkins and Thomas Courtney (U.S.A., 400 m. and 800 m., and 1,600 m. relay). 16 c. Indian team in play (India, hockey). 17 c. Swedish yachts (Sweden, yachting).

**1958.** Inaug. of U.N.E.S.C.O. Headquarters Building, Paris.

758. **175.** 7 c. blue and red .. 15 10

**1958.** Brussels International Exhibition.

759. **176.** 7 c. green (postage) .. 20 15
760. 9 c. grey (air) .. .. 20 15
761. 25 c. violet .. .. 50 30

**1959.** Obligatory Tax. Tuberculosis Relief Fund. As T **170** but inscr. "1959".

763. **170.** 1 c. red and lake .. 15 10

**1959.** I.G.Y. Nos. 748/56 surch. with globe and **ANO GEOFISICO INTERNACIONAL 1957-1958 + 2 c.**

764. 1 c.+2 c. (postage) .. 25 25
765. 2 c.+2 c. .. .. 30 30
766. 3 c.+2 c. .. .. 35 35
767. 5 c.+2 c. .. .. 40 40
768. 7 c.+2 c. .. .. 45 45
770. 11 c.+2 c. (air) .. 50 50
771. 16 c.+2 c. .. .. 70 70
772. 17 c.+2 c. .. .. 1·00 1·00

178. Leonidas R. Trujillo (Team Captain).

179. Gen. Trujillo before National Shrine.

**1959.** Jamaican-Dominican Republic Polo Match, Trujillo City. Inscr. as in T **178.**

774. **178.** 2 c. violet (postage) .. 15 10
775. – 7 c. brown .. .. 30 15
776. – 10 c. green .. .. 35 25
777. – 11 c. orange (air) .. 30 25

DESIGNS—HORIZ. 7 c. Jamaican team. 10 c. Dominican Republic team's captain on horseback. 11 c. Dominican Republic team.

**1959.** 29th Year of Trujillo Era.

778. **179.** 9 c. multicoloured .. 20 10

180. Gen. Trujillo and Cornucopia.

**1959.** National Census of 1960. Centres in black, red and blue. Frame colours given.

780. **180.** 1 c. pale blue .. 15 10
781. 9 c. green .. .. 30 15
782. 13 c. orange .. .. 35 25

181. Trujillo Stadium.

**1959.** 3rd Pan-American Games. Chicago.

783. **181.** 9 c. black and green .. 35 20

**1959.** Third Pan-American Games, Chicago. Nos. 667/71 and 673/5, surch. **III JUEGOS DEPORTIVOS PANAMERICANOS + 2** and runner.

784. **162.** 1 c.+2 c. mult. (post.) 15 15
785. – 3 c.+2 c. mult. .. 15 15
786. 3 c.+2 c. pur. & red 15 15
787. – 5 c.+2 c. mult. .. 15 15
788. – 7 c.+2 c. mult. .. 20 20
789. – 11 c.+2 c. blue, red & orge. (air) .. .. 20 20
790. – 16 c.+2 c. red, green & carmine .. .. 30 30
791. – 17 c.+2 c. mult. .. 30 30

182. Emperor Charles V.

183. Rhadames Bridge.

**1959.** 4th Death Cent. of Emperor Charles V.

792. **182.** 5 c. mauve .. .. 15 10
793. 9 c. blue .. .. 15 10

**1959.** Opening of Rhadames Bridge.

794. – 1 c. black and green .. 10 10
795. **183.** 2 c. black and blue .. 15 10
796. – 2 c. black and red .. 15 10
797. **183.** 5 c. brown and bistre 20 15

DESIGN—Nos. 794, 796, Close-up view of Rhadames Bridge.

184. Douglas DC-4 Airliner, "San Cristobal".

**1960.** Air. Dominican Civil Aviation.

798. **184.** 13 c. multicoloured .. 45 15

185.

**1960.** Obligatory Tax. Tuberculosis Relief Fund.

779. **185.** 1 c. red, blue and cream .. .. 20 15

186. Sosua Refugee Colony.

**1960.** World Refugee Year. Inscr. "ANO MUNDIAL DE LOS REFUGIADOS". Centres in black.

800. **186.** 5 c. grn. & brn. (post.) 10 10
801. 9 c. blue, purple & red 20 10
802. 13 c. grn., brn. & orge. 25 15
803. – 10 c. green, mve. & pur. (air) .. .. .. 35 30
804. – 13 c. green and grey .. 45 35

DESIGN: Nos. 802/803, Refugee children.

**1960.** World Refugee Year Fund. Nos. 800/4 surch. + **5** with **c** below.

805. **186.** 5 c.+5 c. green and brown (postage) .. 15 15
806. 9 c.+5 c. bl., pur. & red 20 20
807. 13 c.+5 c. green, brown and orange .. .. 40 40
808. – 10 c.+5 c. grn., mauve and purple (air) .. 25 25
809. – 13 c.+5 c. grn. & grey 30 30

188. General Post Office, Ciudad Trujillo.

**1960.**

811. **188.** 2 c. black and blue .. 10 10

189. Cattle in Street.

**1960.** Agricultural and Industrial Fair, San Juan de la Maguana.

812. **189.** 9 c. black and red .. 25 15

190. Gholam Takhti (Iran; lightweight wrestling).

192.

**1960.** Olympic Games, 1960. More Winning Athletes of Olympic Games, Melbourne, 1956. Flags in national colours.

813. **190.** 1 c. black, green and red (postage) .. 10 10
814. – 2 c. brn., turq. & orge. 10 10
815. – 3 c. blue and red .. 10 10
816. – 5 c. brown and blue .. 15 15
817. – 7 c. brn., blue & green 15 15
819. – 11 c. brown, grey and blue (air) .. .. 20 20
820. – 16 c. green, brown & red 25 25
821. – 17 c. ochre, blue & blk. 30 30

DESIGNS (each with national flag of athlete): 2 c. Mauru Furukawa (Japan 200 m. breast-stroke swimming). 3 c. Mildred McDaniel (U.S.A., high jump). 5 c. Terence Spinks (spelt "Terrence" on stamp) (Great Britain, feather weight boxing). 7 c. Carlo Pavesi (Italy, fencing). 11 c. Pat McCormick (U.S.A., high diving). 16 c. Mithat Bayrack (Turkey, Greco-Roman welterweight wrestling). 17 c. Ursula Happe (Germany, women's 200 m. breaststroke swimming).

**1961.** Surch. **HABILITADA PARA** and value.

823. – 2 c. on 1 c. black and green (No. 794) .. 15 10
824. **168.** 9 c. on 4 c. red & mauve 45 10
825. 9 c. on 7 c. green & blue 45 15
826. **146.** 36 c. on ½ c. brown .. 1·50 70
827. **127.** 1 p. on 50 c. yellow .. 3·25 1·90

**1961.** Obligatory Tax. Tuberculosis Relief Fund.

828. **192.** 1 c. red and blue .. 10 10

See also No. 876.

193. Madame Trujillo and Houses.

**1961.** Welfare Fund.

829. **193.** 1 c. red .. .. .. 20 10

194.

195. Coffee Plant and Cocoa Beans.

**1961.**

| | | | | |
|---|---|---|---|---|
| 830. | 194. | 1 c. brown .. .. | 10 | 10 |
| 831. | | 2 c. myrtle .. .. | 10 | 10 |
| 832. | | 4 c. purple .. .. | 40 | 35 |
| 833. | | 5 c. blue .. .. | 25 | 10 |
| 834. | | 9 c. orange .. .. | 30 | 20 |

**1961.** Obligatory Tax. Child Welfare. As Nos. 627/8 but with "ERA DE TRUJILLO" omitted.

(a) Size 23½ × 32 mm.

| | | | | |
|---|---|---|---|---|
| 835. | 148a. | 1 c. blue .. .. | 15 | 10 |

(b) Size 21½ × 32 mm.

| | | | | |
|---|---|---|---|---|
| 907. | 148b. | 1 c. blue .. .. | 15 | 10 |

**1961.**

| | | | | |
|---|---|---|---|---|
| 836. | 195. | 1 c. green (postage) .. | 10 | 10 |
| 837. | | 2 c. brown .. .. | 10 | 10 |
| 838. | | 4 c. violet .. .. | 10 | 10 |
| 839. | | 5 c. blue .. .. | 10 | 10 |
| 840. | | 9 c. grey .. .. | 25 | 10 |
| 841. | | 13 c. red (air) .. .. | 25 | 25 |
| 842. | | 33 c. yellow .. .. | 55 | 55 |

**1961.** 15th Anniv. of U.N.E.S.C.O. Nos. 813/21 surch. **XV ANIVERSARIO DE LA UNESCO + 2c.**

| | | | |
|---|---|---|---|
| 843. | 1 c. + 2 c. (postage) .. | 10 | 10 |
| 844. | 2 c. + 2 c. .. .. | 10 | 10 |
| 845. | 3 c. + 2 c. .. .. | 10 | 10 |
| 846. | 5 c. + 2 c. .. .. | 15 | 15 |
| 847. | 7 c. + 2 c. .. .. | 15 | 15 |
| 849. | 11 c. + 2 c. (air) .. | 25 | 25 |
| 850. | 16 c. + 2 c. .. .. | 35 | 35 |
| 851. | 17 c. + 2 c. .. .. | 35 | 35 |

197. Mosquito and Dagger.

198. Plantation.

**1962.** Malaria Eradication.

| | | | | |
|---|---|---|---|---|
| 853. | 197. | 10 c. mauve (postage) | 15 | 10 |
| 854. | | 10 c. + 2 c. mauve .. | 20 | 15 |
| 855. | | 20 c. sepia .. .. | 35 | 30 |
| 856. | | 20 c. + 2 c. sepia .. | 35 | 25 |
| 857. | | 25 c. green .. .. | 45 | 55 |
| 858. | | 13 c. red (air) .. .. | 25 | 20 |
| 859. | | 13 c. + 2 c. red .. | 25 | 25 |
| 860. | | 33 c. orange .. .. | 50 | 50 |
| 861. | | 33 c. + 2 c. orange .. | 60 | 60 |

**1962.** Farming and Industrial Development. Flag in red and blue.

| | | | | |
|---|---|---|---|---|
| 863. | 198. | 1 c. green and blue .. | 10 | 10 |
| 864. | | 2 c. red and blue .. | 10 | 10 |
| 865. | | 3 c. brown and blue .. | 10 | 10 |
| 866. | | 5 c. blue .. .. | 15 | 10 |
| 867. | | 15 c. orange and blue | 25 | 15 |

199. Laurel Sprig and Broken Link.

DESIGNS — VERT. 9 c., 1 p. "Justice" on map. HORIZ. 20 c., 50 c. Flag and flaming torch.

**1962.** 1st Anniv. of Assassination of Pres. Trujillo.

| | | | | |
|---|---|---|---|---|
| 868. | 199. | 1 c. multicoloured (postage) .. .. | 10 | 10 |
| 869. | – | 9 c. red, blue and ochre | 25 | 15 |
| 870. | – | 20 c. red, blue & turq. | 45 | 25 |
| 871. | – | 1 p. red, blue & violet | 2·75 | 1·60 |
| 873. | 199. | 13 c. multicoloured (air) | 25 | 20 |
| 874. | – | 50 c. red, blue & mauve | 1·00 | 70 |

200. Map and Laurel.

201. U.P.A.E. Emblem.

**1962.** Martyrs of June 1959 Revolution.

| | | | | |
|---|---|---|---|---|
| 875. | 200. | 1 c. black .. .. | 25 | 15 |

**1962.** Tuberculosis Relief Fund. As No. 828 but inscr. "1962".

| | | | | |
|---|---|---|---|---|
| 876. | 192. | 1 c. red and blue .. | 10 | 10 |

**1962.** 50th Anniv. of Postal Union of the Americas and Spain.

| | | | | |
|---|---|---|---|---|
| 877. | 201. | 2 c. red (postage) .. | 10 | 10 |
| 878. | | 9 c. orange .. .. | 25 | 15 |
| 879. | | 14 c. turquoise .. | 25 | 20 |
| 880. | | 13 c. blue (air) .. | 35 | 20 |
| 881. | | 22 c. brown .. .. | 45 | 40 |

202. Archbishop Nouel.

203. Globe, Riband and Campaign Emblem.

**1962.** Birth Cent. of Archbishop Adolfo Nouel.

| | | | | |
|---|---|---|---|---|
| 882. | 202. | 2 c. myrtle & grn. (post.) | 10 | 10 |
| 883. | | 9 c. brown and orange | 25 | 15 |
| 884. | | 13 c. purple and brown | 30 | 20 |
| 885. | – | 12 c. blue (air) .. | 35 | 20 |
| 886. | – | 25 c. violet .. .. | 50 | 40 |

DESIGN: Air stamps as Type 202 but different frame.

**1963.** Freedom from Hunger. Riband in red and blue.

| | | | | |
|---|---|---|---|---|
| 888. | 203. | 2 c. green .. .. | 10 | 10 |
| 891. | | 2 c. + 1 c. green .. | 10 | 10 |
| 889. | | 5 c. mauve .. .. | 15 | 10 |
| 892. | | 5 c. + 2 c. mauve .. | 20 | 20 |
| 890. | | 9 c. orange .. .. | 25 | 15 |
| 893. | | 9 c. + 2 c. orange .. | 20 | 20 |

204. Duarte.

205. Espaillat, de Rojas and Bono.

**1963.** 120th Anniv. of Separation from Haiti.

| | | | | |
|---|---|---|---|---|
| 895. | 204. | 2 c. blue (postage) .. | 10 | 10 |
| 896. | – | 7 c. green (Sanchez) .. | 15 | 15 |
| 897. | – | 9 c. purple (Mella) .. | 15 | 15 |
| 898. | – | 15 c. salmon (air) .. | 20 | 15 |

DESIGN—HORIZ. 15 c. Sanchez, Duarte and Mella.

**1963.** "Centenary of the Restoration".

| | | | | |
|---|---|---|---|---|
| 899. | 205. | 2 c. green .. .. | 10 | 10 |
| 900. | – | 4 c. red .. .. | 10 | 10 |
| 901. | – | 5 c. brown .. .. | 10 | 10 |
| 902. | – | 9 c. blue .. .. | 15 | 15 |

DESIGNS: 4 c. Rodriguez, Cabrera and Moncion. 5 c. Capotillo Monument. 9 c. Polanco, Luperon and Salcedo.

206. Nurse tending Patient.

207.

**1963.** Centenary of Red Cross. Cross in red.

| | | | | |
|---|---|---|---|---|
| 904. | 206. | 3 c. grey (postage) .. | 10 | 10 |
| 905. | | 6 c. green .. .. | 15 | 10 |
| 906. | – | 10 c. grey (air) .. | 25 | 20 |

DESIGN—HORIZ. 10 c. Map of continents bordering Atlantic.

**1963.** Obligatory Tax. T.B. Relief Fund.

| | | | | |
|---|---|---|---|---|
| 908. | 207. | 1 c. red and blue .. | 15 | 10 |

208. Scales of Justice and Globe.

**1963.** 15th Anniv. of Declaration of Human Rights.

| | | | | |
|---|---|---|---|---|
| 911. | 208. | 6 c. red (postage) .. | 15 | 10 |
| 912. | | 50 c. green .. .. | 80 | 55 |
| 913. | | 7 c. brown (air) .. | 20 | 15 |
| 914. | | 10 c. blue .. .. | 25 | 15 |

209. Rameses II in War Chariot, Abu Simbel.

**1964.** Nubian Monuments Preservation. Designs as T 209, also surch 2c in circle.

| | | | | |
|---|---|---|---|---|
| 915. | 209. | 3 c. red (postage) .. | 10 | 10 |
| 916. | | 3 c. + 2 c. red .. .. | 15 | 15 |
| 917. | – | 6 c. blue .. .. | 15 | 10 |
| 918. | – | 6 c. + 2 c. blue .. | 15 | 15 |
| 919. | 209. | 9 c. brown .. .. | 20 | 15 |
| 920. | | 9 c. + 2 c. brown .. | 25 | 25 |
| 921. | – | 10 c. violet (air) .. | 25 | 20 |
| 922. | – | 10 c. + 2 c. violet .. | 20 | 20 |
| 923. | – | 13 c. yellow .. .. | 25 | 20 |
| 924. | – | 13 c. + 2 c. yellow .. | 25 | 25 |

DESIGNS—HORIZ. 6 c. Heads of Rameses II. VERT. 10 c., 13 c. As Type 209.

211. M. Gomez (founder).

212. Palm Chat.

**1964.** Bicent. of Bani Foundation.

| | | | | |
|---|---|---|---|---|
| 925. | 211. | 2 c. blue & light blue | 10 | 10 |
| 926. | | 6 c. purple and brown | 15 | 10 |

**1964.** Dominican Birds. Multicoloured.

| | | | |
|---|---|---|---|
| 927. | 1 c. Narrow-billed tody (postage) .. .. | 45 | 20 |
| 928. | 2 c. Hispaniolan emerald .. | 80 | 20 |
| 929. | 3 c. Type 212 .. .. | 95 | 20 |
| 930. | 6 c. Hispaniolan amazon .. | 1·25 | 30 |
| 931. | 6 c. Hispaniolan trogons .. | 1·25 | 30 |
| 932. | 10 c. Hispaniolan woodpecker (air) .. .. | 1·40 | 50 |

The 1 c, 2 c. and 6 c. (No. 931) are smaller (26 × 37½ mm.); the 10 c. is horiz. (43½ × 27½ mm.).

213. Rocket.

214. Pres. Kennedy

**1964.** "Conquest of Space".

| | | | | |
|---|---|---|---|---|
| 933. | – | 1 c. blue (postage) .. | 10 | 10 |
| 934. | 213. | 2 c. green .. .. | 10 | 10 |
| 935. | – | 3 c. blue .. .. | 15 | 10 |
| 936. | 213. | 6 c. blue .. .. | 25 | 15 |
| 937. | 213. | 7 c. green (air) .. | 25 | 25 |
| 938. | – | 10 c. blue .. .. | 35 | 70 |

DESIGNS—VERT. 1 c. Rocket launching. HORIZ. 3 c., 10 c. Capsule in orbit.

**1964.** Air. Pres. Kennedy Commem.

| | | | | |
|---|---|---|---|---|
| 940. | 214. | 10 c. brown and buff .. | 35 | 25 |

215. U.P.U. Monument, Berne.

**1964.** 15th U.P.U. Congress, Vienna.

| | | | | |
|---|---|---|---|---|
| 941. | 215. | 1 c. red (postage) .. | 10 | 10 |
| 942. | | 4 c. green .. .. | 15 | 10 |
| 943. | | 5 c. orange .. .. | 15 | 10 |
| 944. | | 7 c. blue (air) .. .. | 15 | 10 |

216. I.C.Y. Emblem.

217. Hands and Lily.

**1965.** Int. Co-operation Year.

| | | | | |
|---|---|---|---|---|
| 945. | 216. | 2 c. blue and light-blue (postage) .. .. | 10 | 10 |
| 946. | | 3 c. green and emerald | 10 | 10 |
| 947. | | 6 c. red and pink .. | 15 | 10 |
| 948. | | 10 c. violet & lilac (air) | 25 | 20 |

**1965.** 4th Mariological and 11th Int. Marian Congresses. Multicoloured.

| | | | |
|---|---|---|---|
| 949 | 2 c. Type 217 (postage) .. | 10 | 10 |
| 950 | 6 c. Virgin of the Altagracia .. .. | 35 | 25 |
| 951 | 10 c. Douglas DC-8 airliner over Basilica of Virgin of Altagracia (39½ × 31½ mm) (air) .. .. | 30 | 15 |

218. Flags Emblem.

219. Lincoln.

**1965.** 75th Anniv. of Organization of American States.

| | | | | |
|---|---|---|---|---|
| 952. | 218. | 2 c. multicoloured .. | 10 | 10 |
| 953. | | 6 c. multicoloured .. | 15 | 10 |

**1965.** Air. Death Cent. of Abraham Lincoln.

| | | | | |
|---|---|---|---|---|
| 954. | 219. | 17 c. grey and blue .. | 35 | 25 |

220. ½ r. Stamp of 1865.

221. Hibiscus.

**1965.** Stamp Cent.

| | | | | |
|---|---|---|---|---|
| 955 | 220 | 1 c. multicoloured (post.) | 10 | 10 |
| 956 | | 2 c. multicoloured .. | 10 | 10 |
| 957 | | 6 c. multicoloured .. | 15 | 10 |
| 958 | – | 7 c. multicoloured (air) | 25 | 20 |
| 959 | – | 10 c. multicoloured .. | 25 | 25 |

DESIGN: 7 c., 10 c. As Type 220, but showing 1 r. stamp of 1865.

**1966.** Obligatory Tax. Tuberculosis Relief Fund.

| | | | | |
|---|---|---|---|---|
| 963. | 221. | 1 c. red and green .. | 15 | 10 |
| 999. | – | 1 c. mauve, lilac & red | 10 | 10 |
| 1015. | – | 1 c. multicoloured .. | 10 | 10 |
| 1016. | – | 1 c. multicoloured .. | 10 | 10 |
| 1017. | – | 1 c. multicoloured .. | 10 | 10 |

DESIGN: (21½ × 30 mm.). No. 999, Orchid. (20 × 28 mm.). No. 1015, Dogbane. No. 1016, Violets. No. 1017, "Eeanthus capitatus".

222. I.T.U. Emblem and symbols.

223. W.H.O. Building.

**1966.** Air. Cent. (1965) of I.T.U.

| | | | | |
|---|---|---|---|---|
| 964. | 222. | 28 c. red and pink .. | 55 | 40 |
| 965. | | 45 c. green & emerald | 55 | 70 |

**1965.** Inaug. of W.H.O. Headquarters, Geneva.

| | | | | |
|---|---|---|---|---|
| 966. | 223. | 6 c. blue .. .. | 15 | 10 |
| 967. | | 10 c. purple .. .. | 20 | 15 |

224. Man supporting "Republic".

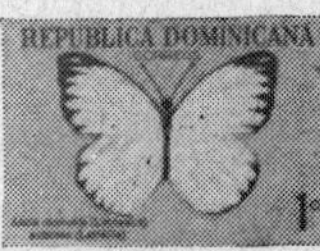

225. "Ascia monuste".

**1966.** General Elections.

| | | | | |
|---|---|---|---|---|
| 968. | 224. | 2 c. black and green .. | 10 | 10 |
| 969. | | 6 c. black and red .. | 15 | 10 |

**1966.** Butterflies. Multicoloured.

| | | | |
|---|---|---|---|
| 970. | 1 c. Type 225 (postage) .. | 10 | 10 |
| 971. | 2 c. "Heliconius charitonius" .. .. | 10 | 10 |
| 972. | 3 c. "Phoebis sennae sennae" .. .. | 15 | 15 |
| 973. | 6 c. "Anteos clorinde clorinde" .. .. | 25 | 25 |
| 974. | 8 c. "Siderone hemesis" .. | 35 | 35 |
| 975. | 10 c. "Eurema gundlachia" (air) .. .. | 45 | 25 |
| 976. | 50 c. "Clothilda pantherata pantherata" .. .. | 2·10 | 1·00 |
| 977. | 75 c. "Papilio androgeus epidaurus" .. .. | 3·00 | 1·50 |

Nos. 975/7 are larger, 35 × 24½ mm.

**1966.** Hurricane Inez Relief. Nos. 970/77. surch. **PRO DAMNIFICADOS CICLON INES** and value.

978. **225.** 1 c.+2 c. mult. (post.) 15 10
979. – 2 c.+2 c. multicoloured 15 10
980. – 3 c.+2 c. multicoloured 15 10
981. – 6 c.+4 c. multicoloured 30 25
982. – 8 c.+4 c. multicoloured 40 30

983. – 10 c.+5 c. mult. (air) .. 40 35
984. – 50 c.+10 c. mult. .. 1·40 1·40
985. – 75 c.+10 c. mult. .. 1·75 1·75

**227.** National Shrine. **228.** Emblem and Map.

**1967.** (a) Postage.

986. **227.** 1 c. blue .. .. 10 10
987. 2 c. red .. .. 10 10
988. 3 c. green .. .. 10 10
989. 4 c. grey .. .. 10 10
990. 5 c. yellow .. .. 10 10
991. 6 c. orange .. .. 10 10

(b) Air. Size 20½ × 25 mm.

992. **227.** 7 c. olive .. .. 15 10
993. 10 c. lilac .. .. 15 15
994. 20 c. brown .. .. 30 25

**1967.** Development Year. Emblem and map in black and blue.

996. **228.** 2 c. orange and yellow 10 10
997. 6 c. orange .. .. 15 10
998. 10 c. green .. .. 25 15

**229.** Rook and Knight. **230.** Civil Defence Emblem.

**1967.** 5th Central American Chess Championship, Santo Domingo.

1000. **229.** 25 c. multicoloured (postage) .. .. 55 40
1001. – 10 c. blk. & olive (air) 35 25

DESIGN: 10 c. Bishop and pawn.

**1967.** Obligatory Tax. Civil Defence Fund.

1003. **230.** 1 c. multicoloured .. 15 15

**231.** Alliance Emblem. **232.** Institute Emblem.

**1967.** 6th Anniv. of "Alliance for Progress".

1004. **231.** 1 c. green (postage) .. 10 10
1005. 8 c. grey (air) .. 15 10
1006. 10 c. blue .. 20 15

**1967.** 25th Anniv. of Inter-American Agricultural Institute.

1007. **232.** 3 c. green (postage) .. 10 10
1008. 6 c. pink .. .. 15 10
1009. – 12 c. mult. (air) .. 20 15

DESIGN: 12 c. Emblem and cornucopia.

**233.** Child and Children's Home. **234.** Hand Holding Invalid.

**1967.** Obligatory Tax. Child Welfare.

1010. **233.** 1 c. red .. .. 25 10
1010a. 1 c. orange .. .. 15 10
1011. 1 c. violet .. .. 10 10
1011a. 1 c. brown .. .. 15 10
1037. 1 c. green .. .. 10 10

See also No. 1278a.

**1968.** Obligatory Tax. Rehabilitation of the Handicapped.

1012. **234.** 1 c. yellow and green 10 10
1013. 1 c. blue .. .. 10 10
1014. 1 c. bright purple .. 10 10
1015. 1 c. brown .. .. 10 10

**236.** W.M.O. Emblem.

**1968.** World Meteorological Day.

1019. **236.** 6 c. mult. (postage) .. 20 15
1020. 10 c. multicoloured (air) 25 20
1021. 15 c. multicoloured 35 25

**237.** Ortiz v. Cruz. **238.** "Lions" Emblem.

**1968.** World Lightweight Boxing Championship. Designs showing similar scenes of the contest.

1024. **237.** 6 c. purple & red (post.) 15 15
1025. – 7 c. green & yellow (air) 15 10
1026. – 10 c. blue and agate .. 25 15

**1968.** Lions Int.

1027. **238.** 6 c. mult. (postage) .. 15 10
1028. 10 c. multicoloured (air) 25 15

**1968.** Obligatory Tax. Anti-Cancer Fund.

1029. **144.** 1 c. green .. .. 10 10
1030. 1 c. orange .. .. 10 10

**239.** Wrestling.

**1968.** Olympic Games, Mexico. Multicoloured.

1031. 1 c. Type **239** (postage) .. 10 10
1032. 6 c. Running .. .. 15 10
1033. 25 c. Boxing .. .. 70 35
1034. 10 c. Weightlifting (air) .. 25 25
1035. 33 c. Pistol-shooting .. 80 70

**240.** Map of Americas and House. **241.** Carved Stool.

**1969.** 7th Inter-American Savings and Loans Congress, Santo Domingo. Multicoloured.

1038. 6 c. Type **240** (postage) .. 15 10
1039. 10 c. Latin-American flags (air) .. .. .. 25 15

**1969.** Taino Art. Multicoloured.

1040. 1 c. Type **241** (postage) .. 10 10
1041. 2 c. Female idol .. .. 10 10
1042. 3 c. Three-cornered foot-stone .. .. 10 10
1043. 4 c. Stone axe .. .. 15 10
1044. 5 c. Clay pot .. .. 15 15
1045. 7 c. Spatula and carved handles (air) .. .. 25 10
1046. 10 c. Breast-shaped vessel 35 25
1047. 20 c. Figured vase .. 35 75

The 2, 4, 7 and 20 c. are vert.

**242.** School Playground and Torch. **243.** Community Emblem.

**1969.** Obligatory Tax. Education Year.

1048. **242.** 1 c. blue .. .. 10 10

**1969.** Community Development Day.

1049. **243.** 6 c. gold and green .. 15 10

**244.** C.O.T.A.L. Emblem. **245.** I.L.O. Emblem.

**1969.** 12th C.O.T.A.L. (Confederation of Latin American Tourist Organizations) Congress, Santo Domingo.

1050. **244** 1 c. blue, red and light blue (post.) .. 10 10
1051. – 2 c. bright grn. & grn. 10 10
1052. – 6 c. red .. .. 15 10
1053. – 10 c. brown (air) .. 30 10

DESIGNS—VERT. 2 c. Boy with flags. HORIZ. (39×31 mm.): 6 c. C.O.T.A.L. Building and emblem. 10 c. "Airport of the Americas", Santo Domingo.

**1969.** 50th Anniversary of I.L.O.

1054. **245.** 6 c. black & turquoise (post) .. .. 25 10
1055. 10 c. black & red (air) 15 15

**246.** Taking a Catch. **247.** Las Damas Hydro-electric Scheme.

**1969.** World Baseball Championships, Santo Domingo.

1056. **246.** 1 c. grey & grn. (post.) 10 10
1057. – 2 c. green .. .. 10 10
1058. – 3 c. brown and violet 10 10
1059. – 7 c. orge. & pur. (air) 20 15
1060. – 10 c. red .. .. 25 15
1061. – 1 p. brown and blue 2·00 1·40

DESIGNS—VERT. 3 c. Making for base. 10 c. Player making strike. HORIZ. (43×30½ mm.): 2 c. Cibao Stadium. 7 c. Tetelo Vargas Stadium. 1 p. Quisqueya Stadium.

**1969.** National Electrification Plan.

1062. **247.** 2 c. mult. (postage) .. 10 10
1063. – 3 c. multicoloured .. 10 10
1064. – 6 c. purple .. .. 15 10
1065. – 10 c. red (air) .. 20 10

DESIGNS—HORIZ. 3 c. Las Damas Dam. 6 c. Arroyo Hondo substation. 10 c. Haina River power station.

**1969.** Obligatory Tax. Anti-Cancer Fund. T **144** re-drawn in larger format and inscriptions.

1066. **144.** 1 c. purple .. .. 10 10
1067. 1 c. green .. .. 15 10

**248.** Tavera Dam.

**1969.** Completion of Dam Projects. Mult.

1068. 6 c. Type **248** (postage) .. 15 10
1069. 10 c. Valdesia Dam (air) 20 10

**249.** Juan Pablo Duarte. **250.** Outline Map, Arms of Census Office and Family.

**1970.** Juan Pablo Duarte (patriot). Commem.

1070. **249.** 1 c. green (postage) .. 10 10
1071. 2 c. red .. .. 10 10
1072. 3 c. purple .. .. 10 10
1073. 6 c. blue .. .. 15 10
1074. 10 c. brown (air) .. 20 15

**1970.** National Census.

1075. **250.** 5 c. blk. & grn. (post.) 10 10
1076. – 6 c. ultram. and blue 15 10
1077. – 10 c. multicoloured (air) 25 15

DESIGNS: 6 c. Arms and quotation. 10 c. Arms and buildings.

**251.** Open Book and Emblem. **252.** Abelardo Urdaneta.

**1970.** Obligatory Tax. Int. Education Year.

1078. **251.** 1 c. purple .. .. 10 10

**1970.** Birth Cent. of A. R. Urdaneta (sculptor).

1079. **252.** 3 c. blue (postage) .. 10 10
1080. – 6 c. green .. .. 15 10
1081. – 10 c. blue (air) .. 20 15

DESIGNS—HORIZ. (39½ × 27 mm.). 6 c. "One of Many" (sculpture.) VERT. (25×39 mm.). 10 c. Prisoner (statue).

**253.** Masonic Symbols. **255.** New U.P.U. Building.

**254.** Telecommunications Satellite.

**1970.** 8th Inter-American Masonic Conf. Santo Domingo.

1082. **253.** 6 c. green (postage) .. 15 10
1083. 10 c. brown (air) .. 20 10

**1970.** World Telecommunications Day.

1084. **254.** 20 c. grey and olive (postage) .. .. 50 30
1085. 7 c. grey and blue (air) 15 10

**1970.** New U.P.U. Headquarters Building, Berne.

1086. **255.** 6 c. brown and grey (postage) .. .. 15 10
1087. 10 c. brn. & yell. (air) 15 10

**256.** I.E.Y. Emblem. **257.** Pedro Alejandrino Pina.

**1970.** Int. Education Year.

1088. **256.** 4 c. purple (postage) 10 10
1089. 15 c. mauve (air) .. 20 15

**1970.** 150th Birth Anniv. and Death Cent. of Pedro A. Pina (writer).

1090. **257.** 6 c. black & brown 15 10

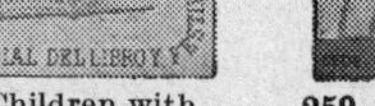

**258.** Children with Book. **259.** Emblem and Stamp Album.

**1970.** 1st World Book Exhibition, and Cultural Festival, Santo Domingo.

1091. **258.** 5 c. green (postage) .. 10 10
1092. – 7 c. multicoloured (air) 15 10
1093. – 10 c. multicoloured .. 20 15

DESIGNS: 7 c. Dancers. 10 c. U.N. emblem within "wheel".

**1970.** Air. "EXFILICA 70" Inter-American Philatelic Exn. Caracas, Venezuela.

1094. **259.** 10 c. multicoloured .. 20 15

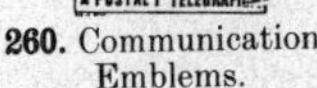

**260.** Communications Emblems. **261.** Virgin of Altagracia.

**1971.** Obligatory Tax. Postal and Telecommunications School.

(a) Size 18 × 20½ mm.

1095. **260.** 1 c. blue and red (white background) 15 10

(b) Size 19 × 22 mm.

1095a. **260.** 1 c. blue and red (red background) 15 10
1095b. 1 c. blue, red and green .. .. 15 10
1095c. 1 c. blue, red and yellow .. .. 15 10
1095d. 1 c. blue, red and mauve .. .. 15 10
1095e. 1 c. blue, red and light blue .. 10 10
1096. 1 c. blue and red (blue background) 10 10

**1971.** Inauguration of Our Lady of Altagracia Basilica. Multicoloured.

1097. 3 c. Type **261** (postage) 10 10
1098. 17 c. Basilica (22½ × 36 mm.) (air) .. 35 25

**262.** Parcel, Emblem and Map. **263.** Manuel Objio.

**1971.** Air. 25th Anniv. of C.A.R.E. (Cooperative for American Relief Everywhere).

1099. **262.** 10 c. green and blue 15 15

**1971.** Death Centenary of Manuel Rodriguez Objio (poet).

1100. **263.** 6 c. blue .. .. 15 10

**264.** Boxing and Canoeing. **265.** Goat and Fruit.

**1971.** 2nd National Games.

1101. **264.** 2 c. brown and orange (postage) .. .. 10 10
1102. – 5 c. brown and green 15 10
1103. – 7 c. purple & grey (air) 15 10

DESIGNS: 5 c. Basketball. 7 c. Volleyball.

**1971.** 6th National Agricultural Census. Multicoloured.

1104. 1 c. Type **265** (postage).. 10 10
1105. 2 c. Cow and goose .. 10 10
1106. 3 c. Cocoa pods and horse 10 10
1107. 6 c. Bananas, coffee beans and pig .. .. 15 10
1108. 25 c. Cockerel and grain (air) .. .. .. 40 30

**266.** Jose Nunez de Caceres. **267.** Shepherds and Star.

**1971.** 150th Anniv. of 1st Declaration of Independence.

1109. **266.** 6 c. bl., vio. & pale bl. (postage) .. .. 15 10
1110. – 10 c. bl., red & yellow (air) .. .. 25 20

DESIGN: 10 c. Flag of the Santo Domingo-Colombia Union.

**1971.** Christmas.

1111. **267.** 6 c. brn. yell. & bl. (post.) 15 10
1112. – 10 c. red, blk. & yell. (air) .. .. 15 15

DESIGN: 10 c. Spanish bell of 1493.

**268.** Child on Beach. **269.** Book Year Emblem.

**1971.** 25th Anniv. of U.N.I.C.E.F.

1113. **268.** 6 c. multicoloured (postage) .. .. 15 10
1114. 15 c. multicoloured (air) .. .. 25 20

**1971.** Int. Book Year.

1115. **269.** 1 c. grn, red & blue (postage) .. .. 10 10
1116. 2 c. brn., red and blue 10 10
1117. 12 c. pur., red & blue (air) .. .. 20 15

**270.** Magnifier on Map. **271.** Orchid.

**1972.** Air. "Exfilima 71" Inter American Philatelic Exn., Lima, Peru.

1118. **270.** 10 c. multicoloured.. 25 15

**1972.** Obligatory Tax. Tuberculosis Relief Fund.

1119. **271.** 1 c. multicoloured .. 10 10

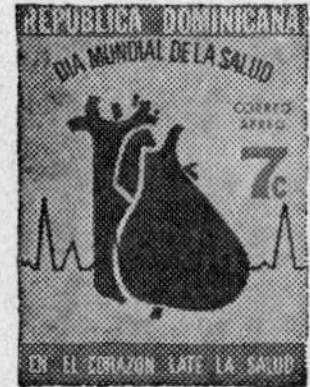

**272.** Heart Emblem. **273.** Mask.

**1972.** Air. World Health Day.

1120. **272.** 7 c. multicoloured .. 15 10

**1972.** Taino Arts and Crafts. Multicoloured.

1121 2 c. Type **273** (postage) .. 10 10
1122 4 c. Spoon and amulet .. 10 10
1123 6 c. Nasal aspirator (horiz) .. .. 10 10
1124 8 c. Ritual vase (horiz) (air) .. .. .. 15 10
1125 10 c. Atlantic trumpet triton (horiz) .. .. 30 10
1126 25 c. Ritual spatulas .. 45 25

**274.** Globe.

**1972.** World Telecommunications Day.

1127. **274.** 6 c. mult. (postage).. 15 10
1128. 21 c. multicoloured (air) 35 20

**275.** Map and "Stamps".

**1972.** 1st Nat. Stamp Exhib., Santo Domingo.

1129. **275.** 2 c. mult. (postage).. 10 10
1130. 33 c. mult. (air) .. 60 35

**276.** Basketball.

**1972.** Olympic Games, Munich. Mult.

1131. 2 c. Type **276** (postage) .. 10 10
1132. 33 c. Running (air) .. 70 40

**277.** Club Badge.

**1972.** 50th Anniv. of Int. Activo 20–30 Club.

1133. **277.** 1 c. mult. (postage).. 10 10
1134. 20 c. mult. (air) .. 35 20

**278.** Emilio Morel and Quotation.

**1972.** Morel (poet and journalist). Commem.

1135. **278.** 6 c. mult. (postage).. 15 10
1136. 10 c. mult. (air) .. 15 10

**279.** Bank Building.

**1972.** 25th Anniv. of Central Bank. Mult.

1137. 1 c. Type **279** .. .. 10 10
1138. 5 c. One-peso banknote.. 10 10
1139. 25 c. 1947 50 c. Coin and Mint .. .. .. 40 25

**280.** Nativity Scene. **281.** Student and Letter-box.

**1972.** Christmas. Multicoloured.

1140. 2 c. Type **280** (postage).. 10 10
1141. 6 c. Poinsettia (horiz.) .. 15 10
1142. 10 c. "La Navidad" Fort 1492 (horiz.) (air) .. 15 10

**1972.** Publicity for Correspondence Schools.

1143. **281.** 2 c. red and pink .. 10 10
1144. 6 c. blue and light blue 15 10
1145. 10 c. grn. and yellow 20 10

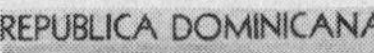

**282.** View of Dam. **283.** Invalid in Wheel-chair.

**1973.** Inaug. of Tavera Dam.

1146. **282.** 10 c. multicoloured.. 20 10

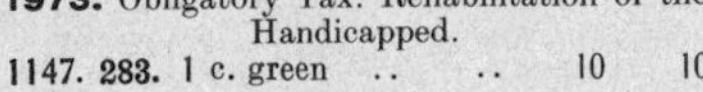

**1973.** Obligatory Tax. Rehabilitation of the Handicapped.

1147. **283.** 1 c. green .. .. 10 10

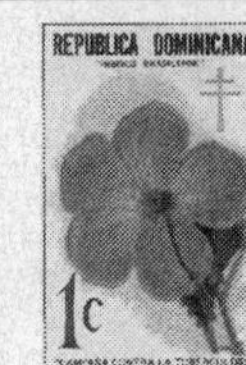

**284.** Long-jumping, Diving, Running, Cycling and Weightlifting. **285.** Hibiscus.

**1973.** 12th Central American and Caribbean Games, Santo Domingo. Multicoloured.

1148. 2 c. Type **284** (postage).. 10 10
1149. 2 c. Boxing, football, wrestling and shooting 10 10
1150. 2 c. Fencing, tennis, high-jumping and sprinting 10 10
1151. 2 c. Putting the shot, throwing the javelin and show-jumping .. 10 10
1152. 25 c. Type **284** .. .. 55 25
1153. 25 c. As No. 1149.. .. 55 25
1154. 25 c. As No. 1150.. .. 55 25
1155. 25 c. As No. 1151.. .. 55 25
1156. 8 c. Type **284** (air) .. 15 10
1157. 8 c. As No. 1149 .. .. 15 10
1158. 8 c. As No. 1150 .. .. 15 10
1159. 8 c. As No. 1151 .. .. 15 10
1160. 10 c. Type **284** .. .. 25 15
1161. 10 c. As No. 1149.. .. 25 15
1162. 10 c. As No. 1150.. .. 25 15
1163. 10 c. As No. 1151.. .. 25 15

**1973.** Obligatory Tax. Tuberculosis Relief Fund.

1164. **285.** 1 c. multicoloured .. 10 10

**286.** Christ carrying the Cross. **287.** Global Emblem.

**1973.** Easter. Multicoloured.

1165. 2 c. Type **286** (postage) 10 10
1166. 6 c. Belfry, Church of Our Lady of Carmen (vert.) 15 10
1167. 10 c. Belfry, Chapel of Our Lady of Succour (vert.) (air) .. 20 10

**1973.** Air. 70th Anniv. of Pan-American Health Organization.

1168. **287.** 7 c. multicoloured .. 15 10

**288.** Weather Zones.

**1973.** Centenary of World Meteorological Organization.

1169. **288.** 6 c. mult. (postage).. 15 10
1170. 7 c. multicoloured (air) 15 10

**289.** Forensic Scientist.

**1973.** Air. 50th Anniv. of International Criminal Police Organization (Interpol).

1171. **289.** 10 c. blue, green and light blue .. .. 20 15

**1973.** Obligatory Tax. Anti-cancer Fund. As T **144** but dated "1973"

1171a. **144.** 1 c. olive .. .. 15 10

See also Nos. 1270a and 1338a.

**290.** Maguey Drum.

**1973.** Opening of Museum of Dominican Man, Santo Domingo. Multicoloured.

1172. 1 c. Type **290** (postage) 10 10
1173. 2 c. Amber carvings .. 10 10
1174. 4 c. Cibao mask (vert.) .. 10 10
1175. 6 c. Pottery (vert.) .. 15 10
1176. 7 c. Model ship in mosaic (vert.) (air) 15 10
1177. 10 c. Maracas rattles .. 20 15

**291.** Nativity Scene.

**1973.** Christmas. Multicoloured.

1178. 2 c. Type **291** (postage).. 10 10
1179. 6 c. " Prayer " (stained-glass window) (vert.).. 15 10
1180. 10 c. Angels beside Crib (air) .. .. .. 20 15

**292.** Scout Badge.

**1973.** 50th Anniv. of Dominican Boy Scouts. Multicoloured.

1181. 1 c. Type **292** (postage).. 10 10
1182. 5 c. Scouts and flag .. 10 10
1183. 21 c. Scouts cooking, and Lord Baden Powell (air) .. .. .. 40 30

No. 1182 is smaller, size 26×36 mm.

**293.** Stadium and Basketball Players.

**294.** Belfry, Santo Domingo Cathedral.

**1974.** 12th Central American and Caribbean Games, Santo Domingo. Multicoloured.

1184. 2 c. Type **293** (postage).. 10 10
1185. 6 c. Arena and cyclist .. 15 10
1186. 10 c. Swimming pool and diver (air) .. .. 20 15
1187. 25 c. Stadium, soccer players and discus-thrower .. 50 35

**1974.** Obligatory Tax. Rehabilitation of the Handicapped. As T **283** but larger, 22×27 mm.

1187a. **283.** 1 c. blue .. .. 15 15

**1974.** Holy Week.

1188. **294.** 2 c. multicoloured (postage) .. .. 10 10
1189. – 6 c. pur., grn. & olive 15 10
1190. – 10 c. multicoloured (air) 20 15

Design—Vert: 6 c. " Sorrowful Mother " (D. Bouts). Horiz. 10 c. " The Last Supper " (R. M. Budi).

**295.** Francisco del Rosario Sanchez Bridge.

**1974.** Dominican Bridges. Multicoloured.

1191. 6 c. Type **295** (postage).. 15 10
1192. 10 c. Higuamo Bridge (air) 20 15

**296.** Emblem and Patient.

**1974.** Anti-Diabetes Campaign. Mult.

1193. 4 c. Type **296** (postage).. 10 10
1194. 5 c. Emblem and pancreas 10 10
1195. 7 c. Emblem and kidney (air) 15 10
1196. 33 c. Emblem, eye and heart 70 45

**1974.** Obligatory Tax. Anti-cancer Fund. As T **144** but dated "1974".

1196a. **144.** 1 c. orange .. .. 15 10

**297.** Steam Train.

**1974.** Centenary of Universal Postal Union. Multicoloured.

1197 2 c. Type **297** (postage) .. 30 45
1198 6 c. Stage-coach .. .. 15 10
1199 7 c. "Eider" mail steamer (air) .. .. .. 40 15
1200 33 c. Boeing 727-200 of Dominicana Airways .. 95 30

**298.** Emblems of World Amateur Golf Council and of Dominican Golf Association.

**1974.** World Amateur Golf Championships.

1202. **298.** 2 c. black and yellow (postage) .. .. 10 10
1203. – 6 c. multicoloured .. 10 10
1204. – 10 c. multicoloured (air) 25 15
1205. – 20 c. multicoloured .. 45 30

Designs—Vert. 6 c. Golfers teeing-off. Horiz. 10 c. Council emblem and golfers. 20 c. Dominican Golf Association emblem, golfer and hand with ball and tee.

**299.** Christmas Decorations.

**301.** Dr. Defillo.

**300.** Tomatoes.

**1974.** Christmas. Multicoloured.

1206. 2 c. Type **299** (postage) .. 10 10
1207. 6 c. Virgin and Child .. 15 10
1208. 10 c. Hand holding dove (horiz.) (air) .. .. 20 15

**1974.** 10th Anniv. of World Food Programme. Multicoloured.

1209. 2 c. Type **300** (postage) .. 10 10
1210. 3 c. Avocado pears .. 10 10
1211. 5 c. Coconuts .. 10 10
1212. 10 c. Bee, hive and cask of honey (air) .. .. 20 15

**1975.** Birth Centenary of Dr. Fernando Defillo (medical scientist).

1213. **301.** 1 c. brown .. .. 10 10
1214. 6 c. green .. .. 15 10

**1975.** Obligatory Tax. Rehabilitation of the Handicapped. As T **283** but dated "1975".

1214a. **283.** 1 c. brown .. .. 15 10

**302.** " I am the Resurrection and the Life ".

**303.** Spanish 6-c. Stamp of 1850 (S.G. 1).

**1975.** Holy Week. Multicoloured.

1215. 2 c. Type **302** (postage).. 10 10
1216. 6 c. Bell tower, Nuestra Senora del Rosario convent .. .. 15 10
1217. 10 c. Catholic emblems (air) .. .. .. 20 15

**1975.** Obligatory Tax. Tuberculosis Relief Fund. As T **221** but dated "1975".

1217a. **221.** 1 c. multicoloured .. 15 10

Design: 1 c. "Catteeyopsis rosea".

**1975.** Air. " Espana 75 " International Stamp Exhibition, Madrid.

1218. **303.** 12 c. blk., red & yell. 25 15

**304.** Hands supporting " Agriculture " and Industry.

**305.** Earth Station.

**1975.** 16th Meeting of Industrial Development Bank Governors, Santo Domingo.

1219. **304.** 6 c. mult. (postage).. 15 10
1220. 10 c. mult. (air) .. 20 15

**1975.** Opening of Satellite Earth Station. Multicoloured.

1221. 5 c. Type **305** (postage).. 10 10
1222. 15 c. Hemispheres and satellites (horiz.) (air).. 30 20

**306.** "Apollo" Spacecraft with Docking Tunnel.

**307.** Father Castellanos.

**1975.** " Apollo-Soyuz " Space Link. Mult.

1223. 1 c. Type **306** (postage).. 10 10
1224. 4 c. " Soyuz " spacecraft 10 10
1225. 2 p. Docking manoeuvre (air) .. .. .. 3·25 2·00

The 2 p. is larger, 42×28 mm.

**1975.** Birth Cent. of Father Rafael C. Castellanos.

1226. **307.** 6 c. brown and buff 15 10

**308.** Women encircling I.W.Y. Emblem.

**309.** Guacanagarix.

**1975.** International Women's Year.

1227. **308.** 3 c. multicoloured .. 10 10

**1975.** Indian Chiefs. Mult.

1228. 1 c. Type **309** (postage).. 10 10
1229. 2 c. Guarionex .. .. 10 10
1230. 3 c. Caonabo .. .. 10 10
1231. 4 c. Bohechio .. .. 10 10
1232. 5 c. Cayacoa .. .. 10 10
1233. 6 c. Anacaona .. .. 15 10
1234. 9 c. Hatuey .. .. 20 15
1235. 7 c. Mayobanex (air) .. 15 10
1236. 8 c. Cotubanama with Juan de Esquivel .. 15 10
1237. 10 c. Enriquillo and wife, Mencia .. .. 20 15

**1975.** Obligatory Tax. Anti-cancer Fund. As T **144** but dated "1975".

1237a. **144.** 1 c. violet .. .. 15 10

**310.** Basketball.

**1975.** 7th Pan-American Games, Mexico City. Multicoloured.

1238. 2 c. Type **310** (postage).. 10 10
1239. 6 c. Baseball .. .. 15 10
1240. 7 c. Volleyball (horiz.) (air) .. .. .. 15 15
1241. 10 c. Weightlifting (horiz.) 25 15

**311.** Carol-singers.

**1975.** Christmas. Multicoloured.

1242. 2 c. Type **311** (postage).. 10 10
1243. 6 c. " Dominican " Nativity 15 10
1244. 10 c. Dove and Peace message (air) .. .. 20 15

**312.** " Abudefdul marginatus ".

**1976.** Fishes. Multicoloured.

1245. 10 c. Type **312** .. .. 20 15
1246. 10 c. " Halichoeres radiata " 20 15
1247. 10 c. " Holocentrus ascensionis " .. .. 20 15
1248. 10 c. " Angelochthys ciliaris " .. .. 20 15
1249. 10 c. " Lutianus aya " .. 20 15

**313.** Valdesia Dam.

**314.** Orchid.

**1976.** Air. Inauguration of Valdesia Dam.

1250. **313.** 10 c. multicoloured.. 15 15

**1976.** Obligatory Tax. Rehabilitation of the Disabled. As T **283** but dated "1976".

1250a. **283.** 1 c. blue .. .. 15 10

**1976.** Obligatory Tax. Tuberculosis Relief Fund.

1251. **314.** 1 c. multicoloured .. 10 10

**315.** "Magdalene" (E. Godoy).

**316.** Schooner "Separacion Dominicana".

**1976.** Holy Week. Multicoloured.

1252. 2 c. Type **315** (postage).. 10 10
1253. 6 c. " The Ascension " (V. Priego) .. .. 10 10
1254. 10 c. " Mount Calvary " (E. Castillo) (air) .. 20 15

**1976.** Navy Day.

1255. **316.** 20 c. multicoloured.. 1·25 30

**317.** National Flower and Maps.

**1976.** American Revolution. Bicentenary, and "Interphil '76" Int. Stamp Exn., Philadelphia.
1256. **317.** 6 c. multicoloured (postage) .. .. 15 10
1257. – 9 c. multicoloured .. 20 10
1258. – 10 c. multicoloured (air) .. .. 50 15
1259. – 75 c. black and orange 1·50 1·00
DESIGNS—HORIZ. 9 c. Maps within cogwheels. 10 c. Maps within hands. VERT. 75 c. George Washington and Philadelphia buildings.

**318.** Flags of Spain and Dominican Republic.

**1976.** Visit of King and Queen of Spain. Multicoloured.
1260. 6 c. Type **318** (postage) .. 35 10
1261. 21 c. King Juan Carlos I and Queen Sophia (air) 1·00 35

**319.** Various Telephones.

**1976.** Telephone Centenary. Multicoloured.
1262. 6 c. Type **319** (postage) .. 15 10
1263. 10 c. A. Graham Bell. (horiz.) (air) .. .. 20 15

**320.** "Duarte's Vision" (L. Desangles).

**1976.** Death Cent. of Juan Duarte (patriot). Multicoloured.
1264. 2 c. Type **320** (postage) .. 10 10
1265. 6 c. "Juan Duarte" (R. Mejia) (vert.) .. .. 15 10
1266. 10 c. Text of Duarte's Declaration (vert.) (air) 20 15
1267. 33 c. "Duarte Sailing to Exile" (E. Godoy) .. 70 45

**321.** Fire Hydrant. **322.** Commemorative Text and Emblem.

**1976.** Dominican Fire Service. Multicoloured.
1268. 4 c. Type **321** (postage) .. 10 10
1269. 6 c. Fire Service emblem 15 10
1270. 10 c. Fire engine (horiz.) (air) .. .. .. 20 15

**1976.** Obligatory Tax. Anti-cancer Fund. As T **144** but dated "1976".
1270a. **144.** 1 c. green .. .. 15 10

**1976.** 50th Anniv. of Dominican Radio Club.
1271. **322.** 6 c. black and red (postage) .. .. 15 10
1272. 10 c. blk. & blue (air) 20 15

**323.** Map and Caravel. **325.** Virgin and Child.

**324.** Boxing.

**1976.** "Hispanidad 1976". Multicoloured.
1273. 6 c. Type **323** (postage) .. 45 15
1274. 21 c. Heads of Spaniard and Dominicans (air) .. 45 30

**1976.** Olympic Games, Montreal. Mult.
1275. 2 c. Type **324** (postage) .. 10 10
1276. 3 c. Weightlifting .. 10 10
1277. 10 c. Running (air) .. 20 15
1278. 25 c. Basketball .. .. 50 35

**1976.** Obligatory Tax. Child Welfare. As T **233** but dated "1976".
1278a. **233.** 1 c. mauve .. .. 15 10

**1976.** Christmas. Multicoloured.
1279. 2 c. Type **325** (postage) .. 10 10
1280. 6 c. The Three Kings (22 × 32 mm.) .. .. 15 10
1281. 10 c. Angel with bells (22 × 32 mm.) (air) .. 20 15

**326.** Cable-car and Beach Scenes.

**1977.** Tourism. Multicoloured.
1282. 6 c. Type **326** (postage) .. 15 10
1283. 10 c. Tourist activities (air) 20 15
1284. 12 c. Fishing and hotel .. 25 15
1285. 25 c. Horse-riding and waterfall .. .. 50 35
No. 1283 measures 36 × 36 mm., No. 1284 35 × 26 mm. and No. 1285 26 × 35 mm.

**327.** Championships Emblem.

**1977.** 10th Central American and Caribbean Children's Swimming Championships, Santo Domingo.
1286. **327.** 3 c. multicoloured (postage) .. .. 10 10
1287. 5 c. multicoloured .. 10 10
1288. 10 c. multicoloured (air) 20 15
1289. 25 c. multicoloured .. 30 35

**1977.** Obligatory Tax. Rehabilitation of the Disabled. As T **283** but dated "1977".
1289a. **283.** 1 c. blue .. .. 15 10

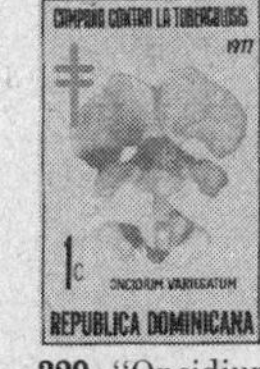


**328.** Allegory of Holy Week. **329.** "Oncidium variegatum" (orchid).

**1977.** Holy Week.
1290. **328.** 2 c. multicoloured (postage) .. .. 10 10
1291. – 6 c. black and mauve 10 10
1292. – 10 c. blk., red & bl. (air) 20 10
DESIGNS: 6 c. Christ crowned with thorns. 10 c. Church and book.

**1977.** Obligatory Tax. Tuberculosis Relief Fund.
1293. **329.** 1 c. multicoloured .. 10 10

**330.** Gulls in Flight.

**1977.** 12th Annual Lions Clubs Convention, Santo Domingo.
1294. **330.** 2 c. multicoloured (postage) .. .. 10 10
1295. 6 c. multicoloured .. 15 10
1296. 7 c. multicoloured (air) 15 10

**331.** "Battle of Tortuguero" (G. Fernandez).

**1977.** Navy Day.
1297. **331.** 20 c. multicoloured .. 75 30

**332.** "Miss Universe" Emblem. **333.** "Nymphaea ampla" ("Nymphea" on stamp).

**1977.** Air. "Miss Universe" Competition.
1298. **332.** 10 c. multicoloured .. 20 15

**1977.** Dominican Flora. Plants in the Dr. Rafael M. Moscoso National Botanical Gardens. Multicoloured.
1299. 2 c. Type **333** (postage) .. 10 10
1300. 4 c. "Broughtonia domingensis" .. 10 10
1301. 6 c. "Cordia sebestena" 15 10
1302. 7 c. "Melocatus lemairei" (cactus) (air) .. 15 10
1303. 33 c. "Coccothrinax argentea" (tree) .. 70 45

**334.** Computers and Graph.

**1977.** Seventh Inter-American Statistics Conference. Multicoloured.
1304. 6 c. Type **334** (postage) .. 15 10
1305. 28 c. Factories and graph (27 × 37 mm) (air) .. 55 35

**335.** Haitian Solenodon.

**1977.** Eighth Inter-American Veterinary Congress. Multicoloured.
1306. 6 c. Type **335** (postage) .. 15 10
1307. 20 c. Iguana .. .. 40 25
1308. 10 c. "Red Roman" stud bull (air) .. .. 20 15
1309. 25 c. Greater Flamingo (vert.) .. .. .. 1·60 40

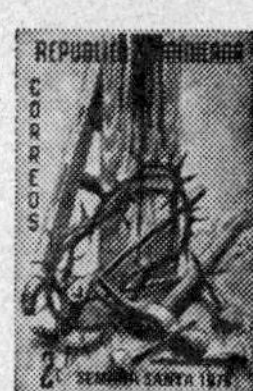


**336.** Main Gateway of Casa del Cordon. **337.** Tools and Crown of Thorns at Foot of Cross.

**1978.** "Hispanidad 1977". Multicoloured.
1310. 6 c. Type **336** (postage) .. 15 10
1311. 21 c. Gothic style window, Casa del Tostado (28 × 41 mm) (air) .. 45 30

**1978.** Holy Week.
1312. **337.** 2 c. multicoloured (postage) .. .. 10 10
1313. – 6 c. green .. .. 15 10
1314. – 7 c. multicoloured (air) 15 10
1315. – 10 c. multicoloured .. 20 15
DESIGNS—(22 × 33 mm.). 6 c. Christ wearing Crown of Thorns. (27 × 37 mm.). 7 c. Facade of Santo Domingo Cathedral. 10 c. Facade of Dominican Convent.

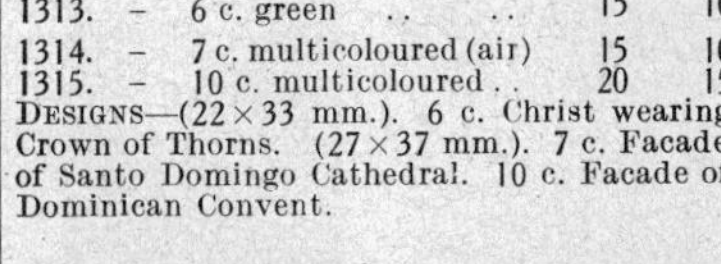


**338.** Schooner "Duarte". **339.** Cardinal Octavio A. Beras Rojas.

**1978.** Air. Navy Day.
1316. **338.** 7 c. multicoloured .. 55 15

**1978.** Consecration of First Cardinal from Dominican Republic.
1317. **339.** 6 c. multicoloured (postage) .. .. 15 10
1318. 10 c. multicoloured (air) 20 15

**340.** Microwave Antenna.

**1978.** Air. Tenth World Telecommunications Day.
1319. **340.** 25 c. multicoloured .. 50 35

**341.** First Dominican Airmail Stamp and Map of First Airmail Service. **342.** Pres. Manuel de Troncoso.

**1978.** Air. 50th Anniv. of First Dominican Airmail Stamp.
1320. **341.** 10 c. multicoloured .. 20 15

**1978.** Birth Cent of President Troncoso.
1321. **342.** 2 c. brn., mve. & blk. 10 10
1322. 6 c. brn., grey & blk. 15 10

**343.** Globe, Football and Emblem. **344.** Father Juan N. Zegri y Moreno (founder).

**1978.** Air. World Cup Football Championship, Argentina. Multicoloured.
1323. 12 c. Type **343** .. .. 25 15
1324. 33 c. Emblem and map on football pitch .. .. 75 45

**1978.** Centenary of Merciful Sisters of Charity. Multicoloured.
1325. 6 c. Type **344** (postage) . . 15 10
1326. 21 c. Symbol of the Order (air) . . . . . . 40 30

**345.** Boxing.

**1978.** 13th Central American and Caribbean Games, Medellin, Colombia. Multicoloured.
1327. 2 c. Type **345** (postage) . . 10 10
1328. 6 c. Weightlifting . . 15 10
1329. 7 c. Baseball (vert.) (air) 15 10
1330. 10 c. Football (vert.) . . 20 15

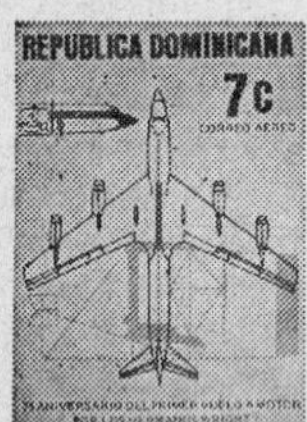

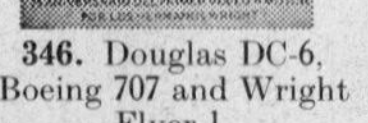

**346.** Douglas DC-6, Boeing 707 and Wright Flyer I.
**347.** Sun over Landscape.

**1978.** Air. 75th Anniv. of First Powered Flight.
1331. **346.** 7 c. multicoloured . . 15 15
1332. – 10 c. brn., yell. & red 35 15
1333. – 13 c. pale blue and deep blue . . 45 20
1334. – 45 c. multicoloured . . 1·25 75
DESIGNS: 10 c. Wright brothers and Wright Glider No. 1. 13 c. Diagram of airflow over wing. 45 c. Wright Flyer I and world map.

**1978.** Tourism. Multicoloured.
1335. 2 c. Type **347** (postage) . . 10 10
1336. 6 c. Sun over beach . . 15 10
1337. 7 c. Sun and musical instruments (air) . . 15 10
1338. 10 c. Sun over Santo Domingo . . . . 20 15

**1978.** Obligatory Tax. Anti-cancer Fund. As T **144** but dated "1977".
1338a. **144.** 1 c. purple . . . . 15 10

**348.** Galleons.
**349.** Flags of Dominican Republic and United Nations.

**1978.** "Hispanidad 1978". Multicoloured.
1339. 2 c. Type **348** (postage) . . 10 10
1340. 21 c. Figures holding hands in front of globe (air) 45 25

**1978.** Air. 33rd Anniv. of United Nations.
1341. **349.** 33 c. multicoloured . . 70 25

**350.** Mother and Child.
**351.** Dove, Lamp and Poinsettia.

**1978.** Obligatory Tax. Child Welfare.
1342. **350.** 1 c. green . . . . 10 10

**1978.** Christmas. Multicoloured.
1343. 2 c. Type **351** (postage) . . 10 10
1344. 6 c. Dominican family and star . . . . 15 10
1345. 10 c. Statue of the Virgin (air) . . . . 20 15
No. 1345 is vert., 22×33 mm.

## MINIMUM PRICE

The minimum price quoted is 10p which represents a handling charge rather than a basis for valuing common stamps. For further notes about prices see introductory pages.

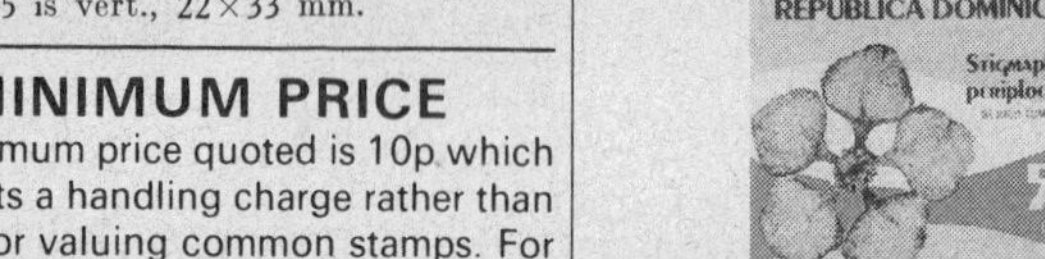

**352.** Pope John Paul II.
**353.** Map of Island, Iguana and Radio Transmitter.

**1979.** Air. Visit of Pope John Paul II.
1346. **352.** 10 c. multicoloured . . 70 20

**1979.** Air. 1st Expedition of Radio Amateurs to Beata Island.
1347. **353.** 10 c. multicoloured . . 20 15

**354.** University Seal.
**355.** Starving Child.

**1979.** Obligatory Tax. 440th Anniv. of Santo Domingo University.
1348. **354.** 2 c. blue . . . . 10 10

**1979.** International Year of the Child.
1349. **355.** 2 c. orge. & blk. (post.) 10 10
1350. – 7 c. multicoloured (air) 15 10
1351. – 10 c. multicoloured . . 20 15
1352. – 33 c. multicoloured . . 70 45
DESIGNS: 7 c. Children reading book. 10 c. Head and protective hands. 33 c. Hands and vases.

**1979.** Obligatory Tax. Rehabilitation of the Disabled. As T **283** but dated "1979".
1353. **283.** 1 c. green . . . . 15 10

**356.** Crucifixion.
**357.** "Turnera ulmifolia".

**1979.** Holy Week. Multicoloured.
1354. 2 c. Type **356** (postage) . . 10 10
1355. 3 c. Christ carrying cross (horiz.) . . . . 10 10
1356. 10 c. Pope John Paul II with Crucifix (air) . . 20 15

**1978.** Obligatory Tax. Tuberculosis Relief Fund. Dated "1978".
1357. **357.** 1 c. multicoloured . . 10 10

**358.** Admiral J. Cambiaso.
**359.** Map, Stamp Album and Philatelic Equipment.

**1979.** Air. 135th Anniv. of Battle of Tortuguero.
1358. **358.** 10 c. multicoloured . . 20 15

**1979.** Air. "Exfilna" Third National Stamp Exhibition.
1359. **359.** 33 c. blue, grn. & blk. 70 45

**360.** "Stigmaphyllon periplocifolium".

**1979.** Flowers from National Botanical Gardens.
1360. **360.** 50 c. grey, yellow and black (postage) . . 1·00 70
1361. – 7 c. multicoloured (air) 15 10
1362. – 10 c. multicoloured . . 20 15
1363. – 13 c. blue, mve. & blk. 25 15
DESIGNS: 7 c. "Passiflora foetida". 10 c. "Isidorea pungens". 13 c. "Calotropis procera".

**362.** Heart and Section through Artery.

**1979.** Dominican Cardiology Institute.
1364. **362.** 3 c. multicoloured (postage) . . . . 10 10
1365. – 1 p. black, red & blue 2·00 1·40
1366. – 10 c. multicoloured (air) 20 15
DESIGNS: VERT. 10 c. Human figure showing blood circulation. HORIZ. 1 p. Cardiology Institute and heart.

**363.** Baseball.

**1979.** 8th Pan-American Games, Puerto Rico. Multicoloured.
1367. 2 c. Type **363** (postage) . . 10 10
1368. 3 c. Cycling (vert.) . . 10 10
1369. 7 c. Running (vert.) (air) 15 10

**364.** Football.
**365.** Sir Rowland Hill and First Dominican Republic Stamp.

**1979.** Third National Games. Multicoloured.
1370. 2 c. Type **364** (postage) . . 10 10
1371. 25 c. Swimming (horiz.) 55 35
1372. 10 c. Tennis (air) . . 20 15

**1979.** Air. Death Cent. of Sir Rowland Hill.
1373. **365.** 2 p. multicoloured . . 4·25 1·10

**366.** Thomas Edison (inventor).
**367.** Hand removing Electric Plug.

**1979.** Centenary of Electric Light-bulb. Mult.
1374. 25 c. Type **366** (postage) 55 30
1375. 10 c. "100" forming lightbulb (horiz.) (air) 20 15

**1979.** "Save Energy". Multicoloured.
1376. 2 c. Type **367** . . 10 10
1377. 6 c. Car being refuelled . . 15 10

**368.** Hispaniolan Conure.
**369.** Lions Emblem.

**1979.** Birds. Multicoloured.
1378 2 c. Type **368** (postage) . . 35 10
1379 6 c. Hispaniolan trogon . . 60 15
1380 7 c. Black-crowned palm tanager (air) . . 60 20
1381 10 c. Chat-tanager . . 85 25
1382 45 c. Black-cowled oriole 2·25 1·00

**1979.** 15th Anniv. of Dominican Republic Lions Club. Multicoloured.
1383. 20 c. Type **369** (postage) 45 20
1384. 10 c. Melvin Jones (founder) (air) . . . . . . 20 10

**371.** Holy Family.
**372.** Christ carrying Cross.

**1979.** Christmas. Multicoloured.
1386. 2 c. Type **371** (postage) . . 10 10
1387. 10 c. Three Kings (air) . . 20 15

**1980.** Holy Week.
1388. **372.** 3 c. black, red and lilac (postage) . . 10 10
1389. – 7 c. blk., red & yell. (air) 15 10
1390. – 10 c. black, red & bistre 20 15
DESIGNS: 7 c. Crucifixion. 10 c. Resurrection.

**1980.** Obligatory Tax. Rehabilitation of the Disabled. As T **283** but dated "1980".
1391. **283.** 1 c. olive and green 10 10

**374.** Navy Crest.
**375.** "Stamp".

**1980.** Air. Navy Day.
1392. **374.** 21 c. multicoloured . . 45 30

**1980.** Air. 25th Anniv. of Dominican Philatelic Society.
1393. **375.** 10 c. multicoloured . . 20 15

**376.** Cocoa Harvest.
**377.** Cotuf Gold Mine, Pueblo Viejo.

**1980.** Agricultural Year. Multicoloured.
1394. 1 c. Type **376** . . . . 10 10
1395. 2 c. Coffee . . . . 10 10
1396. 3 c. Plantain . . . . 10 10
1397. 4 c. Sugar cane . . . . 10 10
1398. 5 c. Maize . . . . 10 10

**1980.** Nationalization of Gold Mines. Mult.
1399. 6 c. Type **377** (postage) . . 15 10
1400. 10 c. Drag line mining (air) 20 15
1401. 33 c. General view of location of gold mines . . 70 45

**378.** Blind Man's Buff.
**379.** "Tourism".

**1980.** Children's Games. Multicoloured.
1402. 3 c. Type **378** . . . . 10 10
1403. 4 c. Marbles . . . . 10 10
1404. 5 c. Spinning top . . 10 10
1405. 6 c. Hopscotch . . . . 15 10

**1980.** Air. World Tourism Conference, Manila, Philippines. Multicoloured.
1406. 10 c. Type **379** . . . . 20 15
1407. 33 c. Conference emblem . . 70 45

380. Cuban Iguana.

**1980.** Animals. Multicoloured.

1408. 20 c. Type **380** (postage) 45 30

1409. 7 c. American crocodile (air) .. .. .. 15 10

1410. 10 c. Hispaniolan hutia 25 15

1411. 25 c. American manatee 65 35

1412. 45 c. Hawksbill turtle .. 95 60

381. " El Merengue " (Jaime Colson).

**1980.** Paintings. Multicoloured.

1413. 3 c. Type **381** (postage) .. 10 10

1414. 50 c. "The Mirror" (G. H. Ortega) .. .. .. 1·10 70

1415. 10 c. "Genesis de un Ganga" (Paul Guidicelli) (air) .. .. .. 20 15

1416. 17 c. "The Countryman" (Yoryi Morel) .. .. 35 25

**1980.** Obligatory Tax. Anti-cancer Fund. As T **144** but dated "1980".

1417. **144.** 1 c. blue and violet 10 10

383. Map of Catalina Island. 384. Rotary Emblem on Globe.

**1980.** Air. Visit of Radio Amateurs to Catalina Island.

1418. **383.** 7 c. green, blue & black 15 10

**1980.** Air. 75th Anniv. of Rotary International. Multicoloured.

1419. 10 c. Type **384**. .. .. 20 15

1420. 33 c. Rotary emblem in "75" .. .. .. 70 45

385. Carrier Pigeons with Letters.

**1980.** Centenary. of U.P.U. Membership. Multicoloured.

1421. 33 c. Type **385** .. .. 70 45

1422. 45 c. Row of stylized pigeons and letter .. 95 60

1423. 50 c. Carrier pigeon with letter and letter .. 1·10 70

**1980.** Obligatory tax. Child Welfare. As T **350** but dated "1980".

1425. **350.** 1 c. blue .. .. 10 10

386. The Three Kings. 387. Arms of Salcedo.

**1980.** Christmas. Multicoloured.

1426. 3 c. Type **386** (postage) 10 10

1427. 6 c. Carol singers .. 15 10

1428. 10 c. The Holy Family (air) 20 15

**1981.** Cent. of Salcedo Province. Mult.

1429. 6 c. Type **387** (postage).. 15 10

1430. 10 c. Arms and map of Salcedo (air) .. .. 20 15

388. Juan Pablo Duarte. 389. Industrial Symbols.

**1981.** Juan Pablo Duarte (patriot). Commemoration.

1431. **388.** 2 c. brown and ochre 10 10

**1981.** Air. Chemical Engineering Seminar.

1432. **389.** 10 c. multicoloured .. 20 15

1433. – 33 c. gold and black 70 45

DESIGN: 33 c. Emblem of Dominican College of Engineering and Architecture (CODIA).

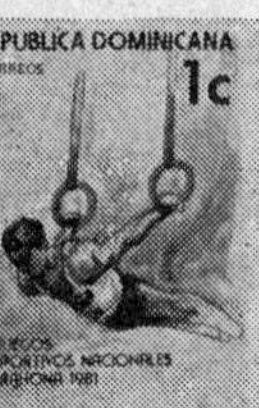

390. Gymnastics. 391. Mother Mazzarello.

**1981.** Fifth National Games (1st issue). Multicoloured.

1434. 1 c. Type **390** (postage) 10 10

1435. 2 c. Running .. .. 10 10

1436. 3 c. Pole-vaulting .. 10 10

1437. 6 c. Boxing .. .. 15 10

1438. 10 c. Baseball (air) .. 20 15

See also Nos. 1463/4.

**1981.** Death Centenary of Mother Mazarello (founder of Daughters of Mary).

1439. **391.** 6 c. brown and black 15 10

392. Admiral Juan Alejandro Acosta. 393. Radio Waves.

**1981.** Air. 137th Anniv. of Battle of Tortuguero.

1440. **392.** 10 c. multicoloured .. 20 15

**1981.** Obligatory Tax. Tuberculosis Relief Fund. Dated "1981".

1441. **357.** 1 c. multicoloured .. 10 10

**1981.** Air. World Telecommunications Day.

1442. **393.** 10 c. multicoloured .. 15 15

394. Pedro Henriquez Urena. 395. Forest.

**1981.** 35th Death Anniv. of Pedro Henriquez Urena.

1443. **394.** 6 c. pale grey and grey .. .. 15 10

**1981.** Forest Conservation. Multicoloured.

1444. 2 c. Type **395** .. .. 10 10

1445. 6 c. Forest river.. .. 15 10

396. Heinrich von Stephan. 397. "Disabled People".

**1981.** Air. 150th Birth Anniv. of Heinrich von Stephan (founder of U.P.U.).

1446. **396.** 33 c. brown & yellow 70 45

**1981.** Air. International Year of Disabled Persons. Multicoloured.

1447. 7 c. Type **397** .. .. 15 10

1448. 33 c. Cobbler in wheelchair 70 45

398. Exhibition Emblem.

**1981.** Air. " Expuridom '81 " International Stamp Exhibition, Santo Domingo.

1149. **398.** 7 c. black, blue & red 15 10

399. Target.

**1981.** Air. Second World Air Gun Shooting Championship. Multicoloured.

1450. 10 c. Type **399** .. .. 20 15

1451. 15 c. Stylized riflemen .. 30 20

1452. 25 c. Stylized pistol shooters .. .. 55 55

400. Family and House. 401. Fruit.

**1981.** National Census. Multicoloured.

1453. 3 c. Type **400** .. .. 10 10

1454. 6 c. Farmer with cow and agricultural produce .. 15 10

**1981.** Obligatory Tax. Anti-cancer Fund. As T **144** but dated "1981".

1455. **144.** 1 c. blue & dp. blue 10 10

**1981.** Air. World Food Day. Multicoloured.

1456. 10 c. Type **401** .. .. 20 15

1457. 50 c. Fish, eggs and vegetables .. .. 1·10 70

402. Gem Stones and Jewellery. 403. Javelin throwing.

**1981.** Air. Exports. Multicoloured.

1458. 7 c. Type **402** .. .. 15 10

1459. 10 c. Handicraft .. .. 20 15

1460. 11 c. Fruit .. .. .. 25 15

1461. 17 c. Cocoa, coffee, tobacco and sugar .. .. 35 25

**1981.** Obligatory Tax. Child Welfare. As T **350** but dated "1981".

1462. **350.** 1 c. green .. .. 10 10

**1981.** Air. Fifth National Games, Barahona (2nd issue). Multicoloured.

1463. 10 c. Type **403** .. .. 20 15

1464. 50 c. Cycling .. .. 1·10 70

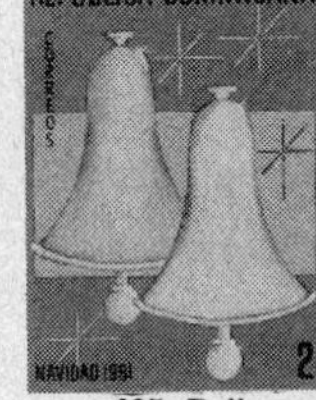


404. "Encyclia cochleata". 405. Bells.

**1981.** Air. Orchids. Multicoloured.

1465. 7 c. Type **404** .. .. 10 15

1466. 10 c. " Broughtonia domingensis " .. .. 15 20

1467. 25 c. " Encyclia truncata " 55 35

1468. 65 c. " Elleanthus capitatus " .. .. 1·60 1·10

**1981.** Christmas. Multicoloured.

1469. 2 c. Type **405** (postage) .. 10 10

1470. 3 c. Holly .. .. .. 10 10

1471. 10 c. Dove and moon (air) 20 15

406. Juan Pablo Duarte.

**1982.** Juan Pablo Duarte (patriot) Commemoration.

1472. **406.** 2 c. light blue and blue 10 10

407. Citizens arriving at Polling Station.

**1982.** National Elections. Multicoloured.

1473. 2 c. Type **407** .. .. 10 10

1474. 3 c. Entering polling booth (vert.) .. .. .. 10 10

1475. 6 c. Casting vote .. 15 10

408. American Air Forces Co-operation Emblem.

**1982.** Air. 22nd American Air Force's Commanders Conference, Buenos Aires.

1476. **408.** 10 c. multicoloured .. 20 15

409. Naval Cadet Parade.

**1982.** Air. Battle of Tortuguero Commem.

1477 **409** 10 c. multicoloured .. 20 15

**410.** Tackling.

**411.** Lord Baden-Powell (statue).

**1982.** Air. World Cup Football Championship, Spain. Multicoloured.
1478. 10 c. Type **410** .. .. 20 15
1479. 21 c. Dribbling .. .. 45 30
1480. 33 c. Heading ball into goal 70 45

**1982.** Air. 75th Anniv. of Boy Scout Movement. Multicoloured.
1481. 10 c. Type **411** .. .. 20 15
1482. 15 c. Scouting emblems (horiz.) .. .. .. 30 20
1483. 25 c. Baden-Powell and scout at camp fire .. 55 35

**412.** "Study of Daylight".

**413.** Cathedral and House.

**1982.** Energy Conservation. Multicoloured.
1484. 1 c. Type **412** .. .. 10 10
1485. 2 c. "Save rural electricity" 10 10
1486. 3 c. "Use wind power" .. 10 10
1487. 4 c. "Switch off lights" .. 10 10
1488. 5 c. "Conserve fuel" .. 15 10
1489. 6 c. "Use solar energy" .. 15 10

**1982.** Air. 25th Congress of Latin-American Tourist Organizations Confederation, Santo Domingo. Multicoloured.
1490. 7 c. Congress emblem .. 15 10
1491. 10 c. Type **413** .. .. 20 15
1492. 33 c. Dancers and beach scene .. .. .. 70 45

**414.** Exhibition Emblem.

**1982.** Air. "Espamer '82" Stamp Exhibition, Puerto Rico. Multicoloured.
1493. 7 c. Stamp bearing map of Puerto Rico (horiz.) .. 15 10
1494. 13 c. Stylized postage stamps (horiz.) .. .. 30 20
1495. 50 c. Type **414** .. .. 1·10 70

**415.** Emilio Prud'Homme and Score of Dominican National Anthem.

**416.** President Guzman.

**1982.** 50th Death Anniv. of Emilio Prud'Homme (composer).
1496. **415.** 6 c. multicoloured .. 15 10

**1982.** President Antonio Guzman Commemoration.
1497. **416.** 6 c. multicoloured .. 15 10

**417.** Baseball.

**1982.** Central American and Caribbean Games, Cuba. Multicoloured.
1498. 3 c. Type **417** (postage) .. 10 10
1499. 10 c. Basketball (air) .. 20 15
1500. 13 c. Boxing .. .. 30 20
1501. 25 c. Gymnastics .. 55 30

**418.** "Harbour" (Alejandro Bonilla).

**1982.** Air. Paintings. Multicoloured.
1502. 7 c. Type **418** .. .. 15 10
1503. 10 c. "Portrait of a Woman" (Leopoldo Navarro) .. .. 20 15
1504. 45 c. "Portrait of Amelia Francasci" (Luis Desangles) .. .. .. 95 65
1505. 2 p. "Portrait" (Abelardo Rodriguez Urdaneta) .. 4·25 2·75

**419.** Horse-drawn Carriage.

**1982.** Centenary of San Pedro de Macoris Province. Multicoloured.
1506. 1 c. Type **419** (postage) .. 10 10
1507. 2 c. Stained-glass window, San Pedro Apostle Church (25 × 34½ mm.) .. 10 10
1508. 5 c. Centenary emblem .. 15 10
1509. 7 c. View of San Pedro de Macoris City (air) .. 45 20

**420.** "Santa Maria" and Map of Voyage.

**1982.** Air. 490th Anniv. of Discovery of America by Columbus. Multicoloured.
1510. 7 c. Type **420** .. .. 75 20
1511. 10 c. "Santa Maria" .. 1·00 30
1512. 21 c. Statue of Columbus, Santo Domingo .. 45 30

**421.** Central Bank.

**1982.** 35th Anniv. of Central Bank.
1513. **421.** 10 c. multicoloured .. 20 15

**422.** St. Theresa of Avila.

**423.** Christmas Tree Decorations.

**1982.** 400th Death Anniv. of St. Theresa of Avila.
1514. **422.** 6 c. multicoloured .. 15 10

**1982.** Christmas. Multicoloured.
1515. 6 c. Type **423** (postage) .. 10 10
1516. 10 c. Tree decorations (different) (air) .. 20 15

**424.** Hand holding Rural and Urban Environments.

**1982.** Environmental Protection. Mult.
1517. 2 c. Type **424** .. .. 10 10
1518. 3 c. Hand holding river in the country .. .. 10 10
1519. 6 c. Hand holding forest 10 10
1520. 20 c. Hand holding swimming fish .. .. 35 25

**425.** Adults writing.

**1983.** National Literacy Campaign. Mult.
1521. Girl and boy writing on blackboard .. .. 10 10
1522. 3 c. Type **425** .. .. 10 10
1523. 6 c. Children, rainbow and pencil .. .. .. 10 10

**426.** Clasped Hands and Eiffel Tower.

**1983.** Air. Centenary of French Alliance (French language-teaching association).
1524. **426.** 33 c. multicoloured .. 50 30

**427.** Arms of Mao City Council.

**428.** Frigate "Mella".

**1983.** Cent. of Mao City Council. Mult.
1525. 1 c. Type **427** .. .. 10 10
1526. 5 c. Centenary monument 10 10

**1983.** Air. Battle of Tortuguero. Commemoration.
1527. **428.** 15 c. multicoloured .. 1·00 30

**429.** Antonio del Monte y Tejada.

**430.** Red Cross.

**1983.** Dominican Historians.
1528. **429.** 2 c. red & brn. (postage) 10 10
1529. – 3 c. pink & brown .. 10 10
1530. – 5 c. blue & brown .. 15 10
1531. – 6 c. lt. brn. & brn. .. 15 10
1532. – 7 c. pink & brn. (air) 15 10
1533. – 10 c. grey & brown .. 20 15

DESIGNS: 3 c. Manuel Ubaldo Gomez. 5 c. Emiliano Tejera. 6 c. Bernardo Pichardo. 7 c. Americo Lugo. 10 c. Jose Gabriel Garcia.

**1983.** Obligatory Tax. Red Cross.
1534. **430.** 1 c. red, gold & blk. 10 10

**431.** Dish Aerial and W.C.Y. Emblem.

**432.** "Simon Bolivar" (Plutarco Andujar).

**1983.** Air. World Communications Year.
1535. **431.** 10 c. lt. blue & blue 20 15

**1983.** Air. Birth Bicent. of Simon Bolivar.
1536. **432.** 9 c. multicoloured .. 15 10

**433.** Pictogram of Rehabilitation.

**434.** Basketball and Gymnastics.

**1983.** Obligatory Tax. Rehabilitation of the Disabled.
1537. **433.** 1 c. blue .. .. 10 10

**1983.** Air. Pan-American Games, Venezuela. Multicoloured.
1538. 7 c. Type **434** .. .. 15 10
1539. 10 c. Boxing and pole vaulting .. .. 20 15
1540. 15 c. Baseball, weightlifting and cycling .. 25 15

**435.** Emilio Prud'Homme and Jose Reyes (composers).

**1983.** Cent. of Dominican National Anthem.
1541. **435.** 6 c. multicoloured .. 10 10

**1983.** Obligatory Tax. Anti-Cancer Fund. As T **144** but dated "1983".
1542. **144.** 1 c. turquoise & green .. .. 10 10

**436.** "Sotavento" (winner of 1982 regatta).

**437.** Arms.

**1983.** Air. Christopher Columbus Regatta and 500th Anniv. (1992) of Discovery of America by Columbus (1st issue).
1543. – 10 c. stone, brn. & blk. 60 40
1544. – 21 c. multicoloured .. 85 55
1545. **436.** 33 c. multicoloured .. 1·40 60

DESIGNS—HORIZ. 10 c. Old map of Greater Antilles. 21 c. Christopher Columbus Regatta trophy.

See also Nos. 1583/5, 1617/20, 1649/52, 1683/6, 1717/20, 1754/7, 1777/80, 1791/4 and 1805/8.

**1983.** 125th Anniv. of Dominican Freemasons.
1547. **437.** 4 c. multicoloured .. 10 10

**438.** Our Lady of Regia Church. **439.** Clocktower.

**1983.** 300th Anniv. of Our Lady of Regla Church.

1548. **438.** 3 c. dp. blue & blue .. 10 10
1549. – 6 c. red & deep red .. 10 10
DESIGN: 6 c. Statue of Our Lady of Regia.

**1983.** 450th Anniv. of Monte Cristi Province.

1550. **439.** 1 c. green & black .. 10 10
1551. – 2 c. multicoloured .. 10 10
1552. – 5 c. grey .. .. 10 10
1553. – 7 c. grey and blue .. 15 10
DESIGNS—VERT. 2 c. Provincial coat of arms. HORIZ. 5 c. Wooden building in which independence of Cuba was signed. 7 c. Men digging out salt crystals.

**1983.** Obligatory Tax. Child Welfare. As T **350** but dated " 1983 ".

1554. **350.** 1 c. green .. .. 10 10

**440.** Commission Emblem.

**1983.** Air. 10th Anniv. of Latin American Civil Aviation Commission.

1555. **440.** 10 c. blue .. .. 15 10

**441.** Baseball, Boxing and Cycling. **442.** Bells and Christmas Tree Decorations.

**1983.** Sixth National Games, San Pedro de Macoris. Multicoloured.

1556. 6 c. Type **441** (postage) 10 10
1557. 10 c. Weightlifting, running and swimming (air) .. .. .. 15 10

**1983.** Air. Christmas.

1558. **442.** 10 c. multicoloured .. 15 10

**443.** "Portrait of a Girl" (Adriana Billini).

**1983.** Air. Paintings. Multicoloured.

1559. 10 c. "The Litter" (Juan Bautista Gomez) (horiz.) .. .. 15 10
1560. 15 c. "The Meeting between Maximo Gomez and Jose Marti at Guayubin" (Enrique Garcia Godoy) (horiz.) 20 15
1561. 21 c. "St. Francis" (Angel Perdomo) .. 30 20
1562. 33 c. Type **443** .. .. 45 30

**444.** Monument to Heroes of Capotillo.

**1983.** 120th Anniv. of Restoration of the Republic.

1563. **444.** 1 c. purple & blue .. 10 10

**445.** Man holding Dominican Flag and Rifle.

**1983.** 67th Anniv. of Battle of Barranquita.

1564. **445.** 5 c. multicoloured .. 10 10

**446.** Matias Ramon Mella and Dominican Flag.

**1984.** 140th Anniv. of Independence. Mult.

1565. 6 c. Type **446** .. .. 10 10
1566. 25 c. Puerta de la Misericordia and Mella's rifle 15 15

**447.** Dr. Heriberto Pieter.

**1984.** Birth Cent. of Dr. Heriberto Pieter.

1567. **447.** 3 c. multicoloured .. 10 10

**448.** Jose Maria Imbert, Fernando Valerio, Cannon and National Flag.

**1984.** 140th Anniv. of Battle of Santiago.

1568. **448.** 7 c. multicoloured .. 10 10

**449.** Coastguard Patrol Boat.

**1984.** 140th Anniv. of Battle of Tortuguero.

1569. **449.** 10 c. multicoloured .. 65 15

**450.** Monument to the Heroes of June 1959.

**1984.** 25th Anniv. of Expedition to Constanza, Maimon and Estero Hondo.

1570. **450.** 6 c. multicoloured .. 10 10

**451.** Salome Urena.

**1984.** Birth Centenary of Pedro Henriquez Urena (poet).

1571. **451.** 7 c. pink and brown 10 10
1572. – 10 c. yellow & brown 10 10
1573. – 22 c. yellow & brown 15 15
DESIGNS: 10 c. Lines from poem "Mi Pedro". 22 c. Pedro H. Urena.

**452.** Running.

**1984.** Olympic Games, Los Angeles. Each in blue, red and black.

1574. 1 p. Type **452** .. .. 55 50
1575. 1 p. Weightlifting .. 55 50
1576. 1 p. Boxing .. .. 55 50
1577. 1 p. Baseball .. .. 55 50

**453.** Stygian Owl. **455.** Pope John Paul II.

**454.** Christopher Columbus landing in Hispaniola.

**1984.** Protection of Wildlife. Multicoloured.

1578. 10 c. Type **453** .. .. 85 30
1579. 15 c. Greater flamingo .. 1·10 30
1580. 25 c. White-lipped peccary .. .. 15 10
1581. 35 c. Haitian solenodon 25 20

**1984.** 500th Anniv (1992) of Discovery of America by Columbus (2nd issue).

1582. **454.** 10 c. multicoloured .. 10 10
1583. – 35 c. multicoloured .. 25 20
1584. – 65 c. brown, yellow and black .. .. 40 35
1585. – 1 p. multicoloured .. 55 50
DESIGNS: 35 c. Destruction of Fort La Navidad. 65 c. First mass in America. 1 p. Battle of Santo Cerro.

**1984.** Papal Visit to Santo Domingo. 500th Anniv. of Christianity in the New World. Multicoloured.

1586. 75 c. Type **455** .. .. 45 40
1587. 75 c. Pope in priest's attire and map .. 45 40
1588. 75 c. Globe and Pope in ceremonial attire .. 45 40
1589. 75 c. Bishop's crosier .. 45 40

**456.** Gomez on Horseback.

**1984.** 150th Birth Anniv. of (1986) Maximo Gomez (leader of Cuban Revolution). Multicoloured.

1590. 10 c. Type **456** .. .. 10 10
1591. 20 c. Maximo Gomez .. 15 10

**457.** "Navidad 1984".

**1984.** Christmas.

1592. **457.** 5 c. mauve, blue and gold .. .. 10 10
1593. – 10 c. blue, gold and mauve .. .. 10 10
DESIGN: 10 c. "Navidad 1984" (different).

**458.** "The Sacrifice of the Kid" (Eligio Pichardo).

**1984.** Art. Multicoloured.

1594. 5 c. Type **458** .. .. 10 10
1595. 10 c. "Pumpkin Sellers" (statuette, Gaspar Mario Cruz) (vert.) .. 10 10
1596. 25 c. "The Market" (Celeste Woss y Gil) .. 15 15
1597. 50 c. "Horses in a Storm" (Dario Suro) .. .. 30 25

**459.** Old Church, Higuey.

**1985.** Our Lady of Altagracia's Day. Mult.

1598. 5 c. Type **459** .. .. 10 10
1599. 10 c. "Our Lady of Altagracia" (1514 painting) 15 10
1600. 25 c. Basilica of Our Lady of Altagracia, Higuey .. .. 35 30

**460.** Sanchez, Durate and Mella.

**1985.** 141st Anniv. of Independence.

1601. **460.** 5 c. multicoloured .. 10 10
1602. 10 c. multicoloured .. 15 10
1603. 25 c. multicoloured .. 35 30

**461.** Gen. Antonia Duverge.

**1985.** 141st Anniv. of Azua Battle.

1604. **461.** 10 c. cream, red and brown .. .. 15 10

**462.** Santo Domingo Lighthouse, 1853. **463.** Flags and Emblem.

**1985.** 141st Anniv. of Battle of Tortuguero.

1605. **462.** 25 c. multicoloured .. 35 30

**1985.** 25th Anniv. of American Airforces Cooperation System.

1606. **463.** 35 c. multicoloured .. 50 45

**464.** Carlos Maria Rojas (first Governor). **465.** Table Tennis Player.

**1985.** Centenary of Espaillat Province.
1607. **464.** 10 c. multicoloured . . 10 10

**1985.** "MOCA 85" (seventh National Games). Multicoloured.
1608. 5 c. Type **465** . . . . 10 10
1609. 10 c. Walking race . . 10 10

**466.** Young People of Different Races.

**1985.** International Youth Year. Mult.
1610. 5 c. Type **466** . . . . 10 10
1611. 25 c. The Haitises . . 15 10
1612. 35 c. Mt. Duarte summit 20 15
1613. 2 p. Mt. Duarte . . . . 90 85

**467.** Evangelina Rodriguez (first Dominican woman doctor). **468.** Emblem.

**1985.** International Decade for Women.
1614. **467.** 10 c. multicoloured . . 10 10

**1985.** 15th Central American and Caribbean Games, Santiago.
1615. **468.** 5 c. multicoloured . . 10 10
1616. 25 c. multicoloured . . 15 10

**469.** Fourth Christopher Columbus Regatta.

**1985.** 500th Anniv. (1992) of Discovery of America by Columbus (3rd issue). Mult.
1617. 35 c. Type **469** . . . . 75 20
1618. 50 c. Foundation of Santo Domingo, 1496 25 20
1619. 65 c. Chapel of Our Lady of the Rosary, 1496 . . 35 30
1620. 1 p. Christopher Columbus's arrival in New World . . . . 45 40

**470.** Bust of Enriquillo. **471.** Arturo de Merino.

**1985.** 450th Death Anniv. of Enriquillo (Indian chief). Multicoloured.
1621. 5 c. Enriquillo in Bahoruco mountains (mural) (46×32 mm.) 10 10
1622. 10 c. Type **470** . . . . 10 10

**1985.** Centenary of Ordination of Fernando Arturo de Merino. (former President).
1623. **471.** 25 c. multicoloured . . 15 10

**472.** Fruit, Candle and Holly.

**1985.** Christmas.
1624. **472.** 10 c, multicoloured . . 10 10
1625. 25 c. multicoloured . . 15 10

**473.** Haina Harbour.

**1985.** 25th Anniv. of Inter-American Development Bank. Multicoloured.
1626. 10 c. Type **473** . . . . 30 10
1627. 25 c. Map and ratio diagram of development activities . . 15 10
1628. 1 p. Tavera-Bao-Lopez hydro-electric complex 45 40

**474.** Mirabal Sisters.

**1985.** 25th Death Anniv. of Minerva, Patria and Maria Mirabal.
1629. **474.** 10 c. multicoloured . . 10 10

**475.** Tomb of Duarte, Sanchez and Mella.

**1986.** National Independence Day.
1630. **475.** 5 c. multicoloured . . 10 10
1631. 10 c. multicoloured . . 10 10

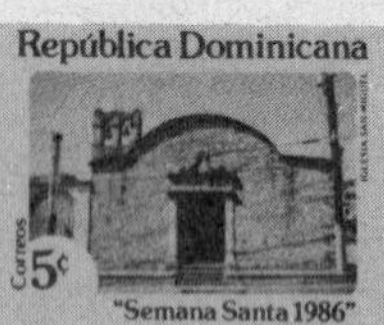


**476.** St. Michael's Church.

**1986.** Holy Week. Santo Domingo Churches. Multicoloured.
1632. 5 c. Type **476** . . . . 10 10
1633. 5 c. St. Andrew's Church 10 10
1634. 10 c. St. Lazarus's Church . . . . 10 10
1635. 10 c. St. Charles's Church 10 10
1636. 10 c. St. Barbara's Church . . . . 10 10

**477.** "Leonor" (schooner) and Dominican Navy Founders. **478.** Voters, Ballot Box and Map.

**1986.** Navy Day.
1637. **477.** 10 c. multicoloured . . 45 10

**1986.** National Elections. Multicoloured.
1638. 5 c. Type **478** . . . . 10 10
1639. 10 c. Hand dropping voting slip into ballot box . . . . 30 10

**479.** Emblem. **480.** Weightlifting.

**1986.** Creation of "Inposdom" (Dominican Postal Institute).
1640. **479.** 10 c. blue, red and gold . . . . 10 10
1641. 25 c. blue, red and silver . . . . 15 10
1642. 50 c. blue, red and black . . . . 25 20

**1986.** 15th Central American and Caribbean Games, Santiago. Multicoloured.
1643. 10 c. Type **480** . . . . 10 10
1644. 25 c. Gymnast on rings 15 10
1645. 35 c. Diving . . . . 20 15
1646. 50 c. Show-jumping . . 25 20

**481.** Ercilia Pepin. **482.** Fifth Christopher Columbus Regatta.

**1986.** Writers' Birth Centenaries. Each brown and silver.
1647. 5 c. Type **481** . . . . 10 10
1648. 10 c. Ramon Emilio Jiminez and Victor Garrido . . . . 10 10

**1986.** 500th Anniv (1992) of Discovery of America by Columbus (4th issue). Mult.
1649. 25 c. Type **482** . . . . 15 10
1650. 50 c. Foundation of Isabela city . . . . 25 20
1651. 65 c. Spanish soldiers . . 35 30
1652. 1 p. Columbus before King of Spain . . 45 40

**483.** Goalkeeper saving Ball. **484.** Maize.

**1986.** World Cup Football Championship, Mexico. Multicoloured.
1654. 50 c. Type **483** . . . . 25 20
1655. 75 c. Footballer and ball 40 35

**1986.** 2nd Caribbean Pharmacopoeia Semina. Medicinal Plants. Multicoloured.
1656. 5 c. Type **484** . . . . 10 10
1657. 10 c. Arnotto . . . . 10 10
1658. 25 c. "Momordica charantia" . . . . 15 10
1659. 50 c. Custard-apple . . 25 20

INDEX
Countries can be quickly located by referring to the index at the end of this volume.

**485.** Town with Christmas Tree.

**1986.** Christmas. Multicoloured.
1660. 5 c. Type **485.** . . . . 15 10
1661. 25 c. Village . . . . 15 10

**486.** Gomez on Horseback. **488.** Emblem.

**1986.** 150th Birth Anniv. of Maximo Gomez.
1662. **486.** 10 c. black & mauve 10 10
1663. – 25 c. black & brown 15 10
DESIGN: 25 c. Head of Gomez.

**1987.** 16th Pan-American Ophthalmology Congress, Santo Domingo.
1676. **488.** 50 c, red blue & blk. 20 15

**489.** "Ascension of Jesus Christ" (stained glass window, St. John Bosco Church). **490.** "Sorghum bicolor".

**1987.** Ascension Day.
1677. **489.** 35 c. multicoloured . . 10 10

**1987.** Edible Plants. Multicoloured.
1678. 5 c. Type **490** . . . . 10 10
1679. 25 c. "Maranta arundinacea" . . . . 10 10
1680. 65 c. "Calathea allouia" 20 15
1681. 1 p. "Voandzeia subterranea" . . . . 35 30

**491.** Emblem and People on Map.

**1987.** 25th Anniv. of Club Activo 20–30 in Dominican Republic.
1682. **491.** 35 c. multicoloured . . 10 10

**492** Sixth Christopher Columbus Regatta

**1987.** 500th Anniv (1992) of Discovery of America by Columbus (5th issue). Mult.
1683 50 c. Type **492** . . . . 10 10
1684 75 c. Columbus writing diary . . . . 15 10
1685 1 p. Foundation of city of Santiago . . . . 20 15
1686 1 p. 50 Columbus and Bobadilla . . . . 30 25

493 Games Emblem

494 Jose Antonio Hungria

**1987.** 50th Anniv of La Vega Province Games.
1688 **493** 40 c. multicoloured .. 10 10

**1987.** Writers' Birth Anniversaries.
1689 **494** 10 c. brown & lt brn 10 10
1690 – 25 c. deep green & grn 10 10
DESIGN: 25 c. Joaquin Sergio Inchaustegui.

495 Baseball

496 Statue

**1987.** 8th National Games, San Cristobal. Multicoloured.
1691 5 c. Type **495** .. .. 10 10
1692 10 c. Boxing .. .. 10 10
1693 50 c. Karate .. .. 10 10

**1987.** 150th Birth Anniv of Fr. Francisco Xavier Billini.
1694 **496** 10 c. deep blue & blue 10 10
1695 – 25 c. green and olive 10 10
1696 – 75 c. brown and pink 15 10
DESIGNS: 25 c. Fr. Billini; 75 c. Ana Hernandez de Billini (mother).

497 Maj. Frank Feliz and Airplane

**1987.** 50th Anniv of Pan-American Flight for Columbus Lighthouse Fund.
1697 **497** 25 c. multicoloured .. 20 10

498 Spit-roasting Pig

**1987.** Christmas. Multicoloured.
1699 10 c. Type **498** .. .. 10 10
1700 50 c. Passsengers disembarking from airplane 20 10

499 "Bromelia pinguin"

**1988.** Flowers. Multicoloured
1701 50 c. Type **499** .. .. 10 10
1702 50 c. "Tillandsia compacta" (vert) .. 10 10
1703 50 c. "Tillandsia fasciculata" .. .. 10 10
1704 50 c. "Tillandsia hotteana" (vert) .. 10 10

500 St. John Bosco

**1988.** Death Centenary of St. John Bosco (founder of Salesian Brothers). Multicoloured.
1705 10 c. Type **500** .. .. 10 10
1706 70 c. Stained glass window 15 10

501 Rainbow, Doves and Cloud

**1988.** 25th Anniv of Dominican Rehabilitation Association.
1707 **501** 20 c. multicoloured .. 10 10

502 Perdomo

503 Emblem

**1988.** Birth Centenary of Dr. Manuel Emilio Perdomo.
1708 **502** 20 c. brown and flesh 10 10

**1988.** 25th Anniv of Dominican College of Engineering and Architecture (CODIA).
1709 **503** 20 c. multicoloured .. 10 10

504 Church and Madonna and Child

505 Flags and Juan Pablo Duarte (Dominican patriot)

**1988.** Centenary of Parish Church of Our Lady of the Carmelites, Duverge.
1710 **504** 50 c. multicoloured .. 10 10

**1988.** Mexican Independence Day. Mult.
1711 50 c. Type **505** .. .. 10 10
1712 50 c. Flags and Miguel Hidalgo (Mexican patriot) .. .. 10 10

506 Athletics

507 Seventh Christopher Columbus Regatta

**1988.** Olympic Games, Seoul. Multicoloured.
1713 50 c. Type **506** .. .. 10 10
1714 70 c. Table tennis .. 15 10
1715 1 p. Judo .. .. 20 15
1716 1 p. 50 "Ying Yang symbol and Balls" (Tete Marella) (horiz) 30 25

**1988.** 500th Anniv of Discovery of America by Columbus (6th issue). Multicoloured.
1717 50 c. Type **507** .. .. 10 10
1718 70 c. Building fort at La Vega Real, 1494 .. 15 10
1719 1 p. 50 Bonao Fort .. 30 25
1720 2 p. Nicolas de Ovando (Governor of Hispaniola) .. .. 40 35

508 Duarte, Mella and Sanchez

509 Parchment, Knife and Pestle and Mortar

**1988.** 150th Anniv of Trinitarian Rebellion.
1722 **508** 10 c. silver, red & blue 10 10
1723 – 1 p. multicoloured .. 20 15
1724 – 5 p. multicoloured .. 95 90
DESIGNS: 1 p. Plaza La Trinitaria; 5 p. Plaza de la Independencia.

**1988.** 13th Panamerican and 16th Central American Congresses of Pharmacy and Biochemistry.
1725 **509** 1 p. multicoloured .. 20 15

510 "Doni Tondo" (Michelangelo)

511 Emblem

**1988.** Christmas. Multicoloured.
1726 10 c. Type **510** .. .. 10 10
1727 20 c. Stained glass window 10 10

**1988.** 50th Anniv. of Dominican Municipal Association.
1728 **511** 20 c. multicoloured .. 10 10

512 Ana Teresa Paradas

513 Birds

**1988.** 28th Death Anniv of Ana Teresa Paradas (lawyer).
1729 **512** 20 c. red .. .. 10 10

**1989.** Bicentenary of French Revolution.
1730 **513** 3 p. red, blue & black 30 25

516 Battle Scene

**1989.** 145th Anniv of Battle of Tortuguero.
1737 **516** 40 c. multicoloured .. 30 15

517 Drug Addict

**1989.** Anti-drugs Campaign.
1738 **517** 10 c. multicoloured .. 10 10
1739 20 c. multicoloured .. 10 10
1740 50 c. multicoloured .. 10 10
1741 70 c. multicoloured .. 10 10
1742 1 p. multicoloured .. 10 10
1743 1 p. 50 multicoloured 15 15
1744 2 p. multicoloured .. 20 15
1745 5 p. multicoloured .. 50 45
1746 10 p. multicoloured .. 1·00 95

518 Breastfeeding Baby

519 Eugenio Maria de Hostos

**1989.** Mothers' Day.
1747 **518** 20 c. multicoloured .. 10 10

**1989.** 150th Birth Anniversaries. Mult.
1748 20 c. Type **519** .. .. 10 10
1749 20 c. Gen. Gregorio Luperon .. .. 10 10

520 Baseball

**1989.** 50th Anniv of Baseball Minor League.
1750 **520** 1 p. multicoloured .. 10 10

521 Map and Human Organs

**1989.** 7th Latin American Diabetes Association Congress.
1751 **521** 1 p. multicoloured .. 10 10

522 Cohoba Artefact and Ritual Dance

**1989.** America. Pre-Columbian Culture. Mult.
1752 20 c. Type **522** .. .. 10 10
1753 1 p. Taina vessel, pounding instrument and Indians preparing manioc cake .. .. 10 10

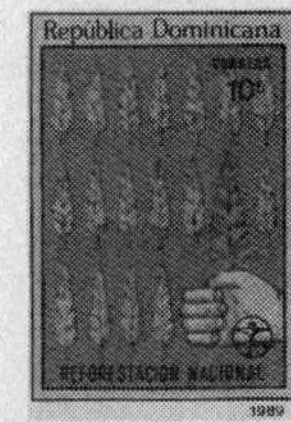


523 Eighth Christopher Columbus Regatta

524 Dead and Living Leaves

**1989.** 500th Anniv (1992) of Discovery of America by Columbus (7th issue). Mult.

1754 50 c. Type **523** .. .. 10 10
1755 70 c. Brother Pedro de Cordoba preaching to Indians (horiz) .. 10 10
1756 1 p. Columbus dividing Indian lands (horiz) .. 10 10
1757 3 p. Brother Antonio Montesinos giving sermon (horiz) .. 30 25

**1989.** National Reafforestation Campaign. Multicoloured.

1758 10 c. Type **524** .. .. 10 10
1759 20 c. Forest .. .. 10 10
1760 50 c. Forest and lake .. 10 10
1761 1 p. Living tree and avenue of dead trees .. 10 10

**525** Map and Cyclist

**526** Mary and Body of Jesus

**1990.** 9th National Games, La Vega. Mult.

1762 10 c. Type **525** .. .. 10 10
1763 20 c. Map and runner .. 10 10
1764 50 c. Map and handball player .. .. .. 10 10

**1990.** Holy Week. Multicoloured.

1765 20 c. Type **526** .. .. 10 10
1766 50 c. Jesus carrying cross 10 10

**527** Cogwheel and Workers

**1990.** International Labour Day.

1767 **527** 1 p. multicoloured .. 10 10

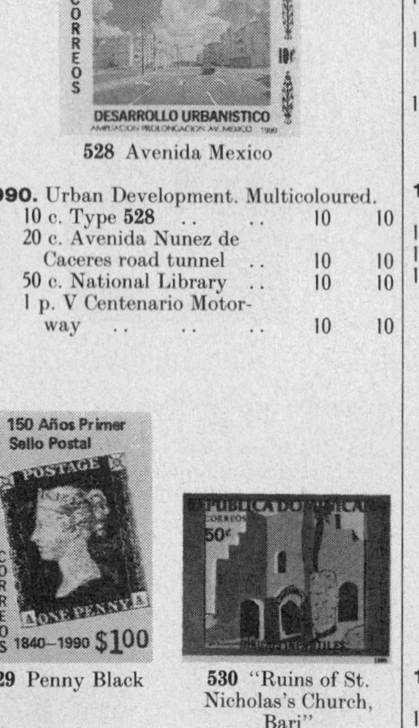

**528** Avenida Mexico

**1990.** Urban Development. Multicoloured.

1768 10 c. Type **528** .. .. 10 10
1769 20 c. Avenida Nunez de Caceres road tunnel .. 10 10
1770 50 c. National Library .. 10 10
1771 1 p. V Centenario Motorway .. .. .. 10 10

**529** Penny Black

**530** "Ruins of St. Nicholas's Church, Bari"

**1990.** 150th Anniv of the Penny Black. Mult.

1772 **529** 1 p. multicoloured .. 10 10

**1990.** Children's Drawings. Multicoloured.

1774 50 c. Type **530** .. .. 10 10
1775 50 c. "House, Tostado" .. 10 10

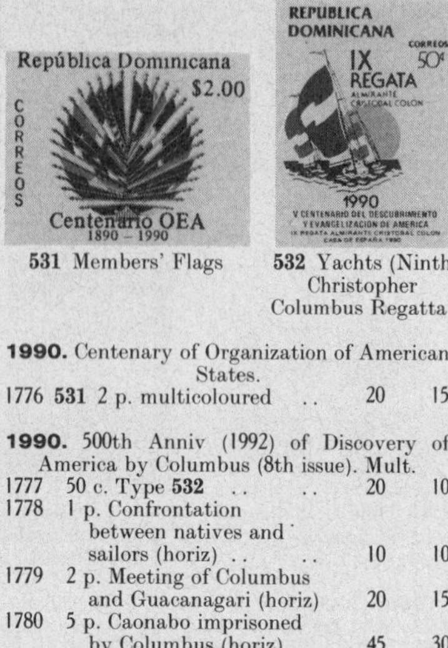

**531** Members' Flags

**532** Yachts (Ninth Christopher Columbus Regatta)

**1990.** Centenary of Organization of American States.

1776 **531** 2 p. multicoloured .. 20 15

**1990.** 500th Anniv (1992) of Discovery of America by Columbus (8th issue). Mult.

1777 50 c. Type **532** .. .. 20 10
1778 1 p. Confrontation between natives and sailors (horiz) .. .. 10 10
1779 2 p. Meeting of Columbus and Guacanagari (horiz) 20 15
1780 5 p. Caonabo imprisoned by Columbus (horiz) .. 45 30

**533** Amerindians in Canoe

**534** Perez Rancier

**1990.** America. Multicoloured.

1781 50 c. Type **533** .. .. 20 10
1782 3 p. Amerindian in hammock .. .. 25 15

**1991.** Birth Centenary of Dr. Tomas Eudoro Perez Rancier (physician).

1783 **534** 2 p. black and yellow 20 10

**535** First Official Mass in America

**536** Boxing

**1991.** Spanish America. Multicoloured.

1784 50 c. Type **535** .. .. 10 10
1785 1 p. Arms (first religious orders) .. .. 10 10
1786 3 p. Map of Hispaniola (first European settlement) (horiz) .. 30 20
1787 4 p. Christopher Columbus (first viceroy and governor) .. .. 45 30

**1991.** 11th Pan-American Games, Havana. Multicoloured.

1788 30 c. Type **536** .. .. 10 10
1789 50 c. Cycling .. .. 10 10
1790 1 p. Putting the shot .. 10 10

**537** Yachts (10th Christopher Columbus Regatta)

**538** Eye and Hands

**1991.** 500th Anniv (1992) of Discovery of America by Columbus (9th issue). Mult.

1791 30 c. Type **537** .. .. 10 10
1792 50 c. Meeting of three cultures (horiz) .. 10 10
1793 3 p. Columbus and Doctor Alvarez Chanco (horiz) 30 20
1794 4 p. Enriquillo's war (horiz) .. .. 45 30

**1991.** Cornea Bank.

1795 **538** 3 p. black and red .. 30 20

**539** "Santa Maria"

**540** Meeting Emblem

**1991.** America. Voyages of Discovery. Mult.

1796 1 p. Type **539** .. .. 10 10
1797 3 p. Columbus and fleet 30 20

**1992.** 33rd Annual Meeting of Governors of Inter-American Development Bank, Santo Domingo.

1798 **540** 1 p. multicoloured .. 10 10

**541** Valentin Salinero (founder)

**542** Flags of Cuba, Dominican Republic and Puerto Rica, and Magnifying Glass

**1992.** Centenary (1991) of Order of the Apostles.

1799 **541** 1 p. brown, black & bl 10 10

**1992.** "Espanola 92" Stamp Exhibition.

1800 **542** 3 p. black, violet & red 30 20

**543** First Monastery in Americas

**1992.** Ruins. Multicoloured.

1801 50 c. Type **543** .. .. 10 10
1802 3 p. First hospital in Americas .. .. 30 20

**544** La Vega Cathedral and Pope

**545** Yacht (11th Christopher Columbus Regatta)

**1992.** Visit of Pope John Paul II. Mult.

1803 50 c. Type **544** .. .. 10 10
1804 3 p. Santo Domingo Cathedral and Pope .. 30 20

**1992.** 500th Anniv of Discovery of America by Columbus (10th issue). Multicoloured.

1805 50 c. Type **545** .. .. 10 10
1806 1 p. Amerindian women preparing food and Columbus (horiz) .. 10 10
1807 2 p. Amerindians demonstrating use of tobacco to Columbus (horiz) .. .. 20 10
1808 3 p. Amerindian woman and Columbus by maize field (horiz) .. .. 30 20

**546** Columbus Lighthouse

**547** Convention Emblem

**1992.**

1809 **546** 30 c. multicoloured .. 10 10
1810 1 p. multicoloured .. 10 10

**1992.** 23rd Pan-American Round Table Convention, Santo Domingo.

1812 **547** 1 p. brn, cream & red 10 10

**548** First Royal Palace in Americas, Santo Domingo

**549** Torch Bearer

**1992.** America. Multicoloured.

1813 50 c. Type **548** .. .. 10 10
1814 3 p. First Vice-regal residence in Americas, Colon .. .. .. 30 20

**1992.** 10th National Games, San Juan.

1815 **549** 30 c. multicoloured .. 10 10
1816 – 1 p. mutlicoloured .. 10 10
1817 – 4 p. black and blue .. 40 25

DESIGNS: 1 p. Emblem of Secretary of State for Sports Education and Recreation; 4 p. Judo.

**550** Emblem

**551** Ema Balaguer

**1993.** 7th Population and Housing Census.

1818 **550** 50 c. blue, blk & pink 10 10
1819 1 p. blue, black & brn 10 10
1820 3 p. blue, black & grey 30 20
1821 4 p. blue, black & grn 40 25

**1993.** Ema Balaguer (humanitarian worker) Commemoration.

1822 **551** 30 c. multicoloured .. 10 10
1823 50 c. multicoloured .. 10 10
1824 1 p. multicoloured .. 10 10

**552** Emblem and Stylized Figures

**1993.** 50th Anniv of Santo Domingo Rotary Club. Multicoloured.

1825 30 c. Type **552** .. .. 10 10
1826 1 p. National flags and rotary emblem .. 10 10

**553** Institute

**1993.** Inauguration of New Dominican Postal Institute Building.

1827 553 1 p. multicoloured .. 10 10
1828 3 p. multicoloured .. 30 20
1829 4 p. multicoloured .. 40 25
1830 5 p. multicoloured .. 50 30
1831 10 p. multicoloured .. 95 60

554 Bird and Books

555 Racketball

**1993.** Ten Year Education Plan.

1833 554 1 p. 50 multicoloured 15 10

**1993.** 17th Central American and Caribbean Games, Ponce (Puerto Rico). Multicoloured.

1834 50 c. Type 555 .. .. 10 10
1835 4 p. Swimming .. .. 40 25

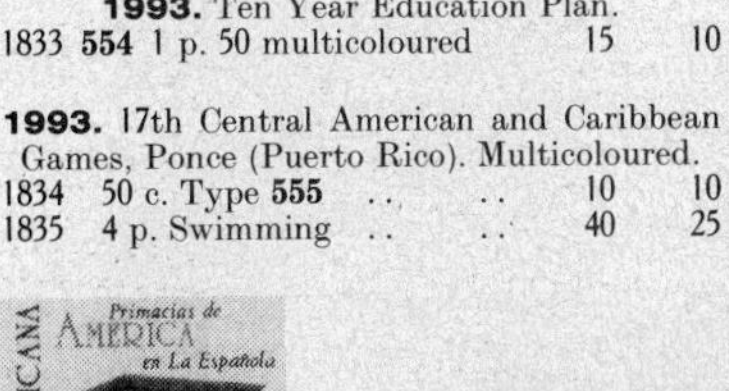

556 Chest (first university)

557 Hispaniolan Conure

**1993.** American Firsts in Hispaniola (1st series). Multicoloured.

1836 50 c. Type 556 .. .. 10 10
1837 3 p. First arms conferred on American city .. 30 20

See also Nos. 1840 and 1882/3.

**1993.** America. Endangered Animals. Mult.

1838 1 p. Type 557 .. .. 10 10
1839 3 p. Rhinoceros iguana .. 30 20

558 Cross and Eucharist (500th anniv of first Mass)

559 State Flag, 1946 15 c. and 1944 3 c. Stamps

**1994.** American Firsts in Hispaniola (2nd series).

1840 558 2 p. multicoloured .. 20 10

**1994.** 5th National Stamp Exhibition.

1841 559 3 p. multicoloured .. 30 20

560 Signing of Independence Treaty (left-hand detail)

**1994.** 150th Anniv of Independence. Mult.

1842 2 p. Type 560 .. .. 20 10
1843 2 p. Signing of Independence Treaty (right-hand detail) .. 20 10
1844 2 p. State flag .. .. 20 10
1845 2 p. Soldier with young woman .. .. 20 10
1846 2 p. Boy helping woman make flag .. .. 20 10
1847 3 p. Revolutionaries (back view of left-hand man) 30 20
1848 3 p. Revolutionaries (window behind men) 30 20
1849 3 p. State arms .. .. 30 20
1850 3 p. Revolutionaries (all turned away from door) 30 20
1851 3 p. Revolutionaries with flag .. .. .. 30 20

Stamps of the same value were issued together, se-tenant, Nos. 1842/3, 1845/6, 1847/8 and 1850/1 forming composite designs.

561 Solenodon on Dead Wood

**1994.** The Haitian Solenodon Multicoloured.

1853 1 p. Type 561 .. .. 10 10
1854 1 p. Solenodon amongst leaves .. .. .. 10 10
1855 1 p. Solenodon on stony ground .. .. 10 10
1856 1 p. Solenodon eating insect .. .. .. 10 10

562 Fusiliers behind Barricade (19 March)

563 Ballot Boxes

**1994.** 150th Anniversaries of Battles of 19 and 30 March. Multicoloured.

1857 2 p. Type 562 .. .. 20 10
1858 2 p. Battle at fort (30 March) .. .. 20 10

**1994.** National Elections.

1859 563 2 p. multicoloured .. 20 10

564 "Virgin of Amparo"

565 Goalkeeper

**1994.** 150th Anniv of Naval Battle of Puerto Tortuguero.

1860 564 3 p. multicoloured .. 30 20

**1994.** World Cup Football Championship, U.S.A. Multicoloured.

1861 4 p. Type 565 .. .. 40 25
1862 6 p. Players contesting possession of ball .. 60 40

566 Figures in Houses

**1994.** Ema Balguer Children's City.

1863 566 1 p. mauve and brown 10 10

567 1866 Medio Real Stamp and Cancellation

**1994.** Stamp Day.

1864 567 5 p. red, black & yell 45 30

## MORE DETAILED LISTS

are given in the Stanley Gibbons Catalogues referred to in the country headings.
For lists of current volumes see Introduction.

568 Postal Carrier on Horseback

571 Writing Desk and Constitution

**1994.** America. Postal Vehicles. Mult.

1865 2 p. Type 568 .. .. 20 10
1866 6 p. Schooner .. .. 55 35

**1994.** 150th Anniv of First Constitution of Dominican Republic.

1876 571 3 p. multicoloured .. 25 15

572 Flight into Egypt

**1994.** Christmas. International Year of the Family. Multicoloured.

1877 2 p. Type 572 .. .. 20 10
1878 3 p. Family .. .. 25 15

573 Ruins of St. Francis's Monastery

**1994.** 500th Anniv of Concepcion de la Vega.

1879 573 3 p. multicoloured .. 25 15

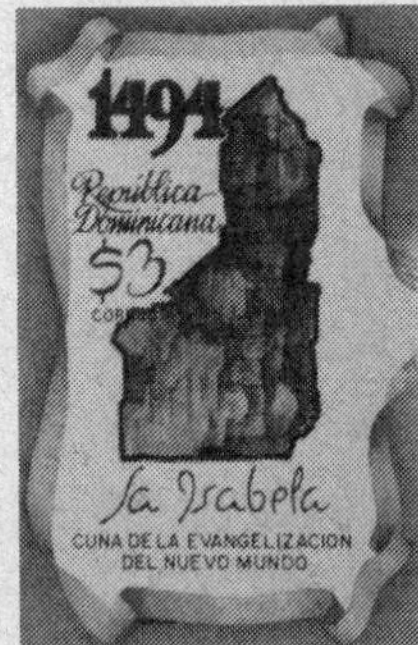


574 Wall of La Isabela Church

**1994.** 500th Anniv of First Church in Dominican Republic. Multicoloured.

1880 3 p. Type 574 .. .. 25 15
1881 3 p. Temple of the Americas .. .. 25 15

Nos. 1880/1 were issued together, se-tenant, forming a composite design.

**1994.** American Firsts in Hispaniola (3rd series). As T 556. Multicoloured.

1882 2 p. First coins, 1505 .. 20 10
1883 5 p. Antonio Montesino (first plea for justice (in Advent sermon), 1511) 45 30

575 "Hypsirhynchus ferox"

**1994.** National Natural History Museum. Snakes. Multicoloured.

1884 2 p. Type 575 .. .. 20 10
1885 2 p. "Antillophis parvifrons" .. .. 20 10
1886 2 p. "Uromacer catesbyi" 20 10
1887 2 p. Bahama boa ("Epicrates striatus") 20 10

Nos. 1884/5 and 1886/7 respectively were issued together, se-tenant, each pair forming a composite design of a tree and the snakes.

576 Taekwondo

**1995.** Pan-American Games, Mar del Plata, Argentine Republic.

1888 576 4 p. blue, red & black 35 20
1889 – 13 p. green, blk & yell 1·25 80

DESIGN: 13 p. Tennis.

577 Allegory of Dominican Agriculture

**1995.** 50th Anniv of F.A.O.

1890 577 4 p. multicoloured .. 35 20

578 Jose Marti, Maximo Gomez and Monte Cristi Clock Tower

579 Emblem

**1995.** Centenaries.

1891 578 2 p. brown, pink & blk 20 10
1892 – 3 p. pink, black & bl 25 15
1893 – 4 p. black and pink .. 35 20

DESIGNS: 3 p. Jose Marti on Cuban national flag (death centenary); 4 p. Gomez and Marti signing Monte Cristi manifesto.

**1995.** "Centrobasket" Basketball Championship, Santo Domingo.

1894 579 3 p. blue, red & black 25 15

580 "Pimenta ozua"

581 San Souci Port

**1995.** Medicinal Plants. Multicoloured.

1895 2 p. Type 580 .. .. 20 10
1896 2 p. "Melocactus communis" .. .. 20 10
1897 3 p. "Smilax sp." .. 25 15
1898 3 p. "Zamia sp." .. 25 15

**1995.** Tourism. Multicoloured.

1899 4 p. Type 581 .. .. 35 20
1900 5 p. Barahona airport .. 45 30
1901 6 p. G. Luperon airport .. 55 35
1902 13 p. Las Americas airport 1·25 80

**582** Ruins of Jacagua Church

**1995.** 500th Anniv of Santiago de los Caballeros.

1903 **582** 3 p. multicoloured .. 25 15

**583** Sei Whale ("Balaenoptera borealis")

**1995.** Natural History Museum. Whales. Multicoloured.

1904 3 p. Type **583** .. .. 25 15

1905 3 p. Humpback whales ("Megaptera nova-eangliae") .. .. 25 15

1906 3 p. Sperm whales ("Physeter macrocephalus") .. .. 25 15

1907 3 p. Cuvier's beaked whales ("Ziphius cavirostris") .. .. 25 15

**584** Rafael Colon **585** Cancelled 1880 2 c. Stamp

**1995.** Singers. Multicoloured.

1908 2 p. Type **584** .. .. 20 10

1909 3 p. Casandra Damiron .. 25 15

**1995.** Stamp Day.

1910 **585** 4 p. multicoloured .. 35 20

**586** Player **587** Anniversary Emblem

**1995.** Centenary of Volleyball.

1911 **586** 6 p. multicoloured .. 55 35

**1995.** 50th Anniv of U.N.O.

1913 **587** 2 p. blue and gold .. 20 10

1914 – 6 p. multicoloured .. 55 35

DESIGN: 33×55 mm—6 p. Allegorical design.

**588** Allegory **589** Columbus Lighthouse

**1995.** 4th World Conference on Women, Peking.

1915 **588** 2 p. multicoloured .. 20 10

**1995.**

1916 **589** 10 p. ultram, bl & blk 90 60

**590** Enriquillo Lake **591** Antonio Mesa (tenor)

**1995.** America. Environmental Protection. Multicoloured.

1917 2 p. Type **590** .. .. 20 10

1918 6 p. Mangrove plantation 55 35

**1995.** Singers. Each red and brown.

1919 2 p. Type **591** .. .. 20 10

1920 2 p. Susano Polanco (tenor) .. .. 20 10

1921 2 p. Julieta Otero (soprano) .. .. 20 10

**592** Cathedral

**1995.** Centenary of Santiago Cathedral.

1922 **592** 3 p. multicoloured .. 25 15

**593** Corsair Fighter **594** Brito

**1995.** 50th Anniv of Dominican Air Force (1st issue). Multicoloured.

1923 2 p. Type **593** .. .. 20 10

1924 2 p. Stearman Pt-17 Kaydett bomber .. 20 10

1925 2 p. North American T-6 Texan trainer .. 20 10

1926 2 p. Consolidated PBY-5A Catalina amphibian .. 20 10

1927 2 p. Bristol Beaufighter fighter .. .. 20 10

1928 2 p. De Havilland Mosquito bomber .. 20 10

1929 2 p. Lockheed P-38 Lightning fighter .. 20 10

1930 2 p. North American P-51 Mustang fighter .. 20 10

1931 2 p. Boeing B-17 Flying Fortress bomber .. 20 10

1932 2 p. Republic P-47 Thunderbolt fighter .. 20 10

1933 2 p. De Havilland Vampire jet fighter .. 20 10

1934 2 p. Curtiss C-46 Commander .. .. 20 10

1935 2 p. Boeing B-26 Invader 20 10

1936 2 p. Douglas C-47 Skytrain transport .. 20 10

1937 2 p. T-28D Trojan .. 20 10

1938 2 p. T-33A Silverstar .. 20 10

1939 2 p. Cessna T-41D .. 20 10

1940 2 p. T-34 Mentor .. 20 10

1941 2 p. Cessna O-2A .. 20 10

1942 2 p. Cessna A-37B Dragonfly fighter .. 20 10

See also Nos. 1958/63.

**1996.** 50th Death Anniv of Eduardo Brito (singer).

1943 **594** 1 p. multicoloured .. 10 10

1944 – 2 p. multicoloured .. 20 10

1945 – 3 p. black and pink .. 25 15

DESIGNS: 55×35 mm—2 p. Brito playing maracas. As T **594**—3 p. Brito (different).

**595** Yachts

**1996.** Hispaniola Cup Yachting Championship.

1946 **595** 5 p. multicoloured .. 45 30

**596** Children

**1996.** 50th Anniv of U.N.I.C.E.F.

1947 **596** 2 p. black and green 20 10

1948 – 4 p. black and green 35 20

DESIGN:—4 p. As T **596** but motif reversed.

**597** Arturo Pallerano, Freddy Gaton and Rafael Herrera

**1996.** National Journalists' Day.

1949 **597** 5 p. multicoloured .. 45 30

**598** Emblem, Astronaut and Biplane

**1996.** "Espamer" Spanish–Latin American and "Aviation and Space" Stamp Exhibitions, Seville, Spain.

1950 **598** 15 p. multicoloured .. 1·40 90

**599** Judo

**1996.** Olympic Games, Atlanta. Each black, blue and red

1951 5 p. Type **599** .. .. 45 30

1952 15 p. Torchbearer .. 1·40 90

**600** Greek 1896 2 l. Olympic Stamp

**1996.** Centenary of Modern Olympic Games.

1953 **600** 6 p. green, red & black 55 35

1954 – 15 p. multicoloured .. 1·40 90

DESIGN: 15 p. Dominican Republic 1937 7 c. Olympic stamp.

**601** "Girl at Postbox"

**1996.** "The Post is your Friend". Winning Entries in Children's Stamp Design Competition. Multicoloured.

1955 3 p. Type **601** .. .. 20 10

1956 3 p. Representations of world post .. .. 20 10

1957 3 p. Postal carrier on horseback delivering letter (vert) .. .. 20 10

**602** Sikorsky S-55

**1996.** 50th Anniv of Air Force (2nd issue). Helicopters. Multicoloured.

1958 3 p. Type **602** .. .. 20 10

1959 3 p. Sud Aviation Alouette II .. .. 20 10

1960 3 p. Sud Aviation Alouette III .. .. 20 10

1961 3 p. OH-6A Cayuse .. 20 10

1962 3 p. Bell 205 A-1 .. 20 10

1963 3 p. Aerospatiale SA.365 Dauphin 2 .. .. 20 10

**603** Workers and Children

**1996.** United Nations Decade against Drug Trafficking.

1964 **603** 15 p. multicoloured .. 1·40 90

## EXPRESS DELIVERY STAMPS

E 40. Biplane.

**1920.**

E 232. **E 40.** 10 c. blue .. .. 5·50 1·00

E 42.

**1925.** Inscr. "ENTREGA ESPECIAL".

E 247. **E 42.** 10 c. blue .. .. 10·00 2·00

**1927.** Inscr. "EXPRESO".

E 250. **E 42.** 10 c brown .. 5·00 1·00
E 459. 10 c. green .. .. 2·00 70

E 123.

**1945.**

E 539. **E 123.** 10 c. blue, red and carmine .. .. 45 20

E 137. Shield, Hand and Letter.

**1950.**

E 594. **E 137.** 10 c. red, grn. & blue 45 20

E 161.

**1956.**

E 663 **E 161** 25c green .. 70 30

E 228. Pigeon and Letter.

**1967.**

E 995. **E 228.** 25 c. blue .. .. 65 25

E 345. Globe, and Pigeon carrying Letter.

E 370. Motorcycle Messenger and Aeroplane.

**1978.**

E 1330. **E 345.** 25 c. multicoloured 55 30

**1979.**

E 1385. **E 370.** 25 c. ultramarine, blue and red .. 55 35

E 514 Motor Cyclist

**1989.** Special Delivery.

E1731 E 514 1 p. multicoloured 10 10

## OFFICIAL STAMPS

**O 23.** Bastion of 27 February.

**O 44.** Columbus Lighthouse.

**1902.**

O 121. **O 23.** 2 c. black and red .. 25 15
O 122. 5 c. black & blue .. 40 15
O 123. 10 c. black & green .. 45 20
O 124. 20 c. black & yellow 55 35

**1910.** As Type O 23, but inscr. "27 DE FEBRERO 1844" and "10 DE AGOSTO 1865" at sides.

O 177. **O 23.** 1 c. black & green .. 15 15
O 178. 2 c. black & red .. 15 15
O 179. 5 c. black and blue .. 25 20
O 180. 10 c. black & green .. 55 40
O 181. 20 c. black & yellow 1·00 55

**1928.**

O 251. **O 44.** 1 c. green .. .. 10 10
O 252. 2 c. red .. .. 10 10
O 253. 5 c. blue .. .. 15 15
O 254. 10 c. blue .. .. 25 25
O 255. 20 c. yellow .. .. 35 35

**1931.** Air. Optd. **CORREO AEREO.**

O 292. **O 44.** 10 c. blue .. .. 12·00 10·00
O 293. 20 c. yellow .. 12·00 10·00

O 82. Columbus Lighthouse.

**1937.** White letters and figures.

O 393. **O 82.** 3 c. violet .. .. 25 10
O 394. 7 c. blue .. .. 35 25
O 395. 10 c. yellow .. .. 45 35

O 88. Columbus Lighthouse.

**1939.** Coloured letters and figures.

O 409. **O 88.** 1 c. green .. .. 10 10
O 410. 2 c. red .. 10 10
O 411. 3 c. violet .. 10 10
O 412. 5 c. blue .. 25 15
O 414. 7 c. blue .. 55 15
O 415. 10 c. orange .. 40 15
O 416. 20 c. brown .. 1·00 25
O 577. 50 c. mauve .. 1·25 70
O 417. 50 c. red .. .. 2·00 85

No. O 417 has smaller figures of value than No. O 577.

**1950.** Values inscr. "CENTAVOS ORO".

O 578. **O 88.** 5 c. blue .. .. 15 10
O 581. 7 c. blue .. .. 15 10
O 579. 10 c. yellow .. 35 15
O 582. 20 c. brown .. 35 25
O 583. 50 c. purple .. 85 55

## POSTAGE DUE STAMPS

D 22. D 110.

**1901.**

D 117. **D 22.** 2 c. sepia .. .. 40 10
D 118. 4 c. sepia .. .. 50 15
D 119. 5 c. sepia .. .. 1·00 20
D 175. 6 c. sepia .. .. 1·40 50
D 120. 10 c. sepia .. .. 1·60 20

**1913.**

D 239. **D 22.** 1 c. olive .. .. 40 35
D 191. 2 c. olive .. .. 35 20
D 192. 4 c. olive .. .. 40 15
D 193. 6 c. olive .. .. 50 15
D 194. 10 c. olive .. .. 70 30

**1942.** Size 20½ × 25½ mm.

D 485. **D 110.** 1 c. red .. .. 15 10
D 486. 2 c. blue .. .. 15 10
D 487. 2 c. blue .. .. 70 50
D 488. 4 c. green .. 15 15
D 489. 6 c. brown & buff 20 20
D 490. 8 c. orge. & yell... 25 20
D 491. 10 c. mauve & pink 35 30

**1966.** Size 21 × 25½ mm. Inscr. larger and in white.

D 492. **D 110.** 1 c. red .. .. 70 70
D 493. 2 c. blue .. .. 70 70
D 494. 4 c. green .. 1·75 1·75

## REGISTRATION STAMPS

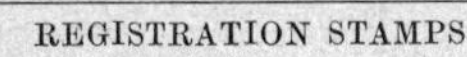

**1935.** De Merino stamps of 1933 surch. **PRIMA VALORES DECLARADOS SERVICIO INTERIOR** and value in figures and words.

R 339. – 8 c. on ½ c. (No. 316) 1·40 1·00
R 340. – 8 c. on 7 c. blue .. 35 15
R 342. **56.** 15 c. on 10 c. orange .. 35 15
R 343. – 30 c. on 8 c. green .. 1·40 50
R 344. – 45 c. on 20 c. red .. 2·00 70
R 345. **57.** 70 c. on 50 c. olive .. 4·75 1·00

R 97. National Coat of Arms. R 98.

**1940.**

R 448. **R 97.** 8 c. black and red .. 45 20
R 449. 15 c. black & orange 85 30
R 450. 30 c. black and green 1·40 15
R 451. 70 c. black & purple 3·25 1·00

**1944.** Redrawn. Larger figures of value and "c" as in Type R **98.**

R 452. **R 98.** 45 c. black and blue 1·60 35
R 453. 70 c. black & olive .. 2·00 30

**1953.**

R 454. **R 98.** 8 c. black & red .. 45 20
R 455. 10 c. black & lake 50 15
R 456. 15 c. black & orange 9·50 2·40

R 155. R 221.

**1955.** Redrawn. Arms and "c" smaller.

R 646. **R 155.** 10 c. black and red .. .. 35 10
R 647. 10 c. black and lilac .. .. 70 25
R 648. 15 c. black and orange .. 1·40 1·10
R 649. 20 c. black and orange .. 60 35
R 650. 20 c. black and red .. 70 45
R 651. 30 c. black and green .. .. 90 20
R 652a. 40 c. black and green .. .. 1·25 55
R 653. 45 c. black and blue .. 2·50 1·10
R 654. 60 c. black and yellow .. 1·60 1·10
R 655. 70 c. black and brown .. 2·50 1·40

**1963.** Redrawn as Type R 97.

R909 10 c. black and orang 40 25
R910 20 c. black and orange 55 45

**1965.**

R 961. **R 221.** 10 c. black & lilac .. 35 20
R 962. 40 c. black & yellow 1·40 85

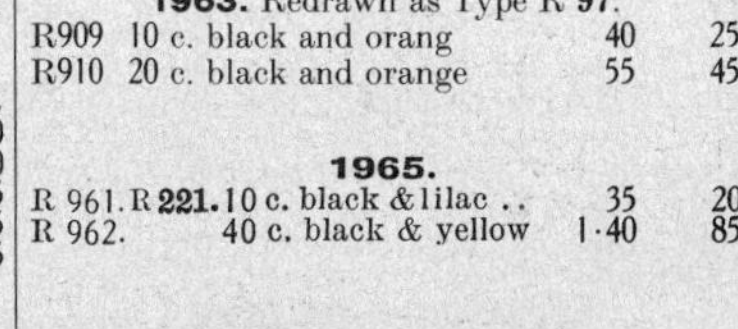

R 282a. R 487.

**1973.**

R 1335. **R 282a.** 10 c. black and violet .. .. 35 15
R 1148. 20 c. black and orange .. 70 55
R 1149. 40 c. black and green .. .. 85 45
R 1150. 70 c. black and blue .. .. 1·60 1·10

**1986.** Redrawn with figures of value and "c" smaller. Inscribed "PRIMA DE VALORES DECLARADOS". Arms in black.

R 1664. **R 487.** 20 c. mauve .. 10 10
R 1665. 60 c. orange .. 20 15
R 1666. 1 p. blue .. 35 30
R 1667. 1 p. 25 pink .. 40 35
R 1668. 1 p. 50 red .. 50 45
R 1669. 3 p. green .. 1·00 95
R 1670. 3 p. 50 bistre .. 1·25 1·10
R 1671. 4 p. yellow .. 1·40 1·25
R 1672. 4 p. 50 green .. 1·50 1·40
R 1673. 5 p. brown .. 1·75 1·50
R 1674. 6 p. grey .. 2·00 1·75
R 1675. 6 p. 50 blue .. 2·25 2·00

R 515

**1989.** Inscribed "PRIMA VALORES DECLARADOS". Arms in black.

R 1732 R 515 20 c. purple .. 10 10
R 1733 60 c. orange .. 10 10
R 1734 1 p. blue .. 10 10
R 1735 1 p. 25 pink .. 15 10
R 1736 1 p. 50 red .. 15 15

R 569

R 570

**1994.** Arms in black.

R1867 R 569 50 c. mauve .. 10 10
R1868 R 570 1 p. blue .. 10 10
R1869 1 p. 50 red .. 15 10
R1870 2 p. pink .. 20 10
R1871 3 p. blue .. 25 15
R1872 5 p. yellow .. 45 30
R1873 6 p. green .. 55 35
R1874 8 p. green .. 70 45
R1875 10 p. silver .. 90 60

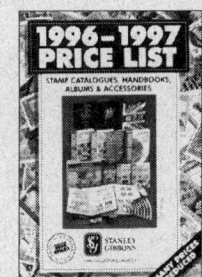

## DUBAI Pt. 19

One of the Trucial States in the Persian Gulf. Formerly used the stamps of Muscat. British control of the postal services ceased in 1963.

On 2 December, 1971, Dubai and six other Gulf Shaikhdoms formed the State of the United Arab Emirates. U.A.E. issues commenced in 1973.

1963. 100 naye paise = 1 rupee.
1966. 100 dirhams = 1 riyal.

**IMPERF STAMPS.** Some of the following issues exist imperf. from limited printings.

1. Hermit Crab.

2. Shaikh Rashid bin Said.

**1963.**

1. 1. 1 n.p. red & blue (post.) 10 10
2. A. 2 n.p. brown and blue .. 10 10
3. B. 3 n.p. sepia and green .. 10 10
4 C 4 n.p. orange and purple 10 10
5. D. 5 n.p. black and violet.. 15 10
6. E. 10 n.p. black and brown 15 15
7. 1. 15 n.p. red and drab .. 20 15
8. A. 20 n.p. orange and red.. 30 20
9. B. 25 n.p. brown and green 30 20
10. C. 30 n.p. red and grey .. 30 25
11. D. 35 n.p. deep blue & lilac 40 25
12. E. 50 n.p. sepia and orange 65 35
13. F. 1 r. salmon and blue .. 1·40 60
14. G. 2 r. brown and bistre .. 3·00 1·40
15. H. 3 r. black and red .. 6·00 3·00
16. I. 5 r. brown and turquoise 10·00 4·75
17. 2. 10 r. black, turq. & purple 22·00 10·00

18. J. 20 n.p. blue & brown (air) 25 15
19. K. 25 n.p. purple & yell. .. 60 15
20. J. 30 n.p. black and red .. 40 15
21. K. 40 n.p. purple and brown 75 25
22. J. 50 n.p. red and green .. 75 25
23. K. 60 n.p. black and brown 2·00 1·00
24. J. 75 n.p. green and violet.. 2·75 1·40
25. K. 1 r. brown and yellow .. 6·25 4·50

DESIGNS (Postage)—HORIZ: A, Common cuttle-fish. B, Edible snail. C, Crab. D, Turban sea urchin. E, Radish murex. F, Mosque. G, Buildings. H, Ancient wall and tower. I, Dubai view. (Air)—HORIZ: J, Falcon in flight over bridge. VERT: K, Peregrine falcon.

3. Dhows.

4. Mosquito.

**1963.** Centenary of Red Cross.

26 3 1 n.p. bl, yell & red (post) 25 25
27 – 2 n.p. brown, yellow & red 25 25
28 – 3 n.p. brown, orange & red 25 25
29 – 4 n.p. brown, red & green 30 25

30 3 20 n.p. brn, yell & red (air) 60 40
31 – 30 n.p. blue, orange & red 75 50
32 – 40 n.p. black, yellow & red 95 95
33 – 50 n.p. violet, red & turq 2·75 1·25

DESIGNS: 2, 30 n.p. First Aid field post. 3, 40 n.p. Camel train. 4, 50 n.p. March moth.

**1963.** Malaria Eradication.

34. 4. 1 n.p. brown & red (post.) 10 10
35. 1 n.p. brown and green .. 10 10
36. 1 n.p. red and blue .. 10 10
37. – 2 n.p. blue and red .. 10 10
38. – 2 n.p. red and brown .. 10 10
39. – 3 n.p. blue and brown .. 10 10

40. 4. 30 n.p. green & purple (air) 25 15
41. – 40 n.p. grey and red .. 35 25
42. – 70 n.p. yellow and purple 70 40

DESIGNS: 2, 40 n.p. Mosquito and snake emblem. 3, 70 n.p. Mosquitoes and swamp.

5. Ears of Wheat.

7. Scout Gymnastics.

6. U.S. Seal and Pres. Kennedy.

**1963.** Air. Freedom from Hunger.

43. 5. 30 n.p. brown and violet.. 25 10
44. – 40 n.p. olive and red .. 35 15
45. – 70 n.p. orange and green.. 70 65
46. – 1 r. blue and brown .. 95 50

DESIGNS: 40 n.p. Palm and campaign emblem. 70 n.p. Emblem within hands. 1 r. Woman bearing basket of fruit.

**1964.** Air. Pres. Kennedy Memorial Issue.

47 6 75 n.p. black & grn on grn 75 50
48 1 r. black & brown on buff 1·10 75
49 1¼ r. black & red on grey 1·60 95

**1964.** World Scout Jamboree, Marathon (1963).

50. 7. 1 n.p. bistre & brn. (post.) 10 10
51. – 2 n.p. brown and red .. 10 10
52. – 3 n.p. brown and blue .. 10 10
53. – 4 n.p. blue and mauve .. 10 10
54. – 5 n.p. turquoise and blue 10 10

55. 7. 20 n.p. brown & green (air) 25 15
56. – 30 n.p. brown and violet.. 35 20
57. – 40 n.p. green and blue .. 55 25
58. – 70 n.p. grey and green .. 70 40
59. – 1 r. red and blue.. .. 1·25 65

DESIGNS: 2, 30 n.p. Bugler. 3, 40 n.p. Wolf cubs. 4, 70 n.p. Scouts on parade. 5 n.p., 1 r. Scouts with standard.

**1964.** Nos. 27/8 surcharged.

59b 20 n.p. on 2 n.p brown, yellow and red .. 18·00
59c 30 n.p. on 3 n.p. brown, orange and red .. 18·00

8. Spacecraft.

**1964.** Air. "Honouring Astronauts". Multicoloured.

60 1 n.p. "Atlas" rocket (vert) 10 10
61 2 n.p. "Mercury" capsule (vert) .. .. 10 10
62 3 n.p. Type 8 .. .. 10 10
63 4 n.p. Two spacecraft .. 10 10
64 5 n.p. As No. 60 .. .. 10 10
65 1 r. As No. 61 .. .. 65 45
66 1½ r. Type 8 .. .. 95 60
67 2 r. As No. 63 .. .. 1·60 95

9. Globe, New York and Dubai Harbours.

**1964.** New York World's Fair.

68 9 1 n.p. red & blue (postage) 10 10
69 – 2 n.p. blue, red and mauve 10 10
70 9 3 n.p. green and brown 10 10
71 – 4 n.p. red, green & turq .. 10 10
72 9 5 n.p. violet, olive & green 10 10
73 – 10 n.p. black, brown & red 10 10

74 – 75 n.p. blk, grn & bl (air) 70 45
75 – 2 r. ochre, turquoise & brn 1·50 90
76 – 3 r. orange, turquoise & ol 2·00 1·25

DESIGNS: 2, 4, 10 n.p. New York skyline and Dubai hotel. 75 n.p., 2, 3 r. Statue of Liberty, New York, and "Rigorous" (tug), Dubai.

10. Flame of Freedom. and Scales of Justice.

**1964.** Air. 15th Anniv. of Human Rights Declaration. Flame in red.

77. 10. 35 n.p. brown and blue.. 25 10
78. 50 n.p. green and blue .. 45 25
79. 1 r. black and turquoise 85 40
80. 3 r. ultramarine and blue 2·25 90

11. Shaikh Rashid bin Said and View of Dubai.

**1964.**

81. 11. 10 n.p. olive, red & brown (postage) .. .. 20 10
82. A. 20 n.p. brown, red & grn. 25 10
83. 11. 30 n.p. black, red & blue 35 15
84. A. 40 n.p. blue, red & cer. 45 25

85. B. 1 r. olive, red & brn. (air) 85 45
86. C. 2 r. brown, red & green.. 2·00 95
87. B. 3 r. black, red and blue.. 3·00 1·60
88. C. 5 r. blue, red and cerise 5·50 3·75

SCENES: A, Waterfront. B, Waterside buildings. C, Harbour.

**1964.** Air. Winter Olympic Games, Innsbruck. Nos. 55/9 optd. with Olympic Rings. Games Emblem and **INNSBRUCK 1964.**

89 7 20 n.p. brown and green 40 40
90 – 30 n.p. brown and violet 55 50
91 – 40 n.p. green and blue .. 75 65
92 – 70 n.p. grey and green .. 1·10 1·00
93 – 1 r. red and blue .. 2·25 1·75

**1964.** Air. 48th Birth Anniv. of Pres. Kennedy. Optd. **MAY 29** (late President's birthday).

94. 6. 75 n.p. blk. & grn. on grn. 1·25 1·25
95. 1 r. black & brown on buff 2·25 1·90
96. 1¼ r. black and red on grey 2·75 2·50

**1964.** Air. Anti-T.B. Campaign. Optd **ANTI TUBERCULOSE** in English and Arabic, and Cross of Lorraine. Perf or roul.

101 3 20 n.p. brn, yell & red 3·25 3·25
102 – 30 n.p. blue, orge & red 3·25 2·25
103 – 40 n.p. blk, yell & red 3·25 3·25
104 – 50 n.p. viol, red & turq 3·25 3·25

15. Gymnastics.

**1964.** Olympic Games, Tokyo.

105. 15. 1 n.p. brown and olive.. 10 10
106. – 2 n.p. sepia & turquoise 10 10
107. – 3 n.p. blue and brown.. 10 10
108. – 4 n.p. violet and yellow 10 10
109. – 5 n.p. ochre and slate.. 10 10
110. – 10 n.p. blue and buff .. 15 15
111. – 20 n.p. olive and red .. 25 15
112. – 30 n.p. blue and yellow 50 25
113. – 40 n.p. green and buff.. 85 50
114. – 1 r. purple and blue .. 2·25 1·25

DESIGNS: 2 n.p. to 1 r. Various gymnastic exercises as Type 12, each with portrait of Ruler.

**1964.** Air. 19th Anniv. of U.N. Nos. 43/6 optd. **U N O 19th ANNIVERSARY** in English and Arabic.

115. 5. 30 n.p. brown and violet 65 40
116. – 40 n.p. olive and red .. 1·25 80
117. – 70 n.p. orange and green 1·75 1·25
118. – 1 r. blue and brown .. 3·00 1·90

17. Shaikh Rasnid and Shaikh Ahmad of Qatar.

**1964.** "Educational Progress". Portraits in black; torch orange.

119. 17. 5 n.p. purple (postage) 15 10
120. 10 n.p. red .. .. 15 10
121. 15 n.p. blue .. .. 20 10
122. – 20 n.p. olive .. .. 25 15

123. – 30 n.p. red (air) .. 90 45
124. – 40 n.p. brown .. .. 2·00 75
125. – 50 n.p. blue .. .. 2·75 90
126. – 1 r. green .. .. 3·75 1·50

DESIGNS: 20, 30, 40 n.p. Shaikh Rashid and Shaikh Abdullah of Kuwait. 50 n.p., 1 r. Shaikh Rashid and Pres. Nasser of Egypt.

**1964.** Air. Outer Space Achievements 1964. Optd. **OUTER SPACE ACHIEVEMENTS 1964** in English and Arabic, **RANGER 7** and space capsule motif.

127. 1 r. multicoloured (No. 65) 2·50 2·50
128. 1½ r. multicoloured (No. 66) 2·50 2·50
129. 2 r. multicoloured (No. 67) 2·50 2·50

19. Globe and Rockets.

**1964.** Space Achievements. Unissued stamps surch as T 19. Multicoloured.

130 10 n.p. on 75 n.p. "Man on Moon" (25 × 78 mm) .. 2·50 2·50
131 20 n.p. on 1 r. 50 Type 19 3·25 3·25
132 30 n.p. on 2 r. "Universe" (25 × 78 mm) .. .. 3·25 3·25

**1964.** Air. 1st Death Anniv. of Pres. J. Kennedy. As No. 47 with colours changed, optd. **22 NOVEMBER.**

133. 6. 75 n.p. black and green.. 8·50 6·25

21. Telephone Handset.

**1966.** Opening of Dubai Automatic Telephone Exchange.

134. 21. 10 n.p. brn. & grn. (post.) 10 10
135. 15 n.p. red and plum .. 20 10
136. 25 n.p. green and blue .. 25 10

137. – 40 n.p. blue & grn. (air) 35 20
138. – 60 n.p. orange and sepia 80 35
139. – 75 n.p. violet and black 90 55
140. – 2 r. green and red .. 3·25 2·10

DESIGN: Nos. 137/40, As Type 21 but showing telephone dial.

22. Sir Winston Churchill and Catafalque.

**1966.** Churchill Commem. (a) Postage.

142. 22. 1 r. black and violet .. 40 30
143. 1 r. 50 black and olive 65 30
144. 3 r. black and blue .. 1·50 1·10
145. 4 r. black and red .. 2·50 1·90

(b) Air. Nos. 142/5 optd. **AIR MAIL** in English and Arabic and with black borders.

147. 22. 1 r. black and violet .. 40 30
148. 1 r. 50 black and olive.. 65 50
149. 3 r. black and blue .. 1·50 1·10
150. 4 r. black and red .. 2·50 1·90

23. Ruler's Palace.

24. Bridge.

**1966.**

152. 23. 5 n.p. brown and blue.. 10 10
153. 10 n.p. black and orange 10 10
154. 15 n.p. blue and brown 15 10
155. A. 20 n.p. blue and brown 20 15
156. 25 n.p. red and blue .. 20 15
157. B. 35 n.p. violet and green 30 20
158. 40 n.p. turquoise & blue 45 25
159. 24. 60 n.p. green and red .. 60 25
160. 1 r. ultramarine and blue 95 50
161. C. 1 r. 25 brown and black 1·25 85
162. D. 1 r. 50 purple and green 2·10 1·10
163. 3 r. brown and violet .. 4·00 2·10
164. E. 5 r. red .. .. 6·75 5·25
165. 10 r. blue .. .. 15·00 11·00

DESIGNS—HORIZ. (28 × 21 mm.): A, Waterfront, Dubai. B, Bridge and dhow. As Type 24: C, Minaret (Ruler's portrait on right). D, Fort Dubai. VERT. (32½ × 42½ mm.): E, Shaikh Rashid bin Said.

25. Oil Rig.

26. "Tasman" (oil rig).

**1966.** Air. Oil Exploration.

(a) "Land" series as T 25.

166. – 5 n.p. black and lilac .. 20 10
167. – 15 n.p. black and bistre 35 15
168. – 25 n.p. black and blue.. 55 30
169. – 35 n.p. black and red.. 70 35
170. – 50 n.p. black and brown 1·00 50
171. 25. 70 n.p. black and red.. 2·25 1·10

DESIGNS—HORIZ. 5 n.p. Map of Dubai. 15 n.p. Surveying 25 n.p. Dubai Petroleum Company building. 35 n.p. Oil drilling. VERT. 50 n.p. Surveying with level.

(b) "Sea" series as T 26.

173. 26. 10 n.p. purple and blue 20 10
174. – 20 n.p. mauve and green 30 10
175. 26. 30 n.p. brown and green 55 10
176. – 40 n.p. lilac and agate.. 55 15
177. 26. 50 n.p. blue and olive.. 85 20
178. – 60 n.p. blue and violet.. 95 35
179. 26. 75 n.p. green and brown 1·50 50
180. – 1 r. green and blue .. 1·75 70

DESIGN: 20, 40, 60 n.p. and 1 r. Ocean well-head.

27. Rulers of Gulf Arab States (reduced size illustration. Actual size 77 × 20 mm.).

**1966.** Gulf Arab States Summit Conf.

182. 27. 35 p. multicoloured .. 85 50
183. 60 p. multicoloured .. 2·25 1·40
184. 150 p. multicoloured .. 4·50 3·50

28. Jules Rimet Cup.

**1966.** World Cup Football Championships. Multicoloured.

185. 40 d. Type **28** .. .. 35 15
186. 60 d. } Various 45 25
187. 1 r. } football 70 35
188. 1 r. 25 } scenes. 90 45
189. 3 r. Wembley Stadium, London .. .. 1·40 1·10

**1966.** England's World Cup Victory. Nos. 185/9 optd. **ENGLAND WINNERS.**

191. **28.** 40 d. multicoloured .. 35 15
192. – 60 d. multicoloured .. 45 25
193. – 1 r. multicoloured .. 70 35
194. – 1 r. 25 multicoloured .. 90 45
195. – 3 r. multicoloured .. 1·40 1·10

29. Rulers of Dubai and Kuwait, and I.C.Y. Emblem.

**1966.** Int. Co-operation Year (1965). Currency expressed in rupees.

197. **29.** 1 r. brown and green .. 1·00 50
198. A. 1 r. green and brown .. 1·00 50
199. B. 1 r. blue and violet .. 1·00 50
200. C. 1 r. blue and violet .. 1·00 50
201. D. 1 r. turquoise and red .. 1·00 50
202. E. 1 r. turquoise and red .. 1·00 50
203. F. 1 r. violet and blue .. 1·00 50
204. G. 1 r. violet and blue .. 1·00 50
205. H. 1 r. red and turquoise .. 1·00 50
206. I. 1 r. red and turquoise .. 1·00 50

Heads of State and Political Leaders (Ruler of Dubai and): A, Pres. John F. Kennedy. B, Prime Minister Harold Wilson. C, Pres. Helou of the Lebanon. D, Pres. De Gaulle. E, Pres. Nasser. F, Pope Paul VI. G, Ruler of Bahrain. H, Pres. Lyndon Johnson. I, Ruler of Qatar.

30. "Gemini" Capsules manoeuvring.

**1966.** "Gemini" Space Rendezvous. Mult.

208. 35 d. Type **30** .. .. 40 15
209. 40 d. "Gemini" capsules linked .. .. 40 15
210. 60 d. "Gemini" capsules separating .. .. 50 25
211. 1 r. Schirra and Stafford in "Gemini 6" .. .. 90 40
212. 1 r. 25 "Gemini" orbits .. 1·25 65
213. 3 r. Borman and Lovell in "Gemini 7" .. .. 2·00 1·25

**1967.** Nos. 197/206 surch. **Riyal** in English and Arabic.

215. **29.** 1 r. on 1 r. .. .. 1·10 65
216. A. 1 r. on 1 r. .. .. 1·10 65
217. B. 1 r. on 1 r. .. .. 1·10 65
218. C. 1 r. on 1 r. .. .. 1·10 65
219. D. 1 r. on 1 r. .. .. 1·10 65
220. E. 1 r. on 1 r. .. .. 1·10 65
221. F. 1 r. on 1 r. .. .. 1·10 65
222. G. 1 r. on 1 r. .. .. 1·10 65
223. H. 1 r. on 1 r. .. .. 1·10 65
224. I. 1 r. on 1 r. .. .. 1·10 65

**1967.** Gemini Flight Success. Nos. 208/13 optd. **SUCCESSFUL END OF GEMINI FLIGHT.**

226. **30.** 35 d. multicoloured .. 45 20
227. – 40 d. multicoloured .. 45 20
228. – 60 d. multicoloured .. 50 25
229. – 1 r. multicoloured .. 90 40
230. – 1 r. 25 multicoloured .. 1·25 65
231. – 3 r. multicoloured .. 2·00 1·25

**1967.** Nos. 152/61, 163/5 with currency names changed by overprinting in English and Arabic (except Nos. 244/5 which have the currency name in Arabic only).

233. **23.** 5 d. on 5 n.p. .. .. 20 10
234. 10 d. on 10 n.p. .. 20 10
235. 15 d. on 15 n.p. .. 30 15
236. A. 20 d. on 20 n.p. .. 45 20
237. 25 d. on 25 n.p. .. 50 20
238. B. 35 d. on 35 n.p. .. 60 20
239. 40 d. on 40 n.p. .. 80 25
240. **24.** 60 d. on 60 n.p. .. 1·25 30
241. 1 r. on 1 r. .. .. 1·90 45
242. C. 1 r. 25 on 1 r. 25 .. 3·50 90
243. D. 3 r. on 3 r. .. .. 6·00 2·50
244. E. 5 r. on 5 r. .. .. 11·00 5·00
245. 10 r. on 10 r. .. .. 17·00 10·00

37. "The Moving Finger writes . . . ".

**1967.** Rubaiyat of Omar Khayyam. Mult.

246. 60 d. Type **37** .. .. 1·10 40
247. 60 d. " Here with a Loaf of Bread . . . " .. .. 1·10 40
248. 60 d. " So, while the Vessels. . . " .. .. 1·10 40
249. 60 d. " Myself when young . . . " .. .. 1·10 40
250. 60 d. " One Moment in Annihilation's Waste . . . " .. 1·10 40
251. 60 d. " And strange to tell . . . " .. .. .. 1·10 40

38. "The Straw Hat" (Rubens).

**1967.** Paintings. Multicoloured.

253. 1 r. Type **38** .. .. 1·60 40
254. 1 r. "Thomas, Earl of Arundel" (Rubens) .. 1·60 40
255. 1 r. "A peasant boy leaning on a sill" (Murillo) .. 1·60 40

See also Nos. 273/5.

39. Ruler and Lanner Falcon.

40. "Bayan" (dhow).

**1967.**

257. **39.** 5 d. red and orange .. 60 25
258. 10 d. sepia and green .. 60 20
259. 20 d. purple and blue .. 75 25
260. 35 d. turquoise & mauve 1·00 25
261. 60 d. blue and green .. 2·00 40
262. 1 r. green and purple .. 2·75 40
263. **40.** 1 r. 25 purple and blue 2·75 55
264. 3 r. purple and blue .. 3·25 1·60
265. 5 r. violet and green .. 6·75 3·25
266. 10 r. green and mauve .. 10·00 6·00

41. Globe and Scout Badge.

**1967.** World Scout Jamboree, Idaho. Mult.

267. 10 d. Type **41** .. .. 35 15
268. 20 d. Dubai scout & dromedaries .. .. .. 70 20
269. 35 d. Bugler .. .. 90 25
270. 60 d. Jamboree emblem and U.S. flags .. .. 1·60 30
271. 1 r. Lord Baden-Powell .. 2·25 60
272. 1 r. 25 Idaho on U.S. Map 3·00 1·25

**1967.** Goya's Paintings in National Gallery, London. As T **38**. Multicoloured.

273. 1 r. " Dr. Peral " .. .. 1·60 45
274. 1 r. " Dona Isabel Cobos de Porcel " .. .. 1·60 45
275. 1 r. " Duke of Wellington " 1·60 45

## MINIMUM PRICE

The minimum price quoted is 10p which represents a handling charge rather than a basis for valuing common stamps. For further notes about prices see introductory pages.

42. Kaiser-i-Hind ("Teinopalpus imperialis").

**1968.** Butterflies and Moths. Multicoloured.

277 60 d. Type **42** .. .. 1·60 25
278 60 d. "Erasmia pulchella" 1·60 25
279 60 d. Gaudy baron ("Euthalia indica") .. 1·60 25
280 60 d. Atlas moth ("Attacus atlas") .. .. 1·60 25
281 60 d. "Dysphania militaris" .. .. 1·60 25
282 60 d. "Neochera butleri" 1·60 25
283 60 d. African monarch ("Danaus chrysippus") 1·60 25
284 60 d. Chestnut tiger ("Danaus tytia") .. 1·60 25

43. " Madonna and Child " (Ferruzi).

**1968.** Arab Mothers' Day. Multicoloured.

285. 60 d. " Games in the Park " (Zandomeneghi) .. .. 40 25
286. 1 r. Type **43** .. .. 65 35
287. 1 r. 25 " Mrs Cockburn and Children " (Reynolds) (wrongly inscr. " Cockburn ") .. .. 85 45
288. 3 r. " Self-portrait with Daughter " (Vigee-Lebrun) 1·90 1·10

44. " Althea rosea ".

**1968.** Flowers. Multicoloured.

289. 60 d. Type **44** .. .. 1·60 25
290. 60 d. " Geranium Lancastriense " .. .. 1·60 25
291. 60 d. " Catharanthus roseus " .. .. 1·60 25
292. 60 d. " Convolvulus minor " 1·60 25
293. 60 d. " Opuntia " .. .. 1·60 25
294. 60 d. " Gaillardia aristata " 1·60 25
295. 60 d. " Heliopsis " .. 1·60 25
296. 60 d. " Centaurea moschata " 1·60 25

45. Running.

**1968.** Olympic Games, Mexico. Multicoloured.

297. 15 d. Type **45** .. .. 70 10
298. 20 d. Swimming .. .. 75 10
299. 25 d. Boxing .. .. 1·25 15
300. 35 d. Water-polo .. .. 1·40 20
301. 40 d. High jump .. .. 1·75 20
302. 60 d. Gymnastics .. .. 2·50 30
303. 1 r. Football .. .. 3·50 40
304. 1 r. 25 Fencing .. .. 4·75 50

46. " Young Girl with Kitten " (Perronneau).

**1968.** Children's Day. Multicoloured.

306. 60 d. " Two Boys with Mastiff " (Goya) .. 50 15
307. 1 r. Type **46** .. .. 80 30
308. 1 r. 25 " Soap Bubbles " (Manet) .. .. .. 1·25 35
309. 3 r. " The Fluyder Boys " (Lawrence) .. .. 2·00 60

47. Ring-necked Pheasant.

**1968.** Arabian Gulf Birds. Multicoloured.

310. 60 d. Type **47** .. .. 1·60 25
311. 60 d. Red turtle dove .. 1·60 25
312. 60 d. Red-footed falcon .. 1·60 25
313. 60 d. European bee eater 1·60 25
314. 60 d. Hoopoe .. .. 1·60 25
315. 60 d. Great egret .. .. 1·60 25
316. 60 d. Little terns .. .. 1·60 25
317. 60 d. Lesser black-backed gulls .. .. .. 1·60 25

48. "Bamora" (freighter), 1914.

**1969.** 60th Anniv of Dubai Postal Service. Multicoloured.

318 25 d. Type **48** .. .. 30 10
319 35 d. De Havilland D.H.66 Hercules airplane, 1930 40 10
320 60 d. "Sirdhana" (liner), 1947 .. .. .. 80 20
321 1 r. Armstrong Whitworth Atalanta airplane, 1938 80 45
322 1 r. 25 "Chandpara" (freighter), 1949 .. 1·25 60
323 3 r. Short Sunderland flying boat, 1943 .. 1·50 80

49. "Madonna and Child" (Bartolome Murillo).

**1969.** Arab Mothers' Day. Multicoloured.

325 60 d. Type **49** .. .. 60 20
326 1 r. "Madonna with Rose" (Francesco Mozzola (Parmigianino)) .. 1·10 30
327 1 r. 25 "Mother and Children" (Peter Paul Rubens) .. .. 1·50 60
328 3 r. "Campori Madonna" (Antonio Correggio) .. 3·50 90

No. 326 wrongly inscribed "Mazzuoli".

50. Pork Fish.

**1969.** Fishes. Multicoloured.

329. 60 d. Type **50** .. .. 1·10 25
330. 60 d. Spotted Grouper .. 1·10 25
331. 60 d. Moonfish .. .. 1·10 25
332. 60 d. Sweetlips .. .. 1·10 25
333. 60 d. Blue Angel .. .. 1·10 25
334. 60 d. Texas Skate .. .. 1·10 25
335. 60 d. Striped butterfly Fish 1·10 25
336. 60 d. Imperial angelfish .. 1·10 25

51. Burton, Doughty, Burckhardt, Thesiger and Map.

**1969.** Explorers of Arabia.

337. 51. 25 d. brown and green 70 20
338. 60 d. blue and brown .. 1·25 35
339. 1 r. green and blue .. 2·50 50
340. 1 r. 25 black and red .. 3·25 1·25

52. Underwater Storage Tank Construction.

**1969.** Oil Industry. Multicoloured.

341 5 d. Type 52 .. .. 20 15
342 20 d. Floating-out storage tank .. .. .. 45 15
343 35 d. Underwater tank in operation .. .. 85 45
344 60 d. Ruler, oil rig and monument .. .. 1·75 60
345 1 r. Fateh marine oilfield 2·40 90

53. Astronauts on Moon.

**1969.** 1st Man on the Moon. Multicoloured.

346. 60 d. Type 53 (postage) .. 50 25
347. 1 r. Astronaut and ladder .. 65 25
348. 1 r. 25 Astronauts planting U.S. flag on Moon (air) 85 35

No. 348 is horiz., size 62 × 38 mm.

54. "Weather Reporter" launching Radio-Sonde and Handley Page Hastings Weather Reconnaissance Airplane.

**1970.** World Meteorological Day. Mult.

349. 60 d. Type 54 .. .. 45 15
350. 1 r. Kew-type radio-sonde and dish aerial .. .. 65 30
351. 1 r. 25 "Tiros" satellite and rocket .. .. 80 40
352. 3 r. "Ariel" satellite and rocket .. .. .. 1·50 90

55. New Headquarters Building.

**1970.** New U.P.U. Headquarters Building, Berne. Multicoloured.

353. 5 d. Type 55 .. .. 25 10
354. 60 d. U.P.U. Monument, Berne .. .. 1·00 25

56. Charles Dickens.

**1970.** Death Cent. of Charles Dickens. Mult.

355. 60 d. Type 56 .. .. 35 15
356. 1 r. Signature, quill and London sky-line (horiz.) 70 35
357. 1 r. 25 Dickens and Victorian street .. .. 90 70
358. 3 r. Dickens and books (horiz.) 1·75 1·40

57. "The Graham Children" (Hogarth).

**1970.** Children's Day. Multicoloured.

359. 35 d. Type 57 .. .. 25 10
360. 60 d. "Caroline Murat and Children" (Gerard) (vert.) 55 20
361. 1 r. "Napoleon as Uncle" (Ducis) .. .. .. 1·00 40

58. Shaikh Rashid.

**1970.** Multicoloured.

362. 5 d. Type 53 .. .. 15 15
363. 10 d. Dhow building (horiz.) 25 10
364. 20 d. Al Maktum Bridge (horiz.) .. .. 45 15
365. 35 d. Great Mosque .. 50 10
366. 60 d. Dubai National Bank (horiz.) .. .. 85 15
367. 1 r. International airport (horiz.) .. .. 1·75 25
368. 1 r. 25 Harbour project (horiz.) .. .. 2·50 65
369. 3 r. Hospital (horiz.) .. 3·50 1·40
370. 5 r. Trade school (horiz.) .. 5·25 2·75
371. 10 r. Television and "Intelsat 4" .. .. .. 9·00 5·00

The riyal values are larger, 40 × 25 or 25 × 40 mm.

59. Terminal Building and Control Tower.

**1971.** Opening of Dubai International Airport. Multicoloured.

372 1 r. Type 59 .. .. 1·90 1·25
373 1 r. 25 Airport entrance 2·40 1·50

60. Telecommunications Map and Satellites.

**1971.** Outer Space Telecommunications Congress, Paris. Multicoloured.

374. 60 d. Type 60 (postage) .. 40 15
375. 1 r. Rocket and "Intelsat 4" (air) .. 55 30
376. 5 r. Eiffel Tower and Goonhilly aerial .. 2·00 1·75

61. Scout Badge, Fan and Map. 62. Albrecht Durer.

**1971.** 13th World Scout Jamboree, Asagiri (Japan). Multicoloured.

377. 60 d. Type 61 .. .. 35 15
378. 1 r. Canoeing .. .. 60 30
379. 1 r. 25 Rock-climbing .. 75 55
380. 3 r. Scouts around campfire (horiz.) .. .. 1·50 1·25

**1971.** Famous People. (1st issue). Mult.

381. 60 d. Type 62 (postage) .. 25 10
382. 1 r. Sir Isaac Newton (air) 65 30
383. 1 r. 25 Avicenna .. .. 90 45
384. 3 r. Voltaire .. .. 1·40 75

See also Nos. 388/91.

63. Boy in Meadow.

**1971.** 25th Anniv. of U.N.I.C.E.F. Mult.

385. 60 d. Type 63 (postage) .. 25 15
386. 5 r. Children with toys (horiz.) .. .. .. 1·75 75
387. 1 r. Mother and children (air) 35 15

**1972.** Famous People (2nd issue). As Type 62. Multicoloured.

388 10 d. Leonardo da Vinci (postage) .. .. 10 10
389 35 d. Beethoven .. .. 30 15
390 75 d. Khalil Gibran (poet) (air) .. .. .. 30 20
391 5 r. Charles de Gaulle 2·75 2·00

65. Nurse supervising children.

**1972.** Air. World Health Day. Multicoloured.

392. 75 d. Type 65 .. .. 70 20
393. 1 r. 25 Doctor treating baby (horiz.) .. .. 1·50 70

67. Gymnastics.

**1972.** Olympic Games, Munich. Multicoloured.

399. 35 d. Type 67 (postage) .. 25 10
400. 40 d. Fencing .. .. 45 10
401. 65 d. Hockey .. .. 65 20
402. 75 d. Water-polo (air) .. 90 25
403. 1 r. Horse-jumping .. 1·10 35
404. 1 r. Athletics .. .. 1·50 60

POSTAGE DUE STAMPS

**1963.** Designs as T 1 but inscr "DUE".

D26 L 1 n.p. red and grey .. 20 20
D27 M 2 n.p. blue and bistre 20 20
D28 N 3 n.p. green and red .. 20 20
D29 L 4 n.p. red and green .. 20 20
D30 M 5 n.p. black and red .. 20 20
D31 N 10 n.p. violet and olive 25 25
D32 L 15 n.p. red and blue .. 85 55
D33 M 25 n.p. green & brown 1·90 1·40
D34 N 35 n.p. orange & blue 4·25 2·75

DESIGNS—HORIZ: L, Common European cockle. M, Common blue mussel. N, Portuguese oyster.

D 66. Shaikh Rashid.

**1972.**

D 394. D 66. 5 d. grey, blue & brn. 55 60
D 395. 10 d. brn., ochre & bl. 80 90
D 396. 20 d. brn., red and blue 1·50 1·60
D 397. 30 d. violet, lilac & blk. 2·00 2·25
D 398. 50 d. brn., ochre & pur. 4·25 4·50

## EAST SILESIA Pt. 5

Special overprints were applied to Czechoslovakian and Polish stamps prior to a plebiscite.

The plebiscite was never held, due to disorders and the area was divided between Czechoslovakia and Poland in 1920.

100 halera = 1 krone.
100 fenni = 1 korona.

**1920.** Stamps of Czechoslovakia optd. **SO 1920.** Imperf. or perf.

23. 3. 1 h. brown .. .. 10 10
2. 2. 3 h. mauve .. .. 10 10
24. 3. 5 h. green .. .. 15 15
25. 10 h. green .. .. 20 20
26. 15 h. red .. .. .. 10 10
6. 2. 20 h. green .. .. 10 10
27. 3. 20 h. red .. .. .. 20 20
28. 25 h. purple .. .. 20 20
9. 2. 30 h. olive .. .. 15 15
35. 3. 30 h. mauve .. .. 25 25
10. 2. 40 h. orange .. .. 15 15
11. 3. 50 h. purple .. .. 40 40
12. 50 h. blue .. .. 1·10 1·10
36. 60 h. orange .. .. 30 30
14. 75 h. green .. .. 30 30
15. 80 h. olive .. .. 40 40
16. 2. 100 h. brown .. .. 50 50
17. 3. 120 h. black .. .. 1·10 1·10
18. 2. 200 h. blue .. .. 1·10 1·10
19. 3. 300 h. green .. .. 1·60 1·60
20. 2. 400 h. violet .. .. 1·40 1·40
21. 3. 500 h. brown .. .. 3·75 3·00
22. 1000 h. purple .. .. 10·00 6·00

**1920.** Stamps of Poland of 1919 optd **S. O. 1920.** Perf.

57. 15. 5 f. green .. .. 10 10
58. 10 f. brown .. .. 10 10
59. 15 f. red .. .. .. 10 10
60. 16. 25 f. olive .. .. 10 10
61. 50 f. green .. .. 10 10
62. 17. 1 k. green .. .. 10 10
63. 1 k. 50 brown .. .. 10 10
64. 2 k. blue .. .. .. 10 10
65. 18. 2 k. 50 purple .. .. 10 10
66. 19. 5 k. blue .. .. .. 15 15

EXPRESS STAMPS FOR PRINTED MATTER

**1920.** Express stamps of Czechoslovakia optd **S O 19 20.**

E 39. E 4. 2 h. purple on yellow 10 10
E 40. 5 h. green on yellow .. 10 10

NEWSPAPER STAMPS

**1920.** Newspaper stamps of Czechoslovakia optd. **SO 1920** Imperf.

N 41. N 4. 2 h. green .. .. 30 30
N 42. 6 h. red .. .. 10 10
N 43. 10 h. lilac .. .. 20 20
N 44. 20 h. blue .. .. 25 25
N 45. 30 h. brown .. .. 25 25

POSTAGE DUE STAMPS

**1920.** Postage Due stamps of Czechoslovakia optd. **SO 1920.** Imperf.

D 46. D 4. 5 h. olive .. .. 10 10
D 47. 10 h. olive .. .. 15 10
D 48. 15 h. olive .. .. 15 10
D 49. 20 h. olive .. .. 25 15
D 50. 25 h. olive .. .. 25 20
D 51. 30 h. olive .. .. 25 20
D 52. 40 h. olive .. .. 40 30
D 53. 50 h. olive .. .. 40 30
D 54. 100 h. brown .. .. 75 55
D 55. 500 h. green .. .. 3·00 2·25
D 56. 1000 h. violet .. .. 6·00 6·00

## EASTERN ROUMELIA (SOUTH BULGARIA) Pt. 3

This area, part of the Turkish Empire, situated south of the Balkan Mts., became semi-autonomous after 1878. In 1885 the population revolted against the Turks, changing the district's name to South Bulgaria. Incorporation into Bulgaria followed in 1886.

40 paras = 1 piastre.

### A. EASTERN ROUMELIA.

**1880.** Stamps of Turkey optd. **RO.**

1. 2. ½ pre. on 20 pa. green (No. 78) .. .. 17·00 17·00
2. 9. 20 pa. pur. & grn. (No. 83) 19·00 19·00
3. 2 pi. blk. & orge. (No. 85) 38·00 38·00
4. 5 pi. red & blue (No. 86) 90·00 90·00

**1881.** Stamp of Turkey optd. **R.O.** and **ROUMELIE ORIENTALE.**

5. 9. 10 pa. black and mauve .. 30·00 30·00

**1881.** As T 9 of Turkey but inscr "ROUMELIE ORIENTALE" at left.

6. 9. 5 pa. black and olive .. 75 25
11. 5 pa. lilac .. .. 15 15
7. 10 pa. black and green .. 2·00 25
12. 10 pa. green .. .. 15 25
8. 20 pa black and red .. 20 25
9. 1 pi. black and blue .. 1·25 1·40
10. 5 pi. red and blue .. 12·00 20·00

### B. SOUTH BULGARIA.

**1885.** As T 9 of Turkey, but inscr. "ROUMELIE ORIENTALE" at left and optd. with lion.

13. 9. 5 pa. black and olive .. — £110
29. 5 pa. lilac .. .. 9·25 21·00
14. 10 pa. black and green .. — £250
30. 10 pa. green .. .. 6·25 12·50
15. 20 pa. black and red .. 90·00
34. 20 pa. red .. .. 14·00 21·00
18. 1 pi. black and blue .. 9·25 21·00
26. 5 pi. red and blue .. £150

**1885.** As T 9 of Turkey, but inscr. "ROUMELIE ORIENTALE" and optd. with lion and inscription in frame.

43. 9. 5 pa. black and olive .. £120 £120
48a. 5 pa. lilac .. .. 6·25 7·75
44. 10 pa. black and green .. £120 £120
49. 10 pa. green .. .. 5·75 9·25
45. 20 pa. black and red .. 38·00 48·00
50. 20 pa. red .. .. 7·75 14·00
46. 1 pi. black and blue .. 25·00 32·00
47. 5 pi. red and blue .. 20·00 25·00

## ECUADOR Pt. 20

A Republic on the W. Coast of S. America. Independent since 1830.

1865. 8 reales = 1 peso.
1881. 100 centavos = 1 sucre.

1. 2.

**1865.** Imperf.

1b. 1. ½ r. blue .. .. .. 11·50 6·25
2d. 1 r. yellow .. .. .. 9·25 6·50
3. 1 r. green .. .. .. £130 15·00
4. 2. 4 r. red .. .. .. £140 70·00

3. 4. 5.

**1872.**

10 3 ½ r. blue .. .. .. 9·25 2·10
11 4 1 r. orange .. .. .. 11·00 3·00
12a 3 1 p. red .. .. .. 2·10 7·00

**1881.** Various frames.

13. 5. 1 c. brown .. .. 10 10
14. 2 c. lake .. .. 10 10
15. 5 c. blue .. .. 1·90 25
16. 10 c. orange .. .. 10 10
17. 20 c. violet .. .. 30 25
18. 50 c. green .. .. 40 1·50

**1883.** Surch. **DIEZ CENTAVOS.**

19. 5. 10 c. on 50 c. green 13·00 11·00

13. 19. Pres. Juan Flores. 20. Pres. Rocafuerte.

**1887.** Various frames.

26. 13. 1 c. green .. .. 10 10
27. 2 c. red .. .. 15 10
28. 5 c. blue .. .. 85 15
29. 80 c. olive .. .. 1·50 4·25

**1892.**

34. 19. 1 c. orange .. .. 10 10
35. 2 c. brown .. .. 10 10
36. 5 c. red .. .. 10 10
37. 10 c. green .. .. 10 10
38. 20 c. brown .. .. 10 10
39. 50 c. red .. .. 10 20
40. 1 s. blue .. .. 10 75
41. 5 s. violet .. .. 25 75

**1893.** Surch. **5 CENTAVOS.**

53. 19. 5 c. on 50 c. red .. 40 35
49. 5 c. on 1 s. blue .. 65 55
50. 5 c. on 5 s. violet .. 3·00 2·75

**1894.** Dated "1894".

57. 20. 1 c. blue .. .. 10 10
58. 2 c. brown .. .. 10 10
59. 5 c. green .. .. 15 10
60. 10 c. red .. .. 30 15
61. 20 c. black .. .. 30 15
62. 50 c. orange .. .. 2·00 75
63. 1 s. red .. .. 3·50 1·50
64. 5 s. blue .. .. 4·25 2·25

**1895.** Dated "1895".

74. 20. 1 c. blue .. .. 25 25
75. 2 c. brown .. .. 25 25
76. 5 c. green .. .. 20 20
77. 10 c. red .. .. 20 10
78. 20 c. black .. .. 30 30
79. 50 c. orange .. .. 1·40 75
80. 1 s. red .. .. 6·50 3·00
81. 5 s. blue .. .. 3·00 1·50

These two series were re-issued in 1897 optd. "1897-1898".

22. F 1.

**1896.** Arms designs, inscr. "U.P.U. 1896".

89. 22. 1 c. green .. .. 30 10
90. 2 c. red .. .. 30 10
91. 5 c. blue .. .. 30 10
92. 10 c. brown .. .. 25 25
93. 20 c. orange .. .. 40 70
94. 50 c. blue .. .. 25 1·25
95. 1 s. brown .. .. 1·25 1·50
96. 5 s. lilac .. .. 5·50 2·10

This series was re-issued in 1897 optd. "1897-1898".

**1896.** Dated "1887 1888". Surch.

112. F1. 5 c. on 10 c. orange .. 75 15
113. 10 c. on 4 c. brown .. 75 30

**1896.** As Type F 1, but dated "1891 1892". Surch.

114. F1. 10 c. on 4 c. brown .. 6·50 5·25

**1896.** As Type F 1, but dated "1893 1894". Surch.

115. F1. 1 c. on 1 c. red .. 40 15
116. 2 c. on 2 c. blue .. 75 50
117. 5 c. on 10 c. orange .. 2·10 1·90

34. V. Roca, D. Noboa and J. Olmedo. (40.)

**1896.** Triumph of Liberal Party. Dated "1845-1895".

118. 34. 1 c. red .. .. 40 40
119. – 2 c. blue .. .. 40 40
120. 34. 5 c. green .. .. 30 50
121. – 10 c. yellow .. .. 30 50
122. 34. 20 c. red .. .. 35 75
123. – 50 c. lilac .. .. 50 1·25
124. 34. 1 s. orange .. .. 95 1·50

DESIGN: 2 c., 10 c., 50 c. Gen. Elizalde.

This series was re-issued in 1897 optd. "1897-1898".

**1896.** Surch.

125. 22. 5 c. on 20 c. orange .. 12·50 12·50
126. 10 c. on 50 c. blue .. 12·50 12·50

**1897.** 1896 Jubilee issue optd. with T 40.

162. 34. 1 c. red .. .. 1·75 1·50
164. – 2 c. blue (No. 119) .. 1·75 1·50
165. 34. 5 c. green .. .. 1·75 1·50
166. – 10 c. yellow (No. 121) .. 1·75 1·50

41. 45. Louis Varags Torres.

**1897.**

173. 41. 1 c. green .. .. 10 10
174. 2 c. red .. .. 10 10
175. 5 c. lake .. .. 10 10
176. 10 c. brown .. .. 10 10
177. 20 c. yellow .. .. 15 25
178. 50 c. blue .. .. 15 40
179. 1 s. grey .. .. 20 50
180. 5 s. purple .. .. 60 75

**1899.** Surch.

191. 41. 1 c. on 2 c. red .. 1·00 50
192. 5 c. on 10 c. brown .. 75 25

**1899.**

193. 45. 1 c. black and grey .. 10 10
205. 1 c. black and red .. 10 10
194. – 2 c. black and brown .. 10 10
206. – 2 c. black and green .. 10 10
195. – 5 c. black and red .. 10 10
207. – 5 c. black and lilac .. 10 10
196. – 10 c. black and lilac .. 10 10
208. – 10 c. black and blue .. 10 10
197. – 20 c. black and green .. 10 10
209. – 20 c. black and grey .. 10 10
198. – 50 c. black and red .. 60 30
210. – 50 c. black and blue .. 35 30
199. – 1 s. black and yellow .. 3·00 1·00
211. – 1 s. black and brown .. 2·10 1·40
200. – 5 s. black and lilac .. 5·00 3·00
212. – 5 s. black and grey .. 3·00 2·25

PORTRAITS: 2 c. A. Calderon. 5 c. J. Montalvo. 10 c. Mejia. 20 c. Espejo. 50 c. Carbo. 1 s. J.J. Olmedo. 5 s. Moncayo.

73. Capt. Abdon Calderon. 76. President Roca.

**1904.** Birth Cent. of Captain Calderon.

310. 73. 1 c. black and red .. 25 20
311. 2 c. black and blue .. 25 20
312. 5 c. black and yellow .. 1·00 70
313. 10 c. black and red .. 1·75 70
314. 20 c. black and blue .. 4·50 1·60
315. 50 c. black and yellow 38·00 23·00

The 5 c. and 50 c. are larger (25 × 30 mm.).

**1907.** Portraits in black.

323. 76. 1 c. red (Roca) .. 20 10
324. – 2 c. blue (Noboa) .. 40 10
325. – 3 c. orange (Robles) .. 50 10
326. – 5 c. purple (Urvina) .. 75 10
327. – 10 c. bl. (Garcia Moreno) 1·50 15
328. – 20 c. green (Carrion) .. 2·25 20
329. – 50 c. lilac (Espinoza) .. 4·50 50
330. – 1 s. green (Borrero) .. 6·25 1·10

84. Steam Locomotive. 86. Mount Chimborazo.

85. Garcia Moreno.

**1908.** Opening of Guayaquil to Quito Railway.

331. 84. 1 c. brown .. .. 50 50
332. 85. 2 c. black and blue .. 85 70
333. – 5 c. black and red .. 1·60 1·40
334. – 10 c. black and yellow .. 1·00 85
335. – 20 c. black and green .. 1·00 1·00
336. – 50 c. black and grey .. 1·00 1·00
337. 86. 1 s. black .. .. 2·00 2·00

PORTRAITS—As Type 85: 5 c. Gen. E. Alfaro. 10 c. A. Moncayo. 20 c. A. Harman. 50 c. Sivewright.

87. Jose Mejia Vallejo. 88. Exhibition Buildings.

**1909.** National Exn. Portraits as T 87.

340. 87. 1 c. green .. .. 15 25
341. – 2 c. blue (Espejo) .. 15 25
342. – 3 c. orange (Ascasubi) .. 15 35
343. – 5 c. lake (Salinas) .. 15 35
344. – 10 c. brown (Alegre) .. 20 35
345. – 20 c. grey (Montufar) .. 20 50
346. – 50 c. red (Morales) .. 20 50
347. – 1 s. olive (Quiroga) .. 20 70
348. 88. 5 s. violet .. .. 70 1·40

**1909.** Surch. **CINCO CENTAVOS.**

349. – 5 c. on 50 c. red (No. 346) 60 50

90. Pres. Roca. 91. Pres. Dr. Noboa. 92. Robles.

98. Valdez. 93. Pres. Gen. Urvina. 94. Pres. Dr. Garcia Moreno.

99. Espinoza. 95. Dr. Borrero.

**1911.**

354. 90. 1 c. black and red .. 25 10
366. 1 c. orange .. .. 25 10
355. 91. 2 c. black and blue .. 25 10
367. 2 c. green .. .. 10 10
356. 92. 3 c. black and orange .. 85 25
368. 3 c. black .. .. 40 10
369. 98. 4 c. black and red .. 10 10
357. 93. 5 c. black and red .. 40 10
370. 5 c. violet .. .. 60 10
358. 94. 10 c. black and blue .. 70 10
371. 10 c. blue .. .. 70 10
373. 99. 50 c. black and violet .. 1·75 35
359. 95. 1 s. black and green .. 3·75 75

See also Nos. 413/6b.

**1912.** Large Fiscal stamps inscr. "TIMBRE CONSULAR" at top. Surch. **POSTAL** and new value.

362. 1 c. on 1 s. green .. 25 25
363. 2 c. on 2 s. red .. 75 35
364. 2 c. on 5 s. blue .. 35 35
365. 2 c. on 10 s. yellow .. 1·50 1·50

**1920.** Optd. **CASA de CORREOS.**

374. 90. 1 c. orange .. .. 25 10

103. 108. Olmedo. 109. Monument to "Fathers of the Country".

**1920.** Obligatory Tax. Optd. **CASA de CORREOS** or surch. also. Dated as shown.

375. 103. 1 c. bl. & red (no date) 40 10
376. 1 c. bl. ("1919–1920") 45 10
379. 1 c. on 2 c. grn. ("1917–1918") 20 10
380. 1 c. on 5 c. grn. ("1911–1912") 30 10
380a. 1 c. on 5 c. grn. ("1913–1914") .. 2·75 35
377. 20 c. bl. ("1913–1914") 85 35
378. 20 c. ol. ("1917–1918") 2·25 40

**1920.** Cent. of Liberation of Guayaquil. Portraits as T **108.**

381. 108. 1 c. green .. .. 15 10
382. – 2 c. red (Ximena) .. 10 10
383. – 3 c. bistre (Roca) .. 10 10
384. – 4 c. green (Vivero) .. 15 10
385. – 5 c. blue (Cordero) .. 15 10
386. – 6 c. orange (Lavayen) .. 30 30
387. – 7 c. brown (Elizalde) .. 85 60
388. – 8 c. green (Garcia) .. 45 25
389. – 9 c. red (Antepara) .. 1·75 75
390. 109. 10 c. blue .. .. 60 10
391. – 15 c. black (Urdaneta) 85 45
392. – 20 c. purple (Villamil) 85 15
393. – 30 c. violet (Letamendi) 1·75 65
394. – 40 c. sepia (Escobedo) 3·00 1·10
395. – 50 c. green (Sucre) .. 1·90 45
396. – 60 c. blue (Illingworth) 3·75 1·10
397. – 70 c. grey (Roca) .. 6·25 2·50
398. – 80 c. yellow (Rocafuerte) 6·50 2·50
399. – 90 c. green (Star and wreath) .. 7·00 2·50
400. – 1 s. blue (Bolivar) .. 9·50 4·25

112. Post Office, Quito. 123.

**1920.** Obligatory Tax. G.P.O. Rebuilding Fund.

401. 112. 1 c. olive .. .. 10 10
402. 2 c. green .. .. 15 10
403. 20 c. brown .. .. 50 10
404. 2 s. violet .. .. 3·00 2·25
405. 5 s. blue .. .. 5·50 3·75

**1921.** Obligatory Tax. Surch. **CASA DE CORREOS. VEINTE CTS. 1921-1922.**

405a. 103. 20 c. on 1 c. blue .. 19·00 2·25
405b. 20 c. on 2 c. green .. 19·00 2·25

**1924.** Obligatory Tax. Surch. **DOS CENTAVOS -2-.**

406. 112. 2 c. on 20 c. brown .. 10 10

**1924.** Oblong Tobacco Tax stamps optd. **CASA-CORREOS.**

407. 1 c. red (Loco.) .. 20 15
408. 2 c. blue (Arms) .. 20 15

**1924.** Telegraph stamps as T **103**, but inscr. "TELEGRAFOS DEL ECUADOR" optd. **CASA—CORREOS.**

(a) Inscr. "TIMBRE FISCAL".

409. 1 c. yellow .. .. 1·50 50
410. 2 c. blue .. .. 25 10

(b) Inscr. "REGION ORIENTAL".

411. 1 c. yellow .. .. 25 20
412. 2 c. blue .. .. 50 20

**1925.**

413. 90. 1 c. blue .. .. 10 10
414. 91. 2 c. violet .. .. 10 10
415. 93. 5 c. red .. .. 15 10
415a. 5 c. brown .. .. 20 10
416. 94. 10 c. green .. .. 15 10
416a. 10 c. black .. .. 50 10
416b. 95. 1 s. black and orange .. 2·75 20

**1925.** Optd. **POSTAL** over ornament.
417. **112.** 20 c. brown .. .. 1·00 35

**1926.** Opening of Quito-Esmeraldas Railway. Optd. **QUITO** and railway train and **ESMERALDAS 1926.**
418. **90.** 1 c. blue .. .. 2·25 1·50
419. **91.** 2 c. violet .. .. 2·25 1·50
420. **92.** 3 c. black .. .. 1·75 1·50
421. – 4 c. green (No. 384) .. 1·75 1·50
422. **93.** 5 c. red .. .. .. 3·00 1·50
423. **94.** 10 c. green .. .. 3·00 1·50

**1927.** Optd. **POSTAL.**
424. **112.** 1 c. olive .. .. 10 10
425. 2 c. green .. .. 10 10
426. 20 c. brown .. .. 70 10

**1927.** Opening of new Post Office. Quito.
427. **123.** 5 c. orange .. .. 20 10
428. 10 c. green .. .. 15 10
429. 20 c. purple .. .. 35 10

**1928.** Opening of Quito-Cayambe Railway. Stamps of 1920 issue surch. **Frril. Norte Julio 8 de 1928 Est. Cayambe** and value.
431. 10 c. on 30 c. (No. 393) 3·00 3·00
432. 50 c. on 70 c. (No. 397) 3·75 3·75
433. 1 s. on 80 c. (No. 398).. 4·50 4·50

**1928.** National Assembly. Stamps of 1920 surch. **ASAMBLEA NCNAL, 1928** and value.
434. **108.** 1 c. on 1 c. green (381).. 6·25 5·25
435. – 1 c. on 2 c. red (382) .. 15 15
436. – 2 c. on 3 c. bistre (383).. 95 95
437. – 2 c. on 4 c. green (384).. 50 50
438. – 2 c. on 5 c. (No. 385) .. 25 25
440. – 5 c. on 6 c. (No. 386) .. 15 10
441. – 10 c. on 2 c. on 7 c. (387) 15 10
442. – 10 c. on 7 c. (No. 387).. 40 40
443. – 20 c. on 8 c. (No. 388).. 15 10
444. **109.** 40 c. on 10 c. (No. 390).. 1·75 1·50
445. – 40 c. on 15 c. (No. 391).. 35 35
446. – 50 c. on 20 c. (No. 392).. 5·75 4·50
447. – 1 s. on 40 c. (No. 394).. 1·40 1·40
448. – 5 s. on 50 c. (No. 395).. 1·90 1·90
449. – 10 s. on 60 c. (No. 396).. 6·75 4·50

**1928.** Opening of Railway at Otavalo, Consular Service stamps inscr. "TIMBRE-CONSULAR" surch. **Postal — Frril Norte Est. OTAVALO** and value.
450. 5 c. on 20 c. lilac .. .. 1·25 95
451. 10 c. on 20 c. lilac .. 1·25 95
452. 20 c. on 1 s. green .. 1·25 95
453. 50 c. on 1 s. green .. 1·40 65
454. 1 s. on 1 s. green .. 2·00 95
455. 5 s. on 2 s. red .. .. 5·75 4·25
456. 10 s. on 2 s. red .. .. 7·25 6·75

**130.** Ryan B-5 Brougham over the River Guayas.

**133.** Ploughing.

**1929.** Air.
458. **130.** 2 c. black .. .. 10 10
459. 5 c. red .. .. 10 10
460. 10 c. brown .. .. 15 10
461. 20 c. purple .. .. 25 10
462. 50 c. green .. .. 60 25
463. 1 s. blue .. .. 1·75 95
467. 1 s. red .. .. .. 1·75 35
709. 1 s. green .. .. 40 10
464. 5 s. yellow .. .. 5·00 3·75
468. 5 s. olive .. .. 2·50 1·90
710. 5 s. violet .. .. 60 10
465. 10 s. red .. .. 25·00 20·00
469. 10 s. black .. .. 7·75 2·75
711. 10 s. blue .. .. 1·10 10

**1929.** As T **103**, but inscr. "MOVILES" and optd. **POSTAL.**
466. **103.** 1 c. blue .. .. 10 10

**1930.** Air. Official Air stamps of 1929 optd. **MENDEZ BOGOTA-QUITO Junio 4 de 1930.**
470. **130.** 1 s. red .. .. .. 13·50 13·50
471. 5 s. olive .. .. 13·50 13·50
472. 10 s. black .. .. 13·50 13·50

**1930.** Independence Cent. Dated "1830 1930".
473. **133.** 1 c. red and yellow .. 10 10
474. – 2 c. green and yellow .. 10 10
475. – 5 c. purple and green .. 10 10
476. – 6 c. red and yellow .. 20 10
477. – 10 c. olive and orange.. 70 15
478. – 16 c. green and red .. 1·25 30
479. – 20 c. yellow and blue .. 35 10
480. – 40 c. sepia and yellow.. 40 10
481. – 50 c. sepia and yellow.. 50 10
482. – 1 s. black and green .. 1·40 10
483. – 2 s. black and deep blue 2·50 35
484. – 5 s. black and purple .. 4·50 50
485. – 10 s. black and red .. 12·50 3·00

DESIGNS—As Type **133**: **1 c.** Labourer and oxen, ploughing. 2 c. Cocoa cultivation. 6 c. Tobacco plantation. 10 c. Exportation of fruit. 10 s. Bolivar's monument (41 × 37½ mm.). LARGER (27 × 42½ mm.): 5 c. Cocoa pod. 20 c. Sugar plantation. 1 s. Olmedo. 2 s. Sucre. 5 s. Bolivar (41½ × 28 mm.): 16 c. Mountaineer, locomotive and airplane. 40, 50 c. Views of Quito.

**1933.** Optd. **CORREOS.**
486. **103.** 10 c. brown .. .. 40 10

**1933.** Optd. **CORREOS—Emision Junio 1933—Dcto. No. 200.**
487. **103.** 10 c. brown .. .. 15 10

**1933.** Nos. 476 and 478 surch.
488. 5 c. on 6 c. red and yellow 20 10
489. 10 c. on 16 c. green and red 30 10

**1934.** Obligatory Tax. Optd. **CASA de Correos y Telegrafos de Guayaquil.**
(a) Fiscal stamp as T **103**, but inscr. "MOVILES" (instead of dates at top).
490. **103.** 2 c. green .. .. 10 10
(b) Centenary stamp of 1930 (No. 479).
491. 20 c. yellow and blue .. 15 10
(c) Telegraph stamp as T **103**, but inscr. "TELEGRAFOS DEL ECUADOR" surch **2 ctvos.** also.
492. **103.** 2 c. on 10 c. brown .. 25 10

**143.** Mount Chimborazo. **144.** Mount Chimborazo.

**1934.**
493. **143.** 5 c. mauve .. .. 10 10
494. 5 c. blue .. .. 15 10
495. 5 c. brown .. .. 15 10
495a. 5 c. grey .. .. 15 10
496. 10 c. red .. .. 15 10
497. 10 c. green .. .. 15 10
498. 10 c. orange .. .. 15 10
499. 10 c. brown .. .. 15 10
500. 10 c. olive .. .. 15 10
500a. 10 c. black .. .. 10 10
500b. 10 c. lilac .. .. 10 10

**1934.**
501. **144.** 1 s. red .. .. .. 75 40

**1934.** Optd. **CASA de Correos y Teleg. de Guayaquil.**
502. **112.** 2 c. green (No. 425) .. 10 10

**146.** Symbol of Telegraphy. **150.** Map of Galapagos Is.

**1934.** G.P.O. Rebuilding Fund.
503. **146.** 2 c. green .. .. 10 10
504. – 20 c. red .. .. 10 10
The symbolic design of the 20 c. is 38 × 18½ mm.

**1935.** Unveiling of Bolivar Monument, Quito. Optd. **INAUGURACION MONUMENTO A BOLIVAR QUITO,** etc., or surch. also.
(a) Postage. On 1930 Independence Issue.
505. 5 c. on 6 c. red and yellow 20 10
506. 10 c. on 6 c. red and yellow 25 10
507. 20 c. yellow and blue .. 25 10
508. 40 c. sepia and yellow .. 35 20
509. 50 sepia and yellow .. 45 35
510. $1 on 5 s. black and purple 1·10 60
511. $2 on 5 s. black and purple 1·50 1·10
512. $5 on 10 s. black and red 2·50 2·50
(b) Air. On Official stamps of 1929.
513. **130.** 50 c. green .. .. 3·25 3·25
514. 50 c. brown .. .. 3·25 3·25
515. $1 on 5 s. olive .. 3·25 3·25
516. $2 on 10 s. black.. 3·25 3·25

**1935.** Fiscal stamp, but without dates and inscr. "TELEGRAFOS DEL ECUADOR", optd. **POSTAL.**
517. **103.** 10 c. brown .. .. 15 10

**1935.** Rural Workers Social Insurance Fund. No. 503 surch. **Seguro Social del Campesino Quito, 16 de Otbre.—1935** and value.
518. **146.** 3 c. on 2 c. green .. 10 10

**1936.** Centenary of Darwin's Visit to the Galapagos Is.
519. **150.** 2 c. black .. .. 10 10
520. – 5 c. olive .. .. 25 10
521. – 10 c. brown .. .. 40 10
522. – 20 c. purple .. .. 1·75 25
523. – 1 s. red .. .. 85 35
524. – 2 s. blue .. .. 1·10 70
DESIGNS—HORIZ. 10 c. Galapagos tortoise. VERT. 5 c. Giant lizard. 20 c. Charles Darwin and H.M.S. "Beagle". 1 s. Columbus. 2 s. View of Galapagos Islands.

**1936.** Oblong Tobacco Tax Stamps.
(a) Charity. Surch. **Seguro Social del Campesino 3 ctvs.**
525. – 3 c. on 1 c. red .. 10 10
(b) Charity. Surch. **SEGURO SOCIAL DEL CAMPESINO 3 ctvs.**
526. – 3 c. on 1 c. red .. 10 10
(c) Optd. **POSTAL.**
527. – 1 c. red .. .. 10 10

**1936.** No. 479 optd. **Casa de Correos y Telegrafos de Guayaquil.**
528. – 20 c. yellow and blue.. 20 10

**160.** Ulloa, La Condamine and Juan. **162.** Woodman.

**1936.** Bicentenary of La Condamine Scientific Expedition. (a) Postage.
529. – 2 c. blue .. .. 10 10
530. **160.** 5 c. green .. .. 10 10
531. – 10 c. orange .. .. 10 10
532. **160.** 20 c. violet .. .. 20 10
533. – 50 c. red .. .. 40 25
(b) Air. Nos. 531/3 optd. **AEREO.**
534. – 10 c. orange .. .. 20 10
535. **160.** 20 c. violet .. .. 20 10
536. – 50 c. red .. .. 35 10
(c) Air. Inscr. "CORREO AEREO".
537. – 70 c. grey .. .. 55 25
DESIGNS: 2 c., 10 c., 50 c. Godin. La Condamine and Bouguer. 70 c. La Condamine, Arms and Maldonado.

**1936.** Building and National Defence Funds. Surch. **5 Centavos Dect. Junio 13 de 1936.**
539. **162.** 5 c. on 3 c. blue .. 10 10

**1936.** Social Insurance.
540. **162.** 3 c. blue.. .. 10 10

**1936.** Oblong Tobacco Tax stamp surch. **TIMBRE PATRIOTICO DIEZ CENTAVOS.**
541. – 10 c. on 1 c. red .. 20 10

**165.** Independence Monument, Quito.

**166.** Condor and Martin M-130 Flying Boat.

**1936.** 1st Int. Philatelic Exn., Quito.
541a **165** 2 c. green (postage) .. 85 20
542 5 c. purple .. .. 85 20
543 10 c. red .. .. 85 25
543a 20 c. black .. .. 85 60
544 50 c. blue .. .. 1·50 1·00
545 1 s. red .. .. 1·75 1·50
546 **166** 70 c. brown (air) .. 90 50
547 1 s. violet .. .. 90 70

**1936.** Air. Optd **AEREA.**
547a **165** 2 c. red .. .. 2·50 2·50
547b 5 c. orange .. .. 2·50 2·50
547c 10 c. brown .. .. 2·50 2·50
547d 20 c. blue .. .. 2·50 2·50
547e 50 c. purple .. .. 2·50 2·50
547f 1 s. green .. .. 2·50 2·50

**167.** Symbolical of Defence. **169.**

**1937.** Obligatory Tax. National Defence Fund. (a) Surch. **POSTAL ADICIONAL** and value in figures.
548. **167.** 5 c. on 10 c. blue .. 40 10
(b) Without surch.
549. **167.** 10 c. blue .. .. 10 10

**1937.** Fiscal stamps inscr. "MOVILES" at top optd. **POSTAL** or surch. also.
550. **169.** 5 c. olive (I) .. .. 40 10
955a. 5 c. olive (II) .. .. 20 10
551. 10 c. blue .. .. 40 10
819. 10 c. orange .. .. 50 10
952. 20 c. on 30 c. blue .. 20 10
953. 30 c. blue .. .. 20 10
954. 40 c. on 50 c. purple .. 10 10
955. 50 c. purple .. .. 30 10
Nos. 952/3 are smaller (19½ × 25½ mm.). Nos. 550 (I) with imprint. 955a (II) without imprint. See also No. 685.

**171.** Andean Landscape.

DESIGNS — VERT. 5 c. Atahualpa. 1 s. Gold washer. HORIZ. 10 c. Straw-hat makers. 20 c. Salinas Beach.

**172.** Andean Condor over El Altar.

**1937.**
(a) Postage.
552. **171.** 2 c. green .. .. 10 10
553. – 5 c. red .. .. 10 10
554. – 10 c. blue .. .. 15 10
555. – 20 c. red .. .. 40 10
556. – 1 s. olive .. .. 55 25
(b) Air.
557. **172.** 10 c. brown .. .. 30 10
558. 20 c. olive .. .. 40 10
558a. 40 c. red .. .. 40 10
559. 70 c. brown .. .. 55 10
560. 1 s. slate .. .. 65 15
561. 2 s. violet .. .. 80 25

**173.**

**1937.** Optd. **TIMBRE PATRIOTICO.**
562. **173.** 5 c. brown .. .. 75 20

**174.** "Liberty" supporting Ecuadorian Flag between American Bald Eagle and Andean Condor.

**1938.** 150th Anniv. of U.S. Constitution. Flags in yellow, blue and red.
563. **174.** 2 c. blue (postage) .. 20 10
564. 5 c. violet .. .. 30 10
565. 10 c. black .. .. 30 10
566. 20 c. purple .. .. 45 15
567. 50 c. black .. .. 65 15
568. 1 s. olive .. .. 1·10 30
569. 2 s. brown .. .. 2·00 45
570. – 2 c. olive (air) .. .. 15 10
571. – 5 c. black .. .. 15 10
572. – 10 c. brown .. .. 20 10
573. – 20 c. blue .. .. 45 10
574. – 50 c. purple .. .. 70 15
575. – 1 s. black .. .. 1·25 15
576. – 2 s. violet .. .. 2·50 65
DESIGN (air): Washington portrait, American bald eagle and flags.

**176.** Ecuador.

**178.** "Road Transport".

**1938.** Obligatory Tax. Social Insurance Fund for Rural Workers and Guayaquil G.P.O. Rebuilding Funds.
577. **176.** 5 c. red .. .. 25 10

**1938.** Obligatory Tax. No. 537 surch. **CASA DE CORREOS Y TELEGRAFOS DE GUAYAQUIL** and **20** in each corner.
578. – 20 c. on 70 c. grey .. 20 10

**1938.** National Progress Exn. Inscr. "1830–1937".
579. **178.** 10 c. blue .. .. 10 10
580. – 50 c. purple .. .. 20 10
581. – 1 s. red .. .. 50 10
582. – 2 s. green .. .. 50 10
DESIGNS—VERT. 50 c. "Railways". 1 s. "Communication" HORIZ. 2 s. "Building" (inscr. "CONSTRUCCION").

**1938.** Air. Surch. **AEREO SEDTA** and value.
582a. **162.** 65 c. on 3 c. blue .. 10 10

**1938.** Obligatory Tax. Int. Anti-Cancer Fund. No. 476 surch. **CAMPANA. CONTRA EL CANCER 5 5.**
583. 5 c. on 6 c. red and yellow 10 10

**181.** Running.

**182.** Ryan B-5 Brougham over Mt. Chimborazo.

**1939.** Ecuadorean Victories at South American Olympic Games, La Paz. Inscr. "EN COMMEMORACION DE LA PRIMERA OLIMPIADA BOLIVARIANA DE 1938".

584. – 5 c. red (postage) .. 1·25 35
585. 181. 10 c. blue .. .. 1·60 40
586. – 50 c. olive .. .. 1·75 50
587. – 1 s. violet .. .. 3·25 50
588. – 2 s. green .. .. 4·50 70

DESIGNS—HORIZ. 5 c. Parade of athletes. 50 c. Basketball. VERT. 1 s. Wrestling. 2 s. Diving.

589. – 5 c. green (air) .. .. 40 10
590. – 10 c. orange .. .. 55 15
591. – 50 c. brown .. .. 2·75 15
592. – 1 s. sepia .. .. 3·25 35
593. – 2 s. red .. .. .. 5·00 70

DESIGNS—HORIZ. 5 c. Riding. 1 s. Boxing. VERT. 10 c. Running. 50 c. Tennis. 2 s. Olympic flame.

**1939.** Air.

594. 182. 1 s. brown .. .. 40 15
595. 2 s. purple .. .. 85 15
596. 5 s. black .. .. 1·25 15

183. Dolores Mission, San Francisco.
184. Golden Gate Bridge and Mountain.

**1939.** San Francisco Int. Exn.

597. 183. 2 c. green (postage) .. 10 10
598. 5 c. red .. .. 10 10
599. 10 c. blue .. .. 10 10
600. 50 c. brown .. .. 25 10
601. 1 s. slate .. .. 45 10
602. 2 s. violet .. .. 80 15
603. 184. 2 c. black (air) .. 10 10
604. 5 c. red .. .. 10 10
605. 10 c. blue .. .. 10 10
606. 50 c. purple .. .. 10 10
607. 1 s. brown .. .. 25 10
608. 2 s. brown .. .. 25 10
609. 5 s. green .. .. 55 10

185. Symbol of N.Y. World's Fair.
186. Empire State Building and Mountain.

**1939.** New York World's Fair.

610. 185. 2 c. olive (postage) .. 10 10
611. 5 c. orange .. .. 10 10
612. 10 c. blue .. .. 10 10
613. 50 c. grey .. .. 40 10
614. 1 s. red .. .. 60 15
615. 2 s. brown .. .. 75 20
616. 186. 2 c. brown (air) .. 10 10
617. 5 c. red .. .. 10 10
618. 10 c. blue .. .. 10 10
619. 50 c. olive .. .. 10 10
620. 1 s. orange .. .. 20 10
621. 2 s. mauve .. .. 35 15
622. 5 s. black .. .. 70 10

**1939.** Obligatory Tax. Social Insurance Fund for Rural Workers. Oblong Tobacco Tax stamps surch. **POSTAL ADICIONAL CINCO CENTAVOS** and value.

623. – 5 c. on 1 c. pink .. 15 10

**1940.** Obligatory Tax. G.P.O. Rebuilding Fund. Oblong Tobacco Tax stamp surch **CASAS DE CORREOS y TELEGRAFOS CINCO CENTAVOS.**

624 5 c. on 1 c. pink .. .. 40 10

**1940.** Obligatory Tax. Guyaquil G.P.O Rebuilding Fund. No. 567 surch. **CASA DE CORREOS y TELEGRAFOS DE GUAYAQUIL 20 20.**

625. 174. 20 c. on 50 c. **Mult.** .. 40 15

**1940.** Obligatory Tax. National Defence Fund. Oblong Tobacco Tax stamps surch. **TIMBRE PATRIOTICO VEINTE CENTAVOS** and value.

625b – 20 c. on 1 c. pink .. 2·25 40

191. Pan-American Union Flags.
192. Allegory of Union.

**1940.** 50th Anniv. of Pan-American Union.

626. 191. 5 c. black & red (post.) 10 10
627. 10 c. black and blue .. 10 10
628. 50 c. black and green .. 35 10
629. 1 s. black and violet .. 50 20
630. 192. 10 c. blue & orange (air) 15 10
631. 70 c. blue and purple .. 25 10
632. 1 s. blue and brown .. 35 10
633. 10 s. blue and black .. 85 50

193. Ploughing.
194. Symbolic of Communications.

**1940.** Obligatory Tax. Social Insurance Fund for Rural Workers and Guayaquil G.P.O. Rebuilding Funds.

634. 193. 5 c. red .. .. .. 15 10

**1940.** Obligatory Tax. G.P.O. Rebuilding Fund.

635. 194. 5 c. brown .. .. 10 10
636. 5 c. green .. .. 10 10

195. Fighter Aircraft.
196. Dr. de Santa Cruz y Espejo.

**1941.** Obligatory Tax. National Defence Fund.

637. 195. 20 c. blue .. .. 40 10

**1941.** 1st National Periodical Exn.

638. 196. 30 c. blue (postage) .. 25 10
639. 1 s. orange .. .. 1·10 10
640. 3 s. red (air) .. .. 70 10
641. 10 s. orange .. .. 1·40 25

197. Francisco de Orellana.
198. Early Map of S. America.

**1942.** 4th Cent. of Discovery of R. Amazon.

642. 197. 10 c. brown (postage) .. 25 10
643. – 40 c. red .. .. 25 10
644. – 1 s. violet .. .. 70 10
645. – 2 s. blue .. .. 95 25
646. 198. 40 c. bistre & black (air) 35 10
647. – 70 c. olive .. .. 60 10
648. – 2 s. green .. .. 70 25
649. – 5 s. red .. .. .. 75 35

DESIGNS—VERT. 40 c. (No. 643). 70 c. Portraits of G. Pizarro and G. Diaz de Pineda. 2 s. (No. 645) Quito. 5 s. Expedition leaving Quito. HORIZ. 1 s. Guayaquil. 2 s. (No. 648) Relief map of R. Amazon.

199. R. Crespo Toral.
201. Mt. Chimborazo.

**1942.**

650. 199. 10 c. green (postage) .. 10 10
651. 50 c. brown .. .. 20 10
652. 10 c. violet (air) .. 25 10

**1942.** As T 199, but portrait of Pres. A. B. Moreno.

653. 10 c. green .. .. 10 10

**1942.**

654. 201. 30 c. brown .. .. 20 10
654a. 30 c. blue .. .. 20 10
654b. 30 c. orange .. .. 10 10
654c. 30 c. green .. .. 20 10

202. "Defence".
203. Guayaquil Riverside.

**1942.** Obligatory Tax. National Defence Fund.

655. 202. 20 c. blue .. .. 40 10
655a. 40 c. brown .. .. 40 10

**1942.** Obligatory Tax. National Defence Fund. As T 173 surch.

655b. 173. 20 c. on 5 c. pink .. — 5·00
655c. 20 c. on 1 s. brown .. — 5·00
655d. 20 c. on 2 s. green .. — 5·00

**1942.** Obligatory Tax. Guayaquil G.P.O. Rebuilding Fund, No. 567 surch. **CASA DE CORREOS Y TELEGRAFOS DE GUAYAQUIL VEINTE CENTAVOS.**

655e. – 20 c. on 50 c. mult. .. 50 15

**1943.**

656. 203. 20 c. red .. .. 20 10
656a. 20 c. blue .. .. 20 10

**1943.** Guayaquil G.P.O. Rebuilding Fund. Surch. **ADICIONAL CINCO CENTAVOS 5 Centavos CASA DE CORREOS DE GQUIL. y.**

657. 162. 5 c.+5 c. on 3 c. blue .. 20 10

**1943.** Surch. **ADICIONAL CINCO CENTAVOS.**

658. 162. 5 c. on 3 c blue .. 20 10

206. Gen. Alfaro.
207. Alfaro's Birthplace.

**1943.** Alfaro Birth Cent.

659. 206. 10 c. black & red (post.) 10 10
660. – 20 c. brown and olive .. 15 10
661. – 30 c. green and olive .. 45 45
662. 207. 1 s. red and grey .. 75 75
663. 206. 70 c. black and red (air) 40 20
664. – 1 s. brown and olive .. 75 50
665. – 3 s. green and olive .. 60 60
666. 207. 5 s. red and grey .. 95 70

DESIGNS—HORIZ. 20 c., 1 s. Devil's Nose Zigzag, Guayaquil-Quito Rly. 30 c., 3 s. Alfaro Military College.

208. Labourers.
213. Arms of Ecuador.

**1943.** Obligatory Tax. Social Insurance Fund for Rural Workers and Guayaquil G.P.O. Rebuilding Funds.

667. 208. 5 c. blue .. .. 30 10

**1943.** Welcome to Henry A. Wallace Vice-President of U.S.A. Optd. **BIENVENIDO-WALLACE Abril 15-1943.**

668. 174. 50 c. multicoloured (post.) 1·50 60
669. 1 s. multicoloured .. 3·25 1·25
670. 2 s. multicoloured .. 4·75 1·90
671. – 50 c. multicoloured (No. 574) (air) .. .. 3·75 70
672. – 1 s. multicoloured (No. 575) .. .. .. 4·75 85
673. – 2 s. multicoloured (No. 576) .. .. .. 6·00 1·25

**1943.** Obligatory Tax. National Defence Fund. Fiscal stamp optd. **TIMBRE PATRIOTICO.**

674. 20 c. orange .. .. 23·00 1·10

**1943.** Air. Visits of Presidents of Bolivia Paraguay and Venezuela to Ecuador.

(a) Optd. **AEREO LOOR A BOLIVIA JUNIO 11-1943.**

675. – 50 c. purple (No. 580) .. 40 40
676. – 1 s. red (No. 581) .. 1·00 60
677. – 2 s. green (No. 582) .. 50 35

(b) Optd. **AEREO LOOR AL PARAGUAY JULIO 5-1943.**

678. – 50 c. purple (No. 580) .. 40 40
679. – 1 s. red (No. 581) .. 1·00 60
680. – 2 s. green (No. 582) .. 50 35

(c) Optd. **AEREO LOOR A VENEZUELA JULIO 23-1943.**

681. – 50 c. purple (No. 580) .. 40 40
682. – 1 s. red (No. 581) .. 1·00 60
683. – 2 s. green (No. 582) .. 50 35

**1943.** Obligatory Tax National Defence Fund. Fiscal stamp surch. **TIMBRE PATRIOTICO VEINTE CENTAVOS.**

684. – 20 c. on 10 c. orange .. 75 20

**1943.** Fiscal stamp as T 169. surch. **POSTAL 30 Centavos** with or without bars.

685. 169. 30 c. on 50 c. brown .. 25 10

As No. 685 but surch. **POSTAL 30 Ctvs.**

780. 169. 30 c. on 50 c. brown .. 10 10

**1943.** Obligatory Tax. National Defence Fund.

686. 213. 20 c. red .. .. 20 10

214. Arms of Ecuador and Map of Central America.

215. Pres. Arroyo del Rio at Washington.

**1943.** President's Visit to Washington.

687. 214. 10 c. violet (postage) .. 20 10
688. 10 c. green .. .. 10 10
688. 20 c. brown .. .. 20 10
699. 20 c. pink .. .. 15 10
689. 30 c. orange .. .. 15 15
700. 30 c. brown .. .. 20 15
690. 50 c. olive .. .. 35 20
701. 50 c. purple .. .. 35 25
691. 1 s. violet .. .. 40 20
702. 1 s. grey .. .. 40 35
692. 10 s. brown .. .. 2·50 2·40
703. 10 s. orange .. .. 2·50 2·50
693. 215. 50 c. brown (air) .. 40 35
704. 50 c. purple .. .. 40 20
694. 70 c. red .. .. 50 50
705. 70 c. brown .. .. 40 35
695. 3 s. blue .. .. 40 50
706. 3 s. green .. .. 40 35
696. 5 s. green .. .. 85 60
707. 5 s. blue .. .. 70 55
697. 10 s. olive .. .. 3·50 3·00
708. 10 s. red .. .. 95 95

**1944.** Nos. 698/708 surch. **Hospital Mendez** and new value.

711a. 214. 10 c.+10 c. grn. (post.) 35 25
711b. 20 c.+20 c. pink .. 35 25
711c. 30 c.+20 c. brown .. 35 35
711d. 50 c.+20 c. purple .. 45 50
711e. 1 s.+50 c. grey .. 75 85
711f. 10 s.+2 s. orange .. 2·75 2·75
711g. 215. 50 c.+50 c. pur. (air) 2·25 2·25
711h. 70 c.+30 c. brown .. 2·25 2·25
711i. 3 s.+50 c. green .. 2·25 2·25
711j. 5 s+1 s. blue .. 2·25 2·25
711k. 10 s.+2 s. red .. 2·25 2·25

**1944.** No. 600. Surch. **30 Centavos.**

712. 183. 30 c. on 50 c. brown .. 15 10

**1944.** Obligatory Tax. National Defence Fund. No. 686 surch. **POSTAL 30 Centavos.**

713. 213. 30 c. on 20 c. red .. 25 10

**1944.** 606 and 619 Surch. **POSTAL 30 Centavos.**

714. 184. 30 c. on 50 c. purple .. 15 10
715. 186. 30 c. on 50 c. olive .. 15 10

218. F. Gonzales Suarez.
219. Cathedral, Quito.

**1944.** Birth Cent. of F. G. Suarez (Archbishop).

716. 218. 10 c. blue (postage) .. 10 10
717. 20 c. green .. .. 10 10
718. 30 c. purple .. .. 20 15
719. 1 s. violet .. .. 40 10
720. 219. 70 c. green (air) .. 50 25
721. 1 s. olive .. .. 50 25
722. 3 s. red .. .. 60 30
723. 5 s. red .. .. 75 35

**1944.** Surch. **CINCO Centavos.**

724. 183. 5 c. on 2 c. green .. 10 10
725. 185. 5 c. on 2 c. green .. 10 10

221. Government Palace, Quito.
222. Red Cross Symbol.

**1944.**

726. 221. 10 c. green (postage) .. 10 10
727. 30 c. blue .. .. 10 10
728. 3 s. orange (air) .. 25 10
729. 5 s. brown .. .. 40 10
730. 10 s. red .. .. 85 10
730a. 10 s. violet .. .. 85 10

**1945.** 80th Anniv. of Int. Red Cross. Cross in red.

731. 222. 30 c. brown (postage) .. 50 10
732. 1 s. brown .. .. 35 20
733. 5 s. green .. .. 75 70
734. 10 s. red .. .. 2·10 1·25
735. 2 s. blue (air) .. .. 40 40
736. 3 s. green .. .. 70 40
737. 5 s. violet .. .. 1·10 70
738. 10 s. red .. .. 2·75 2·10

**1945.** Air. Surch **AEREO 40 Ctvs.**

739 208 40 c. on 5 c. blue .. 15 10

**1945.** Obligatory Tax. Air. No. 726 surch. **FOMENTO - AERO - COMUNICACIONES 20 Ctvs.**

740. 221. 20 c. on 10 c. green .. 25 10

**1945.** Air. Victory. Optd. **V SETIEMBRE 5 1945.**

| | | | | |
|---|---|---|---|---|
| 742. | 221. | 3 s. orange .. .. | 50 | 50 |
| 743. | | 5 s. brown .. .. | 40 | 40 |
| 744. | | 10 s. red .. .. | 1·40 | 1·40 |

**1945.** Visit of Pres. Juan Antonio Rios of Chile. Optd. **LOOR A CHILE OCTUBRE 2 1945** and five-pointed star. Flags in yellow, blue and red.

| | | | | |
|---|---|---|---|---|
| 745. | 174. | 50 c. black (postage) .. | 55 | 25 |
| 746. | | 1 s. olive .. .. | 90 | 40 |
| 747. | | 2 s. brown .. .. | 1·75 | 75 |
| 748. | – | 50 c. pur. (No. 574) (air) | 1·25 | 75 |
| 749. | – | 1 s. black (No. 575) .. | 1·40 | 85 |
| 750. | – | 2 s. violet (No. 576) .. | 1·40 | 85 |

227. Marshal Sucre. 230. Pan-American Highway.

**1945.** 150th Birth Anniv. of Marshal Sucre.

| | | | | |
|---|---|---|---|---|
| 751. | 227. | 10 c. green (postage) .. | 20 | 10 |
| 752. | | 20 c. brown .. .. | 20 | 10 |
| 753. | | 40 c. grey .. .. | 20 | 10 |
| 754. | | 1 s. green .. .. | 20 | 20 |
| 755. | | 2 s. brown .. .. | 45 | 25 |
| 756. | – | 30 c. blue (air) .. | 15 | 10 |
| 757. | – | 40 c. red .. .. | 25 | 10 |
| 758. | – | 1 s. violet .. .. | 50 | 25 |
| 759. | – | 3 s. black .. .. | 60 | 40 |
| 760. | – | 5 s. purple .. .. | 85 | 55 |

DESIGN—Air stamps: Liberty Monument.

**1945.** Surch. **c VEINTE CENTAVOS.**

| | | | | |
|---|---|---|---|---|
| 761. | 221. | 20 c. on 10 c. green .. | 10 | 10 |

**1946.** Completion of Pan-American Highway.

| | | | | |
|---|---|---|---|---|
| 762. | 230. | 20 c. brown (postage) | 10 | 10 |
| 763. | | 30 c. green .. .. | 10 | 10 |
| 764. | | 1 s. blue .. .. | 10 | 10 |
| 765. | | 5 s. purple .. .. | 60 | 60 |
| 766. | | 10 s. red .. .. | 1·10 | 85 |
| 767. | | 1 s. red (air) .. | 35 | 20 |
| 768. | | 2 s. violet .. .. | 45 | 30 |
| 769. | | 3 s. green .. .. | 45 | 35 |
| 770. | | 5 s. orange .. .. | 60 | 50 |
| 771. | | 10 s. blue .. .. | 85 | 45 |

231. Torch of Democracy. 232. Popular Suffrage.

**1946.** 2nd Anniv. of Revolution.

| | | | | |
|---|---|---|---|---|
| 772. | 231. | 5 c. blue (postage) .. | 10 | 10 |
| 773. | 232. | 10 c. green .. .. | 10 | 10 |
| 774. | – | 20 c. red .. .. | 20 | 10 |
| 775. | – | 30 c. brown .. .. | 35 | 10 |
| 776. | 231. | 40 c. red (air) .. | 10 | 10 |
| 777. | 232. | 1 s. brown .. .. | 10 | 10 |
| 778. | – | 2 s. blue .. .. | 40 | 10 |
| 779. | – | 3 s. green .. .. | 55 | 30 |

DESIGNS—VERT. 20 c., 2 s. National flag. 30 c., 3 s. Pres. J.M. Velasco Ibarra.

**1946.** Nos. O 567/8 optd. **POSTAL.**

| | | | | |
|---|---|---|---|---|
| 781. | 172. | 10 c. brown .. .. | 10 | 10 |
| 782. | | 20 c. olive .. .. | 15 | 10 |

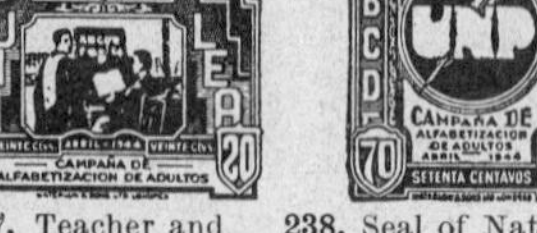

237. Teacher and Scholar. 238. Seal of National Periodicals Union.

**1946.** Adult Instruction.

| | | | | |
|---|---|---|---|---|
| 783. | 237. | 10 c. blue (postage) .. | 10 | 10 |
| 784. | | 20 c. brown .. .. | 10 | 10 |
| 785. | | 30 c. green .. .. | 15 | 10 |
| 786. | | 50 c. black .. .. | 35 | 20 |
| 787. | | 1 s. red .. .. | 50 | 15 |
| 788. | | 10 s. purple .. .. | 2·10 | 50 |
| 789. | 238. | 50 c. violet (air) .. | 35 | 25 |
| 790. | | 70 c. green .. .. | 40 | 25 |
| 791. | | 3 s. red .. .. | 45 | 35 |
| 792. | | 5 s. blue .. .. | 60 | 25 |
| 793. | | 10 s. brown .. .. | 1·75 | 40 |

**INDEX**
Countries can be quickly located by referring to the index at the end of this volume.

239. "Liberty", "Mercury" and Aeroplanes. 240. "Mariana de Jesus Paredes y Flores".

**1946.** Obligatory Tax. Air. National Defence Fund.

| | | | | |
|---|---|---|---|---|
| 794. | 239. | 20 c. brown .. .. | 15 | 10 |

**1946.** 300th Death Anniv. of Blessed Mariana de Jesus Paredes y Flores.

| | | | | |
|---|---|---|---|---|
| 795. | 240. | 10 c. brown (postage) .. | 15 | 10 |
| 796. | | 20 c. green .. .. | 10 | 10 |
| 797. | | 30 c. violet .. .. | 20 | 10 |
| 798. | – | 1 s. brown (Urn) .. | 40 | 30 |
| 799. | – | 40 c. brown (air) .. | 25 | 10 |
| 800. | – | 60 c. blue .. .. | 30 | 30 |
| 801. | – | 3 s. yellow .. .. | 45 | 60 |
| 802. | – | 5 s. green .. .. | 85 | 75 |

DESIGNS: 40 c., 60 c. Mariana teaching children. 3 s., 5 s. Cross and lilies.

244. Vicente Rocafuerte. 245. Jesuit Church, Quito. 250. Andres Bello.

**1947.**

| | | | | |
|---|---|---|---|---|
| 803. | 244. | 5 c. brown (postage) .. | 10 | 10 |
| 804. | | 10 c. purple .. .. | 10 | 10 |
| 805. | | 15 c. black .. .. | 10 | 10 |
| 806. | 245. | 20 c. lake .. .. | 15 | 10 |
| 807. | | 30 c. mauve .. .. | 15 | 10 |
| 808. | | 40 c. blue .. .. | 25 | 10 |
| 809. | – | 45 c. green .. .. | 25 | 10 |
| 810. | – | 50 c. grey .. .. | 35 | 15 |
| 811. | – | 80 c. red .. .. | 40 | 10 |

PORTRAIT: 45 c. to 80 c. F. J. E. de Santa Cruz y Espejo.

| | | | | |
|---|---|---|---|---|
| 812. | – | 60 c. green (air) .. | 10 | 10 |
| 813. | – | 70 c. violet .. .. | 10 | 10 |
| 814. | – | 1 s. brown .. .. | 10 | 10 |
| 815. | – | 1 s. 10 red .. .. | 10 | 10 |
| 816. | – | 1 s. 30 blue .. .. | 10 | 10 |
| 817. | – | 1 s. 90 brown .. .. | 35 | 10 |
| 818. | – | 2 s. olive .. .. | 35 | 10 |

DESIGNS: 60 c. to 1 s. 10, Father J. de Velasco. 1 s. 30 to 2 s. Riobamba Irrigation Canal.

**1948.** 83rd Death Anniv. of Andres Belle (educationalist).

| | | | | |
|---|---|---|---|---|
| 820. | 250. | 20 c. blue (postage) .. | 15 | 10 |
| 821. | | 30 c. pink .. .. | 25 | 10 |
| 822. | | 40 c. green .. .. | 25 | 10 |
| 823. | | 1 s. black .. .. | 50 | 15 |
| 824. | | 60 c. mauve (air.) .. | 20 | 10 |
| 825. | | 1 s. 30 green .. .. | 40 | 25 |
| 826. | | 1 s. 90 red .. .. | 35 | 25 |

**1948.** Economic Conf. Optd. **CONFERENCIA ECONOMICA GRAN-COLOMBIANA MAYO 24 DE 1.948.**

| | | | | |
|---|---|---|---|---|
| 827 | 245 | 40 c. blue (postage) .. | 20 | 10 |
| 828 | – | 70 c. vio (No. 813) (air) | 40 | 25 |

252. The " Santa Maria ". 253. Christopher Columbus.

**1948.** Completion of Columbus Memorial Lighthouse.

| | | | | |
|---|---|---|---|---|
| 829. | 252. | 10 c. green (postage) .. | 40 | 10 |
| 830. | | 20 c. brown .. .. | 70 | 10 |
| 831. | | 30 c. violet .. .. | 90 | 15 |
| 832. | | 50 c. red .. .. | 1·25 | 15 |
| 833. | | 1 s. blue .. .. | 1·75 | 15 |
| 834. | | 5 s. red .. .. | 4·25 | 55 |
| 835. | 253. | 50 c. green (air) .. | 20 | 10 |
| 836. | | 70 c. red .. .. | 20 | 10 |
| 837. | | 3 s. blue .. .. | 40 | 30 |
| 838. | | 5 s. brown .. .. | 70 | 25 |
| 839. | | 10 s. violet .. .. | 95 | 35 |

**1948.** National Fair. Nos. 811 and 816 optd. **Feria Nacional 1948 ECUADOR de hoy y del MANANA.**

| | | | | |
|---|---|---|---|---|
| 840. | | 80 c. red (postage) .. | 25 | 25 |
| 841. | | 1 s. 30 c. blue (air) .. | 40 | 30 |

255. "Telegrafo I" on First Postal Flight. 256. Elia Liut and "Telegrafo I".

**1948.** 25th Anniv. of First Ecuadorian Postal Flight.

| | | | | |
|---|---|---|---|---|
| 842. | 255. | 30 c. orange (postage) | 20 | 10 |
| 843. | | 40 c. mauve .. .. | 20 | 10 |
| 844. | | 60 c. blue .. .. | 25 | 10 |
| 845. | | 1 s. brown .. .. | 35 | 10 |
| 846. | | 3 s. brown .. .. | 1·00 | 20 |
| 847. | | 5 s. black .. .. | 80 | 30 |
| 848. | 256. | 60 c. red (air) .. | 35 | 25 |
| 849. | | 1 s. green .. .. | 45 | 25 |
| 850. | | 1 s. 30 red .. .. | 45 | 30 |
| 851. | | 1 s. 90 violet .. .. | 50 | 30 |
| 852. | | 2 s. brown .. .. | 60 | 35 |
| 853. | | 5 s. blue .. .. | 90 | 55 |

257. "Reading and Writing". 258. "Education For All".

**1948.** National Education Campaign.

| | | | | |
|---|---|---|---|---|
| 854. | 257. | 10 c. claret (postage) .. | 10 | 10 |
| 855. | | 20 c. brown .. .. | 20 | 20 |
| 856. | | 30 c. green .. .. | 10 | 30 |
| 857. | | 50 c. red .. .. | 40 | 20 |
| 858. | | 1 s. violet .. .. | 55 | 40 |
| 859. | | 10 s. blue .. .. | 1·50 | 60 |
| 860. | 258. | 50 c. violet (air) .. | 35 | 20 |
| 861. | | 70 c. blue .. .. | 35 | 20 |
| 862. | | 3 s. green .. .. | 55 | 30 |
| 863. | | 5 s. red .. .. | 70 | 25 |
| 864. | | 10 s. brown .. .. | 1·40 | 45 |

259. "Freedom from Fear". 260. "Freedom of Religion".

261. "Freedom of Speech and Expression". 262. "Freedom from Want".

**1948.** Homage to Franklin D. Roosevelt.

| | | | | |
|---|---|---|---|---|
| 865. | 259. | 10 c. red & grey (post.) | 15 | 10 |
| 866. | | 20 c. olive and blue .. | 15 | 15 |
| 867. | 260. | 30 c. olive and red .. | 25 | 10 |
| 868. | | 40 c. purple and sepia | 35 | 10 |
| 869. | | 1 s. brown and red .. | 40 | 25 |
| 870. | 261. | 60 c. grn. & brn. (air) .. | 10 | 10 |
| 871. | | 1 s. red and black .. | 10 | 10 |
| 872. | 262. | 1 s. 50 green & brown | 25 | 15 |
| 873. | | 2 s. red and black .. | 50 | 15 |
| 874. | | 5 s. blue and black .. | 75 | 20 |

263. Maldonado at Academy of Sciences, Paris. 264. Riobamba Aqueduct.

**1948.** Death Bicentenary of Maldonado (geographer and scientist).

| | | | | |
|---|---|---|---|---|
| 875. | 263. | 5 c. red & blk. (post.) .. | 15 | 10 |
| 876. | 264. | 10 c. black and red .. | 20 | 10 |
| 877. | – | 30 c. blue and brown | 25 | 10 |
| 878. | 264. | 40 c. violet and green | 60 | 10 |
| 879. | 263. | 50 c. red and green .. | 40 | 10 |
| 880. | – | 1 s. blue and brown .. | 75 | 10 |
| 881. | – | 60 c. red & orge. (air) | 25 | 10 |
| 882. | – | 90 c. black and red .. | 25 | 10 |
| 883. | – | 1 s. 30 orange & mauve | 40 | 20 |
| 884. | – | 2 s. green and blue .. | 40 | 20 |

DESIGN—VERT. 30 c., 60 c., 1 s. 30, Maldonado making road to Esmeraldas. 90 c., 1 s., 2 s. P. Vicente Maldonado.

266. Cervantes, Don Quixote and Windmill. 267. Don Quixote and Sheep.

**1949.** 400th Birth Anniv. of Cervantes.

| | | | | |
|---|---|---|---|---|
| 885. | – | 30 c. blue & pur. (post.) | 10 | 10 |
| 886. | 266. | 60 c. brown & purple .. | 25 | 10 |
| 887. | – | 1 s. red and green .. | 75 | 15 |
| 888. | 266. | 2 s. black and red .. | 1·50 | 25 |
| 889. | – | 5 s. green and brown | 2·75 | 75 |
| 890. | – | 1 s. 30 sep. & blue (air) | 1·50 | 1·50 |
| 891. | 267. | 1 s. 90 red and green .. | 40 | 25 |
| 892. | – | 3 s. violet and red .. | 40 | 25 |
| 893. | 267. | 5 s. black and red .. | 95 | 10 |
| 894. | – | 10 s. purple and green | 1·60 | 10 |

DESIGNS—HORIZ. 30 c., 1 s., 5 s. (No. 889) Cervantes, Don Quixote and Sancho Panza. 1 s. 30, 3 s., 10 s. Don Juan Montalvo and Cervantes.

**1949.** 2nd Eucharistic Congress. Stamps of 1947 surch. **II CONGRESO Junio 1949 Eucaristico Ncl.** and values.

(a) Postage. No. 808 surch.

| | | | | |
|---|---|---|---|---|
| 895 | 245 | 10 c. on 40 c. blue .. | 15 | 10 |
| 896 | | 20 c. on 40 c. blue .. | 25 | 10 |
| 897 | | 30 c. on 40 c. blue .. | 25 | 15 |

(b) Air. No. 815 surch.

| | | | | |
|---|---|---|---|---|
| 898 | – | 50 c. on 1 s. 10 red .. | 10 | 10 |
| 899 | – | 60 c. on 1 s. 10 red .. | 10 | 10 |
| 900 | – | 90 c. on 1 s. 10 red .. | 20 | 20 |

269. Equatorial Line Monument. 274. Lake San Pablo.

**1949.**

| | | | | |
|---|---|---|---|---|
| 901. | 269. | 10 c. purple .. .. | 20 | 10 |

**1949.** 75th Anniv. of U.P.U. Surch. **75 ANIVERSARIO** (or **Aniversario**—air stamps) **U.P.U.** and value.

| | | | | |
|---|---|---|---|---|
| 902. | 274. | 10 c. on 50 c. grn. (post.) | 10 | 10 |
| 903. | | 20 c. on 50 c. green .. | 15 | 10 |
| 904. | | 30 c. on 50 c. green .. | 25 | 10 |
| 905. | 221. | 60 c. on 3 s. orge. (air) | 40 | 35 |
| 906. | | 90 c. on 3 s. orange .. | 35 | 25 |
| 907. | | 1 s. on 3 s. orange .. | 40 | 35 |
| 908. | | 2 s. on 3 s. orange .. | 90 | 45 |

For unoverprinted stamp Type **274**, see No. 926.

272. 272a.

**1949.** Consular Service stamps optd. or surch. for postal use.

I. On T **272.**

A. Postage.

(a) Vert. surch **POSTAL** and value before **ct vs.**

| | | | | |
|---|---|---|---|---|
| 908a. | 272. | 5 c. on 10 c. red .. | 10 | 10 |
| 909. | | 20 c. on 25 c. brown .. | 10 | 10 |
| 910. | | 30 c. on 50 c. black .. | 10 | 10 |

(b) Optd. **CORREOS** diag.

| | | | | |
|---|---|---|---|---|
| 927. | 272. | 10 c. red .. .. | 10 | 10 |

(c) Optd. **POSTAL** diag.

| | | | | |
|---|---|---|---|---|
| 929. | 272. | 10 c. red .. .. | 10 | 10 |

(d) Vert. surch. with figs. before and after **Ctvs.**

(i) **CORREOS** upwards.

| | | | | |
|---|---|---|---|---|
| 928. | 272. | 30 c. on 50 c. black .. | 10 | 10 |

(ii) **POSTAL** upwards.

| | | | | |
|---|---|---|---|---|
| 930. | 272. | 20 c. on 25 c. brown .. | 10 | 10 |
| 931. | | 30 c. on 50 c. black .. | 20 | 10 |

(e) Surch. **POSTAL centavos** with figs. between.

| | | | | |
|---|---|---|---|---|
| 969. | 272. | 10 c. on 20 s. blue .. | 15 | 10 |
| 970. | | 20 c. on 10 s. grey .. | 15 | 10 |
| 971. | | 20 c. on 20 s. blue .. | 15 | 10 |
| 972. | | 30 c. on 10 s. grey .. | 15 | 10 |
| 973. | | 30 c. on 20 s. blue .. | 10 | 10 |

B. Air. Surch. **AEREO** and value.

| | | | | |
|---|---|---|---|---|
| 913. | 272. | 60 c. on 50 c. black .. | 20 | 10 |
| 913a. | | 60 c. on 2 s. brown .. | 20 | 10 |
| 913b. | | 1 s. on 2 s. brown (D.) | 30 | 10 |
| 913c. | | 1 s. on 2 s. brown (U.) | 30 | 10 |
| 913d. | | 2 s. on 2 s. brown .. | 30 | 10 |
| 913e. | | 3 s. on 5 s. violet .. | 55 | 15 |

In No. 913b the surch. reads down and in No. 913c it reads up.

II. On T **272a.**

A. Postage. Surch. **POSTAL** and value.

| | | | | |
|---|---|---|---|---|
| 935. | 272a. | 30 c. on 50 c. red .. | 15 | 10 |
| 934. | | 40 c. on 25 c. blue .. | 15 | 10 |
| 936. | | 50 c. on 25 c. blue .. | 15 | 10 |

B. Air. Surch. **AEREO** and value.

| | | | | |
|---|---|---|---|---|
| 913f. | 272a. | 60 c. on 1 s. green .. | 10 | 10 |
| 913g. | | 60 c. on 5 s. sepia .. | 15 | 10 |
| 913h. | | 70 c. on 5 s. sepia .. | 20 | 10 |
| 913i. | | 90 c. on 50 c. red .. | 30 | 10 |
| 913j. | | 1 s. on 1 s. green .. | 20 | 10 |

**1950.** Optd. **POSTAL.**

| | | | | |
|---|---|---|---|---|
| 911. | 194. | 5 c. green .. .. | 10 | 10 |
| 912. | 208. | 5 c. blue .. .. | 10 | 10 |

**1950.** Air. (a) Nos. 816/7 surch. **90 ctvs. 90.**

| | | | | |
|---|---|---|---|---|
| 914. | | 90 c. on 1 s. 30 blue .. | 15 | 10 |
| 914a. | | 90 c. on 1 s. 90 brown .. | 35 | 10 |

(b) No. 816 surch. **90 CENTAVOS.**

| | | | | |
|---|---|---|---|---|
| 914b. | | 90 c. on 1 s. 30 blue .. | 10 | 10 |

**1950.** Literary Campaign. Optd **ALFABETIZACION.** Four values also surch with new values and No. 920 also optd **POSTAL.**

(a) Postage.

915 **269** 10 c. purple 20 20
916 **264** 20 c. on 40 c. (878) 30 30
917 30 c. on 40 c. (878) 40 40
918 **263** 50 c. red and green 60 60
919 – 1 s. blue & brown (880) 70 70
920 **221** 10 s. violet 1·90 95

(b) Air.

921 – 50 c. on 1 s. 10 (815) 25 10
922 – 70 c. on 1 s. 10 (815) 20 25
923 **221** 3 s. orange 45 30
924 5 s. brown 80 40
925 10 s. violet 85 30

**1950.**

926. **274.** 50 c. green 20 10

**1951.** Air. Panagra Airlines' 20,000th Flight across Equator. Optd. **20,000 Cruce** etc., in four lines.

932. **221.** 3 s. orange 50 50
933. 5 s. brown 90 70

**1951.** Adult Education. Surch. **CAMPANA Alfabetizacion** and values. (a) Postage.

937. **272a.** 20 c. on 25 c. blue 10 10
938. 30 c. on 25 c. blue 15 10

(b) Air.

939. – 60 c. on 1 s. 30(890) 20 10
940. **267.** 1 s. on 1 s. 90 (891) 20 10

**278.** Reliquary and St. Peter's, Vatican City. **279.** St. Mariana de Jesus.

**1952.** Canonization of St. Mariana de Jesus.

941. **278.** 10 c. grn. & lake (post.) 20 10
942. 20 c. blue and violet 10 10
943. 30 c. red and green 25 10
944. **279.** 60 c. red & turq. (air) 35 10
945. 90 c. green and blue 40 10
946. 1 s. red and green 45 10
947. 2 s. blue and mauve 45 10

**280.** Presidents Plaza and Truman.

**1952.** Visit of President of Ecuador to U.S.A.

948. **280.** 1 s. blk. & red (postage) 25 15
949. – 2 s. sepia and blue 50 20
950. **280.** 3 s. green & lilac (air) 40 30
951. – 5 s. olive and brown 80 65

DESIGN: 2 s., 5 s. Pres. Plaza addressing U.S. Congress.

**1952.** Consular Service stamps surch. **TIMBRE ESCOLAR 20 ctvs. 20.**

957. **272.** 20 c. on 1 s. red 10 10
958. 20 c. on 2 s. brown 10 10
959. 20 c. on 5 s. violet 10 10

**282.** Pres. Urvina, Slave and "Liberty". **284.** Teacher and Scholars.

**1952.** Cent. of Abolition of Slavery in Ecuador. Roul.

960. **282.** 20 c. grn. & red (post.) 10 10
961. 30 c. red and blue 20 10
962. 50 c. blue and red 35 20
963. – 60 c. red & blue (air) 85 25
964. – 90 c. lilac and red 85 30
965. – 1 s. orange and green 85 10
966. – 2 s. brown and blue 85 20

DESIGN—VERT. Nos. 963/6, Pres. Urvina, condor and freed slave.

**1952.** Obligatory Tax. Literacy Campaign.

967. **284.** 20 c. green 20 10

**1952.** Obligatory Tax. Public Health Fund. Fiscal stamp optd. **PATRIOTICO y SANITARIO.**

968. **103.** 40 c. olive 40 10

**HAVE YOU READ THE NOTES AT THE BEGINNING OF THIS CATALOGUE?**
These often provide answers to the enquiries we receive.

**286.** Learning Alphabet. **287.** Flag-bearer and Health Emblem.

**1953.** Literacy Campaign. Inscr. "UNP LAE".

974. – 5 c. blue (postage) 25 10
975. – 10 c. red 15 10
976. – 20 c. orange 25 10
977. – 30 c. purple 30 10
978. – 1 s. blue (air) 35 10
979. **286.** 2 s. red 60 10

DESIGNS: 5 c. Teacher and pupils. 10 c. Instructor and student. 1 s. Hand and torch. HORIZ. 20 c. Men and ballot-box. 30 c. Teaching the alphabet.

**1953.** Obligatory Tax. Public Health Fund.

980. **287.** 40 c. blue 45 10

**288.** **289.** Equatorial Line Monument.

**1953.** Air. Crossing of Equator by Pan-American Highway.

981. **288.** 60 c. yellow 25 20
982. 90 c. blue 35 20
983. 3 s. red 40 35

**1953.**

984. – 5 c. blue and black 10 10
985 **289.** 10 c. green and black 10 10
986. – 20 c. lilac and black 10 10
987. – 30 c. brown and black 10 10
988. – 40 c. orange and black 10 10
989. – 50 c. red and black 25 10

DESIGNS: 5 c. Cuicocha Lagoon. 20 c. Quininde landscape. 30 c. River Tomebamba. 40 c. La Chilintosa rock. 50 c. Iliniza Mountains.

**290.** Cardinal de la Torre. **291.**

**1954.** 1st Anniv of Elevation of De la Torre to Cardinal.

990. **290.** 30 c. blk. & red (post.) 20 10
991. 50 c. black and purple 15 10
992. **291.** 60 c. blk. & pur. (air) 15 10
993. 90 c. black and green 20 10
994. 3 s. black and orange 35 20

**292.** Isabella the Catholic. **293.**

**1954.** 500th Birth Anniv. of Isabella the Catholic.

995. **292.** 30 c. blk. & bl. (post.) 15 25
996. 50 c. black and yellow 15 10
997. **293.** 60 c. green (air) 10 20
998. 90 c. purple 10 10
999. 1 s. black and pink 25 20
1000. 2 s. black and blue 15 10
1001. 5 s. black and flesh 35 25

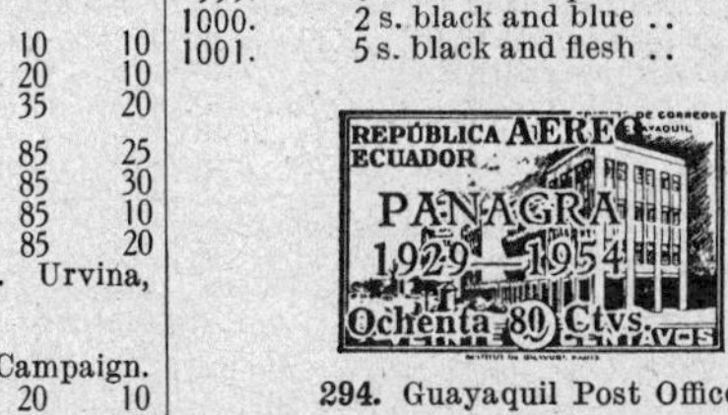


**294.** Guayaquil Post Office.

**1954.** Air. Silver Jubilee of Panagra Air Lines. Unissued stamp surch. as in T **294.**

1002. **294.** 80 c. on 20 c. red 15 10
1003. 1 s. on 20 c. red 20 10

**1954.** Obligatory Tax. Literacy Campaign. Telegraph stamp (18½ × 22½ mm.) surch. **ESCOLAR 20 Centavos.**

1004. 20 c. on 30 c. brown 45 10

**1954.** Obligatory Tax. Literacy Campaign. Fiscal stamp as T **103.** (19½ × 25½ mm.). optd. **ESCOLAR.**

1004a. **103.** 20 c. olive 60 10

**1954.** Obligatory Tax. Tourist Promotion Fund.

(a) Telegraph stamp as No. 1004 but surch. **Pro Turismo 1954 10 ctvs. 10.**

1005. 10 c. on 30 c. brown 60 10

(b) Judicial stamp as T **103.** (19½ × 25½ mm.) optd. **PRO TURISMO 1954.**

1006. 10 c. red 25 10

(c) Fiscal stamp as T **103.** (19½ × 25½ mm.) surch. **PRO TURISMO 1954 10 ctvs. Diez Centavos.**

1006a. **103.** 10 c. on 50 c. red 45 10

(d) Consular Service stamp surch. **PRO TURISMO 1954 10 ctvs.**

1007. **272a.** 10 c. on 25 c. blue 45 10

**1954.** Consular Service stamp surch. **0.20 0.20 ESCOLAR Veinte centavos.**

1007a. **272.** 20 c. on 10 s. grey 60 10

**299.** "Chasqui" (Inca Message Carrier). **300.** Airliner over Building.

**1954.** Postal Employees' Day.

1008. **299.** 30 c. sepia (postage) 20 10
1009. **300.** 80 c. blue (air) 20 10

**301.** Bananas. **302.** Douglas DC-4 over San Pablo Lake.

**1954.**

1010. **301.** 10 c. orange (post.) 10 10
1011. 20 c. red 10 10
1012. 30 c. mauve 10 10
1013. 40 c. myrtle 20 10
1014. 50 c. brown 25 10
1015. **302.** 60 c. orange (air) 20 10
1016. 70 c. mauve 20 10
1017. 90 c. green 20 10
1018. 1 s. myrtle 25 10
1019. 2 s. blue 50 10
1020. 3 s. brown 50 10

**302a.** **303.** Death on Battlefield.

**1954.** Obligatory Tax. Literacy Fund.

1020a. **302a.** 20 c. red 25 10

**1954.** Air. 150th Death Anniv of Captain Calderon Garaicoa.

1021. **303.** 80 c. mauve 20 10
1022. – 90 c. blue 20 10

PORTRAIT—VERT. 90 c. Capt. Calderon.

**304.** El Cebollar College. **305.** "Transport".

**1954.** Air. Birth Cent. of F. F. Cordero.

1023. **304.** 70 c. myrtle 10 10
1024. – 80 c. sepia 10 10
1025. – 90 c. blue 10 10
1026. – 2 s. 50 slate 20 15
1027. – 3 s. lilac 30 25

DESIGNS—VERT. 80 c. Febres Cordero and boys. 90 c. Febres Cordero. 2 s. 50, Tomb. HORIZ. 3 s. Monument.

**1954.** Obligatory Tax. Tourist Promotion Fund.

1028. **305.** 10 c. mauve 25 10

**306.** Kissing the Flag. **308.** La Rotonda, Guayaquil.

**1955.** Obligatory Tax. National Defence Fund.

1029. **306.** 40 c. blue 60 10

**1955.** Air. World Press Exn. No. 730a surch. **E. M. P. 1955** and value.

1030. **221.** 1 s. on 10 s. violet 20 10
1031. 1 s. 70 on 10 s. violet 30 10
1032. 4 s. 20 on 10 s. violet 50 35

**1955.** Air. 50th Anniv. of Rotary Int.

1033. **308.** 80 c. brown 30 20
1034. – 90 c. green 30 25

DESIGN: 90 c. Eugenio Espejo Hospital, Quito.

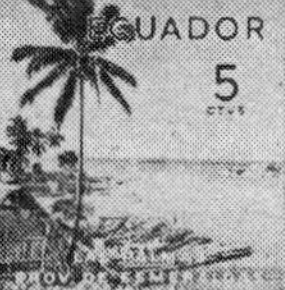


**310.** Castillo and "Telegrafo I". **312.** Palm Trees.

**1955.** Birth Centenary of Jose Abel Castillo (pioneer aviator).

1035. – 30 c. bistre (postage) 10 10
1036. – 50 c. black 10 10
1037. **310.** 60 c. brown (air) 45 10
1038. 90 c. green 45 10
1039. 1 s. mauve 45 10
1040. – 2 s. red 45 15
1041. – 5 s. blue 90 45

DESIGNS—VERT. 30 c., 50 c. Bust of Castillo. HORIZ. 2 s., 5 s. Castillo and map of Ecuador.

**1955.** Air. Surch. **1 SUCRE** over ornamental bar.

1042. **130.** 1 s. on 5 s. violet 20 15

**1955.** Pictorial designs as T **312.**

1043. **312.** 5 c. green (postage) 10 10
1043a. 5 c. blue 10 10
1043b. B. 5 c. green 10 10
1044. C. 10 c. blue 20 10
1044a. 10 c. brown 35 10
1044b. B. 10 c. brown 10 10
1045. A. 20 c. brown 30 10
1045a. 20 c. pink 30 10
1045b. 20 c. green 35 10
1045c. B. 20 c. plum 10 10
1046. D. 30 c. black 10 10
1046a. 30 c. red 10 10
1046b. B. 30 c. blue 10 10
1046c. E. 40 c. blue 2·75 20
1047. F. 50 c. green 30 10
1047a. 50 c. violet 35 10
1048. E. 70 c. olive 3·50 30
1049. G. 80 c. violet 60 10
1049a. B. 80 c. red 10 10
1049b. G. 90 c. blue 20 20
1050. H. 1 s. orange 20 10
1050a. 1 s. sepia 15 10
1050b. I. 1 s. black 50 10
1051. J. 2 s. red 60 15
1051a. 2 s. brown 25 10
1052. K. 50 c. slate (air) 25 10
1052a. 50 c. green 20 10
1053. L. 1 s. blue 50 10
1053a. 1 s. orange 40 10
1054. M. 1 s. 30 red 30 15
1055. N. 1 s. 50 green 20 10
1056. O. 1 s. 70 brown 20 10
1057. P. 1 s. 90 olive 25 25
1058. Q. 2 s. 40 red 30 15
1059. R. 2 s. 50 violet 30 15
1060. S. 4 s. 20 black 40 25
1061. T. 4 s. 80 yellow 50 35

DESIGNS—POSTAGE: A, River Babahoyo. B, "The Virgin of Quito" (after L. y del Arco). C, Manta fisherman. D, Guayaquil. E, Cactus. F, River Pital, G, Orchids. H, Agucate Mission. I, San Pablo. J, Jibaro Indian. AIR: K, Rumichaca Grotto. L, San Pablo. M, "The Virgin of Quito". N, Cotopaxi Volcano. O, Tungurahua Volcano. P, Guanaco. Q, Selling mats. R, Ingapirca ruins. S, El Carmen, Cuenca, T, Santo Domingo Church.

**313.** Vazquez in 1883. **314.** J. A. Schwarz. **315.** Title Page of First Book printed in Ecuador.

**1956.** Air. Birth Cent. of Vazquez.

1062. **313.** 1 s. green 10 10
1063. – 1 s. 50 red 20 10
1064. – 1 s. 70 blue 15 10
1065. – 1 s. 90 slate 20 10

PORTRAITS OF VAZQUEZ: 1 s. 50, 1905. 1 s. 70, 1910. 1 s. 90, 1931.

**1956.** Bicent. of Printing in Ecuador.

1066. **314.** 5 c. green (postage) 10 10
1067. 10 c. red 10 10
1068. 20 c. violet 10 10
1069. 30 c. green 10 10
1070. 40 c. blue 10 10
1071. 50 c. blue 10 10
1072. 70 c. orange 15 10
1073. **315.** 1 s. black (air) 10 10
1074. 1 s. 70 slate 15 10
1075. 2 s. sepia 25 20
1076. 3 s. brown 30 25

**316.** Hands reaching for U.N. Emblem. **317.** Emblem and Girl with Ball.

**1956.** Air. 10th Anniv. of U.N.O.
1077. **316.** 1 s. 70 red .. .. 40 20
For stamp as Type **316** see No. 1095.

**1956.** Air. 6th S. American Women's Basketball Championships.
1078. **317.** 1 s. mauve .. .. 20 10
1079. – 1 s. 70 green .. .. 30 15
DESIGN: 1 s. 70, Map, flags and players.

**318.** Marquis of Canete. **319.** Cuenca Cathedral.

**1957.** 400th Anniv. of Cuenca.
1082. **318.** 5 c. blue on flesh (post.) 10 10
1083. – 10 c. bronze on green 10 10
1084. – 20 c. brown on buff .. 10 10
1085. – 50 c. sep. on cream (air.) 10 10
1086. **319.** 80 c. red on blue .. 10 10
1087. – 1 s. violet on yellow .. 20 10
DESIGNS—HORIZ. 10 c. Gil Ramirez Davalos and Cuenca landscape. 50 c. Early plan of Cuenca. 1 s. Municipal Palace. VERT. 20 c. Father Vicente Solano.

**320.** Delegates to the 1838 Postal Congress. **321.** Gabriela Mistral (Chilean poet).

**1957.** 7th U.P.A.E. Postal Congress, 1955.
1088. **320.** 40 c. yellow .. .. 10 10
1089. 50 c. blue .. .. 10 10
1090. 2 s. red .. .. 40 10

**1957.** Air. Gabriela Mistral Commem.
1091. **321.** 2 s. grey, black & red 20 10

**322.** Arms of Espejo. **323.** Blue and Yellow Macaw.

**1957.** Air. Carchi Cantonal Arms. Inscr. " PROVINCIA DEL CARCHI ". Arms mult.
1092. **322.** 1 s. red .. .. 15 10
1093. – 2 s. black (Montufar) 20 10
1094. – 4 s. 20 blue (Tulcan) 45 30
For other Arms as Type **322** see Nos 1124/7, 1147/51, 1155/9, 1197 and 1220/3.

**1957.** Air. United Nations Day. As T **316** but without dates.
1095. 2 s. blue .. .. 35 25

**1958.** Tropical Birds. Birds in natural colours.
(a) As T **323**.
1096. **323.** 10 c. brown .. .. 60 20
1097. – 20 c. grey and buff .. 60 25
1098. – 30 c. green .. .. 1·60 30
1099. – 40 c. orange .. .. 1·60 35
BIRDS: 20 c. Red-breasted Toucan. 30 c. Andean Condor. 40 c. Sword-billed Hummingbird and Black-tailed Trainbearer.

(b) As T **323** but "ECUADOR" at top in black.
1120. – 20 c. turquoise and red 1·00 20
1121. – 30 c. blue and yellow 1·10 30
1122. – 50 c. orange and green 1·60 45
1123. – 60 c. pink & turquoise 1·90 45
BIRDS: 20 c. Masked Crimson Tanager. 30 c. Andean Cock of the Rock. 50 c. Solitary Cacique. 60 c. Red-fronted Conures.

**324.** The Virgin of Sorrows. **325.** Vice-Pres. Nixon and Flags of Ecuador and the U.S.A.

**1958.** Air. 50th Anniv. of The Miracle of the Virgin of Sorrows of St. Gabriel College, Quito.
1100. **324.** 30 c. purple on purple 10 10
1101. – 30 c. purple on purple 10 10
1102. – 1 s. blue on blue .. 15 10
1103. **324.** 1 s. 70 blue on blue .. 15 15
DESIGN: Nos. 1101/2, Gateway of St. Gabriel College, Quito.

**1958.** Visit of Vice-Pres. of the United States. Flags in red, blue and yellow.
1104. **325.** 2 s. salmon and green 40 10

**1958.** Visit of Pres. Morales of Honduras. As T **325**, but with portrait of Pres. Morales, flags of Ecuador and Honduras, and inscriptions changed. Flags in red, blue and yellow.
1105. 2 s. brown .. .. 40 10

**326.** Dr. C. Sanz de Santamaria.

**1958.** Visit of Chancellor of Colombia.
1106. **326.** 1 s. 80 multicoloured 40 10

**327.** Dr. R. M. Arizaga. **328.** Gonzalo Icaza Cornejo Bridge.

**1958.** Air. Birth Cent. of Arizaga (diplomat.
1107. **327.** 1 s. multicoloured .. 10 10
See also Nos. 1135, 1142 and 1241.

**1958.** Air. Inauguration of Gonzalo Icaza Cornejo Bridge.
1108. **328.** 1 s. 30 green .. .. 20 10

**329.** Steam Locomotive. **330.** Basketball Player.

**1958.** 50th Anniv. of Opening of Guayaquil–Quito Railway.
1109. **329.** 30 c. black .. .. 20 15
1110. – 50 c. red .. .. 30 15
1111. – 5 s. brown .. .. 1·40 1·10
DESIGNS—HORIZ. 50 c. Diesel-electric train. DIAMOND. 5 s. Four founders of the railway.

**1958.** Air. South American Basketball Champions' Tournament, Quito.
1112. **330.** 1 s. 30 green & brown 40 30

**331.** J. C. de Macedo Soares. **332.** Monstrance and Doves.

**1958.** Visit of Brazilian Chancellor.
1113. **331.** 2 s. 20 multicoloured 40 10

**1958.** Air. 3rd National Eucharistic Congress, Guayaquil. Inscr. as in T **332**.
1114. **332.** 10 c. violet and yellow 10 10
1115. — 60 c. violet and salmon 10 10
1116. **332.** 1 s. sepia and turquoise 15 10
DESIGN: 60 c. Guayaquil Cathedral.

**333.** Stamps of 1865 and 1920.

**1958.** Air. National Stamp Exn., Guayaquil.
1117. **333.** 1 s. 30 red and green 20 15
1118. – 2 s. violet and blue .. 35 20
1119. – 4 s. 20 sepia .. .. 45 45
DESIGNS: 2 s. Stamps of 1920 and 1948. 4 s. 20, Guayaquil Municipal Library and Museum.

**1958.** Air. Imbabura Cantonal Arms. As T **322**. Inscr. " PROVINCIA DE IMBABURA ". Arms multicoloured.
1124. 50 c. red and black .. 10 10
1125. 60 c. blue, red and black .. 10 10
1126. 80 c. yellow and black .. 10 10
1127. 1 s. 10 red and black .. 15 10
ARMS: 50 c. Cotacachi. 60 c. Antonio Ante. 80 c. Otavalo. 1 s. 10, Ibarra.

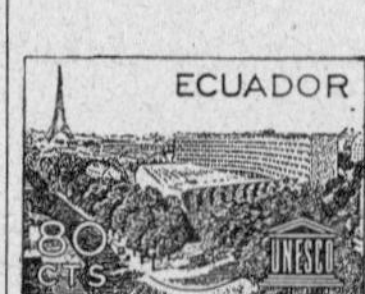

**335.** U.N.E.S.C.O. Headquarters, Paris. **336.** Emperor Charles V (after Titian).

**1958.** Inauguration of U.N.E.S.C.O. Headquarters Building, Paris.
1128 **335** 80 c. brown .. .. 20 10

**1958.** Air. 400th Death Anniv. of Emperor Charles V.
1129. **336.** 2 s. sepia and red .. 20 10
1130. 4 s. 20 brown & black 40 35

**337.** Globe and Satellites. **338.** Paul Rivet (anthropologist).

**1958.** International Geophysical Year.
1131. **337.** 1 s. 80 blue .. .. 60 35

**1958.** Air. Rivet Commem.
1132. **338.** 1 s. sepia .. .. 10 10
See also No. 1134.

**339.** Front page of " El Telegrafo ".

**1959.** Air. 75th Anniv. of "El Telegrafo" (newspaper).
1133. **339.** 1 s. 30 black and green 15 10

**1959.** Air. Death Centenary of Alexander von Humboldt (naturalist). Portrait in design as T **338**.
1134 2 s. grey .. .. .. 20 10

**1959.** Air. Birth Cent. of Dr. Jose L. Tamayo (statesman). Portrait in design as T **327**.
1135. 1 s. 30 multicoloured .. 15 10

**340.** House of M. Canizares. **341.** Pope Pius XII.

**1959.** Air. 150th Anniv of Independence.
1136. **340.** 20 c. brown and blue 10 10
1137. – 80 c. brown and blue 10 10
1138. – 1 s. myrtle and brown 10 10
1139. – 1 s. 30 orange and blue 25 10
1140. – 2 s. brown and blue .. 25 10
1141. – 4 s. 20 blue and red .. 35 30
DESIGNS—HORIZ. 80 c. St. Augustine's chapter-house. 1 s. The Constitution. VERT. 1 s. 30, Condor with broken chains. 2 s. Royal Palace. 4 s. 20, " Liberty " (statue).

**1959.** Air. Birth Cent. of Dr. A. B. Moreno (statesman). Portrait in design as T **327**.
1142. 1 s. multicoloured .. 10 10

**1959.** Air. Pope Pius XII Commem.
1143. **341.** 1 s. 30 multicoloured 25 20

**342.** Flags of Argentina, Bolivia, Brazil, Guatemala, Haiti, Mexico and Peru.

**1959.** Air. Organization of American States Commem. Flag design inscr. " OEA ".
1144. **342.** 50 c. multicoloured .. 10 10
1145. – 80 c. red, blue & yellow 15 10
1146. – 1 s. 30 multicoloured 25 15
FLAGS: 80 c. Chile, Costa Rica, Cuba, Dominican Republic, Panama, Paraguay and U.S.A. 1 s. 30, Colombia, Ecuador, Honduras, Nicaragua, El Salvador, Uruguay and Venezuela.

**1959.** Air. Pichincha Cantonal Arms. As T **322**. Inscr. " PROVINCIA DE PICHINCHA ". Arms multicoloured.
1147. 10 c. red and black .. 10 10
1148. 40 c. yellow and black .. 10 10
1149. 1 s. brown and black .. 10 10
1150. 1 s. 30 green and black .. 10 10
1151. 4 s. 20 yellow and black .. 40 25
ARMS: 10 c. Ruminahui. 40 c. Pedro Moncayo, 1 s. Mejia. 1 s. 30, Cayambe. 4 s. 20, Quito.

**343.** Arms of Quito and Flags. **344.** " Uprooted Tree ".

**1960.** Air. 11th Inter-American Conference, Quito (1st issue). Centres multicoloured within red circle.
1152. **343.** 1 s. 30 turquoise .. 10 10
1153. 2 s. light sepia .. 20 15

**1960.** World Refugee Year.
1154. **344.** 80 c. green and lake .. 10 10

**1960.** Air. Cotopaxi Cantonal Arms. As T **322**. Inscr. " PROVINCIA DE COTOPAXI ". Arms multicoloured.
1155. 40 c. red and black .. 10 10
1156. 60 c. blue and black .. 15 10
1157. 70 c. turquoise and black 20 10
1158. 1 s. red and black .. 25 10
1159. 1 s. 30 orange and black .. 15 30
ARMS: 40 c. Pangua. 60 c. Pujili. 70 c. Saquisili 1 s. Salcedo. 1 s. 30, Latacunga.

DESIGNS: 40 c. Mountain tapir. 80 c. Spectacled bear. 1 s. Puma.

**345.** Giant Ant-eater.

**1960.** 4th Cent. of Baeza. Inscr. as in T **345**.
1160. **345.** 20 c. blk., orge. & grn. 10 10
1161. – 40 c. brown, green and turquoise .. 15 10
1162. – 80 c. blk., blue & brn. 30 10
1163. – 1 s. orge., blue & pur. 50 20

**346.** Quito Airport.

**1960.** 11th Inter-American Conference, Quito. (2nd issue.) Views of Quito. Inscr. as in T **346**.
1164. **346.** 1 s. blue and deep blue 20 10
1165. – 1 s. violet and black .. 15 10
1166. – 1 s. lake and violet .. 15 10
1167. – 1 s. green and blue .. 15 10
1168. – 1 s. blue & violet .. 15 10
1169. – 1 s. brown and blue .. 15 10
1170. – 1 s. brown & violet .. 15 10
1171. – 1 s. red and black .. 15 10
1172. – 1 s. brown & blk. .. 15 10
VIEWS: No. 1165, Legislative Palace. No. 1166, Southern approach motorway and flyover. No. 1167, Government Palace. No. 1168, Foreign Ministry. No. 1169, Students' Quarters, Catholic University. No. 1170, Hotel Quito. No. 1171, Students' Quarters, Central University. No. 1172, Social Security Bank.

**347.** Ambato Railway Bridge. **348.** " Liberty of Expression ".

**1960.** Air. New Bridges.
1173. – 1 s. 30 brown .. 20 10
1174. – 1 s. 30 green .. 20 10
1175. **347.** 2 s. brown .. 60 30
DESIGNS—No. 1173, Bridge of the Juntas. No. 1174, Saracay Bridge.

**1960.** Five Year Development Plan (1st issue). (a) Postage.
1176. **348.** 5 c. blue .. .. 10 10
1177. – 10 c. violet .. .. 10 10
1178. – 20 c. orange .. .. 10 10
1179. – 30 c. turquoise .. 10 10
1180. – 40 c. brown and blue 15 15
DESIGNS—VERT. 10 c. Mother voting. 20 c. People at bus-stop. 30 c. Coins. HORIZ. (37×22 mm.): 40 c. Irrigation project Manabi.

**349.** Road at Chone Bay.

(b) Air.
1181. **349.** 1 s. 30 black and ochre 15 10
1182. – 4 s. 20 lake and green 35 35
1183. – 5 s. brown and lemon 70 40
1184. – 10 s. indigo and blue 70 50
DESIGNS—As Type **349**: 4 s. 20, Ministry of Works and Communications, Cuenca. 5 s. El Coca Airport. 10 s. New port of Guayaquil under construction.
See also Nos. 1214/17.

**350.** Pres. Camilo Ponce Enriquez and Constitution.

**1960.** Air. 5th Anniv. of Constitution.
1185. **350.** 2 s. black and brown 1·10 30

**351.** H. Dunant and Red Cross Buildings, Quito. **352.** "El Belen" Church, Quito.

**1960.** Air. Red Cross Commem.
1186. **351.** 2 s. purple and red .. 30 15

**1961.** Air. 1st Int. Philatelic Congress, Barcelona.
1187. **352.** 3 s. multicoloured .. 40 15

**353.** Map of River Amazon.

**1961.** Air. "Amazon Week". Map in green.
1188. **353.** 80 c. purple and brown 20 10
1189. 1 s. 30 blue and grey 25 15
1190. 2 s. red and grey .. 30 20

**354.** J. Montalvo, J. L. Mera and J. B. Vela.

**1961.** Air. Cent. of Tungurahua Province.
1191. **354.** 1 s. 30 black & salmon 20 10

**355.** 1936 Philatelic Exhibition Air Stamp.

**1961.** Air. 3rd Int. Philatelic Exn., Quito.
1192. **355.** 80 c. violet and orange 25 15
1193. – 1 s. 30 multicoloured 35 20
1194. – 2 s. black and red .. 40 25
DESIGNS: 1 s. 30, San Lorenzo-Belem route map of S. America and 1 r. stamp of 1865 (41×33½ mm.). 2 s., 10 s. Independence stamp of 1930 postmarked "QUITO" (41×36 mm.).

**356.** Statue of H. Ortiz Garces. **357.** Arms of Los Rios and Great Egret.

**1961.** Air. H. Ortiz Garces (national hero). Commem. Multicoloured.
1195. 1 s. 30 Type **356** .. 15 10
1196. 1 s. 30 Portrait .. .. 15 10

**1961.** Air. Centenary of Los Rios Province.
1197 **357** 2 s. multicoloured .. 75 25

**358.** "Graphium pausianus". **359.** Collared Peccary.

**1961.** Butterflies.
1198. **358.** 20 c. yell., grn. blk. and salmon .. 25 10
1198a. 20 c. yell., grey, blk. and green .. .. 15 10
1199. – 30 c. yell., black & blue 35 10
1200. – 50 c. black, grn. & yell. 45 10
1200a. – 50 c. blk., grn. & salmon 25 10
1201. – 80 c. pur., yell., blk. and green .. .. 70 20
1201a. – 80 c. turq., yell., blk. and brown .. 40 15
BUTTERFLIES: 30 c. "Papilio torquatus leptalea". 50 c. "Graphium molops molops". 80 c. "Battus lycidas".

**1961.** 4th Cent. of Tena.
1202. **359.** 10 c. blue, grn. & red 10 10
1203. – 20 c. brn., violet & blue 10 10
1204. – 80 c. orge., blk. & bistre 30 10
1205. – 1 s. brn., orge. & green 20 15
ANIMALS: 20 c. Kinkajou. 80 c. Jaguar. 1 s. Little coatimundi.

**360.** G. G. Moreno. **362.** R. Crespo Toral.

**1961.** Air. Centenary of Re-establishment of "National Integrity".
1206. **360.** 1 s. brown, buff & blue 15 10

**1961.** Opening of Marine Biology Station on Galapagos Is. and 15th Anniv. of U.N.E.S.C.O. Nos. 1/6 of Galapagos Is. optd. **UNESCO 1961 Estacion de Biologia Maritima de Galapagos.**
1207. **1.** 20 c. brown (postage) .. 15 10
1208. – 50 c. violet .. .. 15 15
1209. – 1 s. green .. .. 35 25
1210. – 1 s. blue (air) .. .. 25 20
1211. – 1 s. 80 purple .. .. 35 20
1212. – 4 s. 20 black .. .. 55 30

**1961.** Air. Birth Centenary of Remigio Crespo Toral (writer).
1213 **362** 50 c. multicoloured .. 10 10

**362a.** Soldier and Flag. **363.** Daniel Enrique Proana School, Quito.

**1961.** Obligatory Tax. National Defence Fund.
1213a. **362a.** 40 c. blue .. .. 10 10

**1961.** Five Year Development Plan.
1214 **363** 50 c. black and blue 10 10
1215 – 60 c. black and green 10 10
1216 – 80 c. black and red .. 15 10
1217 – 1 s. black and purple 20 10
DESIGNS—VERT. 60 c. Loja–Zamora Highway. HORIZ. 80 c. Aguirre Abad College, Guayaquil. 1 s. Epiclachima Barracks, Quito.

**364.** Pres. C. Arosemena and Duke of Edinburgh.

**1962.** Air. Visit of Duke of Edinburgh.
1218. **364.** 1 s. 30 multicoloured 20 10
1219. 2 s. multicoloured .. 20 10

**1962.** Air. Tungurahua Cantonal Arms. As T **322**. Inscr. "PROVINCIA DE TUNGURAHUA". Arms mult.
1220. 50 c. black (Pillaro) .. 10 10
1221. 1 s. black (Pelileo) .. 15 10
1222. 1 s. 30 black (Banos) .. 20 10
1223. 2 s. black (Ambato) .. 25 15

**365.** Mountain and Spade in Field. **366.** Mosquito.

**1963.** Air. Freedom from Hunger.
1224. **365.** 30 c. blk., grn. & yell. 10 10
1225. 3 s. black, red & orge. 40 20
1226. 4 s. 20 blk., bl. & yell. 50 35

**1963.** Air. Malaria Eradication.
1227. **366.** 50 c. blk., yell. & red 10 10
1228. 80 c. blk., green & red 10 10
1229. 2 s. blk., pink & pur. 20 20

**367.** Mail Coach and Boeing 707. **370.** Pres. Arosemena and Flags of Ecuador.

**1963.** Air. Cent. of Paris Postal Conf.
1230. **367.** 2 s. red and orange .. 40 15
1231. 4 s. 20 blue and purple 60 30

**1963.** Air. Unissued Galapagos Is. stamps in designs as Ecuador T **321** optd. vert. **ECUADOR** and surch.
1232. **321.** 5 s. on 2 s. mult. .. 40 30
1233. 10 s. on 2 s. mult. .. 80 60

**1963.** Air. Red Cross Cent. Optd. **1863-1963 Centenario de la Fundacion de la Cruz Roja Internacional.**
1234. **351.** 2 s. purple and red .. 25 15

**1963.** Presidential Goodwill Tour. Mult.
1235. 10 c. Type **370** (postage) 10 10
1236. 20 c. Ecuador & Panama flags .. .. .. 10 10
1237. 60 c. Ecuador & U.S.A. flags .. .. .. 10 10
1238. 70 c. Type **370** (air) .. 10 10
1239. 2 s. Ecuador and Panama flags .. .. .. 25 10
1240. 4 s. Ecuador & U.S.A. flags 40 30

**1963.** 150th Birth Anniv. of Dr. M. Cueva (statesman). Portrait in design as T **327**.
1241. 2 s. multicoloured .. 20 10

**371.** "Shield of Security". **372.** Terminal Building.

**1963.** 25th Anniv. of Social Insurance Scheme. Multicoloured.
1242. 10 c. Type **371** (postage) 10 10
1243. 10 s. "Statue of Security" (air) .. .. .. 55 45

**1963.** Air. Inauguration of Simon Bolivar Airport, Guayaquil.
1244. **372.** 60 c. black .. .. 15 10
1245. 70 c. black and blue .. 20 10
1246. 5 s. purple and black 75 25

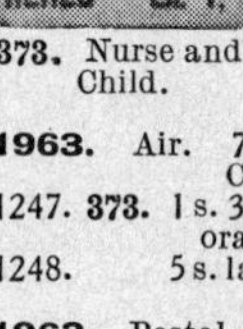


**373.** Nurse and Child. **380.** "Commerce".

**1963.** Air. 7th Pan-American Pediatrics Congress, Quito.
1247. **373.** 1 s. 30 blue, black and orange .. .. 20 15
1248. 5 s. lake, red and grey 45 30

**1963.** Postal Employees' Day. No. 1049a optd. **1961 DIA DEL EMPLEADO POSTAL** and posthorn or surch. also.
1249. B. 10 c. on 80 c. red .. 10 10
1250. 20 c. on 80 c. red .. 10 10
1251. 50 c. on 80 c. red .. 10 10
1252. 60 c. on 80 c. red .. 10 10
1253. 80 c. red .. .. 20 10

**1964.** Nos. 1164, etc., surch.
1254. 10 c. on 1 s. blue & violet 10 10
1255. 10 c. on 1 s. brn. & violet 10 10
1256. 20 c. on 1 s. green & blue 10 10
1257. 20 c. on 1 s. brown & blue 10 10
1258. 30 c. on 1 s. lake & violet 10 10
1259. 40 c. on 1 s. olive & black 10 10
1260. 60 c. on 1 s. red and black 10 10
1261. 80 c. on 1 s. blue & dp. blue 30 10
1262. 80 c. on 1 s. violet & black 20 10

**1964.** Optd. **1961** and ornaments.
1263. **344.** 80 c. green and lake 1·10 75

**1964.** Air. Optd. **AEREO.** Honduras flag in red, blue and yellow.
1264. **326.** 1 s. 80 violet .. 40 25
1265. – 2 s. brown (No. 1105) 40 25
1266. **331.** 2 s. 20 sepia and green 40 25

**1964.** "Columbus Lighthouse". Optd. **FARO DE COLON.**
1267. **337.** 1 s. 80 blue (postage) 1·50 1·50
Optd. **FARO DE COLON AEREO.**
1268. **337.** 1 s. 80 blue (air) .. 1·90 1·25

**1964.** Air. Nos. 1144/6 optd. **1961.**
1269. **342.** 50 c. multicoloured .. 50 20
1270. – 80 c. red, blue & yell. 50 20
1271. – 1 s. 30 multicoloured 50 20

**1964.** O.E.A. Commemoration. Optd. **OEA** with decorative frame across a block of four stamps.
1272. **344.** 80 c. green and lake .. 1·50 25
The unused price is for the block of four.

**1964.** "Alliance for Progress".
1273. – 40 c. bistre and violet 10 10
1274. – 50 c. red and black .. 15 10
1275. **380.** 80 c. blue and brown 15 10
DESIGNS: 40 c. "Agriculture". 50 c. "Industry".

**1964.** Air. 15th Anniv. of Declaration of Human Rights. Optd. **DECLARATION DERECHOS HUMANOS 1964 XV-ANIV.**
1276. **316.** 1 s. 70 red .. .. 30 15

**382.** Banana Tree and Map.

**1964.** Banana Conf., Quito.
1277. **382.** 50 c. olive, brown and grey (postage) .. 10 10
1278. 80 c. olive, blk. & orge. 10 10
1279. 4 s. 20 olive, black and ochre (air) .. 30 20
1280. 10 s. olive, blk. & red 55 40

**383.** Pres. Kennedy and his Son.

**1964.** Air. Pres. Kennedy Commem.
1281. **383.** 4 s. 20 brn., red, blue and green .. .. 70 55
1282. 5 s. brown, blue & vio. 85 70
1283. 10 s. brn., blue & mve. 85 75

DESIGNS: As Type **384** but portrait of Juan de Salinas Loyola (20 c.), Hernando de Santillan (30 c.).

**384.** Old Map of Ecuador and Philip II of Spain.

**1964.** 400th Anniv of Royal High Court, Quito.
1284. 384. 10 c. black, buff & red 10 10
1285. – 20 c. black, buff & grn. 10 10
1286. – 30 c. black, buff & bl. 10 10

385. Pole vaulting. 386. Two-toed Sloth and P. Fleming (missionary).

**1964.** Olympic Games, Tokyo. Mult.
1287. 80 c. Type 385 (postage) 10 10
1288. 1 s. 30 Gymnastics (air) 20 10
1289. 1 s. 80 Hurdling 20 15
1290. 2 s. Basketball 25 15
The 1 s. 30 is vert.

**1965.** Death of Missionaries in Ecuador's Eastern Forests. Multicoloured.
1291 20 c. Nine-banded armadillo and J. Elliot 10 10
1292 30 c. Eurasian red squirrel and E. McCully 10 10
1293 40 c. Peruvian guemal and R. Youderian 10 10
1294 60 c. Piper Vagabond airplane over Napo River, and N. Saint 30 10
1295 80 c. Type 386 40 20

387. Dr. J. B. Vazquez (founder) and College Buildings.

**1965.** Cent. of Benigno Malo College.
1296. 387. 20 c. multicoloured 10 10
1297. 60 c. multicoloured 10 10
1298. 80 c. multicoloured 10 10

388. J. L. Mera (wrongly inscr. "MERAN"), A. Neumane and Part of Anthem.

**1965.** Centenary of National Anthem.
1299. 388. 50 c. black and red 10 10
1300. 80 c. black and green 20 10
1301. 5 s. black and ochre 40 30
1302. 10 s. black and blue 80 60

389. "Olympic" Flame and Athletic Events.

**1965.** 5th Bolivar Games, Quito. Flame in gold and black; athletes in black.
1303. 389. 40 c. orange (postage) 15 10
1304. – 50 c. red 15 10
1305. – 60 c. blue 15 10
1306. 389. 80 c. green 10 10
1307. – 1 s. violet 25 10
1308. – 1 s. 50 mauve 40 25
1309. – 2 s. blue (air) 15 10
1310. – 2 s. 50 orange 20 10
1311. – 3 s. mauve 25 15
1312. – 3 s. 50 violet 25 20
1313. – 4 s. green 30 20
1314. – 5 s. red 35 25
DESIGNS: 50 c., 1 s. Running. 60 c., 1 s. 50, Football. 2 s., 3 s. Diving, gymnastics, etc. 2 s. 50, 4 s. Cycling. 3 s. 50, 5 s. Pole-vaulting, long-jumping, etc.

390. ½ r. and Two 1 r. Stamps of 1865. 391. Golden-headed Trogon.

**1965.** Stamp Cent.
1315. 390. 80 c. multicoloured 15 10
1316. 1 s. 30 multicoloured 20 10
1317. 2 s. multicoloured 25 10
1318. 4 s. multicoloured 75 20

**1966.** Birds. Multicoloured.
1320 40 c. Type 391 (postage) 65 15
1321 50 c. Blue-crowned motmot 65 15
1322 60 c. Paradise tanager 65 15
1323 80 c. Wire-tailed manakin 65 20
1324 1 s. Yellow bellied grosbeak (air) 65 20
1325 1 s. 30 Black-headed caique 80 20
1326 1 s. 50 Scarlet tanager 80 20
1327 2 s. Purple quail dove 95 20
1328 2 s. 50 Violet-tailed sylph 1·10 25
1329 3 s. Lemon-throated barbet 1·25 30
1330 4 s. Yellow-tailed oriole 1·40 40
1331 10 s. Collared puffbird 2·75 1·00

**1967.** Various stamps surch. (a) Postage.
1332. 30 c. on 1 s. 10 (No. 1127) 15 15
1332a. 40 c. on 1 s. 70 (No. 1056) 15 15
1333. 40 c. on 3 s. 50 (No. 1312) 15 10
1334. 80 c. on 1 s. 50 (No. 1308) 10 10
1335. 80 c. on 2 s. 50 (No. 1328) 60 15
1336. 1 s. on 4 s. (No. 1330) 60 15
(b) Air.
1337. 80 c. on 1 s. 50 (No. 1326) 60 15
1338. 80 c. on 2 s. 50 (No. 1310) 15 10

396. Law Books. 399. Pres. Arosemena Gomez.

**1967.** Birth Centenary (1964) of Dr. V. M. Penaherrera (law reformer).
1339. 396. 50 c. blk. & grn. (post.) 10 10
1340. – 60 c. black and red 10 10
1341. – 80 c. black and purple 10 10
1342. – 1 s. 30 blk. & orge. (air) 10 10
1343. – 2 s. black and blue 10 10
DESIGNS—VERT. 60 c. Penaherrera's bust, Central University, Quito. 1 s. 30, Penaherrera's monument, Avenida Patria, Quito. 2 s. Penaherrera's statue, Ibarra. HORIZ. 80 c. Open book and laurel.

**1967.** Nos. 1301/2 surch.
1344. 388. 50 c. on 5 s. blk. & ochre 10 15
1345. 2 s. on 10 s. blk. & blue 30 10

**1968.** No. 1057 surch.
1346. P. 1 s. 30 on 1 s. 90 olive 15 10

**1968.** 1st Anniv. of Dr. Otto Arosemena Gomez as Interim President. Multicoloured.
1347. 80 c. Type 399 (postage) 10 10
1348. 1 s. Page from 1967 Constitution 10 10
1349. 1 s. 30 President's inauguration (air) 10 10
1350. 2 s. President Arosemena Gomez at Punta del Este Conference 15 10

400. Lions Emblem. 404. I.L. Arcaya, Foreign Minister of Venezuela.

**1968.** 50th Anniv (1967) of Lions Int.
1351 400 80 c. multicoloured 15 15
1352 1 s. 30 multicoloured 20 10
1353 2 s. multicoloured 15 10

**1969.** Various stamps surch.
(a) "AEREO" obliterated.
1355. 333. 40 c. on 1 s. 30 20 20
1356. 330. 50 c. on 1 s. 30 20 20
(b) Air. Inscr. "AEREO".
1357. – 80 c. on 10 s. (No. 1331) 60 15
1358. – 1 s. on 10 s. (No. 1331) 60 15
1359. – 2 s. on 10 s. (No. 1331) 60 20

**1969.** Unissued stamp surch or optd only (No. 1363) RESELLO.
1360 404 50 c. on 2 s. mult 15 15
1361 80 c. on 2 s. mult 15 15
1362 1 s. on 2 s. mult 15 15
1363 2 s. multicoloured 10 15

405. Map of Ecuador.

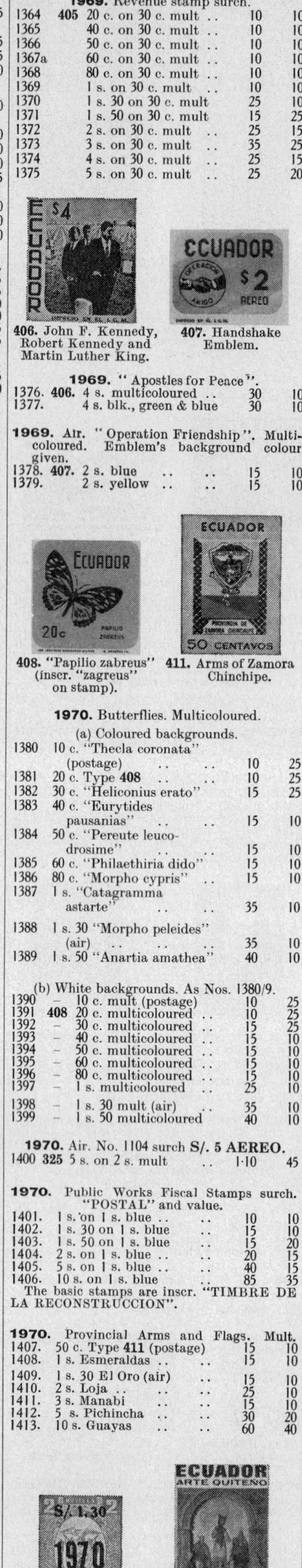

**1969.** Revenue stamp surch.
1364 405 20 c. on 30 c. mult 10 10
1365 40 c. on 30 c. mult 10 10
1366 50 c. on 30 c. mult 10 10
1367a 60 c. on 30 c. mult 10 10
1368 80 c. on 30 c. mult 10 10
1369 1 s. on 30 c. mult 10 10
1370 1 s. 30 on 30 c. mult 25 10
1371 1 s. 50 on 30 c. mult 15 25
1372 2 s. on 30 c. mult 25 15
1373 3 s. on 30 c. mult 35 25
1374 4 s. on 30 c. mult 25 15
1375 5 s. on 30 c. mult 25 20

406. John F. Kennedy, Robert Kennedy and Martin Luther King. 407. Handshake Emblem.

**1969.** "Apostles for Peace".
1376. 406. 4 s. multicoloured 30 10
1377. 4 s. blk., green & blue 30 10

**1969.** Air. "Operation Friendship". Multicoloured. Emblem's background colour given.
1378. 407. 2 s. blue 15 10
1379. 2 s. yellow 15 10

408. "Papilio zabreus" (inscr. "zagreus" on stamp). 411. Arms of Zamora Chinchipe.

**1970.** Butterflies. Multicoloured.
(a) Coloured backgrounds.
1380 10 c. "Thecla coronata" (postage) 10 25
1381 20 c. Type 408 10 25
1382 30 c. "Heliconius erato" 15 25
1383 40 c. "Eurytides pausanias" 15 10
1384 50 c. "Pereute leucodrosime" 15 10
1385 60 c. "Philaethiria dido" 15 10
1386 80 c. "Morpho cypris" 15 10
1387 1 s. "Catagramma astarte" 35 10
1388 1 s. 30 "Morpho peleides" (air) 35 10
1389 1 s. 50 "Anartia amathea" 40 10
(b) White backgrounds. As Nos. 1380/9.
1390 – 10 c. mult (postage) 10 25
1391 408 20 c. multicoloured 10 25
1392 – 30 c. multicoloured 15 25
1393 – 40 c. multicoloured 15 10
1394 – 50 c. multicoloured 15 10
1395 – 60 c. multicoloured 15 10
1396 – 80 c. multicoloured 15 10
1397 – 1 s. multicoloured 25 10
1398 – 1 s. 30 mult (air) 35 10
1399 – 1 s. 50 multicoloured 40 10

**1970.** Air. No. 1104 surch S/. 5 AEREO.
1400 325 5 s. on 2 s. mult 1·10 45

**1970.** Public Works Fiscal Stamps surch. "POSTAL" and value.
1401. 1 s. on 1 s. blue 10 10
1402. 1 s. 30 on 1 s. blue 15 10
1403. 1 s. 50 on 1 s. blue 15 20
1404. 2 s. on 1 s. blue 20 15
1405. 5 s. on 1 s. blue 40 15
1406. 10 s. on 1 s. blue 85 35
The basic stamps are inscr. "TIMBRE DE LA RECONSTRUCCION".

**1970.** Provincial Arms and Flags. Mult.
1407. 50 c. Type 411 (postage) 15 10
1408. 1 s. Esmeraldas 15 10
1409. 1 s. 30 El Oro (air) 15 10
1410. 2 s. Loja 25 10
1411. 3 s. Manabi 15 10
1412. 5 s. Pichincha 30 20
1413. 10 s. Guayas 60 40

412. 413. "Presentation of the Virgin".

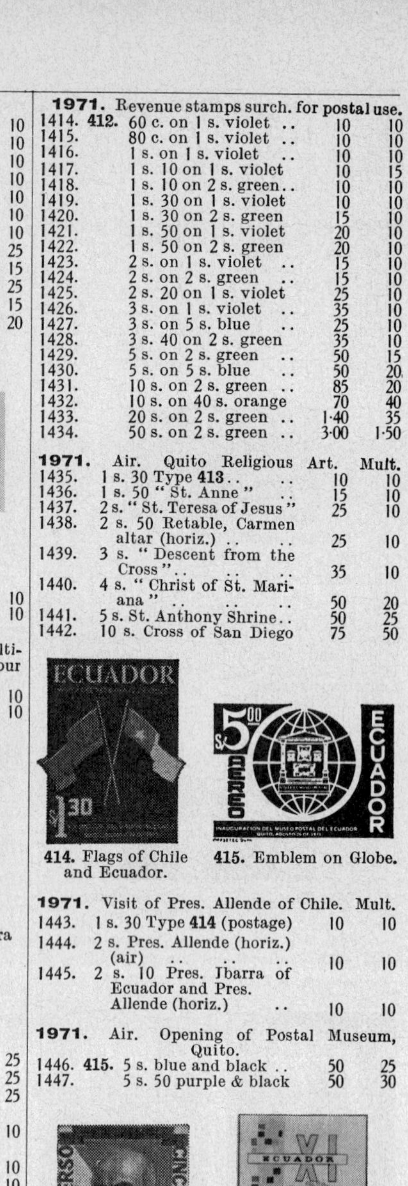

**1971.** Revenue stamps surch. for postal use.
1414. 412. 60 c. on 1 s. violet 10 10
1415. 80 c. on 1 s. violet 10 10
1416. 1 s. on 1 s. violet 10 10
1417. 1 s. 10 on 1 s. violet 10 15
1418. 1 s. 10 on 2 s. green 10 10
1419. 1 s. 30 on 1 s. violet 10 10
1420. 1 s. 30 on 2 s. green 15 10
1421. 1 s. 50 on 1 s. violet 20 10
1422. 1 s. 50 on 2 s. green 20 10
1423. 2 s. on 1 s. violet 15 10
1424. 2 s. on 2 s. green 15 10
1425. 2 s. 20 on 1 s. violet 25 10
1426. 3 s. on 1 s. violet 35 10
1427. 3 s. on 5 s. blue 25 10
1428. 3 s. 40 on 2 s. green 35 10
1429. 5 s. on 2 s. green 50 15
1430. 5 s. on 5 s. blue 50 20
1431. 10 s. on 2 s. green 85 20
1432. 10 s. on 40 s. orange 70 40
1433. 20 s. on 2 s. green 1·40 35
1434. 50 s. on 2 s. green 3·00 1·50

**1971.** Air. Quito Religious Art. Mult.
1435. 1 s. 30 Type 413 10 10
1436. 1 s. 50 "St. Anne" 15 10
1437. 2 s. "St. Teresa of Jesus" 25 10
1438. 2 s. 50 Retable, Carmen altar (horiz.) 25 10
1439. 3 s. "Descent from the Cross" 35 10
1440. 4 s. "Christ of St. Mariana" 50 20
1441. 5 s. St. Anthony Shrine 50 25
1442. 10 s. Cross of San Diego 75 50

414. Flags of Chile and Ecuador. 415. Emblem on Globe.

**1971.** Visit of Pres. Allende of Chile. Mult.
1443. 1 s. 30 Type 414 (postage) 10 10
1444. 2 s. Pres. Allende (horiz.) (air) 10 10
1445. 2 s. 10 Pres. Ibarra of Ecuador and Pres. Allende (horiz.) 10 10

**1971.** Air. Opening of Postal Museum, Quito.
1446. 415. 5 s. blue and black 50 25
1447. 5 s. 50 purple & black 50 30

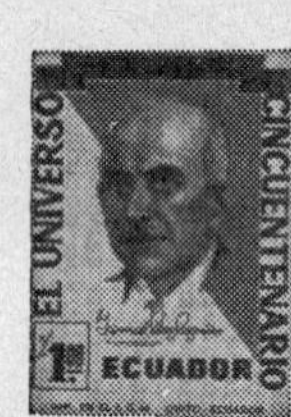

416. Ismael Paz Pazmino (founder).

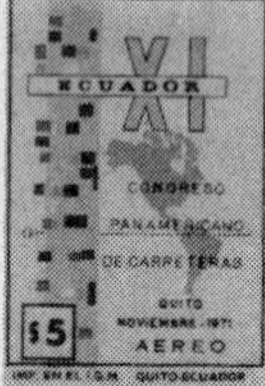

417. Punch-card and Map.

**1971.** 50th Anniv. of "El Universo' (newspaper).
1448. 416. 1 s. multicoloured (postage) 10 10
1449. 1 s. 50 multicoloured (air) 10 10
1450. 2 s. 50 multicoloured 10 10

**1971.** Air. Pan-American Road Conference.
1451. 417. 5 s. multicoloured 50 30
1452. – 10 s. black and orange 90 60
1453. – 20 s. black, red & blue 1·25 65
1454. – 50 s. blk., lilac & blue 1·90 95
DESIGNS: 10 s. Converging roads. 20 s. Globe and equator. 50 s. Mountain road.

418. C.A.R.E. Parcel.

419. Flags of Ecuador and Argentine Republic.

**1972.** 25th Anniv. of C.A.R.E. Organization.
1455. 418. 30 c. purple 10 10
1456. 40 c. green 10 10
1457. 50 c. blue 10 10
1458. 60 c. red 10 10
1459. 80 c. brown 10 10

**1972.** State Visit of President Lanusse of Argentine Republic. Multicoloured.
1460 1 s. Type 419 (postage) 10 10
1461 3 s. Arms of Ecuador and Argentine Republic (horiz) (air) 20 15
1462 5 s. Presidents Velasco Ibarra and Lanusse (horiz) 35 20

**420.** "Jesus giving Keys to St. Peter" (M. de Santiago).

ECUADOR S/1.30 AEREO
XVII conferencia federacion interamericana de abogados
abril 24 1972 quito ecuador

**421.** Map in Flame, and Scales of Justice.

**1972.** Religious Paintings of 18th-century Quito School. Multicoloured.

1463. 50 c. Type **420** (postage) 10 10
1464. 1 s. 10 "Virgin of Mercy" (Quito School) .. .. 20 20
1465. 2 s. "The Immaculate Conception" (M. Samaniego) .. 15 30
1466. 3 s. "Virgin of the Flowers" (M. de Santiago) (air) .. 20 20
1467. 10 s. "Virgin of the Rosary" (Quito School) .. .. 70 50

**1972.** Air. Inter-American Lawyers' Federation Congress, Quito.

1469. **421.** 1 s. 30 blue and red 10 10

**422.** "Our Lady of Sorrow" (Caspicara).

**1972.** 18th-century Ecuador Statues. Mult.

1470. 50 c. Type **422** (postage) 10 10
1471. 1 s. 10 "Nativity" (Quito School) (horiz.) .. 10 20
1472. 2 s. "Virgin of Quito" (anon.) .. .. .. 15 10
1473. 3 s. "St. Dominic" (Quito School) (air) .. .. 20 20
1474. 10 s. "St. Rosa of Lima" (B. de Legarda) .. 70 40

**423.** Juan Ignacio Pareja.

**424.** Woman in Poncho.

**1972.** 150th Anniv. of Battle of Pichincha (1st issue). Multicoloured.

1476. 30 c. Type **423** (postage) 10 10
1477. 40 c. Juan Jose Flores .. 10 10
1478. 50 c. Leon de Febres Cordero .. .. 10 10
1479. 60 c. Ignacio Torres .. 10 10
1480. 70 c. F. de Paula Santander 10 10
1481. 1 s. Jos M. Cordova .. 10 10
1482. 1 s. 30 Jose M. Saenz (air) 10 15
1483. 3 s. Tomas Wright .. 20 15
1484. 4 s. Antonio Farfan .. 25 20
1485. 5 s. A. Jose de Sucre .. 35 25
1486. 10 s. Simon Bolivar .. 35 25
1487. 20 s. Arms of Ecuador .. 75 50

See also Nos. 1508/19.

**1972.** Ecuador Handicrafts and Costumes. Multicoloured.

1488 2 s. Type **424** (postage) .. 15 15
1489 3 s. Girl in striped poncho 25 25
1490 5 s. Girl in embroidered poncho .. .. 40 40
1491 10 s. Copper urn .. 85 75
1492 2 s. Woman in floral poncho (air) .. .. 15 10
1493 3 s. Girl in banded poncho 20 15
1494 5 s. Woman in rose poncho .. .. 35 25
1495 10 s. "Sun" sculpture .. 70 75

**425.** Epidendrum orchid.

**1972.** Air. Ecuador Flowers. Multicoloured.

1497 4 s. Type **425** .. .. 50 20
1498 6 s. Canna .. .. 55 30
1499 10 s. Jimson weed .. 85 75

**426.** Oil Rigs.

**427.** Arms.

**1972.** Air. Oil Industry.

1501. **426.** 1 s. 30 multicoloured 10 10

**1972.** Air. Civic and Armed Forces Day.

1502. **427.** 2 s. multicoloured .. 15 15
1503. 3 s. multicoloured .. 25 15
1504. 4 s. multicoloured .. 35 20
1505. 4 s. 50 multicoloured 35 25
1506. 6 s. 30 multicoloured 40 35
1507. 6 s. 90 multicoloured 40 40

**428.** Statue of Sucre, Santo Domingo.

**429.** Dish Aerial.

**1972.** 150th Anniv. of Battle of Pichincha (2nd issue). Multicoloured.

1508. 1 s. 20 Type **428** (post.) 10 10
1509. 1 s. 80 San Augustin Monastery .. 15 10
1510. 2 s. 30 Independence Square .. .. 20 10
1511. 2 s. 50 Bolivar's statue, La Alameda .. .. 25 15
1512. 4 s. 75 Carved chapel doors .. .. 40 20
1513. 2 s. 40 Cloister, San Augustin Monastery (air) .. .. 15 10
1514. 4 s. 50 La Merced Monastery .. .. 30 25
1515. 5 s. 50 Chapel column .. 40 30
1516. 6 s. 30 Altar, San Augustin Monastery .. 45 35
1517. 6 s. 90 Ceiling San Augustin Monastery .. 45 35
1518. 7 s. 40 Crucifixion, Cantuna Chapel 50 40
1519. 7 s. 90 Ceiling detail, San Agustin Monastery .. 55 45

**1973.** Inauguration (1972) of Satellite Earth Station, Chillotal.

1520 **429** 1 s. multicoloured .. 20 10

**431.** U.N. Emblem.

**432.** O.E.A. Emblem.

**1973.** Air. 25th Anniv of U.N. Economic Committee for Latin America (C.E.P.A.L.).

1521 **431** 1 s. 30 black and blue 15 10

**1973.** Air. "Day of the Americas".

1522 **432** 1 s. 50 multicoloured 15 10

**433.** Presidents Rodriguez Lara and Caldera.

**1973.** Air. Visit of Pres. Caldera of Venezuela.

1523 **433** 3 s. multicoloured .. 30 15

**434.** Blue-footed Boobies.

**1973.** Formation of Galapagos Islands Province. Multicoloured.

1524 30 c. Type **434** (postage) 70 15
1525 40 c. Blue-faced boobies 70 15
1526 50 c. Oystercatcher .. 70 15
1527 60 c. Basking Galapagos fur seals .. .. 50 10
1528 70 c. Giant tortoise .. 50 10
1529 1 s. Californian sealion .. 50 10
1530 1 s. 30 Blue-footed boobies (different) (air) .. 80 15
1531 3 s. Brown pelican .. 1·00 20

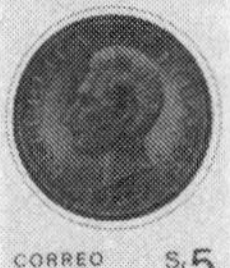


**435.** Silver Coin, 1934.

**436.** Black-chinned Mountain Tanager.

**1973.** Air. Coins. Multicoloured.

1532. 5 s. Type **435** .. .. 35 15
1533. 10 s. Reverse of silver coin, showing arms .. 70 30
1534. 50 s. Gold Coin, 1928 .. 3·00 1·50

**1973.** Birds. Multicoloured.

1536. 1 s. Type **436** .. .. 75 25
1537. 2 s. Epaulet Oriole .. 1·10 40
1538. 3 s. Toucan Barbet (vert.) 1·10 50
1539. 5 s. Masked Crimson Tanager (vert.) .. .. 2·50 90
1540. 10 s. Blue-necked Tanager (vert.) .. .. .. 5·00 1·60

**437.** OPEC Emblem.

**438.** Dr. Marco Tulio Varea Quevedo (botanist).

**1974.** Air. OPEC (Oil exporters) Meeting, Quito.

1542. **437.** 2 s. multicoloured .. 15 10

**1974.** Ecuadorian Personalities (1st series).

1543. **438.** 1 s. blue .. .. 10 10
1544. – 1 s. orange .. .. 10 10
1545. – 1 s. green .. .. 10 10
1546. – 1 s. brown .. .. 10 10

PERSONALITIES: No. 1544, Dr. J. M. Carbo Noboa (medical scientist). No. 1545, Dr. A. J. Valenzuela (physician). No. 1546, Capt. E. Chiriboga (national hero).

See also Nos. 1551/6 and 1565/9.

1974 UPU 1974
ECUADOR

**439.** Flag of Ecuador and U.P.U. Emblem.

**440.** Postman with Letter.

**1974.** Air. Cent. of U.P.U.

1548. **439.** 1 s. 30 multicoloured 10 10

**1974.** Personalities (2nd series). As **438.**

1551. 60 c. red (postage) .. 10 10
1552. 70 c. lilac .. .. .. 10 10
1553. 1 s. 20 green .. .. 10 10
1554. 1 s. 80 blue .. .. 20 10
1555. 1 s. 30 blue and black (air) 10 10
1556. 1 s. 50 grey on pale grey .. 10 10

PERSONALITIES: 60 c. Dr. Pio Jaramillo Alvarado (sociologist). 70 c. Prof. Luciano Andrade Marin (naturalist). 1 s. 20, Dr. Francisco Campos Ruiadaneira (entomologist). 1 s. 30, Teodore Wolf (geographer). 1 s. 50, Capt. Edmundo Chiriboga G. (national hero). 1 s. 80, Luis Vernaza Lazarte (philanthropist).

**1974.** Air. 8th Inter-American Postmasters' Congress, Auibo.

1557. **440.** 5 s. multicoloured .. 30 15

**441.** Map of the Americas and F.I.A.F. Emblem.

**442.** Colonnade.

**1974.** Air. "Exfigua" Stamp Exhibition and Inter-American Philatelic Federation 5th General Assembly, Guayaquil (1973).

1558. **441.** 3 s. multicoloured .. 20 10

**1974.** Colonial Monastery, Tilipulo, Cotopaxi Province. Multicoloured.

1559. 20 c. Type **442** .. .. 10 10
1560. 30 c. Entrance .. .. 10 10
1561. 40 c. Church .. .. 10 10
1562. 50 c. Archway (vert.) .. 10 10
1563. 60 c. Chapel (vert.) .. 10 10
1564. 70 c. Cemetery (vert.) .. 15 10

**1975.** Personalities (3rd series). As T **438.**

1565. 80 c. blue (postage) .. 10 10
1566. 80 c. red and pink .. 10 10
1567. 5 s. red (air) .. .. 40 20
1568. 5 s. grey .. .. .. 40 20
1569. 5 s. violet .. .. 40 20

PORTRAITS: No. 1565, Dr. Angel Polibio Chaves (statesman). No. 1566, Emilio Estrada Ycaza (archaeologist). No. 1567, Manuel J. Calle (journalist). No. 1568, Leopoldo Benites Vinueza (statesman). No. 1569, Adolfo H. Simmonds G. (journalist).

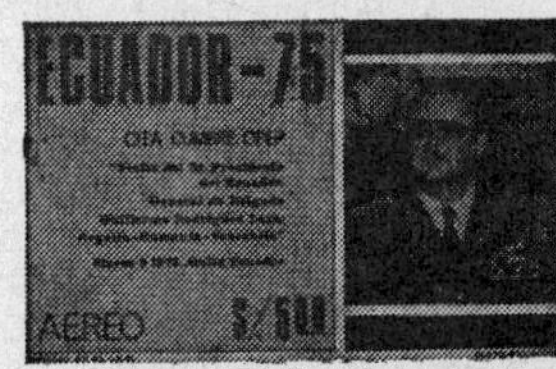


**443.** President Rodriguez Lara.

**1975.** Air. State Visits of President Rodriguez Lara to Algeria, Rumania and Venezuela.

1570. **443.** 5 s. black and red .. 40 20

**444.** Ministerial Greetings.

**445.** "The Sacred Heart".

**1975.** Meeting of Public Works' Ministers of Ecuador and Colombia, Quito. Multicoloured.

1571. 1 s. Type **444** (postage) .. 10 10
1572. 1 s. 50 Ministers at opening ceremony (air) .. .. 15 10
1573. 2 s. Ministers signing treaty 15 10

**1975.** Air. 3rd Eucharistic Congress, Quito. Multicoloured.

1574. 1 s. 30 Type **445** .. .. 10 10
1575. 2 s. Golden monstrance .. 15 10
1576. 3 s. Quito Cathedral .. 20 10

**446.** President Martinez Mera.

**447.** Jorge Delgado Panchana (swimming champion).

**1975.** Air. Birth Centenary of Juan de Dios Martinez Mera (President, 1932–33).

1577. **446.** 5 s. red and black .. 40 20

**1975.** Air. Jorge Delgado Panchana Commemoration. Multicoloured.

1578. 1 s. 30 Type **447** .. .. 15 10
1579. 3 s. Delgado Panchana in water (horiz.) .. .. 30 10

448. "Women of Peace".

449. "Armed Forces".

**1975.** International Women's Year. Mult.
1580. 1 s. Type **448** .. .. 10 10
1581. 1 s. "Women of Action" 10 10

**1975.** 3rd Anniv. of 15th February Revolution.
1582. **449.** 2 s. multicoloured .. 45 15

450. Hurdling.

451. "Phragmipedum candatum".

**1975. 3rd Ecuadorian Games, Quito.**
1583. **450.** 20 c. black and orange (postage) .. .. 10 10
1584. – 20 c. black and yellow 10 10
1585. – 30 c. black and mauve 10 10
1586. – 30 c. black and buff 10 10
1587. – 40 c. black and yellow 10 10
1588. – 40 c. black and mauve 10 10
1589. – 50 c. black and green 10 10
1590. – 50 c. black and red 10 10
1591. – 60 c. black and green 10 10
1592. – 60 c. black and pink 10 10
1593. – 70 c. black and drab 10 10
1594. – 70 c. black and grey 10 10
1595. – 80 c. black and blue 10 10
1596. – 80 c. black and orange 10 10
1597. – 1 s. black and olive 10 10
1598. – 1 s. black and brown 10 10
1599. 1 s. 30 black and orange (air) .. .. 10 10
1600. – 2 s. black and yellow 15 10
1601. – 2 s. 80, black and red 20 10
1602. – 3 s. black and blue 25 10
1603. – 5 s. black and purple 40 20

DESIGNS: No. 1584, Chess. No. 1585, Boxing. No. 1586, Basketball. No. 1587, Showjumping. No. 1588, Cycling. No. 1589, Football. No. 1590, Fencing. No. 1591, Golf. No. 1592, Gymnastics. No. 1593, Wrestling. No. 1594, Judo. No. 1595, Swimming. No. 1596, Weightlifting. No. 1597, Handball. No. 1598, Table tennis. No. 1599, Squash. No. 1600, Rifle shooting. No. 1601, Volleyball. No. 1602, Rafting. No. 1603, Inca mask.

**1975.** Flowers. Multicoloured.
1604. 20 c. Type **451** (postage) 10 10
1605. 30 c. "Genciana" (horiz.) 10 10
1606. 40 c. "Bromeliaeae cactaceae" .. .. 10 10
1607. 50 c. "Cachlioda volcanica" (horiz.) .. 10 10
1608. 60 c. "Odontoglossum hallii (horiz.) .. .. 10 10
1609. 80 c. "Cactaceae sp." (horiz.) .. .. 10 10
1610. 1 s. "Odontoglossum sp." (horiz.) .. .. 10 10
1611. 1 s. 30 "Pitcairnia pungens" (horiz.) (air) .. 15 10
1612. 2 s. "Salvia sp." (horiz.) 25 10
1613. 3 s. "Bomarea" (horiz.) 30 10
1614. 4 s. "Opuntia quitense" (horiz.) .. .. 25 15
1615. 5 s. "Bomarea" (different) (horiz.) .. 30 20

452. Aircraft Tail-fins.
453. Statue of Benalcazar.

**1976.** Air. 23rd Anniv. of TAME Airline. Multicoloured.
1616 1 s. 30 Type **452** .. .. 10 10
1617 3 s. Douglas DC-3 and Lockheed L.188 Electra encircling map .. 40 10

**1976.** Air. Sebastian de Benalcazar Commem.
1618. **453.** 2 s. multicoloured .. 20 10
1619. 3 s. multicoloured .. 30 10

454. "Venus" (Chorrera Culture).

455. Strawberries.

**1976.** Archaeological Discoveries. Mult.
1620. 20 c. Type **454** (postage) 10 10
1621. 30 c. "Venus" (Valdivia) 10 10
1622. 40 c. Seated monkey (Chorrera) .. .. 10 10
1623. 50 c. Man wearing poncho (Panzaleo Tardio) .. 10 10
1624. 60 c. Mythical figure (Cashaloma) .. .. 10 10
1625. 80 c. Musician (Tolita) .. 10 10
1626. 1 s. Chief priest (censer-Mantema) .. .. 10 10
1627. 1 s. Female mask (Tolita) 10 10
1628. 1 s. Gold and platinum brooch (Tolita) .. 10 10
1629. 1 s. "Angry person" mask (Tolita) .. .. 10 10
1630. 1 s. 30 Coconut-dealer (Carchi) (air) .. .. 15 15
1631. 2 s. Funerary urn (Tuncahuan) .. .. .. 15 10
1632. 3 s. Priest (Bahia de Caraquez) .. .. 25 10
1633. 4 s. Seashell (Cuasmal) .. 35 10
1634. 5 s. Bowl supported by figurines (Guangala) .. 40 20

**1976.** Flowers and Fruits Festival, **Ambato.** Multicoloured.
1635. 1 s. Type **455** (postage) .. 10 10
1636. 2 s. Apples (air) .. .. 10 10
1637. 5 s. Rose .. .. .. 40 15

456. S. Cueva Celi.

457. Douglas DC-10 crossing "50" and Dornier Wal Flying Boat.

**1976.** Musical Celebrities. Multicoloured.
1638. 1 s. Type **456** .. .. 10 10
1639. 1 s. C. Ojeda Davila .. 10 10
1640. 1 s. S. Maria Duran .. 10 10
1641. 1 s. C. Amable Ortiz .. 10 10
1642. 1 s. L. Alberto Valencia 10 10

**1976.** Air. 50th Anniv. of Lufthansa Airline.
1643. **457.** 10 s. multicoloured .. 1·25 50

458. Cerros del Carmen y Santa Ana.

459. New Post Office Building.

**1976.** Air. 441st Anniv. of Guayaquil. Mult.
1644. 1 s. 30 Type **458** .. .. 10 10
1645. 1 s. 30 "Pregonero" (vert.) .. .. .. 10 10
1646. 1 s. 30 "Estibador" (vert.) .. .. .. 10 10
1647. 2 s. Sebastian de Benalcazar (vert.) .. .. 15 10
1648. 2 s. Francisco de Orellana (vert.) .. .. 15 10
1649. 2 s. Guayas and Quil (vert.) .. .. .. 15 10

**1976.** Air. Post Office Building Project.
1650 **459** 5 s. multicoloured .. 30 15

460. Emblem and Wreath.

461. The Americas on Globe.

**1976.** Air. 50th Anniv. of Bolivarian Society.
1651. **460.** 1 s. 30 multicoloured 10 10

**1976.** Air. 3rd Pan-American Ministers' Conference on Transport Infrastructure, Quito.
1652. **461.** 2 s. multicoloured .. 10 10

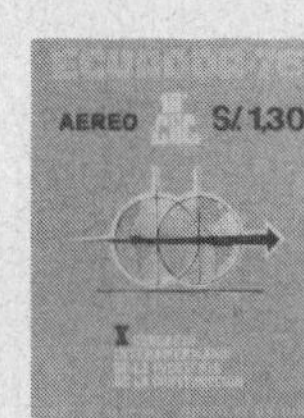
462. Congress Emblem.

463. George Washington.

**1976.** Air. 10th Inter-American Construction Industry Congress, Quito.
1654. **462.** 1 s. 30 multicoloured 10 10
1655. 3 s. multicoloured .. 20 25

**1976.** Air. Bicentenary of American Revolution. Multicoloured.
1657. 3 s. Type **463** .. .. 45 25
1658. 5 s. Battle of Flamborough Head, 1779 (horiz.) .. .. 1·75 40

464. Dr. H. Noguchi.

465. Bolivar Memorial.

**1976.** Air. Birth Centenary of Dr. Hideyo Noguchi (bacteriologist).
1659 **464** 3 c. multicoloured .. 25 10

**1976.** Air. Meeting of Agricultural Ministers of Andean Countries, Quito.
1661 **465** 3 s. multicoloured .. 20 10

466. M. Febres Cordero.

467. Dr. Luis Cordero.

**1976.** Air. Mariuxi Febres Cordero, South American Swimming Champion.
1663 **466** 3 s. multicoloured .. 25 10

**1976.** Air. Pres. Cordero Commemoration.
1664. **467.** 2 s. multicoloured .. 10 10

468. Sister Catalina de Jesus Herrera.

469. General Assembly Emblem.

**1977.** Air. 260th Birth Anniv. of Sister Catalina de Jesus Herrera (religious author).
1665. **468.** 1 s. 30 pink and black 10 10

**1977.** 11th General Assembly of Technical Committees of the Pan-American Historical and Geographical Institute. Multicoloured.
1666. 2 s. Type **469** (postage) .. 10 10
1667. 5 s. Congress Building, Quito (air) .. .. 30 15

470. Mythological Figure ("La Tolita" ceramic).

471. Hands holding Rotary Emblem.

**1977.** Air. 50th Anniv. of Foundation of Central Bank of Ecuador. Multicoloured.
1669. 7 s. Type **470** .. .. 45 20
1670. 9 s. "The Holy Shepherdess Spinning" (B. de Legarda) .. 60 30
1671. 11 s. "The Fruitseller" (B. de Legarda) .. 75 60

**1977.** 50th Anniv. of Guayaquil Rotary Club.
1673. **471.** 1 s. multicoloured .. 15 10
1674. 2 s. multicoloured .. 25 10

472. President Michelsen of Colombia.

**1977.** Air. Meeting of the Presidents of Colombia and Ecuador. Multicoloured.
1676. 2 s. 60 Type **472** .. .. 25 10
1677. 5 s. Ecuador junta .. 45 15
1678. 7 s. Ecuador junta (vert.) 45 20
1679. 9 s. President Michelsen with Ecuador junta 75 40

473. Brother Miguel and St. Peter's, Rome.

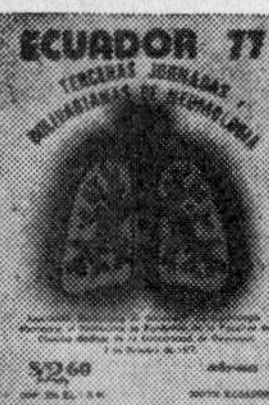
474. Lungs.

**1977.** Air. Beatification of Brother Hermano Miguel.
1681. **473.** 2 s. 60 multicoloured 20 10

**1977.** Air. Third Bolivarian Pneumological Seminar.
1682. **474.** 2 s. 60 multicoloured 25 10

475. Jose Peralta.

476. Blue-faced Booby.

**1977.** 40th Death Anniv. of Jose Peralta (writer).
1683. **475.** 1 s. 80 multicoloured (postage) .. .. 10 10
1684. – 2 s. 40 multicoloured 15 15
1685. – 2 s. 60 blk., red & yell. (air) .. .. 15 10

DESIGNS: 2 s. 40, Statue of Peralta. 2 s. 60, Titles of Peralta's works, and his "ex libris".

**1977.** Birds of the Galapagos Islands. **Mult.**
1686. 1 s. 20 Type **476** .. 50 15
1687. 1 s. 80 Red-footed Booby 60 20
1688. 2 s. 40 Blue-footed Boobies 70 25
1689. 3 s. 40 Dusky Gull .. 1·00 25
1690. 4 s. 40 Galapagos Hawk .. 1·25 60
1691. 5 s. 40 Map of the islands and finches (vert.) .. 1·60 70

477. Broadcast Tower.

478. Dr. Remigio Romero y Cordero.

**1977.** Air. World Telecommunications Day.
1692. **477.** 5 s. multicoloured .. 30 15

**1978.** Air. 10th Death Anniv. of Dr. Remigio Romero y Cordero (poet).

1693. **478.** 3 s. multicoloured .. 15 10
1694. 10 s. 60 multicoloured 60 30

**479.** Children.

**480.** General San Martin.

**1978.** Air. 50th Anniv. of Social Insurance Institute. Multicoloured.

1696. 7 s. Type **479** .. .. 45 20
1697. 9 s. Insurance emblem .. 40 30
1698. 11 s. Hands reaching for sun .. .. .. 70 35

**1978.** Air. Birth Bicent. of General San Martin.

1700. **480.** 10 s. 60 multicoloured 50 40

**481.** Air Survey of Ecuador.

**482.** Dr. Vicente Corral Moscoso Hospital.

**1978.** 50th Anniv of Military Geographical Institute. Multicoloured.

1702 6 s. Type **481** (postage) .. 60 25
1703 7 s. 60 Air survey of mountains (air) .. 80 30

**1978.** Inauguration of Dr. Vicente Corral Moscoso Regional Hospital. Multicoloured.

1705. 3 s. Type **482** (postage) .. 25 10
1706. 7 s. 60 Dr. Moscoso (air) 60 30

**483.** Map of the Americas and Lions Emblem.

**484.** Anniversary Emblem.

**1978.** Seventh Meeting, of Latin American Lions. Multicoloured.

1708. 3 s. Type **483** (postage) .. 25 10
1709. 4 s. 20 Type **483** 35 10
1710. 5 s. As Type **483** but smalle emblem (air) .. .. 40 20
1711. 6 s. 20 As No. 1710 .. 25 25

**1978.** 70th Anniv of Filanbanco (Philanthropic Bank). Multicoloured.

1713 4 s. 20 Type **484** (postage) 30 10
1714 5 s. Bank emblem (air) .. 35 15

**485.** Goal.

**1978.** World Cup Football Championship, Argentina. Multicoloured.

1715. 1 s. 20 Type **485** (postage) 10 10
1716. 1 s. 80 Gauchito and emblem (vert.) .. 15 10
1717. 4 s. 40 Gauchito (vert.) .. 35 15
1718. 2 s. 60 Gauchito, "78" and emblem (air) .. 20 10
1719. 7 s. Football .. .. 30 20
1720. 9 s. Emblem (vert.) .. 40 35

**486.** Old Men of Vilcabamba.

**487.** Bernardo O'Higgins.

**1978.** Air. Vilcabamba (valley of longevity).

1722. **486.** 5 s. multicoloured .. 35 15

**1978.** Air. Birth Bicent. of General Bernardo O'Higgins (national hero of Chile).

1723. **487.** 10 s. 60 multicoloured 50 30

**488.** Hubert Humphrey (former U.S. Vice-President).

**489.** "Virgin and Child".

**1978.** Air. Hubert Humphrey Commem.

1725. **488.** 5 s. multicoloured .. 35 15

**1978.** Air. Christmas. Children's Paintings. Multicoloured.

1726. 2 s. 20 Type **489** .. .. 15 10
1727. 4 s. 60 "Holy Family" 25 15
1728. 6 s. 20 "Candle and Children" .. .. 40 20

**490.** "Village" (Anibal Villacis).

**491.** Male and Female Symbols.

**1978.** Air. Ecuadorian Painters. Mult.

1729. 5 s. Type **490** .. .. 35 20
1730. 5 s. "Mountain Village" (Gilberto Almeida) .. 35 20
1731. 5 s. "Bay" (Roura Oxandaberro) .. .. .. 35 20
1732. 5 s. "Abstract" (Luis Molinari) .. .. 35 20
1733. 5 s. "Statue" (Oswaldo Viteri) .. .. .. 35 20
1734. 5 s. "Tools" (Enrique Tabara) .. .. 35 20

**1979.** 50th Anniv. of Inter-American Women's Commission.

1735. **491.** 3 s. 40 multicoloured 20 10

**492.** House and Monument.

**1979.** Air. 150th Anniv. of Battle of Portete and Tarqui. Multicoloured.

1736. 2 s. 40 Type **492** .. 15 10
1737. 3 s. 40 Monument (vert.) 20 10

**493.** Bank Emblem.

**494.** Deep Sea Trawler and Fish.

**1979.** 16th Anniv. of Ecuadorian Mortgage Bank.

1739. **493.** 4 s. 40 multicoloured 30 15
1740. 5 s. 40 multicoloured 35 15

**1979.** Air. 25th Anniv of Extension to 200-mile Offshore Limit. Multicoloured.

1741. 5 s. Type **494** .. .. 90 25
1742. 7 s. Map of Ecuador and territorial waters (horiz.) 55 25
1743. 9 s. Map of South America 70 35

**495.** Street Scene.

**496.** Coat of Arms.

**1979.** Galapagos Islands. Multicoloured.

1744. 3 s. 40 Type **495** (postage) 25 15
1745. 10 s. 60 Church bells in tower (horiz.) (air) .. 50 20
1746. 13 s. 60 Aerial view of coast .. .. .. 55 20

**1979.** Air. 5th Anniv of Ecuador–American Chamber of Commerce.

1748. **496.** 7 s. 60 multicoloured 45 25
1749. 10 s. 60 multicoloured 65 35

**497.** Young Girl.

**498.** Games Emblem.

**1979.** Air. International Year of the Child.

1751. **497.** 10 s. multicoloured .. 50 40

**1979.** Air. Fifth National Games.

1752. **498.** 28 s. multicoloured .. 1·10 80

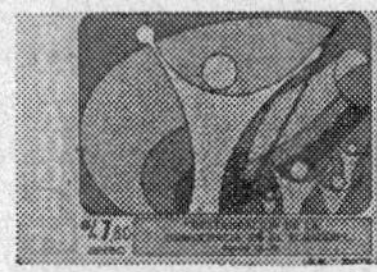
**499.** Rejoicing People with Flags.

**1979.** Air. Restoration of Democracy. Mult.

1753. 7 s. 60 Type **499** .. .. 55 30
1754. 10 s. 60 President Jamie Roldos Aguilera .. 70 35

**500.** CIESPAL Building, Quito.

**1980.** Air. Inauguration of CIESPAL (Ecuadorian Institute of Engineers) Building.

1755. **500.** 10 s. 60 multicoloured 50 35

**501.** Jose Joaquin de Olmedo.

**502.** Enriquillo (Dominican Republic).

**1980.** Birth Bicentenary of Jose Joaquin de Olmedo (physician).

1756. **501.** 3 s. multicoloured (postage) .. .. 25 10
1757. 5 s. multicoloured .. 40 20
1758. 10 s. multicoloured (air) .. .. 50 40

**1980.** Chiefs of the Indo-American Indian Tribes. Multicoloured.

1759. 3 s. Type **502** (postage) .. 25 10
1760. 3 s. 40 Guaycaypuro (Venezuela) .. .. 30 15
1761. 5 s. Abayuba (Uruguay) 40 20
1762. 5 s. Atlacatl (El Salvador) 40 20
1763. 7 s. 60 Cuantemoc (Mexico) (air) .. .. .. 60 30
1764. 7 s. 60 Lempira (Honduras) 60 30
1765. 7 s. 60 Nicaragua (Nicaragua) .. .. .. 60 30
1766. 10 s. Lambare (Paraguay) 50 40
1767. 10 s. Urraca (Panama) .. 50 40
1768. 10 s. 60 Anacaona (Haiti) 50 45
1769. 10 s. 60 Caupolican (Chile) 50 45
1770. 10 s. 60 Tecun-Uman (Guatemala) .. .. 50 45
1771. 12 s. 80 Calarca (Colombia) 65 30
1772. 12 s. 80 Garabito (Costa Rica) .. .. .. 65 30
1773. 12 s. 80 Hatuey (Cuba) .. 65 30
1774. 13 s. 60 Camarao (Brazil) 65 30
1775. 13 s. 60 Tehuelche (Argentina) .. .. .. 65 30
1776. 13 s. 60 Tupaj Katari (Bolivia) .. .. 65 30
1777. 17 s. 80 Sequoyah (U.S.A.) 75 40
1778. 22 s. 80 Ruminahui (Ecuador) .. .. 1·10 55

**503.** King Juan Carlos and Queen Sophia of Spain.

**505.** Cofan Indian (Napo Province).

**506.** U.P.U. Monument.

**504.** Provincial Administration Council Building, Pichincha.

**1980.** Visit of King and Queen of Spain.

1779. **503.** 3 s. 40 multicoloured (postage) .. .. 30 15
1780. 10 s. 60 multicoloured (air) .. .. 50 40

**1980.** Air. Pichincha Provincial Council.

1781. **504.** 10 s. 60 multicoloured 80 40

**1980.** Equatorial Indians. Multicoloured.

1782. 3 s. Type **505** (postage) .. 25 10
1783. 3 s. 40 Zuleta woman (Imbabura) .. .. 30 15
1784. 5 s. Chota negro woman (Imbabura) .. .. 40 20
1785. 7 s. 60 Salasaca boy (Tungurahua) (air) .. 60 30
1786. 10 s. Girl from Amula (Chimborazo) .. .. 50 40
1787. 10 s. 60 Girl from Canar (Canar) .. .. 50 45
1788. 13 s. 60 Colorado Indian (Pichincha) .. .. 65 30

**1980.** Air. Cent. of U.P.U. Membership. Mult.

1789. 10 s. 60 Type **506** .. 70 35
1790. 17 s. 80 Mail box, 1880 .. 95 65

**507.** Our Lady of Mercy Basilica, Quito.

**508.** Olympic Torch.

**1980.** Virgin of Mercy, Patron Saint of Ecuadorian Armed Forces. Multicoloured.

1792. 3 s. 40 Type **507** (postage) 30 15
1793. 3 s. 40 Balcony .. .. 30 15
1794. 3 s. 40 Tower and cupola 30 15
1795. 7 s. 60 Cupola and cloisters (air) .. .. .. 60 30
1796. 7 s. 60 Tower and view of Quito .. .. 60 30
1797. 7 s. 60 Gold screen .. 60 30
1798. 10 s. 60 Retable .. .. 60 45
1799. 10 s. 60 Pulpit .. .. 60 45
1800. 13 s. 60 Cupola .. .. 75 30
1801. 13 s. 60 Statue of Virgin 75 30

**1980.** Olympic Games, Moscow. Multicoloured.

1803. 5 s. Type **508** (postage) 40 20
1804. 7 s. 60 Type **508** .. 35 30
1805. 10 s. 60 Moscow games emblem (air) .. .. 50 45
1806. 13 s. 60 As No. 1805 .. 65 55

**509.** Rotary Anniversary Emlem.

**510.** "Marshal Sucre" (after Marco Salas).

**1980.** Air. 75th Anniv. of Rotary International.

1808. **509.** 10 s. multicoloured .. 75 40

**1980.** Air. 150th Death Anniv. of Marshal Antonio Jose de Sucre

1809. **510.** 10 s. 60 multicoloured 50 45

**511.** J. J. Olmeda, Father de Velasco, Government Building and Constitution.

**512.** The Virgin of the Swans.

**1980.** 150th Anniv of Constitutional Assembly of Riobamba. Multicoloured.

1810 3 s. 40 Type **511** (postage) 25 10
1811 5 s. Type **511** .. .. 40 15
1812 7 s. 60 Monstrance, Riobamba Cathedral (vert) (air) .. .. .. .. 55 25
1813 10 s. 60 As No. 1812 .. 50 35

**1980.** 50th Anniv. of Coronation of the Virgin of the Swans. Multicoloured.

1815. 1 s. 20 Type **512** .. 10 10
1816. 3 s. 40 The Virgin (different) .. .. .. 20 10

**513.** Young Indian.

**514.** O.P.E.C. Emblem and Globe.

**1980.** 1st Anniv. of Return to Democracy. Multicoloured.

1817 1 s. 20 Type **513** (postage) 10 10
1818 3 s. 40 Type **513** .. 20 10
1819 7 s. 60 President Roldos with Indian (air) .. 55 25
1820 10 s. 60 As No. 1819 .. 50 35

**1980.** 20th Anniv. of Organization of Petroleum Exporting Countries. Mult.

1822. 3 s. 40 Type **514** (postage) 30 10
1823. 7 s. 60 Figures supporting O.P.E.C. emblem (air) 60 30

**515.** Dr. Isidro Ayora Cueva.

**516.** Ornamental Hedge, Capitol Gardens.

**1980.** Air. Birth Centenary of Dr. Isidro Ayora Cueva (President, 1926-31).

1824 **515** 18 s. 20 multicoloured 1·10 75

**1980.** Centenary of Carchi Province. Mult.

1825. 3 s. Type **516** (postage).. 20 10
1826. 10 s. 60 Governor's palace (air) .. .. .. 70 35
1827. 17 s. 80 Freedom statue, Zulcan .. .. .. 95 65

**517.** " Cattleya maxima ".

**1980.** Orchids. Multicoloured.

1828. 1 s. 20 Type **517** (postage) 10 10
1829. 3 s. " Comparettia speciosa " .. .. 25 10
1830. 3 s. 40 " Cattleya iricolor " .. .. .. 30 15
1831. 7 s. 60 " Anguloa uniflora " (air) .. .. 60 20
1832. 10 s. 60 " Scuticaria salesiana " .. .. 80 35
1833. 50 s. " Helcia sanguinolenta " (vert.) .. 1·10 85
1834. 100 s. " Anguloa virginalis " .. .. .. 1·50 1·50

## INDEX

Countries can be quickly located by referring to the index at the end of this volume.

**518.** Emblem and Radio Waves.

**519.** Simon Bolivar (after Marco Salas).

**520.** Pope John Paul II.

**1980.** 50th Anniv. of Radio Station HCJB.

1836. 2 s. Type **518** (postage).. 15 10
1837. 7 s. 60 Emblem and radio waves (horiz.) (air) .. 50 25
1838. 10 s. 60 Anniversary emblem .. .. 65 35

**1980.** Air. 150th Death Anniv of Simon Bolivar.

1839 **519** 13 s. 60 multicoloured 1·10 55

**1980.** Christmas. Multicoloured.

1840. 3 s. 40 Pope John Paul II with children (horiz.) (postage) .. .. 30 15
1841. 7 s. 60 Pope blessing crowd (air) .. .. 60 25
1842. 10 s. 60 Type **520** .. 50 35

**521.** Carlos and Jorge Mantilla Ortega (editors).

**1981.** 75th Anniv. of "El Comercio" (newspaper). Multicoloured.

1843. 2 s. Type **521** .. .. 15 10
1844. 3 s. 40 Cesar and Carlos Mantilla Jacome .. 25 15

**522.** Oldest letter-box, Galapagos, 1793.

**1981.** Air. Galapagos Islands.

1845. – 50 s. yellow and black .. .. 3·00 2·25
1846. **522.** 100 s. multicoloured 4·50 3·00

DESIGN—HORIZ. 50 s. Turtle.

**523.** Flag, Map and Soldier.

**1981.** National Defence. Multicoloured.

1847. 3 s. 40 Type **523** .. .. 25 15
1848. 3 s. 40 Flag, map and Pres. Roldos Aguilera .. 25 15

**524.** Theodore E. Gildred and " Ecuador I ".

**525.** Dr. Octavio Cordero Palacios.

**1981.** 50th Anniv. of Flight of "Ecuador I" from San Diego to Quito.

1849. **524.** 2 s. black and blue .. 30 15

**1981.** 50th Death Anniv. (1980) of Dr. Octavio Cordero Palacios.

1850. **525.** 2 s. multicoloured .. 15 10

**526.** Miraculous Painting of the Virgin of Sorrows.

**527.** Football Emblem.

**1981.** 75th Anniv. of Miracle of the Virgin blinking at San Gabriel College. Multicoloured.

1851. 2 s. Type **526** .. .. 15 10
1852. 2 s. San Gabriel College Church .. .. .. 15 10

**1981.** Air. World Cup Football Championship, Spain (1982). Multicoloured.

1853. 7 s. 60 Type **527** .. 60 30
1854. 10 s. 60 Footballer .. 90 45
1855. 13 s. 60 World Cup trophy 1·10 55

**528.** Mendoza Aviles and Bridge.

**1981.** Inauguration of Dr. Rafael Mendoza Aviles Bridge.

1857. **528.** 2 s. multicoloured .. 15 10

**529.** " Still-life ".

**1981.** Air. Birth Centenary of Pablo Picasso (artist). Multicoloured.

1858. 7 s. 60 Type **529**.. .. 35 30
1859. 10 s. 60 " First Communion " .. .. 50 45
1860. 13 s. 60 " Las Meninas " 60 55

Nos. 1859 and 1860 are vert.

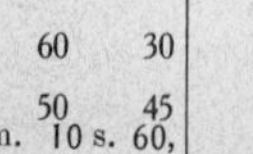

**530.** Ear of Wheat on World Map.

**1981.** World Food Day. Multicoloured.

1862. 5 s. Type **530** (postage).. 40 20
1863. 10 s. 60 Agricultural products and farmer sowing seed (air) .. 50 35

**531.** "Isla Solango" (freighter).

**532.** Person in Wheelchair.

**1982.** 10th Anniv. of Transnave Shipping Company.

1864. **531.** 3 s. 50 multicoloured 90 25

**1982.** International Year of Disabled Persons (1981).

1865. **532.** 3 s. 40 brown, red and black (postage) .. 30 15
1866. – 7 s. 60 silver, green & blue (air) .. .. 60 30
1867. – 10 s. 60 brown, black and red .. .. 50 45

DESIGNS: 7 s. 60, I.Y.D.P. emblem. 10 s. 60, Man breaking crutch.

**533.** Gateway, Quito.

**534.** Flags of Member Countries and Emblem.

**1982.** "Quitex '82" National Stamp Exn.

1868. **533.** 2 s. yellow, brown and black .. .. 15 10
1869. – 3 s. yellow, brown and black .. .. 20 10

DESIGN. 3 s. Old houses, Quito.

**1982.** 22nd American Air Forces' Commanders Conference.

1871 **534** 5 s. multicoloured .. 40 20

**535.** Juan Montalvo. (after C. A. Villacres).

**536.** Swimming Pool.

**1982.** 150th Birth Anniv. of Juan Montalvo (writer).

1872. **535.** 2 s. pink, brown and black (postage) .. 15 10
1873. – 3 s. multicoloured .. 20 10
1874. – 5 s. multicoloured (air) 35 20

DESIGNS—VERT. 3 s. Mausoleum. HORIZ. 5 s., Montalvo's villa.

**1982.** World Swimming Championships, Guayaquil. Multicoloured.

1875. 1 s. 80 Type **536** (postage) 15 10
1876. 3 s. 40 Water polo .. 25 10
1877. 10 s. 20 Games emblem (vert.) (air) .. .. 50 40
1878. 14 s. 20 Diving (vert.) .. 65 50

**537.** Juan Leon Mera (after Victor Mideros).

**538.** " The Ecstasy of St. Theresa " (detail of sculpture by Bernini).

**1982.** 150th Birth Anniv. of Juan Leon Mera (author).

1879. **537.** 5 s. 40 brown, black and light brown .. 30 15
1880. – 6 s. multicoloured .. 40 15

DESIGN: 6 s. Statue of Mera, Ambato.

**1983.** 400th Death Anniv. of St. Theresa of Avila.

1881. **538.** 2 s. multicoloured .. 15 10

**539.** Pres. and Martha Roldos and Independence Monument.

**1983.** Air. 2nd Death Anniv. of President and Martha Roldos.

1882. **539.** 13 s. 60 multicoloured 35 35

**540.** Californian Sealions.

**541.** Statue of Rocafuerte in Guayaquil.

**1983.** 150th Anniv. of Ecuadorian Rule over Galapagos Islands and Death Centenary of Charles Darwin (evolutionary biologist). Multicoloured.

1883. 3 s. Type **540** .. .. 10 10
1884. 5 s. James's Flamingoes and inset portrait of Darwin .. .. 1·75 45

**1983.** Birth Bicentenary of Vicente Rocafuerte Bejarano (President, 1835–39). Mult.

1885. 5 s. Type **541** .. .. 20 10
1886. 20 s. Painting of Rocafuerte .. .. .. 45 35

**542.** Bolivar (after Antonio Salguero).

**543.** Long-distance View of Daniel Palacios Dam.

**1983.** Birth Bicent. of Simon Bolivar.

1887. **542.** 20 s. multicoloured .. 45 35

**1983.** Inauguration of First Stage of Paute Hydro-electric Project. Multicoloured.

1888. 5 s. Type **543** .. .. 20 10
1889. 10 s. Close-up of dam .. 40 15

**544.** W.C.Y. Emblem.

**545.** Bolivar and Bananas.

**1983.** World Communications Year.

1891. **544.** 2 s. multicoloured .. 10 10

**1983.** Centenaries of Provinces of Bolivar and El Oro.

1892. **545.** 3 s. multicoloured .. 10 10

**546.** Atahualpa.

**547.** "Holy Family".

**1984.** 450th Death Anniv (1983) of Atahualpa (last Inca emperor).

1893. **546.** 15 s. multicoloured .. 20 10

**1984.** Christmas. Multicoloured.

1894 5 s. Type **547** .. .. 10 10
1895 5 s. Jesus and the lawyers 10 10
1896 5 s. Marzipan kings .. 10 10
1897 6 s. Marzipan preacher (vert) .. .. .. 10 10

**548.** Visit to Brazil.

**1984.** President Hurtado's International Policies. Multicoloured.

1898 8 s. Type **548** .. .. 10 10
1899 9 s. Visit to China .. 15 10
1900 24 s. Addressing U.N. General Assembly .. 15 10
1901 28 s. Meeting President Reagan of U.S.A. .. 20 15
1902 29 s. Visit to Caracas, Venezuela, for Bolivar's birth bicentenary .. 45 15
1903 37 s. Opening Latin-American Economic Conference, Quito .. 60 20

**549.** Diaz and Scales.

**1984.** Birth Centenary of Miguel Diaz Cueva (lawyer).

1904. **549.** 10 s. multicoloured .. 25 10

**550.** Games Emblem.

**551.** Montgolfier Balloon.

**1984.** Winter Olympic Games, Sarajevo. Multicoloured.

1905 2 s. Type **550** .. .. 10 10
1906 4s . Ice skating .. .. 10 10
1907 6 s. Ice skating (different) 15 10
1908 10 s. Skiing .. .. 15 10

**1984.** Bicent of Manned Fight (1983). Mult.

1910 3 s. Type **551** .. .. 10 10
1911 6 s. Charles's hydrogen balloon .. .. 20 10

**552.** La Marimba (dance).

**1984.** "San Mateo '83" Provincial Stamp Exhibition, Esmeraldas.

1913 **552** 8 s. multicoloured .. 10 10

**553.** Language Academy.

**554.** Yerovi.

**1984.** Canonization of Brother Miguel. Mult.

1915 9 s. Type **553** .. .. 10 10
1916 24 s. Pope, St. Miguel and St. Peter's, Rome (vert) 35 25

**1984.** 165th Birth Anniv of Jose Maria de Jesus Yerovi, Archbishop of Quito.

1918 **554** 5 s. multicoloured .. 15 10

**555.** Pope's Arms.

**556.** Mercedes de Jesus Molina.

**1985.** Visit of Pope John Paul II. Mult.

1919 1 s. 60 Type **555** .. .. 10 10
1920 5 s. Pope holding crucifix 10 10
1921 9 s. Map of papal route .. 15 10
1922 28 s. Pope waving .. 35 20
1923 29 s. Pope .. .. 40 20

**1985.** Beatification of Mercedes de Jesus Molina. Multicoloured.

1925. 1 s. 60 Type **556** .. 10 10
1926. 5 s. "Madonna of Czestochowa" (icon) .. 10 10
1927. 9 s. "Our Lady of La Alborada" (statue) .. 10 10

**557.** Hummingbird.

**558.** Exhibition Emblem.

**1985.** Samuel Valarezo Delgado (ornithologist and former Director of Posts).

1929. **557.** 2 s. red, grn. & brn. 50 10
1930. – 3 s. grn., yell. and bl. 10 10
1931. – 6 s. black and brown 10 10

DESIGNS: 3 s. Swordfish and tunnyfish. 6 s. Valarezo Delgado.

**1985.** "Espana 84" International Stamp Exhibition, Madrid.

1932. **558.** 6 s. brn. & cinnamon 10 10
1933. – 10 s. brown and cinnamon .. .. 15 10

DESIGN: 10 s. Spanish royal family.

**559.** Dr. Pio Jaramallo Alvarado.

**560.** Sugar Cane and Water Tower.

**1985.** Death Centenary (1984) of Dr. Pio Jaramallo Alvardo (historian).

1935. **559.** 6 s. multicoloured .. 15 10

**1985.** Centenary of Valdez Sugar Refinery. Multicoloured.

1936. 50 s. Type **560** .. .. 60 25
1937. 100 s. Rafael Valdez Cervantes (founder) .. 1·25 50

**561.** Emblem.

**1985.** 10th Anniv. of Chamber of Commerce.

1939. **561.** 24 s. multicoloured .. 30 20
1940. 28 s. multicoloured .. 35 25

**562.** Emblem.

**1985.** 50th Anniv. of Ecuador Philatelic Association. Multicoloured.

1942 25 s. Type **562** .. .. 30 15
1943 30 s. Philatelic Exhibition 1 s. stamp, 1936 (horiz) 35 20

**563.** Fire Engine, 1882.

**564.** Children and Tree.

**1985.** 150th Anniv. of Guayaquil Fire Station. Multicoloured.

1944 6 s. Type **563** .. .. 10 10
1945 10 s. Fire-engine, 1899 .. 10 10
1946 20 s. Fire service anniversary emblem .. 20 10

**1985.** Infant Survival Campaign.

1947. **564.** 10 s. multicoloured .. 10 10

**565.** Israeli Aircraft Industry Kfir-C2.

**566.** Boxer.

**1985.** Armed Forces. Multicoloured.

1948 10 s. Type **565** (65th anniv of Air Force) .. .. 30 10
1949 10 s. Seaman and gunboat "Calderon" (centenary of Navy) .. .. 50 20
1950 10 s. Insignia (30th anniv of Parachute Regiment) 35 25

**1985.** Bolivar Games, Cuenca. Each silver, blue and red.

1951. 10 s. Type **566** .. .. 15 10
1952. 25 s. Gymnast .. .. 30 20
1953. 30 s. Discus thrower .. 35 25

**567.** "Royal Audience Quarter, Quito" (J. M. Roura).

**568.** U.N. Emblem.

**1985.** First National Philatelic Congress and "50th Anniv. of Ecuador Philatelic Association" Stamp Exhibition, Quito.

1954. **567.** 5 s. blk., yell. & orge. 10 10
1955. – 10 s. blk., grn. & red 20 10
1956. – 15 s. blk., bl. & red 20 10
1957. – 20 s. blk., red & lilac 30 15

DESIGNS—VERT. 10 s. "Riobamba Cathedral" (O. Munoz). HORIZ. 15 s. "House of a Hundred Windows, Guayaquil" (J. M. Roura). 20 s. "Rural House, near Cuenca" (J. M. Roura).

**1985.** 40th Anniv. of U.N.O. Multicoloured.

1959 10 s. Type **568** .. .. 15 10
1960 20 s. State flag .. .. 30 15

**569.** Child on Donkey.

**570.** "Embotrium grandiforum".

**1985.** Christmas. Multicoloured.

1962. 5 s. Type **569** .. .. 10 10
1963. 10 s. Food display .. 15 10
1964. 15 s. Child seated upon display .. .. 20 10

**1986.** Flowers. Multicoloured.

1966. 24 s. Type **570** .. .. 35 15
1967. 28 s. Orchid ("Topobea" sp.) .. .. .. 35 15
1968. 29 s. "Befaria resinosa mutis" .. .. .. 35 15

**571.** Land Iguana.

**1986.** Galapagos Islands. Multicoloured.

1970 10 s. Type **571** .. .. 15 10
1971 20 s. Californian sealion .. 25 15
1972 30 s. Magnificent frigate birds .. .. .. 1·75 40
1973 40 s. Galapagos penguins 2·00 70
1974 50 s. Tortoise (25th anniv (1984) of Charles Darwin Foundation .. 60 30
1975 100 s. Charles Darwin (150th anniv (1985) of visit) .. 2·00 90
1976 200 s. Bishop Tomas de Berlanga and map (450th anniv (1985) of Islands' discovery) .. 2·10 1·40

**572.** Antonio Ortiz Mena (President). **573.** Andres Gomez Santos.

**1986.** 25th Anniv. (1985) of Inter-American Development Bank. Multicoloured.

1978. 5 s. Type **572** .. .. 10 10
1979. 10 s. Felipe Herrera (President, 1960–71) .. 15 10
1980. 50 s. Emblem .. .. 75 30

**1986.** 75th Anniv. (1985) of Guayaquil Tennis Club. Multicoloured.

1981. 10 s. Type **573** .. .. 15 10
1982. 10 s. Francisco Segura Cano .. .. .. 15 10
1983. 10 s. Emblem (horiz.) .. 15 10

**574.** Prawn.

**1986.** Exports. Seafoods.

1984. **574.** 35 s. red and blue .. 35 20
1985. – 40 s. green and red .. 40 20
1986. – 45 s. yellow & mauve 45 25

Designs: 40 s. Tuna fish. 45 s. Sardines in tin.

**575.** Goalkeeper diving for Ball.

**1986.** World Cup Football Championship, Mexico. Multicoloured.

1988. 5 s. Type **575** .. .. 10 10
1989. 10 s. Player tackling .. 15 10

**576.** Betancourt and Cordero.

**1986.** Rumichaca Meeting of Pres. Belisario Betancourt of Colombia and Pres. Leon Febres Cordero of Ecuador. Multicoloured.

1991. 20 s. Type **576** .. .. 20 15
1992. 20 s. Presidents embracing .. .. 20 15

**577.** Charles-Marie de La Condamine.

**1986.** 250th Anniv. of First Geodetic Expedition (to measure Arcs of Meridian).

1993. **577.** 10 s. green and light green .. .. 15 10
1994. – 15 s. violet and lilac 15 10
1995. – 20 s. green & brown 20 10

Designs: No. 1994, Maldonado. 1995, Centre of World Monument, Quito.

**578.** Emblem of Pichincha Chamber of Trade. **579.** National Railways Emblem.

**1986.** 50th Anniversaries of Chambers of Trade.

1997. **578.** 10 s. black and brn. 10 10
1998. – 10 s. black and blue 10 10
1999. – 10 s. black and green 10 10

Designs: No. 1998, Cuenca. 1999, Guayaquil.

**1986.** 57th Anniv. of Ministry of Public Works and Communications. Multicoloured.

2000. 5 s Type **579** .. .. 10 10
2001. 10 s. Post Office emblem 10 10
2002. 15 s. IETEL (telecommunications) emblem 15 10
2003. 20 s. Ministry of Public Works emblem .. 20 15

**580.** Emblem. **581.** Vargas.

**1987.** 50th Anniv. of First Zone Chamber of Agriculture.

2004. **580.** 5 s. multicoloured .. 10 10

**1988.** Death Centenary of Luis Vargas Torres (revolutionary).

2005. **581.** 50 s. black, gold and green .. .. 40 20
2006. – 100 s. blue, gold and red .. .. 1·00 35

Design: No. 2006, Group of soldiers.

**582.** Las Penas Quarter.

**1988.** 450th Anniv of Guayaquil City. Mult.

2008 15 s. Type **582** .. .. 10 10
2009 30 s. Rafael Mendoza Aviles Bridge of National Unity (horiz) 20 10
2010 40 s. Federico de Orellana (founder) (horiz) .. 15 15

**583.** Family within Hands.

**1988.** 60th Anniv. of Social Security Work. Multicoloured.

2011. 50 s. Type **583** .. .. 30 20
2012. 100 s. Anniversary emblem .. .. 55 35

**584.** Yaguarcocha Lake.

**1988.** Death Centenary of Dr. Pedro Moncayo y Esparza (politician). Multicoloured.

2013. 10 s. Type **584** .. .. 10 10
2014. 15 s. Dr. Moncayo .. 10 10
2015. 20 s. Dr. Moncayo's house .. .. .. 10 10

**585.** Junkers F-13 Seaplane.

**1988.** 60th Anniv. of Avianca National Airline. Multicoloured.

2017 10 s. Type **585** .. .. 10 10
2018 20 s. Dornier Wal flying boat .. .. .. 10 10
2019 30 s. Ford "Tin Goose" .. 15 10
2020 40 s. Boeing 247D .. 20 10
2021 50 s. Boeing 720-059D .. 25 15
2022 100 s. Douglas DC-3 .. 45 25
2023 200 s. Boeing 727-200 .. 1·40 50
2024 300 s. Sikorsky S-38 flying boat .. .. .. 2·00 1·00
2025 500 s. Anniversary emblem (vert) .. 3·25 1·60

586 New Building

**1988.** 125th Anniv of San Gabriel College. Multicoloured.

2026 15 s. Type **586** .. .. 10 10
2027 35 s. Door of old building 25 10

587 Institute 588 St. John Bosco

**1988.** 60th Anniv of Military Geographical Institute, Quito. Multicoloured.

2028 25 s. Type **587** .. .. 25 10
2029 50 s. Inside planetarium 35 20
2030 60 s. Anniversary emblem 40 20
2031 500 s. Mural by E. Kingman .. .. 3·25 1·60

**1988.** Centenary of Salesian Brothers in Ecuador and Death Centenary of St. John Bosco (founder). Multicoloured.

2033 10 s. Type **588** .. .. 10 10
2034 50 s. Group of Brothers .. 25 20

589 Dr. Francisco Campos Coello (founder) 590 Bank

**1988.** Cent of Guayaquil Welfare Society.

2036 **589** 15 s. multicoloured .. 10 10
2037 – 20 s. multicoloured .. 10 10
2038 – 45 s. black, silver & bl 10 10

DESIGNS: 20 s. Eduardo M. Arosemena (first Director); 45 s. Emblem;

**1989.** 75th Anniv (1988) of Azuay Bank, Cuenca. Multicoloured.

2040 20 s. Type **590** .. .. 10 10
2041 40 s. Bank (vert) .. .. 10 10

591 Athletics 592 "Bird" (sculpture, Joaquin Tinta)

**1989.** Olympic Games, Seoul (1988). Designs showing Hodori the Tiger (mascot).

2043 10 s. Type **591** .. .. 10 10
2044 20 s. Boxing .. .. 10 10
2045 30 s. Cycling .. .. 10 10
2046 40 s. Shooting .. .. 10 10
2047 100 s. Swimming .. 20 10
2048 200 s. Weightlifting .. 75 20
2049 300 s. Taekwondo .. 1·10 60

**1989.** 50th Anniv of Ruminahui State. Mult.

2051 50 s. Type **592** .. .. 10 10
2052 70 s. Sangolqui church (horiz) .. .. 15 15

593 Dr. Carrion Mora 594 "The Gilt Mirror" (Myrna Baez)

**1989.** Birth Centenary of Dr. Benjamin Carrion Mora (writer). Multicoloured.

2054 50 s. Type **593** .. .. 10 10
2055 70 s. Loja (horiz) .. 15 15
2056 1000 s. Loja university (horiz) .. .. 3·75 1·90

**1989.** 2nd Art Biennale, Cuenca. Mult.

2058 40 s. Type **594** .. .. 10 10
2059 70 s. "Paraguay III" (Carlos Colombino) (vert) .. .. .. 15 15
2060 180 s. "Modulation 892" (Julio Le Parc) (vert) 75 20

595 Ignacio C. Roca Molestina (founding President) 596 Emblems

**1989.** Centenary of Guayaquil Chamber of Commerce. Multicoloured.

2062 50 s. Type **595** .. .. 10 10
2063 300 s. Chamber building (horiz) .. .. 1·10 60
2064 500 s. Trade and progress symbol (horiz) .. 1·90 95

**1989.** 60th Anniv of Ministry of Public Works and Communications. Multicoloured.

2066 50 s. Type **596** .. .. 10 10
2067 100 s. IETEL emblem (telecommunications) 20 10
2068 200 s. Ministry of Public Works emblem .. 75 20

597 Birds 598 Red Cross Worker

**1989.** Bicent of French Revolution. Mult.

2070 20 s. Type **597** .. .. 10 10
2071 50 s. Cathedral fresco (horiz) .. .. 10 10
2072 100 s. French cock .. 20 10

**1989.** 125th Anniv of Red Cross in Ecuador. Multicoloured.

2074 10 s. Type **598** .. .. 10 10
2075 30 s. Emblem (horiz) .. 10 10
2076 200 s. Masked Red Cross workers (horiz) .. 75 20

599 Montalvo's Tomb

**1989.** Death Cent of Juan Montalvo (writer).

2077 50 s. Type **599** .. .. 10 10
2078 100 s. Photograph of Montalvo .. .. 45 10
2079 200 s. Statue of Montalvo 90 45

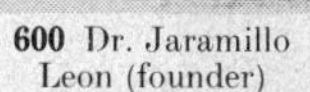

**600** Dr. Jaramillo Leon (founder)
**601** Tolita Head-shaped Censer

**1990.** 70th Anniv of Cuenca Chamber of Commerce. Multicoloured.
2081 100 s. Type **600** .. .. 30 15
2082 100 s. Federico Malo Andrade (first Honorary President) .. 30 15
2083 130 s. Roberto Crespo Toral (first President) 40 20
2084 200 s. Alfonso Jaramillo Leon (founder of savings and credit departments) .. .. 60 25

**1990.** America. Pre-Columbian Artefacts. Multicoloured.
2086 200 s. Type **601** .. .. 25 25
2087 300 s. Carchi plate with warrior design (horiz) 65 20

**602** Mercedes de Jesus Molina
**603** Mascot, Quarter Finalists and Ball

**1990.** Anniversaries. Multicoloured.
2088 100 s. Type **602** (centenary of Marianitas) .. 30 15
2089 200 s. Clock tower and roses on open book (centenary of Santa Mariana de Jesus College) .. .. 60 25

**1990.** World Cup Football Championship, Italy. Multicoloured.
2090 100 s. Type **603** .. .. 30 15
2091 200 s. Finalists' flags and player (vert) .. .. 60 25
2092 300 s. Mascot, map and trophy (vert) .. .. 90 45

**604** Emblem

**1990.** 5th Population Census and 4th Housing Census. Multicoloured.
2094 100 s. Type **604** .. .. 25 10
2095 200 s. Logo of National Statistics and Census Institute (horiz) .. 50 25
2096 300 s. Pencil and population statistics .. 75 20

**605** Iguana (Galapagos)
**606** Members' Flags

**1990.** Tourism. Multicoloured.
2098 100 s. Type **605** .. .. 25 10
2099 200 s. Church of Companionship (Quito) (vert) 50 25
2100 300 s. Old man of Vilcabamba .. .. 75 20

**1990.** 30th Anniv of Organization of Petroleum Exporting Countries. Multicoloured.
2102 200 s. Type **606** .. .. 50 25
2103 300 s. Emblem .. .. 75 20

**607** Anniversary Emblem
**608** "Blakea sp"

**1990.** 25th Anniv of Organization for Preservation of Traditional Handicrafts. Mult.
2104 200 s. Type **607** .. .. 50 25
2105 300 s. Carved and painted parrots .. .. 75 20

**1990.** Flowers. Multicoloured.
2107 100 s. Type **608** .. .. 10 10
2108 100 s. "Loasa sp" .. .. 10 10
2109 100 s. "Cattleya sp" .. .. 10 10
2110 100 s. "Sobralia sp" (horiz) .. .. 10 10

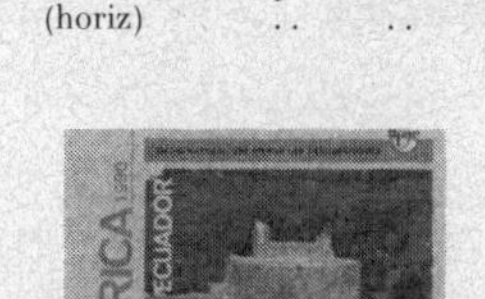


**609** Ingapirca

**1991.** America. World found by the Discoverers. Multicoloured.
2111 100 s. Type **609** .. .. 10 10
2112 200 s. Forest pool .. 50 25

**610** Globe amd Means of Information
**611** Broadcaster

**1991.** 50th Anniv of National Journalists' Federation. Multicoloured.
2113 200 s. Type **610** .. .. 50 25
2114 300 s. Eugenio Espejo .. 75 20
2115 400 s. Emblem .. .. 1·00 50

**1991.** 50th Anniv of Radio Quito. Mult.
2116 200 s. Type **611** .. .. 20 20
2117 500 s. Family listening to radio (horiz) .. .. 90 35

**612** Suarez
**613** Columbus's Ships

**1991.** Birth Cent of Dr. Pablo Arturo Suarez.
2118 **612** 70 s. multicoloured .. 15 10

**1991.** America. Multicoloured.
2119 200 s. Type **613** .. .. 25 25
2120 500 s. Columbus and landing party .. .. 1·10 50

**614** Cat-shaped Censer
**615** Hand and Woman's Face

**1991.** Archaeology. La Tolita Culture (1st series). Multicoloured.
2121 100 s. Type **614** .. .. 10 10
2122 200 s. Head of old man .. 20 10
2123 300 s. Human/animal statuette .. .. 60 20
See also No. 2144.

**1991.** No Violence to Women Day. Mult.
2124 300 s. Type **615** .. .. 60 20
2125 500 s. Woman's profile and hand .. .. 95 30

**616** Presidents Borja and Paz Zamora

**1991.** Visit of President Jaime Paz Zamora of Bolivia.
2126 **616** 500 s. multicoloured .. 95 30

**617** Jijon y Caamano

**1991.** Birth Centenary of Jacinto Jijon y Caamano (historian and geographer).
2127 **617** 200 s. multicoloured 20 10
2128 – 300 s. blue, blk & mve 60 20
DESIGN—HORIZ. 300 s. Books and Jijon y Caamano.

**618** Pres. Borja

**1992.** President Rodrigo Borja's Speech to United Nations. Multicoloured.
2129 100 s. Type **618** .. .. 10 10
2130 1000 s. Map and flags of U.N. Security Council members .. .. 1·60 65

**619** "Calderon" (gunboat) and Rafael Moran Valverde

**1992.** 50th Anniv (1991) of Battle of Jambeli. Multicoloured.
2131 300 s. Type **619** .. .. 50 10
2132 500 s. "Atahualpa" (despatch vessel) and Victor Naranjo Fiallo 85 25

**620** Land Iguana
**621** College

**1992.** Galapagos Islands Animals.
2134 100 s. Type **620** .. .. 15 10
2135 100 s. Giant tortoise .. 15 10
2136 100 s. Swallow-tailed gull 15 10
2137 100 s. Great frigate bird ("Fregata minor") .. 15 10
2138 100 s. Galapagos penguin (vert) .. .. 15 10
2139 100 s. Californian sea-lion (vert) .. .. 15 10

**1992.** 150th Anniv (1991) of Vicente Rocafuerte National College, Guayaquil. Multicoloured.
2140 200 s. Type **621** .. .. 15 10
2141 400 s. Vicente Rocafuerte (Ecuador President 1835–39 and College founder) .. .. 65 15

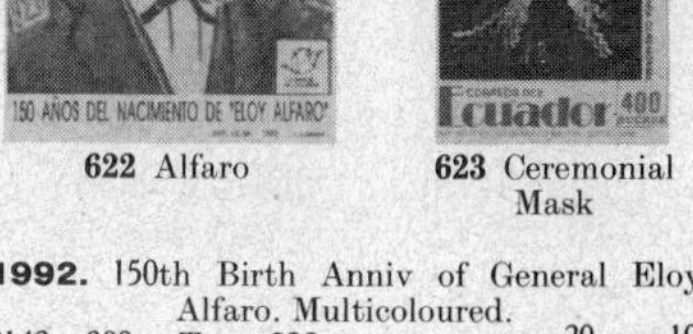

**622** Alfaro
**623** Ceremonial Mask

**1992.** 150th Birth Anniv of General Eloy Alfaro. Multicoloured.
2142 300 s. Type **622** .. .. 20 10
2143 700 s. Alfaro's house (horiz) .. .. 1·00 30

**1992.** Archaeology. La Tolita Culture (2nd series).
2144 **623** 400 s. multicoloured .. 60 15



**624** "Santa Maria"

**1992.** America. 500th Anniv of Discovery of America by Columbus. Multicoloured.
2145 200 s. Type **624** .. .. 15 10
2146 400 s. Columbus and map of Americas (vert) .. 25 15

**625** Cordova
**626** Narcisa de Jesus

**1992.** Birth Centenary of Andres Cordova (President, 1940).
2147 **625** 300 s. multicoloured .. 20 10

**1992.** Beatification of Narcisa de Jesus.
2148 **626** 100 s. multicoloured .. 10 10

**627** Infant Jesus
**628** Velasco (statue)

**1992.** Christmas. Multicoloured.
2149 300 s. Type **627** .. .. 20 10
2150 600 s. Children, lamb and baby Jesus .. .. 40 25

**1992.** Death Bicentenary of Juan de Velasco.
2151 **628** 200 s. multicoloured .. 15 10

**629** "Atelopus bomolochos"
**630** Paez

**1993.** Frogs. Multicoloured.
2152 300 s. Type **629** .. .. 20 10
2153 300 s. Spurrell's tree frog ("Agalychnis spurelli") 20 10
2154 600 s. "Hyla picturata" .. 40 20
2155 600 s. "Gastrotheca plumbea" .. .. 40 20
2156 900 s. Splendid poison-arrow frog ("Dendrobates sp.") .. 60 25
2157 900 s. "Sphaenorhynchus lacteus" .. .. 60 25

**1993.** Birth Centenary of J. Roberto Paez (co-founder of social security system and writer).
2158 **630** 300 s. blue .. .. 20 10

631 1907 3 c. Robles Stamp
632 Arms

**1993.** Death Centenary of Francisco Robles Garcia (President 1856–59).
2159 **631** 500 s. multicoloured .. 35 15

**1993.** National Police.
2160 **632** 300 s. multicoloured .. 20 10

633 Velasco

**1993.** Birth Centenary of Jose Maria Velasco Ibarra (President, 1934–35, 1944–47, 1952–56, 1960–61 and 1968–72).
2161 **633** 500 s. multicolured .. 35 15

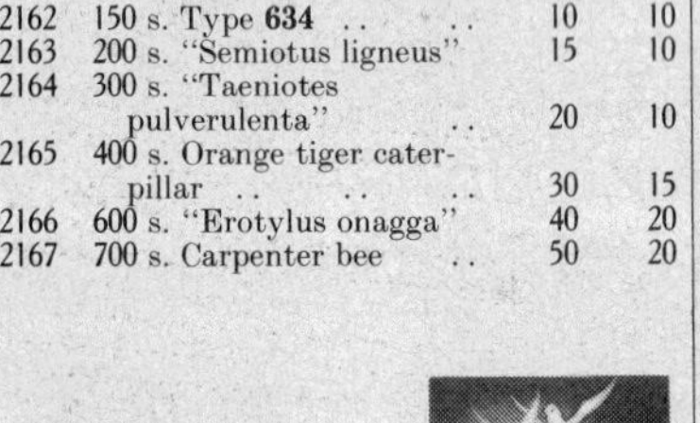

634 Lantern Fly

**1993.** Insects. Multicoloured.
2162 150 s. Type **634** .. .. 10 10
2163 200 s. "Semiotus ligneus" 15 10
2164 300 s. "Taeniotes pulverulenta" .. 20 10
2165 400 s. Orange tiger caterpillar .. .. .. 30 15
2166 600 s. "Erotylus onagga" 40 20
2167 700 s. Carpenter bee .. 50 20

635 Cevallos Villacreces

636 Boy releasing Doves

**1993.** Death Centenary of Pedro Fermin Cevallos Villacreces (historian and founder of Language Academy).
2168 **635** 1000 s. multicoloured 70 30

**1993.** First Latin-American Children's Peace Assembly, Quito.
2169 **636** 300 s. multicoloured .. 20 10

637 Vela Hervas

638 "Cinchonia cordifolia"

**1993.** 150th Birth Anniv of Juan Benigno Vela Hervas (politician).
2170 **637** 2000 s. multicoloured 1·40 60

**1993.** 250th Anniv of Maldonado and La Condamine's Amazon Expedition. Mult.
2171 150 s. Type **638** .. .. 10 10
2172 250 s. Pedro Maldonado 15 10
2173 1500 s. Charles de la Condamine .. .. 1·00 65

639 Anniversary Emblem

**1993.** 300th Anniv of Faculty of Medical Sciences, Ecuador Central University.
2174 **639** 300 s. multicoloured .. 20 10

640 Bustamante

642 Arroyo del Rio

641 Pacarana

**1993.** Birth Centenary of Guillermo Bustamante (writer).
2175 **640** 1500 s. multicoloured 1·00 40

**1993.** America. Endangered Animals. Mult.
2176 400 s. Type **641** .. .. 30 15
2177 800 s. Chestnut-fronted macaw (vert) .. .. 55 25

**1993.** Birth Centenary of Dr. Carlos Arroyo del Rio (President, 1939–44).
2178 **642** 500 s. multicoloured .. 35 15

643 "Nativity" (ivory nut carvings)

644 Scouts Emblem and Map on Wall

**1993.** Christmas. Multicoloured.
2179 600 s. Type **643** .. .. 35 15
2180 900 s. Madonna and Child in landscape (vert) .. 50 20

**1994.** Scouting Movement.
2181 **644** 400 s. multicoloured .. 20 10

645 Emblem

646 Donoso

**1994.** International Year of the Family.
2182 **645** 300 s. red, green & blk 15 10

**1994.** Birth Cent of Dr. Julio Tobar Donoso.
2183 **646** 500 s. multicoloured .. 30 15

647 "Sobralia dichotoma"

648 Cabezas

**1994.** 1st Andean Orchid Conservation Convention. Multicoloured.
2184 150 s. Type **647** .. .. 10 10
2185 150 s. "Dracula hirtzii" .. 10 10
2186 300 s. "Encyclia pulcherrima" .. .. 15 10
2187 300 s. "Lepanthes delhierroi" .. .. 15 10
2188 600 s. "Masdevallia rosea" 35 15
2189 600 s. "Telipogon andicola" .. .. 35 15

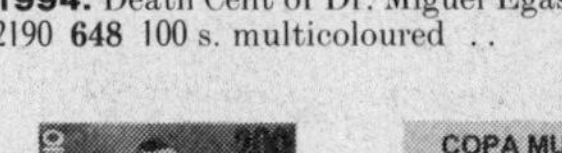

**1994.** Death Cent of Dr. Miguel Egas Cabezas.
2190 **648** 100 s. multicoloured .. 10 10

649 Gonzalez Suarez

650 Earth as Football

**1994.** 150th Birth Anniv of Federico Gonzalez Suarez, Archbishop of Quito.
2191 **649** 200 s. multicoloured .. 10 10

**1994.** World Cup Football Championship, U.S.A. Multicoloured.
2192 300 s. Type **650** .. .. 15 10
2193 600 s. Striker (mascot) .. 35 15
2194 900 s. Footballer .. 50 20

651 Cyclists on "Road" of National Colours to Equator Monument

652 Espinosa Polit

**1994.** International Junior Cycling Championship, Quito. Multicoloured.
2196 300 s. Type **651** .. .. 15 10
2197 400 s. Stylized cyclist and monument (vert) .. 20 10

**1994.** Birth Centenary of Father Aurelio Espinosa Polit (writer).
2198 **652** 200 s. multicoloured .. 10 10

653 Pedro Vicente Maldonado Research Station

**1994.** Ecuador's Presence in Antarctica. Multicoloured.
2199 600 s. Type **653** .. .. 35 15
2200 900 s. "Orion" (survey ship) .. .. .. 50 20

654 Anniversary Emblem

**1994.** Centenary of National Lottery.
2201 **654** 1000 s. multicoloured 45 20

655 Benjamon Carrion (founder)

**1994.** 50th Anniv of House of Ecuadorean Culture. Multicoloured.
2202 700 s. Type **655** .. .. 30 15
2203 900 s. House of Culture (horiz) .. .. 40 20

656 Worker and "75"

**1994.** 75th Anniv of I.L.O.
2204 **656** 100 s. multicoloured .. 10 10

657 Globe and Postal Emblem

**1994.** Christmas. Multicoloured.
2205 600 s. Type **657** .. .. 25 10
2206 900 s. Nativity (vert) 40 20

658 Airplane and Sack of Mail

659 Mera's Country Villa

**1994.** America. Postal Transport. Mult.
2207 600 s. Type **658** .. .. 25 10
2208 600 s. Airplane, ship and van (horiz) .. .. 25 10

**1994.** Death Centenary of Juan Leon Mera (author). Multicoloured.
2209 600 s. Type **659** .. 25 10
2210 900 s. Mera (after Victor Mideros) .. .. 40 20

660 Sucre

**1995.** Birth Bicent of Marshal Antonio Jose de Sucre (first Bolivian President). Mult.
2211 1500 s. Type **660** .. 65 30
2212 2000 s. Sucre (looking to left) .. .. .. 90 40

661 Escriva

663 Girl

662 Eloy Alfaro (President 1897–1901 and 1907–11)

**1995.** 3rd Anniv of Beatification of Josemaria Escriva de Balaguer (founder of Opus Dei).
2214 **661** 900 s. multicoloured .. 40 20

**1995.** Centenary of Alfarist Revolution.
2215 **662** 800 s. multicoloured .. 35 15

**1995.** 50th Anniv of CARE (Co-operative for Assistance and Remittances Overseas).
2216 **663** 400 s. blk, grn & gold 20 10
2217 – 800 s. multicoloured 35 15
DESIGN—HORIZ: 800 s. People working land.

**664** Soldier thinking of Children

**1995.** "Peace with Dignity". Multicoloured.
2218 200 s. Type **664** .. .. 10 10
2219 400 s. Hand holding Ecuador flag (25 × 34 mm) .. .. 20 10
2220 800 s. Soldier amongst bamboo .. .. 35 15

**665** Anniversary Emblem

**666** "Our Lady of Cisne" (statue, Diego de Robles)

**1995.** 25th Anniv of Andean Development Corporation.
2221 **665** 1000 s. multicoloured 45 20

**1995.**
2222 **666** 500 s. multicoloured .. 20 10

**667** Anniversary Emblem

**668** Anniversary Emblem

**1995.** 35th Anniv of INNFA (child welfare organization).
2223 **667** 400 s. multicoloured .. 20 10

**1995.** 50th Anniv of U.N.O.
2224 **668** 1000 s. blue, gold & blk 45 20

**669** Man with Book (preparation for natural disasters)

**1995.** International Decade for the Reduction of Natural Disasters. Ecuador Civil Defence Organization. Multicoloured.
2225 1000 s. Type **669** .. 45 20
2226 1000 s. Family hiding beneath table (protection) .. .. 45 20
2227 1000 s. Couple escaping from flooded house (maintenance of elevated refugee centres) .. .. 45 20
2228 1000 s. Children planting sapling (reforestation) 45 20
2229 1000 s. Family escaping erupting volcano (awareness of warning signs) .. .. .. 45 20

**670** Emblem

**1995.** 50th Anniv of F.A.O.
2230 **670** 1300 s. multicoloured 55 25

**671** Woman, Piano and Book

**1995.** 50th Anniv of Women's Cultural Club.
2231 **671** 1500 s. multicoloured 55 25

**672** Emblem

**1995.** 39th Annual Assembly of Interamerican Philately Federation.
2232 **672** 1000 s. blue and red .. 35 15

**673** Combat Planes flying over Mountains

**674** Long-tailed Sylphs ("Aglaiocercus kingi")

**1995.** 75th Anniv of Ecuadorean Air Force.
2233 **673** 1000 s. multicoloured 35 15

**1995.** Hummingbirds. Multicoloured.
2234 1000 s. Type **674** .. 35 15
2235 1000 s. Collared incas ("Coeligena torquata") 35 15
2236 1000 s. Long-tailed hermits ("Phaethornis superciliosus") .. 35 15
2237 1000 s. Booted racquet-tails ("Ocreatus underwoodii") .. 35 15
2238 1000 s. Chimbarazo hillstars ("Oreotrochilus chimborazo") .. 35 15
2239 1000 s. Violet-tailed sylphs ("Aglaiocercus coelestis") .. .. 35 15

**675** "World Post" (Gishella Alejandro Reyes)

**676** Jaramillo

**1995.** Christmas. Children's Painting Competition Winners. Multicoloured.
2240 2000 s. Type **675** .. 75 30
2241 2600 s. "Procession" (Juan Jaramillo Leon) .. 95 40

**1996.** National Music Year. 60th Birth Anniv of Julio Jaramillo (singer and composer). Multicoloured.
2242 **676** 2000 s. multicoloured 75 30

EXPRESS LETTER STAMPS

**1928.** Oblong Tobacco Tax stamp surch. **CORREOS EXPRESO** and new value.
E 457. 2 c. on 2 c. blue .. 3·00 3·50
E 458. 5 c. on 2 c. blue .. 2·75 3·50
E 459. 10 c. on 2 c. blue .. 2·75 2·25
E 460. 20 c. on 2 c. blue .. 3·75 3·50
E 461. 50 c. on 2 c. blue .. 4·50 3·50

**1945.** Surch. **EXPRESO 20 Ctvs.**
E 742. **194.** 20 c. on 5 c. green 15 10

LATE FEE STAMP

**1945.** Surch **U. H. 10 Ctvs.**
L742 **194** 10 c. on 5 c. green .. 10 10

OFFICIAL STAMPS

**1886.** Stamps of 1881 optd. **OFICIAL.**
O 20 **5** 1 c. brown .. .. 60 60
O 21 2 c. red .. .. 75 75
O 22 5 c. blue .. .. 1·50 1·90
O 23 10 c. orange .. .. 1·10 70
O 24 20 c. violet .. .. 1·10 1·10
O 25 50 c. green .. .. 3·25 2·75

**1887.** Stamps of 1887 optd. **OFICIAL.**
O 30 **13** 1 c. green .. .. 75 10
O 31 2 c. red .. .. 75 10
O 32 5 c. blue .. .. 1·10 50
O 33 80 c. green .. .. 3·75 2·25

**1892.** Stamps of 1892 optd. **FRANQUEO OFICIAL.**
O 42. **15.** 1 c. blue .. .. 10 15
O 43. 2 c. blue .. .. 10 15
O 44. 5 c. blue .. .. 10 15
O 45. 10 c. blue .. .. 10 10
O 46. 20 c. blue .. .. 10 10
O 47. 50 c. blue .. .. 10 25
O 48. 1 s. blue .. .. 20 25

**1894.** Stamps of 1894 (dated "1894") optd. **FRANQUEO OFICIAL.**
O 65. **20.** 1 c. grey .. .. 25 25
O 66. 2 c. grey .. .. 25 25
O 67. 5 c. grey .. .. 25 25
O 68. 10 c. grey .. .. 10 20
O 69. 20 c. grey .. .. 30 35
O 70. 50 c. grey .. .. 75 75
O 71. 1 s. grey .. .. 1·10 1·10
This series was re-issued in 1897 optd. "1897–1898".

**1894.** Postal Fiscals as Type **F 1** but dated "1891-1892", optd. **OFICIAL 1894 y 1895.**
O 72 **F 1** 1c. grey .. .. 6·25 4·00
O 73 2 c. red .. .. 6·25 4·00

**1895.** Stamps of 1895 (dated "1895") optd. **FRANQUEO OFICIAL.**
O 82. **20.** 1 c. grey .. .. 1·10 1·10
O 83. 2 c. grey .. .. 1·60 1·60
O 84. 5 c. grey .. .. 25 25
O 85. 10 c. grey .. .. 1·60 1·60
O 86. 20 c. grey .. .. 2·75 2·75
O 87. 50 c. grey .. .. 6·75 6·75
O 88. 1 s. grey .. .. 75 75
This series was re-issued in 1897 optd. "1897–1898".

**1896.** Stamps of 1896 optd. **FRANQUEO OFICIAL** in oval.
O 97. **22.** 1 c. bistre .. .. 20 15
O 98. 2 c. bistre .. .. 20 15
O 99. 5 c. bistre .. .. 25 15
O 100. 10 c. bistre .. .. 25 15
O 101. 20 c. bistre .. .. 25 15
O 102. 50 c. bistre .. .. 25 15
O 103. 1 s. bistre .. .. 50 35
O 104. 5 s. bistre .. .. 85 80

**F 10.**

**O 245.** Government Building, Quito.

**1898.** Fiscal stamps as Type **F 10,** surch. **CORREOS OFICIAL** and value in frame.
O 181. **F 10.** 5 c. on 50 c. purple 15 15
O 184. 10 c. on 20 s. orange 40 40
O 185. 20 c. on 50 c. purple 1·25 1·25
O 187. 20 c. on 50 s. green 1·25 1·25

**1899.** Stamps as 1899 optd. **OFICIAL.**
O 201. 2 c. black and orange 25 55
O 202. 10 c. black and orange 25 55
O 203. 20 c. black and orange 25 85
O 204. 50 c. black and orange 25 1·10

**1913.** Stamps of 1911 (except No. O 396) optd. **OFICIAL.**
O 374. **90.** 1 c. black and red .. 50 50
O 387. 1 c. orange .. 10 15
O 388. **91.** 2 c. black and blue .. 55 55
O 424. 2 c. green .. 15 15
O 368. **92.** 3 c. black and orange 25 25
O 390. 3 c. black .. 20 15
O 437. **98.** 4 c. black and red .. 15 15
O 369. **93.** 5 c. black and red .. 70 50
O 393. 5 c. violet .. 25 10
O 370. **94.** 10 c. black and blue 70 55
O 395. 10 c. blue .. 10 10
O 396. – 20 c. black and green (No. 328) .. 1·50 60
O 429. **95.** 1 s. black and green .. 1·90 1·90

**1920.** Stamps of 1920 (Nos. 381/400) optd. **OFICIAL.**
O 401. **108.** 1 c. green .. .. 40 40
O 402. – 2 c. red .. .. 30 30
O 403. – 3 c. bistre .. .. 30 30
O 404. – 4 c. green .. .. 10 10
O 405. – 5 c. blue .. .. 10 10
O 406. – 6 c. orange .. .. 40 40
O 407. – 7 c. brown .. .. 60 60
O 408. – 8 c. green .. .. 75 75
O 409. – 9 c. red .. .. 95 95
O 410. **109.** 10 c. blue .. .. 60 60
O 411. – 15 c. black .. .. 3·00 3·00
O 412. – 20 c. purple .. .. 3·75 3·75
O 413. – 30 c. violet .. .. 4·50 4·50
O 414. – 40 c. sepia .. .. 6·25 6·25
O 415. – 50 c. green .. .. 3·75 3·75
O 416. – 60 c. blue .. .. 4·50 4·50
O 417. – 70 c. grey .. .. 4·50 4·50
O 418. – 80 c. yellow .. .. 5·75 5·75
O 419. – 90 c. green .. .. 6·25 6·25
O 420. – 1 s. blue .. .. 11·50 11·50

**1924.** Fiscal stamps of 1919 optd. **OFICIAL.**
O 421. **103.** 1 c. blue .. .. 60 60
O 422. 2 c. green .. .. 3·25 3·25

**1924.** No. O 204 optd. **Acuerdo No. 4,223.**
O 430. 50 c. black and orange 70 70

**1925.** Stamps of 1925 optd. **OFICIAL.**
O 457. **90.** 1 c. blue .. .. 30 30
O 439. **93.** 5 c. red .. .. 15 15
O 440. **94.** 10 c. green .. .. 10 10

**1928.** Stamp of 1927 optd. **OFICIAL.**
O 463. **123.** 20 c. purple .. .. 1·10 75

**1929.** Official Air stamps. Air stamps of 1929 optd. **OFICIAL.**
O 466. **130.** 2 c. black .. .. 40 40
O 467. 5 c. red .. .. 40 40
O 468. 10 c. brown .. .. 40 40
O 469. 20 c. purple .. .. 40 40
O 470. 50 c. green .. .. 95 95
O 474. 50 c. brown .. .. 75 85
O 471. 1 s. blue .. .. 95 95
O 475. 1 s. red .. .. 1·10 1·10
O 472. 5 s. yellow .. .. 4·50 3·75
O 476. 5 s. olive .. .. 2·25 2·25
O 473. 10 s. red .. .. 50·00 38·00
O 477. 10 s. black .. .. 5·75 5·75

**1936.** Stamps of 1936 (Nos. 520/4) optd. **OFICIAL.**
O 525. 5 c. olive .. .. 15 10
O 526. 10 c. brown .. .. 15 10
O 527. 20 c. purple .. .. 1·10 30
O 528. 1 s. red .. .. 25 20
O 529. 2 s. blue .. .. 40 60

**1937.** Stamps of 1937 optd. **OFICIAL.**
O 562. **171.** 2 c. green (postage) .. 10 10
O 563. – 5 c. red .. .. 10 10
O 564. – 10 c. blue .. .. 10 10
O 565. – 20 c. red .. .. 10 10
O 566. – 1 s. olive .. .. 10 10
O 567. **172.** 10 c. brown (air) .. 40 15
O 568. 20 c. olive .. .. 40 15
O 569. 70 c. brown .. .. 40 15
O 570. 1 s. slate .. .. 55 20
O 571. 2 s. violet .. .. 80 25

**1941.** Air stamp of 1939 optd. **OFICIAL.**
O 638. **184.** 5 s. green .. .. 60 60

**1946.** Oblong Tobacco Tax stamp optd. **CORRESPONDENCIA OFICIAL.** Roul.
O 803. 1 c. red .. .. 40 60

**1947.**
O 804. **O 245.** 30 c. blue .. 20 10
O 805. 30 c. brown .. 20 10
O 806. 30 c. violet .. 20 10

**1964.** Air. Nos. 1269/71 optd. **Oficial.**
O 1272. **342.** 50 c. multicoloured 70 70
O 1273. – 80 c. red. bl. & yell. 70 70
O 1274. – 1 s. 30 multicoloured 70 70

**1964.** No. 1272 optd. **oficial** on each stamp.
O 1275. **344.** 80 c. green and lake 1·50 30
The "OEA" overprint is across four stamps, the "oficial" overprint is on each stamp.
The unused price is for a block of four.

POSTAGE DUE STAMPS

D 32.

D 131.

**1896.**
D 105. **D 32.** 1 c. green .. .. 1·50 1·50
D 106. 2 c. green .. .. 1·50 1·50
D 107. 5 c. green .. .. 1·50 1·50
D 108. 10 c. green .. .. 1·90 2·25
D 109. 20 c. green .. .. 1·90 3·00
D 110. 50 c. green .. .. 1·50 3·75
D 111. 100 c. green .. .. 1·50 3·00

**1929.**

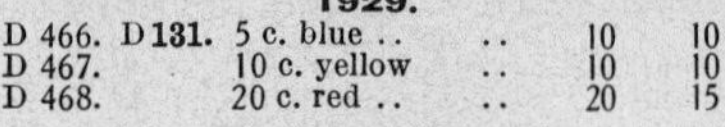

| | | | | |
|---|---|---|---|---|
| D 466. | D131. | 5 c. blue .. .. | 10 | 10 |
| D 467. | | 10 c. yellow .. | 10 | 10 |
| D 468. | | 20 c. red .. .. | 20 | 15 |

D 335.

**1958.**

| | | | | |
|---|---|---|---|---|
| D 1128. | D335. | 10 c. violet .. | 10 | 10 |
| D 1129. | | 50 c. green .. | 10 | 10 |
| D 1130. | | 1 s. brown .. | 15 | 10 |
| D 1131. | | 2 s. red .. .. | 25 | 15 |

## APPENDIX

The following stamps have either been issued in excess of postal needs or have not been available to the public in reasonable quantities at face value. Such stamps may later be given full listing if there is evidence of regular postal use.

**1966.**

Cent. of I.T.U. Postage 10, 10, 80 c.; Air 1 s. 50, 3, 4 s.

Space Achievements. Postage 10 c., 1 s.; Air 1 s. 30, 2 s., 2 s. 50, 3 s. 50.

Dante and Galileo. Postage 10, 80 c.; Air 2, 3 s.

Pope Paul VI. Postage 10 c.; Air 1 s. 30, 3 s. 50.

Famous Persons. Postage 10 c., 1 s.; Air 1 s. 50, 2 s. 50, 4 s.

Olympic Games. Postage 10, 10, 80 c.; Air 1 s. 30, 3 s., 3 s. 50.

Winter Olympics. Postage 10 c., 1 s.; Air 1 s. 50, 2 s., 2 s. 50, 4 s.

Franco-American Space Research. Postage 10 c.; Air 1 s. 50, 4 s.

Italian Space Research. Postage 10 c.; Air 1 s. 30, 3 s. 50.

Exploration of the Moon's Surface. Postage 10, 80 c., 1 s.; Air 2 s., 2 s. 50, 3 s.

**1967.**

Olympic Games, Mexico. Postage 10 c., 1 s.; Air 1 s. 30, 2 s., 2 s. 50, 3 s. 50.

Olympic Games, Mexico. Postage 10, 10, 80 c.; Air 1 s. 50, 3, 4 s.

Eucharistic Conference. Postage 10, 60, 80 c., 1 s.; Air 1 s. 50, 2 s.

Paintings of the Madonna. Postage 10, 40, 50 c.; Air 1 s. 30, 2 s. 50, 3 s.

Famous Paintings. Postage 10 c., 1 s.; Air 1 s. 50, 2 s., 2 s. 50, 4 s.

50th Birth Anniv. of J. F. Kennedy. Postage 10, 10, 80 c.; Air 1 s. 30, 3 s., 3 s. 50.

Christmas Postage 10, 10, 40, 50, 60 c.; Air 2 s. 50.

**1968.**

Religious Paintings and Sculptures. Postage 10, 80 c., 1 s.; Air 1 s. 30, 1 s. 50, 2 s.

COTAL Tourist Organization Congress. Postage 20, 30, 40, 50, 60, 80 c., 1 s.; Air 1 s. 30, 1 s. 50, 2 s.

**1969.**

Visit of Pope Paul VI to Latin America. Postage 40, 40 c.; Air 1 s. 30.

39th Int. Eucharistic Congress, Bogota. Postage 1 s.; Air 2 s.

Paintings of the Virgin Mary. Postage 40, 60 c., 1 s.; Air 1 s. 30, 2 s.

## EGYPT Pt. 19

Formerly a kingdom of N.E. Africa. Turkish till 1914, when it became a British Protectorate. Independent from 1922. A republic from 1953.

In 1958 the United Arab Republic was formed, comprising Egypt and Syria, but separate stamps continued to be issued for each territory as they have different currencies. In 1961 Syria became an independent Arab republic and left the U.A.R. but the title was retained by Egypt until a new federation was formed with Libya and Syria in 1971, when the country's name was changed to Arab Republic of Egypt.

1866. 40 paras = 1 piastre.
1888. 1000 milliemes = 1 piastre.
100 piastres = £1 Egyptian.

1.

4.

**1866.** Designs as T 1. Imperf or perf.

1 1 5 pa. grey .. .. 32·00 24·00
2 10 pa. brown .. .. 50·00 28·00
3 20 pa. blue .. .. 70·00 27·00
4 1 pi. purple .. .. 55·00 4·25
5 2 pi. yellow .. .. 90·00 40·00
6 5 pi. pink .. .. £250 £170
7 10 pi. grey .. .. £275 £250

**1867.**

11. 4. 5 pa. yellow .. .. 20·00 7·50
12b. 10 pa. violet .. .. 42·00 8·50
13 20 pa. green .. .. £100 13·00
14. 1 pi. red .. .. 10·00 90
15. 2 pi. blue .. .. £110 14·00
16. 5 pi. brown .. .. £300 £180

On the piastre values the letters "P" and "E" appear on the upper corners.

7.

10.

**1872.**

28 7 5 pa. brown .. .. 7·00 4·50
29 10 pa. mauve .. .. 6·00 3·00
37 20 pa. blue .. .. 8·00 2·50
38 1 pi. red .. .. .. 4·25 65
39 2 pi. yellow .. .. 5·50 4·75
40 2½ pi. violet .. .. 8·50 5·00
41 5 pi. green .. .. 55·00 19·00

**1875.** As T 7, but "PARA" inscr. left-hand side and figure "5" inverted.

35. – 5 pa. brown .. .. 6·00 3·25

**1879.** Surch. in English and Arabic.

42. 7. 5 pa on 2½ pi. violet .. 6·00 6·00
43. 10 pa. on 2½ pi. violet .. 10·00 10·00

**1879.** Various frames.

44a 10 5 pa. brown .. .. 1·00 15
45 10 pa. lilac .. .. 50·00 3·00
50 10 pa. purple .. .. 48·00 4·75
51 10 pa. grey .. .. 6·50 1·75
52 10 pa. green .. .. 70 40
46 20 pa. blue .. .. 80·00 1·75
53 20 pa. red .. .. 9·50 55
47 1 pi. pink .. .. 24·00 10
54b 1 pi. blue .. .. 2·25 10
55a 2 pi. brown .. .. 12·00 10
55ab 2 pi. orange .. .. 20·00 1·00
49a 5 pi. green .. .. 55·00 6·00
56a 5 pi. grey .. .. 11·00 40

**1884.** Surch **20 PARAS** in English and Arabic.

57 10 20 pa. on 5 pi. green .. 7·00 1·25

18.

**1888.** Various frames.

58b 18 1 m. brown .. .. 45 10
59 2 m. green .. .. 60 10
60 3 m. purple .. .. 2·25 1·00
61ab 3 m. yellow .. .. 2·00 10
62 4 m. red .. .. 85 10
63 5 m. red .. .. 1·25 10
64 10 pi. mauve .. .. 15·00 80

**HAVE YOU READ THE NOTES AT THE BEGINNING OF THIS CATALOGUE?**
These often provide answers to the enquiries we receive.

29. Nile Feluccas.

35. Pylon of Karnak Temple, Luxor.

41. Statue of Rameses II 42.
(Arabic inscriptions differ).

**1914.**

73 29 1 m. brown .. .. 40 40
74 – 2 m. green .. .. 50 20
86 – 2 m. red .. .. 1·00 55
75 – 3 m. orange .. .. 40 35
76 – 4 m. red .. .. 90 65
88 – 4 m. green .. .. 2·25 3·50
77 – 5 m. red .. .. 70 10
90 – 5 m. pink .. .. 2·25 10
78 – 10 m. blue .. .. 1·75 10
92 – 10 m. red .. .. 1·50 15
96 41 15 m. blue .. .. 2·00 15
97 42 15 m. blue .. .. 15·00 2·50
93 35 20 m. green .. .. 6·00 30
80 – 50 m. purple .. .. 8·50 40
81 – 100 m. grey .. .. 10·00 60
82 – 200 m. purple .. .. 24·00 2·25

DESIGNS—As Type **29**: 2 m. Cleopatra in head-dress of Isis. 3 m. Ras-el-Tin Palace, Alexandria. 4 m. Pyramids, Giza. 5 m. Sphinx. 10 m. Colossi of Thebes. As Type **35**: 50 m. Citadel, Cairo. 100 m. Rock Temples, Abu Simbel. 200 m. Aswan Dam.

**1915.** Surch. **2 Milliemes** in English and Arabic.

83. 29. 2 m. on 3 m. orge. (No. 75) 55 90

(43. "The Kingdom of Egypt, 15 March, 1922").

44. King Fuad I.

**1922.** Stamps of 1914 optd with T 43.

98 29 1 m. brown .. .. 75 60
99 – 2 m. red .. .. 65 35
100 – 3 m. orange .. .. 50 60
101 – 4 m. green .. .. 25 55
102 – 5 m. pink .. .. 1·50 10
103 – 10 m. red .. .. 1·50 10
104 41 15 m. blue .. .. 3·00 60
105 42 15 m. blue .. .. 2·50 60
106 35 20 m. green .. .. 3·25 40
107 – 50 m. purple .. .. 4·00 60
108 – 100 m. grey .. .. 14·50 75
110 – 200 m. purple .. .. 13·50 90

**1923.**

111 44 1 m. orange .. .. 15 10
112 2 m. black .. .. 60 10
113 3 m. brown .. .. 55 40
114 4 m. green .. .. 35 15
115 5 m. brown .. .. 25 10
116 10 m. pink .. .. 1·10 10
117 15 m. blue .. .. 1·60 10
118 20 m. green .. .. 3·25 10
119 50 m. green .. .. 5·75 10
120 100 m. purple .. .. 13·50 40
121 200 m. mauve .. .. 25·00 1·10
122 – £E1 violet and blue .. £150 15·00

The 20 m. to £1 values are larger (22½ × 28 mm). The £E1 shows the King in military uniform.

46. Thoth writing name of King Fuad.

**1925.** Int. Geographical Congress, Cairo.

123. 46. 5 m. brown .. .. 3·75 3·75
124. 10 m. red .. .. 7·00 7·75
125. 15 m. blue .. .. 7·50 8·75

47. Ploughing with Oxen.

**1926.** 12th Agricultural Exn., Cairo.

126. 47. 5 m. brown .. .. 1·25 1·25
127. 10 m. red .. .. 1·00 1·25
128. 15 m. blue .. .. 85 1·75
129. 50 m. green .. .. 8·00 5·50
130. 100 m. purple .. .. 9·50 12·50
131. 200 m. violet .. .. 20·00 24·00

49. De Havilland D.H.34 Biplane over Nile.

**1926.** Air.

132 49 27 m. violet .. .. 11·50 14·50
133 27 m. brown .. .. 3·75 1·25

50. King Fuad.

**1926.** King's 58th Birthday.

134 50 50 p. purple .. .. 75·00 16·00

**1926.** Surch.

135. 47. 5 m. on 50 m. green .. 1·90 2·25
136. 10 m. on 100 m. purple 1·10 1·90
137. 15 m. on 200 m. violet .. 1·50 2·25

52. Ancient Egyptian Ship, Temple of Deir-el-Bahari.

**1926.** Int. Navigation Congress.

138. 52. 5 m. black and brown .. 1·50 1·25
139. 10 m. black and red .. 1·75 2·00
140. 15 m. black and blue .. 1·75 2·00

**1926.** Inauguration of Port Fuad. Optd **PORT FOUAD**.

141 52 5 m. black and brown £180 £120
142 10 m. black and red .. £180 £120
143 15 m. black and blue .. £180 £120
144 50 50 p. purple .. .. £1000 £750

55.

**1927.** Int. Cotton Congress, Cairo.

145. 55. 5 m. green and brown .. 80 80
146. 10 m. green and red .. 1·50 2·25
147. 15 m. green and blue .. 1·50 1·75

56.

57.

58.

**1927.**

148. 56. 1 m. orange .. .. 10 10
149. 2 m. black .. .. 10 10
150. 3 m. brown .. .. 10 45
151. 3 m. green .. .. 35 10
153. 4 m. green .. .. 70 60
154. 4 m. brown .. .. 65 50
156. 5 m. brown .. .. 25 10
157. 10 m. red .. .. 75 10
158. 10 m. violet .. .. 2·00 10
159. 13 m. red .. .. 75 15
160a. 15 m. blue .. .. 85 10
161. 15 m. purple .. .. 2·50 10
162. 20 m. blue .. .. 4·25 10
163a. 57. 20 m. olive .. .. 1·75 10
164. 20 m. blue .. .. 5·25 10
165. 40 m. brown .. .. 2·25 10
166a. 50 m. blue .. .. 1·75 10
167a. 100 m. purple .. .. 7·00 25
168a. 200 m. mauve .. .. 6·50 70
171. 58. 500 m. blue and brown 45·00 5·00
172. – £1 brown and green .. 50·00 5·00

DESIGN—VERT. As Type **58**: £1, King Fuad I.
See also Nos. 233/9.

60. Amenhotep.

61. Imhotep.

**1927.** Statistical Congress, Cairo.

173. 60. 5 m. brown .. .. 55 1·10
174. 10 m. red .. .. 65 1·25
175. 15 m. blue .. .. 65 1·10

**1928.** Medical Congress, Cairo.

176. 61. 5 m. brown .. .. 45 55
177. – 10 m. red .. .. 50 55

DESIGN: 10 m. Mohammed Ali Pasha

63. King Farouk when Crown Prince.

64. Ancient Agriculture.

**1929.** Prince's 9th Birthday.

178. 63. 5 m. grey and purple .. 1·25 1·40
179. 10 m. grey and red .. 90 1·40
180. 15 m. grey and blue .. 90 1·75
181. 20 m. grey & turquoise 90 1·75

**1931.** Agricultural and Industrial Exhibition, Cairo.

182. 64. 5 m. brown .. .. 55 60
183. 10 m. red .. .. 60 1·10
184. 15 m. blue .. .. 80 1·10

**1931.** Air. Surch. **GRAF ZEPPELIN AVRIL 1931** and value in English and Arabic.

185 49 50 m. on 27 m. brown 42·00 42·00
186 100 m. on 27 m. brown 42·00 48·00

**1932.** Surch. in English and Arabic.

187 50 50 m. on 50 p. purple 5·00 90
188 – 100 m. on £E1 violet and blue (No. 122) .. £140 £150

67. 2-4-0 Locomotive, 1852.

**1933.** International Railway Congress, Cairo.

189. 67. 5 m. black and brown .. 4·50 5·50
190. – 13 m. black and red .. 10·00 10·00
191. – 15 m. black and violet 10·00 12·00
192. – 20 m. black and blue .. 10·00 10·00

DESIGNS: 13 m. 2-2-2 locomotive, 1859. 15 m. 2-2-2 locomotive, 1862. 20 m. 4-4-2 locomotive, 1932.

68. Handley Page H.P.42 over Pyramids.

**1933. Air.**

| No. | Type | Description | Unused | Used |
|---|---|---|---|---|
| 193. | 68. | 1 m. black and orange | 15 | 50 |
| 194. | | 2 m. black and grey | 65 | 1·40 |
| 195. | | 2 m. black and orange | 2·25 | 2·50 |
| 196. | | 3 m. black and brown | 70 | 35 |
| 197. | | 4 m. black and green | 95 | 1·00 |
| 198. | | 5 m. black and brown | 1·00 | 10 |
| 199. | | 6 m. black and green | 1·25 | 1·40 |
| 200. | | 7 m. black and blue | 1·25 | 1·00 |
| 201. | | 8 m. black and violet | 70 | 25 |
| 202. | | 9 m. black and red | 1·40 | 1·40 |
| 203. | | 10 m. brown and violet | 45 | 80 |
| 204. | | 20 m. brown and green | 60 | 20 |
| 205. | | 30 m. brown and blue | 1·75 | 20 |
| 206. | | 40 m. brown and red | 11·00 | 60 |
| 207. | | 50 m. brown and orange | 11·00 | 15 |
| 208. | | 60 m. brown and grey | 6·00 | 1·10 |
| 209. | | 70 m. green and blue | 2·50 | 1·00 |
| 210. | | 80 m. green and sepia | 2·50 | 1·10 |
| 211. | | 90 m. green and orange | 3·50 | 1·10 |
| 212. | | 100 m. green and violet | 7·50 | 65 |
| 213. | | 200 m. green and red | 9·50 | 1·25 |

See also Nos. 285/8.

69. Armstrong-Whitworth Atalanta of Imperial Airways.

**1933.** Int. Aviation Congress. Inscr. as in T **69.**

| No. | Type | Description | Unused | Used |
|---|---|---|---|---|
| 214. | 69. | 5 m. brown | 3·50 | 2·50 |
| 215. | | 10 m. violet | 13·00 | 9·25 |
| 216. | – | 13 m. red | 12·50 | 16·00 |
| 217. | – | 15 m. purple | 10·00 | 14·00 |
| 218. | – | 20 m. blue | 13·00 | 17·00 |

DESIGNS: 13, 15 m. Dornier Do-X flying boat. 20 m. Airship "Graf Zeppelin".

72. Khedive Ismail Pasha. 73.

**1934.** 10th U.P.U. Congress, Cairo.

| No. | Type | Description | Unused | Used |
|---|---|---|---|---|
| 219 | 72 | 1 m. orange | 30 | 65 |
| 220 | | 2 m. black | 30 | 65 |
| 221 | | 3 m. brown | 35 | 70 |
| 222 | | 4 m. green | 65 | 20 |
| 223 | | 5 m. brown | 75 | 15 |
| 224 | | 10 m. violet | 1·40 | 15 |
| 225 | | 13 m. red | 2·25 | 1·25 |
| 226 | | 15 m. purple | 2·25 | 1·00 |
| 227 | | 20 m. blue | 1·60 | 20 |
| 228 | | 50 m. blue | 5·00 | 35 |
| 229 | | 100 m. green | 11·00 | 75 |
| 230 | | 200 m. violet | 42·00 | 4·00 |
| 231 | 73 | 50 p. brown | £150 | 60·00 |
| 232 | | £E1 blue | £225 | £100 |

**1936.** As T **56** but inscribed "POSTES".

| No. | Type | Description | Unused | Used |
|---|---|---|---|---|
| 233. | 56. | 1 m. orange | 10 | 50 |
| 234. | | 2 m. black | 60 | 10 |
| 235. | | 4 m. green | 80 | 10 |
| 236. | | 5 m. brown | 40 | 30 |
| 237. | | 10 m. violet | 1·25 | 20 |
| 238. | | 15 m. purple | 2·00 | 15 |
| 239. | | 20 m. blue | 2·00 | 15 |

75. Exhibition Entrance.

**1936.** 15th Agricultural and Industrial Exn., Cairo.

| No. | Type | Description | Unused | Used |
|---|---|---|---|---|
| 240. | 75. | 5 m. brown | 1·10 | 1·00 |
| 241. | – | 10 m. violet | 1·25 | 1·40 |
| 242. | – | 13 m. red | 1·00 | 2·25 |
| 243. | – | 15 m. purple | 75 | 1·00 |
| 244. | – | 20 m. blue | 2·00 | 2·50 |

DESIGN—HORIZ. 10 m., 13 m. Palace of Agriculture. 15 m., 20 m. Palace of Industry.

77. Nahas Pasha and Treaty Delegates.

**1936.** Anglo-Egyptian Treaty.

| No. | Type | Description | Unused | Used |
|---|---|---|---|---|
| 245. | 77. | 5 m. brown | 40 | 85 |
| 246. | | 15 m. purple | 25 | 95 |
| 247. | | 20 m. blue | 65 | 1·10 |

78. King Farouk. 79. Medal commemorating Abolition of Capitulations.

**1937.** Investiture of King Farouk.

| No. | Type | Description | Unused | Used |
|---|---|---|---|---|
| 248. | 78. | 1 m. orange | 10 | 10 |
| 249. | | 2 m. red | 10 | 10 |
| 250. | | 3 m. brown | 10 | 10 |
| 251. | | 4 m. green | 10 | 10 |
| 252. | | 5 m. brown | 10 | 10 |
| 253. | | 6 m. green | 55 | 20 |
| 254. | | 10 m. violet | 20 | 10 |
| 255. | | 13 m. red | 20 | 20 |
| 256. | | 15 m. purple | 20 | 10 |
| 257. | | 20 m. blue | 30 | 10 |
| 258. | | 20 m. violet | 55 | 15 |

**1937.** Abolition of Capitulations at the Montreux Conference.

| No. | Type | Description | Unused | Used |
|---|---|---|---|---|
| 259. | 79. | 5 m. brown | 25 | 20 |
| 260. | | 15 m. purple | 35 | 80 |
| 261. | | 20 m. blue | 65 | 1·25 |

80. Nekhbet, Sacred Eye of Horus and Buto.

**1937.** 15th Ophthalmological Congress, Cairo.

| No. | Type | Description | Unused | Used |
|---|---|---|---|---|
| 262. | 80. | 5 m. brown | 25 | 70 |
| 263. | | 15 m. purple | 30 | 1·10 |
| 264. | | 20 m. blue | 30 | 1·10 |

81. King Farouk and Queen Farida.

**1938.** Royal Wedding.

| No. | Type | Description | Unused | Used |
|---|---|---|---|---|
| 265. | 81. | 5 m. brown | 1·75 | 3·75 |

82. Gathering Cotton. 83. Pyramids of Giza and Colossus of Thebes.

**1938.** 18th Int. Cotton Congress, Cairo.

| No. | Type | Description | Unused | Used |
|---|---|---|---|---|
| 266. | 82. | 5 m. brown | 20 | 90 |
| 267. | | 15 m. purple | 40 | 1·50 |
| 268. | | 20 m. blue | 35 | 1·40 |

**1938.** Int. Telecommunications Conf., Cairo.

| No. | Type | Description | Unused | Used |
|---|---|---|---|---|
| 269. | 83. | 5 m. brown | 55 | 1·40 |
| 270. | | 15 m. purple | 90 | 2·00 |
| 271. | | 20 m. blue | 95 | 2·00 |

**1938.** King Farouk's 18th Birthday. Portrait similar to T 81 with inscr. "11 FEVRIER 1938" at foot.

| No. | Type | Description | Unused | Used |
|---|---|---|---|---|
| 272. | – | £E 1 brown and green | £100 | £120 |

84. Hydnocarpus. 85. King Farouk and Pyramids.

86. King Farouk. 87.

**1938.** Leprosy Research Congress.

| No. | Type | Description | Unused | Used |
|---|---|---|---|---|
| 273. | 84. | 5 m. brown | 75 | 80 |
| 274. | | 15 m. purple | 75 | 80 |
| 275. | | 20 m. blue | 75 | 80 |

**1939.**

| No. | Type | Description | Unused | Used |
|---|---|---|---|---|
| 276a | 85 | 30 m. grey | 20 | 10 |
| 277 | | 30 m. green | 20 | 10 |
| 278 | – | 40 m. brown | 25 | 10 |
| 279 | – | 50 m. blue | 85 | 10 |
| 280 | – | 100 m. purple | 1·25 | 10 |
| 281 | – | 200 m. violet | 4·50 | 15 |
| 282 | 86 | 50 p. brown and green | 5·00 | 65 |
| 283 | 87 | £E 1 brown and blue | 11·50 | 1·50 |

DESIGNS (As Type 85): 40 m. Mosque. 50 m. Cairo Citadel. 100 m. Aswan Dam. 200 m. Fuad I University, Giza.

For similar issue with portrait looking to left, see 1947 issue.

88. Princess Ferial (18 months old). 90. King Fuad I.

**1940.** Child Welfare.

| No. | Type | Description | Unused | Used |
|---|---|---|---|---|
| 284 | 88 | 5 m.+5 m. red | 35 | 30 |

**1941.** Air.

| No. | Type | Description | Unused | Used |
|---|---|---|---|---|
| 285 | 68 | 5 m. red | 25 | 20 |
| 286 | | 10 m. violet | 45 | 50 |
| 287a | | 25 m. purple | 35 | 20 |
| 288 | | 30 m. green | 50 | 15 |

**1943.** 5th Birthday of Princess Ferial. Optd **1943** in English and Arabic.

| No. | Type | Description | Unused | Used |
|---|---|---|---|---|
| 289 | 88 | 5 m.+5 m red | 3·25 | 9·00 |

**1944.** 8th Death Anniv. of King Fuad.

| No. | Type | Description | Unused | Used |
|---|---|---|---|---|
| 290. | 90. | 10 m. purple | 50 | 10 |

91. King Farouk. 92. King Farouk. 93. Khedive Ismail Pasha.

**1944.**

| No. | Type | Description | Unused | Used |
|---|---|---|---|---|
| 291 | 91 | 1 m. brown | 10 | 10 |
| 292 | | 2 m. red | 10 | 10 |
| 293 | | 3 m. brown | 25 | 35 |
| 294 | | 4 m. green | 20 | 10 |
| 295 | | 5 m. brown | 20 | 10 |
| 296 | | 10 m. violet | 45 | 10 |
| 297 | | 13 m. red | 8·00 | 3·00 |
| 298 | | 15 m. purple | 85 | 10 |
| 299 | | 17 m. olive | 75 | 10 |
| 300 | | 20 m. violet | 85 | 10 |
| 301 | | 22 m. blue | 85 | 10 |

**1945.** 25th Birthday of King Farouk.

| No. | Type | Description | Unused | Used |
|---|---|---|---|---|
| 302. | 92. | 10 m. violet | 15 | 10 |

**1945.** 50th Death Anniv. of Ismail Pasha.

| No. | Type | Description | Unused | Used |
|---|---|---|---|---|
| 303 | 93 | 10 m. green | 15 | 10 |

94. Flags of the Arab Union. 95. Flags of Egypt and Saudi Arabia.

**1945.** Arab Union.

| No. | Type | Description | Unused | Used |
|---|---|---|---|---|
| 304. | 94. | 10 m. violet | 10 | 10 |
| 305. | | 22 m. green | 15 | 15 |

**1946.** Visit of King of Saudi Arabia.

| No. | Type | Description | Unused | Used |
|---|---|---|---|---|
| 306. | 95. | 10 m. green | 15 | 10 |

96. Reproduction of First Egyptian Stamp.

DESIGNS: 10 m. Khedive Ismail Pasha. 17 m. King Fuad. 22 m. King Farouk.

**1946.** 80th Anniv of First Egyptian Postage Stamp.

| No. | Type | Description | Unused | Used |
|---|---|---|---|---|
| 307. | 96. | 1 m.+1 m. grey | 10 | 10 |
| 308. | – | 10 m.+10 m. purple | 15 | 10 |
| 309. | – | 17 m.+17 m. brown | 15 | 15 |
| 310. | – | 22 m.+22 m. green | 20 | 15 |

98. King Farouk, Egyptian Flag and Citadel.

**1946.** Evacuation of Cairo Citadel.

| No. | Type | Description | Unused | Used |
|---|---|---|---|---|
| 313. | 98. | 10 m. brown and green | 20 | 15 |

**1946.** Air. Cairo Aviation Congress. Optd. **Le Caire 1946** and Arabic characters.

| No. | Type | Description | Unused | Used |
|---|---|---|---|---|
| 314. | 68. | 30 m. green (No. 288) | 20 | 15 |

100. King Farouk and Inshas Palace.

**1946.** Arab League Congress. Portraits.

| No. | Type | Description | Unused | Used |
|---|---|---|---|---|
| 315 | 100 | 1 m. green | 35 | 10 |
| 316 | – | 2 m. brown | 35 | 10 |
| 317 | – | 3 m. blue | 35 | 10 |
| 318 | – | 4 m. brown | 35 | 15 |
| 319 | – | 5 m. red | 35 | 10 |
| 320 | – | 10 m. grey | 40 | 15 |
| 321 | – | 15 m. violet | 50 | 20 |

DESIGNS: 2 m. Prince Abdullah of Yemen. 3 m. President of Lebanon, Beshara al-Khoury. 4 m. King Ibn Saud of Saudi Arabia. 5 m. King Faisal II of Iraq. 10 m. King Abdullah of Jordan. 15 m. Pres of Syria, Shukri Bey al-Quwatli.

101. King Farouk, Delta Barrage and Douglas Dakota Transport. 102. Triad of Mycerinus.

**1947.** Air.

| No. | Type | Description | Unused | Used |
|---|---|---|---|---|
| 322. | 101. | 2 m. red | 10 | 40 |
| 323. | | 3 m. brown | 10 | 45 |
| 324. | | 5 m. red | 10 | 10 |
| 325. | | 7 m. orange | 25 | 15 |
| 326. | | 8 m. green | 25 | 40 |
| 327. | | 10 m. violet | 25 | 10 |
| 328. | | 20 m. blue | 35 | 15 |
| 329. | | 30 m. purple | 45 | 15 |
| 330. | | 40 m. red | 65 | 20 |
| 331. | | 50 m. blue | 85 | 25 |
| 332. | | 100 m. olive | 1·50 | 35 |
| 333. | | 200 m. grey | 2·75 | 1·50 |

**1947.** Int. Exhibition of Fine Arts. Inscr. "EXPOSITION INTERNATIONALE D'ART CONTEMPORIAN".

| No. | Type | Description | Unused | Used |
|---|---|---|---|---|
| 334. | 102. | 5 m.+5 m. grey | 20 | 65 |
| 335. | – | 15 m.+15 m. blue | 30 | 1·10 |
| 336. | – | 30 m.+30 m. red | 45 | 1·40 |
| 337. | – | 50 m.+50 m. brown | 55 | 1·60 |

DESIGNS—HORIZ. 15 m. Temple of Rameses. VERT. 30 m. Queen Nefertiti. 50 m. Tutankhamun.

104. Egyptian Parliament Buildings. 105. King Farouk hoisting Flag.

**1947.** 36th Int. Parliamentary Union Conference, Cairo.

| No. | Type | Description | Unused | Used |
|---|---|---|---|---|
| 338. | 104. | 10 m. green | 15 | 15 |

**1947.** Withdrawal of British Troops from Nile Delta.

| No. | Type | Description | Unused | Used |
|---|---|---|---|---|
| 339. | 105. | 10 m. purple and green | 15 | 15 |

**106.** King Farouk and Sultan Hussein Mosque, Cairo. **107.** King Farouk.

**1947.** Designs as 1939 issue but with portrait altered as T **106** and **107.**

| No. | Type | Description | | |
|---|---|---|---|---|
| 340. | – | 30 m. olive .. .. | 35 | 10 |
| 341. | 106. | 40 m. brown .. .. | 25 | 10 |
| 342. | – | 50 m. blue .. .. | 35 | 10 |
| 343. | – | 100 m. purple .. | 2·75 | 60 |
| 344. | – | 200 m. violet .. | 7·75 | 1·00 |
| 345. | 107. | 50 p. brown and green | 21·00 | 9·25 |
| 346. | – | £E1 brown and blue .. | 23·00 | 2·25 |

DESIGNS—As Type **106**: 30 m. Pyramids. 50 m. Cairo Citadel. 100 m. Aswan Dam. 200 m. Fuad I University, Cairo. As T **107**: £E1, King Farouk (different).

**109.** Cotton Plant. **110.** Egyptian Soldiers Entering Palestine.

**1948.** Int. Cotton Congress.

| | | | | |
|---|---|---|---|---|
| 347. | 109. | 10 m. green .. .. | 15 | 60 |

**1948.** Arrival of Egyptian Troops in Gaza.

| | | | | |
|---|---|---|---|---|
| 348. | 110. | 10 m. green .. .. | 45 | 95 |

**1948.** Air. Air Mail Service to Athens and Rome. Surch **S. A. I. D. E. 23-8-1948** and values in English and Arabic.

| | | | | |
|---|---|---|---|---|
| 349 | 101 | 13 m. on 100 m. olive | 35 | 1·50 |
| 350 | | 22 m. on 200 m. grey .. | 65 | 2·00 |

**112.** Ibrahim Pasha and Battle of Navarino, 1827.

**1948.** Death Centenary of Ibrahim Pasha (statesman and General).

| | | | | |
|---|---|---|---|---|
| 351. | 112. | 10 m. green and red .. | 30 | 25 |

**113.** Reclining Male Figure symbolising River Nile.

**114.** Protection of Industry and Agriculture by Army. **115.** Mohammed Ali and Map.

**1949.** 16th Agricultural and Industrial Exn., Cairo.

| | | | | |
|---|---|---|---|---|
| 352. | 113. | 1 m. green .. .. | 10 | 60 |
| 353. | | 10 m. violet .. .. | 15 | 60 |
| 354. | | 17 m. red .. .. | 15 | 1·00 |
| 355. | | 22 m. blue .. .. | 15 | 25 |
| 356. | 114. | 30 m. sepia .. .. | 20 | 40 |

**1949.** Death Centenary of Mohammed Ali (statesman and General).

| | | | | |
|---|---|---|---|---|
| 358. | 115. | 10 m. green and brown | 15 | 55 |

**116.** Globe. **117.** Scales of Justice.

**1949.** 75th Anniv. of U.P.U.

| | | | | |
|---|---|---|---|---|
| 359. | 116. | 10 m. red .. .. | 65 | 40 |
| 360. | | 22 m. violet .. .. | 75 | 80 |
| 361. | | 30 m. blue .. .. | 85 | 90 |

**1949.** Abolition of Mixed Courts.

| | | | | |
|---|---|---|---|---|
| 362 | 117 | 10 m. green & dp green | 15 | 15 |

**118.** Camels by Water-hole.

**1950.** Inaug. of Fuad I Desert Institute.

| | | | | |
|---|---|---|---|---|
| 363. | 118. | 10 m. brown and violet | 65 | 1·10 |

**119.** King Fuad University.

**1950.** 25th Anniv. of Fuad I University.

| | | | | |
|---|---|---|---|---|
| 364. | 119. | 22 m. purple and green | 65 | 1·25 |

**120.** Khedive Ismail and Globe. **121.** Girl and Cotton.

**1950.** 75th Anniv. of Royal Egyptian Geographical Society.

| | | | | |
|---|---|---|---|---|
| 365. | 120. | 30 m. green and purple | 70 | 2·00 |

**1951.** International Cotton Congress, Cairo.

| | | | | |
|---|---|---|---|---|
| 366 | 121 | 10 m. green .. .. | 25 | 80 |

**122.** King Farouk and Queen Narriman.

**1951.** Royal Wedding.

| | | | | |
|---|---|---|---|---|
| 367. | 122. | 10 m. brown and green | 1·25 | 2·25 |

**123.** Triumphal Arch.

**1951.** 1st Mediterranean Games, Alexandria.

| | | | | |
|---|---|---|---|---|
| 369. | 123. | 10 m. brown .. .. | 85 | 1·25 |
| 370. | – | 22 m. green .. .. | 85 | 1·75 |
| 371. | – | 30 m. blue and green .. | 85 | 2·00 |

DESIGNS—VERT. 22 m. Badge of Alexandria and map of Mediterranean. HORIZ. 30 m. King Farouk and waves.

ملك مصر والسودان
١٦ اكتوبر سنة ١٩٥١

**124.** (" King of Egypt and the Sudan, 16th October 1951 ").

**1952.** Optd as T **124** (different sizes).

| | | | | |
|---|---|---|---|---|
| 373 | 91 | 1 m. brown (postage) | 60 | 70 |
| 374 | | 2 m. red .. .. | 20 | 20 |
| 375 | 78 | 3 m. brown .. .. | 20 | 1·25 |
| 376 | 91 | 4 m. green .. .. | 20 | 20 |
| 377 | 78 | 6 m. green .. .. | 90 | 1·25 |
| 378 | 91 | 10 m. violet .. .. | 30 | 10 |
| 379 | | 13 m. red .. .. | 1·00 | 1·25 |
| 380 | | 15 m. purple .. .. | 1·75 | 1·25 |
| 381 | | 17 m. green .. .. | 1·25 | 20 |
| 382 | | 20 m. violet .. .. | 1·00 | 20 |
| 383 | | 22 m. blue .. .. | 2·00 | 2·25 |
| 384 | – | 30 m. green (No. 340) | 1·50 | 70 |
| 386 | 106 | 40 m. brown .. .. | 50 | 15 |
| 387 | – | 50 m. blue (No. 342) | 1·10 | 20 |
| 388 | – | 100 m. purple (No. 343) | 2·00 | 35 |
| 389 | – | 200 m. violet (No. 344) | 9·75 | 1·60 |
| 390 | 107 | 50 p. brown and green | 10·00 | 5·50 |
| 391 | – | £E1 brown and blue (No. 346) .. .. | 25·00 | 6·00 |
| 392 | 101 | 2 m. red (air) .. | 20 | 20 |
| 393 | | 3 m. brown .. .. | 80 | 1·00 |
| 394 | | 5 m. red .. .. | 30 | 30 |
| 395 | | 7 m. brown .. .. | 35 | 25 |
| 396 | | 8 m. green .. .. | 1·10 | 1·25 |
| 397 | | 10 m. violet .. .. | 80 | 1·00 |
| 398 | | 20 m. blue .. .. | 1·25 | 2·25 |
| 399 | | 30 m. purple .. .. | 90 | 1·50 |
| 400 | | 40 m. red .. .. | 1·25 | 1·75 |
| 401 | | 50 m. blue .. .. | 1·60 | 2·25 |
| 402 | | 100 m. green .. .. | 2·75 | 3·25 |
| 403 | | 200 m. grey .. .. | 6·50 | 5·50 |

**125.** "Egypt". **126.** Egyptian Flag.

**1952.** Abrogation of Anglo-Egyptian Treaty of 1936. Inscr. " 16 Oct. 1951 ".

| | | | | |
|---|---|---|---|---|
| 404. | 125. | 10 m. green .. .. | 15 | 1·00 |
| 405. | – | 22 m. green and purple | 35 | 1·10 |
| 406. | – | 30 m. green and brown | 35 | 1·25 |

DESIGNS: 22 m. King Farouk and map of Nile Valley. 30 m. King Farouk and flag.

**1952.** Birth of Crown Prince Ahmed Fuad.

| | | | | |
|---|---|---|---|---|
| 408. | 126. | 10 m. green, yell. & blue | 25 | 1·25 |

**127.** " Freedom, Hope and Peace ".

**1952.** Revolution of 23 July 1952. Inscr. " 23 JUILLET 1952 ".

| | | | | |
|---|---|---|---|---|
| 410. | 127. | 4 m. orange and green | 20 | 25 |
| 411. | – | 10 m. brown and green | 20 | 80 |
| 412. | – | 17 m. brown and green | 75 | 90 |
| 413. | – | 22 m. green and brown | 1·00 | 60 |

DESIGNS—HORIZ. 10 m. Allegory of Egyptian freedom. VERT. 17 m. Map of Nile Valley, and Egyptian citizens. 22 m. Rejoicing crowd and Egyptian flag.

**129.** "Agriculture". **130.** "Defence".

**131.** Sultan Hussein Mosque, Cairo. **132.** Queen Nefertiti.

**133.** Douglas Dakota Transport over Delta Barrage.

**1953.** Inscr "DEFENCE" (A) or "DEFENSE" (B).

| | | | | |
|---|---|---|---|---|
| 414 | 129 | 1 m. brown (postage) | 40 | 20 |
| 415 | | 2 m. purple .. .. | 25 | 20 |
| 416 | | 3 m. blue .. .. | 40 | 35 |
| 417 | | 4 m. green .. .. | 25 | 25 |
| 418 | 130 | 10 m. brown (A) .. | 25 | 35 |
| 419 | | 10 m. brown (B) .. | 50 | 20 |
| 420 | | 15 m. grey (B) .. | 40 | 25 |
| 421 | | 17 m. blue (B) .. | 50 | 25 |
| 422 | | 20 m. violet (B) .. | 25 | 25 |
| 423 | 131 | 30 m. green .. .. | 25 | 20 |
| 424 | | 32 m. blue .. .. | 60 | 25 |
| 425 | | 35 m. violet .. .. | 50 | 25 |
| 426 | | 37 m. brown .. .. | 85 | 1·00 |
| 427 | | 40 m. brown .. .. | 50 | 25 |
| 428 | | 50 m. purple .. .. | 1·50 | 10 |
| 429 | 132 | 100 m. brown .. | 1·25 | 20 |
| 430 | | 200 m. blue .. .. | 3·50 | 45 |
| 431 | | 500 m. violet .. | 6·50 | 1·00 |
| 432 | | £E1 red and green .. | 10·00 | 1·75 |
| 433 | 133 | 5 m. brown (air) .. | 25 | 50 |
| 434 | | 15 m. green .. .. | 65 | 70 |

See also No. 619.

**1953.** Various issues of King Farouk with portrait obliterated by three horiz bars.

(i) Stamps of 1937.

| | | | | |
|---|---|---|---|---|
| 435 | 78 | 1 m. orange .. .. | 13·50 | 21·00 |
| 436 | | 3 m. brown .. .. | 45 | 60 |
| 437 | | 6 m. green .. .. | 25 | 25 |

(ii) Stamps of 1944.

| | | | | |
|---|---|---|---|---|
| 438 | 91 | 1 m. brown .. .. | 25 | 25 |
| 439 | | 2 m. red .. .. | 25 | 10 |
| 440 | | 3 m. brown .. .. | 50 | 60 |
| 441 | | 4 m. green .. .. | 25 | 20 |
| 442 | | 10 m. violet .. .. | 25 | 20 |
| 443 | | 13 m. red .. .. | 80 | 90 |
| 444 | | 15 m. purple .. .. | 50 | 20 |
| 445 | | 17 m. green .. .. | 45 | 25 |
| 446 | | 20 m. violet .. .. | 50 | 10 |
| 447 | | 22 m. blue .. .. | 70 | 20 |

(iii) Stamps of 1947.

| | | | | |
|---|---|---|---|---|
| 448 | – | 30 m. green (No. 340) | 50 | 25 |
| 449 | 106 | 40 m. brown .. .. | 32·00 | 45·00 |
| 450 | – | 50 m. blue (No. 342) | 80 | 20 |
| 451 | – | 100 m. pur (No. 343) | 1·10 | 50 |
| 452 | – | 200 m. violet (No. 344) | 4·50 | 1·10 |
| 453 | 107 | 50 p. brown and green | 5·00 | 4·00 |
| 454 | – | £E1 brown and blue (No. 346) .. .. | 9·50 | 2·75 |

(iv) Air stamps of 1947.

| | | | | |
|---|---|---|---|---|
| 455 | 101 | 2 m. red .. .. | 1·70 | 2·00 |
| 456 | | 3 m. brown .. .. | 1·25 | 2·75 |
| 457 | | 5 m. red .. .. | 80 | 1·25 |
| 458 | | 7 m. brown .. .. | 20 | 25 |
| 459 | | 8 m. green .. .. | 1·10 | 1·75 |
| 460 | | 10 m. violet .. .. | 30·00 | 32·00 |
| 461 | | 20 m. blue .. .. | 1·25 | 25 |
| 462 | | 30 m. purple .. .. | 1·75 | 85 |
| 463 | | 40 m. red .. .. | 1·75 | 95 |
| 464 | | 50 m. blue .. .. | 3·00 | 1·00 |
| 465 | | 100 m. green .. .. | 4·75 | 2·50 |
| 466 | | 200 m. grey .. .. | 48·00 | 50·00 |

(v) Stamps of 1952 with "Egypt-Sudan" opt T **124**.

| | | | | |
|---|---|---|---|---|
| 467 | 91 | 1 m. brown (postage) | 5·25 | 7·75 |
| 468 | | 2 m. red .. .. | 70 | 1·90 |
| 469 | 78 | 3 m. brown .. .. | 6·00 | 8·25 |
| 470 | 91 | 4 m. green .. .. | 6·50 | 8·25 |
| 471 | 78 | 6 m. green .. .. | 8·75 | 8·75 |
| 472 | 91 | 10 m. violet .. .. | 3·00 | 4·25 |
| 473 | | 13 m. red .. .. | 70 | 1·50 |
| 474 | | 15 m. purple .. .. | 13·00 | 16·00 |
| 475 | | 17 m. green .. .. | 13·00 | 16·00 |
| 476 | | 20 m. violet .. .. | 14·00 | 16·00 |
| 477 | | 22 m. blue .. .. | 38·00 | 42·00 |
| 477a | – | 30 m. green (No. 384) | 17·00 | 17·00 |
| 478 | 106 | 40 m. brown .. .. | 80 | 1·60 |
| 479 | – | 200 m. violet (No. 389) | 3·75 | 3·25 |
| 480 | 101 | 2 m. red (air) .. | 50 | 30 |
| 481 | | 3 m. brown .. .. | 1·00 | 90 |
| 482 | | 5 m. red .. .. | 25 | 25 |
| 483 | | 7 m. brown .. .. | 11·00 | 12·00 |
| 484 | | 8 m. green .. .. | 60 | 1·60 |
| 485 | | 10 m. violet .. .. | 50 | 1·25 |
| 486 | | 20 m. blue .. .. | 45·00 | 48·00 |
| 487 | | 30 m. purple .. .. | 1·10 | 1·10 |
| 488 | | 40 m. red .. .. | 45·00 | 48·00 |
| 489 | | 50 m. blue .. .. | 1·40 | 60 |
| 490 | | 100 m. green .. .. | 2·50 | 2·50 |
| 491 | | 200 m. grey .. .. | 5·00 | 7·00 |

**135.**

**1953.** Electronics Exn., Cairo.

| | | | | |
|---|---|---|---|---|
| 492. | 135. | 10 m. blue .. .. | 40 | 60 |

## INDEX

Countries can be quickly located by referring to the index at the end of this volume.

136. "Young Egypt". 137. "Agriculture".

**1954.** 1st Anniv. of Republic.
493. 136. 10 m. brown .. .. 50 25
494. – 30 m. blue .. .. 80 70
DESIGN: 30 m. Marching crowd, Egyptian flag and eagle.

**1954.**
495. 137. 1 m. brown .. .. 25 20
496. 2 m. purple .. .. 25 20
497. 3 m. blue .. .. 20 25
498. 4 m. green .. .. 90 80
499. 5 m. red .. .. 25 25

138. Flag and Map showing Area watered by Canal.  139.

**1954.** Evacuation of British Troops from Suez Canal. Inscr. "EVACUATION".
500. 138. 10 m. purple and green 35 25
501. – 35 m. green and red .. 55 60
DESIGN: 35 m. Egyptian army bugler, machine-gunner and map.

**1955.** Arab Postal Union.
502. 139. 5 m. brown .. .. 35 25
503. 10 m. green .. .. 35 50
504. 37 m. violet .. .. 60 1·75

140. P. P. Harris and Rotary Emblem. 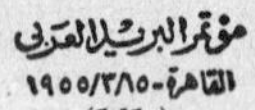 (141.)

**1955.** 50th Anniv of Rotary International.
505 140 10 m. purple .. .. 1·00 25
506 – 35 m. blue .. .. 1·25 60
DESIGN: 35 m. Globe and Rotary emblem.

**1955.** Second Arab Postal Union Conf., Cairo. Optd. with T 141.
507. 139. 5 m. brown .. .. 80 1·25
508. 10 m. green .. .. 1·00 1·10
509. 37 m. violet .. .. 1·25 1·60

142. Scout Badge. 143. Globes and Laurel Branch.

**1956.** 2nd Arab Scout Jamboree, Aboukir (Alexandria). Inscr. "2EME JAMBOREE ARABE", etc.
510. 142. 10 m.+10 m. green .. 60 1·60
511. – 20 m.+10 m. ultram... 70 1·90
512. – 35 m.+15 m. blue .. 60 2·00
DESIGNS: 20 m. Sea Scout badge. 35 m. Air Scout badge.

**1956.** Afro-Asian Festival, Cairo. Inscr. "FESTIVAL ASIATICO-AFRICAIN".
515. 143. 10 m. green and brown 40 25
516. – 35 m. purple and yellow 70 1·50
DESIGN—VERT. 35 m. Globe, lamp, dove and ear of corn.

144. Freighter and Map of Suez Canal.  145. Queen Nefertiti.

**1956.** Nationalisation of Suez Canal.
517. 144. 10 m. blue and buff .. 40 40

**1956.** Int. Museum Week.
518. 145. 10 m. green .. .. 70 1·40

146. Defence of Port Said.

**1956.** "Port Said, Nov. 1956".
519. 146. 10 m. purple .. .. 1·00 1·25

**1957.** Evacuation of British and French Troops from Port Said. Optd EVACUATION 22-12-56 in English and Arabic.
520 146 10 m. purple .. .. 55 1·25

148. Early Locomotive and Modern Express Train.

**1957.** Centenary of Egyptian Railways.
521 148 10 m. purple and brown 50 1·10

149. Mother and Children.

**1957.** Mothers' Day.
522 149 10 m. red .. .. 50 1·10

150. Battle Scene.

**1957.** 150th Anniv. of Victory over British at Rosetta.
523. 150. 10 m. blue .. .. 25 1·10

**1957.** Re-opening of Suez Canal. As T 144 but inscr "REOPENING 1957" in English and Arabic.
524 100 m. blue and green .. 1·10 1·40

151. Al-Azhar University.  152. Map of Gaza.

**1957.** Millenary of Al-Azhar University, Cairo. Unissued stamps of 1942 as T 151 optd. with the present Arabic year (1376).
525. 151. 10 m. violet .. .. 40 1·25
526. 15 m. purple .. .. 60 50
527. 20 m. grey .. .. 90 80

**1957.** Re-occupation of Gaza Strip.
528. 152. 10 m. blue .. .. 75 1·75

153. Motor Ambulance.

**1957.** 50th Anniv. of Public Aid Society.
529. 153. 10 m.+5 m. red .. 30 1·40

154. Shepheard's Hotel.  156. Egyptian Parliament Buildings.

**1957.** Re-opening of Shepheard's Hotel, Cairo.
530. 154. 10 m. violet .. .. 30 1·25

**1957.** Opening of National Assembly.
531. 156. 10 m. brown & yellow 25 1·25

157. Avaris, 1580 B.C.

**1957.** 5th Anniv. of 1952 Revolution.
532. 157. 10 m. red .. .. 70 1·00
533. – 10 m. green .. .. 70 1·00
534. – 10 m. purple .. .. 70 1·00
535. – 10 m. blue .. .. 70 1·00
536. – 10 m. brown .. .. 70 1·00
DESIGNS—HORIZ: No. 533, Saladin at Hattin, A.D. 1187. 534, Ein Galout, A.D. 1260 (Middle East map). 536, Evacuation of Port Said, 1956. VERT: No. 534, Louis IX in chains at Mansourah, A.D. 1250.

159. Ahmed Arabi addressing Revolutionaries.  160. Rameses II.

**1957.** 75th Anniv. of Arabi Revolution.
537. 159. 10 m. violet .. .. 30 40

**1957.**
540 – 1 m. turquoise .. 25 50
541 – 5 m. sepia .. 25 35
539 160 10 m. violet .. .. 40 25
DESIGNS: 1 m. Country woman and cotton plant. 5 m. Factory skyline.
See also Nos. 553/9, 603/19 and 669/72.

162. Ahmed Shawqi.  163. Vickers Viscount Airliner and Airline Badge.

**1957.** 25th Death Anniv of Ahmed Shawqi and Hafez Ibrahim (poets).
543. 162. 10 m. olive .. .. 25 1·10
544. – 10 m. brown (Hafez Ibrahim) .. .. 25 1·10

**1957.** 25th Anniv. of Egyptian Civil Airlines "MISRAIR", and Air Force.
545. 163. 10 m. green .. .. 70 65
546. – 10 m. blue .. .. 30 1·10
DESIGN: No. 546, Ilyushin Il-28 bomber, two Mikoyan Gurevich MiG-17 jet fighters and Air Force emblem.

164. Pyramids, Dove of Peace and Globe. 165. Racing Cyclists.

**1957.** Afro-Asian People's Conference, Cairo.
547. 164. 5 m. brown .. .. 50 1·00
548. 10 m. green .. .. 30 1·00
549. 15 m. violet .. .. 30 1·00

**1958.** 5th Egyptian Int. Cycle Race.
550. 165. 10 m. brown .. .. 30 1·00

166. Mustapha Kamil.

**1958.** 50th Death Anniv. of Mustapha Kamil (patriot).
551. 166. 10 m. slate .. .. 50 25

## UNITED ARAB REPUBLIC

For stamps inscribed "UAR" but with value in piastres, see under Syria.

167. Congress Emblem. 168. Princess Nofret.

**1958.** 1st Afro-Asian Ophthalmology Congress.
552. 167. 10 m. + 5 m. orange.. 65 65

**1958.** Inscr. "U A R EGYPT".
553. – 1 m. red (as No. 538) 20 20
554. – 2 m. blue .. .. 15 15
555. 168. 3 m. brown .. .. 15 15
556. – 4 m. green .. .. 20 15
557. – 5 m. sepia (as No. 541) 20 10
558. 160. 10 m. violet .. .. 50 10
559. – 35 m. blue .. .. 2·75 25
DESIGNS—VERT. 2 m. Ahmed Ibn Toulon Mosque. 4 m. Glass lamp and mosque. 35 m. Ship and crate on hoist.
See also Nos. 603/19, 669/72 and 739.

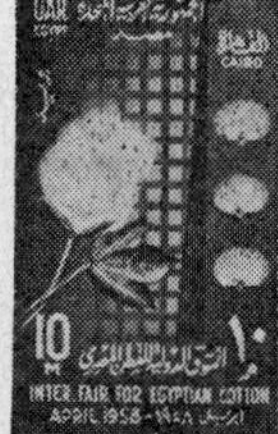


169. Union of Egypt and Syria. 170. Cotton Plant.

**1958.** Birth of United Arab Republic.
560. 169. 10 m. grn. & yell. (post.) 35 25
561. 15 m. brn. & blue (air) 35 25

**1958.** Int. Cotton Fair, Cairo.
562. 170. 10 m. turquoise .. 25 15

171. Qasim Amin.

172. Dove of Peace.

**1958.** 50th Death Anniv. of Qasim Amin (reformer).
563. **171.** 10 m. blue .. .. 40 20

**1958.** 5th Anniv. of Republic.
564. **172.** 10 m. violet .. .. 40 20

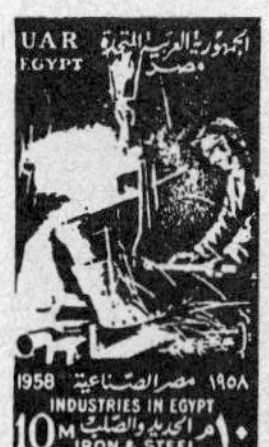

173. "Iron and Steel".

174. Sayed Darwich.

**1958.** 6th Anniv of 1952 Revolution. Egyptian Industries.

| | | | | |
|---|---|---|---|---|
| 565. | – | 10 m. brown .. .. | 35 | 20 |
| 566. | – | 10 m. green .. .. | 35 | 20 |
| 567. | **173.** | 10 m. red .. .. | 35 | 20 |
| 568. | – | 10 m. myrtle .. .. | 35 | 20 |
| 569. | – | 10 m. blue .. .. | 35 | 20 |

DESIGNS: Industrial views representing: No. 565, "Cement". No. 566, "Textiles". No. 568, "Petroleum". No. 569, "Electricity and Fertilizers".

**1958.** 35th Death Anniv. of Sayed Darwich.
580. **174.** 10 m. purple .. .. 40 20

175. Torch and Broken Chains.

176. Cogwheels, Maps and Emblems of Productivity.

**1958.** Republic of Iraq Commem.
581. **175.** 10 m. red .. .. 25 15

**1958.** Afro-Asian Economic Conf., Cairo.
582. **176.** 10 m. blue .. .. 40 20

**1958.** Industrial and Agricultural Fair, Cairo. As No. 582 but colour changed, optd. **INDUSTRIAL & AGRICULTURAL PRODUCTION FAIR** in Arabic and English.
583. **176.** 10 m. brown .. .. 40 25

178. Dr. Mahmoud Azmy (Egyptian U.N.O. representative).

**1958.** 10th Anniv. of Declaration of Human Rights.
584. **178.** 10 m. violet .. .. 35 25
585. 35 m. green .. .. 75 65

179. "Learning".
180. Egyptian Postal Emblem.

**1958.** 50th Anniv. of Cairo University.
586. **179.** 10 m. green .. .. 25 15

**1959.** Post Day and Postal Employees Social Fund.
587. **180.** 10 m. + 5 m. red, black and turquoise .. 25 20

**1959.** Surch **UAR 55** and equivalent in Arabic.
588 **132** 55 m. on 100 m. red .. 45 40

182.

184. State Emblem.

183. Nile Hilton Hotel.

**1959.** Afro-Asian Youth Conf., Cairo.
589. **182.** 10 m. green .. .. 25 15

**1959.** Opening of Nile Hilton Hotel.
590. **183.** 10 m. brown .. .. 25 15

**1959.** 1st Anniv. of United Arab Republic.
591. **184.** 10 m. red, black & grn. 25 15

185. "Telecommunications".

**1959.** Arab Telecommunications Union Commemoration.
592 **185** 10 m. violet .. .. 25 15

186. U.A.R. and Yemeni Flags.

187. Oil Derrick and Pipe-lines.

**1959.** 1st Anniv. of Proclamation of United Arab States (U.A.R. and Yemen).
593. **186.** 10 m. red and green .. 25 15

**1959.** 1st Arab Petroleum Congress.
594 **187** 10 m. blue & turquoise 25 20

188. "Railways" (Diesel-electric Train).
189. "Migration".

**1959.** 7th Anniv. of Revolution and Transport and Communications Commem. Frames in slate. Centre colours given.

| | | | | |
|---|---|---|---|---|
| 595. | **188.** | 10 m. lake .. .. | 70 | 30 |
| 596. | – | 10 m. green .. .. | 70 | 30 |
| 597. | – | 10 m. blue .. .. | 70 | 30 |
| 598. | – | 10 m. violet .. .. | 70 | 30 |
| 599. | – | 10 m. plum .. .. | 70 | 30 |
| 600. | – | 10 m. red .. .. | 70 | 30 |

DESIGNS: No. 596, "Highways" (bus passing bridge). 597, "Seaways" ("Al Mokattam" (freighter)). 598, "Nile Transport" (motorised river barge). 599, "Telecommunications" (telephone and radio mast). 600, "Postal Services" (Post Office H.Q., Cairo).

**1959.** 3rd Arab Emigrants' Association Convention, Middle East.
602. **189.** 10 m. lake .. .. 25 15

**1959.** As Types **132**, **160** and **168**, but inscr "UAR" only.

| | | | | |
|---|---|---|---|---|
| 603 | – | 1 m. red (as No. 553) .. | 10 | 30 |
| 604 | – | 2 m. blue (as No. 554) | 10 | 30 |
| 605 | **168** | 3 m. brown .. .. | 10 | 20 |
| 606 | – | 4 m. green (as No. 556) | 10 | 10 |
| 607 | – | 5 m. black (as No. 557) | 10 | 10 |
| 608 | **160** | 10 m. green .. .. | 20 | 10 |
| 609 | – | 15 m. brown .. .. | 30 | 10 |
| 610 | – | 20 m. red .. .. | 70 | 10 |
| 611 | – | 30 m. purple .. .. | 45 | 10 |
| 612 | – | 35 m. blue (as No. 559) | 55 | 10 |
| 613 | – | 40 m. brown .. .. | 75 | 15 |
| 614 | – | 45 m. blue .. .. | 1·60 | 20 |
| 615 | – | 55 m. green .. .. | 1·25 | 15 |
| 616 | – | 60 m. violet .. .. | 2·00 | 15 |
| 617 | – | 100 m. green & orange | 1·50 | 20 |
| 618 | – | 200 m. brown and blue | 3·00 | 35 |
| 619 | **132** | 500 m. red and blue .. | 9·00 | 1·10 |

DESIGNS—VERT: 15 m. Omayad Mosque, Damascus. 20 m. Tutankhamun's Lamp. 40 m. Statue. 55 m. Cotton and ears of corn. 60 m. Barrage and plant. 100 m. Egyptian eagle and hand holding agricultural products. HORIZ: 30 m. Stone archway. 45 m. Citadel Gate, Aleppo. 200 m. Temple ruins.
See also Nos. 669/72 and No. 739.

191. Airplane over Pyramids.

192. "Shield against Aggression".

**1959.** Air.

| | | | | |
|---|---|---|---|---|
| 620 | **191** | 5 m. red .. .. | 20 | 20 |
| 621 | – | 15 m. purple .. .. | 25 | 25 |
| 622 | – | 60 m. green .. .. | 60 | 50 |
| 623 | – | 90 m. purple .. .. | 1·25 | 1·00 |

DESIGNS: 15 m. Boeing Flying Fortress bomber over Colossi of Thebes. 60 m. Douglas DC-6B airliner over Al-Azhar University. 90 m. Airplane over St. Catherine's Monastery, Sinai.
See also Nos. 758/62.

**1959.** Army Day.
624. **192.** 10 m. red .. .. 25 15

193. Children and U.N. Emblem.
194. Cairo Museum.

**1959.** U.N. Day. UNICEF.
625 **193** 10 m. + 5 m. purple .. 25 25
626 35 m. + 10 m. blue .. 50 35

**1959.** Centenary of Cairo Museum.
627. **194.** 10 m. brown .. .. 25 15

195. Rock Temples of Abu Simbel.

**1959.** U.N.E.S.C.O. Campaign for Preservation of Nubian Monuments (1st issue).
628. **195.** 10 m. brown .. .. 40 30
See also Nos. 650, 676, 728, 754/6, 825/7, 864/6 and 878/9.

196. Mounted Postman.

**1960.** Post Day.
629. **196.** 10 m. blue .. .. 25 20

1960 UAR
ASWAN HIGH DAM MEANS:
10M
197.

198. View of projected Aswan High Dam.

**1960.** Laying of Foundation Stone of Aswan High Dam.
630. **197.** 10 m. lake .. .. 45 50
631. **198.** 35 m. lake .. .. 75 55

199. Aswan Dam Hydro-electric Power Station.

200.

**1960.** Projected Aswan Dam Hydro-Electric Power Station.
632. **199.** 10 m. black .. .. 25 15

**1960.** Industrial and Agricultural Fair.
633. **200.** 10 m. green .. .. 30 20

**1960.** No. 432 optd **UAR** and Arabic equivalent.
634 **132** £E1 red and green .. 12·00 3·00

202. State Emblem with U.A.R. Flag.

203. Sculpture and Palette.

**1960.** 2nd Anniv. of U.A.R.
635. **202.** 10 m. red, black & green 25 20

**1960.** 3rd Fine Arts Biennale. Alexandria.
636. **203.** 10 m. sepia .. .. 25 20

204. Arab League Centre, Cairo.

**1960.** Inaug. of Arab League Centre, Cairo.
637. **204.** 10 m. green and black 25 20

205. Mother and Child pointing to Map of Palestine.

206. Weight-lifting.

**1960.** World Refugee Year.
638. **205.** 10 m. red .. .. 20 20
639. 35 m. turquoise .. 55 55

**1960.** Sports Campaign and Olympic Games.

| | | | | |
|---|---|---|---|---|
| 640 | **206** | 5 m. grey .. .. | 20 | 20 |
| 641 | – | 5 m. brown .. .. | 20 | 20 |
| 642 | – | 5 m. purple .. .. | 20 | 20 |
| 643 | – | 10 m. red .. .. | 20 | 20 |
| 644 | – | 10 m. green .. .. | 20 | 20 |
| 645 | – | 30 m. violet .. .. | 45 | 45 |
| 646 | – | 35 m. blue .. .. | 55 | 50 |

DESIGNS—VERT: No. 641, Basketball. 642, Football. 643, Fencing. 644, Rowing. HORIZ: No. 645, Horse-jumping. 646, Swimming.

## MINIMUM PRICE

The minimum price quoted is 10p which represents a handling charge rather than a basis for valuing common stamps. For further notes about prices see introductory pages.

207. U.N. Emblem within 15 candles.

**1960.** 15th Anniv. of U.N.O.

648. – 10 m. violet .. .. 20 15
649. 207. 35 m. red .. .. 50 40
DESIGN—VERT. 10 m. Dove and U.N. Emblem.

208. Rock Temples of Abu Simbel.

**1960.** U.N.E.S.C.O. Campaign for Preservation of Nubian Monuments (2nd issue).

650. 208. 10 m. brown .. .. 50 35

209. Modern Post Office. 210. State Emblem. and Wreath.

**1961.** Post Day.

651. 209. 10 m. red .. .. 25 20

**1961.** 3rd Anniv. of U.A.R.

652. 210. 10 m. purple .. .. 25 20

211. Globe, Flags and Wheat. 212. Patrice Lumumba and Map of Africa.

**1961.** Int. Agricultural Exn. Cairo.

653. 211. 10 m. red .. .. 25 20

**1961.** 3rd All African Peoples' Conf. Cairo.

654. 212. 10 m. black .. .. 25 20

213. Hands "reading" Braille. 214. Tower of Cairo.

**1961.** World Health Organization Day.

655. 213. 10 m. brown .. .. 30 20
656. 35 m.+15 m. yellow & brown .. .. 65 70

**1961.** Inauguration of Tower of Cairo.

657 214 10 m. blue .. .. 25 20

**1961.** Air. As No. 657, but with aircraft replacing inscr. in upper corners and inscr. "AIR MAIL" in English and Arabic.

658. 214. 50 m. blue .. .. 65 60

215. Refugee Mother and Child, and Map. 216. "Transport and Communications".

**1961.** Palestine Day.

659. 215. 10 m. green .. .. 25 20

**1961.** 9th Anniv. of Revolution and Five Year Plan. Inscr. "1961".

660. 216. 10 m. purple .. .. 25 15
661. – 10 m. red .. .. 20 15
662. – 10 m. blue .. .. 20 15
663. – 35 m. myrtle .. .. 55 35
664. – 35 m. violet .. .. 55 35
DESIGNS: No. 661, Worker turning cogwheel and pylons. No. 662, Apartment houses. No. 663, Cotton plant and dam. No. 664, Family moving towards lighted candle.

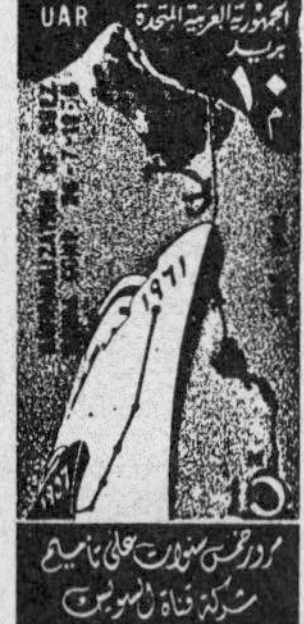

217. Ships and Map of Suez Canal. 218. Mehalla El Kobra Textile Factories.

**1961.** 5th Anniv. of Nationalization of Suez Canal.

666. 217. 10 m. olive .. .. 40 25

**1961.** Misr Bank Organization and 20th Death Anniversary of Talaat Harb (founder).

667. 218. 10 m. brown .. .. 25 20

219. Ship's Wheel and "Al Nasser" (destroyer). 220. "Industrial Worlds".

**1961.** Navy Day.

668. 219. 10 m. blue .. .. 25 20

**1961.** As Nos. 553, etc. Inscr. "UAR" only (in English). New colours.

669. 1 m. turquoise (as No. 603) 15 15
670. 4 m. olive (as No. 606) .. 15 15
671. 10 m. violet .. .. 25 15
672. 35 m. slate (as No. 612) .. 45 15
NEW DESIGN: 10 m. Eagle of Saladin.
See also No. 739.

**1961.** U.N. Technical Co-operation. Programme and 16th Anniv. of U.N.O.

674. – 10 m. black and brown 20 15
675. 220. 35 m. brown and green 50 35
DESIGN—VERT. 10 m. Corncob, wheel and book ("Agriculture, Industry and Education").

221. Philae Temple.

**1961.** 15th Anniv. of U.N.E.S.C.O. and Preservation of Nubian Monuments Campaign (3rd issue).

676. 221. 10 m. blue .. .. 60 30

222. "Fine Arts". 223. "Arts and Sciences".

**1961.** 4th Fine Arts Biennale, Alexandria.

677. 222. 10 m. brown .. .. 25 20

**1961.** Education Day.

678. 223. 10 m. purple .. .. 25 20

224. State Emblem, Torch and Olive Branch. 225. Sphinx and Pyramid.

**1961.** Victory Day.

679. 224. 10 m. green and red .. 25 20

**1961.** "Son et Lumiere" Display.

680. 225. 10 m. black .. .. 35 20

226. Postal Authority Press Building, El Nasr. 227. King of Morocco and Map.

**1962.** Post Day.

681. 226. 10 m. brown .. .. 25 20

**1962.** 1st Anniv. of African Charter of Casablanca.

682. 227. 10 m. blue .. .. 25 20

228. Guide and Badge. 229. Gaza Family with Egyptian Flag

**1962.** Silver Jubilee of Egyptian Girl Guides Association.

683 228 10 m. blue .. .. 30 20

**1962.** 5th Anniv. of Egyptian Occupation of Gaza.

684. 229. 10 m. myrtle .. .. 25 20

230. Mother and Child. 231. League Centre, Cairo, and Emblem.

**1962.** Mothers' Day.

694 230 10 m. purple .. .. 25 15

**1962.** Arab League Week.

695. 231. 10 m.+5 m. black .. 40 35

232. W.M.O. Emblem and Weather-vane. 233. Posthorn on North Africa.

**1962.** World Meteorological Day.

696. 232. 60 m. blue and yellow 65 65

**1962.** African Postal Union Commem.

697. 233. 10 m. brown and red .. 20 15
698. 50 m. brown and blue 60 50

234. Cadets on Parade. 235. Campaign Emblem.

**1962.** 150th Anniv. of Military Academy.

699. 234. 10 m. green .. .. 25 15

**1962.** Malaria Eradication.

700. 235. 10 m. red and sepia .. 20 15
701. – 35 m. blue and myrtle 50 40
DESIGN: 35 m. As Type 235 but with laurel and inscription around emblem.

237. Bilharz and Microscope. 238. Lumumba.

**1962.** Death Cent. of Dr Theodore Bilharz (discoverer of parasitic disease: bilharzia).

702. 237. 10 m. brown .. .. 35 20

**1962.** Lumumba Commem.

703. 238. 10 m. red (postage) .. 25 20
704. – 35 m. multicoloured (air) 65 45
DESIGN: 35 m. Lumumba with laurel sprays and flaming torch.

239. "The Charter". 240. "Birth of the Revolution".

**1962.** Proclamation of National Charter.

705. 239. 10 m. brown and blue 25 15

**1962.** 10th Anniv. of 1952 Revolution.

706. 240. 10 m. brown and pink 30 25
707. A. 10 m. sepia and blue .. 30 25
708. B. 10 m. blue and sepia .. 30 25
709. C. 10 m. blue and olive .. 30 25
710. D. 10 m. red, black & grn. 30 25
711. E. 10 m. slate and brown 30 25
712. F. 10 m. purple and brown 30 25
713. G. 10 m. sepia and orange 30 25
DESIGNS: A, Scroll and book. B, Agricultural Scene. C, Globe and dove. D, Flag and eagle emblem. E, Industrial scene and cogwheel. F, Dam construction. G, Eagle, building, cogwheel and ear of corn.

241. M. Moukhtar (sculptor) and "La Vestale des Secrets".

**1962.** Moukhtar Museum Inaug.

716. 241. 10 m. olive and blue .. 25 15

242. Algerian Flag and map. 243. Rocket.

**1962.** Independence of Algeria.

717. 242. 10 m. red, green & pink 25 15

**1962.** Launching of U.A.R. Rocket.

718. 243. 10 m. red, black & green 30 20

**244.** Table Tennis Bat, Ball and Net.

**1962.** 1st African Table Tennis Tournament, Alexandria, and 38th World Shooting Championships, Cairo.

| | | | | |
|---|---|---|---|---|
| 719. | **244.** | 5 m. red and green .. | 40 | 40 |
| 720. | – | 5 m. red and green .. | 40 | 40 |
| 721. | **244.** | 10 m. blue and ochre .. | 60 | 50 |
| 722. | – | 10 m. blue and ochre .. | 60 | 50 |
| 723. | **244.** | 35 m. red and blue .. | 1·25 | 1·00 |
| 724. | – | 35 m. red and blue .. | 1·25 | 1·00 |

DESIGN: Nos. 720, 722, 724, Rifle and target.

**245.** Dag Hammarskjold and U.N. Emblem.

**246.** Coronation of Queen Nefertari (from small temple of Abu Simbel).

**1962.** 17th Anniv of U.N.O. and Dag Hammarskjold (Secretary-General, 1953–61) Commemoration.

| | | | | |
|---|---|---|---|---|
| 725 | **245** | 5 m. blue and violet .. | 20 | 15 |
| 726 | | 10 m. blue and green | 35 | 20 |
| 727 | | 35 m. blue & ultram .. | 60 | 45 |

**1962.** U.N.E.S.C.O. Campaign for Preservation of Nubian Monuments (4th issue).

| | | | | |
|---|---|---|---|---|
| 728. | **246.** | 10 m. brown and blue | 45 | 25 |

**247.** Al Kahira Jet Trainer, College Emblem and De Havilland Tiger Moth Biplane.

**1962.** Silver Jubilee of U.A.R. Air Force College.

| | | | | |
|---|---|---|---|---|
| 729. | **247.** | 10 m. red and blue .. | 30 | 20 |

**248.** Postal Authority Emblem.

**1963.** Post Day and 1966 Int. Stamp Exn. Insc. "1866 1966".

| | | | | |
|---|---|---|---|---|
| 736. | **248.** | 20 m. + 10 m. red & grn. | 75 | 75 |
| 737. | – | 40 m. + 20 m. sepia and brown .. .. | 1·25 | 1·50 |
| 738. | – | 40 m. + 20 m. brn. & sepia | 1·25 | 1·50 |

DESIGNS—TRIANGULAR: Egyptian stamps of 1866 – No. 737, 5 paras. No. 738, 10 paras.

**1963.** As No. 670 but inscr. "1963" in English and Arabic and new colours.

| | | | | |
|---|---|---|---|---|
| 739. | | 4 m. red, green and sepia .. | 20 | 15 |

**249.** Yemeni Republican Flag and Torch.

**250.** Maritime Station, Alexandria.

**1963.** Proclamation of Yemeni Arab Republic.

| | | | | |
|---|---|---|---|---|
| 740. | **249.** | 10 m. red and olive .. | 20 | 15 |

**1963.** Air.

| | | | | |
|---|---|---|---|---|
| 741. | **250.** | 20 m. sepia .. .. | 45 | 20 |
| 742. | – | 30 m. mauve .. .. | 60 | 35 |
| 743. | – | 40 m. black .. .. | 90 | 75 |

DESIGNS: 30 m. International Airport, Cairo. 40 m. Railway Station, Luxor.

**251.** Tennis-player.

**1963.** 51st Int. Lawn Tennis Championships held in U.A.R.

| | | | | |
|---|---|---|---|---|
| 744. | **251.** | 10 m. brown and black | 50 | 25 |

**252.** Cow and Emblems.

**1963.** Freedom from Hunger.

| | | | | |
|---|---|---|---|---|
| 745 | **252** | 5 m. brown and violet | 25 | 20 |
| 746 | – | 10 m. yellow and blue | 30 | 20 |
| 747 | – | 35 m. yellow and blue | 45 | 45 |

DESIGNS—VERT: 10 m. Corncob and ear of wheat. HORIZ: 35 m. Corncob, ear of wheat, U.N. and F.A.O. emblems.

**253.** Centenary Emblem within Red Crescent.

**254.** "Arab Socialist Union".

**1963.** Centenary of Red Cross.

| | | | | |
|---|---|---|---|---|
| 748. | **253.** | 10 m. red, purple & blue | 30 | 20 |
| 749. | – | 35 m. red and blue .. | 65 | 65 |

DESIGN: 35 m. Emblem, Red Crescent, olive branches and Globe.

**1963.** 11th Anniv. of Revolution.

| | | | | |
|---|---|---|---|---|
| 750. | **254.** | 10 m. mauve and blue | 20 | 15 |

**255.** TV Building, Cairo, and Television Receiver.

**256.** Queen Nefertari.

**1963.** 2nd International Television Festival, Alexandria.

| | | | | |
|---|---|---|---|---|
| 753 | **255** | 10 m. yellow and blue | 20 | 15 |

**1963.** U.N.E.S.C.O. Campaign for preservation of Nubian Monuments (5th issue).

| | | | | |
|---|---|---|---|---|
| 754. | **256.** | 5 m. yellow and blue .. | 35 | 20 |
| 755. | – | 10 m. orange and black | 45 | 35 |
| 756. | – | 35 m. yellow and black | 80 | 60 |

DESIGNS—(28×61 mm.): 10 m. Great Hall of Pillars, Abu Simbel. As Type **256**: 35 m. Heads of Colossi, Abu Simbel.

**257.** Swimmer and Map.

**258.** Ministry Building.

**1963.** Suez Canal Int. Long-distance Swimming Race.

| | | | | |
|---|---|---|---|---|
| 757. | **257.** | 10 m. red and blue .. | 30 | 20 |

**1963.** Air.

| | | | | |
|---|---|---|---|---|
| 758 | | 50 m. brown and blue .. | 2·00 | 80 |
| 759 | | 80 m. purple and blue .. | 2·50 | 1·25 |
| 761 | | 115 m. yellow and brown | 2·75 | 1·10 |
| 762 | | 140 m. red and violet .. | 2·75 | 1·50 |

DESIGNS—VERT: 50 m. Cairo Tower and Arch. HORIZ: 80 m. As No. 622. 115 m. Colossi of Rameses II and Queen Nefertari, Abu Simbel. 140 m. Seated colossi of Rameses II (Great Temple, Abu Simbel).

**1963.** 50th Anniv. of Egyptian Ministry of Agriculture.

| | | | | |
|---|---|---|---|---|
| 763. | **258.** | 10 m. blue and brown | 20 | 15 |

**259.** Map and Blocks of Flats.

**1963.** Afro-Asian Housing Congress.

| | | | | |
|---|---|---|---|---|
| 764 | **259** | 10 m. blue and brown | 20 | 15 |

**259a.** Globe and Scales of Justice.

**259b.** Statuette, Palette and Arms of Alexandria.

**1963.** 15th Anniv of Declaration of Human Rights.

| | | | | |
|---|---|---|---|---|
| 765 | **259a** | 5 m. yellow and green | 20 | 15 |
| 766 | – | 10 m. black, brn & bl | 25 | 15 |
| 767 | – | 35 m. blk, pink & red | 60 | 40 |

DESIGNS: 10, 35 m. As Type **259a** but arranged differently.

**1963.** 5th Fine Arts Biennale, Alexandria.

| | | | | |
|---|---|---|---|---|
| 768. | **259b.** | 10 m. brown and blue | 20 | 15 |

**260.** El Mitwalli Gate, Cairo.

**261.** Glass and Enamel Urn.

**263.** King Osircaf.

**1964.**

| | | | | |
|---|---|---|---|---|
| 769 | – | 1 m. blue and green .. | 10 | 10 |
| 770 | – | 2 m. bistre and purple | 10 | 10 |
| 771 | – | 3 m. bl, orge & salmon | 10 | 10 |
| 772 | – | 4 m. brown, black & bl | 10 | 10 |
| 773 | – | 5 m. brown, lt brn & bl | 10 | 10 |
| 774 | – | 10 m. lt brn, brn & grn | 20 | 10 |
| 775 | – | 15 m. yell, ultram & bl | 20 | 10 |
| 776 | – | 20 m. brown and blue | 50 | 10 |
| 777 | **260** | 20 m. green .. .. | 1·10 | 15 |
| 778 | **261** | 30 m. brown & yellow | 45 | 10 |
| 779 | – | 35 m. brown, bl & orge | 55 | 10 |
| 780 | – | 40 m. blue and yellow | 1·10 | 20 |
| 781 | – | 55 m. violet .. .. | 1·60 | 20 |
| 782 | – | 60 m. brown and blue | 75 | 30 |
| 783 | **263** | 100 m. blue and purple | 2·00 | 45 |
| 784 | – | 200 m. brown and blue | 4·50 | 65 |
| 785 | – | 500 m. orange and blue | 9·75 | 1·90 |

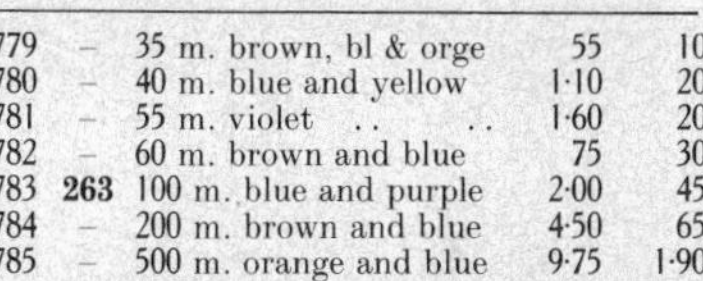

DESIGNS—As Type **260**. 55 m. Kiosk, Sultan Hussein Mosque. As Type **261**— VERT. 1 m. 14th-century glass vase. 4 m. Minaret and archway. 10 m. Eagle emblem and pyramids. 35 m. Queen Nefertari. 40 m. Nile near Agouza. 60 m. Al-Azhar Mosque. HORIZ. 2 m. Ancient Egyptian headrest. 3 m. Alabaster funerary barge. 5 m. Aswan High Dam. 15 m. Window, Ahmed ibn Toulon Mosque. 20 m. (No. 776), Nile Hilton Hotel and Kasr el Nile Bridge. As Type **263**: 200 m. Rameses. 500 m. Tutankhamun.

For the 4 m. in different colours, and with date "1964" added to design see No. 791.

For stamps as Nos. 777 and 781 but larger and in different colours, see Nos. 1042, 1044, 1134/5 and 1137.

**264.** Eagle and Pyramids.

**265.** Emblems on Map of Africa.

**1964.** Post Day.

| | | | | |
|---|---|---|---|---|
| 786. | **264.** | 10 m. + 5 m. grn. & yell. | 1·50 | 1·00 |
| 787. | | 80 m. + 40 m. blk. & bl. | 2·50 | 1·90 |
| 788. | | 115 m. + 55 m. black and brown .. .. | 3·25 | 2·50 |

**1964.** 1st Health, Sanitation and Nutrition Commission Conference, Cairo.

| | | | | |
|---|---|---|---|---|
| 789. | **265.** | 10 m. yellow and blue | 20 | 15 |

**266.** League Emblem and Links.

**1964.** Arab League Heads of State Council, Cairo.

| | | | | |
|---|---|---|---|---|
| 790. | **266.** | 10 m. black and green | 20 | 15 |

**267.** Arch and Minaret.

**268.** Map and Old and New Houses.

**1964.** Ramadan Festival.

| | | | | |
|---|---|---|---|---|
| 791. | **267.** | 4 m. green, red & black | 20 | 10 |

**1964.** Nubians' Resettlement.

| | | | | |
|---|---|---|---|---|
| 792. | **268.** | 10 m. yellow & purple .. | 20 | 15 |

**269.** King Akhnaton and Family (Tutankhamun's tomb).

**270.** Diesel Train and Afro-Asian Map.

**1964.** Mothers' Day.

| | | | | |
|---|---|---|---|---|
| 793. | **269.** | 10 m. brown and blue | 20 | 15 |

**1964.** Asian Railways Conference.

| | | | | |
|---|---|---|---|---|
| 794. | **270.** | 10 m. yellow and blue | 40 | 20 |

271. Office Emblem. 272. W.H.O. Emblem.

**1964.** 10th Anniv. of Arab Postal Union's Permanent Office.
795. 271. 10 m. blue and brown 20 10

**1964.** World Health Day.
796. 272. 10 m. blue and red .. 20 10

273. Statue of Liberty, U.A.R. Pavilion and Pyramids.

**1964.** New York World's Fair.
797. 273. 10 m. grn., brn. & olive 20 10

274. Site of Diversion.

**1964.** Nile High Dam (Diversion of Flow).
798. 274. 10 m. black and blue.. 25 20

275. Map of Africa and Flags.

**1964.** O.A.U. Assembly, Cairo.
799. 275. 10 m. black, bl. & brn. 35 20

DESIGN: No. 801, "Land Reclamation" (tractor and symbols of land cultivation).

276. "Electricity".

**1964.** Aswan Dam Projects.
800. 276. 10 m. blue and green.. 35 20
801. – 10 m. green and yellow 35 20

277. Jamboree Badge.

**1964.** 6th Pan Arab Scout Jamboree Alexandria.
803. 277. 10 m. green and red .. 35 25
804. – 10 m. red and green .. 35 25
DESIGN: No. 804, Air Scout badge.

278. Algerian Flag.

**1964.** 2nd Arab League Heads of State Council. Flags in national colours; inscr. in green (except Sudan, in blue). Each with country name at foot.
805. 10 m. Type 278 .. .. 60 30
806. 10 m. Iraq .. .. 60 30
807. 10 m. Jordan .. .. 60 30
808. 10 m. Kuwait .. .. 60 30
809. 10 m. Lebanon .. .. 60 30
810. 10 m. Libya .. .. 60 30
811. 10 m. Morocco .. .. 60 30
812. 10 m. Saudi Arabia .. 60 30
813. 10 m. Sudan .. .. 60 30
814. 10 m. Syria .. .. 60 30
815. 10 m. Tunisia .. .. 60 30
816. 10 m. U.A.R. .. .. 60 30
817. 10 m. Yemen .. .. 60 30

279. Globe, Dove and Pyramids.

**1964.** Non-aligned Countries Conf., Cairo.
818. 279. 10 m. yellow and blue 20 15

280. Emblem and Map. 281. Gymnastics.

**1964.** 1st Afro-Asian Medical Congress.
819. 280. 10 m. violet and yellow 20 15

**1964.** Olympic Games, Tokyo.
820. – 5 m. orange and green 20 20
821. 281. 10 m. ochre and blue.. 20 20
822. – 35 m. ochre and purple 65 65
823. – 50 m. brown and blue 90 90
DESIGNS—As Type 281—HORIZ. 5 m. Gymnastics. VERT. 35 m. Wrestling. LARGER (61 × 28 mm.): 50 m. Charioteer hunting lions.

282. Emblems of Posts and Telecommunications and Map. 283. Rameses II.

**1964.** Pan-African and Malagasy Posts and Telecommunications Congress. Cairo.
824. 282. 10 m. sepia and green 20 15

**1964.** U.N.E.S.C.O. Campaign for Preservation of Nubian Monuments (6th issue).
825. – 5 m. brown and blue.. 20 15
826. 283. 10 m. yellow and sepia 45 20
827. – 35 m. blue & brown 1·40 95
DESIGNS—SQUARE (40 × 40 mm.) 5 m. Horus and facade of Abu Simbel. 35 m. Wall sculpture, Abu Simbel.

284. Handicrafts and Weaving. 285. U.N. and U.N.E.S.C.O. Emblems.

**1964.** 25th Anniv. of Ministry of Social Affairs.
829. 284. 10 m. blue and yellow 20 15

**1964.** U.N.E.S.C.O. Day.
830 285 10 m. blue and yellow 20 15

286. Emblem and Posthorn.

**1965.** Post Day and 1966 Int. Stamp Exn.
831. 286. 10 m. + 5 m. red, purple and green .. 65 65
832. – 10 m. + 5 m. red, black and blue .. .. 65 65
833. – 80 m. + 40 m. black, green and red .. 2·00 2·00
DESIGNS—As Type 286: No. 832, Posthorn over emblem. As Type 248: 80 m. Bird carrying letter, inscr. "STAMP CENTENARY EXHIBITION".

286a Al-Maridani Mosque Minaaret 287. Police Emblem.

**1965.** Ramadan Festival.
834 286a 4 m. brown and blue 35 20

**1965.** Police Day.
835. 287. 10 m. yellow and sepia 65 20

288. Oil Derrick. 289. Emblem and Flags.

**1965.** 5th Arab Petroleum Congress and 2nd Petroleum Exn.
836. 288. 10 m. sepia and yellow 50 25

**1965.** 20th Anniv. of Arab League.
837. 289. 10 m. green and red .. 65 30
838. – 20 m. brown and blue 85 50
DESIGN—HORIZ. 20 m. Arab League emblem.

290. W.M.O. Emblem and Weather-vane.

**1965.** Air. World Meteorological Day.
839 290 80 m. purple and blue 2·50 1·25

291. W.H.O. Emblem within Red Crescent. 292. Dagger on Deir Yassin, Palestine.

**1965.** World Health Day.
840. 291. 10 m. red and blue .. 45 25

**1965.** Deir Yassin Massacre.
841. 292. 10 m. red and sepia .. 1·10 25

293. I.T.U. Emblem and Symbols.

**1965.** Centenary of I.T.U.
842. 293. 5 m. pur., yell. & blk. 30 25
843. 10 m. rose, yell. & red 45 25
844. 35 m. blue, yellow and deep blue .. .. 1·40 1·10

294. Lamp and Burning Library.

**1965.** Reconstitution of Algiers University Library.
845. 294. 10 m. green, red & black 40 20

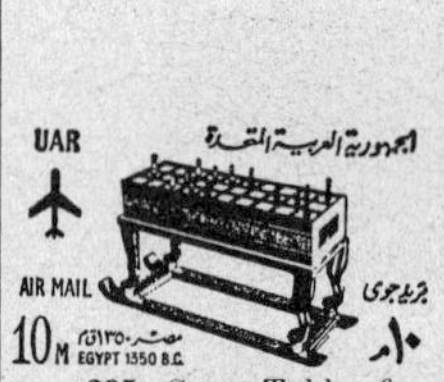

295. Senet Table of 1350 B.C. 296. Shaikh Mohamed Abdo.

**1965.** Air. Re-establishment of Egyptian Civil Airlines, "MISRAIR".
846. 295. 10 m. blue and yellow 1·25 25

**1965.** 60th Death Anniv. of Shaikh Abdo (mufti).
847. 296. 10 m. brown and blue 25 20

297. "Housing".

**1965.** 13th Anniv. of Revolution.
848. 297. 10 m. black and brown 50 30
849. – 10 m. brown & yellow 50 30
850. – 10 m. indigo and blue 50 30
851. – 100 m. black and green 3·75 3·25
DESIGNS—SQUARE: No. 849, "Heavy Industry" (ladle and furnace). 850, "Petroleum and Mining" (refinery and oil rig "Discoverer"). 80 × 80 mm: No. 851, President Nasser.

298. Stadium, Flag and Torch.

**1965.** 4th Pan-Arab Games, Cairo.
857 **298** 5 m. blue & red on blue 30 30
858 – 10 m. brown and blue 60 30
859 – 35 m. brown and green 1·00 95
DESIGNS—As Type **298**: 35 m. Horse "Saadoon". DIAMOND (56×56 mm): 10 m. Map and emblems of Arab countries.

**299.** Swimmers Zeitun and Abd el Gelil.

**1965.** Long-Distance Swimming Championships, Alexandria.
860. **299.** 10 m. sepia and blue . . 50 25

**300.** Map and Arab League Emblem. **301.** Land Forces Emblem.

**1965.** 3rd Arab Summit Conf., Casablanca.
861. **300.** 10 m. sepia and yellow 30 20

**1965.** Land Forces Day.
862. **301.** 10 m. black and brown 45 25

**302.** Flaming Torch on Africa.

**1965.** O.A.U. Assembly, Accra.
863. **302.** 10 m. purple & red . . 30 15

**303.** Rameses II, Abu Simbel.

**1965.** U.N.E.S.C.O. Campaign for Preservation of Nubian Monuments (7th issue).
864. **303.** 5 m. blue and yellow . . 55 30
865. – 10 m. black and blue . . 1·00 35
866. – 35 m. violet and yellow 1·90 1·25
DESIGNS—As Type **303**: 35 m. Colossi, Abu Simbel. VERT. (28×61½ mm.): 10 m. Hall of Pillars, Abu Simbel.

**304.** Al-Maqrizi, Scrolls and Books. **305.** Bust and Flag.

**1965.** 600th Birth Anniv. of Al-Maqrizi (historian).
868. **304.** 10 m. blue and olive . . 30 15

**1965.** 6th Fine Arts Biennale, Alexandria.
869. **305.** 10 m. multicoloured . . 30 15

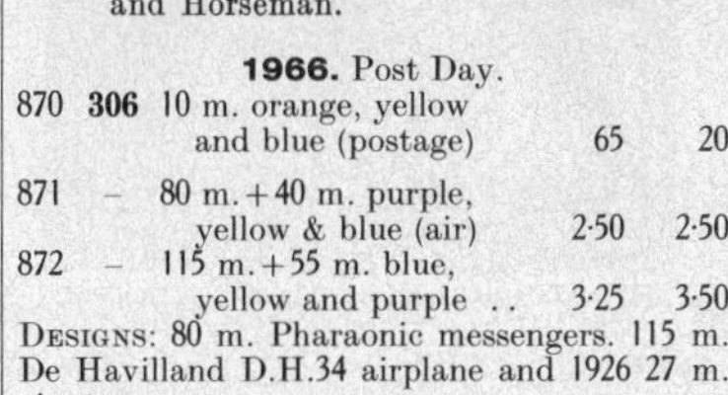

**306.** Pigeon, Parchment and Horseman. **307.** Glass Lamp.

**1966.** Post Day.
870 **306** 10 m. orange, yellow and blue (postage) 65 20
871 – 80 m.+40 m. purple, yellow & blue (air) 2·50 2·50
872 – 115 m.+55 m. blue, yellow and purple . . 3·25 3·50
DESIGNS: 80 m. Pharaonic messengers. 115 m. De Havilland D.H.34 airplane and 1926 27 m. air stamp.

**1966.** Ramadan Festival.
874. **307.** 4 m. orange and violet 30 15

**308.** Exhibition Emblem. **309.** Arab League Emblem.

**1966.** Industrial Exhibition, Cairo.
875 **308** 10 m. black, bl & lt bl 30 15

**1966.** Arab Publicity Week.
876. **309.** 10 m. violet and yellow 30 15

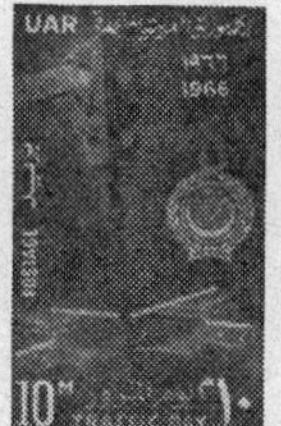

**310.** Torch and Newspapers. **312.** Traffic Signals.

**311.** Rock Temples of Abu Simbel.

**1966.** Cent. of Egyptian National Press.
877. **310.** 10 m. slate and orange 30 15

**1966.** Air. U.N.E.S.C.O. Campaign for Preservation of Nubian Monuments (8th issue).
878. **311.** 20 m. multicoloured . . 65 40
879. 80 m. multicoloured . . 1·60 1·25

**1966.** Traffic Day.
880. **312.** 10 m. red, emer. & grn. 65 25

**313.** Torch. **314.** "Labourers".

**1966.** U.A.R.—Iraq Union Agreement.
881. **313.** 10 m. red, grn. & pur. 30 15

**1966.** 50th Session of I.L.O. Conf.
882. **314.** 5 m. black & turquoise 25 20
883. 10 m. green and purple 25 20
884. 35 m. black and orange 1·00 75

**315.** Emblem, People and City. **316.** Building "Salah-el-Deen".

**1966.** 1st Population Census.
885. **315.** 10 m. purple and brown 25 15

**1966.** 14th Anniv of Revolution.
886 **316** 10 m. black, bl & orge 50 25
887 – 10 m. pur, yell & grn 50 25
888 – 10 m. blue, yell & blk 50 25
889 – 10 m. turq, bl & red . . 50 25
DESIGNS: No. 886, Type **316** (shipbuilding). 887, Transfer of first stones at Abu Simbel. 888, Map (development of Sinai). 889, El Mahdi hospital, nurse and patient.

**318.** Suez Canal H.Q., "Southern Cross" (liner), Freighter and Map.

**1966.** 10th Anniv. of Suez Canal Nationalization.
891. **318.** 10 m. red and blue . . 65 30

**319.** Jamboree Emblem and Camp.

**1966.** Air. 7th Pan-Arab Scout Jamboree, Libya.
892. **319.** 20 m. red and olive . . 95 45

**320.** Cotton.

**1966.** Peasants' Day.
893. **320.** 5 m. violet, yell. & blue 25 20
894. – 10 m. brn. & grn. (Rice) 25 20
895. – 35 m. orge. & bl. (Onions) 1·00 75

**321.** W.H.O. Building.

**1966.** U.N. Day.
896. **321.** 5 m. violet and olive . . 25 20
897. – 10 m. violet & orange 25 20
898. – 35 m. violet and blue . . 75 50
DESIGNS: 10 m. U.N.R.W.A. (Refugees) emblem. 35 m. U.N.I.C.E.F. emblem.

**322.** Globe and Festival Emblem.

**1966.** 5th Int. Television Festival.
899. **322.** 10 m. violet and yellow 30 15

**MINIMUM PRICE**
The minimum price quoted is 10p which represents a handling charge rather than a basis for valuing common stamps. For further notes about prices see introductory pages.

**323.** St. Catherine's Monastery.

**1966.** Air. 1400th Anniv of St. Catherine's Monastery, Mt. Sinai.
900 **323** 80 m. red, yellow & blue 2·25 1·60

**324.** Eagle and Torch.

**1966.** Victory Day.
901. **324.** 10 m. red and green . . 35 15

**325.** Anubis (God).

**1967.** Post Day. Designs showing items from Tutankhamun's Tomb.
902 **325** 10 m. multicoloured . . 50 20
903 – 35 m. brown, pur & bl 75 45
904 – 80 m.+20 m. brown, yellow and blue . . 2·25 2·25
905 – 115 m.+40 m. brown, black and blue . . 3·75 3·50
DESIGNS—As T **325**: 35 m. Alabaster head (stopper from canopic urn). 27×60 mm: 80 m. Ushabti figure. 115 m. Statue of Tutankhamun.

**326.** Carnations. **327.** Tree-planting.

**1967.** Ramadan Festival.
906. **326.** 4 m. violet and olive . . 30 15

**1967.** Tree Festival.
907. **327.** 10 m. lilac and green . . 30 15

**328.** Gamal el-Dine el-Afghani and Arab League Emblem. **329.** Workers, Factories and Census Symbol.

**1967.** Arab Publicity Week.
908. **328.** 10 m. brown and green 30 15

**1967.** 1st Industrial Census.
909. **329.** 10 m. green & orange 30 15

**330.** Hawker Siddeley Comet 4 Aircraft at Cairo Airport.

**1967.** Air.
910. **330.** 20 m. blue and brown 95 30

**331.** " Workers " (rock-carving).

**1967.** Labour Day.
911. **331.** 10 m. orange and olive 35 20

**332.** Nefertari and Rameses II.

**1967.** International Tourist Year.
912 **332** 10 m. red, yellow and green (postage) .. 65 35
913 – 35 m. orange, yell & bl 2·75 95
914 – 20 m. lilac, black and orange (air) .. 65 20
915 – 80 m. brown, yell & bl 1·60 1·10
916 – 115 m. orange, bl & brn 3·00 1·60
DESIGNS—As T **332**: 35 m. Shooting red-breasted geese. 40 × 40 mm: 20 m. Hotel, El Alamein. 80 m. Virgin's Tree. 115 m. Hotel and fishes, Red Sea.

**333.** Pres. Nasser and Map.

**1967.** Arab Solidarity for Palestine Defence.
917. **333.** 10 m. ol., yell. & orge. 1·90 1·25

**334.** " Petroleum " (oil rigs).

**1967.** Air. 15th Anniv. of Revolution.
930. **334.** 50 m. blk., orge. & blue 1·00 65

**336.** Salama Higazi.

**337.** Porcelain Dish.

**1967.** 50th Death Anniv. of Higazi (lyric stage impresario).
932. **336.** 20 m. brown and blue 65 20

**1967.** U.N. Day. Egyptian Art.
933 20 m. blue & red (postage) 55 30
934 55 m. multicoloured .. 1·00 65
935 80 m. red, yellow & bl (air) 1·10 85
DESIGNS: 20 m. Type **337**. 55 m. "Christ in Glory" (painting). 80 m. Tutankhamun and Ankhesenamun (back of throne).

**338.** Savings Bank " Coffer ".

**1967.** World Savings Day.
936. **338.** 20 m. blue and pink 45 25

**339.** Ca d'Oro Palace (Venice) and Santa Maria Cathedral (Florence).

**1967.** " Save the Monuments of Florence and Venice ".
937. **339.** 80 m. + 20 m. brown, yellow and green .. 1·25 1·60
938. – 115 m. + 30 m. blue, yellow and olive .. 2·25 2·40
DESIGN: 115 m. Palace of the Doges and Campanile (Venice) and Vecchio Palace (Florence).

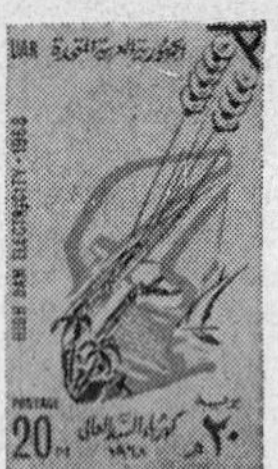
**340.** Rose.

**341.** Isis.

**1967.** Ramadan Festival.
939. **340.** 5 m. purple and green 40 20

**1968.** Post Day. Pharaonic Dress.
940. **341.** 20 m. sepia, green & yell. 65 20
941. – 55 m. brn., yell. & grn. 1·25 75
942. – 80 m. red, bl. & blk.. 1·75 95
DESIGNS: 55 m. Nefertari. 80 m. Isis (different). See also Nos. 970/3.

**342.** High Dam and Power Station.

**1968.** Electrification of High Dam.
943 **342** 20 m. purple, yell & bl 40 20

**343.** Alabaster Vessel (Tutankhamun).

**344.** Head of Woman.

**1968.** International Museums Festival.
944 **343** 20 m. brown, yell & bl 45 15
945 – 80 m. grn, vio & emer 1·10 85
DESIGN—39 × 39 mm: 80 m. Capital of Coptic limestone pillar.

**1968.** 7th Fine Arts Biennale, Alexandria.
946. **344.** 20 m. black and blue .. 25 15

**345.** "The Glorious Koran ".
(Illustration reduced. Actual size 75 × 36 mm.)

**1968.** Air. 1400th Anniv. of The Holy Koran.
947. **345.** 30 m. violet, blue & yell. 95 95
948. 80 m. violet, blue & yell. 1·25 1·25

**346.** Tending Cattle.

**1968.** Arab Veterinary Congress.
949. **346.** 20 m. brn., grn. & yell. 40 20

**347.** St. Mark and St. Mark's Cathedral.

**1968.** Air. 1900th Anniv of Martyrdom of St. Mark.
950 **347** 80 m. sepia, mve & grn 1·25 95

**348.** Human Rights Emblem.

**349.** Open Book and Symbols.

**1968.** Human Rights Year.
951. **348.** 20 m. red, green & olive 30 15
952. 60 m. red, green & blue 65 65

**1968.** 16th Anniv of Revolution.
953 **349** 20 m. green and pink .. 25 15

**351.** W.H.O. Emblem and Imhotep.

**352.** Table Tennis Bats, Net and Ball.

**1968.** 20th Anniv. of W.H.O.
955. **351.** 20 m. sepia, yell. & bl. 50 40
956. – 20 m. turquoise, sepia and yellow 50 40
DESIGN: No. 956, W.H.O. emblem and Avicenna.

**1968.** 1st Mediterranean Table Tennis Tournament.
957. **352.** 20 m. brown and green 65 25

**353.** Industrial Skyline.

**1968.** Int. Industrial Fair, Cairo.
958. **353.** 20 m. red, indigo and blue .. .. .. 35 20

**354.** Philae Temple.

**355.** Scout Badge.

**1968.** United Nations Day.
959. – 20 m. salmon, vio. & blue 45 20
960. – 30 m. blue, orge. & yell. 65 50
961. **354.** 55 m. pur., yell. & blue 1·10 75
DESIGNS (62 × 29 mm.): 20 m. Philae Temples (aerial view). (As Type **354**): 30 m. Refugee women and children.

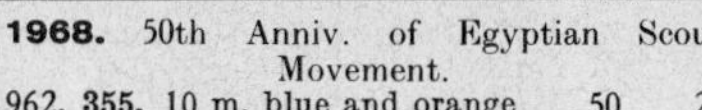
**1968.** 50th Anniv. of Egyptian Scout Movement.
962. **355.** 10 m. blue and orange 50 20

**356.** Ancient Games.

**1968.** Olympic Games Mexico.
963. **356.** 20 m. violet, olive & orge. 45 20
964. – 30 m. violet, bl. & buff 65 50
DESIGN: 30 m. Ancient Games (different).

**357.** Boeing 707 Jetliner and Route Map.

**358.** Ali Moubarek (educator).

**1968.** Air. 1st United Arab Airlines Boeing Flight, Cairo—London.
965. **357.** 55 m. red, blue & orge. 95 65

**1968.** 75th Death Anniv of Ali Moubarek.
966 **358** 20 m. lilac, orge & grn 40 20

**359.** Boy and Girl.

**360.** Lotus.

**1968.** World Children's Day.
967 **359** 20 m. + 10 m. red, blue and brown .. .. 65 65
968 – 20 m. + 10 m. blue, brown and green .. 65 65
DESIGN: No. 968, Group of Children.

**1968.** Ramadan Festival.
969. **360.** 5 m. yellow, bl. & grn. 35 15

**1968.** Post Day. Pharaonic Dress. As T **341**.
970 5 m. brown, yellow & blue 40 20
971 20 m. yellow, red and blue 65 40
972 20 m. brn, cinnamon & bl 75 45
973 55 m. orange, yellow & bl 1·75 1·10
DESIGNS: No. 970, Son of Ramess III. 971, Rameses III. 972, Maiden carrying offerings. 973, Queen Nefertari.

**361.** H. Nassef (poet and writer).

**363.** Teacher at Blackboard.

**362.** Ilyushin Il-18 and Route Map.

**1969.** 50th Death Anniv of Hefni Nassef and Mohamed Farid.
974 **361** 20 m. brown and violet 40 40
975 – 20 m. brown and green 40 40
DESIGN: No. 975, M. Farid (politician).

**1969.** Air. Inauguration of Ilyushin Il-18 Aircraft by United Arab Airlines.
976 **362** 55 m. purple, yell & bl 95 65

**1969.** Arab Teachers' Day.
977. **363.** 20 m. multicoloured .. 35 15

**364.** Flags of Arab Nations. **365.** I.L.O. Emblem and Factory Stacks.

**1969.** Arab Publicity Week.

| | | | | |
|---|---|---|---|---|
| 978 | **364** | 20 m. + 10 m. red, blue and green .. .. | 45 | 45 |

**1969.** 50th Anniv. of I.L.O.

| | | | | |
|---|---|---|---|---|
| 979. | **365.** | 20 m. multicoloured .. | 40 | 20 |

**366.** Algerian Flag.

**1969.** African Tourist Year. Flags of African Nations.

| | | | | |
|---|---|---|---|---|
| 980. | **366.** | 10 m. red and green | 60 | 30 |
| 981. | – | 10 m. blk., blue & grn. | 60 | 30 |
| 982. | – | 10 m. red and green .. | 60 | 30 |
| 983. | – | 10 m. red, yell. & grn. | 60 | 30 |
| 984. | – | 10 m. multicoloured .. | 60 | 30 |
| 985. | – | 10 m. yell., red & blue | 60 | 30 |
| 986. | – | 10 m. brn., red & grn. | 60 | 30 |
| 987. | – | 10 m. red, yellow & bl. | 60 | 30 |
| 988. | – | 10 m. brn., red & grn. | 60 | 30 |
| 989. | – | 10 m. grn., red & blk. | 60 | 30 |
| 990. | – | 10 m. multicoloured .. | 60 | 30 |
| 991. | – | 10 m. multicoloured | 60 | 30 |
| 992. | – | 10 m. yell., grn. & blue | 60 | 30 |
| 993. | – | 10 m. bl., red & green | 60 | 30 |
| 994. | – | 10 m. multicoloured | 60 | 30 |
| 995. | – | 10 m. brn., red & grn. | 60 | 30 |
| 996. | – | 10 m. orange & green | 60 | 30 |
| 997. | – | 10 m. blk., red & green | 60 | 30 |
| 998. | – | 10 m. blue, red & grn. | 60 | 30 |
| 999. | – | 10 m. red and blue .. | 60 | 30 |
| 1000. | – | 10 m. blk., red & green | 60 | 30 |
| 1001. | – | 10 m. red and green .. | 60 | 30 |
| 1002. | – | 10 m. red, blk. & grn. | 60 | 30 |
| 1003. | – | 10 m. brn., red & grn. | 60 | 30 |
| 1004. | – | 10 m. yellow & green | 60 | 30 |
| 1005. | – | 10 m. multicoloured .. | 60 | 30 |
| 1006. | – | 10 m. green and red | 60 | 30 |
| 1007. | – | 10 m. orange & green | 60 | 30 |
| 1008. | – | 10 m. green .. .. | 60 | 30 |
| 1009. | – | 10 m. multicoloured | 60 | 30 |
| 1010. | – | 10 m. grn., brn. & red | 60 | 30 |
| 1011. | – | 10 m. blue and green | 60 | 30 |
| 1012. | – | 10 m. blue and green | 60 | 30 |
| 1013. | – | 10 m. yell., grn. & blue | 60 | 30 |
| 1014. | – | 10 m. multicoloured | 60 | 30 |
| 1015. | – | 10 m. multicoloured | 60 | 30 |
| 1016. | – | 10 m. yell., grn. & red | 60 | 30 |
| 1017. | – | 10 m. red and green .. | 60 | 30 |
| 1018. | – | 10 m. blk., yell. & red | 60 | 30 |
| 1019. | – | 10 m. blk., red & grn. | 60 | 30 |
| 1020. | – | 10 m. multicoloured | 60 | 30 |

FLAGS: No. 981, Botswana. No. 982, Burundi No. 983, Cameroun. No. 984, Central African Republic. No. 985, Chad. No. 986, Congo-Brazzaville. No. 987, Congo-Kinshasa. No. 988, Dahomey. No. 989, Egypt-U.A.R. No. 990, Equatorial Guinea. No. 991, Ethiopia. No. 992, Gabon. No. 993, Gambia. No. 994, Ghana. No. 995, Guinea. No. 996, Ivory Coast. No. 997, Kenya. No. 998, Lesotho. No. 999, Liberia. No. 1000, Libya. No. 1001, Malagasy Republic. No. 1002, Malawi. No. 1003, Mali. No. 1004, Mauritania. No. 1005, Mauritius. No. 1006, Morocco. No. 1007, Niger. No. 1008, Nigeria. No. 1009, Rwanda. No. 1010, Senegal. No. 1011, Sierra Leone. No. 1012, Somalia. No. 1013, Sudan. No. 1014, Swaziland. No. 1015, Tanzania. No. 1016, Togo. No. 1017 Tunisia. No. 1018, Uganda. No. 1019, Upper Volta. No. 1020, Zambia.

**367.** El Fetouh Gate. **368.** Development Bank Emblem.

**1969.** Cairo Millenary.

| | | | | |
|---|---|---|---|---|
| 1021. | **367.** | 10 m. brn., yell & blue | 35 | 15 |
| 1022. | – | 10 m. multicoloured .. | 35 | 15 |
| 1023. | – | 10 m. pink and blue .. | 35 | 15 |
| 1024. | – | 20 m. multicoloured .. | 65 | 30 |
| 1025. | – | 20 m. pur., yell. & blue | 65 | 30 |
| 1026. | – | 20 m. blue, yell. & brn. | 65 | 30 |

DESIGNS—As Type **367**. No. 1022, Al-Azhar University. No. 1023, Citadel. ($57\frac{1}{2} \times 24\frac{1}{2}$ mm.). No. 1024, Two sculptures from Pharaonic period. No. 1025, Carved decorations, Coptic era. No. 1026. Glassware, Fatimid dynasty.

**1969.** 5th Anniv. of African Development Bank.

| | | | | |
|---|---|---|---|---|
| 1028. | **368.** | 20 m. grn., vio. & yell. | 30 | 15 |

**369.** Mahatma Gandhi. **370.** " King and Queen ", Abu Simbel (U.N.E.S.C.O.).

**1969.** Air. Birth Cent of Mahatma Gandhi.

| | | | | |
|---|---|---|---|---|
| 1029 | **369** | 80 m. orange, brn & bl | 2·50 | 1·25 |

**1969.** United Nations Day.

| | | | | |
|---|---|---|---|---|
| 1030. | **370.** | 5 m. yell., blue & brn. | 20 | 20 |
| 1031. | – | 20 m. blue & yellow .. | 40 | 20 |
| 1032. | – | 30 m. + 10 m. mult. .. | 75 | 75 |
| 1033. | – | 55 m. multicoloured | 95 | 50 |

DESIGNS—As T **370**: 20 m. Ancient Egyptian Ship (I.M.C.O.). 36 × 36 m: 30 m. + 10 m. Arab refugees (U.N.R.W.A.). 55 m. Partly submerged temple, Philae (U.N.E.S.C.O.).

**371.** Demonstrators.

**1969.** Anniversaries.

| | | | | |
|---|---|---|---|---|
| 1034. | **371.** | 20 m. purple, red & grn. | 75 | 35 |
| 1035. | – | 20 m. brn., yell. & blue | 75 | 35 |
| 1036. | – | 20 m. multicoloured .. | 75 | 35 |

DESIGNS AND EVENTS: No. 1034, (50th anniv of 1919 Revolution). LARGER (58 × 25 mm). No. 1035, Labourers, merchant ships of 1869 and 1969 and map (Suez Canal Centenary). No. 1036, Performance of "Aida" (Cairo Opera-house Centenary).

**372.** " Ancient Egyptian Accountants ".

**1969.** International Scientific Accounts Congress, Cairo.

| | | | | |
|---|---|---|---|---|
| 1037 | **372** | 20 m. pur, grn & yell | 45 | 20 |

**373.** Poinsettia.

**1969.** Ramadan Festival.

| | | | | |
|---|---|---|---|---|
| 1038 | **373** | 5 m. red, green & yell | 40 | 20 |

**374.** Step Pyramid, Sakkara. **375.** President Nasser.

**1969.**

| | | | | |
|---|---|---|---|---|
| 1039 | **374** | 1 m. brn, ochre & bl | 20 | 30 |
| 1040 | – | 5 m. brown, yell & bl | 30 | 10 |
| 1041 | – | 10 m. pur, ochre & bl | 30 | 10 |
| 1042 | **260** | 20 m. brown ($22 \times 27\frac{1}{2}$ mm) .. .. | 1·60 | 25 |
| 1043 | – | 50 m. brn, ochre & bl | 1·60 | 35 |
| 1044 | – | 55 m. green .. .. | 2·25 | 25 |
| 1045 | **375** | 200 m. blue & purple | 5·00 | 95 |
| 1046 | | 500 m. black and blue | 9·50 | 3·50 |
| 1047 | – | £E1 green and orange | 19·00 | 5·50 |

DESIGNS—As Type **374**: 5 m. Al-Azhar Mosque, Cairo. 10 m. Temple, Luxor. 50 m. Qaitbay Fort, Alexandria. $22 \times 27\frac{1}{2}$ mm: 55 m. As No. 781. As T **375**: £E1, Khafre.

See also Nos. 1131/41.

**376a.** Imam Mohamed El Boukhary. **377.** Azzahir Beybars Mosque.

**1969.** Air. 1100th Death Anniv. of Imam El Boukhary (philosopher and writer).

| | | | | |
|---|---|---|---|---|
| 1048. | **376a.** | 30 m. brown and olive | 45 | 20 |

**1969.** Air. 700th Anniv. of Azzahir Beybars Mosque.

| | | | | |
|---|---|---|---|---|
| 1049. | **377.** | 30 m. purple .. .. | 45 | 20 |

**378.** " Three Veiled Women " (Mahmoud Said).

**1970.** Post Day.

| | | | | |
|---|---|---|---|---|
| 1050. | **378.** | 100 m. multicoloured | 2·75 | 2·25 |

**379.** Parliament Building and Emblems.

**1970.** Int Conf on Middle East Crisis, Cairo.

| | | | | |
|---|---|---|---|---|
| 1051 | **379** | 20 m. ultram, brn & bl | 45 | 20 |

**380.** Human Rights Emblem and " Three Races ".

**1970.** Racial Equality Day.

| | | | | |
|---|---|---|---|---|
| 1052 | **380** | 20 m. + 10 m. yellow, brown and green .. | 65 | 65 |

**381.** Arab League Flag, Arms and Map.

**1970.** 25th Anniv. of Arab League.

| | | | | |
|---|---|---|---|---|
| 1053. | **381.** | 20 m. + 10 m. green, brown and blue .. | 50 | 55 |
| 1054. | | 30 m. grn., plum & orge. | 55 | 25 |

**382.** Mina House Hotel, Giza, and Sheraton Hotel, Cairo.

**1970.** Centenary of Mina House Hotel and Opening of Sheraton Hotel.

| | | | | |
|---|---|---|---|---|
| 1055 | **382** | 20 m. green, orge & bl | 50 | 25 |

**383.** Pharmacists.

**1970.** 30th Anniv of Egyptian Pharmaceutical Industry.

| | | | | |
|---|---|---|---|---|
| 1056 | **383** | 20 m. blue, brn & yell | 85 | 25 |



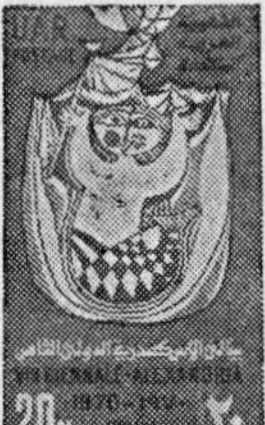

**384.** Mermaid. **385.** Lenin.

**1970.** 8th Fine Arts Biennale, Alexandria.

| | | | | |
|---|---|---|---|---|
| 1057. | **384.** | 20 m. blk., bl. & orge. | 45 | 20 |

**1970.** Air. Birth Cent. of Lenin.

| | | | | |
|---|---|---|---|---|
| 1058. | **385.** | 80 m. brown and green | 1·25 | 95 |

**386.** Emblem and Bombed Factory.

**1970.** Air. Attack on Abu Zaabal Factory.

| | | | | |
|---|---|---|---|---|
| 1059. | **386.** | 80 m. purple, blue and yellow .. .. | 1·25 | 95 |

**387.** Talaat Harb (founder) and Bank. **388.** I.T.U. Emblem.

**1970.** 50th Anniv of Misr Bank.

| | | | | |
|---|---|---|---|---|
| 1060 | **387** | 20 m. brn, ochre & bl | 45 | 20 |

**1970.** World Telecommunications Day.

| | | | | |
|---|---|---|---|---|
| 1061 | **388** | 20 m. blue, yell & brn | 50 | 20 |

**389.** New Headquarters Building. **390.** Basketball Player, Cup and Map.

**1970.** New U.P.U. Headquarters Building, Berne.

| | | | | |
|---|---|---|---|---|
| 1062 | **389** | 20 m. purple, green & yellow (postage) .. | 50 | 20 |
| 1063 | | 80 m. black, green and yellow (air) .. | 95 | 80 |

**1970.** 5th Africa Men's Basketball Championships.

| | | | | |
|---|---|---|---|---|
| 1064 | **390** | 20 m. blue, brn & yell | 75 | 30 |

**391.** Emblems of U.P.U., U.N. and African Postal Union.

**1970.** African Postal Union Seminar.

| | | | | |
|---|---|---|---|---|
| 1065. | **391.** | 20 m. grn. violet & orge. | 50 | 20 |

**392.** Footballer and Cup. **393.** Clenched Fists and Dove.

**1970.** Africa Cup Football Championships.

| | | | | |
|---|---|---|---|---|
| 1066 | **392** | 20 m. brown, yell & bl | 65 | 30 |

**1970.** 18th Anniv. of Revolution.

| | | | | |
|---|---|---|---|---|
| 1067. | 393. | 20 m. orge., blk. & grn. | 60 | 25 |

394. Mosque in Flames.

**1970.** 1st Anniv of Burning of Al Aqsa Mosque, Jerusalem.

| | | | | |
|---|---|---|---|---|
| 1069 | 394 | 20 m. brn, orge & grn | 65 | 30 |
| 1070 | | 60 m. brown, red & bl | 1·75 | 1·25 |

395. Globe, Wheat and Cogwheel.

**1970.** World Standards Day.

| | | | | |
|---|---|---|---|---|
| 1071. | 395. | 20 m. brn., blue & grn. | 50 | 20 |

396. " Peace, Justice and Progress " (25th Anniv. of U.N.).

**1970.** United Nations Day.

| | | | | |
|---|---|---|---|---|
| 1072 | 396 | 5 m. blue, lt bl & mve | 20 | 10 |
| 1073 | – | 10 m. bl, ochre & brn | 20 | 15 |
| 1074 | – | 20 m. multicoloured | 40 | 20 |
| 1075 | – | 20 m. + 10 m. mult .. | 60 | 60 |
| 1076 | – | 55 m. brn, bl & ochre | 90 | 80 |
| 1077 | – | 55 m. brn, bl & ochre | 90 | 80 |

Designs and Events—37 × 37 mm: 10 m. U.N. emblem. 55 m. (2) Philae Temple (composite design) (U.N.E.S.C.O. Campaign for Preservation of Nubian Monuments). 36 × 36 mm: 20 m. Frightened child and bombed school (Int Education Year). 41 × 25 mm: 20 m. + 10 m. Palestinian guerrillas and refugees ("Int support for Palestinians").

397. President Nasser. 398. Medical Association Building.

**1970.** Pres. Gamal Nasser Memorial Issue.

| | | | | |
|---|---|---|---|---|
| 1078 | 397 | 5 m. black and blue (postage) .. .. | 20 | 15 |
| 1079 | – | 20 m. black and green | 45 | 20 |
| 1080 | – | 30 m. black & grn (air) | 65 | 30 |
| 1081 | – | 80 m. black & brown | 1·90 | 95 |

Design—46 × 27 mm: 30, 80 m. Pre Nasser and mosque.

**1970.** Egyptian Anniversaries.

| | | | |
|---|---|---|---|
| 1082 | 20 m. brown, yellow & bl | 60 | 40 |
| 1083 | 20 m. brown, yellow & bl | 60 | 40 |
| 1084 | 20 m. brown and blue .. | 60 | 40 |
| 1085 | 20 m. brown, yellow & bl | 60 | 40 |
| 1086 | 20 m. brown, yellow & bl | 60 | 40 |

Designs and Events: No. 1082, Type **398** (50th anniv of Egyptian Medical Assn). 1083, Old and new library buildings (centenary of National Library). 1084, "The most significant victory..." Pres. Nasser text ("Egyptian Credo"). 1085, Old and new printing works (150th anniv of Govt. Printing Office). 1086, Old and new headquarters (50th anniv of Egyptian Engineering Society).

399. Map of Egypt, Libya and Sudan.

**1970.** Signing of Tripoli Charter.

| | | | | |
|---|---|---|---|---|
| 1087. | 399. | 20 m. green, blk. & red | 50 | 20 |

400. Minaret, Qalawun Mosque. 402. Fair Emblem.

**1970.** Post Day. Mosque Minarets. Each brown, blue and yellow.

| | | | |
|---|---|---|---|
| 1088. | 5 m. Type **400** .. .. | 30 | 25 |
| 1089. | 10 m. As-Salem Mosque | 40 | 30 |
| 1090. | 20 m. Isna Mosque .. | 60 | 50 |
| 1091. | 55 m. Al-Hakim Mosque | 1·25 | 1·00 |

See also Nos. 1142/5 and 1189/92.

**1971.** Cairo International Fair.

| | | | | |
|---|---|---|---|---|
| 1093. | 402. | 20 m. yell., blk. & pur. | 45 | 20 |

403. Map of Arab States and A.P.U. Emblem.

**1971.** 9th Arab Postal Union Congress, Cairo.

| | | | | |
|---|---|---|---|---|
| 1094 | 403 | 20 m. blue, orange and green (postage) .. | 50 | 20 |
| 1095 | | 30 m. brown, orange and green (air) .. | 70 | 35 |

404. Globe and Cotton Symbols.

**1971.** Egyptian Cotton Production.

| | | | | |
|---|---|---|---|---|
| 1096. | 404. | 20 m. brn., bl. & grn. | 50 | 20 |

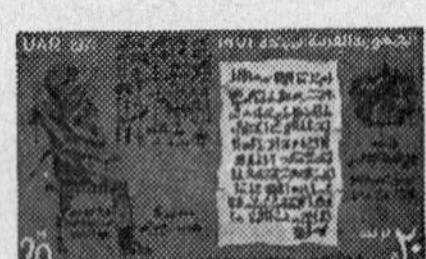

405. Army Emblem. 406. Hesy Ra (ancient physician) and Papyrus.

**1971.** Forces' Mail.

| | | | | |
|---|---|---|---|---|
| 1097. | 405. | 10 m. violet .. .. | 1·00 | 40 |

The above stamp was issued for civilian use on letters addressed to servicemen and was not valid for any other purpose.

**1971.** World Health Day.

| | | | | |
|---|---|---|---|---|
| 1098. | 406. | 20 m. purple and yell. | 65 | 20 |

407. Pres. Gamal Nasser. 408. Map and I.T.U. Emblem.

**1971.**

| | | | | |
|---|---|---|---|---|
| 1099. | 407. | 20 m. blue and purple | 65 | 20 |
| 1100. | | 55 m. plum and blue | 2·25 | 75 |

**1971.** African Telecommunications Year.

| | | | | |
|---|---|---|---|---|
| 1101 | 408 | 20 m. multicoloured .. | 65 | 20 |

409. El Rifaei and Sultan Hussein Mosques.

**1971.** Air. Multicoloured.

| | | | |
|---|---|---|---|
| 1102. | 30 m. Type **409** .. .. | 95 | 45 |
| 1103. | 85 m. Rameses Square, Cairo .. .. | 1·60 | 85 |
| 1104. | 110 m. Sphinx and Pyramids .. .. | 2·25 | 1·90 |

410. "Industrial Progress". 411. A.P.U. Emblem.

**1971.** 19th Anniv of Revolution. Mult.

| | | | |
|---|---|---|---|
| 1105 | 20 m. Type **410** .. .. | 45 | 30 |
| 1106 | 20 m. Ear of Wheat and Laurel ("Land Reclamation") .. | 45 | 30 |

**1971.** 25th Anniv of Founding of Arab Postal Union at Sofar Conference.

| | | | | |
|---|---|---|---|---|
| 1108 | 411 | 20 m. emerald, yellow and green (postage) | 50 | 20 |
| 1109 | | 30 m. mult (air) .. | 85 | 50 |

412. Federal Links. 413. Pres. Gamal Nasser.

**1971.** Inaug. of Confederation of Arab Republics.

| | | | | |
|---|---|---|---|---|
| 1110. | 412. | 20 m. brn., blk. and purple (postage) .. | 50 | 25 |
| 1111. | | 30 m. green, blk. and purple (air) .. | 80 | 40 |

**1971.** 1st Death Anniv of President Nasser.

| | | | | |
|---|---|---|---|---|
| 1112. | 413. | 5 m. blue and purple | 25 | 15 |
| 1113. | | 20 m. purple and blue | 40 | 15 |
| 1114. | | 30 m. blue and brown | 75 | 45 |
| 1115. | | 55 m. brown and green | 1·25 | 75 |

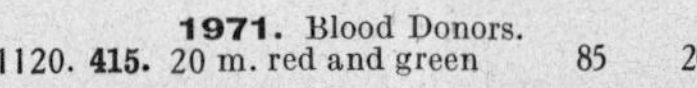

414. " Princess and Child ". 415. " Blood Saves Lives ".

**1971.** United Nations Day.

| | | | | |
|---|---|---|---|---|
| 1116 | 414 | 5 m. black, brown and cinnamon (postage) | 20 | 15 |
| 1117 | – | 20 m. multicoloured | 45 | 20 |
| 1118 | – | 55 m. multicoloured | 1·10 | 85 |
| 1119 | – | 30 m. mult (air) .. | 85 | 45 |

Designs—As Type **414**. vert: 5 m. (U.N.I.C.E.F.). horiz: 20 m. Emblem and four heads (Racial Equality Year). 36 × 36 mm: 30 m. Refugee and Al-Aqsa Mosque (U.N.R.W.A.). 24 × 58 mm: 55 m. Partly submerged pillar, Philae (25th anniv of U.N.E.S.C.O.).

**1971.** Blood Donors.

| | | | | |
|---|---|---|---|---|
| 1120. | 415. | 20 m. red and green | 85 | 20 |

416. New Post Office. 417. Sunflower.

**1971.** Opening of New Head Post Office, Alexandria.

| | | | | |
|---|---|---|---|---|
| 1121. | 416. | 20 m. brown and blue | 75 | 20 |

**1971.** Ramadan Festival.

| | | | | |
|---|---|---|---|---|
| 1122. | 417. | 5 m. multicoloured .. | 30 | 15 |

418. Abdallah El Nadim. 419. Globe and Earth's Strata.

**1971.** 75th Death Anniv. of Abdallah El Nadim (poet and journalist).

| | | | | |
|---|---|---|---|---|
| 1123. | 418. | 20 m. brown & green | 50 | 20 |

**1971.** 75th Anniv. of Egyptian Geological Survey.

| | | | | |
|---|---|---|---|---|
| 1124. | 419. | 20 m. multicoloured | 95 | 25 |

420. A.P.U. Emblem and Dove with Letter.

**1971.** 10th Anniv. of African Postal Union.

| | | | | |
|---|---|---|---|---|
| 1125. | 420. | 5 m. mult. (postage) .. | 25 | 10 |
| 1126 | | 20 m. grn., orge. & blk. | 50 | 15 |
| 1127. | – | 55 m. blk., bl. & red | 1·25 | 80 |
| 1128. | – | 30 m. mult. (air) .. | 65 | 40 |

Design: 30 m., 55 m. A.P.U. emblem and airmail envelope.

421. " Savings Bank ".

**1971.** 70th Anniv of Post Office Savings Bank.

| | | | | |
|---|---|---|---|---|
| 1129 | 421 | 20 m. multicoloured .. | 75 | 25 |

421a. Victory Parade (scene from "Aida"). 423. Cairo Citadel.

**1971.** Air. Centenary of First Performance of Verdi's Opera "Aida", in Cairo.

| | | | | |
|---|---|---|---|---|
| 1130. | 421a. | 110 m. yell., grn. & brn. | 4·50 | 2·50 |

**1972.** Inscr "A.R. EGYPT".

| | | | | |
|---|---|---|---|---|
| 1131 | 374 | 1 m. blue and brown | 10 | 20 |
| 1131a | | 1 m. brown .. | 10 | 20 |
| 1132 | – | 5 m. blue, yellow & brn (as No. 1040) | 25 | 15 |
| 1132a | – | 5 m. green .. .. | 30 | 15 |
| 1132b | – | 5 m. bistre .. .. | 30 | 15 |
| 1133 | – | 10 m. purple, brown & bl (as No. 1041) | 40 | 15 |
| 1133a | – | 10 m. brown .. | 40 | 10 |
| 1134 | 260 | 20 m. green (22 × 27½ mm) .. .. | 65 | 20 |
| 1135 | | 20 m. mauve (22 × 27½ mm) .. .. | 95 | 25 |
| 1136 | – | 50 m. brown, ochre & blue (as No. 1043) | 1·50 | 25 |
| 1136a | – | 50 m. blue .. .. | 1·75 | 25 |
| 1137 | – | 55 m. mauve (as No. 1044) .. .. | 2·25 | 55 |
| 1137a | – | 55 m. green .. | 1·40 | 20 |
| 1138a | 423 | 100 m. blk., red & bl | 1·10 | 45 |
| 1139 | – | 200 m. brown & grn | 4·50 | 95 |
| 1140 | – | 500 m. brown and blue (as No. 1046) | 9·50 | 2·25 |
| 1141 | – | £E1 green & orange (as No. 1047) .. | 19·00 | 5·50 |

Designs—As Type **423**: Nos. 1132a/b, Rameses II. 1133a, Head of Seti I. 1136a, Goddess Hathar. 1137a, Sphinx and pyramid. As Type **375**: No. 1139, Head of Userkaf.

**1972.** Post Day. Mosque Minarets. As T **400**. Multicoloured.

| | | | |
|---|---|---|---|
| 1142. | 5 m. Western minaret, An-Nasir Mosque .. | 35 | 25 |
| 1143. | 20 m. Eastern minaret, An-Nasir Mosque .. | 50 | 45 |
| 1144. | 30 m. Al-Gawli Mosque | 80 | 65 |
| 1145. | 55 m. Ahmed Ibn Toulon Mosque .. .. | 1·25 | 95 |

424a. Police Emblem and Activities.

**1972.** Police Day.

| | | | | |
|---|---|---|---|---|
| 1146. | 424a. | 20 m. yell., bl. & brn. | 1·25 | 25 |

**425.** Book Year Emblem.

**426.** Globe, Glider, Rocket and Emblem.

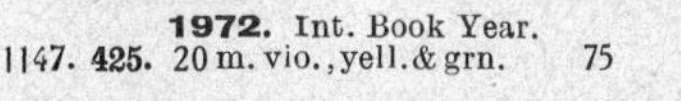

**1972.** Int. Book Year.
1147. **425.** 20 m. vio., yell. & grn. 75 20

**1972.** Air. International Aerospace Education Conference, Cairo.
1148 **426** 30 m. brown, bl & yell 1·25 45

**427.** Monastery Aflame.

**428.** " Palette" (Seif Wanli).

**1972.** Air. Burning of St. Catherine's Monastery, Sinai.
1149 **427** 110 m. blk, brn & red 3·75 3·25

**1972.** 9th Fine Arts Biennial, Alexandria.
1150. **428.** 20 m. red, yell. & blk. 75 20

**429.** Fair Emblem.

**430.** Brig. Abdel Moniem Riad and Battle Scene.

**1972.** Int. Fair, Cairo.
1151. **429.** 20 m. multicoloured 75 20

**1972.** 2nd Death Anniv of Brig. Abdel Moniem Riad.
1152 **430** 20 m. brown, turq & bl 95 25

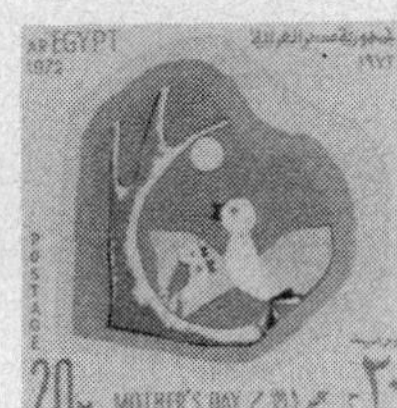

**431.** Birds in Tree.

**1972.** Mothers' Day.
1153. **431.** 20 m. multicoloured .. 75 20

**432.** Head of Tutankhamun (wooden statuette).

**1972.** 50th Anniv. of Discovery of Tutankhamun's Tomb.
1154. **432.** 20 m. mult. (postage) 85 30
1155. – 55 m. multicoloured .. 1·75 80
1156. – 110 m. grn. brn. & bl. (air) .. .. 3·75 2·75
1157. – 110 m. grn., brn. & bl. 3·75 2·75

Designs—As Type **432**: No. 1155, Decorated chairback. 28×62 mm: No. 1156, Tutankhamun. 1157, Ankhesenamun.

Nos. 1156/7 were issued together, se-tenant, forming a composite design.

**433.** Nefertiti.

**434.** Map of Africa.

**1972.** 50th Anniv. of Society of Friends of Art.
1159. **433.** 20 m. blk., gold & red 75 20

**1972.** Africa Day.
1160 **434** 20 m. brown, bl & vio 75 20

**436.** Eagle Emblem.

**1972.** 20th Anniv. of Revolution.
1167. **436.** 20 m. gold, blk. & grn. 75 20
1168. 20 m. red, blk. & blue 75 20

**437.** Al-Azhar Mosque and St. George's Church, Cairo.

**1972.** Air.
1170 **437** 30 m. brn, ochre & bl 1·60 30
1171 – 85 m. brn, ochre & bl 2·75 1·25
1172 – 110 m. brn, ochre & bl 3·25 1·25

Designs: 85 m. Temple, Abu Simbel. 110 m. Pyramids, Giza.

**438.** Boxing.

**1972.** Olympic Games. Munich.
1173 **438** 5 m. mult (postage) .. 20 10
1174 – 10 m. yell, blk & red 25 10
1175 – 20 m. grn, red & orge 40 20
1176 – 30 m. green, buff and red (air) .. .. 75 30
1177 – 30 m. vio, red & turq 75 30
1178 – 50 m. black, bl & grn 1·25 80
1179 – 55 m. red, green & bl 1·50 95

Designs—Horiz. 10 m. Wrestling. 20 m. Basketball. Vert. 30 m. (No. 1176), Weightlifting. 30 m. (No. 1177), Handball. 50 m. Swimming. 55 m. Gymnastics.

**439.** Confederation Flag.

**1972.** 1st Anniv of Confederation of Arab Republics.
1180 **439** 20 m. brown, red & blk 75 25

**440.** J.-F. Champollion and Rosetta Stone.

**1972.** Air. 150th Anniv. of Champollion's Translation of Egyptian Heiroglyphics.
1181. **440.** 110 m. grn., blk. & brn. 5·00 2·00

**441.** Heart (World Health Day).

**1972.** United Nations Day.
1182 – 10 m. red, blue & brn 25 15
1183 **441** 20 m. black, yell & grn 45 15
1184 – 30 m. brown, vio & bl 85 30
1185 – 55 m. gold, brn & bl 1·90 95

Designs—22×40 mm: 10 m. Emblem of 14th Regional Tuberculosis Conference, Cairo. 47×28 mm: 30 m. Refugees (U.N.R.W.A.). 37×37 mm: 55 m. Flooded temple, Philae (UNESCO Campaign for Preservation of Nubian Monuments).

**442.** Hibiscus.

**443.** Work Day Emblem.

**1972.** Ramadan Festival.
1186. **442.** 10 m. pur., grn. & brn. 50 20

**1972.** Social Work Day.
1187 **443** 20 m. blue, brn & grn 75 20

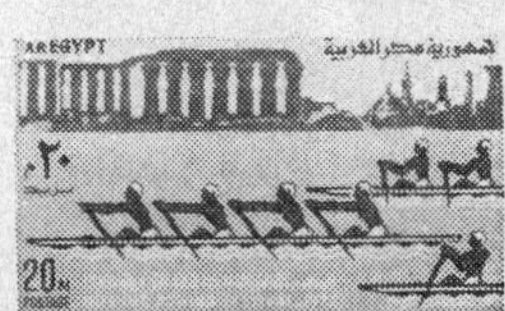

**444.** " Rowing Fours " on Nile.

**1972.** 3rd Nile Rowing Festival, Luxor.
1188. **444.** 20 m. brown and blue 95 25

**1973.** Post Day. Mosque Minarets. As T **400**. Each brown, yellow and green.
1189. 10 m. Al-Maridani Mosque 40 30
1190. 20 m. Bashtak Mosque .. 60 45
1191. 30 m. Qusun Mosque .. 95 65
1192. 55 m. Al-Gashankir Mosque 1·25 90

**445.** Ears of Corn and Globe within Cogwheel.

**446.** Symbolic Family.

**1973.** International Fair, Cairo.
1193 **445** 20 m. blue, blk & grn 55 25

**1973.** Family Planning Week.
1194. **446.** 20 m. blk., orge. & grn. 75 25

**447.** Telecommunications Map.

**1973.** Air. 5th Int Telecommunications Day.
1195 **447** 30 m. blue, blk & brn 1·00 25

**448.** Temple Column, Karnak.

**449.** Bloody Hand and Boeing 727 Jetliner.

**1973.** Air. "Son et Lumiere", Karnak Temples, Luxor.
1196 **448** 110 m. black, mve & bl 3·00 1·90

**1973.** Air. Attack on Libyan Airliner over Sinai.
1197 **449** 110 m. red, black & bis 4·25 1·90

**451.** Rifaa el Tahtawi.

**452.** Mrs. Hoda Sharawi and Sania Girls Secondary School.

**1973.** Death Centenary of Rifaa el Tahtawi (educationist).
1200 **451** 20 m. brown, green and deep green .. 65 25

**1973.** Cent of Egyptian Female Education and 50th Anniv of Women's Union.
1201 **452** 20 m. green, brn & bl 65 25

**453.** Mohamed Korayem.

**454.** Refugees and Map of Palestine.

**1973.** 21st Anniv of Revolution. Leaders of the 1798 Resistance Movement.
1202 **453** 20 m. brown, bl & grn 65 25
1203 – 20 m. brown, bl & grn 65 25
1204 – 20 m. chocolate, pink and brown .. 65 25

Designs: No. 1203, Omar Makram. 1204, Abdel Rahman el Gaberti.

**1973.** Air. Palestinian Refugees.
1206 **454** 30 m. purple, brn & bl 1·90 50

**455.** Rose.

**456.** "Light and Hope".

**1973.** Ramadan Festival.
1207 **455** 10 m. red, yellow & bl 40 15

**1973.** 25th Anniv. of W.H.O.
1208. **456.** 20 m. + 10 m. bl. & gold 60 60

**HAVE YOU READ THE NOTES AT THE BEGINNING OF THIS CATALOGUE?**

These often provide answers to the enquiries we receive.

**457.** Bank Building. **458.** Emblem and Weather-vane.

**1973.** 75th Anniv. of National Bank of Egypt.
1209. **457.** 20 m. blk., grn. & orge. 65 25

**1973.** Air. Centenary of World Meteorological Organization.
1210. **458.** 110 m. gold, vio. & bl. 2·50 1·50

**459.** Global Emblem.

**1973.** 10th Anniv. of World Food Programme.
1211. **459.** 10 m. bl., grn. & brn. 45 25

**460.** Philae Temples.

**1973.** U.N.E.S.C.O. Campaign for the Preservation of Nubian Monuments.
1212. **460.** 55 m. orge., blue & violet 2·50 95

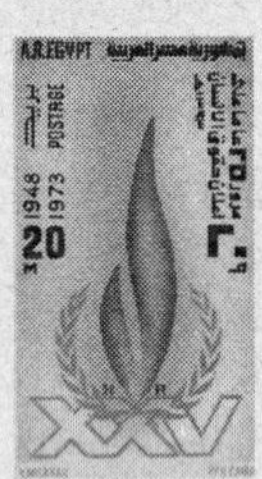

**461.** Interpol Emblem. **462.** Flame Emblem.

**1973.** Air. 50th Anniv of International Criminal Police Organization (Interpol).
1213 **461** 110 m. multicoloured 3·75 1·90

**1973.** 25th Anniv. of Declaration of Human Rights.
1214. **462.** 20 m. red, green & bl. 55 20

**463.** Laurel and Map of Africa. **464.** " Donation ".

**1973.** 10th Anniv of Organization of African Unity.
1215 **463** 55 m. + 20 m. mult .. 2·25 2·50

**1973.** Social Work Day.
1216 **464** 20 m. + 10 m. blue, lilac and red .. 65 75

**465.** Dr. Taha Hussein (scholar). **467.** Egyptian Postal Services Emblem.

**466.** Pres. Sadat and Flag.

**1973.** Hussein Commemoration.
1217. **465.** 20 m. brn., blue & grn. 55 20

**1973.** Crossing of the Suez Canal, 6 October 1973.
1218 **466** 20 m. black, red & brn 1·00 35
See also No. 1233.

**1973.** Air. Post Day.
1219 **467** 20 m. blk, red & grey 25 15
1220 – 30 m. vio, orge & blk 30 15
1221 – 55 m. mve, grn & blk 90 85
1222 – 110 m. gold, bl & blk 1·75 1·60
DESIGNS—As T **467**: 30 m. Arab Postal Union emblem. 55 m. African Postal Union emblem. 37 × 37 mm: 110 m. U.P.U. emblem.

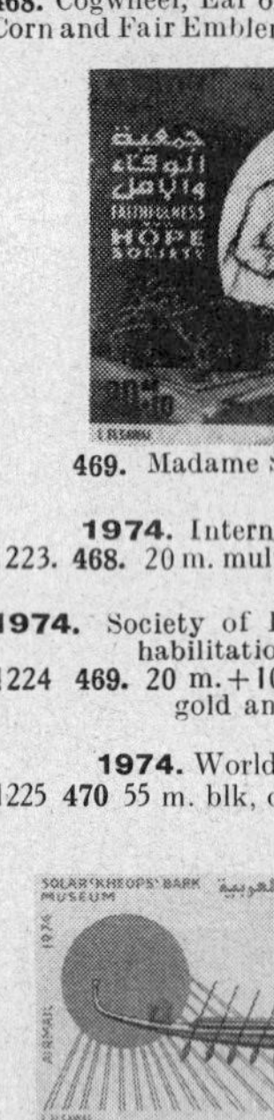

**468.** Cogwheel, Ear of Corn and Fair Emblem. **470.** Emblem and Graph.

**469.** Madame Sadat with Patient.

**1974.** International Fair, Cairo.
1223. **468.** 20 m. multicoloured .. 50 20

**1974.** Society of Faith and Hope (for rehabilitation of the disabled).
1224 **469.** 20 m. + 10 m. purple, gold and green .. 85 85

**1974.** World Population Year.
1225 **470** 55 m. blk, orge & grn 1·10 60

**471.** Solar Boat of Cheops.

**1974.** Air. Inauguration of Solar Boat Museum.
1226. **471.** 110 m. brn., gold & bl. 2·25 1·60

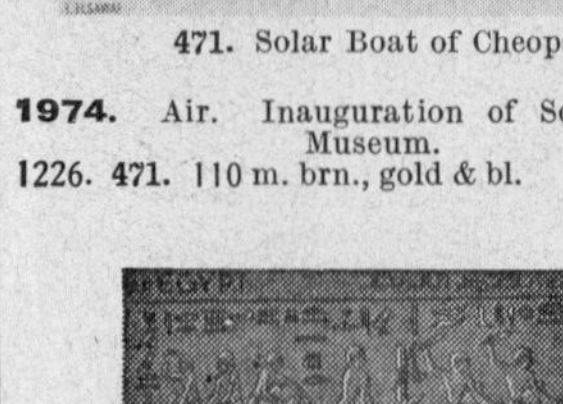

**472.** " Ancient Egyptian Workers " (carving from Queen Tee's tomb, Sakara).

**1974.** Labour Day (1st May).
1227. **472.** 20 m. blk., yell. & blue 55 20

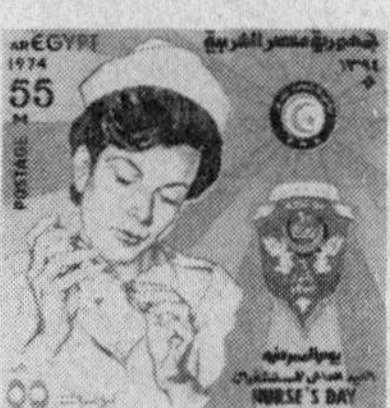

**473.** Nurse with Syringe. **474.** Troops crossing Barlev Line during October War.

**1974.** Nurses' Day.
1228 **473** 55 m. gold, red & green 1·25 40

**1974.** 22nd Anniv of Revolution.
1229 – 20 m. gold, black & bl 65 35
1230 – 20 m. silver, blk & pur 65 35
1231 **474** 20 m. black, orge & bl 65 35
DESIGNS—As T **474**: No. 1229, Map of Suez Canal and "Reconstruction". 36 × 36 mm: No. 1230, Sheet of aluminium.

**476.** Pres. Sadat and Flag.

**1974.** 1st Anniv of Suez Crossing.
1233 **476** 20 m. black, red & yell 1·00 40
See also No. 1218.

**477.** Teachers' Badge. **478.** Artists' Palette.

**1974.** Teachers' Day.
1234. **477.** 20 m. brn., blk. & blue 55 20

**1974.** 6th Plastic Arts Exhibition.
1235. **478.** 30 m. blk., yell. & vio. 95 35

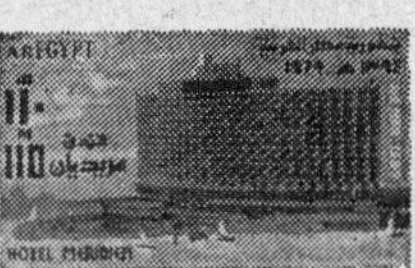

**479.** Meridian Hotel.

**1974.** Air. Opening of Meridian Hotel, Cairo.
1236. **479.** 110 m. multicoloured 1·60 95

**481.** Child and Emblems.

**1974.** Social Work Day.
1238. **481.** 30 m. grn., brn. & bl. 85 30

**482.** Emblems of Standardization.

**1974.** World Standards Day.
1239. **482.** 10 m. orge., bl. & blk. 40 20

**483.** " Aggression Registers ". **484.** Philae Temples.

**1974.** Refugees Propaganda.
1240 **483** 20 m. blue and red .. 60 20

**1974.** U.N.E.S.C.O. Campaign for Preservation of Nubian Monuments.
1241 **484** 55 m. brn, stone & bl 1·90 55

**485.** Arum Lily. **486.** Pile of Coins.

**1974.** Ramadan Festival.
1242 **485** 10 m. multicoloured .. 45 20

**1974.** International Savings Day.
1243. **486.** 20 m. grey, blue & grn. 55 20

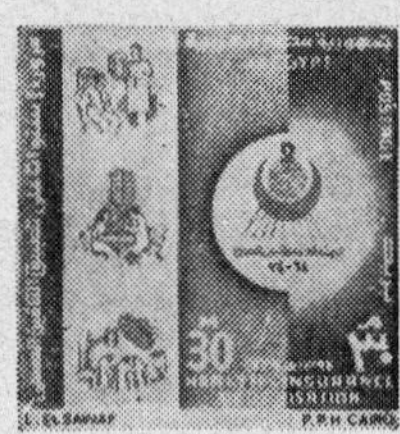

**487.** Organization Emblems and Cameos. **487a** Abbas Mahmoud El Akkad (writer).

**1974.** Health Insurance Organization.
1244 **487** 30 m. violet, red & brn 80 30

**1974.** Famous Egyptians.
1245 **487a** 20 m. blue and brown 50 25
1246 – 20 m. brown and blue 50 25
DESIGNS: No. 1245, (10th death anniv). No. 1246 Mustafa Lutfy El Manfalouty (journalist).

**488.** Sacred Ibis.

**1975.** Post Day. Ancient Treasures.
1247 **488** 20 m. brown, bl & sil 55 20
1248 – 30 m. bl, orge & mve 55 20
1249 – 55 m. brn, gold & grn 1·10 65
1250 – 110 m. yell, brn & bl 1·90 1·40
DESIGNS—HORIZ: 30 m. Glass "fish" vase. VERT: 55 m. Pharaonic gold vase. 110 m. Ankh-shaped mirror.

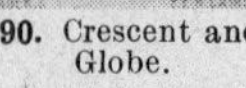

**489.** Om Kolthoum (Arab singer). **490.** Crescent and Globe.

**1975.** Om Kolthoum Commemoration.
1251. **489.** 20 m. brown .. .. 75 25

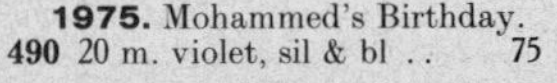

**1975.** Mohammed's Birthday.
1252 **490** 20 m. violet, sil & bl .. 75 25

**491.** Fair Emblem. **492.** Kasr El Ainy Hospital.

**1975.** Cairo International Fair.
1253 **491** 20 m. green, blue & red 45 20

**1975.** World Health Day.
1254. **492.** 20 m. brown & blue . . 75 25

**493.** Children Reading Book. **495.** Belmabgoknis Flower.

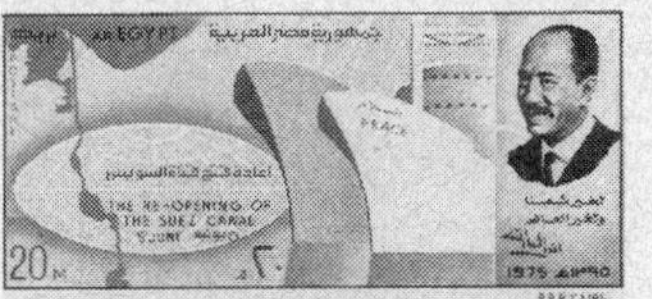

**494.** President Sadat, Ships and Map of Canal.

**1975.** Science Day.
1255 **493** 20 m. blue, red & yell 60 25
1256 – 20 m. black & brown 60 25
DESIGN: No. 1256, Pupils and graph.

**1975.** Re-opening of Suez Canal.
1257 **494** 20 m. brown, blue and black (postage) . . 60 25
1258 30 m. turquoise, green and blue (air) . . 1·25 45
1259 110 m. bl, blk & turq 1·90 1·60

**1975.** Festivals.
1260 **495** 10 m. bl, grn & lt grn 45 20

**496.** I.C.I.D. Emblem. **497.** Spotlight on Village.

**1975.** Air. 25th Anniv of International Commission on Irrigation and Drainage.
1261 **496** 110 m. green, bl & orge 2·25 1·25

**1975.** 23rd Anniv. of Revolution.
1262. **497.** 20 m. blue & brown . . 50 25
1263. – 20 m. orge., blk. & grn. 50 25
1264. – 110 m. multicoloured 2·50 2·50
DESIGNS—38 × 22 mm: No. 1263, "Tourism" (pyramids and sphinx). 70 × 79 mm: No. 1264, Tourist map of Egypt.

**498.** Volleyball. **499.** Flag and Tanks.

**1975.** 6th Arab School Sports Tournament. Each blue, orange and green.
1265. 20 m. Type **498** . . . . 65 40
1266. 20 m. Running . . . . 65 40
1267. 20 m. Tournament emblem 65 40
1268. 20 m. Basketball 65 40
1269. 20 m. Football . . . . 65 40

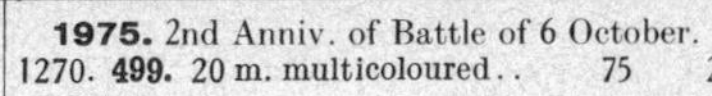

**1975.** 2nd Anniv. of Battle of 6 October.
1270. **499.** 20 m. multicoloured . . 75 25

**1975.** International Symposium on October War, Cairo University. As T **499** but with additonal commemorative inscription at foot and "M" above figures of value.
1271 20 m. multicoloured . . 65 25

**500.** Schistosomiasis Conference Emblem. **501.** University Emblem.

**1975.** United Nations Day.
1272 **500** 20 m. blue, mauve and brown (postage) . . 65 25
1273 – 55 m. purple, yell & bl 1·50 80
1274 – 30 m. brown, green and purple (air) . . 85 40
1275 – 110 m. blk, orge & grn 2·25 1·60
DESIGNS—27 × 47 mm: 55 m. Wall relief (UNESCO Campaign for Preservation of Nubian Monuments). 48 × 40 mm: 30 m. Refugees and barbed wire (U.N.R.W.A.). 22 × 40 mm: 110 m. Women (International Women's Year).

**1975.** 25th Anniv of Ein Shams University.
1276 **501** 20 m. blue, yell & grey 40 20

**501a.** Al-Kanady. **502.** Ibex.

**1975.** Arab Philosophers.
1277 **501a** 20 m. brown, grn & bl 50 35
1278 – 20 m. brown, grn & bl 50 35
1279 – 20 m. brown, grn & bl 50 35
DESIGNS: No. 1278, Al-Farabi, and lute. No. 1279, Al-Biruni, and open book.

**1976.** Post Day. Treasures from Tutankhamun's Tomb. Multicoloured.
1280. 20 m. Type **502** . . . . 50 20
1281. 30 m. Lioness . . . . 85 25
1282. 55 m. Sacred Cow . . 1·40 75
1283. 110 m. Hippopotamus . . 2·00 1·50

**503.** High Dam and Industrial Potential. **504.** Fair Emblem.

**1976.** Filling of High Dam Lake.
1284. **503.** 20 m. multicoloured . . 75 25

**1976.** Cairo International Fair.
1285 **504** 20 m. violet & orange 30 15

**505.** Biennale Commemorative Emblem. **506.** Protective Hands.

**1976.** 11th Fine Arts Biennale, Alexandria.
1286 **505** 20 m. yell, blk & grn 35 15

**1976.** Society of Faith and Hope.
1287 **506** 20 m. yellow, green and deep green . . 35 15

**507.** "Pharaonic Eye" and Emblem. **508.** Scales of Justice.

**1976.** World Health Day.
1288 **507** 20 m. brn, yell & grn 60 15

**1976.** 5th Anniv. of Rectification Movement.
1289. **508.** 20 m. blk., grn. & red 50 15

**509.** Pres. Sadat and Emblem.

**1976.** Cent of Arbitration Service.
1290 **509** 20 m. yellow, grn & ol 50 15

**510.** Front Page of First Issue.

**1976.** Cent of Newspaper "Al-Ahram".
1291 **510** 20 m. brown, blk & red 50 15

**511.** Pres. Sadat and World Map.

**1976.** 24th Anniv. of Revolution.
1292. **511.** 20 yell., blue & black 60 20

**512.** Amaryllis. **513.** Map of Red Sea, Pres. Sadat and Abu Redice Oil Refinery.

**1976.** Festivals.
1294. **512.** 10 m. multicoloured . . 45 10

**1976.** 3rd Anniv of Suez Canal Crossing. Mult.
1295 20 m. Type **513** . . . . 50 25
1296 20 m. Irrigation and Reconstruction. Map of Suez Canal (48 × 40 mm) 50 25
1297 110 m. Monument to Soldier of October 6th, 1973 (65 × 80 mm) . . 2·50 2·50

**514.** Animals on Papyrus Leaf ("Literature for Children").

**1976.** United Nations Day.
1298 **514** 20 m. brn, stone & bl 40 20
1299 – 30 m. brn, grn & blk 50 25
1300 – 55 m. brown and blue 95 40
1301 – 110 m. red, grn & vio 1·50 1·10
DESIGNS—39 × 22 mm: 30 m. Dome of the Rock (Palestinian Refugees). 110 m. UNESCO emblem on figure "30" (30th anniv of UNESCO). 25 × 59 mm: 55 m. Relief showing goddess Isis, Philae Temple (UNESCO Campaign for Preservation of Nubian Monuments).

**515.** Graph, People and Skyline. **516.** Society Medal and Map of the Nile.

**1976.** Population and Housing Census.
1302 **515** 20 m. sepia, blue & brn 50 10

**1976.** Cent of Egyptian Geographical Society.
1303 **516** 20 m. brown, grn & bl 50 10

**517.** King Akhnaton. **518.** Patrolman, Police Car and Map.

**1977.** Post Day.
1304 **517** 20 m. brown & black 30 15
1305 – 30 m. brown & black 45 20
1306 – 55 m. brown & purple 60 30
1307 – 110 m. brown & pur 1·25 95
DESIGNS: 30 m. Head of Akhnaton's daughter. 55 m. Head of Nefertiti, wife of Akhnaton. 110 m. Bust of Akhnaton.

**1977.** Police Day.
1308 **518** 20 m. red, blue & black 95 25

**519.** Pharaonic Ship. **520.** O.A.U. and Arab League Emblems on Map.

**1977.** Cairo International Fair.
1309 **519** 20 m. green, blk & red 45 10

**1977.** 1st Afro-Arab Summit Conference.
1310. **520.** 55 m. blue, blk. & orge. 75 40

**521.** King Faisal. **522.** Healthy Children and Paralysed Child.

**1977.** King Faisal of Saudi Arabia Commemoration.
1311 **521** 20 m. brown and blue 50 10

**1977.** National Campaign for Prevention of Poliomyelitis.
1312 **522** 20 m. deep brown, brown and red . . 75 20

**523.** A.P.U. Emblem and National Flags.

**1977.** Silver Jubilee of Arab Postal Union.
1313. **523.** 20 m. multicoloured . . 35 20
1314. 30 m. multicoloured . . 45 25

**524.** Children's Village. **525.** Earth and Satellite.

**1977.** Inauguration of S.O.S. Children's Village, Cairo.
1315 **524** 20 m. brown, bl & grn 35 20
1316 55 m. red, blue & grn 95 60

**1977.** World Telecommunications Day.
1317 **525** 110 m. bl, yell & blk 1·60 1·00

**526.** Loom, Spindle and Factories.

**1977.** 50th Anniv of Egyptian Spinning and Weaving Company, El Mehalla El Kobra.
1318 **526** 20 m. green, brn & bis 40 10

**527.** Egyptian Flag and Symbol of the Revolution. **528.** Saad Zaghoul.

**1977.** 25th Anniv. of Revolution.
1319. **527.** 20 m. blk., red & silver 35 10

**1977.** 50th Death Anniv. of Saad Zaghoul (revolutionary).
1321. **528.** 20 m. brown & green 25 10

**529.** Archbishop Capucci and Map of Palestine. **530.** Bird of Paradise Flowers.

**1977.** 3rd. Anniv of Arrest of Archbishop Capucci.
1322 **529** 45 m. blk, grey & grn 95 40

**1977.** Festivals.
1323. **530.** 10 m. multicoloured . . 35 10

**531.** Title Deeds over-shadowing Map of Egypt. **532.** Soldier, Tanks and 6th October Medal.

**1977.** 25th Anniv of Agrarian Reform Law.
1324 **531** 20 m. black, bl & grn 25 10

**1977.** 4th Anniv of Suez Canal Crossing.
1325 **532** 20 m. brn, red & orge 35 20
1326 – 140 m. brn, red & gold 3·50 3·50
DESIGN—46 × 55 mm: 140 m. President Sadat.

**533.** Old and Modern Trains.

**1977.** 125th Anniv. of Egyptian Railways.
1327. **533.** 20 m. grn., blue & vio. 85 30

**534.** Refugees and the Al Aqsa Mosque (U.N.R.W.A.).

**1977.** United Nations Day.
1328 **534** 45 m. green, red & blk 50 30
1329 – 55 m. yellow and blue 75 40
1330 – 140 m. ochre & brown 1·60 1·25
DESIGNS—36 × 36 mm: 55 m. Relief from Philae showing Horus and goddess Taueret. As T **534** but vert: 140 m. Relief from Philae in frame of pharaonic column. (UNESCO Campaign for Preservation of Nubian Monuments).

**535.** Ancient Egyptian Symbol for " Vision " and Film. **536.** Natural Gas Rig and Factories.

**1977.** 50th Anniv. of Egyptian Cinema.
1331. **535.** 20 m. blk., gold & grey 65 20

**1977.** National Petroleum Festival.
1332 **536** 20 m. blue, blk & grn 65 20

**537.** President Sadat, Olive Branches and Dome of the Rock, Jerusalem.

**1977.** President Sadat's Peace Mission to Israel.
1333 **537** 20 m. brn, grn & blk 35 20
1334 140 m. blk, grn & brn 1·60 1·25

**538.** The Three Pyramids at Giza. **539.** Statue of Rameses II.

**1978.** Air.
1335 **538** 45 m. yellow & brn 45 20
1335b 60 m. brown . . 1·10 60
1336 – 115 m. brown & blue 80 40
1337 – 140 m. lilac and blue 1·25 70
1337a – 185 m. brown & blue 2·75 1·40
DESIGNS: 115, 185 m. Step Pyramid and temple entrance, Sakkara. 140 m. Nile feluccas.

**1978.** Post Day. Multicoloured.
1338 20 m. Type **539** . . . . 30 20
1339 45 m. Relief showing coronation of Queen Nefertari, Abu Simbel 85 60

**540.** Irrigation Wheels, Fayoum. **541.** Fair Emblem.

**1978.**
1340 **540** 1 m. blue . . . . 10 10
1341 – 5 m. brown . . 10 10
1342 – 10 m. green . . 10 10
1343 – 20 m. brown . . 20 10
1343b – 30 m. brown . . 20 10
1344 – 50 m. blue . . . . 30 15
1345 – 55 m. brown . . 40 25
1346 – 70 m. brown . . 50 25
1346a – 80 m. brown . . 45 10
1347 – 85 m. purple . . 60 30
1348 – 100 m. brown . . 85 25
1349 – 200 m. indigo & blue 1·60 50
1350 – 500 m. brn, bl & yell 4·50 1·60
1351 – £E1 blue, yell & brn 6·50 3·00
DESIGNS—As T **540**: 5 m. Pigeon-loft. 10 m. Statue of Horus. 20, 30 m. El Rifaei Mosque, Cairo. 50 m. Syrian Monastery, Wady el Netroon. 55 m. Edfu temple. 70, 80 m. October Bridge over Suez Canal. 85 m. Medom pyramid. 100 m. Facade of Abu el Abbas el Morsy Mosque, Alexandria. 200 m. El Sawary column and sphinx, Alexandria. 37 × 45 mm: 500 m. Arab horse. £E1, Bird (floor decoration from Akhnaton's palace).

**1978.** 11th Cairo International Fair.
1352. **541.** 20 m. grn., blk. & orge. 30 10

**542.** Old Kasr el Ainy Medical School and New Tower. **543.** Youssef el Sebai.

**1978.** 150th Anniv of Kasr el Ainy Medical School.
1353. **542.** 20 m. brn., blue & gold 40 20

**1978.** Youssef el Sebai (assassination victim) and Commando Heroes Commemoration.
1354 – 20 m. brown . . 35 25
1355 **543** 20 m. blk, brn & yell 35 25
DESIGN: No. 1354, Group of Commandos and emblems.

**544.** Biennial Medal and Statue, Port Said.

**1978.** 12th Fine Arts Biennale, Alexandria.
1356. **544.** 20 m. blk., grn. & blue 40 20

**545.** Child with Smallpox

**1978.** World Health Day.
1357 **545** 20 m. orge, blk & grn 50 25
1358 – 20 m. red, orge & blk 50 25
DESIGN AND EVENT: No. 1357, Type **545** (World Year for the Eradication of Smallpox). 21 × 38 mm: No. 1358, Heart and downwards pointing arrow (World Hypertension Month).

**546.** President Sadat.

**1978.** 7th Anniv. of Rectification Movement.
1359. **546.** 20 m. brn., grn. & gold 20 10

**547.** Emblem, Beneficiaries and Olive-branch.

**1978.** 25th Anniv. of General Organization of Insurance and Pensions.
1360. **547.** 20 m. brown and green 20 10

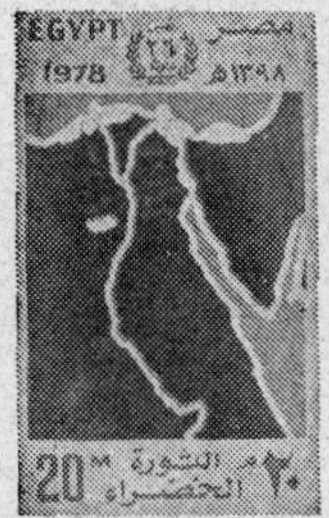

**548.** Map showing New Cities and suitable Regions for Cultivation (The Green Revolution). **549.** Wall of Ministerial Emblems.

**1978.** 26th Anniv. of Revolution.
1361. **548.** 20 m. grn., yell. & blue 30 20
1362. – 45 m. orge., grn. & brn. 60 30
DESIGN: 45 m. Map of Egypt and Sudan with ear of wheat (Economic integration of Egypt and Sudan).

**1978.** Cent of Egyptian Ministerial System.
1363 **549** 20 m. violet, grn & yell 25 10

**550.** President Sadat, Statue of the Crossing and Factories.

**1978.** 5th Anniv. of Suez Canal Crossing.
1364. **550.** 20 m. yell., brn. & grn. 40 10

**551.** Anti-Apartheid Emblem. **552.** Tahtib Folk-dance on Horseback.

**1978.** United Nations Day.
1365 **551** 20 m. orge, blk & grn 25 10
1366 – 45 m. yell, brn & grn 55 35
1367 – 55 m. orange, brn & bl 70 55
1368 – 140 m. orge, blk & grn 1·40 95
DESIGNS—As T **551**. HORIZ: 55 m. Philae temples (UNESCO Campaign for Preservation of Nubian Monuments). VERT: 140 m. Dove, flame and olive branch (30th anniv of Declaration of Human Rights). 37 × 37 mm: 45 m. Kobet al-Sakhra Mosque, refugee camp and U.N. emblem (U.N.R.W.A.).

**1978.** Festivals.
1369 **552** 10 m. orange, brn & bl 20 10
1370 20 m. bistre, brn & bl 35 10

**553.** Pilgrims at Mount Arafat and Script of Islamic Prayer.

**1978.** Islamic Pilgrimage.
1371 **553** 45 m. brown, yell & bl 65 35

**554.** U.N. and Conference Emblems.

**1978.** U.N. Conference on Technical Co-operation amongst Developing Countries.
1372 **554** 20 m. black, grn & yell 25 10

**555.** Oil Pipeline "Sumed", Badge and Map.

**1978.** 1st Anniv. of Inauguration of "Sumed" Oil Pipeline.
1373 **555** 20 m. brown, orge & bl 50 10

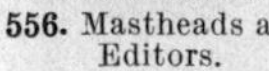

**556.** Mastheads and Editors. **557.** Ibn Roshd.

**1978.** 150th Anniv. of "El Wakaea el Massreya" Newspaper.
1374. **556.** 20 m. black & brown 30 10

**1978.** 800th Death Anniv. of Ibn Roshd (philosopher).
1375 **557** 45 m. blue, emer & grn 40 20

**558.** Old and Modern Observatories and Chart of Planet Movements.

**1978.** 75th Anniv of Helwan Observatory.
1376 **558** 20 m. blue, brn & yell 70 25

**559.** Wright Brothers' Type A Biplane and I.C.A.O. Emblem. **560.** Daughter of Rameses II.

**1978.** Air. 75th Anniv. of First Powered Flight.
1377 **559** 140 m. brown, bl & blk 1·90 1·25

**1979.** Post Day.
1378. **560.** 20 m. yellow & brown 30 20
1379. – 140 m. yell., brn. & blue 95 65
DESIGN:—(37½ × 43 mm.). 140 m. Small temple and statues of Rameses II, Abu Simbel.

**561.** Open Book, Globe and Reader.

**1979.** 11th Cairo International Book Fair.
1380. **561.** 20 m. brown and green 35 10

**562.** Fair Emblem and Symbols of Industry and Agriculture.

**1979.** Cairo International Fair.
1381 **562** 20 m. brown, orge & bl 35 10

**563.** Poppy and Skull.

**1979.** 50th Anniv. of Anti-Narcotics General Administration.
1382. **563.** 70 m. green, red & yell. 1·40 50

**564.** Isis and Horus. **566.** Doves, President Sadat's Signature and "Peace".

**565.** World Map, Koran and Symbols of Arab Accomplishments.

**1979.** Mothers' Day.
1383. **564.** 140 m. yell., brn. & blue 1·10 75

**1979.** The Arabs.
1384. **565.** 45 m. sepia, yellow and turquoise .. 40 20

**1979.** Signing of Egyptian–Israeli Peace Treaty.
1385 **566** 20 m. violet & yellow 25 10
1386 70 m. red and green 75 35
1387 140 m. red and green 1·25 95

**567.** Honeycomb of Food Projects.

**1979.** Food Security.
1388 **567** 20 m. yell, grn & blk 25 10

**568.** Examining 1979 Peace Stamp.

**1979.** 50th Anniv. of Egyptian Philatelic Society.
1389. **568.** 20 m. emerald, black and brown .. 40 20

**569.** Coins of 1954 and 1979.

**1979.** 25th Anniv. of Egyptian Mint.
1390. **569.** 20 m. grey and yellow 30 10

**570.** "Sun of Freedom" and Open Book.

**1979.** 27th Anniv. of Revolution.
1391. **570.** 20 m. brn., orge. & blue 25 10

**571.** Musicians playing Rabab and Arghoul. **572.** Dove and Map of Sinai.

**1979.** Festivals.
1393 **571** 10 m. blk, brn & orge 10 10

**1979.** 6th Anniv. of Suez Canal Crossing.
1394. **572.** 20 m. brown and blue 35 10

**573.** Skeleton of "Arsinotherium ziltelli".

**1979.** 75th Anniv of Egyptian Geological Museum.
1395 **573** 20 m. brown, yell & bl 50 20

**574.** Symbols of Engineering.

**1979.** Engineers' Day.
1396. **574.** 20 m. purple, yellow and emerald .. 40 10

**575.** Human Rights Flame over Globe.

**1979.** United Nations Day.
1397 **575** 45 m. orange, bl & grn 45 20
1398 – 140 m. brn, yell & red 1·10 95
DESIGN: 140 m. Child with flower (International Year of the Child).

**576.** Buildings and Hand placing Coin in Box.

**1979.** International Savings Day.
1399 **576** 70 m. multicoloured .. 60 35

**577.** Championship Emblem. **578.** Figure clothed in Palestinian Flag.

**1979.** 20th International Military Sports Council Shooting Championship.
1400 **577** 20 m. red, blue & yell 35 10

**1979.** International Day of Solidarity with Palestinian People.
1401. **578.** 45 m. multicoloured 55 15

**579.** Dove, Globe and Rotary Club Emblem.

**1979.** 50th Anniv. of Cairo Rotary Club and 75th Anniv. (1980) of Rotary International.
1402 **579** 140 m. green, bl & yell 1·10 75

**580.** Cogs and Factories. **581.** Ali el Garem (educational writer, 1881-1949).

**1979.** 25th Anniv. of Military Factories.
1403. **580.** 20 m. green and brown 25 10

**1979.** Writers.
1404. **581.** 20 m. brn. & deep brn. 20 15
1405. – 20 m. deep brn. & brn. 20 15
DESIGN: No. 1405, Mahmoud el Baroudy (poet, 1839–1904).

**582.** Capital of Pharaonic Column. **583.** Goddess of Writing and Fair Emblem.

**1980.** Post Day. Pharaonic Capitals.
1406. **582.** 20 m. brown and violet 25 25
1407. – 45 m. brown and violet 40 40
1408. – 70 m. brown and violet 50 50
1409. – 140 m. brown and violet 1·10 1·10
DESIGNS: 45 m. Head capital. 70 m. Leaf capital. 140 m. Capital with cartouche.

**1980.** 12th Cairo International Book Fair.
1410 **583** 20 m. brown, bl & yell 25 10

**584.** Exhibition Catalogue and Medal. **585.** Fair Emblem and Branch.

**1980.** 13th Fine Arts Biennial, Alexandria.
1411 **584** 20 m. multicoloured .. 25 10

**1980.** 13th Cairo International Fair.
1412 **585** 20 m. blk, grn & orge 35 10

**586.** Trajan Monument.

**1980.** 20th Anniv of Nubian Monuments Preservation Campaign.
1413 **586** 70 m. orange, brn & bl 80 55
1414 – 70 m. orange, brn & bl 80 55
1415 – 70 m. orange, brn & bl 80 55
1416 – 70 m. orange, brn & bl 80 55
DESIGNS: No. 1414, Qortasi monument. 1415, Kalabasha monument. 1416, Philae temple.

**587.** Doctors' Day Medal.

**588.** President Sadat.

**1980.** Doctors' Day.
1417. **587.** 20 m. grn., blk. & brn. 30 10

**1980.** 9th Anniv. of Rectification Movement.
1418. **588.** 20 m. grn., blk. & red 30 10

**589.** Ship and Figure Symbolizing Peace and Freedom.

**1980.** 5th Anniv. of Re-opening of Suez Canal.
1419 **589** 140 m. black, orge & bl 1·10 75

**590.** Pharaonic Cat.

**1980.** Centenary of Society for the Prevention of Cruelty to Animals.
1420. **590.** 20 m. grey and green 35 15

**591.** Worker pushing Cogwheel.

**1980.** Industry Day.
1421 **591** 20 m. orange, brn & bl 25 10

**592.** Symbolic Tree.

**593.** Erksous Seller and Nakrazan Player.

**1980.** 28th Anniv. of Revolution. Social Security Year.
1422. **592.** 20 m. pur., grn. & brn. 25 10

**1980.** Festivals 1980.
1424. **593.** 10 m. multicoloured 25 10

**594.** " 6 October ", Building Construction and Doves.

**1980.** 7th Anniv. of Suez Crossing.
1425. **594.** 20 m. multicoloured 30 10

**595.** Islamic and Coptic Capitals.

**1980.** United Nations Day.
1426. **595.** 70 m. yellow and blue 60 40
1427. – 140 m. red, grn. & brn. 1·10 90
DESIGN: 140 m. I.T.U. emblem (International Telecommunications Day).

**596.** Spider's Web, Dove and Olive Branch.

**1980.** 1400th Anniv. of Hegira.
1428. **596.** 45 m. yell., brn. & grn. 50 25

**597.** Tankers.

**1980.** Opening of Third Channel of Suez Canal.
1429. **597.** 70 m. blue, turq. & grn. 65 40

**598.** Mustafa Sadek el Rafai (writer).

**599.** Scarab from Tutankhamun Collection.

**1980.** Arab Personalities. Brown and green.
1430. 20 m. Type **598** (birth centenary) .. .. 25 20
1431. 20 m. Dr. Ali Mustafa Mousharafa (scientist, 30th death anniv.) .. 25 20
1432. 20 m. Dr. Ali Ibrahim (surgeon, birth centenary) .. .. .. 25 20

**1981.** Post Day.
1433. **599.** 70 m. multicoloured 65 35
1434. – 70 m. yellow, brown and green .. .. 65 35
DESIGN: No. 1434, Other side of scarab.

**600.** Heinrich von Stephan.

**602.** Symbols of Agriculture and Industry.

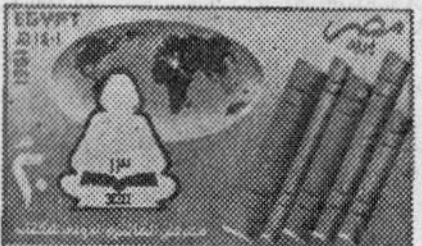


**601.** Fair Emblem, Globe and Books.

**1981.** 150th Birth Anniv. of Heinrich von Stephan (founder of U.P.U.).
1435. **600.** 140 m. brown & blue 1·60 95

**1981.** 13th Cairo International Book Fair.
1436. **601.** 20 m. grn., yell & brn. 35 10

**1981.** 14th Cairo International Fair.
1437. **602.** 20 m. pink, brn. & gr. 35 10

**603.** R.E.A. Emblem, Pylon and Village.

**1981.** 10th Anniv. of Rural Electrification Authority.
1438. **603.** 20 m. yell., grn. & blk. 35 10

**604.** Soldier, Olive Branch and Veteran's Association Emblem.

**605.** Conference Emblem.

**1981.** Veteran's Day.
1439. **604.** 20 m. grn., red & brn. 35 10

**1981.** International Dentistry Conference, Cairo.
1440. **605.** 20 m. brown and red 35 10

**606.** Confederation Emblem.

**607.** Nurse.

**1981.** 25th Anniv. of International Confederation of Arab Trade Unions.
1441. **606.** 20 m. brown and blue 35 10

**1981.** Nurses' Day.
1442. **607.** 20 m. orge., grn. & red 35 10

**608.** Irrigation Spray.

**609.** Rocket and Military Equipment.

**1981.** 10th Anniv. of Rectification Movement.
1443. **608.** 20 m. grn., brn. & yell. 35 10

**1981.** Air Defence Day.
1444. **609.** 20 m. grn., blue & red 40 20

**610.** Map of Afghanistan.

**1981.** Solidarity with Afghan People.
1445. **610.** 20 m. + 10 m. brown, red and black (37 × 36 mm.) .. .. 40 20
1446. 20 m. + 10 m. brown, red and black (27 × 22 mm.) .. .. 40 20

**611.** " 29 " and Social Defence Badge.

**612.** Water Lilies.

**1981.** 29th Anniv. of Revolution.
1447. **611.** 20 m. yell., grn. & brn. 30 10
1448. – 20 m. blue, blk. & red 30 10
DESIGN: No. 1448, Map of Suez Canal and ships on graph surrounded by Egyptian flag. (25th anniv. of Suez Canal nationalization).

**1981.** Festivals 1981.
1449. **612.** 10 m. multicoloured 20 10

**613.** Kemal Ataturk.

**614.** Ahmed Arabi.

**1981.** Birth Centenary of Kemal Ataturk (Turkish statesman).
1450. **613.** 140 m. brn. & grn. .. 1·60 95

**1981.** Centenary of Arabi Revolution.
1451 **614** 20 m. brown and green 25 10

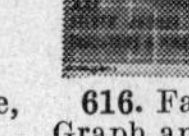

**615.** Muscular Athlete, Sphinx and Pyramids.

**616.** Factory on Graph and Atomic Symbol.

**1981.** World Muscular Athletics Championship, Cairo.
1452. **615.** 45 m. yellow, black and brown .. 45 25

**1981.** 25th Anniv. of Ministry of Industry.
1453. **616.** 45 m. yell, bl. & red 35 20

**617.** Congress Emblem and Imhotep (god of Medicine).

**1981.** 20th International Medical Industries Congress, Cairo.
1454. **617.** 20 m. grn., blk. & orge. 35 15

**618.** Eye.

**1981.** Air.
1455 **618** 230 m. bl, orge & brn 1·90 95

**619.** Olive, Dove, Canal and Wheat.

**1981.** 8th Anniv of Suez Crossing.
1456 **619** 20 m. green, stone & bl 30 10

**620.** I.T.U. and W.H.O. Emblems.

**1981.** United Nations Day.

1457. – 10 m. yell., bl. & brn. 20 10
1458. **620.** 20 m. bl., orge. & blk. 25 15
1459. – 45 m. pur., grn. & blk. 55 35
1460. – 230 m. orge, grn. and black .. .. 2·50 1·60

DESIGNS—HORIZ: 10 m. Food and Agriculture Organization Emblem (World Food Day). 230 m. Olive branches (Racial Discrimination Day). VERT: 20 m. Type **620** (World Telecommunications Day). 45 m. International Year of Disabled Persons emblem.

**621.** President Sadat and Memorial.

**1981.** President Sadat Commemoration.

1461. **621.** 30 m. brn., grn. & red 30 20
1462. 230 m. brn., grn. & red 1·90 1·60

**622.** Dome of Shura Council, Hands and Candle.

**623.** Bank Emblem.

**1981.** 1st Anniv of Shura Council.

1463. **622.** 45 m. yell. and lilac 35 20

**1981.** 50th Anniv. of Bank for Development and Agricultural Credit.

1464. **623.** 20 m. buff, grn. & blk. 25 10

**624.** Ali el Gayati.

**625.** Dove and Globe forming Figure "20".

**1981.** Celebrities.

1465. **624.** 30 m. brn. and grn... 25 25
1466. – 60 m. brn. and grn... 40 40

DESIGNS: Type **624** (journalist, 25th death anniv.). 60 m. Omar Ebn el Fared (poet, 1181–1234).

**1981.** 20th Anniv. of African Postal Union.

1467. **625.** 60 m. yell., bl. & red 65 30

**626.** Book and Writing Materials.

**627.** Federation Emblem.

**1982.** 14th Cairo International Book Fair.

1468. **626.** 3 p. brown & yellow 25 10

**1982.** 25th Anniv. of Egyptian Trade Unions Federation.

1469. **627.** 3 p. blue and green.. 25 10

**628.** Map, " 25 " and Dome of University.

**1982.** 25th Anniv. of Cairo University, Khartoum Branch.

1470 **628** 6 p. green and blue .. 50 35

**629.** Fair Emblem.

**630.** Hilton Ramses Hotel.

**1982.** 15th Cairo International Fair

1471 **629** 3 p. black, grn & orge 25 10

**1982.** Air. Opening of Hilton Ramses Hotel.

1472 **630** 18½ p. brown, yell & bl 1·25 85

**631.** Batfish.

**1982.** International Conference on Marine Science and 50th Anniv of Marine Biological Station, El Ghardaka. Multicoloured.

1473 10 m. Type **631** .. .. 40 35
1474 30 m. Blue-banded sea perch .. .. .. 60 40
1475 60 m. Blue-spotted box fish .. .. .. 65 60
1476 230 m. Lined butterfly fish .. .. .. 1·60 1·25

**632.** Map of Sinai, Olive Branch and Dove.

**1982.** Sinai Restoration.

1477 **632** 3 p. brn, stone & grn 35 15

**633.** De Havilland D.H.86B Dragon Express Biplane and Boeing 737 Jetliner.

**1982.** 50th Anniv of Egyptair (state airline).

1478 **633** 23 p. blue, mve & yell 2·50 1·60

**634.** Minaret.

**635.** Dove.

**1982.** Millenary of El Azhar Mosque.

1479 **634** 6 p. yellow, brn & grn 65 45
1480 – 6 p. yellow, brn & grn 65 45
1481 – 6 p. yellow, brn & grn 65 45
1482 – 6 p. yellow, brn & grn 65 45

DESIGNS: No. 1480, Dome and minaret (different). 1481, Minaret with three stages and one ball on top. 1482, Minaret with two balls on top.

**1982.** 30th Anniv. of Revolution.

1484. **635.** 3 p. green, deep green & orange .. 25 15

**636.** Hotel, Citadel, Sphinx, Pyramid and St. Catherine's.

**1982.** International Tourism Day.

1486 **636** 23 p. blue, orge & brn 2·50 1·60

**637.** Martyrs' Monument, Egyptian Flag and Map.

**1982.** 9th Anniv of Suez Crossing.

1487 **637** 3 p. black, pink & blue 35 15

**638.** Biennale Emblem and Sailboat.

**639.** Trees and Factory Pollution (World Environment Day).

**1982.** 14th Fine Arts Biennale, Alexandria.

1488 **638** 3 p. orange, bl & lilac 35 15

**1982.** United Nations Day.

1489 **639** 3 p. brown, yell & grn 25 15
1490 – 6 p. blue and green .. 50 40
1491 – 6 p. blue and brown 50 40
1492 – 8 p. brown, blue & red 75 65

DESIGNS—HORIZ: No. 1490, Olive branch and dove encircling globe (2nd Conference on the Exploration and Peaceful Uses of Outer Space, Vienna). 1492, Dr. Robert Koch and bacillus (centenary of discovery of tubercle bacillus). 36 × 36 mm: No. 1491, Lord Baden-Powell and scout emblems (125th birth anniv of Lord Baden-Powell (founder) and 75th anniv of boy scout movement).

**640.** Avro Type 618 Ten and General Dynamics Fighting Falcon.

**1982.** 50th Anniv. of Egyptian Air Force.

1493. **640.** 3 p. blue and black.. 40 20

**641.** Ahmed Shawqi and Hafez Ibrahim.

**1982.** 50th Death Annivs. of Ahmed Shawqi and Hafez Ibrahim (poets).

1494. **641.** 6 p. blue and brown 50 35

**642.** Jubilee Emblem.

**643.** Hands holding Flower.

**1982.** 25th Anniv. of National Research Centre.

1495. **642.** 3 p. blue and red .. 25 15

**1982.** Aged People Year.

1496 **643** 23 p. green, red & blue 2·50 1·60

**644.** "Academy" on Open Books.

**1982.** 50th Anniv of Arab League Academy.

1497 **644** 3 p. brown, stone & bl 45 35

**645.** Postal Emblem and Postcoded Letter.

**647.** Emblem, Globe and Open Book.

**646.** Police Emblem.

**1983.** Post Day.

1498. **645.** 3 p. blue, red and blk. 25 20

**1983.** Police Day.

1499 **646** 3 p. blue, black & grn 45 20

**1983.** 15th Cairo International Book Fair.

1500. **647.** 3 p. blue and red .. 25 20

**648.** Satellite and Map of Africa.

**649.** Conference Emblem.

**1983.** Fifth U.N. Regional Conference for African Maps, Cairo.

1501. **648.** 3 p. green and blue.. 25 20

**1983.** Third African Ministers of Transport, Communication and Planning Conference, Cairo.

1502. **649.** 23 p. blue and green 1·10 75

**650.** Emblem, Olive Branch and Cogwheel.

**651.** Footballer heading Ball.

**1983.** 16th Cairo International Fair.

1503. **650.** 3 p. grn., blk. & red.. 25 20

**1983.** Egyptian Football Victories in Africa Cup and African Cup-winners Cup.

1504 **651** 3 p. stone, brn & red 30 25
1505 – 3 p. stone, brn & red 30 25

DESIGNS: No. 1504, Type **651** (African Cup-winners Cup, Arab Contractors Club). No. 1505, Footballer kicking ball (Africa Cup, National Club).

**652.** Emblem within Heart.

**1983.** World Health Day. Blood Donation.

1506. **652.** 3 p. blk., red & grn. 30 20

**653.** Organization. Emblem.

**1983.** 10th Anniv. of Trade Union Unity Organization.

1507. **653.** 3 p. blue and green 25 20

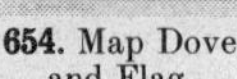

**654.** Map Dove and Flag. **655.** Scarab and Microscope.

**1983.** 1st Anniv. of Restoration of Sinai.

1508. **654.** 3 p. green, blk. & red 35 20

**1983.** 75th Anniv. of Egyptian Entomological Society.

1509. **655.** 3 p. black and blue .. 35 20

**656.** Chrysanthemums.

**1983.** Festivals.

1510. **656.** 20 m. red and green 25 15

**657.** Stadium, Player and Championship Emblem.

**1983.** Fifth African Handball Championship, Cairo.

1511. **657.** 6 p. brown and green 45 25

**658.** Ears of Wheat and "23". **659.** Simon Bolivar (statue).

**1983.** 31st Anniv. of Revolution.

1512. **658.** 3 p. grn., yell. & brn. 25 15

**1983.** Birth Bicentenary of Simon Bolivar (South American revolutionary leader).

1513. **659.** 23 p. brown and blue 1·25 75

**660.** Arabi Pasha, Maps of Egypt and Ceylon and House.

**1983.** Centenary of Exile to Ceylon of Arabi Pasha.

1514 **660** 3 p. brown, grn & orge 35 20

**661.** Jar and Museum.

**1983.** Reopening of Islamic Museum.

1515. **661.** 3 p. light brn., & brn. 35 20

**662.** Monument, Martyrs, Cogwheel, Wheat and Oil Well. **663.** Rally Cars.

**1983.** 10th Anniv. of Suez Crossing.

1516. **662.** 3 p. grn., red and blk. 40 20

**1983.** 2nd International Pharaonic Motor Rally.

1517 **663** 23 p. brown, bl & stone 1·60 75

**664.** Radar, Modern Freighter and Pharaonic Ship.

**1983.** United Nations Day.

1518. **664.** 3 p. blue and black .. 30 15
1519. – 6 p. green and blue .. 50 40
1520. – 6 p. grn., orge. and blk. 50 40
1521. – 23 p. blue and brown 1·25 95

Designs: No. 1518, Type **664** (25th anniv of International Maritime Organization). 1519, Emblems and concentric circles (World Communications Year). 1520, Ear of wheat and emblems (20th anniv of World Food Programme). 1521, Fishing boat and fish (Fishery Resources).

**665.** Karate, Pyramids and Sphinx.

**1983.** Fourth World Karate Championship, Cairo.

1522. **665.** 3 p. multicoloured .. 45 25

**666.** Dome of the Rock, Jerusalem.

**1983.** International Day of Solidarity with Palestinian People.

1523 **666** 6 p. brn, ochre & grn 75 25

**667.** Artist's Palette. **668.** Statue and Cairo University.

**1983.** 75th Anniv of Faculty of Fine Arts, Helwan University.

1524. **667.** 3 p. yell., red and blue 25 20

**1983.** 75th Anniv. of Cairo University.

1525. **668.** 3 p. light brown, brown and blue .. 25 20

**669.** "Mother and Child" and Emblem.

**1983.** International Egyptian Maternity and Child Care Society.

1526 **669** 2 p. blue, black & orge 30 20

**670.** Emblem and Maps. **671.** Rameses II, Thebes.

**1983.** 20th Anniv. of Organization of African Unity.

1527. **670.** 3 p. green and red .. 30 20

**1983.** 10th Anniv (1982) of World Heritage Convention. Each stone, brown and green.

1528. 3 p. Type **671** .. .. 40 30
1529. 3 p. Coptic weaving (detail) .. .. 40 30
1530. 3 p. Islamic carved wooden panel .. .. 40 30

**672.** Qaitbay Fort.

**1984.** Post Day. Multicoloured.

1531 6 p. Type **672** .. .. 50 35
1532 23 p. Mohammed Ali Mosque, Saladin's Citadel .. .. 1·50 95

**673.** Emblem, Family and Insurance Document. **674.** Open Book and Emblem.

**1984.** 50th Anniv. of Misr Insurance Company.

1533. **673.** 3 p. ochre, green and brown .. .. 25 20

**1984.** 16th Cairo International Book Fair.

1534. **674.** 3 p. pink, green and brown .. .. 25 20

**675.** Fair Emblem within Pyramids. **676.** University Emblem and Map.

**1984.** 17th Cairo International Fair.

1535. **675.** 3 p. orange, brown and green .. .. 25 20

**1984.** 25th Anniv. of Assiout University.

1536. **676.** 3 p. orange, blue and lilac .. .. 25 20

**677.** Emblem. **678.** Curtains, Masks and Globe.

**1984.** 75th Anniv of Egyptian Co-operatives.

1537 **677** 3 p. orange, blue & grn 25 20

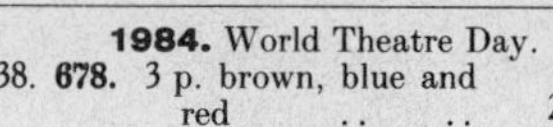

**1984.** World Theatre Day.

1538. **678.** 3 p. brown, blue and red .. .. 25 20

**679.** Mahmoud Moukhtar and Sculptures.

**1984.** 50th Death Anniv. of Mahmoud Moukhtar (sculptor).

1539. **679.** 3 p. brown and green 25 20

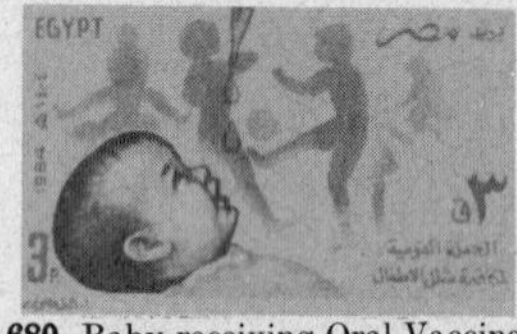

**680.** Baby receiving Oral Vaccine.

**1984.** World Health Day. Anti-poliomyelitis Campaign.

1540. **680.** 3 p. yellow, brown and green .. .. 40 20

**681.** Doves over Sinai. **682.** Map of Africa showing Namibia.

**1984.** 2nd Anniv of Restoration of Sinai.

1541 **681** 3 p. stone, green & bl 30 20

**1984.** Africa Day.

1542. **682.** 3 p. blue and brown 25 20

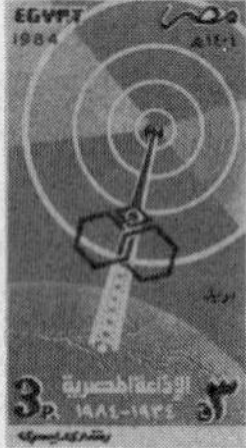

**683.** Globe and Transmitter **684.** Carnation.

**1984.** 50th Anniv. of Egyptian Broadcasting.

1543. **683.** 3 p. blue, black and red .. .. 30 20

**1984.** Festivals.

1544. **684.** 2 p. red and green .. 25 10

**685.** Decorated Mask. **686.** Atomic Power.

**1984.** First Cairo International Biennale.

1545. **685.** 3 p. multicoloured .. 30 20

**1984.** 32nd Anniv. of Revolution.
1546. **686.** 3 p. blue, yellow and red .. .. 25 20

**687.** Boxing.
**688.** Conference Emblem.

**1984.** Olympic Games, Los Angeles.
1547. **687.** 3 p. green, blue and red .. .. 30 20
1548. – 3 p. green, blue and red .. .. 30 20
1549. – 3 p. green, blue and red .. .. 30 20
1550. – 3 p. green, blue and red .. .. 30 20
DESIGNS: No. 1548, Basketball. 1549, Volleyball. 1550, Football.

**1984.** Second Egyptians Abroad Conference, Cairo.
1552. **688.** 3 p. brown, blue and black .. .. 30 20
1553. 23 p. brown, green and black .. .. 1·60 95

**689.** Couple and Emblem.
**690.** Emblem and Sphinx.

**1984.** 30th Anniv. of Egyptian Youth Hostels' Association.
1554. **689.** 3 p. green, black and orange .. .. 25 20

**1984.** 50th Anniv. of Misr Travel Company.
1555. **690.** 3 p. brown, yellow and blue .. .. 25 20

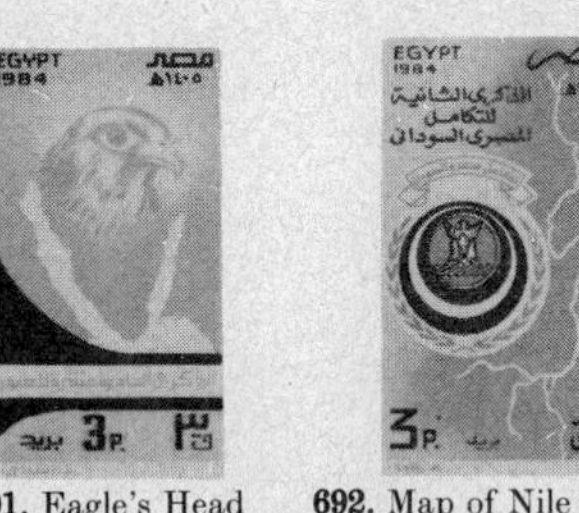

**691.** Eagle's Head and Map of Sinai.
**692.** Map of Nile Valley and Integration Badge.

**1984.** 11th Anniv. of Suez Crossing.
1556. **691.** 3 p. green, red and black .. .. 25 20

**1984.** 2nd Anniv. of Signing of Egypt-Sudan Co-operation Treaty.
1557. **692.** 3 p. red, black and green .. .. 25 20

**693.** Child's Face within Blossom.
**694.** Tank, Anti-aircraft Gun and Emblem.

**1984.** United Nations Children's Fund.
1558. **693.** 3 p. multicoloured .. 25 20

**1984.** Defence Equipment Exhibition, Cairo.
1559. **694.** 3 p. yellow, black and red .. .. 25 20

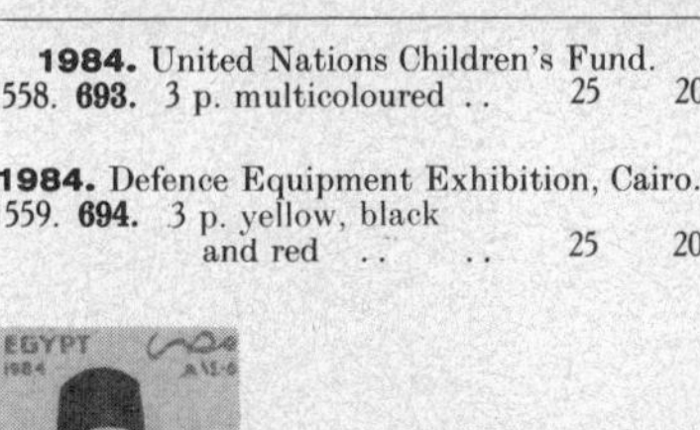

**695.** Kamel Kilany and Books.
**696.** Ahmed ibn Toulon Mosque.

**1984.** 25th Death Anniv. of Kamel Kilany (children's author and poet).
1560. **695.** 3 p. brown, yellow and blue .. .. 25 20

**1984.** 1100th Death Anniv. of Ahmed ibn Toulon (governor of Egypt).
1561. **696.** 3 p. light brown, blue and brown .. 30 20

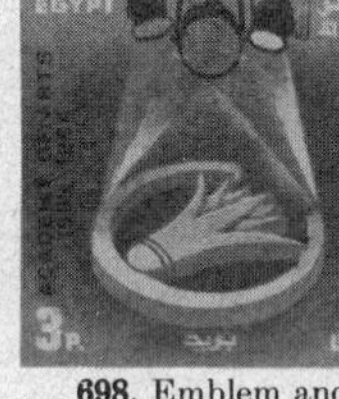

**697.** Congress Emblem.
**698.** Emblem and Spotlights.

**1984.** 29th International History of Medicine Congress, Cairo.
1562. **697.** 3 p. blue, blk. & red 25 20

**1984.** 25th Anniv. of Academy of Art.
1563. **698.** 3 p. multicoloured .. 25 20

**699.** Pharaoh receiving Letter (monument) and Postal Museum.

**1985.** Post Day.
1564. **699.** 3 p. bl., brn. & red .. 25 20

**700.** Cairo Gate and Tower on Scroll and Emblem.
**701.** Scribe (statue) and Emblem.

**1985.** 15th International Union of Architects Conference.
1565 **700** 3 p. lilac and blue .. 25 20

**1985.** 17th Cairo International Book Fair.
1566. **701.** 3 p. blue and orange 25 20

**702.** Edfu Temple.
**703.** Ear of Wheat, Cogwheels and Emblem.

**1985.** Air.
1567 **702** 6 p. green and blue .. 50 25
1568 15 p. brown and blue 75 35
1569 – 18 p. 50 green, yellow and brown .. 95 95
1570 – 23 p. brown, yellow and blue .. .. 1·25 1·25
1571 – 25p. blue, yellow and brown .. .. 1·25 65
1572 – 30 p. brown, orange and blue .. .. 1·60 85
DESIGNS—HORIZ. 23, 30 p. Giza Pyramids. VERT. 18 p. 50, 25 p. Akhnaton.

**1985.** 18th Cairo International Fair.
1573. **703.** 3 p. multicoloured .. 25 20

**704.** Woman holding Heart.
**705.** Priest of god Mout.

**1985.** 3rd Anniv. of Restoration of Sinai.
1574. **704.** 5 p. multicoloured .. 30 20

**1985.** (a) Size 22×27 mm.
1575 **705** 1 p. brown .. .. 10 10
1576 – 2 p. blue .. .. 10 10
1577 – 3 p. brown .. .. 15 10
1578 – 5 p. purple .. .. 25 15
1579 – 8 p. brown and green 35 25
1580 – 10 p. blue and purple 15 15
1581 – 11 p. purple .. .. 45 40
1582 – 15 p. brown and ochre 70 45
1583 – 20 p. green .. .. 1·00 45
1584 – 20 p. green and yellow 30 20
1585 – 30 p. brn & cinnamon 35 10
1586 – 35 p. yellow & brown 1·60 1·00
1587 – 50 p. lilac and brown 55 25

(b) Mosques. Size 22×39 mm
1588 – £E1 brown and orange 1·10 45
1589 – £E2 brown and yellow 2·25 60
DESIGNS: 2, 20 p. (1583) Wading birds (relief sculpture); 3, 5 p. Statue of Rameses II, Luxor; 8, 15 p. Slave kneeling with tray and fruit (wall painting); 10 p. Vase; 11 p. Carved head; 20 p. (1584) Jug; 30 p. Flagon; 35 p. Capitals of pharaonic columns; 50 p. Flask; £E1, Al-Maridani Mosque; £E2, Al-Azhar Mosque, Cairo.
For designs size 18×22 mm, see Nos. 1772/5.

**707.** Treble Clef.
**708.** El Moulid Bride (doll).

**1985.** 50th Anniv. of Helwan University Musical Faculty.
1595. **707.** 5 p. blue and yellow 30 20

**1985.** Festivals 1985.
1596 **708** 2 p. violet, orge & yell 20 10
1597 5 p. red, blue & green 30 20

**709.** Player and Cup.
**710.** Television Headquarters and Radio Waves.

**1985.** Egyptian Football Victories. Mult.
1598. 5 p. Cairo Stadium (left-hand) .. .. .. 50 40
1599. 5 p. Cairo Stadium (right-hand) .. .. 50 40
1600. 5 p. El Zamalek Club player and Africa Cup (winners, 1984) .. 50 40
1601. 5 p. National Club player (red shirt) and African Cup-winners Cup (winners 1984) .. 50 40
1602. 5 p. Type **709** (Arab Contractors Club, African Cup-winners Cup winners, 1983) .. 50 40
Nos. 1598/9 were issued together, forming a composite design.

**1985.** Anniversaries. Multicoloured.
1603. 5 p. Type **710** (25th anniv. of Egyptian television) .. .. 35 20
1604. 5 p. Flag and olive branch entwined, ships and maps of world and Suez Canal (10th anniv. of re-opening) (horiz.) 35 20
1605. 5 p. Cars in Ahmed Hamdi Tunnel under Suez Canal (33rd anniv. of revolution) 35 20

**711.** Map within Heart and Emblem.

**1985.** Third Egyptians Abroad Conference, Cairo.
1607. **711.** 15 p. multicoloured 75 45

**712.** Akhnaton worshipping Aton and Emblem.

**1985.** 50th Anniv. of Tourism Organization.
1608. **712.** 5 p. multicoloured .. 30 20

**713.** Flag and Olive Branch on Map of Sinai.

**1985.** 12th Anniv. of Suez Crossing.
1609. **713.** 5 p. multicoloured .. 30 20

**714.** Air Scouts Emblem.

**1985.** 30th Anniv. of Air Scouts.
1610. **714.** 5 p. blue, red & yell. 50 25

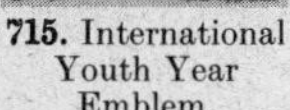

**715.** International Youth Year Emblem.

**716.** Conference and Association Emblems.

**1985.** United Nations Day.

1611 **715** 5 p. lilac, yellow and green .. .. 35 20
1612 – 5 p. multicoloured .. 35 20
1613 – 15 p. blue, yellow and red .. .. 90 60
1614 – 15 p. blue & lt. blue 90 60

DESIGNS: No. 1612. Meteorological map of Egypt (World Meteorology Day). 1613, Dove and U.N. emblem (40th Anniv. of United Nations Organization). 1614. International communications development programme emblem.

**1985.** Second International Conference of Egyptian Association of Dental Surgeons, Cairo.

1615. **716.** 5 p. blue and brown 40 20

**717.** Conference Banner and Koran.

**718.** Squash Player.

**1985.** Fourth International Conference of Biography and Sunna (sayings) of Prophet Mohammed.

1616. **717.** 5 p. blue, yellow and brown .. .. 30 20

**1985.** World Squash Championships, Cairo.

1617. **718.** 5 p. green, yellow and brown .. 45 20

**719.** Emblem, Flag and Hand holding Tools.

**720.** Emblem and Tomb Paintings.

**1985.** First Technical Industrial Education Conference.

1618. **719.** 5 p. blue, red & blk. 30 20

**1985.** 75th Anniv. of Egyptian Olympic Committee.

1619. **720.** 5 p. multicoloured .. 30 20

**721.** Narmer Board.

**722.** Emblem and Relief of Scribe.

**1986.** Air. Post Day. Multicoloured.

1620 15 p. Type **721** .. .. 95 95
1621 15 p. Narmer Board (opposite side) .. 95 95

**1986.** 18th Cairo International Book Fair.

1622. **722.** 5 p. brn., yell. & bl. 30 20

**723.** Conference Emblem.

**1986.** 3rd International Conference for Transport in Developing Countries, Cairo.

1623. **723.** 5 p. bl., grn. & red .. 30 20

**724.** Emblem on Islamic Ornament.

**1986.** 25th Anniv. of Central Bank.

1624. **724.** 5 p. multicoloured .. 30 20

**725.** Globe, Sorting Office and Map.

**1986.** Inauguration of Cairo Postal Sorting Centre.

1625. **725.** 5 p. blue and brown 30 20

**726.** Tomb Painting, Sakkara.

**1986.** 75th Anniv of Cairo University Commerce Faculty.

1626 **726** 5 p. yellow, brn & pur 30 20

**727.** Wheat, Cogwheel, Flags and Emblem.

**728.** Map of Sudan and dead Tree.

**1986.** 19th Cairo International Fair.

1627. **727.** 5 p. multicoloured .. 30 20

**1986.** Relief of Drought Victims in Sudan.

1628. **728.** 15 p.+5 p. blue, brown and yellow 1·25 95

**729.** Map of Africa, Boeing 707 and Emblem.

**1986.** 18th Annual General Assembly of African Airlines Association.

1629. **729.** 15 p. bl., yell. & blk. 85 40

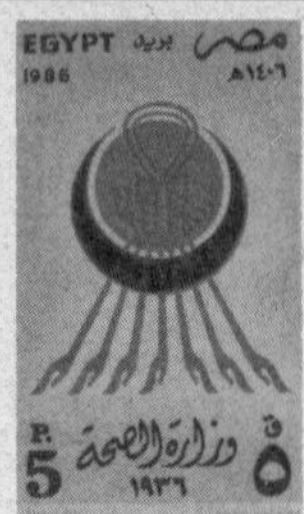

**730.** Ankh, Red Crescent and Hands.

**1986.** 50th Anniv. of Ministry of Health.

1630. **730.** 5 p. multicoloured .. 30 20

**731.** Queen Nefertari and Map of Sinai.

**1986.** 4th Anniv of Restoration of Sinai.

1631 **731** 5 p. blue, red & green 45 20

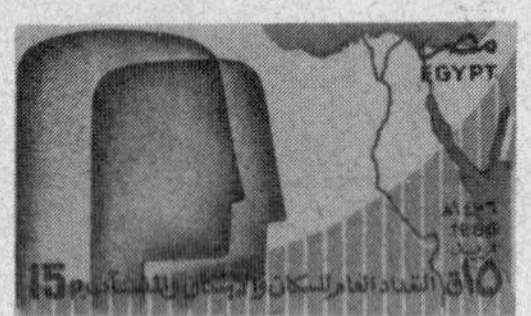

**732.** Profiles and Map.

**1986.** Census.

1632. **732.** 15 p. brown, yellow and blue .. .. 80 30

**733.** Map, Cup and Emblem.

**734.** Roses.

**1986.** Victory in African Nations Cup Football Championship. Multicoloured.

1633. 5 p. Type **733** .. .. 40 25
1634. 5 p. As No. 1633 but emblem inscr. in Arabic .. .. .. 40 25

**1986.** Festivals 1986.

1635. **734.** 5 p. purple, green and lilac .. .. 30 20

**735.** Smoke issuing from Factory.

**736.** Eagle and "23 July".

**1986.** World Environment Day.

1636. **735.** 15 p. blk., grn. & bl. 85 35

**1986.** 34th Anniv. of Revolution.

1637. **736.** 5 p. yell., grn. & red 25 20

**737.** Road on Map of Africa.

**1986.** 6th African Road Conference, Cairo.

1638. **737.** 15 p. multicoloured 75 30

**738.** Map, Eagle, Olive Branch and Flag.

**739.** Workers holding Books and Tools.

**1986.** 13th Anniv. of Suez Crossing.

1639. **738.** 5 p. multicoloured .. 35 20

**1986.** 25th Anniv. of Workers' Cultural Association.

1640. **739.** 5 p. orange and lilac 25 15

**740.** Syndicate Emblem and Engineering Symbols.

**741.** Dove and Emblem (International Peace Year).

**1986.** Engineers' Day. 40th Anniv. of Engineers' Syndicate.

1641. **740.** 5 p. grn., brn. & bl. 25 15

**1986.** United Nations Day.

1642. **741.** 5 p. grn., bl. & red .. 25 15
1643. – 15 p. yell., grn. & brn 75 40
1644. – 15 p. multicoloured 75 40

DESIGNS—HORIZ. As T **741**. No. 1643, Harvester and ears of wheat (40th anniv of Food and Agriculture Organization). 46×27 mm. 1644, Emblem, globe and "U.N.E.S.C.O." in Arabic (40th anniv of U.N.E.S.C.O.).

**742.** Map and Old and New Drilling Towers.

**1986.** Centenary of First Egyptian Oilwell, Gemsa.

1645. **742.** 5 p. grn., yell. & blk. 35 20

**743.** Children holding Flower.

**1986.** Children's Day.

1646. **743.** 5 p. multicoloured .. 35 20

744. Ahmed Amin.

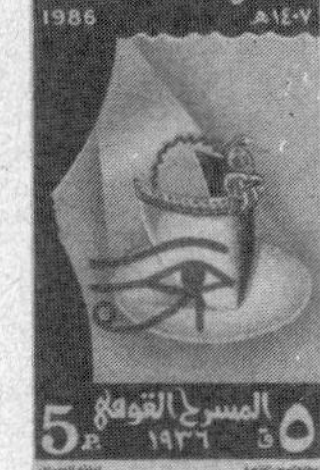
745. Mask and Eye in Spotlight.

**1986.** Birth Centenary of Ahmed Amin (literary researcher).
1647. **744.** 5 p. yell., brn. & grn. 25 20

**1986.** 50th Anniv. of National Theatre.
1648. **745.** 5 p. multicoloured .. 25 20

746. Statue of King Zoser and Step Pyramid, Sakkara.

**1987.** Post Day.
1649. **746.** 5 p. multicoloured .. 30 20

747. Book and Pencil as "19".

**1986.** 19th Cairo International Book Fair.
1650. **747.** 5 p. multicoloured .. 25 20

748. Emblem.

749. Medal.

**1987.** 5th International Conference on Islamic Education.
1651. **748.** 5 p. multicoloured .. 25 20

**1987.** 20th Cairo International Fair.
1652. **749.** 5 p. blk., gold & red 25 20

750. Olive Branch, Profile and National Colours.

**1987.** Veterans' Day.
1653 **750** 5 p. red, green & gold 25 20

751. Plants and Emblem.

**1987.** Air. International Garden Festival, Cairo.
1654. **751.** 15 p. multicoloured 75 40

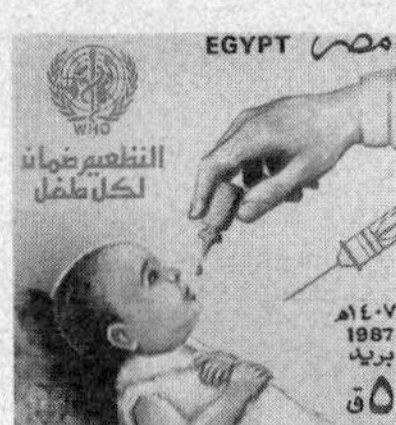
752. Oral Vaccination.

**1987.** International Health Day.
1655. **752.** 5 p. multicoloured .. 30 20
1656. – 5 p. yell., grn. & blk. 30 20
DESIGN: No. 1656, Woman giving baby oral rehydration therapy.

753. Africa Cup.

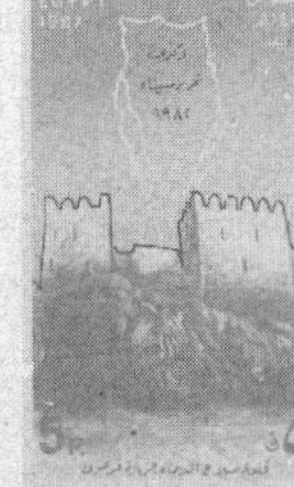
754. Saladin's Citadel and Map.

**1987.** Egyptian Victories in Football Championships. Multicoloured.
1657. 5 p. Type **753** (El Zamalek team) .. 30 25
1658. 5 p. African Nations Cup (national team) .. 30 25
1659. 5 p. African Cup Winners Cup (El Ahly team) .. 30 25

**1987.** 5th Anniv. of Restoration of Sinai.
1661. **754.** 5 p. blue and brown 25 20

755. Dahlia.

**1987.** Festivals 1987.
1662. **755.** 5 p. blue, yellow & mauve .. .. 25 15

756. Pyramid and Camel Train.

**1987.** "Saudi Arabia—Yesterday and Today" Exhibition, Cairo.
1663. **756.** 15 p. multicoloured 75 35

757. El Sawary Column and Sphinx and Qaitbay Fort, Alexandria.

**1987.** Tourism. Multicoloured.
1664. 15 p. Type **757** .. .. 75 65
1665. 15 p. St. Catherine's Monastery, Sinai .. 75 65
1666. 15 p. Colossi of Thebes .. 75 65
1667. 15 p. Temple, Luxor .. 75 65
Nos. 1664/7 were printed together, se-tenant, forming a composite design of a map with each illustrated subject pinpointed.

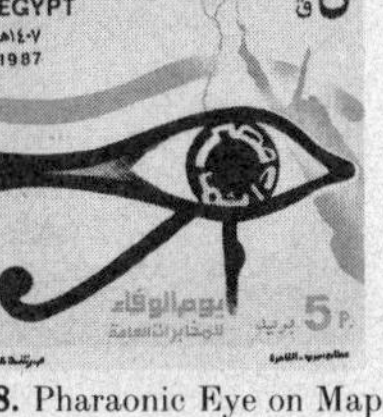
758. Pharaonic Eye on Map.

**1987.** Loyalty Day. 32nd Anniv. of General Intelligence Service.
1669. **758.** 5 p. multicoloured .. 25 15

759. Ears of Wheat and Emblem.

**1987.** Industrial and Agricultural Exhibition, Alexandria.
1670. **759.** 5 p. black, green and orange .. 25 20

760. Emblems.

**1987.** International Year of Shelter for the Homeless. World Architects' Day.
1671. **760.** 5 p. yellow, brown and green .. .. 25 20

761. Scene from Opera and Sphinx.

**1987.** Performance of Verdi's "Aida" (opera) at the Pyramids, Giza.
1672. **761.** 15 p. multicoloured 95 40

762. Train in Station.

**1987.** Inauguration of Cairo Underground Railway.
1674. **762.** 5 p. multicoloured .. 45 20

763. Head composed of Industrial Symbols.

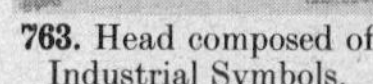
764. Horseman and Map.

**1987.** Production Day.
1675. **763.** 5 p. multicoloured .. 25 15

**1987.** 800th Anniv of Battle of Hattin.
1676 **764** 5 p. multicoloured .. 30 20

765. U.P.U. Emblem.

**1987.** 40th Anniv. of Executive Council and 30th Anniv. of Consultative Council of U.P.U.
1677. **765.** 5 p. blk., orge. & bl. 25 15

766. Eye and Art Materials.

**1987.** 16th Fine Arts Biennale, Alexandria.
1678. **766.** 5 p. multicoloured .. 25 15

767. Emblem and Ancient Egyptians making Weapons.

**1987.** 2nd International Defence Equipment Exhibition, Cairo.
1679. **767.** 5 p. multicoloured .. 25 15

768. Profile and Emblem.

**1987.** 2nd Pan-Arab Anaesthesia and Intensive Care Congress.
1680. **768.** 5 p. multicoloured .. 30 20

769. Globe and Emblem on Skeleton.

770. Selim Hassan (archaeologist) and Hieroglyphics.

**1987.** International Orthopaedic and Traumatology Conference, Luxor.
1681. **769.** 5 p. grey, brn. & bl. 30 20

**1987.** Birth Centenaries. Multicoloured.
1682. 5 p. Type **770** .. .. 25 15
1683. 5 p. Abdel Hamid Badawi (politician and International Court of Justice judge) .. 25 15

771. Mycerinus and Left-hand Pyramid, Giza.

773. Emblem, Hieroglyphics and Scribe.

772. Map.

**1988.** Post Day. Multicoloured.
1684 15 p. Type **771** .. .. 75 65
1685 15 p. Chefren (with beard) and middle pyramid .. 75 65
1686 15 p. Cheops and right-hand pyramid .. 75 65

**1988.** 30th Anniv. of Asia–Africa Organization.
1687. **772.** 15 p. multicoloured 75 35

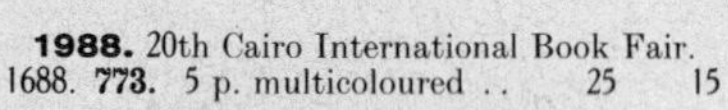

**1988.** 20th Cairo International Book Fair.
1688. **773.** 5 p. multicoloured .. 25 15

774. Container Ship.

**1988.** 25th Anniv of Martrans Shipping Line.
1689. **774.** 5 p. multicoloured .. 35 15

775. Fair Facade, Globe and Emblem.

**1988.** 21st Cairo International Fair.
1690. **775.** 5 p. multicoloured .. 25 15

776. Bowl of Sugar and Emblem.

777. Prince Ossrite and Fig Tree.

**1988.** World Health Day. Diabetic Care.
1691 **776** 5 p. multicoloured .. 30 15

**1988.** Festivals 1988.
1692. **777.** 5 p. orange, green and brown .. 25 15

778. Letters and Emblem.

**1988.** 25th Anniv. of African Postal Union.
1693. **778.** 15 p. blue .. .. 65 30

779. Hands of Different Races reaching for Torch.

**1988.** Anti-Racism Campaign.
1694. **779.** 5 p. multicoloured .. 25 20

780. Maps of Africa around Emblem.

**1988.** 25th Anniv. of Organization for African Unity.
1695. **780.** 15 p. + 10 p. mult. .. 65 50

781. Tawfek el Hakem.

**1988.** 1st Death Anniv. of Tawfek el Hakem (dramatist).
1696. **781.** 5 p. brown and blue 25 20

782. Cubic Art (M. el Razaz).

**1988.** 50th Anniv. of Faculty of Art Education.
1697. **782.** 5 p. multicoloured .. 20 15

783. Games Emblem.

**1988.** Air. Olympic Games, Seoul.
1698. **783.** 15 p. multicoloured 75 35

784. Torch, Flag and Palestinians.

**1988.** Air. Palestinian "Intifida" Movement.
1700. **784.** 25 p. multicoloured 65 35

785. Soldier and Flag.

**1988.** 15th Anniv. of Suez Crossing.
1701. **785.** 5 p. multicoloured .. 20 15

786. Model of Opera House.

**1988.** Inauguration of Opera House.
1702. **786.** 5 p. multicoloured .. 25 20

787. Red Crescent and Red Cross (125th Anniv. of Red Cross).

**1988.** U.N. Day.
1704. **787.** 5 p. black, red and green (postage) .. 25 20
1705. – 20 p. yellow, blue and orange .. 60 30
1706. – 25 p. mult. (air) .. 65 35

DESIGNS—22 × 39 mm. 20 p. Anniversary emblem (40th anniv. of W.H.O.). 47 × 28 mm. 25 p. Globes on scales (40th anniv. of Human Rights Declaration).

788. Naguib Mahfouz.

**1988.** Award of Nobel Prize for Literature to Naguib Mahfouz.
1707. **788.** 5 p. mult. (post.) .. 25 20
1708. 25 p. mult. (air) .. 60 30

789. Tent and "75".

**1988.** 75th Anniv. of Arab Scout Movement.
1709. **789.** 25 p. multicoloured 60 30

790. Ein Shams University and Association Emblems.

**1988.** Egyptian Orthopaedic Association International Conference, Cairo.
1710. **790.** 5 p. yell., brn. & grn. 20 10

791. Pharaonic Eye and Map.

**1988.** Restoration of Taba.
1711. **791.** 5 p. multicoloured .. 20 10

792. "75" in Sun above Plant.

793. Mohamed Hussein Hekal (writer and politician).

**1988.** 75th Anniv. of Ministry of Agriculture.
1712. **792.** 5 p. blue, yellow and orange .. .. 20 10

**1988.** Anniversaries. Each brown and green.
1713. 5 p. Type **793** (birth cent.) .. .. .. 20 10
1714. 5 p. Ahmed Lofty el Sayed (philosopher and politician) (25th death anniv.) .. .. 20 10

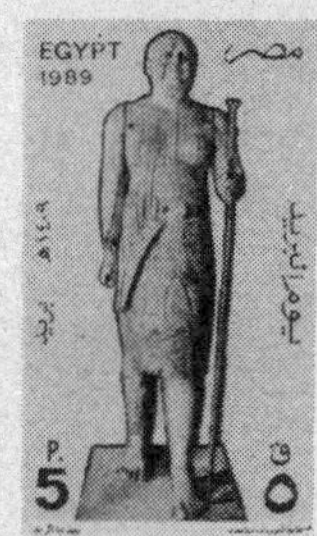


794. Priest. (5th dynasty).

795. Nehru.

**1989.** Post Day. Statues. Multicoloured.
1715. 5 p. Type **794** .. .. 20 15
1716. 25 p. Princess Nefert (4th dynasty) .. .. 60 35
1717. 25 p. Prince Ra-Hoteb (4th dynasty) .. .. 60 35

**1989.** Birth Centenary of Jawaharlal Nehru (Indian statesman).
1718. **795.** 5 p. green .. .. 20 10

796 Nile Hilton

**1989.** 30th Anniv of Nile Hilton Hotel.
1719 **796** 5 p. multicoloured .. 20 10

797 Route Map and Train leaving Tunnel

**1989.** Inauguration of Second Stage of Cairo Underground Railway.
1720 **797** 5 p. multicoloured .. 15 10

**798** Arms and Map. **799** Balcony

**1989.** Restoration of Taba.
1721 **798** 5 p. multicoloured .. 20 10

**1989.** Air.

| | | | | |
|---|---|---|---|---|
| 1722 | **799** | 20 p. pur, brn & bl | 40 | 20 |
| 1723 | – | 25 p. brn, yell & grn | 50 | 25 |
| 1724 | – | 35 p. pur, orge & bl | 60 | 35 |
| 1725 | – | 45 p. yell, blk & red | 70 | 40 |
| 1725a | – | 45 p. pur, orge & grn | 45 | 15 |
| 1726 | – | 50 p. bl, stone & pur | 80 | 50 |
| 1726a | – | 55 p. brn, buff & bl | 80 | 30 |
| 1727 | – | 60 p. pur, stone & bl | 1·10 | 50 |
| 1727a | – | 65 p. pur, brn & grn | 75 | 30 |
| 1728 | **799** | 70 p. pur, brn & orge | 80 | 30 |
| 1729 | – | 85 p. yellow, light yellow and brown | 95 | 45 |

DESIGNS: 25, 35, 45 p. (1725a) Lantern; 45 p. (1725) Carpet; 50, 60, 65 p. Dish with gazelle motif; 55, 85 p. Dish with fluted edge.

**800** Lamp **801** Members' Flags

**1989.** Festivals 1989.
1730 **800** 5 p. multicoloured .. 10 10

**1989.** Air. Formation of Arab Co-operation Council.
1731 **801** 25 p. multicoloured .. 55 25

**802** Olympic Rings, Map and Sports

**1989.** 1st Arab Olympic Day.
1733 **802** 5 p. green, brn & blk 15 10

**803** Pyramids and Parliament Building

**1989.** Cent of Interparliamentary Union.
1734 **803** 25 p. multicoloured .. 55 25

**804** Egyptian and French Flags

**1989.** Air. Bicentenary of French Revolution.
1736 **804** 25 p. multicoloured .. 60 25

**805** Bank Emblem

**1989.** 25th Anniv of African Development Bank.
1737 **805** 10 p. blue, yell & pur 15 10

**806** Conference Centre

**1989.** Cairo International Conference Centre.
1738 **806** 5 p. brown, green & bl 15 10

**807** October Panorama **808** Mohammed Ali Mosque, Saladin's Citadel

**1989.** 16th Anniv of Suez Crossing. Mult.
1739 10 p. Egyptians in El Qantara (47x28 mm) .. 20 10
1740 10 p. Type **807** .. .. 20 10
1741 10 p. Crossing the Suez (47x28 mm) .. .. 20 10
See also No. 1766.

**1989.** Aga Khan Architecture Prize.
1742 **808** 35 p. brown, grn & pur 70 25

**809** Emblem sheltering Family **810** Envelopes forming World Map

**1989.** 25th Anniv of Health Insurance Scheme.
1743 **809** 10 p. red, grey & black 15 10

**1989.** World Post Day.
1744 **810** 35 p. black, blue & yell 45 20

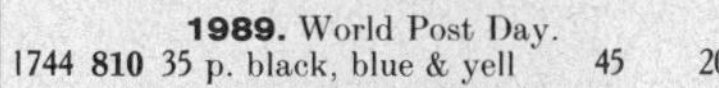

**811** Colossi of Thebes

**1989.** International Congress and Convention Association Meeting, Cairo.
1745 **811** 10 p. lilac, green & blk 20 10

**MORE DETAILED LISTS**
are given in the Stanley Gibbons Catalogues referred to in the country headings.
For lists of current volumes see Introduction.

**812** Faculty Emblem **814** University Emblem

**813** Children at Crossings

**1989.** Centenary of Faculty of Agriculture, Cairo University.
1746 **812** 10 p. purple, grn & yell 20 10

**1989.** 20th Anniv of Egyptian Road Safety Society.
1747 **813** 10 p. multicoloured .. 20 10

**1989.** 50th Anniv of Alexandria University.
1748 **814** 10 p. brown and blue 20 10

**815** Abdel Kader el Mazni (writer) **816** Statue of Priest Renofr

**1989.** Birth Anniversaries.
1749 **815** 10 p. ochre and brown 20 10
1750 – 10 p. olive and green 20 10
1751 – 10 p. multicoloured .. 20 10
DESIGNS—VERT: No. 1750, Abdel Rahman el Rafei (historian and politician). HORIZ: No. 1751, Ibrahim Pasha and statue in Opera Square, Cairo (son of Mohammed Ali and Viceroy of Egypt, July–November 1848).

**1990.** Post Day. Multicoloured.
1752 30 p. Type **816** .. .. 50 25
1753 30 p. Relief of Betah Hoteb from Sakkara .. 50 25

**817** Emblem

**1990.** 1st Anniv of Arab Co-operation Council.
1754 **817** 10 p. multicoloured .. 20 10
1755 35 p. multicoloured .. 60 30

**818** Emblem **819** Road Sign and Steering Wheel

**1990.** African Parliamentary Union Conf.
1756 **818** 10 p. black, red & grn 20 10

**1990.** International Conf. Road Safety and Accidents in Developing Countries.
1758 **819** 10 p. multicoloured .. 20 10

**820** Daisies **821** Doves and Map

**1990.** Festivals 1990.
1759 **820** 10 p. multicoloured .. 20 10

**1990.** 8th Anniv of Restoration of Sinai.
1760 **821** 10 p. blue, yell & blk 20 10

**822** Trophy and Ball **824** Figures forming Pyramid

**823** Pyramid, Sphinx, Mascot and Ball in Basket

**1990.** World Cup Football Championship, Italy.
1761 **822** 10 p. multicoloured .. 20 10

**1990.** World Basketball Championship, Argentina.
1763 **823** 10 p. black, bl & orge 20 10

**1990.** 5th Anniv of National Population Council.
1764 **824** 10 p. brn, lt grn & grn 20 10

**825** Battlefield

**1990.** 17th Anniv of Suez Crossing. Mult.
1765 10 p. Type **825** .. .. 20 10
1766 10 p. As Type **807** but dated "1990" .. .. 20 10
1767 10 p. Egyptian soldiers with flamethrower .. 20 10

**826** Anniversary Emblem

**1990.** 125th Anniv of Egyptian Post.
1768 **826** 10 p. black, red & blue 20 10

827 Faculty Emblem and Al-Azhar Mosque, Cairo

**1990.** Centenary of Dar el Eloum Faculty.
1769 **827** 10 p. multicoloured .. 20 10

828 Emblem and Map (40th anniv of U.N. Development Programme)

**1990.** United Nations Day.
1770 **828** 30 p. blue, grn & yell 45 20
1771 – 30 p. multicoloured .. 45 20
DESIGN—VERT: No. 1771, Cables and emblem forming Arabic "125" (125th anniv of I.T.U).

**1990.** As previous designs and new design as T **705** but size 18 × 22 mm.
1772 5 p. buff and brown .. 10 10
1773 10 p. blue and lilac .. 10 10
1774 30 p. brown and ochre .. 15 10
1775 50 p. brown and yellow .. 20 10
DESIGNS: 5 p. Jar; 10 p. Vase (as No. 1580); 30 p. Flagon (as No. 1585); 50 p. Flask (as No. 1587).

829 Pictogram, Hand and Disabled Person

**1990.** Disabled Persons' Day.
1790 **829** 10 p. multicoloured .. 20 10

830 Fish and Coral

**1990.** Ras Mohamed National Park. Mult.
1791 10 p. Type **830** .. .. 20 10
1792 10 p. Lionfish .. .. 20 10
1793 20 p. Two fishes and sea anemone .. .. 20 10
1794 20 p. Sea anemone, fish and coral .. .. 20 10

831 Nabaweya Moussa (educationist)

832 1866 5 pa. Stamp

**1990.** Birth Centenaries.
1795 **831** 10 p. orge, grey & grn 20 10
1796 – 10 p. orange, brn & bl 20 10
DESIGN: No. 1796, Dr. Mohamed Fahmy Abdel Meguid (pioneer of free medical care).

**1991.** Post Day. 125th Anniv of First Egyptian Stamps (1st issue).
1797 **832** 5 p. grey and black .. 10 10
1798 – 10 p. brown and black 20 10
1799 – 20 p. blue and black 20 10
DESIGNS: 10 p. 1866 10 pa. stamp; 20 p. 1866 20 pa. stamp.
See also Nos. 1815/17 and 1831.

833 Birth of Calf

**1991.** 50th Anniv (1990) of Veterinary Surgeons' Syndicate.
1800 **833** 10 p. multicoloured .. 20 10

834 Newspaper, Quill, Ink and Lens

835 Narcissi

**1991.** 50th Anniv of Journalists' Syndicate.
1801 **834** 10 p. multicoloured .. 20 10

**1991.** Festivals 1991.
1802 **835** 10 p. multicoloured .. 20 10

836 "Procession" and Mohamed Nagi

839 Score and Mohamed Abdel el Wahab

838 Saladin's Citadel and Faculty Building

**1991.** Artists' Anniversaries. Multicoloured.
1803 10 p. Type **836** (35th death) .. .. 20 10
1804 10 p. Mahmoud Mokhtar and sculptures (birth centenary) (horiz) .. 20 10

**1991.** Centenary of Technical Faculty, University of Cairo.
1814 **838** 10 p. multicoloured .. 20 10

**1991.** 125th Anniv of First Egyptian Stamps (2nd issue) and "Cairo 1991" Stamp Exhibition (1st issue). As T **832**.
1815 10 p. orange and black .. 20 10
1816 10 p. yellow and black .. 20 10
1817 10 p. purple and black .. 20 10
DESIGNS: No. 1815, 1866 5 pi. stamp; 1816, 1866 2 pi. stamp; 1817, 1866 1 pi. stamp.

**1991.** Mohamed Abdel el Wahab (composer) Commemoration.
1819 **839** 10 p. multicoloured .. 20 10

840 Session Emblem

**1991.** 48th Session of International Statistics Institute, Nasr.
1820 **840** 10 p. multicoloured .. 20 10

841 Horus (mascot)

842 New Building

**1991.** 5th African Games, Cairo. Mult.
1821 10 p. Type **841** .. .. 20 10
1822 10 p. Running, gymnastics and swimming pictograms (horiz) .. .. 20 10
1823 10 p. Football, basketball and shooting pictograms (horiz) .. .. 20 10
1824 10 p. Taekwondo, karate and judo pictograms (horiz) .. .. 20 10
1825 10 p. Table tennis, hockey and tennis pictograms (horiz) .. .. 20 10
1826 10 p. Boxing, wrestling and weightlifting pictograms (horiz) .. .. 20 10
1827 10 p. Handball, cycling and volleyball pictograms (horiz) .. .. 20 10

**1991.** Opening of Dar El Eftaa's New Building.
1829 **842** 10 p. multicoloured .. 20 10

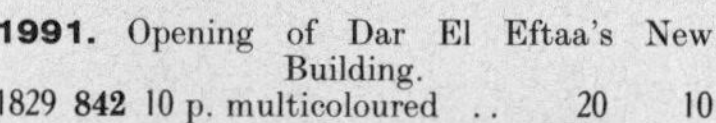

843 Troops in Inflatable Dinghy

**1991.** 18th Anniv of Suez Crossing.
1830 **843** 10 p. multicoloured .. 20 10

**1991.** 125th Anniv of First Egyptian Stamps (3rd issue). As T **832**.
1831 10 p. black and blue .. 20 10
DESIGN: 10 p. 1866 10 pi. stamp.

844 Woman writing

845 Dr. Zaki Mubarak (poet, birth centenary)

**1991.** United Nations Day. Multicoloured.
1833 10 p. Type **844** (Int Literacy Year) .. 20 10
1834 10 p. Brick "hands" sheltering people (World Shelter for the Homeless Day) (horiz) 20 10
1835 10 p. Egyptian and International Standards Organizations emblems (World Standardization Day) (horiz) .. .. 20 10

**1991.** Writers' Anniversaries.
1836 **845** 10 p. brown .. .. 20 10
1837 – 10 p. grey .. .. 20 10
DESIGN: No. 1837, Abd el Kader Hamza (journalist and historian, 50th death anniv).

846 Scarab Pectoral (from Tutankhamun's tomb)

**1992.** Post Day. Multicoloured.
1838 10 p. Type **846** (postage) 15 10
1839 45 p. Eagle pectoral (from Tutankhamun's tomb) (air) .. .. .. 30 15
1840 70 p. Golden saker falcon head (27 × 47 mm) .. 55 25

847 Arabic "40" and Emblem

849 Darwish and Opening Bars of "Stand up O Egyptian"

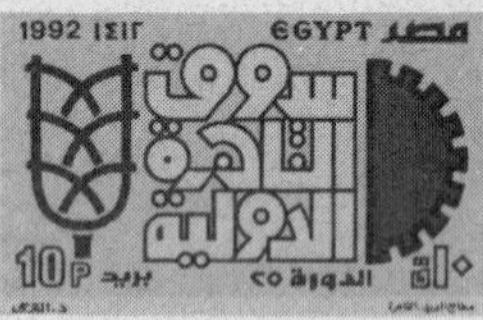
848 Ear of Wheat and Cogwheel

**1992.** Police Day.
1841 **847** 10 p. multicoloured .. 15 10

**1992.** 25th Cairo International Fair.
1842 **848** 10 p. multicoloured .. 15 10

**1992.** Birth Centenary of Sayed Darwish (composer).
1843 **849** 10 p. green and yellow 15 10

850 Hoopoe

**1992.** Festivals 1992.
1844 **850** 10 p. orange, blk & grn 15 10

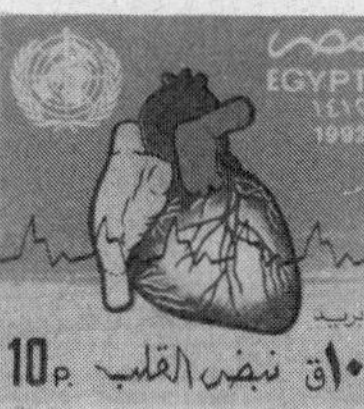
851 Heart and Cardiograph

**1992.** World Health Day.
1845 **851** 10 p. multicoloured .. 15 10

852 Tent, Emblem and Map

**1992.** 20th Arab Scout Jamboree.
1846 **852** 10 p. multicoloured .. 15 10

853 Games Emblem, Mascot and Pictograms

854 U.A.R. 1960 60 m. Dam Stamp

**1992.** Olympic Games, Barcelona. Mult.
1847 **853** 10 p. multicoloured .. 15 10

**1992.** 90th Anniv of Aswan Dam.
1849 **854** 10 p. mauve, yell & blk 15 10

855 "Dar El Helal"

**1992.** Centenary of "El Helal" (periodical).
1850 **855** 10 p. brn, gold & blk 15 10

**856** Sphinx and Pyramids

**1992.** Federation of Travel Companies International Congress, Cairo.
1851 **856** 70 p. multicoloured .. 45 20

**857** World Map, Lighthouse and Pharaonic Ship

**1992.** Alexandria World Festival.
1852 **857** 70 p. multicoloured .. 45 20

**858** U.P.U. Emblem

**1992.** World Post Day.
1853 **858** 10 p. bl, blk & ultram 15 10

**859** Girl **860** Emblem

**1992.** United Nations Day. Multicoloured.
1854 10 p. Type **859** (Children's Day) .. .. .. 15 10
1855 70 p. Wall paintings of agriculture and medicine (International Food, Agriculture and World Health Conference) (36 × 37 mm) .. 45 20

**1992.** 20th Arab Scout Conference, Cairo.
1856 **860** 10 p. multicoloured .. 15 10

## INDEX

Countries can be quickly located by referring to the index at the end of this volume.

**861** Mohamed Taymour **862** Sesostris I

**1992.** Birth Anniversaries.
1857 **861** 10 p. blue, dp bl & bis 15 10
1858 – 10 p. blue, dp bl & bis 15 10
1859 – 10 p. brown, orge & bl 15 10
DESIGNS: No. 1857, Type **861** (dramatist and theatre critic, centenary); 1851, Ahmed Zaki Abu Shadi (physician and poet, centenary); 1859, Talaat Harb (economist, 125th anniv).

**1993.** Post Day. Statues of Pharaohs. Mult.
1860 10 p. Type **862** .. .. 15 10
1861 45 p. Amenemhet III .. 25 10
1862 70 p. Hur I .. .. 40 20

**863** Book and Statue of Scribe **864** Bust

**1993.** 25th Cairo International Book Fair.
1863 **863** 15 p. multicoloured .. 15 10

**1993.** Size 18 × 22 mm.
1864 **864** 5 p. orange and black 10 10
1865 – 15 p. brown and ochre 10 10
1866 – 15 p. brown and ochre 15 10
1867 – 25 p. lt brown & brn 20 10
1868 – 55 p. blue and black 30 15
DESIGNS—15 p. Sphinx*; 25 p. Bust of woman; 55 p. Bust of Pharaoh.
*On No. 1865 the illustration of the sphinx countinues behind the face value; on No. 1866 the sphinx is cropped so that the value appears on a white background.
For same designs but larger, 21 × 26 mm, see Nos. 1916/19.

**865** Plan and Set Square on Drawing Board

**1993.** 75th Anniv (1992) of Architects' Association.
1869 **865** 15 p. black, orge & bl 15 10

**866** Gold Mask of Tutankhamun

**1993.**
1870 – £E1 brown and blue (postage) .. .. 40 20
1871 – £E2 green and brown 75 35
1872 – £E5 gold and brown 1·90 95
1873 **866** 55 p. gold and brown (air) .. .. 20 10
1874 – 80 p. gold and brown 30 15
DESIGNS: 80 p. Side view of Tutankhamun's mask; £E1, Bust of woman; £E2, Head of Queen Tiye; £E5, Carved head captial.

**867** Old and New Foreign Ministry Buildings and Globe **868** Cactus

**1993.** (a) Egyptian Diplomacy Day
1875 **867** 15 p. multicoloured .. 15 10
(b) Air. Inauguration of New Foreign Ministry Building. As T **867** but inscr "AIR MAIL MINISTRY OF FOREIGN AFFAIRS"
1876 **867** 80 p. multicoloured .. 40 20

**1993.** Festivals 1993.
1877 **868** 15 p. multicoloured .. 15 10

**869** First Issue and Emblem

**1993.** Centenary of "Le Progres Egyptien" (newspaper).
1878 **869** 15 p. multicoloured .. 15 10

**870** Dish Aerial, I.T.U. Emblem and Satellite **871** Globe

**1993.** World Telecommunications Day.
1879 **870** 15 p. multicoloured .. 15 10

**1993.** U.N. World Conference on Human Rights, Vienna.
1880 **871** 15 p. ultram, bl & orge 15 10

**872** Emblem, Map of Africa and Stars

**1993.** 30th Anniv of Organization of African Unity.
1881 **872** 15 p. black, silver and green (postage) .. 15 10
1882 80 p. black, gold and mauve (air) .. 40 20

**873** Conference Emblem

**1993.** Int Post, Telegraph and Telecommunications Union Conference, Cairo.
1883 **873** 15 p. multicoloured .. 15 10

**874** Saladin and Dome of the Rock, Jerusalem

**1993.** 800th Death Anniv of Saladin.
1884 **874** 55 p. multicoloured .. 35 15

**875** Soldiers **876** Pres. Mubarak

**1993.** 20th Anniv of Suez Crossing.
1885 **875** 15 p. blk, mve & orge 15 10

**1993.** Mohammed Hosni Mubarak's 3rd Consecutive Term as President.
1886 **876** 15 p. multicoloured .. 15 10
1887 55 p. multicoloured .. 35 15
1888 80 p. multicoloured .. 40 20

**877** Map of Egypt and Electricity Symbol **878** Emblem and Caring Hands

**1993.** Centenary of Electricity in Egypt.
1890 **877** 15 p. multicoloured .. 15 10

**1993.** Air. International Decade for Natural Disaster Reduction.
1891 **878** 80 p. violet, blue & red 40 20

**879** Pyramids, Sphinx and Dam (congress emblem)

**1993.** 2nd International Large Dams Congress, Cairo.
1892 **879** 15 p. yell, mve & blk 15 10

**880** Trophy and Emblem

**1993.** Egyptian Victories in International Sports Competitions. Multicoloured.
1893 15 p. Type **880** (Junior Men's World Handball Championship) .. 15 10
1894 15 p. Trophy and emblem (World Military Football Championship) 15 10

881 Abdel Aziz al Bishry (50th death)

882 Amenhotep III

**1993.** Writers' Anniversaries.

1895 **881** 15 p. blue .. .. 15 10
1896 – 15 p. turquoise .. 15 10
1897 – 15 p. green .. .. 15 10
1898 – 15 p. mauve .. .. 15 10

DESIGNS: No. 1896, Mohamed Fareed Abu Hadeed (birth centenary); 1897, Ali Moubarak (death centenary); 1898, M. Beram al Tunisy (birth centenary).

**1994.** Post Day. Statues of Pharaohs. Multicoloured.

1899 15 p. Type **882** .. .. 10 10
1900 55 p. Queen Hatshepsut 25 10
1901 85 p. Thutmose III .. 40 20

883 Pyramids

**1994.** Egyptian Sedimentary Society Congress.

1902 **883** 15 p. multicoloured .. 10 10

884 Firecrests

885 Scout Salute and Emblem

**1994.** Festivals 1994. Multicoloured.

1903 15 p. Type **884** .. .. 10 10
1904 15 p. Barn swallows (one perching, one flying) .. 10 10
1905 15 p. Alexandrine parakeets (on tree trunk and branch) .. 10 10
1906 15 p. Goldfinches (on blossoming branch) .. 10 10

Nos. 1903/6 were issued together, se-tenant, forming a composite design.

**1994.** 40th Anniv of Arab Scout Movement.

1907 **885** 15 p. black, yell & grn 10 10

886 Emblem

887 Radio Waves over Map of Africa

**1994.** 27th Cairo International Fair.

1908 **886** 15 p. multicoloured .. 10 10

**1994.** "Africa Telecom 94" Exhibition, Cairo.

1909 **887** 15 p. green and brown 10 10

888 Map, Palestine Flag and Olive Branch

**1994.** Signing in Cairo of Israel–Palestine Agreement on Self-rule for Gaza and Jericho.

1910 **888** 15 p. multicoloured .. 10 10

889 Conference Emblem and Oil Well

**1994.** 5th Arab Energy Conference, Cairo.

1911 **889** 15 p. multicoloured .. 10 10

890 Emblem

**1994.** 18th Mediterranean Countries' Biennial Art Exhibition, Alexandria.

1912 **890** 15 p. lilac, yell & blk 10 10

891 Map of Africa and Dove

892 Campaign Emblem Magnfied

**1994.** Africa Day.

1913 **891** 15 p. multicoloured .. 10 10

**1994.** Tree Planting Campaign.

1914 **892** 15 p. blue, green & blk 10 10

893 Library, Family and Open Book

**1994.** "Reading for All" Summer Festival.

1915 **893** 15 p. multicoloured .. 10 10

**1994.** As previous designs but size 21 × 26 mm.

1916 **864** 5 p. red and purple .. 10 10
1917 – 15 p. brown and cinnamon (as No. 1866) .. .. 10 10
1918 – 25 p. orange and brown (as No. 1867) 10 10
1919 – 55 p. blue and black (as No. 1868) .. 20 10

**HAVE YOU READ THE NOTES AT THE BEGINNING OF THIS CATALOGUE?**
These often provide answers to the enquiries we receive.

894 Emblem

**1994.** 75th Anniv of I.L.O.

1925 **894** 15 p. grey, blue & blk 10 10

895 Conference and United Nations Emblems

**1994.** U. N. International Conference on Population and Development, Cairo. Mult.

1926 15 p. Type **895** (postage) 10 10
1927 80 p. Emblems and pharaonic murals (vert) (air) .. .. .. 30 15

896 Player and Trophy

**1994.** Egyptian Victories in Junior World Squash Championship.

1928 **896** 15 p. multicoloured .. 10 10

897 Anniversary Emblem

**1994.** Air. 50th Anniv of Signing of Int Civil Aviation Agreement, Chicago.

1929 **897** 80 p. blue, yell & blk 30 15

898 Map on Envelopes

**1994.** World Post Day.

1930 **898** 15 p. multicoloured .. 10 10

899 Akhenaten and Nefertiti (International Year of the Family)

**1994.** United Nations Day.

1931 **899** 80 p. lilac, red and black (postage) .. 30 15
1932 – 80 p. mult (air) .. 30 15

DESIGN—VERT: No. 1931, Nurses (75th anniv of International Red Crescent/Red Cross Union).

900 Arabic Script over Globes

**1994.** 50th Anniv of "Akhbar El Yom" (newspaper).

1933 **900** 15 p. multicoloured .. 10 10

901 Emblem, Trophy and Ancient Egyptian Players

**1994.** African Clubs Hockey Championship.

1934 **901** 15 p. multicoloured .. 10 10

902 Pharaoh and Radames

903 Centenary Emblem

**1994.** Performance of Verdi's "Aida" (opera) at Deir al-Bahari Temple, Luxor.

1935 **902** 15 p. Type **902** .. 10 10

**1994.** Cent of Int Olympic Committee.

1937 **903** 15 p. multicoloured .. 10 10

904 Map showing Hostels and Association Emblem

906 Emblem as Flower

905 Player and Globe

**1994.** 40th Anniv of Egyptian Youth Hostels Association.

1938 **904** 15 p. multicoloured .. 10 10

**1994.** 10th Anniv of International Speedball Federation.

1939 **905** 15 p. multicoloured .. 10 10

**1994.** 30th Anniv of African Development Bank.

1940 **906** 15 p. multicoloured .. 10 10

907 Route Maps through Canal and around Africa

**1994.** 125th Anniv of Suez Canal. Mult.

1941 15 p. Type **907** .. .. 10 10
1942 80 p. Inauguration ceremony, 1869 .. 30 15

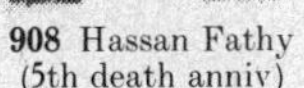

**908** Hassan Fathy (5th death anniv)  **910** Akhenaten (statuette)

**909** Anniversary Emblem

**1994.** Anniversaries.
1943 **908** 15 p. brown and flesh 10 10
1944 – 15 p. red and pink .. 10 10
DESIGN: No. 1944, Mahmoud Taimour (birth centenary).

**1995.** 20th Anniv of World Tourism Organization.
1945 **909** 15 p. multicoloured .. 10 10

**1995.** Post Day. Multicoloured.
1946 15 p. Type **910** .. .. 10 10
1947 55 p. Gold mask of Tutankhamun .. 20 10
1948 80 p. Nefertiti (bust) .. 30 15

**911** Flowers

**1995.** Festivals 1995.
1949 **911** 15 p. multicoloured .. 10 10

**912** Demonstration, 1919

**1995.** National Women's Day.
1950 **912** 15 p. multicoloured .. 10 10

**913** Emblem and Map  **915** Misr Bank

**914** Hotel

**1995.** 50th Anniv of Arab League.
1951 **913** 15 p. green, bl & gold 10 10
1952 55 p. multicoloured .. 20 10

**1995.** 25th Anniv of Cairo Sheraton Hotel.
1953 **914** 15 p. multicoloured .. 10 10

**1995.** 75th Anniv of Misr Bank.
1954 **915** 15 p. multicoloured .. 10 10

**916** Dish Aerial and Globe

**1995.** International Telecommunications Day.
1955 **916** 80 p. orange, blk & bl 30 15

**917** Rontgen and X-ray of Hand  **918** Goddess Hathor

**1995.** Centenary of Discovery of X-rays by Wilhelm Rontgen.
1956 **917** 100 p. multicoloured 10 10

**1995.** 20th Anniv of Membership of World Heritage Committee. Luxor statues. Mult.
1957 15 p. Type **918** (postage) 10 10
1958 15 p. God Atoum .. 10 10
1959 80 p. God Amon with Horemheb (air) .. 30 15
Nos. 1957/8 were issued together, se-tenant, forming a composite design.

**919** Emblem

**1995.** Air. 25th Anniv of Arab Educational, Scientific and Cultural Organization.
1960 **919** 55 p. multicoloured .. 20 10

**920** Children as Flowers  **921** Ozone Bands over Globe

**1995.** 21st Int Pediatrics Conf, Cairo.
1961 **920** 15 p. multicoloured .. 10 10

**1995.** International Ozone Day.
1962 **921** 15 p. multicoloured .. 10 10
1963 55 p. multicoloured .. 20 10
1964 – 80 p. multicoloured .. 30 15
DESIGNS: 80 p. As Type **921** but inscribed "The Ozonaction Protection Programme".
See also Nos. 1994/5.

**922** Pharaonic Ship and Globe

**1995.** World Tourism Day.
1965 **922** 15 p. multicoloured .. 10 10

**923** Emblem and Works, Imbaba

**1995.** 175th Anniv of Government Printing Offices.
1966 **923** 15 p. multicoloured .. 10 10

**924** Sun illuminating Statue

**1995.** Overhead Sun Festival, Abu Simbel.
1967 **924** 15 p. multicoloured .. 10 10

**925** Gold Mask of Tutankhamun  **926** Dam and Ship

**1995.** Air. United Nations Day. 50th Anniversaries.
1968 **925** 80 p. multicoloured .. 30 15
1969 – 80 p. lilac, blue & vio 30 15
1970 – 80 p. multicoloured .. 30 15
DESIGNS—VERT: No. 1968, Type **925** (U.N.E.S.C.O.). HORIZ: No. 1969, Globe, dove, emblem and "50" (U.N.O.); 1970, Farmer and wife working in field (ancient Egyptian mural) (F.A.O.).

**1995.** Inauguration of Esna Dam.
1971 **926** 15 p. black, blue & grn 10 10

**927** Emblem and Pharaonic Mural  **928** Youssef Wahby

**1995.** 75th Anniv of Egyptian Engineers Society.
1972 **927** 15 p. multicoloured .. 10 10

**1995.** Artists.
1973 **928** 15 p. blue and black 10 10
1974 – 15 p. green .. .. 10 10
1975 – 15 p. red and yellow 10 10
DESIGNS: No. 1974, Nagib el Rihany; 1975, Abdel Hallim Hafez.

**929** "100"  **930** Pharaonic Mural (left detail)

**1995.** Centenary of Motion Pictures.
1976 **929** 15 p. multicoloured .. 10 10

**1996.** Post Day. Multicoloured.
1977 55 p. Type **930** .. .. 20 10
1978 80 p. Right detail of Pharaonic mural .. 30 15
Nos. 1977/8 were issued together, se-tenant, forming a composite design.

**931** Convolvulus  **932** Summit Emblem

**1996.** Festivals 1996. Multicoloured.
1980 15 p. Type **931** .. .. 10 10
1981 15 p. Poppies .. .. 10 10

**1996.** Middle East Peace Process Summit, Sharm el Shaikh.
1982 **932** 15 p. multicoloured .. 10 10
1983 80 p. multicoloured .. 30 15

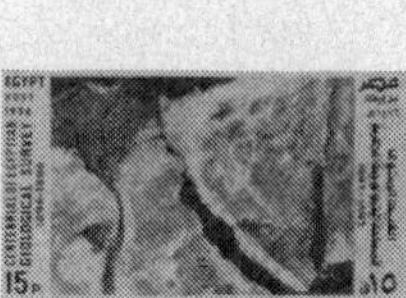

**933** Geological Map  **934** Fair Emblem

**1996.** Centenary of Egyptian Geological Survey Authority.
1984 **933** 15 p. multicoloured .. 10 10

**1996.** 29th Cairo International Fair.
1985 **934** 15 p. multicoloured .. 10 10

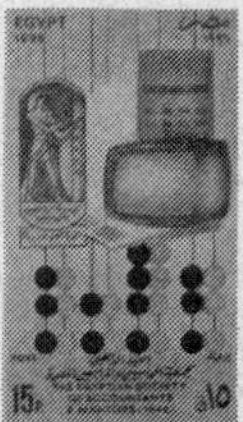

**935** Emblem  **936** Emblem, Calculator, Computer and Abacus

**1996.** Signing of Pelindaba Treaty declaring Africa a Nuclear Weapon-free Zone, Cairo.
1986 **935** 15 p. multicoloured .. 10 10
1987 80 p. multicoloured .. 30 15

**1996.** 50th Anniv of Egyptian Society of Accountants and Auditors.
1988 **936** 15 p. multicoloured .. 10 10

**937** "People" forming Graph  **938** Emblem

**1996.** General Population and Housing Census.
1989 **937** 15 p. multicoloured .. 10 10

**1996.** Arab Summit, Cairo.
1990 **938** 55 p. multicoloured .. 20 10

**939** Games Emblem  **940** Emblems

**1996.** Olympic Games, Atlanta.
1991 **939** 15 p. muticoloured .. 10 10

**1996.** Air. 16th International Congress on Irrigation and Drainage, Cairo.
1993 **940** 80 p. multicoloured .. 30 15

**1996.** International Ozone Day. As T **921** but inscr "2nd ANNUAL OZONE INTERNATIONAL DAY".
1994 **921** 15 p. mult (postage) 10 10
1995 **921** 80 p. mult (air) .. 30 15

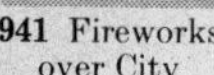

**941** Fireworks over City

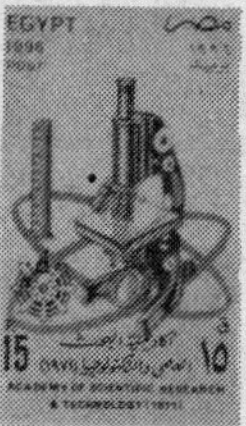

**942** Test Tube, Microscope and Atomic Symbol

**1996.** 2nd Alexandria World Festival.
1996 **941** 80 p. multicoloured .. 30 15

**1996.** 25th Anniv of Academy of Scientific Research and Technology.
1997 **942** 15 p. multicoloured .. 10 10

**943** Pharaonic Boat (Rowing Festival)

**1996.** International Tourism Day.
1998 **943** 15 p. mult (postage) 10 10
1999 – 55 p. grey, black and green (air) .. 20 10
2000 – 80 p. multicoloured .. 30 15
DESIGNS: 20 × 36 mm—55 p. Arab horse (Arabian Horse Festival). 47 × 26 mm—80 p. Egyptian figure and hieroglyphs (Tourism Day).

**944** Route Map and Train

**945** U.P.U. Emblem and Stylized Postal Messengers

**1996.** Inauguration of Second Greater Cairo Metro Line.
2001 **944** 15 p. multicoloured .. 10 10

**1996.** Air. World Post Day.
2002 **945** 80 p. multicoloured .. 30 15

**946** Emblems and Map

**947** Mother and Child (statue)

**1996.** Air. Cairo, Cultural Capital of Arab Region.
2003 **946** 55 p. blue, orge & blk 20 10

**1996.** Air. 50th Anniv of U.N.I.C.E.F.
2004 **947** 80 p. multicoloured .. 30 15

**948** Council of State Courts

**949** Emblem

**1996.** 50th Anniv of Council of State.
2005 **948** 15 p. lilac, ultram & bl 10 10

**1996.** 25th Conference of Int Federation of Training Development Organizations.
2006 **949** 15 p. black, bl & yell 10 10

**950** Emblem

**951** Emblem and Ear of Wheat

**1996.** Economic Summit, Cairo.
2007 **950** 15 p. multicoloured .. 10 10

**1996.** International Nutrition Conf, Rome.
2009 **951** 15 p. green, yell & red 10 10

### EXPRESS LETTER STAMPS

E 52. Postman on Motor-cycle.

**1926.**

| | | | | |
|---|---|---|---|---|
| E 138. | E 52. | 20 m. green | 10·00 | 5·00 |
| E 139. | | 20 m. black and red | 3·25 | 1·25 |

**1943.** As Type E 52, but inscr. "POSTES EXPRES".

| | | | | |
|---|---|---|---|---|
| E 289. | E 52. | 26 m. black and red | 3·25 | 4·50 |
| E 290. | | 40 m. black and brown | 1·60 | 1·60 |

**1952.** No. E 290 optd. as T 124.

| | | | | |
|---|---|---|---|---|
| E 404. | E 52. | 40 m. black & brown | 1·40 | 1·25 |

### OFFICIAL STAMPS

O 25. (O 46.) O 52.

**1893.**

| | | | | |
|---|---|---|---|---|
| O 64. | O 25. | (–) brown | 1·25 | 10 |

**1907.** Stamps of 1879 and 1888 optd **O.H.H.S.** and Arabic equivalent.

| | | | | |
|---|---|---|---|---|
| O73 | 18 | 1 m. brown | 1·75 | 20 |
| O74 | | 2 m. green | 2·75 | 10 |
| O75 | | 3 m. yellow | 2·75 | 95 |
| O86 | | 4 m. red | 2·75 | 1·60 |
| O76 | | 5 m. red | 3·25 | 10 |
| O77 | 10 | 1 p. blue | 1·75 | 10 |
| O87 | | 5 p. grey | 2·75 | 70 |

**1913.** No. 63 optd in English only. (a) Optd **"O.H.H.S."** (with inverted commas).

| | | | | |
|---|---|---|---|---|
| O79 | 18 | 5 m. pink | — | £300 |

(b) Optd **O.H.H.S.** (without inverted commas).

| | | | | |
|---|---|---|---|---|
| O80 | 18 | 5 m. pink | 2·75 | 20 |

**1915.** Stamps of 1914 optd. **O.H.H.S.** and Arabic equivalent.

| | | | | |
|---|---|---|---|---|
| O 83 | 29 | 1 m. sepia | 1·50 | 3·00 |
| O 99 | – | 2 m. red | 6·50 | 10·00 |
| O 85 | – | 3 m. orange | 1·75 | 3·00 |
| O 87 | – | 5 m. lake | 2·75 | 70 |
| O101 | – | 5 m. pink | 14·00 | 3·75 |

**1922.** Stamps of 1914 optd **O.H.E.M.S.** and Arabic equivalent.

| | | | | |
|---|---|---|---|---|
| O111 | 29 | 1 m. brown | 1·60 | 2·75 |
| O112 | | 2 m. red | 1·50 | 3·50 |
| O113 | | 3 m. orange | 2·00 | 4·25 |
| O114 | | 4 m. green | 4·25 | 10·00 |
| O115 | | 5 m. pink | 2·75 | 60 |
| O116 | | 10 m. blue | 4·75 | 5·75 |
| O117 | | 10 m. red | 6·50 | 2·00 |
| O118 | 41 | 15 m. blue | 6·50 | 5·50 |
| O119 | 42 | 15 m. blue | £120 | £120 |
| O120 | – | 50 m. purple | 16·00 | 16·00 |

**1923.** Stamps of 1923 optd. with Type O 46.

| | | | | |
|---|---|---|---|---|
| O 123. | 44. | 1 m. orange | 90 | 2·00 |
| O 124. | | 2 m. black | 1·25 | 3·25 |
| O 125. | | 3 m. brown | 3·25 | 4·75 |
| O 126. | | 4 m. green | 3·75 | 5·50 |
| O 127. | | 5 m. brown | 1·40 | 70 |
| O 128. | | 10 m. red | 2·00 | 2·25 |
| O 129. | | 15 m. blue | 4·00 | 6·00 |
| O 130. | – | 50 m. green | 6·00 | 7·50 |

**1926.**

| | | | | |
|---|---|---|---|---|
| O 138. | O 52. | 1 m. orange | 50 | 25 |
| O 139. | | 2 m. black | 30 | 20 |
| O 140. | | 3 m. brown | 90 | 70 |
| O 141. | | 4 m. green | 85 | 80 |
| O 142. | | 5 m. brown | 95 | 25 |
| O 143. | | 10 m. lake | 2·50 | 25 |
| O 144. | | 10 m. violet | 1·50 | 30 |
| O 145. | | 15 m. blue | 2·50 | 60 |
| O 146. | | 15 m. purple | 2·50 | 35 |
| O 148. | | 20 m. olive | 4·25 | 1·25 |
| O 147. | | 20 m. blue | 2·50 | 75 |
| O 149. | | 50 m. green | 5·50 | 1·10 |

Nos. O 148/9 are larger (22½ × 27½ mm.).

O 85.

O 174.

**1938.**

| | | | | |
|---|---|---|---|---|
| O276 | O 85 | 1 m. orange | 20 | 1·00 |
| O277 | | 2 m. red | 20 | 25 |
| O278 | | 3 m. brown | 85 | 1·25 |
| O279 | | 4 m. green | 55 | 1·25 |
| O280 | | 5 m. brown | 25 | 35 |
| O281 | | 10 m. mauve | 35 | 60 |
| O282 | | 15 m. purple | 85 | 85 |
| O283 | | 20 m. blue | 80 | 80 |
| O284 | | 50 m. green | 2·00 | 1·75 |

**1952.** Optd as T 124.

| | | | | |
|---|---|---|---|---|
| O404 | O 85 | 1 m. orange | 1·00 | 1·10 |
| O405 | | 2 m. red | 85 | 1·10 |
| O406 | | 3 m. brown | 1·10 | 1·10 |
| O407 | | 4 m. green | 1·10 | 1·10 |
| O408 | | 5 m. brown | 1·10 | 1·10 |
| O409 | | 10 m. mauve | 1·65 | 1·10 |
| O410 | | 15 m. purple | 1·50 | 1·10 |
| O411 | | 20 m. blue | 1·75 | 1·25 |
| O412 | | 50 m. green | 4·00 | 2·75 |

**1958.**

| | | | | |
|---|---|---|---|---|
| O685 | O 174 | 1 m. orange | 20 | 30 |
| O686 | | 4 m. green | 40 | 45 |
| O687 | | 5 m. brown | 40 | 15 |
| O571 | | 10 m. purple | 45 | 15 |
| O688 | | 10 m. brown | 40 | 15 |
| O572 | | 35 m. blue | 1·10 | 20 |
| O689 | | 35 m. violet | 1·50 | 35 |
| O690 | | 50 m. green | 2·40 | 40 |
| O691 | | 100 m. lilac | 4·75 | 1·25 |
| O692 | | 200 m. red | 10·50 | 5·75 |
| O693 | | 500 m. black | 15·00 | 11·00 |

O 334. Eagle.

O 435. Eagle.

**1967.**

| | | | | |
|---|---|---|---|---|
| O 918. | O 334. | 1 m. blue | 10 | 20 |
| O 919. | | 4 m. brown | 15 | 20 |
| O 920. | | 5 m. olive | 20 | 10 |
| O 921. | | 10 m. brown | 75 | 45 |
| O 922. | | 10 m. purple | 65 | 25 |
| O 923. | | 20 m. purple | 40 | 20 |
| O 924. | | 35 m. violet | 60 | 25 |
| O 925. | | 50 m. orange | 75 | 30 |
| O 926. | | 55 m. violet | 75 | 30 |
| O 927. | | 100 m. red and green | 1·60 | 70 |
| O 928. | | 200 m. red and blue | 3·25 | 1·25 |
| O 929. | | 500 m. red and olive | 6·50 | 4·50 |

**1972.**

| | | | | |
|---|---|---|---|---|
| O1161a | O 435 | 1 m. blue & blk | 10 | 10 |
| O1162a | | 10 m. red & blk | 10 | 10 |
| O1163 | | 20 m. grn & blk | 60 | 25 |
| O1165 | | 20 m. brn & vio | 10 | 10 |
| O1166 | | 30 m. brn & lilac | 20 | 20 |
| O1294 | | 50 m. orge & blk | 20 | 10 |
| O1295 | | 55 m. lilac & blk | 25 | 10 |
| O1169 | | 60 m. orge & blk | 40 | 20 |
| O1170 | | 70 m. grn & blk | 50 | 30 |
| O1171 | | 80 m. grn & blk | 45 | 25 |

O 706. Eagle.

**1985.** Size 20 × 25 mm.

| | | | | |
|---|---|---|---|---|
| O1589 | O 706 | 1 p. red | 10 | 10 |
| O1590 | | 2 p. brown | 10 | 10 |
| O1591 | | 3 p. brown | 10 | 10 |
| O1592a | | 5 p. orange | 20 | 20 |
| O1593 | | 8 p. green | 35 | 25 |
| O1594 | | 10 p. brown | 10 | 10 |
| O1595 | | 15 p. lilac | 70 | 45 |
| O1596 | | 20 p. blue | 50 | 50 |
| O1597 | | 25 p. red | 55 | 55 |
| O1598 | | 30 p. purple | 40 | 40 |
| O1599 | | 50 p. green | 1·25 | 1·25 |
| O1600 | | 60 p. green | 75 | 75 |

**1991.** As Nos. O1589/1600 but smaller, 17 × 22 mm.

| | | | | |
|---|---|---|---|---|
| O1806 | O 706 | 5 p. orange | 10 | 10 |
| O1807 | | 10 p. brown | 10 | 10 |
| O1808 | | 15 p. brown | 10 | 10 |
| O1809 | | 25 p. lilac | 15 | 15 |
| O1810 | | 30 p. lilac | 15 | 15 |
| O1811 | | 50 p. green | 20 | 20 |
| O1812 | | 55 p. red | 20 | 20 |
| O1813 | | £E1 blue | 40 | 40 |
| O1814 | | £E2 green | 75 | 75 |

### POSTAGE DUE STAMPS

D 16.

D 24.

**1884.**

| | | | | |
|---|---|---|---|---|
| D57 | D 16 | 10 pa. red | 38·00 | 8·50 |
| D58 | | 20 pa. red | £100 | 20·00 |
| D64 | | 1 pi. red | 25·00 | 4·50 |
| D65 | | 2 pi. red | 25·00 | 3·00 |
| D61 | | 5 pi. red | 14·00 | 32·00 |

**1888.** As Type D 16, but values in "Millemes" and "Piastres".

| | | | | |
|---|---|---|---|---|
| D66 | D 16 | 2 m. green | 7·50 | 12·00 |
| D67 | | 5 m. red | 24·00 | 11·00 |
| D68 | | 1 p. blue | £120 | 35·00 |
| D69 | | 2 p. orange | £140 | 12·00 |
| D70 | | 5 p. grey | £190 | £180 |

**1889.** Inscr. "A PERCEVOIR POSTES EGYPTIENNES".

| | | | | |
|---|---|---|---|---|
| D 71 | D 24 | 2 m. green | 7·00 | 50 |
| D 72 | | 4 m. purple | 2·25 | 50 |
| D 73 | | 1 p. blue | 5·50 | 50 |
| D 74 | | 2 p. orange | 5·50 | 50 |

**1898.** Surch. **3 Milliemes** in English and Arabic.

| | | | | |
|---|---|---|---|---|
| D 75 | D 24 | 3 m. on 2 p. orange | 55 | 2·50 |

**1921.** As Type D 24, but inscr "POSTAGE DUE EGYPT POSTAGE".

| | | | | |
|---|---|---|---|---|
| D 98 | D 23 | 2 m. green | 2·75 | 3·00 |
| D 99 | | 2 m. red | 1·00 | 1·50 |
| D100 | | 4 m. red | 5·00 | 10·00 |
| D101 | | 4 m. green | 2·50 | 1·00 |
| D102 | – | 10 m. blue | 4·50 | 13·00 |
| D103 | – | 10 m. red | 5·50 | 70 |

The 10 m. values have "MILLIEMES" in a bar across the figure of value.

**1922.** Optd with T 43 inverted.

| | | | | |
|---|---|---|---|---|
| D 111 | D 24 | 2 m. red (No. D 99) | 90 | 4·00 |
| D 112 | | 4 m. green (No. D 101) | 1·25 | 4·25 |
| D 113 | | 10 m. red (No. D 103) | 1·90 | 1·40 |
| D 114 | | 2 p. orge (No. D 74) | 4·00 | 11·00 |

D 59.

D 298.

**1927.**

| | | | | |
|---|---|---|---|---|
| D173 | D 59 | 2 m. black | 50 | 30 |
| D730 | | 2 m. orange | 45 | 70 |
| D175a | | 4 m. green | 50 | 30 |
| D176 | | 4 m. sepia | 4·25 | 2·75 |
| D177 | | 5 m. brown | 2·50 | 75 |
| D575 | | 6 m. green | 1·60 | 1·25 |
| D179 | | 8 m. purple | 90 | 40 |
| D180a | | 10 m. lake | 65 | 20 |
| D732 | | 10 m. brown | 1·50 | 90 |
| D181 | | 12 m. red | 1·10 | 3·00 |
| D182 | | 20 m. brown | 1·25 | 1·75 |
| D183 | | 30 m. violet | 2·50 | 2·50 |

The 30 m. is larger, 22 × 27½ mm.

**1952.** Optd. as T 124.

| | | | | |
|---|---|---|---|---|
| D 404. | D 59. | 2 m. orange | 1·10 | 1·25 |
| D 405. | | 4 m. green | 1·10 | 1·40 |
| D 406. | | 6 m. green | 1·25 | 2·00 |
| D 407. | | 8 m. purple | 1·50 | 1·60 |
| D 408. | | 10 m. lake | 2·50 | 2·25 |
| D 410. | | 12 m. red | 1·50 | 1·75 |
| D 411. | | 30 m. violet | 2·25 | 2·50 |

**1965.**

| | | | | |
|---|---|---|---|---|
| D 852. | D 298. | 2 m. violet on orange | 85 | 85 |
| D 853. | | 8 m. blue on pale bl. | 1·10 | 1·10 |
| D 854. | | 10 m. grn. on yellow | 1·60 | 1·50 |
| D 855. | | 20 m. vio. on pale bl. | 1·90 | 1·75 |
| D 856. | | 40 m. grn. on orge. | 3·50 | 3·25 |

## ELOBEY, ANNOBON AND CORISCO Pt. 9

A group of Spanish islands off the west coast of Africa in the Gulf of Guinea. In 1909 became part of Spanish Guinea. In 1959 Annobon became part of Fernando Poo, and Elobey and Corisco part of Rio Muni.

100 centimos = 1 peseta.

**1903.** "Curly Head" key-type inscr "ELOBEY, ANNOBON Y CORISCO". Dated "1903".

| | | | | |
|---|---|---|---|---|
| 1 | Z | ¼ c. red | 45 | 30 |
| 2 | | ½ c. purple | 45 | 30 |
| 3 | | 1 c. black | 45 | 30 |
| 4 | | 2 c. red | 45 | 30 |
| 5 | | 3 c. green | 45 | 30 |
| 6 | | 4 c. green | 45 | 30 |
| 7 | | 5 c. lilac | 45 | 30 |
| 8 | | 10 c. red | 85 | 85 |
| 9 | | 15 c. orange | 2·75 | 85 |
| 10 | | 25 c. blue | 4·25 | 3·25 |
| 11 | | 50 c. brown | 5·75 | 5·75 |
| 12 | | 75 c. brown | 5·75 | 7·50 |
| 13 | | 1 p. red | 9·00 | 11·00 |
| 14 | | 2 p. brown | 24·00 | 32·00 |
| 15 | | 3 p. green | 35·00 | 40·00 |
| 16 | | 4 p. purple | 80·00 | 55·00 |
| 17 | | 5 p. green | 95·00 | 55·00 |
| 18 | | 10 p. blue | £180 | 85·00 |

**1905.** "Curly Head" key-type inscr. "ELOBEY, ANNOBON Y CORISCO" and dated "1905".

| | | | | |
|---|---|---|---|---|
| 19 | Z | 1 c. pink | 75 | 50 |
| 20 | | 2 c. purple | 3·25 | 40 |
| 21 | | 3 c. black | 75 | 40 |
| 22 | | 4 c. red | 75 | 40 |
| 23 | | 5 c. green | 75 | 40 |
| 24 | | 10 c. green | 2·75 | 60 |
| 25 | | 15 c. lilac | 3·25 | 3·00 |
| 26 | | 25 c. red | 3·25 | 3·00 |
| 27 | | 50 c. orange | 6·00 | 4·25 |
| 28 | | 75 c. blue | 6·00 | 4·25 |
| 29 | | 1 p. brown | 11·50 | 9·00 |
| 30 | | 2 p. brown | 12·50 | 13·50 |
| 31 | | 3 p. red | 12·50 | 13·50 |
| 32 | | 4 p. brown | 95·00 | 55·00 |
| 33 | | 5 p. green | 95·00 | 55·00 |
| 34 | | 10 p. red | £250 | £170 |

**1906.** Preceding issue surch **1906** and value, with or without ornamental frame.

| | | | | |
|---|---|---|---|---|
| 35d | Z | 10 c. on 1 c. pink | 11·00 | 5·50 |
| 36 | | 15 c. on 2 c. purple | 11·00 | 8·00 |
| 38 | | 25 c. on 3 c. black | 11·00 | 8·00 |
| 40 | | 50 c. on 4 c. red | 11·00 | 8·00 |

3. King Alfonso XIII.

**1907.**

| | | | | |
|---|---|---|---|---|
| 41 | 3 | 1 c. purple | 25 | 25 |
| 42 | | 2 c. black | 25 | 25 |
| 43 | | 3 c. red | 25 | 25 |
| 44 | | 4 c. green | 25 | 25 |
| 45 | | 5 c. green | 25 | 25 |
| 46 | | 10 c. lilac | 3·25 | 2·75 |
| 47 | | 15 c. pink | 1·10 | 1·10 |
| 48 | | 25 c. buff | 1·10 | 1·10 |
| 49 | | 50 c. blue | 1·10 | 1·10 |
| 50 | | 75 c. brown | 3·50 | 1·60 |
| 51 | | 1 p. brown | 5·75 | 2·75 |
| 52 | | 2 p. red | 8·00 | 4·75 |
| 53 | | 3 p. brown | 7·50 | 4·75 |
| 54 | | 4 p. green | 8·00 | 4·75 |
| 55 | | 5 p. red | 12·00 | 4·75 |
| 56 | | 10 p. pink | 28·00 | 15·00 |

**1908.** Surch. **HABILITADO PARA 05 CTMS.**

| | | | | |
|---|---|---|---|---|
| 57. | 3. | 05 c. on 1 c. purple | 1·75 | 80 |
| 58. | | 05 c. on 2 c. black | 1·75 | 80 |
| 59. | | 05 c. on 3 c. red | 1·75 | 80 |
| 60. | | 05 c. on 4 c. green | 1·75 | 80 |
| 61. | | 05 c. on 10 c. lilac | 3·50 | 3·00 |
| 62. | | 25 c. on 10 c. lilac | 16·00 | 8·25 |

**1909.** Fiscal stamps inscr "POSESIONES ESPAÑOLES DE AFRICA OCCIDENTAL", surch **1909 CORREOS 10 cen de peseta**.

| | | | |
|---|---|---|---|
| 63 | 10 c. on 50 c. green | 25·00 | 15·00 |
| 64 | 10 c. on 1 p. 25 lilac | 32·00 | 18·00 |
| 65 | 10 c. on 2 p. brown | £100 | 75·00 |
| 66 | 10 c. on 2 p. 50 blue | £100 | 75·00 |
| 67 | 10 c. on 10 p. brown | £110 | 75·00 |
| 68 | 10 c. on 15 p. grey | £100 | 75·00 |
| 69 | 10 c. on 25 p. brown | £100 | 75·00 |

For later issues see SPANISH GUINEA.

## EL SALVADOR Pt. 15

A republic of C. America, independent since 1838.

1867. 8 reales = 100 centavos = 1 peso.
1912. 100 centavos = 1 colon.

1. San Miguel Volcano. 4.

**1867.**

1. 1. ½ r. blue .. .. .. 90 90
2. 1 r. red .. .. .. 90 90
3. 2 r. green .. .. .. 1·75 2·50
4. 4 r. brown .. .. .. 4·25 4·00

**1874.** Optd. **CONTRA SELLO 1874.** and Arms in circle.

5. 1. ½ r. blue .. .. .. 4·00 4·00
6. 1 r. red .. .. .. 4·00 4·00
7. 2 r. green .. .. .. 4·00 4·00
8. 4 r. brown .. .. .. 11·00 10·50

**1879.**

9. 4. 1 c. green .. .. .. 1·25 75
15. 2 c. red .. .. .. 1·75 1·75
16. 5 c. blue .. .. .. 3·00 1·50
12. 10 c. black .. .. 6·00 4·00
13. 20 c. purple .. .. 15·00 12·00

8. 9. 10.

**1887.**

18. 8. 3 c. brown (perf.) .. .. 40 40
19. 9. 5 c. blue (roul.) .. .. 40 30
20. 10. 10 c. orange (perf.) .. 4·00 1·10

**1889.** Surch. **1 centavo.**

21. 8. 1 c. on 3 c. brown .. .. 1·00 60

A number of postage stamps listed above are found overprinted **1889.**

**1889.** As T 8, but with bar at top. Perf.

22. 8. 1 c. green .. .. .. 50 50

14. 15. 19. Landing of Columbus.

**1890.**

30. 14. 1 c. green .. .. 15 20
31. 2 c. brown .. .. 15 25
32. 3 c. yellow .. .. 15 25
33. 5 c. blue .. .. 15 25
34. 10 c. violet .. .. 15 25
35. 20 c. orange .. .. 15 30
36. 25 c. red .. .. 15 40
37. 50 c. purple .. .. 15 80
38. 1 p. red .. .. .. 15 2·00

**1891.**

39. 15. 1 c. red .. .. .. 15 15
40. 2 c. green .. .. .. 15 15
41. 3 c. violet .. .. .. 15 20
42. 5 c. red .. .. .. 15 20
43. 10 c. blue .. .. .. 15 20
44. 11 c. violet .. .. 15 60
45 20 c. green .. .. .. 15 80
46. 25 c. brown .. .. 15 90
47. 50 c. blue .. .. .. 15 1·75
48. 1 p. brown .. .. .. 20 3·50

**1891.** Surch. **1 centavo.**

49. 15. 1 c. on 2 c. green .. .. 2·00 3·00

**1891.** Surch. **UN CENTAVO**

50. 15. 1 c. on 2 c. green .. .. 1·75 2·50

**1891.** Surch. **5 CENTAVOS.**

51. 15. 5 c. on 3 c. violet .. .. 6·00 4·50

**1892.**

52. 19. 1 c. green .. .. 15 15
53. 2 c. brown .. .. 15 15
54. 3 c. blue .. .. 15 15
55. 5 c. grey .. .. 15 15
56. 10 c. red .. .. 15 20
57. 11 c. brown .. .. 15 1·00
58. 20 c. orange .. .. 15 1·00
59. 25 c. purple .. .. 15 1·50
60. 50 c. yellow .. .. 15 2·00
61. 1 p. red .. .. .. 15 3·00

**1892.** Surch.

62a. 19. 1 c. on 5 c. grey .. .. 75 80
64. 1 c. on 20 c. orange .. 1·00 1·10
66. 1 c. on 25 c. purple .. 1·50 90

23. Gen. Ezeta. 24. Founding the City of Isabella.

**1893.** Dated "1893".

67. 23. 1 c. blue .. .. .. 15 20
68. 2 c. red .. .. .. 15 20
69. 3 c. violet .. .. 15 20
70. 5 c. brown .. .. 15 25
71. 10 c. brown .. .. 15 25
72. 11 c. red .. .. 15 30
73. 20 c. green .. .. 15 40
74. 25 c. black .. .. 15 50
75. 50 c. orange .. .. 15 60
76. 1 p. black .. .. 15 90
77. 24. 2 p. green .. .. 50
78. – 5 p. violet .. .. 50
79. – 10 p. red .. .. .. 50

DESIGNS—VERT. 5 p. Columbus Statue, Genoa. 10 p. Departure from Palos.

**1893.** Surch. **UN CENTAVO.**

80. 23. 1 c. on 2 c. red .. .. 60 60

28. Liberty. 29. Columbus before the Council.

**1894.** Dated "1894".

81. 28. 1 c. brown .. .. 15 20
82. 2 c. blue .. .. 15 20
83. 3 c. purple .. .. 15 20
84. 5 c. brown .. .. 15 30
85. 10 c. violet .. .. 15 30
86. 11 c. red .. .. 15 30
87. 20 c. blue .. .. 15 40
88. 25 c. orange .. .. 15 50
89. 50 c. black .. .. 15 80
90. 1 p. blue .. .. 15 1·10
91. 29. 2 p. blue .. .. 40
92. – 5 p. red .. .. 50
93. – 10 p. brown .. .. 50

DESIGNS—HORIZ. 5 p. Columbus protecting hostages. 10 p. Columbus received by King and Queen.

**1894.** Surch. **1 Centavo.**

94. 28. 1 c. on 11 c. red .. .. 90 60

31. 34.

**1895.** Optd. with Arms obliterating portrait. Various frames.

95. 31. 1 c. olive .. .. 15
96. 2 c. green .. .. 15
97. 3 c. brown .. .. 15
98. 5 c. blue .. .. 15
99. 10 c. orange .. .. 15
100. 12 c. red .. .. 15
101. 15 c. red .. .. 15
102. 20 c. yellow .. .. 15
103. 24 c. violet .. .. 15
104. 30 c. blue .. .. 15
105. 50 c. red .. .. 15
106. 1 p. black .. .. 15

**1895.** Various frames.

115. 34. 1 c. olive .. .. 90 60
116. 2 c. green .. .. 20 20
117. 3 c. brown .. .. 20 20
118. 5 c. blue .. .. 20 20
119. 10 c. orange .. .. 80 40
120. 12 c. red .. .. 80 40
121. 15 c. red .. .. 25 40
122. 20 c. green .. .. 30 60
123. 24 c. lilac .. .. 40 60
124. 30 c. blue .. .. 25 60
125. 50 c. red .. .. 1·25 1·50
126. 1 p. brown .. .. 1·50 2·25

**1895.** Surch.

132. 34. 1 c. on 12 c. red .. 1·25 1·10
133. 1 c. on 24 c. lilac .. 1·25 1·10
134. 1 c. on 30 c. blue .. 1·25 1·10
135. 2 c. on 20 c. green .. 1·25 1·10
136. 3 c. on 30 c. blue .. 1·50 1·40



37. Peace. 38. Arms. 39. Government Building.

**1896.**

137. 37. 1 c. brown .. .. 15 15
138. 2 c. brown .. .. 15 30
139. 3 c. green .. .. 15 20
140. 5 c. olive .. .. 15 30
141. 10 c. yellow .. .. 15 30
142. 12 c. blue .. .. 90 1·10
143. 15 c. violet .. .. 15 30
144. 20 c. red .. .. 70 60
145. 24 c. red .. .. 15 30
146. 30 c. orange .. .. 15 50
147. 50 c. black .. .. 15 60
148. 1 p. red .. .. .. 15 1·10

**1896.** Dated "1896".

158. 38. 1 c. green .. .. 15 15
159. 39. 2 c. lake .. .. 15 15
160. – 3 c. orange .. .. 15 15
161. – 5 c. blue .. .. 15 15
162. – 10 c. brown .. .. 20 25
163. – 12 c. grey .. .. 20 30
164. – 15 c. green .. .. 15 30
165. – 20 c. red .. .. 20 40
166. – 24 c. violet .. .. 15 50
167. – 30 c. green .. .. 15 50
168. – 50 c. orange .. .. 15 50
169. – 100 c. blue .. .. 15 1·00

DESIGNS: 3 c. Locomotive. 5 c. Mt. San Miguel. 10, 12 c. Steamship. 15 c. Post Office. 20 c. Lake Ilopango. 24 c. Magra Falls. 30, 50 c. Arms. 100 c. Columbus.

**1896.** No. 166 surch. **Quince centavos.**

218. 15 c. on 24 c. violet .. 5·00 5·00

**1897.** As Nos. 158/69. New colours.

220. 1 c. red .. .. .. 15 15
221. 2 c. green .. .. 15 15
222. 3 c. brown .. .. 15 15
223. 5 c. orange .. .. 15 15
224. 10 c. green .. .. 15 20
225. 12 c. blue .. .. 50 40
226. 15 c. black .. .. 2·50 2·50
227. 20 c. slate .. .. 15 40
228. 24 c. yellow .. .. 15 50
229. 30 c. red .. .. 15 40
230. 50 c. violet .. .. 25 80
231. 100 c. lake .. .. 3·50 3·50

55. 57. Union of Central America.

**1897.** Federation of Central America.

270. 55. 1 c. multicoloured .. 75 3·00
271. 5 c. multicoloured .. 75 3·50

**1897.** Nos. 228/31 surch. **TRECE centavos.**

272. 13 c. on 24 c. yellow .. 3·00 3·00
273. 13 c. on 30 c. red .. 3·00 3·00
274. 13 c. on 50 c. violet .. 3·00 3·00
275. 13 c. on 100 c. lake .. 3·00 3·00

**1898.**

276. 57. 1 c. red .. .. .. 10 15
277. 2 c. red .. .. .. 10 15
278. 3 c. green .. .. 15 20
279. 5 c. green .. .. 15 15
280. 10 c. blue .. .. 15 20
281. 12 c. violet .. .. 25 30
282. 13 c. lake .. .. 15 20
283. 20 c. blue .. .. 15 40
284. 24 c. blue .. .. 15 50
285. 26 c. brown .. .. 15 50
286. 50 c. orange .. .. 15 90
287. 1 p. yellow .. .. 25 1·25

Some values of the above set exist optd. with a wheel as Type 58.

(58.) 59. Ceres.

**1899.** Optd. with T 58.

318. 59. 1 c. brown .. .. 30 15
319. 2 c. green .. .. 40 10
320. 3 c. blue .. .. 50 25
321. 5 c. orange .. .. 35 15
322. 10 c. brown .. .. 35 15
323. 12 c. green .. .. 85 60
324. 13 c. red .. .. 75 70
325. 24 c. blue .. .. 10·00 10·00
326. 26 c. red .. .. 2·00 1·75
327. 50 c. red .. .. 2·00 1·75
328. 100 c. violet .. .. 2·50 1·25

**1899.** Optd. **1900.**

398. 57. 1 c. red .. .. .. 1·40 1·00

**1900.** Stamps of 1898 surch. **1900** and new value, with or without wheel opt., T 58.

400. 57. 1 c. on 10 c. blue .. 4·00 3·50
401. 1 c. on 13 c. lake .. £225
414. 2 c. on 12 c. violet .. 2·00 2·00
403. 2 c. on 13 c. lake .. 1·25 1·10
404. 2 c. on 20 c. blue .. 1·25 1·25
406b. 3 c. on 12 c. violet .. 42·00 42·00
407. 3 c. on 50 c. orange .. 15·00 15·00
419. 5 c. on 12 c. violet .. 25·00 25·00
409. 5 c. on 24 c. blue .. 13·00 13·00
410a. 5 c. on 26 c. brown .. 42·00 42·00
411. 5 c. on 1 p. yellow .. 15·00 15·00

On Nos. 406b and 410a the surcharge is inverted.

**1900.** Stamps of 1899 surch. **1900** and new value, with or without wheel opt., T 58.

424. 59. 1 c. on 2 c. green .. 25 15
420. 1 c. on 13 c. red .. 40 40
426. 2 c. on 12 c. green .. 85 60
422. 2 c. on 13 c. red .. 85 70
423. 3 c. on 12 c. green .. 85 70
429. 5 c. on 24 c. blue .. 2·00 90
430. 5 c. on 26 c. red .. 80 60

(66.) 70. Columbus Monument.

**1900.** T 59 with date altered to "1900" and optd. as **T 66.**

438. 59. 1 c. green .. .. 15 15
468. 2 c. red .. .. 15 15
469. 3 c. black .. .. 15 15
470. 5 c. blue .. .. 15 10
471. 10 c. blue .. .. 35 20
472. 12 c. green .. .. 35 25
473. 13 c. brown .. .. 15 15
474. 24 c. black .. .. 40 35
475. 26 c. brown .. .. 50 40
447. 50 c. red .. .. 1·60 1·50

**1902.** Nos. 468, 469 & 472 surch. **1 centavo.**

483. 59. 1 c. on 2 c. red .. 2·00 1·60
484. 1 c. on 3 c. black .. 1·40 1·00
485. 1 c. on 5 c. blue .. 90 70

**1903.**

486. 70. 1 c. green .. .. 25 20
487. 2 c. red .. .. 25 20
488. 3 c. orange .. .. 60 50
489. 5 c. blue .. .. 25 20
490. 10 c. purple .. .. 25 20
491. 12 c. grey .. .. 35 20
492. 13 c. brown .. .. 35 25
493. 24 c. red .. .. 1·75 90
494. 26 c. brown .. .. 1·75 90
495. 50 c. yellow .. .. 90 55
496. 100 c. blue .. .. 3·50 1·75

**1905.** Surch. in words or figures and words.

514. 70. 1 c. on 2 c. red .. .. 40 35
517. 5 c. on 12 c. grey .. 55 45

**1905.** Surch. in figures only and two black circles.

515. 70. 1 c. on 13 c. brown .. 1·40 1·40
516. 3 c. on 13 c. brown .. 50 50

**1905.** Surch. in figures twice.

527. 70. 5 c. on 12 c. grey .. 2·00 1·25

**1905.** Surcharged in figures repeated four times.

529. 70. 5 c. on 12 c. grey .. 2·75 2·40

**1905.** Surch. with new value: **1 1** at top of stamp and **1 CENTAVO 1** at foot.

523. 70. 1 c. on 2 c. red .. 25 20
524. 1 c. on 10 c. purple .. 25 20
525. 1 c. on 12 c. grey .. 70 55
526. 1 c. on 13 c. brown .. 3·00 2·50
530. 6 c. on 12 c. grey .. 50 40
531. 6 c. on 13 c. brown .. 85 35

**1905.** Stamps dated "1900", with or without opt. T **66**, and optd. **1905** or **O1905.**

552. 59. 1 c. green .. .. 3·25 2·25
546. 2 c. red .. .. 30 25
543. 3 c. black .. .. 3·50 2·10
547. 5 c. blue .. .. 90 50
548. 10 c. blue .. .. 50 40

**1906.** Stamps dated "1900", with or without opt. T **66**, and optd. **1906** or surch. also.

560. 59. 2 c. on 26 c. brown .. 40 35
562. 3 c. on 26 c. brown .. 2·40 2·00
564. 10 c. blue .. .. 90 90

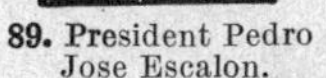
89. President Pedro Jose Escalon.

91. President's Palace.

**1906.**

570. 89. 1 c. black and green .. 15 10
571. 2 c. black and red .. 15 10
572. 3 c. black and yellow .. 15 10
573. 5 c. black and blue .. 15 10
574. 6 c. black and red .. 15 10
575. 10 c. black and violet .. 15 10
576. 12 c. black and violet .. 15 10
577. 13 c. black and brown 15 10
578. 24 c. black and red .. 35 35
579. 26 c. black and brown 35 35
580. 50 c. black and yellow 35 50
581. 100 c. black and blue .. 1·90 1·90

**1907.** Nos. 570/2 optd. as T **66.**

592. 89. 1 c. black and green .. 25 20
593. 2 c. black and red .. 25 20
594. 3 c. black and yellow .. 25 20

**1907.** Surch. with new value and black circles and optd. with shield, T **66.**

595. 89. 1 c. on 5 c. blk. & blue .. 10 10
596. 1 c. on 6 c. black and red 20 15
597. 2 c. on 6 c. black and red 1·40 70
598. 10 c. on 6 c. black & red 50 35

**1907.** Optd. with shield, T **66.**

599. 91. 1 c. black and green .. 15 10
600. 2 c. black and red .. 15 10
601. 3 c. black and yellow .. 15 10
602. 5 c. black and blue .. 15 10
603b. 6 c. black and red .. 15 10
604. 10 c. black and violet .. 15 10
605. 12 c. black and violet .. 15 10
606. 13 c. black and sepia .. 15 10
607. 24 c. black and red .. 15 10
608. 26 c. black and brown .. 35 15
609. 50 c. black and yellow .. 50 25
610. 100 c. black and blue .. 70 50

**1908.** Surch. **UN CENTAVO** and one black circle.

621. 91. 1 c. on 2 c. black and red 35 25

**1909.** Optd. **1821. 15 Septiembre 1909.**

633. 91. 1 c. black and green .. 1·40 1·00

**1909.** Surch. with new value and **1909.**

634. 91. 2 c. on 13 c. blk. & sep. 1·00 90
635. 3 c. on 26 c. blk. & brn. 1·25 1·00

99. Gen. Figueroa.

100. M. J. Arce.

**1910.**

642. 99. 1 c. black and brown .. 15 10
643. 2 c. black and green .. 15 15
644. 3 c. black and orange .. 15 15
645. 4 c. black and red .. 15 15
646. 5 c. black and violet .. 15 15
647. 6 c. black and red .. 15 15
648. 10 c. black and violet .. 20 15
649. 12 c. black and blue .. 20 15
650. 17 c. black and green .. 20 15
651. 19 c. black and brown 20 15
652. 29 c. black and brown 20 15
653. 50 c. black and yellow 15 15
654. 100 c. black and blue .. 20 15

**1911.** Centenary of Insurrection of 1811.

655. – 5 c. brown and blue .. 10 10
656. 100. 6 c. brown and orange 10 10
657. – 12 c. black and mauve 10 10

DESIGNS: 5 c. Portrait of J. M. Delgado. 12 c. Centenary Monument.

**1911.** T 91 without shield opt. T **66.**

658. 91. 1 c. red .. .. .. 10 10
659. 2 c. brown .. .. 35 35
660. 13 c. green .. .. 15 15
661. 24 c. yellow .. .. 20 20
662. 50 c. brown .. .. 20 20

101. Jose Matias Delgado.

107. Independence Monument.

108. National Palace.

110. National Arms.

**1912.**

663. 101. 1 c. black and blue .. 15 10
664. – 2 c. black and brown .. 20 15
665. – 5 c. black and red .. 20 15
666. – 6 c. black and green .. 15 15
667. – 12 c. black and olive .. 60 25
668. – 17 c. grey and purple .. 50 20
669. 107. 19 c. grey and red .. 75 20
670. 108. 29 c. grey and orange .. 90 25
671. – 50 c. grey and blue .. 1·10 50
672. 110. 1 col. grey and black .. 1·50 70

DESIGNS—As Type **101:** 2 c. M. J. Arce. 5 c. F. Morazan. 6 c. R. Campo. 12 c. T. Cabanas. 17 c. Barrios Monument. As Type **108:** 50 c. Rosales Hospital.

111. J. M. Rodriguez.

**1914.**

673. 111. 10 c. brown and orange 1·50 70
674. – 25 c. brown and violet .. 1·50 70

PORTRAIT: 25 c. Dr. M. E. Araujo.

**1915.** Re-issue of T **91.** No shield. Optd. **1915.**

675. 91. 1 c. grey .. .. 15 10
676. 2 c. red .. .. .. 15 10
677. 5 c. blue .. .. 15 10
678. 6 c. blue .. .. 15 10
679. 10 c. yellow .. .. 55 40
680. 12 c. brown .. .. 40 20
681. 50 c. purple .. .. 20 15
682. 100 c. brown .. .. 85 85

113. National Theatre.

114. Pres. Carlos Melendez.

**1916.** Various frames.

683. 113. 1 c. green .. .. 25 10
684. 2 c. red .. .. 25 10
685. 5 c. blue .. .. 25 10
686. 6 c. violet .. .. 30 15
687. 10 c. brown .. .. 30 15
688. 12 c. purple .. .. 2·75 75
689. 17 c. orange .. .. 50 20
690. 25 c. brown .. .. 75 40
691. 29 c. black .. .. 5·00 1·25
692. 50 c. grey .. .. 1·75 1·00
693. 114. 1 col. black and blue .. 70 60

**1917.** Official stamps of 1915, with word "OFICIAL" cancelled with five bars.

694. 91. 2 c. red (No. O 686) .. 40 25
695. 5 c. blue (No. O 687) .. 50 35

**1918.** Official stamps of 1915 optd. **CORRIENTE** and bar.

696. 91. 1 c. grey (No. O 685) .. 1·10 90
697. 2 c. red .. .. 1·10 90
698. 5 c. blue .. .. 7·00 4·50
699. 6 c. blue .. .. 70 50
700. 10 c. yellow .. .. 75 40
701. 12 c. brown .. .. 60 50
702. 50 c. purple .. .. 50 50

**1918.** Official stamps of 1916 optd. **Corriente** and bar or surch. also.

704. 113. 1 c. on 6 c. vio. (No. O 696) 3·00 3·00
705. 5 c. blue .. .. 4·00 4·00
706. 6 c. violet .. .. 6·50 6·50

**1919.** Surch. with new value and square or circles or bars.

710. 113. 1 c. on 6 c. violet .. 3·00 3·00
711. 1 c. on 12 c. purple .. 2·50 2·50
712. 1 c. on 17 c. orange .. 2·50 2·50
713. 2 c. on 10 c. brown .. 2·50 2·50
714. 5 c. on 50 c. grey .. 2·50 2·50
715. 6 c. on 25 c. brown .. 2·50 2·50
716. 15 c. on 29 c. black .. 1·75 1·75
717. 26 c. on 29 c. black .. 3·50 3·50
719. 35 c. on 50 c. grey .. 3·50 3·50
720. 60 c. on 1 col. blk. & bl. 40 35

**1919.** No. O 699 surch. **1 Centavo 1** and black squares.

721. 113. 1 c. on 12 c. purple .. 2·50 2·50

**1920.** Municipal stamps (Arms) surch. **Correos Un centavo 1919.**

722. 1 c. on 1 c. olive .. .. 10 10
723. 1 c. on 5 c. yellow .. 10 10
724. 1 c. on 10 c. blue .. .. 15 10
725. 1 c. on 25 c. green .. 10 10
726. 1 c. on 50 c. olive .. .. 15 15
727. 1 c. on 1 p. black .. .. 25 25

130. F. Menendez.

131. Confederation Coin.

132. Delgado Speaking.

133. Arms of the Confederation.

135. Independence Monument.

139. J. S. Canas.

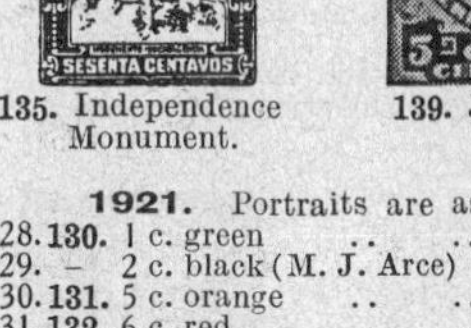

**1921.** Portraits are as T **130.**

728. 130. 1 c. green .. .. 25 10
729. – 2 c. black (M. J. Arce) 25 10
730. 131. 5 c. orange .. .. 60 15
731. 132. 6 c. red .. .. 50 10
732. 133. 10 c. blue .. .. 50 10
733. – 25 c. grn. (F. Morazan) 1·50 15
734. 135. 60 c. violet .. .. 3·75 50
735 – 1 col. sepia (Columbus) 6·00 50

**1921.** Centenary of Independence. Nos. 728/31 optd **CENTENARIO.**

735a. 130. 1 c. green .. .. 4·50 2·40
735b. – 2 c. black .. .. 4·50 2·40
735c. 131. 5 c. orange .. .. 4·50 2·40
735d. 132. 6 c. red .. .. 4·50 2·40

**1923.** As last, surch.

745. 131. 1 c. on 5 c. orange .. 35 25
741. – 1 c. on 25 c. green .. 15 15
746. 131. 2 c. on 5 c. orange .. 35 35
737. 132. 5 c. on 6 c. red .. 35 20
747. 133. 6 c. on 10 c. blue .. 35 25
742. – 6 c. on 25 c. green .. 20 15
738. – 10 c. on 2 c. black .. 50 20
739. 132. 20 c. on 6 c. red .. 35 35
743. – 20 c. on 25 c. green .. 45 35
744. – 20 c. on 1 col. sepia .. 55 25

**1923.** Centenary of Abolition of Slavery.

740. 139. 5 c. blue .. .. 50 35

**1924.** U.P.U. Commem. Surch. **15 Sept. 1874-1924 5 5 U.P.U. CINCO CENTAVOS.**

749. 135. 5 c. on 60 c. violet .. 3·25 3·00

141. Daniel Hernandez.

146. Central America.

150.

**1924.**

750. 141. 1 c. purple .. .. 10 10
751. – 2 c. red .. .. 25 10
752. – 3 c. brown .. .. 20 10
753. – 5 c. black .. .. 20 10
754. – 6 c. blue .. .. 50 10
755. 146. 10 c. orange .. .. 55 20
756. – 20 c. green .. .. 70 35
757. – 35 c. green and red .. 1·75 30
758. – 50 c. brown .. .. 1·50 40
759. 150. 1 col. blue and green .. 2·25 40

DESIGNS—VERT. 2 c. National Gymnasium. 3 c. Atlacatl. 20 c. Balsam tree. 35 c. Senora T. S. Morazan. HORIZ. 5 c. Conspiracy of 1811. 6 c. Bridge over R. Lempa. 50 c. Columbus at La Rabida.

**1925.** 400th Anniv of San Salvador. Surch **1525 2 2 1925 Dos centavos.**

760. 135. 2 c. on 60 c. violet .. 1·60 1·50

152. View of San Salvador.

**1925.**

761. 152. 1 c. blue .. .. 50 50
762. 2 c. green .. .. 50 50
763. 3 c. red .. .. .. 50 50

**1928.** Artistic Industrial Exn. Surch. **Exposicion Santaneca Julio de 1928** and value in figures.

764. 3 c. on 10 c. orange .. 50 40

**1928.** No. 753 surch.

765. 1 c. on 5 c. black .. .. 35 25

155. Dr. P. R. Bosque and Gen. L. Chacon.

**1930.** Inauguration of Railway link between Salvador and Guatemala.

766. 155. 1 c. purple and mauve 1·25 1·00
767. 3 c. purple and brown .. 1·25 1·00
768. 5 c. purple and green .. 1·40 1·25
769. 10 c. purple and orange 1·40 1·25

**1930.** Air. Nos. 755/759 optd. **Servicio Aereo** or surch. also.

770. 146. 15 c. on 10 c. orange 45 45
771. – 20 c. green .. .. 45 45
772. – 25 c. on 35 c. grn. & red 40 40
773. – 40 c. on 50 c. brown .. 55 40
774. 150. 50 c. on 1 col. bl. & grn. 1·00 1·00

158. Curtiss "Jenny" over San Salvador.

**1930.** Air.

775. 158. 15 c. red .. .. 30 10
776. 20 c. green .. .. 35 10
777. 25 c. purple .. .. 35 10
778. 40 c. blue .. .. 70 10

158a. Tomb of F. Menendez.

158b. Simon Bolivar.

**1930.** Birth Cent. of Menendez.

779. 158a. 1 c. violet .. .. 3·00 2·75
780. 3 c. brown .. .. 3·00 2·75
781. 5 c. green .. .. 3·00 2·75
782. 10 c. orange .. .. 3·00 2·75

**1930.** Air. Death Cent. of Bolivar.

783. 158b. 15 c. red .. .. 5·25 4·00
784. 20 c. green .. .. 5·25 4·00
785. 25 c. purple .. .. 5·25 4·00
786. 40 c. blue .. .. 5·25 4·00

**1931.** Air. Optd with Curtiss "Jenny" Biplane.

787 150 1 col. blue and green .. 3·00 2·50

**1931.** New G.P.O. Building Fund. Nos. 756 and 758 surch. **EDIFICIOS POSTALES** and value.

790. 1 c. on 20 c. green .. 15 15
788. 1 c. on 50 c. brown .. 15 15
789. 2 c. on 20 c. green .. 15 15
791. 2 c. on 50 c. brown .. 15 15

162. Church of Mercy, San Salvador.

164. Jose Matias Delgado.

**1931.** Air. 120th Anniv. of Independence.

792. 162. 15 c. red .. .. 3·50 3·00
793. 20 c. green .. .. 3·50 3·00
794. 25 c. purple .. .. 3·50 3·00
795. 40 c. blue .. .. 3·50 3·00

**1932.** Issues of 1924–26 optd **1932**.

| No. | Type | Description | Unused | Used |
|---|---|---|---|---|
| 796. | **141.** | 1 c. purple | 15 | 10 |
| 797. | – | 2 c. red | 20 | 15 |
| 798. | – | 3 c. brown | 25 | 10 |
| 799. | – | 5 c. black | 25 | 10 |
| 800. | – | 6 c. blue | 90 | 15 |
| 801. | **146.** | 10 c. orange | 85 | 20 |
| 802. | – | 20 c. green | 1·10 | 45 |
| 803. | – | 35 c. green and red | 1·60 | 55 |
| 804. | – | 50 c. brown | 2·25 | 70 |
| 805. | **150.** | 1 col. blue and green | 4·00 | 1·60 |

**1932.** Air. Death Cent. of J. M. Delgado.

| No. | Type | Description | Unused | Used |
|---|---|---|---|---|
| 806. | **164.** | 15 c. red and violet | 1·00 | 1·00 |
| 807. | | 20 c. green and blue | 1·50 | 1·50 |
| 808. | | 25 c. violet and red | 1·50 | 1·50 |
| 809. | | 40 c. blue and green | 1·75 | 1·75 |

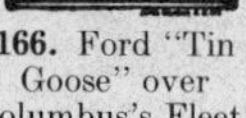
**166.** Ford "Tin Goose" over Columbus's Fleet.

**169.** Police Headquarters.

**1933.** Air. 441st Anniv. of Departure of Columbus from Palos.

| No. | Type | Description | Unused | Used |
|---|---|---|---|---|
| 810. | **166.** | 15 c. orange | 4·00 | 1·75 |
| 811. | | 20 c. green | 6·00 | 3·75 |
| 812. | | 25 c. mauve | 6·00 | 3·75 |
| 813. | | 40 c. blue | 6·00 | 3·75 |
| 814. | | 1 col. bronze | 6·00 | 3·75 |

**1934.** Issues of 1924 and 1926 surch.

| No. | Type | Description | Unused | Used |
|---|---|---|---|---|
| 815. | – | 2 on 5 c. blk. (No. 753) | 15 | 10 |
| 816. | – | 2 on 50 c. brn. (No. 758) | 25 | 15 |
| 817. | **146.** | 3 on 10 c. orange | 15 | 10 |
| 818. | **150.** | 8 on 1 col. blue & green | 15 | 15 |
| 819. | – | 15 on 35 c. green and red (No. 757) | 25 | 25 |

**1934.**

| No. | Type | Description | Unused | Used |
|---|---|---|---|---|
| 820. | **169.** | 2 c. brown | 20 | 10 |
| 821. | | 5 c. red | 20 | 10 |
| 822. | | 8 c. blue | 20 | 10 |

**1934.** Air. Inscr. "**SERVICIO AEREO**".

| No. | Type | Description | Unused | Used |
|---|---|---|---|---|
| 823. | **169.** | 25 c. violet | 45 | 20 |
| 824. | | 30 c. brown | 65 | 30 |
| 825. | | 1 col. black | 1·75 | 55 |

**171.** Discus Thrower.

**172.** Runner breaking the Tape.

**1935.** 3rd Central American Athletic Games.

| No. | Type | Description | Unused | Used |
|---|---|---|---|---|
| 826 | 171 | 5 c. red (postage) | 3·00 | 2·40 |
| 827 | | 8 c. blue | 3·25 | 2·75 |
| 828 | | 10 c. yellow | 4·00 | 3·00 |
| 829 | | 15 c. brown | 4·75 | 3·25 |
| 830 | | 37 c. green | 6·00 | 4·75 |
| 831 | 172 | 15 c. red (air) | 4·00 | 4·00 |
| 832 | | 25 c. violet | 4·00 | 4·00 |
| 833 | | 30 c. brown | 3·50 | 3·00 |
| 834 | | 55 c. blue | 17·00 | 15·00 |
| 835 | | 1 col. black | 13·00 | 12·00 |

**1935.** Nos. 826/35 optd **HABILITADO**.

| No. | Type | Description | Unused | Used |
|---|---|---|---|---|
| 836 | 171 | 5 c. red (postage) | 4·00 | 3·00 |
| 837 | | 8 c. blue | 6·00 | 3·00 |
| 838 | | 10 c. yellow | 6·00 | 3·50 |
| 839 | | 15 c. brown | 6·00 | 3·50 |
| 840 | | 37 c. green | 9·50 | 6·00 |
| 841 | 172 | 15 c. red (air) | 4·00 | 1·75 |
| 842 | | 25 c. violet | 4·00 | 1·75 |
| 843 | | 30 c. brown | 4·00 | 1·75 |
| 844 | | 55 c. blue | 26·00 | 22·00 |
| 845 | | 1 col. black | 13·00 | 12·00 |

**174.** National Flag.

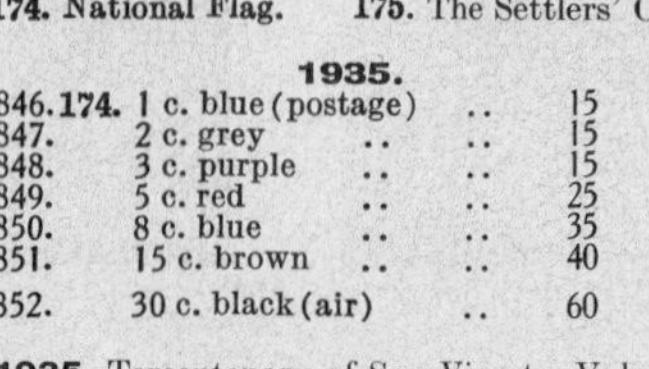
**175.** The Settlers' Oak.

**1935.**

| No. | Type | Description | Unused | Used |
|---|---|---|---|---|
| 846. | **174.** | 1 c. blue (postage) | 15 | 10 |
| 847. | | 2 c. grey | 15 | 10 |
| 848. | | 3 c. purple | 15 | 10 |
| 849. | | 5 c. red | 25 | 10 |
| 850. | | 8 c. blue | 35 | 15 |
| 851. | | 15 c. brown | 40 | 15 |
| 852. | | 30 c. black (air) | 60 | 25 |

**1935.** Tercentenary of San Vicente. Value in black.

| No. | Type | Description | Unused | Used |
|---|---|---|---|---|
| 853. | **175.** | 2 c. grn. & brn. (post.) | 35 | 25 |
| 854. | | 3 c. green | 40 | 25 |
| 855. | | 5 c. green and red | 55 | 35 |
| 856. | | 8 c. green and blue | 55 | 40 |
| 857. | | 15 c. green and brown | 55 | 50 |
| 858. | | 10 c. grn. & yellow (air) | 1·25 | 90 |
| 859. | | 15 c. green and brown | 1·25 | 90 |
| 860. | | 20 c. green | 1·25 | 90 |
| 861. | | 25 c. green and violet | 1·25 | 90 |
| 862. | | 30 c. green and brown | 1·25 | 90 |

**178.** Cutuco Harbour.

**179.** D. Vasconcelos.

**181.** Sugar Refinery.

**182.** Coffee Cargo.

**1935.**

| No. | Type | Description | Unused | Used |
|---|---|---|---|---|
| 863. | – | 1 c. violet | 15 | 10 |
| 864. | **178.** | 2 c. brown | 20 | 10 |
| 865. | **179.** | 3 c. green | 15 | 10 |
| 866. | – | 5 c. red | 40 | 10 |
| 867. | – | 8 c. blue | 15 | 10 |
| 868. | **181.** | 10 c. yellow | 25 | 10 |
| 869. | **182.** | 15 c. bistre | 40 | 20 |
| 870. | – | 50 c. blue | 1·25 | 75 |
| 871. | – | 1 col. black | 3·50 | 2·25 |

DESIGNS—As Type **178**. 1 c. Mt. Izalco. 5 c. Campo de Marte playing-fields. As Type **179**: 8 c. T. G. Palomo. 1 col. Dr. M. Araujo. As Type **181**: 50 c. Balsam tree.

**1937.** Air. Optd. **AEREO** in frame.

| No. | Type | Description | Unused | Used |
|---|---|---|---|---|
| 872. | **182.** | 15 c. bistre | 40 | 25 |

**1937.** Air. No. 844 surch **30** in frame.

| No. | Type | Description | Unused | Used |
|---|---|---|---|---|
| 873 | 172 | 30 on 55 c. blue | 1·25 | 55 |

**186.** Panchimalco Church.

**1937.** Air.

| No. | Type | Description | Unused | Used |
|---|---|---|---|---|
| 874. | **186.** | 15 c. orange | 30 | 15 |
| 875. | | 20 c. green | 30 | 15 |
| 876. | | 25 c. violet | 30 | 15 |
| 877. | | 30 c. brown | 25 | 10 |
| 878. | | 40 c. blue | 45 | 35 |
| 879. | | 1 col. black | 85 | 35 |
| 880. | | 5 col. red | 3·75 | 2·50 |

**1938.** Surch.

| No. | Type | Description | Unused | Used |
|---|---|---|---|---|
| 881. | **178.** | 1 c. on 2 c. brown | 20 | 10 |
| 882. | – | 1 c. on 5 c. (No. 866) | 15 | 10 |
| 883. | **181.** | 3 c. on 10 c. yellow | 15 | 10 |
| 884. | **182.** | 8 c. on 15 c. bistre | 20 | 15 |

**1938.** Death Cent. of J. Simeon Canas. Surch. **3**.

| No. | Type | Description | Unused | Used |
|---|---|---|---|---|
| 885. | **139.** | 3 c. on 5 c. blue | 25 | 30 |

**190.** Flags and Book of Constitution.

**1938.** 150th Anniv. of U.S. Constitution.

(a) Postage (without air liner).

| No. | Type | Description | Unused | Used |
|---|---|---|---|---|
| 886. | **190.** | 8 c. red, yellow and blue | 60 | 50 |

(b) **Air.**

| No. | Type | Description | Unused | Used |
|---|---|---|---|---|
| 887. | | 30 c. multicoloured | 1·50 | 1·00 |

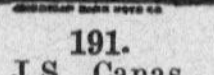
**191.** J.S. Canas.

**192.** Native Women at Washing Pool.

**1938.** Air. Death Cent. of J. S. Canas

| No. | Type | Description | Unused | Used |
|---|---|---|---|---|
| 888. | **191.** | 15 c. orange | 1·00 | 1·00 |
| 889. | | 20 c. green | 1·25 | 1·00 |
| 890. | | 30 c. brown | 1·25 | 1·00 |
| 891. | | 1 col. black | 4·00 | 3·50 |

**1938.**

| No. | Type | Description | Unused | Used |
|---|---|---|---|---|
| 892. | – | 1 c. violet | 15 | 10 |
| 893. | **192.** | 2 c. green | 15 | 10 |
| 894. | – | 3 c. brown | 25 | 10 |
| 895. | – | 5 c. red | 25 | 10 |
| 896. | – | 8 c. blue | 90 | 20 |
| 897. | – | 10 c. orange | 1·50 | 20 |
| 898. | – | 20 c. brown | 1·25 | 25 |
| 899. | – | 50 c. violet | 1·60 | 35 |
| 900. | – | 1 col. black | 1·50 | 60 |

DESIGNS: 1 c. Native sugar-mill. 3 c. Girl at spring. 5 c. Native ploughing. 8 c. Yucca plant. 10 c. Champion cow. 20 c. Extraction of Peruvian balsam. 50 c. Maquilishuat tree in flower. 1 col. G.P.O., San Salvador.

**195.** Golden Gate Bridge.

**1939.** Air. Golden Gate Int. Exn., San Francisco.

| No. | Type | Description | Unused | Used |
|---|---|---|---|---|
| 901. | **195.** | 15 c. black and yellow | 30 | 15 |
| 902. | | 30 c. black and brown | 45 | 15 |
| 903. | | 40 c. black and blue | 65 | 35 |

**1939.** Cent. of Battle of San Pedro Perulapan. Surch. **BATALLA SAN PEDRO PERU-LAPAN** and value.

| No. | Type | Description | Unused | Used |
|---|---|---|---|---|
| 904. | – | 8 c. on 50 c. bl. (No. 870) | 35 | 20 |
| 905. | – | 10 c. on 1 col. black (No. 871) | 50 | 20 |
| 906. | **150.** | 50 c. on 1 col. bl. & grn. | 2·75 | 2·75 |

**197.** Sir Rowland Hill.

**199.** Coffee Tree in Bloom.

**198.** Western Hemisphere and "Peace".

**1940.** Cent. of First Postage Stamps.

| No. | Type | Description | Unused | Used |
|---|---|---|---|---|
| 907. | **197.** | 8 c. black & blue (post.) | 3·00 | 60 |
| 908. | | 30 c. black & brown (air) | 4·75 | 1·75 |
| 909. | | 80 c. black and red | 12·00 | 9·00 |

**1940.** Air. 50th Anniv. of Pan-American Union.

| No. | Type | Description | Unused | Used |
|---|---|---|---|---|
| 910. | **198.** | 30 c. blue and brown | 50 | 35 |
| 911 | | 80 c. black and red | 75 | 50 |

**1940.** Air.

| No. | Type | Description | Unused | Used |
|---|---|---|---|---|
| 912. | **199.** | 15 c. orange | 75 | 25 |
| 913. | | 20 c. green | 90 | 15 |
| 914. | | 25 c. violet | 1·10 | 30 |
| 915. | – | 30 c. brown | 1·25 | 25 |
| 916. | – | 1 col. black | 4·75 | 35 |

DESIGN: 30 c., 1 col. Coffee tree in fruit.

**200.** Dr. Lindo, Gen. Mallespin and New National University of El Salvador.

**1941.** Air. Cent. of El Salvador University.

| No. | Type | Description | Unused | Used |
|---|---|---|---|---|
| 917. | **200.** | 20 c. red and green | 75 | 50 |
| 918. | – | 40 c. orange and blue | 75 | 50 |
| 919. | – | 60 c. brown and violet | 75 | 50 |
| 920. | – | 80 c. green and red | 2·75 | 2·00 |
| 921. | – | 1 col. orange and black | 2·75 | 2·00 |
| 922. | **200.** | 2 col. purple and orange | 2·75 | 2·00 |

PORTRAITS: 40 c., 80 c. Dr. N. Monterey and A. J. Canas. 60 c., 1 col. Dr. I. Menendez and Dr. C. Salazar.

**201.** Map of El Salvador.

DESIGN: 8 c. Patron Saint and Cathedral of San Salvador, in medallions.

**1942.** 1st National Eucharistic Congress. Inscr. "NOVIEMBRE 1942".

| No. | Type | Description | Unused | Used |
|---|---|---|---|---|
| 923. | – | 8 c. blue (postage) | 40 | 25 |
| 924. | **201.** | 30 c. orange (air) | 40 | 30 |

**1943.** Air. Surch. in large figures.

| No. | Type | Description | Unused | Used |
|---|---|---|---|---|
| 925. | **195.** | 15 on 15 c. black & yell. | 35 | 30 |
| 926. | | 20 on 30 c. blk. & brown | 40 | 30 |
| 927. | | 25 on 40 c. black & blue | 50 | 35 |

**1944.** Air. Surch. in small figures.

| No. | Type | Description | Unused | Used |
|---|---|---|---|---|
| 928. | **195.** | 15 on 15 c. black & yell. | 25 | 20 |
| 929. | | 20 on 30 c. black & brn. | 40 | 30 |
| 930. | | 25 on 40 c. black & blue | 50 | 30 |

**205.** Cuscatlan Bridge.

**1944.** Optd. with small shield.

| No. | Type | Description | Unused | Used |
|---|---|---|---|---|
| 931. | **205.** | 8 c. blk. & blue (post.) | 20 | 15 |
| 932. | | 30 c. blk. & red (air) | 45 | 25 |

**206.** Presidential Palace.

**207.** General J. J. Canas.

**1944.** Air.

| No. | Type | Description | Unused | Used |
|---|---|---|---|---|
| 933. | **206.** | 15 c. mauve | 15 | 10 |
| 934. | – | 20 c. green | 25 | 10 |
| 935. | – | 25 c. purple | 25 | 10 |
| 936. | – | 30 c. red | 25 | 10 |
| 937. | – | 40 c. blue | 35 | 25 |
| 938. | – | 1 col. black | 75 | 35 |

DESIGNS: 20 c. National Theatre. 25 c. National Palace. 30 c. Mayan Pyramid. 40 c. Public Gardens. 1 col. Aeronautics School.

**1945.** General J. J. Canas (author of National Anthem).

| No. | Type | Description | Unused | Used |
|---|---|---|---|---|
| 939. | **207.** | 8 c. blue | 15 | 10 |

**1945.** No. 893 surch. **1.**

| No. | Type | Description | Unused | Used |
|---|---|---|---|---|
| 940. | | 1 c. on 2 c. green | 15 | 10 |

**1945.** Air. Optd. **Aereo.**

| No. | Type | Description | Unused | Used |
|---|---|---|---|---|
| 942. | | 1 col. black (No. 900) | 65 | 25 |

**210.** Juan Ramon Uriarte.

**211.** Alberto Masferrer.

**1945.** Air. J. R. Uriarte, former Director General of Posts.

| No. | Type | Description | Unused | Used |
|---|---|---|---|---|
| 943. | **210.** | 12 c. blue | 25 | 15 |
| 944. | | 14 c. orange | 25 | 10 |

**1945.** Air. Alberto Masferrer (writer).

| No. | Type | Description | Unused | Used |
|---|---|---|---|---|
| 945. | **211.** | 12 c. red | 25 | 15 |
| 946. | | 14 c. green | 25 | 10 |

**212.** Lake of Ilapango.

**215.** Isidro Menendez.

**1946.**

| No. | Type | Description | Unused | Used |
|---|---|---|---|---|
| 947. | **212.** | 1 c. blue | 10 | 10 |
| 948. | – | 2 c. green | 25 | 10 |
| 949. | – | 5 c. red | 15 | 10 |

DESIGNS: 2 c. Ceiba tree. 5 c. Water carriers (larger).

**1947.**

| | | | | |
|---|---|---|---|---|
| 950 | 215 | 1 c. red | 10 | 10 |
| 951 | – | 2 c. yellow (Salazar) | 10 | 10 |
| 952 | – | 3 c. violet (Bertis) | 10 | 10 |
| 953 | – | 5 c. grey (Duenas) | 10 | 10 |
| 954 | – | 8 c. blue (Belloso) | 10 | 10 |
| 955 | – | 10 c. bistre (Trigueros) | 15 | 10 |
| 956 | – | 20 c. green (Gonzalez) | 25 | 15 |
| 957 | – | 50 c. black (Castaneda) | 45 | 25 |
| 958 | – | 1 col. red (Castro) | 1·00 | 35 |

217. Alfredo Espino.

218. M. J. Arce.

**1947.** Air.

| | | | | |
|---|---|---|---|---|
| 959. | – | 12 c. brown (F. Soto) | 25 | 15 |
| 960. | 217. | 14 c. blue | 20 | 10 |

**1948.** Death Cent. of M. J. Arce.

| | | | | |
|---|---|---|---|---|
| 961. | 218. | 8 c. blue (postage) | 20 | 15 |
| 962. | | 12 c. green (air) | 20 | 15 |
| 963. | | 14 c. red | 25 | 15 |
| 964. | | 1 col. purple | 2·00 | 1·60 |

219. Mackenzie King, Roosevelt and Churchill.

220. Franklin D. Roosevelt.

DESIGNS—HORIZ. 5 c., 14 c. Pres. Roosevelt bestowing decorations. 8c 25 c. Pres and Mrs. Roosevelt. 20 c. (2) Pres. Roosevelt and Secretary Hull. 50 c., 2 col. Pres. Roosevelt's funeral.

**1948.** 3rd Death Anniv. of Franklin D. Roosevelt.

| | | | | |
|---|---|---|---|---|
| 965. | – | 5 c. blk. & bl. (post.) | 15 | 10 |
| 966. | – | 8 c. black and green | 15 | 10 |
| 967. | 220. | 12 c. black and violet | 25 | 15 |
| 968. | 219. | 15 c. black and red | 25 | 15 |
| 969. | – | 20 c. black and lake | 35 | 30 |
| 970. | – | 50 c. black and grey | 55 | 45 |
| 971. | 220. | 12 c. blk. & grn. (air) | 40 | 25 |
| 972. | – | 14 c. black and olive | 40 | 25 |
| 973. | – | 20 c. black and brown | 40 | 35 |
| 974. | – | 25 c. black and red | 40 | 40 |
| 975. | 219. | 1 col. black and purple | 1·00 | 60 |
| 976. | – | 2 col. black and lilac | 2·00 | 1·25 |

**1948.** Air. Optd. **Aereo.**

| | | | |
|---|---|---|---|
| 977. | 5 c. grey (No. 953) | 10 | 10 |
| 978. | 10 c. bistre (No. 955) | 15 | 10 |
| 979. | 1 col. red (No. 958) | 1·40 | 80 |

**1949.** Air. No. 936 surch. **10.**

| | | | |
|---|---|---|---|
| 980. | 10 c. on 30 c. red | 20 | 10 |

222. Torch and Wings.

**1949.** 75th Anniv. of U.P.U.

| | | | | |
|---|---|---|---|---|
| 981. | 222. | 8 c. blue (postage) | 50 | 25 |
| 982. | | 5 c. brown (air) | 15 | 10 |
| 983. | | 10 c. black | 25 | 10 |
| 984. | | 1 col. violet | 8·50 | 8·50 |

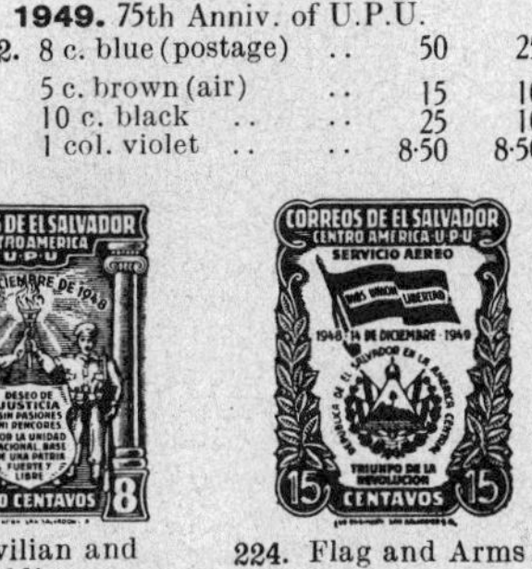

223. Civilian and Soldier. 224. Flag and Arms.

**1949.** 1st Anniv. of Revolution. (a) Postage.

| | | | | |
|---|---|---|---|---|
| 985. | 223. | 8 c. blue | 30 | 10 |

(b) Air. Centres in blue and yellow.

| | | | | |
|---|---|---|---|---|
| 986. | 224. | 5 c. brown | 15 | 10 |
| 987. | | 10 c. green | 25 | 10 |
| 988. | | 15 c. violet | 30 | 10 |
| 989. | | 1 col. red | 40 | 25 |
| 990. | | 5 col. purple | 3·75 | 2·75 |

225. Isabella the Catholic.

**1951.** Air. 500th Birth Anniv. of Isabella the Catholic. Backgrounds in blue, red and yellow.

| | | | | |
|---|---|---|---|---|
| 991. | 225. | 10 c. green | 40 | 10 |
| 992. | | 20 c. violet | 40 | 20 |
| 993. | | 40 c. red | 40 | 20 |
| 994. | | 1 col. brown | 90 | 40 |

226.

227.

**1952.** 1948 Revolution and 1950 Constitution. (a) Postage. Wreath in green.

| | | | | |
|---|---|---|---|---|
| 995. | 226. | 1 c. green | 10 | 10 |
| 996. | | 2 c. purple | 10 | 10 |
| 997. | | 5 c. brown | 10 | 10 |
| 998. | | 10 c. yellow | 10 | 10 |
| 999. | | 20 c. green | 20 | 15 |
| 1000. | | 1 col. red | 70 | 55 |

(b) Air. Flag in blue.

| | | | | |
|---|---|---|---|---|
| 1001. | 227. | 10 c. blue | 10 | 10 |
| 1002. | | 15 c. brown | 20 | 10 |
| 1003. | | 20 c. blue | 20 | 10 |
| 1004. | | 25 c. grey | 20 | 10 |
| 1005. | | 40 c. violet | 40 | 30 |
| 1006. | | 1 col. orange | 50 | 30 |
| 1007. | | 2 col. brown | 1·75 | 1·25 |
| 1008. | | 5 col. blue | 1·75 | 65 |

**1952.** Surch. in figures and words (No. 1009) or in figures only (remainder). (a) Postage.

| | | | | |
|---|---|---|---|---|
| 1009. | – | 2 c. on 3 c. violet (952) | 10 | 10 |
| 1010. | – | 2 c. on 8 c. blue (954) | 15 | 10 |
| 1011. | – | 2 c. on 12 c. brn. (959) | 15 | 10 |
| 1012. | 217. | 2 c. on 14 c. blue | 15 | 10 |
| 1013. | – | 3 c. on 8 c. blue (954) | 15 | 10 |
| 1014. | – | 5 c. on 8 c. blue (954) | 15 | 10 |
| 1015. | – | 5 c. on 12 c. brn. (959) | 15 | 10 |
| 1016. | – | 7 c. on 8 c. blue (954) | 15 | 10 |
| 1017. | 217. | 10 c. on 14 c. blue | 15 | 15 |
| 1018. | – | 10 c. on 50 c. blk. (957) | 20 | 15 |

(b) Air.

| | | | | |
|---|---|---|---|---|
| 1019. | – | 20 c. on 25 c. pur. (935) | 25 | 20 |

230. Jose Marti.

232. Signing Act of Independence.

233. Campanile of Our Saviour.

234. General Barrios.

**1953.** Birth Cent. of Marti.

| | | | | |
|---|---|---|---|---|
| 1020. | 230. | 1 c. red (postage) | 10 | 10 |
| 1021. | | 2 c. green | 15 | 10 |
| 1022. | | 10 c. blue | 15 | 10 |
| 1023. | | 10 c. violet (air) | 20 | 15 |
| 1024. | | 20 c. brown | 20 | 15 |
| 1025. | | 1 col. orange | 50 | 30 |

**1953.** 4th Pan-American Social Medicine Congress. Nos. 952 and 953 optd. **"IV Congreso Medico Social Panamericano 16/19 Abril, 1953".**

| | | | |
|---|---|---|---|
| 1026. | 3 c. violet (postage) | 15 | 10 |
| 1027. | 25 c. purple (air) | 40 | 25 |

**1953.** Independence.

| | | | | |
|---|---|---|---|---|
| 1028. | 232. | 1 c. red (postage) | 10 | 10 |
| 1029. | | 2 c. turquoise | 10 | 10 |
| 1030. | | 3 c. violet | 10 | 10 |
| 1031. | | 5 c. blue | 10 | 10 |
| 1032. | | 7 c. brown | 10 | 10 |
| 1033. | | 10 c. ochre | 10 | 10 |
| 1034. | | 20 c. orange | 25 | 20 |
| 1035. | | 50 c. green | 60 | 25 |
| 1036. | | 1 col. grey | 90 | 65 |
| 1037. | 233. | 5 c. red (air) | 10 | 10 |
| 1038. | | 10 c. turquoise | 10 | 10 |
| 1039. | | 20 c. blue | 20 | 15 |
| 1040. | | 1 col. violet | 50 | 35 |

**1953.** Optd. **C de C.**

| | | | | |
|---|---|---|---|---|
| 1041. | 234. | 1 c. green | 10 | 10 |
| 1042. | | 2 c. blue | 10 | 10 |
| 1043. | – | 3 c. green | 10 | 10 |
| 1044. | 234. | 5 c. red | 10 | 10 |
| 1045. | – | 7 c. blue | 15 | 10 |
| 1046. | – | 10 c. red | 15 | 10 |
| 1047. | 234. | 20 c. violet | 20 | 15 |
| 1048. | – | 22 c. violet | 25 | 20 |

PORTRAIT: 3 c., 7 c., 10 c., 22 c. Gen. Morazan.

235. 236.

237. General Barrios Square.

238. Balboa Park.

**1954.**

| | | | | |
|---|---|---|---|---|
| 1049. | A. | 1 c. red & olive (post.) | 10 | 10 |
| 1050. | 237. | 1 c. violet | 10 | 10 |
| 1051. | B. | 1 c. olive and green | 10 | 10 |
| 1052. | 235. | 2 c. red | 15 | 10 |
| 1053. | 236. | 2 c. red | 15 | 10 |
| 1054. | 237. | 2 c. green and blue | 15 | 10 |
| 1055. | F. | 3 c. slate and blue | 15 | 10 |
| 1056. | C. | 3 c. green and blue | 15 | 10 |
| 1057. | I. | 3 c. lake | 15 | 10 |
| 1058. | F. | 5 c. violet and blue | 15 | 10 |
| 1059. | I. | 5 c. green | 15 | 10 |
| 1060. | C. | 7 c. brown and buff | 15 | 10 |
| 1061. | B. | 7 c. green and blue | 20 | 10 |
| 1062. | 238. | 7 c. red and brown | 15 | 10 |
| 1063. | G. | 10 c. blue, brown & red | 15 | 10 |
| 1064. | 236. | 10 c. turquoise | 15 | 10 |
| 1065. | D. | 10 c. lake and pink | 35 | 15 |
| 1066. | H. | 20 c. orange and buff | 80 | 35 |
| 1067. | E. | 22 c. blue | 45 | 35 |
| 1068. | J. | 50 c. black and drab | | |
| 1069. | G. | 1 col. blue, brown and chestnut | 90 | 55 |
| 1070. | E. | 1 col. blue | 90 | 35 |
| 1071. | 235. | 5 c. red (air) | 20 | 10 |
| 1072. | B. | 5 c. brown and buff | 30 | 10 |
| 1073. | G. | 10 c. blue, green and emerald | 25 | 10 |
| 1074. | 237. | 10 c. olive and grey | 25 | 10 |
| 1075. | E. | 10 c. red | 40 | 10 |
| 1076. | 238. | 10 c. violet and brown | 25 | 10 |
| 1077. | I. | 10 c. blue | 30 | 10 |
| 1078. | D. | 15 c. slate and blue | 40 | 15 |
| 1079. | A. | 20 c. violet and slate | 45 | 15 |
| 1080. | E. | 25 c. green and blue | 70 | 15 |
| 1081. | H. | 30 c. red and pink | 45 | 15 |
| 1082. | J. | 40 c. chestnut & brown | 50 | 35 |
| 1083. | 236. | 80 c. lake | 1·00 | 65 |
| 1084. | C. | 1 col. red and pink | 1·25 | 65 |
| 1085. | 236. | 2 col. orange | 2·25 | 65 |

DESIGNS—$32\frac{1}{2} \times 22\frac{1}{2}$ mm: A, Litoral Bridge. B, Fishing boats. C, Izalco Volcano and Atecosol Baths. D, Lake Ilopango and Apulo Baths. E, "Fle-Ja-Lis" (coastguard cutter). $37\frac{1}{2} \times 22\frac{1}{2}$ mm: F, Guayabo Dam. G, Six Prime Ministers and flag of O.D.E.C.A. H, Workers' houses. $22\frac{1}{2} \times 32\frac{1}{2}$ mm: I, Gen. Arce. $21 \times 25\frac{1}{2}$ mm: J, Sonsonate–Puerto Acajutla Highway.

239. Captain General Barrios.

240. Gathering Coffee Beans.

**1956.**

| | | | | |
|---|---|---|---|---|
| 1086. | 239. | 1 c. red (postage) | 10 | 10 |
| 1087. | | 2 c. green | 15 | 10 |
| 1088. | | 3 c. blue | 15 | 10 |
| 1089. | | 20 c. violet | 20 | 15 |
| 1090. | | 20 c. brown (air) | 20 | 15 |
| 1091. | | 30 c. lake | 25 | 25 |

**1956.** Cent. of Santa Ana.

| | | | | |
|---|---|---|---|---|
| 1092. | 240. | 3 c. brown (postage) | 10 | 10 |
| 1093. | | 5 c. orange | 15 | 10 |
| 1094. | | 10 c. blue | 20 | 15 |
| 1095. | | 2 col. red | 1·25 | 75 |
| 1096. | | 5 c. brown (air) | 10 | 10 |
| 1097. | | 10 c. green | 10 | 10 |
| 1098. | | 40 c. purple | 25 | 20 |
| 1099. | | 80 c. green | 45 | 30 |
| 1100. | | 5 col. slate | 2·50 | 1·50 |

241.

242. Arms of Nueva San Salvador.

**1956.** Centenary of Chalatenango Province.

| | | | | |
|---|---|---|---|---|
| 1101. | 241. | 2 c. blue (postage) | 15 | 10 |
| 1102. | | 7 c. red | 35 | 25 |
| 1103. | | 50 c. brown | 55 | 40 |
| 1104. | | 10 c. red (air) | 10 | 10 |
| 1105. | | 15 c. orange | 15 | 10 |
| 1106. | | 20 c. olive | 15 | 10 |
| 1107. | | 25 c. lilac | 35 | 25 |
| 1108. | | 50 c. brown | 55 | 35 |
| 1109. | | 1 col. blue | 60 | 50 |

**1957.** Centenary of Nueva San Salvador City.

| | | | | |
|---|---|---|---|---|
| 1110. | 242. | 1 c. red (postage) | 10 | 10 |
| 1111. | | 2 c. green | 10 | 10 |
| 1112. | | 3 c. violet | 10 | 10 |
| 1113. | | 7 c. orange | 35 | 35 |
| 1114. | | 10 c. blue | 15 | 10 |
| 1115. | | 50 c. brown | 40 | 40 |
| 1116. | | 1 col. red | 60 | 50 |
| 1117. | | 10 c. salmon (air) | 15 | 10 |
| 1118. | | 20 c. red | 20 | 10 |
| 1119. | | 50 c. red | 35 | 30 |
| 1120. | | 1 col. green | 60 | 35 |
| 1121. | | 2 col. red | 1·50 | 90 |

**1957.** Surch.

| | | | | |
|---|---|---|---|---|
| 1121a. | 242. | 1 c. on 2 c. green | 10 | 10 |
| 1121b. | | 5 c. on 7 c. orange | 20 | 15 |
| 1122. | C. | 6 c. on 7 c. brown and buff (No. 1060) | 25 | 15 |
| 1123. | B. | 6 c. on 7 c. green and blue (No. 1061) | 30 | 15 |
| 1124. | 241. | 6 c. on 7 c. red | 20 | 10 |
| 1125. | 242. | 6 c. on 7 c. orange | 25 | 15 |

244. Salvador Hotel.

**1958.** Salvador Hotel Commem. Centre mult., frame colour below.

| | | | | |
|---|---|---|---|---|
| 1126. | 244. | 3 c. brown | 10 | 10 |
| 1127. | | 6 c. red | 10 | 10 |
| 1128. | | 10 c. blue | 10 | 10 |
| 1129. | | 15 c. green | 15 | 10 |
| 1130. | | 20 c. violet | 25 | 15 |
| 1131. | | 30 c. green | 35 | 25 |

245. Presidents Eisenhower and Lemus.

**1959.** Visit of Pres. Lemus to U.S. Flags in red and blue. Portraits in brown.

| | | | | |
|---|---|---|---|---|
| 1132. | 245. | 3 c. pink & blue (post.) | 15 | 10 |
| 1133. | | 6 c. green and blue | 15 | 10 |
| 1134. | | 10 c. red and blue | 20 | 10 |
| 1135. | | 15 c. orge. & blue (air) | 20 | 15 |
| 1136. | | 20 c. green and blue | 25 | 15 |
| 1137. | | 30 c. red and blue | 35 | 25 |

**1960.** 20th Anniv. of Salvador Philatelic Society. Optd. **5 Enero 1960 XX Aniversario Fundacion Sociedad Filatelica de El Salvador.**

| | | | | |
|---|---|---|---|---|
| 1138. | 242. | 2 c. green | 10 | 10 |

**1960.** Air. World Refugee Year. Optd. **ANO MUNDIAL DE LOS REFUGIADOS 1959-1960.**

| | | | | |
|---|---|---|---|---|
| 1139. | 240. | 10 c. green | 25 | 20 |

248. Block of Flats.

249. Poinsettias.

**1960.** "I.V.U." Building Project. Centres multicoloured.

| | | | | |
|---|---|---|---|---|
| 1140. | 248. | 10 c. red | 10 | 10 |
| 1141. | | 15 c. purple | 15 | 10 |
| 1142. | | 25 c. green | 20 | 15 |
| 1143. | | 30 c. turquoise | 25 | 15 |
| 1144. | | 40 c. olive | 35 | 25 |
| 1145. | | 80 c. blue | 55 | 45 |

**1960.** Christmas. Flowers in yellow, red and green. Background colours given.

| | | | | |
|---|---|---|---|---|
| 1146. | 249. | 3 c. yellow (postage) | 10 | 10 |
| 1147. | | 6 c. orange | 15 | 10 |
| 1148. | | 10 c. blue | 20 | 10 |
| 1149. | | 15 c. blue | 25 | 15 |
| 1150. | | 20 c. mauve (air) | 35 | 15 |
| 1151. | | 30 c. grey | 40 | 25 |
| 1152. | | 40 c. grey | 40 | 35 |
| 1153. | | 50 c. salmon | 65 | 35 |

250. Fathers Nicolas, Vincent and Manuel Aguilar.

**1961.** 150th Anniv. of Patriots' Revolution against Spain.
1154. **250.** 1 c. sepia and grey .. 10 10
1155. 2 c. brown and pink .. 10 10
1156. – 5 c. green and brown 15 10
1157. – 6 c. sepia and mauve 15 10
1158. – 10 c. sepia and blue 15 10
1159. – 20 c. sepia and violet 25 10
1160. – 30 c. mauve and blue 35 15
1161. – 40 c. sepia and brown 50 20
1162. – 50 c. sepia & turquoise 70 40
1163. – 80 c. blue and grey .. 1·00 60
DESIGNS: 5 c., 6 c. Manuel Arce, Jose Delgado and Juan Rodriguez. 10 c., 20 c. Pedro Castillo, Domingo de Lara and Santiago Celis. 30 c., 40 c. Parochial Church of San Salvador, 1808. 50 c., 80 c. Monument, Plaza Libertad.

**1962.** 3rd Central American Industrial Exn. Nos. 1048, 1069, 1116 and 1121 optd. **"III Exposicion Industrial Centroamericana Diciembre de 1962".** Nos. 1166/7 additionally optd. **AEREO.**
1165. – 22 c. violet (postage) 20 15
1166. G. 1 col. blue, brown and chestnut (air) .. 50 45
1167. **242.** 1 col. red .. .. 50 45
1168. 2 col. red .. .. 1·00 85

**1962.** Nos. 1161/2, 1141 and 1070 surch.
1169. – 6 c. on 40 c. sepia and brown .. .. 25 10
1170. – 6 c. on 50 c. sepia and turquoise .. .. 25 10
1164. **248.** 10 c. on 15 c. purple .. 25 10
1171. E. 10 c. on 1 col. blue .. 30 10

**1963.** Surch. in figures.
1172. **248.** 6 c. on 15 c. pur. (post.) 25 10
1173. – 10 c. on 50 c. sepia and turquoise (No. 1162) 25 10
1174. – 10 c. on 80 c. blue and grey (No. 1163) (air) 25 10
1175. **242.** 10 c. on 1 col. green .. 1·10 15
1176. **249.** 10 c. on 30 c. grey .. 15 10
1177. **242.** 10 c. on 1 col. red (No. 1167) .. .. 15 15
1178. **242.** 10 c. on 2 col. red (No. 1168) .. .. 1·10 10

**1963.** Freedom from Hunger. No. 1161 optd. **CAMPANA MUNDIAL CONTRA EL HAMBRE** and Campaign emblem.
1179. 40 c. sepia and brown .. 60 40

**259.** Coyote. **260.** Statue of Christ on Globe.

**1963.** Fauna. Multicoloured.
1180. 1 c. Type **259** (postage) 25 10
1181. 2 c. Black spider monkey 25 10
1182. 3 c. Common racoon .. 25 10
1183. 5 c. King vulture .. 1·00 20
1184. 6 c. Northern coati .. 25 10
1185. 10 c. Kinkajou .. .. 25 10
1186. 5 c. As No. 1183 (air) .. 1·00 20
1187. 6 c. Yellow-crowned amazon .. .. 1·00 20
1188. 10 c. Spotted-breasted oriole .. .. 1·00 20
1189. 20 c. Turquoise-browed motmot .. .. 1·40 30
1190. 30 c. Great-tailed grackle .. .. 1·75 40
1191. 40 c. Great curassow .. 2·75 50
1192. 50 c. White-throated magpie-jay .. 3·25 60
1193. 80 c. Golden-fronted woodpecker .. .. 5·50 1·50
The 2 c. and 5 c. postage and 5 c., 6 c., 40 c. and 80 c. air stamps are vert.

**1964.** 2nd National Eucharistic Congress San Salvador.
1194. **260.** 6 c. bl. & brn. (post.) 10 10
1195. 10 c. blue and bistre .. 10 10
1196. 10 c. slate & blue (air) 10 10
1197. 25 c. blue and red .. 20 15

**261.** President Kennedy. **262.** Water-lily.

**1964.** Pres. Kennedy Commem.
1198. **261.** 6 c. black & stone (post.) 10 10
1199. 10 c. black and drab .. 15 10
1200. 50 c. black and pink 50 30
1201. 15 c. black & grey (air) 20 15
1202. 20 c. black and green 25 15
1203. 40 c. black and yellow 40 30

**1965.** Flora. Multicoloured.
1204. 3 c. Type **262** (postage) .. 10 10
1205. 5 c. "Maquilishuat" .. 10 10
1206. 6 c. "Cinco Negritos" .. 10 10
1207. 30 c. Hydrangea .. .. 20 15
1208. 50 c. "Maguey" .. 60 25
1209. 60 c. Geranium .. .. 70 25
1210. 10 c. Rose (air) .. .. 10 10
1211. 15 c. "Platanillo" .. 15 10
1212. 25 c. "San Jose" .. 20 15
1213. 40 c. Hibiscus .. .. 25 25
1214. 45 c. Bougainvillea .. 40 25
1215. 70 c. "Flor de Fuego" .. 55 45

**263.** I.C.Y. Emblem. **265.** F. A. Gavidia (philosopher).

**1965.** Int. Co-operation Year. Laurel in gold.
1216. **263.** 5 c. brn. & yell. (post.) 10 10
1217. 6 c. brown and red 10 10
1218. 10 c. brown and grey 10 10
1219. 15 c. brn. & blue (air) 10 10
1220. 30 c. brown and violet 25 15
1221. 50 c. brown and orange 35 30

**1965.** Death Cent. of Captain General Barrios. No. 1163 optd. **1 er. Centenario Muerte Cap. Gral. Gerardo Barrios 1865 29 de Agosto 1965.**
1222. 80 c. blue and grey .. 70 40

**1965.** Gavidia Commem.
1223. **265.** 2 c. multicoloured (post.) 15 10
1224. 3 c. multicoloured .. 15 10
1225. 6 c. multicoloured .. 15 10
1226. 10 c. multicoloured (air) 15 10
1227. 20 c. multicoloured .. 25 15
1228. 1 col. multicoloured .. 90 40

**1965.** Birth Cent. of Dr. M. E. Araujo. Optd. **1865 12 de Octubre 1965 Dr. Manuel Enrique Araujo.** Laurel in gold.
1229. **263.** 10 c. brn. & grey (post.) 10 10
1230. 50 c. brown & orge. (air) 45 30

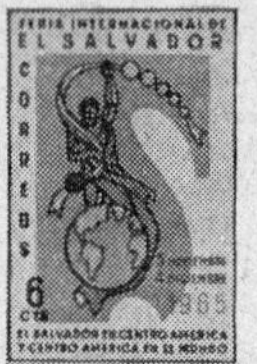

**267.** Fair Emblem. **268.** W.H.O. Building.

**1965.** Int. Fair, El Salvador.
1231. **267.** 6 c. mult. (postage) .. 10 10
1232. 10 c. multicoloured .. 10 10
1233. 20 c. multicoloured .. 20 15
1234. 20 c. multicoloured (air) 15 10
1235. 80 c. multicoloured .. 50 30
1236. 5 col. multicoloured .. 2·50 1·75

**1966.** Inaug. of W.H.O. Headquarters, Geneva.
1237. **268.** 15 c. mult. (postage) 15 10
1238. 50 c. multicoloured (air) 45 30

**1966.** Air. 150th Birth Anniv. of St. Juan Bosco. No. 1197 optd. **1816 1966 150 anos Nacimiento San Juan Bosco.**
1239. **260.** 25 c. blue and red .. 35 25

**1966.** Civic Commem. of Independence Month No. 1163 optd. **Mes de Conmemoracion Civica de la Independencia. Centroamericana 15 Sept. 1821 1966.**
1240. 80 c. ultramarine and grey 55 45

**271.** U.N.E.S.C.O. Emblem.

**1966.** 20th Anniv. of U.N.E.S.C.O.
1241. **271.** 20 c. blue, grey and black (postage) .. 15 15
1242. 1 col. blue, green and black .. .. 60 30
1243. 30 c. blue, brown and black (air) .. .. 35 15
1244. 2 col. blue, green and black .. .. 1·25 75

**272.** Map, Cogwheels and Flags.

**1966.** 2nd Int. Fair, El Salvador.
1245. **272.** 6 c. mult. (postage) .. 10 10
1246. 10 c. multicoloured .. 10 10
1247. 15 c. multicoloured (air) 15 10
1248. 20 c. multicoloured .. 20 15
1249. 60 c. multicoloured .. 50 35

**1967.** Air. 9th Int. Catholic Education Congress No. 1197 optd. **IX-Congreso Interamericano de Educacion Catolica 4 Enero 1967.**
1250. **260.** 25 c. blue and red .. 35 20

**274.** Father Canas pleading for Slaves.

**1967.** Birth Centenary of Father J. S. Canas y Villacorta (slavery emancipator).
1251. **274.** 6 c. mult. (postage) .. 10 10
1252. 10 c. multicoloured .. 10 10
1253. 5 c. mult. (air) .. 10 10
1254. 45 c. multicoloured .. 55 35

**1967.** 15th Lions Convention El Salvador. No. 1161 optd. **"XV Convencion de Clubes de Leones etc.".**
1255. 40 c. sepia and brown .. 45 20

**276.** Central Design of First El Salvador Stamp.

**1967.** Stamp Cent.
1256. **276.** 70 c. brn. & mve. (post.) 75 60
1257. 50 c. brn. & olive (air) 50 30

**1967.** 8th Central-American Pharmaceutical and Biochemical Congress. Nos. 1237/8 optd. **VIII CONGRESO CENTROAMERICANO,** etc.
1258. **268.** 15 c. mult. (postage) 15 10
1259. 50 c. mult. (air) .. 45 30

**1967.** 1st Central American and Caribbean Basket-ball Games, San Salvador. Nos. 1204 and 1212 optd. **1 Juegos Centroamericanos,** etc.
1260. **262.** 3 c. mult. (postage) .. 10 10
1261. – 25 c. mult. (air) .. 25 15

**1968.** Human Rights Year. Nos. 1216, 1220 optd. **1968 AÑO INTERNACIONAL DE LOS DERECHOS HUMANOS.**
1262. **263.** 5 c. mult. (postage) .. 10 10
1263. 30 c. mult. (air) .. 40 25

**280.** Weather Map, Satellite and W.M.O. Emblem.

**1968.** World Meteorological Day.
1264. **280.** 1 c. multicoloured .. 10 10
1265. 30 c. multicoloured .. 30 15

**1968.** 20th Anniv. of W.H.O. Nos. 1237/8 optd. **1968 XX ANIVERSARIO DE LA ORGANIZATION MUNDIAL DE LA SALUD.**
1266. **268.** 15 c. mult. (postage) 20 10
1267. 50 c. mult. (air) .. 50 25

**1968.** Rural Credit Year. Nos. 1231, 1235 optd. **1968 Ano del Sistema de Credito Rural.**
1268. **267.** 6 c. mult. (postage) .. 10 10
1269. 80 c. mult. (air) .. 50 40

**283.** A. Masferrer (philosopher). **284.** Building Construction ("Service to the Community").

**1968.** Birth Cent. of Alberto Masferrer.
1270. **283.** 2 c. mult. (postage) .. 10 10
1271. 6 c. multicoloured .. 10 10
1272. 25 c. multicoloured .. 35 15
1273. 5 c. multicoloured (air) 10 10
1274. 15 c. multicoloured .. 15 10

**1968.** 7th Inter-American Scout Conf., San Salvador.
1275. **284.** 25 c. mult. (postage) 25 15
1276. – 10 c. multicoloured (air) 10 10
DESIGN—HORIZ. 10 c. Scouts and Conference emblem.

**285.** Map, Presidents and Flags.

**1968.** Meeting of President Lyndon B. Johnson (U.S.A.) with Central American Presidents, San Salvador.
1277. **285.** 10 c. mult. (postage) 10 10
1278. 15 c. multicoloured .. 15 10
1279. 20 c. mult. (air) .. 15 10
1280. 1 col. multicoloured .. 55 50

**286.** "Heliconius charithonius".

**1969.** Butterflies. Multicoloured.
1281. 5 c. Type **286** (postage) .. 10 10
1282. 10 c. "Diaethria astala" 15 10
1283. 30 c. "Heliconius hortense" 40 20
1284. 50 c. "Pyrrhogyra arge" .. 55 35
1285. 20 c. "Ageronia amphinome" (air) .. .. 25 10
1286. 1 col. "Smyrna karkwinskii" 1·10 50
1287. 2 col. "Papilio photinus" 2·10 1·10
1288. 10 col. "Papilio consus" .. 9·75 5·00

**287.** Red Cross Activities.

**1969.** 50th Anniv. of League of Red Cross Societies. Multicoloured.
1289. 10 c. Type **287** (postage) 10 10
1290. 20 c. Type **287** .. 15 10
1291. 40 c. Type **287** .. .. 25 15
1292. 30 c. Red Cross emblems (air) .. .. 25 15
1293. 1 col. As No. 1292 .. 60 45
1294. 4 col. As No. 1292 .. 2·40 1·75
Nos. 1292/4 are smaller size 34 × 25 mm.

**1969.** 1st Man on the Moon. Nos. 1200 and 1203 (Kennedy) optd. **"Alunzaje Apolo-11 21 Julio 1969".**
1295. **261.** 50 c. black & pink (post.) 40 25
1297. 40 c. blk. & yellow (air) 30 20

**289.** Social Security Hospital. **290.** I.L.O. Emblem.

**1969.** Salvador Hospitals. Multicoloured.
1299. 6 c. Type **289** (postage) .. 10 10
1300. 10 c. Type **289** .. .. 10 10
1301. 30 c. Type **289** .. .. 25 15
1302. 1 col. Benjamin Bloom Children's Hospital, San Salvador (air) .. .. 60 45
1303. 2 col. As No. 1302 .. 1·25 70
1304. 5 col. As No. 1302 .. 3·00 1·75

**1969.** 50th Anniv. of I.L.O.
1305. **290.** 10 c. mult. (postage) 10 10
1306. 50 c. multicoloured (air) 40 25

**291.** Los Chorros Baths.

**1969.** Tourism. Multicoloured.
1307. 10 c. Type **291** (postage) 10 10
1308. 40 c. Jaltepeque estuary 60 25
1309. 80 c. Fountains Amapulapa .. .. 70 45
1310. 20 c. Devil's Gate (air) .. 15 10
1311. 35 c. Gardens, Ichanmichen .. .. 25 15
1312. 60 c. Port of Acajutla .. 50 25

**292.** "Euchroma gigantea".

**1970.** Insects. Multicoloured.
1313 5 c. Type **292** (postage) .. 10 10
1314 25 c. "Pterophylla sp" .. 15 15
1315 30 c. "Chlorion cyaneum" 30 20
1316 2 col. "Eulema dimidiata" (air) .. .. .. 2·00 95
1317 3 col. "Elaterida" .. 2·75 1·50
1318 4 col. "Tenodora sinensis" 3·50 2·00

**293.** Map, Emblem and Arms.

**1970.** "Human Rights".
1319. **293.** 10 c. mult. (postage) 10 10
1320. 40 c. multicoloured .. 45 20
1321. – 20 c. multicoloured (air) 15 10
1322. – 80 c. multicoloured .. 50 40
**Designs—vert.** Nos. 1321/2 are similar to Type **293**.

**294.** Infantry with National Flag.

**1970.** Army Day. Multicoloured.
1323 10 c. Type **294** (postage) 10 10
1324 30 c. Anti-aircraft gun position .. .. 30 15
1325 20 c. Fighter aircraft (air) 15 10
1326 40 c. Artillery gun and crew .. .. .. 35 15
1327 50 c. "Nohaba" (coast-guard patrol boat) .. 1·25 35

**295.** Brazilian Team.

**1970.** Air. World Cup Football Championships, Mexico. National Teams. Mult.
1328. 1 col. Belgium .. .. 70 50
1329. 1 col. Type **295** .. .. 70 50
1330. 1 col. Bulgaria .. .. 70 50
1331. 1 col. Czechoslovakia .. 70 50
1332. 1 col. El Salvador .. 70 50
1333. 1 col. England .. .. 70 50
1334. 1 col. West Germany .. 70 50
1335. 1 col. Israel .. .. 70 50
1336. 1 col. Italy .. .. 70 50
1337. 1 col. Mexico .. .. 70 50
1338. 1 col. Morocco .. .. 70 50
1339. 1 col. Peru .. .. 70 50
1340. 1 col. Rumania .. .. 70 50
1341. 1 col. Russia .. .. 70 50
1342. 1 col. Sweden .. .. 70 50
1343. 1 col. Uruguay .. .. 70 50

**296.** Lottery Building. **297.** Education Year and U.N. Emblems.

**1970.** Cent. of National Lottery.
1344. **296.** 20 c. multicoloured (postage) .. .. 20 10
1345. 80 c. multicoloured (air) .. .. 50 35

**1970.** Int. Education Year.
1346. **297.** 50 c. multicoloured (postage) .. .. 40 15
1347. 1 col. multicoloured .. 60 40
1348. 20 c. multicoloured (air) 15 10
1349. 2 col. multicoloured .. 1·25 70

**298.** Globe and Fair Symbols.

**1970.** 4th International Fair, El Salvador.
1350. **298.** 5 c. multicoloured (postage) .. .. 10 10
1351. 10 c. multicoloured .. 10 10
1352. 20 c. multicoloured (air) .. .. 25 10
1353. 30 c. multicoloured .. 35 15

**1970.** Cent. of National Library. Nos. 1272/3 optd. **Ano del Centenario de la Biblioteca Nacional 1970.**
1354. **283.** 25 c. mult. (postage) 20 15
1355. 5 c. mult. (air) .. 10 10

**300.** Beethoven and Music.

**1971.** 2nd Int. Music Festival, San Salvador.
1356. **300.** 50 c. brn., yell & green (postage) .. .. 45 25
1357. – 40 c. multicoloured (air) 45 25
**Design:** 40 c. Bach, manuscript and harp.

**301.** Maria Elena Sol. **302.** Michelangelo's "Pieta".

**1971.** Maria Elena Sol's Election as "World Tourism Queen", Punta del Este, Uruguay.
1358. **301.** 10 c. mult. (postage) 10 10
1359. 30 c. multicoloured .. 25 15
1360. 20 c. mult. (air) .. 15 10
1361. 60 c. multicoloured .. 40 30

**1971.** Mothers' Day.
1362. **302.** 10 c. purple and pink (postage) .. .. 10 10
1363. 40 c. pur. & grn (air) 45 20

**1971.** 104th Anniv. of Nat. Police Force. Nos. 1320/1 optd. **1867, C. I. V. Aniversario Fundacion de La Policia Nacional 6-Julio, 1971.**
1364. **293.** 40 c. mult. (postage) 45 25
1365. – 20 c. mult. (air) .. 25 10

**304.** Tiger Shark.

**1971.** Fishes. Multicoloured.
1366. 10 c. Type **304** (postage) 10 10
1367. 40 c. Swordfish .. .. 25 15
1368. 30 c. Sawfish (air) .. 25 10
1369. 1 col. Sailfish .. .. 50 40

**305.** Izalco Church.

**1971.** Churches. Multicoloured.
1370. 20 c. Type **305** (postage) 25 10
1371. 30 c. Sonsonate Church .. 40 15
1372. 15 c. Metapan Church (air) 15 10
1373. 70 c. Panchimalco Church 45 25

**1971.** Air. 20th Anniv. of El Salvador Navy. No. 1327 optd. **1951-12 Octubre-1971 XX Aniversario MARINA NACIONAL.**
1374. 50 c. multicoloured .. 70 30

**307.** Declaration of Independence.

**1971.** 150th Anniv. of Central American Independence.
1375. **307.** 5 c. blk. & grn. (post.) 10 10
1376. – 10 c. black and pur. 10 10
1377. – 15 c. black and red .. 10 10
1378. – 20 c. black & mauve 15 10
1379. – 30 c. blk. & blue (air) 25 15
1380. – 40 c. black & brown .. 40 20
1381. – 50 c. black & yellow .. 30 25
1382. – 60 c. black and grey .. 40 35
**Designs:** Nos. 1376/82 as Type **307**, but showing different manuscripts.

**1972.** Air. 5th Int. Fair, El Salvador. No. 1235 optd. **V Feria Internacional 3-20 Noviembre de 1972.**
1384. **267.** 80 c. multicoloured .. 1·25 40

**1972.** American Tourist Year. No. 1359 optd. **1972. Ano del Turismo de las Americas.**
1385. **301.** 30 c. multicoloured 25 10

**1972.** Air. 30th Anniv. of Inter-American Agricultural Science Institute. No. 1221 optd. **1972-XXX Anniversario Creacion Instituto Interamericano de Ciencias Agricolas.**
1386. **263.** 50 c. multicoloured 30 25

**1973.** 3rd Int. Music Festival. Nos. 1356/7 optd. **III Festival Internacional de Musica 9 - 25 Febrero - 1973.**
1387. **300.** 50 c. brn., yell. & grn. (postage) .. .. 35 20
1388. – 40 c. multicoloured (air) 40 20

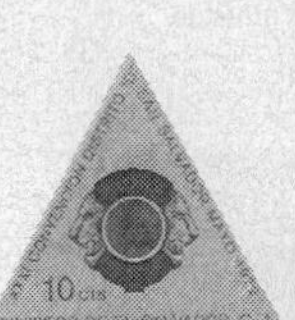

**312.** Lions Emblem. **318.** Institute Emblem.

**314.** Hurdling.

**1973.** 31st Convention of Lions International District D.
1389. **312.** 10 c. mult. (post.) .. 10 10
1390. 25 c. multicoloured .. 15 10
1391. – 20 c. mult. (air) .. 20 10
1392. – 40 c. multicoloured .. 40 15
**Design:** 20 c., 40 c., Map of Central America.

**1973.** 50th Anniv. of El Salvador Air Force. No. 1324 optd. **1923 1973 50 ANOS FUNDACION FUERZA AEREA.**
1393. 30 c. multicoloured .. 25 15

**1973.** Olympic Games, Munich (1972). Multicoloured.
1394. 5 c. Type **314** (postage) .. 10 10
1395. 10 c. High-jumping .. 10 10
1396. 25 c. Running .. .. 15 10
1397. 60 c. Pole-vaulting .. 35 20
1398. 20 c. Throwing the javelin (air) .. .. .. 15 10
1399. 80 c. Throwing the discus 45 35
1400. 1 col. Throwing the hammer 55 40
1401. 2 col. Putting the shot 1·10 65

**1973.** Nos. 1256/7 surch.
1402. **276.** 10 c. on 70 c. brown and mauve (post.) 10 10
1403. 25 c. on 50 c. brown and olive (air) .. 15 10

**1973.** 150th Anniv. of Slaves' Liberation in Central America. Nos. 1251 and 1254 surch. **1823–1973 150 Aniversario Liberacion Esclavos en Centroamerica** and value.
1404. **274.** 5 c. on 6 c. multicoloured 10 10
1405. 10 c. on 45 c. multicoloured 10 10
No. 1405 has the word "AEREO" obliterated.

**1974.** Nos. 1198 and 1238 surch.
1407. **261.** 5 c. on 6 c. black and stone (postage) .. 10 10
1408. **268.** 25 c. on 50 c. multicoloured (air) .. 15 10

**1974.** 10th Anniv. of Institute for the Rehabilitation of Invalids.
1409. **318.** 10 c. multicoloured (post.) 10 10
1410. 25 c. multicoloured (air) 15 10

**1974.** Air. No. 1235 surch.
1411. **267.** 10 c. on 80 c. mult... 10 10

**1974.** Air. West Germany's Victory in World Cup Football Championships. Nos. 1328/43 optd. **ALEMANIA 1974.**
1412. 1 col. Belgium .. .. 60 50
1413. 1 col. Type **158** .. .. 60 50
1414. 1 col. Bulgaria .. .. 60 50
1415. 1 col. Czechoslovakia .. 60 50
1416. 1 col. El Salvador .. 60 50
1417. 1 col. England .. .. 60 50
1418. 1 col. West Germany .. 60 50
1419. 1 col. Israel .. .. 60 50
1420. 1 col. Italy .. .. 60 50
1421. 1 col. Mexico .. .. 60 50
1422. 1 col. Morocco .. .. 60 50
1423. 1 col. Peru .. .. 60 50
1424. 1 col. Rumania .. .. 60 50
1425. 1 col. Russia .. .. 60 50
1426. 1 col. Sweden .. .. 60 50
1427. 1 col. Uruguay .. .. 60 50

**1974.** No. 1271 surch.
1428. **283.** 5 c. on 6 c. multicoloured 10 10

**322.** Interpol Headquarters Paris. **323.** F.A.O. and W.F.P. Emblems.

**1974.** 50th Anniv. of Int. Criminal Police Organization (Interpol).
1429. **322.** 10 c. multicoloured (post.) 10 10
1430. 25 c. multicoloured (air) 15 10

**1974.** 10th Anniv. of World Food Programme.
1431. **323.** 10 c. gold, turquoise & blue (postage) .. 10 10
1432. 25 c. gold, turquoise & blue (air) .. .. 15 10

**1974.** Surch.
1432a. **271.** 25 c. on 1 col. blue, grn. & blk. (postage) 15 10
1433. **276.** 10 c. on 50 c. brown & olive (air) .. .. 10 10
1434. **271.** 25 c. on 2 col. blue, green and black .. 45 25

**1974.** 12th Central American and Caribbean Chess Tournament. Surch. **XII Serie Ajedrez de Centro America y del Caribe Oct. 1974.**
1435 **265** 5 c. on 6 c. mult .. 10 10

**1974.** Surch.
1436. **289.** 5 c. on 6 c. mult. (postage) .. .. 10 10
1437. **265.** 10 c. on 3 c. mult. .. 10 10
1438. – 10 c. on 45 c. mult. (No. 1214) (air) .. 10 10
1439. – 10 c. on 70 c. mult. (No. 1215) .. 10 10
1440. – 25 c. on 2 col. mult. (No. 1287) .. 20 10
1441. – 25 c. on 1 col. mult. (No. 1293) .. 20 15
1442. – 25 c. on 4 col. mult. (No. 1294) .. 20 15
1443. – 25 c. on 5 col. mult. (No. 1304) .. 20 15

**327.** 25-cent Silver Coin, 1914.

**1974.** El Salvador Coins. Multicoloured.
1445. 10 c. Type **327** (postage) .. 10 10
1446. 15 c. 50-cent silver coin, 1953 .. .. .. 10 10
1447. 25 c. 25-cent silver coin, 1943 .. .. .. 15 10
1448. 30 c. 1-centavo copper coin, 1892 .. .. 15 10
1449. 20 c. 1-peso silver coin, 1892 (air) .. .. 10 10
1450. 40 c. 20-cent silver coin, 1828 .. .. .. 20 15
1451. 50 c. 20-peso gold coin, 1892 .. .. .. 25 20
1452. 60 c. 20-col gold coin, 1925 35 25

**328.** U.P.U. Emblem.

**1975.** Centenary of U.P.U.

1453. **328.** 10 c. mult. (postage) .. 10 10
1454. 60 c. multicoloured .. 35 20
1455. 25 c. mult. (air) .. 15 10
1456. 30 c. multicoloured .. 15 15

**329.** Acajutla Harbour. **331.** Central Post Office, San Salvador.

**1975.** Opening of Acajutla Port.

1457. **329.** 10 c. mult. (post.) .. 10 10
1458. 15 c. mult. (air) .. 10 10

**1975.**

1459. **331.** 10 c. mult. (postage) 10 10
1460. 25 c. mult. (air) .. 15 10

**332.** Map of El Salvador and the Americas.

**1975.** " Miss Universe " Contest.

1461. **332.** 10 c. mult. (postage) 10 10
1462. 40 c. multicoloured .. 35 25
1463. 25 c. mult. (air) .. 25 15
1464. 60 c. multicoloured .. 50 35

**333.** Claudia Lars (poet). **334.** Nurses with Patient.

**1975.** International Women's Year.

1465. **333.** 10 c. blue & yellow (post.) 10 10
1466. 15 c. blue & light blue (air) .. .. 10 10
1467. – 25 c. blue & green .. 15 10

DESIGN: 25 c. I.W.Y. emblem.

**1975.** Honouring Nursing Profession.

1468. **334.** 10 c. mult. (postage) 10 10
1469. 25 c. mult. (air) .. 25 15

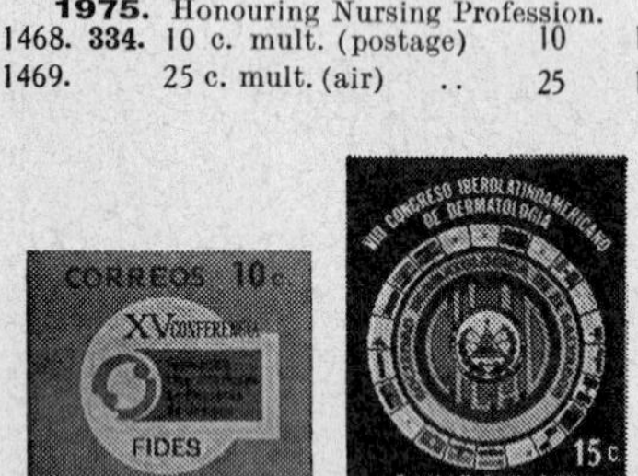

**335.** Conference Emblem. **337.** Congress Emblem and Flags.

**1975.** 15th Conference of Inter-American Security Printers Federation, San Salvador.

1470. **335.** 10 c. mult. (postage) 10 10
1471. 30 c. mult. (air) .. 15 15

**1975.** 16th Central American Medical Congress, San Salvador. Optd. **XVI CONGRESO MEDICO CENTRO-AMERICANO SAN SALVADOR, EL SALVADOR DIC. 10-13, 1975.**

1472. **268.** 15 c. multicoloured .. 15 10

**1975.** 8th Ibero-Latin-American Dermatological Congress, El Salvador.

1473. **337.** 15 c. mult. (postage) 10 10
1474. 50 c. multicoloured .. 25 20
1475. 20 c. mult. (air) .. 15 10
1476. 30 c. multicoloured .. 15 15

**338.** Congress Emblem. **339.** U.N.I.C.E.F. Emblem.

**1975.** 7th Latin-American Charity Congress, San Salvador.

1477. **338.** 10 c. brn & red (post.) 10 10
1478. 20 c. light bl. & bl. (air) 15 10

**1975.** Air. 25th Anniv. (1971) of U.N.I.C.E.F.

1479. **339.** 15 c. silver & green .. 10 10
1480. 20 c silver and red .. 15 10

**1976.** Air. Nos. 1316/18 surch.

1481. 25 c. on 2 col. mult. .. 20 15
1482. 25 c. on 3 col. mult. .. 20 15
1483. 25 c. on 4 col. mult. .. 20 15

**341.** " Caularthron bilamellatum ". **343.** Map of El Salvador.

**1976.** Air. Orchids. Multicoloured.

1484. 25 c. Type **341** .. .. 20 10
1485. 25 c. " Oncidium oliganthum " .. .. 20 10
1486. 25 c. " Epidendrum radicans " .. .. 20 10
1487. 25 c. " Cyrtopodium punctatum " .. .. 20 10
1488. 25 c. " Epidendrum vitellinum " .. .. 20 10
1489. 25 c. " Pleurothallis schiedei " .. .. 20 10
1490. 25 c. " Lycaste cruenta " 20 10
1491. 25 c. " Spiranthes speciosa " .. .. 20 10

**1976.** " Cencamex '76 " 3rd Nurses' Congress. **III CONGRESO ENFERMERIA CENCAMEX '76.**

1492. **334.** 10 c. multicoloured .. 10 10

**1976.** 10th Anniv. of Central Inter-American Tax-collectors Association.

1493. **343.** 10 c. multicoloured (postage) .. .. 10 10
1494. 50 c. multicoloured (air) .. .. 25 20

**344.** Torch and Flags of El Salvador and U.S.A.

**1976.** Bicent. of American Revolution. Mult.

1495. 10 c. Type **344** (postage) 10 10
1496. 40 c. " Spirit of '76 " (A. M. Willard) (vert.) 20 15
1497. 25 c. Type **344** (air) .. 15 10
1498. 5 col. As 40 c. .. .. 2·25 1·50

**345.** "Crocodylus acutus".

**1976.** Reptiles. Multicoloured.

1499. 10 c. Type **345** (postage) 10 10
1500. 20 c. "Iguana iguana rhinolopha" .. .. 10 10
1501. 30 c. "Ctenosaura similis" .. .. 20 15
1502. 15 c. "Sceloporus malachiticus" (air) .. 10 10
1503. 25 c. "Basiliscus vittatus" 15 10
1504. 60 c. "Anolis sp." .. 35 25

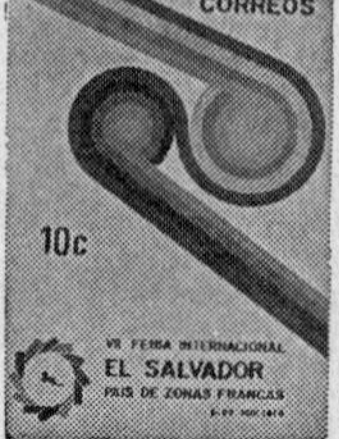

**346.** Fair Emblem. **347.** Post-classical. Lead Vase (San Salvador).

**1976.** 7th International Fair.

1505. **346.** 10 c. mult. (post.) 10 10
1506. 30 c. multicoloured .. 15 10
1507. 25 c. multicoloured (air) 15 10
1508. 70 c. multicoloured .. 35 25

**1976.** Pre-Columbian Art. Multicoloured.

1509. 10 c. Type **347** (postage) 10 10
1510. 15 c. Brazier with classical effigy (Tazumal) .. 10 10
1511. 40 c. Vase with classical effigy (Tazumal) .. 20 15
1512. 25 c. Brazier with pre-classical effigy (El Trapiche) (air) .. .. .. 15 10
1513. 50 c. Kettle with pre-classical effigy (Atiquizaya) 25 20
1514. 70 c. Classical whistling vase (Tazumal) .. 35 30

**348.** Child beside Christmas Tree. **349.** Rotary Emblem on Map of El Salvador.

**1976.** Christmas.

1515. **348.** 10 c. mult. (post.) 10 10
1516. 15 c. multicoloured .. 10 10
1517. 30 c. multicoloured .. 15 10
1518. 40 c. multicoloured .. 20 15
1519. 25 c. multicoloured (air) 15 10
1520. 50 c. multicoloured .. 25 20
1521. 60 c. multicoloured .. 35 25
1522. 75 c. multicoloured .. 40 30

**1977.** 50th Anniv. of San Salvador Rotary Club.

1523. **349.** 10 c. gold, bl. & blk. (postage) .. .. 10 10
1524. 15 c. multicoloured .. 15 10
1525. 25 c. mult. (air) .. 25 15
1526. 1 col. multicoloured .. 60 50

**350.** Hydro-electric Station, Cerron Grande.

**1977.** Industrial Development. Multicoloured.

1527. 10 c. Type **350** (postage) 10 10
1528. 10 c. Sugar refinery, Jiboa .. .. 10 10
1529. 15 c. As No. 1528 .. 10 10
1530. 30 c. Radar station, Izalco (vert.) .. 15 10
1531. 25 c. As No. 1530 (air) .. 15 10
1532. 50 c. As No. 1528 .. 25 20
1533. 75 c. Type **192** .. 40 30

**1977.** Surch.

1534. **283.** 15 c. on 2 c. multicoloured (postage) 10 10
1535. **274.** 25 c. on 6 c. mult. .. 15 10
1536. – 25 c. on 80 c. mult. (No. 1322) (air) .. 30 15
1537. **274.** 30 c. on 5 c. mult. .. 20 15
1538. 40 c. on 5 c. mult. .. 25 15
1539. 50 c. on 5 c. mult. .. 25 20

**352.** Microphone and A.S.D.E.R. Emblem.

**1977.** 50th Anniv. of Broadcasting in El Salvador.

1540. **352.** 10 c. mult. (post.) .. 10 10
1541. 15 c. multicoloured .. 10 10
1542. 20 c. mult. (air) .. 20 10
1543. 25 c. multicoloured .. 25 15

**353.** King, Pawn and Championship Emblem. **354.** Basketball.

**1977.** Air. El Salvador's Victory in Arab Chess Olympiad, Tripoli.

1544. **353.** 25 c. multicoloured .. 15 10
1545. 50 c. multicoloured .. 25 25

**1977.** Air. 2nd Central American Games, San Salvador. Multicoloured.

1546. 10 c. Type **354** .. .. 10 10
1547. 10 c. Football .. .. 10 10
1548. 15 c. Javelin throwing .. 10 10
1549. 15 c. Weightlifting .. 10 10
1550. 20 c. Boxing (horiz.) .. 10 10
1551. 20 c. Volleyball .. .. 10 10
1552. 25 c. Baseball .. .. 15 10
1553. 25 c. Softball (horiz.) .. 15 10
1554. 30 c. Swimming (horiz.) .. 15 10
1555. 30 c. Fencing (horiz.) .. 15 10
1556. 40 c. Cycle-racing (horiz.) 20 15
1557. 50 c. Rifle-shooting (horiz.) .. .. 25 20
1558. 50 c. Tennis (horiz.) .. 25 20
1559. 60 c. Judo .. .. 35 25
1560. 75 c. Wrestling (horiz.) .. 40 30
1561. 1 col. Gymnastics (horiz.) 55 40
1562. 1 col. Horse-jumping (horiz.) .. .. .. 55 40
1563. 2 col. Table-tennis (horiz.) 1·10 80

**1978.** Air. Centenary of Chalchuapa City. No. 1514 optd. **CENTENARIO CIUDAD DE CHALCHUAPA 1878-1978.**

1565. 70 c. Classical whistling vase (Tazumal) .. 35 30

**356.** Map of South America and Emblem.

**1978.** Air. World Cup Football Championship, Argentina.

1566. **356.** 25 c. multicoloured .. 15 10
1567. 60 c. multicoloured .. 35 20
1568. 5 col. multicoloured 2·40 2·00

**357.** Wooden Drum.

**1978.** Musical Instruments. Multicoloured.

1569. 5 c. Type **357** (postage) 10 10
1570. 10 c. Flutes .. .. 10 10
1571. 25 c. Drum (vert.) (air) .. 15 10
1572. 50 c. Rattles .. .. 25 20
1573. 80 c. Xylophone .. 45 30

**358.** " Man and Engineering ".

**1978.** 4th National Engineers' Congress. San Salvador.

1574. **358.** 10 c. mult. (post.) .. 10 10
1575. 25 c. mult. (air) .. 15 10

**359.** Dish Aerials.

**1978.** Inauguration of Izalco Satellite Earth Station.

1576. **359.** 10 c. mult. (post.) 10 10
1577. 75 c. multicoloured (air) 40 30

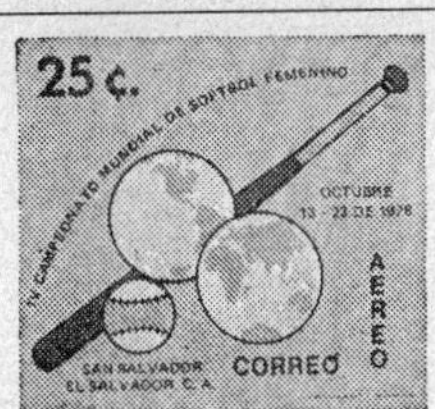

**360.** Softball, Bat and Hemispheres.

**1978.** Air. 4th Women's Softball Championships, San Salvador.
1578. **360.** 25 c. multicoloured . . 15 10
1579. 1 col. multicoloured 55 40

**361.** Henri Dunant. **362.** Fair Poster.

**1978.** 150th Birth Anniv. of Henri Dunant (founder of Red Cross).
1580. **361.** 10 c. yellow, black & red (postage) . . 10 10
1581. 25 c. turquoise, black and red (air) . . 15 10

**1978.** 8th International Fair.
1582. **362.** 10 c. mult. (post.) . . 10 10
1583. 20 c. multicoloured . . 10 10
1584. 15 c. multicoloured (air) 10 10
1585. 25 c. multicoloured . . 15 10

**363.** Globe as Cotton Boll.

**1978.** 37th Plenary Session of Cotton Growers' Association, San Salvador.
1586. **363.** 15 c. mult. (post.) 10 10
1587. 40 c. multicoloured (air) 25 15

**364.** " Nativity with Angel " (stained glass window).

**1978.** Christmas.
1588. **364.** 10 c. mult. (post.) 10 10
1589. 15 c. multicoloured . . 10 10
1590. 25 c. mult. (air). 15 10
1591. 1 col. multicoloured . . 55 40

**365.** Arms of Salvador Athenium.

**1978.** Millenary of Castilian Language.
1592. **365.** 5 c. mult. (post.) . . 10 10
1593. 25 c. mult. (air). . . 15 10

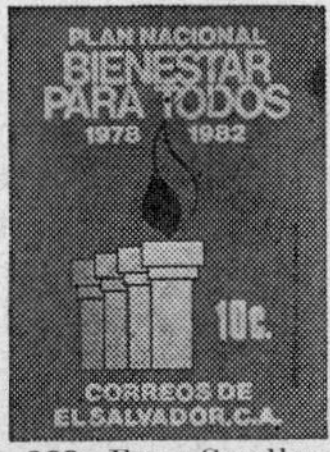

**366.** Four Candles.

**1979.** Four Year Plan " Welfare for All ".
1594. **366.** 10 c. mult. (post.) 10 10
1595. 15 c. multicoloured . . 10 10
1596. 25 c. mult. (air). . . 15 10
1597. 1 col. multicoloured . . 55 40

**367.** Torch and Letter beside U.P.U. Statue.

**1979.** Centenary of U.P.U. Membership.
1598. **367.** 10 c. multicoloured (postage) . . . . 10 10
1599. 75 c. multicoloured (air) . . . . 40 30

**368.** Emblem and " 75 ". **369.** I.S.S.S. Emblem.

**1979.** 75th Anniv. of Pan-American Health Organization.
1600. **368.** 10 c. turq. and yell. (postage) . . . . 10 10
1601. 25 c. turq. & rose (air) 15 10

**1979.** Air. 25th Anniv. of Social Insurance Institute (I.S.S.S.).
1602. **369.** 25 c. blue and black . . 15 10
1603. 60 c. mauve and black 35 25

**370.** Pope John Paul II and Map of Americas. **371.** Games Emblem.

**1979.** Pope John Paul II. Multicoloured.
1604. 10 c. Type **370** (postage) 10 10
1605. 20 c. Type **370** . . 15 10
1606. 60 c. Pope John Paul II and Aztec pyramid (air) . . . . 35 25
1607. 5 col. As 60 c. . . . . 2·75 2·10

**1979.** Air. 8th Panamerican Games, Puerto Rico.
1608. **371.** 25 c. multicoloured . . 15 10
1609. 40 c. multicoloured . . 25 20
1610. 70 c. multicoloured . . 40 30

**372.** Mastodon. **373.** J. Cauas (lyric writer) and Chorus of Anthem.

**1979.** Prehistoric Animals. Multicoloured.
1611. 10 c. Type **372** (postage) 10 10
1612. 20 c. Sabre-toothed Tiger 15 10
1613. 30 c. Toxodon . . . . 15 15
1614. 15 c. Mammoth (air) . . 10 10
1615. 25 c. Giant Sloth (vert.) 15 15
1616. 2 col. Hyenas . . . . 1·10 70

**1979.** Centenary of National Anthem.
1617. 10 c. Type **373** (postage) 10 10
1618. 40 c. J. Aberle (composer) and score (air) 25 15

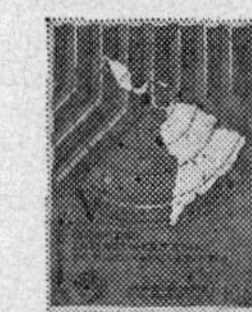

**374.** Cogwheel encircling Central America. **376.** Map of Central and South America.

**375.** Children of Different Races.

**1979.** 8th Mechanical, Electrical and Allied Trade Engineers' Congress, San Salvador.
1619. **374.** 10 c. multicoloured (postage) . . . . 10 10
1620. 50 c. multicoloured (air) 30 20

**1979.** International Year of the Child.
1621. **375.** 10 c. multicoloured (postage) . . . . 10 10
1622. – 15 c. multicoloured . . 10 10
1623. – 25 c. yell., red & blk. (air) . . . . 15 15
1624. – 30 c. blue and black . . 15 15

DESIGNS—HORIZ. 30 c. S.O.S. Children's Village emblem. VERT. 15 c. Children with nurses. 25 c. Children dancing in circle.

**1979.** 5th Latin American Clinical Biochemistry Congress, San Salvador.
1625. **376.** 10 c. orange, red and black (postage) . . 10 10
1626. 25 c. yellow, red and black (air) . . . . 15 10

**377.** Coffee Bushes in Bloom.

**1979.** 50th Anniv. of Salvador Coffee Association. Multicoloured.
1627. 10 c. Type **377** (postage) 10 10
1628. 30 c. Planting coffee bushes (vert.) . . . . 15 15
1629. 40 c. Coffee beans . . 25 15
1630. 50 c. Picking coffee beans (air) . . . . . . 30 20
1631. 75 c. Drying coffee beans (vert.) . . . . . . 45 30
1632. 1 col. Coffee exports . . 90 45

**378.** Dove, Star and Children holding Candles.

**1979.** Christmas.
1633. **378.** 10 c. multicoloured . . 10 10

**379.** Diseased Animal.

**1980.** Campaign against Foot and Mouth Disease.
1634. **379.** 10 c. multicoloured (postage) . . . . 10 10
1635. 60 c. mult. (air) . . 35 25

**380.** Grand Ark.

**1980.** Shells. Multicoloured.
1636 10 c. Type **380** (postage) 15 10
1637 30 c. "Ostrea iridescens" 30 15
1638 40 c. White-mouthed turritella . . . . 50 20
1639 15 c. Regal murex (air) . . 20 10
1640 25 c. Spiral moon . . 30 15
1641 75 c. Jenner's cowrie . . 85 45
1642 1 col. Prostitute venus . . 1·00 65

**381.** Resplendent Quetzal.

**1980.** Birds. Multicoloured.
1643. 10 c. Type **381** (postage) 50 20
1644. 20 c. Highland guan . . 75 35
1645. 25 c. Emerald toucanet (air) . . . . . . 95 55
1646. 50 c. Barred owl . . 1·40 80
1647. 75 c. Slate-coloured solitaire . . . . . . 1·75 1·10

**382.** " Porthidium godmani ". **383.** Corporation Emblem.

**1980.** Snakes. Multicoloured.
1648. 10 c. Type **382** (postage) 10 10
1649. 20 c. " Agkistrodon bilineatus " . . . . 15 10
1650. 25 c. " Crotalus durissus " (air) . . . . . . 15 10
1651. 50 c. " Micrurus nigrocinctus " . . . . 30 20

**1980.** 50th Anniv. of Corporation of Auditors.
1652. **383.** 15 c. multicoloured (postage) . . . . 10 10
1653. 20 c. multicoloured . . 15 10
1654. 50 c. multicoloured (air) . . . . 30 20
1655. 75 c. multicoloured . . 45 30

**384.** Hands releasing Dove (cartoon by " Nando ").

**1980.** " Man and Peace " Caricature Contest Winner.
1656. **384.** 5 c. blue, black and brown (postage) . . 10 10
1657. 10 c. blue, blk. & yell. 10 10
1658. 25 c. blue, black and green (air) . . . . 15 10
1659. 60 c. blue, blk. & orge. 35 25

**385.** Decade Emblem. **386.** Black-handed Spider Monkey.

**1981.** Air. International Decade for Women.
1660. **385.** 25 c. black and green 15 10
1661. 1 col. black & orange 55 45

**1981.** Air Protected Animals. Multicoloured.
1662. 25 c. Type **386** . . . . 15 10
1663. 40 c. Tropical gar . . 25 20
1664. 50 c. Common iguana . . 30 20
1665. 60 c. Hawksbill turtle . . 35 25
1666. 75 c. Ornate hawk eagle 2·50 75

**387.** Heinrich von Stephan. **389.** Dental Association Emblems.

**1981.** Air. 150th Birth Anniv. of Heinrich von Stephan (founder of U.P.U.).
1667. **387.** 15 c. pink and black 10 10
1668. 2 col. blue and black 1·10 70

**1981.** Air. Nos. 1573 and 1610 surch.
1669. – 50 c. on 80 c. mult. 30 20
1670. 371. 1 col. on 70 c. mult. 55 45

**1981.** 50th Anniv. of El Salvador Dental Society, and 25th Anniv. of Odontological Federation of South America and Panama.
1671. 389. 15 c. green and black (postage) .. .. 10 10
1672. 5 col. blue & blk. (air) 2·40 2·10

390. Eye, Hands and Braille Book. 391. Los Proceres Auditorium.

**1981.** International Year of Disabled People.
1673. 390. 10 c. multicoloured (postage) .. .. 10 10
1674. 25 c. multicoloured (air) 15 10
1675. – 50 c. green and blue 30 20
1676. 390. 75 c. multicoloured .. 45 30
1677. – 1 col. black and blue 55 40
DESIGN: 50 c., 1 col. I.Y.D.P. emblem.

**1981.** 25th Anniv. of Roberto Quinonez National Agricultural College.
1678. 391. 10 c. multicoloured (postage) .. .. 10 10
1679. 50 c. multicoloured (air) 30 20

392. Map of El Salvador and Hand holding Maize. 393. Open Book and El Salvador Flags of 1881 and 1981.

**1981.** World Food Day.
1680. 392. 10 c. multicoloured (postage) .. .. 10 10
1681. 25 c. multicoloured (air) 15 10

**1981.** Air. Centenary of Land Registry Office.
1682. 393. 1 col. blk., bl. & red .. 55 40

394. Boeing 737.

**1981.** Air. 50th Anniv. of "TACA" National Airline.
1683. 394. 15 c. multicoloured .. 15 10
1684. 25 c. multicoloured .. 30 15
1685. 75 c. multicoloured .. 90 50

395. Goalkeeper. 396. Salvador Lyceum.

**1981.** World Cup Football Preliminary Round, Honduras. Multicoloured.
1686. 10 c. Type **395** (postage) 10 10
1687. 40 c. World Cup, football and flags of competing countries .. .. 25 20
1688. 25 c. Type **395** (air) .. 15 10
1689. 75 c. As No. 1687 .. 45 30

**1981.** Centenary of Salvador Lyceum.
1690. 396. 10 c. multicoloured (postage) .. .. 10 10
1691. 25 c. multicoloured (air) 15 10

397. Ceremonial Axe.

**1982.** Pre-columbian Stone Sculptures. Multicoloured.
1692. 10 c. Type **397** (postage) 10 10
1693. 20 c. Sun disc .. .. 15 10
1694. 40 c. Stela of Tazumal .. 25 20
1695. 25 c. Ehecatl (god of the winds) (air) .. .. 15 10
1696. 30 c. Rock mask of jaguar .. .. .. 15 15
1697. 80 c. Flint sculpture .. 50 35

398. Scout Salute, Flag and Globe. 399. Dr. Robert Koch.

**1982.** Boy Scout and Girl Guide Movement. Multicoloured.
1698. 10 c. Type **398** (Scout Movement. 75th anniv.) (postage) .. 10 10
1699. 30 c. Girl guide helping old lady .. .. 15 10
1700. 25 c. Scout and Lord Baden-Powell (125th birth anniv.) (air) .. 15 10
1701. 50 c. Girl Guide with emblem and national flag .. .. .. 30 20

**1982.** Air. Centenary of Discovery of Tubercle Bacillus.
1702. 399. 50 c. multicoloured .. 30 20

400. Emblem and Soldier.

**1982.** Armed Forces.
1703. 400. 10 c. black, green and brown (postage) .. 10 10
1704. 25 c. multicoloured (air) 15 10

401. Converging Lines. 402. Hexagonal Pattern.

**1982.** Air. 25th Anniv. of Confederation of Latin American Tourist Organizations.
1705. 401. 75 c. yell., grn. & blk. 45 30

**1982.** Air. World Telecommunications Day.
1706. 402. 15 c. multicoloured .. 10 10
1707. 2 col. multicoloured 1·10 60

403. Salvador Football Team.

**1982.** World Cup Football Championship, Spain (1st issue). Multicoloured.
1708. 10 c. Type **403** (postage) 10 10
1709. 25 c. As 10 c. but different logo (air) .. 15 10
1710. 60 c. Trophy and map of El Salvador .. .. 35 25
1711. 2 col. National team and results of qualifying rounds. (66 × 45 mm.) 1·10 60

404. Flag of Italy.

405. Fair Poster.

**1982.** Air. World Cup Football Championship, Spain (2nd issue). Multicoloured.

(a) Flags.
1712. 15 c. Type **404** .. .. 10 10
1713. 15 c. West Germany .. 10 10
1714. 15 c. Argentine Republic 10 10
1715. 15 c. England .. .. 10 10
1716. 15 c. Spain .. .. 10 10
1717. 15 c. Brazil .. .. 10 10
1718. 15 c. Poland .. .. 10 10
1719. 15 c. Algeria .. .. 10 10
1720. 15 c. Belgium .. .. 10 10
1721. 15 c. France .. .. 10 10
1722. 15 c. Honduras .. .. 10 10
1723. 15 c. Russia .. .. 10 10
1724. 15 c. Peru .. .. 10 10
1725. 15 c. Chile .. .. 10 10
1726. 15 c. Hungary .. .. 10 10
1727. 15 c. Czechoslovakia .. 10 10
1728. 15 c. Yugoslavia .. .. 10 10
1729. 15 c. Scotland .. .. 10 10
1730. 15 c. Cameroun .. .. 10 10
1731. 15 c. Austria .. .. 10 10
1732. 15 c. El Salvador .. 10 10
1733. 15 c. Kuwait .. .. 10 10
1734. 15 c. Northern Ireland .. 10 10
1735. 15 c. New Zealand .. 10 10

(b) Coat of Arms.
1736. 25 c. Italy .. .. 15 10
1737. 25 c. Poland .. .. 15 10
1738. 25 c. West Germany .. 15 10
1739. 25 c. Algeria .. .. 15 10
1740. 25 c. Argentine Republic 15 10
1741. 25 c. Belgium .. .. 15 10
1742. 25 c. Peru .. .. 15 10
1743. 25 c. Cameroun .. .. 15 10
1744. 25 c. Chile .. .. 15 10
1745. 25 c. Austria .. .. 15 10
1746. 25 c. Hungary .. .. 15 10
1747. 25 c. El Salvador .. 15 10
1748. 25 c. England .. .. 15 10
1749. 25 c. France .. .. 15 10
1750. 25 c. Spain .. .. 15 10
1751. 25 c. Honduras .. .. 15 10
1752. 25 c. Brazil .. .. 15 10
1753. 25 c. Russia .. .. 15 10
1754. 25 c. Czechoslovakia .. 15 10
1755. 25 c. Kuwait .. .. 15 10
1756. 25 c. Yugoslavia .. .. 15 10
1757. 25 c. Northern Ireland .. 15 10
1758. 25 c. Scotland .. .. 15 10
1759. 25 c. New Zealand .. 15 10

(c) 89 × 67 mm.
1760. 5 col. El Salvador team, World Cup and flags of competing countries .. 2·40 1·50

**1982.** 10th International Fair. Mult.
1761. 10 c. Type **405** (postage) 10 10
1762. 15 c. Fair emblem (air) .. 10 10

406. Hand supporting Family. 407. St. Francis with Wolf.

**1983.** Air. World Food Day.
1763. 406. 25 c. multicoloured .. 15 10

**1982.** Air. 800th Birth Anniv. of St. Francis of Assisi.
1764. 407. 1 col. multicoloured 55 45

408. Campaign Emblem. 409. Christmas Retable.

**1982.** Air. National Labour Campaign.
1765. 408. 50 c. multicoloured .. 30 20

**1982.** Christmas. Multicoloured.
1766. 5 c. Type **409** (postage) .. 10 10
1767. 25 c. Christmas triptych (air) .. .. .. 15 10

410. Dance.

**1983.** Pre-columbian Ceramics. Mult.
1768. 10 c. Type **410** (postage) 10 10
1769. 20 c. The sower .. .. 15 10
1770. 25 c. Flying man .. 15 10
1771. 60 c. Archer hunting (left) (air) .. .. .. 35 30
1772. 60 c. Archer hunting (right) 35 30
1773. 1 col. Procession (left) .. 55 45
1774. 1 col. Procession (right) 55 45
Nos. 1771/2 and 1773/4 were issued together, each pair forming a composite design.

411. Papal Arms and Maria Auxiliadora Church.

**1983.** Papal Visit. Multicoloured.
1775. 25 c. Type **411** .. .. 15 10
1776. 60 c. Pope John Paul II and Christ on Globe monument .. .. 35 30

412. Ricardo Aberle.

**1983.** 50th Anniv. of Air Force. Mult.
1777. 10 c. Type **412** .. .. 10 10
1778. 10 c. Air Force emblem .. 10 10
1779. 10 c. Enrico Massi .. 10 10
1780. 10 c. Juan Ramon Munes 20 10
1781. 10 c. American Airforces Co-operation emblem .. 10 10
1782. 10 c. Belisario Salazar .. 20 10

413. "Papilio torquatus" (male).

414. Simon Bolivar.

**1983.** Butterflies. Multicoloured.
1783. 5 c. Type **413** .. .. 10 10
1784. 5 c. "Metamorpha stenelès" .. .. .. 10 10
1785. 10 c. "Papilio torquatus" (female) .. .. 10 10
1786. 10 c. "Anaea marthesia" 10 10
1787. 15 c. "Prepona brooksiana" .. .. .. 15 10
1788. 15 c. "Caligo atreus" .. 15 10
1789. 25 c. Emperor .. .. 30 15
1790. 25 c. "Dismorphia praxinoe" .. .. .. 30 15
1791. 50 c. "Morpho polyphemus" .. .. 70 25
1792. 50 c. "Metamorpha epaphus" .. .. .. 70 25

**1983.** Birth Bicent. of Simon Bolivar.
1793. 414. 75 c. multicoloured .. 45 30

415. Dr. Jose Mendoza (founder).

416. "Rural School" (L.A. Caceres Madrid).

**1983.** 40th Anniv. of Medical College.
1794. 415. 10 c. pink, blk. & grn. 10 10

**1983.** Air. Paintings. Multicoloured.
1795. 25 c. Potters of Paleca" (M. Ortiz Villacorta) .. 15 10
1796. 25 c. Type **416** .. .. 15 10
1797. 75 c. "To the Wash" (Julia Diaz) (vert.) .. 45 30
1798. 75 c. "La Pancha" (Mejia Vides) (vert.) .. .. 45 30
1799. 1 col. "Meanguera del Golfo" (Elas Reyes) (vert.) .. .. .. 1·10 60
1800. 1 col. "The Muleteers" (Noe Canjura) (vert.) 55 45

## MINIMUM PRICE

The minimum price quoted is 10p which represents a handling charge rather than a basis for valuing common stamps. For further notes about prices see introductory pages.

**417.** David J. Guzman (founder).

**418.** Gen Juan Jose Canas and Dr Francisco Duenas.

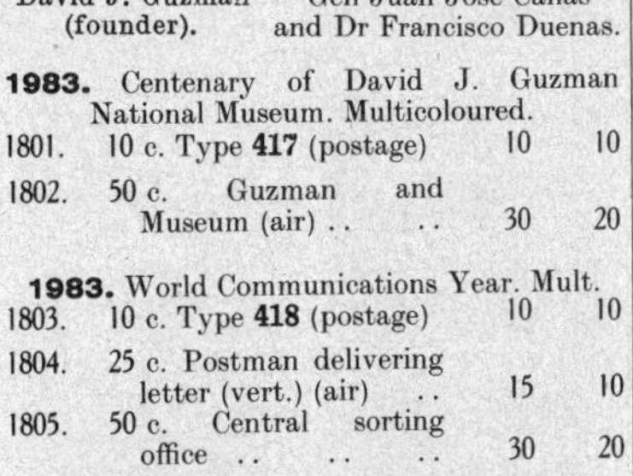

**1983.** Centenary of David J. Guzman National Museum. Multicoloured.

1801. 10 c. Type **417** (postage) 10 10
1802. 50 c. Guzman and Museum (air) .. .. 30 20

**1983.** World Communications Year. Mult.

1803. 10 c. Type **418** (postage) 10 10
1804. 25 c. Postman delivering letter (vert.) (air) .. 15 10
1805. 50 c. Central sorting office .. .. .. 30 20

**419.** Dove and Globe.

**420.** Bus emitting Exhaust Fumes.

**1983.** Christmas. Multicoloured.

1806. 10 c. Type **419** (postage) 10 10
1807. 25 c. Christmas crib (air) 15 10

**1983.** Environmental Protection. Mult.

1808. 10 c. Type **420** (postage) 10 10
1809. 15 c. Fig tree (air) .. 10 10
1810. 25 c. Paca .. .. 20 15

**421.** Fisherman with Catch.

**422.** Tweezers holding First Stamp of El Salvador.

**1983.** Air. Fishery Resources. Multicoloured.

1811. 25 c. Type **421** .. .. 55 20
1812. 75 c. Fish farming .. 55 20

**1984.** Philatelists' Day.

1813. **422.** 10 c. blue, black and orange .. .. 10 10

**423.** Maize.

**424.** Caluco Church.

**1984.** Agricultural Products. Multicoloured.

1814. 10 c. Type **423** .. .. 10 10
1815. 15 c. Cotton .. .. 10 10
1816. 25 c. Coffee .. .. 20 15
1817. 50 c. Sugar .. .. 35 25
1817a. 55 c. Cotton .. .. 20 20
1817b. 70 c. Type **423** .. .. 25 20
1818. 75 c. Kidney bean .. 25 20
1818a. 90 c. Sugar cane .. .. 25 20
1819. 1 col. Agave .. .. 30 25
1819a. 2 col. Beans .. .. 60 50
1820. 5 col. Balsam .. .. 2·40 1·75
1820c. 10 col. Agave .. .. 4·75 3·50

**1984.** Colonial Churches. Multicoloured.

1821. 5 c. Type **424** (postage) 10 10
1822. 10 c. Salcoatitan .. 10 10
1823. 15 c. Huizucar (air) .. 10 10
1824. 25 c. Santo Domingo .. 20 15
1825. 50 c. Pilar .. .. 35 25
1826. 75 c. Nahuizalco .. 40 30

**425.** Banknote.

**426.** Running.

**1984.** 50th Anniv. of General Reserve Bank. Multicoloured.

1827. 10 c. Type **425** (postage) 10 10
1828. 25 c. Bank Building (air) 20 15

**1984.** Olympic Games, Los Angeles. Multicoloured.

1829. 10 c. Boxing (horiz.) (postage) .. .. 10 10
1830. 25 c. Type **426** (air.) .. 20 15
1831. 40 c. Cycling (horiz.) .. 30 20
1832. 50 c. Swimming (horiz.) 35 25
1833. 75 c. Judo .. .. 40 30
1834. 1 col. Pierre de Coubertin (horiz.) .. .. 50 40

**427.** New Building.

**1984.** New Servicios Graficos (Government printer) Building.

1835. **427.** 10 c. multicoloured .. 10 10

**428.** "5th November" Hydro-electric Plant.

**1984.** National Energy Resources. Mult.

1836. 20 c. Type **428** (postage) 10 10
1837. 55 c. "Cerron Grande" Hydro-electric Plant .. 30 20
1838. 70 c. Ahuachapan Geo-thermal Plant (air) .. 40 30
1839. 90 c. Mural, Guajoyo Hydro-electric Plant .. 45 35
1840. 2 col. "15th September" Hydro-electric Plant .. 60 50

**429.** Playing Marbles.

**1984.** Children's Games. Multicoloured.

1841. 55 c. Type **429** .. 30 20
1842. 70 c. Spinning a top .. 40 30
1843. 90 c. Flying a kite .. 45 35
1844. 2 col. "Capirucho" .. 60 50

**430.** Fair Emblem.

**1984.** 11th International Fair, El Salvador. Multicoloured.

1845. 25 c. Type **430** (postage) 15 10
1846. 70 c. Fair building and flags (air) .. .. 40 30

**431.** Los Chorros Tourist Centre.

**1984.** Tourism. Multicoloured.

1847. 15 c. Type **431** .. .. 10 10
1848. 25 c. The Americas Square 15 10
1849. 70 c. El Salvador International Airport .. 70 30
1850. 90 c. El Tunco beach .. 45 35
1851. 2 col. Sihuatehucan Tourist Centre .. 60 50

**432.** "The White Nun" (Salarrue).

**1984.** Paintings. Multicoloured.

1852. 20 c. Type **432** (postage) 10 10
1853. 55 c. "The Paper of Papers" (Roberto Antonio Galicia) (horiz) (air) .. .. 30 20
1854. 70 c. "Supreme Elegy to Masferrer" (Antonio Garcia Ponce) (wrongly inscr "Figuras en Palco") .. 40 30
1854a. 70 c. "Supreme Elegy to Masferrer" (correct inscription) .. .. 40 30
1855. 90 c. "Transmutation" (Armando Solis) (horiz) .. .. .. 45 35
1856. 2 col. "Figures in Theatre Box" (Carlos Canas) (wrongly inscr "Suprema Elegia a Masferrer") .. .. 1·10 90
1856a. 2 col. "Figures in Theatre Box" (correct inscription) .. .. 1·10 90

Nos. 1854a and 1856a are overprinted with the correct inscription.

**433.** Christmas Tree Decoration.

**434.** Spot-crowned Woodcreeper.

**1984.** Christmas. Multicoloured.

1857 25 c. Type **433** (postage) 15 10
1858 70 c. Christmas tree decorations and dove (air) .. .. .. 40 30

**1984.** Birds. Multicoloured.

1859. 15 c. Type **434** (postage) 45 15
1860. 25 c. Slaty finch .. .. 75 40
1861. 55 c. Purple-breasted ground dove (air) .. 1·90 80
1862. 70 c. Tody-motmot .. 2·25 1·25
1863. 90 c. Belted flycatcher .. 1·90 95
1864. 1 col. Red-faced warbler 2·75 1·40

**435.** Emblem and Share Certificate.

**1985.** Centenary of El Salvador Bank.

1865. **435.** 25 c. multicoloured .. 15 10

**436.** Share Certificate and Emblem.

**1985.** 50th Anniv. of El Salvador Mortgage Bank.

1866. **436.** 25 c. multicoloured .. 15 10

**437.** I.Y.Y. Emblem.

**1985.** International Youth Year.

1867. **437.** 25 c. black and green (postage) .. .. 15 10
1868. – 55 c. mult. (air) .. 30 20
1869. – 70 c. mult. .. .. 40 30
1870. – 1 col. 50 mult. .. 50 40

DESIGNS: 55 c. Woodwork class. 70 c. Boys raising tray of equipment by pulley. 1 col. 50, Parade.

**438.** Pre-Classic seated Figurine.

**439.** Red Cross and Hand holding "100".

**1985.** Archaeological Finds. Multicoloured.

1871. 15 c. Type **438** (postage) 10 10
1872. 20 c. Late Classic engraved vase .. 10 10
1873. 25 c. Post-Classic lead animal pot .. .. 15 10
1874. 55 c. Post-classic figurine (air) .. .. .. 30 20
1875. 70 c. Late post-Classic figurine of Xipe Totec 40 30
1876. 1 col. Late post-Classic clay animal on wheels 30 25

**1985.** Cent of El Salvador Red Cross. Mult.

1878 25 c. Type **439** (postage) 15 10
1879 55 c. Red Cross workers and inflatable inshore lifeboat (horiz) (air) .. 70 30
1880 70 c. Blood donor and Red Cross workers (horiz) .. .. 40 30
1881 90 c. Tending injured man 45 35

**440.** Hand holding Pin Figures and Houses.

**1985.** Child Welfare. Multicoloured.

1882. 25 c. Type **440** (postage) 15 10
1883. 55 c. Children outside house (air) .. .. 30 20
1884. 70 c. Children dancing .. 40 30
1885. 80 c. Oral vaccination .. 45 35

**441.** Child and Soldiers on Map.

**1985.** El Salvador Army. Multicoloured.
1886. 25 c. Type **441** (postage) 15 10
1887. 70 c. Armed soldier and flag (air) .. .. 40 30

**442.** Flag, Open Book and Laurel.

**1985.** Election of President Duarte.
1888. **442.** 25 c. multicoloured .. 15 10
1889. – 70 c. black and yell. 40 30
DESIGN: 70 c. Extract from constitution.

**443.** Hydro-electric Station and Emblem.

**1985.** 25th Anniv. of Inter-American Development Bank. Multicoloured.
1890. 25 c. Type **443** (postage) 15 10
1891. 70 c. Emblem and map (air) .. .. .. 25 30
1892. 1 col. Emblem and arms 30 25

**1985.** Air. No. 1829 surch.
1893 1 col. on 10 c. mult .. 55 45

**445.** "Cichlasoma trimaculatum".

**1985.** Fresh Water Fishes. Multicoloured.
1894. 25 c. Type **445** (postage 15 10
1895. 55 c. "Rhamdia guatemalensis" (air) .. 30 20
1896. 70 c. "Poecilia sphenops" 40 30
1897. 90 c. "Cichlasoma nigrofasciatum" .. 45 35
1898. 1 col. "Astyanax fasciatus" .. .. 55 45
1899. 1 col. 50 "Dormitator latifrons" .. .. 85 75

**446.** Food spilling from Basket.

**1985.** 40th Anniv. of Food and Agriculture Organization. Multicoloured.
1900. 20 c. Type **446** .. .. 10 10
1901. 40 c. Centeotl, Nahuat god of maize .. .. 20 15

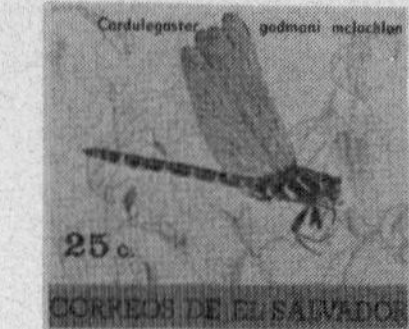


**447.** "Cordulegaster godmani mclachlan".

**1985.** Dragonflies. Multicoloured.
1902. 25 c. Type **447** (postage) 20 15
1903. 55 c. "Libellula herculea karsch" (air) .. .. 45 30
1904. 70 c. "Cora marina selys" 65 45
1905. 90 c. "Aeshna cornigera braver" .. .. 70 50
1906. 1 col. "Mecistogaster ornata rambur" .. 90 60
1907. 1 col. 50 "Hetaerina smaragdalis de marmels" .. .. 1·50 1·00

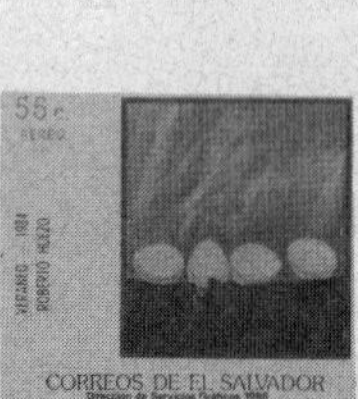
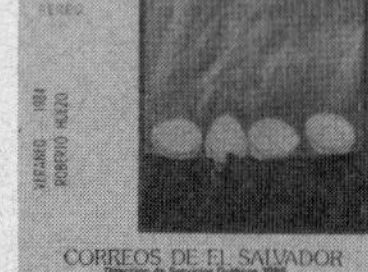


**448.** "Summer Holiday" (Roberto Huezo). **449.** St. Vicente Tower.

**1985.** Paintings. Multicoloured.
1908. 25 c. "Profiles" (Rosa Mena Valenzuela) (vert.) (postage) .. 15 10
1909. 55 c. Type **448** (air) .. 30 20
1910. 70 c. "La Entrega" (Fernando Llort) .. 35 25
1911. 90 c. "For Decorating Pots" (Pedro Acosta Garcia) .. .. 45 35
1912. 1 col. "Still Life" (Miguel Angel Orellana) (vert.) 55 45

**1985.** 350th Anniv. of City of St. Vicente de Austria y Lorenzana. Multicoloured.
1913. 15 c. Type **449** .. .. 10 10
1914. 20 c. St. Vicente Cathedral .. .. 10 10

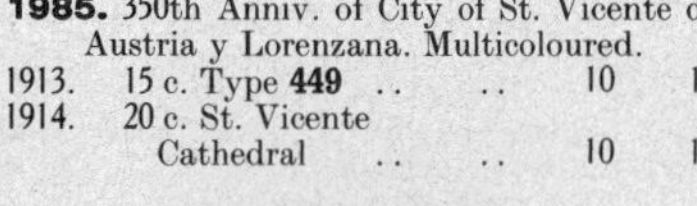

**450.** Emblem.

**1986.** International Peace Year. Mult.
1915. 15 c. Type **450** (postage) 10 10
1916. 70 c. People reaching towards peace dove (air) .. .. .. 20 15

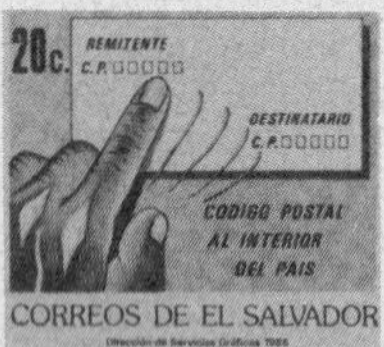


**451.** Hand and Interior Mail Envelope.

**1986.** Introduction of Post Codes. Mult.
1917. 20 c. Type **451** .. .. 10 10
1918. 25 c. Hand and airmail envelope .. .. 10 10

**452.** Microphone.

**1986.** 60th Anniv. of Radio El Salvador. Multicoloured.
1919. 25 c. Type **452** (postage) 10 10
1920. 70 c. "60", map and radio waves (air) .. 20 15

**453.** Margay.

**1986.** Mammals. Multicoloured.
1921. 15 c. Type **453** (postage) 10 10
1922. 20 c. Tamandua .. .. 10 10
1923. 1 col. Nine-banded armadillo (air) .. 30 25
1924. 2 col. Collared peccary .. 95 75

**454.** Flags and Mascot.

**1986.** World Cup Football Championship, Mexico. Multicoloured.
1925. 70 c. Type **454** .. .. 20 15
1926. 1 col. Footballers and Trophy (vert.) .. 30 25
1927. 2 col. Footballer (vert.) 95 75
1928. 5 col. Goal and emblem 2·40 1·90

**455.** Dr. Dario Gonzalez (medicine). **456.** Tlaloc Seal.

**1986.** Teachers (1st series). Multicoloured.
1929. 20 c. Type **455** (postage) 10 10
1930. 20 c. Valero Lecha (art) 10 10
1931. 40 c. Prof. Marcelino Garcia Flamenco .. 10 10
1932. 40 c. Camilo Campos .. 10 10
1933. 70 c. Prof. Saul Flores (educationist) (air) .. 20 15
1934. 70 c. Prof. Jorge Larde (law) .. .. .. 20 15
1935. 1 col. Prof. Francisco Moran .. .. .. 30 25
1936. 1 col. Mercedes Maiti de Luarca .. .. .. 30 25
See also Nos. 1973/80.

**1986.**
1937 **456** 25 c. mult (postage) .. 10 10
1938 55 c. mult (air) .. 15 15
1939 70 c. multicoloured .. 20 15
1940 90 c. multicoloured .. 25 20
1941 1 col. multicoloured .. 30 25
1942 1 col. 50 multicoloured 45 40

**457.** Open Book on "100" as Stand. **458.** "Spathiphyllum phryniifolium".

**1986.** Air. Centenary of Constitution.
1943. **457.** 1 col. multicoloured 30 25

**1986.** Flowers. Multicoloured.
1944. 20 c. Type **458** (postage) 10 10
1945. 25 c. "Asclepias curassavica" (horiz.) .. 10 10
1946. 70 c. "Tagetes tenuifolia" (horiz.) (air) .. 20 15
1947. 1 col. "Ipomoea lilacea" .. .. 30 25

**459.** Unloading Fishing Boat.

**1986.** World Food Day.
1948. **459.** 20 c. multicoloured .. 30 15

**460.** Hugo Lindo. **461.** Emblem.

**1986.** Air. 1st Death Anniv. of Hugo Lindo (writer and poet).
1949. **460.** 1 col. multicoloured 30 25

**1986.** Air. 25th Anniv. of Central American Economic Integration Bank.
1950. **461.** 1 col. 50 black, blue and mauve .. 45 40

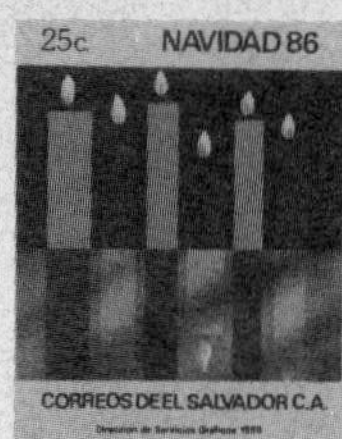


**462.** Candles.

**1986.** Christmas. Multicoloured.
1951. 25 c. Type **462** (postage) 10 10
1952. 70 c. Birds flying towards light (air) .. .. 20 15

**463.** Baskets.

**1986.** Traditional Crafts. Multicoloured.
1953. 25 c. Type **463** .. .. 10 10
1954. 55 c. Pottery .. .. 15 15
1955. 70 c. Guitars (vert.) .. 20 15
1956. 1 col. Eastern reed baskets .. .. 30 25

**464.** "Church" (Mario Araujo Rajo). **465.** Emblem.

**1986.** Paintings. Multicoloured.
1957. 25 c. Type **464** (postage) 10 10
1958. 70 c. "Landscape" (Francisco Reyes) (air) 20 15

**1987.** Air. 12th International Fair, El Salvador.
1959. **465.** 70 c. multicoloured .. 20 15

**466.** Stamps.

**1987.** Philately.
1960. **466.** 25 c. multicoloured .. 15 10

**467.** Maps, Globe and Foodstuffs.

**468.** "Maxillaria tenuifolia".

**1987.** International Solidarity.
1961. **467.** 15 c. multicoloured .. 10 10
1962. 70 c. multicoloured .. 20 15
1963. 1 col. 50 mult .. 40 35
1964. 5 col. multicoloured 1·50 1·00

**1987.** Orchids. Multicoloured.
1965. 20 c. Type **468** (postage) 10 10
1966. 20 c. "Ponthieva maculata" .. .. 10 10
1967. 25 c. "Meiracyllium trinasutum" (horiz.) .. 10 10
1968. 25 c. "Encyclia vagans" (horiz.) .. .. 10 10
1969. 70 c. "Encyclia cochleata" (horiz.) (air) .. .. .. 20 15
1970. 70 c. "Maxillaria atrata" (horiz.) .. .. 20 15
1971. 1 col. 50 "Sobrialia xantholeuca" (horiz.) 40 35
1972. 1 col. 50 "Encyclia microcharis" (horiz.) .. 40 35

**469.** C. de Jesus Alas (music).

**1987.** Teachers (2nd series).
1973. **469.** 15 c. black and blue (postage) .. .. 10 10
1974. – 15 c. black & blue .. 10 10
1975. – 20 c. black & brown 10 10
1976. – 20 c. black & brown 10 10
1977. – 70 c. black & orange (air) .. .. 20 15
1978. – 70 c. black & orange 20 15
1979. – 1 col. 50 blk. & grn. 40 35
1980. – 1 col. 50 blk. & grn. 40 35

DESIGNS: No. 1974. Dr. Luis Edmundo Vasquez (medicine). 1975, Dr. David Rosales (law). 1976. Dr. Guillermo Trigueros (medicine). 1977, Manuel Farfan Castro. 1978, Iri Sol (singing). 1979, Carlos Arturo Imendia (primary education). Dr. Benjamin Orozco (chemistry).

**470.** Man on Roof above Houses.

**1987.** Air. International Year of Shelter for the Homeless.
1981. **470.** 70 c. multicoloured .. 20 15
1982. – 1 col. blue .. .. 25 20
DESIGN: 1 p. Emblem.

**471.** Emblem. **472.** Nicolas Aguilar.

**1987.** 10th Pan-American Games, Indianapolis, U.S.A. Multicoloured.
1983. 20 c. Type **471** (postage) 10 10
1984. 20 c. Table tennis .. 10 10
1985. 25 c. Wrestling (horiz.) .. 10 10
1986. 25 c. Fencing (horiz.) .. 10 10
1987. 70 c. Softball (horiz.) (air) .. .. .. 20 15
1988. 70 c. Showjumping (horiz.) .. .. 20 15
1989. 5 col. Weightlifting .. 1·40 1·10
1990. 5 col. Hurdling .. .. 1·40 1·10

**1987.** Independence Leaders. Multicoloured.
1991. 15 c. Type **472** (postage) 10 10
1992. 20 c. Domingo Antonio de Lara .. .. 10 10
1993. 70 c. Juan Manuel Rodriguez (air) .. 20 15
1994. 1 col. 50 Pedro Pablo Castillo .. .. 40 35

**473.** Man tending Crops.

**1987.** World Food Day.
1995. **473.** 50 c. multicoloured .. 15 10

**474.** The Three Kings (crochet).

**1987.** Christmas. Multicoloured.
1996. 25 c. Stained glass window from Church of Virgin of the Everlasting Succour (postage) .. .. 10 10
1997. 70 c. Type **474** (air) .. 20 15

**475.** "Self-portrait".

**476.** Man with Ceramic Drum.

**1987.** Salvador Salazar Arrue (writer and painter). Multicoloured.
1998. 25 c. Type **475** (postage) 10 10
1999. 70 c. "Lake" (air) .. 20 15

**1987.** Pre-Columbian Musical Instruments. Multicoloured.
2000. 20 c. Type **476** (postage) 10 10
2001. 70 c. Parade of musicians from Saluan ceramic vase (left) (air) .. 20 15
2002. 70 c. Parade of musicians from Saluan ceramic vase (right) .. .. 20 15
2003. 1 col. 50 Conch shell trumpet .. .. 65 45
Nos. 2001/2 are each 31 × 30 mm.

**477.** King Ferdinand of Spain.

**478.** Words and Stamps.

**1987.** 500th Anniv (1992) of Discovery of America by Columbus (1st issue). Mult.
2004. 1 col. Type **477** .. .. 25 20
2005. 1 col. Queen Isabella of Spain .. .. 25 20
2006. 1 col. Banner and North America .. 25 20
2007. 1 col. Islands, coat of arms and ships .. 25 20
2008. 1 col. Caribbean .. .. 25 20
2009. 1 col. Ships and South America .. .. 25 20
2010. 1 col. Native figure and South America .. 25 20
2011. 1 col. South America and compass rose .. .. 25 20
2012. 1 col. Anniversary logo 25 20
2013. 1 col. Columbus .. .. 25 20

Nos. 2004/13 were printed together in se-tenant sheetlets, Nos. 2006/11 forming a composite design of a contemporary map.

See also Nos. 2040/9, 2065/70, 2116/21, 2166/71 and 2206/9.

**1988.** Philately.
2014. **478.** 25 c. multicoloured .. 10 10

**479.** Crowd and Emblem.

**1988.** Empesarios Juveniles (youth education programme).
2015. **479.** 25 c. multicoloured .. 10 10

**480.** Bosco (after N. Musio).

**1988.** Death Centenary of St. John Bosco (founder of Salesian Brothers).
2016. **480.** 20 c. multicoloured .. 10 10

**481.** Felling of Trees and Children Planting Saplings.

**1988.** Environmental Protection. Mult.
2017. 20 c. Type **481** (postage) 10 10
2018. 70 c. Rubbish in river and monkey in forest (air) .. .. .. 20 15

**482.** High Jumping.

**1988.** Olympic Games, Seoul (1988) and Barcelona (1992). Multicoloured.
2019. 1 col. Type **482** .. .. 25 20
2020. 1 col. Throwing the javelin .. .. .. 25 20
2021. 1 col. Pistol shooting .. 25 20
2022. 1 col. Wrestling .. .. 25 20
2023. 1 col. Basketball .. 25 20

**483.** Rural Youth.

**1988.** World Food Day.
2025. **483.** 20 c. multicoloured .. 10 10

**484.** Fair Emblem.

**486.** Father and Son flying Heart-shaped Kite.

**1988.** 13th International Fair, El Salvador.
2026. **484.** 70 c. multicoloured .. 20 15

**1988.** "Prenfil '88" International Philatelic Literature and Press Exhibition, Buenos Aires. No. 1905 surch. **C5.00 PRENFIL '88 EXPOSICION MUNDIAL DE LITERATURA Y PRENSA FILATELICA BUENOS AIRES ARGENTINA DEL 25 DE NOVIEMBRE AL 2 DE DICEMBRE** and emblem.
2027. 5 col. on 90 c. mult. .. 1·40 1·25

**1988.** Infant Protection Campaign. Mult.
2028. 15 c. Type **486** .. .. 10 10
2029. 20 c. Happy child hugging adult's leg .. 10 10

**487.** "Virgin and Child with St. John and St. Anthony".

**1988.** Christmas. 500th Birth Anniv. of Titian (painter). Multicoloured.
2030. 25 c. Type **487** (postage) 10 10
2031. 70 c. "Virgin and Child in Glory with St. Francis and St. Alvise" (vert.) (air) .. .. .. 20 15

**488.** Emblems.

**1988.** Air. 18th Organization of American States General Assembly.
2032. **488.** 70 c. multicoloured .. 20 15

**489.** Hands holding Scroll.

**490.** "Esperanza de los Soles" (Victor Rodriguez Preza).

**1988.** "Return to Moral Values".
2033. **489.** 25 c. multicoloured .. 10 10

**1988.** Paintings. Multicoloured.
2034. 40 c. Type **490** (postage) 10 10
2035. 1 col. "Pastoral" (Luis Angel Salinas) (horiz.) (air) .. .. .. 25 20
2036. 2 col. "Children" (Julio Hernandez Aleman) (horiz.) .. .. 60 45
2037. 5 col. "El Nino de las Alcancias" (Camilo Minero) .. .. 1·50 1·25

491 Emblem within Laurel Wreath, People and Map

**1988.** 40th Anniv. of Declaration of Human Rights. Multicoloured.
2038 25 c. Type **491** (postage) 10 10
2039 70 c. U.N. and Human Rights emblems and map (air) (horiz) .. 20 15

492 El Tazumal

**1988.** 500th Anniv (1992) of Discovery of America by Columbus (2nd issue). Mult.
2040 1 col. Type **492** .. .. 25 20
2041 1 col. Earthenware bowl 25 20
2042 1 col. San Andres .. 25 20
2043 1 col. Dish for burning aromatic substances .. 25 20
2044 1 col. Sihuatan .. .. 25 20
2045 1 col. Effigy of rain god 25 20
2046 1 col. Cara Sucia .. 25 20
2047 1 col. Monkey-shaped pot 25 20
2048 1 col. San Lorenzo .. 25 20
2049 1 col. Round pot with monkey-head spout .. 25 20

**493** Margay

**494** Flag, Map and Compass Rose

**1989.** Endangered Animals. Multicoloured.
2051 25 c. Type **493** .. .. 10 10
2052 25 c. Margay (different) .. 10 10
2053 55 c. Ocelot in tree .. 15 10
2054 55 c. Ocelot resting .. 15 10

**1989.** Centenary of El Salvador Meteorological Services. Multicoloured.
2055 15 c. Type **494** .. .. 10 10
2056 20 c. Sea, land and measuring equipment 20 10

**495** El Salvador Philatelic Society Emblem

**496** Basketball

**1989.** Philately.
2057 **495** 25 c. grey, black & bl 10 10

**1989.** Olympic Games, Barcelona (1992). Mult.
2058 20 c. Type **496** (postage) 10 10
2059 25 c. Boxing .. .. 10 10
2060 25 c. Athletics .. .. 10 10
2061 40 c. Showjumping .. 10 10
2063 55 c. Badminton (horiz) (air) .. .. .. 15 10
2064 55 c. Handball (horiz) .. 15 10

**497** 1893 10 p. Columbus Stamp

**1989.** 500th Anniv (1992) of Discovery of America by Columbus (3rd issue). El Salvador Stamps featuring Columbus.
2065 **497** 50 c. orange .. .. 15 10
2066 – 50 c. blue .. .. 15 10
2067 – 50 c. green .. .. 15 10
2068 – 50 c. red .. .. 15 10
2069 – 50 c. violet .. .. 15 10
2070 – 50 c. brown .. .. 15 10
DESIGNS: No. 2066, 1894 2 p. stamp; 2067, 1893 2 p. stamp; 2068, 1894 5 p. stamp; 2069, 1893 5 p. stamp; 2070, 1894 10p. stamp.

**498** Fire Engine

**1989** 106th Anniv of Fire Service. Mult.
2072 25 c. Type **498** .. .. 10 10
2073 70 c. Firemen fighting fire 15 10

**499** Birds

**1989.** Bicent of French Revolution. Mult.
2074 90 c. Type **499** .. .. 25 20
2075 1 col. Storming the Bastille .. .. 25 20

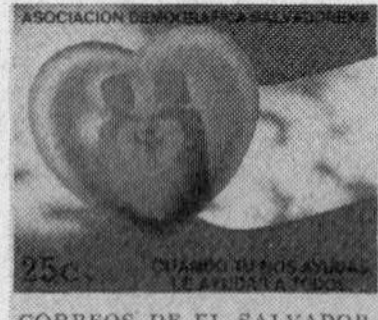

**500** People within Heart

**1989.** 27th Anniv of El Salvador Demographic Association.
2076 **500** 25 c. multicoloured .. 10 10

**501** "Signing the Act of Independence" (Luis Vergara Ahumada)

**1989.** 168th Anniv of Independence. Mult.
2077 25 c. Type **501** (postage) 10 10
2078 70 c. Flag, independence leaders and arms (air) 15 10

**502** Flags of El Salvador and United States

**1989.** World Cup Football Championship, Italy (1990) (1st issue). Preliminary Rounds. Multicoloured.
2079 20 c. Type **502** .. .. 10 10
2080 20 c. Flags of El Salvador and Guatemala .. 10 10
2081 25 c. Flags of El Salvador and Costa Rica .. 10 10
2082 25 c. Flags of El Salvador and Trinidad and Tobago .. .. 10 10
2083 55 c. Flags and ball .. 15 10
2084 1 col. Ball and Cuscatlan Stadium .. .. 25 20
See also Nos. 2109/15.

**503** Marcelino Champagnat and Arms of Order

**1989.** Birth Bicent of Jose Benito Marcelino Champagnat (founder of Maristas Brothers).
2085 **503** 20 c. multicoloured .. 10 10

**504** "The Farmer" (bowl decoration)

**1989.** America. Multicoloured.
2086 25 c. Type **504** .. .. 10 10
2087 70 c. Pre-Columbian pottery production .. 15 10

**505** Man tending Crops

**1989.** World Food Day. "One Land, One Community, One Future". Multicoloured.
2088 15 c. Type **505** .. .. 10 10
2089 55 c. Food production activities in chain links 15 10

**506** Children under Umbrella

**507** Holy Family in Stable

**1989.** Children's Rights.
2090 **506** 25 c. multicoloured .. 10 10

**1989.** Christmas. Multicoloured.
2091 25 c. Type **507** .. .. 10 10
2092 70 c. Holy family .. 15 10

**508** King Vulture

**509** Treasury, Map and "50"

**1989.** Birds. Multicoloured.
2093 70 c. Type **508** .. .. 25 15
2094 1 col. Common caracara (horiz) .. .. 45 30
2095 2 col. Sharp-shinned hawk 90 55
2096 10 col. Ferruginous pygmy owl (horiz) .. .. 5·00 3·25

**1990.** 50th Anniv of Treasury.
2097 **509** 50 c. blue, gold & blk 15 10

**510** Baden-Powell

**511** Young Girl

**1990.** 133rd Birth Anniv of Lord Baden-Powell (founder of Boy Scouts Movement).
2098 **510** 25 c. multicoloured .. 10 10

**1990.** International Women's Day.
2099 **511** 25 c. multicoloured .. 10 10

**512** Hourglass

**513** "No to Alcoholic Drinks"

**1990.** 50th Anniv of El Salvador Philatelic Society.
2100 **512** 25 c. mult (postage) .. 10 10
2101 55 c. mult (air) .. 10 10

**1990.** Problems of Addiction. Multicoloured.
2103 20 c. Type **513** (postage) 10 10
2104 25 c. "No to Tobacco" .. 10 10
2105 1 col. 50 "No to Drugs" (air) .. .. .. 25 20

**514** Player

**515** First Page and Map

**1990.** Air. Victory by El Salvador at Fourth International Football Championship for Amputees (1989).
2106 **514** 70 c. multicoloured .. 15 10

**1990.** 75th Anniv of "La Prensa Grafica" (newspaper). Multicoloured.
2107 15 c. Type **515** .. .. 10 10
2108 25 c. Newspaper as diamond and "75" .. 10 10

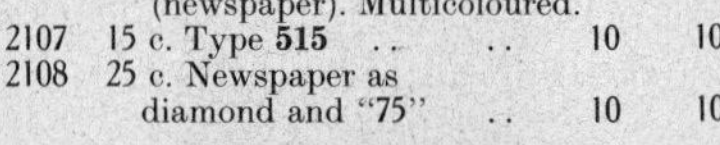

**516** Group A

**1990.** World Cup Football Championship, Italy (2nd issue). Multicoloured.
2109 55 c. Type **516** .. .. 10 10
2110 55 c. Group B .. .. 10 10
2111 70 c. Group C .. .. 15 10
2112 70 c. Group D .. .. 15 10
2113 1 col. Group E .. .. 15 10
2114 1 col. Group F .. .. 15 10
2115 1 col. 50 Winner's medal (vert) .. .. .. 25 20

**517** Ferdinand the Catholic

**1990.** 500th Anniv (1992) of Discovery of America by Columbus (4th issue). Mult.
2116 1 col Type **517** .. .. 15 10
2117 1 col. Isabella the Catholic 15 10
2118 1 col. Arms and topsail .. 15 10
2119 1 col. Anniversary emblem .. .. 15 10
2120 1 col. "Santa Maria" .. 30 15
2121 1 col. "Pinta" and "Nina" 30 15

**1990.** Germany, World Cup Football Championship Winner. No. 2112 surch **90c. ALEMANIA CAMPEON.**
2123 90 c. on 70 c. mult .. 15 10

**519** Globe and Figures

**1990.** World Summit on Children, New York.
2124 **519** 5 col. blue, bis & blk 85 80

**520** Sir Rowland Hill (instigator of first postage stamps)

**1990.** 150th Anniv of the Penny Black.
2125 **520** 2 col. multicoloured .. 30 25
2126 – 2 col. multicoloured .. 30 25
2127 – 2 col. mulitcoloured .. 30 25
2128 – 2 col. multicoloured .. 30 25
2129 – 2 col. multicoloured .. 30 25
2130 – 2 col. multicoloured .. 30 25
DESIGNS: No. 2126, 1 d. Black; 2127, El Salvador 1889 1 c. stamp; 2128, Post Headquarters; 2129, United Kingdom and El Salvador flags; 2130, El Salvador 1949 1 col. U.P.U. stamp.

**521** Chichontepec Volcano

**1990.** America. Natural World. Multicoloured.
2131 25 c. Type **521** .. .. 20 15
2132 70 c. Coatepeque Lake .. 45 15

**522** "Food for the Future"

**524** Road Signs

**523** Light Bulb

**1990.** World Food Day.
2133 **522** 5 col. multicoloured .. 85 80

**1990.** Centenary of San Salvador Electric Light Company. Multicoloured.
2134 20 c. Type **523** .. .. 10 10
2135 90 c. Maintenance of overhead power lines .. 15 10

**1990.** 8th Anniv of National Commission for Education and Road Safety. Multicoloured.
2136 25 c. Type **524** .. .. 10 10
2137 40 c. Family at road junction (horiz) .. 10 10

**525** Anniversary Emblem

**1990.** 75th Anniv of Chamber of Trade and Commerce.
2138 **525** 1 col. blue, gold & blk 15 10

**526** "Papilio garamas amerias"

**1990.** Butterflies. Multicoloured.
2139 15 c. "Eurytides calliste" 10 10
2140 20 c. Type **526** .. .. 10 10
2141 25 c. "Papilio garamas" 10 10
2142 55 c. "Hypanartia godmani" (vert) .. 10 10
2143 70 c. "Anaea (Consul) excellens" (vert) .. 10 10
2144 1 col. "Papilio pilumnus" (vert) .. .. .. 15 10

**527** Children

**1990.** Christmas. Multicoloured.
2146 25 c. Type **527** .. .. 10 10
2147 70 c. Nativity (vert) .. 10 10

**528** Elderly Couple

**529** University Emblem

**1991.** Month of the Third Age.
2148 **528** 15 c. black and violet 10 10

**1991.** 150th Anniv of El Salvador University.
2149 **529** 25 c. black and silver 10 10
2150 – 70 c. multicoloured .. 10 10
2151 – 1 col. 50 multicoloured .. 20 15
DESIGNS: 70 c. Footsteps leading to light; 1 col. 50, Pencil, pen and dove on globe.

**530** Auditorium

**1991.** Restoration of Santa Ana Theatre. Multicoloured.
2152 20 c. Type **530** .. .. 10 10
2153 70 c. Facade .. .. 10 10

**531** Mexican Tree Frog

**1991.** Frogs. Multicoloured.
2154 25 c. Type **531** .. .. 10 10
2155 70 c. Robber frog .. 10 10
2156 1 col. "Plectrohyla guatemalensis" .. 15 10
2157 1 col. 50 Morelet's frog .. 20 15

**532** National Colours, Map and Child

**1991.** S.O.S. Children's Villages. Mult.
2158 20 c. Type **532** .. .. 10 10
2159 90 c. Children playing in village .. .. 15 10

**533** Family building Map

**534** Blue and White Mockingbird

**1991.** Family Unity Month.
2160 **533** 50 c. multicoloured .. 10 10

**1991.** Birds. Multicoloured.
2161 20 c. Type **534** .. .. 10 10
2162 25 c. Red-winged blackbird .. .. .. 10 10
2163 70 c. Rufous-naped wren 10 10
2164 1 col. Bushy-crested jay 15 10
2165 5 col. Long-tailed manakin .. .. .. 75 50

**535** Hourglass and Atlas

**1991.** 500th Anniv (1992) of Discovery of America by Columbus (5th issue). Mult.
2166 1 col. Type **535** .. .. 15 10
2167 1 col. "Santa Maria's" sails and atlas .. 30 15
2168 1 col. Map and caravel .. 30 15
2169 1 col. Caravels and edge of atlas .. .. 30 15
2170 1 col. Compass rose and map .. .. .. 15 10
2171 1 col. Map and anniversary emblem .. 15 10
Nos. 2166/71 were issued together, se-tenant, forming a composite design.

**536** Battle of Acaxual

**537** Tree-globe and Plant and Animal Life

**1991.** America. Voyages of Discovery. Mult.
2173 25 c. Type **536** .. .. 10 10
2174 70 c. First Mass in Cuzcatlan .. .. 10 10

**1991.** World Food Day. "The Tree, Fountain of Life for the World".
2175 **537** 50 c. multicoloured .. 10 10

**538** Manuscript and Mozart

**1991.** Death Bicentenary of Wolfgang Amadeus Mozart (composer).
2176 **538** 1 col. multicoloured .. 15 10

**539** Nativity

**1991.** Christmas. Multicoloured.
2177 25 c. Type **539** .. .. 10 10
2178 70 c. Carol singers (horiz) 10 10

**540** Moon and Left Half of Eclipse

**1991.** Total Eclipse of the Sun. Mult.
2179 70 c. Type **540** .. .. 10 10
2180 70 c. Right half of eclipse and moon .. .. 10 10
Nos. 2179/80 were issued together, se-tenant, forming a composite design.

**541** Lifeguards with rescued Swimmer

**1992.** Red Cross Lifeguards. Multicoloured.
2181 3 col. Type **541** .. .. 45 30
2182 4 col. 50 Lifeguards in sea 75 45

**542** St. Vincent de Paul and Sick Man

**543** Anniversary Emblem

**1992.** Centenary of St. Vincent de Paul Society of Sisters of Charity.
2183 **542** 80 c. multicoloured .. 10 10

**1992.** 50th Anniv of Lions International in El Salvador.
2184 **543** 90 c. multicoloured .. 15 10

**544** Cyclist ("Non-polluting Transport")
**545** Roberto Orellana Valdes (gynaecologist)

**1992.** Ecology. Multicoloured.
2185 60 c. Type **544** .. .. 10 10
2186 80 c. Children and butterfly ("Fauna, ecology and education") .. 10 10
2187 1 col. 60 Man working on allotment ("Harmony with nature") .. .. 15 10
2188 2 col. 20 Animals beside clean river ("Do not pollute rivers") .. 30 20
2189 3 col. Fruits ("Eat natural foods") .. .. 45 30
2190 5 col. Recycling bins ("Energy without contamination") .. 75 50
2191 10 col. Landscape ("Conserve nature") .. 1·50 1·00
2192 25 col. Wild animals ("Do not destroy fauna") .. 3·50 2·40

**1992.** Doctors. Multicoloured.
2193 80 c. Type **545** .. .. 10 10
2194 1 col. Carlos Gonzalez Bonilla (surgeon) .. 15 10
2195 1 col. 60 Andres Gonzalez Funes (paediatrician) 25 20
2196 2 col. 20 Joaquin Coto (anaesthetist) .. .. 30 20

**546** Mascot and Census Document
**548** Simon Bolivar

**1992.** 5th Population and Fourth Housing Census. Multicoloured.
2197 60 c. Type **546** .. .. 10 10
2198 80 c. Graph and globe .. 10 10

**1992.**
2205 **548** 2 col. 20 multicoloured 30 20

**549** Carvings

**1992.** 500th Anniv of Discovery of America by Columbus (6th series). Multicoloured.
2206 1 col. Type **549** .. .. 15 10
2207 1 col. Caravel reflected in human eye .. .. 30 15
2208 1 col. Caravel and Mexican pyramids .. 30 15
2209 1 col. "500", caravel and satellite .. .. 30 15

**550** Footprints on Globe

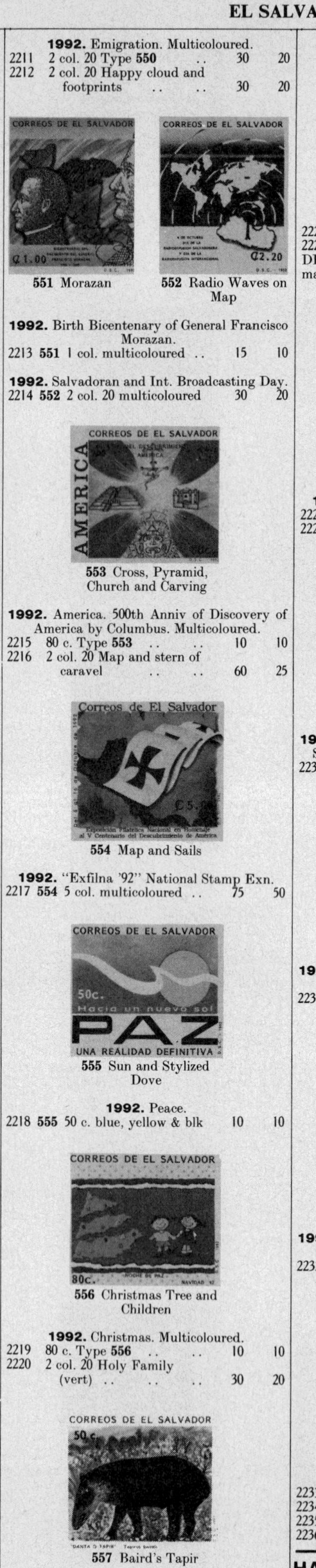

**1992.** Emigration. Multicoloured.
2211 2 col. 20 Type **550** .. 30 20
2212 2 col. 20 Happy cloud and footprints .. .. 30 20

**551** Morazan
**552** Radio Waves on Map

**1992.** Birth Bicentenary of General Francisco Morazan.
2213 **551** 1 col. multicoloured .. 15 10

**1992.** Salvadoran and Int. Broadcasting Day.
2214 **552** 2 col. 20 multicoloured 30 20

**553** Cross, Pyramid, Church and Carving

**1992.** America. 500th Anniv of Discovery of America by Columbus. Multicoloured.
2215 80 c. Type **553** .. .. 10 10
2216 2 col. 20 Map and stern of caravel .. .. 60 25

**554** Map and Sails

**1992.** "Exfilna '92" National Stamp Exn.
2217 **554** 5 col. multicoloured .. 75 50

**555** Sun and Stylized Dove

**1992.** Peace.
2218 **555** 50 c. blue, yellow & blk 10 10

**556** Christmas Tree and Children

**1992.** Christmas. Multicoloured.
2219 80 c. Type **556** .. .. 10 10
2220 2 col. 20 Holy Family (vert) .. .. .. 30 20

**557** Baird's Tapir

**1993.** Mammals. Multicoloured.
2221 50 c. Type **557** .. .. 10 10
2222 70 c. Water opossum .. 10 10
2223 1 col. Tayra .. .. 15 10
2224 3 col. Jaguarundi .. 45 30
2225 4 col. 50 White-tailed deer 65 45

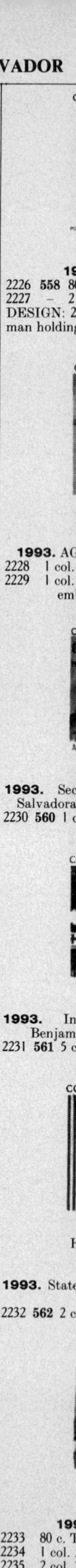

**558** Head

**1993.** "Third Age" Month.
2226 **558** 80 c. black .. .. 10 10
2227 – 2 col. 20 multicoloured 30 20
DESIGN: 2 col. 20, Young boy beside elderly man holding tree.

**559** Church of the Divine Providence

**1993.** AGAPE (social organization). Mult.
2228 1 col. Type **559** .. .. 15 10
2229 1 col. Family and AGAPE emblem .. .. 15 10

**560** Secretary

**1993.** Secretary's Day. 25th Anniv of Salvadoran Assn of Executive Secretaries.
2230 **560** 1 col. multicoloured .. 15 10

**561** Hospital

**1993.** Inauguration of Reconstructed Benjamin Bloom Children's Hospital.
2231 **561** 5 col. multicoloured .. 80 55

**562** Flags, Clasped Hands and Chapultepec Castle

**1993.** State Visit of Pres. Carlos Salinas de Gortari of Mexico.
2232 **562** 2 col. 20 multicoloured 35 25

**563** White Ibis

**1993.** Birds. Multicoloured.
2233 80 c. Type **563** .. .. 10 10
2234 1 col. American wood ibis 15 10
2235 2 col. 20 Great blue heron 35 25
2236 5 col. Roseate spoonbill .. 80 55

HAVE YOU READ THE NOTES AT THE BEGINNING OF THIS CATALOGUE?
These often provide answers to the enquiries we receive.

**564** Anniversary Emblem

**1993.** Centenary of Pharmaceutical Industry Standards Council.
2237 **564** 80 c. mauve, blk & yell 10 10

**565** Agouti

**1993.** America. Endangered Animals. Mult.
2238 80 c. Type **565** .. .. 10 10
2239 2 col. 20 Common racoon 30 20

**566** Pulgarcito (mascot)
**568** Masferrer

**567** Holy Family

**1993.** 5th Central American Games, El Salvador (1994). Multicoloured.
2240 50 c. Type **566** .. .. 10 10
2241 1 col. 60 Games emblem, flags and Olympic rings 25 20
2242 2 col. 20 Mascot and map of Central America (horiz) .. .. 30 20
2243 4 col. 50 Mascot and map of El Salvador (horiz) 65 45

**1993.** Christmas. Multicoloured.
2244 80 c. Type **567** .. .. 10 10
2245 2 col. 20 Nativity scene and Christmas tree .. 30 20

**1993.** 125th Birth Anniv of Alberto Masferrer (sociologist).
2246 **568** 2 col. 20 multicoloured 30 20

**569** "Solanum mammosum"
**570** I.Y.F. and United Nations Emblems

**1993.** Medicinal Plants. Multicoloured.
2247 1 col. Type **569** .. .. 15 10
2248 1 col. "Hamelia patens" 15 10
2249 1 col. "Tridax procumbens" .. .. 15 10
2250 1 col. "Calea urticifolia" 15 10
2251 1 col. "Ageratum conyzoides" .. .. 15 10
2252 1 col. "Pluchea odorata" 15 10

**1994.** International Year of the Family.
2253 **570** 2 col. 20 multicoloured 30 20

571 Hospital

**1994.** Centenary of Military Hospital. Mult.

| | | | |
|---|---|---|---|
| 2254 | 1 col. Type **571** .. .. | 15 | 10 |
| 2255 | 1 col. Medical corps soldier treating wounded .. .. | 15 | 10 |

572 Santa Ana Arms

**1994.** Centenary of Uprising of the 44 at Santa Ana. Multicoloured.

| | | | |
|---|---|---|---|
| 2256 | 60 c. Type **572** .. .. | 10 | 10 |
| 2257 | 80 c. Commemorative inscription, laurel wreath and ribbon .. | 10 | 10 |

573 Goalkeeper and Flags of U.S.A., Switzerland, Colombia and Rumania

**1994.** World Cup Football Championship, U.S.A. Various footballing scenes and flags of participating countries. Multicoloured.

| | | | |
|---|---|---|---|
| 2258 | 60 c. Type **573** .. .. | 10 | 10 |
| 2259 | 80 c. Brazil, Russia, Cameroun and Sweden | 10 | 10 |
| 2260 | 1 col. Germany, Bolivia, South Korea and Spain | 15 | 10 |
| 2261 | 2 col. 20 Argentina, Greece, Nigeria and Bulgaria .. .. | 30 | 20 |
| 2262 | 4 col. 50 Italy, Ireland, Norway and Mexico .. | 65 | 45 |
| 2263 | 5 col. Belgium, Morocco, Holland and Saudi Arabia .. .. | 75 | 50 |

574 Order of Malta Square, Santa Elena, Cuscatlan

**1994.** Work of Sovereign Military Order of Malta in El Salvador.

| | | | |
|---|---|---|---|
| 2264 | **574** 2 col. 20 multicoloured | 30 | 20 |

575 Tiger and the Stag (San Juan Nonualco)

**1994.** Traditional Dances. Multicoloured.

| | | | |
|---|---|---|---|
| 2265 | 1 col. Type **575** .. .. | 15 | 10 |
| 2266 | 2 col. 20 The Speckled Bull (Santa Cruz Analquito and Estanzuelas) .. .. | 30 | 20 |

576 Sweet Pepper

**1994.** Edible Plants. Multicoloured.

| | | | |
|---|---|---|---|
| 2267 | 70 c. Type **576** .. .. | 10 | 10 |
| 2268 | 80 c. Cacao .. .. | 10 | 10 |
| 2269 | 1 col. Sweet potato .. | 15 | 10 |
| 2270 | 5 col. Pacaya .. .. | 75 | 50 |

577 Mail Van

**1994.** America. Postal Vehicles. Mult.

| | | | |
|---|---|---|---|
| 2271 | 80 c. Type **577** .. .. | 10 | 10 |
| 2272 | 2 col. 20 Train .. .. | 30 | 20 |

578 Cyclists

579 National Colours and Globe as Crate

**1994.** 22nd Tour of El Salvador Cycling Championship.

| | | | |
|---|---|---|---|
| 2273 | **578** 80 c. multicoloured .. | 10 | 10 |

**1994.** 16th International Fair.

| | | | |
|---|---|---|---|
| 2274 | **579** 5 col. multicoloured .. | 75 | 50 |

580 Holy Family and Donkey

**1994.** Christmas. Multicoloured.

| | | | |
|---|---|---|---|
| 2275 | 80 c. Type **580** .. .. | 10 | 10 |
| 2276 | 2 col. 20 Wise men and baby Jesus .. .. | 30 | 20 |

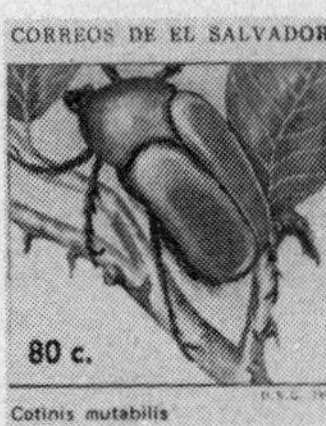
581 "Cotinis mutabilis"

582 Books

**1994.** Beetles. Multicoloured.

| | | | |
|---|---|---|---|
| 2277 | 80 c. Type **581** .. .. | 10 | 10 |
| 2278 | 1 col. "Phyllophaga sp." | 15 | 10 |
| 2279 | 2 col. 20 "Galofa sp." .. | 30 | 20 |
| 2280 | 5 col. Longhorn beetle .. | 75 | 50 |

**1995.** 40th Anniv of Cultural Centre. Anniversary emblems. Multicoloured.

| | | | |
|---|---|---|---|
| 2281 | 70 c. Type **582** .. .. | 10 | 10 |
| 2282 | 1 col. "40" and arrows .. | 15 | 10 |

583 Vase

584 Menendez

**1995.** World Heritage Site. Joya de Ceren. Multicoloured.

| | | | |
|---|---|---|---|
| 2283 | 60 c. Type **583** .. .. | 10 | 10 |
| 2284 | 70 c. Three-footed dish .. | 10 | 10 |
| 2285 | 80 c. Two-handled pot .. | 10 | 10 |
| 2286 | 2 col. 20 Jug .. .. | 35 | 25 |
| 2287 | 4 col. 50 Building No. 3 .. | 65 | 45 |
| 2288 | 5 col. Building No. 4 .. | 75 | 50 |

**1995.** Birth Bicentenary of Isidro Menendez (politician).

| | | | |
|---|---|---|---|
| 2289 | **584** 80 c. multicoloured .. | 10 | 10 |

585 Anniversary Emblem

**1995.** 80th Anniv of La Centro Americana, S. A. (welfare organization). Multicoloured.

| | | | |
|---|---|---|---|
| 2290 | 80 c. Type **585** (safeguarding the future of the child) .. .. | 10 | 10 |
| 2291 | 2 col. 20 "Child in Fancy Dress" (Jorge Driottez) (first "Expresiones" painting competition) | 35 | 25 |

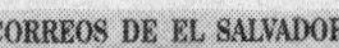

586 College and Map of Founding Sisters' Voyage

**1995.** Cent of College of the Sacred Heart.

| | | | |
|---|---|---|---|
| 2292 | **586** 80 c. multicoloured .. | 10 | 10 |

587 Emblem

**1995.** 50th Anniv of F.A.O.

| | | | |
|---|---|---|---|
| 2293 | **587** 2 col. 20 multicoloured | 35 | 25 |

588 Los Almendros Beach, Sonsonate

**1995.** 20th Anniv of World Tourism Organization. Multicoloured.

| | | | |
|---|---|---|---|
| 2294 | 50 c. Type **588** .. ..i | 10 | 10 |
| 2295 | 60 c. Apaneca Lake .. | 10 | 10 |
| 2296 | 2 col. 20 Guerrero Beach, La Union .. .. | 35 | 25 |
| 2297 | 5 col. Usulutan Volcano | 75 | 50 |

589 National Arms and Symbols of Development

**1995.** 174th Anniv of Central American Independence. Multicoloured.

| | | | |
|---|---|---|---|
| 2298 | 80 c. Type **589** .. .. | 10 | 10 |
| 2299 | 25 col. El Salvador exports (sustained economic development) | 3·75 | 2·50 |

590 "Lemboglossum stellatum"

**1995.** Orchids. Multicoloured.

| | | | |
|---|---|---|---|
| 2300 | 60 c. "Pleurothallis glandulosa" .. .. | 10 | 10 |
| 2301 | 60 c. "Pleurothallis grobyi" .. .. | 10 | 10 |
| 2302 | 70 c. Type **590** .. .. | 10 | 10 |
| 2303 | 70 c. "Pleurothallis fuegii" | 10 | 10 |
| 2304 | 1 col. "Pleurothallis hirsuta" .. .. | 15 | 10 |
| 2305 | 1 col. "Lepanthes inaequalis" .. .. | 15 | 10 |
| 2306 | 3 col. "Hexadesmia micrantha" .. .. | 45 | 30 |
| 2307 | 3 col. "Pleurothallis segoviense" .. .. | 45 | 30 |
| 2308 | 4 col. 50 "Stelis aprica" .. | 65 | 45 |
| 2309 | 4 col. 50 "Platystele stenostachya" .. | 65 | 45 |
| 2310 | 5 col. "Stelis barbata" .. | 75 | 50 |
| 2311 | 5 col. "Pleurothallis schiedeii" .. .. | 75 | 50 |

591 Pygmy Kingfisher

**1995.** America. Conservation. Multicoloured.

| | | | |
|---|---|---|---|
| 2312 | 80 c. Type **591** .. .. | 10 | 10 |
| 2313 | 2 col. Green kingfisher .. | 30 | 20 |

592 Anniversary Emblem

**1995.** 50th Anniv of U.N.O. Multicoloured.

| | | | |
|---|---|---|---|
| 2314 | 80 c. Type **592** .. .. | 10 | 10 |
| 2315 | 2 col. 20 Hands supporting emblem .. | 35 | 25 |

593 Children with Sparklers

**1995.** Christmas. Multicoloured.

| | | | |
|---|---|---|---|
| 2316 | 80 c. Type **593** .. .. | 10 | 10 |
| 2317 | 2 col. 20 Family celebrating at midnight | 35 | 25 |

594 Great Horned Owl ("Bubo virginianus")

**1995.** Wildlife of Montecristo. Multicoloured.
2318 80 c. Type **594** .. .. 10 10
2319 80 c. Kinkajou ("Potos flavus") .. .. 10 10
2320 80 c. "Porthidium godmani" (snake) .. 10 10
2321 80 c. Ocelot ("Felis pardalis") .. .. 10 10
2322 80 c. "Deliathis bifurcata" (longhorn beetle) .. 10 10
2323 80 c. Puma ("Felis concolor") .. .. 10 10
2324 80 c. Red brocket ("Mazama americana") 10 10
2325 80 c. "Leptophobia aripa" (butterfly) .. .. 10 10
2326 80 c. Salamander ("Bolitoglossa salvinii") 10 10
2327 80 c. Rivoli's hummingbird ("Eugenes fulgens") .. .. 10 10

Nos. 2318/27 were issued together, se-tenant, forming a composite design of a forest.

595 Pope John Paul II in Mitre

**1996.** 2nd Papal Visit. Multicoloured.
2328 1 col. 50 Type **595** .. 20 15
2329 5 col. 40 Pope and Metropolitan Cathedral 75 50

596 Arrival of Spaniards

**1996.** 450th Anniv of Grant of City Status to San Salvador. Multicoloured.
2330 2 col. 50 Type **596** .. 35 25
2331 2 col. 70 Diego de Holguin (first governor) and chapel .. .. 40 30
2332 3 col. 30 Former National Palace, 1889 .. .. 45 30
2333 4 col. Boulevard de los Heroes 55 40

597 ANTEL Emblem incorporating Globes

**1996.** Telecommunications Workers' Day. Multicoloured.
2334 1 col. 50 Dish aerial and hand holding optic fibres (horiz) .. .. 20 15
2335 5 col. Type **597** .. .. 70 50

598 Rey Avila (El Chele) (singer)

**1996.** Entertainers' Death Anniversaries. Multicoloured.
2336 1 col. Type **598** (1st death) 15 10
2337 1 col. 50 Maria Moreira (Dona Teresfora) (singer, 1st death) .. 20 15
2338 2 col. 70 Francisco Lara (Pancho Lara) (musician and composer, 7th death) .. 40 30
2339 4 col. Carlos Pineda (Aniceto Porsisoca) (singer, 3rd death) .. 55 40

599 Anniversary Emblem

**1996.** 40th Anniv of YSKL Radio Station.
2340 **599** 1 col. 40 multicoloured 20 15

600 Throwing the Discus

**1996.** Centenary of Modern Olympic Games and Olympic Games, Atlanta. Ancient Greek athletes. Multicoloured.
2341 1 col. 50 Type **600** .. 20 15
2342 3 col. Hurdling .. .. 45 30
2343 4 col. Wrestling .. .. 55 40
2344 5 col. Throwing the javelin .. .. 70 50

ACKNOWLEDGEMENT OF RECEIPT STAMP

AR 53.

**1897.**
AR 264. **AR 53.** 5 c. green .. 15

EXPRESS STAMPS

E 547 Throwing the Hammer

**1992.** Olympic Games, Barcelona. Mult.
E2199 60 c. Type E **547** .. 10 10
E2200 80 c. Volleyball .. 10 10
E2201 90 c. Putting the shot (decathlon) .. .. 15 10
E2202 2 col. 20 Long jumping 30 20
E2203 3 col. Gymnastics (vaulting) .. .. 45 30
E2204 5 col. Gymnastics (floor exercise) .. .. 75 50

OFFICIAL STAMPS

**1896.** Stamps of 1896 (first issue) optd. **FRANQUEO OFICIAL** in oval.
O 170. **37.** 1 c. blue .. .. 10
O 171. 2 c. brown .. .. 10
O 172. 3 c. green .. .. 40
O 173. 5 c. olive .. .. 10
O 174. 10 c. yellow .. .. 10
O 175. 12 c. blue .. .. 20
O 176. 15 c. violet .. .. 10
O 177. 20 c. red .. .. 40
O 178. 24 c. red .. .. 10
O 179. 30 c. orange .. 40
O 180. 50 c. black .. .. 30
O 181. 1 p. red .. .. 20

**1896.** Stamps of 1896 (second issue) optd. **FRANQUEO OFICIAL** in oval.
O 182. **38.** 1 c. green .. .. 10
O 183. **39.** 2 c. lake .. .. 10
O 184. 3 c. orange .. 25
O 185. 5 c. blue .. .. 20
O 186. 10 c. brown .. 10
O 187. 12 c. grey .. .. 25
O 188. 15 c. green .. .. 25
O 189. 20 c. red .. .. 25
O 190. 24 c. violet .. .. 25
O 191. 30 c. green .. .. 15
O 192. 50 c. orange .. 25
O 193. 100 c. blue .. .. 30

**1896.** Stamps of 1895 (first issue) optd. **CORREOS DE EL SALVADOR DE OFICIO** in circle and band.
O 194. **37.** 1 c. blue .. .. 8·50
O 195. 2 c. brown .. .. 8·50
O 196. 3 c. green .. .. 8·50
O 197. 5 c. olive .. .. 8·50
O 198. 10 c. yellow .. .. 10·00
O 199. 12 c. blue .. .. 13·00
O 200. 15 c. violet .. .. 13·00
O 201. 20 c. red .. .. 13·00
O 202. 24 c. red .. .. 13·00
O 203. 30 c. orange .. 13·00
O 204. 50 c. black .. .. 17·00
O 205. 1 p. red .. .. 17·00

**1896.** Stamps of 1896 (second issue) optd. **CORREOS DE EL SALVADOR DE OFICIO** in circle and band.
O 206. **38.** 1 c. green .. .. 7·00
O 207. **39.** 2 c. lake .. .. 7·00
O 208. 3 c. orange .. .. 20·00
O 209. 5 c. blue .. .. 7·00
O 210. 10 c. brown .. 7·00
O 211. 12 c. grey .. .. 12·00
O 212. 15 c. green .. .. 12·00
O 219. 15 c. on 24 c. violet (No. 218) .. .. 12·00
O 213. 20 c. red .. .. 12·00
O 214. 24 c. violet .. .. 12·00
O 215. 30 c. green .. .. 12·00
O 216. 50 c. orange .. 12·00
O 217. 100 c. blue .. .. 12·00

**1897.** Stamps of 1897 optd. **FRANQUEO OFICIAL** in oval.
O 232. 1 c. red .. .. .. 10 10
O 233. 2 c. green .. .. 70
O 234. 3 c. brown .. .. 35
O 235. 5 c. orange .. .. 20 25
O 236. 10 c. green .. .. 25
O 237. 12 c. blue .. .. 30
O 238. 15 c. black .. .. 35 45
O 239. 20 c. grey .. .. 15
O 240. 24 c. yellow .. .. 25 35
O 241. 30 c. red .. .. 25 65
O 242. 50 c. violet .. .. 90
O 243. 100 c. lake .. .. 80 1·75

**1897.** Stamps of 1897 optd. **CORREOS DE EL SALVADOR DE OFICIO** in circle and band.
O 244. 1 c. red .. .. .. 9·00 9·00
O 245. 2 c. green .. .. 9·00 9·00
O 246. 3 c. brown .. .. 20·00 20·00
O 247. 5 c. orange .. .. 9·00 9·00
O 248. 10 c. green .. .. 10·00 10·00
O 249. 12 c. blue .. .. 13·00
O 250. 15 c. black .. .. 13·00
O 251. 20 c. grey .. .. 15·00
O 252. 24 c. yellow .. .. 20·00
O 253. 30 c. red .. .. 17·00
O 254. 50 c. violet .. .. 22·00
O 255. 100 c. lake .. .. 20·00

**1898.** Stamps of 1898 optd. **FRANQUEO OFICIAL** in oval.
O 288. **57.** 1 c. red .. .. 10
O 289. 2 c. red .. .. 15
O 290. 3 c. green .. .. 1·75
O 291. 5 c. green .. .. 15
O 292. 10 c. blue .. .. 10
O 293. 12 c. violet .. .. 1·75
O 294. 13 c. lake .. .. 15
O 295. 20 c. blue .. .. 15
O 296. 24 c. blue .. .. 10
O 297. 26 c. brown .. .. 15
O 298. 50 c. orange .. .. 15
O 299. 1 p. yellow .. .. 15

**1899.** Stamps of 1899, with wheel opt. **T 58.** optd. **FRANQUEO OFICIAL** in fancy letters.
O 329. **59.** 1 c. brown .. .. 40 40
O 330. 2 c. green .. .. 70 70
O 331. 3 c. blue .. .. 40 40
O 332. 5 c. orange .. .. 40 40
O 333. 10 c. brown .. .. 50 50
O 334. 12 c. green .. ..
O 335. 13 c. red .. .. 95 95
O 336. 24 c. blue .. .. 18·00 18·00
O 337. 26 c. red .. .. 50 50
O 338. 50 c. red .. .. 1·00 1·00
O 339. 100 c. violet .. .. 1·00 1·00

**1900.** Federation issue of 1897 optd. **CORREOS DE EL SALVADOR DE OFICIO** in circle and band.
O 355. **55.** 1 c. multicoloured .. 20·00 20·00
O 356. 5 c. multicoloured .. 20·00 20·00

**1900.** Stamps of 1900, dated "1900", optd. **FRANQUEO OFICIAL** in oval, and with or without shield optd. T **66.**
O 448. **59.** 1 c. green (No. 438) .. 35 35
O 449. 2 c. red .. .. 40 35
O 450. 3 c. black .. .. 25 25
O 451. 5 c. blue .. .. 25 25
O 452. 10 c. blue .. .. 50 50
O 453. 12 c. green .. .. 50 50
O 454. 13 c. brown .. .. 50 50
O 455. 24 c. black .. .. 30 50
O 461. 26 c. brown .. .. 35 35
O 462. 50 c. red .. .. 55 40

**1903.** As T **70,** but inscr. "FRANQUEO OFICIAL" across statue.
O 497. 1 c. green .. .. 35 25
O 498. 2 c. red .. .. 35 15
O 499. 3 c. orange .. .. 70 60
O 500. 5 c. blue .. .. 35 15
O 501. 10 c. purple .. .. 50 35
O 502. 13 c. brown .. .. 50 35
O 503. 15 c. brown .. .. 2·50 1·25
O 504. 24 c. red .. .. 35 35
O 505. 50 c. brown .. .. 50 25
O 506. 100 c. blue .. .. 50 55

**1905.** Nos. O 500/502 surch. with new value and two black circles.
O 518. 2 c. on 5 c. blue .. 2·40 2·00
O 519. 3 c. on 5 c. blue ..
O 520. 3 c. on 10 c. purple .. 6·50 4·50
O 521. 3 c. on 13 c. brown .. 60 50

**1905.** No. O 450 optd. **1905.**
O 558. **59.** 3 c. black .. .. 1·25 1·10

**1906.** Nos. O 449/50 optd. **1906.**
O 567. **59.** 2 c. red .. ..
O 568. 3 c. black .. .. 90 70

**1906.** As T **89,** but inscr. "FRANQUEO OFICIAL" at foot of portrait.
O 582. 1 c. black and green .. 15 10
O 583. 2 c. black and red .. 15 10
O 584. 3 c. black and yellow .. 15 10
O 585. 5 c. black and blue .. 15 35
O 586. 10 c. black and violet .. 15 10
O 587. 13 c. black and brown 15 10
O 588. 15 c. black and red .. 20 10
O 589. 24 c. black and red .. 25 25
O 590. 50 c. black and orange 25 50
O 591. 100 c. black and blue .. 25 1·50

**1908.** As T **91,** but inscr. "FRANQUEO OFICIAL" below building.
O 611. 1 c. black and green .. 10 10
O 612. 2 c. black and red .. 10 10
O 613. 3 c. black and yellow .. 10 10
O 614. 5 c. black and blue .. 10 10
O 615. 10 c. black and violet .. 10 10
O 616. 13 c. black and violet .. 15 15
O 617. 15 c. black and sepia .. 15 15
O 618. 24 c. black and red .. 15 15
O 619. 50 c. black and yellow .. 15 15
O 620. 100 c. black and blue .. 25 15

These stamps also exist optd. with shield, Type **66.**

**1910.** As T **99** but inscr. "OFICIAL" below portrait.

| No. | Type | Description | | |
|---|---|---|---|---|
| O 655. | | 2 c. black and green .. | 15 | 15 |
| O 656. | | 3 c. black and orange .. | 15 | 15 |
| O 657. | | 4 c. black and red | 15 | 15 |
| O 658. | | 5 c. black and violet .. | 15 | 15 |
| O 659. | | 6 c. black and red .. | 15 | 15 |
| O 660. | | 10 c. black and violet .. | 15 | 15 |
| O 661. | | 12 c. black and blue .. | 15 | 15 |
| O 662. | | 17 c. black and green .. | 15 | 15 |
| O 663. | | 19 c. black and brown .. | 15 | 15 |
| O 664. | | 29 c. black and brown .. | 15 | 15 |
| O 665. | | 50 c. black and yellow .. | 15 | 15 |
| O 666. | | 100 c. black and blue .. | 15 | 15 |

**1911.** Stamps of 1900, dated "1900", optd. **OFICIAL** and black circles or surch. also.

| No. | Type | Description | | |
|---|---|---|---|---|
| O 667. | **59.** | 1 c. green .. .. | 10 | 10 |
| O 668. | | 3 c. on 13 c. brown .. | 10 | 10 |
| O 669. | | 5 c. on 10 c. green .. | 10 | 10 |
| O 670. | | 10 c. green .. .. | 10 | 10 |
| O 671. | | 12 c. green .. .. | 10 | 10 |
| O 672. | | 13 c. brown .. | 10 | 10 |
| O 673. | | 50 c. on 10 c. green .. | 10 | 10 |
| O 674. | | 1 col. on 13 c. brown | 15 | 15 |

O 112. O 113.

**1914.** Words of background in green, shield and word "PROVISIONAL" in black.

| No. | Type | Description | | |
|---|---|---|---|---|
| O 675. | **O 112.** | 2 c. brown .. .. | 10 | 10 |
| O 676. | | 3 c. yellow .. .. | 10 | 10 |
| O 677. | | 5 c. blue .. .. | 10 | 10 |
| O 678. | | 10 c. red .. .. | 10 | 10 |
| O 679. | | 12 c. green .. .. | 10 | 10 |
| O 680. | | 17 c. violet .. | 10 | 10 |
| O 681. | | 50 c. brown .. | 10 | 10 |
| O 682. | | 100 c. brown .. | 10 | 10 |

**1915.**

| No. | Type | Description | | |
|---|---|---|---|---|
| O 683. | **O 113.** | 2 c. green .. .. | 10 | 10 |
| O 684. | | 3 c. orange .. .. | 10 | 10 |

**1915.** Stamps of 1915, with optd. **1915** optd. **OFICIAL.**

| No. | Type | Description | | |
|---|---|---|---|---|
| O 685. | **91.** | 1 c. grey (No. 675) .. | 25 | 20 |
| O 686. | | 2 c. red .. .. | 25 | 20 |
| O 687. | | 5 c. blue .. .. | 25 | 20 |
| O 688. | | 6 c. blue .. .. | 50 | 40 |
| O 689. | | 10 c. yellow .. .. | 25 | 25 |
| O 690. | | 12 c. brown .. .. | 60 | 60 |
| O 691. | | 50 c. purple .. .. | 60 | 50 |
| O 692. | | 100 c. brown .. .. | 90 | 70 |

**1916.** Stamps of 1916 optd. **OFICIAL.**

| No. | Type | Description | | |
|---|---|---|---|---|
| O 694. | **113.** | 1 c. green .. .. | 40 | 65 |
| O 695. | | 2 c. red .. .. | 1·50 | 1·50 |
| O 696. | | 5 c. blue .. .. | 1·10 | 1·50 |
| O 697. | | 6 c. violet .. .. | 40 | 65 |
| O 698. | | 10 c. brown .. | 40 | 65 |
| O 699. | | 12 c. purple .. .. | 1·75 | 2·75 |
| O 700. | | 17 c. orange .. | 40 | 65 |
| O 701. | | 25 c. brown .. | 40 | 65 |
| O 702. | | 29 c. black .. .. | 40 | 65 |
| O 703. | | 50 c. grey .. .. | 40 | 65 |

**1922.** Stamps of 1921 optd. **OFICIAL.**

| No. | Type | Description | | |
|---|---|---|---|---|
| O 736. | **130.** | 1 c. green .. .. | 15 | 10 |
| O 737. | – | 2 c. black .. .. | 15 | 10 |
| O 738. | **131.** | 5 c. orange .. .. | 20 | 15 |
| O 739. | **132.** | 6 c. red .. .. | 15 | 10 |
| O 740. | **133.** | 10 c. blue .. .. | 25 | 20 |
| O 741. | – | 25 c. green .. .. | 40 | 35 |
| O 742. | **135.** | 60 c. sepia .. .. | 50 | 50 |
| O 743. | – | 1 col. sepia .. .. | 50 | 60 |

**1925.** Stamps of 1924 optd. **OFICIAL.**

| No. | Type | Description | | |
|---|---|---|---|---|
| O 768. | **141.** | 1 c. purple .. .. | 15 | 10 |
| O 769. | – | 2 c. red .. .. | 35 | 10 |
| O 770. | – | 5 c. black .. .. | 15 | 10 |
| O 765. | – | 6 c. blue .. .. | 7·00 | 5·75 |
| O 766. | **146.** | 10 c. orange .. .. | 35 | 15 |
| O 767. | **150.** | 1 col. blue and green | 1·10 | 70 |

**1947.** Stamps of 1947 optd. **OFICIAL.**

| No. | Type | Description | | |
|---|---|---|---|---|
| O 959. | **155.** | 1 c. red .. .. | 30·00 | 14·00 |
| O 960. | – | 2 c. yellow .. .. | 30·00 | 14·00 |
| O 961. | – | 5 c. grey .. .. | 30·00 | 14·00 |
| O 962. | – | 10 c. yellow .. | 30·00 | 14·00 |
| O 963. | – | 20 c. green .. .. | 30·00 | 14·00 |
| O 964. | – | 50 c. black .. .. | 30·00 | 14·00 |

**1964.** No. O 963 further surch. **1 CTS XX.**

| No. | Type | Description | | |
|---|---|---|---|---|
| O 1198. | | 1 c. on 20 c. green .. .. | | |

OFFICIAL REGISTRATION STAMP

**1897.** Registration stamp optd. **FRANQUEO OFICIAL** in oval.

| No. | Type | Description | | |
|---|---|---|---|---|
| OR 268. | R **54.** | 10 c. blue .. .. | 20 | |

PARCEL POST STAMPS

P **35.** Hermes.

**1895.**

| No. | Type | Description | | |
|---|---|---|---|---|
| P 127. | P **35.** | 5 c. orange .. .. | 30 | 50 |
| P 128. | | 10 c. blue .. .. | 30 | 50 |
| P 129. | | 15 c. red .. .. | 30 | 75 |
| P 130. | | 20 c. orange .. .. | 30 | 75 |
| P 131. | | 50 c. green .. .. | 30 | 75 |

POSTAGE DUE STAMPS

D **33.** D **72.** Columbus Monument.

**1895.**

| No. | Type | Description | | |
|---|---|---|---|---|
| D 107. | D **33.** | 1 c. green .. .. | 10 | 15 |
| D 108. | | 2 c. green .. .. | 10 | 15 |
| D 109. | | 3 c. green .. .. | 10 | 15 |
| D 110. | | 5 c. green .. .. | 10 | 20 |
| D 111. | | 10 c. green .. .. | 10 | 20 |
| D 112. | | 15 c. green .. .. | 10 | 25 |
| D 113. | | 25 c. green .. .. | 10 | 50 |
| D 114. | | 50 c. green .. .. | 30 | 50 |

**1896.**

| No. | Type | Description | | |
|---|---|---|---|---|
| D 150. | D **33.** | 1 c. red .. .. | 10 | 15 |
| D 151. | | 2 c. red .. .. | 10 | 15 |
| D 152. | | 3 c. red .. .. | 10 | 15 |
| D 153. | | 5 c. red .. .. | 10 | 15 |
| D 154. | | 10 c. red .. .. | 10 | 20 |
| D 155. | | 15 c. red .. .. | 15 | 30 |
| D 156. | | 25 c. red .. .. | 15 | 30 |
| D 157. | | 50 c. red .. .. | 15 | 40 |

**1897.**

| No. | Type | Description | | |
|---|---|---|---|---|
| D 256. | D **33.** | 1 c. blue .. .. | 10 | 15 |
| D 257. | | 2 c. blue .. .. | 10 | 15 |
| D 258. | | 3 c. blue .. .. | 10 | 15 |
| D 259. | | 5 c. blue .. .. | 10 | 15 |
| D 260. | | 10 c. blue .. .. | 15 | 20 |
| D 261. | | 15 c. blue .. .. | 15 | 25 |
| D 262. | | 25 c. blue .. .. | 10 | 30 |
| D 263. | | 50 c. blue .. .. | 10 | 40 |

**1898.**

| No. | Type | Description | | |
|---|---|---|---|---|
| D 302. | D **33.** | 1 c. violet .. .. | 15 | 15 |
| D 303. | | 2 c. violet .. .. | 15 | 15 |
| D 304. | | 3 c. violet .. .. | 15 | 15 |
| D 305. | | 5 c. violet .. .. | 15 | 15 |
| D 306. | | 10 c. violet .. .. | 30 | 50 |
| D 307. | | 15 c. violet .. .. | 15 | 20 |
| D 308. | | 25 c. violet .. .. | 15 | 25 |
| D 309. | | 50 c. violet .. .. | 20 | 50 |

**1899.** Optd. with T **35.**

| No. | Type | Description | | |
|---|---|---|---|---|
| D 347. | D **33.** | 1 c. orange .. .. | 35 | 35 |
| D 348. | | 2 c. orange .. .. | 35 | 35 |
| D 349. | | 3 c. orange .. .. | 35 | 35 |
| D 350. | | 5 c. orange .. .. | 55 | 55 |
| D 351. | | 10 c. orange .. .. | 70 | 70 |
| D 352. | | 15 c. orange .. .. | 70 | 70 |
| D 353. | | 25 c. orange .. .. | 90 | 90 |
| D 354. | | 50 c. orange .. .. | 1·00 | 1·00 |

**1903.**

| No. | Type | Description | | |
|---|---|---|---|---|
| D 507. | D **72.** | 1 c. green .. .. | 90 | 70 |
| D 508. | | 2 c. red .. .. | 1·50 | 1·10 |
| D 509. | | 3 c. orange .. .. | 1·50 | 1·10 |
| D 510. | | 5 c. blue .. .. | 1·50 | 1·10 |
| D 511. | | 10 c. purple .. .. | 1·50 | 1·10 |
| D 512. | | 25 c. green .. .. | 1·50 | 1·10 |

**1908.** Stamps of 1907 optd. **Deficiencia de franqueo.**

| No. | Type | Description | | |
|---|---|---|---|---|
| D 623. | **91.** | 1 c. black and green | 20 | 20 |
| D 624. | | 2 c. black and red | 20 | 20 |
| D 625. | | 3 c. black & yellow | 25 | 25 |
| D 626. | | 5 c. black & blue .. | 40 | 40 |
| D 627. | | 10 c. blk. & violet .. | 70 | 70 |

**1908.** Stamps of 1907 optd. **DEFICIENCIA DE FRANQUEO.**

| No. | Type | Description | | |
|---|---|---|---|---|
| D 628. | **91.** | 1 c. black and green | 30 | 30 |
| D 629. | | 2 c. black and red .. | 20 | 20 |
| D 630. | **91.** | 5 c. black and blue | 55 | 40 |
| D 631. | | 10 c. black & mauve | 80 | 70 |
| D 632. | – | 3 c. black & yellow (No. O 613) | 55 | 50 |

**1910.** As T **99**, but inscr. "FRANQUEO DEFICIENTE" below portrait.

| No. | Type | Description | | |
|---|---|---|---|---|
| D 655. | | 1 c. black and brown .. | 15 | 15 |
| D 656. | | 2 c. black and green .. | 15 | 15 |
| D 657. | | 3 c. black and yellow .. | 15 | 15 |
| D 658. | | 4 c. black and red .. | 15 | 15 |
| D 659. | | 5 c. black and violet .. | 15 | 15 |
| D 660. | | 12 c. black and blue .. | 15 | 15 |
| D 661. | | 24 c. black and red .. | 15 | 15 |

REGISTRATION STAMP

R **54.** Gen. R. A. Gutierrez.

**1897.**

| No. | Type | Description | | |
|---|---|---|---|---|
| R 266. | R **54.** | 10 c. lake .. .. | 20 | 30 |



## EQUATORIAL GUINEA Pt. 12

The former Spanish Overseas Provinces of Fernando Poo and Rio Muni united on 12 October 1968, to become the Republic of Equatorial Guinea.

1968. 100 centimos = 1 peseta.
1973. 100 centimos = 1 ekuele (plural: bipkwele).
1985. 100 centimos = 1 franc (CFA).

**1.** Clasped Hands. **2.** President Macias Nguema.

**1968.** Independence.

| No. | Type | Description | | |
|---|---|---|---|---|
| 1. | **1.** | 1 p. sepia, gold and blue .. | 10 | 10 |
| 2. | | 1 p. 50 sepia, gold & green | 10 | 10 |
| 3. | | 6 p. sepia, gold and red .. | 15 | 10 |

**1970.** 1st Anniv. (12.10.69) of Independence.

| No. | Type | Description | | |
|---|---|---|---|---|
| 4. | **2.** | 50 c. red, purple & orange | 10 | 10 |
| 5. | | 1 p. purple, green & mauve | 10 | 10 |
| 6. | | 1 p. 50 green and purple .. | 10 | 10 |
| 7. | | 2 p. green and buff .. | 10 | 10 |
| 8. | | 2 p. 50 blue and green .. | 10 | 10 |
| 9. | | 10 p. purple, blue & brown | 60 | 10 |
| 10. | | 25 p. brown, black & grey | 1·10 | 15 |

**3.** Pres. Macias Nguema and Cockerel.

**1971.** 2nd Anniv. of Independence.

| No. | Type | Description | | |
|---|---|---|---|---|
| 11. | **3.** | 3 p. multicoloured .. | 10 | 10 |
| 12. | | 5 p. multicoloured .. | 15 | 10 |
| 13. | | 10 p. multicoloured .. | 25 | 10 |
| 14. | | 25 p. multicoloured .. | 40 | 20 |

**5.** Flaming Torch.

**1972.** 3rd Year of Independence.

| No. | Type | Description | | |
|---|---|---|---|---|
| 17. | **5.** | 50 p. multicoloured .. | 1·00 | 35 |

**6.** Pres. Macias Nguema, Hands and Fruit.

**1979.** 4th Anniv. of Independence (1972). Multicoloured.

| No. | Type | Description | | |
|---|---|---|---|---|
| 18. | | 1 p. 50, Type **6** .. .. | 10 | 10 |
| 19. | | 2 p. Classroom .. .. | 10 | 10 |
| 20. | | 3 p. Soldiers and sailors on parade .. .. | 10 | 10 |
| 21. | | 4 p. As No. 19 .. .. | 10 | 10 |
| 22. | | 5 p. As No. 20 .. .. | 15 | 10 |

**7.** Party Emblem.

**1979.** United National Workers' Party.

| No. | Type | Description | | |
|---|---|---|---|---|
| 23. | **7.** | 1 p. multicoloured .. | 10 | 10 |
| 24. | | 1 p. 50 multicoloured .. | 10 | 10 |
| 25. | | 2 p. multicoloured .. | 10 | 10 |
| 26. | | 4 p. multicoloured .. | 10 | 10 |
| 27. | | 5 p. multicoloured .. | 15 | 10 |

**8.** Ekuele Coin.

**1979.** 5th Anniv. of Independence (1973) (1st issue).

| No. | Type | Description | | |
|---|---|---|---|---|
| 28. | **8.** | 1 e. multicoloured .. | 10 | 10 |

**9.** State Palace. **10.** Pres. Macias Nguema.

**1979.** Independence (1973) (2nd issue). National Enterprises. Multicoloured.

| No. | Type | Description | | |
|---|---|---|---|---|
| 29. | | 1 e. Bata harbour .. .. | 15 | 10 |
| 30. | | 1 e. 50 Type **9** .. .. | 10 | 10 |
| 31. | | 2 e. Bata Central Bank | 10 | 10 |
| 32. | | 2 e. 50 Nguema Biyogo bridge | 10 | 10 |
| 33. | | 3 e. Pres. Nguema and scenes as on Nos. 29/32 .. .. | 15 | 10 |

**1979.** 3rd Congress of United National Workers' Party.

| No. | Type | Description | | |
|---|---|---|---|---|
| 34. | **10.** | 1 e. 50 multicoloured .. | 10 | 10 |

**11.** Salvador Ndongo Ekang. **12.** Hands cupping Seedling.

**1979.** Martyrs of Independence. Mult.

| No. | Type | Description | | |
|---|---|---|---|---|
| 35. | | 1 e. Enrique Nvo .. .. | 10 | 10 |
| 36. | | 1 e. 50 Type **11** .. .. | 10 | 10 |
| 37. | | 2 e. Acacio Mane .. .. | 10 | 10 |

**1979.** Experimental Agriculture Year.

| No. | Type | Description | | |
|---|---|---|---|---|
| 38. | **12.** | 1 e. multicoloured .. | 10 | 10 |
| 39. | | 1 e. 50 multicoloured .. | 10 | 10 |

**12a.** Boy and Bells.

**1980.** Christmas.

| No. | Type | Description | | |
|---|---|---|---|---|
| 39b | **12a** | 25 b. multicoloured .. | 70 | 50 |

**13.** Obiang Esono Nguema. **14.** King Juan Carlos and Pres. Obiang Nguema.

**1981.** National Heroes.

| No. | Type | Description | | |
|---|---|---|---|---|
| 40. | **13.** | 5 b. blue, yellow & black | 10 | 10 |
| 41. | – | 15 b. purple, brown and black .. .. | 10 | 10 |
| 42. | – | 25 b. red, grey and black | 20 | 10 |
| 43. | – | 35 b. green, pink & black | 30 | 15 |
| 44. | – | 50 b. blue, green & black | 40 | 20 |
| 45. | – | 100 b. multicoloured .. | 75 | 40 |

DESIGNS: 15 b. Fernando Nvara Engonga. 25 b. Ela Edjodjomo Mangue. 35 b. Lt.-Col. Obiang Nguema Mbasogo. 50 b. Hipolito Micha Eworo. 100 b. National coat of arms

**1981.** Visit of King and Queen of Spain. Mult.

| No. | Type | Description | | |
|---|---|---|---|---|
| 46. | | 50 b. Royal couple and President at reception .. | 40 | 20 |
| 47. | | 100 b. Official welcoming ceremony at airport .. | 1·00 | 50 |
| 48. | | 150 b. Type **14** .. .. | 1·00 | 60 |

**15.** Choristers. **16.** Pope John Paul II.

**1981.** Christmas.

49. **15.** 100 b. multicoloured .. 75 90
50. – 150 b. brn., blue & yell. 1·00 60

DESIGN: 150 b. Three Kings on camels and head of African.

**1982.** Papal Visit. Multicoloured.

51. 100 b. Arms of Pope and Equatorial Guinea .. 75 40
52. 200 b. President Obiang Nguema greeting Pope .. 1·25 75
53. 300 b. Type **16** .. .. 1·75 1·25

**17.** Footballer and Emblem.

**1982.** World Cup Football Championship, Spain. Multicoloured.

54. 40 b. Type **17** .. .. 35 15
55. 60 b. Footballer and championship mascot .. 45 25
56. 100 b. World Cup and footballer .. .. 75 40
57. 200 b. Footballers .. .. 1·25 75

**18.** Stars.

**1982.** Christmas. Multicoloured.

58. 100 b. Type **18** .. .. 75 40
59. 200 b. King offering gift .. 1·25 75

**19.** Gorilla.

**1982.** Protected Animals. Multicoloured.

60. 40 b. Type **19** .. .. 40 15
61. 60 b. Hippopotamus .. 55 30
62. 80 b. African brush-tailed porcupine .. .. .. 65 35
63. 120 b. Leopard .. .. 90 60

**20.** Postal Runner.

**1983.** World Communications Year. Mult.

64. 150 b. Type **20** .. .. 1·00 60
65. 200 b. Drummer and microwave station .. .. 1·25 75

**21.** Tropical Flowers.

**1983.** Multicoloured.

66. 300 b. Type **21** .. .. 1·25 80
67. 400 b. Forest .. .. 1·60 1·25

**22.** Great Egret, Dancer and Musical Instruments.

**1983.** Christmas. Multicoloured.

68. 80 b. Type **22** .. .. 1·50 40
69. 100 b. Holy Family .. 40 25

**23.** Annobon and Bioko.

**1984.** Constitution of State Powers. Multicoloured

70. 50 b. Type **23** .. .. 20 10
71. 100 b. Mainland regions .. 40 25

**24.** Hunting Sperm Whales.

**1984.** Marine Resources. Multicoloured.

72. 125 b. Type **24** .. .. 1·25 75
73. 150 b. Capturing a turtle .. 1·25 75

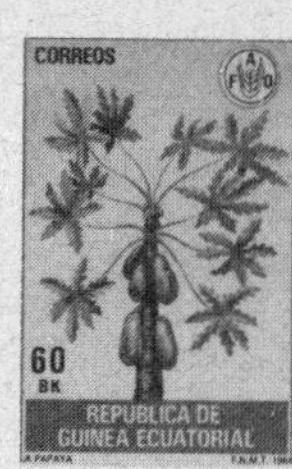

**25.** Pawpaw. **26.** Mother and Child.

**1984.** World Food Day. Multicoloured.

74. 60 b. Type **25** .. .. 30 20
75. 80 b. Malanga .. .. 40 25

**1984.** Christmas. Multicoloured.

76. 60 b. Type **26** .. .. 30 20
77. 100 b. Musical instruments 50 30

**27.** "Black Gazelle" and Anxiety" (wood carvings).

**1985.** Art.

78. **27.** 25 b. multicoloured .. 15 10
79. – 30 b. multicoloured .. 15 10
80. – 60 b. multicoloured .. 30 20
81. – 75 b. black, red & yellow 40 25
82. – 100 b. multicoloured .. 50 30
83. – 150 b. multicoloured .. 75 45

DESIGNS—HORIZ. 30 b. "Black Gazelle" (different) and "Woman" (wood carvings). 150 b. "Man and Woman" and "Bust of Woman" (wood carvings). VERT. 60 b. "Man and Woman" (different). 75 b. Poster. 100 b. "Mother and Child" (wood carving).

**28.** Mission Emblem. **29.** Postal Emblem.

**1985.** Immaculate Conception Mission. Centenary. Multicoloured.

84. 50 f. Type **28** .. .. 20 15
85. 60 f. Nun teaching children in African village .. 20 15
86. 80 f. First Guinean nuns .. 30 20
87. 125 f. Nuns landing on Bata beach .. .. .. 45 25

**1985.** Postal Service. Multicoloured.

88. 50 f. Type **29** .. .. 20 15
89. 80 f. Jose Mavule Ndjong, first Guinean postman .. 30 20

**30.** Nativity.

**1985.** Christmas. Multicoloured.

90. 40 f. Type **30** .. .. 15 10
91. 70 f. Musicians, dancer and woman with baby .. 30 20

**31.** Crab and Snail.

**1986.** Nature Protection. Multicoloured.

92. 15 f. Type **31** .. .. 20 10
93. 35 f. Butterflies, bees, chaffinch and grey-headed kingfisher .. 1·25 25
94. 45 f. Plants .. .. .. 20 15
95. 65 f. Men working on cacao crop .. .. .. 30 20

**32.** Mekuyo Dancers.

**1986.** Folk Customs. Multicoloured.

96. 10 f. Type **32** .. .. 10 10
97. 50 f. Kokom dancers .. 20 15
98. 65 f. Bisila girl .. .. 30 20
99. 80 f. Ndong-Mba man .. 35 20

**33.** Footballers and Emblem.

**1986.** World Cup Football Championship, Mexico. Designs showing various footballing scenes.

100. **33.** 50 f. multicoloured .. 20 15
101. – 100 f. multicoloured .. 45 25
102. – 150 f. mult. (vert.) .. 65 40
103. – 200 f. mult. (vert.) .. 85 50

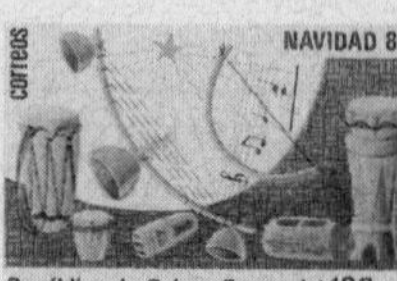


**34.** Musical Instruments.

**1986.** Christmas. Multicoloured.

104. 100 f. Type **34** .. .. 40 25
105. 150 f. Mother breast-feeding baby .. .. 60 35

**35.** Map and Member Countries' Flag. **36.** Coins and Hen with Chick.

**1986.** Union of Central African States Conference. Multicoloured.

106. 80 f. Type **35** .. .. 35 20
107. 100 f. Maps .. .. .. 40 25

**1987.** Campaign against Hunger.

108. **36.** 60 f. pur., orge. & blk. 25 15
109. – 80 f. blue, orge. & blk. 35 20
110. – 100 f. brown, orange and black .. .. 40 25

DESIGNS: 80 f. Coins and fish in net. 100 f. Coins and ear of wheat.

**37.** Dove and Open Door.

**1987.** International Peace Year. Mult.

111. 100 f. Type **37** .. .. 40 25
112. 200 f. Hands holding dove 80 50

**38.** Night Sky and Envelope.

**1987.** World Stamp Day. Multicoloured.

113. 150 f. Type **38** .. .. 60 35
114. 300 f. Banner of national colours and envelope .. 1·10 75

**39.** Mother and Child. **40** Man climbing Palm Tree

**1987.** Christmas. Wood Sculptures. Mult.

115. 80 f. Type **39** .. .. 30 15
116. 100 f. Mother and child (different) .. .. 40 20

**1988.** International Labour Day. Mult.

117 50 f. Type **40** .. .. 20 15
118 75 f. Woman with catch of fish .. .. .. 30 20
119 150 f. Chopping down tree 60 35

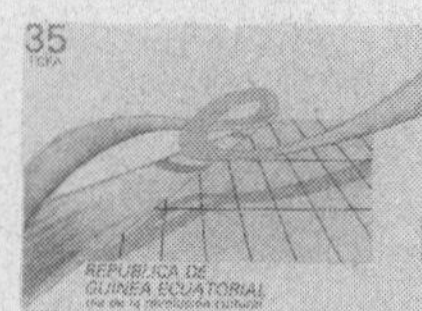


**41** Ribbons

**1988.** Cultural Revolution Day. Mult.

120 35 f. Type **41** .. .. 15 10
121 50 f. Cubes and sphere .. 20 15
122 100 f. Stylized dove .. 40 25

**42** Party Badge    **43** Musician

**1988.** 1st Anniv of Democratic Party of Equatorial Guinea. Multicoloured.

123 40 f. Type **42** .. .. 15 10
124 75 f. Torch and concentric circles (horiz) .. .. 30 20
125 100 f. Torch (horiz) .. 40 25

**1988.** Christmas. Multicoloured.

126 50 f. Type **43** .. .. 20 15
127 100 f. Mother, child and stars .. .. .. 40 25

**44** Lorry loaded with Logs

**1989.** 20th Anniv of Independence. Mult.

128 10 f. Type **44** .. .. 10 10
129 35 f. Traditional folk gathering .. .. 15 10
130 45 f. President at official function .. .. 20 15

**45** Bathers at Ilachi Waterfall    **47** Stringed Instrument

**46** Palace of Congresses

**1989.** Water. Multicoloured.

131 15 f. Type **45** .. .. 10 10
132 25 f. La Selva waterfall .. 10 10
133 60 f. Boy drinking from green coconut and youths in water .. 25 15

**1989.** 1st Democratic Party Congress. Mult.

134 25 f. Type **46** .. .. 10 10
135 35 f. Torch (party emblem) (vert) .. .. 15 10
136 40 f. Pres. Obiang Nguema Mbasogo (vert) .. 15 10

**1989.** Christmas. Multicoloured.

137 150 f. Type **47** .. .. 60 35
138 300 f. Mother with child and drummer (horiz) .. 1·25 80

**48** Sir Robert Baden-Powell (founder)

**1990.** Boy Scout Movement. Multicoloured.

139 100 f. Type **48** .. .. 40 25
140 250 f. Scout saluting .. 1·00 70
141 350 f. Scout with bugle .. 1·40 90

**49** Player and Map of Italy

**1990.** World Cup Football Championship, Italy. Multicoloured.

142 100 f. Type **49** .. .. 40 25
143 250 f. Goalkeeper and ball in net .. .. .. 1·00 70
144 350 f. Trophy and globe .. 1·40 90

**50** Drums and Horn (Ndowe tribe)

**1990.** Musical Instruments. Multicoloured.

145 100 f. Type **50** .. .. 40 25
146 250 f. Drums, horn, pipes and stringed instruments (Fang) .. .. 1·00 70
147 350 f. Flute and cup, bell and horn (Bubi) .. 1·40 90

**51** Arrival in America of Columbus

**1990.** 500th Anniv (1992) of Discovery of America by Columbus (1st issue). Mult.

148 170 f. Type **51** .. .. 90 50
149 300 f. "Santa Maria", "Pinta" and "Nina" .. 1·60 1·00

See also Nos. 165/7.

**52** Mother and Child

**1990.** Christmas. Multicoloured.

150 170 f. Type **52** .. .. 70 40
151 300 f. Bubi man ringing handbell .. .. 1·25 80

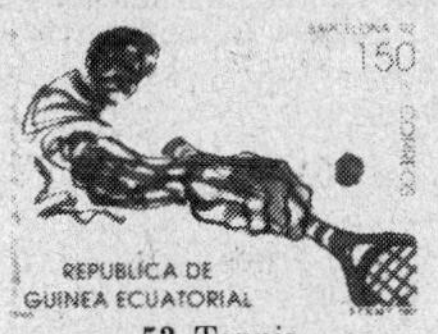


**53** Tennis

**1991.** Olympic Games, Barcelona (1992) (1st issue). Multicoloured.

152 150 f. Type **53** .. .. 70 45
153 250 f. Cycling .. .. 1·10 70

See also Nos. 168/9.

**54** "The Naked Maja" (Francisco de Goya)

**1991.** Paintings. Multicoloured

155 100 f. Type **54** .. .. 45 25
156 250 f. "Eve" (Albrecht Durer) (vert) .. .. 1·10 70
157 350 f. "The Three Graces" (Peter Paul Rubens) (vert) .. .. .. 1·60 1·00

**55** Mandrill

**1991.** The Mandrill. Multicoloured.

158 25 f. Type **55** .. .. 10 10
159 25 f. Close-up of face .. 10 10
160 25 f. On all fours (horiz) .. 10 10
161 25 f. With foreleg raised .. 10 10

**56** Japanese Electric Locomotive, 1932

**1991.** Railway Locomotives. Multicoloured.

162 150 f. Type **56** .. .. 70 45
163 250 f. U.S.A. locomotive, 1873 .. .. .. 1·10 70

**57** Vicente Pinzon and "Nina"

**1991.** 500th Anniv (1992) of Discovery of America by Columbus (2nd issue). Mult.

165 150 f. Type **57** .. .. 70 45
166 250 f. Martin Pinzon and "Pinta" .. .. 1·10 70
167 350 f. Christopher Columbus and "Santa Maria" .. .. .. 1·60 1·00

**58** Basketball

**1992.** Olympic Games, Barcelona (2nd issue). Multicoloured.

168 200 f. Type **58** .. .. 90 60
169 300 f. Swimming .. .. 1·40 90

**60** Blue-breasted Kingfisher and Black-winged Stilt    **62** "Termitomyces globulus"

**61** Scene from "Casablanca"

**1992.** Nature Protection. Multicoloured.

172 150 f. Type **60** .. .. 40 25
173 250 f. Great blue turaco and grey parrot .. 65 40

**1992.** Centenary of Motion Pictures.

175 **61** 100 f. blue and black .. 25 15
176 – 250 f. green and black .. 65 40
177 – 350 f. brown and black 90 60

DESIGNS: 250 f. Scene from "Viridiana"; 350 f. Scene from "A Couple of Gypsies".

**1992.** Fungi. Multicoloured.

178 75 f. Type **62** .. .. 35 15
179 125 f. "Termitomyces letestui" .. .. 55 30
180 150 f. "Termitomyces robustus" .. .. 65 35

**63** "Virgin and Child amongst the Saints" (Claudio Coello)

**1993.** Painters' Anniversaries. Multicoloured.

181 200 f. Type **63** (300th death anniv) .. .. .. 50 30
182 300 f. "Apollo, Conqueror of Marsyas" (Jacob Jordaens) (400th birth anniv) .. .. .. 80 50

**64** Scene from "Romeo and Juliet" and Pyotr Ilyich Tchaikovsky

**1993.** Composers' Death Centenaries. Mult.

184 100 f. Type **64** .. .. 25 15
185 200 f. Scene from "Faust" (opera) and Charles Gounod .. .. 50 30

**65** Quincy Watts (400 m.)

**1993.** Gold Medal Winners at Olympic Games, Barcelona, and Winter Olympic Games, Albertville. Multicoloured.

186 100 f. Type **65** .. .. 25 15
187 250 f. Martin Lopez Zubero (200 m. backstroke) .. 65 40
188 350 f. Petra Kronbreger (slalom and combined) 90 60
189 400 f. "Flying Dutchman" class yacht (Luis Doreste and Domingo Manrique) 1·00 65

**66** Ford's First Motor Car

**1993.** 130th Birth Anniv of Henry Ford (motor car manufacturer).

190 **66** 200 f. multicoloured .. 50 30
191 – 300 f. multicoloured .. 80 50
192 – 400 f. black and red .. 1·00 65

DESIGNS—HORIZ: 300 f. Model "T" motor car. VERT: 400 f. Henry Ford.

**67** Pres. Obiang Nguema Mbasogo

**1993.** 25th Anniv of Independence. Mult.

193 150 f. Type **67** .. .. 40 25
194 250 f. Oil refinery, ship, map and radio mast (horiz) .. .. 65 40
195 300 f. Hydro-electric station, Riaba, and waterfall (horiz) .. 80 50
196 350 f. Woman, bridge and man (horiz) .. .. 90 60

68 Lunar Module "Eagle"

**1994.** 25th Anniv of First Manned Moon Landing. Multicoloured.

| | | | |
|---|---|---|---|
| 197 | 500 f. Type **68** .. .. | 1·25 | 80 |
| 198 | 700 f. Buzz Aldrin, Michael Collins and Neil Armstrong (astronauts) | 1·75 | 1·10 |
| 199 | 900 f. Footprint on Moon and module reflected in astronaut's visor .. | 2·25 | 1·50 |

69 German Team (1990 champions)

**1994.** World Cup Football Championship, U.S.A. Multicoloured.

| | | | |
|---|---|---|---|
| 200 | 200 f. Type **69** .. .. | 50 | 30 |
| 201 | 300 f. Rose Bowl Stadium, Los Angeles .. .. | 75 | 45 |
| 202 | 500 f. Player dribbling ball (vert) .. .. .. | 1·25 | 80 |

70 "Chasmosauraus belli"

**1994.** Prehistoric Animals. Multicoloured.

| | | | |
|---|---|---|---|
| 203 | 300 f. Type **70** .. .. | 75 | 45 |
| 204 | 500 f. "Tyrannosaurus rex" | 1·25 | 80 |
| 205 | 700 f. "Triceratops horridus" .. .. | 1·75 | 1·10 |

71 Gold Calcite

**1994.** Minerals. Multicoloured.

| | | | |
|---|---|---|---|
| 207 | 300 f. Type **71** .. .. | 75 | 45 |
| 208 | 400 f. Pyromorphite .. | 95 | 60 |
| 209 | 600 f. Fluorite .. .. | 1·40 | 90 |
| 210 | 700 f. Halite .. .. | 1·75 | 1·10 |

72 Poster for "Elena y los Hombres" and Jean Renoir (film director)

**1994.** Anniversaries. Multicoloured.

| | | | |
|---|---|---|---|
| 211 | 300 f. Type **72** (birth cent) | 75 | 45 |
| 212 | 500 f. Map and Ferdinand Marie de Lesseps (director of Suez Canal development, death centenary) .. .. | 1·25 | 80 |
| 213 | 600 f. Illustration from "The Little Prince" and Antoine de Saint-Exupery (pilot and writer, 50th death anniv) | 1·40 | 90 |
| 214 | 700 f. Bauhaus (75th anniv) and Walter Gropius (architect) .. .. | 1·75 | 1·10 |

## INDEX

Countries can be quickly located by referring to the index at the end of this volume.

EXPRESS LETTER STAMPS

E 4. Guinea Archer.

**1971.** 3rd Anniv. of Independence.

| | | | |
|---|---|---|---|
| E 15. | E **4.** 4 p. multicoloured .. | 10 | 10 |
| E 16. | 8 p. multicoloured .. | 10 | 10 |

## APPENDIX

The following stamps have either been issued in excess of postal needs or have not been available to the public in reasonable quantities at face value. Such stamps may later be given full listing if there is evidence of regular postal use.

### 1972.

Space Flight of "Apollo 15". Postage 1, 3, 5, 8, 10 p.; Air 15, 25 p.

Winter Olympic Games, Sapporo, Japan. Postage 1, 2, 3, 5, 8 p.; Air 15, 50 p.

Christmas 1971. Paintings. Postage 1, 3, 5, 8, 10 p.; Air 15, 25 p.

Easter. Postage 1, 3, 5, 8, 10 p.; Air 15, 25 p.

Olympic Games, Munich 1972. Augsburg Events. Postage 1, 2, 3, 5, 8 p.; Air 15, 50 p.

Winter Olympic Games, Sapporo, Japan. Gold medal winners. Postage 1, 2, 3, 5, 8 p.; Air 15, 50 p.

Olympic Games, Munich 1972. Buildings and previous medal winners. Postage 1, 2, 3, 5, 8 p.; Air 15, 50 p.

Olympic Games. Sailing and rowing, Kiel. Postage 1, 2, 3, 5, 8 p.; Air 15, 50 p.

Olympic Games Munich. Modern sports. Postage 1, 2, 3, 5, 8 p.; Air 15, 50 p.

Olympic Games, Munich. Equestrian events. Postage 1, 2, 3, 5, 8 p.; Air 15, 50 p.

Centenary of Japanese Railway. Various steam locomotives. Postage 1, 3, 5, 8, 10 p.; Air 15, 25 p.

Olympic Games, Munich. Gold medal winners. Postage 1, 2, 3, 5, 8 p.; Air 15, 50 p.

Christmas 1972. Paintings by Cranach. Postage 1, 3, 5, 8, 10 p.; Air 15, 25.

Cosmonauts Memorial. Designs with black borders. Postage 1, 3, 5, 8, 10 p.; Air 15, 25 p.

### 1973.

Transatlantic Yacht Race 1972. Postage 1, 2, 3, 5, 8 p.; Air 15, 50 p.

Renoir Paintings. Postage 1, 2, 3, 5, 8 p.; Air 15, 50 p.

Conquest of Venus. Postage 1, 3, 5, 8, 10 p.; Air 15, 25 p.

Easter. Religious Paintings by Old Masters. Postage 1, 3, 5, 8, 10 p.; Air 15, 25 p.

"Tour de France" Cycle Race. Postage 1, 2, 3, 5, 8 p.; Air 15, 50 p.

Paintings by European Old Masters. Postage 1, 2, 3, 5, 8 p.; Air 15, 50 p.

World Football Cup Championships, West Germany (1974) (1st issue). Previous Finals. Postage 5, 10, 15, 20, 25, 60 c.; Air 5, 70 p.

Paintings by Rubens. Postage 1, 2, 3, 5, 8 p.; Air 15, 50 p.

Christmas. Religious Paintings. Postage 1, 3, 5, 8, 10 p.; Air 15, 25 p.

World Cup Football Championships, West Germany (1974) (2nd issue). Famous players. Postage 30, 35, 40, 45, 50, 65, 70 c.; Air 8, 60 p.

Paintings by Picasso. Postage 30, 35, 40, 45, 50 c.; Air 8, 60 e.

### 1974.

500th Birth Anniv. of Nicolas Copernicus (astronomer). Postage 5, 10, 15, 20 c.; Air 4, 10, 70 e.

World Cup Football Championships, West Germany (3rd issue). Venues of Qualifying Matches. Postage 75, 80, 85, 90, 95 c., 1 e. 1 e. 25; Air 10, 50 e.

Easter. Postage 1, 3, 5, 8, 10 p.; Air 15, 25 p.

Holy Year. Postage 5, 10, 15, 20 c., 3 e. 50; Air 10, 70 e.

World Cup Football Championships, West Germany (4th issue). Famous Players. Postage 1 e. 50, 1 e. 75, 2 e., 2 e. 25, 2 e. 50, 3 e., 3 e. 50; Air 10, 60 e.

Centenary of U.P.U. (1st issue). Postage 60, 70, 80 c., 1 e. 50; Air 30, 50 e.

First Death Anniv. of Picasso. Postage 55, 60, 65, 70, 75 c.; Air 10, 50 e.

"The Wild West". Postage 30, 35, 40, 45, 50 c.; Air 8, 60 p.

Protected Flowers. Postage 5, 10, 15, 20, 25 c., 1, 3, 5, 8, 10 p.; Air 5, 15, 25, 70 p.

Christmas. Postage 60, 70, 80 c., 1 e., 1 e. 50; Air 30, 50 e.

75th Anniv. of FC Barcelona. Postage 1, 3, 5, 8, 10 e.; Air 15, 60 e.

Centenary of U.P.U. (2nd issue) and "Espana '75" International Stamp Exhibition, Madrid. Postage 1 e, 25, 1 e. 50, 1 e. 75, 2 e., 2 e. 25.; Air 35, 60 e.

Nature Protection (1st series). Australian Animals. Postage 80, 85, 90, 95 c., 1 e.; Air 15, 40 e.

Nature Protection (2nd series).African Animals. Postage 50, 60, 65, 70, 75 c.; Air 10, 70 e.

Nature Protection (3rd series). South American and Australian Birds. Postage 1 p. 25, 1 p. 50, 1 p. 75, 2 p., 2 p. 25, 2 p. 50, 2 p. 75, 3 p., 3 p. 50, 4 p.; Air 20, 25, 30, 35 p.

Nature Protection (4th series). Endangered Species. Postage 10, 15, 20, 25, 30, 35, 40, 45, 50, 55, 60 c., 1 e.; Air 2, 10, 70 e.

### 1975.

Paintings by Picasso. Postage 5, 10, 15, 20, 25 c.; Air 5, 70 e.

Easter. Postage 60, 70, 80 c., 1 e. 1 e. 50; Air 30, 50 e.

Winter Olympic Games, Innsbruck (1976). 5, 10, 15, 20, 25, 30, 35, 40, 45 c., 25, 70 e.

Paintings of Don Quixote. Postage 30, 35, 40, 45, 50 c.; Air 25, 60 e.

Bicent. of American Revolution (1st issue). Postage 5, 20, 40, 75 c., 2, 5, 8 e.; Air 25, 30 e.

Bullfighting. Postage 80, 85, 90 c., 8 e.; Air 35, 40 e.

"Apollo–Soyuz" Space Test Project. Postage 1, 2, 3, 5 e., 5 e. 50, 7 e., 7 e. 50, 9, 15 e.; Air 20, 30 e.

Bicent. of American Revolution (2nd issue). Postage 10, 30, 50 c., 1, 3, 6, 10 e.; Air 12, 40 e.

Nude Paintings. Postage 5, 10, 15, 20, 25, 30, 35, 40, 45, 50, 55, 60 c., 1, 2 e.; Air 10, 70 e.

Ships. Postage 30, 35, 40, 45, 50, 55, 60, 65, 70, 75 c.; Air 8, 10, 50, 60 e.

Christmas. Postage 60, 70, 80 c., 1 e., 1 e. 50; Air 30, 50 e.

Olympic Games, Montreal (1st issue). Postage 50, 60, 70, 80, 90 c.; Air 35, 60 e.

Bicent. of American Revolution (3rd issue). Presidents. Postage 5, 10, 20, 30, 40, 50, 75 c., 1, 2, 3, 5, 6, 8, 10 e.; Air 12, 25, 30, 40 e.

Monkeys. Postage 5, 10, 15, 20, 25 30, 35, 40, 45, 50, 55, 60 c., 1, 2 e.; Air 10, 70 e.

Butterflies (1st series). Postage 5, 10, 15, 20, 25, 30, 35, 40, 45, 50, 55, 60 c., 1, 2 e.; Air 10, 70 e.

Fishes (1st series). Postage 5, 10, 15, 20, 25, 30, 35, 40, 45, 50, 55, 60 c., 1, 2 e.; Air 10, 70 e.

Cats (1st series). Postage 5, 10, 15, 20, 25, 30, 35, 40, 45, 50, 55, 60 c., 1, 2 e.; Air 10, 70 e.

Pres. Francisco Macias Nguema. Postage 1 e. 50, 3 e. 50, 7 e.; Air 300 e.

Arms. Postage 3 e.; Air 100 e.

Government House. 5 e.

International Women's Year. 10 e.

### 1976.

Winter Olympic Games, Innsbruck (1st issue). Postage 50, 55, 60, 65, 70, 75, 80, 85, 90 c.; Air 35, 60 e.

Winter Oympic Games, Innsbruck (2nd issue). Postage 3, 5, 50 e.; Air 200 e.

Bicent of American Revolution (4th issue). Flora and Fauna. Postage 1 e. 50, 3, 5, 7, 25, 100 e.; Air 200 e.

Apollo–Soyuz Project. Optd. on Arms issue. Air 100 e.

Concorde's First Commercial Flight. Optd. on Arms issue. Air 100 e.

Nude Paintings. 7, 10, 25 e.

Easter. Air 200 e.

Olympic Games, Montreal (2nd issue). Postage 7, 10, 25 e.; Air 200 e.

Apollo–Soyuz Project, Concorde, and Telephone Centenary. Postage 3, 5, 50 e.; Air 200 e.

Bicent. of American Revolution (5th issue). Fauna. Postage 1 e. 50, 3, 5, 7, 25, 100 e.; Air 200 e.

Cavalry Officers. Postage 5, 10, 15, 20, 25 c.; Air 5, 70p.

Paintings by El Greco. Postage 1, 3, 5, 8, 10p.; Air 15, 25p.

Olympic Games, Montreal (3rd issue). Rowing and Sailing events. Postage 50, 60, 70, 80, 90c.; Air 30, 60 e.

Olympic Games, Montreal (4th issue). Postage 50, 55, 60, 65, 70, 75, 80, 85, 90c.; Air 35, 60 e.

Veteran Cars. Postage 1, 3, 5, 8, 10p.; Air 15, 25p.

Nature Protection (5th series). European animals. Postage 5, 10, 15, 20, 25c.; Air 5, 70p.

Racing Motorcyclists. 1, 2, 3, 4, 5, 10, 30, 40 e.

Nature Protection (6th series). Flowers of South America and Oceania. Postage 30, 35, 40, 45, 50, 80, 85, 90, 95c., 1p.; Air 8, 15, 40, 60p.

Nature Protection (7th series). Asian animals and birds. Postage 30, 35, 40, 45, 55, 60, 65, 70, 75c., 8p.; Air 50c., 10, 50, 60p.

Nature Protection (8th series). African birds and flowers. Postage 30, 35, 40, 45, 50, 55, 60, 65, 70, 75c.; Air 8, 10, 50, 60p.

Steamships. Postage 80, 85, 90, 95c., 1p.; Air 15, 40p.

Nature Protection (9th series). European birds. Postage 5, 10, 15, 20, 25c.; Air 5, 70p.

Paintings of Ships. Postage 5, 10, 15, 20, 25, 30 e.; Air 50, 60, 65, 70 e.

### 1977.

Nature Protection (10th series). Birds of North America. Postage 80, 85, 90, 95c., 1p.; Air 15, 40p.

Cats (2nd series). Postage 5, 10, 15, 20, 25c.; Air 15, 70 e.

Silver Jubilee of Queen Elizabeth II. Postage 2, 4, 5, 8, 10, 15 e.; Air 20, 35 e.

Nude Drawings. Postage 5, 10, 50, 50 e.; Air 15, 200 e.

Dogs (1st series). Postage 5, 10, 15, 20, 25, 30, 35, 40, 45, 50, 55, 60c., 1, 2 e.; Air 10, 70 e.

World War Air Aces. Postage 5, 10, 15, 20, 25, 30, 35, 40, 45, 50, 55, 60c.; Air 10, 70 e.

Football. Postage 2, 4, 5, 8, 10, 15 e.; Air 20, 35 e.

Butterflies (2nd series). Postage 80, 85, 90, 95c., 8 e.; Air 35, 40 e.

Cars. Postage 5, 10, 15, 20, 25, 30, 35, 40, 45, 50, 55, 60c., 1, 2 e.; Air 10, 70 e.

Chinese Art. Postage 60, 70, 80c., 1e., 1e.50; Air 30, 50 e.

African Masks. Postage 5, 10, 15, 20, 25c.; Air 5, 70 e.

Nature Protection (11th series). Animals of North America. Postage 1 e. 25, 1 e.50, 1 e.75, 2 e., 2 e. 25; Air 20, 50 e.

Napoleon. Scenes from his life. Postage 5, 10, 15, 20, 25, 30, 35, 40, 45, 50, 55, 60c., 1, 2 e.; Air 10, 70 e.

Napoleon. Military uniforms. Postage 5, 10, 15, 20, 25, 30, 35, 40, 45, 50, 55, 60c., 1, 2 e.; Air 10, 70 e.

Nature Protection (12th series). Animals of South America. Postage 2 e. 50, 2 e. 75, 3 e., 3 e.50, 4 e.; Air 25, 35 e.

Nature Protection (13th series). European flowers. Postage 2 e.50, 2 e.75, 3 e.50, 4 e.; Air 25, 30 e.

### 1978.

25th Anniv. of Queen Elizabeth II's Coronation. Members of Royal Family. Postage 2, 5, 8, 10, 12, 15 e.; Air 30, 50, 150 e.

Knights. Postage 5, 10, 15, 20, 25 c.; Air 15, 70 e.

Cats (3rd series). 1, 3, 5, 8, 15, 30, 60, 100 e.

American Astronauts. 1, 3, 5, 8, 15, 30, 60, 100 e.

25th Anniv. of Queen Elizabeth II's Coronation. Medals. 1, 3, 5, 8, 25, 50, 75, 200 e.

Queen Elizabeth II's Coronation. 25th Anniv. Scenes from previous coronations. Air 1, 3, 5, 8, 15, 30, 60, 100 e.

Dogs (2nd series). 1, 3, 5, 8, 15, 30, 60, 100 e.

World Famous Paintings. 1, 3, 5, 8, 25, 50, 75, 200 e.

Butterflies (3rd series). 1, 3, 5, 8, 15, 30, 60, 100 e.

Nature Protection (14th series). Asian flowers. Postage 1 e. 25, 1 e. 50, 1 e. 75, 2 e., 2 e. 25; Air 20, 50 e.

Flowers. 1, 3, 5, 8, 15, 30, 60, 100 e.

Water Birds. 1, 3, 5, 8, 15, 30, 60, 100 e.

World Cup Football Championship. Air 150 e.

Belgrade Conference. Air 250 e.

"Eurphila 78" Exhibition. Air 250 e.

Winter Olympic Games, Lake Placid (1980). Postage 5, 10, 20, 25 e.; Air 70 e.

150th Death Anniv. of Goya. Air 150 e.

Christmas. Painting by Titian. Air 150 e.

Prehistoric Animals. Postage 30, 35, 40, 45, 50 c.; Air 25, 60 e.

Cats (4th series). Postage 2 e. 50, 2 e. 75, 3 e., 3 e. 50, 4 e.; Air 25, 40 e.

### 1979.

Death Centenary of Sir Rowland Hill (1st series). 3, 5, 8, 15, 30, 75, 220 e.

Wright Brothers. 1, 3, 5, 8, 15, 30, 60, 100 e.

Death Bicentenary of Capt. James Cook. Air 100 e.

Fishes (2nd series). Postage 5, 10, 20, 25 c., 1 e. 50; Air 15, 70 e.

Death Centenary of Sir Rowland Hill (2nd series). Stamps. Postage 8, 15, 20, 20, 30 e.; Air 50 e.

International Year of the Child (1st series). Postage 5, 7, 11, 24 e.; Air 75 e.

Death Anniversaries of Schubert, Voltaire, Rousseau and Cranach. Air 100, 100, 100, 100 e.

10th Anniv. (1972) of "Apollo XI" Space Flight."Apollo 15" stamps each surch. 50 e. and inscription. Postage 50 e. on 1, 3, 5, 8, 10 p.; Air 50 e. on 15, 25 p.

European Space Agency Satellite. 200 e.

Fairy Tales. Postage 2, 3, 5, 10, 15, 18 e.; Air 24, 35 e.

Automobiles. Air 35, 50 e.

Fishes (3rd series). 5, 10, 15, 20, 25, 30, 35, 40, 45, 50, 55, 60, 70 c., 1, 2, 10 e.

International Year of the Child (2nd series). Various 1978 stamps optd. with I.Y.C. emblem. On Cats (3rd series). 1, 3, 5, 8, 15, 30, 60, 100 e. On Dogs. 1, 3, 5, 8, 15, 30, 60, 100 e. On Butterflies. 1, 3, 5, 8, 15, 30, 60, 100 e. On Water Birds. 1, 3, 5, 8, 15, 30, 60, 100 e.

"London 1980" Stamp Exhibition. Rowland Hill (1st series) stamps optd. 1, 3, 5, 8, 15, 30, 75, 200 e.

Olympic Games, Moscow (1st series). Postage 2, 3, 5, 8, 10, 15 e.; Air 30, 50 e.

Olympic Games, Moscow (2nd series). Water sports. Postage 5, 10, 20, 25 e.; Air 70 e.

## ERITREA — Pt. 8

A former Italian colony on the Red Sea, north-east Africa. Under British Administration from 1942 to September 1952, when Eritrea was federated with Ethiopia.

Eritrea was declared an independent state in May 1993.

1893. 100 centesimi = 1 lira.
1991. 100 cents = 1 birr.

### ITALIAN COLONY

**1893.** Stamps of Italy optd **Colonia Eritrea** (1 to 5 c.) or **COLONIA ERITREA** (others).

| | | | | |
|---|---|---|---|---|
| 1. | 4. | 1 c. green | 1·50 | 1·25 |
| 2. | 5. | 2 c. brown | 60 | 60 |
| 3. | 23. | 5 c. green | 18·00 | 2·50 |
| 4. | 12. | 10 c. red | 12·00 | 2·00 |
| 5. | | 20 c. orange | 60·00 | 2·00 |
| 6. | | 25 c. blue | £180 | 7·00 |
| 7. | 14. | 40 c. brown | 2·40 | 4·00 |
| 8. | | 45 c. green | 3·00 | 5·50 |
| 9. | | 60 c. mauve | 3·00 | 6·00 |
| 10. | | 1 l. brown and orange | 8·00 | 7·50 |
| 11. | 29. | 5 l. red and blue | £150 | 75·00 |

**1895.** Stamps of Italy optd **Colonia Eritrea** (1 to 5 c.) or **COLONIA ERITREA** (others).

| | | | | |
|---|---|---|---|---|
| 12. | 21. | 1 c. brown | 2·75 | 3·75 |
| 13. | 22. | 2 c. brown | 50 | 70 |
| 14. | 24. | 5 c. green | 50 | 70 |
| 15. | 25. | 10 c. lake | 55 | 70 |
| 16. | 26. | 20 c. orange | 70 | 1·00 |
| 17. | 27. | 25 c. blue | 1·00 | 1·25 |
| 18. | | 45 c. olive | 4·00 | 6·50 |

**1903.** Stamps of Italy optd **Colonia Eritrea**.

| | | | | |
|---|---|---|---|---|
| 19. | 30. | 1 c. brown | 30 | 50 |
| 20. | 31. | 2 c. brown | 30 | 40 |
| 21. | | 5 c. green | 12·00 | 50 |
| 22. | 33. | 10 c. red | 16·00 | 50 |
| 30. | | 15 c. on 20 c. orange | 8·50 | 1·60 |
| 23. | | 20 c. orange | 40 | 60 |
| 24. | | 25 c. blue | 80·00 | 5·00 |
| 25. | | 40 c. brown | 80·00 | 7·50 |
| 26. | | 45 c. olive | 1·00 | 4·00 |
| 27. | | 50 c. violet | 42·00 | 6·00 |
| 28. | 34. | 1 l. brown and green | 75 | 60 |
| 29. | | 5 l. blue and red | 12·00 | 6·00 |

**1908.** Stamps of Italy optd **ERITREA** (20 c.) or **Colonia Eritrea** (others).

| | | | | |
|---|---|---|---|---|
| 31 | 37 | 5 c. green | 15 | 10 |
| 32 | | 10 c. red | 15 | 10 |
| 41 | | 15 c. grey | 2·75 | 1·75 |
| 42 | 41 | 20 c. orange | 1·75 | 6·00 |
| 33 | 39 | 25 c. blue | 1·25 | 80 |
| 43 | | 40 c. brown | 11·00 | 17·00 |
| 44 | | 50 c. violet | 1·60 | 60 |
| 45 | | 60 c. red | 6·00 | 8·50 |
| 46 | 34 | 10 l. green and red | £130 | £275 |

**3.** Ploughing.

**1910.**

| | | | | |
|---|---|---|---|---|
| 34 | 3 | 5 c. green | 50 | 40 |
| 35 | | 10 c. red | 1·00 | 1·60 |
| 40 | – | 15 c. grey | 21·00 | 20·00 |
| 37 | – | 25 c. blue | 1·00 | 1·60 |

DESIGN: 15, 25 c. Government Palace, Massawa.

**1916.** Red Cross Society stamps of Italy optd **ERITREA**.

| | | | | |
|---|---|---|---|---|
| 47 | 53 | 10 c.+5 c. red | 1·00 | 4·00 |
| 48 | 54 | 15 c.+5 c. grey | 4·75 | 9·00 |
| 49 | | 20 c. on 15 c.+5 c. grey | 4·75 | 9·00 |
| 50 | | 20 c.+5 c. orange | 1·75 | 5·50 |

**1916.** No. 40 surch with new value and bars or crosses.

| | | | | |
|---|---|---|---|---|
| 51 | – | 5 c. on 15 c. grey | 2·50 | 7·50 |
| 52 | – | 20 c. on 15 c. grey | 75 | 1·00 |

**1922.** Victory stamps of Italy optd **ERITREA**.

| | | | | |
|---|---|---|---|---|
| 53. | 62. | 5 c. green | 50 | 1·90 |
| 54. | | 10 c. red | 50 | 1·90 |
| 55. | | 15 c. grey | 50 | 3·00 |
| 56. | | 25 c. blue | 50 | 3·00 |

**1922.** Stamps of Somalia optd **ERITREA** and bars.

| | | | | |
|---|---|---|---|---|
| 57 | 1 | 2 c. on 1 b. brown | 3·00 | 5·50 |
| 58 | | 5 c. on 2 b. green | 3·00 | 4·50 |
| 59 | 2 | 10 c. on 1 a. red | 3·00 | 1·25 |
| 60 | | 15 c. on 2 a. brown | 3·00 | 2·00 |
| 61 | | 25 c. on 2½ a. blue | 3·00 | 1·40 |
| 62 | | 50 c. on 5 a. orange | 5·00 | 2·50 |
| 63 | | 1 l. on 10 a. lilac | 6·00 | 6·00 |

**1923.** Propagation of the Faith stamps of Italy optd **ERITREA**.

| | | | | |
|---|---|---|---|---|
| 64. | 66. | 20 c. orange and green | 1·50 | 6·00 |
| 65. | | 30 c. orange and red | 1·50 | 6·00 |
| 66. | | 50 c. orange and violet | 1·25 | 6·00 |
| 67. | | 1 l. orange and blue | 1·25 | 6·00 |

**1923.** Fascist March on Rome stamps of Italy optd **ERITREA**.

| | | | | |
|---|---|---|---|---|
| 68. | 73. | 10 c. green | 1·40 | 6·00 |
| 69. | | 30 c. violet | 1·40 | 6·00 |
| 70. | | 50 c. red | 1·40 | 6·00 |
| 71. | 74. | 1 l. blue | 1·40 | 6·00 |
| 72. | | 2 l. brown | 1·40 | 6·00 |
| 73. | 75. | 5 l. black and blue | 1·40 | 7·00 |

**1924.** Manzoni stamps of Italy optd **ERITREA**.

| | | | | |
|---|---|---|---|---|
| 74 | 77 | 10 c. black and purple | 1·00 | 11·00 |
| 75 | – | 15 c. black and green | 1·00 | 11·00 |
| 76 | – | 30 c. black | 1·00 | 11·00 |
| 77 | – | 50 c. black and brown | 1·00 | 11·00 |
| 78 | – | 1 l. black and blue | 15·00 | 90·00 |
| 79 | – | 5 l. black and purple | £275 | £900 |

**1924.** Stamps of Italy optd **ERITREA**.

| | | | | |
|---|---|---|---|---|
| 80 | 30 | 1 c. brown | 1·75 | 5·50 |
| 81 | 31 | 2 c. orange | 1·25 | 5·00 |
| 82 | 37 | 5 c. green | 2·50 | 4·75 |

**1925.** Holy Year stamps of Italy optd **ERITREA**.

| | | | | |
|---|---|---|---|---|
| 90. | – | 20 c.+10 c. brn. & green | 1·00 | 4·00 |
| 91. | 81. | 30 c.+15 c. brn. & choc. | 1·00 | 6·00 |
| 92. | – | 50 c.+25 c. brn. & violet | 1·00 | 4·00 |
| 93. | – | 60 c.+30 c. brown & red | 1·00 | 6·00 |
| 94. | – | 1 l.+50 c. pur. and blue | 1·00 | 8·00 |
| 95. | – | 5 l.+2 l. 50 purple & red | 1·00 | 8·00 |

**1925.** Stamps of Italy optd **Colonia Eritrea**.

| | | | | |
|---|---|---|---|---|
| 123 | 92 | 7½ c. brown | 8·00 | 28·00 |
| 124 | 39 | 20 c. purple | 4·00 | 3·25 |
| 96 | | 20 c. green | 3·50 | 4·75 |
| 97 | | 30 c. grey | 3·50 | 4·75 |
| 125 | 92 | 50 c. mauve | 28·00 | 20·00 |
| 126 | 39 | 60 c. orange | 35·00 | 70·00 |
| 127 | 34 | 75 c. red and carmine | 35·00 | 5·50 |
| 128 | | 1 l. 25 blue & ultram | 24·00 | 3·25 |
| 98 | | 2 l. green and orange | 11·00 | 29·00 |
| 129 | | 2 l. 50 green and orange | 65·00 | 30·00 |

**1925.** Royal Jubilee stamps of Italy optd **ERITREA**.

| | | | | |
|---|---|---|---|---|
| 99 | 82 | 60 c. red | 20 | 3·00 |
| 100 | | 1 l. blue | 25 | 3·00 |
| 101 | | 1 l. 25 blue | 45 | 9·50 |

**1926.** St. Francis of Assisi stamps of Italy optd **ERITREA** (20 to 60 c.) or **Eritrea** (others).

| | | | | |
|---|---|---|---|---|
| 102. | 83. | 20 c. green | 1·00 | 4·00 |
| 103. | – | 40 c. violet | 1·00 | 4·00 |
| 104. | – | 60 c. red | 1·00 | 4·00 |
| 105. | – | 1 l. 25 blue | 1·00 | 4·00 |
| 106. | – | 5 l.+2 l. 50 brown | 2·00 | 5·50 |

**1926.** Colonial Propaganda stamps as T 6 of Cyrenaica, but inscr. "ERITREA".

| | | | | |
|---|---|---|---|---|
| 107. | | 5 c.+5 c. brown | 20 | 3·25 |
| 108. | | 10 c.+5 c. olive | 20 | 3·25 |
| 109. | | 20 c.+5 c. green | 20 | 3·25 |
| 110. | | 40 c.+5 c. red | 20 | 3·25 |
| 111. | | 60 c.+5 c. orange | 20 | 3·25 |
| 112. | | 1 l.+5 c. blue | 20 | 3·25 |

**1926.** Portrait stamps of Italy optd **ERITREA**.

| | | | | |
|---|---|---|---|---|
| 113 | 34 | 75 c. red and carmine | 16·00 | 4·75 |
| 114 | | 1 l. 25 blue & ultram | 11·00 | 1·75 |
| 115 | | 2 l. 50 green and orange | 30·00 | 14·00 |

**1927.** 1st National Defence issue of Italy optd **ERITREA**.

| | | | | |
|---|---|---|---|---|
| 116. | 89. | 40 c.+20 c. black & brn. | 1·40 | 16·00 |
| 117. | | 60 c.+30 c. brown & red | 1·40 | 16·00 |
| 118. | | 1 l. 25+60 c. black and blue | 1·40 | 28·00 |
| 119. | | 5 l.+2 l. 50 blk. & grn. | 1·75 | 40·00 |

**1927.** Centenary of Volta issue of Italy optd **Eritrea**.

| | | | | |
|---|---|---|---|---|
| 120. | 90. | 20 c. violet | 4·00 | 18·00 |
| 121. | | 50 c. orange | 5·00 | 14·00 |
| 122. | | 1 l. 25 blue | 7·00 | 24·00 |

**1928.** Portrait stamps of Italy optd **Eritrea** (130) or **ERITREA** (others).

| | | | | |
|---|---|---|---|---|
| 130. | 91. | 50 c. grey and brown | 8·00 | 2·50 |
| 131. | 92. | 50 c. mauve | 24·00 | 20·00 |
| 132. | 91. | 1 l. 75 brown | 35·00 | 14·00 |

**1928.** 45th Anniv. of the Italian-African Society. As T 8 of Cyrenaica but inscr. "ERITREA".

| | | | | |
|---|---|---|---|---|
| 133. | | 20 c.+5 c. green | 1·00 | 4·00 |
| 134. | | 30 c.+5 c. red | 1·00 | 4·00 |
| 135. | | 50 c.+10 c. violet | 1·00 | 4·00 |
| 136. | | 1 l. 25+20 c. blue | 1·00 | 4·00 |

**1929.** 2nd National Defence issue of Italy (colours changed) optd **ERITREA**.

| | | | | |
|---|---|---|---|---|
| 137 | 89 | 30 c.+10 c. black & red | 1·40 | 5·00 |
| 138 | | 50 c.+20 c. grey & lilac | 1·40 | 5·00 |
| 139 | | 1 l. 25+50 c. blue & brn | 1·40 | 6·00 |
| 140 | | 5 l.+2 l. black and green | 1·40 | 12·00 |

**1929.** Montecassino stamps of Italy (colours changed) optd **Eritrea** (10 l.) or **ERITREA** (others).

| | | | | |
|---|---|---|---|---|
| 141 | 104 | 20 c. green | 1·75 | 6·00 |
| 142 | – | 25 c. red | 1·75 | 6·00 |
| 143 | – | 50 c.+10 c. red | 1·75 | 9·00 |
| 144 | – | 75 c.+15 c. brown | 1·75 | 9·00 |
| 145 | 104 | 1 l. 25+25 c. purple | 4·00 | 10·00 |
| 146 | – | 5 l.+1 l. blue | 4·00 | 12·00 |
| 147 | – | 10 l.+2 l. brown | 4·00 | 15·00 |

**1930.** Royal Wedding stamps of Italy (colours changed) optd **ERITREA**.

| | | | | |
|---|---|---|---|---|
| 148 | 109 | 20 c. green | 45 | 1·60 |
| 149 | | 50 c.+10 c. red | 35 | 2·50 |
| 150 | | 1 l. 25+25 c. red | 35 | 3·50 |

**21.** Telegraph Linesman. **22.** **24.** King Victor Emmanuel III.

**1930.**

| | | | | |
|---|---|---|---|---|
| 151 | – | 2 c. black and blue | 35 | 1·25 |
| 152 | – | 5 c. black and violet | 50 | 55 |
| 153 | – | 10 c. black and brown | 50 | 25 |
| 154 | 21 | 15 c. black and green | 50 | 45 |
| 155 | – | 25 c. black and green | 50 | 25 |
| 156 | – | 35 c. black and red | 1·60 | 4·00 |
| 157 | – | 1 l. black and blue | 50 | 40 |
| 158 | – | 2 l. black and brown | 3·75 | 3·50 |
| 159 | – | 5 l. black and green | 3·50 | 7·50 |
| 160 | – | 10 l. black and blue | 4·00 | 9·50 |

DESIGNS—VERT: 2, 35 c. Lancer; 5, 10 c. Postman; 25 c. Rifleman. HORIZ: 1 l. Massawa; 2 l. Railway Bridge; 5 l. Asmara Deghe Selam; 10 l. Camel transport.

**1930.** Ferrucci issue of Italy (colours changed) optd **ERITREA**.

| | | | | |
|---|---|---|---|---|
| 161. | 114. | 20 c. violet | 40 | 1·75 |
| 162. | – | 25 c. green (283) | 40 | 1·75 |
| 163. | – | 50 c. black (284) | 40 | 1·75 |
| 164. | – | 1 l. 25 c. blue (285) | 40 | 1·75 |
| 165. | – | 5 l.+2 l. red (286) | 1·60 | 6·00 |

**1930.** 3rd National Defence issue of Italy (colours changed) optd **ERITREA**.

| | | | | |
|---|---|---|---|---|
| 166 | 89 | 30 c.+10 c. grn & dp grn | 5·00 | 15·00 |
| 167 | | 50 c.+10 c. purple & grn | 5·00 | 15·00 |
| 168 | | 1 l. 25+30 c. light brown and brown | 5·00 | 15·00 |
| 169 | | 5 l.+1 l. 50 green & blue | 12·00 | 50·00 |

**1930.** 25th Anniv of Italian Colonial Agricultural Institute.

| | | | | |
|---|---|---|---|---|
| 170. | 22. | 50 c.+20 c. brown | 1·10 | 4·75 |
| 171. | | 1 l. 25+20 c. blue | 1·10 | 4·75 |
| 172. | | 1 l. 75+20 c. green | 1·10 | 6·00 |
| 173. | | 2 l. 55+50 c. violet | 1·50 | 10·50 |
| 174. | | 5 l.+1 l. red | 1·50 | 14·00 |

**1930.** Bimillenary of Virgil issue of Italy (colours changed) optd **ERITREA**.

| | | | | |
|---|---|---|---|---|
| 175 | | 15 c. grey | 25 | 1·50 |
| 176 | | 20 c. brown | 25 | 1·50 |
| 177 | | 25 c. green | 25 | 1·50 |
| 178 | | 30 c. brown | 25 | 1·50 |
| 179 | | 50 c. purple | 25 | 1·50 |
| 180 | | 75 c. red | 25 | 1·50 |
| 181 | | 1 l. 25 blue | 25 | 1·50 |
| 182 | | 5 l.+1 l. 50 purple | 1·75 | 8·00 |
| 183 | | 10 l.+2 l. 50 brown | 1·75 | 8·00 |

**1931.** St. Antony of Padua issue of Italy (colours changed) optd **ERITREA**.

| | | | | |
|---|---|---|---|---|
| 184. | 121. | 20 c. brown | 60 | 2·50 |
| 185. | – | 25 c. green | 60 | 2·50 |
| 186. | – | 30 c. brown | 60 | 2·50 |
| 187. | – | 50 c. purple | 60 | 1·40 |
| 188. | – | 75 c. grey | 60 | 2·50 |
| 189. | – | 1 l. 25 blue | 60 | 2·50 |
| 190. | – | 5 l.+2 l. 50 brown | 2·00 | 15·00 |

**1931.**

| | | | | |
|---|---|---|---|---|
| 191. | 24. | 7½ c. brown | 20 | 65 |
| 192. | | 20 c. red and blue | 20 | 10 |
| 193. | | 30 c. purple and olive | 25 | 10 |
| 194. | | 40 c. green and blue | 35 | 10 |
| 195. | | 50 c. olive and brown | 10 | 10 |
| 196. | | 75 c. red | 70 | 10 |
| 197. | | 1 l. 25 blue and purple | 85 | 10 |
| 198. | | 2 l. 50 green | 1·40 | 90 |

**25.** Dromedary.

**1933.**

| | | | | |
|---|---|---|---|---|
| 199. | 25. | 2 c. blue | 30 | 90 |
| 200. | – | 5 c. black | 40 | 40 |
| 201. | 25. | 10 c. brown | 55 | 20 |
| 202. | – | 15 c. brown | 70 | 70 |
| 203. | – | 25 c. green | 45 | 15 |
| 204. | – | 35 c. violet | 1·40 | 3·00 |
| 205. | – | 1 l. blue | 20 | 10 |
| 206. | – | 2 l. olive | 5·50 | 90 |
| 207. | – | 5 l. red | 2·50 | 1·60 |
| 208. | – | 10 l. orange | 3·50 | 2·00 |

DESIGNS—HORIZ. 5 c., 15 c. Fish wharf. 25 c. Baobab tree. 35 c. Native village. 2 l. African Elephant. VERT. 1 l. Ruins at Cholloe. 5 l. Eritrean man. 10 l. Eritrean woman.

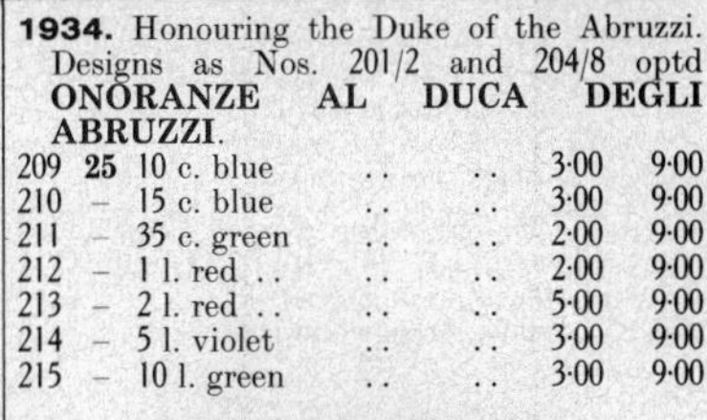

**1934.** Honouring the Duke of the Abruzzi. Designs as Nos. 201/2 and 204/8 optd **ONORANZE AL DUCA DEGLI ABRUZZI**.

| | | | | |
|---|---|---|---|---|
| 209 | 25 | 10 c. blue | 3·00 | 9·00 |
| 210 | – | 15 c. blue | 3·00 | 9·00 |
| 211 | – | 35 c. green | 2·00 | 9·00 |
| 212 | – | 1 l. red | 2·00 | 9·00 |
| 213 | – | 2 l. red | 5·00 | 9·00 |
| 214 | – | 5 l. violet | 3·00 | 9·00 |
| 215 | – | 10 l. green | 3·00 | 9·00 |

**30.** Grant's Gazelle.

**1934.** 2nd International Colonial Exn, Naples.

| | | | | |
|---|---|---|---|---|
| 216 | 30 | 5 c. brown & grn (post) | 2·00 | 6·00 |
| 217 | | 10 c. black and brown | 2·00 | 6·00 |
| 218 | | 20 c. slate and red | 2·00 | 6·00 |
| 219 | | 50 c. brown and violet | 2·00 | 6·00 |
| 220 | | 60 c. blue and brown | 2·00 | 6·00 |
| 221 | | 1 l. 25 green and blue | 2·00 | 6·00 |
| 222 | – | 25 c. orange & blue (air) | 2·00 | 6·00 |
| 223 | – | 50 c. blue and green | 2·00 | 6·00 |
| 224 | – | 75 c. orange and brown | 2·00 | 6·00 |
| 225 | – | 80 c. green and brown | 2·00 | 6·00 |
| 226 | – | 1 l. green and red | 2·00 | 6·00 |
| 227 | – | 2 l. brown and blue | 2·00 | 6·00 |

DESIGNS—36×43 mm: Nos. 222/4, Caproni Ca 101 airplane over landscape. 225/7, Savoia Marchetti S-66 flying boat over globe.

**31.** King Victor Emmanuel III and Caproni Ca 101 Airplane.

**1934.** Air. Rome–Mogadiscio Flight.

| | | | | |
|---|---|---|---|---|
| 228 | 31 | 25 c.+10 c. green | 2·00 | 5·00 |
| 229 | | 50 c.+10 c. brown | 2·00 | 5·00 |
| 230 | | 75 c.+15 c. red | 2·00 | 5·00 |
| 231 | | 80 c.+15 c. black | 2·00 | 5·00 |
| 232 | | 1 l.+20 c. brown | 2·00 | 5·00 |
| 233 | | 2 l.+20 c. blue | 2·00 | 5·00 |
| 234 | | 3 l.+25 c. violet | 16·00 | 40·00 |
| 235 | | 5 l.+25 c. red | 16·00 | 40·00 |
| 236 | | 10 l.+30 c. purple | 16·00 | 40·00 |
| 237 | | 25 l.+2 l. green | 16·00 | 40·00 |

**33.** Macchi Castoldi MC-94 Flying Boat over Zebu-drawn Plough.

**1936.** Air.

| | | | | |
|---|---|---|---|---|
| 238. | 33. | 25 c. green | 55 | 1·00 |
| 239. | – | 50 c. brown | 30 | 20 |
| 240. | – | 60 c. orange | 85 | 2·75 |
| 241. | – | 75 c. brown | 70 | 70 |
| 242. | – | 1 l. blue | 15 | 10 |
| 243. | 33. | 1 l. 50 violet | 45 | 25 |
| 244. | – | 2 l. blue | 65 | 55 |
| 245. | – | 3 l. lake | 6·50 | 6·50 |
| 246. | – | 5 l. green | 2·75 | 1·10 |
| 247. | – | 10 l. red | 7·25 | 2·00 |

DESIGNS: 50 c., 2 l. Caproni Ca 101 airplane over Massawa–Asmara Railway. 60 c., 5 l. Savoia Marchetti S-74 airplane over Dom palm trees. 75 c., 10 l. Savoia Marchetti S-73 airplane over roadway through cactus trees. 1, 3 l. Caproni Ca 101 airplane over bridge.

### INDEPENDENT STATE

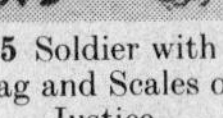

**35** Soldier with Flag and Scales of Justice

**36** Map on Ballot Box

**1991.** 30th Anniv of Liberation Struggle.

(a) As T **35**. Size 26×36 mm.

| No. | Type | Description | Unused | Used |
|---|---|---|---|---|
| 250 | | 5 c. black, orange and blue | | |
| 251 | | 15 c. black, orange & green | | |
| 252 | | 20 c. black, orange & yell | | |

(b) As T **35**, but redrawn with dates added either side of "30". Size 24×33 mm.

| No. | Type | Description | Unused | Used |
|---|---|---|---|---|
| 253 | | 3 b. black, orange & silver | | |
| 254 | | 5 b. black, orange and gold | | |

**1993.** Independence Referendum.

| No. | Type | Description | Unused | Used |
|---|---|---|---|---|
| 255 | **36** | 15 c. multicoloured | 10 | 10 |
| 256 | – | 60 c. red, violet & green | 15 | 10 |
| 257 | – | 75 c. black, red and blue | 15 | 10 |
| 258 | – | 1 b. multicoloured | 20 | 15 |
| 259 | – | 2 b. blue, black & green | 45 | 30 |

DESIGNS—60 c. Arrows; 75 c. "YES" and "NO" signpost; 1 b. Candle; 2 b. Dove, posthorn and map.

**38** Eritrean Flag

**1993.** Multicoloured, colour of frame given.

| No. | Type | Description | Unused | Used |
|---|---|---|---|---|
| 260 | **38** | 5 c. brown | 10 | 10 |
| 261 | | 5 c. blue | 10 | 10 |
| 262 | | 15 c. red | 10 | 10 |
| 263 | | 20 c. gold | 10 | 10 |
| 264 | | 20 c. blue | 10 | 10 |
| 265 | | 25 c. blue | 10 | 10 |
| 266 | | 35 c. blue | 10 | 10 |
| 267 | | 40 c. blue | 10 | 10 |
| 268 | | 50 c. blue | 10 | 10 |
| 269 | | 60 c. yellow | 15 | 10 |
| 270 | | 70 c. mauve | 15 | 10 |
| 271 | | 70 c. blue | 15 | 10 |
| 272 | | 80 c. blue | 20 | 15 |
| 273 | | 3 b. green | 65 | 45 |
| 274 | | 5 b. silver | 1·10 | 80 |

**39** National Flag and Map

**1994.** Multicoloured, colour of frame given.

| No. | Type | Description | Unused | Used |
|---|---|---|---|---|
| 275 | **39** | 5 c. yellow | 10 | 10 |
| 276 | | 10 c. green | 10 | 10 |
| 277 | | 20 c. orange | 10 | 10 |
| 278 | | 25 c. red | 10 | 10 |
| 279 | | 40 c. mauve | 10 | 10 |
| 280 | | 60 c. turquoise | 15 | 10 |
| 281 | | 70 c. green | 15 | 10 |
| 282 | | 1 b. orange | 20 | 15 |
| 283 | | 2 b. orange | 45 | 30 |
| 284 | | 3 b. blue | 65 | 45 |
| 285 | | 5 b. mauve | 1·10 | 80 |
| 286 | | 10 b. lilac | 2·25 | 1·60 |

**40** Fishermen

**1995.** 20th Anniv of World Tourism Organization. Multicoloured.

| No. | Type | Description | Unused | Used |
|---|---|---|---|---|
| 287 | | 10 c. Type **40** | 10 | 10 |
| 288 | | 35 c. Monument (vert) | 10 | 10 |
| 289 | | 85 c. Mountain road | 20 | 15 |
| 290 | | 2 b. Archaeological site (vert) | 45 | 30 |

**41** Horned Butterflyfish

**1995.** Marine Life. Multicoloured.

| No. | Type | Description | Unused | Used |
|---|---|---|---|---|
| 291 | | 30 c. Type **41** | 10 | 10 |
| 292 | | 55 c. "Gonochaetodon larvatus" | 10 | 10 |
| 293 | | 70 c. Shrimp and lobster | 15 | 10 |
| 294 | | 1 b. Blue-stripe snapper | 20 | 15 |

**42** Mountain and broken Manacles

**1995.** Independence Day. Multicoloured.

| No. | Type | Description | Unused | Used |
|---|---|---|---|---|
| 295 | | 25 c. Type **42** | 10 | 10 |
| 296 | | 40 c. Planting national flag on mountain top (vert) | 10 | 10 |
| 297 | | 70 c. Men with national flag and scimitar (vert) | 15 | 10 |
| 298 | | 3 b. National flag and fireworks (vert) | 65 | 45 |

**43** Construction Works

**44** Dove flying around Map

**1995.** "Towards the Bright Future".

| No. | Type | Description | Unused | Used |
|---|---|---|---|---|
| 299 | **43** | 60 c. black, orange & red | 15 | 10 |
| 300 | – | 80 c. multicoloured | 20 | 15 |
| 301 | – | 90 c. black, orange & red | 20 | 15 |
| 302 | – | 1 b. brown, orange & red | 20 | 15 |

DESIGNS: 80 c. Tree; 90 c. Village; 1 b. Camels.

**1995.** Council for Mutual Economic Assistance in Africa. Multicoloured.

| No. | Type | Description | Unused | Used |
|---|---|---|---|---|
| 303 | | 40 c. Type **44** | 10 | 10 |
| 304 | | 50 c. Tree with member countries' names on leaves | 10 | 10 |
| 305 | | 60 c. Emblem and handshake | 15 | 10 |
| 306 | | 3 b. Emblem and flags of member countries (horiz) | 65 | 45 |

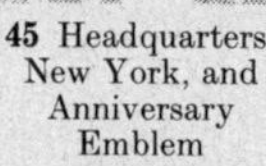

**45** Headquarters, New York, and Anniversary Emblem

**46** Bowl and Spoon

**1995.** 50th Anniv of U.N.O. Multicoloured.

| No. | Type | Description | Unused | Used |
|---|---|---|---|---|
| 307 | | 40 c. Type **45** | 10 | 10 |
| 308 | | 60 c. U.N. Emblem forming tree | 15 | 10 |
| 309 | | 70 c. Anniversary emblem and peace dove | 15 | 10 |
| 310 | | 2 b. Type **45** | 45 | 30 |

**1995.** 50th Anniv of F.A.O. Multicoloured.

| No. | Type | Description | Unused | Used |
|---|---|---|---|---|
| 311 | | 5 c. Type **46** | 10 | 10 |
| 312 | | 25 c. Agriculture | 10 | 10 |
| 313 | | 80 c. Bird feeding young | 20 | 15 |
| 314 | | 3 b. Cornucopia of crops | 65 | 45 |

**47** Eritreans raising Flag

**1996.** Martyrs' Day. Multicoloured.

| No. | Type | Description | Unused | Used |
|---|---|---|---|---|
| 315 | | 40 c. Type **47** | 10 | 10 |
| 316 | | 60 c. Man laying wreath on grave | 10 | 10 |
| 317 | | 70 c. Breastfeeding | 15 | 10 |
| 318 | | 80 c. Planting seedlings | 15 | 10 |

**48** Adult and Young

**1996.** Endangered Animals. Multicoloured.

(a) Gemsbok.

| No. | Type | Description | Unused | Used |
|---|---|---|---|---|
| 319 | | 3 b. Type **48** | 60 | 45 |
| 320 | | 3 b. Adult eating | 60 | 45 |
| 321 | | 3 b. Encounter between two males | 60 | 45 |
| 322 | | 3 b. Gemsbok | 60 | 45 |

(b) Mammals.

| No. | Type | Description | Unused | Used |
|---|---|---|---|---|
| 323 | | 3 b. Savanna (inscr "Green") monkey | 60 | 45 |
| 324 | | 3 b. Aardwolf | 60 | 45 |
| 325 | | 3 b. Dugong | 60 | 45 |
| 326 | | 3 b. Maned rat | 60 | 45 |

(c) White-eyed Gull.

| No. | Type | Description | Unused | Used |
|---|---|---|---|---|
| 327 | | 3 b. Preening | 60 | 45 |
| 328 | | 3 b. Flying | 60 | 45 |
| 329 | | 3 b. Pair of gulls on rock | 60 | 45 |
| 330 | | 3 b. Gull on rock | 60 | 45 |

## CONCESSIONAL LETTER POST

**1939.** No. CL267 of Italy optd **ERITREA**.

| No. | Type | Description | Unused | Used |
|---|---|---|---|---|
| CL248 | CL **109** | 10 c. brown | 10·00 | 14·00 |

## EXPRESS LETTER STAMPS

Italian Issues.

**1907.** Express Letter stamps of Italy optd. **Colonia Eritrea.**

| No. | Type | Description | Unused | Used |
|---|---|---|---|---|
| E 31. | E **35.** | 25 c. red | 10·00 | 7·50 |
| E 34. | E **41.** | 30 c. blue and red | 42·00 | 65·00 |
| E 53. | E **35.** | 50 c. red | 1·75 | 12·00 |

E 13

**1924.**

| No. | Type | Description | Unused | Used |
|---|---|---|---|---|
| E83 | E **13** | 60 c. brown and red | 3·50 | 9·50 |
| E84 | | 2 l. pink and blue | 6·50 | 15·00 |

**1926.** Surch.

| No. | Type | Description | Unused | Used |
|---|---|---|---|---|
| E113 | E **13** | 70 on 60 c. brn & red | 3·25 | 9·50 |
| E116 | | 1 l. 25 on 60 c. brown and red | 8·00 | 2·00 |
| E114 | | 2 l. 50 on 2 l. pink and blue | 6·25 | 14·50 |

## OFFICIAL AIR STAMP

**1934.** Optd **SERVIZIO DI STATO** and Crown.

| No. | Type | Description | Unused | Used |
|---|---|---|---|---|
| O238 | **31** | 25 l. + 2 l. red | £1500 | |

## PARCEL POST STAMPS

**PRICES:** Unused prices are for complete stamps, used prices for a half stamp.

**1916.** Parcel Post stamps of Italy optd **ERITREA** on each half of stamp.

| No. | Type | Description | Unused | Used |
|---|---|---|---|---|
| P61 | P **53** | 5 c. brown | 1·00 | 1·00 |
| P62 | | 10 c. blue | 1·00 | 1·00 |
| P63 | | 20 c. black | 1·00 | 1·00 |
| P64 | | 25 c. red | 1·00 | 1·00 |
| P65 | | 50 c. orange | 3·00 | 1·00 |
| P66 | | 1 l. violet | 3·00 | 1·00 |
| P67 | | 2 l. green | 3·00 | 1·25 |
| P68 | | 3 l. yellow | 3·50 | 1·50 |
| P69 | | 4 l. grey | 3·50 | 1·75 |
| P70 | | 10 l. purple | 35·00 | 4·00 |
| P71 | | 12 l. brown | 80·00 | 4·25 |
| P72 | | 15 l. green | 80·00 | 6·00 |
| P73 | | 20 l. purple | 80·00 | 12·00 |

**1927.** Parcel Post stamps of Italy optd. **ERITREA** on each half of stamp.

| No. | Type | Description | Unused | Used |
|---|---|---|---|---|
| P 123. | P **92.** | 10 c. blue | £3500 | 4·25 |
| P 124. | | 25 c. red | £180 | 80 |
| P 125. | | 30 c. blue | 80 | 30 |
| P 126. | | 50 c. orange | £180 | 1·00 |
| P 127. | | 60 c. red | 80 | 30 |
| P 128. | | 1 l. violet | £160 | 30 |
| P 129. | | 2 l. green | £130 | 30 |
| P 130. | | 3 l. yellow | 3·25 | 30 |
| P 131. | | 4 l. grey | 3·25 | 30 |
| P 132. | | 10 l. mauve | £250 | 5·50 |
| P 133. | | 20 l. purple | £250 | 8·50 |

## POSTAGE DUE STAMPS

**1903.** Postage Due stamps of Italy optd **Colonia Eritrea**.

| No. | Type | Description | Unused | Used |
|---|---|---|---|---|
| D53 | D **12** | 5 c. mauve & orange | 30 | 1·75 |
| D54 | | 10 c. mauve & orge | 55 | 1·75 |
| D32 | | 20 c. mauve & orge | 5·00 | 7·50 |
| D33 | | 30 c. mauve & orge | 7·00 | 10·00 |
| D57 | | 40 c. mauve & orge | 9·00 | 15·00 |
| D58 | | 50 c. mauve & orge | 6·50 | 15·00 |
| D36 | | 60 c. mauve & orge | 7·00 | 15·00 |
| D116 | | 60 c. brown & orge | 22·00 | 48·00 |
| D37 | | 1 l. mauve and blue | 5·00 | 2·00 |
| D38 | | 2 l. mauve and blue | 38·00 | 42·00 |
| D39 | | 5 l. mauve and blue | 85·00 | 95·00 |
| D63 | | 10 l. mauve and blue | 4·25 | 20·00 |
| D41 | D **13** | 50 l. yellow | £190 | 80·00 |
| D42 | | 100 l. blue | £110 | 32·00 |

**1934.** Postage Due stamps of Italy optd. **ERITREA.**

| No. | Type | Description | Unused | Used |
|---|---|---|---|---|
| D 216. | D **141.** | 5 c. brown | 15 | 1·25 |
| D 217. | | 10 c. blue | 15 | 1·25 |
| D 218. | | 20 c. red | 1·60 | 1·40 |
| D 219. | | 25 c. green | 1·60 | 1·40 |
| D 220. | | 30 c. orange | 1·60 | 2·40 |
| D 221. | | 40 c. brown | 1·60 | 3·25 |
| D 222. | | 50 c. violet | 1·60 | 40 |
| D 223. | | 60 c. blue | 2·25 | 4·50 |
| D 224. | D **142.** | 1 l. orange | 1·60 | 45 |
| D 225. | | 2 l. green | 14·00 | 20·00 |
| D 226. | | 5 l. violet | 17·00 | 22·00 |
| D 227. | | 10 l. blue | 19·00 | 24·00 |
| D 228. | | 20 l. red | 21·00 | 27·00 |

For British Administration see BRITISH OCCUPATION OF ITALIAN COLONIES in Volume 3.

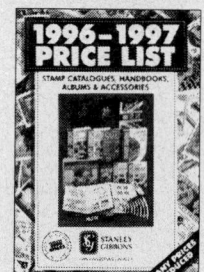

## ESTONIA Pt. 10

A former province of the Russian Empire on the S. Coast of the Gulf of Finland. Under Russian rule until 1918 when it became an independent republic. The area was incorporated into the Soviet Union from 1940; for issues made during 1941 see GERMAN OCCUPATION OF ESTONIA.

Estonia once again became independent in 1991.

1918. 100 kopeks = 1 rouble.
1919. 100 penni = 1 Estonian mark.
1928. 100 senti = 1 kroon.
1991. 100 kopeks = 1 rouble.
1992. 100 senti = 1 kroon.

**Note.** An Asterisk * after the date indicates that the stamps have a network background in colour.

2.

4. Seagulls.

**1918.** Imperf.
1. 2. 5 k. pink .. .. .. 50 50
2. 15 k. blue .. .. .. 50 50
3. 35 p. brown .. .. 75 70
4. 70 p. olive .. .. .. 1·40 1·40

**1919.** Imperf.
5. 4. 5 p. yellow .. .. 2·00 2·00

5.

6.

7.

9. Viking Longship.

10. L.V.G. Schneider Biplane.

**1919.** Imperf. (10 p., 15 m. and 25 m. also perf).
6 5 5 p. orange .. .. 10 10
7a 10 p. green .. .. 15 10
8 6 15 p. red .. .. 15 10
9 7 35 p. blue .. .. 25 10
10 70 p. lilac .. .. 30 20
11 9 1 m. blue and brown .. 1·50 2·00
12a 5 m. yellow and black .. 1·50 1·25
33 15 m. green and violet .. 2·00 40
34 25 m. blue and brown .. 2·75 1·50

**1920.** Air. Imperf.
15. 10. 5 m. black, blue & yellow 3·00 5·00

11. Tallinn.

12. Wounded Soldier.

13.

**1920.** Imperf.
16. 11. 25 p. green .. .. 25 10
17. 25 p. yellow .. .. 25 20
18. 35 p. red .. .. .. 35 15
19. 50 p. green .. .. 30 15
20. 1 m. red .. .. .. 1·00 50
21. 2 m. blue .. .. 50 25
23. 2 m. 50 blue .. .. 1·00 50

**1920.** War Victims' Fund. Imperf.
24 12 35+10 p. grey and red .. 50 1·10
25 13 70+15 p. bistre and blue 50 1·10

**1920.** Surch.
26 6 1 m. on 15 p. red .. 25 20
27 11 1 m. on 35 p. red .. 50 20
29 12 1 m. on 35+10 p. grey and red .. .. 25 35
28 7 2 m. on 70 p. lilac .. 75 40
30 13 2 m. on 70+15 p. bistre and blue .. .. 25 35

17.

18. Weaver.

19. Blacksmith.

**1921.** Red Cross. Imperf. or perf.
31. 17. 2½—3½ m. brown, red and orange .. .. .. 2·50 5·00
32. 5—7 m. brn., red & blue 2·50 5·00

**1922.** Imperf. or perf.
35. 18. ½ m. orange .. .. 1·25 75
36. 1 m. brown .. .. 2·50 75
37. 2 m. green .. .. 2·50 10
38. 2½ m. red .. .. 5·00 75
39. 3 m. green .. .. 2·50 10
40. 19. 5 m. red .. .. .. 5·00 10
41. 9 m. red .. .. .. 5·00 1·25
42. 10 m. blue .. .. 6·25 10
72. 10 m. grey .. .. 3·75 5·00
42a. 12 m. red .. .. 6·25 1·10
42b. 15 m. purple .. .. 5·00 75
42c. 20 m. blue .. .. 10·00 20

20. Map of Estonia.

**1923.***
43. 20. 100 m. blue and olive .. 10·00 2·50
43a. 300 m. blue and brown .. 75·00 12·50

**1923.** Air. No. 15 optd **1923** or surch **15 Marka 1923**.
44 10 5 m. black, blue & yell .. 10·00 25·00
45 15 m. on 5 m. black, blue and yellow .. .. 9·00 16·00

**1923.** Air. Pairs of No. 15 surch **1923** and new value.
46. 10. 10 m. on 5 m. .. .. 12·50 25·00
47. 20 m. on 5 m. .. .. 20·00 38·00
48. 45 m. on 5 m. .. .. 75·00 £130

**1923.** Red Cross stamps optd. **Aita hadalist.** Imperf. or perf.
49. 17. 2½—3½ m. brown, red and orange .. .. 50·00 75·00
50. 5—7 m. brn., red & blue 50·00 75·00

24. Junkers F 13 with Floats.

**1924.*** Air. Various planes. Imperf. or perf.
51. – 5 m. black and yellow .. 1·25 3·75
52. – 10 m. black and blue .. 1·25 3·75
53. 24. 15 m. black and red .. 1·25 6·25
54. 20 m. black and green .. 1·25 3·75
55. 45 m. black and violet .. 1·25 10·00
DESIGNS—5 m. Sabaltnig PIII. 10 m. Sabaltnig PIII with floats. 20 m. Junkers F 13 with wheels. 45 m. Junkers F 13 with skis.

25. National Theatre.

DESIGN: 40 m. Wanemuine Theatre, Tartu.

**1924*.** Perf.
57. 25. 30 m. black and violet .. 12·50 3·75
58. – 40 m. sepia and blue .. 7·50 2·50
59. 25. 70 m. black and red .. 19·00 6·25

**1926.** Red Cross stamps surch. in figures only. Perf.
60. 17. 5—6 on 2½—3½ brown, red and orange .. 3·75 6·25
61. 10—12 on 5—7 m. brown, red and blue .. 3·75 6·25

28. Arensburg Castle.

30. Tallinn.

32. Arms of Estonia.

**1927.** Liberation War Commemoration Fund.
62. 28. 5 m.+5 m. brn. & green 75 2·50
63. – 10 m.+10 m. brn. & blue 75 2·50
64. – 12 m.+12 m. olive & red 60 2·50
65. – 20 m.+20 m. pur. & blue 65 3·75
66. 30. 40 m.+40 m. grey & brn. 75 3·75
DESIGNS—As Type **28**: 10 m. Tartu Cathedral. 12 m. Parliament House, Tallinn. As Type **30**: 20 m. Narva Fortress.

**1928.** 10th Anniv. of Independence. Surch. **1918 24/11 1928 S.S.** Perf.
67. 18. 2 s. on 2 m. green .. 1·25 1·00
68. 19. 5 s. on 5 m. red .. .. 1·25 1·00
69. 10 s. on 10 m. blue .. 2·50 1·25
70. 15 s. on 15 m. purple .. 3·75 1·00
71. 20 s. on 20 m. blue .. 3·75 1·00

**1928.***
73. 32. 1 s. grey .. .. .. 25 10
74. 2 s. green .. .. 25 10
75. 4 s. green .. .. 70 15
76. 5 s. red .. .. .. 75 10
77. 8 s. purple .. .. 2·00 20
78. 10 s. blue .. .. 85 10
79. 12 s. red .. .. .. 1·25 10
80. 15 s. yellow .. .. 1·50 10
80a. 15 s. red .. .. .. 15·00 75
81. 20 s. blue .. .. 2·00 10
82. 25 s. mauve .. .. 5·00 15
83. 25 s. blue .. .. 15·00 75
84. 40 s. orange .. .. 3·75 50
86. 60 s. grey .. .. 5·00 40
87. 80 s. sepia .. .. 6·25 60

**1930.*** Surch in **KROON**.
88. 25. 1 k. on 70 m. black & red 12·50 6·25
89. 20. 2 k. on 300 m. blue & brn. 25·00 25·00
90. 3 k. on 300 m. blue & brn. 50·00 38·00

35. "Succour".

37. Tartu Observatory.

**1931.** Red Cross Fund.
91. 35. 2 s.+3 s. green and red .. 6·25 7·50
92. – 5 s.+3 s. rose and red .. 6·25 7·50
93. – 10 s.+3 s. blue and red .. 6·25 7·50
94. 35. 20 s.+3 s. blue and red .. 10·00 15·00
DESIGN: 5 s., 10 s. "The Light of Hope".

**1932.*** 300th Anniv of Tartu University.
95. 37. 5 s. red .. .. .. 7·50 20
96. – 10 s. blue .. .. 3·75 10
97. 37. 12 s. red .. .. .. 12·50 3·75
98. – 20 s. blue .. .. 7·50 75
DESIGN: 10 s., 20 s. Tartu University.

39. Narva Falls.

40. Ancient Bard.

41. Invalid and Nurse.

**1933.**
99. 39. 1 k. black .. .. 6·25 3·75
99a. 1 k. green .. .. 1·25 6·25

**1933.*** 10th All-Eastonian Choral Festival.
100. 40. 2 s. green .. .. 2·50 20
101. 5 s. red .. .. .. 3·75 20
102. 10 s. blue .. .. 5·00 15

**1933.*** Anti-tuberculosis Fund.
103. 41. 5 s.+3 s. red .. .. 6·75 6·75
104. – 10 s.+3 s. blue .. 6·75 6·75
105. – 12 s.+3 s. red .. .. 7·50 7·50
106. – 20 s.+3 s. blue .. 10·00 10·00
DESIGNS—HORIZ. 10 s. 20 s. Taagepera Sanatorium. VERT. 12 s. Cross of Lorraine.

43. Harvesting. 44. Arms of Narva.

**1935.**
107. 43. 3 k. brown .. .. 1·25 5·00

**1936.*** Charity. Social Relief Fund.
108. 44. 10 s.+10 s. blue & green 3·75 7·50
109. – 15 s.+15 s. blue and red 5·00 10·00
110. – 25 s.+25 s. orge. & blue 7·50 12·50
111. – 50 s.+50 s. yell. & blk. 25·00 38·00
DESIGNS—Arms of Parnu (15 s.), Tartu (25 s.), and Tallinn (50 s.).

45. Pres. Konstantin Pats.

46. Tallinn Harbour.

**1936.**
112. 45. 1 s. brown .. .. 1·00 10
113. 2 s. green .. .. 1·00 10
113a. 3 s. orange .. .. 12·50 6·25
114. 4 s. purple .. .. 2·50 75
115. 5 s. green .. .. 2·25 10
116. 6 s. red .. .. 2·00 15
117. 6 s. green .. .. 30·00 25·00
118. 10 s. blue .. .. 2·50 10
119. 15 s. red .. .. 3·75 50
119a. 15 s. blue .. .. 6·25 1·25
120. 18 s. red .. .. 25·00 6·75
121. 20 s. mauve .. .. 3·75 10
122. 25 s. blue .. .. 15·00 1·25
123. 30 s. yellow .. .. 15·00 1·25
123a. 30 s. blue .. .. 25·00 6·75
124. 50 s. brown .. .. 12·50 90
125. 60 s. mauve .. .. 12·50 5·00
127. 46. 2 k. blue .. .. 1·25 6·25

47. St. Brigitte Abbey.

48. Paide.

**1936.*** 500th Anniv of St. Brigitte Abbey.
128. 47. 5 s. green .. .. 75 45
129. – 10 s. blue .. .. 75 75
130. – 15 s. red .. .. 2·00 3·75
131. – 25 s. blue .. .. 2·50 5·00
DESIGNS: 5 s. Restored portal. 10 s. Ruins of the Abbey. 15 s. Ruined facade. 25 s. Old seal.

**1937.*** Social Relief Fund. Inscr. "CARITAS 1937".
132. 48. 10 s.+10 s. green .. 3·75 5·00
133. – 15 s.+15 s. red .. 3·75 5·00
134. – 25 s.+25 s. blue .. 5·00 7·50
135. – 50 s.+50 s. purple .. 12·50 20·00
DESIGNS—Arms of Rakvere (15 s.). Valga (25 s.). Viljandi (50 s.).

49. Paldiski (Port Baltic).

50. Dr. F. R. Faehlmann.

51. Arms of Viljandi.

**1938.*** Social Relief Fund. Inscr. "CARITAS 1938".
136. 49. 10 s.+10 s. brown .. 2·50 3·75
137. – 15 s.+15 s. grn. & red 2·50 5·00
138. – 25 s.+25 s. red & blue 5·00 10·00
139. – 50 s.+50 s. yell. & blue 12·50 25·00
DESIGNS: Arms of Voru (15 s). Haapsalu (25 s.). Kuresaare (50 s.).

**1938.** Centenary of Estonian Literary Society. Designs showing Society founders.
140. 50. 5 s. green .. .. 30 25
141. – 10 s. brown .. .. 55 30
142. – 15 s. red .. .. 1·25 5·00
143. 50. 25 s. blue .. .. 2·50 6·25
DESIGN: 10 s. ,15 s. Dr. F. R. Kreutzwald.

**1939.*** Social Relief. Inscr. "CARITAS 1939".
144. 51. 10 s.+10 s. green .. 3·75 5·00
145. – 15 s.+15 s. red (Parnu) 3·75 5·00
146. – 25 s.+25 s. blue (Tartu) 7·50 12·50
147. – 50 s.+50 s. pur. (Harju) 19·00 32·00

52. Sanatorium, Parnu.

53. Laanemaa.

**1939.** Centenary of Parnu.
148. 52. 5 s. green .. .. 1·90 1·25
149. – 10 s. violet .. .. 1·25 1·25
150. 52. 18 s. red .. .. 2·50 5·00
151. – 30 s. blue .. .. 2·50 5·00
DESIGNS—10 s., 30 s. Beach Hotel, Parnu.

**1940.** Social Relief Fund. Arms. Inscr. "CARITAS 1940".
152. – 10 s.+10 s. grn. & bl. (Vorumaa) .. .. 2·50 7·50
153. – 15 s.+15 s. red & blue (Jarvemaa) .. .. 2·50 7·50
154. 53. 25 s.+25 s. blue & red 3·75 12·50
155. – 50 s.+50 s. orge. & bl. (Saaremaa) .. .. 10·00 19·00

54 Carrier Pigeon and Airplane
55 National Arms

**1940.** Cent of 1st Adhesive Postage Stamps.

156. **54.** 3 s. orange .. .. 20 25
157. 10 s. violet .. .. 20 15
158. 15 s. brown .. .. 20 15
159. 30 s. blue .. .. 1·40 1·25

**1991.**

161 **55** 5 k. red and orange .. 10 10
162 10 k. green & emerald .. 20 20
163 15 k. blue and light blue 35 35
164 30 k. black and grey .. 25 25
165 50 k. brown and orange 40 40
166 70 k. purple and mauve 50 50
167 90 k. magenta & mauve 65 65
168 1 r. brown (21 × 27 mm) 75 75
169 2 r. blue (21 × 27 mm) .. 1·50 1·50
See also Nos. 194/205.

56 Flag
57 Estonian Arms

**1991.**

170 **56** 1 r. 50 multicoloured .. 1·25 1·25
171 – 2 r. 50 black, grey & grn 1·90 1·90
DESIGN—HORIZ. 2 r. 50, Map of Europe showing Estonia.

**1992.** Value expressed by letter.

172 **57** E (1 r.) green and yellow 15 15
173 R (10 r.) red and pink .. 50 50
174 I (20 r.) green & blue 1·00 1·00
175 A (40 r.) blue & lt blue 2·00 2·00
See also Nos. 179/81 and 182/4.

58 Olympic Rings and Pattern
59 Osprey ("Pandion haliaetus")

**1992.** Olympic Games, Barcelona.

176 **58** 1 k. + 50 s. red .. .. 15 15
177 – 3 k. + 1 k. 50 green .. 45 45
178 – 5 k. + 2 k. 50 black & bl 75 75
DESIGNS: 3 k. Olympic rings and pattern (different); 5 k. Estonian flag, rings and pattern.

**1992.** As Nos. 172 and 174/5 but colours changed.

179 **57** E (10 s.) orange & yell 10 10
180 I (1 k.) green .. .. 10 10
181 A (2 k.) blue .. .. 20 20

**1992.** Value expressed by letter. Size 21 × 27 mm.

182 **57** X (10 s.) brown .. 10 10
183 X (10 s.) green .. 10 10
184 X (10 s.) black .. 10 10

**1992.** Birds of the Baltic.

185 **59** 1 k. black and red .. 10 10
186 – 1 k. brown, black & red 10 10
187 – 1 k. sepia, brown & red 10 10
188 – 1 k. brown, black & red 10 10
DESIGNS: No. 186, Black-tailed godwit ("Limosa limosa"); 187, Goosander ("Mergus merganser"); 188, Common shelducks ("Tadorna tadorna").

**1992.** Value expressed by letter. Size 21 × 27 mm.

189 **57** Z (30 s.) mauve .. 10 10
190 Z (30 s.) red .. .. 10 10
191 Z (30 s.) black .. .. 10 10

60 Decorated Christmas Tree
61 Birds, Flowers and Envelope within Heart

**1992.** Christmas.

192 **60** 30 s. multicoloured .. 10 10
193 2 k. multicoloured .. 20 20

**1993.** As Nos. 161/9 but face values in senti.

194 **55** 10 s. grey and blue (18 × 21 mm) .. 10 10
195 20 s. black and green (21 × 27 mm) .. 10 10
197 30 s. purple and grey (21 × 27 mm) .. 10 10
199 50 s. blue and brown (18 × 21 mm) .. 10 10
200 60 s. green and purple (18 × 21 mm) .. 10 10
205 60 s. brown (21 × 27 mm) 10 10
201 80 s. blue and mauve (21 × 27 mm) .. 10 10
202 5 k. mauve and brown (23 × 28 mm) .. 50 50
203 10 k. green and blue (23 × 28 mm) .. 60 60
204 20 k. green and lilac (23 × 28 mm) .. 1·25 1·25

**1993.** Friendship.

210 **61** 1 k. multicoloured .. 10 10

62 Anniversary Emblem
64 Wrestling

**1993.** 75th Anniv of Republic.

211 **62** 60 s. multicoloured .. 10 10
212 1 k. multicoloured .. 10 10
213 2 k. multicoloured .. 20 20

**1993.** No. 163 surch **0.60.**

214 **55** 60 s. on 15 k. blue and light blue .. .. 10 10

**1993.** Baltic Sea Games. Multicoloured.

215 60 s. Type **64** .. .. 10 10
216 1 k. + 25 s. Ship with map of Baltic on sail and colours of participating countries as shields .. 10 10
217 2 k. Athlete putting the rock and sports pictograms .. .. 20 20

65 Toompea Castle, Tallinn
66 1918 5 k. Stamp and Anniversary Emblem

**1993.**

218 – 1 k. black & brown 10 10
219 **65** 2 k. brown & lt brn 20 20
219a – 2 k. 50 deep lilac and lilac .. .. 25 25
219b – 2 k. 50 grey .. 25 25
220 – 2 k. 70 blue & cobalt 25 25
221 – 2 k. 90 dp grn & grn 30 30
222 – 3 k. brown and pink 30 30
222a – 3 k. 20 dp grn & grn 35 35
223 – 4 k. violet and lilac 40 40
DESIGNS—HORIZ: 1 k. Toolse Castle; 2 k. 70, Hermann's Castle, Narva; 2 k. 90, Haapsalu Castle; 3 k. 20, Rakvere Castle; 4 k. Kuressaare Castle. VERT: 2 k. 50 (219a), Paide Castle; 2 k. 50 (219b), Purtse Castle; 3 k. Kiiu Castle.

**1993.** 75th Anniv of First Estonian Stamps.

225 **66** 1 k. multicoloured .. 10 10

68 Haapsalu Church
69 Lydia Koidula

**1993.** Christmas.

228 **68** 80 s. red .. .. 10 10
229 – 2 k. blue .. .. 20 20
DESIGN—VERT. 2 k. Tallinn church.

**1993.** 150th Birth Anniv of Lydia Koidula (writer).

230 **69** 1 k. multicoloured .. 10 10

70 Ski Jumping
71 Tartu 1869 Emblem

**1994.** Winter Olympic Games, Lillehammer, Norway. Multicoloured.

231 1 k. + 25 s. Type **70** .. 15 15
232 2 k. Speed skating .. 20 20

**1994.** 125th Song Festival. Multicoloured.

233 **71** 1 k. + 25 s. yellow, brown and green .. .. 15 15
234 – 2 k. brown and blue .. 20 20
235 – 3 k. bistre, brown and stone .. .. 30 30
DESIGNS: 2 k. Tallinn 1923 emblem; 3 k. Tallinn 1969 emblem.

72 Squirrel
73 Mill (Patent No. 1, Aleksander Mikiver)

**1994.** The Siberian Flying Squirrel. Mult.

237 1 k. Type **72** .. .. 10 10
238 2 k. Squirrel on broad-leafed branch .. .. 20 20
239 3 k. Squirrel on pine branch .. .. 30 30
240 4 k. Squirrel with young .. 40 40

**1994.** Europa. Inventions. Multicoloured.

241 1 k. Type **73** .. .. 10 10
242 2 k. 70 "Minox" mini camera (Patent No. 2628, Walter Zapp) .. 30 30

74 Mustjala Woman
75 Kadriorg Palace

**1994.** Costumes (1st series). Multicoloured.

243 1 k. Type **74** .. .. 10 10
244 1 k. Jamaja couple .. 10 10
See also Nos. 254/5 and 274/5.

**1994.** 75th Anniv of Estonian Art Museum, Tallinn.

245 **75** 1 k. 70 multicoloured .. 15 15

76 "The Holy Family" (Lichtenstein Master)
77 Ruhnu Church

**1994.** International Year of the Family.

246 **76** 1 k. 70 multicoloured .. 15 15

**1994.** Christmas.

247 **77** 1 k. 20 brown .. .. 10 10
248 – 2 k. 50 green .. .. 25 25
DESIGN—HORIZ: 2 k. 50, Urvaste Church.

**1994.** Victims of the Estonia Ferry Disaster Fund. No. 248 surch + **20 kr 28. 09. 1994 59°23 POHJALAIUST 21°42 ÎDAPIKKUST "ESTONIA" laevahuku ohvrite fondi.**

249 2 k. 50 + 20 k. green .. 30 30

79 Gustav II Adolphus
80 Barnacle Geese

**1994.** 400th Birth Anniv of King Gustav II Adolphus of Sweden.

250 **79** 2 k. 50 purple .. .. 25 25

**1995.** Matsalu Wetland Reserve. Mult.

251 1 k. 70 Type **80** .. .. 15 15
252 3 k. 20 Greylag geese .. 35 35

81 'Labourer's Family at Table" (Efraim Allsalu)
82 Beach Hotel, Parnu (Estonia)

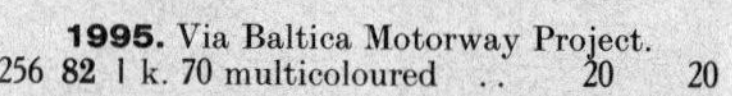

**1995.** 50th Anniv of F.A.O.

253 **81** 2 k. 70 multicoloured .. 30 30

**1995.** Costumes (2nd series). As T **74.** Multicoloured.

254 1 k. 70 Muhu couple .. 20 20
255 1 k. 70 Muhu women .. 20 20

**1995.** Via Baltica Motorway Project.

256 **82** 1 k. 70 multicoloured .. 20 20

83 Broken Barbed Wire
84 U.N. Emblem and Landscape

**1995.** Europa. Peace and Freedom.

258 **83** 2 k. 70 brown and mauve 30 30

**1995.** 50th Anniv of U.N.O.

259 **84** 4 k. multicoloured .. 45 45

85 Lighthouse and Chart
86 Vanemuine Theatre

**1995.** Pakri Lighthouse.

260 **85** 1 k. 70 multicoloured .. 20 20

**1995.** 125th Anniv of Vanemuine Theatre.

261 **86** 1 k. 70 orange, blk & grn 20 20

87 White-tailed Sea Eagle
88 Pasteur and Bacteria

**1995.** "Keep the Estonian Sea Clean".

262 **87** 2 k. + 25 s. black & blue 25 25

**1995.** Death Cent of Louis Pasteur (chemist).

263 **88** 2 k. 70 multicoloured .. 30 30

89 Bronze Bear Amulet (Samoyedic group) 90 Kunileid and Music

**1995.** Finno-Ugric Peoples. Multicoloured.

| No. | Description | | |
|---|---|---|---|
| 264 | 2 k. 50 Shaman's drum (Saami group) | 30 | 30 |
| 265 | 2 k. 50 Karelian writing (Baltic-Finnic group) | 30 | 30 |
| 266 | 3 k. 50 Duck brooch of Kama area (Volga group) | 40 | 40 |
| 267 | 3 k. 50 Type **89** | 40 | 40 |
| 268 | 4 k. 50 Duck-feet pendant (Permic group) | 50 | 50 |
| 269 | 4 k. 50 Khanty band ornament (Ugric group) | 50 | 50 |

**1995.** 150th Birth Anniv of Aleksandr Kunileid (composer).

| No. | Description | | |
|---|---|---|---|
| 270 **90** | 2 k. blue | 20 | 20 |

91 St. Martin's Church, Turi 92 "Lembit" (submarine)

**1995.** Christmas.

| No. | Description | | |
|---|---|---|---|
| 271 **91** | 2 k. yellow | 20 | 20 |
| 272 – | 3 k. 50 red | 40 | 40 |

DESIGN: 3 k. 50, Charles's Church, Tallinn.

**1996.** 60th Anniv of "Lembit".

| No. | Description | | |
|---|---|---|---|
| 273 **92** | 2 k. 50 multicoloured | 25 | 25 |

**1996.** Costumes (3rd series). As T **74**. Mult.

| No. | Description | | |
|---|---|---|---|
| 274 | 2 k. 50 Emmaste mother and bride | 25 | 25 |
| 275 | 2 k. 50 Reigi women | 25 | 25 |

94 Marie Under (poet) 95 Marconi and Wireless Telegraph

**1996.** Europa. Famous Women.

| No. | Description | | |
|---|---|---|---|
| 277 **94** | 2 k. 50 multicoloured | 25 | 25 |

**1996.** Centenary of Guglielmo Marconi's Patented Wireless Telegraph.

| No. | Description | | |
|---|---|---|---|
| 278 **95** | 3 k. 50 multicoloured | 35 | 35 |

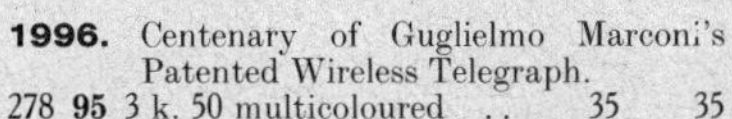

96 "Surr Toll" 97 Lighthouse and Chart

**1996.** 82nd Anniv of "Suur Toll" (ice-breaker).

| No. | Description | | |
|---|---|---|---|
| 279 **96** | 2 k. 50 multicoloured | 25 | 25 |

**1996.** 125th Anniv of Vaindloo Lighthouse.

| No. | Description | | |
|---|---|---|---|
| 280 **97** | 2 k. 50 multicoloured | 25 | 25 |

98 Class "Gk" Steam Locomotive

**1996.** Cent of Narrow-gauge Railway. Mult.

| No. | Description | | |
|---|---|---|---|
| 281 | 3 k. 20 Type **98** | 35 | 35 |
| 282 | 3 k. 50 Class "DeM" diesel railcar | 35 | 35 |
| 283 | 4 k. 50 Class "Sk" steam locomotive | 45 | 45 |

# ETHIOPIA Pt. 12

Formerly called Abyssinia. An ancient empire on the E. coast of Africa. From 1936 to 1941, part of Italian East Africa. Since 1952 Eritrea has been federated with Ethiopia. In 1974 Emperor Haile Selassie was deposed and a republic proclaimed.

1894 and 1907. 16 guerche = 1 Maria Theresa-Thaler.
1905. 100 centimes = 1 franc.
1908. 16 piastres = 1 thaler.
1928. 16 mehaleks = 1 thaler.
1936. 100 centimes = 1 thaler.
1936. 100 centesimi = 1 lira.
1946. 100 cents = 1 Ethiopian dollar.
1976. 100 cents = 1 birr.

## INDEPENDENT EMPIRE

**1.** Menelik II. **2.** Lion of the Tribe of Judah.

**1894.**

| No. | Type | Description | | |
|---|---|---|---|---|
| 1. | **1.** | ¼ g. green | 3·25 | 5·00 |
| 2. | | ½ g. red | 1·90 | 3·75 |
| 3. | | 1 g. blue | 1·90 | 3·75 |
| 4. | | 2 g. brown | 1·90 | 5·00 |
| 5. | **2.** | 4 g. red | 1·90 | 5·00 |
| 6. | | 8 g. mauve | 1·90 | 5·00 |
| 7. | | 16 g. black | 2·75 | 5·00 |

**1901.** Optd. **Ethiopie.**

| No. | Type | Description | | |
|---|---|---|---|---|
| 15. | **1.** | ¼ g. green | 9·25 | 9·25 |
| 16. | | ½ g. red | 9·25 | 9·25 |
| 17. | | 1 g. blue | 10·00 | 10·00 |
| 18. | | 2 g. brown | 10·00 | 10·00 |
| 19. | **2.** | 4 g. red | 10·00 | 10·00 |
| 20. | | 8 g. mauve | 13·50 | 13·50 |
| 21. | | 16 g. black | 18·00 | 18·00 |

በስጣ:: (4.) መልክት:: (5.)

**1902.** Optd. with T **4.**

| No. | Type | Description | | |
|---|---|---|---|---|
| 22. | **1.** | ¼ g. green | 5·25 | 5·25 |
| 23. | | ½ g. red | 5·25 | 5·25 |
| 24. | | 1 g. blue | 7·25 | 7·25 |
| 25. | | 2 g. brown | 7·25 | 7·25 |
| 26. | **2.** | 4 g. red | 11·50 | 11·50 |
| 27. | | 8 g. mauve | 15·00 | 15·00 |
| 28. | | 16 g. black | 30·00 | 30·00 |

**1903.** Optd. with T **5.**

| No. | Type | Description | | |
|---|---|---|---|---|
| 29. | **1.** | ¼ g. green | 4·50 | 4·50 |
| 30. | | ½ g. red | 4·50 | 4·50 |
| 31. | | 1 g. blue | 7·00 | 7·00 |
| 32. | | 2 g. brown | 8·25 | 8·25 |
| 33. | **2.** | 4 g. red | 8·25 | 8·25 |
| 34. | | 8 g. mauve | 20·00 | 20·00 |
| 35. | | 16 g. black | 28·00 | 28·00 |

ምልክት (6.) ምኒልክ (10.)

**1904.** Optd. with T **6.**

| No. | Type | Description | | |
|---|---|---|---|---|
| 36. | **1.** | ¼ g. green | 8·25 | 8·25 |
| 37. | | ½ g. red | 10·00 | 10·00 |
| 38. | | 1 g. blue | 13·50 | 13·50 |
| 39. | | 2 g. brown | 15·00 | 15·00 |
| 40. | **2.** | 4 g. red | 17·00 | 17·00 |
| 41. | | 8 g. mauve | 32·00 | 32·00 |
| 42. | | 16 g. black | 50·00 | 50·00 |

**1905.** Surch. in figures.

| No. | Type | Description | | |
|---|---|---|---|---|
| 43. | **1.** | 05 on ¼ g. green | 6·00 | 6·00 |
| 44. | | 10 on ½ g. red | 6·00 | 6·00 |
| 45. | | 20 on 1 g. blue | 6·00 | 6·00 |
| 46. | | 40 on 2 g. brown | 7·75 | 8·00 |
| 47. | **2.** | 80 on 4 g. red | 13·50 | 13·50 |
| 48. | | 1.60 on 8 g. mauve | 12·00 | 17·00 |
| 49. | | 3.20 on 16 g. black | 24·00 | 24·00 |

The above surcharge was also applied to some stamps optd. with **Ethiopie** and Types **4**, **5** and **6**.

**1905.** Surch. in figures and words.

| No. | Type | Description | | |
|---|---|---|---|---|
| 90. | **2.** | 5 c. on 16 g. blk. (No. 28) | 85·00 | £100 |

**1905.** No. 2 divided diagonally and surch. **5c/m.**

| No. | Type | Description | | |
|---|---|---|---|---|
| 86. | **1.** | 5 c. on half of ½ g. red | 4·25 | 4·25 |

**1905.** Surch. **5c/m.**

| No. | Type | Description | | |
|---|---|---|---|---|
| 71. | **1.** | 5 c. on ¼ g. grn. (No. 22) | 10·00 | 11·50 |

**1906.** Optd. with T **10** and surch. in figures.

| No. | Type | Description | | |
|---|---|---|---|---|
| 94. | **1.** | 05 on ¼ g. green | 5·25 | 5·25 |
| 95. | | 10 on ½ g. red | 7·00 | 7·00 |
| 96. | | 20 on 1 g. blue | 7·00 | 7·00 |
| 97. | | 40 on 2 g. brown | 7·00 | 7·00 |
| 98. | **2.** | 80 on 4 g. red | 8·75 | 8·75 |
| 99. | | 1.60 on 8 g. mauve | 12·00 | 12·00 |
| 100. | | 3.20 on 16 g. black | 32·00 | 32·00 |

**1906.** Surch. with figures and native word.

| No. | Type | Description | | |
|---|---|---|---|---|
| 101. | **1.** | 05 on ¼ g. green | 5·75 | 5·75 |
| 102. | | 10 on ½ g. red | 7·00 | 7·00 |
| 103. | | 20 on 1 g. blue | 9·75 | 9·75 |
| 104. | | 40 on 2 g. brown | 9·75 | 9·75 |
| 105. | **2.** | 80 on 4 g. red | 13·50 | 13·50 |
| 106. | | 1.60 on 8 g. mauve | 13·50 | 13·50 |
| 107. | | 3.20 on 16 g. black | 32·00 | 32·00 |

ዳግማዊ:: (13.)

**1907.** Optd. with T **13** and surch. in figures between stars.

| No. | Type | Description | | |
|---|---|---|---|---|
| 115. | **1.** | ¼ on ¼ g. green | 6·00 | 6·00 |
| 116. | | ½ on ½ g. red | 6·00 | 6·00 |
| 117. | | 1 on 1 g. blue | 7·25 | 7·25 |
| 118. | | 2 on 2 g. brown | 8·75 | 8·75 |
| 119. | **2.** | 4 on 4 g. red | 8·75 | 8·75 |
| 120. | | 8 on 8 g. mauve | 18·00 | 18·00 |
| 121. | | 16 on 16 g. black | 25·00 | 25·00 |

**1908.** Entry into U.P.U. Nos. 1/7 surch. in figures and words.

| No. | Type | Description | | |
|---|---|---|---|---|
| 133. | **1.** | ¼ pi. on ¼ g. green | 2·10 | 2·10 |
| 134. | | ½ pi. on ½ g. red | 2·10 | 2·10 |
| 129. | | 1 pi. on ½ g. red | 7·75 | 7·75 |
| 135. | | 1 pi. on 1 g. blue | 2·75 | 2·75 |
| 136. | | 2 pi. on 2 g. brown | 4·75 | 4·75 |
| 137. | **2.** | 4 pi. on 4 g. red | 6·75 | 6·75 |
| 138. | | 8 pi. on 8 g. mauve | 13·50 | 13·50 |
| 139. | | 16 pi. on 16 g. black | 18·00 | 18·00 |

**19.** Throne of Solomon. **20.** Emperor Menelik.

**1909.**

| No. | Type | Description | | |
|---|---|---|---|---|
| 147. | **19.** | ¼ g. green | 85 | 85 |
| 148. | | ½ g. red | 85 | 65 |
| 149. | | 1 g. orange and green | 2·75 | 2·75 |
| 150. | **20.** | 2 g. blue | 3·25 | 2·75 |
| 151. | | 4 g. red and green | 5·00 | 4·25 |
| 152. | – | 8 g. grey and red | 8·25 | 5·75 |
| 153. | – | 16 g. red | 12·50 | 9·25 |

DESIGN: 8 g., 16 g. Another portrait.

**1911.** T 1 and 2 optd. **AFF EXCEP FAUTE TIMB** and surch. in manuscript.

| No. | Type | Description | | |
|---|---|---|---|---|
| 154. | **1.** | ¼ g. on ¼ g. green | £110 | 60·00 |
| 155. | | ½ g. on ½ g. red | £110 | 60·00 |
| 156. | | 1 g. on 1 g. blue | £110 | 60·00 |
| 157. | | 2 g. on 2 g. brown | £110 | 60·00 |
| 158. | **2.** | 4 g. on 4 g. red | £110 | 60·00 |
| 159. | | 8 g. on 8 g. mauve | £110 | 60·00 |
| 160. | | 16 g. on 16 g. black | £110 | 60·00 |

(22.)

ተፈሪ::
11/2/1917.

(24.)

**1917.** Coronation. Optd. with T **22** (and similar type).

| No. | Type | Description | | |
|---|---|---|---|---|
| 161. | **19.** | ¼ g. green | 4·25 | 5·00 |
| 162. | | ½ g. red | 4·25 | 5·00 |
| 163. | **20.** | 2 g. blue | 5·00 | 6·00 |
| 164. | | 4 g. red and green | 8·25 | 8·25 |
| 165. | – | 8 g. grey and red (No. 152) | 15·00 | 15·00 |
| 166. | – | 16 g. red (No. 153) | 23·00 | 25·00 |

**1917.** Optd. with T **24** (and similar type).

| No. | Type | Description | | |
|---|---|---|---|---|
| 168. | **19.** | ¼ g. green | 25 | 25 |
| 169. | | ½ g. red | 25 | 25 |
| 170. | | 1 g. orange and green | 2·10 | 2·10 |
| 171. | **20.** | 2 g. blue | 70 | 70 |
| 174. | | 4 g. red and green | 1·40 | 1·40 |
| 175. | – | 8 g. grey & red (No. 152) | 1·10 | 1·10 |
| 176. | – | 16 g. red (No. 153) | 2·10 | 2·10 |

**1917.** Nos. 175/6 surch. with large figure.

| No. | Description | | |
|---|---|---|---|
| 177. | ¼ on 8 g. grey and red | 3·00 | 3·00 |
| 178. | ½ on 8 g. grey and red | 3·00 | 3·00 |
| 179. | 1 on 16 g. red | 7·00 | 7·00 |
| 180. | 2 on 16 g. red | 7·00 | 7·00 |

**28.** Gerenuk. **29.** Ras Tafari, later Emperor Haile Selassie.

**30.** African Buffalo.

**1919.**

| No. | Type | Description | | |
|---|---|---|---|---|
| 181. | **28.** | ⅛ g. brown and violet | 15 | 10 |
| 182. | – | ¼ g. grey and green | 15 | 10 |
| 183. | – | ½ g. green and red | 15 | 10 |
| 184. | – | 1 g. black and purple | 10 | 10 |
| 185. | **29.** | 2 g. brown and blue | 10 | 10 |
| 186. | – | 4 g. orange and blue | 20 | 20 |
| 187. | – | 6 g. orange and blue | 25 | 25 |
| 188. | – | 8 g. black and olive | 40 | 40 |
| 189. | – | 12 g. grey and purple | 80 | 85 |
| 190. | – | $1 black and red | 1·40 | 1·10 |
| 191. | **30.** | $2 brown and black | 3·25 | 3·00 |
| 192. | – | $3 red and green | 5·00 | 5·00 |
| 193. | – | $4 pink and brown | 5·00 | 5·00 |
| 194. | – | $5 grey and red | 6·75 | 6·75 |
| 195. | – | $10 yellow and olive | 10·00 | 10·00 |

DESIGNS—VERT. As Type **28:** ¼ g. Giraffes. ½ g. Leopard. As Type **29:** 1 g. Ras Tafari. 4 g. ditto (different portrait). $4, $5, $10, Empress Zauditu (different portraits). HORIZ. As Type **30:** 6 g. St. George's Cathedral, Addis Ababa. 8 g. Black rhinoceros. 12 g. Ostriches. $1, African elephant. $3, Lions.

**1919.** Stamps of 1919 variously surch.

| No. | Type | Description | | |
|---|---|---|---|---|
| 197 | **28.** | ½ g. on ⅛ g. brn. & violet | 50 | 50 |
| 207 | – | ½ g. on 8 g. blk. & olive | 1·00 | 80 |
| 202 | – | ½ g. on $1 black and red | 50 | 50 |
| 203 | – | ½ g. on $5 grey and red | 1·00 | 1·00 |
| 198 | – | 1 g. on ¼ g. grey & green | 1·40 | 1·40 |
| 204 | – | 1 g. on 6 g. orge. & blue | 85 | 85 |
| 208 | – | 1 g. on 12 g. grey & pur. | 1·50 | 1·40 |
| 205 | – | 1 g. on $3 red and green | 90 | 90 |
| 206 | – | 1 g. on $10 yell. & olive | 1·40 | 1·40 |
| 198c | – | 2 g. on 1 g. black & pur. | 50 | 50 |
| 199 | – | 2 g. on $4 pink & brown | 18·00 | 18·00 |
| 200 | – | 2½ g. on ½ g. grn. & red | 90 | 90 |
| 201 | **29.** | 4 g. on 2 g. brn. & blue | 90 | 90 |
| 196 | – | 4 g. on $4 pink & brown | 1·40 | 1·40 |

**39.** Ras Tafari, later Emperor Haile Selassie. **40.** Empress Zauditu.

(41.) (46. "The Emperor of the Kings of Ethiopia, 2 Nov., 1930, Haile Selassie").

**1928.** Opening of P.O. at Addis Ababa. Optd. with T **41.**

| No. | Type | Description | | |
|---|---|---|---|---|
| 213. | **39.** | ⅛ m. blue and orange | 1·60 | 2·50 |
| 214. | **40.** | ¼ m. red and blue | 1·60 | 2·50 |
| 215. | **39.** | ½ m. black and green | 1·60 | 2·50 |
| 216. | **40.** | 1 m. black and red | 1·60 | 2·50 |
| 217. | **39.** | 2 m. black and blue | 1·60 | 2·50 |
| 218. | **40.** | 4 m. olive and yellow | 1·60 | 2·50 |
| 219. | **39.** | 8 m. olive and mauve | 1·60 | 2·40 |
| 220. | **40.** | 1 t. mauve and brown | 2·00 | 3·00 |
| 221. | **39.** | 2 t. brown and green | 2·75 | 4·25 |
| 222. | **40.** | 3 t. green and purple | 2·75 | 4·25 |

**1928.**

| No. | Type | Description | | |
|---|---|---|---|---|
| 223. | **39.** | ⅛ m. blue and orange | 85 | 95 |
| 224. | **40.** | ¼ m. red and blue | 50 | 85 |
| 225. | **39.** | ½ m. black and green | 95 | 1·10 |
| 226. | **40.** | 1 m. black and red | 45 | 50 |
| 227. | **39.** | 2 m. black and blue | 45 | 50 |
| 228. | **40.** | 4 m. olive and yellow | 45 | 50 |
| 229. | **39.** | 8 m. olive and mauve | 1·40 | 1·75 |
| 230. | **40.** | 1 t. mauve and brown | 1·75 | 2·10 |
| 231. | **39.** | 2 t. brown and green | 2·50 | 2·75 |
| 232. | **40.** | 3 t. green and purple | 3·25 | 4·25 |

**1928.** Elevation of Ras Tafari to Negus. Optd. with Crown and **NEGOUS TEFERI.**

| No. | Type | Description | | |
|---|---|---|---|---|
| 233. | **39.** | ⅛ m. blue and orange | 2·75 | 5·00 |
| 234. | | ½ m. black and green | 2·75 | 5·00 |
| 235. | | 2 m. black and blue | 2·75 | 6·75 |
| 236. | | 8 m. olive and mauve | 2·75 | 6·75 |
| 237. | | 2 t. brown and green | 2·75 | 6·75 |

**1929.** Air. Arrival of First Airplane of the Ethiopian Government. Optd with airplane and Amharic text (= "16 Aug 1929. Ethiopian Government Air Mail").

| No. | Type | Description | | |
|---|---|---|---|---|
| 238. | **39.** | ⅛ m. blue and orange | 1·40 | 1·90 |
| 239. | **40.** | ¼ m. red and blue | 1·40 | 1·90 |
| 240. | **39.** | ½ m. black and green | 1·50 | 2·00 |
| 241. | **40.** | 1 m. black and red | 1·50 | 2·00 |
| 242. | **39.** | 2 m. black and blue | 1·50 | 2·00 |
| 243. | **40.** | 4 m. olive and yellow | 1·50 | 2·00 |
| 244. | **39.** | 8 m. olive and mauve | 1·50 | 2·00 |
| 245. | **40.** | 1 t. mauve and brown | 2·00 | 3·25 |
| 246. | **39.** | 2 t. brown and green | 3·25 | 4·25 |
| 247. | **40.** | 3 t. green and purple | 3·25 | 4·25 |

**1930.** Accession of Ras Taffari as Emperor Haile Selassie. Optd. **HAYLE** (or **HAILE**) **SELASSIE 1er 3 Avril 1930** and native inscriptions.

| No. | Type | Description | | |
|---|---|---|---|---|
| 248. | **39.** | ⅛ m. blue and orange | 65 | 65 |
| 249. | **40.** | ¼ m. red and blue | 65 | 65 |
| 250. | **39.** | ½ m. black and green | 65 | 65 |
| 261. | **40.** | 1 m. black and red | 50 | 50 |
| 262. | **39.** | 2 m. black and blue | 50 | 50 |
| 263. | **40.** | 4 m. olive and yellow | 1·00 | 1·00 |
| 264. | **39.** | 8 m. olive and mauve | 1·40 | 1·40 |
| 265. | **40.** | 1 t. mauve and brown | 2·40 | 2·40 |
| 266. | **39.** | 2 t. brown and green | 2·75 | 2·75 |
| 267. | **40.** | 3 t. green and purple | 4·25 | 4·25 |

**1930.** Coronation of Emperor Haile Selassie (1st issue). Optd. with T **46.**

268. **39.** 1/8 m. blue and orange .. 50 70
269. **40.** 1/4 m. red and blue .. 50 70
270. **39.** 1/2 m. black and green .. 50 70
271. **40.** 1 m. black and red .. 50 70
272. **39.** 2 m. black and blue .. 50 70
273. **40.** 4 m. olive and yellow .. 50 70
274. **39.** 8 m. olive and mauve .. 85 85
275. **40.** 1 t. mauve and brown 1·40 1·40
276. **39.** 2 t. brown and green .. 2·10 2·10
277. **40.** 3 t. green and purple .. 3·25 3·25

**47.** The Ethiopian Lion and Symbols.

**1930.** Coronation of Emperor Haile Selassie (2nd issue).

278. **47.** 1 g. orange .. .. 25 25
279. 2 g. blue .. .. 25 25
280. 4 g. purple .. .. 40 50
281. 8 g. green .. .. 40 55
282. 1 t. brown .. .. 50 65
283. 3 t. green .. .. 1·10 1·10
284. 5 t. brown .. .. 1·50 1·50

**1931.** Issue of 1928 surch. in Mehaleks.

285. **40.** 1/8 m. on 1 m. blk. & red 45 85
286. **39.** 1/8 m. on 2 m. blk. & blue 45 85
287. **40.** 1/8 m. on 4 m. olive & yell. 45 85
288. 1/4 m. on 1 m. blk. & red 45 85
289. **39.** 1/4 m. on 2 m. blk. & blue 1·00 1·40
290. **40.** 1/4 m. on 4 m. olive & yell. 1·00 1·40
291. 1/2 m. on 1 m. blk. & red 1·00 1·40
292. **39.** 1/2 m. on 2 m. blk. & blue 1·00 1·40
293. **40.** 1/2 m. on 4 m. olive & yell. 1·00 1·40
294. 1/2 m. on 3 t. grn. & pur. 6·75 8·25
295. **39.** 1 m. on 2 m. blk. & blue 1·40 1·60

**49.** Potez 25A2 over Map of Ethiopia.

**50.** Ras Makonnen.

**1931.** Air.

296. **49.** 1 g. red .. .. 30 50
297. 2 g. blue .. .. 30 50
298. 4 g. mauve .. .. 45 65
299. 8 g. green .. .. 1·00 1·10
300. 1 t. brown .. .. 1·60 1·60
301. 2 t. red .. .. .. 4·00 5·25
302. 3 t. green .. .. 6·00 7·25

Reprints. See note below No. 284.

**1931.**

303. **50.** 1/8 g. red .. .. .. 15 40
304. – 1/4 g. olive .. .. 40 40
305. **50.** 1/2 g. purple .. .. 45 45
306. – 1 g. orange .. .. 45 45
307. – 2 g. blue .. .. 45 45
308. – 4 g. lilac .. .. 95 1·00
309. – 8 g. green .. .. 2·00 2·00
310. – 1 t. brown .. .. 5·25 5·25
311. – 3 t. green .. .. 5·75 6·00
312. – 5 t. brown .. .. 8·25 8·25

DESIGNS—HORIZ. 1/4 g. Railway Bridge over R. Awash. VERT. 1 g. Empress Menen (profile). 2 g., 8 g. Haile Selassie (profile). 4 g., 1 t. Statue of Menelik II. 3 t. Empress Menen (full face). 5 t. Haile Selassie (full face).

**1936.** Red Cross. As T **50** optd with red cross.

313. 1 g. green .. .. 90 90
314. 2 g. pink .. .. 90 90
315. 4 g. blue .. .. 90 90
316. 8 g. brown .. .. 1·10 1·10
317. 1 t. violet .. .. 1·10 1·10

**1936.** As T **50** surch with value and Amharic text.

318 **50** 1 c. on 1/8 g. red .. 1·40 1·40
319 – 2 c. on 1/4 g. green .. 1·40 1·40
320 **50** 3 c. on 1/2 g. purple .. 1·40 1·40
321 – 5 c. on 1 g. orange .. 1·10 1·10
322 – 10 c. on 2 g. blue .. 1·10 1·00

**54.** King Victor Emmanuel III.

**56.** Haile Selassie I in Coronation Robes.

## ITALIAN COLONY

**1936.** Annexation of Ethiopia.

322a. **54.** 10 c. brown .. .. 40 95
322b. – 20 c. violet .. .. 40 95
322c. – 25 c. green .. .. 15 35
322d. – 30 c. brown .. .. 30 85
322e. – 50 c. red .. .. 15 25
322f. – 75 c. orange .. .. 40 95
322g. – 1 l. 25 blue .. .. 40 1·10

DESIGNS—VERT. 25 c., 30 c., 50 c. Victor Emmanuel III. HORIZ. Victor Emmanuel III and 20 c. Mountain scenery. 75 c. Gonder Castle. 1 l. 25, Tomb of Scec Hussen and Dordola Hills.

## INDEPENDENCE RESTORED

**1942.** 1st issue. "Centimes" with capital initial and small letters.

323. **56.** 4 c. black and green .. 1·40 75
324. 10 c. black and red .. 2·75 1·10
325. 20 c. black and blue .. 4·00 2·00

**1942.** 2nd issue. "CENTIMES" in block capital letters.

326. **56.** 4 c. black and green .. 85 25
327. 8 c. black and orange.. 90 25
328. 10 c. black and red .. 1·25 30
329. 12 c. black and violet.. 1·25 60
330. 20 c. black and blue .. 1·60 85
331. 25 c. black and green.. 2·40 1·40
332. 50 c. black and brown.. 4·00 1·60
333. 60 c. black and mauve.. 5·25 2·40

**1943.** Restoration of Obelisk and 13th Anniv. of Coronation of Haile Selassie. Stamps of 1942 inscr. "CENTIMES" surch. **OBELISK 3 NOV. 1943** and value.

334. **56.** 5 c. on 4 c. black & grn. 50·00 50·00
335. 10 c. on 8 c. blk. & orge. 50·00 50·00
336. 15 c. on 10 c. blk. & red 50·00 50·00
337. 20 c. on 12 c. blk. & vio. 50·00 50·00
338. 30 c. on 20 c. blk. & bl. 50·00 50·00

In No. 338 the figure "3" is surcharged on the "2" of "20" to make "30" and this value is confirmed by the Amharic characters.

**58.** Royal Palace, Addis Ababa.

**59.** Menelik II.

**1944.** Birth Cent. of Emperor Menelik II.

339. **58.** 5 c. green .. .. 1·60 85
340. **59.** 10 c. red .. .. 2·50 1·25
341. – 20 c. blue .. .. 4·75 3·00
342. – 50 c. violet .. .. 5·25 3·25
343. – 65 c. orange .. .. 9·25 4·25

DESIGNS—VERT. 20 c. Equestrian statue of Menelik II. 65 c. Menelik in royal robes. HORIZ. 50 c. Menelik's mausoleum.

**60.** Patient and Nurse (Amharic characters = "Victory").

**64.** Postal Transport by Mule and by Bus.

**1945.** Victory. Optd. V in red.

344. – 5 c. green .. .. 3·25 2·00
345. – 10 c. red .. .. 4·00 3·25
346. **60.** 25 c. blue .. .. 5·00 4·75
347. – 50 c. brown .. .. 6·75 5·00
348. – 1 t. violet .. .. 8·25 8·25

DESIGNS: 5 c. Nurse and baby. 10 c. Native soldier. 50 c. Nurse and child. 1 t. "Supplication". The above stamps without the "V" were not issued for postal purposes.

**1946.** Air. Resumption of National Air Mail Services. (a) Surch. at sides and top in Amharic, with **20-4-39** and value below.

349. **56.** 12 c. on 4 c. blk. & grn. 55·00 55·00

(b) Surch. **REPRISE POSTE AERIENNE ETHIOPIENNE** at sides and top, with **29.12.46** and values below.

350. **56.** 0.50 on 25 c. blk. & grn. 55·00 55·00
351. $2 on 60 c. blk. & mve. 75·00 75·00

**1947.** 50th Anniv. of Postal Service.

352. **64.** 10 c. yellow .. .. 2·50 2·00
353. – 20 c. blue .. .. 3·25 2·40
354. **63.** 30 c. brown .. .. 4·75 3·25
355. – 50 c. green .. .. 12·50 6·75
356. – 70 c. mauve .. .. 19·00 10·50

DESIGNS—VERT. 20 c. Menelik II (as in Type 1). HORIZ. 50 c. G.P.O., Addis Ababa. 70 c. Menelik and Haile Selassie.

**65.** Negus Sahle Selassie.

**1947.** 150th Anniv. of Selassie Dynasty.

357. **65.** 20 c. blue .. .. 2·50 1·60
358. – 30 c. purple .. .. 3·25 2·75
359. – $1 green .. .. 9·25 4·00

DESIGNS—HORIZ. 30 c. View of Ancober. VERT. $1, Negus Sahle Selassie.

**67.** Emperor Haile Selassie and Pres. Roosevelt.

**1947.** 2nd Death Anniv. of Pres. Roosevelt.

360. **67.** 12 c. grn. & lake (post.) 1·40 1·60
361. 25 c. red and blue .. 2·75 3·25
362. – 65 c. blue, red and black 5·00 6·25
363. – $1 sepia & purple (air) 10·00 12·00
364. – $2 blue and red .. 20·00 23·00

DESIGNS—HORIZ. 65 c. Pres. Roosevelt and U.S. flags. VERT. $1, Pres. Roosevelt. $2, Haile Selassie.

**1947.** Surch. **12 centimes** in French and Amharic with six bars.

365. **56.** 12 c. on 25 c. blk. & grn. 50·00 50·00

**69.** Lake Tana.

**1947.** Views with medallion portrait of Haile Selassie inset. (a) Postage.

366. – 1 c. purple .. .. 15 10
367. – 2 c. violet .. .. 15 15
368. – 4 c. green .. .. 20 15
369. – 5 c. green .. .. 15 10
370. **69.** 8 c. orange .. .. 50 15
371. 12 c. red .. .. 40 15
371a. – 15 c. olive .. .. 50 25
372. – 20 c. blue .. .. 65 30
373. – 30 c. brown .. .. 1·10 50
373a. – 60 c. red .. .. 1·90 60
374. – 70 c. mauve .. .. 2·40 65
375. – $1 red .. .. .. 4·75 55
376. – $3 blue .. .. .. 12·00 3·25
377. – $5 olive .. .. .. 18·00 5·75

DESIGNS: 1 c. Amba Alagi. 2 c. Trinity Church, Addis Ababa. 4 c. Debra Sina. 5 c. Mecan mountain pathway, near Ashangi. 12 c., 15 c. Parliament Building, Addis Ababa. 20 c. Aiba mountain scenery, near Mai Chio. 30 c. Nile Bridge. 60 c., 70 c. Canoe on Lake Tana. $1, Omo Falls. $3, Mt. Alamata. $5, Ras Dashan Mountains.

**70.** Douglas DC 3 over Zoquala Volcano.

(b) Air.

378. – 8 c. purple .. .. 15 10
379. **70.** 10 c. green .. .. 25 10
379a. – 25 c. purple .. .. 50 20
380. – 30 c. orange .. .. 75 25
380a. – 35 c. blue .. .. 1·00 40
380b. – 65 c. purple .. .. 75 35
381. – 70 c. red .. .. 1·75 40
382. – $1 blue .. .. .. 2·75 65
383. – $3 mauve .. .. 8·25 4·00
384. – $5 brown .. .. 13·00 6·50
385. – $10 violet .. .. 24·00 16·00

DESIGNS: 8 c. Ploughing with oxen. 30 c., 35 c. Tehis Isat Falls, Blue Nile. 65 c., 70 c. Amba Alagi. $1, Sacala source of River Nile. $3, Gorgora and Dembia on Lake Tana. $5, Magdala Fort. $10, Ras Dasnan Mountains and Lake.

**72.** Emperor, Empress, Lion and Map.

**1949.** 8th Anniv. of Liberation.

386. – 20 c. blue .. .. 1·40 30
387. **72.** 30 c. orange .. .. 1·40 65
388. – 50 c. violet .. .. 3·00 1·60
389. – 80 c. green .. .. 4·25 2·10
390. – $1 red .. .. .. 7·00 3·25

DESIGNS—20 c. Emperor and Empress with sceptres and orb. 50 c. Coat of arms. 80 c. Shield and spears. $1, Star of Solomon.

**1949.** Industrial and Agricultural Exn. Nos. 370/1 and 373/5 surch. **EXPOSITION 1949** and new value and two lines of Amharic characters.

391. 8 c.+8 c. orange .. 3·25 3·25
392. 12 c.+5 c. red .. .. 3·25 3·25
393. 30 c.+15 c. brown .. 6·75 6·75
394. 70 c.+70 c. mauve .. 17·00 17·00
395. $1+80 c. red .. .. 20·00 20·00

**74.** Emperor and U.P.U. Monument, Berne.

**1950.** Air. 75th Anniv. of U.P.U.

396. **74.** 5 c. red and green .. 90 70
397. 15 c. red and blue .. 1·10 70
398. 25 c. green and yellow 1·75 90
399. 50 c. blue and red .. 3·00 2·10

**1950.** Red Cross Fund. As Nos. 344/8 but without V opt. and surch. + **10 ct.** below a cross.

399a. 5 c.+10 c. green .. 1·40 1·40
399b. 10 c.+10 c. red .. 1·60 1·60
399c. 25 c.+10 c. blue .. 3·25 3·25
399d. 50 c.+10 c. brown .. 5·25 5·25
399e. $1+10 c. violet .. 12·50 12·50

**75.** Lion of the Tribe of Judah.

**76.** Emperor and Abbaye Bridge.

**1950.** 20th Anniv. of Coronation.

400. – 5 c. violet .. .. 1·40 45
401. – 10 c. mauve .. .. 2·75 1·00
402. – 20 c. red .. .. 3·25 1·50
403. **75.** 30 c. green .. .. 4·00 2·00
404. – 50 c. blue .. .. 5·00 3·25

DESIGNS—HORIZ. 5 c. Dejach Balcha Hospital. 50 c. Emperor, Empress and palace. VERT. 10 c. Abuna Petros. 20 c. Emperor hoisting flag.

**1951.** Opening of Abbaye Bridge.

405. **76.** 5 c. brown and green .. 3·25 1·00
406. 10 c. black and orange.. 5·00 1·60
407. 15 c. brown and blue .. 6·75 2·50
408. 30 c. mauve and olive 10·00 3·25
409. 60 c. blue and brown .. 13·50 5·00
410. 80 c. green and violet.. 20·00 6·75

**1951.** 55th Anniv. of Battle of Adwa. As T **76**, but Emperor and Tomb of Ras Makonnen.

411. 5 c. black and green .. 1·60 1·00
412. 10 c. black and blue .. 2·00 1·40
413. 15 c. black and blue .. 3·00 2·00
414. 30 c. black and red .. 4·00 2·40
415. 80 c. black and red .. 6·00 3·25
416. $1 black and brown .. 10·00 4·00

**1951.** Industrial and Agricultural Exhibition. Nos. 391/5 further optd **1951** with Amharic characters above.

417. 8 c.+8 c. orange .. 1·00 1·00
418. 12 c.+5 c. red .. .. 1·00 1·00
419. 30 c.+15 c. brown .. 1·40 1·40
420. 70 c.+70 c. mauve .. 11·50 11·50
421. $1+80 c. red .. .. 18·00 18·00

**79.** "Tree of Health".

**80.** Haile Selassie I.

**56.** Haile Selassie I in Coronation Robes.

**63.** Lion of the Tribe of Judah.

**1968.** Death Cent. of Emperor Theodore II.
690. – 10 c. brn., lilac & yellow 20 10
691. **137.** 20 c. lilac, brn. & mauve 35 20
692. – 50 c. red, orge. & green 1·10 85
DESIGNS—VERT. 10 c. Emperor Theodore. 50 c. Imperial crown.

**138.** Human Rights Emblem.

**1968.** Human Rights Year.
693. **138.** 15 c. black and red .. 55 15
694. $1 black and blue .. 2·40 1·60

**139.** Shah of Iran and Haile Selassie I.

**1968.** State Visit of Shah of Iran.
695. **139.** 5 c. multicoloured .. 20 10
696. 15 c. multicoloured .. 35 20
697. 30 c. multicoloured .. 1·00 75

**140.** Haile Selassie I and Addressing League of Nations, 1936.

**1968.** "Ethiopia's Struggle for Peace".
698. **140.** 15 c. multicoloured .. 20 20
699. – 35 c. multicoloured .. 40 45
700. – $1 multicoloured .. 2·40 1·40
HAILE SELASSIE and: 35 c. Africa Hall. $1, World map ("International Relations").

**141.** W.H.O. Emblem.

**1968.** 20th Anniv. of W.H.O.
701. **141.** 15 c. black and green .. 20 15
702. 60 c. black and purple 1·00 65

**142.** Running. **143.** Arrussi Costume.

**1968.** Olympic Games, Mexico. Multicoloured.
703. 10 c. Type **142** .. .. 15 10
704. 15 c. Football .. .. 20 15
705. 20 c. Boxing .. .. 25 20
706. 40 c. Basketball .. .. 85 55
707. 50 c. Cycling .. .. 1·10 85

**1968.** Ethiopian Costume (1st series). Mult.
708. 5 c. Type **143** .. .. 10 10
709. 15 c. Gemu Gofa .. .. 20 10
710. 20 c. Godjam .. .. 25 10
711. 30 c. Kaffa .. .. 30 20
712. 35 c. Harar .. .. 45 25
713. 50 c. Illubabor .. .. 95 35
714. 60 c. Eritrea .. .. 1·10 85
See also Nos. 768/74.

**144.** Postal Service Emblem and Initials.

**1969.** 75th Anniv. of Ethiopian Postal Service.
715. **144.** 10 c. blk., brn. & green 15 10
716. 15 c. blk., brn. & yell. 50 50
717. 35 c. black, brn. & red 90 90

**145.** I.L.O. Emblem.

**146.** Red Cross Emblems. **147.** Silver Coin of Endybis (3rd cent.).

**1969.** 50th Anniv. of I.L.O.
718. **145.** 15 c. orange and black 25 15
719. 60 c. green and black 1·40 1·40

**1969.** 50th Anniv. of League of Red Cross Societies.
720. **146.** 5 c. red, black and blue 20 15
721. 15 c. red, green & blue 65 50
722. 30 c. red, ultram & blue 1·10 1·00

**1969.** Ancient Ethiopian Coins.
723. **147.** 5 c. silver, black & blue 15 15
724. – 10 c. gold, black & red 30 25
725. – 15 c. gold, blk. & brown 25 35
726. – 30 c. bronze, blk. & red 85 65
727. – 40 c. bronze, blk. & grn. 95 85
728. – 50 c. silver, blk. & violet 1·25 1·10
COINS: 10 c. Gold coin of Ezana (4th century). 15 c. Gold coin of Kalob (6th century). 30 c. Bronze coin of Armah (7th century). 40 c. Bronze coin of Wazena (7th century). 50 c. Silver coin of Gersem (8th century).

**148.** "Hunting".

**1969.** African Tourist Year. Multicoloured.
729. 5 c. Type **148** .. .. 10 10
730. 10 c. "Camping" .. .. 10 10
731. 15 c. "Fishing" .. .. 55 10
732. 20 c. "Watersports" .. .. 65 65
733. 25 c. "Mountaineering" (vert.) .. .. .. 1·10 1·00

**149.** Dove of Peace.

**1969.** 25th Anniv. of U.N. Mult.
734. 10 c. Type **149** .. .. 10 10
735. 30 c. Stylised flowers (vert.) 50 65
736. 60 c. Peace dove and emblem 1·25 1·25

**150.** Ancient Cross, and "Holy Family".

**1969.** Ancient Ethiopian Crosses (2nd series).
737. **150.** 5 c. black, yell. & green 10 10
738. – 10 c. black and yellow 10 10
739. – 25 c. black, grn. & yell. 75 60
740. – 60 c. black and yellow 1·90 1·40
DESIGNS—VERT. 10 c., 25 c. and 60 c. show different crosses and drawings similar to Type 150.

**151.** Ancient Figurines.

**1970.** Ancient Ethiopian Pottery. Mult.
741. 10 c. Type **151** .. .. 10 10
742. 20 c. Decorated jar, Yeha 45 45
743. 25 c. Axum Pottery .. 60 60
744. 35 c. "Bird" jug, Matara 75 75
745. 60 c. Christian pottery, Adulis .. .. .. 1·40 1·40

**152.** Medhane Alem Church.

**1970.** Rock Churches of Lalibela. Mult.
746. 5 c. Type **152** .. .. 10 10
747. 10 c. Bieta Amanuel .. 10 10
748. 15 c. Four churches .. 20 35
749. 20 c. Bieta Mariam .. 55 55
750. 50 c. Bieta Giorgis .. 1·40 1·40

**153.** Sail-finned Surgeon.

**1970.** Fishes. Multicoloured.
751. 5 c. Type **153** .. .. 15 15
752. 10 c. Undulate triggerfish 35 35
753. 15 c. Red striped butterfly 60 60
754. 25 c. Ghost butterfly .. 95 95
755. 50 c. Imperial angelfish .. 1·40 1·40

**154.** I.E.Y. Emblem. **156.** Haile Selassie I.

**155.** O.A.U. Emblem.

**1970.** International Education Year.
756. **154.** 10 c. multicoloured .. 15 10
757. 20 c. multicoloured .. 25 15
758. 50 c. multicoloured .. 65 85

**1970.** Organization of African Unity. Mult.
759. 20 c. Type **155** .. .. 20 15
760. 30 c. O.A.U. flag .. .. 50 50
761. 40 c. O.A.U. Headquarters, Addis Ababa .. .. 85 85

**1970.** 40th Anniv. of Haile Selassie's Coronation.
762. **156.** 15 c. multicoloured .. 15 10
763. 50 c. multicoloured .. 70 70
764. 60 c. multicoloured .. 1·25 1·25

**157.** Ministry Buildings.

**1970.** Inaug. of New Posts and Telecommunications Buildings, Addis Ababa.
765. **157.** 10 c. multicoloured .. 15 10
766. 50 c. multicoloured .. 95 95
767. 80 c. multicoloured .. 1·25 1·25

**1971.** Ethiopian Costumes (2nd series). Multicoloured designs similar to T **143**.
768. 5 c. Begemedir and Semain Costume .. .. 10 10
769. 10 c. Bale .. .. 15 10
770. 15 c. Wolega .. .. 20 10
771. 20 c. Showa .. .. 40 40
772. 25 c. Sidamo .. .. 50 50
773. 40 c. Tigre .. .. 75 75
774. 50 c. Wello .. .. 95 95

**159.** Tail of Boeing 707. **160.** "Fountain of Life" (15th-cent. Gospel).

**1971.** Air. 25th Anniv. of Ethiopian Airlines. Multicoloured.
775 5 c. Type **159** .. .. 10 10
776 10 c. "Ethiopian Life" .. 10 10
777 20 c. Nose of Boeing 707 and control tower .. 40 40
778 60 c. Airliner's flight deck and jet engine .. .. 1·10 1·10
779 80 c. Route map .. .. 1·60 1·60

**1971.** Ethiopian Paintings. Multicoloured.
780. 5 c. Type **160** .. .. 10 10
781. 10 c. "King David" (15th-cent. manuscript) .. 10 10
782. 25 c. "St. George" (17th-cent. canvas) .. .. 45 45
783. 50 c. "King Kaleb" (18th-cent. triptych, Lalibela) 95 95
784. 60 c. "Yared singing to King Kaleb" (18th-cent. mural, Axum) .. .. 1·60 1·60

**161.** Black and White Heads.

**1971.** Racial Equality Year.
785. **161.** 10 c. blk., red & orange 15 10
786. – 60 c. multicoloured .. 75 75
787. – 80 c. multicoloured .. 1·25 1·25
DESIGN: 60 c. Black and white hands holding Globe. 80 c. Heads of four races.

**162.** Emperor Menelik II and Proclamation.

**1971.** 75th Anniv. of Victory of Adwa. Multicoloured.
788. 10 c. Type **162** .. .. 15 10
789. 30 c. Ethiopian army on the march .. .. .. 55 55
790. 50 c. Battle of Adwa .. 85 85
791. 60 c. Ethiopian soldiers .. 90 1·00

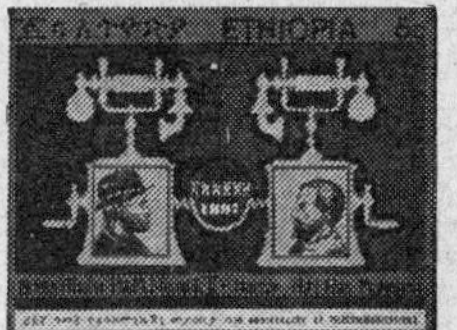


**163.** Emperor Menelik II, Ras Makonnen and Early Telephones.

**1971.** 75th Anniv. of Ethiopian Telecommunications. Multicoloured.
792. 5 c. Type **163** .. .. 10 10
793. 10 c. Emperor Haile Selassie and radio masts .. 10 10
794. 30 c. T.V. set & Ethiopians 55 55
795. 40 c. Microwave equipment 65 65
796. 60 c. Telephone dial and part of Globe .. .. 1·00 1·00

164. Mother and Child.

**1971.** 25th Anniv. of U.N.I.C.E.F. Mult.

797. 5 c. Type **164** .. .. 10 10
798. 10 c. Refugee children .. 10 10
799. 15 c. Man embracing child 35 35
800. 30 c. Children with toys .. 60 60
801. 50 c. Students .. .. 90 90

165. Lion's Head.

**1971.** Tourism. Embossed on gold foil.

802. **165.** $15 gold .. .. 20·00
803. – $15 gold .. .. 20·00

DESIGN: No. 803, Visit of Queen of Sheba to King Solomon.

**1972.** 1st U.N. Security Council Meeting in Africa (1st issue). Nos. 615/8 Optd. **U.N. SECURITY COUNCIL FIRST MEETING IN AFRICA 1972.**, in English and Amharic.

804. 20 c. multicoloured .. 25 15
805. 25 c. multicoloured .. 40 25
806. 30 c. multicoloured .. 2·10 2·10
807. 35 c. multicoloured .. 2·10 2·10

See also Nos. 832/4.

167. Reed Raft, Lake Haik.

**1972.** Ethiopian River Craft. Multicoloured.

808. 10 c. Type **167** .. .. 10 10
809. 20 c. Canoes, Lake Abaya 45 45
810. 30 c. Punts, Lake Tana .. 75 75
811. 60 c. Dugout canoes, Baro River .. .. .. 2·50 95

168. Cuneiform Proclamation of Cyrus the Great.

**1972.** 2500th Anniv. of Persian Empire.

812. **168.** 10 c. multicoloured .. 20 20
813. – 60 c. multicoloured .. 1·00 1·00
814. – 80 c. multicoloured .. 1·50 1·50

169. "Beehive" Hut, Sidamo Province.

**1972.** Architecture of Ethiopian Provinces.

815. **169.** 5 c. multicoloured .. 10 10
816. – 10 c. blk., grey & brn. 10 10
817. – 20 c. multicoloured .. 55 55
818. – 40 c. multicoloured .. 90 90
819. – 80 c. multicoloured .. 1·60 1·60

DESIGNS: 10 c. Two-storey houses, Tigre Province. 20 c. House with veranda, Eritrea Province. 40 c. Town house, Addis Ababa. 80 c. Thatched huts, Shoa Province.

170. "Development" within Cupped Hands.

171. Running.

**1972.** Emperor Haile Selassie's 80th Birthday. Multicoloured.

820. 5 c. Type **170** .. .. 10 10
821. 10 c. Ethiopians within cupped hands .. .. 10 10
822. 25 c. Map, hands and O.A.U. emblem .. .. .. 45 45
823. 50 c. Handclasp and U.N. emblem .. .. .. 90 90
824. 60 c. Peace dove within hands .. .. .. 1·25 1·25

**1972.** Olympic Games, Munich. Mult.

825. 10 c. Type **171** .. .. 20 20
826. 30 c. Football .. .. 60 60
827. 50 c. Cycling .. .. 95 95
828. 60 c. Boxing .. .. 1·40 1·40

172. Cross and Open Bible.

**1972.** World Assembly of United Bible Societies, Addis Ababa. Multicoloured.

829. 20 c. Type **172** .. .. 35 35
830. 50 c. First office of B.F.B.S., and new H.Q. (vert.) .. 75 75
831. 80 c. Amharic Bible .. 1·40 1·40

173. Council in Session.

**1972.** 1st U.N. Security Council Meeting in Africa (2nd issue). Multicoloured.

832. 10 c. Type **173** .. .. 10 10
833. 60 c. Africa Hall, Addis Ababa .. .. .. 1·00 1·00
834. 80 c. Map of Africa and flags .. .. .. 1·50 1·50

174. "Polluted Waters".

**1973.** World Campaign against Sea Pollution Multicoloured.

835. 20 c. Type **174** .. .. 25 10
836. 30 c. Fishing in polluted sea 40 25
837. 80 c. Beach pollution .. 1·10 1·10

175. Interpol and Ethiopian Police Badges.

**1973.** 50th Anniv. of Int. Criminal Police Organization (Interpol).

838. **175.** 40 c. black and orange 65 65
839. – 50 c. blk., brown & blue 85 85
840. – 60 c. black and red .. 1·00 1·00

DESIGNS: 50 c. Interpol badge and Headquarters, Paris. 60 c. Interpol badge.

176. "The Virgin and Child" (Fere Seyoum Zana Yacob period).

**1973.** Ethiopian Fine Arts. Multicoloured.

841. 5 c. Type **176.** .. .. 10 10
842. 15 c. "The Crucifixion" (Zara Yacob period) .. 15 15
843. 30 c. "St. Mary" (Entoto Mariam church painting) 65 65
844. 40 c. "Saint" mosaic (Addis Ababa Art School) 75 75
845. 80 c. Sculptured relief (Addis Ababa Art School) 1·60 1·60

177. African Colonial Maps, 1963 and 1973.

178. Ethiopian Scout Flags.

**1973.** 10th Anniv. of Organization of African Unity. Multicoloured.

846. 5 c. Type **177** .. .. 15 15
847. 10 c. Map, Headquarters and flags .. .. 10 10
848. 20 c. Map and emblems .. 40 40
849. 40 c. Map and "population" ranks .. .. .. 85 85
850. 80 c. Map on globe, O.A.U. and U.N. emblems .. 1·60 1·60

**1973.** 40th Anniv. of Scouting in Ethiopia. Multicoloured.

851. 5 c. Type **178** .. .. 10 10
852. 15 c. "Scout" sign on highway .. .. .. 15 15
853. 30 c. Guide teaching old man to read .. .. 65 65
854. 40 c. "First Aid" .. .. 90 90
855. 60 c. Ethiopian scout .. 1·90 1·90

179. W.M.O. Emblem. 180. Old Wall, Harar.

**1973.** Centenary of World Meteorological Organization.

856. **179.** 40 c. blk., blue & new blue 75 75
857. – 50 c. black and blue .. 95 95
858. – 60 c. multicoloured .. 1·10 1·10

DESIGNS: 50 c. Wind gauge and emblem. 60 c. Weather satellite.

**1973.** Inauguration of Prince Makonnen Memorial Hospital. Multicoloured.

859. 5 c. Type **180** .. .. 10 10
860. 10 c. Prince Makonnen, equipment and patients 10 10
861. 20 c. Operating Theatre .. 40 40
862. 40 c. Scouts giving first-aid 70 70
863. 80 c. Prince Makonnen .. 1·40 1·40

181. Haile Selassie I. 182. Flame Emblem.

**1973.**

864. **181.** 5 c. multicoloured .. 10 10
865. 10 c. multicoloured .. 10 10
866. 15 c. multicoloured .. 10 10
867. 20 c. multicoloured .. 15 10
868. 25 c. multicoloured .. 20 10
869. 30 c. multicoloured .. 25 15
870. 35 c. multicoloured .. 30 15
871. 40 c. multicoloured .. 35 15
872. 45 c. multicoloured .. 35 20
873. 50 c. multicoloured .. 40 20
874. 55 c. multicoloured .. 50 35
875. 60 c. multicoloured .. 65 45
876. 70 c. multicoloured .. 70 45
877. 90 c. multicoloured .. 1·10 60
878. $1 multicoloured .. 1·40 1·00
879. $2 multicoloured .. 3·25 1·90
880. $3 multicoloured .. 4·75 2·40
881. $5 multicoloured .. 8·00 4·25

**1973.** 25th Anniv. of Declaration of Human Rights.

882. **182.** 40 c. gold, grn. & yell. 65 65
883. 50 c. gold, grn. & emerald 85 85
884. 60 c. gold, grn. & orge. 1·00 1·00

183. Wicker Furniture. 184. Cow, Calf and Syringe.

**1974.** Ethiopian Wicker-work. Various Wicker handicrafts.

885. **183.** 5 c. multicoloured .. 10 10
886. – 10 c. multicoloured .. 10 10
887. – 30 c. multicoloured .. 45 45
888. – 50 c. multicoloured .. 80 80
889. – 60 c. multicoloured .. 1·00 1·00

**1974.** Campaign Against Rinderpest. Mult.

890. 5 c. Type **184** .. .. 10 10
891. 15 c. Inoculation .. .. 10 10
892. 20 c. Bullock and syringe 40 40
893. 50 c. Laboratory technician 95 95
894. 60 c. Symbolic map .. 1·40 1·40

185. Umbrella Manufacture.

**1974.** 20th Anniv. of Haile Selassie I Foundation. Multicoloured.

895. 10 c. Type **185** .. .. 10 10
896. 30 c. Weaving .. .. 50 50
897. 50 c. Children with books and toys .. .. .. 95 95
898. 60 c. Foundation building 1·10 1·10

186. Bitwoded Robe.

**1974.** Traditional Ceremonial Robes. Mult.

899. 15 c. Type **186** .. .. 10 10
900. 25 c. Wagseyoum .. .. 25 20
901. 35 c. Ras .. .. .. 35 35
902. 40 c. Leol Ras .. .. 45 45
903. 60 c. Negusenegest .. 1·00 1·00

187. "Population Growth".

188. U.P.U. and Ethiopian P.T.T. Emblems.

**1974.** World Population Year. Multicoloured.

904. 40 c. Type **187** .. .. 35 35
905. 50 c. Diagram with large family .. .. .. 45 45
906. 60 c. "Rising Population" 1·00 1·00

**1974.** Centenary of Universal Postal Union. Multicoloured.

907. 15 c. Type **188** .. .. 10 10
908. 50 c. Emblem and letters .. 75 75
909. 60 c. U.P.U. emblem .. 90 90
910. 70 c. U.P.U. emblem and H.Q., Berne .. .. 1·00 1·00

189. Landscape.

190. "Nymphalidae precis clelia CR".

**1974.** Meskel Festival.
911. **189.** 5 c. multicoloured 10 10
912. – 10 c. multicoloured 10 10
913. – 20 c. multicoloured 20 20
914. – 80 c. multicoloured 1·10 1·10
DESIGNS: Nos. 912/4, Various festive scenes similar to Type **189**.

**1975.** Butterflies (2nd series). Multicoloured.
915. 10 c. Type **190** 15 15
916. 25 c. "Nymphalidae charaxes achaemenes F." 30 30
917. 45 c. "Papilionidae P. dardanus" 80 80
918. 50 c. "Nymphalidae charaes druceanus B." 1·10 1·10
919. 60 c. "Papilionidae P. demodocus" 1·25 1·25

**191.** "The Magi". **192.** Warthog.

**1975.** Religious Paintings in Ethiopian Churches. Multicoloured.
920. 5 c. Type **191** 10 10
921. 10 c. "The Entombment" 10 10
922. 15 c. "Christ with the Apostles" 10 10
923. 30 c. "The Miracle of the Blind" 25 20
924. 40 c. "The Crucifixion" 55 55
925. 80 c. "Christ in Majesty" 1·10 1·10

**1975.** Animals. Multicoloured.
926. 5 c. Type **192** 10 10
927. 10 c. Aardvark 10 10
928. 20 c. Simien jackal 20 15
929. 40 c. Gelada 85 85
930. 80 c. African civet 1·60 1·60

**193.** Dove crossing Globe. **194.** Reception Desk.

**1975.** International Women's Year. Mult.
931. 40 c. Type **193** 50 50
932. 50 c. I.W.Y. emblem and symbols 65 65
933. 90 c. "Equality" 1·10 1·10

**1975.** Opening of National Postal Museum.
934. **194.** 10 c. multicoloured 10 10
935. – 30 c. multicoloured 25 15
936. – 60 c. multicoloured 85 85
937. – 70 c. multicoloured 1·00 1·00
DESIGNS: 30 c. to 70 c. Views of museum display area.

**195.** Map Emblem. **196.** U.N. Emblem.

**1975.** 1st Anniv. of Socialist Government.
938. **195.** 5 c. multicoloured 10 10
939. 10 c. multicoloured 10 10
940. 25 c. multicoloured 15 15
941. 50 c. multicoloured 65 65
942. 90 c. multicoloured 1·10 1·10

**1975.** 30th Anniv. of United Nations.
943. **196.** 40 c. multicoloured 55 55
944. 50 c. multicoloured 65 65
945. 90 c. multicoloured 1·10 1·10

**197.** Illubabor. **198.** "Delphinium wellbyi".

**1975.** Regional Hairstyles. (1st series). Mult.
946. 5 c. Type **197** 10 10
947. 15 c. Arussi 10 10
948. 20 c. Eritrea 20 15
949. 30 c. Bale 25 20
950. 35 c. Kaffa 45 45
951. 50 c. Begemder 55 65
952. 60 c. Shoa 85 85
See also Nos. 1027/33.

**1975.** Ethiopian Flowers. Multicoloured.
953. 5 c. Type **198** 10 10
954. 10 c. "Plectocephalus varians" 10 10
955. 20 c. "Brachystelma asmarensis" (horiz.) 35 35
956. 40 c. "Ceropegia inflata" 80 80
957. 80 c. "Erythrina brucei" 1·25 1·25

**199.** Goalkeeper diving. **200.** Early and Modern Telephones.

**1976.** 10th African Football "Cup of Nations" Championships. Multicoloured.
958. 5 c. Type **199** 10 10
959. 10 c. Footballers in tackle 10 10
960. 25 c. Player shooting at goal 15 15
961. 50 c. Defender clearing ball 85 85
962. 90 c. Ball and Ethiopian flag 1·40 1·40

**1976.** Telephone Cent. Multicoloured.
963. 30 c. Type **200** 25 15
964. 60 c. A. Graham Bell 90 90
965. 90 c. Aerial complex 1·10 1·10

**201.** Amulets. **202.** Boxing.

**1976.** Ethiopian Jewellery.
966. **201.** 5 c. multicoloured 10 10
967. – 10 c. multicoloured 10 10
968. – 20 c. multicoloured 35 35
969. – 40 c. multicoloured 65 65
970. – 80 c. multicoloured 1·10 1·10
Nos. 967/70 are similar to Type **201** showing models with jewellery.

**1976.** Olympic Games, Montreal. Mult.
971. 10 c. Type **202** 10 10
972. 80 c. Shot-putting 1·10 1·10
973. 90 c. Cycling 1·10 1·10

**203.** Campaign Emblem. **204.** Map Emblem.

**1976.** "Development Through Co-operation" Campaign.
974. **203.** 5 c. multicoloured 10 10
975. 10 c. multicoloured 10 10
976. 25 c. multicoloured 15 15
977. 50 c. multicoloured 65 65
978. 90 c. multicoloured 1·00 1·00

**1976.** 2nd Anniv. of Republic.
979. **204.** 5 c. multicoloured 10 10
980. 10 c. multicoloured 10 10
981. 25 c. multicoloured 30 30
982. 50 c. multicoloured 65 65
983. 90 c. multicoloured 1·00 1·00

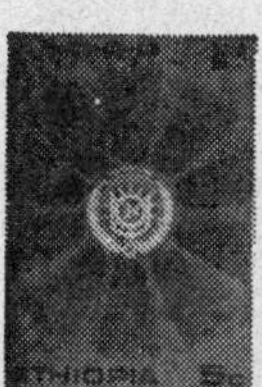

**205.** Crest with Sunburst. **206.** Donkey Boy and Aircraft.

**1976.**
984. **205.** 5 c. gold, grn. & blk. 10 10
985. 10 c. gold, orge. & blk. 10 10
986. 15 c. gold, blue & blk. 10 10
987. 20 c. gold, lilac & blk. 15 10
988. 25 c. gold, grn. & blk. 15 10
989. 30 c. gold, red & blk. 20 15
990. 35 c. gold, yell. & blk. 25 15
991. 40 c. gold, olive & blk. 55 20
992. 45 c. gold, grn. & blk. 65 50
993. 50 c. gold, mve. & blk. 75 55
994. 55 c. gold, blue & blk. 85 65
995. 60 c. gold, brn. & blk. 90 65
996. 70 c. gold, pink & blk. 1·00 75
997. 90 c. gold, blue & blk. 1·10 85
998. $1 gold, grn. & blk. 1·40 1·00
999. $2 gold, grey & black 2·50 2·00
1000. $3 gold, purple & blk. 3·75 2·75
1001. $5 gold, blue & black 6·75 4·75
See also Nos. 1263a/c.

**1976.** 30th Anniv. of Ethiopian Airlines. Multicoloured.
1002. 5 c. Type **206** 10 10
1003. 10 c. Crescent on globe 15 15
1004. 25 c. "Star" of crew and passengers 35 35
1005. 50 c. Propeller and jet engines 65 65
1006. 90 c. Aircraft converging on map 1·10 1·10

**207.** Tortoise. **208.** Cessna 170A dropping Supplies.

**1976.** Reptiles. Multicoloured.
1007. 10 c. Type **207** 10 10
1008. 20 c. Chameleon 15 10
1009. 30 c. Python 25 45
1010. 40 c. Monitor (lizard) 75 75
1011. 80 c. Crocodile 1·25 1·25

**1976.** Relief and Rehabilitation. Mult.
1012. 5 c. Type **208** 10 10
1013. 10 c. Carved hand with hammer 10 10
1014. 45 c. Child supported by banknote 65 65
1015. 60 c. Map of Ogaden region and desert tracks 85 85
1016. 80 c. Waif within broken eggshell, camera & film 1·10 1·10

**209.** Dengour Ruins and Elephant Figurine. **210.** Route Map.

**1977.** Ethiopian Archaeology. Multicoloured.
1017. 5 c. Type **209** 10 10
1018. 10 c. Yeha temple and bronze ibex 10 10
1019. 25 c. Sourre Kabanawa dolmen and ancient pot 20 10
1020. 50 c. Melka Kontoure site and stone axe 75 75
1021. 80 c. Omo Valley, skull and jawbone 1·10 1·10

**1977.** Inauguration of Trans-East African Highway.
1022. **210.** 10 c. multicoloured 10 10
1023. 20 c. multicoloured 20 15
1024. 40 c. multicoloured 50 50
1025. 50 c. multicoloured 65 65
1026. 60 c. multicoloured 85 85

**1977.** Regional Hairstyles (2nd series). As T **197**. Multicoloured.
1027. 5 c. Wollega 10 10
1028. 10 c. Godjam 10 10
1029. 15 c. Tigre 10 10
1030. 20 c. Harrar 40 40
1031. 25 c. Gemu Gofa 40 40
1032. 40 c. Sidamo 80 80
1033. 50 c. Wollo 90 90

**211.** Addis Ababa. **212.** "Terebratula abyssinica".

**1977.** Ethiopian Towns. Multicoloured.
1034. 5 c. Type **211** 10 10
1035. 10 c. Asmara 10 10
1036. 25 c. Harrar 20 15
1037. 50 c. Jimma 75 75
1038. 90 c. Dessie 1·25 1·25

**1977.** Fossil Shells. Multicoloured.
1039. 5 c. Type **212** 10 10
1040. 10 c. "Terebratula subalata" 10 10
1041. 25 c. "Cuculloea lefeburiaua" 40 40
1042. 50 c. "Ostrea (gryphea) plicatissima" 75 75
1043. 90 c. "Trigonia cousobrina" 1·40 1·40

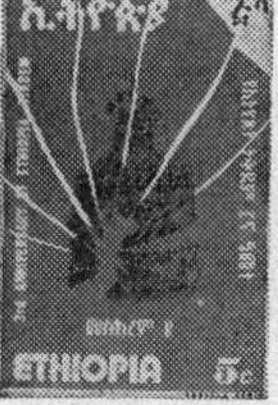

**213.** Shattered Imperial Crown. **214.** "Cicindela petitii".

**1977.** 3rd Anniv. of Republic. Mult.
1044. 5 c. Type **213** 10 10
1045. 10 c. Emblem of revolutionary regime 10 10
1046. 25 c. Warriors with hammer and sickle 20 15
1047. 60 c. Soldiers and map 50 40
1048. 80 c. Crest of revolutionary regime 1·10 1·10

**1977.** Insects. Multicoloured.
1049. 5 c. Type **214** 10 10
1050. 10 c. "Heliocopris dillonii" 10 10
1051. 25 c. "Poekilocerus vignaudii" 30 20
1052. 50 c. "Pepsis heros" 80 80
1053. 90 c. "Pepsis dedjaz" 1·40 1·40

**215.** Lenin, Globe and Map of Ethiopia. **216.** "Chondrostoma dilloni".

**1977.** 60th Anniv. of Russian Revolution.
1054. **215.** 5 c. multicoloured 10 10
1055. 10 c. multicoloured 10 10
1056. 25 c. multicoloured 20 15
1057. 50 c. multicoloured 65 65
1058. 90 c. multicoloured 1·10 1·10

**1978.** Fishes. Multicoloured.
1059. 5 c. Type **216** 10 10
1060. 10 c. "Ostracion cubicus" 10 10
1061. 25 c. "Serranus summana" 45 45
1062. 50 c. "Serranus luti" 85 85
1063. 90 c. "Tetraodon maculatus" 1·40 1·40

**217.** Cattle. **218.** Emblem and Weapons.

**1978.** Domestic Animals. Multicoloured.
1064. 5 c. Type **217** 10 10
1065. 10 c. Donkeys 10 10
1066. 25 c. Sheep 20 15
1067. 50 c. Camels 85 85
1068. 90 c. Horses 1·40 1·40

**1978.** "Call of the Motherland". Mult.
1069. 5 c. Type **218** 10 10
1070. 10 c. Armed workers 10 10
1071. 25 c. Map of Africa 20 15
1072. 60 c. Soldiers 50 65
1073. 80 c. Nurse and blood donor 70 90

**219.** Ibex. **220.** Globe and Emblem.

**1978.** Ancient Bronzes. Multicoloured.
1074. 5 c. Type **219** 10 10
1075. 10 c. Lion (horiz.) 10 10
1076. 25 c. Lamp. 40 40
1077. 50 c. Goat (horiz.) 90 90
1078. 90 c. Axe, chisel and sickle 1·50 1·50

**1978.** World Cup Football Championship, Argentina. Multicoloured.

| | | | |
|---|---|---|---|
| 1079. | 5 c. Type **220** | 10 | 10 |
| 1080. | 20 c. Player kicking ball | 20 | 15 |
| 1081. | 30 c. Ball in net | 25 | 20 |
| 1082. | 55 c. F.I.F.A. emblem and ball | 80 | 80 |
| 1083. | 70 c. World Cup emblem and pitch (vert.) | 90 | 90 |

**221.** Man under Thumb. **222.** Armed Forces.

**1978.** Namibia Day. Multicoloured.

| | | | |
|---|---|---|---|
| 1084. | 5 c. Type **221** | 10 | 10 |
| 1085. | 10 c. Man with pistol | 10 | 10 |
| 1086. | 25 c. Soldier | 20 | 20 |
| 1087. | 60 c. Bound figure | 65 | 65 |
| 1088. | 80 c. Head of African | 90 | 90 |

**1978.** 4th Anniv. of Revolution. Mult.

| | | | |
|---|---|---|---|
| 1089. | 80 c. Type **222** | 90 | 90 |
| 1090. | 1 b. Revolutionaries | 1·10 | 1·10 |

**223.** Open Globe filled with Tools.

**1978.** U.N. Conference on Technical Co-operation among Developing Countries. Mult.

| | | | |
|---|---|---|---|
| 1091. | 10 c. Type **223** | 10 | 10 |
| 1092. | 15 c. Symbols | 10 | 10 |
| 1093. | 25 c. World map and gear wheels | 20 | 20 |
| 1094. | 60 c. Hands passing spanner over globe | 65 | 65 |
| 1095. | 70 c. Geese and tortoise over world map | 85 | 85 |

**224.** Human Rights Emblem. **225.** Manacled Hands and Anti-Apartheid Emblem.

**1978.** 30th Anniv. of Human Rights Declaration.

| | | | | |
|---|---|---|---|---|
| 1096. | **224.** | 5 c. multicoloured | 10 | 10 |
| 1097. | | 15 c. multicoloured | 10 | 10 |
| 1098. | | 25 c. multicoloured | 20 | 20 |
| 1099. | | 35 c. multicoloured | 40 | 40 |
| 1100. | | 1 b. multicoloured | 1·25 | 1·25 |

**1978.** International Anti-Apartheid Year.

| | | | | |
|---|---|---|---|---|
| 1101. | **225.** | 5 c. multicoloured | 10 | 10 |
| 1102. | | 20 c. multicoloured | 15 | 10 |
| 1103. | | 30 c. multicoloured | 20 | 20 |
| 1104. | | 55 c. multicoloured | 65 | 65 |
| 1105. | | 70 c. multicoloured | 75 | 75 |

**226.** Stone Monument at Osole.

**1979.** Ancient Carved Stones from Soddo. Multicoloured.

| | | | |
|---|---|---|---|
| 1106. | 5 c. Type **226** | 10 | 10 |
| 1107. | 10 c. Garashino | 10 | 10 |
| 1108. | 25 c. Wado | 20 | 20 |
| 1109. | 60 c. Ambeut | 90 | 90 |
| 1110. | 80 c. Detail of decoration, Tiya | 1·00 | 1·00 |

**227.** Cotton Plant. **228.** Grar.

**1979.** Cotton Industry. Multicoloured.

| | | | |
|---|---|---|---|
| 1111. | 5 c. Type **227** | 10 | 10 |
| 1112. | 10 c. Women spinning cotton | 10 | 10 |
| 1113. | 20 c. Reeling cotton onto poles | 45 | 45 |
| 1114. | 65 c. Weaving | 90 | 90 |
| 1115. | 80 c. Shemma work | 1·10 | 1·10 |

**1979.** Trees. Multicoloured.

| | | | |
|---|---|---|---|
| 1116. | 5 c. Type **228** | 10 | 10 |
| 1117. | 10 c. Weira | 10 | 10 |
| 1118. | 25 c. Tidh | 20 | 20 |
| 1119. | 50 c. Shola | 75 | 75 |
| 1120. | 90 c. Zigba | 1·10 | 1·10 |

**229.** Plough and Sickle (agriculture). **230.** Family holding Hands.

**1979.** National Revolutionary Development Campaign. Multicoloured.

| | | | |
|---|---|---|---|
| 1121. | 10 c. Type **229** | 10 | 10 |
| 1122. | 15 c. Industry | 10 | 10 |
| 1123. | 25 c. Transport and communications | 60 | 25 |
| 1124. | 60 c. Education and Health | 85 | 85 |
| 1125. | 70 c. Commerce | 90 | 90 |

**1979.** International Year of the Child. Multicoloured.

| | | | |
|---|---|---|---|
| 1126. | 10 c. I.Y.C. Emblem | 10 | 10 |
| 1127. | 15 c. Type **230** | 10 | 10 |
| 1128. | 25 c. Helping a crippled child | 40 | 40 |
| 1129. | 60 c. Circle of children | 90 | 90 |
| 1130. | 70 c. Black and white children embracing | 1·00 | 1·00 |

**231.** Revolutionaries and Emblem.

**1979.** 5th Anniv. of Revolution. Mult.

| | | | |
|---|---|---|---|
| 1131. | 10 c. Type **231** | 10 | 10 |
| 1132. | 15 c. Soldiers and agriculture | 10 | 10 |
| 1133. | 25 c. Emblem of revolution | 20 | 20 |
| 1134. | 60 c. Students with torch | 65 | 65 |
| 1135. | 70 c. Citizens and emblems | 75 | 75 |

**232** " Communications ". **233.** Incense Container.

**1979.** Third World Telecommunications Exhibition, Geneva.

| | | | | |
|---|---|---|---|---|
| 1136. | **232.** | 5 c. blue, mauve and black | 10 | 10 |
| 1137. | – | 30 c. multicoloured | 50 | 50 |
| 1138. | – | 35 c. multicoloured | 50 | 50 |
| 1139. | – | 45 c. multicoloured | 70 | 70 |
| 1140. | – | 65 c. multicoloured | 90 | 90 |

DESIGN: 30 c. Telephone handset. 35 c. Communications satellite. 45 c. Ground receiving aerial. 65 c. Television camera.

**1979.** Wickerwork. Multicoloured.

| | | | |
|---|---|---|---|
| 1141. | 5 c. Type **233** | 10 | 10 |
| 1142. | 10 c. Flower vase | 10 | 10 |
| 1143. | 25 c. Earthenware cover | 40 | 40 |
| 1144. | 60 c. Milk container | 90 | 90 |
| 1145. | 80 c. Storage container | 1·10 | 1·10 |

**234.** Dish. **235.** Lappet-faced Vulture.

**1980.** Woodwork. Multicoloured.

| | | | |
|---|---|---|---|
| 1146. | 5 c. Type **234** | 10 | 10 |
| 1147. | 30 c. Table and chair | 50 | 50 |
| 1148. | 35 c. Pestles and Mortars | 50 | 50 |
| 1149. | 45 c. Stools | 70 | 70 |
| 1150. | 65 c. Pots | 90 | 90 |

**1980.** Birds of Prey. Multicoloured.

| | | | |
|---|---|---|---|
| 1151. | 10 c. Type **235** | 55 | 25 |
| 1152. | 15 c. Long-crested eagle | 65 | 35 |
| 1153. | 25 c. Secretary bird | 80 | 40 |
| 1154. | 60 c. Abyssinian long-eared owl | 2·10 | 90 |
| 1155. | 70 c. Lanner falcon | 2·50 | 1·10 |

**236.** W.H.D Emblem and Cigarette. **237.** Lenin in Hiding at Rasliv.

**1980.** Anti-Smoking Campaign. Multicoloured

| | | | |
|---|---|---|---|
| 1156. | 20 c. Skull superimposed on cigarette packet | 40 | 40 |
| 1157. | 60 c. Type **236** | 85 | 85 |
| 1158. | 1 b. Pipe, cigarette and infected lungs | 1·25 | 1·25 |

**1980.** 110th Birth Anniv. of Lenin. Mult.

| | | | |
|---|---|---|---|
| 1159. | 5 c. Lenin's House, Pskov | 10 | 10 |
| 1160. | 15 c. Type **237** | 10 | 10 |
| 1161. | 20 c. Lenin as student | 20 | 15 |
| 1162. | 40 c. Lenin returns to Russia | 50 | 50 |
| 1163. | 1 b. Lenin speaking on the Goerlo plan | 1·10 | 1·10 |

**238.** Grevy's Zebra. **239.** Running.

**1980.** Endangered Animals. Multicoloured.

| | | | |
|---|---|---|---|
| 1164. | 10 c. Type **238** | 10 | 10 |
| 1165. | 15 c. Dibatag | 15 | 10 |
| 1166. | 25 c. Hunting dog | 40 | 40 |
| 1167. | 60 c. Hartebeest | 1·00 | 1·00 |
| 1168. | 70 c. Cheetahs | 1·10 | 1·10 |

**1980.** Olympic Games, Moscow. Multicoloured.

| | | | |
|---|---|---|---|
| 1169. | 30 c. Type **239** | 45 | 45 |
| 1170. | 70 c. Cycling | 95 | 95 |
| 1171. | 80 c. Boxing | 1·10 | 1·10 |

**240.** Man cutting Blindfold. **241.** Meal Basket.

**1980.** 6th Anniv. of Revolution. Mult

| | | | |
|---|---|---|---|
| 1172. | 30 c. Type **240** | 35 | 35 |
| 1173. | 40 c. Crowd | 50 | 50 |
| 1174. | 50 c. Woman cutting chain | 65 | 65 |
| 1175. | 70 c. Crowd and flags | 1·00 | 1·00 |

**1980.** Bamboo Folk Craft. Multicoloured.

| | | | |
|---|---|---|---|
| 1176. | 5 c. Type **241** | 10 | 10 |
| 1177. | 15 c. Hand basket | 10 | 10 |
| 1178. | 25 c. Stool | 40 | 40 |
| 1179. | 35 c. Fruit compote | 65 | 65 |
| 1180. | 1 b. Lamp shade | 1·40 | 1·40 |

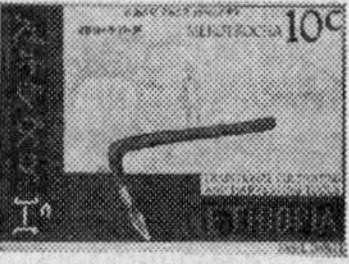


**242.** Mekotkocha (weeding tool).

**1980.** Traditional Cultivating and Harvesting Tools. Multicoloured.

| | | | |
|---|---|---|---|
| 1181. | 10 c. Type **242** | 10 | 10 |
| 1182. | 15 c. Layda | 10 | 10 |
| 1183. | 40 c. Mensh | 50 | 50 |
| 1184. | 45 c. Medekdekia | 60 | 60 |
| 1185. | 70 c. Mofer and kenber | 1·00 | 1·00 |

**243.** Baro River.

**1981.** Baro River Bridge. Multicoloured.

| | | | |
|---|---|---|---|
| 1186. | 15 c. Type **243** | 20 | 10 |
| 1187. | 65 c. Bridge under construction | 90 | 90 |
| 1188. | 1 b. Bridge | 1·40 | 1·40 |

**244.** Wawel Castle, Poland.

**1981.** World Heritage (1st series). Mult.

| | | | |
|---|---|---|---|
| 1189. | 5 c. Type **244** | 10 | 10 |
| 1190. | 15 c. Quito Cathedral, Ecuador | 10 | 10 |
| 1191. | 20 c. Island of Goree, Senegal | 10 | 10 |
| 1192. | 30 c. Messa Verde, U.S.A. | 35 | 35 |
| 1193. | 80 c. Simien National Park, Ethiopia | 1·00 | 1·00 |
| 1194. | 1 b. L'Anse aux Meadows, Canada | 1·10 | 1·10 |

See also Nos. 1200/1205.

**245.** Drinking Vessel.

**1981.** Ancient Pottery. Multicoloured.

| | | | |
|---|---|---|---|
| 1195. | 20 c. Type **245** | 15 | 10 |
| 1196. | 25 c. Spice container | 15 | 10 |
| 1197. | 35 c. Jug | 45 | 45 |
| 1198. | 40 c. Cooking apparatus | 55 | 55 |
| 1199. | 60 c. Animal figurine | 90 | 90 |

**246.** Biet Medhani Alem Church, Ethiopia.

**1981.** World Heritage (2nd series). Mult.

| | | | |
|---|---|---|---|
| 1200. | 10 c. Type **246** | 10 | 10 |
| 1201. | 15 c. Nehanni National Park, Canada | 10 | 10 |
| 1202. | 20 c. Lower Falls of the Yellowstone River, U.S.A. | 15 | 10 |
| 1203. | 30 c. Aachen Cathedral, West Germany | 45 | 45 |
| 1204. | 80 c. Kicker Rock, San Cristobel Island, Ecuador | 1·00 | 1·00 |
| 1205. | 1 b. Holy Cross Chapel, Poland (vert.) | 1·40 | 1·40 |

**247.** Disabled Child learning to write. **248.** Children at Work and Play.

**1981.** International Year of Disabled Persons. Multicoloured.

| | | | |
|---|---|---|---|
| 1206. | 5 c. Disabled, artificial limbs and crutch | 10 | 10 |
| 1207. | 15 c. Type **247** | 10 | 10 |
| 1208. | 20 c. Artificial limbs | 15 | 15 |
| 1209. | 40 c. Disabled hands learning to knit | 50 | 50 |
| 1210. | 1 b. Disabled people learning to weave | 1·25 | 1·25 |

**1981.** 7th Anniv. of Revolution. Mult.

| | | | |
|---|---|---|---|
| 1211. | 20 c. Type **248** | 15 | 15 |
| 1212. | 60 c. Disabled revolutionaries | 75 | 75 |
| 1213. | 1 b. Printing and distributing " Serto Ader Gazette " | 1·10 | 1·10 |

**249.** Ploughing by Oxen, Tilling and Harvesting by hand. **250.** Animal-shaped Pitcher.

**1981.** World Food Day. Multicoloured.
1214. 5 c. Air-drop of food and starving Ethiopians 10 10
1215. Type **249** 10 10
1216. 20 c. Desert and agricultural scenes 15 15
1217. 40 c. Agricultural lecture and farmlands 55 55
1218. 1 b. Cattle and corn 1·40 1·40

**1981.** Ancient Bronze Implements.
1219. **250.** 15 c. multicoloured 10 10
1220. – 45 c. silver, black and brown 60 60
1221. – 50 c. multicoloured 65 65
1222. – 70 c. multicoloured 90 90
DESIGNS: 45 c. Tsenatsil. 50 c. Pitcher. 70 c. Pot.

**251.** Cup. **252.** Coffee Plantation.

**1981.** Horn Work. Multicoloured.
1223 10 c. Tobacco container 10 10
1224 15 c. Type **251** 10 10
1225 40 c. Tej container 50 50
1226 45 c. Goblet 60 60
1227 70 c. Spoon 1·00 1·00

**1982.** Ethiopian Coffee. Multicoloured.
1228. 5 c. Type **252** 10 10
1229. 15 c. Coffee bush 10 10
1230. 25 c. Mature plantation 15 10
1231. 35 c. Picking coffee 45 45
1232. 1 b. Pouring and drinking coffee 1·40 1·40

**253.** Players and Football.

**1982.** World Cup Football Championship, Spain. Multicoloured.
1233. 5 c. Type **253** 10 10
1234. 15 c. Player with ball 10 10
1235. 20 c. Goalkeeper saving ball 15 15
1236. 40 c. Player kicking ball 60 60
1237. 1 b. Ball, clasped hands and shirts 1·40 1·40

**254.** Cattle. **255.** Preventing Theft

**1982.** Centenary of Discovery of Tubercle Bacillus. Multicoloured.
1238. 15 c. Type **254** 10 10
1239. 20 c. Magnifying glass and bacillus 15 15
1240. 30 c. Koch with microscope 20 15
1241. 35 c. Dr. Robert Koch 45 45
1242. 80 c. T.B. patient and Dr. Koch 1·10 1·10

**1982.** 8th Anniv. of Revolution. Mult.
1243. 80 c. Type **255** 1·00 1·00
1244. 1 b. Voting 1·25 1·25

**256.** Primitive Measurements of Length.

**1982.** World Standards Day. Multicoloured.
1245. 5 c. Type **256** 10 10
1246. 15 c. Primitive balance 10 10
1247. 20 c. Metric measurement 15 10
1248. 40 c. Weights and scales 50 50
1249. 1 b. Ethiopian standards emblem 1·40 1·40

**257.** Wildlife Conservation.

**1982.** 10th Anniv. of U.N. Environment Programme. Multicoloured.
1250. 5 c. Type **257** 10 10
1251. 15 c. Village (Environmental health and settlement) 10 10
1252. 20 c. Forest protection 15 10
1253. 40 c. National literacy campaign 50 50
1254. 1 b. Soil and water conservation 1·40 1·40

**258.** Grand Gallery.

**1983.** Sof Omar Caves. Multicoloured.
1255. 5 c. Type **258** 10 10
1256. 10 c. Chamber of Columns 10 10
1257. 15 c. Route through cave 10 10
1258. 70 c. Map of caves 90 90
1259. 80 c. Entrance to cave 1·00 1·00

**259.** " 25 " on Emblem. **260.** I.M.O. Emblem and Waves.

**1983.** 25th Anniv. of Economic Commission for Africa.
1260. **259.** 80 c. multicoloured 1·10 1·10
1261. 1 b. multicoloured 1·40 1·40

**1983.** 25th Anniv. of International Maritime Organization. Multicoloured.
1262. 85 c. Type **260** 1·10 1·10
1263. 1 b. Lighthouse and liner 1·75 1·60

**1983.** As Nos. 998/1000 but with value expressed in "BIRR".
1263a **205** 1 b. grn, gold & blk
1263b 2 b. grey, gold & blk
1263c 3 b. pur, gold & blk

**261.** U.P.U. Monument, Berne. **262.** Peace Dove on Globe.

**1983.** World Communications Year. Mult.
1264. 25 c. Type **261** 15 10
1265. 55 c. Antenna, satellite and drum 65 65
1266. 1 b. River bridge and railway tunnel 2·10 2·10

**1983.** 9th Anniv. of Revolution. Mult.
1267. 25 c. Type **262** 15 10
1268. 55 c. Red star 75 75
1269. 1 b. Crest 1·10 1·10

**263.** Hura and Shepherd. **264.** "Charaxes galawadiwosi".

**1983.** Musical Instruments. Multicoloured.
1270. 5 c. Type **263** 10 10
1271. 15 c. Dinke and funeral 10 10
1272. 20 c. Meleket and announcing royal proclamation 35 35
1273. 40 c. Embilta and royal procession 65 65
1274. 1 b. Tom and dancers 1·50 1·50

**1983.** Butterflies. Multicoloured.
1275 10 c. Type **264** 15 10
1276 15 c. "Epiphora elianae" 30 10
1277 55 c. "Batiama rougeoti" 1·00 1·00
1278 1 b. "Achaea saboeaereginae" 1·90 1·90

**265.** I.A.A.Y Emblem (horiz). **266.** "Protea gaguedi".

**1984.** International Anti-Apartheid Year.
1279. **265.** 5 c. multicoloured 10 10
1280. 15 c. multicoloured 10 10
1281. 20 c. multicoloured 15 10
1282. 40 c. multicoloured 55 55
1283. 1 b. multicoloured 1·40 1·40

**1984.** Flowers. Multicoloured.
1284 5 c. Type **266** 10 10
1285 25 c. "Sedum epidendrum" 55 55
1286 50 c. "Echinops amplexicaulis" 95 95
1287 1 b. "Canarina eminii" 1·90 1·90

**267.** Konso House. **268.** Torch on Map and Crowd of Workers.

**1984.** Ethiopian House Architecture. Mult.
1288. 15 c. Type **267** 15 15
1289. 65 c. Dorze house 95 95
1290. 1 b. Harer houses 1·50 1·50

**1984.** 10th Anniv. of Revolution. Mult.
1291. 5 c. Type **268** 10 10
1292. 10 c. Countrywoman and ploughing with oxen 10 10
1293. 15 c. Crowd with flag 15 10
1294. 20 c. Pres. Mengistu, flag, map and crowd 20 15
1295. 25 c. Soldiers ploughing with oxen 25 20
1296. 40 c. Workers writing 60 60
1297. 45 c. Pres. Mengistu addressing Party conference 65 65
1298. 50 c. Schoolchildren 75 75
1299. 70 c. Pres. Mengistu and statue 1·00 1·00
1300. 1 b. Pres. Mengistu addressing Organization of African Unity meeting 1·40 1·40

**269.** "Gugs". **270.** Harwood's Francolin.

**1984.** Traditional Games. Multicoloured.
1301. 5 c. Type **269** 10 10
1302. 25 c. Tigil (wrestling) 35 35
1303. 50 c. Gerna (hockey) 75 75
1304. 1 b. Gebeta (board game) 1·40 1·40

**1985.** Birds. Multicoloured.
1305 5 c. Type **270** 40 20
1306 15 c. Rouget's rail 70 35
1307 80 c. Little bee eater 4·00 2·25
1308 85 c. Red-headed weaver 4·75 2·50

**271.** Hippopotami.

**1985.** Mammals. Multicoloured.
1309. 20 c. Type **271** 20 15
1310. 25 c. Gerenuk 20 15
1311. 40 c. Common duiker 65 65
1312. 1 b. Gunther's dik-dik 1·90 1·90

**272.** "Barbus degeni".

**1985.** Fishes. Multicoloured.
1313. 10 c. Type **272** 10 10
1314. 20 c. "Labeo cylindricus" 15 10
1315. 55 c. African lungfish 85 85
1316. 1 b. "Alestes dentex" 1·60 1·60

**273.** "Securidaca longepedunculata". **274.** "50" and First Aid.

**1985.** Medicinal Plants. Multicoloured.
1317. 10 c Type **273** 10 10
1318. 20 c. "Plumbago zeylanicum" 15 10
1319. 55 c. "Brucea antidysenteric" 85 85
1320. 1 b. "Dorstenia barminiana" 1·60 1·60

**1985.** 50th Anniv. of Ethiopian Red Cross. Multicoloured.
1321 35 c. Type **274** 50 50
1322 55 c. Community aid scenes 85 85
1323 1 b. Nursing scenes 1·60 1·60

**275.** Kombolcha Textile Mills. **276.** U.N. Emblem.

**1985.** 11th Anniv. of Revolution. Mult.
1324. 10 c. Type **275** 10 10
1325. 80 c. Mugher cement factory 1·10 1·10
1326. 1 b. Views of famine and drought and resettlement of victims 1·60 1·60

**1985.** 40th Anniv. of U.N.O.
1327. **276.** 25 c. multicoloured 15 10
1328. 55 c. multicoloured 85 85
1329. 1 b. multicoloured 1·60 1·60

**277.** Man with Caliper, Boy, Microscope and Crutch.

**1986.** Anti-polio Campaign. Multicoloured.
1330. 5 c. Type **277** 10 10
1331. 10 c. Child on crutches 10 10
1332. 20 c. Doctor fitting child with caliper 15 10
1333. 55 c. Man with caliper working sewing machine 85 85
1334. 1 b. Doctor vaccinating baby 1·60 1·60

**278.** "Millettia ferruginea". **279.** Ginger.

**1986.** Trees. Multicoloured.
1335. 10 c. Type **278** 10 10
1336. 30 c. "Syzyigum guineense" 45 45
1337. 50 c. "Cordia africana" 80 80
1338. 1 b. "Hagenia abyssinica" 1·60 1·60

**1986.** Spices and Herbs. Multicoloured.
1339. 10 c. Type **279** .. .. 10 10
1340. 15 c. Basil .. .. 10 10
1341. 55 c. Mustard .. .. 85 85
1342. 1 b. Cumin .. .. 1·60 1·60

**280.** One Cent Coin. **281.** Globe, Map and Skeleton.

**1986.** Coins. Multicoloured.
1343. 5 c. Type **280** .. .. 10 10
1344. 10 c. 25 cents .. .. 10 10
1345. 35 c. 5 cents .. .. 50 50
1346. 50 c. 50 cents .. .. 75 75
1347. 1 b. 10 cents .. .. 1·60 1·60

**1986.** 12th Anniv. of Discovery of Oldest Known Hominid Skeleton.
1348. **281.** 2 b. multicoloured .. 3·75 3·75

**282.** Military Training.

**1986.** 12th Anniv. of Revolution. Mult.
1349. 20 c. Type **282** .. .. 15 10
1350. 30 c. Tiglachin Monument, Addis Ababa .. .. .. 40 40
1351. 55 c. Emblem of Delachin Historical Exhibition .. .. 85 85
1352. 85 c. Merti food-processing plant .. .. .. 1·10 1·10

**283.** Boeing 767. **284.** Emblem.

**1986.** 40th Anniv of Ethiopian Airlines. Mult.
1353 10 c. Type **283** .. .. 15 10
1354 20 c. Douglas DC-3 .. 20 10
1355 30 c. Emblem on tail-fin of airplane and crew .. 20 40
1356 40 c. Mechanic working on engine .. .. 60 60
1357 1 b. Map and Boeing 727 airliner .. .. 1·60 1·60

**1986.** International Peace Year.
1358. **284.** 10 c. multicoloured .. 15 15
1359. 80 c. multicoloured .. 1·10 1·10
1360. 1 b. multicoloured .. 1·60 1·60

**285.** Mother breastfeeding Baby.

**1986.** U.N.I.C.E.F. Child Survival Campaign. Multicoloured.
1361. 10 c. Type **285** .. .. 10 10
1362. 35 c. Doctor vaccinating child and vaccination chart .. .. .. 50 50
1363. 50 c. Fly on feeding bottle and oral rehydration therapy formula .. .. 75 75
1364. 1 b. Baby on scales and growth chart .. .. 1·60 1·60

**286.** Auxum, Tigray. **287.** "Affar".

**1987.** Traditional Umbrellas. Multicoloured.
1365. 35 c. Type **286** .. .. 50 50
1366. 55 c. Negele-Borena, Sidamo .. .. 85 85
1367. 1 b. Jimma, Kafa .. 1·50 1·50

**1987.** "Defender of his Country". Paintings by Afewerk Tekle. Multicoloured.
1368. 50 c. Type **287** .. .. 75 75
1369. 2 b. "Adwa" .. .. 2·75 2·75

**288.** People behind Man holding Torch.

**1987.** "The Struggle of the African People" (stained glass windows) by Afewerk Tekle. Multicoloured.
1370. Type **288** .. .. .. 75 75
1371. 80 c. Robed skeleton, dragon and men covering their faces (23 × 36 mm.) .. .. 1·10 1·10
1372. 1 b. Robed skeleton, man killing dragon and people on map of Africa (23 × 36 mm.) .. 1·50 1·50

**289.** Simien Fox.

**1987.**
1373. **289.** 5 c. multicoloured .. 10 10
1374. 10 c. multicoloured .. 10 10
1375. 15 c. multicoloured .. 10 10
1376. 20 c. multicoloured .. 25 20
1377. 25 c. multicoloured .. 15 10
1378. 45 c. multicoloured .. 60 45
1379. 55 c. multicoloured .. 75 55

**290.** Finfine, Empress Taitu and Emperor Menelik II in "100".

**1987.** Centenary of Addis Ababa. Mult.
1380. 5 c. Type **290** .. .. 10 10
1381. 10 c. Traditional housing 10 10
1382. 80 c. Central Addis Ababa .. .. .. 1·10 1·10
1383. 1 b. Aerial view of city 1·50 1·50

**291.** Newspaper and People on Map.

**1987.** 13th Anniv of Revolution. Mult.
1384 5 c. Type **291** .. .. 10 10
1385 10 c. People queuing by ballot box and open book .. .. .. 10 10
1386 80 c. Ballot paper and map .. .. .. 1·10 1·10
1387 1 b. Boeing 727 airliner on runway at Bahir Dar airport .. .. 1·50 1·50

**292.** Spoon fron Hurso, Harerge.

**1987.** Wooden Spoons. Multicoloured.
1388. 85 c. Type **292** .. .. 95 95
1389. 1 b. Spoon from Borena, Sidamo .. .. 1·10 1·10

**293.** Village Programme.

**1988.** International Year of Shelter for the Homeless (1987). Multicoloured.
1390. 10 c. Type **293** .. .. 10 10
1391. 35 c. Resettlement programme .. .. 20 15
1392. 50 c. Urban improvement programme .. .. 50 50
1393. 1 b. Co-operative and Government housing 1·00 1·00

**294.** Lenin and Delegates.

**1988.** 70th Anniv. of Russian Revolution.
1394. **294.** 1 b. multicoloured .. 1·10 1·10

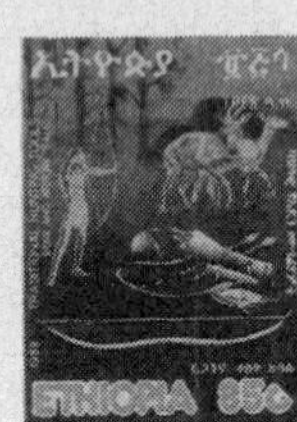

**295.** Bow and Arrows. **296.** Anniversary Emblem.

**1988.** Traditional Hunting Weapons. Mult.
1395. 85 c. Type **295** .. .. 90 90
1396. 1 b. Double-pronged spear .. .. .. 1·10 1·10

**1988.** 125th Anniv. of Red Cross.
1397. **296.** 85 c. multicoloured .. 85 85
1398. 1 b. multicoloured .. 1·10 1·10

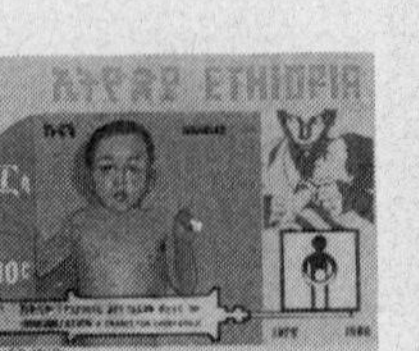

**297.** Measles. **298.** "Let there be Peace in Africa and the World" (detail, Afewerk Tekle).

**1988.** U.N.I.C.E.F. Child Vaccination Campaign. Multicoloured.
1399. 10 c. Type **297** .. .. 10 10
1400. 35 c. Tetanus .. .. 20 15
1401. 50 c. Whooping cough .. 45 45
1402. 1 b. Diphtheria .. .. 85 85

**1988.** 25th Anniv. of Organization of African Unity.
1403. **298.** 2 b. multicoloured .. 1·90 1·90

**299.** Mikoyan Gurevich MiG-23 above Simien Mountains and Farmland.

**1988.** "The Victory of Ethiopia" (triptych) by Afewerk Tekle. Details of the mural in Heroes' Centre, Debre Zeit. Multicoloured.
1404 10 c. Type **299** .. .. 20 10
1405 20 c. Coffee plantation, rural homelife and farmers going to work 15 10
1406 35 c. New Ethiopia rising above flags and people 20 15
1407 55 c. Mikoyan Gurevich MiG-21 over port of Assab (horiz) .. .. 40 45
1408 80 c. Worker in foundry (horiz) .. .. 50 65
1409 1 b. Villagers engaged in cottage industries (horiz) .. .. 85 85

**300.** Sidamo Bracelet.

**1988.** Bracelets. Multicoloured.
1410. 15 c. Type **300** .. .. 10 10
1411. 85 c. Arsi bracelet .. 85 85
1412. 1 b. Harerge bracelet .. 1·00 1·00

**301.** Dollars on Map.

**1988.** International Agricultural Development Fund. Multicoloured.
1413. 15 c. Type **301** .. .. 10 10
1414. 85 c. Agricultural activities .. .. 85 85
1415. 1 b. Farmer and produce 1·00 1·00

**302.** First Session of National Shengo (assembly).

**1988.** 1st Anniv. of People's Democratic Republic of Ethiopia. Multicoloured.
1416. 5 c. Type **302** .. .. 10 10
1417. 10 c. President Lt.-Col. Mengistu Haile Mariam 10 10
1418. 80 c. State emblem and flag .. .. .. 85 85
1419. 1 b. State Council building .. .. 1·00 1·00

**303** One Birr Note

**1988.** Banknotes. Multicoloured.
1420 5 c. Type **303** .. .. 10 10
1421 10 c. Five birr note .. 10 10
1422 20 c. Ten birr note .. 15 10
1423 75 c. 50 birr note .. 75 75
1424 85 c. 100 birr note .. 85 85

**1988.** World Aids Day. Nos. 1376/9 optd **WORLD AIDS DAY**.

| | | | | |
|---|---|---|---|---|
| 1425 | 289 | 20 c. multicoloured | 15 | 10 |
| 1426 | | 25 c. multicoloured | 15 | 10 |
| 1427 | | 45 c. multicoloured | 60 | 60 |
| 1428 | | 55 c. multicoloured | 75 | 75 |

**305** Emblem within "40"

**1988.** 40th Anniv of W.H.O.

| | | | | |
|---|---|---|---|---|
| 1429 | 305 | 50 c. multicoloured | 50 | 50 |
| 1430 | | 65 c. multicoloured | 65 | 65 |
| 1431 | | 85 c. multicoloured | 85 | 85 |

**306** Gambella Gere (leg rattle)

**1989.** Musical Instruments. Multicoloured.

| | | | |
|---|---|---|---|
| 1432 | 30 c. Type **306** | 35 | 35 |
| 1433 | 40 c. Konos fanfa (pipes) | 40 | 40 |
| 1434 | 50 c. Konso chancha (waist rattle) | 50 | 50 |
| 1435 | 85 c. Gendeberet negareet (drum) | 85 | 85 |

**307** "Abyot" (container ship)

**1989.** 25th Anniv of Ethiopian Shipping Lines. Multicoloured.

| | | | |
|---|---|---|---|
| 1436 | 15 c. Type **307** | 20 | 10 |
| 1437 | 30 c. "Wolwol" (container ship) | 35 | 15 |
| 1438 | 55 c. "Queen of Sheba" (freighter) | 55 | 30 |
| 1439 | 1 b. "Abbay Wonz" under construction | 1·10 | 80 |

**308** Yellow-faced Parrot

**1989.** Birds. Multicoloured.

| | | | |
|---|---|---|---|
| 1440 | 10 c. Type **308** | 15 | 10 |
| 1441 | 35 c. White-winged cliffchat | 75 | 65 |
| 1442 | 50 c. Yellow-rumped seedeater | 95 | 90 |
| 1443 | 1 b. Dark-headed oriole | 2·10 | 1·90 |

**309** Making Vellum

**310** Greater Kudu

**1989.** Ethiopian Manuscripts. Multicoloured.

| | | | |
|---|---|---|---|
| 1444 | 5 c. Type **309** | 10 | 10 |
| 1445 | 10 c. Making inks, ink horns and pens | 10 | 10 |
| 1446 | 20 c. Preparing writing materials and scribe | 10 | 10 |
| 1447 | 75 c. Binding books | 75 | 75 |
| 1448 | 85 c. Finished books | 85 | 85 |

**1989.** Wildlife. Multicoloured.

| | | | |
|---|---|---|---|
| 1449 | 30 c. Type **310** | 40 | 40 |
| 1450 | 40 c. Lesser kudu | 50 | 50 |
| 1451 | 50 c. Roan antelope | 50 | 50 |
| 1452 | 85 c. Nile lechwe | 85 | 85 |

**311** Melka Wakana Hydro-electric Power Station

**312** Bank Emblem

**1989.** 2nd Anniv of People's Democratic Republic of Ethiopia. Multicoloured.

| | | | |
|---|---|---|---|
| 1453 | 15 c. Type **311** | 10 | 10 |
| 1454 | 75 c. Adea Berga Dairy Farm | 75 | 75 |
| 1455 | 1 b. Pawe Hospital | 1·00 | 1·00 |

**1989.** 25th Anniv of African Development Bank.

| | | | | |
|---|---|---|---|---|
| 1456 | 312 | 20 c. multicoloured | 15 | 10 |
| 1457 | | 80 c. multicoloured | 85 | 85 |
| 1458 | | 1 b. multicoloured | 1·00 | 1·00 |

**313** Emblem

**314** Unhappy Man with Newspaper Upside Down

**1990.** 10th Anniv of Pan-African Postal Union.

| | | | | |
|---|---|---|---|---|
| 1459 | 313 | 50 c. multicoloured | 50 | 50 |
| 1460 | | 70 c. multicoloured | 70 | 70 |
| 1461 | | 80 c. multicoloured | 80 | 80 |

**1990.** International Literacy Year. Mult.

| | | | |
|---|---|---|---|
| 1462 | 15 c. Type **314** | 10 | 10 |
| 1463 | 85 c. Adults learning to read | 90 | 90 |
| 1464 | 1 b. Happy man reading newspaper | 1·00 | 1·00 |

**315** Marathon Race

**1990.** Abebe Bikila (marathon runner). Mult.

| | | | |
|---|---|---|---|
| 1465 | 5 c. Type **315** | 10 | 10 |
| 1466 | 10 c. Bikila carrying national flag during Olympic opening ceremony | 10 | 10 |
| 1467 | 20 c. Bikila running in number 11 vest | 10 | 10 |
| 1468 | 75 c. Bikila running in number 69 vest | 80 | 80 |
| 1469 | 85 c. Bikila with medals and cups (vert) | 90 | 90 |

**316** Revolutionary Flag

**1990.**

| | | | | |
|---|---|---|---|---|
| 1470 | 316 | 5 c. multicoloured | 10 | 10 |
| 1471 | | 10 c. multicoloured | 10 | 10 |
| 1472 | | 15 c. multicoloured | 10 | 10 |
| 1473 | | 20 c. multicoloured | 10 | 10 |
| 1474 | | 25 c. multicoloured | 15 | 10 |
| 1475 | | 30 c. multicoloured | 15 | 10 |
| 1476 | | 35 c. multicoloured | 15 | 15 |
| 1477 | | 40 c. multicoloured | 20 | 15 |
| 1478 | | 45 c. multicoloured | 45 | 40 |
| 1479 | | 50 c. multicoloured | 40 | 40 |
| 1480 | 316 | 55 c. multicoloured | 45 | 45 |
| 1481 | | 60 c. multicoloured | 50 | 50 |
| 1482 | | 70 c. multicoloured | 60 | 60 |
| 1483 | | 80 c. multicoloured | 65 | 65 |
| 1484 | | 85 c. multicoloured | 70 | 70 |
| 1485 | | 90 c. multicoloured | 75 | 75 |
| 1486 | | 1 b. multicoloured | 85 | 85 |
| 1487 | | 2 b. multicoloured | 1·60 | 1·60 |
| 1488 | | 3 b. multicoloured | 2·50 | 2·50 |

**317** Ploughing and Sowing

**1990.** Teff. Multicoloured.

| | | | |
|---|---|---|---|
| 1489 | 5 c. Type **317** | 10 | 10 |
| 1490 | 10 c. Harvesting | 10 | 10 |
| 1491 | 20 c. Oxen threshing grain underfoot | 10 | 10 |
| 1492 | 75 c. Grinding teff flour and making starter batter | 75 | 75 |
| 1493 | 85 c. Family eating baked injera | 85 | 85 |

**318** Male and Female Ibexes

**319** Deterioration in Victim's Health

**1990.** Walia Ibex. Multicoloured.

| | | | |
|---|---|---|---|
| 1494 | 5 c. Type **318** | 10 | 10 |
| 1495 | 15 c. Male ibex | 10 | 10 |
| 1496 | 20 c. Male ibex (different) | 10 | 10 |
| 1497 | 1 b. Male ibexes fighting (horiz) | 1·00 | 1·00 |

**1991.** World Aids Day. Multicoloured.

| | | | |
|---|---|---|---|
| 1498 | 15 c. Type **319** | 10 | 10 |
| 1499 | 85 c. Aids education | 80 | 80 |
| 1500 | 1 b. Preventive measures and family sheltered by umbrella | 95 | 95 |

**320** Volcano

**1991.** International Decade for Natural Disaster Reduction. Multicoloured.

| | | | |
|---|---|---|---|
| 1501 | 5 c. Type **320** | 10 | 10 |
| 1502 | 10 c. Earthquake | 10 | 10 |
| 1503 | 15 c. Drought | 10 | 10 |
| 1504 | 30 c. Flood | 15 | 10 |
| 1505 | 50 c. W. H. O. hygiene instruction | 30 | 45 |
| 1506 | 1 b. Red Cross workers helping disaster victims | 95 | 95 |

**321** Constructing Cannon

**1991.** Emperor Theodor's Cannon "Sevastopol". Multicoloured.

| | | | |
|---|---|---|---|
| 1507 | 15 c. Type **321** | 10 | 10 |
| 1508 | 85 c. Completed cannon on carriage | 80 | 80 |
| 1509 | 1 b. Hauling cannon uphill | 95 | 95 |

**INDEX**

Countries can be quickly located by referring to the index at the end of this volume.

**322** Diadem Squirrelfish

**323** Balambaras

**1991.** Fishes. Multicoloured.

| | | | |
|---|---|---|---|
| 1510 | 5 c. Type **322** | 10 | 10 |
| 1511 | 15 c. Black-finned butter-fly fish | 10 | 10 |
| 1512 | 80 c. Royal angelfish | 75 | 75 |
| 1513 | 1 b. Grey reef shark | 95 | 95 |

**1992.** Traditional Ceremonial Robes (military group). Multicoloured.

| | | | |
|---|---|---|---|
| 1514 | 5 c. Type **323** | 10 | 10 |
| 1515 | 15 c. Kegnazmatch | 10 | 10 |
| 1516 | 80 c. Fitawurari (Army Commander) | 75 | 75 |
| 1517 | 1 b. Dedjazmatch | 90 | 90 |

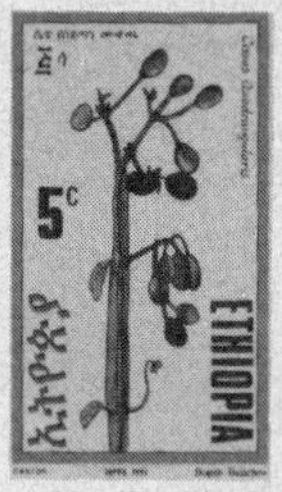

**324** Devil's Mortar

**326** Plate

**325** Afar House

**1992.** Flowers. Multicoloured.

| | | | |
|---|---|---|---|
| 1518 | 5 c. Type **324** | 10 | 10 |
| 1519 | 15 c. "Delphinium dasycaulon" | 10 | 10 |
| 1520 | 80 c. Cow's salt | 65 | 65 |
| 1521 | 1 b. Red hot poker | 85 | 85 |

**1992.** Ethiopian Houses. Multicoloured.

| | | | |
|---|---|---|---|
| 1522 | 15 c. Type **325** | 10 | 10 |
| 1523 | 35 c. Anuak house | 20 | 15 |
| 1524 | 50 c. Gimira house | 30 | 20 |
| 1525 | 1 b. Oromo house | 85 | 85 |

**1992.** Pottery from Sixth Tomb, Yeha. Mult.

| | | | |
|---|---|---|---|
| 1526 | 15 c. Type **326** | 10 | 10 |
| 1527 | 85 c. Milk jar | 50 | 35 |
| 1528 | 1 b. Wine vessel | 55 | 40 |

**327** Campaign Emblem

**328** Catchel (hand rattle)

**1992.** Pan-African Rinderpest Campaign.

| | | | | |
|---|---|---|---|---|
| 1529 | 327 | 20 c. gold, green & blk | 10 | 10 |
| 1530 | | 80 c. multicoloured | 45 | 30 |
| 1531 | | 1 b. multicoloured | 55 | 40 |

**1993.** Traditional Musical Instruments. Multicoloured.

| | | | |
|---|---|---|---|
| 1532 | 15 c. Type **328** | 10 | 10 |
| 1533 | 35 c. Huldudwa (wind instrument) | 10 | 10 |
| 1534 | 50 c. Dita (stringed instrument) | 15 | 10 |
| 1535 | 1 b. Atamo (drum) | 30 | 20 |

**329** Banded Barbets

**331** Caraway Seed

**330** Honey Badger

**1993.** Birds. Multicoloured.

1536 15 c. Type **329** .. .. 10 10
1537 35 c. Ruppell's chats .. .. 10 10
1538 50 c. Abyssinian catbirds 15 10
1539 1 b. White-billed starling 30 20

**1993.** Mammals. Multicoloured.

1540 15 c. Type **330** .. .. 10 10
1541 35 c. Spotted-necked otter 10 10
1542 50 c. Rock hyrax .. 15 10
1543 1 b. White-tailed mongoose .. .. 30 20

**1993.** Spicy Herbs. Multicoloured.

1544 5 c. Type **331** .. .. 10 10
1545 15 c. Garlic .. .. 10 10
1546 80 c. Turmeric .. .. 20 15
1547 1 b. Capsicum peppers .. 30 20

**332** Southern White-banded Papilio

**333** "C. variabilis"

**1993.** Butterflies. Multicoloured.

1548 20 c. Type **332** .. .. 10 10
1549 30 c. King swallowtail .. 10 10
1550 50 c. Small striped swallowtail .. .. 15 10
1551 1 b. Veined swallowtail .. 30 20

**1993.** Beetles. Multicoloured.

1552 15 c. Type **333** .. .. 10 10
1553 35 c. "Lycus trabeatus" 10 10
1554 50 c. "Malachius bifasciatus" .. .. 15 10
1555 1 b. "Homoeogryllus xanthographus" .. 30 20

**334** "Euphorbia amliphylla"

**1993.** Trees. Multicoloured.

1556 15 c. Type **334** .. .. 10 10
1557 35 c. "Erythrina brucei" 10 10
1558 50 c. "Draceana steudneri" .. .. 15 10
1559 1 b. "Allophylus abbyssinicus" .. .. 30 20

**335** Lake Wonchi

**1993.** Lakes. Multicoloured.

1560 15 c. Type **335** .. .. 10 10
1561 35 c. Lake Zuquala .. 10 10
1562 50 c. Lake Ashengi .. 10 10
1563 1 b. Lake Tana .. .. 25 15

**336** Simien Fox

**1994.** Dated "1991". Multicoloured, frame colours given.

1564 **336** 5 c. lilac .. ..
1565 10 c. brown .. ..
1566 15 c. yellow .. ..
1567 20 c. pink .. ..
1568 40 c. pink .. ..
1569 55 c. green .. ..
1570 60 c. blue .. ..
1571 80 c. blue .. ..
1572 85 c. green .. ..
1573 1 b. green .. ..

**337** Flag and Fighter

**338** Emblem

**1994.** 3rd Anniv of Ethiopian People's Revolutionary Democratic Front Transitional Government. Multicoloured.

1574 15 c. Type **337** (control of Addis Ababa, May 1991) 10 10
1575 35 c. Peaceful and Democratic Transition Conference, Addis Ababa, July 1991 .. 10 10
1576 50 c. Elections, June 1994 10 10
1577 1 b. Flag and Government arms .. .. .. 25 15

**1994.** International Year of the Family.

1578 **338** 15 c. multicoloured .. 10 10
1579 85 c. multicoloured .. 20 15
1580 1 b. multicoloured .. 25 15

**339** Postal Messengers

**1994.** Centenary of Postal Services in Ethiopia. Multicoloured.

1581 60 c. Postal workers, magnifying glass over 1st Ethiopian stamp and early postal messenger .. .. 15 10
1582 75 c. Type **339** .. .. 20 15
1583 80 c. Old post office and early mechanized post transport .. .. 20 15
1584 85 c. Rural service .. 20 15
1585 1 b. Express Mail Service 25 15

**340** Plant

**341** Iron Ornament, Gamo Gofa

**1994.** The Enset Plant. Multicoloured.

1587 10 c. Type **340** .. .. 10 10
1588 15 c. Enset growing beside house .. .. .. 10 10
1589 25 c. Gathering and preparation .. .. 10 10
1590 50 c. Plantation .. .. 10 10
1591 1 b. Prepared food .. 20 15

**1994.** Hair Ornaments. Multicoloured.

1592 5 c. Type **341** .. .. 10 10
1593 15 c. Aluminium beads, Sidamo .. .. .. 10 10
1594 80 c. Metal ornament, Gamo Gofa (different) 20 15
1595 1 b. Silver hairpin, Wello 20 15

**342** Simien Fox

**1994.** Dated "1993". Multicoloured, frame colours given.

1597 **342** 10 c. brown .. ..
1598 15 c. yellow .. ..
1606 55 c. green .. ..
1607 60 c. blue .. ..
1614 1 b. green .. ..
1615 2 b. brown .. ..

**344** Anniversary Emblem

**1994.** 50th Anniv of I.C.A.O.

1620 **344** 20 c. blue, yell & mve 10 10
1621 80 c. blue and yellow 20 15
1622 1 b. bl, yell & ultram 20 15

**346** Erbo (dish)

**1995.** Traditional Food Serving Utensils. Multicoloured.

1627 30 c. Type **346** .. .. 10 10
1628 70 c. Sedieka (round table) 15 10
1629 1 b. Tirar (rectangular table) .. .. .. 20 15

**347** Kuncho (young boys and girls)

**1995.** Traditional Hairstyles. Multicoloured.

1630 25 c. Type **347** .. .. 10 10
1631 75 c. Gamme (unmarried women) .. .. 15 10
1632 1 b. Sadulla (married women until birth of first child) .. .. 20 15

**348** Anniversary Emblem

**1995.** 50th Anniv of F.A.O.

1633 **348** 20 c. multicoloured .. 10 10
1634 80 c. multicoloured .. 15 10
1635 1 b. multicoloured .. 20 15

**349** Dangora (digging tool)

**1995.** Traditional Agricultural Tools. Mult.

1636 15 c. Type **349** .. .. 10 10
1637 35 c. Gheso (hoe) .. 10 10
1638 50 c. Akafa (hoe) .. 10 10
1639 1 b. Ankasse (digging tool) .. .. .. 20 15

**350** Anniversary Emblem

**1995.** 50th Anniv of U.N.O.

1640 **350** 20 c. multicoloured .. 10 10
1641 80 c. multicoloured .. 15 10
1642 1 b. multicoloured .. 20 10

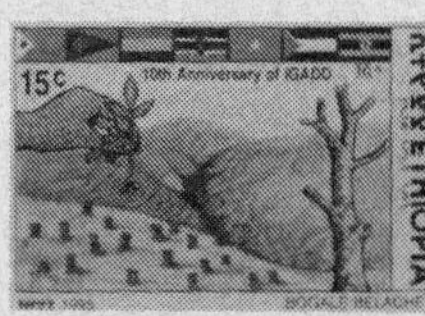

**351** Reforestation

**1995.** 10th Anniv of Intergovernmental Authority on Drought and Development. Multicoloured.

1643 15 c. Type **351** .. .. 10 10
1644 35 c. People moving from drought area .. .. 10 10
1645 50 c. Boy picking fruit .. 10 10
1646 1 b. Member countries' flags and map of East Africa .. .. .. 20 15

**352** Map of Battle Site

**1996.** Cent of Victory at Battle of Adwa. Mult.

1647 40 c. Type **352** .. .. 10 10
1648 50 c. Map of Africa and emblem .. .. 10 10
1649 60 c. Ship and Italian soldiers .. .. 10 10
1650 70 c. Battle scenes .. 15 10
1651 80 c. Soldiers surrendering and frontline .. .. 15 10
1652 1 b. Emperor Menelik II and Empress Zauditu 20 10

**353** Village

**1996.** 25th Anniv of United Nations Volunteers' Service. Multicoloured.

1654 20 c. Type **353** .. .. 10 10
1655 30 c. Planting .. .. 10 10
1656 50 c. Teacher and pupils 10 10
1657 1 b. Parents and child .. 20 10

**354** Boxing

**1996.** Olympic Games, Atlanta. Unissued stamps (for 1984 Olympics) optd with Atlanta Olympics emblem as in T **354**. Multicoloured.

1658 15 c. Type **354** .. .. 10 10
1659 20 c. Swimming .. .. 10 10
1660 40 c. Cycling .. .. 10 10
1661 85 c. Running .. .. 20 10
1662 1 b. Football .. .. 20 10

EXPRESS LETTER STAMPS

DESIGN: 50 c. G.P.O., Addis Ababa.

E 65. Motor-cycle Messenger.

**1947.** Inscr. "EXPRESS".

| | | | | |
|---|---|---|---|---|
| E 357. | E 65. | 30 c. brown .. | 2·75 | 75 |
| E 358. | – | 50 c. blue .. | 3·25 | 90 |

POSTAGE DUE STAMPS

(D 3.)

D 77.

**1896.** Optd with Type D 3.

| | | | | |
|---|---|---|---|---|
| D 8. | 1. | ¼ g. green .. .. | 1·25 | |
| D 9. | | ½ g. red .. .. | 1·25 | |
| D 10. | | 1 g. blue .. .. | 1·25 | |
| D 11. | | 2 g. brown .. .. | 1·25 | |
| D 12. | | 4 g. red .. .. | 90 | |
| D 13. | | 8 g. mauve .. .. | 90 | |
| D 14. | | 16 g. black .. .. | 90 | |

**1905.** Optd. Taxe a Percevoir T.

| | | | | |
|---|---|---|---|---|
| D 108. | 1. | ¼ g. green .. .. | 10·00 | 10·00 |
| D 109. | | ½ g. red .. .. | 10·00 | 10·00 |
| D 110. | | 1 g. blue .. .. | 10·00 | 10·00 |
| D 111. | | 2 g. brown .. .. | 10·00 | 10·00 |
| D 112. | 2. | 4 g. red .. .. | 10·00 | 10·00 |
| D 113. | | 8 g. mauve .. .. | 15·00 | 15·00 |
| D 114. | | 16 g. black .. .. | 17·00 | 17·00 |

**1907.** As above further optd. with value in figures between stars.

| | | | | |
|---|---|---|---|---|
| D 122. | 1. | ¼ g. green .. .. | 17·00 | 17·00 |
| D 123. | | ½ g. red .. .. | 17·00 | 17·00 |
| D 124. | | 1 g. blue .. .. | 17·00 | 17·00 |
| D 125. | | 2 g. brown .. .. | 17·00 | 17·00 |
| D 126. | 2. | 4 g. red .. .. | 17·00 | 17·00 |
| D 127. | | 8 g. mauve .. .. | 17·00 | 17·00 |
| D 128. | | 16 g. black .. .. | 25·00 | 25·00 |

**1908.** Optd. with Amharic inscription and large T in triangle.

| | | | | |
|---|---|---|---|---|
| D 140. | 1. | ¼ g. green .. .. | 1·60 | 1·60 |
| D 141. | | ½ g. red .. .. | 1·60 | 1·60 |
| D 142. | | 1 g. blue .. .. | 1·60 | 1·60 |
| D 143. | | 2 g. brown .. .. | 2·00 | 2·00 |
| D 144. | 2. | 4 g. red .. .. | 3·00 | 3·00 |
| D 145. | | 8 g. mauve .. .. | 7·50 | 7·50 |
| D 146. | | 16 g. black .. .. | 13·50 | 13·50 |

**1913.** Stamps of 1909 and the 1 g. of 1919 optd. with Amharic inscription and large T in triangle.

| | | | | |
|---|---|---|---|---|
| D 161. | 19. | ½ g. green .. .. | 75 | 75 |
| D 162. | | ½ g. red .. .. | 1·10 | 1·10 |
| D 163. | | 1 g. orange and green .. | 2·50 | 2·50 |
| D 210. | – | 1 g. black and purple (No. 184) .. .. | 3·75 | 3·75 |
| D 164. | 20. | 2 g. blue .. .. | 3·00 | 3·00 |
| D 165. | | 4 g. red and green .. | 4·75 | 4·75 |
| D 166. | – | 8 g. grey and red (No. 152) .. .. | 6·00 | 6·00 |
| D 167. | – | 16 g. red (No. 153) .. | 16·00 | 16·00 |

**1951.**

| | | | | |
|---|---|---|---|---|
| D 417. | D 77. | 1 c. green .. .. | 10 | 15 |
| D 418. | | 5 c. red .. .. | 20 | 20 |
| D 419. | | 10 c. violet .. | 55 | 55 |
| D 420. | | 20 c. brown .. | 80 | 85 |
| D 421. | | 50 c. blue .. .. | 2·00 | 2·25 |
| D 422. | | $1 purple .. .. | 4·00 | 4·00 |

# FAROE ISLANDS Pt. 11

A Danish possession in the North Atlantic Ocean.

Under British Administration during the German Occupation of Denmark, 1940/5.

100 ore = 1 krone.

**1940.** Stamps of Denmark surch with new value (twice on Type 43).

| | | | | |
|---|---|---|---|---|
| 2 | 43 | 20 ore on 1 ore green .. | 25·00 | 65·00 |
| 3 | | 20 ore on 5 ore purple .. | 25·00 | 20·00 |
| 1 | 40 | 20 ore on 15 ore red .. | 45·00 | 12·00 |
| 4 | 43 | 50 ore on 5 ore purple .. | £160 | 50·00 |
| 5 | | 60 ore on 6 ore orange .. | 70·00 | £160 |

2. 1673 Map of the Faroe Islands.

3. "Vidoy and Svinoy" (E. Nohr).

**1975.**

| | | | | |
|---|---|---|---|---|
| 6 | 2 | 5 ore brown .. .. | 10 | 10 |
| 7 | – | 10 ore blue and green .. | 10 | 10 |
| 8 | 2 | 50 ore blue .. .. | 20 | 20 |
| 9 | – | 60 ore brown and blue .. | 1·50 | 1·25 |
| 10 | – | 70 ore black and blue .. | 1·00 | 1·00 |
| 11 | – | 80 ore brown and blue .. | 35 | 35 |
| 12 | 2 | 90 ore red .. .. | 80 | 80 |
| 13 | – | 120 ore blue and deep blue | 50 | 35 |
| 14 | – | 200 ore black and blue .. | 50 | 70 |
| 15 | – | 250 ore green, brown & bl | 50 | 70 |
| 16 | – | 300 ore green, brown & bl | 4·75 | 1·40 |
| 17 | 3 | 350 ore multicoloured .. | 70 | 90 |
| 18 | – | 450 ore multicoloured .. | 80 | 90 |
| 19 | – | 500 ore multicoloured .. | 80 | 90 |

DESIGNS—As Type 2 but HORIZ: 10, 60, 80, 120 ore Northern map (A. Ortelius). 70, 200 ore West Sandoy. 250, 300 ore Streymoy and Vagar. As Type 3: 450 ore "Nes" (R. Smith). 500 ore "Hvitanes and Skalafjordur" (S. Joensen-Mikines).

4. Rowing Boat.

5. Motor Fishing Boat.

**1976.** Inauguration of Faroese Post Office.

| | | | | |
|---|---|---|---|---|
| 20. | 4. | 125 ore red .. .. | 2·00 | 1·25 |
| 21. | – | 160 ore multicoloured .. | 30 | 30 |
| 22. | – | 800 ore green .. .. | 1·50 | 1·00 |

DESIGNS—24 × 34 mm: 160 ore Faroese flag. 24 × 31 mm: 800 ore Faroese postman.

**1977.** Faroese Fishing Vessels.

| | | | | |
|---|---|---|---|---|
| 23. | 5. | 100 ore blk., lt. grn. & grn. | 6·75 | 4·25 |
| 24. | – | 125 ore blk., rose and red | 90 | 65 |
| 25. | – | 160 ore blk., lt. bl. & bl. | 1·25 | 85 |
| 26. | – | 600 ore blk., ochre & brn. | 1·75 | 1·00 |

DESIGNS: 125 ore "Niels Pauli" (inshore fishing cutter). 160 ore Modern seine fishing boat. 600 ore "Polarfisk" (deep-sea trawler).

6. Common Snipe. 7. Atlantic Puffins over North Coast.

**1977.** Birds. Multicoloured.

| | | | |
|---|---|---|---|
| 27. | 70 ore Type 6 .. .. | 30 | 20 |
| 28. | 180 ore Oystercatcher .. | 45 | 40 |
| 29. | 250 ore Whimbrel .. .. | 55 | 50 |

**1978.** Views of Mykines Island. Multicoloured.

| | | | |
|---|---|---|---|
| 30. | 100 ore Type 7 .. .. | 25 | 25 |
| 31. | 130 ore Mykines village (horiz.) .. .. | 30 | 30 |
| 32. | 140 ore Cultivated fields (horiz.) .. .. | 50 | 50 |
| 33. | 150 ore Aerial view of Mykines .. .. | 50 | 50 |
| 34. | 180 ore Map of Mykines (37 × 26 mm) .. | 50 | 50 |

8. Northern Gannet.

9. Old Library Building.

**1978.** Sea Birds. Multicoloured.

| | | | |
|---|---|---|---|
| 35. | 140 ore Type 8 .. .. | 60 | 60 |
| 36. | 180 ore Atlantic puffin .. | 80 | 80 |
| 37. | 400 ore Common guillemot | 80 | 80 |

**1978.** 150th Anniv. of National Library.

| | | | | |
|---|---|---|---|---|
| 38. | 9. | 140 ore olive and blue .. | 60 | 60 |
| 39. | – | 180 ore brown and flesh | 65 | 40 |

DESIGN: 180 ore New National Library building.

10. Guide, Tent and Campfire.

11. Ram.

**1978.** 50th Anniv. of Girl Guides.

| | | | | |
|---|---|---|---|---|
| 40. | 10. | 140 ore multicoloured .. | 70 | 55 |

**1979.** Sheep-rearing.

| | | | | |
|---|---|---|---|---|
| 41. | 11. | 25 k. multicoloured .. | 4·75 | 2·40 |

12. Bisect of Denmark 4 ore Blue, 1919.

13. Girl in Festive Costume.

**1979.** Europa. Multicoloured.

| | | | | |
|---|---|---|---|---|
| 42. | 12. | 140 ore blue and yellow on stone .. .. | 50 | 50 |
| 43. | – | 180 ore olive and mauve on stone .. .. | 50 | 50 |

DESIGN: 180 ore Denmark 1919 2 ore surcharge on 5 ore.

**1979.** International Year of the Child. Multicoloured designs showing childrens' drawings.

| | | | |
|---|---|---|---|
| 44. | 110 ore Type 13 .. .. | 30 | 30 |
| 45. | 150 ore Man fishing from boat .. .. | 30 | 30 |
| 46. | 200 ore Two friends .. | 40 | 40 |

14. Sea Plantain.

15. Jakob Jakobsen (linguist and folklorist).

**1980.** Flowers. Multicoloured.

| | | | |
|---|---|---|---|
| 47 | 90 ore Type 14 .. .. | 20 | 20 |
| 48 | 110 ore Glacier buttercup .. | 20 | 20 |
| 49 | 150 ore Purple saxifrage .. | 30 | 30 |
| 50 | 200 ore Starry saxifrage .. | 40 | 40 |
| 51 | 400 ore Faroese lady's mantle .. .. .. | 70 | 70 |

**1980.** Europa.

| | | | | |
|---|---|---|---|---|
| 52. | 15. | 150 ore green .. .. | 30 | 30 |
| 53. | – | 200 ore brown .. .. | 40 | 40 |

DESIGN: 200 ore Vensel Ulrich Hammershaimb (theologian and linguist).

16. Virgin and Child.

17. Timber Houses, Torshavn.

**1980.** Pews of Kirkjubour Church (1st series).

| | | | | |
|---|---|---|---|---|
| 54 | 16 | 110 ore multicoloured .. | 25 | 25 |
| 55 | – | 140 ore multicoloured .. | 25 | 25 |
| 56 | – | 150 ore multicoloured .. | 25 | 25 |
| 57 | – | 200 ore black and buff .. | 30 | 30 |

DESIGNS: 140 ore St. John the Baptist. 150 ore St. Peter. 200 ore St. Paul.

See also Nos. 90/3.

**1981.** Old Torshavn. Designs show different views.

| | | | | |
|---|---|---|---|---|
| 58. | 17. | 110 ore green .. .. | 15 | 15 |
| 59. | – | 140 ore black .. .. | 25 | 25 |
| 60. | – | 150 ore brown .. .. | 25 | 25 |
| 61. | – | 200 ore blue .. .. | 30 | 30 |

18. Garter Dance.

**1981.** Europa.

| | | | | |
|---|---|---|---|---|
| 62. | 18. | 150 ore green and brown | 25 | 30 |
| 63. | – | 200 ore brown and green | 30 | 40 |

DESIGN: 200 ore Ring dance.

19. Rune Stone.

20. Map of Viking Voyages in North Atlantic.

**1981.** Historic Writings of the Faroes.

| | | | | |
|---|---|---|---|---|
| 64. | 19. | 10 ore blue, black and grey | 10 | 10 |
| 65. | – | 1 k. light brown, black and brown .. .. | 15 | 15 |
| 66. | – | 3 k. grey, black and red | 75 | 50 |
| 67. | – | 6 k. red, black and grey .. | 1·50 | 85 |
| 68. | – | 10 k. stone, brown and black .. .. | 2·00 | 1·75 |

DESIGNS: 1 k. Score of folksong, 1846. 3 k. Manuscript of Sheep Farming Law, 1298. 6 k. Seal showing heraldic ram, 1533. 10 k. Title page of "Faeroae et Faeroa Reserata" and library.

**1982.** Europa.

| | | | | |
|---|---|---|---|---|
| 69. | 20. | 1 k. 50 blue .. .. | 30 | 60 |
| 70. | – | 2 k. black .. .. | 40 | 50 |

DESIGN: 2 k. Archaeological excavations at Kvivik village.

21. Gjogv.

22. Elinborg's Promise to remain Faithful.

**1982.** Villages.

| | | | | |
|---|---|---|---|---|
| 71. | 21. | 180 ore black and blue .. | 30 | 30 |
| 72. | – | 220 ore black and brown | 85 | 45 |
| 73. | – | 250 ore black and brown | 45 | 45 |

DESIGNS: 220 ore Hvalvik. 250 ore Kvivik.

**1982.** The Ballad of Harra Paetur and Elinborg. Multicoloured.

| | | | |
|---|---|---|---|
| 74. | 220 ore Type 22 .. .. | 40 | 40 |
| 75. | 250 ore Elinborg longing for Paetur .. .. .. | 50 | 50 |
| 76. | 350 ore Paetur in disguise greets Elinborg .. | 70 | 70 |
| 77. | 450 ore Elinborg and Paetur sail away .. .. | 90 | 90 |

**23.** "Arcturus". **24.** King.

**1983.** Old Cargo Liners on the Faroes Run. Multicoloured.
78 220 ore Type **23** .. .. 60 55
79 250 ore "Laura" .. .. 75 65
80 700 ore "Thyra" .. .. 1·90 1·60

**1983.** 19th-century Chess Pieces by Pol i Bud from Nolsoy.
81 **24** 250 ore brown and black 2·00 2·00
82 – 250 ore blue and black 2·00 2·00
DESIGN: No. 82, Queen.

**25.** Niels R. Finsen (founder of phototherapy).

**1983.** Europa.
83 **25** 250 ore blue .. .. 65 50
84 – 400 ore purple .. .. 85 95
DESIGN: 400 ore Sir Alexander Fleming (discoverer of penicillin).

**26.** Tusk.

**1983.** Fishes. Multicoloured.
85. 250 ore Type **26** .. .. 40 40
86. 280 ore Haddock .. .. 75 75
87. 500 ore Halibut .. .. 1·40 1·25
88. 900 ore Catfish .. .. 2·25 2·25

**1984.** Pews of Kirkjubour Church (2nd series). As T **16**.
90. 250 ore multicoloured .. 65 65
91. 300 ore lt. brn., blk. & brn. 75 75
92. 350 ore brn., grey & blk. .. 85 70
93. 400 ore multicoloured .. 95 80
DESIGNS: 250 ore St. John. 300 ore St. Jacob. 350 ore St Thomas. 400 ore Judas Taddeus.

**28.** Bridge.

**1984.** Europa. 25th Anniv. of European Post and Telecommunications Conference.
94. **28.** 250 ore red .. .. 50 60
95. 500 ore blue .. .. 1·40 1·40

**29.** Sverri Patursson. **30.** Fisherman.

**1984.** Writers.
96. **29.** 200 ore green .. .. 30 40
97. – 250 ore red .. .. 40 50
98. – 300 ore blue .. .. 75 60
99. – 450 ore violet .. .. 1·10 1·10
DESIGNS: 250 ore Joannes Patursson. 300 ore, Janus Djurhuus. 450 ore Hans Andrias Djurhuus.

**1984.** Fishing Industry.
100. – 280 ore blue .. .. 50 50
101. – 300 ore brown .. .. 60 70
102. **30.** 12 k. olive .. .. 3·00 3·00
DESIGNS—HORIZ. 280 ore Fishing ketch "Westward Ho". VERT. 300 ore Fishermen on deck.

**31.** "Beauty of the Veils". **32.** Torshavn.

**1984.** Fairy Tales. Designs showing woodcuts by Elinborg Lutzen.
103. **31.** 140 ore blue, olive and brown .. .. 3·75 3·75
104. – 280 ore olive & brown 3·75 3·75
105. – 280 ore olive, deep olive and brown .. 3·75 3·75
106. – 280 ore brown & olive 3·75 3·75
107. – 280 ore olive, deep olive and brown .. 3·75 3·75
108. – 280 ore brown, olive and deep brown .. 3·75 3·75
DESIGNS: No. 104, "Beauty of the Veils" (different). 105, "The Shy Prince". 106, "The Glass Sword". 107, "Little Elin". 108, "The Boy and the Ox".

**1985.** J. T. Stanley's Expedition to the Faroes, 1789. Paintings by Edward Dayes.
109 **32** 250 ore brown and blue 55 55
110 – 280 ore brown, grn & bl 70 70
111 – 550 ore green, brn & bl 1·50 1·50
112 – 800 ore brown, grn & bl 1·90 1·90
DESIGNS: 280 ore Mount Skaeling. 550 ore Hoyvik. 800 ore The Rocking Stones, Eysturoy.

**33.** Cellist, Pianist and Flautist.

**1985.** Europa. Music Year. Multicoloured.
113. 280 ore Type **33** .. .. 1·10 1·10
114. 550 ore Drummer, guitarist and saxophonist .. 2·25 2·25

**34.** "Self-portrait" (Ruth Smith).

**1985.** Paintings. Multicoloured.
115. 280 ore "The Garden, Hoyvik" (Tummas Arge) (horiz.) .. .. 95 95
116. 450 ore Type **34** .. .. 1·40 1·40
117. 550 ore "Winter's Day in Nolsoy" (Steffan Danielsen) (horiz.) .. 2·10 2·10

**35.** Nolsoy Lighthouse.

**1985.** Lighthouses. Multicoloured.
118. 270 ore Type **35** .. .. 1·25 1·25
119. 320 ore Torshavn .. .. 1·50 1·50
120. 350 ore Mykines .. .. 1·75 1·75
121. 470 ore Map of the Faroes showing lighthouse sites 2·00 2·00

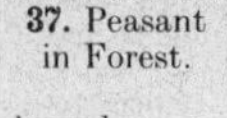

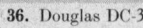

**36.** Douglas DC-3. **37.** Peasant in Forest.

**1985.** Aircraft. Multicoloured.
122 300 ore Type **36** .. .. 1·90 1·90
123 300 ore Fokker Friendship 1·90 1·90
124 300 ore Boeing 737 Special 1·90 1·90
125 300 ore Beech Twin Bonanza inter-island airplane .. .. 1·90 1·90
126 300 ore Bell 212 helicopter 1·90 1·90

**1986.** Skrimsla (dancing ballad). Mult.
127 300 ore Type **37** .. .. 75 75
128 420 ore Giant challenges peasant to chess game .. 1·25 1·25
129 550 ore Peasant beats giant 1·50 1·50
130 650 ore Peasant and castle 1·75 1·75

**38.** Ship dumping Dangerous Canisters at Sea. **39.** Birds escaping from Cage.

**1986.** Europa. Multicoloured.
131. 3 k. Type **38** .. .. 1·75 1·75
132. 5 k. 50 Contents of damaged canister escaping into sea .. .. 3·00 3·00

**1986.** 25th Anniv. of Amnesty International. Multicoloured.
133. 3 k. Type **39** .. .. 85 85
134. 4 k. 70 Faces (horiz.) .. 1·25 1·25
135. 5 k. 50 Man behind bars and woman with children .. .. .. 1·75 1·75

**41.** Glyvrar Bridge, Eysturoy.

**1986.** Bridges.
137. **41.** 2 k. 70 brown .. .. 1·90 1·90
138. – 3 k. blue .. .. 1·75 1·75
139. – 13 k. green .. .. 3·75 3·75
DESIGNS—VERT. 3 k. Leypanagjogv, Vagar. HORIZ. 13 k. Skaelingur, Streymoy.

**42.** Farmhouse, Depli. **43.** Windows.

**1987.** Farm Buildings.
140. **42.** 300 ore dp. bl. & bl. .. 95 90
141. – 420 ore brn. & lt. brn. 2·40 2·40
142. – 470 ore grn & lt. grn .. 1·90 1·90
143. – 650 ore black & grey .. 2·40 2·40
DESIGNS: 420 ore Barn, Depli. 470 ore Cowshed and blacksmith's, Frammi vid Gjonna. 650 ore Farmhouse, Frammi vid Gjonna.

**1987.** Europa. Architecture. Details of Nordic House, Torshavn (by O. Steen and K. Ragnarsdottir).
144. **43.** 300 ore blue .. .. 1·25 1·25
145. – 550 ore brown .. .. 2·40 2·40
DESIGN: 550 ore Entrance.

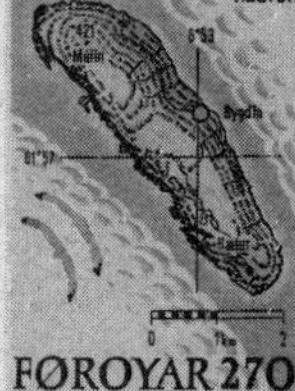


**44.** "Joannes Patursson". **45.** Map.

**1987.** Trawlers. Multicoloured.
146. 300 ore Type **44** .. .. 90 80
147. 550 ore "Magnus Heinason" (side trawler) 2·00 2·00
148. 800 ore "Sjurdarberg" (stern trawler) .. .. 3·50 3·50

**1987.** Hestur Island. Multicoloured.
149. 270 ore Type **45** .. .. 80 90
150. 300 ore Harbour (horiz.) .. 80 70
151. 420 ore Alvastakkur needle .. .. .. 1·75 1·75
152. 470 ore Fagradalsvatn Lake (horiz.) .. .. 1·90 1·90
153. 550 ore Bygdin village .. 1·90 1·90

**47.** "West Bay".

**1987.** Torshavn Views. Collages by Zacharias Heinesen. Multicoloured.
155 4 k. 70 "East Bay" .. 1·90 1·90
156 6 k. 50 Type **47** .. .. 2·40 2·40

**48.** Daisy. **49.** Container Ship and Dockside Scene.

**1988.** Flowers. Multicoloured.
157. 2 k. 70 Type **48** .. .. 1·10 1·10
158. 3 k. Heath spotted orchid 1·25 1·25
159. 4 k. 70 Tormentil .. .. 1·75 1·75
160. 9 k. Common butterwort .. 2·50 2·50

**1988.** Europa. Transport and Communications. Multicoloured.
161. 3 k. Dish aerial and satellite .. .. .. 1·40 1·40
162. 5 k. 50 Type **49** .. .. 2·40 2·40

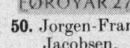

**50.** Jorgen-Frantz Jacobsen. **51.** Notice of Christmas Meeting and Conveners.

**1988.** Writers.
163. **50.** 270 ore green .. .. 1·40 1·40
164. – 300 ore red .. .. 80 80
165. – 470 ore blue .. .. 1·75 1·75
166. – 650 ore brown .. .. 2·40 2·40
DESIGNS: 300 ore Christian Matras. 470 ore William Heinesen. 650 ore Hedin Bru.

**1988.** Centenary of Christmas Meeting to Establish National Movement. Mult.
167 3 k. Type **51** .. .. 80 80
168 3 k. 20 Drawing by William Heinesen of a People's Meeting, 1908, and conveners .. 1·25 1·25
169 12 k. Opening words of Joannes Patursson's poem "Now the Hour has Come", conveners and oystercatcher .. 4·25 4·25

**52.** Exterior View of Cathedral.

**1988.** Kirkjubour Cathedral Ruins.
170. **52.** 270 ore green .. .. 1·40 1·40
171. – 300 ore blue .. .. 1·10 1·10
172. – 470 ore brown .. .. 1·75 1·75
173. – 550 ore purple .. .. 2·00 2·00
DESIGNS—VERT. 300 ore Window. 470 ore Crucifixion (relief). HORIZ. 550 ore Nave.

**53** Church

**1989.** Bicentenary of Torshavn Church.
174 **53** 350 ore green .. .. 1·00 1·00
175 – 500 ore brown .. .. 1·75 1·75
176 – 15 k. blue .. .. 3·25 3·25
DESIGNS—VERT: 500 ore "The Last Supper" (altarpiece); 15 k. Bell from "Norske Love" (shipwreck).

**54** Wooden Toy Boat **55** Sjostuka Man

**1989.** Europa. Children's Toys. Multicoloured.
177 3 k. 50 Type **54** .. .. 1·50 1·50
178 6 k. Wooden horse .. 2·00 2·00

**1989.** Nordic Countries' Postal Co-operation. Traditional Costumes. Multicoloured.
179 350 ore Type **55** .. .. 1·00 1·00
180 600 ore Stakkur woman .. 1·40 1·40

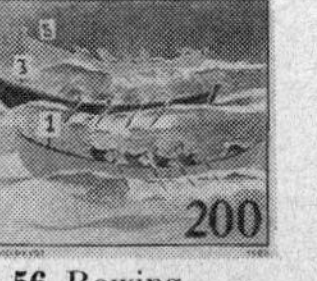


**56** Rowing **57** Tvoran

**1989.** Sports. Multicoloured.
181 200 ore Type **56** .. .. 50 50
182 350 ore Handball .. .. 1·00 1·00
183 600 ore Football .. .. 1·60 1·60
184 700 ore Swimming .. 2·00 2·00

**1989.** Bird Cliffs of Suduroy. Each brown, green and blue.
185 320 ore Type **57** .. .. 80 80
186 350 ore Skuvanes .. .. 1·00 1·00
187 500 ore Beinisvord .. 1·40 1·40
188 600 ore Asmundarstakkur 1·60 1·60

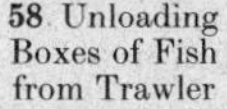

**58** Unloading Boxes of Fish from Trawler **59** Old Post Office, Gjogv

**1990.** Fish Processing Industry. Mult.
189 3 k. 50 Type **58** .. .. 70 70
190 3 k. 70 Cleaning fish .. 1·00 1·00
191 5 k. Filleting fish .. 1·25 1·25
192 7 k. Deep-freezing fish .. 1·75 1·75

**1990.** Europa. Post Office Buildings. Mult.
193 3 k. 50 Type **59** .. .. 1·40 1·40
194 6 k. Klaksvik post office .. 1·90 1·90

**61** Sowerby's Beaked Whale

**1990.** Whales. Multicoloured.
196 320 ore Type **61** .. .. 95 95
197 350 ore Bowhead whale .. 1·10 1·10
198 600 ore Black right whale 1·75 1·75
199 700 ore Northern bottle-nosed whale .. .. 1·90 1·90

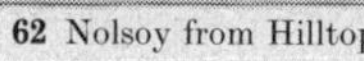

**62** Nolsoy from Hilltop **63** Ribwort Plantain

**1990.** Nolsoy. Paintings by Steffan Danielsen. Multicoloured.
200 50 ore Type **62** .. .. 10 10
201 350 ore Church .. .. 95 95
202 500 ore Village .. .. 1·25 1·25
203 1000 ore Cliffs by moonlight .. .. .. 2·50 2·50

**1991.** Anthropochora. Multicoloured.
204 3 k. 70 Type **63** .. .. 1·00 1·00
205 4 k. Northern dock .. 1·10 1·10
206 4 k. 50 Black beetle .. 1·25 1·25
207 6 k. 50 Earthworm .. 1·75 1·75

**64** Town Hall

**1991.** 125th Anniv of Torshavn as Capital. Multicoloured.
208 3 k. 70 Type **64** .. .. 1·00 1·00
209 3 k. 70 Eastern Tinganes (old part of Torshavn) 1·00 1·00

**65** Satellite, Earth and Weather Map **66** Arctic Terns

**1991.** Europa. Europe in Space. Mult.
210 3 k. 70 Type **65** .. .. 1·10 1·10
211 6 k. 50 Chart of Plough constellation and Pole Star, and sailors navigating by stars .. 1·75 1·75

**1991.** Birds. Multicoloured.
212 3 k. 70 Type **66** .. .. 1·00 1·00
213 3 k. 70 Kittiwakes .. 1·00 1·00

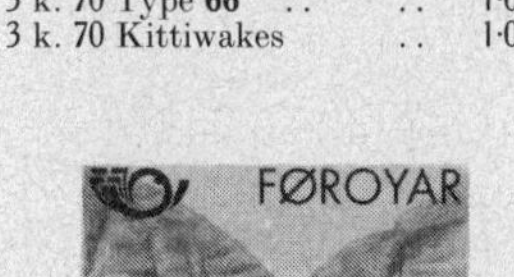


**67** Saksun

**1991.** Nordic Countries' Postal Co-operation. Tourism. Multicoloured.
214 370 ore Type **67** .. .. 1·00 1·00
215 650 ore Vestmanna cliffs 1·75 1·75

**68** "Handanagardur"

**1991.** 85th Birth Anniv of Samal Joensen-Mikines (painter). Multicoloured.
216 340 ore "Funeral Procession" .. .. 70 70
217 370 ore "The Farewell" .. 1·00 1·00
218 550 ore Type **68** .. .. 1·40 1·40
219 1300 ore "Winter Morning" 3·25 3·25

**69** "Ruth"

**1991.** Mail Ships. Multicoloured.
220 200 ore Type **69** .. .. 40 40
221 370 ore "Ritan" .. .. 1·00 1·00
222 550 ore "Sigmundur" .. 1·50 1·50
223 800 ore "Masin" .. .. 2·10 2·10

**70** Map and Viking Ship (Leif Eriksson)

**1992.** Europa. 500th Anniv of Discovery of America by Columbus. Multicoloured.
224 3 k. 70 Type **70** .. .. 85 85
225 6 k. 50 Map and "Santa Maria" .. .. .. 1·50 1·50

**71** Grey Seal ("Halichoerus grypus")

**1992.** Seals. Multicoloured.
227 3 k. 70 Type **71** .. .. 80 80
228 3 k. 70 Common seal ("Phoca vitulina") .. 80 80

**72** Desmine **73** Glyvra Hanus's House.

**1992.** Minerals. Multicoloured.
229 370 ore Type **72** .. .. 1·00 1·00
230 650 ore Mesolite .. .. 1·75 1·75

**1992.** Old Houses in Nordragota, Eysturoy. Multicoloured.
231 3 k. 40 Type **73** .. .. 70 70
232 3 k. 70 Village and church 75 75
233 6 k. 50 Blasastova .. 1·75 1·75
234 8 k. Jakupsstova .. .. 2·10 2·10

**74** Musicians at Jazz, Folk and Blues Festival

**1993.** 10th Anniv of Nordic House, Torshavn. Multicoloured.
235 400 ore "The Lost Musicians" (William Heinesen) .. .. 80 80
236 400 ore Joannes Andreassen (pianist) .. 80 80
237 400 ore Type **74** .. .. 80 80

**75** Landscape **76** "Reflection"

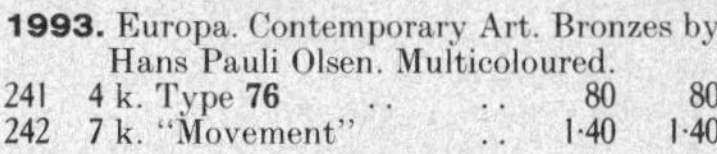

**1993.** Nordic Countries' Postal Co-operation. Gjogv. Multicoloured.
239 4 k. Type **75** .. .. 80 80
240 4 k. Village .. .. 80 80

**1993.** Europa. Contemporary Art. Bronzes by Hans Pauli Olsen. Multicoloured.
241 4 k. Type **76** .. .. 80 80
242 7 k. "Movement" .. 1·40 1·40

**77** Horse's Head

**1993.** Horses.
243 **77** 400 ore brown .. .. 80 80
244 – 20 k. lilac .. .. 5·25 5·25
DESIGN—HORIZ. 20 k. Mare and foal.

**78** "Apamea zeta"

**1993.** Butterflies and Moths. Multicoloured.
245 350 ore Type **78** .. .. 95 95
246 400 ore "Hepialus humuli" 1·10 1·10
247 700 ore Red admiral .. 1·90 1·90
248 900 ore "Perizoma albulata" .. .. 2·25 2·25

**79** Three-spined Stickleback

**1994.** Fishes. Multicoloured.
249 10 ore Type **79** .. .. 10 10
250 4 k. False boarfish .. 1·10 1·10
251 7 k. Brown trout .. .. 1·90 1·90
252 10 k. Orange roughy .. 2·50 2·50

**80** St. Brendan discovering Faroe Islands

**1994.** Europa. St. Brendan's Voyages. Mult.
253 4 k. Type **80** .. .. 85 85
254 7 k. St. Brendan visiting Iceland .. .. 1·50 1·50

**81** Sailing Ship and Sailor using Sextant

**1994.** Centenary (1993) of Faroese Nautical School, Torshavn. Multicoloured.
256 3 k. 50 Type **81** .. .. 1·00 1·00
257 7 k. Modern ship and sailor using modern equipment 1·90 1·90

82 Dog and Sheep

83 Ship

**1994.** Sheepdogs. Multicoloured.
258 4 k. Type **82** .. .. 85 85
259 4 k. Dog's head (18 × 25 mm) .. .. 85 85

**1994.** Brusajokil's Lay (traditional song). Multicoloured.
260 1 k. Type **83** .. .. 20 20
261 4 k. Asbjorn at entrance to Brusajokil's cave .. 1·10 1·10
262 6 k. Trolls appearing after Ormar had killed cat .. 1·50 1·50
263 7 k. Ormar pulling off Brusajokil's beard .. 1·90 1·90

84 First to Tenth Days

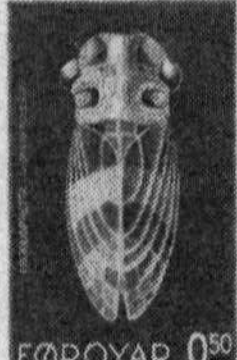

85 "Ulopa reticulata"

**1994.** Christmas. Designs illustrating "On the First Day of Christmas St. Martin gave to Me". Multicoloured.
264 400 ore Type **84** .. .. 85 85
265 400 ore 11th to 15th days 85 85

**1995.** Leafhoppers. Multicoloured.
266 50 ore Type **85** .. .. 10 10
267 4 k. "Streptanus sordidus" 1·10 1·10
268 5 k. "Anoscopus flavostriatus" .. .. 1·40 1·40
269 13 k. "Macrosteles alpinus" 3·75 3·75

86 Vatnsdalur

**1995.** Nordic Countries' Postal Co-operation. Tourism. Multicoloured.
270 400 ore Type **86** .. .. 1·25 1·25
271 400 ore Famjin .. .. 1·25 1·25

87 Vidar, Vali and Baldur

**1995.** Europa. Peace and Freedom. Mult.
272 4 k. Type **87** .. .. 1·25 1·25
273 7 k. Liv and Livtrasir .. 2·00 2·00

88 Museum of Art, Torshavn

**1995.** 50th Anniv of Nordic Artists Association. Multicoloured.
274 2 k. Type **88** .. .. 45 45
275 4 k. "Woman" (Frimod Joensen) (vert) .. 1·25 1·25
276 5 k. 50 Self-portrait (Joensen) (vert) .. 1·60 1·60

89 Common Raven

**1995.** The Raven. Multicoloured.
277 400 ore Type **89** .. .. 1·25 1·25
278 400 ore White speckled raven .. .. .. 1·25 1·25

90 St. Olaf

**1995.**
279 **90** 4 k. multicoloured .. 1·25 1·25

91 Dairy Maids

92 St. Mary's Church

**1995.** Rural Life.
280 **91** 4 k. green .. .. 1·25 1·25
281 – 6 k. brown .. .. 1·75 1·75
282 – 15 k. blue .. .. 4·25 4·25
DESIGNS—VERT: 6 k. Sheep shearing; 15 k. Fishermen.

**1995.** The Catholic Church. Multicoloured.
283 400 ore Type **92** .. .. 1·25 1·25
284 400 ore Stained glass window, St. Mary's Church .. .. 1·25 1·25

93 Risin and Kellingin

94 "Ptilota plumosa"

**1996.**
285 **93** 450 ore multicoloured .. 1·00 1·00

**1996.** Seaweed. Multicoloured.
286 4 k. Type **94** .. .. 95 95
287 5 k. 50 Flat wrack .. 1·25 1·25
288 6 k. Knotted wrack .. 1·40 1·40
289 9 k. Forest kelp .. .. 2·10 2·10

95 "Young Girl"

96 Bohemian Waxwing

**1996.** Europa. Famous Women. Paintings by Samal Joensen-Mikines. Multicoloured.
290 4 k. 50 Type **95** .. 1·00 1·00
291 7 k. 50 "Old Woman" (vert) .. .. .. 1·75 1·75

**1996.** Birds. Multicoloured.
292 4 k. 50 Type **96** .. .. 1·00 1·00
293 4 k. 50 Red crossbill ("Loxia curvirostra") 1·00 1·00

97 Faroe Islands and Compass Rose

99 "Flock of Sheep"

**1996.** Maps.
311 **97** 10 k. multicoloured .. 2·10 2·10
313 16 k. multicoloured .. 3·50 3·50

**1996.** Paintings by Janus Kamban. Mult.
315 4 k. 50 Type **99** .. .. 95 95
316 6 k. 50 "Fishermen on way Home" .. .. 1·40 1·40
317 7 k. 50 "View from Torshavn's Old Quarter" 1·60 1·60

100 Klaksvik Church

**1996.** Christmas. Multicoloured.
318 4 k. 50 Type **100** .. .. 95 95
319 4 k. 50 Altarpiece depicting biblical scenes (21 × 38 mm) .. .. .. 95 95

## FERNANDO POO Pt. 9

A Spanish island off the west coast of Africa, in the Gulf of Guinea. Became part of Spanish Guinea in 1909. In 1959 Fernando Poo became an overseas province of Spain, comprising the island and Annobon. On 12 October 1968 became independent and joined Rio Muni to form Equatorial Guinea.

1868. Currencies stated below issue.
1894. 1000 milesimas = 100 centavos = 1 peso.
1901. 100 centimos = 1 peseta.

1. Isabella II.

(3)

**1868.**
1 **1** 20 c. brown .. .. £400 £120

**The face value of No. 1 is expressed in centimos de escudo. It was in use until Dec. 1868. Stamps of Cuba were then used until 1879.**

**1879.** "Alfonso XII" key-type inscr. "FERNANDO POO".
**5. X. 1 c. green** .. .. .. 7·50 4·50
**6. 2 c. red** .. .. .. 11·00 8·00
**2. 5 c. green** .. .. .. 40·00 11·00
**7. 5 c. lilac** .. .. .. 35·00 11·00
**3. 10 c. red** .. .. .. 20·00 11·00
**8. 10 c. brown** .. .. .. 55·00 5·75
**4. 50 c. blue** .. .. .. 70·00 11·00

**Nos. 2, 3 and 4 have face values expressed in centimos de peseta and the remainder are in centavos de peso.**

**1884.** Nos. 5, 6 and 7 surch as T **3**.
9 X 50 c. on 1 c. green .. 75·00 21·00
10 50 c. on 2 c. red .. .. 22·00 6·50
11 50 c. on 5 c. lilac .. 85·00 26·00

**1893.** On plain paper.
12 **3** 50 c. on blue .. .. 10·00 9·00

**1894.** "Baby" key-type inscr "FERNANDO POO".
13 Y ⅛ c. grey .. .. 18·00 3·25
14 2 c. red .. .. .. 13·00 2·50
15 5 c. green .. .. 13·00 2·50
16 6 c. purple .. .. 11·50 3·25
18 10 c. red .. .. 42·00 10·00
19 10 c. brown .. .. 8·75 2·50
20 12½ c. brown .. .. 9·75 3·25
21 20 c. blue .. .. 9·75 3·25
22 25 c. red .. .. 18·00 3·25

**1896.** Nos. 13 etc surch **HABILITADO 5 C. DE PESO** in circle.
23 Y 5 c. on ⅛ c. grey .. 65·00 13·00
24 5 c. on 2 c. red .. .. 32·00 8·00
25 5 c. on 6 c. purple .. £100 21·00
26a 5 c. on 10 c. brown .. 42·00 12·50
28 5 c. on 12½ c. brown .. 25·00 6·50
29 5 c. on 20 c. blue .. £100 21·00
30 5 c. on 25 c. red .. £100 17·00

7.

**1896.** Fiscal stamps optd or surch **HABILITADO —PARA— CORREOS** (Nos. 60/1) or **CORREOS 5 CENTAVOS** (59).
59 **7** 5 c. on 10 c. red .. .. 20·00 13·00
60 10 c. red .. .. .. 20·00 12·00
61 15 c. 10 c. green .. .. 20·00 13·00

**1897.** Nos. 13 etc surch **5 Cen.** in circle.
31 Y 5 c. on ⅛ c. grey .. 19·00 6·00
32 5 c. on 2 c. red .. .. 19·00 6·00
33a 5 c. on 5 c. green .. 90·00 19·00
34c 5 c. on 6 c. purple .. 14·00 11·50
35 5 c. on 10 c. brown .. £110 23·00
36 5 c. on 10 c. red .. £250 55·00
38 5 c. on 12½ c. brown .. 42·00 5·00
39a 5 c. on 20 c. blue .. 23·00 8·50
40 5 c. on 25 c. red .. 25·00 9·25

**1898.** Nos. 13 etc surch as T **3**.
41 Y 50 c. on ⅛ c. grey .. £180 38·00
42 50 c. on 2 c. red .. 50·00 9·50
43 50 c. on 5 c. green .. £130 28·00
44 50 c. on 10 c. brown .. £120 28·00
45a 50 c. on 10 c. red .. £130 28·00
47 50 c. on 12½ c. brown .. £100 17·00
48 50 c. on 25 c. red .. £120 24·00

10.

**1899.** Fiscal stamps variously optd. (a) Surch **FERNANDO POO 1899 Habilitado para Corrreos** and new value.

62 **10** 10 c. on 25 c. green .. 55·00 38·00
63 15 c. on 25 c. green .. 85·00 55·00

(b) Optd or surch **CORREOS**

65 **10** 15 c. on 25 c. green .. £1600 £1000
64 25 c. green .. .. £350 £170

**1899.** "Curly Head" key-type inscr "FERNANDO POO 1899".

66 Z 1 m. brown .. .. 1·50 55
67 2 m. brown .. .. 1·50 55
68 3 m. brown .. .. 1·50 55
69 4 m. brown .. .. 1·50 55
70 5 m. brown .. .. 1·50 55
71 1 c. purple .. .. 1·50 55
72 2 c. green .. .. 1·50 55
73 3 c. brown .. .. 1·50 55
74 4 c. orange .. .. 9·25 1·40
75 5 c. red .. .. .. 1·50 55
76 6 c. blue .. .. 1·50 55
77 8 c. brown .. .. 5·50 55
78 10 c. red .. .. 3·50 55
79 15 c. grey .. .. 3·50 55
80 20 c. purple .. .. 9·75 1·40
81 40 c. lilac .. .. 65·00 23·00
82 60 c. black .. .. 65·00 23·00
83 80 c. brown .. .. 65·00 23·00
84 1 p. green .. .. £225 £110
85 2 p. blue .. .. £225 £110

**1900.** No. 80 surch **HABILITADO 5 C. DE PESO**.

86 Z 5 c. on 20 c. purple .. £225 15·00

**1900.** No. 80 surch **5 Cen.** in circle.

87 Z 5 c. on 20 c. purple .. 7·50 4·00

**1900.** No. 80 surch with T **3**.

88 Z 50 c. on 20 c. purple .. 9·00 4·00

**1900. " Curly Head " key-type inscr. "FERNANDO POO 1900".**

91. Z. 1 m. black .. .. 2·40 60
92. 2 m. black .. .. 2·40 60
93. 3 m. black .. .. 2·40 60
94. 4 m. black .. .. 2·40 60
95. 5 m. black .. .. 2·40 60
96. 1 c. green .. .. 2·40 60
97. 2 c. lilac .. .. .. 2·40 60
98. 3 c. pink .. .. 2·40 60
99. 4 c. brown .. .. 2·40 60
100. 5 c. blue .. .. .. 2·40 60
101. 6 c. orange .. .. 2·40 2·40
102. 8 c. green .. .. 2·40 2·40
103. 10 c. red .. .. 2·40 60
104. 15 c. purple .. .. 2·40 60
105. 20 c. brown .. .. 2·40 60
106. 40 c. brown .. .. 6·00 2·50
107. 60 c. green .. .. 12·50 2·50
108. 80 c. blue .. .. 12·50 4·25
109. 1 p. brown .. .. 70·00 32·00
110. 2 p. orange .. .. £120 65·00

**1900.** Fiscal stamps as T **7** but dated 1900 optd or surch. (a) **CORREOS** and **5 Cen.** in circle

111 **7** 5 c. on 10 c. blue .. 55·00 24·00

(b) **CORREOS CORREOS** and **5 Cen.** in circle

113 **7** 5 c. on 10 c. blue .. £130 85·00

(c) **CORREOS**

114a **7** 10 c. blue .. .. 30·00 8·00

**1900.** Fiscal stamp as T **7** but dated 1900 surch **CORREOS 5 CENTAVOS**.

115 **7** 5 c. on 10 c. blue .. £550 £375

**1900.** Nos. 74 and 105 surch with T **3**.

116a Z 50 c. on 4 c. orange .. 12·00 6·00
117 50 c. on 20 c. brown .. 9·00 3·50

14a.

**1900.** Fiscal stamp surch. (a) **CORREOS** and **5 Cen.** in circle

118 **14a** 5 c. on 25 c. brown .. £600 £350

(b) **CORREOS HABILITADO 5 C. DE PESO**

119 **14a** 5 c. on 25 c. brown .. £600 £350

**1901.** "Curly Head" key-type inscr "FERNANDO POO 1901".

124 Z 1 c. black .. .. 1·60 95
125 2 c. brown .. .. 1·60 95
126 3 c. purple .. .. 1·60 95
127 4 c. lilac .. .. 1·60 95
128 5 c. red .. .. .. 1·00 95
129 10 c. brown .. .. 1·00 95
130 25 c. blue .. .. 1·00 95
131 50 c. purple .. .. 1·60 95
132 75 c. brown .. .. 1·25 95
133 1 p. green .. .. 35·00 7·50
134 2 p. brown .. .. 22·00 12·00
135 3 p. green .. .. 22·00 16·00
136 4 p. red .. .. .. 22·00 16·00
137 5 p. green .. .. 27·00 16·00
138 10 p. orange .. .. 60·00 45·00

**1902.** "Curly Head" key-type inscr "FERNANDO POO 1902". With control figures on back.

140 Z 5 c. green .. .. 1·40 25
141 10 c. grey .. .. 1·40 25
142 25 c. red .. .. 3·50 70
143 50 c. brown .. .. 8·00 2·75
144 75 c. lilac .. .. 8·00 2·75
145 1 p. red .. .. .. 10·00 4·00
146 2 p. green .. .. 21·00 10·00
147 5 p. red .. .. .. 30·00 23·00

**1903.** "Curly Head" key-type inscr "FERNANDO POO PARA 1903". With control figures on back.

154 Z ¼ c. purple .. .. 20 20
155 ½ c. black .. .. 20 20
156 1 c. red .. .. .. 20 20
157 2 c. green .. .. 20 20
158 3 c. green .. .. 20 20
159 4 c. lilac .. .. 20 20
160 5 c. red .. .. .. 30 20
161 10 c. orange .. .. 35 30
162 15 c. green .. .. 1·50 1·00
163 25 c. brown .. .. 1·60 1·60
164 50 c. brown .. .. 2·50 2·75
165 75 c. red .. .. 9·75 5·25
166 1 p. brown .. .. 14·00 7·50
167 2 p. green .. .. 19·00 11·50
168 3 p. purple .. .. 19·00 11·50
169 4 p. blue .. .. 23·00 20·00
170 5 p. blue .. .. 32·00 24·00
171 10 p. orange .. .. 70·00 35·00

**1905.** "Curly Head" key-type inscr "FERNANDO POO PARA 1905". With control figures on back.

172 Z 1 c. purple .. .. 25 25
173 2 c. black .. .. 25 25
174 3 c. red .. .. .. 25 25
175 4 c. green .. .. 25 25
176 5 c. green .. .. 30 25
177 10 c. lilac .. .. 1·00 50
178 15 c. red .. .. 1·00 50
179 25 c. orange .. .. 8·50 1·75
180 50 c. green .. .. 6·00 2·50
181 75 c. brown .. .. 7·50 7·50
182 1 p. brown .. .. 8·50 7·50
183 2 p. red .. .. 15·00 11·00
184 3 p. brown .. .. 23·00 12·50
185 4 p. green .. .. 27·00 17·00
186 5 p. red .. .. .. 42·00 26·00
187 10 p. blue .. .. 65·00 38·00

17. King Alfonso XIII.

24. Woman at Prayer.

**1907.** With control figures on back.

188 **17** 1 c. black .. .. 15 15
189 2 c. pink .. .. 15 15
190 3 c. purple .. .. 15 15
191 4 c. black .. .. 15 15
192 5 c. buff .. .. 15 15
193 10 c. purple .. .. 90 50
194 15 c. black .. .. 25 15
195 25 c. brown .. .. 14·50 11·00
196 50 c. green .. .. 15 15
197 75 c. red .. .. 20 15
198 1 p. blue .. .. 1·50 55
199 2 p. brown .. .. 6·00 4·50
200 3 p. pink .. .. 6·00 4·50
201 4 p. lilac .. .. 6·00 4·50
202 5 p. brown .. .. 6·00 4·50
203 10 p. brown .. .. 6·00 4·50

**1908.** Surch **HABILITADO PARA 05 CTMS.**

204 **17** 05 c. on 10 c. purple .. 3·00 2·00

**1929.** Seville and Barcelona Exhibition stamps of Spain (Nos. 504, etc.) optd. **FERNANDO POO.**

209. 5 c. red .. .. .. 20 20
210. 10 c. green .. .. 20 20
211. 15 c. blue .. .. 25 25
212. 20 c. violet .. .. 20 20
213. 25 c. red .. .. 25 25
214. 30 c. brown .. .. 20 20
215. 40 c. blue .. .. .. 55 55
216. 50 c. orange .. .. 1·10 1·10
217. 1 p. grey .. .. .. 4·25 4·25
218. 4 p. red .. .. .. 22·00 22·00
219. 10 p. brown .. .. 27·00 27·00

**1960.**

220. **24.** 25 c. grey .... .. 10 10
221. 50 c. drab .. .. 10 10
222. 75 c. brown .. .. 10 10
223. 1 p. red .. .. .. 10 10
224. 1 p. 50 turquoise .. 10 10
225. 2 p. purple .. .. 10 10
226. 3 p. blue .. .. .. 2·00 70
227. 5 p. brown .. .. 15 10
228. 10 p. olive .. .. 30 10

25. De Falla (composer).

**1960.** Child Welfare.

229 **25** 10 c.+5 c. purple .. 10 10
230 – 15 c.+5 c. brown .. 10 10
231 – 35 c. green .. .. 10 10
232 **25** 80 c. green .. .. 10 10

Designs—vert. (De Falla's ballets): 15 c. Spanish dancer ("Love, the Magician"). 35 c. Tricorne, stick and windmill ("Three-cornered Hat").

26. Sperm Whale.

27. "The Blessing".

**1960.** Stamp Day.

233 **26** 10 c.+5 c. red .. .. 10 10
234 – 20 c.+5 c. green .. 10 10
235 **26** 30 c.+10 c. brown .. 10 10
236 – 50 c.+20 c. brown .. 30 10

Design: 20, 50 c. Natives harpooning humpback whale.

**1961.** Child Welfare. Inscr. "PRO-INFANCIA 1961".

237. **27.** 10 c.+5 c. lake .. 10 10
238. – 25 c.+10 c. violet .. 10 10
239. **27.** 80 c.+20 c. green .. 10 10

**Design**: 25 c. African kneeling before Cross.

28.

**1961.** 25th Anniv. of Gen. Franco as Head of State.

240. – 25 c. grey .. .. 10 10
241. **28.** 50 c. brown .. .. 10 10
242. – 70 c. green .. .. 10 10
243. **28.** 1 p. orange .. .. 10 10

Designs—vert: 25 c. Map. 70 c. St. Isabel Cathedral.

29. Great Turtle

**1961.** Stamp Day. Inscr. "DIA DEL SELLO 1961".

244. **29.** 10 c.+5 c. red .. 10 10
245. – 25 c.+10 c. plum .. 10 10
246. **29.** 30 c.+10 c. purple .. 10 10
247. – 1 p.+10 c. orange .. 10 10

Design: 25 c., 1 p. Native porters, palm trees and shore.

30. Spanish Freighter " Okume ".

**1962.** Child Welfare. Inscr. "PRO-INFANCIA 1962".

248. **30.** 25 c. violet .. .. 10 10
249. – 50 c. olive .. .. 10 10
250. **30.** 1 p. brown .. .. 20 20

Design: 50 c. Spanish freighter "San Francisco".

31. Postman.

32. Native Shrine.

33. Sister and Child.

**1962.** Stamp Day. Inscr. "DIA DEL SELLO 1962".

251. **31.** 15 c. green .. .. 10 10
252. – 35 c. mauve .. .. 35 25
253. **31.** 1 p. brown .. .. 10 10

Design—horiz. 35 c. Mail transport.

**1963.** Seville Flood Relief

254 **32** 50 c. brown .. .. 10 10
255 1 p. purple .. .. 10 10

**1963.** Child Welfare.

256 – 25 c. purple .. .. 10 10
257 **33** 50 c. green .. .. 10 10
258 – 1 p. red .. .. 10 10

Design—horiz: 25 c., 1 p. Two sisters.

34. Child and Arms.

**1963.** "For Barcelona".

259 **34** 50 c. brown .. .. 10 10
260 1 p. red .. .. 10 10

35. Governor Chacon.

36. Canoe.

**1964.** Stamp Day.

261 **35** 25 c. violet .. .. 15 10
262 – 50 c. brown .. .. 15 10
263 **35** 1 p. red .. .. 15 10

Design—vert: 50 c. Orange blossom.

**1964.** Child Welfare. Inscr. "PRO-INFANCIA 1964".

264. **36.** 25 c. violet .. .. 10 10
265. – 50 c. olive (Pineapple) 10 10
266. **36.** 1 p. purple .. .. 10 10

37. Ring-necked Francolin.

38. " The Three Kings ".

**1964.** Birds.

267 **37** 15 c. brown .. .. 15 10
268 – 25 c. violet .. .. 25 10
269 – 50 c. green .. .. 35 10
270 **37** 70 c. green .. .. 40 10
271 – 1 p. brown .. .. 45 15
272 – 1 p. 50 blue .. .. 55 20
273 **37** 3 p. blue .. .. 1·75 35
274 – 5 p. purple .. .. 4·50 40
275 – 10 p. green .. .. 6·00 1·25

Designs: 25 c., 1, 5 p. Mallard. 50 c., 1 p. 50, 10 p. Great blue turaco.

**1964.** Stamp Day.

276. – 50 c. green .. .. 10 10
277. **38.** 1 p. red .. .. 10 10
278. – 1 p. 50 green .. .. 15 10
279. **38.** 3 p. blue .. .. 1·00 60

DESIGNS—VERT. 50 c., 1 p. 50, King presenting gift to Infant Jesus.

**39.** Native. **40.** "Metopodontus savagei" (stag beetle).

**1965.** 25th Anniv. of End of Spanish Civil War.

280. **39.** 50 c. blue .. .. 10 10
281. – 1 p. red .. .. .. 10 10
282. – 1 p. 50 turquoise .. .. 10 10

DESIGNS: 1 p. "Agriculture" (fruit farming). 1 p. 50, "Education" (child writing).

**1965.** Child Welfare. Insects.

283 – 50 c. green .. .. 10 10
284 **40** 1 p. red .. .. 15 10
285 – 1 p. 50 blue .. .. 15 10

DESIGN—VERT: 50 c., 1 p. 50, "Plectrocnemia cruciata" (squashbug).

**41.** Pole Vaulting.

**1965.** Stamp Day.

286. **41.** 50 c. green .. .. 10 10
287. – 1 p. brown .. .. 10 10
288. **41.** 1 p. 50 blue .. .. 10 10

DESIGN—VERT. 1 p. Arms of Fernando Poo.

**42.** European and African Women.

**1966.** Child Welfare.

289 **42** 50 c. green .. .. 10 10
290 1 p. red .. .. 10 10
291 – 1 p. 50 blue .. .. 10 10

DESIGN—VERT. 1 p. 50, St. Isabel of Hungary.

**43.** Greater White-nosed Monkey. **44.** Flowers.

**1966.** Stamp Day.

292. **43.** 10 c. blue and yellow .. 10 10
293. – 40 c. blue and brown .. 10 10
294. **43.** 1 p. 50 olive and brown 10 10
295. – 4 p. brown and green .. 20 10

DESIGN—VERT. 40 c., 4. p. Moustached Monkey.

**1967.** Child Welfare and similar floral design.

296. **44.** 10 c. red and green .. 10 10
297. – 40 c. brown and orange 10 10
298. **44.** 1 p. 50 purple & brown 10 10
299. – 4 p. blue and green .. 15 10

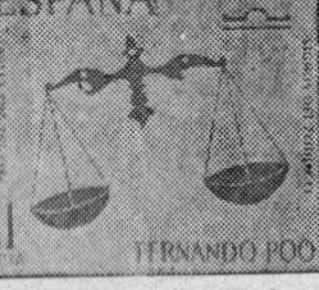


**45.** African Linsang. **47.** Libra (scales).

**46.** Arms of San Carlos and Stamp of 1868.

**1967.** Stamp Day.

300. **45.** 1 p. black and bistre .. 10 10
301. – 1 p. 50 brown and olive 10 10
302. – 3 p. 50 purple & green 15 15

DESIGNS—VERT. 1 p. 50, Western needle-clawed bush-baby. HORIZ. 3 p. 50, Lord Derby's flying squirrel.

**1968.** Stamp Centenary.

303 **46** 1 p. brown and purple 10 10
304 – 1 p. 50 brown and blue 10 10
305 – 2 p. 50 chestnut & brn 15 10

DESIGNS—Each with stamp of 1868: 1 p. 50, Arms of Santa Isabel. 2 p. 50, Arms of Fernando Poo.

**1968.** Child Welfare. Signs of the Zodiac.

306. **47.** 1 p. mauve on yellow .. 10 10
307. – 1 p. 50 brown on pink .. 10 10
308. – 2 p. 50 violet on yellow 15 10

DESIGNS: 1 p. 50, Lion (Leo). 2 p. 50, Water-carrier (Aquarius).

For later issues see **EQUATORIAL GUINEA.**

## FEZZAN Pt. 6

A desert territory in N. Africa taken from Turkey by Italy and captured by French forces in 1943. Algerian stamps used from April 1944, until 1946, and then under French control until the end of 1951 when it was incorporated in the independent kingdom of Libya.

100 centimes = 1 franc.

### (a) Issues for Fezzan and Ghadames

**1943.** Optd **FEZZAN Occupation Francaise** or surch in addition.

(a) Postage.

No. 247 of Italy optd.

1 **103** 50 c. violet .. .. 35·00 35·00

Stamps of Libya surch.

2 **4** 0 f. 50 on 5 c. grn & blk 95·00 95·00
3 **5** 1 f. on 10 c. pink & blk £140 £130
4 **6** 2 f. on 30 c. brown & blk £250 £225
5 **9** 3 f. on 20 c. green .. 55·00 48·00
6 **5** 3 f. 50 on 25 c. blue and deep blue .. .. 70·00 55·00
7 **6** 5 f. on 50 c. green & blk 13·50 14·00
8 10 f. on 1 l. 25 blue and indigo .. .. £750 £650
9 **9** 20 f. on 1 l. 75 orange .. £2750 £2750
10 **7** 50 f. on 75 c. red & pur £3250 £3000

(b) Air.

No. 271 of Italy optd.

11. **10.** 50 c. brown .. .. 55·00 55·00

No. 72 of Libya surch.

12. **18.** 7 f. 50 on 50 c. red .. 60·00 60·00

**1943.** Handstamped locally. (a) Postage.

No. 247 of Italy handstamped **R.F. O, 50 FEZZAN** around circle and within dotted circle.

13. **103.** 0 f. 50 on 50 c. violet .. — £250

No. 27 of Libya handstamped **R.F. 1 Fr FEZZAN** in two lines.

14 **5** 1 f. on 25 c. blue & dp blue — £210

(b) Air.

No. 271 of Italy handstamped as No. 13.

15. **110.** 0 f. 50 on 50 c. brown — £625

**1943.** Parcel Post stamps of Libya handstamped across each half as No. 14.

16 **P 53** 1 f. on 5 c. brown .. £475 £190
17 **P 92** 1 f. on 10 c. blue .. £475 £190
18 1 f. on 50 c. orange .. £475 £190
19 1 f. on 1 l. violet .. £475 £190
20 1 f. on 2 l. green .. — £800
21 1 f. on 3 l. bistre .. — £1250
22 1 f. on 4 l. black .. — £800

The prices are for each half of the Parcel Post stamps.

**4.** Fort of Sebha.

**6.** Map and Fort of Sebha.

**1946.**

23. **4.** 10 c. black .. .. 25 40
24. 50 c. red .. .. .. 25 40
25. 1 f. brown .. .. .. 25 40
26. 1 f. 50 green .. .. 25 40
27. 2 f. blue .. .. .. 30 60
28. – 2 f. 50 violet .. .. 40 75
29. – 3 f. red .. .. .. 40 75
30. – 5 f. brown .. .. .. 60 90
31. – 6 f. green .. .. .. 60 80
32. – 10 f. blue .. .. .. 60 80
33. **6.** 15 f. violet .. .. 70 1·00
34. 20 f. red .. .. .. 1·00 1·50
35. 25 f. brown .. .. 1·00 1·50
36. 40 f. green .. .. 1·25 1·75
37. 50 f. blue .. .. .. 1·25 1·75

DESIGN—36 × 21½ mm: 2 f. 50 to 10 f. Turkish fort and mosque at Murzuk.

### (b) Issues for Fezzan only

**7.** Douglas C-47B Skytrain at Fezzan Airfield.

**1948.** Air.

38. **7.** 100 f. red .. .. 3·00 4·75
39. – 200 f. blue .. .. 5·00 7·00

DESIGN—VERT. 200 f. Airplane over Fezzan.

**9.** Djerma. **10.** Well at Gorda.

**1949.**

40. **9.** 1 f. black .. .. .. 50 75
41. 2 f. pink .. .. .. 50 75
42. – 4 f. brown .. .. .. 1·25 1·50
43. – 5 f. green .. .. .. 1·25 1·50
44. **10.** 8 f. blue .. .. .. 1·00 1·40
45. 10 f. brown .. .. 2·00 2·25
46. 12 f. green .. .. 2·75 4·00
47. – 15 f. red .. .. .. 3·00 4·50
48. – 20 f. black .. .. 2·00 2·50
49. – 25 f. blue .. .. .. 2·75 3·00
50. – 50 f. red .. .. .. 4·00 4·50

DESIGNS—HORIZ. 4 f., 5 f. Beni Khettab tombs. 15 f., 20 f. Col. Colonna d'Ornano and fort. 25 f., 50 f. Gen. Leclerc and map of Europe and N. Africa.

**11.** "Charity". **12.** Mother and Child.

**1950.** Charity.

51. **11.** 15 f. + 5 f. lake .. .. 1·75 1·90
52. **12.** 25 f. + 5 f. blue .. .. 1·75 1·90

**14.** Camel Breeding. **15.** Ahmed Bey.

**1951.**

59 **14** 30 c. brown (postage) .. 70 70
60 1 f. blue .. .. 70 90
61 2 f. red .. .. 70 90
62 – 4 f. red .. .. 70 90
63 – 5 f. green .. .. 85 1·00
64 – 8 f. blue .. .. 80 1·00
65 – 10 f. brown .. .. 2·75 3·25
66 – 12 f. green .. .. 3·00 3·50
67 – 15 f. red .. .. 3·50 4·00
68 **15** 20 f. brown .. .. 3·50 4·00
69 25 f. blue and deep blue 4·25 5·00
70 50 f. brown and blue .. 4·00 5·00
71 – 100 f. blue (air) .. .. 6·25 7·25
72 – 200 f. red .. .. 7·75 9·00

DESIGNS—HORIZ. 4 f. to 8 f. Arab hoeing. 100 f. Brak Oasis. 200 f. Sebha Fort. VERT. 10 f. to 15 f. Artesian well.

POSTAGE DUE STAMPS

**1943.** Postage Due stamps of Libya optd. **FEZZAN Occupation Francaise** or surch. in addition with bars obliterating old inscr. and values.

D 13. **D141.** 0 f. 50 on 5 c. brown .. £750 £675
D 14. 1 f. on 10 c. blue .. £750 £675
D 15. 2 f. on 25 c. green .. £750 £675
D 16. 3 f. on 50 c. violet .. £750 £675
D 17. **D142.** 5 f. on 1 l. orange .. £6000 £5500

**D 13.** Brak Oasis.

**1950.**

D 53. **D13.** 1 f. black .. .. 65 85
D 54. 2 f. green .. .. 65 85
D 55. 3 f. lake .. .. 90 1·00
D 56. 5 f. violet .. .. 1·00 1·25
D 57. 10 f. red .. .. 2·25 2·50
D 58. 20 f. blue .. .. 3·50 4·00

## FIJI BC

An island group in the S. Pacific. A member of the Commonwealth until September 1987. Earlier issues are listed in vol 3.

100 cents = 1 dollar.

**211.** The Nativity.

**1987.** Christmas. Multicoloured.

766. 8 c. Type **211** .. .. 30 10
767. 40 c. The Shepherds (horiz.) .. .. .. 1·00 40
768. 50 c. The Three Kings (horiz.) .. .. .. 1·10 90
769. $1 The Three Kings presenting gifts .. .. 1·75 2·00

**212** Windsurfer and Beach

**1988.** "Expo '88" World Fair, Brisbane.

770 **212** 30 c. multicoloured .. 70 50

**213** Woman using Fiji "Nouna" (stove)

**1988.** Centenary of International Council of Women.

771 **213** 45 c. multicoloured .. 90 60

**214** Pottery Bowl

**1988.** Ancient Fijian Pottery. Multicoloured.
772 9 c. Type **214** .. .. 15 10
773 23 c. Cooking pot .. 25 25
774 58 c. Priest's drinking vessel .. .. 50 80
775 63 c. Drinking vessel .. 55 90
776 69 c. Earthenware oil lamp 60 95
777 75 c. Cooking pot with relief pattern (vert) .. 70 1·10

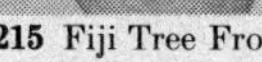

**215** Fiji Tree Frog **216** "Dendrobium mohlianum"

**1988.** Fiji Tree Frog. Multicoloured.
778 18 c. Type **215** .. .. 70 35
779 23 c. Frog climbing grass stalks .. .. .. 85 75
780 30 c. On leaf .. .. 1·00 1·50
781 45 c. Moving from one leaf to another .. .. 1·40 2·50

**1988.** Native Flowers. Multicoloured.
782 9 c. Type **216** .. .. 35 15
783 30 c. "Dendrobium cattilare" .. .. 60 45
784 45 c. "Degeneria vitiensis" 70 60
785 $1 "Degeneria roseiflora" 1·25 1·75

**217** Battle of Solferino, 1859

**1989.** 125th Anniv of International Red Cross.
786 **217** 58 c. multicoloured .. 80 80
787 – 63 c. multicoloured .. 90 90
788 – 69 c. multicoloured .. 1·10 1·00
789 – $1 black and red .. 1·40 1·40
DESIGNS—VERT. 63 c. Henri Dunant (founder); $1 Anniversary logo. HORIZ. 69 c. Fijian Red Cross worker with blood donor.

**218** Plan of "Bounty's" Launch

**1989.** Bicentenary of Captain Bligh's Boat Voyage. Multicoloured.
790 45 c. Type **218** .. .. 1·00 50
791 58 c. Cup, bowl and Bligh's journal .. .. 1·10 1·10
792 80 c. Bligh and extract from journal .. .. 1·60 2·50
793 $1 "Bounty's" launch and map of Fiji .. .. 2·25 2·75

**219** "Platygyra daedalea"

**1989.** Corals. Multicoloured.
794 46 c. Type **219** .. .. 1·25 75
795 60 c. "Caulastrea furcata" 1·60 1·75
796 75 c. "Acropora echinata" (vert) .. .. .. 1·90 2·25
797 90 c. "Acropora humilis" (vert) .. .. .. 2·25 2·75

**220** Goalkeeper

**1989.** World Cup Football Championship, Italy (1990). Multicoloured.
798 35 c. Type **220** .. .. 75 40
799 63 c. Goalkeeper catching ball .. .. .. 1·25 1·50
800 70 c. Player with ball .. 1·40 1·60
801 85 c. Tackling .. .. 1·60 2·25

**221** Congregation in Church

**1989.** Christmas. Multicoloured.
802 9 c. Type **221** .. .. 25 10
803 45 c. "Delonix regia" (Christmas tree) .. 75 35
804 $1 The Nativity .. .. 1·50 1·75
805 $1.40 Fijian children under tree .. .. .. 1·75 2·75

**222** Mangrove Jack

**1990.** Freshwater Fishes. Multicoloured.
806 50 c. Type **222** .. .. 1·50 70
807 70 c. Orange-spotted therapon perch .. 2·00 2·00
808 85 c. Spotted scat .. 2·25 2·25
809 $1 Flagtail .. .. 2·75 3·25

**224** Vertiver Grass Contours **225** "Dacrydium nidulum"

**1990.** Soil Conservation. Multicoloured.
811 50 c. Type **224** .. .. 60 50
812 70 c. Mulching .. .. 80 1·00
813 90 c. Hillside contour cultivation .. .. 1·00 1·50
814 $1 Land use rotation (vert) 1·25 1·75

**1990.** Timber Trees. Multicoloured.
815 25 c. Type **225** .. .. 55 20
816 35 c. "Decussocarpus vitiensis" .. .. 65 30
817 $1 "Agathis vitiensis" .. 2·00 2·25
818 $1.55 "Santalum yasi" .. 2·75 3·75

**226** "Hark the Herald Angels sing"

**1990.** Christmas. Carols. Multicoloured.
819 10 c. Type **226** .. .. 25 10
820 35 c. "Still the Night, Holy the Night" .. .. 60 30
821 65 c. "Joy to the World!" 1·00 1·50
822 $1 "The Race that long in Darkness pined" .. 1·75 2·25

**227** Sigatoka Sand Dunes

**1991.** Environmental Protection. Mult.
823 35 c. Type **227** .. .. 75 30
824 50 c. Monu and Monuriki Islands .. .. .. 1·00 80
825 65 c. Ravilevu Nature Reserve, Taveuni .. 1·10 1·60
826 $1 Colo-I-Suva Forest Park 1·75 2·50

**228** H.M.S. "Pandora" (frigate)

**1991.** Bicentenary of Discovery of Rotuma Island. Multicoloured.
827 54 c. Type **228** .. .. 1·50 85
828 70 c. Map of Rotuma .. 1·60 2·00
829 75 c. Natives welcoming H.M.S. "Pandora" .. 1·60 2·00
830 $1 Mount Soloroa and Uea Island .. .. .. 2·50 3·00

**229** "Scylla serrata"

**1991.** Mangrove Crabs. Multicoloured.
831 38 c. Type **229** .. .. 60 35
832 54 c. "Metopograpsus messor" .. .. 85 85
833 96 c. "Parasesarma erythrodactyla" .. 1·50 2·25
834 $1.65 "Cardisoma carnifex" 2·50 3·50

**230** Mary and Joseph travelling to Bethlehem

**1991.** Christmas. Multicoloured.
835 11 c. Type **230** .. .. 25 10
836 75 c. Manger scene .. 1·00 1·25
837 96 c. Presentation in the Temple .. .. 1·25 2·25
838 $1 Infant Jesus with symbols .. .. 1·40 2·25

**231** De Havilland D.H.89 Dragon Rapide of Fiji Airways.

**1991.** 40th Anniv of Air Pacific. Mult.
839 54 c. Type **231** .. .. 1·00 80
840 75 c. Douglas DC-3 .. 1·60 1·75
841 96 c. Aerospatial/Aeritalia ATR 42 .. .. 1·75 2·25
842 $1.40 Boeing 767 .. .. 2·00 2·75

**232** Ethnic Dancers

**1992.** "Expo 92" World's Fair, Seville, Spain. Multicoloured.
843 27 c. Type **232** .. .. 55 35
844 75 c. Peoples of Fiji .. 1·25 1·40
845 96 c. Gold bars and sugar cane train .. .. 2·50 2·75
846 $1.40 "Queen Elizabeth 2" (cruise liner) at Suva .. 2·75 3·75

**233** "Tabusoro"

**1992.** Inter-Islands Shipping. Multicoloured.
847 38 c. Type **233** .. .. 1·00 55
848 54 c. "Degei II" .. .. 1·50 1·25
849 $1.40 "Dausoko" .. .. 2·50 3·00
850 $1.65 "Nivanga" .. .. 2·75 3·25

**234** Running **235** European War Memorial, Levuka

**1992.** Olympic Games, Barcelona. Mult.
851 20 c. Type **234** .. .. 45 20
852 86 c. Yachting .. .. 1·60 1·75
853 $1.34 Swimming .. .. 2·25 2·50
854 $1.50 Judo .. .. 2·40 2·75

**1992.** Historic Levuka (former capital). Mult.
855 30 c. Type **235** .. .. 30 30
856 42 c. Map of Fiji .. .. 45 55
857 59 c. Beach Street .. 65 90
858 77 c. Sacred Heart Church (vert) .. .. .. 80 1·25
859 $2 Deed of Cession site (vert) .. .. .. 1·75 2·50

**236** The Nativity

**1992.** Christmas. Multicoloured.
860 12 c. Type **236** .. .. 25 10
861 77 c. Shepherds and family giving presents .. 1·10 1·25
862 83 c. Shepherds at manger and giving presents to pensioners .. .. 1·25 1·40
863 $2 Wise Men and collecting Fiji produce .. .. 2·50 3·50

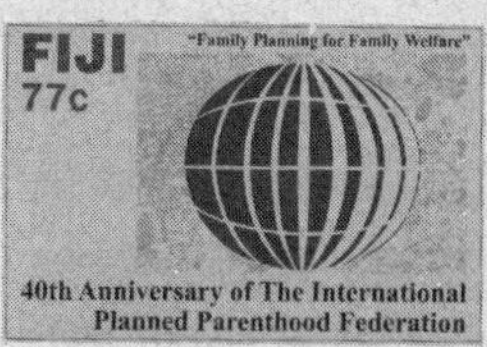


**237** International Planned Parenthood Federation Logo

**1992.** 40th Anniv of International Planned Parenthood Federation. Multicoloured.
864 77 c. Type **237** .. .. 85 85
865 $2 Man weeping and pregnant mother with children .. .. 2·50 3·25

**238** Dove and Peace Corps Emblem

**1993.** 25th Anniv of Peace Corps in Fiji. Mult.
866 59 c. Type **238** .. .. 85 75
867 77 c. Handshake .. .. 1·10 1·40
868 $1 Educational symbols .. 1·50 1·75
869 $2 Symbols of home businesses scheme .. 2·25 3·25

**239** Fijian Players performing Cibi (traditional dance)

**1993.** Hong Kong Rugby Sevens Competition. Multicoloured.

| | | | |
|---|---|---|---|
| 870 | 77 c. Type **239** | 1·10 | 1·25 |
| 871 | $1.06 Players and map of Pacific | 1·50 | 2·25 |
| 872 | $2 Scrum and stadium | 2·50 | 3·00 |

**239a** Gloster Gauntlet II

**1993.** 75th Anniv of Royal Air Force. Mult.

| | | | |
|---|---|---|---|
| 873 | 59 c. Type **239a** | 90 | 75 |
| 874 | 77 c. Armstrong Whitworth Whitley Mk V | 1·10 | 1·25 |
| 875 | 83 c. Bristol F2B "Brisfit" | 1·25 | 1·40 |
| 876 | $2 Hawker Tempest Mk V | 1·90 | 2·75 |

**240** "Chromodoris fidelis"

**1993.** Nudibranchs. Multicoloured.

| | | | |
|---|---|---|---|
| 878 | 12 c. Type **240** | 35 | 10 |
| 879 | 42 c. "Halgerda carlsoni" | 80 | 55 |
| 880 | 53 c. "Chromodoris lochi" | 1·00 | 90 |
| 881 | 83 c. Blue sea lizard | 1·10 | 1·75 |
| 882 | $1 "Phyllidia bourguini" | 1·75 | 2·00 |
| 883 | $2 Spanish dancer | 2·75 | 3·25 |

**241** Mango

**1993.** Tropical Fruits. Multicoloured.

| | | | |
|---|---|---|---|
| 884 | 30 c. Type **241** | 65 | 45 |
| 885 | 42 c. Guava | 85 | 55 |
| 886 | $1 Lemon | 1·75 | 1·75 |
| 887 | $2 Soursop | 3·00 | 3·50 |

**243** The Last Supper

**1994.** Easter. Multicoloured.

| | | | |
|---|---|---|---|
| 890 | 59 c. Type **243** | 70 | 60 |
| 891 | 77 c. The Crucifixion (vert) | 90 | 1·10 |
| 892 | $1 The Resurrection | 1·40 | 1·75 |
| 893 | $2 Examining Christ's wounds (vert) | 2·50 | 3·50 |

## MINIMUM PRICE

The minimum price quoted is 10p which represents a handling charge rather than a basis for valuing common stamps. For further notes about prices see introductory pages.

**244** Sagati

**247** Father Ioane Batita

**1994.** Edible Seaweeds. Multicoloured.

| | | | |
|---|---|---|---|
| 894 | 42 c. Type **244** | 55 | 45 |
| 885 | 83 c. Nama | 1·00 | 1·25 |
| 896 | $1 Lumicevata | 1·40 | 1·75 |
| 897 | $2 Lumiwawa | 2·50 | 3·50 |

**1994.** 150th Anniv of Arrival of Catholic Missionaries in Fiji. Multicoloured.

| | | | |
|---|---|---|---|
| 900 | 23 c. Type **247** | 25 | 25 |
| 901 | 31 c. Local catechist | 30 | 30 |
| 902 | 44 c. Sacred Heart Cathedral, Suva | 40 | 60 |
| 903 | 63 c. Lomary Church | 55 | 75 |
| 904 | 81 c. Pope Gregory XVI | 90 | 1·00 |
| 905 | $2 Pope John Paul II | 2·00 | 2·50 |

**247a** Fijian soldiers guarding crashed Japanese Mitsubishi A6M Zero-Sen aircraft

**249** Red-headed Parrot Finch

**1995.** 50th Anniv of End of Second World War. Multicoloured.

| | | | |
|---|---|---|---|
| 907 | 13 c. Type **247a** | 20 | 10 |
| 908 | 63 c. American spotter plane landing on Kameli Airstrip, Solomon Islands | 85 | 90 |
| 909 | 87 c. Corporal Sukanaivalu and Victoria Cross | 1·25 | 1·75 |
| 910 | $1.12 H.M.S. "Fiji" (cruiser) | 1·50 | 2·00 |

**1995.** Birds. Multicoloured.

| | | | |
|---|---|---|---|
| 912 | 1 c. Type **249** | 10 | 10 |
| 913 | 2 c. Golden whistler | 10 | 10 |
| 914 | 3 c. Versicoloured flycatcher ("Ogea Flycatcher") | 10 | 10 |
| 915 | 4 c. Peale's pigeon | 10 | 10 |
| 916 | 6 c. Blue-headed flycatcher ("Blue-crested Broadbill") | 10 | 10 |
| 917 | 13 c. Island thrush | 10 | 10 |
| 918 | 23 c. Many-coloured fruit dove | 20 | 25 |
| 919 | 31 c. Green heron ("Mangrove heron") | 25 | 30 |
| 920 | 44 c. Purple swamphen | 40 | 45 |
| 921 | 63 c. Fiji goshawk | 55 | 60 |
| 922 | 81 c. Kandavu fantail | 70 | 75 |
| 923 | 87 c. Collard lory | 75 | 80 |
| 924 | $1 Scarlet robin | 90 | 95 |
| 925 | $2 Peregrine falcon | 1·75 | 1·90 |
| 926 | $3 Barn owl | 2·75 | 3·00 |
| 927 | $5 Masked shining parrot ("Yellow-breasted musk parrot") | 4·50 | 4·75 |

No. 922 is inscribed "Kadavu" in error.

**251** Pres. Ratu Sir Kamisese Mara, Parliament Building and National Flag

**1995.** 25th Anniv of Independence. Mult.

| | | | |
|---|---|---|---|
| 930 | 81 c. Type **251** | 90 | 1·00 |
| 931 | 87 c. Young citizens of Fiji | 95 | 1·10 |
| 932 | $1.06 Rugby players | 1·25 | 1·60 |
| 933 | $2 Boeing 747 "Island of Viti Levu" | 2·25 | 2·75 |

**252** "Praying Madonna with the Crown of Stars" (workshop of Correggio)

**253** Trolling Lure

**1995.** Christmas. Multicoloured.

| | | | |
|---|---|---|---|
| 934 | 10 c. Type **252** | 15 | 10 |
| 935 | 63 c. "Madonna and Child with Crowns" (on porcelain) | 70 | 75 |
| 936 | 87 c. "The Holy Virgin with Holy Child and St. John" (after Titian) | 95 | 1·10 |
| 937 | $2 "The Holy Family and St. John" (workshop of Rubens) | 2·25 | 3·00 |

**1996.** 50th Anniv of Resettlement of Banabans (inhabitants of Ocean Island) in Fiji. Multicoloured.

| | | | |
|---|---|---|---|
| 938 | 81 c. Type **253** | 90 | 1·00 |
| 939 | 87 c. Banaban fishing canoes | 95 | 1·10 |
| 940 | $1.12 Banaban warrior (vert) | 1·25 | 1·60 |
| 941 | $2 Great frigate bird (vert) | 2·75 | 3·00 |

**254** L2B Portable Tape Recorder

**255** Winged Monster and Ring (bronze), c. 450 B.C.

**1996.** Centenary of Radio. Multicoloured.

| | | | |
|---|---|---|---|
| 942 | 44 c. Type **254** | 55 | 45 |
| 943 | 63 c. Broadcasting House, Fiji | 75 | 60 |
| 944 | 81 c. Communications satellite | 90 | 1·00 |
| 945 | $3 Guglielmo Marconi | 3·50 | 3·75 |

**1996.** "CHINA '96" 9th Asian International Stamp Exhibition, Peking. Multicoloured.

| | | | |
|---|---|---|---|
| 946 | 63 c. Type **255** | 75 | 65 |
| 947 | 81 c. Archer (terracotta sculpture), 210 B.C. | 90 | 1·00 |
| 948 | $1 Dragon plate, 1426–35 | 1·25 | 1·40 |
| 949 | $2 Central Asian horseman (sculpture), 706 | 2·75 | 3·00 |

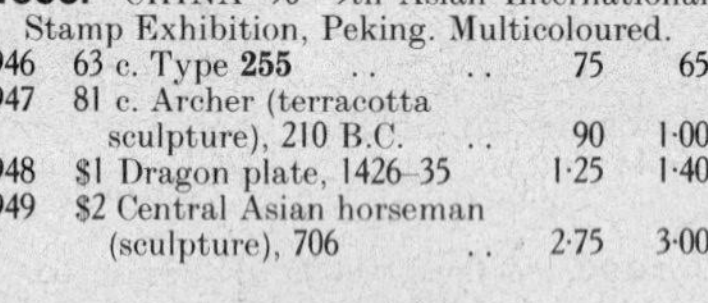

**256** Hurdling

**1996.** Cent of Modern Olympic Games. Mult.

| | | | |
|---|---|---|---|
| 951 | 31 c. Type **256** | 25 | 30 |
| 952 | 63 c. Judo | 55 | 60 |
| 953 | 87 c. Sailboarding | 80 | 85 |
| 954 | $1.12 Swimming | 1·00 | 1·10 |

**257** Computerised Telephone Exchange

**1996.** Innauguration of Independent Postal and Telecommunications Companies. Mult.

| | | | |
|---|---|---|---|
| 956 | 31 c. Type **257** | 35 | 30 |
| 957 | 44 c. Unloading mail from aircraft | 60 | 55 |
| 958 | 81 c. Manual telephone exchange (vert) | 90 | 1·00 |
| 959 | $1 Postman on motorbike (vert) | 1·25 | 1·40 |

**258** "Our Children Our Future"

**1996.** 50th Anniv of U.N.I.C.E.F. Children's Paintings. Multicoloured.

| | | | |
|---|---|---|---|
| 961 | 81 c. Type **258** | 80 | 75 |
| 962 | 87 c. "Village Scene" | 90 | 95 |
| 963 | $1 "Living in Harmony the World over" | 1·10 | 1·25 |
| 964 | $2 "Their Future" | 2·10 | 2·40 |

**259** First Seaplane in Fiji, 1921

**1996.** 50th Anniv of Nadi International Airport. Multicoloured.

| | | | |
|---|---|---|---|
| 965 | 31 c. Type **259** | 40 | 30 |
| 966 | 44 c. Nadi Airport in 1946 | 60 | 50 |
| 967 | 63 c. Arrival of first jet airliner, 1959 | 80 | 75 |
| 968 | 87 c. Airport entrance | 1·10 | 1·10 |
| 969 | $1 Control tower | 1·40 | 1·50 |
| 970 | $2 Diagram of Global Positioning System | 2·25 | 2·50 |

**260** The Annunciation and Fijian beating Lali (drum)

**1996.** Christmas. Multicoloured.

| | | | |
|---|---|---|---|
| 971 | 13 c. Type **260** | 20 | 15 |
| 972 | 81 c. Shepherds with sheep, and canoe | 90 | 75 |
| 973 | $1 Wise men on camels, and people on cross | 1·25 | 1·25 |
| 974 | $3 The Nativity, and Fijian blowing conch | 3·25 | 3·50 |

## FINLAND Pt. 11

A country to the east of Scandinavia. A Russian Grand-Duchy until 1917, then a Republic.

1856. 100 kopeks = 1 rouble.
1865. 100 pennia = 1 markka.

1.

2.

**1856.** Imperf.

| | | | | |
|---|---|---|---|---|
| 4 | 1 | 5 k. blue | £5000 | £1500 |
| 2 | | 10 k. pink | £7000 | £425 |

Used prices are for stamps with penmark cancellation only. Stamps with postmark as well are worth more.

**1860.** Values in "KOP". Roul.

| | | | | |
|---|---|---|---|---|
| 11 | 2 | 5 k. blue on blue | £600 | £150 |
| 13 | | 10 k. pink on pink | £425 | 48·00 |

**1866.** As T **2**, but values in "PEN" and "MARK". Roul.

| | | | | |
|---|---|---|---|---|
| 54 | 2 | 5 p. brown on grey | £250 | £130 |
| 46 | | 8 p. black on green | £225 | £140 |
| 30 | | 10 p. black on buff | £425 | £140 |
| 38 | | 20 p. blue on blue | £400 | 48·00 |
| 42 | | 40 p. pink on lilac | £375 | 60·00 |
| 49 | | 1 m. brown | £1200 | £700 |

5.

6.

**1875.** Perf.

| | | | | |
|---|---|---|---|---|
| 81 | 5 | 2 p. grey | 9·75 | 12·00 |
| 82 | | 5 p. yellow | 48·00 | 4·75 |
| 83 | | 5 p. red | 55·00 | 8·25 |
| 97 | | 5 p. green | 14·50 | 30 |
| 71 | | 8 p. green | £180 | 48·00 |
| 85 | | 10 p. brown | 95·00 | 14·50 |
| 99 | | 10 p. pink | 20·00 | 2·40 |
| 87 | | 20 p. blue | 45·00 | 1·40 |
| 102 | | 20 p. orange | 27·00 | 25 |
| 89 | | 25 p. red | 35·00 | 7·25 |
| 103 | | 25 p. blue | 48·00 | 2·40 |
| 79 | | 32 p. red | £325 | 29·00 |
| 90 | | 1 m. mauve | £300 | 35·00 |
| 105 | | 1 m. grey and pink | 27·00 | 17·00 |
| 106 | | 5 m. green and pink | £350 | £275 |
| 107 | | 10 m. brown and pink | £500 | £500 |

**1889.**

| | | | | |
|---|---|---|---|---|
| 108 | 6 | 2 p. grey | 30 | 65 |
| 148 | | 5 p. green | 35 | 35 |
| 149 | | 10 p. red | 40 | 35 |
| 150 | | 20 p. yellow | 40 | 10 |
| 151 | | 25 p. blue | 60 | 30 |
| 119 | | 1 m. grey and pink | 3·50 | 3·00 |
| 120a | | 5 m. green and red | 22·00 | 60·00 |
| 122 | | 10 m. brown and red | 32·00 | 80·00 |

7.

8.

9.

10.

11.

**1891.** Similar to Russian types, but with circles added in designs.

| | | | | |
|---|---|---|---|---|
| 133 | 7 | 1 k. yellow | 4·00 | 8·75 |
| 134 | | 2 k. green | 4·75 | 7·25 |
| 135 | | 3 k. pink | 9·75 | 13·00 |
| 136 | 8 | 4 k. pink | 12·00 | 12·00 |
| 137 | 7 | 7 k. blue | 5·00 | 2·00 |
| 138 | 8 | 10 k. blue | 12·00 | 12·50 |
| 139 | 9 | 14 k. red and blue | 17·00 | 19·00 |
| 140 | 8 | 20 k. red and blue | 14·50 | 13·50 |
| 141 | 9 | 35 k. green and purple | 24·00 | 45·00 |
| 142 | 8 | 50 k. green and purple | 26·00 | 29·00 |
| 143 | 10 | 1 r. orange and brown | 70·00 | 80·00 |
| 144 | 11 | 3½ r. grey and black | £275 | £375 |
| 145 | | 7 r. yellow and black | £200 | £250 |

12.

13.

14.

15.

**1901.** Similar to Russian types, but value in Finnish currency.

| | | | | |
|---|---|---|---|---|
| 161. | 12. | 2 p. orange | 35 | 55 |
| 162b. | | 5 p. green | 1·25 | 10 |
| 169a. | 13. | 10 p. red | 30 | 10 |
| 170. | 12. | 20 p. blue | 30 | 10 |
| 165a. | 14. | 1 m. green and purple | 65 | 20 |
| 166. | 15. | 10 m. grey and black | £120 | 40·00 |

16. 17.

18.

**1911.**

| | | | | |
|---|---|---|---|---|
| 176 | 16 | 2 p. orange | 10 | 15 |
| 177 | | 5 p. green | 10 | 10 |
| 180 | 17 | 10 p. red | 15 | 10 |
| 181 | 16 | 20 p. blue | 15 | 10 |
| 182 | 18 | 40 p. blue & purple | 10 | 10 |

19.

20.

23.

**1917.**

| | | | | |
|---|---|---|---|---|
| 187a | 19 | 5 p. green | 10 | 10 |
| 188 | | 5 p. grey | 10 | 10 |
| 189 | | 10 p. red | 10 | 10 |
| 190 | | 10 p. green | 1·25 | 10 |
| 191a | | 10 p. blue | 10 | 10 |
| 192 | | 20 p. orange | 10 | 10 |
| 193 | | 20 p. red | 30 | 10 |
| 194 | | 20 p. brown | 40 | 20 |
| 195 | | 25 p. blue | 20 | 10 |
| 196 | | 25 p. brown | 10 | 10 |
| 234 | | 30 p. green | 10 | 10 |
| 198a | | 40 p. purple | 10 | 10 |
| 246 | | 40 p. green | 10 | 10 |
| 200 | | 50 p. brown | 15 | 10 |
| 201 | | 50 p. blue | 30·00 | 10 |
| 247 | | 50 p. green | 10 | 15 |
| 237 | | 60 p. purple | 10 | 10 |
| 204 | | 75 p. yellow | 20 | 30 |
| 205 | | 1 m. black and pink | 11·00 | 10 |
| 248 | | 1 m. orange | 10 | 10 |
| 207a | | 1½ m. purple and green | 10 | 10 |
| 208 | | 2 m. black and green | 2·25 | 40 |
| 250 | | 2 m. blue | 30 | 20 |
| 251 | | 3 m. black and blue | 30 | 20 |
| 242 | | 5 m. black and purple | 20 | 20 |
| 212 | | 10 m. black and bistre | 55 | 1·00 |
| 213 | | 25 m. orange and red | 70 | 20·00 |

**1918.** With white circle round figure of value.

| | | | | |
|---|---|---|---|---|
| 214 | 20 | 5 p. green | 20 | 30 |
| 215 | | 10 p. pink | 20 | 30 |
| 216 | | 30 p. grey | 60 | 1·40 |
| 217 | | 40 p. lilac | 20 | 30 |
| 218 | | 50 p. brown | 30 | 90 |
| 219 | | 70 p. brown | 1·60 | 12·00 |
| 220 | | 1 m. black and red | 25 | 50 |
| 221 | | 5 m. black and lilac | 35·00 | 70·00 |

**1919.** Surch with new figure of value three times.

| | | | | |
|---|---|---|---|---|
| 222. | 19. | 10 on 5p. green | 20 | 25 |
| 223. | | 20 on 10p. red | 20 | 25 |
| 224. | | 50 on 25 p. blue | 90 | 25 |
| 225. | | 75 on 20 p. orange | 15 | 25 |

**1921.** Surch. with value, **P** and bars.

| | | | | |
|---|---|---|---|---|
| 226. | 19. | 30 p. on 10 p. green | 40 | 15 |
| 227. | | 60 p. on 40 p. purple | 2·75 | 30 |
| 228. | | 90 p. on 20 p. red | 15 | 15 |
| 229. | | 1½ m. on 50 p. blue | 1·00 | 10 |

**1922.** Red Cross.

| | | | | |
|---|---|---|---|---|
| 230. | 23. | 1 m.+50 p. red & grey | 60 | 8·25 |

26.

28. Freighter "Bore" leaving Turku (Abo).

**1927.** 10th Anniv of Independence.

| | | | | |
|---|---|---|---|---|
| 255 | 26 | 1½ m. mauve | 10 | 15 |
| 256 | | 2 m. blue | 20 | 1·25 |

**1928.** Philatelic Exhibition. Optd **Postim. naytt. 1928 Frim. utstalln.**

| | | | | |
|---|---|---|---|---|
| 258. | 19. | 1 m. orange | 5·00 | 16·00 |
| 259. | | 1½ m. purple and green | 5·00 | 16·00 |

**1929.** 700th Anniv. of Abo.

| | | | | |
|---|---|---|---|---|
| 260. | 28. | 1 m. olive | 1·90 | 3·50 |
| 261. | – | 1½ m. brown | 2·00 | 3·00 |
| 262. | – | 2 m. grey | 60 | 3·75 |

DESIGNS—VERT. 1½ m. Cathedral. HORIZ. 2 m. Castle.

31.

32. Olavinlinna.

35.

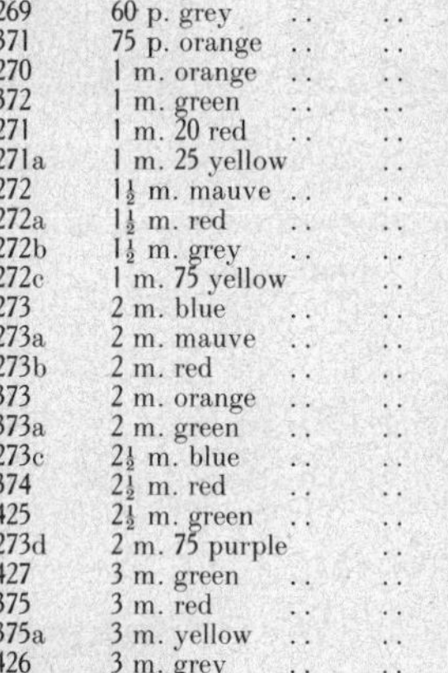

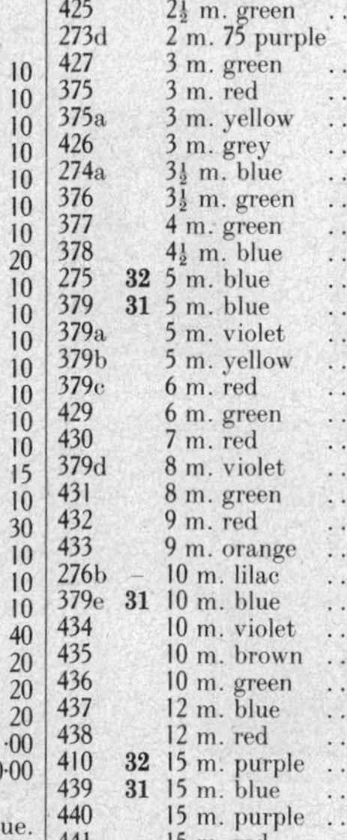

**1930.**

| | | | | |
|---|---|---|---|---|
| 263 | 31 | 5 p. brown | 10 | 10 |
| 264 | | 10 p. lilac | 10 | 10 |
| 265 | | 20 p. green | 20 | 25 |
| 266 | | 25 p. brown | 10 | 10 |
| 267 | | 40 p. green | 1·50 | 10 |
| 268 | | 50 p. yellow | 50 | 15 |
| 268a | | 50 p. green | 10 | 10 |
| 269 | | 60 p. grey | 35 | 30 |
| 371 | | 75 p. orange | 30 | 35 |
| 270 | | 1 m. orange | 30 | 10 |
| 372 | | 1 m. green | 10 | 10 |
| 271 | | 1 m. 20 red | 50 | 40 |
| 271a | | 1 m. 25 yellow | 30 | 10 |
| 272 | | 1½ m. mauve | 1·75 | 10 |
| 272a | | 1½ m. red | 20 | 10 |
| 272b | | 1½ m. grey | 10 | 10 |
| 272c | | 1 m. 75 yellow | 50 | 15 |
| 273 | | 2 m. blue | 30 | 10 |
| 273a | | 2 m. mauve | 4·25 | 10 |
| 273b | | 2 m. red | 30 | 10 |
| 373 | | 2 m. orange | 30 | 10 |
| 373a | | 2 m. green | 20 | 10 |
| 273c | | 2½ m. blue | 2·50 | 10 |
| 374 | | 2½ m. red | 15 | 10 |
| 425 | | 2½ m. green | 40 | 10 |
| 273d | | 2 m. 75 purple | 10 | 10 |
| 427 | | 3 m. green | 2·50 | 15 |
| 375 | | 3 m. red | 30 | 10 |
| 375a | | 3 m. yellow | 50 | 40 |
| 426 | | 3 m. grey | 40 | 10 |
| 274a | | 3½ m. blue | 6·75 | 10 |
| 376 | | 3½ m. green | 15 | 10 |
| 377 | | 4 m. green | 55 | 10 |
| 378 | | 4½ m. blue | 10 | 15 |
| 275 | 32 | 5 m. blue | 30 | 10 |
| 379 | 31 | 5 m. blue | 50 | 10 |
| 379a | | 5 m. violet | 60 | 10 |
| 379b | | 5 m. yellow | 1·40 | 10 |
| 379c | | 6 m. red | 50 | 10 |
| 429 | | 6 m. green | 1·00 | 30 |
| 430 | | 7 m. red | 75 | 10 |
| 379d | | 8 m. violet | 30 | 10 |
| 431 | | 8 m. green | 1·60 | 1·60 |
| 432 | | 9 m. red | 1·25 | 15 |
| 433 | | 9 m. orange | 1·40 | 25 |
| 276b | – | 10 m. lilac | 35 | 10 |
| 379e | 31 | 10 m. blue | 1·00 | 10 |
| 434 | | 10 m. violet | 2·00 | 10 |
| 435 | | 10 m. brown | 5·00 | 70 |
| 436 | | 10 m. green | 2·25 | 10 |
| 437 | | 12 m. blue | 2·00 | 10 |
| 438 | | 12 m. red | 1·00 | 10 |
| 410 | 32 | 15 m. purple | 1·25 | 15 |
| 439 | 31 | 15 m. blue | 4·00 | 10 |
| 440 | | 15 m. purple | 12·00 | 10 |
| 441 | | 15 m. red | 3·00 | 10 |
| 442 | | 20 m. blue | 5·75 | 10 |
| 443 | | 24 m. purple | 1·25 | 20 |
| 277 | – | 25 m. brown | 75 | 10 |
| 444 | 31 | 25 m. blue | 4·00 | 10 |
| 445 | 32 | 35 m. violet | 8·50 | 10 |
| 445a | – | 40 m. brown | 3·50 | 10 |

DESIGNS—As Type **32**: 10 m. Lake Saimaa. 25, 40 m. Wood-cutter.

**1930.** Red Cross Fund.

| | | | | |
|---|---|---|---|---|
| 278 | 35 | 1 m.+10 p. red & orange | 1·25 | 8·75 |
| 279 | – | 1½ m.+15 p. red & green | 1·10 | 7·25 |
| 280 | – | 2 m.+20 p. red and blue | 2·50 | 45·00 |

DESIGNS: 1½ m. Drapery. 2 m. Viking longship.

**1930.** Air. No. 276b optd. **ZEPPELIN 1930.**

| | | | | |
|---|---|---|---|---|
| 281. | – | 10 m. lilac | £100 | £200 |

39. Church at Hattula. 40. Elias Lonnrot.

**1931.** Red Cross Fund.

| | | | | |
|---|---|---|---|---|
| 282. | 39. | 1 m.+10 p. grn. & red | 1·60 | 5·50 |
| 283. | – | 1½ m.+15 p. brn. & red | 5·50 | 8·75 |
| 284. | – | 2 m.+20 p. blue & red | 1·10 | 13·00 |

DESIGNS: 1½ m. Hameen Castle. 2 m. Viipuri Castle.

**1931.** Finnish Literary Society's Centenary.

| | | | | |
|---|---|---|---|---|
| 285. | 40. | 1 m. brown | 2·00 | 4·75 |
| 286. | – | 1½ m. blue | 9·75 | 4·75 |

DESIGN—HORIZ: 1½ m. Society's seal with inscr as T **40**.

42.

**1931.** 75th Anniv. of First Finnish Postage Stamps.

| | | | | |
|---|---|---|---|---|
| 287. | 42. | 1½ m. red | 2·00 | 7·75 |
| 288. | | 2 m. blue | 2·00 | 9·75 |

43.

45.

**1931.** Granberg Collection Fund.

| | | | | |
|---|---|---|---|---|
| 289. | 43. | 1 m.+4 m. black | 7·75 | 45·00 |

**1931.** Surch.

| | | | | |
|---|---|---|---|---|
| 290 | 31 | "50 PEN." on 40 p. grn | 1·00 | 15 |
| 291 | | "1,25 Mk." on 50 p. yell | 2·50 | 95 |

**1931.** President Svinhufvud's 70th Birthday.

| | | | | |
|---|---|---|---|---|
| 292. | 45. | 2 m. black and blue | 1·00 | 3·25 |

47. St. Nicholas Cathedral.

48. Magnus Tawast.

**1932.** Red Cross Fund.

| | | | | |
|---|---|---|---|---|
| 293 | – | 1½ m.+10 p. bistre & red | 1·50 | 9·75 |
| 294 | 47 | 2 m.+20 p. purple & red | 35 | 4·75 |
| 295 | – | 2½ m.+25 p. blue & red | 1·00 | 17·00 |

DESIGNS—HORIZ: 1½ m. University Library, Helsinki. 2½ m. Houses of Parliament.

**1933.** Red Cross Fund.

| | | | | |
|---|---|---|---|---|
| 296 | 48 | 1¼ m.+10 p. brn & red | 2·00 | 7·75 |
| 297 | – | 2 m.+20 p. purple & red | 50 | 2·40 |
| 298 | – | 2½ m.+25 p. blue & red | 70 | 3·00 |

DESIGNS: 2 m. Michael Agricola. 2½ m. Isacus Rothovius.

51. Evert Horn.

52. Aleksis Kivi, after medallion by V. Aaltonen.

**1934.** Red Cross Fund.

| | | | | |
|---|---|---|---|---|
| 299 | 51 | 1¼ m.+10 p. brn & red | 60 | 1·75 |
| 300 | – | 2 m.+20 p. mauve & red | 1·40 | 4·50 |
| 301 | – | 2½ m.+25 p. blue & red | 60 | 2·25 |

DESIGNS: 2 m. Torsten Stalhandske. 2½ m. Jacob de la Gardie ("Lazy Jack").

**1934.** Birth Cent. of Kivi (poet).

| | | | | |
|---|---|---|---|---|
| 302. | 52. | 2 m. purple | 1·00 | 3·25 |

53. M. Calonius.

54. Finnish Bards.

**1935.** Red Cross Fund. Cross in red.

| | | | | |
|---|---|---|---|---|
| 303 | 53 | 1¼ m.+15 p. brown | 60 | 2·40 |
| 304 | – | 2 m.+20 p. mauve | 1·40 | 4·50 |
| 305 | – | 2½ m.+25 p. blue | 60 | 2·25 |

PORTRAITS: 2 m. H. G. Porthan. 2½ m. A. Chydenius.

**1935.** Cent. of Publication of "Kalevala" (Finnish National Poems).

306. **54.** 1½ m. red .. .. 1·00 1·10
307. – 2 m. brown .. .. 2·50 1·40
308. – 2½ m. blue .. .. 2·50 1·75

**DESIGNS: 2 m. Louhi's failure to recover the "Sampo". 2½ m. Kullervo's departure to war.**

**57.** R. H. Rehbinder. **58.** "Lodbrok", 1771. **60.** Marshal Mannerheim.

**1936.** Red Cross Fund. Cross in red.

309 **57** 1¼ m.+15 p. brown .. 60 1·90
310 – 2 m.+20 p. purple .. 2·40 5·75
311 – 2½ m.+25 p. blue .. 60 3·00

PORTRAITS: 2 m. G. M. Armfeldt. 2½ m. Arvid Horn.

**1937.** Red Cross Fund. Warships. Cross in red.

312 – 1¼ m.+15 p. brown .. 80 2·00
313 **58** 2 m+20 p. red .. .. 14·00 7·25
314 – 3½ m.+35 p. blue .. 70 3·00

DESIGNS—HORIZ. 1¼ m. "Thorborg" (inscr "Uusiman"). 3½ m. "Styrbjorn" (inscr "Hameenmaa").

**1937.** Surch **2 MARKKAA**.

315 **31** 2 m. on 1½ m. red .. 4·25 65

**1937. Marshal Mannerheim's 70th Birthday.**

**316. 60. 2 m. blue .. .. 55 75**

**61.** A. Makipeska. **62.** Cross-country Skiing. **63.** War Veteran.

**1938.** Red Cross Fund. Cross in red.

317. **61.** 50 p.+5 p. green .. 40 90
318. – 1¼ m.+15 p. brown .. 75 2·00
319. – 2 m.+20 p. red .. 4·75 6·00
320. – 3½ m.+35 p. blue .. 45 3·00

PORTRAITS: 1¼ m. R. I. Orn. 2 m. E. Bergenheim. 3½ m. J. M. Nordenstam.

**1938.** Int Skiing Contest, Lahti.

321 **62** 1 m. 25+75 p. black .. 3·75 11·00
322 – 2 m.+1 m. red .. 3·75 11·00
323 – 3 m. 50+1 m. 50 blue and light blue .. 3·75 11·00

DESIGNS: 2 m. Ski jumping. 3 m. 50, Downhill skiing contest.

**1938.** Disabled Soldiers' Relief Fund. 20th Anniv. of Independence.

324. **63.** 2 m.+½ m. blue .. 1·25 3·75

**64.** Colonizers felling Trees. **65.** Ahvenkoski P.O. 1787.

**1938.** Tercentenary of Scandinavian Settlement in America.

325. **64.** 3½ m. brown .. .. 80 2·40

**1938.** Tercent. of Finnish Postal Service.

326. **65.** 50 p. green .. .. 25 65
327. – 1¼m. blue .. .. 1·25 2·75
328. – 2 m. red .. .. 1·50 95
329. – 3½ m. slate .. .. 5·50 7·25

DESIGNS: 1¼ m. Sledge-boat. 2 m. Junkers Ju 52/3m mail plane. 3½ m. G.P.O., Helsinki.

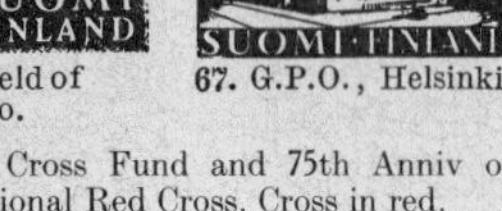

**66.** Battlefield of Solferino. **67.** G.P.O., Helsinki.

**1939.** Red Cross Fund and 75th Anniv of International Red Cross. Cross in red.

330. **66.** 50 p.+5 p. green .. 55 1·50
331. 1¼ m.+15 p. brown .. 80 2·00
332. 2 m.+20 p. red .. 9·75 10·50
333. 3½ m.+35 p. blue .. 65 2·40

**1939.**

334. **67.** 4 m. brown .. .. 40 25

See also Nos. 382/4.

**68.** Crossbowman. **69.** Lion of Finland.

**1940.** Red Cross Fund. Cross in red.

335. **68.** 50 p.+5 p. green .. 40 1·25
336. – 1¼ m.+15 p. brown .. 1·10 2·00
337. – 2 m.+20 p. red .. 1·75 2·25
338. – 3½ m.+35 p. blue .. 1·10 3·50

DESIGNS: 1¼ m. Mounted cavalrymen. 2 m. Unmounted cavalrymen. 3½ m. Officer and infantryman.

**1940.** National Defence Fund.

339. **69.** 2 m.+2 m. blue .. 30 1·40

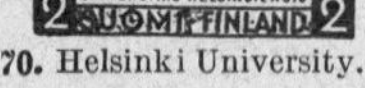

**70.** Helsinki University. **72.** Builder.

**1940.** 300th Anniv. of Founding of Helsinki University.

340 **70** 2 m. deep blue and blue 30 75

**1940.** Surch.

341. **31.** 1 m. 75 on 1 m. 25 yellow 75 90
342. 2 m. 75 on 2 m. red .. 1·75 15

**1941.** Red Cross Fund. Cross in red.

343. **72.** 50 p.+5 p. green .. 25 35
344. – 1 m. 75+15 p. sepia .. 90 2·40
345. – 2 m. 75+25 p. brown .. 5·75 7·75
346. – 3 m. 50+35 p. blue .. 1·40 2·40

DESIGNS: 1 m. 75, Farmer. 2 m. 75, Mother and child. 3 m. 50, Flag.

See also Nos. 405/8.

**73.** Farewell Review. **74.** Knight.

**1941.** President Kallio Memorial.

347. **73.** 2 m. 75 black .. .. 30 60

**1941.** "Brothers-in-Arms" Welfare Fund.

348. **74.** 2 m. 75+25 p. blue .. 70 1·00

**75.** Viipuri Castle.

**1941.** Reconquest of Viipuri.

349. **75.** 1 m. 75 orange .. .. 30 70
350. 2 m. 75 purple .. .. 50 70
351. 3 m. 50 blue .. .. 55 1·40

**76.** Pres. Risto Ryti. **77.** Marshal Mannerheim.

**1941.** (a) President Ryti.

352. **76.** 50 p. green .. .. 70 75
353. 1 m. 75 brown .. .. 85 1·25
354. 2 m. red .. .. 65 1·25
355. 2 m. 75 violet .. .. 85 1·25
356. 3 m. 50 blue .. .. 65 1·25
357. 5 m. grey .. .. 85 1·25

(b) Marshal Mannerheim.

358. **77.** 50 p. green .. .. 60 75
359. 1 m. 75 brown .. .. 85 1·25
360. 2 m. red .. .. 85 1·25
361. 2 m. 75 violet .. .. 85 1·25
362. 3 m. 50 blue .. .. 85 1·25
363. 5 m. grey .. .. 75 1·25

**79.** Aland. **80.** Tampere.

**1942.** Red Cross Fund. Cross in red.

364. **79.** 50 p.+5 p. green .. 1·10 1·10
365. – 1 m. 75+15 p. brown .. 1·25 2·00
366. – 2 m. 75+25 p. red .. 1·10 2·00
367. – 3 m. 50+35 p. blue .. 1·25 2·00
368. – 4 m. 75+45 p. grey .. 95 2·75

ARMS: 1 m. 75, Uusimaa (Nyland). 2 m. 75, Finland Proper. 3 m. 50, Karelia. 4 m. 75, Satakunta.

**1942.**

369. **80.** 50 m. violet .. .. 1·50 10
370. – 100 m. blue .. .. 2·00 10

DESIGN: 100 m. Helsinki Harbour.

For 100 m. in green without "mk" see No. 557b.

**81.** New Testament. **82.** Mediaeval Press. **83.** Lapland.

**1942.** Tercentenary of Introduction of Printing into Finland.

380. **81.** 2 m. 75 brown .. .. 20 75
381. **82.** 3 m. 50 blue .. .. 35 1·25

**1942.**

382. **67.** 7 m. brown .. .. 50 10
383. 9 m. mauve .. .. 50 10
384. 20 m. brown .. .. 1·25 10

**1943.** Red Cross Fund. **Cross in red.**

385. **83.** 50 p.+5 p. green .. 20 70
386. – 2 m.+20 p. brown .. 75 1·75
387. – 3 m. 50+35 p. red .. 75 1·75
388. – 4 m. 50+45 p. blue .. 1·75 4·75

ARMS: 2 m. Hame (Tavastland). 3 m. 50, Pohjanmaa Osterbotten). 4 m. 50, Savo (Savolaks).

**1943.** Surch **3½mk**.

389 **31** 3½ m. on 2 m. 75 purple 30 10

**85.** Military Tokens.

**1943.** National Relief Fund.

390 **85** 2 m.+50 p. brown .. 25 70
391 – 3 m. 50+1 m. purple .. 25 70

DESIGN—VERT: 3 m. 50, Widow and Orphans.

**87.** Red Cross Train.

**1944.** Red Cross Fund. Inscr. "1944" Cross in red.

392. **87.** 50 p.+25 p. green .. 40 40
393. – 2 m.+50 p. violet .. 50 70
394. – 3 m. 50+75 p. red .. 50 70
395. – 4 m. 50+1 m. blue .. 95 3·00

DESIGNS: 2 m. Ambulance. 3 m. 50, Hospital, Helsinki. 4 m. 50, Airplane.

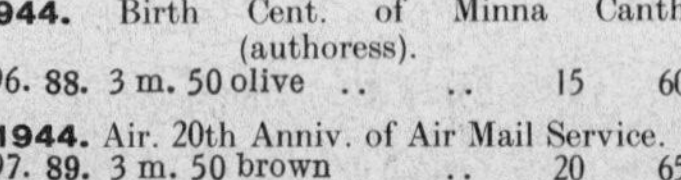

**88.** Minna Canth. **89.** Douglas DC-2 Mail Plane.

**1944.** Birth Cent. of Minna Canth (authoress).

396. **88.** 3 m. 50 olive .. .. 15 60

**1944.** Air. 20th Anniv. of Air Mail Service.

397. **89.** 3 m. 50 brown .. 20 65

**90.** Pres. Svinhufvud. **91.** **92.** Wrestling.

**1944.** Mourning for Pres. P. E. Svinhufvud.

398 **90** 3½ m. black .. .. 15 60

**1944.** National Relief Fund.

399. **91.** 3 m. 50+1 m. 50 brown 20 70

**1945.** Sports Fund.

400. **92.** 1 m.+50 p. green .. 25 70
401. – 2 m.+1 m. red .. 25 70
402. – 3 m. 50+1 m. 75 vio.. 25 70
403. – 4 m. 50+2 m. 25 blue 50 1·00
404. – 7 m.+3 m. 50 brown 60 1·90

DESIGNS: 2 m. Vaulting. 3 m. 50, Running. 4 m. 50, Skiing. 7 m. Throwing the javelin.

**1945.** Red Cross Fund. As Nos. 343/6, but dated "1945". Cross in red.

405. 1 m.+25 p. green .. 25 55
406. 2 m.+50 p. brown .. 25 70
407. 3 m. 50+75 p. brown .. 25 70
408. 4 m. 50+1 m. blue .. 45 90

DESIGNS: 1 m. Builder. 2 m. Farmer. 3 m. 50, Mother and child. 4 m. 50, Flag.

**93.** Pres. Stahlberg. **94.** Sibelius. **95.** Fishermen.

**1945.** 80th Birth Anniv of Pres. K. J. Stahlberg.

409 **93** 3 m. 50 violet .. .. 30 30

**1945.** 80th Birthday of Sibelius (composer).

411. **94.** 5 m. green .. .. 30 30

**1946.** Red Cross Fund. Cross in red.

412. **95.** 1 m.+25 p. green .. 20 40
413. – 3 m.+75 p. purple .. 20 40
414. – 5 m.+1 m. 25 red .. 20 40
415. – 10 m.+2 m. 50 blue .. 20 90

DESIGNS: 3 m. Butter-making. 5 m. **Harvesting.** 10 m. Logging.

**1946. Surch. with bold figures and bars.**

**416. 31. 8 m. on 5 m. violet .. 30 15**
**416a. 12 m. on 10 m. violet .. 85 15**

**97.** Athletes. **98.** Nurse and Children. **99.** Uto Lighthouse, and Sailing Ship.

**1946.** National Games.

417. **97.** 8 m. purple .. .. 20 35

**1946.** Anti-tuberculosis Fund.

418 **98** 5 m.+1 m. green .. 25 40
419 – 8 m.+2 m. purple .. 25 40

DESIGN: 8 m. Lady doctor examining child.

**1946.** 250th Anniv. of Foundation of Pilotage Institution.

420. **99.** 8 m. violet .. .. 40 40

**100.** Postal Motor Coach. **101.** Town Hall.

**1946.**

421. **100.** 16 m. black .. .. 70 60
421a. 30 m. black .. .. 1·50 10

**1946.** 600th Anniv. of Founding of Porvoo (Borga).

422. **101.** 5 m. black .. .. 25 40
423. – 8 m. purple .. .. 25 40

DESIGN—VERT. 8 m. Bridge and church.

103. Tammisaari.

104. Pres. Paasikivi.

**1946.** 400th Anniv. of Tammisaari (Ekenas).
424. **103.** 8 m. green .. .. 20 40

**1947.**
446. **104.** 10. m black .. .. 20 30

**1947.** Anti-tuberculosis Fund. Nos. 418/19 surch.
447 **98** 6+1 on 5 m.+1 m. grn 20 65
448 – 10+2 on 8 m.+2 m. pur 20 65

106. Bank Emblem.

107. Athletes.

**1947.** 60th Anniv of Finnish Postal Savings Bank.
449 **106** 10 m. purple .. .. 20 30

**1947.** National Sports Festival.
450. **107.** 10 m. blue .. .. 30 40

108. Ilmarinen Ploughing.

109. Emblem of Savings Bank Association.

**1947.** Conclusion of Peace Treaty.
451. **108.** 10 m. black .. .. 15 30

**1947.** 125th Anniv. of Savings Bank Assn.
452. **109.** 10 m. brown .. .. 20 30

110. Physical Exercise.

111. Sower

**1947.** Anti-tuberculosis Fund.
453. **110.** 2 m. 50+1 m. green .. 30 70
454. – 6 m.+1 m. 50 red .. 40 1·40
455. – 10 m.+2 m. 50 brown .. 40 1·40
456. – 12 m.+3 m. blue .. 95 1·75
457. – 20 m.+5 m. mauve .. 1·40 2·40
DESIGNS—VERT: 6, 10, 20 m. Various child exercises. HORIZ: 12 m. Mme. Paasikivi and child.

**1947.** 150th Anniv of Central League of Agricultural Societies.
458 **111** 10 m. grey .. .. 20 30

112. Heights of Koli.

113. Z. Topelius.

**1947.** 60th Anniv. of Tourist Society.
459. **112.** 10 m. blue .. .. 20 30

**1948.** Red Cross Fund. Dated "1948" Cross in red.
460. **113.** 3 m.+1 m. green .. 40 70
461. – 7 m.+2 m. red .. .. 50 1·40
462. – 12 m.+3 m. blue .. 50 1·40
463. – 20 m.+5 m. violet .. 65 1·60
PORTRAITS: 7 m. Fr. Pacius. 12 m. J. L. Runeberg. 20 m. F. R. Cygnaeus.

**1948.** Anti-tuberculosis Fund. Nos. 454/5 and 457 surch.
464 7 m.+2 m. on 6 m.+ 1 m. 50 red .. .. 1·25 2·25
465 15 m.+3 m. on 10 m.+ 2 m. 50 brown .. 1·50 2·25
466 24 m.+6 m. on 20 m.+5 m. mauve .. .. 2·00 4·00

115. Michael Agricola. (after sculpture by C. Sjostrand).

116. King's Gate, Suomenlinna.

**1948.** 400th Anniv of Translation of New Testament into Finnish by Michael Agricola.
467 **115** 7 m. purple .. .. 90 1·25
468 – 12 m. blue .. .. 90 1·25
DESIGN: 12 m. Agricola translating New Testament (after painting by A. Edelfelt).

**1948.** Bicent of Suomenlinna (Sveaborg).
469 **116** 12 m. green .. .. 90 1·90

117. Finnish Mail-carrier's Badge.

118. Girl Bundling Twigs.

119. Anemone.

**1948.** Helsinki Philatelic Exn.
470. **117.** 12 m. green .. .. 7·25 19·00
**Sold only at the Exn., at 62 m. (including 50 m. entrance fee).**

**1949.** Red Cross Fund. Inscr. "SAUNA BASTU 1949". Cross in red.
471. **118.** 5 m.+2 m. green .. 40 60
472. – 9 m.+3 m. red .. 70 1·10
473. – 15 m.+5 m. blue .. 70 1·10
474. – 30 m.+10 m. brown .. 1·40 2·40
DESIGNS: 9 m. Bathing scene. 15 m. Heating sauna in winter. 30 m. Bathers leaving sauna for plunge in lake.

**1949.** Tuberculosis Relief Fund.
475. **119.** 5 m.+2 m. green .. 75 85
476. – 9 m.+3 m. red .. 75 1·00
477. – 15 m.+5 m. brown .. 75 1·10
DESIGNS: 9 m. Rose. 15 m. Coltsfoot.

120. Trees and Papermill.

121. Girl with Torch.

**1949.** 3rd World Forestry Congress. Inscr. "IIIE CONGRES FORESTIER MONDIAL 1949".
478. **120.** 9 m. brown .. .. 2·00 2·75
479. – 15 m. green (Tree and Globe) .. .. 2·00 2·75

**1949.** 50th Anniv. of Labour Movement.
480. **121.** 5 m. green .. .. 3·50 7·75
481. – 15 m. red (Man with mallet) .. .. 3·50 7·75

122. Kristiinankaupunki.

123. Lappeenranta.

**1949.** Tercentenary of Kristiinankaupunki (Kristinestad).
482. **122.** 15 m. blue .. .. 1·75 2·25

**1949.** Tercent. of Lappeenranta (Villmanstrand).
483. **123.** 5 m. green .. .. 90 70

124. Church, Raahe.

125. Seal of Technical High School.

126. Hannes Gebhard (founder).

**1949.** Tercent. of Raahe (Brahestad).
484. **124.** 9 m. purple .. .. 1·00 1·25

**1949.** Cent. of Technical High School, Helsinki.
485. **125.** 15 m. blue .. .. 80 1·00

**1949.** 50th Anniv. of Finnish Co-operative Movement.
486. **126.** 15 m. green .. .. 80 1·00

127.

128. Douglas DC-6.

129. White Water-lily.

**1949.** 75th Anniv. of U.P.U.
487. **127.** 15 m. blue .. .. 95 1·25

**1950.** Air.
488. **128.** 300 m. blue .. .. 22·00 7·00
For 300 m. stamp without "mk" see No. 585 and for 3 m. stamp see No. 679.

**1950.** Tuberculosis Relief Fund.
489. **129.** 5 m.+2 m. green .. 2·40 2·40
490. – 9 m.+3 m. mauve .. 1·75 1·75
491. – 15 m.+5 m. blue .. 1·75 1·75
DESIGNS: 9 m. Pasque flower. 15 m. Clustered bellflower.

130. Plan of Helsinki, 1550.

131. President Paasikivi.

**1950.** 400th Anniv. of Helsinki.
492. **130.** 5 m. green .. .. 30 70
493. 9 m. brown .. .. 75 1·10
494. – 15 m. blue .. .. 60 75
DESIGNS: 9 m. J. A. Ehrenstrom and C. L. Engel. 15 m. Town Hall and Cathedral.

**1950.** President's 80th Birthday.
495. **131.** 20 m. blue .. .. 30 20

132. Hospital, Helsinki.

133. Town Hall.

134. Capercaillie.

**1951.** Red Cross Fund. Cross in red.
496. **132.** 7 m.+2 m. brown .. 1·40 2·00
497. – 12 m.+3 m. violet .. 1·40 2·00
498. – 20 m.+5 m. red .. 1·75 2·00
DESIGNS: 12 m. Blood donor and nurse. 20 m. Blood donor's badge.

**1951.** 300th Anniv of Kajaani (Kajana).
499 **133** 20 m. brown .. .. 55 65

**1951.** Tuberculosis Relief Fund.
500. **134.** 7 m.+2 m. green .. 2·50 2·75
501. – 12 m.+3 m. lake .. 2·50 2·75
502. – 20 m.+5 m. blue .. 2·50 2·75
DESIGNS: 12 m. Common Cranes. 20 m. Caspian Terns.

135. Diving.

138 Marshal Mannerheim.

139. Arms of Pietarsaari.

**1951.** 15th Olympic Games, Helsinki.
503. **135.** 12 m.+2 m. red .. 95 1·10
504. – 15 m.+2 m. green .. 1·75 1·60
505. – 20 m.+3 m. blue .. 1·40 1·50
506. – 25 m.+4 m. brown .. 2·00 2·10
DESIGNS—HORIZ. 15 m. Football. 25 m. Running. VERT. 20 m. Olympic stadium.

**1952.** Red Cross Fund. Cross in red.
507. **138.** 10 m.+2 m. black .. 1·10 1·50
508. 15 m.+3 m. purple .. 1·25 2·00
509. 25 m.+5 m. blue .. 1·25 2·00

**1952.** 300th Anniv. of Founding of Pietarsaari (Jakobstad).
510. **139.** 25 m. blue .. .. 60 1·00

140. Vaasa.

141. Knight, Rook and Chessboard.

142. Great Tit.

**1952.** Centenary of Fire of Vaasa (Vasa).
511. **140.** 25 m. brown .. .. 60 95

**1952.** 10th Chess Olympiad, Helsinki.
512. **141.** 25 m. black .. .. 2·50 2·25

**1952.** Tuberculosis Relief Fund. Birds.
513. **142.** 10 m.+2 m. green .. 2·25 2·25
514. – 15 m.+3 m. red .. 2·25 2·25
515. – 25 m.+5 m. blue .. 2·25 2·25
BIRDS: 15 m. Spotted Flycatchers. 25 m. Common Swifts.

143. "Flame of Temperance".

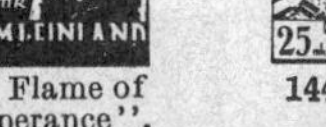

144. Aerial view of Hamina.

**1953.** Cent. of Finnish Temperance Movement.
516. **143.** 25 m. blue .. .. 95 95

**1953.** 300th Anniv. of Hamina (Fredrikshamn).
517. **144.** 25 m. slate .. .. 80 75

DESIGNS: 15 m. Brown bear. 25 m. Elk.

145. Eurasian Red Squirrel.

**1953.** Tuberculosis Relief Fund.
518. **145.** 10 m.+2 m. brown .. 2·75 2·75
519. – 15 m.+3 m. violet .. 2·75 2·75
520. – 25 m.+5 m. green .. 2·75 2·75

146. I. Wilskman.

147. Mother and Children.

**1954.** Birth Cent. of Wilskman (gymnast).
521. **146.** 25 m. blue .. .. 65 70

**1954.** Red Cross Fund. Cross in red.
522. **147.** 10 m.+2 m. green .. 1·00 1·00
523. – 15 m.+3 m. blue .. 1·25 1·25
524. – 25 m.+5 m. brown .. 1·25 1·25
DESIGNS: 15 m. Old lady knitting. 25 m. Blind man and dog.

148.

149. "In the Outer Archipelago" (after Edelfelt).

**1954.**
525 **148** 1 m. brown .. .. 50 10
526 2 m. green .. .. 50 10
527 3 m. orange .. .. 55 10
527a 4 m. grey .. .. 70 30
528 5 m. blue .. .. 1·00 10
529 10 m. green .. .. 1·00 10
530 15 m. red .. .. 3·00 10
530a 15 m. orange .. .. 6·75 10
531 20 m. purple .. .. 9·75 10
531a 20 m. red .. .. 2·00 10
532 25 m. blue .. .. 3·25 10
532a 25 m. purple .. .. 9·75 10
532b 30 m. blue .. .. 2·00 10
See also Nos. 647, etc.

**1954.** Birth Cent of A. Edelfelt (painter).
533 **149** 25 m. black .. .. 40 45

150. White-tailed Bumble Bees collecting Pollen.

151. J. J. Nervander

**1954.** Tuberculosis Relief Fund. Cross in red.
534. 150. 10 m.+2 m. brown .. 1·90 1·90
535. – 15 m.+3 m. red .. 2·25 2·25
536. – 25 m.+5 m. blue .. 2·25 2·25
DESIGNS: 15 m. Apollo (butterfly) and wild rose. 25 m. "Aeshna juncea" (dragonfly).

**1955.** 150th Birth Anniv. of Nervander. (astronomer and poet).
537. 151. 25 m. blue .. .. 70 50

**152.** Parliament Building.

**153.** St. Henry.

**1955.** National Philatelic Exn, Helsinki.
538 152 25 m. black .. .. 13·00 15·00

**1955.** 800th Anniv. of Establishment of Christianity in Finland.
539. 153. 15 m. purple .. .. 95 60
540. – 25 m. green .. .. 95 60
DESIGN: 25 m. Arrival of Christian preachers in 1155.

**154.** Conference in Session.

**155.** Barque "Ilma" and Cargo.

**1955.** Interparliamentary Conf., Helsinki.
541. 154. 25 m. green .. .. 95 1·40

**1955.** 350th Anniv. of Oulu (Uleaborg).
542. 155. 25 m. brown .. .. 1·75 1·75

**156.** Perch.

**157.** Town Hall, Lahti.

**1955.** Tuberculosis Relief Fund. Cross in red.
543. 156. 10 m.+2 m. green .. 1·40 1·40
544. – 15 m.+3 m. brn.(Pike) 2·25 2·25
545. – 25 m.+5 m. bl.(Salmon) 2·25 2·25

**1955.** 50th Anniv. of Lahti.
546. 157. 25 m. blue .. .. 95 1·40

**158.** J. Z. Duncker.

**159.** "Telegraphs".

**1955.** Red Cross. Cross in red.
547. – 10 m.+2 m. blue .. 90 90
548. 158. 15 m.+3 m. brown .. 1·25 1·25
549. – 25 m.+5 m. green .. 1·25 1·25
DESIGNS: 10 m. Von Dobeln on horseback. 25 m. Young soldier.

**1955.** Cent. of Telegraphs in Finland. Inscr. "1855-1955 Telegrafen".
550. 159. 10 m. green .. .. 1·25 1·25
551. – 15 m. violet .. .. 1·25 80
552. – 25 m. blue .. .. 1·75 1·25
DESIGNS: 15 m. Otto Nyberg. 25 m. Telegraph pole.

**160.** Lighthouse at Porkkala.

**161.** Lammi Church.

**1956.** Return of Porkkala to Finland.
553 160 25 m. blue .. .. 75 45

**1956.** Value expressed as "5" etc.
553a – 5 m. green (postage) 30 10
554 161 30 m. green .. .. 1·25 10
555 – 40 m. lilac .. .. 2·75 10
556 161 50 m. green .. .. 6·25 10
557 – 60 m. purple .. .. 9·75 10
557a – 75 m. black .. .. 4·50 10
557b – 100 m. green .. .. 27·00 10
557c – 125 m. green .. .. 17·00 30

DESIGNS: 5 m. View of lake, Keuru. 40 m. Houses of Parliament. 60 m. Olavinlinna. 75 m. Pyhakoski Dam. 100 m. Helsinki Harbour. 125 m. Turku Castle.
No. 557b differs from No. 370 in that "FINLAND" is without the scroll, the figures "100" are upright and "mk" is omitted.
See also Nos. 660, etc.

**162.** J. V. Snellman (after sculpture by E. Wikstrom).

**163.** Athletes.

**1956.** 150th Birth Anniv. of Snellman (statesman).
558. 162. 25 m. brown .. .. 35 40

**1956.** Finnish Games.
559 163 30 m. blue .. .. 95 80

**164.**

**165.** Bohemian Waxwing.

**1956.** Centenary of First Finnish Postage Stamp and International Philatelic Exhibition, Helsinki. Roul.
560 164 30 m. blue .. .. 3·00 4·75

**1956.** Tuberculosis Relief Fund. Cross in red.
561. 165. 10 m.+2 m. brown .. 1·75 1·75
562. – 20 m.+3 m. green .. 2·10 2·10
563. – 30 m.+5 m. blue .. 2·50 2·50
DESIGNS: 20 m. Eagle Owl. 30 m. Mute Swan.

**166.** Vaasa Town Hall.

**167.** P. Aulin.

**1956.** 350th Anniv. of Vaasa.
564. 166. 30 m. blue .. .. 95 85

**1956.** Northern Countries' Day. As T 100 of Denmark.
565. 20 m. red .. .. 3·50 1·40
566. 30 m. blue .. .. 12·50 1·40

**1956.** Red Cross. Inscr. "1956". Cross in red.
567. 167. 5 m.+1 m. green .. 80 80
568. – 10 m.+2 m. brown .. 1·25 1·25
569. – 20 m.+3 m. red .. 1·50 1·50
570. – 30 m. +5 m. blue .. 1·50 1·50
PORTRAITS: 10 m. L. von Pfaler. 20 m. G. Johansson. 30 m. V. M. von Born.

**168.** University Hospital, Helsinki.

**169.** Scout Badge and Saluting Hand.

**1956.** Bicent. of National Health Service.
571. 168. 30 m. green .. .. 1·40 70

**1957.** 50th Anniv. of Boy Scout Movement.
572. 169. 30 m. blue .. .. 1·90 1·00

**171.** "In Honour of Work".

**172.** "Lex" (sculpture by W. Runeberg).

**1957.** 50th Anniv. of Finnish Trade Union Movement.
573. 171. 30 m. red .. .. 95 50

**1957.** 50th Anniv. of Finnish Parliament.
574. 172. 30 m. olive .. .. 1·10 95

**173.** Wolverine.

**174.** Factories within Cogwheel.

**1957.** Tuberculosis Relief Fund. Inscr. "1957". Cross in red.
575. 173. 10 m.+2 m. purple .. 1·40 1·40
576. – 20 m.+3 m. sepia .. 2·25 2·25
577. – 30 m.+5 m. blue .. 2·25 2·25
DESIGNS: 20 m. Lynx. 30 m. Reindeer.
See also Nos. 642/4.

**1957.** 50th Anniv. of Central Federation of Finnish Employers.
578. 174. 20 m. blue .. .. 80 45

**175.** Red Cross Flag.

**176.** Ida Aalberg (after Edelfelt).

**1957.** Red Cross Fund and 80th Anniv. of Finnish Red Cross. Cross in red.
579 175. 10 m.+2 m. green .. 1·50 1·60
580. 20 m.+3 m. lake .. 1·50 1·90
581. 30 m.+5 m. blue .. 1·50 1·90

**1957.** Birth Cent of Ida Aalberg (actress).
582 176 30 m. maroon & purple 85 85

**177.** Arms of Finland.

**178.** Bust of Sibelius (Waino Aaltonen).

**1957.** 40th Anniv. of Independence.
583. 177. 30 m. blue .. .. 95 85

**1957.** Death of Sibelius (composer).
584. 178. 30 m. black .. .. 95 55

**1958.** Air. As No. 488 but with "mk" omitted.
585. 128. 300 m. blue .. .. 38·00 80
See also No. 679.

**179.** Ski Jumping.

**180.** "March of the Bjorneborgienses" (after Edelfelt).

**1958.** World Ski Championships.
586. 179. 20 m. green .. .. 75 75
587. – 30 m. blue .. .. 95 45
DESIGN—VERT. 30 m. Cross-country skiing.

**1958.** 400th Anniv. of Founding of Pori (Bjorneborg).
588. 180. 30 m. purple .. .. 1·40 70

**181.** Lily of the Valley.

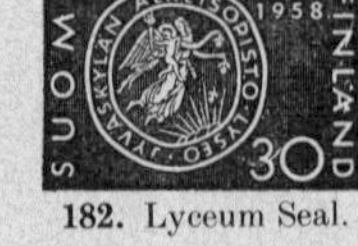

**182.** Lyceum Seal.

**1958.** Tuberculosis Relief Fund. Cross in red.
589. 181. 10 m.+2 m. green .. 1·60 1·60
590. – 20 m.+3 m. red .. 1·90 1·90
591. – 30 m.+5 m. blue .. 2·10 2·10
DESIGNS: 20 m. Red clover. 30 m. Anemone.

**1958.** Centenary of Jyvaskyla Lyceum (secondary school).
592. 182. 30 m. red .. .. 1·40 95

**183.** Convair CV 340 over Lakes.

**184.** Cloudberry.

**1958.** Air.
593 183 34 m. blue .. .. 80 80
594 45 m. blue .. .. 2·25 1·40
See also Nos. 678/a.

**1958.** Red Cross Fund. Cross in red
595. 184. 10 m.+2 m. orange .. 1·40 1·40
596. – 20 m.+3 m. red .. 1·75 1·75
597. – 30 m.+5 m. blue .. 1·75 1·75
DESIGNS: 20 m. Cowberry. 30 m. Blueberry.

**185.** Missionary Emblem and Globe.

**186.** Opening of Diet, 1809.

**1959.** Cent. of Finnish Missionary Society.
598. 185. 30 m. purple .. .. 65 65

**1959.** 150th Anniv. of Re-convening of Finnish Diet at Porvoo.
599. 186. 30 m. blue .. .. 50 40

**1959.** Air. No. 593 surch 45.
600 45 m. on 34 m. blue .. 2·50 2·00

**188.** Multiple Saws.

**189.** Gymnast.

**1959.** Centenaries of Kestila Sawmill (10 m.) and Finnish Forestry Department (30 m.)
601. 188. 10 m. brown .. .. 50 35
602. – 30 m. grn. (Forest firs) 50 35

**1959.** Tuberculosis Relief Fund. As T 181 but inscr. "1959". Cross in red.
603. 10 m.+2 m. green .. 3·00 1·40
604. 20 m.+3 m. brown .. 3·50 2·25
605. 30 m.+5 m. blue.. .. 3·50 2·25
DESIGNS: 10 m. Marguerite. 20 m. Cowslip. 30 m. Cornflower.

**1959.** Birth Centenary of Elin Oihonna Kallio (Women's Gymnastics pioneer).
606. 189. 30 m. purple .. .. 95 80

**190.** Oil Lamp.

**191.** Arms of the Towns.

**1959.** Cent. of Trade Freedom in Finland.
607. 190. 30 m. blue .. .. 85 65

**1960.** Extra Privileges for Finnish Towns—Hyvinkaa, Kouvola, Riihimaki, Rovaniemi, Salo and Seinajoki.
608. 191. 30 m. violet .. .. 80 1·40

**192.** 5 k. "Serpentine Roulette" Stamp of 1860.

**1960.** Stamp Exn., Helsinki, and Cent. of "Serpentine Roulette" stamps. Roul.
609. 192. 30 m. blue and grey .. 5·00 6·50

193. Refugees and Symbol.

194. J. Gadolin.

**1960.** World Refugee Year.
610. **193.** 30 m. red .. .. 45 40
611. 40 m. blue .. .. 45 40

**1960.** Birth Bicent. of Johan Gadolin (chemist).
612. **194.** 30 m. brown .. .. 75 70

195. H. Nortamo.

196. European Cuckoo.

**1960.** Birth Cent. of H. Nortamo (writer).
613. **195.** 30 m. green .. .. 80 65

**1960.** Karelian National Festival, Helsinki.
614. **196.** 30 m. red .. .. 80 65

197. "Geodesy" (Geodetic instrument).

198. Pres. Kekkonen.

**1960.** 12th International Geodesy and Geophysics Union Assembly, Helsinki.
615. **197.** 10 m. sepia and blue .. 60 50
616. – 30 m. brn., red & verm. 80 40
DESIGN: 30 m. "Geophysics" (representation of Northern Lights).

**1960.** President Kekkonen's 60th Birthday.
617. **198.** 30 m. blue .. .. 85 20

**1960.** Europa. As T **373** of Belgium but size 31 × 20½ mm.
618. 30 m. blue and ultramarine 70 45
619. 40 m. purple and sepia .. 70 45

199. Pastor Cygnaeus.

200. Reindeer.

**1960.** 150th Birth Anniv of Pastor Uno Cygnaeus (founder of elementary schools).
620 **199** 30 m. purple .. .. 65 40

**1960.** Red Cross Fund. Cross in red.
621 **200** 10 m. + 2 m. purple .. 1·00 1·00
622 – 20 m. + 3 m. violet .. 1·40 1·40
623 – 30 m. + 5 m. purple .. 1·40 1·40
DESIGNS: 20 m. Hunter with lasso. 30 m. Mountain and lake.

201. "Pommern" (barque).

202. Savings Bank's New Emblem.

**1961.** Cent of Marianhamina (Mariehamn).
624 **201** 30 m. blue .. .. 2·75 1·40

**1961.** 75th Anniv of Finnish Postal Savings Bank.
625 **202** 30 m. blue .. .. 65 25

203. Symbol of Standardization.

204. J. Aho.

**1961.** General Assembly of Int. Organization for Standardization, Helsinki.
626. **203.** 30 m. green & orange .. 30 40

**1961.** Tuberculosis Relief Fund. As T **173**. Cross in red.
627 10 m. + 2 m. purple .. 1·40 1·00
628 20 m. + 3 m. blue .. .. 1·90 1·40
629 30 m. + 5 m. green .. 1·90 1·40
ANIMALS: 10 m. Muskrat. 20 m. European otter. 30 m. Ringed seal.

**1961.** Birth Centenary of Aho (writer).
630. **204.** 30 m. brown .. .. 65 40

205. Public Buildings.

206. A. Jarnefelt.

**1961.** 150th Anniv. of Finnish Central Building Board.
631. **205.** 30 m. black .. .. 65 40

**1961.** Birth Cent. of Arvid Jarnefelt (writer).
632. **206.** 30 m. purple .. .. 65 40

207. Bank Facade.

208. First locomotive, "Ilmarinen".

**1961.** 150th Anniv. of Bank of Finland.
633. **207.** 30 m. purple .. .. 65 40

**1962.** Centenary of Finnish Railways.
634. **208.** 10 m. green .. .. 1·25 35
635. – 30 m. blue .. .. 2·10 60
636. – 40 m. purple .. .. 3·75 70
LOCOMOTIVES: 30 m. Class "Hr 1" steam locomotive. 40 m. Class "Hr 12" diesel.

209. Mora Stone.

210. Senate Place, Helsinki.

**1962.** 600th Anniv. of Finnish People's Political Rights.
637. **209.** 30 m. purple .. .. 65 40

**1962.** 150th Anniv. of Proclamation of Helsinki as Finnish Capital.
638. **210.** 30 m. brown .. .. 65 40

211. Customs Board Crest.

212. Emblem of Commerce.

**1962.** 150th Anniv. of Finnish Customs Board.
639. **211.** 30 m. red .. .. 65 40

**1962.** Cent of 1st Finnish Commercial Bank.
640 **212** 30 m. green .. .. 65 40

213. S. Alkio.

214. Finnish Labour Emblem on Conveyor Belt.

**1962.** Birth Cent of Santeri Alkio (writer and founder of Young People's Societies' Movement).
641 **213** 30 m. purple .. .. 70 40

**1962.** Tuberculosis Relief Fund. As T **173**. Cross in red.
642 10 m. + 2 m. black .. 1·40 1·40
643 20 m. + 3 m. purple .. 1·90 1·75
644 30 m. + 5 m. blue .. 1·90 1·75
DESIGNS: 10 m. Brown hare. 20 m. Pine marten. 30 m. Stoat.

**1962.** Home Production.
645. **214.** 30 m. purple .. 65 25

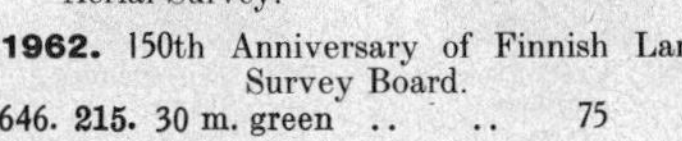
215. Hunting Pembroke making Aerial Survey.

216.

**1962.** 150th Anniversary of Finnish Land Survey Board.
646. **215.** 30 m. green .. .. 75 40

Currency reform. 100 (old) markkaa = 1 (new) markka.

**1963.** (a) Lion Type.
647 **216** 1 p. brown .. .. 20 10
648 2 p. green .. .. 20 10
649 4 p. grey .. .. 30 30
650c 5 p. blue .. .. 35 10
651c 10 p. green .. .. 35 10
652 15 p. orange .. .. 85 10
653 20 p. red .. .. 40 10
654a 25 p. purple .. .. 80 10
656a 30 p. blue .. .. 70 10
657 35 p. blue .. .. 1·10 10
657a 35 p. yellow .. .. 45 10
658a 40 p. blue .. .. 95 10
658b 40 p. orange .. .. 70 10
659 50 p. blue .. .. 2·00 10
659a 50 p. purple .. .. 60 10
659b 60 p. blue .. .. 55 10

(b) Views. Values expressed as "0,05" (pennia values) or "1,00" (mark values).
660 – 5 p. green (As No. 553a) (postage) .. 20 10
661 – 25 p. multicoloured .. 45 10
662 – 30 p. multicoloured .. 95 10
663 – 40 p. lilac (As No. 555) 3·00 10
664 **161** 50 p. green .. .. 2·75 10
665 – 60 p. purple (As No. 557) .. .. 6·25 10
666 – 65 p. purple (As No. 557) .. .. 90 10
667 – 75 p. black (As No. 557a) .. .. 1·25 10
668 – 80 p. multicoloured .. 3·00 10
669 – 90 p. multicoloured .. 1·10 10
670 – 1 m. green (As No. 557b) .. .. 70 10
671 – 1 m. 25 green (As No. 557c) .. .. 1·75 20
672 – 1 m. 30 multicoloured 1·00 10
673 – 1 m. 50 green .. 1·00 10
674 – 1 m. 75 blue .. 1·00 10
675 – 2 m. green .. .. 8·00 10
676 – 2 m. 50 blue & yellow 6·50 10
677 – 5 m. green .. .. 13·00 20
678 **183** 45 p. blue (air) .. 1·50 10
678a 57 p. blue .. .. 1·50 50
679 – 3 m. blue (585) .. 2·75 10
NEW DESIGNS: As Type **161**—VERT: 30 p. Nasinneula Tower, Tampere. 80 p. Keuruu church. 1 m. 30, Helsinki Railway Station. HORIZ: 25 p. Country mail bus. 90 p. Hameen Bridge, Tampere. 1 m. 50, Loggers afloat. 1 m. 75, Parainen Bridge. 2 m. Country house by lake. 2 m. 50, Aerial view of Punkaharju. 5 m. Ristikallio gorge.
No. 679 is as No. 585, but with a comma after "3".

217. Mother and Child.

218. Hands reaching for Red Cross.

**1963.** Freedom from Hunger.
680. **217.** 40 p. brown .. .. 40 35

**1963.** Centenary of Red Cross.
681 **218** 10 p. + 2 p. brn & red 60 70
682 20 p. + 3 p. violet & red 80 1·00
683 30 p. + 5 p. green & red 80 1·00

219. Crown of Thorns.

220. "Co-operation".

**1963.** Lutheran World Federation Assembly, Helsinki.
684. **219.** 10 p. lake .. .. 20 15
685. – 30 p. green .. .. 30 30
DESIGN: 30 p. Head of Christ.

**1963.** Europa.
686. **220.** 40 p. purple .. 95 65

221. House of Estates, Helsinki.

222. Convair CV 440 Metropolitan Airliner.

**1963.** Centenary of Finnish Representative Assembly.
687. **221.** 30 p. purple .. .. 65 30

**1963.** 40 Years of Finnish Civil Aviation.
688. **222.** 35 p. green .. .. 90 50
689. – 40 p. blue .. .. 90 40
DESIGN: 40 p. Sud-Aviation Caravelle in flight.

223. M. A. Castren (after E. J. Lofgren).

224. Soapstone Elk's Head.

**1963.** 150th Birth Anniv of M. A. Castren (explorer and scholar).
690 **223** 35 p. blue .. .. 65 30

**1964.** "For Art" (centenary of Finnish Artists' Society).
691 **224** 35 p. green and buff .. 65 30

225. E. N. Setala.

226. Doctor tending Patient on Sledge.

**1964.** Birth Centenary of Emil Setala (philologist and statesman).
692. **225.** 35 p. brown .. .. 65 30

**1964.** Red Cross Fund. Cross in red.
693 **226** 15 p. + 3 p. blue .. 70 70
694 – 25 p. + 4 p. green .. 1·40 1·10
695 – 35 p. + 5 p. purple .. 1·00 1·00
696 – 40 p. + 7 p. green .. 1·00 1·00
DESIGNS: 25 p. Red Cross hospital ship. 35 p. Military sick parade. 40 p. Distribution of Red Cross parcels.

227. Emblem of Medicine.

228. Ice Hockey Players.

**1964.** 18th General Assembly of World Medical Association.
697 **227** 40 p. green .. .. 95 30

**1965.** World Ice Hockey Championships.
698. **228.** 35 p. blue .. .. 70 30

229. Centenary Medal.

230. K. J. Stahlberg and Runeberg's sculpture, "Lex".

**1965.** Centenary of Finnish Communal Self-Government.
699. **229.** 35 p. green .. .. 65 30

**1965.** Birth Centenary of K. J. Stahlberg (statesman).
700. **230.** 35 p. brown .. .. 65 30

231. I.C.Y. Emblem

232. "The Fratricide".

**1965.** Int. Co-operation Year.
701. **231.** 40 p. multicoloured .. 65 30

**1965.** Birth Cent. of A. Gallen-Kallela (artist). Multicoloured.
702. 25 p. Type **232** .. .. 1·10 50
703. 35 p. "Head of a Young Girl" .. .. .. 1·10 50

233. Spitz.

234. Piano, Profile and Score of "Finlandia".

**1965.** Tuberculosis Relief Fund. Dogs.
704. 233. 15 p.+3 p. brn., & red 1·50 1·25
705. – 25 p.+4 p. blk. & red 2·25 1·75
706. – 35 p.+5 p. sep. & red 2·25 1·75
FINNISH DOGS: 25 p. Karelian bear dog. 35 p. Finnish stovare.

**1965.** Birth Cent. of Sibelius (composer).
707. 234. 25 p. violet .. .. 1·00 40
708. – 35 p. green .. .. 1·00 40
DESIGN: 35 p. Part of score of "Finlandia" and dove.

235. Dish Aerial.

236. "Winter Day" (after P. Halonen).

**1965.** Centenary of I.T.U.
709. 235. 35 p. blue .. .. 80 30

**1965.** Birth Cent. of Pekka Halonen (painter).
710. 236. 35 p. multicoloured .. 45 30

237. Europa "Sprig".

238. " Kiss of Life".

**1965.** Europa.
711. 237. 40 p. multicoloured .. 1·10 30

**1966.** Red Cross Fund. Multicoloured.
712 15 p.+3 p. Type 238 .. 1·00 1·00
713 25 p.+4 p. Diver and submerged car .. .. 1·00 1·00
714 35 p.+5 p. Sud-Aviation Alouette II Red Cross helicopter .. .. 1·00 1·00

239. "Growing Up".

240. Old Post Office.

**1966.** Centenary of Finnish Elementary School Decree.
715 239 35 p. bl & ultramarine 65 20

**1966.** "Nordia 1966" Stamp Exn., Helsinki, and Centenary of 1st Postage Stamps in Finnish Currency.
716 240 35 p. blue, brown & yell 3·75 6·75

241. Globe and U.N.E.S.C.O. Emblem.

242. Police Emblem.

**1966.** 20th Anniv. of U.N.E.S.C.O.
717. 241. 40 p. multicoloured .. 65 30

**1966.** 150th Anniv. of Finnish Police Force.
718. 242. 35 p. silver, blk. & bl. 80 30

243. Anniversary Medal (after K. Kallio).

244. U.N.I.C.E.F Emblem.

**1966.** 150th Anniv. of Finnish Insurance.
719. 243. 35 p. olive and lake .. 65 30

**1966.** 20th Anniv of U.N.I.C.E.F.
720 244 15 p. violet, green & bl 20 15

245. FINEFTA Symbol.

246. Windmill.

**1967.** Abolition of Industrial Customs Tariffs by European Free Trade Association.
721 245 40 p. blue .. .. 75 20

**1967.** 350th Anniv. of Uusikaupunki (Nystad).
722. 246. 40 p. multicoloured .. 65 20

247. Birch Tree and Foliage.

248. Mannerheim Statue (A. Tukiainen).

**1967.** Tuberculosis Relief Fund. Mult.
723. 20 p.+3 p. Type 247 .. 50 70
724. 25 p.+4 p. Pine and foliage 60 85
725. 40 p.+7 p. Spruce and foliage .. .. .. 60 85
See also Nos. 753/5.

**1967.** Birth Cent. of Marshal Mannerheim.
726. 248. 40 p multicoloured .. 65 20

249. "Solidarity".

250. Watermark of Thomasbole Factory.

**1967.** Finnish Settlers in Sweden.
727. 249. 40 p. multicoloured .. 65 20

**1967.** 300th Anniv. of Finnish Paper Industry.
728. 250. 40 p. blue and bistre .. 65 20

251. Martin Luther (from painting by Lucas Cranach the Elder).

252. Horse-drawn Ambulance.

**1967.** 450th Anniv. of the Reformation.
729. 251. 40 p. multicoloured .. 65 20

**1967.** Red Cross Fund. Multicoloured.
730. 20 p.+3 p. Type 252 .. 60 70
731. 25 p.+4 p. Modern ambulance .. .. 70 85
732. 40 p.+7 p. Red Cross emblem .. .. 70 85

253. Northern Lights.

254. Z. Topelius and " Bluebird ".

**1967.** 50th Anniv. of Independence.
733 253 20 p. green and blue .. 65 15
734 – 25 p. blue & light blue 65 15
735 – 40 p. mauve and blue 65 15
DESIGNS: 25 p. Flying swan. 40 p. Ear of wheat.

**1968.** 150th Anniv. of Zacharias Topelius (writer).
736. 254. 25 p. multicoloured .. 65 30

255. Skiing.

**1968.** Winter Tourism.
737. 255. 25 p. multicoloured .. 75 30

256. " Paper-making" (from wood relief by H. Autere).

257. W.H.O. Emblem.

**1968.** 150th Anniv. of Tervakoski Paper Factory.
738. 256. 45 p. brown, buff & red 65 30

**1968.** 20th Anniv. of W.H.O.
739. 257. 40 p. multicoloured .. 65 30

258. " Infantryman " (statue by L. Leppanen, Vaasa).

259. Holiday Camp.

**1968.** 50th Anniv. of Finnish Army. Mult.
740. 20 p Type 258 .. .. 85 15
741. 25 p. Memorial (V. Aaltonen), Hietaniemi cemetery .. .. 85 15
742. 40 p. Modern soldier .. 85 15

**1968.** Tourism.
743. 259. 25 p. multicoloured .. 75 30

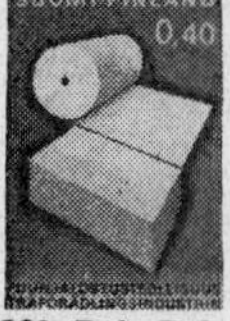

260. Pulp Bale (with outline of tree in centre) and Paper Reel.

261. O. Merikanto.

**1968.** Finnish Wood-processing Industry.
744. 260. 40 p. multicoloured .. 65 30

**1968.** Birth Cent. of Oskar Merikanto (composer).
745. 261. 40 p. multicoloured .. 65 30

262. Mustola Lock.

263. Dock Cranes, "Ivalo" (container ship) and Chamber of Commerce Emblem.

**1968.** Opening of Saima Canal.
746. 262. 40 p. multicoloured .. 65 30

**1968.** "Finnish Economic Life". 50th Anniv. of Finnish Central Chamber of Commerce.
747. 263. 40 p. multicoloured .. 90 30

264. Welding.

265. Lyre Emblem.

**1968.** Finnish Metal Industry.
748. 264. 40 p. multicoloured .. 65 30

**1968.** Finnish Student Unions.
749 265 40 p. brn, bl & ultram 65 30

**1969.** 50th Anniv. of Northern Countries' Union. As T 159 of Denmark.
750. 40 p. blue .. .. .. 1·50 30

266. City Hall and Arms, Kemi.

267. Colonnade.

**1969.** Cent. of Kemi (Kemin).
751. 266. 40 p. multicoloured .. 65 30

**1969.** Europa.
752. 267. 40 p. multicoloured .. 3·00 55

**1969.** Tuberculosis Relief Fund. As T 247, but inscr. " 1969 ". Multicoloured.
753. 20 p.+3 p. Juniper and berries .. .. .. 80 80
754. 25 p.+4 p. Aspen and catkins .. .. .. 1·00 1·00
755. 40 p.+7 p. Wild cherry and flowers .. .. .. 1·00 1·00

268. I.L.O. Emblem.

**1969.** 50th Anniv of I.L.O.
756 268 40 p. blue, lt blue & red 65 30

269. A. Jarnefelt (after V. Sjostrom).

270. Fairs Symbol.

**1969.** Birth Centenary of Armas Jarnefelt (composer).
757. 269. 40 p. multicoloured .. 80 30

**1969.** Finnish National and Int. Fairs.
758. 270. 40 p. multicoloured .. 65 30

271. J. Linnankoski.

272. Board Emblems.

**1969.** Birth Centenary of Johannes Linnankoski (writer).
759 271 40 p. multicoloured .. 65 30

**1969.** Cent of Central Schools Board.
760 272 40 p. violet, grn & grey 65 30

273. Douglas DC-8-62F over Helsinki Airport.

274. Golden Eagle and Eyrie.

**1969.** Aviation.
761. 273. 25 p. multicoloured .. 90 65

**1970.** Nature Conservation Year.
762. 274. 30 p. multicoloured .. 4·50 95

275. " Fabric " Factories.

276. " Molecular Structure " and Factories, Nysta.

**1970.** Finnish Textile Industry.
763. 275. 50 p. multicoloured .. 75 30

**1970.** Finnish Chemical Industry.
764. 276. 50 p. multicoloured .. 75 30

277. U.N.E.S.C.O. Emblem and Lenin.

278. " The Seven Brothers ".

**1970.** Finnish Co-operation with United Nations.
765. 277. 30 p. multicoloured .. 70 30
766. – 30 p. multicoloured .. 70 30
767. – 50 p. gold, ultram. & bl. 70 30
DESIGNS—VERT. 30 p. (No. 765), Type 277 (Lenin Symposium of U.N.E.S.C.O., Tampere). 30 p. (No. 766), " Nuclear data " (Int. Atomic Energy Agency Conference, Otaniemi). HORIZ. 50 p. U.N. emblem and globe (United Nations 25th Anniv.).

**1970.** Red Cross Fund. Multicoloured.
768. 25 p.+5 p. Type 278 .. 80 80
769. 30 p.+6 p. "Juhani on top of Impivaara" (vert.) .. 1·00 1·00
770. 50 p.+10 p. "The Pale Maiden" .. .. .. 1·00 1·00

279. Invalid playing Handball.

280. " Aurora Society Meeting " (E. Jarnefelt).

**1970.** 30th Anniv of Finnish Invalids League.
771 279 50 p. black, red & orge 80 30

**1970.** Bicent of Aurora Society.
772 280 50 p. multicoloured .. 65 30

**281.** City Hall and Old Schoolhouse, Uusikaarlepyy.
**282.** Pres. Kekkonen (from medal by A. Tukiainen).

**1970.** 350th Anniv of Uusikaarlepyy (Nykarleby) and Kokkola (Gamlakarleby) (towns). Multicoloured.
773 50 p. Type **281** .. .. 75 30
774 50 p. Kokkola and arms .. 75 30

**1970.** President Urho Kekkonen's 70th Birthday.
775. **282.** 50 p. silver and blue .. 65 20

**283.** "S.A.L.T." and Globe.
**284.** Pres. Paasikivi (after sculpture by E. Renvall).

**1970.** Strategic Arms Limitation Talks, Helsinki.
776. **283.** 50 p. multicoloured. .. 80 20

**1970.** Birth Cent. of President Paasikivi.
777. **284.** 50 p. blk. blue & gold .. 95 20

**285.** Cogwheels.
**286.** Felling Trees.

**1971.** Finnish Industry.
778. **285.** 50 p. multicoloured .. 65 30

**1971.** Tuberculosis Relief Fund. Timber Industry. Multicoloured.
779. 25 p.+5 p. Type **286** .. 75 75
780. 30 p.+6 p. Floating log-"train" .. .. .. 1·00 1·00
781. 50 p.+10 p. Sorting logs .. 1·00 1·00

**287.** Europa Chain.
**288.** Tornio Church.

**1971.** Europa.
782. **287.** 50 p. yell., pink & blk. 3·00 30

**1971.** 350th Anniv. of Tornio (Torneaa).
783. **288.** 50 p. multicoloured .. 85 30

**289.** "Front-page News" (in Swedish, Finnish and French).
**290.** Hurdling, High-jumping and Discus-throwing.

**1971.** Bicentenary of Finnish Press.
784. **289.** 50 p. multicoloured .. 70 30

**1971.** European Athletic Championships, Helsinki. Multicoloured.
785. 30 p. Type **290** .. .. 1·40 55
786. 50 p. Throwing the javelin and running .. .. 2·10 55
These two designs form a composite picture when placed side by side.

**291.** "Lightning" Class Yachts.
**292.** Silver Pot, Seal and Tools.

**1971.** Int. "Lightning" Class Sailing Championships, Helsinki.
787. **291.** 50 p. multicoloured .. 1·25 30

**1971.** 60th Anniv. of Jewellery and Precious-metal Crafts.
788. **292.** 50 p. multicoloured .. 90 30

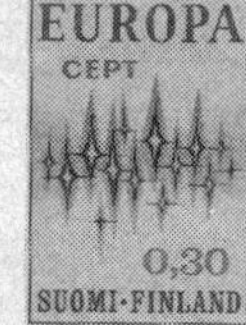


**293.** Plastic Buttons.
**294.** "Communications".

**1971.** Finnish Plastics Industry.
789. **293.** 50 p. multicoloured .. 80 30

**1972.** Europa.
790. **294.** 30 p. multicoloured .. 2·75 45
791. 50 p. multicoloured .. 3·25 45

**295.** National Theatre Building.
**296.** Globe.

**1972.** Cent. of Finnish National Theatre.
792. **295.** 50 p. multicoloured .. 80 30

**1972.** Conclusion of the Strategic Arms Limitation Talks, Helsinki.
793. **296.** 50 p. multicoloured .. 90 30

**297.** Map and Arms.
**298.** Cadet Ship "Suomen Joutsen".

**1972.** 50th Anniv of Local Self-government for the Aland Islands.
794 **297** 50 p. multicoloured .. 3·75 70

**1972.** Start of the Tall Ships' Race, Helsinki.
795. **298.** 50 p. multicoloured .. 1·40 35

**299.** Post Office, Tampere.
**301.** Blood Donation.

**1972.** Multicoloured.
797 40 p. Type **299** .. .. 70 10
798 60 p. National Museum (25 × 37 mm) .. .. 70 10
799 70 p. Market Place, Helsinki (39 × 27 mm) .. 70 10
800 80 p. As 70 p. .. .. 50 10

**1972.** Red Cross Fund. Blood Service. Multicoloured.
820. 25 p.+5 p. Type **301** .. 75 75
821. 30 p.+6 p. Laboratory research (vert.) .. .. 1·00 1·00
822. 50 p.+10 p. Blood transfusion 1·00 1·00

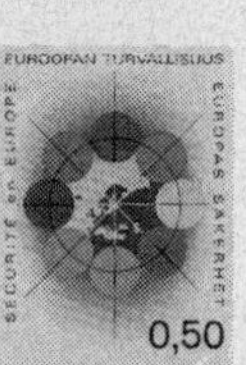


**302.** Voyri Man.
**303.** "European Co-operation".

**1972.** Ancient and National Costumes. Multicoloured.
823. 50 p. Pernio woman .. 2·00 60
824. 50 p. Married couple, Tenala 2·00 60
825. 50 p. Nastola girl .. 2·00 60
826. 50 p. Type **302** .. 2·00 60
827. 50 p. Lapp winter costumes 2·00 60
828. 60 p. Kaukola girl .. 4·75 60
829. 60 p. Jaaski woman .. 4·75 60
830. 60 p. Koivisto couple .. 4·75 60
831. 60 p. Mother and son, Sakyla 4·75 60
832. 60 p. Heinavesi girl .. 4·75 60

**1972.** European Security and Co-operation Conf., Helsinki (1st issue).
833. **303.** 50 p. multicoloured .. 2·25 35
See also No. 839.

**304.** "Treaty" and National Colours.
**305.** Pres. K. Kallio.

**1973.** 25th Anniv. of Friendship Treaty with Russia.
834. **304.** 60 p. multicoloured .. 75 25

**1973.** Birth Cent. of Pres. Kyosti Kallio.
835. **305.** 60 p. multicoloured .. 85 20

**306.** Europa "Posthorn".
**307.** "EUROPA" on Map.

**1973.** Europa.
836. **306.** 60 p. grn., turq. & blue 1·10 20

**1973.** Nordic Countries' Postal Co-operation. As T **201** of Denmark.
837. 60 p. multicoloured .. 85 15
838. 70 p. multicoloured .. 85 25

**1973.** European Security and Co-operation Conf., Helsinki (2nd issue).
839. **307.** 70 p. multicoloured .. 50 20

**308.** Canoe Paddle.
**309.** Radiosonde Balloon.

**1973.** World Canoeing Championships, Tampere.
840. **308.** 60 p. multicoloured .. 65 20

**1973.** Centenary of World Meteorological Organization.
841. **309.** 60 p. multicoloured .. 40 20

**310.** E. Saarinen.
**311.** "Young Girl with Lamb" (H. Simberg).

**1973.** Birth Cent. of Eliel Saarinen (architect).
842. **310.** 60 p. multicoloured .. 40 20

**1973.** Tuberculosis Relief Fund. Artists' Birth Centenaries. Multicoloured.
843. 30 p.+5 p. Type **311** .. 75 75
844. 40 p.+10 p. "Summer Evening" (W. Sjostrom) 1·25 1·25
845. 60 p.+15 p. "At a Mountain Spring" (J. Rissanen) 1·25 1·25

**312.** Douglas DC-10-30.
**313.** Santa Claus.

**1973.** 50th Annivs. of Finnair (airline) and Regular Air Services in Finland.
846. **312.** 60 p. multicoloured .. 60 25

**1973.** Christmas.
847. **313.** 30 p. multicoloured .. 65 10

**314.** Scene from "The Barber of Seville".

**1973.** Centenary of Finnish State Opera Company.
848. **314.** 60 p. multicoloured .. 70 20

## MINIMUM PRICE

The minimum price quoted is 10p which represents a handling charge rather than a basis for valuing common stamps. For further notes about prices see introductory pages.

**315.** Porcelain Products.
**316.** "Paavo Nurmi" (Statue by W. Aaltonen).

**1973.** Finnish Porcelain Industry.
849. **315.** 60 p. grn., blk. & bl.. .. 45 20

**1973.** Paavo Nurmi (Olympic athlete) Commemoration.
850 **316** 60 p. multicoloured .. 45 15

**317.** Hanko Casino, Harbour and Map.
**318.** Arms of Finland, 1581.

**1974.** Centenary of Hanko (Hango).
851. **317.** 60 p. multicoloured .. 75 25

**1974.**
852. **318.** 10 m. multicoloured 2·75 10
852a. – 20 m. multicoloured 6·75 35
DESIGN: 20 m. Arms as in T **318** but different border.

**319.** Ice Hockey Players.

**1974.** World and European Ice Hockey Championships.
853. **319.** 60 p. multicoloured .. 90 25

**320.** Herring Gulls.

**1974.** Baltic Area Marine Environmental Conference, Helsinki.
854. **320.** 60 p. multicoloured .. 1·10 55

**321.** "Goddess of Victory bestowing Wreath on Youth" (W. Aaltonen).
**322.** Ilmari Kianto.

**1974.** Europa.
855. **321.** 70 p. multicoloured .. 2·75 30

**1974.** Birth Centenary of Ilmari Kianto ("Iki Kianto") (writer).
856. **322.** 60 p. multicoloured .. 70 25

**323.** Society Emblem.
**324.** "Rationalisation".

**1974.** Finnish Society for Popular Education.
857. **323.** 60 p. multicoloured .. 70 25

**1974.** Finnish Rationalisation in Social Development.
858. **324.** 60 p. multicoloured .. 70 25

**325.** Beefsteak Morel. **326.** U.P.U. Emblem.

**1974.** Red Cross Fund. Mushrooms (1st series). Multicoloured.

859 35 p.+5 p. Type **325** .. 1·50 1·10
860 50 p.+10 p. Chanterelle .. 1·50 1·25
861 60 p.+15 p. Cep .. .. 1·50 1·25
See also Nos. 937/9 and 967/9.

**1974.** Cent. of Universal Postal Union.

862. **326.** 60 p. multicoloured .. 50 25
863. 70 p. multicoloured .. 50 25

**327.** Christmas Gnomes. **328.** Aunessilta Granite Bridge and Modern Reinforced Concrete Bridge.

**1974.** Christmas.

864. **327.** 35 p. multicoloured .. 95 10

**1974.** 175th Anniv. of Finnish Road and Waterways Board.

865. **328.** 60 p. multicoloured .. 50 20

**329.** National Arms. **330.** Finnish 32 p. Stamp of 1875.

**1975.**

865a 329 10 p. purple .. 10 10
865c 20 p. yellow .. 10 10
865d 30 p. red .. .. 10 10
866 40 p. orange .. 10 10
867 50 p. green .. 10 10
868 60 p. blue .. .. 20 10
869 70 p. brown .. 20 10
1155 80 p. red and green 20 10
871a 90 p. violet .. 25 10
872 1 m. brown .. 30 10
873 1 m. 10 yellow .. 30 10
874 1 m. 20 blue .. 30 10
875 1 m. 30 green .. 30 10
875a 1 m. 40 violet .. 30 10
875b 1 m. 50 blue .. 35 10
875c 1 m. 60 red .. 35 10
875d 1 m. 70 grey .. 40 10
875e 1 m. 80 green .. 45 10
875f 1 m. 90 orange .. 45 10
1157 2 m. green .. 50 10

**1975.** "Nordia 1975" Stamp Exhibition.

876. **330.** 70 p. brn., blk. & buff 2·50 3·50

**331.** " A Girl Combing Her Hair " (M. Enckell). **332.** Office Seal.

**1975.** Europa. Multicoloured.

877. 70 p. Type **331** .. .. 1·90 35
878. 90 p. " Washerwomen " (T. Sallinen) .. .. 1·90 35

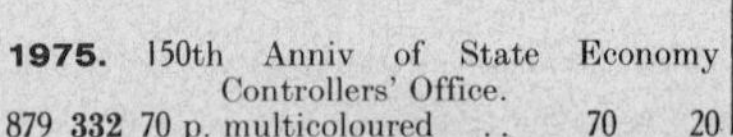

**1975.** 150th Anniv of State Economy Controllers' Office.

879 332 70 p. multicoloured .. 70 20

**333.** "Niilo Saarinen" (lifeboat) and Sinking Ship.

**1975.** 12th International Salvage Conference, Helsinki.

880. **333.** 70 p. multicoloured .. 1·10 40

**334.** "Pharmacology". **335.** Olavinlinna Castle.

**1975.** 6th International Pharmacological Congress, Helsinki.

881. **334.** 70 p. multicoloured .. 75 20

**1975.** 500th Anniv. of Olavinlinna Castle.

882. **335.** 70 p. multicoloured .. 70 20

**336.** Finlandia Hall (Conference Head-quarters) and Barn Swallows. **337.** " Echo " (E. Thesleff).

**1975.** European Security and Co-operation Conference, Helsinki.

883. **336.** 90 p. multicoloured .. 1·10 30

**1975.** Tuberculosis Relief Fund. Paintings by female artists. Multicoloured.

884. 40 p.+10 p. Type **337** .. 70 70
885. 60 p.+15 p. "Portrait of Hilda Wiik" (Maria Wiik) .. .. 1·10 1·10
886. 70 p.+20 p. "At Home" (Helene Schjerfbeck) .. 1·40 1·40

**338.** Men and Women supporting Globe. **339.** Graphic Quarter-circle.

**1975.** International Women's Year.

887. **338.** 70 p. multicoloured .. 75 20

**1975.** Centenary of Finnish Society of Industrial Art.

888. **339.** 70 p. multicoloured .. 70 20

**340.** Nativity Play. **341.** State Debenture.

**1975.** Christmas.

889. **340.** 40 p. multicoloured .. 95 10

**1975.** Cent. of Finnish State Treasury.

890. **341.** 80 p. multicoloured .. 70 20

**342.** Finnish Glider. **343.** Disabled Ex-servicemen's Association Emblem.

**1976.** 15th World Gliding Championships, Rayskala.

891. **342.** 80 p. multicoloured .. 60 15

**1976.** Finnish War Invalids Fund.

892. **343.** 70 p.+30 p. mult. .. 90 80

**344.** Cheese Frames. **345.** Heikki Klemetti.

**1976.** Traditional Finnish Arts.

893 – 1 m. 50 multicoloured 75 10
893a – 2 m. multicoloured .. 50 10
893b – 2 m. 20 multicoloured 75 20
894 344 2 m. 50 multicoloured 95 10
895 – 3 m. multicoloured .. 95 10
896 – 4 m. 50 multicoloured 1·50 10
897 – 5 m. multicoloured .. 1·60 10
898 – 6 m. multicoloured 1·90 10
899 – 7 m. multicoloured .. 2·25 20
899a – 8 m. brown and black 2·75 20
899b – 9 m. black and blue 2·90 20
899c – 12 m. ochre, drab and brown .. .. 3·75 30

DESIGNS—VERT. 1 m. 50, Rusko drinking bowl, 1542. 4 m. 50, Spinning distaffs. 5 m. Weathercock, Kirvu (metalwork). 6 m. Kaspaikka (Karelian towel). 7 m. Bridal rug, 1815. 8 m. Arsenal door, Hollola church (iron forging). HORIZ. 2 m. Old-style sauna. 2 m. 20, Kerimaki Church and belfry (peasant architecture). 3 m. Shuttle and raanu (patterned cover). 9 m. Four-pronged fish spear, c. 1000. 12 m. Damask with tulip pattern.

**1976.** Birth Centenary of Professor Heikki Klemetti (composer).

900. **345.** 80 p. multicoloured .. 90 20

**346.** Map of Finnish Dialect Regions. **347.** " Aino Ackte in Paris " (A. Edelfelt).

**1976.** Cent. of Finnish Language Society.

901. **346.** 80 p. multicoloured .. 50 20

**1976.** Birth Cent. of Aino Ackte (opera singer).

902. **347.** 70 p. multicoloured .. 60 20

**348.** Ancient Knives and Belts. **349.** " Radio Broadcasting ".

**1976.** Europa.

903. **348.** 80 p. multicoloured .. 2·75 30

**1976.** 50th Anniv of Radio Broadcasting in Finland.

904 349 80 p. multicoloured .. 75 20

**350.** Wedding Dance.

**1976.** Tuberculosis Relief Fund. Traditional Wedding Customs. Multicoloured.

905. 50 p.+10 p. Wedding procession (horiz.) .. 75 75
906. 70 p.+15 p. Type **350** .. 1·00 1·00
907. 80 p.+20 p. Wedding breakfast (horiz.) .. 1·00 1·00

**351.** Sleigh arriving at Church.

**1976.** Christmas.

908. **351.** 50 p. multicoloured .. 70 10

**352.** Medieval Seal and Text.

**1976.** 700th Anniv. of Cathedral Chapter, Turku.

909. **352.** 80 p. multicoloured .. 70 20

**353.** Hugo Alvar Aalto and Finlandia Hall, Helsinki.

**1976.** Hugo Alvar Aalto (architect) Commemoration.

910. **353.** 80 p. multicoloured .. 70 20

**354.** " Disaster Relief ". **355.** Figure Skating.

**1977.** Red Cross Fund. Centenary of Finnish Red Cross. Multicoloured.

911. 50 p.+10 p. Type **354** .. 45 45
912. 80 p.+15 p. " Community Work " .. .. 55 55
913. 90 p.+20 p. " Blood Transfusion Service " .. 55 55

**1977.** European Figure Skating Championships, Helsinki.

914. **355.** 90 p. multicoloured .. 75 20

**1977.** Northern Countries' Co-operation in Nature Conservation and Environment Protection. As T **229** of Denmark.

915 90 p. multicoloured .. 80 25
916 1 m. multicoloured .. 80 25

**356.** Ice-breaker and Freighter.

**1977.** Centenary of Winter Navigation between Finland and Sweden.

917. **356.** 90 p. multicoloured .. 90 40

**357.** " Nuclear Reactor ".

**1977.** Inauguration of Hastholm Island Nuclear Power Station.

918. **357.** 90 p. multicoloured .. 70 20

**358.** Autumn Landscape.

**1977.** Europa.

919. **358.** 90 p. multicoloured .. 1·60 20

**359.** Tree with Nest. **360.** New Church of Valamo Cloister, Heinavesi.

**1977.** 75th Anniv. of Co-operative Banks.

920. **359.** 90 p. multicoloured .. 70 20

**1977.** 800th Anniv. of Finnish Orthodoxy and Inauguration of Valamo Cloister.

921. **360.** 90 p. multicoloured .. 70 20

361. Paavo Ruotsalainen. 362. " Defence and Protection ".

**1977.** Birth Centenary of Paavo Ruotsalaninen (leader of Pietistic Movement).
922. **361.** 90 p. multicoloured .. 70 20

**1977.** Civil Defence.
923. **362.** 90 p. multicoloured .. 70 20

363. Volleyball. 364. Women's Relay Skiing.

**1977.** European Volleyball Championships.
924. **363.** 90 p. multicoloured .. 90 20

**1977.** World Ski Championships, Lahti. Multicoloured.
925. 80 p.+40 p. Type **364** .. 2·00 2·75
926. 1 m.+50 p. Ski jumper .. 1·50 1·50

365. Children taking Water to the Sauna. 366. Finnish Flag.

**1977.** Christmas.
927. **365.** 50 p. multicoloured .. 90 10

**1977.** 60th Anniv. of Independence.
928. **366.** 80 p. multicoloured .. 70 15
929. 1 m. multicoloured (37 × 25½ mm.) .. 90 20

367. Early and Modern Telephones. 368. Kotka Harbour.

**1977.** Centenary of Finnish Telephone.
930. **367.** 1 m. multicoloured .. 70 20

**1978.** Centenary of Kotka.
931. **368.** 1 m. multicoloured .. 1·10 20

369. Sanatorium, Paimio.

**1978.** Europa. Multicoloured.
932. 1 m. Type **369** .. .. 5·25 95
933. 1 m. 20 Studio House, Hvittrask (37 × 25½ mm) 6·25 7·25

370. Buses.

**1978.** Provincial Bus Service.
934. **370.** 1 m. multicoloured .. 80 15

371. Eino Leino.

**1978.** Birth Cent. of Eino Leino (poet).
935. **371.** 1 m. multicoloured .. 90 20

372. Function Theory Diagram. 373. Girl feeding Corn to Great Tits.

**1978.** International Congress of Mathematicians, Finland.
936. **372.** 1 m. multicoloured .. 70 20

**1978.** Red Cross Fund. Mushrooms (2nd series). As T **325**. Multicoloured.
937 50 p.+10 p. "Lactarius deterrimus" .. .. 90 90
938 80 p.+15 p. Parasol mushroom (vert) .. 1·40 1·40
939 1 m.+20 p. The gypsy .. 1·40 1·40

**1978.** Christmas.
940. **373.** 50 p. multicoloured .. 65 10

374. Child, Hearts and Flowers. 375. Orienteer.

**1979.** International Year of the Child.
941. **374.** 1 m. 10 multicoloured .. 95 15

**1979.** 8th World Orienteering Championships.
942. **375.** 1 m. 10 multicoloured 55 20

376. Old Training College, Hamina, and Academy Flag. 377. Turku Buildings.

**1979.** Bicent. of Officer Training.
943. **376.** 1 m. 10 multicoloured 40 20

**1979.** 750th Anniv. of Turku (Abo).
944. **377.** 1 m. 10 multicoloured 40 20

378. Tram in City Street. 379. " Tammerkoski Waterfall " (lithograph, P. Gaimard).

**1979.** Helsinki Tram Service.
945. **378.** 1 m. 10 multicoloured 75 20

**1979.** Bicentenary of Tampere (Tammerfors) (1st issue).
946 **379** 90 p. brown, buff & blk 40 15
See also No. 953.

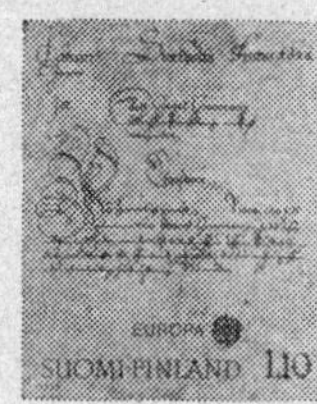


380. Letter establishing Finnish Postal Service, 1638.

**1979.** Europa.
947 **380** 1 m. 10 grey, ochre and brown .. .. .. 1·50 25
948 – 1 m. 30 multicoloured 2·40 1·25
Design—horiz: 1 m. 30, A. E. Edelcrantz's optical telegraph, 1796.

381. Pehr Kalm and Title Page. 382. Town Street with Trade-signs.

**1979.** Tuberculosis Relief Fund. Finnish Scientists. Multicoloured.
949. 60 p.+10 p. Type **381** .. 50 50
950. 90 p.+15 p. Wheat and title page of Pehr Gadd's " Svenska Landt-skotselen " (vert.) .. .. 55 55
951. 1 m. 10+20 p. Petter Forsskaal and title page 55 55

**1979.** Cent. of Business and Industry Law.
952. **382.** 1 m. 10 multicoloured 40 15

383. Stylised View of Tampere.

**1979.** Bicentenary of Tampere (2nd issue).
953 **383** 1 m. 10 multicoloured 60 15

384. Early and Modern Cars at Pedestrian Crossing. 385. House of Korppi, Lapinjarvi, Uusimaa.

**1979.** The Private Car.
954. **384.** 1 m. 10 multicoloured 50 20

**1979.** Peasant Architecture. Mult.
955. 1 m. 10 Type **385** .. 40 40
956. 1 m. 10 House of Syrjala, Tammela, Hame (left-hand part) .. .. 40 40
957. 1 m. 10 House of Syrjala (right-hand part) .. 40 40
958. 1 m. 10 House of Murtovaara, Valtimo, North Karelia 40 40
959. 1 m. 10 House of Antila, Lapua, Pohjanmaa .. 40 40
960. 1 m. 10 Gable loft of Luukila, Haukipudas and loft of Keskikangas, Yliharma, Pohjanmaa 40 40
961. 1 m. 10 Gate, house of Kanajarvi, Kalvola, Hame .. .. .. 40 40
962. 1 m. 10 Porch, house of Havuselka, Kauhajoki, Pohjanmaa .. .. 40 40
963. 1 m. 10 Dinner bell and House of Maki-Rasinpera, Kuortane, Pohjanmaa 40 40
964. 1 m. 10 Gable and eaves of granary of Rasula, Kuortane, Pohjanmaa .. 40 40
See also Nos. 1024/33.

386. " Brownies " feeding Horse. 387. Maria Jotuni.

**1979.** Christmas.
965. **386.** 60 p. multicoloured .. 65 10

**1980.** Birth Cent. of Maria Jotuni (writer).
966. **387.** 1 m. 10 multicoloured 40 15

**1980.** Finnish Red Cross Fund. Mushrooms (3rd series). As T **325**. Multicoloured.
967 60 p.+10 p. Woolly milk cap .. .. .. 80 80
968 90 p.+15 p. Red cap .. 1·40 1·40
969 1 m. 10+20 p. "Russula paludosa" .. .. 1·40 1·40

388. Frans Eemil Sillanpaa.

**1980.** Europa. Finnish Nobel Prize Winners. Multicoloured.
970. 1 m. 10 Type **388** (literature, 1939) .. .. .. 1·25 30
971. 1 m. 30 Artturi Ilmari Virtanen (Chemistry, 1945) (vert.) 1·50 95

389. Pres. Kekkonen. 390. Back-piece Harness.

**1980.** President Urho Kekkonen's 80th Birthday.
973. **389.** 1 m. 10 multicolured .. 60 15

**1980.** Nordic Countries' Postal Co-operation. Multicoloured.
974 1 m. 10 Type **390** .. .. 65 15
975 1 m. 30 Collar harness (vert) .. .. .. 65 25

391. Biathlon. 392. Trials of Strength.

**1980.** Biathlon World Championship Lahti.
976. **391.** 1 m. 10 multicoloured 70 20

**1980.** Christmas. Multicoloured.
977. 60 p. Type **392** .. .. 55 10
978. 1 m. 10 " To put out the shoemaker's eye " (children's game) .. 70 15

393. Kauhaneva Swamps, Kauhajoki.

**1981.** National Parks.
979 **393** 70 p. pink, brn & grn 15 10
980 – 1 m. 60 multicoloured 60 10
981 – 1 m. 80 multicoloured 1·40 20
982 – 2 m. 40 multicoloured 75 15
Designs—vert. 1 m. 60, Forest of Multiharju, Seitseminen National Park. horiz. 1 m. 80, Razorbills, Eastern Gulf National Park. 2 m. 40, Urho Kekkonen National Park.

394. Boxing. 395. Glass-blowing and 19th century Bottle.

**1981.** European Boxing Championships, Tampere.
990. **394.** 1 m. 10 multicoloured 45 20

**1981.** 300th Anniv. of Finnish Glass Industry.
991. **395.** 1 m. 10 multicoloured 45 20

396. "Furst Menschikoff" (paddle-steamer).

**1981.** " Nordia 1981 " Stamp Exhibition, Helsinki.
992. **396.** 1 m. 10 brn. and stone 4·25 4·25

397. Rowing to Church.

**1981.** Europa. Multicoloured.
993. 1 m. 10 Type **397** .. 75 15
994. 1 m. 50 Midsummer Eve celebrations .. .. 90 25

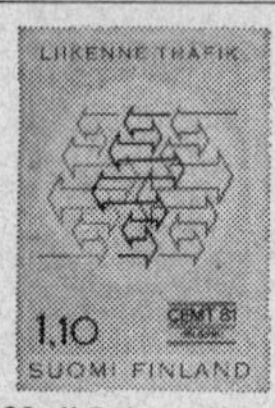

**398.** " International Traffic Movement ".

**399.** Children on Winged Horse.

**1981.** Council Session of European Conference of Ministers of Transport, Finland.
995. **398.** 1 m. 10 multicoloured 45 20

**1981.** Cent. of Finnish Youth Associations.
996. **399.** 1 m. multicoloured .. 40 20

**400.** Fuchsia.

**401.** Face on Graph.

**1981.** Tuberculosis Relief Fund. Potted Plants. Multicoloured.
997. 70 p. + 10 p. Type **400** .. 70 70
998. 1 m. + 15 p. African Violet (" Saintpaulia ionantha ") 95 95
999. 1 m. 10 + 20 p. Pelargonium 95 95

**1981.** International Year of Disabled Persons.
1000. **401.** 1 m. 10 multicoloured 45 20

**402.** Children bringing Home Christmas Tree.

**404.** Hame Castle.

**1981.** Christmas. Multicoloured.
1001. 70 p. Type **402** .. .. 70 10
1002. 1 m. 10 Decorating the Christmas tree (vert.) 70 10

**1982.**
1007 **404** 90 p. brown .. .. 25 10
1008 – 1 m. brown and blue 25 10
DESIGN—VERT. 1 m. Windmill, Harrstrom.

**405.** First Issue of " Om konsten att ratt Behaga " and Modern Periodical.

**406.** Kuopio Cathedral and Puijo Tower.

**1982.** Bicent. of Finnish Periodicals.
1015. **405.** 1 m. 20 multicoloured 45 20

**1982.** Bicentenary of Kuopio.
1016. **406.** 1 m. 20 multicoloured 45 20

**407.** Neck of Stringed Instrument and Staves of Music.

**408** Flats, Factories and Houses.

**1982.** Music Jubilee.
1017. **407.** 1 m. 20 multicoloured 45 20

**1982.** Centenary of Electricity in Finland.
1018 **408** 1 m. 20 multicoloured 70 20

**409.** Vegetable and Fruit Garden.

**410.** Cover of " Abckiria " and sculpture of M. Agricola by O. Jauhiainen.

**1982.** Cent. of First Finnish Horticultural Society.
1019. **409.** 1 m. 10 multicoloured 45 20

**1982.** Europa. Multicoloured.
1020 1 m. 20 Type **410** .. 90 15
1021 1 m. 50 "Turku Academy Inaugural Procession in 1640" (fresco copied by Johannes Gebhard from painting by Albert Edelfelt) (47 × 31 mm) 1·40 40

**411.** Emblems and Symbolic Design.

**1982.** Int Monetary Fund and World Bank Committees' Meetings, Helsinki.
1022 **411** 1 m. 60 multicoloured 70 20

**412.** Interior of Parliament and " Future " (sculpture by W. Aaltonen).

**1982.** 75th Anniv of Single Chamber Parliament.
1023 **412** 2 m. 40 bl, dp bl & blk 70 25

**1982.** Manor Houses. As T **385**. Mult.
1024. 1 m. 20 Kuitia, 1490s .. 70 30
1025. 1 m. 20 Louhisaari, 1655 70 30
1026. 1 m. 20 Frugard, 1780 .. 70 30
1027. 1 m. 20 Jokioinen, 1798 .. 70 30
1028. 1 m. 20 Moisio, 1820 .. 70 30
1029. 1 m. 20 Sjundby, 1560s 70 30
1030. 1 m. 20 Fagervik, 1773 .. 70 30
1031. 1 m. 20 Mustio, 1792 .. 70 30
1032. 1 m. 20 Fiskars, 1818 .. 70 30
1033. 1 m. 20 Kotkaniemi, 1836 70 30

**413.** Garden Dormouse.

**1982.** Red Cross Fund. Endangered Mammals. Multicoloured.
1034. 90 p. + 10 p. Type **413** .. 70 70
1035. 1 m. 10 + 15 p. Siberian flying squirrel (vert.) .. 90 90
1036. 1 m. 20 + 20 p. European mink .. .. .. 90 90

**414.** Brownie Children feeding Forest Animals

**1982.** Christmas. Multicoloured.
1037. 90 p. Type **414** .. .. 65 10
1038. 1 m. 20 Brownie children eating porridge .. 65 10

**415.** Gold Prospector.

**1983.** Nordic Countries' Postal Co-operation. " Visit the North ". Multicoloured.
1039. 1 m. 20 Type **415** .. 45 20
1040. 1 m. 30 Descending the Kitajoki river rapids 70 15

**416.** Postman, Letters and Computer.

**418.** Flash Smelting.

**1983.** World Communications Year. Mult.
1041. 1 m. 30 Type **416** .. 45 20
1042. 1 m. 70 Modulated wave, pulse stream and optical cables .. 45 30

**1983.** Europa. Multicoloured.
1044. 1 m. 30 Type **418** .. 2·10 15
1045. 1 m. 70 Interior of Temppeliaukio Church (Timo and Tuomo Suomalainen) .. .. 2·10 85

**419.** President Relander.

**420.** Throwing the Javelin.

**1983.** Birth Cent. of Lauri Kristian Relander (President, 1925–1931).
1046. **419.** 1 m. 30 multicoloured 45 20

**1983.** World Athletics Championships, Helsinki. Multicoloured.
1047. 1 m. 20 Type **420** .. .. 45 20
1048. 1 m. 30 Running (vert.) .. 45 15

**421.** Kuula and Ostrobothnia.

**422.** Chickweed Wintergreen.

**1983.** Birth Cent. of Toivo Kuula (composer).
1049. **421.** 1 m. 30 multicoloured 45 20

**1983.** Tuberculosis Relief Fund. Wild Flowers. Multicoloured.
1050. 1 m. + 20 p. Type **422** .. 75 75
1051. 1 m. 20 + 25 p. Marsh Violet .. .. .. 95 95
1052. 1 m. 30 + 30 p. Marsh Marigold .. .. 95 95

**423.** "Santa Claus" (Eija Myllyviita).

**424.** Koivisto.

**1983.** Christmas. Children's Drawings.
1053 **423** 1 m. blue & deep blue 60 10
1054 – 1 m. 30 multicoloured 60 10
DESIGN—VERT: 1 m. 30, "Two Candles" (Camilla Lindberg).

**1983.** President Mauno Henrik Koivisto's 60th Birthday.
1055 **424** 1 m. 30 bl, blk & dp bl 45 15

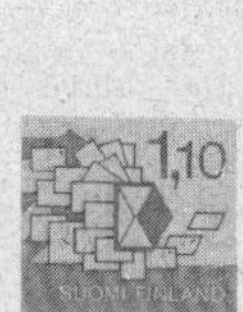

**425.** Second Class Letters.

**426.** Hydraulic Turbine Manufacture.

**1984.** Re-classification of Postal Items.
1056 **425** 1 m. 10 green .. 40 10
1057 – 1 m. 40 orange & red 40 10
DESIGN—VERT: 1 m. 40, First class letter.

**1984.** "Work and Skill" Centenary of Workers' Associations.
1058 **426** 1 m. 40 multicoloured 70 20

**427.** Crossbow, Pot and Chalice.

**428.** Bridge.

**1984.** Museum Activities.
1059. **427.** 1 m. 40 multicoloured 70 20

**1984.** Europa. 25th Anniv. of European Post and Telecommunications Conference.
1060. **428.** 1 m. 40 orange, deep orange and black 1·25 10
1061. 2 m. blue, violet and black .. .. 1·50 85

**429.** Globe as Jigsaw Puzzle.

**430.** Teeth and Dentist treating Patient.

**1984.** Finnish Red Cross Fund. Multicoloured.
1062. 1 m. 40 + 35 p. Type **429** .. 80 80
1063. 2 m. + 40 p. Spheres around globe .. .. .. 80 80

**1984.** International Dental Federation Congress, Helsinki.
1064 **430** 1 m. 40 multicoloured 90 20

**431.** Observatory, Planets and Sun.

**432.** Statute Book and Title Page.

**1984.** Centenary of University of Helsinki Observatory.
1065. **431.** 1 m. 10 multicoloured 45 20

**1984.** 250th Anniv. of 1734 Common Law.
1066. **432.** 2 m. multicoloured .. 65 20

**433.** "Mother and Child" (Waino Aaltonen) and Lines from "Song of my Heart".

**434.** Father Christmas and Brownie.

**1984.** 150th Birth Anniv. of Aleksis Kivi (writer).
1067. **433.** 1 m. 40 grey and black .. .. 70 20

**1984.** Christmas.
1068. **434.** 1 m. 10 multicoloured 65 10

**435.** Symbolic Representation of International Trade.

**1985.** 25th Anniversary of European Free Trade Association.
1069. **435.** 1 m. 20 multicoloured 70 20

**436.** Medal of Johan Ludwig Runeberg (by Walter Runeberg) and Emblem.

**437.** "Saints Sergei and Herman" (icon, Petros Sasaki).

**1985.** Centenary of Society of Swedish Literature in Finland.
1070. **436.** 1 m. 50 multicoloured 60 20

**1985.** Centenary of Saint Sergei and Saint Herman Order (home missionary organization of Finnish Orthodox Church).
1071. **437.** 1 m. 50 multicoloured 70 20

**438.** Pedri Semeikka (rune singer). **439.** "Mermaid" (Ville Vallgren).

**1985.** 150th Anniv of "Kalevala" (Karelian poems collected by Elias Lonnrot). Mult.

1072. 1 m. 50 Type **438** .. 60 15

1073. 2 m. 10 Larin Paraske (legend teller) (after Albert Edelfelt) .. 65 25

**1985.** "Nordia 1985" International Stamp Exhibition, Helsinki.

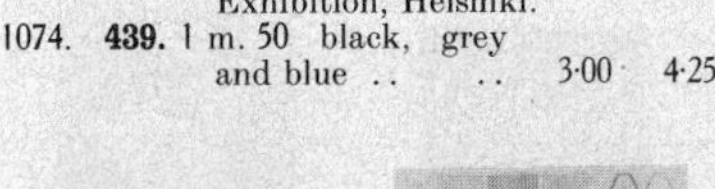

1074. **439.** 1 m. 50 black, grey and blue .. .. 3·00 4·25

**440.** 1886 5 m. Banknote. **441.** Children playing Recorders.

**1985.** Centenary of Finnish Banknote Printing. Multicoloured.

1075 1 m. 50 Type **440** .. 70 40

1076 1 m. 50 1909 50 m. banknote showing sailing ship (horiz) .. 70 40

1077 1 m. 50 50 m. banknote showing waterfall 70 40

1078 1 m. 50 1000 m. banknote showing lake (left side) 70 40

1079 1 m. 50 1000 m. banknote showing lake (right side) .. .. .. 70 40

1080 1 m. 50 500 m. banknote showing harvesters .. 70 40

1081 1 m. 50 1000 m. banknote showing arms and tree, and part of 50 m. banknote (horiz) .. 70 40

1082 1 m. 50 1955 5000 m. banknote showing J. V. Snellman .. .. 70 40

**1985.** Europa. Music Year. Multicoloured.

1083 1 m. 50 Type **441** .. 1·90 15

1084 2 m. 10 Cathedral columns and score of "Ramus Virens Olivarum" .. 2·10 85

**442.** Finlandia Hall and Barn Swallows. **443.** Provincial Arms and Seal of Per Brahe.

**1985.** 10th Anniv. of European Security and Co-operation Conference, Helsinki.

1085. **442.** 2 m. 10 multicoloured 80 30

**1985.** 350th Anniv. of Provincial Administration.

1086. **443.** 1 m. 50 multicoloured 70 20

**445.** I.Y.Y. Emblem. **446.** Bird Decoration and Tulips.

**1985.** International Youth Year.

1088. **445.** 1 m. 50 multicoloured 70 20

**1985.** Christmas. Multicoloured.

1089. 1 m. 20 Type **446.** .. 65 10

1090. 1 m. 20 St. Thomas's cross and hyacinths .. 65 10

**447.** Orbicular Granite. **449.** Baghdad Conference Palace (Kaija and Heikki Siren).

**448.** Saimaa Ringed Seal.

**1986.** Centenary of Geological Society. Multicoloured.

1091. 1 m. 30 Type **447** .. 1·10 25

1092. 1 m. 60 Rapakivi (granite) .. .. 1·10 25

1093. 2 m. 10 Veined gneiss .. 1·10 25

**1986.** Europa. Multicoloured.

1094. 1 m. 60 Type **448** .. 1·75 20

1095. 2 m 20 Landscape seen through window .. 1·75 85

**1986.** Modern Architecture. Multicoloured.

1096 1 m. 60 Type **449** .. 70 35

1097 1 m. 60 Lahti Theatre (Pekka Salminen and Esko Koivisto) (value in blue) .. .. 70 35

1098 1 m. 60 Kuusamo Municipal Offices (Marja and Keijo Petaja) (value in red) 70 35

1099 1 m. 60 Hamina police and court building (Timo and Tuomo Suomalainen) and Greek church (value in green) .. .. .. 70 35

1100 1 m. 60 Finnish Embassy, New Delhi (Raili and Reima Pietila) (value in green) .. .. 70 35

1101 1 m. 60 Day care centre, Western Sakyla (Kari Jarvinen and Timo Airas) (value in red) .. 70 35

**450.** Orange-tip. **451.** Auditorium, Joensuu.

**1986.** Finnish Red Cross Fund. Butterflies. Multicoloured.

1102 1 m. 60+40 p. Type **450** 1·10 1·00

1103 2 m. 10+45 p. Camberwell beauty .. .. 1·40 1·40

1104 5 m.+50 p. Apollo .. 2·25 2·25

**1986.** Nordic Countries' Postal Co-operation. Twinned Towns. Multicoloured.

1105. 1 m. 60 Type **451** .. 75 15

1106. 2 m. 20 Emblem of University of Jyvaskyla 75 25

**453.** Maupertuis, Globe, Quadrant and Sledge.

**1986.** 250th Anniv of Measurement of Arcs of Meridian.

1108 **453** 1 m. 60 blue, ultramarine and black .. 75 20

**454.** Kekkonen. **455.** Cloud, Rainbow and Emblem.

**1986.** Urho Kekkonen (President, 1956–81). Commemoration.

1109. **454.** 5 m. black .. .. 1·50 65

**1986.** International Peace Year.

1110. **455.** 1 m. 60 multicoloured 70 20

**456.** Angels and Garland.

**1986.** Christmas. Multicoloured.

1111. 1 m. 30 Type **456** .. 70 10

1112. 1 m. 30 Angels and garland (different) at 70 10

1113. 1 m. 60 Brownies and garland .. .. 70 10

**457.** Microchip. **458.** Prototype Metre Measuring Bar as Parcel.

**1987.** Centenary of Postal Savings Bank.

1114. **457.** 1 m. 70 multicoloured 50 20

**1987.** Centenary of Metric System in Finland.

1115. **458.** 1 m. 40 multicoloured 45 15

**459.** Cruise Liner, Diesel Train, Snow Scene and Skier. **460.** Wrestlers.

**1987.** Tourism. Multicoloured.

1116 1 m. 70 Type **459** .. 90 15

1117 2 m. 30 Douglas DC-10 airplane, bus, yachts on lake and hiker .. 90 25

**1987.** European Wrestling Championships, Helsinki.

1118. **460.** 1 m. 70 multicoloured 80 20

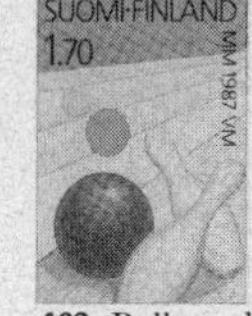


**461.** Madetoja and Score of Cradlesong. **462.** Balls and Pins.

**1987.** Birth Centenary of Leevi Madetoja (composer).

1119. **461.** 2 m. 10 multicoloured 95 20

**1987.** 11th World Ten Pin Bowling Championships.

1120. **462.** 1 m. 70 multicoloured 85 20

**463.** Profiles. **465.** "Strawberry Girl" (Nils Schillmark).

**1987.** 90th Anniv. of Finnish Association for Mental Health.

1121. **463.** 1 m. 70 multicoloured 85 20

**1987.** Centenary of Ateneum Art Museum. Paintings. Multicoloured.

1123. 1 m. 70 Type **465** .. 1·25 45

1124. 1 m. 70 "Still Life on a Lady's Work-table" (Ferdinand von Wright) .. .. 1·25 45

1125. 1 m. 70 "Old Woman with Basket" (Albert Edelfelt) .. .. 1·25 45

1126. 1 m. 70 "Boy and Crow" (Akseli Gallen-Kallela) 2·00 45

1127. 1 m. 70 "Late Winter" (Tyko Sallinen) .. 1·25 45

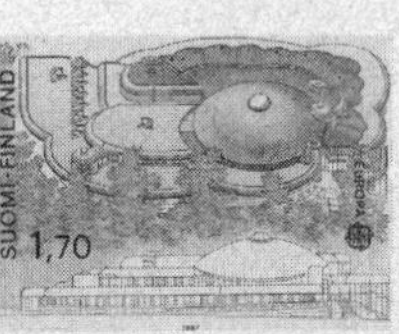


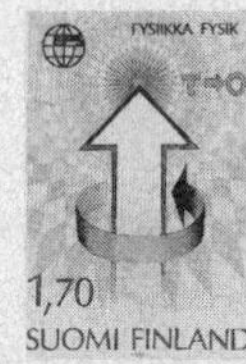


**466.** Tampere Main Library. (Railia and Reima Pietila). **467.** Arrows.

**1987.** Europa. Art and Architecture. Mult.

1128 1 m. 70 Type **466** .. 1·25 15

1129 2 m. 30 "Stoa" (Hannu Siren) .. .. .. 1·75 95

**1987.** 7th European Physics Society General Conference.

1130. **467.** 1 m. 70 multicoloured 45 20

**468.** Outline Maps of Finland. **469.** Baby with Ball and Prof. Ylppo.

**1987.** 70th Anniv of Independence.

1131 **468** 1 m. 70 silver, grey and blue .. .. 60 10

1132 10 m. silver, blue and azure (26 × 37 mm) 3·50 1·40

**1987.** 100th Birthday of Arvo Ylppo (paediatrician).

1133. **469.** 1 m. 70 multicoloured 70 20

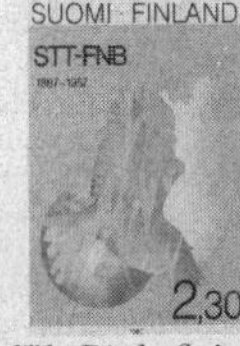


**470.** Father Christmas and Brownies. **471.** Birds flying from Globe to Finland.

**1987.** Christmas. Multicoloured.

1134. 1 m. 40 Type **470** .. 70 10

1135. 1 m. 70 Mother Christmas and brownie (vert.) 70 10

**1987.** Centenary of Finnish News Agency.

1136. **471.** 2 m. 30 multicoloured 70 25

**472.** Pihkala. **473.** Telephone and Mail Boxes.

**1988.** Birth Centenary of Lauri Pihkala ("Tahko") (writer and sport organizer).

1137. **472.** 1 m. 80 deep blue, blue and black .. 65 20

**1988.** 350th Anniv. of Posts and Telecommunications Services (1st issue). Mult.

1138. 1 m. 80 Type **473** .. 65 40

1139. 1 m. 80 Airplane and lorry .. .. .. 65 40

1140. 1 m. 80 Fork-lift truck carrying parcels .. 65 40

1141. 1 m. 80 Postman .. 65 40

1142. 1 m. 80 Woman receiving letter .. .. 65 40

Nos. 1138/42 were printed together, se-tenant, Nos. 1141/2 forming a composite design.

See also Nos. 1165/70.

**474.** Conifer Branches (Christmas).

**475.** Weather Chart and Measuring Equipment.

**1988.** Finnish Red Cross Fund. Festivals. Multicoloured.

| | | | |
|---|---|---|---|
| 1143. | 1 m. 40+40 p. Type **474** | 75 | 75 |
| 1144. | 1 m. 80+45 p. Narcissi (Easter) .. .. | 80 | 80 |
| 1145. | 2 m. 40+50 p. Rose (Midsummer) .. .. | 1·00 | 1·00 |

**1988.** 150th Anniv. of Meteorological Institute.

1146. **475.** 1 m. 40 multicoloured 45 15

**476.** Map, Settlers, Indians, "Calmare Nyckel" and "Fagel Grip".

**1988.** 350th Anniv. of Founding of New Sweden (Finnish and Swedish settlement in North America).

1147. **476.** 3 m. multicoloured .. 1·40 65

**477.** Matti Nykanen (triple gold medal winner).

**478.** Agathon Faberge (philatelist).

**1988.** Finnish Success at Winter Olympic Games, Calgary.

1148. **477.** 1 m. 80 multicoloured 65 30

**1988.** "Finlandia 88" International Stamp Exhibition, Helsinki.

1149. **478.** 5 m. multicoloured .. 13·50 13·50

**479.** Paper Airplanes between VDUs.

**1988.** Europa. Transport and Communications. Multicoloured.

| | | | |
|---|---|---|---|
| 1150. | 1 m. 80 Type **479** .. | 85 | 10 |
| 1151. | 2 m. 40 Horse-drawn tram, 1890 .. .. | 1·60 | 95 |

**481.** Steam-driven Fire Pump, Turku Fire Brigade.

**482.** "Missale Aboense" and Illuminated Page.

**1988.** 150th Anniv. of Fire Brigades in Finland.

1163 **481** 2 m. 20 multicoloured 60 35

**1988.** 500th Anniv of Publishing of "Missale Aboense" (first printed book for Finland).

1164 **482** 1 m. 80 multicoloured 45 10

**483.** 1638 Postal Tariffs.

**484.** Teacher with Children.

**1988.** 350th Anniv. of Posts and Telecommunications Services (2nd issue). Mult.

| | | | |
|---|---|---|---|
| 1165 | 1 m. 80 Type **483** .. | 50 | 25 |
| 1166 | 1 m. 80 Rural postman, 1860s .. .. .. | 50 | 25 |
| 1167 | 1 m. 80 Postman delivering from mail van .. | 50 | 25 |
| 1168 | 1 m. 80 Malmi Post Office | 50 | 25 |
| 1169 | 1 m. 80 Skiers using mobile telephone .. | 50 | 25 |
| 1170 | 1 m. 80 Communications satellite .. .. | 50 | 25 |

**1988.** Church Playgroups.

1171 **484.** 1 m. 80 multicoloured 45 10

**485** Decorations

**486** Market Place, Town Plan and Arms

**1988.** Christmas.

| | | | | |
|---|---|---|---|---|
| 1172 | **485** | 1 m. 40 multicoloured | 75 | 10 |
| 1173 | | 1 m. 80 multicoloured | 75 | 10 |

**1989.** 350th Anniv of Hameenlinna Town Charter.

1174 **486** 1 m. 90 multicoloured 50 10

**487** Skier

**488** Photographer with Box Camera on Tripod

**1989.** World Skiing Championships, Lahti.

1175 **487** 1 m. 90 multicoloured 50 10

**1989.** 150th Anniv of Photography.

1176 **488** 1 m. 50 multicoloured 35 10

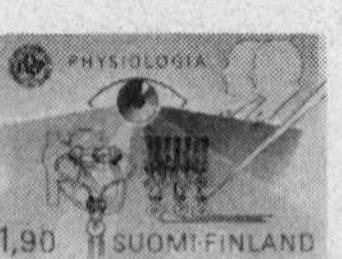

**489** Christmas Collection

**490** Professors Tigerstedt and Granit and Research Fields

**1989.** Cent of Salvation Army in Finland.

1177 **489** 1 m. 90 multicoloured 50 10

**1989.** 31st International Physiological Sciences Congress, Helsinki.

1178 **490** 1 m. 90 multicoloured 50 10

**491** Skiing

**1989.** Sport. Multicoloured.

| | | | |
|---|---|---|---|
| 1179 | 1 m. 90 Type **491** .. | 50 | 25 |
| 1180 | 1 m. 90 Jogging .. .. | 50 | 25 |
| 1181 | 1 m. 90 Cycling .. .. | 50 | 25 |
| 1182 | 1 m. 90 Canoeing .. | 50 | 25 |

**493** Hopscotch

**1989.** Europa. Children's Activities. Mult.

| | | | |
|---|---|---|---|
| 1184 | 1 m. 90 Type **493** .. | 1·40 | 10 |
| 1185 | 2 m. 50 Sledging .. | 1·40 | 65 |

**494** Man from Sakyla

**495** Foxglove and Pharmaceutical Equipment

**1989.** Nordic Countries' Postal Co-operation. Traditional Costumes. Multicoloured.

| | | | |
|---|---|---|---|
| 1186 | 1 m. 90 Type **494** .. | 50 | 10 |
| 1187 | 2 m. 50 Woman from Veteli .. .. .. | 70 | 25 |

**1989.** 300th Anniv of Pharmacies in Finland.

1188 **495** 1 m. 90 multicoloured 50 10

**496** Snow Leopard

**497** Savonlinna

**1989.** Cent of Helsinki Zoo. Multicoloured.

| | | | |
|---|---|---|---|
| 1189 | 1 m. 90 Type **496** .. | 60 | 10 |
| 1190 | 2 m. 50 Markhor goat .. | 70 | 35 |

**1989.** 350th Anniv of Savonlinna.

1191 **497** 1 m. 90 multicoloured 50 10

**498** Brown Bear

**499** Open Book and Mercury's Staff

**1989.**

1192 **498** 50 m. multicoloured .. 12·00 6·50

**1989.** 150th Anniv of Commercial Studies in Finland.

1193 **499** 1 m. 50 multicoloured 45 10

**500** Emblem and Columns in Finland's Parliament

**501** Bridges

**1989.** Cent of Interparliamentary Union.

1194 **500** 1 m. 90 multicoloured 50 10

**1989.** Accession of Finland to, and 40th Anniv of, Council of Europe.

1195 **501** 2 m. 50 multicoloured 70 10

**502** Kolehmainen winning 5000 m., Olympic Games, 1912

**503** Students, Open Book and Keyboard

**1989.** Birth Cent of Hannes Kolehmainen (runner).

1196 **502** 1 m. 90 multicoloured 50 10

**1989.** Centenary of Folk High Schools.

1197 **503** 1 m. 90 multicoloured 50 10

**504** Decorated Street

**505** Emblem and Lake Paijanne

**1989.** Christmas. Multicoloured.

| | | | |
|---|---|---|---|
| 1198 | 1 m. 50 Type **504** .. | 35 | 10 |
| 1199 | 1 m. 90 Sodankyla Church, Lapland .. | 1·40 | 20 |

**1990.** Formation of Posts and Telecommunications into State Commercial Company.

| | | | | |
|---|---|---|---|---|
| 1200 | **505** | 1 m. 90 multicoloured | 70 | 70 |
| 1201 | | 2 m. 50 multicoloured | 95 | 95 |

**506** Wood Anemone (Uusimaa province)

**507** Erik Ferling (first orchestra leader) conducting

**1990.** Provincial Plants. Multicoloured.

| | | | |
|---|---|---|---|
| 1205 | 2 m. Type **506** .. .. | 50 | 10 |
| 1206 | 2 m. 10 Rowan (Northern Savo) .. .. | 50 | 10 |
| 1208 | 2 m. 70 Heather (Kainuu) | 95 | 25 |
| 1209 | 2 m. 90 Shrub sea buckthorn (Satakunta) .. | 95 | 25 |
| 1213 | 3 m. 50 Oak (Varsinais Suomi) .. .. | 1·10 | 35 |

No. 1206 also comes self-adhesive and imperforate.

See also Nos. 1273/4, 1303, 1309, 1327 and 1354.

**1990.** Bicentenary of Foundation of Turku Musical Society (first Finnish orchestra).

1220 **507** 1 m. 90 multicoloured 50 10

**508** Snowflake

**509** Disabled Ex-serviceman

**1990.** 50th Anniv of End of Russo-Finnish Winter War.

1221 **508** 2 m. blue & ultramaine 50 10

**1990.** 50th Anniv of Disabled Ex-servicemen's Association.

1222 **509** 2 m. multicoloured .. 50 10

**510** Nuvvus Postal Agency

**1990.** Europa. Post Office Buildings. Mult.

| | | | |
|---|---|---|---|
| 1223 | 2 m. Type **510** .. .. | 95 | 10 |
| 1224 | 2 m. 70 Turku Postal Centre .. .. | 1·25 | 65 |

**511** Queen Christina

**1990.** 350th Anniv of Grant of Charter to Turku Academy (later Helsinki University). Multicoloured.
1225 2 m. Type **511** .. .. 50 10
1226 3 m. 20 Main building of Helsinki University .. 85 35

**512** Scarce Copper on Goldrod

**1990.** Finnish Red Cross Fund. Butterflies. Multicoloured.
1227 1 m. 50+40 p. Type **512** 80 80
1228 2 m.+50 p. Amanda's blue on meadow vetchling .. .. 1·10 1·10
1229 2 m. 70+60 p. Peacock on tufted vetch .. .. 1·40 1·40
See also Nos. 1279/81.

**513** Postman at Larsmo, 1890, and Modern Address Sign
**514** "Ali Baba and the Forty Thieves"

**1990.** Compilation of Address Register and Centenary of Rural Postal Service.
1230 **513** 2 m. multicoloured .. 50 10

**1990.** Birth Cent of Rudolf Koivu (artist). Designs showing Koivu's illustrations of fairy tales. Multicoloured.
1231 2 m. Type **514** .. .. 95 20
1232 2 m. "The Great Musician" (Raul Roine) 95 20
1233 2 m. "The Giants, the Witches and the Daughter of the Sun" (Koivu) .. .. 95 20
1234 2 m. "The Golden Bird, the Golden Horse and the Princess" (Grimm Brothers) .. .. 95 20
1235 2 m. "Lamb Brother" (Koivu) .. .. 95 20
1236 2 m. "The Snow Queen" (Hans Christian Andersen) .. 95 20

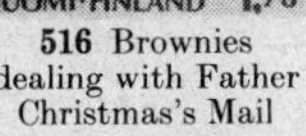

**516** Brownies dealing with Father Christmas's Mail
**517** Player and Turku Castle

**1990.** Christmas. Multicoloured.
1238 1 m. 70 Type **516** .. 45 10
1239 2 m. Father Christmas and reindeer .. .. 50 10

**1991.** World Ice Hockey Championship, Turku, Tampere and Helsinki.
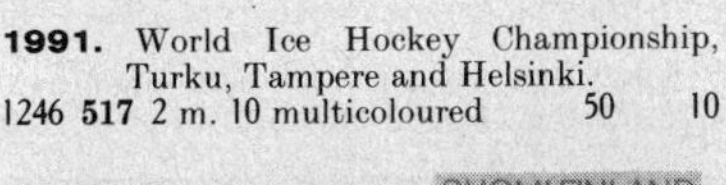
1246 **517** 2 m. 10 multicoloured 50 10

**518** Teacher and Pupils preparing Meal
**519** "Green Still Life"

**1991.** Cent of Domestic Science Teacher Training.
1247 **518** 2 m. 10 multicoloured 50 10

**1991.** Pro Filatelia. Paintings by Helene Schjerfbeck. Multicoloured.
1248 2 m. 10+50 p. Type **519** 75 75
1249 2 m. 10+50 p. "The Little Convalescent" .. 75 75

**520** Great Tit
**521** Fly-fishing for Trout

**1991.** Birds. (1st series). Multicoloured
1250 10 p. Type **520** .. .. 10 10
1251 60 p. Pair of chaffinches 15 10
1252 2 m. 10 Bullfinch .. 85 10
See also Nos. 1282/4 and 1322/4.

**1991.** Centenary of Central Fishery Organization. Multicoloured.
1253 2 m. 10 Type **521** .. 60 35
1254 2 m. 10 Angling for perch 60 35
1255 2 m. 10 Crayfish .. 60 35
1256 2 m. 10 Trawling for baltic herring .. .. 60 35
1257 2 m. 10 Restocking with powan .. .. 60 35

**522** Seurasaari Island
**523** Map of Europe and Human Figures

**1991.** Nordic Countries' Postal Co-operation. Multicoloured.
1258 2 m. 10 Type **522** .. 50 10
1259 2 m. 90 Saimaa ferry .. 80 35

**1991.** Europa. Europe in Space. Mult.
1260 2 m. 10 Type **523** .. 1·10 10
1261 2 m. 90 Map of Europe, satellites and dish aerials .. .. 1·40 60

**524** Iris Vase
**525** Kittens and "Kiss-Kiss" Sweet

**1991.** 61st Death Anniv of Alfred Finch (painter and ceramic artist). Multicoloured.
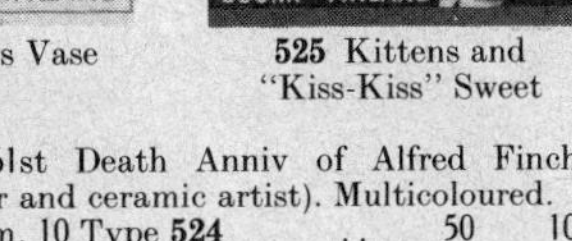
1262 2 m. 10 Type **524** .. 50 10
1263 2 m. 90 "The English Coast at Dover" .. 70 30

**1991.** Centenary of Opening of Karl Fazer's Confectionery (beginning of Finnish Sweet Industry).
1264 **525** 2 m. 10 multicoloured 50 10

**528** Iisalmi
**529** Forest Animals and Elf

**1991.** Centenary of Granting of Town Rights to Iisalmi.
1267 **528** 2 m. 10 multicoloured 50 10

**1991.** Christmas. Multicoloured.
1268 1 m. 80 Type **529** .. 95 10
1269 2 m. 10 Father Christmas in sleigh over new Arctic Circle post office (vert) .. .. .. 1·25 20

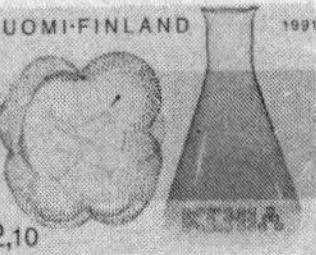

**530** Camphor Molecule and Erlenmeyer Flask
**531** Skiing

**1991.** Cent of Organized Chemistry in Finland.
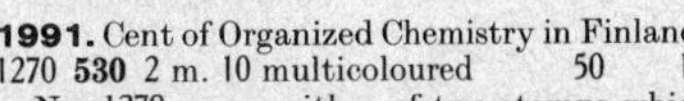
1270 **530** 2 m. 10 multicoloured 50 10
No. 1270 covers either of two stamps which were issued together as a horizontal gutter pair, the stamps differing very slightly in the diagram of the molecule. The gutter pair is stated to produce a three-dimensional image without use of a special viewer.

**1992.** Winter Olympic Games, Albertville (1271) and Summer Games, Barcelona (1272). Multicoloured.
1271 2 m. 10 Type **531** .. 95 10
1272 2 m. 90 Swimming .. 1·10 30

**532** Globe Flower (Lapland)
**533** Finnish Exhibition Emblem

**1992.** Provincial Plants. With service indicator. Multicoloured.
1273 2 klass (1 m. 60) Type **532** 65 10
1274 1 klass (2 m. 10) Hepatica (Hame) .. .. 85 10
See also Nos. 1303, 1309, 1327 and 1354.

**1992.** "Expo '92" World's Fair, Seville.
1275 **533** 3 m. 40 multicoloured 80 35

**534** Map of Europe

**1992.** 3rd Meeting of Council of Foreign Ministers of European Security and Co-operation Conference, Helsinki.
1276 **534** 16 m. multicoloured .. 5·25 2·40

**535** Church of the Holy Cross, Town Hall and Brigantine
**536** Thoughts within Head

**1992.** 550th Anniv of Rauma Town Charter.
1277 **535** 2 m. 10 multicoloured 55 10

**1992.** Healthy Brains Campaign.
1278 **536** 3 m. 50 multicoloured 1·10 75

**1992.** Finnish Red Cross Fund. Centenary of Training of Visually Handicapped. Moths. As T **512**. Multicoloured.
1279 1 m. 60+40 p. Taiga dart 50 50
1280 2 m. 10+50 p. Fjeld tiger 65 65
1281 5 m.+60 p. Baneberry looper moth .. .. 1·90 1·90

**537** Pied Wagtail
**538** "Santa Maria" and Route Map

**1992.** Birds (2nd series). Multicoloured.
1282 10 p. Type **537** .. 10 10
1283 60 p. European robin .. 15 10
1284 2 m. 10 Three Bohemian waxwings .. .. 50 10

**1992.** Europa. 500th Anniv of Discovery of America by Columbus. Multicoloured.
1285 2 m. 10 Type **538** .. 85 10
1286 2 m. 10 Route map and Columbus .. .. 85 10
Nos. 1285/6 were issued together, se-tenant, forming a composite design.

**539** Blowing Machine (first Finnish patent, 150th anniv)
**540** Currant Harvesting

**1992.** Technology. Multicoloured.
1287 2 m. 10 Type **539** (50th anniv of National Board of Patents and Registration of Trademarks) .. .. 50 10
1288 2 m. 90 Triangles and circuits (Finnish chairmanship of EUREKA (European technology development scheme)) .. 70 40
1289 3 m. 40 Inverted triangles (50th anniv of Government Technology Research Centre) .. 1·10 50

**1992.** Cent of National Board of Agriculture.
1290 **540** 2 m. 10 multicoloured 55 10

**541** Aurora Karamzin
**542** Flag in Garden (Niina Pennanen)

**1992.** Notable Finnish Women. Mult.
1291 2 m. 10 Type **541** (founder of Helsinki Deaconesses' Institution) .. 50 20
1292 2 m. 10 Sophie Mannerheim (nursing pioneer) 50 20
1293 2 m. 10 Laimi Leidenius (Professor of Obstetrics and Gynaecology, Helsinki University) .. 50 20
1294 2 m. 10 Miina Sillanpaa (first woman Cabinet Minister) .. .. 50 20
1295 2 m. 10 Edith Sodergran (poet) .. .. .. 50 20
1296 2 m. 10 Kreetta Haapasalo (folk singer) .. 50 20

**1992.** 75th Anniv of Independence.
1297 **542** 2 m. 10 multicoloured 50 10

**543** Moomin looking into River ("Moominland Midwinter")
**544** Rosebay Willowherb (Etela-Pohjanmaa)

**1992.** "Nordia 1993" International Stamp Exhibition. Stamp Day. Designs showing illustrations from her stories by Tove Jansson. Multicoloured.
1299 2 m. 10 Type **543** .. 85 35
1300 2 m. 10 Moomin and trolls ("Moominland Midwinter") .. .. 85 35
1301 2 m. 10 Theatre performance on water ("Moomin Summer Madness") .. .. 85 35
1302 2 m. 10 Moomin and inhabitants ("Tales from Moomin Valley") 85 35

**1992.** Provincial Plants. With service indicator. Self-adhesive. Imperf.
1303 **544** 1 klass (2 m. 10) mult 85 10

545 Computerized and Hot Metal Typesetting

546 St. Lawrence's Church, Vantaa

**1992.** 350th Anniv of Printing in Finland.
1304 **545** 2 m. 10 multicoloured .. 50 10

**1992.** Christmas. Multicoloured.
1305 1 m. 80 Type **546** .. .. 45 10
1306 2 m. 10 Stained glass window, Karkkila Church (vert) .. .. 50 10

547 Couple

548 Birds, Flowers and Envelope within Heart

**1993.** 75th Anniv of Central Chamber of Commerce.
1307 **547** 1 m. 60 multicoloured 40 10

**1993.** Friendship.
1308 **548** 1 klass (2 m. 10) mult 95 10

549 Iris (Kymenlaakso)

550 Fox in Winter Coat

**1993.** Provincial Plants. With service indicator. Self-adhesive. Imperf.
1309 **549** 2 klass (1 m. 90) mult 75 10

**1993.** The Arctic Fox. Multicoloured.
1310 2 m. 30 Type **550** .. .. 55 10
1311 2 m. 30 Two foxes in winter coat .. .. 55 10
1312 2 m. 30 Mother with young in summer coat 55 10
1313 2 m. 30 Two foxes in summer coat .. .. 55 10

551 "Autumn Landscape of Lake Pielisjarvi" (left half)

**1993.** Pro Filatelia. 130th Birth Anniv of Eero Jarnefelt (painter). Multicoloured.
1314 2 m. 30+70 p. Type **551** 75 75
1315 2 m. 30+70 p. "Autumn Landscape of Lake Pielisjarvi" (right half) 75 75

Nos. 1314/15 were issued together, se-tenant, forming a composite design of the entire painting.

552 "Rumba" (Martti Aiha)

553 Burnet Rose

**1993.** Europa Contemporary Art. Sculptures. Multicoloured.
1316 2 m. Type **552** .. .. 1·90 10
1317 2 m. 90 "Complete Works" (Kari Caven) 1·40 30

**1993.** Centenary of Helsinki Philatelic Association.
1318 **553** 2 m. 30 multicoloured 55 10

554 Castle and Courier Route Map

**1993.** 700th Anniv of Vyborg Castle.
1319 **554** 2 m. 30 multicoloured 55 10

555 Naantali

556 Tengmalm's Owl

**1993.** Nordic Countries' Postal Co-operation. Tourism. Multicoloured.
1320 2 m. 30 Type **555** .. .. 55 10
1321 2 m. 90 Imatra .. .. 70 30

**1993.** Birds (3rd series). Multicoloured.
1322 10 p. Type **556** .. .. 10 10
1323 20 p. Redstart .. .. 10 10
1324 2 m. 30 White-backed woodpecker .. .. 55 10

557 Finnish Landscape in Soldier's Silhouette

558 Labrador Tea (Northern Ostrobothnia)

**1993.** 75th Anniv of Military Forces. Mult.
1325 2 m. 30 Type **557** .. .. 55 10
1326 3 m. 40 Checkpoint of Finnish soldiers serving with U.N. peacekeeping force .. .. .. 1·10 35

**1993.** Provincial Plants. With service indicator. Self-adhesive. Imperf.
1327 **558** 1 klass (2 m. 30) mult 1·10 10

559 Child skiing (cover illustration from "Kotiliesi")

561 Gymnastics and Football

560 Flock of Black-throated Divers

**1993.** Birth Centenary of Martta Wendelin (artist). Multicoloured.
1328 2 m. 30 Type **559** .. .. 55 25
1329 2 m. 30 Mother and daughter knitting (illustration from "First Book of the Home and School") .. .. 55 25
1330 2 m. 30 Children making snowman (illustration from "First Book of the Home and School") .. 55 25
1331 2 m. 30 Rural scene (postcard) .. .. 55 25
1332 2 m. 30 Young girl and lamb (cover illustration from "Kotiliesi") .. 55 25

**1993.** Water Birds. Multicoloured.
1333 2 m. 30 Type **560** .. .. 55 25
1334 2 m. 30 Pair of black-throated divers ("Gavia arctica") (53 × 28 mm) 55 25
1335 2 m. 30 Goosander ("Mergus merganser") (26 × 39 mm) .. .. 55 25
1336 2 m. 30 Mallards ("Anas platyrhynchos") (26 × 39 mm) .. .. 55 25
1337 2 m. 30 Red-breasted merganser ("Mergus serrator") (26 × 39 mm) 55 25

**1993.** 150th Anniv of Compulsory Physical Education in Schools.
1338 **561** 2 m. 30 multicoloured 55 10

563 Brownies and Christmas Tree (Anna Kymalainen)

564 Koivisto

**1993.** Christmas. Children's Drawings. Mult.
1340 1 m. 80 Type **563** .. 45 10
1341 2 m. 30 Three angels and star (Taina Tuomola) 55 10

**1993.** 70th Birthday of President Mauno Koivisto.
1342 **564** 2 m. 30 multicoloured 55 10

565 "Moominland Winter"

567 "Peace"

**1994.** Moomin. With service indicator. Illustrations from her stories by Tove Jansson. Multicoloured.
1343 1 klass (2 m. 30) Type **565** 85 25
1344 1 klass (2 m. 30) "Moominland Storm" .. 85 25

**1994.** Birth Centenary of Waino Aaltonen (sculptor). Multicoloured.
1346 2 m. Type **567** .. .. 50 10
1347 2 m. "Muse" .. .. 50 10

568 Postal Clerk and Customer

569 Ploughing

**1994.** Centenary of Postal Service Civil Servants Federation.
1348 **568** 2 m. 30 multicoloured 55 10

**1994.** Finnish Red Cross Fund. Finn Horses. Multicoloured.
1349 2 m. Type **569** .. .. 55 10
1350 2 m. 30 Marinka (trotting horse) .. .. .. 85 10
1351 4 m. 20 Soldiers on horseback (vert) .. 1·40 1·40

570 Paper Roll, Nitrogen-fixing Technique, Padlock and "Fennica" (ice-breaker)

571 Rose (North Karelia)

**1994.** Europa. Discoveries and Inventions. Multicoloured.
1352 2 m. 30 Type **570** .. 60 10
1353 4 m. 20 Balloon, radiosonde, mobile telephone, fishing lure and lake oxygenation equipment .. .. 1·90 75

**1994.** Provincial Plants. With service indicator. Self-adhesive. Imperf.
1354 **571** 1 klass (2 m. 30) mult 95 10

573 Seven-spotted Ladybirds

**1994.** "Finlandia 95" International Stamp Exhibition, Helsinki (1st issue).
1356 **573** 16 m. multicoloured .. 4·75 4·75
See also No. 1393.

574 Perforate St. John's Wort ("Hypericum perforatum")

575 Patrik Sjoberg (high jump)

**1994.** Flowers. With service indicator. Mult.
1357 1 klass (2 m. 30) Type **574** 85 10
1358 1 klass (2 m. 30) Sticky catchfly ("Lychnis viscaria") .. .. 85 10
1359 1 klass (2 m. 30) Harebell ("Campanula rotundifolia") .. .. 85 10
1360 1 klass (2 m. 30) Clustered bellflower ("Campanula glomerata") .. .. 85 10
1361 1 klass (2 m. 30) Bloody cranesbill ("Geranium sanguineum") .. 85 10
1362 1 klass (2 m. 30) Wild strawberry ("Fragaria vesca") .. .. 85 10
1363 1 klass (2 m. 30) Germander speedwell ("Veronica chamaedrys") .. 85 10
1364 1 klass (2 m. 30) Meadow saxifrage ("Saxifraga granulata)" .. .. 85 10
1365 1 klass (2 m. 30) Wild pansy ("Viola tricolor") 85 10
1366 1 klass (2 m. 30) Silver-weed ("Potentilla anserina") .. .. 85 10

**1994.** Sweden–Finland Athletics Meeting, Stockholm. Multicoloured.
1367 2 m. 40 Sepo Raty (javelin) .. .. 65 10
1368 2 m. 40 Type **575** .. 65 10

576 Crowd on Registration List

577 Emblem

**1994.** 450th Anniv of Population Registers.
1369 **576** 2 m. 40 multicoloured 65 10

**1994.** International Year of the Family.
1370 **577** 3 m. 40 multicoloured 90 40

579 Bullfinches on Reindeer's Antlers

580 Postman delivering Letter to Alien

**1994.** Christmas. Multicoloured.

1372 2 m. 10 Type **579** .. 65 10
1373 2 m. 80 Father and son selecting Christmas tree (vert) .. .. .. 85 10

**1995.** Greetings stamps. Multicoloured.

1374 2 m. 80 Type **580** .. 85 35
1375 2 m. 80 Cat writing letter 85 35
1376 2 m. 80 Postman delivering letter to elderly dog .. .. 85 35
1377 2 m. 80 Teenage dog writing letter .. .. 85 35
1378 2 m. 80 Dog receiving postcard .. .. 85 35
1379 2 m. 80 Dog on train reading letter .. .. 85 35
1380 2 m. 80 Guitarist dog with Valentine greeting .. 85 35
1381 2 m. 80 Baby dog .. 85 35

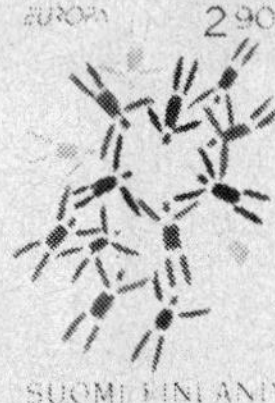

582 Shooting Star and Stars

584 Figures forming Parachute

583 "Boys playing on the Shore"

**1995.** Admission of Finland to European Union.

1383 **582** 3 m. 50 bl, yell & blk 1·00 40

**1995.** Pro Filatelia. Paintings by Albert Edelfelt. Multicoloured.

1384 2 m. 40+60 p. Type **583** 90 90
1385 2 m. 40+60 p. "Queen Blanche" (21 × 30½ mm) 90 90

**1995.** Europa. Peace and Freedom.

1386 **584** 2 m. 90 multicoloured 85 35

585 Lynx

586 Daisy (Keski-Suomi)

**1995.** Endangered Animals. Multicoloured.

1387 2 m. 90 Type **585** .. 85 35
1388 2 m. 90 Landscape .. 85 35
1389 2 m. 90 Shoreline .. 85 35
1390 2 m. 90 Ringed seal .. 85 35

**1995.** Provincial Plants. With service indicator. Self-adhesive. Imperf.

1391 **586** 1 klass (2 m. 80) mult 85 10

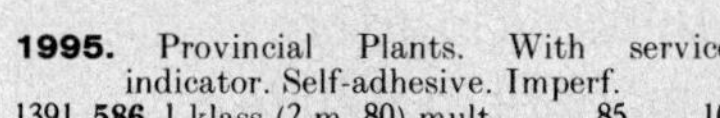

588 Dung Beetle

**1995.** "Finlandia 95" International Stamp Exhibition, Helsinki (2nd issue).

1393 **588** 19 m. multicoloured .. 5·75 5·75

589 Linnanmaki Amusement Park, Helsinki

590 Loviisa Market and Church

**1995.** Nordic Countries' Postal Co-operation. Tourism. Multicoloured.

1394 2 m. 80 Type **589** .. 85 10
1395 2 m. 90 Mantyharju church (400th anniv of parish) .. .. 85 35

**1995.** 250th Anniv of Loviisa.

1396 **590** 3 m. 20 multicoloured 95 40

591 Silver Birch (Betula pendula)

592 Rontgen Tube and X-Ray Theory

**1995.** 20th International Union of Forestry Research Organizations World Congress, Tampere. Leaves and flowers of trees. Multicoloured.

1397 2 m. 80 Type **591** .. 85 35
1398 2 m. 80 Scots pine ("Pinus sylvestris") .. .. 85 35
1399 2 m. 80 Norway spruce ("Picea abies") .. 85 35
1400 2 m. 80 Propagating tree from needle .. .. 85 35

**1995.** Centenary of Discovery of X-Rays by Wilhelm Rontgen.

1401 **592** 4 m. 30 multicoloured 1·25 95

593 Somali

594 Handshake

**1995.** Cats. Multicoloured.

1402 2 m. 80 Type **593** .. 85 35
1403 2 m. 80 Siamese .. .. 85 35
1404 2 m. 80 Domestic cat in grass (58 × 35 mm) .. 85 35
1405 2 m. 80 Norwegian forest cat .. .. .. 85 35
1406 2 m. 80 Colourpoint Persian .. .. 85 35
1407 2 m. 80 Kittens playing in grass (58 × 35 mm) .. 85 35

Nos. 1404 and 1407 form a composite design.

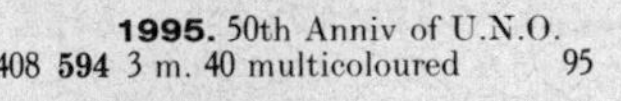

**1995.** 50th Anniv of U.N.O.

1408 **594** 3 m. 40 multicoloured 95 40

595 Father Christmas on Skates

596 "O"

**1995.** Christmas. Multicoloured.

1409 2 m. Type **595** .. .. 55 10
1410 2 m. 80 Poinsettias in snow (horiz) .. .. 75 10

**1996.** Greeting Stamps. Letters of the Alphabet.

1411 **596** 1 m. violet, green and black ("M") .. 25 10
1412 1 m. blue, mauve and black (Type **596**) .. 25 10
1413 1 m. red, yellow and black ("i") .. 25 10
1414 1 m. blue, red and black ("H") .. 25 10
1415 **596** 1 m. red, green and black ("E") .. 25 10
1416 1 m. yellow, blue and black ("J") .. 25 10
1417 1 m. green, red and black ("A") .. 25 10
1418 1 m. yellow, mauve and black ("N") .. 25 10
1419 1 m. yellow, green and black ("T") .. 25 10
1420 1 m. red, blue and black ("P") .. 25 10
1421 1 m. light blue, blue and black ("U") .. 25 10
1422 1 m. yellow, mauve and black ("S") .. 25 10

Nos. 1411/22 were intended to be arranged on envelopes to spell out a desired message.

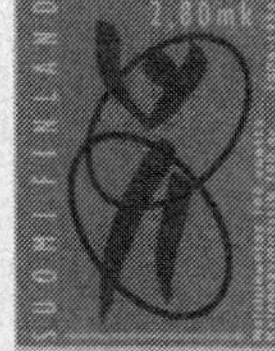

597 "Smile" (Mauno Paavola)

598 Hoop Exercise

**1996.** 50th Anniv of U.N.I.C.E.F.

1423 **597** 2 m. 80 multicoloured 75 10

**1996.** Centenary of Women's Gymnastics Associations in Finland.

1424 **598** 2 m. 80 multicoloured 75 10

599 Mother and Children at Polling Station

**1996.** Europa. 90th Anniv of Women's Suffrage in Finland.

1425 **599** 3 m. 20 multicoloured 85 35

600 Chicks

**1996.** Finnish Red Cross Fund. Chickens. Multicoloured.

1426 2 m. 80+60 p. Type **600** 95 95
1427 3 m. 20+70 p. Hens 1·10 1·10
1428 3 m. 40+70 p. Cock (vert) 1·10 1·10

601 J. Gronroos (circus director) at Film Projector

**1996.** Centenary of Motion Pictures. Mult.

1429 2 m. 80 Valle Saikko and Irma Seikkula in "Juha" .. .. 75 30
1430 2 m. 80 Alli Riks and Theodor Tugai in "Wide Road" ("Den Breda Vagen") .. 75 30
1431 2 m. 80 Ake Lindman in "The Unknown Soldier" ("Okand Soldat") .. .. 75 30
1432 2 m. 80 Type **601** .. 75 30
1433 2 m. 80 Antti Litja in "Year of the Hare" ("Harens Ar") .. 75 30
1434 2 m. 80 Mirjami Kuosmanen in "The White Forest" ("Den Vita Renen") .. .. 75 30
1435 2 m. 80 Ansa Ikonen and Tauno Palo in "Complete Love" ("Alla Alskar") .. 75 30
1436 2 m. 80 Matti Pellonpaa in "Shadow in Paradise" ("Skuggor i Paradiset") 75 30

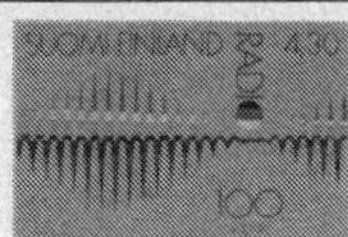

602 Radio Waves

**1996.** Centenary (1995) of First Radio Transmission.

1437 **602** 4 m. 30 multicoloured 1·25 50

603 Canoeing

604 White Water Lily

**1996.** Centenary of Modern Olympic Games. Watersports. Multicoloured.

1438 3 m. 40 Type **603** .. 95 40
1439 3 m. 40 Yachting .. 95 40
1440 3 m. 40 Rowing .. .. 95 40
1441 3 m. 40 Swimming .. 95 40

**1996.** Provincial Plants. With service indicator. Self-adhesive. Imperf.

1442 **604** 1 klass (2 m. 80) mult 75 10

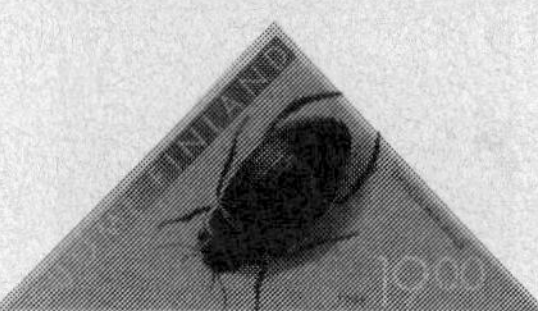

605 Great Diving Beetle

**1996.**

1443 **605** 19 m. multicoloured .. 5·25 2·10

607 Professor Itikaisen (Ilmari Vainio)

**1996.** Centenary of Comic Strips. Each red and black.

1445 2 m. 80 Type **607** .. 75 30
1446 2 m. 80 Pekka Puupaa (Peter Blockhead) (Ola Fogelberg) .. .. 75 30
1447 2 m. 80 Joonas (Veikko Savolainen) .. .. 75 30
1448 2 m. 80 Posti-Aune from "Mammila" (Tarmo Koivisto) .. .. 75 30
1449 2 m. 80 Rymy-Eetu (Erkki Tanttu) .. 75 30
1450 2 m. 80 Kieku (Asmo Alho) .. .. .. 75 30
1451 2 m. 80 Pikku Risunen from "Hyvissa naimisissa" (Well-married) (Riitta Uusitalo) .. .. 75 30
1452 2 m. 80 Kiti from "Vihrea rapsodia" (Green Rhapsody) (Kati Kovacs) .. .. 75 30

608 Father Christmas and Musicians

**1996.** Christmas. Multicoloured.

1453 2 m. Type **608** .. .. 55 10
1454 2 m. 80 Reindeer and hare 75 10
1455 3 m. 20 Father Christmas reading letters (vert) .. 85 35

MILITARY FIELD POST.

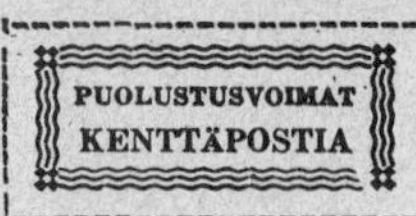

M 76.

**1941.** No value indicated. Imperf.
M 352. M **76.** (–) black on red .. 15 40

M 86.

M 222.

**1943.** No value indicated.
M392 M **86** (–) green .. .. 15 25
M393 (–) purple .. 15 25

**1943.** Optd KENTTA-POSTI FALTPOST.
M394 **31** 2 m. orange .. 20 45
M395 3½ m. blue .. .. 20 50

**1944.** As Type M **86**, but smaller (20 × 16 mm) and inscr "1944".
M 396. (–) violet .. .. .. 15 15
M 397. (–) green .. .. .. 15 15

**1963.** No value indicated.
M 688. M **222.** (–) violet .. .. £120 £120

**1983.** No. M 688 optd **1983.**
M 1043. M **222.** (–) violet .. £160 90·00

PARCEL POST STAMPS

P 118.

**1949.** Printed in black on coloured backgrounds. Roul.
P 471. P. **118.** 1 m. green .. 95 2·75
P 472. 5 m. red .. .. 14·50 14·50
P 473. 20 m. orange .. 24·00 24·00
P 474. 50 m. blue .. 9·50 11·50
P 475. 100 m brown .. 8·75 11·50

P 137.

P 216.

**1952.**
P 507. P **137.** 5 m. red .. .. 2·75 2·75
P 508. 20 m. orange .. 14·00 4·75
P 509. 50 m. blue .. .. 19·00 7·75
P 510. 100 m. brown .. 29·00 15·00

**1963.** Figures of value in black.
P 647. P **216.** 5 p. mauve .. 2·00 2·40
P 648. 20 p. orange .. 3·50 3·00
P 649. 50 p. blue .. 4·75 3·00
P 650. 1 m. brown .. 80 1·90

P 403. " SISU " Bus.

**1981.** Figures of values in black.
P1003 P **403** 50 p. blue .. 30 4·25
P1004 1 m. brown .. 45 4·25
P1005 5 m. green .. 1·50 12·00
P1006 10 m. purple .. 2·40 24·00

## FINNISH OCCUPATION OF EASTERN KARELIA Pt. 10

Part of Russia, extending East to Lake Onega occupied by Finland from 1941 to 1944.
100 penni = 1 markka.

**1941.** Types of Finland in unissued colours optd **ITA-KARJALA Sot. hallinto.**

(a) Arms and pictorial issue.

1 31 50 p. green .. .. 35 1·00
2 1 m. 75 grey .. .. 55 1·40
10 2 m. orange .. .. 80 3·00
11 2 m. 75 orange .. .. 55 1·25
12 3½ m. blue .. .. 75 2·25
13 32 5 m. purple .. .. 1·40 3·50
14 – 10 m. brown (as No. 276b) 2·75 8·00
15 – 25 m. green (as No. 277) 3·25 10·00

(b) President Ryti.

16. 76. 50 p. green .. .. 35 1·25
17. 1 m. 75 slate .. .. 35 1·25
18. 2 m. red .. .. 35 1·25
19. 2 m. 75 brown .. .. 45 1·25
20. 3 m. 50 blue .. .. 45 1·25
21. 5 m. purple .. .. 45 1·25

(c) Marshal Mannerheim.

22. 77. 50 p. green .. .. 45 1·25
23. 1 m. 75 slate .. .. 45 1·25
24. 2 m. red .. .. 45 1·25
25. 2 m. 75 brown .. .. 35 1·25
26. 3 m. 50 blue .. .. 35 1·25
27. 5 m. purple .. .. 35 1·25

4. Arms of E. Karelia.

**1943.** National Relief Fund.

28. 4. 3 m. 50+1 m. 50 olive .. 45 2·50

## FIUME Pt. 8

A seaport and territory on the Adriatic Sea formerly belonging to Hungary and occupied by the Allies in 1918/19. Between 1919 and 1924 the territory was a Free State, controlled by D'Annunzio and his legionaries, until annexation to Italy in 1924. For later issues see Fiume and Kupa Zone; Venezia Giulia. Ceded to Yugoslavia in 1947 and now known as Rijeka.

1918. 100 filler = 1 krone.
1919. 100 centesimi = 1 corona.
1920. 100 centesimi = 1 lira.

**1918.** Various issues of Hungary optd. **FIUME.**

On "Harvesters" and "Parliament" issue of 1916.

1. 18. 2 f. brown .. .. 25 20
2. 3 f. red .. .. 25 20
3. 5 f. green .. .. 25 20
4. 6 f. green .. .. 25 20
5. 10 f. red (No. 250) .. 38·00 12·50
6. 10 f. red (No. 243) .. 48·00 18·00
7. 15 f. violet (No. 251) .. 60 20
8. 15 f. violet (No. 244) .. 18·00 6·50
9. 20 f. brown .. .. 70 20
10. 25 f. blue .. .. 80 30
11. 35 f. brown .. .. 90 45
12. 40 f. olive .. .. 12·00 2·40
13. 19. 50 f. purple .. .. 80 30
14. 75 f. blue .. .. 2·75 50
15. 80 f. green .. .. 2·75 35
16. 1 k. lake .. .. 8·00 1·60
17. 2 k. brown .. .. 80 40
18. 3 k. grey and violet .. 8·00 2·40
19. 5 k. brown .. .. 13·50 4·00
20. 10 k. lilac and brown .. £140 £100

On "Charles" and "Zita" issue of 1918.

21. 27. 10 f. red .. .. 1·25 50
22. 20 f. brown .. .. 80 50
23. 28. 40 f. olive .. .. 4·75 1·75

On War charity issue of 1916.

24. 20. 10+2 f. red .. .. 1·50 70
25. – 15+2 f. violet .. .. 1·50 70
26. 22. 40+2 f. lake .. .. 1·50 70

On Newspaper issue of 1900.

27. N 9. (2 f.) orange .. .. 50 35

On Express Letter stamp of 1916.

28. E 18. 2 f. olive and red .. 50 40

On Saving Bank stamp and surch. **FRANCO** and value.

29. B 17. 15 on 10 f. purple .. 1·60 1·25

On Postage Due stamps of 1915 with figures in red and surch. **FRANCO** and value.

30. D 9. 45 on 6 f. green .. 1·10 1·60
31. 45 on 20 f. green .. 2·40 1·60

2. Liberty.

3. Clock Tower over Market in Fiume.

4.

5. Port of Fiume.

**1919.** Inscr. "FIUME".

32 2 2 c. blue .. .. .. 15 25
33 3 c. brown .. .. .. 20 25
34 5 c. green .. .. .. 25 25
36 3 10 c. red .. .. .. 65 30
57 15 c. violet .. .. .. 20 25
39 20 c. green .. .. .. 40 35
59 4 25 c. blue .. .. .. 35 30
60 5 30 c. violet .. .. .. 35 30
42 4 40 c. brown .. .. .. 55 55
62 45 c. orange .. .. .. 50 40
63 5 50 c. green .. .. .. 55 45
46 60 c. lake .. .. .. 60 40
65 1 cor. brown .. .. .. 85 55
48 2 cor. blue .. .. .. 1·10 80
49 3 cor. red .. .. .. 1·25 85
50 5 cor. brown .. .. .. 1·25 1·00
51 10 cor. olive .. .. .. 1·75 1·60

6. Statue of Romulus, Remus and Wolf.

9. Dr. Grossich.

**1919.** Students' Education Fund. 200th day of peace.

71. 6. 5 c.+5 l. green .. .. 2·75 2·75
72. 10 c.+5 l. red .. .. 2·75 2·75
73. 15 c.+5 l. grey .. .. 2·75 2·75
74. 20 c.+5 l. orange .. .. 2·75 2·75
75. – 45 c.+5 l. olive .. .. 2·75 2·75
76. – 60 c.+5 l. red .. .. 2·75 2·75
77. – 80 c.+5 l. violet .. .. 2·75 2·75
78. – 1 cor.+5 l. grey .. .. 2·75 2·75
79. – 2 cor.+5 l. red .. .. 2·75 2·75
80. – 3 cor.+5 l. brown .. .. 2·75 2·75
81. – 5 cor.+5 l. brown .. .. 2·75 2·75
82. – 10 cor.+5 l. violet .. .. 2·75 2·75

DESIGNS—HORIZ. 45, 60, 80 c., 1 cor. 13th-century Venetian war galley. 2, 3, 5, 10 cor. Piazza of St. Mark, Venice.

**1919.** As T 2 to 5, but inscr. "POSTA FIUME".

83. 2. 5 c. green .. .. .. 15 15
84. 3. 10 c. red .. .. .. 30 30
85. 5. 30 c. violet .. .. .. 50 50
86. 4. 40 c. brown .. .. .. 85 85
87. 45 c. orange .. .. .. 50 50
88. 5. 50 c. green .. .. .. 50 50
89. 60 c. lake .. .. .. 50 50
90. 10 cor. olive .. .. .. 1·60 1·60

**1919.** Dr. Grossich Foundation.

91 9 25 c.(+2 cor.) blue .. .. 50 75

**1919.** Stamps of 1919 surch **FRANCO** and value. (a) Inscr "FIUME".

92. 3. 5 on 20 c. green .. .. 15 20
93. 4. 10 on 45 c. orange .. .. 15 20
94. 5. 25 on 50 c. green .. .. 5·50 7·50
95. 55 on 1 cor. brown .. .. 1·75 2·10
96. 55 on 2 cor. blue .. .. 1·25 2·00
97. 55 on 3 cor. red .. .. 1·25 2·00
98. 55 on 5 cor. brown .. .. 1·25 2·00

(b) Inscr "POSTA FIUME".

99. 4. 5 on 25 c. blue .. .. 15 20
100. 5. 15 on 30 c. violet .. .. 15 20
101. 4. 15 on 45 c. orange .. .. 15 20
102. 5. 15 on 60 c. lake .. .. 25 35
103. 25 on 50 c. green .. .. 25 35
104. 55 on 10 cor. olive .. .. 1·25 2·00

**1919.** Nos. 71/82 and 91 surch **Valore globale** and value.

105 6 5 c. on 5 c. green .. .. 15 20
106 10 c. on 10 c. red .. .. 15 20
107 15 c. on 15 c. grey .. .. 15 20
108 20 c. on 20 c. orange .. .. 15 20
122 9 25 c. on 25 c. blue .. .. 20 30
109 – 45 c. on 45 c. green .. .. 20 25
110 – 60 c. on 60 c. red .. .. 20 25
111 – 80 c. on 80 c. violet .. .. 25 30
112 – 1 cor. on 1 cor. grey .. .. 25 30
113 – 2 cor. on 2 cor. brown .. .. 35 45
114 – 3 cor. on 3 cor. brown .. .. 65 90
115 – 5 cor. on 5 cor. brown .. .. 80 1·10
130 – 10 cor. on 10 cor. violet .. 1·25 1·10

16. Gabriele d'Annunzio.

21. Medieval Ship.

**1920.** Background in ochre.

131. 16. 5 c. green .. .. 20 35
132. 10 c. red .. .. 20 35
133. 15 c. grey .. .. 35 45
134. 20 c. orange .. .. 35 45
135. 25 c. blue .. .. 50 65
136. 30 c. brown .. .. 70 85
137. 45 c. olive .. .. 85 1·00
138. 50 c. lilac .. .. 85 1·00
139. 16. 55 c. yellow .. .. 85 1·00
140. 1 l. black .. .. .. 4·25 5·00
141. 2 l. red .. .. .. 4·75 6·00
142. 3 l. green .. .. .. 4·75 6·00
143. 5 l. brown .. .. .. 4·75 6·00
144. 10 l. lilac .. .. .. 4·75 6·00

**1920.** Nos. M145/8 optd **Reggenza Italiana del Carnaro** or surch also.

146. M 17. 1 on 5 c. green .. 20 30
147. – 2 on 25 c. blue .. 20 30
148. M 17. 5 c. green .. .. 20 30
149. – 10 c. red .. .. 25 35
150. – 15 on 10 c. red .. 25 35
151. – 15 on 20 c. brown .. 25 35
152. – 15 on 25 c. blue .. 30 40
153. – 20 c. brown .. .. 30 40
154. – 25 c. blue .. .. 30 40
155. – 25 on 10 c. red .. 1·40 1·60
156. – 50 on 20 c. brown .. 80 90
157. M 17. 55 on 5 c. green .. 80 90
158. – 1 l. on 10 c. red .. 4·50 5·50
159. – 1 l. on 25 c. blue .. 55·00 50·00
160. M 17. 2 l. on 5 c. green .. 7·00 8·50
161. – 5 l. on 10 c. red .. 40·00 48·00
162. – 10 l. on 20 c. brown .. £200 £140

**1921.** Issue of d'Annunzio optd. **Governo Provvisorio** or also surch. **LIRE UNA** (No. 173).

163. 16. 5 c. green .. .. 20 35
164. 10 c. red .. .. 20 35
165. 15 c. grey .. .. 30 45
166. 20 c. orange .. .. 30 45
167. 25 c. blue .. .. 40 55
168. 30 c. brown .. .. 40 55
169. 45 c. olive .. .. 70 85
170. 50 c. lilac .. .. 70 85
171. 55 c. yellow .. .. 70 85
172. 1 l. black .. .. 30·00 35·00
173. 1 l. on 30 c. brown .. 70 85
174. 2 l. red .. .. 3·25 4·00
175. 3 l. green .. .. 4·50 4·75
176. 5 l. brown .. .. 4·75 5·50
177. 10 l. lilac .. .. 6·50 7·25

**1921.** Charity Stamps of 1919 optd **24-IV-1921 Costituente Fiumana** (and "L" over "Cor." in high values).

178. 5 c. green .. .. 60 85
179. 10 c. red .. .. 60 85
180. 15 c. grey .. .. 60 85
181. 20 c. orange .. .. 60 85
182. 45 c. green .. .. 1·10 1·60
183. 60 c. red .. .. 1·40 1·90
184. 80 c. violet .. .. 2·25 2·75
185. 1 l. on 1 cor. grey .. 3·00 3·75
186. 1 l. on 2 cor. brown .. 11·00 70
187. 3 l. on 3 cor. brown .. 13·00 16·00
188. 5 l. on 5 cor. brown .. 14·00 85
189. 10 l. on 10 cor. violet .. 15·00 18·00

**1922.** Charity Stamps of 1919 optd **24-IV-1921 Costituente Fiumana 1922** (and "L" over "Cor." in high values).

190. 5 c. green .. .. 2·25 45
191. 10 c. red .. .. 25 30
192. 15 c. grey .. .. 8·00 70
193. 20 c. orange .. .. 25 30
194. 45 c. green .. .. 25 70
195. 60 c. red .. .. 25 70
196. 80 c. violet .. .. 25 70
197. 1 l. on 1 cor. grey .. 25 55
198. 2 l. on 2 cor. brown .. 60 1·00
199. 3 l. on 3 cor. brown .. 60 85
200. 5 l. on 5 cor. brown .. 60 85

**1923.**

201. 21. 5 c. green .. .. 30 35
202. 10 c. mauve .. .. 30 35
203. 15 c. brown .. .. 30 35
204. – 20 c. red .. .. 30 35
205. – 25 c. grey .. .. 30 35
206. – 30 c. green .. .. 30 35
207. – 50 c. blue .. .. 30 35
208. – 60 c. red .. .. 40 85
209. – 1 l. blue .. .. 40 40
210. – 2 l. brown .. .. 6·50 4·00
211. – 3 l. olive .. .. 14·50 9·50
212. – 5 l. brown .. .. 12·00 11·00

DESIGNS: 20, 25, 30 c. Roman Arch. 50, 60 c. 1 l. St. Vitus. 2, 3, 5 l. Tarsatic Column.

**1924.** Issue of 1923 optd. **REGNO D'ITALIA** in frame.

213. 21. 5 c. green .. .. 20 1·40
214. 10 c. mauve .. .. 20 1·40
215. 15 c. brown .. .. 20 1·40
216. – 20 c. red .. .. 20 1·40
217. – 25 c. grey .. .. 20 1·40
218. – 30 c. green .. .. 20 1·40
219. – 50 c. blue .. .. 20 1·40
220. – 60 c. red .. .. 20 1·40
221. – 1 l. blue .. .. 20 1·40
222. – 2 l. brown .. .. 65 4·75
223. – 3 l. olive .. .. 1·75 4·75
224. – 5 l. brown .. .. 1·75 4·75

**1924.** Issue of 1923 optd **ANNESSIONE ALL'ITALIA** in frame with **22 Febb 1924** below.

225. 21. 5 c. green .. .. 20 95
226. 10 c. mauve .. .. 20 95
227. 15 c. brown .. .. 20 95
228. – 20 c. red .. .. 20 95
229. – 25 c. grey .. .. 20 95
230. – 30 c. green .. .. 20 95
231. – 50 c. blue .. .. 20 95
232. – 60 c. red .. .. 20 95
233. – 1 l. blue .. .. 20 95
234. – 2 l. brown .. .. 60 2·75
235. – 3 l. olive .. .. 60 2·75
236. – 5 l. brown .. .. 60 2·75

EXPRESS LETTER STAMPS

E 17.

**1920.**

E145 E 17 30 c. green .. .. 5·00 7·00
E146 50 c. red .. .. 5·00 7·00

**1920.** Nos. M147 and M145 surch **Reggenza Italiana del Carnaro ESPRESSO** and new value.

E163 30 c. on 20 c. bistre .. 35·00 29·00
E164 50 c. on 5 c. green .. 24·00 20·00

**1921.** Optd. **Governo Provvisorio.**

E 178. E 17. 30 c. blue .. .. 6·00 7·50
E 179. 50 c. red .. .. 6·00 7·50

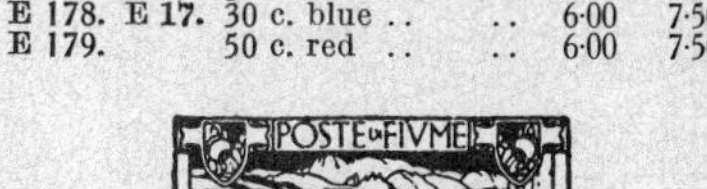

E 25. Fiume in 16th Century.

**1923.**

E 213. E 25. 60 c. red .. .. 4·00 3·00
E 214. 2 l. blue .. .. 4·00 6·00

**1924.** Optd **REGNO D'ITALIA** in frame with arms between the two words.

E225 E 25 60 c. red .. .. 80 4·75
E226 2 l. blue .. .. 80 4·75

**1924.** Optd **ANNESSIONE ALL'ITALIA** in frame with **22 Febbraio 1924** below.

E237 E 25 60 c. red .. .. 80 4·75
E238 2 l. blue .. .. 80 4·75

MILITARY POST STAMPS

M 17. Severing the Gordian Knot.

**1920.** 1st Anniv of Capture of Fiume by D'Annunzio's "legionaries".

M145 M 17 5 c. green .. .. 10·00 10·00
M146 – 10 c. red .. .. 8·00 8·00
M147 – 20 c. bistre .. 10·00 10·00
M148 – 25 c. blue .. .. 22·00 22·00

DESIGNS: 10 c. Arms of Fiume. 20 c. "Crown of Thorns". 25 c. Daggers raised in clenched fists.

NEWSPAPER STAMPS

N 9.

**1919.**

N91 N 9 2 c. brown .. .. 1·10 1·40

N 17. Mail Steamer.

**1920.**

N 145. N 17. 1 c. green .. .. 15 35

POSTAGE DUE STAMPS

**1918.** Postage Due stamps of Hungary of 1903 (figures in black), optd. **FIUME.**

D 29. D 9. 6 f. green (D 21) .. 38·00 19·00
D 30. 12 f. green (D 31) .. £190 80·00
D 31. 50 f. green (D 33) .. 60·00 45·00

**1918.** Postage Due stamps of Hungary of 1915 (figures in red), optd. **FIUME.**

D 32. D 9. 1 f. green .. .. 12·00 6·50
D 33. 2 f. green .. .. 20 20
D 34. 5 f. green .. .. 3·75 1·25
D 35. 6 f. green .. .. 20 20
D 36. 10 f. green .. .. 4·75 1·60
D 37. 12 f. green .. .. 30 30
D 38. 15 f. green .. .. 8·50 8·00
D 39. 20 f. green .. .. 30 30
D 40. 30 f. green .. .. 12·00 8·00

D 9.

**1919.**

D 91. **D 9.** 2 c. brown .. .. 30 30
D 92. 5 c. brown .. .. 40 40

**1921.** Nos. 105/30 surch **Segnatasse**, new value and device obliterating old surch.

D191 **6** 2 c. on 15 c. grey .. 30 40
D192 4 c. on 10 c. red .. 25 30
D193 **9** 5 c. on 25 c. blue .. 25 30
D194 **6** 6 c. on 20 c. orange .. 25 30
D195 10 c. on 20 c. orange .. 65 65
D188 – 20 c. on 45 c. green .. 30 70
D183 – 30 c. on 1 cor. grey .. 30 40
D184 – 40 c. on 80 c. violet .. 25 35
D185 – 50 c. on 60 c. red .. 25 35
D189 – 60 c. on 45 c. green .. 30 70
D190 – 80 c. on 45 c. green .. 30 70
D201 – 1 l. on 2 cor. brown .. 1·10 1·25

For stamps of Italy surch. **3-V-1945 FIUME RIJEKE** and new value, see Venezia Giulia and Istria, Nos. 18/24.

## FIUME AND KUPA ZONE Pt. 3

The zone comprised Fiume (Rijeka), Susak and Kupa River area.

100 pares = 1 dinar.

**1941.** Nos. 414, etc. of Yugoslavia optd. **ZONA OCCUPATA FIUMANO KUPA.**

1. **99.** 25 p. black .. .. 1·75 1·75
2. 50 p. orange .. .. 80 80
3. 1 d. green .. .. 80 80
4. 1 d. 50 red .. .. 80 80
5. 3 d. brown .. .. 1·25 1·25
6. 4 d. blue .. .. 2·25 2·25
7. 5 d. blue .. .. 4·00 4·00
8. 5 d. 50 violet .. .. 4·00 4·00
9. 6 d. blue .. .. 14·50 14·50
10. 8 d. brown .. .. 10·00 10·00
11. 12 d. violet .. .. £160 £160
12. 16 d. purple .. .. 50·00 50·00
13. 20 d. blue .. .. £800 £800
14. 30 d. pink .. .. £3500 £3500

**1941.** Maternity and Child Welfare Fund. Nos. 2/4 further optd. **O.N.M.I.** (=Opera Nazionale Maternita e Infanzia).

15. **99.** 50 p. orange .. .. 1·25 3·00
16. 1 d. green .. .. 1·25 3·00
17. 1 d. 50 red .. .. 1·25 3·00

**1941.** Italian Naval Exploit at Buccari (Bakar) 1918. No. 415 of Yugoslavia surch. **MEMENTO AVDERE** and value etc.

18. **99.** 1 l. on 50 p. orange .. 10·00 24·00

**1942.** Maternity and Child Welfare. Nos. 15/17 further optd. **Pro Maternita—infanzia.**

19. **99.** 50 p. orange .. .. 2·40 6·00
20. 1 d. green .. .. 2·40 6·00
21. 1 d. 50 red .. .. 2·40 6·00

Nos. 1/21 were valid until 26.5.42 after which unoverprinted Italian stamps were used until the Italian Occupation ended.

## FRANCE Pt. 6

A republic in the W. of Europe.

100 centimes = 1 franc

**NOTE.** Stamps in types of France up to the 1877 issue were also issued for the French Colonies and where the values and colours are the same they can only be distinguished by their shade or postmark or other minor differences which are outside the scope of this Catalogue. They are priced here by whichever is the lower of the quotations under France or French Colonies in the Stanley Gibbons Catalogue, Part 6 (France).

Numbers with asterisks are French Colonies numbers.

1. Ceres.

2. Louis Napoleon, President. 3. Napoleon III, Emperor of the French.

**1849.** Imperf.

157 **1** 5 c. green .. .. £225 £160
15* 10 c. bistre .. .. £200 £130
4 15 c. green .. .. £17000 £1100
6 20 c. black .. .. £325 32·00
17* 20 c. blue .. .. £475 £110
18* 25 c. blue .. .. £130 9·50
22* 30 c. brown .. .. 90·00 16·00
19* 40 c. orange .. .. £225 10·50
23* 80 c. red .. .. £500 £120
17 1 f. orange .. .. £50000 £16000
19 1 f. red .. .. £9000 £950

For 10 c. brown on pink and 15 c. bistre, imperf, see French Colonies Nos. 16 and 20.

**1852.** Imperf.

37a. **2.** 10 c. yellow .. .. £30000 £700
39. 25 c. blue .. .. £3000 48·00

**1853.** Imperf.

42a **3** 1 c. olive .. .. £200 85·00
45 5 c. green .. .. £750 95·00
50a 10 c. yellow .. .. £375 8·25
51 20 c. blue .. .. £170 90
63 25 c. blue .. .. £2750 £275
64 40 c. orange .. .. £2500 13·00
70 80 c. red .. .. £1600 50·00
72 1 f. red .. .. £5500 £3750

**1862.** Perf.

87 **3** 1 c. green .. .. £160 38·00
89 5 c. green .. .. £190 10·00
91 10 c. bistre .. .. £1600 3·75
95 20 c. blue .. .. £250 75
97 40 c. orange .. .. £1600 6·50
98 80 c. pink .. .. £1100 35·00

4. 5.
Head with Laurel Wreath.

**1863.** Perf.

102 **4** 1 c. green .. .. 23·00 13·00
104 2 c. brown .. .. 75·00 23·00
109 4 c. grey .. .. £200 50·00
113a **5** 10 c. bistre .. .. £275 5·25
115a 20 c. blue .. .. £200 1·00
116 30 c. brown .. .. £850 16·00
119 40 c. orange .. .. £850 10·00
121 80 c. pink .. .. £1000 19·00

For imperforate stamps in these designs see French Colonies.

6

7. Ceres.

**1869.**

131 **6** 5 f. lilac .. .. .. £6000 £1100

**1870.** Imperf.

146 **7** 1 c. green .. .. 90·00 90·00
152 2 c. brown .. .. £200 £225
156 4 c. grey .. .. £225 £225

For 1 c. green on blue, 2 c. brown on yellow and 5 c. green as Type **7** and imperf, see French Colonies.

**1870.** Perf.

185 **7** 1 c. green .. .. 35·00 11·50
187 2 c. brown .. .. 75·00 11·50
189 4 c. grey .. .. £350 40·00
191 5 c. green .. .. £160 7·00
136 **1** 10 c. bistre .. .. £400 70·00
194 10 c. bistre on pink .. £425 9·50
204 15 c. bistre .. .. £425 3·75
137 20 c. blue .. .. £275 6·50
198 25 c. blue .. .. £110 75
205 30 c. brown .. .. £700 5·75
140 40 c. orange .. .. £700 5·25
142 40 c. red .. .. £700 5·25
208 80 c. red .. .. £850 14·50

10. Peace and Commerce.

**1876.**

212 **10** 1 c. green .. .. £160 65·00
245 1 c. black on blue .. 3·25 60
225 2 c. green .. .. £100 18·00
248 2 c. brown on buff .. 4·50 1·25
249 3 c. brown on yellow .. £200 42·00
251 3 c. grey .. .. 3·25 1·50
214 4 c. green .. .. £160 50·00
252 4 c. brown on grey .. 5·25 1·75
254 4 c. purple on blue .. 6·50 3·25
282 5 c. green .. .. 10·00 80
216 10 c. green .. .. £850 45·00
284 10 c. black on lilac .. 18·00 2·50
232 15 c. lilac .. .. £600 1·50
279 15 c. blue .. .. 11·50 10
219 20 c. brown on yellow .. £500 16·00
260 20 c. red on green .. 35·00 3·25
234 25 c. blue .. .. £450 95
262 25 c. black on red .. £1000 21·00
263 25 c. bistre on yellow .. £300 4·50
266 25 c. black on pink .. 80·00 65
237 30 c. brown .. .. 95·00 95
268 35 c. brown on yellow .. £500 32·00
269 40 c. red on yellow .. £110 1·25
273 50 c. red .. .. £200 1·50
223 75 c. red .. .. £1000 10·00
274 75 c. brown on orange .. £225 29·00
239 1 f. green .. .. £150 6·25
287 2 f. brown on blue .. £100 35·00
277 5 f. mauve on lilac .. £500 80·00

For imperforate stamps in this design see French Colonies.

For 5 f. red, perf, see No. 412.

11. "Blanc" type.

12. "Mouchon" type.

13. "Olivier Merson" type.

**1900.**

288 **11** 1 c. grey .. .. 60 35
289 2 c. purple .. .. 75 10
290 3 c. red .. .. 35 10
292a 4 c. brown .. .. 2·50 1·25
295 5 c. green .. .. 1·90 10
300 **12** 10 c. red .. .. 22·00 75
301 15 c. orange .. .. 8·25 35
297 20 c. brown .. .. 60·00 13·00
302 25 c. blue .. .. 70·00 1·50
299 30 c. mauve .. .. 60·00 5·25
303 **13** 40 c. red and blue .. 13·00 65
304 45 c. green and blue .. 38·00 1·40
305 50 c. brown and lilac .. 90·00 1·25
306 1 f. red and green .. 25·00 60
369 1 f. red and yellow .. 45·00 1·10
307 2 f. lilac and buff .. £750 70·00
308 5 f. blue and buff .. 80·00 3·75

See also Nos. 413 etc.

14. "Mouchon" type redrawn.

15. Sower.

**1902.**

309. **14.** 10 c. red .. .. 22·00 75
310. 15 c. red .. .. 8·50 35
311. 20 c. brown .. .. 65·00 13·00
312. 25 c. blue .. .. 70·00 1·50
313. 30 c. mauve .. .. £190 14·00

**1903.**

314 **15** 10 c. red .. .. 7·75 10
316 15 c. green .. .. 3·75 10
317 20 c. purple .. .. 60·00 1·50
320 25 c. blue .. .. 70·00 1·25
321 30 c. lilac .. .. £150 5·25

16. Ground below Feet.

18. No Ground.

20.

**1906.**

325. **16.** 10 c. red .. .. 2·50 1·10

**1906.**

331 **18** 5 c. green .. .. 1·50 10
334 10 c. red .. .. 1·50 10
337 20 c. brown .. .. 2·50 10
341 25 c. blue .. .. 2·50 10
365 30 c. orange .. .. 13·00 85
346 35 c. violet .. .. 7·75 75

See also Nos. 497 etc. and 454/a.

**1914.** Red Cross Fund. Surch with red cross and **5c.**

351 **18** 10 c. + 5c. red .. .. 5·25 5·25

**1914.** Red Cross Fund.

353. **20.** 10 c. + 5 c. red .. .. 32·00 3·25

21. War Widow.

26. Spirit of War.

23. Woman replaces Man.

27. Sinking of "Charles Roux" Hospital Ship, and Bombed Hospital.

**1917.** War Orphans' Fund.

370 **21** 2 c. + 3 c. red .. .. 4·50 3·75
371 – 5 c. + 5 c. green .. 16·00 5·75
372 **23** 15 c. + 10 c green .. 21·00 19·00
373 25 c. + 15 c. blue .. 80·00 48·00
374 – 35 c. + 25 c. violet & grey £130 £110
375 – 50 c. + 50 c. brown .. £200 £160
376 **26** 1 f. + 1 f. red .. £350 £300
377 5 f. + 5 f. blue and black £1300 £1100

DESIGNS— As Type **21**: 5 c. Orphans. As Type **26**: 35 c. Front line trench. 50 c. Lion of Belfort.

See also Nos. 450/3.

**1918.** Red Cross Fund.

378. **27.** 15 c. + 5 c. red & green .. £120 55·00

**1919.** Surch. ½ **centime.**

379. **11.** ½ c. on 1 c. grey .. 10 10

**1920.**

497 **18** 1 c. bistre .. .. 10 10
497a 1 c. brown .. .. 10 10
498 2 c. green .. .. 10 10
499 3 c. red .. .. 10 10
380 5 c. orange .. .. 1·10 10
500 5 c. mauve .. .. 10 10
413 **11** 7½ c. mauve* .. .. 1·00 45
381 **18** 10 c. green .. .. 40 10
501 10 c. blue .. .. 1·60 15
413a **11** 10 c. lilac .. .. 2·25 15
414 **18** 15 c. brown .. .. 10 10
415 20 c. mauve .. .. 25 10
415b 25 c. brown .. .. 20 10
503 30 c. red .. .. 1·00 10
382a 30 c. mauve .. .. 90 10
416 30 c. blue .. .. 1·25 25
505 35 c. green .. .. 50 15
417 40 c. green .. .. 1·25 25
418 40 c. red .. .. 2·75 20
418a 40 c. violet .. .. 1·10 20
418b 40 c. blue .. .. 1·25 15
419 **15** 45 c. violet .. .. 5·75 1·00
592 50 c. blue .. .. 80 10
420 50 c. green .. .. 6·50 75
421 50 c. red .. .. 1·25 10
384 **13** 60 c. violet and blue .. 80 70
385 **15** 60 c. violet .. .. 5·75 1·25
385a 65 c. red .. .. 2·50 90
422 65 c. green .. .. 6·25 1·60
423 75 c. mauve .. .. 5·25 20
424 80 c. red .. .. 26·00 7·00
386 85 c. red .. .. 12·50 1·50
425 1 f. blue .. .. 5·75 35
426 **18** 1 f. 05 red .. .. 8·25 3·75
427 1 f. 10 mauve .. .. 10·00 1·75
428 1 f. 40 mauve .. .. 16·00 17·00
387 **13** 2 f. orange and green .. 42·00 10
428a **18** 2 f. green .. .. 12·50 90
429 **13** 3 f. violet and blue .. 24·00 6·50
430 3 f. mauve and red .. 50·00 1·90
431 10 f. green and red .. £100 14·00
432 20 f. mauve and green £160 32·00

***PRECANCEL.** No. 413 was issued only pre-cancelled. The "unused" price is for stamps with full gum and the used price for stamps without gum.

**1922.** War Orphans' Fund. Nos. 370/7 surch with new value, cross and bars.

388 **21** 1 c. on 2 c. + 3 c. red .. 20 30
389 – 2½ c. on 5 c. + 5 c. green 60 60
390 **23** 5 c. on 15 c. + 10 c. green 1·10 1·10
391 5 c. on 25 c. + 15 c. blue 2·40 2·40
392 – 5 c. on 35 c. + 25 c. violet and grey .. 13·00 13·00
393 – 10 c. on 50 c. + 50 c. brn 18·00 18·00
394 **26** 25 c. on 1 f. + 1 f. red .. 29·00 29·00
395 1 f. on 5 f. + 5 f. blue and black .. .. £140 £140

30. Pasteur.

31. Stadium and Arc de Triomphe.

**1923.**

396. **30.** 10 c. green .. .. 50 10
396a. 15 c. green .. .. 1·50 10
396b. 20 c. green .. .. 2·75 15
397. 30 c. red .. .. 75 20
397a. 30 c. green .. .. 60 10
398. 45 c. red .. .. 1·75 1·00
399. 50 c. blue .. .. 4·50 10
400. 75 c. blue .. .. 3·75 10
400a. 90 c. red .. .. 11·00 3·25
400b. 1 f. blue .. .. 20·00 10
400c. 1 f. 25 blue .. .. 24·00 7·00
400d. 1 f. 50 blue .. .. 5·25 10

**1923.** Optd. **CONGRES PHILATELIQUE DE BORDEAUX 1923.**

400e. **13.** 1 f. red and green .. £350 £425

**1924.** Olympic Games.

401 **31** 10 c. green & light green 1·60 90
402 – 25 c. deep red and red .. 2·40 25
403 – 30 c. red and black .. 7·75 8·50
404 – 50 c. ultramarine & blue 23·00 3·75

DESIGNS—HORIZ. 25 c. Notre Dame and Pont Neuf. VERT. 30 c. Milan de Crotone (statue). 50 c. The victor.

35. Ronsard.

36.

**1924.** 400th Birth Anniv. of Ronsard.

405. **35.** 75 c. blue .. .. 1·90 1·25

**1924.** Int. Exn. of Modern Decorative Arts. Dated "1925".
406. **36.** 10 c. yellow and green 45 35
407. – 15 c. grn. & dp. grn. .. 45 35
408. – 25 c. red and purple .. 45 35
409. – 25 c. mauve and blue 1·25 75
410. – 75 c. blue and grey .. 2·40 1·50
411. **36.** 75 c. blue & deep blue 17·00 5·75
DESIGNS—HORIZ. 25 c. (No. 408), 75 c. (No. 410) Potter and vase. 25 c. (No. 409), Chateau and steps. VERT. 15 c. Stylized vase.

**1925.** Paris Int. Philatelic Exn.
412. **10.** 5 f. red .. .. .. 95·00 95·00

**1926.** Surch. with new value and bars.
433. **18.** 25 c. on 30 c. blue .. 20 15
434. 25 c. on 35 c. violet .. 20 10
436. **15.** 50 c. on 60 c. violet .. 90 45
437. 50 c. on 65 c. red .. 55 20
438. **30.** 50 c. on 75 c. blue .. 3·00 75
439. **15.** 50 c. on 80 c. red .. 80 80
440. 50 c. on 85 c. red .. 1·90 75
441. **18.** 50 c. on 1 f. 05 red .. 1·00 45
442. **30.** 50 c. on 1 f. 25 blue .. 2·50 1·10
443. **15.** 55 c. on 60 c. violet* .. £120 45·00
444. **18.** 90 c. on 1 f. 05 red .. 2·50 2·50
445. 1 f. 10 on 1 f. 40 red .. 1·10 90
***PRECANCEL.** See note below **No. 432.**

**1926.** War Orphans' Fund.
450 21 2 c.+1 c. purple .. 1·25 1·25
451 – 50 c.+10 c. brown (as No. 375) .. .. 18·00 10·00
452 26 1 f.+25 c. red .. .. 45·00 32·00
453 5 f.+1 f. blue and black 90·00 85·00

**1927. Strasbourg Philatelic Exn.**
454. **18.** 5 f. blue .. .. £200 £200
454a. 10 f. red .. .. £200 £200

**1927.** Air. 1st International Display of Aviation and Navigation, Marseilles. Optd with Bleriot XI airplane and **Poste Aerienne**.
455. **13.** 2 f. red and green .. £170 £170
456. 5 f. blue and yellow .. £170 £170

**44.** Marcelin Berthelot.

**45.** Lafayette, Washington, "Paris" (liner) and Lindbergh's Airplane "Spirit of St. Louis".

**1927.** Birth Centenary of Berthelot.
457. **44.** 90 c. red .. .. 1·90 35

**1927.** Visit of American Legion.
458. **45.** 90 c. red .. .. 1·10 1·10
459. 1 f. 50 blue .. .. 3·75 1·25

**1927.** Sinking Fund. Surch. **Caisse d'Amortissement** or **C A** and premium.
460. **18.** 40 c.+10 c. blue .. 5·00 5·00
461. **15.** 50 c.+25 c. green .. 7·75 7·75
462. **30.** 1 f. 50+50 c. orange .. 11·50 11·50
See also Nos. 466/8, 476/8, 485/7 and 494/6.

**48.**

**50.** Joan of Arc.

**1928.** Sinking Fund.
463. **48.** 1 f. 50+8 f. 50 blue .. £120 £120

**1928.** Air ("Ile de France"). Surch. **10 FR.** and bars.
464. **44.** 10 f. on 90 c. red .. £1500 £1500
465. **30.** 10 f. on 1 f. 50 blue .. £8000 £8000

**1928.** Sinking Fund. Surch as Nos. 460/2.
466. **18.** 40 c.+10 c. violet .. 16·00 14·00
467. **15.** 50 c.+25 c. red.. .. 29·00 24·00
468. **30.** 1 f. 50+50 c. mauve .. 50·00 48·00

**1929.** 500th Anniv. of Relief of Orleans.
469. **50.** 50 c. blue .. .. 1·90 20

**1929.** Optd **EXPOSITION LE HAVRE 1929 PHILATELIQUE.**
470 13 2 f. red and green .. £500 £500

**52.** Reims Cathedral.

**53.** Mont St. Michel.

**1929.** Views.
470a – 90 c. mauve .. .. 3·00 90
471 – 2 f. red .. .. 32·00 55
472 **52** 3 f. blue .. .. 60·00 2·50
473a **53** 5 f. brown .. .. 19·00 35
474b – 10 f. blue .. .. 75·00 6·50
475 – 20 f. brown .. .. £250 35·00
DESIGNS—HORIZ. 90 c. Le Puy-en-Velay. 2 f. Arc de Triomphe. 10 f. Port de la Rochelle. 20 f. Pont du Gard.

**1929.** Sinking Fund. Surch. as Nos. 460/2.
476. **18.** 40 c.+10 c. green .. 16·00 14·00
477. **15.** 50 c.+25 c. mauve .. 29·00 24·00
478. **30.** 1 f. 50+50 c. brown .. 50·00 48·00

**54.** Bay of Algiers.

**1930.** Cent. of French Conquest of Algeria.
479. **54.** 50 c. red and blue .. 2·50 35

**55.** " Le Sourire de Reims ".

**1930.** Sinking Fund.
480. **55.** 1 f. 50+3 f. 50 purple 75·00 75·00

**1930.** I.L.O. Session, Paris. Optd. **CONGRES du B.I.T. 1930.**
481. **15.** 50 c. red .. .. 2·25 1·90
482. **30.** 1 f. 50 blue .. .. 17·00 12·50

**57.** Notre Dame de la Garde, Marseilles.

**1930.** Air.
483. **57.** 1 f. 50 red .. .. 20·00 2·50
484. 1 f. 50 blue .. .. 18·00 1·50

**1930.** Sinking Fund. Surch. as Nos. 460/2.
485. **18.** 40 c.+10 c. red .. 16·00 16·00
486. **15.** 50 c.+25 c. brown .. 32·00 29·00
487. **18.** 1 f. 50+50 c. violet .. 55·00 55·00

**58.** Woman of the Fachi tribe.

**59.** " French Colonies ".

**1930.** Int. Colonial Exn.
488. **58.** 15 c. black .. .. 1·00 10
489. 40 c. brown .. .. 2·10 20
490. 50 c. red .. .. 60 10
491. 1 f. 50 blue .. .. 9·00 45
492. **59.** 1 f. 50 blue .. .. 42·00 1·75

**60.** " French Provinces ".

**1931.** Sinking Fund.
493. **60.** 1 f. 50+3 f. 50 green .. £120 £120

**1931.** Sinking Fund. Surch as Nos. 460/2.
494. **18.** 40 c.+10 c. green .. 38·00 32·00
495. **15.** 50 c.+25 c. violet .. 80·00 80·00
496. **18.** 1 f. 50+50 c. red .. 80·00 80·00

**61.** Peace.

**62.** Briand.

**65.** Dove of Peace.

**1932.**
502. **61.** 30 c. green .. .. 65 20
506. 40 c. mauve .. .. 20 10
507. 45 c. brown .. .. 1·40 55
508. 50 c. red .. .. 10 10
508d. 55 c. violet .. .. 45 20
508e. 60 c. bistre .. .. 10 10
509. 65 c. purple .. .. 25 15
509a. 65 c. blue .. .. 20 10
510. 75 c. green .. .. 10 10
510a. 80 c. orange .. .. 10 10
511. 90 c. red .. .. 30·00 1·40
511a. 90 c. green .. .. 10 10
511b. 90 c. blue .. .. 45 10
512. 1 f. orange .. .. 3·00 15
512a. 1 f. pink .. .. 3·00 20
513. 1 f. 25 olive .. .. 65·00 3·75
513a. 1 f. 25 red .. .. 1·50 1·60
513b. 1 f. 40 mauve .. .. 5·75 4·50
514. 1 f. 50 blue .. .. 10 10
515. 1 f. 75 mauve .. .. 4·00 10

**1933.** Surch ½ **centime.**
515a 18 ½ c. on 1 c. bistre .. 20 25
515b ½ c. on 1 c. brown .. 75 1·10

**1933. Portraits.**
516. **62.** 30 c. green .. .. 16·00 7·75
517. – 75 c. mauve (Doumer).. 23·00 65
518. – 1 f. 25 red (Victor Hugo) 5·75 1·90

**1934.**
519 **65** 1 f. 50 blue .. .. 50·00 14·00

**66.** J. M. Jacquard.

**67.** Jacques Cartier, "Grande Hermine" and "Petite Hermine".

**1934.** Death Centenary of Jacquard.
520. **66.** 40 c. blue .. .. 3·00 75

**1934.** 4th Cent. of Cartier's Discovery of Canada.
521. **67.** 75 c. mauve .. .. 19·00 1·60
522. 1 f. 50 blue .. .. 38·00 2·50

**68.** Bleriot XI.

**1934.** Air. 25th Anniv. of Channel Flight.
523. **68.** 2 f. 25 violet .. .. 19·00 5·75

**1934.** Surch. in figures and bars.
524. **61.** 50 c. on 1 f. 25 olive .. 3·75 35
524a. 80 c. on 1 f. orange .. 30 30

**69.** Breton River Scene.

**1935.**
525. **69.** 2 f. green .. .. 32·00 75

**70.** "Normandie".

**71.** St. Trophime, Arles.

**1935.** Maiden Trip of Liner "Normandie".
526 **70** 1 f. 50 blue .. .. 13·00 1·50

**1935.**
527. **71.** 3 f. 50 brown .. .. 25·00 3·25

**72.** B. Delessert.

**73.** Victor Hugo.

**1935.** Opening of Int. Savings Bank Congress.
528. **72.** 75 c. green .. .. 17·00 1·00

**1935.** 50th Death Anniv. of Victor Hugo.
529. **73.** 1 f. 25 purple .. .. 4·50 1·10

**74.** Cardinal Richelieu.

**1935.** Tercentenary of French Academy by Richelieu.
530. **74.** 1 f. 50 red .. .. 19·00 1·25

**75.** Jacques Callot.

**77.** Symbolic of Art.

**1935.** Death Tercentenary of Callot (engraver).
531. **75.** 75 c. red .. .. 10·00 35

**1935.** Unemployed Intellectuals' Relief Fund. Inscr. " POUR L'ART ET LA PENSEE ".
532. – 50 c.+10 c. blue .. 2·50 2·50
533. **77.** 50 c.+2 f. red .. .. 50·00 45·00
DESIGN—HORIZ. No. 532, Help for intellectuals (inscr. " POUR LES CHOMEURS INTELLECTUELS ".

**78.** Caudron C-635 Simoun over Paris.

**1936.** Air.
534. **78.** 85 c. green .. .. 2·50 2·00
535. 1 f. 50 blue .. .. 9·00 4·00
536. 2 f. 25 violet .. .. 20·00 6·50
537. 2 f. 50 red .. .. 32·00 7·75
538. 3 f. blue .. .. 25·00 90
539. 3 f. 50 brown .. .. 60·00 20·00
540. 50 f. green .. .. £850 £325

**79.** Caudron C-635 Simoun over Paris.

**1936.** Air.
541 **79** 50 f. blue and pink .. £650 £300

**80.** Statue of Liberty.

**81.** Andre-Marie Ampere.

**1936.** Nansen (Refugee) Fund.
541a. **80.** 50 c.+25 c. blue .. 3·25 3·75
542. 75 c.+50 c. violet .. 9·00 9·00

**1936.** Death Centenary of Ampere.
543 **81** 75 c. brown .. .. 16·00 1·90

**82.** Daudet's Mill, Fontvieille.

**1936.**
544. **82.** 2 f. blue .. .. 3·75 30

## INDEX

Countries can be quickly located by referring to the index at the end of this volume.

83. Children of the Unemployed. 84. Pilatre de Rozier.

**1936.** Children of the Unemployed Fund.
545. **83.** 50 c.+10 c. red .. 4·50 4·50

**1936.** 150th Death Anniv. of Pilatre de Rozier.
546. **84.** 75 c. blue .. .. 16·00 2·50

85. Rouget de Lisle. 87. Canadian War Memorial, Vimy.

**1936.** Death Centenary of Rouget de Lisle. Composer of the "Marseillaise."
547. **85.** 20 c. green .. .. 3·00 1·90
548. – 40 c. brown .. .. 5·00 2·50
DESIGN—HORIZ. 40 c. Female figure inscr. "LA MARSEILLAISE".

**1936.** Unveiling of Canadian War Memorial, Vimy Ridge.
549. **87.** 75 c. red .. .. 7·75 1·90
550. 1 f. 50 blue .. .. 14·00 8·25

The 1 f. 50 has a head and shoulders portrait of Jaures.

88. Jean Jaures as an Orator.

**1936.** Jaures Commemoration.
551. **88.** 40 c. brown .. .. 3·25 1·25
552. – 1 f. 50 blue .. .. 11·50 2·50

91. Latecoere 300 Flying Boat.

**1936.** 100th Flight between France and S. America.
553. – 1 f. 50 blue .. .. 14·00 3·25
554. **91.** 10 f. green .. .. £250 £110
DESIGN—VERT. 1 f. 50, Airplane and old-time sailing ship.

92. Herald. 93. "World Exhibition".

**1936.** Paris Int. Exn.
555. **92.** 20 c. mauve .. .. 50 45
556. 30 c. green .. .. 2·50 1·50
557. 40 c. blue .. .. 95 20
558. 50 c. orange .. .. 1·10 10
559. **93.** 90 c. red .. .. 11·00 7·25
560. 1 f. 50 blue .. .. 29·00 2·75

94. "Vision of Peace".

**1936.** Universal Peace Propaganda.
561. **94.** 1 f. 50 blue .. .. 12·50 3·25

**1936.** Unemployed Intellectuals' Fund. No. 533 surch **+20c**.
562 **77** 20 c. on 50 c.+2 f. red .. 3·25 3·25

96. Jacques Callot.

**1936.** Unemployed Intellectuals' Fund. Inscr. as in T **96**.
563. **96.** 20 c.+10 c. lake .. 1·90 2·50
564. – 40 c.+10 c. green .. 2·50 3·25
565. – 50 c.+10 c. red .. 3·25 3·25
566. – 1 f. 50+50 c. blue .. 18·00 16·00
DESIGNS: 40 c. Hector Berlioz. 50 c. Victor Hugo. 1 f. 50, Louis Pasteur.
See also Nos. 603/5 and 607.

97. Ski Jumper.

**1937.** Chamonix-Mont Blanc Skiing Week.
567. **97.** 1 f. 50 blue .. .. 6·50 1·50

98. Pierre Corneille (author). 99. France and Minerva.

**1937.** 300th Anniv of First Performance of "Le Cid" (play).
568 **98** 75 c. red .. .. 1·90 1·25

**1937.** Paris Int. Exn.
569 **99** 1 f. 50 blue .. .. 2·25 55

100. Mermoz. 101. Jean Mermoz Memorial.

**1937.** Mermoz Commem.
570. **100.** 30 c. green .. .. 35 35
571. **101.** 3 f. violet .. .. 5·25 3·25

102. Electric Train.

**1937.** 13th Int. Railway Congress, Paris.
572. **102.** 30 c. green .. .. 1·50 1·25
573. – 1 f. 50 blue .. .. 8·00 7·00
DESIGN: 1 f. 50, Streamlined steam locomotive.

103. Rene Descartes.

**1937.** 300th Anniv. of Publication of "Discours". (a) Wrongly inscr. "DISCOURS SUR LA METHODE".
574. **103.** 90 c. red .. .. 1·90 1·25

(b) Corrected to "DISCOURS DE LA METHODE".
575. **103.** 90 c. red .. .. 5·75 1·50

104. Anatole France. 107. Ramblers.

**1937.** Unemployed Intellectuals' Relief Fund.
576. **104.** 30 c.+10 c. green .. 1·90 1·90
577. – 90 c.+10 c. red .. 5·00 5·00
DESIGN—HORIZ. 90 c. Auguste Rodin.
See also Nos. 602 and 606.

**1937.** Postal Workers' Sports Fund.
578. – 20 c.+10 c. brown .. 1·50 1·90
579. – 40 c.+10 c. lake .. 1·50 1·90
580. **107.** 50 c.+10 c. purple .. 1·50 1·90
DESIGNS—HORIZ. 20 c. Tug-of-War. 40 c. Runners and discus thrower.

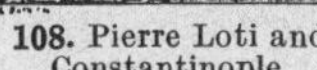

108. Pierre Loti and Constantinople. 109. "Victory" of Samothrace.

**1937.** Pierre Loti Memorial Fund.
585. **108.** 50 c.+20 c. red .. 3·25 3·75

**1937.** National Museums.
586 **109** 30 c. green .. .. 70·00 38·00
587 55 c. red .. .. 70·00 38·00

110. "France" and Child.

**1937.** Public Health Fund.
588. **110.** 65 c.+25 c. purple .. 3·25 2·50
588a. 90 c.+30 c. blue .. 1·90 2·50

111. France congratulating U.S.A.

**1937.** 150th Anniv. of U.S. Constitution.
589. **111.** 1 f. 75 blue .. .. 2·50 1·40

112. Iseran Pass. 113. Ceres.

**1937.** Opening of Col de l'Iseran Road.
590. **112.** 90 c. green .. .. 1·90 20

**1938.**
591 **113** 1 f. 75 blue .. .. 45 15
591a 2 f. red .. .. 10 10
591b 2 f. 25 blue .. .. 9·00 35
591c 2 f. 50 green .. .. 1·40 10
591d 2 f. 50 blue .. .. 35 35
591e 3 f. mauve .. .. 45 15

**1938.** Shipwrecked Mariners Society. As T **104** but portrait of Jean Charcot.
593. 65 c.+35 c. green .. 1·25 2·50
593a. 90 c.+35 c. purple .. 10·50 10·50

113a. Gambetta. 113b. Champagne Girl.

**1938.** Birth Centenary of Leon Gambetta (politician).
594 **113a** 55 c. lilac .. .. 25 40

**1938.**
594a – 90 c. red on blue .. 75 90
595 **113b** 1 f. 75 blue .. .. 3·00 3·50
596 – 2 f. brown .. .. 60 90
597 – 2 f. 15 purple .. .. 3·75 60
598 – 3 f. red .. .. 10·00 3·50
599 – 5 f. blue .. .. 35 20
600 – 10 f. purple on blue .. 1·10 1·25
601 – 20 f. green .. .. 38·00 16·00
DESIGNS—VERT. 2 f. 15, Coal miners. 10 f. Vincennes. HORIZ. 90 c. Chateau de Pau. 2 f. Arc de Triomphe at Orange. 3 f. Papal Palace, Avignon. 5 f. Carcassonne. 20 f. St. Malo.

**1938.** Unemployed Intellectuals' Relief Fund. As Nos. 563/6 and 576/7, inscr. "POUR LES CHOMEURS INTELLECTUELS".
602. 30 c.+10 c. red .. .. 1·90 1·90
603. 35 c.+10 c. green .. .. 2·50 2·50
604. 55 c.+10 c. violet .. .. 5·75 3·75
605. 65 c.+10 c. blue .. .. 5·75 3·75
606. 1 f.+10 c. red .. .. 5·75 4·50
607. 1 f. 75+25 c. blue .. 16·00 15·00
PORTRAITS—As Type **96**: 35 c. Callot. 55 c. Berlioz. 65 c. Victor Hugo. 1 f. 75, Louis Pasteur. As No. 577: 1 f. Auguste Rodin. As Type **104**: 30 c. Anatole France.

114. Palais de Versailles. 115. Soldier in Trench.

**1938.** French National Music Festivals.
608. **114.** 1 f. 75+75 c. blue .. 18·00 17·00

**1938.** Infantry Monument Fund.
609. **115.** 55 c.+70 c. purple .. 4·50 4·50
610. 65 c.+1 f. 10 blue .. 4·50 4·50

116. Medical Corps Monument at Lyons. 117. Saving a Goal.

**1938.** Military Medical Corps' Monument Fund.
611. **116.** 55 c.+45 c. red .. 10·00 10·00

**1938.** World Football Cup.
612. **117.** 1 f. 75 blue .. .. 11·50 11·50

117a. Clement Ader. 118. Jean de La Fontaine.

**1938.** Clement Ader (air pioneer).
612a. **117a.** 50 f. blue .. .. 85·00 65·00

**1938.** La Fontaine (writer of fables).
613. **118.** 55 c. green .. .. 65 95

**1938.** Reims Cathedral Restoration Fund. As T **52**, but inscr "REIMS 10.VII.1938".
614 65 c.+35 c. blue .. .. 7·75 9·50

119. Houses of Parliament, "Friendship" and Arc de Triomphe. 120. "France" welcoming Frenchmen repatriated from Spain.

**1938.** Visit of King George VI and Queen Elizabeth to France.
615. **119.** 1 f. 75 blue .. .. 50 90

**1938.** French Refugees' Fund.
616. **120.** 65 c.+60 c. red .. 3·75 5·25

121. Pierre and Marie Curie.

**1938.** Int. Anti-Cancer Fund. 40th Anniv. of Discovery of Radium.
617. **121.** 1 f. 75+50 c. blue .. 8·50 10·50

122. Arc de Triomphe and Allied Soldiers. 123. Mercury.

**1938.** 20th Anniv. of 1918 Armistice.
618. **122.** 65 c.+35 c. red .. 3·25 3·75

**1938.** Inscr. "REPUBLIQUE FRANCAISE".

| | | | | |
|---|---|---|---|---|
| 618a | 123 | 1 c. brown | 10 | 10 |
| 619 | | 2 c. green | 10 | 10 |
| 620 | | 5 c. red | 10 | 15 |
| 621 | | 10 c. blue | 10 | 10 |
| 622 | | 15 c. orange | 10 | 15 |
| 622a | | 15 c. brown | 35 | 15 |
| 623 | | 20 c. mauve | 10 | 10 |
| 624 | | 25 c. green | 10 | 10 |
| 625 | | 30 c. red | 10 | 15 |
| 626 | | 40 c. violet | 10 | 15 |
| 627 | | 45 c. green | 35 | 20 |
| 627c | | 50 c. blue | 15 | 10 |
| 627b | | 50 c. green | 30 | 10 |
| 628 | | 60 c. orange | 20 | 10 |
| 629 | | 70 c. mauve | 20 | 10 |
| 629a | | 75 c. brown | 3·75 | 1·90 |

For similar stamps inscr. "POSTES FRANCAISES", see Nos. 750/3.

124. Nurse and Patient.

125. Blind Radio Listener.

**1938.** Students' Fund.

630. **124.** 65 c.+60 c. blue .. 7·75 7·75

**1938.** "Radio for the Blind" Fund.

631. **125.** 90 c.+25 c. purple .. 7·75 8·25

126. Monument to Civilian War Victims, Lille.

127. Paul Cezanne.

**1939.** War Victims' Monument Fund.

632. **126.** 90 c.+35 c. brown .. 7·75 9·00

**1939.** Birth Cent of Paul Cezanne (painter).

633 **127** 2 f. 25 blue .. .. 3·25 2·50

128. Red Cross Nurse.

129. Military Engineer.

**1939.** 75th Anniv. of Red Cross Society. Cross in red.

634. **128.** 90c.+35c. bl. & blk... 5·75 7·00

**1939.** To the Glory of French Military Engineers.

635. **129.** 70 c.+50 c. red .. 5·75 6·50

130. Ministry of Posts, Telegraphs and Telephones.

**1939.** P.T.T. Orphans' Fund.

636 **130** 90 c.+35 c. blue .. 18·00 18·00

131. "Dunkerque" Class Battleship.

**1939.** Laying down Keel of Battleship "Clemenceau".

637 **131** 90 c. blue .. .. 50 30

132. French Pavilion, New York Exn.

**1939.** New York World's Fair.

| | | | | |
|---|---|---|---|---|
| 638. | **132.** | 2 f. 25 blue | 7·75 | 5·75 |
| 638a. | | 2 f. 50 blue | 6·25 | 6·25 |

133. Mother and Child.

134. Niepce and Daguerre.

**1939.** Children of the Unemployed Fund.

639. **133.** 90 c.+35 c. red .. 2·50 2·50

**1939.** Photographic Cent.

640. **134.** 2 f. 25 blue .. .. 6·25 5·75

135. Eiffel Tower.

136. Iris.

**1939.** 50th Anniv. of Erection of Eiffel Tower.

641. **135.** 90 c.+50 c. purple .. 7·75 7·75

**1939.**

| | | | | |
|---|---|---|---|---|
| 642. | **136.** | 80 c. brown | 10 | 10 |
| 643. | | 1 f. green | 30 | 10 |
| 643a. | | 1 f. red | 15 | 10 |
| 643b. | | 1 f. 30 blue | 10 | 15 |
| 643c. | | 1 f. 50 orange | 10 | 15 |

See also Nos. 861/8.

137. Marly Water Works.

**1939.** Int. Water Exn. Liege.

644. **137.** 2 f. 25 blue .. .. 9·00 3·75

138. Balzac.

**1939.** Unemployed Intellectuals' Fund.

| | | | | |
|---|---|---|---|---|
| 645. | – | 40 c.+10 c. red | 90 | 90 |
| 646. | – | 70 c.+10 c. purple | 3·25 | 2·10 |
| 647. | **138.** | 90 c.+10 c. mauve | 2·25 | 2·50 |
| 648. | – | 2 f. 25+25 c. blue | 12·50 | 10·50 |

PORTRAITS—VERT. 40 c. Puvis de Chavannes. HORIZ. 70 c. Claude Debussy. 2 f. 25, Claude Bernard.

See also Nos 667b/d.

139. St. Gregory of Tours.

140. Mother and Children.

**1939.** 1400th Birth Anniv. of St. Gregory of Tours.

649. **139.** 90 c. red .. .. 35 45

**1939.** Birth-rate Development Fund.

| | | | | |
|---|---|---|---|---|
| 650. | – | 70 c.+80 c. violet, blue and green | 3·25 | 3·75 |
| 651. | **140.** | 90 c.+60 c. brown, purple and sepia | 4·50 | 5·25 |

DESIGN: 70 c. Mother and children admiring infant in cot.

141. Oath of the Tennis Court.

142. Strasbourg Cathedral.

**1939.** 150th Anniv. of French Revolution.

652. **141.** 90 c. green .. .. 1·90 1·60

**1939.** 5th Cent. of Completion of Strasbourg Cathedral Spire.

653. **142.** 70 c. red .. .. 80 1·25

143. Porte Chaussee, Verdun.

144. "The Letter".

**1939.** 23rd Anniv. of Battle of Verdun.

654. **143.** 90 c. grey .. .. 50 90

**1939.** Postal Museum Fund.

655. **144.** 40 c.+60 c. brown and purple .. .. 2·50 3·25

145. Statue to Sailors lost at Sea.

146 Languedoc.

**1939.** Boulogne Monument Fund.

656. **145.** 70 c.+30 c. plum .. 10·00 9·75

**1939.**

657. **146.** 70 c. black on blue .. 30 25

147. Lyons.

**1939.**

658. **147.** 90 c. purple .. .. 75 75

148. French Soldier and Strasbourg Cathedral.

**1940.** Soldiers' Comforts Fund.

| | | | | |
|---|---|---|---|---|
| 659 | **148** | 40 c.+60 c. purple | 1·90 | 2·50 |
| 660 | – | 1 f.+50 c. blue | 1·90 | 2·50 |

DESIGN: 1 f. Veteran French colonial soldier and African village.

149. French Colonial Empire.

**1940.** Overseas Propaganda Fund.

661. **149.** 1 f.+25 c. red .. 1·50 1·90

See also Nos. 708 and 953.

DESIGNS — HORIZ. 1 f. 50, General Gallieni. 2 f. 50, Ploughing. VERT. 1 f. Marshal Foch.

150. Marshal Joffre.

**1940.** War Charities. Inscr. as in T 150.

| | | | | |
|---|---|---|---|---|
| 662. | **150.** | 80 c.+45 c. brown | 3·25 | 5·75 |
| 663. | – | 1 f.+50 c. violet | 3·25 | 5·75 |
| 664. | – | 1 f. 50+50 c. red | 2·50 | 3·75 |
| 665. | – | 2 f. 50+50 c. blue | 6·25 | 10·00 |

151. Nurse and Wounded Soldier.

**1940.** Red Cross. Cross in red.

| | | | | |
|---|---|---|---|---|
| 666 | – | 80 c.+1 f. green | 4·50 | 5·75 |
| 667 | **151** | 1 f.+2 f. brown | 5·75 | 5·75 |

DESIGN: 80 c. Doctor, nurse, soldier and family.

152. G. Guynemer (pilot).

153. Nurse, wounded Soldier and Family.

**1940.**

667a. **152.** 50 f. blue .. .. 8·50 8·25

**1940.** Unemployed Intellectuals' Fund. As T 138. inscr. "POUR LES CHOMEURS INTELLECTUELS".

| | | | |
|---|---|---|---|
| 667b. | 80 c.+10 c. brown | 3·25 | 5·50 |
| 667c. | 1 f.+10 c. purple | 3·25 | 5·50 |
| 667d. | 2 f. 50+25 c. blue | 3·25 | 5·50 |

PORTRAITS: 80 c. Debussy. 1 f. Balzac. 2 f. 50 c. Bernard.

**1940.** War Victims' Fund.

667e. **153.** 1 f.+2 f. violet .. 75 75

154. Harvesting.

DESIGNS: 1 f. Sowing. 1 f. 50, Gathering grapes. 2 f. 50, Cattle.

**1940.** National Relief Fund. Inscr. "SECOURS NATIONAL".

| | | | | |
|---|---|---|---|---|
| 668. | **154.** | 80 c.+2 f. sepia | 1·50 | 2·00 |
| 669. | – | 1 f.+2 f. brown | 1·50 | 2·00 |
| 670. | – | 1 f. 50+2 f. violet | 1·50 | 2·00 |
| 671. | – | 2 f. 50+2 f. green | 2·00 | 2·00 |

**1940.** Surch. with new value and with bars, on all except T 113.

| | | | | |
|---|---|---|---|---|
| 672. | **18.** | 30 c. on 35 c. green. | 15 | 15 |
| 673. | **61.** | 50 c. on 55 c. violet | 15 | 15 |
| 674. | | 50 c. on 65 c. blue | 10 | 10 |
| 675. | | 50 c. on 75 c. green | 20 | 20 |
| 676. | **123.** | 50 c. on 75 c. brown | 20 | 20 |
| 677. | **61.** | 50 c. on 80 c. orange | 15 | 15 |
| 678. | | 50 c. on 90 c. blue | 10 | 10 |
| 679. | | 1 f. on 1 f. 25 red | 20 | 20 |
| 680. | | 1 f. on 1 f. 40 mauve | 15 | 15 |
| 681. | | 1 f. on 1 f. 50 blue | 75 | 75 |
| 682. | **113.** | 1 f. on 1 f. 75 blue | 15 | 15 |
| 683. | – | 1 f. on 2 f. 15 purple (No. 597) | 20 | 20 |
| 684. | **113.** | 1 f. on 2 f. 25 blue | 15 | 15 |
| 685. | | 1 f. on 2 f. 50 green | 60 | 90 |
| 686. | – | 2 f. 50 on 5 f. blue (No. 599) | 20 | 20 |
| 687. | – | 5 f. on 10 f. purple on blue (No. 600) | 1·50 | 1·75 |
| 688. | – | 10 f. on 20 f. green (No. 601) | 1·50 | 1·50 |
| 689. | **117a.** | 20 f. on 50 f. blue | 32·00 | 35·00 |

155. Marshal Petain.

156. Prisoners of War.

**1940.**

| | | | | |
|---|---|---|---|---|
| 690. | **155.** | 40 c. brown | 30 | 25 |
| 691. | | 80 c. green | 50 | 40 |
| 692. | | 1 f. red | 20 | 15 |
| 693. | | 2 f. 50 blue | 95 | 80 |

See also Nos. 774/5.

**1941.** Prisoners of War Fund.

| | | | | |
|---|---|---|---|---|
| 696. | **156.** | 80 c.+5 f. green | 1·00 | 1·25 |
| 697. | – | 1 f.+5 f. red | 1·00 | 1·25 |

DESIGN: 1 f. Group of soldiers.

157. Frederic Mistral.

158. Science against Cancer.

**1941.** Mistral (poet) Commem.

698. **157.** 1 f. red .. .. 15 15

**1941.** Anti-Cancer Fund.

699. **158.** 2 f. 50+50 c. black and brown .. .. 1·00 1·50

159. Beaune Hospital, 1443.

**1941.** Views.

700 159 5 f. brown .. .. 25 20
701 – 10 f. violet .. .. 50 30
702 159 15 f. red .. .. 75 95
703 – 20 f. brown .. .. 1·00 1·25

DESIGNS: 10 f. Angers. 20 f. Ramparts of St. Louis, Aigues-Mortes.

**1941.** National Relief Fund. Surch +**10c**.

704 155 1 f.+10 c. red .. .. 15 15

DESIGN: 2 f. 50, "Charity" helping a pauper.

**160.**

**1941.** Winter Relief Fund. Inscr. as in T **160.**

705. 160. 1 f.+2 f. purple .. 1·50 1·25
706. – 2 f. 50+7 f. 50 blue .. 4·75 2·50

**162.** Liner "Pasteur".

**1941.** Seamen's Dependants Relief Fund. Surch.

707. 162. 1 f.+1 f. on 70 c. green 25 25

**1941.** As No. 661, but without "R.F." and dated "1941".

708. 149. 1 f.+1 f. multicoloured 50 50

**163.** **164.** **165.**
Marshal Petain.

**1941.** Frame in Type **164** is 17 × 20½ mm.

709 163 20 c. purple .. .. 10 10
710 30 c. red .. .. 10 10
711 40 c. blue .. .. 15 10
712 164 50 c. green .. .. 10 10
713 60 c. violet .. .. 10 10
714 70 c. blue .. .. 10 10
715 70 c. orange .. .. 10 10
716 80 c. brown .. .. 15 15
717 80 c. green .. .. 10 15
718 1 f. red .. .. 10 10
719 1 f. 20 brown .. .. 10 10
720 165 1 f. 50 pink .. .. 15 10
721 1 f. 50 brown .. .. 10 10
722 2 f. green .. .. 10 10
723 2 f. 40 red .. .. 10 10
724 2 f. 50 blue .. .. 60 40
725 3 f. orange .. .. 15 10
725a 164 4 f. blue .. .. 15 10
725b 4 f. 50 green .. .. 80 30

See also Nos. 740/1.

**166.** Fisherman. **167.** Arms of Nancy.

**1941.** National Seamen's Relief Fund.

726. 166. 1 f.+9 f. green .. 70 70

**1942.** National Relief Fund.

727. 167. 20 c.+30 c. black .. 1·60 2·50
728. – 40 c.+60 c. brown .. 1·60 2·50
729. – 50 c.+70 c. blue .. 1·60 2·75
730. – 70 c.+80 c. red .. 1·60 2·75
731. – 80 c.+1 f. red .. 1·60 2·75
732. – 1 f.+1 f. black .. 1·60 2·75
733. – 1 f. 50+2 f. blue .. 1·60 2·75
734. – 2 f.+2 f. violet .. 1·60 2·75
735. – 2 f. 50+3 f. green .. 1·60 2·75
736. – 3 f.+5 f. brown .. 1·60 2·75
737. – 5 f.+6 f. blue .. .. 1·60 2·75
738. – 10 f.+10 f. red .. 1·60 2·75

DESIGNS—As Type **167**. Nos. 728/38 show respectively the Arms of Lille, Rouen, Bordeaux, Toulouse, Clermont-Ferrand, Marseilles, Lyons, Rennes, Reims, Montpellier and Paris.
See also Nos. 757/68.

**168.** Jean-Francois de La Perouse, "L'Astrolabe" and "La Boussole".

**1942.** Birth Bicent. of La Perouse (navigator and explorer) and National Relief Fund.

739. 168. 2 f. 50+7 f. 50 blue .. 1·50 1·50

**1942.** As T **164**. Frame 18 × 21½ mm.

740. 164. 4 f. blue .. .. 25 25
741. 4 f. 50 green .. .. 25 25

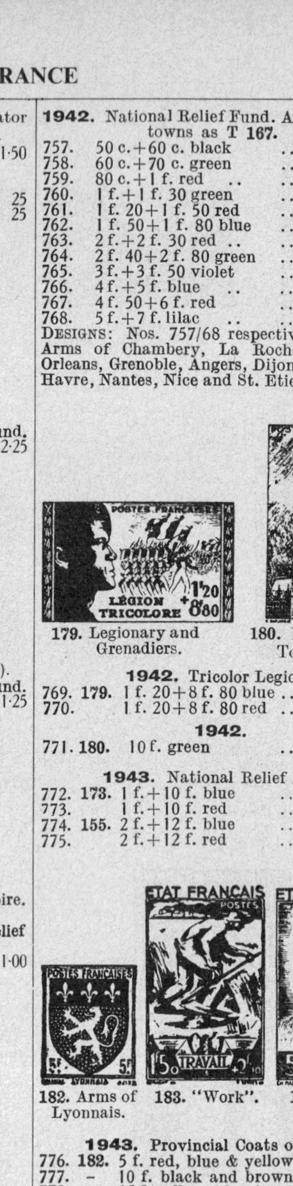

**169.** Potez 63–11 Bombers.

**1942.** Air Force Dependants Relief Fund.

742. 169. 1 f. 50+3 f. 50 violet .. 1·50 2·25

**170.** Alexis Emmanuel Chabrier.

**1942.** Birth Cent. of Chabrier (composer). and Musicians' Mutual Assistance Fund.

743. 170. 2 f.+3 f. brown .. 60 1·25

**171.** Symbolical of French Colonial Empire.

**1942.** Empire Fortnight and National Relief Fund.

744. 171. 1 f. 50+8 f. 50 black .. 1·00 1·00

**172.** Marshal Petain. **173.**

**1942.**

745. 172. 5 f. green .. .. 20 20
746. 173. 50 f. black .. .. 2·75 3·75

See also Nos. 772/3.

**174.** Jean de Vienne. **175.** Jules Massenet.

**1942.** 600th Birth Anniv. of Jean de Vienne (admiral) and Seamen's Relief Fund.

748. 174. 1 f. 50+8 f. 50 brown 70 1·00

**1942.** Birth Cent. of Massenet (composer).

749. 175. 4 f. green .. .. 25 25

**1942.** As T 123, but inscr. "POSTES FRANCAISES".

750. 10 c. blue .. .. 10 10
751. 30 c. red .. .. 10 10
752. 40 c. violet .. .. 15 15
753. 50 c. blue .. .. 10 10

**1942.** National Relief Fund. Surch + **50 S N.**

754 165 1 f. 50+50 c. blue .. 15 15

**177.** Stendhal (Marie Henri Beyle). **178.** Andre Blondel.

**1942.** Death Cent. of Stendhal (novelist).

755. 177. 4 f. brown and red .. 30 30

**1942.** Andre Blondel (physicist).

756. 178. 4 f. blue .. .. 30 30

**1942.** National Relief Fund. Arms of French towns as T **167.**

757. 50 c.+60 c. black .. 2·40 3·75
758. 60 c.+70 c. green .. 1·90 3·25
759. 80 c.+1 f. red .. 1·90 3·25
760. 1 f.+1 f. 30 green .. 1·90 3·25
761. 1 f. 20+1 f. 50 red .. 1·90 3·50
762. 1 f. 50+1 f. 80 blue .. 1·90 3·50
763. 2 f.+2 f. 30 red .. 1·90 3·50
764. 2 f. 40+2 f. 80 green .. 2·10 3·50
765. 3 f.+3 f. 50 violet .. 2·10 3·50
766. 4 f.+5 f. blue .. 2·50 3·75
767. 4 f. 50+6 f. red .. 2·50 3·75
768. 5 f.+7 f. lilac .. 2·50 3·75

DESIGNS: Nos. 757/68 respectively show the Arms of Chambery, La Rochelle, Poitiers, Orleans, Grenoble, Angers, Dijon, Limoges, Le Havre, Nantes, Nice and St. Etienne.

**179.** Legionary and Grenadiers. **180.** Belfry, Arras Town Hall.

**1942.** Tricolor Legion.

769. 179. 1 f. 20+8 f. 80 blue .. 5·75 10·50
770. 1 f. 20+8 f. 80 red .. 5·75 10·50

**1942.**

771. 180. 10 f. green .. 20 20

**1943.** National Relief Fund.

772. 173. 1 f.+10 f. blue .. 2·50 2·50
773. 1 f.+10 f. red .. 2·50 2·50
774. 155. 2 f.+12 f. blue .. 2·50 2·50
775. 2 f.+12 f. red .. 2·50 2·50

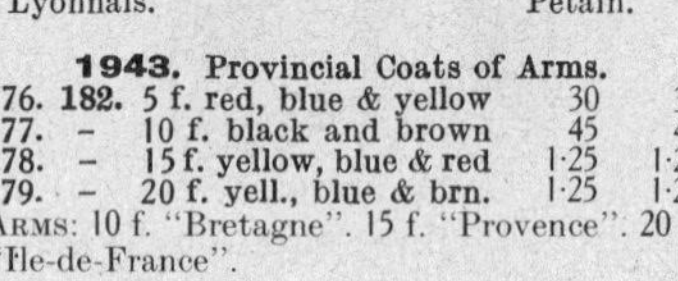

**182.** Arms of Lyonnais. **183.** "Work". **184.** Marshal Petain.

**1943.** Provincial Coats of Arms.

776. 182. 5 f. red, blue & yellow 30 30
777. – 10 f. black and brown 45 45
778. – 15 f. yellow, blue & red 1·25 1·25
779. – 20 f. yell., blue & brn. 1·25 1·25

ARMS: 10 f. "Bretagne". 15 f. "Provence". 20 f. "Ile-de-France".

For other provinces in this series, see Nos. 814/7, 971/4, 1049/53, 1121/5, 1178/83, 1225/31, 1270/3. For arms of French towns, see Nos. 1403/10, etc.

**1943.** National Relief Fund.

780. – 1 f. 20+1 f. 40 purple 16·00 16·00
781. 183. 1 f. 50+2 f. 50 red .. 16·00 16·00
782. – 2 f. 40+7 f. brown .. 16·00 16·00
783. – 4 f.+10 f. violet .. 16·00 16·00
784. 184. 5 f.+15 f. brown .. 16·00 16·00

DESIGNS: 1 f. 20, Marshal Petain bareheaded. 2 f. 40, "Family". 4 f. "Country".

**185.** Lavoisier. **186.** Lake Lerie and the Meije Peak.

**1943.** Birth Bicentenary of Lavoisier (chemist).

785. 185. 4 f. blue .. .. 15 15

**1943.**

786. 186. 20 f. green .. .. 55 55

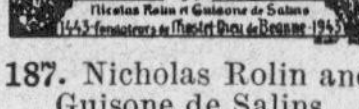

**187.** Nicholas Rolin and Guisone de Salins. **188.** Victims of Bombed Towns.

**1943.** 500th Anniv. of Beaune Hospital.

787. 187. 4 f. blue .. .. 25 25

**1943.** National Relief Fund.

788. 188. 1 f. 50 +3 f. 50 black 40 40

**189.** Prisoners' Families' Relief Work. **190.** Chevalier de Bayard.

**1943.** Prisoners' Families Relief Fund. Inscr. as in T **189.**

789. – 1 f. 50+8 f. 50 brown .. 1·10 1·10
790. 189. 2 f. 40+7 f. 60 green .. 1·10 1·10

DESIGN—VERT. 1 f. 50, Prisoner's family.

**1943.** National Relief Fund.

791. – 60 c.+80 c. green .. 2·00 2·00
792. – 1 f. 20+1 f. 50 black .. 2·00 2·00
793. – 1 f. 50+3 f. blue .. 2·00 2·00
794. 190. 2 f. 40+4 f. red .. 2·00 2·00
795. – 4 f.+6 f. brown .. 2·25 2·25
796. – 5 f.+10 f. green .. 2·25 2·25

PORTRAITS: 60 c. Michel de Montaigne (essayist). 1 f. 20, Francois Clouet (painter). 1 f. 50, Ambroise Pare (surgeon). 4 f. Duc de Sully (King Henri IV's finance minister). 5 f. King Henri IV.

**191.** Picardy. **196.** Admiral de Tourville.

**1943.** National Relief Fund. Provincial costumes.

797. 191. 60 c.+1 f. 30 brown .. 2·00 2·00
798. – 1 f. 20+2 f. violet .. 2·00 2·00
799. – 1 f. 50+4 f. blue .. 2·00 2·00
800. – 2 f. 40+5 f. red .. 2·00 2·00
801. – 4 f.+6 f. blue .. .. 3·00 3·00
802. – 5 f.+7 f. red .. .. 3·00 3·00

DESIGNS: 1 f. 20, "Bretagne". 1 f. 50, "Ile de France". 2 f. 40, "Bourgogne". 4 f. "Auvergne". 5 f. "Provence".

**1944.** 300th Birth Anniv. of Admiral de Tourville.

810. 196. 4 f.+6 f. red .. .. 55 55

**197.** Branly. **198.** Gounod.

**1944.** Birth Cent. of Branly (physicist).

811. 197. 4 f. blue .. .. 20 20

**1944.** 50th Death Anniv of Gounod (composer).

812. 198. 1 f. 50+3 f. 50 brown 95 95

**200.** Flanders. **202.** Petain gives France Workers' Charter.

**201.** Marshal Petain.

**1944.** Provincial Coats of Arms.

814. 200. 5 f. black, orge. & red 20 20
815. – 10 f. yellow, red & brn. 20 20
816. – 15 f. yellow, blue & brn. 80 80
817. – 20 f. yellow, red & blue 1·25 1·10

ARMS: 10 f. "Languedoc". 15 f. "Orleanais". 20 f. "Normandie".

**1944.** Petain's 88th Birthday.

| | | | | |
|---|---|---|---|---|
| 818. | 201. | 1 f. 50+3 f. 50 brown | 3·75 | 3·75 |
| 819. | – | 2 f.+3 f. blue.. | 50 | 50 |
| 820. | 202. | 4 f.+6 f. red .. .. | 50 | 50 |

DESIGN—As Type **202**: 2 f. inscr. "Le Marechal institua la Corporation Paysanne" (Trans. "The Marshal set up the Peasant Corporation").

**203.** Mobile Post Office.

**1944.** Centenary of Mobile Post Office.

| | | | | |
|---|---|---|---|---|
| 821. | 203. | 1 f. 50 green .. .. | 40 | 50 |

**204.** Chateau of Chenonceaux.

**1944.**

| | | | | |
|---|---|---|---|---|
| 822. | 204. | 15 f. brown .. .. | 35 | 35 |
| 823. | | 25 f. black .. .. | 40 | 40 |

The 15 f. is inscr. "FRANCE".

**205.** Louis XIV. **206.** Old and Modern Locomotives.

**1944.** National Relief Fund.

| | | | | |
|---|---|---|---|---|
| 824. | – | 50 c.+1 f. 50 red .. | 1·00 | 1·50 |
| 825. | – | 80 c.+2 f. 20 green .. | 75 | 1·40 |
| 826. | – | 1 f. 20+2 f. 80 black | 75 | 1·40 |
| 827. | – | 1 f. 50+3 f. 50 blue .. | 75 | 1·40 |
| 828. | – | 2 f.+4 f. brown | 1·00 | 1·50 |
| 829. | 205. | 4 f.+6 f. orange .. | 1·00 | 1·60 |

DESIGNS: 50 c. Moliere (dramatist). 80 c. Jean Hardouin-Manzart (scholar). 1 f. 20, Blaise Pascal (mathematician). 1 f. 50, Louis, Prince de Conde. 2 f. Jean-Baptiste Colbert (King Louis XIV's chief minister).

**1944.** National Relief Fund. Cent. of Paris-Orleans and Paris-Rouen Railways.

| | | | | |
|---|---|---|---|---|
| 830. | 206. | 4 f.+6 f. black .. | 2·25 | 2·25 |

**207.** Claude Chappe. **208.** Gallic Cock. **209.** "Marianne".

**1944.** 150th Anniv. of Invention of Semaphore Telegraph.

| | | | | |
|---|---|---|---|---|
| 831. | 207. | 4 f. blue .. .. | 20 | 20 |

**1944.**

| | | | | |
|---|---|---|---|---|
| 832. | 208. | 10 c. green .. .. | 10 | 10 |
| 833. | | 30 c. lilac .. .. | 20 | 20 |
| 834. | | 40 c. blue .. .. | 10 | 10 |
| 835. | | 50 c. red .. .. | 10 | 10 |
| 836. | 209. | 60 c. brown .. .. | 10 | 10 |
| 837. | | 70 c. mauve .. .. | 10 | 10 |
| 838. | | 80 c. green .. .. | 90 | 90 |
| 839. | | 1 f. violet .. .. | 15 | 15 |
| 840. | | 1 f. 20 red .. .. | 15 | 15 |
| 841. | | 1 f. 50 blue .. .. | 10 | 10 |
| 842. | 208. | 2 f. blue .. .. | 10 | 10 |
| 843. | 209. | 2 f. 40 red .. .. | 1·50 | 1·50 |
| 844. | | 3 f. green .. .. | 15 | 15 |
| 845. | | 4 f. blue .. .. | 15 | 15 |
| 846. | | 4 f. 50 black .. .. | 15 | 15 |
| 847. | | 5 f. blue .. .. | 4·50 | 4·50 |
| 848. | 208. | 10 f. violet .. .. | 4·50 | 4·50 |
| 849. | | 15 f. brown .. .. | 5·75 | 5·75 |
| 850. | | 20 f. green .. .. | 4·50 | 4·50 |

**210.** Arc de Triomphe, Paris. **211.** "Marianne".

**1944.**

| | | | | |
|---|---|---|---|---|
| 851 | 210 | 5 c. purple .. .. | 10 | 10 |
| 852 | | 10 c. grey .. .. | 10 | 10 |
| 853 | | 25 c. brown .. .. | 10 | 10 |
| 854 | | 50 c green .. .. | 10 | 10 |
| 855 | | 1 f. green .. .. | 10 | 10 |
| 856 | | 1 f. 50 pink .. .. | 10 | 10 |
| 857 | | 2 f. 50 violet .. .. | 15 | 15 |
| 858 | | 4 f. blue .. .. | 15 | 15 |
| 859 | | 5 f. black .. .. | 20 | 20 |
| 860 | | 10 f. orange .. .. | 18·00 | 23·00 |

See also Nos. 936/45.

**1944.** New colours and values.

| | | | | |
|---|---|---|---|---|
| 861. | 136. | 80 c. green .. .. | 15 | 15 |
| 862. | | 1 f. blue .. .. | 10 | 10 |
| 863. | | 1 f. 20 violet .. | 10 | 10 |
| 864. | | 1 f. 50 brown .. .. | 10 | 10 |
| 865. | | 2 f. brown .. .. | 10 | 10 |
| 866. | | 2 f. 40 red .. .. | 15 | 15 |
| 867. | | 3 f. orange .. .. | 15 | 15 |
| 868. | | 4 f. blue .. .. | 20 | 20 |

**1944.**

| | | | | |
|---|---|---|---|---|
| 869. | 211. | 10 c. blue .. .. | 10 | 10 |
| 870. | | 30 c. brown .. .. | 10 | 10 |
| 871. | | 40 c. blue .. .. | 10 | 10 |
| 872. | | 50 c. orange .. .. | 10 | 10 |
| 873. | | 60 c. blue .. .. | 10 | 10 |
| 874. | | 70 c. brown .. .. | 10 | 10 |
| 875. | | 80 c. green .. .. | 10 | 10 |
| 876. | | 1 f. lilac .. .. | 10 | 10 |
| 877. | | 1 f. 20 green .. .. | 10 | 10 |
| 878. | | 1 f. 50 red .. .. | 10 | 10 |
| 879. | | 2 f. brown .. .. | 15 | 15 |
| 880. | | 2 f. 40 red .. .. | 15 | 15 |
| 881. | | 3 f. olive .. .. | 15 | 15 |
| 882. | | 4 f. blue .. .. | 15 | 15 |
| 883. | | 4 f. 50 grey .. .. | 15 | 15 |
| 884. | | 5 f. orange .. .. | 20 | 20 |
| 885. | | 10 f. green .. .. | 20 | 20 |
| 886. | | 15 f. red .. .. | 25 | 25 |
| 887. | | 20 f. orange .. .. | 1·75 | 1·00 |
| 888. | | 50 f. violet .. .. | 3·25 | 2·40 |

**212.** St. Denis Basilica.

**1944.** 8th Cent. of St. Denis Basilica.

| | | | | |
|---|---|---|---|---|
| 889. | 212. | 2 f. 40 brown .. .. | 20 | 20 |

**213.** Marshal Bugeaud. **214.** Angouleme Cathedral.

**1944.** Centenary of Battle of Isly.

| | | | | |
|---|---|---|---|---|
| 890. | 213. | 4 f. green .. .. | 25 | 25 |

**1944.** Cathedrals of France (1st issue).

| | | | | |
|---|---|---|---|---|
| 891. | 214. | 50 c.+1 f. 50 black .. | 30 | 30 |
| 892. | – | 80 c.+2 f. 20 purple.. | 40 | 40 |
| 893. | – | 1 f. 20+2 f. 80 red .. | 60 | 60 |
| 894. | – | 1 f. 50+3 f. 50 blue .. | 90 | 90 |
| 895. | – | 4 f.+6 f. red .. .. | 90 | 90 |

DESIGNS: 80 c. Chartres. 1 f. 20 Amiens. 1 f. 50 Beauvais. 4 f. Albi.

**1944.** Nos. 750/3 optd. **RF.**

| | | | | |
|---|---|---|---|---|
| 896. | | 10 c. blue .. .. | 10 | 10 |
| 897. | | 30 c. red .. .. | 10 | 10 |
| 898. | | 40 c. violet .. .. | 10 | 10 |
| 899. | | 50 c. blue .. .. | 10 | 10 |

**215.** Arms of De Villayer. **216.** "France" exhorting Resistance Forces.

**1944.** Stamp Day.

| | | | | |
|---|---|---|---|---|
| 900. | 215. | 1 f. 50+3 f. 50 brown | 15 | 15 |

**1945.** Liberation.

| | | | | |
|---|---|---|---|---|
| 901. | 216. | 4 f. blue .. .. | 30 | 25 |



**217.** Shield and Broken Chains. **218.** Ceres. **219.** Marianne.

**220.** Marianne. **221.** Arms of Strasbourg.

**1945.**

| | | | | |
|---|---|---|---|---|
| 902 | 217 | 10 c. brown .. | 10 | 10 |
| 903 | | 30 c. green .. .. | 10 | 10 |
| 904 | | 40 c. mauve .. | 15 | 15 |
| 905 | | 50 c. blue .. .. | 10 | 10 |
| 906 | 218 | 60 c. blue .. .. | 10 | 10 |
| 907 | | 80 c. green .. .. | 15 | 15 |
| 908 | | 90 c. green* .. | 55 | 55 |
| 909 | | 1 f. red .. .. | 10 | 10 |
| 910 | | 1 f. 20 black .. | 20 | 20 |
| 997 | | 1 f. 30 blue .. | 25 | 15 |
| 911 | | 1 f. 50 purple .. | 10 | 10 |
| 912 | 219 | 1 f. 50 red .. .. | 10 | 10 |
| 913 | | 2 f. green .. .. | 15 | 15 |
| 914 | 218 | 2 f. green .. .. | 15 | 15 |
| 915 | 219 | 2 f. 40 red .. .. | 25 | 25 |
| 916 | 218 | 2 f. 50 brown .. | 15 | 15 |
| 997a | 219 | 2 f. 50 brown* .. | 2·25 | 1·40 |
| 917 | | 3 f. brown .. .. | 10 | 10 |
| 918 | | 3 f. red .. .. | 10 | 10 |
| 998 | | 3 f. green .. .. | 1·90 | 15 |
| 999 | | 3 f. mauve .. .. | 15 | 15 |
| 1000 | | 3 f. 50 red .. .. | 30 | 20 |
| 919 | | 4 f. blue .. .. | 15 | 15 |
| 920 | | 4 f. violet .. .. | 10 | 10 |
| 1001 | | 4 f. green .. .. | 20 | 15 |
| 1001a | | 4 f. orange .. .. | 3·25 | 30 |
| 1002 | | 4 f. 50 blue .. .. | 10 | 10 |
| 921 | | 5 f. green .. .. | 10 | 10 |
| 1003 | | 5 f. red .. .. | 10 | 10 |
| 1004 | | 5 f. blue .. .. | 15 | 10 |
| 1004b | | 5 f. violet .. .. | 35 | 10 |
| 922 | | 6 f. blue .. .. | 25 | 25 |
| 1005 | | 6 f. red .. .. | 65 | 30 |
| 1005a | | 6 f. green .. .. | 7·25 | 30 |
| 1006 | | 8 f. blue .. .. | 25 | 15 |
| 924 | | 10 f. orange .. | 25 | 25 |
| 928 | | 10 f. blue .. .. | 75 | 25 |
| 1007 | | 10 f. violet .. .. | 15 | 10 |
| 1007a | | 12 f. blue .. .. | 3·25 | 15 |
| 1007b | | 12 f. orange .. | 1·00 | 20 |
| 926 | | 15 f. purple .. | 3·25 | 1·40 |
| 1007c | | 15 f. red .. .. | 60 | 10 |
| 1007d | | 15 f. blue .. .. | 15 | 10 |
| 1007e | | 18 f. red .. .. | 18·00 | 1·25 |
| 930 | | 20 f. green .. .. | 95 | 30 |
| 932 | 220 | 20 f. green .. .. | 1·00 | 95 |
| 931 | 219 | 25 f. red .. .. | 7·75 | 1·50 |
| 933 | 220 | 25 f. violet .. .. | 1·75 | 1·00 |
| 934 | | 50 f. brown .. | 1·90 | 1·75 |
| 935 | | 100 f. red .. .. | 13·00 | 5·75 |

***PRECANCELS.** See note below No. 432.

**1945.**

| | | | | |
|---|---|---|---|---|
| 936 | 210 | 30 c. black and orange | 10 | 15 |
| 937 | | 40 c. black and grey .. | 10 | 15 |
| 938 | | 50 c. black and green | 10 | 10 |
| 939 | | 60 c. black and violet | 10 | 15 |
| 940 | | 80 c. black and green | 10 | 15 |
| 941 | | 1 f. 20 black and brown | 10 | 15 |
| 942 | | 1 f. 50 black and red .. | 10 | 10 |
| 943 | | 2 f. black and yellow | 10 | 15 |
| 944 | | 2 f. 40 black and red .. | 10 | 15 |
| 945 | | 3 f. black and purple | 10 | 15 |

**1945.** Liberation of Metz and Strasbourg.

| | | | | |
|---|---|---|---|---|
| 946. | – | 2 f. 40 blue .. | 20 | 20 |
| 947. | 221. | 4 f. brown .. .. | 20 | 20 |

DESIGN: 2 f. 40, Arms of Metz.

**222.** Patient in Deck Chair. **223.** Refugee Employee and Family.

**1945.** Anti-Tuberculosis Fund

| | | | | |
|---|---|---|---|---|
| 948. | 222. | 2 f.+1 f. orange .. | 15 | 15 |

**1945.** Postal Employees War Victims Fund.

| | | | | |
|---|---|---|---|---|
| 949. | 223. | 4 f.+6 f. brown .. | 15 | 15 |

**224.** Sarah Bernhardt. **225.** Alsatian and Lorrainer in Native Dress.

**1945.** Birth Cent. of Sarah Bernhardt (actress).

| | | | | |
|---|---|---|---|---|
| 950. | 224. | 4 f.+1 f. brown .. | 20 | 20 |

**1945.** Liberation of Alsace-Lorraine.

| | | | | |
|---|---|---|---|---|
| 951. | 225. | 4 f. brown .. .. | 20 | 20 |

**226.** Children in Country. **227.** Destruction of Oradour.

**1945.** Fresh Air Crusade.

| | | | | |
|---|---|---|---|---|
| 952. | 226. | 4 f.+2 f. green .. | 15 | 15 |

**1945.** As No. 661 but incorporating Cross of Lorraine and inscr "1945".

| | | | | |
|---|---|---|---|---|
| 953 | 149 | 2 f. blue .. .. | 15 | 15 |

**1945.** Destruction of Oradour-sur-Glane.

| | | | | |
|---|---|---|---|---|
| 954. | 227. | 4 f.+2 f. brown .. | 15 | 15 |

**228.** Louis XI.

**1945.** Stamp Day.

| | | | | |
|---|---|---|---|---|
| 955. | 228. | 2 f.+3 f. blue.. .. | 40 | 40 |

**229.** Dunkirk. **230.** Alfred Fournier.

**1945.** Devastated Towns.

| | | | | |
|---|---|---|---|---|
| 956. | 229. | 1 f. 50+1 f. 50 red .. | 65 | 65 |
| 957. | – | 2 f.+2 f. violet .. | 65 | 65 |
| 958. | – | 2 f. 40+2 f. 60 blue .. | 65 | 65 |
| 959. | – | 4 f.+4 f. black .. | 65 | 65 |

DESIGNS: 2 f. Rouen. 2 f. 40 c. Caen. 4 f. St. Malo.

**1946.** Prophylaxis Fund.

| | | | | |
|---|---|---|---|---|
| 960. | 230. | 2 f.+3 f. red .. .. | 25 | 25 |
| 961. | | 2 f.+3 f. blue.. .. | 25 | 25 |

**231.** Henri Becquerel. **233.** "Les Invalides".

**1946.**

| | | | | |
|---|---|---|---|---|
| 962. | 231. | 2 f.+3 f. violet .. | 15 | 15 |

**1946.** Surcharged **3F.**

| | | | | |
|---|---|---|---|---|
| 963. | 222. | 3 f. on 2 f.+1 f. orange | 15 | 15 |

**1946.** War Invalids' Relief Fund.

| | | | | |
|---|---|---|---|---|
| 964. | 233. | 4 f.+6 f. brown .. | 30 | 30 |

234. "Emile Bertin" (cruiser) and "Lorraine" (battleship).

235. "The Letter".

**1946.** Naval Charities.

965. 234. 2 f.+3 f. black .. .. 65 65

**1946.** Postal Museum Fund.

966. 235. 2 f.+3 f. red .. .. .. 45 45

236. Iris.

237. Jupiter carrying off Egine.

**1946.** Air.

967. – 40 f. green .. .. 50 10
968. 236. 50 f. pink .. .. 50 10
969. 237. 100 f. blue .. .. 7·75 90
970. – 200 f. red .. .. 5·75 1·25

DESIGNS—VERT. 40 f. Centaur. HORIZ. 200 f. Apollo and chariot.

239. Arms of Corsica.

241. Fouquet de la Varane.

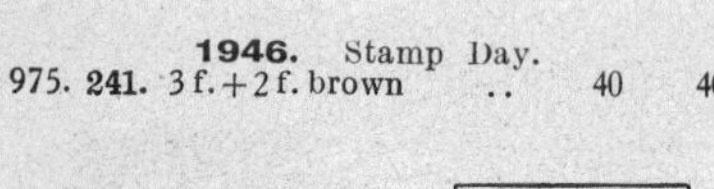

**1946.** Provincial Coats of arms.

971. 239. 10 c. black and blue .. 10 10
972. – 30 c. blk., red and yell. 10 10
973. – 50 c. brn., yell. & red 10 10
974. – 60 c. red, blue & black 10 10

DESIGNS: 30 c. Alsace. 50 c. Lorraine. 60 c. Nice.

**1946.** Stamp Day.

975. 241. 3 f.+2 f. brown .. 40 40

244. Luxembourg Palace.

245. Roc-Amadour.

**1946.** Views.

976 – 5 f. mauve .. .. 15 15
977 – 6 f. red .. .. 1·25 65
978 244 10 f. blue .. .. 15 15
979 12 f. red .. .. 3·25 30
980 245 15 f. purple .. 4·50 50
980a 244 15 f. red .. .. 50 35
981 – 20 f. blue .. .. 1·25 15
982 – 25 f. brown .. 5·25 15
982a – 25 f. blue .. .. 13·00 90

DESIGNS—HORIZ. 5 f. Vezelay. 6 f. Cannes. 20 f. Pointe du Raz. 25 f. (both) Stanislas Place, Nancy.

248. "Peace".

**1946.** Peace Conf.

983. 248. 3 f. green .. .. 15 15
984. – 10 f. blue .. .. 15 15

DESIGN: 10 f. Woman releasing dove.

250. Francois Villon.

251.

**1946.** National Relief Fund. 15th century Figures.

985. 250. 2 f.+1 f. blue .. 1·60 1·60
986. – 3 f.+1 f. blue .. 1·60 1·60
987. – 4 f.+3 f. red .. 1·60 1·60
988. – 5 f.+4 f. blue .. 1·75 1·75
989. – 6 f.+5 f. brown .. 1·75 1·75
990. – 10 f.+6 f. orange .. 1·75 1·75

DESIGNS: 3 f. Jean Fouquet. 4 f. Philippe de Commynes. 5 f. Joan of Arc. 6 f. Jean Gerson. 10 f. Charles VII.

**1946.** U.N.E.S.C.O. Conf., Paris.

991. 251. 10 f. blue .. .. 15 15

252. St. Julien Cathedral, Le Mans.

253. Louvois.

**1947.** National Relief Fund. Cathedrals of France (2nd issue). As T 214 and 252.

992. – 1 f.+1 f. red .. 90 90
993. – 3 f.+2 f. black .. 3·25 3·25
994. – 4 f.+3 f. red .. 1·50 1·50
995. 252. 6 f.+4 f. blue .. 1·90 1·90
996. – 10 f.+6 f. green .. 3·25 3·25

DESIGNS—VERT. 1 f. St. Sernin, Toulouse. 3 f. Notre-Dame du Port, Clermont-Ferrand. 10 f. Notre-Dame, Paris. HORIZ. 4 f. St. Front, Perigueux.

**1947.** Stamp Day.

1008. 253. 4 f. 50+5 f. 50 red .. 1·40 1·40

254. The Louvre Colonnade.



255. Herring Gull over Ile de la Cite.

**1947.** 12th U.P.U. Congress.

1009. 254. 3 f. 50 purple (postage) 30 30
1010. – 4 f. 50 grey .. .. 30 30
1011. – 6 f. red .. .. 1·10 70
1012. – 10 f. blue .. .. 1·10 70
1013. 255. 500 f. green (air) .. 55·00 45·00

DESIGNS—As Type 254: 4 f. 50, La Conciergerie. 6 f. La Cite. 10 f. Place de la Concorde.

256. Auguste Pavie.

257. Fenelon.

**1947.** Birth Cent. of Auguste Pavie (explorer).

1014. 256. 4 f. 50 purple .. 25 25

**1947.** Fenelon, Archbishop of Cambrai.

1015. 257. 4 f. 50 brown .. 25 25

258. St. Nazaire Monument.

259.

**1947.** 5th Anniv. of British Commando Raid on St. Nazaire.

1016. 258. 6 f.+4 f. blue .. 65 65

**1947.** Boy Scouts' Jamboree.

1017. 259. 5 f. brown .. .. 25 25

260. Milestone on Road of Liberty.

261. "Resistance."

**1947.** Road Maintenance Fund.

1018. 260. 6 f.+4 f. green .. 1·10 1·10

**1947.** Resistance Movement.

1019. 261. 5 f. purple .. .. 25 25

**1947.** No. 997 surch 1F.

1020 218 1 f. on 1 f. 30 blue .. 15 15

263. Conques Abbey.

264. Louis Braille.

**1947.**

1021 263 15 f. red .. .. 5·25 40
1022 18 f. blue .. .. 3·75 20

No. 1022 is inscribed "FRANCE".

**1948.** Louis Braille (inventor of system of writing and printing for the blind).

1023 264 6 f.+4 f. violet .. 25 25

265. A. de St.-Exupery (pilot and writer).

267. Etienne Arago.

**1948.** Air. Famous Airmen.

1026. – 40 f.+10 f. blue .. 1·50 1·50
1024. 265. 50 f.+30 f. purple .. 3·25 3·25
1025. – 100 f.+70 f. blue .. 3·75 3·75

DESIGNS: 40 f. "Avion III" and Douglas DB-7 (Clement Ader). 100 f. Jean Dagnaux.

**1948.** Stamp Day and Centenary of First French Adhesive Postage Stamps.

1027. 267. 6 f.+4 f. violet .. 40 40

268. Lamartine.

269. Dr. Calmette.

**1948.** National Relief Fund and Cent. of 1848 Revolution. Dated "1848 1948".

1028. 268. 1 f.+1 f. green .. 1·25 1·25
1029. – 3 f.+2 f. red .. 1·25 1·25
1030. – 4 f.+3 f. purple .. 1·25 1·25
1031. – 5 f.+4 f. blue .. 3·25 3·25
1032. – 6 f.+5 f. blue .. 2·75 2·75
1033. – 10 f.+6 f. red .. 2·75 2·75
1034. – 15 f.+7 f. blue .. 3·00 3·00
1035. – 20 f.+8 f. violet .. 3·00 3·00

PORTRAITS: 3 f. Alexandre-Auguste Ledru-Rollin. 4 f. Louis Blanc. 5 f. A. M. Albert. 6 f. Pierre Joseph Proudhon. 10 f. Louis- Auguste Blanqui. 15 f. Armand Barbes. 20 f. Denis-Auguste Affre.

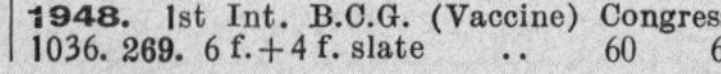

**1948.** 1st Int. B.C.G. (Vaccine) Congress.

1036. 269. 6 f.+4 f. slate .. 60 60

270. Gen. Leclerc.

**1948.** Gen. Leclerc Memorial.

1037. 270. 6 f. black .. .. 30 30

See also Nos. 1171/a.

271. Chateaubriand.

**1948.** Death Cent. of Chateaubriand.

1038. 271. 18 f. blue .. .. 25 25

272. Genissiat Barrage.

**1948.** Inaug. of Genissiat Barrage.

1039. 272. 12 f. red .. .. 40 40

273. Aerial View of Chaillot Palace.

274. Paul Langevin.

**1948.** U.N. Assembly, Paris.

1040. – 12 f. red .. .. 35 35
1041. 273. 18 f. blue .. .. 35 35

DESIGN: 12 f. Ground level view of Chaillot Palace.

**1948.** Transfer of Ashes of Paul Langevin and Jean Perrin to the Pantheon.

1042. 274. 5 f. brown .. .. 15 15
1043. – 8 f. green (Perrin) .. 15 15

**1949.** Surch 5F.

1044 219 5 f. on 6 f. red .. 15 15

276. Ploughing.

277. Arms of Burgundy.

**1949.** Workers.

1045. 276. 3 f.+1 f. purple .. 70 70
1046. – 5 f.+3 f. blue .. 70 70
1047. – 8 f.+4 f. blue .. 80 80
1048. – 10 f.+6 f. red .. 1·25 1·00

DESIGNS: 5 f. Fisherman. 8 f. Miner. 10 f. Industrial worker.

**1949.** Provincial Coats of Arms.

1049. 277. 10 c. red, yellow & blue 10 10
1050. – 50 c. yellow, red & blue 10 10
1051. – 1 f. red and brown .. 45 20
1052. – 2 f. red, yellow & green 50 20
1053. – 4 f. blue, yellow & red 35 30

ARMS: 50 c. "Guyenne". 1 f. "Savoie". 2 f. "Auvergne". 4 f. "Anjou".

See also Nos. 1121/5, 1178/83, 1225/31 and 1270/3.

278. Duc de Choiseul.

279. Lille.

279a. Paris.

**1949.** Stamp Day.

1054. **278.** 15 f.+5 f. green .. 90 90

**1949.** Air. Views.

1055. **279.** 100 f. purple.. .. 1·25 20

1056. – 200 f. green .. .. 12·00 60

1057. – 300 f. violet .. .. 18·00 10·00

1058. – 500 f. red .. .. 65·00 5·50

1059. **279a.** 1000 f. purple & black £100 23·00

DESIGNS—As Type **279**. 200 f. Bordeaux. 300 f. Lyons. 500 f. Marseilles.

**280.** Polar Scene. **281.** Collegiate Church of St. Bernard, Romans.

**1949.** Polar Expeditions.

1060. **280.** 15 f. blue .. .. 40 20

**1949.** French Stamp Cent. (a) Imperf.

1061. **1.** 15 f. red .. .. 3·75 3·75

1062. 25 f. blue .. .. 3·75 3·75

(b) Perf.

1063. **219.** 15 f. red .. .. 3·75 3·75

1064. 25 f. blue .. .. 3·75 3·75

**1949.** 600th Anniv. of Cession of Dauphiny to King of France.

1065. **281.** 12 f. brown .. .. 25 20

**282.** Emblems of U.S.A. and France.

**1949.** Franco-American Amity.

1066. **282.** 25 f. blue and red .. 65 50

**284.** St. Wandrille Abbey. **285.** Jean Racine.

**1949.** Views.

1067 – 20 f. red .. .. 25 20

1068 **284** 25 f. blue .. .. 25 15

1068a 30 f. blue .. .. 5·75 4·50

1068b – 30 f. blue .. .. 1·00 30

1069 – 40 f. green .. .. 17·00 25

1070 – 50 f. purple .. .. 2·50 15

DESIGNS: 20 f. St. Bertrand de Comminges. 30 f. (1068b) Arbois (Jura). 40 f. Valley of the Meuse (Ardennes). 50 f. Mt. Gerbier-de-Jonc, Vivarais.

**1949.** 250th Death Anniv. of Racine (dramatist).

1071. **285.** 12 f. purple .. .. 25 25

**286.** Claude Chappe. **288.** Allegory of Commerce.

**287.** Alexander III Bridge and "Petit Palais".

**1949.** International Telephone and Telegraph Congress, Paris.

1072 **286** 10 f. red (postage) .. 90 90

1073 – 15 f. violet .. .. 1·10 95

1074 – 25 f. red .. .. 3·00 4·50

1075 – 50 f. blue .. .. 5·25 4·50

1076 **287** 100 f. red (air) .. 8·25 6·50

PORTRAITS—As Type **286**: 15 f. Arago and Ampere. 25 f. Emile Baudot. 50 f. Gen. Ferrie.

**1949.** French Chambers of Commerce.

1077. **288.** 15 f. red .. .. 20 20

**289.** Allegory. **290.** Montesquieu.

**1949.** 75th Anniv. of U.P.U.

1078. **289.** 5 f. green .. .. 20 20

1079. 15 f. red .. .. 25 20

1080. 25 f. blue .. .. 1·00 70

**1949.** National Relief Fund.

1081 **290** 5 f.+1 f. green .. 3·75 3·75

1082 – 8 f.+2 f. blue .. 3·75 3·75

1083 – 10 f.+3 f. brown .. 3·75 3·75

1084 – 12 f.+4 f. violet .. 3·75 3·75

1085 – 15 f.+5 f. red .. 5·75 5·75

1086 – 25 f.+10 f. blue .. 7·00 7·00

PORTRAITS: 8 f. Voltaire. 10 f. Watteau. 12 f. Buffon. 15 f. Dupleix. 25 f. Turgot.

**291.** "Spring".

DESIGNS: 8 f. "Summer". 12 f. "Autumn". 15 f. "Winter".

**1949.** National Relief Fund. Seasons.

1087. **291.** 5 f.+1 f. green .. 2·25 2·25

1088. – 8 f.+2 f. yellow .. 2·25 2·25

1089. – 12 f.+3 f. violet .. 2·50 2·50

1090. – 15 f.+4 f. blue .. 3·75 3·75

**292.** Postman.  **293.** Raymond Poincare.

**1950.** Stamp Day.

1091. **292.** 12 f.+3 f. blue .. 3·75 3·25

**1950.** Honouring Poincare.

1092. **293.** 15 f. blue .. .. 25 20

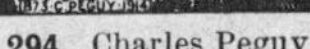

**294.** Charles Peguy.  **295.** Francois Rabelais.

**1950.** Honouring Charles Peguy (writer).

1093. **294.** 12 f. purple .. .. 30 30

**1950.** Honouring Francois Rabelais (writer).

1094. **295.** 12 f. lake .. .. 75 75

**296.** Andre Chenier. **297.** Chateaudun.

**1950.** National Relief Fund. Frames in blue.

1095. **296.** 5 f.+2 f. purple .. 11·00 11·00

1096. – 8 f.+3 f. sepia .. 11·00 11·00

1097. – 10 f.+4 f. red .. 11·50 11·50

1098. – 12 f.+5 f. brown .. 11·50 11·50

1099. – 15 f.+6 f. green .. 12·50 12·50

1100. – 20 f.+10 f. blue .. 12·50 12·50

PORTRAITS: 8 f. Louis David. 10 f. Lazare Carnot. 12 f. Danton. 15 f. Robespierre. 20 f. Hoche.

**1950.**

1101 **297** 8 f. brown & lt brown 65 40

1102 – 12 f. brown .. .. 40 40

DESIGN: 12 f. Palace of Fontainebleau.

**298.** Madame Recamier. **299.** "L'Amour" (after Falconet).

**1950.**

1103. **298.** 12 f. green .. .. 30 30

1104. – 15 f. blue .. .. 30 30

PORTRAIT: 15 f. Madame de Sevigne.

**1950.** Red Cross. Cross in red.

1105. – 8 f.+2 f. blue .. 2·50 2·50

1106. **299.** 15 f.+3 f. purple .. 3·25 3·25

DESIGN: 8 f. Bust of Alexandre Brongniart (after Houdon).

**300.** T.P.O. Sorting Van. **301.** J. Ferry (statesman).

**1951.** Stamp Day.

1107. **300.** 12 f.+3 f. violet .. 3·75 3·75

**1951.**

1108. **301.** 15 f. red .. .. 40 35

**302.** Shuttle. **303.** De La Salle.

**1951.** Textile Industry.

1109. **302.** 25 f. blue .. .. 95 60

**1951.** Birth Tercentenary of Jean Baptiste de la Salle (educational reformer).

1110. **303.** 15 f. brown .. .. 40 40

**304.** Anchor and Map.

**1951.** 50th Anniv. of Formation of Colonial Troops.

1111. **304.** 15 f. blue .. .. 40 40

**305.** Vincent D'Indy.

**1951.** Birth Centenary of Vincent D'Indy (composer).

1112. **305.** 25 f. green .. .. 1·90 1·50

**306.** A. de Musset. **307.** Nocard, Bouley and Chauveau.

**1951.** National Relief Fund. Frames in sepia.

1113. **306.** 5 f.+1 f. green .. 7·75 7·75

1114. – 8 f.+2 f. purple .. 8·25 8·25

1115. – 10 f.+3 f. green .. 8·25 8·25

1116. – 12 f.+4 f. brown .. 8·25 8·25

1117. – 15 f.+5 f. red .. 9·00 9·00

1118. – 30 f.+10 f. blue .. 13·00 13·00

PORTRAITS: 8 f. Delacroix. 10 f. Gay-Lussac. 12 f. Surcouf. 15 f. Talleyrand. 30 f. Napoleon.

**1951.** French Veterinary Research.

1119. **307.** 12 f. mauve .. .. 40 35

**308.** Picque, Roussin and Villemin. **309.** St. Nicholas.

**1951.** Military Health Service.

1120. **308.** 15 f. purple .. .. 45 35

**1951.** Provincial Coats of Arms as T **277**.

1121. 10 c. yellow, blue and red 10 10

1122. 50 c. black, red and green 10 10

1123. 1 f. red, yellow and blue.. 25 20

1124. 2 f. yellow, blue and red.. 85 20

1125. 3 f. yellow, blue and red.. 1·00 25

ARMS: 10 c. "Artois". 50 c. "Limousin". 1 f. "Bearn". 2 f. "Touraine". 3 f. "Franche-Comte".

**1951.** Popular Pictorial Art Exn., Epinal. Multicoloured centre.

1126. **309.** 15 f. blue .. .. 70 40

**310.** Seal of Mercantile Guild. **311.** M. Nogues.

**1951.** Bimillenary of Paris.

1127. **310.** 15 f. brn., blue & red 35 30

**1951.** M. Nogues (aviator).

1128. **311.** 12 f. indigo and blue 90 35

**312.** C. Baudelaire.

**1951.** Famous French Poets.

1129 **312** 8 f. violet .. .. 35 35

1130 – 12 f. grey .. .. 45 45

1131 – 15 f. green .. .. 50 50

DESIGNS: 12 f. Paul Verlaine. 15 f. Arthur Rimbaud.

313. Eiffel Tower and Chaillot Palace.

314. L. G. Clemenceau (statesman).

**1951.** U.N.O. General Assembly.
1132. **313.** 18 f. red .. .. 1·10 60
1133. 30 f. blue .. .. 2·00 90

**1951.** 110th Birth Anniv. of Clemenceau and 33rd Anniv. of Armistice.
1134. **314.** 15 f. sepia .. .. 25 25

315. Chateau Clos-Vougeot.

316. 15th century Child.

**1951.** 400th Anniv of Chateau Clos-Vougeot.
1135 **315** 30 f. dp brn & brown 5·75 2·25

**1951.** Red Cross. Cross in red.
1136. **316.** 12 f.+3 f. brown .. 3·25 3·25
1137. – 15 f.+5 f. blue .. 3·75 3·75
DESIGN: 15 f. 18th century child (De La Tour).

317. Observatory, Pic du Midi de Bigorre.

**1951.**
1138. **317.** 40 f. violet .. .. 6·50 20
1139. – 50 f. brown .. .. 5·25 15
VIEW—VERT. 50 f. Church of St. Etienne, Caen.

319. 19th-cent. Mail Coach.

**1952.** Stamp Day.
1140. **319.** 12 f.+3 f. green .. 5·75 5·75

320. Marshal de Lattre de Tassigny.

321. Gate of France, Vaucouleurs.

**1952.**
1140a **320** 12 f. indigo and blue 1·90 1·25
1141 15 f. brown .. 90 60

**1952.**
1142 **321** 12 f. brown .. .. 1·50 1·00

322. French Monument, Narvik.

**1952.** Battle of Narvik.
1143. **322.** 30 f. blue .. .. 3·00 1·90

323. Chambord Chateau.

**1952.**
1144 **323** 20 f. violet .. .. 40 20

324. Council of Europe Building, Strasbourg.

**1952.** Council of Europe Assembly.
1145. **324.** 30 f. green .. .. 9·00 6·50

325. Bir Hakeim Monument.

326. Abbey of the Holy Cross, Poitiers.

**1952.** 10th Anniv. of Battle of Bir Hakeim.
1146. **325.** 30 f. lake .. .. 3·25 1·90

**1952.** 1400th Anniv of Abbey of the Holy Cross, Poitiers.
1147 **326** 15 f. red .. .. 30 30

327. Medaille Militaire, in 1852 and 1952.

328. Garabit Railway Viaduct.

**1952.** Centenary of Medaille Militaire.
1148. **327.** 15 f. brn., yell. & grn. 35 30

**1952.**
1149 **328** 15 f. blue .. .. 60 45

329. Leonardo, Amboise Chateau and Town of Vinci.

330. Flaubert (after E. Giraud).

**1952.** 500th Birth Anniv. of Leonardo da Vinci.
1150. **329.** 30 f. blue .. .. 9·00 7·00

**1952.** National Relief Fund. Frames in sepia.
1151. **330.** 8 f.+2 f. blue .. 5·75 5·75
1152. – 12 f.+3 f. blue .. 6·50 6·50
1153. – 15 f.+4 f. green .. 6·50 6·50
1154. – 18 f.+5 f. sepia .. 8·25 8·25
1155. – 20 f.+6 f. red .. 9·00 9·00
1156. – 30 f.+7 f. violet .. 9·00 9·00
PORTRAITS: 12 f. Manet. 15 f. Saint-Saens. 18 f. H. Poincare. 20 f. Haussmann (after Yvon). 20 f. Thiers.

331. R. Laennec (physician).

332. "Cherub" (bas-relief).

**1952.**
1157. **331.** 12 f. green .. .. 35 30

**1952.** Red Cross Fund. Sculptures from Basin of Diana, Versailles. Cross in red.
1158. **332.** 12 f.+3 f. green .. 5·25 5·25
1159. – 15 f.+5 f. blue .. 5·25 5·25
DESIGN: 15 f. "Cherub" (facing left).

333. Versailles Gateway.

334. Count D'Argenson.

**1952.**
1160 **333** 18 f. purple .. 2·50 2·00
1160a 18 f. indigo, bl & brn 11·00 6·50

**1953.** Stamp Day.
1161 **334** 12 f.+3 f. blue .. 3·25 3·25

335. "Gargantua" (Rabelais).

337. Mannequin and Place Vendome, Paris.

**1953.** Literary Figures and National Industries.
1162. **335.** 6 f. lake and red .. 20 20
1163. – 8 f. blue and indigo .. 20 20
1164. – 12 f. green and brown 15 15
1165. – 18 f. sepia and purple 70 30
1166. – 25 f. sepia, red & brn. 14·50 30
1166a. – 25 f. blue and black .. 70 15
1167. **337.** 30 f. violet and blue .. 1·25 10
1167a. – 30 f. blue & turquoise 1·60 30
1168. – 40 f. brown & chocolate 4·50 15
1169. – 50 f. brn., turq. & blue 1·50 10
1170. – 75 f. lake and red .. 14·50 1·10
DESIGNS—As Types **335/337**: 8 f. "Celimene" (Moliere). 12 f. "Figaro" (Beaumarchais). 18 f. "Hernani" (Victor Hugo). 25 f. (No. 1166) Tapestry. 25 f. (No. 1166a) Mannequin modelling gloves. 30 f. (No. 1167a) Rare books and book-binding. 40 f. Porcelain and cut-glass. 50 f. Gold plate and jewellery. 75 f. Flowers and perfumes.

**1953.** General Leclerc. As T **270** but inscr. "GENERAL LECLERC MARECHAL DE FRANCE".
1171. **270.** 8 f. brown .. .. 90 75
1171a. 12 f. turq. and green 2·75 1·50

338. Olivier de Serres.

339. Cyclists and Map.

**1953.** National Relief Fund.
1172. – 8 f.+2 f. blue .. 6·50 6·50
1173. **338.** 12 f.+3 f. green .. 6·50 6·50
1174. – 15 f.+4 f. lake .. 10·00 10·00
1175. – 18 f.+5 f. blue .. 10·00 10·00
1176. – 20 f.+6 f. violet .. 10·00 10·00
1177. – 30 f.+7 f. brown .. 14·00 14·00
PORTRAITS: 8 f. St. Bernard. 15 f. Rameau. 18 f. Monge. 20 f. Michelet. 30 f. Marshal Lyautey.

**1953.** Provincial Coats of Arms as T **277.**
1178. 50 c. yellow, red and blue 20 20
1179. 70 c. yellow, blue and red 20 20
1180. 80 c. yellow, red and blue 20 20
1181. 1 f. yellow, red and black 20 15
1182. 2 f. yellow, blue and brown 20 20
1183. 3 f. yellow, blue and red .. 50 25
ARMS: 50 c. "Picardie". 70 c. "Gascogne". 80 c. "Berri" 1 f. "Poitou". 2 f. "Champagne". 3 f. "Dauphine".

**1953.** 50th Anniv. of "Tour de France" Cycle Race.
1184. **339.** 12 f. blk., bl. & red 2·10 90

340. Swimming.

341. Mme. Vigee-Lebrun and Daughter (self -portrait).

**1953.** Sports.
1185. **340.** 20 f. brown and red 2·50 15
1186. – 25 f. brown and green 14·00 30
1187. – 30 f. brown and blue 2·50 30
1188. – 40 f. indigo and brown 14·00 30
1189. – 50 f. brown and green 5·25 15
1190. – 75 f. lake and orange 35·00 12·50
SPORTS: 25 f. Running. 30 f. Fencing. 40 f. Canoeing. 50 f. Rowing. 75 f. Horse-jumping.
See also Nos. 1297/1300.

**1953.** Red Cross Fund. Cross in red.
1191. **341.** 12 f.+3 f. brown .. 7·75 7·75
1192. – 15 f.+5 f. blue .. 9·50 9·00
DESIGN: 15 f. "The Return from the Baptism" (L. Le Nain).

**1953.** Surch **15F.**
1193 **219** 15 f. on 18 f. red .. 50 40

343. Air Fouga Magister.

**1954.** Air.
1194. – 100 f. brown & blue .. 3·25 15
1195. – 200 f. purple & blue .. 12·00 20
1196. **343.** 500 f. red & orange .. £130 11·50
1197. – 1000 f. bl., pur. & turq. £120 17·00
AIRCRAFT: 100 f. Dassault Mystere IVA. 200 f. Nord 2501 Noratlas. 1000 f. Breguet Provence.
See also No. 1457.

344. Harvester.

345. Gallic Cock.

346. Lavallette.

**1954.** (a) Precancelled*
1198 **344** 4 f. blue .. .. 25 25
1198a **345** 5 f. brown .. .. 25 25
1199 **344** 8 f. red .. .. 5·25 1·00
1199a **345** 8 f. violet .. .. 65 20
1199b 10 f. blue .. .. 2·10 25
1200 12 f. mauve .. .. 4·25 35
1200b 15 f. purple .. .. 2·50 75
1200c 20 f. green .. .. 2·00 75
1201 24 f. green .. .. 21·00 4·75
1201a 30 f. red .. .. 5·25 1·50
1201b 40 f. red .. .. 4·50 2·75
1201c 45 f. green .. .. 30·00 16·00
1201d 55 f. green .. .. 19·00 12·00

(b) Without precancel.
1201e **344** 6 f. brown .. .. 10 10
1201f 10 f. green .. .. 80 10
1201g 12 f. purple .. .. 15 15
***PRECANCELS.** See note below No. 432.
See also Nos. 1470/3.

**1954.** Stamp Day.
1202 **346** 12 f.+3 f. green & brn 5·25 3·75

347. Exhibition Buildings.

348. "D-Day".

**1954.** 50th Anniv. of Paris Fair.
1203. **347.** 15 f. lake and blue .. 55 55

**1954.** 10th Anniv. of Liberation.
1204. **348.** 15 f. red and blue .. 1·75 1·10

349. Lourdes.

350. Jumieges Abbey.

**1954.** Views.

| | | | | |
|---|---|---|---|---|
| 1205 | 349 | 6 f. indigo, bl & grn | 25 | 20 |
| 1206 | – | 8 f. green and blue | 25 | 15 |
| 1207 | – | 10 f. brown and blue | 25 | 15 |
| 1208 | – | 12 f. lilac and violet | 35 | 10 |
| 1209 | – | 12 f. brn & chocolate | 1·50 | 1·25 |
| 1210 | – | 18 f. indigo, bl & grn | 3·25 | 90 |
| 1211 | – | 20 f. brown, chestnut and blue . . . . | 2·75 | 20 |
| 1211a | 349 | 20 f. brown and blue | 40 | 15 |

VIEWS—HORIZ. 8 f. Seine Valley at Andelys. 10 f. Royan. 12 f. (No. 1209), Limoges. 18 f. Cheverny Chateau. 20 f. (No. 1211), Ajaccio Bay. VERT. 12 f. (No. 1208), Quimper.

**1954.** 13th Cent. of Jumieges Abbey.

| | | | | |
|---|---|---|---|---|
| 1212. | 350. | 12 f. indigo, bl. & grn. | 1·75 | 1·25 |

**351.** Abbey Church of St. Philibert, Tournus. **352.** Stenay.

**1954.** 1st Conference of Romanesque Studies, Tournus.

| | | | | |
|---|---|---|---|---|
| 1213. | 351. | 30 f. blue and indigo | 7·75 | 5·25 |

**1954.** Tercent. of Return of Stenay to France.

| | | | | |
|---|---|---|---|---|
| 1214. | 352. | 15 f. brown and sepia | 75 | 50 |

**353.** St. Louis. **354.** Villandry Chateau.

**1954.** National Relief Fund.

| | | | | |
|---|---|---|---|---|
| 1215. | 353. | 12 f.+4 f. blue . . | 19·00 | 19·00 |
| 1216. | – | 15 f.+5 f. violet . . | 20·00 | 20·00 |
| 1217. | – | 18 f.+6 f. sepia . . | 20·00 | 20·00 |
| 1218. | – | 20 f.+7 f. red . . | 27·00 | 27·00 |
| 1219. | – | 25 f.+8 f. blue . . | 27·00 | 27·00 |
| 1220. | – | 30 f.+10 f. purple . . | 27·00 | 27·00 |

PORTRAITS: 15 f. Bossuet. 18 f. Sadi Carnot. 20 f. A. Bourdelle. 25 f. Dr. E. Roux. 30 f. Paul Valery.

**1954.** Four Centuries of Renaissance Gardens.

| | | | | |
|---|---|---|---|---|
| 1221. | 354. | 18 f. green and blue . . | 5·25 | 3·75 |

**355.** Cadet and Flag.

**1954.** 150th Anniv. of St. Cyr Military Academy.

| | | | | |
|---|---|---|---|---|
| 1222. | 355. | 15 f. indigo, blue & red | 1·50 | 1·10 |

**356.** Napoleon Conferring Decorations. **357.** " Basis of Metric System."

**1954.** 150th Anniv. of First Legion of Honour Presentation.

| | | | | |
|---|---|---|---|---|
| 1223. | 356. | 12 f. red . . . . | 1·50 | 1·10 |

**1954.** 150th Anniv. of Metric System.

| | | | | |
|---|---|---|---|---|
| 1224. | 357. | 30 f. sepia and blue . . | 7·75 | 5·25 |

**1954.** Provincial Coats of Arms as T **277.**

| | | | |
|---|---|---|---|
| 1225. | 50 c. yellow, bl. & blk. . . | 15 | 15 |
| 1226. | 70 c. yellow, red & grn. | 20 | 20 |
| 1227. | 80 c. yellow, blue and red | 20 | 20 |
| 1228. | 1 f. yellow, blue and red | 15 | 15 |
| 1229. | 2 f. yellow, red and black | 10 | 10 |
| 1230. | 3 f. yell., red & brn. . . | 10 | 10 |
| 1231. | 5 f. yellow and blue . . | 10 | 10 |

ARMS: 50 c. " Maine ". 70 c. " Navarre ". 80 c. " Nivernais ". 1 f. " Bourbonnais ". 2 f. " Angoumois ". 3 f. " Aunis ". 5 f. " Saintonge ".

**359.** " Young Girl with Doves " (J.-B. Greuze). **360.** Saint-Simon.

**1954.** Red Cross Fund. Cross in red.

| | | | | |
|---|---|---|---|---|
| 1232 | – | 12 f.+3 f. indigo and blue . . . . | 9·00 | 9·00 |
| 1233 | 359 | 15 f.+5 f. brown and deep brown . . | 10·00 | 10·00 |

DESIGN: 12 f. "The Sick Child" (E. Carriere).

**1955.** Death Bicent. of Saint-Simon (writer).

| | | | | |
|---|---|---|---|---|
| 1234. | 360. | 12 f. purple & brown | 80 | 40 |

**361.** " Industry ", " Agriculture" and Rotary Emblem. **362.** " France ".

**1955.** 50th Anniv of Rotary International.

| | | | | |
|---|---|---|---|---|
| 1235 | 361 | 30 f. orange, blue and deep blue . . . . | 2·25 | 1·40 |

**1955.**

| | | | | |
|---|---|---|---|---|
| 1236 | 362 | 6 f. brown . . | 3·50 | 1·90 |
| 1237 | | 12 f. green . . | 3·50 | 1·25 |
| 1238 | | 15 f. red . . . . | 20 | 10 |
| 1238ab | | 18 f. green . . | 30 | 20 |
| 1238b | | 20 f. blue . . . . | 30 | 10 |
| 1238c | | 25 f. red . . . . | 90 | 10 |

**363.** Thimonnier and Sewing-machines.

**1955.** French Inventors (1st series).

| | | | | |
|---|---|---|---|---|
| 1239. | – | 5 f. blue & lt. blue | 85 | 60 |
| 1240. | 363. | 10 f. brn. & chestnut | 75 | 60 |
| 1241. | – | 12 f. green . . | 1·25 | 60 |
| 1242. | – | 18 f. blue and grey . . | 3·25 | 2·75 |
| 1243. | – | 25 f. violet and plum | 3·25 | 2·50 |
| 1244. | – | 30 f. vermilion & red | 3·25 | 2·50 |

DESIGNS: 5 f. Le Bon (gaslight). 12 f. Appert (food canning). 18 f. Sainte-Claire Deville (aluminium). 25 f. Martin (steel). 30 f. Chardonnet (artificial silk).

See also Nos. 1324/7.

**364.** Mail Balloon "Armand Barbes", 1870.

**1955.** Stamp Day.

| | | | | |
|---|---|---|---|---|
| 1245. | 364. | 12 f.+3 f. brown, green and blue . . | 5·75 | 4·50 |

**365.** Florian and Pastoral scene.

**1955.** Birth Bicent. of Florian (fabulist).

| | | | | |
|---|---|---|---|---|
| 1246. | 365. | 12 f. turquoise . . | 80 | 50 |

**366.** Eiffel Tower and Television Aerials.

**1955.** Television Development.

| | | | | |
|---|---|---|---|---|
| 1247. | 366. | 15 f. blue and dp. blue. | 85 | 50 |

**367.** Observation Tower and Fence.

**1955.** 10th Anniv of Liberation of Concentration Camps.

| | | | | |
|---|---|---|---|---|
| 1248 | 367 | 12 f. black and grey . . | 1·00 | 90 |

**368.** Electric Train. **369.** The "Jacquemart" (campanile), Moulins.

**1955.** Electrification of Valenciennes–Thionville Railway Line.

| | | | | |
|---|---|---|---|---|
| 1249 | 368 | 12 f. brown and grey | 2·10 | 1·50 |

**1955.**

| | | | | |
|---|---|---|---|---|
| 1250 | 369 | 12 f. brown . . . . | 1·60 | 70 |

**370.** Jules Verne and Capt. Nemo on the " Nautilus ".

**1955.** 50th Death Anniv. of Jules Verne (author).

| | | | | |
|---|---|---|---|---|
| 1251. | 370. | 30 f. blue . . . . | 8·25 | 6·50 |

**371.** Maryse Bastie (airwoman). **372.** Vauban.

**1955.** Air. Maryse Bastie Commemoration.

| | | | | |
|---|---|---|---|---|
| 1252. | 371. | 50 f. claret and red . . | 7·00 | 4·50 |

**1955.** National Relief Fund.

| | | | | |
|---|---|---|---|---|
| 1253. | – | 12 f.+5 f. violet . . | 16·00 | 16·00 |
| 1254. | – | 15 f.+6 f. blue . . | 16·00 | 16·00 |
| 1255. | 372. | 18 f.+7 f. green . . | 17·00 | 17·00 |
| 1256. | – | 25 f.+8 f. slate . . | 22·00 | 20·00 |
| 1257. | – | 30 f.+9 f. lake . . | 24·00 | 24·00 |
| 1258. | – | 50 f.+15 f. turquoise | 28·00 | 28·00 |

PORTRAITS: 12 f. King Philippe-Auguste. 15 f. Malherbe. 25 f. Vergennes. 30 f. Laplace. 50 f. Renoir.

**373.** A. and L. Lumiere.

**1955.** 60th Anniv. of French Cinema Industry.

| | | | | |
|---|---|---|---|---|
| 1259. | 373. | 30 f. brown . . . . | 6·50 | 4·50 |

**374.** Jacques Cœur (merchant prince).

**1955.**

| | | | | |
|---|---|---|---|---|
| 1260. | 374. | 12 f. violet . . . . | 2·25 | 1·60 |

## INDEX

Countries can be quickly located by referring to the index at the end of this volume.

**375.** "La Capricieuse".

**1955.** Centenary of Voyage of "La Capricieuse" (sail warship).

| | | | | |
|---|---|---|---|---|
| 1261 | 375 | 30 f. blue & turquoise | 6·50 | 5·25 |

**376.** Marseilles. **377.** Gerard de Nerval.

**1955.** Views.

| | | | | |
|---|---|---|---|---|
| 1262 | – | 6 f. red . . . . | 20 | 20 |
| 1263 | 376 | 8 f. blue . . . . | 35 | 15 |
| 1264 | – | 10 f. blue . . . . | 25 | 10 |
| 1265 | – | 12 f. brown and grey | 25 | 10 |
| 1265a | – | 15 f. indigo and blue | 35 | 35 |
| 1266 | – | 18 f. blue and green | 60 | 20 |
| 1267 | – | 20 f. violet & dp vio | 3·75 | 20 |
| 1268 | – | 25 f. brown & chest | 90 | 15 |
| 1268a | – | 35 f. turquoise & grn | 4·50 | 60 |
| 1268b | – | 70 f. black and green | 17·00 | 1·90 |

DESIGNS—HORIZ. 6 f., 35 f. Bordeaux. 10 f. Nice. 12 f., 70 f. Valentre Bridge, Cahors. 18 f. Uzerche. 20 f. Mount Pele, Martinique. 25 f. Ramparts of Brouage. VERT. 15 f. Douai Belfry.

**1955.** Death Cent. of De Nerval (writer).

| | | | | |
|---|---|---|---|---|
| 1269. | 377. | 12 f. sepia and red . . | 35 | 20 |

**1955.** Provincial Coats of Arms as T **277.**

| | | | |
|---|---|---|---|
| 1270. | 50 c. multicoloured | 10 | 10 |
| 1271. | 70 c. yellow, blue and red | 10 | 10 |
| 1272. | 80 c. yell., red and brown | 10 | 10 |
| 1273. | 1 f. yellow, red and blue | 10 | 10 |

ARMS: 50 c. " Comte de Foix ". 70 c. " Marche ". 80 c. " Roussillon ". 1 f. " Comtat Venaissin ".

**379.** " Child and Cage " (after Pigalle). **380.**

**1955.** Red Cross Fund. Cross in red.

| | | | | |
|---|---|---|---|---|
| 1274. | 379. | 12 f.+3 f. lake . . | 7·00 | 7·00 |
| 1275. | – | 15 f.+5 f. blue . . | 5·25 | 5·25 |

DESIGN: 15 f. " Child and goose " (Greek sculpture).

**1956.** National Deportation Memorial.

| | | | | |
|---|---|---|---|---|
| 1276 | 380 | 15 f. sepia and brown | 45 | 45 |

**381.** Colonel Driant. **382.** Trench Warfare.

**1956.** Birth Centenary of Col. Driant.

| | | | | |
|---|---|---|---|---|
| 1277. | 381. | 15 f. blue . . . . | 25 | 25 |

**1956.** 40th Anniv. of Battle of Verdun.

| | | | | |
|---|---|---|---|---|
| 1278. | 382. | 30 f. blue and brown | 2·10 | 1·50 |

**383.** Francis of Taxis.

**1956.** Stamp Day.

| | | | | |
|---|---|---|---|---|
| 1279. | 383. | 12 f.+3 f. brown, green and blue | 3·25 | 3·25 |

384. J. H. Fabre (entomologist).

DESIGNS: 15 f. C. Tellier (refrigeration engineer). 18 f. C. Flammarion (astronomer). 30 f. P. Sabatier (chemist).

**1956.** French Scientists.

1280. **384.** 12 f. dp. brn. & brn. 60 45
1281. – 15 f. black and grey 95 45
1282. – 18 f. blue .. .. 2·25 1·90
1283. – 30 f. grn. & dp. grn. 4·25 2·50

385. Grand Trianon, Versailles.

**1956.**

1284 **385** 12 f. brown, grn & blk 1·25 80

386. "Latin America" and "France".

**1956.** Franco-Latin American Friendship.

1285. **386.** 30 f. brown and sepia 1·60 1·10

387. "Reims" and "Florence". 388. Order of Malta and Leper Colony.

**1956.** Reims-Florence Friendship.

1286. **387.** 12 f. green and black 60 50

**1956.** Order of Malta Leprosy Relief.

1287. **388.** 12 f. red, brn. & sepia 35 20

389. St. Yves de Treguier. 390. Marshal Franchet d'Esperey.

**1956.** St. Yves de Treguier Commemoration.

1288. **389.** 15 f. black and grey .. 25 20

**1956.** Birth Centenary of Marshal d'Esperey.

1289 **390** 30 f. purple .. .. 2·75 1·50

391. Monument. 392. Bude.

**1956.** Centenary of Montceau-les-Mines.

1290. **391.** 12 f. sepia .. .. 35 30

**1956.** National Relief Fund.

1291. **392.** 12 f.+3 f. blue .. 5·75 5·75
1292. – 12 f.+3 f. grey .. 6·50 6·50
1293. – 12 f.+3 f. red .. 7·00 7·00
1294. – 15 f.+5 f. green .. 7·75 7·75
1295. – 15 f.+5 f. brown .. 9·00 9·00
1296. – 15 f.+5 f. violet .. 9·00 9·00

PORTRAITS: No. 1292, Goujon. No. 1293, Champlain. No. 1294, Chardin. No. 1295, Barres. No. 1296, Ravel.

393. Pelota.

395. Donzere-Mondragon Barrage.

**1956.** Sports.

1297 – 30 f. black and grey 1·60 10
1298 **393** 40 f. purple and brown 5·50 20
1299 – 50 f. violet and purple 2·00 20
1300 – 75 f. grn, black & blue 11·50 1·60

DESIGNS: 30 f. Basketball. 50 f. Rugby. 75 f. Alpine climbing.

**1956.** Europa. As T **320** of Belgium.

1301 15 f. red and pink .. 1·00 20
1302 30 f. ultramarine and blue 6·50 1·10

**1956.** Technical Achievements.

1303. **395.** 12 f. grey and brown 1·40 1·00
1304. – 18 f. blue .. .. 3·50 2·25
1305. – 30 f. blue and indigo 14·00 6·50

DESIGNS—VERT. 18 f. Aiguille du Midi cable railway. HORIZ. 30 f. Port of Strasbourg.

396. A. A. Parmentier (agronomist). 397. Petrarch.

**1956.** Parmentier Commemoration.

1306. **396.** 12 f. brown and sepia 65 30

**1956.** Famous men.

1307. **397.** 8 f. green .. .. 50 40
1308. – 12 f. purple (Lully).. 50 40
1309. – 15 f. red (Rousseau).. 75 50
1310. – 18 f. blue (Franklin) 2·50 1·90
1311. – 20 f. violet (Chopin).. 3·75 1·50
1312. – 30 f. turq. (Van Gogh) 5·50 3·25

398. Pierre de Coubertin (reviver of Olympic Games). 399. "Jeune Paysan" (after Le Nain).

**1956.** Coubertin Commemoration.

1313. **398.** 30 f. purple and grey 1·75 1·10

**1956** Red Cross Fund. Cross in red.

1314. **399.** 12 f.+3 f. olive .. 3·25 3·25
1315. 15 f.+5 f. lake .. 3·25 3·25

DESIGN: 15 f. "Gilles" (after Watteau).

400. Pigeon and Loft.

**1957.** Pigeon-fanciers' Commemoration.

1316 **400** 15 f. blue, indigo & pur 25 25

401. Sud Aviation Caravelle.

402. Victor Schoelcher (slavery abolitionist).

**1957.** Air.

1318. – 300 f. olive & turq... 6·50 2·50
1319. **401.** 500 f. black & blue .. 38·00 3·25
1320. – 1000 f. black, violet and sepia .. .. 60·00 22·00

AIRCRAFT: 300 f. Morane Saulnier Paris I airplane. 1000 f. Sud Aviation Alouette II helicopter.

See also Nos. 1458/60.

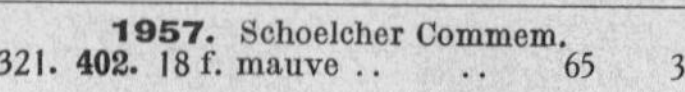

**1957.** Schoelcher Commem.

1321. **402.** 18 f. mauve .. .. 65 30

403. 18th Cent. Felucca.

**1957.** Stamp Day.

1322 **403** 12 f+3 f. black & grey 1·90 1·40

404. "La Baigneuse" (after Falconet) and Sevres Porcelain.

**1957.** Bicentenary of National Porcelain Industry at Sevres.

1323. **404.** 30 f. blue & light bl. 60 50

405. Plante and Accumulators.

DESIGNS: 12 f. Beclere (radiology). 18 f. Terrillon (antiseptics). 30 f. Oehmichen (helicopter).

**1957.** French Inventors (2nd series).

1324. **405.** 8 f. purple and sepia 30 30
1325. – 12 f. blk., blue & grn. 35 35
1326. – 18 f. lake and red .. 1·50 1·50
1327. – 30 f. myrtle and green 2·25 2·25

406. Uzes Chateau. 407. Jean Moulin.

**1957.**

1334 – 8 f. green .. .. 15 15
1328 **406** 12 f. black, brn & bl 25 25
1335 – 15 f. black and green 15 15

DESIGNS—VERT. 8 f., 15 f. Le Quesnoy.

**1957.** Heroes of the Resistance (1st issue). Inscr. as in T **407**.

1329. **407.** 8 f. chocolate & brn. 1·00 35
1330. – 10 f. blue and black.. 1·00 35
1331. – 12 f. green and brown 1·00 90
1332. – 18 f. black and violet 1·90 1·50
1333. – 20 f. blue & turquoise 1·40 1·00

PORTRAITS: 10 f. H. d'Estienne d'Orves. 12 f. R. Keller. 18 f. P. Brossolette. 20 f. J.-B. Lebas.

See also Nos. 1381/4, 1418/22, 1478/82 and 1519/22.

409. Emblems of Auditing. 410. Joinville.

**1957.** 150th Anniv of Court of Accounts.

1336 **409** 12 f. blue and green .. 20 20

**1957.** National Relief Fund.

1337. **410.** 12 f.+3 f. olive & sage 2·50 2·50
1338. – 12 f.+3 f. black and turquoise 2·75 2·75
1339. – 15 f.+5 f. lake and vermilion 3·25 3·25
1340. – 15 f.+5 f. blue and ultramarine 3·50 3·50
1341. – 18 f.+7 f. blk. & grn. 3·75 3·75
1342. – 18 f.+7 f. chocolate and brown 4·50 4·50

PORTRAITS: No. 1338, Bernard Palissy. No. 1339, Quentin de la Tour. No. 1340, Lamennais. No. 1341, George Sand. No. 1342, Jules Guesde.

See also Nos. 1390/5.

411. "Public Works".

**1957.** French Public Works.

1343. **411.** 30 f. brown, deep brown and green.. 2·25 1·40

412. Port of Brest.

**1957.**

1344 **412** 12 f. green and brown 55 35

413. Leo Lagrange (founder) and Stadium. 414. Auguste Comte.

**1957.** Universities World Games.

1345. **413.** 18 f. black and grey.. 40 35

**1957.** Death Centenary of Auguste Comte (philosopher).

1346. **414.** 35 f. sepia and brown 40 40

415. "Agriculture and Industry". 416. Roman Theatre, Lyons.

**1957.** Europa.

1347. **415.** 20 f. green and brown 35 20
1348. 35 f. blue and sepia.. 1·50 75

**1957.** Bimillenary of Lyons.

1349. **416.** 20 f. purple & brown 35 30

417. Sens River, Guadeloupe. 418. Copernicus.

**1957.** Tourist Publicity Series.

1350 **417** 8 f. brown and green 10 10
1351 – 10 f. chocolate & brn 10 10
1351a – 15 f. multicoloured 25 25
1352 – 18 f. brown and blue 20 10
1353 – 25 f. brown and grey 65 15
1353a – 30 f. green .. 2·50 20
1354 – 35 f. mauve and red 25 10
1355 – 50 f. brown & green 35 10
1356 – 65 f. blue and indigo 60 20
1356a – 85 f. purple .. 3·75 20
1356b **417** 100 f. violet 32·00 25

DESIGNS—HORIZ. 10 f., 30 f., Palais de l'Elysee, Paris. 15 f. Chateau de Foix. 25 f. Chateau de Valencay. 50 f. Les Antiques, Saint Remy. 65 f., 85 f. Evian-les-Bains. VERT. 18 f. Beynac-Cazenac (Dordogne). 35 f. Rouen Cathedral.

**1957.** Famous Men.

1357 **418** 8 f. brown .. .. 60 40
1358 – 10 f. green .. .. 65 40
1359 – 12 f. violet .. .. 70 40
1360 – 15 f. brown & dp brn 80 30
1361 – 18 f. blue .. .. 1·50 80
1362 – 25 f. purple and lilac 1·60 1·00
1363 – 35 f. blue .. .. 1·90 1·40

PORTRAITS: 10 f. Michelangelo. 12 f. Cervantes. 15 f. Rembrandt. 18 f. Newton. 25 f. Mozart. 35 f. Goethe.

See also Nos. 1367/74.

419. L.-J. Thenard.

420. " The Blind Man and the Beggar " (after J. Callot).

**1957.** Death Cent. of Thenard (chemist).
1364. **419.** 15 f. green and bistre 30 30

**1957.** Red Cross Fund. Cross in red.
1365. **420.** 15 f.+7 f. blue .. 3·25 3·25
1366. – 20 f.+8 f. brown .. 4·50 4·50
DESIGN: 20 f. " The Beggar and the One-eyed Woman " (after J. Callot).

**1958.** French Doctors. As T **418.**
1367. 8 f. brown .. .. 70 50
1368. 12 f. violet .. .. 70 50
1369. 15 f. blue .. .. 1·40 60
1370. 35 f. black .. .. 2·00 1·25
PORTRAITS: 8 f. Dr. Pinel. 12 f. Dr. Widal. 15 f. Dr. C. Nicolle. 35 f. Dr. R. Leriche.

**1958.** French Scientists. As T 418.
1371 8 f. violet and blue .. 1·00 50
1372 12 f. grey and brown .. 1·10 90
1373 15 f. green and deep green 2·25 85
1374 35 f. red and lake .. 2·50 1·40
PORTRAITS: 8 f. Lagrange (mathematician). 12 f. Le Verrier (astonomer). 15 f. Foucault (physicist). 35 f. Berthollet (chemist).

421. Rural Postal Services.

**1958.** Stamp Day.
1375 421 15 f.+5 f. deep green, green and brown .. 1·75 1·40

422. Le Havre.

DESIGNS—VERT. 15 f. Maubeuge. 18 f. Saint-Die. HORIZ. 25 f. Sete.

**1958.** Municipal Reconstruction.
1376. **422.** 12 f. red and olive .. 50 40
1377. – 15 f. brown and violet 80 40
1378. – 18 f. indigo and blue 85 70
1379. – 25 f. brn.,turq. & blue 1·40 70

423. French Pavilion.

**1958.** Brussels Int. Exn.
1380. **423.** 35 f. grn.,blue & brn. 25 25

**1958.** Heroes of the Resistance (2nd issue). Portraits inscr. as in T **407.**
1381. 8 f. black and violet .. 60 30
1382. 12 f. green and blue .. 60 30
1383. 15 f. grey and sepia .. 1·75 80
1384. 20 f. blue and brown .. 1·40 1·10
PORTRAITS: 8 f. Jean Cavailles. 12 f. Fred Scamaroni. 15 f. Simone Michel-Levy. 20 f. Jacques Bingen.

424. Boules.

425. Senlis Cathedral.

**1958.** French Traditional Games.
1385 424 12 f. brown and red .. 1·40 90
1386 – 15 f. deep green, green and blue 1·40 90
1387 – 18 f. brown and green 2·50 1·00
1388 – 25 f. blue and brown 3·75 2·00
DESIGNS–HORIZ. 15 f. Nautical jousting. VERT. 18 f. Archery. 25 f. Breton wrestling.

**1958.** Senlis Cathedral Commem.
1389. **425.** 15 f. blue and indigo 25 25

**1958.** Red Cross Fund. French Celebrities as T **410.**
1390 12 f.+4 f. green .. .. 1·90 1·90
1391 12 f.+4 f. blue .. .. 1·90 1·90
1392 15 f.+5 f. purple .. 2·25 2·25
1393 15 f.+5 f. blue .. .. 2·50 2·50
1394 20 f.+8 f. red .. .. 2·50 2·50
1395 35 f.+15 f. green .. 2·75 2·75
PORTRAITS: No. 1390, J. du Bellay. No. 1391, Jean Bart. No. 1392, D. Diderot. No. 1393, G. Courbet. No. 1394, J. B. Carpeaux. No. 1395, Toulouse-Lautrec.

426. Fragment of the Bayeux Tapestry.

**1958.**
1396. **426.** 15 f. red and blue .. 30 25

**1958.** Europa. As T **345** of Belgium. Size 22×36 mm.
1397. 20 f. red .. .. .. 30 20
1398. 35 f. blue .. .. .. 90 80

427. Town Halls of Paris and Rome.

**1958.** Paris-Rome Friendship.
1399. **427.** 35 f. grey, blue & red 35 30

428. U.N.E.S.C.O. Headquarters, Paris.

429. Flanders Grave.

**1958.** Inaug. of U.N.E.S.C.O. Building.
1400. **428.** 20 f. bistre and turq. 15 15
1401. – 35 f. red and myrtle.. 15 15
DESIGN: 35 f. Different view of building.

**1958.** 40th Anniv. of First World War Armistice.
1402. **429.** 15 f. blue and green.. 20 20

430. Arms of Marseilles.

431. St. Vincent de Paul.

**1958.** Arms of French Towns.
1403 430 50 c. blue & deep blue 10 10
1404 – 70 c. multicoloured .. 10 10
1405 – 80 c. red, yellow & bl 10 10
1406 – 1 f. red, yellow & blue 10 10
1407 – 2 f. red, green & blue 10 10
1408 – 3 f. multicoloured .. 10 10
1409 – 5 f. red and brown .. 10 10
1410 – 15 f. multicoloured .. 10 10
ARMS: 70 c. "Lyon". 80 c. "Toulouse". 1 f. "Bordeaux". 2 f. "Nice". 3 f. "Nantes". 5 f. "Lille". 15 f. "Alger".
See also Nos. 1452, 1454, 1498a/99f, 1700/1 and 1735.

**1958.** Red Cross Fund. Cross in red.
1411. **431.** 15 f.+7 f. green .. 1·25 1·25
1412. – 20 f.+8 f. violet .. 1·25 1·25
PORTRAIT: 20 f. J. H. Dunant (founder).

## MINIMUM PRICE

The minimum price quoted is 10p which represents a handling charge rather than a basis for valuing common stamps. For further notes about prices see introductory pages.

432. Arc du Carrousel and Flowers.

433. Symbols of Learning and " Academic Palms ".

**1959.** Paris Flower Festival.
1413. **432.** 15 f. multicoloured.. 25 20

**1959.** 150th Anniv. of "Academic Palms".
1414. **433.** 20 f. blk., vio. & lake 15 15

434. Father Charles de Foucauld (missionary).

**1959.** Charles de Foucauld Commem.
1415. **434.** 50 f. multicoloured .. 45 35

435. Douglas DC-3 Mail Plane making Night-landing.

**1959.** Stamp Day.
1416 435 20 f.+5 f. mult .. 40 40
See also No. 1644.

436. Miner's Lamp, Picks and School Building.

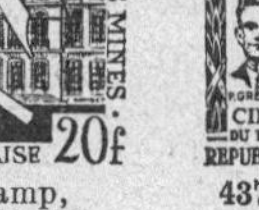

437. " Five Martyrs ".

**1959.** 175th Anniv. of School of Mines.
1417. **436.** 20 f. turq., blk. & red 15 15

**1959.** Heroes of the Resistance (3rd series).
1418. **437.** 15 f. black and violet 25 20
1419. – 15 f. violet & purple 30 30
1420. – 20 f. brown & chestnut 35 30
1421. – 20 f. turquoise & green 55 40
1422. – 30 f. violet and purple 90 40
PORTRAITS—As T **407.** No. 1419, Yvonne Le Roux. No. 1420, Martin Bret. No. 1421, Mederic-Vedy. No. 1422, Moutardier.

438. Foum el Gherza Dam.

**1959.** French Technical Achievements.
1423. **438.** 15 f. turq. and brown 25 20
1424. – 20 f. pur., red & brn. 35 25
1425. – 30 f. brn., turq. & blue 50 25
1426. – 50 f. blue and green.. 90 60
DESIGNS—VERT. 20 f. Marcoule Atomic Power Station. 30 f. Oil derrick and pipe-line at Hassi-Messaoud, Sahara. HORIZ. 50 f. National Centre of Industry and Technology, Paris.

439. C. Goujon and C. Rozanoff (test pilots).

**1959.** Goujon and Rozanoff Commem.
1427. **439.** 20 f. brn., red & blue 30 30

440. Villehardouin (chronicler).

**1959.** Red Cross Fund.
1428. **440.** 15 f.+5 f. blue .. 1·40 1·40
1429. – 15 f.+5 f. myrtle .. 1·40 1·40
1430. – 20 f.+10 f. bistre .. 1·60 1·60
1431. – 20 f.+10 f. grey .. 1·60 1·60
1432. – 30 f.+10 f. lake .. 2·00 2·00
1433. – 30 f.+10 f. brown .. 2·00 2·00
PORTRAITS: No. 1429, Le Notre (Royal gardener). No. 1430, D'Alembert (philosopher). No. 1431, D'Angers (sculptor). No. 1432, Bichat (physiologist). No. 1433, Bartholdi (sculptor).

441. M. Desbordes-Valmore.

442. " Marianne " in Ship of State.

**1959.** Death Centenary of Marceline Desbordes-Valmore (poetess).
1434. **441.** 30 f. brn., blue & grn. 20 20

**1959.**
1437. **442.** 25 f. red and black .. 30 10
See also No. 1456.

443. Tancarville Bridge.

**1959.** Inaug. of Tancarville Bridge.
1438. **443.** 30 f. grn., brn. & blue 25 20

444. Jean Jaures.

445. " Giving Blood ".

**1959.** Birth Centenary of Jean Jaures (socialist leader).
1439. **444.** 50 f. brown .. .. 35 25

**1959.** Europa. As T **360** of Belgium but size 22×36 mm.
1440. 25 f. green .. .. 30 20
1441. 50 f. violet .. .. 1·10 30

**1959.** Blood Donors.
1442 445 20 f. grey and red .. 20 20

446. Clasped Hands of Friendship.

447. Youth throwing away Crutches.

**1959.** Tercent of Treaty of the Pyrenees.
1443 446 50 f. red, blue & mauve 45 30

**1959.** Infantile Paralysis Relief Campaign.
1444. **447.** 20 f. blue .. .. 15 15

448. Henri Bergson.

449. Avesnes-sur-Helpe.

**1959.** Birth Cent. of Bergson (philosopher).
1445. **448.** 50 f. brown .. .. 35 25

**1959.**
1446. **449.** 20 f. blue, brn. & blk. 25 15
1447. – 30 f. brn., pur. & blue 30 20
DESIGN: 30 f. Perpignan Castle.

**450.** Abbe C. M. de l'Epee (teacher of deaf mutes). **451.** N.A.T.O. Headquarters, Paris.

**1959.** Red Cross Fund. Cross in red.
1448. **450.** 20 f.+10 f. purple and black .. .. 2·10 2·10
1449. – 25 f.+10 f. blk. & t.l. 2·25 2·25
PORTRAIT: 25 f. V. Hauy (teacher of the blind)

**1959.** 10th Anniv. of N.A.T.O.
1450. **451.** 50 f. brn., grn. & blue 90 45

**1959.** Frejus Disaster Fund. Surch **FREJUS +5f.**
1451 **442** 25 f.+5 f. red & black 25 25

(New currency. 100 (old) francs = 1 (new) franc.)

**453.** Sower. **454.** Laon Cathedral.

**1960.** T **453** and previous designs but new currency.
1452 – 5 c. red and brown (as 1409) .. .. 9·25 20
1453 **344** 10 c. green .. .. 35 10
1454 – 15 c. multicoloured (as 1410) .. .. 1·10 20
1455 **453** 20 c. red & turquoise 20 10
1456 **442** 25 c. blue and red .. 2·50 15
1456a **453** 30 c. blue and indigo 2·10 30

**1960.** Air. As previous designs but new currency and new design (No. 1457b).
1457 – 2 f. purple and black (as 1195) .. .. 1·50 15
1457b – 2 f. indigo and blue 1·90 10
1458 – 3 f. brown and blue (as 1318) .. .. 1·90 10
1459 **401** 5 f. black and blue 3·25 30
1460 – 10 f. black, violet & brown (as 1320) .. 16·00 2·00
DESIGN: No. 1457b, Mystere "20" jetliner.

**1960.** Tourist Publicity.
1461. **454.** 15 c. indigo and blue 30 25
1462. – 30 c. pur., grn. & blue 3·25 25
1463. – 45 c. vio., pur. & sepia 60 15
1464. – 50 c. purple and green 2·75 15
1465. – 65 c. brn., grn. & blue 1·60 20
1466. – 85 c. sep., grn. & blue 3·00 25
1467. – 1 f. vio., grn. & turq. 3·00 15
DESIGNS—HORIZ. 30 c. Fougeres Chateau. 65 c. Valley of the Sioule. 85 c. Chaumont Railway Viaduct. VERT. 45 c. Kerrata Gorges, Algeria. 50 c. Tlemcen Mosque, Algeria. 1 f. Cilaos Church and Great Bernard Mountains, Reunion.
See also Nos. 1485/7.

**455.** Pierre de Nolhac.

**1960.** Birth Centenary (1959) of Pierre de Nolhac (historian).
1468 **455** 20 c. black .. .. 50 35

**456.** St. Etienne Museum.

**1960.** Museum of Art and Industry, St. Etienne.
1469. **456.** 30 c. brn., red & blue 60 45

**1960.** As T **345** but with values in new currency.
1470 **345** 8 c. violet .. .. 40 40
1471 20 c. green .. .. 3·00 45
1472 40 c. red .. .. 12·00 2·50
1473 55 c. green .. .. 32·00 16·00
Nos. 1470/3 were only issued precancelled (see note below No. 432).

**457.** Assembly Emblem and View of Cannes.

**1960.** 5th Meeting of European Mayors Assembly.
1474. **457.** 50 c. brown and green 1·00 75

**458.** "Ampere" (cable-laying ship)

**1960.** Stamp Day.
1475. **458.** 20 c.+5 c. blue and turquoise .. .. 1·50 1·50

**459.** Girl of Savoy. **460.** Child Refugee.

**1960.** Cent. of Attachment of Savoy and Nice to France.
1476. **459.** 30 c. green .. .. 55 55
1477. – 50 c. brn., red & yellow (Girl of Nice) .. 45 30

**1960.** Heroes of the Resistance (4th series). Portraits as T **407**.
1478 20 c. black and brown .. 2·75 1·60
1479 20 c. lake and red .. 2·25 1·60
1480 30 c. violet & deep violet 2·25 1·60
1481 30 c. blue and indigo .. 3·25 2·50
1482 50 c. brown and green .. 3·50 3·00
PORTRAITS: No. 1478, E. Debeaumarche. No. 1479, P. Masse. No. 1480, M. Ripoche. No. 1481, L. Vieljeux. No. 1482, Abbe Rene Bonpain.

**1960.** World Refugee Year.
1483. **460.** 25 c.+10 c. bl., brn. & grn. 25 25

**461.** "The Road to Learning".

**1960.** 150th Anniv. of Strasbourg Teachers' Training College.
1484. **461.** 20 c. vio., pur. & blk. 25 20

**1960.** Views as T **454**.
1485. 15 c. sepia, grey and blue 25 25
1485a. 20 c. blue, green and buff 25 20
1486. 30 c. sepia, green and blue 55 30
1487. 50 c. brown, green & red 70 50
DESIGNS: 15 c. Lisieux Basilica. 20 c. Bagnoles de l'Orne. 30 c. Chateau de Blois. 50 c. La Bourboule.

**462.** L'Hospital (statesman). **463.** "Marianne".

**1960.** Red Cross Fund.
1488. **462.** 10 c.+5 c. vio. & red 2·50 2·50
1489. – 20 c.+10 c. turquoise and green .. 3·50 3·50
1490. – 20 c.+10 c. olive and brown .. .. 3·75 3·75
1491. – 30 c.+10 c. blue and violet .. .. 5·75 5·75
1492. – 30 c.+10 c. crimson and red .. .. 6·50 6·50
1493. – 50 c.+15 c. blue and slate .. .. 7·00 7·00
DESIGNS: No. 1489, Boileau (poet). No. 1490, Turenne (military leader). No. 1491, Bizet (composer). No. 1492, Charcot (neurologist). No. 1493, Degas (painter).

**1960.**
1494. **463.** 25 c. grey and red .. 15 10

**464.** Cross of Lorraine. **465.** Jean Bouin and Olympic Stadium.

**1960.** 20th Anniv. of De Gaulle's Appeal.
1495. **464.** 20 c. brn., grn. & sep. 95 30

**1960.** Olympic Games.
1496. **465.** 20 c. brn., red & bl. 30 25

**1960.** Europa. As T **373** of Belgium, but size 36×22½ mm.
1497. 25 c. turquoise and green 15 10
1498. 50 c. purple and red .. 25 20

**1960.** Arms. As T **430**.
1498a 1 c. blue and yellow .. 10 10
1498b 2 c. yellow, green & blue 10 10
1499 5 c. multicoloured .. 10 10
1499a 5 c. red, yellow & blue 10 10
1499b 10 c. blue, yellow & red 10 10
1499c 12 c. red, yellow & black 10 10
1499d 15 c. yellow, blue & red 10 10
1499e 18 c. multicoloured .. 25 25
1499f 30 c. red and blue .. 30 15
ARMS: 1 c. "Niort". 2 c. "Gueret". 5 c. (No. 1499) "Oran". 5 c. (No. 1499a) "Amiens". 10 c. "Troyes". 12 c. "Agen". 15 c. "Nevers". 18 c. "Saint-Denis (Reunion)". 30 c. "Paris".

**466.** Madame de Stael (after Gerard). **467.** Gen. Estienne, Morane Saulnier Type L Airplane and Tank.

**1960.** Madame de Stael (writer).
1500. **466.** 30 c. olive and purple 25 20

**1960.** Birth Cent. of Gen. Estienne.
1501. **467.** 15 c. sepia and lilac .. 25 25

**468.** Sangnier. **469.** Order of the Liberation.

**1960.** 10th Death Anniv of Marc Sangnier (patriot).
1502 **468** 20 c. black, violet & bl 15 15

**1960.** 20th Anniv. of Order of the Liberation.
1503. **469.** 20 c. green and black 35 30

DESIGN: 50 c. European bee eaters, Camargue.

**470.** Atlantic Puffins at Les Sept Iles.

**1960.** Nature Protection.
1504. **470.** 30 c. multicoloured .. 25 20
1505. – 50 c. multicoloured .. 60 25

**471.** A. Honnorat. **472.** Mace of St. Martin's Brotherhood.

**1960.** 10th Death Anniv. of Andre Honnorat (philanthropist).
1506. **471.** 30 c. blk., grn. & blue 25 25

**1960.** Red Cross Fund. Cross in red.
1507. **472.** 20 c.+10 c. lake .. 3·25 3·25
1508. – 25 c.+10 c. blue .. 3·25 3·25
DESIGN: 25 c. St. Martin (after 16th-cent. wood-carving).

**473.** St. Barbe and College.

**1960.** 500th Anniv. of St. Barbe College.
1509. **473.** 30 c. multicoloured .. 30 25

DESIGN: 45 c. Green-winged teal.

**474.** Lapwings.

**1960.** Study of Bird Migration. Inscr. "ETUDE DES MIGRATIONS".
1510. **474.** 20 c. multicoloured .. 25 20
1511. – 45 c. multicoloured .. 85 50

**475.** "Mediterranean" (after Maillol). **476.** "Marianne".

**1961.** Birth Cent. of Aristide Maillol (sculptor).
1512. **475.** 20 c. blue and red .. 20 20

**1961.**
1513. **476.** 20 c. red and blue .. 15 10

**477.** Orly Airport.

**1961.** Opening of New Installations at Orly Airport.
1514. **477.** 50 c. turq., blue & blk. 35 30

**478.** Georges Melies. **479.** Postman of Paris "Little Post" 1760.

**1961.** Birth Centenary of Georges Melies (cinematograph pioneer).
1515. **478.** 50 c. blue, olive & vio. 90 50

**1961.** Stamp Day and Red Cross Fund.
1516. **479.** 20 c.+5 c. green, red and brown .. 70 35

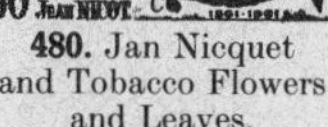

**480.** Jan Nicquet and Tobacco Flowers and Leaves. **481.** Father Lacordaire (after Chasseriau).

**1961.** 400th Anniv. of Introduction of Tobacco into France.
1517. **480.** 30 c. red, brn. & grn. 20 20
The portrait on No. 1517 is of Jan Nicquet, a Flemish merchant, and not Jean Nicot as inscribed.

**1961.** Death Centenary of Father Lacordaire (theologian).
1518 **481** 30 c. black and brown 25 25

**1961.** Heroes of the Resistance (5th issue). Portrait inscr. as in T **407.**

1519. 20 c. violet and blue .. 60 50
1520. 20 c. blue and green .. 95 50
1521. 30 c. black and brown .. 1·50 90
1522. 30 c. black and blue .. 1·25 1·00

PORTRAITS: No. 1519, J. Renouvin. No. 1520, L. Dubray. No. 1521, P. Gateaud. No. 1522, Mother Elisabeth.

**482.** Dove, Globe and Olive Branch.

**483.** Deauville, 1861.

**1961.** World Federation of Old Soldiers Meeting, Paris.

1523. **482.** 50 c. red, bl. & grn. 25 25

**1961.** Centenary of Deauville.

1524. **483.** 50 c. lake .. .. 1·60 1·40

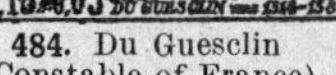
**484.** Du Guesclin (Constable of France).

**485.** Champmesle ("Roxane").

**1961.** Red Cross Fund.

1525. **484.** 15 c.+5 c. blk. & pur. 2·50 2·50
1526. – 20 c.+10 c. grn. & blue 2·50 2·50
1527. – 20 c.+10 c. crim. & red 2·50 2·50
1528. – 30 c.+10 c. blk. & brn. 3·25 3·25
1529. – 45 c.+10 c. brn. & grn. 4·50 4·50
1530. – 50 c.+15 c. vio. & lake 4·50 4·50

PORTRAITS: No. 1526, Puget (sculptor). No. 1527, Coulomb (physicist). No. 1528, General Drouot. No. 1529, Daumier (caricaturist). No. 1530, Apollinaire (writer).

**1961.** French Actors and Actresses. Frames in red.

1531. **485.** 20 c. brown & green 1·00 20
1532. – 30 c. brown and red .. 1·00 25
1533. – 30 c. myrtle and green 1·00 25
1534. – 50 c. brown and turq. 1·40 35
1535. – 50 c. brown and olive 1·25 45

PORTRAITS: No. 1532, Talma ("Oreste"). No. 1533, Rachel ("Phedre"). No. 1534, Raimu ("Cesar"). No. 1535, Gerard Philipe ("Le Cid").

**486.** Mont Dore, Snow Crystal and Cable Rly. **487.** Thann. **488.** Pierre Fauchard.

**1961.** Mont Dore.

1536 **486** 20 c. purple and orange 25 20

**1961.** 800th Anniv. of Thann.

1537. **487.** 20 c. violet, brown and green .. .. 50 30

**1961.** Birth Bicentenary of Pierre Fauchard (dentist).

1538 **488** 50 c. black and green 45 40

**489.** Doves.

**1961.** Europa.

1539. **489.** 25 c. red .. .. 15 10
1540. 50 c. blue .. .. 25 25

**490.** Sully-sur-Loire.

**1961.** Tourist Publicity.

1541. – 15 c. slate, pur. & turq. 10 10
1542. – 20 c. brown and green 20 45
1543. – 30 c. bl., myrt. & sepia 20 15
1544. – 30 c. blk., grey & grn. 1·10 90
1545. **490.** 45 c. brn., grn. & blue 25 15
1546. – 50 c. myrt., turq. & grn. 1·50 15
1547. – 65 c. blue, brn. & myrt. 35 15
1548. – 85 c. blue, brn. & myrt. 50 15
1549. – 1 f. brn., blue & myrt. 5·75 20
1550. – 1 f. brn., grn. & blue 45 10

VIEWS—HORIZ. 15 c. Saint-Paul. 30 c. (No. 1543), Arcachon. 30 c. (No. 1544), Law Courts, Rennes. 50 c. Cognac. 65 c. Dinan. 85 c. Calais. 1 f. (No. 1549), Medea, Algeria. 1 f. (No. 1550), Le Touquet-Paris-Plage, golf-bag and Handley Page Dart Herald airplane. VERT. 20 c. Laval, Mayenne.

See also Nos. 1619/23, 1654/7, 1684/8, 1755/61, 1794, 1814/18, 1883/5, 1929/33, 1958/61, 2005/8, 2042/4, 2062/4, 2115/20, 2187/97, 2258/64, 2310/15, 2360/5, 2403/10, 2503/8, 2566/70, 2630/4, 2652/6, 2710/14, 2762/6, 2834/6, 2883/6, 2973/6, 3024/6, 3077/80, 3124/9, 3180/3, 3240/3 and 3330/3.

**491.** "14th July" (R. de la Fresnaye).

**1961.** Modern French Art.

1551. – 50 c. multicoloured .. 3·25 2·00
1552. – 65 c. blue, green & violet 5·25 2·50
1553. – 85 c. red, bistre and blue 1·90 1·90
1554. **491.** 1 f. multicoloured .. 5·25 3·25

PAINTINGS: 50 c. "The Messenger" (Braque). 65 c. "Blue Nudes" (Matisse). 85 c. "The Cardplayers" (Cezanne).

See also Nos. 1590/2, 1603/6, 1637/9, 1671/4, 1710/4 1742/5, 1786/9, 1819/22, 1877/80, 1908/10, 1944/7, 1985/8, 2033/6, 2108/13, 2159/60, 2243, 2290/2, 2338/41, 2398/9, 2531/4, 2580/2, 2608/12, 2672/6, 2721/5, 2773/6, 2850/3, 2858/60, 2966/8, 3008/9, 3085, 3245/7 and 3306/7.

**493.** "It is so sweet to love" (Wood-carving from Rouault's "Miserere").

**494.** Liner "France".

**1961.** Red Cross Fund. Cross in red.

1555. **493.** 20 c.+10 c. black and purple .. .. 2·25 2·25
1556. – 25 c.+10 c. black and purple .. .. 2·75 2·75

DESIGN: 25 c. "The blind leading the blind" (from Rouault's "Miserere").

**1962.** Maiden Voyage of Liner "France".

1557. **494.** 30 c. blk., red & blue 80 30

**495.** Skier at Speed. **496.** M. Bourdet.

**1962.** World Ski Championships, Chamonix.

1558. **495.** 30 c. violet and blue 20 20
1559. – 50 c. grn., blue & vio. 35 25

DESIGN: 50 c. Slalom-racer.

**1962.** 60th Birth Anniv. of Maurice Bourdet (journalist and radio commentator).

1560. **496.** 30 c. grey .. .. 30 25

**497.** Dr. P.-F. Bretonneau.

**498.** Gallic Cock.

**1962.** Death Centenary of Dr. Pierre-Fidele Bretonneau (medical scientist).

1561. **497.** 50 c. violet and blue 30 20

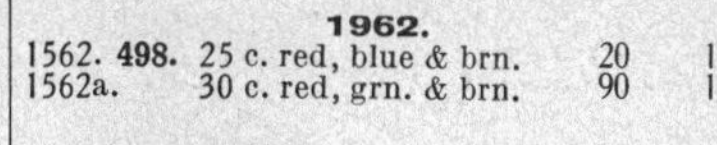

**1962.**

1562. **498.** 25 c. red, blue & brn. 20 10
1562a. 30 c. red, grn. & brn. 90 10

**499.** Royal Messenger of late Middle Ages.

**500.** Vannes.

**1962.** Stamp Day.

1563. **499.** 20 c.+5 c. brown, blue and red .. 70 50

**1962.**

1564. **500.** 30 c. blue .. .. 1·10 90

**501.** Globe and Stage Set. **502.** Harbour Installations.

**1962.** World Theatre Day.

1565. **501.** 50 c. lake, grn. & ochre 35 30

**1962.** 300th Anniv. of Cession of Dunkirk to France.

1566. **502.** 95 c. pur., bis. & grn. 1·25 30

**503.** Mount Valerien Memorial. **504.** Emblem and Swamp.

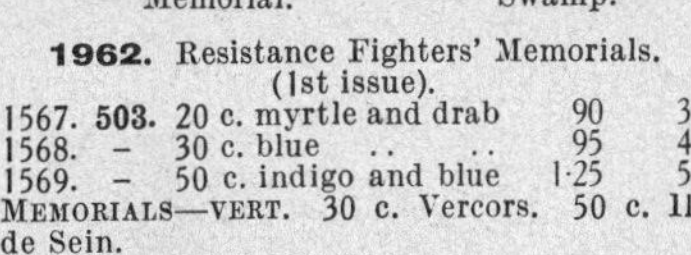

**1962.** Resistance Fighters' Memorials. (1st issue).

1567. **503.** 20 c. myrtle and drab 90 35
1568. – 30 c. blue .. .. 95 40
1569. – 50 c. indigo and blue 1·25 50

MEMORIALS—VERT. 30 c. Vercors. 50 c. Ile de Sein.

See also Nos. 1609/10.

**1962.** Malaria Eradication.

1570. **504.** 50 c. red, blue & green 30 25

**505.** Nurses and Child.

**506.** Gliders and Stork.

**1962.** National Hospitals Week.

1571. **505.** 30 c. brn., grey & grn. 15 15

**1962.** Civil and Sports Aviation.

1572. **506.** 15 c. brown and chest. 35 35
1573. – 20 c. red and purple .. 35 35

DESIGN: 20 c. Jodel Ambassadeur and early aircraft.

**507.** Emblem and School of Horology.

**508.** "Selecting a Tapestry".

**1962.** Cent. of School of Horology, Besancon.

1574. **507.** 50 c. vio., brown & red 35 35

**1962.** Tercentenary of Manufacture of Gobelin Tapestries.

1575. **508.** 50 c. turq., red & grn. 40 35

**509.** Pascal

**510.** Denis Papin (inventor).

**1962.** Death Tercent. of Pascal (philosopher).

1576. **509.** 50 c. red and green .. 55 15

**1962.** Red Cross Fund.

1577. 15 c.+5 c. sepia & turq. 2·50 2·50
1578. 20 c.+10 c. brown & red 2·50 2·50
1579. 20 c.+10 c. blue and grey 2·50 2·50
1580. 30 c.+10 c. indigo & blue 3·75 3·75
1581. 45 c.+15 c. pur. and brn. 4·50 4·50
1582. 50 c.+20 c. black & blue 4·50 4·50

DESIGNS: No. 1577, Type **510.** 1578, Edme Bouchardon (sculptor). 1579, Joseph Lakanal (politician). 1580, Gustave Charpentier (composer). 1581, Edouard Estauni (writer). 1582, Hyacinthe Vincent (scientist).

**511.** "Modern" Rose.

**512.** Europa "Tree".

**1962.** Rose Culture.

1583. **511.** 20 c. red, green & olive 65 25
1584. – 30 c. red, myrt. & olive 75 35

DESIGN: 30 c. "Old fashioned" rose.

**1962.** Europa.

1585. **512.** 25 c. violet .. .. 15 15
1586. 50 c. brown .. .. 25 20

**513.** Telecommunications Centre, Pleumeur-Bodou.

**1962.** 1st Trans-Atlantic Telecommunications Satellite Link.

1587. **513.** 25 c. buff, green & grey 20 20
1588. – 50 c. bl., grn. & indigo 35 25
1589. – 50 c. brown and blue 35 30

DESIGN: 50 c. (No. 1588), "Telstar" satellite, globe and television receiver. 50 c. (No. 1589), Radio telescope, Nancay (Cher).

**1962.** French Art. As T **491.**

1590. 50 c. multicoloured .. 4·25 2·50
1591. 65 c. multicoloured .. 3·00 1·90
1592. 1 f. multicoloured .. 6·50 3·75

PAINTINGS—HORIZ. 50 c. "Bonjour, Monsieur Courbet" (Courbet). 65 c. "Madame Manet on a Blue Sofa" (Manet). VERT. 1 f. "Officer of the Imperial Horse Guards" (Gericault).

**514.** "Rosalie Fragonard" (after Fragonard).

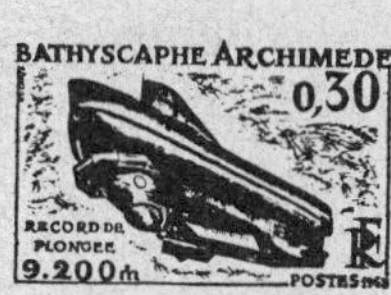

**515.** Bathyscaphe "Archimede".

**1962.** Red Cross Fund. Cross in red.

1593. **514.** 20 c.+10 c. brown .. 1·60 1·60
1594. – 25 c.+10 c. green .. 2·10 2·10

PORTRAIT: 25 c. "Child as Pierrot" (after Fragonard).

**1963.** Record Undersea Dive.

1595. **515.** 30 c. black and blue .. 25 20

**516.** Flowers and Nantes Chateau.

**1963.** Nantes Flower Show.

1596. **516.** 30 c. blue, red & green 25 25

**517.** Jacques Amyot (Bishop of Auxerre).

**1963.** Red Cross Fund.

1597 **517** 20 c.+10 c. purple, violet and grey .. 1·25 1·25
1598 – 20 c.+10 c. dp brown, brown & blue .. 1·60 1·60
1599 – 30 c.+10 c. grn & pur 1·25 1·25
1600 – 30 c.+10 c. black, green and brown .. 1·40 1·40
1601 – 50 c.+ 20 c. green, brown & blue .. 1·25 1·25
1602 – 50 c.+20 c. black, blue and brown .. 2·10 2·10

Designs: No. 1598, Etienne Mehul (composer). No. 1599 Pierre de Marivaux (dramatist). No. 1600, N.-L. Vauquelin (chemist). No. 1601, Jacques Daviel (oculist). No. 1602, Alfred de Vigny (poet).

**1963.** French Art. As T **491.**

1603. 50 c. multicoloured .. 4·50 3·25
1604. 85 c. multicoloured .. 2·50 1·40
1605. 95 c. multicoloured .. 50 50
1606. 1 f. multicoloured .. 6·50 4·50

Designs—vert. 50 c. " Jacob's Struggle with the Angel " (Delacroix). 85 c. " The Married Couple of the Eiffel Tower " (Chagall). 95 c. " The Fur Merchants " (stained glass window, Chartres Cathedral). 1 f. " St. Peter and the Miracle of the Fishes " (stained glass window, Church of St. Foy de Conches).

**518.** Roman Post Chariot.

**1963.** Stamp Day.

1607. **518.** 20 c.+5 c. purple and brown .. 25 25

**519.** Woman reaching for Campaign Emblem.

**520.** Glieres Memorial.

**1963.** Freedom from Hunger.

1608. **519.** 50 c. brown & myrtle 25 25

**1963.** Resistance Fighters' Memorials (2nd issue).

1609. **520.** 30 c. olive and brown 35 35
1610. – 50 c. black .. .. 40 40

Design: 50 c. Deportees Memorial, Ile de la Cite (Paris).

**521.** Beethoven (West Germany).

**1963.** Celebrities of European Economic Community Countries.

1611. **521.** 20 c. blue, brn. & grn. 30 30
1612. – 20 c. blk., vio. & red 30 30
1613. – 20 c. blue, pur. & olive 30 30
1614. – 20 c. brn., pur. & brn. 30 30
1615. – 30 c. sep., vio. & brn. 30 30

Portraits and views: No. 1611, Birthplace and modern Bonn). No. 1612, Emile Verhaeren (Belgium: Family grave and residence, Roisin). No. 1613, Giuseppe Mazzini (Italy: Marcus Aurelius statue and Appian Way, Rome). No. 1614, Emile Mayrisch (Luxembourg: Colpach Chateau and Steel Plant, Esch). No. 1615, Hugo de Groot (Netherlands: Palace of Peace, The Hague, and St. Agatha's Church, Delft).

## MORE DETAILED LISTS

are given in the Stanley Gibbons Catalogues referred to in the country headings.

For lists of current volumes see Introduction.

**522.** Hotel des Postes, Paris.

**523.** College Building.

**1963.** Centenary of Paris Postal Conf.

1616. **522.** 50 c. sepia .. .. 30 30

**1963.** 400th Anniv. of Louis the Great College, Paris.

1617. **523.** 30 c. myrtle .. .. 25 20

**524.** St. Peter's Church and Castle Keep, Caen.

**1963.** 36th French Philatelic Societies Federation Congress, Caen.

1618. **524.** 30 c. brown and blue 25 25

**1963.** Tourist Publicity. As T **490.** Inscr. " 1963 ".

1619. 30 c. ochre, blue & green 25 15
1620. 50 c. red, blue & turquoise 35 10
1621. 60 c. red, turquoise & blue 50 30
1622. 85 c. purple, turq. & grn. 1·75 25
1623. 95 c. black .. .. 60 20

Designs—horiz. 30 c. Amboise Chateau. 50 c. Cote d'Azur, Var. 85 c. Vittel. vert. 60 c. Saint-Flour. 95 c. Church and cloisters, Moissac.

**525.** Water-skiing.

**1963.** World Water-skiing Championships, Vichy.

1624. **525.** 30 c. blk., red & turq. 25 20

**526.** " Co-operation ".

**527.** " Child with Grapes " (Angers).

**1963.** Europa.

1625. **526.** 25 c. brown .. .. 15 15
1626. 50 c. green .. .. 25 25

**1963.** Red Cross Fund. Cross in red.

1627. **527.** 20 c.+10 c. black .. 90 90
1628. – 25 c.+10 c. green .. 90 90

Design: 25 c. " The Piper " (Manet).

**528.** " Philately ".

**1963.** " PHILATEC 1964 " Int. Stamp Exn., Paris (1st issue).

1629. **528.** 25 c. red, green & grey 15 10

See also Nos. 1640/3 and 1651.

**529.** Radio—T.V. Centre.

**1963.** Opening of Radio—T.V. Centre, Paris.

1630. **529.** 20 c. slate, olive and brown .. .. 15 15

**530.** Emblems of C.P. Services.

**531.** Paralytic at Work in Invalid Chair.

**1964.** Civil Protection.

1631. **530.** 30 c. blue, red & orge. 35 30

**1964.** Professional Rehabilitation of Paralytics.

1632. **531.** 30 c. brown, chestnut and green .. .. 20 20

**532.** 18th-century Courier.

**533.** " Deportation ".

**1964.** Stamp Day.

1633. **532.** 20 c.+5 c. myrtle .. 20 20

**1964.** 20th Anniv. of Liberation (1st issue).

1634. **533.** 20 c.+5 c. slate .. 50 50
1635. – 50 c.+5 c. green .. 70 70

Design: 50 c. " Resistance " (memorial).

See also Nos. 1652/3 and 1658.

**534.** Pres. Rene Coty.

**535.** " Blanc " 2 c. Stamp of 1900.

**1964.** Pres. Coty Commem.

1636. **534.** 30 c.+10 c. sep. & lake 25 25

**1964.** French Art. As T **491.**

1637. 1 f. multicoloured .. 2·50 1·60
1638. 1 f. multicoloured .. 1·90 1·40
1639. 1 f. multicoloured .. 75 50

Designs—vert. No. 1637, Jean le Bon (attributed to Girard of Orleans). No. 1638, Tomb plaque of Geoffrey IV (12th-century " champleve " (grooved) enamel from Limousin). No. 1639, " The Lady with the Unicorn " (15th-century tapestry).

**1964.** "PHILATEC 1964" International Stamp Exhibition, Paris (2nd issue).

1640 – 30 c. blue, black & brn 25 25
1641 **535** 25 c. purple and bistre 25 25
1642 – 25 c. blue and bistre 25 25
1643 – 30 c. red, black & blue 25 25

Designs: No. 1640, " Postal Mechanization " (letter-sorting equipment and parcel conveyor). No. 1642, " Mouchon " 25 c. stamp of 1900. No. 1643, " Telecommunications " (telephone dial, teleprinter and T.V. tower).

**1964.** 25th Anniv. of Night Airmail Service. As T **435** but additionally inscr. "25E ANNIVERSAIRE" and colours changed.

1644. **435.** 25 c. multicoloured .. 20 15

**536.** Stained Glass Window.

**537.** Calvin.

**1964.** 800th Anniv. of Notre Dame, Paris.

1645. **536.** 60 c. multicoloured .. 50 50

**1964.** 400th Death Anniv. of Calvin (reformer).

1646. **537.** 30 c.+10 c. brown, sepia and turquoise 25 25

**538.** Gallic Coin.

**539.** Pope Sylvester II.

**1964.** Pre-cancels.

1647. **538.** 10 c. brown and green 90 20
1647a. 15 c. brown & orange 30 20
1647b. 22 c. violet and green 70 30
1647c. 25 c. brown and violet 50 25
1647d. 26 c. brown & purple 50 20
1647e. 30 c. brn. & light brn. 80 20
1647f. 35 c. blue and red .. 1·90 45
1648. 45 c. brown and green 2·10 40
1648a. 50 c. brown and blue 1·25 60
1648b. 70 c. brown and blue 6·75 3·25
1649a. 90 c. brown and red .. 2·50 1·25

See note below No. 432 (1920).

For stamps as Type **538** but inscribed "FRANCE", see Nos. 2065a/l.

**1964.** Pope Sylvester II Commemoration.

1650. **539.** 30 c.+10 c. pur. & grey 30 30

**540.** Rocket and Horseman.

**1964.** " PHILATEC 1964 " Int. Stamp Exn., Paris (3rd issue).

1651. **540.** 1 f. blue, red & brown 32·00 24·00

Sold at 4 f. incl. entrance fee to Exn.

**541.** Landings in Normandy and Provence.

**1964.** 20th Anniv. of Liberation (2nd issue).

1652. **541.** 30 c.+5 c. sepia, brn. and blue .. .. 90 90
1653. – 30 c.+5 c. red, sepia and brown .. 95 95

Design: No. 1653, Taking prisoners in Paris, and tank in Strasbourg.

**1964.** Tourist Publicity. As T **490.** Inscr. " 1964 ".

1654. 40 c. brn., grn. and chest. 20 15
1655. 70 c. purple, turq. & blue 30 15
1656. 1 f. 25 myrt., blue & bistre 60 35
1657. 1 f. 30 chest., choc. & brn. 1·25 30

Designs—horiz. 40 c. 1 f. 25, Notre-Dame Chapel, Haut-Ronchamp (Haute-Saone). vert. 70 c. Caesar's Tower, Provins. 1 f. 30, Joux Chateau (Doubs).

**542.** De Gaulle's Appeal of 18th June, 1940.

**543.** Judo.

**1964.** 20th Anniv. of Liberation (3rd issue).

1658. **542.** 25 c.+5 c. black, red and blue .. .. 70 70

**1964.** Olympic Games, Tokyo.

1659. **543.** 50 c. purple and blue 20 20

**544.** G. Mandel

**545.** Soldiers departing for the Marne by Taxi-cab.

**1964.** 20th Death Anniv. of Georges Mandel (statesman).

1660. **544.** 30 c. purple .. .. 15 15

**1964.** 50th Anniv. of Victory of the Marne.
1661. **545.** 30 c. black, red & blue 25 20

**546.** Europa " Flower ". **547.** Co-operation.

**1964.** Europa.
1662. **546.** 25 c. lake, brn. & grn. 15 15
1663. 50 c. lake, grn. & vio. 25 20

**1964.** French, Africa and Malagasy Co-operation.
1664. **547.** 25 c. choc., blue & brn. 15 15

**548.** J. N. Corvisart (physician). **549.** La Rochefoucauld.

**1964.** Red Cross Fund.
1665. **548.** 20 c.+10 c. black and red .. .. 30 25
1666. – 25 c.+10 c. black and red .. .. 30 25
DESIGN: 25 c. D. Larrey (military surgeon).

**1965.** Red Cross Fund. Inscr. "1965".
1667. **549.** 30 c.+10 c. blue and brown .. 35 35
1668. – 30 c.+10 c. brown and red .. 45 45
1669. – 40 c.+10 c. slate and brown .. 50 50
1670. – 40 c.+10 c. brown, blue & chestnut 50 50
PORTRAITS: No. 1668, Nicolas Poussin (painter). No. 1669, Paul Dukas (composer). No. 1670, Charles d'Orleans.

**1965.** French Art. As T **491.**
1671. 1 f. multicoloured .. 50 50
1672. 1 f. multicoloured .. 35 35
1673. 1 f. multicoloured .. 35 35
1674. 1 f. black, rose and red .. 35 35
DESIGNS—VERT. No. 1671, " L'Anglaise du 'Star' au Havre " (Toulouse-Lautrec). No. 1673, " The Apocalypse " (14th-century tapestry). HORIZ. No. 1672, " Hunting with Falcons " (miniature from manuscript " Les Tres Riches Heures du Duc de Berry ", by the Limbourg brothers). No. 1674, " The Red Violin " (R. Dufy).

**550.** "La Guienne" (steam packet). **551.** Deportees.

**1965.** Stamp Day.
1675. **550.** 25 c.+10 c. black, green and blue .. 60 60

**1965.** 20th Anniv. of Return of Deportees.
1676. **551.** 40 c. green .. .. 45 35

**552.** Youth Club. **553.** Girl with Bouquet.

**1965.** 20th Anniv. of Youth Clubs ("Maisons des Jeunes et de la Culture").
1677. **552.** 25 c. blue, brn. & grn. 25 20

**1965.** " Welcome and Friendship " Campaign.
1678. **553.** 60 c. red, orge. & grn. 30 25

**554.** Allied Flags and Broken Swastika. **555.** I.T.U. Emblem, " Syncom ", Morse Key and Pleumeur-Bodou Centre.

**1965.** 20th Anniv. of Victory in World War II.
1679. **554.** 40 c. red, blue & black 35 30

**1965.** I.T.U. Cent.
1680. **555.** 60 c. brown, blk. & bl. 40 35

**556.** Croix de Guerre. **557.** Bourges Cathedral.

**1965.** 50th Anniv. of Croix de Guerre.
1681. **556.** 40 c. brown, red & grn. 45 35

**1965.** National Congress of Philatelic Societies, Bourges.
1682. **557.** 40 c. brown and blue 30 20

**558.** Stained Glass Window.

**1965.** 800th Anniv. of Sens Cathedral.
1683. **558.** 1 f. multicoloured .. 35 35

**1965.** Tourist Publicity. As T **490.** Inscr. "1965".
1684. 50 c. blue, green and bistre 20 15
1685. 60 c. brown and blue .. 50 20
1686. 75 c. brown, grn. & blue .. 1·00 90
1687. 95 c. brown, green & blue 7·75 90
1688. 1 f. grey, green and brown 1·40 30
DESIGNS—HORIZ. 50 c. Moustiers Ste. Marie (Basses-Alpes). 95 c. Landscape, Vendee. 1 f. Monoliths, Carnac. VERT. 60 c. Yachting, Aix-les-Bains. 75 c. Tarn gorges.

**559.** Mont Blanc from Chamonix. **560.** Europa "Sprig".

**1965.** Opening of Mont Blanc Road Tunnel.
1689. **559.** 30 c. violet, blue & plum 20 15

**1965.** Europa.
1690. **560.** 30 c. red .. .. 20 15
1691. 60 c. grey .. .. 90 75

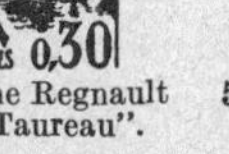

**561.** Etienne Regnault and "Le Taureau". **562.** "One Million Hectares".

**1965.** Tercent. of Colonisation of Reunion.
1692. **561.** 30 c. blue and red .. 20 20

**1965.** Reafforestation.
1693. **562.** 25 c. brn., yell. & grn. 20 15

**563.** Atomic Reactor and Emblems. **564.** Aviation School, Salon-de-Provence.

**1965.** 20th Anniv. of Atomic Energy Commission.
1694. **563.** 60 c. black and blue .. 50 40

**1965.** 30th Anniv of Aviation School.
1695 **564** 25 c. green, indigo & bl 20 15

**565.** Rocket " Diamant ".

**1965.** Launching of 1st French Satellite.
1696. **565.** 30 c. blue, turquoise and indigo .. 15 15
1697. – 60 c. blue, turquoise and indigo .. 25 25
DESIGN: 60 c. Satellite " A1 ".

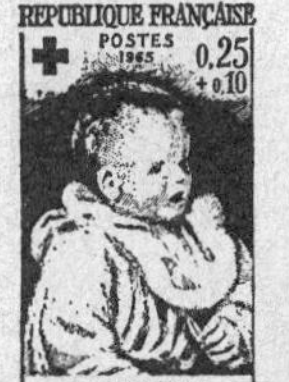

**566.** "Le Bebe a la Cuiller". **568.** St. Pierre Fourier and Basilica, Mattaincourt (Vosges).

**1965.** Red Cross Fund. Paintings by Renoir.
1698. **566.** 25 c.+10 c. blue and red .. .. 20 20
1699. – 30 c.+10 c. brown and red .. .. 25 25
DESIGN: 30 c. " Coco ecrivant " (portrait of Renoir's small son writing).

**1966.** Arms. As T **430.**
1700 5 c. red and blue .. 10 10
1701 25 c. blue and brown .. 80 15
DESIGNS: 5 c. "Auch". 25 c. "Mont-de-Marsan".

**1966.** Red Cross Fund.
1702. **568.** 30 c.+10 c. sepia and green .. .. 35 35
1703. – 30 c.+10 c. purple and green .. .. 35 35
1704. – 30 c.+10 c. blue, brn. and green .. .. 35 35
1705. – 30 c.+10 c. bl. & brn. 35 35
1706. – 30 c.+10 c. brown and green .. .. 35 35
1707. – 30 c.+10 c. black and brown .. .. 35 35
DESIGNS: No. 1703, F. Mansart (architect) and Carnavalet House, Paris. No. 1704, M. Proust (writer) and St. Hilaire Bridge, Illiers (Eure-et-Loir). No. 1705, G. Faure (composer), statuary and music. No. 1706, Hippolyte Taine (philosopher) and birthplace. No. 1707, Elie Metchnikoff (scientist), microscope and Pasteur Institute.

**569.** Satellite " D1 ".

**1966.** Launching of Satellite " D1 ".
1708. **569.** 60 c. red, blue & grn. 20 20

**570.** Engraving a die. **571.** Knight and Chessboard.

**1966.** Stamp Day.
1709. **570.** 25 c.+10 c. choc., slate and brown 30 30

**1966.** French Art. As T **491.**
1710. 1 f. bronze, green & purple 35 35
1711. 1 f. multicoloured .. 35 35
1712. 1 f. multicoloured .. 35 35
1713. 1 f. multicoloured .. 35 35
1714. 1 f. multicoloured .. 35 35
DESIGN—HORIZ. No. 1710, Detail of Vix Crater (wine-bowl). No. 1711, " The New-born Child " (G. de la Tour). No. 1712, " Baptism of Judas " (stained glass window, Sainte Chapelle, Paris). No. 1714, " Crispin and Scapin " (after H. Daumier). VERT. No. 1713, " The Moon and the Bull " (Lurcat tapestry).

**1966.** Int. Chess Festival, Le Havre.
1715. **571.** 60 c. grey, brn. & vio. 45 15

**572.** Pont St. Esprit Bridge. **573.** St. Michel.

**1966.** 700th Anniv. of Pont St. Esprit.
1716. **572.** 25 c. black and blue .. 15 15

**1966.** Millenary of Mont St. Michel.
1717. **573.** 25 c. multicoloured .. 20 15

**574.** King Stanislas, Arms and Palace.

**1966.** Bicentenary of Reunion of Lorraine and Barrois with France.
1718. **574.** 25 c. brn., grn. & blue 15 15

**575.** Niort. **576.** "Angel of Verdun".

**1966.** National Congress of Philatelic Societies, Niort.
1719. **575.** 40 c. slate, green & blue 20 20

**1966.** 50th Anniv. of Verdun Victory.
1720. **576.** 30 c.+5 c. slate, blue and green .. .. 20 20

**577.** Fontenelle.

**1966.** Tercent. of Academy of Sciences.
1721. **577.** 60 c. brown and lake 25 25

**578.** William the Conqueror, Castle and Landings.

**1966.** 900th Anniv. of Battle of Hastings.
1722. **578.** 60 c. brown and blue 30 30

**579.** Globe and Railway Track.

**1966.** 19th Int. Railway Congress, Paris.
1723. **579.** 60 c. brown, blue & lake 80 45

**580.** Oleron Bridge. **581.** Europa "Ship".

**1966.** Opening of Oleron Bridge.
1724. **580.** 25 c. brn., grn. & bl. 15 15

**1966.** Europa.
1725. **581.** 30 c. blue .. .. 15 15
1726. 60 c. red .. .. 65 30

**582.** Vercingetorix.

**1966.** History of France (1st series). Inscr. "1966".
1727. **582.** 40 c. brn., blue & grn. 25 25
1728. – 40 c. brown and black 25 25
1729. – 60 c. red, brn. & violet 25 30
DESIGNS—VERT. 40 c. (No. 1728), Clovis. 60 c. Charlemagne.
See also Nos. 1769/71, 1809/11, 1850/2, 1896/8, 1922/4, 1975/7 and 2017/19.

**583.** Route Map. **584.** Chateau de Val.

**1966.** Centenary of Paris Pneumatic Post.
1730. **583.** 1 f. 60 blue, lake & brn. 90 65

**1966.** Chateau de Val.
1731. **584.** 2 f. 30 brn., grn. & bl. 3·00 20

**585.** Rance Barrage. **586.** Nurse tending wounded soldier (1859).

**1966.** Inauguration of Rance River Tidal Power Station.
1732. **585.** 60 c. slate, grn. & brn. 40 40

**1966.** Red Cross Fund. Cross in red.
1733. **586.** 25 c.+10 c. green .. 30 30
1734. – 30 c.+10 c. blue .. 30 30
DESIGN: 30 c. Nurse tending young girl (1966).

**1966.** Arms. As T **430**. Multicoloured.
1735 20 c. "Saint-Lo" .. 15 10

**588.** Beaumarchais (playwright). **589.** Congress Emblem.

**1967.** Red Cross Fund.
1736. **588.** 30 c.+10 c. violet and lake .. .. 35 35
1737. – 30 c.+10 c. bl. & ind. 50 40
1738. – 30 c.+10 c. pur. & brn. 35 35
1739. – 30 c.+10 c. vio. & bl. 25 25
PORTRAITS: No. 1737, Emile Zola (writer). No. 1738, A. Camus (writer). No. 1739, St. Francois de Sales (reformer).

**1967.** 3rd Int. Congress of European Broadcasting Union (U.E.R.).
1740. **589.** 40 c. red and blue .. 20 20

**590.** Postman of the Second Empire. **591.** Winter Olympics Emblem.

**1967.** Stamp Day.
1741. **590.** 25 c.+10 c. green, red and blue .. 25 25

**1967.** French Art. As T **491**.
1742. 1 f. multicoloured .. 45 20
1743. 1 f. multicoloured .. 45 20
1744. 1 f. brown, blue and black 40 40
1745. 1 f. multicoloured .. 40 40
DESIGNS—HORIZ. No. 1742, "Old Juniet's Trap" (after H. Rousseau). No. 1745, "The Window-makers" (stained glass window, St. Madeleine's Church, Troyes). VERT. No. 1743, "Francois I" (after Jean Clouet). No. 1744, "The Bather" (Ingres).

**1967.** Publicity for Winter Olympic Games, Grenoble (1968).
1746. **591.** 60 c. red, light blue and blue .. .. 30 30

**592.** French Pavilion. **593.** Cogwheels.

**1967.** World Fair, Montreal.
1747. **592.** 60 c. green and blue 25 20

**1967.** Europa.
1748. **593.** 30 c. blue and grey .. 20 15
1749. 60 c. brown and blue 75 65

**594.** Nungesser, Coli and L'Oiseau Blanc".

**1967.** 40th Anniv. of Trans-Atlantic Flight Attempt by Nungesser and Coli.
1750. **594.** 40 c. blue, brn. & pur. 50 25

**595.** Great Bridge, Bordeaux. **596.** Gouin Mansion, Tours.

**1967.** Inaug. of Great Bridge, Bordeaux.
1751. **595.** 25 c. black, olive & brn. 20 15

**1967.** National Congress of Philatelic Societies, Tours.
1752. **596.** 40 c. brown, blue & red 50 30

**597.** Gaston Ramon (vaccine pioneer) and College Gates.

**1967.** Bicent. of Alfort Veterinary School.
1753. **597.** 25 c. brown, grn. & bl. 15 10

**598.** Esnault-Pelterie, Rocket and Satellite.

**1967.** 10th Death Anniv. of Robert Esnault-Pelterie (rocket pioneer).
1754. **598.** 60 c. indigo and blue 45 30

**1967.** Tourist Publicity. As T **490**. Inscr "1967".
1755 50 c. brown, dp blue & bl 30 10
1756 60 c. brown, dp blue & bl 50 20
1757 70 c. brown, blue and red 30 10
1758 75 c. blue, red and brown 3·00 1·10
1759 95 c. violet, green & blue 1·60 1·00
1760 1 f. blue .. .. .. 70 10
1761 1 f. 50 red, blue and green 1·40 25
DESIGNS—VERT. 50 c. Town Hall, St. Quentin (Aisne). 60 c. Clock-tower and gateway, Vire (Calvados). 1 f. Rodez Cathedral. 1 f. 50, Morlaix—views and carved buttress. HORIZ. 70 c. St. Germain-en-Laye Chateau. 75 c. La Baule. 95 c. Boulogne-sur-Mer.

**599.** Orchids. **600.** Scales of Justice.

**1967.** Orleans Flower Show.
1762. **599.** 40 c. red, pur. & violet 1·00 60

**1967.** 9th Int. Accountancy Congress, Paris.
1763. **600.** 60 c. brn., blue & pur. 70 25

**601.** Servicemen and Cross of Lorraine. **602.** Marie Curie and Pitchblende.

**1967.** 25th Anniv. of Battle of Bir-Hakeim.
1764. **601.** 25 c. ult., blue & brn. 15 15

**1967.** Birth Cent. of Marie Curie.
1765. **602.** 60 c. ultramarine & bl. 30 30

**603.** Lions Emblem. **604.** "Republique".

**1967.** 50th Anniv. of Lions Int.
1766. **603.** 40 c. violet and lake 1·40 55

**1967.**
1767. **604.** 25 c. blue .. .. 40 20
1768. 30 c. purple .. .. 45 10
1843. 30 c. green .. .. 20 10
1768b. 40 c. red .. .. 40 10
See also No. 1882.

**1967.** History of France (2nd series). As T **582**, but inscr. "1967".
1769. 40 c. ultram., slate & blue 25 10
1770. 40 c. black and slate .. 25 15
1771. 60 c. green and brown .. 40 20
DESIGNS—HORIZ. No. 1769, Hugues Capet elected King of France. VERT. No. 1770, Philippe-Auguste at Bouvines. 1771, Saint-Louis receiving poor.

**605.** "Flautist". **606.** Anniversary Medal.

**1967.** Red Cross Fund. Ivories in Dieppe Museum. Cross in red.
1772 **605** 25 c.+10 c. brown and violet .. .. 40 40
1773 – 30 c.+10 c. brown and green .. .. 40 40
DESIGN: 30 c. "Violinist".

**1968.** 50th Anniv. of Postal Cheques Service.
1774. **606.** 40 c. bistre and green 10 10

**607.** Cross-country Skiing and Ski Jumping. **608.** Road Signs.

**1968.** Winter Olympic Games, Grenoble.
1775 30 c.+10 c. brown, grey and red .. .. 25 25
1776 40 c.+10 c. purple, bistre and deep purple .. 35 35
1777 60 c.+20 c. red, purple and green .. .. 45 45
1778 75 c.+25 c. brown, green and purple .. .. 55 55
1779 95 c.+35 c. brown, mauve and blue .. .. 60 60
DESIGNS: 30 c. Type **607**. 40 c. Ice hockey. 60 c. Olympic flame. 75 c. Figure skating. 95 c. Slalom.

**1968.** Road Safety.
1780. **608.** 25 c. red, blue and purple .. .. 20 15

**609.** Rural Postman of 1830. **610.** F. Couperin (composer) and Concert Instruments.

**1968.** Stamp Day.
1781. **609.** 25 c.+10 c. indigo, blue and red .. 20 20

**1968.** Red Cross Fund. Inscr. "1968"
1782. **610.** 30 c.+10 c. lilac and violet .. .. 25 25
1783. – 30 c.+10 c. brown and green .. .. 25 25
1784. – 30 c.+10 c. red and brown .. .. 25 25
1785. – 30 c.+10 c. purple and lilac .. .. 25 25
DESIGN: No. 1783, General Desaix, and death scene at Marengo. No. 1784, Saint Pol-Roux (poet) and "Evocation of Golgotha". No. 1785, Paul Claudel (poet) and "Joan of Arc".

**1968.** French Art. As T **491**.
1786. 1 f. multicoloured .. 40 20
1787. 1 f. multicoloured .. 95 30
1788. 1 f. olive and red .. 75 30
1789. 1 f. multicoloured .. 1·25 30
DESIGNS—HORIZ. No. 1786, Wall painting, Lascaux. No. 1787, "Arearea" (Gauguin). VERT. No. 1788, "La Danse" (relief by Bourdelle in Champs-Elysees Theatre, Paris). No. 1789, "Portrait of a Model" (Renoir).

**611.** Congress Palace, Royan.

**1968.** World Co-operation Languages Conf., Royan.
1790. **611.** 40 c. blue, brn. & grn. 25 25

**612.** Europa "Key". **613.** Alain R. Le Sage.

**1968.** Europa.
1791. **612.** 30 c. brown and purple 25 15
1792. 60 c. red and brown .. 1·00 60

**1968.** 300th Birth Anniv. of Le Sage (writer).
1793. **613.** 40 c. purple and blue 20 20

**1968.** Tourist Publicity. As T **490**, but inscr. "1968".
1794. 60 c. blue, purple & green 75 50
DESIGN—HORIZ. 60 c. Langeais Chateau.

**614.** Pierre Larousse (encyclopedist). **615.** Forest Trees.

**1968.** Larousse Commem.
1795. **614.** 40 c. brown & violet 25 25

**1968.** Link of Black and Rambouillet Forests.
1796. **615.** 25 c. brn., grn. & blue 50 25

**616.** Presentation of the Keys, and Map.

**1968.** 650th Anniv. of Papal Enclave, Valreas.
1797. **616.** 60 c. vio., bistre & brn. 40 30

**617.** Louis XIV, and Arms of Flanders and France.

**1968.** 300th Anniv. of (First) Treaty of Aix-la-Chapelle.
1798. **617.** 40 c. lake, bistre & grey 20 15

**618.** Martrou Bridge, Rochefort.

**1968.** Inaug. of Martrou Bridge.
1799. **618.** 25 c. blk., brn. & blue 20 20

**619.** Letord Lorraine Bomber and Route Map. **620.** Tower of Constance, Aigues-Mortes.

**1968.** 50th Anniv. of 1st Regular Internal Airmail Service.
1800. **619.** 25 c. indigo, blue & red 45 25

**1968.** Bicent. of Release of Huguenot Prisoners.
1801. **620.** 25 c. pur., brn. & blue 20 20

**621.** Cathedral and Old Bridge, Beziers.

**1968.** National Congress of Philatelic Societies, Beziers.
1802. **621.** 40 c. ochre, grn. & bl. 1·10 20

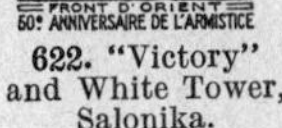

**622.** "Victory" and White Tower, Salonika. **623.** Louis XV and Arms of Corsica and France.

**1968.** 50th Anniv. of Armistice on Salonika Front.
1803. **622.** 40 c. pur. & bright pur. 20 15

**1968.** Bicent. of Union of Corsica and France.
1804. **623.** 25 c. bl., grn. & blk. 15 15

**624.** Relay-racing. **626.** "Ball of the Little White Beds" (opera) and Bailby.

**625.** Polar Landscape.

**1968.** Olympic Games, Mexico.
1805. **624.** 40 c. bl., grn. & brn 40 30

**1968.** French Polar Exploration.
1806. **625.** 40 c. turq., red & blue 30 25

**1968.** 50th Anniv. of "Little White Beds" Children's Hospital Charity.
1807. **626.** 40 c. lake, orge. & brn. 20 15

**627.** "Angel of Victory" over Arc de Triomphe. **628.** "Spring".

**1968.** 50th Anniv. of Armistice on Western Front.
1808. **627.** 25 c. blue and red .. 15 15

**1968.** History of France (3rd series). Designs as T **582**, but inscr. "1968".
1809. 40 c. grn., grey & red .. 25 20
1810. 40 c. blue, grn. & brown 25 20
1811. 60 c. brown, blue & ultram. 50 20
DESIGN—HORIZ. No. 1809, Philip the Good presiding over States-General. VERT. No. 1810, Death of Du Guesclin. 1811, Joan of Arc.

**1968.** Red Cross Fund. Cross in red.
1812. **628.** 25 c. + 10 c. blue and violet .. .. 30 30
1813. – 30 c. + 10 c. red and brown .. .. 30 30
DESIGN: 30 c. "Autumn".
See also Nos. 1853/4.

**1969.** Tourist Publicity. Similar to T **490** but inscr "1969".
1814 45 c. green, brown & blue 25 10
1815 70 c. brown, indigo & blue 40 20
1816 80 c. brown, purple & bis 40 10
1817 85 c. grey, blue and green 1·25 1·10
1818 1 f. 15 lt brown, brn & bl 1·40 75
DESIGNS—HORIZ. 45 c. Brou Church, Bourg-en-Bresse (Ain). 70 c. Hautefort Chateau. 80 f. Vouglans Dam, Jura. 85 f. Chantilly Chateau. 1 f. 15, La Trinite-sur-Mer, Morbihan.

**1969.** French Art. As T **491**.
1819. 1 f. brown and black .. 45 20
1820. 1 f. multicoloured .. 45 20
1821. 1 f. multicoloured .. 45 20
1822. 1 f. multicoloured .. 1·25 65
DESIGNS—VERT. No. 1819, "February" (bas-relief, Amiens Cathedral). No. 1820, "Philippe le Bon" (Rogier de la Pasture, called Van der Weyden). No. 1822, "The Circus" (Georges Seurat). HORIZ. No. 1821, "Savin and Cyprien appearing before Ladicius" (Romanesque painting, Church of St. Savin, Vienne).

**629.** Concorde in Flight.

**1969.** Air. 1st Flight of Concorde.
1823 **629** 1 f. indigo and blue .. 1·25 15

**HAVE YOU READ THE NOTES AT THE BEGINNING OF THIS CATALOGUE?**
These often provide answers to the enquiries we receive.

**630.** Postal Horse-bus of 1890.

**1969.** Stamp Day.
1824. **630.** 30 c. + 10 c. green, brown and black 20 20

**631.** A. Roussel (composer). **632.** Irises.

**1969.** Red Cross Fund. Celebrities.
1825. **631.** 50 c. + 10 c. blue .. 45 45
1826. – 50 c. + 10 c. red .. 45 45
1827. – 50 c. + 10 c. grey .. 45 45
1828. – 50 c. + 10 c. brown .. 45 45
1829. – 50 c. + 10 c. purple .. 45 45
1830. – 50 c. + 10 c. green .. 45 45
PORTRAITS: No. 1826, General Marceau. No. 1827, C. A. Sainte-Beuve (writer). No. 1828, Marshal Lannes. No. 1829, G. Cuvier (anatomist and naturalist). No. 1830, A. Gide (writer).

**1969.** Int. Flower Show, Paris.
1831. **632.** 45 c. multicoloured .. 30 30

**633.** Colonnade.

**1969.** Europa.
1832. **633.** 40 c. mauve .. .. 20 15
1833. 70 c. blue .. .. 30 20

**634.** Battle of the Garigliano (Italy).

**1969.** 25th Anniv. of "Resistance and Liberation".
1834 **634** 45 c. black and violet 30 30
1835 – 45 c. ultram, bl & grey 1·25 40
1836 – 45 c. grey, blue & grn 1·25 30
1837 – 45 c. brown and grey 1·25 40
1838 – 45 c. indigo, bl & red 1·25 40
1839 – 45 c. + 10 c. grn & grey 1·10 1·10
1840 – 70 c. + 10 c. green, purple and brown 3·00 2·50
DESIGNS—VERT. No. 1835, Parachutists and Commandos ("D-Day Landings"). 1836, Memorial and Resistance fighters (Battle of Mont Mouchet). HORIZ. No. 1837, Troops storming beach (Provence Landings). 1838, French pilot, Soviet mechanic and Yakovlev Yak-9 fighter aircraft (Normandy-Niemen Squadron). 1839, General Leclerc, troops and Les Invalides (Liberation of Paris). 1840, As No. 1839 but showing Strasbourg Cathedral (Liberation of Strasbourg).

**635.** "Miners" (I.L.O. Monument, Geneva) and Albert Thomas (founder). **636.** Chalons-sur-Marne.

**1969.** 50th Anniv of I.L.O.
1841 **635** 70 c. brown, blue and deep brown .. 35 30

**1969.** National Congress of Philatelic Societies, Chalons-sur-Marne.
1842. **636.** 45 c. ochre, blue & grn. 45 25

**637.** Canoeing. **639.** "Diamond Crystal" in Rain Drop.

**638.** Napoleon as Young Officer, and Birthplace.

**1969.** World Kayak-Canoeing Championships, Bourg-St. Maurice.
1844. **637.** 70 c. brown, olive & bl. 35 25

**1969.** Birth Bicent. of Napoleon Bonaparte.
1845. **638.** 70 c. grn., violet & blue 40 25

**1969.** European Water Charter.
1846. **639.** 70 c. black, grn. & bl. 45 30

**640.** Mouflon. **641.** Aerial View of College.

**1969.** Nature Conservation.
1847. **640.** 45 c. black, brn. & grn. 1·00 1·00

**1969.** College of Arts and Manufactures, Chatenay-Malabry.
1848 **641** 70 c. green, orange and deep green .. 35 30

**642.** "Le Redoutable".

**1969.** 1st French Nuclear Submarine "Le Redoutable".
1849 **642** 70 c. green, emerald and blue .. .. 30 20

**1969.** History of France (4th series). As T **582** but inscr "1969".
1850 80 c. bistre, brown & grn 40 25
1851 80 c. brown, black and light brown .. .. 40 25
1852 80 c. blue, black & violet 60 25
DESIGNS—HORIZ. No. 1850, Louis XI and Charles the Bold. 1852, Henry IV and Edict of Nantes. VERT. No. 1851, Bayard at the Battle of Brescia.

**1969.** Red Cross Fund. Paintings by N. Mignard. As T **628**. Cross in red.
1853 40 c. + 15 c. brown & choc 35 35
1854 40 c. + 15 c. blue & violet 35 35
DESIGNS: No. 1853, "Summer". 1854, "Winter".

**643.** Gerbault aboard "Firecrest".

**1970.** Alain Gerbault's World Voyage, 1923–29.
1855 **643** 70 c. indigo, grey & bl 55 30

**644.** Gendarmerie Badge and Activities.

**1970.** National Gendarmerie.
1856. **644.** 45 c. blue, grn. & brown 1·90 40

**645.** L. Le Vau (architect). **646.** Handball Player.

**1970.** Red Cross Fund.
1857. **645.** 40 c.+10 c. lake .. 45 45
1858. – 40 c.+10 c. blue .. 45 45
1859. – 40 c.+10 c. green .. 45 45
1860. – 40 c.+10 c. brown .. 45 45
1861. – 40 c.+10 c. slate .. 45 45
1862. – 40 c.+10 c. blue .. 45 45
DESIGNS: No. 1858, Prosper Merimee (writer). 1859, Philbert de l'Orme (architect). 1860, Edouard Branly (scientist). 1861, Maurice de Broglie (physicist). 1862, Alexandre Dumas (pere) (writer).

**1970.** 7th World Handball Championship.
1863. **646.** 80 c. green .. .. 40 30

**647.** Marshal Alphonse Juin and Les Invalides, Paris.

**1970.** Marshal Juin Commem.
1864. **647.** 45 c. brown & blue .. 30 20

**648.** Hovertrain "Orleans" 1–80. **649.** Postman of 1830 and Paris Scene.

**1970.** 1st "Hovertrain" in Service.
1865. **648.** 80 c. drab and violet 55 35

**1970.** Stamp Day.
1866. **649.** 40 c.+10 c. black, blue and red .. 30 30

**650.** P.-J. Pelletier and J. B. Caventou with Formula.

**1970.** 150th Anniv. of Discovery of Quinine.
1870. **650.** 50 c. grn., mve. & blue 30 20

**651.** Greater Flamingo. **652.** Rocket and Dish Aerial.

**1970.** Nature Conservation Year.
1871. **651.** 45 c. mve., slate & grn. 40 20

**1970.** Launching of "Diamant B" Rocket from Guyana.
1872. **652.** 45 c. green .. .. 75 30

**653.** "Health and Sickness". **654.** "Flaming Sun".

**1970.** W.H.O. "Fight Cancer" Day (7th April).
1873. **653.** 40 c.+10 c. mauve, brown and blue .. 25 20

**1970.** Europa.
1874. **654.** 40 c. red .. .. 20 15
1875. 80 c. blue .. .. 35 25

**655.** Marshal de Lattre de Tassigny and Armistice Meeting.

**1970.** 25th Anniv. of Berlin Armistice.
1876. **655.** 40 c.+10 c. blue and turquoise .. .. 70 60

**1970.** French Art. As T **491.**
1877. 1 f. multicoloured .. 45 30
1878. 1 f. chestnut .. .. 60 30
1879. 1 f. multicoloured .. 1·50 40
1880. 1 f. multicoloured .. 1·25 40
DESIGNS—VERT. No. 1877, 15-cent. Savoy Primitive painting on wood. No. 1880, "The Ballet-dancer" (Degas). HORIZ. No. 1878, "The Triumph of Flora" (sculpture by J. B. Carpeaux). No. 1879, "Diana's Return from the Hunt" (F. Boucher).

**656.** Arms of Lens, Miner's Lamp and Pithead.

**1970.** 43rd French Federation of Philatelic Societies Congress, Lens.
1881. **656.** 40 c. red .. .. 20 15

**657.** "Republique" and Perigueux. **658.** Javelin-thrower in Wheel-chair.

**1970.** Transfer of French Govt. Printing Works to Perigueux.
1882. **657.** 40 c. red .. .. 40 25
The above stamp and label which together comprise No. 1882 were issued together se-tenant in sheets for which special printing plates were laid down. The stamp is virtually indistinguishable from the normal 40 c. definitive, No. 1768b.

**1970. Tourist Publicity. As T 490, but inscr. "1970".**
1883. 50 c. purple, blue & green 30 10
1884. 95 c. brown, red and olive 1·90 90
1885. 1 f. green, blue and red .. 40 10
DESIGNS: 50 c. Diamond Rock, Martinique. 95 c. Chancelade Abbey (Dordogne). 1 f. Gosier Island, Guadeloupe.

**1970.** World Games for the Physically Handicapped, St-Etienne.
1886. **658.** 45 c. red, grn. & blue 40 25

**659.** Hand and Broken Chain. **660.** Observatory and Nebula.

**1970.** 25th Anniv. of Liberation from Concentration Camps.
1887. **659.** 45 c. brown, ultra-marine and blue .. 35 20

**1970.** Haute-Provence Observatory.
1888. **660.** 1 f. 30 vio., bl. & grn. 3·00 1·00

**661.** Pole Vaulting. **663.** Bath-House, Arc-et-Senans (Doubs).

**662.** Didier Daurat, Raymond Vanier and Douglas DC-4.

**1970.** First European Junior Athletic Championships. Paris.
1889. **661.** 45 c. indigo, blue & pur. 35 25

**1970.** Air. Pioneer Aviators.
1890. **662.** 5 f. brn., grn. & blue 2·50 10
1891. – 10 f. grey, vio. & red 5·25 20
1892. – 15 f. grey, mve. & brn. 7·75 50
1893. – 20 f. indigo and blue 10·00 55
DESIGNS: 10 f. Helene Boucher, Maryse Hilsz and De Havilland Gipsy Moth and Caudron aircraft. 15 f. Henri Guillaumet, Paul Cordes, "Lieutenant de Vaisseau Paris" (flying boat) and wreck of Potez 25A2 airplane. 20 f. Jean Mermoz, Antoine de Saint-Exupery and Concorde airplane.

**1970.** Royal Salt Springs, Chaux (founded by N. Ledoux).
1895. **663.** 80 c. brn., grn. & bl. 1·75 65

**1970.** History of France (5th series). As T **582**, but inscr. "1970".
1896. 45 c. mauve, grey & black 90 55
1897. 45 c. brown, green & yell. 90 55
1898. 45 c. grey, brn. & orange 1·10 75
DESIGNS: No. 1896, Richelieu and siege of La Rochelle, 1628. 1897, King Louis XIV. 1898, King Louis XV at Battle of Fontenoy (after painting by H. Vernet).

**664.** U.N. Emblem, New York Headquarters and Palais des Nations, Geneva.

**1970.** 25th Anniv. of United Nations.
1899. **664.** 80 c. vio., grn. & blue 35 25

**665.** Bordeaux and "Ceres" Stamp.

**1970.** Centenary of Bordeaux "Ceres" Stamp Issue.
1900. **665.** 80 c. violet and blue 35 25

**666.** Col. Denfert-Rochereau and "Lion of Belfort" (after Bartholdi).

**1970.** Centenary of Belfort Siege.
1901. **666.** 45 c. blue, brn. & grn. 30 20

**667.** "Lord and Lady" (circa 1500.) **668.** "Marianne."

**1970.** Red Cross Fund. Frescoes from Dissay Chapel, Vienne. Cross in red.
1902. **667.** 40 c.+15 c. green .. 65 60
1903. – 40 c.+15 c. red .. 65 60
DESIGN: No. 1903, "Angel with instruments of mortification".

**1971.**
1904 **668** 45 c. blue .. .. 30 10
1905 50 c. red .. .. 35 10
1904ap 60 c. green .. 90 10
1905bp 80 c. red .. 50 10
1904b 80 c. green .. 35 10
1905d 1 f. red .. .. 40 10

**669.** Balloon "Ville d'Orleans" leaving Paris. **670.** Ice Skaters.

**1971.** Air. Cent. of Paris Balloon Post.
1907. **669.** 95 c. multicoloured .. 90 60

**1971. French Art. As T 491.**
1908. 1 f. brown .. .. 90 40
1909. 1 f. multicoloured .. 90 40
1910. 1 f. multicoloured .. 60 40
DESIGNS: No. 1908, "St. Matthew" (sculpture, Strasbourg Cathedral). No. 1909, "The Winnower" (Millet). No. 1910, "Songe Creux" (G. Rouault).

**1971.** World Ice Skating Championships, Lyon.
1911 **670** 80 c. ultramarine, blue and indigo .. 50 40

**671.** Diver and Bathysphere. **672.** General D. Brosset and Fourviere Basilica, Lyon.

**1971.** "Oceanexpo" Exhibition, Bordeaux.
1912. **671.** 80 c. turq. & blue .. 40 25

**1971.** Red Cross Fund. Celebrities.
1913. **672.** 50 c.+10 c. brn. & grn. 80 80
1914. – 50 c.+10 c. brn. & choc 80 80
1915. – 50 c.+10 c. brn. & red 80 80
1916. – 50 c.+10 c. lilac & bl. 80 80
1917. – 50 c.+10 c. pur. & plum 90 90
1918. – 50 c.+10 c. bl. & indigo 90 90
DESIGNS: No. 1914, Esprit Auber (composer) and manuscript of "Fra Diavolo". 1915, Victor Grignard (chemist) and Nobel Prize for Chemistry. 1916, Henri Farman (aviation pioneer) and Farman Voisin No. 1 bis (airplane). 1917, General C. Delestraint (Resistance leader) and "Secret Army" proclamation. 1918, J. Robert-Houdin (magician) and levitation act.

**673.** Field Post Office, World War I.

**1971.** Stamp Day.
1919. **673.** 50 c. + 10 c. blue, brown and bistre 35 30

674. Barque "Antoinette".

**1971.** French Sailing Ships.
1920 674 80 c. violet, indigo & bl 1·25 60
See also Nos. 1967, 2011 and 2100.

675. Chamois. 676. Basilica of Santa Maria, Venice.

**1971.** Inauguration of Western Pyrenees National Park.
1921. 675. 65 c. brn., bl. & choc. 60 25

**1971.** History of France (Sixth series). As T 582 but inscr. "1971".
1922. 45 c. purple, blue & red 55 25
1923. 45 c. red, brown & blue.. 55 25
1924. 65 c. brn., purple & blue.. 1·25 40
DESIGNS: No. 1922, Cardinal, noble and commoner (Opening of the States-General, 1789). No. 1923, Battle of Valmy, 1792. No. 1924, Fall of the Bastille, 1789.

**1971.** Europa.
1925. 676. 50 c. brown and blue 30 10
1926. – 80 c. purple .. .. 40 15
DESIGN: 80 c. Europa chain.

677. View of Grenoble. 678. A.F.R. Emblem and Town.

**1971.** 44th French Federation of Philatelic Societies Congress, Grenoble.
1927. 677. 50c. red, pink & brown 25 10

**1971.** 25th Anniv. (1970) of Rural Family Aid.
1928. 678. 40 c. blue, vio. & green 20 15

**1971.** Tourist Publicity. As T 490, but inscr. "1971".
1929. 60 c. black, blue & green 30 10
1930. 65 c. blk., violet & brown 55 10
1931. 90 c. brown, green & ochre 40 10
1932. 1 f. 10 brown, blue & grn. 50 30
1933 1 f. 40 pur., blue & green 60 10
DESIGNS—VERT. 60 c. Sainte Chapelle, Riom. 65 c. Church and fountain, Dole. 90 c. Gate-tower and houses, Riquewihr. 1 f. 40, Ardeche gorges. HORIZ. 1 f. 10, Fortress, Sedan.

679. Bourbon Palace, Paris.

**1971.** 59th Interparliamentary Union Conference, Paris.
1934 679 90 c. blue .. .. 1·10 30

680. Embroidery and Instrument-making.

**1971.** 40th Anniv. of 1st Meeting of Crafts Guilds Assn.
1935. 680. 90 c. purple and red.. 50 25

681. Reunion Chameleon. 682. De Gaulle in Uniform (June 1940).

**1971.** Nature Conservation.
1936. 681. 60 c. grn., brn. & yell. 1·25 75

**1971.** 1st Death Anniv of General Charles de Gaulle.
1937. 682. 50 c. black .. .. 1·40 75
1938. – 50 c. blue .. .. 1·40 75
1939. – 50 c. red .. .. 1·40 75
1940. – 50 c. black .. .. 1·40 75
DESIGNS: No. 1938, De Gaulle at Brazzaville, 1944. No. 1939, Liberation of Paris, 1944. No. 1940, De Gaulle as President of the French Republic, 1970.

683. Baron Portal (1st President) and First Assembly.

**1971.** 150th Anniv. of National Academy of Medicine.
1941. 683. 45 c. plum and purple 25 20

684. "Young Girl with Little Dog". 685. King Penguin, Map and Antarctic Exploration Ship.

**1971.** Red Cross Fund. Paintings by J.-B. Greuze. Cross in red.
1942 684 30 c.+10 c. blue .. 55 55
1943 – 50 c.+10 c. red .. 55 55
DESIGN: No. 1943. "The Dead Bird".

**1972.** French Art. As T 491. Multicoloured.
1944. 1 f. "L'Etude" (portrait of a young girl) (Fragonard) .. .. 75 40
1945. 1 f. "Women in a Garden" (Monet) .. .. 2·50 40
1946. 2 f. "St. Peter presenting Pierre de Bourbon" (Master of Moulins) .. 2·50 1·25
1947. 2 f. "The Barges" (A. Derain).. .. 3·75 1·50
No. 1947 is horiz. the rest are vert.

**1972.** Bicentenary of Discovery of Crozet Islands and Kerguelen (French Southern and Antarctic Territories).
1948. 685. 90 c. black, blue and orange .. .. 80 40

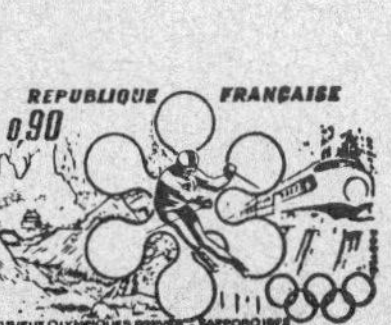
686. Skier and Emblem 687. Aristide Berges (hydro-electric engineer).

**1972.** Winter Olympic Games, Sapporo, Japan.
1949. 686. 90 c. red and deep olive 50 25

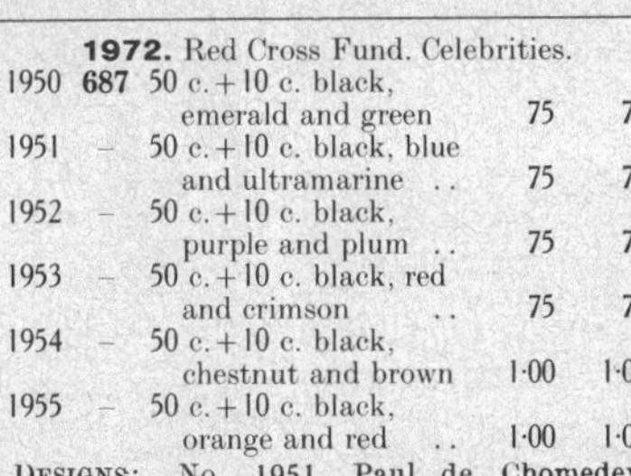

**1972.** Red Cross Fund. Celebrities.
1950 687 50 c.+10 c. black, emerald and green 75 75
1951 – 50 c.+10 c. black, blue and ultramarine .. 75 75
1952 – 50 c.+10 c. black, purple and plum .. 75 75
1953 – 50 c.+10 c. black, red and crimson .. 75 75
1954 – 50 c.+10 c. black, chestnut and brown 1·00 1·00
1955 – 50 c.+10 c. black, orange and red .. 1·00 1·00
DESIGNS: No. 1951, Paul de Chomedey, Sieur de Maisonneuve (founder of Montreal). No. 1952, Edouard Belin (communications scientist). No. 1953, Louis Bleriot (pioneer airman). No. 1954, Theophile Gautier (writer). No. 1955, Admiral Francois de Grasse.

688. Rural Postman of 1894. 689. Heart and W.H.O. Emblems.

**1972.** Stamp Day.
1956. 688. 50 c.+10 c. blue, drab and yellow .. 1·00 70

**1972.** World Heart Month.
1957. 689. 45 c. red, orge & slate 30 30

**1972.** Tourist Publicity. As Type 490, but inscr "1972".
1958 1 f. brown and yellow .. 50 20
1959 1 f. 20 blue and brown .. 45 15
1960 2 f. purple and green .. 85 15
1961 3 f. 50 brown, red & blue 2·10 30
DESIGNS—VERT. 1 f. Red deer stag and forest, Sologne Nature Reserve. HORIZ. 1 f. 20, Charlieu Abbey. 2 f. Bazoches-du-Morvand Chateau. 3 f. 50, St. Just Cathedral, Narbonne.

690. Eagle Owl. 691. "Communications".

**1972.** Nature Conservation.
1962. – 60 c. black, green and blue .. .. 3·75 1·25
1963. 690. 65 c. brn., bis. & grey 2·00 80
DESIGN—HORIZ. 60 c. Salmon.

**1972.** Europa.
1964. – 50 c. pur., yell. & brn. 30 15
1965. 691. 90 c. multicoloured.. 45 30
DESIGN: 50 c. Aix-la-Chapelle Cathedral.

692. "Tree of Hearts". 693. "Cote d'Emeraude" Grand Banks Fishing barquentine.

**1972.** 20th Anniv. of Post Office Employees' Blood-Donors Association.
1966. 692. 40 c. red .. .. 25 20

**1972.** French Sailing Ships.
1967 693 90 c. blue, grn & orge 1·00 75

694. St.-Brieuc Cathedral (from lithograph of 1840).

**1972.** 45th French Federation of Philatelic Societies Congress, St.-Brieuc.
1968. 694. 50 c. red .. .. 25 15

695. Hand and Code Emblems. 696. Old and New Communications.

**1972.** Postal Code Campaign.
1969. 695. 30 c. red, blk. & grn. 15 10
1970. 50 c. yell., blk. & red 25 10

**1972.** 21st World Congress of Post Office Trade Union Federation (I.P.T.T.), Paris.
1971. 696. 45 c. blue and grey.. 40 20

697. Hurdling. 698. Hikers on Road.

**1972.** Olympic Games, Munich.
1972. 697. 1 f. green .. .. 50 20

**1972.** "Walking Tourism Year".
1973. 698. 40 c. multicoloured.. 1·90 75

699. Cycling. 701. Nicholas Desgenettes (military physician).

700. J.-F. Champollion and Hieroglyphics.

**1972.** World Cycling Championships.
1974. 699. 1 f. brn., pur. & grey 2·50 1·00

**1972.** History of France (7th series). The Directory. As T 582 but dated "1972".
1975. 45 c. purple, olive & grn. 40 25
1976. 60 c. blue, red and black.. 1·00 35
1977. 65 c. pur., brn. & blue .. 85 60
DESIGNS—VERT. 45 c. "Incroyables et Merveilleuses" (fashionable Parisians), 1794. 60 c. Napoleon Bonaparte at the Bridge of Arcole, 1796. 65 c. Discovery of antiquities, Egyptian Expedition, 1798.

**1972.** 150th Anniv. of Champollion's Translation of Egyptian Hieroglyphics.
1978. 700. 90 c. brn., blue & blk. 50 30

**1972.** Red Cross Fund. Doctors of the 1st Empire. Cross in red.
1979. 701. 30 c.+10 c. green and bronze .. 90 55
1980. – 50 c.+10 c. red & brn. 90 55
DESIGN: No. 1980, Francois Broussais (pathologist).

702. St. Theresa and Porch of Notre Dame, Alencon.

703. Anthurium.

**1973.** Birth Cent. of St. Theresa of Lisieux.
1981. **702.** 1 f. indigo & turquoise 60 40

**1973.** Martinique Flower Cultivation.
1982. **703.** 50 c. multicoloured .. 35 20

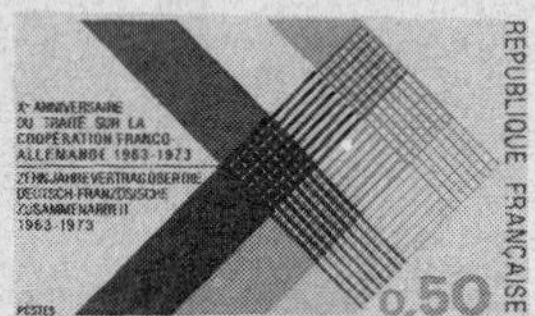

704. National Colours of France and West Germany.

**1973.** 10th Anniv. of Franco-German Co-operation Treaty.
1983. **704.** 50 c. multicoloured .. 35 20

705. Polish Immigrants.

**1973.** 50th Anniv. of Polish Immigration.
1984. **705.** 40 c. red, green & brn. 25 15

**1973.** French Art. As T **491.**
1985. 2 f. multicoloured .. 2·10 1·25
1986. 2 f. red and yellow .. 2·25 1·25
1987. 2 f. maroon and brown .. 2·10 1·25
1988. 2 f. multicoloured .. 3·25 1·25
DESIGNS: No. 1985, "The Last Supper" (carved capital, St. Austremoine Church, Issoire). No. 1986, "Study of a Kneeling Woman" (Charles le Brun). No. 1987, Wood-carving, Moutier d'Ahun. No. 1988, "La Finette" (girl with lute) (Watteau).

706. Admiral G. de Coligny (Protestant leader).

707. Mail Coach, circa 1835.

**1973.** Red Cross Fund. Celebrities' Annivs.
1989 **706** 50 c. + 10 c. blue, brown and purple 80 70
1990 – 50 c. + 10 c. mauve, grey and orange .. 80 70
1991 – 50 c. + 10 c. green, purple and yellow 80 70
1992 – 50 c. + 10 c. red, purple and bistre .. 80 70
1993 – 50 c. + 10 c. grey, purple and brown 80 70
1994 – 50 c. + 10 c. brown, lilac and blue .. 80 70
1995 – 50 c. + 10 c. blue, purple and brown 80 70
DESIGNS: No. 1989, (400th death anniv (1972)). 1990, Ernest Renan (philologist and writer, 150th birth anniv). 1991, Santos-Dumont (pioneer aviator, birth centenary). 1992, Colette (writer, birth centenary). 1993, Duguay-Trouin (naval hero, 300th birth anniv). 1994, Louis Pasteur (scientist, 150th birth anniv 1972). 1995, Tony Gariner (architect, 25th death anniv).

**1973.** Stamp Day.
1996. **707.** 50 c. + 10 c. blue .. 35 30

## MINIMUM PRICE

The minimum price quoted is 10p which represents a handling charge rather than a basis for valuing common stamps. For further notes about prices see introductory pages.

708. Tuileries Palace and New Telephone Exchange.

709. Town Hall, Brussels.

**1973.** French Technical Achievements.
1997. **708.** 45 c. blue, grey & green 30 20
1998. – 90 c. blk., bl. & pur... 70 20
1999. – 3 f. blk., bl. & grn. .. 2·10 1·25
DESIGNS: 90 c. Francois I Lock, Le Havre. 3 f. Airbus Industrie A300B2-100 airplane.

**1973.** Europa.
2000. **709.** 50 c. brown and red .. 35 15
2001. – 90 c. multicoloured .. 1·90 90
DESIGN—HORIZ. 90 c. Europa "Posthorn".

710. Guadeloupe Racoon.

**1973.** Nature Conservation.
2002 **710** 40 c. maroon, green and purple .. 30 20
2003 – 60 c. black, red & blue 80 40
DESIGN: 60 c. White storks.

711. Masonic Emblem.

712. Globe and "Heart".

**1973.** Bicentenary of Masonic Grand Orient Lodge of France.
2004. **711.** 90 c. blue and purple 55 25

**1973.** Tourist Publicity. As T **490**, but inscr. "1973".
2005. 60 c. blue, green and light blue .. .. 20 10
2006. 65 c. violet and red .. 30 10
2007. 90 c. brown, deep blue and blue .. .. 35 10
2008. 1 f. green, brown & blue 35 10
DESIGNS—VERT. 60 c. Waterfall, Doubs. 1 f. Clos-Luce Palace, Amboise. HORIZ. 65 c. Palace of the Dukes of Burgundy, Dijon. 90 c. Gien Chateau.

**1973.** 50th Anniv. of Academy of Overseas Sciences.
2009. **712.** 1 f. green, brn. & pur. 40 20

713. Racing-car at Speed.

715. Bell-tower, Toulouse.

714. Five-masted Barque "France II".

**1973.** 50th Anniv. of Le Mans 24-hour Endurance Race.
2010. **713.** 60 c. blue and brown 70 45

**1973.** French Sailing Ships.
2011 **714** 90 c. lt bl, indigo & bl 1·10 30

**1973.** 46th French Federation of Philatelic Societies Congress, Toulouse.
2012. **715.** 50 c. brown and violet 25 20

716. Dr. G. Hansen.

717. Eugene Ducretet (radio pioneer).

**1973.** Centenary of Hansen's Identification of Leprosy Bacillus.
2013. **716.** 45 c. brn., olive & grn. 30 15

**1973.** 75th Anniv of Eiffel Tower–Pantheon Experimental Radio Link.
2014 **717** 1 f. green and red .. 45 25

718. Moliere as "Sganarelle".

719. Pierre Bourgoin (parachutist) and Philippe Kieffer (Marine Commando).

**1973.** 300th Death Anniv. of Moliere (playwright).
2015. **718.** 1 f. brown and red .. 60 25

**1973.** Heroes of World War II.
2016. **719.** 1 f. claret, blue & red 50 30

**1973.** History of France (8th series). As Type **582**, but inscr. "1973".
2017. 45 c. purple, grey & blue 35 30
2018. 60 c. brn., bistre & green 55 40
2019. 1 f. red, brown and green 60 30
DESIGNS—HORIZ. 45 c. Napoleon and Portalis (Preparation of Civil Code, 1800–1804). 60 c. Paris Industrial Exhibition, Les Invalides, 1806. VERT. 1 f. "The Coronation of Napoleon, 1804" (David).

720. Eternal Flame, Arc de Triomphe.

721. "Mary Magdalene".

**1973.** 50th Anniv. of Tomb of the Unknown Soldier, Arc de Triomphe.
2020. **720.** 40 c. red, blue and lilac 25 15

**1973.** Red Cross Fund. Tomb Figures, Tonnerre.
2021. **721.** 30 c. + 10 c. grn. & red 40 40
2022. – 50 c. + 10 c. blk. & red 50 50
DESIGN: 50 c. Female saint.

722. Weathervane.

723. Figure and Human Rights Emblem.

**1973.** 50th Anniv. of French Chambers of Agriculture.
2023. **722.** 65 c. blk., blue & grn. 35 20

**1973.** 25th Anniv. of Declaration of Human Rights.
2024. **723.** 45 c. brn., orge. & red 25 20

724. Facade of Museum.

725. Exhibition Emblem.

**1973.** Opening of New Postal Museum Building.
2025. **724.** 50 c. bistre, purple and brown .. 20 15

**1974.** "ARPHILA 75" International Stamp Exhibition, Paris.
2026 **725** 50 c. brown, bl & pur 25 15

726. St. Louis-Marie Grignion de Montfort.

727. Automatic Letter-sorting.

**1974.** Red Cross Fund. Celebrities.
2027 **726** 50 c. + 10 c. brown, green and red .. 1·40 1·40
2028 – 50 c. + 10 c. red, purple and blue 1·00 1·00
2029 – 80 c. + 15 c. purple, deep purple & blue 80 80
2030 – 80 c. + 15 c. blue, black and purple .. 80 80
DESIGNS: No. 2028, Francis Poulenc (composer). No. 2029, Jean Giraudoux (writer). No. 2030, Jules Barbey d'Aurevilly (writer).

**1974.** Stamp Day.
2031. **727.** 50 c. + 10 c. brn., red and green .. .. 25 25

728. Concorde over Airport.

730. "The Brazen Age" (Rodin).

729. French Alps and Gentian.

**1974.** Opening of Charles de Gaulle Airport, Roissy.
2032. **728.** 60 c. violet and brown 40 25

**1974.** "Arphila 1975" Stamp Exhibition. French Art. As Type **491.** Multicoloured.
2033. 2 f. "Cardinal Richelieu" (P. de Champaigne) .. 1·50 1·10
2034. 2 f. "Abstract after Original Work" (J. Miro) .. 2·00 1·50
2035. 2 f. "Loing Canal" (A. Sisley) .. .. 2·25 1·10
2036. 2 f. "Homage to Nicolas Fouquet" (E. de Mathieu) 2·00 1·25

**1974.** Cent. of French Alpine Club.
2037. **729.** 65 c. vio., grn. & blue 40 25

**1974.** Europa. Sculptures.
2038. **730.** 50 c. black & purple 30 15
2039. – 90 c. brown and bistre 60 25
DESIGN—HORIZ. 90 c. "The Expression" (reclining woman) (A. Maillol).

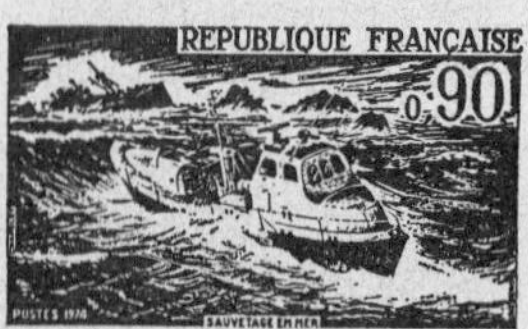

731. Shipwreck and Modern Lifeboat.

**1974.** French Lifeboat Service.
2040. **731.** 90 c. blue, red & bistre 45 25

732. Council Headquarters, Strasbourg.

**1974.** 25th Anniv. of Council of Europe.
2041. **732.** 45 c. bl., bright bl. & brn. 25 25

733. " Cornucopia of St. Florent " (Corsica).

**1974.** Tourist Publicity.

2042 – 65 c. brown and green 25 20
2043 – 1 f. 10 brown & green 45 30
2044 – 2 f. purple and blue .. 80 15
2045 733 3 f. blue, red & green 1·40 35

DESIGNS—As Type **49C**. HORIZ. 65 c. Salers. 1 f. 10, Lot Valley. VERT. 2 f. Basilica of St. Nicolas-de-Port.

734. European Bison.

**1974.** Nature Conservation.

2046. 734. 40 c. pur., bl. & brn. 30 20
2047. – 65 c. grey, grn. & blk. 30 20

DESIGN: 65 c. Giant Armadillo of Guiana.

735. Normandy Landings.

**1974.** 30th Anniv of Liberation.

2048 735 45 c. blue, red & green 85 25
2049 – 1 f. red, brown & vio 45 25
2050 – 1 f. brown, blk & red 50 25
2051 – 1 f. + 10 c. brown, green and black .. 90 45

DESIGNS—HORIZ. No. 2050, Resistance medal and torch. 2051, Order of Liberation and honoured towns. VERT. No. 2049, General Koenig and liberation monuments.

736. Colmar.

737. Board and Chess Pieces.

**1974.** 47th Congress of French Philatelic Societies.

2052 736 50 c. red, purple & brn 20 10

**1974.** 21st Chess Olympiad, Nice.

2053 737 1 f. red, brown & blue 85 35

738. Commemorative Medallion.

**1974.** 300th Anniv. of "Hotel des Invalides".

2054. 738. 40 c. black, brown and blue .. .. 20 15

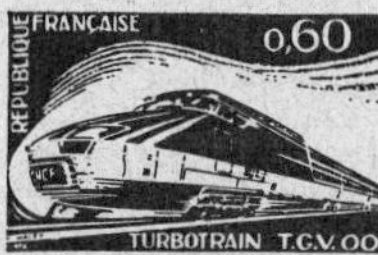


739. French Turbotrain.

**1974.** Completion of Turbotrain "TGV001" Project.

2055 739 60 c. red, black & blue 1·25 75

740. " Nuclear Power "

**1974.** Completion of Phenix Nuclear Generator.

2056. 740. 65 c. brn., mve. & red 30 20

741. Peacocks with Letter.

**1974.** Cent. of Universal Postal Union.

2057. 741. 1 f. 20 red, grn. & blue 45 30

742. Copernicus and Heliocentric System.

**1974.** 500th Birth Anniv (1973) of Nicolas Copernicus (astronomer).

2058 742 1 f. 20 mauve, brown and black .. .. 45 30

743. Children playing on Beach.

744. Dr. Albert Schweitzer.

**1974.** Red Cross Fund. Seasons. Cross in red.

2059. 743. 60 c. + 15 c. red, brown and blue .. 45 45
2060. – 80 c. + 15 c. red, brown and blue .. 55 55

DESIGN: 80 c. Child in garden looking through window.

See also 2098/9.

**1975.** Birth Cent. of Dr. Albert Schweitzer.

2061. 744. 80 c. + 20 c. brown, red and green .. .. 40 40

**1975.** Tourist Publicity. As Type **490** but inscr "1975".

2062 85 c. blue and brown .. 35 15
2063 1 f. 20 brown, dp brn & bl 40 15
2064 1 f. 40 blue, brown & grn 50 15

DESIGNS—HORIZ. 85 c. Law Courts, Rouen. 1 f. 40, Chateau de Rochechouart. VERT. 1 f. 20, St. Pol-de-Leon.

745. Little Egrets.

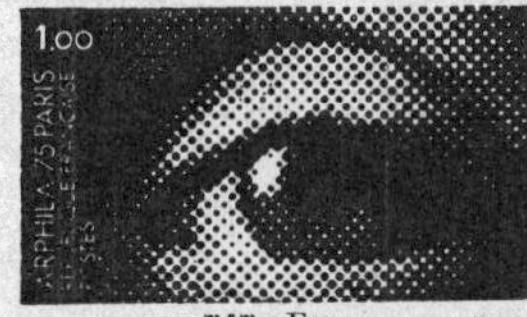


746. Edmond Michelet (politician).

**1975.** Nature Conservation.

2065. 745. 70 c. brown and blue 50 30

**1975.** Precancels. As T **538**, but inscribed " France ".

2065a. 42 c. red and orange .. 1·40 65
2065b. 48 c. red and turquoise 1·75 1·10
2065c. 50 c. brown and turq. 1·40 1·25
2065d. 52 c. brown and red .. 85 55
2065e. 60 c. brown and mauve 2·00 1·50
2065f. 62 c. brn. and deep mve. 1·50 1·25
2065g. 70 c. red and mauve .. 2·75 1·25
2065h. 90 c. brown and pink .. 2·75 1·40
2065i. 95 c. brown and sepia .. 1·90 1·50
2065j. 1 f. 35 lake and green .. 3·50 1·40
2065k. 1 f. 60 brown and violet 5·25 3·25
2065l. 1 f. 70 brown and blue .. 3·50 1·90

See note below No. 432 (1920).

**1975.** Red Cross Fund. Celebrities.

2066. 746. 80 c. + 20 c. ind. & bl. 50 40
2067. – 80 c. + 20 c. blk. & bl. 55 55
2068. – 80 c. + 20 c. blk. & bl. 50 40
2069. – 80 c. + 20 c. blk., turq. and blue .. .. 50 40

DESIGNS—VERT. No. 2067, Robert Schuman (statesman). No. 2068, Eugene Thomas (former Telecommunications Minister). HORIZ. No. 2069, Andre Siegfried (geographer and humanist).

747. Eye.

**1975.** " Arphila 75 " International Stamp Exhibition, Paris.

2070. 747. 1 f. orge., vio. & red .. 45 25
2071. – 2 f. blk., red & grn... 70 35
2072. – 3 f. grn., slate & brn. 1·25 75
2073. – 4 f. grn., red & orge. 1·75 1·10

DESIGNS: 2 f. Capital. 3 f. " Arphila 75 Paris ". 4 f. Head of Ceres.

748. Postman's Badge.

749. Pres. G. Pompidou.

**1975.** Stamp Day.

2075. 748. 80 c. + 20 c. blk., yell. and blue .. .. 35 35

**1975.** Pres. Georges Pompidou Commem.

2076. 749. 80 c. black and blue .. 30 15

750. "Paul as Harlequin" (Picasso).

**1975.** Europa. Multicoloured.

2077. 80 c. Type **750** .. .. 45 15
2078. 1 f. 20 "In the Square" or "Woman leaning on Balcony" (Van Dongen) (horiz.) .. 65 30

751. Machine Tools and Emblem.

**1975.** 1st World Machine-Tools Exhibition, Paris.

2079. 751. 1 f. 20 blk., red & blue 40 25

752. First Assembly at Luxembourg Palace.

**1975.** Centenary of French Senate.

2080 752 1 f. 20 bistre, brn & red 45 25

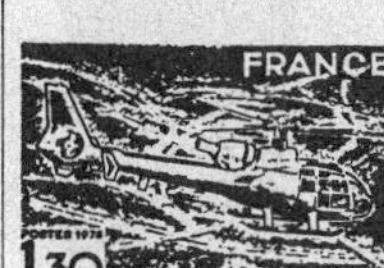


753. Seals, Signatures and Symbols.

**1975.** Cent. of Metre Convention.

2081. 753. 1 f. purple, mauve and brown .. 40 25

754. Sud Aviation Gazelle Helicopter.

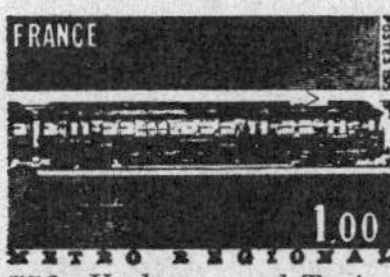


755. Youth and Health Symbols.

**1975.** Development of Gazelle Helicopter.

2082 754 1 f. 30 green and blue 65 50

**1975.** Students' Health Foundation.

2083. 755. 70 c. blk., pur. & red 25 15

756. Underground Train.

**1975.** Opening of Metro Regional Express Service.

2084. 756. 1 f. deep blue and blue 1·00 40

757. Bussang Theatre and M. Pottecher (founder).

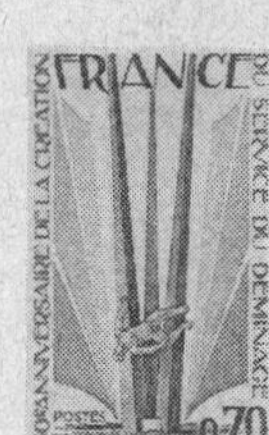


758. Picardy Rose.

**1975.** 80th Anniv. of People's Theatre, Bussang.

2085. 757. 85 c. lilac, brn. & bl. 30 20

**1975.** Regions of France.

2086. 758. 85 c. orge., turq. & blue 70 30
2087. – 1 f. lake, red & yellow 75 20
2088. – 1 f. 15 grn., bl. & ochre 70 30
2089. – 1 f. 30 blk., red & bl. 70 20
2090. – 1 f. 90 bl., bistre & blk. 80 30
2091. – 2 f. 80 bl., red, & blk. 1·75 1·10

DESIGNS—VERT. 1 f. Bourgogne agriculture emblems. 1 f. 15, Loire scene. 1 f. 30, Auvergne (bouquet of carnations). 1 f. 90, Allegory, Poitou-Charentes. HORIZ. 2 f. 80, " Nord-Pas-de-Calais ".

See also Nos. 2102/6, 2150/7, 2246/8, 2329, 2508, 2555 and 2613.

759. Concentration Camp Victims.

760. "Ballon d'Alsace" (Mine-clearers Monument).

**1975.** 30th Anniv of Liberation of Concentration Camps.

2092 759 1 f. green, blue and red 35 25

**1975.** 30th Anniv of Mine Clearance Service.

2093 760 70 c. green, bistre & bl 20 15

761. " Urban Development ".

**1975.** New Towns.

2094. 761. 1 f. 70 bl., grn. & brn. 70 45

762. St. Nazaire Bridge.

763. Rainbow over Women's Faces.

**1975.** Opening of St. Nazaire Bridge.
2095. **762.** 1 f. 40 blk., bl. & grn. 60 25

**1975.** International Women's Year.
2096. **763.** 1 f. 20 multicoloured 45 25

764. French and Russian Flags.

765. Cadet Ship "La Melpomene".

**1975.** 50th Anniv. of Franco-Soviet Diplomatic Relations.
2097. **764.** 1 f. 20 yell., red & bl. 50 25

**1975.** Red Cross Fund. "The Seasons". As T **743.**
2098. 60 c. + 15 c. red & grn. .. 35 35
2099. 80 c. + 20 c. brn., orge. & red 65 65
DESIGNS: 60 c. Child on swing. 80 c. Rabbits under umbrella.

**1975.** French Sailing Ships.
2100. **765.** 90 c. bl., orge. & red .. 1·25 65

766. Concorde.

767. French Stamp Design of 1876.

**1976.** Air. Concorde's First Commercial Flight, Paris–Rio de Janeiro.
2101 **766** 1 f. 70 black, bl & red 80 30

**1976.** Regions of France. As T **758.**
2102. 25 c. green and blue .. 20 10
2103. 60 c. green, blue & pur. .. 25 10
2104. 70 c. blue, grn., & black .. 50 15
2105. 1 f. 25 blue, brn. & grn. .. 90 75
2106. 2 f. 20 multicoloured .. 1·10 1·00
DESIGNS—HORIZ. 25 c. Industrial complex in the Central region. 60 c. Aquitaine. 2 f. 20, Pyrenees. VERT. 70 c. Limousin. 1 f. 25, Guiana.

**1976.** French Art. As T **491.**
2108. 2 f. grey and blue .. 1·60 60
2109. 2 f. yellow and brown .. 90 60
2110. 2 f. multicoloured .. 1·25 70
2111. 2 f. multicoloured .. 80 50
2112. 2 f. multicoloured .. 80 50
2113. 2 f. multicoloured .. 90 60
DESIGNS—VERT. No. 2108, "The Two Saints", St.-Genis-des-Fontaines (wood-carving). No. 2109, "Venus of Brassempouy" (ivory sculpture). No. 2110, "La Joie de Vivre" (Robert Delaunay). HORIZ. No. 2111, Rameses II in war-chariot (wall-carving). No. 2112, Painting by Carzou. No. 2113, "Still Life with Fruit" Maurice de Vlaminck).

**1976.** International Stamp Day.
2114. **767.** 80 c. + 20 c. lilac & blk. 40 35

**1976.** Tourist Publicity. As T **490,** but but dated "1976".
2115. 1 f. brn., grn. & red .. 30 10
2116. 1 f. 10 blue .. .. 40 10
2117. 1 f. 40 blue, grn. & brn. .. 50 15
2118. 1 f. 70 pur., grn. & blue .. 60 15
2119. 2 f. mauve, lake & brn. 80 25
2120. 3 f. brn., blue & green .. 90 25
DESIGNS—HORIZ. 1 f. Chateau Bonaguil. 1 f. 40, Basque coast, Biarritz. 3 f. Chateau de Malmaison. VERT. 1 f. 10, Lodeve Cathedral. 1 f. 70, Thiers. 2 f. Ussel.

768. Old Rouen.

769. "Duguay Trouin VIII" (cruiser), "Duguay Trouin IX" (destroyer) and Naval Emblem.

**1976.** 49th Congress of French Philatelic Societies.
2121. **768.** 80 c. green and brown 30 15

**1976.** 50th Anniv of Central Marine Officers' Reserve Association.
2122 **769** 1 f. yellow, blue & red 50 25

770. Youth.

771. Strasbourg Jug.

**1976.** "Juvarouen 76" Youth Stamp Exhibition, Rouen.
2123 **770** 60 c. indigo, blue & red 30 15

**1976.** Europa. Multicoloured.
2124. 80 c. Type **771** .. .. 40 20
2125. 1 f. 20 Sevres plate .. 60 35

772. Vergennes and Franklin.

**1976.** Bicent. of American Revolution.
2126. **772.** 1 f. 20 blk., red & blue 40 30

773. Marshal Moncey.

774. People talking.

**1976.** Red Cross. Celebrities.
2127. **773.** 80 c. + 20 c. purple, black and brown .. 45 45
2128. – 80 c. + 20 c. grn. & brn. 45 45
2129. – 80 c. + 20 c. mve. & grn. 45 45
2130. – 1 f. + 20 c. blk., pale blue and blue .. 50 50
2131. – 1 f. + 20 c. blue, mauve and purple .. .. 50 50
2132. – 1 f. + 20 c. grey & red 50 50
DESIGNS: No. 2128, Max Jacob (poet). No. 2129, Mounet-Sully (tragedian). No. 2130, General Daumesnil. No. 2131, Eugene Fromentin (writer and painter). No. 2132, Anna de Noailles.

**1976.** "Communication".
2133. **774.** 1 f. 20 blk., red & yell. 40 30

775. Verdun Memorial. 776. Troncais Forest.

**1976.** 60th Anniv. of Verdun Offensive.
2134. **775.** 1 f. red, brown & green 45 30

**1976.** Nature Conservation.
2135. **776.** 70 c. brn., grn. & blue 30 20

777. Cross of Lorraine Emblem.

778. Satellite "Symphonie".

**1976.** 30th Anniv. of Free French Association.
2136. **777.** 1 f. red, deep bl. & bl. 55 25

**1976.** Launch of "Symphonie No. 1" Satellite.
2137 **778** 1 f. 40 brown, chocolate and violet 70 30

779. Carnival Figures.

780. Yachting.

**1976.** "La Fete" (Summer Festivals Exhibition, Tuileries, Paris).
2138. **779.** 1 f. red, green & blue 75 20

**1976.** Olympic Games, Montreal.
2139 **780** 1 f. 20 indigo, ultramarine & blue 45 25

781. Officers in Military and Civilian Dress.

**1976.** Cent. of Reserve Officers Corps.
2140. **781.** 1 f. grey, red & blue .. 35 20

782. Early and Modern Telephones.

**1976.** Telephone Centenary.
2141. **782.** 1 f. grey, brn. & blue 40 15

783. Bronze Statue and Emblem.

784. Police and Emblems.

**1976.** 10th Anniv. of International Tourist Film Association.
2142. **783.** 1 f. 40 brn., red & grn. 50 30

**1976.** 10th Anniv. of National Police Force.
2143. **784.** 1 f. 10 grn., red & blue 50 30

785. Symbol of Nuclear Science.

**1976.** European Research into Nuclear Science.
2144. **785.** 1 f. 40 multicoloured 70 30

786. Fair Emblem.

787. St. Barbara.

**1976.** 50th Anniv. of French Fairs and Exhibitions Federation.
2145. **786.** 1 f. 50 blue, grn. & brn. 80 35

**1976.** Red Cross Fund. Statuettes in Brou Church.
2146. **787.** 80 c. + 20 c. vio. & red 50 50
2147. – 1 f. + 25 c. brn. & red 60 60
DESIGN: 1 f. Cumaean Sybil.

788. "Douane" Symbol.

**1976.** French Customs Service.
2148. **788.** 1 f. 10 multicoloured 45 25

789. Museum and "Duchesse Anne" (cadet ship).

**1976.** Atlantic Museum, Port Louis.
2149. **789.** 1 f. 45 brn., blue & blk. 60 30

**1977.** Regions of France. As T **758.**
2150. 1 f. 45 mauve and green 60 20
2151. 1 f. 50 multicoloured .. 55 20
2152. 2 f. 10 yellow, blue & grn. 80 70
2153. 2 f. 40 brn., green & blue 1·25 20
2154. 2 f. 50 multicoloured .. 1·25 70
2155. 2 f. 75 green .. .. 1·75 70
2156. 3 f. 20 brn., grn. and blue 1·75 1·00
2157. 3 f. 90 lake, brown & blue 3·00 1·25
DESIGN—HORIZ. 1 f. 45, Birds and flowers (Reunion). 2 f. 40, Coastline (Bretagne). 2 f. 75 Mountains (Rhone–Alpes). VERT. 1 f. 50, Banana tree (Martinique). 2 f. 10, Arms and transport (Franche–Comte). 2 f. 50, Fruit and yachts (Languedoc–Roussillon). 3 f. 20, Champagne and scenery (Champagne–Ardenne). 3 f. 90, Village church (Alsace).

790. Centre Building.

**1977.** Opening of Georges-Pompidou National Centre of Arts and Culture, Paris.
2158. **790.** 1 f. red, blue & green 35 15

**1977.** French Art. As T **491.**
2159. 2 f. multicoloured .. 1·25 75
2160. 2 f. multicoloured .. 1·75 90
DESIGN—HORIZ. No. 2159, "Mantes Bridge" (Corot). VERT. No. 2160, "Virgin and Child" (Rubens).

791. Dunkirk Harbour.

792. Torch and Dagger Emblem.

**1977.** Dunkirk Port Extensions.
2161 **791** 50 c. blue, ind & brn 25 15

**1977.** 90th Anniv. of "Le Souvenir Francais" (French War Graves Organization).
2162. **792.** 80 c. brn., red & blue 50 25

793. Marckolsheim Post Relay Sign.
794. " Pisces ".

**1977.** Stamp Day.
2163. 793. 1 f.+20 c. grey & blue 40 40

**1977.** Precancels. Signs of the Zodiac.
2164. 794. 54 c. violet .. .. 60 30
2165. – 58 c. green .. .. 90 35
2166. – 61 c. blue .. .. 50 30
2167. – 68 c. brown .. .. 75 40
2168. – 73 c. red .. .. 1·60 65
2169. – 78 c. orange .. .. 65 40
2170. – 1 f. 05 mauve .. 1·40 1·25
2171. – 1 f. 15 orange .. 2·75 1·90
2172. – 1 f. 25 green .. .. 1·10 80
2173. – 1 f. 85 green .. .. 3·00 1·75
2174. – 2 f. turquoise .. 3·50 3·25
2175. – 2 f. 10 mauve .. 1·75 1·50
DESIGNS: 58 c. Cancer. 61 c. Sagittarius. 68 c. Taurus. 73 c. Aries. 78 c. Libra. 1 f. 05, Scorpio. 1 f. 15, Capricorn. 1 f. 25, Leo. 1 f. 85, Aquarius. 2 f. Virgo. 2 f. 10, Gemini.
See note below No. 432 (1920).

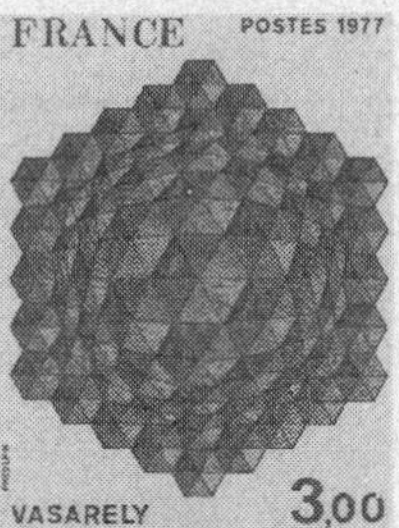
795. " Geometric Design " (Victor Vasarely).

**1977.** Philatelic Creations. Works of Art by Modern Artists.
2176 795 3 f. green and lilac .. 1·75 90
2177 – 3 f. black and red .. 2·50 1·50
2178 – 3 f. multicoloured .. 2·75 1·10
DESIGNS—VERT. No. 2177, Profile heads of man and hawk (Pierre-Yves Tremois). HORIZ. No. 2178, Abstract in Blue (R. Excoffon).
See also Nos. 2249, 2331/2, 2346/8, 2434/5, 2547 and 2578/9.

796. Flowers and Ornamental Garden.

**1977.** 50th Anniv. of National Horticultural Society.
2179. 796. 1 f. 70 lake, brn. & grn. 70 30

797. Provencal Village.

**1977.** Europa.
2180 797 1 f. red, brown & blue 45 15
2181 – 1 f. 40 black, brown and green .. .. 80 25
DESIGN: 1 f. 40, Breton port.

798. Stylized Plant.

**1977.** International Flower Show, Nantes.
2182. 798. 1 f. 40 mauve, yellow and blue .. .. 55 40

799. Battle of Cambrai.

**1977.** 300th Anniv. of Reunification of Cambrai with France.
2183. 799. 80 c. mve., brn. & blue 35 20

800. Church, School and Map.
801. Modern Constructions.

**1977.** Centenary of French Catholic Institutes.
2184 800 1 f. 10 blue, brown and chocolate .. 55 20

**1977.** Meeting of European Civil Engineering Federation, Paris.
2185. 801. 1 f. 10 red, bistre & bl. 55 25

802. Annecy.

**1977.** 50th Congress of French Philatelic Societies.
2186. 802. 1 f. brn., grn. & olive 65 15

**1977.** Tourist Publicity. As T **490**.
2187. 1 f. 25 grey, brn. and red 50 15
2188. 1 f. 40 blue, purple & pink 50 15
2189. 1 f. 45 sepia, brn. & blue 50 15
2190. 1 f. 50 olive, red & brown 50 20
2191. 1 f. 90 yellow and black .. 65 25
2192. 2 f. 40 bistre, grn. and blk. 80 25
DESIGNS—HORIZ. 1 f. 25, Premontres Abbey, Pont-a-Mousson. 1 f. 50, Statue and cloisters, Fontenay Abbey, Cote d'Or. 2 f. 40, Chateau de Vitre. VERT. 1 f. 40, Abbey tower of St. Amand-les-Eaux, Nord. 1 f. 45, Le Dorat Church, Haute-Vienne. 1 f. 90, Bayeux Cathedral.

803. School Building.

**1977.** Polytechnic School, Palaiseau.
2193. 803. 1 f. 70 grn., red & blue 60 20

804. "Spirit of St. Louis" and "L'Oiseau Blanc".

**1977.** Air. 50th Anniv of North Atlantic Flights.
2194 804 1 f. 90 indigo, bl & grn 80 40

805. French Football Cup and Players.

**1977.** 60th Anniv. of French Football Cup.
2195 805 80 c. bistre, blue & red 1·25 25

**HAVE YOU READ THE NOTES AT THE BEGINNING OF THIS CATALOGUE?**
These often provide answers to the enquiries we receive.

806. De Gaulle Memorial.
807. " Map of France ".

**1977.** 5th Anniv. of General de Gaulle Memorial.
2196. 806. 1 f. multicoloured .. 90 20

**1977.** 25th Anniv. of Junior Chambers of Commerce.
2197. 807. 1 f. 10 blue and red .. 60 25

808. Battle of Nancy.
809. Seal of Burgundy.

**1977.** 500th Anniv. of Battle of Nancy.
2198. 808. 1 f. 10 slate and blue 1·40 40

**1977.** 500th Anniv. of Union of Burgundy with France.
2199. 809. 1 f. 25 green and olive 50 25

810. Compass on Globe.
811. Red Cicada.

**1977.** 10th Anniv. of International Association of French Language Parliaments.
2200. 810. 1 f. 40 red and blue 45 25

**1977.** Nature Protection.
2201. 811. 80 c. multicoloured .. 50 20

812. Hand and Examples of Craftsmanship
813. Edouard Herriot (statesman).

**1977.** French Craftsmanship.
2202. 812. 1 f. 40 brown and olive 50 25

**1977.** Red Cross Fund. Celebrities.
2203. 813. 1 f.+20 c. black .. 60 60
2204. – 1 f.+20 c. brn. & grn. 50 50
2205. – 1 f.+20 c. brn., bistre and green .. .. 50 50
2206. – 1 f.+20 c. blue, light blue and red .. 50 50
DESIGNS: No. 2204, Abbe Breuil (archaeologist). No. 2205, Guillaume de Machault (poet). No. 2206, Charles Cros (poet).

814. "Agriculture and Industry".
815. " Old Man ".

**1977.** 30th Anniv. of Economic and Social Council.
2207. 814. 80 c. bistre, ol. & brn. 30 15

**1977.** Red Cross Fund. Carved Christmas Crib Figures from Provence.
2208. 815. 80 c.+20 c. black & red 45 45
2209. – 1 f.+25 c. grn. & red 55 55
DESIGN: 1 f. " Old Woman ".

816. " Sabine " (after Louis David).
817. Table Tennis.

**1977.** Inscr "FRANCE".
2210 816 1 c. black .. .. 10 10
2211 2 c. blue .. .. 10 10
2212 5 c. green .. .. 10 10
2213 10 c. red .. .. 10 10
2214 15 c. blue .. .. 15 15
2215 20 c. green .. .. 10 10
2216 30 c. orange .. .. 10 10
2216a 40 c. brown .. .. 15 10
2217 50 c. violet .. .. 15 10
2217a 60 c. red .. .. 25 10
2218 70 c. blue .. .. 20 10
2219 80 c. green .. .. 1·25 25
2220 80 c. yellow .. .. 25 10
2221 90 c. mauve .. .. 30 15
2222 1 f. red .. .. 1·40 10
2223 1 f. emerald .. 50 10
2224 1 f. olive .. .. 25 10
2225 1 f. 10 green .. 65 10
2226 1 f. 20 red .. .. 50 10
2226a 1 f. 20 green .. 40 10
2227 1 f. 30 red .. .. 65 10
2228 1 f. 40 blue .. .. 2·10 25
2228a 1 f. 40 red .. .. 45 10
2229 1 f. 60 violet .. 80 20
2230 1 f. 70 blue .. .. 90 20
2230a 1 f. 80 brown .. 65 10
2231 2 f. green .. .. 60 10
2232 2 f. 10 purple .. 90 10
2233 3 f. brown .. .. 90 30
2233a 3 f. 50 green .. 1·25 60
2234 4 f. red .. .. 1·50 50
2234a 5 f. blue .. .. 1·90 25
For values inscr "REPUBLIQUE FRANCAISE" see Nos. 2423/5.

**1977.** 50th Anniv. of French Table Tennis Federation.
2240. 817. 1 f. 10 grn., pur. & orge. 4·00 60

818. Percheron.

**1978.** Nature Conservation.
2241. 818. 1 f. 70 multicoloured 90 75
2242. – 1 f. 80 brn., olive & grn. 1·25 40
DESIGN—VERT. (23×37 mm.) 1 f. 80, Osprey.

**1978.** French Art. As T **491**.
2243. 2 f. black .. .. .. 3·50 1·50
DESIGN: 2 f. Tournament under Louis XIV, Les Tuileries, 1662.

819. Flags of France and Sweden of 1878.
820. College Building.

**1978.** Centenary of Return of St. Barthelemy Island to France.
2244. 819. 1 f. 10 brn., red & mve. 45 20

**1978.** Centenary of National Telecommunications College.
2245 820 80 c. blue .. .. 55 15

**1978.** Regions of France. As T **758**.
2246 1 f. red, blue and black .. 45 15
2247 1 f. 40 blue, orange & grn 55 20
2248 1 f. 70 gold, red and black 1·25 65
DESIGNS—VERT. 1 f. Symbol of Ile de France. HORIZ. 1 f. 40, Flower and port (Haute-Normandie) 1 f. 70, Ancient Norman ship (Basse-Normandie).

**1978.** "Philatelic Creations". As T **795**.
2249 3 f. multicoloured .. 3·50 1·00
2250 3 f. multicoloured .. 2·25 1·00
DESIGNS—HORIZ. No. 2249 "Institut de France and Pont des Arts, Paris" (B. Buffet). 2250, "Camargue Horses" (Yves Brayer).

**821.** Marie Noel (poet).

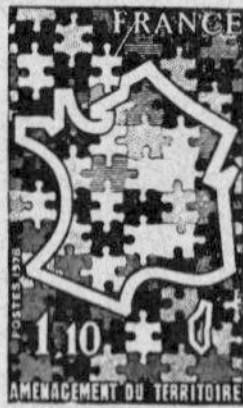

**822.** Jigsaw Map of France.

**1978.** Red Cross Fund. Celebrities.
2251 **821** 1 f.+20 c. indigo & bl 50 50
2252 – 1 f.+20 c. green, brown and blue .. 50 50
2253 – 1 f.+20 c. mve & vio 50 50
2254 – 1 f.+20 c. green & brn 50 50
2255 – 1 f.+20 c. mve & red 50 50
2256 – 1 f.+20 c. black, brown and red .. 50 50
DESIGNS: No. 2252, Georges Bernanos (writer). No. 2253, Leconte de Lisle (poet). No. 2254, Leo Tolstoy (novelist). No. 2255, Voltaire and J.-J. Rousseau. No. 2256, Claude Bernard (physician).

**1978.** 15th Anniv. of Regional Planning Boards.
2257. **822.** 1 f. 10 green & violet 45 20

**1978.** Tourist Publicity. As T **490**.
2258 50 c. blue, deep blue & grn 20 10
2259 80 c. deep green, bl & grn 35 10
2260 1 f. black .. .. 35 10
2261 1 f. 10 violet, brown & grn 45 20
2262 1 f. 10 brown, blue & grn 35 20
2263 1 f. 25 brown and red .. 50 20
2264 1 f. 70 black and brown .. 90 30
DESIGNS—VERT. 50 c. Verdon Gorge. 1 f. Church of St. Saturnin, Puy de Dome. HORIZ. 80 c. Pont-Neuf, Paris. 1 f. 10 (No. 2261), Notre-Dame du Bec-Hellouin Abbey. 1 f. 10 (No. 2262), Chateau d'Esquelbecq. 1 f. 25, Abbey Church of Aubazine. 1 f. 70, Fontevraud Abbey.

**823.** Head of Girl.

**824.** Postman emptying Pillar Box, 1900.

**1978.** "Juvexniort" Youth Philately Exhibition, Niort.
2265 **823** 80 c. brown, chocolate and mauve .. 25 10

**1978.** Stamp Day.
2266. **824.** 1 f.+20 c. grn. & blue 45 40

**825.** Underwater Scene.

**826.** Floral Arch and Garden.

**1978.** Port Cros National Park.
2267. **825.** 1 f. 25 multicoloured 1·25 1·00

**1978.** " Make France Bloom ".
2268. **826.** 1 f. 70 red, blue & grn. 3·25 30

**827.** Hands encircling Sun.

**828.** War Memorial Notre Dame de Lorette.

**1978.** Energy Conservation.
2269. **827.** 1 f. yell., brn. & bistre 55 20

**1978.** Hill of Notre Dame de Lorette (War Cemetery).
2270. **828.** 2 f. brown and bistre 1·25 55

**829.** Fontaine des Innocents, Paris.

**830.** Hotel de Mauroy, Troyes.

**1978.** Europa. Fountains.
2271. **829.** 1 f. blk., bistre & blue 40 10
2272. – 1 f. 40 brn., grn. & blue 55 15
DESIGNS: 1 f. 40, Fontaine du Parc Floral, Paris.

**1978.** 51st Congress of French Philatelic Societies.
2273. **830.** 1 f. black, red & blue 35 15

**831.** Tennis Player and Stadium.

**1978.** 50th Anniv. of Roland Garros Tennis Stadium.
2274. **831.** 1 f. slate, brn. & blue 3·25 50

**832.** Open Hand.

**833.** Citadel and Church.

**1978.** Handicrafts.
2275. **832.** 1 f. 30 brn., grn. & red 50 20

**1978.** 300th Anniv. of Reunification of Franche-Comte with France.
2276. **833.** 1 f. 20 slate, blue & grn. 45 15

**834.** Emblem.

**835.** Valenciennes and Maubeuge.

**1978.** State Printing Office.
2277 **834** 1 f. green, black & bl 35 10

**1978.** 300th Anniv. of Return of Valenciennes and Maubeuge to France.
2278. **835.** 1 f. 20 brn., vio. & slate 45 20

**836.** Sower.

**837.** Morane-Saulnier Type H and Route.

**1978.** 50th Anniv. of Academie de Philatelie.
2279. **836.** 1 f. blue, pur. & violet 35 15

**1978.** Air. 65th Anniv. of First Airmail Flight Villacoublay-Pauillac.
2280. **837.** 1 f. 50 brn., blue & grn. 90 30

**INDEX**

Countries can be quickly located by referring to the index at the end of this volume.

**838.** Gymnasts, White Stork and Strasbourg Cathedral.

**839.** Sporting Activities.

**1978.** 19th World Gymnastics Championships, Strasbourg.
2281. **838.** 1 f. red, sepia & brn. 65 20

**1978.** Sport for All.
2282. **839.** 1 f. violet, mauve & blue 1·40 30

**840.** "Freedom holding Dying Warrior" (A. Greck).

**841.** Railway Carriage, Rethondes and Armistice Monument.

**1978.** Polish Fighters' War Memorial.
2283 **840** 1 f. 70 lake, red & grn 60 40

**1978.** 60th Anniv. of Armistice.
2284. **841.** 1 f. 20 black .. .. 65 15

**842.** Symbols of Readaptation.

**1978.** Help for Convalescents.
2285. **842.** 1 f. red, brn. and orge. 35 15

**843.** " The Hare and the Tortoise ".

**844.** Human Figures balanced on Globe.

**1978.** Red Cross Fund. Fables of La Fontaine.
2286. **843.** 1 f.+25 c. brown, red and green .. .. 60 50
2287. – 1 f. 20+30 c. green, red and brown .. 70 60
DESIGN: 1 f. 20, "The Town and the Country Mouse".

**1978.** 30th Anniv. of Human Rights.
2288. **844.** 1 f. 70 blue and brown 70 25

**845.** Seated Child.

**846.** Marshal de Bercheny (Cavalry leader).

**1979.** International Year of the Child.
2289. **845.** 1 f. 70 red, violet and brown .. .. 5·25 3·25

**1979.** French Art. As T **491**.
2290. 2 f. multicoloured .. 1·75 75
2291. 2 f. brn., blk. & deep brn. 1·90 85
2292. 2 f. multicoloured .. 6·50 1·00
DESIGNS—HORIZ. No. 2290, "Music" (15th-century miniature by Robinet Testart). VERT. No. 2291, "Diana in her Bath" (mantelpiece originally from Chalons-sur-Marne, now in Chateau d'Ecouen). 2292, "Auvers-sur-Oise Church" (Vincent van Gogh).

**1979.** Red Cross Fund. Celebrities.
2293. **846.** 1 f. 20+30 c. brown, blue and deep blue 55 55
2294. – 1 f. 20+30 c. blk. and yellow .. .. 65 65
2295. – 1 f. 20+30 c. deep brown, red & brown 55 50
2296. – 1 f. 20+30 c. blue, mauve and red .. 55 55
2297. – 1 f. 30+30 c. red and brown .. .. 60 60
2298. – 1 f. 30+30 c. blue and ultramarine .. 60 60
DESIGNS. No. 2294, Leon Jouhaux (Nobel Peace Prize winner). No. 2295, Abelard and Heloise. No. 2296, Georges Courteline (playwright). No. 2297, Simone Weil (social philosopher). No. 2298, Andre Malraux (writer and politician).

**847.** Caesar's Mushroom.

**848.** Segalen, Pirogue, Pagoda and "Durance".

**1979.** Precancelled. Mushrooms.
2299. **847.** 64 c. red .. .. 50 25
2300. – 83 c. brown .. .. 65 35
2301. – 1 f. 30 yellow .. 1·00 60
2302. – 2 f. 25 lilac .. .. 1·40 1·00
DESIGNS: 83 c. Death trumpet. 1 f. 30, Olive-wood pleurotus. 2 f. 20, Cauliflower clavaria.
See note below No. 432 (1920).

**1979.** 60th Death Anniv. of Victor Segalen (writer and explorer).
2303. **848.** 1 f. 50 turquoise, brown and red .. 50 20

**849.** Hibiscus Flower.

**850.** Seated Buddha.

**1979.** International Flower Show, Martinique.
2304. **849.** 35 c. lilac, mauve and green .. .. 15 10

**1979.** Borobudur Temple Preservation.
2305. **850.** 1 f. 80 turq. and olive 60 30

**851.** Head Post Office, Paris.

**852.** Street Urchin.

**1979.** Stamp Day.
2306. **851.** 1 f. 20+30 c. blue, red and brown .. 45 35

**1979.** Birth Centenary of Francisque Poulbot (artist).
2307. **852.** 1 f. 30 multicoloured 45 20

**853.** "Apis mellifera".

**1979.** Nature Conservation.
2308. **853.** 1 f. grn., brn. & orge. 50 15

**854.** St.-Germain-des-Pres Abbey.

**1979.** St.-Germain-des-Pres Abbey Restoration.
2309. **854.** 1 f. 40 red, grey and blue .. .. 60 20

**1979.** Tourist Publicity. As T **490**.

| | | | |
|---|---|---|---|
| 2310 | 45 c. violet, blue & ultram | 20 | 10 |
| 2311 | 1 f. green, deep green and light green .. .. | 30 | 15 |
| 2312 | 1 f. sepia, brown and lilac | 30 | 15 |
| 2313 | 1 f. 20 brn, blue and green | 50 | 15 |
| 2314 | 1 f. 50 sepia, red & brown | 55 | 25 |
| 2315 | 1 f. 70 blue and brown .. | 55 | 30 |

DESIGNS—VERT: No. 2311, Interiors of Abbeys of Bernay and St. Pierre-sur-Dives, Normandy. No. 2312, Auray. No. 2313, Windmill at Steenvoorde, Dunkirk (after Pierre Spas). HORIZ.—No. 2310, Chateau de Maisons-Laffitte. No. 2314, Niaux Grotto. No. 2315, Palace of Kings of Majorca, Perpignan.

**855.** Caudron Simoun C.635 Monoplanes.

**1979.** Europa.

| | | | |
|---|---|---|---|
| 2316. **855.** | 1 f. 20 blue, green and turquoise .. .. | 60 | 15 |
| 2317. – | 1 f. 70 green, turquoise and red .. .. | 1·40 | 55 |

DESIGN: 1 f. 70, Boule de Moulins (floating container used to carry letters during the Siege of Paris).

**856.** Sailing Ship at Nantes.

**1979.** Federation of French Philatelic Societies Congress, Nantes.

| | | |
|---|---|---|
| 2318 **856** 1 f. 20 blue, violet and grey .. .. | 45 | 15 |

**857.** " Camille Desmoulins addressing Crowd " (engraving by Huyot).

**1979.** 190th Anniv of Palais Royal, Paris.

| | | |
|---|---|---|
| 2319 **857** 1 f. red and violet .. | 40 | 25 |

**858.** Flags of Member Countries and Strasbourg Cathedral.

**1979.** First Direct Elections to European Assembly.

| | | |
|---|---|---|
| 2320. **858.** 1 f. 20 multicoloured | 45 | 15 |

**859.** Joan of Arc Monument, Rouen.

**1979.** National Monument.

| | | |
|---|---|---|
| 2321. **859.** 1 f. 70 mauve .. | 70 | 25 |

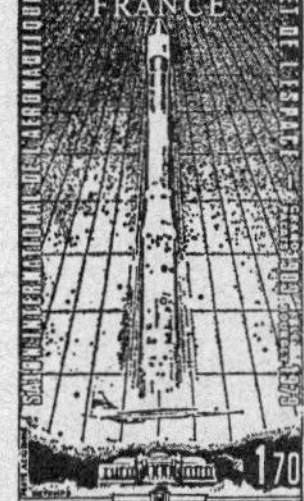

**860.** "Ariane" Rocket and Concorde over Grand Palais, Paris and Le Bourget Airport.

**862.** Lantern Tower, La Rochelle.

**861.** Felix Guyon (urologist).

**1979.** Air. International Aeronautics and Space Exhibition, Le Bourget.

| | | |
|---|---|---|
| 2322 **860** 1 f. 70 blue, orange and brown .. | 1·90 | 1·25 |

**1979.** 18th Congress of International Society of Urologists, Paris.

| | | |
|---|---|---|
| 2323. **861.** 1 f. 80 blue and brown | 60 | 25 |

**1979.** Pre-cancelled. Historic Monuments (1st series).

| | | | |
|---|---|---|---|
| 2324. **862.** | 68 c. lilac .. .. | 35 | 30 |
| 2325. – | 88 c. blue .. .. | 45 | 30 |
| 2326. – | 1 f. 40 green .. .. | 70 | 60 |
| 2327. – | 2 f. 35 brown .. | 1·25 | 80 |

DESIGNS: 88 c. Cathedral towers, Chartres. 1 f. 40, Cathedral towers, Bourges. 2 f. 35, Cathedral towers, Amiens.

See note below No. 432 (1920).

See also Nos. 2342/5, 2383/6 and 2509/12.

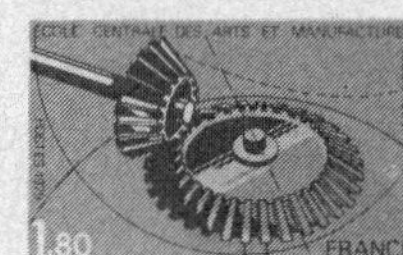


**863.** " Telecom 79 ". **864.** Gear-wheels.

**1979.** Third World Telecommunications Exhibition, Geneva.

| | | |
|---|---|---|
| 2328. **863.** 1 f. 10 brown, turq. and green .. .. | 35 | 15 |

**1979.** Regions of France. As T **758**.

| | | |
|---|---|---|
| 2329. 2 f. 30 black, yell. and red | | |

DESIGN: 2 f. 30, Thistle, Lorraine. 1·10 25

**1979.** 150th Anniv. of Central Technical School, Paris.

| | | |
|---|---|---|
| 2330. **864.** 1 f. 80 yell., blk. & grn. | 65 | 40 |

**1979.** " Philatelic Creations ". As T **795**.

| | | |
|---|---|---|
| 2331. 3 f. multicoloured .. | 1·60 | 90 |
| 2332. 3 f. brown and green .. | 1·50 | 90 |

DESIGNS: No. 2331, "Marianne" (Salvador Dali). No. 2332, "Fire Dancer from 'The Magic Flute' " (Chapelain-Midy).

**865.** Judo.

**866.** Women's Head.

**1979.** World Judo Championships, Paris.

| | | |
|---|---|---|
| 2333. **865.** 1 f. 60 black, light green and green .. | 75 | 25 |

**1979.** Red Cross Fund. Stained Glass Windows, Church of St. Joan of Arc, Rouen.

| | | | |
|---|---|---|---|
| 2334. **866.** | 1 f. 10+30 c. brown, green and red .. | 45 | 40 |
| 2335. – | 1 f. 30+30 c. brown, green and red .. | 45 | 45 |

DESIGN: 1 f. 30, Simon the Magician.

The windows came originally from the Church of St. Vincent, Rouen, destroyed during the Second World War.

**867.** Violins. **868.** Eurovision Satellite.

**1979.** Handicrafts. Violin Manufacture.

| | | |
|---|---|---|
| 2236 **867** 1 f. 30 black, red and lake .. .. | 60 | 20 |

**1980.** 25th Anniv. of Eurovision (European Broadcasting Union).

| | | |
|---|---|---|
| 2337. **868.** 1 f. 80, blue, deep blue and black .. | 1·40 | 45 |

**1980.** French Art. Design similar to T **491**.

| | | |
|---|---|---|
| 2338. 3 f. brown, ochre & green | 2·10 | 1·00 |
| 2339. 3 f. multicoloured .. | 1·60 | 90 |
| 2340. 3 f. multicoloured .. | 1·50 | 90 |
| 2341. 4 f. multicoloured .. | 3·75 | 1·10 |

DESIGNS—VERT. No. 2338, " Woman with Fan " (sculpture by Ossip Zadkine). No. 2340, " The Peasant Family " (Louis le Nain). No. 2341, " Woman with Blue Eyes " (Modigliani). HORIZ. No. 2339, " Homage to J. S. Bach " (tapestry by Jean Picart Le Doux).

**1980.** Pre-cancelled. Historic Monuments (2nd series). Designs as T **862**.

| | | |
|---|---|---|
| 2342. 76 c. turquoise .. .. | 25 | 25 |
| 2343. 99 c. green .. .. | 35 | 30 |
| 2344. 1 f. 60 red .. .. | 60 | 70 |
| 2345. 2 f. 65 brown .. .. | 1·25 | 80 |

DESIGNS: 76 c. Chateau d'Angers. 99 c. Chateau de Kerjean. 1 f. 60, Chateau de Pierrefonds. 2 f. 65, Chateau de Tarascon.

See note below No. 432 (1920).

**1980.** Philatelic Creations. Design similar to T **795**.

| | | |
|---|---|---|
| 2346. 3 f. blue, black & brn. | 1·90 | 1·00 |
| 2347. 4 f. multicoloured .. | 3·00 | 95 |
| 2348. 4 f. black and blue .. | 4·50 | 95 |

DESIGNS—As T **795**: HORIZ. No. 2346, Abstract (Raoul Ubac). VERT. No. 2348, Abstract (Hans Hartung). 43×49 mm. No. 2347, "Message of Peace" (Yaacov Agam).

**869.** Processional Figures and Carnival Crowd.

**870.** Viollet-le-Duc (architect and writer).

**1980.** " Giants of the North " Festival.

| | | |
|---|---|---|
| 2349. **869.** 1 f. 60, red, grn. & blue | 80 | 40 |

**1980.** Red Cross Fund. Celebrities.

| | | | |
|---|---|---|---|
| 2350 **870** | 1 f. 30+30 c. black and grey .. .. | 80 | 50 |
| 2351 – | 1 f. 30+30 c. brown and green .. .. | 1·25 | 1·25 |
| 2352 – | 1 f. 40+30 c. deep blue and blue .. | 55 | 50 |
| 2353 – | 1 f. 40+30 c. black .. | 55 | 50 |
| 2354 – | 1 f. 40+30 c. grey and black .. .. | 55 | 50 |
| 2355 – | 1 f. 40+30 c. turquoise and green .. .. | 55 | 50 |

DESIGN—VERT. No. 2351, Jean Monnet (statesman). No. 2352, Jean-Marie de la Mennais (Christian educationalist) (portrait after Paulin-Guerin). 2353, Frederic Mistral (poet). 2355, Saint-John Perse (poet and diplomat). HORIZ. No. 2354, Pierre Paul de Riquet (constructor of Canal du Midi).

**871.** French Cuisine.

**873.** "Woman Embroidering" (Toffoli).

**872.** " The Letter to Melie " (Mario Avati).

**1980.** French Gastronomical Exn, Paris.

| | | |
|---|---|---|
| 2356 **871** 90 c. brown and red .. | 90 | 30 |

**1980.** Stamp Day.

| | | |
|---|---|---|
| 2357. **872.** 1 f. 30+30 c. mult. .. | 55 | 40 |

**1980.** Handicrafts. Embroidery.

| | | |
|---|---|---|
| 2358. **873.** 1 f. 10 blue, yellow and brown .. | 50 | 15 |

**874.** Smoker and Non-smoker (poster).

**875.** Aristide Briand (statesman).

**1980.** Anti-Smoking Campaign.

| | | |
|---|---|---|
| 2359. **874.** 1 f. 30 blue, red & black .. .. | 40 | 15 |

**1980.** Tourist Publicity. Designs as T **490**.

| | | |
|---|---|---|
| 2360. 1 f. 50 orge., brn. & blue | 50 | 15 |
| 2361. 2 f. black and red .. | 60 | 20 |
| 2362. 2 f. 20 brn., blue & green | 85 | 20 |
| 2363. 2 f. 30 grn., brn. & blue | 80 | 20 |
| 2364. 2 f. 50, blue, violet and mauve .. .. | 80 | 15 |
| 2365. 3 f. 20 brown and blue .. | 1·40 | 25 |

DESIGNS—VERT. 1 f. 50, Cordes. 2 f. 30, Montauban. 2 f. 50, Praying nun and St. Peter's Abbey, Solesmes. 3 f. 20, Puy Cathedral. HORIZ. 2 f. Chateau de Maintenon. 2 f. 20, Chateau de Rambouillet.

**1980.** Europa.

| | | |
|---|---|---|
| 2366. **875.** 1 f. 30 multicoloured | 45 | 15 |
| 2367. – 1 f. 80 red and brown | 90 | 25 |

DESIGN: 1 f. 80, St. Benedict (illuminated letter from manuscript).

**876.** La Rouchefoucauld-Liancourt (founder) and Map.

**1980.** Bicentenary of National Technical High School.

| | | |
|---|---|---|
| 2368. **876.** 2 f. green and violet | 90 | 20 |

**877.** Town Hall and Cranes, Dunkirk.

**878.** Isabel.

**1980.** Federation of French Philatelic Societies Congress, Dunkirk.

| | | |
|---|---|---|
| 2369. **877.** 1 f. 30 blue, red and ultramarine .. | 45 | 15 |

**1980.** Nature Conservation.

| | | |
|---|---|---|
| 2370. **878.** 1 f. 10 multicoloured | 65 | 25 |

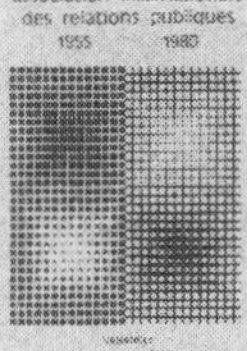


**879.** Albert Durer (self portrait).

**880.** Symbolic Design.

**1980.** " Philexfrance 82 " International Stamp Exhibition, Paris (1st issue).

| | | |
|---|---|---|
| 2371. **879.** 2 f. multicoloured .. | 1·50 | 75 |

See also Nos. 2415/16 and 2520/1.

**1980.** 25th Anniv. of International Public Relations Association.

| | | |
|---|---|---|
| 2372. **880.** 1 f. 30 blue and red .. | 40 | 15 |

**881.** " Marianne " and Architecture.

**1980.** Heritage Year.
2373. **881.** 1 f. 50 blue and black 55 25

**882.** Sources of Energy.

**1980.** 26th International Geological Congress, Paris.
2374. **882.** 1 f. 60 red, brown and olive .. .. 50 25

**883.** Rochambeau landing at Newport.

**1980.** Bicentenary of Rochambeau's arrival at Newport, Rhode Island.
2375. **883.** 2 f. 50 mauve, red and grey .. .. 1·60 40

**884.** Breguet Biplane "Point d'Interrogation".

**1980.** Air. 50th Anniv. of First Non-stop Paris–New York Flight.
2376. **884.** 2 f. 50 purple and blue 1·10 25

**885.** Golf.

**1980.** French Golf Federation.
2377. **885.** 1 f. 40 brown & green 50 20

**886.** Comedie-Francaise.

**1980.** 300th Anniv. of Comedie-Francaise.
2378. **886.** 2 f. blue, red and grey 70 30

**887.** Abstract based on Lorraine Cross and French Flag.

**1980.** 40th Anniv. of Appeal by, and 10th Death Anniv. of, General de Gaulle.
2379. **887.** 1 f. 40 multicoloured 1·25 50

**888.** Guardsman. **889.** "Filling the Granaries".

**1980.** Centenary of Reorganization and Naming of Republican Guard.
2380. **888.** 1 f. 70 blue and red 80 30

**1980.** Red Cross Fund. Stall Carvings from Amiens Cathedral.
2381. **889.** 1 f. 20+30 c. brown and red .. .. 55 50
2382. – 1 f. 40+30 c. brown and red .. .. 60 55
DESIGN: 1 f. 40, "Grapes from the Promised Land".

**1981.** Pre-cancelled. Historic Monuments (3rd series). HORIZ. designs as T **862.**
2383. 88 c. mauve .. .. 30 20
2384. 1 f. 14 blue .. .. 40 25
2385. 1 f. 84 green .. .. 70 60
2386. 3 f. 05 brown .. .. 1·40 1·10
DESIGNS: 88 c. Imperial Chapel, Ajaccio. 1 f. 14, Astronomical Clock, Besancon. 1 f. 84, Castle ruins, Coucy-le-Chateau. 3 f. 05, Cave paintings, Font-de Gaume, Les Eyzies-de Tayac.
See note below No. 432 (1920).

**890.** Micro-electronics. **891.** Louis Armand (engineer and Academician).

**1981.** Technology.
2387. **890.** 1 f. 20 multicoloured 90 15
2388. – 1 f. 20 multicoloured 40 15
2389. – 1 f. 40 multicoloured 50 20
2390. – 1 f. 80 deep blue, blue and yellow .. 65 30
2391. – 2 f. blue, red and black .. .. 80 25
DESIGNS: No. 2388, Biology. No. 2389, New energy sources. No. 2390, Sea bed exploitation. No. 2391, Telematics.

**1981.** Red Cross Fund. Celebrities.
2392 **891** 1 f. 20+30 c. green and brown .. 60 60
2393 – 1 f. 20+30 c. mult .. 60 60
2394 – 1 f. 40+30 c. deep green and green .. 90 90
2395 – 1 f. 40+30 c. blue and black .. .. 90 90
2396 – 1 f. 40+30 c. blue and violet .. .. 90 90
2397 – 1 f. 40+30 c. brown and bistre .. 1·25 1·25
DESIGNS—VERT. No. 2393, Louis Jouvet (theatre and film director and actor). No. 2396, R. P. Pierre Teilhard de Chardin (palaeontologist and philosopher). HORIZ. No. 2394, Anne-Marie Javouhey (missionary). No. 2395, Jacques Offenbach (composer). No. 2397, Pastor Marc Boegner.

**1981.** French Art. Designs similar to T **491.** Multicoloured.
2398. 2 f. "The Footpath" (Camille Pissarro) (horiz.) .. .. .. 1·50 75
2399. 4 f. "Composition 1920/23" (Albert Gleizes) (vert.) .. 2·25 90

**892.** "The Love Letter" (Goya).

**1981.** Stamp Day.
2400 **892** 1 f. 40+30 c. mult .. 90 50

**893.** Angel pouring Water on France. **894.** Bookbinding Press.

**1981.** Water.
2401. **893.** 1 f. 40 red, blue & blk. 50 15

**1981.** Tourist Publicity. Designs similar to T **490.**
2403 1 f. 40 brown and red .. 70 15
2404 1 f. 70 brown, green & bl 90 25
2405 2 f. black and red 80 25
2406 2 f. 20 black and blue .. 1·00 25
2407 2 f. 20 sepia and brown .. 80 30
2408 2 f. 50 brown, blue & grn 85 20
2409 2 f. 60 red and green .. 90 20
2410 2 f. 90 green .. .. 1·25 15
DESIGNS—VERT. 1 f. 40, St. John's Cathedral, Lyon. 1 f. 70, Maison Carree, Nimes. 2 f. 20 (2406), St. Anne's Church, Auray. 2 f. 90, Crest. HORIZ. 2 f. Interior, Notre Dame Abbey, Vaucelles. 2 f. 20 (2407), Notre Dame Church, Louviers. 2 f. 50, Chateau de Sully, Rosny-sur-Seine. 2 f. 60, Saint-Emilion.

**1981.** Handicrafts. Bookbinding.
2411. **894.** 1 f. 50 olive and red 70 25

**895.** Bourree Croisee dance. **896.** Military and Sporting Scenes.

**1981.** Europa.
2412. **895.** 1 f. 40 brn., blk. & green 50 15
2413. – 2 f. black, brn. & blue 1·60 20
DESIGN: 2 f. Sardane (Catalan dance).

**1981.** Cent. of Saint-Maixent Military Academy.
2414. **896.** 2 f. 50 mauve, bl. & vio 80 15

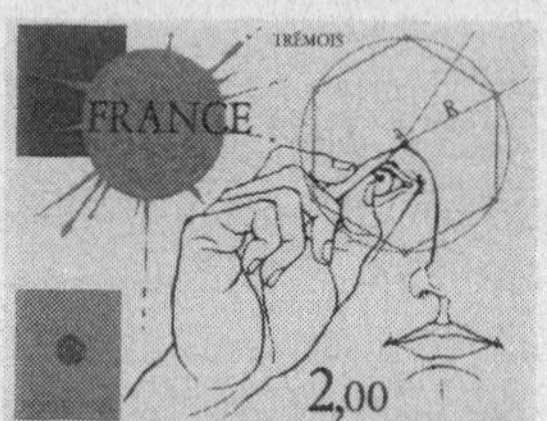

**897.** "France".

**1981.** "Philexfrance 82" International Stamp Exhibition, Paris (2nd issue). Multicoloured.
2415. 2 f. Type **897** .. .. 1·90 75
2416. 2 f. "Paris" .. .. 1·90 75

**898.** Theophraste Renaudot and Emile de Girardin. **899.** Thermal Waters of Vichy.

**1981.** 350th Anniv of First French Newspaper "La Gazette", Death Centenary of Emile de Girardin (founder of newspaper "La Presse") and Cent of Law on Freedom of the Press.
2417 **898** 2 f. 20 black and red .. 80 20

**1981.** Federation of French Philatelic Societies Congress, Vichy.
2418. **899.** 1 f. 40 brn., bl. and grn. 60 20

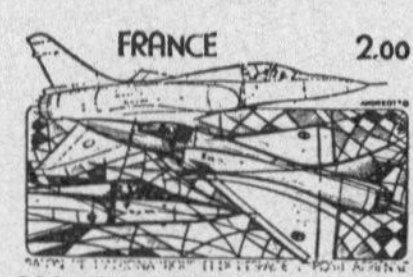

**900.** Dassault Mirage 2000 Aircraft.

**1981.** Air. 34th International Aeronautics and Space Exhibition.
2419 **900** 2 f. mauve, blue & vio 2·50 25

**901.** "HEC".

**1981.** Cent. of Paris Commercial College.
2420. **901.** 1 f. 40 blue, grn. and red 50 15

**902.** Grey Heron and La Palissade, Camargue.

**1981.** Conservation of Littoral Regions.
2421. **902.** 1 f. 60 grn., brn. & red 80 25

**903.** Fencing.

**1981.** World Fencing Championships, Clermont-Ferrand.
2422. **903.** 1 f. 80 black and brn. 80 25

**1981.** Vert designs as T **816** but inscr. "REPUBLIQUE FRANCAISE".
2423. 1 f. 40 green .. .. 45 10
2424. 1 f. 60 red .. .. 50 10
2425. 2 f. 30 blue .. .. 3·00 90

**904.** Car colliding with Glass.

**1981.** Campaign against Drinking and Driving.
2428. **904.** 1 f. 60 brn., red & olive 75 20

**905.** Costes, Le Brix and Airplane "Nungesser et Coli".

**1981.** Air. Dieudonne Costes and Joseph Le Brix (pilots of first non-stop South Atlantic flight) Commemoration.
2429. **905.** 10 f. blk., brn. and red 5·75 15

**906.** Bird. **907.** Stylized Bird.

**1981.** 45th International Congress of P.E.N. Club, Lyon and Paris.
2430. **906.** 2 f. blk., vio. and grn. 65 20

**1981.** Cent. of National Savings Bank.
2431. **907.** 1 f. 40 grn., bl. & red 50 15
2432. 1 f. 60 red, bl. & lt. red 55 15

**908.** Jules Ferry (education reformer). **909.** "Borda" (warship) and Naval School, Lanveoc-Poulmic.

**1981.** Cent. of National Education System.
2433. **908.** 1 f. 60 vio., brn. & blk. 90 15

**1981.** Philatelic Creations. As T **795.** Mult.
2434. 4 f. "The Divers" (Edouard Pignon) (horiz.) .. 2·10 75
2435. 4 f. "Alleluia" (Alfred Manessier) .. .. 2·10 75

**1981.** 150th Anniv. of Naval School.
2436. **909.** 1 f. 40 brn., bl. and red 55 20

910. "Vision of St. Hubert" (15th-cent. sculpture).

911. J. Moulin, J. Jaures, V. Schoelcher and Pantheon.

**1981.** Hunting and Nature Museum, Hotel de Guenegaud, Paris.

2437. **910.** 1 f. 60 brown & stone 55 15

**1981.** Pantheon.

2438. **911.** 1 f. 60 purple & bl. 60 15

**912.** Disabled Draughtsman.

**1981.** International Year of Disabled Persons.

2439. **912.** 1 f. 60 blk., bl. & red 50 15

**913.** Pastoral Scene (2nd century mosaic).

**1981.** 2000th Death Anniv of Virgil (poet)

2440. **913.** 2 f. multicoloured .. 1·40 75

**914.** " Scourges of the Passion ".

**915.** Memorial (Antoine Rohal).

**1981.** Red Cross Fund. Stained Glass Windows by Fernand Leger from the Church of the Sacred Heart, Audincort. Multicoloured.

2441. 1 f. 40+30 c. Type **914** .. 60 60
2442. 1 f. 60+30 c. " Peace " .. 65 65

**1981.** Martyrs of Chateaubriant (World War II victims).

2443. **915.** 1 f. 40 blk., pur. & bl. 45 15

**916.** " Liberty " (from " Liberty guiding the People " by Delacroix).

**918.** Guillaume Postel (scholar).

**1982.**

| | | | | |
|---|---|---|---|---|
| 2444 | **916.** 5 c. green .. | .. | 20 | 10 |
| 2445 | 10 c. red .. | .. | 10 | 10 |
| 2446 | 15 c. purple | .. | 30 | 10 |
| 2447 | 20 c. green .. | .. | 10 | 10 |
| 2448 | 30 c. orange | .. | 10 | 10 |
| 2449 | 40 c. brown | .. | 15 | 10 |
| 2450 | 50 c. mauve | .. | 15 | 10 |
| 2451 | 60 c. brown.. | .. | 15 | 10 |
| 2452 | 70 c. blue .. | .. | 25 | 10 |
| 2453 | 80 c. green .. | .. | 25 | 10 |
| 2454 | 90 c. mauve | .. | 30 | 10 |
| 2455 | 1 f. green .. | .. | 30 | 10 |
| 2456 | 1 f. 40 green | .. | 60 | 10 |
| 2457 | 1 f. 60 red .. | .. | 65 | 10 |
| 2458 | 1 f. 60 green | .. | 50 | 10 |
| 2484 | **916.** 1 f. 70 green | .. | 35 | 15 |
| 2460 | 1 f. 80 red .. | .. | 75 | 10 |
| 2461 | 1 f. 80 green | .. | 90 | 10 |
| 2487 | 1 f. 90 green | .. | 80 | 15 |
| 2465 | 2 f. green .. | .. | 55 | 10 |
| 2464 | 2 f. red .. | .. | 60 | 10 |
| 2466 | 2 f. 10 red .. | .. | 90 | 10 |
| 2467 | 2 f. 20 red .. | .. | 90 | 10 |
| 2468 | 2 f. 30 blue .. | .. | 2·75 | 1·00 |
| 2469 | 2 f. 60 blue .. | .. | 3·50 | 90 |
| 2470 | 2 f. 80 blue .. | .. | 2·50 | 90 |
| 2471 | 3 f. brown .. | .. | 80 | 10 |
| 2472 | 3 f. blue .. | .. | 2·50 | 50 |
| 2473 | 3 f. 20 blue .. | .. | 3·00 | 60 |
| 2474 | 3 f. 40 blue .. | .. | 2·75 | 75 |
| 2475 | 3 f. 60 blue .. | .. | 1·60 | 35 |
| 2476 | 3 f. 70 purple | .. | 1·40 | 25 |
| 2477 | 4 f. red .. | .. | 1·25 | 15 |
| 2478 | 5 f. blue .. | .. | 1·90 | 15 |
| 2479 | 10 f. violet .. | .. | 3·75 | 10 |

**1982.** Tourist Publicity. As T **490**.

2503. 1 f. 60 bl., grn. and blk. 60 15
2504. 2 f. red and mauve .. 70 15
2505. 2 f. 90 green, deep brown and brown .. .. 90 15
2506. 3 f. deep blue and blue .. 90 25
2507. 3 f. red, yellow and blue 90 25

DESIGNS—VERT. No. 2503, Fishing boats and map of St. Pierre et Miquelon. HORIZ. No. 2504, Aix-en-Provence. No. 2505, Chateau de Ripaille, Haute-Savoie. No. 2506, Chateau Henri IV, Pau. No. 2507, Collonges-la-Rouge.

**1982.** Regions of France. As T **758**.

2508. 1 f. 90 blue and red .. 1·10 45

DESIGN: 1 f. 90, Map of Corsica, containing sun and sea, superimposed on mountain.

**1982.** Pre-cancelled. Historic Monuments (4th series). As T **862**.

2509. 97 c. green .. .. 35 25
2510. 1 f. 25 red .. .. 40 30
2511. 2 f. 03 brown .. .. 90 60
2512. 3 f. 36 blue .. .. 1·40 90

DESIGNS: 97 c. Chateau de Tanlay. 1 f. 25, Salses Fort. 2 f. 03, Montlhery Tower. 3 f. 36, Chateau d'If.

See note below No. 432 (1920).

**1982.** Red Cross Fund. Celebrities.

2513. **918.** 1 f. 40+30 c. black & brown .. .. 90 90
2514. – 1 f. 40+30 c. brown & grey .. .. 90 90
2515. – 1 f. 60+30 c. lilac, violet and purple 95 95
2516. – 1 f. 60+40 c. blue & brown .. .. 95 95
2517. – 1 f. 60+40 c. blue .. 95 95
2518. – 1 f. 80+40 c. brown 1·25 1·25

DESIGNS: No. 2514, Henri Mondor (doctor and writer). 2515, Andre Chantemesse (doctor and bacteriologist). 2516, Louis Pergaud (writer). 2517, Robert Debre (professor of medicine). 2518, Gustave Eiffel (engineer).

**919.** St. Francis of Assisi.

**1982.** 800th Birth Anniv. of St. Francis of Assisi.

2519. **919.** 2 f. black and blue .. 1·00 25

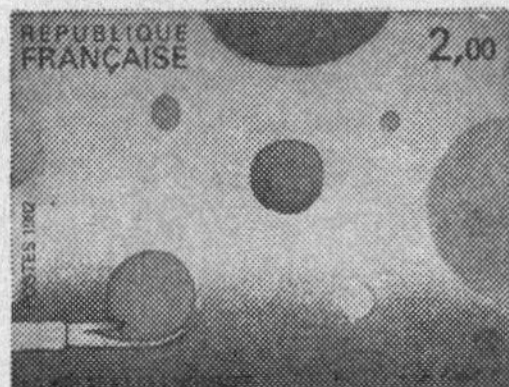

**920.** " The Post and Man ".

**1982.** "Philexfrance 82" International Stamp Exhibition, Paris (3rd issue). Multicoloured.

2520. 2 f. Type **920** .. .. 5·25 1·90
2521. 2 f. Cogwheels ("The Post and Technology") 5·25 1·90

**921.** Lord Baden-Powell and Scouts.

**922.** "Marianne" on Map of France.

**1982.** 75th Anniv. of Boy Scout Movement and 125th Birth Anniv. of Lord Baden-Powell (founder).

2522. **921.** 2 f. 30 black & green 80 35

**1982.** Population Census.

2523. **922.** 1 f. 60 multicoloured 50 15

**923.** Basel-Mulhouse Airport.

**1982.**

2524. **923.** 1 f. 90 bl., brn. & red 1·10 30

**924.** Clasped Wrists.

**1982.** Anti-racism Campaign.

2525. **924.** 2 f. 30 orge. & brn. 90 35

**925.** "Woman Reading" (Picasso).

**1982.** Stamp Day.

2526. **925.** 1 f. 60+40 c. mult.. . 90 45

**926.** " Blacksmith " (Toffoli).

**927.** Map of Europe and Seal (Treaty of Rome).

**1982.** Handicrafts. Iron Work.

2527. **926.** 1 f. 40 yell., red & blk. 50 25

**1982.** Europa.

2528. **927.** 1 f. 60 blue .. .. 85 15
2529. – 2 f. 30 brn., blk. & grn. 1·00 25

DESIGN: 2 f. 30, Seal of Charles the Bald (Treaty of Verdun, 843).

**928.** Goalkeeper and Stadium.

**1982.** World Cup Football Championship, Spain.

2530. **928.** 1 f. 80 grn., red & bl. 1·60 20

**1982.** Art. Designs as T **491**.

2531. 4 f. yell., blue and brown 2·25 80
2532. 4 f. multicoloured .. 2·25 80
2533. 4 f. multicoloured .. 2·25 80
2534. 4 f. pink and grey .. 2·25 80

DESIGNS—VERT. No. 2531, "Ephebus of Agde" (ancient Greek bronze sculpture). 2533, "The Lacemaker" (Vermeer). 2534, "The Family" (sculpture, Marc Boyan). HORIZ. 2532, "Embarkation of St. Paul at Ostia" (Claude Gellee (Le Lorrain)).

**929.** Festival Poster (Federico Fellini).

**930.** "Eole" Satellite, "Ariane" Rocket and Antenna.

**1982.** 35th International Film Festival, Cannes.

2535. **929.** 2 f. 30 multicoloured 80 45

**1982.** 20th Anniv of National Space Studies Centre.

2536 **930** 2 f. 60 dp bl, bl & red 1·25 75

**931.** Interlocking Lines.

**932.** Valles.

**1982.** Industrialized Countries Summit, Versailles.

2537. **931.** 2 f. 60 multicoloured 80 45

**1982.** 150th Birth Anniv. of Jules Valles (journalist).

2538. **932.** 1 f. 60 dp. grn. & grn. 60 15

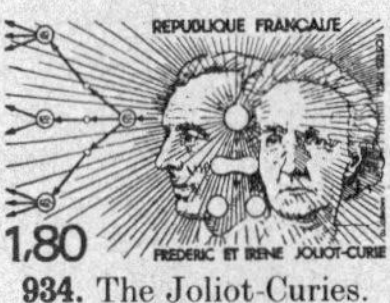

**934.** The Joliot-Curies.

**1982.** Frederic and Irene Joliot-Curie (nuclear physicists) Commemoration.

2540. **934.** 1 f. 80 purple, mauve and violet .. 1·00 15

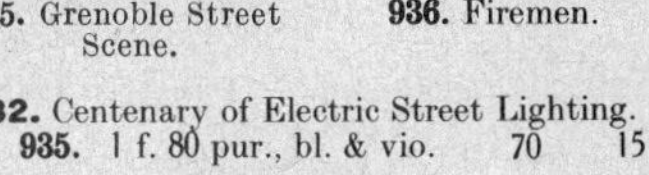

**935.** Grenoble Street Scene.

**936.** Firemen.

**1982.** Centenary of Electric Street Lighting.

2541. **935.** 1 f. 80 pur., bl. & vio. 70 15

**1982.** Centenary of National Federation of Fire Fighters.

2542. **936.** 3 f. 30 brown and red 1·90 20

**937.** Marionnettes.

**1982.**

2543 **937** 1 f. 80 red, blue & lilac 90 15

**938.** Rugby.

**1982.**

2544. **938.** 1 f. 60 bl., grn. & red 2·50 20

**939.** Lecture Room.

**940.** Lille.

**1982.** Teacher Training Colleges.

2545. **939.** 1 f. 80 grey & brn. 60 15

**1982.**

2546. **940.** 1 f. 80 red and green 60 15

**1982.** Philatelic Creations. Horiz. design similar to T **795.** Multicoloured.
2547. 4 f. "The Turkish Room" (Balthus) .. .. 2·25 1·00

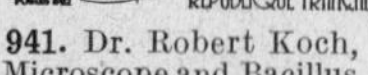

**941.** Dr. Robert Koch, Microscope and Bacillus. **942.** " Five Weeks in a Balloon ".

**1982.** Cent. of Discovery of Tubercle Bacillus.
2548. **941.** 2 f. 60 black and red 1·00 60

**1982.** Red Cross Fund. Works by Jules Verne.
2549. **942.** 1 f. 60 + 30 c. brown and red .. .. 90 65
2550. – 1 f. 80 + 40 c. green and red .. .. 90 65
Design: 1 f. 80, " 20,000 Leagues Under the Sea ".

**943.** St. Theresa of Avila.

**1982.** 400th Death Anniv. of St. Theresa of Avila.
2551. **943.** 2 f. 10 brown, black and green .. .. 90 20

**944.** Latecoere 300 Flying Boat "Croix du Sud".

**1982.** Air. 46th Anniv. of Disappearance of "Croix du Sud".
2552. **944.** 1 f. 60 lilac and blue 95 75

**945.** Cavelier de la Salle and Map of Louisiana. **946.** Leon Blum.

**1982.** 300th Anniv. of Discovery of Louisiana.
2553. **945.** 3 f. 25 brn., red & grn. 1·25 40

**1982.** 110th Birth Anniv. of Leon Blum (politician).
2554. **946.** 1 f. 80 brn. & light brn. 55 15

**1983.** Regions of France. As T **758.**
2555. 1 f. multicoloured .. 45 10
Design—horiz. 1 f. Map and coastline, Provence, Alpes, Cote d'Azur.

**947.** Andre Messager (composer). **948.** Budding Plant (spring).

**1983.** Red Cross Fund. Celebrities.
2556. **947.** 1 f. 60+30 c. blk. & bl. 90 90
2557. – 1 f. 60+30 c. blk. & yell 65 65
2558. – 1 f. 80+40 c. blk. & vio. 80 80
2559. – 1 f. 80+40 c. blk & red 80 80
2560. – 2 f. +40 c. blk. & grn. 80 80
2561. – 2 f. + 40 c. blk. & bl. 80 80
Designs: No. 2557, Jacques-Ange Gabriel (architect). 2558, Hector Berlioz (composer). 2559, Max-Pol Fouchet (writer). 2560, Rene Cassin (diplomat). 2561, Stendhal (writer).

**1983.** Pre-cancelled. The Four Seasons.
2562 **948** 1 f. 05 green .. .. 35 20
2563 – 1 f. 35 red .. .. 45 25
2564 – 2 f. 19 brown .. 1·00 60
2565 – 3 f. 63 violet .. .. 1·50 1·25
Designs: 1 f. 35, Wheat (summer). 2 f. 19, Berries (autumn). 3 f. 63, Tree in snow (winter).
See note below No. 432 (1920).

**949.** Charleville Mezieres. (½-size illustration).

**1983.** Tourist Publicity.
2566. – 1 f. 80 brn., grn. & bl. 60 10
2567. – 2 f. brown and black 60 15
2568. – 3 f. brown and blue 90 15
2569. **949.** 3 f. 10 brown and red 1·40 60
2570. – 3 f. 60 blk., brn. & bl. 1·50 25
Designs: As T **490.** 1 f. 80 Brantome, Perigord. 2 f. Jarnac. 3 f. Concarneau. 3 f. 60 Noirlac Abbey.
See also No. 2838.

**950.** Martin Luther. **951.** Woman reading and Globe.

**1983.** 500th Birth Anniv. of Martin Luther (Protestant reformer).
2571. **950.** 3 f. 30 brn. & stone 1·25 20

**1983.** Centenary of French Alliance (language-teaching and cultural institute).
2572. **951.** 1 f. 80 bl., red & brn. 60 15

**952.** "Man dictating Letter" (Rembrandt).

**1983.** Stamp Day.
2573. **952.** 1 f. 80+40 c. stone & black .. .. 90 55

**953.** Danielle Casanova (resistance leader).

**1983.** International Women's Day.
2574. **953.** 3 f. brown and black 90 20

**954.** Figure within Globe releasing Dove. **955.** Montgolfier Brothers' Hot-air Balloon.

**1983.** World Communications Year.
2575. **954.** 2 f. 60 multicoloured 80 25

**1983.** Bicent. of Manned Flight. Mult.
2576. 2 f. Type **955** (first manned flight by Pilatre de Rozier and Marquis d'Arlandes, Nov. 1783) .. .. 1·00 45
2577. 3 f. Hydrogen balloon over Tuileries, Paris (flight by J. Charles and M. N. Robert, Dec 1783) .. .. .. 1·25 80

**1983.** Philatelic Creations. As T **795.** Mult.
2578. 4 f. "Aurora-Set" (Dewasne) (horiz.) .. 1·90 90
2579. 4 f. "Marianne" licking envelope (Jean Effel) (vert.) .. .. .. 2·00 90

**1983.** Art. As T **491.**
2580. 4 f. brown and buff .. 1·90 1·00
2581. 4 f. black and red .. 1·90 1·00
2582. 4 f. multicoloured .. 2·10 90
Designs—vert. No. 2580. "Venus and Psyche" (preparatory sketch for fresco, Raphael). 2581, "Blue-beard giving Keys to his wife" from Perrault's "Tales" (engraving by Gustave Dore). horiz. 2582, "The agile Rabbit Inn" (Utrillo).

**956.** Thistle. **957.** Camera Diaphgragm (photography).

**1983.** Flowers. Engravings from Paris Natural History Museum Library. Mult.
2583. 1 f. Type **956** .. .. 30 15
2584. 2 f. Turk's cap lily (after Nicolas Robert) .. 70 15
2585. 3 f. Aster (after Nicolas Robert) .. .. 1·25 30
2586. 4 f. Aconite .. .. 1·90 30

**1983.** Europa. Each brown and deep brown.
2587. 1 f. 80 Type **957** .. .. 3·25 25
2588. 2 f. 60 Light rays entering eye and film (cinema) 3·25 30

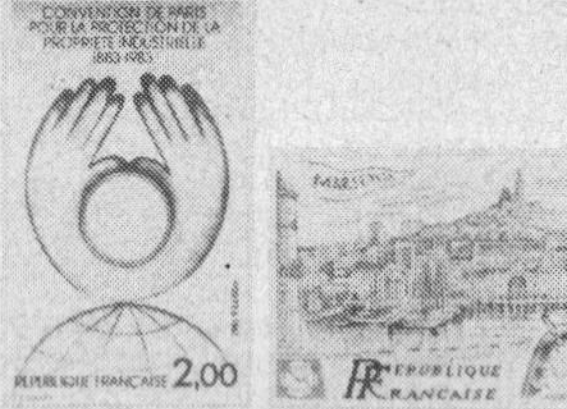

**958.** Hands on Globe. **959.** Marseille.

**1983.** Centenary of Paris Convention for the Protection of Industrial Property.
2589. **958.** 2 f. multicoloured .. 60 15

**1983.** Federation of French Philatelic Societies Congress, Marseille.
2590. **959.** 1 f. 80 red and blue 70 15

**960.** Air France Colours and Emblem.

**1983.** 50th Anniv. of Air France.
2591. **960.** 3 f. 45 bl., red & blk. 1·50 75

**961.** "France defending U.S.A. from England" (medal by Augustin Dupre).

**1983.** Bicentenary of Treaties of Versailles and Paris.
2592. **961.** 2 f. 80 brown & black 1·25 40

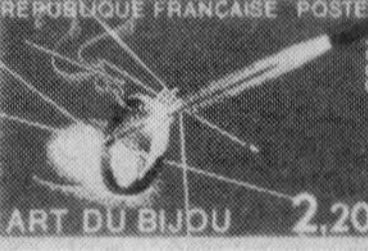

**962.** Forging a Ring.

**1983.** Handicrafts. Jewellery.
2593. **962.** 2 f. 20 multicoloured 1·00 25

**963.** Customs Museum, Bordeaux.

**1983.** 30th Anniv. of Customs Co-operation Council.
2594 **963** 2 f. 30 black, deep green and green .. 70 20

**964.** Pierre and Ernest Michaux's Bicycle. **965.** Globe and Weather-Satellite and Map.

**1983.** The Bicycle.
2595. **964.** 1 f. 60 blk., bl. & red 1·25 20

**1983.** National Meteorology.
2596 **965** 1 f. 50 deep blue, brown and blue .. 95 10

**966.** Renee Levy. **967.** Virgin and Child, Baillon.

**1983.** Heroines of the Resistance.
2597. **966.** 1 f. 60 brown & blue 50 15
2598. – 1 f. 60 brown and green .. .. 50 15
Design: No. 2598, Berthie Albrecht.

**1983.** Red Cross Fund. Wood Sculptures.
2599 **967** 1 f. 60+40 c. brown and red .. .. 90 55
2600 – 2 f. +40 c. blue & red 90 55
Design: 2 f. Virgin and Child, Genainville.

**968.** Pierre Mendes France. **969.** Emile Littre (lexicographer and writer).

**1983.** 1st Death Anniv. of Pierre Mendes France (statesman).
2601. **968.** 2 f. black and red .. 60 15

**1984.** Red Cross Fund. Celebrities.
2602. **969.** 1 f. 60+40 c. purple and black .. .. 60 60
2603. – 1 f. 60+40 c. green and black .. .. 60 60
2604. – 1 f. 70+40 c. violet and black .. .. 70 70
2605. – 2 f. +40 c. grey and black .. .. 70 70
2606. – 2 f. 10+40 c. brown and black .. .. 70 70
2607. – 2 f. 10+40 c. blue and black .. .. 70 70
Designs: No. 2603, Jean Zay (politician). 2604, Pierre Corneille (dramatist). 2605, Gaston Bachelard (philosopher and poet). 2606, Jean Paulhan (writer). 2607, Evariste Galois (mathematician).

**1984.** Art. As T **491**. Multicoloured.
2608. 4 f. "Cesar" film award (Cesar Baldaccini) (vert.) .. .. .. 2·50 90
2609. 4 f. "The Four Corners of Heaven" (Jean Messagier) (horiz.) .. 2·10 1·00
2610. 4 f. "Corner of Dining Room at Cannet" (Pierre Bonnard) (horiz.) .. .. 2·25 1·00
2611. 5 f. "Pythia" (Andre Masson) (vert.) .. 2·50 1·00
2612. 5 f. "The Painter trampled by his Model" (Jean Helion) (vert.) .. .. .. 2·50 10·00

**1984.** Regions of France. As T **758**.
2613. 2 f. 30 vio., purp. & red 1·00 15
DESIGN—HORIZ. 2 f. 30, Map and dancers, Guadeloupe.

**970.** Farman Goliath.

**1984.** Air.
2614a **970** 15 f. blue .. .. 7·00 65
2614ba – 20 f. red .. .. 8·50 65
2614ca – 30 f. violet .. 11·50 60
2614d – 50 f. green .. 12·00 3·00
DESIGNS: 20 f. CAMS 53 flying boat. 30 f. Wibault 283 trimotor. 50 f. Dewoitine D-338 trimotor.

**971.** Flora Tristan. **972.** "Diderot" (L. M. van Loo).

**1984.** International Women's Day.
2615. **971.** 2 f. 80 purple and black .. .. 90 30

**1984.** Stamp Day.
2616. **972.** 2 f. + 40 c. blue and black .. .. 1·25 50

**973.** Pierre Waldeck-Rousseau (politician). **974.** Emblem.

**1984.** Cent. of Trade Union Legislation.
2617. **973.** 3 f. 60 black and blue 1·40 25

**1984.** 2nd Direct Elections to European Parliament.
2618. **974.** 2 f. orange, yellow and blue .. .. 70 10

**975.** Hearts.

**976.** Jacques Cartier and "Grande Hermine".

**1984.** Precancels. Playing Cards.
2619. **975.** 1 f. 14 violet and red 35 30
2620. – 1 f. 47 blue and black 45 40
2621. – 2 f. 38 brown and red 1·10 60
2622. – 3 f. 95 green and black 1·50 1·25
DESIGNS: 1 f. 47, Spades. 2 f. 38, Diamonds. 3 f. 95, Clubs.
See note below No. 432 (1920).

**1984.** 450th Anniv. of Jacques Cartier's Voyage to Canada.
2623. **976.** 2 f. multicoloured .. 65 10

**977.** Children and "Sower" Stamp.

**1984.** "Philex-Jeunes 84" Stamp Exhibition, Dunkirk.
2624. **977.** 1 f. 60 brown, red and violet .. 50 15

**978.** Bridge.

**1984.** Europa. 25th Anniv. of European Post and Telecommunications Conference.
2625. **978.** 2 f. red .. .. 80 15
2626. 2 f. 80 blue .. .. 1·50 25

**979.** Legionnaires at Camerone, Mexico, 1863.

**1984.** Foreign Legion.
2627. **979.** 3 f. 10 red, green and black .. .. 1·25 30

**980.** Resistance Fighter.

**1984.** 40th Anniv. of Liberation.
2628. **980.** 2 f. red, brown and black .. .. 90 30
2629. – 3 f. red, brown and black .. .. 1·25 40
DESIGN: 3 f. Soldiers disembarking.

**1984.** Tourist Publicity. As T **490**.
2630. 1 f. 70 blue and red .. 60 10
2631. 2 f. 10 brn., grn. & red .. 70 10
2632. 2 f. 50 brown, grn. & bl. 80 15
2633. 3 f. 50 purple and black 1·75 15
2634. 3 f. 70 pur., vio. & red .. 1·50 15
DESIGNS—HORIZ. 1 f. 70, Monastery of Grande, Chartreuse. 2 f. 10, Cheval's Ideal Palace, Hauterives. 2 f. 50, Vauban's Citadel, Belle-Ile-en-Mer, Brittany. 3 f. 70, Chateau de Montsegur. VERT. 3 f. 50, Cordouan lighthouse, Gironde.

**981.** Olympic Sports. (½-size illustration).

**1984.** Olympic Games, Los Angeles, and 90th Anniv. of International Olympic Committee.
2635. **981.** 4 f. lilac, bl. & grn. 1·90 90

**982.** Engraver.

**983.** Bordeaux.

**1984.** Handicrafts. Engraving.
2636. **982.** 2 f. brown, black and green .. .. 60 15

**1984.** Federation of French Philatelic Societies Congress, Bordeaux.
2637. **983.** 2 f. red .. .. 60 15

**984.** Anniversary Emblem.

**1984.** 40th Anniv. of National Centre for Telecommunications Studies.
2638 **984** 3 f. blue and deep blue 90 20

**985** Contour Map of Alps. (½-size illustration).

**1984.** 25th International Geography Congress, Paris.
2639. **985.** 3 f. blue, black and orange .. .. 1·40 40

**986.** "Telecom 1".

**1984.** "Telecom 1" Communications Satellite.
2640. **986.** 3 f. 20 multicoloured 1·60 30

**987.** "TGV" Mail Train. **988.** Marx Dormoy.

**1984.** Inauguration of "TGV" High-speed Paris-Lyon Mail Service.
2641. **987.** 2 f. 10 multicoloured 1·40 25

**1984.** Marx Dormoy (politician). Commemoration.
2642. **988.** 2 f. 40 black and blue 1·00 15

**989.** Lammergeier.

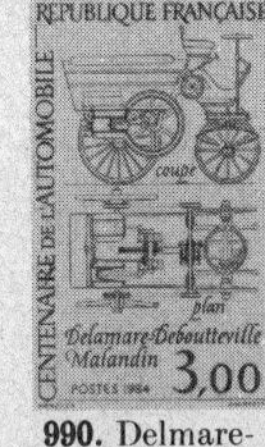

**990.** Delmare-Debouteville Malandin Automobile.

**1984.** Birds of Prey. Multicoloured.
2643 1 f. Type **989** .. .. 35 50
2644 2 f. Short-toed eagle .. 80 50
2645 3 f. European sparrow hawk .. .. 1·40 1·00
2646 5 f. Peregrine falcon .. 2·25 1·00

**1984.** Centenary of Motor Car.
2647. **990.** 3 f. brn., bl. & red 1·75 15

**991.** Vincent Auriol.

**992.** "The Pink Basket" (Caly).

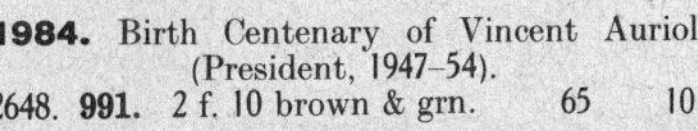
**1984.** Birth Centenary of Vincent Auriol (President, 1947–54).
2648. **991.** 2 f. 10 brown & grn. 65 10

**1984.** Red Cross Fund.
2649 **992** 2 f. 10 + 50 c. mult .. 80 70

**993.** Emblem.

**994.** Four Heads.

**1984.** Ninth Five-year Plan.
2650. **993.** 2 f. 10 blue, red and black .. .. 70 15

**1985.** Promotion of French Language.
2651. **994.** 3 f. deep blue & bl. 1·25 15

**1985.** Tourist Publicity. As T **490**.
2652. 1 f. 70 green, ol. & brn. 60 10
2653. 2 f. 10 brown and orange 65 10
2654. 2 f. 20 multicoloured .. 65 10
2655. 3 f. brown, red and blue 1·25 50
2656. 3 f. 90 brown, red & bl. 1·50 15
DESIGNS—HORIZ. 1 f. 70 Vienne, Isere. 2 f. 10 Montpellier Cathedral. 3 f. Talmont Church. 3 f. 90, Solutre. VERT. 2 f. 20, St. Michael of Cuxa Abbey.

**995.** Coloured Dots.

**1985.** 50th Anniv. of French Television.
2657. **995.** 2 f. 50 multicoloured 1·00 20

**996.** Snowflake (January).

**997.** Couple, Heart-shaped Letter-box and Cherubs.

**1985.** Precancels. Months of the Year (1st series).
2658. **996.** 1 f. 22 violet and lilac 80 30
2659. – 1 f. 57 grey and blue 1·25 75
2660. – 2 f. 55 brown & grn. 1·50 1·25
2661. – 4 f. 23 green & orge. 2·50 1·90
DESIGNS: 1 f. 57, Bare branch and bird (February). 2 f. 55, Rain-drops and sun-rays (March). 4 f. 23, Flowers (April).
See note below No. 432 (1920).
See also Nos. 2699/2702 and 2750/3.

**1985.** Saint Valentine's Day.
2662. **997.** 2 f. 10 multicoloured 90 20

**998.** Jean-Paul Sartre.

**1985.** Red Cross Fund. Writers.
2663. **998.** 1 f. 70 + 40 c. violet and purple .. 3·75 3·75
2664. – 1 f. 70 + 40 c. purple and violet .. 3·75 3·75
2665. – 1 f. 70 + 40 c. violet and deep violet .. 3·75 3·75
2666. – 2 f. 10 + 50 c. deep violet and violet .. 3·75 3·75
2667. – 2 f. 10 + 50 c. violet and purple .. 3·75 3·75
2668. – 2 f. 10 + 50 c. purple and violet .. 3·75 3·75
DESIGNS: No. 2664, Romain Rolland. 2665, Jules Romains. 2666, Francois Mauriac. 2667, Victor Hugo. 2668, Roland Dorgeles.

**1000.** Pauline Kergomard.

**1001.** Daguin Cancelling Machine.

**1985.** International Women's Day. 60th Death Anniv. of Pauline Kergomard (reformer of infant schools).
2670. **1000.** 1 f. 70 blue & brn. 55 15

**1985.** Stamp Day.
2671. **1001.** 2 f. 10+50 c. brown grey and black .. 70 50

**1985.** Art. As T **491.**
2672. 5 f. multicoloured .. 4·50 1·10
2673. 5 f. multicoloured .. 4·50 1·00
2674. 5 f. multicoloured .. 3·25 75
2675. 5 f. red, green and black 3·25 75
2676. 5 f. black and yellow .. 3·25 1·00
DESIGNS—VERT. No. 2672, "Judgement of Solomon" (stained glass window, Strasbourg Cathedral). 2675, Painting by Pierre Alechinsky. HORIZ. No. 2673, "Still Life with Candlestick" (Nicholas de Stael). 2674, Painting by Dubuffet. 2676, "The Dog" (sculpture by Alberto Giacometti).

**1002.** Landevennec Abbey.

**1985.** 1500th Anniv of Landevennec Abbey.
2677. **1002.** 1 f. 70 grn. & pur. 60 10

**1003.** Modern Housing, Givors (Jean Renaudie).

**1985.** Contemporary Architecture.
2678. **1003.** 2 f. 40 black, green and orange .. 1·00 50

**1004.** Adam de la Halle (composer). **1005.** Soldier with Rifle.

**1985.** Europa. Music Year.
2679. **1004.** 2 f. 10 deep blue, blue and black .. 70 15
2680. – 3 f. black, blue and deep blue .. 1·75 35
DESIGN: 3 f. Darius Milhaud (composer).

**1985.** 40th Anniv. of V.E. (Victory in Europe) Day.
2681. **1005.** 2 f. black, red & bl. 60 25
2682. – 3 f. black, red & bl. 90 35
DESIGN: 3 f. Prisoners of war.

**1006.** Tours Cathedral. **1007.** Vaccinating Patient (after Le Riverend).

**1985.** Federation of French Philatelic Societies Congress, Tours.
2683 **1006** 2 f. 10 indigo and blue 65 15

**1985.** Cent. of Anti-rabies Vaccination.
2684. **1007.** 1 f. 50 brown, green and red .. .. 50 15

**HAVE YOU READ THE NOTES AT THE BEGINNING OF THIS CATALOGUE?**
These often provide answers to the enquiries we receive.

**1008.** Dassault Breguet Mystere Falcon 900.

**1985.** 36th International Aeronautics and Space Exhibition, Le Bourget.
2685 **1008** 10 f. blue .. .. 5·75 1·90

**1009.** Capsized Boat and Lifeboat. **1010.** U.N. Emblem.

**1985.** Centenary of Lake Geneva International Life-Saving Society.
2686. **1009.** 2 f. 50 blk., red & bl. 1·10 50

**1985.** 40th Anniv. of U.N.O.
2687. **1010.** 3 f. blue, grey and deep blue .. 1·25 20

**1011.** Huguenot Cross. **1012.** Beech.

**1985.** French Huguenots (300th Anniv. of Revocation of Edict of Nantes).
2688. **1011.** 2 f. 50 brn., red & bl. 1·10 20

**1985.** Trees.
2689. **1012.** 1 f. blk., grn. & bl. 40 10
2690. – 2 f. blk., grn. & red 80 10
2691. – 3 f. blk., grn. & vio. 1·40 60
2692. – 5 f. blk., grn. & brn. 2·10 35
DESIGNS: 2 f. Scotch elm. 3 f. Pedunculate oak. 5 f. Norwegian spruce.

**1013.** "Marianne". **1014.** Dullin and Theatre.

**1985.** National Memorial Day.
2693. **1013.** 1 f. 80 purple, orange and black .. 1·00 15

**1985.** Birth Centenary of Charles Dullin (actor).
2694. **1014.** 3 f. 20 black & blue 1·40 20

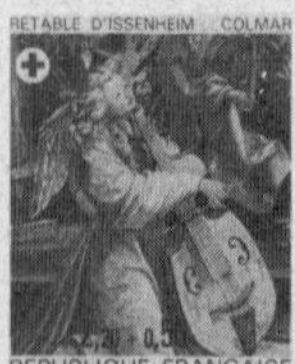

**1015.** World Map on Open Book and Keyboard. **1016.** "Concert of Angels" (M. Grunewald) (detail, Isenheim Altarpiece).

**1985.** 40th Anniv. of French Information Service.
2695. **1015.** 2 f. 20 black and red 95 10

**1985.** Red Cross Fund.
2696 **1016** 2 f. 20+50 c. mult .. 1·00 60

**1017.** Siamese Envoys before King Louis XIV.

**1986.** 300th Anniv. of Diplomatic Relations with Thailand.
2697. **1017.** 3 f. 20 purple & blk. 1·40 60

**1018.** "Leisure Activities" (Fernand Leger). **1019.** Masked Revellers.

**1986.** 50th Anniv. of Popular Front.
2698. **1018.** 2 f. 20 multicoloured 1·00 10

**1986.** Precancels. Months of the Year (2nd series). As T **996.**
2699. 1 f. 28 pink and green .. 80 75
2700. 1 f. 65 green & turq. .. 1·25 1·00
2701. 2 f. 67 blue and red .. 1·50 1·25
2702. 4 f. 44 orange and brown 2·50 2·10
DESIGNS: 1 f. 28 Butterflies (May). 1 f. 65 Flowers (June). 2 f. 67 Phrygian cap (July). 4 f. 44 Sun (August).
See note below No. 432 (1920).

**1986.** Venetian Carnival in Paris.
2703. **1019.** 2 f. 20 multicoloured 70 10

**1020.** Francois Arago (physicist and politician). **1021.** Woman's Head.

**1986.** Red Cross Fund. Celebrities.
2704. **1020.** 1 f. 80+40 c. black, blue & turquoise 75 40
2705. – 1 f. 80+40 c. black, blue & turquoise 75 75
2706. – 1 f. 80+40 c. black, blue & turquoise 75 75
2707. – 2 f. 20+50 c. black, turquoise & blue 1·00 1·00
2708. – 2 f. 20+50 c. black, turquoise & blue 1·00 1·00
2709. – 2 f. 20+50 c. brown 1·00 1·00
DESIGNS. No. 2705, Henri Moissan (chemist). 2706, Henri Fabre (engineer). 2707, Marc Seguin (engineer). 2708, Paul Heroult (chemist). 2709, Pierre Cot (politician).

**1986.** Tourist Publicity. As T **490** and **949.**
2710. 1 f. 80 multicoloured .. 60 10
2711. 2 f. blue and black .. 90 10
2712. 2 f. 20 brown, bl. & grn. 70 10
2713. 2 f. 50 dp. brown & brn. 80 10
2714. 3 f. 90 orange and black 2·25 75
DESIGNS—As T **490.** HORIZ. 1 f. 80, Filitosa, Corsica. 2 f. Chateau de Loches. 2 f. 20, Manor of St. Germain de Livet, Calvados. VERT. 2 f. 50, Cloisters, Notre Dame en Vaux, Marne. As T **949**—3 f. 90, Monpazier, Dordogne.

**1986.** Typography.
2715. **1021.** 5 f. black and red .. 3·25 90

**1022.** Louise Michel (writer).

**1986.** International Women's Day.
2716. **1022.** 1 f. 80 black and red 60 10

**1023.** La Villette.

**1986.** Science and Industry City, La Villette.
2717. **1023.** 3 f. 90 multicoloured 1·60 50

**1024.** Britska Mail Coach.

**1986.** Stamp Day.
2718. **1024.** 2 f. 20+60 c. pink and brown .. 1·10 1·00
2719. 2 f. 20+60 c. yellow and black .. 1·50 1·10

**1025.** Map and Latitude Lines.

**1986.** 50th Anniv. of African and Asian Studies Centre.
2720. **1025.** 3 f. 20 multicoloured 1·25 15

**1986.** Art. As T **491.**
2721. 5 f. multicoloured .. 3·00 1·10
2722. 5 f. multicoloured .. 3·00 1·10
2723. 5 f. multicoloured .. 2·50 1·10
2724. 5 f. multicoloured .. 3·00 1·10
2725. 5 f. grey, black & violet 2·00 1·10
DESIGNS—HORIZ. No. 2721, "Skibet" (Maurice Esteve). 2722, "Virginia" (Alberto Magnelli). 2725, Abstract by Pierre Soulages. VERT. 2723, "The Dancer" (Hans Arp). 2724, "Isabelle d'Este" (Leonardo da Vinci).

**1026.** Genet. **1027.** Victor Basch.

**1986.** Europa.
2726. **1026.** 2 f. 20 black and red 1·10 10
2727. – 3 f. 20 black and red 1·60 15
DESIGN: 3 f. 20, Lesser horseshoe bat.

**1986.** International Peace Year.
2728. **1027.** 2 f. 50 black & green 1·25 15

**1028.** Vianney. **1029.** City Gate.

**1986.** Birth Bicentenary of Saint J.M.B. Vianney, Cure d'Ars.
2729. **1028.** 1 f. 80 brown, deep brown and orange 60 10

**1986.** Federation of French Philatelic Societies Congress, Nancy.
2730. **1029.** 2 f. blue & green .. 1·00 10

**1030.** Players. **1031.** Head of Statue.

**1986.** Men's World Volleyball Championships.
2731. **1030.** 2 f. 20 purple, violet and red .. 1·00 10

**1986.** Centenary of Statue of Liberty.
2732. **1031.** 2 f. 20 blue and red 90 10

**1032.** "Liberty" (after Delacroix). **1033.** Mont Blanc, J. Balmat and M. G. Paccard.

**1986.** No value expressed.
2733. **1032.** (1 f. 90) green .. 75 10
See also Nos. 2784 and 2949/50.

**1986.** Bicentenary of First Ascent of Mont Blanc.
2734. **1033.** 2 f. blue, deep blue and brown .. 1·00 15

**1034.** Maupertuis and La Condamine.

**1986.** 250th Anniv. of Measurement of Arcs of Meridian.
2735. **1034.** 3 f. black, light blue and blue .. .. 1·25 15

**1035.** Marcasite. **1037.** Woman's Head, Printed Circuit and Drawing Instruments.

**1986.** Minerals.
2736. **1035.** 2 f. multicoloured .. 80 15
2737. – 3 f. multicoloured .. 1·50 15
2738. – 4 f. bl., brn. & mve. 2·10 75
2739. – 5 f. turq., mve. & bl. 2·25 60
DESIGNS: 3 f. Quartz. 4 f. Calcite. 5 f. Fluorite.

**1986.** Centenary of Technical Education.
2741. **1037.** 1 f. 90 bl. & mve. .. 90 10

**1038.** Scene from "Le Grand Meaulnes". **1039.** Emblem.

**1986.** Birth Centenary of Henri Alain-Fournier (writer).
2742. **1038.** 2 f. 20 brown & red 1·00 15

**1986.** World Energy Conference, Cannes.
2743. **1039.** 3 f. 40 blue, mauve and red .. .. 1·40 65

**1041.** Detail of Window by Vieira da Silva, St. John's Church, Rheims. **1042.** Car, Locomotive and Carpet.

**1986.** Red Cross Fund.
2745 **1041** 2 f. 20+60 c. mult .. 1·10 90

**1986.** Mulhouse Technical Museums.
2746. **1042.** 2 f. 20 red, blk. & bl. 1·60 20

**1043.** Museum Facade.

**1986.** Quai d'Orsay Museum.
2747. **1043.** 3 f. 70 dp. blue & bl. 1·50 50

**1044.** Underground Train in Tunnel. **1045.** Raoul Follereau.

**1987.** 50th Death Anniv. (1986) of Fulgence Bienvenue (designer of Paris metro).
2748. **1044.** 2 f. 50 purple, green and brown .. 1·25 15

**1987.** 10th Death Anniv. of Raoul Follereau (leprosy pioneer).
2749. **1045.** 1 f. 90 deep green and green .. 60 10

**1987.** Precancels. Months of the Year (3rd series). As T **996.**
2750 1 f. 31 brown and orange 1·10 60
2751 1 f. 69 orange and purple 1·50 90
2752 2 f. 74 grey and blue .. 1·75 1·60
2753 4 f. 56 green and mauve 3·25 2·50
DESIGNS: 1 f. 31, Grapes (September). 1 f. 69, Posthorn (October). 2 f. 74, Falling leaves (November). 4 f. 56, Christmas tree (December).
See note below No. 432 (1920).

**1046.** Charles Richet (physiologist). **1047.** Grinding Blades.

**1987.** Red Cross Fund. Medical Celebrities.
2754. **1046.** 1 f. 90+50 c. blue .. 70 70
2755. – 1 f. 90+50 c. lilac .. 70 70
2756. – 1 f. 90+50 c. grey .. 70 70
2757. – 2 f. 20+50 c. grey .. 80 80
2758. – 2 f. 20+50 c. blue .. 80 80
2759. – 2 f. 20+50 c. lilac .. 80 80
DESIGNS: No. 2755, Eugene Jamot (sleeping sickness pioneer). 2756, Bernard Halpern (immunologist); 2757, Alexandre Yersin (bacteriologist, discoverer of plague bacillus). 2758, Jean Rostand (geneticist). 2759, Jacques Monod (molecular biologist).

**1987.** Handicrafts. Thiers Cutlery.
2760. **1047.** 1 f. 90 black and red 60 10

**1048.** "Liberty" and "Philexfrance 89".

**1987.** "Philexfrance 89" International Stamp Exhibition, Paris (1st issue).
2761. **1048.** 2 f. 20 red .. .. 1·10 10
The stamp and label which together comprise No. 2761 were printed together se-tenant. For stamp without label, see No. 2466.
See also No. 2821.

**1987.** Tourist Publicity. As T **490** and **949**.
2762 2 f. 20 green, grey & mve 1·00 10
2763 2 f. 20 multicoloured .. 1·00 10
2764 2 f. 50 green and blue .. 1·10 75
2765 2 f. 50 black, red and blue 1·00 25
2766 3 f. brown and violet .. 1·25 25
2767 3 f. 70 blue, lilac & brown 5·25 1·00
DESIGNS—As T **490**: No. 2762, Redon Abbey. 2763, Etretat (after Eugene Delacroix). 2764, Azay-le-Rideau Chateau. 2765, Montbenoit le Saugeais. 2766, Les Baux-de-Provence. As T **949**: No. 2767, Cotes de Meuse.

**1049.** Berlin.

**1987.** Stamp Day.
2768. **1049.** 2 f. 20+60 c. brown and yellow .. 1·10 90
2769. 2 f. 20+60 c. deep blue and blue .. 1·40 1·10

**1050.** "Divine Proportion".

**1987.** Birth Centenary of Charles-Edouard Jeanneret, "Le Corbusier" (architect).
2770. **1050.** 3 f. 70 multicoloured 1·50 55

**1051.** "57 Metal", Boulogne-Billancourt (Claude Vasconi). **1052.** Gaspard of the Mountains.

**1987.** Europa. Architecture.
2771. **1051.** 2 f. 20 blue and green 1·90 15
2772. – 3 f. 40 brn. & green 2·50 25
DESIGN: 3 f. 40, Rue Mallet-Stevens, Paris (Robert Mallet-Stevens).

**1987.** Art. As T **491.**
2773. 5 f. multicoloured .. 2·25 90
2774. 5 f. multicoloured .. 2·75 65
2775. 5 f. multicoloured .. 1·90 55
2776. 5 f. brown, light brown and black .. .. 1·90 55
DESIGNS—HORIZ. No. 2773, "Abstract" (Bram van Velde). 2774, "Woman with Parasol" (Eugene Boudin). 2776, "World" (sculpture, Antoine Pevsner). VERT. No. 2775, "Pre-Cambrian" (Camille Bryen).

**1987.** Birth Centenary of Henri Pourrat (writer).
2777. **1052.** 1 f. 90 brown and green .. .. 60 15

**1053.** Lens.

**1987.** Federation of French Philatelic Societies Congress, Lens.
2778. **1053.** 2 f. 20 red & brn. 90 10



**1054.** Gen. Pershing, Soldiers and U.S. Flag. **1055.** Cable Cars.

**1987.** 70th Anniv of Entry of U.S. Troops into First World War.
2779 **1054** 3 f. 40 red, blue & grn 1·40 65

**1987.** 6th International Cable Transport Congress, Grenoble.
2780. **1055.** 2 f. black, blue and green .. .. 55 15

**1056.** Noyon Cathedral and Symbol. **1057.** Prytanee.

**1987.** Millenary of Election of Hugues Capet as King of France.
2781. **1056.** 1 f. 90 black and blue .. .. 90 15

**1987.** Prytanee National Military School (for French Soldiers' Children), La Fleche.
2782. **1057.** 2 f. 20 black, green and red .. .. 90 10

**1058.** Black Footprints on Map of France. **1059.** Globe and Wrestlers.

**1987.** "25 Years After" World Assembly of Repatriated French-Algerians, Nice.
2783. **1058.** 1 f. 90 multicoloured 80 20

**1987.** No value expressed. As T **1032** but inscr "B".
2784. (2 f.) green .. .. 90 50

**1987.** World Wrestling Championship, Clermont-Ferrand.
2785. **1059.** 3 f. brown, grey and violet .. .. 1·25 20

**1060.** Indigo Boletus. **1061.** Bayeux Tapestry (detail).

**1987.** Fungi.
2786 **1060** 2 f. multicoloured .. 60 10
2787 – 3 f. multicoloured .. 85 15
2788 – 4 f. black, bis & brn 1·40 50
2789 – 5 f. multicoloured .. 1·60 35
DESIGNS: 3 f. "Gomphus clavatus". 4 f. Morel. 5 f. Cracked green russula.

**1987.** 900th Death Anniv. of William the Conqueror.
2790. **1061.** 2 f. multicoloured .. 55 10

**1062.** Institute. **1063.** Cendrars (after Modigliani).

**1987.** Centenary of Pasteur Institute.
2791. **1062.** 2 f. 20 red and blue 90 10

**1987.** Birth Centenary of Blaise Cendrars (writer).
2792. **1063.** 2 f. buff, black and green .. .. 90 10

**1064.** "Flight into Egypt" (Melchior Broederlam) (detail, Champmol Charterhouse retable).

**1987.** Red Cross Fund.
2793 1064 2 f. 20+60 c. mult .. 1·00 70

**1065.** Leclerc, Oasis, Tank, Pantheon and Strasbourg Cathedral. **1066.** Treaty Document, Brunehaut, Childebert II and King Guntram of Burgundy.

**1987.** 40th Death Anniv. of Marshal Leclerc.
2794. **1065.** 2 f. 20 black, brown and deep brown 1·00 10

**1987.** 1400th Anniv. of Treaty of Andelot.
2795. **1066.** 3 f. 70 black, deep blue and blue .. 1·75 50

**1067.** Dr. Konrad Adenauer (West German Chancellor) and Charles de Gaulle (French President).

**1988.** 25th Anniv of Franco-German Co-operation Treaty.
2796 1067 2 f. 20 purple & black 1·50 20

**1068.** Dassault and Airplanes.

**1988.** 2nd Death Anniv of Marcel Dassault (aircraft engineer).
2797 1068 3 f. 60 brn, red & bl 2·25 60

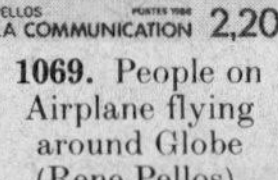

**1069.** People on Airplane flying around Globe (Rene Pellos). **1070.** Bird flying (Air).

**1988.** Communications. Designs by comic strip artists. Multicoloured.
2798 2 f. 20 Type **1069** .. 1·00 60
2799 2 f. 20 Monkey writing in light from table lamp (Jean-Marc Reiser) .. 1·00 60
2800 2 f. 20 Sitting Bull and smoke signals (Marijac (Jacques Dumas)) .. 1·00 60
2801 2 f. 20 Couple with love letter (Fred (Othon Aristides)) .. .. 1·00 60
2802 2 f. 20, Man watching levitating letter (Moebius (Jean Giraud)) 1·00 60
2803 2 f. 20 Globe and astronaut (Paul Gillon) 1·00 60
2804 2 f. 20 Man playing letter and pen "guitar" (Claire Bretecher) .. 1·00 60
2805 2 f. 20 Hand posting letter in talking letter-box (Jean-Claude Forest) .. 1·00 60
2806 2 f. 20 Rocket behind astronaut reading letter (Jean-Claude Mezieres) 1·00 60
2807 2 f. 20 Woman with mystery letter (Jacques Tardi) .. .. .. 1·00 60
2808 2 f. 20 Baby reading letter in pram with attached letter-box (Jacques Lob) .. .. .. 1·00 60
2809 2 f. 20 Woman pilot with letters (Enki Bilal) .. 1·00 60

**1988.** Precancels. The Elements.
2810 1070 1 f. 36 blue and black 1·10 50
2811 – 1 f. 75 blue and black 1·50 60
2812 – 2 f. 83 red and black 1·90 1·40
2813 – 4 f. 75 green & black 3·25 2·50
Designs: 1 f. 70, Splash of water (Water). 2 f. 83, Flames (Fire). 4 f. 75, Tree (Earth).
See note below No. 432 (1920).

**1071.** Dove and Interior. **1072** Abraham Duquesne and Map.

**1988.** Rue Victoire Synagogue, Paris.
2814. **1071.** 2 f. black and gold 90 10

**1988.** Red Cross Fund. Explorers. Each blue, brown and black.
2815 2 f.+50 c. Type **1072** .. 90 90
2816 2 f.+50 c. Pierre Andre de Suffren Saint Tropez .. 90 90
2817 2 f.+50 c. Jean Francois de Galaup, Comte de La Perouse .. .. 90 90
2818 2 f.+50 c. Bertrand Francois Mahe de La Bourdonnais .. 90 90
2819 2 f. 20+50 c. Louis Antoine de Bougainville 90 90
2820 2 f. 20+50 c. Jules Dumont d'Urville .. 90 90

**1073.** "Liberty" and Emblem.

**1988.** "Philexfrance 89" International Stamp Exhibition, Paris (2nd issue).
2821. **1073.** 2 f. 20 red, black and blue .. .. 90 10

**1074.** Mail Coach.

**1988.** Stamp Day.
2822. **1074.** 2 f. 20+60 c. purple and mauve .. 1·10 1·00
2823. 2 f. 20+60 c. brown and flesh .. .. 1·10 1·00

**1075.** Emblem.

**1988.** Centenary of Post Office National College.
2824. **1075.** 3 f. 60 blue, green and red .. .. 1·40 40

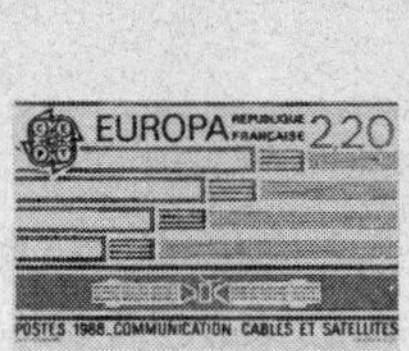


**1076.** "Stamps". **1077.** Blood Drop.

**1988.** "Philex-Jeunes 88" Stamp Exhibition, Nevers.
2825. **1076.** 2 f. blue, violet and mauve .. .. 60 15

**1988.** Blood Donation Service.
2826. **1077.** 2 f. 50 red, black and yellow .. 1·10 20

**1988.** No. 2467 surch **ECU 0,31**.
2827 **916** 0.31 ECU on 2 f. 20 red 1·40 20
ECU stands for European Currency Unit.

**1079.** Cable and Satellite Communications. **1080.** Monnet.

**1988.** Europa. Transport and Communications.
2828. **1079.** 2 f. 20 grey, black and blue .. .. 1·90 10
2829. – 3 f. 60 purple, black and light purple 2·50 20
Design: 3 f. 60, Two-car electric train.

**1988.** Birth Centenary of Jean Monnet (statesman).
2830 **1080** 2 f. 20 blue and brown 1·00 10

**1081.** Town Hall and Roman Carved Stone Heads.

**1988.** Federation of French Philatelic Societies Congress, Valence.
2831. **1081.** 2 f. 20 orange, deep blue and blue .. 90 10

**1082.** Rod of Aesculapius, Globes and Rainbows.

**1988.** International Medical Assistance.
2832. **1082.** 3 f. 60 multicoloured 1·50 50

**1083.** Typical Access Routes. **1084.** Otters.

**1988.** Easy Access for the Handicapped.
2833. **1083.** 3 f. 70 multicoloured 1·50 50

**1988.** Tourist Publicity.
2834. 2 f. multicoloured .. 1·00 10
2835. 2 f. 20 brown, blue and turquoise .. .. 90 10
2836. 2 f. 20 blue, turquoise and green .. .. 95 10
2837. 3 f. violet, green and brown .. .. .. 1·10 20
2838. 3 f. 70 black, blue and red .. .. .. 2·00 75
DESIGNS—As T **490**. HORIZ: No. 2834, Ship Museum, Douarnenez; 2836, Perouges; 2837, Cirque de Gavarnie (rock formation). VERT: No. 2835, Sedieres Chateau, Correze. As T **949**: No. 2838, "Double-headed Hermes of Frejus" (Roman sculpture).

**1988.** Animals. Illustrations from "Natural History" by Comte de Buffon.
2839. **1084.** 2 f. black and green 1·10 10
2840. – 3 f. black and red .. 1·10 10
2841. – 4 f. black & mauve 1·50 75
2842. – 5 f. black and blue 1·90 50
Designs: 3 f. Stag. 4 f. Fox. 5 f. Badger.

**1085.** "Assembly of the Three Estates, Vizille" (Alexandre Debelle).

**1988.** Bicentenary of French Revolution (1st issue). Each black, blue and red.
2843. 3 f. Type **1085** .. .. 1·10 1·00
2844. 4 f. "Day of the Tiles, Grenoble" (Alexandre Debelle) .. .. 1·40 1·10
See also Nos. 2857, 2863/8 and 2871/3.

**1086.** Soldiers of 1888 and 1988. **1087.** Bleriot XI Monoplane.

**1988.** Centenary of Alpine Troops.
2845. **1086.** 2 f. 50 deep blue, blue and red .. 1·40 60

**1988.** Birth Centenary of Roland Garros (aviator).
2846. **1087.** 2 f. green, olive and blue .. .. 1·10 20

**1088.** Soldiers.

**1988.** 70th Anniv. of Armistice.
2847. **1088.** 2 f. 20 multicoloured 1·00 10

**1089.** "Tribute to Leon Degand" (Robert Jacobsen). **1090.** City Arms.

**1988.** French–Danish Cultural Year.
2848 **1089** 5 f. red and black on grey .. .. 2·50 55

**1988.** 2000th Anniv. of Strasbourg.
2849. 1090. 2 f. 20 multicoloured .. 90 15

**1988.** Art. As T **491**.
2850. 5 f. brown .. .. 1·90 75
2851. 5 f. multicoloured .. 1·90 80
2852. 5 f. multicoloured .. 4·50 1·10
2853. 5 f. multicoloured .. 2·25 1·00

DESIGNS—48 x 38 mm: No. 2850, St. Mihiel's Sepulchre (Ligier Richier); 2851, "Composition" (Serge Poliakoff); 2852, "Meta" (Tinguely). 48 x 43 mm: No. 2853, "Pieta de Villeneuve-les-Avignon" (Enguerrand Quarton).

**1091.** Activities at Spas.

**1988.** Thermal Spas.
2854. 1091. 2 f. 20 red, blue and green .. .. 90 10

**1092.** Cross.

**1988.** Red Cross Fund.
2855. 1092. 2 f. 20+60 c. red, blue and black .. 1·00 65

**1093.** Earth.

**1988.** 40th Anniv of Universal Declaration of Human Rights.
2856 1093 2 f. 20 dp blue & blue 1·75 10

**1094.** Birds.

**1989.** Bicentenary of French Revolution (2nd issue).
2857. 1094. 2 f. 20 blue, red and black .. .. 1·00 10

**1989.** Art. As T **491**. Multicoloured.
2858 5 f. "Anthropometry of the Blue Era" (Yves Klein) .. .. .. 1·90 55
2859 5 f. "Oath of the Tennis Court" (sketch, David) 2·00 55
2860 5 f. "Regatta with Wind Astern" (Lapicque) (vert) .. .. .. 2·50 55

**1095.** Page of Braille.

**1989.** The Blind.
2861. 1095. 2 f. 20, blue, orange and mauve .. 1·00 20

**1096** "E" **1097** Comte de Sieyes

**1989.** Centenary of Estienne School.
2862 1096 2 f. 20 blk, grey & red 80 20

**1989.** Red Cross Fund. Bicentenary of French Revolution (3rd issue). Personalities. Mult.
2863 2 f. 20+50 c. Type **1097** 1·00 1·00
2864 2 f. 20+50 c. Comte de Mirabeau .. .. 1·00 1·00
2865 2 f. 20+50 c. Vicomte de Noailles .. .. 1·00 1·00
2866 2 f. 20+50 c. Marquis de Lafayette .. .. 1·00 1·00
2867 2 f. 20+50 c. Antoine Barnave .. .. 1·00 1·00
2868 2 f. 20+50 c. Jean Baptiste Drouet .. 1·00 1·00

**1098** Emblem on Spectrum

**1989.** Direct Elections to European Parliament.
2869 1098 2 f. 20 multicoloured 90 15

**1099** Flags, Astronauts and Satellite

**1989.** French–Soviet Space Flight.
2870 1099 3 f. 60 multicoloured 2·25 20

**1100** "Liberty"

**1989.** Bicentenary of French Revolution (4th issue) and Declaration of Rights of Man. Paintings by Roger Druet. Multicoloured.
2871 2 f. 20 Type **1100** .. 90 15
2872 2 f. 20 "Equality" .. 90 15
2873 2 f. 20 "Fraternity" .. 90 15

**1101** Paris–Lyon Stage Coach

**1989.** Stamp Day.
2874 1101 2 f.20+60 c. deep blue and blue .. 1·10 70
2875 2 f. 20+60 c. lilac and mauve .. 1·25 80

**1102** Arche de la Defense **1103** Hopscotch

**1989.** Paris Panorama. Multicoloured.
2876 2 f. 20 Type **1102** .. 1·10 75
2877 2 f. 20 Eiffel Tower .. 1·10 75
2878 2 f. 20 Pyramid, Louvre 1·10 75
2879 2 f. 20 Notre Dame Cathedral .. .. .. 1·10 75
2880 2 f. 20 Bastille Opera House .. .. .. 1·10 75

**1989.** Europa. Children's Games. Mult.
2881 2 f. 20 Type **1103** .. 1·00 10
2882 3 f. 60 Ball game .. 1·60 50

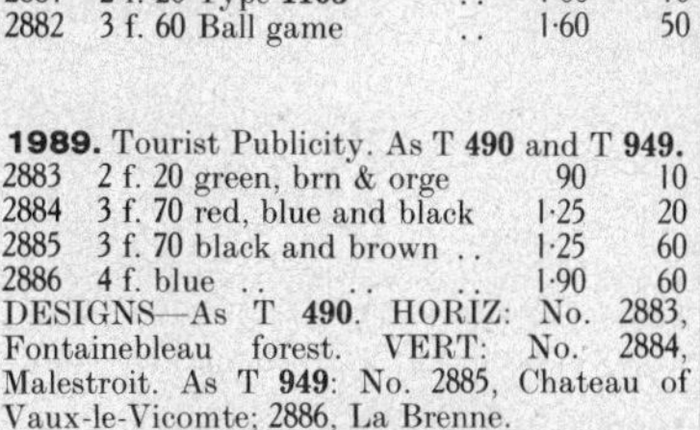

**1989.** Tourist Publicity. As T **490** and T **949**.
2883 2 f. 20 green, brn & orge 90 10
2884 3 f. 70 red, blue and black 1·25 20
2885 3 f. 70 black and brown .. 1·25 60
2886 4 f. blue .. .. .. 1·90 60

DESIGNS—As T **490**. HORIZ: No. 2883, Fontainebleau forest. VERT: No. 2884, Malestroit. As T **949**: No. 2885, Chateau of Vaux-le-Vicomte; 2886, La Brenne.

**1104** Emblems and Buildings

**1989.** International Telecommunications Union Plenipotentiaries Conference, Nice.
2887 1104 3 f. 70 red, bl & orge 1·25 20

**1105** Cyclists

**1989.** International Cycling Championships, Chambery.
2888 1105 2 f. 20 multicoloured 1·25 20

**1108** Arche de la Defense

**1989.** Summit Conference of Industrialised Countries, Paris.
2891 1108 2 f. 20 multicoloured 90 15

**1109** Preamble

**1989.** Bicentenary of Declaration of Rights of Man (3rd issue). Multicoloured.
2892 2 f. 50 Type **1109** .. 1·00 90
2893 2 f. 50 Articles II to VI .. 1·00 90
2894 2 f. 50 Articles VII to XI 1·00 90
2895 2 f. 50 Articles XII to XVII .. .. .. 1·00 90

**1110** Harp **1111** Train

**1989.** Precancels. Musical Instruments (1st series).
2896 1110 1 f. 39 lt blue & blue 1·00 50
2897 – 1 f. 79 brown and light brown .. 1·25 75
2898 – 2 f. 90 orange & brn 2·10 1·90
2899 – 4 f. 84 orange & brn 3·25 2·50

DESIGNS: 1 f. 79, Piano; 2 f. 90, Trumpet; 4 f. 84, Violin.
See note below No. 432 (1920).
See also Nos. 2993/9, 3052/62, 3095/8 and 3145/8.

**1989.** "TGV" Atlantique Express Train.
2900 1111 2 f. 50 bl, silver & red 2·25 40

**1112** Tram **1113** King Francois I

**1989.** Cent of Clermont–Ferrand Electric Tramway.
2901 1112 3 f. 70 black & brown 1·90 20

**1989.** 450th Anniv of Villers-Cotterets Ordinance.
2902 1113 2 f. 20 red and black 90 15

**1114** Cauchy, Graphs and Formula

**1989.** Birth Bicentenary of Augustin Louis Cauchy (mathematician).
2903 1114 3 f. 60 blue, blk & red 1·25 50

**1115** Marshal Lattre de Tassigny

**1989.** Birth Centenary of Marshal Jean de Lattre de Tassigny.
2904 1115 2 f. 20 black, bl & red 1·00 10

**1116** Bird feeding Chicks (18th-century silk painting)

**1989.** Red Cross Fund.
2905 1116 2 f. 20+60 c. mult .. 1·00 1·00

**1117** Harkis **1118** "Marianne"

**1989.** Harkis (French North African troops).
2906 1117 2 f. 20 multicoloured 1·25 20

**1989.** Imperf (2943), perf or imperf (2910, 2915, 2916), perf (others).

| No. | Type | Value | | | |
|---|---|---|---|---|---|
| 2907 | 1118 | 10 c. brown | .. | 10 | 10 |
| 2908 | | 20 c. green | .. | 10 | 10 |
| 2909 | | 50 c. violet | .. | 10 | 10 |
| 2943 | | 70 c. brown | .. | 15 | 10 |
| 2910 | | 1 f. orange | .. | 20 | 10 |
| 2911 | | 2 f. green .. | .. | 75 | 10 |
| 2911a | | 2 f. blue .. | .. | 45 | 10 |
| 2912 | | 2 f. 10 green | .. | 75 | 10 |
| 2913 | | 2 f. 20 green | .. | 50 | 10 |
| 2915 | | 2 f. 30 red .. | .. | 90 | 10 |
| 2915b | | 2 f. 40 green | .. | 55 | 10 |
| 2916 | | 2 f. 50 red .. | .. | 90 | 10 |
| 2916b | | 2 f. 70 green | .. | 80 | 20 |
| 2917 | | 3 f. 20 blue | .. | 1·50 | 20 |
| 2918 | | 3 f. 40 blue | .. | 1·25 | 50 |
| 2918a | | 3 f. 50 green | .. | 1·10 | 20 |
| 2919 | | 3 f. 80 mauve | .. | 85 | 20 |
| 2919a | | 3 f. 80 blue | .. | 1·00 | 40 |
| 2920 | | 4 f. mauve | .. | 2·00 | 15 |
| 2921 | | 4 f. 20 mauve | .. | 1·25 | 20 |
| 2922 | | 4 f. 40 blue | .. | 1·00 | 25 |
| 2923 | | 4 f. 50 mauve | .. | 1·10 | 25 |
| 2924 | | 5 f. blue .. | .. | 1·10 | 20 |
| 2928 | | 10 f. violet | .. | 2·50 | 20 |

The imperforate stamps are self-adhesive.
For designs as T **1118** but inscr "D" for face value, see Nos. 3036/7, and with no value at all see No. 3121.

**1990.** No value expressed. As T **1032** but inscr "C".
2949 (2 f.10) green .. .. 90 15
2950 (2 f. 30) red .. .. 1·00 15

**1119** Lace

**1120** Games Emblem

**1990.**
2951 **1119** 2 f. 50 white and red 1·00 15

**1990.** Winter Olympic Games, Albertville (1992) (1st issue).
2952 **1120** 2 f. 50 multicoloured 1·00 15
See also Nos. 2953/62 and 3048.

**1121** Emblem and Ice Skaters

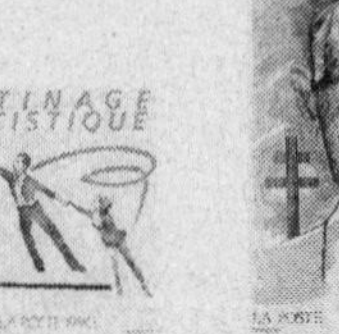
**1122** Cross of Lorraine and De Gaulle

**1990.** Winter Olympic Games, Albertville (1992) (2nd issue). Each black, blue and red.
2953 2 f. 30+20 c. Type **1121** 1·00 60
2954 2 f. 30+20 c. Ski jumping 1·00 60
2955 2 f. 30+20 c. Speed skiing 1·00 60
2956 2 f. 30+20 c. Slalom .. 1·00 60
2957 2 f. 30+20 c. Cross-country skiing .. 1·00 60
2958 2 f. 30+20 c. Ice hockey 1·00 60
2959 2 f. 50+20 c. Luge .. 1·00 65
2960 2 f. 50+20 c. Curling .. 1·00 65
2961 2 f. 50+20 c. Artistic skiing .. .. .. 1·00 65
2962 2 f. 50+20 c. Downhill skiing .. .. .. 1·00 65

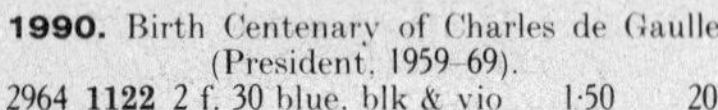

**1990.** Birth Centenary of Charles de Gaulle (President, 1959–69).
2964 **1122** 2 f. 30 blue, blk & vio 1·50 20

**1123** Aircraft and Hymans

**1124** Eyes and Keyboard

**1990.** 90th Birth Anniv of Max Hymans (civil aviation pioneer).
2965 **1123** 2 f. 30 green, vio & bl 90 10

**1990.** Art. As T **491**.
2966 5 f. multicoloured .. 2·00 90
2967 5 f. blue, brown and ochre 2·00 1·00
2968 5 f. multicoloured .. 3·25 90
2969 5 f. multicoloured .. 1·90 90
DESIGNS—VERT. No. 2966, "Woman's Profile" (Odilon Redon); 2967, "Seated Cambodian Woman" (Auguste Rodin); 2968, "Head of Christ of Wissembourg"; 2969, "Yellow and Grey" (Roger Bissiere).

**1990.** Stamp Day.
2970 **1124** 2 f. 30+60 c. blue, ultramarine & yell 1·00 70
2971 2 f. 30+60 c. deep green, green, blue and yellow 1·10 85

**1125** Guehenno

**1126** Macon Post Office

**1990.** Birth Cent of Jean Guehenno (writer).
2972 **1125** 3 f. 20 brown & lt brn 90 20

**1990.** Tourist Publicity. As T **490**.
2973 2 f. 30 orange, blue & blk 1·00 15
2974 2 f. 30 black, blue & green 1·00 10
2975 3 f. 80 brown and green .. 1·50 20
2976 3 f. 80 purple, brown & bl 1·50 20
DESIGNS: No. 2973, Cluny; 2974, Aqueduct, Briare Canal; 2975, Flaran-Gers Abbey; 2976, Cap Canaille Cassis.

**1990.** Europa. Post Office Buildings.
2978 **1126** 2 f. 30 black, ochre and blue .. .. 90 20
2979 – 3 f. 20 multicoloured 1·25 35
DESIGN: 3 f. 20, Cerizay post office.

**1127** Crowd

**1990.** Centenary of Labour Day.
2980 **1127** 2 f. 30 multicoloured 1·00 15

**1128** Quimper Faience Plate

**1129** Institute Building

**1990.** Red Cross Fund.
2981 **1128** 2 f. 30+60 c. mult .. 1·10 85

**1990.** Arab World Institute.
2982 **1129** 3 f. 80 dp bl, bl & red 1·50 35

**1130** Detail of Stonework, Notre Dame des Marais

**1131** "La Poste"

**1990.** Federation of French Philatelic Societies Congress, Villefranche-sur-Saone.
2983 **1130** 2 f. 30 blk, grn & red 90 15

**1990.** Round the World Yacht Race.
2984 **1131** 2 f. 30 multicoloured 90 20

**1132** Georges Brassens

**1133** Cross of Lorraine and Marianne

**1990.** Red Cross Fund. French Singers. Mult.
2985 2 f. 30+50 c. Aristide Bruant .. .. 1·10 1·10
2986 2 f. 30+50 c. Maurice Chevalier .. .. 1·10 1·10
2987 2 f. 30+50 c. Tino Rossi 1·10 1·10
2988 2 f. 30+50 c. Edith Piaf 1·10 1·10
2989 2 f. 30+50 c. Jacques Brel 1·10 1·10
2990 2 f. 30+50 c. Type **1132** 1·10 1·10

**1990.** 50th Anniv of De Gaulle's Call to Resist.
2991 **1133** 2 f. 30 red, blue & blk 55 15

**1134** Aerial View of House

**1990.** 5th Anniv of France–Brazil House, Rio de Janeiro.
2992 **1134** 3 f. 20 multicoloured 1·10 35

**1990.** Precancels. Musical Instruments (2nd series). As T **110**.
2993 1 f. 46 emerald and green 1·00 75
2994 1 f. 89 brown and orange 1·25 1·00
2995 1 f. 93 green & deep green 1·25 75
2996 2 f. 39 mauve and purple 1·50 1·10
2997 2 f. 74 violet and blue .. 1·90 1·50
2998 3 f. 06 blue and deep blue 2·50 2·00
2999 5 f. 10 violet and purple 2·75 2·50
DESIGNS: 1 f. 46, Accordion; 1 f. 89, Breton bagpipe; 1 f. 93, Harp; 2 f. 39, Piano; 2 f. 74, Violin; 3 f. 06, Provencal drum; 5 f. 10, Hurdy-gurdy.
See note below No. 432 (1920).

**1135** Relief Map of France

**1136** Roach

**1990.** 50th Anniv of National Geographical Institute.
3000 **1135** 2 f. 30 multicoloured 1·25 20

**1990.** Freshwater Fishes. Multicoloured.
3001 2 f. Type **1136** .. 75 15
3002 3 f. River perch .. 1·10 20
3003 4 f. Atlantic salmon .. 1·90 60
3004 5 f. Northern pike .. 1·90 30

**1138** Genevoix

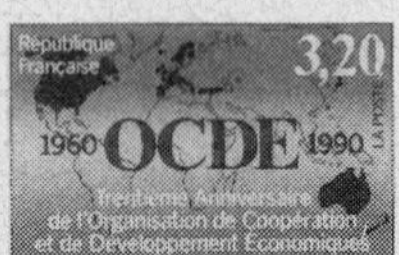
**1139** World Map

**1990.** Birth Centenary of Maurice Genevoix (writer).
3006 **1138** 2 f. 30 green & black 90 15

**1990.** 30th Anniv of Organization for Economic Co-operation and Development.
3007 **1139** 3 f. 20 blue & ultram 1·25 20

**1991.** Art. As T **491**.
3008 5 f. multicoloured .. 2·25 55
3009 5 f. black and stone .. 2·25 55
3010 5 f. black .. .. 1·90 45
3011 5 f. multicoloured .. 1·90 45
DESIGNS—VERT: No. 3008, "The Swing" (Auguste Renoir); 3009, "The Black Knot" (Georges Seurat); 3010, "Volta faccia" (Francois Rouan). HORIZ: No. 3011, "Oh Black Painting" (Roberto Matta).

**1140** Paul Eluard (after Pablo Picasso)

**1991.** Red Cross Fund. French Poets. Each grey, black and blue.
3013 2 f. 50+50 c. Type **1140** 1·10 1·10
3014 2 f. 50+50 c. Andre Breton (after Man Ray) 1·10 1·10
3015 2 f. 50+50 c. Louis Aragon (after Henri Matisse) .. .. 1·10 1·10
3016 2 f. 50+50 c. Francis Ponge (after Stella Mertens) .. .. 1·10 1·10
3017 2 f. 50+50 c. Jacques Prevert (after Picasso) 1·10 1·10
3018 2 f. 50 + 50 c. Rene Char (after Valentine Hugo) 1·10 1·10

**1141** Mail Sorting by Hand and by Machine

**1991.** Stamp Day. Multicoloured, colour of machine given.
3019 **1141** 2 f. 50+60 c. blue .. 1·10 1·00
3020 2 f. 50+60 c. violet 1·25 1·10

**1142** Children, Bicycle and Dove

**1991.** "Philexjeunes 91" Youth Stamp Exhibition, Cholet.
3021 **1142** 2 f. 50 multicoloured 1·00 15

**1143** Mozart and Globe

**1144** Eyes and Forms of Writing

**1991.** Death Bicentenary of Wolfgang Amadeus Mozart (composer).
3022 **1143** 2 f. 50 black, bl & red 1·00 50

**1991.** 350th Anniv of State Printing Office.
3023 **1144** 4 f. multicoloured .. 1·50 30

**1991.** Tourist Publicity. As T **490**.
3024 2 f. 50 multicoloured .. 1·00 10
3025 2 f. 50 multicoloured .. 1·40 10
3026 4 f. lilac .. .. 1·60 35
DESIGNS—VERT: No. 3024, Chevire Bridge, Nantes. HORIZ: No. 3025, Carennac; 3026, Munster Valley.

**1145** Poster

**1146** "Ariane" Rocket and Map of French Guiana

**1991.** 90th Anniv of Concours Lepine (French Association of Small Manufacturers and Inventors).
3028 **1145** 4 f. multicoloured .. 1·50 35

**1991.** Europa. Europe in Space. Each blue, red and green
3029 2 f. 50 Type **1146** .. 1·00 20
3030 3 f. 50 "TDF-1" broadcasting satellite, eyes and globe .. .. 1·50 40

**1147** Perpignan

**1148** Painting by Joan Miro

**1991.** Federation of French Philatelic Societies Congress, Perpignan.
3031 **1147** 2 f. 50 red, grey & bl 1·00 10

**1991.** Centenary of French Open Tennis Championships.
3032 **1148** 3 f. 50 multicoloured 1·50 55

**1150** Organ Pipes

**1151** Illustration from Gaston's "Book of Hunting"

**1991.** Organ of St. Nicholas's, Wasquehal.
3034 **1150** 4 f. buff and brown 1·60 35

**1991.** 600th Death Anniv of Gaston III Phoebus, Count of Foix.
3035 **1151** 2 f. 50 multicoloured 90 20

**1991.** No value expressed. As T **1118** but inscr "D". Imperf (self-adhesive) or perf (3037), perf (3036).
3036 (2 f. 20) green .. .. 1·00 10
3037 (2 f. 50) red .. .. 1·00 10

**1152** Brown Bear

**1991.** Nature. Multicoloured.
3039 2 f. Type **1152** .. .. 90 15
3040 3 f. Hermann's tortoise .. 1·10 30
3041 4 f. Eurasian beaver .. 1·60 65
3042 5 f. Common kingfisher .. 2·00 65

**1153** Forest

**1991.** 10th World Forestry Congress, Paris.
3043 **1153** 2 f. 50 green, bl & blk 1·10 20

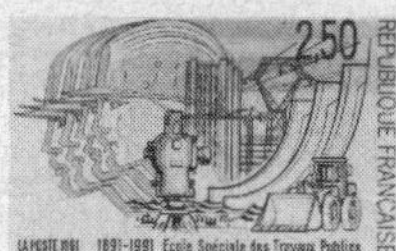

**1154** Aspects of Public Works

**1991.** Centenary of School of Public Works.
3044 **1154** 2 f. 50 multicoloured 1·00 15

## MINIMUM PRICE

The minimum price quoted is 10p which represents a handling charge rather than a basis for valuing common stamps. For further notes about prices see introductory pages.

**1155** "Bird Monument" (detail)

**1991.** Birth Centenary of Max Ernst (painter).
3045 **1155** 2 f. 50 multicoloured 1·25 50

**1156** Cerdan

**1991.** 75th Birth Anniv of Marcel Cerdan (boxer).
3046 **1156** 2 f. 50 black and red 1·00 20

**1157** "Amnesty International"

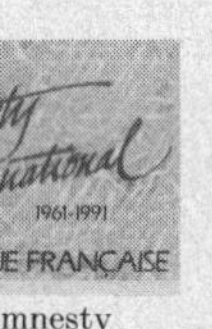

**1158** Stylized Flame

**1991.** 30th Anniv of Amnesty International.
3047 **1157** 3 f. 40 bl, mve & blk 1·50 50

**1991.** Winter Olympic Games, Albertville (1992) (3rd issue).
3048 **1158** 2 f. 50 blue, blk & red 1·00 15

**1159** "Toulon" (Francois Nardi)

**1160** Bird

**1991.** Red Cross Fund.
3049 **1159** 2 f. 50+60 c. mult .. 80 80

**1991.** 5th Paralympic Games, Tignes (1992).
3050 **1160** 2 f. 50 blue .. .. 60 15

**1161** Shore

**1991.** 150th Anniv of Voluntary Adhesion of Mayotte to France.
3051 **1161** 2 f. 50 multicoloured 1·00 15

**1992.** Precancels. Musical Instruments (3rd series). As T **1110**.
3052 1 f. 60 brown and orange 6·50 3·75
3053 1 f. 98 bistre and ochre .. 3·75 2·75
3054 2 f. 08 orange and yellow 1·90 1·50
3055 2 f. 46 violet .. .. 1·90 1·50
3056 2 f. 98 lilac and mauve .. 1·90 1·50
3057 3 f. 08 purple and red .. 4·50 3·50
3058 3 f. 14 green and turquoise 2·50 1·90
3059 3 f. 19 grey and black .. 5·00 3·00
3060 5 f. 28 green and lt green 4·50 3·00
3061 5 f. 30 ultramarine & blue 3·00 2·50
3062 5 f. 32 brown & dp brown 3·00 2·50
DESIGNS: 1 f. 60, Guitar; 1 f. 98, Accordion; 2 f. 08, Saxophone; 2 f. 46, Breton bagpipe; 2 f. 98, Banjo; 3 f. 08, Provencal drum; 3 f. 14, Hurdy-gurdy; 3 f. 19, Harp; 5 f. 28, Xylophone; 5 f. 30, Piano; 5 f. 32, Violin.
See note below No. 432 (1920).

**1162** Plan of French Pavilion

**1992.** "Expo '92" World's Fair, Seville.
3063 **1162** 2 f. 50 blue, blk & grn 1·00 15

**1163** Post Office, Reception Area and Postal Self-service Machines

**1992.** Stamp Day.
3064 **1163** 2 f. 50+60 c. black, blue and yellow .. 1·10 80
3065 2 f. 50+60 c. red, blue, black & yell 1·10 80

**1164** Runner

**1165** Cesar Franck

**1992.** Olympic Games, Barcelona.
3066 **1164** 2 f. 50 multicoloured 1·60 10

**1992.** Red Cross Fund. Composers. Mult.
3067 2 f. 50+50 c. Type **1165** 1·10 1·10
3068 2 f. 50+50 c. Erik Satie .. 1·10 1·10
3069 2 f. 50+50 c. Florent Schmitt .. .. 1·10 1·10
3070 2 f. 50+50 c. Arthur Honegger .. .. 1·10 1·10
3071 2 f. 50+50 c. Georges Auric .. .. 1·10 1·10
3072 2 f. 50+50 c. Germaine Tailleferre .. .. 1·10 1·10

**1166** Marguerite d'Angouleme (after Clouet)

**1167** "Madonna, Child and Angel" (Botticelli)

**1992.** 500th Birth Anniv of Marguerite d'Angouleme, Queen of Navarre.
3073 **1166** 3 f. 40 multicoloured 1·40 60

**1992.** 500th Anniv of Ajaccio.
3074 **1167** 4 f. multicoloured .. 1·50 25

**1168** Navigational Instruments and Map

**1169** Wheat, Poppies and Loaves

**1992.** Europa. 500th Anniv of Discovery of America by Columbus. Multicoloured.
3075 2 f. 50 Type **1168** .. 1·00 15
3076 3 f. 40 Caravel, map and compass rose .. .. 1·50 45

**1992.** Tourist Publicity. As T **490**.
3077 2 f. 50 brown, blue & grn 1·00 10
3078 3 f. 40 brown, green & bl 1·40 50
3079 4 f. blue, black and green 1·50 25
3080 4 f. green, lt green & brn 1·50 25

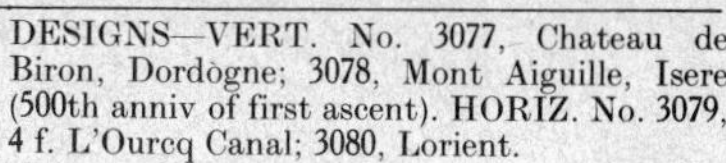

DESIGNS—VERT. No. 3077, Chateau de Biron, Dordogne; 3078, Mont Aiguille, Isere (500th anniv of first ascent). HORIZ. No. 3079, 4 f. L'Ourcq Canal; 3080, Lorient.

**1992.** International Bread and Cereals Congress.
3081 **1169** 3 f. 40 multicoloured 1·40 60

**1170** Couple leaping through Stamp

**1992.** Federation of French Philatelic Societies Congress, Niort.
3082 **1170** 2 f. 50 multicoloured 1·00 50

**1171** Olympic Rings

**1992.** Winter Olympic Games, Albertville, and Summer Games, Barcelona.
3083 **1171** 2 f. 50 multicoloured 1·90 35

**1172** Tautavel Man

**1173** Sand Lily

**1992.**
3084 **1172** 3 f. 40 multicoloured 1·40 20

**1992.** Art. As T **491**.
3085 5 f. black and stone .. 1·25 35
DESIGN—VERT. 5 f. "Portrait of Claude Deruet" (Jacques Callot).

**1992.** Flowers. Multicoloured.
3086 2 f. Type **1173** .. .. 45 15
3087 3 f. Sundew .. .. 65 20
3088 4 f. "Orchis palustris" .. 90 25
3089 5 f. Yellow water lily .. 1·10 30

**1174** Marianne and National Colours

**1175** Marianne

**1992.** Bicentenary of Year One of First Republic.
3090 **1174** 2 f. 50 multicoloured 1·00 15

**1992.** Bicentenary of Declaration of First Republic. Each red.
3091 2 f. 50 Type **1175** .. 1·00 15
3092 2 f. 50 Tree of Liberty .. 1·00 15
3093 2 f. 50 Marianne as cockerel .. .. 1·00 15
3094 2 f. 50 "Republique Francaise" .. .. 1·00 15

**1992.** Precancels. Musical Instruments (4th series). As T **1110**.
3095 1 f. 73 deep green & green 75 50
3096 2 f. 25 red and orange .. 1·00 75
3097 3 f. 51 ultramarine & blue 1·60 1·25
3098 5 f. 40 red and mauve .. 2·25 1·90
DESIGNS: 1 f. 73, Guitar; 2 f. 25, Saxophone; 3 f. 51, Banjo; 5 f. 40, Xylophone.
See note below No. 432 (1920).

**1176** Symbol of Market

**1992.** European Single Market.
3099 **1176** 2 f. 50 multicoloured 1·00 15

**1177** Farman M.F.7 Type Biplane and Boeing 737-500

**1178** Paul and Electricity Pylon

**1992.** 80th Anniv of Nancy–Luneville Air Mail Service.
3100 **1177** 2 f. 50 multicoloured 1·00 50

**1992.** 10th Death Anniv of Marcel Paul (politician).
3101 **1178** 4 f. 20 blue & purple 1·60 25

**1179** "Woman at Window" (Paul Delvaux)

**1992.** Contemporary Art.
3102 **1179** 5 f. multicoloured .. 1·10 75
3103 – 5 f. multicoloured .. 1·10 75
3104 – 5 f. black, mve & yell 1·10 75
3105 – 5 f. black and yellow 1·10 75
DESIGNS: No. 3103, "Portrait of Man" (Francis Bacon); 3104, Abstract (Alberto Burri); 3105, Abstract (Antoni Tapies).
See also Nos. 3154, 3176, 3285 and 3301/2.

**1180** Birds holding Strings (T. Ungerer)

**1181** Horse, Guitar and Dancer

**1992.** Red Cross Fund. Mutual Aid Meeting, Strasbourg.
3106 **1180** 2 f. 50+60 c. mult .. 1·10 70

**1992.** Gypsies.
3107 **1181** 2 f. 50 multicoloured 1·10 15

**1182** Smew Pair

**1184** Memorial

**1183** "La Poste" (yacht) and Globe

**1993.** Ducks. Multicoloured.
3108 2 f. Type **1182** .. .. 75 10
3109 3 f. Ferruginous duck and drake .. .. .. 1·25 20
3110 4 f. Common sheldrake pair .. .. .. 1·60 60
3111 5 f. Red-breasted merganser pair .. 2·00 30

**1993.** "Postmen around the World". Post Office Team Participation in Around the World Yacht Race.
3112 **1183** 2 f. 50 yellow, ultramarine & blue 1·00 15
3113 2 f. 80 yellow, ultramarine & blue 1·90 20

**1993.** Indo-China Wars Memorial, Frejus.
3114 **1184** 4 f. multicoloured .. 1·50 50

**1185** Postman with Bicycle

**1186** Yacht and Runner

**1993.** Stamp Day.
3115 **1185** 2 f. 50 multicoloured 1·25 60
3116 2 f. 50+60 c. mult .. 1·10 70

**1993.** Mediterranean Games, Agde and Roussillon (Languedoc).
3117 **1186** 2 f. 50 multicoloured 1·00 15

**1187** Maria Deraismes and Georges Martin (founders)

**1189** Guy de Maupassant

**1188** "Red Rhythm Blue" (Olivier Debre)

**1993.** Centenary of Le Droit Humain (International Mixed Freemasons Order).
3118 **1187** 3 f. 40 black and blue 1·25 50

**1993.** Europa. Contemporary Art. Mult.
3119 2 f. 50 Type **1188** .. 80 50
3120 3 f. 40 "Le Griffu" (bronze, Germaine Richier) (vert) .. 1·25 60

**1993.** As T **1118** but no value expressed. Imperf (self-adhesive) or perf.
3121 **1118** (–) red .. .. 55 15
No. 3121 was sold at the current inland rate (at time of issue 2 f. 50).

**1993.** Tourist Publicity. As T **490** and **949**.
3124 2 f. 80 green, brown & bl 1·00 20
3125 3 f. 40 red, green & blue 1·25 20
3126 4 f. 20 dp green, grn & brn 1·50 25
3127 4 f. 20 brown and green .. 1·60 50
3128 4 f. 40 black, green & red 1·50 25
3129 4 f. 40 multicoloured .. 1·50 25
DESIGNS—As T **490**: HORIZ. No. 3124, La Chaise-Dieu Abbey, Haute-Loire; 3128, Montbeliard-Doubs. VERT. No. 3125, Artouste train, Laruns; 3126, Minerve-Herault; 3129, Le Jacquemard, Lambesc. As T **949**: No. 3127, Chinon.

**1993.** Red Cross Fund. Writers. Mult.
3131 2 f. 50+50 c. Type **1189** 1·00 1·00
3132 2 f. 50+50 c. Alain .. 1·00 1·00
3133 2 f. 50+50 c. Jean Cocteau .. 1·00 1·00
3134 2 f. 50+50 c. Marcel Pagnol .. 1·00 1·00
3135 2 f. 50+50 c. Andre Chamson .. 1·00 1·00
3136 2 f. 50+50 c. Marguerite Yourcenar .. .. 1·00 1·00

**1190** Map of Europe and Liberty

**1993.** 9th European Constitutional Court Conference on Human Rights.
3137 **1190** 2 f. 50 multicoloured 1·00 15

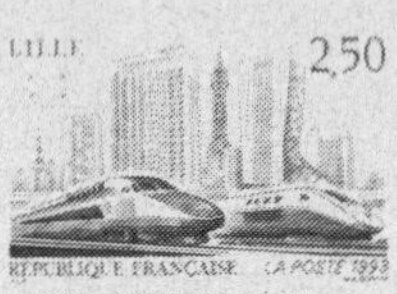

**1191** Reinhardt

**1192** Weiss

**1993.** 40th Death Anniv of Django Reinhardt (guitarist).
3138 **1191** 4 f. 20 multicoloured 1·50 40

**1993.** Birth Centenary of Louise Weiss (women's rights campaigner).
3139 **1192** 2 f. 50 black, orange and red .. .. 1·00 40



**1193** "TGV" Trains at Lille

**1993.** Federation of French Philatelic Societies Congress, Lille.
3140 **1193** 2 f. 50 light blue, blue and mauve .. 1·00 15



**1194** Emblem

**1993.** Bicentenary of National Natural History Museum, Paris.
3141 **1194** 2 f. 50 multicoloured 1·00 15

**1195** Bas-relief (Georges Jeanclos) (left half)

**1196** Central Telegraph Tower, Paris

**1993.** Martyrs and Heroes of the Resistance. Multicoloured.
3142 2 f. 50 Type **1195** .. 1·00 40
3143 4 f. 20 Right half of bas-relief .. .. .. 1·50 50
Nos. 3142/3 were issued together, se-tenant, forming a composite design.

**1993.** Bicentenary of Chappe's Optical Telegraph.
3144 **1196** 2 f. 50 black, stone and blue .. .. 1·00 15

**1993.** Precancels. Musical Instruments (5th series). As T **1110**.
3145 1 f. 82 grey and black .. 75 50
3146 2 f. 34 brown and orange 1·00 75
3147 3 f. 86 red and pink .. 1·60 1·25
3148 5 f. 93 violet and mauve 2·25 1·90
DESIGNS: 1 f. 82, Trumpet; 2 f. 34, Drum; 3 f. 86, Hurdy-gurdy; 5 f. 93, Xylophone.

**1197** Map of Corsica and "Casabianca" (submarine)

**1198** Le Val-de-Grace, Paris

**1993.** 50th Anniv of Liberation of Corsica.
3149 **1197** 2 f. 80 black, red & bl 1·25 20

**1993.** Art. As T **491**. Multicoloured.
3150 5 f. "Saint Thomas" (Georges de la Tour) (vert) .. 1·90 75
3151 5 f. "The Muses" (Maurice Denis) (vert) .. .. 1·90 75

**1993.** Bicentenary of Conversion of Monastery of Le Val-de-Grace to Military Hospital (now museum).
3152 **1198** 3 f. 70 blk, grn & brn 1·25 25

**1199** Clowns

**1200** Girl studying Flower ("Happy Holiday") (C. Wendling)

**1993.** National Centre for Circus Arts, Chalons-sur-Marne.
3153 **1199** 2 f. 80 multicoloured 1·00 20

**1993.** Contemporary Art. As T **1179**.
3154 5 f. red and black .. 1·10 60
3155 5 f. multicoloured .. 1·10 60
DESIGNS: No. 3154, Abstract (Takis); 3155, "Enhanced Engraving" (Maria Elena Vieira da Silva).

**1993.** Greetings Stamps. "The Pleasure of Writing". Designs by comic strip artists. Multicoloured.
3156 2 f. 80 Type **1200** .. 1·00 20
3157 2 f. 80 Clowns ("Happy Holiday") (B. Olivie) .. 1·00 20
3158 2 f. 80 Cat on birthday cake ("Happy Birthday") (S. Colman) 1·00 20
3159 2 f. 80 Girl with cake ("Happy Birthday") (G. Sorel) .. 1·00 20
3160 2 f. 80 Man courting woman on balcony ("With Passion") (J.-M. Thiriet) .. .. 1·00 20
3161 2 f. 80 Man playing large fountain pen ("Pleasure of Writing") (E. Davodeau) .. 1·00 20
3162 2 f. 80 Pig with letter ("Greetings") (J. de Moor) .. .. 1·00 20
3163 2 f. 80 Jester in horseshoe ("Good Luck") (Mezzo) 1·00 20
3164 2 f. 80 Clowns running ("Best Wishes") (N. de Crecy) .. 1·00 20
3165 2 f. 80 Girl and cat watching tree fairy ("Best Wishes") (F. Magnin) .. .. 1·00 20
3166 2 f. 80 Cards tumbling from Santa Claus's sack ("Happy Christmas") (T. Robin) .. 1·00 20
3167 2 f. 80 Mouse dressed as Santa Claus ("Happy Christmas") (P. Prugne) 1·00 20

**1202** Louvre, 1793

**1993.** Bicentenary of Louvre Museum. Mult.
3169 2 f. 80 Type **1202** .. 1·10 50
3170 4 f. 40 Louvre, 1993 .. 1·60 60
Nos. 3169/70 were issued together, se-tenant, forming a composite design.

1203 "St. Nicholas"

1204 Cast-iron Subway Entrance (detail, Hector Guimard)

**1993.** Red Cross Fund. Metz Engravings.
3171 **1203** 2 f. 80+60 c. mult .. 1·10 90

**1994.** Art Nouveau. Multicoloured.
3172 2 f. 80 Type **1204** .. 1·00 20
3173 2 f. 80 "Roses of France Cup" (vase, Emile Galle) .. .. 1·00 20
3174 4 f. 40 Drawing-room table with bronze water-lily decoration (Louis Majorelle) .. 1·50 25
3175 4 f. 40 Stoneware teapot (Pierre-Adrien Dalpayrat) .. .. 1·50 25

**1994.** Contemporary Art. As T **1179**. Mult.
3176 6 f. 70 Abstract (Sean Scully) .. .. 1·75 90
3177 6 f. 70 "Couple" (Georg Baselitz) .. .. 1·75 90

1205 "Death of St. Stephen"

**1994.** 12th-century Stained Glass Window, Le Mans Cathedral.
3179 **1205** 6 f. 70 multicoloured 2·50 90

**1994.** Tourist Publicity. As T **490**.
3180 2 f. 80 multicoloured .. 1·00 20
3181 2 f. 80 blue .. .. 1·00 20
3182 3 f. 70 brown, deep green and green .. .. 1·25 25
3183 4 f. 40 brown and blue .. 1·40 50
3184 4 f. 40 brown and red .. 1·40 50
DESIGNS—HORIZ: No. 3180, "Mount Sainte Victoire" (Paul Cezanne); 3181, Bridge at Rupt aux Nonains, Saulx Region, Meuse. 3184, Argentat. VERT: No. 3182, La Grand Cascade, Saint-Cloud Park; 3183, Old port and St. John the Baptist Church, Bastia.

1206 European Union Flag

**1994.** European Parliament Elections.
3185 **1206** 2 f. 80 bl, yell & grey 1·00 20

1207 Mourguet and Guignol

**1994.** 150th Death Anniv of Laurent Mourguet (creator of Guignol (puppet)).
3186 **1207** 2 f. 80 multicoloured 1·00 20

**HAVE YOU READ THE NOTES AT THE BEGINNING OF THIS CATALOGUE?**
These often provide answers to the enquiries we receive.

1208 Emblem

**1994.** Bicent of Polytechnic Institute, Paris.
3187 **1208** 2 f. 80 multicoloured 1·00 20

1209 "Marianne"

1210 "The Vikings" (detail, Bayeux Tapestry)

**1994.** Stamp Day. 50th Anniv of Edmond Dulac's "Marianne" Design.
3189 **1209** 2 f. 80 red and blue 1·90 90
3188 2 f. 80+60 c. red & bl 1·40 1·10

**1994.** Franco-Swedish Cultural Relations. Multicoloured.
3191 2 f. 80 Type **1210** .. 1·90 50
3192 2 f. 80 Viking longships (different detail) .. 1·90 50
3193 2 f. 80 Costume design for sailor by Fernand Leger in Swedish Ballet production of "Skating Rink" .. .. 1·90 50
3194 2 f. 80 Costume design for gentleman in "Skating Rink" .. .. 1·90 50
3195 3 f. 70 "Banquet for Gustav III at the Trianon, 1784" (Niclas Lafrensen the younger) 2·50 1·10
3196 3 f. 70 Swedish and French flags .. .. 2·50 1·10
Nos. 3195/6 are larger, 49 × 37 mm.

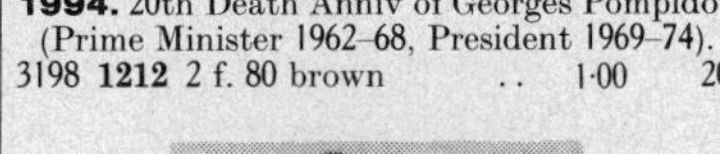

1211 Mountain Ambush

1212 Pompidou

**1994.** 50th Anniv of Liberation. The Maquis (resistance movement).
3197 **1211** 2 f. 80 multicoloured 1·00 20

**1994.** 20th Death Anniv of Georges Pompidou (Prime Minister 1962–68, President 1969–74).
3198 **1212** 2 f. 80 brown .. 1·00 20

1213 Boy netting Stamps

**1994.** "Philex Jeunes 94" Youth Stamp Exhibition, Grenoble.
3199 **1213** 2 f. 80 multicoloured 1·00 20

1214 AIDS Virus

**1994.** Europa. Discoveries. Multicoloured.
3200 2 f. 80 Type **1214** (11th anniv of discovery) .. 1·10 20
3201 3 f. 70 Wavelength formula (70th anniv of Louis de Broglie's proof of undulatory theory of matter) .. .. 1·40 60

1215 Bank Emblem

**1994.** 27th Assembly of Asian Development Bank, Nice.
3202 **1215** 2 f. 80 multicoloured 1·00 20

1216 British Lion and French Cockerel over Tunnel

**1994.** Opening of Channel Tunnel. Mult.
3203 2 f. 80 Type **1216** .. 1·00 20
3204 2 f. 80 Symbolic hands over train .. .. 1·00 20
3205 4 f. 30 Type **1216** .. 1·50 50
3206 4 f. 30 As No. 3204 .. 1·50 50

1217 Martigues inside Fish

**1994.** Federation of French Philatelic Societies Congress, Martigues.
3207 **1217** 2 f. 80 violet, bl & grn 1·00 20

1218 Court Building, Ile de la Cite, Paris

**1994.** Court of Cassation.
3208 **1218** 2 f. 80 multicoloured 1·00 20

1219 Landing Forces and Beach Defences

**1994.** 50th Anniv of Normandy Landings.
3209 **1219** 4 f. 30 red, indigo and blue .. .. 1·50 25

1220 Allied Forces

**1994.** 50th Anniv of Liberation.
3210 **1220** 4 f. 30 multicoloured 1·50 25

1221 Sorbonne University and Pierre de Coubertin (founder)

1222 Organ Pipes

**1994.** Centenary of International Olympic Committee.
3211 **1221** 2 f. 80 multicoloured 1·00 25

**1994.** Poitiers Cathedral Organ.
3212 **1222** 4 f. 40 multicoloured 1·50 20

1223 Flag, Map and Soldier

1224 Oak

**1994.** 50th Anniv of Allied Landings in Southern France.
3213 **1223** 2 f. 80 multicoloured 65 20

**1994.** Precancels. Leaves.
3321 – 1 f. 87 brown & green 50 25
3214 **1224** 1 f. 91 olive & green 75 25
3322 – 2 f. 18 red and lake 65 50
3215 – 2 f. 46 green & lt grn 1·00 30
3216 – 4 f. 24 red and orange 1·50 1·10
3323 – 4 f. 66 yellow & green 1·40 1·00
3217 – 6 f. 51 turquoise & bl 2·40 1·90
3324 – 7 f. 11 turquoise & bl 2·40 1·75
DESIGNS: 1 f. 87, Ash; 2 f. 18, Beech; 2 f. 46, Plane; 4 f. 24, Chestnut; 4 f. 66, Walnut; 6 f. 51, Holly; 7 f. 11, Elm.

1225 "Moses and the Daughters of Jethro" (drawing) (½-size illustration)

**1994.** 400th Birth Anniv of Nicolas Poussin (artist).
3218 **1225** 4 f. 40 brown & black 1·60 50

1226 Yvonne Printemps (singer and actress)

1227 Map and Foucault's Pendulum

**1994.** Entertainers. Multicoloured.
3219 2 f. 80+60 c. Type **1226** 1·10 1·10
3220 2 f. 80+60 c. Fernandel (Fernand Contandin) (actor) .. .. 1·10 1·10
3221 2 f. 80+60 c. Josephine Baker (music hall performer) .. .. 1·10 1·10
3222 2 f. 80+60 c. Bourvil (Andre Raimbourg) (actor) .. .. 1·10 1·10
3223 2 f. 80+60 c. Yves Montand (singer and actor) .. .. 1·10 1·10
3224 2 f. 80+60 c. Coluche (Michel Colucci) (comedian) .. .. 1·10 1·10

**1994.** Bicentenary of National Conservatory of Arts and Craft.
3225 **1227** 2 f. 80 pur, bl & red 1·00 20

1228 Doorway

1229 Simenon and Quai des Orfevres, Paris

**1994.** Bicent of Ecole Normale Superieure.
3226 **1228** 2 f. 80 blue and red 90 20

**1994.** 5th Death Anniv of Georges Simenon (novelist).
3227 **1229** 2 f. 80 multicoloured 1·00 20

**1230** Headless Drug Addict (after Vladimir Velickovic)

**1232** Lodge Emblem and Symbols of Freemasonry

**1994.** National Drug Addiction Prevention Day.
3228 **1230** 2 f. 80 multicoloured 1·00 20

**1994.** Centenary of Grand Lodge of France.
3230 **1232** 2 f. 80 brn, red & bl 1·00 20

**1233** Stormy Sea and Colas

**1994.** 16th Death Anniv of Alain Colas (yachtsman).
3231 **1233** 3 f. 70 black, green and emerald .. 1·25 25

**1234** St. Vaast

**1994.** Red Cross Fund. 15th-century Arras Tapestry.
3232 **1234** 2 f. 80+60 c. mult .. 1·25 80

**1235** AIDS Virus (½-size illustration)

**1994.** A.I.D.S. Day.
3233 **1235** 2 f. 80 multicoloured 1·00 60

The stamp and se-tenant label, as illustrated, comprise No. 3233. For stamp without attached label, see No. 3200.

**1236** Slogan

**1994.** 50th Anniv of National Press Federation.
3234 **1236** 2 f. 80 purple & yell 1·00 20

**1237** Champ Elysees (½-size illustration)

**1994.** New Year.
3235 **1237** 4 f. 40 multicoloured 1·90 30

**1239** Normandy Bridge (½-size illustration)

**1995.** Inauguration of Normandy Bridge (over Seine between Le Havre and Honfleur).
3237 **1239** 4 f. 40 multicoloured 1·90 30

**1240** Emblem

**1241** Pasteur

**1995.** European Public Notaries.
3238 **1240** 2 f. 80 multicoloured 90 20

**1995.** Death Centenary of Louis Psateur (chemist).
3239 **1241** 3 f. 70 multicoloured 1·25 50

**1995.** Tourist Publicity. As T **490**.
3240 2 f. 80 green and olive .. 1·00 20
3241 2 f. 80 green, brown & bl 1·00 20
3242 4 f. 40 multicoloured .. 1·50 30
3243 4 f. 40 black, lilac & green 1·50 30

DESIGNS—HORIZ: No. 3240, Malt works, Stenay; 3241, Remiremont, Vosges; 3242, Nyons Bridge, Drome. VERT: No. 3143, Margot gate and St. Martial's Church, Correze.

**1995.** Art. As T **491**.
3245 6 f. 70 black, yellow & red 2·25 75
3246 6 f. 70 black, blue & dp bl 2·25 75
3247 6 f. 70 multicoloured .. 2·25 75
3248 6 f. 70 multicoloured .. 2·25 90

DESIGNS—VERT: No. 3245, Reliquary of St. Taurin, Evereux; 3248, "The Cradle" (Berthe Morisot). HORIZ: No. 3246, Study for "The Dream of Happiness" (Pierre Prud'hon); 3247, Seascape (Zao Wou-Ki).

**1242** Band-tailed Pigeons

**1995.** Bird Paintings by John James Audubon (ornithologist). Multicoloured.
3249 2 f. 80 Type **1242** .. 1·00 20
3250 2 f. 80 Snowy egret .. 1·00 20
3251 4 f. 30 Common tern .. 1·40 30
3252 4 f. 40 Rough-legged buzzards .. .. 1·40 30

**1243** "Marianne"

**1995.** Stamp Day. 50th Anniv of Pierre Gandon's "Marianne" Design.
3255 **1243** 2 f. 80 green, bl & red 75 75
3254 2 f. 80+60 c. green, ultramarine & red 90 90

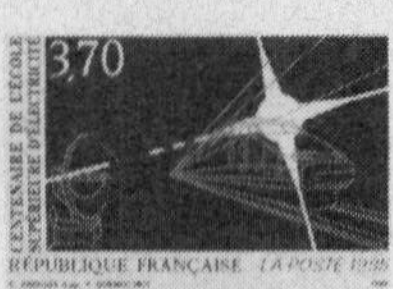


**1244** Hour Glass

**1245** Means of Communications

**1995.** 50th Anniv of Works Councils.
3257 **1244** 2 f. 80 brn, lt bl & bl 75 20

**1995.** Centenary (1994) of Advanced Institute of Electricity.
3258 **1245** 3 f. 70 lt bl, bl & red 1·25 50

**1246** Forms of Writing

**1995.** Bicentenary of School of Oriental Languages.
3259 **1246** 2 f. 80 multicoloured 1·00 20

**1247** Giono

**1248** "Ariane" Rocket and Map of French Guiana

**1995.** Birth Centenary of Jean Giono (writer).
3260 **1247** 3 f. 70 blk, blue & red 1·25 50

**1995.** French Space Centre in French Guiana.
3261 **1248** 2 f. 80 blue, grn & red 1·00 20

**1249** Steel and Worker

**1995.** Lorraine's Iron and Steel Industry.
3262 **1249** 2 f. 80 multicoloured 1·00 20

**1250** "Freedom"

**1995.** Europa. Peace and Freedom. Mult.
3263 2 f. 80 Type **1250** .. 1·00 20
3264 3 f. 70 "Peace" .. .. 1·25 25

**1251** Lumberjack

**1252** Paris Landmarks and Charles de Gaulle

**1995.** Forestry in the Ardennes.
3265 **1251** 4 f. 40 brn, blk & grn 1·40 30

**1995.** 50th Anniv of End of Second World War.
3266 **1252** 2 f. 80 multicoloured 1·00 20

**1253** Marianne in Assembly Building

**1995.** National Assembly.
3267 **1253** 2 f. 80 multicoloured 1·00 20

**1254** "King Louis XIII on Horseback" (Saumur tapestry)

**1995.** Red Cross Fund.
3268 **1254** 2 f. 80+60 c. mult .. 90 90

**1255** Winged Hand

**1256** Brittany

**1995.** 50th Anniv of French People's Relief Association (welfare organization).
3270 **1255** 2 f. 80 multicoloured 75 20

**1995.** Landscapes.
3271 **1256** 2 f. 40 green .. 65 20
3272 – 2 f. 40 green .. 65 20
3273 – 2 f. 80 red .. .. 75 20
3274 – 2 f. 80 red .. .. 75 20

DESIGNS: No. 3272, Vosges; 3273, Auvergne; 3274, Carmargue.

**1257** Orleans

**1258** "The Grasshopper and The Ant"

**1995.** Federation of French Philatelic Societies Congress, Orleans.
3275 **1257** 2 f. 80 multicoloured 75 20

**1995.** 300th Death Anniv of Jean de la Fontaine (writer of fables). Multicoloured.
3276 2 f. 80 Type **1258** .. 1·00 20
3277 2 f. 80 "The Fat Frog and the Ox" .. .. 1·00 20
3278 2 f. 80 "The Wolf and the Lamb" .. .. 1·00 20
3279 2 f. 80 "The Raven and the Fox" .. .. 1·00 20
3280 2 f. 80 "The Cat, the Weasel and the Little Rabbit" .. .. 1·00 20
3281 2 f. 80 "The Hare and the Tortoise" .. .. 1·00 20

**1259** Flower, Star and Wire

**1260** Maginot and Roof

**1995.** 53rd Anniv of Internment of Jews in Velodrome d'Hiver, Paris.
3282 **1259** 2 f. 80 multicoloured 1·00 20

**1995.** 63th Death Anniv of Andre Maginot (politician and instigator of Maginot Line (fortifications on French–German border)).
3283 **1260** 2 f 80 brn, grn & red 75 20

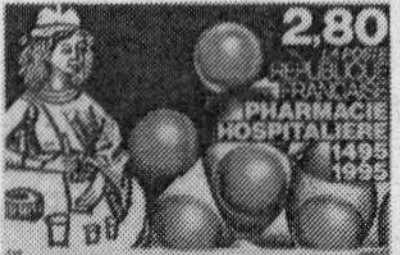


**1261** Lodge Emblem

**1262** Apothecary and Molecules

**1995.** 50th Anniv of Women's Grand Masonic Lodge of France.
3284 1261 2 f. 80 multicoloured 75 20

**1995.** Contemporary Art. As T **1179**. Mult.
3285 6 f. 70 Abstract (Kirkeby) 1·75 90

**1995.** 500th Anniv of Hospital Pharmacies.
3286 1262 2 f. 80 multicoloured 75 20

1263 "Thatched Cottages in Barbizon" (Narcisse Diaz de la Pena)

1264 Institute Emblem

**1995.** 170th Anniv of Barbizon School (artists' settlement).
3287 1263 4 f. 40 multicoloured 1·10 30

**1995.** 50th Anniv of National Civil Servants' Training Institute, Paris.
3288 1264 2 f. 80 multicoloured 75 20

1265 Institute Building

1266 New and Old Motor Vehicles and Headquarters

**1995.** Bicentenary of French Institute, Paris.
3289 1265 2 f. 80 blk, red & grn 75 20

**1995.** Centenary of French Automobile Club.
3290 1266 4 f. 40 black, bl & red 1·10 30

1267 Dove, Blue Helmet and Anniversary Emblem

1268 Shepherd

**1995.** 50th Anniv of U.N.O.
3291 1267 4 f. 30 multicoloured 1·40 30

**1995.** Red Cross Fund. Crib Figures from Provence. Multicoloured.
3292 2 f. 80+60 c. Type **1268** 90 90
3293 2 f. 80+60 c. Miller .. 90 90
3294 2 f. 80+60 c. Simpleton and tambourine player 90 90
3295 2 f. 80+60 c. Fishmonger 90 90
3296 2 f. 80+60 c. Knife-grinder .. .. 90 90
3297 2 f. 80+60 c. Elderly couple .. .. 90 90

1269 Jammes

**1995.** 127th Birth Anniv of Francis Jammes (poet).
3298 1269 3 f. 70 black and blue 95 25

1270 Architect's Plans

1271 Pitch and Balls

**1995.** Completion of Evry Cathedral.
3299 1270 2 f. 80 multicoloured 75 20

**1995.** World Cup Football Championship, France (1998).
3300 1271 2 f. 80 multicoloured 75 20

**1996.** Contemporary Art. As T **1179**.
3301 6 f. 70 black, red and blue 1·75 90
3302 6 f. 70 multicoloured .. 1·75 90
DESIGNS: No. 3301, "Sculpture" (Lucien Wercollier); 3302, "Horizon" (Jan Dibbets).

1272 Pottery Dog

1273 "St. Patrick" (stained glass window, Evie Hone)

**1996.** Completion of Archaeological Excavations in Saint-Martin Island, Guadeloupe.
3305 1272 2 f. 80 multicoloured 75 20

**1996.** Art. As T **491**.
3306 6 f. 70 multicoloured .. 1·60 40
3307 6 f. 70 multicoloured .. 1·60 40
3308 6 f. 70 gold, copper & blk 1·60 40
DESIGNS: No. 3306, "Narni Bridge" (Camille Corot); 3308, "Cellos" (Arman). VERT: No. 3307, Bronze horse (found at Neuvy-en-Sullias).

**1996.** "L'imaginaire Irlandais" Festival of Contemporary Irish Arts, France.
3311 1273 2 f. 80 multicoloured 75 20

1274 "The Sower"

1276 Descartes (after Frans Hals)

1275 Rueff and New 1 Franc Coin of 1960

**1996.** Stamp Day. 93rd Anniv of Louis-Oscar Roty's "The Sower" design.
3312 1274 2 f. 80+60 c. mauve and violet .. 90 90
3313 2 f. 80 mauve & vio 75 75

**1996.** Birth Centenary of Jacques Rueff (economist)
3315 1275 2 f. 80 black, bl & brn 75 20

**1996.** 400th Birth Anniv of Rene Descartes (philosopher and scientist).
3316 1276 4 f. 40 red .. .. 1·10 30

1277 Lightbulb and Flame

**1996.** 50th Anniv of Electricite de France and Gaz de France.
3317 1277 3 f. multicoloured .. 75 20

1278 Eurasian Beaver and Columbine, Cevennes

1280 Mme. de Sevigne (writer)

**1996.** National Parks. Multicoloured.
3318 3 f. Type **1278** .. .. 75 20
3319 4 f. 40 Bearded vulture and saxifrage, Mercantour .. .. 1·10 30
3320 4 f. 40 Ibex and gentian, Vanoise .. .. 1·10 30

**1996.** Europa. Famous Women.
3325 1280 3 f. multicoloured .. 75 20

1281 Test Tubes and Flower held with Tweezers

**1996.** 50th Anniv of National Institute for Agronomic Research.
3326 1281 3 f. 80 multicoloured 90 25

1282 Joan of Arc's Cottage, Domremy la Pucelle, Vosges

**1996.** 75th Anniv (1995) of Canonization of Joan of Arc.
3327 1282 4 f. 50 multicoloured 1·10 30

1283 Fishes, Sea and Coastline

**1996.** 20th Anniv of Ramoge Agreement on Environmental Protection of the Mediterranean.
3328 1283 3 f. multicoloured .. 75 20

1284 Notre-Dame de Clermont and the Jacquemart (Cathedral clock)

**1996.** Federation of French Philatelic Societies Congress, Clermont-Ferrand.
3329 1284 3 f. green, brn & red 75 20

**1996.** Tourist Publicity. As T **490**.
3330 3 f. multicoloured .. 75 20
3331 3 f. multicoloured .. 75 20
3332 3 f. 80 brown and mauve 90 25
3333 4 f. 50 multicoloured .. 1·10 30
DESIGN—HORIZ: 3 f. (No. 3330), Bitche Castle, Moselle; 3 f. (No. 3331), Sanguinaires Islands, Corsica; 3 f. 80, Cloisters, Thoronet Abbey, Var; 4 f. 50, Detail of trompe l'oeil by Casimir Vicario, Chambery Cathedral.

1285 Lens

1286 Throwing the Discus

**1996.** World Cup Football Championship, France (1998) (1st issue). Host Cities. Multicoloured.
3335 3 f. Type **1285** .. .. 75 20
3336 3 f. Montpellier .. .. 75 20
3337 3 f. Saint-Etienne .. 75 20
3338 3 f. Toulouse .. .. 75 20

**1996.** Centenary of Modern Olympic Games.
3339 1286 3 f. multicoloured .. 75 70

1287 Marette

1288 Railway

**1996.** 12th Death Anniv of Jacques Marette (journalist and politician).
3340 1287 4 f. 40 lilac .. .. 1·10 30

**1996.** Centenary of Ajaccio–Vizzavona Railway, Corsica.
3341 1288 3 f. multicoloured .. 75 20

1289 Basilica

**1996.** Centenary of Our Lady of Fourviere Basilica, Lyon.
3342 1289 3 f. black and yellow 75 20

1290 Baptism of Clovis (illus from "Grandes Chroniques de France")

1291 Arsene Lupin (Maurice Leblanc)

**1996.** Inauguration of Committee for Commemoration of Origins: from Gaul to France. 1500th Anniv of Baptism of Clovis.
3343 1290 3 f. multicoloured .. 75 30

**1996.** Red Cross Fund. Heroes of Crime Novels. Multicoloured.
3344 3 f.+60 c. Rocambole (Pierre Ponson du Terrail) .. .. 85 85
3345 3 f.+60 c. Type **1291** .. 85 85
3346 3 f.+60 c. Joseph Rouletabille (Gaston Leroux) .. .. 85 85
3347 3 f.+60 c. Fantomas (Pierre Souvestre and Marcel Allain) .. 85 85
3348 3 f.+60 c. Commissioner Maigret (Georges Simenon) .. .. 85 85
3349 3 f.+60 c. Nestor Burma (Leo Malet) .. .. 85 85

1292 School Building

1293 Children of Different Nations

**1996.** Bicentenary of Henri IV School, Paris.
3350 1292 4 f. 50 blue, brn & grn 1·10 30

**1996.** 50th Anniv of U.N.I.C.E.F.
3351 1293 4 f. 50 multicoloured 1·10 30

1294 Iena Palace (headquarters)

1295 Headquarters, Paris

**1996.** 50th Anniv of Economic and Social Council.

| | | | | |
|---|---|---|---|---|
| 3352 | 1294 | 3 f. black, red & blue | 75 | 20 |

**1996.** 50th Anniv of U.N.E.S.C.O.

| | | | | |
|---|---|---|---|---|
| 3353 | 1295 | 3 f. 80 multicoloured | 90 | 25 |

1296 Magnifying Glass over Eiffel Tower

1297 "Woman"

**1996.** 50th Anniv of Autumn Stamp Show, Paris.

| | | | | |
|---|---|---|---|---|
| 3354 | 1296 | 3 f. multicoloured .. | 75 | 20 |

**1996.** 50th Anniv of Creation of French Overseas Departments of Martinique, Guadeloupe, Guiana and La Reunion.

| | | | | |
|---|---|---|---|---|
| 3355 | 1297 | 3 f. multicoloured .. | 75 | 20 |

1298 Snowman and Polar Bear in Hot-air Balloon

**1996.** Red Cross Fund. Christmas.

| | | | | |
|---|---|---|---|---|
| 3356 | 1298 | 3 f.+60 c. mult .. | 85 | 85 |

1299 Temple, Delphi

**1996.** 150th Anniv of French School in Athens.

| | | | | |
|---|---|---|---|---|
| 3357 | 1299 | 3 f. multicoloured .. | 75 | 20 |

1300 Malraux

**1996.** 20th Death Anniv of Andre Malraux (writer and politician).

| | | | | |
|---|---|---|---|---|
| 3358 | 1300 | 3 f. blue .. .. | 75 | 20 |

MILITARY FRANK STAMPS

**1901.** Optd **F. M.**

| | | | | |
|---|---|---|---|---|
| M309 | 12 | 15 c. orange .. .. | 50·00 | 6·50 |

**1903.** Optd **F. M.**

| | | | | |
|---|---|---|---|---|
| M314 | 14 | 15 c. red .. .. | 50·00 | 5·75 |

**1904.** Optd **F. M.**

| | | | | |
|---|---|---|---|---|
| M323 | 15 | 10 c. red .. .. | 22·00 | 7·00 |
| M324 | | 15 c. green .. .. | 35·00 | 5·75 |

**1907.** Optd **F. M.**

| | | | | |
|---|---|---|---|---|
| M348 | 18 | 10 c. red .. .. | 1·25 | 50 |

**1929.** Optd **F. M.**

| | | | | |
|---|---|---|---|---|
| M471 | 15 | 50 c. red .. .. | 4·50 | 65 |

**1933.** Optd **F. M.**

| | | | | |
|---|---|---|---|---|
| M516 | 61 | 50 c. red .. .. | 3·25 | 35 |
| M517 | | 65 c. blue .. .. | 30 | 25 |
| M508 | | 90 c. blue .. .. | 35 | 30 |

**1939.** Optd **F.**

| | | | | |
|---|---|---|---|---|
| M519 | 61 | 90 c. blue .. .. | 1·90 | 2·50 |

M 236.

M 545. Flag.

**1946.** No value indicated.

| | | | | |
|---|---|---|---|---|
| M 967. | M 236. | green .. .. | 1·50 | 1·00 |
| M 968. | | red .. .. | 30 | 30 |

**1964.** No value indicated.

| | | | | |
|---|---|---|---|---|
| M 1661. | M 545. | multicoloured .. | 30 | 30 |

NEWSPAPER STAMPS

J 6

**1868.** With or without gum. (a) Imperf

| | | | | |
|---|---|---|---|---|
| J131 | J 6 | 2 c. mauve .. .. | £275 | 60·00 |
| J132 | | 2 c. blue .. .. | £550 | £275 |

(b) Perf

| | | | | |
|---|---|---|---|---|
| J133 | J 6 | 2 c. mauve .. .. | 38·00 | 19·00 |
| J134 | | 2 c. blue .. .. | 70·00 | 29·00 |
| J135 | | 2 c. pink .. .. | £200 | 95·00 |
| J136 | | 5 c. mauve .. .. | £1100 | £600 |

POSTAGE DUE STAMPS

D 4. D 11. D 19.

**1859.**

| | | | | |
|---|---|---|---|---|
| D 87. | D 4. | 10 c. black .. .. | 20·00 | 16·00 |
| D 88. | | 15 c. black .. .. | 23·00 | 12·50 |
| D 212. | | 25 c. black .. .. | £120 | 45·00 |
| D 213. | | 30 c. black .. .. | £190 | £110 |
| D 214. | | 40 c. blue .. .. | £275 | £300 |
| D 216. | | 60 c. yellow .. .. | £450 | £1000 |
| D 217. | | 60 c. blue .. .. | 55·00 | 90·00 |

**1882.**

| | | | | |
|---|---|---|---|---|
| D279 | D 11 | 1 c. black .. .. | 1·90 | 1·90 |
| D280 | | 2 c. black .. .. | 22·00 | 22·00 |
| D281 | | 3 c. black .. .. | 22·00 | 22·00 |
| D282 | | 4 c. black .. .. | 45·00 | 35·00 |
| D283 | | 5 c. black .. .. | 95·00 | 25·00 |
| D297 | | 5 c. blue .. .. | 25 | 10 |
| D284 | | 10 c. black .. .. | 90·00 | 1·90 |
| D298 | | 10 c. brown .. .. | 25 | 10 |
| D285 | | 15 c. black .. .. | 60·00 | 9·00 |
| D317 | | 15 c. green .. .. | 25·00 | 25 |
| D286 | | 20 c. black .. .. | £300 | £120 |
| D300 | | 20 c. green .. .. | 5·75 | 35 |
| D301 | | 25 c. red .. .. | 6·25 | 3·75 |
| D287 | | 30 c. black .. .. | £180 | 1·90 |
| D302 | | 30 c. red .. .. | 25 | 10 |
| D288 | | 40 c. black .. .. | £100 | 55·00 |
| D304 | | 40 c. red .. .. | 11·00 | 3·75 |
| D305 | | 45 c. green .. .. | 8·50 | 4·50 |
| D289 | | 50 c. black .. .. | £500 | £160 |
| D306 | | 50 c. purple .. .. | 25 | 10 |
| D307 | | 60 c. green .. .. | 75 | 10 |
| D290 | | 60 c. black .. .. | £500 | 45·00 |
| D291 | | 1 f. black .. .. | £700 | £300 |
| D310 | | 1 f. brown .. .. | 1·00 | 35 |
| D308 | | 1 f. pink on yellow | £450 | £375 |
| D309 | | 1 f. brown on yellow | 8·50 | 35 |
| D293 | | 2 f. black .. .. | £1200 | £750 |
| D294 | | 2 f. brown .. .. | £170 | £120 |
| D311 | | 2 f. red .. .. | £200 | 60·00 |
| D312 | | 2 f. mauve .. .. | 55 | 75 |
| D313 | | 3 f. mauve .. .. | 55 | 75 |
| D295 | | 5 f. black .. .. | £300 | £1500 |
| D296 | | 5 f. brown .. .. | £450 | £300 |
| D314 | | 5 f. orange .. .. | 2·25 | 2·25 |

**1908.**

| | | | | |
|---|---|---|---|---|
| D 348. | D 19. | 1 c. olive .. .. | 1·00 | 90 |
| D 349. | | 10 c. violet .. .. | 1·25 | 10 |
| D 350. | | 20 c. bistre .. .. | 32·00 | 90 |
| D 351. | | 30 c. bistre .. .. | 12·00 | 15 |
| D 352. | | 50 c. red .. .. | £225 | 50·00 |
| D 353. | | 60 c. red .. .. | 3·00 | 2·50 |

**1917.** Surch.

| | | | | |
|---|---|---|---|---|
| D 378. | D 19. | 20 c. on 30 c. bistre | 20·00 | 2·50 |
| D 379. | | 40 c. on 50 c. red .. | 9·50 | 2·50 |
| D 433. | | 50 c. on 10 c. violet | 3·00 | 1·90 |
| D 434. | | 60 c. on 1 c. olive .. | 5·25 | 2·50 |
| D 435. | | 1 f. on 60 c. red .. | 14·00 | 7·75 |
| D 436. | | 2 f. on 60 c. red .. | 14·00 | 7·75 |

D 43. D 187. Wheat Sheaves. D 457.

**1927.**

| | | | | |
|---|---|---|---|---|
| D454. | D 43. | 1 c. green .. .. | 1·00 | 1·25 |
| D455. | | 10 c. red .. .. | 1·90 | 1·25 |
| D456. | | 30 c. bistre .. .. | 5·25 | 30 |
| D457. | | 60 c. red .. .. | 4·75 | 20 |
| D458. | | 1 f. purple .. .. | 14·00 | 3·00 |
| D459. | | 1 f. green .. .. | 16·00 | 45 |
| D460. | | 2 f. blue .. .. | 45·00 | 40·00 |
| D461. | | 2 f. brown .. .. | £140 | 25·00 |

**1929.** Surch.

| | | | | |
|---|---|---|---|---|
| D471. | D 43. | 1 f. 20 on 2 f. blue .. | 32·00 | 10·00 |
| D472. | | 5 f. on 1 f. purple .. | 45·00 | 10·00 |

**1931.** Surch. **UN FRANC.**

| | | | | |
|---|---|---|---|---|
| D 494. | D 43. | 1 f. on 60 c. red .. | 20·00 | 1·10 |

**1943.** Inscr. " CHIFFRE-TAXE ".

| | | | | |
|---|---|---|---|---|
| D 787. | D 187. | 10 c. brown .. | 10 | 10 |
| D 788. | | 30 c. purple .. | 10 | 10 |
| D 789. | | 50 c. green .. | 10 | 10 |
| D 790. | | 1 f. blue .. | 10 | 10 |
| D 791. | | 1 f. 50 red .. | 25 | 20 |
| D 792. | | 2 f. blue .. | 25 | 20 |
| D 793. | | 3 f. red .. | 25 | 20 |
| D 794. | | 4 f. violet .. | 3·25 | 2·75 |
| D 794. | | 5 f. red .. | 30 | 30 |
| D 796. | | 10 f. orange .. | 2·00 | 1·10 |
| D 797. | | 20 f. bistre .. | 6·50 | 1·25 |

**1946.** As Type D 187 but inscr "TIMBRE TAXE".

| | | | |
|---|---|---|---|
| D985 | 10 c. brown .. .. | 90 | 80 |
| D986 | 30 c. purple .. .. | 70 | 60 |
| D987 | 50 c. green .. .. | 20·00 | 7·75 |
| D988 | 1 f. blue .. .. | 20 | 20 |
| D989 | 2 f. blue .. .. | 20 | 20 |
| D990 | 3 f. red .. .. | 20 | 20 |
| D991 | 4 f. violet .. .. | 20 | 20 |
| D992 | 5 f. pink .. .. | 20 | 20 |
| D993 | 10 f. red .. .. | 20 | 20 |
| D994 | 20 f. brown .. .. | 1·50 | 20 |
| D995 | 50 f. green .. .. | 23·00 | 20 |
| D996 | 100 f. green .. .. | 70·00 | 6·50 |

**1960.** New Currency.

| | | | | |
|---|---|---|---|---|
| D 1474. | D 457. | 5 c. mauve .. | 3·25 | 50 |
| D 1475. | | 10 c. red .. | 5·25 | 40 |
| D 1476. | | 20 c. brown .. | 4·50 | 20 |
| D 1477. | | 50 c. green .. | 12·50 | 90 |
| D 1478. | | 1 f. green .. | 55·00 | 1·90 |

D 539. Poppies.

D 917. " Ampedus cinnabarinus ".

**1964.**

| | | | | |
|---|---|---|---|---|
| D 1650. | – | 5 c. red. grn. & purple .. | 10 | 10 |
| D 1651. | – | 10 c. blue, green and purple .. | 10 | 10 |
| D 1652. | D 539. | 15 c. red, green, and brown .. | 25 | 25 |
| D 1653. | – | 20 c. purple, green and turq. .. | 10 | 10 |
| D 1654. | – | 30 c. blue, green and brown .. | 15 | 10 |
| D 1655. | – | 40 c. yellow, red and turq. | 20 | 20 |
| D 1656. | – | 50 c. red, green and blue .. | 25 | 15 |
| D 1657. | – | 1 f. violet, green and blue .. | 50 | 15 |

DESIGNS: 5 c. Knapweed. 10 c. Gentian. 20 c. Little periwinkle. 30 c. Forget-me-not. 40 c Columbine. 50 c. Clover. 1 f. Soldanella.

**1982.** Beetles.

| | | | | |
|---|---|---|---|---|
| D 2493. | D 917. | 10 c. brown and black .. .. | 15 | 10 |
| D 2494. | – | 20 c. black .. | 15 | 10 |
| D 2495. | – | 30 c. red, brown and black .. | 25 | 10 |
| D 2496. | – | 40 c. blue, brown and black .. | 25 | 10 |
| D 2497. | – | 50 c. red and black .. | 25 | 10 |
| D 2498. | – | 1 f. black .. | 35 | 20 |
| D 2499. | – | 2 f. yellow and black .. | 60 | 20 |
| D 2500. | – | 3 f. black and red | 1·25 | 25 |
| D 2501. | – | 4 f. brown and black .. | 1·60 | 35 |
| D 2502. | – | 5 f. blue, red and black .. | 2·00 | 35 |

DESIGNS: 20 c. "Dorcadion fuliginator". 30 c. "Leptura cordigera". 40 c. "Paederus littoralis". 50 c. "Pyrochroa coccinea". 1 f. "Scarites laevigatus". 2 f. "Trichius gallicus". 3 f. "Adalia alpina". 4 f. "Apoderus coryli". 5 f. "Trichodes alvearius.

COUNCIL OF EUROPE STAMPS

Until March 25th, 1960, these stamps could only be used by delegates and permanent officials of the Council of Europe on official correspondence at Strasbourg. From that date they could be used on all correspondence posted within the Council of Europe building.

**1950.** No. 1354 optd. **CONSEIL DE L'EUROPE.**

| | | | |
|---|---|---|---|
| C 1. | 35 f. mauve and red .. | 60 | 2·00 |

C 2. Council Flag.

**1958.**

| | | | | |
|---|---|---|---|---|
| C 2. | C 2. | 8 f. blue, orge. & pur. | 10 | 15 |
| C 3. | | 20 f. blue, yell. & brn. | 20 | 15 |
| C 4. | | 25 f. blue, pur. & myrtle | 90 | 40 |
| C 5. | | 35 f. blue and red .. | 75 | 75 |
| C 6. | | 50 f. blue and purple .. | 1·50 | 1·50 |

(New currency. 100 (old) francs = 1 (new) franc).

**1963.**

| | | | | |
|---|---|---|---|---|
| C 7. | C 2. | 20 c. blue, yell. & brn. | 1·10 | 75 |
| C 8. | | 25 c. blue, pur. & myrt. | 3·00 | 1·50 |
| C 9. | | 25 c. multicoloured .. | 1·00 | 75 |
| C 10. | | 30 c. blue, yell. & red | 1·00 | 75 |
| C 11. | | 40 c. multicoloured .. | 1·60 | 1·10 |
| C 12. | | 50 c. blue and purple | 2·50 | 2·10 |
| C 13. | | 50 c. multicoloured .. | 3·25 | 1·60 |
| C 14. | | 60 c. multicoloured .. | 1·25 | 90 |
| C 15. | | 70 c. multicoloured .. | 4·75 | 3·00 |

**1975.** As Type C 2, but inscr. " FRANCE ".

| | | | |
|---|---|---|---|
| C 16. | 60 c. multicoloured .. | 1·60 | 70 |
| C 17. | 80 c. yellow, blue and red | 2·10 | 1·40 |
| C 18. | 1 f. multicoloured .. | 6·50 | 4·50 |
| C 19. | 1 f. 20 multicoloured .. | 8·25 | 3·75 |

C 3. New Council of Europe Building, Strasbourg.

**1977.**

| | | | | |
|---|---|---|---|---|
| C20 | C 3 | 80 c. red, lt brn & brn | 1·50 | 60 |
| C21 | | 1 f. brown, blue & grn | 30 | 30 |
| C22 | | 1 f. 40 grey, grn & brn | 3·75 | 2·00 |
| C23 | | 1 f. 40 green .. .. | 55 | 55 |
| C24 | | 2 f. blue .. .. | 65 | 65 |

**1978.** 25th Anniv. of European Convention on Human Rights. As Type C 3 with the addition of the Human Rights emblem.

| | | | |
|---|---|---|---|
| C 25. | 1 f. 20 blk., purple & grn. | 45 | 40 |
| C 26. | 1 f. 70 turq., blue & grn. | 65 | 55 |

C 5. Exterior and Interior of New Council of Europe Building, Strasbourg.

**1981.**

| | | | | |
|---|---|---|---|---|
| C27. | C 5. | 1 f. 40 vio., bl. & pur. | 50 | 50 |
| C28. | | 1 f. 60 green & brown | 50 | 50 |
| C29. | | 1 f. 70 green .. | 1·00 | 1·00 |
| C30. | | 1 f. 80 red, green and purple .. | 70 | 70 |
| C31. | | 2 f. red, grn. & blue | 70 | 70 |
| C32. | | 2 f. 10 red .. | 1·10 | 1·10 |
| C33. | | 2 f. 30 green, turquoise and blue .. | 1·00 | 1·00 |
| C34. | | 2 f. 60 purple, blue and grey .. | 90 | 90 |
| C35. | | 2 f. 80 brn., deep blue and blue .. | 90 | 90 |
| C36. | | 3 f. blue .. | 1·60 | 1·60 |

C 6. Foot Breaking through Shell.

**1985.**

| | | | | |
|---|---|---|---|---|
| C37. | C 6. | 1 f. 80 green .. | 1·00 | 1·00 |
| C38. | | 2 f. 20 red .. | 1·10 | 1·10 |
| C39. | | 3 f. 20 blue .. | 1·60 | 1·60 |

C 7. Council of Europe Building, Strasbourg.

**1986.**

C40 C 7 1 f. 90 green .. .. 1·25 1·25
C41 2 f. green .. .. 1·25 1·25
C42 2 f. 20 red .. .. 1·25 1·25
C43 3 f. 40 blue .. .. 2·50 2·50
C44 3 f. 60 blue .. .. 2·50 2·50

C 8 Stars, Doves and Girl

**1989.** 40th Anniv of Council of Europe.

C45 C 8 2 f. 20 multicoloured .. 2·25 2·25
C46 3 f. 60 multicoloured .. 3·50 3·50

C 9 Map of Europe

C 10 "36 Heads" (Friedensreich Hundertwasser)

**1990.**

C47 C 9 2 f. 30 multicoloured 1·25 1·25
C48 2 f. 50 multicoloured 1·00 1·00
C49 3 f. 20 multicoloured 1·90 1·90
C50 3 f. 40 multicoloured 1·50 1·50

**1994.**

C51 C 10 2 f. 80 multicoloured 1·10 1·10
C52 3 f. 70 multicoloured 1·50 1·50

C 11 Palace of Human Rights, Strasbourg

**1996.**

C53 C 11 3 f. multicoloured .. 75 75
C54 3 f. 80 multicoloured 90 90

U.N.E.S.C.O. STAMPS

For use on correspondence posted within the U.N.E.S.C.O. Headquarters building.

U 1. Buddha and Hermes.

**1961.**

U 1 U 1 20 c. bistre, blue & brn 20 15
U 2 25 c. purple, grn & blk 20 15
U 3 30 c. brown, & dp brn 1·50 1·00
U 4 50 c. red, violet & blk 1·50 1·40
U 5 60 c. brown, mve & bl 2·50 1·90

U 2. Open Book and Globe.

U 3. "Human Rights".

**1966.**

U 6. U 2. 25 c. brown .. .. 60 60
U 7. 30 c. red .. .. 75 75
U 8. 60 c. green .. .. 1·40 1·40

**1969.**

U 9. U 3. 30 c. red, grn. & brn. 60 40
U 10. 40 c. red, mve. & brn. 90 60
U 11. 50 c. red, bl. & brn. 2·50 1·90
U 12. 70 c. red, vio. & blue 3·75 3·25

**1975.** As Type U **3**, but inscribed "France".

U 13. 60 c. red, grn. & brown .. 1·40 75
U 14. 80 c. red, brn. & lake .. 2·10 1·40
U 15. 1 f. 20 red, blue & purple .. 8·25 3·75

U 4. " Leaf ".

**1976.**

U 16. U 4. 80 c. bl., brn. & pur. 1·25 75
U 17. 1 f. orge., grn. & blue 30 25
U 18. 1 f. 20 bl., red & grn. 45 30
U 19. 1 f. 40 brown. mauve and orange .. 2·75 2·00
U 20. 1 f. 70 red, grn. & brn. 55 45

U 5. Old Slave Dungeons, Goree, Senegal.

U 6. Gateway, Fez, Morocco.

**1980.** Sites in Need of Protection.

U 21. U 5. 1 f. 20 blue, grn. & lake 45 35
U 22. – 1 f. 40 mve., blue & grn. 50 35
U 23. – 2 f. vio., grn. & lake 80 60

DESIGNS: 1 f. 40, Moenjodaro, Pakistan. 2 f. Palace of Sans-Souci, Haiti.

**1981.** Sites in need of Preservation.

U 24. U 6. 1 f. 40 brown, blue and red .. .. 50 50
U 25. – 1 f. 60 blue, red and green .. .. 50 50
U 26. – 1 f. 80 violet, purple and blue .. .. 70 70
U 27. – 2 f. 30 brown, green and blue .. .. 80 80
U 28. – 2 f. 60 black, blue and red .. .. 90 90

DESIGNS—VERT. 1 f. 60, Seated Buddha Sukhotai, Thailand. 1 f. 80, Hue, Vietnam. 2 f. 60, Sao Miguel Cathedral, Brazil. HORIZ. 2 f. 30, Fort St. Elmo, Malta.

U 7. Chinguetti Mosque Mauritania.

U 8. Amphitheatre, Carthage.

**1983.** Sites in need of Preservation.

U 29. – 1 f. 70 brown and green .. .. 60 60
U 30. U 7. 2 f. brown, blue and black .. 70 70
U 31. – 2 f. 10 brown, blue and turquoise .. 70 70
U 32. – 2 f. 80 black, blue and brown .. 90 90
U 33. – 3 f. orange, brown and green .. 1·50 1·50

DESIGNS: 1 f. 70, Lalibela Church, Ethiopia. 2 f. 10, Sana'a, Yemen Arab Republic. 2 f. 80, City walls, Istanbul, Turkey. 3 f. St. Mary's Church, Kotor, Yugoslavia.

**1985.** Protected Sites. Each grey, green and blue.

U 34. 1 f. 80 Type U **8** .. .. 1·40 1·40
U 35. 2 f. 20 Old Square, Havana, Cuba .. 1·40 1·40
U 36. 3 f. 20 Temple of Anuradhapura, Sri Lanka .. .. .. 2·50 2·50

U 9. Temple of Tikal, Guatemala.

U 10. Acropolis, Athens.

**1986.** Protected Sites. Each grey, brown and green.

U 37. 1 f. 90. Type U **9** .. 1·50 1·50
U 38. 3 f. 40 Bagerhat Mosque, Bangladesh .. .. 2·50 2·50

**1987.** Protected Sites. Each brown, chestnut and blue.

U39 2 f. Type U **10** .. .. 1·25 1·25
U40 3 f. 60 Philae Temple, Egypt .. .. .. 2·50 2·50

U 11 St. Francis's Monastery, Lima, Peru

U 12 Temple of Bagdaon, Nepal

**1990.** Protected Sites.

U41 U 11 2 f. 30 brown, green and black .. 1·00 1·00
U42 – 3 f. 20 brown, orange and blue .. .. 1·50 1·50

DESIGN—HORIZ. 3 f. 20 Shibam, People's Democratic Republic of Yemen.

**1991.** Protected Sites.

U43 U 12 2 f. 50 brown and red 1·00 1·00
U44 – 3 f. 40 brown & green 1·50 1·50

DESIGN—HORIZ. 3 f. 40, Herat Fort, Afghanistan.

U 13 Angkor, Cambodia

U 14 Ayers Rock, Uluru, Australia

**1993.** Protected Sites. Multicoloured.

U45 2 f. 80 Type U **13** .. 1·10 1·10
U46 3 f. 70 Cave paintings, Tassili n'Ajjer National Park, Algeria (horiz) .. 1·50 1·50

**1996.** Protected Sites. National Parks. Mult.

U47 3 f. Type U **14** .. .. 75 75
U48 3 f. 80 Glacier, Los Glaciares, Argentine Republic .. .. 90 90

## FREE FRENCH FORCES IN THE LEVANT Pt. 19

After British and Free French troops had occupied Syria and Lebanon in June 1941 the following stamps were issued for the use of Free French forces in those areas.

100 centimes = 1 franc.

**1942.** Surch. with Lorraine Crosses **FORCES FRANCAISES LIBRES LEVANT** and value.

(i) On No. 252 of Syria.

1. – 50 c. on 4 p. orange .. 5·25 6·25

(ii) On Nos. 251 and 212 of Lebanon.

2. 16a. 1 f. on 5 p. blue .. 4·75 6·00
3. 22. 2 f. 50 on 12½ p. blue .. 5·00 6·00

**1942.** Air. Nos. 269/70 of Syria surch. with Lorraine Crosses, **LIGNES AERIENNES F.A.F.L.** and value.

4. 4 f. on 50 p. black .. 4·75 5·00
5. 6 f. 50 on 50 p. black .. 4·75 5·25
6. 8 f. on 50 p. black .. 4·50 5·25
7. 10 f. on 100 p. mauve .. 4·50 5·25

3. Camelry and Ruins at Palmyra.

4. Wings bearing Lorraine Crosses.

**1942.** Buff background.

8. 3. 1 f. red (postage) .. 30 1·40
9. 1 f. 50 violet .. 30 1·40
10. 2 f. orange .. 40 1·40
11. 2 f. 50 brown .. 35 1·40
12. 3 f. blue .. .. 40 1·40
13. 4 f. green .. 75 1·90
14. 5 f. purple .. 65 1·90
15. 4. 6 f. 50 red (air) .. 65 1·90
16. 10 f. purple and blue .. 70 1·90

**1942.** Air. No. 15 surch **4.**

17 4 4 f. on 6 f. 50 red 1·40 2·00

**1943.** Surch. **RESISTANCE** and premium.

18. 3. 1 f.+9 f. red (postage) .. 1·40 1·40
19. 5 f.+20 f. purple .. 1·40 1·40
20. 4. 6 f. 50+48 f. 50 red (air) 23·00 23·00
21. 10 f.+100 f. pur. & bl.. 23·00 23·00

**1943.** Air. No. 12 surch **4F** and airplane.

22 3 4 f. on 3 f. blue and buff .. 1·10 1·60

## FRENCH COLONIES Pt. 6

General issues for use in French Colonies which had no special stamps.

100 centimes = 1 franc.

**NOTE.** For other stamps issued for the French Colonies see the note at the beginning of France.

A. Eagle.

B. Laureated. D. Laureated.

**1859.** Imperf.

1. A. 1 c. green .. .. .. 18·00 20·00
2. 5 c. green .. .. .. 20·00 12·50
3. 10 c. brown .. .. 23·00 7·00
4. 20 c. blue .. .. .. 28·00 12·50
5. 40 c. orange .. .. 20·00 7·75
6. 80 c. red .. .. .. 95·00 55·00

**1871.** Imperf.

7. B. 1 c. green .. .. 55·00 55·00
9. D 30 c. brown .. .. £130 38·00
10. 80 c. red .. .. £900 £100

E. Ceres.

F. Ceres.

**1871.** Imperf.

11 E 1 c. green on blue .. 11·50 12·50
12 2 c. brown on buff .. £450 £750
14 5 c. green .. .. 11·50 8·25
20 F 10 c. brown on pink .. £200 15·00
16 15 c. bistre .. .. £275 9·50

H. Peace and Commerce.

J. Commerce.

**1877.** Imperf.

24 H 1 c. green .. .. 23·00 35·00
25 2 c. green .. .. 10·50 9·00
26 4 c. green .. .. 14·00 10·00
27 5 c. green .. .. 14·00 3·75
28 10 c. green .. .. 75·00 9·00
29 15 c. grey .. .. £225 65·00
30 20 c. brown on yellow .. 45·00 5·75
31a 25 c. blue .. .. 32·00 7·75
32 30 c. brown .. .. 32·00 32·00
33 35 c. black on yellow .. 38·00 22·00
34 40 c. red on yellow .. 21·00 18·00
35a 75 c. red .. .. 70·00 52·00
36 1 f. green .. .. 42·00 18·00

**1878.** Imperf.

37 H 1 c. black on blue .. 15·00 15·00
38 2 c. brown on buff .. 14·00 10·00
39 4 c. brown on grey .. 19·00 19·00
40 10 c. black on lilac .. 95·00 16·00
41 15 c. blue on blue .. 24·00 10·00
42 20 c. red on green .. 65·00 10·00
43 25 c. black on red .. £550 £250
44 25 c. brown on yellow .. £650 22·00

**1881.** Perf.

45 J 1 c. black on blue .. 3·75 3·00
46 2 c. brown on buff .. 3·75 3·75
47 4 c. brown on grey .. 3·00 3·75
48 5 c. green on green .. 3·00 1·90
49 10 c. black on lilac .. 7·75 3·00
50 15 c. blue on blue .. 11·50 1·90
51 20 c. red on green .. 48·00 16·00
52 25 c. brown on yellow .. 10·00 3·00
53 25 c. black on pink .. 10·00 1·90
54 30 c. brown on drab .. 32·00 16·00
55 35 c. black on orange .. 35·00 24·00
56 40 c. red on yellow .. 35·00 25·00
57 75 c. red on pink .. £100 50·00
58 1 f. green .. .. 60·00 32·00

K. Map of France.

L. Colonies offering France Aid.

M. Resisters.

**1943.** Aid to Resistance Movement.

82. K. 50 c.+4 f. 50 green .. 60 85
83. 1 f. 50+8 f. 50 red .. 60 85
84. 3 f.+12 f. blue .. .. 60 85
85. 5 f.+15 f. grey .. .. 70 90
86. L. 9 f.+41 f. purple .. 2·00 2·40

**1943.** Aid to Resistance Movement. Roul.

87. M. 1 f. 50+98 f. 50 bl. & grey 32·00 45·00

N.

O.

**1943.** French Solidarity Fund.

88. N. 10 f.+40 f. blue .. 3·75 5·00

**1944.** Air. Aviation Fund.

89. O 10 f.+40 f. green .. 3·75 5·75

POSTAGE DUE STAMPS

U

V

**1884.** Imperf.

D 59. U 1 c. black .. .. 2·50 2·50
D 60. 2 c. black .. .. 2·50 2·50
D 61. 3 c. black .. .. 2·50 2·50
D 62. 4 c. black .. .. 3·00 2·50
D 63. 5 c. black .. .. 4·50 3·75
D 64. 10 c. black .. .. 6·25 4·50
D 65. 15 c. black .. .. 6·75 7·00
D 66. 20 c. black .. .. 9·50 8·50
D 67. 30 c. black .. .. 11·00 6·50
D 68. 40 c. black .. .. 16·00 6·50
D 69. 60 c. black .. .. 24·00 14·00
D 70. 1 f. brown .. .. 24·00 15·00
D 71. 2 f. brown .. .. 20·00 12·50
D 72. 5 f. brown .. .. 80·00 48·00

**1893.** Imperf.

D 73. U 5 c. blue .. .. 75 40
D 74. 10 c. brown .. .. 75 40
D 75. 15 c. green .. .. 60 65
D 76. 20 c. olive .. .. 65 70
D 77. 30 c. red .. .. 1·25 70
D 78. 50 c. red .. .. 1·40 1·00
D 79. 60 c. brown on yellow 2·50 1·90
D 81. 1 f. red on yellow .. 4·50 3·00

**1945.** Perf.

D 90. V 10 c. blue .. .. 20 30
D 91. 15 c. green .. .. 20 30
D 92. 25 c. orange .. .. 25 30
D 93. 50 c. black .. .. 35 40
D 94. 60 c. brown .. .. 40 40
D 95. 1 f. red .. .. 40 50
D 96. 2 f. red .. .. 45 55
D 97. 4 f. grey .. .. 1·90 1·90
D 98. 5 f. blue .. .. 1·75 1·75
D 99. 10 f. violet .. .. 13·50 10·00
D 100. 20 f. brown .. .. 2·00 2·00
D 101. 50 f. green .. .. 4·50 4·50

## FRENCH CONGO Pt. 6

A French colony in central Africa. in 1903 divided into Gabon, Middle Congo, Ubangi-Shari and Chad.

100 centimes = 1 franc.

**1891.** Stamps of French Colonies, "Commerce" type, surch. **Congo francais** and value in figures.

2. J 5 c. on 1 c. black on blue £100 55·00
3. 5 c. on 15 c. blue .. .. £180 80·00
4. 5 c. on 25 c. black on red .. 65·00 22·00
11. 10 c. on 25 c. black on red £120 60·00
12. 15 c. on 25 c. black on red £150 48·00

**1892.** Stamps of French Colonies, "Commerce" type, surch **COngo Francais** and value in figures.

5. J 5 c. on 20 c. red on green .. £700 £250
6. 5 c. on 25 c. black on red .. £100 45·00
7. 10 c. on 25 c. black on red £110 30·00
8. 10 c. on 40 c. red on yellow £1300 £225
9. 15 c. on 25 c. black on red £100 22·00

**1892.** Postage Due stamps of French Colonies surch. **Congo francais Timbre poste** and value in figures.

13. U 5 c. on 5 c. black .. 90·00 80·00
14. 5 c. on 20 c. black .. 95·00 80·00
15. 5 c. on 30 c. black .. £130 95·00
16. 10 c. on 1 f. brown .. £110 80·00

**1892.** "Tablet" key-type inscr "CONGO FRANCAIS" in red (1, 5, 15, 25, 50 (No. 31), 75 c. and 1 f.) or blue (others).

17 D 1 c. black on blue .. 85 1·00
18 2 c. brown on buff .. 1·10 1·10
19 4 c. brown on grey .. 1·25 1·25
20 5 c. green on light green 2·75 2·50
21 10 c. black on lilac .. 11·00 7·75
22 10 c. red .. .. 1·25 1·40
23 15 c. blue .. .. 30·00 5·00
24 15 c. grey .. .. 4·00 4·00
25 20 c. red on green .. 11·00 8·00
26 25 c. black on pink .. 12·50 7·50
27 25 c. blue .. .. 5·25 4·25
28 30 c. brown on drab .. 16·00 9·75
29 40 c. red on yellow .. 29·00 15·00
30 50 c. red on pink .. 30·00 14·00
31 50 c. brown on blue .. 3·75 6·00
32 75 c. brown on orange .. 21·00 13·00
33 1 f. green .. .. 35·00 10·00

6. Leopard in Ambush.

8. Woman of the Bakalois Tribe.

**1900.**

36c 6 1 c. brown and grey .. 40 60
37 2 c. brown and yellow .. 40 35
38 4 c. red and grey .. 50 40
39 5 c. green and light green 85 40
40 10 c. red and light red .. 3·00 1·25
41 15 c. violet and green .. 1·00 50
42 8 20 c. green and red .. 75 80
43a 25 c. blue and light blue 1·25 1·00
44 30 c. red and yellow .. 1·25 1·00
45 40 c. brown and green .. 2·25 2·00
46 50 c. violet and lilac .. 2·75 2·50
47 75 c. red and orange .. 5·00 4·75
48 – 1 f. grey and green .. 9·50 8·25
49 – 2 f. red and brown .. 20·00 12·50
50 – 5 f. orange and black .. 50·00 38·00

Design—28 × 40 mm: 1, 2, 5 f. Coconut palms, Libreville.

**1903.** Surch in figures.

51 8 5 c. on 30 c. red & yellow £200 95·00
52 – 0,10 on 2 f. red and brown (No. 49) .. .. £250 95·00

PARCEL POST STAMPS

P 3.

**1891.**

P13 P 3 10 c. black on blue .. £140 £100

**1893.** Receipt stamp of France optd **Congo Francais COLIS POSTAUX.**

P34 10 c. grey .. .. £100 £100

## FRENCH EQUATORIAL AFRICA Pt. 6

In 1910 Gabon, Middle Congo and Ubangi-Shari-Chad were federated to form French Equatorial Africa; each colony continued to issue its own stamps until 1936.

In 1958 the four constituent colonies became autonomous republics as Gabon, Congo Republic, Central African Republic (formerly Ubangi-Shari) and Chad.

100 centimes = 1 franc.

**1936.** Middle Congo stamps of 1933 optd **AFRIQUE EQUATORIALE FRANCAISE.**

1 15 1 c. brown .. .. 15 50
2 2 c. blue .. .. 15 50
3 4 c. green .. .. 40 75
4 5 c. purple .. .. 55 65
5 10 c. green .. .. 80 90
6 15 c. purple .. .. 1·25 90
7 20 c. red on pink .. 1·25 90
8 25 c. orange .. .. 2·75 1·75
9 – 40 c. brown .. .. 1·75 1·90
10 – 50 c. purple .. .. 1·40 65
11 – 75 c. black on pink .. 2·50 1·25
12 – 90 c. red .. .. 1·40 1·60
13 – 1 f. 50 blue .. .. 1·25 1·00
14 – 5 f. blue .. .. 35·00 19·00
15 – 10 f. black .. .. 18·00 10·00
16 – 20 f. brown .. .. 18·00 14·00

**1936.** Gabon Stamps of 1933 optd. **AFRIQUE EQUATORIALE FRANCAISE.**

17. 21. 1 c. red .. .. 15 30
18. 2 c. black on pink .. 15 25
19. 4 c. green .. .. 40 60
20. 5 c. blue .. .. 40 55
21. 10 c. red on yellow .. 40 40
22. 22. 40 c. purple .. .. 95 1·00
23. 50 c. brown .. .. 95 50
24. 1 f. green on blue .. 19·00 6·50
25. 1 f. 50 blue .. .. 1·60 1·00
26. 2 f. red .. .. 9·00 3·50

**1937.** International Exhibition, Paris. As Nos. 110/15 of Cameroun.

27 20 c. violet .. .. 1·25 1·25
28 30 c. green .. .. 1·25 1·10
29 40 c. red .. .. 90 1·25
30 50 c. brown and blue .. 85 1·00
31 90 c. red .. .. 90 1·25
32 1 f. 50 blue .. .. 90 1·50

8. Logging near Mayumba.

9. Chad Family.

10. Count Savorgnan de Brazza.

12. Savoia Marchetti S-73 over Stanley Pool.

**1937.**

34 8 1 c. brown & yell (post) 15 50
35 2 c. violet and green .. 15 50
36 3 c. blue and yellow .. 25 50
37 4 c. mauve and blue .. 15 40
38 5 c. deep green & green 20 75
39 9 10 c. mauve and blue .. 15 20
40 15 c. blue and pink .. 15 15
41 20 c. brown and yellow .. 20 30
42 25 c. red and blue .. 25 10
44 10 30 c. deep green & green 25 35
45 30 c. blue and pink .. 25 30
46 9 35 c. green & light green 60 50
47 10 40 c. red and blue .. 15 15
48 45 c. blue and green .. 2·25 2·00
49 45 c. green & light green 40 50
50 50 c. brown and yellow .. 40 50
51 55 c. violet and blue .. 35 50
52 60 c. purple and blue .. 25 35
53 A 65 c. blue and green .. 30 25
54 70 c. violet and orange .. 35 45
55 75 c. black and yellow .. 3·25 3·25
56 80 c. brown and yellow .. 30 40
57 90 c. red and orange .. 25 40
58 1 f. violet and green .. 75 35
59 10 1 f. red and orange .. 1·25 80
60 A 1 f. green and blue .. 25 40
61 B 1 f. 25 red and orange .. 55 40
62 1 f. 40 brown and green 40 50
63 1 f. 50 blue and light blue 90 90
64 1 f. 60 violet and orange 40 55
65 1 f. 75 brown and yellow 90 85
66 A 1 f. 75 blue and light blue 40 55
67 B 2 f. green and light green 75 30
68 C 2 f. 15 violet and yellow 40 55
69 2 f. 25 blue and light blue 75 90
70 2 f. 50 purple and orange 40 50
71 3 f. blue and pink .. 45 15
72 5 f. green and light green 75 60
73 10 f. violet and blue .. 1·75 1·25
74 20 f. black and yellow .. 2·25 1·40

75 D 1 f. 50 black & yell (air) 40 60
76 2 f. mauve and blue .. 50 70
77 2 f. 50 green and pink .. 35 25
78 3 f. 75 brown and green 50 60
79 12 4 f. 50 red and blue .. 45 30
80 6 f. 50 blue and green .. 70 80
81 8 f. 50 red and orange .. 70 70
82 10 f. 75 violet and green 70 80

Designs: A, Emile Gentil. B, Paul Crampel. C, Victor Liotard. D, Latecoere 300 flying boat over Pointe Noire.

**1938.** Anti-Cancer Fund. As T **19** of Cameroun.

94. 1 f. 75+50 c. blue .. 7·00 11·00

**1978.** Social Welfare. Surch. with premium in figures.

95. A. 65 c.+35 c. (No. 53) .. 80 1·25
96. – 1 f. 75+50 c. (No. 66) .. 80 1·25

16. Bouet-Willaumez and "La Malouine".

**1938.** Centenary of Landing of Bouet-Willaumez in Gabon.

97. 16. 65 c. brown .. .. 55 60
98. 1 f. red .. .. 55 50
99. 1 f. 75 blue .. .. 1·00 1·00
100. 2 f. violet .. .. 1·25 1·10

**1939.** New York World's Fair. As T **20** of Cameroun.

101. 1 f. 25 red .. .. 80 90
102. 2 f. 25 blue .. .. 80 90

**1939.** 150th Anniv of French Revolution. As T **25** of Cameroun.

103 45 c.+25 c. grn & blk (post) 6·00 8·25
104 70 c.+30 c. brown & black 6·00 8·25
105 90 c.+35 c. orange & black 6·00 8·25
106 1 f. 25+1 f. red and black 6·00 8·25
107 2 f. 25+2 f. blue and black 6·00 8·25
108 4 f. 50+4 f. blk & orge (air) 12·00 18·00

**1940.** Adherence to General de Gaulle.
A. Postage stamps of 1936 and 1937.

(a) Optd **AFRIQUE FRANCAISE LIBRE**.

| | | | | |
|---|---|---|---|---|
| 109 | 8 | 1 c. brown and yellow | 55 | 1·00 |
| 110 | | 2 c. violet and green | 65 | 1·00 |
| 111 | | 3 c. blue and yellow | 55 | 1·00 |
| 112 | | 5 c. green & light green | 50 | 80 |
| 113 | 9 | 10 c. mauve and blue | 75 | 90 |
| 114 | | 15 c. blue and pink | 70 | 90 |
| 115 | | 20 c. brown and yellow | 75 | 1·25 |
| 116 | | 25 c. red and blue | 2·50 | 4·75 |
| 117 | | 35 c. green & lt green | 80 | 1·10 |

(b) Optd **LIBRE**.

| | | | | |
|---|---|---|---|---|
| 118 | – | 4 c. green (No. 3) | 6·50 | 6·00 |
| 119a | 10 | 30 c. deep green & grn | 1·40 | 1·40 |
| 120a | | 30 c. blue and pink | 4·25 | 4·50 |
| 121 | | 40 c. red and blue | 35 | 45 |
| 122a | | 45 c. green & lt green | 65 | 50 |
| 123a | | 50 c. brown and yellow | 1·00 | 1·90 |
| 124 | | 55 c. violet and blue | 50 | 80 |
| 125 | | 60 c. purple and blue | 35 | 35 |
| 126 | A | 65 c. blue and green | 35 | 45 |
| 127 | | 70 c. violet and orange | 35 | 50 |
| 128 | | 75 c. black and yellow | 30·00 | 30·00 |
| 129 | | 80 c. brown and yellow | 35 | 40 |
| 130 | | 90 c. red and orange | 50 | 60 |
| 131 | 10 | 1 f. red and orange | 80 | 90 |
| 132 | A | 1 f. green and blue | 2·25 | 3·00 |
| 133 | B | 1 f. 40 brown and green | 35 | 55 |
| 134 | | 1 f. 50 blue & light blue | 40 | 40 |
| 135 | | 1 f. 60 violet & orange | 35 | 50 |
| 136 | | 1 f. 75 brown & yellow | 70 | 85 |
| 137 | C | 2 f. 15 violet and yellow | 50 | 75 |
| 138 | | 2 f. 25 blue & light blue | 60 | 80 |
| 139 | | 2 f. 50 purple & orange | 45 | 65 |
| 140 | | 3 f. blue and pink | 60 | 70 |
| 141 | | 5 f. green & light green | 1·50 | 1·50 |
| 142 | | 10 f. violet and blue | 90 | 75 |
| 143 | | 20 f. black and yellow | 75 | 65 |

(c) Surch **LIBRE** and value in figures.

| | | | | |
|---|---|---|---|---|
| 144 | 10 | 75 c. on 50 c. brown and yellow | 40 | 40 |
| 145 | A | 1 f. on 65 c. blue & grn | 30 | 30 |

(d) Optd **Afrique Francaise Libre.**

| | | | | |
|---|---|---|---|---|
| 146 | 8 | 1 c. brown and yellow | 80 | 80 |
| 147 | | 2 c. violet and green | 85 | 80 |
| 148 | | 3 c. blue and yellow | 85 | 80 |
| 149 | | 5 c. blue and green | 80 | 80 |
| 150 | 9 | 10 c. mauve and blue | 85 | 80 |
| 151 | | 15 c. blue and pink | 85 | 80 |
| 152 | | 20 c. brown and yellow | 80 | 80 |
| 153 | | 25 c. red and blue | 2·50 | 2·50 |
| 154 | | 35 c. green & lt green | 2·50 | 2·00 |

B. Air stamps of 1937 optd **Afrique Francaise Libre** or surch also.

| | | | | |
|---|---|---|---|---|
| 155 | D | 1 f. 50 black and yellow | £140 | £140 |
| 156 | | 2 f. 50 green and pink | 65 | 80 |
| 157 | | 3 f. 75 brown and green | £140 | £140 |
| 158 | 12 | 4 f. 50 red and blue | 75 | 90 |
| 159 | | 6 f. 50 blue and green | 85 | 1·00 |
| 160 | | 8 f. 50 red and orange | 75 | 90 |
| 161 | D | 10 f. on 2 f. 50 green and pink | 60·00 | 60·00 |
| 162 | 12 | 50 f. on 10 f. 75 violet and green | 5·00 | 6·75 |

C. No. 71 of Middle Congo optd **AFRIQUE FRANCAISE LIBRE.**

| | | | | |
|---|---|---|---|---|
| 163 | 15 | 4 c. green | 30·00 | 28·00 |

**1940.** Arrival of Gen. de Gaulle in Brazzaville. Optd. **LIBRE 24-10-40.**

| | | | | |
|---|---|---|---|---|
| **164.** | **A.** | 80 c. brown and yellow | 10·00 | 10·00 |
| **165.** | **10.** | 1 f. red and orange | 10·00 | 10·00 |
| **166.** | **A.** | 1 f. green and blue | 10·00 | 10·00 |
| **167.** | **B.** | 1 f. 50 blue and pale blue | 10·00 | 10·00 |

**23.** Phoenix.

**25.** Count Savorgnan de Brazza and Stanley Pool.

**1941.** Free French Issue. (a) Postage.

| | | | | |
|---|---|---|---|---|
| 168. | **23.** | 5 c. brown | 10 | 25 |
| 169. | | 10 c. blue | 10 | 25 |
| 170. | | 25 c. green | 10 | 25 |
| 171. | | 30 c. orange | 10 | 25 |
| 172. | | 40 c. green | 15 | 30 |
| 173. | | 80 c. purple | 10 | 25 |
| 174. | | 1 f. mauve | 20 | 10 |
| 175. | | 1 f. 50 red | 15 | 10 |
| 176. | | 2 f. black | 10 | 10 |
| 177. | | 2 f. 50 blue | 40 | 25 |
| 178. | | 4 f. violet | 35 | 25 |
| 179. | | 5 f. yellow | 40 | 20 |
| 180. | | 10 f. brown | 35 | 40 |
| 181. | | 20 f. green | 55 | 40 |

(b) Air. As T **32** of Cameroun.

| | | | | |
|---|---|---|---|---|
| 182. | – | 1 f. orange | 30 | 20 |
| 183. | – | 1 f. 50 red | 40 | 45 |
| 184. | – | 5 f. purple | 80 | 70 |
| 185. | – | 10 f. black | 75 | 70 |
| 186. | – | 25 f. blue | 60 | 60 |
| 187. | – | 50 f. green | 55 | 55 |
| 188. | – | 100 f. red | 80 | 80 |

**1941.** De Brazza Memorial Fund.

| | | | | |
|---|---|---|---|---|
| 189. | **25.** | 1 f.+2 f. brown and red | 55 | 45 |

**1943.** Free French Funds. Nos. 69, 73 and 82 surch. **Afrique Francaise Combattante,** cross and value.

| | | | |
|---|---|---|---|
| 190. | 2 f. 25+50 f. blue and pale blue (postage) | 7·25 | 7·25 |
| 191. | 10 f.+100 f. violet and blue | 22·00 | 22·00 |
| 192. | 10 f. 75+200 f. violet and green (air) | £100 | £100 |

**1944.** French Aid Fund. Various stamps surch. **RESISTANCE** and value.

| | | | | |
|---|---|---|---|---|
| 195. | **23.** | 5 c.+10 f. brown (No. 168) | 4·00 | 4·00 |
| 196. | | 10 c.+10 f. blue (No. 169) | 4·00 | 4·00 |
| 197. | | 25 c.+10 f. grn. (No. 170) | 4·00 | 4·00 |
| 198. | | 30 c.+10 f. orge. (No. 171) | 4·00 | 4·00 |
| 199. | | 40 c.+10 f. grn. (No. 172) | 4·00 | 4·00 |
| 193. | A. | 80 c.+10 f. brown and yellow (No. 164) | 12·50 | 12·50 |
| 200. | **23.** | 1 f.+10 f. mve. (No. 174) | 4·00 | 4·00 |
| 194. | B. | 1 f. 50+15 f. blue and pale blue (No. 167) | 12·50 | 12·50 |
| 201. | **23.** | 2 f.+20 f. black (No. 176) | 4·00 | 4·00 |
| 202. | | 2 f. 50+25 f. blue (No. 177) | 4·00 | 4·00 |
| 203. | | 4 f.+40 f. violet (No. 178) | 4·00 | 4·00 |
| 204. | | 5 f.+50 f. yell. (No. 179) | 4·00 | 4·00 |
| 205. | | 10 f.+100 f. brn. (No. 180) | 5·50 | 5·50 |
| 206. | | 20 f.+200 f. grn. (No. 181) | 5·50 | 5·50 |

**1944.** French Aid Fund. Nos. 164, 167, 168/72, 174 and 176/7 surch **LIBERATION** and value.

| | | | | |
|---|---|---|---|---|
| 209. | **23.** | 5 c.+10 f. brown | 4·25 | 4·25 |
| 210. | | 10 c.+10 f. blue | 4·25 | 4·25 |
| 211. | | 25 c.+10 f. green | 4·25 | 4·25 |
| 212. | | 30 c.+10 f. orange | 4·25 | 4·25 |
| 213. | | 40 c.+10 f. green | 4·25 | 4·25 |
| 207. | A. | 80 c.+10 f. brown & yell. | 12·50 | 12·50 |
| 214. | **23.** | 1 f.+10 f. mauve | 4·25 | 4·25 |
| 208. | B. | 1 f. 50+15 f. bl. & pale bl. | 12·50 | 12·50 |
| 215. | **23.** | 2 f.+20 f. black | 4·25 | 4·25 |
| 216. | | 2 f. 50+25 f. blue | 4·25 | 4·25 |

**1944.** Mutual Aid and Red Cross Funds. As T **33** of Cameroun.

| | | | |
|---|---|---|---|
| 217. | 5 f.+20 f. blue | 60 | 65 |

**1945.** Surch. with new values and bars.

| | | | | |
|---|---|---|---|---|
| 218. | **23.** | 50 c. on 5 c. brown | 40 | 60 |
| 219. | | 60 c. on 5 c. brown | 40 | 60 |
| 220. | | 70 c. on 5 c. brown | 40 | 60 |
| 221. | | 1 f. 20 on 5 c. brown | 40 | 60 |
| 222. | | 2 f. 40 on 25 c. green | 60 | 80 |
| 223. | | 3 f. on 25 c. green | 65 | 80 |
| 224. | | 4 f. 50 on 25 c. green | 65 | 80 |
| 225. | | 15 f. on 2 f. 50 blue | 65 | 80 |

**1945.** Eboue. As T **34** of Cameroun.

| | | | |
|---|---|---|---|
| 226. | 2 f. black | 25 | 25 |
| 227. | 25 f. green | 1·00 | 1·00 |

**1946.** Air. Victory. As T **35** of Cameroun.

| | | | |
|---|---|---|---|
| 228. | 8 f. red | 50 | 75 |

**1946.** Air. From Chad to the Rhine. As Nos. 226/31 of Cameroun.

| | | | |
|---|---|---|---|
| 229. | 5 f. purple | 85 | 1·00 |
| 230. | 10 f. green | 85 | 1·00 |
| 231. | 15 f. blue | 1·00 | 1·25 |
| 232. | 20 f. red | 1·00 | 1·25 |
| 233. | 25 f. black | 1·10 | 1·25 |
| 234. | 50 f. red | 1·10 | 1·25 |

**34.** Black Rhinoceros.

**36.** Boatman.

**37.** Caudron Goeland over Beach.

**1947.**

| | | | | |
|---|---|---|---|---|
| 235. | **34.** | 10 c. blue (postage) | 10 | 25 |
| 236. | | 30 c. violet | 10 | 25 |
| 237. | | 40 c. orange | 10 | 25 |
| 238. | – | 50 c. blue | 10 | 25 |
| 239. | – | 60 c. red | 15 | 35 |
| 240. | – | 80 c. green | 20 | 45 |
| 241. | – | 1 f. orange | 20 | 15 |
| 242. | – | 1 f. 20 red | 25 | 50 |
| 243. | – | 1 f. 50 green | 30 | 70 |
| 244. | – | 2 f. brown | 20 | 15 |
| 245. | – | 3 f. red | 15 | 15 |
| 246. | – | 3 f. 60 brown | 1·25 | 1·50 |
| 247. | – | 4 f. blue | 20 | 10 |
| 248. | **36.** | 5 f. purple | 35 | 45 |
| 249. | | 6 f. blue | 30 | 40 |
| 250. | | 10 f. black | 35 | 45 |
| 251. | – | 15 f. brown | 50 | 40 |
| 252. | – | 20 f. red | 60 | 15 |
| 253. | – | 25 f. black | 75 | 15 |
| 254. | – | 50 f. brown (air) | 1·25 | 60 |
| 255. | **37.** | 100 f. green | 2·50 | 1·50 |
| 256. | – | 200 f. blue | 4·50 | 2·50 |

DESIGNS—As Type **36**: 50 c. to 80 c. Palms and cataract. 1 f. to 1. f. 50, River view. 2 f. to 4 f. Tropical forest. 15 f. to 25 f. Bakongo girl. As Type **37**: 50 f. Savoia Marchetti S.M.75 airplane over village. 200 f. Savoia Marchetti S.M.75 over column of porters.

**1949.** Air. 75th Anniv. of U.P.U. As T **46** of Cameroun.

| | | | |
|---|---|---|---|
| 267. | 25 f. green | 5·50 | 6·50 |

**1950.** Colonial Welfare Fund. As T **47** of Cameroun.

| | | | |
|---|---|---|---|
| 268. | 10 f.+2 f. purple & grn. | 2·50 | 3·00 |

**42.** De Brazza and Landscape.

**1951.** Birth Centenary of Count Savorgnan de Brazza.

| | | | | |
|---|---|---|---|---|
| 269 | – | 10 f. green & blue (post) | 65 | 15 |
| 270 | **42** | 15 f. red, bl & brn (air) | 3·00 | 2·25 |

DESIGN—22 × 31½ mm: 10 f. De Brazza.

**43.** Monseigneur Augouard.

**1952.** Air. Birth Centenary of Mgr. Augouard (First Bishop of the Congo).

| | | | | |
|---|---|---|---|---|
| 271. | **43.** | 15 f. sepia, purple & olive | 3·25 | 1·40 |

**1952.** Military Medal Cent. As T **48** of Cameroun.

| | | | |
|---|---|---|---|
| 272. | 15 f. multicoloured | 3·25 | 3·00 |

**45.** Sailing Canoe.

**1953.** Air.

| | | | | |
|---|---|---|---|---|
| 273. | – | 50 f. brn., green & blue | 1·00 | 35 |
| 274. | **45.** | 100 f. grn., turq. & sepia | 4·00 | 40 |
| 275. | – | 200 f. red and lake | 4·75 | 2·00 |
| 276. | – | 500 f. blue, blk. & grn. | 40·00 | 6·50 |

DESIGNS: 50 f. Logs in river. 200 f. Native driver and docks. 500 f. African darters.

**1954.** Air. 10th Anniv. of Liberation. As T **52** of Cameroun.

| | | | |
|---|---|---|---|
| 277 | 15 f. brown and violet | 3·25 | 4·00 |

**47.** Lieut.-Governor Cureau.

**1954.**

| | | | | |
|---|---|---|---|---|
| 278. | **47.** | 15 f. brown and green | 80 | 30 |

**48.** Felix Eboue.

**1955.** Air. Governor General Eboue Commem.

| | | | | |
|---|---|---|---|---|
| 279. | **48.** | 15 f. sepia, brn. & blue | 2·50 | 1·60 |

**49.** Lizard.

**1955.** Nature Protection.

| | | | | |
|---|---|---|---|---|
| 280 | **49** | 8 f. green and purple | 75 | 70 |

**50.** Boali Waterfall and Power Station.

DESIGNS: 10 f. Cotton production, Chad. 15 f. Brazzaville Hospital, Middle Congo. 20 f. Libreville harbour, Gabon.

**1956.** Economic and Social Development Fund.

| | | | | |
|---|---|---|---|---|
| 281. | **50.** | 5 f. purple and sepia | 25 | 10 |
| 282. | – | 10 f. green and black | 30 | 15 |
| 283. | – | 15 f. grey and blue | 35 | 10 |
| 284. | – | 20 f. vermilion and red | 40 | 20 |

**51.** Coffee.

**1956.** Coffee.

| | | | | |
|---|---|---|---|---|
| 285 | **51** | 10 f. violet and lilac | 50 | 20 |

**52.** Riverside Hospital.

**1957.** Order of Malta Leprosy Relief.

| | | | | |
|---|---|---|---|---|
| 286. | **52.** | 15 f. turquoise, grn. & red | 85 | 45 |

**54.** Lion and Lioness.

**53.** Gen. Faidherbe and African Trooper.

**1957.** Air. Centenary of African Troops.

| | | | | |
|---|---|---|---|---|
| 287. | **53.** | 15 f. brown & chestnut | 1·75 | 2·00 |

**1957.**

| | | | | |
|---|---|---|---|---|
| 288. | – | 1 f. brown and green | 20 | 25 |
| 289. | **54.** | 2 f. olive and green | 20 | 30 |
| 290. | – | 3 f. black, blue & green | 25 | 30 |
| 291. | – | 4 f. brown and grey | 25 | 30 |

DESIGNS—HORIZ. 1 f. Giant eland. VERT. 3 f. African elephant. 4 f. Greater Kudu.

**55.** Regional Bureau, Brazzaville.

**56.** "Euadania".

**1958.** 10th Anniv. of W.H.O.

| | | | | |
|---|---|---|---|---|
| 292. | **55.** | 20 f. brown and green | 50 | 60 |

**1958.** Tropical Flora.

| | | | | |
|---|---|---|---|---|
| 293. | **56.** | 10 f. yell., grn. & violet | 40 | 30 |
| 294. | – | 25 f. red, yellow & green | 50 | 50 |

DESIGN: 25 f. "Spathodea".

**1958.** 10th Anniv. of Declaration of Human Rights. As T **10** of Comoro Is.

| | | | |
|---|---|---|---|
| 295. | 20 f. turquoise and blue | 1·00 | 80 |

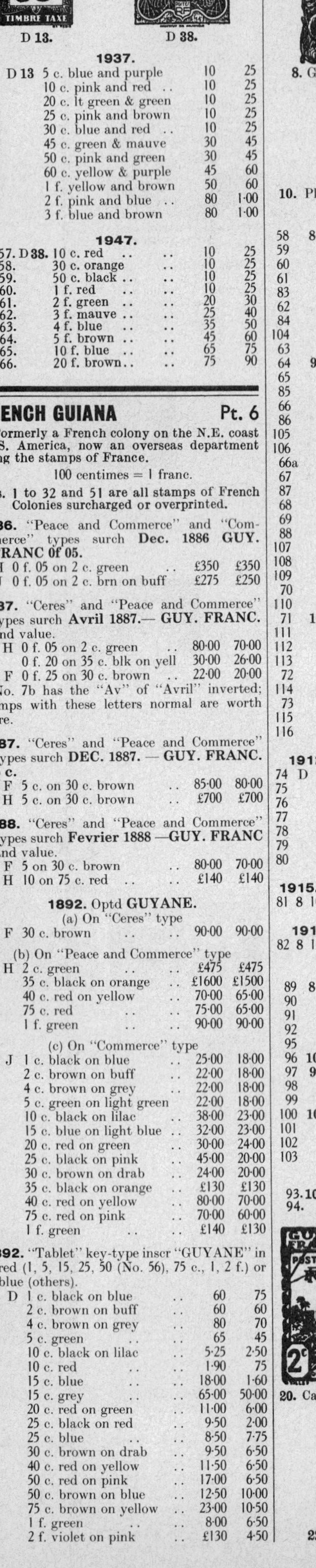

POSTAGE DUE STAMPS

D 13. D 38.

**1937.**

| | | | | |
|---|---|---|---|---|
| D83 | D 13 | 5 c. blue and purple | 10 | 25 |
| D84 | | 10 c. pink and red .. | 10 | 25 |
| D85 | | 20 c. lt green & green | 10 | 25 |
| D86 | | 25 c. pink and brown | 10 | 25 |
| D87 | | 30 c. blue and red .. | 10 | 25 |
| D88 | | 45 c. green & mauve | 30 | 45 |
| D89 | | 50 c. pink and green | 30 | 45 |
| D90 | | 60 c. yellow & purple | 45 | 60 |
| D91 | | 1 f. yellow and brown | 50 | 60 |
| D92 | | 2 f. pink and blue .. | 80 | 1·00 |
| D93 | | 3 f. blue and brown | 80 | 1·00 |

**1947.**

| | | | | |
|---|---|---|---|---|
| D 257. | D38. | 10 c. red .. .. | 10 | 25 |
| D 258. | | 30 c. orange .. | 10 | 25 |
| D 259. | | 50 c. black .. .. | 10 | 25 |
| D 260. | | 1 f. red .. .. | 10 | 25 |
| D 261. | | 2 f. green .. .. | 20 | 30 |
| D 262. | | 3 f. mauve .. .. | 25 | 40 |
| D 263. | | 4 f. blue .. .. | 35 | 50 |
| D 264. | | 5 f. brown .. .. | 45 | 60 |
| D 265. | | 10 f. blue .. .. | 65 | 75 |
| D 266. | | 20 f. brown.. .. | 75 | 90 |

## FRENCH GUIANA Pt. 6

**Formerly a French colony on the N.E. coast of S. America, now an overseas department using the stamps of France.**

100 centimes = 1 franc.

**Nos. 1 to 32 and 51 are all stamps of French Colonies surcharged or overprinted.**

**1886.** "Peace and Commerce" and "Commerce" types surch **Dec. 1886 GUY. FRANC 0f 05.**

| | | | | |
|---|---|---|---|---|
| 2 | H | 0 f. 05 on 2 c. green .. | £350 | £350 |
| 5 | J | 0 f. 05 on 2 c. brn on buff | £275 | £250 |

**1887.** "Ceres" and "Peace and Commerce" types surch **Avril 1887.— GUY. FRANC.** and value.

| | | | | |
|---|---|---|---|---|
| 6 | H | 0 f. 05 on 2 c. green .. | 80·00 | 70·00 |
| 7b | | 0 f. 20 on 35 c. blk on yell | 30·00 | 26·00 |
| 8 | F | 0 f. 25 on 30 c. brown .. | 22·00 | 20·00 |

No. 7b has the "Av" of "Avril" inverted; stamps with these letters normal are worth more.

**1887.** "Ceres" and "Peace and Commerce" types surch **DEC. 1887. — GUY. FRANC. 5 c.**

| | | | | |
|---|---|---|---|---|
| 9 | F | 5 c. on 30 c. brown .. | 85·00 | 80·00 |
| 10 | H | 5 c. on 30 c. brown .. | £700 | £700 |

**1888.** "Ceres" and "Peace and Commerce" types surch **Fevrier 1888 —GUY. FRANC** and value.

| | | | | |
|---|---|---|---|---|
| 11 | F | 5 on 30 c. brown .. | 80·00 | 70·00 |
| 12 | H | 10 on 75 c. red .. .. | £140 | £140 |

**1892.** Optd **GUYANE.**

(a) On "Ceres" type

| | | | | |
|---|---|---|---|---|
| 14 | F | 30 c. brown .. .. | 90·00 | 90·00 |

(b) On "Peace and Commerce" type

| | | | | |
|---|---|---|---|---|
| 15 | H | 2 c. green .. .. | £475 | £475 |
| 16 | | 35 c. black on orange .. | £1600 | £1500 |
| 17 | | 40 c. red on yellow .. | 70·00 | 65·00 |
| 18 | | 75 c. red .. .. | 75·00 | 65·00 |
| 19 | | 1 f. green .. .. | 90·00 | 90·00 |

(c) On "Commerce" type

| | | | | |
|---|---|---|---|---|
| 20 | J | 1 c. black on blue .. | 25·00 | 18·00 |
| 21 | | 2 c. brown on buff .. | 22·00 | 18·00 |
| 22 | | 4 c. brown on grey .. | 22·00 | 18·00 |
| 23 | | 5 c. green on light green | 22·00 | 18·00 |
| 24 | | 10 c. black on lilac .. | 38·00 | 23·00 |
| 25 | | 15 c. blue on light blue .. | 32·00 | 23·00 |
| 26 | | 20 c. red on green .. | 30·00 | 24·00 |
| 27 | | 25 c. black on pink .. | 45·00 | 20·00 |
| 28 | | 30 c. brown on drab .. | 24·00 | 20·00 |
| 29 | | 35 c. black on orange .. | £130 | £130 |
| 30 | | 40 c. red on yellow .. | 80·00 | 70·00 |
| 31 | | 75 c. red on pink .. | 70·00 | 60·00 |
| 32 | | 1 f. green .. .. | £140 | £130 |

**1892.** "Tablet" key-type inscr "GUYANE" in red (1, 5, 15, 25, 50 (No. 56), 75 c., 1, 2 f.) or blue (others).

| | | | | |
|---|---|---|---|---|
| 38 | D | 1 c. black on blue .. | 60 | 75 |
| 39 | | 2 c. brown on buff .. | 60 | 60 |
| 40 | | 4 c. brown on grey .. | 80 | 70 |
| 52 | | 5 c. green .. .. | 65 | 45 |
| 42 | | 10 c. black on lilac .. | 5·25 | 2·50 |
| 53 | | 10 c. red .. .. | 1·90 | 75 |
| 43 | | 15 c. blue .. .. | 18·00 | 1·60 |
| 54 | | 15 c. grey .. .. | 65·00 | 50·00 |
| 44 | | 20 c. red on green .. | 11·00 | 6·00 |
| 45 | | 25 c. black on red .. | 9·50 | 2·00 |
| 55 | | 25 c. blue .. .. | 8·50 | 7·75 |
| 46 | | 30 c. brown on drab .. | 9·50 | 6·50 |
| 47 | | 40 c. red on yellow .. | 11·50 | 6·50 |
| 48 | | 50 c. red on pink .. | 17·00 | 6·50 |
| 56 | | 50 c. brown on blue .. | 12·50 | 10·00 |
| 49 | | 75 c. brown on yellow .. | 23·00 | 10·50 |
| 50 | | 1 f. green .. .. | 8·00 | 6·50 |
| 57 | | 2 f. violet on pink .. | £130 | 4·50 |

**1892.** "Commerce" type surch **DEC. 92. 0f 05 GUYANE.**

| | | | | |
|---|---|---|---|---|
| 51 | J | 0 f. 05 on 15 c. blue on bl | 18·00 | 14·50 |

**8.** Giant Anteater. **9.** Gold-washer.

**10.** Plantation of Coconut Palms, Cayenne.

**1904.**

| | | | | |
|---|---|---|---|---|
| 58 | 8 | 1 c. black .. .. | 15 | 15 |
| 59 | | 2 c. blue .. .. | 15 | 15 |
| 60 | | 4 c. brown .. .. | 15 | 15 |
| 61 | | 5 c. green .. .. | 35 | 45 |
| 83 | | 5 c. orange .. .. | 15 | 25 |
| 62 | | 10 c. red .. .. | 25 | 15 |
| 84 | | 10 c. green .. .. | 20 | 30 |
| 104 | | 10 c. red on blue .. | 20 | 25 |
| 63 | | 15 c. violet .. .. | 70 | 50 |
| 64 | 9 | 20 c. brown .. .. | 25 | 30 |
| 65 | | 25 c. blue .. .. | 75 | 45 |
| 85 | | 25 c. violet .. .. | 40 | 35 |
| 66 | | 30 c. black .. .. | 65 | 50 |
| 86 | | 30 c. red .. .. | 30 | 30 |
| 105 | | 30 c. orange .. .. | 20 | 30 |
| 106 | | 30 c. green .. .. | 55 | 60 |
| 66a | | 35 c. black on yellow | 25 | 20 |
| 67 | | 40 c. red .. .. | 25 | 25 |
| 87 | | 40 c. black .. .. | 30 | 30 |
| 68 | | 45 c. brown .. .. | 45 | 35 |
| 69 | | 50 c. lilac .. .. | 1·25 | 1·25 |
| 88 | | 50 c. blue .. .. | 15 | 30 |
| 107 | | 50 c. grey .. .. | 40 | 45 |
| 108 | | 60 c. mauve on pink | 20 | 30 |
| 109 | | 65 c. green .. .. | 35 | 40 |
| 70 | | 75 c. green .. .. | 60 | 40 |
| 110 | | 85 c. purple .. .. | 35 | 35 |
| 71 | 10 | 1 f. red .. .. | 35 | 35 |
| 111 | | 1 f. blue on light blue | 40 | 40 |
| 112 | | 1 f. blue on green .. | 1·00 | 1·25 |
| 113 | | 1 f. 10 pink .. .. | 65 | 75 |
| 72 | | 2 f. blue .. .. | 50 | 45 |
| 114 | | 2 f. red on yellow .. | 1·10 | 1·00 |
| 73 | | 5 f. black .. .. | 3·75 | 2·75 |
| 115 | | 10 f. green on yellow | 7·00 | 7·00 |
| 116 | | 20 f. red .. .. | 9·75 | 9·25 |

**1912.** "Tablet" key-type surch in figures.

| | | | | |
|---|---|---|---|---|
| 74 | D | 05 on 2 c. brown on buff | 35 | 45 |
| 75 | | 05 on 4 c. brown on grey | 35 | 40 |
| 76 | | 05 on 20 c. red on green | 50 | 60 |
| 77 | | 05 on 25 c. black on pink | 1·60 | 1·75 |
| 78 | | 05 on 30 c. brown on drab | 50 | 75 |
| 79 | | 10 on 40 c. red on yellow | 35 | 45 |
| 80 | | 10 on 50 c. red .. | 1·25 | 1·40 |

**1915.** Red Cross. Surch with red cross and **5.**

| | | | | |
|---|---|---|---|---|
| 81 | 8 | 10 c.+5 c. red .. .. | 8·00 | 8·00 |

**1915.** Red Cross. Surch **5c** and red cross.

| | | | | |
|---|---|---|---|---|
| 82 | 8 | 10 c.+5 c. red .. .. | 40 | 55 |

**1922.** Surch in figures with bars.

| | | | | |
|---|---|---|---|---|
| 89 | 8 | 0,01 on 15 c. violet .. | 15 | 35 |
| 90 | | 0,02 on 15 c. violet .. | 15 | 35 |
| 91 | | 0,04 on 15 c. violet .. | 15 | 35 |
| 92 | | 0,05 on 15 c. violet .. | 20 | 35 |
| 95 | | 25 c. on 15 c. violet .. | 20 | 30 |
| 96 | 10 | 25 c. on 2 f. blue .. | 25 | 30 |
| 97 | 9 | 65 on 45 c. brown .. | 65 | 65 |
| 98 | | 85 on 45 c. brown .. | 65 | 65 |
| 99 | | 90 on 75 c. red .. | 75 | 75 |
| 100 | 10 | 1 f. 05 on 2 f. brown .. | 60 | 65 |
| 101 | | 1 f. 25 on 1 f. blue on bl | 60 | 65 |
| 102 | | 1 f. 50 on 1 f. blue .. | 90 | 95 |
| 103 | | 3 f. on 5 f. violet .. | 85 | 90 |

**1924.** Surch. in words.

| | | | | |
|---|---|---|---|---|
| 93. | 10. | 10 f. on 1 f. green on yell. | 8·00 | 8·25 |
| 94. | | 20 f. on 5 f. mauve on red | 7·75 | 8·25 |

**20.** Carib Archer. **21.** Shooting the Rapids, R. Maroni.

**22.** Government Building, Cayenne.

**1929.**

| | | | | |
|---|---|---|---|---|
| 117 | 20 | 1 c. blue and lilac .. | 15 | 25 |
| 118 | | 2 c. green and red | 15 | 25 |
| 119 | | 3 c. green and violet .. | 15 | 25 |
| 120 | | 4 c. mauve and brown | 15 | 30 |
| 121 | | 5 c. red and blue .. | 20 | 30 |
| 122 | | 10 c. brown and mauve | 15 | 25 |
| 123 | | 15 c. red and brown .. | 20 | 30 |
| 124 | | 20 c. green and blue .. | 15 | 25 |
| 125 | | 25 c. brown and red .. | 30 | 40 |
| 126 | 21 | 30 c. lt green & green | 30 | 45 |
| 127 | | 30 c. brown and green .. | 15 | 25 |
| 128 | | 35 c. green and blue .. | 35 | 45 |
| 129 | | 40 c. drab and brown .. | 25 | 30 |
| 130 | | 45 c. brown and green .. | 45 | 55 |
| 131 | | 45 c. green and olive .. | 25 | 30 |
| 132 | | 50 c. brown and blue .. | 20 | 30 |
| 133 | | 55 c. red and blue .. | 65 | 75 |
| 134 | | 60 c. green and red .. | 25 | 30 |
| 135 | | 65 c. green and red .. | 45 | 60 |
| 136 | | 70 c. green and blue .. | 55 | 70 |
| 137 | | 75 c. light blue and blue | 75 | 90 |
| 138 | | 80 c. blue and black .. | 30 | 40 |
| 139 | | 90 c. red and carmine .. | 45 | 50 |
| 140 | | 90 c. brown and mauve | 60 | 60 |
| 141 | | 1 f. brown and mauve .. | 45 | 50 |
| 142 | | 1 f. red and carmine .. | 1·40 | 1·25 |
| 143 | | 1 f. blue and black .. | 35 | 45 |
| 144 | 22 | 1 f. 05 green and red .. | 2·75 | 2·75 |
| 145 | | 1 f. 10 mauve and brown | 2·25 | 2·50 |
| 146 | | 1 f. 25 green and brown | 50 | 60 |
| 147 | | 1 f. 25 red and carmine | 25 | 35 |
| 148 | | 1 f. 40 mauve and brown | 50 | 60 |
| 149 | | 1 f. 50 light blue & blue | 20 | 30 |
| 150 | | 1 f. 60 green and brown | 25 | 35 |
| 151 | | 1 f. 75 brown and red .. | 1·25 | 1·25 |
| 152 | | 1 f. 75 ultramarine & bl | 50 | 60 |
| 153 | | 2 f. red and green .. | 25 | 30 |
| 154 | | 2 f. 25 ultramarine & bl | 60 | 65 |
| 155 | | 2 f. 50 brown and red .. | 55 | 65 |
| 156 | | 3 f. mauve and brown .. | 35 | 45 |
| 157 | | 5 f. green and violet .. | 35 | 45 |
| 158 | | 10 f. blue and brown .. | 65 | 80 |
| 159 | | 20 f. red and blue .. | 1·10 | 1·40 |

**1931.** "Colonial Exhibition" key-types inscr "GUYANE FRANCAISE".

| | | | | |
|---|---|---|---|---|
| 160 | E | 40 c. black and green .. | 2·25 | 2·25 |
| 161 | F | 50 c. black and mauve | 2·25 | 2·25 |
| 162 | G | 90 c. black and red .. | 2·25 | 2·50 |
| 163 | H | 1 f. 50 black and blue .. | 2·25 | 2·50 |

**25.** Cayenne.

**1933.** Air.

| | | | | |
|---|---|---|---|---|
| 164. | 25. | 50 c. brown .. .. | 25 | 30 |
| 165. | | 1 f. green .. .. | 20 | 30 |
| 166. | | 1 f. 50 blue .. .. | 20 | 30 |
| 167. | | 2 f. orange .. .. | 20 | 30 |
| 168. | | 3 f. black .. .. | 45 | 50 |
| 169. | | 5 f. violet .. .. | 30 | 40 |
| 170. | | 10 f. olive .. .. | 40 | 45 |
| 171. | | 20 f. red .. .. | 50 | 55 |

**26.** Cayenne recaptured by D'Estrees, 1676.

**27.** Local Products.

**1935.** West Indies Tercent.

| | | | | |
|---|---|---|---|---|
| 172. | 26. | 40 c. brown .. .. | 2·50 | 2·75 |
| 173. | | 50 c. red .. .. | 5·75 | 4·00 |
| 174. | | 1 f. 50 blue .. .. | 2·50 | 2·75 |
| 175. | 27. | 1 f. 75 red .. .. | 7·50 | 7·50 |
| 176. | | 5 f. brown .. .. | 5·50 | 5·00 |
| 177. | | 10 f. green .. .. | 6·00 | 5·00 |

**1937.** International Exhibition, Paris. As Nos. 110/15 of Cameroun.

| | | | |
|---|---|---|---|
| 178 | 20 c. violet .. .. | 45 | 60 |
| 179 | 30 c. green .. .. | 45 | 60 |
| 180 | 40 c. red .. .. | 45 | 60 |
| 181 | 50 c. brown and agate | 45 | 60 |
| 182 | 90 c. red .. .. | 50 | 65 |
| 183 | 1 f. 50 blue .. .. | 50 | 65 |

**1938.** Int. Anti-Cancer Fund. As T **19** of Cameroun.

| | | | |
|---|---|---|---|
| 184. | 1 f. 75+50 c. blue .. | 5·50 | 6·25 |

**1939.** New York World's Fair. As T **20** of Cameroun.

| | | | |
|---|---|---|---|
| 185. | 1 f. 25 red .. .. | 50 | 60 |
| 186. | 2 f. 25 blue .. .. | 50 | 60 |

**1939.** 150th Anniv. of French Revolution. As T **25** of Cameroun.

| | | | |
|---|---|---|---|
| 187. | 45 c.+25 c. grn. & blk. (post) .. .. .. | 5·25 | 5·50 |
| 188. | 70 c.+30 c. brn. & blk.. | 5·25 | 5·50 |
| 189. | 90 c.+35 c. orge. & blk. | 5·25 | 5·50 |
| 190. | 1 f. 25+1 f. red & black | 5·25 | 5·50 |
| 191. | 2 f. 25+2 f. blue & black | 5·25 | 5·50 |
| 192. | 5 f.+4 f. black & orange (air) .. .. .. | 9·25 | 10·00 |

**28.** View of Cayenne and Marshal Petain.

**1941.** Marshal Petain Issue.

| | | | | |
|---|---|---|---|---|
| 192a | 28 | 1 f. purple .. .. | 20 | 40 |
| 192b | | 2 f. 50 blue .. .. | 20 | 40 |

**1944.** Mutual Aid and Red Cross Funds. As T **33** of Cameroun.

| | | | |
|---|---|---|---|
| 193. | 5 f.+20 f. purple .. | 50 | 60 |

**1945.** Felix Eboue. As T **34** of Cameroun.

| | | | |
|---|---|---|---|
| 194. | 2 f. black .. .. | 35 | 50 |
| 195. | 25 f. green .. .. | 35 | 70 |

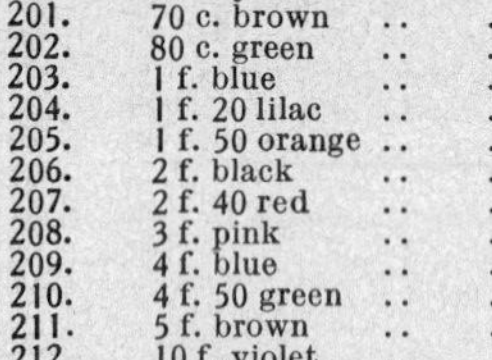

**28a.** Arms of French Guiana.

**1945.**

| | | | | |
|---|---|---|---|---|
| 196. | 28a. | 10 c. blue .. .. | 15 | 30 |
| 197. | | 30 c. brown .. .. | 15 | 30 |
| 198. | | 40 c. blue .. .. | 20 | 30 |
| 199. | | 50 c. purple .. .. | 15 | 30 |
| 200. | | 60 c. yellow .. .. | 15 | 30 |
| 201. | | 70 c. brown .. .. | 20 | 30 |
| 202. | | 80 c. green .. .. | 20 | 30 |
| 203. | | 1 f. blue .. .. | 15 | 30 |
| 204. | | 1 f. 20 lilac .. .. | 20 | 30 |
| 205. | | 1 f. 50 orange .. .. | 35 | 40 |
| 206. | | 2 f. black .. .. | 45 | 50 |
| 207. | | 2 f. 40 red .. .. | 45 | 50 |
| 208. | | 3 f. pink .. .. | 45 | 50 |
| 209. | | 4 f. blue .. .. | 45 | 50 |
| 210. | | 4 f. 50 green .. .. | 45 | 50 |
| 211. | | 5 f. brown .. .. | 45 | 50 |
| 212. | | 10 f. violet .. .. | 40 | 45 |
| 213. | | 15 f. red .. .. | 55 | 60 |
| 214. | | 20 f. olive .. .. | 60 | 65 |

**1945.** Air. As T **32** of Cameroun.

| | | | |
|---|---|---|---|
| 215. | 50 f. green .. .. | 70 | 75 |
| 216. | 100 f. red .. .. | 1·25 | 1·25 |

**1946.** Air. Victory. As T **35** of Cameroun.

| | | | |
|---|---|---|---|
| 217. | 8 f. black .. .. | 65 | 85 |

**1946.** Air. From Chad to the Rhine. As Nos. 226/31 of Cameroun.

| | | | |
|---|---|---|---|
| 218. | 5 f. blue .. .. | 50 | 60 |
| 219. | 10 f. red .. .. | 55 | 65 |
| 220. | 15 f. purple .. .. | 55 | 65 |
| 221. | 20 f. green .. .. | 70 | 75 |
| 222. | 25 f. purple .. .. | 70 | 85 |
| 223. | 50 f. mauve .. .. | 1·00 | 1·10 |

**29.** Hammock.

**33.** Cuvier's Toucans.

**35.** Yellow-throated Caracara.

**1947.**

| | | | | |
|---|---|---|---|---|
| 224. | 29. | 10 c. green (postage) .. | 15 | 25 |
| 225. | | 30 c. red .. .. | 15 | 25 |
| 226. | | 50 c. purple .. .. | 15 | 30 |
| 227. | – | 60 c. grey .. .. | 15 | 30 |
| 228. | – | 1 f. brown .. .. | 15 | 30 |
| 229. | – | 1 f. 50 brown .. .. | 15 | 30 |
| 230. | – | 2 f. green .. .. | 30 | 40 |
| 231. | – | 2 f. 50 blue .. .. | 35 | 40 |
| 232. | – | 3 f. brown .. .. | 40 | 50 |
| 233. | – | 4 f. brown .. .. | 1·10 | 55 |
| 234. | – | 5 f. blue .. .. | 65 | 55 |
| 235. | – | 6 f. brown .. .. | 70 | 55 |

236. **33.** 10 f. blue .. .. 5·50 2·25
237. 15 f. brown .. .. 5·50 2·50
238. 20 f. brown .. .. 5·50 2·25
239. – 25 f. green .. .. 7·00 3·00
240. – 40 f. brown .. .. 8·50 3·00
241. **35.** 50 f. green (air) .. 12·00 7·50
242. – 100 f. lake .. .. 8·00 8·75
243. – 200 f. blue .. .. 29·00 21·00

DESIGNS—As Types **29** and **33**—HORIZ. 60 c. to 1 f. 50, Riverside village. 2 f. to 3 f. Pirogue. 25 f., 40 f. Blue and yellow macaw, military macaw and white-eyed conure. VERT. 4 f. to 6 f. Girl. As Type **35**—VERT. 100 f. Airplane over peccary and palms. HORIZ. 200 f. Sud Ouest Corse II airplane, channel-billed toucan, Cuvier's toucan and black-necked aracari.

POSTAGE DUE STAMPS

**1925.** Postage Due stamps of France optd. **GUYANE FRANCAISE** or surch. also **centimes a percevoir and value in figures.**
D 117. **D 11** 5 c. blue .. .. 15 30
D 118. 10 c. brown .. .. 15 35
D 119. 15 c. on 20 c. olive .. 15 35
D 120. 20 c. olive .. .. 25 35
D 121. 25 c. on 5 c. blue .. 35 50
D 122. 30 c. on 20 c. olive .. 45 60
D 123. 45 c. on 10 c. brown 30 40
D 124. 50 c. red .. .. 40 50
D 125. 60 c. on 5 c. blue .. 35 45
D 126. 1 f. on 20 c. olive .. 70 85
D 127. 2 f. on 50 c. red .. 90 1·10
D 128. 3 f. mauve .. .. 5·00 5·50

D **23.** Palm trees. D **36.**

**1929.**
D160 **D 23** 5 c. blue & dp blue 15 30
D161 10 c. blue & brown 15 30
D162 20 c. red and green 15 30
D163 30 c. red and brown 15 30
D164 50 c. brown & mve 30 40
D165 60 c. brown and red 50 55
D166 – 1 f. red and blue .. 75 80
D167 – 2 f. green and red .. 1·10 1·10
D168 – 3 f. grey and mauve 1·75 2·25

DESIGN: 1 f. to 3 f. Creole girl.

**1947.**
D 244. **D 36.** 10 c. red .. .. 15 25
D 245. 30 c. green .. .. 15 30
D 246. 50 c. black .. .. 15 30
D 247. 1 f. blue .. .. 20 30
D 248. 2 f. lake .. .. 20 30
D 249. 3 f. violet .. .. 30 40
D 250. 4 f. red .. .. 50 55
D 251. 5 f. purple .. .. 60 75
D 252. 10 f. green .. .. 1·10 1·40
D 253. 20 f. purple .. .. 1·50 1·75

## FRENCH GUINEA Pt. 6

A French colony on the W. coast of Africa incorporated in French West Africa in 1944. Became completely independent in 1958 (see Guinea).

100 centimes = 1 franc.

**1892.** "Tablet" key-type inscr "GUINEE FRANCAISE" in red (1, 5, 15, 50 (No. 17), 75 c., 1 f.) or blue (others).
1 D 1 c. black on blue .. 60 70
2 2 c. brown on buff .. 75 85
3 4 c. brown on grey .. 80 1·00
4 5 c. green on light green 2·50 2·00
5 10 c. black on lilac .. 3·25 2·50
14 10 c. red .. .. 25·00 19·00
6 15 c. blue .. .. 3·75 2·25
15 15 c. grey .. .. 65·00 60·00
7 20 c. red on green .. 9·00 6·50
8 25 c. black on pink .. 5·25 3·00
16 25 c. blue .. .. 13·00 11·00
9 30 c. brown on drab .. 19·00 12·50
10 40 c. red on yellow .. 19·00 13·00
11 50 c. red on pink .. 24·00 17·00
17 50 c. brown on blue .. 19·00 14·00
12 75 c. brown on yellow .. 35·00 26·00
13 1 f. green .. .. 25·00 19·00

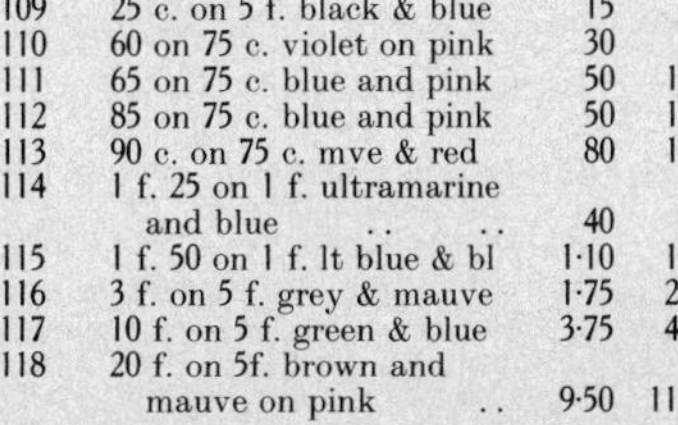

**1.** Fulas Shepherd. **3.** Ford at Kitim.

**1904.**
18 1 1 c. black on green .. 35 35
19 2 c. brown on yellow .. 30 40
20 4 c. red on blue .. 60 65
21 5 c. green on light green 60 60
22 10 c. red .. .. 1·40 75
23 15 c. lilac on pink .. 3·75 2·00
24 20 c. red on green .. 6·25 5·25
25 25 c. blue .. .. 6·75 5·25
26 30 c. brown .. .. 11·00 9·75
27 40 c. red on yellow .. 13·00 13·50
28 50 c. brown on green .. 14·00 13·00
29 75 c. blue on yellow .. 20·00 16·50
30 1 f. green .. .. 26·00 21·00
31 2 f. red on orange .. 55·00 50·00
32 5 f. blue on green .. 70·00 70·00

**1906.** "Faidherbe", "Palms" and "Balay" key-types inscr "GUINEE" in blue (10 c., 5 f.) or red (others).
33. I. 1 c. slate .. .. 30 30
34. 2 c. brown .. .. 50 40
35. 4 c. brown on blue .. 65 50
36. 5 c. green .. .. 1·40 75
37. 10 c. red .. .. 9·00 95
38. J. 20 c. black on blue .. 2·25 2·00
39. 25 c. blue .. .. 3·25 2·75
40. 30 c. brown on pink .. 3·00 2·00
41. 35 c. black on yellow .. 1·25 95
43. 45 c. brown on green .. 2·50 2·25
44. 50 c. violet .. .. 5·50 5·50
45. 75 c. green on orange .. 3·00 2·25
46. K. 1 f. black on blue .. 12·00 11·00
47. 2 f. blue on pink .. 25·00 23·00
48. 5 f. red on yellow .. 35·00 35·00

**1912.** Surch in figures.
49 D 05 on 2 c. brown on buff 50 70
50 05 on 4 c. brown on grey 45 50
51 05 on 15 c. blue .. .. 40 45
52 05 on 20 c. red on green 1·10 2·00
53 05 on 30 c. brown on drab 2·00 2·50
54 10 on 40 c. red on yellow 75 1·10
55 10 on 75 c. brown on yell 3·50 3·75

**1912.** Surch in figures.
56 1 05 on 2 c. brown on yell 35 50
57 05 on 4 c. red on blue .. 35 50
58 05 on 15 c. lilac on pink 35 50
59 05 on 20 c. red on green 35 50
60 05 on 25 c. blue .. .. 50 65
61 05 on 30 c. brown .. 55 65
62 10 on 40 c. red on yellow 60 85
63 10 on 50 c. brown on grn 1·50 2·25

**1913.**
64 **3** 1 c. blue and violet .. 10 10
65 2 c. chocolate and brown 10 10
66 4 c. black and grey .. 10 10
67 5 c. green and light green 20 15
83 5 c. green and purple .. 10 25
68 10 c. pink and red .. 25 20
84 10 c. green & light green 15 25
85 10 c. red and lilac .. 10 25
69 15 c. red and purple .. 15 20
86 15 c. green & light green 15 30
87 15 c. mauve and purple 15 25
70 20 c. violet and brown .. 10 20
88 20 c. green .. .. 40 60
89 20 c. brown and red .. 20 25
71 25 c. blue & ultramarine 65 55
90 25 c. violet and black .. 40 30
72 30 c. green and purple .. 40 55
91 30 c. pink and red .. 25 35
92 30 c. green and red .. 20 35
93 30 c. green and olive .. 75 80
73 35 c. pink and blue .. 15 30
74 40 c. grey and green .. 50 40
75 45 c. red and brown .. 65 75
76 50 c. black and blue .. 3·25 1·90
94 50 c. blue & ultramarine 50 65
95 50 c. green and brown .. 20 15
96 60 c. violet on pink .. 25 35
97 65 c. blue and brown .. 1·10 1·00
77 75 c. blue and pink .. 80 70
98 75 c. light blue and blue 35 50
99 75 c. green and mauve .. 70 85
100 85 c. purple and green .. 55 65
101 90 c. mauve and red .. 1·75 3·00
78 1 f. black and violet .. 65 40
102 1 f. 10 brown and violet 2·50 3·50
103 1 f. 25 brown and violet 85 90
104 1 f. 50 light blue and blue 2·50 1·40
105 1 f. 75 mauve and brown 1·50 1·50
79 2 f. brown and orange .. 1·25 1·00
106 3 f. mauve on pink .. 4·00 3·50
80 5 f. violet and black .. 4·00 6·50
107 5 f. black and blue .. 1·60 1·25

**1915.** Surch **5c** and red cross.
81 **3** 10 c.+5 c. pink and red 60 80

**1922.** Surch in figures and bars.
108 **3** 25 c. on 2 f. brown & orge 15 30
109 25 c. on 5 f. black & blue 15 30
110 60 on 75 c. violet on pink 30 50
111 65 on 75 c. blue and pink 50 1·10
112 85 on 75 c. blue and pink 50 1·10
113 90 c. on 75 c. mve & red 80 1·10
114 1 f. 25 on 1 f. ultramarine and blue .. .. 40 65
115 1 f. 50 on 1 f. lt blue & bl 1·10 1·40
116 3 f. on 5 f. grey & mauve 1·75 2·50
117 10 f. on 5 f. green & blue 3·75 4·25
118 20 f. on 5f. brown and mauve on pink .. 9·50 11·50

**1931.** "Colonial Exhibition" key-types inscr. "GUINEE FRANCAISE".
119. E. 40 c. black and green .. 2·00 2·25
120. F. 50 c. black and purple .. 2·00 2·25
121. G. 90 c. black and red .. 2·00 2·25
122. H. 1 f. 50 black and blue .. 1·90 2·00

**1937.** International Exhibition, Paris. As Nos. 110/15 of Cameroun.
123 20 c. violet .. .. 50 90
124 30 c. green .. .. 50 90
125 40 c. red .. .. 50 1·00
126 50 c. brown and agate .. 50 1·00
127 90 c. red .. .. 50 1·00
128 1 f. 50 blue .. .. 50 1·00

**4.** Native Village. **7.** Ford at Kitim and Marshal Petain.

**1938.**
129. **4.** 2 c. red .. .. .. 10 25
130. 3 c. blue .. .. .. 10 25
131. 4 c. green .. .. .. 10 25
132. 5 c. red .. .. .. 10 25
133. 10 c. blue .. .. .. 10 20
134. 15 c. purple .. .. .. 10 25
135. – 20 c. red .. .. .. 10 15
136. – 25 c. blue .. .. .. 15 20
137. – 30 c. blue .. .. .. 15 10
138. – 35 c. green .. .. .. 25 25
139. – 40 c. brown .. .. .. 20 25
140. – 45 c. green .. .. .. 35 45
141. – 50 c. red .. .. .. 15 25
142. – 55 c. blue .. .. .. 40 55
143. – 60 c. blue .. .. .. 50 60
144. – 65 c. green .. .. .. 45 50
145. – 70 c. green .. .. .. 50 65
146. – 80 c. purple .. .. .. 25 40
147. – 90 c. purple .. .. .. 50 65
148. – 1 f. red .. .. .. 1·00 1·00
149. – 1 f. brown .. .. .. 35 45
150. – 1 f. 25 red .. .. .. 65 75
151. – 1 f. 40 brown .. .. .. 65 80
152. – 1 f. 50 brown .. .. .. 90 1·25
153. – 1 f. 60 red .. .. .. 70 90
154. – 1 f. 75 blue .. .. .. 35 50
155. – 2 f. mauve .. .. .. 50 60
156. – 2 f. 25 blue .. .. .. 1·00 1·25
157. – 2 f. 50 brown .. .. .. 75 90
158. – 3 f. blue .. .. .. 25 35
159. – 5 f. purple .. .. .. 35 50
160. – 10 f. green .. .. .. 60 50
161. – 20 f. brown .. .. .. 1·10 85

DESIGNS—HORIZ. 20 c. to 50 c. Wooden pot makers. 55 c. to 1 f. 50, Waterfall. VERT. 1 f. 60, to 20 f. Native women.

**1938.** Int. Anti-Cancer Fund. As T **19** of Cameroun.
162. 1 f. 75+50 c. blue .. 3·75 5·25

**1939.** Death Cent. of R. Caillie. As T **11** of Dahomey.
163. 90 c. orange .. .. 50 65
164. 2 f. violet .. .. 50 65
165. 2 f. 25 blue .. .. 50 65

**1939.** New York World's Fair. As T **20** of Cameroun.
166. 1 f. 25 red .. .. 55 60
167. 2 f. 25 blue .. .. 55 60

**1939.** 150th Anniv. of French Revolution. As T **25** of Cameroun.
168. 45 c.+25 c. green & black 3·75 4·00
169. 70 c.+30 c. brown & black 3·50 4·00
170. 90 c.+35 c. orange & black 3·75 4·00
171. 1 f. 25+1 f. red & black 3·75 4·00
172. 2 f. 25+2 f. blue & black 3·75 4·00

**1940.** Air. As T **12** of Dahomey.
173. 1 f. 90 blue .. .. 30 40
174. 2 f. 90 red .. .. 30 40
175. 4 f. 50 green .. .. 40 60
176. 4 f. 90 olive .. .. 45 60
177. 6 f. 90 orange .. .. 65 80

**1941.** National Defence Fund. Surch. **SECOURS NATIONAL** and value.
178. +1 f. on 50 c. (No. 141) .. 2·00 2·00
179. +2 f. on 80 c. (No. 146) .. 3·00 3·00
180. +2 f. on 1 f. 50 (No. 152) .. 3·00 3·00
181. +3 f. on 2 f. (No. 155) .. 3·00 3·00

**1941.**
182 **7** 1 f. green .. .. 20 25
183 2 f. 50 blue .. .. 20 25

**1942** Air. Colonial Child Welfare. As Nos. 143g/i of Dahomey.
184. 1 f. 50+3 f. 50 green .. 20 50
185. 2 f.+6 f. brown .. 20 50
186. 3 f.+9 f. red .. 20 50

**1942.** Air. As T **14e** of Dahomey.
187 50 f. olive and green .. 65 1·50

POSTAGE DUE STAMPS

D **2.** Woman of Futa Jallon. D **7.** Native Idol.

**1905.**
D 33. **D 2.** 5 c. blue .. .. 60 65
D 34. 10 c. brown .. .. 60 65
D 35. 15 c. green .. .. 1·50 1·90
D 36. 30 c. red .. .. 2·50 2·50
D 37. 50 c. black .. .. 4·75 5·25
D 38. 60 c. orange .. .. 7·25 6·00
D 39. 1 f. lilac .. .. 23·00 21·00

**1906.** "Natives" key-type inscr "GUINEE".
D49 L 5 c. green .. .. 8·00 8·00
D50 10 c. purple .. .. 3·00 3·25
D51 15 c. blue on blue .. 2·25 3·25
D52 20 c. black on yellow .. 2·25 2·75
D53 30 c. red on cream .. 17·00 14·00
D54 50 c. violet .. .. 9·00 14·00
D55 60 c. black on buff .. 6·50 13·00
D56 1 f. black on pink .. 4·75 8·00

**1914.** "Figure" key-type inscr. "GUINEE".
D 81. M. 5 c. green .. .. 15 25
D 82. 10 c. red .. .. 15 25
D 83. 15 c. grey .. .. 25 40
D 84. 20 c. brown .. .. 25 40
D 85. 30 c. blue .. .. 25 40
D 86. 50 c. black .. .. 40 60
D 87. 60 c. orange .. .. 90 1·10
D 88. 1 f. violet .. .. 1·00 1·25

**1927.** Surch. in figures.
D 119. M. 2 F. on 1 f. mauve .. 3·00 4·25
D 120. 3 F. on 1 f. brown .. 3·25 4·75

**1938.**
D 162. **D 7.** 5 c. violet .. .. 10 25
D 163. 10 c. red .. .. 10 25
D 164. 15 c. green .. .. 10 25
D 165. 20 c. brown .. .. 10 25
D 166. 30 c. purple .. .. 20 30
D 167. 50 c. brown .. .. 35 50
D 168. 60 c. blue .. .. 55 65
D 169. 1 f. red .. .. 55 70
D 170. 2 f. blue .. .. 65 80
D 171. 3 f. black .. .. 85 1·00

For later issues see **GUINEA.**

## FRENCH INDIAN SETTLEMENTS Pt. 6

A group of five small French settlements in India. The inhabitants voted to join India in 1954.

1892. 100 centimes = 1 franc.
1923. 24 caches = 1 fanon. 8 fanons = 1 rupee.

**1892.** "Tablet" key-type inscr "ETABLISSEMENTS DE L'INDE" in red (1, 5, 15, 25, 35, 45, 50 (No. 19), 75 c., 1 f.) or blue (others).
1 D 1 c. black on blue .. 65 55
2 2 c. brown on buff .. 80 70
3 4 c. brown on grey .. 90 85
4 5 c. green on light green 2·25 1·60
5 10 c. black on lilac .. 4·50 1·60
14 10 c. red .. .. 1·60 1·40
6 15 c. blue .. .. 4·25 3·00
15 15 c. grey .. .. 16·00 15·00
7 20 c. red on green .. 3·75 2·75
8 25 c. black on pink .. 1·75 1·40
16 25 c. blue .. .. 7·00 5·50
9 30 c. brown on drab .. 35·00 30·00
17 35 c. black on yellow .. 7·25 4·75
10 40 c. red on yellow .. 2·50 2·50
18 45 c. black on green .. 2·75 2·00
11 50 c. red on pink .. 3·25 2·50
19 50 c. brown on blue .. 6·50 5·00
12 75 c. brown on yellow .. 4·00 4·25
13 1 f. green .. .. 4·00 6·25

**1903.** Surch in figures.
20 D 0,05 on 25 c. blk on pink £200 £140
21 0,10 on 25 c. blk on pink £200 £140
22 0,15 on 25 c. blk on pink 70·00 70·00
23 0,40 on 50 c. red on pink £325 £275

**1903.** Fiscal stamp bisected and each half surch. **Inde Fcaise POSTES 0.05.**
24. 0.05 black and blue .. 12·50 12·50

3 Brahma.

**4.** Temple near Pondicherry.

**1914.**
26 3 1 c. black and grey .. 15 15
27 2 c. black and purple .. 15 15
52 2 c. purple and green .. 15 30
28 3 c. black and brown .. 15 25
29 4 c. black and orange .. 20 30
30 5 c. black and green .. 30 45
53 5 c. black and purple .. 20 30
31 10 c. black and red .. 40 45
54 10 c. black and green .. 25 35
32 15 c. black and violet .. 40 40
33 20 c. black and red .. 65 70
34 25 c. black and blue .. 65 65
55 25 c. red and blue .. 40 45
35 30 c. black and blue .. 70 70
56 30 c. black and red .. 45 50
36 4 35 c. black and brown .. 70 75
37 40 c. black and red .. 75 70
38 45 c. black and green .. 70 75
39 50 c. black and red .. 50 50
57 50 c. blue and ultramarine 50 55
40 75 c. black and blue .. 1·25 1·40
41 1 f. black and yellow .. 1·40 1·40
42 2 f. black and violet .. 3·00 2·75
43 5 f. black and blue .. 1·10 1·25
58 5 f. black and red .. 1·60 1·75
See also Nos. 88/107.

**1916.** Surch with plain cross and premium.
50 3 10 c.+5 c. black and red .. 60 70

**1916.** Surch. **5** and Maltese cross.
48. 3. 10 c.+5 c. black and red 7·00 8·25

**1916.** Surch. with Maltese cross and **5 C.**
49. 3. 10 c.+5 c. black and red 75 1·50

**1922.** Surch. in figures and bars.
59. 3. 0.01 on 15 c. black & violet 35 45
60. 0.02 on 15 c. black & violet 25 45
61. 0.05 on 15 c. black & violet 25 45

**1923.** Surch in new currency (caches, fanons and rupees) in figures and words.
62 3 1 c. on 1 c. black and grey 15 30
63 2 c. on 5 c. black & purple 20 25
64 3 c. on 3 c. black & brown 25 35
65 4 c. on 4 c. black & orange 40 40
66 6 c. on 10 c. black & green 45 45
67 4 6 c. on 45 c. black & green 40 45
68 3 10 c. on 20 c. green & red 1·25 1·25
69 12 c. on 15 c. black & vio 55 55
70 15 c. on 20 c. black & red 50 65
71 4 16 c. on 35 c. brown & blue 1·25 1·25
72 3 18 c. on 30 c. black & red 75 60
73 4 20 c. on 45 c. pink & green 65 65
74 3 1 f. on 25 c. red and green 1·75 1·75
75 4 1 f. 3 on 35 c. black & brn 55 75
76 1 f. 6 on 40 c. black & red 75 60
77 1 f. 12 on 50 c. bl & ultram 70 65
78 1 f. 12 on 75 c. black & bl 70 70
79 1 f. 16 on 75 c. green & red 1·25 1·40
80 3 2 f. 9 on 25 c. red and blue 65 65
81 4 2 f. 12 on 1 f. brn & mve 1·40 1·50
82 3 f. 3 on 1 f. black & yell 70 85
83 6 f. 6 on 2 f. black & violet 3·00 2·50
84 1 r. on 1 f. blue and green 3·75 3·25
85 2 r. on 5 f. black and red 3·75 3·25
86 3 r. on 2 f. violet and grey 9·00 7·00
87 5 r. on 5 f. black and pink on green .. .. 12·50 10·00

**1929.** As T **3** and **4** but with value in caches, fanons or rupees.
88 3 1 c. black and brown .. 15 30
89 2 c. black and purple .. 15 25
90 3 c. black and brown .. 15 30
91 4 c. black and orange .. 15 30
92 6 c. green and deep green 15 30
93 10 c. green and red .. 20 30
94 4 12 c. green & deep green 35 40
95 3 16 c. black and blue .. 40 50
96 18 c. red and carmine .. 40 55
97 20 c. green & bl on azure 40 45
98 4 1 f. red and green .. 35 40
99 1 f. 6 black and orange .. 35 40
100 1 f. 12 blue and deep blue 35 40
101 1 f. 16 green and red .. 40 55
102 2 f. 12 brown and mauve 65 60
103 6 f. 6 black and violet .. 65 65
104 1 r. blue and green .. 45 50
105 2 r. black and red .. 80 45
106 3 r. lilac and black .. 1·40 90
107 5 r. black & red on green 1·90 1·75

**1931.** "Colonial Exhibition" key-types inscr "ETS FRANCAIS DANS L'INDE".
108. E. 10 c. green .. .. 1·60 1·75
109. F. 12 c. mauve .. .. 1·60 1·75
110. G. 18 c. red .. .. 1·75 1·90
111. H. 1 f. 12 blue .. .. 1·75 1·75

**1937.** International Exn., Paris. As Nos. 110/15 of Cameroun.
112. 8 c. violet .. .. 65 95
113. 12 c. green .. .. 75 95
114. 16 c. red .. .. 50 95
115. 20 c. brown .. .. 50 95
116. 1 f. 12 red .. .. 60 95
117. 2 f. 12 blue .. .. 60 95

**1938.** Int. Anti-Cancer Fund. As T **19** of Cameroun.
118. 2 f. 12+20 c. blue .. .. 5·50 6·25

**1939.** New York World's Fair. As T **20** of Cameroun.
119. 1 f. 12 red .. .. .. 80 80
120. 2 f. 12 blue .. .. .. 95 95

**1939.** 150th Anniv. of French Revolution. As T **25** of Cameroun.
121. 18 c.+10 c. grn. & blk. .. 4·00 4·00
122. 1 f. 6+12 c. brn. & blk. .. 4·00 4·00
123. 1 f. 12+16 c. orge. & blk. 4·00 4·00
124. 1 f. 16+1 f. 16 red & blk. 4·00 4·00
125. 2 f. 12+3 f. blue & blk. .. 4·00 4·00

**1941.** Optd **FRANCE LIBRE**
(a) Stamps of 1923.
126 3 15 c. on 20 c. black & red 45·00 45·00
127 18 c. on 30 c. black & red 1·40 1·40
129 4 1 f. 3 on 35 c. black & brn 55·00 55·00
132 3 2 f. 9 on 25 c. red & blue £525 £575

(b) Stamps of 1929.
133 3 2 c. black and purple .. 5·50 5·50
134 3 c. black and brown .. 1·40 1·40
135 4 c. black and orange .. 3·50 3·00
136 6 c. green and deep green 95 95
137 10 c. green and red .. 1·10 1·10
139 4 12 c. green & deep green 1·10 1·10
140 3 16 c. black and blue .. 1·40 1·40
141 18 c. red and carmine .. £425 £400
142 20 c. green & bl on azure 1·10 1·10
143 4 1 f. red and green .. 95 95
144 1 f. 6 black and red .. 1·40 1·25
145 1 f. 12 blue and deep blue 2·50 2·25
146 1 f. 16 green and red .. 1·10 1·00
147 2 f. 12 brown and mauve 1·10 1·00
148 6 f. 6 black and violet .. 1·10 1·10
149 1 r. blue and green .. 1·10 1·10
150 2 r. black and red .. 1·10 1·10
151 3 r. lilac and black .. 1·50 1·40
152 5 r. black & red on green 5·75 4·00

(c) Paris Exn. stamps of 1937.
154. 8 c. violet (No. 112) 3·75 3·75
157. 12 c. green .. .. 2·50 2·50
158. 16 c. red .. .. .. 2·50 2·50
159. 1 f. 12 red .. .. .. 2·50 2·50
160. 2 f. 12 blue .. .. 2·50 2·50

(d) New York Fair stamps of 1939.
161. 1 f. 12 red .. .. .. 1·75 1·75
162. 2 f. 12 blue .. .. 1·75 1·75

**1942.** Optd **FRANCE LIBRE** and Cross of Lorraine.
(a) No. 72 and stamps of 1929.
165 3 2 c. black and purple .. 50 55
166 3 c. black and brown .. 60 60
169 6 c. green and deep green 65 70
170 4 12 c. green & deep green 1·50 1·50
171 3 16 c. black and blue .. 75 75
172 18 c. red and carmine .. 70 75
173 18 c. on 30 c. black and red (No. 72) .. .. £160 £140
174 20 c. green & bl on azure 65 75
176 4 1 f. red and green .. 65 75
178 1 f. 6 black and red .. 95 95
179 1 f. 12 blue and deep blue 85 85
180 1 f. 16 green and red .. 75 75
182 2 f. 12 brown and mauve 80 90
183 6 f. 6 black and violet .. 1·40 1·50
184 1 r. blue and green .. 3·00 3·50
185 2 r. black and red .. 2·50 2·75
187 3 r. lilac and black .. 3·00 3·25
188 5 r. black & red on green 3·25 3·25

(b) Paris Exn. stamps of 1937.
189. 8 c. violet .. .. 4·00 3·75
190. 12 c. green .. .. 3·75 3·75
191. 16 c. red .. .. £625 £625
192. 1 f. 12 red .. .. 75 75
193. 2 f. 12 blue .. .. 1·75 1·75

(c) New York Fair stamps of 1939.
194. 1 f. 12 red .. .. .. 1·40 1·40
195. 2 f. 12 blue .. .. 2·25 2·25

**1942.** Stamps of 1929 surch **FRANCE LIBRE**, Cross of Lorraine and new value.
196 3 1 c. on 16 c. black & blue 48·00 27·00
203 4 1 c. on 6 f. 6 black & vio 5·75 4·50
204 1 c. on 1 r. blue and green 2·75 2·50
205 2 c. on 1 r. blue and green 75 80
197 3 4 c. on 16 c. black & blue 48·00 22·00
206 4 4 c. on 6 f. 6 black & vio 6·75 6·75
207 4 c. on 1 r. blue and green 75 75
208 6 c. on 2 r. black and red 65 70
198 3 10 c. on 16 c. black & bl 29·00 12·50
209 4 10 c. on 6 f. 6 black & vio 1·40 1·10
210 10 c. on 2 r. black and red 95 1·10
211 12 c. on 2 r. black and red 65 70
199 3 15 c. on 16 c. black & bl 27·00 12·50
212 4 15 c. on 6 f. 6 black & vio 2·75 1·25
213 15 c. on 3 r. lilac & black 60 70
214 16 c. on 3 r. lilac & black 60 70
200 3 1 f. 3 on 16 c. black & bl 48·00 25·00
215 4 1 f. 3 on 6 f. 6 black & vio 4·00 2·25
216 1 f. 3 on 3 r. lilac & black 65 75
217 1 f. 6 on 5 r. black and red on green .. 95 1·10
218 1 f. 12 on 5 r. black and red on green .. 95 90
219 1 f. 16 on 5 r. black and red on green .. 95 85
201 3 2 f. 9 on 16 c. black & bl 40·00 35·00
220 4 2 f. 9 on 6 f. 6 black & vio 3·25 3·00
202 3 3 f. 3 on 16 c. black & bl 32·00 16·00
221 4 3 f. 3 on 6 f. 6 black & vio 5·25 3·50

**1943.** No. 103 surch with value only.
222. 4. 1 c. on 6 f. 6 blk. & violet 16·00 10·00
223. 4 c. on 6 f. 6 blk. & violet 16·00 10·00
224. 10 c. on 6 f. 6 blk. & violet 5·25 3·75
225. 15 c. on 6 f. 6 blk. & violet 5·25 3·75
226. 1 f. 3 c. on 6 f. 6 blk. & vio. 12·50 12·00
227. 2 f. 9 c. on 6 f. 6 blk. & vio. 12·50 12·00
228. 3 f. 3 c. on 6 f. 6 blk. & vio. 15·00 13·00

20. Lotus Flowers. 22. Apsara.

**1942.** Free French issue. (a) Postage.
229. 20. 2 c. brown .. .. 15 30
230. 3 c. blue .. .. .. 15 30
231. 4 c. green .. .. 15 30
232. 6 c. orange .. .. 15 30
233. 12 c. green .. .. 15 30
234. 16 c. purple .. .. 15 30
235. 20 c. purple .. .. 20 40
236. 1 f. red .. .. .. 20 40
237. 1 f. 18 black .. .. 30 40
238. 6 f. 6 blue .. .. 35 60
239. 1 r. violet .. .. 40 60
240. 2 r. bistre .. .. 45 75
241. 3 r. brown .. .. 50 80
242. 5 r. green .. .. 60 1·10

(b) Air. As T **32** of Cameroun.
243. 4 f. orange .. .. 50 60
244. 1 r. red .. .. .. 50 60
245. 2 r. purple .. .. 70 80
246. 5 r. black .. .. 80 90
247. 8 r. blue .. .. 1·40 1·50
248. 10 r. green .. .. 1·40 1·60

**1944.** Mutual Aid and Red Cross Funds. As T **33** of Cameroun.
249. 3 f.+1 r. 4 f. bistre .. 65 75

**1945.** Eboue. As T **34** of Cameroun.
250. 3 f. 8 black .. .. 30 45
251. 5 r. 1 f. 16 green .. .. 60 75

**1946.** Air. Victory. As T **35** of Cameroun.
252. 4 f. green .. .. .. 50 75

**1946.** Air. From Chad to the Rhine. As Nos. 226/31 of Cameroun.
253. 2 f. 12 brown .. .. 60 70
254. 5 f. blue .. .. .. 60 70
255. 7 f. 12 violet .. .. 70 80
256. 1 r. 2 f. green .. .. 70 80
257. 1 r. 4 f. 12 red .. .. 95 1·00
258. 3 r. 1 f. purple .. .. 95 1·00

**1948.**
259. 22. 1 c. olive (postage) .. 15 30
260. 2 c. brown .. .. 15 30
261. 4 c. violet on cream .. 15 30
262. A. 6 c. orange .. .. 35 45
263. 8 c. slate .. .. 50 55
264. 10 c. green on green .. 55 55
265. B. 12 c. purple .. .. 30 35
266. 15 c. blue .. .. 30 30
267. C. 18 c. lake .. .. 70 75
268. B. 1 f. violet on red .. 60 40
269. D. 1 f. 6 red .. .. 50 55
270. C. 1 f. 15 violet .. 1·10 1·10
271. D. 2 f. green .. .. 50 35
272. 2 f. 2 blue on cream .. 80 75
273. E. 2 f. 12 brown .. .. 80 75
274. 3 f. red .. .. .. 1·00 80
275. C. 4 f. olive .. .. 1·50 1·50
276. E. 5 f. purple on red .. 1·00 90
277. F. 7 f. 12 brown .. .. 80 85
278. 1 r. 2 f. black .. .. 2·50 2·50
279. 1 r. 4 f. 12 c. green .. 2·50 3·00
DESIGNS—As Type **22**: A, Dvarabalagar standing erect. B, Vishnu. C, Brahmin idol. D, Dvarabalagar with leg raised. E, Temple Guardian. F, One of the Tigoupalagar.

25. Douglas DC-4 and Bas-relief.

**1949.** Air.
281 25 1 r. red and yellow .. 2·50 2·00
282 – 2 r. deep green & green 3·25 3·50
283 – 5 r. purple and blue .. 22·00 12·00
DESIGNS—VERT. 2 r. Wing and temple. 5 r. Short-toed eagle and palm trees.

**1949.** Air. 75th Anniv. of U.P.U. As T **46** of Cameroun.
284. 6 f. red .. .. .. 3·00 4·50

**1950.** Colonial Welfare Fund. As T **47** of Cameroun.
285. 1 f.+10 c. blue & slate .. 95 1·00

**1952.** Cent. of Military Medal. As T **48** of Cameroun.
286. 1 f. brown, yellow & green 2·25 2·25

**1954.** Air. 10th Anniv. of Liberation. As T **52** of Cameroun.
287. 1 f. purple and sepia .. 3·25 3·50

POSTAGE DUE STAMPS

**1923.** Postage Due stamps of France surch. in figures and letters.
D 88. D 11. 4 c. on 20 c. violet .. 55 60
D 89. 6 c. on 10 c. brown .. 55 60
D 90. 12 c. on 25 c. red .. 55 60
D 91. 15 c. on 20 c. olive .. 70 75
D 92. 1 f. on 30 c. orange .. 90 95
D 93. 1 f. 6 on 30 c. red .. 4·75 5·00
D 94. 1 f. 12 on 50 c. purple 90 1·00
D 95. 1 f. 15 on 5 c. blue .. 1·25 1·40
D 96. 1 f. 16 on 5 c. black .. 1·00 1·10
D 97. 3 f. on 1 f. green .. 1·60 1·75
D 98. 3 f. 3 on 1 f. brown on yellow .. 1·50 1·90

D 14. D 24.

**1929.**
D108 D 14 4 c. red .. .. 25 45
D109 6 c. blue .. .. 30 50
D110 12 c. green .. .. 45 50
D111 1 f. brown .. .. 65 70
D112 1 f. 12 violet .. 65 70
D113 1 f. 16 brown .. 80 85
D114 3 f. mauve .. .. 1·25 1·40

**1948.**
D 280. D 24. 1 c. violet .. .. 15 30
D 281. 2 c. brown .. .. 15 30
D 282. 6 c. green .. .. 15 30
D 283. 12 c. red .. .. 20 40
D 284. 1 f. mauve .. .. 25 45
D 285. 1 f. 12 brown .. 35 55
D 286. 2 f. blue .. .. 55 70
D 287. 2 f. 12 lake .. .. 60 85
D 288. 5 f. green .. .. 85 1·40
D 289. 1 r. violet .. .. 1·00 1·90

## FRENCH MOROCCO Pt. 6

Part of the Sultanate of Morocco which was a French protectorate from 1912 until independence was granted on 2 March 1956. For issues before 1912 see French Post Offices in Morocco, and for stamps used in the International Zone see French Post Offices in Tangier.

100 centimes = 1 franc.

**1914.** Surcharged "Blanc", "Mouchon" and "Merson" key-types of French Post Offices in Morocco optd **PROTECTORAT FRANCAIS**.
40. A. 1 c. on 1 c. grey .. .. 15 15
41. 2 c. on 2 c. red .. .. 15 35
42. 3 c. on 3 c. orange .. 20 45
43. 5 c. on 5 c. green .. .. 40 10
44. B. 10 c. on 10 c. red .. .. 35 10
45. 15 c. on 15 c. orange .. 35 10
46. 20 c. on 20 c. red .. .. 50 1·25
47. 25 c. on 25 c. blue .. 40 10
48. 25 c. on 25 c. brown .. 60 10
49. 30 c. on 30 c. brown .. 7·75 7·00
50. 35 c. on 35 c. lilac .. 85 1·50
51. C. 40 c. on 40 c. red and blue 2·50 4·00
52. 45 c. on 45 c. green & blue 25·00 22·00
53. 50 c. on 50 c. brn. & lilac .. 25 15
54. 1 p. on 1 f. red and green .. 50 15
55. 2 p. on 2 f. lilac and yellow 75 60
56. 5 p. on 5 f. blue & yellow .. 3·25 3·50

**1914.** Surch **5c** and red cross.
(a) No. 32 of French Post Offices in Morocco.
65 5 10 c.+5 c. on 10 c. red .. 60 1·25

(b) As No. 43 but without previous surcharge.
62 4 5 c.+5 c. green .. .. 25 90

(c) No. 44.
59 5 10 c.+5 c. on 10 c. red .. 75 2·75

**1915.** No. 352 of France optd. **MAROC** and Arabic.
63. 20. 10 c.+5 c. red .. .. 70 3·00

13.

**1915.** Optd. **PROTECTORAT FRANCAIS.**
64. 13. 10 c.+5 c. red .. .. 65 1·25

**15.** Tower of Hassan, Rabat. **16.** Fez.

**1917.**

| No. | Type | Description | Unused | Used |
|---|---|---|---|---|
| 76 | 15 | 1 c. black | 45 | 60 |
| 123 | | 1 c. green | 10 | 10 |
| 124 | | 2 c. purple | 10 | 15 |
| 125 | | 3 c. brown | 10 | 20 |
| 79 | 16 | 5 c. green | 40 | 10 |
| 126 | | 5 c. yellow | 10 | 10 |
| 80 | | 10 c. red | 25 | 10 |
| 127 | | 10 c. green | 10 | 10 |
| 128 | | 15 c. grey | 25 | 10 |
| 129 | A | 20 c. purple | 10 | 10 |
| 131 | | 25 c. blue | 10 | 10 |
| 84 | | 30 c. lilac | 2·25 | 2·00 |
| 132 | | 30 c. red | 10 | 10 |
| 133 | | 30 c. blue | 15 | 15 |
| 85 | B | 35 c. orange | 1·50 | 1·50 |
| 134 | | 35 c. purple | 30 | 50 |
| 86 | | 40 c. blue | 85 | 35 |
| 135 | | 40 c. orange | 10 | 10 |
| 136 | | 45 c. green | 30 | 20 |
| 88 | C | 50 c. brown | 3·00 | 2·00 |
| 137 | | 50 c. blue | 15 | 30 |
| 138 | B | 50 c. green | 35 | 15 |
| 139 | C | 60 c. mauve | 15 | 15 |
| 140a | | 75 c. purple | 20 | 20 |
| 89 | | 1 f. grey | 3·50 | 3·00 |
| 141 | | 1 f. brown | 20 | 35 |
| 142 | | 1 f. 05 brown | 60 | 60 |
| 143 | | 1 f. 40 pink | 20 | 15 |
| 144 | | 1 f. 50 blue | 15 | 15 |
| 145 | D | 2 f. brown | 30 | 40 |
| 146 | | 3 f. red | 60 | 40 |
| 147 | | 5 f. green | 60 | 60 |
| 148 | | 10 f. brown | 1·75 | 2·75 |

Designs—vert: A, Chella. B, Marrakesh. Horiz: C, Meknes. D, Volubilis.

**22.** Breguet 14T Biplane over Casablanca.

**1922.** Air.

| No. | Type | Description | Unused | Used |
|---|---|---|---|---|
| 112. | 22. | 5 c. orange | 20 | 20 |
| 113. | | 25 c. blue | 55 | 25 |
| 114. | | 50 c. blue | 35 | 15 |
| 115. | | 75 c. blue | 45·00 | 5·00 |
| 116. | | 75 c. green | 1·25 | 25 |
| 117. | | 80 c. brown | 35 | 30 |
| 118. | | 1 f. red | 75 | 15 |
| 119. | | 1 f. 40 red | 1·00 | 1·00 |
| 120. | | 1 f. 90 blue | 1·00 | 1·50 |
| 121. | | 2 f. violet | 50 | 70 |
| 122. | | 3 f. black | 50 | 60 |

**23.** Ploughing with Camel and Donkey.

**1928.** Air. Flood Relief.

| No. | Type | Description | Unused | Used |
|---|---|---|---|---|
| 149. | – | 5 c. blue | 2·75 | 3·00 |
| 150. | 23. | 25 c. orange | 2·50 | 3·00 |
| 151. | – | 50 c. red | 2·50 | 3·00 |
| 152. | – | 75 c. brown | 2·50 | 3·00 |
| 153. | – | 80 c. green | 2·50 | 3·00 |
| 154. | – | 1 f. orange | 2·50 | 3·00 |
| 155. | – | 1 f. 50 blue | 2·50 | 3·00 |
| 156. | – | 2 f. brown | 2·50 | 3·00 |
| 157. | – | 3 f. purple | 3·75 | 4·50 |
| 158. | – | 5 f. black | 2·50 | 3·00 |

Designs: 5 c. Moorish tribesmen. 50 c. Caravan nearing Safi. 75 c. Walls of Marrakesh. 80 c. Sheep grazing at Azrou. 1 f. Gateway at Fez. 1 f. 50, Aerial view of Tangier. 2 f. Aerial view of Casablanca. 3 f. White storks at Rabat. 5 f. "La Hedia", a Moorish entertainment.

**1930.** Stamps of 1917 surch.

| No. | Type | Description | Unused | Used |
|---|---|---|---|---|
| 163 | B | 15 c. on 40 c. orange | 35 | 70 |
| 164 | A | 25 c. on 30 c. blue | 50 | 1·25 |
| 165 | C | 50 c. on 60 c. mauve | 45 | 15 |
| 166 | | 1 f. on 1 f. 40 pink | 95 | 75 |

**1931.** Air. Surch.

| No. | Type | Description | Unused | Used |
|---|---|---|---|---|
| 167. | 22. | 1 f. on 1 f. 40 red | 95 | 80 |
| 168. | | 1 f. 50 on 1 f. 90 blue | 80 | 1·00 |

**27.** Sultan's Palace, Tangier. **28.** Saadian Tombs, Marrakesh.

**1933.**

| No. | Type | Description | Unused | Used |
|---|---|---|---|---|
| 169. | 27. | 1 c. black | 10 | 10 |
| 170. | | 2 c. mauve | 10 | 10 |
| 171. | – | 3 c. brown | 10 | 40 |
| 172. | – | 5 c. lake | 10 | 10 |
| 173. | – | 10 c. green | 20 | 10 |
| 174. | – | 15 c. black | 15 | 10 |
| 175. | – | 20 c. purple | 20 | 15 |
| 176. | – | 25 c. blue | 10 | 10 |
| 177. | – | 30 c. green | 15 | 10 |
| 178. | – | 40 c. sepia | 15 | 15 |
| 179. | – | 45 c. purple | 20 | 35 |
| 180. | – | 50 c. green | 50 | 10 |
| 181. | – | 65 c. red | 10 | 10 |
| 182. | – | 75 c. purple | 15 | 10 |
| 183. | – | 90 c. red | 15 | 10 |
| 184. | – | 1 f. brown | 45 | 10 |
| 185. | – | 1 f. 25 black | 50 | 35 |
| 186. | – | 1 f. 50 blue | 50 | 10 |
| 187. | – | 1 f. 75 green | 25 | 10 |
| 188. | – | 2 f. brown | 1·50 | 10 |
| 189. | – | 3 f. red | 38·00 | 3·00 |
| 190. | 28. | 5 f. lake | 60 | 65 |
| 191. | | 10 f. black | 2·50 | 2·00 |
| 192. | | 20 f. grey | 2·00 | 5·00 |

Designs—Horiz. 3 c., 5 c. Agadir Bay. 10 c. to 20 c. G.P.O., Casablanca. 25 c. to 40 c. Moulay Idriss. 45 c. to 65 c. Rabat. 1 f. 50 to 3 f. Quarzazat. vert. 75 c. to 1 f. 25, Attarine College, Fez.

**29.** Hassan Tower, Rabat. **30.** Marshal Lyautey.

**1933.** Air.

| No. | Type | Description | Unused | Used |
|---|---|---|---|---|
| 193. | 29. | 50 c. blue | 60 | 75 |
| 194. | | 80 c. brown | 75 | 25 |
| 195. | | 1 f. 50 lake | 25 | 25 |
| 196. | – | 2 f. 50 red | 75 | 75 |
| 197. | – | 5 f. violet | 1·25 | 75 |
| 198. | – | 10 f. green | 40 | 80 |

Design: 2 f. 50 to 10 f. Casablanca.

**1935.** Lyautey Memorial Fund.

| No. | Type | Description | Unused | Used |
|---|---|---|---|---|
| 199. | 30. | 50 c.+50 c. red (post.) | 5·50 | 6·25 |
| 200. | | 1 f.+1 f. green | 5·50 | 6·25 |
| 201. | | 5 f.+5 f. brown | 25·00 | 30·00 |
| 202. | – | 1 f. 50+1 f. 50 blue (air) | 14·00 | 14·00 |

Design—Horiz. 1 f. 50, Lyautey in profile.

**1938.** Child Welfare Fund. Stamps of 1933 surch **O.S.E.** and value.

| No. | Type | Description | Unused | Used |
|---|---|---|---|---|
| 203. | 27. | 2 c.+2 c. mauve (post.) | 1·00 | 3·00 |
| 204. | – | 3 c.+3 c. brown | 1·00 | 3·00 |
| 205. | – | 20 c.+20 c. purple | 1·00 | 3·00 |
| 206. | – | 40 c.+40 c. sepia | 1·00 | 3·00 |
| 207. | – | 65 c.+65 c. red | 2·00 | 4·00 |
| 208. | – | 1 f. 25+1 f. 25 black | 1·00 | 3·00 |
| 209. | – | 2 f.+2 f. brown | 1·00 | 3·00 |
| 210. | 28. | 5 f.+5 f. lake | 1·00 | 3·00 |
| 211. | 29. | 50 c.+50 c. blue (air) | 1·00 | 3·00 |
| 212. | – | 10 f.+10 f. green | 1·00 | 3·00 |

**1939.** No. 180 surch **40c.**

| No. | Type | Description | Unused | Used |
|---|---|---|---|---|
| 213 | | 40 c. on 50 c. green | 1·75 | 60 |

**34.** Mosque at Sale. **36.** Shepherd and Arganier Trees.

**42.** Dewoitine D-338 Trimotor over Morocco.

**1939.**

| No. | Type | Description | Unused | Used |
|---|---|---|---|---|
| 214 | 34 | 1 c. mauve (postage) | 10 | 25 |
| 215 | A | 2 c. green | 10 | 25 |
| 216 | | 3 c. blue | 10 | 20 |
| 217 | 34 | 5 c. green | 10 | 15 |
| 218 | A | 10 c. purple | 10 | 15 |
| 219 | B | 15 c. green | 10 | 25 |
| 220 | | 20 c. brown | 10 | 25 |
| 221 | 36 | 30 c. blue | 10 | 15 |
| 222 | | 40 c. brown | 10 | 20 |
| 223 | | 45 c. green | 15 | 50 |
| 224 | E | 50 c. red | 55 | 75 |
| 293 | | 50 c. green | 75 | 10 |
| 226 | | 60 c. blue | 50 | 75 |
| 227 | | 60 c. brown | 20 | 10 |
| 228 | C | 70 c. violet | 10 | 15 |
| 229 | F | 75 c. green | 15 | 40 |
| 230 | | 80 c. blue | 10 | 40 |
| 231 | | 80 c. green | 10 | 35 |
| 232 | E | 90 c. blue | 15 | 25 |
| 233 | B | 1 f. brown | 15 | 10 |
| 234 | F | 1 f. 20 mauve | 15 | 40 |
| 295 | | 1 f. 20 brown | 10 | 15 |
| 235 | | 1 f. 25 red | 15 | 65 |
| 296 | A | 1 f. 30 blue | 25 | 40 |
| 236 | F | 1 f. 40 purple | 15 | 40 |
| 238 | E | 1 f. 50 pink | 45 | 10 |
| 297 | | 1 f. 50 red | 10 | 10 |
| 239 | D | 2 f. green | 10 | 10 |
| 240 | | 2 f. 25 blue | 15 | 25 |
| 241 | 34 | 2 f. 40 red | 10 | 10 |
| 242 | | 2 f. 50 red | 15 | 15 |
| 243 | | 2 f. 50 blue | 15 | 25 |
| 299 | D | 3 f. brown | 10 | 10 |
| 300 | 36 | 3 f. 50 red | 25 | 30 |
| 245 | 34 | 4 f. blue | 25 | 20 |
| 246 | F | 4 f. 50 green | 15 | 25 |
| 301 | C | 4 f. 50 mauve | 10 | 10 |
| 302 | | 5 f. blue | 15 | 30 |
| 303 | F | 6 f. blue | 10 | 10 |
| 248 | C | 10 f. red | 35 | 40 |
| 305 | | 15 f. green | 40 | 50 |
| 306 | | 20 f. purple | 40 | 90 |
| 307 | | 25 f. brown | 40 | 65 |

Designs—vert. A, Mosque at Sefrou. B, Horseman and Cedar tree. C, Scimitar oryxes. D, Fez. horiz. E, Ramparts at Sale. F, Draa Valley.

| No. | Type | Description | Unused | Used |
|---|---|---|---|---|
| 251. | G. | 80 c. green (air) | 10 | 15 |
| 252. | | 1 f. brown | 10 | 10 |
| 253. | 42. | 1 f. 90 blue | 10 | 30 |
| 254. | | 2 f. purple | 10 | 20 |
| 255. | | 3 f. brown | 20 | 25 |
| 256. | G. | 5 f. violet | 45 | 70 |
| 257. | 42. | 10 f. blue | 40 | 65 |

Design—vert. G, Storks and Mosque at Chella.

**1940.** Alternate horiz rows of No. 181 surch **35c.**

| No. | Type | Description | Unused | Used |
|---|---|---|---|---|
| 258 | | 35 c. on 65 c. red | 1·00 | 1·00 |

**1942.** French Child Refugees in Morocco Fund. Types of 1939 surch **Enfants de France au Maroc** and premium.

| No. | Type | Description | Unused | Used |
|---|---|---|---|---|
| 259 | 36 | 45 c.+2 f. green | 1·00 | 3·00 |
| 260 | E | 90 c.+4 f. blue | 2·00 | 3·00 |
| 261 | F | 1 f. 25+6 f. red | 1·00 | 3·00 |
| 262 | 34 | 2 f. 50+8 f. red | 1·00 | 3·00 |

**1943.** As T **35** of Algeria.

| No. | Type | Description | Unused | Used |
|---|---|---|---|---|
| 263. | | 1 f. 50 blue | 50 | 60 |

**46.** Tower of Hassan.

**1943.**

| No. | Type | Description | Unused | Used |
|---|---|---|---|---|
| 264. | 46. | 10 c. lilac | 10 | 10 |
| 265. | | 30 c. blue | 10 | 25 |
| 266. | | 40 c. red | 10 | 10 |
| 267. | | 50 c. green | 10 | 10 |
| 268. | | 60 c. brown | 10 | 10 |
| 269. | | 70 c. lilac | 10 | 15 |
| 270. | | 80 c. green | 10 | 15 |
| 271. | | 1 f. red | 10 | 20 |
| 272. | | 1 f. 20 violet | 10 | 15 |
| 273. | | 1 f. 50 red | 10 | 15 |
| 274. | | 2 f. green | 20 | 30 |
| 275. | | 2 f. 40 red | 15 | 25 |
| 276. | | 3 f. brown | 10 | 15 |
| 277. | | 4 f. blue | 15 | 10 |
| 278. | | 4 f. 50 black | 15 | 10 |
| 279. | | 5 f. blue | 20 | 10 |
| 280. | | 10 f. brown | 25 | 10 |
| 281. | | 15 f. green | 25 | 25 |
| 282. | | 20 f. purple | 30 | 35 |

**47.** Sud Est Languedoc over Desert. **49.** Potez 56 over Minarets.

**1944.** Air.

| No. | Type | Description | Unused | Used |
|---|---|---|---|---|
| 283. | 47. | 50 c. green | 10 | 20 |
| 284. | | 2 f. blue | 15 | 20 |
| 285. | | 5 f. red | 20 | 15 |
| 286. | | 10 f. violet | 30 | 30 |
| 287. | | 50 f. black | 40 | 75 |
| 288. | | 100 f. blue and red | 2·25 | 2·25 |

**1944.** Air. Mutual Aid Fund. Surch **ENTR'AIDE FRANCAISE +98F 50.**

| No. | Type | Description | Unused | Used |
|---|---|---|---|---|
| 289 | 47 | 1 f. 50+98 f. 50 red & bl | 50 | 1·10 |

**1945.** Air.

| No. | Type | Description | Unused | Used |
|---|---|---|---|---|
| 290. | 49. | 50 f. brown | 15 | 50 |

**1945.** Anti-tuberculosis Fund. No. 239 surch **AIDEZ LES TUBERCULEUX +1f.**

| No. | Type | Description | Unused | Used |
|---|---|---|---|---|
| 308 | D | 2 f.+1 f. green | 15 | 35 |

**51.** Mausoleum. **54.** Marshal Lyautey Statue, Casablanca.

**1945.** Solidarity Fund. Marshal Lyautey's Mausoleum.

| No. | Type | Description | Unused | Used |
|---|---|---|---|---|
| 309a | 51 | 2 f+3 f. blue | 20 | 35 |

**1946.** No. 308 surch **3f.**

| No. | Type | Description | Unused | Used |
|---|---|---|---|---|
| 310 | D | 3 f. on 2 f.+1 f green | 10 | 35 |

**1946.** Air. 6th Anniv of Gen. De Gaulle's Call to Arms. Surch **+5 F 18 Juin 1940 18 Juin 1946.**

| No. | Type | Description | Unused | Used |
|---|---|---|---|---|
| 311 | 47 | 5 f.+5 f. red | 20 | 55 |

**1946.** Solidarity Fund.

| No. | Type | Description | Unused | Used |
|---|---|---|---|---|
| 312. | 54. | 2 f.+10 f. black (post.) | 30 | 80 |
| 313. | | 3 f.+15 f. red | 30 | 1·00 |
| 314. | | 10 f.+20 f. blue | 30 | 1·25 |
| 315. | | 10f. +30f. green(air) | 35 | 1·25 |

**1947.** Stamp Day. Stamp of 1939 surch **JOURNEE DU TIMBRE 1947 +5F50.**

| No. | Type | Description | Unused | Used |
|---|---|---|---|---|
| 316 | C | 4 f. 50+5 f. 50 mauve (No. 301) | 75 | 90 |

**56.** Coastline and Symbols of Prosperity.

**1947.** 25th Anniv. of Sherifian Phosphates Office.

| No. | Type | Description | Unused | Used |
|---|---|---|---|---|
| 317. | 56. | 3 f. 50+5 f. 50 green | 65 | 85 |

**58.** Coastal Fortress.

**57.** The Terraces.

**65.** La Medina Barracks. **59.** Barracks on the Mountains.

**1947.** (a) Postage.

| No. | Type | Description | Unused | Used |
|---|---|---|---|---|
| 318. | 57. | 10 c. brown | 10 | 25 |
| 319. | | 30 c red | 10 | 25 |
| 320. | | 30 c. violet | 10 | 25 |
| 321. | | 50 c. blue | 10 | 15 |
| 322. | | 60 c. purple | 10 | 25 |
| 323. | 58. | 1 f. black | 10 | 10 |
| 324. | | 1 f. 50 blue | 10 | 10 |
| 325. | 59. | 2 f. green | 15 | 30 |
| 325a. | 58. | 2 f. purple | 35 | 35 |
| 326. | 59. | 3 f. lake | 10 | 10 |
| 327. | – | 4 f. violet | 10 | 15 |
| 328. | – | 4 f. green | 30 | 50 |
| 329. | – | 5 f. green | 20 | 40 |
| 329a. | – | 5 f. green | 15 | 20 |
| 330. | – | 6 f. red | 10 | 10 |
| 330a. | – | 8 f. orange | 15 | 30 |
| 331. | – | 10 f. blue | 10 | 15 |
| 332a. | – | 10 f. red | 30 | 20 |
| 333. | 58. | 12 f. red | 15 | 25 |
| 334. | – | 15 f. green | 10 | 35 |
| 334a. | – | 15 f. red | 10 | 20 |
| 335. | – | 18 f. blue | 15 | 30 |
| 336. | – | 20 f. red | 15 | 20 |
| 337. | – | 25 f. violet | 25 | 60 |
| 337a. | – | 25 f. blue | 25 | 40 |
| 337b. | – | 25 f. violet | 80 | 1·00 |
| 337c. | – | 30 f. blue | 30 | 50 |
| 337d. | – | 35 f. brown | 20 | 30 |
| 337e. | – | 50 f. slate | 60 | 10 |

Designs—horiz. 4 f., 6 f. Marrakesh. 5 f. (No. 329), 8 f., 10 f. blue, The Gardens, Fez. 5 f. (No. 329a) Fortified oasis. 15 f. red, 25 f. (Nos. 337a/b), Walled city. 30 f., 35 f., 50 f. Todra Valley. vert. 10 f. red, 15 f. green, 18 f., 20 f., 25 f. (No. 337), Barracks in oasis.

(b) Air.

| No. | Type | Description | Unused | Used |
|---|---|---|---|---|
| 338. | – | 9 f. red | 20 | 20 |
| 339. | – | 40 f. blue | 15 | 50 |
| 340. | – | 50 f. purple | 30 | 30 |
| 341. | 65. | 100 f. blue | 60 | 60 |
| 342. | | 200 f. red | 70 | 1·50 |
| 342a. | – | 300 f. violet | 3·75 | 6·50 |

Designs—vert. 9, 40, 50 f. Sud Est Languedoc airplane over Moulay Idriss. horiz. 300 f. Oudayas Kasbah, Rabat.

67. " Energy ".

68. Marshal Lyautey's Mausoleum.

**1947.** Solidarity Fund. Inscr. "SOLIDARITE 1947".
343. **67.** 6 f.+9 f. red (postage) 50 1·50
344. – 10 f.+20 f. blue .. 50 1·50
345. – 9 f.+16 f. green (air) .. 1·00 1·50
346. – 20 f.+35 f. brown .. 65 1·10
DESIGNS—VERT. 10 f. Red Cross unit ("Health"). HORIZ. 9 f. Freighter at quayside and Sud Est Languedoc airplane ("Supplies"). 20 f. Sud Est Languedoc airplane over landscape ("Agriculture").

**1948.** Stamp Day. View of Meknes (as No. 88) inscr. "JOURNEE DU TIMBRE 1948" below central vignette.
347. 6 f.+4 f. brown .. 40 60

**1948.** Air. Lyautey Exn., Paris.
348. **68.** 10 f.+25 f. green .. 35 75

69. P.T.T. Clubhouse, Ifrane.

**1948.** Air. P.T.T. Employees' Holiday Camp Fund.
349. **69.** 6 f.+34 f. green .. 75 1·25
350. 9 f.+51 f. red .. .. 75 1·25

70. "Dunkerque" (battleship) and Coastline.

**1948.** Naval Charities.
351 **70** 6 f.+9 f. violet .. .. 50 1·00

**1948.** Stamp of 1939 surch 8f.
352 C 8 f. on 20 f. purple (No. 306) .. .. 25 45

72. Wheat and View of Mekens.

**1949.** Solidarity Fund. Inscr. "SOLIDARITE 1948".
353. **72.** 1 f.+2 f. orange (post).. 35 80
354. – 2 f.+5 f. red .. .. 35 85
355. – 3 f.+7 f. blue .. .. 35 85
356. – 5 f.+10 f. purple .. 35 85
357. – 5 f.+5 f. green (air) .. 35 85
358. – 6 f.+9 f. red .. .. 35 85
359. – 9 f.+16 f. brown .. 35 85
360. – 15 f.+25 f. slate .. 35 85
DESIGNS—HORIZ. (postage): 2 f. Olive grove and Taroudant. 3 f. Trawling. 5 f. Plums and Aguedal Gardens, Marrakesh. VERT (air): Airplane over—5 f. Agadir. 6 f. Fez. 9 f. Atlas Mountains. 15 f. Draa Valley.

74. Gazelle Hunter.

75. Soldiers with Flag.

**1949.** Stamp Day and 50th Anniv. of Mazagan-Marrakesh Local Postage Stamp.
361. **74.** 10 f.+5 f. red and purple 55 95

**1949.** Army Welfare Fund.
362. **75.** 10 f.+10 f. red.. .. 35 85

76. Oudayas Gate, Rabat.

77. Nejjarine Fountain, Fez.

78. Gardens at Meknes.

**1949.**
363. **76.** 10 c. black .. .. 10 25
364. 50 c. lake .. .. 10 25
365. 1 f. violet .. .. 10 20
366. **77.** 2 f. red .. .. .. 10 15
367. 3 f. blue.. .. .. 10 10
368. 5 f. green .. .. 10 10
369. **78.** 8 f. green .. .. 20 20
370. 10 f. red .. .. 20 10

79. Post Office, Meknes.

80. Breguet 14T Biplane over Globe.

**1949.** 75th Anniv. of U.P.U.
371. **79.** 5 f. green .. .. 50 1·00
372. 15 f. red .. .. 50 1·00
373. 25 f. blue .. .. 50 1·40

**1950.** Air. Stamp Day and 25th Anniv of First Mail Flight from Casablanca to Dakar.
374 **80** 15 f.+10 f. blue, green and red .. .. 1·50 2·00

81. Carpets.

83. Ruins of Sala-Colonia (Chella.)

**1950.** Solidarity Fund. Inscr. "SOLIDARITE 1949".
375. **81.** 1 f.+2 f. red (postage) 50 1·25
376. – 2 f.+5 f. blue .. 50 1·25
377. – 3 f.+7 f. violet .. 50 1·25
378. – 5 f.+10 f. brown .. 50 1·25
379. – 5 f.+5 f. blue (air) .. 80 1·10
380. – 6 f.+9 f. green .. 60 1·10
381. – 9 f.+16 f. brown .. 60 1·10
382. – 15 f.+25 f. brown .. 60 1·10
DESIGNS—VERT. Postage: 2 f. Pottery. 3 f Books. 5 f. Copperware. HORIZ. Air—(Maps of Morocco): 5 f. N.W. 6 f. N.E., 9 f. S.W., 15 f. S.E.

**1950.** Army Welfare Fund. Inscr. "ŒUVRES SOCIALES DE L'ARMEE".
383. **83.** 10 f.+10 f. red (post.).. 60 80
384. 15 f.+15 f. slate .. 60 80
385. – 10 f.+10 f. sepia (air).. 60 80
386. – 15 f.+15 f. green .. 90 1·10
DESIGN: 10 f., 15 f. Triumphal Arch of Caracalla, Volubilis.

**1950.** Stamps of 1939 and 1947 surch.
387 F 1 f. on 1 f. 20 brown (No. 295) .. .. 10 25
388 A 1 f. on 1 f. 30 blue (No. 296) .. .. 10 25
389 – 5 f. on 6 f. red (No. 330) 15 10

84. General Leclerc.

85. New Hospital, Meknes.

**1951.** Gen. Leclerc Monument, Casablanca.
390. **84.** 10 f. green (postage) .. 50 80
391. 15 f. red .. .. 35 1·00
392. 25 f. blue .. .. 45 1·10
393. 50 f. violet (air) .. 50 1·50

**1951.** Solidarity Fund. Inscr. "SOLIDARITE 1950".
394. – 10 f. violet & bl. (post) 35 80
395. **85.** 15 f. brown and green.. 35 1·00
396. – 25 f. blue and brown .. 35 1·25
397. – 50 f. green & violet (air) 35 1·40
DESIGNS: 10 f. Loustau Hospital, Oujda. 25 f. New Hospital, Rabat. 50 f. Sanatorium, Ben Smine.

86. Fountain and Doves.

87. Karaouine Mosque, Fez.

88. Old Moroccan Courtyard.

**1951.**
398. **86.** 5 f. purple (A) .. 10 10
434. 5 f. purple (B) .. 30 40
399. **87.** 6 f. green .. .. 15 30
400. **86.** 8 f. brown .. .. 15 25
401. **87.** 10 f. red .. .. 30 15
402. 12 f. blue .. .. 30 10
403. – 15 f. brown (A) .. 25 50
404. – 15 f. brown (B) .. 25 10
405. – 15 f. violet (A) .. 20 15
435. – 15 f. violet (B) .. 30 50
406. **86.** 15 f. green .. .. 30 15
407. – 18 f. red .. .. 75 75
408. **88.** 20 f. blue .. .. 45 20
DESIGNS—As Type 86/7: 15 f. brown (2) Oudayas Courtyard. 15 f. violet (2), 18 f. Oudayas Point, Rabat.
Two types each of: 5 f. (A) 18×22 mm, (B) 17×21½ mm; 15 f. brown (A) "MAROC" not in tablet, (B) "MAROC" in white tablet; 15 f. violet (A) 18×22½ mm, (B) 16½×21½ mm.

89. Casablanca P.O. and Reproduction of T 22.

90. Saadian Capital.

**1952.** Air Stamp Day and 30th Anniv. of First Moroccan Air Stamps.
409. **89.** 15 f.+5 f. blue & brown 2·25 3·00

**1952.** Solidarity Fund. Inscr. "SOLIDARITE 1951". Column capitals as T 90.
410. – 15 f. blue (Omeiyad) 1·00 1·60
411. – 20 f. red (Almohad) .. 1·00 1·75
412. – 25 f. violet (Merinid) .. 1·00 1·50
413. **90.** 50 f. green .. .. 1·00 1·50

91. Ramparts of Chella, Rabat.

92. War Memorial, Casablanca.

**1952.** Air.
414. **91.** 10 f. green .. .. 25 40
415. – 40 f. red .. .. 30 40
416. – 100 f. brown .. .. 50 60
417. – 200 f. violet .. 1·25 2·00
DESIGN: Lockheed Constellation over—HORIZ. 40 f. Marrakesh. VERT. 100 f. Fort in Anti-Atlas Mts. 200 f. Fez.

**1952.** Cent. of Military Medal.
418. **92.** 15 f. brown, yellow & grn. 75 1·00

93. Jewellery from Fez.

94. Arab Courier and Scribe.

**1953.** Solidarity Fund. Inscr. "SOLIDARITE 1952".
419. – 15 f. red (postage) .. 1·40 1·60
420. **93.** 20 f. brown .. .. 1·40 1·50
421. – 25 f. blue .. .. 1·40 1·40
422. – 50 f. green (air).. .. 1·25 1·50
DESIGNS: 15 f. Daggers from S. Morocco. 25 f. Jewellery from Anti-Atlas. 50 f. Jewellery from N. Morocco.

**1953.** Stamp Day.
423. **94.** 15 f. purple .. .. 1·10 1·40

95. Bine el Ouidane Barrage.

96. Mogador Battlements.

**1953.** Inauguration of Barrage.
424. **95.** 15 f. blue .. .. 80 1·00
424a. 15 f. blue and brown .. 50 45

**1953.** Army Welfare Fund.
425. **96.** 15 f. green .. .. 80 1·00
426. – 30 f. brown .. .. 50 90
DESIGN: 30 f. Moorish horsemen.

**1954.** Nos. 324 and 335 surch.
427 **58** 1 f. on 1 f. 50 blue .. 10 20
428 – 15 f. on 18 f. blue .. 20 40

98. Meknes.

**1954.** Air. Solidarity Fund. Inscr. "1953".
429. **98.** 10 f. olive .. .. 1·40 1·40
430. – 20 f. violet (Rabat) .. 1·25 1·50
431. – 40 f. brn. (Casablanca) 1·25 1·50
432. – 50 f. green (Fedala) .. 1·25 1·40

99. Mail Van and Postmen.

**1954.** Stamp Day.
433. **99.** 15 f. green .. .. 60 70

100. Schooner and Destroyer.

101. Marshal Lyautey at Khenifra.

**1954.** Air. Naval Welfare Fund.
436. **100.** 15 f. green .. .. 95 1·00
437. 30 f. blue .. .. 1·10 1·25

**1954.** Birth Cent. of Marshal Lyautey.
438. – 5 f. blue .. .. 1·00 1·40
439. **101.** 15 f. green .. .. 1·00 1·60
440. – 30 f. lake .. .. 1·00 1·90
441. – 50 f. brown .. .. 1·00 1·90
DESIGNS—HORIZ. 5 f. Lyautey receiving Moroccan notables at Rabat. VERT. 30 f. Lyautey in dockyards. 50 f. Portrait of Lyautey (after Laszlo).

102. Moroccan Scholar.

103. Mazagan P.O.

**1955.** Solidarity Fund.
442. – 5 f. blue.. .. .. 50 70
443. **102.** 15 f. red .. .. 50 90
444. – 30 f. brown .. .. 50 60
445. – 50 f. green .. .. 60 1·00
DESIGNS—HORIZ. 5 f. French and Moroccan schoolchildren. 30 f. Muslim School, Camp-Boulhaut. VERT. 50 f. Moulay Idriss College, Fez.

**1955.** Day of the Stamp.
446. **103.** 15 f. red .. .. 75 90

104. Map of Morocco.

105. Bab el Mrissa, Sale.

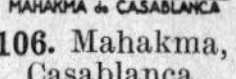

106. Mahakma, Casablanca. 107. Bou Regreg Estuary.

**1955.** 50th Anniv. of Rotary International.

| No. | Type | Description | Unused | Used |
|---|---|---|---|---|
| 447. | 104. | 15 f. blue and brown .. | 1·00 | 1·25 |

**1955.**

| No. | Type | Description | Unused | Used |
|---|---|---|---|---|
| 448. | 105. | 50 c. purple .. .. | 10 | 25 |
| 449. | | 1 f. blue .. .. .. | 10 | 10 |
| 450. | | 2 f. purple .. .. | 10 | 10 |
| 451. | | 3 f. blue .. .. .. | 25 | 20 |
| 452. | – | 5 f. red .. .. .. | 45 | 20 |
| 453. | – | 6 f. green .. .. | 25 | 30 |
| 454. | – | 8 f. brown .. .. | 40 | 50 |
| 455. | – | 10 f. purple .. .. | 60 | 50 |
| 456. | – | 12 f. turquoise .. .. | 35 | 25 |
| 457. | – | 15 f. lake .. .. | 60 | 10 |
| 458. | 106. | 18 f. myrtle .. .. | 35 | 50 |
| 459. | | 20 f. lake .. .. | 30 | 10 |
| 460. | – | 25 f. blue .. .. | 1·00 | 25 |
| 461. | – | 30 f. green .. .. | 1·00 | 25 |
| 462. | – | 40 f. red .. .. | 50 | 15 |
| 463. | – | 50 f. sepia .. .. | 85 | 20 |
| 464. | – | 75 f. turquoise .. .. | 50 | 60 |

DESIGNS—As Type **105**. **5 f., 6 f., 8 f. Bab Chorfa, Fez. 10 f., 12 f., 15 f. Chella Minaret, Rabat.** As Type **106** — HORIZ. **25 f. Coastal castle, Safi. 30 f. Menara, Marrakesh. 40 f. Tafraout. 50 f. Portuguese cistern, Mazagan.** VERT. **75 f. Oudaya gardens, Rabat.**

**1955.** Air.

| No. | Type | Description | Unused | Used |
|---|---|---|---|---|
| 465. | – | 100 f. violet .. .. | 1·40 | 20 |
| 466. | 107. | 200 f. red .. .. | 1·90 | 40 |
| 467. | – | 500 f. blue .. .. | 2·75 | 2·25 |

DESIGNS—VERT. **100 f. Village in the Anti-Atlas.** HORIZ. **500 f. Ksar es Souk.**

PARCEL POST STAMPS

P 21.

**1917.**

| No. | Type | Description | Unused | Used |
|---|---|---|---|---|
| P 101. | P 21. | 5 c. green .. .. | 35 | 20 |
| P 102. | | 10 c. red .. .. | 40 | 25 |
| P 103. | | 20 c. brown .. .. | 65 | 30 |
| P 104. | | 25 c. blue .. .. | 50 | 35 |
| P 105. | | 40 c. brown .. .. | 1·25 | 50 |
| P 106. | | 50 c. red .. .. | 1·40 | 40 |
| P 107. | | 75 c. grey .. .. | 1·50 | 80 |
| P 108. | | 1 f. blue .. .. | 1·50 | 30 |
| P 109. | | 2 f. grey .. .. | 1·50 | 45 |
| P 110. | | 5 f. violet .. .. | 2·50 | 45 |
| P 111. | | 10 f. black .. .. | 3·50 | 40 |

POSTAGE DUE STAMPS

**1915.** Postage Due stamps of France surch. with figure and Arabic word, and further optd. **PROTECTORAT FRANCAIS.**

| No. | Type | Description | Unused | Used |
|---|---|---|---|---|
| D 66. | D 11. | 1 c. on 1 c. black .. | 15 | 40 |
| D 67. | | 5 c. on 5 c. blue .. | 40 | 55 |
| D 68. | | 10 c. on 10 c. brown | 90 | 1·00 |
| D 69. | | 20 c. on 20 c. green.. | 60 | 90 |
| D 70. | | 30 c. on 30 c. red .. | 1·00 | 2·75 |
| D 71. | | 50 c. on 50 c. purple | 1·25 | 1·25 |

**1915.** Postage Due stamps of France with surch. and optd. as above.

| No. | Type | Description | Unused | Used |
|---|---|---|---|---|
| D 72. | D 19. | 1 c. on 1 c. olive .. | 35 | 55 |
| D 73. | | 10 c. on 10 c. violet | 80 | 1·00 |
| D 74. | | 30 c. on 30 c. bistre | 50 | 1·10 |
| D 75. | | 50 c. on 50 c. red .. | 60 | 1·25 |

D 21.

**1917.**

| No. | Type | Description | Unused | Used |
|---|---|---|---|---|
| D93 | D 21 | 1 c. black .. .. | 10 | 30 |
| D94 | | 5 c. blue .. .. | 10 | 30 |
| D95 | | 10 c. brown .. .. | 10 | 25 |
| D96 | | 20 c. green .. .. | 15 | 45 |
| D97 | | 30 c. red .. .. | 20 | 15 |
| D98 | | 50 c. brown .. .. | 10 | 10 |
| D99 | | 1 f. purple on yellow | 15 | 40 |
| D100 | | 2 f. violet .. .. | 20 | 40 |
| D308 | | 1 f. red .. .. | 15 | 40 |
| D310 | | 3 f. blue .. .. | 20 | 50 |
| D311 | | 4 f. orange .. .. | 20 | 50 |
| D312 | | 5 f. green .. .. | 20 | 40 |
| D313 | | 10 f. bistre .. .. | 75 | 15 |
| D314 | | 20 f. red .. .. | 75 | 50 |
| D315 | | 30 f. brown .. .. | 1·40 | 1·25 |

**1944.** Surch.

| No. | Type | Description | Unused | Used |
|---|---|---|---|---|
| D 289. | D 21. | 50 c. on 30 c. red .. | 1·50 | 3·00 |
| D 290. | | 1 f. on 10 c. brown.. | 2·25 | 3·00 |
| D 291. | | 3 f. on 10 c. brown.. | 5·50 | 7·00 |

For later issues see **MOROCCO.**

## FRENCH OCCUPATION OF HUNGARY Pt. 2

### ARAD

Arad later became part of Rumania.

100 filler = 1 korona.

**1919.** Stamps of Hungary Optd. **Occupation francaise** or surch. also.

(a) War Charity stamps of 1916.

| No. | Type | Description | Unused | Used |
|---|---|---|---|---|
| 1. | 20. | 11 f. (+2 f.) red .. | 20·00 | 20·00 |
| 2. | – | 15 f. (+2 f.) lilac .. | 1·00 | 1·00 |
| 3. | 22. | 40 f. (+2 f.) red .. | 1·75 | 1·75 |

(b) Harvesters and Parliament Types.

| No. | Type | Description | Unused | Used |
|---|---|---|---|---|
| 4. | 18. | 2 f. brown .. .. | 25 | 25 |
| 5. | | 3 f. red .. .. | 20 | 20 |
| 6. | | 5 f. green .. .. | 1·00 | 1·00 |
| 7. | | 6 f. blue .. .. | 25 | 25 |
| 8. | | 10 f. red .. .. | 35 | 35 |
| 9. | | 15 f. purple .. .. | 25 | 25 |
| 10. | | 15 f. violet (No. 244) .. | 42·00 | 42·00 |
| 11. | | 20 f. brown .. .. | 8·00 | 8·00 |
| 12. | | 35 f. brown .. .. | 20·00 | 20·00 |
| 13. | | 40 f. green .. .. | 6·50 | 6·50 |
| 14. | | 45 on 2 f. brown .. | 1·00 | 1·00 |
| 15a. | | 45 on 3 f. red .. | 17·00 | |
| 16. | | 50 on 3 f. red .. | 1·00 | 1·00 |
| 18. | 19. | 50 f. purple .. .. | 75 | 75 |
| 19. | | 75 f. blue .. .. | 35 | 35 |
| 20. | | 80 f. green .. .. | 60 | 60 |
| 21. | | 1 k. red .. .. | 4·00 | 4·00 |
| 22. | | 2 k. brown .. .. | 65 | 65 |
| 23. | | 3 k. grey and violet .. | 3·50 | 3·50 |
| 24. | | 5 k. brown .. .. | 3·50 | 3·50 |
| 25. | | 10 k. mauve and brown | 38·00 | 38·00 |

(c) Charles and Zita stamps.

| No. | Type | Description | Unused | Used |
|---|---|---|---|---|
| 26. | 27. | 10 f. red .. .. | 11·00 | 11·00 |
| 27. | | 20 f. brown .. .. | 15 | 15 |
| 28. | | 25 f. blue .. .. | 50 | 50 |
| 29. | 28. | 40 f. green .. .. | 60 | 60 |

(d) Harvester stamps inscr. "MAGYAR POSTA".

| No. | Type | Description | Unused | Used |
|---|---|---|---|---|
| 30. | 18. | 5 f. green .. .. | 70 | 70 |
| 31. | | 10 f. red .. .. | 70 | 70 |
| 32. | | 20 f. brown .. .. | | |

(e) Stamps of 1919 optd **KOZTARSASAG**.

(i) Harvesters and Parliament Types.

| No. | Type | Description | Unused | Used |
|---|---|---|---|---|
| 33. | 18. | 2 f. brown .. .. | 40 | 40 |
| 34. | | 3 f. red .. .. | 2·75 | 2·75 |
| 35. | | 4 f. grey .. .. | 40 | 40 |
| 36. | | 5 f. green .. .. | 15 | 15 |
| 37. | | 6 f. blue .. .. | 2·25 | 2·25 |
| 38. | | 10 f. red .. .. | 20·00 | 20·00 |
| 39. | | 20 f. brown .. .. | 3·50 | 3·50 |
| 40. | | 40 f. green .. .. | 40 | 40 |
| 41. | 19. | 1 k. red .. .. | 50 | 50 |
| 42. | | 3 k. grey and violet .. | 3·50 | 3·50 |
| 43. | | 10 (k) on 1 k. red .. | 3·50 | 3·50 |

(ii) Charles and Zita stamps.

| No. | Type | Description | Unused | Used |
|---|---|---|---|---|
| 44. | 27. | 25 f. blue .. .. | 50 | 50 |
| 45. | 28. | 40 f. green .. .. | 18·00 | 18·00 |
| 46. | | 50 f. violet .. .. | 50 | 50 |

EXPRESS LETTER STAMP

**1919.** No. E245 optd **Occupation francaise.**

| No. | Type | Description | Unused | Used |
|---|---|---|---|---|
| E48 | E 18 | 2 f. green and red .. | 15 | 15 |

NEWSPAPER STAMP

**1919.** No. N 136 optd. **Occupation francaise.**

| No. | Type | Description | Unused | Used |
|---|---|---|---|---|
| N 47. | N 9. | (2 f.) orange .. | 25 | 25 |

POSTAGE DUE STAMPS

**1919.** (a) No. D191 of Hungary optd **Occupation francaise**.

| No. | Type | Description | Unused | Used |
|---|---|---|---|---|
| D 49. | D 9. | 2 f. red and green .. | 60 | 60 |
| D 50. | | 10 f. red and green.. | 50 | 50 |
| D 51. | | 12 f. red and green.. | 9·00 | 9·00 |
| D 52. | | 15 f. red and green.. | 9·00 | 9·00 |
| D 53. | | 20 f. red and green.. | 6·00 | 6·00 |

(b) No. N47 of Arad surch **Porto** and new value.

| No. | Type | Description | Unused | Used |
|---|---|---|---|---|
| D 54. | N 9. | 12 on (2 f.) orange .. | 2·00 | 2·00 |
| D 55. | | 15 on (2 f.) orange .. | 2·00 | 2·00 |
| D 56. | | 30 on (2 f.) orange .. | 2·00 | 2·00 |
| D 57. | | 50 on (2 f.) orange .. | 2·00 | 2·00 |
| D 58. | | 100 on (2 f.) orange | 2·00 | 2·00 |

## FRENCH POLYNESIA Pt. 6

The French Settlements in the South Pacific, formerly called Oceanic Settlements.

100 centimes = 1 franc.

1. Girl playing Guitar. 2. Polynesian.

3. "The Women of Tahiti" (after Gauguin).

**1958.**

| No. | Type | Description | Unused | Used |
|---|---|---|---|---|
| 1. | 1. | 10 c. brown, green and turquoise (postage) .. | 30 | 45 |
| 2. | | 25 c. purple, red and green | 30 | 45 |
| 3. | | 1 f. sepia, red and blue .. | 40 | 50 |
| 4. | | 2 f. violet, choc. & brown | 50 | 50 |
| 5. | 2. | 4 f. myrtle, green & yellow | 75 | 65 |
| 6. | – | 5 f. brown, violet & green | 80 | 80 |
| 7. | 2. | 7 f. brown, green & orange | 1·90 | 1·25 |
| 8. | | 9 f. purple, green & orange | 2·50 | 1·75 |
| 9. | – | 10 f. red, blue and brown | 3·50 | 1·90 |
| 10. | – | 16 f. multicoloured .. | 4·25 | 2·50 |
| 11. | – | 17 f. brown, blue & turq. | 4·00 | 2·00 |
| 12. | – | 20 f. brown, violet & pink | 5·25 | 2·75 |
| 13. | – | 13 f. brn., grn. & drab (air) | 5·50 | 3·00 |
| 14. | 3. | 50 f. multicoloured .. | 8·00 | 3·75 |
| 15. | – | 100 f. multicoloured .. | 12·00 | 6·00 |
| 16. | – | 200 f. slate and lilac .. | 32·00 | 18·00 |

DESIGNS: As Types **1/2**—VERT. **5 f. Spear-fishing. 10 f., 20 f. Polynesian girl on beach.** HORIZ. **16 f. Post Office, Papeete. 17 f. Tahitian dancers.** As Type **3**—VERT. **13 f. Mother-of-Pearl engraver. 100 f. "The White Horse" (after Gauguin).** HORIZ. **200 f. Night-fishing off Moorea.**

**1958.** 10th Anniv. of Declaration of Human Rights. As T **10** of Comoro Is.

| No. | Type | Description | Unused | Used |
|---|---|---|---|---|
| 17. | | 7 f. grey and blue .. | 8·00 | 6·25 |

**1959.** Tropical Flora. As T **56** of French Equatorial Africa. Multicoloured.

| No. | Type | Description | Unused | Used |
|---|---|---|---|---|
| 18. | | 4 f. "Artocarpus" .. | 4·00 | 3·00 |

7. Douglas DC-8 over Papeete Airport.

**1960.** Air. Inaug. of Papeete Airport.

| No. | Type | Description | Unused | Used |
|---|---|---|---|---|
| 19. | 7. | 13 f. violet, purple & green | 3·00 | 1·75 |

8. "Saraca indica". 11. Squirrel Fish.

9. Pacific Map and Palms.

**1962.** Flowers.

| No. | Type | Description | Unused | Used |
|---|---|---|---|---|
| 20. | | 15 f. Type **8** .. .. | 11·00 | 7·25 |
| 21. | | 25 f. Hibiscus .. .. | 13·00 | 10·00 |

**1962.** 5th South Pacific Conference, Pago-Pago.

| No. | Type | Description | Unused | Used |
|---|---|---|---|---|
| 22. | 9. | 20 f. multicoloured .. | 8·50 | 5·50 |

**1962.** Air. 1st Trans-Atlantic TV Satellite Link. As Type F **23** of Andorra (French).

| No. | Type | Description | Unused | Used |
|---|---|---|---|---|
| 23 | | 50 f. blue, brown and purple | 9·50 | 5·50 |

**1962.** Fishes. Multicoloured.

| No. | Type | Description | Unused | Used |
|---|---|---|---|---|
| 24. | | 5 f. Type **11** .. .. | 2·75 | 1·60 |
| 25. | | 10 f. One Spot Butterfly .. | 3·75 | 2·25 |
| 26. | | 30 f. Scorpion Fish .. | 7·75 | 4·50 |
| 27. | | 40 f. Cowfish .. .. | 11·50 | 7·75 |

12. Football.

**1962.** 1st South Pacific Games, Suva, Fiji.

| No. | Type | Description | Unused | Used |
|---|---|---|---|---|
| 28. | 12. | 20 f. brown and blue .. | 7·25 | 5·50 |
| 29. | – | 50 f. blue and red .. | 10·50 | 6·50 |

DESIGN: **50 f. Throwing the javelin.**

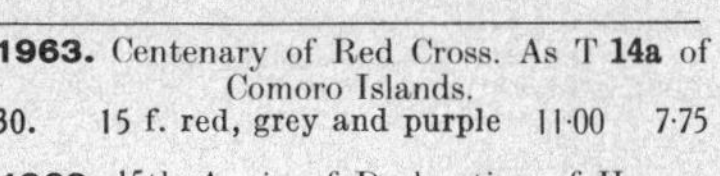

**1963.** Centenary of Red Cross. As T **14a** of Comoro Islands.

| No. | Type | Description | Unused | Used |
|---|---|---|---|---|
| 30. | | 15 f. red, grey and purple | 11·00 | 7·75 |

**1963.** 15th Anniv of Declaration of Human Rights. As T **15** of Comoro Islands.

| No. | Type | Description | Unused | Used |
|---|---|---|---|---|
| 31 | | 7 f. violet and green .. | 9·50 | 6·50 |

**1964.** "PHILATEC 1964" Int. Stamp Exn., Paris. As T **528** of France.

| No. | Type | Description | Unused | Used |
|---|---|---|---|---|
| 32. | | 25 f. red, black and green | 12·00 | 7·50 |

16. Dancer. 17. Tahitian Volunteers.

**1964.** Tahitian Dancers.

| No. | Type | Description | Unused | Used |
|---|---|---|---|---|
| 33. | 16. | 1 f. multicoloured (post.) | 50 | 55 |
| 34. | | 3 f. orange, sepia & purple | 70 | 55 |
| 35. | – | 15 f. multicoloured (air).. | 4·00 | 1·75 |

DESIGN—VERT. (27 × 46½ mm.): **15 f. Dancer in full costume.**

**1964.** Polynesia's War Effort in Second World War. Multicoloured.

| No. | Type | Description | Unused | Used |
|---|---|---|---|---|
| 36 | | 5 f. Type **17** (postage) .. | 7·25 | 3·75 |
| 37 | | 16 f. Badges and map of Tahiti (48 × 27 mm) (air) | 10·00 | 5·50 |

18. Tuamotu Lagoon (after J. D. Lajoux).

**1964.** Landscapes. Multicoloured.

| No. | Type | Description | Unused | Used |
|---|---|---|---|---|
| 38 | | 2 f. Type **18** (postage) .. | 55 | 45 |
| 39 | | 4 f. Bora-Bora (after Lajoux) .. .. | 90 | 65 |
| 40 | | 7 f. Papeete (after A. Sylvain) .. .. | 1·90 | 1·10 |
| 41 | | 8 f. Marquesas (Gauguin's grave) .. .. | 2·25 | 1·25 |
| 42 | | 20 f. Gambier (after Mazellier) .. .. | 5·50 | 2·25 |
| 43 | | 23 f. Moorea (after Sylvain) (48 × 27 mm) (air) .. | 6·00 | 2·75 |

**1965.** Air. Centenary of I.T.U. As T **20** of Comoro Islands.

| No. | Type | Description | Unused | Used |
|---|---|---|---|---|
| 44. | | 50 f. brown, blue & violet | 75·00 | 38·00 |

20. Museum Buildings.

**1965.** Air. Gauguin Museum.

| No. | Type | Description | Unused | Used |
|---|---|---|---|---|
| 45. | 20. | 25 f. green .. .. | 5·50 | 3·50 |
| 46. | – | 40 f. turquoise .. .. | 11·00 | 5·50 |
| 47. | – | 75 f. brown .. .. | 20·00 | 11·00 |

DESIGNS: **40 f. Statues and hut. 75 f. Gauguin.**

21. Skin-diver with Harpoon.

**1965.** Air. World Under-water Swimming Championships, Tuamoto.

| No. | Type | Description | Unused | Used |
|---|---|---|---|---|
| 48. | 21. | 50 f. blue, brown & green | 70·00 | 45·00 |

22. Tropical Foliage. 23. Aerial, Globe and Palm.

**1965.** Schools Canteen Art.
49. **22.** 20 f. red, green and brown (postage) .. .. 14·00 9·50
50. – 80 f. red, blue and brown (27×48 mm.) (air) .. 18·00 13·50
DESIGN: 80 f. Totem, and garland in harbour.

**1965.** Air. 50th Anniv. of 1st Radio Link with France.
51. **23.** 60 f. brn., green & orange 16·00 13·50

**1966.** Air. Launching of 1st French Satellite. As Nos. 1696/7 (plus se-tenant label) of France.
52. 7 f. brown, purple & green 5·00 5·00
53. 10 f. brown, purple & green 5·00 5·00

**1966.** Air. Launching of Satellite "D1". As T **569** of France.
54. 20 f. red, brown and green 6·00 4·00

26. Papeete Port.

**1966.** Air.
55. **26.** 50 f. multicoloured .. 12·50 9·00

27. Pirogue.

**1966.** Polynesian Boats.
56. **27.** 10 f. red, green and blue 1·40 90
57. – 11 f. red, green and blue 1·60 1·10
58. – 12 f. purple, green & blue 2·25 1·40
59. – 14 f. brown, blue & green 3·75 1·75
60. – 19 f. green, red and blue 4·50 1·75
61. – 22 f. green, blue & purple 5·50 3·00
DESIGNS—VERT. 11 f. Schooner. 19 f. Early schooner. HORIZ. 12 f. Fishing launch. 14 f. Pirogues. 22 f. Coaster, "Oiseau des Iles II".

28. Tahitian Dancer and Band.

**1966.** Air. "Vive, Tahiti!" (tourist publicity).
62. **28.** 13 f. multicoloured .. 8·25 5·00

29. High-jumping. 30. Stone Pestle.

**1966.** 2nd South Pacific Games. Noumea.
63. **29.** 10 f. bistre and red .. 1·60 1·40
64. – 20 f. green and blue .. 3·50 2·00
65. – 40 f. purple and green .. 6·00 1·90
66. – 60 f. blue and brown .. 11·00 7·00
DESIGNS—VERT. 20 f. Pole-vaulting. 40 f. Basketball. HORIZ. 60 f. Hurdling.

**1967.** 50th Anniv. of Oceanic Studies Society.
67. **30.** 50 f. blue and orange .. 11·50 7·25

31. Spring Dance.

**1967.** July Festival.
68. **31.** 5 f. blue, purple and drab 2·25 90
69. – 13 f. purple, violet & grn. 2·75 1·40
70. – 15 f. brown, purple & grn. 3·25 1·60
71. – 16 f. purple, grn. & blue 3·25 2·25
72. – 21 f. brown, green & blue 6·00 3·50
DESIGNS—VERT. 13 f. Javelin-throwing. 16 f. Fruit-porters' race. HORIZ. 15 f. Horse-racing. 21 f. Pirogue-racing.

32. Ear-ring.

**1967.** Ancient Art of the Marquesas Islands.
73. – 10 f. blue, red & purple 2·50 75
74. – 15 f. black and green .. 3·00 1·10
75. **32.** 20 f. brown, green & lake 3·50 1·50
76. – 23 f. brown and ochre .. 4·75 3·00
77. – 25 f. brown, purple & blue 4·75 3·00
78. – 30 f. brown and purple .. 5·75 3·50
79. – 35 f. blue and brown .. 10·00 5·50
80. – 50 f. brown, blue & green 10·00 5·50
DESIGNS: 10 f. Sculpture on mother-of-pearl. 15 f. Paddle-blade. 23 f. Receptacle for anointing oil. 25 f. Hunting stirrups. 30 f. Fan handles. 35 f. Tattooed man. 50 f. "Tikis".

33. Ship's Stern and Canoe ("Wallis, 1767").

**1968.** Air. Bicent. of Discovery of Tahiti.
81. **33.** 40 f. brown, blue & green 6·00 4·00
82. – 60 f. orge., black & blue 8·00 5·00
83. – 80 f. salmon, lake & pur. 11·00 6·50
DESIGNS—HORIZ. 60 f. Ship and witch-doctor ("Cook, 1769"). VERT. 80 f. "Bougainville, 1768" (portrait).

**1968.** 20th Anniv of World Health Organization. As T **26** of Comoro Islands.
85 15 f. violet, red and green .. 7·25 4·50
86 16 f. green, purple & orange 7·25 6·00

35. "The Meal" (Gauguin).

**1968.** Air.
87. **35.** 200 f. multicoloured .. 30·00 22·00

**1968.** Human Rights Year. As T **28** of Comoro Islands.
88. 15 f. red, blue and brown 6·50 4·50
89. 16 f. blue, brown & purple 7·25 5·50

37. Putting the Shot. 38. Tiare Apetahi.

**1968.** Air. Olympic Games, Mexico.
90. **37.** 35 f. grn., pur. & lake 12·00 6·50

**1969.** Flowers. Multicoloured.
91. 9 f. Type **38** .. .. 2·00 1·10
92. 17 f. Tiare Tahiti .. .. 7·25 5·50

**1969.** Air. 1st Flight of "Concorde". As T **32** of Comoro Islands.
93. 40 f. brown and red .. 48·00 27·00

40. Polynesian with Guitar.

**1969.** Air. Pacific Area Travel Association (P.A.T.A.) Congress, Tahiti (1970) (1st issue).
94. **40.** 25 f. multicoloured .. 12·00 5·50
See also Nos. 109/11.

41. Diver and Fish.

**1969.** Air. World Underwater Hunting Championships.
95. **41.** 48 f. black, purple & turq. 19·00 7·75
96. – 52 f. black, red and blue 20·00 14·50
DESIGN—VERT. 52 f. "Flag" Fish.

42. Boxing.

**1969. 3rd South Pacific Games, Port Moresby, New Guinea.**
97. **42.** 9 f. brown and violet .. 2·75 1·60
98. – 17 f. brown and red .. 3·25 1·60
99. – 18 f. brown and blue .. 4·50 2·25
100. – 22 f. purple and green .. 6·50 4·00
DESIGNS—VERT. 17 f. High jumping. 18 f. Running. 22 f. Long jumping.

**1969.** Air. Birth Bicentenary of Napoleon Bonaparte. As T **144** of Cameroun.
101 100 f. "Bonaparte as Commander-in-Chief, Italy" (Rouillard) (vert) .. 75·00 60·00

**1969.** 50th Anniv. of Int. Labour Organization. As T **33** of Comoro Islands.
102. 17 f. drab, green & orange 6·00 4·50
103. 18 f. blue, brown & orange 7·00 5·50

45. Territorial Assembly Building. 46. Tiki holding P.A.T.A. Emblem.

**1969.** Polynesian Buildings. Multicoloured.
104. 13 f. Type **45** .. .. 1·60 1·40
105. 14 f. Governor's residence 2·25 1·40
106. 17 f. Tourist offices .. 3·25 1·60
107. 18 f. Maeva Hotel .. 4·50 1·75
108. 24 f. Taharaa Hotel .. 6·00 4·50

**1970.** P.A.T.A. Congress (2nd issue).
109. **46.** 20 f. blue, brn. & purple 5·00 2·75
110. – 40 f. blue, purple & grn. 7·00 4·00
111. – 60 f. choc., blue & brn. 12·00 7·25
DESIGNS—HORIZ. 40 f. Globe, Airliner and "tourists". VERT. 60 f. Polynesian holding globe.

**1970.** New U.P.U. Headquarters Building. As T **156** of Cameroun.
112 18 f. light brown, vio & brn 5·50 2·75
113 20 f. blue, brown & purple 6·00 3·50

48. Tower of the Sun and Mt. Fuji.

**1970.** Air. "EXPO 70" World Fair, Osaka, Japan. Multicoloured.
114. 30 f. Type **48** .. .. 9·00 5·50
115. 50 f. Eiffel Tower and Torii Gate (vert.) .. .. 17·00 7·50

49. Diver and Basket.

**1970.** Air. Pearl-diving.
116. **49.** 2 f. brn., ind. & bl. 1·10 55
117. – 5 f. ultramarine, orange and blue .. 2·25 1·10
118. – 18 f. grey, orge. & pur. 3·25 1·60
119. – 27 f. lilac, brn. & pur. 5·50 4·00
120. – 50 c. orge., grey & brn. 11·00 6·00
DESIGNS—VERT: 5 f. Diver gathering black-lipped pearl oysters. 27 f. Pearl in opened oyster. 50 f. Woman with pearl jewellery. HORIZ: 18 f. Opening oyster-shell.

50. I.E.Y. Emblem, Open Book and "The Thinker" (statue).

**1970.** Air. International Education Year.
121. **50.** 50 f. blue, brn. & new bl. 10·00 7·50

51. "Polynesian Woman" (Y. de St. Front).

**1970.** Air. Paintings by Polynesian Artists (1st series). Multicoloured.
122 20 f. Type **51** .. .. 5·50 3·25
123 40 f. "Harbour Scene" (F. Fay) .. .. 9·50 5·50
124 60 f. "Niu" (abstract, J. Guillois) .. .. 14·00 4·00
125 80 f. "Beach Hut" (J. Masson) .. .. 18·00 11·00
126 100 f. "Polynesian Girl" (J.-C. Bouloc) (vert) .. 25·00 17·00
See also Nos. 147/51, 160/4, 172/6, 189/93 and 205/9.

52. Games Emblem. 53. Flame of Remembrance.

**1971.** Air. 4th South Pacific Games, Tahiti (1st issue).
127 **52** 20 f. multicoloured .. 6·50 4·00

**1971.** Air. Erection of General de Gaulle Monument.
128. **53.** 5 f. multicoloured .. 6·00 3·00

54. Volunteer, Crest and Tricolour.

**1971.** Air. 30th Anniv. of Departure of Tahitian "Free French" Volunteers.
129. **54.** 25 f. multicoloured .. 8·50 5·50

55. Marara Fisherman.

**1971.** Water Sports. Multicoloured.

130 10 f. Type **55** (postage) .. 9·00 3·50
131 15 f. Surfing (vert) (air) .. 4·50 2·75
132 16 f. Skin-diving (vert) .. 5·50 3·50
133 20 f. Paragliding .. .. 7·25 5·00

56. Red Flower. 57. Yachting.

**1971.** "Day of the 1,000 Flowers". Mult.

134. 8 f. Type **56** .. .. 1·40 1·10
135. 12 f. Hibiscus (horiz.) .. 2·50 1·40
136. 22 f. Porcelain rose .. 4·00 2·25

**1971.** Air. 4th South Pacific Games, Tahiti (2nd issue). Multicoloured.

137. 15 f. Type **57** .. .. 4·00 2·75
138. 18 f. Golf .. .. .. 5·00 3·50
139. 27 f. Archery .. .. 6·50 4·50
140. 53 f. Tennis .. .. 12·00 8·50

58. Water-skiing.

**1971.** 1st World Water-ski Championships, Papeete.

142. **58.** 10 f. red, green & brown 4·00 2·00
143. – 20 f. red, brown & green 6·00 4·00
144. – 40 f. purple, brn. & grn. 13·00 7·00

DESIGNS—VERT. 20 f. Ski-jumping. HORIZ. 40 f. Acrobatics on one ski.

**1971.** 1st Death Anniv. of General de Gaulle. As Nos. 1937 and 1940 of France.

145. 30 f. black and purple .. 8·50 6·00
146. 50 f. black and purple .. 12·00 9·00

**1971.** Air. Paintings by Polynesian Artists (2nd series). As T **51.** Multicoloured.

147. 20 f. "Polynesian Village" (I. Wolf) .. .. 5·00 4·00
148. 40 f. "Lagoon" (A. Dobrowolski) .. .. 8·50 5·50
149. 60 f. "Polynesian Woman" (F. Seli) (vert.) .. .. 11·00 7·50
150. 80 f. "The Holy Family" (P. Heymann) (vert.) .. 15·00 9·50
151. 100 f. "Faces in a Crowd" (N. Michoutouchkine) .. 28·00 18·00

60. Cross Emblem.

**1971.** 2nd French Pacific Scouts and Guides Rally, Taravao.

152. **60.** 28 f. multicoloured .. 11·00 6·50

61. Harbour, Papeete.

**1972.** Air. 10th Anniv. of Autonomous Port of Papeete.

153. **61.** 28 f. multicoloured .. 8·50 5·50

## INDEX

Countries can be quickly located by referring to the index at the end of this volume.

62. Figure-skating.

**1972.** Air. Winter Olympic Games, Sapporo, Japan.

154. **62.** 20 f. red, green & vio. 7·75 5·00

63. Commission H.Q., Noumea, New Caledonia.

**1972.** Air. 25th Anniv. of South Pacific Commission.

155. **63.** 21 f. multicoloured .. 7·75 4·50

64. Alcoholic behind Bars. 65. Floral Emblem.

**1972.** Campaign Against Alcoholism.

156. **64.** 20 f. multicoloured .. 7·75 4·50

**1972.** Air. South Pacific Arts Festival, Fiji.

157. **65.** 36 f. orge., grn. & blue 6·50 4·50

66. Raft "Kon-Tiki" and Route-map.

**1972.** Air. 25th Anniv. of Arrival of "Kon-Tiki" Expedition in French Polynesia.

158. **66.** 16 f. multicoloured .. 5·50 3·50

67. De Gaulle and Monument.

**1972.** Air. Completion of De Gaulle Monument.

159. **67.** 100 f. grey .. .. 48·00 30·00

**1972.** Air. Paintings by Polynesian Artists (3rd series). As Type **51.** Multicoloured.

160. 20 f. "Horses" (G. Bovy) 6·00 3·50
161. 40 f. "Harbour" (R. Juventin) (vert.) .. 9·00 5·00
162. 60 f. "Landscape" (A. Brooke) .. .. 16·00 7·00
163. 80 f. "Polynesians" (D. Adam) (vert.) .. .. 22·00 10·00
164. 100 f. "Dancers" (A. Pilioko) (vert.) .. .. 25·00 18·00

68. St. Theresa and Lisieux Basilica.

**1973.** Air. Birth Centenary of St. Theresa of Lisieux.

165. **68.** 85 f. multicoloured .. 22·00 13·00

69. Copernicus and Planetary System.

**1973.** Air. 500th Birth Anniv. of Nicolas Copernicus (astronomer).

166. **69.** 100 f. violet, brn. & pur. 25·00 15·00

70. Aeroplane and Flying Fish.

**1973.** Air. Inauguration of "Air France" Round-the-World Service via Tahiti.

167. **70.** 80 f. multicoloured .. 18·00 11·00

71. Douglas DC-10 over Papeete Airport.

**1973.** Air. Inaug. of "DC-10" Service.

168. **71.** 20 f. blue, grn. & light bl. 11·00 6·00

72. "Ta Matete" (Gauguin).

**1973.** Air. 125th Birth Anniv. of Gauguin.

169. **72.** 200 f. multicoloured .. 22·00 16·00

73. Loti, Fishermen and Polynesian Girl.

**1973.** Air. 50th Death Anniv. of Pierre Loti (writer).

170. **73.** 60 f. multicoloured .. 35·00 16·00

74. Polynesian Mother and Child. 75. "Teeing Off".

**1973.** Opening of Tahitian Women's Union Creche.

171. **74.** 28 f. multicoloured .. 6·50 3·50

**1973.** Air. Paintings by Polynesian Artists (4th series). As Type **51.** Multicoloured.

172. 20 f. "Sun God" (J.-F. Favre) (vert.) .. .. 4·50 2·75
173. 40 f. "Polynesian Girl" (E. de Gennes) (vert.) .. 7·50 4·50
174. 60 f. "Abstract" (A. Sidet) (vert.) .. .. 11·00 6·50
175. 80 f. "Bus Passengers" (F. Ravello) (vert.) .. 18·00 11·00
176. 100 f. "Boats" (J. Bourdin) 25·00 14·00

**1974.** Atimaono Golf Course, Tahiti. Mult.

177 16 f. Type **75** .. .. 3·50 1·60
178 24 f. View of golf course .. 4·75 2·25

76. "A Helping Hand".

**1974.** Polynesian Animal Protection Society.

179. **76.** 21 f. multicoloured .. 8·75 4·50

77. Mountains and Lagoon. 78. Bird, Fish, Leaf and Flower.

**1974.** Polynesian Landscapes. Multicoloured.

180 2 f. Type **77** .. .. 45 35
181 5 f. Beach games .. .. 55 45
182 6 f. Canoe fishing .. 75 55
183 10 f. Mountain peak (vert) 1·00 65
184 15 f. "Regina Maris" (schooner) in sunset scene .. .. .. 2·25 90
185 20 f. Island and lagoon .. 2·75 1·50

**1974.** Air. Protection of Nature.

186. **78.** 12 f. multicoloured .. 6·00 4·00

79. Catamarans. 80. Polynesian Woman.

**1974.** Air. 2nd World Catamaran Sailing Championships, Papeete.

187. **79.** 100 f. multicoloured .. 20·00 11·00

**1974.** Cent. of Universal Postal Union.

188. **80.** 65 f. multicoloured .. 8·50 5·50

**1974.** Air. Paintings by Polynesian Artists (5th series). As Type **51.** Multicoloured.

189. 20 f. "Flower arrangement" (R. Temarui-Masson) vert.) 7·00 5·00
190. 40 f. "Palms on Beach" M. Chardon) (vert.) .. 12·00 6·50
191. 60 f. "Portrait of Man" (M. F. Avril) (vert.) .. 20·00 9·00
192. 80 f. "Polynesian Girl" (H. Robin (vert.) .. .. 30·00 12·00
193. 100 f. "Lagoon at Night" (D. Farsi) .. .. 42·00 22·00

81. "The Travelling Gods".

**1975.** Air. "50 Years of Tahitian Aviation".

194. **81.** 50 f. vio., red & brn. 6·50 4·50
195. – 75 f. bl., red & grn. 10·00 6·50
196. – 100 f. brn., mve. & grn. 17·00 11·00

DESIGNS: 75 f. Tourville's flying-boat. 100 f. Boeing 707 airliner.

82. Polynesian Girl and French " Ceres " Stamp of 1870.

83. Tahiti Lions' Emblem.

**1975.** Air. " Arphila 75 " International Stamp Exhibition, Paris.

197. **82.** 32 f. red, brn. & blk. .. 5·50 3·50

**1975.** 15th Anniv. of Tahiti Lions' Club.

198. **83.** 26 f. multicoloured .. 8·50 5·50

84. " Protect Nature ".

**1975.** Nature Protection.

199. **84.** 19 f. blue and green .. 6·50 3·50

85. Putting the Shot. 86. Athlete and View of Montreal.

**1975.** Air. Fifth South Pacific Games, Guam. Multicoloured.

200. 25 f. Type **85** .. .. 3·50 6·50
201. 30 f. Volleyball .. .. 5·00 3·50
202. 40 f. Swimming .. .. 6·00 4·50

**1975.** Air. Olympic Games, Montreal (1976).

203. **86.** 44 f. black, blue & red 7·00 4·50

87. Boeing 737 Airliner and Letters.

**1975.** Air. World U.P.U. Day.

204. **87.** 100 f. bl., ol. and brn. 17·00 10·00

**1975.** Air. Paintings by Polynesian Artists (6th series). As T **51**. Multicoloured.

205 20 f. "Beach Scene" (R. Marcel-Marius) .. 1·60 1·25
206 40 f. "Rooftop Aerials" (M. Anglade) .. .. 3·50 2·25
207 60 f. "Street Scene" (J. Day) .. .. .. 5·00 3·50
208 80 f. "Tropical Waters" (J. Steimetz) (vert) .. 7·50 5·00
209 100 f. "Portrait of a Woman" (A. van der Heyde) (vert) .. .. 11·00 7·50

88. Concorde.

**1976.** Air. Concorde's First Commercial Flight.

210 88 100 f. dp blue, bl & mve 15·00 10·00

89. President Pompidou. 91. King Pomare I.

90. Battle of the Saints.

**1976.** 2nd Death Anniv of Georges Pompidou (President of France, 1969–74).

211 89 49 f. grey and blue .. 6·50 5·00

**1976.** Air. Bicent of American Revolution.

212 90 24 f. blue, brown & blk 4·00 2·00
213 – 31 f. purple, red & bistre 4·50 2·50

DESIGN: 31 f. Sea battle of The Chesapeake.

**1976.** Air. Pomare Dynasty. Multicoloured.

214. 18 f. Type **91** .. .. 1·10 55
215. 21 f. King Pomare II .. 1·40 75
216. 26 f. Queen Pomare IV .. 1·75 1·00
217. 30 f. King Pomare V .. 2·25 1·40

See also Nos. 234/7.

92. Gerbault and " Firecrest ".

**1976.** 50th Anniv. of Alain Gerbault's Arrival at Bora-Bora.

218. **92.** 90 f. multicoloured .. 10·00 7·50

93. Turtle.

**1976.** World Ecology Day. Multicoloured.

219. 18 f. Type **93** .. .. 6·50 3·50
220. 42 f. Doves in hand .. 11·00 6·00

94. Legs of Runner.

**1976.** Air. Olympic Games, Montreal.

221. **94.** 26 f. brn., pur. and blue 2·75 1·60
222. – 34 f. pur., brn. and blue 4·00 2·25
223. – 50 f. brn., blue and pur. 7·75 4·50

DESIGNS: VERT. 34 f. Runners. HORIZ. 50 f. Olympic Flame and flowers.

95. A. Graham Bell, early Telephone and Dish Aerial.

**1976.** Telephone Centenary.

225. **95.** 37 f. red, bl. & brn. 6·00 3·50

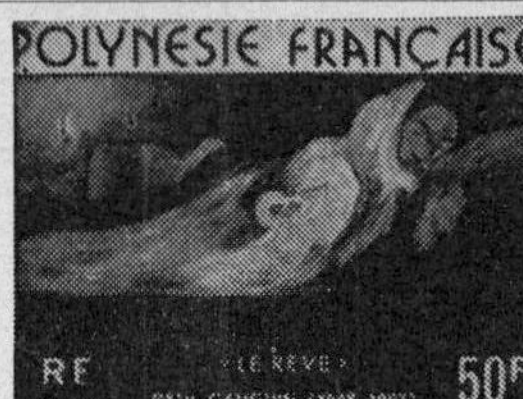


96. " The Dream " (Gauguin).

**1976.** Air.

226. **96.** 50 f. multicoloured .. 9·00 5·50

97. Marquesas Pirogue.

**1976.** Ancient Pirogues. Multicoloured.

227. 25 f. Type **97** .. .. 2·00 1·10
228. 30 f. Raiatea pirogue .. 2·50 1·40
229. 75 f. Tahiti pirogue .. 4·50 2·75
230. 100 f. Tuamotu pirogue .. 6·00 4·00

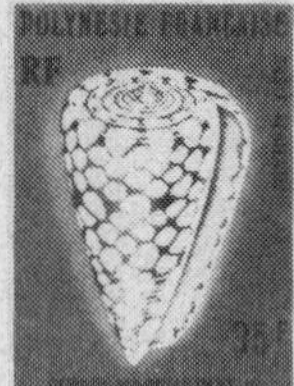


98. Marquesas Cone.

**1977.** Air. Sea Shells (1st series). Mult.

231 25 f. Maurus murex .. 1·60 90
232 27 f. Gaugin's cone .. 2·25 1·10
233 35 f. Type **98** .. .. 2·75 1·40

See also Nos. 268/70 and 307/9.

**1977.** Air. " Sovereigns of Archipelago ". As T **91**. Multicoloured.

234. 19 f. Maputeoa (Mangareva) 90 55
235. 33 f. Tamatoa V (Raiatea) 1·25 90
236. 39 f. Vaekehu (Marquesas 1·75 1·10
237. 43 f. Teuruarii III (Rurutu) 2·00 1·10

99. " Acropora ". 101. Dancer.

**1977.** Air. 3rd Coral Reefs Symposium, Miami.

238. 25 f. Type **99** .. 1·50 75
239. 33 f. " Pocillopora " (vert). 2·00 1·25

**1977.** Air. 5th Anniv. of General de Gaulle Memorial. As T **806** of France.

255. 40 f. multicoloured .. 3·50 2·25

**1977.** Air. Polynesian Dancer.

256. **101.** 27 f. multicoloured .. 2·50 1·25

102. Lindbergh and " Spirit of St. Louis ".

**1977.** Air. 50th Anniv. of Lindbergh's Transatlantic Flight.

257. **102.** 28 f. multicoloured .. 4·50 3·00

103. "Hibiscus tiliaceus".

**1977.** Air. Polynesian Flowers (1st series). Multicoloured.

258. 8 f. Type **103** .. .. 75 55
259. 12 f. " Plumeria acuminata " 1·25 80

See also 276/7 and 288/9.

104. Palm Tree. 105. " Portrait of Rubens' Son, Albert ".

**1977.** Air. Forest Conservation.

260. **104.** 32 f. multicoloured .. 4·50 2·50

**1977.** Air. 400th Birth Anniv. of Peter Paul Rubens.

261. **105.** 100 f. red and blue .. 8·00 6·00

106. Cutter.

**1977.** Sailing Ships. Multicoloured.

262 20 f. Type **106** .. .. 2·25 1·10
263 50 f. "Tiare Taporo" (schooner) .. .. 3·00 1·40
264 85 f. Barque .. .. 4·50 2·25
265 120 f. Full-rigged ship .. 6·50 3·50

107. Captain Cook and H.M.S. " Discovery ".

**1978.** Air. Bicent. of Discovery of Hawaii.

266. **107.** 33 f. mve., red & blue 2·50 1·50
267. – 39 f. grn., bl., & mauve 3·00 2·00

DESIGN: 39 f. Captain Cook and H.M.S. "Resolution".

**1978.** Air. Sea Shells (2nd series). As T **98**. Multicoloured.

268 22 f. Walled cowrie .. 1·50 75
269 24 f. Ventral cowrie .. 1·50 75
270 31 f. False scorpion conch 2·25 1·10

108. " Tahitian Woman and Boy " (Gauguin).

**1978.** Air. 75th Death Anniv. of Paul Gauguin. Multicoloured.

271. **108.** 50 f. multicoloured .. 6·50 4·50

109. Microwave Antenna.

**1978.** Air. World Telecommunications Day.

272. **109.** 80 f. multicoloured .. 4·50 3·00

110. Match Scene.

**1978.** Air. World Cup Football Championship, Argentina.
273. **110.** 28 f. multicoloured .. 2·50 1·75

**111.** Fungia. **112.** " Hibiscus aros sinensis ".

**1978.** Air. Coral (1st series). Multicoloured.
274. 26 f. Type **111** .. .. 1·25 90
275. 34 f. Millepora (vert.) .. 1·50 90
See also Nos. 292/3.

**1978.** Flowers (2nd series). Multicoloured.
276. 13 f. Type **112** .. .. 1·25 75
277. 16 f. " Fagraea berteriana " 1·50 1·00

**113.** Polynesian Girl and Aerial. **115.** Polynesian Girl on Beach.

**114.** Bird and Rainbow over Tropical Island.

**1978.** Air. Papenoo Ground Receiving Station.
278. **113.** 50 f. black and blue .. 2·75 1·60

**1978.** Air. Nature Protection.
279. **114.** 23 f. multicoloured .. 1·75 1·10

**1978.** 20th Anniv. of First French Polynesian Stamps.
280. **115.** 20 f. brn., violet & red 1·75 1·10
281. – 28 f. brn., grn. & yellow 2·50 1·40
282. – 36 f. brn., red and blue 3·50 1·50
Designs: 28 f. Polynesian (as T **2**). 36 f. Girl playing guitar (as T **1**).

**116.** "Tahiti" (inter-island ship).

**1978.** Ships. Multicoloured.
284 15 f. Type **116** .. .. 1·25 90
285 30 f. "Monowai" (liner) .. 2·00 90
286 75 f. "Tahitien" (inter-island ship) .. 3·50 1·75
287 100 f. "Mariposa" (cargo liner) .. .. 5·00 3·00

**1979.** Flowers (3rd series). As T **112**. Mult.
288 10 f. "Vanda sp." .. 75 40
289 22 f. "Gardenia tahitensis" 1·00 65

**1979.** Air. Death Bicentenary of Captain James Cook (explorer). Nos. 266/7 optd **"1779–1979" BICENTENAIRE DE LA MORT DE.**
290 **107** 33 f. mauve, red & blue 2·00 1·10
291 – 39 f. green, blue & mve 2·50 1·60

**1979.** Coral (2nd series). As T **111. Mult.**
292. 32 f. Porytes .. .. 1·50 75
293. 27 f. Montipora .. .. 2·25 1·10

**118.** Raiatea.

**1979.** Landscapes.
468a 1 f. Bora Bora .. .. 10 10
469 2 f. Ua Pou .. .. 10 10
470 3 f. Motu Tapu .. .. 10 10
470a 4 f. Type **118** .. .. 10 10
471 5 f. Motu .. .. .. 10 10
472 6 f. Case au Taumotu .. 10 10

**119.** Children and Toys.

**1979.** Air. International Year of the Child.
300. **119.** 150 f. mve., bl. & turq. 8·00 5·50

**120.** " You are waiting for a Letter? " (Gauguin).

**1979.** Air.
301. **120.** 200 f. multicoloured .. 9·00 6·00

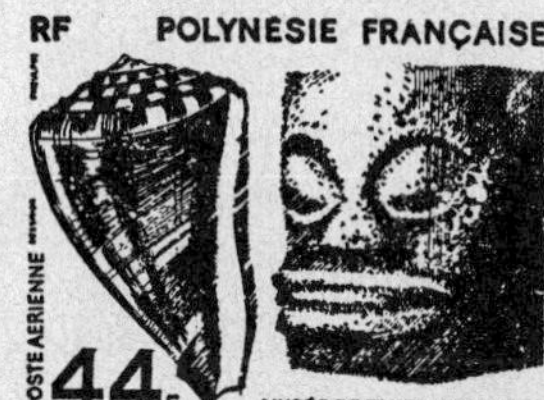

**121.** Conch and Stone Head of a Tiki.

**1979.** Air. Tahiti and the Islands Museum.
302. **121.** 44 f. brn., red & lake 2·50 1·75

**122.** Fetia.

**1979.** Traditional Dancing Costumes. Multicoloured.
303. 45 f. Type **122** .. .. 1·25 75
304. 51 f. Teanuanua .. .. 1·60 75
305. 74 f. Temaeva .. .. 3·25 1·75

**123.** Sir Rowland Hill, British and Polynesian Stamps.

**1979.** Death Cent. of Sir Rowland Hill.
306. **123.** 100 f. mve., vio. & grn. 3·75 2·75

**1979.** Sea Shells (3rd series). As T **98**. Mult.
307 20 f. Strigate auger .. 90 55
308 28 f. Snake mitre .. .. 1·40 55
309 35 f. Wavy-edge spindle .. 1·75 1·10

**124.** Arrows converging on Tahiti. **125.** Carving and Rotary Emblem.

**1979.** Air. 19th South Pacific Conference, Tahiti.
310. **124.** 23 f. multicoloured .. 1·90 1·00

**1979.** 20th Anniv. of Papeete Rotary Club.
311. **125.** 47 f. multicoloured .. 3·00 1·75

**126.** Short Sandringham 7 Bermuda Flying Boat.

**1979.** Air. Aircraft (1st series). Multicoloured.
312 24 f. Type **126** .. .. 75 45
313 40 f. Douglas DC-4 .. 1·25 70
314 60 f. Britten Norman Islander .. .. 1·90 1·10
315 80 f. Fokker/Fairchild Friendship .. .. 2·75 1·75
316 120 f. Douglas DC-8 .. 4·50 2·75
See also Nos. 335/8.

**127.** Emperor Angelfish.

**1980.** Fishes (1st series). Multicoloured.
317. 7 f. Soldier Fish .. .. 90 65
318. 8 f. Napoleon lumphead wrasse .. .. .. 90 65
319. 12 f. Type **127** .. .. 1·25 75
See also Nos. 339/41, 360/2 and 386/8.

**128.** "Window in Tahiti".

**1980.** Air. 50th Anniv. of Henri Matisse's Visit to Tahiti.
320. **128.** 150 f. multicoloured .. 5·50 4·00

**1980.** 75th Anniv. of Rotary International. No. 311 surch. **75eme ANNIVERSAIRE 1905–1980 77F.**
321. **125.** 77 f. on 47 f. mult. .. 4·25 2·75

**130.** National Centre for Exploitation of Oceans.

**1980.** Aquaculture (1st series). Multicoloured.
322. 15 f. Type **130** .. .. 1·25 70
323. 22 f. Sea-water shrimp .. 1·40 1·00
See also Nos. 343/4.

**131.** General Post Office, Papeete.

**1980.** Opening of New General Post Office.
324. **131.** 50 f. multicoloured .. 1·75 1·10

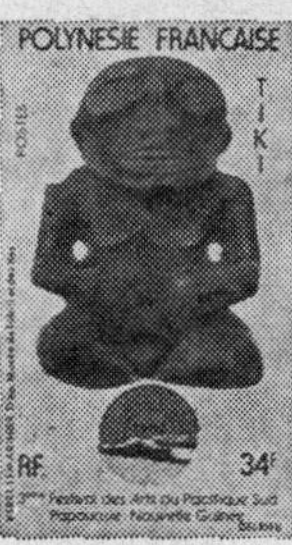

**132.** Tiki Statuette, Marquesas Islands.

**1980.** 3rd South Pacific Arts Festival, Papua New Guinea.
325. 34 f. Type **132** .. .. 1·40 90
326. 39 f. Pahu (drum), Marquesas Islands .. .. 1·50 90
327. 49 f. Adze, Society Islands 2·00 1·25

**133.** " Tehamana's Ancestors " (Gauguin).

**1980.** Air.
329. **133.** 500 f. multicoloured .. 15·00 10·00

**134.** Sydney Town Hall and 1955 Oceanic Settlements 9 f. stamp.

**1980.** Air. "Sydpex 80" Stamp Exhibition, Sydney.
330. **134.** 70 f. multicoloured .. 7·25 4·50

**135.** White Tern. **136.** Charles de Gaulle.

**1980.** Birds. (1st series). Multicoloured.
331. 25 f. Type **135** .. .. 1·25 60
332. 35 f. Tahitian Lory (vert.) 1·50 60
333. 45 f. Great Frigate Bird .. 1·75 1·10
See also Nos. 350/52 and 379/81.

**1980.** 10th Death Anniv. of Charles de Gaulle (French statesman).
334. **136.** 100 f. multicoloured .. 4·00 2·75

**1980.** Air. Aircraft (2nd series). As T **126**. Multicoloured.
335 15 f. Consolidated Catalina amphibian .. .. 60 35
336 26 f. De Havilland Twin Otter .. .. .. 80 40
337 30 f. CAMS 55 flying boat 90 60
338 50 f. Douglas DC-6 .. 1·75 1·00

**1981.** Fishes (2nd series). As T **127**. Mult.
339. 13 f. Zebra unicorn .. 65 35
340. 16 f. Yellow-striped snapper 65 35
341. 24 f. Purple-spotted grouper .. .. .. 1·25 65

**137.** " And the Gold of their Bodies " (Gauguin).

**1981.** Air.
342. **137.** 100 f. multicoloured .. 3·50 2·00

**1981.** Aquaculture (2nd series). As T **130**. Multicoloured.
343 23 f. Shrimp hatching room, National Centre for Exploitation of Oceans.. 1·00 60
344 41 f. Green mussels .. 1·40 75

**138.** Yury Gagarin and Alan Shepard.

**1981.** Air. 20th Anniv. of First Men in Space.
345. **138.** 300 f. multicoloured .. 7·00 5·00

139. Dancers.

**1981.** Folklore. Multicoloured.

346. 26 f. Type **139** .. .. 70 40
347. 28 f. Drummer .. .. 75 40
348. 44 f. Two dancers (vert.) 1·50 1·00

140. Racing Pirogue.

**1981.** Air. First International Pirogue Championship, Polynesia.

349. **140.** 200 f. multicoloured .. 5·00 3·50

141. Common Waxbill.

**1981.** Birds (2nd series). Multicoloured.

350. 47 f. Crested terns .. .. 1·60 80
351. 53 f. Grey-green fruit dove 2·00 90
352. 65 f. Type **141** .. .. 2·50 1·40

142. Huahine.

**1981.** French Polynesian Islands (1st series). Multicoloured.

353 34 f. Type **142** .. .. 65 45
354 134 f. Maupiti .. .. 2·50 1·40
355 136 f. Bora Bora .. .. 2·50 1·40

See also Nos. 376/8.

143. " Matavai Bay " (William Hodges).

**1981.** Air. 18th-century Paintings. Mult.

356 40 f. Type **143** .. .. 85 60
357 60 f. "Poedea" (John Webber) (wrongly inscr "Weber") (vert) .. 1·10 80
358 80 f. "Omai" (Sir Joshua Reynolds) (vert) .. 2·00 1·25
358 120 f. "Point Venus" (Georges Tobin) .. 2·75 1·75

**1982.** Fishes (3rd series). As T **127.** Mult.

360. 30 f. Parrot fish .. .. 70 50
361. 31 f. Regal angel fish .. 75 50
362. 45 f. Spotted bass .. .. 1·10 60

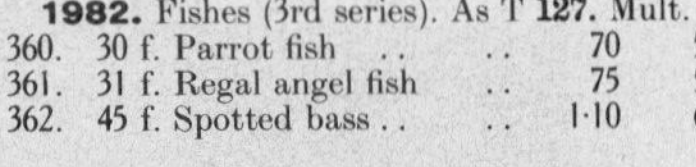

144. Family, Bacillus and Dr Robert Koch.

**1982.** Air. Centenary of Discovery of Tubercle Bacillus.

363. **144.** 200 f. bl., grey & brn. 4·50 2·75

145. Oyster Farm.

**1982.** Pearl Industry. Multicoloured.

364. 7 f. Type **145** .. .. 40 20
365. 8 f. Grafting oysters .. 45 30
366. 10 f. Pearls .. .. .. 1·00 40

146. Girl and Tahiti 25 c. stamp.

**1982.** "Philexfrance 82" International Stamp Exhibition, Paris.

367. **146.** 15 f. brn., grn. & bl... 5·50 5·50

147. Footballers.

148. Priest.

**1982.** Air. World Cup Football Championship, Spain.

369. **147.** 250 f. multicoloured .. 6·00 4·00

**1982.** Polynesian Folklore. King's Enthroning. Multicoloured.

370. 12 f. Type **148** .. .. 35 25
371. 13 f. Enthroning ceremony 45 25
372. 17 f. Priest and King .. 60 35

149. "Hobie Cat 16" Class Catamaran.

**1982.** 4th World "Hobie Cat" Championship, Tahiti.

373 **149** 90 f. multicoloured .. 2·00 1·50

150. Island Scene.

151. Sun, Man and Pacific Scene.

**1982.** Air. Overseas Week.

374. **150.** 110 f. brn., bl & grn... 2·25 1·40

**1982.** First South Pacific Commission Conference on New Energy Sources, Tahiti.

375. **151.** 46 f. multicoloured .. 1·25 80

**1982.** French Polynesian Islands (2nd series). As T **142.** Multicoloured.

376. 20 f. Motu .. .. .. 60 30
377. 33 f. Tupai Atoll .. .. 75 40
378. 35 f. Gambier .. .. 75 40

**1982.** Birds (3rd series). As T **141.** Mult.

379 37 f. Eastern reef heron (horiz) .. .. 1·40 95
380 39 f. American golden plover .. .. 1·50 1·00
381 42 f. Chestnut-breasted mannikins .. .. 1·75 1·10

152. "Tahitian Girl" (Maximilien Radiguet).

**1982.** Air. 19th-century Paintings. Mult.

382 50 f. Type **152** .. .. 1·00 60
383 70 f. "Tahiti Souvenir" (Charles Giraud) (horiz) 1·40 80
384 100 f. "Pounding Material" (Jules Louis Le Jeune) (horiz) .. .. .. 2·00 1·50
385 160 f. "Papeete Harbour" (Constance Gordon Cumming) (horiz) .. 3·50 2·50

**1983.** Fishes (4th series). As T **127.** **Mult.**

386. 8 f. " Acanthurus lineatus " 35 25
387. 10 f. " Caranx melampygus " 60 25
388. 12 f. " Carcharhinus melanopterus " .. .. 70 35

153. "The Way of the Cross".

154. "The Axeman".

**1983.** Religious Sculptures by Damien Haturau. Multicoloured.

389. 7 f. Type **153** .. .. 25 15
390. 21 f. " The Virgin and the Infant Jesus " .. .. 55 25
391. 23 f. " Christ " .. .. 70 35

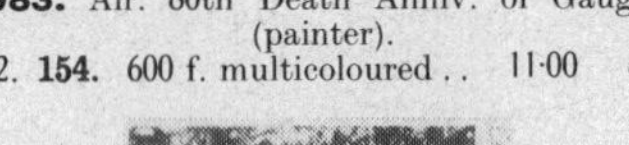

**1983.** Air. 80th Death Anniv. of Gauguin (painter).

392. **154.** 600 f. multicoloured .. 11·00 8·50

155. Acacia and Pandanus Hat.

**1983.** Polynesian Hats (1st series). Mult.

393. 11 f. Type **155** .. .. 20 15
394. 13 f. High-crowned hat made from coconut leaves .. .. .. 25 15
395. 25 f. Coffee-coloured openwork hat .. .. 40 25
396. 35 f. Bamboo hat .. .. 80 45

See also Nos. 423/6.

156. Bligh, Route Map and Breadfruit.

**1983.** Air. Re-enactment of Captain William Bligh's Open-boat Voyage after the "Bounty" Mutiny.

397. **156.** 200 f. multicoloured .. 4·00 2·75

157. Chief of St. Christine.

**1983.** Costumes (1st series). Multicoloured.

398. 15 f. Type **157** .. .. 35 30
399. 15 f. St. Christine man .. 40 35
400. 28 f. St. Christine woman 60 36

See also Nos. 427/9 and 454/6.

158. Polynesian Girls.

**1983. Air. " Brasiliana 83 " International Stamp Exhibition, Rio de Janeiro.**

401. **158.** 100 f. multicoloured .. 2·50 1·75

159. Polynesian and Thai Girls.

**1983.** Air. "Bangkok 1983" International Stamp Exhibition.

403. **159.** 110 f. multicoloured .. 2·50 1·75

160. Fragrant Fern Headdress.

**1983.** Floral Headdresses (1st series). Multicoloured.

405. 41 f. Type **160** .. .. 80 55
406. 44 f. Gardenias .. .. 90 60
407. 45 f. Mixed flowers .. 1·00 60

See also Nos. 433/5.

161. Luther and Church.

**1983.** 500th Birth Anniv. of Martin Luther (Protestant reformer).

408. **161.** 90 blk., blue & brown 2·00 1·25

162. "Arrival of Escort Ship" (Nicolas Mordvinoff).

163. Me'ae of Peke, Nuku-Hiva.

**1983.** Air. 20th-century Paintings. Mult.

409. 40 f. "View of Moorea" (William MacDonald) (horiz.) .. .. .. 1·00 60
410. 60 f. "Fei Porter" (Adrian Herman Gouwe) .. 90 80
411. 80 f. Type **162** .. .. 1·50 90
412. 100 f. "Women on the Veranda" (Charles Lemoine) (horiz.) .. 2·00 1·25

**1984.** Marquesian Tikis. Multicoloured.

413. 14 f. Type **163** .. .. 30 25
414. 16 f. Me'ae of Paeke (different) .. .. .. 40 25
415. 19 f. Me'ae Oipona, Hiva-Oa 45 25

**165.** Island Canoeists.

**1984.** Air. "Espana 84" International Stamp Exhibition, Madrid.

420. **165.** 80 f. red and blue .. 2·00 1·40

**166.** "Woman with Mango" (Gauguin).

**1984.** Air.

422 **166** 400 f. multicoloured .. 8·00 5·50

**1984.** Polynesian Hats (2nd series). As T **155.** Multicoloured.

423. 20 f. Reed hat .. .. 35 25
424. 24 f. Pandanus leaves hat 40 35
425. 26 f. Fei and bamboo hat 40 35
426. 33 f. Pandanus hat decorated with toetoe flowers .. .. .. 75 40

**1984.** Costumes (2nd series). As T **157.** Multicoloured.

427. 34 f. Tahitian boy playing nose flute .. .. 60 35
428. 35 f. Priest from Oei-Eitia 70 40
429. 39 f. Tahitian woman and her son .. .. .. 80 40

**167.** "Human Sacrifice" (detail, John Webber).

**1984.** Air. "Ausipex 84" International Stamp Exhibition, Melbourne. Multicoloured.

430. 120 f. Type **167** .. .. 3·50 2·50
431. 120 f. Different detail of "Human Sacrifice" .. 3·50 2·50

**1984.** Floral Headdresses (2nd series). As T **160.** Multicoloured.

433. 46 f. Ylang ylang .. .. 80 40
434. 47 f. Garden vine .. .. 90 55
435. 53 f. Bougainvillea .. 1·00 60

**168.** Tiki and Native.

**1984.** Fourth South Pacific Arts Festival, Noumea, New Caledonia.

436. **168.** 150 f. multicoloured .. 3·00 2·00

See No. 453.

**169.** "Tahitian Girls on the Beach" (Pierre Heyman).

**1984.** 20th-century Paintings. Multicoloured.

437 50 f. "After Church" (Jacques Boulaire) (vert) 90 65
438 65 f. "Anaa Countryside" (Jean Masson) .. .. 1·00 75
439 75 f. "Festival" (Robert Tatin) .. .. .. 1·40 90
440 85 f. Type **169** .. .. 1·40 1·25

**170.** Pair of Tikis. **171.** Girl wearing Lei.

**1985.** Wooden Tikis. Multicoloured.

441. 30 f. Type **170** .. .. 55 30
442. 36 f. Joined tikis .. .. 65 55
443. 40 f. Tiki .. .. .. 80 55

**1985.** Polynesian Faces (1st series). Multicoloured.

444. 22 f. Type **171** .. .. 35 25
445. 39 f. Girl's profile .. .. 70 50
446. 44 f. Girl wearing shell necklace .. .. .. 85 65

See also Nos. 473/5 and 498/500.

**172.** "Where Have We come From? What are We? Where are We Going?" (Gauguin). (½-size illustration).

**1985.** Air.

447. **172.** 550 f. multicoloured .. 10·00 7·50

**173.** East Bridge, Papeete.

**1985.** Tahiti in Olden Days (1st series). Multicoloured.

448. 42 f. Type **173** .. .. 80 40
449. 45 f. Inhabitants of Papeete (vert.) .. .. 80 45
450. 48 f. Papeete market .. 1·00 65

See also Nos. 477/9, 528/30, 703/5 and 742/4.

**174.** Coral Reef.

**1985.** Fifth International Coral Reefs Congress, Tahiti.

451 **174.** 140 f. multicoloured .. 2·50 1·75

**175.** National Flag.

**1985.**

452. **175.** 9 f. multicoloured .. 20 15

**1985.** 4th Pacific Arts Festival, Papeete. As T **168** but with "Sud Noumea" omitted, different emblem, inscr. "29 juin au 15 juillet" and dated "1985".

453. 200 f. multicoloured .. 3·50 2·25

The Festival was originally to be held in New Caledonia in 1984 but was cancelled and subsequently held in Tahiti in 1985.

**1985.** Costumes (3rd series). As T **157.** Multicoloured.

454. 38 f. Tahitian dancer .. 70 45
455. 55 f. Tahitian couple .. 90 55
456. 70 f. Tahitian king .. 1·40 80

**176.** Couple holding Blue-faced Booby.

**1985.** Air. International Youth Year.

457. **176.** 250 f. multicoloured .. 5·00 3·00

**177.** 19th-century French Warship in Papeete Harbour.

**1985.** Air. "Italia '85" International Stamp Exhibition, Rome.

458. **177.** 130 f. green .. .. 3·00 2·00

**178.** Traditional Foods.

**1985.** Tahitian Oven Pit. Multicoloured.

460. 25 f. Type **178** .. .. 60 30
461. 35 f. Man tending oven .. 70 40

**179.** St. Michael's Cathedral, Rikitea (Gambier Island).

**1985.** Catholic Churches. Multicoloured.

462. 90 f. St Anne's Church, Otepipi (Anaa) .. .. 1·50 1·00
463. 100 f. Interior of St. Michael's Cathedral, Rikitea (Gambier Island) .. .. .. 2·00 1·10
464. 120 f. Type **179** .. .. 2·25 1·50

**180.** Fiddler Crab.

**1986.** Crabs. Multicoloured.

465. 18 f. Type **180** .. .. 35 25
466. 29 f. Hermit land crab .. 55 35
467. 31 f. Coconut crab .. .. 55 35

**181.** Youth with Fish.

**1986.** Polynesian Faces (2nd series). Multicoloured.

473 43 f. Type **181** .. .. 80 40
474 49 f. Boy holding coral .. 80 40
475 51 f. Youth and turtle (vert.) .. .. .. 90 45

**182.** Marlin and Emblem. **183.** Tiki, Punaei Valley.

**1986.** Air. 1st International Marlin Fishing Contest.

476. **182.** 300 f. multicoloured 5·50 3·50

**1986.** Tahiti in Olden Days (2nd series). As T **173.** Multicoloured.

477. 52 f. Papeete .. .. 80 40
478. 56 f. Harpoon fishing .. 90 55
479. 57 f. King's Palace, Papeete .. .. .. 1·00 55

**1986.** Rock Carvings (1st series). Mult.

480. 58 f. Type **183** .. .. 1·00 55
481. 59 f. Human figure, Hane Valley .. .. .. 1·00 55

See also Nos. 507/8.

**184.** Fish in Coconut Milk.

**1986.** Polynesian Food Dishes (1st series). Multicoloured.

482. 80 f. Type **184** .. .. 1·60 1·10
483. 110 f. Fafaru .. .. 2·25 1·60

See also Nos. 504/5 and 524/5.

**185.** Arrival of Sailing Ships, 1880.

**1986.** Air.

484. **185.** 400 f. blue .. .. 7·50 4·50

**186.** "Tifaifai" (sewn collage).

**1986.** Polynesian Folklore. Traditional Crafts. Multicoloured.

485. 8 f. Type **186** .. .. 10 10
486. 10 f. Wickerwork .. .. 20 15
487. 12 f. Making "mores" (dance skirts) .. .. 30 20

**187.** Map of Tahiti, Daniel Carl Solander and Anders Sparrmann.

**1986.** Air. "Stockholmia 86" International Stamp Exhibition.
488. **187.** 150 f. green, deep blue and blue .. .. 2·75 2·00

**188.** Building a Pirogue. **189.** Metuapua.

**1986.** Pirogue Construction. Multicoloured.
490. 46 f. Type **188** .. .. 80 45
491. 50 f. Constructing the hull 90 55

**1986.** Medicinal Plants (1st series). Designs showing illustrations by Gilles Cordonnier.
492. **189.** 40 f. green .. .. 80 40
493. – 41 f. green .. .. 80 40
494. – 60 f. green .. .. 1·10 65
DESIGNS: 41 f. Hotu. 60 f. Miri.
See also Nos. 514/6 and 545/7.

**190.** Tiva Church.

**1986.** Air. Protestant Churches. Mult.
495. 80 f. Type **190** .. .. 1·40 90
496. 200 f. Avera church .. 3·50 2·00
497. 300 f. Papetoai church .. 5·50 2·75

**191.** Old Man. **192.** Reef Crab.

**1987.** Polynesian Faces (3rd series). Mult.
498. 28 f. Type **191** .. .. 65 30
499. 30 f. Girl holding baby .. 65 35
500. 37 f. Elderly woman .. 80 35

**1987.** Crustaceans. Multicoloured.
501. 34 f. Type **192** .. .. 65 35
502. 35 f. "Parribacus antarcticus" .. .. 65 40
503. 39 f. "Justitia longimana" 80 55

**1987.** Polynesian Food Dishes (2nd series). As T **184**. Multicoloured.
504. 33 f. Papaya po'e .. .. 65 40
505. 65 f. Chicken fafa .. .. 1·25 80

**193.** Broche Barracks.

**1987.** Air. Centenary of Broche Army Barracks.
506 **193** 350 f. multicoloured .. 6·00 4·50

**1987.** Rock Carvings (2nd series). As T **183**. Multicoloured.
507. 13 f. Double-headed figure, Tipaerui .. .. .. 20 15
508. 21 f. Turtle, Raiatea .. 40 25

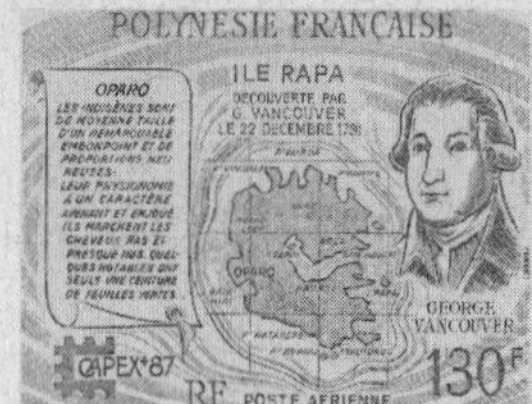

**194.** George Vancouver, Map of Rapa Island and Quotation.

**1987.** Air. "Capex '87" International Stamp Exhibition, Toronto.
509. **194.** 130 f. brown and red 2·50 1·60

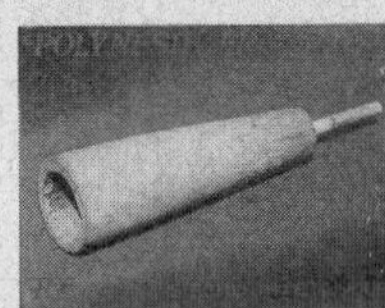

**195.** Marquesas Islands Miro Wood and Bamboo Horn.

**1987.** Musical Instruments. Multicoloured.
511 20 f. Type **195** .. .. 20 35
512 26 f. Trumpet triton horn with coconut fibre cord 45 35
513 33 f. Bamboo flutes .. 65 45

**1987.** Medicinal Plants (2nd series). As T **189** showing illustrations by Gilles Cordonnier.
514. 46 f. green .. .. .. 90 45
515. 53 f. mauve .. .. 1·00 55
516. 54 f. black .. .. .. 1·00 55
DESIGNS: 46 f. Miro. 53 f. Tiapito. 54 f. Taataahiara.

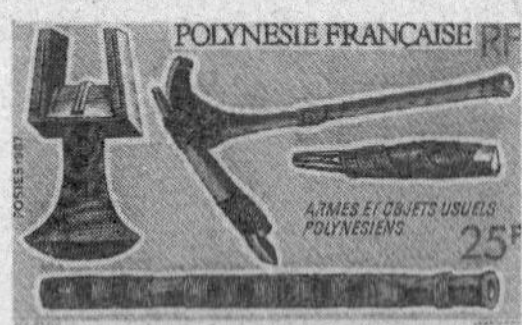

**196.** Penu, War Club, Adze and Nose Flute.

**1987.** Tools and Weapons. Designs showing plates from "The Voyages of Captain Cook".
517. **196.** 25 f. black and green 45 35
518. – 27 f. blue & turq. .. 45 35
519. – 32 f. deep brown and brown .. .. 65 35
DESIGNS: 27 f. War club, tattooing comb, paddle and chisels. 32 f. Head bands, head and chest ornaments and adze.

**197.** "Soyez Mysterieuses". (wood sculpture, Paul Gauguin). (illustration half-size).

**1987.** Air.
520. **197.** 600 f. multicoloured .. 10·50 7·25

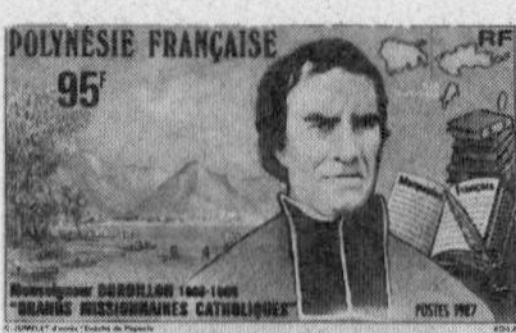

**198.** Mgr. Rene Dordillon, Bishop of Marquesas Islands.

**1987.** Catholic Missionaries. Multicoloured.
521 95 f. Type **198** .. .. 1·60 1·10
522 105 f. Mgr. Tepano Jaussen 1·75 1·10
523 115 f. Mgr. Paul Maze, Archbishop of Papeete 2·75 1·40

**1988.** Polynesian Food Dishes (3rd series). As T **184**. Multicoloured.
524 40 f. Crayfish (vert) .. 65 45
525 75 f. Bananas in coconut milk (vert) .. .. 1·40 90

**199.** James Norman Hall.

**1988.** Birth Centenaries (1987) of Nordhoff and Hall (writers).
526. **199.** 62 f. black, cream and silver .. .. 1·10 65
527. – 85 f. black, grey and silver .. .. 1·50 90
DESIGN: 85 f. Charles Bernard Nordhoff.

**1988.** Tahiti in Olden Days (3rd series). As T **173**. Multicoloured.
528 11 f. Taranpoo hut on raft, Raiatea .. .. 30 20
529 15 f. Small Tahitian huts 35 20
530 17 f. Large Tahitian hut .. 35 20

**200.** Lighthouse and Anchor.

**1988.** 120th Anniv. of Venus Point Lighthouse.
531. **200.** 400 f. multicoloured .. 7·00 4·00

**201.** "River Scene".

**1988.** Tapa (cloth made from beaten bark) Paintings by Paul Engdahl. Multicoloured.
532. 52 f. Type **201** .. .. 90 65
533. 54 f. "River scene" (different) .. .. 90 65
534. 64 f. "Jungle" .. .. 1·10 90

**202.** Dish Aerial, Papenoo, Tahiti.

**1988.** Polysat Satellite Communications Network.
535. **202.** 300 f. multicoloured .. 5·00 3·25

**203.** Doll in More Skirt. **204.** Carved Figures (detail).

**1988.** Polynesian Folklore. Tahitian Dolls. Multicoloured.
536. 42 f. Type **203** .. .. 80 45
537. 45 f. Doll in city clothing 80 45
538. 48 f. Doll in city clothing (different) .. .. 90 65

**1988.** "Sydpex 88" International Stamp Exhibition, Australia. Engraving by J. and E. Verreaux from Atlas by Baron von Krusenstern (explorer).
539 **204** 68 f. brown .. .. 1·40 90

**205.** Route Map.

**1989.** 30th Death Anniv of Eric de Bisschop (leader of "Tahiti Nui" expedition).
541 **205** 350 f. blue, black & brn 6·00 3·25

**206.** "Kermia barnardi".

**1988.** Sea Shells (1st series). Multicoloured.
542. 24 f. Type **206** .. .. 45 35
543. 35 f. "Vexillum suavis" .. 55 45
544. 44 f. "Berthelinia" sp. .. 65 55
See also Nos. 573/5.

**1988.** Medicinal Plants (3rd series). As T **189** showing illustrations by Gilles Cordonnier.
545. 23 f. red .. .. .. 45 20
546. 36 f. brown .. .. .. 65 45
547. 49 f. blue .. .. .. 90 55
DESIGNS: 23 f. Tiatiamona. 36 f. Patoa purahi. 49 f. Haehaa.

**207** Henry Nott and "Duff"

**1988.** Protestant Missionaries. Multicoloured.
548 80 f. Type **207** .. .. 1·40 90
549 90 f. Papeiha .. .. 1·60 1·00
550 100 f. Samuel Raapoto .. 1·75 1·10

**208** Papeete Post Office, 1875

**1989.** Taihitian Postal History.
551 **208** 30 f. brown, green & bl 55 35
552 – 40 f. brown, green & bl 65 45
DESIGN: 40 f. Papeete Post Office, 1915.

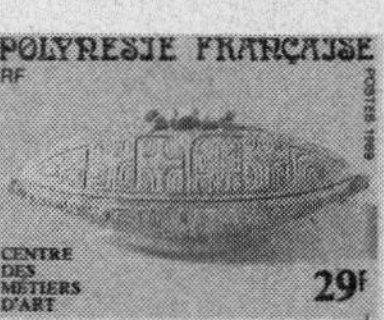

**209** Bowl with Wooden Cover, Marquesas Islands

**1989.** 8th Anniv of Arts and Crafts Centre. Multicoloured.
553 29 f. Type **209** .. .. 55 35
554 31 f. Mother-of-pearl pendant, Marquesas Islands .. .. .. 55 35

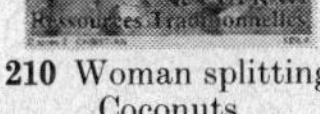

**210** Woman splitting Coconuts — **211** Wooden Statue with Tapa Covering

**1989.** Copra Production. Multicoloured.
555 55 f. Type **210** .. .. 45·00
556 70 f. Drying copra (horiz) 1·25 90

**1989.** Tapa (bark of paper-mulberry tree) Decorations. Multicoloured.
557 43 f. Type **211** .. .. 80 55
558 51 f. Fern leaf decoration, Society Islands (horiz) 90 55
559 56 f. Concentric circles decoration, Austral Islands (horiz) .. .. 1·00 65

**212** Woman playing Ukulele — **213** Lifting Stone

**1989.** Polynesian Environment. Mult.
560 120 f. Type **212** .. .. 2·10 1·40
561 140 f. Diver collecting marlin-spike auger shells 2·40 1·60

**1989.** Polynesian Folklore. July Festivals. Multicoloured.
562 47 f. Type **213** .. .. 90 55
563 61 f. Dancer .. .. 1·10 65
564 67 f. Group of singers (horiz) .. .. .. 1·25 80

**214** "Mutineers casting Bligh adrift" (detail, Robert Dodd)

**1989.** Bicentenaries of French Revolution and Mutiny on the "Bounty".
565 **214** 100 f. deep blue, blue and green .. 1·75 1·25

**215** Fr. O'Reilly

**1989.** 1st Death Anniv of Father Patrick O'Reilly (founder of Gauguin Museum).
567 **215** 52 f. green & brown .. 90 55

**216** "Get Well Soon"

**1989.** Greetings Stamps. Multicoloured.
568 42 f. Type **216** .. .. 1·25 90
569 42 f. Horseshoe ("Good Luck") .. .. 1·25 90
570 42 f. Cake ("Happy Anniversary") .. .. 1·25 90
571 42 f. Letters and telephone ("In Touch") .. 1·25 90
572 42 f. Presents ("Congratulations") .. 1·25 90

**1989.** Sea Shells (2nd series). As T **206**. Mult.
573 60 f. "Triphoridae" .. 1·00 65
574 69 f. "Favartia" .. .. 1·10 80
575 73 f. Checkerboard engina and grape drupe .. 1·25 80

**217** "Te Faaturuma" (Paul Gauguin) — **218** "Legend of Maui: Birth of the Islands"

**1989.**
576 **217** 1000 f. multicoloured 16·00 12·00

**1989.** Polynesian Legends (1st series). Mult.
577 66 f. Type **218** .. .. 1·10 65
578 82 f. "Legend of the Pierced Mountain" (horiz) .. .. .. 1·40 85
579 88 f. "Legend of Hina, the Eel from Lake Vaihiria" 1·40 90
See also Nos. 599/601.

**219** Flower — **220** Spotted Flagtail

**1990.** Traditional Resources. Vanilla. Mult.
580 34 f. Type **219** .. .. 60 35
581 35 f. Pods .. .. 60 35

**1990.** Fresh Water Animals. Multicoloured.
582 40 f. Type **220** .. .. 70 45
583 50 f. Shrimp .. .. 85 55

**221** Sandwich Islands Man and Hawaiian Islands

**1990.** Maori World (1st series).
584 **221** 58 f. black .. .. 90 55
585 – 59 f. blue .. .. 12·00 9·00
586 – 63 f. green .. .. 90 55
587 – 71 f. blue .. .. 1·00 65
DESIGNS: 59 f. Easter Island man and map; 63 f. New Zealand man and map; 71 f. Octopus and Tahiti.
See also Nos. 610/12 and 644/6.

**222** Old Town Hall

**1990.** Centenary of Township of Papeete. Multicoloured.
588 150 f. Type **222** .. .. 2·25 1·40
589 250 f. New Town Hall .. 4·25 2·40

**223** Sooty Crake — **224** Young People reading

**1990.** Birds. Multicoloured.
590 13 f. Type **223** .. .. 40 20
591 20 f. Ultramarine lory .. 50 30

**1990.** 30th Anniv of Papeete Lions Club.
592 **224** 39 f. multicoloured .. 65 45

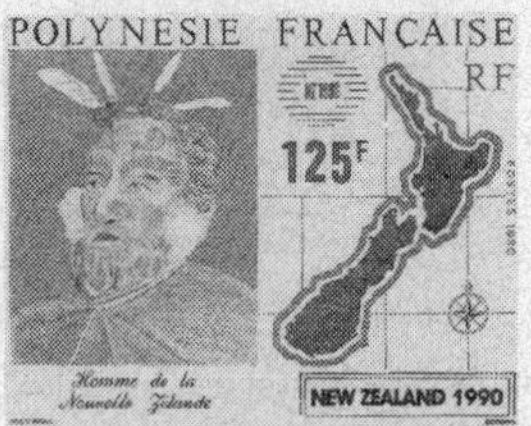


**225** New Zealand Man and Map

**1990.** "New Zealand 1990" International Stamp Exhibition, Auckland.
593 **225** 125 f. blue, green & pur 2·25 1·40

**226** De Gaulle and Globe

**1990.** Birth Centenary of Charles de Gaulle (French statesman).
595 **226** 200 f. blue, brown & red 3·25 2·25

**227** Girls in Pareos — **228** Girl wearing Tiare Headdress

**1990.** World Tourism Day.
596 **227** 8 f. multicoloured .. 15 10
597 – 10 f. multicoloured .. 15 10
598 – 12 f. multicoloured .. 20 15
DESIGNS: 10, 12 f. Girls in pareos (different).

**1990.** Polynesian Legends (2nd series). As T **218**. Multicoloured.
599 170 f. "Legend of Uru" (horiz) .. .. .. 2·75 1·90
600 290 f. "Legend of Pipiri-Ma" .. .. .. 4·50 2·50
601 375 f. "Legend of Hiro, God of Thieves" .. 6·00 4·00

**1990.** Tiare Flower. Multicoloured.
602 28 f. Type **228** .. .. 50 35
603 30 f. Tiare bush .. .. 50 35
604 37 f. Girl wearing flower over ear and lei .. 65 35

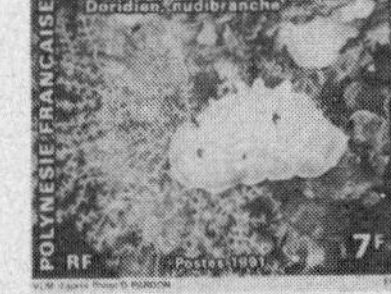

**229** Pineapple Plants — **230** Doridian Nudibranch

**1991.** Traditional Resources. The Pineapple. Multicoloured. Self-adhesive. Backing paper perf.
605 42 f. Type **229** .. .. 65 45
606 44 f. Plantation .. .. 65 45

**1991.** Undersea Wonders. Multicoloured.
607 7 f. Type **230** .. .. 15 10
608 9 f. "Galaxaura tenera" (red alga) .. .. 15 10
609 11 f. Cuming's cowrie .. 20 15

**1991.** Maori World (2nd series). As T **221** showing 18th-century engravings.
610 68 f. green .. .. 17·00
611 84 f. black .. .. 1·50 85
612 94 f. brown .. .. 1·75 1·25
DESIGNS—VERT. 68 f. Woman, child and statues, Easter Island. HORIZ. 84 f. Sandwich Islands pirogue race; 94 f. Maori village, New Zealand.

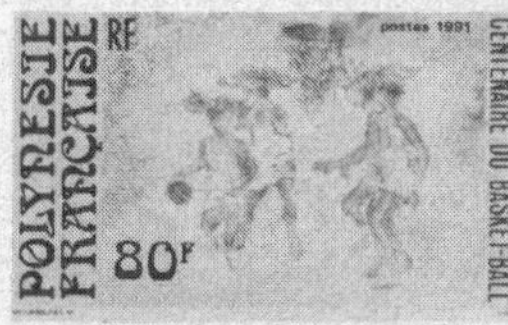


**231** Basketball Players

**1991.** Centenary of Basketball.
613 **231** 80 f. multicoloured .. 1·25 70

**232** Tuamotu Kingfisher — **234** "Tuava"

**233** "Oranges of Tahiti" (Gauguin)

**1991.** Protected Birds. Multicoloured.
614 17 f. Type **232** .. .. 70 20
615 21 f. Kuhl's lory .. 80 45

**1991.** Centenary of Paul Gauguin's Arrival in Tahiti.
616 **233** 700 f. multicoloured .. 12·00 5·50

**1991.** Marquesas Islands Sculptures. Mult.
617 56 f. Type **234** .. .. 90 45
618 102 f. "Te Hina o Motu Haka" .. .. 1·60 90
619 110 f. "Kooka" (horiz) .. 1·75 1·00

**235** Pianist's Hands, Conductor and Orchestra

**1991.** Death Bicentenary of Wolfgang Amadeus Mozart (composer).
620 **235** 100 f. multicoloured .. 1·60 90

236 Fishing Canoes

**1991.** Stone Fishing. Multicoloured.

| | | | |
|---|---|---|---|
| 621 | 25 f. Type **236** .. .. | 45 | 25 |
| 622 | 57 f. Fisherman swinging stone (used to beat the water) .. .. .. | 85 | 55 |
| 623 | 62 f. Fish in entrapment area (horiz) .. .. | 1·00 | 60 |

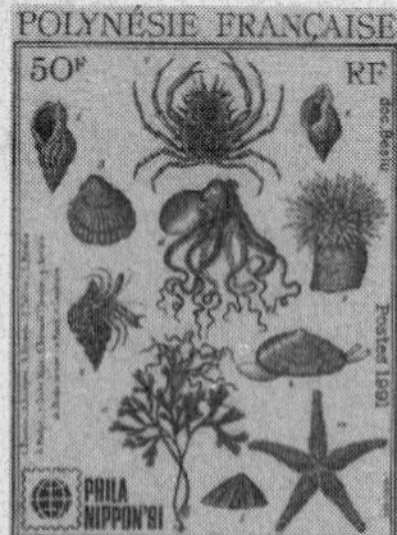
237 Sketches of Shells and Marine Life by Rene Lesson

**1991.** "Phila Nippon '91" International Stamp Exhibition, Tokyo.

| | | | | |
|---|---|---|---|---|
| 624 | **237** | 50 f. brown, red & vio | 80 | 45 |
| 625 | – | 70 f. blue, red & green | 1·25 | 75 |

DESIGN—HORIZ. 70 f. "View of Venus Point at Matavae, Tahiti".

238 Financed Projects

**1991.** 50th Anniv of Central Economic Co-operation Bank.

| | | | | |
|---|---|---|---|---|
| 627 | **238** | 307 f. multicoloured .. | 5·00 | 2·75 |

239 Father Christmas

**1991.** "Christmas under the Sea". Mult.

| | | | |
|---|---|---|---|
| 628 | 55 f. Type **239** .. .. | 90 | 45 |
| 629 | 83 f. Corals decorated with baubles .. .. | 1·40 | 80 |
| 630 | 86 f. Crib among corals (vert) .. .. .. | 1·40 | 90 |

240 Setting Nets along Shore

**1992.** Tourist Activities. Multicoloured.

| | | | |
|---|---|---|---|
| 631 | 1 f. Type **240** .. .. | 10 | 10 |
| 632 | 2 f. Horse riding along beach .. .. .. | 10 | 10 |
| 633 | 3 f. Woman holding sailfish | 10 | 10 |
| 634 | 4 f. Exploring waterfall (vert) .. .. .. | 10 | 10 |
| 635 | 5 f. Yachting .. .. | 15 | 10 |
| 636 | 6 f. Sikorsky S-61N helicopter flight to waterfall (vert) .. | 15 | 10 |

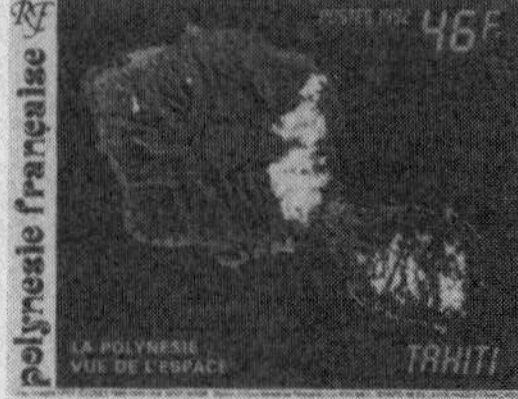
241 Tahiti

**1992.** "SPOT" Satellite Pictures of French Polynesia. Multicoloured.

| | | | |
|---|---|---|---|
| 637 | 46 f. Type **241** .. .. | 70 | 45 |
| 638 | 72 f. Mataiva .. .. | 90 | 60 |
| 639 | 76 f. Bora-Bora .. .. | 95 | 65 |

242 "Orange Carriers" (L. Taerea)

**1992.** World Health Day. "Health in Rhythm with the Heart".

| | | | | |
|---|---|---|---|---|
| 641 | **242** | 136 f. multicoloured .. | 1·75 | 1·25 |

243 Sailor asking for Directions

**1992.** "World Columbian Stamp Expo '92" Exhibition, Chicago.

| | | | | |
|---|---|---|---|---|
| 642 | **243** | 130 f. multicoloured .. | 2·25 | 1·40 |

244 Dancers, Tahiti

**1992.** Maori World (3rd series). Traditional Dances.

| | | | | |
|---|---|---|---|---|
| 644 | **244** | 95 f. brown .. .. | 1·25 | 85 |
| 645 | – | 105 f. brown .. .. | 1·40 | 95 |
| 646 | – | 115 f. green, brn & choc | 1·50 | 1·00 |

DESIGNS: 105 f. Hawaiian dancers; 115 f. Night Dance by Tongan women.

245 Tattooed Hand

**1992.** Tattoos. Multicoloured.

| | | | |
|---|---|---|---|
| 647 | 61 f. Type **245** .. .. | 85 | 55 |
| 648 | 64 f. Tattooed man (vert) | 90 | 60 |

246 Sailing Model Outrigger Canoes

247 Melville and Books

**1992.** Children's Pastimes. Multicoloured.

| | | | |
|---|---|---|---|
| 649 | 22 f. Type **246** .. .. | 45 | 25 |
| 650 | 31 f. String game .. .. | 50 | 35 |
| 651 | 45 f. Stilt walking (vert) .. | 65 | 45 |

**1992.** Writers of the South Seas. 150th Anniv of Arrival in Polynesia of Herman Melville (novelist).

| | | | | |
|---|---|---|---|---|
| 652 | **247** | 78 f. multicoloured .. | 1·50 | 85 |

248 Raft, Gambier Islands

**1992.** 6th Pacific Arts Festival, Rarotonga, Cook Islands.

| | | | | |
|---|---|---|---|---|
| 653 | **248** | 40 f. red .. .. | 70 | 45 |
| 654 | – | 65 f. ultramarine .. | 1·10 | 80 |

DESIGN: 65 f. Pirogues off Taihiti.

249 Arrival of Mail at Cercle Bougainville Post Office, Papeete

**1992.** Centenary of First French Oceanic Settlements Stamp.

| | | | | |
|---|---|---|---|---|
| 655 | **249** | 200 f. multicoloured .. | 2·50 | 1·75 |

250 "Fare Tamarii" (Erhard Lux)

252 Cast-net Fisherman

**1992.** Artists in Polynesia. Multicoloured.

| | | | |
|---|---|---|---|
| 656 | 55 f. Type **250** .. .. | 70 | 45 |
| 657 | 60 f. "Symphonie de Monettes" (Uschi) .. | 75 | 50 |
| 658 | 75 f. "Spear Fisherman" (Pierre Kienlen) .. | 95 | 65 |
| 659 | 85 f. "Maternity" (Octave Morillot) .. .. | 1·10 | 75 |

**1993.** Fishing in Couleur Lagoon. Self-adhesive. Imperf. (a) Size 26 × 36 mm.

| | | | | |
|---|---|---|---|---|
| 670 | **252** | 46 f. multicoloured .. | 60 | 40 |

(b) Size 17 × 23 mm.

| | | | | |
|---|---|---|---|---|
| 671 | **252** | 46 f. multicoloured .. | 60 | 40 |

253 Hanging Bonito on Rack

**1993.** Bonito Fishing. Multicoloured.

| | | | |
|---|---|---|---|
| 672 | 68 f. Bone hook and line .. | 85 | 55 |
| 673 | 84 f. Fishing launch (horiz) | 1·00 | 65 |
| 674 | 86 f. Type **253** .. .. | 1·10 | 75 |

254 U.S. Flag, Pilot and Airstrip

**1993.** 50th Anniv of Bora-Bora Airfield.

| | | | | |
|---|---|---|---|---|
| 675 | **254** | 120 f. multicoloured .. | 1·50 | 1·00 |

255 "Pahi Moorea"

**1993.** Birth Centenary of Jacques Boullaire (artist).

| | | | | |
|---|---|---|---|---|
| 676 | **255** | 32 f. brown .. .. | 40 | 25 |
| 677 | – | 36 f. orange .. .. | 45 | 30 |
| 678 | – | 39 f. violet .. .. | 50 | 35 |
| 679 | – | 51 f. brown .. .. | 65 | 45 |

DESIGNS: 36 f. "Pahi Tuamoto"; 39 f. "Pahi Rurutu"; 51 f. "Pahi Nuku-hiva".

256 Sportsman 257 Contestant

**1993.** Sports Festival.

| | | | | |
|---|---|---|---|---|
| 680 | **256** | 30 f. multicoloured .. | 40 | 25 |

**1993.** 15th Anniv of Australian Mathematics Competition.

| | | | | |
|---|---|---|---|---|
| 681 | **257** | 70 f. multicoloured .. | 90 | 60 |

258 Pele, Goddess of Volcanoes

259 Red Junglefowl crowing

**1993.** International Symposium on Intra-plate Volcanism, Punaauia (Tahiti).

| | | | | |
|---|---|---|---|---|
| 682 | **258** | 140 f. pink, brn & blk | 1·75 | 1·10 |

**1993.** "Taipei 93" International Stamp Exhibition, Taipeh.

| | | | | |
|---|---|---|---|---|
| 683 | **259** | 46 f. multicoloured .. | 60 | 40 |

260 Sight-seeing Canoe Trip

**1993.** International Tourism Day. Mult.

| | | | |
|---|---|---|---|
| 684 | 14 f. Type **260** .. .. | 20 | 15 |
| 685 | 20 f. Tahitian women decorating tourist (vert) | 25 | 15 |
| 686 | 29 f. Beach picnic .. | 40 | 25 |

261 Municipal Guard of 1843 and Modern Gendarme

**1993.** 150th Anniv of Arrival of First Gendarme in Tahiti.

| | | | | |
|---|---|---|---|---|
| 687 | **261** | 100 f. multicoloured .. | 1·40 | 95 |

262 Gerbault and "Firecrest"

**1993.** Birth Centenary of Alain Gerbault (round the world sailor).
688 **262** 150 f. blue, red & green .. 2·00 1·40

263 Woman Dancing to Guitar Music (Vaea Sylvain)

**1993.** Artists in Polynesia. Multicoloured.
689 40 f. Type **263** .. .. 50 35
690 70 f. Portrait of Polynesian woman (Andre Marere) (vert) .. .. .. 90 60
691 80 f. Four generations of women (Jean Shelsher) 1·00 65
692 90 f. Woman in hat (Paul-Emile Victor) (vert) .. 1·25 85

264 Relief (Vahineroo Terupe)

**1993.** 30th Anniv of French Pacific School.
693 **264** 200 f. multicoloured .. 2·60 1·75

265 Spinner Dolphins

**1994.** Marine Mammals. Multicoloured.
694 25 f. Spinner dolphin .. 30 20
695 68 f. Type **265** .. .. 90 60
696 72 f. Humpback whales (vert) .. .. .. 95 65

266 Spaniel

267 Sister Germaine Bruel and Child

**1994.** "Hong Kong '94" Int Stamp Exn.
697 **266** 51 f. multicoloured .. 65 45

**1994.** 150th Anniv of Arrival of Sisters of St. Joseph of Cluny Congregation.
698 **267** 180 f. multicoloured .. 2·40 1·60

268 Tahiti Temple

**1994.** 150th Anniv of Arrival in Polynesia of Church of Jesus Christ of Latter Day Saints.
699 **268** 154 f. multicoloured .. 2·00 1·40

269 Father Gregoire (founder) and Polynesians

**1994.** Bicentenary of National Conservatory of Arts and Crafts, Paris, and 15th Anniv of Papeete Regional Associated Centre.
700 **269** 316 f. multicoloured .. 4·25 2·90

270 Emblem and Polynesians

**1994.** 10th Anniv of Internal Autonomy.
701 **270** 500 f. multicoloured .. 6·50 4·50

271 "Fare Vana'a"

**1994.** 20th Anniv of Tahiti Academy.
702 **271** 136 f. black, red & blue 1·90 1·25

272 Papara

**1994.** Tahiti in Olden Days (4th series). Mult.
703 22 f. Type **272** .. .. 30 20
704 26 f. Mataiea coast .. 35 25
705 51 f. Bamboo forest, Taravao (vert) .. .. 65 45

273 "Faaturuma" (Paul Gauguin)

**1994.**
706 **273** 1000 f. multicoloured .. . 14·50 9·75

274 "Epiphyllum oxipetalum"

**1994.** Beauty of the Night (cactus).
707 **274** 51 f. multicoloured .. 75 50

275 Bow of Pirogue No. 27

**1994.** "Hawaiki Nui Va'a 94" Pirogue Race. Multicoloured.
708 52 f. Type **275** .. .. 75 50
709 76 f. Pirogue (detail) .. 1·10 75
710 80 f. Pirogue (different detail) .. .. 1·10 75
711 94 f. Stern of pirogue and pirogue No. 60 .. .. 1·40 95

Nos. 708/11 were issued together, se-tenant, forming a composite design.

276 Portrait by Michelle Villemin

**1994.** Artists in Polynesia. Paintings by artists named. Multicoloured.
712 62 f. Type **276** .. .. 90 60
713 78 f. Michele Dallet .. 1·10 75
714 102 f. Johel Blanchard .. 1·40 95
715 110 f. P. Lacouture (horiz) 1·60 1·10

277 Don Domingo de Boenechea and Frigate

**1995.** 220th Anniv of Spanish Expeditions to Tautira.
716 **277** 92 f. multicoloured .. 1·25 85

278 Girls in Pareos

280 Emblem

279 Pigs

**1995.** Tourism.
717 **278** 92 f. multicoloured .. 1·25 85

**1995.** Chinese New Year. Year of the Pig.
718 **279** 51 f. multicoloured .. 75 50

**1995.** Pacific University Teachers' Training Institute.
719 **280** 59 f. multicoloured .. 85 55

281 Head of Green Turtle

**1995.** Protected Species. Multicoloured.
720 22 f. Type **281** .. .. 30 20
721 29 f. Green turtle .. 40 25
722 91 f. Black coral .. .. 1·25 85

282 Pasteur

**1995.** Death Centenary of Louis Pasteur (chemist).
723 **282** 290 f. blue and lt blue 4·25 2·75

283 Scene from Novel

**1995.** 113th Anniv of Publication of "Le Mariage de Loti" by Pierre Loti.
724 **283** 66 f. multicoloured .. 95 65

284 Woman with bowl of Monoi

285 Rapa Island Fruit Dove

**1995.** Tahiti Monoi (blend of coconut oil and tiare flower).
725 **284** 150 f. multicoloured .. 2·10 1·40

**1995.** "Unique Birds of the World". Mult.
726 22 f. Type **285** .. .. 30 20
727 44 f. Marquesas pigeon .. 65 45

286 Black Pearls

**1995.** Tahitian Pearls. Multicoloured.
728 66 f. Type **286** .. .. 95 65
729 84 f. Coloured pearls .. 1·25 85

287 Alvaro de Mendana de Neira and Galleon

**1995.** 400th Anniv of Discovery of Marquesas Islands. Multicoloured.
730 161 f. Type **287** .. .. 2·25 1·50
731 195 f. Pedro Fernandez de Quiros and map of islands .. .. .. 2·75 1·90

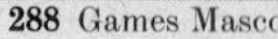

288 Games Mascot

289 Pandanus Tree

**1995.** 10th South Pacific Games, Tahiti.

| | | | | |
|---|---|---|---|---|
| 732 | **288** | 83 f. multicoloured .. | 1·25 | 85 |

**1995.** "Singapore'95" International Stamp Exhibition. Multicoloured.

| | | | |
|---|---|---|---|
| 733 | 91 f. Type **289** .. .. | 1·25 | 85 |
| 734 | 91 f. Pandanus (flower) .. | 1·25 | 85 |
| 735 | 91 f. Pandanus (fruit) .. | 1·25 | 85 |
| 736 | 91 f. Plaiting leaves .. | 1·25 | 85 |

290 Man and Woman wearing Headdresses and Emblem

**1995.** 50th Anniv of U.N.O.

| | | | | |
|---|---|---|---|---|
| 737 | **290** | 420 f. multicoloured .. | 5·50 | 3·75 |

291 "Oarsman with Yellow Dog" (Philippe Dubois)

**1996.** Artists in Polynesia. Multicoloured.

| | | | |
|---|---|---|---|
| 738 | 57 f. Type **291** .. .. | 75 | 50 |
| 739 | 76 f. "Afternoon in Vaitape" (Maui Seaman) | 1·00 | 65 |
| 740 | 79 f. "Woman with White Hat" (Simone Testeguide) (horiz) .. | 1·10 | 75 |
| 741 | 100 f. "Kellum House in Moorea" (Christian Deloffre) (horiz) .. | 1·40 | 95 |

**1996.** Tahiti in Olden Days (5th series). As T **272**. Multicoloured.

| | | | |
|---|---|---|---|
| 742 | 18 f. La Fautana .. .. | 25 | 15 |
| 743 | 30 f. Punaauia Grove .. | 40 | 25 |
| 744 | 35 f. Coconut palm forest, Tautira .. .. | 45 | 30 |

292 Rats

293 Queen Pomare

**1996.** Chinese New Year. Year of the Rat.

| | | | | |
|---|---|---|---|---|
| 745 | **292** | 51 f. multicoloured .. | 70 | 45 |

**1996.** No value expressed. (a) Size 26 × 36 mm.

| | | | | |
|---|---|---|---|---|
| 746 | **293** | (51 f.) multicoloured .. | 70 | 45 |

(b) Size 12 × 23 mm. Self-adhesive.

| | | | | |
|---|---|---|---|---|
| 747 | **293** | (51 f.) multicoloured .. | 70 | 45 |

294 Victor and Hemispheres

**1996.** Paul-Emile Victor (polar explorer) Commemoration.

| | | | | |
|---|---|---|---|---|
| 748 | **294** | 500 f. multicoloured .. | 6·75 | 4·50 |

295 Pertusus Cone

**1996.** Sea Shells. Multicoloured.

| | | | |
|---|---|---|---|
| 749 | 10 f. Type **295** .. .. | 15 | 10 |
| 750 | 15 f. "Cypraea alisonae" (cowrie) .. .. | 20 | 15 |
| 751 | 25 f. "Vexillum roseo-tinctum" (ribbed mitre) | 35 | 25 |

296 Badge, Soldiers and Troopship

**1996.** 50th Anniv of Return of Pacific Battalion from Second World War.

| | | | | |
|---|---|---|---|---|
| 752 | **296** | 100 f. multicoloured .. | 1·40 | 95 |

297 Dancers

**1996.** "China'96" Int Stamp Exn, Peking.

| | | | | |
|---|---|---|---|---|
| 753 | **297** | 50 f. multicoloured .. | 65 | 45 |

298 Red-footed Booby

**1996.** Marine Birds. Multicoloured.

| | | | |
|---|---|---|---|
| 755 | 66 f. Type **298** .. .. | 90 | 60 |
| 756 | 79 f. Great frigate bird .. | 1·10 | 75 |
| 757 | 84 f. Common noddy .. | 1·10 | 75 |

299 Pahu, Ukulele and Toere

**1996.** Musical Instruments. Multicoloured.

| | | | |
|---|---|---|---|
| 758 | 5 f. Type **299** .. .. | 10 | 10 |
| 759 | 9 f. Toere .. .. | 10 | 10 |
| 760 | 14 f. Pu and vivo (wind instruments) .. | 20 | 15 |

300 Polynesian Cicada

**1996.**

| | | | | |
|---|---|---|---|---|
| 761 | **300** | 66 f. multicoloured .. | 90 | 60 |

301 Ruahatu, God of the Ocean

302 Lemasson's 1913 Tahitian Girl Stamp Design

**1996.** 7th Pacific Arts Festival.

| | | | | |
|---|---|---|---|---|
| 762 | **301** | 70 f. black and blue .. | 95 | 65 |

**1996.** Stamp Day. 40th Death Anniv of Henri Lemasson (photographer and stamp designer).

| | | | | |
|---|---|---|---|---|
| 763 | **302** | 92 f. multicoloured .. | 1·25 | 85 |

OFFICAL STAMPS

O 100. Uru.

O 251 1840 French Colonies 40 c. Stamps

**1977.** Native Fruits.

| | | | | |
|---|---|---|---|---|
| O 240. | O **100.** | 1 f. multicoloured | 10 | 10 |
| O 241. | | 2 f. multicoloured | 10 | 10 |
| O 242. | | 3 f. multicoloured | 10 | 10 |
| O 243. | | 5 f. multicoloured | 10 | 10 |
| O 244. | – | 7 f. multicoloured | 35 | 20 |
| O 245. | – | 8 f. multicoloured | 35 | 20 |
| O 246. | – | 10 f. multicoloured | 45 | 35 |
| O 247. | – | 15 f. multicoloured | 55 | 45 |
| O 248. | – | 19 f. multicoloured | 65 | 55 |
| O 249. | – | 20 f. multicoloured | 75 | 65 |
| O 250. | – | 25 f. multicoloured | 1·25 | 1·10 |
| O 251. | – | 35 f. multicoloured | 1·50 | 1·40 |
| O 252. | – | 50 f. multicoloured | 2·00 | 1·75 |
| O 253. | – | 100 f. multicoloured | 4·00 | 3·50 |
| O 254. | – | 200 f. multicoloured | 6·50 | 5·00 |

DESIGNS: 7 f., 8 f., 10 f., 15 f., **Vi Tahiti**. 19 f., 20 f., 25 f., 35 f., Avocat. 50 f., 100 f., 200 f., Vi Popaa.

**1993.**

| | | | | |
|---|---|---|---|---|
| O660 | O **251** | 1 f. red, brown and black .. | 10 | 10 |
| O661 | – | 2 f. multicoloured | 10 | 10 |
| O662 | – | 3 f. blk, red & yell | 10 | 10 |
| O663 | – | 5 f. blk, red & yell | 10 | 10 |
| O664 | – | 10 f. mult .. | 15 | 10 |
| O665 | – | 20 f. mult .. | 25 | 20 |
| O666 | – | 46 f. mult .. | 60 | 45 |
| O666a | – | 51 f. mult .. | 65 | 50 |
| O667 | – | 70 f. mult .. | 90 | 70 |
| O668 | – | 100 f. mult .. | 1·25 | 95 |
| O669 | – | 200 f. mult .. | 2·50 | 1·90 |

DESIGNS: 2 f. French Colonies 1877 Peace and Commerce 40 c. and 1872 Ceres 25 c. stamps; 3 f. French Colonies Peace and Commerce stamp with Papeete 1884 postmark; 5 f. 1884 Papeete postmark; 10 f. Oceanic Settlements 1892 5 c. stamp and 1894 postmark; 20 f. Oceanic Settlements 1892 10 and 15 c. stamps with Tahiti postmark; 46 f. Oceanic Settlements 1930 90 c. Kanakas stamps; 51 f. Oceanic Settlements 1942 5 and 10 f. Free French stamps with Vaitepaua postmark; 70 f. "Visit Tahiti" postmark; 100 f. Oceanic Settlements 1956 3 f. Dry dock stamp; 200 f. Oceanic Settlements 1953 14 f. Gauguin stamp.

POSTAGE DUE STAMPS

D 4 Polynesian Mask

D 164 Mother of Pearl Fish-hook

**1958.**

| | | | | |
|---|---|---|---|---|
| D 17 | D **4.** | 1 f. green and brown .. | 65 | 65 |
| D 18. | | 3 f. red and indigo .. | 75 | 75 |
| D 19. | | 5 f. blue and brown .. | 1·00 | 1·00 |

**1984.** Multicoloured.

| | | | |
|---|---|---|---|
| D416 | 1 f. Type D **164** .. | 10 | 10 |
| D417 | 3 f. Tahitian bowl (horiz) | 10 | 10 |
| D418 | 5 f. Marquesian fan (horiz) .. | 10 | 10 |
| D419 | 10 f. Lamp stand .. | 15 | 10 |
| D420 | 20 f. Wooden head-rest (horiz) .. | 35 | 20 |
| D421 | 50 f. Scoop (horiz) .. | 80 | 65 |

## FRENCH POST OFFICES IN CHINA Pt. 6

General issues for the French post offices in China, which were closed in 1922.

1894. 100 centimes = 1 franc.
1907. 100 cents = 1 piastre.

Stamps of Indo-China optd. **CHINE** are listed under Indo-Chinese Post Offices in China.

**1894.** Stamps of France optd **Chine**.

| | | | | |
|---|---|---|---|---|
| 1 | **10** | 5 c. green .. .. | 1·10 | 80 |
| 4 | | 10 c. black on lilac .. | 2·75 | 70 |
| 6 | | 15 c. blue .. .. | 3·50 | 1·10 |
| 8 | | 20 c. red on green .. | 2·75 | 1·25 |
| 9 | | 25 c. black on pink .. | 2·75 | 1·25 |
| 10 | | 30 c. brown .. .. | 2·75 | 1·75 |
| 11 | | 40 c. red on yellow .. | 3·75 | 2·00 |
| 12 | | 50 c. red .. .. | 8·75 | 2·50 |
| 14 | | 75 c. brown on orange .. | 50·00 | 30·00 |
| 15 | | 1 f. green .. .. | 6·00 | 1·90 |
| 16 | | 2 f. brown on blue .. | 22·00 | 13·50 |
| 17 | | 5 f. mauve on lilac .. | 45·00 | 30·00 |

**1900.** No. 15 surch **25**.

| | | | | |
|---|---|---|---|---|
| 18 | **10** | 25 on 1 f. green .. .. | 40·00 | 25·00 |

**1901.** No. 9 surch.

| | | | | |
|---|---|---|---|---|
| 19 | **10** | 2 c. on 25 c. blk on pink | £625 | £160 |
| 20 | | 4 c. on 25 c. blk on pink | £550 | £160 |
| 21 | | 6 c. on 25 c. blk on pink | £600 | £250 |
| 22 | | 16 c. on 25 c. blk on pink | £170 | £130 |

**1902.** "Blanc", "Mouchon" and "Merson" key-types inscr "CHINE".

| | | | | |
|---|---|---|---|---|
| 37a | A | 5 c. green .. .. | 90 | 75 |
| 38 | B | 10 c. red .. .. | 85 | 75 |
| 39 | | 15 c. red .. .. | 1·25 | 85 |
| 40 | | 20 c. brown .. .. | 2·50 | 2·75 |
| 41 | | 25 c. blue .. .. | 2·25 | 1·10 |
| 42 | | 30 c. mauve .. .. | 2·75 | 2·75 |
| 43 | C | 40 c. red and blue .. | 6·25 | 5·50 |
| 44 | | 50 c. brown and lilac .. | 8·25 | 6·00 |
| 45 | | 1 f. red and green .. | 11·50 | 6·00 |
| 46 | | 2 f. lilac and buff .. | 32·00 | 24·00 |
| 47 | | 5 f. blue and buff .. | 45·00 | 35·00 |

**1903.** No. 39 surch **5**.

| | | | | |
|---|---|---|---|---|
| 48 | B | 5 on 15 c. red .. .. | 8·25 | 4·50 |

**1907.** Stamps of 1902 surch with new value in French and Chinese.

| | | | | |
|---|---|---|---|---|
| 92 | A | 1 c. on 5 c. orange .. | 1·60 | 95 |
| 84 | | 2 c. on 5 c. green .. | 60 | 35 |
| 93 | B | 2 c. on 10 c. green .. | 2·75 | 2·50 |
| 94 | | 3 c. on 15 c. orange .. | 4·00 | 3·50 |
| 77 | | 4 c. on 10 c. red .. | 55 | 50 |
| 95 | | 4 c. on 20 c. brown .. | 5·50 | 4·00 |
| 96 | | 5 c. on 25 c. purple .. | 3·25 | 1·75 |
| 78 | | 6 c. on 15 c. red .. | 1·00 | 65 |
| 97 | | 6 c. on 30 c. red .. | 6·25 | 5·00 |
| 87 | | 8 c. on 20 c. brown .. | 95 | 45 |
| 80 | | 10 c. on 25 c. blue .. | 60 | 35 |
| 98 | | 10 c. on 50 c. blue .. | 6·75 | 5·00 |
| 81 | C | 20 c. on 50 c. brown and lilac .. .. .. | 1·50 | 90 |
| 89 | B | 20 c. on 50 c. blue .. | 32·00 | 23·00 |
| 99 | C | 20 c. on 1 f. red & green | 19·00 | 15·00 |
| 90 | | 40 c. on 1 f. red & green | 1·60 | 1·50 |
| 100 | | 40 c. on 2 f. red & green | 19·00 | 15·00 |
| 101 | | 1 pi. on 5 f. blue & buff | 95·00 | 95·00 |
| 83 | | 2 pi. on 5 f. blue & buff | 11·50 | 7·25 |
| 91 | | $2 on 5 f. blue and buff | £100 | 80·00 |

POSTAGE DUE STAMPS

**1901.** Postage Due stamps of France optd **Chine.**

| | | | | |
|---|---|---|---|---|
| D 23. | D **11.** | 5 c. blue .. .. | 2·25 | 1·50 |
| D 24. | | 10 c. brown .. | 4·00 | 3·00 |
| D 25. | | 15 c. green .. .. | 4·00 | 3·00 |
| D 26. | | 20 c. olive .. .. | 4·25 | 3·75 |
| D 27. | | 30 c. red .. .. | 7·50 | 6·00 |
| D 28. | | 50 c. red .. .. | 7·50 | 6·50 |

**1903.** Stamps of 1894 and 1902 optd **A PERCEVOIR**.

| | | | | |
|---|---|---|---|---|
| D58 | **10** | 5 c. green .. .. | £1100 | £225 |
| D62 | A | 5 c. green .. .. | £700 | £400 |
| D51 | **10** | 10 c. black on lilac .. | £4000 | £3500 |
| D63 | B | 10 c. red .. .. | £300 | 55·00 |
| D60 | **10** | 15 c. blue .. .. | £650 | 60·00 |
| D64 | B | 15 c. red .. .. | £400 | 65·00 |
| D53 | **10** | 30 c. brown .. .. | 60·00 | 60·00 |

**1911.** Postage Due stamps of France surch with new value in French and Chinese.

| | | | | |
|---|---|---|---|---|
| D 102. | D **11.** | 1 c. on 5 c. blue .. | 45·00 | 40·00 |
| D 92. | | 2 c. on 5 c. blue .. | 65 | 60 |
| D 103. | | 2 c. on 10 c. brown | 60·00 | 55·00 |
| D 93. | | 4 c. on 10 c. brown | 75 | 60 |
| D 104. | | 4 c. on 20 c. olive .. | 60·00 | 55·00 |
| D 94. | | 8 c. on 20 c. olive .. | 95 | 85 |
| D 105. | | 10 c. on 50 c. red .. | 60·00 | 55·00 |
| D 95. | | 20 c. on 50 c. red .. | 1·10 | 90 |

## MINIMUM PRICE

The minimum price quoted is 10p which represents a handling charge rather than a basis for valuing common stamps. For further notes about prices see introductory pages.

## FRENCH POST OFFICES IN CRETE Pt. 6

These offices were closed in 1914.
100 centimes = 1 franc.
25 centimes = 1 piastre.

**1902.** "Blanc", "Mouchon" and "Merson" key-types inscr. "CRETE".

| No. | Type | Description | Unused | Used |
|---|---|---|---|---|
| 1. | A. | 1 c. grey | 70 | 85 |
| 2. | | 2 c. red | 60 | 1·00 |
| 3. | | 3 c. red | 75 | 95 |
| 4. | | 4 c. brown | 80 | 1·00 |
| 5. | | 5 c. green | 80 | 80 |
| 6. | B. | 10 c. red | 1·10 | 1·00 |
| 7. | | 15 c. orange | 1·50 | 1·00 |
| 8. | | 20 c. red | 1·40 | 1·40 |
| 9. | | 25 c. blue | 2·00 | 1·75 |
| 10. | | 30 c. mauve | 3·25 | 3·00 |
| 11. | C. | 40 c. red and blue | 5·50 | 4·75 |
| 12. | | 50 c. brown and lavender | 8·00 | 7·50 |
| 13. | | 1 f. red and green | 11·50 | 11·50 |
| 14. | | 2 f. lilac and buff | 17·00 | 18·00 |
| 15. | | 5 f. blue and buff | 30·00 | 27·00 |

**1903.** Surch. in figures and words.

| No. | Type | Description | Unused | Used |
|---|---|---|---|---|
| 16. | B. | 1 pi. on 25 c. blue | 21·00 | 19·00 |
| 17. | C. | 2 pi. on 50 c. brown & lav. | 42·00 | 35·00 |
| 18. | | 4 pi. on 1 f. red and green | 65·00 | 60·00 |
| 19. | | 8 pi. on 2 f. lilac and buff | 75·00 | 70·00 |
| 20. | | 20 pi. on 5 f. blue and buff | £120 | £110 |

## FRENCH POST OFFICES IN MOROCCO Pt. 6

French Post Offices were first established in Morocco in 1862, using the stamps of France. For stamps used by French Post Offices in Tangier after 1912 see under that heading.

100 centimos = 1 peseta.

**1891.** Stamps of France surch in Spanish currency (centimos on equivalent centime values).

| No. | Type | Description | Unused | Used |
|---|---|---|---|---|
| 1 | 10 | 5 c. on 5 c. green | 4·50 | 50 |
| 5 | | 10 c. on 10 c. blk on lilac | 16·00 | 1·75 |
| 6 | | 20 c. on 20 c. red on grn | 20·00 | 3·00 |
| 7 | | 25 c. on 25 c. blk on pink | 14·50 | 60 |
| 8a | | 50 c. on 50 c. red | 55·00 | 9·00 |
| 10 | | 1 p. on 1 f. green | 50·00 | 38·00 |
| 11 | | 2 p. on 2 f. brown on bl | £150 | £150 |

**1893.** Postage Due stamps of France optd. **TIMBRE POSTE** and bar.

| No. | Type | Description | Unused | Used |
|---|---|---|---|---|
| 12. | D11. | 5 c. black | £1300 | £575 |
| 13. | | 10 c. black | £1100 | £350 |

**1902.** "Blanc", "Mouchon" and "Merson" key types inscr. "MAROC" and surch. in Spanish currency in figures and words.

| No. | Type | Description | Unused | Used |
|---|---|---|---|---|
| 14 | A | 1 c. on 1 c. grey | 40 | 20 |
| 15 | | 2 c. on 2 c. red | 40 | 25 |
| 16 | | 3 c. on 3 c. red | 35 | 35 |
| 17 | | 4 c. on 4 c. brown | 3·75 | 4·00 |
| 18a | | 5 c. on 5 c. green | 2·75 | 65 |
| 19 | B | 10 c. on 10 c. red | 1·75 | 25 |
| 20 | | 20 c. on 20 c. red | 12·00 | 1·50 |
| 21 | | 25 c. on 25 c. blue | 13·00 | 25 |
| 22 | | 35 c. on 35 c. lilac | 15·00 | 4·50 |
| 23 | C | 50 c. on 50 c. brn. & lilac | 18·00 | 1·75 |
| 24 | | 1 p. on 1 f. red and green | 50·00 | 35·00 |
| 25 | | 2 p. on 2 f. lilac & yellow | 60·00 | 40·00 |

**1903.** Postage Due stamps of 1896 optd **P. P.** in box.

| No. | Type | Description | Unused | Used |
|---|---|---|---|---|
| 26 | D 11 | 5 c. on 5 c. blue | £750 | |
| 27 | | 10 c. on 10 c. brown | £1500 | |

**1911.** Key-types surch with figure of value and Arabic word.

| No. | Type | Description | Unused | Used |
|---|---|---|---|---|
| 28. | A. | 1 c. on 1 c. grey | 15 | 20 |
| 29. | | 2 c. on 2 c. red | 15 | 20 |
| 30. | | 3 c. on 3 c. orange | 15 | 20 |
| 31. | | 5 c. on 5 c. green | 15 | 15 |
| 32. | B. | 10 c. on 10 c. red | 15 | 10 |
| 33. | | 15 c. on 15 c. orange | 1·00 | 2·00 |
| 34. | | 20 c. on 20 c. red | 70 | 2·00 |
| 35. | | 25 c. on 25 c. blue | 40 | 45 |
| 36. | | 35 c. on 35 c. lilac | 2·25 | 35 |
| 37. | C. | 40 c. on 40 c. red and blue | 3·00 | 3·00 |
| 38. | | 50 c. on 50 c. brn. & lilac | 8·50 | 2·50 |
| 39. | | 1 p. on 1 f. red and green | 2·50 | 5·00 |

POSTAGE DUE STAMPS

**1896.** Postage Due stamps of France surch. in Spanish currency in figures and words.

| No. | Type | Description | Unused | Used |
|---|---|---|---|---|
| D14 | D11 | 5 c. on 5 c. blue | 3·50 | 60 |
| D15 | | 10 c. on 10 c. brown | 5·25 | 50 |
| D16 | | 30 c. on 30 c. red | 13·50 | 5·00 |
| D17a | | 50 c. on 50 c. red | 13·50 | 3·50 |
| D18 | | 1 p. on 1 f. brown | £200 | £180 |

**1909.** Postage Due stamps of France surch in Spanish currency.

| No. | Type | Description | Unused | Used |
|---|---|---|---|---|
| D 28. | D19. | 1 c. on 1 c. olive | 30 | 90 |
| D 29. | | 10 c. on 10 c. violet | 20·00 | 16·00 |
| D 30. | | 30 c. on 30 c. bistre | 10·00 | 22·00 |
| D 31. | | 50 c. on 50 c. red | 35·00 | 35·00 |

**1911.** Postage Due stamps of France surch. with figure and Arabic word.

| No. | Type | Description | Unused | Used |
|---|---|---|---|---|
| D 40. | D11. | 5 c. on 5 c. blue | 40 | 1·75 |
| D 41. | | 10 c. on 10 c. brown | 1·50 | 6·25 |
| D 42. | | 50 c. on 50 c. purple | 2·00 | 8·25 |

**1911.** Postage Due stamps of France surch. in figures and Arabic.

| No. | Type | Description | Unused | Used |
|---|---|---|---|---|
| D 43. | D19. | 1 c. on 1 c. olive | 30 | 60 |
| D 44. | | 10 c. on 10 c. violet | 75 | 1·50 |
| D 45. | | 30 c. on 30 c. bistre | 85 | 2·50 |
| D 46. | | 50 c. on 50 c. red | 2·00 | 7·00 |

For later issues see **FRENCH MOROCCO.**

## FRENCH POST OFFICES IN TANGIER Pt. 6

By Franco-Spanish Treaty of 27 November 1912, Tangier was given a special status outside the protectorates. After the Tangier Convention of 1924 the zone was administered by an international commission. Tangier was occupied by Spain in 1940 and the French P.O's. closed in 1942.

100 centimes = 1 franc.

**1918.** "Blanc", "Mouchon" and "Merson" key-types of French Post Offices in Morocco optd **TANGER**.

| No. | Type | Description | Unused | Used |
|---|---|---|---|---|
| 1a | A | 1 c. grey | 20 | 35 |
| 2 | | 2 c. red | 20 | 35 |
| 3 | | 3 c. orange | 25 | 40 |
| 4 | | 5 c. green | 35 | 40 |
| 5 | | 5 c. orange | 60 | 55 |
| 6 | B | 10 c. red | 35 | 30 |
| 7 | | 10 c. green | 35 | 50 |
| 8 | | 15 c. orange | 65 | 50 |
| 9 | | 20 c. red | 85 | 1·00 |
| 10 | | 25 c. blue | 1·25 | 20 |
| 11 | | 30 c. red | 1·25 | 1·50 |
| 12 | | 35 c. lilac | 85 | 1·10 |
| 13 | C | 40 c. red and blue | 1·40 | 1·50 |
| 14 | | 50 c. brown and lilac | 8·00 | 8·50 |
| 15 | B | 50 c. blue | 8·00 | 5·25 |
| 16 | C | 1 f. red and green | 3·00 | 3·50 |
| 17 | | 2 f. red and green | 45·00 | 42·00 |
| 18 | | 5 f. blue and yellow | 38·00 | 40·00 |

**1928.** Air. Nos. 149/58 of French Morocco optd. **Tanger.**

| No. | Type | Description | Unused | Used |
|---|---|---|---|---|
| 30. | | 5 c. blue | 1·00 | 3·00 |
| 31. | | 25 c. orange | 1·00 | 3·00 |
| 32. | | 50 c. red | 1·00 | 3·00 |
| 33. | | 75 c. brown | 1·00 | 3·00 |
| 34. | | 80 c. green | 1·00 | 3·00 |
| 35. | | 1 f. orange | 1·00 | 3·00 |
| 36. | | 1 f. 50 blue | 1·00 | 3·00 |
| 37. | | 2 f. brown | 1·00 | 3·00 |
| 38. | | 3 f. purple | 3·00 | 4·50 |
| 39. | | 5 f. black | 1·00 | 3·00 |

POSTAGE DUE STAMPS

**1918.** Postage Due stamps of France optd. **TANGER.**

| No. | Type | Description | Unused | Used |
|---|---|---|---|---|
| D 19. | D11. | 1 c. black | 10 | 35 |
| D 20. | | 5 c. blue | 45 | 50 |
| D 21. | | 10 c. brown | 60 | 70 |
| D 22. | | 15 c. green | 60 | 2·00 |
| D 23. | | 20 c. olive | 1·50 | 2·75 |
| D 24. | | 30 c. red | 3·00 | 6·25 |
| D 25. | | 50 c. purple | 3·75 | 9·75 |

**1918.** Postage Due stamps of France optd. **TANGER.**

| No. | Type | Description | Unused | Used |
|---|---|---|---|---|
| D 26. | D19. | 1 c. olive | 60 | 75 |
| D 27. | | 10 c. violet | 60 | 70 |
| D 28. | | 20 c. bistre | 3·25 | 3·75 |
| D 29. | | 40 c. red | 7·75 | 9·00 |

## FRENCH POST OFFICES IN THE TURKISH EMPIRE Pt. 6

General issues for the French Post Offices in the Turkish Empire.

1885. 25 centimes = 1 piastre.
1921. 40 paras = 1 piastre.

**1885.** Stamps of France surch in figures and words.

| No. | Type | Description | Unused | Used |
|---|---|---|---|---|
| 1 | 10 | 1 pi. on 25 c. bistre on yellow | £300 | 6·50 |
| 4 | | 1 pi. on 25 c. blk on pink | 1·00 | 40 |
| 5 | | 2 pi. on 50 c. pink | 8·25 | 1·10 |
| 2 | | 3 pi. on 75 c. red | 13·50 | 5·50 |
| 3 | | 4 pi. on 1 f. green | 11·50 | 4·75 |
| 7 | | 8 pi. on 2 f. brown on blue | 22·00 | 12·50 |
| 8 | | 20 pi. on 5 f. mauve | 55·00 | 25·00 |

**1902.** "Blanc", "Mouchon" and "Merson" key-types inscr "LEVANT".

| No. | Type | Description | Unused | Used |
|---|---|---|---|---|
| 9 | A | 1 c. grey | 25 | 25 |
| 10 | | 2 c. purple | 40 | 30 |
| 11 | | 3 c. red | 25 | 40 |
| 12 | | 4 c. brown | 75 | 50 |
| 13a | | 5 c. green | 40 | 30 |
| 14 | B | 10 c. red | 50 | 20 |
| 15 | | 15 c. red | 95 | 60 |
| 16 | | 20 c. brown | 95 | 70 |
| 17 | | 30 c. lilac | 2·00 | 1·40 |
| 18 | C | 40 c. red and blue | 2·25 | 1·60 |

**1902.** Surch. in figures and words.

| No. | Type | Description | Unused | Used |
|---|---|---|---|---|
| 19. | B. | 1 pi. on 25 c. blue | 55 | 20 |
| 20. | C. | 2 pi. on 50 c. brn. & lav. | 1·40 | 40 |
| 21. | | 4 pi. on 1 f. red & green | 1·60 | 55 |
| 22. | | 8 pi. on 2 f. lilac & yellow | 10·00 | 5·50 |
| 23. | | 20 pi. on 5 f. blue & yell. | 3·50 | 1·75 |

**1905.** Surch. **1 Piastre Beyrouth.**

| No. | Type | Description | Unused | Used |
|---|---|---|---|---|
| 24. | B. | 1 pi. on 15 c. orange | £900 | £200 |

**1906.** For use in Ethiopia.

| No. | Type | Description | Unused | Used |
|---|---|---|---|---|
| 25. | A. | 25 c. blue | 30·00 | 22·00 |
| 26. | B. | 50 c. brown and lavender | £110 | £110 |
| 27. | | 1 f. red and green | £250 | £250 |

**1921.** Stamps of France surch. in figures and words.

| No. | Type | Description | Unused | Used |
|---|---|---|---|---|
| 28. | 18. | 30 par. on 5 c. green | 40 | 45 |
| 29. | | 30 par. on 5 c. orange | 45 | 45 |
| 30. | | 1 pi. 20 on 10 c. red | 40 | 45 |
| 31. | | 1 pi. 20 on 10 c. green | 45 | 25 |
| 39. | | 3 pi. 30 on 15 c. green | 12·50 | 12·50 |
| 32. | | 3 pi. 30 on 25 c. blue | 45 | 30 |
| 33. | | 4 pi. 20 on 30 c. orange | 45 | 40 |
| 40. | | 7 pi. 20 on 35 c. violet | 13·50 | 13·50 |
| 34. | 15. | 7 pi. 20 on 50 c. blue | 45 | 25 |
| 35. | 13. | 15 pi. on 1 f. red & green | 65 | 45 |
| 36. | | 30 pi. on 2 f. red & green | 6·50 | 4·25 |
| 37. | | 75 pi. on 5 f. blue & yell. | 4·25 | 2·50 |

For stamps issued by the Free French forces during 1942/3 see under **FREE FRENCH FORCES IN THE LEVANT.**

## FRENCH POST OFFICES IN ZANZIBAR Pt. 6

The French post office in Zanzibar operated from 1889 to 1904.

16 annas = 1 rupee.

Stamps of France surcharged.

**1894.** Surch. in figures and words.

| No. | Type | Description | Unused | Used |
|---|---|---|---|---|
| 1a | 10 | ½ a. on 5 c. green | 3·00 | 2·75 |
| 3 | | 1 a. on 10 c. black on lilac | 6·25 | 4·75 |
| 4 | | 1½ a. on 15 c. blue | 16·00 | 14·00 |
| 6 | | 2 a. on 20 c. red on green | 6·25 | 4·75 |
| 7 | | 2½ a. on 25 c. black on red | 5·25 | 3·25 |
| 8 | | 3 a. on 30 c. brown | 10·00 | 8·75 |
| 9 | | 4 a. on 40 c. red on yellow | 10·00 | 9·00 |
| 10 | | 5 a. on 50 c. red | 15·00 | 13·00 |
| 11 | | 7½ a. on 75 c. brn. on orge. | £250 | £200 |
| 12a | | 10 a. on 1 f. olive | 28·00 | 22·00 |
| 14 | | 50 a. on 5 f. mve. on lilac | £170 | £150 |

**1894.** Surch **Zanzibar** and value both in Indian currency (in figures and words) and in corresponding French currency (in figures only on Nos. 15/18).

| No. | Type | Description | Unused | Used |
|---|---|---|---|---|
| 15. | 10. | ½ a. & 5 on 1 c. blk. on bl. | £100 | £110 |
| 16. | | 1 a. & 10 on 3 c. grey | 90·00 | 95·00 |
| 17. | | 2½ a. and 25 on 4 c. lilac on grey | £120 | £130 |
| 18. | | 5 a. and 50 and 20 c. red on green | £120 | £130 |
| 19. | | 10 a. and 1 f. on 40 c. red on yellow | £225 | £225 |

**1896.** Surch **ZANZIBAR** and new value in Indian currency only.

| No. | Type | Description | Unused | Used |
|---|---|---|---|---|
| 20a | 10 | ½ a. on 5 c. green | 3·50 | 2·50 |
| 24 | | 1 a. on 10 c. black on lilac | 3·75 | 3·00 |
| 26 | | 1½ a. on 15 c. blue | 3·50 | 3·50 |
| 28 | | 2 a. on 20 c. red on green | 3·25 | 3·25 |
| 29 | | 2½ a. on 25 c. black on red | 5·00 | 3·50 |
| 30 | | 3 a. on 30 c. brown | 4·25 | 3·50 |
| 31 | | 4 a. on 40 c. red on yellow | 4·25 | 3·75 |
| 32 | | 5 a. on 50 c. red | 18·00 | 14·50 |
| 35 | | 10 a. on 1 f. olive | 10·00 | 7·00 |
| 37 | | 20 a. on 2 f. brown on blue | 13·50 | 8·25 |
| 38 | | 50 a. on 5 f. mve. on lilac | 35·00 | 23·00 |

**1897.** Nos. 1/4 and 8/9 further surch. with new figures of value in French and Indian currency and optd. **ZANZIBAR** vert.

| No. | Type | Description | Unused | Used |
|---|---|---|---|---|
| 42. | 10. | 2½ and 25 on ½ a. on 5 c. | £675 | 95·00 |
| 43. | | 2½ and 25 on 1 a. on 10 c. | £2250 | £525 |
| 44. | | 2½ and 25 on 1½ a. on 15 c. | £2250 | £400 |
| 45. | | 5 and 50 on 3 a. on 30 c. | £2250 | £375 |
| 46. | | 5 and 50 on 4 a. on 40 c. | £2250 | £500 |

PosteFrance ZANZIBAR
5
Annas
50c

4

**1897.**

| No. | Type | Description | Unused | Used |
|---|---|---|---|---|
| 47 | 4 | 2½ a. and 25 c. black on green and white | — | £600 |
| 48 | | 2½ a. and 25 c. black on lilac and white | — | £2000 |
| 49 | | 2½ a. and 25 c. black on blue and white | — | £1500 |
| 50 | | 5 a. and 50 c. black on buff and white | — | £1500 |
| 51 | | 5 a. and 50 c. black on yellow and white | — | £2000 |
| 52 | | 5 a. and 50 c. on white | — | £2000 |

**1902.** "Blanc", "Mouchon" and "Merson" key-types inscr. "ZANZIBAR" and surch. in figures and words.

| No. | Type | Description | Unused | Used |
|---|---|---|---|---|
| 53. | A. | ½ a. on 5 c. green | 2·25 | 1·90 |
| 54. | B. | 1 a. on 10 c. red | 3·25 | 3·00 |
| 55. | | 1½ a. on 15 c. orange | 6·50 | 6·00 |
| 56. | | 2 a. on 20 c. red | 9·00 | 7·25 |
| 57. | | 2½ a. on 25 c. blue | 8·75 | 7·25 |
| 58. | | 3 a. on 30 c. mauve | 6·00 | 5·00 |
| 59. | C. | 4 a. on 40 c. red and blue | 12·50 | 10·00 |
| 60. | | 5 a. on 50 c. brown & lav. | 10·00 | 7·75 |
| 61. | | 10 a. on 1 f. red and green | 16·00 | 13·00 |
| 62. | | 20 a. on 2 f. lilac & yellow | 35·00 | 30·00 |
| 63. | | 50 a. on 5 f. blue & yellow | 50·00 | 50·00 |

**1904.** Nos. 30/31 further surch with both currencies in figures on either side of bars.

| No. | Type | Description | Unused | Used |
|---|---|---|---|---|
| 65 | 10 | "25 c. 2½" on 4 a. on 40 c. | — | £525 |
| 66 | | "50 5" on 3 a. on 30 c. | — | £625 |
| 67 | | "50 5" on 4 a. on 40 c. | — | £625 |
| 68 | | "1 fr 10" on 3 a. on 30 c. | — | £1100 |
| 69 | | "1 fr 10" on 4 a. on 40 c. | — | £1100 |

**1904.** "Blanc" key-type surch. with both currencies in large figures.

| No. | Type | Description | Unused | Used |
|---|---|---|---|---|
| 70. | A. | "2 25" on ½ a. on 5 c. green (No. 53) | — | 65·00 |

**1904.** "Mouchon" key-type surch. with both currencies in figures or in figures and words.

| No. | Type | Description | Unused | Used |
|---|---|---|---|---|
| 71. | B. | "25 c 2½" on 1 a. on 10 c. red (No. 54) | — | 75·00 |
| 72. | | "25 c 2½" on 3 a. on 30 c. mauve (No. 58) | — | £1200 |
| 73. | | "50 c cinq" on 3 a. on 30 c. mauve (No. 58) | — | £625 |
| 74. | | "1 fr dix" on 3 a. on 30 c. mauve (No. 58) | — | £800 |

**1904.** Postage Due stamps optd.

(a) **Timbre**

| No. | Type | Description | Unused | Used |
|---|---|---|---|---|
| 75 | D 11 | ½ a. on 5 c. blue | — | £210 |

(b) **Affrancht.**

| No. | Type | Description | Unused | Used |
|---|---|---|---|---|
| 76 | D 11 | 1 a. on 10 c. brown | — | £210 |

(c) With red line at top and bottom obliterating words "CHIFFRE" and "TAXE".

| No. | Type | Description | Unused | Used |
|---|---|---|---|---|
| 77 | D 11 | 1½ a. on 15 c. green | — | £525 |

POSTAGE DUE STAMPS

**1897.** Postage Due stamps of France surch **ZANZIBAR** and value in figures and words

| No. | Type | Description | Unused | Used |
|---|---|---|---|---|
| D 39. | D 11. | ½ a. on 5 c. blue | 9·50 | 3·00 |
| D 40. | | 1 a. on 10 c. brown | 9·50 | 4·50 |
| D 41. | | 1½ a. on 15 c. green | 12·50 | 6·25 |
| D 42. | | 3 a. on 30 c. red | 15·00 | 12·50 |
| D 43. | | 5 a. on 50 c. purple | 14·50 | 12·00 |

## FRENCH SOMALI COAST Pt. 6

A French colony on the Gulf of Aden, E. coast of Africa. Renamed French Territory of the Afars and the Issas in 1967.

100 centimes = 1 franc.

23. Mosque at Tajurah.

24. Mounted Somalis. 25. Somali Warriors.

**1902.**

| No. | Type | Description | Unused | Used |
|---|---|---|---|---|
| 121 | 23 | 1 c. orange and purple | 40 | 45 |
| 137 | | 1 c. black and brown | 40 | 40 |
| 122 | | 2 c. green and brown | 40 | 40 |
| 138 | | 2 c. black and brown | 70 | 40 |
| 123 | | 4 c. red and blue | 40 | 90 |
| 139 | | 4 c. black and red | 85 | 50 |
| 124 | | 5 c. green & deep green | 1·50 | 85 |
| 140a | | 5 c. black and green | 2·25 | 55 |
| 125 | | 10 c. orange and red | 3·00 | 2·50 |
| 141a | | 10 c. black and red | 5·00 | 1·00 |
| 126 | | 15 c. blue and orange | 3·00 | 2·50 |
| 142 | | 15 c. black and brown | 10·00 | 8·50 |
| 127 | 24 | 20 c. green and lilac | 5·00 | 5·00 |
| 143 | | 20 c. black and lilac | 9·00 | 12·50 |
| 128 | | 25 c. blue | 10·00 | 9·00 |
| 129 | | 25 c. blue and indigo | 16·00 | 6·00 |
| 144 | | 25 c. black and blue | 3·75 | 3·75 |
| 130 | | 30 c. black and red | 4·25 | 4·00 |
| 131 | | 40 c. blue and yellow | 10·00 | 10·00 |
| 145 | | 40 c. black and orange | 4·50 | 4·50 |
| 132 | | 50 c. red and green | 35·00 | 30·00 |
| 146 | | 50 c. black and green | 10·00 | 9·00 |
| 133 | | 75 c. mauve and orange | 4·50 | 3·00 |
| 147 | | 75 c. black and brown | 6·00 | 7·00 |
| 134 | 25 | 1 f. purple and red | 12·00 | 12·00 |
| 148 | | 1 f. black and red | 7·50 | 9·75 |
| 135 | | 2 f. red and green | 22·00 | 20·00 |
| 149 | | 2 f. black and green | 4·50 | 5·50 |
| 136 | | 5 f. blue and orange | 16·00 | 14·00 |
| 150 | | 3 f. black and orange | 9·00 | 11·00 |

26. Mosque at Tajurah. 27. Mounted Somalis.

**1909.**

| No. | Type | Description | Unused | Used |
|---|---|---|---|---|
| 151 | 26 | 1 c. brown and purple | 20 | 20 |
| 152 | | 2 c. green and violet | 20 | 30 |
| 153 | | 4 c. blue and brown | 40 | 40 |
| 154 | | 5 c. olive and green | 65 | 30 |
| 155 | | 10 c. orange and red | 1·50 | 80 |
| 156 | | 20 c. brown and black | 2·75 | 3·25 |
| 157 | 27 | 25 c. blue and deep blue | 2·50 | 1·25 |
| 158 | | 30 c. red and brown | 3·00 | 4·00 |
| 159 | | 35 c. green and violet | 4·00 | 2·50 |
| 160 | | 40 c. violet and pink | 3·75 | 3·25 |
| 161 | | 45 c. green and brown | 5·00 | 3·50 |
| 162 | | 50 c. brown and purple | 4·50 | 4·50 |
| 163 | | 75 c. green and red | 7·00 | 7·75 |
| 164 | 25 | 1 f. brown and violet | 12·50 | 12·50 |
| 165 | | 2 f. pink and brown | 22·00 | 22·00 |
| 166 | | 5 f. green and brown | 42·00 | 30·00 |

**1915.** No. 172 surch **5c** and red cross.

| No. | Type | Description | Unused | Used |
|---|---|---|---|---|
| 167 | 29 | 10 c. + 5 c. red & carmine | 2·50 | 4·75 |

28. Drummer.

29. Somali Woman.

30. Railway Bridge at Holl-Holli.

**1915.**

168 28 1 c. brown and violet .. 10 25
169 2 c. blue and bistre .. 10 15
170 4 c. red and brown .. 10 35
171 5 c. green & light green 30 50
195 5 c. red and orange .. 10 40
172 29 10 c. red and carmine .. 40 45
196 10 c. green & light green 15 50
214 10 c. green and red .. 10 25
173 15 c. pink and lilac .. 40 40
174 20 c. brown and orange 15 30
215 20 c. light green & green 25 35
216 20 c. red and green .. 20 25
175 25 c. blue & ultramarine 45 40
197 25 c. green and black .. 30 20
176 30 c. green and black .. 65 60
198 30 c. brown and red .. 50 60
217 30 c. green and violet .. 10 25
218 30 c. olive and green .. 20 25
177 35 c. pink and green .. 25 40
178 40 c. lilac and blue .. 25 40
179 45 c. blue and brown .. 50 65
180 50 c. black and pink .. 6·25 4·25
199 50 c. blue & ultramarine 65 80
219 50 c. purple and brown 20 15
220 60 c. purple and green 20 30
221 65 c. green and red .. 40 15
181 75 c. brown and lilac .. 55 40
222 75 c. blue and deep blue 10 20
223 75 c. brown and mauve 75 1·25
224 85 c. green and purple 15 50
225 90 c. carmine and red .. 2·50 3·75
182 30 1 f. red and brown .. 75 50
226 1 f. 10 blue and brown 3·50 3·50
227 1 f. 25 brown and blue 5·75 5·50
228 1 f. 50 blue & light blue 1·00 60
229 1 f. 75 red and green .. 4·00 3·00
183 2 f. black and violet .. 2·00 1·25
230 3 f. mauve on pink .. 7·50 4·25
184 5 f. black and red .. 3·75 1·75

**1922.** Surch **1922** and value in figures in frame.
193 28 10 on 5 c. green & lt grn 30 50
194 29 50 on 25 c. bl & ultram 30 50

**1922.** Surch in figures.
200 29 0.01 on 15 c. pink and lilac .. .. .. 10 30
201 0.02 on 15 c. pink and lilac .. .. .. 10 30
202 0.04 on 15 c. pink and lilac .. .. .. 15 30
203 0.05 on 15 c. pink and lilac .. .. .. 10 25
204 30 25 c. on 5 f. black & red 40 55
205 29 60 on 75 c. violet & grn 15 30
206 65 on 15 c. pink and lilac 30 55
207 85 on 40 c. lilac and blue 40 70
208 90 on 75 c. red .. .. 50 2·00
209 30 1 f. 25 on 1 f. ultra-marine and blue .. 45 55
210 1 f. 50 on 1 f. bl & lt bl 60 70
211 3 f. on 5 f. mauve & red 2·25 2·50
212 10 f. on 5 f. brown & red 5·00 4·75
213 20 f. on 5 f. pink & green 7·75 7·50

**1931.** "Colonial Exhibition" key-types inscr. "COTE FR. DES SOMALIS".
233 E 40 c. green and black .. 3·00 3·00
234 F 50 c. mauve and black .. 3·00 3·25
235 G 90 c. red and black .. 3·00 3·25
236 H 1 f. 50 blue and black .. 3·00 3·25

**1937.** Int. Exn., Paris. As Nos. 110/15 of Cameroun.
237. 20 c. violet .. .. 50 75
238. 30 c. green .. .. 50 80
239. 40 c. red .. .. 40 75
240. 50 c. brown and blue .. 40 80
241. 90 c. red .. .. 50 1·00
242. 1 f. 50 blue .. .. 50 1·00

**1938.** Int. Anti-Cancer Fund. As T **19** of Cameroun.
244. 1 f. 75+50 c. blue .. 2·00 4·50

34. Mosque at Djibouti.

35. Somali Warriors.

37. Djibouti.

**1938.**

245 34 2 c. purple .. .. 10 25
246 3 c. green .. .. 10 25
247 4 c. brown .. .. 10 25
248 5 c. red .. .. 10 25
249 10 c. blue .. .. 10 25
250 15 c. black .. .. 10 25
251 20 c. red .. .. 25 40
252 35 25 c. brown .. .. 40 60
253 30 c. blue .. .. 25 45
254 35 c. green .. .. 50 60
255 34 40 c. brown .. .. 30 40
256 45 c. green .. .. 40 55
257 35 50 c. red .. .. 25 40
258 55 c. purple .. .. 55 70
259 60 c. black .. .. 40 70
260 65 c. brown .. .. 40 55
261 70 c. violet .. .. 90 1·10
262 – 80 c. black .. .. 1·00 1·25
263 35 90 c. mauve .. .. 1·00 1·25
264 – 1 f. red .. .. 1·10 1·25
265 – 1 f. black .. .. 40 60
266 – 1 f. 25 red .. .. 70 90
267 – 1 f. 40 blue .. .. 70 90
268 – 1 f. 50 green .. .. 55 75
269 – 1 f. 60 red .. .. 70 90
270 – 1 f. 75 blue .. .. 55 75
271 – 2 f. red .. .. 55 75
272 – 2 f. 25 blue .. .. 1·00 1·25
273 – 2 f. 50 brown .. .. 1·25 1·50
274 – 3 f. purple .. .. 70 90
275 37 5 f. brown & deep brown 90 1·25
276 10 f. light blue and blue 90 1·25
277 20 f. blue and red .. 95 1·60
DESIGN—VERT. 80 c. and 1 f. to 3 f. Governor L. Lagarde.

**1939.** New York World's Fair. As T **20** of Cameroun.
288. 1 f. 25 red .. .. 80 95
289. 2 f. 25 blue .. .. 80 95

**1939.** 150th Anniv of French Revolution. As T **25** of Cameroun.
290 45 c.+25 c. green & black 4·00 4·50
291 70 c.+30 c. brown & blk 4·00 4·50
292 90 c.+35 c. orange & blk 4·25 4·50
293 1 f. 25+1 f. red and black 5·50 5·50
294 2 f. 25+2 f. blue & black 6·00 6·25

**1941.** Air. Free French Issue. As T **32** of Cameroun, but inscr. " DJIBOUTI ".
295. 32. 1 f. orange .. .. 40 60
296. 1 f. 50 red .. .. 50 65
297. 5 f. purple .. .. 50 65
298. 10 f. black .. .. 75 90
299. 25 f. blue .. .. 90 1·40
300. 50 f. green .. .. 90 1·25
301. 100 f. red .. .. 1·25 1·75

**1942.** Optd or surch also **FRANCE LIBRE** or **France Libre**.
302 28 1 c. brown and violet .. 65 80
303 2 c. blue and bistre .. 85 1·00
304 34 2 c. purple .. .. 80 1·25
305 3 c. green .. .. 1·25 1·40
306 28 4 c. red and brown .. 15·00 16·00
307 34 4 c. brown .. .. 1·40 1·40
308 28 5 c. red and orange .. 85 95
309 34 5 c. red .. .. 1·25 1·40
310 10 c. blue .. .. 50 55
311 29 15 c. pink and lilac .. 4·00 4·50
312 34 15 c. black .. .. 1·25 1·40
313 29 20 c. red and green .. 1·40 1·40
314 34 20 c. red .. .. 1·25 1·40
315 35 25 c. brown .. .. 1·25 1·75
316 29 30 c. olive and green .. 1·00 1·25
317 35 30 c. blue .. .. 60 75
318 35 c. green .. .. 1·50 1·60
319 34 40 c. brown .. .. 60 75
320 45 c. green .. .. 90 1·40
321 29 50 c. purple and brown 1·40 1·40
322 35 50 c. on 65 c. brown .. 45 65
323 55 c. purple .. .. 1·25 1·40
324 60 c. black .. .. 50 65
325 29 65 c. green and red .. 1·40 1·40
326 35 70 c. violet .. .. 45 65
327 – 80 c. black (No. 262) .. 40 65
328 35 90 c. mauve .. .. 40 50
329 – 1 f. 25 red (No. 266) .. 60 75
330 – 1 f. 40 blue (No. 267) .. 45 65

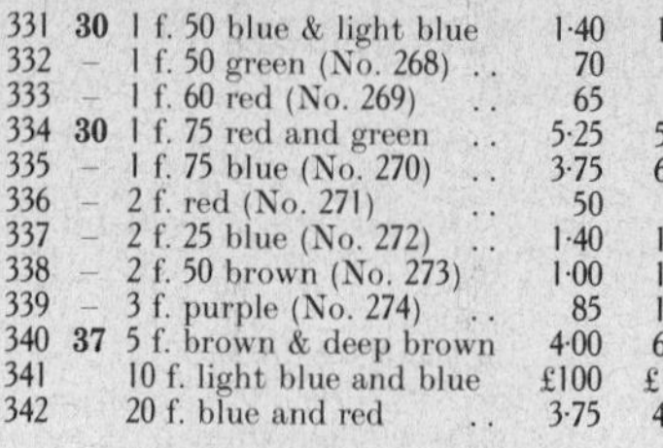

331 30 1 f. 50 blue & light blue 1·40 1·40
332 – 1 f. 50 green (No. 268) .. 70 70
333 – 1 f. 60 red (No. 269) .. 65 70
334 30 1 f. 75 red and green .. 5·25 5·25
335 – 1 f. 75 blue (No. 270) .. 3·75 6·00
336 – 2 f. red (No. 271) .. 50 70
337 – 2 f. 25 blue (No. 272) .. 1·40 1·25
338 – 2 f. 50 brown (No. 273) 1·00 1·00
339 – 3 f. purple (No. 274) .. 85 1·25
340 37 5 f. brown & deep brown 4·00 6·00
341 10 f. light blue and blue £100 £100
342 20 f. blue and red .. 3·75 4·25

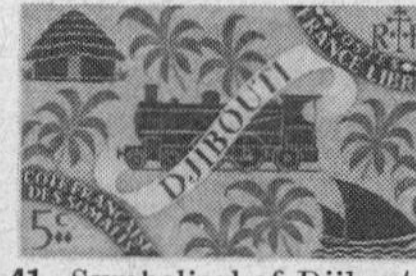

41. Symbolical of Djibouti.

**1943.** Free French issue.
361. 41. 5 c. blue .. .. 10 25
362. 10 c. red .. .. 10 25
363. 25 c. green .. .. 10 25
364. 30 c. black .. .. 10 25
365. 40 c. violet .. .. 15 25
366. 80 c. purple .. .. 20 35
367. 1 f. blue .. .. 20 30
368. 1 f. 50 red .. .. 20 30
369. 2 f. bistre .. .. 25 35
370. 2 f. 50 blue .. .. 40 45
371. 4 f. orange .. .. 40 50
372. 5 f. mauve .. .. 40 55
373. 10 f. blue .. .. 65 75
374. 20 f. green .. .. 65 75

**1944.** Mutual Aid and Red Cross Funds. As T **33** of Cameroun.
375. 5 f.+20 f. green .. .. 75 1·10

**1945.** Eboue. As T **34** of Cameroun.
376. 2 f. black .. .. .. 25 45
377. 25 f. green .. .. .. 70 90

**1945.** Surch.
378. 41. 50 c. on 5 c. blue .. 35 50
379. 60 c. on 5 c. blue .. 15 25
380. 70 c. on 5 c. blue .. 20 25
381. 1 f. 20 on 5 c. blue .. 40 55
382. 2 f. 40 on 25 c. green .. 50 60
383. 3 f. on 25 c. green .. 35 50
384. 4 f. 50 on 25 c. green .. 50 60
385. 15 f. on 2 f. 50 blue .. 75 90

**1946.** Air. Victory. As T **35** of Cameroun.
386. 8 f. blue .. .. .. 50 90

**1946.** Air. From Chad to the Rhine. As Nos. 226/31 of Cameroun.
387. 5 f. black .. .. .. 1·00 1·40
388. 10 f. red .. .. .. 90 1·10
389. 15 f. brown .. .. .. 90 1·10
390. 20 f. mauve .. .. .. 1·00 1·40
391. 25 f. green .. .. .. 1·00 1·40
392. 50 f. blue .. .. .. 1·25 1·75

44. Outpost at Khor-Angar.

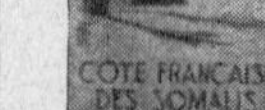

43. Danakil Tent. 45. Somali.

46. Government Palace, Djibouti.

**1947.**
393. 43. 10 c. orge. & vio. (post.) 10 25
394. 30 c. orange and green 10 25
395. 40 c. orange and purple 10 25
396. 44. 50 c. orange and green 10 25
397. 60 c. yellow and brown 10 25
398. 80 c. orange and violet 15 25
399. – 1 f. brown and blue .. 15 25
400. – 1 f. 20 green and grey .. 20 40
401. – 1 f. 50 blue and orange 20 40
402. – 2 f. mauve and grey .. 30 35
403. – 3 f. blue and brown .. 40 55
404. – 3 f. 60 brown and red .. 90 1·00
405. – 4 f. brown and grey .. 80 70
406. – 5 f. orange and brown .. 45 60
407. – 6 f. blue and grey .. 50 65
408. – 10 f. purple and blue .. 35 45
409. – 15 f. brown, blue & buff 80 80
410. – 20 f. blue, orange & blue 90 80
411. – 25 f. red, blue & pur... 90 75
412. 45. 50 f. brown & blue (air) 1·50 1·00
413. – 100 f. yellow and green 2·00 1·60
414. 46. 200 f. green, yell. & blue 2·50 2·50
DESIGNS—HORIZ. As Type **44**: 1 f. to 1 f. 50, Obock Tajurah road. 2 f. to 4 f. Woman carrying dish. 5 f. to 10 f. Somali village. 15 f. to 25 f. Mosque. Djibouti. As Type **46**: 100 f. Frontier post, Loyada.

**1949.** Air. 75th Anniv of U.P.U. As T **46** of Cameroun.
425 30 f. multicoloured .. 2·50 6·00

**1950.** Colonial Welfare Fund. As T **47** of Cameroun.
426 10 f.+2 f. red and brown 1·50 3·00

**1952.** Centenary of Medaille Militaire. As T **48** of Cameroun.
427. 15 f. violet, yellow & green 3·50 3·75

**1954.** Air. 10th Anniv of Liberation. As T **52** of Cameroun.
428 15 f. violet and blue .. 4·50 5·00

48. Ras-Bir Lighthouse

50. Freighter at Wharf, Djibouti.

49. Aerial Map of Djibouti.

**1956.**
429 48 40 f. blue and deep blue (postage) .. 2·00 90
430 49 500 f. purple & vio (air) 55·00 42·00

**1956.** Economic and Social Development Fund.
431. 50. 15 f. violet .. .. 1·40 1·00

51. Warthog

**1958.** Animals, Fishes and Birds.
432. 51. 30 c. brown & red (postage) .. .. 25 25
433. – 40 c. brown and bistre 25 30
434. – 50 c. purple, grey & grn. 35 35
435. – 1 f. orge., blue & brown 50 50
436. – 2 f. multicoloured .. 25 25
437. – 3 f. brown and violet .. 50 50
438. – 4 f. brn., orange & blue 65 60
439. – 5 f. black and blue .. 85 60
440. – 10 f. red, brown & green 2·25 1·25
441. – 15 f. yell., grn. & mauve 3·50 1·25
442. – 20 f. pur., red and blue 2·00 1·10
443. – 25 f. blue, red & green .. 3·25 1·65
444. – 30 f. blk., red and blue 7·00 2·75
445. – 60 f. green and blue .. 8·00 2·50
446. – 75 f. yell., brn. and green 15·00 5·50
447. – 100 f. brn., grn. & bl. (air) 5·00 4·00
448. – 200 f. brn., blk. & orge. 32·00 14·00
449. – 500 f. multicoloured .. 22·00 17·00
DESIGNS—HORIZ. As Type **51**: 40 c. Cheetah. 1 f. Parrot fish. 3 f. Black marlin. 4 f. Spotted trunkfish. 5 f. Eagle ray. 15 f. Little bee eater. 20 f. Triggerfish. 25 f. Red-toothed file fish. 30 f. Sacred ibis. 60 f. Hammerhead shark. 48×27 mm: 100 f. Bohar reedbucks and airplane. 200 f. Great bustard. 500 f. Salt caravan, Lake Assal. VERT. As Type **51**: 50 c. Gerenuks. 2 f. Angelfish. 10 f. Greater flamingo. 75 f. Pink-backed pelican.

**1958.** Tropical Flora. As T **56** of French Equatorial Africa.
450. 10 f. red, green and yellow 1·50 1·25
DESIGN—HORIZ. 10 f. " Haemanthus ".

**1958.** 10th Anniv of Declaration of Human Rights. As T **10** of Comoro Islands.
451. 20 f. violet and blue .. 1·10 1·50

**53.** Governor Bernard.

**1960.** Air. 25th Death Anniv. of Governor Bernard.

| | | | | |
|---|---|---|---|---|
| 452. | **53.** | 55 f. brown, blue & red | 2·25 | 1·40 |

**54.** "Forbin", Obock, 1862.

**1962.** Air. Centenary of Obock.

| | | | | |
|---|---|---|---|---|
| 453. | **54.** | 100 f. brown and blue .. | 3·75 | 2·40 |

**55.** Dragon Tree. **56.** Black-lip Pearl Oyster.

**1962.** Fauna and Flora.

| | | | | |
|---|---|---|---|---|
| 454. | | 2 f. multicoloured .. .. | 1·60 | 75 |
| 455. | | 4 f. brown and ochre .. | 1·60 | 90 |
| 456. | | 6 f. multicoloured .. .. | 2·75 | 1·75 |
| 457. | | 25 f. bistre, green and red | 6·00 | 3·00 |
| 458. | | 40 f. brown, black & blue | 16·00 | 5·00 |
| 459. | | 50 f. brown, purple & blue | 10·00 | 6·25 |

DESIGNS—HORIZ. 2 f. Type **55.** 4 f. Large-toothed rock hyrax. 6 f. Large carangue (fish). 25 f. Fennec foxes. 40 f. Griffon Vulture. VERT. 50 f. Klipspringer.

**1962.** Malaria Eradication. As T **70** of Cameroun.

| | | | | |
|---|---|---|---|---|
| 460. | | 25 f. + 5 f. blue .. .. | 5·50 | 5·50 |

**1962.** Shells of the Red Sea. Multicoloured.
(a) Postage as T **56.**

| | | | | |
|---|---|---|---|---|
| 461 | | 8 f. Type **56** .. .. | 1·00 | 55 |
| 462 | | 10 f. Fluted giant clam (horiz) .. .. .. | 1·00 | 55 |
| 463 | | 25 f. Three knobbed conch (horiz) .. .. .. | 2·75 | 1·40 |
| 464 | | 30 f. Knobbed top .. | 2·75 | 1·25 |
| | | (b) Air. 50 × 28 mm. | | |
| 465 | | 60 f. Arabian tibia .. | 5·00 | 2·50 |
| 466 | | 100 f. Giant spider conch | 7·25 | 3·50 |

**1962.** Air. 1st Trans-Atlantic TV Satellite Link. As Type F **23** of Andorra (French).

| | | | | |
|---|---|---|---|---|
| 467 | | 20 f. purple and green .. | 90 | 90 |

**1963.** Red Cross Centenary. As T **14a** of Comoro Islands.

| | | | | |
|---|---|---|---|---|
| 468 | | 50 f. red, grey and brown .. | 5·00 | 5·00 |

**57.** Large Star Coral. **58.** Houri.

**1963.** Corals. Multicoloured.
(a) Postage as T **57.**

| | | | | |
|---|---|---|---|---|
| 469 | | 5 f. Type **57** .. .. | 90 | 80 |
| 470 | | 6 f. Organ-pipe coral .. | 1·00 | 80 |
| | | (b) Air Horiz. (48 × 27 mm) | | |
| 471 | | 40 f. Stinging coral .. | 2·25 | 1·00 |
| 472 | | 55 f. Brain coral .. .. | 4·75 | 2·25 |
| 473 | | 200 f. Branched coral .. | 8·25 | 4·50 |

**1963.** 15th Anniv. of Declaration of Human Rights. As T **15** of Comoro Islands.

| | | | | |
|---|---|---|---|---|
| 474. | | 70 f. blue and brown .. | 7·25 | 7·25 |

**1964.** "PHILATEC 1964" Int. Stamp Exn., Paris. As T **528** of France.

| | | | | |
|---|---|---|---|---|
| 475. | | 80 f. brown, green & purple | 7·25 | 7·25 |

**1964.** Local Dhows. Multicoloured.
(a) Postage as T **58.**

| | | | | |
|---|---|---|---|---|
| 476 | | 15 f. Type **58** .. .. | 1·00 | 75 |
| 477 | | 25 f. Sambuk .. .. | 2·00 | 1·40 |
| | | (b) Air. Size 48 × 27 mm. | | |
| 478 | | 50 f. Building sambuk .. | 3·00 | 1·60 |
| 479 | | 85 f. Zaruk .. .. | 4·25 | 2·50 |
| 480 | | 300 f. Ziema .. .. | 13·00 | 5·75 |

**59.** Rameses II and Nefertari Temple, Philae.

**1964.** Air. Nubian Monuments Preservation.

| | | | | |
|---|---|---|---|---|
| 481. | **59.** | 25 f. + 5 f. brown, green and red .. .. | 7·75 | 7·75 |

**60.** "The Discus Thrower". (Ancient Greece).

**1964.** Air. Olympic Games, Tokyo.

| | | | | |
|---|---|---|---|---|
| 482. | **60.** | 90 f. purple, red & black | 9·50 | 7·75 |

**1965.** Air. Centenary of I.T.U. As T **20** of Comoro Islands.

| | | | | |
|---|---|---|---|---|
| 483. | | 95 f. blue, brown & purple | 15·00 | 9·00 |

**61.** Ghoubet Kharab.

**1965.** Landscapes.

| | | | | |
|---|---|---|---|---|
| 484 | – | 6 f. brown, blue and green (postage) .. | 75 | 50 |
| 485 | – | 20 f. green, blue & brn | 1·00 | 75 |
| 486 | – | 45 f. brown, blue and deep blue (air) .. | 2·25 | 2·50 |
| 487 | **61** | 65 f. brown, ochre & bl | 2·75 | 1·50 |

VIEWS—26 × 22 mm: 6 f. Dadwayya. 20 f. Tajurah. As Type **61**: 45 f. Lake Abbe.

**62.** "Life and Death".

**1965.** Anti-Tuberculosis Campaign.

| | | | | |
|---|---|---|---|---|
| 488. | **62.** | 25 f. + 5 f. brown, green and turquoise .. | 2·50 | 1·75 |

**1966.** Air. Launching of 1st French Satellite. As Nos. 1696/7 (plus se-tenant label) of France.

| | | | | |
|---|---|---|---|---|
| 489. | | 25 f. brown, bistre and red | 2·50 | 2·50 |
| 490. | | 30 f. brown, bistre and red | 3·00 | 3·00 |

**63.** Senna. **64.** Feather Star and Flame Coral.

**1966.** Flowers.

| | | | | |
|---|---|---|---|---|
| 491. | **63.** | 5 f. orange, green and brown (postage) .. | 1·00 | 50 |
| 492. | – | 8 f. orange, green & brn. | 1·00 | 50 |
| 493. | – | 25 f. red, blue and green | 1·40 | 1·00 |
| 494. | – | 55 f. lake, green & myrtle (air) .. .. | 4·00 | 2·00 |

FLOWERS—VERT. 8 f. Poinciana. 25 f. Aloes. HORIZ. ($48\frac{1}{2}$ × 27 mm.); 55 f. Stapelia.

**1966.** Air. Marine Life. Multicoloured.

| | | | | |
|---|---|---|---|---|
| 495. | | 8 f. Type **64** .. .. | 1·75 | 1·75 |
| 496. | | 25 f. Regal angel fish .. | 3·00 | 3·00 |
| 497. | | 40 f. Purple moon angel fish | 4·50 | 4·50 |
| 498. | | 50 f. Cardinal coral fish .. | 6·25 | 6·25 |
| 499. | | 70 f. Squirrel fish .. .. | 10·00 | 10·00 |
| 500. | | 80 f. Majestic surgeon fish | 10·50 | 10·50 |
| 501. | | 100 f. Scorpion fish .. | 16·00 | 16·00 |

**1966.** Air. Launching of Satellite "D1". As T **569** of France.

| | | | | |
|---|---|---|---|---|
| 502. | | 48 f. green, brown & blue | 3·25 | 2·25 |

**65.** Grey Monitor.

**1967.** Somali Fauna.

| | | | | |
|---|---|---|---|---|
| 503. | **65.** | 20 f. purple, chest. & brn. | 3·25 | 2·25 |

POSTAGE DUE STAMPS

**D 31.** Somali Spears. **D 47.**

**1915.**

| | | | | |
|---|---|---|---|---|
| D278 | D **31** | 5 c. blue .. .. | 10 | 25 |
| D279 | | 10 c. red .. .. | 10 | 25 |
| D280 | | 15 c. black .. .. | 10 | 25 |
| D281 | | 20 c. violet .. | 15 | 25 |
| D282 | | 30 c. yellow .. | 20 | 40 |
| D190 | | 50 c. red .. .. | 50 | 1·00 |
| D283 | | 50 c. brown .. | 20 | 45 |
| D284 | | 60 c. green .. .. | 30 | 70 |
| D285 | | 1 f. blue .. .. | 50 | 1·50 |
| D286 | | 2 f. red .. .. | 40 | 80 |
| D287 | | 3 f. sepia .. .. | 60 | 85 |

**1927.** Surch. in figures.

| | | | | |
|---|---|---|---|---|
| D 231. | D **31.** | "2 F" on 1 f. red | 2·50 | 4·50 |
| D 232. | | "3 F" on 1 f. mve. | 2·50 | 4·50 |

**1942.** (a) Optd. **FRANCE LIBRE.**

| | | | | |
|---|---|---|---|---|
| D 343. | D **31.** | 5 c. blue .. .. | 1·00 | 1·00 |
| D 344. | | 10 c. red .. .. | 1·00 | 1·00 |
| D 345. | | 15 c. black .. .. | 1·00 | 1·00 |
| D 346. | | 20 c. violet .. | 1·00 | 1·00 |
| D 347. | | 30 c. yellow .. | 1·00 | 1·00 |
| D 348. | | 50 c. red .. .. | 1·00 | 1·00 |
| D 349. | | 60 c. green .. .. | 1·00 | 1·00 |
| D 350. | | 1 f. blue .. .. | 4·75 | 4·75 |
| | | (b) Optd. **France Libre.** | | |
| D 351. | D **31.** | 5 c. blue .. .. | 1·00 | 1·00 |
| D 352. | | 10 c. red .. .. | 1·00 | 1·00 |
| D 353. | | 15 c. black .. .. | 1·00 | 1·00 |
| D 354. | | 20 c. violet .. | 85 | 1·00 |
| D 355. | | 30 c. yellow .. | 85 | 1·00 |
| D 356. | | 50 c. brown .. | 85 | 1·00 |
| D 357. | | 60 c. green .. .. | 1·00 | 1·00 |
| D 358. | | 1 f. blue .. .. | 1·00 | 1·00 |
| D 359. | | 2 f. red .. .. | 1·00 | 1·00 |
| D 360. | | 3 f. sepia .. .. | 1·00 | 1·00 |

**1947.**

| | | | | |
|---|---|---|---|---|
| D 415. | D **47.** | 10 c. mauve .. | 10 | 25 |
| D 416. | | 30 c. brown .. | 10 | 25 |
| D 417. | | 50 c. green .. .. | 10 | 25 |
| D 418. | | 1 f. brown .. .. | 10 | 25 |
| D 419. | | 2 f. red .. .. | 10 | 25 |
| D 420. | | 3 f. brown .. .. | 20 | 35 |
| D 421. | | 4 f. blue .. .. | 20 | 45 |
| D 422. | | 5 f. red .. .. | 25 | 45 |
| D 423. | | 10 f. green .. | 45 | 70 |
| D 424. | | 20 f. blue .. .. | 20 | 80 |

For later issues see **FRENCH TERRITORY OF THE AFARS AND THE ISSAS.**



## FRENCH SOUTHERN AND ANTARCTIC TERRITORIES Pt. 6

Stamps issued for use in the French settlements in the southern Indian Ocean and in the Antarctic.

100 centimes = 1 franc.

**1955.** No. 324 of Madagascar optd **TERRES AUSTRALES ET ANTARCTIQUES FRANCAISES.**

| | | | | |
|---|---|---|---|---|
| 1 | **39** | 15 f. blue and green .. | 18·00 | 28·00 |

**2.** Rockhopper Penguins. **5.** Polar Camp and Meteorologist.

**4.** Emperor Penguins and South Pole.

**1956.**

| | | | | |
|---|---|---|---|---|
| 2. | – | 30 c. brn., grn. & bl. (post.) | 50 | 1·50 |
| 3. | – | 40 c. blk., purple and blue | 50 | 1·50 |
| 4. | **2.** | 50 c. blue, ochre & brn. | 50 | 1·50 |
| 5. | | 1 f. blue, orange and grey | 50 | 1·50 |
| 6. | – | 2 f. black, brown & blue | 1·25 | 1·50 |
| 7. | – | 4 f. brown, green & blue | 8·00 | 8·25 |
| 8. | – | 5 f. blue and light blue | 2·00 | 3·00 |
| 9. | – | 8 f. brown and grey .. | 14·00 | 15·00 |
| 10. | – | 10 f. blue .. .. | 4·00 | 5·00 |
| 11. | – | 12 f. black and blue .. | 12·00 | 10·00 |
| 12. | – | 15 f. purple and blue .. | 6·00 | 6·75 |
| 13. | – | 20 f. blue, yell. & pale blue | 17·00 | 17·00 |
| 14. | – | 25 f. blk., brown & green | £100 | 75·00 |
| 15. | – | 85 f. orge., blue and black | 22·00 | 22·00 |
| 16. | **4.** | 50 f. green and olive (air) | 35·00 | 30·00 |
| 17. | | 100 f. indigo and blue .. | 32·00 | 30·00 |
| 18. | – | 200 f. black, blue & purple | 38·00 | 27·00 |

DESIGNS—VERT. As Type **2.** 30 c. Light-mantled sooty albatross. 2 f. Black-faced sheathbills. 12 f. Kerguelen Cormorants. 20 f. Territorial arms. 85 f. King penguin. HORIZ. (36 × 22 mm.). 40 c. Great skuas. 4 f. Leopard seal. 5 f., 8 f. Kerguelen fur seal and settlement. 10 f., 15 f. Southern elephant-seal. 25 f. Kerguelen fur seal. As Type **4.** 200 f. Wandering albatross.

See also Nos. 26/34.

**1957.** Int. Geophysical Year.

| | | | | |
|---|---|---|---|---|
| 19. | **5.** | 5 f. black and violet .. | 4·50 | 4·50 |
| 20. | | 10 f. red .. .. | 5·00 | 5·50 |
| 21. | | 15 f. blue .. .. | 5·00 | 5·50 |

**1959.** Tropical Flora. As T **56** of French Equatorial Africa.

| | | | | |
|---|---|---|---|---|
| 22. | | 10 f. multicoloured .. | 8·00 | 7·00 |

DESIGN—HORIZ. 10 f. "Pringlea".

**6.** Yves-Joseph Kerguelen-Tremarec and "Dauphine".

**1960.** Kerguelen Archipelago Discovery. Commemoration.

| | | | | |
|---|---|---|---|---|
| 23. | **6.** | 25 f. brown, chest. & blue | 27·00 | 22·00 |

**7.** Jean Charcot, Compass and "Pourquoi Pas?"

**1962.** 25th Anniv. of Disappearance of Jean Charcot.

| | | | | |
|---|---|---|---|---|
| 24. | **7.** | 25 f. brown, red & green | 23·00 | 18·00 |

**1962.** Air. 1st Trans-Atlantic TV Satellite Link. As Type F **23** of Andorra (French).

| | | | | |
|---|---|---|---|---|
| 25 | | 50 f. green, olive and blue .. | 24·00 | 21·00 |

**1963.** Designs as T 2 and 4.

26. 5 f. violet and blue (postage) 16·00 12·00
35. 5 f. brown, black and blue.. 45·00 32·00
27. 8 f. indigo, purple and blue 10·00 8·00
28. 10 f. black, blue and brown 24·00 19·00
29. 12 f. green, blue and brn. 16·00 10·00
30. 15 f. blue, black and brown 9·00 5·00
31. 20 f. grey, orange and green £325 £200
32. 45 f. green, brown and blue 8·00 6·00
33. 25 f. pur., brn. & blue (air) 25·00 19·00
34. 50 f. black, purple and blue 38·00 38·00

DESIGNS—HORIZ. As Type 2. 5 f. (No. 26) Blue whale. 5 f. (No. 35) Crozet Archipelago. 8 f. Southern elephant-seals in combat. 12 f. Phylica (tree), New Amsterdam island. 15 f. Killer whale, Crozet islands. As Type 4. 50 f. Adelie penguins. VERT. As Type 2. 10 f. Pintado petrel. 20 f. Black-browed albatross. 45 f. Kerguelen cabbage. As Type 4. 25 f. Ionospheric research pylon, Adelie Land.

9. Observation Station.

**1963.** "Int. Year of the Quiet Sun".

36. 9. 20 f. slate, brown and violet (postage) .. .. 55·00 38·00
37. – 100 f. red, blue & blk. (air) 90·00 80·00

DESIGN—VERT. (27×48 mm.): 100 f. Pylons and Adelie penguins.

10. Landfall of Dumont d'Urville.

**1965.** Air. Discovery of Adelie Land, 1840.

38. 10. 50 f. indigo and blue .. £110 £100

**1965.** Air. Centenary of I.T.U. As T 20 of Comoro Islands.

39. 30 f. brown, mauve & blue £225 £170

**1966.** Air. Launching of 1st French Satellite. As Nos. 1696/7 of France.

40. 25 f. blue, green and brown 11·00 10·50
41. 30 f. blue, green and brown 11·00 10·50

**1966.** Air. Launching of Satellite "D1". As T 569 of France.

42. 50 f. violet, purple & orge. 40·00 15·00

11. Space Probe.

12. Dumont D'Urville, "L'Astrolabe" and "Zelee".

**1967.** Launching of 1st Space Probe, Adelie Land.

43. 11. 20 f. black, purple & blue 24·00 22·00

**1968.** Dumont D'Urville Commem.

44. 12. 30 f. brn., dp. blue & lt. bl. £110 80·00

13. Port-aux-Francais.

**1968.** Air.

45. – 40 f. slate and blue .. 35·00 28·00
46. 13. 50 f. black, green & blue £130 90·00

DESIGN: 40 f. Aerial View of St. Paul Island.

14. Kerguelen and Rocket.

**1968.** Air. Launching of "Dragon" Space Rockets.

47. 14. 25 f. brown, green & blue 14·50 14·00
48. – 30 f. blue, brown & green 14·50 14·00

DESIGN: 30 f. Adelie Land and rocket.

**1968.** 20th Anniv. of W.H.O. As T 26 of Comoro Islands, but inscr. "TERRES AUSTRALIS ET ANTARCTIQUES FRANCAISES".

49. 30 f. blue, yellow and red.. 50·00 35·00

**1968.** Human Rights Year. As T 28 of Comoro Islands.

50. 30 f. red, blue and brown .. 45·00 38·00

15. Eiffel Tower and Badge of Paris, and Ship in Antarctica.

**1969.** Air. 5th Antarctic Treaty Consultative Meeting, Paris.

51. 15. 50 f. blue.. .. .. 38·00 30·00

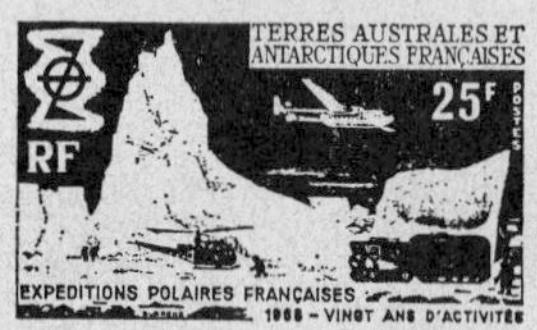


16. Antarctic Scene.

**1969.** French Polar Exploration.

52. 16. 25 f. blue, red & turq. 17·00 15·00

**1969.** Air. 1st Flight of Concorde. As T 32 of Comoro Islands.

53 85 f. turquoise and blue .. 40·00 30·00

17. Possession Island, Crozet Archipelago.

**1969.** Air.

54. 17. 50 f. green, red and blue 16·00 10·00
55. – 100 f. black, grey and blue 60·00 40·00
56. – 200 f. brn., green and blue 55·00 32·00
57. – 500 f. blue .. 14·00 11·00

DESIGNS-HORIZ. 100 f. Relief Map of Kerguelen. VERT. 200 f. Cape Geology Archipelago map. 500 f. Territorial arms.

**1970.** 50th Anniv. of Int. Labour Organization. As T 33 of Comoro Islands.

58. 20 f. purple, blue and red.. 18·00 13·00

18. Relief Map of New Amsterdam Island.

**1970.** Air. 20th Anniv. of Meteorological Station, New Amsterdam Island.

59. 18. 30 f. brown .. .. 14·00 10·00

**1970.** New U.P.U. Headquarters Building, Berne. As T 156 of Cameroun.

60. 50 f. brown, purple and blue 29·00 21·00

19. "Chaenichthys rhinoceratus".

**1971.** Fishes.

61. 19. 5 f. blue, yell. and green 3·00 2·50
62. – 10 f. brn., violet and blue 4·00 3·00
63. – 20 f. grn., orge. & purple 4·00 3·00
64. – 22 f. red, violet & brown 6·00 5·00
65. – 25 f. blue, yell. & green.. 4·00 3·00
66. – 30 f. grey, blue & brown 6·00 5·00
67. – 35 f. multicoloured .. 6·00 5·00
68. – 135 f. red, brn. and blue 7·00 6·00

DESIGNS: 10 f. "Notothenia rossii". 20 f. "Notothenia coriiceps". 22 f. "Trematomus hansoni". 25 f. "Notothenia macrocephala". 30 f. "Notothenia cyanobrancha". 35 f. "Trematomus bernacchii". 135 f. "Zanchlorhynchus spinifer".

20. Port-aux-Francais, 1950.

**1971.** Air. 20th Anniv. of Port-aux-Francais, Kerguelen.

69. 20. 40 f. brown, green & blue 16·00 12·50
70. – 50 f. green, blue & brown 19·00 14·50

DESIGN: 50 f. Port-aux-Francais, 1970.

21. Treaty Emblem.

22. "Christiansenia dreuxi".

**1971.** 10th Anniv. of Antarctic Treaty.

71. 21. 75 f. red .. .. .. 26·00 19·00

**1972.** Insects.

72. 22. 15 f. brn. pur. and red .. 11·00 8·00
73. – 22 f. yell. blue and green 11·00 8·00
74. – 25 f. violet, purple & grn. 8·00 5·00
75. – 30 f. multicoloured .. 15·00 9·00
76. – 40 f. black, brn. & choc. 9·00 7·00
77. – 140 f. brn., green & blue 10·00 8·00

DESIGNS: 22 f. "Phtirocoris antarcticus". 25 f. "Microzetia mirabilis" (midge). 30 f. "Antarctophytosus atriceps" (rove beetle). 40 f. "Paractora dreuxi". 140 f. "Pringleophaga kerguelenensis" (scavenger moth).

23. Landing on Crozet Islands.

**1972.** Air. Bicentenary of Discovery of Crozet Islands and Kerguelen.

78. 23. 100 f. black .. .. 38·00 27·00
79. – 250 f. black and brown.. 70·00 38·00

DESIGN: 250 f. Hoisting the flag on Kerguelen.

**1972.** 1st Death Anniv. of General De Gaulle. As Nos. 1937 and 1940 of France.

80. 50 f. black and green .. 15·00 13·00
81. 100 f. black and green .. 20·00 15·00

24. "Gallieni".

**1973.** Air. Antarctic Voyages of the "Gallieni" (supply ship).

82 24 100 f. black and blue .. 24·00 21·00

25. "Azorella selago".

**1973.** Plants.

83. 25. 61 f. green, slate & brown 3·00 2·50
84. – 87 f. green, blue and red 4·00 3·00

DESIGN: 87 f. "Acaena ascendens".

26. "Mascarin", 1772.

**1973.** Air. Antarctic Ships.

85. 26. 120 f. brown .. .. 6·00 4·00
86. – 145 f. blue .. .. 7·00 5·00
87. – 150 f. blue .. .. 8·00 6·00
88. – 185 f. brown .. .. 9·00 7·00

DESIGNS: 145 f. "L'Astrolabe", 1840. 150 f. "Roland", 1774. 185 f. "Vitoria", 1522.

See also Nos. 93/4.

27. Part of Alfred Faure Base.

**1974.** 10th Anniv. of Alfred Faure Base, Crozet Archipelago.

89. 27. 75 f. brn., blue & ultram. 10·00 4·00
90. – 110 f. brn., blue & ultram. 10·00 5·00
91. – 150 f. brn., blue & ultram. 14·00 10·00

Nos. 89/91 were issued together se-tenant within the sheet, making a composite picture of the base.

28. Emperor Penguin, Globe and Letters.

**1974.** Air. Cent. of Universal Postal Union.

92. 28. 150 f. brown, blk. & blue 10·00 7·50

**1974.** Air. Charcot's Antarctic Voyages. As T 26.

93. 100 f. blue .. .. .. 5·50 3·50
94. 200 f. red .. .. .. 7·00 4·50

DESIGN: 100 f. "Francais" (1903–05 voyage). 200 f. "Pourquoi Pas?" (1908–10 voyage).

29. Mail Ship "Sapmer".

**1974.** 25th Anniv. of Postal Service.

95. 29. 75 f. black, blue & mauve 8·00 7·00

30. Rockets over Kerguelen Islands.

**1975.** Air. "ARAKS" Franco–Soviet Magnetosphere Research Project.

96. 30. 45 f. red, blue and lilac.. 9·00 4·50
97. – 90 f. red, lilac and blue.. 11·00 6·50

DESIGN: 90 f. Map of North Coast of U.S.S.R.

31. Swallow-tailed Tern.

32. "La Curieuse" (topsail schooner).

**1976.**

| | | | | |
|---|---|---|---|---|
| 98 | 31 | 40 c. black, blue and orange (postage) .. | 4·50 | 4·00 |
| 99 | – | 50 c. brown, lt blue & bl | 6·00 | 5·00 |
| 100 | – | 90 c. brown and blue .. | 7·00 | 4·00 |
| 101 | – | 1 f. brown, blue & violet | 11·00 | 7·50 |
| 102 | – | 1 f. 20 green, blue & brn | 14·00 | 11·00 |
| 103 | – | 1 f. 40 blue, green & orge | 15·00 | 15·00 |
| 104 | 32 | 1 f. 90 blue, ultramarine and brown (air) .. | 5·00 | 3·50 |
| 105 | – | 2 f. 70 brown, blue and ultramarine .. .. | 6·00 | 4·50 |
| 106 | – | 4 f. blue and red .. | 8·00 | 5·50 |

DESIGNS—As T **31**. HORIZ: 50 c. Antarctic petrel. 90 c. Kerguelen fur seal. 1 f. Weddell seal. VERT: 1 f. 20, Kerguelen cormorant. 1 f. 40, Gentoo penguin. As T **32**. 2 f. 70, "Commandant Charcot" (ice patrol ship). 4 f. "Marion Dufresne" (Antarctic supply ship).

**33.** Dumont d'Urville Base, 1956.

**1976.** Air. 20th Anniv. of Dumont d'Urville Base, Adelie Land.

| | | | | |
|---|---|---|---|---|
| 107. | **33.** | 1 f. 20 brn., orge. & blue | 9·00 | 5·50 |
| 108. | – | 4 f. orge., blue & brown | 11·00 | 7·00 |

DESIGNS: 4 f. Dumont d'Urville Base, 1976.

**34.** Kerguelen Island.

**1976.** Air. Bicentenary of Cook's Passage to Kerguelen.

| | | | | |
|---|---|---|---|---|
| 109. | **34.** | 3 f. 50 slate and blue .. | 12·00 | 9·00 |

**35.** Captain Cook.

**36.** First Ascent of Mt. Ross (5 Jan 1975).

**1976.** Cook Commemoration.

| | | | | |
|---|---|---|---|---|
| 110. | **35.** | 70 c. bl., brn. & yell. | 13·00 | 10·00 |

**1976.** Ross Commemoration.

| | | | | |
|---|---|---|---|---|
| 111. | **36.** | 30 c. red, brown & blue | 5·00 | 4·00 |
| 112. | – | 3 f. violet, brown & blue | 5·00 | 4·00 |

DESIGN: 3 f. Sir James Clark Ross.

**37.** Blue Whale.

**1977.** Marine Mammals.

| | | | | |
|---|---|---|---|---|
| 113. | **37.** | 1 f. 10 deep blue & blue | 5·00 | 4·00 |
| 114. | – | 1 f. 50 indigo, blue & brown .. .. | 5·00 | 4·00 |

DESIGN: 1 f. 50, Commerson's dolphin.

**38.** Seaweed, "Macrocystis".

**1977.**

| | | | | |
|---|---|---|---|---|
| 115. | **38.** | 40 c. brown and bistre | 80 | 90 |
| 116. | – | 70 c. grn., brn. and blk. | 90 | 90 |
| 117. | – | 1 f. grey .. .. | 1·25 | 1·00 |
| 118. | – | 1 f. 20 red, grn. and blue | 3·00 | 3·00 |
| 119. | – | 1 f. 40 red, blue & grey | 3·00 | 3·00 |

DESIGNS—HORIZ. 70 c. Seaweed "Durvillea". 1 f. 20 "Magga Dan" (Antarctic supply ship). 1 f. 40, "Thala Dan" (Antarctic supply ship). VERT. 1 f. Oceanology.

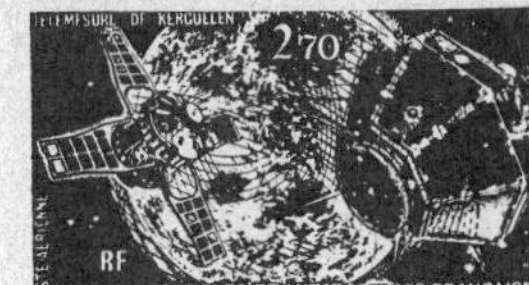


**39.** Kerguelen Satellite.

**1977.** Air. Satellites.

| | | | | |
|---|---|---|---|---|
| 120 | 39 | 2 f. 70 multicoloured .. | 3·50 | 3·00 |
| 121 | – | 3 f. blue and light blue | 4·00 | 3·50 |

DESIGN: 3 f. Adelie Land satellite.
See also No. 143.

**40.** Polar Explorer with Flags.

**42.** R. Rallier du Baty.

**41.** Salmon and Breeding Tanks.

**1977.** 30th Anniv. of French Polar Expeditions.

| | | | | |
|---|---|---|---|---|
| 122. | **40.** | 1 f. 90 orge., red & bl. | 8·00 | 6·00 |

**1977.** Antarctic Fauna.

| | | | | |
|---|---|---|---|---|
| 123. | **41.** | 50 c. violet & blue (postage) .. .. | 1·75 | 1·40 |
| 124. | – | 90 c. brn., blue & grn. | 1·75 | 1·40 |
| 125. | – | 10 f. brown, blue and red (air) .. .. | 12·00 | 10·00 |

DESIGNS—As T **41**: 90 c. Head of light-mantled sooty albatross. 36 × 48 mm: 10 f. Kerguelen fur seal and cub.

**1979.** R. Rallier du Baty Commemoration.

| | | | | |
|---|---|---|---|---|
| 126. | **42.** | 1 f. 20 blue and bistre | 1·90 | 1·90 |

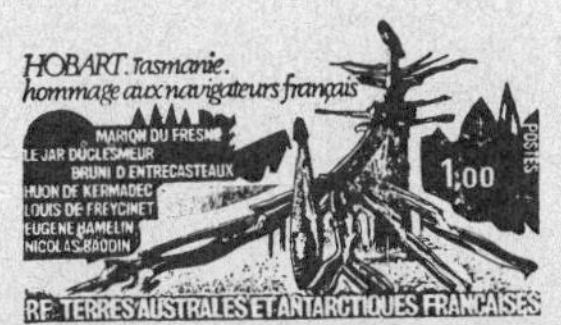


**43.** Memorial and Names of French Navigators.

**1979.** French Navigators' Memorial, Hobart.

| | | | | |
|---|---|---|---|---|
| 127. | **43.** | 1 f. brown, turq. & blue | 1·25 | 1·25 |

**44.** "Argos" Satellite and Geophysical Laboratory.

**1979.** Air. Satellite Research.

| | | | | |
|---|---|---|---|---|
| 128. | **44.** | 70 c. turq, violet & olive | 1·25 | 1·25 |
| 129. | – | 1 f. 90 blk., bistre & mve. | 2·00 | 1·25 |

DESIGN: 1 f. 90, Satellite and Kerguelen Receiving Station.

**45.** Kerguelen Cormorant.

**1979.** Antarctic Fauna.

| | | | | |
|---|---|---|---|---|
| 130. | **45.** | 1 f. 40 green, blue and sepia (postage) .. | 2·00 | 2·00 |
| 131. | – | 4 f. ultramarine, blue and green (air) .. | 3·50 | 2·50 |
| 132. | – | 10 f. brn., grn. & blk. | 9·00 | 6·50 |

DESIGNS—VERT. (36 × 48 mm.). 4 f. As No. 125, (27 × 48 mm.). 10 f. Southern elephant-seal.
See also Nos. 138/9.

**46.** Destroyer "Forbin".

**1979.** Ships.

| | | | | |
|---|---|---|---|---|
| 133. | **46.** | 40 c. blk., turq. & green | 1·75 | 1·50 |
| 134. | – | 50 c. blk., turq. and grn. | 1·75 | 1·50 |

DESIGN: 50 c. Helicopter Carrier "Jeanne d'Arc".
See also Nos. 136/7.

**47.** H.M.S. "Challenger" in the Antarctic (from engraving in "Illustrated London News").

**1979.** Air. Expedition of the "Challenger", 1872–6.

| | | | | |
|---|---|---|---|---|
| 135. | **47.** | 2 f. 70 black and blue .. | 2·50 | 1·75 |

**1980.** Frigates. Designs similar to T **46**.

| | | | | |
|---|---|---|---|---|
| 136. | | 1 f. 10 blue, ultramarine and violet .. .. | 1·25 | 1·10 |
| 137. | | 1 f. 50 black, blue and deep blue .. .. | 1·25 | 1·25 |

DESIGNS—VERT. 1 f. 10, "Doudart de Lagree". HORIZ. 1 f. 50, "Commandant Bourdais".

**1980.** Antarctic Fauna. Designs similar to T **45**.

| | | | | |
|---|---|---|---|---|
| 138. | | 70 c. black, red and blue .. | 1·75 | 1·10 |
| 139. | | 1 f. brown and blue .. | 1·60 | 1·10 |

DESIGNS—VERT. 70 c. Royal penguins. HORIZ. 1 f. Head of Soyeux petrel.

**50.** Admiral d'Entrecasteaux.

**51.** El Cano.

**1980.** Admiral d'Entrecasteaux Commemoration.

| | | | | |
|---|---|---|---|---|
| 140. | **50.** | 1 f. 20 blk., violet & blue | 1·75 | 1·25 |

**1980.** Sebastian de El Cano (discoverer of Amsterdam Island) Commemoration.

| | | | | |
|---|---|---|---|---|
| 141 | 51 | 1 f. 40 grey, orge & red | 1·25 | 1·10 |
| 142 | – | 4 f. multicoloured .. | 2·75 | 2·00 |

DESIGN: 4 f. El Cano's ship "Vitoria".

**1980.** Air. Kerguelen Satellite.

| | | | | |
|---|---|---|---|---|
| 143 | 39 | 50 c. grey, blue & brown | 1·10 | 1·10 |

**52.** Lion Rock.

**1980.** Air. Dumont d'Urville Base.

| | | | | |
|---|---|---|---|---|
| 144. | **52.** | 90 c. multicoloured .. | 1·10 | 1·10 |

**53.** "La Recherche" and "L'Esperance" (after Roux).

**1980.** Air. Arrival at Amsterdam Island of D'Entrecasteaux and De Kermadec Commemoration.

| | | | | |
|---|---|---|---|---|
| 145 | 53 | 1 f. 90 blue .. .. | 2·50 | 2·25 |

**54.** "Terror" (bomb ketch) at Arched Rock, Kerguelen (after Williams).

**1980.** Air.

| | | | | |
|---|---|---|---|---|
| 146. | **54.** | 2 f. 70 blk., grn. & brn. | 1·75 | 1·75 |

**55.** "Phylica nitida".

**1980.** Air.

| | | | | |
|---|---|---|---|---|
| 147. | **55.** | 10 f. blk., grn. and brn. | 7·00 | 5·50 |

**56.** Charles de Gaulle. **57.** Adelie Penguins.

**1980.** Air. 10th Death Anniv. of Charles de Gaulle.

| | | | | |
|---|---|---|---|---|
| 148. | **56.** | 5 f. 40 pur., bl. & red | 12·00 | 11·00 |

**1981.** Antarctic Fauna.

| | | | | |
|---|---|---|---|---|
| 149. | **57.** | 50 c. lilac .. .. | 1·75 | 1·60 |
| 150. | – | 60 c. bl., grn. & turq. | 1·25 | 1·10 |
| 151. | **57.** | 1 f. 20 blk., bl. & vio. | 1·60 | 1·25 |
| 152. | – | 1 f. 30 blk., brn. & blue | 1·60 | 1·25 |
| 153. | – | 1 f. 80 brown green and bistre .. .. | 2·00 | 1·25 |

DESIGNS—HORIZ. 1 f. 30, 1 f. 80, Leopard seal. (48 × 28 mm.) 60 c. Head of Adelie Penguin.

**58.** "HB 40 Castor".

**1981.** Air. Antarctic Transport.

| | | | | |
|---|---|---|---|---|
| 154. | **58.** | 2 f. 40 blue, orge. & vio. | 1·75 | 1·25 |

**59.** "Saint Marcouf".

**1981.** Air. Antarctic Supply Ships.

| | | | | |
|---|---|---|---|---|
| 155. | **59.** | 3 f. 50 grey, blue & red | 1·75 | 1·25 |
| 156. | – | 7 f. 30 blue, turq. & lilac | 3·00 | 2·50 |

DESIGN: 7 f. 30, "Norsel".

**60.** Map of Antarctica.

**1981.** 20th Anniv. of Antarctic Treaty.

| | | | | |
|---|---|---|---|---|
| 157. | **60.** | 1 f. 80 bl., dp. bl. & brn. | 5·50 | 5·50 |

**61.** Sud Aviation Alouette II Helicopter.

**1981.**

158 **61** 55 c. blue, turq & brown 1·00 80
159 65 c. turquoise, grn & bl 1·00 80

**62.** Compacted Ice, Dumont d'Urville.

**1981.** Air.

160. **62.** 1 f. 30 dp. bl., bl. & grey 1·25 80

**63.** Loranchet.

**1981.** Jean Loranchet Commemoration.

161. **63.** 1 f. 40 dp. grn., grn. & ol. 1·25 1·10

**64.** Black-faced Sheathbill.

**1981.** Air.

162. **64.** 1 f. 50 black .. .. 1·25 1·10

**65.** " Adele Dumont d'Urville " (Michele Garreau).

**1981.** Air.

163. **65.** 2 f. brown and black .. 1·25 1·25

**66.** " Arcad III " Satellite over Antarctic.

**1981.** Air.

164. **66.** 3 f. 85 green, blue & deep blue .. .. 2·75 2·50

**67.** Charcot Station.

**1981.** Air. 25th Anniv. of Charcot Antarctic Station.

165. **67.** 5 f. red, blue and violet 2·75 2·25

**68.** "Antares" (dispatch vessel).

**1981.** Air.

166. **68.** 8 f. 40 purple, grey & bl. 2·75 2·50

**69.** Rockhopper, Gentoo and King Penguins.

**1982.** Air. " Philexfrance 82 " International Stamp Exhibition, Paris.

167. **69.** 8 f. brown, blue & black 6·00 6·00

**70.** "Commandant Charcot" (ice patrol ship).

**1982.** Air. Overseas Week.

168. **70.** 5 f. blue and green .. 2·75 2·50

**71.** Lighter " Le Gros Ventre ".

**1983.**

169. **71.** 55 c. dp. brn., grn. & bl. 1·25 1·10

**72.** Apostles Islands.

**1983.** Air.

170. **72.** 65 c. dp. bl., brn. & bl. 1·00 1·00

**73.** Church and Statue of Virgin and Child.

**1983.** Church of Our Lady of the Winds, Kerguelen.

171 **73** 1 f. 40 blue, brown & grn 1·25 1·25

**74.** Pintails. **75.** Vivies.

**1983.**

172. **74.** 1 f. 50 dp. brn., brn. & bl. 1·40 1·25
173. 1 f. 80 brown & green .. 1·40 1·25

**1983.** Paul Martin de Vivies Commemoration.

174. **75.** 1 f. 60 blue .. .. 1·25 1·25

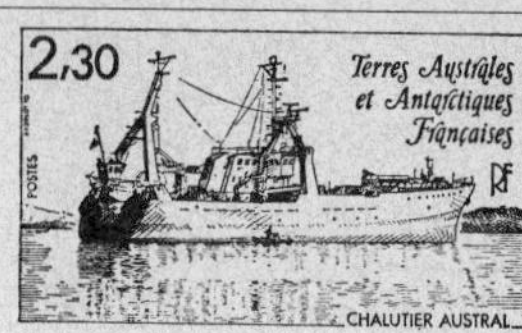


**76.** Trawler " Austral ".

**1983.**

175. **76.** 2 f. 30 brn., blue & pur. 1·75 1·60

**77.** Dog Sledge.

**1983.** Air.

176. **77.** 4 f. 55 blue .. .. 4·50 3·50

**78.** "Sputnik I" Satellite. **80.** "Lady Franklin" (Antarctic supply ship).

**79.** "Antarctica" (Georges Mathieu) (illustration reduced to half-size).

**1983.** Air. Anniversaries. Each black, blue and brown.

177 1 f. 50 Type **78** (25th anniv of International Geophysical Year) .. .. 50 40
178 3 f. 30 Orange Bay, Cape Horn (cent of first Polar Year) (49 × 36 mm.) .. 1·00 80
179 5 f. 20 Scoresby Sound, Greenland (50th anniv of second Polar Year) (49 × 36 mm.) .. .. 1·50 1·25

**1983.** Air.

180. **79.** 25 f. blue, blk. & red 12·00 10·00

**1983.**

181. **80.** 5 f. bl., dp. bl. & blk... 5·50 5·50

**81. Drilling for Samples.**

**1984.** Glaciology.

182. **81.** 15 c. brn., orge. & bl. 50 50
183. 1 f. 70 bl., orge. & red 1·00 1·00

**82.** Crabeater Seal.

**1984.** Antarctic Wildlife.

184. **82.** 60 c. green, grey & brn. 1·00 1·00
185. – 70 c. bl., dp. bl. & brn. 1·25 1·00
186. – 2 f. green, blue & brn. 1·75 1·60
187. **82.** 5 f. 90 blk., blue & red 3·00 2·50

Designs: 70 c., 2 f. Rockhopper penguins.

**83.** Faure.

**1984.** Alfred Faure Commemoration.

188. **83.** 1 f. 80 blk., brn. & red 1·50 1·50

**84.** "Erebus" (bomb ketch) in Antarctic (after Davis).

**1984.** Air.

189. **84.** 2 f. 60 dp. blue & blue.. 1·50 1·50

**85.** Balloons and Airships.

**1984.** Air. Bicent. of Manned Flight.

190. **85.** 3 f. 50 red, brn. & blue 1·50 1·50
191. – 7 f. 80 brn., bl. & vio. 3·50 3·50

Design: 7 f. 80, Montgolfier balloon, Renard and Krebs' airship "La France", balloon "Zodiac" and other balloons and airships.

**86. Polar Aurora.**

**1984.** Air.

192. **86.** 3 f. 50 multicoloured .. 2·50 2·50

**87.** Joan of Arc Port, Kerguelen, 1930.

**1984.** Air.

193. **87.** 4 f. 70 turquoise, blue & deep blue.. .. 3·00 3·00

**88.** "Albatros". **90.** Mouflons.

**89.** Survey Barquentine "Gauss".

**1984.** Air. Commissioning of Patrol Boat "Albatros".
194. **88.** 11 f. 30 deep blue, red and blue .. .. 5·00 5·00

**1984.** Air. "Nordposta" International Stamp Exhibition, Hamburg.
195. **89.** 9 f. maroon and blue .. 5·50 5·50

**1985.** Antarctic Wildlife.
196 – 1 f. 70 black, brown and orange (postage) .. 1·75 1·75
197 – 2 f. 80 turquoise, black and blue .. .. 1·75 1·75
198 **90** 70 c. brn, bl & mve (air) 1·00 1·00
199 – 3 f. 90 brn, grey & orge 2·75 2·75
DESIGNS—HORIZ. 1 f. 70, Emperor penguins. 2 f. 80, Snow petrel. VERT. 3 f. 90, Amsterdam albatross.

**91.** Emblem, Humpback Whales, Krill and Research Vessel.

**1985.** Biomass.
200. **91.** 1 f. 80 deep blue, mauve and blue .. 1·75 1·75
201. 5 f. 20 blue, light blue and red .. .. 2·75 2·75

**92.** Liotard. **93.** Port Martin Base, Adelie Land.

**1985.** Andre-Frank Liotard (explorer) Commemoration.
202. **92.** 2 f. purple and violet 1·25 1·10

**1985.**
203. **93.** 2 f. 20 blue, brown and deep blue .. .. 1·40 1·40

**94.** "La Novara" (frigate) at Saint Paul (after J. Noel).

**1985.** Air.
204. **94.** 12 f. 80 black & orange 7·50 7·50

**95.** "Explorer and Fur Seal". (½-size illustration.)

**1985.** Air.
205. **95.** 30 f. multicoloured .. 12·00 12·00

**96.** Various Motifs, Rope and Kerguelen's Ships.

**1985.** Air. 30th Anniv of French Southern and Antarctic Territories. Each blue, green and black.
206. 2 f. Type **96** .. .. 75 75
207. 12 f. 80 Motifs, rope and ships (different) .. .. 4·75 4·75

**97.** Southern Fulmars.

**1986.** Birds.
208. **97.** 1 f. blue & black (postage) .. .. 80 80
209. – 1 f. 70 black, green and brown .. .. 1·00 1·00
210. – 4 f. 60 brown, yellow and red (air) .. 2·75 2·75
DESIGNS: 1 f. 70, Giant petrels. 4 f. 60, Southern black-backed gull.

**98.** Echinoderms.

**1986.**
211. **98.** 1 f. 90 brown and blue 1·10 1·10

**99.** "Polarbjorn" (Antarctic supply ship). **101.** "Cotula plumosa".

**100.** Charcot and "Pourquoi Pas?" leaving Harbour.

**1986.** Ships.
212. – 2 f. 10 deep blue and blue .. .. 1·25 1·25
213. **99.** 3 f. red, light blue and blue .. .. 1·60 1·60
DESIGN: 2 f. 10, B.C.A. "Var A 608" (patrol boat).

**1986.** Air. 50th Death Anniv. of Jean Charcot (explorer). Each brown, blue and red.
214. 2 f. 10 Type **100** .. .. 75 75
215. 14 f. Charcot and "Pourquoi Pas?" in heavy seas .. .. 5·25 5·25

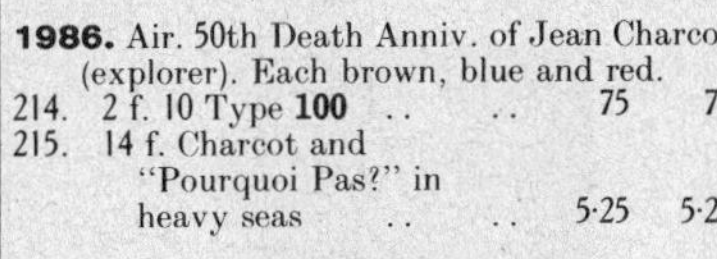

**1986.** Plants.
216. **101.** 2 f. 30 green, yellow and black .. .. 1·40 1·25
217. – 6 f. 20 green and red 3·00 2·75
DESIGN: 6 f. 20, "Lycopodium saururus."

**102.** Airplane, Parachutes and Aerial.

**1986.** Scientific Research.
218 **102** 14 f. red, black & orge 6·00 6·00

**103.** Satellite over Antarctic.

**1986.** Air. "SPOT" Surveillance Satellite.
219. **103.** 8 f. brown, grn & bl. 4·00 4·00

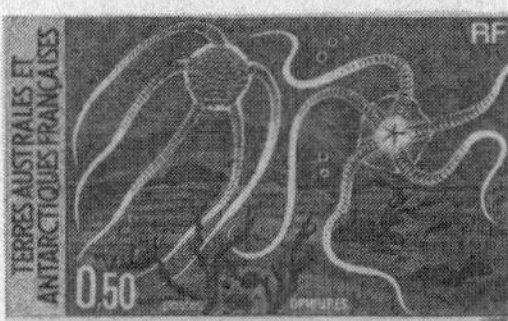


**104.** Starfish.

**1987.**
220. **104.** 50 c. blue, orge. & grn. 40 30

**105.** "Poa cookii".

**1987.** Plants.
221. **105.** 1 f. 80 green and blue 1·10 90
222. – 6 f. 50 green, red & bl. 2·75 2·25
DESIGN: 6 f. 50, Lichen.

**106.** Marret Base, Adélie Land.

**1987.**
223. **106.** 2 f. brown, bl. & pur. 1·25 1·25

**107.** Admiral Mouchez.

**1987.**
224. **107.** 2 f. 20 bl., blk. & brn. 1·40 1·40

**108.** Reindeer.

**1987.** Antarctic Wildlife.
225. **108.** 2 f. 50 black .. .. 1·25 1·10
226. – 4 f. 80 multicoloured 2·50 2·25
DESIGN: 4 f. 80, Macaroni penguins.

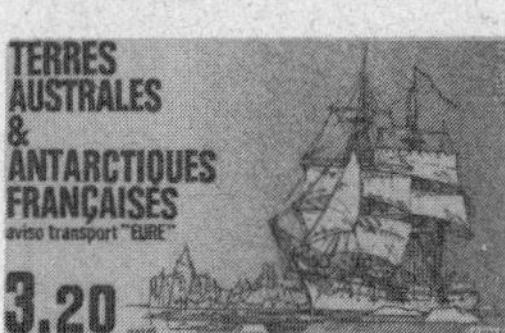


**109.** Dispatch Vessel "Eure".

**1987.**
227. **109.** 3 f. 20 turquoise, blue and green .. .. 1·40 1·40

**110.** "J. B. Charcot" (schooner).

**1987.** Air.
228. **110.** 14 f. 60 purple, blue and brown .. .. 6·00 5·50

**111.** Globe and Research Vessels.

**1987.** Air. Scientific Research.
229. **111.** 16 f. 80 deep blue, blue and brown .. .. 6·00 5·50

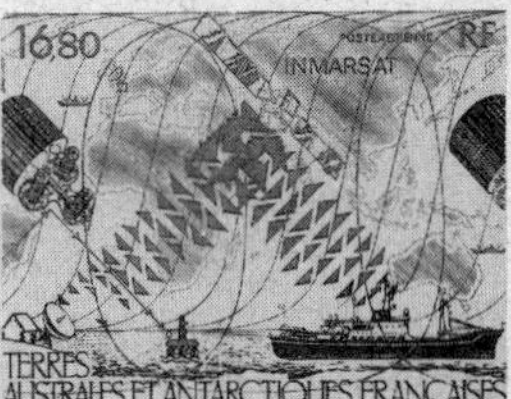


**112.** "Inmarsat" Satellite.

**1987.** Air.
230. **112.** 16 f. 80 brown and black .. .. 6·00 5·50

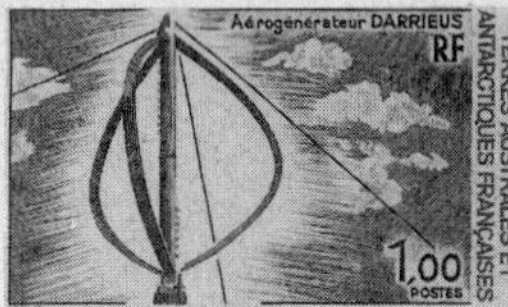


**113.** Darrieus Wind Generator.

**1988.**
231. **113.** 1 f. blue, indigo and light blue .. .. 65 55

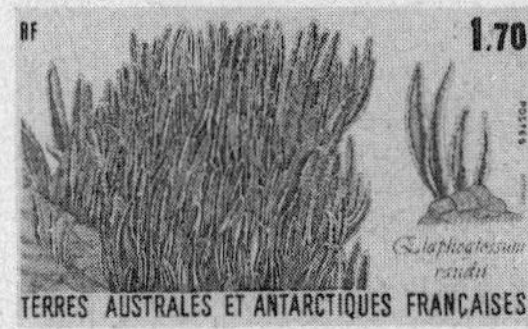


**114.** Elephant Grass.

**1988.**
232 **114** 1 f. 70 green, bistre and deep green .. 80 55

**115.** Globe and Father Lejay. **117.** Gessain.

**116.** Geological Sections of Volcanoes.

**1988.**
233. **115.** 2 f. 20 black and violet 1·00 65

**1988.** Antarctic Geology. Multicoloured.
234. 2 f. 20 Type **116** .. .. 55 45
235. 15 f. 10 Geological map of Kerguelen Islands .. 4·50 4·00

**1988.** 2nd Death Anniv of Robert Gessain (explorer).
236 **117** 3 f. 40 red, grey & grn 1·10 90

**118.** "Le Gros Ventre" (frigate).

**1988.** Ships.
237. **118.** 3 f. 50 brown, green and blue .. .. 1·10 80
238. – 4 f. 90 blue and black 1·60 1·25
239. – 5 f. blue and black .. 1·60 1·25
DESIGNS—HORIZ. 4 f. 90, Mermaid with anvil and "Jules Verne" (Antarctic supply ship). VERT. 5 f. "La Fortune" (sail warship).

**119.** Penguin Island.

**1988.** Air. Penguin Island.
240 **119** 3 f. 90 brown and blue 1·50 1·10
241 – 15 f. 10 blue, brown and green .. .. 4·75 4·00
DESIGN: 15 f. 10, Views of island from sea and air.

**120.** Wilson's Petrels.

**1988.**
242. **120.** 6 f. 80 blue, black and brown .. .. 2·50 1·90

**121.** Igloos.

**1988.** Air. 40th Anniv. of French Polar Expeditions.
243. **121.** 20 f. green, purple and red .. .. .. 6·75 5·50

**122.** Crab.

**1989.** Flora and Fauna.
244. **122.** 1 f. 10 light brown, blue and brown .. 35 20
245. – 2 f. black, brown and green 65 55
246. – 2 f. 80 green, red and brown .. .. 90 55
247. – 3 f. 60 blue, deep blue and black .. 1·25 1·00
DESIGNS: 2 f. Kerguelen sheep. 2 f. 80, "Blechnum penna marina". 3 f. 60, Blue petrel.

**123.** Diver.

**1989.** Diving off Adelie Land.
248. **123.** 1 f. 70 brn., grn. & bl. 65 55

**124.** Henry and Rene Bossiere.

**1989.** Kerguelen Islands Pioneers.
249. **124.** 2 f. 20 brn., ol. & bl. 65 55

**125.** "La Curieuse" (topsail schooner), 1913.

**1989.** Air. Ships. Each blue, black and red.
250 2 f. 20 Type **125** .. .. 1·00 1·00
251 15 f. 50 "La Curieuse" (supply ship), 1989 .. 4·50 4·50

**126.** Mesotype.

**1989.** Crystals.
252. **126.** 5 f. 10 turq., blk. & bl. 1·60 1·40
253. – 7 f. 30 mauve, green and grey .. .. 2·25 2·00
DESIGN: 7 f. 30, Analcime.

**127.** Map.

**1989.** Air. Apostles Islands.
254 **127** 8 f. 40 blue, grey & grn 2·75 1·60

**128.** Buildings.

**1989.** Air. 40th Anniv. of Establishment of Permanent Antarctic Bases.
255. **128.** 15 f. 50 brown .. 5·00 3·50

**129** Allegory

**1989.** Air. Bicentenary of French Revolution.
256 **129** 5 f. blue, green & mve 4·00 2·75

**130** Figures around Map

**1989.** Air. 15th Antarctic Treaty Consultative Meeting, Paris.
258 **130** 17 f. 70 red, purple & bl 5·50 4·50

**131** "Chonotriches", "Copepodes" and Map of Kerguelen

**1990.** Protistology.
259 **131** 1 f. 10 blue, brn & blk 50 45

**132** Cattle

**1990.** Restoration of Amsterdam Island.
260 **132** 1 f. 70 brown, grn & bl 70 70

**133** Quoy and Decollate Planaxis Shell

**135** Dumont d'Urville

**134** Yellow-nosed Albatrosses

**1990.** Birth Bicentenary of Jean Rene C. Quoy (doctor and naturalist).
261 **133** 2 f. 20 bl, dp brn & brn 80 65

**1990.**
262 **134** 2 f. 80 multicoloured .. 1·50 1·25

**1990.** Birth Bicentenary of Jules Dumont d'Urville (explorer).
263 **135** 3 f. 60 brown and blue 1·10 90

**136** Aragonite

**1990.** Minerals.
264 **136** 5 f. 10 brown and blue 1·60 1·40

**137** Pigs Island

**1990.** Air.
265 **137** 7 f. 30, green, brn & bl 2·25 1·60

**138** "Ranunculus pseudo trullifolius"

**1990.**
266 **138** 8 f. 40 green, bl & orge 2·50 2·00

**139** "L'Astrolabe"

**1990.** Air. 150th Anniv of Discovery of Adelie Land by Dumont d'Urville.
267 **139** 15 f. 50 brown and red 3·00 3·00

**140** "L'Astrolabe" (fishery control vessel), 1988

**1990.** Air. Ships. Each blue, green and red.
268 2 f. 20 Type **140** .. .. 75 75
269 15 f. 50 "L'Astrolabe" (Dumont d'Urville's ship), 1840 .. .. 4·75 4·75

**141** Bird
(½ size illustration)

**1990.** Air.
270 **141** 30 f. multicoloured .. 9·00 5·50

**142** Map, Emperor Penguin and Envelopes

**1991.** 30th Anniv of Postal Service to Crozet.
271 **142** 50 c. blue, ultram & blk 50 20

**143** Moss Balls in Shingle

**1991.**
272 **143** 1 f. 70 grey, brn & blk 50 35

144 Wandering Albatrosses and "Argos" Satellite

**1991.** Air.

273 **144** 2 f. 10 brown, bl & red 1·25 95

**145** Douguet and Flag

**1991.** Admiral Max Douguet Commemoration.

274 **145** 2 f. 30 blue, blk & orge 70 70

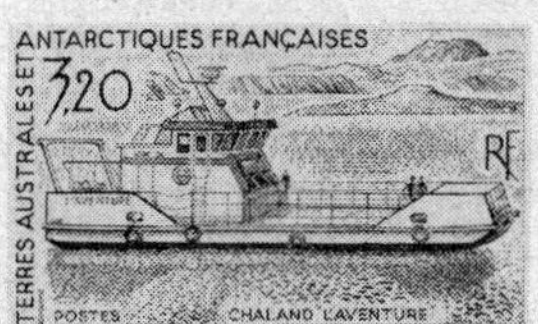


**146** "L'Aventure" (landing craft)

**1991.**

275 **146** 3 f. 20 brown, bl & grn 1·00 1·00

**147** Fur Seals

**1991.**

276 **147** 3 f. 60 brown and blue 1·10 65

**148** Infra-red Image and Measuring Equipment (study of ozone layer)

**1991.** Air. Climatic Research. Each green, violet and orange.

277 3 f. 60 Type **148** .. .. 1·00 1·00
278 20 f. Research vessel and rock samples (palaeo-climatology) .. .. 5·75 5·75

**149** Mordenite

**1991.**

279 **149** 5 f. 20 blue, grn & blk 1·50 80

**150** Mackerel Icefish

**1991.**

280 **150** 7 f. 80 green and blue 2·25 1·60

**151** Map **152** De Gaulle and Map

**1991.** 30th Anniv of Antarctic Treaty.

281 **151** 9 f. 30 green, deep green and red .. 2·75 1·90

**1991.** Air. Birth Centenary of Charles de Gaulle (French statesman).

282 **152** 18 f. 80 black, bl & red 5·50 3·25

**153** Research Worker greeting Penguin (Antarctic)

**1991.** Air. French Institute for Polar Research and Technology. Multicoloured.

283 15 f. Type **153** .. .. 4·25 4·25
284 15 f. Research worker greeting polar bear (Arctic) .. .. 4·25 4·25

Nos. 283/4 were printed together, se-tenant, forming a composite design.

**154** Arms **155** "Colobanthus kerguelensis"

**1992.**

| | | | | | |
|---|---|---|---|---|---|
| 285 | **154** | 10 c. black .. .. | 10 | 10 |
| 286 | | 20 c. blue .. .. | 10 | 10 |
| 287 | | 30 c. red .. .. | 10 | 10 |
| 288 | | 40 c. green .. .. | 10 | 10 |
| 289 | | 50 c. orange .. .. | 10 | 10 |

**1992.**

295 **155** 1 f. brown, green & blue 30 15

**156** Yacht and Antarctic Route

**1992.** "Globe Challenge" Round the World Sailing Race.

296 **156** 2 f. 20 multicoloured .. 75 75

**157** Antarctic Blenny

**1992.**

297 **157** 2 f. 30 green, blue & brn 65 35

**158** Paul Tchernia (scientist)

**1992.**

298 **158** 2 f. 50 green, brown and deep brown .. 70 35

**159** Pintado Petrels **160** Marion-Dufresne (after Meryon)

**1992.** Air.

299 **159** 3 f. 40 brown, blk & grn 1·25 1·00

**1992.** 220th Death Anniv of Marion-Dufresne (explorer).

300 **160** 3 f. 70 black, red & blue 1·10 45

**161** "Tottan" (supply ship)

**1992.**

301 **161** 14 f. brown, turq & blue 4·00 4·00

**162** Columbus's Fleet, Montgolfier Balloon and Columbus

**1992.** Air. 500th Anniv of Discovery of America by Columbus.

302 **162** 22 f. brn, pur & dp brn 7·00 7·00

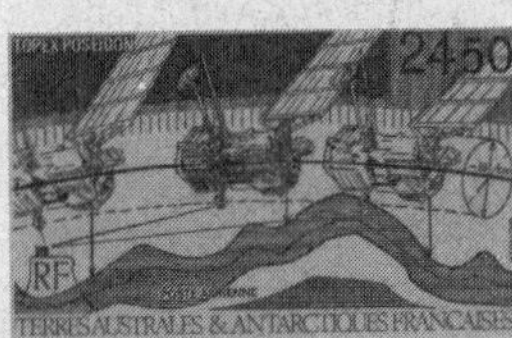


**163** Satellite in Orbit

**1992.** Air. "Topex Poseidon" Satellite.

303 **163** 24 f. 50 red, black & bl 6·75 2·75

**164** Ocean Currents, Research Vessel and Pipes

**1992.** WOCE Research Programme.

304 **164** 25 f. 40 brown, orange and blue .. .. 7·50 7·50

**165** Adelie and Emperor Penguins on Landing Strip (½-size illustration)

**1992.** Air. Completion of Landing Strip at Dumont D'Urville Research Station, Adelie Land.

305 **165** 25 f. 70 multicoloured 7·25 5·25

**166** Violet-tinted Garnet

**1993.**

306 **166** 1 f. purple, green & blk 20 10

**167** Radio Equipment, Handshake and Globe

**1993.** Air. Amateur Radio Enthusiasts.

307 **167** 2 f. black, red & mauve 45 20

**168** "Marion Dufresne" **169** "Lyallia kerguelensis"

**1993.** 20th Anniv of the "Marion Dufresne" (Antarctic supply ship).

308 **168** 2 f. 20 mauve, blk & bl 50 35

**1993.**

309 **169** 2 f. 30 blue, green & yell 50 20

**170** Killer Whale

**1993.**

310 **170** 2 f. 50 black and purple 55 25

171 Great Skuas

**1993.**
311 171 2 f. 50 black .. .. 55 25

172 Andre Prud'homme (meteorologist)

**1993.** 43rd Anniv of Meteo France (weather service) in the Antarctic. Each black, blue and red.
312 2 f. 50 Type 172 .. .. 55 25
313 22 f. Meteorologists recording wind speed on Adelie Land (35 × 37mm) 4·75 2·00

173 Red-banded Bellowfish

**1993.**
314 173 3 f. 40 red, brown & bl 75 30

174 "Italo Marsano"

**1993.** 43rd Anniv of Chartering of the "Italo Marsano" (freighter).
315 174 3 f. 70 purple, brn & bl 80 50

175 King Penguins on Television and Platform

**1993.** ECOPHY Research Programme.
316 175 14 f. brown, blue & blk 3·00 1·25

176 "L'Astrolabe" and Route Map

**1993.** Voyage of "L'Astrolabe" (fishery control ship) through North-East Passage.
317 176 22 f. red and blue .. 4·75 3·00

177 Scientists examining Arctic Tern and using Microscope

**1993.** Air. Animal Biology Laboratory, Adelie Land.
318 177 25 f. 40 brown, green and deep green .. 5·75 2·25

178 Camp, Snow Vehicles and Map

**1993.** Air. Antarctic Expedition Base D 10.
319 178 25 f. 70 brown, red & bl 5·75 2·25

179 Lockheed Hercules over Adelie Land

**1993.** Air. Inauguration of Air Strip, Adelie Land.
320 179 30 f. black, blue & grn 6·75 2·75

180 Cordierite

**1994.**
321 180 1 f. blue, green & black 20 10

181 Domestic Cat

**1994.**
322 181 2 f. blk, grn & emerald 45 20

182 Lowering Probe into Sea

**1994.** 1000th Sea-bed Sample.
323 182 2 f. 40 black and blue .. 55 25

183 Pommier and Dog

**1994.** 75th Birth Anniv of Robert Pommier (explorer).
324 183 2 f. 80 blue, pur & orge 65 30

184 Salvin's Prion

**1994.**
325 184 2 f. 80 blue .. .. 65 30

185 C. A. Vincendon Dumoulin (hydrographic engineer)

**1994.** Navy Hydrographic and Oceanographic Service. Each black and blue.
326 2 f. 80 Type 185 .. .. 65 30
327 23 f. Measuring magnetic force (35 × 36 mm) .. 5·25 2·10

186 Yellow Gurnard

**1994.**
328 186 3 f. 70 orange and green 85 35

187 "Kerguelen de Tremarec" (trawler)

**1994.**
329 187 4 f. 30 lilac, red & green 1·00 40

188 "Copepoda"

**1994.** Air.
330 188 15 f. black .. .. 3·50 1·40

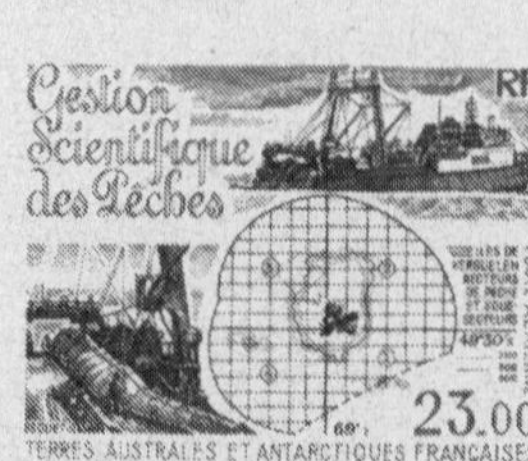
189 Trawler and Chart of Fishing Sectors around Kerguelen Islands

**1994.** Air. Scientific Management of Fishing Industry.
331 189 23 f. purple, blue & red 5·25 2·10

190 Map of Antarctic, Satellite and Earth Station

**1994.** Air. National Centre for Space Study Satellite Station, Kerguelen.
332 190 26 f. 70 lilac, blue and ultramarine .. 6·00 2·40

191 Lidar Station and Map

**1994.** Air. Lidar Research Station, Adelie Land.
333 191 27 f. 30 blue, grn & mve 6·25 2·50

192 Penguins (½-size illustration)

**1994.** Air. Migration of Emperor Penguins.
334 192 28 f. black and blue .. 6·25 2·50

193 Olivine

**1995.**
335 193 1 f. olive, green & lilac 25 10

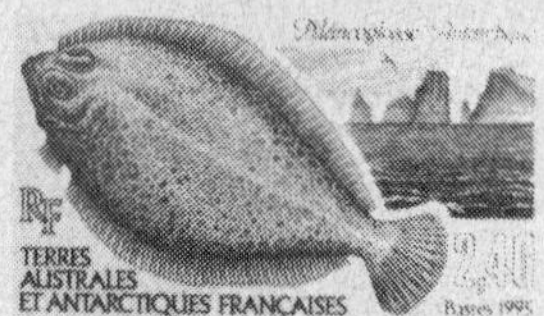
194 Antarctic Mancoglosse

**1995.**
336 194 2 f. 40 brown, bl & mve 60 25

195 Andree and Edgar Aubert de la Rue (naturalists)

**1995.**
337 195 2 f. 80 brown, bl & mve 65 25

196 SODAR Station (wind study centre)

**1995.**
338 196 2 f. 80 mauve, red & vio 65 25

**197** Mont d'Alsace, Kerguelen

**1995.**
339 **197** 3 f. 70 brown, vio & bl 90 35

**198** Research Vessel

**1995.** Air. Mt. Erebus Expedition.
340 **198** 4 f. 30 blue, grn & mve 1·00 40

**199** Waving Farewell

**1995.** Air. Departure of Winter Residents from Charcot Station.
341 **199** 15 f. multicoloured .. 3·50 1·40

**200** Minke Whale

**1995.**
342 **200** 23 f. dp blue, bl & pur 5·50 2·25

**201** "Tamaris" and Tagged Grey-headed Albatross

**1995.** Voyage of "Tamaris" (full-rigged ship).
343 **201** 25 f. 80 brn, turq & bl 6·25 2·50

**202** "Heroine" (full-rigged ship)

**1995.** Expedition of "Heroine" to Crozet Islands in 1837.
344 **202** 27 f. 30 blue .. 6·50 2·75

**203** Seals
(½-size illustration)

**1995.** 165th Death Anniv of G. Lesquin.
345 **203** 28 f. multicoloured .. 6·75 2·75

**204** Amazonite

**1996.**
347 **204** 1 f. blue, green & black 25 10

**205** White-chinned Petrel

**1996.**
348 **205** 2 f. 40 blue .. .. 65 30

**206** "Yves de Kerguelen" (expedition ship)

**1996.**
349 **206** 2 f. 80 brown, bl & pur 75 30

**207** Station

**209** Jacquinot

**208** Victor crossing Greenland, 1936

**1996.** Benedict Point Scientific Research Station, Amsterdam Island.
350 **207** 2 f. 80 brown, deep green and green .. 75 30

**1996.** Paul-Emile Victor Commemoration. Each black, blue and red.
351 2 f. 80. Type **208** .. .. 75 30
352 23 f. Victor, penguins and Dumont d'Urville Base, Terre Adelie .. .. 6·00 2·40

**1996.** Birth Bicentenary of Admiral Jacquinot.
353 **209** 3 f. 70 ultramarine & bl 95 40

**210** "Austral" (trawler)

**1996.**
354 **210** 4 f. 30 black, blue & grn 1·10 45

**211** "Lycopodium magellanicum"

**1996.**
355 **211** 7 f. 70 green and purple 2·00 80

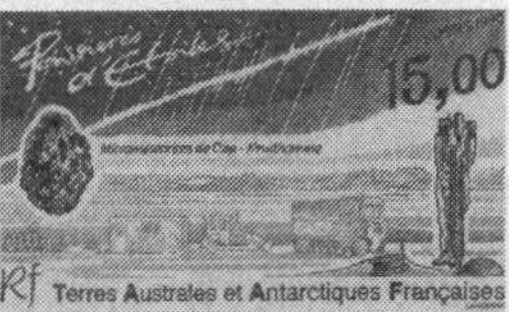

**212** Drilling and Micrometeorite

**1996.** Micrometeorites of Cape Prudhomme.
356 **212** 15 f. black, violet & bl 4·00 1·60

**213** East Island

**1996.** Air.
357 **213** 20 f. brown, bl & lt brn 5·25 2·10

**214** Tractor and Camp

**1996.** Air. Raid Dome/C.
358 **214** 23 f. blue .. .. 6·00 2·40

**215** Blue Rorqual and Map of Sanctuary Area

**1996.** Air. Southern Whale Sanctuary.
359 **215** 26 f. 70 pur, bl & orge 7·00 3·00

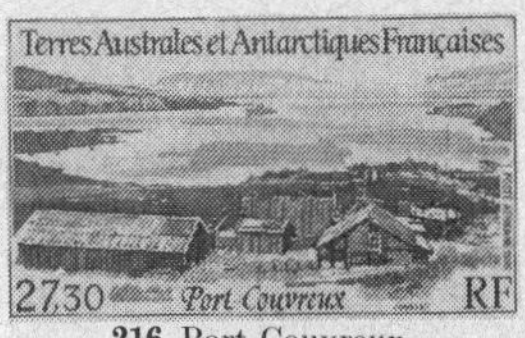

**216** Port-Couvreux

**1996.** Air.
360 **216** 27 f. 30 blue, grn & brn 7·25 3·00

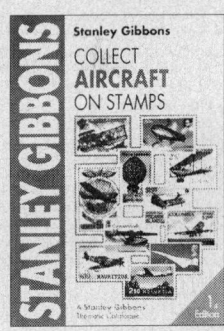

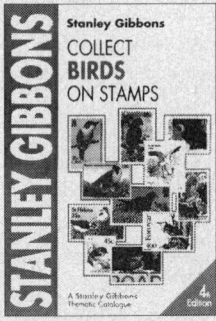

## FRENCH SUDAN Pt. 6

A territory in central Africa. In 1899 parts of the colony were detached and added to neighbouring coastal colonies with the remainder becoming Senegambia and Niger (subsequently renamed Upper Senegal and Niger). In 1920 Niger became a separate colony and Upper Senegal reverted to the name of French Sudan.

From 1944 to 1959 French Sudan used the stamps of French West Africa. In 1959 French Sudan combined with Senegal to form the Mali Federation.

100 centimes = 1 franc.

**1894.** Stamps of French Colonies, "Commerce" type, surch. **SOUDAN Fais and value.**

| | | | | |
|---|---|---|---|---|
| 1. | J. | 0.15 on 75 c. red .. .. | £2250 | £1250 |
| 2. | | 0.25 on 1 f. olive .. .. | £2750 | £900 |

**1894.** "Tablet" key-type inscr "SOUDAN FRANÇAIS" in red (1, 5, 15, 25, 50 (No. 21), 75c., 1 f.) or blue (others).

| | | | | |
|---|---|---|---|---|
| 3 | D | 1 c. black on blue .. | 85 | 1·00 |
| 4 | | 2 c. brown on buff .. | 1·00 | 80 |
| 5 | | 4 c. brown on grey .. | 2·50 | 3·00 |
| 6 | | 5 c. green on light green | 2·00 | 2·00 |
| 7 | | 10 c. black on lilac .. | 8·50 | 8·50 |
| 18 | | 10 c. red .. | 2·50 | 2·50 |
| 8 | | 15 c. blue .. .. | 2·25 | 2·25 |
| 19 | | 15 c. grey .. .. | 3·50 | 4·00 |
| 9 | | 20 c. red on green .. | 10·00 | 13·50 |
| 10 | | 25 c. black on pink .. | 13·50 | 13·00 |
| 20 | | 25 c. blue .. .. | 3·00 | 3·25 |
| 11 | | 30 c. brown on drab .. | 28·00 | 28·00 |
| 12 | | 40 c. red on yellow .. | 15·00 | 15·00 |
| 13 | | 50 c. red on pink .. | 30·00 | 30·00 |
| 21 | | 50 c. brown on blue .. | 6·00 | 6·25 |
| 14 | | 75 c. brown on yellow .. | 20·00 | 20·00 |
| 15 | | 1 f. green .. .. | 4·50 | 5·50 |

**1921.** Stamps of Upper Senegal and Niger optd **SOUDAN FRANCAIS.**

| | | | | |
|---|---|---|---|---|
| 85 | 7 | 1 c. violet and purple .. | 10 | 25 |
| 86 | | 2 c. purple and grey .. | 10 | 25 |
| 87 | | 4 c. blue and black .. | 10 | 25 |
| 88 | | 5 c. chocolate and brown | 10 | 25 |
| 89 | | 10 c. green & light green | 10 | 25 |
| 121 | | 10 c. blue and mauve .. | 10 | 25 |
| 90 | | 15 c. orange and purple | 15 | 25 |
| 122 | | 15 c. green & light green | 10 | 25 |
| 123 | | 15 c. mauve and brown | 70 | 90 |
| 91 | | 20 c. black and purple | 15 | 20 |
| 92 | | 25 c. green and black .. | 25 | 20 |
| 93 | | 30 c. carmine and red .. | 25 | 35 |
| 124 | | 30 c. black and green .. | 20 | 35 |
| 125 | | 30 c. green and olive .. | 70 | 1·10 |
| 94 | | 35 c. violet and red .. | 10 | 25 |
| 95 | | 40 c. red and grey .. | 40 | 55 |
| 96 | | 45 c. brown and blue .. | 40 | 50 |
| 97 | | 50 c. blue & ultramarine | 50 | 70 |
| 126 | | 50 c. blue and orange .. | 35 | 35 |
| 127 | | 60 c. violet on pink .. | 20 | 45 |
| 128 | | 65 c. blue and brown .. | 75 | 75 |
| 98 | | 75 c. brown and yellow | 50 | 70 |
| 129 | | 90 c. carmine and red .. | 3·00 | 3·00 |
| 99 | | 1 f. purple and brown .. | 60 | 70 |
| 130 | | 1 f. 10 mauve and blue | 1·40 | 1·40 |
| 131 | | 1 f. 50 blue .. .. | 3·00 | 3·00 |
| 100 | | 2 f. blue and green .. | 1·40 | 1·40 |
| 132 | | 3 f. mauve on pink .. | 5·50 | 4·75 |
| 101 | | 5 f. black and violet .. | 3·25 | 3·00 |

**1922.** Surch in figures and bars.

| | | | | |
|---|---|---|---|---|
| 110 | 7 | 25 c. on 45 c. brown & bl | 45 | 60 |
| 111 | | 60 on 75 c. violet on pink | 20 | 40 |
| 112 | | 65 on 75 c. brown & yell | 60 | 75 |
| 113 | | 85 on 2 f. blue and green | 85 | 1·00 |
| 114 | | 85 on 5 f. black & violet | 95 | 1·25 |
| 115 | | 90 c. on 75 c. red and carmine .. .. | 1·00 | 1·25 |
| 116 | | 1 f. 25 on 1 f. lt bl & bl | 55 | 75 |
| 117 | | 1 f. 50 on 1 f. ultramarine and blue .. | 65 | 65 |
| 118 | | 3 f. on 5 f. buff and pink | 2·25 | 1·90 |
| 119 | | 10 f. on 5 f. green & red | 8·00 | 9·00 |
| 120 | | 20 f. on 5 f. red & violet | 9·50 | 12·50 |

**14.** Sudanese Woman marketing.

**15.** Djenne Gateway.

**1931.**

| | | | | |
|---|---|---|---|---|
| 135 | 14 | 1 c. black and red .. | 10 | 20 |
| 136 | | 2 c. red and blue .. | 10 | 25 |
| 137 | | 3 c. black and red .. | 10 | 25 |
| 138 | | 4 c. red and lilac .. | 10 | 25 |
| 139 | | 5 c. green and blue .. | 10 | 25 |
| 140 | | 10 c. red and green .. | 10 | 15 |
| 141 | | 15 c. violet and black .. | 10 | 10 |
| 142 | | 20 c. blue and brown .. | 10 | 10 |
| 143 | | 25 c. pink and mauve .. | 15 | 20 |
| 144 | 15 | 30 c. light green & green | 15 | 25 |
| 145 | | 30 c. red and blue .. | 30 | 40 |
| 146 | | 35 c. green and olive .. | 20 | 35 |
| 147 | | 40 c. red and green .. | 10 | 25 |
| 148 | | 45 c. red and blue .. | 45 | 45 |
| 149 | | 45 c. green and olive .. | 20 | 35 |
| 150 | | 50 c. black and red .. | 40 | 10 |
| 151 | | 55 c. red and blue .. | 25 | 40 |
| 152 | | 60 c. brown and blue .. | 15 | 45 |
| 153 | | 65 c. black and violet .. | 35 | 30 |
| 154 | | 70 c. red and blue .. | 60 | 60 |
| 155 | | 75 c. brown and blue .. | 1·00 | 70 |
| 156 | | 80 c. brown and red .. | 30 | 45 |
| 157 | | 90 c. orange and red .. | 40 | 50 |
| 158 | | 90 c. black and violet .. | 50 | 65 |
| 159 | | 1 f. green and blue .. | 4·00 | 90 |
| 160 | | 1 f. red .. .. | 2·25 | 1·00 |
| 161 | | 1 f. brown and red .. | 20 | 40 |
| 162 | – | 1 f. 25 mauve and violet | 1·25 | 50 |
| 163 | – | 1 f. 25 red and scarlet .. | 40 | 50 |
| 164 | – | 1 f. 40 black and violet | 50 | 60 |
| 165 | – | 1 f. 50 blue and indigo | 50 | 50 |
| 166 | – | 1 f. 60 blue and brown | 60 | 60 |
| 167 | – | 1 f. 70 blue and brown | 60 | 50 |
| 168 | – | 1 f. 75 blue .. .. | 45 | 50 |
| 169 | – | 2 f. green and brown .. | 40 | 35 |
| 170 | – | 2 f. 25 ultramarine & bl | 50 | 50 |
| 171 | – | 2 f. 50 brown .. .. | 60 | 60 |
| 172 | – | 3 f. brown and green .. | 40 | 25 |
| 173 | – | 5 f. black and red .. | 85 | 60 |
| 174 | – | 10 f. green and blue .. | 1·25 | 1·25 |
| 175 | – | 20 f. brown and mauve | 1·75 | 1·75 |

Design: 1 f. 25 to 20 f. Niger boatman.

**1931.** "Colonial Exhibition" key-types inscr "SOUDAN FRANCAIS".

| | | | | |
|---|---|---|---|---|
| 186 | E | 40 c. green and black .. | 1·10 | 1·25 |
| 187 | F | 50 c. mauve and black .. | 1·10 | 1·10 |
| 188 | G | 90 c. red and black .. | 1·00 | 1·10 |
| 189 | H | 1 f. 50 blue and black .. | 1·10 | 1·10 |

**1937.** International Exhibition, Paris. As Nos. 110/15 of Cameroun.

| | | | |
|---|---|---|---|
| 190 | 20 c. violet .. .. | 65 | 70 |
| 191 | 30 c. green .. .. | 65 | 70 |
| 192 | 40 c. red .. .. | 45 | 65 |
| 193 | 50 c. brown and agate .. | 45 | 70 |
| 194 | 90 c. red .. .. | 45 | 60 |
| 195 | 1 f. 50 blue .. .. | 45 | 65 |

**1938.** Int. Anti-Cancer Fund. As T **19** of Cameroun.

| | | | |
|---|---|---|---|
| 197. | 1 f. 75+50 c. blue .. | 2·50 | 6·00 |

**1939.** Caillie. As T **11** of Dahomey.

| | | | |
|---|---|---|---|
| 198. | 90 c. orange .. .. | 30 | 40 |
| 199. | 2 f. violet .. .. | 30 | 40 |
| 200. | 2 f. 25 blue .. .. | 30 | 45 |

**1939.** New York World's Fair. As T **20** of Cameroun.

| | | | |
|---|---|---|---|
| 201. | 1 f. 25 red .. .. | 55 | 60 |
| 202. | 2 f 25 blue .. .. | 50 | 60 |

**1939.** 150th Anniv of French Revolution. As T **25** of Cameroun.

| | | | |
|---|---|---|---|
| 203 | 45 c.+25 c. green & black | 4·25 | 4·25 |
| 204 | 70 c.+30 c. brown & black | 4·25 | 4·75 |
| 205 | 90 c.+35 c. orange & black | 4·25 | 4·75 |
| 206 | 1 f. 25+1 f. red and black | 4·25 | 4·25 |
| 207 | 2 f. 25+2 f. blue and black | 4·25 | 4·75 |

**1940.** Air. As T **12** of Dahomey.

| | | | |
|---|---|---|---|
| 208. | 1 f. 90 blue .. .. | 50 | 60 |
| 209. | 2 f. 90 red .. .. | 50 | 60 |
| 210. | 4 f. 50 green .. .. | 60 | 70 |
| 211. | 4 f. 90 olive .. .. | 60 | 70 |
| 212. | 6 f. 90 orange .. .. | 70 | 80 |

**1941.** National Defence Fund. Surch **SECOURS NATIONAL** and value.

| | | | |
|---|---|---|---|
| 213. | +1 f. on 50 c. (No. 150) .. | 2·00 | 2·00 |
| 214. | +2 f. on 80 c. (No. 156) .. | 3·75 | 3·75 |
| 215. | +2 f. on 1 f. 50 (No. 165) .. | 3·75 | 3·75 |
| 216. | +3 f. on 2 f. (No. 169) .. | 3·75 | 3·75 |

**1941. Marshal Petain Issue. As T 14b of Dahomey.**

| | | | |
|---|---|---|---|
| 217. | 1 f. green .. .. | 15 | 40 |
| 218. | 2 f. 50 blue .. .. | 20 | 40 |

**Designs—vert. Gate at Djenne and Marshal Petain.**

**1942.** Air. Colonial Child Welfare Fund. As Nos. 143g/i of Dahomey.

| | | | |
|---|---|---|---|
| 219 | 1 f. 50+3 f. 50 green .. | 15 | 85 |
| 220 | 2 f.+6 f. brown .. .. | 15 | 85 |
| 221 | 3 f.+9 f. red .. .. | 15 | 85 |

**1942.** Air. Imperial Fortnight. As T **14d** of Dahomey.

| | | | |
|---|---|---|---|
| 222 | 1 f. 20+1 f. 80 blue and red | 20 | |

**1942.** Air. As T **14e** of Dahomey.

| | | | |
|---|---|---|---|
| 223 | 50 f. blue and green .. | 90 | 1·40 |

### POSTAGE DUE STAMPS

**1921.** Postage Due stamps of Upper Senegal and Niger optd. **SOUDAN FRANCAIS.**

| | | | | |
|---|---|---|---|---|
| D 102. | M. | 5 c. green .. .. | 20 | 35 |
| D 103. | | 10 c. red .. .. | 25 | 35 |
| D 104. | | 15 c. grey .. .. | 30 | 45 |
| D 105. | | 20 c. brown .. .. | 35 | 55 |
| D 106. | | 30 c. blue .. .. | 55 | 60 |
| D 107. | | 50 c. black .. .. | 70 | 80 |
| D 108. | | 60 c. orange .. .. | 95 | 1·40 |
| D 109. | | 1 f. violet .. .. | 1·00 | 1·40 |

**1927.** Postage Due stamps of Upper Senegal and Niger surch. **SOUDAN FRANCAIS** and value.

| | | | | |
|---|---|---|---|---|
| D 133. | M. | "2 F." on 1 f. mauve | 2·50 | 3·25 |
| D 134. | | "3 F." on 1 f. brown | 2·50 | 3·25 |

**1931.** "Figure" key-type inscr. "SOUDAN FRANCAIS".

| | | | | |
|---|---|---|---|---|
| D 176. | M. | 5 c. green .. .. | 10 | 25 |
| D 177. | | 10 c. red .. .. | 10 | 25 |
| D 178. | | 15 c. grey .. .. | 10 | 25 |
| D 179. | | 20 c. brown .. .. | 10 | 30 |
| D 180. | | 30 c. blue .. .. | 15 | 30 |
| D 181. | | 50 c. black .. .. | 20 | 35 |
| D 182. | | 60 c. orange .. .. | 25 | 40 |
| D 183. | | 1 f. violet .. .. | 50 | 65 |
| D 184. | | 2 f. mauve .. .. | 65 | 75 |
| D 185. | | 3 f. brown .. .. | 75 | 70 |

## FRENCH TERRITORY OF THE AFARS AND THE ISSAS Pt. 6

Formerly French Somali Coast. Became independent in 1977 as Djibouti Republic.

100 centimes = 1 franc.

**66.** Grey-headed Kingfisher.

**1967.** Fauna.

| | | | |
|---|---|---|---|
| 504. 66. | 10 f. multicoloured (post.) | 2·75 | 1·75 |
| 505. – | 15 f. multicoloured .. | 3·25 | 2·75 |
| 506. – | 50 f. purple, brown & grn. | 9·50 | 8·00 |
| 507. – | 55 f. blue, violet and grey | 11·00 | 9·25 |
| 508. – | 60 f. orge., emer. & grn. | 15·00 | 13·00 |
| 509. – | 200 f. sepia, bistre and blue (air) .. .. .. | 40·00 | 19·00 |

Designs—horiz. 15 f. Oystercatcher. 50 f. Greenshank. 55 f. Abyssinian roller. vert. (22×36 mm.). 60 f. Unstriped ground squirrel. (27×48 mm.). 200 f. Tawny eagles.

**67.** Footballers.

**1967.** Sports.

| | | | |
|---|---|---|---|
| 510. 67. | 25 f. brn., grn. & bl. (post.) | 2·25 | 1·25 |
| 511. – | 30 f. brown, blue & purple | 3·00 | 2·50 |
| 512. – | 48 f. pur., bl. & bistre (air) | 3·75 | 1·60 |
| 513. – | 85 f. brown, blue & bistre | 5·50 | 3·50 |

Designs—horiz. 30 f. Basketball. **vert.** (27×48 mm.) 48 f. Parachute-jumping. **85 f.** Aquatic sports.

**1968.** 20th Anniv. of W.H.O. As T **26** of Comoro Islands.

| | | | |
|---|---|---|---|
| 514. | 15 f. multicoloured .. | 1·40 | 1·00 |

**68.** Damerdjog Fort.

**1968.** Administrative Outposts.

| | | | |
|---|---|---|---|
| 515. 68. | 20 f. blue, brown & green | 1·00 | 75 |
| 516. – | 25 f. blue, green & brown | 1·00 | 75 |
| 517. – | 30 f. blue, bistre & orange | 1·25 | 1·00 |
| 518. – | 40 f. blue, brown & green | 2·50 | 1·75 |

Designs—forts. 25 f. Ali Adde. 30 f. Dorra. 40 f. Assamo.

**1968.** Human Rights Year. As T **28** of Comoro Islands.

| | | | |
|---|---|---|---|
| 519. | 10 f. red, violet and yellow | 1·40 | 1·00 |
| 520. | 70 f. purple, green & orange | 2·25 | 1·75 |

**69.** Broadcasting Station.

**70.** Relief Map of Territory.

**1968.** Buildings and Landmarks.

| | | | | |
|---|---|---|---|---|
| 521 | 69 | 1 f. blue, turquoise and red (postage) .. | 25 | 20 |
| 522 | – | 2 f. blue, green & lt blue | 25 | 20 |
| 523 | – | 5 f. brown, green & blue | 40 | 25 |
| 524 | – | 8 f. brown, blue & green | 40 | 25 |
| 525 | – | 15 f. brown, green & bl | 3·00 | 1·75 |
| 526 | – | 40 f. grey, brown & turq | 2·00 | 1·40 |
| 527 | – | 60 f. multicoloured .. | 2·25 | 1·60 |
| 528 | – | 70 f. brown, grn & grey | 3·00 | 2·25 |
| 529 | – | 85 f. green, blue & brn | 4·50 | 3·00 |
| 530 | – | 85 f. grey, blue & green | 3·75 | 3·25 |
| 531 | – | 100 f. brown, green and blue (air) .. .. | 3·25 | 1·60 |
| 532 | – | 200 f. blue, brown & pur | 6·50 | 2·75 |
| 533 | 70 | 500 f. orange, brn & bl | 30·00 | 9·50 |

Designs—As T **69**. horiz: 2 f. Courts of Justice. 5 f. Chamber of Deputies. 8 f. Great Mosque. 40 f. Post Office, Djibouti. 70 f. Governor's Residence, Obock. 85 f. (No. 529) Port Administration Building, Djibouti. 85 f. (No. 530) Airport. vert. 15 f. Free French Forces' Monument. As T **70**. horiz: 60 f. French High Commission, Djibouti. vert: 100 f. Djibouti Cathedral. 200 f. Sayed Hassan Mosque.

**1969.** Air. 1st Flight of Concorde. As T **32** of Comoro Islands.

| | | | |
|---|---|---|---|
| 534 | 100 f. red and drab .. | 22·00 | 14·00 |

**71.** Desert Locust.

**1969. Anti-Locust Campaign.**

| | | | |
|---|---|---|---|
| 535. 71. | 15 f. brown, slate & green | 2·00 | 1·00 |
| 536. – | 50 f. brn., green & blue | 2·25 | 1·25 |
| 537. – | 55 f. brown, blue & lake | 2·50 | 1·75 |

Designs: 50 f. Sud Aviation Alouette II helicopter spraying crops. 55 f. Piper Super Cub spraying crops.

**1969.** 50th Anniv. of Int. Labour Organization. As T **33** of Comoro Islands.

| | | | |
|---|---|---|---|
| 538. | 30 f. mauve, slate and red | 1·75 | 1·00 |

**73.** Afar Dagger.

**74.** Ionospheric Station, Arta.

**1970.**

| | | | |
|---|---|---|---|
| 543. 73. | 10 f. brn., grn. & myrtle | 60 | 40 |
| 544. | 15 f. brown, green & blue | 75 | 40 |
| 545. | 20 f. brown, green & red | 1·00 | 60 |
| 546. | 25 f. brown, green & violet | 1·40 | 60 |

**1970. Air. Opening of Ionospheric Station, Arta.**

| | | | |
|---|---|---|---|
| 547. 74. | 70 f. red, green and blue | 3·50 | 2·75 |

**1970.** New U.P.U. Headquarters Building. As T **156**. of Cameroun.

| | | | |
|---|---|---|---|
| 548. | 25 f. brown, green & bistre | 1·50 | 1·00 |

**75.** Clay-pigeon Shooting.

**1970.** Sports.

| | | | |
|---|---|---|---|
| 549. 75. | 30 f. brn., blue & green .. | 1·90 | 1·00 |
| 550. – | 48 f. brn., purple & blue | 2·25 | 1·50 |
| 551. – | 50 f. red, violet & blue .. | 2·25 | 1·00 |
| 552. – | 55 f. brn., bistre & blue .. | 2·25 | 1·50 |
| 553. – | 60 f. black, brn. & green | 3·50 | 2·50 |

Designs—horiz. 48 f. Speedboat racing. 50 f. Show jumping. 60 f. Pony-trekking. vert. 55 f. Yachting.

**76.** "Fish" Sword-guard.

**77.** "Goubet".

**1970.** Air "Expo 70" World Fair, Osaka, Japan.
554 76 100 f. violet, blue and green on gold .. 8·25 5·00
555 – 200 f. violet, green and red on gold .. .. 10·50 6·00
Design: 200 f. "Horse" sword-guard.

**1970.** Inauguration of Car Ferry, Tajurah.
556. 77. 48 f. brown, blue and grn. 2·00 1·50

78. Dolerite Basalt.

**1971.** Geology. Multicoloured.
557. 10 f. Type 78 .. .. 60 40
558. 15 f. Olivine basalt .. 90 1·25
559. 25 f. Volcanic geode .. 2·25 1·40
560. 40 f. Diabase and chrysolite 2·75 1·75

79. Manta Rays.

81. Mantle Clanculus

80. Aerial View of Port.

**1971.** Marine Fauna. Multicoloured.
(a) Postage. As T 79
561 4 f. Type 79 .. .. 1·00 60
562 5 f. Dolphin fish .. .. 1·00 60
563 9 f. Common sailfish .. 1·50 1·00

(b) Air. Size 46 × 27 mm (30 f.) or 48 × 27 mm (others)
564 30 f. Queen parrot fish .. 3·00 2·25
565 40 f. Long-armed octopus 1·40 1·25
566 60 f. Dugong .. .. 3·50 2·00

**1971.** De Gaulle Commemoration. As Nos. 1937 and 1940 of France.
567. 60 f. black and blue .. 3·25 2·25
568. 85 f. black and blue .. 4·50 2·75

**1971.** Air. New Harbour, Djibouti.
569. 80. 100 f. multicoloured .. 4·50 2·75

**1972.** Sea Shells. Multicoloured.
570 4 f. Type 81 .. .. 50 40
571 9 f. Panther cowrie .. 60 50
572 20 f. Bull-mouth helmet 2·00 1·00
573 50 f. Melon shell .. .. 3·00 1·75

82. Lichtenstein's Sandgrouse.

**1972.** Air. Birds. Multicoloured.
574. 30 f. Type 82 .. .. 2·75 2·10
575. 49 f. Hoopoe .. .. 3·75 2·25
576. 66 f. Great Snipe .. 6·00 3·50
577. 500 f. Pale-bellied Francolin 26·00 12·00

83. Swimming.

**1972.** Air. Olympic Games, Munich.
578. – 5 f. brn., grn. and violet 50 25
579. – 10 f. brn., grn. & lake .. 50 25
580. 83. 55 f. brn., blue & green 2·00 1·00
581. – 60 f. violet, lake & green 2·40 1·00
Designs—Vert. 5 f. Running. 10 f. Basketball. Horiz. 60 f. Olympic flame, rings and ancient frieze.

84. Pasteur and Equipment.

**1972.** Air. "Famous Medical Scientists".
582. 84. 20 f. brn., green and red 1·25 60
583. – 100 f. brn., green & lake 3·50 2·75
Design: 100 f. Calmette and Guerin (B.C.G. pioneers).

85. Mosque, Map and Transport.

**1973.** Air. Visit of President Pompidou. Multicoloured.
584. 30 f. Type 85 .. .. 5·50 3·25
585. 200 f. Mosque and street scene, Djibouti (vert.) .. 10·00 7·50

86. Gemsbok.

**1973.** Air. Wild Animals. Multicoloured.
587. 30 f. Type 86 .. .. 1·75 1·25
588. 50 f. Salt's dik-dik .. 3·00 1·50
590. 66 f. Caracal .. .. 3·50 2·50
See also Nos. 603/5, 641/3, 659/60 and 662/4.

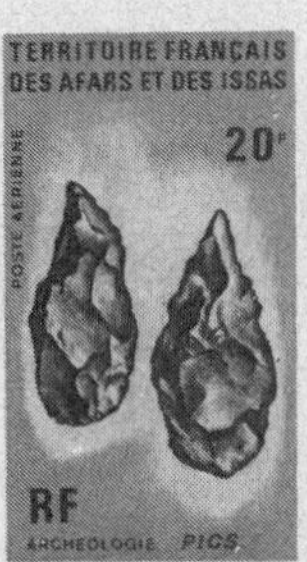

87. Flint Pick-heads.

89. Nicolas Copernicus (500th Birth Anniv.).

88. Shepherd watering Sheep.

**1973.** Air. Archaeological Discoveries. Mult.
592. 20 f. Type 87 .. .. 1·50 1·25
593. 40 f. Arrow-heads and blade (horiz.) .. 2·00 1·25
594. 49 f. Biface flint tool .. 3·50 2·00
595. 60 f. Flint axe-head and scraper (horiz.) 3·00 2·00

**1973.** Pastoral Economy. Multicoloured.
596. 9 f. Type 88 .. .. 60 60
597. 10 f. Camel herd .. 60 60

**1973.** Air. Celebrities' Anniversaries.
598 89 8 f. black, brown & pur 60 35
599 – 9 f. purple, orange & brn 70 40
600 – 10 f. purple, brn & red 75 45
615 – 10 f. maroon, blue & pur 75 60
601 – 49 f. pur, grn & dp grn 2·75 1·60
658 – 50 f. brown, blue & grn 2·50 75
611 – 55 f. indigo, brown & bl 1·90 1·50
602 – 85 f. dp blue, blue & vio 3·75 2·25
607 – 100 f. purple, blue & grn 3·50 1·25
657 – 150 f. turq, blue & brn 4·00 2·75
656 – 250 f. brown, light brown and green .. 6·00 3·75
Designs: 9 f. Wilhelm Rontgen (X-ray pioneer) (50th death anniv). 10 f. (600) Edward Jenner (smallpox vaccination pioneer) (150th death anniv). 10 f. (615) Marie Curie (physicist) (40th death anniv). 49 f. Robert Koch (bacteriologist) (130th birth anniv). 50 f. Clement Ader (aviation pioneer) (50th death anniv). 55 f. Guglielmo Marconi (radio pioneer) (birth centenary). 85 f. Moliere (playwright) (300th death anniv). 100 f. Henri Farman (aviation pioneer) (birth centenary). 150 f. Ampere (physicist) (birth bicentenary). 250 f. Michelangelo (500th birth anniv).

**1973.** Air. Wild Animals (2nd series). As Type 86. Multicoloured.
603. 20 f. Olive baboon (vert.) 1·25 75
604. 50 f. Large-spotted genet 2·50 1·25
605. 66 f. Abyssinian hare (vert.) .. .. .. 3·50 2·00

90. Afar Dagger.

**1974.**
606 90 30 f. purple and green .. 1·40 70

91. Greater Flamingoes.

**1974.** Lake Abbe. Multicoloured.
608. 5 f. Type 91 .. .. 80 25
609. 15 f. Two Greater Flamingoes 55 40
610. 50 f. Greater Flamingoes in flight .. .. .. 1·90 1·10

92. Underwater Hunting.

**1974.** Air. Third Underwater Hunting Trophy.
612. 92. 200 f. blue, green & red 7·25 5·50
No. 612 has part of the original inscription blocked out.

93. Various Animals.

**1974.** Air. Balho Rock Paintings.
613 93 200 f. black and red .. 7·75 6·00

94. Football and Emblem.

**1974.** World Cup Football Championships.
614. 94. 25 f. green and black .. 1·60 1·00

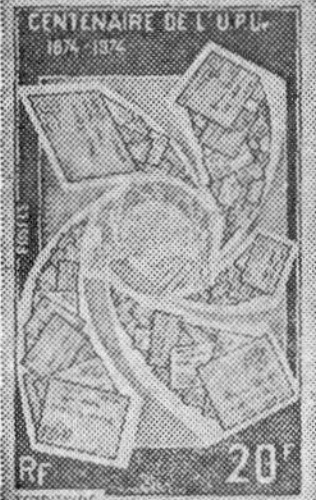

95. U.P.U. Emblem and Letters.

97. "Oleo chrysophylla".

96. Sunrise over Lake.

**1974.** Cent. of Universal Postal Union.
616. 95. 20 f. violet, blue & ind. 1·40 70
617. 100 f. brown, light brown and red .. .. 3·00 2·50

**1974.** Air. Lake Assal. Multicoloured.
618. 49 f. Type 96 .. .. 1·40 1·00
619. 50 f. Rocky shore .. 1·60 1·10
620. 85 f. Crystallisation on dead wood .. .. .. 3·25 2·50

**1974.** Forest Plants. Multicoloured.
621. 10 f. Type 97 .. .. 75 55
622. 15 f. "Fiscus" (tree) .. 1·00 70
623. 20 f. "Solanum adoense" (shrub) .. .. 2·25 1·40

**1975.** Surch 40F.
624 90 40 f. on 30 f. pur & grn 1·60 1·10

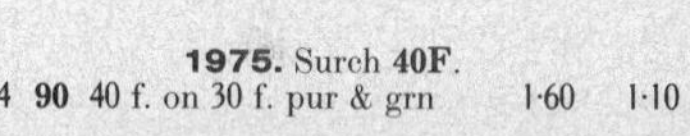

99. Treasury Building.

**1975.** Administrative Buildings, Djibouti.
625. 99. 8 f. grey, blue and red .. 55 35
626. – 25 f. grey, blue and red 1·00 70
Design: 25 f. "Government City" complex.

100. Textile Cone.

**1975.** Sea Shells.
627 100 5 f. brown and green .. 45 35
628 – 5 f. brown and blue .. 45 20
629 – 5 f. brown, mauve and violet .. .. 70 55
630 – 10 f. brown and purple 70 40
631 – 15 f. brown and blue .. 1·00 55
632 – 20 f. brown and violet 1·75 55
633 – 20 f. brown and green 55 35
634 – 30 f. brown, purple and green .. .. 90 55
635 – 40 f. brown and green 2·40 1·40
636 – 45 f. brown, green & bl 1·75 1·25
637 – 55 f. brown and blue .. 1·50 90
638 – 60 f. black and brown 2·00 1·40
639 – 70 f. brown, blue & blk 2·75 1·75
640 – 85 f. purple, blue & blk 4·25 2·75
Designs: 5 f. (628) Rose-branch murex. 5 f. (629) Tiger cowrie. 10 f. Sumatran cone. 15 f. Lovely cowrie. 20 f. (632), 45 f. Woodcock murex. 20 f. (633) Burnt cowrie. 30 f. Beech cowrie. 40 f. Spiny frog shell. 55 f. Red Sea cowrie. 60 f. Ringed cone. 70 f. Striate cone. 85 f. Humpback cowrie.

**1975.** Wild Animals (3rd series). As T 86. Mult.
641 50 f. White-tailed mongoose .. 2·40 1·40
642 60 f. North African crested porcupine (vert) .. 3·00 1·75
643 70 f. Zorilla .. .. 4·25 2·40

101. African Monarch.

**1975.** Butterflies and Moths (1st series). Mult.

| | | | |
|---|---|---|---|
| 644 | 25 f. Type **101** .. .. | 1·40 | 90 |
| 645 | 40 f. Narrow blue-banded swallowtail .. .. | 1·75 | 1·00 |
| 646 | 70 f. Citrus butterfly .. | 3·00 | 2·25 |
| 647 | 100 f. Mocker swallowtail | 3·75 | 2·75 |

See also Nos. 666/7 and 675/6.

**102.** Speckled Pigeon. **103.** Palm Trees.

**1975.** Birds. Multicoloured.

| | | | |
|---|---|---|---|
| 648. | 20 f. Pin-tailed whydah (postage) .. .. | 1·10 | 80 |
| 649. | 25 f. Rose-ringed parakeet | 1·25 | 80 |
| 650. | 50 f. Variable sunbird .. | 2·75 | 1·75 |
| 651. | 60 f. Goliath heron .. | 3·75 | 2·25 |
| 652. | 100 f. Hammerkop .. | 5·25 | 3·00 |
| 653. | 100 f. Namaqua dove .. | 3·50 | 2·25 |
| 654. | 300 f. African spoonbill .. | 10·00 | 5·50 |
| 655. | 500 f. Type **102** (air) .. | 22·00 | 10·50 |

**1975.** Wild Animals (4th series). As T **86.** Multicoloured.

| | | | |
|---|---|---|---|
| 659 | 15 f. Savanna monkeys (vert.) .. .. .. | 90 | 45 |
| 660 | 200 f. Aardvarks .. .. | 5·75 | 3·25 |

**1975.**

| | | | |
|---|---|---|---|
| 661. **103.** | 20 f. multicoloured .. | 70 | 45 |

**1976.** Wild Animals (5th series). As T **86.** Multicoloured.

| | | | |
|---|---|---|---|
| 662. | 10 f. Striped hyena .. | 70 | 35 |
| 663. | 15 f. African ass (vert.) .. | 75 | 45 |
| 664. | 30 f. Beira antelope .. | 1·25 | 70 |

**104.** Alexander Graham Bell and Satellite.

**1976.** Telephone Centenary.

| | | | |
|---|---|---|---|
| 665.**104.** | 200 f. blue, grn. & orge. | 3·75 | 2·75 |

**1976.** Butterflies and Moths (2nd series). As T **101.** Multicoloured.

| | | | |
|---|---|---|---|
| 666 | 65 f. Variable prince .. | 2·25 | 1·50 |
| 667 | 100 f. "Balachowsky gonimbrasia" .. | 3·25 | 2·00 |

**105.** Basketball.

**1976.** Olympic Games, Montreal. Mult.

| | | | |
|---|---|---|---|
| 668. | 10 f. Type **105** .. .. | 35 | 25 |
| 669. | 15 f. Cycling .. .. | 45 | 35 |
| 670. | 40 f. Football .. .. | 1·00 | 70 |
| 671. | 60 f. Running .. .. | 1·50 | 1·00 |

**106.** Lion Fish.

**1976.** Marine Life.

| | | | |
|---|---|---|---|
| 672.**106.** | 45 f. multicoloured .. | 1·60 | 1·40 |

**107.** Black-necked Cobra. **108.** Motor Cyclist on Course.

**1976.** Snakes. Multicoloured.

| | | | |
|---|---|---|---|
| 673. | 70 f. Type **107** .. .. | 2·40 | 1·75 |
| 674. | 80 f. Elegant sand snake .. | 3·00 | 2·00 |

**1976.** Butterflies and Moths (3rd series). As T **101.** Multicoloured.

| | | | |
|---|---|---|---|
| 675 | 50 f. Broad bordered acraea .. .. .. | 1·90 | 1·50 |
| 676 | 150 f. Painted lady .. | 3·50 | 2·75 |

**1977.** Moto-Cross.

| | | | |
|---|---|---|---|
| 677 **108** | 200 f. multicoloured .. | 5·00 | 3·00 |

**109.** Air Terminal.

**1977.** Air. Inauguration of New Djibouti Airport.

| | | | |
|---|---|---|---|
| 678.**109.** | 500 f. multicoloured .. | 11·00 | 8·25 |

**110.** Sweetlips.

**1977.** Fishes. Multicoloured.

| | | | |
|---|---|---|---|
| 679. | 15 f. Type **110** .. .. | 75 | 65 |
| 680. | 65 f. Barracuda .. .. | 2·00 | 1·10 |

**111.** Edison and Phonograph.

**1977.** Air. Celebrities.

| | | | |
|---|---|---|---|
| 681.**111.** | 55 f. red, slate and green | 2·75 | 1·75 |
| 682. – | 75 f. red, brown & olive | 5·25 | 3·75 |

DESIGN: 75 f. Volta and electric train.

POSTAGE DUE STAMPS

D 72. Nomadic Milk-jug.

**1969.**

| | | | |
|---|---|---|---|
| D 539. D **72.** | 1 f. slate, brn. & pur. | 25 | 25 |
| D 540. | 2 f. slate, brn. & grn. | 25 | 25 |
| D 541. | 5 f. slate, brn. & blue | 50 | 50 |
| D 542. | 10 f. slate, lake & brn. | 1·00 | 1·00 |

For later issues see **DJIBOUTI REPUBLIC.**

# FRENCH WEST AFRICA Pt. 6

The territory in north-west Africa comprising Senegal, French Guinea, Ivory Coast, Dahomey, French Sudan, Mauritania, Niger and Upper Volta. French Sudan and Senegal became the Mali Federation and the rest independent republics.

100 centimes = 1 franc.

**1944.** Mutual Aid and Red Cross Funds. As T **33** of Cameroun.

| | | | |
|---|---|---|---|
| 1. | 5 f.+20 f. purple.. .. | 2·75 | 3·50 |

**1945.** Eboue. As T **34** of Cameroun.

| | | | |
|---|---|---|---|
| 2. | 2 f. black .. .. .. | 30 | 60 |
| 3. | 25 f. green .. .. .. | 85 | 1·00 |

1. Soldiers.

**1945.**

| | | | |
|---|---|---|---|
| 4. **1.** | 10 c. blue and pink .. | 10 | 20 |
| 5. | 30 c. olive and cream .. | 25 | 35 |
| 6. | 40 c. blue and pink .. | 25 | 40 |
| 7. | 50 c. orange and grey .. | 10 | 20 |
| 8. | 60 c. olive and grey .. | 30 | 40 |
| 9. | 70 c. mauve and cream .. | 30 | 45 |
| 10. | 80 c. green and cream .. | 15 | 25 |
| 11. | 1 f. purple and olive .. | 10 | 10 |
| 12. | 1 f. 20 c. brown and olive | 50 | 1·25 |
| 13. | 1 f. 50 c. brown and red.. | 20 | 25 |
| 14. | 2 f. yellow and grey .. | 20 | 30 |
| 15. | 2 f. 40 c. red and grey .. | 25 | 60 |
| 16. | 3 f. red and olive.. .. | 15 | 10 |
| 17. | 4 f. blue and red .. .. | 15 | 25 |
| 18. | 4 f. 50 c. brown and olive | 25 | 35 |
| 19. | 5 f. violet and olive .. | 25 | 10 |
| 20. | 10 f. green and red .. | 40 | 50 |
| 21. | 15 f. brown and cream .. | 60 | 80 |
| 22. | 20 f. green and grey .. | 70 | 1·00 |

**1945.** Stamp Day. As T **228** of France (Louis XI) but optd. **A O F.**

| | | | |
|---|---|---|---|
| 23. | 2 f.+3 f. red .. .. | 40 | 60 |

**1945.** Air. As T **32** of Cameroun.

| | | | |
|---|---|---|---|
| 24. | 5 f. 50 c. blue .. .. | 65 | 60 |
| 25. | 50 f. green .. .. .. | 1·00 | 1·00 |
| 26. | 100 f. red .. .. .. | 1·00 | 1·00 |

**1946.** Air. Victory. As T **35** of Cameroun.

| | | | |
|---|---|---|---|
| 27. | 8 f. mauve .. .. .. | 50 | 65 |

**1946.** Air. From Chad to the Rhine. As Nos. 226/31 of Cameroun.

| | | | |
|---|---|---|---|
| 28. | 5 f. red .. .. .. | 1·00 | 1·25 |
| 29. | 10 f. blue .. .. .. | 1·00 | 1·25 |
| 30. | 15 f. mauve .. .. .. | 1·00 | 1·25 |
| 31. | 20 f. green .. .. .. | 1·00 | 1·25 |
| 32. | 25 f. brown.. .. .. | 1·00 | 1·25 |
| 33. | 50 f. brown.. .. .. | 1·25 | 1·75 |

3. War Dance. 6. Sudanese Carving.

9. Natives and Airplane.

**1947.**

| | | | |
|---|---|---|---|
| 34 **3** | 10 c. blue (postage) .. | 10 | 25 |
| 35 – | 30 c. brown .. .. | 10 | 25 |
| 36 – | 40 c. green .. .. | 10 | 25 |
| 37 – | 50 c. red .. .. | 10 | 25 |
| 38 – | 60 c. grey .. .. | 25 | 35 |
| 39 – | 80 c. lilac .. .. | 40 | 55 |
| 40 – | 1 f. red .. .. | 10 | 10 |
| 41 – | 1 f. 20 c. green .. | 60 | 75 |
| 42 – | 1 f. 50 c. blue .. | 85 | 95 |
| 43 **6** | 2 f. orange .. .. | 10 | 10 |
| 68 – | 3 f. brown.. .. | 35 | 10 |
| 45 – | 3 f. 60 c. red .. | 1·25 | 1·40 |
| 46 – | 4 f. blue .. .. | 15 | 15 |
| 47 – | 5 f. green .. .. | 20 | 10 |
| 48 – | 6 f. blue .. .. | 25 | 15 |
| 49 – | 10 f. red .. .. | 25 | 15 |
| 50 – | 15 f. brown .. .. | 75 | 20 |
| 51 – | 20 f. brown .. .. | 35 | 15 |
| 52 – | 25 f. black .. .. | 70 | 25 |
| 53 – | 8 f. red (air) .. .. | 50 | 60 |
| 54 – | 50 f. violet .. .. | 1·40 | 90 |
| 55 – | 100 f. blue .. .. | 9·50 | 2·25 |
| 56 **9** | 200 f. grey .. .. | 3·25 | 1·90 |

DESIGNS—As TYPE **3/6**—HORIZ. 30 c. Girl and bridge. 40 c. Canoe. 50 c. Niger landscape. 80 c. Dahomey weaver. 1 f. Donkey caravan. 1 f. 20, Crocodile and hippopotamus. 10 f. Djenne Mosque. 15 f. Renault railcar. VERT. 60 c. Coconuts 1 f. 50, Palm trees. 3 f. Togo girl. 3 f. 60, Sudanese market. 4 f. Dahomey labourer. 5 f. Mauritanian woman. 6 f. Guinea headdress. 20 f. Ivory Coast girl. 25 f. Niger washerwoman. As Type **9**—VERT. 8 f. Antoine de Saint-Exupery. HORIZ. 50 f. Caudron Goeland airplane over Dakar (Senegal). 100 f. Flight of great egrets (Niger).

**1949.** 75th Anniv. of U.P.U. As T **46** of Cameroun.

| | | | |
|---|---|---|---|
| 69. | 25 f. multicoloured .. | 2·50 | 4·50 |

**1950.** Colonial Welfare Fund. As T **47** of Cameroun.

| | | | |
|---|---|---|---|
| 70 | 10 f.+2 f. dp brown & brn | 1·75 | 3·50 |

**10.** Medical Research.

**11.** T. Laplene and Map of Ivory Coast.

**12.** Logging Camp.

**1951.**

| | | | |
|---|---|---|---|
| 71. – | 8 f. blue and brown (post.) | 80 | 40 |
| 72. **10.** | 15 f. green, brown & sepia | 60 | 10 |
| 73. – | 20 f. myrtle and turquoise | 1·00 | 1·25 |
| 74. – | 25 f. sepia, blue and purple | 85 | 25 |
| 75. **11.** | 40 f. red .. .. .. | 95 | 35 |
| 76. **12.** | 50 f. brown and green (air) | 1·50 | 60 |
| 77. – | 100 f. brown, blue & green | 3·00 | 50 |
| 78. – | 200 f. green, turq. & lake.. | 6·75 | 1·40 |
| 79. – | 500 f. green, blue & orange | 15·00 | 6·00 |

DESIGNS—As Type **11**: 8 f. Governor-General Ballay. 20 f. Abidjan Bridge. 25 f. Africans, animals and sailing canoe. As Type **12**: 100 f. Telephonist, Lockheed Constellation airplane and pylons. 200 f. Baobab trees. 500 f. Vridi Canal, Abidjan.

**1952.** Cent. of Military Medal. As T **48** of Cameroun.

| | | | |
|---|---|---|---|
| 80. | 15 f. sepia, yellow & green | 2·00 | 3·00 |

**1954.** Air. 10th Anniv. of Liberation. As T **52** of Cameroun.

| | | | |
|---|---|---|---|
| 81. | 15 f. blue and indigo .. | 2·50 | 3·00 |

**13.** Chimpanzee. **14.**

**1955.** Nature Protection. Inscr. as in T **13.**

| | | | |
|---|---|---|---|
| 82. **13.** | 5 f. sepia and grey .. | 85 | 45 |
| 83. – | 8 f. sepia and green .. | 50 | 45 |

DESIGN—HORIZ. 8 f. Giant ground pangolin.

**1955.** 50th Anniv. of Rotary International.

| | | | |
|---|---|---|---|
| 84. **14.** | 15 f. blue .. .. | 85 | 40 |

**15.** Mossi Railways.

DESIGNS — HORIZ. 1 f. Date palms. 2 f. Milo River bridge. 4 f. Herdsman and cattle. 15 f. Combine harvester. 17 f. Woman and aerial view. 20 f. Palm oil factory. 30 f. Abidjan-Abengourou road.

**1955.** Economic and Social Development Fund. Inscr. "F.I.D.E.S.".

| | | | |
|---|---|---|---|
| 85. – | 1 f. green and myrtle .. | 35 | 25 |
| 86. – | 2 f. myrtle and turquoise | 40 | 35 |
| 87. **15.** | 3 f. sepia and brown .. | 90 | 50 |
| 88. – | 4 f. red .. .. .. | 70 | 40 |
| 89. – | 15 f. blue and indigo .. | 65 | 25 |
| 90. – | 17 f. blue and indigo .. | 65 | 30 |
| 91. – | 20 f. purple .. .. | 65 | 30 |
| 92. – | 30 f. purple and lilac .. | 85 | 45 |

**1956.** Coffee. As T **51** of French Equatorial Africa.

| | | | |
|---|---|---|---|
| 93 | 15 f. green and turquoise .. | 20 | 20 |

**16.** Medical Station and Ambulance.

**17.** Map of Africa.

**1957.** Order of Malta Leprosy Relief.

| | | | |
|---|---|---|---|
| 94. **16.** | 15 f. claret, purple & red | 80 | 75 |

**1957.** Air. Centenary of African Troops. As T **53** of French Equatorial Africa.

| | | | |
|---|---|---|---|
| 95 | 15 f. blue and indigo .. | 1·25 | 1·50 |

**1958.** 6th African Int Tourist Congress.

| | | | |
|---|---|---|---|
| 96 **17** | 20 f. red and green .. | 45 | 55 |

**18.** " Communication ".

**1958.** Stamp Day.

| | | | |
|---|---|---|---|
| 97. **18.** | 15 f. brown, blue & orge. | 45 | 55 |

**19.** Isle of Goree and West African.

**1958.** Air. Dakar Cent. Inscr. " CENTENAIRE DE DAKAR ".

| | | | |
|---|---|---|---|
| 98. **19.** | 15 f. multicoloured .. | 85 | 40 |
| 99. – | 20 f. red, brown and blue | 85 | 60 |
| 100. – | 25 f. multicoloured .. | 60 | 40 |
| 101. – | 40 f. brown, green & blue | 60 | 40 |
| 102. – | 50 f. violet, brn. & grn. | 1·00 | 60 |
| 103. – | 100 f. grn., blue & brn. | 3·00 | 1·50 |

DESIGNS: 20 f. Map of Dakar, liner, freighters and Lockheed Super Constellation and Douglas DC-6 aircraft. 25 f. Town construction. 40 f. Council house. 50 f. Groundnuts, artisan and "L'Arachide" (freighter) at quayside. 100 f. Bay of N'Gor.

**20.** Banana Plant and Fruit.

**1958.** Banana Production.

| | | | |
|---|---|---|---|
| 105. **20.** | 20 f. purple, green & olive | 30 | 35 |

**1958.** Tropical Flora. As T **56** of French Equatorial Africa.

| | | | |
|---|---|---|---|
| 118. | 10 f. multicoloured .. | 50 | 30 |
| 119. | 25 f. yellow, green and red | 55 | 30 |
| 120. | 30 f. brown, green & blue | 70 | 40 |
| 121. | 40 f. yellow, green & sepia | 1·00 | 75 |
| 122. | 65 f. multicoloured .. | 1·00 | 75 |

DESIGNS—VERT. 10 f. " Gloriosa ". 25 f. " Adenopus ". 30 f. " Cyrtosperma ". 40 f. " Cistanche ". 65 f. " Crinum moorei ".

**22.** Moro Naba Sagha and Map of Upper Volta.

**1958.** 10th Anniv. of Upper Volta Scheme.

| | | | |
|---|---|---|---|
| 123. **22.** | 20 f. multicoloured .. | 80 | 65 |

**23.** Native Chief and Musician.

**1958.** Air. Inauguration of Nouakchott, Capital of Mauritania.

| | | | |
|---|---|---|---|
| 124. **23.** | 20 f. sep, brn. & grey | 75 | 60 |

**1958.** 10th Anniv. of Declaration of Human Rights. As T **10** of Comoro Is.

| | | | |
|---|---|---|---|
| 125. | 20 f. purple and blue .. | 55 | 1·00 |

**1959.** Stamp Day. As T **18** but inscr. " DAKAR-ABIDJAN " in place of " AFRIQUE OCCIDENTALE FRANCAISE ".

| | | | |
|---|---|---|---|
| 126. | 20 f. green, blue and red .. | 1·60 | 1·50 |

No. 126 was for use in Ivory Coast and Senegal.

OFFICIAL STAMPS.

**O 21.**

**1958.** Inscr. " OFFICIEL ".

| | | | | |
|---|---|---|---|---|
| O 106. | **O. 21** | 1 f. brown .. | 40 | 40 |
| O 107. | | 3 f. green .. | 30 | 40 |
| O 108. | | 5 f. red .. | 35 | 30 |
| O 109. | | 10 f. blue .. | 40 | 30 |
| O 110. | – | 20 f. red .. | 50 | 25 |
| O 111. | – | 25 f. violet .. | 50 | 25 |
| O 112. | – | 30 f. green .. | 70 | 50 |
| O 113. | – | 45 f. black .. | 90 | 55 |
| O 114. | – | 50 f. red .. | 1·40 | 45 |
| O 115. | – | 65 f. blue .. | 1·75 | 55 |
| O 116. | – | 100 f. olive .. | 3·25 | 45 |
| O 117. | – | 200 f. green .. | 6·75 | 1·75 |

DESIGNS—VERT. 20 f. to 45 f. Head as Type O 21 but with female face. 50 f. to 200 f. Head as Type O 21 but with hooped headdress, portrait being diagonal on stamp.

POSTAGE DUE STAMPS.

**D 10.**

**1947.**

| | | | | |
|---|---|---|---|---|
| D 57. | **D 10.** | 10 c. red .. | 10 | 25 |
| D 58. | | 30 c. orange .. | 10 | 25 |
| D 59. | | 50 c. black .. | 10 | 25 |
| D 60. | | 1 f. red .. | 10 | 25 |
| D 61. | | 2 f. green .. | 10 | 25 |
| D 62. | | 3 f. mauve .. | 10 | 25 |
| D 63. | | 4 f. blue .. | 30 | 45 |
| D 64. | | 5 f. brown .. | 30 | 75 |
| D 65. | | 10 f. blue .. | 50 | 1·25 |
| D 66. | | 20 f. brown .. | 70 | 2·00 |

## FUJEIRA Pt. 19

One of the Trucial States in the Persian Gulf. With six other shaikdoms formed the State of the United Arab Emirates on 18 July 1971. Fujeira stamps were replaced by issues of United Arab Emirates on 1 January 1973.

100 naye paise = 1 rupee.
1967. 100 dirhams = 1 riyal.

**1.** Shaikh Mohamed bin Hamad al Sharqi and Great Crested Grebe.

**1964.** Multicoloured.

(a) Size as T **1**.

| | | | |
|---|---|---|---|
| 1. | 1 n.p. Type **1** .. | 30 | 15 |
| 2. | 2 n.p. Arabian oryx | 15 | 15 |
| 3. | 3 n.p. Hoopoe .. | 40 | 15 |
| 4. | 4 n.p. Asiatic wild ass | 15 | 15 |
| 5. | 5 n.p. Great Egrets | 40 | 15 |
| 6. | 10 n.p. Arab horses .. | 15 | 15 |
| 7. | 15 n.p. Cheetah .. | 15 | 15 |
| 8. | 20 n.p. Dromedaries | 15 | 15 |
| 9. | 30 n.p. Lanner falcon | 80 | 15 |

(b) Size $43\frac{1}{2} \times 28\frac{1}{2}$ mm.

| | | | |
|---|---|---|---|
| 10. | 40 n.p. Type **1** .. | 80 | 20 |
| 11. | 50 n.p. Arabian oryx | 30 | 15 |
| 12. | 70 n.p. Hoopoe .. | 1·50 | 30 |
| 13. | 1 r. Asiatic wild ass | 50 | 35 |
| 14. | 1 r. 50 Great egrets .. | 1·75 | 50 |
| 15. | 2 r. Arab horses | 1·00 | 60 |

(c) Size $53\frac{1}{2} \times 35\frac{1}{2}$ mm.

| | | | |
|---|---|---|---|
| 16. | 3 r. Leopard .. | 2·50 | 1·50 |
| 17. | 5 r. Dromedaries .. | 3·75 | 2·75 |
| 18. | 10 r. Lanner falcon .. | 8·00 | 6·00 |

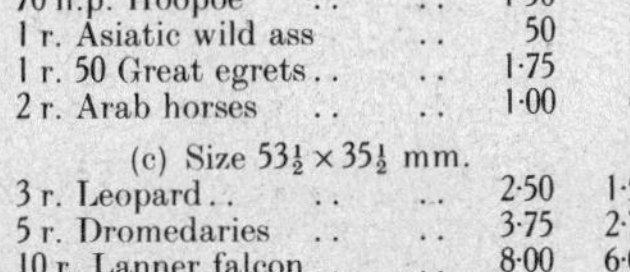


**2.** Shaikh Mohamed and Putting the Shot.

**1964.** Olympic Games, Tokyo. Multicoloured.

(a) Size as T **2**.

| | | | |
|---|---|---|---|
| 19 | 25 n.p. Type **2** .. | 15 | 15 |
| 20 | 50 n.p. Throwing the discus | 20 | 20 |
| 21 | 75 n.p. Fencing .. | 25 | 25 |
| 22 | 1 r. Boxing .. | 40 | 35 |
| 23 | 1 r. 50 Relay-racing .. | 65 | 60 |
| 24 | 2 r. Football .. | 95 | 85 |

(b) Size $53 \times 35\frac{1}{2}$ mm.

| | | | |
|---|---|---|---|
| 25 | 3 r. High jumping .. | 1·90 | 1·60 |
| 26 | 5 r. Hurdling .. | 3·00 | 2·75 |
| 27 | 7 r. 50 Horse-riding .. | 5·00 | 4·50 |

**3.** Kennedy as a Boy.

**4.** Queen Nefertiti.

**1965.** Pres. Kennedy Commem. Each black and gold on coloured paper as given below.

| | | | |
|---|---|---|---|
| 28 **3** | 5 n.p. blue .. | 15 | 15 |
| 29 – | 10 n.p. yellow .. | 15 | 15 |
| 30 – | 15 n.p. pink .. | 15 | 15 |
| 31 – | 20 n.p. green .. | 15 | 15 |
| 32 – | 25 n.p. blue .. | 20 | 15 |
| 33 – | 50 n.p. flesh .. | 20 | 20 |
| 34 – | 1 r. lilac .. | 60 | 45 |
| 35 – | 2 r. yellow .. | 1·40 | 90 |
| 36 – | 3 r. blue .. | 1·90 | 1·25 |
| 37 – | 5 r. buff .. | 3·75 | 2·75 |

DESIGNS (Kennedy): 10 n.p. As student. 15 n.p. As cadet. 20 n.p. As Senator. 25 n.p. Sailing. 50 n.p. As President. 33 × 51 mm: 1 r. With Mrs. Kennedy and guest. 2 r. With Pres. Eisenhower. 3 r. With family. 5 r. Full face portrait.

**1965.** Air. Designs similar to Nos. 1/9, but with "FUJEIRA" and value transposed, and inscr "AIR MAIL". Multicoloured.

(a) Size $43\frac{1}{2} \times 28\frac{1}{2}$ mm.

| | | | |
|---|---|---|---|
| 39. | 15 n.p. Type **1** .. | 40 | 15 |
| 40. | 25 n.p. Arabian oryx .. | 15 | 15 |
| 41. | 35 n.p. Hoopoe .. | 75 | 15 |
| 42. | 50 n.p. Asiatic wild ass .. | 25 | 20 |
| 43. | 75 n.p. Great egrets .. | 1·00 | 35 |
| 44. | 1 r. Arab horses .. | 50 | 40 |

(b) Size $53\frac{1}{2} \times 35\frac{1}{2}$ mm.

| | | | |
|---|---|---|---|
| 45. | 2 r. Leopard .. | 1·25 | 95 |
| 46. | 3 r. Dromedaries .. | 2·75 | 1·60 |
| 47. | 5 r. Lanner falcon .. | 4·25 | 2·75 |

**1966.** Stamp Cent Exn., Cairo. Mult.

| | | | |
|---|---|---|---|
| 57 | 3 n.p. Type **4** .. | 15 | 15 |
| 58 | 5 n.p. Colossi, Abu Simbel .. | 15 | 15 |
| 59 | 10 n.p. Tutankhamun's mask .. | 15 | 15 |
| 60 | 15 n.p. Sphinx, Gezir .. | 15 | 15 |
| 61 | 25 n.p. Statues of Prince Rahotep and his wife Nofret .. | 20 | 15 |
| 62 | 50 n.p. Ancient Church .. | 25 | 15 |
| 63 | 1 r. Colonnade, Great Temple of Isis, Philae | 55 | 25 |
| 64 | 2 r. Nile sphinxes .. | 1·10 | 55 |
| 65 | 5 r. Pyramids, Giza | 3·25 | 1·25 |

The 50 n.p. to 5 r. are horiz.

**5.** Sir Winston Churchill as Harrow Schoolboy.

**1966.** Churchill Commem. Each design black and gold; frame in colours given.

| | | | |
|---|---|---|---|
| 67. **5.** | 10 n.p. yellow (postage) .. | 15 | 15 |
| 68. – | 15 n.p. blue .. | 15 | 15 |
| 69. – | 25 n.p. buff .. | 15 | 15 |
| 70. – | 50 n.p. blue .. | 15 | 15 |
| 71. – | 75 n.p. mauve .. | 25 | 20 |
| 72. – | 1 r. blue .. | 50 | 25 |
| 73. – | 2 r. gold (air) .. | 1·25 | 45 |
| 74. – | 3 r. gold .. | 1·90 | 90 |

DESIGNS — CHURCHILL: 15 n.p. Wearing Hussars' uniform. 25 n.p. As Boer War correspondent. 50 n.p. In morning dress. 75 n.p. With Eisenhower. 1 r. Painting. 2 r. With grandson. 3 r. Giving " V " sign.

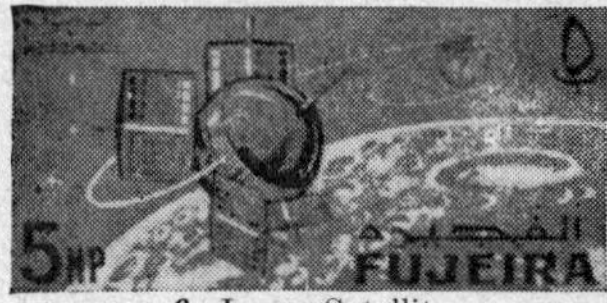


**6.** Lunar Satellite.

**1966.** Space Achievements. Multicoloured.

| | | | |
|---|---|---|---|
| 76. | 5 n.p. Type **6** .. | 15 | 15 |
| 77. | 10 n.p. Satellite approaching Moon | 15 | 15 |
| 78. | 15 n.p. Satellite and planets | 15 | 15 |
| 79. | 25 n.p. Satellite and Solar System .. | 15 | 15 |
| 80. | 50 n.p. Communications satellite .. | 15 | 15 |
| 81. | 75 n.p. Venus probe .. | 40 | 15 |
| 82. | 1 r. " Telstar " .. | 60 | 25 |
| 83. | 2 r. " Relay " .. | 1·25 | 60 |

**1967.** Various stamps with currency names changed by overprinting.

(i) Nos. 1/18 (Definitives).

| | | | |
|---|---|---|---|
| 85. | 1 d. on 1 n.p. .. | 2·50 | 40 |
| 86. | 2 d. on 2 n.p. .. | 1·00 | 20 |
| 87. | 3 d. on 3 n.p. .. | 2·50 | 40 |
| 88. | 4 d. on 4 n.p. .. | 1·00 | 20 |
| 89. | 5 d. on 5 n.p. .. | 2·50 | 40 |
| 90. | 10 d. on 10 n.p. .. | 90 | 20 |
| 91. | 15 d. on 15 n.p. .. | 1·50 | 30 |
| 92. | 20 d. on 20 n.p. .. | 1·00 | 20 |
| 93. | 30 d. on 30 n.p. .. | 2·50 | 40 |
| 94. | 40 d. on 40 n.p. .. | 3·25 | 40 |
| 95. | 50 d. on 50 n.p. .. | 1·50 | 20 |
| 96. | 70 d. on 70 n.p. .. | 4·50 | 40 |
| 97. | 1 r. on 1 r. .. | 1·50 | 40 |
| 98. | 1 r. 50 on 1 r. 50 .. | 5·00 | 1·00 |
| 99. | 2 r. on 2 r. .. | 1·00 | 1·00 |
| 100. | 3 r. on 3 r. .. | 1·50 | 1·25 |
| 101. | 5 r. on 5 r. .. | 2·25 | 2·25 |
| 102. | 10 r. on 10 r. .. | 24·00 | 6·00 |

(ii) Air. Nos. 39/47 (Definitives).

| | | | |
|---|---|---|---|
| 123. | 15 d. on 15 n.p. .. | 2·50 | 40 |
| 124. | 25 d. on 25 n.p. .. | 1·00 | 15 |
| 125. | 35 d. on 35 n.p. .. | 3·00 | 40 |
| 126. | 50 d. on 50 n.p. .. | 1·50 | 40 |
| 127. | 75 d. on 75 n.p. .. | 4·50 | 1·00 |
| 128. | 1 r. on 1 r. .. | 1·00 | 50 |
| 129. | 2 r. on 2 r. .. | 1·25 | 1·00 |
| 130. | 3 r. on 3 r. .. | 2·25 | 2·00 |
| 131. | 5 r. on 5 r. .. | 9·50 | 2·75 |

Nos. 19/37 and 57/83 were also surcharged in the new currency in limited quantities, but they had little local usage.

**9.** "Pararge felix".

**1967.** Butterflies. Multicoloured.

(a) Postage. (i) Size 32 × 32 mm.

| | | | |
|---|---|---|---|
| 167 | 1 d. Type **9** .. | 10 | 10 |
| 168 | 2 d. African clouded yellow (male) .. | 10 | 10 |
| 169 | 3 d. African clouded yellow (female) .. | 10 | 10 |
| 170 | 4 d. "Spindasis scotti" .. | 10 | 10 |
| 171 | 5 d. "Pararge felix" (different) .. | 10 | 10 |
| 172 | 10 d. "Lepidochrysops arabicus" .. | 10 | 10 |
| 173 | 15 d. "Eumenis tewfiki" | 20 | 10 |
| 174 | 20 d. "Euchrysops philbyi" | 30 | 10 |
| 175 | 30 d. "Mylothris arabicus" | 35 | 10 |

(ii) Size 40 × 40 mm.

| | | | |
|---|---|---|---|
| 176 | 40 d. Type **9** .. | 50 | 10 |
| 177 | 50 d. As No. 168 .. | 55 | 10 |
| 178 | 70 d. As No. 169 .. | 65 | 15 |
| 179 | 1 r. As No. 170 .. | 70 | 20 |
| 180 | 1 r. 50 As No. 171 .. | 1·10 | 35 |
| 181 | 2 r. As No. 172 .. | 1·50 | 60 |

(iii) Size 42 × 42 mm.

| | | | |
|---|---|---|---|
| 182 | 3 r. As No. 173 .. | 1·75 | 75 |
| 183 | 5 r. As No. 174 .. | 3·00 | 1·10 |
| 184 | 10 r. As No. 175 .. | 5·25 | 2·25 |

(b) Air. Size 45 × 45 mm.

| | | | |
|---|---|---|---|
| 185 | 15 d. Type **9** .. | 15 | 10 |
| 186 | 25 d. As No. 168 .. | 25 | 10 |
| 187 | 35 d. As No. 169 .. | 40 | 10 |
| 188 | 50 d. As No. 170 .. | 50 | 10 |
| 189 | 75 d. As No. 171 .. | 65 | 15 |
| 190 | 1 r. As No. 172 .. | 85 | 20 |
| 191 | 2 r. As No. 173 .. | 1·25 | 40 |
| 192 | 3 r. As No. 174 .. | 3·00 | 65 |
| 193 | 5 r. As No. 175 .. | 5·00 | 1·10 |

**10.** Shaikh Mohamed bin Hamad al Sharqi and Veil-tailed Goldfish.

**1971.** Multicoloured.

| | | | |
|---|---|---|---|
| 194. | 5 d. Type **10** (postage) .. | 35 | 20 |
| 195. | 20 d. Shaikh and fish (different) (air) .. | 25 | 10 |
| 196. | 35 d. Shaikh and fish (different) .. .. | 30 | 10 |
| 197. | 40 d. Shaikh and fish (different) .. .. | 35 | 10 |
| 198. | 60 d. Shaikh and daisy .. | 40 | 10 |
| 199. | 1 r. Shaikh and rose .. | 60 | 15 |
| 200. | 2 r. Shaikh and gentian .. | 90 | 35 |
| 201. | 3 r. Shaikh and wild rose | 1·40 | 50 |

OFFICIAL STAMPS

**1965.** Designs similar to Nos. 1/9, but with "FUJEIRA" and value transposed, additionally inscr. "ON STATE'S SERVICE". Multicoloured.

(i) Postage. Size 43½ × 28½ mm.

| | | | |
|---|---|---|---|
| O 48. | 25 n.p. Type **1** .. .. | 40 | 15 |
| O 49. | 40 n.p. Arabian oryx .. | 40 | 15 |
| O 50. | 50 n.p. Hoopoe .. .. | 90 | 20 |
| O 51. | 75 n.p. Asiatic wild ass .. | 75 | 20 |
| O 52. | 1 r. Great egrets .. .. | 1·00 | 70 |

(ii) Air. (a) Size 43½ × 28½ mm.

| | | | |
|---|---|---|---|
| O 53. | 75 n.p. Arab horses .. | 40 | 25 |

(b) Size 53½ × 35½ mm.

| | | | |
|---|---|---|---|
| O 54. | 2 r Leopard .. .. | 95 | 65 |
| O 55. | 3 r. Dromedaries .. | 1·90 | 1·00 |
| O 56. | 5 r. Lanner falcon .. | 3·75 | 2·25 |

**1967.** Nos. 48/56 with currency name changed by overprinting.

| | | | |
|---|---|---|---|
| O 158. | 25 d. on 25 n.p. (postage) | 40 | 10 |
| O 159. | 40 d. on 40 n.p. .. .. | 20 | 15 |
| O 160. | 50 d. on 50 n.p. .. | 90 | 25 |
| O 161. | 75 d. on 75 n.p. .. .. | 50 | 35 |
| O 162. | 1 r. on 1 r. .. | 1·00 | 45 |
| O 163. | 75 d. on 75 n.p. (air) .. | 45 | 30 |
| O 164. | 2 r. on 2 r. .. .. | 1·40 | 70 |
| O 165. | 3 r. on 3 r. .. .. | 2·00 | 1·25 |
| O 166. | 5 r. on 5 r. .. .. | 4·00 | 2·75 |

## APPENDIX

The following stamps have either been issued in excess of postal needs or have not been available to the public in reasonable quantities at face value. Such stamps may later be given full listing if there is evidence of regular postal use.

**1967.**

"One Thousand and One Nights". Postage 10, 15, 30, 75 d., 1 r., 1 r. 50; Air 25, 50, 75 d., 1 r., 1 r. 25, 2 r.

Famous Paintings. Postage 25, 50, 75 d., 1, 1 r. 50 ; Air 2, 3, 5 r.

Cats. Postage 10, 35, 50 d., 1, 1 r. 50; Air 1 r. 25, 2 r. 75, 3 r. 50.

**1968.**

Winter Olympic Games, Grenoble. 25, 50, 75 d., 1, 1 r. 50, 2, 3 r.

Famous Paintings (square designs). Postage 50, 75 d., 1, 2, 3 r.; Air 1 r. 50, 2 r. 50, 3 r. 50, 4, 5 r.

Ships. Postage 15, 25, 50, 75 d., 1 r.; Air 2, 3, 4, 5 r.

Olympic Games, Mexico. Optd. on Nos. 22/6 and four values of 1968 Winter Olympics issue. Postage 1, 1 r. 50, 2, 3, 5 r.; Air 1, 1 r. 50, 2, 3 r.

Prehistoric Animals. Postage 15, 25, 50, 75 d., 1 r. 50; Air 1, 2 r. 50, 3, 4, 5 r.

Robert Kennedy Memorial issue. Optd. on Nos. 34/7. 1, 2, 3, 5 r.

Olympic Games, Mexico. Postage 15, 25, 35, 50, 75 d., 1 r.; Air 1 r. 50, 2, 3, 5 r.

International Letter-writing Week. Paintings. Postage 25, 50, 75 d., 1 r.: Air 1 r. 50, 2, 3, 5 r.

"EFIMEX" Int. Stamp Exhibition, Mexico. Optd on 1968 Letter-writing Week issue. Postage 25, 50, 75 d.; 1r. Air 1 r. 50, 2, 3, 5 r.

Gold Medal Winners, Olympic Games, Mexico. Optd. on 1968 Olympic Games, Mexico issue. Postage 15, 25, 35, 50 75 d., 1 r.; Air 1 r. 50, 2, 3, 5 r.

**1969.**

Wild Animals of the World. Postage 15, 25, 50, 75 d., 1 r.; Air 1 r. 50, 2, 3, 5 r.

Scenes from Shakespeare's Plays. Postage 25, 50, 75 d., 1, 2 r.; Air 1 r. 25, 2 r. 50, 3, 5 r.

Olympic Games, Munich (1969). Optd. on 1968 Olympic Games, Mexico issue. Postage 15, 25, 35, 50, 75 d., 1 r.; Air 1 r. 50, 2 r. 50, 3, 5 r.

Famous Railway Locomotives. Postage 15, 25, 50, 75 d., 1 r.; Air 2, 3, 5 r.

Moon Flight of "Apollo 8". Optd. or surch. on Nos. 76/83. 50, 75 n.p., 1, 2, 2 r. 50 on 25 n.p., 3 r on 15 n.p., 4 r. on 10 n.p., 5 r. on 5 n.p.

Winter Olympic Games, Sapporo, Japan (1972). Optd. on 1968 Winter Olympic Games, Grenoble issue. 25, 50, 75 d., 1, 1 r. 50, 2, 3 r.

Birds. Postage 25, 50 d., 1 r., 1 r. 50, 2 r.; Air 1 r. 25, 2 r. 50, 3, 5 r.

Pres. Eisenhower Memorial issue. Postage 25, 50 d., 1 r., 1 r. 50, 2 r.; Air 1 r. 25, 2 r. 50, 3, 5 r.

Champions of Peace. 25, 50, 75 d., 1, 2, 3, 5 r.

Human Rights Year. Optd. on 1969 Champions of Peace issue. 25, 50, 75 d., 1, 2, 3, 5 r.

Flowers. Postage 25, 50 d., 1, 1 r. 50, 2 r.; Air 1 r. 25, 2 r. 50, 3, 5 r.

"Apollo" Space Flights. Postage 10, 25, 50 d., 1, 2 r.; Air 2 r. 50, 3, 4, 5 r.

Space Flight of "Apollo 10". Optd. on 1969 "Apollo" Space Flights issue. Postage 10, 25, 50 d., 1, 2 r.; Air 2 r. 50, 3, 4, 5 r.

Moon Landing. Optd. on 1969 "Apollo" Space Flights issue. Postage 10, 25, 50 d., 1, 2 r.; Air 2 r. 50, 3, 4, 5 r.

First Man on the Moon. 1969 'Apollo" Space Flights issue optd. with various commemoration inscriptions. Postage 10, 25, 50 d., 1, 2 r.; Air 2 r. 50, 3, 4, 5 r.

**1970.**

Birth Bicentenary of Napoleon Bonaparte. 15, 25, 50, 75 d., 1, 1 r. 50, 2 r.

General De Gaulle Commemoration. Air 35, 60, 75 d., 1 r. 25, 2 r. 50, 3, 5 r.

Bible Stories. Postage 15 d., 1 r.; Air 35, 75 d., 1 r. 25, 1 r. 50, 2 r. 50, 3 r.

"Expo 70" World Fair, Osaka, Japan. Japanese Art. Postage 15, 25, 50, 75 d., 1, 2 r.; Air 75 d., 1 r. 25, 2 r. 50, 4 r.

Exploration of the Moon. 25, 50 d., 1, 2, 3, 4, 5 r.

Space Flight of "Apollo 13". Optd. on 1970 Moon Exploration issue. 25, 50 d., 1, 2, 3, 4, 5 r.

Moon Mission of "Apollo 14". Optd on 1970 Moon Exploration issue. 25, 50 d., 1, 2, 3, 4, 5 r.

"Expo 70" World Fair, Osaka, Japan. Pavilions. 10, 20, 70 d., 1 r. × 2, 2 r.

World Football Cup, Mexico. 10, 20, 70 d., 1 r. × 2, 2 r.

Pres. Gamal Nasser Memorial issue. Postage 10, 20, 30, 40, 50 d.; Air 5 r.

Horses. Postage 10, 20 d.; Air 70 d., 1, 2 r.

Cats. Postage 30, 70 d.; Air 1, 2, 3 r.

Dogs. Postage 30, 70 d.; Air 1, 2, 3 r.

Paintings of the Madonna. 30, 70 d., 1, 2, 3 r.

Stations of the Cross. 1 r. × 15.

Christmas. Paintings. Postage 30, 70 d., 1 r.; Air 2, 3 r.

**1971.**

American and European Cars. Postage 5, 20, 30 d., 4 r.; Air 30, 50, 70 d., 1 r. 50, 2 r. 50, 4 r

Space Exploration. Air 40, 60 d., 1, 2, 5 r.

History of Railways. 10, 20, 70 d., 2, 3 r.

General De Gaulle Memorial issue. Air 30, 70 d., 1, 2, 3 r.

Moon Mission of "Apollo 14" Air 70 d., 1, 2, 3, 4 r.

Wild Animals. Air 20, 40, 60 d., 1, 2, 3 r.

Olympic Games, Munich (1972) (square designs). Postage 50 d., 1 r.; Air 2, 3, 4 r.

Winter Olympic Games, Sapporo, Japan (1972). Postage 5, 10, 15, 20, 30, 50 d.; Air 70 d., 4 r.

500th Birth Anniv. of Durer. Paintings. Air 70 d., 1, 2, 3, 4 r.

Birth Bicentenary of Beethoven. Portraits and instruments. Postage 30, 70 d.; Air 1, 3, 4 r.

Mozart Commemoration. Postage 30, 70 d. 1 r.; Air 3, 4 r.

Frazier v Mohammed Ali World Heavyweight Boxing Championship Fight. Air 1, 2, 3 r.

World Scout Jamboree, Asagiri, Japan. Postage 20, 30, 50, 70 d., 1 r. × 2, 2 r. × 2; Air 3, 4 r.

Butterflies. Air. 70 d., 1, 2, 3, 5 r.

Cats and Dogs. 10, 20, 30 d., 1, 2, 3 r.

Monkeys. 30, 70 d., 1, 2, 3 r.

Wild Animals. 30, 70 d., 1, 2, 3 r.

Horses. 70 d., 1, 2, 3, 4 r.

Olympic Games, Munich, Sports. 1, 2, 3, 4, 5, 6, 7, 8, 9, 10, 11, 12, 13, 14, 15, 16, 17, 18, 19, 20, 21, 22, 23, 24, 25, 26, 27, 28, 29, 30 d.

Olympic Games, Munich. Sports and Arenas. Postage 35, 60 d., 2, 3 r.; Air 4 r.

Christmas. Postage 40, 60 d., 2 r.; Air 3, 4 r.

International Labour Day. Paintings. Postage 40, 60 d., 2, 3 r.; Air 2, 3, 4 r.

**1972.**

400th Birth Anniv. of Kepler. Postage 35, 75 d., 1, 2 r.; Air 3, 5 r.

Moon Mission of "Apollo 15". Postage 30, 70 d.; Air 1, 2, 5 r.

2500th Anniv. of The Persian Empire. Postage 35, 65, 75 d.; Air 1 r. 25, 2, 3 r.

Historical Costumes. 30, 70 d., 1, 2, 3 r.

Winter Olympic Games, Sapporo, Japan. Postage 25, 30, 70 d.; Air 1 r. 25, 2, 3 r.

Tropical Birds 30, 70 d., 1, 2, 3 r.

Children's Day. Paintings. Postage 10, 30, 60 d.; Air 4, 5 r.

Sculptures. Postage 30, 70 d.; Air 1, 2, 6 r.

Paintings of the Madonna. Postage 20, 30 50 d.; Air 4, 5 r.

Nude Paintings. 50 d., 1, 2, 3, 4 r.

Gold Medal Winners, Winter Olympic Games, Sapporo. Optd. on 1972 Winter Olympic Games, Sapporo issue. Postage 25, 30, 70 d.; Air 1 r. 25, 2, 3 r.

Olympic Games, Munich. Discus-thrower. Air 8 r.

Space Exploration. Postage 5, 10, 15, 20, 25, 30, 35, 40, 45, 50, 55, 60 d.; Air 65, 70, 75 d., 1, 2, 3, 4, 5 r.

Walt Disney Cartoon Characters. Postage 1, 2, 3, 4, 5, 10, 15, 20, 25, 30 d.; Air 45, 55, 65, 70 d., 1, 1 r. 50, 2, 3, 4, 5 r.

History of the Olympic Games Postage 1, 2, 3, 4, 5, 10, 15, 20, 25, 30, 45, 55 d.; Air 65, 70 d., 1, 1 r. 50, 2, 3, 5 r.

Summit Meeting of Pres. Nixon and Mao Tse-tung. Air 2, 3, 5 r.

Pres. Nixon's Visit of Russia. Optd. on 1972 Nixon-Mao Tse-tung Meeting issue. Air 2, 3, 5 r.

150th Death Anniv. (1971) of Napoleon Bonaparte. Air 10 r.

2nd Death Anniv. of General De Gaulle. Air 10 r.

Olympic Games, Munich, Javelin-thrower. Air 10 r.

Gold Medal Winners, Olympic Games, Munich. Optd. on 1972 Discus-thrower issue. Air 8 r.

Moon Mission of "Apollo 16". Air 10 r.

European Birds. 30, 70 d., 1, 2, 3 r.

A number of issues on gold and silver foil also exist, but it is understood that these were mainly for presentation purposes, although valid for postage.

During 1970 a number of other sets came on to the market, but their official status is in doubt.

The United Arab Emirates Ministry of Communications took over the Fujeira postal service on 1 August 1972. Further stamps were released without authority and had no validity.

# FUNCHAL Pt. 9

The District of Funchal (the chief town) was the administrative title of Madeira from 1892 to 1905. From 1905 the name reverted to Madeira.

1000 reis = 1 milreis.

**4.**

**1892.**

| | | | | |
|---|---|---|---|---|
| 85 | 4 | 5 r. yellow .. .. | 2·50 | 1·60 |
| 86 | | 10 r. mauve .. .. | 2·25 | 1·60 |
| 87 | | 15 r. brown .. .. | 3·00 | 2·25 |
| 89 | | 20 r. lilac .. .. | 3·00 | 2·25 |
| 83 | | 25 r. green .. .. | 4·00 | 1·00 |
| 84 | | 50 r. blue .. .. | 5·25 | 2·25 |
| 92 | | 75 r. pink .. .. | 6·50 | 5·25 |
| 93 | | 80 r. green .. .. | 11·50 | 10·00 |
| 95 | | 100 r. brown on buff .. | 7·75 | 4·00 |
| 107 | | 150 r. red on pink .. | 45·00 | 27·00 |
| 96 | | 200 r. blue on blue .. | 50·00 | 40·00 |
| 97 | | 300 r. blue on brown .. | 60·00 | 48·00 |

**1897.** "King Carlos" key-type inscr "FUNCHAL". Name and value in red (Nos. 123, 130) or black (others).

| | | | | |
|---|---|---|---|---|
| 110 | S | 2½ r. grey .. .. | 45 | 35 |
| 111 | | 5 r. red .. .. | 45 | 35 |
| 112 | | 10 r. green .. .. | 45 | 35 |
| 113 | | 15 r. brown .. .. | 5·00 | 4·00 |
| 126 | | 15 r. green .. .. | 3·00 | 2·25 |
| 114 | | 20 r. lilac .. .. | 1·25 | 80 |
| 115 | | 25 r. green .. .. | 2·50 | 80 |
| 127 | | 25 r. red .. .. | 1·25 | 55 |
| 128 | | 50 r. blue .. .. | 1·25 | 90 |
| 129 | | 65 r. blue .. .. | 1·00 | 90 |
| 117 | | 75 r. pink .. .. | 1·40 | 1·00 |
| 130 | | 75 r. brown on yellow .. | 1·60 | 1·00 |
| 118 | | 80 r. mauve .. .. | 1·40 | 1·10 |
| 119 | | 100 r. blue on blue .. | 1·40 | 1·10 |
| 131 | | 115 r. red on pink .. | 2·00 | 1·25 |
| 132 | | 130 r. brown on cream .. | 2·00 | 1·25 |
| 120 | | 150 r. brown on yellow .. | 2·40 | 1·25 |
| 133 | | 180 r. grey on pink .. | 2·00 | 1·25 |
| 121 | | 200 r. purple on pink .. | 2·50 | 2·25 |
| 122 | | 300 r. blue on pink .. | 2·50 | 2·25 |
| 123 | | 500 r. black on blue .. | 2·50 | 2·25 |

# GABON Pt. 6; Pt. 13

A French colony on the W. coast of equatorial Africa. Became part of Fr. Equatorial Africa in 1937 and a republic within the French Community in 1958.

100 centimes = 1 franc.

**1886.** Stamps of French Colonies, "Commerce" type, surch. **GAB** surrounded by dots, and value in figures.

| | | | | |
|---|---|---|---|---|
| 1 | J | 5 on 20 c. red on green .. | £275 | £275 |
| 2 | | 10 on 20 c. red on green .. | £275 | £275 |
| 3 | | 25 on 20 c. red on green .. | £275 | £275 |
| 4 | | 50 on 15 c. blue on lt blue | £850 | £850 |
| 5 | | 75 on 15 c. blue on lt blue | £1000 | £1000 |

**1888.** Stamps of French Colonies, "Commerce" type, surch. in figures.

| | | | | |
|---|---|---|---|---|
| 6. | J. | 15 on 10 c. black on lilac | £3250 | £750 |
| 7. | | 15 on 1 f. olive .. .. | £1300 | £600 |
| 8. | | 25 on 5 c. green .. .. | £850 | £160 |
| 9. | | 25 on 10 c. black on lilac .. | £3250 | £1000 |
| 10. | | 25 on 75 c. red .. .. | £1800 | £850 |

**1889.** Postage Due stamps of French Colonies surch. **GABON TIMBRE** and value in figures.

| | | | | |
|---|---|---|---|---|
| 11. | U. | 15 on 5 c. black .. | £160 | £140 |
| 12. | | 15 on 30 c. black .. | £3250 | £2250 |
| 13. | | 25 on 20 c. black .. | 70·00 | 50·00 |

**6.**

**1889.** Imperf.

| | | | | |
|---|---|---|---|---|
| 14. | **6.** | 15 c. black on pink .. | £1000 | £675 |
| 15. | | 25 c. black on green .. | £650 | £525 |

**1904.** "Tablet" key-type inscr "GABON" in red (1, 5, 15, 25, 35, 45, 75 c., 1, 2 f.) or blue (others).

| | | | | |
|---|---|---|---|---|
| 16 | D | 1 c. black on blue .. | 50 | 55 |
| 17 | | 2 c. brown on buff .. | 50 | 40 |
| 18 | | 4 c. brown on grey .. | 70 | 70 |
| 19 | | 5 c. green .. .. | 80 | 60 |
| 20 | | 10 c. red .. .. | 2·50 | 65 |
| 21 | | 15 c. grey .. .. | 3·75 | 75 |
| 22 | | 20 c. red on green .. | 5·00 | 4·00 |
| 23 | | 25 c. blue .. .. | 4·00 | 3·00 |
| 24 | | 30 c. brown on drab .. | 8·25 | 7·00 |
| 25 | | 35 c. black on yellow .. | 14·00 | 12·50 |
| 26 | | 40 c. red on yellow .. | 9·50 | 9·00 |
| 27 | | 45 c. black on green .. | 18·00 | 18·00 |
| 28 | | 50 c. brown on blue .. | 7·00 | 6·50 |
| 29 | | 75 c. brown on orange .. | 11·00 | 12·00 |
| 30 | | 1 f. green .. .. | 22·00 | 20·00 |
| 31 | | 2 f. violet on pink .. | 48·00 | 50·00 |
| 32 | | 5 f. mauve on lilac .. | 95·00 | 90·00 |

**7.** Gabon Warrior. **9.** Bantu Woman.

**8.** View of Libreville.

**1910.**

| | | | | |
|---|---|---|---|---|
| 33. | **7.** | 1 c. brown and orange .. | 50 | 50 |
| 34. | | 2 c. black and brown .. | 1·00 | 50 |
| 35. | | 4 c. violet and blue .. | 70 | 50 |
| 36. | | 5 c. olive and green .. | 50 | 50 |
| 37. | | 10 c. red and lake .. | 1·25 | 1·00 |
| 38. | | 20 c. brown and violet .. | 1·50 | 3·00 |
| 39. | **8.** | 25 c. brown and blue .. | 2·00 | 2·75 |
| 40. | | 30 c. red and grey .. | 15·00 | 19·00 |
| 41. | | 35 c. green and violet .. | 9·00 | 9·00 |
| 42. | | 40 c. blue and brown .. | 13·00 | 16·00 |
| 43. | | 45 c. violet and red .. | 21·00 | 21·00 |
| 44. | | 50 c. grey and green .. | 40·00 | 42·00 |
| 45. | | 75 c. brown and orange .. | 60·00 | 65·00 |
| 46. | **9.** | 1 f. yellow and brown .. | 65·00 | 65·00 |
| 47. | | 2 f. brown and red .. | £180 | £180 |
| 48. | | 5 f. brown and blue .. | £180 | £180 |

**1910.** As last but inscr "AFRIQUE EQUATORIALE GABON".

| | | | | |
|---|---|---|---|---|
| 49 | 7 | 1 c. brown and orange .. | 10 | 10 |
| 50 | | 2 c. black and brown .. | 10 | 10 |
| 51 | | 4 c. violet and blue .. | 20 | 20 |
| 52 | | 5 c. grey and green .. | 35 | 20 |
| 82 | | 5 c. black and yellow .. | 30 | 45 |
| 53 | | 10 c. red and lake .. | 50 | 40 |
| 83 | | 10 c. light green and green | 30 | 50 |
| 54 | | 15 c. purple and pink .. | 30 | 50 |
| 55 | | 20 c. brown and violet .. | 5·00 | 6·75 |
| 56 | 8 | 25 c. brown and blue .. | 55 | 50 |
| 84 | | 25 c. black and green .. | 75 | 85 |
| 57 | | 30 c. red and grey .. | 50 | 50 |
| 85 | | 30 c. red and carmine .. | 65 | 70 |
| 58 | | 35 c. green and violet .. | 55 | 55 |

59 40 c. blue and brown .. 70 50
60 45 c. violet and red .. 55 50
86 45 c. red and black .. 65 80
61 50 c. grey and green .. 65 70
87 50 c. blue and deep blue 45 50
62 75 c. brown and red .. 1·90 3·00
63 **9** 1 f. bistre and brown .. 1·50 1·75
64 2 f. brown and red .. 2·50 2·25
65 5 f. brown and blue .. 4·50 4·50

**1912.** "Tablet" key-type surch in figures.

66 D 05 on 2 c. brown on buff 50 55
67 05 on 4 c. brown on grey 50 55
68 05 on 15 c. grey .. .. 15 15
69 05 on 20 c. red on green 25 40
70 05 on 25 c. blue .. .. 20 25
71 05 on 30 c. brown on drab 50 65
72 10 on 40 c. red on yellow 25 40
73 10 on 45 c. black on green 30 55
74 10 on 50 c. brown on blue 70 85
75 10 on 75 c. brown on orge 40 60
76 10 on 1 f. green .. .. 40 60
77 10 on 2 f. violet on pink 40 60
78 10 on 5 f. mauve on lilac 1·75 2·00

**1915.** Surch with red cross and **5c**.

79 **7** 10 c.+5 c. (No. 37) .. 10·00 10·50
81 10 c.+5 c. (No. 53) .. 30 65

**1924.** Inscr "AFRIQUE EQUATORIALE GABON" and optd **AFRIQUE EQUATORIALE FRANCAISE**.

88 **7** 1 c. brown and orange .. 10 20
89 2 c. black and brown .. 10 30
90 4 c. violet and blue .. 10 25
91 5 c. black and yellow .. 10 20
92 10 c. light green & green 30 40
93 10 c. blue and brown .. 15 20
94 15 c. purple and pink .. 20 40
95 15 c. pink and purple .. 40 55
96 20 c. brown and violet .. 20 40
97 **8** 25 c. black and green .. 15 30
98 30 c. red and carmine .. 25 40
99 30 c. yellow and black .. 25 40
100 30 c. green .. .. 65 65
101 35 c. green and violet .. 20 35
102 40 c. blue and brown .. 30 25
103 45 c. red and black .. 45 50
104 50 c. blue and deep blue 30 35
105 50 c. green and red .. 30 20
106 65 c. red and blue .. 1·00 2·00
107 75 c. brown and orange 50 80
108 90 c. red and scarlet .. 1·25 1·40
109 **9** 1 f. bistre and brown .. 50 60
110 1 f. 10 red and green .. 3·25 3·50
111 1 f. 50 blue and light blue 1·00 60
112 2 f. brown and red .. 80 80
113 3 f. mauve on pink .. 3·00 4·25
114 5 f. brown and blue .. 3·25 4·00

**1925.** As last, surch in figures.

115 **9** 65 on 1 f. brown & green 35 55
116 85 on 1 f. brown & green 35 55
117 **8** 90 c. on 75 c. pink & red 65 1·10
118 **9** 1 f. 25 on 1 f. ultram & bl 45 50
119 1 f. 50 on 1 f. dp bl & bl 65 80
120 3 f. on 5 f. brown & mve 1·50 3·75
121 10 f. on 5 f. green & brn 8·00 8·25
122 20 f. on 5 f. red & purple 8·25 8·25

**1931.** "Colonial Exn." key-types inscr. "GABON".

123. E. 40 c. green .. .. 1·40 1·60
124. F. 50 c. mauve .. .. 1·25 1·40
125. G. 90 c. orange .. .. 1·40 1·60
126. H. 1 f. 50 blue .. .. 2·25 2·50

**21.** Log Raft on the River Ogowe. **22.** Count de Brazza.

**1932.**

127. **21.** 1 c. red .. .. .. 15 25
128. 2 c. black on red .. 20 30
129. 4 c. green .. .. 20 30
130. 5 c. blue .. .. 20 30
131. 10 c. red on yellow .. 20 30
132. 15 c. red on green .. 50 60
133. 20 c. red .. .. 50 65
134. 25 c. brown .. .. 35 45
135. **22.** 30 c. green .. .. 80 80
136. 40 c. purple .. .. 65 65
137. 45 c. black on green .. 85 85
138. 50 c. brown .. .. 60 40
139. 65 c. blue .. .. 3·25 3·00
140. 75 c. black on orange .. 1·75 1·75
141. 90 c. red .. .. 2·00 1·90
142. 1 f. green on blue .. 10·00 11·00
143. – 1 f. 25 violet .. 1·25 85
144. – 1 f. 50 blue .. 2·00 1·00
145. – 1 f. 75 green .. 1·60 75
146. – 2 f. red .. .. 13·50 10·50
147. – 3 f. green on blue .. 3·25 2·75
148. – 5 f. brown .. .. 4·00 4·00
149. – 10 f. black on orange .. 17·00 14·00
150. – 20 f. purple .. .. 30·00 24·00

DESIGN—HORIZ. 1 f. 25 to 20 f. Gabon Village.

**25.** Prime Minister Leon Mba.

**1959.** 1st Anniv. of Republic.

161. **25.** 15 f. brown .. .. 40 30
162. – 25 f. green and sepia .. 40 25

PORTRAIT: 25 f. Prime Minister Mba (profile).

**1960.** 10th Anniv. of African Technical Co-operation Commission. As T **62** of Cameroun.

163. 50 f. blue and purple .. 85 75

**27.** Dr. Albert Schweitzer (philosopher and missionary), Organ and View of Lambarene.

**1960.** Air.

164. **27.** 200 f. brn., grn. & bl. .. 5·00 4·00

**1960.** Air. Olympic Games. No. 192 of French Equatorial Africa optd. with Olympic rings, **XVIIe OLYMPIADE 1960. REPUBLIQUE GABONAISE** and surch. **250F** and bars.

165. 250 f. on 500 F. blue, black and green .. .. 6·75 6·75

**29.** Tree Felling.

**1960.** Air. 5th World Forestry Congress, Seattle.

166. **29.** 100 f. brown, black & grn. 3·00 1·40

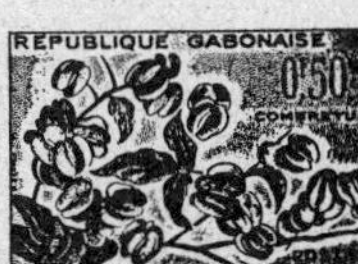

**30.** Flag, Map and U.N. Emblem. **32.** Combretum.

**31.** Lyre-tailed Honeyguide in flight.

**1961.** Admission into U.N.

167. **30.** 15 f. multicoloured .. 30 20
168. 25 f. multicoloured .. 35 25
169. 85 f. multicoloured .. 1·25 80

**1961.** Air. Birds. Multicoloured.

170. 50 f. Type **31** .. .. 3·25 1·40
171. 100 f. Madame Verreaux's sunbird .. .. 6·25 2·00
172. 200 f. Blue-headed bee eater .. .. 12·00 4·25
173. 250 f. Crowned eagle .. 15·00 5·75
174. 500 f. Narina trogon .. 30·00 11·00

The 200 f., 250 f.. and 500 f. are vert. designs.

**1961.**

175. **32.** 50 c. red, purple & grn. 10 10
176. – 1 f. red, turq. and bistre 10 10
177. – 2 f. yellow and green .. 10 10
178. – 3 f. yellow, green & olive 20 15
179. – 5 f. multicoloured .. 25 20
180. **32.** 10 f. red, grn. & turquoise 30 25

FLOWERS—VERT. 1 f., 5 f. Gabonese tulip (tree). HORIZ. 2 f., 3 f. Yellow cassia.

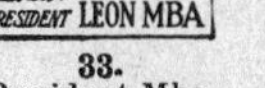

**33.** President Mba. **39.** Capt. Ntchorere and Flags.

**37.** Breguet 14 Biplane.

**1962.**

181. **33.** 15 f. blue, red & grn. .. 20 10
182. 20 f. sepia, red & green 35 15
183. 25 f. brown, red & green 40 15

**1962.** Air. "Air Afrique" Airline. As T **69** of Cameroun.

184. 500 f. green, ochre & blk. 9·50 5·50

**1962.** Malaria Eradication. As T **70** of Cameroun.

185. 25 f.+5 f. green .. .. 80 80

**1962.** Sports. As T **12** of Central African Republic. Inscr. "JEUX SPORTIFS".

186. 20 f. multicoloured (post.) 45 20
187. 50 f. multicoloured .. 95 60
188. 100 f. multicoloured (air) 2·50 1·10

DESIGNS—HORIZ. 20 f. Start of race. 50 f. Football. VERT. (26×47 mm.): 100 f. long-jump.

**1962.** Air. Evolution of Air Transport.

189. **37.** 10 f. blue and red .. 50 20
190. – 20 f. indigo, blue & brn. 70 35
191. – 60 f. blue, pur. & green 1·90 85
192. – 85 f. indigo, blue & orge. 2·75 1·40

AIRCRAFT: 20 f. De Havilland Dragon Rapide. 60 f. Sud Aviation Caravelle. 85 f. Rocket.

**1962.** 1st Anniv of Union of African and Malagasy States. As No. 328 of Cameroun.

194. 30 f. green .. .. .. 1·10 80

**1962.** Capt. Ntchorere Commem.

195. **39.** 80 f. multicoloured .. 1·10 70

**1963.** Freedom from Hunger. As T **76** of Cameroun.

196. 25 f.+5 f. grn., brn. & red 60 60

**1963.** Air. 50th Anniv. of Arrival of Dr Schweitzer in Gabon. Surch. **100 F JUBILE GABONAIS 1913-1963.**

197. **27.** 100 f. on 200 f. brown, green and blue .. 2·50 1·40

**43.** Libreville Post Office.

**1963.** Air. Cent of Gabon Postal Services.

198 **43** 100 f. multicoloured .. 1·40 85

**1963.** Air. African and Malagasy Posts and Telecommunications Union. As T **18** of Central African Republic.

199. 85 f. multicoloured .. 1·40 80

**1963.** Space Telecommunications. As Nos. 37/8 of Central African Republic.

200. 25 f. orange, blue & green 40 35
201. 100 f. brown, green & blue 1·60 1·40

**1963.** Air. 1st Anniv. of "Air Afrique" and Inauguration of "DC-8" Service. As T **11** of Congo Republic.

202. 50 f. multicoloured .. 90 55

**1963.** Air. European-African Economic Convention. As T **24** of Central African Republic.

203. 50 f. multicoloured .. 1·25 65

**1963.** 15th Anniv. of Declaration of Human Rights. As T **26** of Central African Republic.

204. 25 f. slate green and brown 45 30

**49.** Rameses and Gods, Wadi-es-Sebua.

**1964.** Air. Nubian Monuments.

205. **49.** 10 f.+5 f. brown & blue 85 85
206. 25 f.+5 f. blue and red 1·00 1·00
207. 50 f.+5 f. pur. & myrtle 1·50 1·50

**1964.** World Meteorological Day. As T **14** of Congo Republic.

208. 25 f. green, blue and bistre 55 35

**51.** Arms of Gabon.

**1964.**

209. **51.** 25 f. multicoloured .. 50 30

**1964.** Air. 5th Anniv. of Equatorial African Heads of State Conf. As T **31** of Central African Republic.

210. 100 f. multicoloured .. 1·50 85

**53.** Tarpon. **54.** Ear of Wheat, Cogwheel and Globe.

**1964.** Gabon Fauna.

211. **53.** 30 f. black, blue & brown 70 40
212. – 60 f. brown, chest. & grn. 1·50 60
213. – 80 f. brown, green & blue 1·60 85

DESIGNS—VERT. 60 f. Gorilla. HORIZ. 80 f. African buffalo.

**1964.** Air. 1st Anniv. of "Europafrique".

214. **54.** 50 f. blue, olive and red 1·25 80

**55.** Start of Race.

**1964.** Air. Olympic Games, Tokyo.

215. **55.** 25 f. grn., brn. and orge. 60 35
216. – 50 f. brn., orge. & green 1·10 45
217. – 100 f. violet, pur. & olive 2·25 90
218. – 200 f. brn., purple & red 3·50 2·25

DESIGNS—VERT. 50 f. Massaging athlete. 100 f. Anointing before the Games. HORIZ. 200 f. Athletes.

**1964.** Air. Pan-African and Malagasy Posts and Telecommunications Congress, Cairo. As T **23** of Congo Republic.

220. 25 f. sepia, red and green 55 30

**1964.** French, African and Malagasy Co-operation. As T **547** of France.

221. 25 f. brown, blue and slate 55 40

**58.** "Dissotis rotundifolia". **59.** Pres. Kennedy.

**1964.** Flowers. Multicoloured.

222. 3 f. Type **58** .. .. 20 10
223. 5 f. "Gloriosa superba" .. 30 15
224. 15 f. "Eulophia horsfallii" 55 25

**1964.** Air. Pres. Kennedy Commem.

225. **59.** 100 f. black, orge. & grn. 1·60 1·40

60. Women in Public Service.

**1964.** Air. Social Evolution of Gabonese Women.
227. **60.** 50 f. brown, blue & red 85 45

61. Sun and I.Q.S.Y. Emblem.

**1965.** Int. Quiet Sun Year.
228. **61.** 85 f. multicoloured .. 1·40 85

62. Globe and I.C.Y. Emblem.

**1965.** Air. Int. Co-operation Year.
229. **62.** 50 f. orge., turq. & blue 85 45

63. 17th-cent. Merchantman.

**1965.** Air. Old Ships. Multicoloured.
230. 25 f. 16th-cent. galleon .. 40 55
231. 50 f. Type **63** .. .. 1·75 85
232. 85 f. 18th-cent. frigate .. 3·25 1·40
233. 100 f. 19th-cent. brig .. 4·75 1·60
The 25 f. and 85 f. are vert.

64. Morse Telegraph Apparatus.

**1965.** Centenary of I.T.U.
234. **64.** 30 f. green, orge. & blue 55 35

65. Manganese Mine, Moanda. 67. Football.

66. Nurse holding Child.

**1965.** "Mining Riches".
235. **65.** 15 f. red, violet and blue 40 20
236. – 60 f. red and blue .. 1·25 60
DESIGN: 60 f. Uranium mine, Mounana.

**1965.** Air. Gabon Red Cross.
237. **66.** 100 f. brown, red & grn. 1·60 85

**1965.** 1st African Games, Brazzaville.
238. **67.** 25 f. blk., red & grn. (post.) 55 35
239. – 100 f. purple, red & brown (air) .. .. 1·90 85
DESIGN (27 × 48½ mm.): 100 f. Basketball.

68. "Globe", Pylon and "Sun".

**1965.** Air. "Europafrique".
240. **68.** 50 f. multicoloured .. 1·40 55

69. President Mba.

**1965.** Air. 5th Anniv. of Independence.
241. **69.** 25 f. multicoloured .. 50 30

70. Okoukoue Dance. 71. Abraham Lincoln.

**1965.** Gabon Dances.
242. **70.** 25 f. yellow, brown & grn. 45 20
243. – 60 f. black, red & brown 1·25 60
DESIGN: 60 f. Makudji dance.

**1965.** Death Cent. of Abraham Lincoln.
244. **71.** 50 f. multicoloured .. 80 45

72. Sir Winston Churchill.

**1965.** Air. Churchill Commem.
245. **72.** 100 f. multicoloured .. 1·60 85

73. Dr. A. Schweitzer and Map.

**1965.** Air. Schweitzer Commem.
246. **73.** 1000 f. gold .. .. 48·00 48·00

74. Pope John XXIII.

**1965.** Air. Pope John Commem.
247. **74.** 85 f. multicoloured .. 1·10 80

75. Mail Carrier, Post Office and Van. 76. Nurse and Patients.

**1965.** Stamp Day.
248. **75.** 30 f. brown, green & blue 50 40

**1966.** Air. Red Cross. Multicoloured.
249. 50 f. Type **76** .. .. 95 55
250. 100 f. Bandaging patient 1·90 85

77. Balumbu Mask. 78. W.H.O. Building.

**1966.** World Festival of Negro Arts, Dakar. Multicoloured.
253. 5 f. Type **77** .. .. 20 15
254. 10 f. Statuette—"Ancestor of the Fang (tribe), Byeri" .. .. .. 30 20
255. 25 f. Fang mask .. .. 70 30
256. 30 f. Okuyi Myene mask .. 90 50
257. 85 f. Bakota copper mask 2·10 1·10

**1966.** Inaug. of W.H.O. Headquarters, Geneva.
258. **78.** 50 f. black, yellow & blue 85 40

79. Satellite "A1" and Rocket.

**1966.** Air. "Conquest of Space".
259. **79.** 30 f. lake, plum and blue 55 30
260. – 90 f. plum, red and purple 1·40 60
DESIGN: 90 f. Satellite "FR1" and rocket.

80. "Learning the Alphabet". 81. Footballer.

**1966.** U.N.E.S.C.O. Literacy Campaign.
261. **80.** 30 f. multicoloured .. 55 30

**1966.** World Cup Football Championships England.
262. **81.** 25 f. blue, green & lake (postage) .. 40 20
263. – 90 f. purple and blue .. 1·60 70
264. – 100 f. slate and red (air) 1·90 90
DESIGNS—VERT. 90 f. Footballer (different). HORIZ. 100 f. Footballers on world map (47½ × 27 mm.).

82. Industrial Scenes within leaves of "Plant". 83. Plywood Mill.

**1966.** Air. "Europafrique".
265. **82.** 50 f. multicoloured .. 85 45

**1966.** Economic Development.
266. **83.** 20 f. lake, purple & grn. 45 30
267. – 85 f. brown, blue & grn. 2·40 1·10
DESIGN: 85 f. "Roger Butin" (oil rig).

**1966.** Air. Inauguration of Douglas DC-8F Air Services. As T **54** of Central African Republic.
268 30 f. grey, black and orange 40 20

85. Making Deposit.

**1966.** Savings Bank.
269. **85.** 25 f. brown, green & blue 55 30

86. Scouts and Camp Fire. 87. Gabonese Scholar.

**1966.** Scouting.
270. **86.** 30 f. brown, red & slate 55 35
271. – 50 f. brown, lake & blue 1·00 45
DESIGN—VERT. 50 f. Scouts taking oath.

**1966.** Air. 20th Anniv. of U.N.E.S.C.O.
272. **87.** 100 f. black, buff & blue 1·40 65

88. Libreville Airport.

**1966.** Air.
273. **88.** 200 f. brown, red & blue 3·25 1·10

89. Sikorsky S-43 Amphibian, Map and Flag (Aeromaritime's First Airmail Service, 1937).

**1966.** Stamp Day.
274. **89.** 30 f. multicoloured .. 85 40

90. Hippopotami.

**1967.** Gabon Fauna. Multicoloured.
275. 1 f. Type **90** .. .. 10 10
276. 2 f. Crocodiles .. .. 15 10
277. 3 f. Water chevrotains .. 15 10
278. 5 f. Chimpanzees .. .. 20 10
279. 10 f. African elephants .. 65 30
280. 20 f. Leopards .. .. 1·25 40

91. Lions Emblem and Anniversary Dates.

**1967.** 50th Anniv. of Lions Int. Mult.
281. 30 f. Type **91** .. .. 55 30
282. 50 f. Lions emblem, map and globe .. .. 90 40

92. Masked Faces. 93. I.T.Y. Emblem and Transport.

**1967.** Libreville Carnival.
283. **92.** 30 f. blue, brown & yell. 60 30

**1967.** Int. Tourist Year.
284. **93.** 30 f. multicoloured .. 65 35

94. Diving-board (Mexico City).

96. Atomic Symbol Dove and Globe.

95. Farman F.190.

**1967.** Publicity for 1968 Olympic Games, Mexico.
285. **94.** 25 f. turq., blue & violet 45 20
286. – 30 f. purple, lake & green 65 30
287. – 50 f. blue, green & purple 1·10 60
DESIGNS: 30 f. Sun and snow crystal. 50f. Ice rink, Grenoble.

**1967.** Air. Famous Aircraft.
288. **95.** 200 f. plum, blue & turq. 3·25 1·10
289. – 300 f. blue, pur. & brn. 5·50 1·40
290. – 500 f. blue, pur. & grn. 9·50 4·25
AIRCRAFT: 300 f. De Havilland Heron 2. 500 f. Potez 56.

**1967.** Int. Atomic Energy Agency.
291. **96.** 30 f. red, blue and green 65 30

97. Aircraft on Flight-paths.

**1967.** Air. I.C.A.O. Commem.
292. **97.** 100 f. pur., blue & green 1·50 70

98. Pope Paul VI. 99. Blood Donor and Bank.

**1967.** Papal Encyclical "Populorum Progressio".
293. **98.** 30 f. black, blue & green 65 35

**1967.** Air. Red Cross.
294. **99.** 50 f. multicoloured .. 1·10 45
295. – 100 f. multicoloured .. 1·90 95
DESIGN: 100 f. Heart and blood-transfusion apparatus.

100. Indigenous Emblems. 101. "Europafrique".

**1967.** World Fair, Montreal.
297. **100.** 30 f. brn., green & lake 55 30

**1967.** Europafrique.
298. **101.** 50 f. multicoloured .. 85 35

102. Orientation Diagram and Sun. 103. U.N. Emblem, Gabon Women and Child.

**1967.** Air. World Scout Jamboree, Idaho.
299. **102.** 50 f. green, orge. & blue 80 50
300. – 100 f. red, green & blue 1·40 90
DESIGN: 100 f. U.S. scout greeting Gabon scout on map.

**1967.** U.N. Status of Women Commission.
301. **103.** 75 f. blue, green & brn. 1·40 55

**1967.** Air. 5th Anniv. of U.A.M.P.T. As T **66** of Central African Republic.
302. 100 f. red, blue and olive .. 1·40 65

105. Baraka Mission, Libreville.

**1967.** Air. 125th Anniv. of American Missionaries Arrival.
303. **105.** 100 f. black, grn. & blue 1·60 85

106. U.N. Emblem and Book with Supporters. 107. "Draconea fragans".

**1967.** Air. U.N. Int. Rights Commission.
304. **106.** 60 f. multicoloured .. 90 55

**1967.** Gabon Trees.
305. **107.** 5 f. brown, green and blue (postage) 20 15
306. – 10 f. green, bronze & blue 35 20
307. – 20 f. red, green & brown 55 30
308. – 50 f. green, bistre and blue (air) .. .. 95 40
309. – 100 r. multicoloured .. 1·90 70
DESIGNS: 10 f. "Pycnanthus angolensis" 20 f. "Disthemonanthus benthamianus". (27 × 48 mm.). 50 f. "Baillonella toxisperma". 100 f. "Aucoumea klaineana".

108. "Belgrano" and "Jean Guiton" (19th-century steam packets).

**1967.** Stamp Day. Multicoloured.
311 30 f. Type **108** .. .. 70 45
312 30 f. "Ango" and "Lucie Delmas" (modern mail carriers) .. .. 70 45
Nos. 311/12 were issued together, se-tenant, forming a composite design.

109. Chancellor Adenauer. 110. African W.H.O. Building.

**1968.** Air. Adenauer Commem.
313. **109.** 100 f. sepia, red & yellow 1·90 65

**1968.** 20th Anniv. of W.H.O.
315. **110.** 20 f. purple, blue & grn. 55 30

111. Dam and Power-station. 112. President Bongo.

**1968.** Int. Hydrological Decade.
316. **111.** 15 f. blue, orange & lake 45 20

**1968.**
317 **112** 25 f. black, yell & grn 40 20
318 – 30 f. black, turq & pur 45 20
DESIGN: 30 f. Pres. Bongo (half-length portrait)

113. "Madonna and Child with Rosary" (Murillo).

**1968.** Air. Religious Paintings. Multicoloured.
319. 60 f. Type **113** .. .. 90 45
320. 90 f. "Christ in Bonds" (Luis de Morales) .. 1·40 65
321. 100 f. "St. John at Patmos" (Juan Mates) (horiz.) .. 1·60 85

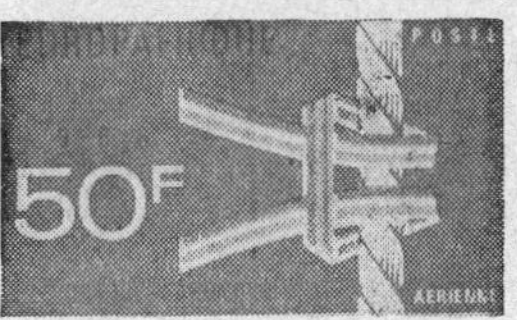


114. Beribboned Rope.

**1968.** Air. 5th Anniv. of Europafrique.
322. **114.** 50 f. multicoloured .. 80 40

**1968.** Inauguration of Petroleum Refinery, Port Gentil, Gabon. As T **80** of Central African Republic.
323. 30 f. multicoloured .. 55 30

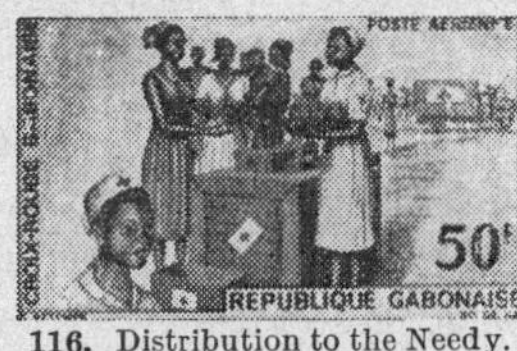


116. Distribution to the Needy.

**1968.** Air. Red Cross. Multicoloured.
324. 50 f. Type **116** .. .. 85 35
325. 100 f. "Support the Red Cross" .. .. 1·60 65

117. High-jumping.

**1968.** Air. Olympic Games, Mexico.
327. **117.** 25 f. brown, slate & red 50 30
328. – 30 f. brown, blue & red 60 35
329. – 100 f. brown, yell. & blue 1·60 80
330. – 200 f. brn., slate & grn. 3·00 1·40
DESIGNS—VERT. 30 f. Cycling. 100 f. Judo. HORIZ. 200 f. Boxing.

118. Open Book. 120. Coffee.

**1968.** Literacy Day.
332. **118.** 25 f. brown, red & blue 40 20

**1968.** Agricultural Produce.
333. **120.** 20 f. red, myrtle and green 45 15
334. – 40 f. orange, brn. & grn. 75 35
DESIGNS: 40 f. Cocoa.

121. "Junon" (sail/steam warship). 123. Advocate holding "Charter".

122. President Mba and Flag.

**1968.** Stamp Day.
335. **121.** 30 f. violet, grn. & orge. 1·10 55

**1968.** Air. 1st Death Anniv. of Pres. Mba.
336. **122.** 1,000 f. multicoloured .. 18·00 18·00

**1968.** Human Rights Year.
337. **123.** 20 f. black, grn. & red .. 45 30

124. President Bongo, Maps of Gabon and Owendo Port.

**1968.** Air. "Laying of 1st Stone". Owendo Port. Multicoloured.
338. 25 f. Type **124** .. .. 60 25
339. 30 f. Harbour Project .. 70 25

**1969.** Air. "Philexafrique" Stamp Exn., Abidjan, Ivory Coast (1st issue). As T **86** of Central African Republic.
340. 100 f. multicoloured .. 2·50 2·50
DESIGN: 100 f. "The Cloisters of Ste. Marie des Anges" (F. M. Granet).
See also No. 346.

126. Mahatma Gandhi. 128. View of Okanda Gates.

**1969.** Air. "Apostles of Peace".
341. **126.** 25 f. black and pink .. 45 15
342. – 30 f. black and green .. 55 30
343. – 50 f. black and blue .. 85 35
344. – 100 f. black and mauve 1·50 60
DESIGNS: 30 f. J. F. Kennedy. 50 f. R. F. Kennedy. 100 f. Martin Luther King.

**1969.** Air. "Philexafrique" Stamp Exn., Abidjan, Ivory Coast (2nd issue). As Type **137** of Cameroun.
346. 50 f. blue, red and green .. 1·50 1·50
DESIGN: 50 f. Oil refinery. Port Gentil and Gabon stamp of 1932.

**1969.** African Tourist Year.

| | | | |
|---|---|---|---|
| 347. 128. | 10 f. brown, grn. & blue | 20 | 10 |
| 348. – | 15 f. blue, green and red | 80 | 20 |
| 349. – | 25 f. pur., blue & brown | 40 | 20 |
| 350. – | 30 f. brn., choc. & blue | 85 | 35 |

DESIGNS—HORIZ. 15 f. Barracuda. VERT. 25 f. Kinguele Falls. 30 f. Hunting Trophies.

129. "Battle of Rivoli" (Philippoteaux).

**1969.** Air. Birth Bicent. of Napoleon Bonaparte. Multicoloured.

| | | | |
|---|---|---|---|
| 351. | 50 f. Type 129 | 1·60 | 1·10 |
| 352. | 100 f. "Oath of the Army" (J. L. David) | 1·90 | 1·60 |
| 353. | 250 f. "The Emperor Napoleon I on the Terrace at St. Cloud" (Ducis) | 7·50 | 4·50 |

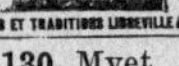
130. Mvet.

132. "Aframomum polyanthum".

131. Refugees and Red Cross Plane.

**1969.** Traditional Musical Instruments from Folk Art Museum, Libreville.

| | | | |
|---|---|---|---|
| 354. 130. | 25 f. lake, drab & purple | 40 | 15 |
| 355. – | 30 f. brown, drab & red | 45 | 20 |
| 356. – | 50 f. lake, drab & purple | 85 | 35 |
| 357. – | 100 f. brn., drab & red | 1·60 | 65 |

DESIGNS: 30 f. Ngombi harp. 50 f. Ebele and Mbe drums. 100 f. Medzang xylophone.

**1969.** Air. Red Cross. Aid for Biafra. Multicoloured.

| | | | |
|---|---|---|---|
| 359. | 15 f. Type 131 | 40 | 20 |
| 360. | 20 f. Hospital and supplies van | 45 | 25 |
| 361. | 25 f. Doctor and nurse tending children | 50 | 25 |
| 362. | 30 f. Children and hospital | 60 | 30 |

**1969.** Flowers. Multicoloured.

| | | | |
|---|---|---|---|
| 364. | 1 f. Type 132 | 10 | 10 |
| 365. | 2 f. "Chlamydocola chlamydantha" | 15 | 10 |
| 366. | 5 f. "Costus dinklagei" | 20 | 10 |
| 367. | 10 f. "Cola rostrata" | 45 | 20 |
| 368. | 20 f. "Dischistocalyx grandifolius" | 70 | 45 |

133. Astronauts and Module on Moon.

**1969.** Air. 1st Man on the Moon. Embossed on gold foil.

| | | | |
|---|---|---|---|
| 369. 133. | 1000 f. gold | 18·00 | 18·00 |

134. Tree and Insignia.

135. Oil Derrick.

**1969.** "National Renovation".

| | | | |
|---|---|---|---|
| 370. 134. | 25 f. multicoloured | 40 | 30 |

**1969.** 20th Anniv. of Elf/Spafe Petroleum Consortium.

| | | | |
|---|---|---|---|
| 371 | 25 f. Type 135 | 35 | 10 |
| 372 | 50 f. Oil rig | 65 | 30 |

136. African Workers.

137. Arms of Lambarene.

**1969.** 50th Anniv. of I.L.O.

| | | | |
|---|---|---|---|
| 373. 136. | 30 f. green, blue and red | 55 | 30 |

**1969.** Town Arms (1st series).

| | | | |
|---|---|---|---|
| 374. 137. | 20 f. multicoloured | 50 | 15 |
| 375. – | 25 f. gold, black & blue | 55 | 15 |
| 376. – | 30 f. multicoloured | 60 | 20 |

ARMS: 25 f. Port-Gentil. 30 f. Libreville.
See also Nos. 405/7, 460/2, 504/6, 510/12, 539/41, 596/8, 618/20, 669/71, 684/6, 729/31, 800/2, 898/900, 953/4, 1083 and 1128.

138. Adoumas Mail Pirogue.

**1969.** Stamp Day.

| | | | |
|---|---|---|---|
| 377. 138. | 30 f. brown, emer. & grn. | 80 | 35 |

139. Satellite and Globe.

**1970.** World Telecommunications Day.

| | | | |
|---|---|---|---|
| 378. 139. | 25 f. blue, black & lake | 55 | 35 |

**1970.** New U.P.U. Headquarters Building Berne. As T 156 of Cameroun.

| | | | |
|---|---|---|---|
| 379. | 30 f. green, purple & brown | 50 | 30 |

140. Japanese Geisha and African.

**1970.** "EXPO 70" World Fair, Osaka, Japan.

| | | | |
|---|---|---|---|
| 380. 140. | 30 f. multicoloured | 50 | 30 |

141. "Co-operation".

142. Icarus and the Sun.

**1970.** Air. "Europafrique".

| | | | |
|---|---|---|---|
| 381. 141. | 50 f. multicoloured | 85 | 35 |

**1970.** Air. History of Flight.

| | | | |
|---|---|---|---|
| 382. 142. | 25 f. blue, yell. and red | 55 | 35 |
| 383. – | 100 f. grn., brn. & pur. | 1·40 | 70 |
| 384. – | 200 f. blue, red & slate | 3·00 | 1·40 |

DESIGNS: 100 f. Leonardo da Vinci's design for wings. 200 f. Jules Verne's rocket approaching Moon.

143. U.A.M.P.T. Emblem.

**1970.** Air. U.A.M.P.T. Conf., Libreville.

| | | | |
|---|---|---|---|
| 386. 143. | 200 f. gold, grn. & blue | 2·75 | 1·25 |

144. Throwing-knives.

**1970.** Air. Gabonaise Weapons, Folk Art Museum, Libreville. All values blue, red and green.

| | | | |
|---|---|---|---|
| 387 | 25 f. Type 144 | 45 | 30 |
| 388 | 30 f. Assegai and crossbow | 55 | 35 |
| 389 | 50 f. War knives | 80 | 40 |
| 390 | 90 f. Dagger and sheath | 1·60 | 55 |

Nos. 388/9 are vert.

145. Japanese Masks, Gateway and Mt. Fuji.

**1970.** Air. "Expo. 70" World Fair, Osaka, Japan. Embossed on gold foil.

| | | | |
|---|---|---|---|
| 392. 145. | 1000 f. red, black, green and gold | 17·00 | 17·00 |

146. President Bongo.

148. "Portrait of Young Man" (School of Raphael).

**1970.** Air. 10th Anniv. of Independence.

| | | | |
|---|---|---|---|
| 393. 146. | 200 f. multicoloured | 3·25 | 1·60 |

**1970.** 10th Anniv. (1969) of Aerial Navigation Security Agency for Africa and Madagascar. As T 150 of Cameroun.

| | | | |
|---|---|---|---|
| 394. | 100 f. green and blue | 1·40 | 65 |

**1970.** Air. 450th Death Anniv. of Raphael. Multicoloured.

| | | | |
|---|---|---|---|
| 395. | 50 f. Type 148 | 90 | 40 |
| 396. | 100 f. "Jeanne d'Aragon" (Raphael) | 1·60 | 70 |
| 397. | 200 f. "The Virgin of the Blue Diadem" (Raphael) | 3·25 | 1·60 |

149. U.N. Emblem, Globe, Dove and Wheat.

**1970.** 25th Anniv. of United Nations.

| | | | |
|---|---|---|---|
| 398. 149. | 30 f. multicoloured | 55 | 35 |

150. Bushbucks.

**1970.** Wild Fauna. Multicoloured.

| | | | |
|---|---|---|---|
| 399. | 5 f. Type 150 | 35 | 25 |
| 400. | 15 f. Pel's flying squirrel | 55 | 30 |
| 401. | 25 f. White-cheeked mangabey (vert.) | 1·40 | 55 |
| 402. | 40 f. African golden cat | 1·90 | 85 |
| 403. | 60 f. Servaline genet | 3·00 | 1·40 |

151. Presidents Bongo and Pompidou.

**1971.** Air. Visit of Pres. Pompidou of France to Gabon.

| | | | |
|---|---|---|---|
| 404. 151. | 50 f. multicoloured | 1·60 | 85 |

**1971.** Town Arms (2nd series). Vert. designs as T 137. Multicoloured.

| | | | |
|---|---|---|---|
| 405. | 20 f. multicoloured | 40 | 15 |
| 406. | 25 f. black, green & gold | 40 | 15 |
| 407. | 30 f. multicoloured | 55 | 20 |

ARMS: 20 f. Mouila. 25 f. Bitam. 30 f. Oyem.

152. Four Races and Emblem.

154. Freesias.

153. Telecommunications Map.

**1971.** Racial Equality Year.

| | | | |
|---|---|---|---|
| 408. 152. | 40 f. black, orge. & yell. | 55 | 30 |

**1971.** Pan-African Telecommunications Network.

| | | | |
|---|---|---|---|
| 409. 153. | 30 f. multicoloured | 50 | 30 |

**1971.** Air. "Flowers by Air". Mult.

| | | | |
|---|---|---|---|
| 410. | 15 f. Type 154 | 35 | 20 |
| 411. | 25 f. Carnations | 50 | 20 |
| 412. | 40 f. Roses | 85 | 35 |
| 413. | 55 f. Daffodils | 95 | 35 |
| 414. | 75 f. Orchids | 1·90 | 60 |
| 415. | 120 f. Tulips | 2·25 | 80 |

155. Napoleon's Death Mask.

**1971.** Air. 150th Death Anniv. of Napoleon. Multicoloured.

| | | | |
|---|---|---|---|
| 417. | 100 f. Type 155 | 2·25 | 80 |
| 418. | 200 f. "Longwood House" (after Marchand) (horiz.) | 3·25 | 1·40 |
| 419. | 500 f. Napoleon's Tomb | 8·25 | 3·50 |

156. "Charaxes smaragdalis".

157. Hertzian Communications Centre, Nkol Ogoum.

**1971.** Butterflies. Multicoloured.

| | | | |
|---|---|---|---|
| 420. | 5 f. Type 156 | 40 | 30 |
| 421. | 10 f. "Euxanthe crossleyi" | 65 | 40 |
| 422. | 15 f. "Epiphora rectifascia" | 1·10 | 45 |
| 423. | 25 f. "Imbrasia bouvieri" | 1·50 | 70 |

**1971.** World Telecommunications Day.

| | | | |
|---|---|---|---|
| 424. 157. | 40 f. red, blue & green | 60 | 35 |

159. Red Crosses.

**1971.** Air. Red Cross.
426. **159.** 50 f. multicoloured .. 95 40

160. Uranium.

**1971.** Air. Minerals Multicoloured.
427. 85 f. Type **160** .. .. 3·00 1·40
428. 90 f. Manganese.. .. 3·25 1·90

161. Landing Module above Moon's Surface.

**1971.** Air. Moon Flight of "Apollo 15". Embossed on gold foil.
429. **161.** 1500 f. multicoloured 19·00 19·00

162. Mother feeding Child. 163. U.N. Emblem and New York Headquarters.

**1971.** 15th Anniv. of Social Welfare Fund.
430. **162.** 30 f. brown, bistre & mauve 50 30

**1971.** 10th Anniv. of Gabon's Admission to United Nations.
431. **163.** 30 f. multicoloured .. 45 30

164. Great Egret.

**1971.** Birds. Multicoloured.
432 30 f. Type **164** .. .. 2·00 1·00
433 40 f. Grey parrot .. .. 2·75 1·25
434 50 f. Woodland kingfisher 3·00 1·50
435 75 f. Grey-necked bald crow .. .. .. 4·25 1·75
436 100 f. Knysna turaco .. 5·75 2·25

**1971.** Air. 10th Anniv. of African and Malagasy Posts and Telecommunications Union. As T **184** of Cameroun. Mult.
439. 100 f. U.A.M.P.T. building & Bakota copper mask 1·40 65

167. Ski-jumping.

**1972.** Air. Winter Olympic Games, Sapporo. Japan.
440. **167.** 40 f. violet, brn. & grn. 65 35
441. – 130 f. grn., violet & brn. 1·90 80
DESIGN: 130 f. Speed-skating.

168. "Santa Maria della Salute" (Vanvitelli).

**1972.** Air. U.N.E.S.C.O. "Save Venice" Campaign. Multicoloured.
443. 60 f. "The Basin and Grand Canal" (Vanvitelli) (horiz.) .. .. .. 1·10 55
444. 70 f. "Rialto Bridge" (Canaletto) .. .. 1·60 85
445. 140 f. Type **168** .. .. 2·75 1·10
On the stamp the design of No. 445 wrongly attributed to Caffi.

170. Hotel Intercontinental.

**1972.** Air. Opening of Hotel Intercontinental.
447. **170.** 40 f. brn., grn. & blue 60 30

**1972.** Air. Visit of the Grand Master, Sovereign Order of Malta. No. 289 surch **VISITE OFFICIELLE GRAND MAITRE ORDRE SOUVERAIN DE MALTE 3 MARS 1972 50F** and emblem.
448 50 f. on 300 f. blue, purple and brown .. .. 80 40

172. "Asystasia vogeliana".

**1972.** Flowers. Varieties of Acanthus. Multicoloured.
449. 5 f. Type **172** .. .. 20 20
450. 10 f. "Stenandriopsis guineensis" .. .. 35 25
451. 20 f. "Thomandersia hensii" .. .. 55 35
452. 30 f. "Thomandersia laurifolia" .. .. 85 50
453. 40 f. "Physacanthus batanganus" .. .. 1·40 65
454. 65 f. "Physacanthus nematosiphon" .. 2·25 85

173. "The Discus-thrower" (Alcamene). 174. Pasteur with Microscope.

**1972.** Air. Olympic Games, Munich. Ancient Sculptures.
455. **173.** 30 f. grey and red .. 60 50
456. – 100 f. grey and red .. 1·40 70
457. – 140 f. grey and red .. 1·90 1·00
DESIGNS: 100 f. "Doryphoros" (Polyclete). 140 f. "Gladiator" (Agasias).

**1972.** 150th Anniv. of Louis Pasteur (scientist).
459. **174.** 80 f. purple, grn. & red 65 35

**1972.** Town Arms (3rd series). Vert. designs as T **137**. Multicoloured.
460. 30 f. multicoloured .. 40 20
461. 40 f. multicoloured .. 55 20
462. 60 f. silver, black & green 90 30
ARMS: 30 f. Franceville. 40 f. Makokou. 60 f. Tchibanga.

175. Global Emblem.

**1972.** World Telecommunications Day.
463. **175.** 40 f. blk., orge. & yell. 55 30

176. Nat King Cole.

**1972.** Famous Negro Musicians. Mult.
464. 40 f. Type **176** .. .. 60 30
465. 60 f. Sidney Bechet .. 90 45
466. 100 f. Louis Armstrong .. 1·60 65

177. "Boiga blandingi".

**1972.** Reptiles. Multicoloured.
467. 1 f. Type **177** .. .. 10 10
468. 2 f. Sand snake .. .. 15 10
469. 3 f. Egg-eating snake .. 20 15
470. 15 f. Pit viper .. .. 70 25
471. 25 f. Jameson's tree asp.. 1·00 30
472. 50 f. Gabon viper .. 1·60 50

178. "The Adoration of the Magi" (Bruegel the Elder).

**1972.** Air. Christmas. Multicoloured.
473. 30 f. Type **178** .. .. 60 35
474. 40 f. "Madonna and Child" (Basaiti) (vert.) .. 85 45

**1972.** Air. Olympic Gold Medal Winners. Nos. 455/7 surch. as listed below.
475. **125.** 40 f. on 30 f. grey & red 70 40
476. – 120 f. on 100 f. grey & red .. .. .. 1·40 65
477. – 170 f. on 140 f. grey & red .. .. .. 2·10 90
SURCHARGES: No. 475, **MORELON.** No. 476, **KEINO.** No. 477, **SPITZ.**

180. Dr. G. A. Hansen and Hospital, Lambarene. 182. "Charaxes candiope".

181. "Thematic Collecting".

**1973.** Centenary of Dr Hansen's Discovery of Leprosy Bacillus.
478. **180.** 30 f. brn., grn. & blue 65 35

**1973.** Air. "PHILEXGABON 73" Int. Stamp Exhibition, Libreville.
479. **181.** 100 f. multicoloured .. 1·40 70

**1973.** Butterflies. Multicoloured.
481. 10 f. Type **182** .. .. 40 15
482. 15 f. "Eunica pechueli" 50 15
483. 20 f. "Cyrestis camillus" 80 30
484. 30 f. "Charaxes castor".. 1·10 40
485. 40 f. "Charaxes ameliae" 1·25 55
486. 50 f. "Pseudacrea boisduvali" .. .. 1·40 80

183. Douglas DC-10-30 over Libreville Airport.

**1973.** Air. Libreville-Paris Air Service by "Air Afrique" "DC 10 Libreville". No gum.
487. **183.** 40 f. multicoloured .. 1·10 55

184. Montgolfier's Balloon, 1783. 186. Interpol Emblem.

185. Power Station.

**1973.** History of Flight.
488. **184.** 1 f. grn., myrtle & brn. 10 10
489. – 2 f. green and blue .. 10 10
490. – 3 f. new bl., bl. & orge. 10 10
491. – 4 f. vio. & reddish vio. 25 15
492. – 5 f. green and orange.. 30 20
493. – 10 f. purple and blue.. 45 20
493a. – 10 f. blue .. .. 45 45
DESIGNS—HORIZ. 2 f. Santos-Dumont's airship "Ballon No. 6", 1901. 3 f. Chanute's glider, 1896. 4 f. Clement Ader's "Avion III" flying-machine, 1897. 5 f. Bleriot's cross-Channel flight, 1909. 10 f. (both) Fabre's seaplane "Hydravion", 1910.

**1973.** Air. Kinguele Hydro-electric Project.
494. **185.** 30 f. green and brown 50 25
495. – 40 f. blue, green & brn. 60 25
DESIGN: 40 f. Dam.

**1973.** 50th Anniv. Int. Criminal Police Organization (Interpol).
496. **186.** 40 f. blue and red .. 55 35

187. Dish Aerial and Station. 188. Gabon Woman.

**1973.** Inauguration of "2 Decembre" Satellite Earth Station.
497. **187.** 40 f. brn., blue & grn. 55 30

**1973.** Air. M'Bigou Stone Sculptures.
498. **188.** 100 f. brown, bl. & blk. 1·50 80
499. – 200 f. green and brown 2·75 1·40
DESIGN: 200 f. Gabon man wearing head-dress.

**1973.** Air. Pan-African Drought Relief. No. 426 surch. **SECHERESSE SOLIDARITE AFRICAINE** and value.
500. **159.** 100 f. on 50 f. mult. .. 1·40 85

190. Party Headquarters.

**1973.** Gabonaise Democratic Party Headquarters, Libreville.
501. **190.** 30 f. multicoloured .. 40 20

**191.** Astronauts and Lunar Rover.

**1973.** Air. Moon Flight of "Apollo 17".
502. **191.** 500 f. multicoloured .. 6·75 3·25

**1973.** 10th Anniv. of African and Malagasy Posts and Telecommunications Union. As T **216** of Cameroun.
503. 100 f. plum, purple & blue 90 55

**1973.** Town Arms (4th series). Vert. designs as T **137** dated "1973". Multicoloured.
504. 30 f. Kango .. .. 55 20
505. 40 f. Booue .. .. 65 30
506. 60 f. Koula-Moutou .. 1·00 35

**193.** St. Theresa of Lisieux. **194.** Flame Emblem.

**1973.** Birth Cent. of St. Theresa of Lisieux. Stained-glass windows in the Basilica at Lisieux. Multicoloured.
507. 30 f. Type **193** .. .. 55 25
508. 40 f. "St. Theresa with Saviour" .. .. 65 30

**1973.** 25th Anniv. of Declaration of Human Rights.
509. **194.** 20 f. red, blue & green 40 20

**1974.** Town Arms (5th series). Vert. designs as T **137** dated "1974". Multicoloured.
510. 5 f. Gamba.. .. .. 15 10
511. 10 f. Ogooue-Lolo.. .. 15 10
512. 15 f. Fougamou .. .. 20 15

**195.** White-collared Mangabey.

**1974.** Monkeys. Multicoloured.
513. 40 f. Type **195** .. .. 55 30
514. 60 f. Moustached Monkey 85 35
515. 80 f. Mona Monkey .. 1·40 50

**196.** De Gaulle and Houphouet-Boigny.

**1974.** Air. 30th Anniv. of Brazzaville Conference.
516. **196.** 40 f. blue and purple.. 1·00 55

**197.** "Pleasure Boats" (Monet).

**1974.** Air. Impressionist Paintings. Multicoloured.
517. 40 f. Type **197** .. .. 90 45
518. 50 f. "End of an Arabesque" (Degas) (vert.) .. 1·40 65
519. 130 f. "Young Girl with Flowers" (Renoir) (vert.) 2·25 1·10

**198.** American Bald Eagle, and Astronaut on Moon. **199.** Ogooue River, Lambarene.

**1974.** Air. 5th Anniv. of First Manned Moon Landing.
520. **198.** 200 f. blue, brn. & ind. 2·75 1·25

**1974.** Gabon Views. Multicoloured.
521. 30 f. Type **199** .. .. 35 25
522. 50 f. Cape Esterias .. 50 30
523. 75 f. Rope bridge, Poubara 85 45

**200.** U.P.U. Emblem and Letters.

**1974.** Air. Cent. of U.P.U.
524. **200.** 150 f. turq. and blue.. 1·90 80
525. – 300 f. red and orange 3·25 1·60
DESIGN: 300 f. Similar to Type **200**, but with design reversed.

**201.** "Apollo" and "Soyuz" Spacecraft, Flight Badge and Maps of U.S.A. and U.S.S.R.

**1974.** Air. Soviet-American Co-operation in Space.
526. **201.** 1000 f. grn., red & blue 7·75 5·50

**202.** Ball and Footballers.

**1974.** Air. World Cup Football Championships, Munich.
527. **202.** 40 f. red, green & brown 50 30
528. – 65 f. green, brown & red 65 40
529. – 100 f. brown, red & grn. 1·10 65
DESIGNS: 65 f., 100 f. Football scenes similar to Type **202**.

**203.** Manioc Plantation.

**1974.** Agriculture. Multicoloured.
531. 40 f. Type **203** .. 50 20
532. 50 f. Palm-tree grove .. 60 20

**1974.** 10th Anniv of Central African Customs and Economic Union. As Nos. 734/5 of Cameroun.
533. 40 f. mult. (postage) .. 50 30
534. 100 f. multicoloured (air).. 85 45

**205.** "The Visitation".

**1974.** Air. Christmas. Details from 15th century tapestry of Notre Dame, Beaune. Multicoloured.
535. 40 f. Type **205** .. .. 80 35
536. 50 f. "The Annunciation" (horiz.) .. .. .. 90 45

**206.** Dr. Schweitzer and Lambarene Hospital.

**1978.** Air. Birth Centenary of Dr. Albert Schweitzer.
537. **206.** 500 f. grn., lilac & brn. 5·50 3·25

**207.** Dialogue Hotel.

**1975.** Inauguration of "Hotel du Dialogue", Libreville.
538. **207.** 50 f. multicoloured .. 55 30

**1975.** Town Arms (6th series). Vert. designs as T **137** dated "1975". Multicoloured.
539. 5 f. Ogooue-Ivindo .. 10 10
540. 10 f. Moabi .. .. 15 10
541. 15 f. Moanda .. .. 25 10

**208.** "The Crucifixion" (Bellini).

**1975.** Air. Easter. Multicoloured.
542. 140 f. Type **208** .. .. 1·40 55
543. 150 f. "The Resurrection" (Burgundian School) (36 × 49 mm.) .. 1·90 80

**209.** Locomotive "Marc Seguin"
(Illustration reduced. Actual size 100 × 27 mm.)

**1975.** Air. Scale Drawings of Steam Locomotives.
544. **209.** 20 f. bl., brn. & brt. bl. 65 50
545. – 25 f. red, yell. & blue.. 80 1·25
546. – 40 f. blue, pur. & grn. 1·10 1·75
547. – 50 f. pur., blue & grn. 1·40 90
Locomotives. 25 f. "Iron Duke" (1847). 40 f. "Thomas Rogers" (1895). 50 f. Soviet Type "LA-272" (1934).

**210.** Congress Emblem.

**1975.** 17th Lions Club Congress, Libreville.
548. **210.** 50 f. multicoloured .. 70 30

**211.** Aerial and Network Map.

**1975.** Gabonese Development of Hertzian Wave Radio Links.
549. **211.** 40 f. grn., brn. & blue 55 35

**212.** Man and Woman and I.W.Y. Emblem.

**1975.** International Women's Year.
550. **212.** 50 f. brn., red and blue 55 30

**213.** Ange M'ba (founder of Gabonaise Scouts).

**1975.** "Nordjamb 75" World Scout Jamboree, Norway.
551. **213.** 40 f. blk., pur. and grn. 45 30
552. – 50 f. pur., grn. and red 55 30
DESIGN: 50 f. Scout camp.

**214.** "Lutjanus goreensis".

**1975.** Fishes. Multicoloured.
553. 30 f. Type **214** .. .. 45 20
554. 40 f. "Galeoides decadactylus" .. .. .. 55 30
555. 50 f. "Sardinella aurita" 95 30
556. 120 f. "Scarus hoefleri" 1·60 65

**215.** Swimming Pool.

**1975.** Air. Olympic Games, Montreal (1976). (1st issue). Multicoloured.
557. 100 f. Type **215** .. .. 1·00 45
558. 150 f. Boxing ring .. 1·40 65
559. 300 f. Aerial view of Games complex .. .. 2·75 1·40
See also Nos. 591/3.

**1975.** Air. "Apollo-Soyuz" Space Link. Optd. **JONCTION 17 Juillet 1975.**
561. **201.** 1000 f. grn., red & blue 7·25 4·00

**217.** "The Annunciation" (M. Denis).

**1975.** Air. Christmas. Multicoloured.
562. 40 f. Type **217** .. .. 60 30
563. 50 f. "Virgin and Child with Two Saints" (Fra Filippo Lippi) .. .. .. 80 40

**218.** Franceville Complex.

**1975.** Inauguration of Agro-Industrial Complex, Franceville.
564. **218.** 60 f. multicoloured .. 65 35

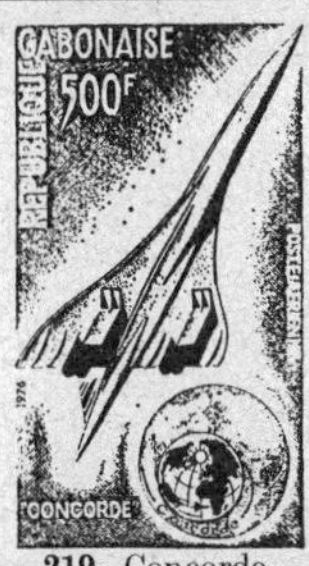


219. Concorde.

**1975.** Air.
565 **219** 500 f. ultram, bl & red 7·75 4·50

**1975.** Air. Concorde's First Commercial Flight. Surch **1000 F 21 Janv. 1976, 1er Vol Commercial de CONCORDE**.
566 **219** 1000 f. on 500 f. ultram, blue and red .. 14·00 9·00

221. Tchibanga Bridge.

**1975.** Gabon Bridges. Multicoloured.
567. 5 f. Type **221** .. .. 15 10
568. 10 f. Mouila Bridge .. 20 15
569. 40 f. Kango Bridges .. 45 20
570. 50 f. Lambarene Bridges (vert.) .. .. .. 60 30

222. A. G. Bell and Early and Modern Telephones.

**1976.** Telephone Centenary.
571. **222.** 60 f. grey, grn. & blue 60 30

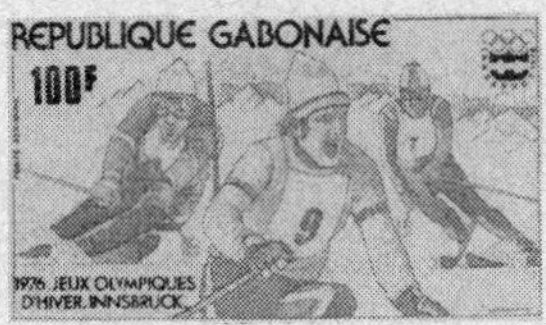


223. Skiing (slalom).

**1976.** Air. Winter Olympic Games, Innsbruck.
572. **223.** 100 f. brn., blue & blk. 95 45
573. – 250 f. brn., blue & blk. 2·10 1·25
DESIGN: 250 f. Speed skating.

224. " The Crucifixion between Thieves " (wood-carving).

**1976.** Air. Easter. Multicoloured.
575. 120 f. Type **224** .. .. 1·10 60
576. 130 f. " Thomas placing finger in Jesus' wounds " (wood-carving) .. .. 1·40 80

225. Monseigneur Jean-Remy Bessieux.

**1976.** Death Centenary of Bessieux.
577. **225.** 50 f. brn., blue & grn. 50 30

226. Boston Tea Party.

**1976.** Air. Bicent. of American Revolution.
578. **226.** 100 f. brn., orge. & blue 90 50
579. – 150 f. brn., orge. & blue 1·40 65
580. – 200 f. brn., orge. & blue 2·00 1·00
DESIGNS: 150 f. Battle scenes at Hudson Bay and New York. 200 f. Wrecking of King George III's statue in New York.

227. Games Emblem.

**1976.** 1st Central African Games.
581. **227.** 50 f. multicoloured .. 45 20
582. 60 f. multicoloured .. 55 30

**1976.** Air. U.S. Independence Day. Nos. 578/80 optd **4 JUILLET 1976**.
583. **226.** 100 f. brn., orge. & blue 95 55
584. – 150 f. brn., orge. & blue 1·40 65
585. – 200 f. brn., orge. & blue 2·00 1·00

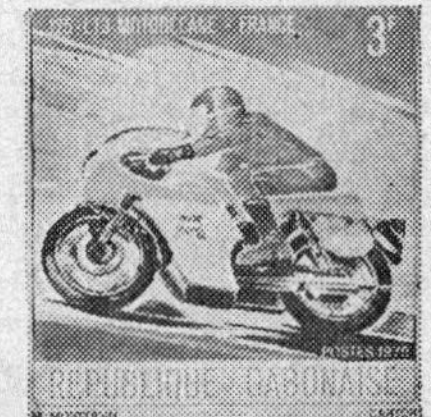


229. Motobecane 125–LT3 (France).

**1976.** Motorcycles.
586. **229.** 3 f. black, green & blue 15 10
587. – 5 f. blk., mve. & yell. 15 15
588. – 10 f. blk., grn. & blue 35 15
589. – 20 f. blk., grn. & red .. 65 15
590. – 100 f. blk., blue & red 2·00 70
MOTORCYCLES: 5 f. Bultaco 125 (Spain). 10 f. Suzuki 125 (Japan). 20 f. Kawasaki H2R (Japan). 100 f. Harley-Davidson 750–TX (USA).

230. Running.

**1976.** Air. Olympic Games, Montreal. (2nd issue). Multicoloured.
591. **230.** 100 f. brn., blue & violet 85 45
592. – 200 f. multicoloured .. 1·60 90
593. – 260 f. brn., grn. & myrtle 2·25 1·10
DESIGNS: 200 f. Football. 260 f. High Jumping.

231. Presidents Giscard d'Estaing and Bongo.

**1976.** Air. Visit of Pres. Giscard d'Estaing to Gabon.
595. **231.** 60 f. multicoloured .. 90 40

**1976.** Town Arms (7th series). Vert. designs as T **137** dated " 1976 "
596. 15 f. multicoloured .. 15 10
597. 25 f. multicoloured .. 20 10
598. 50 f. black, gold and red .. 50 15
ARMS: 15 f. Nyanga. 25 f. Mandji. 50 f. Mekambo.

232. Ricefield and Plant.

**1976.** Agriculture. Multicoloured.
599. 50 f. Type **232** .. 55 20
600. 60 f. Pepper grove and plant 65 30

233. " Presentation at the Temple ".

**1976.** Air. Christmas. Wood-carvings. Multicoloured.
601. 50 f. Type **233** .. .. 60 30
602. 60 f. " The Nativity " .. 70 35

234. Photograph of Site.

**1976.** Air. Discovery of Oklo Fossil Reactor.
603. **234.** 60 f. multicoloured .. 65 35

235. " The Last Supper " (Juste de Gand).

**1977.** Air. Easter. Multicoloured.
604. 50 f. Type **235** .. .. 80 45
605. 100 f. " The Deposition " (N. Poussin) .. .. 1·40 65

**1977.** Agriculture. As T **232** but dated " 1977 ". Multicoloured.
606. 50 f. Banana plantation .. 55 20
607. 60 f. Groundnuts and market 65 30

236. Printed Circuit and Telephone.

**1977.** 9th World Telecommunications Day.
608. **236.** 60 f. multicoloured .. 55 30

237. "Air Gabon" Insignia and Boeing 747.

**1977.** Air. First " Air Gabon " Intercontinental Air Service.
609. **237.** 60 f. blue, yell. and green 70 40

238. Cap Lopez.

**1977.** Gabon Views and Features. Mult.
610. 50 f. Type **238** .. .. 45 20
611. 60 f. Oyem .. .. 45 20
612. 70 f. Lebamba grotto .. 60 25

239. Beethoven and Musical Score.

**1977.** Air. 150th Death Anniv. of Beethoven.
613. **239.** 260 f. blue .. .. 2·25 1·40

240. Palais des Congres.

**1977.** Organization of African Unity Conference.
614. **240.** 100 f. multicoloured .. 85 55

241. Gabon Coat of Arms.

**1977.**
615. **241.** 50 f. blue (22 × 36 mm.) 65 30
616. 60 f. orange .. .. 60 30
617. 80 f. red .. .. 70 35

**1977.** Town Arms (8th series). As T **137** but dated " 1977 ". Multicoloured.
618. 50 f. Omboue .. .. 45 20
619. 60 f. Minvoul .. .. 50 20
620. 90 f. Mayumba .. .. 85 35

242. Parliament Building, Libreville.

**1977.** National Festival.
621. **242.** 50 f. multicoloured .. 50 20

243. Renault " Voiturette " of 1902.

**1977.** Birth Centenary of Louis Renault (motor pioneer).
622. **243.** 5 f. blue, red and brown 20 15
623. – 10 f. brown and red .. 20 15
624. – 30 f. red, green & drab 65 30
625. – 40 f. green, yell. & brn. 1·10 35
626. – 100 f. blk., turq. & blue 2·25 1·00
DESIGNS: 10 f. Coupe of 1921. 30 f. " Torpedo Scaphandrier " of 1925. 40 f. " Reinastella " of 1929. 100 f. " Nerva Grand Sport " of 1937.

244. Lindbergh and " Spirit of St. Louis ".

**1977.** Air. 50th Anniv. of Lindbergh's Transatlantic Flight.
628. **244.** 500 f. blue, brown and light blue .. .. 5·50 3·25

245. Footballer.

**1977.** Air. World Cup Football Championship Qualifying Rounds.
629. **245.** 250 f. multicoloured .. 2·25 1·25

**246.** "Viking" on Mars.

**1977.** Air. "Operation Viking".
630. **246.** 1000 f. multicoloured 8·25 8·25

**1977.** Air. First Commercial Paris-New York Flight by "Concorde". Optd. **PARIS NEW-YORK PREMIER VOL 22.11.77.**
631. **219.** 500 f. ultram., bl. & red 7·25 5·00

**248.** "Study of a Head".

**1977.** Air. 400th Birth Anniv. of Peter Paul Rubens. Multicoloured.
632. 60 f. "Lion Hunt" (horiz.) 65 25
633. 80 f. "Hippopotamus Hunt" (horiz.) .. .. 85 40
634. 200 f. Type **248** .. .. 2·25 1·00

**249.** "Adoration of the Magi" (Rubens).

**1977.** Air. Christmas. Multicoloured.
636 60 f. Type **249** .. .. 65 35
637 80 f. "The Flight into Egypt" (Rubens) .. 90 45

**250.** "Still Life and Maori Statue".

**1978.** Air. 75th Death Anniv. of Paul Gauguin. Multicoloured.
638. 150 f. Type **250** .. .. 1·90 65
639. 300 f. "Self-Portrait" .. 3·25 1·40

**251.** Globe.

**1978.** World Leprosy Day.
640. **251.** 80 f. grn., bl. & red. 55 30

**MINIMUM PRICE**

The minimum price quoted is 10p which represents a handling charge rather than a basis for valuing common stamps. For further notes about prices see introductory pages.

**252.** Boeing 747 Airplane, Locomotive and President.

**1978.** 10th Anniv. of National Renewal.
641. **252.** 500 f. multicoloured .. 5·75 4·00

**253.** Citroen "Cabriolet", 1922.

**1978.** Birth Centenary of Andre Citroen (motor pioneer).
642. **253.** 10 f. pur., grn. and red 30 15
643. – 50 f. green, blue & turq. 65 20
644. – 60 f. grey, brn. & blue 1·00 40
645. – 80 f. blue, slate & lilac 1·10 45
646. – 200 f. brn., slate & orge. 2·75 1·00
DESIGNS: 50 f. "B 14" Taxi, 1927. 60 f. 8 h.p. "Berline", 1932. 80 f. 7 h.p. "Berline" saloon, 1934. 200 f. 2 h.p. "Berline", 1948.

**254.** Ndjole and L'Ogooue.

**1978.** Views of Gabon. Multicoloured.
648. 30 f. Type **254** .. .. 20 15
649. 40 f. Lambarene, Lake District .. .. .. 35 15
650. 50 f. Owendo Port .. 45 15

**255.** "Sternotomis mirabilis".

**1978.** Beetles. Multicoloured.
651. 20 f. Type **255** .. .. 20 15
652. 60 f. "Analeptes trifasciata" .. .. .. 65 40
653. 75 f. "Homoderus mellyi" 85 45
654. 80 f. "Stephanorrhina guttata" .. .. 1·00 55

**257.** Players heading Ball.

**1978.** Air. World Cup Football Championship, Argentina.
660. **257.** 100 f. brn., red & grn. 70 35
661. – 120 f. brn., red & grn. 85 45
662. – 200 f. brown and red .. 1·50 70
DESIGNS: 120 f. Players tackling. VERT. 200 f. F.I.F.A. World Cup.

**258.** Anti-Apartheid Emblem.

**260.** "Self-portrait at 13 years".

**1978.** International Anti-Apartheid Year.
664. **258.** 80 f. orge., brn. & blue 55 35

**1978.** Air. Argentina's Victory in World Cup Football Championship. Nos. 660/2 optd.
665. **257.** 100 f. brn., red & grn. 70 40
666. – 120 f. brn., red & grn. 90 50
667. – 200 f. brown and red .. 1·40 80
OVERPRINTS: 100 f. **ARGENTINE HOLLAND 3 - 1.** 120 f. **BRESIL ITALIE 2 - 1.** 200 f. **CHAMPION DU MONDE 1978. ARGENTINE.**

**1978.** Town Arms (9th series). As T **137**, but dated "1978".
669. 5 f. multicoloured .. 15 10
670. 40 f. multicoloured .. 30 15
671. 60 f. gold, black and blue 45 15
DESIGNS: 5 f. Oyem. 40 f. Okandja. 60 f. Mimongo.

**1978.** Air. 450th Death Anniv of Albrecht Durer (artist).
672. **260.** 100 f. grey and red .. 85 40
673. – 250 f. red and grey .. 2·25 1·00
DESIGN: 250 f. "Lucas de Leyde".

**261.** Parthenon.

**1978.** U.N.E.S.C.O. Campaign for the Preservation of the Acropolis.
674. **261.** 80 f. brown, orange and blue .. .. 55 35

**1978.** Air. "Philexafrique" Exhibitions Libreville, Gabon and Int. Stamp Fair Essen, W. Germany. As T **237** of Benin. Multicoloured.
675. 100 f. White Stork and Saxony 1850 3 f. stamp 1·60 1·40
676. 100 f. Gorilla and Gabon 1971 40 f. Grey Parrot stamp .. .. .. 1·60 1·40

**263.** Sir Alexander Fleming, Chemical Formula and Laboratory Equipment.

**1978.** 50th Anniv. of Fleming's Discovery of Antibiotics.
677. **263.** 90 f. brn., orge. & grn. 80 40

**264.** "The Visitation".

**1978.** Christmas. Sculptures from the Church of St. Michel de Libreville. Multicoloured.
678. 60 f. Type **264** .. .. 50 20
679. 80 f. "Massacre of the Innocents" .. .. 60 35

**265.** Wright Brothers and Flyer I.

**1978.** Air. 75th Anniv. of First Powered Flight.
680. **265.** 380 f. brn., bl. & red 3·25 1·40

**266.** Diesel Train.

**1978.** Inauguration of First Section of Trans-Gabon Railway, Libreville-Njole.
681. **266.** 60 f. multicoloured .. 75 30

**267.** Pope John Paul II.

**1979.** Air. The Popes of 1978. Multicoloured.
682. 100 f. Type **267** .. .. 1·10 65
683. 200 f. Popes Paul VI and John Paul I with St. Peter's .. .. .. 2·25 90

**1979.** Town Arms (10th series). As T **137**, but dated "1979". Multicoloured.
684. 5 f. Ogooue-Maritime .. 15 10
685. 10 f. Lastoursville .. 15 10
686. 15 f. M'Bigou .. .. 20 10

**268.** "The Two Disciples".

**1979.** Air. Easter. Wood-carvings from St. Michel de Libreville Church. Mult.
687. 100 f. Type **268** .. .. 75 55
688. 150 f. "Jesus appearing to Mary Magdalene" .. 1·25 65

**269.** Long Jumping.

**1979.** Pre-Olympic Year.
689. – 60 f. red, brown & turq. 45 15
690. **269.** 80 f. brown, turq. & red 55 30
691. – 100 f. turq., red & brn. 65 35
DESIGNS—HORIZ. 60 f. Horse Riding. 100 f. Yachting.

**270.** Sir Rowland Hill, Postal Messenger and Stamp.

**1979.** "Philexafrique 2" Exhibition, Libreville.
693. **270.** 50 f. multicoloured .. 70 55
694. – 80 f. multicoloured .. 1·25 85
695. – 150 f. grn., blue & brn. 1·90 1·40
DESIGNS—VERT. 80 f. Bakota mask and tulip flower. HORIZ. 150 f. Canoeist, mail van, U.P.U. emblem and stamps.

**272.** Child holding Bird.

**1979.** International Year of the Child.
697. **272.** 100 f. brn., vio. & blue 80 40

**273.** Captain Cook.

**1979.** Air. Death Bicent. of Captain Cook.
698. **273.** 500 f. multicoloured .. 4·50 2·25

**274.** Louis Bleriot and Channel Flight Route.

**1979.** Air. Aviation History. Multicoloured.
699. 250 f. Type **274** (First Channel Flight, 70th anniv.) .. .. .. 2·25 1·40
700. 1000 f. Astronauts and module on Moon and Gabon S.G. 369 (Moon Landing, 10th anniv.) .. 7·25 4·00

**275.** " Telecom 79 ". **276.** Carved Head, Map and Rotary Emblem.

**1979.** Third World Telecommunications Exhibition, Geneva.
701. **275.** 80 f. blue, orange and deep blue .. .. 50 30

**1979.** Air. 75th Anniv. of Rotary International.
702. **276.** 80 f. multicoloured .. 60 35

**277.** Harvesting Sugar Cane. **278.** Judo.

**1979.** Agriculture. Multicoloured.
703. 25 f. Type **277** .. .. 25 10
704. 30 f. Igname .. .. 35 10

**1979.** World Judo Championships, Paris.
705. **278.** 40 f. olive, brn. & orge. 1·00 45

**279.** Eugene Jamot and Tsetse Fly.

**1979.** Air. Birth Centenary of Eugene Jamot (discovery of sleeping sickness cure).
706. **279.** 300 f. blk., brn. & violet 2·50 1·40

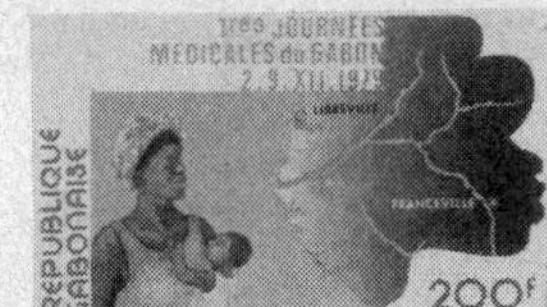


**280.** Mother with Child and Map of Gabon.

**1979.** First Gabon Medical Days.
707. **280.** 200 f. multicoloured .. 1·50 65

**281.** " The Flight into Egypt ". **282.** Statue of President Bongo.

**1979.** Christmas. Carvings from St. Michael's Church, Libreville. Multicoloured.
708. 60 f. Type **281** .. .. 50 30
709. 80 f. " The Circumcision ". 60 30

**1979.** 44th Anniv. of President Bongo.
710. **282.** 60 f. multicoloured .. 55 20
See also No. 714.

**283.** Bob Sleighing. **284.** Oil Derrick.

**1980.** Air. Winter Olympic Games, Lake Placid. Multicoloured.
711. 100 f. Type **283** .. .. 70 40
712. 200 f. Ski jumping .. 1·50 70

**1980.** Investiture of President. As No. 710 but inscr. " INVESTITURE 27 FEVRIER 1980 ".
714. **282.** 80 f. multicoloured .. 1·60 1·00

**1980.** 20th Anniv. of O.P.E.C.
715. **284.** 50 f. multicoloured .. 60 30

**285.** Donguila Church.

**1980.** Easter. Multicoloured.
716. 60 f. Type **285** .. .. 45 15
717. 80 f. Bizangobibere Church 55 30

**286.** Dominique Ingres (artist).

**1980.** Air. Celebrities' Anniversaries.
718. **286.** 100 f. sepia, grn. & brn. 85 40
719. – 200 f. brn., pur. & grey 2·25 1·00
720. – 360 f. brn., grn. & sepia 2·50 1·40
DESIGNS: 100 f. Type **286** (birth cent). 200 f. Jacques Offenbach (composer, death cent). 360 f. Gustave Flaubert (author, death cent).

**287.** Telephone.

**1980.** Air. World Telecommunications Day.
721. **287.** 80 f. multicoloured .. 60 30

**288.** Savorgnan de Brazza and Map.

**1980.** Centenary of Franceville.
722. **288.** 165 f. multicoloured .. 1·40 80

**289.** Dieudonne Costes, Maurice Bellonte and "Point d'Interrogation".

**1980.** Air. Aviation Anniversaries.
723 **289** 165 f. red, blue & green 1·10 55
724 – 1000 f. green, red & bl 7·25 3·25
DESIGNS: 165 f. Type **289** (50th anniv of first North Atlantic flight). 1000 f. Jean Mermoz and seaplane "Comte de la Vaulx" (50th anniv of first South Atlantic airmail).

**290.** Running.

**1980.** Air. Olympic Games, Moscow.
725. **290.** 50 f. multicoloured .. 40 15
726. – 100 f. black, red & grn. 70 40
727. – 250 f. multicoloured .. 1·60 85
DESIGNS: 100 f. Pole vaulting. 250 f. Boxing.

**1980.** District Arms (1st series). Vert. designs as T **137** but dated " 1980 ".
729. 10 f. silver, black and gold 15 10
730. 20 f. multicoloured .. 20 15
731. 30 f. black, silver and red 20 15
DESIGNS: 10 f. Haut-Ogooue. 20 f. L'Estuaipe. 30 f. Bitam.

**291.** Leon Mba and El Hadj Omar Bongo.

**1980.** 20th Anniv. of Independence.
732. **291.** 60 f. multicoloured .. 60 30

**292.** Peacock Emblem and Tourist Attractions.

**1980.** World Tourism Conference, Manila.
733. **292.** 80 f. blue, violet & brn. 60 30

**1980.** 20th Anniv. of Organization of Petroleum Exporting Countries. Mult.
734. 90 f. Globe and O.P.E.C. Emblem (horiz.) .. 85 35
735. 120 f. Type **293** .. .. 1·10 50

**1980.** Air. Olympic Medal Winners. Nos. 725/7 optd.
736. 50 f. **YIFTER (Eth.) NYAMBUI (Tanz.) MAANINKA (Finl.) 5000 metres** .. 40 20
737. 100 f. **KOZIAKIEWICZ (Pol.) (record du monde) VOLKOV (Urss) et SLUSARSKI (Pol.)** .. 70 45
738. 250 f. **WELTERS ALDAMA (Cuba) MUGABI (Oug.) KRUBER (Rda) et SZCZERDA (Pol.)** .. 1·60 1·00

**1980.** Birds. Multicoloured.
740. 50 f. Type **295** .. .. 1·00 35
741. 60 f. White-fronted bee eater .. .. 1·25 50
742. 80 f. African pitta .. .. 1·50 70
743. 150 f. Pel's fishing owl .. 2·40 1·25

**296.** Charles de Gaulle. **297.** St. Matthew.

**1980.** Air. 10th Death Anniv. of Charles de Gaulle. Multicoloured.
744. 100 f. Type **296** .. .. 95 55
745. 200 f. Charles and Mme. de Gaulle .. 1·90 95

**1980.** Christmas. Carvings from Bizangobibere Church. Multicoloured.
747. 60 f. St. Luke .. .. 45 20
748. 80 f. Type **297** .. .. 65 35

**298.** Heinrich von Stephan. **299.** Shooting at Goal.

**1981.** 150th Birth Anniv. of Heinrich von Stephan (founder of U.P.U.).
749. **298.** 90 f. deep brown, light brown and brown.. 65 35

**1981.** Air. World Cup Football Championship Eliminators. Multicoloured.
750. 60 f. Type **299** .. .. 45 30
751. 190 f. Players with ball .. 1·40 85

**300.** Palais Renovation.

**1981.** 13th Anniv. of National Renewal.
752. **300.** 60 f. multicoloured .. 55 20

**293.** Figures supporting O.P.E.C. Emblem. **295.** African River Martin.

**301.** W. Herschel. (Discovery of Uranus Bicent.). **302.** Lion (St. Mark).

**1981.** Air. Space Anniversaries. Mult.

753. 150 f. Type **301** .. .. 1·10 45
754. 250 f. Yuri Gagarin. First man in space (20th anniv.) 1·60 95
755. 500 f. Alan Shepard. First American in space (20th anniv.) .. .. .. 3·25 1·60

**1981.** Easter. Wood Carvings from Bizangobibere Church. Multicoloured.

757. 75 f. Type **302** .. .. 55 20
758. 100 f. Eagle (St. John) .. 80 30

**303.** Port Gentil. **304.** Caduceus.

**1981.** 23rd Congress of Lions Club District 403 Libreville. Multicoloured.

759. 60 f. Type **303** .. .. 45 20
760. 75 f. District 403 .. 55 20
761. 80 f. Libreville Cocotiers 55 30
762. 100 f. Libreville Hibiscus 80 35
763. 165 f. Ekwata .. .. 1·25 55
764. 200 f. Haute-Ogooue .. 1·40 65

**1981.** World Telecommunications Day.

765. **304.** 125 f. multicoloured .. 80 40

**305.** Map of Africa and Emblems of Gabon Electricity and Water Society and U.P.D.E.A.

**1981.** Air. 7th Congress of African Electricity Producers and Suppliers.

766. **305.** 100 f. multicoloured .. 70 40

**306.** Japanese " D–51 " Locomotive and French High-speed Train.

**1981.** Air. Birth Bicent. of George Stephenson.

767. **306.** 75 f. grey, orge. & brn. 1·00 40
768. – 100 f. grn., blk. and blue 1·10 55
769. – 350 f. grn., brn. and red 2·75 1·60

DESIGNS: 100 f. Baltimore & Ohio " Mallet 7100 " and Prussian State Railways " T–3 " locomotives. 350 f. George Stephenson with " Rocket " and " BB Alsthom " electric locomotive.

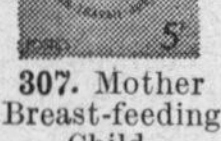

**307.** Mother Breast-feeding Child. **308.** R. P. Klaine (70th death anniv.).

**1981.**

| | | | | |
|---|---|---|---|---|
| 772 | 307 | 5 f. brown and black | 10 | 10 |
| 773 | | 10 f. mauve and black | 10 | 10 |
| 774 | | 15 f. green and black | 10 | 10 |
| 775 | | 20 f. pink and black | 10 | 10 |
| 776 | | 25 f. blue and black | 15 | 10 |
| 777 | | 40 f. pink and black | 25 | 10 |
| 778 | | 50 f. green and black | 35 | 10 |
| 779 | | 75 f. brown and black | 45 | 20 |
| 779a | | 90 f. blue and black | 55 | 20 |
| 780 | | 100 f. yellow & black | 60 | 25 |
| 780a | | 125 f. green and black | 85 | 30 |
| 780b | | 150 f. purple & black | 1·00 | 25 |

**1981.** Religious Personalities. Multicoloured

781. 70 f. Type **308** .. .. 50 20
782. 90 f. Mgr. Walker (110th birth anniv.) .. .. 70 30

**309.** Scout Badge on Map of Gabon. **311.** " Helping the Disabled ".

**1981.** 4th Panafrican Scout Congress, Abidjan.

783. **309.** 75 f. multicoloured .. 60 30

**1981.** 28th World Scout Conference, Dakar. Optd. **DAKAR 28e CONFERENCE MONDIALE DU SCOUTISME.**

784. **309.** 75 f. multicoloured .. 60 30

**1981.** International Year of Disabled People.

785. **311.** 100 f. red, dp. grn. & grn. 65 35

**312.** " Hypolimnas salmacis ".

**1981.** Butterflies. Multicoloured.

786. 75 f. Type **312** .. .. 90 45
787. 100 f. " Euphaedra themis " 1·10 45
788. 150 f. " Amauris niavius " 1·40 90
789. 250 f. " Cymothoe lucasi " 2·25 1·25

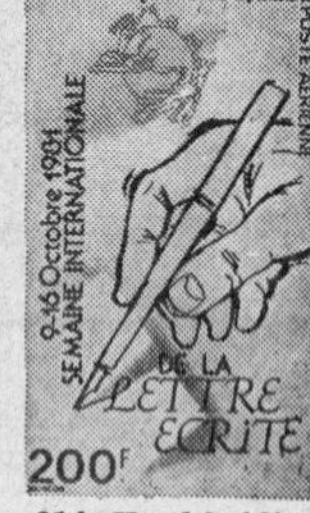

**313.** " Paul as Harlequin ". **314.** Hand holding Pen.

**1981.** Birth Centenary of Pablo Picasso.

790. **313.** 500 f. multicoloured .. 4·50 1·90

**1981.** Air. International Letter-writing Week.

791. **314.** 200 f. multicoloured .. 1·40 65

**315.** Agricultural Scenes, Wheat and F.A.O. Emblem.

**1981.** World Food Day.

792. **315.** 350 f. brn., dp. brn. & bl. 2·75 1·40

**316.** Traditional Hairstyle.

**1981.** Traditional Hairstyles.

793. **316.** 75 f. red, yellow & blk. 70 35
794. – 100 f. grn. lilac & blk. 85 40
795. – 125 f. lt. grn., grn. & blk. 1·10 60
796. – 200 f. pink, vio. & blk. 1·75 90

DESIGNS: 100 f. to 200 f. Different hairstyles. See also Nos. 964a and 1046.

**317.** Dancers around Fire.

**1981.** Christmas. Multicoloured.

798. 75 f. Type **317** .. .. 55 20
799. 100 f. Christmas meal .. 80 35

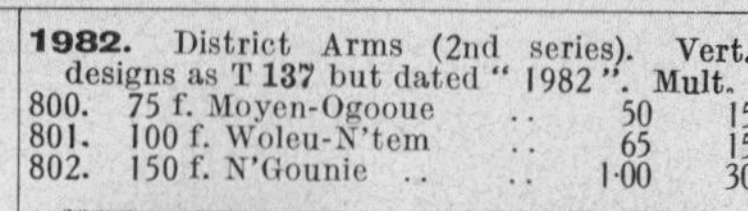

**1982.** District Arms (2nd series). Vert. designs as T **137** but dated " 1982 ". Mult.

800. 75 f. Moyen-Ogooue .. 50 15
801. 100 f. Woleu-N'tem .. 65 15
802. 150 f. N'Gounie .. .. 1·00 30

**318.** Pope John Paul II. **319.** Alfred de Musset.

**1982.** Papal Visit.

803. **318.** 100 f. multicoloured .. 1·10 65

**1982.** 125th Death Anniv. of Alfred de Musset (writer).

804. **319.** 75 f. black .. .. 55 20

**320.** "Leonce Veilvieux" (freighter).

**1982.** Merchant Ships. Multicoloured.

805 75 f. Type **320** .. .. 50 45
806 100 f. "Correze" (container ship) .. .. .. 65 45
807 200 f. Oil tanker .. .. 1·50 75

**321.** Dr. Robert Koch, Microscope, Bacillus and Guinea Pig.

**1982.** Centenary of Discovery of Tubercle Bacillus.

808. **321.** 100 f. multicoloured .. 90 45

**322.** Rope Bridge, Poubara. **323.** Hexagonal Pattern.

**1982.** "Philexfrance 82" International Stamp Exhibition, Paris. Multicoloured.

809. 100 f. Type **322** .. .. 65 35
810. 100 f. Bapounou sculpture 1·40 55

**1982.** World Telecommunications Day.

811. **323.** 75 f. multicoloured .. 60 35

**324.** Footballer (Brazil).

**1982.** World Cup Football Championship, Spain. Multicoloured.

812. 100 f. Type **324** .. .. 65 30
813. 125 f. Footballer (Argentina) 85 35
814. 200 f. Footballer (England) 1·25 50

**325.** " Caprice des Dames " (Morning).

**1982.** Flower " Caprice des Dames ". Mult.

816. 75 f. Type **325** .. .. 60 35
817. 100 f. Midday .. .. 80 35
818. 175 f. Evening .. .. 1·40 65

**326.** Satellites.

**1982.** Second U.N. Conference on Exploration and Peaceful Uses of Outer Space.

819. **326.** 250 f. bl., dp. bl. & red 1·90 1·10

**1982.** World Cup Football Championship Winners. Nos. 812/14 optd.

821. **324.** 100 f. multicoloured .. 65 35
822. – 125 f. multicoloured .. 85 40
823. – 200 f. multicoloured .. 1·40 60

OPTS: 100 f. **DEMIE-FINALE POLOGNE 0—ITALIE 2.** 125 f. **DEMIE-FINALE R. F. ALLEMAGNE 3—FRANCE 3.** 200 f. **FINALE ITALIE 3—R. F. ALLEMAGNE 1.**

**329.** Duplex Murex.

**1982.** Shells. Multicoloured.

825. 75 f. Type **329** .. .. 80 50
826. 100 f. " Chama crenulata " 1·40 60
827. 125 f. " Cardium hians " .. 2·00 1·10

**330.** " Still-life with Mandolin " (Braque birth centenary).

**1982.** Painters' Anniversaries. Mult.

828. 300 f. Type **330** .. .. 2·25 70
829. 350 f. " Boy blowing Soap Bubbles " (Manet—death cent.) (vert.) .. .. 3·25 1·10

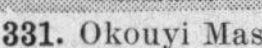

**331.** Okouyi Mask. **332.** St. Francis Xavier Church, Lambarene.

**1982.** Artifacts. Multicoloured.

830. 75 f. Type **331** .. .. 45 20
831. 100 f. Ondoumbo reliquary 65 20
832. 150 f. Tsogho statuette .. 1·10 40
833. 250 f. Forge bellows .. 1·60 60

**1982.** Christmas.

834. **332.** 100 f. multicoloured .. 65 35

**333.** Presidents Bongo and Mitterand, Route Map and Train.

**1983.** Inauguration of Second Stage of Trans-Gabon Railway.

835. **333.** 75 f. multicoloured .. 65 35

**334.** Stylised Highway and Map of Africa.

**1983.** 5th African Highway Conference.

836 **334** 100 f. multicoloured .. 65 30

**335.** Gymnast with Hoop.

**336.** " Epitorium trochiformis " (Estuaire).

**1983.** Air. Olympic Games, Los Angeles. Multicoloured.
837. 90 f. Type **335** .. .. 60 30
838. 350 f. Wind-surfing .. 2·50 1·00

**1983.** Provinces. Multicoloured.
839. 75 f. Bakota mask (Ogooue Ivindo) .. .. .. 50 25
840. 90 f. African buffalo (Nyanga) .. .. 60 30
841. 90 f. "Charaxes druceanus" (Ogooue Lolo) .. .. 60 30
842. 100 f. Isogho hairstyle (Ngounie) .. .. 65 35
843. 125 f. Manganese (Haut Ogooue) .. .. .. 85 45
844. 125 f. Crocodiles (Moyen Ogooue) .. .. .. 85 45
845. 125 f. Tarpon (Ogooue Maritime) .. .. 85 45
846. 135 f. Type **336** .. .. 1·25 60
847. 135 f. Coffee flowers (Woleu Ntem) .. .. .. 1·25 60

**337.** "Ville de Rouen" (container ship) and I.M.O. Emblem.

**1983.** 25th Anniv. of International Maritime Organization.
848. **337.** 125 f. multicoloured .. 90 45

**338.** Water Chevrotain.

**1983.** Fauna. Multicoloured.
849. 90 f. Type **338** .. .. 60 30
850. 125 f. Pink-backed Pelican 2·25 90
851. 225 f. African elephant .. 1·90 70
852. 400 f. Iguana .. .. 2·75 1·40

**339.** E.C.A. Anniversary Emblem.

**1983.** 25th Anniv. of Economic Commission for Africa.
854. **339.** 125 f. multicoloured .. 85 40

**340.** Telephones.

**341.** " Double Eagle II " crossing Atlantic.

**1983.** World Telecommunications Day. Mult.
855. 90 f. Type **340** .. .. 85 45
856. 90 f. As No. 855 but design inverted .. .. 85 45

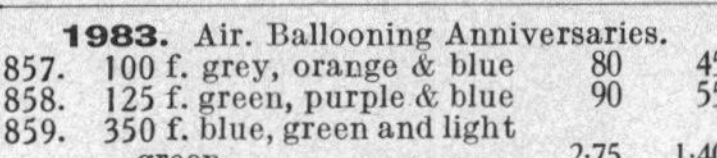
**1983.** Air. Ballooning Anniversaries.
857. 100 f. grey, orange & blue 80 45
858. 125 f. green, purple & blue 90 55
859. 350 f. blue, green and light green .. .. .. 2·75 1·40
DESIGNS: 100 f. Type **341** (5th anniv of first Atlantic crossing). 125 f. Hot-air balloons (Bicentenary of Montgolfier Brothers' balloon). 350 f. Pilatre de Rozier and Montgolfier balloon (Bicentenary of manned flight).

**342.** " Lady with Unicorn ".

**1983.** Air. 150th Birth Anniv. of Raphael.
860. **342.** 1000 f. multicoloured 7·25 3·25

**343.** Nkoltang Satellite Receiving Station.

**1983.** World Communications Year.
861. **343.** 125 f. multicoloured .. 85 35

**344.** Rapids on the Ivindo River.

**1983.** Tourism.
862. **344.** 90 f. blue, brn. & grn. 55 30
863. – 125 f. brn., grn. & grey 85 45
864. – 185 f. grey, orge. and grn. 1·25 45
865. – 350 f. brn., grn. & blue 2·40 1·10
DESIGNS: 125 f. Pirogue on the Ogooue River. 185 f. Wonga Wongue Game Reserve. 350 f. Coastal beach.

**345.** Mahongwe Drum.

**1983.** Music and Dance. Multicoloured.
866. 90 f. Type **345** .. .. 55 30
867. 125 f. Okoukoue dance .. 85 45
868. 135 f. Ngomi bateke .. 1·25 45
869. 260 f. Ndoumou dancer .. 2·40 1·25

**346.** "Glossinidae".

**347.** "The Adulterous Woman".

**1983.** Harmful Insects. Multicoloured.
870. 90 f. Type **346** .. .. 90 45
871. 125 f. " Belonogaster junceus " .. .. .. 1·10 50
872. 300 f. " Aedes aegypti " .. 2·25 1·25
873. 350 f. " Mylabris " .. 3·00 1·40

**1983.** Christmas. Wood carvings from St. Michel Church, Libreville. Mult.
874. 90 f. Type **347** .. .. 55 30
875. 125 f. " Parable of the Good Samaritan " .. .. 85 40

**348.** Boeing 747-200 Airliner and Gabon Stamp of 1966.

**1984.** World Post Congress Stamp Exhibition, Hamburg. Multicoloured.
876 125 f. Type **348** .. .. 95 45
877 225 f. Douglas DC-10 and German airmail stamp of 1919 .. .. .. 1·90 90

**349.** Pylons and Buildings.

**1984.** 3rd Anniv. of "Africa 1".
878. **349.** 125 f. multicoloured .. 85 35

**350.** Ice Hockey.

**1984.** Air. Winter Olympic Games, Sarajevo.
879. **350.** 125 f. grn., pur. & blk. 1·10 55
880. – 350 f. blue, brn. & blk. 2·50 1·10
DESIGN: 350 f. Ice-dancing.

**351.** Coconut.

**1984.** Fruit Trees. Multicoloured.
881. 90 f. Type **351** .. .. 70 35
882. 100 f. Pawpaw .. .. 80 35
883. 125 f. Mango .. .. 1·00 45
884. 250 f. Banana .. .. 1·90 85

**352.** Robin Dauphin and Piper Cherokee Six Aircraft.

**1984.** Air. Paris-Libreville Air Rally.
885. **352.** 500 f. multicoloured .. 3·25 1·90

**353.** "Racehorses".

**1984.** Air. 150th Birth Anniv. of Degas.
886. **353.** 500 f. multicoloured .. 4·25 2·25

**354.** Water Lily.

**355.** Spectrum.

**1984.** Flowers. Multicoloured.
887. 90 f. Type **354** .. .. 80 30
888. 125 f. Water hyacinth .. 80 40
889. 135 f. Hibiscus .. .. 1·10 45
890. 350 f. Bracteate orchid .. 2·50 1·40

**1984.** World Telecommunications Day.
891. **355.** 125 f. multicoloured .. 85 35

**356.** Basketball.

**358.** Lionel Hampton.

**1984.** Air. Olympic Games, Los Angeles. Multicoloured.
892. 90 f. Type **356** .. .. 55 35
893. 125 f. Steeple-chase .. 85 45

**1984.** Jazz Musicians. Multicoloured.
895. 90 f. Type **358** .. .. 1·10 55
896. 125 f. Charlie Parker .. 1·40 55
897. 260 f. Erroll Garner .. 2·50 1·40

**1984.** District Arms (3rd series). As T **137** but dated "1984". Multicoloured.
898. 90 f. Cocobeach .. .. 55 15
899. 125 f. Mouila .. .. 80 15
900. 135 f. N'Djole .. .. 90 20

**359.** Medouneu.

**1984.** Tourism. Multicoloured.
901. 90 f. Type **359** .. .. 65 35
902. 125 f. Sunset over Ogooue 1·00 50
903. 165 f. Trans-Gabon train .. 1·75 1·25

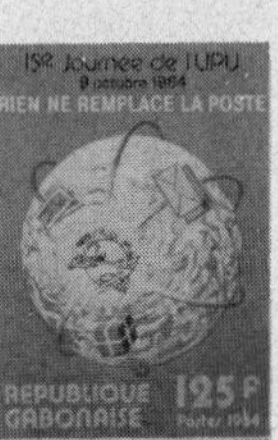


**360.** Globe, Post and Emblem.

**360a.** Kota Reliquary.

**1984.** Universal Postal Union Day.
905. **360.** 125 f. multicoloured .. 85 35

**1984.** Traditional Art. Multicoloured.
905a 90 f. Kouble mask
905b 125 f. Pounou fan
905c 150 f. Mahongoue reliquary
905d 250 f. Type **360a**

**361.** "Icarus" (Hans Herni).

**1984.** 40th Anniv. of International Civil Aviation Organization.
906. **361.** 125 f. deep blue, green and blue .. .. 85 35

**362.** Tympanum of Saint Michael's Church (left side).

**1984.** Christmas. Multicoloured.
907. 90 f. Type **362** .. .. 55 25
908. 125 f. Tympanum of Saint Michael's church (right side) .. .. .. 85 35
Nos. 907/8 were printed together se-tenant forming a composite design.

**363.** South African Crowned Cranes.

**1984.** Birds. Multicoloured.
909. 90 f. Type **363** .. .. 1·50 75
910. 125 f. Snowy-breasted hummingbird .. .. 2·50 1·40
911. 150 f. Keel-billed toucan .. 2·75 1·50

**364.** Leper Colony, Libreville.

**1985.** World Lepers' Day.
912. **364.** 125 f. multicoloured .. 85 40

**365.** I.Y.Y. Emblem.

**367.** Profiles and Emblem.

**1985.** International Youth Year.
913. **365.** 125 f. multicoloured .. 85 35

**1985.** 15th Anniv. of Cultural and Technical Co-operation Agency.
914. **367.** 125 f. blue, red and deep blue .. .. 85 35

**368.** Water Rat.

**1985.** Animals. Multicoloured.
915. 90 f. Type **368** .. .. 90 35
916. 100 f. Porcupine .. .. 90 35
917. 125 f. Giant pangolin .. 1·25 55
918. 350 f. Antelope .. .. 2·75 1·40

**369.** Score and Aleka.

**1985.** Georges Damas Aleka (composer) Commemoration.
920. **369.** 90 f. multicoloured .. 80 35

**370.** Emblem and Coloured Lines.

**371.** Shield.

**1985.** World Telecommunications Day.
921. **370.** 125 f. multicoloured .. 85 35

**1985.** 30th Anniv. of Christian Youth Workers' Movement in Gabon.
922. **371.** 90 f. multicoloured .. 60 30

**372.** "La Mpassa" (freighter).

**1985.**
923. **372.** 185 f. multicoloured .. 1·50 70

**373.** Building and Dish Aerials.

**1985.** 25th Anniv. of Posts and Telecommunications Administration.
924. **373.** 90 f. multicoloured .. 60 30

**374.** President Bongo.

**375.** Dr. Albert Schweitzer.

**1985.** 25th Anniv. of Independence.
925. **374.** 250 f. multicoloured .. 1·90 1·10
926. 500 f. multicoloured .. 4·25 2·50

**1985.** Air. 20th Death Anniv. of Dr. Albert Schweitzer.
928. **375.** 350 f. multicoloured .. 2·50 1·25

**376.** Hand holding U.N. and Gabon Flags.

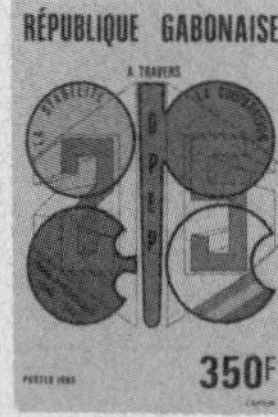


**377.** O.P.E.C. Emblem.

**1985.** Air. 20th Anniv. of Membership of United Nations Organization.
929. **376.** 225 f. multicoloured .. 1·50 70

**1985.** 25th Anniv. of Organization of Petroleum Exporting Countries.
930. **377.** 350 f. multicoloured .. 2·50 1·40

**378.** Boy Scouts around Campfire and Elephant.

**1985.** Air. "Philexafrique" Stamp Exhibition, Lome, Togo. Multicoloured.
931. 100 f. Type **378** .. .. 85 45
932. 150 f. Diesel train, satellite and dish aerial .. .. 1·50 65

**379.** Central Post Office, Libreville, Gabon Posts and U.P.U. Emblems.

**1985.** Air. World Post Day.
933. **379.** 300 f. multicoloured .. 2·25 1·00

**380.** Hand holding Globe.

**381.** Centre.

**1985.** Air. 40th Anniv. of U.N.O.
934. **380.** 350 f. multicoloured .. 2·50 1·10

**1985.** International Centre of Bantu Civilisations.
935. **381.** 185 f. multicoloured .. 1·40 60

**381a.** Interior of Church.

**1985.** Christmas. St. Andrew's Church, Libreville. Multicoloured.
935a 90 f. Exterior of church
935b 125 f. Type **381a**

**382.** Young People within Laurel Wreath.

**1986.** 25th Anniv. of U.N.E.S.C.O. National Commission.
936. **382.** 100 f. multicoloured .. 65 30

**383.** "Mother and Child".

**385.** Key as Emblem and Map.

**384.** Savorgnan de Brazza and Canoe.

**1986.** Air. Gabon's Gift to United Nations Organization.
937. **383.** 350 f. multicoloured .. 2·50 1·10

**1986.** Air. Centenary of Lastoursville.
938. **384.** 100 f. multicoloured .. 85 45

**1986.** 4th Rotary International District 915 Conference, Libreville.
939. **385.** 150 f. multicoloured .. 1·10 50

**386.** Communications Equipment.

**1986.** World Telecommunications Day.
940. **386.** 300 f. multicoloured .. 2·00 1·00

**387.** Goalkeeper saving Ball.

**1986.** Air. World Cup Football Championship, Mexico. Multicoloured.
941. 100 f. Type **387** .. .. 65 35
942. 150 f. Footballers and Mexican statue .. .. 1·00 45
943. 250 f. World Cup trophy, footballers and map .. 1·60 65
944. 350 f. Flags, ball and stadium .. .. .. 2·25 1·00

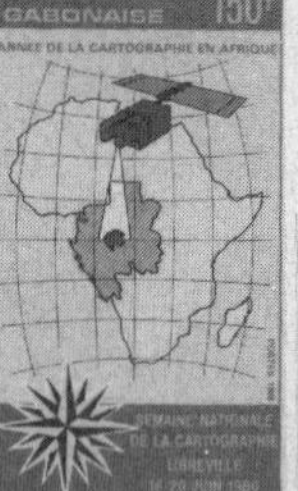

**388.** Map and Satellite.

**389.** "L'Abanga" (container ship).

**1986.** African Cartography Year and National Cartography Week, Libreville.
946. **388.** 150 f. multicoloured .. 1·10 55

**1986.**
947. **389.** 250 f. multicoloured .. 2·25 1·50

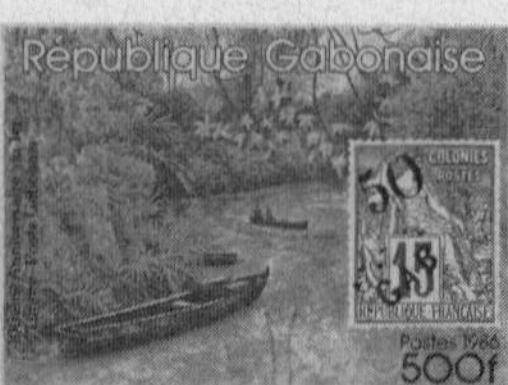


**390.** River and Gabon 1886 50 c. Stamp.

**1986.** Centenary of First Gabon Stamps.
948. **390.** 500 f. multicoloured .. 4·25 2·00

**391.** "Allamanda neriifolia". **392.** Arms of Lambarn.

**1986.** Flowers. Multicoloured.
949. 100 f. Type **391** .. .. 65 35
950. 150 f. "Musa cultivar" .. 1·00 50
951. 350 f. "Dissotis decumbens" .. .. 1·10 55
952. 350 f. "Campylospermum laeve" .. .. .. 2·50 1·10

**1986.** District Arms (4th series). Mult.
953. 100 f. Type **392** .. .. 65 20
954. 160 f. Leconi .. .. 1·10 35

**393.** Coffee Berries, Flowers and Beans.

**1986.** 25th Anniv. of African and Malagasy Coffee Producers Organization.
955. **393.** 125 f. multicoloured .. 95 55

**394.** "Machaon". **395.** Dove and U.P.U. Emblem.

**1986.** Butterflies. Multicoloured.
956. 150 f. Type **394** .. .. 1·90 1·25
957. 290 f. "Urania" .. .. 2·75 2·25

**1986.** Air. World Post Day.
958. **395.** 500 f. multicoloured .. 3·25 1·60

**1986.** Air. World Cup Football Championship Winners. Nos 941/4 optd. **ARGENTINE 3-R.F.A. 2.** Multicoloured.
959. 100 f. Type **387** .. .. 65 45
960. 150 f. Footballers and Mexican statue .. .. 1·00 55
961. 250 f. World Cup trophy, footballers and map .. 1·60 1·00
962. 350 f. Flags, ball and stadium .. .. .. 2·25 1·60

**397.** St. Peter's Church, Libreville.

**1986.** Christmas.
963. **397.** 500 f. multicoloured .. 3·25 1·60

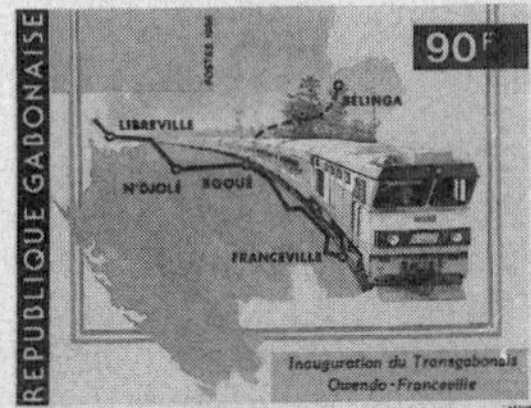


**398.** Train and Route Map.

**1986.** Inauguration of Owendo–Franceville Trans-Gabon Railway.
964. **398.** 90 f. multicoloured .. 1·10 45

**1986.** Traditional Hairstyles. As T **316**.
964a 150 f. black, red and grey 3·25 1·10

**399.** "Adioryx bastatus".

**1987.** Fishes. Multicoloured.
966. 90 f. Type **399** .. .. 60 35
967. 125 f. "Scarus boefleri" .. 85 45
968. 225 f. "Cephalacanthus volitans" .. .. 1·40 90
969. 350 f. "Dasyatis marmorata" .. .. 2·25 1·10

**400.** Raoul Follereau (leprosy pioneer). **401.** Man and Child in front of Map.

**1987.** World Leprosy Day.
971. **400.** 125 f. multicoloured .. 1·00 65

**1987.** Air. 19th Anniv. of National Renewal.
972. **401.** 500 f. multicoloured .. 3·50 1·60

**402.** Pres. Bongo receiving Prize.

**1987.** Award of Dag Hammarskjold Peace Prize to Pres. Omar Bongo.
973. **402.** 125 f. multicoloured .. 85 55

**403.** Konrad Adenauer. **404.** Symbols of Communication.

**1987.** Air. 20th Death Anniv. of Konrad Adenauer (German statesman).
974. **403.** 300 f. multicoloured .. 2·50 1·25

**1987.** World Telecommunications Day.
975. **404.** 90 f. multicoloured .. 60 35

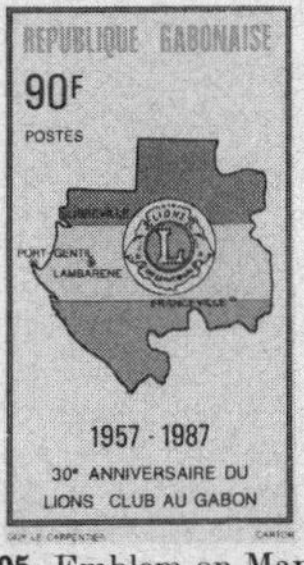


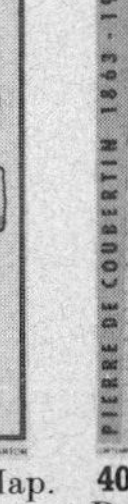


**405.** Emblem on Map. **406.** Coubertin and Runner with Torch.

**1987.** 30th Anniv. of Lions Club of Gabon.
976. **405.** 90 f. multicoloured .. 60 35

**1987.** 50th Death Anniv. of Pierre de Coubertin (founder of modern Olympic Games).
977. **406.** 200 f. multicoloured .. 1·40 65

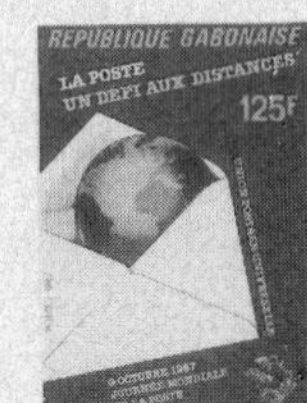


**407.** Map, Emblems and People. **408.** Globe in Envelope.

**1987.** 70th Anniv. of Lions International.
978. **407.** 165 f. multicoloured .. 1·25 65

**1987.** World Post Day.
979. **408.** 125 f. multicoloured .. 85 35

**409.** Pres. Bongo and Sam Nujoma. **410.** Fanel Moon.

**1987.** Solidarity with South-West African Peoples' Organization.
980. **409.** 225 f. multicoloured .. 1·40 55

**1987.** Sea Shells. Multicoloured.
981 90 f. Type **410** .. .. 1·25 70
982 125 f. Lightning moon ("Natica fulminea cruentata") .. .. 1·50 70
See also Nos. 1018a/b.

**411.** Man, House and Machinery.

**1987.** International Year of Shelter for the Homeless. World Shelter Day.
984. **411.** 90 f. multicoloured .. 60 35

**412.** Mission. **413.** Nurse vaccinating Child.

**1987.** Centenary of St. Anne of Odimba Mission.
985. **412.** 90 f. multicoloured .. 65 35

**1987.** Universal Vaccination for Children.
986. **413.** 100 f. multicoloured .. 80 40

**414.** President making Address.

**1987.** 20th Anniv. of Installation of President Omar Bongo.
987. **414.** 1000 f. multicoloured 6·75 3·25

**415.** St. Theresa's Church, Oyem. **417.** "Cassia occidentalis".

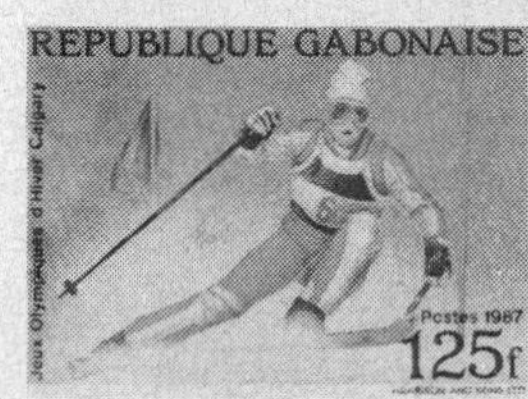


**416.** Skier.

**1987.** Christmas.
988. **415.** 90 f. multicoloured .. 65 35

**1987.** Winter Olympic Games, Calgary (1988).
989. **416.** 125 f. multicoloured .. 85 45

**1988.** Medicinal Plants. Multicoloured.
990. 90 f. Type **417** .. .. 65 45
991. 125 f. "Tabernanthe iboga" 90 45
992. 225 f. "Cassia alata" .. 1·50 80
993. 350 f. "Anthocleista schweinfurthii" .. .. 2·75 1·60

**418.** Obamba Rattle.

**1988.** Traditional Musical Instruments. Mult.
995. 90 f. Type **418** .. .. 60 35
996. 100 f. Fang sanza (vert.) .. 80 45
997. 125 f. Mitsogho harp (vert.) 90 55
998. 165 f. Fang xylophone .. 1·40 65

**419.** Elephant with raised Trunk.

**1988.** Endangered Animals. African Elephant. Multicoloured.
1000. 25 f. Type **419** .. .. 30 15
1001. 40 f. Elephant family .. 45 20
1002. 50 f. Elephant in vegetation .. .. 55 20
1003. 100 f. Elephant .. .. 95 55

420. Postal Delta Building.

**1988.** Inauguration of Postal Delta.
1004. **420.** 90 f. multicoloured .. 65 35

421. Village and Dr. Schweitzer.

**1988.** Air. 75th Anniv. of Arrival in Gabon of Dr. Albert Schweitzer.
1005. **421.** 500 f. multicoloured 3·50 1·60

422. Players.

**1988.** World Cup Rugby Championship (1987).
1006. **422.** 350 f. multicoloured 2·75 1·60

423. Opposing Arrows.

**1988.** World Telecommunications Day.
1007. **423.** 125 f. multicoloured 85 40

424. Storming the Bastille, 1789.

**1988.** "Philexfrance 89" Stamp Exhibition, Paris.
1008. **424.** 125 f. multicoloured 1·10 55

425. Crops and Agricultural Activities.

**1988.** 10th Anniv. of International Agricultural Development Fund.
1009. **425.** 350 f. multicoloured 2·50 1·10

426. Emblem and Theatre Staff.

**1988.** 125th Anniv. of Red Cross.
1010. **426.** 125 f. multicoloured 85 35

427. Refinery.

**1988.** Air. 20th Anniv. of Port Gentil Oil Refinery.
1011. **427.** 350 f. multicoloured 2·25 1·10

428 Tennis

**1988.** Olympic Games, Seoul. Multicoloured.
1012 90 f. Type **428** .. 65 35
1013 100 f. Swimming .. 65 35
1014 350 f. Running .. 2·25 1·00
1015 500 f. Hurdling .. 3·25 1·10

429 Envelopes forming World Map

**1988.** World Post Day.
1017 **429** 125 f. black, bl & yell 85 35

430 Medouneu Church

431 Map and Emblem

**1988.** Christmas.
1018 **430** 200 f. multicoloured .. 1·40 65

**1988.** Sea Shells. As T **410**. Multicoloured.
1018a 90 f. Fanel moon ("Natica fanel var") 1·25 55
1018b 125 f. "Natica variolaria"(inser "Natica sp.") .. 1·50 85

**1989.** 10th Anniv of Chaine de Rotisseurs in Gabon.
1019 **431** 175 f. multicoloured .. 1·10 65

432 Map

434 African Tiger Bittern

433 Boys playing

**1989.** Inauguration of Rabi Kounga Oil Field.
1020 **432** 125 f. multicoloured .. 85 50

**1989.** Traditional Games.
1021 **433** 90 f. multicoloured .. 60 40

**1989.** Birds. Multicoloured.
1022 100 f. Type **434** .. .. 65 35
1023 175 f. Grey parrot .. 1·10 65
1024 200 f. Red-billed dwarf hornbill .. .. 1·40 70
1025 500 f. Blue-breasted kingfisher .. .. .. 3·25 1·75

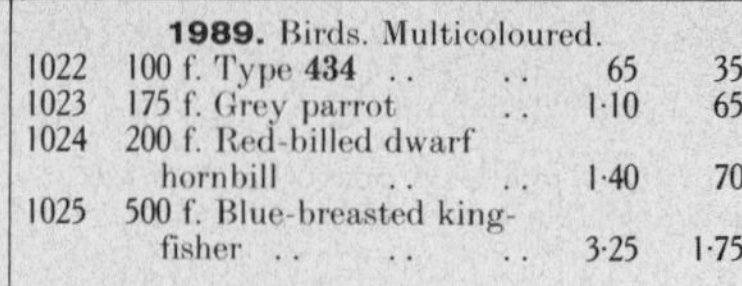

435 Map and Emblem

436 Arrows and Dish Aerials

**1989.** 8th Lions Club International Multidistrict 403 Convention, Libreville.
1027 **435** 125 f. multicoloured .. 85 45

**1989.** World Telecommunications Day.
1028 **436** 300 f. multicoloured .. 1·90 90

437 Palm-nuts

**1989.** Fruits. Multicoloured.
1029 90 f. Type **437** .. .. 60 35
1030 125 f. Cabosse .. .. 85 35
1031 175 f. Pineapple .. .. 1·40 55
1032 250 f. Breadfruit .. 1·60 1·00

438 "Apples and Oranges"

**1989.** 150th Birth Anniv of Paul Cezanne (painter).
1034 **438** 500 f. multicoloured 3·25 2·25

439 Phrygian Cap on Tree of Liberty and Sans-culotte

**1989.** "Philexfrance '89" International Stamp Exhibition, Paris.
1035 **439** 175 f. multicoloured .. 1·40 65

440 Soldier and Sans-culotte

**1989.** Bicentenary of French Revolution.
1036 **440** 500 f. multicoloured .. 3·50 2·50

441 Town Hall

**1989.** 10th Anniv of International Association of French-speaking Town Halls.
1037 **441** 100 f. multicoloured .. 65 40

442 Emblem and Map showing Development Programmes

444 Footballers

443 Post Office

**1989.** 25th Anniv of African Development Bank.
1038 **442** 100 f. multicoloured .. 65 40

**1989.** 125th Anniv (1987) of Gabon Postal Service.
1039 **443** 90 f. multicoloured .. 65 35

**1989.** World Cup Football Championship, Italy (1990). Multicoloured.
1040 100 f. Type **444** .. .. 65 35
1041 175 f. Player tackling .. 1·25 55
1042 300 f. Goalkeeper catching ball .. .. .. 2·00 80
1043 500 f. Goalkeeper catching ball (different) .. 3·25 1·40

445 Woman and Child posting Letter

447 St. Louis' Church, Port-Gentil

**1989.** World Post Day.
1045 **445** 175 f. multicoloured .. 1·10 45

**1989.** Traditional Hairstyles. As T **316**.
1046 175 f. black, lilac & grey 1·40 55

**1989.** Christmas.
1047 **447** 100 f. multicoloured .. 65 30

448 L' Ogooue, N'Gomo

**1989.**
1048 **448** 100 f. multicoloured .. 50 25

**HAVE YOU READ THE NOTES AT THE BEGINNING OF THIS CATALOGUE?**
These often provide answers to the enquiries we receive.

**449** Axehead

**1990.** Prehistory. Stone Weapons. Mult.
1049 100 f. Type **449** .. .. 90 45
1050 175 f. Paring knife .. 1·40 65
1051 300 f. Flint arrowhead .. 2·25 1·10
1052 400 f. Double-edged knife 3·25 1·90

**450** Arms of Libreville

**1990.** 22nd Anniv of National Renovation.
1054 **450** 100 f. multicoloured .. 65 30

**451** Penny Black and Beach

**1990.** 150th Anniv of the Penny Black.
1055 **451** 500 f. multicoloured .. 4·50 2·75

**452** Doctor and Nurse Examining Patient

**453** Monkey

**1990.** World Health Day.
1056 **452** 400 f. multicoloured .. 2·75 1·40

**1990.** Animals of Gabon. Multicoloured.
1057 100 f. Type **453** .. .. 90 45
1058 175 f. Bush pig (horiz) .. 1·40 65
1059 200 f. Antelope (horiz) .. 1·60 1·10
1060 500 f. Mandrill .. .. 4·50 2·75

**454** De Gaulle and Map

**1990.** Air. 50th Anniv of De Gaulle's Call to Resist.
1062 **454** 500 f. multicoloured .. 3·75 1·90

**455** Map and Arms on Flag

**1990.** 30th Anniv of Independence.
1063 **455** 100 f. multicoloured .. 65 45

**456** Morel

**1990.** Fungi.
1064 **456** 100 f. multicoloured .. 1·10 55
1065 – 175 f. multicoloured .. 2·25 1·10
1066 – 300 f. multicoloured .. 3·25 2·25
1067 – 500 f. multicoloured .. 4·50 3·25
DESIGNS: 175 f. to 500 f. Various fungi.

**457** Flags of Member Countries

**458** Envelopes as World Map

**1990.** 30th Anniv of Organization of Petroleum Exporting Countries.
1068 **457** 200 f. multicoloured .. 1·40 80

**1990.** World Post Day
1069 **458** 175 f. blue, yell & blk 1·25 65

**459** Makokou Church

**1990.** Christmas.
1070 **459** 100 f. multicoloured .. 65 45

**460** Frangipani

**1991.** Flowers. Multicoloured.
1071 100 f. Type **460** .. .. 65 45
1072 175 f. Burning bush .. 1·10 65
1073 200 f. Flame tree .. 1·40 90
1074 300 f. Porcelain rose .. 1·90 1·40

**461** "Marseilles Harbour"

**1991.** Air. Death Cent of Johan Barthold Jongkind (artist).
1076 **461** 500 f. multicoloured .. 3·25 1·60

**462** Lizard

**463** Collecting Resin from Rubber Trees

**1991.** Prehistory. Petroglyphs. Multicoloured.
1077 100 f. Type **462** .. .. 70 45
1078 175 f. Triangular figure .. 1·10 65
1079 300 f. Abstract pattern .. 2·10 1·10
1080 500 f. Circles and chains 3·25 2·25

**1991.** Agriculture.
1082 **463** 100 f. multicoloured .. 65 45

**1991.** District Arms (5th series). As T **392**.
1083 100 f. silver, black & green 65 20
DESIGN: 100 f. Port-Gentil.

**464** Couple and Arrows

**465** Basket Weaving

**1991.** World Telecommunications Day.
1084 **464** 175 f. multicoloured .. 1·10 55

**1991.** Arts and Crafts. Multicoloured.
1085 100 f. Type **465** .. .. 65 45
1086 175 f. Stone carving .. 1·40 80
1087 200 f. Weaving .. .. 1·40 80
1088 500 f. Straw plaiting .. 3·25 1·90

**466** Women at Riverbank

**467** Knight

**1991.** Washerwomen of the Ngounie.
1089 **466** 100 f. multicoloured .. 65 45

**1991.** Order of the Equatorial Star. Mult.
1090 100 f. Type **467** .. .. 65 45
1091 175 f. Officer .. .. 1·10 65
1092 200 f. Commander .. 1·40 90

**468** Inspecting Fish Traps

**469** Post Box and Globe

**1991.** Fishing. Multicoloured.
1093 100 f. Type **468** .. .. 65 45
1094 175 f. Fishing from canoe 1·10 65
1095 200 f. Casting net .. 1·40 90
1096 300 f. Pulling in net .. 1·90 1·40

**1991.** World Post Day.
1098 **469** 175 f. blue, blk & red 1·10 45

**470** "Phalloid"

**471** Dibwangui Church

**1991.** Termitaries. Multicoloured.
1099 100 f. Type **470** .. .. 85 55
1100 175 f. "Cathedral" .. 1·40 85
1101 200 f. "Mushroom" .. 1·60 1·10
1102 300 f. "Treehouse" .. 2·25 1·60

**1991.** Christmas.
1103 **471** 100 f. multicoloured .. 65 45

**INDEX**
Countries can be quickly located by referring to the index at the end of this volume.

**472** Neolithic Ceramic Pot

**473** Stripping Wood

**1992.** Prehistory. Pottery. Multicoloured.
1104 100 f. Type **472** .. .. 65 45
1105 175 f. Ceramic bottle (8th century) .. .. 1·10 65
1106 200 f. Ceramic vase (late 8th century) .. .. 1·40 90
1107 300 f. Ceramic vase (early 8th century) .. .. 1·90 1·40

**1992.** Arts and Crafts. Multicoloured.
1109 100 f. Type **473** .. .. 65 45
1110 175 f. Metalwork .. 1·10 65
1111 200 f. Boat building .. 1·40 80
1112 300 f. Hairdressing .. 1·90 1·40

**474** Grand Officer of Order of Equatorial Star

**475** Konrad Adenauer

**1992.** Gabonese Honours. Multicoloured.
1114 100 f. Type **474** .. .. 65 45
1115 175 f. Grand Cross of Order of Equatorial Star .. .. .. 1·10 65
1116 200 f. Order of Merit .. 1·40 90

**1992.** 25th Death Anniv of Konrad Adenauer (German statesman).
1117 **475** 500 f. blk, stone & grn 3·25 2·25

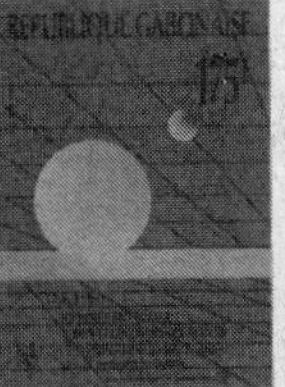

**476** Earth and Moon

**477** Small Striped Swallowtail

**1992.** World Telecommunications Day.
1118 **476** 175 f. multicoloured .. 1·10 45

**1992.** Butterflies. Multicoloured.
1119 100 f. Type **477** .. .. 65 45
1120 175 f. "Acraea egina" .. 1·10 65

**478** Fang Mask

**479** Cycling

**1992.** Gabonese Masks. Multicoloured.
1121 100 f. Type **478** .. .. 65 45
1122 175 f. Mpongwe mask .. 1·10 65
1123 200 f. Kwele mask .. 1·40 95
1124 300 f. Pounou mask .. 1·90 1·40

**1992.** Olympic Games, Barcelona. Mult.
1125 100 f. Type **479** .. .. 65 45
1126 175 f. Boxing .. .. 1·10 65
1127 200 f. Pole vaulting .. 1·40 90

**1992.** District Arms (6th series). As T **392**.
1128 100 f. silver, black & blue 65 20
DESIGN: 100 f. Medouneu.

**1992.** World Post Day. As No. 1098 but dated "1992".
1129 **469** 175 f. multicoloured .. 1·10 55

480 Columbus and Fleet

**1992.** Air. 500th Anniv of Discovery of America by Columbus.
1130 **480** 500 f. multicoloured .. 3·25 1·90

481 African Owl
482 Cattle

**1992.** Birds. Multicoloured.
1131 100 f. Type **481** .. .. 65 35
1132 175 f. Speckled mousebird 1·10 55
1133 200 f. Palm-nut vulture .. 1·40 80
1134 300 f. Giant kingfisher .. 1·90 1·10

**1992.** Beef Production.
1136 **482** 100 f. multicoloured .. 65 45
1137 – 175 f. multicoloured .. 1·10 65
1138 – 200 f. multicoloured .. 1·40 85
DESIGNS: 175, 200 f. Cattle (different).

483 Tchibanga Church

484 Emblems

**1992.** Christmas.
1139 **483** 100 f. multicoloured .. 65 35

**1992.** International Nutrition Conference, Rome.
1140 **484** 100 f. multicoloured .. 65 45

485 "Giant Hairy Melongena"

**1993.** Shells. Multicoloured.
1141 100 f. Type **485** .. .. 50 30
1142 175 f. Butterfly cone .. 85 60
1143 200 f. Carpat's spindle .. 1·00 70
1144 300 f. "Cymatium linatella" .. .. 1·50 1·10

486 Crowd with Banner outside Hospital

**1993.** World Leprosy Day.
1146 **486** 175 f. multicoloured .. 80 50

487 Fritz the Elephant

**1993.** Fernan-Vaz Mission.
1147 **487** 175 f. multicoloured .. 80 50

488 Claude Chappe

489 Schweitzer feeding Animals

**1993.** Bicentenary of Chappe's Optical Telegraph. Multicoloured.
1148 100 f. Type **488** .. .. 45 25
1149 175 f. Signals and table of signs .. .. .. 80 50
1150 200 f. Emile Baudot (inventor of five-unit code telegraph printing system) .. .. 90 55
1151 300 f. Satellite and fibre-optics .. .. .. 1·40 85

**1993.** 80th Anniv of First Visit of Albert Schweitzer (medical missionary) to Lambarene. Multicoloured.
1153 250 f. Type **489** .. .. 1·10 65
1154 250 f. Schweitzer holding babies .. .. .. 1·10 65
1155 500 f. Schweitzer (36×49 mm) .. .. 2·25 1·40

490 Copernicus (astronomer) and illustration from "De Revolutionibus"

491 Emblem

**1993.** "Polska'93" International Stamp Exhibition, Poznan.
1156 **490** 175 f. multicoloured .. 80 50

**1993.** World Telecommunications Day.
1157 **491** 175 f. multicoloured .. 80 50

492 Making Sugar-cane Wine

493 Lobster

**1993.** Traditional Wine-making. Mult.
1158 100 f. Type **492** .. .. 45 25
1159 175 f. Filling bottle with palm wine .. .. 80 50
1160 200 f. Gathering ingredients for palm wine .. 90 55

**1993.** Crustaceans. Multicoloured.
1162 100 f. Type **493** .. .. 45 25
1163 175 f. Crab .. .. 80 50
1164 200 f. Crayfish .. .. 90 55
1165 300 f. Sea spider .. .. 1·40 85

## MINIMUM PRICE

The minimum price quoted is 10p which represents a handling charge rather than a basis for valuing common stamps. For further notes about prices see introductory pages.

494 Magnifying Glass, Flowers, Stamp and Emblem

**1993.** 1st First European Stamp Salon, Flower Gardens, Paris.
1166 **494** 100 f. multicoloured .. 45 25

495 Squirrel Trap

496 Post Box and Globe

**1993.** Trapping. Multicoloured.
1167 100 f. Type **495** .. .. 45 25
1168 175 f. Small game trap .. 80 50
1169 200 f. Large game trap .. 90 55
1170 300 f. Palm squirrel trap 1·40 85

**1993.** World Post Day.
1171 **496** 175 f. multicoloured .. 80 50

497 Making Model Airplane

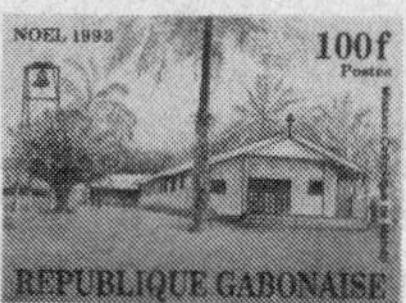

499 Mandji Catholic Mission

498 Leconi Canyon

**1993.** Bamboo Toys.
1172 **497** 100 f. multicoloured .. 45 25

**1993.** Tourism. Multicoloured.
1173 100 f. Type **498** .. .. 45 25
1174 175 f. La Lope tourist site 80 50

**1993.** Christmas.
1175 **499** 100 f. multicoloured .. 45 25

OFFICIAL STAMPS

O **119.** Map of Gabon River.

**1968.**
O 333. O **119.** 1 f. multicoloured .. 10 10
O 334. 2 f. multicoloured .. 10 10
O 335. 5 f. multicoloured .. 10 10
O 336. 10 f. multicoloured 15 10
O 337. – 25 f. multicoloured 35 15
O 338. – 30 f. multicoloured 40 20
O 339. – 50 f. multicoloured 55 20
O 340. – 85 f. multicoloured 1·10 40
O 341. – 100 f. multicoloured 1·40 55
O 342. – 200 f. multicoloured 2·50 1·10
DESIGNS: 25 f., 30 f. Gabon flag. 50 f. to 200 f. Gabon coat of arms.

O **165.** Gabon Flag.

**1971.** Flag in actual colours; inscription in blue; background as below.
O 436. O **165.** 5 f. blue .. .. 10 10
O 437. 10 f. grey .. 15 15
O 437a. 20 f. orange .. 15 10
O 437b. 25 f. yellow .. 20 15
O 438. 30 f. cobalt .. 30 10
O 439. 40 f. orange .. 55 30
O 440. 50 f. red .. .. 60 20
O 441. 60 f. brown .. 70 30
O 441a. 75 f. grey .. 55 15
O 442. 80 f. mauve .. 1·10 50
O 443. 100 f. mauve .. 80 30
O 444. 500 f. green .. 4·50 1·40

POSTAGE DUE STAMPS

**1928.** Postage Due type of French Colonies optd **GABON A. E. F.**
D 123. U. 5 c. blue .. .. 10 30
D 124. 10 c. brown .. .. 10 30
D 125. 20 c. olive .. .. 40 60
D 126. 25 c. red .. .. 15 60
D 127. 30 c. red .. .. 15 60
D 128. 45 c. green .. .. 45 90
D 129. 50 c. red .. .. 15 90
D 130. 60 c. brown .. .. 15 90
D 131. 1 f. purple .. .. 15 90
D 132. 2 f. red .. .. 25 1·00
D 133. 3 f. violet .. .. 40 2·00

D **19.** Local Chief.

D **24.** Pahquin Woman.

**1930.**
D134 D **19** 5 c. drab and blue 55 80
D135 10 c. brown and red 65 80
D136 20 c. brown & green 95 1·25
D137 25 c. brown and blue 90 1·40
D138 30 c. green & brown 90 1·40
D139 45 c. drab and green 1·25 1·90
D140 50 c. brown & mve 1·40 2·00
D141 60 c. black & violet 1·25 3·50
D142 – 1 f. black and brown 1·25 5·25
D143 – 2 f. brown & mauve 5·00 7·75
D144 – 3 f. brown and red 5·00 8·25
DESIGN—VERT. 1 f. to 3 f. Count Savorgnan de Brazza.

**1932.**
D 151. D **24.** 5 c. blue on blue .. 15 50
D 152. 10 c. brown .. 50 70
D 153. 20 c. brown .. 60 1·40
D 154. 25 c. green on blue 85 1·00
D 155. 30 c. red .. .. 1·25 2·00
D 156. 45 c. red on yellow 3·00 4·50
D 157. 50 c. purple .. 2·00 3·00
D 158. 60 c. blue .. .. 2·00 3·00
D 159. 1 f. blk. on orange 1·75 3·00
D 160. 2 f. green .. .. 6·25 7·00
D 161. 3 f. red .. .. 5·50 7·00

D **40.** Pineapple.

**1962.** Fruits.
D 196. 50 c. red, yell. and grn. 10 10
D 197. 50 c. red, yell. and grn. 10 10
D 198. 1 f. mauve, yell. & grn. 10 10
D 199. 1 f. mauve, yell. & grn. 10 10
D 200. 2 f. yell., brn. and grn. 10 10
D 201. 2 f. yell., brn. and grn. 10 10
D 202. 5 f. yell., grn. and brn. 30 30
D 203. 5 f. yell., grn. and brn. 30 30
D 204. 10 f. multicoloured .. 60 60
D 205. 10 f. multicoloured .. 60 60
D 206. 25 f. yell., grn. and pur. 80 80
D 207. 25 f. yell., grn. and pur. 80 80
FRUITS: No. D 196, Type D **40.** D 197, Mangoes D 198, Mandarin oranges. D 199, Avocado pears. D 200, Grapefruit. D 201, Coconuts D 202. Oranges. D 203, Papaws. D 204, Breadfruit. D 205, Guaves. D 206, Lemons D 207, Bananas.

D **256.** "Charaxes candiope".

**1978.** Butterflies. Multicoloured.
D 655. 5 f. Type D **256.** .. 10 10
D 656. 10 f. "Charaxes ameliae" 10 10
D 657. 25 f. "Cyrestis camillus" 30 15
D 658. 50 f. "Charaxes castor" 60 35
D 659. 100 f. "Pseudacrea boisduvali" .. .. 1·10 65

## GALAPAGOS ISLANDS Pt. 20

These islands, noted for their fauna and flora, were annexed by Ecuador, and later (1973) became a province of that country.

100 centavos = 1 sucre.

1. Californian Sealions.

DESIGNS—VERT. 50 c. Map of Ecuador coastline. HORIZ. 1 s. (No. 3) Iguana. 1 s. (No. 4) Santa Cruz Island. 1 s. 80, Map of Galapagos Is. 4 s. 20, Giant tortoise.

**1957.** Inscr. " ISLAS GALAPAGOS ".

1. 1. 20 c. brown (postage) .. 40 15
2. – 50 c. violet .. .. .. 40 15
3. – 1 s. green .. .. .. 1·25 45
4. – 1 s. blue (air) .. .. 30 15
5. – 1 s. 80 purple .. .. 65 30
6. – 4 s. 20 black .. .. 1·75 75

**1959.** Air. United Nations Commem. Triangular design as T **316** of Ecuador but insc. " ISLAS GALAPAGOS ".

7. 2 s. green .. .. .. 50 35

## GAZA Pt. 19

### EGYPTIAN OCCUPATION

A strip of territory along the coast from Gaza to the Egyptian frontier, seized by Egypt when the British Mandate for Palestine ended in May 1948.

In 1967 Israeli troops seized the Gaza Strip and from that date Israeli stamps were used.

In May 1994 the area became autonomous under the Palestinian National Authority.

1000 milliemes = £1 (Egyptian).

**1948.** Various stamps of Egypt optd **PALESTINE** in English and Arabic.

1 **91** 1 m. brown (postage) .. 40 55
2 2 m. red .. .. 40 55
3 **78** 3 m. brown .. .. 40 55
4 **91** 4 m. green .. .. 40 55
5 5 m. brown .. .. 40 60
6 **78** 6 m. green .. .. 55 60
7 **91** 10 m. violet .. .. 40 60
8 **78** 13 m. red .. .. 80 1·00
9 **91** 15 m. purple .. .. 50 60
10 17 m. green .. .. 60 65
11 20 m. violet .. .. 75 1·10
12 22 m. blue .. .. 80 1·10
13 – 30 m. green (No. 340) .. 80 1·10
14 **106** 40 m. brown .. .. 1·25 1·40
15 – 50 m. blue (No. 342) .. 1·75 1·75
16 – 100 m. purple (No. 280) 6·00 6·50
17 – 200 m. violet (No. 281) 12·00 14·00
18 **86** 50 p. brown and green 17·00 18·00
19 **87** £E1 brown and blue .. 30·00 32·00
20 **101** 2 m. red (air) .. .. 40 55
21 3 m. brown .. .. 40 55
22 5 m. red .. .. 40 45
23 7 m. brown .. .. 40 45
24 8 m. green .. .. 40 45
25 10 m. violet .. .. 40 45
26 20 m. blue .. .. 60 65
27 30 m. purple .. .. 80 85
28 40 m. red .. .. 1·40 1·50
29 50 m. blue .. .. 1·60 1·75
30 100 m. green .. .. 2·25 2·75
31 200 m. grey .. .. 18·00 22·00

**1953.** As above but with portrait obliterated by three horiz bars. (a) Postage.

32 **91** 1 m. brown .. .. 40 50
33 2 m. red .. .. 40 50
34 **78** 3 m. brown .. .. 40 50
35 **91** 4 m. green .. .. 40 50
36 5 m. brown .. .. 40 50
37 **78** 6 m. green .. .. 40 50
38 **91** 10 m. violet .. .. 40 60
39 **78** 13 m. red .. .. 80 95
40 **91** 15 m. purple .. .. 80 95
41 17 m. green .. .. 80 95
42 20 m. violet .. .. 80 95
43 22 m. blue .. .. 1·25 1·40
44 – 30 m. green .. .. 2·00 2·25
45 **106** 40 m. brown .. .. 2·75 3·00
46 – 50 m. blue .. .. 4·00 4·25
47 – 100 m. purple .. .. 8·00 10·00
48 – 200 m. violet .. .. 16·00 22·00
49 **86** 50 p. brown and green 32·00 38·00
50 **87** £E1 brown and blue .. 90·00 95·00

(b) Air.

51 **101** 2 m. red .. .. 1·75 2·10
52 3 m. brown .. .. 45 75
53 5 m. red .. .. 10·00 11·00
54 7 m. brown .. .. 65 90
55 8 m. green .. .. 1·75 1·90
56 10 m. violet .. .. 1·75 1·90
57 20 m. blue .. .. 1·75 1·90
58 30 m. purple .. .. 1·75 1·90
59 40 m. red .. .. 1·40 1·50
60 50 m. blue .. .. 14·00 15·00
61 100 m. green .. .. 55·00 60·00
62 200 m. grey .. .. 14·00 19·00

**1953.** Air. Nos. 480/2, 485 and 489/90 of Egypt optd **PALESTINE** in English and Arabic.

63 **101** 2 m. red .. .. 40 55
64 3 m. brown .. .. 8·75 10·00
65 5 m. red .. .. 60 65
66 10 m. violet .. .. 20·00 21·00
67 50 m. blue .. .. 4·00 4·50
68 100 m. olive .. .. 33·00 38·00

**1955.** Stamps of Egypt, 1953/4, optd **PALESTINE** in English and Arabic.

69. **137.** 1 m. brown (postage) .. 40 45
70. 2 m. purple .. .. 40 45
71. 3 m. blue .. .. 40 45
72. 4 m. green .. .. 40 45
73. 5 m. red .. .. 40 45
74. **130.** 10 m. sepia (B) .. 40 45
75. 15 m. grey .. .. 60 70
76. 17 m. turquoise .. 60 70
77. 20 m. violet .. .. 60 70
78. **131.** 30 m. green .. .. 1·00 1·10
79. 32 m. blue .. .. 1·00 1·10
80. 35 m. violet .. .. 1·00 1·10
81. 40 m. brown .. .. 1·75 1·90
82. 50 m. purple .. .. 2·00 2·10
83. **132.** 100 m. brown .. .. 5·00 5·25
84. 200 m. turquoise .. 11·00 11·50
85. 500 m. violet .. .. 40·00 40·00
86. £E1 red and green .. 70·00 70·00

**1955.** Air. Nos. 433/4 of Egypt optd **PALESTINE** in English and Arabic.

86a **133** 5 m. brown .. .. 4·00 5·25
86b 15 m. green .. .. 5·00 6·00

Types of Egypt (sometimes with colours changed) overprinted **PALESTINE** in English and Arabic.

**1957.** Re-occupation of Gaza Strip.

87. **152.** 10 m. green .. .. 3·00 3·25

**1958.** Stamps of 1957.

88. – 1 m. turq. (No. 538) .. 10 20
89. – 5 m. sepia (No. 541) .. 40 40
90. **160.** 10 m. violet .. .. 40 40

### UNITED ARAB REPUBLIC

**1958.** Stamps of 1958 (inscr. " U A R EGYPT ").

91. – 1 m. red (No. 553) .. 10 10
92. – 2 m. blue (No. 554) .. 10 10
93. **168.** 3 m. brown .. .. 15 15
94. – 4 m. green (No. 556) .. 15 15
95. – 5 m. sepia (No. 557) .. 20 20
96. **160.** 10 m. violet (No. 558) 20 20
96a. – 35 m. blue (No. 559) .. 2·75 1·75

**1958.** 5th Anniv. of Republic.

97. **172.** 10 m. brown .. .. 1·75 1·75

**1958.** 10th Anniv of Declaration of Human Rights.

98. **178.** 10 m. purple .. .. 2·00 3·25
99. 35 m. brown .. .. 5·00 5·50

**1959.** No. 588.

100 **132** 55 m. on 100 m. red .. 3·00 4·50

Types of Egypt with some colours changed and additionally inscribed " PALESTINE " in English and Arabic.

**1960.** As Nos. 603, etc.

101 **160** 1 m. orange .. .. 10 10
104 – 4 m. brown .. .. 10 10
105 – 5 m. violet .. .. 15 15
106 – 10 m. green .. .. 20 20

**1960.** World Refugee Year.

109. **205.** 10 m. brown .. .. 30 30
110. 35 m. black .. .. 1·50 1·25

**1961.** World Health Day.

111. **213.** 10 m. blue .. .. 1·00 1·00

**1961.** Palestine Day.

112. **215.** 10 m. violet .. .. 25 20

**1961.** U.N. Technical Co-operation Programme and 16th Anniv. of U.N.O.

113. – 10 m. blue & orange 50 30
114. **220.** 35 m. purple and red 80 50

**1961.** Education Day.

115. **223.** 10 m. brown .. .. 80 50

**1961.** Victory Day.

116. **224.** 10 m. brown & chest. 30 25

**1962.** 5th Anniv. of Egyptian Occupation of Gaza.

117. **229.** 10 m. brown .. .. 30 25

**1962.** Arab League Week.

118. **231.** 10 m. purple .. .. 30 25

**1962.** Malaria Eradication.

119 **235** 10 m. red and brown .. 25 25
120 – 35 m. yellow and black 1·00 75

**1962.** 17th Anniv of U.N.O. and Hammarskjold Commemoration.

121. **245.** 5 m. blue and pink .. 20 20
122. 10 m. blue and brown 35 30
123. 35 m. indigo and blue 1·00 80

**1963.** As No. 739.

124. 4 m. blue, orge. & blk. 20 20

**1963.** Freedom from Hunger.

125 **252** 5 m. brown and green 15 10
126 – 10 m. yellow and green 30 20
127 – 35 m. yellow & purple 1·25 80

**1963.** Centenary of Red Cross.

128. **253.** 10 m. red, purple & blue 50 30
129. – 35 m. ultra., blue & red 1·00 80

**1963.** U.N.E.S.C.O. Campaign for Preservation of Nubian Monuments (4th issue).

130. **256.** 5 m. yellow and purple 15 10
131. – 10 m. yellow and black 20 15
132. – 35 m. yellow and violet 1·00 80

**1963.** Air. As Nos. 758, 760 and 761/2.

133. 50 m. purple and blue .. 80 75
134. 80 m. indigo and blue .. 1·25 1·10
135. 115 m. yellow and black .. 2·00 1·75
136. 140 m. red and blue .. 2·50 2·25

**1963.** 15th Anniv of Declaration of Human Rights.

137. **259a.** 5 m. yellow and sepia 15 15
138. – 10 m. blk., grey & pur. 20 20
139. – 35 m. black, green and turquoise .. .. 80 80

**1964.** As No. 769, etc.

140 – 1 m. violet and green 10 10
141 – 2 m. blue and orange 10 10
142 – 3 m. blue, brown and light blue .. .. 10 10
143 – 4 m. green, brn & pink 15 10
144 – 5 m. red, blue and pink 15 10
145 – 10 m. red, brown & grn 20 15
146 – 15 m. yell, vio & lilac 20 15
147 – 20 m. green and violet 40 15
148 **261** 30 m. blue and orange 80 15
149 – 35 m. brn, grn & orge 60 30
150 – 40 m. blue and green 80 30
151 – 60 m. brown and blue 1·25 70
152 **263** 100 m. brown and blue 1·75 1·40

**1964.** Arab League Heads of State Congress, Cairo.

153. **266.** 10 m. black and olive .. 15 15

**1964.** Ramadan Festival.

154. **267.** 4 m. olive, red & lake .. 15 15

**1964.** 10th Anniv of Arab Postal Union's Permanent Office.

155 **271** 10 m. blue and green .. 15 10

**1964.** World Health Day.

156. **272.** 10 m. purple and red .. 15 10

**1965.** Ramadan Festival. As No. 834.

157. – 4 m. brown and green 30 15

**1965.** 20th Anniv. of Arab League.

158. **289.** 10 m. green and red .. 15 15
159. – 20 m. brown & green .. 20 20

**1965.** Air. World Meteorological Day.

160 **290** 80 m. orange and blue 2·00 1·50

**1965.** World Health Day.

161. **291.** 10 m. red and green .. 30 20

**1965.** Deir Yassin Massacre.

162. **292.** 10 m. red and blue .. 50 20

**1965.** Cent. of I.T.U.

163. **293.** 5 m. blue, yell. & grn. 30 15
164. 10 m. rose, blue and red 40 20
165. 35 m. blue, yellow and ultramarine .. 1·00 60

**1965.** Air. Re-establishment of Egyptian Civil Airlines "MISRAIR".

166 **295** 10 m. green and orange 40 30

**1966.** U.N. Day.

167. **321.** 5 m. violet and red .. 10 10
168. – 10 m. violet & brown .. 20 15
169. – 35 m. violet and green 60 30

**1966.** Victory Day.

170. **324.** 10 m. red and olive .. 15 10

**1967.** Arab Publicity Week.

171. **328.** 10 m. brown and blue 15 10

**1967.** Labour Day.

172. **331.** 10 m. sepia and olive .. 15 10

### EXPRESS LETTER STAMP

**1948.** Express Letter stamp of Egypt optd. **PALESTINE** in English and Arabic.

E 32. **E 52** 40 m. black & brown 7·00 7·50

### POSTAGE DUE STAMPS

**1948.** Postage Due stamps of Egypt optd. **PALESTINE** in English and Arabic.

D 32. **D 59.** 2 m. orange .. .. 1·25 1·40
D 33. 4 m. green .. .. 1·00 1·10
D 34. 6 m. green .. .. 1·00 1·10
D 35. 8 m. purple .. .. 1·00 1·10
D 36. 10 m. lake .. .. 1·00 1·10
D 37. 12 m. red .. .. 1·00 1·10
D 38. 30 m. violet .. .. 3·00 5·50

**This area was occupied by Israel on 6th June 1967. Post Offices were opened in July 1967 and Israeli stamps are now used.**



## GEORGIA Pt. 10

Formerly part of Russia, Georgia declared its independence after the Russian Revolution. In 1921 it became a Soviet Republic and in 1922 joined with Armenia and Azerbaijan to form the Transcaucasian Federation, whose stamps were used from September 1923. After absorption into the U.S.S.R. Russian stamps were used from 1924.

With the dissolution of the Soviet Union in 1991 Georgia again became an independent state.

100 kopeks = 1 rouble.

1\. St. George.

3\. Queen Tamara (A.D. 1184-1212).

**1919.** Imperf. or perf

10. **1.** 10 k. blue .. .. .. 10 55
11. 40 k. red .. .. .. 10 55
12. 50 k. green .. .. .. 10 55
13. 60 k. red .. .. .. 10 50
14. 70 k. purple .. .. .. 10 50
15. – 1 r. brown (20 × 25 mm.) 10 50
16. **3.** 2 r. brown .. .. .. 15 35
17a. 3 r. blue .. .. .. 10 50
18. 5 r. yellow .. .. .. 20 50

4\. Soldier.

6\. Industry and agriculture.

7\.

**1922.** Perf.

28a. **4.** 500 r. red .. .. .. 1·40 3·00
29. – 1000 r. brown (Sower) .. 2·00 2·50
30. **6.** 2000 r. grey .. .. 2·25 2·50
31. 3000 r. brown .. .. 2·25 2·50
32. 5000 r. green .. .. 2·25 2·50

**1922.** Famine Relief. Designs as T **7**. Surch.

33 – 100 r. on 50 r. violet .. 30 2·00
34 – 3000 r. on 100 r. red .. 30 2·00
35 – 5000 r. on 250 r. green .. 30 2·00
36 **7** 10,000 r. on 25 r. blue .. 30 3·00

**1923.** Surch.

37 – 10,000 r. on 1000 r. (No. 29) .. .. .. 1·50 70
38 **6** 15,000 r. on 2000 r. grey 1·60 85
44 **4** 20,000 r. on 500 r. red .. 45 75
40a **6** 40,000 r. on 5000 r. green 90 75
46 80,000 r. on 3000 r. brown 1·00 1·50

**1923.** Surch. (a) On Arms types of Russia.

47 **22** 10,000 r. on 7 k. blue .. 21·00 25·00
48 **10** 15,000 r. on 15 k. bl & brn 1·75 2·50

(b) On No. 75B of Armenia.

49 **10** 1,5000 r. on 5 r. on 15 k. blue and brown .. 16·00 18·00

**1923.** Arms types of Russia surch with hammer and sickle and value. Imperf or perf.

50 **22** 75,000 r. on 1 k. orange .. 2·75 3·75
52 20,0000 r. on 5 k. red .. 1·60 3·00
53 **14** 30,0000 r. on 20 k. red and blue .. .. .. 1·40 2·25
54 **22** 35,0000 r. on 3 k. red .. 2·50 3·50
57 700,000 r. on 2 k. green .. 3·00 4·00

12 Map, National Flag and U.N. Emblem

13 Arms and Flag

**1993.** 1st Anniv of Admission to U.N.O.

58 **12** 25 r. multicoloured .. 75 75
59 50 r. multicoloured .. 1·25 1·25
60 100 r. multicoloured .. 2·50 2·50

**1993.**

62 **13** 50 k. multicoloured .. 4·00 4·00

14 18th-century Fresco in Gold

15 "Apostle Simon" (icon)

**1993.** Treasures of the National Museum.

| | | | | |
|---|---|---|---|---|
| 63 | 14 | 50 k. multicoloured .. | 4·50 | 4·50 |

**1993.** Ancient Art.

| | | | | |
|---|---|---|---|---|
| 64 | 15 | 1 r. multicoloured .. | 4·50 | 4·50 |

16 "Three Women" (Lado Gudiashvili)

17 Mtskheta Church

**1993.** National Paintings.

| | | | | |
|---|---|---|---|---|
| 65 | 16 | 1 r. multicoloured .. | 4·50 | 4·50 |

**1993.** Places of Worship.

| | | | | |
|---|---|---|---|---|
| 66 | 17 | 30 r. blue .. .. | 55 | 55 |
| 67 | – | 40 r. brown .. .. | 75 | 75 |
| 68 | – | 50 r. brown .. .. | 95 | 95 |
| 69 | – | 60 r. red .. .. | 1·10 | 1·10 |
| 70 | – | 70 r. lilac .. .. | 1·40 | 1·40 |
| 71 | – | 80 r. green .. .. | 1·50 | 1·50 |
| 72 | – | 90 r. black .. .. | 1·75 | 1·75 |

DESIGNS: 40 r. Gelati Church; 50 r. Nikortsminda Church; 60 r. Ikorta Church; 70 r. Samtavisi church; 80 r. Bolnisi Zion Synagogue; 90 r. Gremi Citadel Church.

18 Emblem

19 Emblem

**1994.** 2nd Anniv of International Olympic Committee Recognition of Georgian National Olympic Committee.

| | | | | |
|---|---|---|---|---|
| 73 | 18 | 100 r. + 50 r. multicoloured | 40 | 40 |

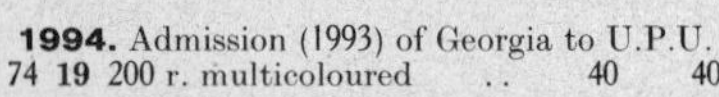

**1994.** Admission (1993) of Georgia to U.P.U.

| | | | | |
|---|---|---|---|---|
| 74 | 19 | 200 r. multicoloured .. | 40 | 40 |

20 Window and Nikoladze

**1994.** 150th Birth Anniv (1993) of Niko Nikoladze (journalist).

| | | | | |
|---|---|---|---|---|
| 75 | 20 | 150 r. multicoloured .. | 40 | 40 |

**1994.** Nos. 62/5 surch.

| | | | | |
|---|---|---|---|---|
| 76 | 13 | 5000 r. on 50 k. mult .. | 10 | 10 |
| 77 | 14 | 5000 r. on 50 k. mult .. | 10 | 10 |
| 78 | 15 | 10000 r. on 1 r. mult .. | 30 | 30 |
| 79 | 16 | 10000 r. on 1 r. mult .. | 30 | 30 |

22 Man wrestling Lion

24 Olympic Rings and Colours

**1994.** All-Georgian Congress.

| | | | | |
|---|---|---|---|---|
| 80 | 22 | 100 r. brown and pink | 50 | 50 |
| 81 | – | 200 r. deep blue & blue | 50 | 50 |

DESIGN: 200 r. Equestrian statue

**1994.** Nos. 63/5 surch **Georgia** and new value.

| | | | | |
|---|---|---|---|---|
| 82 | 14 | 200 r. on 50 k. mult .. | 50 | 50 |
| 83 | 15 | 300 r. on 1 r. mult .. | 75 | 75 |
| 84 | 16 | 500 r. on 1 r. mult .. | 1·25 | 1·25 |

**1995.** Centenary of International Olympic Committee. Multicoloured.

| | | | |
|---|---|---|---|
| 85 | 10 r. Type **24** (International Year of Sport) .. .. | 45 | 45 |
| 86 | 15 r. Emblem symbolising founding congress .. | 70 | 70 |
| 87 | 20 r. Anniversary emblem | 90 | 90 |
| 88 | 25 r. Olympic rings and peace dove ("Olympic Truce") .. .. .. .. | 1·25 | 1·25 |

## GERMAN COMMANDS Pt. 7

**EASTERN COMMAND.**

German occupation of Estonia, Latvia and Lithuania during the war of 1914-18.

100 pfennig = 1 mark.

**1916.** Stamps of Germany inscr "DEUTSCHES REICH" optd **Postgebiet Ob. Ost.**

| | | | | |
|---|---|---|---|---|
| 1. | 24. | 2½ pf. grey | 30 | 40 |
| 2. | 10. | 3 pf. brown | 25 | 25 |
| 3. | | 5 pf. green | 30 | 40 |
| 4. | 24. | 7½ pf. orange | 30 | 40 |
| 5. | 10. | 10 pf. red | 45 | 80 |
| 6. | 24. | 15 pf. brown | 4·50 | 3·00 |
| 7. | | 15 pf. violet | 25 | 35 |
| 8. | 10. | 20 pf. blue | 50 | 60 |
| 9. | | 25 pf. black & red on yell. | 30 | 50 |
| 10. | | 40 pf. black and red | 1·00 | 2·75 |
| 11. | | 50 pf. black & pur. on buff | 1·00 | 1·25 |
| 12a. | 12. | 1 m. red | 10·00 | 3·25 |

**WESTERN COMMAND.**

For Forces in Belgium and Northern France.

100 centimes = 1 franc.

**1916.** Stamps of Germany surch with new values as **2 Cent. 1 F.** or **1 F. 25 Cent.**

| | | | | |
|---|---|---|---|---|
| 1 | 10 | 3 c. on 3 pf. brown | 25 | 50 |
| 2 | | 5 c. on 5 pf. green | 25 | 55 |
| 3 | 24 | 8 c. on 7½ pf. orange | 40 | 80 |
| 4 | 10 | 10 c. on 10 pf. red | 1·25 | 3·00 |
| 5 | 24 | 15 c. on 15 pf. brown | 25 | 45 |
| 6 | 10 | 25 c. on 20 pf. blue | 85 | 2·00 |
| 7 | | 40 c. on 30 pf. black and orange on buff | 70 | 1·40 |
| 8 | | 50 c. on 40 pf. blk & red | 1·00 | 2·00 |
| 9 | | 75 c. on 60 pf. purple | 3·25 | 6·50 |
| 10 | | 1 f. on 80 pf. black and red on red | 4·00 | 7·50 |
| 11a | 12 | 1 f. 25 on 1 m. red | 18·00 | 18·00 |
| 12 | 13 | 2 f. 50 on 2 m. blue | 18·00 | 16·00 |

## GERMAN EAST AFRICA Pt. 7

A German colony on the east coast of Africa. Placed under British mandate after the First World War.

1893. 64 pesa = 1 rupee.
1905. 100 heller = 1 rupee.

**1893.** Stamps of Germany surch. with value in "PESA".

| | | | | |
|---|---|---|---|---|
| 1. | 8. | 2 p. on 3 pf. brown | 42·00 | 65·00 |
| 2. | | 3 p. on 5 pf. green | 55·00 | 65·00 |
| 4. | 9. | 5 p. on 10 pf. red | 30·00 | 17·00 |
| 5. | | 10 p. on 20 pf. blue | 23·00 | 14·00 |
| 6. | | 25 p. on 50 pf. brown | 40·00 | 35·00 |

**1896.** Stamps of Germany surch. **Deutsch-Ostafrika** and value in "PESA".

| | | | | |
|---|---|---|---|---|
| 7. | 8. | 2 p. on 3 pf. brown | 1·60 | 6·50 |
| 10. | | 3 p. on 5 pf. green | 2·25 | 4·50 |
| 11. | 9. | 5 p. on 10 pf. red | 2·25 | 4·50 |
| 13. | | 10 p. on 20 pf. blue | 5·50 | 6·00 |
| 14. | | 25 p. on 50 pf. brown | 22·00 | 32·00 |

**1901.** "Yacht" key-type inscr "DEUTSCH-OSTAFRIKA". Currency in pesa and rupees.

| | | | | |
|---|---|---|---|---|
| 15 | N | 2 p. brown | 3·00 | 2·25 |
| 16 | | 3 p. green | 3·00 | 2·25 |
| 17 | | 5 p. red | 3·25 | 3·00 |
| 18 | | 10 p. blue | 4·75 | 5·50 |
| 19 | | 15 p. black & orge. on buff | 4·75 | 7·00 |
| 20 | | 20 p. black and red | 7·50 | 18·00 |
| 21 | | 25 p. black & pur. on buff | 7·50 | 18·00 |
| 22 | | 40 p. black & red on rose | 8·00 | 26·00 |
| 23 | O | 1 r. red | 23·00 | 65·00 |
| 24 | | 2 r. green | 11·00 | £120 |
| 44 | | 3 r. black and red | 40·00 | £225 |

**1905.** "Yacht" key-types inscr. "DEUTSCH-OSTAFRIKA". Currency in heller.

| | | | | |
|---|---|---|---|---|
| 34 | N | 2½ h. brown | 90 | 80 |
| 35 | | 4 h. green | 90 | 60 |
| 36 | | 7½ h. red | 1·00 | 50 |
| 37 | | 15 h. blue | 2·25 | 1·00 |
| 38 | | 20 h. blk. & red on yellow | 2·75 | 14·00 |
| 39 | | 30 h. black and red | 2·75 | 8·00 |
| 32a | | 45 h. black and mauve | 15·00 | 32·00 |
| 33 | | 60 h. black & red on rose | 20·00 | £110 |

For stamps issued for this territory under British auspices since 1915 see under Tanganyika in Volume 3.

## GERMAN NEW GUINEA Pt. 7

A German Colony, part of the island of New Guinea.

100 pfennig = 1 mark.

**1898.** Stamps of Germany optd. **Deutsch-New-Guinea.**

| | | | | |
|---|---|---|---|---|
| 1a. | 8. | 3 pf. brown | 7·00 | 11·00 |
| 2. | | 5 pf. green | 3·00 | 5·00 |
| 3. | 9. | 10 pf. red | 6·00 | 8·50 |
| 4. | | 20 pf. blue | 9·00 | 13·00 |
| 5. | | 25 pf. orange | 32·00 | 60·00 |
| 6. | | 50 pf. brown | 32·00 | 50·00 |

**1901.** "Yacht" key-types inscr "DEUTSCH-NEU-GUINEA".

| | | | | |
|---|---|---|---|---|
| 7 | N | 3 pf. brown | 1·00 | 1·10 |
| 8 | | 5 pf. green | 9·00 | 1·10 |
| 9 | | 10 pf. red | 35·00 | 1·75 |
| 10 | | 20 pf. blue | 1·00 | 2·25 |
| 11 | | 25 pf. blk. & red on yell. | 1·00 | 15·00 |
| 12 | | 30 pf. blk. & orge. on buff | 1·00 | 22·00 |
| 13 | | 40 pf. black and red | 1·00 | 26·00 |
| 14 | N | 50 pf. blk. & pur. on buff | 1·75 | 22·00 |
| 15 | | 80 pf. black & red on rose | 3·25 | 30·00 |
| 16 | O | 1 m. red | 3·50 | 60·00 |
| 17 | | 2 m. blue | 5·00 | 85·00 |
| 18 | | 3 m. black | 7·50 | £190 |
| 19 | | 5 m. red and black | £130 | £500 |

Australian forces occupied German New Guinea in 1914 and it was administered as a League of Nations mandate from 1920. For stamps issued since 1914 see under New Guinea in Volume 3.

## GERMAN OCCUPATION OF ALSACE Pt. 7

100 pfennig = 1 mark.

**1940.** Stamps of Germany optd. **Elsass.**

| | | | | |
|---|---|---|---|---|
| 1. | 94. | 3 pf. brown | 20 | 40 |
| 2. | | 4 pf. slate | 30 | 1·00 |
| 3. | | 5 pf. green | 20 | 45 |
| 4. | | 6 pf. green | 20 | 45 |
| 5. | | 8 pf. orange | 20 | 45 |
| 6. | | 10 pf. brown | 25 | 70 |
| 7. | | 12 pf. red | 25 | 60 |
| 8. | | 15 pf. red | 35 | 90 |
| 9. | | 20 pf. blue | 35 | 90 |
| 10. | | 25 pf. blue | 40 | 1·25 |
| 11. | | 30 pf. olive | 90 | 1·40 |
| 12. | | 40 pf. mauve | 90 | 1·40 |
| 13. | | 50 pf. black and green | 1·40 | 2·00 |
| 14. | | 60 pf. black and red | 1·50 | 3·00 |
| 15. | | 80 pf. black and blue | 1·75 | 4·25 |
| 16. | | 100 pf. black and yellow | 3·00 | 3·25 |

## GERMAN OCCUPATION OF BELGIUM Pt. 4

German occupation of E. Belgium during the war of 1914-18.

100 centimes = 1 franc.

Stamps of Germany inscr. "DEUTSCHES REICH" surcharged.

**1914.** Surch **Belgien** and value thus: **3 Centimes**, or **1 Franc** or **1 Fr. 25 C.**

| | | | | |
|---|---|---|---|---|
| 1. | 10. | 3 c. on 3 pf. brown | 25 | 30 |
| 2. | | 5 c. on 5 pf. green | 25 | 30 |
| 3. | | 10 c. on 10 pf. red | 50 | 30 |
| 4. | | 25 c. on 20 pf. blue | 60 | 35 |
| 5. | | 50 c. on 40 pf. black & red | 2·00 | 1·25 |
| 6. | | 75 c. on 60 pf. purple | 1·00 | 1·10 |
| 7. | | 1 f. on 80 pf. black and red on rose | 2·25 | 2·00 |
| 8. | 12. | 1 f. 25 on 1 m. red | 17·00 | 15·00 |
| 9. | 13. | 2 f. 50 on 2 m. blue | 16·00 | 17·00 |

**1916.** Surch. **Belgien** and value, thus: **2 Cent., 1 F. or 1 F. 25 Cent.**

| | | | | |
|---|---|---|---|---|
| 10 | 24 | 2 c. on 2 pf. grey | 15 | 30 |
| 11 | 10 | 3 c. on 3 pf. brown | 15 | 20 |
| 12 | | 5 c. on 5 pf. green | 25 | 30 |
| 13 | 24 | 8 c. on 7½ pf. orange | 40 | 50 |
| 14 | 10 | 10 c. on 10 pf. red | 25 | 40 |
| 15 | 24 | 15 c. on 15 pf. brown | 25 | 30 |
| 16 | | 15 c. on 15 pf. violet | 20 | 40 |
| 17 | 10 | 20 c. on 25 pf. black and red on yellow | 15 | 25 |
| 18 | | 25 c. on 20 pf. blue | 15 | 25 |
| 19 | | 40 c. on 30 pf. black and orange on buff | 15 | 20 |
| 20 | | 50 c. on 40 pf. blk. & red | 30 | 35 |
| 21 | | 75 c. on 60 pf. mauve | 1·40 | 1·40 |
| 22 | | 1 f. on 80 f. black and red on rose | 1·40 | 4·50 |
| 23a | 12 | 1 f. 25 on 1 m. red | 2·75 | 2·50 |
| 24 | 13 | 2 f. 50 on 2 m. blue | 25·00 | 25·00 |
| 25 | 15 | 6 f. 25 on 5 m. red & black | 26·00 | 30·00 |

## GERMAN OCCUPATION OF DALMATIA Pt. 3

Areas formerly under Italian control which were occupied by the Germans in 1943.

### A. ZARA (Zadar)

100 centesimi = 1 lira

**1943.** Imperial series of Italy, 1929, optd **Deutsche Besetzung Zara.**

| | | | | |
|---|---|---|---|---|
| 1 | 98 | 5 c. brown | 25·00 | 60·00 |
| 2 | – | 10 c. brown | 2·00 | 3·75 |
| 3 | – | 15 c. green | 3·25 | 7·50 |
| 4 | 99 | 20 c. red | 2·00 | 5·00 |
| 5 | – | 25 c. green | 2·00 | 5·00 |
| 6 | 103 | 30 c. brown | 2·00 | 5·00 |
| 7 | – | 35 c. blue | 80·00 | £200 |
| 8 | – | 75 c. red | 5·00 | 15·00 |
| 9 | 99 | 1 l. violet | 2·00 | 5·00 |
| 10 | – | 1 l. 25 blue | 3·25 | 8·50 |
| 11 | – | 1 l. 75 red | 9·00 | 24·00 |
| 12 | – | 2 l. red | 18·00 | 40·00 |
| 13 | 98 | 2 l. 55 green | £110 | £200 |
| 14 | – | 3 l. 70 violet | £800 | £1500 |
| 15 | – | 5 l. red | 20·00 | 40·00 |
| 16 | – | 10 l. violet | £250 | £425 |
| 17 | 99 | 20 l. green | £3000 | £5000 |
| 18 | – | 25 l. black | £9000 | £13000 |
| 19 | – | 50 l. violet | £5500 | £8500 |

**1943.** War Propaganda stamps of Italy (Nos. 571/4) optd **Deutsche Besetzung Zara** on stamp and label.

| | | | | |
|---|---|---|---|---|
| 20 | 103 | 50 c. violet (Navy) | 2·75 | 8·00 |
| 21 | | 50 c. violet (Army) | 2·75 | 8·00 |
| 22 | | 50 c. violet (Air Force) | 2·75 | 8·00 |
| 23 | | 50 c. violet (Militia) | 2·75 | 8·00 |

**1943.** Air. Nos. 270/7 of Italy optd **Deutsche Besetzung Zara.**

| | | | | |
|---|---|---|---|---|
| 26 | – | 25 c. green | 3·00 | 7·50 |
| 27 | 110 | 50 c. brown | 3·00 | 7·50 |
| 28 | – | 75 c. brown | £110 | £225 |
| 29 | – | 80 c. red | 14·00 | 30·00 |
| 30 | – | 1 l. violet | 3·00 | 7·50 |
| 31 | 113 | 2 l. blue | 10·00 | 18·00 |
| 32 | 110 | 5 l. green | £1500 | £2500 |
| 33 | | 10 l. red | £5500 | £8500 |

**1943.** Imperial series of Italy, 1929, optd **ZARA.**

| | | | | |
|---|---|---|---|---|
| 46 | 103 | 50 c. violet | 1·75 | 5·00 |
| 47 | – | 75 c. red | 1·75 | 5·00 |
| 48 | – | 1 l. 25 blue | 17·00 | 40·00 |

**1943.** War Propaganda stamps of Italy (Nos. 563/70) optd **ZARA ZARA.**

| | | | | |
|---|---|---|---|---|
| 49 | – | 25 c. green (Navy) | 2·50 | 7·00 |
| 50 | – | 25 c. green (Army) | 2·50 | 7·00 |
| 51 | – | 25 c. green (Air Force) | 2·50 | 7·00 |
| 52 | – | 25 c. green (Militia) | 2·50 | 7·00 |
| 53 | 103 | 30 c. brown (Navy) | 2·50 | 7·00 |
| 54 | | 30 c. brown (Army) | 2·50 | 7·00 |
| 55 | | 30 c. brown (Air Force) | 2·50 | 7·00 |
| 56 | | 30 c. brown (Militia) | 2·50 | 7·00 |

EXPRESS LETTER STAMPS

**1943.** Nos. E350/1 of Italy optd **Deutsche Besetzung Zara.**

| | | | | |
|---|---|---|---|---|
| E24 | E 132 | 1 l. 25 green | 2·75 | 8·00 |
| E25 | | 2 l. 50 orange | 25·00 | 50·00 |

**1943.** Air. No. E370 of Italy optd **Deutsche Besetzung Zara.**

| | | | | |
|---|---|---|---|---|
| E34 | E 133 | 2 l. black | 10·00 | 22·00 |

**1943.** Nos. E350/1 of Italy optd **ZARA.**

| | | | | |
|---|---|---|---|---|
| E57 | E 132 | 1 l. 25 green | 4·00 | 11·00 |
| E58 | | 2 l. 50 orange | 30·00 | 60·00 |

POSTAGE DUE STAMPS

**1943.** Italian Postage Due stamps optd **Deutsche Besetzung Zara.**

| | | | | |
|---|---|---|---|---|
| D35 | D 141 | 5 c. brown | 8·50 | 20·00 |
| D36 | | 10 c. blue | 8·50 | 20·00 |
| D37 | | 20 c. red | 8·50 | 20·00 |
| D38 | | 25 c. green | £160 | £350 |
| D39 | | 30 c. red | 8·50 | 20·00 |
| D40 | | 40 c. brown | 8·50 | 20·00 |
| D41 | | 50 c. violet | 8·50 | 20·00 |
| D42 | | 60 c. blue | £160 | £350 |
| D43 | D 142 | 1 l. orange | £160 | £350 |
| D44 | | 2 l. green | £200 | £400 |
| D45 | | 5 l. violet | £160 | £350 |

### B. GULF OF KOTOR

Italian and German currency

**1944.** Imperial series of Italy, 1929, surch **Deutsche Militar- verwaltung Kotor** and new value in lire.

| | | | | |
|---|---|---|---|---|
| 1 | – | 0.50 LIT. on 10 c. brown | 24·00 | 35·00 |
| 2 | – | 1 LIT. on 25 c. green | 24·00 | 35·00 |
| 3 | 103 | 1.50 LIT. on 50 c. violet | 24·00 | 35·00 |
| 4 | | 3 LIT. on 30 c. brown | 24·00 | 35·00 |
| 5 | 99 | 4 LIT. on 20 c. red | 24·00 | 35·00 |
| 6 | | 10 LIT. on 20 c. red | 24·00 | 35·00 |

**1944.** Nos. 419/20 of Yugoslavia (King Peter II) surch **Boka Kotorska** and new value in marks.

| | | | | |
|---|---|---|---|---|
| 7 | 99 | 0,10 R.M. on 3 d. brown | 1·50 | 3·25 |
| 8 | | 0,15 R.M. on 3 d. brown | 1·50 | 3·25 |
| 9 | | 0,25 R.M. on 4 d. blue | 3·25 | 5·00 |
| 10 | | 0,50 R.M. on 4 d. blue | 3·75 | 8·50 |

## GERMAN OCCUPATION OF ESTONIA Pt. 10

100 kopeks = 1 rouble.

1.

2. "Long Hermann" Tower, Reval (Tallinn).

**1941.** Tartu issue.

| | | | | |
|---|---|---|---|---|
| 3. | 1. | 15 (k.) brown | 7·50 | 10·00 |
| 4. | | 20 (k.) green | 7·50 | 10·00 |
| 5. | | 30 (k.) blue | 7·50 | 10·00 |

Originally issued for local use, the above were made available for use throughout Estonia from 29.9.41 to 30.4.42. However, not many were used since the German **OSTLAND** stamps were used from 1 December 1941.

**1941.** Reconstruction Fund.

| | | | | |
|---|---|---|---|---|
| 6. | 2. | 15+15 (k.) sepia & brown | 15 | 3·00 |
| 7. | – | 20+20 (k.) purple & brown | 15 | 3·00 |
| 8. | – | 30+30 (k.) blue & brown | 15 | 3·00 |
| 9. | – | 50+50 (k.) green and brown | 20 | 5·00 |
| 10. | – | 60+60 (k.) red and brown | 30 | 5·00 |
| 11. | – | 100+100 (k.) slate & brown | 55 | 5·00 |

DESIGNS—HORIZ. 20 k. Stone Bridge, Tartu. 30 k. Narva Castle. 50 k. View of Tallinn. VERT. 60 k. Tartu University. 100 k. Narva Castle.

German stamps optd **OSTLAND** (see German Occupation of Russia, Nos. 1/20) were used from 1 December 1941 until the Russian re-occupation of Estonia in 1944. Since then Russian stamps have been in use.

## GERMAN OCCUPATION OF LATVIA Pt. 10

100 kopeks = 1 rouble.

**1941.** Russian stamps of 1936-39 optd **LATVIJA 1941. 1. VII.**

| | | | |
|---|---|---|---|
| 1 | 5 k. red (No. 847a) | 50 | 3·00 |
| 2 | 10 k. blue (No. 727f) | 50 | 3·00 |
| 3 | 15 k. green (No. 847c) | 15·00 | 60·00 |
| 4 | 20 k. green (No 727h) | 50 | 3·00 |
| 5 | 30 k. blue (No. 847d) | 50 | 3·00 |
| 6 | 50 k. brown on buff (No. 727m) | 1·00 | 7·50 |

German stamps optd **OSTLAND** (see German Occupation of Russia Nos. 1/20) were used from 4th November, 1941, until the Russian re-occupation of Latvia in 1944-45. Since then Russian stamps have been in use.

## GERMAN OCCUPATION OF LITHUANIA Pt. 10

100 kopeks = 1 rouble.

**1941.** Russian stamps of 1936-40 optd. **NEPRIKLAUSOMA LIETUVA 1941-V1-23.**

| | | | |
|---|---|---|---|
| 1 | 2 k. green (No. 542) | 22·00 | £125 |
| 2 | 5 k. red (No. 847a) | 60 | 10·00 |
| 3 | 10 k. blue (No. 727f) | 60 | 10·00 |
| 4 | 15 k. green (No. 847c) | 60 | 10·00 |
| 5 | 20 k. green (No. 727h) | 60 | 10·00 |
| 6 | 30 k. blue (No. 847d) | 60 | 10·00 |
| 7 | 50 k. brown on buff (No. 727m) | 1·50 | 16·00 |
| 8 | 60 k. red (No. 847f) | 4·00 | 30·00 |
| 9 | 80 k. blue (No. 905) | 9·00 | 40·00 |

**1941.** Issue for Vilnius and South Lithuania. Russian stamps of 1936-39 optd **VILNIUS.**

| | | | |
|---|---|---|---|
| 10 | 5 k. red (No. 847a) | 1·10 | 3·00 |
| 11 | 10 k. blue (No. 727f) | 1·10 | 3·00 |
| 12 | 15 k. green (No. 847c) | 1·10 | 3·00 |
| 13 | 20 k. green (No. 727h) | 4·00 | 11·00 |
| 14 | 30 k. blue (No. 847d) | 2·25 | 7·00 |
| 15 | 50 k. brown on buff (No. 727m) | 3·25 | 7·00 |
| 16 | 60 k. red (No. 847f) | 4·00 | 8·50 |
| 17 | 80 k. red and deep red (No. 772) | £150 | £225 |
| 18 | 1 r. black and red (No. 779) | £475 | £650 |

German stamps optd. OSTLAND (see German Occupation of Russia Nos. 1/20) were used from 4th November, 1941, till the Russian re-occupation of Lithuania in 1944. Since then Russian stamps have been in use.

## GERMAN OCCUPATION OF LORRAINE Pt. 7

100 pfennig = 1 mark.

**1940.** Stamps of Germany optd. **Lothringen.**

| | | | | |
|---|---|---|---|---|
| 1. | 94. | 3 pf. brown | 30 | 75 |
| 2. | | 4 pf. slate | 35 | 75 |
| 3. | | 5 pf. green | 35 | 75 |
| 4. | | 6 pf. green | 35 | 35 |
| 5. | | 8 pf. orange | 35 | 75 |
| 6. | | 10 pf. brown | 35 | 50 |
| 7. | | 12 pf. red | 40 | 50 |
| 8. | | 15 pf. lake | 50 | 90 |
| 9. | | 20 pf. blue | 50 | 1·10 |
| 10. | | 25 pf. blue | 60 | 1·10 |
| 11. | | 30 pf. olive | 75 | 1·25 |
| 12. | | 40 pf. mauve | 75 | 1·25 |
| 13. | | 50 pf. black and green | 1·25 | 2·25 |
| 14. | | 60 pf. black and red | 1·25 | 2·75 |
| 15. | | 80 pf. black and blue | 1·60 | 3·25 |
| 16. | | 100 pf. black and yellow | 2·00 | 5·50 |

## GERMAN OCCUPATION OF POLAND Pt. 5

German occupation of Poland, 1915-1918.

100 pfennig = 1 mark.

**1915.** Stamps of Germany inscr. "DEUTSCHES REICH" optd. **Russisch-Polen.**

| | | | | |
|---|---|---|---|---|
| 1. | 10. | 3 pf. brown | 60 | 30 |
| 2. | | 5 pf. green | 75 | 35 |
| 3. | | 10 pf. red | 75 | 35 |
| 4. | | 20 pf. blue | 1·10 | 50 |
| 5. | | 40 pf. black and red | 6·00 | 2·50 |

**1916.** Stamps of Germany inscr. "DEUTSCHES REICH" optd. **Gen.-Gouv. Warschau.**

| No. | Description | | |
|---|---|---|---|
| 6. 24. | 2½ pf. grey | 25 | 30 |
| 7. 10. | 3 pf. brown | 70 | 1·00 |
| 8. | 5 pf. green | 70 | 70 |
| 9. 24. | 7½ pf. orange | 40 | 25 |
| 10. 10. | 10 pf. red | 55 | 50 |
| 11. 24. | 15 pf. brown | 2·50 | 2·50 |
| 12. | 15 pf. violet | 35 | 90 |
| 13. 10. | 20 pf. blue | 1·00 | 90 |
| 14. | 30 pf. blk. & orge. on buff | 3·75 | 4·00 |
| 15. | 40 pf. black and red | 1·40 | 30 |
| 16. | 60 pf. purple | 2·00 | 2·00 |

## GERMAN OCCUPATION OF RUMANIA — Pt. 3

German occupation of Rumania, 1917-1918.

100 bani = 1 leu.

Stamps of Germany inscr. "DEUTSCHES REICH".

**1917.** Surch. **M.V.i.R.** in frame and value in "bani".

| No. | Description | | |
|---|---|---|---|
| 1 24 | 15 b. on 15 pf. violet | 70 | 1·00 |
| 2 10 | 25 b. on 20 pf. blue | 70 | 1·00 |
| 3a | 40 b. on 30 pf. black and orange on buff | 15·00 | 28·00 |

**1917.** Surch. **M.V.i.R.** (not in frame) and value in "bani".

| No. | Description | | |
|---|---|---|---|
| 4. 10. | 10 b. on 10 pf. red | 1·00 | 1·25 |
| 5. 24. | 15 b. on 15 pf. violet | 3·00 | 5·50 |
| 6. 10. | 25 b. on 20 pf. blue | 1·00 | 1·25 |
| 7. | 40 b. on 30 pf. black and orange on buff | 1·25 | 1·10 |

**1918.** Surch. **Rumanien** and value in "bani".

| No. | Description | | |
|---|---|---|---|
| 8. 10. | 5 b. on 5 pf. green | 25 | 30 |
| 9 | 10 b. on 10 pf. red | 25 | 40 |
| 10. 24. | 15 b. on 15 pf. violet | 10 | 15 |
| 11. 10. | 25 b. on 20 pf. blue | 50 | 1·00 |
| 12. | 40 b. on 30 pf. black and orange on buff | 30 | 30 |

**1918.** Stamps of Germany inscr. "DEUTSCHES REICH" optd. **Gultig 9 Armee** in frame.

| No. | Description | | |
|---|---|---|---|
| 13. 10. | 10 pf. red | 9·00 | 20·00 |
| 14 24. | 15 pf. violet | 16·00 | 28·00 |
| 15 10. | 20 pf. blue | 1·25 | 2·00 |
| 16. | 30 pf. blk. & orge. on buff | 12·00 | 22·00 |

POSTAGE DUE STAMPS

**1918.** Postage Due stamps of Rumania optd. **M.V.i.R.** in frame.

| No. | Description | | |
|---|---|---|---|
| D 1. D 38. | 5 b. blue on green | 7·50 | 7·50 |
| D 2. | 10 b. blue on green | 7·50 | 7·50 |
| D 3. | 20 b. blue on green | 6·00 | 6·00 |
| D 4. | 30 b. blue on green | 6·00 | 6·00 |
| D 5. | 50 b. blue on green | 6·00 | 6·00 |

## GERMAN OCCUPATION OF RUSSIA — Pt. 10

100 pfennig = 1 reichsmark.

**1941.** Issue for Ostland. Stamps of Germany of 1941 optd. **OSTLAND.**

| No. | Description | | |
|---|---|---|---|
| 1. 173. | 1 pf. grey | 10 | 15 |
| 2. | 3 pf. brown | 10 | 15 |
| 3. | 4 pf. slate | 10 | 15 |
| 4. | 5 pf. green | 10 | 15 |
| 5. | 6 pf. violet | 10 | 15 |
| 6. | 8 pf. red | 10 | 15 |
| 7. | 10 pf. brown | 60 | 1·25 |
| 9. | 12 pf. red | 60 | 1·25 |
| 11. | 15 pf. lake | 10 | 15 |
| 12. | 16 pf. green | 10 | 25 |
| 13. | 20 pf. blue | 10 | 15 |
| 14. | 24 pf. brown | 10 | 25 |
| 15. | 25 pf. blue | 10 | 15 |
| 16. | 30 pf. olive | 10 | 15 |
| 17. | 40 pf. mauve | 10 | 20 |
| 18. | 50 pf. green | 10 | 20 |
| 19. | 60 pf. brown | 10 | 20 |
| 20. | 80 pf. blue | 10 | 45 |

**1941.** Issue for Ukraine. Stamps of Germany of 1941 optd. **UKRAINE.**

| No. | Description | | |
|---|---|---|---|
| 21. 173. | 1 pf. grey | 10 | 15 |
| 22. | 3 pf. brown | 10 | 15 |
| 23. | 4 pf. slate | 10 | 15 |
| 24. | 5 pf. green | 10 | 15 |
| 25. | 6 pf. violet | 10 | 15 |
| 26. | 8 pf. red | 10 | 15 |
| 27. | 10 pf. brown | 50 | 1·60 |
| 29. | 12 pf. red | 50 | 1·60 |
| 31. | 15 pf. lake | 10 | 15 |
| 32. | 16 pf. green | 10 | 20 |
| 33. | 20 pf. blue | 10 | 15 |
| 34. | 24 pf. brown | 10 | 20 |
| 35. | 25 pf. blue | 10 | 15 |
| 36. | 30 pf. olive | 10 | 15 |
| 37. | 40 pf. mauve | 10 | 20 |
| 38. | 50 pf. green | 10 | 15 |
| 39. | 60 pf. brown | 10 | 20 |
| 40. | 80 pf. blue | 10 | 25 |

## GERMAN OCC. OF ZANTE — Pt. 3

German occupation of Ionian Islands, 1943-44.

100 centesimi = 1 lira = 8 drachma.

ΕΛΛΑΣ
2-X-43

(1.)

**1943.** Stamps of Italian Occupation of Ionian Islands further optd. with T **1.**

| No. | Description | | |
|---|---|---|---|
| 1. – | 25 c. green (postage) | 15·00 | 50·00 |
| 2. 103. | 50 c. violet | 15·00 | 50·00 |
| 3. 110. | 50 c. brown (air) | 50·00 | £160 |

## GERMAN POST OFFICES IN CHINA — Pt. 7

German post offices in China, now closed.

1898. 100 pfennig = 1 mark.
1905. 100 cents = 1 dollar.

**1898.** Stamps of Germany optd. **China.**

| No. | Description | | |
|---|---|---|---|
| 7. 8. | 3 pf. brown | 6·00 | 6·00 |
| 8. | 5 pf. green | 3·50 | 3·00 |
| 9. 9. | 10 pf. red | 8·00 | 7·50 |
| 4. | 20 pf. blue | 18·00 | 10·00 |
| 11. | 25 pf. orange | 35·00 | 32·00 |
| 12. | 50 pf. brown | 18·00 | 14·00 |

**1901.** Stamps of Germany inscr "REICHSPOST" optd **China.**

| No. | Description | | |
|---|---|---|---|
| 22 10 | 3 pf. brown | 1·50 | 1·75 |
| 23 | 5 pf. green | 1·50 | 1·00 |
| 24 | 10 pf. red | 2·50 | 1·00 |
| 25 | 20 pf. blue | 2·75 | 1·25 |
| 26 | 25 pf. blk & red on yell | 12·00 | 18·00 |
| 27 | 30 pf. blk & orge on pink | 13·00 | 14·00 |
| 28 | 40 pf. black and red | 12·00 | 11·00 |
| 29 | 50 pf. blk & pur on pink | 12·00 | 11·00 |
| 30 | 80 pf. blk & red on pink | 14·00 | 12·00 |
| 31 12 | 1 m. red | 35·00 | 35·00 |
| 32 13 | 2 m. blue | 30·00 | 32·00 |
| 33 14 | 3 m. black | 45·00 | 60·00 |
| 35a 15 | 5 m. red and black | £180 | £325 |

**1905.** Stamps of Germany inscr "DEUTSCHES REICH" surch **China** and new value.

| No. | Description | | |
|---|---|---|---|
| 46 10 | 1 c. on 3 pf. brown | 35 | 75 |
| 47 | 2 c. on 5 pf. green | 35 | 70 |
| 48 | 4 c. on 10 pf. red | 35 | 70 |
| 39 | 10 c. on 20 pf. blue | 3·00 | 1·40 |
| 50 | 20 c. on 40 pf. blk & red | 1·00 | 3·00 |
| 51 | 40 c. on 80 pf. black and red on rose | 1·25 | 45·00 |
| 42 12 | ½ d. on 1 m. red | 18·00 | 25·00 |
| 53 13 | 1 d. on 2 m. blue | 12·00 | 32·00 |
| 44a 14 | 1½ d. on 3 m. black | 24·00 | 50·00 |
| 55 15 | 2½ d. on 5 m. red & blk | 60·00 | £110 |

## GERMAN POST OFFICES IN MOROCCO — Pt. 7

German Post Offices in Morocco, now closed.

100 centimos = 1 peseta.

Stamps of Germany surcharged **Marocco** (or **Marokko**) and new value.

**1889.** Spelt **Marocco.**

| No. | Description | | |
|---|---|---|---|
| 1. 8. | 3 c. on 3 pf. brown | 2·75 | 3·00 |
| 2. | 5 c. on 5 pf. green | 2·75 | 3·00 |
| 3. 9. | 10 c. on 10 pf. red | 5·50 | 6·00 |
| 4. | 25 c. on 20 pf. blue | 12·00 | 16·00 |
| 5. | 30 c. on 25 pf. orange | 23·00 | 35·00 |
| 6. | 60 c. on 50 pf. brown | 18·00 | 45·00 |

**1900.** Inscr "REICHSPOST" surch **Marocco** (3 c. to 1 p.) or **Marocco Marocco** (others).

| No. | Description | | |
|---|---|---|---|
| 7 10 | 3 c. on 3 pf. brown | 1·10 | 1·75 |
| 8 | 5 c. on 5 pf. green | 1·10 | 80 |
| 9 | 10 c. on 10 pf. red | 1·75 | 80 |
| 10 | 25 c. on 20 pf. blue | 2·25 | 2·25 |
| 11 | 30 c. on 25 pf. black and red on yellow | 9·00 | 14·00 |
| 12 | 35 c. on 30 pf. black and orange on rose | 6·50 | 5·50 |
| 13 | 50 c. on 40 pf. blk & red | 6·50 | 5·50 |
| 14 | 60 c. on 50 pf. black and purple on rose | 15·00 | 32·00 |
| 15 | 1 p. on 80 pf. black and red on rose | 11·00 | 11·00 |
| 16 12 | 1 p. 25 c. on 1 m. red | 28·00 | 40·00 |
| 17 13 | 2 p. 50 c. on 2 m. blue | 30·00 | 48·00 |
| 18 14 | 3 p. 75 c. on 3 m. black | 40·00 | 60·00 |
| 19b 15 | 6 p. 25 c. on 5 m. red and black | £160 | £300 |

**1905.** Inscr "DEUTSCHES REICH" surch **Marocco** (3 c. to 1 p.) or **Marocco Marocco** (others).

| No. | Description | | |
|---|---|---|---|
| 26 10 | 3 c. on 3 pf. brown | 2·50 | 2·50 |
| 27 | 5 c. on 5 pf. green | 5·00 | 85 |
| 28 | 10 c. on 10 pf. red | 10·00 | 65 |
| 42 | 25 c. on 20 pf. blue | 19·00 | 3·50 |
| 30 | 30 c. on 25 pf. black and red on yellow | 6·00 | 4·50 |
| 31 | 35 c. on 30 pf. black and orange on buff | 10·00 | 5·50 |
| 32 | 50 c. on 40 pf. black & red | 9·50 | 8·50 |
| 46 | 60 c. on 50 pf. black and purple on buff | 25·00 | 15·00 |
| 34 | 1 p. on 80 pf. black and red on rose | 32·00 | 20·00 |
| 35a 12 | 1 p. 25 on 1 m. red | 40·00 | 30·00 |
| 36 13 | 2 p. 50 on 2 m. blue | 80·00 | £140 |
| 37a 14 | 3 p. 75 on 3 m. black | 45·00 | 42·00 |
| 38 15 | 6 p. 25 on 5 m. red and black | £120 | £160 |

**1911.** Inscr. "DEUTSCHES REICH". Spelt **Marokko.**

| No. | Description | | |
|---|---|---|---|
| 51. 10. | 3 c. on 3 pf. brown | 45 | 65 |
| 52. | 5 c. on 5 pf. green | 45 | 75 |
| 53. | 10 c. on 10 pf. red | 45 | 80 |
| 54. | 25 c. on 20 pf. blue | 55 | 85 |
| 55. | 30 c. on 25 pf. black and red on yellow | 1·25 | 17·00 |
| 56. | 35 c. on 30 pf. black and orange on buff | 1·10 | 8·50 |
| 57. | 50 c. on 40 pf. black & red | 1·10 | 4·50 |
| 58. | 60 c. on 50 pf. black and purple on buff | 1·50 | 35·00 |
| 59. | 1 p. on 80 pf. black and red on rose | 1·60 | 28·00 |
| 60. 12. | 1 p. 25 c. on 1 m. red | 3·00 | 65·00 |
| 61. 13. | 2 p. 50 c. on 2 m. blue | 4·50 | 55·00 |
| 62. 14. | 3 p. 75 c. on 3 m. black | 9·00 | £250 |
| 63. 15. | 6 p. 25 c. on 5 m. red and black | 16·00 | £325 |

## GERMAN POST OFFICES IN THE TURKISH EMPIRE — Pt. 7

German Post Offices in the Turkish Empire, now closed.

1884. 40 para = 1 piastre.
1908. 100 centimes = 1 franc.

**1884.** Stamps of Germany surch. with new value. ("PFENNIG" without final "E".)

| No. | Description | | |
|---|---|---|---|
| 1. 5. | 10 pa. on 5 pf. mauve | 30·00 | 24·00 |
| 2. 6. | 20 pa. on 10 pf. red | 65·00 | 60·00 |
| 3. | 1 pi. on 20 pf. blue | 48·00 | 2·25 |
| 4. | 1¼ pi. on 25 pf. brown | £120 | £190 |
| 6. | 2½ pi. on 50 pf. green | £100 | 65·00 |

**1889.** Stamps of Germany surch.

| No. | Description | | |
|---|---|---|---|
| 10. 8. | 10 pa. on 5 pf. green | 2·75 | 3·25 |
| 11. 9. | 20 pa. on 10 pf. red | 7·00 | 1·50 |
| 12. | 1 pi. on 20 pf. blue | 4·50 | 85 |
| 13. | 1¼ pi. on 25 pf. orange | 27·00 | 15·00 |
| 16. | 2½ pi. on 50 pf. brown | 32·00 | 23·00 |

**1900.** Stamps of Germany inscr "REICHSPOST" surch in **PARA** or **PIASTER.**

| No. | Description | | |
|---|---|---|---|
| 17. 10. | 10 pa. on 5 pf. green | 1·40 | 1·40 |
| 18. | 20 pa. on 10 pf. red | 1·75 | 1·75 |
| 19. | 1 pi. on 20 pf. blue | 3·50 | 1·25 |
| 20. | 1¼ pi. on 25 pf. black and red on yellow | 7·00 | 4·00 |
| 21. | 1½ pi. on 30 pf. black and orange on buff | 7·00 | 4·00 |
| 22. | 2 pi. on 40 pf. black & red | 7·00 | 4·00 |
| 23. | 2½ pi. on 50 pf. black and purple on buff | 13·00 | 13·00 |
| 24. | 4 pi. on 80 pf. black and red on rose | 17·00 | 13·00 |
| 25. 12. | 5 pi. on 1 m. red | 32·00 | 40·00 |
| 26. 13. | 10 pi. on 2 m. blue | 32·00 | 45·00 |
| 27. 14. | 15 pi. on 3 m. black | 55·00 | £100 |
| 28b. 15. | 25 pi. on 5 m. red & black | £160 | £275 |

**1905.** Stamps of Germany inscr "DEUTSCHES REICH" surch in **Para** or **Piaster.**

| No. | Description | | |
|---|---|---|---|
| 47 10 | 10 pa. on 5 pf. green | 1·60 | 40 |
| 48 | 20 pa. on 10 pf. red | 2·00 | 40 |
| 49 | 1 pi. on 20 pf. blue | 3·25 | 40 |
| 38 | 1¼ pi. on 25 pf. black and red on yellow | 11·00 | 7·00 |
| 51 | 1½ pi. on 30 pf. black and orange on buff | 10·00 | 6·50 |
| 52 | 2 pi. on 40 pf. black & red | 4·50 | 1·00 |
| 53 | 2½ pi. on 50 pf. black and purple on buff | 11·00 | 7·00 |
| 54 | 4 pi. on 80 pf. black and red on pink | 10·00 | 18·00 |
| 55 12 | 5 pi. on 1 m. red | 18·00 | 32·00 |
| 56 13 | 10 pi. on 2 m. blue | 18·00 | 48·00 |
| 45 14 | 15 pi. on 3 m. black | 50·00 | 50·00 |
| 58 15 | 25 pi. on 5 m. red & black | 24·00 | 60·00 |

**1908.** Stamps of Germany inscr. "DEUTSCHES REICH", surch. in **Centimes.**

| No. | Description | | |
|---|---|---|---|
| 60. 10. | 5 c. on 5 pf. green | 1·25 | 2·00 |
| 61. | 10 c. on 10 pf. red | 3·25 | 5·00 |
| 62. | 25 c. on 20 pf. blue | 7·00 | 35·00 |
| 63. | 50 c. on 40 pf. black & red | 32·00 | 70·00 |
| 64. | 100 c. on 80 pf. black and red on rose | 70·00 | 90·00 |

## GERMAN SOUTH WEST AFRICA — Pt. 7

A German colony in S.W. Africa.

100 pfennig = 1 mark.

**1897.** Stamps of Germany optd.

(a) **Deutsch- Sudwest-Afrika** (with hyphen)

| No. | Description | | |
|---|---|---|---|
| 1 8 | 3 pf. brown | 6·00 | 12·00 |
| 2 | 5 pf. green | 3·25 | 3·75 |
| 3 9 | 10 pf. red | 16·00 | 17·00 |
| 4 | 20 pf. blue | 3·50 | 4·50 |

(b) **Deutsch- Sudwestafrika** (without hyphen)

| No. | Description | | |
|---|---|---|---|
| 5 8 | 3 pf. brown | 6·00 | 12·00 |
| 6 | 5 pf. green | 2·75 | 2·25 |
| 7 9 | 10 pf. red | 2·75 | 3·00 |
| 8 | 20 pf. blue | 13·00 | 16·00 |
| 9 | 25 pf. orange | £325 | £475 |
| 10 | 50 pf. brown | 12·00 | 12·00 |

**1900.** "Yacht" key-types inscr. "DEUTSCH-SUDWESTAFRIKA".

| No. | Description | | |
|---|---|---|---|
| 24 N | 3 pf. brown | 75 | 1·25 |
| 25 | 5 pf. green | 75 | 1·25 |
| 26 | 10 pf. red | 75 | 1·50 |
| 27 | 20 pf. blue | 90 | 4·00 |
| 15 | 25 pf. blk. & red on yell. | 1·40 | 5·00 |
| 16 | 30 pf. black and orange on buff | 12·00 | 2·75 |
| 17 | 40 pf. black and red | 1·40 | 3·25 |
| 18 | 50 pf. blk. & pur. on buff | 1·75 | 2·25 |
| 19 | 80 pf. black & red on rose | 1·75 | 8·00 |
| 29 O | 1 m. red | 12·00 | 32·00 |
| 30 | 2 m. blue | 11·00 | 32·00 |
| 22 | 3 m. black | 32·00 | 55·00 |
| 32 | 5 m. red and black | 22·00 | £300 |

South Africa occupied the colony in 1914 and administered the territory under a League of Nations mandate from 1920. For stamps issued from 1923 see under South West Africa in Volume 3.

## GERMANY — Pt. 7

A country in Northern Central Europe. A federation of states forming the German Reich. An empire till November 1918 and then a republic until the collapse of Germany in 1945. Until 1949 under Allied Military Control when the German Federal Republic was set up for W. Germany and the German Democratic Republic for E. Germany. See also notes before No. 899.

### I. GERMANY 1871–1945

1872. Northern areas including Alsace and Lorraine: 30 groschen = 1 thaler. Southern areas: 90 kreuzer = 1 gulden.

1875. Throughout Germany: 100 pfennig = 1 mark.

1923. 100 renten-pfennig = 1 rentenmark (gold currency).

1928. 100 pfennig = 1 reichsmark.

1.

A.

**1872.** Arms embossed as Type A.

| No. | Description | | |
|---|---|---|---|
| 1 1 | ¼ g. violet | £170 | 80·00 |
| 2 | ⅓ g. green | £325 | 30·00 |
| 3 | ½ g. red | £1000 | 35·00 |
| 4 | ½ g. yellow | £1000 | 40·00 |
| 5 | 1 g. red | £250 | 3·00 |
| 6 | 2 g. blue | £900 | 9·00 |
| 7 | 5 g. bistre | £475 | 80·00 |
| 8 | 1 k. green | £500 | 50·00 |
| 9 | 2 k. red | £550 | £250 |
| 10 | 2 k. yellow | 30·00 | £160 |
| 11 | 3 k. red | £1000 | 9·75 |
| 12 | 7 k. blue | £1800 | 80·00 |
| 13 | 18 k. bistre | £500 | £350 |

2.

B.

**1872.**

| No. | Description | | |
|---|---|---|---|
| 14. 2. | 10 g. grey | 55·00 | £100 |
| 15. – | 30 g. blue | £100 | £400 |
| 38d. 2. | 2 m. purple | 45·00 | 1·75 |

On the 30 g. the figures are in a rectangular frame.

**1872.** Arms embossed as Type B.

| No. | Description | | |
|---|---|---|---|
| 16. 1. | ¼ g. purple | 55·00 | £100 |
| 17. | ⅓ g. green | 25·00 | 12·00 |
| 18. | ½ g. orange | 27·00 | 3·50 |
| 19. | 1 g. red | 38·00 | 1·00 |
| 20. | 2 g. blue | 20·00 | 3·75 |
| 21. | 2½ g. brown | £2000 | 50·00 |
| 22. | 5 g. olive | 26·00 | 28·00 |
| 23. | 1 k. green | 30·00 | 28·00 |
| 24. | 2 k. orange | £400 | £2250 |
| 25. | 3 k. red | 20·00 | 3·00 |
| 26. | 7 k. blue | 28·00 | 65·00 |
| 27. | 9 k. brown | £225 | £170 |
| 28. | 18 k. olive | 30·00 | £2000 |

**1874.** Surch. with bold figures over arms.

| No. | Description | | |
|---|---|---|---|
| 29. 1. | "2½" on 2½ g. brown | 28·00 | 32·00 |
| 30. | "9" on 9 k. brown | 60·00 | £300 |

5.

6.

**1875.** "PFENNIGE" with final "E".

| No. | Description | | |
|---|---|---|---|
| 31. 5. | 3 pf. green | 60·00 | 5·00 |
| 32. | 5 pf. mauve | 95·00 | 2·00 |
| 33. 6. | 10 pf. red | 38·00 | 30 |
| 34. | 20 pf. blue | £300 | 90 |
| 35. | 25 pf. brown | £450 | 16·00 |
| 36a. | 50 pf. grey | £900 | 10·00 |
| 37. | 50 pf. green | £1600 | 15·00 |

**1880.** "PFENNIG" without final "E".

| | | | | |
|---|---|---|---|---|
| 39a. | 5. | 3 pf. green | 2·75 | 40 |
| 40a. | | 5 pf. purple | 1·50 | 30 |
| 41b. | 6. | 10 pf. red | 9·00 | 10 |
| 42a. | | 20 pf. blue | 7·00 | 10 |
| 43b. | | 25 pf. brown | 17·00 | 2·75 |
| 44a. | | 50 pf. green | 7·00 | 65 |

8. 9.

**1889.**

| | | | | |
|---|---|---|---|---|
| 45. | 8. | 2 pf. grey | 50 | 70 |
| 46. | | 3 pf. brown | 1·75 | 10 |
| 47a. | | 5 pf. green | 1·25 | 20 |
| 48b. | 9. | 10 pf. red | 1·75 | 20 |
| 49. | | 20 pf. blue | 9·00 | 20 |
| 50b. | | 25 pf. yellow | 35·00 | 1·25 |
| 51b. | | 50 pf. brown | 35·00 | 30 |

10. "Germania". 12. General Post Office, Berlin.

13. Allegory of Union of N. and S. Germany (after Anton von Werner).

14. Unveiling of Kaiser Wilhelm I Memorial in Berlin (after W. Pape).

15. 25th Anniv. of German Empire Address by Wilhelm II (after W. Pape).

**1899.** Types **10** to **15** inscr "REICHSPOST".

| | | | | |
|---|---|---|---|---|
| 52 | 10 | 2 pf. grey | 50 | 60 |
| 53 | | 3 pf. brown | 50 | 30 |
| 54 | | 5 pf. green | 1·00 | 30 |
| 55 | | 10 pf. red | 1·75 | 30 |
| 56 | | 20 pf. blue | 6·00 | 30 |
| 57 | | 25 pf. blk & red on yell | 12·00 | 6·00 |
| 58 | | 30 pf. blk & orge on rose | 22·00 | 60 |
| 59 | | 40 pf. black and red | 26·00 | 1·40 |
| 60 | | 50 pf. blk & pur on rose | 26·00 | 1·00 |
| 61 | | 80 pf. blk & red on rose | 35·00 | 2·25 |
| 62 | 12 | 1 m. red | 60·00 | 1·40 |
| 63 | 13 | 2 m. blue | 65·00 | 5·00 |
| 64 | 14 | 3 m. black | 90·00 | 42·00 |
| 65b | 15 | 5 m. red and black | £300 | £325 |

**1902.** T **10** to **15** inscr "DEUTSCHES REICH".

| | | | | |
|---|---|---|---|---|
| 67 | 10 | 2 pf. grey | 1·25 | 60 |
| 83a | | 3 pf. brown | 25 | 10 |
| 84a | | 5 pf. green | 25 | 10 |
| 85a | | 10 pf. red | 60 | 10 |
| 86d | | 20 pf. blue | 30 | 10 |
| 87 | | 25 pf. blk & red on yell | 30 | 15 |
| 88a | | 30 pf. blk & orge on buff | 30 | 15 |
| 89a | | 40 pf. black and red | 65 | 15 |
| 90a | | 50 pf. blk & pur on buff | 30 | 10 |
| 91a | | 60 pf. purple | 1·00 | 50 |
| 92a | | 80 pf. blk & red on rose | 70 | 1·90 |
| 93 | 12 | 1 m. red | 1·75 | 40 |
| 94 | 13 | 2 m. blue | 3·50 | 4·50 |
| 95 | 14 | 3 m. black | 1·00 | 3·75 |
| 96 | 15 | 5 m. red and black | 80 | 2·75 |

24. Unshaded background.

**1916.** Inscr "DEUTSCHES REICH".

| | | | | |
|---|---|---|---|---|
| 97 | 24 | 2 pf. grey | 15 | 2·40 |
| 98 | | 2½ pf. grey | 15 | 40 |
| 140 | 10 | 5 pf. brown | 15 | 1·00 |
| 99a | 24 | 7½ pf. yellow | 20 | 70 |
| 141a | 10 | 10 pf. orange | 10 | 50 |
| 100 | 24 | 15 pf. brown | 2·25 | 80 |
| 101 | | 15 pf. violet | 15 | 50 |
| 102 | | 15 pf. purple | 20 | 85 |
| 142 | 10 | 20 pf. green | 10 | 80 |
| 143a | | 30 pf. blue | 10 | 75 |
| 103 | 24 | 35 pf. brown | 15 | 1·00 |
| 144a. | 10. | 40 pf. red | 10 | 75 |
| 145a. | | 50 pf. purple | 40 | 1·60 |
| 146. | | 60 pf. olive | 10 | 60 |
| 104. | | 75 pf. black and green | 15 | 60 |
| 147a. | | 75 pf. purple | 10 | 1·00 |
| 148a. | | 80 pf. blue | 10 | 1·10 |
| 149. | | 1 m. green and violet | 10 | 65 |
| 150. | | 1¼ m. purple and red | 10 | 70 |
| 114. | 12. | 1 m. 25 green | 1·50 | 1·00 |
| 115. | | 1 m. 50 brown | 15 | 1·10 |
| 151. | 10. | 2 m. blue and red | 45 | 85 |
| 116a. | 13. | 2 m. 50 red | 10 | 1·00 |
| 152. | 10. | 4 m. red and black | 10 | 1·40 |

**1919.** War Wounded Fund. Surch **5 Pf. fur Kriegs-beschadigte**.

| | | | | |
|---|---|---|---|---|
| 105 | 10 | 10 pf. + 5 pf. (No. 85a) | 50 | 6·00 |
| 106 | 24 | 15 pf. + 5 pf. (No. 101) | 50 | 7·00 |

26. 27. 28.

**1919.** National Assembly, Weimar.

| | | | | |
|---|---|---|---|---|
| 107. | 26. | 10 pf. red | 10 | 1·25 |
| 108. | 27. | 15 pf. blue and brown | 10 | 1·25 |
| 109. | 28. | 25 pf. red and green | 10 | 1·25 |
| 110. | | 30 pf. red and purple | 10 | 1·25 |

29. 30. L.V.G. Schneider Biplane.

**1919.** Air.

| | | | | |
|---|---|---|---|---|
| 111. | 29. | 10 pf. orange | 10 | 2·50 |
| 112. | 30. | 40 pf. green | 10 | 2·50 |

**1920.** Stamps of Bavaria optd **Deutsches Reich**.

| | | | | |
|---|---|---|---|---|
| 117 | 26 | 5 pf. green | 10 | 1·25 |
| 118 | | 10 pf. orange | 10 | 1·10 |
| 119 | | 15 pf. red | 10 | 1·10 |
| 120 | 27 | 20 pf. purple | 10 | 80 |
| 121 | | 30 pf. blue | 10 | 80 |
| 122 | | 40 pf. brown | 10 | 80 |
| 123 | 28 | 50 pf. red | 10 | 2·00 |
| 124 | | 60 pf. green | 10 | 80 |
| 125 | | 75 pf. purple | 35 | 4·00 |
| 126 | | 80 pf. blue | 20 | 2·50 |
| 127 | 29 | 1 m. red and grey | 30 | 2·00 |
| 128 | | 1¼ m. blue and bistre | 35 | 1·60 |
| 129 | | 1½ m. green and grey | 30 | 2·00 |
| 130 | | 2 m. violet and bistre | 65 | 3·50 |
| 131 | | 2½ m. black and grey | 10 | 2·25 |
| 132 | 30 | 3 m. blue | 2·75 | 6·50 |
| 133 | | 4 m. red | 3·25 | 12·00 |
| 134 | | 5 m. yellow | 2·50 | 8·50 |
| 135 | | 10 m. green | 3·00 | 12·00 |
| 136 | | 20 m. black | 5·25 | 15·00 |

**1920.** Surch. with new value and stars.

| | | | | |
|---|---|---|---|---|
| 137. | 12. | 1 m. 25 on 1 m. green | 30 | 7·00 |
| 138. | | 1 m. 50 on 1 m. brown | 30 | 7·00 |
| 139. | 13. | 2 m. 50 on 2 m. purple | 7·00 | £200 |

35. 36. Blacksmiths. 37. Miners.

38. Reapers. 40.

41. Ploughman. 39. Posthorn.

**1921.**

| | | | | |
|---|---|---|---|---|
| 153. | 35. | 5 pf. red | 10 | 1·40 |
| 154. | | 10 pf. olive | 10 | 80 |
| 155. | | 15 pf. blue | 10 | 60 |
| 156. | | 25 pf. brown | 10 | 50 |
| 157. | | 30 pf. green | 10 | 50 |
| 158. | | 40 pf. orange | 10 | 45 |
| 182. | | 50 pf. purple | 10 | 80 |
| 160. | 36. | 60 pf. red | 10 | 60 |
| 184. | 35. | 75 pf. blue | 10 | 3·25 |
| 161. | 36. | 80 pf. red | 10 | 7·00 |
| 186. | 37. | 100 pf. green | 10 | 55 |
| 163. | | 120 pf. blue | 10 | 60 |
| 188. | 38. | 150 pf. orange | 10 | 70 |
| 165. | | 160 pf. green | 10 | 11·00 |
| 193. | 40. | 5 m. orange | 15 | 1·25 |
| 170. | | 10 m. red | 30 | 1·50 |
| 195. | 41. | 20 m. blue and green | 10 | 3·00 |

**1921.** 1902 stamps surch.

| | | | | |
|---|---|---|---|---|
| 172. | 10. | 1 m. 60 on 5 pf. brown | 10 | 1·10 |
| 173. | | 3 m. on 1¼ m. pur. & red | 10 | 1·10 |
| 174. | | 5 m. on 75 pf. purple | 10 | 1·10 |
| 175. | | 10 m. on 75 pf. purple | 30 | 1·50 |

**1921.**

| | | | | |
|---|---|---|---|---|
| 190 | 39 | 2 m. violet and pink | 10 | 60 |
| 204 | | 2 m. purple | 10 | 90 |
| 191 | | 3 m. red and yellow | 15 | 85 |
| 205 | | 3 m. red | 10 | 60 |
| 192 | | 4 m. green & light green | 10 | 85 |
| 206 | | 4 m. green | 10 | 80 |
| 207 | | 5 m. orange and yellow | 10 | 1·40 |
| 208 | | 5 m. orange | 10 | 80 |
| 209 | | 6 m. blue | 10 | 90 |
| 210 | | 8 m. green | 10 | 80 |
| 211 | | 10 m. red and pink | 10 | 60 |
| 212 | | 20 m. violet and red | 10 | 90 |
| 213 | | 20 m. violet | 10 | 95 |
| 214 | | 30 m. brown and yellow | 10 | 80 |
| 215 | | 30 m. brown | 15 | 6·50 |
| 216 | | 40 m. green | 10 | 1·00 |
| 217 | | 50 m. green and purple | 10 | 80 |

47. Arms of Munich. 48.

**1922.** Munich Exhibition.

| | | | | |
|---|---|---|---|---|
| 198. | 47. | 1¼ m. red | 20 | 1·25 |
| 199. | | 2 m. violet | 20 | 1·25 |
| 200. | | 3 m. red | 30 | 1·40 |
| 201. | | 4 m. blue | 20 | 1·40 |
| 202. | | 10 m. brown on buff | 50 | 2·25 |
| 203. | | 20 m. red on rose | 2·75 | 10·00 |

**1922.** Air.

| | | | | |
|---|---|---|---|---|
| 218. | 48. | 25 pf. brown | 30 | 17·00 |
| 219. | | 40 pf. orange | 30 | 25·00 |
| 220. | | 50 pf. purple | 15 | 10·00 |
| 221. | | 60 pf. red | 35 | 20·00 |
| 222. | | 80 pf. green | 35 | 18·00 |
| 223. | – | 1 m. green | 10 | 4·00 |
| 224. | – | 2 m. red and grey | 10 | 4·00 |
| 225. | – | 3 m. blue and grey | 10 | 4·50 |
| 226. | – | 5 m. orange and yellow | 10 | 4·00 |
| 227. | – | 10 m. purple and red | 15 | 12·00 |
| 228. | – | 25 m. brown and yellow | 15 | 10·00 |
| 229. | – | 100 m. olive and red | 15 | 8·50 |

The mark values are larger (21×27 mm.).

See also Nos. 269/73 and 358/64.

**1922.** New values.

| | | | | |
|---|---|---|---|---|
| 235 | 40 | 50 m. black | 10 | 1·40 |
| 230 | | 100 m. purple on buff | 20 | 1·00 |
| 237 | | 200 m. red on buff | 10 | 65 |
| 238 | | 300 m. green on buff | 10 | 60 |
| 239 | | 400 m. brown on buff | 10 | 60 |
| 240 | | 500 m. orange on buff | 10 | 60 |
| 241 | | 1000 m. grey | 10 | 60 |
| 242 | | 2000 m. blue | 10 | 80 |
| 243 | | 3000 m. brown | 10 | 1·25 |
| 244 | | 4000 m. violet | 20 | 1·40 |
| 245 | | 5000 m. green | 30 | 1·75 |
| 246 | | 100000 m. red | 10 | 1·40 |

8 Mark für Alters- und Kinderhilfe

50. Allegory of Charity. 51. Miners. 54.

**1922.** Fund for the Old and for Children.

| | | | | |
|---|---|---|---|---|
| 247. | 50. | 6 m. + 4 m. bl. & bistre | 15 | 20·00 |
| 248. | | 12 m. + 8 m. red & lilac | 15 | 20·00 |

**1923.**

| | | | | |
|---|---|---|---|---|
| 249 | 51 | 5 m. orange | 10 | 16·00 |
| 250 | 38 | 10 m. blue | 10 | 55 |
| 251 | | 12 m. red | 10 | 1·00 |
| 252 | 51 | 20 m. purple | 10 | 85 |
| 253 | 38 | 25 m. bistre | 10 | 40 |
| 254 | 51 | 30 m. olive | 10 | 1·75 |
| 255 | 38 | 40 m. green | 10 | 95 |
| 256 | 51 | 50 m. blue | 25 | £120 |

**1923.** Relief Fund for Sufferers in the Rhine and Ruhr Occupation Districts. Surch **Rhein = Ruhr = Hilfe** and premium.

| | | | | |
|---|---|---|---|---|
| 257 | 51 | 5 + 100 m. orange | 10 | 10·00 |
| 258 | 38 | 25 + 500 m. bistre | 10 | 26·00 |
| 259 | 41 | 20 + 1000 m. blue & grn | 1·75 | £100 |

**1923.** T = Tausend (thousand).

| | | | | |
|---|---|---|---|---|
| 261 | 54 | 100 m. purple | 10 | 60 |
| 262 | | 200 m. red | 10 | 75 |
| 263 | | 300 m. green | 10 | 1·00 |
| 264 | | 400 m. brown | 10 | 6·00 |
| 265 | | 500 m. red | 10 | 5·50 |
| 266 | | 1000 m. grey | 10 | 1·10 |
| 312 | | 5 T. blue | 10 | 16·00 |
| 313 | | 50 T. brown | 10 | 60 |
| 314 | | 75 T. purple | 10 | 12·00 |

55. Wartburg Castle. 62.

**1923.**

| | | | | |
|---|---|---|---|---|
| 267. | 55. | 5000 m. blue | 15 | 2·50 |
| 268. | – | 10,000 m. olive | 15 | 3·50 |

DESIGN—VERT. 10,000 m. Cologne Cathedral.

**1923.** Air. As T **48**, but larger (21×27 mm.)

| | | | | |
|---|---|---|---|---|
| 269. | | 5 m. orange | 10 | 45·00 |
| 270. | | 10 m. purple | 10 | 9·50 |
| 271. | | 25 m. brown | 10 | 10·00 |
| 272. | | 100 m. green | 10 | 8·50 |
| 273. | | 200 m. blue | 10 | 40·00 |

**1923.** Surch. with new value in **Tausend** or **Millionen** (marks). Perf. or rouletted.

| | | | | |
|---|---|---|---|---|
| 274 | 35 | 5 T. on 40 pf. orange | 10 | 1·50 |
| 275a | | 8 T. on 30 pf. green | 10 | 1·75 |
| 276 | 38 | 15 T. on 40 m. green | 10 | 90 |
| 277 | | 20 T. on 12 m. red | 10 | 1·25 |
| 278 | | 20 T. on 25 m. brown | 10 | 2·25 |
| 279 | 54 | 20 T. on 200 m. red | 10 | 1·25 |
| 280 | 38 | 25 T. on 25 m. brown | 10 | 18·00 |
| 281 | | 30 T. on 10 m. blue | 10 | 1·00 |
| 282 | 54 | 30 T. on 200 m. blue | 10 | 1·40 |
| 283 | | 75 T. on 300 m. green | 10 | 19·00 |
| 284 | | 75 T. on 400 m. green | 10 | 85 |
| 285 | | 75 T. on 1000 m. green | 10 | 85 |
| 286 | | 100 T. on 100 m. purple | 10 | 1·75 |
| 287 | | 100 T. on 400 m. green | 10 | 70 |
| 288 | | 125 T. on 1000 m. red | 10 | 1·40 |
| 289 | | 250 T. on 200 m. red | 10 | 4·00 |
| 290 | | 250 T. on 300 m. green | 10 | 18·00 |
| 291 | | 250 T. on 400 m. brown | 10 | 20·00 |
| 292 | | 250 T. on 500 m. pink | 10 | 70 |
| 293 | | 250 T. on 500 m. orange | 10 | 20·00 |
| 306 | 35 | 400 T. on 15 pf. brown | 10 | 4·00 |
| 307 | | 400 T. on 25 pf. brown | 10 | 4·00 |
| 308 | | 400 T. on 30 pf. brown | 10 | 4·00 |
| 309 | | 400 T. on 40 pf. brown | 10 | 4·00 |
| 294 | | 800 T. on 5 pf. green | 10 | 5·00 |
| 295 | | 800 T. on 10 pf. green | 10 | 5·00 |
| 296 | 54 | 800 T. on 200 m. red | 10 | 60·00 |
| 297 | | 800 T. on 300 m. green | 10 | 4·50 |
| 298 | | 800 T. on 400 m. green | 10 | 4·00 |
| 299 | | 800 T. on 400 m. brown | 10 | 18·00 |
| 300 | | 800 T. on 500 m. green | 20 | £1200 |
| 301 | | 800 T. on 1000 m. green | 10 | 90 |
| 302 | | 2 M. on 200 m. red | 10 | 85 |
| 303 | | 2 M. on 300 m. green | 10 | 2·00 |
| 304 | | 2 M. on 500 m. red | 15 | 6·00 |
| 305 | | 2 M. on 5 T. red | 10 | 1·00 |

**1923.** Perf. or rouletted.

| | | | | |
|---|---|---|---|---|
| 315. | 62. | 500 T. brown | 10 | 3·00 |
| 316. | | 1 M. blue | 10 | 70 |
| 317. | | 2 M. purple | 10 | 25·00 |
| 318. | | 4 M. green | 10 | 2·00 |
| 319. | | 5 M. red | 10 | 65 |
| 320. | | 10 M. red | 10 | 65 |
| 321. | | 20 M. blue | 10 | 75 |
| 322. | | 30 M. purple | 10 | 10·00 |
| 323. | | 50 M. green | 10 | 80 |
| 324. | | 100 M. grey | 10 | 80 |
| 325. | | 200 M. brown | 10 | 1·00 |
| 326. | | 500 M. olive | 10 | 90 |

**1923.** As T **62**, but value in **"Milliarden"**. Perf. or roul.

| | | | | |
|---|---|---|---|---|
| 327 | 62 | 1 Md. brown | 10 | 1·00 |
| 328 | | 2 Md. green and flesh | 10 | 1·00 |
| 329 | | 5 Md. brown and yellow | 10 | 1·00 |
| 330 | | 10 Md. green & lt green | 10 | 1·25 |
| 331 | | 20 Md. brown and green | 10 | 1·60 |
| 332 | | 50 Md. blue | 40 | 30·00 |

**1923.** Surch. in **"Milliarden"**. Perf. or roul.

| | | | | |
|---|---|---|---|---|
| 342. | 54. | 1 Md. on 100 m. purple | 10 | 26·00 |
| 343. | 62. | 5 Md. on 2 M. purple | 20 | £140 |
| 344. | | 5 Md. on 4 M. green | 10 | 27·00 |
| 345. | | 5 Md. on 10 M. red | 10 | 2·25 |
| 346. | | 10 Md. on 20 M. blue | 25 | 2·50 |
| 347. | | 10 Md. on 50 M. green | 10 | 2·25 |
| 348. | | 10 Md. on 100 M. grey | 10 | 2·50 |

**1923.** As T **62**, but without value in words and tablet blank.

| | | | | |
|---|---|---|---|---|
| 352. | 62. | 3 pf. brown | 40 | 20 |
| 353. | | 5 pf. green | 40 | 20 |
| 354. | | 10 pf. red | 40 | 20 |
| 355. | | 20 pf. blue | 90 | 25 |
| 356. | | 50 pf. orange | 2·75 | 60 |
| 357. | | 100 pf. purple | 8·00 | 70 |

The values of this and the following issues are expressed on the basis of the gold mark.

**1924.** Air.

| | | | | |
|---|---|---|---|---|
| 358. | 48. | 5 pf. green | 1·50 | 1·25 |
| 359. | | 10 pf. red | 1·50 | 1·60 |
| 360. | | 20 pf. blue | 3·25 | 5·00 |
| 361. | | 50 pf. orange | 12·00 | 20·00 |
| 362. | | 100 pf. purple | 30·00 | 55·00 |
| 363. | | 200 pf. blue | 60·00 | 75·00 |
| 364. | | 300 pf. grey | 95·00 | £110 |

65. 66.

**1924.** Welfare Fund.

| | | | | |
|---|---|---|---|---|
| 365. | 65. | 5 + 15 pf. green | 1·00 | 2·00 |
| 366. | – | 10 + 30 pf. red | 1·00 | 2·00 |
| 367. | – | 20 + 60 pf. blue | 6·00 | 7·00 |
| 368. | – | 50 + 1 m. 50 pf. brown | 26·00 | 60·00 |

DESIGNS: St. Elizabeth feeding the hungry (5 pf.), giving drink to the thirsty (10 pf.) clothing the naked (20 pf.) and caring for the sick (50 pf.).

**1924.**

| | | | | |
|---|---|---|---|---|
| 369. | 66. | 3 pf. brown | 20 | 15 |
| 370. | | 5 pf. green | 20 | 10 |
| 371. | | 10 pf. red | 30 | 10 |
| 372. | | 20 pf. blue | 1·50 | 15 |
| 373. | | 30 pf. red | 2·25 | 40 |
| 374. | | 40 pf. olive | 15·00 | 80 |
| 375. | | 50 pf. orange | 15·00 | 1·50 |

67. Rheinstein.

DESIGNS: 2 m. Cologne. (A) inscr. "Zwei Mark"; (B) inscr. "ZWEI REICHSMARK". 3 m. Marienburg. 5 m. Speyer Cathedral.

**1924.**

376. 67. 1 m. green .. .. 15·00 2·00
377. – 2 m. blue (A) .. .. 21·00 2·00
458. – 2 m. blue (B) .. .. 30·00 14·00
378. – 3 m. red .. .. 23·00 5·50
379. – 5 m. green .. .. 32·00 15·00

71. Dr. von Stephan. 73. German Eagle and Rhine. 74.

**1924.** 50th Anniv. of U.P.U.

380. 71. 10 pf. green .. .. 50 15
381. 20 pf. blue .. .. 1·00 50
382. – 60 pf. brown .. .. 5·00 20
383. – 80 pf. deep green .. 10·00 1·40

DESIGNS: Nos. 382/3. Similar to Type 71 but with border changed.

**1925.** Rhineland Millenary.

384. 73. 5 pf. green .. .. 40 20
385. 10 pf. red .. .. 80 20
386. 20 pf. blue .. .. 4·50 90

**1925.** Munich Exhibition.

387. 74. 5 pf. green .. .. 3·00 6·50
388. 10 pf. red .. .. 4·00 9·00

75. Arms of Prussia. 76. 78. Goethe.

**1925.** Welfare Fund. Arms dated "1925".

389. 75. 5 pf.+5 pf. yellow, black and green .. .. 35 85
390. – 10 pf.+10 pf. brown, blue and red .. 1·00 1·00
391. – 20 pf.+20 pf. brown, green and blue .. 6·00 16·00

ARMS: 10 pf. Bavaria. 20 pf. Saxony.
See also Nos. 413/16a, 446/50 and 451/5.

**1926.** Air.

392. 76. 5 pf. green .. .. 65 50
393. 10 pf. red .. .. 65 50
394. 15 pf. purple .. .. 1·50 1·00
395. 20 pf. blue .. .. 1·50 1·25
396. 50 pf. orange .. .. 20·00 5·00
397. 1 m. red and black .. 18·00 6·00
398. 2 m. blue and black .. 19·00 22·00
399. 3 m. olive and black .. 55·00 70·00

**1926.** Portraits.

400. 78. 3 pf. brown .. .. 40 15
402. – 5 pf. green (Schiller) .. 90 15
404. – 8 pf. green (Beethoven) 2·00 15
405. – 10 pf. red (Frederick the Great) .. .. 90 15
406. – 15 pf. red (Kant) .. 2·00 20
407. – 20 pf. deep green (Beethoven) .. .. 18·00 1·00
408. 78. 25 pf. blue .. .. 3·25 50
409. – 30 pf. olive (Lessing) .. 6·50 25
410. – 40 pf. violet (Leibniz) .. 14·00 50
411. – 50 pf. brown (Bach) .. 23·00 8·00
412. – 80 pf. brown (Durer) .. 32·00 6·00

**1926.** Welfare Fund. As T 75. Arms, dated "1926".

413. 5 pf.+5 pf. mult. .. 1·00 1·10
414. 10 pf.+10 pf. red, gold and rose .. .. 1·50 2·00
415. 25 pf.+25 pf. blue, yellow and red .. 12·00 22·00
416a. 50 pf+50 pf. mult. .. 50·00 85·00

ARMS: 5 pf. Wurttemberg. 10 pf. Baden. 25 pf. Thuringia. 50 pf. Hesse.

79. Pres. von Hindenburg. 81. Pres. Ebert. 82. Pres. von Hindenburg.

**1927.** Welfare Fund. President's 80th Birthday.

417. 79. 8 pf.+7 pf. green .. 65 1·40
418. 15 pf.+15 pf. red .. 80 2·00
419. 25 pf.+25 pf. blue .. 8·00 20·00
420. 50 pf.+50 pf. brown .. 12·00 24·00

**1927.** International Labour Office Session, Berlin. Optd. **I.A.A. 10-15.10.1927.**

421 – 8 pf. green (No. 404) .. 20·00 60·00
422 – 15 pf. red (No. 406) .. 20·00 60·00
423 78 25 pf. blue .. .. 20·00 60·00

**1928.**

424 81 3 pf. brown .. .. 20 15
425 82 4 pf. blue .. .. 40 20
426 5 pf. green .. .. 25 10
427 81 6 pf. olive .. .. 50 15
428 8 pf. green .. .. 15 10
429 10 pf. red .. .. 1·75 1·60
430 10 pf. purple .. .. 1·00 25
431 82 12 pf. orange .. .. 1·00 20
432 15 pf. red .. .. 45 10
433 81 20 pf. deep green .. 6·00 2·75
434 20 pf. grey .. .. 7·00 30
435 82 25 pf. blue .. .. 10·00 40
436 81 30 pf. olive .. .. 6·00 25
437 82 40 pf. violet .. .. 17·00 40
438 81 45 pf. orange .. .. 10·00 3·00
439 82 50 pf. brown .. .. 10·00 1·25
440 81 60 pf. brown .. .. 13·00 2·75
441 82 80 pf. brown .. .. 28·00 6·00
442 80 pf. yellow .. .. 12·00 1·50

83. Airship "Graf Zeppelin".

**1928.** Air.

443. 83. 1 m. red .. .. 28·00 40·00
444. 2 m. blue .. .. 45·00 55·00
445. 4 m. brown .. .. 27·00 35·00

**1928.** Welfare Fund. As T 75, dated "1928".

446. 5 pf.+5 pf. grn., red & yell. 50 2·75
447. 8 pf.+7 pf. multicoloured 50 2·75
448. 15 pf.+15 pf. red, blue and yellow .. .. .. 1·40 2·75
449. 25 pf.+25 pf. bl., red & yell. 9·00 30·00
450. 50 pf.+50 pf. mult. .. 45·00 80·00

ARMS: 5 pf. Hamburg. 8 pf. Mecklenburg-Schwerin. 15 pf. Oldenburg. 25 pf. Brunswick. 50 pf. Anhalt.

**1929.** Welfare Fund. As T 75, dated "1929".

451 5 pf.+2 pf. grn, yell & red 50 1·75
452 8 pf.+4 pf. yell, red & grn 50 1·75
453 15 pf.+5 pf. yell, blk & red 60 1·75
454 25 pf.+10 pf. mult .. 12·00 32·00
455 50 pf.+40 pf. yellow, red and brown .. .. 45·00 85·00

ARMS: 5 pf. Bremen. 8 pf. Lippe. 15 pf. Lubeck. 25 pf. Mecklenburg-Strelitz. 50 pf. Schaumburg-Lippe.

**1930.** Air. "Graf Zeppelin" 1st S. American Flight. T 83 inscr. "I. SUDAMERIKA FAHRT".

456. 2 m. blue .. .. £170 £275
457a. 4 m. brown .. .. £225 £275

**1930.** Evacuation of Rhineland by Allied Forces. Optd. **30 JUNI 1930.**

459. 81. 8 pf. green .. .. 70 30
460. 82. 15 pf. red .. .. 80 50

86. Aachen. 92. Heidelberg Castle.

**1930.** Welfare Fund.

465 86 8 pf.+4 pf. green .. 40 60
466 – 15 pf.+5 pf. red .. 60 80
467 – 25 pf.+10 pf. blue .. 8·50 20·00
468 – 50 pf.+40 pf. brown .. 23·00 50·00

DESIGNS: 15 pf. Berlin. 25 pf. Marienwerder. 50 pf. Wurzburg.

**1931.** Air. "Graf Zeppelin" Polar Flight. Optd. **POLAR-FAHRT 1931.**

469. 83. 1 m. red .. .. 90·00 75·00
470. 2 m. blue .. .. £140 £190
471. 4 m. brown .. .. £300 £600

**1931.** Welfare Fund.

472. – 8 pf.+4 pf. green .. 40 80
473. – 15 pf.+5 pf. red .. 40 90
474. 92. 25 pf.+10 pf. blue .. 10·00 22·00
475. – 50 pf.+40 pf. brown .. 30·00 70·00

DESIGNS—VERT. 8 pf. The Zwinger, Dresden. 15 pf. Town Hall, Breslau. 50 pf. The Holstentor, Lubeck.
See also Nos. 485/9.

**1932.** Welfare Fund. Nos. 472/3 surch.

476. 6+4 pf. on 8 pf.+4 pf. grn. 5·00 12·00
477. 12+3 pf. on 15 pf.+5 pf. red 6·00 14·00

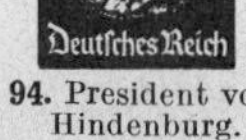

94. President von Hindenburg. 96. Frederick the Great. (after A. von Menzel).

**1932.** 85th Birthday of Pres. von Hindenburg.

478 94 4 pf. blue .. .. 60 25
496B 5 pf. green .. .. 10 20
480 12 pf. orange .. .. 5·00 20
481 15 pf. red .. .. 4·00 12·00
503B 25 pf. blue .. .. 35 20
483 40 pf. violet .. .. 17·00 2·00
484 50 pf. brown .. .. 9·00 12·00

See also Nos. 493/509 and 545/50.

**1932.** Welfare Fund. As T 92.

485. 4 pf.+2 pf. blue .. .. 30 60
486. 6 pf.+4 pf. olive .. .. 30 60
487. 12 pf.+3 pf. red .. .. 50 90
488. 25 pf.+10 of. blue .. 8·00 18·00
489. 40 pf.+40 pf. purple .. 28·00 60·00

CASTLES: 4 pf. Wartburg. 6 pf. Stolzenfels. 12 pf. Nuremberg. 25 pf. Lichtenstein. 40 pf. Marburg.

**1933.** Opening of Reichstag in Potsdam.

490. 96. 6 pf. green .. .. 50 90
491. 12 pf. red .. .. 50 90
492. 25 pf. blue .. .. 35·00 20·00

**1933.**

493B 94 1 pf. black .. .. 30 20
494B 3 pf. brown .. .. 10 20
495B 4 pf. grey .. .. 10 20
497B 6 pf. green .. .. 10 20
498B 8 pf. orange .. .. 10 20
499B 10 pf. brown .. .. 30 20
500B 12 pf. red .. .. 20 20
501B 15 pf. red .. .. 30 20
502B 20 pf. blue .. .. 35 20
504B 30 pf. green .. .. 70 20
505B 40 pf. mauve .. .. 70 30
506B 50 pf. black and green 1·00 35
507B 60 pf black and red .. 90 40
508B 80 pf. black and blue 2·50 1·25
509B 100 pf. black & yellow 5·50 75

**1933.** Air. "Graf Zeppelin" Chicago World Exhibition Flight. Optd. **Chicagofahrt Weltausstellung 1933.**

510. 83. 1 m. red .. .. £425 £275
511. 2 m. blue .. .. 48·00 £150
512. 4 m. brown .. .. 45·00 £150

99. Tannhauser.

**1933.** Welfare Fund. Wagner's Operas.

513. 99. 3 pf.+2 pf. brown .. 1·90 5·50
514. – 4 pf.+2 pf. blue .. 1·50 1·75
515. – 5 pf.+2 pf. green .. 3·75 6·50
516. – 6 pf.+4 pf. green .. 1·40 1·25
517. – 8 pf.+4 pf. orange .. 2·25 3·25
518. – 12 pf.+3 pf. red .. 2·25 1·75
519. – 20 pf.+10 pf. light blue £150 £160
520. – 25 pf.+15 pf. blue .. 34·00 35·00
521. – 40 pf.+35 pf. mauve .. £125 £120

OPERAS: 4 pf. "The Flying Dutchman". 5 pf. "Rhinegold". 6 pf. "The Mastersingers". 8 pf. "The Valkyries". 12 pf. "Siegfried". 20 pf. "Tristan and Isolde". 25 pf. "Lohengrin". 40 pf. "Parsifal".

**1933.** Welfare Fund. Stamps as 1924, issued together in sheets of four, each stamp optd. **1923-1933.**

522. 65. 5+15 pf. green .. 75·00 £225
523. – 10+30 pf. red .. .. 75·00 £225
524. – 20+60 pf. blue .. 75·00 £225
525. – 50 pf.+1·50 m. brn. .. 75·00 £225

100. Golden Eagle, Globe and Swastika. 101. Count Zeppelin and "Graf Zeppelin".

**1934.** Air.

526A 100 5 pf. green .. .. 75 40
527A 10 pf. red .. .. 75 55
528A 15 pf. blue .. .. 1·10 60
529A 20 pf. blue .. .. 2·00 1·40
530A 25 pf. brown .. .. 2·75 1·25
531A 40 pf. mauve .. .. 5·50 1·00
532A 50 pf. green .. .. 4·00 65
533A 80 pf. yellow .. .. 5·00 4·50
534A 100 pf. black .. .. 6·00 2·50
535A – 2 m. grey and green .. 16·00 20·00
536A 101 3 m. grey and blue .. 35·00 38·00

DESIGN—As Type 101: 2 m. Otto Lilienthal and biplane glider.

103. Franz A. E. Luderitz. 104. "Saar Ownership". 105. Nuremberg Castle.

**1934.** German Colonizers' Jubilee.

537 103 3 pf. brn & chocolate 2·75 6·50
538 – 6 pf. brown and green 1·00 1·00
539 – 12 pf. brown and red 1·50 65
540 – 25 pf. brown and blue 8·50 16·00

DESIGNS: 6 pf. Gustav Nachtigal. 12 pf. Karl Peters. 25 pf. Hermann von Wissmann.

**1934.** Saar Plebiscite.

541. 104. 6 pf. green .. .. 3·00 30
542. – 12 pf. red .. .. 5·00 30

DESIGN: 12 pf. Eagle inscribed "Saar" in rays from a swastika-eclipsed sun.

**1934.** Nuremberg Congress.

543. 105. 6 pf. green .. .. 2·75 30
544. 12 pf. red .. .. 4·00 30

**1934.** Hindenburg Memorial. Portrait with black borders.

545. 94. 3 pf. brown .. .. 90 35
546. 5 pf. green .. .. 90 50
547. 6 pf. green .. .. 1·40 30
548. 8 pf. orange .. .. 2·50 30
549. 12 pf. red .. .. 2·25 25
550. 25 pf. blue .. .. 9·00 7·50

106. Blacksmith. 107. Friedrich von Schiller. 108. "The Saar comes home".

**1934.** Welfare Fund.

551 – 3 pf.+2 pf. brown .. 90 1·25
552 106 4 pf.+2 pf. black .. 70 1·00
553 – 5 pf.+2 pf. green .. 4·75 7·00
554 – 6 pf.+4 pf. green .. 40 35
555 – 8 pf.+4 pf. red .. 70 1·00
556 – 12 pf.+3 pf. red .. 40 40
557 – 20 pf.+10 pf. green .. 15·00 22·00
558 – 25 pf.+15 pf. blue .. 15·00 22·00
559 – 40 pf.+35 pf. lilac .. 40·00 65·00

DESIGNS: 3 pf. Merchant. 5 pf. Mason. 6 pf. Miner. 8 pf. Architect. 12 pf. Farmer. 20 pf. Scientist. 25 pf. Sculptor. 40 pf. Judge.

**1934.** 175th Birth Anniv. of Schiller.

560. 107. 6 pf. green .. .. 2·75 30
561. 12 pf. red .. .. 4·50 30

**1935.** Saar Restoration.

562. 108. 3 pf. brown .. .. 75 1·00
563. 6 pf. green .. .. 75 30
564. 12 pf. red .. .. 5·00 30
565. 25 pf. blue .. .. 8·50 6·00

109. "Steel helmet". 110. "Victor's Crown".

**1935.** War Heroes' Day.

566. 109. 6 pf. green .. .. 1·00 1·60
567. 12 pf. red .. .. 1·00 1·60

**1935.** Apprentices Vocational Contest.

568. 110. 6 pf. green .. .. 75 1·25
569. 12 pf. red .. .. 1·00 1·25

111. Heinrich Schutz. 112. Allenstein Castle.

**1935.** Musicians' Anniversaries.

570. 111. 6 pf. green .. .. 1·25 20
571. – 12 pf. red (Bach) .. 1·40 20
572. – 25 pf. blue (Handel) .. 2·00 80

**1935.** Int. Philatelic Exn., Konigsberg. In miniature sheets.

573. 112. 3 pf. brown .. .. 35·00 40·00
574. – 6 pf. green .. .. 35·00 40·00
575. – 12 pf. red .. .. 35·00 40·00
576. – 25 pf. blue .. .. 35·00 40·00

DESIGNS: 6 pf. Tannenberg Memorial. 12 pf. Konigsberg Castle. 25 pf. Heilsberg Castle.

113. "Der Adler". 114. Trumpeter.

**1935.** German Railway Cent. Locomotive types inscr. "1835–1935".

577. 113. 6 pf. green .. .. 1·50 40
578. – 12 pf. red .. .. 1·50 40
579. – 25 pf. blue .. .. 12·00 1·50
580. – 40 pf. purple .. .. 14·00 1·75

DESIGNS: 12 pf. Steam train. 25 pf. Diesel train "The Flying Hamburger". 40 pf. Streamlined steam train.

**1935.** World Jamboree of "Hitler Youth".

581. 114. 6 pf. green .. .. 1·50 2·25
582. 15 pf. red .. .. 1·75 2·75

**115.** Nuremberg. **116.** East Prussia.

**1935.** Nuremberg Congress.
583. **115.** 6 pf. green .. .. 80 40
584. 12 pf. red .. .. 1·25 40

**1935.** Welfare Fund. Provincial Costumes.
585 **116** 3 pf.+2 pf. brown .. 20 25
586 – 4 pf.+3 pf. blue .. 1·25 1·00
587 – 5 pf.+3 pf. green .. 20 50
588 – 6 pf.+4 pf. green .. 25 20
589 – 8 pf.+4 pf. brown .. 2·00 1·25
590 – 12 pf.+6 pf. red .. 20 20
591 – 15 pf.+10 pf. brown .. 5·00 5·00
592 – 25 pf.+15 pf. blue .. 7·50 5·00
593 – 30 pf.+20 pf. grey .. 19·00 20·00
594 – 40 pf.+35 pf. mauve .. 14·00 14·00
Costumes: 4 pf. Silesia. 5 pf. Rhineland. 6 pf. Lower Saxony. 8 pf. Kurmark. 12 pf. Black Forest. 15 pf. Hesse. 25 pf. Upper Bavaria. 30 pf. Friesland. 40 pf. Franconia.

**117.** S.A. Man and Feldherrnhalle, Munich. **118.** Skating.

**1935.** 12th Anniv. of 1st Hitler Putsch.
595. **117.** 3 pf. brown .. .. 1·00 60
596. 12 pf. red .. .. 1·50 50

**1935.** Winter Olympic Games, Garmisch-Partenkirchen.
597. **118.** 6 pf.+4 pf. green .. 70 50
598. – 12 pf.+6 pf. red .. 1·50 75
599. – 25 pf.+15 pf. blue .. 7·00 8·75
Designs: 12 pf. Ski jumping. 25 pf. Bobsleighing.

**119.** Heinkel He 70 Blitz. **120.** Gottlieb Daimler.

**1936.** 10th Anniv of Lufthansa Airways.
600 **119** 40 pf. blue .. .. 7·00 1·50

**1936.** Berlin Motor Show. 50th Anniv. of Invention of First Motor Car.
601. **120.** 6 pf. green .. .. 50 40
602. – 12 pf. red (Carl Benz) 75 60

**121.** Airship "Hindenburg". **122.** Otto von Guericke.

**1936.** Air.
603. **121.** 50 pf. blue .. .. 15·00 60
604. 75 pf. green .. .. 20·00 60

**1936.** 250th Death Anniv. of Otto von Guericke (scientist).
605. **122.** 6 pf. green .. .. 30 45

**123.** Gymnastics. **124.** Symbolical of Local Government.

**1936.** Summer Olympic Games, Berlin.
606. **123.** 3 pf.+2 pf. brown .. 20 30
607. – 4 pf.+3 pf. blue .. 20 65
608. – 6 pf.+4 pf. green .. 30 15
609. – 8 pf.+4 pf. red .. 4·50 1·40
610. – 12 pf.+6 pf. red .. 40 15
611. – 15 pf.+10 pf. red .. 8·50 3·75
612. – 25 pf.+15 pf. blue .. 11·00 7·50
613. – 40 pf.+35 pf. violet .. 26·00 15·00
Designs: 4 pf. Diver. 6 pf. Footballer. 8 pf. Javelin thrower. 12 pf. Olympic torchbearer. 15 pf. Fencer. 25 pf. Double scullers. 40 pf. Show jumper.

**1936.** 6th Int. Local Government Congress.
614. **124.** 3 pf. brown .. .. 25 20
615. 5 pf. green .. .. 30 20
616. 12 pf. red .. .. 40 30
617. 25 pf. blue .. .. 1·00 85

**125.** "Brown Ribbon" Race. **126** "Leisure Time".

**1936.** "Brown Ribbon of Germany". Single stamp in miniature sheet.
MS 618. **125.** 42 pf. brown .. 7·50 16·00

**1936.** Int. Recreational Congress, Hamburg.
619. **126.** 6 pf. green .. .. 50 60
620. 15 pf. red .. .. 75 80

**127.** Saluting the Swastika. **128.** Luitpoldhain Heroes Memorial, Nuremberg.

**1936.** Nuremberg Congress.
621. **127.** 6 pf. green .. .. 50 40
622. 12 pf. red .. .. 75 60

**1936.** Winter Relief Fund.
623 – 3 pf.+2 pf. brown .. 15 20
624 – 4 pf.+3 pf. black .. 30 70
625 **128** 5 pf.+3 pf. green .. 20 20
626 – 6 pf.+4 pf. green .. 20 20
627 – 8 pf.+4 pf. brown .. 1·00 1·75
628 – 12 pf.+6 pf. red .. 20 20
629 – 15 pf.+10 pf. brown .. 3·00 5·50
630 – 25 pf.+15 pf. blue .. 2·75 3·25
631 – 40 pf.+35 pf. mauve .. 3·75 6·00
Designs: 3 pf. Munich frontier road. 4 pf. Air Ministry, Berlin. 6 pf. Bridge over River Saale. 8 pf. Deutschlandhalle, Berlin. 12 pf. Alpine road. 15 pf. Fuhrerhaus, Munich. 25 pf. Bridge over River Mangfall. 40 pf. German Art Museum, Munich.

**129.** R(eichs) L(uftschutz) B(und)=Civil Defence Union.

**1937.** 4th Anniv. of Civil Defence Union.
632. **129.** 3 pf. brown .. .. 20 30
633. 6 pf. green .. .. 40 25
634. 12 pf. red .. .. 60 60

**131.** Fishing Smacks. **132.** Hitler Youth.

**1937.** Winter Relief Fund.
639. – 3 pf.+2 pf. brown .. 20 30
640. – 4 pf.+3 pf. black .. 1·00 1·00
641. **131.** 5 pf.+3 pf. green .. 20 30
642. – 6 pf.+4 pf. green .. 20 45
643. – 8 pf.+4 pf. orange .. 1·40 1·50
644. – 12 pf.+6 pf. red .. 30 25
645. – 15 pf.+10 pf. brown .. 6·00 4·25
646. – 25 pf.+15 pf. blue .. 9·00 4·00
647. – 40 pf.+35 pf. purple .. 7·50 9·00
Designs: 3 pf. Lifeboat "Bremen". 4 pf. Lightship "Elbe I". 6 pf. Liner "Wilhelm Gustloff". 8 pf. Barque "Padua". 12 pf. Liner "Tannenberg". 15 pf. Train ferry "Schwerin". 25 pf. Liner "Hamburg". 40 pf. Liner "Europa".

**1938.** Hitler Culture Fund. 5th Anniv. of Hitler's Leadership.
648. **132.** 6 pf.+4 pf. green .. 85 1·00
649. 12 pf.+8 pf. red .. 1·40 1·60

**133.** "Unity". **134.** Adolf Hitler.

**1938.** Austrian Plebiscite.
650. **133.** 6 pf. green .. .. 15 40

**1938.** Hitler's Culture Fund and 49th Birthday.
652. **134.** 12 pf.+38 pf. red .. 2·50 2·50
See also No. 660.

**135.** Breslau Cathedral. **136.** Airship Gondola and "Graf Zeppelin".

**1938.** 16th German Sports Tournament Breslau. Inscr. as in T **135**.
653. **135.** 3 pf. brown .. .. 25 30
654. – 6 pf. green .. .. 40 30
655. – 12 pf. red .. .. 60 30
656. – 15 pf. brown .. .. 90 1·00
Designs: 6 pf. Hermann Goering Stadium. 12 pf. Breslau Town Hall. 15 pf. Centenary Hall.

**1938.** Air. Birth Cent of Count Zeppelin.
657 – 25 pf. blue .. .. 4·25 1·00
658 **136** 50 pf. green .. .. 5·75 1·00
Design: 25 pf. Count Zeppelin in primitive airship gondola and airship LZ-5.

**137.** Horsewoman. **138.** Saarpfalz Gautheater, Saarbrucken.

**1938.** "Brown Ribbon of Germany".
659. **137.** 42 pf.+108 pf. brown .. 32·00 40·00

**1938.** Nuremberg Congress and Hitler's Culture Fund. As No. 652, but inscr. "Reichsparteitag 1938".
660. **134.** 6 pf.+19 pf. green .. 30·00 70·00

**1938.** Opening of Gautheater and Hitler's Culture Fund.
661. **138.** 6 pf.+4 pf. green .. 1·50 2·00
662. 12 pf.+8 pf. red .. 2·25 3·00

**139.** Forchtenstein Castle, Burgenland. **140.** Sudeten Miner and Wife.

**1938.** Winter Relief.
663. **139.** 3 pf.+2 pf. brown .. 20 30
664. – 4 pf.+3 pf. blue .. 2·40 1·75
665. – 5 pf.+3 pf. green .. 15 40
666. – 6 pf.+4 pf. green .. 15 20
667. – 8 pf.+4 pf. red .. 2·00 1·75
668. – 12 pf.+6 pf. red .. 25 30
669. – 15 pf.+10 pf. red .. 5·00 5·75
670. – 25 pf.+15 pf. blue .. 4·00 5·75
671. – 40 pf.+35 pf. mauve .. 10·00 11·00
Designs: 4 pf. Flexenstrasse. 5 pf. Zell am See. 6 pf. Grossglockner. 8 pf. Augstein Castle, Wachau. 12 pf. Wien (Prince Eugene Statue, Vienna). 15 pf. Erzberg, Steiermark. 25 pf. Hall i. Tirol. 40 pf. Braunau.

**1938.** Acquisition of Sudetenland and Hitler's Culture Fund.
672. **140.** 6 pf.+4 pf. green .. 1·25 2·75
673. 12 pf.+8 pf. red .. 2·50 4·75

**141.** Racing Cars. **142.** Eagle and Laurel Wreath.

**1939.** Int. Motor Show, Berlin, and Hitler's Culture Fund. Inscr. "Internationale Automobil—und Motorrad—Ausstellung Berlin 1939".
674. – 6 pf.+4 pf. green .. 3·75 3·50
675. **141.** 12 pf.+8 pf. red .. 4·00 3·75
676. – 25 pf.+10 pf. blue .. 11·00 6·50
Designs: 6 pf. Early Benz and Daimler cars. 25 pf. Volkswagen car.

**1939.** Apprentices' Vocational Contest.
677. **142.** 6 pf. green .. .. 1·75 3·25
678. 12 pf. red .. .. 2·00 3·25

**143.** Adolf Hitler in Braunau. **144.** Horticultural Exhibition Entrance and Arms of Stuttgart.

**1939.** Hitler's 50th Birthday and Culture Fund.
679. **143.** 12 pf.+38 pf. red .. 2·50 5·50

**1939.** Stuttgart Horticultural Exhibition and Hitler's Culture Fund.
680. **144.** 6 pf.+4 pf. green .. 1·50 2·25
681. 15 pf.+5 pf. red .. 1·50 2·25

**145.** Adolf Hitler Speaking. **147.** "Investment" and Jockey.

**1939.** National Labour Day and Hitler's Culture Fund.
682. **145.** 6 pf.+19 pf. brown .. 2·75 5·75
See also No. 689.

**1939.** Nurburgring Races and Hitler's Culture Fund. Nos. 674/6 optd. **Nurburgring-Rennen.**
683. – 6 pf.+4 pf. green .. 30·00 32·00
684. **141.** 12 pf.+8 pf. red .. 30·00 32·00
685. – 25 pf.+10 pf. blue .. 30·00 32·00

**1939.** 70th Anniv. of German Derby.
686. **147.** 25 pf.+50 pf. blue .. 20·00 20·00

**148.** Training Thoroughbred Horses. **149.** "Young Venetian Woman" after Durer.

**1939.** "Brown Ribbon of Germany" and Hitler's Culture Fund.
687. **148.** 42 pf.+108 pf. brown 17·00 30·00

**1939.** German Art Day.
688. **149.** 6 pf.+19 pf. green .. 5·50 9·00

**1939.** Nuremberg Congress and Hitler's Culture Fund. As T **145**, but inscr. "REICHS-/PARTEITAG/1939"
689. 6 pf.+19 pf. brown .. 3·75 9·00

**150.** Mechanics at Work and Play. **151.** St. Mary's Church, Danzig.

**1939.** Postal Employees' and Hitler's Culture Funds. Inscr. "Kameradschaftsblock der Deutschen Reichspost".
690. – 3 pf.+2 pf. brown .. 4·00 6·00
691. – 4 pf.+3 pf. blue .. 4·00 6·00
692. **150.** 5 pf.+3 pf. green .. 1·00 1·50
693. – 6 pf.+4 pf. green .. 1·00 1·50
694. – 8 pf.+4 pf. orange .. 1·00 1·75
695. – 10 pf.+5 pf. brown .. 1·00 2·25
696. – 12 pf.+6 pf. red .. 1·00 2·25
697. – 15 pf.+10 pf. red .. 1·00 2·50
698. – 16 pf.+10 pf. green .. 1·25 2·25
699. – 20 pf.+10 pf. blue .. 1·00 2·25
700. – 24 pf.+10 pf. olive .. 3·50 4·00
701. – 25 pf.+15 pf. blue .. 3·50 5·00
Designs: 3 pf. Postal employees' rally. 4 pf. Review in Vienna. 6 pf. Youths on parade. 8 pf. Flag bearers. 10 pf. Distributing prizes. 12 pf. Motor race. 15 pf. Women athletes. 16 pf. Postal police. 20 pf. Glider workshop. 24 pf. Mail coach. 25 pf. Sanatorium, Konigstein.
See also Nos. 761/6 and 876/81.

**1939.** Occupation of Danzig. Inscr. "DANZIG IST DEUTSCH".
702. **151.** 6 pf. green .. .. 30 50
703. – 12 pf. red (Crane Gate) 40 60

**1939.** Stamps of Danzig surch. **Deutsches Reich** and new Values.
704. **28.** 3 Rpf. on 3 pf. brown 1·00 2·25
705. 4 Rpf. on 35 pf. blue .. 1·00 2·25
706. Rpf. on 5 pf. orange 1·00 2·25
707. Rpf. on 8 pf. green 1·75 4·00
708. Rpf. on 10 pf. green 2·00 4·00
709. 12 Rpf. on 7 pf. green .. 1·25 2·25
710. Rpf. on 15 pf. red .. 6·00 12·00
711. Rpf. on 20 pf. grey .. 3·50 8·00
712. Rpf. on 25 pf. red .. 6·00 12·00
713. Rpf. on 30 pf. purple 1·75 4·50
714. Rpf. on 40 pf. blue .. 1·90 5·50
715. Rpf. on 50 pf. red and blue .. .. 4·00 8·00
716. **42.** 1 Rm on 1 g. black and orange .. .. 14·00 28·00
717. – 2 Rm. on 2 g. black & red (No. 206) .. 20·00 45·00

**155.** Elbogen Castle. **156.** Leipzig Library and Gutenberg.

**1939.** Winter Relief Fund.

718 **155** 3 pf.+2 pf. brown .. 15 30
719 – 4 pf.+3 pf. black .. 2·00 2·25
720 – 5 pf.+3 pf. green .. 20 40
721 – 6 pf.+4 pf. green .. 20 30
722 – 8 pf.+4 pf. red .. 2·00 1·40
723 – 12 pf.+6 pf. red .. 25 30
724 – 15 pf.+10 pf. brown .. 3·75 6·00
725 – 25 pf.+15 pf. blue .. 2·75 5·75
726 – 40 pf.+35 pf. purple .. 4·00 7·50

DESIGNS: 4 pf. Drachenfels. 5 pf. Goslar Castle. 6 pf. Clocktower, Graz. 8 pf. The Romer, Frankfurt. 12 pf. City Hall, Klagenfurt. 15 pf. Ruins of Schreckenstein Castle. 25 pf. Salzburg Fortress. 40 pf. Hohentwiel Castle.

**1940.** Leipzig Fair.

727. **156.** 3 pf. brown .. .. 25 60
728. – 6 pf. green .. .. 30 60
729. – 12 pf. red .. .. 30 60
730. – 25 pf. blue .. .. 60 1·25

DESIGNS: 6 pf. Augustusplatz. 12 pf. Old Town Hall. 25 pf. View of Fair.

**157.** Courtyard of Chancellery, Berlin. **158.** Hitler and Child.

**1940.** 2nd Berlin Philatelic Exhibition.

731. **157.** 24 pf.+76 pf. green .. 7·50 16·00

**1940.** Hitler's 51st Birthday.

732. **158.** 12 pf.+38 pf. red .. 3·50 7·00

**159.** Wehrmacht Symbol. **160.** Horseman.

**1940.** National Fete Day and Hitler's Culture Fund.

733. **159.** 6 pf.+4 pf. green .. 40 85

**1940.** Hamburg Derby and Hitler's Culture Fund.

734. **160.** 25 pf.+100 pf. blue .. 4·50 12·00

**161.** Chariot. **162.** Malmedy.

**1940.** Hitler's Culture Fund and "Brown Ribbon" Race.

735. **161.** 42 pf.+108 pf. brown 18·00 30·00

**1940.** Eupen and Malmedy reincorporated in Germany, and Hitler's Culture Fund. Inscr. "Eupen-Malmedy wieder deutsch".

736. **162.** 6 pf.+4 pf. green .. 80 2·75
737. – 12 pf.+8 pf. red .. 80 2·75

DESIGN: 12 pf. View of Eupen.

**163.** Heligoland. **164.** Artushof, Danzig.

**1940.** 50th Anniv. of Cession of Heligoland to Germany and Hitler's Culture Fund.

738. **163.** 6 pf.+94 pf. red & green 4·50 8·50

**1940.** Winter Relief Fund.

739 **164** 3 pf.+2 pf. brown .. 15 30
740 – 4 pf.+3 pf. blue .. 1·00 1·00
741 – 5 pf.+3 pf. green .. 20 50
742 – 6 pf.+4 pf. green .. 25 15
743 – 8 pf.+4 pf. orange .. 1·50 1·00
744 – 12 pf.+6 pf. red .. 20 15
745 – 15 pf.+10 pf. brown .. 1·50 2·75
746 – 25 pf.+15 pf. blue .. 2·00 3·00
747 – 40 pf.+35 pf. purple .. 3·00 6·00

DESIGNS: 4 pf. Town Hall, Thorn. 5 pf. Kaub Castle. 6 pf. City Theatre, Posen. 8 pf. Heidelberg Castle. 12 pf. Porta Nigra, Trier. 15 pf. New Theatre, Prague. 25 pf. Town Hall, Bremen. 40 pf. Town Hall, Munster.

**165.** Emil von Behring (bacteriologist). **166.** Postilion and Globe.

**1940.** 50th Anniv. of Development of Diphtheria Antitoxin.

748 **165** 6 pf.+4 pf. green .. 80 1·40
749 25 pf.+10 pf. blue .. 1·25 3·00

**1941.** Stamp Day.

750. **166.** 6 pf.+24 pf. green .. 75 2·00

**167.** Mussolini and Hitler. **168.** House of Nations, Leipzig.

**1941.** Hitler's Culture Fund.

751. **167.** 12 pf.+38 pf. red .. 1·50 3·50

**1941.** Leipzig Fair. Buildings. Inscr. "REICHSMESSE LEIPZIG 1941".

752. **168.** 3 pf. brown .. .. 30 60
753. – 6 pf. green .. .. 30 60
754. – 12 pf. red .. .. 40 90
755. – 25 pf. blue .. .. 80 1·25

DESIGNS: 6 pf. Cloth Hall. 12 pf. Exhibition Building. 25 pf. Railway Station.

**169.** Dancer. **170.** Adolf Hitler.

**1941.** Vienna Fair.

756. **169.** 3 pf. brown .. .. 25 60
757. – 6 pf. green .. .. 25 60
758. – 12 pf. red .. .. 35 70
759. – 25 pf. blue .. .. 80 2·00

DESIGNS: 6 pf. Arms and Exhibition Building. 12 pf. Allegory and Municipal Theatre. 25 pf. Prince Eugene's Equestrian Monument.

**1941.** Hitler's 52nd Birthday and Culture Fund.

760. **170.** 12 pf.+38 pf. red .. 2·00 3·00

**1941.** Postal Employees' and Hitler's Culture Funds. Inscr. "Kameradschaftsblock der Deutschen Reichspost" as Nos. 693/4, 696 and 698/700, but premium values and colours changed.

761. 6 pf.+9 pf. green .. 80 1·40
762. 8 pf.+12 pf. red .. 80 1·25
763. 12 pf.+18 pf. red .. 80 1·25
764. 16 pf.+24 pf. black .. 1·50 3·50
765. 20 pf.+30 pf. blue .. 1·50 3·50
766. 24 pf.+36 pf. violet .. 4·00 12·50

**171.** Racehorse. **172.** Two Amazons.

**1941.** 72nd Anniv. of Hamburg Derby.

767. **171.** 25 pf.+100 pf. blue .. 4·50 7·50

**1941.** "Brown Ribbon of Germany".

768 **172** 42 pf.+108 pf. brown .. 3·00 5·75

**173.** Adolf Hitler. **174.** Brandenburg Gate, Berlin.

**1941.**

769. **173.** 1 pf. grey .. .. 10 15
770. 3 pf. brown .. .. 10 15
771. 4 pf. slate .. .. 10 15
772. 5 pf. green .. .. 10 15
773. 6 pf. violet .. .. 10 15
774. 8 pf. red .. .. 10 15
775. 10 pf. brown .. .. 15 30
776. 12 pf. red .. .. 10 30
779. 15 pf. lake .. .. 10 20
780. 16 pf. green .. .. 20 1·25
781. 20 pf. blue .. .. 10 20
782. 24 pf. brown .. .. 10 1·25
783. 25 pf. blue .. .. 10 20
784. 30 pf. olive .. .. 10 20
785. 40 pf. mauve .. .. 15 20
786. 50 pf. green .. .. 15 20
787. 60 pf. brown .. .. 15 20
788. 80 pf. blue .. .. 15 20

Nos. 783/8 are larger (21½×26 mm.)

**1941.** Berlin Grand Prix and Hitler's Culture Fund.

789. **174.** 25 pf.+50 pf. blue .. 3·00 6·50

**175.** Belvedere Palace, Vienna. **176.** Belvedere Gardens, Vienna.

**1941.** Vienna Fair and Hitler's Culture Fund.

790. **175.** 12 pf.+8 pf. red .. 75 2·50
791. **176.** 15 pf.+10 pf. violet .. 1·00 2·75

**177.** Marburg. **178.** Veldes.

**1941.** Annexation of Northern Slovenia, and Hitler's Culture Fund.

792. **177.** 3 pf.+7 pf. brown .. 80 1·25
793. **178.** 6 pf.+9 pf. violet .. 70 1·60
794. – 12 pf.+13 pf. red .. 80 1·75
795. – 25 pf.+15 pf. blue .. 2·00 3·50

DESIGNS: 12 pf. Pettau. 25 pf. Triglav.

**179.** Mozart. **180.** Philatelist.

**1941.** 150th Death Anniv. of Mozart and Hitler's Culture Fund.

796. **179.** 6 pf.+4 pf. purple .. 30 50

**1942.** Stamp Day and Hitler's Culture Fund.

797. **180.** 6 pf.+24 pf. violet .. 55 2·50

**181.** Symbolical of Heroism. **182.** Adolf Hitler.

**1942.** Heroes' Remembrance Day and Hitler's Culture Fund.

798. **181.** 12 pf.+38 pf. slate .. 40 1·50

**1942.**

799. **182.** 1 m. green .. .. 20 75
800. 2 m. violet .. .. 70 1·50
801. 3 m. red .. .. 70 1·75
802. 5 m. blue .. .. 1·25 4·00

**183.** Adolf Hitler. **184.** Jockey and Three-year-old Horse.

**1942.** Hitler's 53rd Birthday and Culture Fund.

803. **183.** 12 pf.+38 pf. red .. 3·00 6·00

**1942.** Hamburg Derby and Hitler's Culture Fund.

804. **184.** 25 pf.+100 pf. blue .. 6·00 14·00

**185.** Equine Trio. **186.** Cream Jug and Loving Cup.

**1942.** "Brown Ribbon of Germany" and Hitler's Culture Fund.

805. **185.** 42 pf.+108 pf. brown 2·25 7·00

**1942.** 10th Anniv. of National Goldsmiths' Institution.

806. **186.** 6 pf.+4 pf. red .. 30 1·00
807. 12 pf.+88 pf. green .. 50 2·00

**187.** Badge of Armed S.A. **188.** Peter Henlein.

**1942.** S.A. Military Training Month.

808. **187.** 6 pf. violet .. .. 20 90

**1942.** 400th Death Anniv. of Henlein (inventor of the watch).

809. **188.** 6 pf.+24 pf. violet .. 50 1·25

DESIGNS—HORIZ. 3 pf. Postilion and map of Europe. VERT. 6 pf. Mounted postilion and globe.

**189.** Mounted Postilion.

**1942.** European Postal Congress, Vienna.

810. – 3 pf.+7 pf. blue .. 30 1·75
811. – 6 pf.+14 pf. brn. & bl. 40 1·75
812. **189.** 12 pf.+38 pf. brown and red .. 75 2·75

**1942.** Signing of European Postal Union Agreement. Nos. 810/2 optd. **19. Okt. 1942.**

813. – 3 pf.+7 pf. blue .. 75 2·75
814. – 6 pf.+14 pf. brown and blue .. .. 75 2·75
815. **189.** 12 pf.+38 pf. brown and red .. .. 1·00 5·50

**191.** Mail Coach. **192.** Brandenburg Gate and Torchlight Parade.

**1943.** Stamp Day and Hitler's Culture Fund.

816. **191.** 6 pf.+24 pf. brown, yellow and blue .. 25 80

**1943.** 10th Anniv. of Third Reich.

817. **192.** 54 pf.+96 pf. red .. 35 2·00

**193.** **194.** Machine Gunners.

**1943.** Philatelic Cancellation Premium.

818. **193.** 3 pf.+2 pf. bistre .. 20 60

**1943.** Armed Forces' and Heroes' Day.

819 – 3 pf.+2 pf. brown .. 50 1·25
820 **194** 4 pf.+3 pf. brown .. 40 60
821 – 5 pf.+4 pf. green .. 40 70
822 – 6 pf.+9 pf. violet .. 50 70
823 – 8 pf.+7 pf. red .. 50 70
824 – 12 pf.+8 pf. red .. 50 80
825 – 15 pf.+10 pf. purple .. 50 80
826 – 20 pf.+14 pf. blue .. 60 1·00
827 – 25 pf.+15 pf. blue .. 70 1·00
828 – 30 pf.+30 pf. green .. 75 1·40
829 – 40 pf.+40 pf. purple .. 75 2·00
830 – 50 pf.+50 pf. green .. 1·00 3·00

DESIGNS: 3 pf. U-boat Type VIIA. 5 pf. Armed motor cyclists. 6 pf. Wireless operators. 8 pf. Engineers making pontoon. 12 pf. Grenade thrower. 15 pf. Heavy artillery. 20 pf. Anti-aircraft gunners. 25 pf. Junkers Ju 87B "Stuka" dive bombers. 30 pf. Parachutists. 40 pf. Tank. 50 pf. Motor torpedo-boat.

**195.** Hitler Youth. **196.** Adolf Hitler.

**1943.** Youth Dedication Day.

831. **195.** 6 pf.+4 pf. green .. 25 90

**1943.** Hitler's 54th Birthday and Culture Fund.

832. **196.** 3 pf.+7 pf. black .. 40 1·00
833. 6 pf.+14 pf. green .. 40 1·00
834. 8 pf.+22 pf. blue .. 40 1·00
835. 12 pf.+38 pf. red .. 40 1·00
836. 24 pf.+76 pf. purple .. 1·00 3·00
837. 40 pf.+160 pf. olive .. 1·00 3·50

**197.** Attestation. **198.** Huntsman.

**1943.** Labour Corps.

838. **197.** 3 pf.+7 pf. brown .. 15 50
839. – 5 pf.+10 pf. green .. 15 50
840. – 6 pf.+14 pf. blue .. 15 65
841. – 12 pf.+18 pf. red .. 30 1·25

DESIGNS: 5 pf. Harvester sharpening scythe. 6 pf. Labourer wielding sledge-hammer. 12 pf. "Pick and shovel fatigue".

**1943.** "Brown Ribbon of Germany".

842. **198.** 42 pf.+108 pf. brown 30 1·25

**199.** Birthplace of Peter Rosegger. **200.** Peter Rosegger.

**1943.** Birth Cent. of Peter Rossegger (poet).

843. **199.** 6 pf.+4 pf. green .. 20 50
844. **200.** 12 pf.+8 pf. red .. 20 70

**201.** Racehorse. **202.** Mother and Children.

**1943.** Grand Prix, Vienna.

845. **201.** 6 pf.+4 pf. violet .. 20 1·00
846. 12 pf.+88 pf. red .. 20 1·00

**1943.** 10th Anniv. of Winter Relief Fund.

847. **202.** 12 pf.+38 pf. red .. 25 1·00

**203.** St. George and the Dragon. **204.** Lubeck.

**1943.** 11th Anniv. of National Goldsmiths' Institution.

848. **203.** 6 pf.+4 pf. green 20 60
849. 12 pf.+88 pf. purple 20 1·00

**1943.** 800th Anniv. of Lubeck.

850. **204.** 12 pf.+8 pf. red .. 20 75

**205.**

**1943.** 20th Anniv. of Munich Rising.

851. **205.** 24 pf.+26 pf. red .. 20 80

**206.** Dr. Robert Koch. **207.** Adolf Hitler.

**1944.** Birth Centenary of Dr. Robert Koch (bacteriologist).

852. **206.** 12 pf.+38 pf. sepia .. 25 80

**1944.** 11th Anniv. of Third Reich.

853. **207.** 54 pf.+96 pf. brown 25 1·25

**208.** Focke Wulf Condor over Tempelhof Airport. **209.** Dornier Do-26 Flying Boat.

**1944.** 25th Anniv of Air Mail Services.

854 **208** 6 pf.+4 pf. green .. 20 60
855 **209** 12 pf.+8 pf. purple .. 20 90
856 – 42 pf.+108 pf. blue .. 30 2·25

DESIGN—VERT. 42 pf. Junkers Ju 90B airplane seen from above.

**210.** Day Nursery. **211.** "Mothers' Help".

**1944.** 10th Anniv. of "Mother and Child" Organization.

857. **210.** 3 pf.+2 pf. brown .. 15 35
858. **211.** 6 pf.+4 pf. green .. 15 35
859. – 12 pf.+8 pf. red .. 20 35
860. – 15 pf.+10 pf. purple .. 25 65

DESIGNS: 12 pf. Child auscultation. 15 pf. Mothers at convalescent home.

**212.** Landing Craft. **213.** Fulda Monument.

**1944.** Armed Forces' and Heroes' Day.

861. **212.** 3 pf.+2 pf. brown .. 50 1·25
862. – 4 pf.+3 pf. blue .. 30 60
863. – 5 pf.+3 pf. green .. 30 60
864. – 6 pf.+4 pf. violet .. 30 60
865. – 8 pf.+4 pf. red .. 30 60
866. – 10 pf.+5 pf. brown .. 30 60
867. – 12 pf.+6 pf. red .. 30 60
868. – 15 pf.+10 pf. purple .. 30 60
869. – 16 pf.+10 pf. green .. 40 1·25
870. – 20 pf.+10 pf. blue .. 45 1·25
871. – 24 pf.+10 pf. brown .. 50 1·25
872. – 25 pf.+15 pf. blue .. 1·00 1·25
873. – 30 pf.+20 pf. olive .. 1·00 3·75

DESIGNS: 4 pf. Caterpillar tricar. 5 pf. Parachutists. 6 pf. Submarine officer. 8 pf. Mortar-firing party. 10 pf. Searchlight unit. 12 pf. Machine gunners. 15 pf. Tank. 16 pf. Motor torpedo-boat. 20 pf. Arado Ar 196A seaplane. 24 pf. Armoured train. 25 pf. Rocket projectiles. 30 pf. Alpine trooper.

**1944.** 1200th Anniv. of Fulda.

874. **213.** 12 pf.+38 pf. brown 25 85

**214.** Adolf Hitler. **215.** Postwoman.

**1944.** Hitler's 55th Birthday.

875. **214.** 54 pf.+96 pf. red .. 40 1·60

**1944.** Postal Employees' and Hitler's Culture Funds. Inscr. "Kameradschaftsblock der Deutschen Reichspost".

876 **215** 6 pf.+9 pf. blue .. 15 35
877 – 8 pf.+12 pf. grey .. 15 35
878 – 12 pf.+18 pf. mauve 15 55
879 – 16 pf.+24 pf. green .. 15 60
880 – 20 pf.+30 pf. blue .. 25 1·25
881 – 24 pf.+36 pf. violet .. 25 1·40

DESIGNS: As Type **150**—8 pf. Mail coach. 16 pf. Motor-car race. 20 pf. Postal police march. 24 pf. Glider workshop. As Type **215**—12 pf. The Field Post on Eastern Front.

**216.** Girl Worker. **217.** Labourer.

**1944.** Labour Corps.

882. **216.** 6 pf.+4 pf. green .. 10 55
883. **217.** 12 pf.+8 pf. red .. 10 65

**218.** Riflemen. **219.** Duke Albrecht.

**1944.** 7th Innsbruck Shooting Competition.

884. **218.** 6 pf.+4 pf. green .. 10 55
885. 12 pf.+8 pf. red .. 35 65

**1944.** 400th Anniv. of Albert University, Konigsberg.

886. **219.** 6 pf.+4 pf. green .. 25 1·25

**220.** Racehorse and Foal.

**1944.** "Brown Ribbon of Germany".

887. **220.** 42 pf.+108 pf. brown 30 1·40

**221.** Racehorse and Laurel Wreath. **222.** Chambered Nautilus Beaker.

**1944.** Vienna Grand Prix.

888. **221.** 6 pf.+4 pf. green .. 10 1·25
889. 12 pf.+88 pf. red .. 15 1·50

**1944.** National Goldsmiths' Institution.

890. **222.** 6 pf.+4 pf. green .. 10 1·25
891. 12 pf.+88 pf. red .. 20 1·50

**223.** Posthorn. **224.** Eagle and Dragon.

**1944.** Stamp Day.

892. **223.** 6 pf.+24 pf. green .. 25 1·25

**1944.** 21st Anniv. of Munich Rising.

893. **224.** 12 pf.+8 pf. red .. 25 1·25

**225.** Adolf Hitler. **226.** Count Anton Gunther.

**1944.**

894. **225.** 42 pf. green .. .. 15 1·25

**1945.** 600th Anniv. of Oldenburg.

895. **226.** 6 pf.+14 pf. purple .. 25 1·40

**227.** "Home Guard." **228.** S.S. Troopers.

**1945.** Mobilization of "Home Guard".

896. **227.** 12 pf.+8 pf. red .. 40 1·75

**1945.** 12th Anniv. of Third Reich.

897. **228.** 12 pf.+38 pf. red .. 12·00 35·00
898. – 12 pf.+38 pf. red .. 12·00 40·00

DESIGN: No. 898, S.A. man with torch.

For Nos. 899 onwards see section B of Allied Occupation.

MILITARY FIELDPOST STAMPS

M 184. Junkers Ju 52/3m. M 185.

**1942.** Air. No value indicated. Perf. or roul.

M 804. M **184.** (–) blue .. .. 20 20

**1942.** Parcel Post. Size 28×23 mm. No value indicated. Perf. or roul.

M 805. M **185.** (–) brown .. 20 40

Nos. M 804/5 also exist overprinted **INSEL-POST** in various types for use in Crete and the Aegean Islands and there are various other local fieldpost issues.

**1944.** Christmas Parcel Post. Size 22½ × 18 mm. No value indicated. Perf.

M 895. M **185.** (–) green .. 50 1·50

**1944.** For 2 kilo parcels. No value indicated. No. 785 optd. **FELDPOST 2 kg.**

M 896. (–) on 40 pf. mauve .. 50 1·60

NEWSPAPER STAMPS

N 156. Newspaper Messenger and Globe.

**1939.**

N 727. N **156.** 5 pf. green .. 50 2·75
N 728. 10 pf. brown .. 50 2·75

OFFICIAL STAMPS

O 23. O 24.

**1903.**

O 82. O **23.** 2 pf. grey .. .. 1·25 6·00
O 83. 3 pf. brown .. .. 1·25 6·00
O 84. 5 pf. green .. .. 30 30
O 85. 10 pf. red .. .. 30 30
O 86. 20 pf. blue .. .. 30 30
O 87. 25 pf. black and red on yellow .. .. 30 30
O 88. 40 pf. black and red .. 30 1·50
O 89. 50 pf. black and purple on buff .. .. 40 1·75

**1905.**

O 90. O **24.** 2 pf. grey .. .. 60·00 75·00
O 91. 3 pf. brown .. .. 6·00 6·00
O 92. 5 pf. green .. .. 4·00 5·00
O 93. 10 pf. red .. .. 1·00 2·25
O 94. 20 pf. blue .. .. 1·40 2·25
O 95. 25 pf. black and red on yellow .. .. 35·00 40·00

O 31. O 32.

**1920.** Numeral designs as Types O **31** and O **32**.

O117 5 pf. green .. .. 30 2·50
O118 10 pf. red .. .. 60 1·25
O119 15 pf. brown .. .. 20 1·00
O120 20 pf. blue .. .. 20 70
O121 30 pf. orange on pink .. 15 80
O122 50 pf. violet on pink .. 35 75
O123 1 m. red on pink .. 8·00 4·50

**1920.** Similar designs but without figures "21".

O124 5 pf. green .. .. 1·00 10·00
O125 10 pf. red .. .. 10 40
O126 10 pf. orange .. .. 35 £350
O127 15 pf. purple .. .. 10 65
O128 20 pf. blue .. .. 10 50
O129 30 pf. orange on pink .. 10 50
O130 40 pf. red .. .. 10 50
O131 50 pf. violet on pink .. 10 50
O132 60 pf. brown .. .. 10 1·00
O133 1 m. red on pink .. 10 50
O134 1 m. 25 blue on yellow 10 90
O135a 2 m. blue .. .. 10 50
O136 5 m. brown on yellow .. 10 90

**1920.** Official stamps of Bavaria optd. **Deutsches Reich.**

O137 O **31** 5 pf. green .. 10 2·00
O138 10 pf. orange .. 10 1·50
O139 15 pf. red .. .. 10 1·50
O140 20 pf. purple .. 10 1·10
O141 30 pf. blue .. 10 50
O142 40 pf. brown .. 10 50
O143 O **32** 50 pf. red .. .. 10 50
O144 60 pf. green .. 10 50
O145 70 pf. violet .. 1·60 2·75
O146 75 pf. red .. .. 35 1·10
O147 80 pf. blue .. 10 85
O148 90 pf. olive .. 1·40 6·75
O149 O **33** 1 m. brown .. 10 45
O150 1¼ m. green .. 10 45
O151 1½ m. red .. .. 10 45
O152 2½ m. blue .. 15 85
O153 3 m. red .. .. 15 95
O154 5 m. black .. 8·50 30·00

**1920.** Municipal Service stamps of Wurttemberg optd. **Deutsches Reich.**

O 155. M **5.** 5 pf. green .. 3·50 7·00
O 156. 10 pf. red .. .. 2·00 4·25
O 157. 15 pf. violet .. 2·00 4·25
O 158. 20 pf. blue .. 3·50 10·00
O 159. 50 pf. purple .. 5·00 14·00

**1920.** Official stamps of Wurttemberg optd. **Deutsches Reich.**

O 160. O **5.** 5 pf. green .. .. 25 2·50
O 161. 10 pf. red .. .. 10 1·25
O 162. 15 pf. purple .. 10 1·00
O 163. 20 pf. blue .. .. 10 1·00
O 164. 30 pf. black & orange 10 1·0[illegible]
O 165. 40 pf. black and red 15 [illegible]
O 166. 50 pf. purple .. 1[illegible]
O 167. 1 m. black and grey 2[illegible]

O 48.

O 50.

O 81.

**1922.** Figure designs.

O249 O 48 75 pf. blue .. 10 5·00
O247 – 3 m. brown on red 10 1·00
O248 O 50 10 m. green on red 10 80
O251 20 m. blue on red 10 50
O252 50 m. violet on red 10 50
O253 100 m. red on rose 10 50

**1923.** Postage stamps optd. **Dienstmarke.**

O 274. **51.** 20 m. purple .. 10 6·00
O 275. 30 m. olive .. .. 10 20·00
O 276. **38.** 40 m. green .. 10 3·00
O 277. **54.** 200 m. red .. .. 10 55
O 278. 300 m. green .. 10 55
O 279. 400 m. brown .. 10 55
O 280. 500 m. orange .. 10 55
O 342. **62.** 100 M. grey .. 15 £120
O 343. 200 M. brown .. 15 £110
O 344. 2 Md. green & pink 15 £100
O 345. 5 Md. brown & yell. 15 60·00
O 346. 10 Md. green and light green .. 2·25 £110
O 347. 20 Md. brown & grn. 2·25 £130
O 348. 50 Md. blue .. 1·50 £180

**1923.** Official stamps of 1920 and 1922 surch. **Tausend** or **Millionen** and figure.

O 312. – 5 T. on 5 m. brn. on yellow .. .. 10 2·50
O 313. – 20 T. on 30 pf. orge. on rose (No. O 129) 10 2·50
O 317. O **50.** 75 T. on 50 m. vio. on rose .. .. 10 2·50
O 314. – 100 T. on 15 pf. pur. 10 2·50
O 315. – 250 T. on 10 pf. red (No. O 125) .. 10 2·50
O 318. – 400 T. on 15 pf. pur. 10 32·00
O 319. – 800 T. on 30 pf. orge. on rose (No. O 129) 10 2·75
O 320. O **48.** 1 M. on 75 pf. blue 10 42·00
O 321. – 2 M. on 10 pf. red (No. O 125) .. 10 3·00
O 322. O **50.** 5 M. on 100 m. red on rose .. .. 10 5·00

**1923.** Nos. 352/7 optd. **Dienstmarke.**

O 358. **64.** 3 pf. brown .. .. 15 20
O 359. 5 pf. green .. .. 15 20
O 360. 10 pf. red .. .. 25 10
O 361. 20 pf. blue .. .. 55 20
O 362. 50 pf. orange .. 55 65
O 363. 100 pf. purple .. 3·00 5·50

**1924.** Optd. **Dienstmarke.**

O 376. **66.** 3 pf. brown .. 30 60
O 377. 5 pf. green .. .. 30 20
O 378. 10 pf. red .. .. 30 20
O 379. 20 pf. blue .. .. 30 20
O 380. 30 pf. red .. .. 60 40
O 381. 40 pf. olive .. .. 60 40
O 382. 50 pf. orange .. 3·00 1·75
O 384. **72.** 60 pf. brown .. 1·50 2·50
O 385. 80 pf. grey .. .. 7·75 27·00

**1927.**

O424 O 81 3 pf. brown .. 30 10
O425 4 pf. blue .. .. 25 15
O427 5 pf. green .. 15 10
O428 6 pf. green .. 25 10
O429 8 pf. green .. 15 10
O430 10 pf. red .. .. 8·00 6·00
O432 10 pf. mauve .. 30 25
O433 10 pf. brown .. 2·00 3·25
O434 12 pf. orange .. 30 10
O436 15 pf. red .. .. 30 10
O437 20 pf. green .. 3·00 1·50
O438 20 pf. grey .. 50 30
O439 30 pf. green .. 85 15
O440 40 pf. violet .. 85 20
O441 60 pf. brown .. 1·00 80

O 100.

**1934.**

O526 O 100. 3 pf. brown .. 15 30
O527 4 pf. blue .. 15 30
O528 5 pf. green .. 15 30
O529 6 pf. green .. 15 30
O812 6 pf. violet .. 15 30
O530 8 pf. red .. .. 30 30
O531 10 pf. brown .. 25 30
O532 12 pf. red .. 65 30
O533 15 pf. red .. 65 2·25
O534 20 pf. blue .. 20 35
O818 30 pf. green .. 20 60
O819 40 pf. mauve .. 20 60
O537 50 pf. yellow .. 30 35
O820 50 pf. green .. 2·00 5·50

SPECIAL STAMPS FOR USE BY OFFICIALS OF THE NATIONAL SOCIALIST GERMAN WORKERS' PARTY.

P 132. Party Badge.

**1938.**

O 798. P **132.** 1 pf. black .. 50 1·25
O 799. 3 pf. brown .. 20 30
O 800. 4 pf. blue .. 20 30
O 801. 5 pf. green .. 20 1·50
O 652. 6 pf. green .. 60 75
O 802. 6 pf. violet .. 20 30
O 803. 8 pf. red .. 20 30
O 804. 12 pf. red .. 25 30
O 655. 16 pf. grey .. 1·00 14·00
O 805. 16 pf. blue .. 3·00 6·00
O 656. 24 pf. green .. 2·00 6·00
O 806. 24 pf. brown .. 45 1·00
O 807. 30 pf. green .. 45 1·50
O 808. 40 pf. mauve .. 70 2·00

## II. ALLIED OCCUPATION

The defeat of Germany in May 1945 resulted in the division of the country into four zones of occupation (British, American, French and Russian), while Berlin was placed under joint allied control. Allied Military Post Stamps came into use in the British and American zones, the French issued special stamps in their zone and in the Russian zone the first issues were made by local administrations.

The territory occupied by the Anglo-American and French Zones subsequently became the German Federal Republic (West Germany) which was set up in September 1949. By the Nine Power Agreement of 3 October 1954, the occupation of West Germany was ended and full sovereignty was granted to the German Federal Government as from 5 May 1955 (see Section III).

The territory in the Russian Zone became the German Democratic Republic (East Germany) which was set up on 7 October 1949 (see Section V).

Separate issues for the Western Sectors of Berlin came into being in 1948 (see Section IV). The Russian Zone issues inscribed "STADT BERLIN" were for use in the Russian sector of the city and Brandenburg and these were superseded first by the General Issues of the Russian Zone and then by the stamps of East Germany.

100 pfennige = 1 Reichsmark.

21.6.48. 100 pfennige = 1 Deutsche Mark (West).
24.6.48. 100 pfennige = 1 Deutsche Mark (East).

### A. Allied Military Post (British and American Zones)

A 1.

**1945.**

A 16. A **1.** 1 pf. black .. .. 20 50
A 1. 3 pf. violet .. .. 20 20
A 2. 4 pf. grey .. .. 20 20
A 3. 5 pf. green .. .. 20 20
A 4. 6 pf. yellow .. .. 20 20
A 5. 8 pf. orange .. .. 20 20
A 6. 10 pf. brown .. 20 20
A 7. 12 pf. purple .. 20 20
A 8. 15 pf. red .. .. 20 20
A 25. 16 pf. green .. .. 20 20
A 26. 20 pf. blue .. .. 20 20
A 27. 24 pf. brown .. .. 30 20
A 9. 25 pf. blue .. .. 20 20
A 29. 30 pf. olive .. .. 25 60
A 30. 40 pf. mauve .. .. 25 50
A 31. 42 pf. green .. .. 25 50
A 32. 50 pf. slate .. .. 25 60
A 33. 60 pf. plum .. .. 25 1·50
A 34. 80 pf. blue .. .. 22·00 30·00
A 35. 1 m. green .. .. 3·50 7·50

Values 30 pf. to 80 pf. are size 22 × 25 mm. and 1 m. size 25 × 29½ mm.

Nos. A 36 etc continue in Section C.



### B. American, British and Russian Zones 1946–48

From February 1946 to June 1948 these zones used the same stamps (Nos. 899/956). It had been intended that they should be used throughout all four zones but until the creation of the German Federal Republic, in September 1949, the French Zone always had its own stamps, while after the revaluation of the currency in June 1948 separate stamps were again issued for the Russian Zone.

229. Numeral. 231. 1160: Leipzig obtains Charter.

**1946.**

899 **229** 1 pf. black .. .. 10 60
900 2 pf. black .. .. 10 10
901 3 pf. brown .. .. 10 60
902 4 pf. blue .. .. 10 70
903 5 pf. green .. .. 10 10
904 6 pf. violet .. .. 10 10
905 8 pf. red .. .. 10 10
906 10 pf. brown .. .. 10 10
907 12 pf. red .. .. 10 10
908 12 pf. grey .. .. 10 10
909 15 pf. red .. .. 15 1·00
910 15 pf. green .. .. 10 10
911 16 pf. green .. .. 10 10
912 20 pf. blue .. .. 10 10
913 24 pf. brown .. .. 15 10
914 25 pf. blue .. .. 10 1·25
915 25 pf. orange .. .. 10 50
916 30 pf. green .. .. 10 25
917 40 pf. purple .. .. 10 25
918 42 pf. green .. .. 1·25 7·50
919 45 pf. red .. .. 10 30
920 50 pf. green .. .. 10 20
921 60 pf. red .. .. 15 30
922 75 pf. blue .. .. 20 30
923 80 pf. blue .. .. 15 30
924 84 pf. green .. .. 10 30
925 1 m. green (24 × 30 mm) 15 60

**1947.** Leipzig Spring Fair. Inscr. "**LEIPZIGER MESSE 1947**".

926. **231.** 24 pf. + 26 pf. brown .. 25 1·00
927. – 60 pf. + 40 pf. blue .. 35 1·50

DESIGN: 60 pf. 1268: Foreign merchants at Leipzig Fair.

See also Nos. 951/4.

233. Gardener. 237. "Dove of Peace".

**1947.**

928 **233** 2 pf. black .. .. 10 40
929 6 pf. violet .. .. 10 15
930 A 8 pf. red .. .. 10 15
931 10 pf. green .. .. 10 30
932 B 12 pf. grey .. .. 10 15
933 **233** 15 pf. brown .. .. 20 1·25
934 C 16 pf. green .. .. 10 15
935 A 20 pf. blue .. .. 10 20
936 C 24 pf. brown .. .. 10 15
937 **233** 25 pf. orange .. .. 10 25
938 B 30 pf. red .. .. 30 50
939 A 40 pf. mauve .. .. 10 30
940 C 50 pf. blue .. .. 30 60
941 B 60 pf. red .. .. 10 50
942 60 pf. brown .. .. 15 50
943 80 pf. blue .. .. 10 30
944 C 84 pf. green .. .. 30 30
945 **237** 1 m. green .. .. 10 30
946 2 m. violet .. .. 15 50
947 3 m. lake .. .. 15 1·10
948 5 m. blue .. .. 1·25 2·00

DESIGNS: A, Sower. B, Labourer. C, Bricklayer and reaper.

238. Dr. von Stephan.

**1947.** 50th Death Anniv. of Von Stephan.

949. **238.** 24 pf. brown .. .. 15 35
950. 75 pf. blue .. .. 20 55

**1947.** Leipzig Autumn Fair. As T **231.**

951. 12 pf. red .. .. .. 20 60
952. 75 pf. blue .. .. .. 20 80

DESIGNS: 12 pf. 1497: Maximilian I granting Charter. 75 pf. 1365: Assessment and Collection of Ground Rents.

**1948.** Leipzig Spring Fair. As T **231** but dated "1948".

953. 50 pf. blue .. .. 20 65
954. 84 pf. green .. .. 20 85

DESIGNS: 50 pf. 1388: At the customs barrier. 84 pf. 1433: Bringing merchandise.

For similar types, dated "1948", "1949" or "1950", but with premium values, see Nos. R31/2, R51/2, R60/1 of Russian Zone and E7/8 of East Germany.

239. Weighing Goods.

**1948.** Hanover Trade Fair.

955. **239.** 24 pf. red .. .. 10 55
956. 50 pf. blue .. .. 20 75

### C. British and American Zones 1948–49

(A 2.)

**1948.** Currency Reform. Optd. I with Type A 2 or II with multiple posthorns over whole stamp.

(a) On Pictorial issue of 1947, Nos. 928/44.

| | | I. | | II. | |
|---|---|---|---|---|---|
| A36 | 2 pf. black | 10 | 10 | 1·00 | 1·40 |
| A37 | 6 pf. violet | 10 | 10 | 1·25 | 1·40 |
| A38 | 8 pf. red .. | 10 | 10 | 1·00 | 1·25 |
| A39 | 10 pf. green | 20 | 20 | 15 | 15 |
| A40 | 12 pf. grey | 20 | 10 | 1·25 | 1·25 |
| A41 | 15 pf. brown | 8·00 | 13·00 | 30 | 35 |
| A42 | 16 pf. green | 1·25 | 2·00 | 30 | 20 |
| A43 | 20 pf. blue | 60 | 60 | 30 | 20 |
| A44 | 24 pf. brown | 15 | 10 | 75 | 1·00 |
| A45 | 25 pf. orange | 40 | 40 | 8·50 | 13·00 |
| A46 | 30 pf. red .. | 2·25 | 4·00 | 30 | 40 |
| A47 | 40 pf. mauve | 80 | 90 | 40 | 30 |
| A48 | 50 pf. blue | 80 | 80 | 50 | 25 |
| A49 | 60 pf. brown | 80 | 80 | 50 | 25 |
| A50 | 60 pf. red .. | 55·00 | £225 | 2·25 | 3·00 |
| A51 | 80 pf. blue | 1·40 | 2·00 | 45 | 25 |
| A52 | 84 pf. green | 4·25 | 6·00 | 1·00 | 1·40 |

(b) On Numeral issue of 1946, Nos. 900 to 924.

| | | | I. | | II. | |
|---|---|---|---|---|---|---|
| A 53. | **229.** | 2 pf. blk | 6·00 | 20·00 | 22·00 | 55·00 |
| A 54. | | 8 pf. red | 14·00 | 50·00 | 42·00 | 95·00 |
| A 55. | | 10 pf. brn. | 1·00 | 3·50 | 35·00 | 95·00 |
| A 56. | | 12 pf. red | 10·00 | 35·00 | 14·00 | 42·00 |
| A 57. | | 12 pf. grey | £160 | £450 | £300 | £800 |
| A 58. | | 15 pf. red | 11·00 | 35·00 | 16·00 | 35·00 |
| A 59. | | 15 pf. grn. | 3·50 | 12·00 | 90 | 6·00 |
| A 60. | | 16 pf. grn. | 50·00 | £150 | 48·00 | £130 |
| A 61. | | 24 pf. brn. | 95·00 | £170 | 55·00 | £170 |
| A 62. | | 25 pf. blue | 18·00 | 48·00 | 18·00 | 45·00 |
| A 63. | | 25 pf. orge. | 1·75 | 6·50 | 48·00 | £140 |
| A 64. | | 30 pf. olive | 1·50 | 4·75 | 1·75 | 3·25 |
| A 65. | | 40 pf. pur. | 70·00 | £170 | 65·00 | £190 |
| A 66. | | 45 pf. red | 2·40 | 7·00 | 3·00 | 9·00 |
| A 67. | | 50 pf. grn. | 2·10 | 4·00 | 3·00 | 9·00 |
| A 68. | | 75 pf. blue | 6·00 | 12·00 | 3·50 | 8·00 |
| A 69. | | 84 pf. grn. | 6·00 | 20·00 | 3·00 | 11·00 |

A 4. Crowned Head. A 6. Cologne Cathedral.

**1948.** 700th Anniv. of Cologne Cathedral and Restoration Fund.

A 70. A **4.** 6 pf. + 4 pf. brown .. 60 70
A 71. – 12 pf. + 8 pf. blue .. 1·40 1·50
A 72. – 24 pf. + 16 pf. red .. 3·25 3·50
A 73. A **6.** 50 pf. + 50 pf. blue .. 7·50 8·00

DESIGNS—As Type A **4.** 12 pf. The Three Wise Men. 24 pf. Cologne Cathedral.

A 9. The Romer, Frankfurt-on-Main. A 10. Frauenkirche, Munich. A 13. Holstentor Lubeck.

**1948.** Various designs.

| No. | Type | Description | Unused | Used |
|---|---|---|---|---|
| A 74 | A 9 | 2 pf. black | 10 | 10 |
| A 75 | A 10 | 4 pf brown | 20 | 10 |
| A 76a | A | 5 pf. blue | 20 | 10 |
| A 77 | A 10 | 6 pf. brown | 15 | 40 |
| A 78 | | 6 pf. orange | 30 | 10 |
| A 79 | A 9 | 8 pf. yellow | 35 | 40 |
| A 80 | A 10 | 8 pf. slate | 30 | 10 |
| A 81a | A | 10 pf. green | 35 | 10 |
| A 82 | A 10 | 15 pf. orange | 2·00 | 3·00 |
| A 83 | A 9 | 15 pf. violet | 1·25 | 10 |
| A 84 | | 16 pf. green | 40 | 60 |
| A 85 | | 20 pf. blue | 75 | 1·25 |
| A 86 | B | 20 pf. red | 65 | 10 |
| A 87 | | 24 pf. red | 25 | 25 |
| A 88 | A | 25 pf. red | 1·00 | 10 |
| A 89 | B | 30 pf. blue | 1·40 | 10 |
| A 90 | A 10 | 30 pf. red | 2·75 | 3·25 |
| A 91 | A | 40 pf. mauve | 2·00 | 10 |
| A 92 | B | 50 pf. blue | 1·00 | 1·50 |
| A 93 | A 10 | 50 pf. green | 2·00 | 10 |
| A 94 | A | 60 pf. purple | 2·75 | 10 |
| A 95 | B | 80 pf. mauve | 3·00 | 10 |
| A 96 | A 10 | 84 pf. purple | 2·75 | 3·75 |
| A 97 | A | 90 pf. mauve | 3·00 | 10 |
| A 98 | A 13 | 1 Dm. green | 29·00 | 60 |
| A 99 | | 2 Dm. violet | 25·00 | 60 |
| A100 | | 3 Dm. mauve | 28·00 | 2·75 |
| A101 | | 5 Dm. blue | 45·00 | 18·00 |

Designs—As Type A 9/10: A, Cologne Cathedral. B, Brandenburg Gate.

A 15. Brandenburg Gate, Berlin.

**1948.** Aid to Berlin.

| No. | Type | Description | Unused | Used |
|---|---|---|---|---|
| A106 | A 15 | 10 pf.+5 pf. green | 5·50 | 6·00 |
| A107 | | 20 pf.+10 pf. red | 5·50 | 6·00 |

A 16. Herman Hillebrant Wedigh (after Holbein).

A 17. Racing Cyclists.

**1949.** Hanover Trade Fair.

| No. | Type | Description | Unused | Used |
|---|---|---|---|---|
| A108 | A 16 | 10 pf. green | 3·00 | 3·00 |
| A109 | | 20 pf. red | 3·00 | 3·00 |
| A110 | | 30 pf. blue | 4·00 | 4·00 |

**1949.** Trans-Germany Cycle Race.

| No. | Type | Description | Unused | Used |
|---|---|---|---|---|
| A112 | A 17 | 10 pf.+5 pf. green | 5·00 | 5·00 |
| A113 | | 20 pf.+10 pf. brown | 14·00 | 16·00 |

A 18. Goethe in Italy.

A 19. Goethe.

**1949.** Birth Bicentenary of Goethe (poet).

| No. | Type | Description | Unused | Used |
|---|---|---|---|---|
| A114 | A 18 | 10 pf.+5 pf. green | 4·00 | 7·50 |
| A115 | A 19 | 20 pf.+10 pf. red | 5·00 | 8·00 |
| A116 | – | 30 pf.+15 pf. blue | 18·00 | 15·00 |

Design—vert. 30 pf. Profile portrait.

OBLIGATORY TAX STAMPS

AT 14.

**1948.** Aid for Berlin. Perf or imperf.

| No. | Type | Description | Unused | Used |
|---|---|---|---|---|
| T1103 | AT 14 | 2 pf. blue | 20 | 10 |

The Anglo-American Zones, together with the French Zone, became the Federal German Republic (West Germany) in September, 1949.

## D. French Zone.

(a) General Issues, 1945-46.

F 1. Arms of the Palatinate.

F 2. Goethe.

**1945.** (a) Arms.

| No. | Type | Description | Unused | Used |
|---|---|---|---|---|
| F1 | F 1 | 1 pf. green, blk & yell | 10 | 25 |
| F2 | – | 3 pf. yellow, blk & red | 10 | 10 |
| F3 | – | 5 pf. black, yell & brn | 10 | 10 |
| F4 | – | 8 pf. red, yellow & brn | 10 | 10 |
| F5 | F 1 | 10 pf. grn, brn, & yell | 5·00 | 16·00 |
| F6 | – | 12 pf. yell, blk & red | 10 | 10 |
| F7 | – | 15 pf. blue, blk & red | 10 | 10 |
| F8 | – | 20 pf. black, yell & red | 10 | 20 |
| F9 | – | 24 pf. blue, blk & red | 10 | 10 |
| F10 | – | 30 pf. red, yell & blk | 10 | 20 |

Arms: 3, 12 pf. Rhineland. 5, 20 pf. Wurttemberg. 8, 30 pf. Baden. 15, 24 pf. Saar.

(b) Poets.

| No. | Type | Description | Unused | Used |
|---|---|---|---|---|
| F11 | F 2 | 1 m. brown | 1·50 | 6·00 |
| F12 | – | 2 m. blue (Schiller) | 1·00 | 10·00 |
| F13 | – | 5 m. red (Heine) | 1·25 | 10·00 |

(b) Baden, 1947-49.

FB 1. J. P. Hebel.

FB 2. Rastatt Castle.

FB 3. Höllental Black Forest.

FB 4. Freiburg Cathedral.

**1947.** Inscr. "BADEN".

| No. | Type | Description | Unused | Used |
|---|---|---|---|---|
| FB 1. | FB 1. | 2 pf. grey | 10 | 15 |
| FB 2. | – | 3 pf. brown | 10 | 15 |
| FB 3. | – | 10 pf. blue | 10 | 15 |
| FB 4. | FB 1. | 12 pf. green | 10 | 15 |
| FB 5. | – | 15 pf. violet | 10 | 30 |
| FB 6. | FB 2. | 16 pf. green | 10 | 90 |
| FB 7. | – | 20 pf. blue | 10 | 20 |
| FB 8. | FB 2. | 24 pf. red | 10 | 25 |
| FB 9. | – | 45 pf. mauve | 10 | 30 |
| FB 10. | FB 1. | 60 pf. orange | 10 | 20 |
| FB 11. | – | 75 pf. blue | 10 | 60 |
| FB 12. | FB 3. | 84 pf. green | 15 | 1·00 |
| FB 13. | FB 4. | 1 m. brown | 15 | 30 |

Designs—18×23 mm: 3, 15, 45 pf. Badensian girl and yachts. 10, 20, 75 pf. Hans Baldung Grien.

**1948.** Currency Reform. As 1947 issue.

(a) Value in "PF."

| No. | Type | Description | Unused | Used |
|---|---|---|---|---|
| FB 14. | FB 1. | 2 pf. orange | 25 | 35 |
| FB 15. | – | 6 pf. brown | 25 | 15 |
| FB 16. | – | 10 pf. brown | 45 | 15 |
| FB 17. | FB 1. | 12 pf. red | 45 | 15 |
| FB 18. | – | 15 pf. blue | 50 | 35 |
| FB 19. | FB 2. | 24 pf. green | 70 | 10 |
| FB 20. | – | 30 pf. mauve | 1·40 | 85 |
| FB 21. | – | 50 pf. blue | 1·40 | 15 |

(b) New currency. Value in "D.PF" or "D.M."(="Deutschpfennig" or "Deutschmark").

| No. | Type | Description | Unused | Used |
|---|---|---|---|---|
| FB 22. | – | 8 dpf. green | 70 | 1·25 |
| FB 23. | FB 2. | 16 dpf. violet | 1·00 | 1·75 |
| FB 24. | – | 20 dpf. brown | 4·50 | 1·10 |
| FB 25. | FB 1. | 60 dpf. grey | 4·00 | 20 |
| FB 26. | FB 3. | 84 dpf. red | 7·00 | 3·00 |
| FB 27. | FB 4. | 1 dm. blue | 7·00 | 2·75 |

Designs—As Types FB 1/2: 6, 15 pf. Badensian girl. 10, 20 dpf. Hans Baldung Grien. 8 dpf., 30 pf. Black Forest girl in festive headdress. 50 pf. Grand-Duchess Stephanie of Baden.

Nos. FB 14/21 were sold on the new currency basis though not inscribed "D.PF.".

**1948.** As 1947 issue, but "PF" omitted.

| No. | Type | Description | Unused | Used |
|---|---|---|---|---|
| FB 28. | FB 1. | 2 pf. orange | 70 | 50 |
| FB 29. | – | 4 pf. violet | 35 | 35 |
| FB 30. | – | 5 pf. blue | 1·00 | 70 |
| FB 31. | – | 6 pf. brown | 24·00 | 12·00 |
| FB 32. | – | 8 pf. brown | 1·00 | 80 |
| FB 33. | – | 10 pf. green | 1·00 | 15 |
| FB 34. | – | 20 pf. mauve | 1·75 | 25 |
| FB 35. | – | 40 pf. brown | 55·00 | 60·00 |
| FB 36. | FB 1. | 80 pf. red | 11·00 | 7·00 |
| FB 37. | FB 3. | 90 pf. red | 60·00 | 80·00 |

Designs—18×23 mm: 4 pf., 40 pf. Rastatt. 5 pf., 6 pf. Badensian girl and yachts. 8 pf. Black Forest girl in festive headdress. 10 pf., 20 pf. Portrait of Hans Baldung Grien.

FB 5. Cornhouse, Freiburg.

FB 6. Arms of Baden.

**1949.** Freiburg Rebuilding Fund.

| No. | Type | Description | Unused | Used |
|---|---|---|---|---|
| FB 38. | FB 5. | 4 pf.+16 pf. vio. | 7·50 | 30·00 |
| FB 39. | – | 10 pf.+20 pf. grn. | 11·00 | 30·00 |
| FB 40. | – | 20 pf.+30 pf. red | 14·00 | 30·00 |
| FB 41. | – | 30 pf.+50 pf. blue | 19·00 | 40·00 |

Designs: 10 pf. Freiburg Cathedral. 20 pf. Trumpeting angel, Freiburg. 30 pf. "Fischbrunnen," Freiburg.

**1949.** Red Cross Fund.

| No. | Type | Description | Unused | Used |
|---|---|---|---|---|
| FB 42. | FB 6. | 10 pf.+20 pf. grn. | 18·00 | 75·00 |
| FB 43. | | 20 pf.+40 pf. lilac | 18·00 | 75·00 |
| FB 44. | | 30 pf.+60 pf. bl. | 18·00 | 75·00 |
| FB 45. | | 40 pf.+80 pf. grey | 18·00 | 75·00 |

FB 7. Seehof Hotel, Constance.

**1949.** Engineers' Congress, Constance.

| No. | Type | Description | Unused | Used |
|---|---|---|---|---|
| FB 46. | FB 7. | 30 pf. blue | 24·00 | 65·00 |

FB 8. Goethe.

FB 10. Conradin Kreutzer.

FB 9. Carl Schurz and Revolutionary Scene.

**1949.** Birth Bicentenary of Goethe (poet).

| No. | Type | Description | Unused | Used |
|---|---|---|---|---|
| FB 47. | FB 8. | 10 pf.+5 pf. grn. | 8·50 | 17·00 |
| FB 48. | – | 20 pf.+10 pf. red | 8·50 | 17·00 |
| FB 49. | – | 30 pf.+15 pf. blue | 10·00 | 35·00 |

**1949.** Cent. of Rastatt Insurrection.

| No. | Type | Description | Unused | Used |
|---|---|---|---|---|
| FB 50. | FB 9. | 10 pf.+5 pf. grn. | 11·00 | 24·00 |
| FB 51. | | 20 pf.+10 pf. mve. | 11·00 | 24·00 |
| FB 52. | | 30 pf.+15 pf. blue | 11·00 | 24·00 |

**1949.** Death Centenary of Conradin Kreutzer (composer).

| No. | Type | Description | Unused | Used |
|---|---|---|---|---|
| FB53. | FB10. | 10 pf. green | 3·00 | 6·00 |

FB 11. 1849 Mail Coach.

FB 12. Posthorn and Globe.

**1949.** German Stamp Centenary.

| No. | Type | Description | Unused | Used |
|---|---|---|---|---|
| FB 54. | FB 11. | 10 pf. green | 5·50 | 10·00 |
| FB 55. | – | 20 pf. brown | 5·50 | 10·00 |

Design: 20 pf. Postal motor-coach with trailer and Douglas DC-4 airliner.

**1949.** 75th Anniv. of U.P.U.

| No. | Type | Description | Unused | Used |
|---|---|---|---|---|
| FB 56. | FB 12. | 20 pf. red | 5·50 | 10·00 |
| FB 57. | | 30 pf. blue | 5·50 | 8·25 |

(c) Rhineland Palatinate, 1947-49.

FR 1. "Porta Nigra" Trier.

FR 2. Karl Marx.

FR 4. Statue of Charlemagne. FR 5. St. Martin.

**1947.** Inscr. "RHEINLAND-PFALZ".

| No. | Type | Description | Unused | Used |
|---|---|---|---|---|
| FR 1. | – | 2 pf. grey | 10 | 15 |
| FR 2. | – | 3 pf. brown | 10 | 15 |
| FR 3. | – | 10 pf. blue | 10 | 15 |
| FR 4. | FR 1. | 12 pf. green | 10 | 10 |
| FR 5. | FR 2. | 15 pf. violet | 10 | 15 |
| FR 6. | – | 16 pf. green | 10 | 20 |
| FR 7. | – | 20 pf. blue | 10 | 10 |
| FR 8. | – | 24 pf. red | 10 | 10 |
| FR 9. | – | 30 pf. mauve | 10 | 80 |
| FR 10. | – | 45 pf. mauve | 10 | 20 |
| FR 11. | – | 50 pf. blue | 10 | 90 |
| FR 12. | – | 60 pf. orange | 10 | 15 |
| FR 13. | – | 75 pf. blue | 10 | 30 |
| FR 14. | – | 84 pf. green | 10 | 70 |
| FR 15. | FR 4. | 1 m. brown | 10 | 30 |

Designs—small size: 2 pf., 60 pf. Beethoven's death mask. 3 pf. Baron von Ketteler, Bishop of Mainz. 10 pf. Girl vintager. 16 pf. Rocks at Arnweiler. 20 pf. Palatinate village house. 24 pf. Worms Cathedral. 30 pf., 75 pf. Gutenberg (printer). 45 pf., 50 pf. Mainz Cathedral. Large size—horiz. 84 pf. Gutenfels Castle and Rhine.

**1948.** Currency Reform. As 1947 issue.

(a) Value in "PF."

| No. | Type | Description | Unused | Used |
|---|---|---|---|---|
| FR 16. | – | 2 pf. orange | 25 | 40 |
| FR 17. | – | 6 pf. brown | 25 | 30 |
| FR 18. | – | 10 pf. brown | 60 | 10 |
| FR 19. | FR 1. | 12 pf. red | 50 | 10 |
| FR 20. | FR 2. | 15 pf. blue | 1·10 | 70 |
| FR 21. | – | 24 pf. green | 65 | 10 |
| FR 22. | – | 30 pf. mauve | 1·10 | 30 |
| FR 23. | – | 50 pf. blue | 1·60 | 30 |

(b) New currency. Value in "D.PF." or "D.M." (= "Deutschpfennig" or "Deutschmark").

| No. | Type | Description | Unused | Used |
|---|---|---|---|---|
| FR 24. | FR 1. | 8 dpf. green | 75 | 1·50 |
| FR 25. | – | 16 dpf. violet | 80 | 1·25 |
| FR 26. | – | 20 dpf. brown | 2·50 | 40 |
| FR 27. | – | 60 dpf. grey | 11·00 | 30 |
| FR 28. | – | 84 dpf. red | 5·00 | 4·00 |
| FR 29. | FR 4. | 1 dm. blue | 5·50 | 4·00 |

Designs—small size: 6 pf. Baron von Ketteler. 30 pf. Mainz Cathedral. 50 pf. Gutenberg (printer). Others as 1947 issue.

Nos. FR 16/23 were sold on the new currency basis though not inscribed "D.PF.".

**1948.** Ludwigshafen Explosion Relief Fund.

| No. | Type | Description | Unused | Used |
|---|---|---|---|---|
| FR 30. | FR 5. | 20 pf.+30 pf. mve. | 1·40 | 20·00 |
| FR 31. | – | 30 pf.+50 pf. blue | 1·40 | 20·00 |

Design: 30 pf. St. Christopher.

**1948.** Inscr. "RHEINLAND-PFALZ". As 1947 issue, but "PF" omitted.

| No. | Type | Description | Unused | Used |
|---|---|---|---|---|
| FR 32. | – | 2 pf. orange | 30 | 35 |
| FR 33. | – | 4 pf. violet | 40 | 20 |
| FR 34. | FR 2. | 5 pf. blue | 75 | 50 |
| FR 35. | – | 6 pf. brown | 28·00 | 14·00 |
| FR 36. | FR 1. | 8 pf. red | 75·00 | £150 |
| FR 37. | – | 10 pf. green | 80 | 15 |
| FR 38. | – | 20 pf. mauve | 85 | 15 |
| FR 39. | – | 40 pf. brown | 2·25 | 3·00 |
| FR 40. | FR 1. | 80 pf. red | 3·00 | 4·50 |
| FR 41. | – | 90 pf. red | 5·00 | 14·00 |

Designs—small size: 4 pf. Rocks at Arnweiler. 40 pf. Worms Cathedral. Large size—horiz. 90 pf. Gutenfels Castle and Rhine. Others as 1947-48 issues.

**1949.** Red Cross Fund. As Type FB 6 of Baden, but Arms of Rhineland and inscr. "RHEINLAND/PFALZ".

| No. | Description | Unused | Used |
|---|---|---|---|
| FR 42. | 10 pf.+20 pf. green | 20·00 | 85·00 |
| FR 43. | 20 pf.+40 pf. lilac | 20·00 | 85·00 |
| FR 44. | 30 pf.+60 pf. blue | 20·00 | 85·00 |
| FR 45. | 40 pf.+80 pf. grey | 20·00 | 85·00 |

**1949.** Birth Bicent. of Goethe. As Nos. FB 47/9 of Baden.

| No. | Description | Unused | Used |
|---|---|---|---|
| FR 46. | 10 pf.+5 pf. green | 6·00 | 16·00 |
| FR 47. | 20 pf.+10 pf. mauve | 6·00 | 16·00 |
| FR 48. | 30 pf.+15 pf. blue | 12·00 | 38·00 |

**1949.** Centenary of German Postage Stamp. As Nos. FB 54/5 of Baden.

| No. | Description | Unused | Used |
|---|---|---|---|
| FR 49. | 10 pf. green | 8·75 | 19·00 |
| FR 50. | 20 pf. brown | 8·75 | 19·00 |

**1949.** 75th Anniv. of U.P.U. As Nos. FB 56/7 of Baden.

| No. | Description | Unused | Used |
|---|---|---|---|
| FR 51. | 20 pf. red | 5·00 | 10·00 |
| FR 52. | 30 pf. blue | 5·00 | 9·00 |

(d) Saar, 1945–7.

The Saar District, from 1945 to 1947 part of the French Zone, also had its own stamps, but as it was in a different political category, we list its stamps for convenience of reference all together under Saar.

(e) Wurttemberg, 1947-49.

FW 1. Fr. von Schiller.

FW 2. Bebenhausen Monastery.

FW 3. Lichtenstein Castle.

**1947.** Inscr. "WURTTEMBERG".
FW 1. FW 1. 2 pf. grey .. 10 10
FW 2. – 3 pf. brown .. 10 10
FW 3. – 10 pf. blue .. 10 10
FW 4. FW 1. 12 pf. green .. 10 10
FW 5. – 15 pf. violet .. 10 20
FW 6. FW 2. 16 pf. green .. 10 50
FW 7. – 20 pf. blue .. 10 50
FW 8. FW 2. 24 pf. red .. 10 10
FW 9. – 45 pf. mauve .. 15 30
FW 10. FW 1. 60 pf. orange .. 15 45
FW 11. – 75 pf. blue .. 15 50
FW 12. FW 3. 84 pf. green .. 20 60
FW 13. – 1 m. brown .. 20 45
DESIGNS—SMALL SIZE: 3 pf., 15 pf., 45 pf. Holderlin (poet). 10 pf., 20 pf., 75 pf. Wangen Gate. LARGE SIZE—VERT. 1 m. Zwiefalten Monastery Church.

**1948.** Currency Reform. As 1947 issue.
(a) Value in "PF."
FW 14. FW 1. 2 pf. orange .. 20 55
FW 15. – 6 pf. brown .. 20 15
FW 16. – 10 pf. brown .. 25 30
FW 17. FW 1. 12 pf. red .. 25 10
FW 18. – 15 pf. blue .. 70 35
FW 19. FW 2. 24 pf. green .. 80 10
FW 20. – 30 pf. mauve .. 1·25 30
FW 21. – 50 pf. blue .. 2·00 30

(b) Value in "D.PF" (= Deutsch Pfennig) or "D.M." (= Deutsch Mark).
FW 22. – 8 dpf. green .. 1·00 2·00
FW 23. FW 2. 16 dpf. violet .. 90 1·75
FW 24. – 20 dpf. brown .. 1·90 1·10
FW 25. FW 1. 60 dpf. grey .. 13·00 30
FW 26. FW 3. 84 dpf. red .. 4·25 4·00
FW 27. – 1 dm. blue .. 4·25 4·00
DESIGNS—SMALL SIZE: 6 pf., 15 pf. Fr. Holderlin (poet). 8 dpf., 30 pf. Waldsee Castle. 50 pf. Ludwig Uhland (poet). Others as 1947 issue.
Nos. FW 14/21 were sold on the new currency basis though not inscribed "D.PF."

**1948.** Inscr. "WURTTEMBERG". As 1947 issue, but "PF" omitted.
FW 28. FW 1. 2 pf. orange .. 1·25 40
FW 29. FW 2. 4 pf. violet .. 1·00 30
FW 30. – 5 pf. blue .. 5·00 1·75
FW 31. – 6 pf. brown .. 8·00 4·25
FW 32. – 8 pf. red .. 7·00 1·75
FW 33. – 10 pf. green .. 7·00 10
FW 34. – 20 pf. mauve .. 7·00 10
FW 35. FW 2. 40 pf. brown .. 23·00 40·00
FW 36. FW 1. 80 pf. red .. 50·00 40·00
FW 37. FW 3. 90 pf. red .. 70·00 £100
DESIGNS—SMALL SIZE: 5 pf., 6 pf. Holderlin. Others as 1947=48 issues.

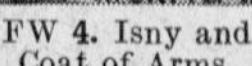
FW 4. Isny and Coat of Arms.
FW 5. Gustav Werner.

**1949.** Ski Championships (Northern Combination) at Isny/Allgau.
FW 38. FW 4. 10 pf.+4 pf. grn. 5·00 14·00
FW 39. – 20 pf.+6 pf. lake 5·00 14·00
DESIGN: 20 pf. Skier and view of Isny.

**1949.** Red Cross Fund. As Type FB 6 of Baden, but Arms of Wurttemberg and inscr. "WURTTEMBERG".
FW 40. 10 pf.+20 pf. green .. 28·00 85·00
FW 41. 20 pf.+40 pf. lilac .. 28·00 85·00
FW 42. 30 pf.+60 pf. blue .. 28·00 85·00
FW 43. 40 pf.+80 pf. grey .. 28·00 85·00

**1949.** Birth Bicent. of Goethe. As Nos. FB 47/9 of Baden.
FW 44. 10 pf.+5 pf. green .. 7·50 14·00
FW 45. 20 pf.+10 pf. mauve .. 8·00 22·00
FW 46. 30 pf.+15 pf. blue .. 11·00 30·00

**1949.** Cent. of Christian Institution "Zum Bruderhaus".
FW 47. FW 5. 10 pf.+5 pf. grn. 5·00 12·00
FW 48. 20 pf.+10 pf. pur. 5·00 12·00

**1949.** German Stamp Centenary. As Nos. FB 54/5 of Baden.
FW 49. 10 pf. green .. .. 6·00 10·00
FW 50. 20 pf. brown .. .. 6·00 13·00

**1949.** 75th Anniv. of U.P.U. As Nos. FB 56/7 of Baden.
FW 51. 20 pf. red .. .. 5·00 10·00
FW 52. 30 pf. blue .. .. 5·00 7·50
The French Zone was incorporated in West Germany in September, 1949.

## INDEX

Countries can be quickly located by referring to the index at the end of this volume.

## E. Russian Zone.

For a list of the stamps issued by the Russian Zone Provincial Administrations of Berlin (Brandenburg), Mecklenburg – Vorpommern, Saxony (Halle, Leipzig and Dresden) and Thuringia, see Stanley Gibbons Part 7 (Germany) Catalogue.

General Issues.

In February 1946, the Provincial Issues were replaced by the General Issues, Nos. 899/956 until the revaluation of the currency in June 1948, when Nos. 928/44 were brought into use handstamped with District names and numbers as a control measure pending the introduction of the following overprinted stamps on 3rd July. There are over 1,900 different types of district handstamp.

R 1. Arms of Berlin.

R 3. Kathe Kollwitz.

**1948.** Optd. **Sowjetische Besatzungs Zone.**

(a) On Pictorial issue of 1947, Nos. 928/44.
R 1 2 pf. black .. .. 15 25
R 2 6 pf. violet .. .. 15 20
R 3 8 pf. red .. .. .. 15 20
R 4 10 pf. green .. .. 15 20
R 5 12 pf. grey .. .. 15 20
R 6 15 pf. brown .. .. 15 25
R 7 16 pf. green .. .. 15 30
R 8 20 pf. blue .. .. 15 20
R 9 24 pf. brown .. .. 15 20
R10 25 pf. orange .. .. 15 30
R11 30 pf. red .. .. 30 30
R12 40 pf. mauve .. .. 30 30
R13 50 pf. blue .. .. 30 50
R14 60 pf. brown .. .. 50 50
R15 60 pf. red .. .. 40·00 70·00
R16 80 pf. blue .. .. 70 70
R17 84 pf. green .. .. 70 90

(b) On Numerical issue of 1946, Nos. 903, etc.
R 18. 229. 5 pf. green .. .. 25 30
R 19. 30 pf. olive .. .. 50 1·10
R 20. 45 pf. red .. .. 30 50
R 21. 75 pf. blue .. .. 30 50
R 22. 84 pf. green .. .. 70 50

(c) On stamps inscr. "STADT BERLIN".
R 23. R 1. 5 pf. green .. .. 20 50
R 25. – 6 pf. violet .. .. 20 50
R 26. – 8 pf. orange .. .. 20 30
R 27. – 10 pf. brown .. .. 20 50
R 28. – 12 pf. red .. .. 20 30
R 29. – 20 pf. blue .. .. 50 1·00
R 30. – 30 pf. olive .. .. 35 60
DESIGNS: 6 pf. Bear with spade. 8 pf. Bear on shield. 10 pf. Bear holding brick. 12 pf. Bear carrying plank. 20 pf. Bear on small shield. 30 pf. Oak sapling amid ruins.

**1948.** Leipzig Autumn Fair. As T 231 but dated "1948".
R 31. 16 pf.+9 pf. purple .. 30 40
R 32. 50 pf.+25 pf. blue .. 30 40
DESIGNS: 16 pf. 1459: The first Spring Fair. 50 pf. 1469: Foreign merchants displaying cloth.

**1948.** Politicians, Artists and Scientists.
R 33. R 3. 2 pf. grey .. .. 15 15
R 34. – 6 pf. violet .. .. 20 15
R 35. – 8 pf. red .. .. 45 25
R 36. – 10 pf. green .. .. 20 25
R 37. – 12 pf. blue .. .. 4·00 25
R 38. – 15 pf. brown .. .. 55 1·10
R 39. – 16 pf. blue .. .. 40 35
R 40. R 3. 20 pf. purple .. 40 70
R 41. – 24 pf. red .. .. 5·00 25
R 42. – 25 pf. olive .. .. 80 1·40
R 43. – 30 pf. red .. .. 80 1·00
R 44. – 40 pf. purple .. .. 55 60
R 45. – 50 pf. blue .. .. 55 40
R 46. – 60 pf. green .. .. 2·00 40
R 47. – 80 pf. blue .. .. 1·10 40
E 95. – 80 pf. red .. .. 8·25 9·00
R 48. – 84 pf. brown .. .. 2·00 2·00
PORTRAITS: 6, 40 pf. Gerhart Hauptmann. 8, 50 pf. Karl Marx. 10, 84 pf. August Bebel. 12, 30 pf. Friedrich Engels. 15, 60 pf. G. F. W. Hegel. 16, 25 pf. Rudolf Virchow. 24, 80 pf. Ernst Thalmann.

R 4.

R 5. Liebknecht and Rosa Luxemburg.

**1948.** Stamp Day.
R 49. R 4. 12 pf.+3 pf. red .. 20 40

**1949.** 30th Death Anniv. of Karl Liebknecht and Rosa Luxemburg (revolutionaries).
R 50. R 5. 24 pf. red .. .. 30 60

**1949.** Leipzig Spring Fair. As T 231 but dated "1949".
R 51. 30 pf.+15 pf. red .. 2·75 3·25
R 52. 50 pf.+25 pf. blue .. 3·00 3·75
DESIGNS: 30 pf. 1st Neubau Town Hall bazaar, 1556. 50 pf. Italian merchants at Leipzig, 1536.

R 6. Dove.

R 8. Goethe.

**1949.** 3rd German Peoples' Congress.
R 53. R 6. 24 pf. red .. .. 80 1·25

**1949.** Optd. **3. Deutscher Volkskongress 29.–30 Mai 1949.**
R 54. R 6. 24 pf. red .. .. 1·00 1·40

**1949.** Birth Bicent. of Goethe. Portraits of Goethe.
R 55. R 8. 6 pf.+4 pf. violet 2·00 2·00
R 56. – 12 pf.+8 pf. brn. 2·00 2·00
R 57. – 24 pf.+16 pf. lake 1·75 1·75
R 58. – 50 pf.+25 pf. blue 1·75 1·75
R 59. – 84 pf.+36 pf. grey 3·00 3·00

**1949.** Leipzig Autumn Fair. As T 231 but dated "1949".
R 60. 12 pf.+8 pf. slate .. 3·00 5·00
R 61. 24 pf.+16 pf. lake .. 4·00 7·50
DESIGNS: 12 pf. Russian merchants, 1650. 24 pf. Goethe at Fair, 1765.

The Russian Zone was incorporated in East Germany in October, 1949.

## III. GERMAN FEDERAL REPUBLIC

The Federal Republic was set up on 23 May, 1949. Until October 1990 it comprised the territory which formerly came under the British, American and French Zones. On 3 October 1990 the former territory of East Germany (German Democratic Republic) was absorbed into the Federal Republic.

100 pfennig = 1 Deutsche Mark (West)

257. Constructing Parliament Building.

258. Reproduction of T 1 of Bavaria.

**1949.** Opening of West German Parliament, Bonn.
1033. 257. 10 pf. green .. .. 45·00 24·00
1034. 20 pf. red .. .. 60·00 28·00

**1949.** Cent. of 1st German Stamps.
1035. 258. 10 pf.+2 pf. blk.& grn. 10·00 12·00
1036. – 20 pf. blue and red 40·00 35·00
1037. – 30 pf. brown and blue 60·00 70·00
DESIGNS: 20 pf., 30 pf. Reproductions of T 2 of Bavaria.

259. Dr. von Stephan, Old G.P.O., Berlin and Standehaus, Berne.


260. St. Elisabeth of Thuringia.

**1949.** 75th Anniv. of U.P.U.
1038. 259. 30 pf. blue .. .. 70·00 48·00

**1949.** Refugees' Relief Fund. Inscr. as in T 260.
1039. 260. 8 pf.+2 pf. purple .. 20·00 24·00
1040. – 10 pf.+5 pf. green 15·00 14·00
1041. – 20 pf.+10 pf. red .. 15·00 14·00
1042. – 30 pf.+15 pf. blue 85·00 60·00
PORTRAITS: 10 pf. Paracelsus von Hohenheim. 20 pf. F. W. A. Froebel. 30 pf. J. H. Wichern.

261. J. S. Bach's Seal.

262. Numeral and Posthorn.

**1950.** Death Bicent. of Bach (composer).
1043. 261. 10 pf.+2 pf. green .. 60·00 38·00
1044. 20 pf.+3 pf. red .. 65·00 48·00

**1951.**
1045. 262. 2 pf. green .. .. 2·00 75
1046. 4 pf. brown .. .. 85 10
1047. 5 pf. purple .. .. 7·00 10
1048. 6 pf. orange .. .. 16·00 3·00
1049. 8 pf. grey .. .. 18·00 10·00
1050. 10 pf. green .. .. 2·00 10
1051. 15 pf. violet .. .. 30·00 90
1052. 20 pf. red .. .. 2·00 10
1053. 25 pf. plum .. .. 85·00 4·00
1054. 30 pf. blue .. .. 45·00 20
1055. 40 pf. purple .. £120 20
1056. 50 pf. grey .. .. £150 20
1057. 60 pf. brown .. £120 20
1058. 70 pf. yellow .. £500 12·00
1059. 80 pf. red .. .. £400 1·75
1060. 90 pf. green .. .. £600 2·00
The 30 pf. to 90 pf. are 20×24½ mm.

264. Figures.

265. Stamps under Magnifier.

**1951.** 700th Anniv. of St. Mary's Church, Lubeck.
1065. 264. 10 pf.+5 pf. black and green .. £100 70·00
1066. 20 pf.+5 pf. black and red .. £100 80·00

**1951.** National Philatelic Exn., Wuppertal.
1067. 265. 10 pf.+2 pf. yellow, black and green .. 50·00 50·00
1068. 20 pf.+3 pf. yellow, black and red .. 50·00 50·00

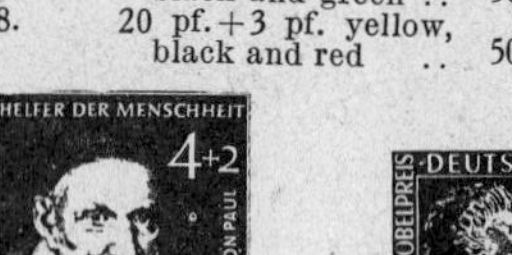

266. St. Vincent de Paul.

267. W. C. Rontgen (physicist).

**1951.** Humanitarian Relief Fund.
1069. 266. 4 pf.+2 pf. brown 8·00 12·00
1070. – 10 pf.+3 pf. green 14·00 8·00
1071. – 20 pf.+5 pf. red .. 14·00 7·00
1072. – 30 pf.+10 pf. blue £120 80·00
PORTRAITS: 10 pf. F. Von Bodelschwingh. 20 pf. Elsa Brandstrom. 30 pf. J. H. Pestalozzi.

**1951.** 50th Anniv of Award to Rontgen of 1st Nobel Prize for Physics.
1073 267 30 pf. blue 70·00 10·00

268. Mona Lisa.

269. Martin Luther.

**1952.** 500th Birth Anniv. of Leonardo da Vinci.
1074. 268. 5 pf. multicoloured .. 1·00 60

**1952.** Lutheran World Federation Assembly, Hanover.
1075. 269. 10 pf. green .. .. 13·00 4·00

270. A. N. Otto and Diagram.

271. Nuremberg Madonna.

**1952.** 75th Anniv. of Otto Gas Engine.
1076. 270. 30 pf. blue .. .. 35·00 8·00

**1952.** Cent. of German National Museum, Nuremberg.
1077. 271. 10 pf.+5 pf. green .. 18·00 17·00

272. Trawler "Senator Schaffer" off Heligoland.

273. Carl Schurz.

**1952.** Rehabilitation of Heligoland.
1078. 272. 20 pf. red .. .. 16·00 7·00

**1952.** Centenary of Arrival of Schurz in America.
1079. **273.** 20 pf. pink, blk. & bl. 20·00 6·00

274. Boy Hikers.

275. Elizabeth Fry.

**1952.** Youth Hostels Fund. Inscr. "JUGENDMARKE 1952".
1080. **274.** 10 pf.+2 pf. green .. 24·00 25·00
1081. – 20 pf.+3 pf. red .. 24·00 25·00
DESIGN: 20 pf. Girl hikers.

**1952.** Humanitarian Relief Fund.
1082. **275.** 4 pf.+2 pf. brown .. 8·00 6·00
1083. – 10 pf.+5 pf. green .. 6·50 3·50
1084. – 20 pf.+10 pf. lake .. 18·00 9·00
1085. – 30 pf.+10 pf. blue .. 85·00 60·00
PORTRAITS: 10 pf. Dr. C. Sonnenschein. 20 pf. T. Fliedner. 30 pf. H. Dunant.

276. Postman, 1852.

277. P. Reis.

**1952.** Thurn and Taxis Stamp Cent.
1086. **276.** 10 pf. multicoloured 7·50 2·50

**1952.** 75th Anniv. of German Telephone Service.
1087. **277.** 30 pf. blue .. .. 35·00 12·00

278. Road Accident Victim.

279.

**1953.** Road Safety Campaign.
1088. **278.** 20 pf. multicoloured 18·00 3·00

**1953.** 50th Anniv. of Science Museum, Munich.
1089. **279.** 10 pf.+5 pf. green .. 30·00 30·00

280. Red Cross and Compass.

281. Prisoner of War.

**1953.** 125th Birth Anniv. of Henri Dunant (founder of Red Cross).
1090. **280.** 10 pf. red and green .. 18·00 5·00

**1953.** Commemorating Prisoners of War.
1091. **281.** 10 pf. black and grey 4·00 20

282. J. von Liebig.

283. "Rail Transport".

**1953.** 150th Birth Anniv. of Liebig (chemist).
1092. **282.** 30 pf. blue .. .. 40·00 12·00

**1953.** Transport Exn., Munich. Inscr. as in T **283**.
1093. **283.** 4 pf. brown .. .. 8·50 6·00
1094. – 10 pf. green .. .. 15·00 6·00
1095. – 20 pf. red .. .. 18·00 8·00
1096. – 30 pf. blue .. .. 40·00 14·00
DESIGNS: 10 pf. "Air" (dove and aeroplanes). 20 pf. "Road" (traffic lights and cars). 30 pf. "Sea" (buoy and ships).

284. Gateway, Thurn and Taxis Palace.

285. A. H. Francke.

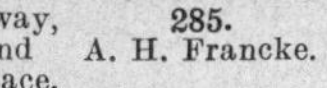
286. Pres. Heuss.

**1953.** Int. Philatelic Exhibition, Frankfurt-on-Main. Inscr. "IFRABA 1953".
1097 **284** 10 pf.+2 pf. brown, black and green .. 28·00 30·00
1098 – 20 pf.+3 pf. grey, blue and red .. .. 30·00 32·00
DESIGN: 20 pf. Telecommunications Buildings, Frankfurt-on-Main.

**1953.** Humanitarian Relief Fund.
1099. **285.** 4 pf.+2 pf. brown .. 5·00 6·00
1100. – 10 pf.+5 pf. green .. 8·00 5·00
1101. – 20 pf.+10 pf. red .. 12·00 7·00
1102. – 30 pf.+10 pf. blue .. 50·00 40·00
PORTRAITS: 10 pf. S. Kneipp. 20 pf. J. C. Senckenberg. 30 pf. F. Nansen.

**1954.** (a) Size 18½×22½ mm. or 18×22 mm.
1103. **286.** 2 pf. green .. .. 10 10
1104. 4 pf. brown .. 30 10
1105. 5 pf. mauve .. .. 20 10
1106. 6 pf. brown .. 10 60
1107. 7 pf. green .. .. 25 10
1108. 8 pf. grey .. .. 20 30
1109. 10 pf. green .. .. 15 10
1110. 15 pf. blue .. .. 70 20
1111. 20 pf. red .. .. 20 10
1112. 25 pf. purple .. 1·00 20
1122a. 30 pf. green .. .. 50 50
1122c. 40 pf. blue .. .. 2·00 10
1122e. 50 pf. olive .. .. 1·50 10
1122f. 60 pf. brown .. .. 3·75 10
1122g. 70 pf. violet .. .. 12·00 10
1122h. 80 pf. orange .. .. 8·00 90
1122i. 90 pf. green .. .. 24·00 20

(b) Size 20×24 mm.
1113. **286.** 30 pf. blue .. .. 15·00 3·00
1114. 40 pf. purple .. .. 6·50 10
1115. 50 pf. slate .. .. £200 10
1116. 60 pf. brown .. .. 50·00 15
1117. 70 pf. olive .. .. 17·00 1·50
1118. 80 pf. red .. .. 4·00 5·00
1119. 90 pf. green .. .. 18·00 2·00

(c) Size 25×30 mm.
1120. **286.** 1 Dm. olive .. .. 2·00 10
1121. 2 Dm. lavender .. 3·25 70
1122. 3 Dm. purple .. .. 7·00 1·50

287. P. Ehrlich and E. von Behring.

288. Gutenburg and Printing-press.

**1954.** Birth Centenaries of Ehrlich and Von Behring (bacteriologists).
1123. **287.** 10 pf. green .. .. 11·00 3·00

**1954.** 500th Anniv. of Gutenberg Bible.
1124. **288.** 4 pf. brown .. .. 85 30

289. Sword-pierced Mitre.

290. Kathe Kollwitz.

**1954.** 1,200th Anniv. of Martyrdrom of St. Boniface.
1125. **289.** 20 pf. red and brown 7·00 3·50

**1954.** Humanitarian Relief Fund.
1126. **290.** 7 pf.+3 pf. brown .. 3·00 3·75
1127. – 10 pf.+5 pf. green .. 2·25 1·75
1128. – 20 pf.+10 pf. red .. 10·00 2·75
1129. – 40 pf.+10 pf. blue .. 35·00 30·00
PORTRAITS: 10 pf. L. Werthmann. 20 pf. J. F. Oberlin. 40 pf. Bertha Pappenheim.

291. C. F. Gauss.

292. "Flight."

**1955.** Death Cent. of Gauss (mathematician).
1130. **291.** 10 pf. green .. .. 4·00 30

**1955.** Re-establishment of "Lufthansa" Airways.
1131. **292.** 5 pf. mauve and black 1·00 70
1132. 10 pf. green and black 1·40 1·00
1133. 15 pf. blue and black 5·50 4·00
1134. 20 pf. red and black .. 20·00 6·50

**HAVE YOU READ THE NOTES AT THE BEGINNING OF THIS CATALOGUE?**
These often provide answers to the enquiries we receive.

293. O. von Miller.

295. Schiller.

**1955.** Birth Centenary of Von Miller (electrical engineer).
1135. **293.** 10 f. green .. .. 4·50 1·10

**1955.** 150th Death Anniv. of Schiller (poet).
1136. **295.** 40 pf. blue .. .. 12·00 5·00

296. Motor-coach, 1906.

297. Arms of Baden-Wurttemburg.

**1955.** 50th Anniv. of Postal Motor Transport.
1137. **296.** 20 pf. black and red 10·00 4·50

**1955.** Baden-Wurttemberg Agricultural Exhibition, Stuttgart.
1138. **297.** 7 pf. blk. brn. & bistre 2·50 3·00
1139. 10 pf. blk. grn. & bistre 4·00 2·00

298. "Earth and Atom".

299. Refugees.

**1955.** Cosmic Research.
1140. **298.** 20 pf. lake .. .. 6·00 45

**1955.** 10th Anniv. of Expulsion of Germans from beyond the Oder-Neisse Line.
1141. **299.** 20 pf. red .. .. 3·25 30
See also No. 1400.

300. Orb, Arrows and Waves.

301. Magnifying Glass and Carrier Pigeon.

**1955.** Millenary of Battle of Lechfeld.
1142. **300.** 20 pf. purple .. 8·00 4·00

**1955.** West European Postage Stamp Exn.
1143. **301.** 10 pf.+2 pf. green .. 5·00 7·00
1144. – 20 pf.+3 pf. red .. 10·00 12·00
DESIGN: 20 pf. Tweezers and posthorn.

302. Railway Signal.

303. Stifter Monument.

**1955.** Railway Timetable Conference.
1145. **302.** 20 pf. black and red 10·00 1·00

**1955.** 150th Birth Anniv. of Stifter (Austrian poet).
1146. **303.** 10 pf. green .. .. 3·50 1·00

304. U.N. Emblem.

305. Amalie Sieveking.

**1955.** U.N. Day.
1147. **304.** 10 pf. green and brn. 3·75 4·25

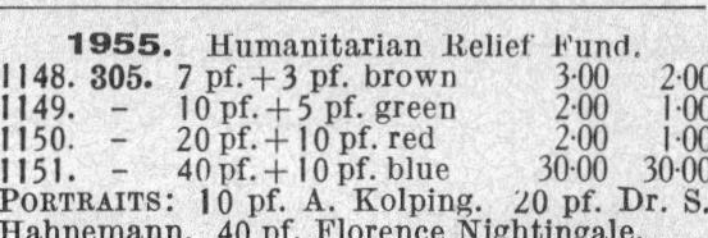
**1955.** Humanitarian Relief Fund.
1148. **305.** 7 pf.+3 pf. brown 3·00 2·00
1149. – 10 pf.+5 pf. green 2·00 1·00
1150. – 20 pf.+10 pf. red 2·00 1·00
1151. – 40 pf.+10 pf. blue 30·00 30·00
PORTRAITS: 10 pf. A. Kolping. 20 pf. Dr. S. Hahnemann. 40 pf. Florence Nightingale.

306.

307. Von Stephan's Signature.

**1955.**
1152. **306.** 1 pf. grey .. .. 10 10

**1955.** 125th Birth Anniv. H. von Stephan.
1153. **307.** 20 pf. red .. .. 6·00 2·00

308. Spinet and Opening Bars of Minuet.

309. Heinrich Heine.

**1956.** Birth Bicent. of Mozart (composer).
1154. **308.** 10 pf. black and lilac 60 10

**1956.** Death Cent. of Heine (poet).
1155. **309.** 10 pf. green & black 1·75 1·60

310. Old Houses and Crane.

311.

**1956.** Millenary of Luneburg.
1156. **310.** 20 pf. red .. .. 8·00 6·00

**1956.** Olympic Year.
1157. **311.** 10 pf. green .. .. 45 15

312. Boy and Dove.

313. Robert Schumann.

**1956.** Youth Hostels' Fund. Inscr. "JUGEND".
1158. **312.** 7 pf.+3 pf. grey, black and brown .. 2·50 4·00
1159. – 10 pf.+5 pf. grey black and green .. .. 6·00 9·00
DESIGN: 10 pf. Girl playing flute and flowers.

**1956.** Death Cent. of Schumann (composer).
1160. **313.** 10 pf. black, red and bistre .. .. 50 20

314.

315. T. Mann (author).

**1956.** Evangelical Church Convention, Frankfurt-on-Main.
1161. **314.** 10 pf. green .. .. 2·75 2·75
1162. 20 pf. red .. .. 3·00 3·00

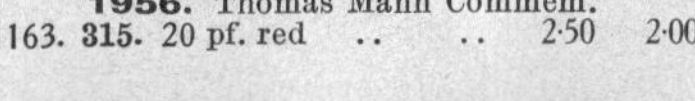
**1956.** Thomas Mann Commem.
1163. **315.** 20 pf. red .. .. 2·50 2·00

316.

317. Ground Plan of Cologne Cathedral and Hand.

**1956.** 800th Anniv of Maria Laach Abbey.
1164 **316** 20 pf. grey and red .. 1·50 1·00

**1956.** 77th Meeting of German Catholics, Cologne.

1165. **317.** 10 pf. green and brown 1·50 1·25

**318.** **320.** Nurse and Baby.

**1956.** Int. Police Exhibition, Essen.

1166. **318.** 20 pf. green, orange and black .. .. 2·50 1·50

**1956.** Europa. As T **320** of Belgium.

1167. 10 pf. green .. .. 1·00 10

1168. 40 pf. blue .. .. 7·50 1·00

**1956.** Humanitarian Relief Fund. Centres in black.

1169. **320.** 7 pf.+3 pf. brown .. 1·25 2·00

1170. – 10 pf.+5 pf. green .. 80 55

1171. – 20 pf.+10 pf. red .. 1·00 40

1172. – 40 pf.+10 pf. blue .. 15·00 16·00

DESIGNS: 10 pf. I. P. Semmelweis and cot. 20 pf. Mother, and baby in cradle. 40 f. Nursemaid and children.

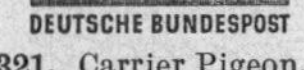
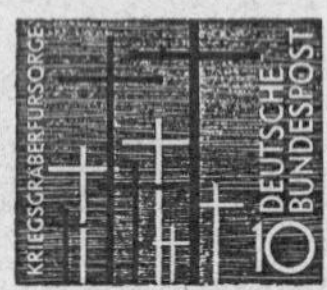

**321.** Carrier Pigeon. **322.** "Military Graves."

**1956.** Stamp Day.

1173. **321.** 10 pf. green .. .. 1·25 40

**1956.** War Graves Commission.

1174. **322.** 10 pf. green .. .. 1·00 30

**323.** Arms. **324.** Children with Luggage.

**1957.** Return of the Saar to West Germany.

1175. **323.** 10 pf. brown & green 40 30

**1957.** Berlin Children's Holiday Fund.

1176. **324.** 10 pf.+5 pf. orange and green .. .. 1·75 3·00

1177. – 20 pf.+10 pf. blue and orange .. 2·75 4·50

DESIGN: 20 pf. Girl returning from holiday.

**325.** Heinrich Hertz. **326.** Paul Gerhardt.

**1957.** Birth Cent. of Hertz (physicist).

1178. **325** 10 pf. black & green 1·00 40

**1957.** 350th Birth Anniv. of Paul Gerhardt (hymn-writer).

1179. **326.** 20 pf. red .. .. 40 30

**327.** "Flora and Philately." **328.** Emblem of Aschaffenburg.

**1957.** Exhibition and 8th Congress of Int. Federation of "Constructive Philately".

1180. **327.** 20 pf. orange .. 40 30

**1957.** Millenary of Aschaffenburg.

1181. **328.** 20 pf. red and black .. 40 30

**329.** University Class.

**1957.** 500th Anniv. of Freiburg University.

1182. **329.** 10 pf. blk. red & grn. 25 10

**330.** "Bayernstein" (freighter).

**1957.** German Merchant Shipping Day.

1183. **330.** 15 pf. blk., red & blue 1·25 1·25

**331.** Justus Liebig University. **332.** Albert Ballin.

**1957.** 350th Anniv of Justus Liebig University, Giessen.

1184. **331.** 10 pf. green .. .. 30 20

**1957.** Birth Cent. of Albert Ballin (director of Hamburg-America Shipping Line).

1185. **332.** 20 pf. black and red 80 30

**333.** Television Screen. **334.** "Europa" Tree.

**1957.** Publicizing West German Television Service.

1186. **333.** 10 pf. green and blue 30 20

**1957.** Europa.

1187. **334.** 10 pf. green and blue 40 10

1188. 40 pf. blue .. .. 4·00 30

**335.** Young Miner. **336.** Water Lily.

**1957.** Humanitarian Relief Fund.

1189. **335.** 7 pf.+3 pf. blk. & brn. 1·60 2·00

1190. – 10 pf.+5 pf. blk. & grn. 90 55

1191. – 20 pf.+10 pf. blk. & red 1·10 55

1192. – 40 pf.+10 pf. blk. & bl. 15·00 18·00

DESIGNS: 10 pf. Miner drilling coal-face. 20 pf. Miner with coal-cutting machine. 40 pf. Operator at mine lift-shaft.

**1957.** Nature Protection Day.

1193. **336.** 10 pf. orange, yellow and green .. .. 30 20

1194. – 20 pf. multicoloured 60 40

DESIGN—VERT. 20 pf. European robin.

**337.** Carrier Pigeons. **338.** Baron von Stein.

**1957.** Int. Correspondence Week.

1195. **337.** 20 pf. black and red 80 30

**1957.** Birth Bicentenary of Baron von Stein (statesman).

1196. **338.** 20 pf. red .. .. 1·25 30

**339.** Dr. Leo Baeck (philosopher). **340.** Wurttemberg Parliament House.

**1957.** 1st Death Anniv. of Dr. Leo Baeck.

1197. **339.** 20 pf. red .. .. 1·25 30

**1957.** 500th Anniv. of First Wurttemberg Parliament.

1198. **340.** 10 pf. olive and green 40 30

**341.** Stage Coach. **342.** "Max and Moritz" (cartoon characters).

**1957.** Death Centenary of Joseph von Eichendorff (novelist).

1199. **341.** 10 pf. green .. .. 40 30

**1958.** 50th Death Anniv. of Wilhelm Busch (writer and illustrator).

1200. **342.** 10 pf. olive and black 20 20

1201. – 20 pf. red and black 40 30

DESIGN: 20 pf. Wilhelm Busch.

**343.** "Prevent Forest Fires".

**1958.** Forest Fires Prevention Campaign.

1202. **343.** 20 pf. black and red 45 30

**344.** Rudolf Diesel and First Oil Engine. **345.** "The Fox who stole the Goose".

**1958.** Birth Cent. of Rudolf Diesel (engineer).

1203. **344.** 10 pf. myrtle .. 25 20

**1958.** Berlin Students' Fund. Inscr "Fur die Jugend".

1204. **345.** 10 pf.+5 pf. red black and green .. 1·25 2·50

1205. – 20 pf.+10 pf. brn. green and red .. 3·00 3·50

DESIGN: 20 pf. "A hunter from the Palatinate" (horseman).

**346.** Giraffe and Lion. **347.** Old Munich.

**1958.** Cent. of Frankfurt-am-Main Zoo.

1206. **346.** 10 pf. black & green 40 30

**1958.** 800th Anniv. of Munich.

1207. **347.** 20 pf. red .. .. 40 20

**348.** Trier and Market Cross. **349.** Deutsche Mark (coin).

**1958.** Millenary of Trier Market.

1208. **348.** 20 pf. red and black 40 20

**1958.** 10th Anniv. of Currency Reform.

1209. **349.** 20 pf. black & orange 40 20

**350.** Emblem of Gymnastics. **351.** H. Schulze-Delitzsch.

**1958.** 150th Anniv. of German Gymnastics.

1210. **350.** 10 pf. black, green. & grey .. .. 20 20

**1958.** 150th Birth Anniv. of Schulze-Delitzsch (pioneer of German co-operative movement).

1211. **351.** 10 pf. green .. .. 30 10

**1958.** Europa. As T **345** of Belgium. Size 24½×30 mm.

1212. 10 pf. blue and green .. 20 10

1213. 40 pf. red and blue .. 2·00 40

**352.** Friedrich Raiffeisen (philanthropist). **353.** Dairymaid.

**1958.** Humanitarian Relief and Welfare Funds.

1214 **352** 7 pf.+3 pf. brown, dp brown and chestnut 40 70

1215 **353** 10 pf.+5 pf. red, yellow and green .. 35 20

1216 – 20 pf.+10 pf. blue, green and red .. 45 30

1217 – 40 pf.+10 pf. yellow, orange and blue .. 5·00 7·00

DESIGNS: As Type **353**: 20 pf. Vine-dresser. 40 pf. Farm labourer.

**354.** Cardinal Nicholas of Cues (founder). **355.** Jakob Fugger (merchant prince).

**1958.** 500th Anniv. of Hospice of St. Nicholas.

1218. **354.** 20 pf. black & mauve 30 10

**1959.** As Type B **53** of West Berlin but without "BERLIN".

1219. 7 pf. green .. .. 30 10

1220. 10 pf. green .. .. 40 10

1221. 20 pf. red .. .. 50 10

1222. 40 pf. blue .. .. 12·00 45

1223. 70 pf. violet .. .. 3·75 20

**1959.** 500th Birth Anniv. of Jakob Fugger.

1224. **355.** 20 pf. black and red 30 20

**356.** Adam Riese (mathematician). **357.** A. von Humboldt (naturalist).

**1959.** 400th Death Anniv. of Adam Riese.

1225. **356.** 10 pf. black & green 15 15

**1959.** Death Cent. of Alexander von Humboldt.

1226. **357.** 40 pf. blue .. .. 80 60

**358.** First Hamburg Stamp of 1859. **359.** Buxtehude.

**1959.** International Stamp Exhibition, Hamburg, and Centenary of First Stamps of Hamburg and Lubeck.

1228. **358.** 10 pf.+5 pf. brown and green .. .. 20 25

1230. – 20 pf.+10 pf. brn. and red .. .. 20 60

DESIGN: 20 pf. First Lubeck stamp of 1859.

**1959.** Millenary of Buxtehude.

1231. **359.** 20 pf. red, black and blue .. .. 20 20

**360.** Holy Tunic of Trier. **361.** Congress Emblem.

**1959.** Holy Tunic of Trier Exhibition.

1232 **360** 20 pf. blk, buff & pur 20 20

**1959.** German Evangelical Church Day and Congress, Munich.

1233. **361.** 10 pf. vio., grn. & blk. 10 10

**1959.** Europa. As T **360** of Belgium but size 24½×30 mm.

1234. 10 pf. green .. .. 15 10

1235. 40 pf. blue .. .. 80 40

362. "Feeding the Poor". 363. "Uprooted Tree".

**1959.** Humanitarian Relief and Welfare Funds.
1236. **362.** 7 pf.+3 pf. sepia and yellow .. .. 15 40
1237. – 10 pf.+5 pf. green and yellow .. .. 20 20
1238. – 20 pf.+10 pf. red and yellow .. .. 30 20
1239. – 40 pf.+10 pf. mult 3·00 4·00
DESIGNS: 10 pf. "Clothing the Naked". 20 pf. "Bounty from Heaven" (scenes from the Brothers Grimm story "The Star Thaler"). 40 pf. The Brothers Grimm.

**1960.** World Refugee Year.
1240. **363.** 10 pf. blk., pur. & grn. 20 10
1241. 40 pf. blk., red & blue 1·00 1·25

364. P. Melanchthon. 365. Cross and Symbols of the Crucifixion.

**1960.** 400th Death Anniv. of Philip Melanchthon. (Protestant reformer).
1242. **364.** 20 pf. black and red 75 60

**1960.** Oberammergau Passion Play.
1243. **365.** 10 pf. grey, ochre and blue .. .. 20 20

366. 367. Wrestling.

**1960.** 37th World Eucharistic Congress, Munich.
1244. **366.** 10 pf. green .. .. 50 30
1245. 20 pf. red .. .. 70 40

**1960.** Olympic Year. Inscr. as in T **367**.
1246. **367.** 7 pf. brown .. .. 15 20
1247. – 10 pf. green .. .. 25 15
1248. – 20 pf. red .. .. 30 10
1249. – 40 pf. blue .. .. 50 75
DESIGNS: 10 pf. Running. 20 pf. Javelin and discus-throwing. 40 pf. Chariot-racing.

368. Hildesheim Cathedral. 369. Little Red Riding Hood meeting Wolf.

**1960.** Birth Millenary of Bishops St. Bernward and St. Godehard.
1250. **368.** 20 pf. purple .. .. 40 40

**1960.** Europa. As T **373** of Belgium.
1251. 10 pf. green & olive .. 20 10
1252. 20 pf. vermilion and red .. 60 20
1253. 40 pf. light blue and blue 1·10 60

**1960.** Humanitarian Relief and Welfare Funds.
1254. **369.** 7 pf.+3 pf. black, red and bistre .. 30 50
1255. – 10 pf.+5 pf. black, red and green .. 30 15
1256. – 20 pf.+10 pf. black, green and red .. 30 20
1257. – 40 pf.+20 pf. black, red and blue .. 2·10 3·25
DESIGNS: 10 pf. Red Riding Hood and wolf disguised as grandmother. 20 pf. Woodcutter and dead wolf. 40 pf. Red Riding Hood with grandmother.

**1960.** 1st Death Anniv. of Gen. George C. Marshall. Portrait as T **364**.
1258. 40 pf. black and blue .. 1·00 70

371. "Der Adler" 1835. 372. St. George and the Dragon.

**1960.** 125th Anniv. of German Railway.
1259. **371.** 10 pf. black & bistre 50 20

**1961.** Pathfinders (German Boy Scouts). Commemoration.
1260. **372.** 10 pf. green .. .. 10 10

**1961.** Famous Germans. As Nos. B 194, etc. of West Berlin but without "BERLIN".
1261 5 pf. olive .. .. 10 10
1262 7 pf. brown .. .. 10 10
1263 8 pf. violet .. .. 10 15
1264 10 pf. green .. .. 10 10
1265 15 pf. blue .. .. 10 10
1266 20 pf. red .. .. 10 10
1267 25 pf. brown .. .. 15 10
1268 30 pf. sepia .. .. 20 10
1269 40 pf. blue .. .. 20 10
1270 50 pf. brown .. .. 45 10
1271 60 pf. red .. .. 35 20
1272 70 pf. green .. .. 35 10
1273 80 pf. brown .. .. 60 20
1274 90 pf. bistre .. .. 60 40
1275 1 Dm. violet .. .. 75 10
1276 2 Dm. green .. .. 3·00 30
PORTRAIT: 90 pf. Franz Oppenheimer (economist).

373. Early Daimler Motor Car. 374. Nuremberg Messenger of 1700.

**1961.** 75th Anniv. of Daimler-Benz Patent.
1277. **373.** 10 pf. green and black 10 10
1278. – 20 pf. red and black 20 15
DESIGN: 20 pf. Early Benz motor car.

**1961.** "The Letter during Five Centuries" Exhibition, Nuremberg.
1279. **374.** 7 pf. black and red .. 10 10

375. Speyer Cathedral. 376. Doves.

**1961.** 900th Anniv. of Speyer Cathedral.
1280. **375.** 20 pf. red .. .. 20 10

**1961.** Europa.
1281. **376.** 10 pf. green .. .. 10 10
1282. 40 pf. blue .. .. 40 40

377. Hansel and Gretel in the Wood. 378. Telephone Apparatus.

**1961.** Humanitarian Relief and Welfare Funds. Multicoloured.
1283. 7 pf.+3 pf. Type **377** .. 20 30
1284. 10 pf.+5 pf. Hansel, Gretel and the Witch .. 15 15
1285. 20 pf.+10 pf. Hansel in the Witch's cage .. 15 15
1286. 40 pf.+20 pf. Hansel and Gretel reunited with their father .. 1·00 1·75

**1961.** Cent. of Philipp Reis's Telephone.
1287. **378.** 10 pf. green .. .. 15 10

379. Baron W. E. von Ketteler. 380. Drusus Stone.

**1961.** 150th Birth Anniv. of Baron W. E. von Ketteler (Catholic leader).
1288. **379.** 10 pf. black & green 10 10

**1962.** Bimillenary of Mainz.
1289. **380.** 20 pf. purple .. .. 10 10

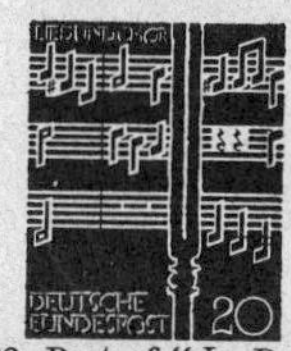

381. Apollo. 382. Part of "In Dulci Jubilo", from "Musæ Sionæ" (M. Praetorius).

**1962.** Child Welfare. Butterflies. Mult.
1290 7 pf.+3 pf. Type **381** .. 35 45
1291 10 pf.+5 pf. Camberwell beauty .. .. 40 45
1292 20 pf.+10 pf. Small tortoiseshell .. .. 1·00 90
1293 40 pf.+20 pf. Scarce swallowtail .. .. 1·40 1·40

**1962.** "Song and Choir" (Summer Music Festivals).
1294. **382.** 20 pf. red and black 20 10

383. "Belief, Thanksgiving and Service". 384. Open Bible.

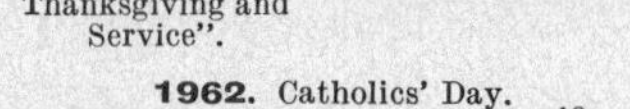

**1962.** Catholics' Day.
1295. **383.** 20 pf. mauve .. 10 10

**1962.** 150th Anniv. of Wurttembergische Bibelanstalt (Bible publishers).
1296. **384.** 20 pf. black and red .. 10 10

385. Europa "Tree". 386. Snow White and Seven Dwarfs.

**1962.** Europa.
1297. **385.** 10 pf. green .. .. 10 10
1298. 40 pf. blue .. .. 25 15

**1962.** Humanitarian Relief and Welfare Funds. Scenes from "Snow White and the Seven Dwarfs" (Brothers Grimm). Multicoloured.
1299. 7 pf.+3 pf. The "Magic Mirror" .. .. 20 30
1300. 10 pf.+5 pf. Type **386** .. 20 10
1301. 20 pf.+10 pf. "The Poisoned Apple" .. 20 15
1302. 40 pf.+20 pf. Snow White and Prince Charming 95 1·25

387. "Bread for the World". 388. Relief Distribution.

**1963.** Freedom from Hunger.
1303. **387.** 20 pf. brown & black 10 10

**1963.** CRALOG and CARE Relief Organizations.
1304. **388.** 20 pf. red .. .. 10 10

389. Ears of Wheat, Cross and Globe. 390. Snake's Head Lily.

**1963.** Freedom from Hunger.
1305. **389.** 20 pf. black, red & grey 15 15

**1963.** "Flora and Philately" Exhibition, Hamburg. Multicoloured.
1306 10 pf. Type **390** .. 15 10
1307 15 pf. Lady's slipper orchid .. .. 15 10
1308 20 pf. Columbine .. 15 10
1309 40 pf. Sea holly .. 30 20

391. "Heidelberger Catechismus". 392. Cross, Sun and Moon.

**1963.** 400th Anniv. of Heidelberg Catechism.
1310. **391.** 20 pf. black, red and orange .. .. 15 15

**1963.** Consecration of Regina Martyrum Church, Berlin.
1311. **392.** 10 pf. multicoloured 10 10

393. Emblems of Conference Participating Countries. 394. Map and Flags.

**1963.** Cent. of Paris Postal Conference.
1312. **393.** 40 pf. blue .. .. 10 15

**1963.** Opening of Denmark—Germany Railway ("Vogelfluglinie").
1313. **394.** 20 pf. multicoloured 20 15

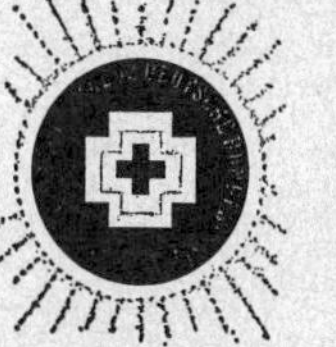

395. Red Cross Emblem. 396. Hoopoe.

**1963.** Red Cross Cent.
1314. **395.** 20 pf. red, purple and yellow .. .. 10 10

**1963.** Child Welfare. Bird designs inscr. "FUR DIE JUGEND 1963". Multicoloured.
1315. 10 pf.+5 pf. Type **396** .. 70 70
1316. 15 pf.+5 pf. Golden Oriole 50 60
1317. 20 pf.+10 pf. Bullfinch .. 55 70
1318. 40 pf.+20 pf. Common Kingfisher .. .. 1·90 2·25

397. Congress Emblem. 398. "Co-operation".

**1963.** German Evangelical Church Day and Congress, Dortmund.
1319. **397.** 20 pf. black & brown 15 20

**1963.** Europa.
1320. **398.** 15 pf. green .. .. 10 10
1321. 20 pf. red .. .. 10 10

399. Mother Goat warning kids. 400. Herring.

**1963.** Humanitarian Relief and Welfare Funds.
1322. **399.** 10 pf.+5 pf. mult .. 10 20
1323. – 15 pf.+5 pf. mult .. 10 15
1324. – 20 pf.+10 pf. mult 15 15
1325. – 40 pf.+20 pf. mult 40 90
DESIGNS: 15 pf. Wolf entering house. 20 pf. Wolf in house, threatening kids. 40 pf. Mother Goat and kids dancing round wolf in well. From Grimm's "Wolf and the Seven Kids".

**1964.** Child Welfare. Fish designs inscr. "Fur die Jugend 1964". Multicoloured.
1326. 10 pf.+5 pf. Type **400** .. 20 40
1327. 15 pf.+5 pf. Sea-perch .. 20 30
1328. 20 pf.+10 pf. Carp .. 40 30
1329. 40 pf.+20 pf. Cod .. 1·10 1·50

401. Old Town Hall, Hanover. 402. Ottobeuren Abbey.

**1964.** Capitals of the Federal Lands. Mult.
1330. 20 pf. Type **401** .. 20 15
1331. 20 pf. Hamburg .. 20 15
1332. 20 pf. Kiel .. 20 15
1333. 20 pf. Munich .. 20 15
1334. 20 pf. Wiesbaden .. 20 15
1335. 20 pf. Berlin .. 20 15
1336. 20 pf. Mainz .. 20 15
1337. 20 pf. Dusseldorf .. 20 15
1338. 20 pf. Bonn .. 20 15
1339. 20 pf. Bremen .. 20 15
1340. 20 pf. Stuttgart .. 20 15
1340a. 20 pf. Saarbrucken .. 20 15
DESIGNS: No. 1331, Liner "Lichtenfels" and St. Michael's Church (775th anniv.). No. 1332, Ferry "Kronprinz Harald". No. 1333, National Theatre. No. 1334, Kurhaus. No. 1335, Reichstag. No. 1336, Gutenberg Museum. No. 1337, Jan Wellen's Monument and Town Hall. No. 1338, Town Hall. No. 1339, Market Hall. No. 1340, Town view. No. 1340a, Ludwig's Church.

**1964.** 1200th Anniv. of Benedictine Abbey, Ottobeuren.
1341. **402.** 20 pf. black, red & pink .. .. 10 10

**1964.** Re-election of Pres. Lubke. As Type B **67** of West Berlin, inscr. "DEUTSCHE BUNDESPOST" only.
1342. 20 pf. red .. .. 10 10
1343. 40 pf. blue .. .. 10 10

**402b.** Sophie Scholl

**1964.** 20th Anniv. of Attempt on Hitler's Life. Anti-Hitlerite Martyrs. Each black and grey.
1343a. 20 pf. Type **402b** .. 90 1·40
1343b. 20 pf. Ludwig Beck .. 90 1·40
1343c. 20 pf. Dietrich Bonhoeffer 90 1·40
1343d. 20 pf. Alfred Delp .. 90 1·40
1343e. 20 pf. Karl Friedrich Goerdeler .. .. 90 1·40
1343f. 20 pf. Wilhelm Leuschner 90 1·40
1343g. 20 pf. Helmuth James (Von Moltke) .. .. 90 1·40
1343h. 20 pf. Claus Schenk (Von Stauffenberg) .. 90 1·40

**403.** Calvin.

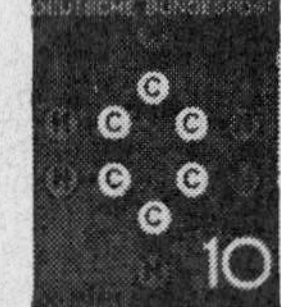

**404.** Diagram of Benzene Formula.

**1964.** World Council of Reformed Churches.
1344. **403.** 20 pf. black and red .. 10 10

**1964.** Scientific Anniversaries (1st series).
1345. 10 pf. green, black & brn. 10 10
1346. 15 pf. multicoloured .. 10 10
1347. 20 pf. green, black and red 10 10
DESIGNS: 10 pf. Type **404** (centenary of publication of Kekule's benzene formula). 15 pf. Diagram of nuclear reaction (25th anniv. of publication of Hahn-Strassman treatise on splitting the nucleus of the atom). 20 pf. Gas engine (centenary of Otto-Langen internal-combustion engine),.
See also Nos. 1426/7 and 1451/3.

**405.** F. Lassalle.

**406.** "The Sun".

**1964.** Death Centenary of Ferdinand Lassalle (Socialist founder and leader).
1348. **405.** 20 pf. black and blue 10 10

**1964.** 80th Catholics' Day.
1349. **406.** 20 pf. red and blue .. 10 10

**407.** Europa "Flower".

**408.** "The Sleeping Beauty".

**1964.** Europa.
1350. **407.** 15 pf. violet and green 10 20
1351. 20 pf. violet and red .. 10 10

**1964.** Humanitarian Relief and Welfare Funds.
1352. **408.** 10 pf. + 5 pf. mult. .. 15 20
1353. – 15 pf. + 5 pf. mult. .. 15 15
1354. – 20 pf. + 10 pf. mult... 15 15
1355. – 40 pf. + 20 pf. mult... 45 90
DESIGNS: 15 pf., 20 pf., 40 pf. Various scenes from Grimm's "The Sleeping Beauty".

**409.** Judo.

**410.** Prussian Eagle.

**1964.** "Olympic Year".
1356. **409.** 20 pf. multicoloured 20 10

**1964.** 250th Anniv. of German Court of Accounts.
1357. **410.** 20 pf. orange & black 30 10

**411.** Pres. Kennedy.

**412.** Castle Gateway Ellwangen (Jagst).

**1964.** Pres. Kennedy Commem.
1358. **411.** 40 pf. blue .. .. 20 10

**1964.** Twelve Centuries of German Architecture.
(a) Size $18\frac{1}{2} \times 22$ mm. Plain background.
1359. – 10 pf. brown .. .. 15 10
1360. – 15 pf. green .. .. 15 10
1361. – 20 pf. brown .. 15 10
1362. – 40 pf. blue .. .. 55 10
1363. **412.** 50 pf. brown .. 85 10
1364. – 60 pf. red .. .. 1·00 45
1365. – 70 pf. green .. .. 1·25 45
1366. – 80 pf. brown .. 1·25 10
(b) Size $19\frac{1}{2} \times 24$ mm. Coloured background.
1367. – 5 pf. brown .. .. 10 10
1368. – 10 pf. brown .. 10 10
1369. – 20 pf. green .. 20 10
1370. – 30 pf. green .. .. 15 10
1371. – 30 pf. red .. .. 30 10
1372. – 40 pf. brown .. 35 10
1373. – 50 pf. blue .. .. 50 10
1374. – 60 pf. orange .. 2·25 1·25
1375. – 70 pf. green .. .. 85 10
1376. – 80 pf. brown .. 2·25 1·25
1377. – 90 pf. black .. .. 70 10
1378. – 1 Dm. blue .. .. 85 10
1379. – 1 Dm. 10 brown .. 1·25 15
1380. – 1 Dm. 30 green .. 2·75 60
1381. – 2 Dm. purple .. 1·40 30
BUILDINGS: 5 pf. Berlin Gate, Stettin. 10 pf. Zwinger pavilion, Dresden. 15 pf. Tegel Castle, Berlin. 20 pf. Monastery Gate, Lorsch. 30 pf. North Gate, Flensburg. 40 pf. Trifels Castle (Palatinate). 60 pf. Treptow Portal, Neubrandenburg. 70 pf. Osthofen Gate, Soest. 80 pf. Ellingen Portal, Weissenburg (Bavaria). 90 pf. Zschokk's Convent, Konigsberg. 1 Dm. Melanchthon House, Wittenberg. 1 Dm. 10, Trinity Hospital, Hildesheim. 1 Dm. 30, Tegel Castle, Berlin (diff). 2 Dm. Burghers' Hall, Lowenberg Town Hall (Silesia).

**413.** Owl, Hat, Walking-stick and Satchel.

**414.** Woodcock.

**1965.** 150th Death Anniv of Matthias Claudius (poet).
1383 **413** 20 pf. black and red on grey .. .. 15 10

**1965.** Child Welfare. Inscr. "FUR DIE JUGEND 1965". Multicoloured.
1384. 10 pf. + 5 pf. Type **414** .. 20 20
1385. 15 pf. + 5 pf. Ring-necked Pheasant .. .. 20 25
1386. 20 pf. + 10 pf. Black Grouse .. .. .. 30 25
1387. 40 pf. + 20 pf. Capercaillie 60 70

**415.** Bismarck (statesman).

**416.** Boeing 727-100 Airliner and Space Capsule.

**1965.** 150th Birth Anniv. of Otto von Bismarck.
1388. **415.** 20 pf. black and red 10 10

**1965.** Int. Transport Exn., Munich. Mult.
1389 5 pf. Traffic lights and road signs .. .. 10 10
1390 10 pf. "Syncom" satellite and tracking station .. 10 10
1391 15 pf. Old and modern postal buses .. .. 10 10
1392 20 pf. Old semaphore station and modern signal tower .. .. 10 10
1393 40 pf. Old steam engine & modern electric loco 25 15
1394 60 pf. Type **416** .. .. 30 20
1395 70 pf. "Bremen" (liner) and "Hammonia" (19th-century steamship) .. 50 15
No. 1394 was also issued to mark the 10th anniv. of Lufthansa's renewed air services.

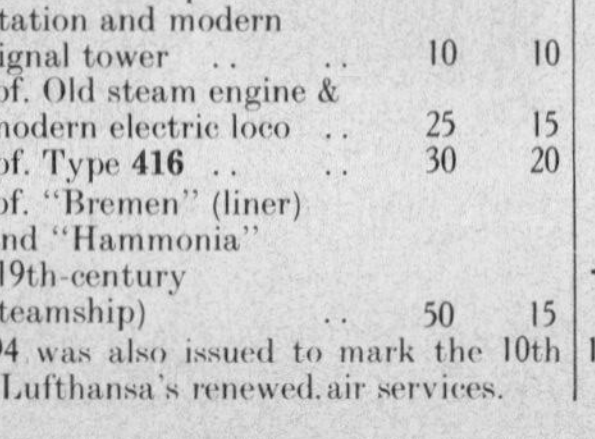

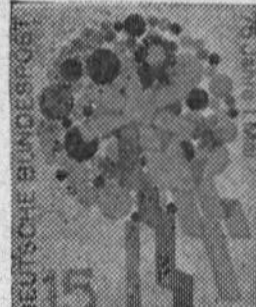

**417.** Bouquet.

**418.** I.T.U. Emblem.

**1965.** 75th Anniv. of "May 1st" (Labour Day).
1396. **417.** 15 pf. multicoloured 10 10

**1965.** Centenary of I.T.U.
1397. **418.** 40 pf. black and blue 25 10

**419.** A. Kopling.

**420.** Rescue Vessel "Theodor Heuss".

**1965.** Death Centenary of Adolf Kolping (miners' padre).
1398. **419.** 20 pf. black, red & grey .. .. 10 10

**1965.** Cent. of German Sea-Rescue Service.
1399. **420.** 20 pf. vio, blk. & red 20 10

**1965.** 20th Anniv of Influx of East German Refugees. As T **299** but inscr "ZWANZIG JAHRE VERTREIBUNG 1945 1965".
1400 20 pf. purple .. .. 10 10

**421.** Evangelical Church. Emblem.

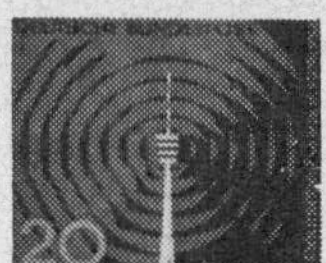

**422.** Radio Tower.

**1965.** German Evangelical Church Day and Synod, Cologne.
1401. **421.** 20 pf. black, turq. & bl. 10 10

**1965.** Radio Exhib., Stuttgart.
1402. **422.** 20 pf. blk., blue & mve. 10 10

**423.** Thurn and Taxis 1, 2, and 5 sgr. Stamps of 1852.

**424.** Europa "Sprig".

**1965.** 125th Anniv. of 1st Postage Stamp.
1403. **423.** 20 pf. multicoloured 10 10

**1965.** Europa.
1404. **424.** 15 pf. green .. .. 20 10
1405. 20 pf. red .. .. 20 10

**425.** Cinderella with Birds.

**426.** N. Soderblom.

**1965.** Humanitarian Relief Funds. Mult.
1406. 10 pf. + 5 pf. Type **425** .. 15 10
1407. 15 pf. + 5 pf. Cinderella and birds with dress 15 10
1408. 20 pf. + 10 pf. Prince offering slipper to Cinderella .. .. 20 10
1409. 40 pf. + 20 pf. Cinderella and Prince on horse 50 70

**1966.** Birth Centenary of Nathan Soderblom (Archbishop of Uppsala).
1410. **426.** 20 pf. black and lilac 10 10

**427.** Cardinal von Galen.

**428.** Brandenburg Gate, Berlin.

**1966.** 20th Death Anniv. of Cardinal Clemens von Galen.
1411. **427.** 20 pf. red, mauve & black .. .. 10 10

**1966.**
1412. **428.** 10 pf. brown .. .. 10 10
1413. 20 pf. green .. .. 15 10
1414. 30 pf. red .. .. 25 10
1415. 50 pf. blue .. .. 90 10
1415a. 100 pf. blue .. .. 6·00 20

**429.** Roe deer.

**430.** Christ and Fishermen (Miracle of the Fishes).

**1966.** Child Welfare. Multicoloured.
1416. 10 pf. + 5 pf. Type **429** 15 25
1417. 20 pf. + 10 pf. Chamois 15 15
1418. 30 pf. + 15 pf. Fallow deer 25 35
1419. 50 pf. + 25 pf. Red deer 55 1·00

**1966.** Catholics' Day.
1420 **430.** 30 pf. black & salmon 10 10

**431.** 19th-cent. Postman.

**432.** G. W. Leibniz.

**1966.** F.I.P. Meeting, Munich. Multicoloured.
1421 30 pf. + 15 pf. Bavarian mail coach .. .. 30 70
1422 50 pf. + 25 pf. Type **431** .. 20 55

**1966.** 250th Death Anniv. of Gottfried Leibniz (scientist).
1423. **432.** 30 pf. black & mauve 10 10

**433.** Europa "Ship".

**434.** Diagram of A.C. Transmission (75th Anniv.).

**1966.** Europa.
1424. **433.** 20 pf. multicoloured 10 15
1425. 30 pf. multicoloured 10 10

**1966.** Scientific Annivs. (2nd series). Mult.
1426. 20 pf. Type **434** .. 10 10
1427. 30 pf. Diagram of electric dynamo (cent.) .. 10 10

**435.** Princess and Frog.

**436.** U.N.I.C.E.F. Emblem.

**1966.** Humanitarian Relief Funds. Mult
1428. 10 pf. + 5 pf. Type **435** .. 10 20
1429. 20 pf. + 10 pf. Frog dining with Princess .. 10 10
1430. 30 pf. + 15 pf. Prince and Princess .. .. 15 20
1431. 50 pf. + 25 pf. In coach .. 35 90
Designs from Grimm's "The Frog Prince".

**1966.** Award of Nobel Peace Prize to United Nations Children's Fund.
1432 **436** 30 pf. sepia, blk & red 10 10

**437.** W. von Siemens (electrical engineer).

**438.** Common rabbit.

**1966.** 150th Birth Anniv of Werner von Siemens (electrical engineer).
1433 **437** 30 pf. red .. .. 20 15

**1967.** Child Welfare. Multicoloured.
1434. 10 pf. + 5 pf. Type **438** .. 20 40
1435. 20 pf. + 10 pf. Stoat .. 20 25
1436. 30 pf. + 15 pf. Common hamster .. .. 30 50
1437. 50 pf. + 25 pf. Red fox .. 80 1·25
See also Nos. 1454/7.

439. Cogwheels.

440. Francis of Taxis.

**1967.** Europa.
1438. 439. 20 pf. multicoloured 10 20
1439. 30 pf. multicoloured 10 10

**1967.** 450th Death Anniv. of Francis of Taxis.
1440. 440. 30 pf. black & orange 10 10

441. Evangelical Symbols.

442. Friedrich von Bodelschwingh (Head of Hospital 1910–46).

**1967.** 13th German Evangelical Churches Day.
1441. 441. 30 pf. black & mauve 10 10

**1967.** Cent of Bethel Hospital, Bielefeld.
1442 442 30 pf. black and brown 10 10

443. Frau Holle at Spinning-wheel.

444. Wartburg (castle), Eisenach.

**1967.** Humanitarian Relief Funds. Mult.
1443. 10 pf.+5 pf. Type 443 15 30
1444. 20 pf.+10 pf. In the clouds 15 15
1445. 30 pf.+15 pf. With shopping-basket and cockerel 20 30
1446. 50 pf.+25 pf. Covered with soot 40 75
Designs from Grimm's "Frau Holle" ("Mother Carey").

**1967.** Re-election of Pres. Lubke. As Type B 67 of West Berlin, but inscr. "DEUTSCHE BUNDESPOST".
1447. 30 pf. red 10 10
1448. 50 pf. blue 15 10

**1967.** 450th Anniv. of Luther's "Theses" and the Reformation.
1449. 444. 30 pf. red 10 10

445. Cross on South American Map.

446. Koenig's Printing Machine.

**1967.** "Adveniat" (Aid for Catholic Church in Latin America).
1450. 445. 30 pf. multicoloured 10 10

**1968.** Scientific Anniv. (3rd series). Mult.
1451. 10 pf. Type 446 10 10
1452. 20 pf. Ore Crystals 10 10
1453. 30 pf. Lens Refraction 10 10
ANNIVS: 10 pf. 150th anniv. 20 pf. Millenary of ore mining in Harz Mountains. 30 pf. Centenary of Abbe-Zeiss Scientific Microscope.

**1968.** Child Welfare. As T 438 but inscr. "1968". Multicoloured.
1454. 10 pf.+5 pf. Wildcat 30 55
1455. 20 pf.+10 pf. European otter 35 40
1456. 30 pf.+15 pf. Eurasian badger 65 85
1457. 50 pf.+25 pf. Eurasian beaver 1·50 2·25

447. Trade Symbols.

**1968.** German Crafts and Trades.
1458. 447. 30 pf. multicoloured 10 10

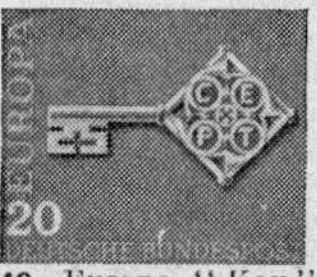
449. Europa "Key".

450. Karl Marx.

**1968.** Europa.
1460. 449. 20 pf. yell., brn. & grn. 10 10
1461. 30 pf. yellow, brn. & red 10 10

**1968.** 150th Birth Anniv. of Karl Marx.
1462. 450. 30 pf. red, black & grey 10 10

451. F. von Langen (horseman).

**1968.** Olympic Games (1972) Promotion Fund (1st series).
1463. 451. 10 pf.+5 pf. black and green 30 30
1464. – 20 pf.+10 pf. black and green. 30 30
1465. – 30 pf. black & lilac 20 10
1466. – 30 pf.+15 pf. black and red 40 40
1467. – 50 pf.+25 pf. black and blue 60 70
DESIGN: 20 pf. R. Harbig (runner). 30 pf. (No. 1465) Pierre de Coubertin (founder of Olympics). 30 pf. (No. 1466) Helene Mayer (fencer). 50 pf. Carl Diem (sports organiser).
See also Nos. 1493/6, 1524/7, 1589/92, 1621/4 and 1629/32.

452. Opening Bars of "The Mastersingers".

453. Dr. Adenauer.

**1968.** Cent. of 1st Performance of Richard Wagner's Opera "The Mastersingers".
1468. 452. 30 pf. multicoloured 30 15

**1968.** Adenauer Commem.
1469. 453. 30 pf. black & orange 20 10

454. Cross, Dove and "The Universe".

455. Northern District 1 g. and Southern District 7 k. stamps of 1868.

**1968.** Catholics' Day.
1470. 454. 20 pf. violet, yellow and green 20 10

**1968.** Cent. of North German Postal Confederation and First Stamps.
1471. 455. 30 pf. red, blue & blk. 20 10

456. Arrows.

457. Doll of 1878.

**1968.** Cent. of German Trade Unions.
1472. 456. 30 pf. multicoloured 10 10

**1968.** Humanitarian Relief Funds. Mult
1473. 10 pf.+5 pf. Type 457 10 20
1474. 20 pf.+10 pf. Doll of 1850 10 15
1475. 30 pf.+15 pf. Doll of 1870 15 20
1476. 50 pf.+25 pf. Doll of 1885 40 90

458. Human Rights Emblem.

459. Pony.

**1968.** Human Rights Year.
1477. 458. 30 pf. multicoloured 10 10

**1969.** Child Welfare.
1478. 459. 10 pf.+5 pf. brown, black and yellow 30 35
1479. – 20 pf.+10 pf. brown black and buff 40 30
1480. – 30 pf.+15 pf. brown, black and red 80 90
1481. – 50 pf.+25 pf. mult 1·75 1·75
HORSES: 20 pf. Draught-horse. 30 pf. Saddle-horse. 50 pf. Thoroughbred.

460. Junkers Ju 52/3m "Boelke".

**1969.** 50th Anniv of German Airmail Services. Multicoloured.
1482 20 pf. Type 460 30 10
1483 30 pf. Boeing 707 airliner 40 10

461. Colonnade.

462. "The Five Continents".

**1969.** Europa.
1484 461 20 pf. yellow, grn & bl 10 10
1485 30 pf. yell, red & vio 15 10

**1969.** 50th Anniv. of I.L.O.
1486. 462. 30 pf. multicoloured 15 10

463. Eagle Emblems of Weimar and Federal Republics.

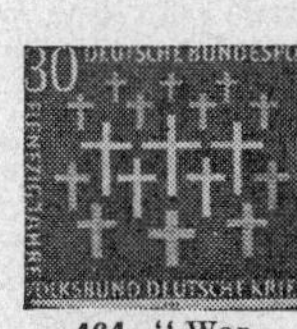
464. "War Graves".

**1969.** 20th Anniv. of German Federal Republic.
1487. 463. 30 pf. black, gold & red 15 10

**1969.** 50th Anniv. of German War Graves Commission.
1488. 464. 30 pf. blue and yell. 20 10

465. Lakeside Landscape.

466. "Running Track".

**1969.** Nature Protection. Multicoloured.
1489. 10 pf. Type 465 10 10
1490. 20 pf. Highland landscape 30 20
1491. 30 pf. Alpine landscape 20 15
1492. 50 pf. River landscape 35 35

**1969.** Olympic Games (1972). Promotion Fund (2nd series). Multicoloured.
1493. 10 pf.+5 pf. Type 466 20 20
1494. 20 pf.+15 pf. "Hockey" 30 40
1495. 30 pf.+15 pf. "Shooting target" 45 45
1496. 50 pf.+25 pf. "Sailing" 80 75

467. "Longing for Justice".

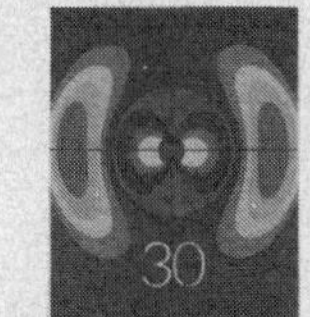
468. "Electro-magnetic Field".

**1969.** 14th German Protestant Congress, Stuttgart.
1497. 467. 30 pf. multicoloured 15 10

**1969.** German Radio Exn., Stuttgart.
1498. 468. 30 pf. multicoloured 15 10

470. Maltese Cross Symbol.

471. Bavaria 3 k. Stamp of 1867.

**1969.** "Malteser Hilfsdienst" (welfare organization).
1500. 470. 30 pf. red and black 15 10

**1969.** German Philatelic Federation Congress and Exn., Garmisch-Partenkirchen.
1501. 471. 30 pf. red and slate 15 10

472. Map of Pipeline.

**1969.** 350th Anniv. of Bad Reichenhall-Traunstein Brine Pipeline.
1502. 472. 20 pf. multicoloured 10 10

473. Rothenburg ob der Tauber.

**1969.** Tourism.
1503. 473. 30 pf. black and red 15 10
See also Nos. 1523, 1558, 1564, 1587, 1606, 1641/2, 1655/6 and 1680/2.

474. Mahatma Gandhi.

475. Pope John XXIII.

**1969.** Birth Cent. of Mahatma Gandhi.
1504. 474. 20 pf. black & green 15 10

**1969.** Pope John XXIII Commem.
1505. 475. 30 pf. red 15 10

476. Locomotive (1835).

477. E. M. Arndt.

**1969.** Humanitarian Relief Funds. Pewter Figurines. Multicoloured.
(a) Inscr. "WOHLFAHRTSMARKE".
1506. 10 pf.+5 pf. Type 476 25 20
1507. 20 pf.+10 pf. Woman watering flowers (1780) 20 15
1508. 30 pf.+15 pf. Bird salesman (1850) 30 25
1509. 50 pf.+25 pf. Mounted dignitary (1840) 70 70
(b) Christmas. Inscr. "WEIHNACHTSMARKE".
1510. 10 pf.+5 pf. "Child Jesus in crib" (1850) 10 15

**1969.** Birth Bicent. of Ernst Arndt (writer).
1511. 477. 30 pf. lake and bistre 15 10

478. "H. von Rugge".

**1970.** Child Welfare. Minnesinger Themes. Multicoloured.
1512. 10 pf.+5 pf. Type 478 40 40
1513. 20 pf.+10 pf. "W. von Eschenbach" 50 40
1514. 30 pf.+15 pf. "W. von Metz" 60 55
1515. 50 pf.+25 pf. "W. von der Vogelweide" 1·25 1·10

479. Beethoven. 480. Saar 1 m. Stamp of 1947.

**1970.** Birth Bicents.

1516. **479.** 10 pf. black & blue . . 50 15
1517. – 20 pf. black & olive 20 10
1518. – 30 pf. black and pink 30 10

DESIGNS: 20 pf. G. W. Hegel (philosopher). 30 pf. F. Holderlin (poet).

**1970.** "Sabria 70" Stamp Exn., Saarbrucken.

1519. **480.** 30 pf. grn., blk. & red 15 10

481. "Flaming Sun". 482. Von Munchhausen on Severed Horse.

**1970.** Europa.

1520. **481.** 20 pf. green . . . . 20 10
1521. 30 pf. red . . . . 40 10

**1970.** 250th Birth Anniv. of Baron H. von Munchhausen.

1522. **482.** 20 pf. multicoloured 15 10

**1970.** Tourism. Horiz. design as T **473**, but with view of Oberammergau.

1523. 30 pf. black and orange . . 15 10

483. Royal Palace.

**1970.** Olympic Games (1972). Promotion Fund (3rd series).

1524. **483.** 10 pf. + 5 pf. brown . . 20 30
1525. – 20 pf. + 10 pf. turq. . . 30 40
1526. – 30 pf. + 15 pf. red . . 50 50
1527. – 50 pf. + 25 pf. blue . . 80 80

DESIGNS (Munich buildings): 20 pf. Propylaea. 30 pf. Glyptothek. 50 pf. "Bavaria" (statue and colonnade).

484. Liner and Road-tunnel. 485. Nurse with Invalid.

**1970.** 75th Anniv. of Kiel Canal.

1528. **484.** 20 pf. multicoloured 25 10

**1970.** Voluntary Relief Services. Mult.

1529 5 pf. Oxygen-lance operator . . . . 10 10
1530 10 pf. Mountain rescue . . 15 10
1531 20 pf. Type **485** . . . . 15 10
1532 30 pf. Fireman with hose 35 10
1533 50 pf. Road-accident casualty . . . . 35 55
1534 70 pf. Rescue from drowning . . . . 40 55

486. President Heinemann. 487. Illuminated Cross.

**1970.**

1535. **486.** 5 pf. black . . . . 10 10
1536. 10 pf. brown . . . . 15 10
1537. 20 pf. green . . . . 15 10
1538. 25 pf. green . . . . 30 10
1539. 30 pf. brown . . 35 10
1540. 40 pf. orange . . 35 10
1541. 50 pf. blue . . . . 2·00 10
1542. 60 pf. blue . . . . 80 10
1543. 70 pf. brown . . 60 10
1544. 80 pf. green . . . . 70 15
1545. 90 pf. red . . . . 2·10 1·75
1546. 1 Dm. green . . . . 60 10
1547. 110 pf. grey . . . . 2·00 50
1548. 120 pf. brown . . 90 55
1549. 130 pf. brown . . 90 60
1550. 140 pf. green . . 1·60 1·00
1551. 150 pf. red . . . . 1·40 40
1552. 160 pf. orange . . 1·50 75
1553. 170 pf. orange . . 1·60 70
1554. 190 pf. purple . . 3·00 1·25
1555. 2 Dm. violet . . 1·60 15

**1970.** Catholic Church World Mission.

1556. **487.** 20 pf. yellow & green 15 10

488. Stylised Cross. 489. "Jester".

**1970.** Catholics Day and 83rd German Catholic Congress, Trier.

1557. **488.** 20 pf. multicoloured 15 10

**1970.** Tourism. As T **473**.

1558. 20 pf. black and green . . 20 10

DESIGN: 20 pf. View of Cochem.

**1970.** Humanitarian Relief Funds. Puppets. Multicoloured.

(a) Relief Funds

1559. 10 pf. + 5 pf. Type **489** 15 15
1560. 20 pf. + 10 pf. "Buffoon" 20 20
1561. 30 pf. + 15 pf. "Clown" 30 30
1562. 50 pf. + 25 pf. "Harlequin" . . . . 60 85

(b) Christmas.

1563. 10 pf. + 5 pf. "Angel" 10 15

**1970.** Tourism. Horiz design as T **473**, but with view of Freiburg im Breisgau.

1564. 20 pf. brown and green 20 10

490. A. J. Comenius (scholar). 491. Engels as Young Man.

**1970.** Int. Education Year and 300th Death Anniv. of Comenius (Jan Komensky).

1565. **490.** 30 pf. red and black 20 10

**1970.** 150th Birth Anniv. of Friedrich Engels.

1566. **491.** 50 pf. blue and red . . 50 35

492. German Eagle. 493. "Ebert" Stamp of 1928 and inscr. "To the German People".

**1971.** Cent. of German Unification.

1567. **492.** 30 pf. black, red & orange . . . . 40 10

**1971.** Birth Centenary of Friedrich Ebert (Chancellor 1918 and President 1919–25).

1568 **493** 30 pf. green, blk & red 50 10

494. "King of Blackamoors". 495. Molecular Chain.

**1971.** Child Welfare. Children's Drawings. Multicoloured.

1569. 10 pf. + 5 pf. Type **494** . . 30 35
1570. 20 pf. + 10 pf. "Flea" . . 40 50
1571. 30 pf. + 15 pf. "Puss-in-Boots" . . 70 85
1572. 50 pf. + 25 pf. "Serpent" 1·25 1·50

**1971.** 125 Years of Chemical Fibre Research.

1573. **495.** 20 pf. black, red & grn. 15 10

496. Road-crossing Patrol. 497. Luther before Charles V.

**1971.** New Road Traffic Regulations (1st series).

1574. **496.** 10 pf. blk., blue & red 15 10
1575. – 20 pf. blk., red & grn. 30 15
1576. – 30 pf. red, blk. & grey 45 15
1577. – 50 pf. blk., blue & red 50 50

ROAD SIGNS: 20 pf. "Right-of-way across junction". 30 pf. "STOP". 50 pf. "Pedestrian Crossing".

See also Nos. 1579/82.

**1971.** 450th Anniv. of Diet of Worms.

1578. **497.** 30 pf. black and red . . 30 10

**1971.** New Traffic Regulations (2nd series). Horiz designs similar to T **496**.

1579. 5 pf. red, black and blue . . 10 10
1580. 10 pf. multicoloured . . 15 10
1581. 20 pf. red, black & green 25 15
1582. 30 pf. yellow, black & red 40 25

NEW HIGHWAY CODE: 5 pf. Overtaking. 10 pf. Warning of obstruction. 20 pf. Lane discipline. 30 pf. Pedestrian Crossing.

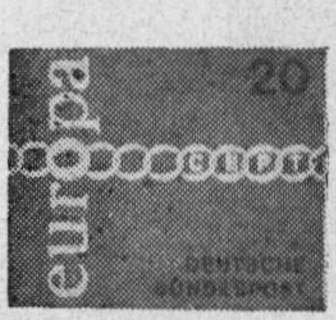

498. Europa Chain. 499. Thomas a Kempis writing "The Imitation of Christ".

**1971.** Europa.

1583. **498.** 20 pf. gold, grn. & blk. 30 10
1584. 30 pf. gold, red & blk. 35 10

**1971.** 500th Death Anniv. of Thomas a Kempis (devotional writer).

1585. **499.** 30 pf. black and red 20 10

500. Durer's Monogram. 501. Meeting Emblem.

**1971.** 500th Birth Anniv. of Albrecht Durer.

1586. **500.** 30 pf. brown & red . . 30 10

**1971.** Tourism. As T **473**, but with view of Nuremburg.

1587. 30 pf. black and red . . 30 10

**1971.** Whitsun Ecumenical Meeting, Augsburg.

1588. **501.** 30 pf. black, orange & red 20 10

502. Ski Jumping. 503. Astronomical Calculus.

**1971.** Olympic Games (1972). Promotion Fund (4th series). Winter Games, Sapporo.

1589. **502.** 10 pf. + 5 pf. blk. & brn. 30 40
1590. – 20 pf. + 10 pf. blk. & grn. 55 75
1591. – 30 pf. + 15 pf. blk. & red 70 85
1592. – 50 pf. + 25 pf. blk. & bl. 1·40 1·60

DESIGNS: 20 pf. Ice dancing. 30 pf. Skiing start. 50 pf. Ice hockey.

**1971.** 400th Birth Anniv. of Johann Kepler (astronomer).

1594. **503.** 30 pf. gold, red & blk. 30 10

504. Dante. 505. Alcohol and front of Car. ("Don't Drink and Drive").

**1971.** 650th Death Anniv. of Dante Alighieri.

1595. **504.** 10 pf. black . . . . 10 10

**1971.** Accident Prevention.

1596. – 5 pf. orange . . . . 30 10
1597. – 10 pf. brown . . . . 15 10
1598. – 20 pf. violet . . . . 30 10
1599. **505.** 25 pf. green . . . . 50 10
1600. – 30 pf. red . . . . 30 10
1601. – 40 pf. mauve . . . . 40 10
1602. – 50 pf. blue . . . . 3·00 10
1603. – 60 pf. blue . . . . 1·50 10
1603a. – 70 pf. blue and green 70 10
1604. – 1 Dm. green . . . . 1·40 10
1605. – 1 Dm. 50 brown . . 5·00 70

DESIGNS: 5 pf. Man within flame, and spent match ("Fire Prevention"). 10 pf. Fall from ladder. 20 pf. Unguarded machinery ("Factory Safety"). 30 pf. Falling brick and protective helmet. 40 pf. Faulty electric plug. 50 pf. Protruding nail in plank. 60 pf., 70 pf. Ball in front of car ("Child Road Safety"). 1 Dm. Crate on hoist. 1 Dm. 50, Open manhole.

**1971.** Tourism. As T **473** but with view of Goslar.

1606 20 pf. black & green . . 30 10

506. Women churning Butter. 507. Deaconess and Nurse.

**1971.** Humanitarian Relief Funds. Wooden Toys. Multicoloured.

(a) Inscr. "WOHLFAHRTSMARKE".

1607. 20 pf. + 10 pf. Type **506** . . 20 25
1608. 25 pf. + 10 pf. Horseman on wheels . . . . 20 25
1609. 30 pf. + 15 pf. Nutcracker man . . . . 30 30
1610. 60 pf. + 30 pf. Dovecote . . 90 1·10

(b) Christmas. Inscr. "WEIHNACHTSMARKE".

1611. 20 pf. + 10 pf. Angel with three candles . . . . 20 20

**1972.** Death Cent. of Johann Wilhelm Lohe (founder of Deaconesses Mission, Neuendettelsau).

1612. **507.** 25 pf. slate, black & green . . . . 15 10

508. Ducks crossing Road. 509. Senefelder's Press.

**1972.** Child Welfare. Annimal Protection. Multicoloured.

1613. 20 pf. + 10 pf. Type **508** 70 70
1614. 25 pf. + 10 pf. Hunter scaring deer . . . . 80 80
1615. 30 pf. + 15 pf. Child protecting bird from cat 95 95
1616. 60 pf + 30 pf. Boy annoying mute swans 1·90 1·90

**1972.** "175 Years of Offset Lithography".

1617. **509.** 25 pf. multicoloured 15 10

510. "Communications". 511. Lucas Cranach.

**1972.** Europa.

1618. **510.** 25 pf. multicoloured 30 15
1619. 30 pf. multicoloured 40 15

**1972.** 500th Birth Anniv. of Lucas Cranach the Elder (painter).

1620. **511.** 25 pf. black, stone & green . . . . 25 10

512. Wrestling. 514. Invalid Archer.

**1972.** Olympic Games, Munich (5th series). Multicoloured.

1621 20 pf. + 10 pf. Type **512** . . 50 65
1622 25 pf. + 10 pf. Yachting . . 60 75
1623 30 pf. + 15 pf. Gymnastics 75 85
1624 60 pf. + 30 pf. Swimming 1·75 2·00

See also Nos. 1629/32.

**1972.** 21st Int. Games for the Paralysed, Heidelberg.

1626. **514.** 40 pf. red, blk. & yell. 30 15

515. Posthorn and Decree. 516. K. Schumacher.

**1972.** Cent. of German Postal Museum.

1627. **515.** 40 pf. multicoloured 30 10

**1972.** 20th Death Anniv. of Kurt Schumacher (politician).

1628. **516.** 40 pf. black and red 60 10

**1972.** Olympic Games, Munich (7th series). As Type **512**. Multicoloured.

| | | | |
|---|---|---|---|
| 1629 | 25 pf.+5 pf. Long jumping | 1·50 | 1·75 |
| 1630 | 30 pf.+10 pf. Basketball | 1·50 | 1·75 |
| 1631 | 40 pf.+10 pf. Throwing the discus | 1·50 | 1·75 |
| 1632 | 70 pf.+10 pf. Canoeing | 1·50 | 1·75 |

**517.** Open Book.

**518.** Music and Signature.

**1972.** Int. Book Year.

1634. **517.** 40 pf. multicoloured 30 10

**1972.** 300th Death Anniv. of Heinrich Schutz (composer).

1635. **518.** 40 pf. multicoloured 40 10

**519.** Knight.

**520.** Revellers.

**1972.** Humanitarian Relief Funds. Mult.

(a) 19th-century Faience Chessmen. Inscr "WOHLFAHRTSMARKE".

| | | | |
|---|---|---|---|
| 1636 | 25 pf.+10 pf. Type **519** | 40 | 40 |
| 1637 | 30 pf.+15 pf. Rook | 50 | 50 |
| 1638 | 40 pf.+20 pf. Queen | 60 | 60 |
| 1639 | 70 pf.+35 pf. King | 2·00 | 2·00 |

(b) Christmas. Inscr "WEIHNACHTSMARKE".

1640 30 pf.+15 pf. "The Three Wise Men" (horiz) 30 40

**1972.** Tourism. As T **473**.

1641. 30 pf. black and green 30 15
1642. 40 pf. black and orange 40 15

VIEWS: 30 pf. Heligoland. 40 pf. Heidelberg.

**1972.** 150th Anniv. of Cologne Carnival.

1643. **520.** 40 pf. multicoloured 60 10

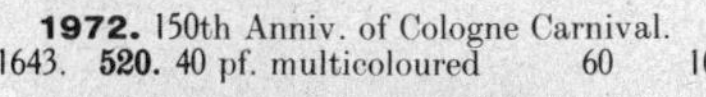

**521.** H. Heine.

**1972.** 175th Birth Anniv. of Heinrich Heine (poet).

1644. **521.** 40 pf. blk., red & pink 50 10

**522.** "Brot fur die Welt".

**523.** Wurzburg Cathedral (seal).

**1972.** Freedom from Hunger Campaign.

1645. **522.** 30 pf. red and green 30 30

**1972.** Catholic Synod '72.

1646. **523.** 40 pf. blk., pur. & red 30 10

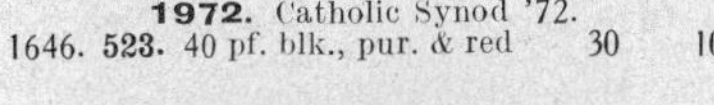

**524.** National Colours of France and Germany.

**1973.** 10th Anniv. of Franco-German Treaty.

1647. **524.** 40 pf. multicoloured 50 15

**525.** Osprey.

**527.** Radio Mast and Transmission.

**526.** Copernicus.

**1973.** Youth Welfare. Birds of Prey. Multicoloured.

| | | | |
|---|---|---|---|
| 1648. | 25 pf.+10 pf. Type **525** | 2·00 | 1·90 |
| 1649. | 30 pf.+15 pf. Common Buzzard | 3·00 | 2·50 |
| 1650. | 40 pf.+20 pf. Red Kite | 3·75 | 3·50 |
| 1651. | 70 pf.+35 pf. Montagu's Harrier | 9·00 | 8·00 |

**1973.** 500th Birth Anniv. of Copernicus.

1652. **526.** 40 pf black and red 50 10

**1973.** 50th Anniv of Interpol.

1653 **527** 40 pf. blk, red & grey 40 10

**528.** Weather Chart.

**529.** "Gymnast" (poster).

**1973.** Cent. of Int. Meteorological Organization.

1654. **528.** 30 pf. multicoloured 30 10

**1973.** Tourism. As T **473**.

1655. 40 pf. black and red 60 15
1656. 40 pf. black and orange 50 15

VIEWS: No. 1655, Hamburg. No. 1656, Rudesheim.

**1973.** Gymnastics Festival, Stuttgart.

1657. **529.** 40 pf. multicoloured 30 10

**530.** Kassel (Hesse) Sign.

**532.** "R" Motif.

**531.** Europa "Posthorn".

**1973.** "I.B.R.A. Munchen 73" Int. Stamp Exhib., Munich. F.I.P. Congress. Posthouse Signs. Multicoloured.

1658. 40 pf.+20 pf. Type **530** 80 1·25
1659. 70 pf.+35 pf. Prussia 1·00 1·60

**1973.** Europa.

1661. **531.** 30 pf. yell., myrtle & grn. 40 20
1662. 40 pf. yell., lake & pink 60 10

**1973.** 1000th Death Anniv. of Roswitha von Gandersheim (poetess).

1663. **532.** 40 pf. yellow, black and red 30 10

**533.** M. Kolbe.

**534.** "Profile" (from poster).

**1973.** Father Maximilian Kolbe (Concentration camp victim) Commemoration.

1664 **533** 40 pf. red, brown & blk 40 10

**1973.** 15th German Protestant Church Conference.

1665. **534.** 30 pf. multicoloured 25 10

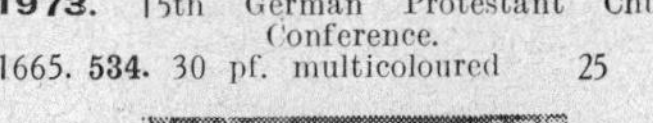

**535.** Environmental Conference Emblem and Waste.

**1973.** "Protection of the Environment". Multicoloured.

| | | | |
|---|---|---|---|
| 1666. | 25 pf. Type **535** | 30 | 15 |
| 1667. | 30 pf. Emblem and "Water" | 35 | 15 |
| 1668. | 40 pf. Emblem and "Noise" | 50 | 15 |
| 1669. | 70 pf. Emblem and "Air" | 95 | 75 |

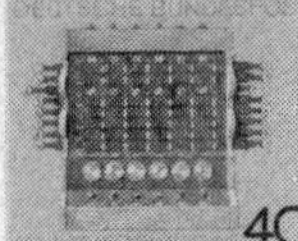
**536.** Schickard's Calculating Machine.

**537.** Otto Wels.

**1973.** 350th Anniv. of Schickard's Calculating Machine.

1670. **536.** 40 pf. black, red and orange 45 40

**1973.** Birth Centenary of Otto Wels (Social Democratic Party leader).

1671. **537.** 40 pf. purple and lilac 40 10

**538.** Lubeck Cathedral.

**1973.** 800th Anniv. of Lubeck Cathedral

1672. **538.** 40 pf. multicoloured 50 10

**539.** U.N. and German Eagle Emblems.

**1973.** Admission of German Federal Republic to U.N. Organization.

1673. **539.** 40 pf. multicoloured 80 10

**540.** French Horn.

**1973.** Humanitarian Relief Funds. Multicoloured.

(a) Musical Instruments. Inscr. "WOHLFAHRTSMARKE".

| | | | |
|---|---|---|---|
| 1674. | 25 pf.+10 pf. Type **540** | 50 | 35 |
| 1675. | 30 pf+15 pf. Grand piano | 50 | 30 |
| 1676. | 40 pf.+20 pf. Violin | 60 | 45 |
| 1677. | 70 pf.+70 pf. Harp | 1·75 | 1·75 |

(b) Christmas. Inscr. "WEIHNACHTSMARKE".

1678. 30 pf.+15 pf. Christmas star 50 40

**541.** Radio set of 1923.

**1973.** "50 Years of German Broadcasting".

1679. **541.** 30 pf. multicoloured 25 15

**1974.** Tourism. As Type **473**.

1680. 30 pf. black and green 50 15
1681. 40 pf. black and red 50 15
1682. 40 pf. black and red 50 15

VIEWS: No. 1680, Saarbrucken. No. 1681, Aachen. No. 1682, Bremen.

**542.** Louise Otto-Peters.

**1974.** Women in German Politics. Each black and orange.

| | | | |
|---|---|---|---|
| 1683. | 40 pf. Type **542** | 50 | 45 |
| 1684. | 40 pf. Helene Lange | 50 | 45 |
| 1685. | 40 pf. Rosa Luxemburg | 50 | 45 |
| 1686. | 40 pf. Gertrud Baumer | 50 | 45 |

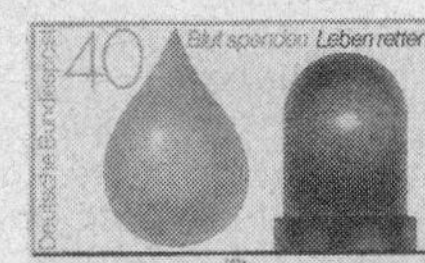
**543.** Drop of Blood and Emergency Light.

**1974.** Blood Donor and Accident/Rescue Services.

1687. **543.** 40 pf. red and blue 50 15

**544.** "Deer in Red" (Franz Marc).

**1974.** German Expressionist Paintings. Multicoloured.

| | | | |
|---|---|---|---|
| 1688. | 30 pf. Type **544** | 35 | 15 |
| 1689. | 30 pf. "Girls under Trees" (A. Macke) | 50 | 15 |
| 1690. | 40 pf. "Portrait in Blue" (A. von Jawlensky) (vert.) | 50 | 20 |
| 1691. | 50 pf. "Pechstein asleep" (E. Heckel) (vert.) | 45 | 25 |
| 1692. | 70 pf. "Still Life with Telescope" (Max Beckmann) | 65 | 50 |
| 1693. | 120 pf. "Old Peasant" (L. Kirchner) (vert.) | 1·40 | 1·50 |

**545.** St. Thomas teaching Pupils.

**1974.** 700th Death Anniv. of St. Thomas Aquinas.

1694. **545.** 40 pf. black and red 30 10

**546.** Disabled Persons in Outline.

**1974.** Rehabilitation of the Handicapped.

1695. **546.** 40 pf. red and black 30 15

**547.** Construction (Bricklayer).

**548.** "Ascending Youth". (W. Lehmbruck).

**1974.** Youth Welfare. Youth Activities. Multicoloured.

| | | | |
|---|---|---|---|
| 1696 | 25 pf.+10 pf. Type **547** | 90 | 1·10 |
| 1697 | 30 pf.+15 pf. Folk dancing | 1·40 | 1·50 |
| 1698 | 40 pf.+20 pf. Study | 1·75 | 2·00 |
| 1699 | 70 pf.+35 pf. Research | 2·75 | 3·00 |

**1974.** Europa.

1700. **548.** 30 pf. blk., grn. & silver 25 20
1701. – 40 pf. blk., red & lilac 35 15

DESIGN: 40 pf. "Kneeling Woman" (W. Lehmbruck).

**549.** Immanuel Kant.

**551.** Country Road.

**1974.** 250th Birth Anniv. of Immanuel Kant (philosopher).

1702. **549.** 90 pf. red 1·00 20

**1974.** Rambling, and Birth Centenaries of Richard Schirrman and Wilhelm Munker (founders of Youth Hostelling Assn.).

1704. **551.** 30 pf. multicoloured 30 15

**552.** Friedrich Klopstock.

**553.** "Crowned Cross" Symbol.

**1974.** 250th Birth Anniv. of Friedrich Gottlieb Klopstock (poet).

1705. **552.** 40 pf. black and red 40 15

**1974.** 125th Anniv. of German Protestant Church Diaconal Association (charitable organization).

1706. **553.** 40p. multicoloured .. 30 15

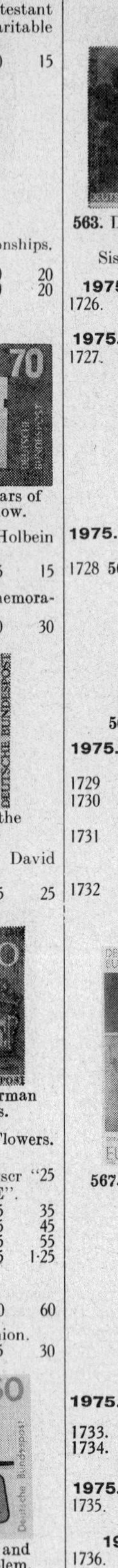

**554.** Goalkeeper saving Goal.

**1974.** World Cup Football Championships. Multicoloured.

1707. 30 pf. Type **554** .. .. 80 20
1708. 40 pf. Mid-field melee .. 1·10 20

**555.** Hans Holbein (self-portrait). **556.** Broken Bars of Prison Window.

**1974.** 450th Death Anniv. of Hans Holbein the Elder (painter).

1709. **555.** 50 pf. black and red 55 15

**1974.** Amnesty International Commemoration.

1710. **556.** 70 pf. black and blue 80 30

**557.** "Man and Woman looking at the Moon".

**1974.** Birth Bicentenary of Caspar David Friedrich (artist).

1711 **557** 50 pf. multicoloured .. 75 25

**558.** Campion. **559.** Early German Post-boxes.

**1974.** Humanitarian Relief Funds. Flowers. Multicoloured.

(a) 25th Anniv of Welfare Stamps. Inscr "25 JAHRE WOHLFAHRTSMARKE".

1712. 30 pf.+15 pf. Type **558** 35 35
1713. 40 pf.+20 pf. Foxglove 45 45
1714. 50 pf.+25 pf. Mallow .. 55 55
1715. 70 pf.+35 pf. Campanula 1·25 1·25

(b) Christmas. Inscr. "WEIHNACHTSMARKE".

1716. 40 pf.+20 pf. Poinsettia 60 60

**1974.** Cent. of Universal Postal Union.

1717. **559.** 50 pf. multicoloured 55 30

**560.** Annette Kolb. **562.** Mother and Child and Emblem.

**561.** Hans Bockler (Trade Union leader).

**1975.** International Women's Year. Women Writers.

1718. 30 pf. Type **560** .. .. 35 25
1719. 40 pf. Ricarda Huch .. 45 20
1720. 50 pf. Else Lasker-Schuler 55 20
1721. 70 pf. Gertrud von le Fort 90 90

**1975.** Birth Centenaries.

1722. **561.** 40 pf. black and green 40 15
1723. – 50 pf. black and red .. 50 15
1724. – 70 pf. black and blue 1·25 40

Designs: 50 pf. Matthias Erzberger (statesman). 70 pf. Albert Schweitzer (medical missionary).

**1975.** 25th Anniv. of Organization for the Rest and Recuperation of Mothers.

1725. **562.** 50 pf. multicoloured 40 15

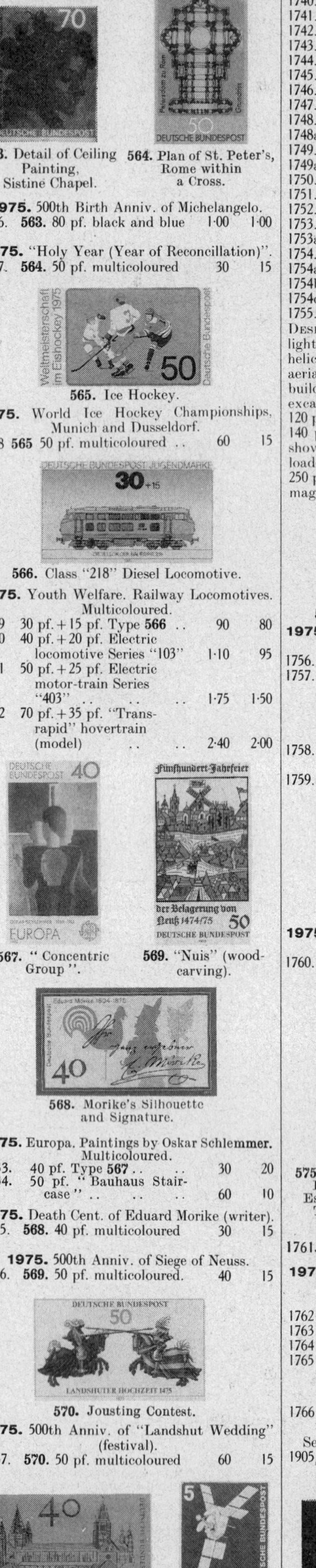

**563.** Detail of Ceiling Painting, Sistine Chapel. **564.** Plan of St. Peter's, Rome within a Cross.

**1975.** 500th Birth Anniv. of Michelangelo.

1726. **563.** 80 pf. black and blue 1·00 1·00

**1975.** "Holy Year (Year of Reconcillation)".

1727. **564.** 50 pf. multicoloured 30 15

**565.** Ice Hockey.

**1975.** World Ice Hockey Championships, Munich and Dusseldorf.

1728 **565** 50 pf. multicoloured .. 60 15

**566.** Class "218" Diesel Locomotive.

**1975.** Youth Welfare. Railway Locomotives. Multicoloured.

1729 30 pf.+15 pf. Type **566** .. 90 80
1730 40 pf.+20 pf. Electric locomotive Series "103" 1·10 95
1731 50 pf.+25 pf. Electric motor-train Series "403" .. .. 1·75 1·50
1732 70 pf.+35 pf. "Trans-rapid" hovertrain (model) .. .. 2·40 2·00

**567.** "Concentric Group". **569.** "Nuis" (wood-carving).

**568.** Morike's Silhouette and Signature.

**1975.** Europa. Paintings by Oskar Schlemmer. Multicoloured.

1733. 40 pf. Type **567** .. .. 30 20
1734. 50 pf. "Bauhaus Staircase" .. .. .. 60 10

**1975.** Death Cent. of Eduard Morike (writer).

1735. **568.** 40 pf. multicoloured 30 15

**1975.** 500th Anniv. of Siege of Neuss.

1736. **569.** 50 pf. multicoloured. 40 15

**570.** Jousting Contest.

**1975.** 500th Anniv. of "Landshut Wedding" (festival).

1737. **570.** 50 pf. multicoloured 60 15

**571.** Mainz Cathedral. **572.** Telecommunication Satellite.

**1975.** Millenary of Mainz Cathedral.

1738. **571.** 40 pf. multicoloured. 60 15

**1975.** Industry and Technology.

1739. **572.** 5 pf. green .. .. 10 10
1740. – 10 pf. mauve .. 15 10
1741. – 20 pf. red .. .. 20 10
1742. – 30 pf. lilac .. .. 30 10
1743. – 40 pf. green .. 40 10
1744. – 50 pf. mauve .. 45 10
1745. – 60 pf. red .. .. 65 10
1746. – 70 pf. blue .. .. 55 10
1747. – 80 pf. green .. 65 10
1748. – 100 pf. brown .. 80 10
1748a. – 110 pf. purple .. 1·40 25
1749. – 120 pf. blue .. 1·00 25
1749a. – 130 pf. red .. .. 1·60 25
1750. – 140 pf. red .. .. 1·10 30
1751. – 150 pf. red .. .. 2·00 50
1752. – 160 pf. green .. 1·75 40
1753. – 180 pf. brown .. 1·75 60
1753a. – 190 pf. brown .. 2·25 60
1754. – 200 pf. purple .. 1·50 15
1754a. – 230 pf. purple .. 2·40 60
1754b. – 250 pf. green .. 3·00 80
1754c. – 300 pf. green .. 3·50 1·00
1755. – 500 pf. black .. 4·00 50

Designs: 10 pf. Rail motor-train. 20 pf. Modern lighthouse. 30 pf. MBB-Bolkow Bo 105C rescue helicopter. 40 pf. Space laboratory. 50 pf. Dish aerial. 60 pf. X-ray apparatus. 70 pf. Shipbuilding. 80 pf. Farm tractor. 100 pf. Lignite excavator. 110 pf. Colour television camera. 120 pf. Chemical plant. 130 pf. Brewery plant. 140 pf. Power station. 150, 190 pf. Mechanical shovel. 160 pf. Blast furnace. 180 pf. Wheel loader. 200 pf. Marine drilling platform. 230, 250 pf. Frankfurt Airport. 300 pf. Electro-magnetic monorail. 500 pf. Radio telescope.

**573.** Town Hall and Market, Alsfeld.

**1975.** European Architectural Heritage Year. German Buildings. Multicoloured.

1756. 50 pf. Type **573** .. .. 60 60
1757. 50 pf. Plonlein corner, Siebers tower and Kobelzeller gate, Rothenburg-on-Tauber .. .. 60 60
1758. 50 pf. Town Hall ("The Steipe") Trier .. 60 60
1759. 50 pf. View of Xanten .. 60 60

**574.** Effects of Drug-taking.

**1975.** Campaign to Fight the Abuse of Drugs and Intoxicants.

1760. **574.** 40 pf. multicoloured 40 15

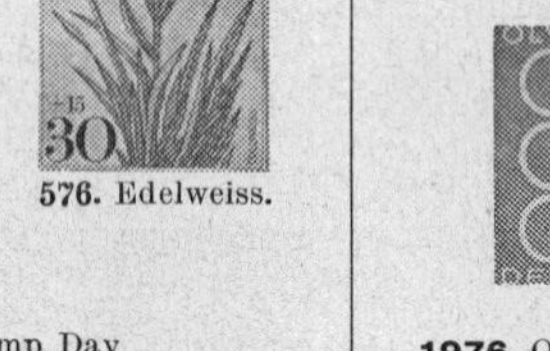

**575.** Posthouse Sign, Royal Prussian Establishment for Transport 1776. **576.** Edelweiss.

**1975.** Stamp Day.

1761. **575.** 10 pf. multicoloured 15 10

**1975.** Humanitarian Relief Funds. Alpine Flowers. Multicoloured.

(a) Inscr "Wohlfartsmarke 1975".

1762 30 pf.+15 pf. Type **576** .. 35 35
1763 40 pf.+20 pf. Trollflower 50 50
1764 50 pf.+25 pf. Alpine rose 60 60
1765 70 pf.+35 pf. Pasque-flower .. .. .. 1·40 1·40

(b) Inscr "Weihnachtsmarke 1975".

1766 **576** 40 pf.+20 pf. Christmas rose .. .. 55 55

See also Nos. 1796/9, 1839/42, 1873/6 and 1905/8.

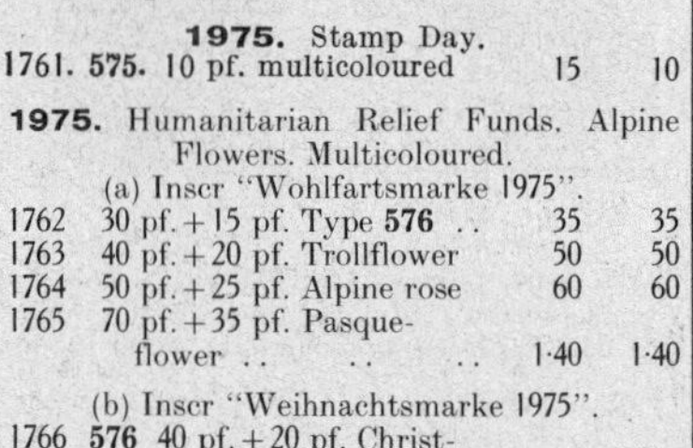

**578.** Stylised Ski-runners. **579.** Konrad Adenauer.

**1975.** Winter Olympic Games, Innsbruck.

1768. **578.** 50 pf. multicoloured 50 15

**1976.** Birth Centenary of Konrad Adenauer (Chancellor 1949–63).

1769 **579** 50 pf. green .. 80 15

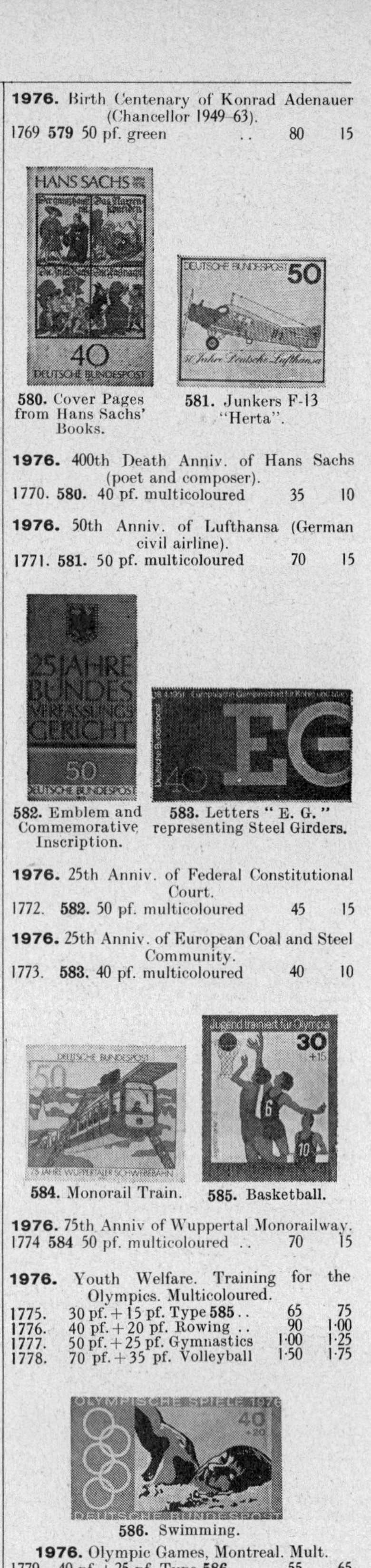

**580.** Cover Pages from Hans Sachs' Books. **581.** Junkers F-13 "Herta".

**1976.** 400th Death Anniv. of Hans Sachs (poet and composer).

1770. **580.** 40 pf. multicoloured 35 10

**1976.** 50th Anniv. of Lufthansa (German civil airline).

1771. **581.** 50 pf. multicoloured 70 15

**582.** Emblem and Commemorative Inscription. **583.** Letters "E. G." representing Steel Girders.

**1976.** 25th Anniv. of Federal Constitutional Court.

1772. **582.** 50 pf. multicoloured 45 15

**1976.** 25th Anniv. of European Coal and Steel Community.

1773. **583.** 40 pf. multicoloured 40 10

**584.** Monorail Train. **585.** Basketball.

**1976.** 75th Anniv of Wuppertal Monorailway.

1774 **584** 50 pf. multicoloured .. 70 15

**1976.** Youth Welfare. Training for the Olympics. Multicoloured.

1775. 30 pf.+15 pf. Type **585** .. 65 75
1776. 40 pf.+20 pf. Rowing .. 90 1·00
1777. 50 pf.+25 pf. Gymnastics 1·00 1·25
1778. 70 pf.+35 pf. Volleyball 1·50 1·75

**586.** Swimming.

**1976.** Olympic Games, Montreal. Mult.

1779 40 pf.+25 pf. Type **586** .. 55 65
1780 50 pf.+25 pf. High jumping .. .. .. 70 80

**587.** Girl selling Trinkets and Copperplate Prints. **588.** Carl Sonnenschein.

**1976.** Europa. Ludwigsburg China Figures. Multicoloured.

1782. 40 pf. Type **587** .. .. 40 15
1783. 50 pf. Boy selling copper-plate prints .. .. 60 10

**1976.** Birthday Centenary of Dr. Carl Sonnenschein (clergyman).

1784. **588.** 50 pf. multicoloured 35 15

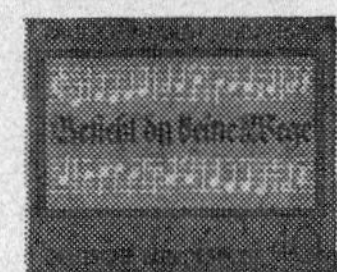

**589.** Opening bars of Hymn "Entrust Yourself to God".

**1976.** 300th Birth Anniv. of Paul Gerhardt (composer).

1785. **589.** 40 pf. multicoloured 40 15

**590** Carl Maria von Weber conducting.

**1976.** 150th Death Anniv. of Carl Maria von Weber (composer).

1786. **590.** 50 pf. black & brown 65 15

**591.** Carl Schurz.

**1976.** Bicent. of American Revolution.

1787. **591.** 70 pf. multicoloured 65 30

**592.** Wagnerian Stage.

**1976.** Centenary of Bayreuth Festival.

1788. **592.** 50 pf. multicoloured 50 15

**593.** Bronze Ritual Chariot.

**1976.** Archaeological Heritage. Mult.

1789. 30 pf. Type **593** .. .. 35 20

1790. 40 pf. Gold-ornamental bowl .. .. .. 45 20

1791. 50 pf. Silver necklet .. 60 25

1792. 120 pf. Roman gold goblet .. .. .. 1·75 1·75

**594.** Golden Plover. **595.** Mythical Creature.

**1976.** Bird Protection.

1793. **594.** 50 pf. multicoloured 1·00 20

**1976.** 300th Death Anniv. of J. J. C. von Grimmelshausen (writer).

1794. **595.** 40 pf. multicoloured 75 15

**596.** 18th-century Posthouse Sign, Hochst-am-Main. **597.** Sophie Schroder ("Sappho").

**1976.** Stamp Day.

1795. **596.** 10 pf. multicoloured 10 10

**1976.** Humanitarian Relief Funds. Garden Flowers. Designs similar to T **576.** Mult.

1796. 30 pf. + 15 pf. Phlox .. 40 40

1797. 40 pf. + 20 pf. Marigolds 50 50

1798. 50 pf. + 25 pf. Dahlias .. 65 65

1799. 70 pf. + 35 pf. Pansies .. 1·00 1·00

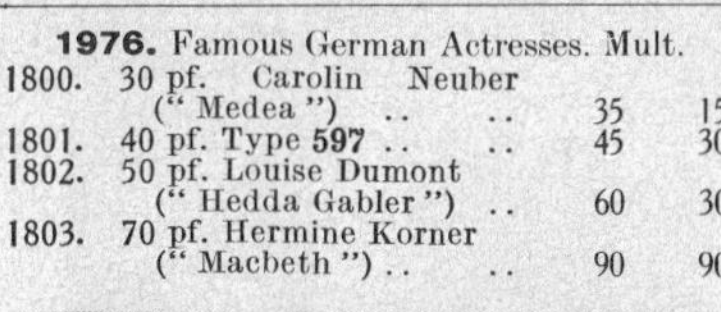

**1976.** Famous German Actresses. Mult.

1800. 30 pf. Carolin Neuber ("Medea") .. .. 35 15

1801. 40 pf. Type **597** .. .. 45 30

1802. 50 pf. Louise Dumont ("Hedda Gabler") .. 60 30

1803. 70 pf. Hermine Korner ("Macbeth") .. .. 90 90

**599.** Eltz Castle. **600.** Palais de l'Europe.

**1977.** German Castles.

| No. | Type | Description | Unused | Used |
|---|---|---|---|---|
| 1805 | – | 10 pf. blue .. .. | 10 | 10 |
| 1805c | – | 20 pf. orange .. | 15 | 10 |
| 1805d | – | 25 pf. red .. .. | 25 | 10 |
| 1806 | – | 30 pf. bistre .. | 25 | 10 |
| 1806c | – | 35 pf. red .. .. | 50 | 10 |
| 1807 | 599 | 40 pf. green .. | 50 | 10 |
| 1807a | – | 40 pf. brown .. | 35 | 10 |
| 1808 | – | 50 pf. red .. .. | 70 | 10 |
| 1808b | – | 50 pf. green .. | 50 | 10 |
| 1809 | – | 60 pf. brown .. | 75 | 15 |
| 1809a | – | 60 pf. red .. .. | 70 | 10 |
| 1810 | – | 70 pf. blue .. .. | 85 | 15 |
| 1810a | – | 80 pf. green .. | 80 | 20 |
| 1810c | – | 90 pf. blue .. .. | 90 | 25 |
| 1810d | – | 120 pf. violet .. | 1·00 | 30 |
| 1811 | – | 190 pf. red .. .. | 1·50 | 50 |
| 1812 | – | 200 pf. green .. | 1·75 | 55 |
| 1812a | – | 210 pf. brown .. | 2·40 | 70 |
| 1812b | – | 230 pf. green .. | 2·00 | 70 |
| 1812c | – | 280 pf. blue .. | 2·50 | 50 |
| 1812d | – | 300 pf. orange .. | 3·00 | 50 |

DESIGNS: 10 pf. Glucksburg. 20, 190 pf. Pfaueninsel, Berlin. 25 pf. Gemen. 30 pf. Ludwigstein, Werratal. 35 pf. Lichtenstein. 40 pf. (1807a) Wolfsburg. 50 pf. (1808) Neuschwanstein. 50 pf. (1808b) Inzlingen. 60 pf. (1809) Marksburg. 60 pf. (1809a) Rheydt. 70 pf. Mespelbrunn. 80 pf. Wilhelmsthal. 90 pf. Vischering. 120 pf. Charlottenburg, Berlin. 200 pf. Burresheim. 210 pf. Schwanenburg. 230 pf. Lichtenberg. 280 pf. Ahrensburg. 300 pf. Herrenhausen, Hanover.

**1977.** Inauguration of Palais de l'Europe (Council of Europe buildings), Strasbourg.

1813. **600.** 140 pf. green and black 1·25 40

**601.** Book Illustrations. **603.** Jean Monnet.

**1977.** "Till Eulenspiegel" (popular fable).

1814. **601.** 50 pf. multicoloured 50 15

**1977.** Award of "Citizen of Europe" honour to Jean Monnet (French statesman).

1816. **603.** 50 pf. blk., grey & yell. 40 15

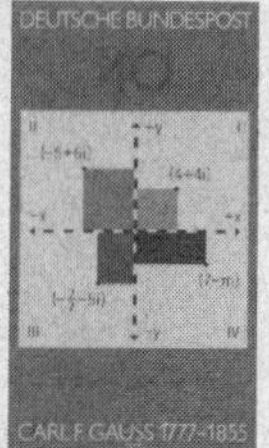

**604.** "Flower". **605.** Plane of Complex Numbers.

**1977.** 25th Anniv. of Federal Horticultural Show.

1817. **604.** 50 pf. multicoloured 40 15

**1977.** Birth Bicentenary of Carl Friedrich Gauss (mathematician).

1818. **605.** 40 pf. multicoloured 50 15

**606.** "Wappen von Hamburg" (warship). **607** Head of Barbarossa.

**1977.** Youth Welfare. Ships. Multicoloured.

1819 30 pf. + 15 pf. Type **606** .. 75 85

1820 40 pf. + 20 pf. "Preussen" (full-rigged sailing ship) 1·00 1·10

1821 50 pf. + 25 pf. "Bremen" (liner) .. .. .. 1·25 1·50

1822 70 pf. + 35 pf. "Sturmfels" (container ship) .. 1·60 1·75

**1977.** Staufer Year, Baden-Wurttemberg.

1823. **607.** 40 pf. multicoloured 80 15

**608.** Rhon Autobahn. **609.** "Self-Portrait" (Rubens).

**1977.** Europa.

1824. **608.** 40 pf. black and green 40 15

1825. – 50 pf. black and red .. 55 10

DESIGN: 50 pf. Rhine landscape.

**1977.** 400th Birth Anniv. of Peter Paul Rubens.

1826. **609.** 30 pf. black .. .. 40 10

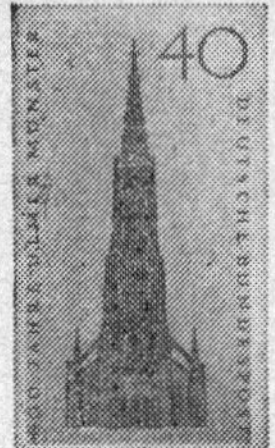

**610.** Ulm Cathedral. **611.** Rector's Seal, Mainz University (500th Anniv.).

**1977.** 600th Anniv. of Ulm Cathedral.

1827. **610.** 40 pf. brn., grn. & bl. 30 15

**1977.** University Anniversaries.

1828. **611.** 50 pf. black and red .. 40 15

1829. – 50 pf. black and red .. 40 15

1830. – 50 pf. black and red .. 40 15

DESIGNS: No. 1829, Great Seal, Marburg University (450th anniv). No. 1830, Great Seal, Tubingen University (500th anniv).

**612.** "Morning".

**1977.** Birth Bicentenary of Phillipp Otto Runge (artist).

1831. **612.** 60 pf. multicoloured 55 30

**613.** Ketteler's Coat of Arms. **614.** Fritz von Bodelschwingh.

**1977.** Death Centenary of Bishop Wilhelm Emmanuel von Ketteler.

1832. **613.** 50 pf. multicoloured 50 15

**1977.** Birth Centenary of Pastor Fritz von Bodelschwingh (pioneer of welfare work for the disabled).

1833. **614.** 50 pf. multicoloured 50 15

**615.** Golden Hat.

**1977.** Archaeological Heritage. Multicoloured.

1834. 30 pf. Type **615** .. .. 50 10

1835. 120 pf. Gilt helmet .. 90 1·10

1836. 200 pf. Bronze centaur head .. .. .. 1·40 1·75

**616.** Operator and Switchboard. **617.** 19th-century Posthouse Sign, Hamburg.

**1977.** Centenary of Telephone in Germany.

1837. **616.** 50 pf. multicoloured 80 15

**1977.** Stamp Day.

1838. **617.** 10 pf. multicoloured 15 10

**1977.** Humanitarian Relief Funds. Meadow Flowers. As T **576.** Multicoloured.

1839. 30 pf. + 15 pf. Caraway 35 40

1840. 40 pf. + 20 pf. Dandelion 50 55

1841. 50 pf. + 25 pf. Red clover 60 70

1842. 70 pf. + 35 pf. Meadow sage 1·00 1·10

**618.** Travelling Surgeon. **619.** Wilhelm Hauff.

**1977.** 250th Death Anniv. of Dr. Johann Andreas Eisenbarth.

1843. **618.** 50 pf. multicoloured 55 15

**1977.** 150th Death Anniv. of Wilhelm Hauff (poet and novelist).

1844. **619.** 40 pf. multicoloured 40 15

**621.** Book Cover Designs. **622.** Refugees.

**1978.** Birth Centenary of Rudolph Alexander Schroder (writer).

1846. **621.** 50 pf. multicoloured 40 15

**1978.** 20th Anniv. of Friedland Aid Society.

1847. **622.** 50 pf. multicoloured 40 15

**623.** Skiing.

**1978.** Sport Promotion Fund. Multicoloured.

1848. 50 pf. + 25 pf. Type **623** .. 1·75 1·75

1849. 70 pf. + 35 pf. Show jumping .. .. 4·25 4·25

**624.** Gerhart Hauptmann. **625.** Martin Buber.

**1978.** German Winners of Nobel Prize for Literature. Multicoloured.

1850. 30 pf. Type **624** .. .. 25 25

1851. 50 pf. Hermann Hesse .. 45 45

1852. 70 pf. Thomas Mann .. 60 60

**1978.** Birth Centenary of Martin Buber (religious philosopher).

1854. **625.** 50 pf. multicoloured 40 15

626. Museum Tower and Cupola.

627. Wilhelmine Reichart's Balloon, Munich October Festival, 1820

**1978.** 75th Anniv. of German Scientific and Technical Museum, Munich.

1855. 626. 50 pf. blk., yell. & red 40 15

**1978.** Youth Welfare. Aviation History (1st series). Multicoloured.

1856 30 pf. + 15 pf. Type 627 .. 70 80
1857 40 pf. + 20 pf. Airship LZ-1, 1900 .. .. 80 90
1858 50 pf. + 25 pf. Bleriot XI monoplane, 1909 .. 75 75
1859 70 pf. + 35 pf. Hans Grade's monoplane, 1909 .. .. .. 1·00 1·00

See also Nos. 1886/9 and 1918/21.

628. Old Town Hall, Bamberg.

**1978.** Europa. Multicoloured.

1860 40 pf. Type 628 .. .. 60 15
1861 50 pf. Old Town Hall, Regensburg .. .. 75 10
1862 70 pf. Old Town Hall, Esslingen am Neckar .. 1·00 50

629. Piper and Children.

**1978.** Pied Piper of Hamelin.

1863. 629. 50 pf. multicoloured 70 15

630. Janusz Korczak. 631. Fossil Bat.

**1978.** Birth Centenary of Janusz Korczak (educational reformer).

1864. 630. 90 pf. multicoloured 70 35

**1978.** Archaeological Heritage, Fossils. Multicoloured.

1865. 80 pf. Type 631 .. .. 2·00 2·00
1866. 200 pf. Horse ("eohippus") skeleton .. .. 2·00 1·75

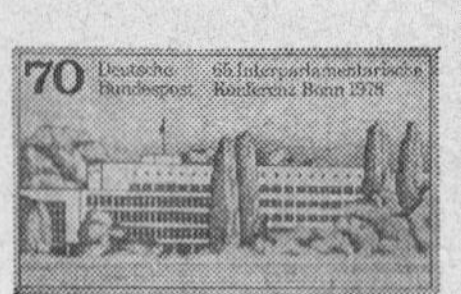

632. Parliament Building, Bonn. 633. Rose Window, Freiburg Minster.

**1978.** 65th Interparliamentary Union Conference, Bonn.

1867. 632. 70 pf. multicoloured 55 30

**1978.** 85th Conference of German Catholics, Freiburg.

1868 633 40 pf. multicoloured .. 40 15

634. Silhouette. 635. Text.

**1978.** Birth Bicent. of Clemens Brentano (poet).

1869. 634. 30 pf. multicoloured 25 15

**1978.** 25th Anniv. of European Convention for the protection of Human Rights.

1870. 635. 50 pf. multicoloured 40 15

636. Baden Post-house Sign. 639. Child.

637. " Easter at the Walchensee " (Lovis Corinth).

**1978.** Stamp Day and World Philatelic Movement. Multicoloured.

1871. 40 pf. Type 636 .. .. 50 25
1872. 50 pf. 1850 3 pf. stamp of Saxony .. .. 50 25

**1978.** Humanitarian Relief Funds. Woodland Flowers. As T 576. Multicoloured.

1873. 30 pf. + 15 pf. Arum .. 35 35
1874. 40 pf. + 20 pf. Weasel-snout .. .. .. 45 45
1875. 50 pf. + 25 pf. Turk's-cap lily .. .. .. 60 60
1876. 70 pf. + 35 pf. Liverwort 95 95

**1978.** Impressionist Paintings. Multicoloured.

1877 50 pf. Type 637 .. .. 50 30
1878 70 pf. "Horseman on the Shore turning Left" (Max Liebermann) (vert) .. .. .. 75 60
1879 120 pf. "Lady with a Cat" (Max Slevogt) (vert) .. 1·40 1·40

**1979.** International Year of the Child.

1881. 639. 60 pf. multicoloured 60 15

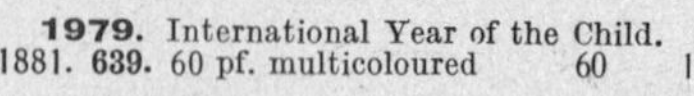

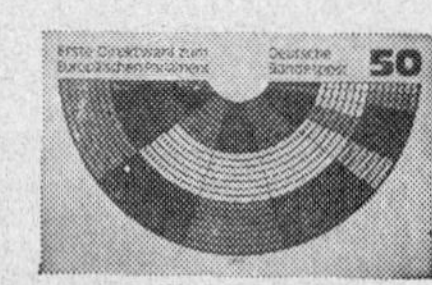

640. Agnes Miegel. 641. Seating Plan.

**1979.** Birth Cent. of Agnes Miegel (poet).

1882. 640. 60 pf. multicoloured 40 15

**1979.** First Direct Elections to European Parliament.

1883. 641. 50 pf. multicoloured 45 15

642. Film. 643. Rescue Services Emblems.

**1979.** 25th West German Short Film Festival.

1884. 642. 50 pf. black and turq. 35 15

**1979.** Rescue Services on the Road.

1885. 643. 50 pf. multicoloured 55 15

**1979.** Youth Welfare. History of Aviation (2nd series). As T 627. Multicoloured.

1886 40 pf. + 20 pf. Dornier Do-J Wal flying boat, 1922 .. 80 80
1887 50 pf. + 25 pf. Heinkel He 70 Blitz, 1932 .. 90 1·00
1888 60 pf. + 30 pf. Junkers W.33 "Bremen", 1928 1·25 1·25
1889 90 pf. + 45 pf. Focke Achgelis Fa 61 helicopter, 1936 .. 1·75 1·60

644. Handball.

**1979.** Sport Promotion Fund. Multicoloured.

1890. 60 pf. + 30 pf. Type 644 1·00 1·40
1891. 90 pf. + 45 pf. Canoeing 1·40 1·60

645. Telegraph Office, 1863. 646. Anne Frank.

**1979.** Europa. Multicoloured.

1892. 50 pf. Type 645.. .. 50 15
1893. 60 pf. Post Office counter, 1854 .. .. .. 60 10

**1979.** 50th Birth Anniv. of Anne Frank (concentration camp victim and diary writer).

1894. 646. 60 pf. black, grey & red .. .. 60 15

647. First Electric Railway, 1879,

**1979.** International Transport Exhibition. Hamburg.

1895. 647. 60 pf. multicoloured 75 15

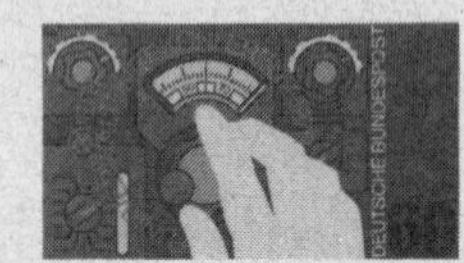

648. Hand operating Radio Dial.

**1979.** World Administrative Radio Conference, Geneva.

1896. 648. 60 f. multicoloured .. 40 15

649. " Moses receiving the Tablets of the Law " (woodcut, Cranach the Elder). 650. Cross and Orb.

**1979.** 450th Anniv. of Publication of Martin Luther's Catechisms.

1897. 649. 50 pf. black & green 75 15

**1979.** Pilgrimage to Aachen.

1898. 650. 50 pf. multicoloured 40 15

651. Hildegard von Bingen.

**1979.** 800th Death Anniv. of Hildegard von Bingen (writer and mystic).

1899. 651. 110 pf. multicoloured 1·00 55

652. Photo-electric Effect.

**1979.** Birth Centenaries of Nobel Prize Winners. Multicoloured.

1900 60 pf. Type 652 (Albert Einstein, Physics, 1921) 70 35
1901 60 pf. Splitting of uranium nucleus (Otto Hahn, Chemistry, 1944) 70 35
1902 60 pf. Diffraction pattern of X-rays passed through crystal (Max von Laue, Physics, 1914) .. .. .. 70 35

## INDEX

Countries can be quickly located by referring to the index at the end of this volume.

653. Pilot and Helmsman. 654. Posthouse Sign, Altheim, Saar (German side), 1754.

**1979.** 300th Anniv. of 1st Pilotage Regulations.

1903. 653. 60 pf. brown & claret 55 15

**1979.** Stamp Day.

1904 654 60 pf. + 30 pf. mult .. 1·00 1·25

**1979.** Humanitarian Relief Funds. Woodland Flowers and Fruit. As T 576. Multicoloured.

1905 40 pf. + 20 pf. Red beech (horiz) .. .. 60 50
1906 50 pf. + 25 pf. English oak (horiz) .. .. 75 65
1907 60 pf. + 30 pf. Hawthorn (horiz) .. .. 80 70
1908 90 pf. + 45 pf. Mountain pine (horiz) .. .. 1·25 1·10

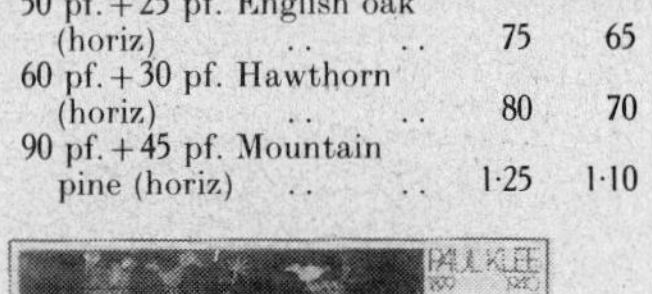

656. " Bird Garden ".

**1979.** Birth Cent. of Paul Klee (artist).

1909. 656. 90 pf. multicoloured 80 45

657. Faust and Mephistopheles. 658. Lightbulb.

**1979.** Doctor Johannes Faust.

1910. 657. 60 pf. multicoloured 60 15

**1979.** " Save Energy ".

1911. 658. 40 pf. multicoloured 40 15

659. " Nativity " (Altenberg medieval manuscript).

**1979.** Christmas.

1912 659 60 pf. + 30 pf. mult .. 65 65

660. "Iphigenia".

**1980.** Death Centenary of Anselm Feuerbach (artist).

1913 660 50 pf. multicoloured .. 55 15

661. Flags of NATO Members.

**1980.** 25th Anniv. of NATO Membership.

1914. 661. 100 pf. multicoloured 1·25 60

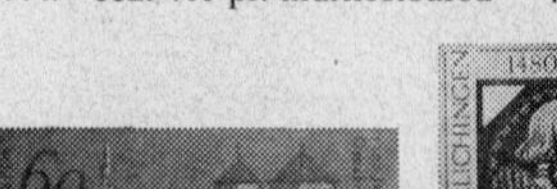

662. Town Hall, St. Mary's Church, and St. Peter's Cathedral. 663. " Gotz von Berlichingen " (glass picture).

**1980.** 1200th Anniv. of Osnabruck Town and Bishopric.

1915. 662. 60 pf. multicoloured 55 20

**1980.** 500th Birth Anniv. of Gotz von Berlichingen (Frankish knight).
1916. **663.** 60 pf. multicoloured 45 20

**664.** Texts from 1880 and 1980 Duden Dictionaries.

**1980.** Centenary of Konrad Duden's 1st Dictionary.
1917. **664.** 60 pf. multicoloured 65 15

**1980.** Youth Welfare. Aviation History (3rd series). As T **627.** Multicoloured.
1918 40 pf. + 20 pf. Phoenix FS 24 glider, 1957 .. 60 50
1919 50 pf. + 25 pf. Lockheed L.1049G Super Constellation .. .. 80 70
1920 60 pf. + 30 pf. Airbus Industrie A300B2, 1972 90 90
1921 90 pf. + 45 pf. Boeing 747-100, 1969 .. .. 1·40 1·40
No. 1919 is incorrectly dated "1950".

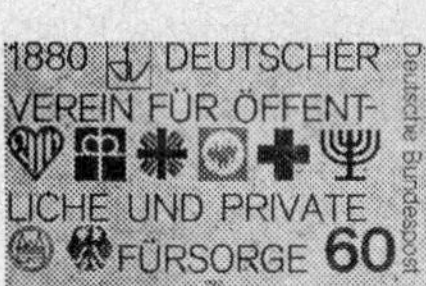

**665.** Emblems of Association Members. **666.** "Frederick I with his sons" (Welf Chronicle).

**1980.** Centenary of German Association of Welfare Societies.
1922 **665** 60 pf. blue, red & black 45 15

**1980.** 800th Anniv. of Imperial Diet of Gelnhausen.
1923. **666.** 60 pf. multicoloured 60 15

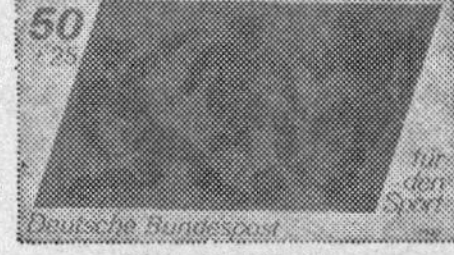

**667.** Football.

**1980.** Sport Promotion Fund. Multicoloured.
1924. 50 pf. + 25 pf. Type **667** 60 70
1925. 60 pf. + 30 pf. Dressage .. 75 75
1926. 90 pf. + 45 pf. Skiing .. 1·25 1·25

**668.** Albertus Magnus (scholar). **669.** Reading the Augsburg Confession (engraving, G. Kohler).

**1980.** Europa. Multicoloured.
1927. 50 pf. Type **668** .. .. 60 10
1928. 60 pf. Gottfried Leibniz (philosopher) .. .. 80 15

**1980.** 450th Anniv. of Augsburg Confession.
1929. **669.** 50 pf. black, yellow and green .. .. 45 15

**670.** Nature Reserve.

**1980.** Nature Conservation.
1930. **670.** 40 pf. multicoloured 50 15

**671.** Ear and Oscillogram Pulses.

**1980.** International Congress for the Training and Education of the Hard of Hearing, Hamburg.
1931. **671.** 90 pf. multicoloured 65 30

**672.** First Book of Daily Bible Readings, 1731. **673.** St. Benedict.

**1980.** 250th Anniv. of Moravian Brethren's Book of Daily Bible Readings.
1932. **672.** 50 pf. multicoloured 55 15

**1980.** 1500th Birth Anniv. of St. Benedict of Nursia (founder of Benedictine Order).
1933. **673.** 50 pf. multicoloured 55 15

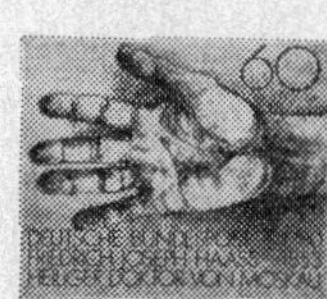

**674.** Helping Hand. **675.** Marie von Ebner-Eschenbach.

**1980.** Birth Bicentenary of Friedrich Joseph Haass (philanthropist).
1934. **674.** 60 pf. multicoloured 60 15

**1980.** 150th Birth Anniv. of Marie von Ebner-Eschenbach (novelist).
1935. **675.** 60 pf. buff, black & orange .. .. 60 15

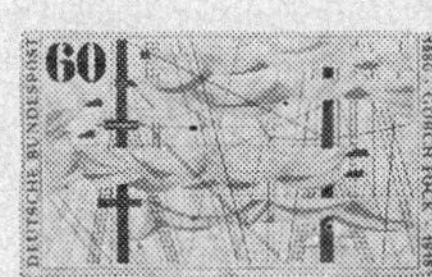

**676.** Rigging.

**1980.** Birth Centenary of Johan Kinau ("Gorch Fock") (poet).
1936. **676.** 60 pf. multicoloured 70 15

**677.** Positioning Keystone of South Tower Finial (engraving). **678.** "Ceratocephalus falcatus".

**1980.** Centenary of Completion of Cologne Cathedral.
1937. **677.** 60 pf. multicoloured 85 15

**1980.** Humanitarian Relief Funds. Endangered Wildflowers. Multicoloured.
1938. 40 pf. + 20 pf. Type **678** .. 50 50
1939. 50 pf. + 25 pf. Yellow Vetchling .. .. 65 65
1940. 60 pf. + 30 pf. Corn Cockle 90 90
1941. 90 pf. + 45 pf. Tassel Hyacinth .. .. 1·25 1·25
See also Nos. 1972/5.

**679.** Wine-making (woodcuts).

**1980.** Bimillenary of Vine Growing in Central Europe.
1942. **679.** 50 pf. multicoloured 55 15

**680.** Posthouse Sign, Altheim, Saar, 1754 (French side). **681.** "Nativity" (Altomunster manuscript).

**1980.** 49th International Philatelic Federation Congress. Essen.
1943. **680.** 60 pf. + 30 pf. mult. 45 60

**1980.** Christmas.
1944. **681.** 60 pf. + 30 pf. mult. 80 70

**682.** "Landscape with Two Fir Trees" (etching). **683.** Elly Heuss-Knapp.

**1980.** 500th Birth Anniv of Albrecht Altdorfer (painter, engraver and architect).
1945 **682** 40 pf. lt brn, blk & brn 40 15

**1981.** Birth Centenary of Elly Heuss-Knapp (social reformer).
1946. **683.** 60 pf. multicoloured 50 15

**684.** Society accepting the Handicapped.

**1981.** International Year of Disabled Persons.
1947. **684.** 60 pf. multicoloured 50 15

**685.** Old Town Houses.

**1981.** European Campaign for Urban Renaissance.
1948. **685.** 60 pf. multicoloured 55 15

**686.** Telemann and Title Page of "Singet dem Herrn".

**1981.** 300th Birth Anniv. of Georg Philipp Telemann (composer).
1949. **686.** 60 pf. multicoloured 70 15

**687.** Visiting a Foreign Family.

**1981.** Integration of Guest Worker Families.
1950. **687.** 50 pf. multicoloured 55 15

**688.** Polluted Butterfly, Fish and Plant.

**1981.** Preservation of the Environment.
1951. **688.** 60 pf. multicoloured 75 15

**689.** Patent Office Emblem and Scientific Signs.

**1981.** Establishment of European Patent Office, Munich.
1952. **689.** 60 pf. grey, red & black .. .. 60 15

**690.** Scintigram showing Distribution of Radioactive Isotope. **691.** Borda Circle, 1800.

**1981.** Cancer Prevention through Medical Check-ups.
1953. **690.** 40 pf. multicoloured 40 15

**1981.** Youth Welfare. Optical Instruments. Multicoloured.
1954. 40 pf. + 20 pf. Type **691** 60 60
1955. 50 pf. + 25 pf. Reflecting telescope, 1770 .. 90 70
1956. 60 pf. + 30 pf. Binocular microscope, 1860 .. 90 80
1957. 90 pf. + 45 pf. Octant, 1775 .. .. .. 1·50 1·40

**692.** Rowing. **693.** South German Dancers.

**1981.** Sport Promotion Fund. Multicoloured
1958. 60 pf. + 30 pf. Type **692** 75 70
1959. 90 pf. + 45 pf. Gliding .. 1·00 90

**1981.** Europa. Multicoloured.
1960. 50 pf. Type **693** .. .. 60 15
1961. 60 pf. North German dancers .. .. 70 15

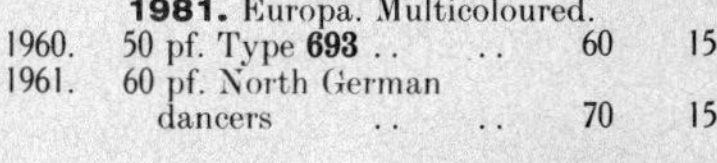

**694.** Convention Cross. **695.** Group from Crucifixion Altar.

**1981.** 19th German Protestant Convention, Hamburg.
1962. **694.** 50 pf. multicoloured 50 15

**1981.** 450th Death Anniv. of Tilman Riemenschneider (woodcarver).
1963. **695.** 60 pf. multicoloured 60 15

**696.** Georg von Neumayer Antarctic Research Station. **697.** Solar Generator.

**1981.** Polar Research.
1964. **696.** 110 pf. multicoloured 1·75 50

**1981.** Energy Research.
1965. **697.** 50 pf. multicoloured 55 15

**698.** Hand holding Baby Coot. **700.** Wilhelm Raabe.

**699.** Arms of different Races forming Square.

**1981.** Animal Protection.
1966. **698.** 60 pf. multicoloured 1·00 15

**1981.** Co-operation with Developing Countries.
1967. **699.** 90 pf. multicoloured 80 40

**1981.** 150th Birth Anniv. of Wilhelm Raabe (poet).
1968. **700.** 50 pf. lt. grn. & grn. 50 15

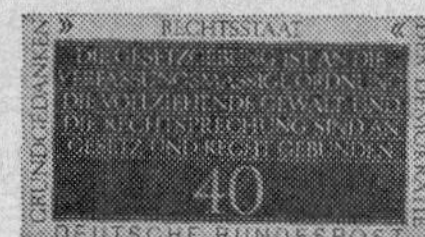


**701.** Constitutional Freedom.

**1981.** Fundamental Concepts of Democracy. Article 20 of the Basic Law. Multicoloured.

1969 40 pf. Type **701** .. .. 40 15
1970 50 pf. Separation of Powers .. .. 50 15
1971 60 pf. Sovereignty of the People .. .. 60 20

**1981.** Humanitarian Relief Funds. Endangered Wildflowers. As T **678**. Mult.

1972. 40 pf. + 20 pf. Water nut 60 50
1973. 50 pf. + 25 pf. Floating Heart .. .. 75 60
1974. 60 pf. + 30 pf. Water gilly-flower .. .. .. 80 75
1975. 90 pf. + 45 pf. Water lobelia 1·40 1·25

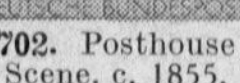

**702.** Posthouse Scene. c. 1855. **703.** "Nativity" (glass painting).

**1981.** Stamp Day.

1976. **702.** 60 pf. multicoloured 80 15

**1981.** Christmas.

1977. **703.** 60 pf. + 30 pf. mult... 60 65

**704.** St. Elisabeth. **705.** Clausewitz (after W. Wach).

**1981.** 750th Death Anniv. of St. Elisabeth of Thuringia.

1978. **704.** 50 pf. multicoloured 50 15

**1981.** 150th Death Anniv. of General Carl von Clausewitz (military writer).

1979. **705.** 60 pf. multicoloured 65 15

**706.** People forming Figure " 100 ". **707.** Map of Antarctica.

**1981.** Cent. of Social Insurance.

1980. **706.** 60 pf. multicoloured 60 15

**1981.** 20th Anniv. of Antarctic Treaty.

1981. **707.** 100 pf. blue, light blue and black .. 1·50 40

**708.** Pot with Lid. **709.** Insulated Wall.

**1982.** 300th Birth Anniv. of Johann Friedrich Bottger (founder of Meissen China Works).

1982. **708.** 60 pf. multicoloured 55 15

**1982.** Energy Conservation.

1983. **709.** 60 pf. multicoloured 60 15

**710.** Silhouette (Dora Brandenburg-Polster). **711.** Goethe (after Georg Melchior Kraus).

**1982.** "The Town Band of Bremen" (German fairy tale).

1984. **710.** 40 pf. black and red .. 50 15

**1982.** 150th Death Anniv. of Johann Wolfgang von Goethe (writer).

1985. **711.** 60 pf. multicoloured 85 20

**712.** Robert Koch.

**1982.** Centenary of Discovery of Tubercle Bacillus.

1986. **712.** 50 pf. multicoloured 1·00 15

**713.** Benz Patent "Motorwagen", 1886.

**1982.** Youth Welfare. Motor Cars. Mult.

1987. 40 pf. + 20 pf. Type **713** 70 65
1988. 50 pf. + 25 pf. Mercedes "Tourenwagen", 1913 80 70
1989. 60 pf. + 30 pf. Hannomag "Kommissbrot", 1925 1·10 1·00
1990. 90 pf. + 45 pf. Opel "Olympia", 1937 .. 1·60 1·40

**714.** Jogging.

**1982.** Sport Promotion Fund. Multicoloured.

1991. 60 pf. + 30 pf. Type **714** 1·00 95
1992. 90 pf. + 45 pf. Disabled archers .. .. 1·50 1·25

**715.** "Good Helene".

**1982.** 150th Birth Anniv. of Wilhelm Busch (writer and illustrator).

1993. **715.** 50 pf. black, green & yellow .. .. 65 15

**716.** "Procession to Hambach Castle, 1832" (wood engraving).

**1982.** Europa.

1994. **716.** 50 pf. black, yellow & red .. .. 90 20
1995. – 60 pf. multicoloured 1·25 20

DESIGN: 60 pf. Excerpt from Treaty of Rome (instituting European Economic Community), 1957, and flags.

**717.** Racing Yachts.

**1982.** Centenary of Kiel Regatta Week,

1996. **717.** 60 pf. multicoloured 1·00 25

**718.** Young Couple.

**1982.** Centenary of Young Men's Christian Association in Germany.

1997. **718.** 50 pf. multicoloured 55 15

**719.** Polluted Sea.

**1982.** " Prevent the Pollution of the Sea ".

1998. **719.** 120 pf. multicoloured 1·40 40

**720.** Battered Licence Plate.

**1982.** " Don't Drink and Drive ".

1999. **720.** 80 pf. multicoloured 1·00 25

**721.** Doctor examining Leper. **722.** Franck and Born.

**1982.** 25th Anniv of German Lepers' Welfare Organization.

2000 **721** 80 pf. multicoloured .. 95 25

**1982.** Birth Centenaries of James Franck and Max Born (physicists and Nobel Prize Winners).

2001. **722.** 80 pf. grey, black and red .. .. 95 25

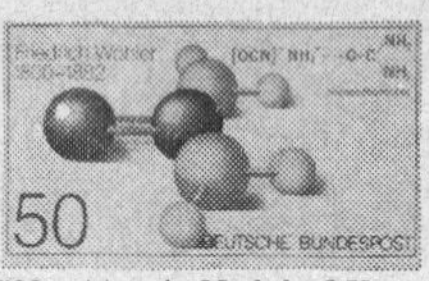


**723.** Atomic Model of Urea.

**1982.** Death Centenary of Friedrich Wohler (chemist).

2002. **723.** 50 pf. multicoloured 55 10

**724.** " St. Francis preaching to the Birds " (fresco by Giotto.) **725.** Hybrid Tea. Rose.

**1982.** 87th German Catholics' Congress, Dusseldorf and 800th Birth Anniv. of St. Francis of Assisi.

2003. **724.** 60 pf. multicoloured 70 20

**1982.** Humanitarian Relief Funds. Roses. Multicoloured.

2004. 50 pf. + 20 pf. Type **725** 60 60
2005. 60 pf. + 30 pf. Floribunda 70 70
2006. 80 pf. + 40 pf. Bourbon .. 90 90
2007. 120 pf. + 60 pf. Polyantha hybrid .. .. 1·50 1·75

**726.** Letters on Desk. **727.** Gregorian Calendar by Johannes Rasch, 1586.

**1982.** Stamp Day.

2008. **726.** 80 pf. multicoloured 1·25 25

**1982.** 400th Anniv. of Gregorian Calendar.

2009. **727.** 60 pf. multicoloured 65 20

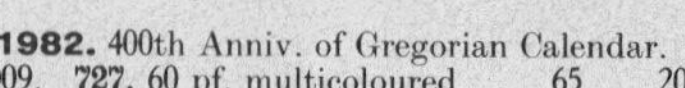
**HAVE YOU READ THE NOTES AT THE BEGINNING OF THIS CATALOGUE?**

These often provide answers to the enquiries we receive.

**729.** "Nativity" (detail from St. Peter Altar by Master Bertram). **730.** Edith Stein.

**1982.** Christmas.

2011. **729.** 80 pf. + 40 pf. mult. 1·25 95

**1983.** 40th Death Anniv. (1982) of Edith Stein (philosopher).

2012. **730.** 80 pf. light grey, grey and black .. .. 1·10 25

**731.** White Rose and Barbed Wire.

**1983.** Persecution and Resistance 1933-1945.

2013. **731.** 80 pf. multicoloured 1·00 25

**732.** "Light Space Modulator" (Laszlo Moholy-Nagy).

**1983.** Birth Cent. of Walter Gropius (founder of Bauhaus School of Art, Weimar). Bauhaus Art. Multicoloured.

2014. 50 pf. Type **732** .. .. 55 20
2015. 60 pf. " Sanctuary " (lithograph by Josef Albers) 65 25
2016. 80 pf. Skylights from Bauhaus Archives, Berlin (Walter Gropius) .. 90 30

**733.** Federahannes (Rottweil carnival figure). **734.** Daimler-Maybach, 1885.

**1983.** Carnival.

2017. **733.** 60 pf. multicoloured 65 20

**1983.** Youth Welfare. Motor Cycles. Mult.

2018. 50 pf. + 20 pf. Type **734** 75 75
2019. 60 pf. + 30 pf. N.S.U., 1901 90 85
2020. 80 pf. + 40 pf. Megola "Sport", 1922 .. 1·75 1·50
2021. 120 pf. + 60 pf. B.M.W. world record holder, 1936 .. .. .. 2·50 2·50

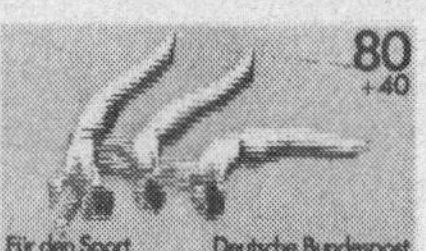

**735.** Gymnastics (German Festival, Frankfurt am Main).

**1983.** Sports Promotion Fund. Multicoloured.

2022. 80 pf. + 40 pf. Type **735** 1·25 1·00
2023. 120 pf. + 60 pf. Modern pentathlon (world championships, Warendorf) .. .. 1·75 1·40

**736.** Stylized Flower.

**1983.** 4th International Horticultural Show, Munich.

2024. **736.** 60 pf. multicoloured 80 20

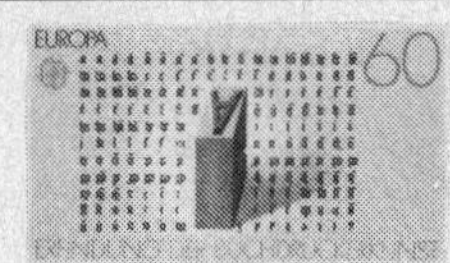

**737. Modern Type and Gutenberg Letters.**

**1983. Europa. Multicoloured.**

2025. 60 pf. Type 737 .. .. 1·50 20
2026. 80 pf. Resonant circuit and electric flux lines .. 1·50 20

**738. Johannes Brahms.**

**1983.** 150th Birth Anniv. of Johannes Brahms (composer).

2027. **738.** 80 pf. multicoloured 1·50 25

**739.** Kafka's Signature and Teyn Church, Prague.

**1983.** Birth Cent. of Franz Kafka (writer).

2028. **739.** 80 pf. multicoloured 1·10 25

**740.** Brewing (frontispiece of 1677 treatise).

**1983.** 450th Anniv. of Beer Purity Law.

2029. **740.** 80 pf. multicoloured 1·10 25

**741. " Concord ".**

**1983.** 300th Anniv. of First German Settlers in America.

2030. **741.** 80 pf. multicoloured 1·40 25

**742. Children crossing Road.**

**1983.** Children and Road Traffic.

2031. **742.** 80 pf. multicoloured 1·40 25

**743.** Flags forming Car.

**1983.** 50th International Motor Show, Frankfurt-on-Main.

2032 743 60 pf. multicoloured .. 75 20

**744.** Warburg (after Oberland).

**745.** Wieland (after G. B. Bosio).

**1983.** Birth Centenary of Otto Warburg (physiologist and chemist).

2033. **744.** 50 pf. multicoloured 60 20

**1983.** 250th Birth Anniv. of Cristoph Martin Wieland (writer).

2034. **745.** 80 pf. multicoloured 90 25

**746.** Rosette in National Colours.

**1983.** 10th Anniv. of U.N. Membership.

2035. **746.** 80 pf. multicoloured 1·10 30

**747. " Das Rauhe Haus " and Children.**

**1983.** 150th Anniv. of "Das Rauhe Haus" (children's home, Hamburg).

2036. **747.** 80 pf. multicoloured 1·00 25

**748. Surveying Maps.**

**1983.** International Geodesy and Geophysics Union General Assembly, Hamburg.

2037. **748.** 120 pf. multicoloured 1·60 60

**749. Swiss Androsace.**

**750.** Horseman with Posthorn.

**1983. Humanitarian Relief Funds. Endangered Alpine Flowers. Multicoloured.**

2038. 50 pf.+20 pf. Type 749 .. 70 70
2039. 60 pf.+30 pf. Krain groundsel .. .. 95 95
2040. 80 pf.+40 pf. Fleischer's willow herb .. .. 1·25 1·25
2041. 120 pf.+60 pf. Alpine sow-thistle .. .. 2·00 2·00

**1983. Stamp Day.**

2042. **750.** 80 pf. multicoloured 1·40 25

**751.** Luther (engraving by G. Konig after Cranach).

**1983.** 500th Birth Anniv. of Martin Luther (Protestant reformer).

2043. **751.** 80 pf. multicoloured 2·00 25

**752. Interwoven National Colours.**

**1983. Federation, Lander and Communities Co-operation.**

2044. **752.** 80 pf. multicoloured 1·10 25

**753. Customs Stamps.**

**754. Epiphany Carol Singers.**

**1983.** 150th Anniv. of German Customs Union.

2045 753 60 pf. multicoloured .. 1·25 20

**1983. Christmas.**

2046 754 80 pf.+40 pf. mult .. 1·60 1·40

**755.** Black Gate, Trier.

**756.** Reis and Telephone Apparatus.

**1984.** 2000th Anniv. of Trier.

2047. **755.** 80 pf. multicoloured 1·10 30

**1984.** 150th Birth Anniv. of Philipp Reis (telephone pioneer).

2048. **756.** 80 pf. multicoloured 1·10 30

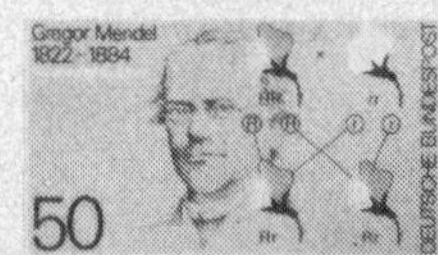

**757.** Mendel and Genetic Diagram.

**1984.** Death Cent. of Gregor Mendel (geneticist).

2049. **757.** 50 pf. multicoloured 80 20

**758.** Town Hall.

**759.** Cloth draped on Cross.

**1984.** 500th Anniv. of Michelstadt Town Hall.

2050. **758.** 60 pf. multicoloured 75 20

**1984.** 350th Anniv. of Oberammergau Passion Play.

2051. **759.** 60 pf. multicoloured 75 20

**760.** Bee-eating Beetle.

**761.** Throwing the Discus.

**1984.** Youth Welfare. Pollinating Insects. Multicoloured.

2052 50 pf.+20 pf. Type 760 .. 80 80
2053 60 pf.+30 pf. Red admiral 1·10 1·10
2054 80 pf.+40 pf. Honey bee 1·40 1·40
2055 120 pf.+60 pf. "Chrysotoxum festivium" (hover fly) .. .. 2·25 2·25

**1984.** Sport Promotion Fund. Multicoloured.

2056. 60 pf.+30 pf. Type 761 1·00 90
2057. 80 pf.+40 pf. Rhythmic gymnastics .. .. 1·40 1·25
2058. 120 pf.+60 pf. Windsurfing .. .. .. 2·50 2·25

**762.** Parliament Emblem.

**763.** Bridge.

**1984.** Second Direct Elections to European Parliament.

2059. **762.** 80 pf. yellow, blue and light blue .. 1·10 25

**1984.** Europa. 25th Anniv. of European Post and Telecommunications Conference.

2060 **763.** 60 pf. blue, light blue and black .. .. 95 25
2061. 80 pf. purple, red and black .. .. 1·40 25

**764.** St. Norbert (sculpture).

**765.** Nursery Rhyme Illustration.

**1984.** 850th Death Anniv. of St. Norbert von Xanten.

2062 764 80 pf. green & dp green 85 25

**1984.** Death Centenary of Ludwig Richter (illustrator).

2063. **765.** 60 pf. black & brown 60 20

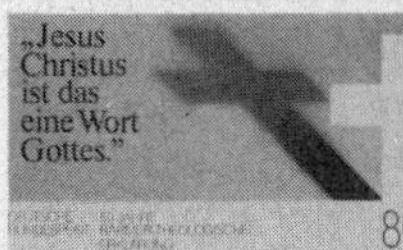

**766.** Cross and Shadow.

**1984.** 50th Anniv. of Protestant Churches' Barmen Theological Declaration.

2064. **766.** 80 pf. multicolured .. 85 20

**768.** Groom leading Horse (detail from tomb of Oclatius).

**769.** Bessel.

**1984.** 2000th Anniv. of Neuss.

2066. **768.** 80 pf. multicoloured 85 20

**1984.** Birth Bicentenary of Friedrich Wilhelm Bessel (astronomer and mathematician).

2067. **769.** 80 pf. grey, black and red .. .. 95 20

**770.** Eugenio Pacelli (Pope Pius XII).

**1984.** 88th German Catholics' Congress, Munich.

2068. **770.** 60 pf. multicoloured 65 20

**771.** Town Hall.

**772.** Medieval Document and Visual Display Unit.

**1984.** 750th Anniv. of Duderstadt Town Hall.

2069. **771.** 60 pf. multicoloured 65 20

**1984.** 10th International Archives Congress, Bonn.

2070. **772.** 70 pf. multicoloured 90 20

**773.** Knoop Lock.

**1984.** Bicent. of Schleswig-Holstein Canal.

2071. **773.** 80 pf. multicoloured 1·00 20

**774.** Research Centre and Storage Rings.

**1984.** 25th Anniv. of German Electron Synchrotron (physics research centre), Hamburg–Bahrenfeld.

2072. **774.** 80 pf. multicoloured 90 20

**775.** "Aceras anthropophorum".

**1984.** Humanitarian Relief Funds. Orchids. Multicoloured.

2073. 50 pf.+20 pf. Type 775 1·00 80
2074. 60 pf.+30 pf. "Orchis ustulata" .. .. 1·10 1·10
2075. 80 pf.+40 pf. "Limodorum abortivum" .. 1·60 1·40
2076. 120 pf.+60 pf. "Dactylorhiza sambucina" .. 2·40 2·25

776. Taxis Posthouse, Augsburg.

**1984.** Stamp Day.
2077. **776.** 80 pf. multicoloured 1·25 30

777. Burning Match.

**1984.** Anti-smoking Campaign.
2078. **777.** 60 pf. multicoloured 90 30

778. Male and Female Symbols.

**1984.** Equal Rights for Men and Women.
2079. **778.** 80 pf. black, mauve and blue .. .. 90 30

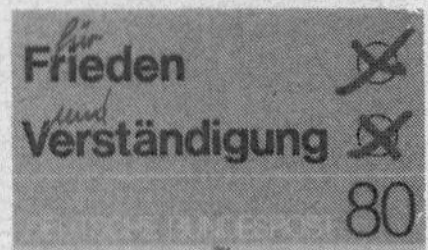

779. Ballot Slip.

**1984.** For Peace and Understanding.
2080. **779.** 80 pf. grey, black and blue .. .. 90 30

780. St. Martin giving Cloak to Beggar.

**1984.** Christmas.
2081 **780** 80 pf. + 40 pf. mult .. 1·25 1·25

781. Emperor Augustus (bust), Buildings and Arms.

**1985.** 2000th Anniv. of Augsburg.
2082. **781.** 80 pf. multicoloured 90 30

782. Spener (engraving by Bartholome Kilian after Johann Georg Wagner).

**1985.** 350th Birth Anniv. of Philipp Jakob Spener (church reformer).
2083. **782.** 80 pf. black & green 90 30

783. Grimm Brothers (engraving by Lazarus Sichling).

**1985.** Birth Bicentenaries of Grimm Brothers (folklorists) and 7th International Union for German Linguistics and Literature Congress, Gottingen.
2084. **783.** 80 pf. black, grey and red .. .. 90 30

784. Romano Guardini.

**1985.** Birth Centenary of Romano Guardini (theologian).
2085. **784.** 80 pf. multicoloured 90 30

785. Verden.

**1985.** Millenary of Market and Coinage Rights in Verden.
2086. **785.** 60 pf. multicoloured 80 20

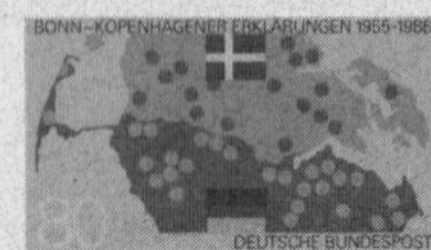

786. Flags and German-Danish Border.

**1985.** 30th Anniv. of Bonn-Copenhagen Declarations.
2087. **786.** 80 pf. multicoloured 1·00 30

787. Bowling.

**1985.** Sport Promotion Fund. Multicoloured.
2088. 80 pf. + 40 pf. Type **787** (cent. of German Nine-pin Bowling Association) .. .. 1·40 1·25
2089. 120 pf. + 60 pf. Kayak (world rapid-river and slalom canoeing championships) .. 2·50 2·25

788. Kisch.

789. "Hebel and the Margravine".

**1985.** Birth Centenary of Egon Erwin Kisch (journalist).
2090. **788.** 60 pf. multicoloured 75 20

**1985.** 225th Birth Anniv. of Johann Peter Hebel (poet).
2091. **789.** 80 pf. multicoloured 1·00 30

790. Draisienne Bicycle, 1817.

791. Handel.

**1985.** Youth Welfare International Youth Year. Cycles. Multicoloured.
2092. 50 pf. + 20 pf. Type **790**.. 1·10 1·00
2093. 60 pf. + 30 pf. NSU Germania "ordinary", 1866 .. .. .. 1·60 1·40
2094. 80 pf. + 40 pf. Cross-frame low bicycle, 1887 .. 2·00 1·75
2095. 120 pf. + 60 pf. Adler tricycle, 1888 .. .. 3·25 3·00

**1985.** Europa. Composers' 300th Birth Anniversaries. Multicoloured.
2096. 60 pf. Type **791** .. .. 1·75 30
2097. 80 pf. Bach .. .. 1·75 30

792. Saint George's Cathedral.

793. Capital (presbytery, "Wies" Church).

**1985.** 750th Anniv. of Limburg Cathedral.
2098. **792.** 60 pf. multicoloured 90 20

**1985.** 300th Birth Anniv. of Dominikus Zimmermann (architect).
2099. **793.** 70 pf. multicoloured 90 25

794. Josef Kentenich.

**1985.** Birth Centenary of Father Josef Kentenich (founder of International Schonstatt (Catholic laymen's) Movement).
2100. **794.** 80 pf. multicoloured 1·00 30

795. Clock and Forest.

**1985.** Save the Forests.
2101. **795.** 80 pf. multicoloured 1·40 30

796. Tug of War and Scouting Emblem.

**1985.** 30th World Scouts Conference, Munich.
2102 **796** 60 pf. multicoloured .. 85 20

797. "Sunday Walk".

**1985.** Death Cent. of Carl Spitzweg (artist).
2103. **797.** 60 pf. multicoloured 80 20

798. Horses and Postilion.

**1985.** "Mophila 1985" Stamp Exhibition, Hamburg. Multicoloured.
2104. 60 pf. + 20 pf. Type **798**.. 2·50 2·50
2105. 80 pf. + 20 pf. Mail coach 2·75 2·75
Nos. 2104/5 were printed se-tenant, forming a composite design.

799. Stock Exchange.

**1985.** 400th Anniv. of Frankfurt Stock Exchange.
2106. **799.** 80 pf. black, red and grey .. .. 95 30

800. Flowers and Butterfly. 801. Fritz Reuter.

**1985.** Humanitarian Relief Funds. Designs depict motifs from borders of medieval prayer book. Multicoloured.
2107. 50 pf. + 20 pf. Type **800**.. 1·00 85
2108. 60 pf. + 30 pf. Flowers, bird and butterfly .. 1·40 1·25
2109. 80 pf. + 40 pf. Flowers, berries and snail .. 2·00 2·25
2110. 120 pf. + 60 pf. Flowers, snail and butterfly .. 2·25 2·50

**1985.** 175th Death Anniv. of Fritz Reuter (writer).
2111. **801.** 80 pf. black, grey and blue .. .. 95 30

802. "Inauguration of First German Railway" (Heim).

**1985.** 150th Anniv. of German Railways and Birth Bicent. of Johannes Scharrer (joint founder).
2112. **802.** 80 pf. multicoloured 1·40 30

803. Carpentry Joint in National Colours. 805. "Nativity" (detail, High Altar, Freiburg).

804. Iron Cross and National Colours.

**1985.** 40th Anniv. of Integration of Refugees.
2113. **803.** 80 pf. multicoloured 90 30

**1985.** 30th Anniv. of Federal Armed Forces.
2114. **804.** 80 pf. red, black and yellow .. .. 1·40 30

**1985.** Christmas. 500th Birth Anniversary of Hans Baldung Grien (artist).
2115 **805** 80 pf. + 40 pf. mult .. 1·40 1·40

806. Early and Modern Cars.

**1986.** Centenary of Motor Car.
2116. **806.** 80 pf. multicoloured 1·25 30

807. Town Buildings.

808. "Self-portrait".

**1986.** 1250th Anniv. of Bad Hersfeld.
2117. **807.** 60 pf. multicoloured 95 30

**1986.** Birth Centenary of Oskar Kokoschka (artist and writer).
2118. **808.** 80 pf. black, grey and red .. .. 95 30

**809.** Comet and "Giotto" Space Probe.

**1986.** Appearance of Halley's Comet.
2119. **809.** 80 pf. multicoloured 1·25 30

**810.** Running.

**1986.** Sport Promotion Fund. Multicoloured.
2120. 80 pf.+40 pf. Type **810** (European Athletics Championships, Stuttgart) .. .. 1·50 1·50
2121. 120 pf.+55 pf. Bobsleigh (World Championships, Konigsee) .. 2·00 2·00

**811.** Optician.

**1986.** Youth Welfare. Trades (1st series). Multicoloured.
2122. 50 pf.+25 pf. Type **811** 1·25 1·25
2123. 60 pf.+30 pf. Bricklayer 1·50 1·50
2124. 70 pf.+35 pf. Hairdresser .. .. .. 1·75 1·75
2125. 80 pf.+40 pf. Baker .. 2·00 2·00
See also Nos. 2179/82.

**812.** Walsrode Monastery.

**1986.** Millenary of Walsrode.
2126. **812.** 60 pf. multicoloured 95 20

**813.** Ludwig and Neuschwanstein Castle.

**1986.** Death Centenary of King Ludwig II of Bavaria.
2127. **813.** 60 pf. multicoloured 1·10 25

**814.** Mouth.

**1986.** Europa. Details of "David" (sculpture) by Michelangelo. Multicoloured.
2128. 60 pf. Type **814** .. .. 1·00 20
2129. 80 pf. Nose .. .. 1·40 25

**815.** Karl Barth. **817.** Weber and Score of "Gloria".

**816.** Ribbons.

**1986.** Birth Centenary of Karl Barth (theologian).
2130. **815.** 80 pf. black, red and purple .. .. 1·00 30

**1986.** Union of German Catholic Students' Societies 100th Assembly, Frankfurt am Main.
2131. **816.** 80 pf. multicoloured 1·00 30

**1986.** Birth Bicentenary of Carl Maria von Weber (composer).
2132. **817.** 80 pf. brown, black and red .. .. 1·40 30

**818.** "TV-Sat" and Earth.

**1986.** Launch of German "TV-Sat" and French "TDF-1" Broadcasting Satellites.
2133. **818.** 80 pf. multicoloured 1·40 30

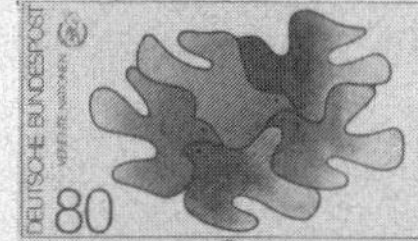

**819.** Doves.

**1986.** International Peace Year.
2134. **819.** 80 pf. multicoloured 1·25 30

**820.** Liszt.

**1986.** Death Centenary of Franz Liszt (composer).
2135. **820.** 80 pf. blue & orange 1·50 30

**822.** Pollution Damage of Stained Glass Window.

**1986.** Protection of Monuments.
2137. **822.** 80 pf. multicoloured 1·25 30

**823.** Frederick the Great (after Anton Graff). **824.** Congress Card.

**1986.** Death Bicentenary of Frederick the Great.
2138. **823.** 80 pf. multicoloured 1·25 30

**1986.** Centenary of First German Skat Congress and 24th Congress, Cologne.
2139. **824.** 80 pf. multicoloured 1·25 30

**825.** Opposing Arrows.

**1986.** 25th Anniv. of Organization for Economic Co-operation and Development.
2140. **825.** 80 pf. multicoloured 1·00 30

**826.** Old University.

**1986.** 600th Anniv. of Heidelberg University.
2141. **826.** 80 pf. multicoloured 1·25 30

**827.** Fan of Stamps behind Stagecoach.

**1986.** 50th Anniv. of Stamp Day.
2142. **827.** 80 pf. multicoloured 1·50 35

**828.** Ornamental Flask, 300 A.D. **829.** "Dance in Silence" from "Autumnal Dances".

**1986.** Humanitarian Relief Funds. Glassware. Multicoloured.
2143. 50 pf.+25 pf. Type **828** 70 70
2144. 60 pf.+30 pf. Goblet with decorated stem, 1650 .. .. .. 85 85
2145. 70 pf.+35 pf. Imperial Eagle tankard, 1662 .. 1·00 1·00
2146. 80 pf.+40 pf. Engraved goblet, 1720 .. .. 1·25 1·25

**1986.** Birth Centenary of Mary Wigman (dancer).
2147. **829.** 70 pf. multicoloured 90 25

**830.** Cross over Map.

**1986.** 25th Anniv. of Adveniat (Advent collection for Latin America).
2148. **830.** 80 pf. green, blue and black .. .. 85 30

**831.** "Adoration of the Infant Jesus" (Ortenberg altarpiece). **832.** Christine Teusch (politician).

**1986.** Christmas.
2149 **831** 80 pf.+40 pf. mult .. 1·25 1·25

**1986.** Famous German Women.
2150 – 5 pf. brown and grey 20 10
2151 – 10 pf. brown & violet 20 10
2152 – 20 pf. blue and red 25 10
2152a – 30 pf. bistre & purple 30 10
2153 – 40 pf. red and blue 40 10
2154 **832** 50 pf. green & brown 50 10
2155 – 60 pf. lilac and green 50 15
2155a – 70 pf. green and red 60 20
2156 – 80 pf. brown & green 65 20
2156a – 80 pf. brown & blue 65 25
2157 – 100 pf. grey and red 80 25
2157a – 100 pf. bistre & lilac 85 30
2158 – 120 pf. green & brn 90 25
2159 – 130 pf. violet & blue 1·00 30
2160 – 140 pf. ochre & blue 1·10 30
2161 – 150 pf. blue and red 1·25 35
2162 – 170 pf. purple & grn 1·40 35
2163 – 180 pf. purple & blue 1·50 40
2164 – 200 pf. red & brown 1·60 45
2165 – 240 pf. brown & grn 1·75 50
2166 – 250 pf. blue & mauve 2·00 55
2167 – 300 pf. green & pur 2·50 65
2168 – 350 pf. brown & blk 2·75 80
2168a – 400 pf. black and red 3·00 95
2168b – 450 pf. ultram & blue 2·75 1·90
2169 – 500 pf. red and green 4·00 1·10

DESIGNS: 5 pf. Emma Ihrer (politician and trade unionist). 10 pf. Paula Modersohn-Becker (painter). 20 pf. Cilly Aussem (tennis player). 30 pf. Kathe Kollwitz (artist). 40 pf. Maria Sibylla Merian (artist and naturalist). 60 pf. Dorothea Erxleben (first German woman Doctor of Medicine). 70 pf. Elisabet Boehm (founder of Agricultural Association of Housewives). 80 pf. (2156), Clara Schumann (pianist and composer). 80 pf. (2156a), Rahel Varnhagen von Ense (humanist) (after Wilhelm Hensel). 100 pf. (2157), Therese Giehse (actress). 100 pf. (2157a), Luise Henriette of Orange (mother of King Friedrich I of Prussia) (after Gerhard von Honthorst). 120 pf. Elisabeth Selbert (politician). 130 pf. Lise Meitner (physicist). 140 pf. Cecile Vogt (medical researcher). 150 pf. Sophie Scholl (resistance member). 170 pf. Hannah Arendt (sociologist). 180 pf. Lotte Lehmann (opera singer). 200 pf. Bertha von Suttner (novelist and pacifist). 240 pf. Mathilda Franziska Anneke (women's rights activist). 250 pf. Queen Louise of Prussia. 300 pf. Fanny Hensel (composer) (after Eduard Magnus). 350 pf. Hedwig Dransfeld (politician). 400 pf. Charlotte von Stein (friend of Goethe). 450 pf. Hedwig Courths-Mahler (novelist). 500 pf. Alice Salomon (women's rights activist).

**833.** Berlin Landmarks.

**1987.** 750th Anniv. of Berlin.
2170. **833.** 80 pf. multicoloured 1·25 35

**834.** Staircase, Residenz Palace, Wurzburg. **835.** Erhard.

**1987.** 300th Birth Anniv. of Balthasar Neumann (architect).
2171. **834.** 80 pf. grey, black and red .. .. 1·00 30

**1987.** 90th Birth Anniv. of Ludwig Erhard (former Chancellor).
2172. **835.** 80 pf. multicoloured 1·25 30

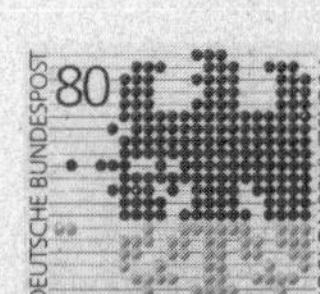

**836.** Abacus Beads forming Eagle. **838.** Chief Winnetou (from book cover).

**837.** Clemenswerth Castle.

**1987.** Census.
2173. **836.** 80 pf. multicoloured 1·00 30

**1987.** 250th Anniv. of Clemenswerth Castle.
2174. **837.** 60 pf. multicoloured 90 30

**1987.** 75th Death Anniv. of Karl May (writer).
2175. **838.** 80 pf. multicoloured 1·00 30

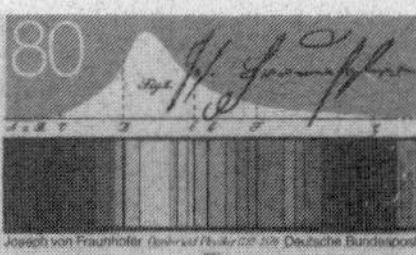

**839.** Solar Spectrum.

**1987.** Birth Bicentenary of Joseph von Fraunhofer (optician and physicist).
2176. **839.** 80 pf. multicoloured 90 30

**840.** World Sailing Championships, Kiel.

**1987.** Sport Promotion Fund. Multicoloured.
2177 80 pf.+40 pf. Type **840** .. 1·25 1·25
2178 120 pf.+55 pf. World Nordic Skiing Championships, Oberstdorf .. 1·75 1·75

**1987.** Youth Welfare. Trades (2nd series). As T **811**. Multicoloured.
2179. 50 pf.+25 pf. Plumber .. 1·25 1·10
2180. 60 pf.+30 pf. Dental technician .. .. 1·50 1·25
2181. 70 pf.+35 pf. Butcher .. 1·75 1·50
2182. 80 pf.+40 pf. Bookbinder .. .. .. 2·00 1·60

**841.** Clefs, Notes and Leaves.

**1987.** 125th Anniv. of German Choir Association.
2183. **841.** 80 pf. multicoloured 1·00 30

**842.** Pope's Arms, Madonna and Child and Kevelaer.

**1987.** Visit of Pope John Paul II to Kevelaer (venue for 17th Marian and 10th Mariological Congresses).
2184. **842.** 80 pf. multicoloured 1·00 30

**843.** Dulmen's Wild Horses.

**1987.** European Environment Year.
2185 **843** 60 pf. multicoloured .. 1·25 35

**844.** German Pavilion, International Exhibition, Barcelona, 1929 (Ludwig Mies van der Rohe).

**1987.** Europa. Architecture. Multicoloured.
2186. 60 pf. Type **844** .. .. 85 25
2187. 80 pf. Kohlbrand Bridge, Hamburg (Thyssen Engineering) .. .. 1·10 30

**845.** Emblem and Globe.

**1987.** Rotary International Convention, Munich.
2188 **845** 70 pf. ultram, yell & bl 1·00 30

**846.** "Without Title (With an Early Portrait)".

**847.** Organ Pipes and Signature.

**1987.** Birth Centenary of Kurt Schwitters (artist and writer).
2189 **846** 80 pf. multicoloured .. 1·00 30

**1987.** 350th Birth Anniv. of Dietrich Buxtehude (composer).
2190. **847.** 80 pf. black, stone and red .. .. 1·00 30

**848.** Bengel.

**849.** Wilhelm Kaisen.

**1987.** 300th Birth Anniv. of Johann Albrecht Bengel (theologian).
2191 **848** 80 pf. brn, ochre & blk 1·00 30

**1987.** Birth Centenary of Wilhelm Kaisen (Senate president and Mayor of Bremen).
2192 **849** 80 pf. multicoloured .. 1·00 30

**850.** Charlemagne, Bishop Willehad, Bremen Cathedral and City Arms (after mural).

**1987.** 1200th Anniv. of Bremen Bishopric.
2193. **850.** 80 pf. multicoloured 90 30

**851.** Target, Crossed Rifles and Wreath.

**1987.** 7th European Riflemen's Festival, Lippstadt.
2194 **851** 80 pf. multicoloured .. 80 30

**852.** 4th-century Roman Bracelet.

**1987.** Humanitarian Relief Funds. Precious Metal Work. Multicoloured.
2195 50 pf. + 25 pf. Type **852** .. 1·00 65
2196 60 pf. + 30 pf. 6th-century East Gothic buckle .. 1·10 75
2197 70 pf. + 35 pf. 7th-century Merovingian disc fibula 1·25 95
2198 80 pf. + 40 pf. 8th-century reliquary .. .. 1·60 1·10

**853.** Loading and Unloading Mail Train, 1897.

**854.** Corner Tower, Celle Castle.

**1987.** Stamp Day.
2199. **853.** 80 pf. multicoloured 70 30

**1987.** Tourist Sights. Inscr "DEUTSCHE BUNDESPOST".

| | | | | |
|---|---|---|---|---|
| 2200 | – | 5 pf. blue and grey | 10 | 10 |
| 2201 | – | 10 pf. blue & indigo | 10 | 10 |
| 2202 | – | 20 pf. pink and blue | 15 | 10 |
| 2203 | **854** | 30 pf. brown & green | 20 | 10 |
| 2204 | – | 33 pf. green and red | 40 | 10 |
| 2205 | – | 38 pf. grey and blue | 60 | 10 |
| 2206 | – | 40 pf. brn, red & bl | 30 | 10 |
| 2206a | – | 41 pf. grey & yellow | 30 | 10 |
| 2207 | – | 45 pf. pink and blue | 30 | 10 |
| 2208 | – | 50 pf. brown & blue | 35 | 10 |
| 2209 | – | 60 pf. green & black | 40 | 15 |
| 2210 | – | 70 pf. pink and blue | 85 | 20 |
| 2210a | – | 70 pf. brown & blue | 50 | 20 |
| 2211 | – | 80 pf. grey and green | 55 | 20 |
| 2212 | – | 90 pf. bistre & yellow | 1·10 | 20 |
| 2213 | – | 100 pf. green & orge | 80 | 25 |
| 2214 | – | 120 pf. green and red | 1·40 | 25 |
| 2215 | – | 140 pf. bistre & yell | 1·60 | 30 |
| 2216 | – | 170 pf. grey & yellow | 1·25 | 35 |
| 2216a | – | 200 pf. blue & brown | 1·10 | 1·10 |
| 2217 | – | 280 pf. grey and blue | 3·00 | 60 |
| 2218 | – | 300 pf. pink & brown | 2·40 | 65 |
| 2219 | – | 350 pf. grey and blue | 2·50 | 80 |
| 2220 | – | 400 pf. red & brown | 3·25 | 90 |
| 2220a | – | 450 pf. blue & brown | 2·75 | 1·90 |
| 2220b | – | 500 pf. stone & pur | 3·00 | 3·00 |
| 2220c | – | 550 pf. brown & blue | 4·50 | 1·50 |
| 2220d | – | 700 pf. green & yell | 5·50 | 1·90 |

DESIGNS: 5 pf. Brunswick Lion. 10 pf. Frankfurt airport. 20, 70 (2210) pf. Head of Nefertiti, Berlin Museum. 33, 120 pf. Schleswig Cathedral. 38, 280 pf. Statue of Roland, Bremen. 40 pf. Chile House, Hamburg. 41, 170 pf. Russian Church, Wiesbaden. 45 pf. Rastatt Castle. 50 pf. Freiburg Cathedral. 60 pf. "Bavaria" (bronze statue), Munich. 70 pf. (2210a) Heligoland. 80 pf. Zollern II Dortmund Mine Industrial Museum, Westphalia. 90, 140 pf. Bronze flagon, Reinheim. 100 pf. Pilgrimage Chapel, Altotting. 200 pf. Magdeburg Cathedral. 300 pf. Hambach Castle. 350 pf. Externsteine (rock formation), Horn-Bad Meinberg. 400 pf. Dresden Opera House. 450 pf. New Gate, Neubrandenburg. 500 pf. Cottbus State Theatre. 550 pf. Suhl-Heinrichs Town Hall, Thuringia. 700 pf. National Theatre, Berlin.

The 10, 60, 80 and 100 pf. also exist imperforate and self-adhesive from booklets.

For similar designs inscribed "DEUTSCHLAND", see Nos. 2665/6.

**855.** Gluck and Score of "Armide".

**1987.** Death Bicentenary of Christoph Willibald Gluck (composer).
2221. **855.** 60 pf. black, grey and red .. .. 75 20

**856.** Poster by Emil Orlik for "The Weavers".

**1987.** 125th Birth Anniv. of Gerhart Hauptmann (playwright).
2222. **856.** 80 pf. light red, black and red .. .. 1·00 30

**857.** Paddy Field.

**1987.** 25th Anniv. of German Famine Aid.
2223. **857.** 80 pf. multicoloured 1·00 30

**858.** "Birth of Christ" (13th-century Book of Psalms).

**1987.** Christmas.
2224. **858.** 80 pf. + 40 pf. mult .. 1·00 1·10

**859.** Jester.

**860.** Kaiser.

**1988.** 150th Anniv. of Mainz Carnival.
2225. **859.** 60 pf. multicoloured 80 20

**1988.** Birth Centenary of Jakob Kaiser (trade unionist and politician).
2226. **860.** 80 pf. black and grey 85 30

**861.** Stein and Mayer.

**1988.** Beatification of Edith Stein and Father Rupert Mayer.
2227 **861** 80 pf. multicoloured .. 75 30

**862.** Dr. Konrad Adenauer (West German Chancellor) and Charles de Gaulle (French President).

**1988.** 25th Anniv. of Franco-German Co-operation Treaty.
2228. **862.** 80 pf. purple & black 1·00 35

**863.** "Solitude of the Green Woods" (woodcut of poem, Ludwig Richter).

**865.** Schopenhauer.

**864.** Raiffeisen and Ploughed Field.

**1988.** Birth Bicentenary of Joseph von Eichendorff (writer).
2229. **863.** 60 pf. multicoloured 80 20

**1988.** Death Centenary of Friedrich Wilhelm Raiffeisen (philanthropist and agricultural co-operative founder).
2230 **864** 80 pf. green and black 1·25 30

**1988.** Birth Bicentenary of Arthur Schopenhauer (philosopher).
2231 **865** 80 pf. brown and black 90 30

**866.** Football (European Championship).

**1988.** Sport Promotion Fund. Multicoloured.
2232. 60 pf. + 30 pf. Type **866** 1·25 75
2233. 80 pf. + 40 pf. Tennis (Olympic Games) .. 1·60 1·00
2234. 120 pf. + 55 pf. Diving (Olympic Games) .. 2·25 1·60

**867.** Buddy Holly.

**1988.** Youth Welfare. Pop Music. Mult.
2235. 50 pf. + 25 pf. Type **867** 1·75 1·00
2236. 60 pf. + 30 pf. Elvis Presley .. .. 4·00 2·00
2237. 70 pf. + 35 pf. Jim Morrison .. .. 2·00 1·00
2238. 80 pf. + 40 pf. John Lennon .. .. 3·75 1·50

**868.** Hutten (wood engraving from "Conquestiones").

**1988.** 500th Birth Anniv of Ulrich von Hutten (writer).
2239 **868** 80 pf. multicoloured .. 90 30

**869.** City Buildings and Jan Wellem Monument.

**1988.** 700th Anniv. of Dusseldorf.
2240. **869.** 60 pf. multicoloured 75 20

**870.** Airbus Industrie A320 and Manufacturing Nations' Flag.

**1988.** Europa. Transport and Communications. Multicoloured.
2241. 60 pf. Type **870** .. .. 1·25 30
2242. 80 pf. Diagram of Integrated Services Digital Network .. 85 35

**871.** University Buildings and City Landmarks. **872.** Monnet.

**1988.** 600th Anniv. of Cologne University.
2243. **871.** 80 pf. multicoloured 90 30

**1988.** Birth Centenary of Jean Monnet (statesman).
2244. **872.** 80 pf. multicoloured 90 30

**873.** Storm.

**1988.** Death Centenary of Theodor Storm (writer).
2245. **873.** 80 pf. multicoloured 80 30

**874.** Tree supported by Stake in National Colours. **876.** Gmelin.

**875.** Meersburg.

**1988.** 25th Anniv. of German Volunteer Service.
2246. **874.** 80 pf. multicoloured 80 30

**1988.** Millenary of Meersburg.
2247. **875.** 60 pf. multicoloured 65 20

**1988.** Birth Bicentenary of Leopold Gmelin (chemist).
2248. **876.** 80 pf. multicoloured 80 30

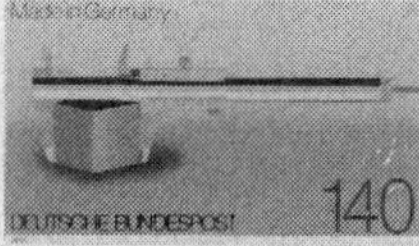

**877.** Vernier Caliper Rule in National Colours.

**1988.** "Made in Germany".
2249. **877.** 140 pf. multicoloured 1·60 55

**878.** Bebel.

**1988.** 75th Death Anniv. of August Bebel (Social Democratic Labour Party co-founder).
2250. **878.** 80 pf. mauve, blue and silver . . . . 1·00 30

**879.** Carrier Pigeon. **880.** 13th-century Rock Crystal Reliquary.

**1988.** Stamp Day.
2251. **879.** 20 pf. multicoloured 50 10

**1988.** Humanitarian Relief Funds. Precious Metal Work. Multicoloured.
2252. 50 pf. + 25 pf. Type **880** 70 55
2253. 60 pf. + 30 pf. 14th-century bust of Charlemagne . . . . 85 70
2254. 70 pf. + 35 pf. 10th-cent. crown of Otto III 1·00 85
2255. 80 pf. + 40 pf. 17th-cent. jewelled flowers . . 1·25 1·10

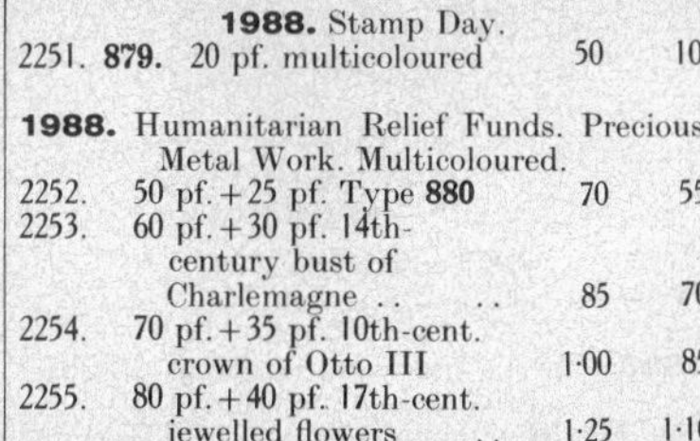

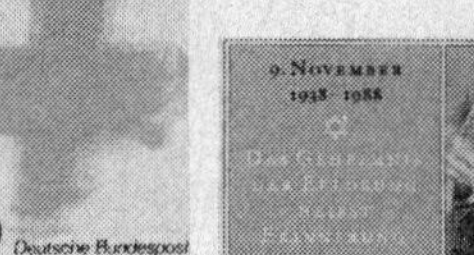

**881.** Red Cross. **882.** Burning Synagogue, Baden-Baden.

**1988.** 125th Anniv. of Red Cross.
2256. **881.** 80 pf. red and black 1·00 30

**1988.** 50th Anniv. of "Kristallnacht" (Nazi pogrom).
2257. **882.** 80 pf. purple & blk. 85 30

**883.** Cancelled Postage Stamps.

**1988.** Centenary of Collection of Used Stamps for the Bethel Charity.
2258 **883** 60 pf. multicoloured . . 90 20

**884.** Linked Arms.

**1988.** Centenary of Samaritan Workers' (first aid) Association.
2259. **884.** 80 pf. multicoloured 85 30

**885.** "Adoration of the Magi" (illus. from Henry the Lion's Gospel Book).

**1988.** Christmas.
2260 **885** 80 pf. + 40 pf. mult . . 1·40 1·00

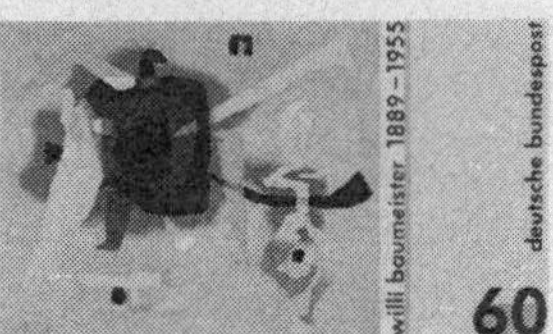

**886** "Bluxao I"

**1989.** Birth Centenary of Willi Baumeister (painter).
2261 **886** 60 pf. multicoloured . . 70 20

**887** Bonn

**1988.** 2000th Anniv of Bonn.
2262 **887** 80 pf. multicoloured . . 1·00 30

**888** Grass growing from Dry, Cracked Earth

**1989.** 30th Anniversaries of Misereor and Bread for the World (Third World relief organizations).
2263 **888** 80 pf. multicoloured . . 80 30

**889** "Cats in the Attic" (woodcut)

**1989.** Birth Cent of Gerhard Marcks (artist).
2264 **889** 60 pf. blk, stone & red 65 20

**890** Table Tennis (World Championships)

**1989.** Sport Promotion Fund. Multicoloured.
2265 100 pf. + 50 pf. Type **890** 2·00 1·25
2266 140 pf. + 60 pf. Gymnastics (World Championships) 3·00 2·00

**891** Elephants

**1989.** Youth Welfare. Circus. Multicoloured.
2267 60 pf. + 30 pf. Type **891** . . 1·50 80
2268 70 pf. + 30 pf. Acrobat on horseback . . . . 1·60 90
2269 80 pf. + 35 pf. Clown . . 2·00 1·40
2270 100 pf. + 50 pf. Caravans and Big Top . . . . 3·00 1·90

**892** Posthorn and Book of Stamps

**1989.** "IPHLA '89" International Philatelic Literature Exhibition, Frankfurt.
2271 **892** 100 pf. + 50 pf. mult . . 2·00 1·25

**893** European and Members' Flags

**1989.** 3rd Direct Elections to European Parliament.
2272 **893** 100 pf. multicoloured 1·60 60

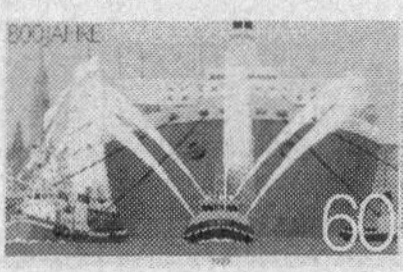

**894** Shipping

**1989.** 800th Anniv of Hamburg Harbour.
2273 **894** 60 pf. multicoloured . . 75 20

**895** Asam (detail of fresco, Weltenburg Abbey)

**1989.** 250th Death Anniv of Cosmas Damian Asam (painter and architect).
2274 **895** 60 pf. multicoloured . . 75 20

**896** Kites

**1989.** Europa. Children's Toys. Multicoloured.
2275 60 pf. Type **896** . . . . 85 20
2276 100 pf. Puppet show . . 1·40 30

**897** Emblem, National Colours and Presidents' Signatures

**1989.** 40th Anniv of German Federal Republic.
2277 **897** 100 pf. multicoloured 1·50 35

**898** Council Assembly and Stars

**1989.** 40th Anniv of Council of Europe.
2278 **898** 100 pf. blue and gold 1·25 35

**899** Gabelsberger and Shorthand

**1989.** Birth Bicentenary of Franz Xaver Gabelsberger (shorthand pioneer).
2279 **899** 100 pf. multicoloured 1·10 35

**900** Score of "Lorelei" and Silhouette of Silcher

**1989.** Birth Bicentenary of Friedrich Silcher (composer).
2280 **900** 80 pf. multicoloured . . 1·00 30

**901** Saints Kilian, Totnan and Colman (from 12th-century German manuscript)

**1989.** 1300th Death Anniversaries of Saints Kilian, Colman and Totnan (Irish missionaries to Franconia).
2281 **901** 100 pf. multicoloured 1·25 35

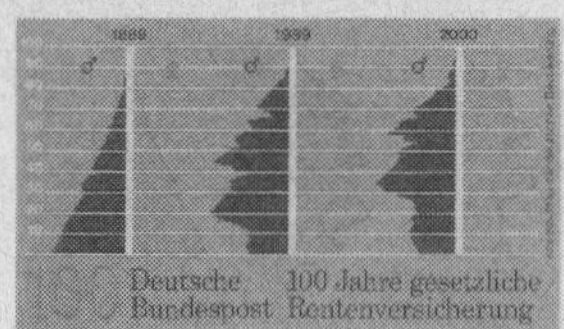


**902** Age Graphs of Men and Women

**1989.** Centenary of National Insurance.
2282 **902** 100 p. blue, red & ltbl 1·25 35

**903** "Summer Evening" (Heinrich Vogler)

**1989.** Cent of Worpswede Artists' Village.
2283 **903** 60 pf. multicoloured .. 80 20

**904** Schneider **905** List (after Kriehuber and Train)

**1989.** 50th Death Anniv of Reverend Paul Schneider (concentration camp victim).
2284 **904** 100 pf. black, light grey and grey .. 1·25 35

**1989.** Birth Bicentenary of Friedrich List (economist).
2285 **905** 170 pf. black and red 2·00 60

**906** Cathedral **907** Children building House

**1989.** 750th Anniv of Frankfurt Cathedral.
2286 **906** 60 pf. multicoloured .. 75 20

**1989.** "Don't Forget the Children".
2287 **907** 100 pf. multicoloured 1·25 35

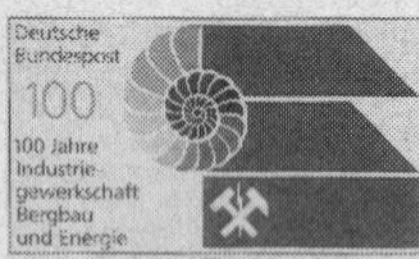


**908** Ammonite and Union Emblem

**1989.** Centenary of Mining and Power Industries Trade Union.
2288 **908** 100 pf. multicoloured 1·50 45

**909** 18th-century Mounted Courier, Thurn and Taxis **910** Maier

**1989.** Humanitarian Relief Funds. Postal Deliveries. Multicoloured.
2289 60 pf. + 30 pf. Type **909** .. 1·10 1·00
2290 80 pf. + 35 pf. Hamburg postal messenger, 1808 1·60 1·50
2291 100 pf. + 50 pf. Bavarian mail coach, 1900 .. 2·00 1·75

**1989.** Birth Centenary of Reinhold Maier (politician).
2292 **910** 100 pf. multicoloured 1·10 35

**911** Organ Pipes

**1989.** 300th Anniv of Arp Schnitger Organ, St. James's Church, Hamburg.
2293 **911** 60 pf. multicoloured .. 75 20

**912** Angel

**1989.** Christmas. 16th-century Carvings by Veit Stoss, St. Lawrence's Church, Nuremberg. Multicoloured.
2294 60 pf. + 30 pf. Type **912** .. 90 90
2295 100 pf. + 50 pf. "Nativity" 1·60 1·60

**913** Speyer **914** "Courier" (Albrecht Durer)

**1990.** 2000th Anniv of Speyer.
2296 **913** 60 pf. multicoloured .. 70 20

**1990.** 500th Anniv of Regular European Postal Services.
2297 **914** 100 pf. deep brown, lt brown and brown 1·25 35

**915** Vine forming Initial "R"

**1990.** 500 Years of Riesling Grape Cultivation.
2298 **915** 100 pf. multicoloured 1·00 35

**916** Old Lubeck

**1990.** U.N.E.S.C.O. World Heritage Site. Old Lubeck.
2299 **916** 100 pf. multicoloured 1·00 35

**917** 15th-century Seal and Grand Master's Arms

**1990.** 800th Anniv of Teutonic Order.
2300 **917** 100 pf. multicoloured 1·00 35

**HAVE YOU READ THE NOTES AT THE BEGINNING OF THIS CATALOGUE?**
These often provide answers to the enquiries we receive.

**918** Frederick II's Seal and Fair Entrance Hall

**1990.** 750th Anniv of Granting of Fair Privileges to Frankfurt.
2301 **918** 100 pf. multicoloured 1·00 35

**919** Maze

**1990.** 25th Anniv of Youth Research Science Competition.
2302 **919** 100 pf. multioloured .. 1·00 35

**920** Wildlife

**1990.** North Sea Protection.
2303 **920** 100 pf. multicoloured 1·40 45

**921** Handball

**1990.** Sport Promotion Fund. Multicoloured.
2304 100 pf. + 50 pf. Type **921** 2·00 1·40
2305 140 pf. + 60 pf. Keep-fit .. 2·50 1·60

**922** Widow Bolte

**1990.** Youth Welfare. 125th Anniv of Max and Moritz (characters from books by Wilhelm Busch). Multicoloured.
2306 60 pf. + 30 pf. Type **922** .. 1·00 80
2307 70 pf. + 30 pf. Max asleep 1·25 1·00
2308 80 pf. + 35 pf. Moritz watching Max sawing through bridge .. 1·25 1·10
2309 100 pf. + 50 pf. Max and Moritz .. .. 1·60 1·40

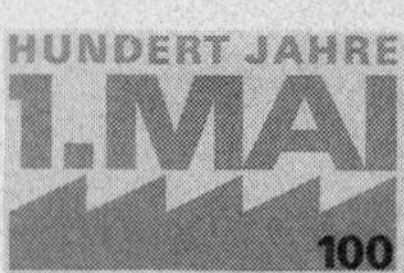


**923** "1.MAI" and Factory Silhouette

**1990.** Centenary of Labour Day.
2310 **923** 100 pf. red and black 1·00 35

**924** Woman's Face

**1990.** 75th Anniv of German Association of Housewives.
2311 **924** 100 pf. multicoloured 1·00 35

**925** Collection Box

**1990.** 125th Anniv of German Lifeboat Institution.
2312 **925** 60 pf. multicoloured .. 60 20

**926** Thurn and Taxis Palace, Frankfurt

**1990.** Europa. Post Office Buildings. Mult.
2313 60 pf. Type **926** .. .. 60 20
2314 100 pf. Postal Giro Office, Frankfurt .. .. 1·00 35

**927** St. Philip's Church, Protestant Church Flag and Candle Flames

**1990.** Centenary of Rummelsberg Diaconal Institution.
2315 **927** 100 pf. multicoloured 1·00 35

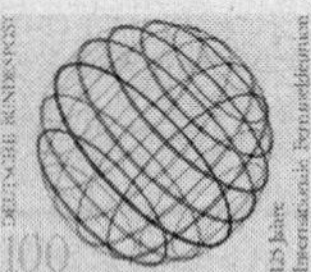

**928** Leuschner **929** Globe

**1990.** Birth Centenary of Wilhelm Leuschner (trade unionist and member of anti-Hitler Resistance).
2316 **928** 100 pf. black and lilac 1·00 35

**1990.** 125th Anniv of I.T.U.
2317 **929** 100 pf. multicoloured 1·00 35

**930** National Colours and Students

**1990.** 175th Anniv of German Students' Fraternity and of their Colours (now national colours).
2318 **930** 100 pf. multicoloured 1·00 35

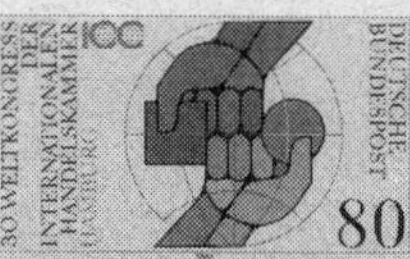


**931** Hands exchanging Money and Goods

**1990.** 30th World Congress of International Chamber of Commerce, Hamburg.
2319 **931** 80 pf. multicoloured .. 70 25

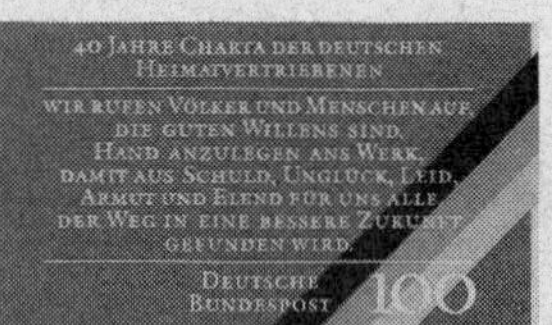


**932** Closing Sentence of Charter

**1990.** 40th Anniv of Expelled Germans Charter.
2320 **932** 100 pf. multicoloured 90 30

**934** Claudius

**935** Mail Motor Wagon, 1900

**1990.** 250th Birth Anniv of Matthias Claudius (writer).
2322 **934** 100 pf. blue, blk & red 1·10 30

**1990.** Humanitarian Relief Funds. Posts and Telecommunications. Multicoloured.
2323 60 pf + 30 pf. Type **935** .. 1·00 75
2324 80 pf. + 35 pf. Telephone exchange, 1890 .. 1·25 90
2325 100 pf. + 50 pf. Parcel sorting office, 1900 .. 1·40 1·25

**936** "German Unity" and National Colours

**1990.** Reunification of Germany.
2326 **936** 50 pf. blk, red & yell 60 15
2327 100 pf. blk, red & yell 1·25 30

**937** Schliemann and Lion Gate, Mycenae

**1990.** Death Centenary of Heinrich Schliemann (archaeologist).
2328 **937** 60 pf. multicoloured .. 70 20

**938** Penny Black, Bavaria 1 k. and West Germany 1989 100 pf. Stamps

**1990.** Stamp Day. 150th Anniv of the Penny Black.
2329 **938** 100 pf. multicoloured 1·25 30

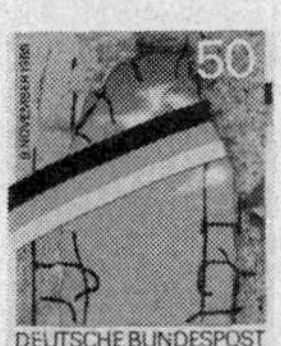


**939** National Colours spanning Breach in Wall

**940** Angel with Candles

**1990.** 1st Anniv of Opening of Berlin Wall.
2330 50 pf. Type **939** .. .. 50 15
2331 100 pf. Brandenburg Gate and crowd .. .. 1·00 30

**1990.** Christmas. Multicoloured.
2333 50 pf. + 20 pf. Type **940** .. 90 60
2334 60 pf. + 30 pf. Figure of man smoking .. .. 1·10 70
2335 70 pf. + 30 pf. "Soldier" nutcrackers .. .. 1·25 85
2336 100 pf. + 50 pf. Tinsel angel .. .. .. 1·75 1·25

**941** Kathe Dorsch in "Mrs. Warren's Profession"

**942** View of City

**1990.** Birth Centenary of Kathe Dorsch (actress).
2337 **941** 100 pf. violet and red 1·00 30

**1991.** 750th Anniv of Hanover.
2338 **942** 60 pf. multicoloured .. 60 20

**943** "Three Golden Circles with a Full Circle in Blue" (relief in wood)

**944** Miniature from 13th-century French Code

**1991.** Birth Centenary of Erich Buchholz (artist).
2339 **943** 60 pf. multicoloured .. 50 20

**1991.** 750th Anniv of Promulgation of Pharmaceutical Ethics in Germany.
2340 **944** 100 pf. multicoloured 90 30

**945** Brandenburg Gate (from "Old Engravings of Berlin")

**1991.** Bicentenary of Brandenburg Gate.
2341 **945** 100 pf. blk, red & grey 90 30

**946** Eucken

**947** Globe and "25" (poster)

**1991.** Birth Centenary of Walter Eucken (economist).
2342 **946** 100 pf. multicoloured 90 30

**1991.** 25th International Tourism Fair, Berlin.
2343 **947** 100 pf. multicoloured 90 30

**949** Weightlifting (World Championships)

**1991.** Sport Promotion Fund. Multicoloured.
2345 70 pf. + 30 pf. Type **949** .. 90 75
2346 100 pf. + 50 pf. Cycling (world championships) 1·25 1·10
2347 140 pf. + 60 pf. Basketball (centenary) .. .. 1·75 1·50
2348 170 pf. + 80 pf. Wrestling (European championships) .. .. .. 2·00 1·75

**950** Title Page of "Cautio Criminalis" (tract against witch trials), Langenfeld and Score of "Trutz-Nachtigall"

**1991.** 400th Birth Anniv of Friedrich Spee von Langenfeld (poet and human rights pioneer).
2349 **950** 100 pf. multicoloured 90 30

**951** Androsace

**952** Werth (attr. Wenzel Hollar)

**1991.** Plants in Rennsteiggarten (botanical garden), Oberhof. Multicoloured.
2350 30 pf. Type **951** .. .. 35 15
2351 50 pf. Primula .. .. 50 20
2352 80 pf. Gentian .. .. 70 25
2353 100 pf. Cranberry .. 90 30
2354 350 pf. Edelweiss .. 3·00 1·00

**1991.** 400th Birth Anniv of Jan von Werth (military commander).
2355 **952** 60 pf. multicoloured .. 50 20

**953** Windthorst

**955** Mountain Clouded Yellow

**954** Junkers F-13, 1930

**1991.** Death Centenary of Ludwig Windthorst (politician).
2356 **953** 100 pf. multicoloured 90 30

**1991.** Historic Mail Aircraft. Multicoloured.
2357 30 pf. Type **954** .. .. 40 20
2358 50 pf. Hans Grade's monoplane, 1909 .. 60 30
2359 100 pf. Fokker F.III, 1922 1·00 40
2360 165 pf. Airship "Graf Zeppelin", 1928 .. 1·40 60

**1991.** Youth Welfare. Endangered Butterflies. Multicoloured.
2361 30 pf. + 15 pf. Type **955** .. 40 40
2362 50 pf. + 25 pf. Poplar admiral .. .. 60 60
2363 60 pf. + 30 pf. Purple emperor .. .. 70 60
2364 70 pf. + 30 pf. Violet copper .. .. 80 70
2365 80 pf. + 35 pf. Swallowtail 90 80
2366 90 pf. + 45 pf. Small apollo 1·00 90
2367 100 pf. + 50 pf. Moorland clouded yellow .. 1·25 1·00
2368 140 pf. + 60 pf. Large copper .. .. 1·60 1·40

See also Nos. 2449/53.

**956** Academy Building, 1830

**1991.** Bicentenary of Choral Academy, Berlin.
2369 **956** 100 pf. multicoloured 90 30

**957** Typesetting School, 1875

**1991.** 125th Anniv of Lette Foundation (institute for professional training of women).
2370 **957** 100 pf. multicoloured 90 30

**958** Battle (detail of miniature, Schlackenwerth Codex, 1350)

**1991.** 750th Anniv of Battle of Legnica.
2371 **958** 100 pf. multicoloured 90 40

**959** Arms

**1991.** 700th Anniv of Granting of Charters to Six Towns of Trier.
2372 **959** 60 pf. multicoloured 50 20

**960** Speeding Train

**1991.** Inauguration of Inter-City Express (ICE) Railway Service.
2373 **960** 60 pf. multicoloured 50 20

**961** "ERS-1" European Remote Sensing Satellite

**1991.** Europa. Europe in Space. Mult.
2374 60 pf. Type **961** .. .. 50 15
2375 100 pf. "Kopernikus" telecommunications satellite 90 40

**962** Reger and Organ Pipes

**963** Ruffs

**1991.** 75th Death Anniv of Max Reger (composer).
2376 **962** 100 pf. multicoloured 90 30

**1991.** Seabirds. Multicoloured.
2390 60 pf. Type **963** .. .. 75 25
2391 80 pf. Little terns .. 95 40
2392 100 pf. Brent geese .. 1·25 45
2393 140 pf. White-tailed sea eagles .. .. .. 1·75 1·40

**964** Wilhelm August Lampadius (gas pioneer)

**1991.** 18th World Gas Congress, Berlin. Each black and blue.
2394 60 pf. Type **964** .. .. 50 20
2395 100 pf. Gas street lamp, Berlin .. .. .. 90 30

**965** Wallot (after Franz Wurbel) and Reichstag Building, Berlin

**1991.** 150th Birth Anniv of Paul Wallot (architect).

| | | | | |
|---|---|---|---|---|
| 2396 | **965** | 100 pf. multicoloured | 90 | 40 |

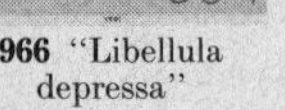

**966** "Libellula depressa" **967** Hand clutching Cloak

**1991.** Dragonflies. Multicoloured.

| | | | |
|---|---|---|---|
| 2397 | 50 pf. Type **966** .. .. | 50 | 20 |
| 2398 | 60 pf. Type **966** .. .. | 60 | 40 |
| 2399 | 60 pf. "Sympetrum sanguineum" .. .. | 60 | 40 |
| 2400 | 60 pf. "Cordulegaster boltonii" .. .. | 60 | 40 |
| 2401 | 60 pf. "Aeshna viridis" .. | 60 | 40 |
| 2402 | 70 pf. As No. 2399 .. | 70 | 30 |
| 2403 | 80 pf. As No. 2400 .. | 80 | 40 |
| 2404 | 100 pf. As No. 2401 .. | 1·00 | 50 |

**1991.** 40th Anniv of Geneva Convention on Refugees.

| | | | | |
|---|---|---|---|---|
| 2405 | **967** | 100 pf. lilac and black | 90 | 30 |

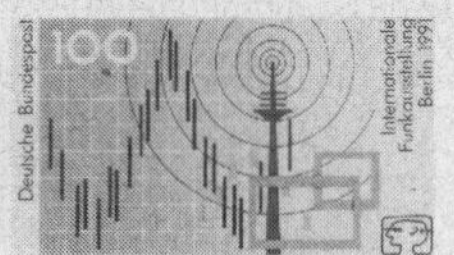

**968** Radio Waves and Mast

**1991.** International Radio Exhibition, Berlin.

| | | | | |
|---|---|---|---|---|
| 2406 | **968** | 100 pf. multicoloured | 90 | 30 |

**969** Pedestrians and Traffic

**1991.** Road Safety Campaign.

| | | | | |
|---|---|---|---|---|
| 2407 | **969** | 100 pf. multicoloured | 90 | 40 |

**971** August Heinrich Hoffmann von Fallersleben (lyricist) and Third Verse

**1991.** 150th Anniv of "Song of the Germans" (national anthem).

| | | | | |
|---|---|---|---|---|
| 2409 | **971** | 100 pf. red, blk & grn | 1·00 | 30 |

**972** Thadden-Trieglaff

**1991.** Birth Cent of Reinold von Thadden-Trieglaff (founder of German Protestant Convention).

| | | | | |
|---|---|---|---|---|
| 2410 | **972** | 100 pf. multicoloured | 1·00 | 30 |

## MORE DETAILED LISTS

are given in the Stanley Gibbons Catalogues referred to in the country headings.
For lists of current volumes see Introduction.

**973** Transmission Test between Lauffen-on-Neckar and Frankfurt-on-Main

**1991.** Centenary of Three-phase Energy Transmission.

| | | | | |
|---|---|---|---|---|
| 2411 | **973** | 170 pf. multicoloured | 1·75 | 60 |

**975** Albers in "The Winner"

**1991.** Birth Centenary of Hans Albers (actor).

| | | | | |
|---|---|---|---|---|
| 2413 | **975** | 100 pf. multicoloured | 1·00 | 30 |

**976** Harbour

**1991.** 275th Anniv of Rhine-Ruhr Port, Duisburg.

| | | | | |
|---|---|---|---|---|
| 2414 | **976** | 100 pf. multicoloured | 1·25 | 35 |

**977** Bethel Post Office **978** Postal Delivery in Spreewald Region

**1991.** Humanitarian Relief Funds. Postal Buildings. Multicoloured.

| | | | |
|---|---|---|---|
| 2415 | 30 pf. + 15 pf. Type **977** .. | 50 | 40 |
| 2416 | 60 pf. + 30 pf. Budingen post station .. .. | 80 | 70 |
| 2417 | 70 pf. + 30 pf. Stralsund post office .. .. | 1·10 | 90 |
| 2418 | 80 pf. + 35 pf. Lauscha post office .. .. | 1·40 | 1·00 |
| 2419 | 100 pf. + 50 pf. Bonn post office .. .. .. | 1·75 | 1·40 |
| 2420 | 140 pf. + 60 pf. Weilburg post office .. .. | 2·10 | 1·75 |

**1991.** Stamp Day.

| | | | | |
|---|---|---|---|---|
| 2421 | **978** | 100 pf. multicoloured | 1·25 | 40 |

**979** "Bird Monument" (detail) **980** "Portrait of the Dancer Anita Berber"

**1991.** Birth Centenary of Max Ernst (painter).

| | | | | |
|---|---|---|---|---|
| 2422 | **979** | 100 pf. multicoloured | 1·00 | 30 |

**1991.** Birth Cent of Otto Dix (painter). Mult.

| | | | |
|---|---|---|---|
| 2423 | 60 pf. Type **980** .. .. | 75 | 25 |
| 2424 | 100 pf. "Self-portrait in Right Profile" .. | 1·25 | 30 |

**981** "The Violinist and the Water Sprite" **982** Angel (detail of "The Annunciation")

**1991.** Sorbian Legends. Multicoloured.

| | | | |
|---|---|---|---|
| 2425 | 60 pf. Type **981** .. .. | 70 | 15 |
| 2426 | 100 pf. "The Midday Woman and the Woman from Nochten" | 1·00 | 30 |

**1991.** Christmas. Works by Martin Schongauer. Multicoloured.

| | | | |
|---|---|---|---|
| 2427 | 60 pf. + 30 pf. Type **982** .. | 90 | 70 |
| 2428 | 70 pf. + 30 pf. Virgin Mary (detail of "The Annunciation") .. | 1·25 | 90 |
| 2429 | 80 pf. + 35 pf. Angel (detail of "Madonna in a Rose Garden") .. | 1·40 | 90 |
| 2430 | 100 pf. + 50 pf. "Nativity" | 2·00 | 1·40 |

**983** Leber **984** Nelly Sachs

**1991.** Birth Cent of Julius Leber (politician).

| | | | | |
|---|---|---|---|---|
| 2431 | **983** | 100 pf. multicoloured | 1·25 | 30 |

**1991.** Birth Centenary of Nelly Sachs (writer).

| | | | | |
|---|---|---|---|---|
| 2432 | **984** | 100 pf. dp violet & vio | 1·00 | 30 |

**986** Base of William I Monument and City Silhouette

**1992.** 2000th Anniv of Koblenz.

| | | | | |
|---|---|---|---|---|
| 2434 | **986** | 60 pf. multicoloured .. | 80 | 20 |

**987** Niemoller **988** Child's Eyes

**1992.** Birth Centenary of Martin Niemoller (theologian).

| | | | | |
|---|---|---|---|---|
| 2435 | **987** | 100 pf. multicoloured | 1·00 | 30 |

**1992.** 25th Anniv of Terre des Hommes (child welfare organization) in Germany.

| | | | | |
|---|---|---|---|---|
| 2436 | **988** | 100 pf. multicoloured | 1·00 | 30 |

**989** Arms of Baden-Wurttemberg

**1992.** Lander of the Federal Republic.

| | | | | |
|---|---|---|---|---|
| 2437 | **989** | 100 pf. multicoloured | 1·50 | 40 |

See also Nos. 2448, 2465, 2470, 2474, 2479, 2506, 2526, 2527, 2534, 2539, 2556, 2567, 2580, 2584 and 2597.

**990** Fencing **991** Honegger and Score of Ballet "Semiramis"

**1992.** Sport Promotion Fund. Olympic Games, Albertville and Barcelona. Mult.

| | | | |
|---|---|---|---|
| 2438 | 60 pf. + 30 pf. Type **990** .. | 1·00 | 70 |
| 2439 | 80 pf. + 40 pf. Rowing eight .. .. .. | 1·40 | 1·00 |
| 2440 | 100 pf. + 50 pf. Dressage | 1·75 | 1·25 |
| 2441 | 170 pf. + 80 pf. Skiing (slalom) .. .. | 2·40 | 1·50 |

**1992.** Birth Centenary of Arthur Honegger (composer).

| | | | | |
|---|---|---|---|---|
| 2442 | **991** | 100 pf. black & brown | 1·00 | 30 |

**992** Zeppelin and "Graf Zeppelin"

**1992.** 75th Death Anniv of Ferdinand von Zeppelin (airship manufacturer).

| | | | | |
|---|---|---|---|---|
| 2443 | **992** | 165 pf. multicoloured | 2·40 | 60 |

**993** Kiel City and Harbour

**1992.** 750th Anniv of Kiel.

| | | | | |
|---|---|---|---|---|
| 2444 | **993** | 60 pf. multicoloured .. | 65 | 25 |

**994** Andreas Marggraf, Beet, Franz Achard and Carl Scheibler

**1992.** 125th Anniv of Berlin Sugar Institute.

| | | | | |
|---|---|---|---|---|
| 2445 | **994** | 100 pf. multicoloured | 90 | 35 |

The stamp depicts the discoverer of beet sugar, the founder of the beet sugar industry and the founder of the Institute respectively.

**995** Horses and Renz **996** Adenauer

**1992.** Death Centenary of Ernst Jakob Renz (circus director).

| | | | | |
|---|---|---|---|---|
| 2446 | **995** | 100 pf. multicoloured | 90 | 35 |

**1992.** 25th Death Anniv of Konrad Adenauer (Chancellor, 1949–63).

| | | | | |
|---|---|---|---|---|
| 2447 | **996** | 100 pf. brown and cinnamon .. .. | 1·00 | 35 |

**1992.** Lander of the Federal Republic. As T **989**. Multicoloured.

| | | | |
|---|---|---|---|
| 2448 | 100 pf. Bavaria .. .. | 85 | 40 |

**1992.** Youth Welfare. Endangered Moths. As T **955**. Multicoloured.

| | | | |
|---|---|---|---|
| 2449 | 60 pf. + 30 pf. Purple tiger moth .. .. .. | 1·00 | 1·00 |
| 2450 | 70 pf. + 30 pf. Hawk moth | 1·10 | 1·10 |
| 2451 | 80 pf. + 40 pf. "Noctuidae sp." .. .. .. | 1·25 | 1·25 |
| 2452 | 100 pf. + 50 pf. Tiger moth | 1·40 | 1·40 |
| 2453 | 170 pf. + 80 pf. "Arichanna melanaria" .. .. | 2·00 | 2·00 |

**997** Schall

**1992.** 400th Birth Anniv of Adam Schall (missionary astronomer).

| | | | | |
|---|---|---|---|---|
| 2454 | **997** | 140 pf. black, yell & bl | 1·25 | 55 |

**998** Cathedral and St. Severus's Church **999** Woodcut from 1493 Edition of Columbus's Letters

**1992.** 1250th Anniv of Erfurt.

| | | | | |
|---|---|---|---|---|
| 2455 | **998** | 60 pf. multicoloured .. | 60 | 25 |

**1992.** Europa. 500th Anniv of Discovery of America by Columbus. Multicoloured.
2456 60 pf. Type **999** .. .. 65 25
2457 100 pf. "Rene de Laudonniere and Chief Athore" (Jacques le Moyne de Morgues, 1564) .. .. .. 90 40

**1000** "Consecration of St. Ludgerus" (from "Vita Liudgeri" by Altfridus)

**1001** Arithmetic Sum

**1992.** 1250th Birth Anniv of St. Ludgerus (first Bishop of Munster).
2458 **1000** 100 pf. multicoloured 85 35

**1992.** 500th Birth Anniv of Adam Riese (mathematician).
2459 **1001** 100 pf. multicoloured 90 40

**1002** Order of Merit

**1992.** 150th Anniv of Civil Class of Order of Merit (for scientific or artistic achievement).
2460 **1002** 100 pf. multicoloured 85 35

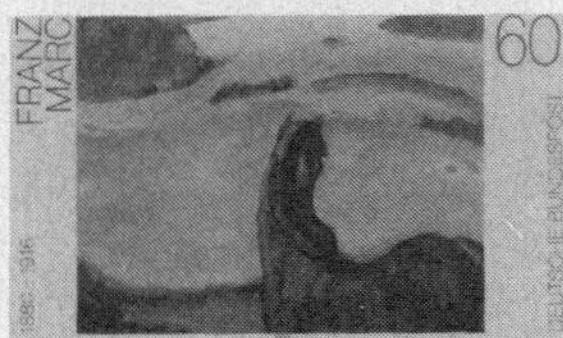

**1003** "Landscape with Horse" (Franz Marc)

**1992.** 20th-century German Paintings (1st series). Multicoloured.
2461 60 pf. Type **1003** .. 50 25
2462 100 pf. "Fashion Shop" (August Macke) .. 85 40
2463 170 pf. "Murnau with Rainbow" (Wassily Kandinsky) .. .. 1·40 65
See also Nos. 2507/9, 2590/2, 2615/17 and 2704/6.

**1004** Lichtenberg

**1005** Rainforest

**1992.** 250th Birth Anniv of Georg Christoph Lichtenberg (physicist and essayist).
2464 **1004** 100 pf. multicoloured 90 40

**1992.** Lander of the Federal Republic. As T **989**. Multicoloured.
2465 100 pf. Berlin .. .. 85 40

**1992.** "Save the Tropical Rain Forest".
2466 **1005** 100 pf.+50 pf. mult 1·25 1·10
The premium was for the benefit of environmental projects.

**1006** Garden

**1992.** Leipzig Botanical Garden.
2467 **1006** 60 pf. multicoloured 60 25

**1007** Stylized House and Globe

**1992.** 17th International Home Economics Congress, Hanover.
2468 **1007** 100 pf. multicoloured 90 40

**1008** Family

**1009** "Assumption of the Virgin Mary" (Rohr Monastery Church)

**1992.** Family Life.
2469 **1008** 100 pf. multicoloured 90 40

**1992.** Lander of the Federal Republic. As T **989**. Multicoloured.
2470 100 pf. Brandenburg .. 85 40

**1992.** 300th Birth Anniv of Egid Quirin Asam (sculptor).
2471 **1009** 60 pf. multicoloured 60 25

**1010** Opera House (Georg von Knobelsdorff)

**1011** Masked Actors

**1992.** 250th Anniv of German State Opera House, Berlin.
2472 **1010** 80 pf. multicoloured 75 35

**1992.** Centenary of German Amateur Theatres Federation.
2473 **1011** 100 pf. multicoloured 90 40

**1992.** Lander of the Federal Republic. As T **989**. Multicoloured.
2474 100 pf. Bremen .. .. 85 40

**1012** Globe

**1013** 1890 Pendant and 1990 Clock

**1992.** 500th Anniv of Martin Behaim's Terrestrial Globe.
2475 **1012** 60 pf. multicoloured 65 25

**1992.** 225th Anniv of Jewellery and Watch-making in Pforzheim.
2476 **1013** 100 pf. multicoloured 90 40

**1014** Bergengruen (after Hanni Fries)

**1015** Neue Holzbrucke Bridge, nr. Essing

**1992.** Birth Centenary of Werner Bergengruen (writer).
2477 **1014** 100 pf. grey, bl & blk 90 40

**1992.** Inauguration of Main–Donau Canal.
2478 **1015** 100 pf. multicoloured 90 40

**1992.** Lander of the Federal Republic. As T **989**. Multicoloured.
2479 100 pf. Hamburg .. 85 40

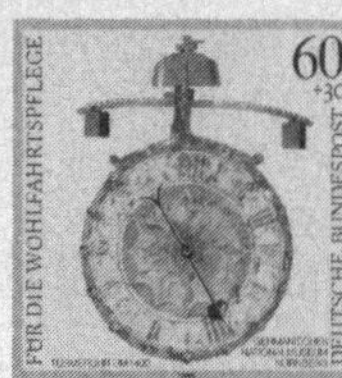

**1016** Turret Clock, 1400

**1992.** Humanitarian Relief Funds. Clocks. Multicoloured.
2480 60 pf.+30 pf. Type **1016** 85 85
2481 70 pf.+30 pf. Astronomical mantel clock, 1738 1·00 1·00
2482 80 pf.+40 pf. Flute clock, 1790 .. .. 1·10 1·10
2483 100 pf.+50 pf. Figurine clock, 1580 .. .. 1·25 1·25
2484 170 pf.+80 pf. Table clock, 1550 .. .. 1·90 1·90

**1017** Distler and Score of "We Praise Our Lord Jesus Christ"

**1018** Balloon Post

**1992.** 50th Death Anniv of Hugo Distler (composer).
2485 **1017** 100 pf. black & violet 90 40

**1992.** Stamp Day.
2486 **1018** 100 pf. multicoloured 90 40

**1019** Otto Engine, 1892, Cogwheel and Laser Beam

**1992.** Centenary of German Plant and Machine Builders Association.
2487 **1019** 170 pf. multicoloured 1·40 65

**1020** "Adoration of the Magi"

**1021** Blucher (after Simon Meister)

**1992.** Christmas. Carvings by Franz Maidburg, St. Anne's Church, Annaberg-Buchholz. Multicoloured.
2488 60 pf.+30 pf. Type **1020** 75 75
2489 100 pf.+50 pf. "Birth of Christ" .. .. 1·10 1·10

**1992.** 250th Birth Anniv of Field Marshal Gebhard Leberecht von Blucher.
2490 **1021** 100 pf. multicoloured 90 40

**1022** Werner von Siemens

**1023** Klepper

**1992.** Death Centenary of Werner von Siemens (industrialist).
2491 **1022** 100 pf. brn & dp brn 90 40

**1992.** 50th Death Anniv of Jochen Klepper (writer).
2492 **1023** 100 pf. multicoloured 90 40

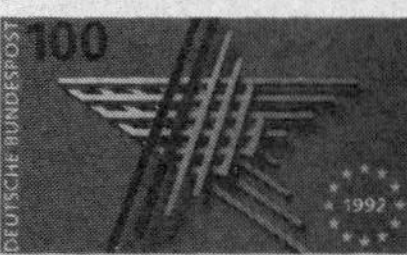

**1024** Star in German Colours

**1992.** European Single Market.
2493 **1024** 100 pf. multicoloured 90 40

**1025** Cathedral and Uberwasser Church

**1993.** 1200th Anniv of Munster.
2494 **1025** 60 pf. multicoloured 60 35

**1026** Newton, Sketch of Refraction of Light and Formula

**1993.** 350th Birth Anniv of Sir Isaac Newton (scientist).
2495 **1026** 100 pf. multicoloured 90 40

**1027** Route Map and Compass Rose

**1028** Emblem and Safety Stripes

**1993.** 125th Anniv of North German Naval Observatory, Hamburg.
2496 **1027** 100 pf. multicoloured 90 40

**1993.** European Year of Health, Hygiene and Safety in the Workplace.
2497 **1028** 100 pf. bl, yell & blk 90 40

**1029** Wires and Wall Socket forming House

**1030** Ski-jumping Hill, Garmisch-Partenkirchen

**1993.** Centenary of German Association of Electrical Engineers.
2498 **1029** 170 pf. multicoloured 1·40 65

**1993.** Sport Promotion Fund. German Olympic Venues. Multicoloured.
2499 60 pf.+30 pf. Type **1030** 85 85
2500 80 pf.+40 pf. Olympia-park, Munich .. .. 1·00 1·00
2501 100 pf.+50 pf. Olympic Stadium, Berlin .. 1·10 1·10
2502 170 pf.+80 pf. Olympic Harbour, Kiel .. 2·00 2·00

**1031** Stylised Sound Vibration

**1993.** 250th Anniv of Leipzig Gewandhaus Orchestra.
2503 **1031** 100 pf. gold and black 90 40

**1032** Statue of St. John and Charles Bridge, Prague

**1993.** 600th Death Anniv of St. John of Nepomuk.
2504 **1032** 100 pf. multicoloured 90 40

**1033** Diagram explaining New Postcodes

**1993.** Introduction of Five-digit Postcode System.
2505 **1033** 100 pf. multicoloured 90 40

**1993.** Lander of the Federal Republic. As T **989**. Multicoloured.
2506 100 pf. Hesse .. .. 85 40

**1993.** 20th-century German Paintings (2nd series). As T **1003**. Multicoloured.
2507 100 pf. multicoloured .. 90 40
2508 100 pf. black, grey & mve 90 40
2509 100 pf. multicoloured .. 90 40
DESIGNS: No. 2507, "Cafe" (George Grosz); 2508, "Sea and Sun" (Otto Pankok); 2509, "Audience" (Andreas Paul Weber).

**1034** Abbeys

**1993.** 900th Anniversaries of Maria Laach and Bursfelde Benedictine Abbeys.
2510 **1034** 80 pf. multicoloured 60 30

**1035** Alpine Longhorn Beetle

**1993.** Youth Welfare. Endangered Beetles. Multicoloured.
2511 80 pf. + 40 f. Type **1035** .. 1·10 1·10
2512 80 pf. + 40 pf. Rose chafer 1·10 1·10
2513 100 pf. + 50 pf. Stag beetle 1·40 1·40
2514 100 pf. + 50 pf. Tiger beetle .. .. .. 1·40 1·40
2515 200 pf. + 50 pf. Cockchafer 1·90 1·90

**1036** Plants

**1993.** 5th International Horticultural Show, Stuttgart.
2516 **1036** 100 pf. multicoloured 90 40

**1037** Horse Race

**1993.** 125th Anniv of Hoppegarten Race-course.
2517 **1037** 80 pf. multicoloured 60 30

**1038** "Storage Place" (Joseph Beuys)

**1993.** Europa. Contemporary Art. Mult.
2518 80 pf. Type **1038** .. 65 30
2519 100 pf. "Homage to the Square" (Josef Albers) 85 40

**1039** Church and Pupils

**1993.** 450th Anniv of Pforta School.
2520 **1039** 100 pf. multicoloured 90 40

**1040** Students, Flag, City Hall and Castle

**1993.** 125th Anniv of Coburg Association of University Student Unions.
2521 **1040** 100 pf. blk, grn & red 90 40

**1041** "Hohentwiel" (lake steamer) and Flags

**1993.** Lake Constance European Region.
2522 **1041** 100 pf. multicoloured 90 40

**1042** "Old Market—View of St. Nicholas's Church" (detail, Ferdinand von Arnim)

**1043** Holderlin (after Franz Hiemer)

**1993.** Millenary of Potsdam.
2523 **1042** 80 pf. multicoloured 90 40

**1993.** 150th Death Anniv of Friedrich Holderlin (poet).
2524 **1043** 100 pf. multicoloured 90 40

**1044** "If People can fly to the Moon, why can't they do anything about so many Children dying?"

**1993.** 40th Anniv of German United Nations Children's Fund Committee.
2525 **1044** 100 pf. multicoloured 90 40

**1993.** Lander of the Federal Republic. As T **989**. Multicoloured.
2526 100 pf. Mecklenburg–Vorpommern .. .. 85 40

**1993.** Lander of the Federal Republic. As T **989**. Multicoloured.
2527 100 pf. Lower Saxony .. 85 40

**1045** Fallada (after E. O. Plauen)

**1993.** Birth Centenary of Hans Fallada (writer).
2528 **1045** 100 pf. grn, brn & red 90 40

**1046** Harz Mountain Range

**1993.** Landscapes (1st series). Multicoloured.
2529 100 pf. Type **1046** .. 85 40
2530 100 pf. Rugen .. .. 85 40
2531 100 pf. Hohe Rhon .. 85 40
See also Nos. 2585/8, 2646/9 and 2709/12.

**1047** Stages of Manufacture

**1993.** 250th Death Anniv of Mathias Klotz (violin maker).
2532 **1047** 80 pf. multicoloured 65 30

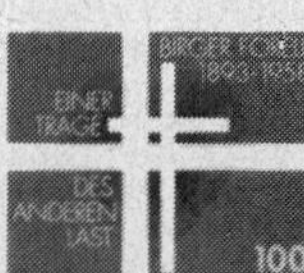


**1048** George as Gotz von Berlichingen in Goethe's "Urgotz"

**1050** Swedish Flag, Heart and Cross

**1993.** Birth Centenary of Heinrich George (actor).
2533 **1048** 100 pf. multicoloured 85 40

**1993.** Lander of the Federal Republic. As T **989**. Multicoloured.
2534 100 pf. Nordrhein–Westfalen .. .. 85 40

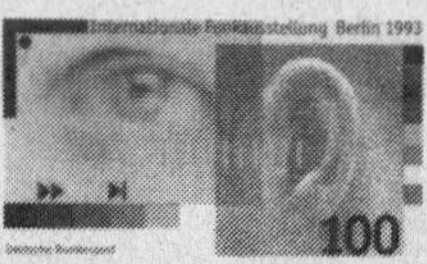


**1049** Digitalised Eye and Ear

**1993.** International Radio Exhibition, Berlin.
2535 **1049** 100 pf. multicoloured 85 40

**1993.** Birth Centenary of Birger Forell (founder of Espelkamp (town for war refugees)).
2536 **1050** 100 pf. yellow, ultramarine & blue 85 40

**1051** "Tuledu Bridge" (engraving)

**1993.** Birth Centenary of Hans Leip (writer and artist).
2537 **1051** 100 pf. black, red & bl 85 40

**1993.** Lander of the Federal Republic. As T **989**. Multicoloured.
2539 100 pf. Rheinland–Pfalz 85 40

**1053** Postman delivering Letter

**1993.** Stamp Day.
2540 **1053** 100 pf. + 50 pf. mult 1·10 1·10

**1054** "Swan Lake"

**1993.** Death Centenary of Pyotr Tchaikovsky (composer).
2541 **1054** 80 pf. multicoloured 65 30

**1055** Fohr, Schleswig-Holstein

**1056** St. Jadwiga (miniature, Schlackenwerther Codex)

**1993.** Humanitarian Relief Funds. Traditional Costumes (1st series). Mult.
2542 80 pf. + 40 pf. Type **1055** 1·00 1·00
2543 80 pf. + 40 pf. Rugen, Mecklenburg–Vorpommern .. .. 1·00 1·00
2544 100 pf. + 50 pf. Oberndorf, Bavaria .. .. 1·40 1·40
2545 100 pf. + 50 pf. Schwalm, Hesse .. .. 1·40 1·40
2546 200 pf. + 40 pf. Ernstroda, Thuringia .. .. 2·00 2·00
See also Nos. 2598/2602.

**1993.** 750th Death Anniv of St. Jadwiga of Silesia.
2547 **1056** 100 pf. multicoloured 85 40

**1058** image: 

**1057** Reinhardt on Stage

**1058** Brandt

**1993.** 50th Death Anniv of Max Reinhardt (theatrical producer).
2548 **1057** 100 pf. blk, brn & red 85 40

**1993.** 80th Birth Anniv of Willy Brandt (statesman).
2549 **1058** 100 pf. multicoloured 85 40

**1059** Monteverdi

**1993.** 350th Death Anniv of Claudio Monteverdi (composer).
2550 **1059** 100 pf. multicoloured 85 40

**1060** Paracelsus (after Augustin Hirschvogel)

**1061** "Adoration of the Magi"

**1993.** 500th Birth Anniv of Paracelsus (physician and philosopher).
2551 **1060** 100 pf. ochre, brown and green .. 85 40

**1993.** Christmas. Carvings from Altar Triptych, Blaubeuren Minster. Mult.
2552 80 pf.+40 pf. Type **1061** 1·00 1·00
2553 100 pf.+50 pf. "Birth of Christ" .. .. 1·10 1·10

**1062** Quayside Buildings, Town Hall and St. Cosmas's Church

**1994.** Millenary of Stade.
2554 **1062** 80 pf. red, brown & bl 65 35

**1063** "FAMILIE"

**1994.** International Year of the Family.
2555 **1063** 100 pf. multicoloured 85 40

**1994.** Lander of the Federal Republic. As T **989**. Multicoloured.
2556 100 pf. Saarland .. .. 85 40

**1064** Hertz and Electromagnetic Waves

**1994.** Death Centenary of Heinrich Hertz (physicist).
2557 **1064** 200 pf. black, red and drab .. .. 2·00 1·00

**1065** Frankfurt am Main

**1994.** 1200th Anniv of Frankfurt am Main.
2558 **1065** 80 pf. multicoloured 70 35

**1066** Ice Skating

**1994.** Sport Promotion Fund. Sporting Events and Anniversaries. Multicoloured.
2559 80 pf.+40 pf. Type **1066** (Winter Olympic Games, Lillehammer, Norway) .. .. 1·10 1·10
2560 100 pf.+50 pf. Football and trophy (World Cup Football Championship, U.S.A.) .. .. 1·40 1·40
2561 100 pf.+50 pf. Flame (cent of International Olympic Committee) .. 1·40 1·40
2562 200 pf.+80 pf. Skier (Winter Paralympic Games, Lillehammer) 2·50 2·50

**1067** Cathedral, St. Michael's Church and Castle

**1994.** 1250th Anniv of Fulda.
2563 **1067** 80 pf. multicoloured 70 35

**1068** Council Emblem

**1994.** Cent of Federation of German Women's Associations–German Women's Council.
2564 **1068** 100 pf. blk, red & yell 85 40

**1069** Members' Flags as Stars

**1994.** 4th Direct Elections to European Parliament.
2565 **1069** 100 pf. multicoloured 85 40

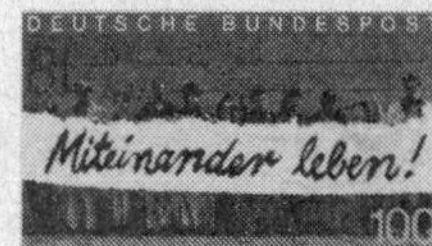


**1070** People holding Banner

**1994.** "Living Together" (integration of foreign workers in Germany).
2566 **1070** 100 pf. multicoloured 85 40

**1994.** Lander of the Federal Republic. As T **989**. Multicoloured.
2567 100 pf. Saxony .. .. 85 40

**1071** Johnny Head-in-the-Air

**1994.** Youth Welfare. Death Centenary of Heinrich Hoffmann (writer). Designs illustrating characters from "Slovenly Peter". Multicoloured.
2568 80 pf.+40 pf. Type **1071** 1·10 1·10
2569 80 pf.+40 pf. Little Pauline .. .. 1·10 1·10
2570 100 pf.+50 pf. Naughty Friederich .. .. 1·25 1·25
2571 100 pf.+50 pf. Slovenly Peter .. .. .. 1·25 1·25
2572 200 pf.+80 pf. Fidget-Philipp .. .. 2·50 2·50

**1072** Frauenkirche

**1994.** 500th Anniv of Frauenkirche, Munich.
2573 **1072** 100 pf. multicoloured 85 40

**1073** Resistor and Formula

**1074** Pfitzner (after Emil Orlik)

**1994.** Europa. Discoveries. Multicoloured.
2574 80 pf. Type **1073** (Ohm's Law) .. .. .. 70 35
2575 100 pf. Radiation from black body and formula (Max Planck's Quantum Theory) .. 85 40

**1994.** 125th Birth Anniv of Hans Pfitzner (composer).
2576 **1074** 100 pf. deep blue, blue and red .. 85 40

**1076** Spandau Castle

**1994.** 400th Anniv of Spandau Castle.
2578 **1076** 80 pf. multicoloured 70 35

**1077** Village Sign showing Society Emblem

**1994.** Centenary of Herzogsagmuhle (Society for the Domestic Missions welfare village).
2579 **1077** 100 pf. multicoloured 85 40

**1994.** Lander of the Federal Republic. As T **989**. Multicoloured.
2580 100 pf. Saxony-Anhalt .. 85 40

**1078** Heart inside Square

**1079** Friedrich II (13th-century miniature, "Book of Falcons")

**1994.** Environmental Protection.
2581 **1078** 100 pf.+50 pf. green and black .. 1·25 1·25

**1994.** 800th Birth Anniv of Emperor Friedrich II.
2582 **1079** 400 pf. multicoloured 3·50 3·50

**1994.** Lander of the Federal Republic. As T **989**. Multicoloured.
2584 100 pf. Schleswig-Holstein 85 40

**1994.** Landscapes (2nd series). As T **1046**. Multicoloured.
2585 100 pf. The Alps .. 85 40
2586 100 pf. Erzgebirge .. 85 40
2587 100 pf. Main valley .. 85 40
2588 100 pf. Mecklenburg lakes 85 40

**1081** Herder (after Anton Graff)

**1994.** 250th Birth Anniv of Johann Gottfried Herder (philosopher).
2589 **1081** 80 pf. multicoloured 70 35

**1994.** 20th-century German Paintings (3rd series). As T **1003**. Multicoloured.
2590 100 pf. "Maika" (Christian Schad) .. .. 85 40
2591 200 pf. "Dresden Landscape" (Erich Heckel) .. .. 1·75 85
2592 300 pf. "Aleksei Javlensky and Marianne Werefkin" (Gabriele Munter) .. .. 2·75 1·25

**1082** Early 20th-century Makonde Mask (Tanzania)

**1994.** 125th Anniv of Leipzig Ethnology Museum.
2593 **1082** 80 pf. multicoloured 70 30

**1083** Helmholtz, Eye and Colour Triangle

**1994.** Death Centenary of Hermann von Helmholtz (physicist).
2594 **1083** 100 pf. multicoloured 85 40

**1084** Richter

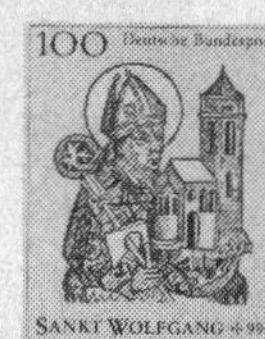

**1086** St. Wolfgang with Church Model (woodcut)

**1994.** Birth Cent of Willi Richter (President of Confederation of German Trade Unions).
2595 **1084** 100 pf. brown, purple and black .. 85 40

**1994.** Lander of the Federal Republic. As T **989**. Multicoloured.
2597 100 pf. Thuringia .. 85 40

**1994.** Humanitarian Relief Funds. Traditional Costumes (2nd series). As T **1055**. Multicoloured.
2598 80 pf.+40 pf. Buckeburg 1·10 1·10
2599 80 pf.+40 pf. Halle an der Saale .. .. .. 1·10 1·10
2600 100 pf.+50 pf. Minden .. 1·25 1·25
2601 100 pf.+50 pf. Hoyerswerda .. .. .. 1·25 1·25
2602 200 pf.+70 pf. Betzingen 2·40 2·40

**1994.** Death Millenary of St. Wolfgang, Bishop of Regensburg.
2603 **1086** 100 pf. gold, cream and black .. 85 40

**1087** Sachs

**1088** Spreewald Postman, 1900

**1994.** 500th Birth Anniv of Hans Sachs (mastersinger and poet).
2604 **1087** 100 pf. purple and green on greyish .. 85 40

**1994.** Stamp Day.
2605 **1088** 100 pf. multicoloured 85 40

**1089** Quedlinburg

**1090** "Adoration of the Magi"

**1994.** Millenary of Quedlinburg.
2606 **1089** 80 pf. multicoloured 70 35

**1994.** Christmas. 500th Death Anniv of Hans Memling (painter). Details of his triptych in St. John's Hospice, Bruges. Multicoloured.
2607 80 pf.+40 pf. Type **1090** 1·10 1·10
2608 100 pf.+50 pf. "Nativity" 1·25 1·25

**1091** Steuben and "Surrender of Cornwallis at Yorktown" (detail, John Trumbull)

**1994.** Death Bicentenary of Gen. Friedrich Wilhelm von Steuben (Inspector General of Washington's Army).
2609 **1091** 100 pf. multicoloured 85 40

**1092** Cemetery

**1994.** 75th Anniv of National Assn for the Preservation of German Graves Abroad.
2610 **1092** 100 pf. black and red 85 40

**1093** Obersuhl Checkpoint, 11 November 1989

**1994.** 5th Anniv of Opening of Borders between East and West Germany.
2611 **1093** 100 pf. multicoloured 85 40

**1094** Fontane (after Max Liebermann) and Lines from "Prussian Song"

**1095** Simson Fountain, Town Hall and St. Mary's and St. Salvator's Churches

**1994.** 175th Birth Anniv of Theodor Fontane (writer).
2612 **1094** 100 pf. green, black and mauve .. 85 40

**1995.** Millenary of Gera.
2613 **1095** 80 pf. multicoloured 70 35

**1096** Emperor Friedrich III, First Page of "Libellus" and Zur Munze (venue)

**1995.** 500th Anniv of Diet of Worms.
2614 **1096** 100 pf. black and red 85 40

**1995.** 20th-century German Paintings (4th series). As T **1003**. Multicoloured.
2615 100 pf. "The Water Tower, Bremen" (Franz Radziwill) .. .. 85 40
2616 200 pf. "Still Life with Cat" (Georg Schrimpf) 1·75 1·75
2617 300 pf. "Estate in Dangast" (Karl Schmidt-Rottluff) .. 2·75 2·75

**1097** Canoeing

**1098** Friedrich Wilhelm (after A. Romandon)

**1995.** Sport Promotion Fund. Multicoloured.
2618 80 pf. + 40 pf. Type **1097** (27th World Canoeing Championships, Duisburg) .. .. 1·10 1·10
2619 100 pf. + 50 pf. Hoop exercises (10th Int Gymnastics Festival, Berlin) .. .. 1·25 1·25
2620 100 pf. + 50 pf. Boxing (8th World Amateur Boxing Championships, Berlin) .. .. 1·25 1·25
2621 200 pf. + 80 pf. Volleyball (centenary) .. .. 2·50 2·50

**1995.** 375th Birth Anniv of Friedrich Wilhelm of Brandenburg, The Great Elector.
2622 **1098** 300 pf. multicoloured 2·75 2·75

**1099** Deed of Donation (995) and Arms of Mecklenburg-Vorpommern

**1995.** Millenary of Mecklenburg.
2623 **1099** 100 pf. multicoloured 85 40

**1100** Computer Image of Terminal and Lion

**1995.** 250th Anniv of Carolo-Wilhelmina Technical University, Braunschweig.
2624 **1100** 100 pf. multicoloured 85 40

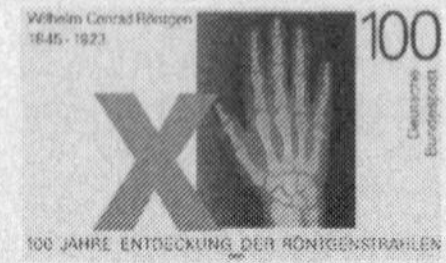

**1101** X-ray of Hand

**1995.** 150th Birth Anniv of Wilhelm Rontgen and Centenary of his Discovery of X-rays.
2625 **1101** 100 pf. multicoloured 85 40

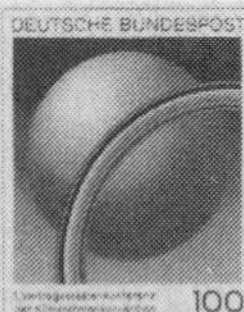

**1102** Globe and Rainbow

**1995.** 1st Conference of Signatories to General Convention on Climate, Berlin.
2626 **1102** 100 pf. multicoloured 85 40

**1103** Old Town Hall Reliefs

**1995.** 750th Anniv of Regensburg.
2627 **1103** 80 pf. multicoloured 70 35

**1104** Bonhoeffer

**1995.** 50th Death Anniv of Dietrich Bonhoeffer (theologian).
2628 **1104** 100 pf. blk, bl & grey 85 40

**1105** Symbols of Speech, Writing and Pictures

**1995.** Freedom of Expression.
2629 **1105** 100 pf. multicoloured 85 40

**1106** St. Clement's Church, Munster

**1995.** 300th Birth Anniv of Johann Conrad Schlaun (architect).
2630 **1106** 200 pf. multicoloured 1·75 85

**1107** Friedrich Schiller, Signature and Schiller Museum, Marbach

**1108** St. Vincent de Paul

**1995.** Centenary of German Schiller Society.
2631 **1107** 100 pf. multicoloured 90 45

**1995.** 150th Anniv of Vincent Conferences (charitable organization) in Germany.
2632 **1108** 100 pf. multicoloured 90 45

**1111** Returning Soldiers ("End of War")

**1112** Shipping Routes before and after 1895

**1995.** Europa. Peace and Freedom.
2635 **1111** 100 pf. black and red 90 45
2636 – 200 pf. bl, yell & blk 1·75 85
DESIGN: 200 pf. Emblem of European Community ("Moving towards Europe").

**1995.** Centenary of Kiel Canal.
2637 **1112** 80 pf. multicoloured 70 35

**1113** Guglielmo Marconi and Wireless Equipment

**1995.** 100 Years of Radio.
2638 **1113** 100 pf. multicoloured 90 45

**1114** U.N. Emblem

**1995.** 50th Anniv of U.N.O.
2639 **1114** 100 pf. lilac, gold and grey .. .. 90 45

**1115** Munsterlander

**1116** Opening Bars of "Carmina Burana" and Characters

**1995.** Youth Welfare. Dogs (1st series). Mult.
2640 80 pf. + 40 pf. Type **1115** 1·10 1·10
2641 80 pf. + 40 pf. Giant schnauzer .. 1·10 1·10
2642 100 pf. + 50 pf. Wire-haired dachshund .. 1·25 1·25
2643 100 pf. + 50 pf. German shepherd .. .. 1·25 1·25
2644 200 pf. + 80 pf. Keeshund 2·50 2·50
See also Nos. 2696/2700.

**1995.** Birth Centenary of Carl Orff (composer).
2645 **1116** 100 pf. multicoloured 90 45

**1995.** Landscapes (3rd series). As T **1046**. Multicoloured.
2646 100 pf. Franconian Switzerland .. .. 90 45
2647 100 pf. River Havel, Berlin .. .. 90 45
2648 100 pf. Oberlausitz .. 90 45
2649 100 pf. Sauerland .. 90 45

**1117** Lion (from 12th-century coin)

**1118** Kaiser Wilhelm Memorial Church

**1995.** 800th Death Anniv of Henry the Lion, Duke of Saxony and Bavaria.
2650 **1117** 400 pf. multicoloured 3·50 3·50

**1995.** Centenary of Kaiser Wilhelm Memorial Church, Berlin.
2651 **1118** 100 pf. multicoloured 90 45

**1119** Werfel and Signature

**1995.** 50th Death Anniv of Franz Werfel (writer).
2652 **1119** 100 pf. mve, bl & blk 90 45

**1995.** Tourist Sights. As T **854** but inscr "DEUTSCHLAND".
2665 640 pf. blue and brown .. 4·25 2·50
2666 690 pf. black and green .. 5·50 2·75
DESIGNS: 640 pf. Speyer Cathedral; 690 pf. St. Michael's Church, Hamburg.

**1120** Strauss

**1995.** 80th Birth Anniv of Franz Josef Strauss (politician).
2675 **1120** 100 pf. multicoloured 90 45

**1121** Postwoman

**1995.** Stamp Day.
2676 **1121** 200 pf. + 100 pf. mult 2·75 2·75

1123 Eifel

**1995.** Humanitarian Relief Funds. Farmhouses (1st series). Multicoloured.
2678 80 pf.+40 pf. Type **1123** 1·10 1·10
2679 80 pf.+40 pf. Saxony .. 1·10 1·10
2680 100 pf.+50 pf. Lower Germany .. .. 1·25 1·25
2681 100 pf.+50 pf. Upper Bavaria .. .. 1·25 1·25
2682 200 pf.+70 pf. Mecklenburg .. .. .. 2·40 2·40
See also Nos. 2742/6.

1124 Schumacher

1126 Ranke

**1995.** Birth Centenary of Kurt Schumacher (politician).
2683 **1124** 100 pf. multicoloured 90 45

**1995.** Birth Bicentenary of Leopold von Ranke (historian).
2685 **1126** 80 pf. multicoloured 70 35

1127 Hindemith

**1995.** Birth Centenary of Paul Hindemith (composer).
2686 **1127** 100 pf. multicoloured 90 45

1128 Alfred Nobel and Will

**1995.** Centenary of Nobel Prize Trust Fund.
2687 **1128** 100 pf. multicoloured 90 45

1129 "CARE" in American Colours

**1995.** 50th Anniv of CARE (Co-operative for Assistance and Remittances Overseas).
2688 **1129** 100 pf. multicoloured 90 45

1130 Berlin Wall

**1995.** Commemorating Victims of Political Oppression, 1945–89.
2689 **1130** 100 pf. multicoloured 90 45

1131 "The Annunciation"

**1995.** Christmas. Stained Glass Windows in Augsburg Cathedral. Multicoloured.
2690 80 pf.+40 pf. Type **1131** 1·10 1·10
2691 100 pf.+50 pf. "Nativity" 1·25 1·25

1132 Dribbling

**1995.** Borussia Dortmund, German Football Champion.
2692 **1132** 100 pf. multicoloured 90 45

1133 Auguste von Sartorius (founder)

**1996.** 150th Anniv of German Institute for Children's Missionary Work.
2693 **1133** 100 pf. multicoloured 90 45

1134 Bodelschwingh

**1996.** 50th Death Anniv of Friedrich von Bodelschwingh (theologian).
2694 **1134** 100 pf. black and red 90 45

1135 Luther (after Lucas Cranach)

**1996.** 450th Death Anniv of Martin Luther (Protestant reformer).
2695 **1135** 100 pf. multicoloured 90 45

**1996.** Youth Welfare. Dogs (2nd series). As T **1115**. Multicoloured.
2696 80 pf.+40 pf. Borzoi .. 1·10 1·10
2697 80 pf.+40 pf. Chow chow 1·10 1·10
2698 100 pf.+50 pf. St. Bernard 1·25 1·25
2699 100 pf.+50 pf. Rough collie .. .. .. 1·25 1·25
2700 200 pf.+80 pf. Briard .. 2·50 2·50

1136 Siebold

**1996.** Birth Bicentenary of Philipp Franz von Siebold (physician and Japanologist).
2701 **1136** 100 pf. multicoloured 90 45

1137 Cathedral Square

**1996.** Millenary of Cathedral Square, Halberstadt.
2702 **1137** 80 pf. multicoloured 70 35

1138 Galen

**1996.** 50th Death Anniv of Cardinal Count Clemens von Galen, Bishop of Munster.
2703 **1138** 100 pf. grey, bl & gold 90 45

**1996.** 20th-century German Paintings (5th series). As T **1003**. Multicoloured.
2704 100 pf. "Seated Female Nude" (Max Pechstein) 90 45
2705 200 pf. "For Wilhelm Runge" (Georg Muche) 1·75 85
2706 300 pf. "Still Life with Guitar, Book and Vase" (Helmut Kolle) .. 2·75 1·25

1139 Detail of Ceiling Fresco, Prince-bishop's Residence, Wurzburg

**1996.** 300th Birth Anniv of Giovanni Battista Tiepolo (artist).
2707 **1139** 200 pf. multicoloured 1·75 85

**1996.** Landscapes (4th series). As T **1046**. Multicoloured.
2709 100 pf. Eifel .. .. 80 40
2710 100 pf. Holstein Switzerland .. .. 80 40
2711 100 pf. Saale .. .. 80 40
2712 100 pf. Spreewald .. 80 40

1141 Paula Modersohn-Becker (self-portrait)

**1996.** Europa. Famous Women.
2713 **1141** 80 pf. multicoloured 65 30
2714 – 100 pf. black, grey and mauve .. 80 40
DESIGN: 100 pf. Kathe Kollwitz (self-portrait).

1142 Opening Lines of Document and Town (1642 engraving, Matthaeus Merian)

**1996.** Millenary of Granting to Freising the Right to hold Markets.
2715 **1142** 100 pf. multicoloured 80 40

1143 Borchert

**1996.** 75th Birth Anniv of Wolfgang Borchert (writer).
2716 **1143** 100 pf. multicoloured 80 40

1144 Emblem

**1996.** 50th Anniv of Ruhr Festival, Recklinghausen.
2717 **1144** 100 pf. multicoloured 80 40

1145 Ticket and Stage Curtain

**1996.** 150th Anniv of German Theatre Assn.
2718 **1145** 200 pf. multicoloured 1·60 80

1146 Leibniz and Mathematical Diagram

**1996.** 350th Birth Anniv of Gottfried Leibniz.
2719 **1146** 100 pf. red and black 80 40

1147 Kneeling Figure and Motto forming "A"

**1996.** 300th Anniv of Berlin Academy of Arts.
2720 **1147** 100 pf. multicoloured 80 40

1148 Carl Schuhmann (wrestling, equestrian sports and gymnastics, 1896)

**1996.** Sport Promotion Fund. Centenary of Modern Olympic Games. German Olympic Champions. Multicoloured.
2721 80 pf.+40 pf. Type **1148** 1·00 1·00
2722 100 pf.+50 pf. Josef Neckermann (dressage, 1964 and 1968) .. 1·25 1·25
2723 100 pf.+50 pf. Annie Hubler-Horn (ice skating, 1908) .. .. 1·25 1·25
2724 200 pf.+80 pf. Alfred and Gustav Flatow (gymnastics, 1896) .. 2·25 2·25

1149 Townscape

**1996.** 800th Anniv of Heidelberg.
2725 **1149** 100 pf. multicoloured 80 40

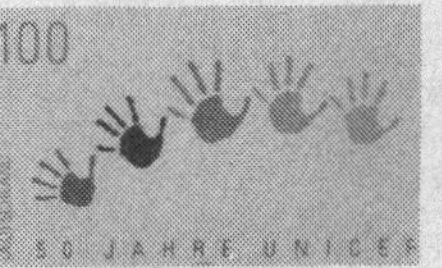

1150 Children's Handprints

**1996.** 50th Anniv of U.N.I.C.E.F.
2726 **1150** 100 pf. multicoloured 80 40

**1151** "Wedding" (illustration by Bruno Paul)

**1996.** 75th Death Anniv of Ludwig Thoma (satirist).
2727 **1151** 100 pf. multicoloured 80 40

**1153** Map and Tropical Wildlife

**1996.** Environmental Protection. Preservation of Tropical Habitats.
2729 **1153** 100 pf. + 50 pf. mult 1·25 1·25

**1154** Volklingen Blast Furnace

**1996.** U.N.E.S.C.O World Heritage Sites.
2730 **1154** 100 pf. multicoloured 80 40

**1155** Lincke

**1996.** 50th Death Anniv of Paul Lincke (composer and conductor).
2731 **1155** 100 pf. multicoloured 80 40

**1156** Gendarmenmarkt, Berlin

**1996.**
2732 **1156** 100 pf. multicoloured 80 40

**1157** "50" comprising Stamp under Magnifying Glass

**1996.** 50th Anniv of Association of German Philatelists.
2733 **1157** 100 pf. multicoloured 80 40

**1158** Book

**1996.** Centenary of German Civil Code.
2734 **1158** 300 pf. multicoloured 2·50 1·25

**1159** Players

**1996.** Borussia Dortmund, German Football Champion.
2735 **1159** 100 pf. multicoloured 80 40

**1160** Bamburg Old Town

**1996.** U.N.E.S.C.O World Heritage Sites.
2736 **1160** 100 pf. multicoloured 80 40

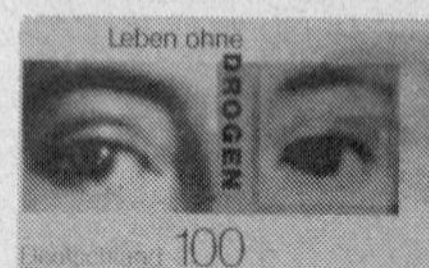

**1161** Eyes

**1996.** "Life without Drugs".
2737 **1161** 100 pf. multicoloured 80 40

**1162** "Like will Cure Like" and Samuel Hahnemann (developer of principle)

**1163** Bruckner and Symphony No. III

**1996.** Bicentenary of Homeopathy.
2738 **1162** 400 pf. multicoloured 3·25 1·60

**1996.** Death Centenary of Anton Bruckner (composer).
2739 **1163** 100 pf. multicoloured 80 40

**1164** Mueller, Map and Plants

**1996.** Death Centenary of Baron Ferdinand von Mueller (botanist).
2740 **1164** 100 pf. multicoloured 80 40

**1165** Score by John Cage

**1996.** 75th Anniv of Donaueschingen Music Festival.
2741 **1165** 100 pf. bl, blk & mve 80 40

**1996.** Humanitarian Relief Funds. Farmhouses (2nd series). As T **1123**. Mult.
2742 80 pf. + 40 pf. Spree Forest 1·00 1·00
2743 80 pf. + 40 pf. Thuringia 1·00 1·00
2744 100 pf. + 50 pf. Black Forest . . . . 1·25 1·25
2745 100 pf. + 50 pf. Westphalia 1·25 1·25
2746 200 pf. + 70 pf. Schleswig-Holstein . . . . 2·25 1·10

## IV. WEST BERLIN.

The Russian Government withdrew from the four-power control of Berlin on 1 July 1948, with the Western Sectors remaining under American, British and French control. West Berlin was constituted a "Land" of the Federal Republic in 1 September 1950.

**The Russian Zone issues inscribed "STADT BERLIN" (which we do not list unoverprinted in this Catalogue), were not intended for use throughout Berlin, but were for the Russian sector of the city and for Brandenburg.**

**The first stamps to be used in the Western Sectors were Nos. A 4/5 and A 7 of the Anglo-American Zones, followed by Nos. A 36/52, which were on sale from 24 June to 31 August 1948, and remained valid until 19 September 1948.**

1948. 100 pfennig = 1 Deutsche Mark (East).
1949. 100 pfennig = 1 Deutsche Mark (West).

**1948.** Pictorial issue of 1947 (Nos. 928/48) optd. **BERLIN.**

| | | | |
|---|---|---|---|
| B21 | 2 pf. black | 2·75 | 1·40 |
| B2 | 6 pf. violet | 85 | 3·00 |
| B3 | 8 pf. red | 85 | 2·75 |
| B4 | 10 pf. green | 60 | 80 |
| B5 | 12 pf. grey | 60 | 40 |
| B25 | 15 pf. brown | 8·00 | 2·00 |
| B7 | 16 pf. green | 1·00 | 1·75 |
| B26 | 20 pf. blue | 2·75 | 50 |
| B9 | 24 pf. brown | 90 | 40 |
| B10 | 25 pf. orange | 22·00 | 45·00 |
| B11 | 30 pf. red | 3·50 | 7·00 |
| B12 | 40 pf. mauve | 4·00 | 3·00 |
| B13 | 50 pf. blue | 8·00 | 24·00 |
| B14 | 60 pf. brown | 2·25 | 20 |
| B15 | 80 pf. blue | 8·00 | 22·00 |
| B16 | 84 pf. green | 15·00 | 90·00 |
| B17 | 1 m. olive | 40·00 | £150 |
| B18 | 2 m. violet | 55·00 | £450 |
| B19 | 3 m. red | 65·00 | £600 |
| B20 | 5 m. blue | 80·00 | £650 |

B 2. Schoneberg.

B 3. Douglas C-54 Skymaster Transport over Tempelhof Airport.

**1949.** Insc. "DEUTSCHE POST". Berlin Views. (a) Small size.

| | | | | |
|---|---|---|---|---|
| B35 | – | 1 pf. grey | 15 | 10 |
| B36 | B 2 | 4 pf. brown | 30 | 10 |
| B36c | – | 4 pf. brown | 2·25 | 1·60 |
| B37 | – | 5 pf. green | 50 | 10 |
| B38 | – | 6 pf. purple | 80 | 80 |
| B39 | B 2 | 8 pf. orange | 1·25 | 1·25 |
| B40 | – | 10 pf. green | 1·00 | 10 |
| B41 | B 3 | 15 pf. brown | 12·00 | 50 |
| B42 | – | 20 pf. red | 5·50 | 10 |
| B42b | – | 20 pf. red | 60·00 | 30 |
| B43 | – | 25 pf. yellow | 25·00 | 90 |
| B44 | – | 30 pf. blue | 14·00 | 60 |
| B45 | B 2 | 40 pf. lake | 18·00 | 30 |
| B46 | – | 50 pf. olive | 20·00 | 20 |
| B47 | – | 60 pf. red | 50·00 | 20 |
| B48 | – | 80 pf. blue | 16·00 | 70 |
| B49 | – | 90 pf. green | 17·00 | 80 |

(b) Large size.

| | | | | |
|---|---|---|---|---|
| B50 | B 3 | 1 Dm. olive | 26·00 | 50 |
| B51 | – | 2 Dm. purple | 65·00 | 90 |
| B52 | – | 3 Dm. red | £250 | 10·00 |
| B53 | – | 5 Dm. blue | £140 | 10·00 |

DESIGNS—As Type B 2: 1 pf. Brandenburg Gate. 4 pf. (B36c) Exhibition Building. 5, 25 pf. "Tegel Schloss". 6, 50 pf. Reichstag Building. 10, 30 pf. "Kleistpark". 20 (B42), 80, 90 pf. Technical High School. 20 pf. (B42b) Olympia Stadium. 60 pf. National Gallery. As Type B 3: 2 Dm. "Gendarmenmarkt". 3 Dm. Brandenburg Gate. 5 Dm. "Tegel Schloss".

For similar views inscribed "DEUTSCHE POST BERLIN" see Nos. B118/19.

B 4. Stephen Monument and Globe.

B 5. Heinrich von Stephen Monument.

**1949.** 75th Anniv. of U.P.U.

| | | | | |
|---|---|---|---|---|
| B54 | B 4 | 12 pf. grey | 12·00 | 6·00 |
| B55 | | 16 pf. green | 20·00 | 10·00 |
| B56 | | 24 pf. orange | 14·00 | 30 |
| B57 | | 50 pf. olive | £130 | 20·00 |
| B58 | | 60 pf. brown | £160 | 28·00 |
| B59 | B 5 | 1 Dm. olive | £100 | £100 |
| B60 | | 2 Dm. purple | £100 | 55·00 |

B 6. Goethe and Scene from "Iphigenie".

B 9. Alms Bowl and Bear.

**1949.** Birth Bicent. of Goethe (poet). Portraits of Goethe and scenes from his works.

| | | | | |
|---|---|---|---|---|
| B 61. | B 6. | 10 pf. green | 85·00 | 50·00 |
| B 62. | – | 20 pf. red | 90·00 | 55·00 |
| B 63. | – | 30 pf. blue | 24·00 | 24·00 |

DESIGNS: Scenes from—20 pf. "Reineke Fuchs" or—30 pf. "Faust".

**1949.** Numeral and pictorial issues of 1946/7 surch. **BERLIN** and bold figures.

| | | | | |
|---|---|---|---|---|
| B 64. | **229.** | 5 pf. on 45 pf. red | 3·25 | 10 |
| B 65. | C. | 10 pf. on 24 pf. brn. | 10·00 | 20 |
| B 66. | B. | 20 pf. on 80 pf. blue | 55·00 | 16·00 |
| B 67. | **237.** | 1 m. on 3 m. lake | £120 | 18·00 |

**1949.** Berlin Relief Fund.

| | | | | |
|---|---|---|---|---|
| B 68. | B **9.** | 10 pf. + 5 pf. green | 90·00 | £150 |
| B 69. | | 20 pf. + 5 pf. red | 90·00 | £150 |
| B 70. | | 30 pf. + 5 pf. blue | 90·00 | £150 |

B 10.

B 11. Harp.

**1950.** European Recovery Programme.

| | | | | |
|---|---|---|---|---|
| B 71. | B **10.** | 20 pf. red | 75·00 | 34·00 |

**1950.** Restablishment of Berlin Philharmonic Orchestra.

| | | | | |
|---|---|---|---|---|
| B 72. | B **11.** | 10 pf. + 5 pf. green | 40·00 | 38·00 |
| B 73. | – | 30 pf. + 5 pf. blue | 75·00 | 70·00 |

DESIGN: 30 pf. "Singing Angels" (after H. and J. van Eyck).

B 13. G. A. Lortzing.

B 14. Freedom Bell.

**1951.** Death Cent. of Lortzing (composer).

| | | | | |
|---|---|---|---|---|
| B 74. | B **13.** | 20 pf. brown | 50·00 | 42·00 |

**1951.** (a) Clapper at left.

| | | | | |
|---|---|---|---|---|
| B 75. | B **14.** | 5 pf. brown | 2·00 | 2·75 |
| B 76. | | 10 pf. green | 10·00 | 14·00 |
| B 77. | | 20 pf. red | 3·25 | 10·00 |
| B 78. | | 30 pf. blue | 28·00 | 35·00 |
| B 79. | | 40 pf. purple | 14·00 | 28·00 |

(b) Clapper at right.

| | | | | |
|---|---|---|---|---|
| B 82. | B **14.** | 5 pf. green | 3·25 | 1·40 |
| B 83. | | 10 pf. green | 7·50 | 4·50 |
| B 84. | | 20 pf. red | 22·00 | 15·00 |
| B 85. | | 30 pf. blue | 35·00 | 35·00 |
| B 86. | | 40 pf. red | 80·00 | 16·00 |

(c) Clapper in centre.

| | | | | |
|---|---|---|---|---|
| B 101. | B **14.** | 5 pf. brown | 1·00 | 85 |
| B 102. | | 10 pf. green | 3·25 | 1·40 |
| B 103. | | 20 pf. red | 6·50 | 3·75 |
| B 104. | | 30 pf. blue | 12·00 | 9·50 |
| B 105. | | 40 pf. violet | 42·00 | 28·00 |

B 15. Boy Stamp Collectors.

B 16. Mask of Beethoven (taken from life, 1812).

**1951.** Stamp Day.

| | | | | |
|---|---|---|---|---|
| B 80. | B **15.** | 10 pf. + 3 pf. green | 18·00 | 20·00 |
| B 81. | | 20 pf. + 2 pf. red | 27·00 | 30·00 |

**1952.** 125th Death Anniv. of Beethoven (composer).

| | | | | |
|---|---|---|---|---|
| B 87. | B **16.** | 30 pf. blue | 42·00 | 25·00 |

B 17. Olympic Torch.

B 18. W. von Siemens (electrical engineer).

**1952.** Olympic Games Festival, Berlin.

| | | | | |
|---|---|---|---|---|
| B 88. | B **17.** | 4 pf. brown | 1·00 | 1·40 |
| B 89. | | 10 pf. green | 7·50 | 12·00 |
| B 90. | | 20 pf. red | 14·00 | 18·00 |

**1952.** Famous Berliners.

| | | | | |
|---|---|---|---|---|
| B 91. | – | 4 pf. brown | 30 | 15 |
| B 92. | – | 5 pf. blue | 40 | 30 |
| B 93. | – | 6 pf. purple | 5·00 | 12·00 |
| B 94. | – | 8 pf. brown | 2·00 | 2·00 |
| B 95. | – | 10 pf. green | 1·50 | 30 |
| B 96. | – | 15 pf. lilac | 13·00 | 14·00 |
| B 97. | B **18.** | 20 pf. red | 2·50 | 60 |
| B 98. | – | 25 pf. green | 44·00 | 4·00 |
| B 99. | – | 30 pf. purple | 16·00 | 8·00 |
| B 100. | – | 40 pf. black | 24·00 | 2·00 |

PORTRAITS: 4 pf. Zelter (musician). 5 pf. Lilienthal (aviator). 6 pf. Rathenau (statesman). 8 pf. Fontane (writer). 10 pf. Von Menzel (artist). 15 pf. Virchow (pathologist). 25 pf. Schinkel (architect). 30 pf. Planck (physicist). 40 pf. W. von Humboldt (philologist).

B 19. Church before Bombing.

B 20. Chainbreaker.

**1953.** Kaiser Wilhelm Memorial Church Reconstruction Fund.

| | | | | |
|---|---|---|---|---|
| B 106. | B **19.** | 4 pf. + 1 pf. brown | 30 | 7·50 |
| B 107. | | 10 pf. + 5 pf. green | 1·20 | 25·00 |
| B 108. | – | 20 pf. + 10 pf. red | 2·00 | 32·00 |
| B 109. | – | 30 pf. + 15 pf. blue | 13·00 | 80·00 |

DESIGN: 20 pf., 30 pf. Church after bombing.

**1953.** East German Uprising. Inscr. "17 JUNI 1953".

| | | | | |
|---|---|---|---|---|
| B 110. | B **20.** | 20 pf. black | 3·75 | 1·40 |
| B 111. | – | 30 pf. red | 24·00 | 17·00 |

DESIGN: 30 pf. Brandenburg Gate.

B 21. Ernst Reuter.

B 22. Conference Buildings.

**1954.** Death of Ernst Reuter (Mayor of West Berlin).

| | | | | |
|---|---|---|---|---|
| B 112. | B **21.** | 20 pf. brown | 7·50 | 1·75 |

**1954.** Four-Power Conference, Berlin.

| | | | | |
|---|---|---|---|---|
| B113 | B **22** | 20 pf. red | 7·50 | 3·75 |

B 23. O. Mergenthaler and Linotype Machine.

B 25. "Germany in Bondage".

**1954.** Birth Cent. of Mergenthaler (inventor).

| | | | | |
|---|---|---|---|---|
| B114. | B **23.** | 10 pf. green | 2·25 | 2·00 |

**1954.** West German Presidential Election. No. B 103 optd. **Wahl des Bundespräsidenten in Berlin 17. Juli 1954.**

| | | | | |
|---|---|---|---|---|
| B115. | B **14.** | 20 pf. red | 2·75 | 4·00 |

**1954.** 10th Anniv. of Attempt on Hitler's Life.

| | | | | |
|---|---|---|---|---|
| B116. | B **25.** | 20 pf. grey and red | 4·75 | 4·50 |

B 26. Prussian Postilion, 1827.

B 27. Memorial Library.

**1954.** National Stamp Exhibition.

| | | | | |
|---|---|---|---|---|
| B 117. | B **26.** | 20 pf. + 10 pf. mult. | 14·00 | 26·00 |

**1954.** Berlin Views. As Type B 4 but inscr. "DEUTSCHE POST BERLIN".

| | | | | |
|---|---|---|---|---|
| B 118. | | 7 pf. green | 7·00 | 30 |
| B 119. | | 70 pf. olive | 90·00 | 19·00 |

DESIGNS: 7 pf. Exhibition building. 70 pf. Grunewald hunting lodge.

**1954.**

| | | | | |
|---|---|---|---|---|
| B 120. | B **27.** | 40 pf. purple | 10·00 | 2·50 |

B 28. Richard Strauss.

B 29. Blacksmiths at Work.

**1954.** 5th Death Anniv. of Strauss (composer).

| | | | | |
|---|---|---|---|---|
| B121. | B **28.** | 40 pf. blue | 15·00 | 3·00 |

**1954.** Death Cent. of A. Borsig (industrialist).

| | | | | |
|---|---|---|---|---|
| B122. | B **29.** | 20 pf. brown | 6·00 | 1·25 |

B 30. Liner "Berlin".

B 31. Wilhelm Furtwangler (conductor).

**1955.**

| | | | | |
|---|---|---|---|---|
| B 123. | B **30.** | 10 pf. green | 1·00 | 30 |
| B 124. | | 25 pf. blue | 5·50 | 3·50 |

**1955.** 1st Death Anniv. of Furtwangler.

| | | | | |
|---|---|---|---|---|
| B 125. | B **31.** | 40 pf. blue | 20·00 | 14·00 |

B 32.

B 33. Prussian Rural Postilion, 1760.

**1955.** Federal Parliament Session, Berlin.

| | | | | |
|---|---|---|---|---|
| B 126. | B **32.** | 10 pf. black, yellow and red | 30 | 25 |
| B 127. | | 20 pf. black, yellow and red | 3·25 | 6·50 |

**1955.** Stamp Day and Philatelic Fund.

| | | | | |
|---|---|---|---|---|
| B 128. | B **33.** | 25 pf. + 10 pf. mult. | 5·50 | 14·00 |

B 34. St. Otto.

B 35. Radio Tower and Exhibition Hall.

**1955.** 25th Anniv. of Berlin Bishopric.

| | | | | |
|---|---|---|---|---|
| B 129. | B **34.** | 7 pf. + 3 pf. brown | 60 | 2·00 |
| B 130. | – | 10 pf. + 5 pf. green | 1·25 | 2·75 |
| B 131. | – | 20 pf. + 10 pf. mve. | 1·25 | 3·75 |

DESIGNS: 10 pf. St. Hedwig. 20 pf. St. Peter.

**1956.** Berlin Buildings and Monuments.

| | | | | |
|---|---|---|---|---|
| B 133 | – | 1 pf. grey | 10 | 10 |
| B 133b. | – | 3 pf. violet | 15 | 10 |
| B 134. | – | 5 pf. mauve | 15 | 10 |
| B 132. | B **35.** | 7 pf. turq. (A) | 8·50 | 2·40 |
| B 135. | – | 7 pf. turq. (B) | 20 | 10 |
| B 136. | – | 8 pf. grey | 30 | 55 |
| B 136a. | – | 8 pf. red | 30 | 20 |
| B 137. | – | 10 pf. green | 15 | 10 |
| B 138. | – | 15 pf. blue | 25 | 30 |
| B 139. | – | 20 pf. red | 15 | 10 |
| B 140. | – | 25 pf. brown | 35 | 30 |
| B 141. | – | 30 pf. green | 50 | 55 |
| B 142. | – | 40 pf. blue | 8·50 | 7·00 |
| B 143. | – | 50 pf. green | 50 | 50 |
| B 144. | – | 60 pf. brown | 65 | 1·00 |
| B 145. | – | 70 pf. violet | 26·00 | 12·00 |
| B 146. | – | 1 Dm. green | 2·00 | 2·25 |
| B 146a. | – | 3 Dm. red | 5·00 | 12·00 |

7 pf. (A) Type B 35. (B) As Type B 35 but with inscription at top.

DESIGNS—As Type B 35 (B)—HORIZ. 1 pf., 3 pf. Brandenburg Gate. 5 pf. P.O. Headquarters. 20 pf. Free University. 40 pf. Charlottenburg Castle. 60 pf. Chamber of Commerce and Bourse. 70 pf. Schiller Theatre. VERT. 8 pf. Town Hall, Neukollin. 10 pf. Kaiser Wilhelm Memorial Church. 15 pf. Airlift Monument. 25 pf. Lilienthal Monument. 30 pf. Pfaueninsel Castle. 50 pf. Reuter Power-station. LARGER (24 × 30 mm): 1 Dm. "The Great Elector" (statue, after Schluter). (29½ × 25 mm.): 3 Dm. Congress Hall, Berlin.

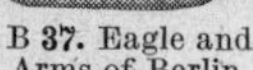

B **37.** Eagle and Arms of Berlin.

B **38.**

**1956.** Federal Council Meeting.
B 147. B **37.** 10 pf. black, yellow and red .. 85 40
B 148. 25 pf. black, yellow and red .. 3·75 4·00

**1956.** Cent. of German Engineers' Union.
B 149. B **38.** 10 pf. green .. 1·75 1·10
B 150. 20 pf. red .. .. 3·75 4·00

**1956.** Flood Relief Fund. As No. B 77 (colour changed) surch. **+10 Berlinhilfe fur die Hochwassergeschadigten. DEUTSCHE BUNDESPOST BERLIN** and bar.
B 151. B **14.** 20 pf. + 10 pf. bistre 2·00 3·00

B **40.** P. Lincke.

B **41.** Wireless Transmitter.

**1956.** 10th Death Anniv. of Lincke (composer).
B 152. B **40.** 20 pf. red .. .. 2·50 3·00

**1956.** Industrial Exhibition.
B 153. B **41.** 25 pf. brown .. 5·00 7·50

B **42.** Brandenburg Postilion, 1700.

B **43.** Spandau.

**1956.** Stamp Day and Philatelic Fund.
B 154. B **42.** 25 pf. + 10 pf. multicoloured .. 2·00 3·25

**1957.** 725th Anniv. of Spandau.
B 155. B **43.** 20 pf. olive & brn. 40 60

B **44.** Model of Hansa District.

B **45.** Friedrich K. von Savigny (jurist).

**1957.** Int. Building Exn., Berlin
B 156. B **44.** 7 pf. brown .. 30 20
B 157. – 20 pf. red .. .. 70 60
B 158. – 40 pf. blue .. 80 1·25
DESIGNS—HORIZ. 20 pf. Aerial view of Exhibition. 40 pf. Exhibition Congress Hall.

**1957.** Portraits as Type B **45.**
B 159. – 7 pf. brown & green 10 10
B 160. – 8 pf. brown & grey 10 25
B 161. – 10 pf. brn. & green 10 10
B 162. – 15 pf. sepia and blue 75 50
B 163. – 20 pf. + 10 pf. sepia and red .. 20 60
B 164. – 20 pf. brown & red 15 15
B 165. – 25 pf. sepia and lake 40 65
B 166. B **45.** 30 pf. sepia & grn. 1·25 1·40
B 167. – 40 pf. sepia & blue 40 30
B 168. – 50 pf. sepia & olive 3·00 5·00
PORTRAITS—VERT. 7 pf. T. Mommsen (historian). 8 pf. H. Zille (painter). 10 pf. E. Reuter (Mayor of Berlin). 15 pf. F. Haber (chemist). 20 pf. (No. B 164), F. Schleiermacher (theologian). 20 pf. (B 163), L. Heck (zoologist). 25 pf. Max Reinhardt (theatrical producer). 40 pf. A. von Humboldt (naturalist). 50 pf. C. D. Rauch (sculptor).

The premium on No. B 163 was for the Berlin Zoo. No. B 167 commemorates Humboldt's death centenary.

## INDEX

Countries can be quickly located by referring to the index at the end of this volume.

B **46.** Uta von Naumburg (statue).

B **47.** "Unity Justice and Freedom."

**1957.** German Cultural Congress.
B 169. B **46.** 25 pf. brown .. 50 60

**1957.** 3rd Federal Parliament Assembly.
B 170. B **47.** 10 pf. black, ochre and red .. .. 30 40
B 171. 20 pf. black, ochre and red .. .. 1·25 2·00

B **48.** Postilion, 1897-1925.

B **49.** Torch of Remembrance.

**1957.** Stamp Day.
B 172. B **48.** 20 pf. multicoloured 45 75

**1957.** 7th World War Veterans Congress.
B 173. B **49.** 20 pf. myrtle, yellow and green .. 50 60

B **50.** Elly Heuss-Knapp (social worker).

B **51.** Christ and Symbols of the Cosmos.

**1957.** Mothers' Convalescence Fund.
B 174. B **50.** 20 pf. + 10 pf. red 90 1·25

**1958.** German Catholics' Day.
B 175. B **51.** 10 pf. blk. and grn.. 25 50
B 176. 20 pf. blk. and mve. 50 1·00

B **52.** Otto Suhr.

B **53.** Pres. Heuss.

**1958.** 1st Death Anniv. of Burgomaster Otto Suhr.
B 177. B **52.** 20 pf. red .. .. 60 1·10
See also Nos. B 187 and B 193.

**1959.**
B 178. B **53.** 7 pf. green .. 40 30
B 179. 10 pf. green .. 30 10
B 180. 20 pf. red .. .. 75 10
B 181. 40 pf. blue .. 3·00 2·40
B 182. 70 pf. violet .. 12·00 12·00

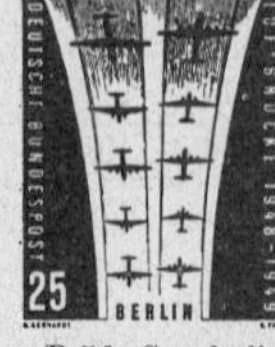

B **54.** Symbolic Airlift.

B **55.** Brandenburg Gate, Berlin.

**1959.** 10th Anniv. of Berlin Airlift.
B 183. B **54.** 25 pf. blk. and red 50 35

**1959.** 14th World Communities Congress, Berlin.
B 184. B **55.** 20 pf. blue, red and light blue .. 30 30

B **56.** Schiller.

B **57.** Robert Koch.

**1959.** Birth Bicent. of Schiller (poet).
B 185. B **56.** 20 pf. brn. & red .. 20 20

**1960.** 50th Death Anniv. of Robert Koch (bacteriologist).
B 186. B **57.** 20 pf. purple .. 20 25

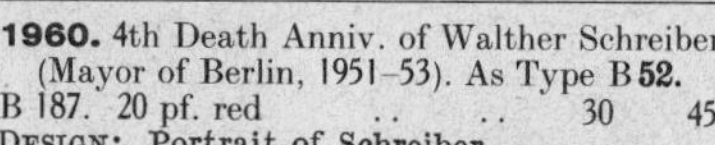

**1960.** 4th Death Anniv. of Walther Schreiber (Mayor of Berlin, 1951–53). As Type B **52.**
B 187. 20 pf. red .. .. 30 45
DESIGN: Portrait of Schreiber.

B **58.** Boy at Window.

B **59.** Hans Boeckler.

**1960.** Berlin Children's Holiday Fund. Inscr. "FERIENPLATZE FUR BERLINER KINDER".
B 188 B **58** 7 pf. + 3 pf. dp brn, brown & lt brn .. 15 40
B 189 – 10 pf. + 5 pf. deep green, olive & grn 15 50
B 190 – 20 pf. + 10 pf. brown, red and pink .. 25 65
B 191 – 40 pf. + 20 pf. deep blue, blue & lt bl 80 3·00
DESIGNS: 10 pf. Girl in street. 20 pf. Girl blowing on Alpine flower. 40 pf. Boy on beach.

**1961.** 10th Anniv. of Hans Boeckler (politician).
B 192. B **59.** 20 pf. black and red 10 10

**1961.** Louise Schroeder Commemoration. As Type B **52.**
B 193. 20 pf. brown .. .. 15 25
DESIGN: Portrait of Schroeder.

B **60.** Durer.

B **61.** "Five Crosses" Symbol and St. Mary's Church.

B **62.** Exhibition Emblem.

**1961.** Famous Germans.
B 194. 5 pf. olive (Magnus) .. 10 15
B 195. 7 pf. brown (St. Elizabeth of Thuringia) .. .. 10 30
B 196. 8 pf. violet (Gutenberg) 10 30
B 197. 10 pf. green (Type B **60**) .. .. 10 10
B 198. 15 pf. blue (Luther) .. 20 25
B 199. 20 pf. red (Bach) .. 30 10
B 200. 25 pf. brown (Neumann) .. 20 35
B 201. 30 pf. brown (Kant) .. 20 25
B 202. 40 pf. blue (Lessing) .. 40 55
B 203. 50 pf. brown (Goethe) 40 60
B 204. 60 pf. red (Schiller) .. 40 70
B 205. 70 pf. green (Beethoven) .. 90 70
B 206. 80 pf. brown (Kleist) .. 3·50 5·25
B 207. 1 Dm. violet (Annette von Droste-Hulshoff) .. 1·60 2·00
B 208. 2 Dm. green (Hauptmann) .. 1·75 3·00

**1961.** 10th Evangelical Churches' Day. Crosses in violet.
B 210. B **61.** 10 pf. green .. 10 15
B 211. 20 pf. purple .. 10 20
DESIGN: 20 pf. "Five Crosses" and Kaiser Wilhelm Memorial Church.

**1961.** West Berlin Radio and Television Exn.
B 212. B **62.** 20 pf. brown & red 10 15

B **63.** "Die Linden" (1650).

B **64.** Euler Gelberhund Biplane, 1912, and Boeing 707 Airliner.

**1962.** " Old Berlin " series.
B 213. B **63.** 7 pf. sepia & brown 10 10
B 214. – 10 pf. sepia & grn. 10 10
B 215. – 15 pf. black & blue 15 10
B 216. – 20 pf. sepia & brn. 25 10
B 217. – 25 pf. sepia & olive 20 30
B 218. – 40 pf. black & blue 30 25
B 219. – 50 pf. sepia & purple 40 35
B 220. – 60 pf. sepia & mve. 35 50
B 221. – 70 pf. black & pur. 30 80
B 222. – 80 pf. sepia and red 40 60
B 223. – 90 pf. sepia & brn. 70 80
B 224. – 1 Dm. sepia & grn. 65 1·00
DESIGNS: 10 pf. "Waisenbrucke" (Orphans' Bridge), 1783. 15 pf. Mauerstrasse, 1780. 20 pf. Berlin Castle, 1703. 25 pf. Potsdamer Platz, 1825. 40 pf. Bellevue Castle, circa 1800. 50 pf. Fischer Bridge, 1830. 60 pf. Halle Gate, 1880. 70 pf. Parochial Church, 1780. 80 pf. University, 1825. 90 pf. Opera House, 1780. 1 Dm. Grunewald Lake, circa 1790.

**1962.** 50th Anniv. of German Airmail Transport.
B 225. B **64.** 60 pf. black & blue 40 40

B **65.** Exhibition Emblem.

B **66.** Town Hall Schoneberg.

**1963.** West Berlin Broadcasting Exn.
B 226. B **65.** 20 pf. ultramarine, grey and blue .. 15 20

**1964.** 700th Anniv. of Schoneberg.
B 227. B **66.** 20 pf. brown .. 15 15

B **67.** Pres. Lubke.

B **68.** Kaiser Wilhelm Memorial Church.

**1964.** Re-election of Pres. Lubke.
B 228. B **67.** 20 pf. red .. .. 10 10
B 229. 40 pf. blue .. 20 25
See also Nos. B 308/9.

**WEST GERMAN DESIGNS.** Except where illustrated the following are the same or similar designs to West Germany additionally inscr "BERLIN".

**1964.** Capitals of the Federal Lands. As No. 1335.
B 230. 20 pf. multicoloured. .. 20 25

**1964.** Humanitarian Relief and Welfare Funds. As Nos. 1352/5.
B 231. 10 pf. + 5 pf. mult. .. 15 20
B 232. 15 pf. + 5 pf. mult. .. 15 20
B 233. 20 pf. + 10 pf. mult. .. 20 20
B 234. 40 pf. + 20 pf. mult. .. 50 90

**1964.** Pres. Kennedy Commem. As Type **411.**
B 235. 40 pf. blue .. .. 20 30

**1964.** Twelve Centuries of German Architecture.

(a) Size 18½ × 22½ mm. As Nos. 1359/66. Plain backgrounds.
B 236. 10 pf. brown .. .. 10 10
B 237. 15 pf. green .. .. 20 15
B 238. 20 pf. red .. .. 20 15
B 239. 40 pf. blue .. .. 70 80
B 240. 50 pf. bistre .. .. 1·40 1·50
B 241. 60 pf. red .. .. 1·00 90
B 242. 70 pf. green .. .. 2·00 2·75
B 243. 80 pf. brown .. .. 1·25 1·25

(b) Size 19½ × 24 mm. As Nos. 1367/81. Coloured backgrounds.
B 244. 5 pf. bistre .. .. 10 15
B 245. 8 pf. red .. .. 10 30
B 246. 10 pf. purple .. .. 15 10
B 247. 20 pf. green .. .. 20 15
B 248. 30 pf. olive .. .. 30 30
B 249. 30 pf. red .. .. 25 10
B 250. 40 pf. bistre .. .. 55 1·00
B 251. 50 pf. blue .. .. 40 55
B 252. 60 pf. red .. .. 1·50 2·00
B 253. 70 pf. bronze .. .. 70 80
B 254. 80 pf. brown .. .. 1·25 2·00
B 255. 90 pf. black .. .. 70 90
B 256. 1 Dm. blue .. .. 60 40
B 257. 1 Dm. 10 brown .. 1·25 1·50
B 258. 1 Dm. 30 green .. 1·50 2·00
B 259. 2 Dm. purple .. .. 1·75 1·60
BUILDINGS: 8 pf. Palatine Castle, Kaub. Others as Nos. 1359/81 of West Germany.

**1965.** Child Welfare. As Nos. 1384/7.
B 261. 10 pf. + 5 pf. Woodcock 15 20
B 262. 15 pf. + 5 pf. Ring-necked pheasant .. 15 20
B 263. 20 pf. + 10 pf. Black grouse .. .. 25 25
B 264. 40 pf. + 20 pf. Capercaillie .. .. 60 65

**1965.** "New Berlin". Multicoloured.

B 265. 10 pf. Type B **68** .. 15 10
B 266. 15 pf. Opera House .. 15 10
B 267. 20 pf. Philharmonic Hall .. .. .. 15 10
B 268. 30 pf. Jewish Community Centre 30 10
B 269. 40 pf. Regina Martyrum Memorial Church .. .. 25 20
B 270. 50 pf. Ernst-Reuter Square .. .. 30 20
B 271. 60 pf. Europa Centre .. 30 40
B 272. 70 pf. Technical University, Charlottenburg .. 45 60
B 273. 80 pf. City Motorway 40 25
B 274. 90 pf. Planetarium .. 50 30
B 275. 1 Dm. Telecommunications, Tower .. 50 60
B 276. 1 Dm. 10 University Clinic, Steglitz .. 50 60

Nos. B 266/270, B 272, B 274 and B 276 are horiz.

**1965.** Humanitarian Relief Funds. As Nos. 1406/9.

B 277. 10 pf. + 5 pf. Type **425** 10 30
B 278. 15 pf. + 5 pf. Cinderella and birds with dress 10 30
B 279. 20 pf. + 10 pf. Prince offering slipper to Cinderella .. .. 15 30
B 280. 40 pf. + 20 pf. Cinderella and Prince on horse .. 40 75

**1966.** As Nos. 1412/5a.

B 281. 10 pf. brown .. .. 10 10
B 282. 20 pf. green .. .. 30 15
B 283. 30 pf. red .. .. 30 10
B 284. 50 pf. blue .. .. 80 55
B 284a. 100 pf. blue .. .. 5·00 3·25

**1966.** Child Welfare. As Nos. 1416/9.

B 285. 10 pf. + 5 pf. Type **429** 20 30
B 286. 20 pf. + 10 pf. Chamois 20 30
B 287. 30 pf. + 15 pf. Fallow deer .. .. 30 50
B 288. 50 pf. + 25 pf. Red deer 50 1·10

**1966.** Humanitarian Relief Funds. As Nos. 1428/31.

B 289. 10 pf. + 5 pf. Type **435** 15 30
B 290. 20 pf. + 10 pf. Frog dining with Princess .. 15 30
B 291. 30 pf. + 15 pf. Frog Prince and Princess .. 20 30
B 292. 50 pf. + 25 pf. In coach 35 80

Designs from Grimm's "The Frog Prince".

**1967.** Child Welfare. As Nos. 1434/7.

B 293. 10 pf. + 5 pf. Common rabbit .. .. 25 40
B 294. 20 pf. + 10 pf. Stoat .. 30 40
B 295. 30 pf. + 15 pf. Common hamster .. .. 40 50
B 296. 50 pf. + 25 pf. Red fox 65 1·25

B **69.** "Bust of a Young Man" (after C. Meit).

B **70.** Broadcasting Tower and TV Screen.

**1967.** Berlin Art Treasures.

B 297. B **69.** 10 pf. sepia & bistre 15 15
B 298. – 20 pf. olive and blue 20 20
B 299. – 30 pf. brown & olive 20 30
B 300. – 50 pf. sepia and grey 30 40
B 301. – 1 Dm. black & blue 50 65
B 302. – 1 Dm. 10 brown and chestnut .. 75 90

DESIGNS: 20 pf. Head of "The Elector of Brandenburg" (statue by Schluter). 30 pf. "St. Mark" (statue by Riemenschneider). 50 pf. Head from Quadriga, Brandenburg Gate. 1 Dm. "Madonna" (carving by Feuchtmayer). (22½ × 39 mm.) 1 Dm. 10, "Christ and St. John" (after carving from Upper Swabia, circa 1320).

**1967.** West Berlin Broadcasting Exn.

B 303. B **70.** 30 pf. multicoloured 20 30

**1967.** Humanitarian Relief Funds. As Nos. 1443/6.

B 304. 10 pf. + 5 pf. mult. .. 20 30
B 305. 20 pf. + 10 pf. mult. .. 20 30
B 306. 30 pf. + 15 pf. mult. .. 30 40
B 307. 50 pf. + 25 pf. mult. .. 50 90

**1967.** Re-election of President Lubke. As Type B **67.**

B 308. B **67.** 30 pf. red .. .. 20 30
B 309. 50 pf. blue .. .. 30 40

**1968.** Child Welfare. As Nos. 1454/7.

B 310. 10 pf. + 5 pf. Wild cat 30 65
B 311. 20 pf. + 10 pf. European otter .. 40 65
B 312. 30 pf. + 15 pf. Eurasian badger .. .. 65 85
B 313. 50 pf. + 25 pf. Eurasian beaver .. .. 1·50 2·50

B **71.** Former Court-house.

B **72.** Festival Emblems.

**1968.** 500th Anniv. of Berlin Magistrate's Court.

B 314. B **71.** 30 pf. black .. 20 30

**1968.** Athletics Festival, Berlin.

B 315. B **72** 20 f. red, blk. & grey 15 30

**1968.** Humanitarian Relief Funds. As Nos. 1473/6.

B 316. 10 pf. + 5 pf. Doll of 1878 15 25
B 317. 20 pf. + 10 pf. Doll of 1850 20 15
B 318. 30 pf. + 15 pf. Doll of 1870 25 20
B 319. 50 pi. + 25 pf. Doll of 1885 60 80

B **74.** "The Newspaper Seller" (C. W. Allers, 1889).

**1969.** 19th-Cent. Berliners. Contemporary Art.

B 320. – 5 pf. black .. 10 15
B 321. B **74.** 10 pf. purple .. 15 20
B 322. – 10 pf. brown .. 15 20
B 323. – 20 pf. green .. 15 20
B 324. – 20 pf. turquoise .. 15 20
B 325. – 30 pf. brown .. 40 60
B 326. – 30 pf. brown .. 40 50
B 327. – 50 pf. blue .. 1·50 1·60

DESIGNS—HORIZ. 5 pf. "The Cab-driver" (H. Zille, 1875). VERT. 10 pf. "The Bus-driver" (C.W. Allers, 1890). 20 pf. (No. B 323) "The Cobblers Boy" (F. Kruger, 1839). 20 pf. (No. B 324) "The Cobbler" (A. von Menzel, 1833). 30 pf. (No. B325) "The Borsig Forge" (P. Meyerheim, 1878). 30 pf. (No. B 326) "Three Berlin Ladies" (F. Kurger, 1839). 50 pf. "At the Brandenburg Gate" (C.W. Allers, 1889).

**1969.** Child Welfare. As Nos. 1478/81.

B 328. 10 pf. + 5 pf. brown, black and yellow .. 25 40
B 329. 20 pf. + 10 pf. brown, black and buff .. 35 50
B 330. 30 pf. + 15 pf. brown, black and red .. 50 70
B 331. 50 pf. + 25 pf. grey, yellow, black and blue .. .. .. 1·25 1·75

B **76.** Postman.

B **77.** J. Joachim (violinist & director; after A. von Menzel).

**1969.** 20th Congress of Post Office Trade Union Federation (I.P.T.T.), Berlin.

B 333. B **76.** 10 pf. olive .. 15 25
B 334. – 20 pf. brown & buff 25 35
B 335. – 30 pf. vio. & ochre 60 60
B 336. – 50 pf. bl. & lt. bl. 80 80

DESIGNS: 20 pf. Telephonist. 30 pf. Technician. 50 pf. Airmail Handlers.

**1969.** Anniversaries. Multicoloured.

B 337. 30 pf. Type B **77** .. 50 40
B 338. 50 pf. Alexander von Humboldt (after J. Stieler) .. .. 60 40

ANNIVERSARIES: 30 pf. Centenary of Berlin Academy of Music. 50 pf. Birth bicentenary of Humboldt.

B **78.** Railway Carriage (1835).

B **79.** T. Fontane.

**1969.** Humanitarian Relief Funds. Pewter Figurines. Multicoloured.

(a) Inscr. "WOHLFAHRTSMARKE".

B 339. 10 pf. + 5 pf. Type B **78** 25 30
B 340. 20 pf. + 10 pf. Woman feeding chicken (1850) 25 30
B 341. 30 pf. + 15 pf. Market stall (1850) .. 40 50
B 342. 50 pf. + 25 pf. Mounted postilion (1860) .. 80 90

(b) Christmas. Inscr. "WEIHNACHTSMARKE".

B 343. 10 pf. + 5 pf. "The Three Kings" .. 20 30

**1970.** 150th Birth Anniv. of Theodor Fontane (writer).

B 344. B **79.** 20 pf. multicoloured 25 25

B **80.** Heinrich von Stretlingen.

B **81.** Film "Title".

**1970.** Miniatures of Minnesingers. Mult.

B345 10 pf. + 5 pf. Type B **80** 20 40
B346 20 pf. + 10 pf. Meinloh von Sevelingen .. 35 50
B347 30 pf. + 15 pf. Burkhart von Hohenfels .. 60 85
B348 50 pf. + 25 pf. Albrecht von Johannsdorf .. 1·00 1·40

**1970.** 20th Int. Film Festival, Berlin.

B 349. B **81.** 30 pf. multicoloured 20 30

**1970.** Pres. Heinemann. As Nos. 1535/1555.

B 350. **486.** 5 pf. black .. 15 10
B 351. 8 pf. brown .. 85 1·50
B 352. 10 pf. brown .. 15 10
B 353. 15 pf. bistre .. 25 50
B 354. 20 pf. green .. 15 10
B 355. 25 pf. green .. 80 90
B 356. 30 pf. brown .. 1·00 30
B 357. 40 pf. orange .. 35 25
B 358. 50 pf. blue .. 40 25
B 359. 60 pf. blue .. 70 40
B 360. 70 pf. brown .. 50 40
B 361. 80 pf. green .. 75 1·00
B 362. 90 pf. red .. 2·25 2·75
B 363. 1 Dm. green .. 55 20
B 364. 1 Dm. 10 grey .. 1·25 1·50
B 365. 1 Dm. 20 brown .. 1·10 1·25
B 366. 1 Dm. 30 brown .. 1·50 1·50
B 367. 1 Dm. 40 green .. 1·50 2·00
B 368. 1 Dm. 50 red .. 1·50 65
B 369. 1 Dm. 60 orange .. 1·50 2·00
B 370. 1 Dm. 70 orange .. 1·75 1·75
B 371. 1 Dm. 90 purple .. 1·75 1·75
B 372. 2 Dm. violet .. 1·60 1·50

B **82.** Allegory of Folklore.

B **83.** "Caspar".

**1970.** 20th Berlin Folklore Week.

B 373. B **82.** 30 pf. multicoloured 30 30

**1970.** Humanitarian Relief Funds. Puppets. Multicoloured.

(a) Relief Funds.

B 374. 10 pf. + 5 pf. Type B **83** 15 20
B 375. 20 pf. + 10 pf. "Polichinelle" .. 20 35
B 376. 30 pf. + 15 pf. "Punch" 30 35
B 377. 50 pf. + 25 pf. "Pulcinella" .. 60 90

(b) Christmas.

B 378. 10 pf. + 5 pf. "Angel" 20 20

B **84.** L. von Ranke (after painting by J. Schrader).

B **85.** City Train (1933).

**1970.** 175th Birth Anniv. of Leopold von Ranke (historian).

B 379. B **84.** 30 pf. multicoloured 25 30

**1971.** Centenary of German Unification.

B380 **492** 30 pf. blk, red & orge 30 40

**1971.** Berlin Rail Transport. Multicoloured.

B381 5 pf. Local steam train (1925) .. .. .. 20 25
B382 10 pf. Electric tram, 1890 30 25
B383 20 pf. Horse-drawn tram-car, 1880 .. .. 45 40
B384 30 pf. Type B **85** .. 50 55
B385 50 pf. Electric tram-car, 1950 .. .. .. 1·50 2·00
B386 1 Dm. Underground train, 1971 .. .. 1·90 2·50

B **86.** "Fly".

B **87.** "The Bagpiper" (copper engraving, Durer, c. 1514).

**1971.** Child Welfare Children's Drawings. Multicoloured.

B 387. 10 pf. + 5 pf. Type B **86** 30 40
B 388. 20 pf. + 10 pf. "Fish" .. 30 45
B 389. 30 pf. + 15 pf. "Porcupine" 40 70
B 390. 50 pf. + 25 pf. "Cockerel" 90 1·25

**1971.** 500th Birth Anniv. of Albrecht Durer.

B 391. B **87.** 10 pf. blk. & brn. 30 20

B **88.** Communications Tower and Dish Aerials.

B **89.** Bach and part of 2nd Brandenburg Concerto.

**1971.** West Berlin Broadcasting Exhib.

B 392. B **88.** 30 pf. ind., bl. & red 40 35

**1971.** 250th Anniv. of Bach's Brandenburg Concertos.

B 393. B **89.** 30 pf. multicoloured 80 35

B **90.** H. von Helmholtz (from painting by K. Morell-Kramer).

B **92.** Dancing Men.

**1971.** 150th Anniv. of Hermann von Helmholtz (scientist).

B 394. B **90.** 25 pf. multicoloured 35 40

**1971.** Accident Prevention. As Nos. 1596/1605.

B 396. 5 pf. orange .. .. 30 35
B 397. 10 pf. brown .. .. 30 20
B 398. 20 pf. violet .. .. 30 30
B 399. 25 pf. green .. .. 60 55
B 400. 30 pf. red .. .. 40 15
B 401. 40 pf. mauve .. .. 40 20
B 402. 50 pf. blue .. .. 2·00 80
B 403. 60 pf. blue .. .. 1·75 1·40
B 404. 70 pf. blue and green .. 1·00 75
B 405. 100 pf. green .. .. 1·50 90
B 406. 150 pf. brown .. .. 4·50 3·00

**1971.** Humanitarian Relief Funds. Wooden Toys. Multicoloured.

(a) Inscr. "WOHLFAHRTSMARKE".

B 407. 10 pf. + 5 pf. Type B **92** 15 20
B 408. 25 pf. + 10 pf. Horse-man on wheels .. 25 35
B 409. 30 pf. + 15 pf. Acrobat 50 50
B 410. 60 pf. + 30 pf. Nurse and babies .. .. 75 90

(b) Christmas. Inscr. "WEIHNACHTSMARKE".

B 411. 10 pf. + 5 pf. Angel with two candles .. 20 30

B **93.** Microscope.

B **94.** F. Gilly (after bust by Schadow).

**1971.** Birth Centenary of Material-Testing Laboratory, Berlin.

| | | | | |
|---|---|---|---|---|
| B412 | B **93** | 30 pf. multicoloured | 30 | 30 |

**1972.** Birth Bicentenary of Friedrich Gilly (architect).

| | | | | |
|---|---|---|---|---|
| B 413. | B **94.** | 30 pf. black & blue | 30 | 30 |

**B 95.** Boy raiding Bird's-nest.

**B 97.** E. T. A. Hoffman.

**B 96.** " Grunewaldsee " (A. von Riesen).

**1972.** Child Welfare. Animal Protection. Multicoloured.

| | | | |
|---|---|---|---|
| B 414. | 10 pf.+5 pf. Type B **95** | 25 | 30 |
| B 415. | 25 pf.+10 pf. Care of kittens .. .. | 40 | 50 |
| B 416. | 30 pf.+15 pf. Man beating watch-dog .. | 60 | 75 |
| B 417. | 60 pf.+30 pf. Animals crossing road at night | 1·50 | 1·75 |

**1972.** Paintings of Berlin Lakes. Mult.

| | | | |
|---|---|---|---|
| B 418. | 10 pf. Type B **96** .. | 15 | 10 |
| B 419. | 25 pf. " Wannsee " (Max Liebermann) .. | 35 | 30 |
| B 420. | 30 pf. " Schlachtensee " (W. Leistikow) .. | 50 | 45 |

**1972.** 150th Death Anniv. of E. T. A. Hoffman (poet and musician).

| | | | | |
|---|---|---|---|---|
| B 421. | B **97.** | 60 pf. blk. & violet | 50 | 60 |

**B 98.** Max Liebermann (self-portrait).

**B 99.** Stamp Printing-press.

**1972.** 125th Birth Anniv. of Max Liebermann (painter).

| | | | | |
|---|---|---|---|---|
| B 422. | B **98.** | 40 pf. multicoloured | 40 | 30 |

**1972.** Stamp Day.

| | | | | |
|---|---|---|---|---|
| B 423. | B **99.** | 20 pf. blue, blk. & red | 25 | 15 |

**1972.** Humanitarian Relief Funds. Multicoloured. (a) 19th-century Faience Chessmen. As Nos. 1636/40 of West Germany. Inscr "WOLHFAHRTSMARKE".

| | | | |
|---|---|---|---|
| B 424 | 20 pf.+10 pf. Knight | 30 | 30 |
| B 425 | 30 pf.+15 pf. Rook .. | 40 | 40 |
| B 426 | 40 pf.+20 pf. Queen .. | 80 | 80 |
| B 427 | 70 pf.+35 pf. King .. | 1·25 | 90 |

(b) Christmas. Inscr. " WEIHNACHTSMARKE ".

| | | | |
|---|---|---|---|
| B 428. | 20 pf.+10 pf. " The Holy Family " .. .. | 35 | 40 |

**B 100.** Prince von Hardenberg (after Tischbein).

**B 101.** Northern Goshawk.

**1972.** 150th Death Anniv. of Karl August von Hardenberg (statesman).

| | | | | |
|---|---|---|---|---|
| B 429. | B **100.** | 40 pf. multicoloured | 45 | 30 |

**1973.** Youth Welfare. Birds of Prey. Mult.

| | | | |
|---|---|---|---|
| B 430. | 20 pf.+10 pf. Type B **101** .. .. | 75 | 75 |
| B 431. | 30 pf.+15 pf. Peregrine falcon .. .. | 1·10 | 1·10 |
| B 432. | 40 pf.+20 pf. European sparrow hawk .. .. | 1·75 | 1·75 |
| B 433. | 70 pf.+35 pf. Golden eagle .. .. .. | 2·50 | 2·50 |

B **102.** Horse-bus, 1907.

**1973.** Berlin Buses. Multicoloured.

| | | | |
|---|---|---|---|
| B 434. | 20 pf. Type B **102** .. | 30 | 20 |
| B 435. | 20 pf. Trolley bus, 1933 | 30 | 20 |
| B 436. | 30 pf. Motor bus, 1919 | 50 | 60 |
| B 437. | 30 pf. Double-decker, 1970 .. .. .. | 60 | 45 |
| B 438. | 40 pf. Double-decker, 1925 .. .. .. | 80 | 75 |
| B 439. | 40 pf. "Standard" bus, 1973 .. .. .. | 80 | 65 |

**B 103.** L. Tieck.

**B 104.** J. J. Quantz.

**1973.** Birth Bicentenary of Ludwig Tieck (poet and writer).

| | | | | |
|---|---|---|---|---|
| B 440. | B **103.** | 40pf. multicoloured | 40 | 30 |

**1973.** Death Bicentenary of Johann Quantz (composer).

| | | | | |
|---|---|---|---|---|
| B 441. | B **104.** | 40 pf. black .. | 85 | 50 |

B **106.** 17th-Century Hurdy-Gurdy.

B **107.** G. W. Knobelsdorff.

**1973.** Humanitarian Relief Funds. Mult. (a) Musical Instruments. Inscr. " WOHLFAHRTSMARKE ".

| | | | |
|---|---|---|---|
| B 443. | 20 pf.+10 pf. Type B **106** | 35 | 30 |
| B 444. | 30 pf.+15 pf. 16th century drum .. .. | 50 | 40 |
| B 445. | 40 pf.+20 pf. 18th century lute .. | 80 | 50 |
| B 446. | 70 pf.+35 pf. 16th century organ .. .. | 1·25 | 1·10 |

(b) Christmas. Inscr. " WEIHNACHTSMARKE ".

| | | | |
|---|---|---|---|
| B 447. | 20 pf.+10 pf. Christmas star .. .. .. | 40 | 30 |

**1974.** 275th Birth Anniv. of Georg W. von Knobelsdorff (architect).

| | | | | |
|---|---|---|---|---|
| B 448. | B **107.** | 20 pf. brown .. | 25 | 20 |

B **108.** G. R. Kirchoff.

B **109.** A. Slaby.

**1974.** 150th Birth Anniv. of Gustav R. Kirchhoff (physicist).

| | | | | |
|---|---|---|---|---|
| B 449. | B **108.** | 30 pf. grn. & grey | 30 | 25 |

**1974.** 125th Birth Anniv. of Adolf Slaby (radio pioneer).

| | | | | |
|---|---|---|---|---|
| B 450. | B **109.** | 40 pf. black & red | 40 | 40 |

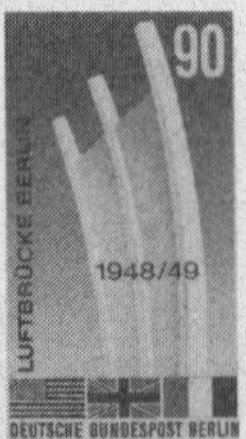


B **110.** Airlift Memorial.

B **111.** Photography.

**1974.** 25th Anniv. of Berlin Airlift.

| | | | | |
|---|---|---|---|---|
| B 451 | B **110** | 90 pf. mult .. | 1·25 | 1·00 |

**1974.** Youth Welfare. Youth Activities. Multicoloured.

| | | | |
|---|---|---|---|
| B 452. | 20 pf.+10 pf. Type B **111** | 50 | 55 |
| B 453. | 30 pf.+15 pf. Athletics .. | 60 | 40 |
| B 454. | 40 pf.+20 pf. Music .. | 1·10 | 1·40 |
| B 455. | 70 pf.+35 pf. Voluntary service (Nurse) .. | 1·75 | 2·00 |

B **112.** School Seal.

B **113.** Spring Bouquet.

**1974.** 400th Anniv. of Evangelical Grammar School, Berlin.

| | | | | |
|---|---|---|---|---|
| B 456. | B **112.** | 50 pf. grey, brn. & gold | 40 | 35 |

**1974.** Humanitarian Relief Funds. Flowers. Multicoloured. (a) 25th Anniv of Humanitarian Relief Stamps. Inscr "25 JAHRE WOHLFAHRTSMARKE".

| | | | |
|---|---|---|---|
| B 457. | 30 pf.+15 pf. Type B **113** | 30 | 40 |
| B 458. | 40 pf.+20 pf. Autumn bouquet .. .. | 40 | 45 |
| B 459. | 50 pf.+25 pf. Bouquet of roses .. .. | 45 | 55 |
| B 460. | 70 pf.+35 pf. Winter bouquet .. .. | 80 | 85 |

(b) Christmas. Inscr. " WEIHNACHTSMARKE."

| | | | |
|---|---|---|---|
| B 461. | 30 pf.+15 pf. Christmas bouquet .. .. | 60 | 40 |

B **114.** Tegel Airport.

B **115.** "Venus" (F. E. Meyer).

**1974.** Opening of Tegel Airport. Berlin.

| | | | | |
|---|---|---|---|---|
| B462 | B **114** | 50 pf. vio, bl & grn | 90 | 45 |

**1974.** Berlin Porcelain Figures. Mult.

| | | | |
|---|---|---|---|
| B 463. | 30 pf. Type B **115** .. | 35 | 25 |
| B 464. | 40 pf. "Astronomy" (W. C. Meyer) .. | 40 | 45 |
| B 465. | 50 pf. "Justice" (J. G. Muller) .. | 50 | 50 |

B **116.** Gottfried Schadow.

B **117.** "Prinzess Charlotte".

**1975.** 125th Death Anniv. of Gottfried Schadow (sculptor).

| | | | | |
|---|---|---|---|---|
| B 466. | B **116.** | 50 pf. brown .. | 45 | 40 |

**1975.** Berlin Pleasure Boats. Multicoloured.

| | | | |
|---|---|---|---|
| B 467. | 30 pf. Type B **117** .. | 50 | 35 |
| B 468. | 40 pf. "Siegfried" .. | 50 | 60 |
| B 469. | 50 pf. "Sperber" .. | 60 | 40 |
| B 470. | 60 pf. "Vaterland" .. | 70 | 75 |
| B 471. | 70 pf. "Moby Dick" .. | 1·00 | 85 |

B **118.** "Drache" Steam Locomotive of 1840.

**1975.** Youth Welfare. Railway Locomotives. Multicoloured.

| | | | |
|---|---|---|---|
| B472 | 30 pf.+15 pf. Type B **118** | 1·00 | 80 |
| B473 | 40 pf.+20 pf. Tank locomotive Series "89" .. | 1·25 | 1·10 |
| B474 | 50 pf.+25 pf. Steam locomotive Series "050" .. | 1·90 | 1·60 |
| B475 | 70 pf.+35 pf. Steam locomotive Series "010" .. | 2·75 | 2·75 |

B **119.** Ferdinand Sauerbruch (surgeon).

B **120.** Gymnastics Emblem.

**1975.** Birth Cent. of Ferdinand Sauerbruch.

| | | | | |
|---|---|---|---|---|
| B 476. | B **119.** | 50 pf. deep brown, brown and pink | 55 | 40 |

**1975.** Gymnaestrada (Gymnastic Games), Berlin.

| | | | | |
|---|---|---|---|---|
| B 477. | B **120.** | 40 pf. black, gold and green .. | 45 | 35 |

**1975.** Industry and Technology. As Nos. 1742/55.

| | | | | |
|---|---|---|---|---|
| B 478. | – | 5 pf. green .. .. | 10 | 10 |
| B 479. | – | 10 pf. purple .. | 10 | 10 |
| B 480. | – | 20 pf. red .. .. | 25 | 10 |
| B 481. | – | 30 pf. violet .. | 30 | 15 |
| B 482. | **572.** | 40 pf. green .. | 45 | 25 |
| B 483. | – | 50 pf. red .. .. | 55 | 15 |
| B 483a. | – | 60 pf. red .. .. | 1·00 | 25 |
| B 484. | – | 70 pf. blue .. .. | 70 | 25 |
| B 485. | – | 80 pf. green .. | 80 | 20 |
| B 486. | – | 100 pf. brown .. | 90 | 35 |
| B 486a. | – | 110 pf. purple .. | 1·25 | 60 |
| B 487. | – | 120 pf. blue .. | 1·25 | 70 |
| B 487a. | – | 130 pf. red .. | 1·75 | 95 |
| B 488. | – | 140 pf. red .. .. | 1·25 | 25 |
| B 488a. | – | 150 pf. red .. | 2·25 | 90 |
| B 489. | – | 160 pf. green .. | 1·75 | 90 |
| B 489a. | – | 180 pf. brown .. | 1·75 | 1·10 |
| B 489b. | – | 190 pf. brown .. | 2·50 | 1·25 |
| B 490. | – | 200 pf. purple .. | 1·75 | 50 |
| B 490a. | – | 230 pf. purple .. | 2·25 | 1·40 |
| B 490b. | – | 250 pf. green .. | 3·00 | 1·25 |
| B 490c. | – | 300 pf. green .. | 3·75 | 2·00 |
| B 491. | – | 500 pf. black .. | 5·75 | 2·50 |

B **121.** " Lovis Corinth " (self-portrait).

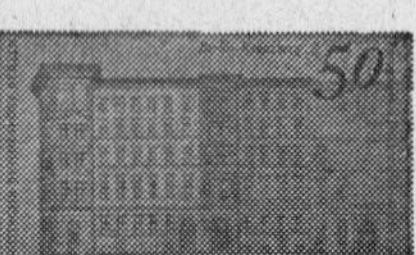

B **122.** Buildings in Naunynstrasse, Berlin-Kreuzberg.

**1975.** 50th Death Anniv of Lovis Corinth (painter).

| | | | | |
|---|---|---|---|---|
| B 492. | B **121.** | 50 pf. multicoloured | 60 | 40 |

**1975.** European Architectural Heritage Year.

| | | | | |
|---|---|---|---|---|
| B 493. | B **122.** | 50 pf. multicoloured | 50 | 35 |

B **123.** Yellow Gentian.

B **124.** Paul Lobe.

**1975.** Humanitarian Relief Funds. Alpine Flowers. Multicoloured.

| | | | |
|---|---|---|---|
| B 494. | 30 pf.+15 pf. Type B **123** | 45 | 35 |
| B 495. | 40 pf.+20 pf. Arnica .. | 50 | 45 |
| B 496. | 50 pf.+25 pf. Cyclamen | 65 | 60 |
| B 497. | 70 pf.+35 pf. Blue gentian | 1·25 | 95 |

**1975.** Christmas. As Type B **123.** inscr. " WEIHNACHTSMARKE ". Mult.

| | | | |
|---|---|---|---|
| B 498. | 30 pf.+15 pf. Snow heather | 55 | 55 |

See also Nos. B508/11, B540/3 and B557/60.

**1975.** Birth Cent. of Paul Lobe (politician).

| | | | | |
|---|---|---|---|---|
| B 499. | B **124** | 50 pf. red .. | 55 | 45 |

B **125.** Ears of Wheat, with inscription " Grune Woche ".

B **126.** Putting the Shot.

**1976.** "International Agriculture Week", Berlin.

| | | | | |
|---|---|---|---|---|
| B 500. | B **125.** | 70 pf. yell. & grn. | 60 | 60 |

**1976.** Youth Welfare. Training for the Olympics. Multicoloured.

| | | | |
|---|---|---|---|
| B 501. | 30 pf.+15 pf. Type B **126** | 60 | 60 |
| B 502. | 40 pf.+20 pf. Hockey .. | 70 | 70 |
| B 503. | 50 pf.+25 pf. Handball | 90 | 90 |
| B 504. | 70 pf.+35 pf. Swimming | 1·40 | 1·40 |

B 127. Hockey.

B 128. Treble Clef.

**1976.** Women's World Hockey Championships.
B 505. **B 127.** 30 pf. green .. 60 35

**1976.** German Choristers' Festival.
B 506. **B 128.** 40 pf. multicoloured 70 40

B 129. Fire Service Emblem.

B 130. Julius Tower, Spandau.

**1976.** 125th Anniv of Berlin Fire Service.
B507 **B 129** 50 pf. multicoloured 65 75

**1976.** Humanitarian Relief Funds. Garden Flowers. As Type **B 123.** Multicoloured.

| | | | |
|---|---|---|---|
| B 508. | 30 pf. + 15 pf. Iris .. | 40 | 40 |
| B 509. | 40 pf. + 20 pf. Wallflower | 50 | 50 |
| B 510. | 50 pf. + 25 pf. Dahlia .. | 60 | 60 |
| B 511. | 70 pf. + 35 pf. Larkspur | 1·00 | 1·00 |

**1976.** Berlin Views (1st series).

| | | | | |
|---|---|---|---|---|
| B 512. | – | 30 pf. blk. and blue | 50 | 25 |
| B 513. | **B 130.** | 40 pf. blk. and brn. | 60 | 35 |
| B 514. | – | 50 pf. blk. and grn. | 70 | 50 |

DESIGNS: 30 pf. Yacht on the Havel. 50 pf. Lake and Victory Column, Tiergarten park.

See also Nos. B 562/4, B 605/7 and B 647/9.

**1977.** Coil Stamps. German Castles. As Nos. 1805/12d. of Germany.

| | | | |
|---|---|---|---|
| B516 | 10 pf. blue .. .. | 10 | 10 |
| B517 | 20 pf. orange .. .. | 20 | 10 |
| B517a | 25 pf. red .. .. | 50 | 20 |
| B518 | 30 pf. brown .. .. | 30 | 10 |
| B518c | 35 pf. red .. .. | 55 | 15 |
| B519 | 40 pf. green .. .. | 45 | 15 |
| B519a | 40 pf. brown .. .. | 35 | 15 |
| B520 | 50 pf. red .. .. | 55 | 15 |
| B520b | 50 pf. green .. .. | 45 | 15 |
| B521 | 60 pf. brown .. .. | 1·25 | 20 |
| B521a | 60 pf. red .. .. | 60 | 15 |
| B522 | 70 pf. blue .. .. | 90 | 30 |
| B522a | 80 pf. green .. .. | 75 | 25 |
| B522b | 90 pf. blue .. .. | 1·00 | 40 |
| B522c | 120 pf. violet .. .. | 1·10 | 50 |
| B523 | 190 pf. red .. .. | 1·60 | 80 |
| B524 | 200 pf. green .. .. | 2·00 | 80 |
| B524a | 210 pf. brown .. .. | 2·50 | 1·25 |
| B524b | 230 pf. green .. .. | 2·50 | 1·00 |
| B524c | 280 pf. blue .. .. | 2·25 | 95 |
| B524d | 300 pf. orange .. .. | 2·75 | 1·00 |

B 132. "Eugenie d' Alton" (Cristian Rauch).

B 133. "Eduard Gaertner" (self-portrait).

**1977.** Birth Bicentenary of Christian Daniel Rauch (sculptor).
B525. **B 132.** 50 pf. black .. 60 45

**1977.** Death Cent. of Eduard Gaertner (artist).
B 526. **B 133.** 40 pf. black, green & deep green .. 50 35

B 134. Bremen Kogge, 1380.

B 135. Female Figure.

**1977.** Youth Welfare. Ships. Multicoloured.

| | | | |
|---|---|---|---|
| B 527. | 30 pf. + 15 pf. Type **B 134** | 50 | 55 |
| B 528. | 40 pf. + 20 pf. "Helena Sloman" (steamship), 1850 .. .. .. | 60 | 65 |
| B 529. | 50 pf. + 25 pf. "Cap Polonio" (liner), 1914 | 90 | 85 |
| B 530. | 70 pf. + 35 pf. "Widar" (bulk carrier), 1971 .. | 1·10 | 1·10 |

**1977.** Birth Cent. of Georg Kolbe (sculptor).
B 531. **B 135.** 30 pf. grn. & blk. 30 30

B 136. Crosses and Text.

B 137. Telephones of 1905 and 1977.

**1977.** 17th Evangelical Churches Day.
B 532. **B 136.** 40 pf. yell., black and green .. 30 35

**1977.** International Telecommunications Exhibition and Centenary of German Telephone Service.
B 533. **B 137.** 50 pf. buff, black and red .. 45 55

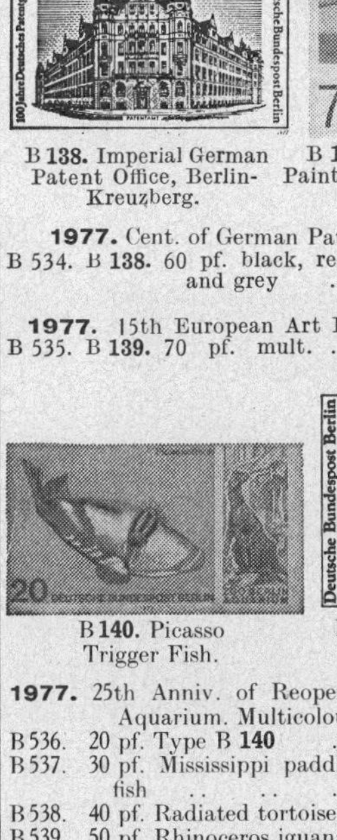

B 138. Imperial German Patent Office, Berlin-Kreuzberg.

B 139. Untitled Painting (G. Grosz).

**1977.** Cent. of German Patent Office.
B 534. **B 138.** 60 pf. black, red and grey .. 60 55

**1977.** 15th European Art Exhibition.
B 535. **B 139.** 70 pf. mult. .. 60 65

B 140. Picasso Trigger Fish.

B 142. Walter Kollo.

**1977.** 25th Anniv. of Reopening of Berlin Aquarium. Multicoloured.

| | | | |
|---|---|---|---|
| B 536. | 20 pf. Type **B 140** .. | 40 | 25 |
| B 537. | 30 pf. Mississippi paddle fish .. .. .. | 50 | 40 |
| B 538. | 40 pf. Radiated tortoise | 80 | 50 |
| B 539. | 50 pf. Rhinoceros iguana | 1·10 | 70 |

**1977.** Humanitarian Relief Funds. Meadow Flowers. As Type **B 123.** Multicoloured.

| | | | |
|---|---|---|---|
| B 540. | 30 pf. + 15 pf. Daisy .. | 35 | 35 |
| B 541. | 40 pf. + 20 pf. Marsh marigold .. .. | 50 | 50 |
| B 542. | 50 pf. + 25 pf. Sainfoin .. | 60 | 60 |
| B 543. | 70 pf. + 35 pf. Forget-me-not .. .. .. | 95 | 95 |

**1978.** Birth Cent. of Walter Kollo (composer).
B 545. **B 142.** 50 pf. brn. & red 90 60

B 143. Emblem of U.S. Chamber of Commerce.

**1978.** 75th Anniv. of U.S. Chamber of Commerce in Germany.
B 546. **B 143.** 90 pf. blue & red 95 80

**1978.** Youth Welfare. Aviation History (1st series). As T **627.** Multicoloured.

| | | | |
|---|---|---|---|
| B547 | 30 pf. + 15 pf. Montgolfier balloon, 1783 .. .. | 55 | 55 |
| B548 | 40 pf. + 20 pf. Lilienthal glider, 1891 .. .. | 65 | 65 |
| B549 | 50 pf. + 25 pf. Wright Type A, 1909 .. .. | 75 | 75 |
| B550 | 70 pf. + 35 pf. Etrich/Rumpler Taube, 1910 | 1·40 | 1·00 |

See also Nos. B567/70 and 589/92.

**1978.** Sport Promotion Fund. As T **623.** Multicoloured.

| | | | |
|---|---|---|---|
| B 551. | 50 pf. + 25 pf. Cycling .. | 65 | 70 |
| B 552. | 70 pf. + 35 pf. Fencing .. | 95 | 95 |

B 146. Albrecht von Graefe.

B 147. Friedrich Ludwig Jahn.

**1978.** 150th Birth Anniv. of Albrecht von Graefe (pioneer of medical eye services).
B 553. **B 146.** 30 pf. blk. & brn. 40 25

**1978.** Birth Bicentenary of F. L. Jahn (pioneer of physical education).
B 554. **B 147.** 50 pf. red .. 50 45

B 148. Swimming.

**1978.** Third World Swimming Championships.
B 555. **B 148.** 40 pf. multicoloured 45 35

B 149. "The Boat" (Karl Hofer).

**1978.** Birth Centenary of Karl Hofer (Impressionist painter).
B 556. **B 149.** 50 pf. multicoloured 50 50

**1978.** Humanitarian Relief Funds. Woodland Flowers. Multicoloured designs as Type **B 123.**

| | | | |
|---|---|---|---|
| B 557. | 30 pf. + 15 pf. Solomon's seal .. .. .. | 40 | 40 |
| B 558. | 40 pf. + 20 pf. Wood primrose .. .. | 50 | 50 |
| B 559. | 50 pf. + 25 pf. Red helleborine .. .. .. | 60 | 60 |
| B 560. | 70 pf. + 35 pf. Bugle .. | 95 | 95 |

B 150. Prussian State Library.

**1978.** Opening of New Prussian State Library Building.
B 561. **B 150.** 90 pf. olive & red 1·00 1·10

**1978.** Berlin Views (2nd series). As Type **B 130.**

| | | | |
|---|---|---|---|
| B 562. | 40 pf. black and green .. | 50 | 35 |
| B 563. | 50 pf. black and purple | 60 | 50 |
| B 564. | 60 pf. black and brown | 75 | 60 |

DESIGNS: 40 pf. Belvedere. 50 pf. Landwehr Canal. 60 pf. Village church, Lichtenrade.

B 152. Congress Centre.

B 154. Old and New Arms.

B 153. Relay Runners.

**1979.** Opening of International Congress Centre, Berlin.
B 566. **B 152.** 60 pf. black, blue and red .. 80 60

**1979.** Youth Welfare. History of Aviation (2nd series). As T **627.** Multicoloured.

| | | | |
|---|---|---|---|
| B567 | 40 pf. + 20 pf. Vampyr glider, 1921 .. .. | 60 | 55 |
| B568 | 50 pf. + 25 pf. Junkers Ju 52/3m "Richthafen", 1932 .. | 75 | 70 |
| B569 | 60 pf. + 30 pf. Messerschmitt Bf 108, 1934 .. | 1·00 | 90 |
| B570 | 90 pf. + 45 pf. Douglas DC-3, 1935 .. .. | 2·00 | 1·75 |

**1979.** Sport Promotion Fund. Multicoloured.

| | | | |
|---|---|---|---|
| B 571. | 60 pf. + 30 pf. Type **B 153** .. .. | 75 | 85 |
| B 572. | 90 pf. + 45 pf. Archers | 1·25 | 1·00 |

**1979.** Centenary of State Printing Works, Berlin.
B 573. **B 154.** 60 pf. multicoloured 70 50

B 155. Arrows and Target.

**1979.** World Archery Championships.
B 574. **B 155.** 50 pf. mult. .. 60 45

B 156. Television Screen.

B 157. Moses Mendelssohn.

**1979.** International Telecommunications Exhibition, Berlin.
B 575. **B 156.** 60 pf. black, grey and red .. 70 50

**1979.** 250th Birth Anniv. of Moses Mendelssohn (philosopher).
B 576. **B 157.** 90 pf. black .. 1·25 85

B 158. Venus Slipper Orchid and Great Tropical House.

**1979.** 300th Anniv. of Berlin Botanical Gardens.
B 577. **B 158.** 50 pf. multicoloured 70 40

B 159. Gas Lamp, Kreuzberg District.

**1979.** 300th Anniv. of Street Lighting.

| | | | | |
|---|---|---|---|---|
| B 578. | **B 159.** | 10 pf. green, blue and grey .. | 20 | 10 |
| B 579. | – | 40 pf. green, bistre and grey .. | 55 | 35 |
| B 580. | – | 50 pf. green, brown and grey .. | 80 | 50 |
| B 581. | – | 60 pf. green, red and grey .. | 90 | 55 |

DESIGN: 40 pf. Electric carbon-arc lamp, Hardenbergstrasse. 50 pf. Gas Lamps, Wittenberg-platz. 60 pf. Five-armed chandelier, Charlottenburg.

**1979.** Humanitarian Relief Funds. Woodland Flowers and Fruit. Multicoloured. As Type **B 123,** but horiz.

| | | | |
|---|---|---|---|
| B 582. | 40 pf. + 20 pf. Larch .. | 60 | 50 |
| B 583. | 50 pf. + 25 pf. Hazelnut | 70 | 60 |
| B 584. | 60 pf. + 30 pf. Horse chestnut .. .. | 90 | 80 |
| B 585. | 90 pf. + 45 pf. Blackthorn | 1·40 | 1·25 |

B 161. Advertisement Pillar.

B 162. "Nativity" (Altenberg medieval manuscript).

**1979.** 125th Anniv. of Advertisement Pillars.
B 586. B **161.** 50 pf. red and lilac 75 60

**1979.** Christmas.
B 587 B **162** 40 pf. + 20 pf. mult 60 70

B **163.** Map showing Wegener's Theory of Continental Drift.

**1980.** Birth Cent. of Alfred Wegener (explorer and geophysicist).
B 588. B **163.** 60 pf. black, orange and blue 1·10 80

**1980.** Youth Welfare. Aviation History (3rd series). As T **627.** Multicoloured.
B589 40 pf. + 20 pf. Vickers Viscount 810 .. .. 75 75
B590 50 pf. + 25 pf. Fokker Friendship "Condor" 90 90
B591 60 pf. + 30 pf. Sud Aviation Caravelle, 1955 .. 1·25 1·25
B592 90 pf. + 45 pf. Sikorsky S-55 helicopter, 1949 .. 1·75 1·75
Nos. B589/90 are incorrectly dated.

B **164.** Throwing the Javelin.

**1980.** Sport Promotion Fund. Multicoloured.
B 593. 50 pf. + 25 pf. Type B **164** 60 70
B 594. 60 pf. + 30 pf. Weight-lifting .. .. 80 85
B 595. 90 pf. + 45 pf. Water polo 1·25 1·40

B **165.** Cardinal Preysing.
B **166.** "Operatio" (enamel medallion).

**1980.** 86th German Catholics Congress.
B 596. B **165.** 50 pf. red & black 40 45

**1980.** 150th Anniv. of Prussian Museums. Multicoloured.
B 597. 40 pf. Type B **166** .. 60 30
B 598. 60 pf. "Monks Reading" (oak sculpture, Ernst Barlach) .. .. 75 55

B **167.** Robert Stolz.
B **168.** Von Steuben.

**1980.** Birth Centenary of Robert Stolz (composer).
B599. B **167.** 60 pf. multicoloured 1·25 70

**1980.** 250th Birth Anniv. of Friedrich Wilhelm von Steuben (American general).
B600. B **168.** 40 pf. multicoloured 60 45

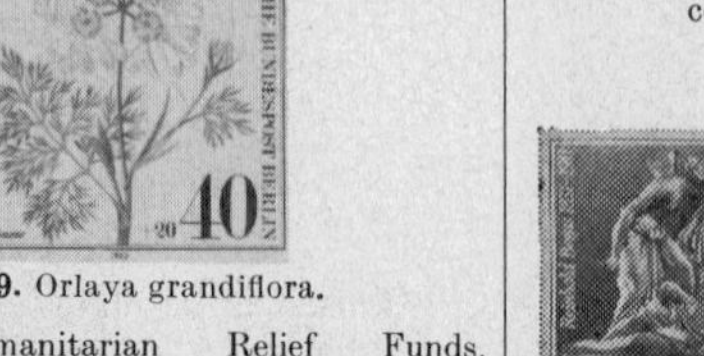

B **169.** Orlaya grandiflora.

**1980.** Humanitarian Relief Funds. Endangered Wildflowers. Multicoloured.
B601. 40 pf. + 20 pf. Type B **169** .. .. .. 60 60
B602. 50 pf. + 25 pf. Yellow gagae .. .. .. 65 65
B603. 60 pf. + 30 pf. Summer pheasant's-eye .. 85 85
B604. 90 p. + 45 pf. Venus's looking-glass .. .. 1·25 1·25
See also Nos. B 622/5

**1980.** Berlin Views (3rd series). As Type B **130.**
B605 40 pf. black and green .. 50 35
B606 50 pf. black and brown .. 65 45
B607 60 pf. black and blue .. 80 60
DESIGNS: 40 pf. Lilienthal Monument. 50 pf. "Grosse Neugierde". 60 pf. Grunewald Tower.

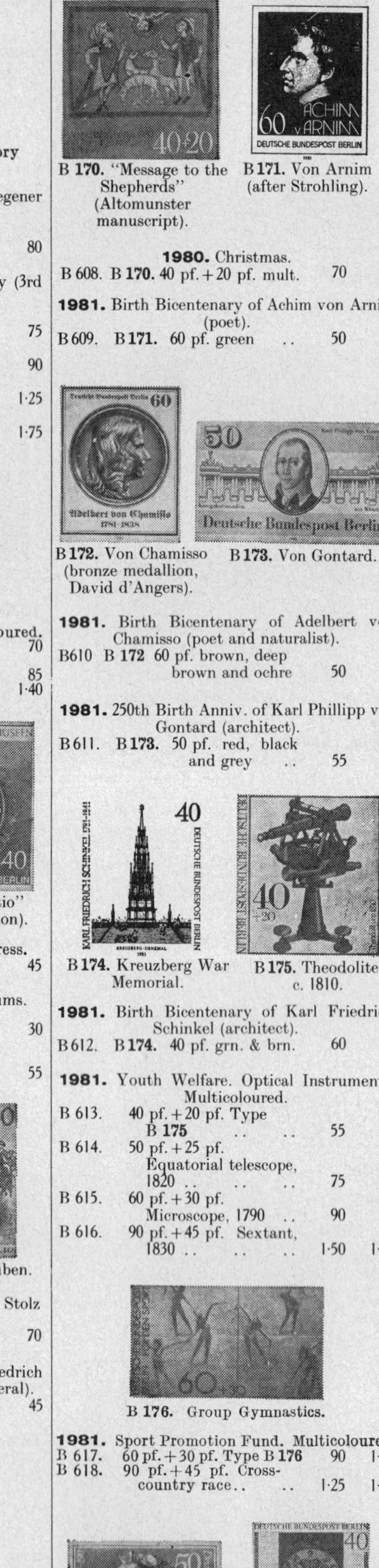

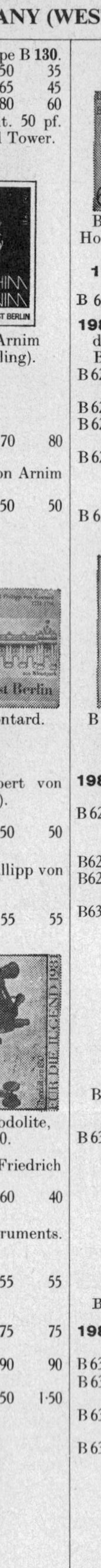

B **170.** "Message to the Shepherds" (Altomunster manuscript).
B **171.** Von Arnim (after Strohling).

**1980.** Christmas.
B 608. B **170.** 40 pf. + 20 pf. mult. 70 80

**1981.** Birth Bicentenary of Achim von Arnim (poet).
B609. B **171.** 60 pf. green .. 50 50

B **172.** Von Chamisso (bronze medallion, David d'Angers).
B **173.** Von Gontard.

**1981.** Birth Bicentenary of Adelbert von Chamisso (poet and naturalist).
B610 B **172** 60 pf. brown, deep brown and ochre 50 50

**1981.** 250th Birth Anniv. of Karl Phillipp von Gontard (architect).
B611. B **173.** 50 pf. red, black and grey .. 55 55

B **174.** Kreuzberg War Memorial.
B **175.** Theodolite, c. 1810.

**1981.** Birth Bicentenary of Karl Friedrich Schinkel (architect).
B612. B **174.** 40 pf. grn. & brn. 60 40

**1981.** Youth Welfare. Optical Instruments. Multicoloured.
B 613. 40 pf. + 20 pf. Type B **175** .. .. 55 55
B 614. 50 pf. + 25 pf. Equatorial telescope, 1820 .. .. .. 75 75
B 615. 60 pf. + 30 pf. Microscope, 1790 .. 90 90
B 616. 90 pf. + 45 pf. Sextant, 1830 .. .. 1·50 1·50

B **176.** Group Gymnastics.

**1981.** Sport Promotion Fund. Multicoloured.
B 617. 60 pf. + 30 pf. Type B **176** 90 1·00
B 618. 90 pf. + 45 pf. Cross-country race .. .. 1·25 1·40

B **177.** "Cupid and Psyche."
B **178.** Badge of Order "Pour le Merite".

**1981.** 150th Birth Anniv. of Reinhold Begas (sculptor).
B619 B **177** 50 pf. black & blue 50 40

**1981.** Prussian Exhibition, Berlin-Krevzberg.
B 620. B **178.** 40 pf. multicoloured 50 30

B **179.** Broadcasting House, Charlottenburg.
B **180.** "Three Kings" (glass painting).

**1981.** International Telecommunications Exhibition, Berlin.
B 621. B **179.** 60 pf. multicoloured 70 65

**1981.** Humanitarian Relief Funds. Endangered Wildflowers. Designs as Type B **169.** Multicoloured.
B622. 40 pf + 20 pf. Common bistort .. .. .. 60 60
B623. 50 pf. + 25 pf. Moor-king 70 70
B624. 60 pf. + 30 pf. "Gladiolus palustris" .. .. 90 90
B625. 90 pf. + 45 pf. Siberian iris .. .. .. 1·60 1·60

**1981.** Christmas.
B 626. B **180.** 40 pf. + 20 pf. mult. 55 55

B **181.** Peter Beuth.
B **182.** "Dancer Nijinsky" (Georg Kolbe).

**1981.** Birth Bicentenary of Peter Beuth (constitutional lawyer).
B627. B **181.** 60 pf. blk. & brn. 55 55

**1981.** 20th Century Sculptures. Mult.
B628 40 pf. Type B **182** .. 40 30
B629 60 pf. "Mother Earth II" (Ernst Barlach) .. 70 55
B630 90 pf. "Flora Kneeling" (Richard Scheibe) .. 1·25 85

B **183.** Arms and View of Spandau, c. 1700.

**1982.** 750th Anniv. of Spandau.
B631. B **183.** 60 pf. multicoloured 90 90

B **184.** Daimler Steel-wheeled Car, 1889.

**1982.** Youth Welfare Fund. Motor Cars. Multicoloured.
B632. 40 pf. + 20 pf. Type B **184** 80 65
B633. 50 pf. + 25 pf. Wanderer "Puppchen", 1911 .. 95 70
B634. 60 pf. + 30 p. Adler limousine, 1913 .. 1·25 1·00
B635. 90 pf. + 45 pf. DKW "F 1", 1913 .. .. 1·75 1·40

B **185.** Sprinting.

**1982.** Sport Promotion Fund. Multicoloured.
B 636. 60 pf. + 30 pf. Type B **185** 1·00 85
B 637. 90 pf. + 45 pf. Volleyball 1·40 1·10

B **186.** Harp.
B **187.** "Emigrants reaching Prussian Frontier" (woodcut after drawing by Adolph von Menzel).

**1982.** Centenary of Berlin Philharmonic Orchestra.
B638 B **186** 60 pf. grey, red and green .. .. 80 70

**1982.** 250th Anniv. of Salzburg Emigrants' Arrival in Prussia.
B639. B **187.** 50 pf. stone, deep brown and brn. 50 40

B **188.** "Italian Stone Carriers" (Max Pechstein).

**1982.** Paintings. Multicoloured.
B 640. 50 pf. Type B **188** .. 60 45
B 641. 80 pf. "Two Girls Bathing" (Otto Mueller) .. .. 1·00 75

B **189.** Floribunda-Grandiflora.
B **191.** "Adoration of the Kings" (detail from St. Peter altar by Master Bertram).

B **190.** Castle Theatre, Charlottenburg.

**1982.** Humanitarian Relief Funds. Roses. Multicoloured.
B 642. 50 pf. + 20 pf. Type B **189** .. .. 75 65
B 643. 60 pf. + 30 pf. Hybrid tea .. .. .. 1·00 90
B 644. 80 pf. + 40 pf. Floribunda .. .. 1·25 1·10
B 645. 120 pf. + 60 pf. Miniature rose .. 2·00 1·75

**1982.** 250th Birth Anniv. of Carl Gotthard Langhans (architect).
B 646. B **190.** 80 pf. red, grey and black .. .. 1·00 90

**1982.** Berlin Views (4th series). As Type B **130.**
B 647. 50 pf. black and blue .. 75 40
B 648. 60 pf. black and red .. 80 70
B 649. 80 pf. black and brown 1·25 95
DESIGNS: 50 pf. Villa Borsig. 60 pf. Sts. Peter and Paul Church. 80 pf. Villa von der Heydt.

**1982.** Christmas.
B 650. B **191.** 50 pf. + 20 pf. multicoloured .. 80 1·00

B **192.** Water Pump, Klausenerplatz.
B **193.** Royal Prussian Telegraphy Inspectors at St. Anne's Church.

**1983.** Street Water Pumps. Multicoloured.
B 651. 50 pf. Type B **192** 80 45
B 652. 60 pf. Chamissoplatz .. 1·00 60
B 653. 80 pf. Schloss-strasse .. 1·25 85
B 654. 120 pf. Kuerfurstendamm 2·00 1·25

**1983.** 150th Anniv. of Berlin-Coblenz Optical-Mechanical Telegraph.
B655. B **193.** 80 pf. brown .. 1·50 1·00

B **194.** Hildebrand & Wolfmuller, 1894.

**1983.** Youth Welfare. Motor Cycles. Mult.

B 656. 50 pf.+20 pf. Type B **194** .. .. 1·00 80
B 657. 60 pf.+30 pf. Wanderer, 1908 .. 1·40 1·10
B 658. 80 pf.+40 pf. D.K.W.-Lomos, 1922 .. 1·50 1·25
B 659. 120 pf.+60 pf. Mars, 1925 .. .. .. 2·25 1·90

B **195**. Latin-American Dancing.

**1983. Sport Promotion Fund. Multicoloured.**

**B 660. 80 pf.+40 pf. Type B 195 1·60 1·40**
**B 661. 120 pf.+60 pf. Ice hockey 2·40 2·25**

**B 196. " La Barbarina " (painting of Barbara Campanini).** B **197**. Ringelnatz (silhouette by E. M. Engert).

**1983.** 300th Birth Anniv. of Antoine Pesne (artist).

B662. B **196**. 50 pf. multicoloured 70 60

**1983.** Birth Centenary of Joachim Ringelnatz (poet and painter).

B 663. B **197**. 50 pf. green, brown and red 70 60

**B 198. Paul Nipkow's Picture Transmission System, 1884.**

**1983.** International Broadcasting Exn, Berlin.

B664 B **198** 80 pf. multicoloured 1·10 90

**B 199. Mountain Windflower.** **B 200. Nigerian Yoruba Crib.**

**1983. Humanitarian Relief Funds. Endangered Alpine Flowers. Multicoloured.**

B 665. 50 pf.+20 pf. Type B **199** 1·00 1·00
B 666. 60 pf.+30 pf. Alpine auricula .. .. 1·25 1·25
B 667. 80 pf.+40 pf. Little primrose .. .. 2·00 2·00
B 668. 120 pf.+60 pf. Einsele's aquilegia .. .. 2·40 2·10

**1983. Christmas.**

**B 669. B 200. 50 pf.+20 pf. mult. 90 70**

B **201**. Queen Cleopatra VII (Antikenmuseum).

**1984.** Art Objects in Berlin Museums. Multicoloured.

B670. 30 pf. Type B **201** .. 1·00 1·00
B671. 50 pf. Statue of seated couple from Giza Necropolis (Egyptian Museum) .. .. 1·25 1·10
B672. 60 pf. Goddess with pearl turban (Ethnology Museum) .. .. 1·40 1·25
B673. 80 pf. Majolica dish (Applied Arts Museum) .. .. 2·00 1·75

B **202**. Bee Chafer. B **203**. Hurdling.

**1984.** Youth Welfare. Pollinating Insects. Multicoloured.

B674 50 pf.+20 pf. Type B **202** 1·25 1·00
B675 60 pf.+30 pf. Common burnet (moth) .. 1·25 1·25
B676 80 pf.+40 pf. Buff-tailed bumble bee .. .. 2·00 1·50
B677 120 pf.+60 pf. Drone-fly 2·25 2·25

**1984.** Sport Promotion Fund. Multicoloured.

B 678. 60 pf.+30 pf. Type B **203** 1·25 1·10
B 679. 80 pf.+40 pf. Cycling .. 2·00 1·60
B 680. 120 pf.+60 pf. Four-seater kayaks .. .. 2·50 2·25

B **204**. Klausener. B **205**. "Electric Power" (K. Sutterlin).

**1984.** 50th Death Anniv. of Dr. Erich Klausener (chairman of Catholic Action).

B 681. B **204**. 80 pf. green and deep green .. 80 80

**1984.** Cent. of Berlin Electricity Supply.

B 682. B **205**. 50 pf. yellow, orange & black 60 50

B **206**. Conference Emblem. B **207**. Brehm and White Stork.

**1984.** 4th European Ministers of Culture Conference, Berlin.

B 683. B **206**. 60 pf. multicoloured 70 60

**1984.** Death Centenary of Alfred Brehm (zoologist).

B 684. B **207**. 80 pf. multicoloured 1·75 1·10

B **208**. Heim (bust, Friedrich Tieck). B **209**. "Listera cordata".

**1984.** 150th Death Anniv. of Ernst Ludwig Heim (medical pioneer).

B 685. B **208**. 50 pf. black and red .. .. 70 60

**1984.** Humanitarian Relief Funds. Orchids. Multicoloured.

B686. 50 pf.+20 pf. Type B **209** 1·25 1·25
B687. 60 pf.+30 pf. "Ophrys insectifera" .. .. 1·40 1·40
B688 80 pf.+40 pf. "Epipactis palustris" .. .. 2·25 2·25
B689. 120 pf.+60 pf. "Ophrys coriophora" .. .. 3·25 3·25

B **210**. "Sunflowers on Grey Background". B **211**. St. Nicholas.

**1984.** Birth Centenary of Karl Schmidt-Rottluff (artist).

B 690. B **210**. 60 pf. multicoloured 90 70

**1984.** Christmas.

B 691. B **211**. 50 pf.+20 pf. mult. 1·00 1·00

B **212**. Bettina von Arnim. B **213**. Humboldt (statue, Paul Otto).

**1985.** Birth Bicentenary of Bettina von Arnim (writer).

B 692. B **212**. 50 pf. black, brown and red .. 80 60

**1985.** 50th Death Anniv. of Wilhelm von Humboldt (philologist).

B 693. B **213**. 80 pf. black, blue and red .. 1·25 90

B **214**. Ball in Net.

**1985.** Sport Promotion Fund. Multicoloured.

B 694. 80 pf.+40 pf. Type B **214** (50th anniv. of basketball in Germany and European championships, Stuttgart) .. 1·75 1·60
B 695. 120 pf.+60 pf. Table tennis (60th anniv. of German Table Tennis Association) .. .. 2·50 2·25

B **215**. Stylized Flower. B **216**. Bussing Bicycle, 1868.

**1985.** Federal Horticultural Show, Berlin.

B 696. B **215**. 80 pf. multicoloured 1·00 80

**1985.** Youth Welfare. International Youth Year. Bicycles. Multicoloured.

B 697. 50 pf.+20 pf. Type B **216** .. .. 1·25 1·00
B 698. 60 pf.+30 pf. Child's tricycle, 1885 .. 1·40 1·25
B 699. 80 pf.+40 pf. Jaray bicycle, 1925 .. 1·75 1·50
B 700. 120 pf.+60 pf. Opel racing bicycle, 1925 2·75 2·25

B **217**. Stock Exchange, 1863–1945.

**1985.** 300th Anniv of Berlin Stock Exchange.

B701 B **217** 50 pf. multicoloured 75 55

B **218**. Otto Klemperer.

**1985.** Birth Centenary of Otto Klemperer (orchestral conductor).

B702 B **218** 60 pf. blue .. 1·50 90

B **219**. Association Emblem.

**1985.** 11th International Gynaecology and Obstetrics Association Congress, Berlin.

B 703. B **219**. 60 pf. multicoloured 75 60

B **220**. "FE 3" Television Camera, 1935.

**1985.** International Broadcasting Exn, Berlin.

B704 B **220** 80 pf. multicoloured 1·50 1·10

B **221**. Seal of Brandenburg-Prussia and Preamble of Edict.

**1985.** 300th Anniv. of Edict of Potsdam (admitting Huguenots to Prussia).

B 705. B **221**. 50 pf. lilac & blk. 60 45

B **222**. Flowers, Strawberries and Ladybirds.

**1985.** Humanitarian Relief Funds. Designs depict motifs from borders of Medieval Prayer book. Multicoloured.

B 706. 50 pf.+20 pf. Type B **222** .. .. 90 80
B 707. 60 pf.+30 pf. Flowers, bird and butterfly .. 1·25 1·00
B 708. 80 pf.+40 pf. Flowers, bee and butterfly .. 1·50 1·25
B 709. 120 pf.+60 pf. Flowers, berries, butterfly and snail .. .. .. 2·25 2·50

B **223**. "Adoration of the Kings" (detail, Epiphany Altar). B **224**. Kurt Tucholsky.

**1985.** Christmas. 500th Birth Anniv. of Hans Baldung Grien (artist).

B710. B **223**. 50 pf.+20 pf. mult. 1·00 1·00

**1985.** 50th Death Anniv. of Kurt Tucholsky (writer and journalist).

B711. B **224**. 80 pf. multicoloured 1·00 90

B **225**. Furtwangler and Score.

**1986.** Birth Centenary of Wilhelm Furtwangler (composer and conductor).

B712. B **225**. 80 pf. multicoloured 1·50 1·00

B **226**. Rohe and National Gallery.

**1986.** Birth Centenary of Ludwig Mies van der Rohe (architect).

B713. B **226**. 50 pf. multicoloured 85 60

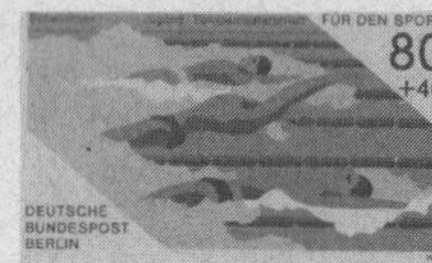

B 227. Swimming.

**1986.** Sport Promotion Fund. Multicoloured.
B714. 80 pf.+40 pf. Type B 227 (European Youth Championships, Berlin) .. .. 2·00 2·00
B715. 120 pf.+55 pf. Show-jumping (World Championships, Aachen) .. .. 2·25 2·25

B 228. Glazier.

**1986.** Youth Charity. Trades (1st series). Multicoloured.
B716. 50 pf.+25 pf. Type B 228 1·00 90
B717. 60 pf.+30 pf. Locksmith 1·50 1·40
B718. 70 pf.+35 pf. Tailor .. 1·75 1·60
B719. 80 pf.+40 pf. Carpenter 1·90 1·75
See also Nos. B 765/8.

B 229. Flags.

**1986.** 16th European Communities Day.
B720. B 229. 60 pf. multicoloured 75 55

B 230. Ranke. B 231. Benn.

**1986.** Death Centenary of Leopold von Ranke (historian).
B721. B 230. 80 pf. brn. & grey 1·25 1·00

**1986.** Birth Centenary of Gottfried Benn (poet).
B722. B 231. 80 pf. blue .. 1·25 1·00

B 232. Charlottenburg Gate. B 233. "The Flute Concert" (detail, Adolph von Menzel).

**1986.** Gateways. Multicoloured.
B723. 50 pf. Type B 232 .. 80 40
B724. 60 pf. Griffin Gate, Glienicke Palace .. 90 70
B725. 80 pf. Elephant Gate, Berlin Zoo .. .. 1·25 95

**1986.** Death Bicentenary of Frederick the Great.
B726. B 233. 80 pf. multicoloured 1·25 80

B 234. Cantharus, 1st century A.D. B 235. "Adoration of the Three Kings" (Ortenberg altarpiece).

**1986.** Humanitarian Relief Funds. Glassware. Multicoloured.
B727. 50 pf.+25 pf. Type B 234 1·00 75
B728. 60 pf.+30 pf. Beaker, 200 A.D. .. .. 1·40 1·00
B729. 70 pf.+35 pf. Jug, 3rd century A.D. .. 1·50 1·25
B730. 80 pf.+40 pf. Diatreta 4th century A.D. .. 1·75 1·40

**1986.** Christmas.
B731. B 235. 50 pf.+25 pf. mult. 1·00 1·00

**1986.** Famous German Women. As Nos. 2149a/2154, 2158, 2161, 2166/9a.

| | | | |
|---|---|---|---|
| B732 | 5 pf. brown and grey | 15 | 40 |
| B733 | 10 pf. brown and violet | 25 | 30 |
| B734 | 20 pf. blue and red .. | 20 | 50 |
| B735 | 40 pf. red and blue .. | 35 | 80 |
| B736 | 50 pf. green and brown | 70 | 40 |
| B737 | 60 pf. lilac and green | 60 | 75 |
| B738 | 80 pf. brown and green | 80 | 50 |
| B739 | 100 pf. grey and red .. | 1·25 | 1·00 |
| B740 | 130 pf. violet and blue | 1·75 | 4·00 |
| B741 | 140 pf. brown and blue | 3·00 | 3·25 |
| B742 | 170 pf. purple & green | 2·00 | 2·40 |
| B743 | 180 pf. purple and blue | 2·60 | 3·25 |
| B744 | 240 pf. brown and blue | 2·40 | 3·25 |
| B745 | 250 pf. blue and mauve | 3·25 | 5·00 |
| B746 | 300 pf. green and plum | 4·75 | 6·00 |
| B747 | 350 pf. brown & black | 4·75 | 5·00 |
| B748 | 500 pf. red and green | 8·00 | 12·00 |

**1987.** 750th Anniv. of Berlin. As No. 2170.
B760. 833. 80 pf. multicoloured 1·40 1·00

B 237. Louise Schroeder. B 239. "Bohemian Refugees" (detail of relief, King Friedrich Wilhelm Monument, Berlin-Neukolln).

B 238. German Gymnastics Festival, Berlin.

**1987.** Birth Centenary of Louise Schroeder (Mayor of Berlin).
B762. B 237. 50 pf. brown and orange on light brown .. 80 70

**1987.** Sport Promotion Fund. Multicoloured.
B763 80 pf.+40 pf. Type B 238 2·00 1·75
B764 120 pf.+55 pf. World Judo Championships, Essen .. .. 2·50 2·00

**1987.** Youth Welfare. Trades (2nd series). As Type B 228. Multicoloured.
B765. 50 pf.+25 pf. Cooper .. 1·25 90
B766. 60 pf.+30 pf. Stonemason .. .. 1·40 1·25
B767. 70 pf.+35 pf. Furrier 1·60 1·40
B768. 80 pf.+40 pf. Painter/lacquerer .. .. 1·75 1·50

**1987.** 250th Anniv. of Bohemian Settlement, Rixdorf.
B769. B 239. 50 pf. brown and green .. .. 60 45

B 240. New Buildings.

**1987.** International Building Exhibition, Berlin.
B770 B 240 80 pf. silver, black and blue .. 95 60

B 241. Tree in Arrow Circle. B 242. Compact Disc and Gramophone.

**1987.** 14th International Botanical Congress, Berlin.
B771. B 241. 60 pf. multicoloured 80 60

**1987.** International Broadcasting Exhibition, Berlin. Centenary of Gramophone Record.
B772 B 242 80 pf. multicoloured 1·00 70

B 243. 5th-century Bonnet Ornament.

**1987.** Humanitarian Relief Funds. Precious Metal Work. Multicoloured.
B773. 50 pf+25 pf. Type B 243 .. .. 90 80
B774. 60 pf.+30 pf. Athene plate, 1st-century B.C. .. .. .. 1·00 90
B775. 70 pf.+35 pf. "Armilla" armlet, 1180 .. .. .. 1·25 1·00
B776. 80 pf.+40 pf. Snake bracelet, 300 B.C. .. 1·40 1·25

**1987.** Tourist Sights. As Nos. 2200/19.

| | | | |
|---|---|---|---|
| B777 | 5 pf. blue and grey .. | 20 | 30 |
| B778 | 10 pf. blue and indigo .. | 15 | 25 |
| B779 | 20 pf. flesh and blue .. | 30 | 40 |
| B780 | 30 pf. brown and green .. | 80 | 70 |
| B781 | 40 pf. brown, red & blue | 75 | 1·25 |
| B782 | 50 pf. ochre and blue .. | 1·00 | 60 |
| B783 | 60 pf. green and black .. | 1·00 | 40 |
| B784 | 70 pf. flesh and blue .. | 1·00 | 1·25 |
| B785 | 70 pf. brown and blue .. | 2·00 | 3·00 |
| B786 | 80 pf. grey and green .. | 1·00 | 50 |
| B787 | 100 pf. green and orange | 1·00 | 1·00 |
| B788 | 120 pf. green and red .. | 1·25 | 1·75 |
| B789 | 140 pf. bistre and yellow | 2·00 | 2·50 |
| B790 | 300 pf. flesh and brown | 4·00 | 6·00 |
| B791 | 350 pf. brown and blue .. | 4·00 | 5·00 |

B 244. "Adoration of the Magi" (13th-century Book of Psalms). B 245. Heraldic Bear.

**1987.** Christmas.
B797. B 244. 50 pf.+25 pf. mult. 80 75

**1988.** Berlin, European City of Culture.
B798 B 245 80 pf. multicoloured 1·25 1·00

B 246. Old and New Buildings.

**1988.** Centenary of Urania Science Museum.
B799. B 246. 50 pf. multicoloured 75 70

B 247. "Large Pure-bred Foal" (bronze).

**1988.** Birth Centenary of Rene Sintenis (sculptor).
B800. B 247. 60 pf. multicoloured 75 60

B 248. Clay-pigeon Shooting.

**1988.** Sport Promotion Fund. Olympic Games. Multicoloured.
B801 60 pf.+30 pf. Type B 248 1·25 1·25
B802 80 pf.+40 pf. Figure skating (pairs) .. 2·00 1·40
B803 120 pf.+55 pf. Throwing the hammer .. .. 2·50 2·00

B 249. Piano, Violin and Cello.

**1988.** Youth Welfare. Music. Multicoloured.
B804. 50 pf.+25 pf. Type B 249 1·25 1·25
B805. 60 pf.+30 pf. Wind quintet .. .. 1·50 1·50
B806. 70 pf.+35 pf. Guitar, recorder and mandolin 1·60 1·60
B807. 80 pf.+40 pf. Children's choir .. .. .. 2·00 2·00

B 250. Great Elector and Family in Berlin Castle Gardens.

B 251. Globe.

**1988.** 300th Death Anniv of Friedrich Wilhelm, Great Elector of Brandenburg.
B808 B 250 50 pf. multicoloured 90 80

**1988.** International Monetary Fund and World Bank Boards of Governors Annual Meetings, Berlin.
B809. B 251. 70 pf. multicoloured 1·00 80

B 252. First Train leaving Potsdam Station.

**1988.** 150th Anniv. of Berlin–Potsdam Railway.
B810. B 252. 10 pf. multicoloured 60 40

B 253 "The Collector" (bronze statue).

B 254. 18th-century Breast Ornament.

**1988.** 50th Death Anniv. of Ernst Barlach (artist).
B811. B 253. 40 pf. multicoloured 60 40

**1988.** Humanitarian Relief Funds. Precious Metal Work. Multicoloured.
B812 50 pf.+25 pf. Type B 254 1·00 1·00
B813 60 pf.+30 pf. 16th-century lion-shaped jug .. 1·25 1·25
B814 70 pf.+35 pf. 16th-century goblet .. .. 1·25 1·25
B815 80 pf.+40 pf. 15th-century cope clasp .. 1·50 1·50

B 255. "Annunciation to the Shepherds" (illus from Henry the Lion's Gospel Book).

**1988.** Christmas.
B816 B 255 50 pf.+25 pf. mult 1·00 90

B **256** Volleyball (European Championships)

**1989.** Sport Promotion Fund. Multicoloured.
B817 100 pf. + 50 pf. Type B **256** 2·75 2·75
B818 140 pf. + 60 pf. Hockey (Champions Trophy) 3·00 3·00

B **257** Tigers and Tamer

**1989.** Youth Welfare. Circus. Multicoloured.
B819 60 pf. + 30 pf. Type B **257** 1·50 1·50
B820 70 pf. + 30 pf. Trapeze artistes .. .. 1·60 1·60
B821 80 pf. + 35 pf. Sealions .. 1·75 1·75
B822 100 pf. + 50 pf. Jugglers 2·00 2·00

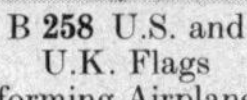

B **258** U.S. and U.K. Flags forming Airplane  B **259** Emblem

**1989.** 40th Anniv of Berlin Airlift.
B823 B **258** 60 pf. multicoloured 75 50

**1989.** 13th International Organization of Chief Accountants Congress.
B824 B **259** 80 pf. multicoloured 1·00 50

B **260** Reuter

**1989.** Birth Centenary of Ernst Reuter (politician and Mayor of Berlin).
B825 B **260** 100 pf. mult .. 1·25 1·00

B **261** Satellite, Radio Waves and T.V. Screen

**1989.** International Broadcasting Exn, Berlin.
B826 B **261** 100 pf. mult .. 1·25 85

B **262** Plan of Berlin Zoo and Lenne

**1989.** Birth Bicentenary of Peter Joseph Lenne (landscape designer).
B827 B **262** 60 pf. multicoloured 1·25 80

B **263** Ossietzky and Masthead of "Die Weltbuhne"

**1989.** Birth Centenary of Carl von Ossietzky (journalist and peace activist).
B828 B **263** 100 pf. mult .. 1·25 80

B **264** Former School Building  B **265** St. Nicholas's Church, Berlin-Spandau

**1989.** 300th Anniv of Berlin Lycee Francais.
B829 B **264** 40 pf. multicoloured 75 60

**1989.** 450th Anniv of Reformation.
B830 B **265** 60 pf. multicoloured 75 60

B **266** 15th-century Letter Messenger  B **267** "Journalists"

**1989.** Humanitarian Relief Funds. Postal Deliveries. Multicoloured.
B831 60 pf. + 30 pf. Type B **266** 2·00 2·00
B832 80 pf. + 35 pf. Brandenburg mail coach, 1700 2·50 2·50
B833 100 pf. + 50 pf. 19th-century Prussian postal messengers .. .. 3·00 3·00

**1989.** Birth Centenary of Hannah Hoch (painter).
B834 B **267** 100 pf. mult .. 1·60 1·25

B **268** Angel

**1989.** Christmas. 16th-century Carvings by Veit Stoss, St. Lawrence's Church, Nuremberg. Multicoloured.
B835 40 pf. + 20 pf. Type B **268** 1·00 1·00
B836 60 pf. + 30 pf. "Adoration of the Magi" .. .. 1·50 1·50

B **269** Horse-drawn Passenger Vehicle

**1990.** 250th Anniv of Public Transport in Berlin.
B837 B **269** 60 pf. multicoloured 1·50 1·00

B **270** Rudorff

**1990.** 150th Birth Anniv of Ernst Rudorff (founder of conservation movement).
B838 B **270** 60 pf. multicoloured 1·50 1·00

**1990.** 500th Anniv of Regular European Postal Services. As No. 2297.
B839 **914** 100 pf. deep brown, lt brown & brown .. 1·50 1·00

## MINIMUM PRICE

The minimum price quoted is 10p which represents a handling charge rather than a basis for valuing common stamps. For further notes about prices see introductory pages.

B **271** Curtain and Theatre

**1990.** Cent of National Free Theatre, Berlin.
B840 B **271** 100 pf. mult .. 2·00 1·25

B **272** Facade

**1990.** 40th Anniv of Bundeshaus, Berlin.
B841 B **272** 100 pf. mult .. 2·25 1·75

B **273** Water Polo

**1990.** Sport Promotion Fund. Multicoloured.
B842 100 pf. + 50 pf. Type B **273** 3·00 3·00
B843 140 pf. + 60 pf. Wheelchair basketball .. .. 4·00 4·00

B **274** Moritz filling Pipe with Gunpowder

**1990.** Youth Welfare. 125th Anniv of Max and Moritz (characters from books by Wilhelm Busch). Multicoloured.
B844 60 pf. + 30 pf. Type B **274** 1·75 1·75
B845 70 pf. + 30 pf. Max and Moritz running off .. 2·00 2·00
B846 80 pf. + 35 pf. Moritz slashing sack open .. 2·25 2·25
B847 100 pf. + 50 pf. Insect on Uncle Fritz's nose .. 2·50 2·50

B **275** Poster  B **276** "Street Singer" (etching, Ludwig Knaus)

**1990.** 90th German Catholic Day.
B848 B **275** 60 pf. multicoloured 1·25 1·00

**1990.** Bicentenary of Barrel-organ.
B849 B **276** 100 pf. mult .. 1·40 1·00

B **277** Pestle and Mortar and Diagram of Aspirin Molecule  B **278** Diesterweg

**1990.** Centenary of German Pharmaceutical Society.
B850 B **277** 100 pf. mult .. 3·75 2·50

**1990.** Birth Bicentenary of Adolph Diesterweg (educationist).
B851 B **278** 60 pf. multicoloured 2·00 1·75

B **279** Travelling Post Office, 1900

**1990.** Humanitarian Relief Funds. Posts and Telecommunications. Multicoloured.
B852 60 pf. + 30 pf. Type B **279** 2·00 2·00
B853 80 pf. + 35 pf. Installing telephone lines, 1900 .. 2·75 2·75
B854 100 pf. + 50 pf. Electric parcels van, 1930 .. 3·50 3·50

With the absorption of East Germany into the Federal Republic of Germany on 3 October 1990, separate issues for West Berlin ceased.

## V. GERMAN DEMOCRATIC REPUBLIC (East Germany)

The German Democratic Republic was set up in October 1949 and comprised the former Russian Zone. Its stamps were used in East Berlin.

On 3 October 1990 the territory was absorbed into the German Federal Republic.

1949. 100 pfennig = 1 Deutsche mark (East).
1990. 100 pfennig = 1 Deutsche mark (West).

E **1.** Pigeon and Globe.  E **2.** Postal Workers and Globe.

**1949.** 75th Anniv. of U.P.U.
E1. E**1.** 50 pf. blue & deep bl. 7·00 5·50

**1949.** Postal Workers' Congress.
E 2. E **2.** 12 pf. blue .. .. 7·00 7·50
E 3. 30 pf. red .. .. 12·00 12·50

E **3.** T **1** of Bavaria and Magnifying Glass.  E **4.** Skier.

**1949.** Stamp Day.
E 4. E **3.** 12 pf. + 3 pf. black .. 5·00 4·50

**1950.** 1st Winter Sports Meeting, Schierke.
E 5. E **4.** 12 pf. violet .. .. 6·00 4·00
E 6. – 24 pf. blue .. .. 8·00 7·50
DESIGN: 24 pf. Girl skater.

**1950.** Leipzig Spring Fair. As T **231** but dated "1950".
E 7. 24 pf. + 12 pf. purple .. 7·00 8·00
E 8. 30 pf. + 14 pf. red .. 9·00 10·00
DESIGNS: 24 pf. First Dresden China Fair, 1710. 30 pf. First Sample Fair, 1894.

E **5.** Globe and Sun.  E **6.** Wilhelm Pieck.

E **7.** Wilhelm Pieck.  E **8.** Shepherd Playing Pipes

**1950.** 60th Anniv. of Labour Day.
E9. E**5.** 30 pf. red .. .. 16·00 12·00

**1950.**
E 68. E **6.** 5 pf. green .. 8·00 1·25
E 10. 12 pf. blue .. 15·00 2·00
E 70. 24 pf. brown .. 19·00 45
E 12. E **7.** 1 Dm. olive .. 24·00 2·40
E 13. 2 Dm. red .. .. 14·00 2·40
E 14. 5 Dm. blue .. 6·00 60

For 1 and 2 Dm. with different portrait of president, see Nos. E 320/1 (1953).

**1950.** Death Bicentenary of J. S. Bach (composer).

E 15. E 8. 12 pf.+4 pf. green .. 5·00 4·00
E 16. – 24 pf.+6 pf. olive .. 5·00 4·00
E 17. – 30 pf.+8 pf. red .. 10·00 8·00
E 18. – 50 pf.+16 pf. blue .. 13·50 10·00

DESIGNS: 24 pf. Girl playing hand-organ. 30 pf. Bach. 50 pf. Three singers.

E 9. Dove, Globe and Stamp.

E 10. L. Euler.

**1950.** Philatelic Exhibition (DEBRIA), Leipzig.

E 19. E 9. 84 pf.+41 pf. red .. 35·00 12·00

**1950.** 250th Anniv. of Academy of Science, Berlin.

E 20. E 10. 1 pf. grey .. .. 3·25 1·75
E 21. – 5 pf. green .. .. 5·00 5·00
E 22. – 6 pf. violet .. .. 8·00 4·00
E 23. – 8 pf. brown .. .. 14·00 11·00
E 24. – 10 pf. green .. 12·00 11·00
E 25. – 12 pf. blue .. .. 3·00 1·50
E 26. – 16 pf. blue .. .. 17·00 15·00
E 27. – 20 pf. purple .. 14·00 12·00
E 28. – 24 pf. red .. .. 15·00 2·50
E 29. – 50 pf. blue .. .. 22·00 13·00

PORTRAITS: 5 pf. A. von Humboldt. 6 pf. T. Mommsen. 8 pf. W. von Humboldt. 10 pf. H. von Helmholtz. 12 pf. M. Planck. 16 pf. J. Grimm. 20 pf. W. Nernst. 24 pf. G. W. Leibniz. 50 pf. A. von Harnack.

E 11. Miner.

E 12. Ballot Box.

**1950.** 750th Anniv of Mansfeld Copper Mines.

E30 E 11 12 pf. blue .. .. 4·00 4·00
E31 – 24 pf. red .. .. 6·00 6·00

DESIGN: 24 pf. Copper smelting.

**1950.** East German Elections.

E 32. E 12. 24 pf. brown .. 10·00 3·50

E 13. Hand, Dove and Burning Buildings.

E 14. Tobogganing.

**1950.** Peace Propaganda. Inscr. "ERKAMPFT DEN FRIEDEN".

E 33. – 6 pf. blue .. .. 3·50 4·00
E 34. E 13. 8 pf. brown .. 3·00 1·50
E 35. – 12 pf. blue .. 5·50 3·00
E 36. – 24 pf. red .. .. 5·00 1·50

DESIGNS (all include hand and dove): 6 pf. Tank. 12 pf. Atom bomb Explosion. 24 pf. Rows of gravestones.

**1951.** 2nd Winter Sports Meeting, Oberhof.

E37 E 14 12 pf. blue .. .. 8·00 6·00
E38 – 24 f. red (ski jumper) 10·00 8·00

E 15.

**1951.** Leipzig Spring Fair.

E 39. E 15. 24 pf. red .. .. 15·00 14·00
E 40. 50 pf. blue .. .. 15·00 14·00

E 16. Presidents Pieck and Bierut.

**1951.** Visit of Polish President to Berlin.

E 41. E 16. 24 pf. red .. .. 18·00 15·00
E 42. 50 pf. blue .. .. 18·00 15·00

E 17. Mao Tse-tung.

E 18. Chinese Land Reform.

**1951.** Friendship with China.

E 43. E 17. 12 pf. green .. £100 24·00
E 44. E 18. 24 pf. red .. .. £150 32·00
E 45. E 17. 50 pf. blue .. .. £100 24·00

E 19. Youth Hoisting Flag.

E 20. Symbols of Agriculture & Industry

**1951.** 3rd World Youth Festival. Inscr. as in Type E 19. On coloured papers.

E 46. E 19. 12 pf. brown .. 10·00 5·00
E 47. – 24 pf. green & red .. 10·00 4·00
E 48. E 19. 30 pf. buff and green 12·00 7·50
E 49. – 50 pf. red and blue .. 12·00 6·00

DESIGN: 24 pf., 50 pf. Three girls dancing.

**1951.** Five Year Plan.

E 50. E 20. 24 pf. multicoloured 4·00 1·50

E 21. K. Liebknecht.

E 22. Instructing Young Collectors.

**1951.** 80th Birth Anniv. of Liebknecht (revolutionary).

E 51. E 21. 24 pf. slate and red 4·00 1·75

**1951.** Stamp Day.

E 52. E 22. 12 pf. blue .. .. 4·00 2·00

E 23. P. Bykow and E. Wirth.

**1951.** German-Soviet Friendship.

E 53. E 23. 12 pf. blue .. .. 3·50 3·00
E 54. – 24 pf. red .. .. 4·00 4·00

DESIGN: 24 pf. Stalin and Pres. Pieck.

E 24. Skier.

E 25. Beethoven.

**1952.** 3rd Winter Sports Meeting, Oberhof.

E 55. E 24. 12 pf. green .. 4·75 3·00
E 56. – 24 pf. blue .. .. 4·75 3·00

DESIGN: 24 pf. Ski jumper.

**1952.** 125th Death Anniv. of Beethoven (composer).

E 57. – 12 pf. bl. & lt. bl. 1·75 50
E 58. E 25. 24 pf. brn. & grey 3·00 70

DESIGN: 12 pf. Full face portrait.

E 26. President Gottwald.

E 27. Bricklayers.

**1952.** Czechoslovak-German Friendship.

E 59. E 26. 24 pf. blue .. .. 2·00 1·40

**1952.** National Reconstruction Fund.

E 60. – 12 pf.+3 pf. violet .. 60 40
E 61. E 27. 24 pf.+6 pf. red .. 1·10 50
E 62. – 30 pf.+10 pf. green 1·40 75
E 63. – 50 pf.+10 pf. blue 2·25 1·00

DESIGNS: 12 pf. Workers clearing debris. 30 pf. Carpenters. 50 pf. Architect and workmen.

E 28. Cyclists.

E 29. Handel.

**1952.** 5th Warsaw–Berlin–Prague Cycle Race.

E64 E 28 12 pf. blue .. .. 2·50 1·00

**1952.** Handel Festival, Halle.

E 65. E 29. 6 pf. brown .. 1·60 1·00
E 66. – 8 pf. red .. .. 2·50 1·25
E 67. – 50 pf. blue .. .. 3·25 1·40

COMPOSERS: 8 pf. Lortzing. 50 pf. Weber.

E 31. Victor Hugo.

E 32. Machinery Dove and Globe.

**1952.** Cultural Anniversaries.

E 73. E 31. 12 pf. brown .. 2·50 3·00
E 74. – 20 pf. green .. 2·50 3·00
E 75. – 24 pf. red .. .. 2·50 3·00
E 76. – 35 pf. blue .. .. 3·50 4·50

PORTRAITS: 20 pf. Leonardo da Vinci. 24 pf. N. Gogol. 35 pf. Avicenna.

**1952.** Leipzig Autumn Fair.

E 77. E 32. 24 pf. red .. .. 1·40 30
E 78. 35 pf. blue .. .. 1·40 1·50

E 33. F. L. Jahn.

E 34. University Building.

**1952.** Death Cent. of Jahn (patriot).

E 79. E 33. 12 pf. blue .. .. 1·40 65

**1952.** 450th Anniv. of Halle-Wittenberg University.

E 80. E 34. 24 pf. green .. 1·75 60

E 35. Dove, Stamp and Flags.

E 36. Dove, Globe and St. Stephen's Cathedral, Vienna.

**1952.** Stamp Day.

E 81. E 35. 24 pf. brown .. 1·60 80

**1952.** Vienna Peace Congress.

E 97. E 36. 24 pf. red .. .. 1·00 1·60
E 98. 35 pf. blue .. .. 1·50 2·00

E 37. President Pieck.

E 38. Karl Marx.

**1953.** President's Birthday.

E 320. E 37. 1 Dm. olive .. 1·50 10
E 321. 2 Dm. brown .. 4·50 10

**1953.** 70th Death Anniv. of Marx.

E 102. – 6 pf. red & green .. 60 30
E 103. – 10 pf. brn. & green 4·00 50
E 104. – 12 pf. red & green 60 50
E 105. – 16 pf. blue and red 2·50 1·50
E 106. – 20 pf. brown & yell. 80 80
E 107. E 38. 24 pf. brown & red 2·75 60
E 108. – 35 pf. yell. & purple 3·00 2·25
E 109. – 48 pf. brn. & green 1·25 60
E 110. – 60 pf. red & brown 4·00 2·50
E 111. – 84 pf. brown & blue 3·00 1·50

DESIGNS—VERT: 6 pf. Flag and foundry. 12 pf. Flag and Spassky Tower, Kremlin. 20 pf. Marx reading from "Das Kapital". 35 pf. Marx addressing meeting. 48 pf. Marx and Engels. HORIZ: 10 pf. Marx, Engels and "Communist Manifesto". 16 pf. Marching crowd. 60 pf. Flag and workers. 84 pf. Marx in medallion and Stalin Avenue, Berlin.

In each case the flag shows heads of Marx, Engels, Lenin and Stalin.

E 39. Gorky.

E 40. Cyclists.

**1953.** 85th Birth Anniv of Maksim Gorky (writer).

E112 E 39 35 pf. brown .. 20 20

**1953.** 6th Int. Cycle Race.

E 113. E 40. 24 pf. green .. 1·90 1·75
E 114. – 35 pf. blue .. 1·00 1·00
E 115. – 60 pf. brown .. 1·25 1·25

DESIGNS—VERT. 35 pf. Cyclists and countryside. 60 pf. Cyclists in town.

E 41. H. Von Kleist.

E 42. Miner.

**1953.** 700th Anniv. of Frankfurt-on-Oder.

E 116. E 41. 16 pf. brown .. 1·00 1·00
E 117. – 20 pf. green .. 75 75
E 118. – 24 pf. red .. .. 1·25 1·25
E 119. – 35 pf. blue .. 1·00 1·25

DESIGNS—HORIZ. 20 pf. St. Mary's Church. 24 pf. Frankfurt from R. Oder. 35 pf. Frankfurt Town Hall and coat of arms.

**1953.** Five Year Plan. (a) Design in minute dots.

E 120. E 42. 1 pf. black .. 80 20
E 121. – 5 pf. green .. 1·75 60
E 122. – 6 pf. violet .. 1·75 40
E 123. – 8 pf. brown .. 2·00 60
E 124. – 10 pf. green .. 1·75 50
E 125. – 12 pf. blue .. 1·75 40
E 126. – 15 pf. violet .. 2·50 80
E 127. – 16 pf. violet .. 2·75 1·00
E 128. – 20 pf. green .. 3·00 1·50
E 129. – 24 pf. red .. .. 8·00 40
E 130. – 25 pf. green .. 5·00 2·00
E 131. – 30 pf. red .. .. 5·00 2·00
E 132. – 35 pf. blue .. 10·00 2·50
E 133. – 40 pf. red .. .. 10·00 1·60
E 134. – 48 pf. mauve .. 10·00 2·00
E 135. – 60 pf. blue .. 10·00 2·75
E 136. – 80 pf. turquoise .. 12·00 2·75
E 137. – 84 pf. brown .. 12·00 2·75

(b) Design in lines.

E 153. E 42. 1 pf. black .. 70 10
E 310. – 5 pf. green .. 10 10
E 155. – 6 pf. violet .. 2·50 30
E 156. – 8 pf. brown .. 2·75 30
E 312. – 10 pf. green .. 45 10
E 311. – 10 pf. blue .. 15 30
E 159. – 12 pf. turquoise .. 3·00 20
E 160. – 15 pf. lilac .. 6·50 40
E 313. – 15 pf. violet .. 10 10
E 162. – 16 pf. violet .. 3·00 50
E 163. – 20 pf. green .. 8·50 50
E 314. – 20 pf. red .. .. 25 10
E 165. – 24 pf. red .. .. 6·00 20
E 315. – 25 pf. green .. 50 20
E 316. – 30 pf. red .. .. 10 10
E 168. – 35 pf. blue .. 2·75 55
E 169. – 40 pf. red .. .. 9·00 40
E 317. – 40 pf. mauve .. 10 15
E 171. – 48 pf. mauve .. 10·00 1·00
E 318. – 50 pf. blue .. 15 40
E 173. – 60 pf. blue .. 12·00 1·25
E 319. – 70 pf. brown .. 15 40
E 175. – 80 pf. turquoise .. 3·00 1·25
E 176. – 84 pf. brown .. 17·00 1·25

DESIGNS—VERT. 5 pf. Woman turning wheel. 6 pf. Workmen shaking hands. 8 pf. Students. 10 pf. Engineers. 10 pf. bl. and 12 pf. Agricultural and industrial workers. 15 pf. mve. Tele-typist. 15 pf. vio. and 16 pf. Foundry worker. 20 pf. grn. Workers' health centre, Elster. 20 pf. red and 24 pf. Stalin Avenue, Berlin. 25 pf. Railway engineers. 30 pf. Folk dancers. 35 pf. Stadium. 40 pf. red, Scientist. 40 pf. mve., 48 pf. Zwinger, Dresden. 50 pf., 60 pf. Launching ship. 80 pf. Farm workers. 70 pf., 84 pf. Workman and family.

E 43. Mechanical Grab. E 44. G. W. von Knobelsdorff and Opera House, Berlin.

**1953.** Leipzig Autumn Fair.
E 138. E 43. 24 pf. brown .. 1·40 80
E 139. – 35 pf. green .. 1·60 1·40
DESIGN: 35 pf. Potato-harvester.

**1953.** German Architects.
E 140. E 44. 24 pf. mauve .. 1·00 50
E 141. – 35 pf. slate .. 1·50 1·10
DESIGN: 35 pf. B. Neumann and Wurzburg Palace.

E 45. Lucas Cranach. E 46. Nurse and Patient.

**1953.** 400th Death Anniv. of Cranach (painter).
E 142. E 45. 24 pf. brown .. 2·75 1·00

**1953.** Red Cross.
E 143. E 46. 24 pf. red & brown 2·00 1·25

E 47. Postman delivering Letters. E 48. Lion and Lioness.

**1953.** Stamp Day.
E 144. E 47. 24 pf. blue .. 2·00 75

**1953.** 75th Anniv. of Leipzig Zoo.
E 145. E 48. 24 pf. brown .. 1·40 50

E 49. Muntzer and Peasants. E 50. Franz Schubert.

**1953.** German Patriots.
E 146. E 49. 12 pf. brown .. 1·00 50
E 147. – 16 pf. brown .. 1·00 50
E 148. – 20 pf. red .. .. 90 20
E 149. – 24 pf. blue .. 1·00 20
E 150. – 35 pf. green .. 2·00 1·25
E 151. – 48 pf. sepia .. 2·00 90
DESIGNS: 16 pf. Baron vom Stein and scroll. 20 pf. Von Schill and cavalry. 24 pf. Blucher and infantry. 35 pf. Students marching. 48 pf. Barricade, 1848 Revolution.

**1953.** 125th Death Anniv of Schubert.
E152 E 50 48 pf. brown .. 2·50 1·10

E 52. G. E. Lessing (writer). E 53. Conference Table and Crowd.

**1954.** 225th Birth Anniv. of Lessing.
E 177. E 52. 20 pf. green .. 1·40 60

**1954.** Four-Power Conference, Berlin.
E178 E 53 12 pf. blue .. .. 1·25 50

E 54. Stalin. E 55. Racing Cyclists.

**1954.** 1st Death Anniv. of Stalin.
E 179. E 54. 20 pf. brown, orange & grey .. 2·00 60

**1954.** 7th International Cycle Race.
E 180. E 55. 12 pf. brown .. 1·25 80
E 181. – 24 pf. green .. 1·60 1·00
DESIGN: 24 pf. Cyclists racing through countryside.

E 56. Folk Dancing. E 57. F. Reuter.

**1954.** 2nd German Youth Assembly.
E 182. E 56. 12 pf. green .. 80 55
E 183. – 24 pf. red .. .. 80 55
DESIGN: 24 pf. Young people and flag.

**1954.** 80th Death Anniv. of Reuter (author).
E 184. E 57. 24 pf. brown .. 1·00 80

E 58. Dam and Forest. E 59. E. Thalmann.

**1954.** Flood Relief Fund.
E 185. E 58. 24 pf.+6 pf. green 30 30

**1954.** 10th Death Anniv. of Thalmann (politician)
E 186. E 59. 24 pf. brown, blue and orange .. 75 40

E 60. Exhibition Buildings.

**1954.** Leipzig Autumn Fair.
E 187. E 60. 24 pf. red .. .. 40 20
E 188. 35 pf. blue .. 70 35

**1954.** (a) Nos. E155, etc, surch in figures.
E 189 5 pf. on 6 pf. violet .. 40 10
E 190 5 pf. on 8 pf. brown .. 40 10
E 191 10 pf. on 12 pf. turq .. 60 20
E 192 15 pf. on 16 pf. lilac .. 50 20
E 194 20 pf. on 24 pf. red .. 50 20
E 195 40 pf. on 48 pf. mauve 2·00 1·00
E 196 50 pf. on 60 pf. blue .. 1·60 1·00
E 197 70 pf. on 84 pf. brown 5·00 1·00

(b) No. E129 similarly surch
E 193a 20 pf. on 24 pf. red .. 50 25

E 62. President Pieck.

**1954.** 5th Anniv. of German Democratic Republic.
E 198. E 62. 20 pf. brown .. 2·40 80
E 199. 35 pf. blue .. 2·75 70

E 63. Stamp of 1953. E 64. Russian Pavilion.

**1954.** Stamp Day.
E 200. E 63. 20 pf. mauve .. 1·00 50

**1955.** Leipzig Spring Fair.
E 201. E 64. 20 pf. purple .. 50 30
E 202. – 35 pf. blue (Chinese Pavilion) .. 90 80

**1955.** Flood Relief Fund. Surch. in figures.
E 203. E 58. 20+5 pf. on 24 pf.+6 pf. green .. 60 40

E 66. "Women of All Nations".

**1955.** 45th Anniv. of Int. Women's Day.
E 204. E 66. 10 pf. green .. 60 30
E 205. 20 pf. red .. .. 70 40

E 67. Parade of Workers. E 68. Monument to Fascist Victims, Brandenburg.

**1955.** International Conference of Municipal Workers, Vienna.
E 206. E 67. 10 pf. black & red 80 60

**1955.** Int. Liberation Day.
E 207. E 68. 10 pf. blue .. 60 80
E 208. 20 pf. mauve .. 80 1·00

E 69. Monument to Russian Soldiers, Treptow. E 70. Schiller (poet).

**1955.** 10th Anniv. of Liberation.
E 209. E 69. 20 pf. mauve .. 1·00 80

**1955.** 150th Death Anniv. of Schiller.
E 210. E 70. 5 pf. green .. 2·75 2·25
E 211. – 10 pf. blue .. 30 20
E 212. – 20 pf. brown .. 30 20
PORTRAITS OF SCHILLER: 10 pf. Full-face. 20 pf. Facing left.

E 71. Cyclists. E 72. Karl Liebknecht.

**1955.** 8th Int. Cycle Race.
E 213. E 71. 10 pf. turquoise .. 60 30
E 214. 20 pf. red .. .. 70 50

**1955.** German Labour Leaders.
E 215. E 72. 5 pf. green .. 15 20
E 216. – 10 pf. blue .. 20 20
E 217. – 15 pf. violet .. 7·00 3·00
E 218. – 20 pf. red .. .. 20 10
E 219. – 25 pf. blue .. 30 10
E 220. – 40 pf. red .. .. 70 10
E 221. – 60 pf. brown .. 30 20
PORTRAITS: 10 pf. A. Bebel. 15 pf. F. Mehring 20 pf. E. Thalmann. 25 pf. Clara Zetkin. 40 pf. Wilhelm Liebknecht. 60 pf. Rosa Luxemburg.

E 73. Pottery. E 74. Workers and Charter.

**1955.** Leipzig Autumn Fair.
E 222. – 10 pf. blue .. 50 30
E 223. E 73. 20 pf. green .. 50 30
DESIGN: 10 pf. Camera and microscope.

**1955.** 10th Anniv. of Land Reform.
E 224. E 74. 5 pf. green .. 5·00 4·50
E 225. – 10 pf. blue .. 60 20
E 226. – 20 pf. red .. .. 70 20
DESIGNS–VERT. 10 pf. Bricklayers at work. HORIZ. 20 pf. Combine-harvesters.

E 75. "Solidarity". E 76. Engels Speaking.

**1955.** 10th Anniv. of People's Solidarity Movement.
E 227. E 75. 10 pf. blue .. 50 20

**1955.** 135th Birth Anniv. of Engels.
E 228. E 76. 5 pf. blue & yell. .. 30 10
E 229. – 10 pf. vio. & yell. 60 10
E 230. – 15 pf. grn. & yell. 70 10
E 231. – 20 pf. brn. & orge. 1·40 20
E 232. – 30 pf. brn. & grey 8·00 6·00
E 233. – 70 pf. green & red 2·50 30
DESIGNS: 10 pf. Engels and Marx. 15 pf. Engels and newspaper. 20 pf. Portrait facing right. 30 pf. Portrait facing left. 70 pf. 1848 Revolution scene.

E 77. Magdeburg Cathedral. E 78. Georg Agricola.

**1955.** Historic Buildings.
E 234. E 77. 5 pf. sepia .. .. 40 10
E 235. – 10 pf. green .. 40 10
E 236. – 15 pf. purple .. 40 10
E 237. – 20 pf. red .. .. 40 10
E 238. – 30 pf. brown .. 12·00 10·00
E 239. – 40 pf. blue .. 80 50
DESIGNS: 10 pf. State Opera House, Berlin. 15 pf. Old Town Hall, Leipzig. 20 pf. Town Hall, Berlin. 30 pf. Erfurt Cathedral. 40 pf. Zwinger, Dresden.

**1955.** 400th Death Anniv. of Agricola (scholar).
E 240. E 78. 10 pf. brown .. 50 30

E 79. "Portrait of a Young Man" (Durer). E 80. Mozart.

**1955.** Dresden Gallery Paintings. (1st series).
E 241. E 79. 5 pf. brown .. 60 10
E 242. – 10 pf. brown .. 60 10
E 243. – 15 pf. purple .. 30·00 24·00
E 244. – 20 pf. sepia .. 85 20
E 245. – 40 pf. green .. 85 40
E 246. – 70 pf. blue .. 2·50 80
PAINTINGS: 10 pf. "The Chocolate Girl" (Liotard). 15 pf. "Portrait of a Boy" (Pinturicchio). 20 pf. "Self-portrait with Saskia" (Rembrandt). 40 pf. "Maiden with Letter" (Vermeer). 70 pf. "Sistine Madonna" (Raphael).
See also Nos. E 325/30 and E 427/31.

**1956.** Birth Bicent of Mozart (composer).
E 247. E 80. 10 pf. green .. 10·00 8·00
E 248. – 20 pf. brown .. 3·00 1·60
PORTRAIT: 20 pf. Facing left.

E 81. Ilyushin Il-14P. E 82. Heinrich Heine (poet).

**1956.** Establishment of East German Lufthansa Airways.
E249 – 5 pf. multicoloured 12·00 9·00
E250 E 81 10 pf. green .. 30 10
E251 – 15 pf. blue .. 30 10
E252 – 20 pf. red .. .. 30 10
DESIGNS: 5 pf. Lufthansa flag. 15 pf. View of Ilyushin Il-14P airplane from below. 20 pf. Ilyushin Il-14P airplane facing left.

**1956.** Death Cent. of Heine.
E 253. E **82.** 10 pf. green .. 9·50 5·50
E 254. – 20 pf. red .. .. 2·25 50
PORTRAIT: 20 pf. Full-face.

E **83.** Mobile Cranes. E **84.** E. Thalmann.

**1956.** Leipzig Spring Fair.
E 255. E **83.** 20 pf. red .. .. 60 30
E 256. 35 pf. blue .. 80 60

**1956.** 70th Birth Anniv. of Thalmann (communist leader).
E 257. E **84.** 20 pf. black, brown and red .. .. 50 20

E **85.** Hand, Laurels and Cycle Wheel. E **86.** New Buildings, Old Market-place.

**1956.** 9th Int. Cycle Race.
E 258. E **85.** 10 pf. green .. 50 15
E 259. – 20 pf. red .. .. 50 15
DESIGN: 20 pf. Arms of Warsaw, Berlin and Prague and cycle wheel.

**1956.** 750th Anniv. of Dresden.
E 260. E **86.** 10 pf. green .. 30 15
E 261. – 20 pf. red .. 30 10
E 262. – 40 pf. violet .. 2·40 2·25
DESIGNS: 20 pf. Elbe Bridge. 40 pf. Technical High School.

E **87.** Workman.

**1956.** 10th Anniv. of Industrial Reforms.
E 263. E **87.** 20 pf. red .. 30 20

E **88.** Robert Schumann. E **88a.**

**1956.** Death Cent. of Schumann (composer).
(a) Type E **88** (wrong music).
E 264. E **88.** 10 pf. green .. 2·00 1·25
E 265. 20 pf. red .. .. 50 15
(b) Type E **88a** (correct music).
E 266. E **88a.** 10 pf. green .. 3·00 1·40
E 267. 20 pf. red .. .. 1·50 35

E **89.** Footballers. E **90.** T. Mann (author).

**1956.** 2nd Sports Festival, Leipzig.
E 268. E **89.** 5 pf. green .. 20 10
E 269. – 10 pf. blue .. 20 10
E 270. – 15 pf. purple .. 1·60 1·10
E 271. – 20 pf. red .. .. 20 10
DESIGNS: 10 pf. Javelin thrower. 15 pf. Hurdlers. 20 pf. Gymnast.

**1956.** 1st Anniv. of Death of Thomas Mann.
E 272. E **90.** 20 pf. black .. 90 40

E **91.** J. B. Cisinski. E **92.** Lace.

**1956.** Birth Cent. of Cisinski (poet).
E 273. E **91.** 50 pf. brown .. 80 25

**1956.** Leipzig Autumn Fair.
E274 E **92** 10 pf. green & black 15 10
E275 – 20 pf. pink & black (Sailing dinghy) 20 15

E **93.** Buchenwald Memorial.

**1956.** Concentration Camp Memorials Fund.
E 276. E **93.** 20 pf.+80 pf. red.. 1·00 1·40
For similar stamp see No. E 390.

E **94.** Torch and Olympic Rings. E **95.**

**1956.** Olympic Games.
E 277. E **94.** 20 pf. brown .. 30 10
E 278. – 35 pf. slate .. 40 20
DESIGN: 35 pf. Greek athlete.

**1956.** 500th Anniv. of Greifswald University.
E 279. E **95.** 20 pf. red .. .. 40 15

E **96.** Postal Carrier, 1450. E **97.** E. Abbe.

**1956.** Stamp Day.
E 280. E **96.** 20 pf. red .. .. 40 15

**1956.** 110th Anniv. of Zeiss Factory, Jena.
E 281. E **97.** 10 pf. green .. 15 10
E 282. – 20 pf. brown .. 15 10
E 283. – 25 pf. blue .. 25 15
DESIGNS—HORIZ. 20 pf. Factory buildings. 25 pf. Carl Zeiss.

E **98.** "Negro". E **99.** Indian Elephants.

**1956.** Human Rights Day.
E 284. – 5 pf. green on olive 1·00 1·00
E 285. E **98.** 10 pf. brown on pink 15 10
E 286. – 25 pf. blue on lav. 15 10
DESIGNS: 5 pf. "Chinese". 25 pf. "European".

**1956.** Berlin Zoological Gardens. Centres in grey.
E 287. E **99.** 5 pf. black 15 10
E 288. – 10 pf. green .. 30 10
E 289. – 15 pf. purple .. 4·00 3·00
E 290. – 20 pf. red .. .. 20 10
E 291. – 25 pf. brown .. 30 15
E 292. – 30 pf. blue .. 30 15
DESIGNS: 10 pf. Greater Flamingoes. 15 pf. Black rhinoceros. 20 pf. Mouflon. 25 pf. European bison. 30 pf. Polar bear.

**1956.** Egyptian Relief Fund. No. E 237 surch. **HELFT AGYPTEN+10.**
E 293. 20 pf.+10 pf. red .. 40 20

**1956.** Hungarian Socialists' Relief Fund. No. E 237 surch. **HELFT DEM SOZIALISTISCHEN UNGARN+10.**
E 294. 20 pf.+10 pf. red .. 40 20

DESIGN: 25 pf. Electric locomotive.

E **103.** "Frieden" (freighter).

**1957.** Leipzig Spring Fair.
E 295. E **103.** 20 pf. red .. 25 10
E 296. – 25 pf. blue .. 25 15

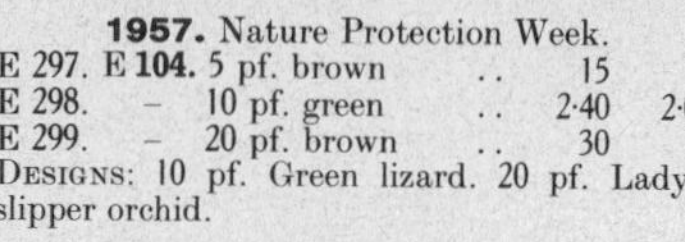

E **104.** Silver Thistle. E **105.** Friedrich Froebel and Children.

**1957.** Nature Protection Week.
E 297. E **104.** 5 pf. brown .. 15 10
E 298. – 10 pf. green .. 2·40 2·00
E 299. – 20 pf. brown .. 30 10
DESIGNS: 10 pf. Green lizard. 20 pf. Lady's slipper orchid.

**1957.** 175th Birth Anniv. of Froebel (educator).
E 300. – 10 pf. blk. & grn... 1·00 1·00
E 301. E **105.** 20 pf. blk. & brn. 20 10
DESIGN: 10 pf. Children at play.

DESIGN—HORIZ. 20 pf. Memorial and environs.

E **106.** Ravensbruck Memorial. E **107.** Cycle Race Route.

**1957.** Concentration Camp Memorials Fund.
E 302. E **106.** 5 pf.+5 pf. green 15 15
E 303. – 20 pf.+10 pf. red.. 20 30
DESIGN: Memorial and environs.
For similar stamp to No. E 303 see No. E 453.

**1957.** 10th Int. Cycle Race.
E 304. E **107.** 5 pf. orange .. 30 15

E **108.** Miner. E **109.** Henri Dunant and Globe.

**1957.** Coal Mining Industry.
E 305. – 10 pf. green .. 15 10
E 306. – 20 pf. brown .. 15 10
E 307. E **108.** 25 pf. blue .. 2·00 80
DESIGNS: (39×21 mm.): 10 pf. Mechanical shovel. 20 pf. Gantry.

**1957.** Int. Red Cross Day. Cross in red.
E 308. E **109.** 10 pf. brown & grn. 15 10
E 309. – 25 pf. brn. & blue 20 15
DESIGN: 25 pf. H. Dunant wearing hat, and globe.

E **110.** Joachim Jungius (botanist). E **111.** Clara Zetkin and Flower.

**1957.** Scientists' Anniversaries.
E 322. E **110.** 5 pf. brown .. 1·00 75
E 323. – 10 pf. green .. 15 10
E 324. – 20 pf. brown .. 15 10
PORTRAITS: 10 pf. L. Euler (mathematician). 20 pf. H. Hertz (physicist).

**1957.** Dresden Gallery Paintings (2nd series). As Type E **79**.
E 325. 5 pf. sepia .. .. 15 10
E 326. 10 pf. green .. .. 15 10
E 327. 15 pf. brown .. .. 15 10
E 328. 20 pf. red .. .. 15 10
E 329. 25 pf. purple .. .. 30 10
E 330. 40 pf. grey .. .. 3·50 2·00
PAINTINGS—VERT. 5 pf. "The Holy Family" (Mantegna). 10 pf. "The Dancer, Barbarina Campani" (Carriera). 15 pf. "Portrait of Morette" (Holbein the Younger). 20 pf. "The Tribute Money" (Titian). 25 pf. "Saskia with a Red Flower" (Rembrandt). 40 pf. "A Young Standard-bearer" (Piazetta).

**1957.** Birth Cent. of Clara Zetkin (patriot).
E 331. E **111.** 10 pf. green & red 50 20

E **112.** Bertolt Brecht (dramatist). E **113.** Congress Emblem.

**1957.** 1st Death Anniv. of Bertolt Brecht.
E 332. E **112.** 10 pf. green .. 20 15
E 333. 25 pf. blue .. 40 15

**1957.** 4th World Trade Unions Congress.
E 334. E **113.** 20 pf. black & red 50 25

E **114.** Fair Emblem. E **115.** Savings Bank Book.

**1957.** Leipzig Autumn Fair.
E 335. E **114.** 20 pf. red .. 20 10
E 336. 25 pf. blue .. 25 10

**1957.** Savings Week.
E337 E **115** 10 pf. black and green on grey .. 75 65
E338 20 pf. black and mauve on grey 25 15

E **116.** Postrider of 1563. E **117.** Revolutionary's Rifle and Red Flag.

**1957.** Stamp Day.
E 339. E **116.** 5 pf. blue on brown 40 15

**1957.** 40th Anniv. of Russian Revolution.
E 340. E **117.** 10 pf. green & red 15 10
E 341. 25 pf. blue & red.. 25 20

E. **118** Artificial Satellite. E **119.** Professor Ramin.

**1957.** Int. Geophysical Year.
E 342. E **118.** 10 pf. blue .. 30 15
E 343. – 20 pf. red .. 30 15
E 344. – 25 pf. blue .. 1·90 1·00
DESIGNS: 20 pf. Stratosphere balloon. 25 pf. Ship using echo-sounder.

**1957.** "National Prize" Composers.
E 345. E **119.** 10 pf. black & grn. 75 75
E 346. – 20 pf. black & orge. 25 25
PORTRAIT: 20 pf. Professor Abendroth.

PORTRAITS: 25 pf. R. Breitscheid. 40 pf. Father P. Schneider. For other stamps as Type E **120** see Nos. E 374/8, E 448/52, E 485/7, E 496/500, E 540/4 and E 588/92.

E **120.** Ernst Thalmann.

**1957.** National Memorials Fund. East German War Victims. Portraits in grey.
E 347. E **120.** 20 pf.+10 pf. mve. 10 15
E 348. – 25 pf.+15 pf. blue 15 20
E 349. – 40 pf.+20 pf. violet 30 35

E **121.** E **122.**

**1957.** Air.
E 350. E **121.** 5 pf. black & grey 50 10
E 351. 20 pf. black & red 30 10
E 352. 35 pf. black & vio. 15 10
E 353. 50 pf. black & brn. 20 15
E 354. E **122.** 1 Dm. olive & yell. 1·50 10
E 355. 3 Dm. brn. & yell. 3·00 20
E 356. 5 Dm. blue & yell. 4·25 25

E 123. Fair Emblem.

**1958.** Leipzig Spring Fair.
E 357. E 123. 20 pf. red .. 25 15
E 358. 25 pf. blue .. 25 15

E 124. Transmitting Aerial and Posthorn.

E 125. "Zille at play".

**1958.** Communist Postal Conf., Moscow.
E 359. E 124. 5 pf. black and grey 65 55
E 360. – 20 pf. red .. 25 10
DESIGN—HORIZ. 20 pf. Aerial as in 5 pf. but posthorn above figures of value.

**1958.** Birth Cent. of Heinrich Zille (painter).
E 361. E 125. 10 pf. drab & grn. 2·40 1·25
E 362. – 20 pf. drab and red 65 15
DESIGN—VERT. 20 pf. Self-portrait of Zille.

E 126. Max Planck.

E 127. Breeding Cow.

**1958.** Birth Cent. of Max Planck (physicist).
E 363. – 10 pf. olive .. 1·10 1·10
E 364. E 126. 20 pf. mauve .. 30 15
DESIGN—VERT. 10 pf. "h" (symbol of Planck's Constant).

**1958.** 6th Markkleeberg Agricultural Exn. Inscr. "6 Landwirtschaftausstellung der DDR in Markkleeberg".
E 365. E 127. 5 pf. grey .. 1·60 1·25
E 366. – 10 pf. green .. 15 10
E 367. – 20 pf. red .. 15 10
DESIGNS (39×22½ mm.): 10 pf. Chaff-cutter. 20 pf. Beet-harvester.

E 128. Charles Darwin.

E 129. Congress Emblem.

**1958.** Cent. of Darwin's Theory of Evolution and Bicent. of Linnaeus's Plant Classification System. Portraits in black.
E 368. E 128. 10 pf. green .. 1·10 1·10
E 369. – 20 pf. red .. 15 15
PORTRAIT—HORIZ. 20 pf. Linnaeus (Carl von Linne) inscr. "200 JAHRE SYSTEMA NATURAE".

**1958.** 5th German Socialist Unity Party Congress.
E 370. E 129. 10 pf. red .. 25 20

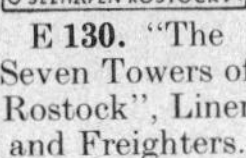
E 130. "The Seven Towers of Rostock", Liner and Freighters.

E 131. Mare and Foal.

**1958.** Rostock Port Reconstruction.
E 371. – 10 pf. green .. 20 10
E 372. E 130. 20 pf. orange .. 30 10
E 373. – 25 pf. blue .. 1·00 1·25
DESIGNS: 10 pf. "Freundschaft" (freighter) at quayside. 25 pf. "Frieden" (freighter) in Rostock harbour.

**1958.** "Resistance Fighters". As Type E 120. Portraits in grey.
E 374. 5 pf.+5 pf. brown .. 10 15
E 375. 10 pf.+5 pf. green .. 10 15
E 376. 15 pf.+10 pf. violet .. 15 1·75
E 377. 20 pf.+10 pf. brown .. 15 40
E 378. 25 pf.+15 pf. black .. 55 5·50
PORTRAITS—VERT. 5 pf. A. Kuntz. 10 pf. R. Arndt. 15 pf. Dr. K. Adams. 20 pf. R. Renner. 25 pf. W. Stoecker.

**1958.** "Grand Prix of the D.D.R." Horse Show.
E 379. E 131. 5 pf. sepia .. 4·50 2·50
E 380. – 10 pf. green .. 15 10
E 381. – 20 pf. brown .. 15 10
DESIGNS: 10 pf. Horse-trotting. 20 pf. Racing horses.

E 132. J. A. Komensky ("Comenius").

E 133. Camp Bugler.

**1958.** Komensky Commem. Centres in black.
E 382. E 132. 10 pf. green .. 1·40 1·10
E 383. – 20 pf. brown .. 15 10
DESIGN: 20 pf. Komensky with pupils (from an old engraving).

**1958.** 10th Anniv. of East German "Pioneer" Organization.
E 384. E 133. 10 pf.+5 pf. green 25 15
E 385. – 20 pf.+10 pf. red 25 20
DESIGN—VERT. 20 pf. Young Pioneer saluting.

E 134. University Seal.

DESIGN: 20 pf. University building.

**1958.** 400th Anniv. of Friedrich Schiller University, Jena.
E 386. E 134. 5 pf. black & grey 1·40 1·10
E 387. – 20 pf. grey and red 35 10

E 135. Model with Hamster-lined Coat, and Leipzig Railway Station.

E 136. Soldier climbing Wall.

**1958.** Leipzig Autumn Fair.
E 388. E 135. 10 pf. brn. & grn. 15 10
E 389. – 25 pf. black & blue 20 20
DESIGN: 25 pf. Model with Karakul fur coat, and Leipzig Old Town Hall.

**1958.** Concentration Camp Memorials Fund. As Type E 93 but additionally inscr. "14. SEPTEMBER 1958" in black.
E 390. 20 pf.+20 pf. red .. 35 35

**1958.** 1st Summer Military Games. Leipzig.
E 391. E 136. 10 pf. brn. & green 1·10 1·00
E 392. – 20 pf. yell. & brown 10 10
E 393. – 25 pf. red & blue 10 10
DESIGNS: 20 pf. Games emblem. 25 pf. Marching athletes with banner.

E 137. Warding off the Atomic Bomb.

E 138. 17th-century Mail Cart.

**1958.** Campaign Against Atomic Warfare.
E 394. E 137. 20 pf. red .. 20 10
E 395. 25 pf. blue .. 40 15

**1958.** Stamp Day.
E 396. E 138. 10 pf. green .. 1·90 1·40
E 397. – 20 pf. red .. 30 10
DESIGN: 20 pf. Modern postal sorting train and Baade-Bonin 152 jetliner.

E 139. Revolutionary and Soldier.

E 140. Brandenburg Gate, Berlin.

**1958.** 40th Anniv. of November Revolution.
E 398. E 139. 20 pf. purple & red 7·50 12·00

**1958.** Brandenburg Gate Commem.
E 399. E 140. 20 pf. red .. 35 10
E 400. 25 pf. blue .. 2·40 1·75

E 142. Negro and European Youths.

E 141. "Girl's Head" (bas-relief).

**1958.** Antique Art Treasures.
E 401. E 141. 10 pf. black & grn. 1·00 1·00
E 402. – 20 pf. black & red 35 15
DESIGN: 20 pf. "Large Head" (from Pergamon frieze).
See also Nos. E 475/8.

**1958.** 10th Anniv. of Declaration of Human Rights.
E 403. E 142. 10 pf. black & grn. 15 15
E 404. – 25 pf. black & blue 1·00 1·00
DESIGN: 25 pf. Chinese and European girls.

E 143. O. Nuschke.

E 144. "The Red Flag" (Party Newspaper).

**1958.** 1st Death Anniv. of Vice-Premier Otto Nuschke.
E 405. E 143. 20 pf. red .. 25 15

**1958.** 40th Anniv. of German Communist Party.
E 406. E 144. 20 pf. red .. 30 10

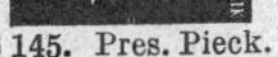
E 145. Pres. Pieck.

E 146. Rosa Luxemburg (revolutionary).

**1959.** Pres. Pieck's 83rd Birthday.
E 407. E 145. 20 pf. red .. 30 15
For 20 pf. black see No. E 517.

**1959.** 40th Death Anniv. of Rosa Luxemburg and Karl Liebknecht. Centres in black.
E 408. E 146. 10 pf. green .. 1·75 1·40
E 409. – 20 pf. red .. 35 15
DESIGN—HORIZ. 20 pf. Liebknecht (revolutionary).

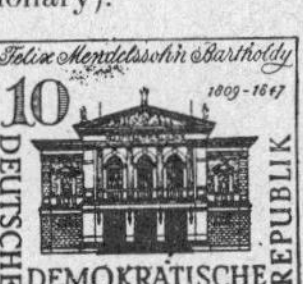
E 147. Concert Hall, Leipzig.

DESIGN—HORIZ. 25 pf. Opening theme of Symphony in A Major ("The Italian").

**1959.** 150th Birth Anniv. of Felix Mendelssohn-Bartholdy (composer).
E 410. E 147. 10 pf. green on grn 25 35
E 411. – 25 pf. blue on blue 1·50 2·00

E 148. "Schwarze Pumpe" plant.

E 149. Boy holding Book for Girl.

**1959.** Leipzig Spring Fair. Inscr. as in Type E 148.
E 412. E 148. 20 pf. red .. 10 10
E 413. – 25 pf. blue .. 30 15
DESIGN—HORIZ. 25 pf. Various cameras.

**1959.** 5th Anniv. of "Youth Consecration".
E 414. E 149. 10 pf. black on grn. 1·40 1·00
E 415. – 20 pf. blk. on salm. 15 10
DESIGN: 20 pf. Girl holding book for boy.

E 150. Handel's Statue, Oboe and Arms of Halle.

E 151. A. von Humboldt and Jungle Scene.

**1959.** Death Bicentenary of Handel. Centre in black.
E 416. E 150. 10 pf. green .. 1·50 1·10
E 417. – 20 pf. red .. 15 10
DESIGN: 20 pf. Portrait of Handel (after oil painting by Thomas Hudson).

**1959.** Death Centenary of Alexander von Humboldt (naturalist).
E 418. E 151. 10 pf. green .. 1·40 1·00
E 419. – 20 pf. red .. 20 45
DESIGN: 20 pf. As Type E 151 but with view of sleigh in forest.

E 152. Posthorn.

E 153. Grey Heron.

**1959.** Socialist Countries' Postal Ministers Conference, Berlin.
E420 E 152 20 pf. black, yellow and red .. 15 10
E421 25 pf. blk. yell & bl 75 75

**1959.** Nature Preservation.
E 422. E 153. 5 pf. lilac, black and blue .. 40 10
E 423. – 10 pf. brown, sepia and turquoise .. 40 10
E 424. – 20 pf. multicoloured 25 10
E 425. – 25 pf. multicoloured 35 15
E 426. – 40 pf. yellow, black and grey .. 4·75 3·00
DESIGNS: 10 pf. Eurasian bittern. 20 pf. Lily of the valley and peacock (butterfly). 25 pf. Eurasian beaver. 40 pf. Honey bee and willow catkin.

**1959.** Dresden Gallery Paintings as Type E 79 (3rd series).
E 427. 5 pf. olive .. .. 10 10
E 428. 10 pf. green .. .. 10 10
E 429. 20 pf. orange .. .. 10 10
E 430. 25 pf. brown .. .. 20 10
E 431. 40 pf. red .. .. 3·75 2·75
PAINTINGS—VERT. 5 pf. "The Vestal Virgin" (Kauffman). 10 pf. "The Needlewoman" (Metsu). 20 pf. "Mlle. Lavergne reading a letter" (Liotard). 25 pf. "Old woman with a brazier" (Rubens). 40 pf. "Young man in black coat" (Hals).

E 154. Common Cormorant.

E 155.

**1959.** "Birds of the Homeland". Centres and inscriptions in black.
E 432. E 154. 5 pf. yellow .. 10 10
E 433. – 10 pf. green .. 15 10
E 434. – 15 pf. violet .. 5·00 2·50
E 435. – 20 pf. pink .. 20 10
E 436. – 25 pf. blue .. 25 10
E 437. – 40 pf. red .. 55 15
BIRDS: 10 pf. Black Stork. 15 pf. Eagle Owl. 20 pf. Black Grouse. 25 pf. Hoopoe. 40 pf. Peregrine Falcon.

**1959.** 7th World Youth Festival, Vienna.
E 438. E 155. 20 pf. red .. 20 20
E 439. – 25 pf. blue .. 45 35
DESIGN—HORIZ. 25 pf. White girl embracing negro girl.

E 156. Hoop Exercises.

E 157. Modern Leipzig Building.

**1959.** 3rd German Gymnastic and Sports Festival, Leipzig.
E 440. E 156. 5 pf.+5 pf. brown 10 10
E 441. – 10 pf.+5 pf. green 10 10
E 442. – 20 pf.+10 pf. red 10 10
E 443. – 25 pf.+10 pf. blue 20 10
E 444. – 40 pf.+20 pf. pur. 2·00 75
DESIGNS: 10 pf. High jumping. 20 pf. Vaulting. 25 pf. Club exercises. 40 pf. Fireworks over Leipzig Stadium.

**1959.** Leipzig Autumn Fair.
E 445. E 157. 20 pf. grey & red 20 15
See also Nos. E 483/4.

E 158. Glass Tea-set.

**1959.** 75 Years of Jena Glassware.
E 446. E 158. 10 pf. turquoise .. 25 10
E 447. – 25 pf. blue .. 1·10 75
DESIGN—VERT. 25 pf. Laboratory retorts.

**1959.** Ravensbruck Concentration Camp Victims. As Type E **120.** Portraits in black.

E 448. 5 pf.+5 pf. brown .. 10 10
E 449. 10 pf.+5 pf. green .. 15 10
E 450. 15 pf.+10 pf. violet .. 15 10
E 451. 20 pf.+10 pf. mauve .. 15 10
E 452. 25 pf.+15 pf. blue .. 50 1·00

PORTRAITS: 5 pf. T. Klose. 10 pf. K. Niederkirchner 15 pf. C. Eisenblatter. 20 pf. O. Benario-Prestes. 25 pf. M. Grollmuss.

**1959.** Concentration Camp Memorials Fund. As No. E 303 but inscr. "12. SEPTEMBER 1959" in black.

E 453. 20 pf.+10 pf. red .. 35 15

E **159.** "Russian Pennant on the Moon".

**1959.** Landing of Russian Rocket on the Moon.

E 454. E **159.** 20 pf. red .. 55 25

E **160.** E. German Flag & Combine-harvester. E **161.** J. R. Becher.

**1959.** 10th Anniv. of German Democratic Republic. Designs as Type E **160** showing E. German Flag in black, red and yellow. Inscriptions in black and red on coloured paper.

E 455. E **160.** 5 pf. buff.. .. 10 10
E 456. – 10 pf. grey .. 10 10
E 457. – 15 pf. pale yellow 10 10
E 458. – 20 pf. lilac .. 10 10
E 459. – 25 pf. pale olive.. 15 15
E 460. – 40 pf. yellow .. 20 20
E 461. – 50 pf. salmon .. 25 25
E 462. – 60 pf. turquoise 25 25
E 463. – 70 pf. pale green 25 25
E 464. – 1 Dm. brown .. 50 50

DESIGNS—East German flag and: 10 pf. "Fritz Heckert" convalescent home. 15 pf. Zwinger Palace, Dresden. 20 pf. Steel worker. 25 pf. Industrial chemist. 40 pf. Leipzig Stadium. 50 pf. Woman tractor-driver. 60 pf. Ilyushin Il-14M airplane. 70 pf. Shipbuilding. 1 Dm. East Germany's first atomic reactor.

**1959.** 1st Death Anniv. of Becher (poet).

E 465. E **161.** 20 pf. slate and red 85 15

E **162.** Schiller. E **163.** 18th-century Courier and Milestone.

**1959.** Birth Bicent. of Schiller (poet).

E 466. – 10 pf. grn. on grn. 1·50 1·10
E 467. E **162.** 20 pf. lake on pink 50 10

DESIGN: 10 pf. Schiller's house, Weimar.

**1959.** Stamp Day.

E 468. E **163.** 10 pf. green .. 1·10 75
E 469. – 20 pf. lake .. 15 10

DESIGN: 20 pf. Postwoman on motor cycle.

E **164.** Eurasian Red Squirrels. E. **165.** Boxing.

**1959.** Forest Animals.

E 470. E **164.** 5 pf. red, brn. & grey 15 10
E 471. – 10 pf. light brown, brown and green 15 10
E 472. – 20 pf. multicoloured 15 10
E 473. – 25 pf. multicoloured 15 10
E 474. 40 pf. yellow, brown and blue .. 6·00 2·75

ANIMALS: 10 pf. Brown hares. 20 pf. Roe deer. 25 pf. Red deer. 40 pf. Lynx.

**1959.** Antique Art Treasures (2nd series). As Type E **141.**

E 475. 5 pf. black and yellow.. 10 10
E 476. 10 pf. black and green.. 10 10
E 477. 20 pf. black and red .. 10 10
E 478. 25 pf. black and blue .. 1·10 50

DESIGNS: 5 pf. Attic goddess (about 580 B.C.). 10 pf. Princess of Tell el-Amarna (about 1360 B.C.). 20 pf. Bronze horse of Toprak-Kale, Armenia (7th-century B.C.). HORIZ. (49 × 28 mm.): 25 pf. Altar of Zeus, Pergamon (about 160 B.C.).

**1960.** Olympic Games. As Type E **165** inscr. "OLYMPISCHE SOMMERSPIELE 1960" or "WINTERSPIELE" etc. (20 pf). Centres and inscriptions in bistre.

E 479. E **165.** 5 pf. brown .. 4·50 1·75
E 480. – 10 pf. green .. 10 10
E 481. – 20 pf. red .. 10 10
E 482. – 25 pf. blue .. 15 10

DESIGNS: 10 pf. Running. 20 pf. Ski jumping. 25 pf. Yachting.

**1960.** Leipzig Spring Fair. As Type E **157** but inscr. "LEIPZIGER FRUHJAHRSMESSE 1960".

E 483. 20 pf. grey and red .. 15 10
E 484. 25 pf. grey and blue .. 20 10

DESIGNS: 20 pf. Northern Entrance, Technical Fair. 25 pf. Ring Fair Building.

**1960.** Sachsenhausen Concentration Camp Victims (1st issue). As Type E **120.** Portraits in black.

E 485. 5 pf.+5 pf. drab .. 10 10
E 486. 10 pf.+5 pf. myrtle .. 10 10
E 487. 20 pf.+10 pf. purple .. 10 10

PORTRAITS: 5 pf. L. Erdmann. 10 pf. E. Schneller. 20 pf. L. Horn.

See also Nos. E 496/500.

E **166.** Purple Foxglove. E **167.** Lenin.

**1960.** Medicinal Flowers. Background in pale drab.

E 488. E **166.** 5 pf. red and green 10 10
E 489. – 10 pf. olive & green 10 10
E 490. – 15 pf. red & green 15 10
E 491. – 20 pf. violet & turq. 15 10
E 492. – 40 pf. red, green and brown .. 4·00 2·10

FLOWERS: 10 pf. Camomile. 15 pf. Peppermint. 20 pf. Poppy. 40 pf. Wild Rose.

**1960.** 90th Birth Anniv. of Lenin.

E 493. E **167.** 20 pf. red .. .. 20 10

**1960.** Re-opening of Rostock Port. No. E 371. optd **Inbetriebnahme des Hochseehafens 1. Mai 1960.**

E494 10 pf. green .. .. 25 20

E **169.** Russian Soldier and Liberated Prisoner.

**1960.** 15th Anniv. of Liberation.

E 495. E **169.** 20 pf. red .. 75 15

**1960.** Sachsenhausen Concentration Camp Victims (2nd issue). As Type E **120.** Portraits in black.

E 496. 10 pf.+5 pf. green .. 10 10
E 497. 15 pf.+5 pf. violet .. 70 65
E 498. 20 pf.+10 pf. lake .. 10 10
E 499. 25 pf.+10 pf. blue .. 20 15
E 500. 40 pf.+20 pf. brown .. 1·75 1·60

PORTRAITS: 10 pf. M. Lademann. 15 pf. L. Breunig. 20 pf. M. Thesen. 25 pf. G. Sandtner. 40 pf. H. Rothbarth.

E **170.** Model and Plan of Liner.

**1960.** Launching of Cruise Liner "Fritz Heckert".

E 501. E **170.** 5 pf. slate, red and yellow .. .. 15 10
E 502. – 10 pf.+5 pf. black, red and yellow 15 10
E 503. – 20 pf.+10 pf. black, red and blue .. 20 10
E 504. – 25 pf. black, yellow and blue .. 4·25 4·00

DESIGNS: 10 pf. Liner under construction at Wismar. 20 pf. Liner off Stubbenkammer. 25 pf. Liner and Russian cruiser "Aurora" at Leningrad.

E **171.** Lenin Statue, Eisleben. E **172.** Masked Dancer (statuette).

**1960.** Lenin-Thalmann Statues.

E 505. E **171.** 10 pf. green .. 15 15
E 506. – 20 pf. red .. 25 25

DESIGN: 20 pf. Thalmann statue, Pushkin. U.S.S.R.

**1960.** 250th Anniv of Porcelain Industry, Meissen. Centres and inscriptions in blue. Figures in colours given.

E 507. E **172.** 5 pf. orange .. 10 10
E 508. – 10 pf. green .. 10 10
E 509. – 15 pf. purple .. 4·00 3·00
E 510. – 20 pf. red .. 15 10
E 511. – 25 pf. olive .. 15 10

DESIGNS: 10 pf. Dish inscr. with swords and years "1710 1960". 15 pf. Otter. 20 pf. Potter. 25 pf. Coffee-pot.

E **173.** Racing Cyclist. E **174.** Opera House, Leipzig.

**1960.** World Cycling Championships.

E 512. E **173.** 20 pf.+10 pf. mult. 25 15
E 513. – 25 pf.+10 pf. brn., drab and blue.. 1·40 2·10

DESIGN ($38\frac{1}{2}$ × 21 mm.): 25 pf. Racing cyclists on track.

**1960.** Leipzig Autumn Fair.

E 514. E **174.** 20 pf. grey and red 15 10
E 515. – 25 pf. brn. & blue 35 20

DESIGN: 25 pf. Export goods.

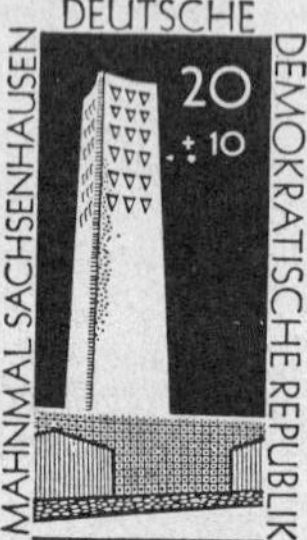

E **175.** Sachsenhausen Memorial. E **176.** 18th-century Rook.

**1960.** Concentration Camp Memorials Fund.

E 516. E **175.** 20 pf.+10 pf. red 30 20

**1960.** President Pieck Mourning issue

E 517. E **145.** 20 pf. black .. 35 20

**1960.** 14th Chess Olympiad, Leipzig. German Chessmen.

E518 E **176** 10 pf.+5 pf. green 20 15
E519 – 20 pf.+10 pf. pur 20 15
E520 – 25 pf.+10 pf. blue 1·75 1·75

DESIGNS: 20 pf. 18th-century knight. 25 pf. 14th-century knight.

E **177.** Mail Vans.

**1960.** Stamp Day.

E521 E **177** 20 pf. yellow, black and mauve .. 30 10
E522 – 25 pf. mve, blk & bl 2·00 1·60

DESIGN: 25 pf. 19th-cent railway mail-coach.

E **178.** Medal of 1518 showing Hans Burgkmair (painter). E **179.** Count N. von Gneisenau.

**1960.** 400th Anniv. of Dresden Art Collections.

E 523. E **178.** 20 pf. ochre, green and buff 10 10
E 524. – 25 pf. black & blue 1·40 1·40

DESIGN: 25 pf. "Dancing Peasants" (after Durer).

**1960.** Birth Bicent. of Count N. von Gneisenau.

E 525. E **179.** 20 pf. black & red 15 10
E 526. – 25 pf. blue 1·10 90

DESIGN: 25 pf. Similar portrait but vert.

E **180.** R. Virchow. E **181.** Scientist with notebook.

**1960.** 250th Anniv. of Berlin Charity and 150th Anniv. of Humboldt University, Berlin. Centres in black.

E 527. E **180.** 5 pf. ochre .. 15 10
E 528. – 10 pf. green .. 15 10
E 529. – 20 pf. brown .. 15 10
E 530. – 25 pf. blue .. 15 15
E 531. – 40 pf. red .. 3·00 1·00

DESIGNS—As Type E **180** (Berlin Charity): 10 pf. Robert Koch. 40 pf. W. Griesinger. (Humboldt University): 20 pf. University building and statues of William and Alexander von Humboldt. 25 pf. Plaque with profiles of Von Humboldt brothers.

**1960.** Chemical Workers' Day.

E 532. E **181.** 5 pf. grey & red 10 10
E 533. – 10 pf. green and orange 10 10
E 534. – 20 pf. red & bl. 10 10
E 535. – 25 pf. bl. & yell. 1·90 1·40

DESIGNS: 10 pf. Chemical worker with fertiliser. 20 pf. Girl worker with jar, and Trabant car. 25 pf. Laboratory assistant and synthetic dress.

E **182.** "Young Socialist Express" (double-decker train). E **183.** President Pieck.

**1960.** 125th Anniv. of German Railways.

E 536. E **182.** 10 pf. black and green .. .. 15 10
E 537. – 20 pf. blk. & red.. 15 10
E 538. – 25 pf. blk. & bl. 4·00 3·75

DESIGNS—As Type E **182**: 25 pf. Locomotive "Der Adler" of 1835 and modern diesel locomotive No. V 180 with train. (43 × $25\frac{1}{2}$ mm): 20 pf. Sassnitz Harbour station and train ferry "Sassnitz".

**1961.** 85th Birth Anniv. of President Pieck.

E 539. E **183.** 20 pf. red & blk. 35 20

**1961.** Concentration Camp Victims. As Type E **120.** Portraits in black.

E 540. 5 pf.+5 pf. green .. 10 10
E 541. 10 pf.+5 pf. green .. 10 10
E 542. 15 pf.+5 pf. violet .. 1·00 2·75
E 543. 20 pf.+10 pf. red .. 10 10
E 544. 25 pf.+10 pf. blue .. 10 10

PORTRAITS: 5 pf. W. Kube. 10 pf. H. Gunther. 15 pf. Elvira Eisenschneider. 20 pf. Hertha Lindner. 25 pf. H. Tschape.

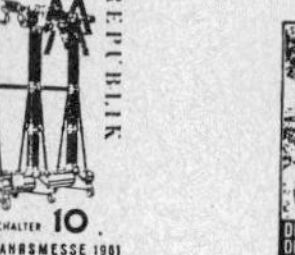


E **184.** High-voltage Switchgear. E **185.** Lilienstein Saxony.

**1961.** Leipzig Spring Fair. Inscr. as in Type E **184.**

E 545. E **184.** 10 pf. slate & grn. 15 10
E 546. – 25 pf. slate & blue 35 20

DESIGN: 25 pf. Fair Press Centre.

**1961.** Landscapes and Historical Buildings.

E 547. – 5 pf. grey .. 10 10
E 548. – 10 pf. green .. 10 10
E 549. E **185.** 20 pf. brown .. 10 10
E 550. – 20 pf. red .. 10 10
E 551. – 25 pf. blue .. 15 10

DESIGNS—VERT. 5 pf. Ruins of Rudelsburg. 10 pf. Wartburg. 20 pf. (No. E 550), Town Hall, Wernigerode. HORIZ. 25 pf. Brocken, Oberharz.

DESIGNS: 20 pf. Hauling nets. 25 pf. Trawler "Robert Koch". 40 pf. Fish-processing machine.

E **186.** Trawler.

**1961.** Deep Sea Fishing Industry.

E 552. E **186.** 10 pf. green .. 10 10
E 553. – 20 pf. purple .. 10 10
E 554. – 25 pf. blue .. 10 10
E 555. – 40 pf. violet .. 2·50 1·60

E 187. Cosmonaut in Capsule.

**1961.** 1st Manned Space Flight. Inscr "12.4.1961".
E556 – 10 pf. red & green 25 10
E557 E 187 20 pf. red .. 25 10
E558 – 25 pf. blue .. 4·00 3·75
DESIGNS: 10 pf. Space rocket leaving globe. 25 pf. Capsule's parachute descent.

E 188. Marx, Engels, Lenin and Demonstrators.

**1961.** 15th Anniv of German Socialist Unity Party.
E559 E 188 20 pf. red .. .. 40 20

DESIGN: 20 pf. Eastern black-and-white colobus.

E 189. Common Zebra.

**1961.** Centenary of Dresden Zoo.
E 560. E 189. 10 pf. blk. and grn. 4·00 3·50
E 561. – 20 pf. blk. and mve. 30 30

E 190. Pioneers playing Volleyball.

**1961.** Young Pioneers Meeting, Erfurt. Multicoloured.
E562 10 pf.+5 pf. Type E 190 10 10
E563 20 pf.+10 pf. Folk dancing .. .. .. 10 10
E564 25 pf.+10 pf. Model airplane construction .. 2·25 2·25

E 191. High Jump. E 192. Salt Miners and Castle.

**1961.** 3rd European Women's Gymnastic Championships, Leipzig.
E 565. E 191. 10 pf. green .. 15 10
E 566. – 25 pf. mauve .. 15 10
E 567. – 25 pf. blue .. 4·25 3·75
DESIGNS—VERT. 20 pf. Gymnast. HORIZ. 25 pf. Exercise on parallel bars.

**1961.** Halle (Saale) Millenary.
E 568. E 192. 10 pf.black,yellow and green .. 1·75 1·25
E 569. – 20 pf.black, yellow and red .. 15 10
DESIGNS: 20 pf. Scientist and Five Towers of Halle.

DESIGNS: 5 pf. Folding canoe. 20 pf. Canadian two-seater canoe.

E 193. Canadian Canoe.

**1961.** World Canoeing Championships.
E 570. – 5 pf. blue & grey 2·50 2·50
E 571. E 193. 10 pf. grn. & grey 10 10
E 572. – 20 pf. pur. & grey 10 10

E 194. Line-casting. E 195. Old Weigh-house, Leipzig.

**1961.** World Angling Championships.
E 573. E 194. 10 pf. grn. & blue 2·10 1·75
E 574. 20 pf. lake & blue 15 15
DESIGN: 20 pf. River-fishing.

**1961.** Leipzig Autumn Fair.
E 575. E 195. 10 pf. olive & grn. 20 10
E 576. – 25 pf. blue & ultram. 60 10
DESIGNS: 25 pf. Old Stock Exchange, Leipzig.
See also Nos. E 612/14.

E 196. Walter Ulbricht. E 197. Dahlia.

**1961.** Type E 196 or larger, 24 × 29 mm. (Dm. values).
E 577. 5 pf. blue .. .. 10 10
E 578. 10 pf. green .. .. 15 10
E 579. 15 pf. purple .. .. 20 15
E 580. 20 pf. red .. .. 65 30
E 581. 25 pf. turquoise .. 15 10
E 582. 30 pf. red .. .. 20 10
E 582a. 35 pf. green .. .. 30 10
E 583. 40 pf. violet .. .. 20 10
E 584. 50 pf. blue .. .. 30 10
E 584a. 60 pf. green .. .. 40 10
E 585. 70 pf. brown .. .. 40 10
E 585a. 80 pf. blue .. .. 55 10
E 586. 1 DM. green .. .. 1·00 15
E 587. 2 DM. brown .. .. 1·90 15
See also Nos. E 805/6, E 1197/8 and E 1255.

**1961.** Concentration Camps Memorials Fund. As Type E 120. Portraits in grey and black.
E 588. 5 pf.+5 pf. green .. 10 15
E 589. 10 pf.+5 pf. green .. 10 15
E 590. 20 pf.+10 pf. mauve .. 15 30
E 591. 25 pf.+10 pf. blue .. 25 30
E 592. 40 pf.+20 pf. lake .. 2·00 3·25
PORTRAITS: 5 pf. C. Schonhaar. 10 pf. H. Baum. 20 pf. Liselotte Herrmann. HORIZ. (41×32½ mm.): 25 pf. Sophie and Hans Scholl. 40 pf. Hilde and Hans Coppi.

**1961.** Int. Horticultural Exn.
E 593. – 10 pf. red, yellow and green .. 15 10
E 594. E 197. 20 pf. red, yellow and brown .. 30 15
E 595. – 40 pf. red, yellow and blue .. 8·00 8·50
FLOWERS: 10 pf. Tulip. 40 pf. Rose.

E 198. Liszt and Berlioz (after Von Kaulbach and Prinzhofer). E 199. TV Camera and Screen.

**1961.** 150th Birth Anniv. of Liszt (composer).
E 596. E 198. 5 pf. black .. 15 15
E 597. – 10 pf. green .. 1·90 1·75
E 598. – 20 pf. red .. 15 15
E 599. – 25 pf. blue .. 2·25 2·00
DESIGNS: 10 pf. Young hand of Liszt (from French sculpture, Liszt Museum, Budapest). 20 pf. Liszt (after Rietschel). 25 pf. Liszt and Chopin (after Bartolini and Bovy).

**1961.** Stamp Day.
E 600. E 199. 10 pf. black & green 1·10 1·90
E 601. – 20 pf. black & red 15 15
DESIGNS: 20 pf. Studio microphone and radio tuning-scale.

E 200. G. S. Titov with Young Pioneers.

**1961.** 2nd Russian Manned Space Flight.
E 602. E 200. 5 pf. violet & red 15 10
E 603. – 10 pf. green & red 15 10
E 604. – 15 pf. mve. & blue 7·50 8·00
E 605. – 20 pf. red and blue 15 10
E 606. – 25 pf. blue and red 15 10
E 607. – 40 pf. blue and red 1·00 15
DESIGNS—HORIZ. 15 pf. Titov in space-suit. 20 pf. Titov receiving Karl Marx Order from Ulbricht. 25 pf. "Vostok 2" rocket in flight. 40 pf. Titov and Ulbricht in Berlin. VERT. 10 pf. Titov in Leipzig.

DESIGNS: 10 pf. Weasels. 20 pf. Eurasian common shrews. 40 pf. Common long-eared bat.

E 201. Red Wood Ants.

**1962.** Fauna Protection Campaign (1st series).
E 608. E 201. 5 pf. yellow, brown and black .. 3·25 3·75
E 609. – 10 pf. brn. & grn. 15 10
E 610. – 20 pf. brn. & red 15 10
E 611. – 40 pf. yellow, black and violet .. 50 10
See also Nos. E 699/703.

**1962.** Leipzig Spring Fair. As Type E 195.
E 612. 10 pf. sepia and green .. 20 10
E 613. 20 pf. black and red .. 25 10
E 614. 25 pf. purple and blue .. 75 50
BUILDINGS: 10 pf. Zum Kaffeebaum. 20 pf. Gobliser Schlosschen. 25 pf. Romanus-Haus.

E 203. Pilot and Mikoyan Gurevich MiG-17 Jet Fighters. E 204. Danielle Casanova.

**1962.** 6th Anniv. of East German People's Army.
E 615. E 203. 5 pf. blue .. .. 10 10
E 616. – 10 pf. green .. 10 10
E 617. – 20 pf. red .. 15 10
E 618. – 25 pf. blue .. 15 15
E 619. – 40 pf. brown .. 1·60 1·25
DESIGNS: 10 pf. Soldier and armoured car. 20 pf. Factory guard. 25 pf. Sailor and destroyer "Ernst Thalmann". 40 pf. Tank and driver.

**1962.** Concentration Camps Memorial Fund. Camp Victims.
E 620. E 204. 5 pf.+5 pf. black 10 15
E 621. – 10 pf.+5 pf. grn. 10 15
E 622. – 20 pf.+10 pf. pur. 10 15
E 623. – 25 pf.+10 pf. blue 20 25
E 624. – 40 pf.+20 pf. pur. 1·60 1·60
PORTRAITS: 10 pf. Julius Fucik. 20 pf. Johanna J. Schaft. 25 pf. Pawel Finder. 40 pf. Soja A. Kosmodemjanskaja.

E 205. Racing Cyclists and Prague Castle. E 206. Johann Fichte.

**1962.** 15th Int. Peace Cycle Race. Mult.
E 625. 10 pf. Type E 205 .. 10 10
E 626. 20 pf.+10 pf. Cyclists and Palace of Culture and Science, Warsaw 10 10
E 627. 25 pf. Cyclist and Town Hall, East Berlin .. 1·50 1·50

**1962.** Birth Bicent. of Fichte (philosopher).
E 628. – 10 pf. grn. & blk. 1·25 1·50
E 629. E 206. 20 pf. red and blk. 15 15
DESIGNS: 10 pf. Fichte's birthplace Ramenau.

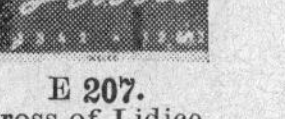

E 207. Cross of Lidice. E 208. Dimitrov at Leipzig.

**1962.** 20th Anniv. of Destruction of Lidice.
E 630. E 207. 20 pf. red & black 15 10
E 631. 25 pf. blue & black 1·00 70

**1962.** 80th Birth Anniv. of G. Dimitrov (Bulgarian statesman).
E 632. E 208. 5 pf. black & turq. 55 55
E 633. – 20 pf. black & red 10 10
DESIGN: 20 pf. Dimitrov as Premier of Bulgaria.

E 209. Maize-planting machine. E 210. Freighter "Frieden".

**1962.** 10th D.D.R. Agricultural Exn., Markkleeberg. Multicoloured.
E 634. 10 pf. Type E 209 .. 15 10
E 635. 20 pf. Milking shed .. 15 10
E 636. 40 pf. Combine-harvester 1·40 1·40

**1962.** 5th Baltic Sea Week, Rostock.
E 637. – 10 pf. turq. & blue 15 10
E 638. – 20 pf. red & yellow 15 10
E 639. E 210. 25 pf. bistre & blue 2·50 2·00
DESIGNS—HORIZ. 10 pf. Map of Baltic Sea inscr. "Meer des Friedens" ("Sea of Peace"). VERT. 20 pf. Railway-station hotel, Rostock.

E 215. Dove. E 216. National Theatre, Helsinki.

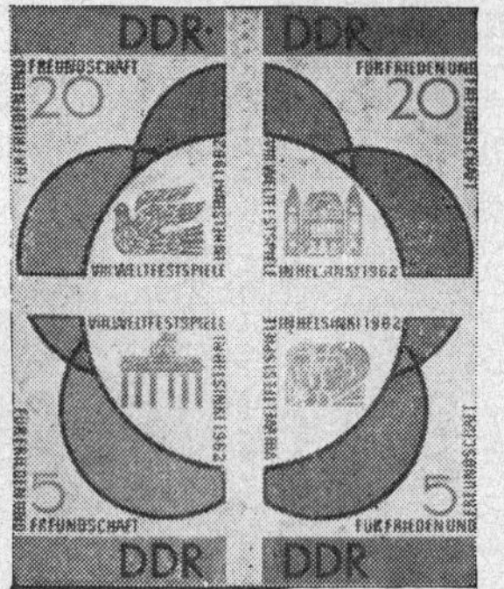

E 211. Brandenburg Gate, Berlin. E 212. Youth of Three Races.

E 213. Folk Dancers. E 214. Youth of Three Nations.

**1962.** World Youth Festival Games, Helsinki. Multicoloured.
E 640. E 211. 5 pf. .. .. 1·75 6·00
E 641. E 212. 5 pf. .. .. 1·75 6·00
E 642. E 213. 10 pf.+5 pf. .. 50 25
E 643. E 214. 15 pf.+5 pf. .. 50 25
E 644. E 215. 20 pf. .. .. 1·75 6·00
E 645. E 216. 20 pf. .. .. 1·75 6·00

E 217. Free-style Swimming. E 218 Municipal Store, Leipzig.

**1962.** 10th European Swimming Championships, Leipzig. Design in blue: value colours given.
E 646. E 217. 5 pf. orange .. 10 10
E 647. – 10 pf. blue .. 10 10
E 648. – 20 pf.+10 pf. mve. 10 10
E 649. – 25 pf. blue .. 10 10
E 650. – 40 pf. violet .. 1·75 1·75
E 651. – 70 pf. brown .. 15 10
DESIGNS: 10 pf. Back stroke. 20 pf. High diving. 25 pf. Butterfly stroke. 40 pf. Breast stroke. 70 pf. Water-polo. On Nos. E 649/51 the value, etc., appears at the foot of the design.

**1962.** Leipzig Autumn Fair.
E 652. E 218. 10 pf. blk. & green 20 15
E 653. – 20 pf. black & red 30 15
E 654. – 25 pf. black & blue 50 30
DESIGNS: 20 pf. Madler Arcade, Leipzig. 25 pf. Leipzig Airport and Ilyushin Il-14M airplane.

E 219. "Transport and Communications". E 220. Rene Blieck.

**1962.** 10th Anniv. of "Friedrich List" Transport High School, Dresden.
E 655. E 219. 5 pf. black & blue 30 20

**1962.** Concentration Camp Victims. Memorials Fund.
E 656. E 220. 5 pf.+5 pf. blue .. 10 10
E 657. – 10 pf.+5 pf. green 10 10
E 658. – 15 pf.+5 pf. violet 15 15
E 659. – 20 pf.+10 pf. pur. 15 15
E 660. – 70 pf.+30 pf. brn. 1·90 2·10
PORTRAITS—As Type E 220: 10 pf. Dr. A. Klahr. 15 pf. J. Diaz. 20 pf. J. Alpari. HORIZ. (39 × 21 mm.): 70 pf. Seven Cervi brothers.

E 221. Television Screen and Call-sign. E 222. G. Hauptmann.

**1962.** Stamp Day and 10th Anniv. of German Television.

E 661. E **221.** 20 pf. pur. & grn. 15 10
E 662. – 40 pf. pur. & mve. 1·75 1·75
DESIGN: 40 pf. Children with stamp album (inscr. "TAG DER BRIEFMARKE 1962").

**1962.** Birth Centenary of Gerhart Hauptmann (author).

E 663. E **222.** 20 pf. black and red 35 15

E **223.** Pierre de Coubertin.

E **224.** Party Flag.

**1963.** Birth Cent. of Pierre de Coubertin (reviver of Olympic Games).

E 664. E **223.** 20 pf. red & grey 10 10
E 665. – 25 pf. bl. & ochre 1·25 1·60
DESIGN: 25 pf. Stadium.

**1963.** 6th Socialists Unity Party Day.

E 666. E **224.** 10 pf. red, black and yellow .. 30 10

E **225.** Insecticide Sprayer.

DESIGNS: 25 pf. Rod of Aesculapius. 50 pf. Mosquito. Map is common to all values.

**1963.** Malaria Eradication.

E 667. E **225.** 20 pf. black, red and orange .. 10 10
E 668. – 25 pf. multicoloured 10 10
E 669. – 50 pf. multicoloured 1·25 1·10

E **226.** Red Fox.

E **227.** Barthels Hof, Leipzig (1748–1872).

**1963.** Int. Fur Auctions, Leipzig.

E 670. E **226.** 20 pf. blue and red .. .. 20 15
E 671. – 25 pf. indigo & blue .. .. 1·40 1·60
DESIGN: 25 pf. Karakul lamb.

**1963.** Leipzig Spring Fair.

E 672. E **227.** 10 pf. blk. & yell. 15 10
E 673. – 20 pf. blk. & brn. 25 25
E 674. – 25 pf. black & blue 95 95
LEIPZIG BUILDINGS: 20 pf. New Town Hall. 25 pf. Clock-tower, Karl-Marx Square.

E **228.** J. G. Seume (poet) and Scene from "Syracuse Walk" (Birth Bicent.).

**1963.** Cultural Anniversaries. Design and portrait in black.

E 675. E **228.** 5 pf. yellow .. 15 10
E 676. – 10 pf. turquoise .. 15 10
E 677. – 20 pf. orange .. 15 10
E 678. – 25 pf. blue .. 1·75 1·60
DESIGNS: 10 pf. F. Hebbel (poet) and scene from "Mary Magdalene" (150th birth anniv.) 20 pf. G. Buchner (poet) and scene from "Woyzeck" (150th birth anniv.). 25 pf. R. Wagner (composer) and scene from "The Flying Dutchman" (150th birth anniv.).

E **229.** Nurse bandaging Patient.

E **230.** W. Bohne (runner).

**1963.** Centenary of Red Cross.

E 679. E **229.** 10 pf. mult. .. 95 75
E 680. – 20 pf. black, grey and red .. .. 10 10
DESIGNS. 20 pf. Barkas type "B 1000" ambulance.

**1963.** Concentration Camps Memorial Fund. Sportsmen Victims (1st series). Designs in black.

E 681. E **230.** 5 pf.+5 pf. yellow 15 10
E 682. – 10 pf.+5 pf. grn. 15 10
E 683. – 15 pf.+5 pf. mve. 15 15
E 684. – 20 pf.+10 pf. pink 15 15
E 685. – 25 pf.+10 pf. blue 1·90 2·75
SPORTSMAN: 10 pf. W. Seelenbinder (wrestler). 15 pf. A. Richter (cyclist). 20 pf. H. Steyer (footballer). 25 pf. K. Schlosser (mountaineer).

See also Nos. E 704/8.

E **231.** Gymnastics.

E **232.** E. Pottier (lyricist) and Opening Bars of the "Internationale".

**1963.** 4th East German Gymnastics and Sports Festival, Leipzig. Inscr. in black.

E 686. E **231.** 10 pf.+5 pf. yell. and green .. 15 10
E 687. – 20 pf.+10 pf. vio. and red .. 20 15
E 688. – 25 pf.+10 pf. grn. and blue .. 3·25 3·00
DESIGNS: 20 pf. Dederon kerchief exercises. 25 pf. Relay-racing.

**1963.** 75th Anniv. of "Internationale" (song).

E 689. E **232.** 20 pf. black & red 15 10
E 690. – 25 pf. blk. & blue 95 1·25
DESIGN: 25 pf. As 20 pf. but portrait of P.-C. Degeyter.

E **233.** V. Tereshkova and "Vostok 6". E **234.** V. Bykovsky and "Vostok 5".

**1963.** 2nd "Team" Manned Space Flights.

E 691. E **233.** 20 pf. black, grey and blue .. 65 10
E 692. E **234.** 20 pf. black, grey and blue .. 65 10
Nos. E 691/2 were printed together, se-tenant, forming a composite design.

E **235.** Motor Cyclist competing in "Motocross", Apolda.

E **236.** Treblinka Memorial.

**1963.** World Motor Cycle Racing Championships.

E693 E **235** 10 pf. emer & grn 3·00 3·50
E694 – 20 pf. red and pink 25 15
E695 – 25 pf. blue & lt bl 25 20
DESIGNS—HORIZ. (39×22 mm): 20 pf. Motor cyclist. 25 pf. Two motor cyclists cornering.

**1963.** Erection of Treblinka Memorial, Poland.

E 696. E **236.** 20 pf. blue & red .. 25 15

E **237.** Transport. E **238.**

**1963.** Leipzig Autumn Fair.

E 697. E **237.** 10 pf. multicoloured 75 10
E 698. E **238.** 10 pf. multicoloured 75 10
Nos. E 697/8 were printed together, se-tenant, forming a composite design.

**1963.** Fauna Protection Campaign (2nd series). As Type E **201.** Fauna in natural colours, background colours given.

E 699. 10 pf. green .. .. 20 10
E 700. 20 pf. red .. .. 20 10
E 701. 30 pf. red .. .. 30 10
E 702. 50 pf. blue .. .. 4·00 3·50
E 703. 70 pf. brown .. .. 40 30
DESIGNS: 10 pf. Stag-beetle. 20 pf. Salamander. 30 pf. European pond tortoise. 50 pf. Green toad. 70 pf. West European hedgehogs.

**1963.** Concentration Camps Memorial Fund. Sportsmen Victims (2nd series). As Type E **230.** Designs in black.

E 704. 5 pf.+5 pf. yellow .. 15 15
E 705. 10 pf.+5 pf. green .. 15 15
E 706. 15 pf.+5 pf. violet .. 15 20
E 707. 20 pf. 10 pf. red .. 15 20
E 708. 40 pf.+20 pf. blue .. 2·75 7·00
SPORTSMEN: 5 pf. H. Tops (Gymnast). 10 pf. Kate Tucholla (hockey-player). 15 pf. R. Seiffert (swimmer). 20 pf. E. Grube (athlete). 40 pf. K. Biedermann (canoeist).

E **239.** N. von Gneisenau and G. L. von Blucher.

**1963.** 150th Anniv. of German War of Liberation.

E 709. E **239.** 5 pf. black, buff and yellow .. 15 10
E 710. – 10 pf. black, buff and green .. 15 10
E 711. – 20 pf. black, buff and orange .. 15 10
E 712. – 25 pf. black, buff and blue .. 15 10
E 713. – 40 pf. black, buff and red .. 1·50 50
DESIGNS: 10 pf. "Cossacks and (German) Soldiers in Berlin" (Ludwig Wolf). 20 pf. E. M. Arndt and Baron vom Stein. 25 pf. Lutzow corps in battle order (detail from painting by Hans Kohlschein). 40 pf. G. von Scharnhorst and Prince Kutuzov.

E **240.** V. Tereshkova.

E **241.** Synagogue aflame.

**1963.** Visit of Soviet Cosmonauts to East Berlin.

E 714. E **240.** 10 pf. green & blue 15 10
E 715. – 20 pf. black, red and buff .. 15 10
E 716. – 20 pf. green, red and buff .. 15 10
E 717. – 25 pf. orange and blue .. .. 3·25 2·00
DESIGNS—SQUARE: No. E 717, Tereshkova in capsule. VERT. (24×32 mm.). No. E 715, Tereshkova with bouquet. No. E 716, Gagarin (visit to Berlin).

**1963.** 25th Anniv. of "Kristallnacht" (Nazi pogrom).

E718 E **241** 10 pf. multicoloured 25 15

E **242.** Letter-sorting Machine.

**1963.** Stamp Day. Multicoloured.

E719 10 pf. Type E **242** .. 1·10 1·10
E720 20 pf. Fork-lift truck loading mail train .. 20 10

E **243.** Ski Jumper commencing Run.

E **244.** Red Admiral.

**1963.** Winter Olympic Games, Innsbruck, 1964. Rings in different colours: skier in black.

E 721. E **243.** 5 pf. yellow .. 20 10
E 722. – 10 pf. green .. 20 10
E 723. – 20 pf.+10 pf. red .. .. 20 10
E 724. – 25 pf. blue .. 2·40 1·25
DESIGNS: Ski jumper—10 pf. Taking-off. 20 pf. In mid-air. 25 pf. Landing.

**1964.** Butterflies. Butterflies in natural colours; inscr. in black.

E 725. E **244.** 10 pf. olive .. 15 10
E 726. – 15 pf. lilac .. .. 15 10
E 727. – 20 pf. orange .. 20 10
E 728. – 25 pf. blue .. 30 10
E 729. – 40 pf. blue .. 4·50 2·50
BUTTERFLIES: 15 pf. Small apollo. 20 pf. Swallowtail. 25 pf. Clouded yellow. 40 pf. Large tortoiseshell.

E **245.** Shakespeare. (b. 1564).

E **246.** "Elektrotecknik" Hall.

**1964.** Cultural Anniversaries.

E 730. – 20 pf. blue & pink 15 10
E 731. – 25 pf. purple & blue 15 10
E 732. E **245.** 40 pf. blue & lilac 1·00 90
DESIGNS: 20 pf. Quadriga, Brandenburg Gate (J. G. Schadow, sculptor, b. 1764). 25 pf. Portal keystone, German Historical Museum (A. Schluter, sculptor, b. 1664).

**1964.** Leipzig Spring Fair.

E 733. E **246.** 10 pf. blk. & grn. 1·75 10
E 734. – 20 pf. black & red 2·50 10
DESIGNS: 20 pf. Braunigkes Hof, c. 1700.

E **247.** A. Saefkow.

**1964.** Concentration Camp Victims. Memorials Fund.

E 735. E **247.** 5 pf.+5 pf. brown and blue .. 15 10
E 736. – 10 pf.+5 pf. brn. and olive .. 15 10
E 737. – 15 pf.+5 pf. brn. and violet .. 15 10
E 738. – 20 pf.+5 pf. olive and red .. 15 10
E 739. – 25 pf.+10 pf. blue and olive .. 20 15
E 740. – 40 pf.+10 pf. olive and brown .. 1·25 1·50
PORTRAITS—As Type E **247**: 10 pf. F. Jacob. 15 pf. B. Bastlein. 20 pf. H. Schulze-Boysen. 25 pf. Dr. A. Kuckhoff. (49×27½ mm.): 40 pf. Dr. A. and Mildred Harnack.

E **248.** Mr. Khrushchev with East German Officials.

E **249.** Boys and Girls.

**1964.** Mr. Khrushchev's 70th Birthday.

E 741. E **248.** 25 pf. blue .. 15 10
E 742. – 40 pf. black & pur. 2·25 2·25
DESIGN: 40 pf. Mr. Khrushchev with cosmonauts Tereshkova and Gagarin.

**1964.** German Youth Meeting, Berlin. Multicoloured.

E 743. 10 pf. Type E **249** .. 10 10
E 744. 20 pf. Young gymnasts 20 10
E 745. 25 pf. Youth with accordion and girl with flowers .. .. 1·00 65

E **250.** Flax, Krumel and Struppi, the dog.

**The designs show characters from children's T.V. programmes.**

**1964.** Children's Day. Multicoloured.

E 746. 5 pf. Type E **250** .. 10 10
E 747. 10 pf. Master Nadelohr 10 10
E 748. 15 pf. Pittiplatsch .. 10 10
E 749. 20 pf. Sandmannschen (sandman) .. .. 10 10
E 750. 40 pf. Bummi (teddy bear) and Schnatterinchen (duckling) .. 1·50 1·50

E 251. Governess and Child (with portrait of Jenny Marx).

**1964.** East German Women's Congress. Multicoloured.
E 751. 20 pf. Type E 251 .. 10 10
E 752. 25 pf. Switchboard technicians .. .. 1·10 80
E 753. 70 pf. Farm girls .. 15 10

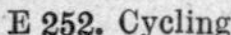

E 252. Cycling. E 253. Diving.

**1964.** Olympic Games, Tokyo. Multicoloured.
(a) 1st Series. As Type E 252.
E 754. 5 pf. Type E 252 .. 10 10
E 755. 10 pf. Volleyball .. 10 10
E 756. 20 pf. Judo .. .. 10 10
E 757. 25 pf. Diving .. .. 10 10
E 758. 40 pf.+20 pf. Running 30 10
E 759. 70 pf. Horse-jumping .. 1·60 1·50
(b) 2nd Series. As Type E 253.
E 760. 10 pf. Type E 253 .. 2·10 2·25
E 761. 10 pf. +5 pf. Horse-jumping .. .. 2·10 2·25
E 762. 10 pf. Volleyball .. 2·10 2·25
E 763. 10 pf. Cycling .. .. 2·10 2·25
E 764. 10 pf.+5 pf. Running .. 2·10 2·25
E 765. 10 pf. Judo .. .. 2·10 2·25
Nos. E 760/5 were printed together in se-tenant blocks of six (3×2) within sheets of 60 (6×10), and with an overall pattern of the five Olympic "rings" in each block.

E 254. Young Artists.

**1964.** 5th Young Pioneer's Meeting, East Berlin. Multicoloured.
E 766. 10 pf.+5 pf. Type E 254 .. .. 20 10
E 767. 20 pf.+10 pf. Planting tree .. .. .. 50 10
E 768. 25 pf.+10 pf. Playing with ball .. .. 2·00 1·10

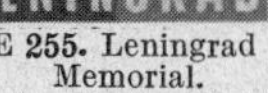

E 255. Leningrad Memorial. E 256. F. Joliot-Curie.

**1964.** Victims of Leningrad Siege Commem.
E 769. E 255. 25 pf. black, yell. and blue .. 60 15

**1964.** "World Peace".
E 770. E 256. 20 pf. sepia & red 15 10
E 771. – 25 pf. black & blue 15 10
E 772. – 50 pf. blk. & lilac 1·10 65
PORTRAITS: (Campaigners for "World Peace"): 25 pf. B. von Suttner. 50 pf. C. von Ossietzky.

E 257. Ancient Glazier's Shop. E 258. I.W.M.A. Cachet.

**1964.** Leipzig Autumn Fair. Multicoloured.
E773 10 pf. Type E 257 .. 55 10
E774 15 pf. Jena glass factory 55 10

**1964.** Centenary of "First International".
E 775. E 258. 20 pf. black & red 10 10
E 776. 25 pf. black & blue 70 60

E 259. "Rostock Port" Stamp of 1958. E 260. Modern Buildings and Flag ("Reconstruction").

**1964.** National Stamp Exn., East Berlin.
E 777. E 259. 10 pf.+5 pf. green and orange .. 20 10
E 778. – 20 pf.+10 pf. blue and purple .. 20 10
E 779. – 50 pf. brown and grey .. .. 3·25 1·50
DESIGNS: 20 pf., 12 pf. "Peace" stamp of 1950. 50 pf., 5 pf. "Dresden Paintings" stamp of 1955.

**1964.** 15th Anniv. of German Democratic Republic. Multicoloured.
E 780. 10 pf. Type E 260 .. 20 15
E 781. 10 pf. Surveyor and conveyor ("Coal") .. 20 15
E 782. 10 pf. Scientist and chemical works ("Chemical Industry") .. .. 20 15
E 783. 10 pf. Guard and chemical works ("Chemical Industry") .. .. 20 15
E 784. 10 pf. Milkmaid and dairy pen ("Agriculture") .. .. 20 15
E 785. 10 pf. Furnaceman and mills ("Steel") .. 20 15
E 786. 10 pf. Student with microscope, and lecture hall ("Education") .. 20 15
E 787. 10 pf. Operator and lathe ("Engineering") .. 20 15
E 788. 10 pf. Scientist and planetarium" (Optics") .. 20 15
E 789. 10 pf. Girl with cloth, and loom ("Textiles") .. 20 15
E 790. 10 pf. Docker and ship at quayside ("Shipping") 20 15
E 791. 10 pf. Leipzig buildings and "businessmen" formed of Fair emblem ("Exports") .. 20 15
E 792. 10 pf. Building worker and flats ("New Construction") .. 20 15
E 793. 10 pf. Sculptor modelling and Dresden gateway ("Culture") .. 20 15
E 794. 10 pf. Girl skier and holiday resort ("Recreation") .. 20 15

E 261. Monchgut (Rugen) Costume. E 262. Dr. Schweitzer and Lambarene River.

**1964.** Provincial costumes (1st series). Mult.
E 795. 5 pf. Type E 261 .. 8·25 6·25
E 796. 5 pf. Monchgut (male) .. 8·25 6·25
E 797. 10 pf. Spreewald (female) 35 15
E 798. 10 pf. Spreewald (male) 35 15
E 799. 20 pf. Thuringen (female) 65 30
E 800. 20 pf. Thuringen (male) 65 30
See Nos. E 932/7 and E 1073/6.

**1965.** 90th Birthday of Dr. Albert Schweitzer.
E 802. E 262. 10 pf. yellow, black and green .. 15 10
E 803. – 20 pf. yellow, black and red .. 15 10
E 804. – 25 pf. yellow, black and blue .. 2·75 1·75
DESIGNS: 20 pf. Schweitzer and "nuclear disarmament" marchers. 25 pf. Schweitzer and part of a Bach organ prelude.

**1965.** As Nos. E 586/7 but values expressed in "MDN" (Deutschen Notenbank Marks) instead of "DM".
E 805. 1 MDN. green .. .. 35 10
E 806. 2 MDN. brown .. .. 55 10

## MINIMUM PRICE

The minimum price quoted is 10p which represents a handling charge rather than a basis for valuing common stamps. For further notes about prices see introductory pages.

E 263. A. Bebel. E 264. Fair Medal (obverse).

**1965.** 125th Birth Anniv. of August Bebel (founder of Social Democratic Party).
E 807. E 263. 20 pf. yellow, brn. and red .. 35 10
See also Nos. E 814/5, E 839, E 842 and E 871.

**1965.** Leipzig Spring Fair and 800th Anniv. of Leipzig Fair.
E 808. E 264. 10 pf. gold & mve. 15 10
E 809. – 15 pf. gold & mve. 20 10
E 810. – 25 pf. mult. .. 50 15
DESIGNS: 15 pf. Fair medal (reverse). 25 pf. Chemical Works.

E 265. Giraffe. E 266. Belyaev and Leonov.

**1965.** 10th Anniv. of East Berlin Zoo.
E811. E 265. 10 pf. grey & grn. 20 10
E812. – 25 pf. grey & blue 30 15
E813. – 30 pf. grey & sepia .. .. 2·10 1·25
ANIMALS—HORIZ. 25 pf. Iguana. 30 pf. Black wildebeest.

**1965.** 120th Birth Anniv. of W. C. Rontgen (physicist). As Type E 263 but portrait of Rontgen.
E 814. 10 pf. yellow, brn. & grn. 40 10

**1965.** 700th Birth Anniv. of Dante. As Type E 263 but portrait of Dante.
E 815. 50 pf. yellow, brown and lemon .. .. 1·00 15

**1965.** Space Flight of "Voskhod 2".
E 816. E 266. 10 pf. red .. 20 10
E 817. – 25 pf. blue .. 2·40 1·60
DESIGN: 25 pf. Leonov in space.

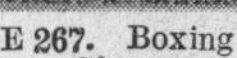

E 267. Boxing Gloves. E 269. Transmitter Aerial and Globe.

E 268. Dimitrov denouncing Fascism.

**1965.** European Boxing Championships, Berlin.
E 818. E 267. 10 pf.+5 pf. mult. 15 10
E 819. – 20 pf. gold, black and red .. 75 75
DESIGN: 20 pf. Boxing glove.

**1965.** 20th Anniv. of Liberation. Mult.
E 820. 5 pf.+5 pf. Type E 268 10 10
E 821. 10 pf.+5 pf. Distributing "Communist Manifesto" .. .. 10 10
E 822. 15 pf.+5 pf. Soldiers of International Brigade fighting in Spain .. 10 10
E 823. 20 pf.+10 pf. "Freedom for Ernst Thalmann" demonstration .. 10 10
E 824. 25 pf.+10 pf. Founding of "Free Germany" National Committee (Moscow) .. .. 10 10
E 825. 40 pf. Ulbricht and Weinert distributing "Manifesto" on Eastern Front .. .. 15 10
E 826. 50 pf. Liberation of concentration camps .. 15 10
E 827. 60 pf. Hoisting Red Flag on Reichstag .. 2·00 1·75
E 828. 70 pf. Bilateral demonstration of Communist and Socialist parties 20 10

**1965.** 20th Anniv. of East German Broadcasting Service.
E 829. E 269. 20 pf. black, red and cerise .. 20 10
E 830. – 40 pf. black & blue 1·25 40
DESIGN: 40 pf. Radio workers.

E 270. I.T.U. Emblem and Radio Circuit Diagram. E 271. F.D.G.B. Emblem.

**1965.** Centenary of I.T.U.
E 831. E 270. 20 pf. blk., yellow and olive .. 30 10
E 832. – 25 pf. black, mauve and violet .. 1·75 40
DESIGN: 25 pf. I.T.U. emblem and switch diagram.

**1965.** 20th Anniv. of Free German (F.D.G.B.) and World Trade Unions.
E 833. E 271. 20 pf. gold and red 15 10
E 834. – 25 pf. black, blue and gold .. 75 50
DESIGN—HORIZ. (39×21½ mm.): 25 pf. Workers of "two hemispheres" (inscr. "20 JAHRE WELTGEWERKSCHAFTSBUND").

E 272. Industrial Machine. E 273. Marx and Lenin.

**1965.** 800th Anniv of Karl-Marx-Stadt (formerly Chemnitz).
E 835. E 272. 10 pf. green & gold 15 10
E 836. – 20 pf. red and gold 20 10
E 837. – 25 pf. blue & gold 70 30
DESIGNS: 20 pf. Red Tower, Chemnitz. 25 pf. Town Hall, Chemnitz.

**1965.** Socialist Countries' Postal Ministers Conference, Peking.
E838 E 273 20 pf. black, yellow and red .. 25 10

**1965.** 90th Birth Anniv. of Dr Wilhelm Kulz (politician). As Type E 263 but portrait of Kulz.
E839. 25 pf. yellow, brn. and bl. 65 10

E 274. Congress Emblem.

**1965.** World Peace Congress, Helsinki.
E 840. E 274. 10 pf.+5 pf. green and blue .. 10 10
E 841. 20 pf.+5 pf. blue and red .. 60 40

**1965.** 75th Birth Anniv. of Erich Weinert (poet). As Type E 263, but portrait of Weinert.
E 842. 40 pf. yell., brn. & red 40 10

**1965.** "Help for Vietnam". Surch. **Hilfe fur VIETNAM+10.**
E 843. E 260. 10 pf.+10 pf. mult. 35 10

E 276. Rebuilt Weigh-house and Modern Buildings, Katharinenstrasse.

**1965.** 800th Anniv. of Leipzig.
E 844. E 276. 10 pf. purple, blue and gold .. 10 10
E 845. – 25 pf. orange, sepia and gold .. 10 10
E 846. – 40 pf. multicoloured 10 10
E 847. – 70 pf. blue & gold 1·50 1·00
DESIGNS: 25 pf. Old Town Hall. 40 pf. Opera House and new G.P.O. 70 pf. "Stadt Leipzig" Hotel.

E 277. "Praktica" and "Praktisix" Cameras.

E 278. Show Jumping.

**1965.** Leipzig Autumn Fair.

E 848. E 277. 10 pf. black, gold and green .. 10 10
E 849. – 15 pf. mult. .. 10 10
E 850. – 25 pf. mult. .. 60 15

DESIGNS: 15 pf. Clavichord and electric guitar. 25 pf. "Zeiss" microscope.

**1965.** World Modern Pentathlon Championships, Leipzig. Multicoloured.

E 852. 10 pf. Type E **278** .. 20 10
E 853. 10 pf. Swimming .. 20 10
E 854. 10 pf. Running .. 3·00 2·25
E 855. 10 pf.+5 pf. Fencing .. 20 10
E 856. 10 pf.+5 pf. Pistol-shooting .. .. 20 10

E 279. E. Leonov.

E 280. Memorial at Putten, Netherlands.

**1965.** Soviet Cosmonauts Visit to East Germany.

E 857. E 279. 20 pf. blue, silver and red .. 50 50
E 858. – 20 pf. blue, silver and red .. 50 50
E 859. – 25 pf. multicoloured 50 50

DESIGNS—As Type E 275. No. E858, Belyaev. HORIZ. (48×29 mm). No. E859, "Voskhod 2" and Leonov in space.

**1965.** Putten War Victims Commem.

E 860. E 280. 25 pf. black, yellow and blue .. 45 10

E 281. Stoking Furnace (from old engraving).

E 282. Red Kite.

**1965.** Bicent. of Mining School, Freiberg. Multicoloured.

E 861. 10 pf. Type E **281** .. 10 10
E 862. 15 pf. Mining ore (old engraving) .. .. 60 60
E 863. 20 pf. Ore .. .. 15 10
E 864. 25 pf. Sulphur .. .. 15 10

**1965.** Birds of Prey. Multicoloured.

E 865. 5 pf. Type E **282** .. 10 10
E 866. 10 pf. Lammergeier .. 15 10
E 867. 20 pf. Common Buzzard 20 10
E 868. 25 pf. Common Kestrel 20 10
E 869. 40 pf. Northern Goshawk 30 10
E 870. 70 pf. Golden Eagle .. 5·75 2·40

**1965.** 150th Birth Anniv. of A. von Menzel (painter). As Type E 263 but portrait of Menzel.

E 871. 10 pf. yellow, brown and red .. .. 45 10

E 283. Otto Grotewohl.

E 285. Ladies' Single-seater.

**1965.** Grotewohl Commem.

E 872. E 283. 20 f. black .. 45 10

**1966.** World Tobogganing Championships, Friedrichroda.

E 874. E 285. 10 pf. green & ol. 10 10
E 875. – 20 pf. blue & red 25 10
E 876. – 25 pf. indigo & blue 1·40 1·00

DESIGNS: 20 pf. Men's double-seater. 25 pf. Men's single seater.

E 286. Electronic Punch-card Computer.

**1966.** Leipzig Spring Fair. Multicoloured.

E 877. 10 pf. Type E **286** .. 25 10
E 878. 15 pf. Drilling and milling plant .. .. .. 50 10

E 287. Soldier and National Gallery Berlin.

E 288. J. A. Smoler (Sorb patriot and savant).

**1966.** 10th Anniv. of National People's Army.

E 879. E 287. 5 pf. black, olive and yellow .. 10 10
E 880. – 10 pf. black, olive and yellow .. 10 10
E 881. – 20 pf. black, olive and yellow .. 20 10
E 882. – 25 pf. black, olive and yellow .. 1·10 75

DESIGNS: Soldier and—10 pf. Brandenburg Gate. 20 pf. Industrial plant. 25 pf. Combine-harvester.

**1966.** 150th Birth Anniv. of Jan Smoler.

E 883. E 288. 20 pf. black, red and blue .. 10 10
E 884. – 25 pf. black, red and blue .. 40 45

DESIGN: 25 pf. House of the Sorbs, Bautzen.

E 289. "Good Knowledge" Badge.

E 290. "Luna 9" on Moon.

**1966.** 20th Anniv of "Freie Deutsche Jugend" (Socialist Youth Movement).

E885 E 289 20 pf. multicoloured 35 10

**1966.** Moon Landing of "Luna 9".

E 886. E 290. 20 pf. multicoloured 1·50 25

E 291. Road Signs.

**1966.** Road Safety.

E 887. E 291. 10 pf. red, blue and ultramarine .. 10 10
E 888. – 15 pf. black, yell. and green .. 10 10
E 889. – 25 pf. black, blue and bistre .. 10 10
E 890. – 50 pf. black, yellow, and red .. 1·10 50

DESIGNS: 15 pf. Child on scooter crossing in front of car. 25 pf. Cyclist and hand-signal. 50 pf. Motor cyclist, glass of beer and ambulance.

E 292. Marx and Lenin Banner.

**1966.** 20th Anniv. of Socialist Unity Party (S.E.D.).

E 891. – 5 pf. multicoloured 10 10
E 892. E 292. 10 pf. yellow, black and red .. 10 10
E 893. – 15 pf. blk. & green 10 10
E 894. – 20 pf. black & red 15 10
E 895. – 25 pf. black, yellow and red .. 1·25 1·00

DESIGNS—VERT. 5 pf. Party badge and demonstrators. 15 pf. Marx. Engels and manifesto. 20 pf. Pieck and Grotewohl. HORIZ. 25 pf. Workers greeting Ulbricht.

E 293. W.H.O. Building.

**1966.** Inaug. of W.H.O. Headquarters, Geneva.

E 896. E 293. 20 pf. multicoloured 30 20

E 294. Spreewald.

**1966.** National Parks. Multicoloured.

E 897. 10 pf. Type E **294** .. 10 10
E 898. 15 pf. Konigsstuhl (Isle of Rugen) .. .. 10 10
E 899. 20 pf. Sachsische Schweiz 10 10
E 900. 25 pf. Westdarss .. 20 10
E 901. 30 pf. Teufelsmauer .. 20 10
E 902. 50 pf. Feldberg Lakes .. 1·60 1·00

E 295. Lace "Flower".

E 296. Lily of the Valley.

**1966.** Plauen Lace. Floral Patterns as Type E 295.

E 903. E 295. 10 pf. myrtle & grn. 10 10
E 904. – 20 pf. indigo & bl. 20 10
E 905. – 25 pf. red & rose 25 10
E 906. – 50 pf. violet & lilac 3·00 1·40

**1966.** Int. Horticultural Show, Erfurt. Multicoloured.

E 907. 20 pf. Type E **296** .. 10 10
E 908. 25 pf. Rhododendrons .. 20 10
E 909. 40 pf. Dahlias .. .. 20 10
E 910. 50 pf. Cyclamen .. 3·50 3·00

E 297. Parachutist on Target.

DESIGNS: 15 pf. Group descent. 20 pf. Free fall.

**1966.** 8th World Parachute Jumping Championships, Leipzig.

E911 E 297 10 pf. blue, black, & bistre .. .. 10 10
E912 – 15 pf. mult. .. 50 50
E913 – 20 pf. black, bistre & blue .. .. 10 10

E 298. Hans Kahle and Music of "The Thalmann Column".

**1966.** 30th Anniv. of Int. Brigade in Spain. Multicoloured.

E 914. 5 pf. Type E **298** .. 10 10
E 915. 10 pf.+5 pf. W. Bredel and open-air class .. 10 10
E 916. 15 pf. H. Beimler and Madrid street-fighting 10 10
E 917. 20 pf.+10 pf. H. Rau and march-past after Battle of Brunete .. .. 20 10
E 918. 25 pf.+10 pf. H. Marchwitza and soldiers .. 25 10
E 919. 40 pf.+10 pf. A. Becker and Ebro battle .. 1·50 95

E 299. Canoeing.

**1966.** World Canoeing Championships, Berlin. Multicoloured.

E 920. 10 pf.+5 pf. Type E **299** 10 10
E 921. 15 pf. Kayak doubles .. 1·00 1·00

E 300. Television Set.

E 302. "Blood Donors".

E 301. Oradour Memorial.

**1966.** Leipzig Autumn Fair. Multicoloured.

E 922. 10 pf. Type E **300** .. 30 10
E 923. 15 pf. Electric typewriter 50 10

**1966.** Oradour-sur-Glane War Victims. Commem.

E 924. E 301. 25 pf. blk., bl. & red 20 10

**1966.** Int. Health Co-operation.

E 925. E 302. 5 pf. red and green 10 10
E 926. – 20 pf.+10 pf. red and violet .. 10 10
E 927. – 40 pf. red and blue 1·10 40

DESIGNS—HORIZ. 20 pf. I.C.Y. emblem. VERT. 40 pf. Health symbol.

E 303. Weightlifting ("snatch").

E 304. Congress Hall.

**1966.** World and European Weightlifting Championships, Berlin.

E 928. E 303. 15 pf. black & brn. 1·10 1·25
E 929. – 20 pf.+5 pf. black and blue .. 15 10

DESIGN: 20 pf. Weightlifting ("jerk").

**1966.** 6th Int. Journalists' Congress, Berlin.

E 930. E 304. 10 pf. multicoloured 35 20
E 931. – 20 pf. yellow & blue 15 10

DESIGN—VERT. 20 pf. Emblem of Int. Organization of journalists.

**1966.** Provincial Costumes (2nd series). As Type E 261. Multicoloured.

E 932. 5 pf. Altenburg (female) 15 15
E 933. 10 pf. Altenburg (male) 15 15
E 934. 10 pf. Mecklenburg (female) .. .. 15 15
E 935. 15 pf. Mecklenburg (male) 15 15
E 936. 20 pf. Magdeburger Borde (female) .. 2·25 2·50
E 937. 30 pf. Magdeburger Borde (male) .. .. 2·25 2·50

E 305. "Vietnam is Invincible".

**1966.** Aid for Vietnam.

E 938. E 305. 20 pf.+5 pf. black and pink .. 25 10

E 306. Oil Rigs and Pipeline Map.

**1966.** Inaug. of Int. "Friendship" Oil Pipeline.
E 939. E **306.** 20 pf. black & red 10 10
E 940. – 25 pf. black & blue 50 30
DESIGN: 25 pf. "Walter Ulbricht" Oil Works, Leuna and pipeline map.

E **307.** Black Phantom Tetra.

**1966.** Aquarium Fishes. Multicoloured.
E 941. 5 pf. Type E **307** .. 10 10
E 942. 10 pf. Cardinal tetra .. 10 10
E 943. 15 pf. Texas cichlid .. 2·40 2·00
E 944. 20 pf. Blue gularis .. 15 10
E 945. 25 pf. Butterfly dwarf cichlid .. .. 20 10
E 946. 40 pf. Honey gourami 30 15

E **308.** "Horse" (detail from Ishtar Gate).

**1966.** Babylonian Art Treasures, Vorderasiatisches Museum, Berlin. Multicoloured.
E 947. 10 pf. Type E **308** .. 10 10
E 948. 20 pf. Mythological animal, Ishtar Gate 10 10
E 949. 25 pf. Lion facing right (vert.) .. .. 10 10
E 950. 50 pf. Lion facing left (vert.) .. .. 85 85

E **309.** The Wartburg from the East. E **310.** "Gentiana pneumonanthe".

**1966.** 900th Anniv. of Wartburg Castle.
E 951. E **309.** 10 pf.+5 pf. slate 10 10
E 952. – 20 pf. green .. 10 10
E 953. – 25 pf. purple .. 60 35
DESIGNS: 20 pf. Castle bailiwick. 25 pf. Residence.

**1966.** Protected Plants (1st series). Mult.
E 954. 10 pf. Type E **310** .. 10 10
E 955. 20 pf. "Cephalanthera rubra" .. 15 10
E 956. 25 pf. "Arnica montana" 1·40 80
See also Nos. E 1177/82 and E 1284/9.

E **311.** Son leaves Home. E **312.** Worlitz Castle.

**1966.** Fairy Tales (1st series). "The Wishing Table". Multicoloured.
E 957. 5 pf. Type E **311** .. 30 30
E 958. 10 pf. Setting the table 30 30
E 959. 20 pf. The thieving innkeeper .. .. 30 30
E 960. 25 pf. The magic donkey 30 30
E 961. 30 pf. The cudgel in the sack .. .. .. 30 30
E 962. 50 pf. Return of the son 30 30
See also Nos. E 1045/50, E 1147/52, E 1171/6, E 1266/71, E 1437/42, E 1525/30, E 1623/8, E 1711/16, E 1811/13, E 1902/7, E 1996/2001 and E 2092/7.

**1967.** Principal East German Buildings. (1st series). Multicoloured.
E 964. 5 pf. Type E **312** .. 10 10
E 965. 10 pf. Stralsund Town Hall .. .. .. 10 10
E 966. 15 pf. Chorin Monastery .. .. 10 10
E 967. 20 pf. Ribbeck House, Berlin .. .. 10 10
E 968. 25 pf. Moritzburg, Zeitz .. .. .. 10 10
E 969. 40 pf. Old Town Hall Potsdam .. .. 1·10 90
The 10 pf., 15 pf., 25 pf. and 40 pf. are vert.
See also Nos. E 1100/3 and E 1155/60.

E **313.** Rifle-shooting.

**1967.** World Biathlon Championships, Altenburg.
E 970. E **313.** 10 pf. blue, drab and mauve .. 10 10
E 971. – 20 pf. olive, blue and green .. 15 10
E 972. – 25 pf. green, blue and olive .. 1·00 65
DESIGNS: 20 pf. Shooting on skis. 25 pf. Riflemen racing on skis.

E **314.** "Multilock" Loom.

**1967.** Leipzig Spring Fair.
E 973. E **314.** 10 pf. green grey and purple .. 15 10
E 974. – 15 pf. bistre & blue 35 10
DESIGN: 15 pf. Zeiss tracking telescope.

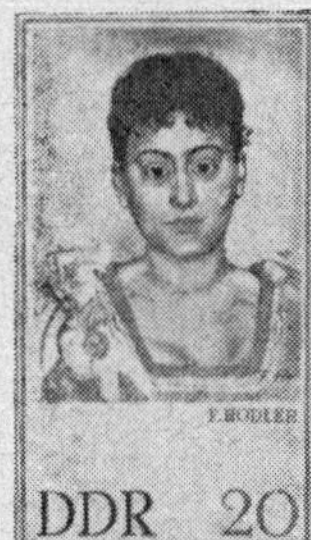

E **315.** Mother and Child. E **317.** "Portrait of a Girl" (after F. Hodler).

E **316.** Industrial Control Desk.

**1967.** 20th Anniv. of German Democratic Women's Federation.
E 975. E **315.** 20 pf. grey, red and purple .. 10 10
E 976. – 25 pf. brown, turq. and brown .. 75 60
DESIGN: 25 pf. Professional woman.

**1967.** Socialist Party Rally. Multicoloured. (a) 1st series.
E 977. 10 pf. Type E **316** .. 10 10
E 978. 20 pf. Ulbricht meeting workers .. .. 10 10
E 979. 25 pf. Servicemen guarding industrial plants .. 10 10
E 980. 40 pf. Agricultural workers and harvesters .. 65 55
Each with inset portraits of Marx, Engels and Lenin.

(b) 2nd series. As Type E **316** but vert.
E 981. 5 pf. Agricultural worker 10 10
E 982. 10 pf. Teacher and pupil 10 10
E 983. 15 pf. Socialist family .. 40 40
E 984. 20 pf. Servicemen .. 10 10
Each with inset portraits as above.

**1967.** Dresden Gallery Paintings (1st series). Multicoloured.
E 985. 20 pf. Type E **317** .. 10 10
E 986. 25 pf. "Peter at the Zoo" (H. Hakenbeck) .. 10 10
E 987. 30 pf. "Venetian Episode" (R. Bergander) .. 10 10
E 988. 40 pf. "Tahitian Women" (Gauguin) .. .. 10 10
E 989. 50 pf. "The Grandchild" (J. Scholtz) .. .. 2·00 1·60
E 990. 70 pf. "Cairn in the Snow" (C. D. Friedrich) 15 15
The 40 pf. and 70 pf. are horiz.
See also Nos. E 1114/19 and E 1249/54.



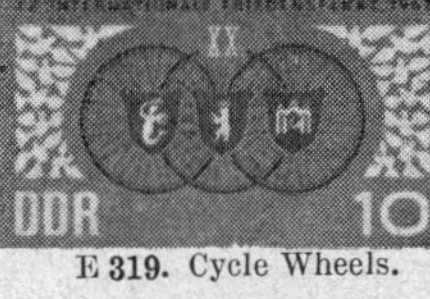

E **319.** Cycle Wheels.

E **318.** Barn Owl. E **320.** "Tom Cat".

**1967.** Protected Birds. Multicoloured.
E 991. 5 pf. Type E **318** .. 20 10
E 992. 10 pf. Common Crane .. 20 10
E 993. 20 pf. Peregrine Falcon 30 10
E 994. 25 pf. Bullfinches .. 40 10
E 995. 30 pf. Common Kingfisher 4·75 2·50
E 996. 40 pf. Common Roller .. 25 10

**1967.** 20th Warsaw-Berlin-Prague Cycle Race.
E 997. E **319.** 10 pf. violet, black and yellow .. 10 10
E 998. – 25 pf. red and blue 45 35
DESIGN: 25 pf. Racing cyclists.

**1967.** Int. Children's Day. Multicoloured.
E 999. 5 pf. Type E **320** .. 10 10
E 1000. 10 pf. "Snow White" 10 10
E 1001. 15 pf. "Fire Brigade" 10 10
E 1002. 20 pf. "Cockerel" .. 10 10
E 1003. 25 pf. "Vase of Flowers" 15 15
E 1004. 30 pf. "Children Playing with Ball" .. 1·00 65

E **321.** "Girl with Grapes" (Gerard Dou). E **322.** Exhibition Emblem.

**1967.** Paintings Missing from German National Galleries (after World War II).
E 1005. 5 pf. blue .. .. 10 10
E 1006. 10 pf. brown .. .. 10 10
E 1007. 20 pf. green .. .. 10 10
E 1008. 25 pf. purple .. .. 10 10
E 1009. 40 pf. olive .. .. 15 10
E 1010. 50 pf. sepia .. .. 1·60 1·40
DESIGNS—VERT. 10 pf. Type E **321.** 25 pf. "Portrait of W. Schroeder-Devrient" (after K. Begas). 40 pf. "Young Girl in Straw Hat" (after S. Bray). 50 pf. "The Four Evangelists" (after Jordaens). HORIZ. 5 pf. "Three Horsemen" (after Rubens). 20 pf. "Spring Idyll" (after H. Thoma).

**1967.** 15th Agricultural Exn., Markkleeberg.
E 1011. E **322.** 20 pf. red, green and yellow .. 20 10

E **323.** Marie Curie (Birth Cent.). E **324.** Jack of Diamonds.

**1967.** Birth Anniversaries.
E 1012. – 5 pf. brown .. 10 10
E 1013. E **323.** 10 pf. blue .. 10 10
E 1014. – 20 pf. red .. 10 10
E 1015. – 25 pf. sepia .. 10 10
E 1016. – 40 pf. green .. 80 55
PORTRAITS: 5 pf. G. Herwegh (poet—150th). 20 pf. Kathe Kollwitz (artist—cent). 25 pf. J. J. Winckelmann (archaeologist—250th). 40 pf. T. Storm (poet—150th).

**1967.** German Playing-Cards. Multicoloured.
E 1017. 5 pf. Type E **324** .. 15 10
E 1018. 10 pf. Jack of Hearts 15 10
E 1019. 20 pf. Jack of Spades 35 10
E 1020. 25 pf. Jack of Clubs .. 3·00 2·75

E **325.** Mare and Filly.

**1967.** Thoroughbred Horse Meeting, Berlin. Multicoloured.
E1021. 5 pf. Type E **325** .. 10 10
E1022. 10 pf. Stallion .. 10 10
E1023. 20 pf. Horse-racing .. 30 10
E1024. 50 pf. Two fillies (vert.) 3·00 1·75

E **326.** Kitchen Equipment. E **328.** Kragujevac Memorial.

E **327.** Max Reichpietsch and "Friedrich der Grosse" (battleship).

**1967.** Leipzig Autumn Fair. Multicoloured.
E 1025. 10 pf. Type E **326** .. 40 10
E 1026. 15 pf. Fur coat and "Interpelz" brand-mark 60 15

**1967.** 50th Anniv. of Revolutionary Sailors' Movement. Multicoloured.
E1027 10 pf. Type E **327** .. 15 10
E1028 15 pf. Albin Kobis and battleship "Prinz-regent Luitpold" .. 1·00 40
E1029 20 pf. Sailors' demonstration with battle cruiser "Seydlitz" .. 30 10

**1967.** Victims of Kragujevac (Yugoslavia) Massacre.
E 1030. E **328.** 25 pf. black, yellow & red .. 45 20

E **329.** Worker and Dam ("Electrification"). E **330.** Martin Luther (from engraving by Lucas Cranach the Elder).

**1967.** 50th Anniv. of October Revolution.
E 1031. 5 pf. black, orge. & red 10 10
E 1032. 10 pf. black, red & bistre 10 10
E 1033. 15 pf. black, red & grey 10 10
E 1034. 20 pf. black, red & orge. 20 10
E 1035. 40 pf. black, red & orge. 2·25 1·90
DESIGNS: 5 pf. Worker and newspaper headline "Hands off Soviet Russia!". 10 pf. Type E **329.** 15 pf. Treptow Memorial ("Victory over Fascism"). 20 pf. German and Soviet soldiers ("Friendship"). 40 pf. Lenin and cruiser "Aurora". Each with hammer and sickle.

**1967.** 450th Anniv. of Reformation.
E 1037. E **330.** 20 pf. black & mve. 10 10
E 1038. – 25 pf. black & blue 10 10
E 1039. – 40 pf. blk. & bistre 1·60 1·00
DESIGNS—HORIZ. 25 pf. Luther's house, Wittenberg. VERT. 40 pf. Castle church, Wittenberg.

E **331.** Young Workers. E **332.** Goethe's House Weimar.

**1967.** 10th "Masters of Tomorrow" Fair, Leipzig.
E 1040. 20 pf. black, gold & blue 40 35
E 1041. 20 pf. black, gold & blue 40 35
E 1042. 25 pf. multicoloured .. 40 35
DESIGNS—VERT. No. E 1040, Type E **331.** No. E 1041, Young man and woman. HORIZ.—(51 × 29 mm.) No. E 1042, Presentation of awards.

**1967.** Cultural Places.
E 1043. E **332** 20 pf. black, brn. and grey .. 15 10
E 1044. – 25 pf. olive, brn. and yellow .. 1·10 50
DESIGN: 25 pf. Schiller's House, Weimar.

E 333. Queen and Courtiers.  E 335. Nutcracker and Two "Smokers".

E 334. Peasants and Modern Farm Buildings.

**1967.** Fairy Tales (2nd series). "King Thrushbeard". Designs showing different scenes.

E 1045. E **333.** 5 pf. mult. .. 25 25
E 1046. – 10 pf. mult. .. 25 25
E 1047. – 15 pf. mult. .. 25 25
E 1048. – 20 pf. mult. .. 25 25
E 1049. – 25 pf. mult. .. 25 25
E 1050. – 30 pf. mult. .. 25 25

**1967.** 15th Anniv. of Agricultural Co-operatives.

E 1052. E **334.** 10 pf. sepia, green and olive .. 20 10

**1967.** Popular Art of the Erzgebirge. Multicoloured.

E 1053. 10 pf. Type E **335** .. 55 25
E 1054. 20 pf. "Angel" and miner with candles (carved figures) .. .. 10 10

E 336. Ice Skating.  E 337. Actinometer.

**1968.** Winter Olympic Games, Grenoble.

E1055 E **336** 5 pf. blue, red and light blue .. 10 10
E1056 – 10 pf.+5 pf. blue, red & turquoise 10 10
E1057 – 15 pf. mult .. 20 10
E1058 – 20 pf. ultramarine, red and blue .. 20 10
E1059 – 25 pf. mult .. 30 10
E1060 – 30 pf. ultram, red and blue .. 2·50 1·60

Designs: 10 pf. Tobogganing. 15 pf. Slalom. 20 pf. Ice hockey. 25 pf. Figure skating (pairs). 30 pf. Cross-country skiing.

**1968.** 75th Anniv. of Potsdam Meteorological Observatory and World Meteorological Day (23 March).

E1061 E **337** 10 pf. black, red and purple .. 35 35
E1062 – 20 pf. mult .. 35 35
E1063 – 25 pf. black, yellow & green 35 35

Designs—Vert. 25 pf. Cornfield by day and night. Horiz—(50×28 mm.): 20 pf. Satellite picture of clouds.

E 338. "Venus 4".

**1968.** Soviet Space Achievements. Mult.

E 1064. 20 pf. Type E **338** .. 20 10
E 1065. 25 pf. Coupled satellites "Cosmos 186" and "188" 1·00 30

E 339. "Illegal Struggle" (man, wife and child).  E 341. Gorky.

E 340. Diesel Locomotive.

**1968.** Stained-glass Windows, Sachsenhausen National Memorial Museum. Multicoloured.

E 1066. 10 pf. Type E **339** .. 10 10
E 1067. 20 pf. "Liberation" .. 10 10
E 1068. 25 pf. "Partisans' Struggle" .. 50 40

**1968.** Leipzig Spring Fair. Multicoloured.

E 1069. 10 pf. Type E **340** .. 40 15
E 1070. 15 pf. Deep sea trawler 60 30

**1968.** Birth Cent of Maksim Gorky (writer).

E 1071. E **341.** 20 pf. pur. & red 10 10
E 1072. – 25 pf. pur. & red 60 40

Design: 25 pf. Fulmar (from "Song of the Stormy Petrel"—poem).

**1968.** Provincial Costumes (3rd series). As Type E **261.** Multicoloured.

E 1073. 10 pf. Hoyerswerda (female) .. .. 10 10
E 1074. 20 pf. Schleife (female) .. 10 10
E 1075. 40 pf. Crostwitz (female) 10 10
E 1076. 50 pf. Spreewald (female) 1·60 90

E 342. Ring-necked Pheasants.  E 343. Karl Marx.

**1968.** Small Game. Multicoloured.

E 1077. 10 pf. Type E **342** .. 40 10
E 1078. 15 pf. Grey Partridges 40 10
E 1079. 20 pf. Mallards .. 40 10
E 1080. 25 pf. Greylag Geese .. 40 10
E 1081. 30 pf. Wood Pigeon .. 50 15
E 1082. 40 pf Brown hares .. 3·50 2·25

**1968.** 150th Birth Anniv. of Karl Marx.

E 1083. – 10 pf. blk. & grn. 75 75
E 1084. E **343.** 20 pf. black, yellow and red 75 75
E 1085. – 25 pf. black, brn. and yellow .. 75 75

Designs: 10 pf. Title-page of "Communist Manifesto". 25 pf. Title-page of "Das Kapital".

E 344. "Fritz Heckert" (after E. Hering).  E 345. Hammer and Anvil ("The right to work").

**1968.** 7th Confederation of Free German Trade Unions Congress. Multicoloured.

E 1087. 10 pf. Type E **344** .. 15 10
E 1088. 20 pf. Young workers and new tenements 20 20

**1968.** Human Rights Year.

E 1089. E **345.** 5 pf. mve. & pur. 10 10
E 1090. – 10 pf. bistre & brn. 10 10
E 1091. – 25 pf. blue and turquoise .. 60 35

Designs: 10 pf. Tree and Globe ("The right to live"). 25 pf. Dove and Sun ("The right to peace").

E 346. Vietnamese Mother and Child.

**1968.** Aid for Vietnam.

E 1092. E **346.** 10 pf.+5 pf. mult. 15 10

E 347. Angling (World Angling Championships, Gustrow).

**1968.** Sporting Events.

E 1093. E **347.** 20 pf. blue, green and red .. 70 70
E 1094. – 20 pf. blue, turq. and green .. 10 10
E 1095. – 20 pf. purple, red and blue .. 10 10

Designs: No. E 1094, Sculling (European Women's Rowing Championships, Berlin). No. E 1095, High jumping (2nd European Youth Athletic Competitions).

E 348. Brandenburg Gate and Torch.  E 349. Festival Emblem.

**1968.** German Youth Sports Day. Mult.

E 1096. 10 pf. Type E **348** .. 10 10
E 1097. 25 pf. Stadium plan and torch .. .. 90 65

**1968.** Peace Festival, Sofia.

E 1098. E **349.** 20 pf.+5 pf. mult. 10 10
E 1099. 25 pf. multicoloured 70 35

**1968.** Principal East German Buildings (2nd series). As Type E **312.** Multicoloured.

E 1100. 10 pf. Town Hall, Wernigerode .. 10 10
E 1101. 20 pf. Moritzburg Castle, Dresden .. .. 10 10
E 1102. 25 pf. Town Hall, Greifswald .. .. 10 10
E 1103. 30 pf. New Palace, Potsdam .. .. 80 85

Design sizes—vert. 10 pf., 25 pf. (24×29 mm.). horiz: 20 pf., 30 pf. (51½×29½ mm.).

E 350. Walter Ulbricht.

E 351. Ancient Rostock.  E 352. Dr. K. Landsteiner (physician and pathologist, birth cent).

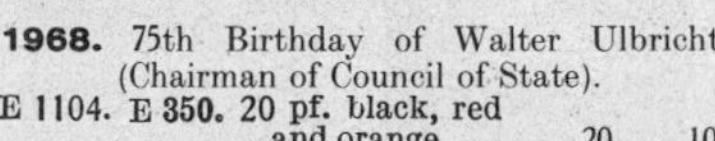

**1968.** 75th Birthday of Walter Ulbricht (Chairman of Council of State).

E 1104. E **350.** 20 pf. black, red and orange .. 20 10

**1968.** 750th Anniv. of Rostock. Mult.

E 1105. 20 pf. Type E **351** .. 10 10
E 1106. 25 pf. Rostock, 1968 .. 50 50

**1968.** Celebrities' Annivs. (1st series).

E 1107. E **352.** 10 pf. grey .. 10 10
E 1108. – 15 pf. black .. 20 10
E 1109. – 20 pf. brown .. 10 10
E 1110. – 25 pf. blue .. 10 10
E 1111. – 40 pf. red .. 80 65

Designs: 15 pf. Emanuel Lasker (chess master, birth cent). 20 pf. Hans Eisler (composer, 70th birth anniv). 25 pf. Ignaz Semmelweis (physician, 150th birth anniv). 40 pf. Max von Pettenkofer (hygienist, 150th birth anniv).

See also Nos. E1161/4 and E1256/61.

E 353. Zlin Z-226 Trener 6 looping.  E 354. "At the Seaside" (Womacka).

**1968.** Aerobatics World Championships, Magdeburg. Multicoloured.

E 1112. 10 pf. Type E **353** .. 10 10
E 1113. 25 pf. Stunt flying .. 60 50

**1968.** Dresden Gallery Paintings (2nd series). Multicoloured.

E 1114. 10 pf. Type E **354** .. 10 10
E 1115. 15 pf. "Peasants Mowing Mountain Meadow" (Egger-Lienz) .. .. 10 10
E 1116. 20 pf. "Portrait of a Farmer's Wife" (Liebl) .. .. 10 10
E 1117. 40 pf. "Portrait of my Daughter" (Venturelli) .. .. 15 10
E 1118. 50 pf. "High-School Girl" (Michaelis) .. 15 15
E 1119. 70 pf. "Girl with Guitar" (Castelli) .. 2·10 1·40

The 20 pf. to 70 pf. are vert.

E 355. Model Trains.

**1968.** Leipzig Autumn Fair.

E 1120. E **355.** 10 pf. multicoloured 20 10

E 356. Spremberg Dam.

**1968.** East German Post-War Dams. Multicoloured.

E 1121. 5 pf. Type E **356** .. 10 10
E 1122. 10 pf. Pohl Dam .. 10 10
E 1123. 15 pf. Ohra Valley Dam 50 50
E 1124. 20 pf. Rappbode Dam 10 10

The 10 pf. and 15 pf. are vert.

E 357. Sprinting.

**1968.** Olympic Games, Mexico. Multicoloured.

E 1125. 5 pf. Type E **357** .. 10 10
E 1126. 10 pf.+5 pf. Pole-vaulting .. .. 10 10
E 1127. 20 pf.+10 pf. Football 10 10
E 1128. 25 pf. Gymnastics .. 20 10
E 1129. 40 pf. Water-polo .. 30 10
E 1130. 70 pf. Sculling .. 1·50 1·50

The 10, 20, 25 and 40 pf. are vert.

E 358. Breendonk Memorial, Belgium.  E 359. Green Tiger Beetle.

**1968.** Breendonk War Victims. Commem.

E 1131. E **358.** 25 pf. mult. .. 20 10

**1968.** "Useful Beetles". Multicoloured.

E1132 10 pf. Type E **359** .. 10 10
E1133 15 pf. Cyprus beetle .. 10 10
E1134 20 pf. Two spotted lady-bird .. .. .. 20 10
E1135 25 pf. Field ground beetle .. .. 3·00 1·60
E1136 30 pf. Hister beetle .. 30 10
E1137 40 pf. "Pseudoclerops mutillarius" .. .. 40 10

E 360. Lenin and Letter to Spartacus Group.

**1968.** 50th Anniv. of German November Revolution.

E 1138. 10 pf. black, red and yellow .. .. 10 10
E 1139. 20 pf. black, red and yellow .. .. 10 10
E 1140. 25 pf. black, red and yellow .. .. 40 40

Designs: 10 pf. Type E **360.** 20 pf. Revolutionaries and title of Spartacus newspaper "Die Rote Fahne". 25 pf. Karl Liebknecht and Rosa Luxemburg.

E 361. "Lailio-cattleya alba rubra" ("Maggie Raphaela").

**1968.** Orchids. Multicoloured.

E 1141. 5 pf. Type E **361** .. 10 10
E 1142. 10 pf. "Paphiopedilum albertianum" .. 10 10
E 1143 15 pf. "Cattleya fabia" .. .. 10 10
E 1144. 20 pf. "Cattleya aclaniae" .. .. 15 10
E 1145. 40 pf. "Sobralia macrantha" .. .. 15 15
E 1146. 50 pf. "Dendrobium alpha" .. .. 2·00 1·60

E 362. Trying on the Boots.

**1968.** Fairy Tales (3rd series). "Puss in Boots". As Type E **362**. Designs showing different scenes.

E 1147. 5 pf. multicoloured .. 35 35
E 1148. 10 pf. multicoloured .. 35 35
E 1149. 15 pf. multicoloured .. 35 35
E 1150. 20 pf. multicoloured .. 35 35
E 1151. 25 pf. multicoloured .. 35 35
E 1152. 30 pf. multicoloured .. 35 35

E **363** Young Pioneers.

**1968.** 20th Anniv. of Ernst Thalmann's "Young Pioneers." Multicoloured.

E 1153. 10 pf. Type E **363** .. 10 10
E 1154. 15 pf. Young pioneers (diff.) .. .. 35 25

**1969.** Principal East German Buildings (3rd series). As Type E **312**. Mult.

E 1155. 5 pf. Town Hall, Tangermunde .. 10 10
E 1156. 10 pf. State Opera House, Berlin .. 10 10
E 1157. 20 pf. Rampart Pavilion, Dresden Castle .. 10 10
E 1158. 25 pf. Patrician's House, Luckau .. .. 1·00 80
E 1159. 30 pf. Dornburg Castle 15 10
E 1160. 40 pf. "Zum Stockfisch" Inn, Erfurt.. .. 15 15

The 5, 20, 25 and 40 pf. are vert.

**1969.** Celebrities' Annivs. (2nd series). As Type E **352**.

E 1161. 10 pf. olive .. .. 10 10
E 1162. 20 pf. brown .. .. 10 10
E 1163. 25 pf. blue .. .. 80 55
E 1164. 40 pf. brown .. .. 10 10

DESIGNS: 10 pf. M. A. Nexo (Danish poet—birth cent.). 20 pf. O. Nagel (painter—75th birth anniv.). 25 pf. A. von Humboldt (naturalist—bicent. of birth). 40 pf. T. Fontane writer—150th birth anniv.).

E **364**. Pedestrian Crossing. E 365. "E-512" Combine-harvester.

**1969.** Road Safety. Multicoloured.

E 1165. 5 pf. Type E **364** .. 10 10
E 1166. 10 pf. Traffic lights .. 10 10
E 1167. 20 pf. Level-crossing sign .. .. .. 10 10
E 1168. 25 pf. Motor-vehicle overtaking.. .. 55 35

**1969.** Leipzig Spring Fair. Multicoloured.

E 1169. 10 pf. Type E **365** .. 10 10
E 1170. 15 pf. "Planeta-Varianii" lithograph printing-press .. 15 15

E **366**. Jorinde and Joringel. E 367. Spring Snowflake.

**1969.** Fairy Tales (4th series). "Jorinde and Joringel". As Type E **366**, showing different scenes.

E 1171. 5 pf. multicoloured .. 25 25
E 1172. 10 pf. multicoloured .. 25 25
E 1173. 15 pf. multicoloured .. 25 25
E 1174. 20 pf. multicoloured .. 25 25
E 1175. 25 pf. multicoloured .. 25 25
E 1176. 30 pf. multicoloured .. 25 25

**1969.** Protected Plants (2nd series). Mult.

E1177 5 pf. Type E **367** .. 10 10
E1178 10 pf. Yellow pheasant's-eye ("Adonis vernalis") .. 10 10
E1179 15 pf. Globe flower ("Trollius europaeus") 10 10
E1180 20 pf. Martagon lily ("Lilium martagon") 15 10
E1181 25 pf. Sea holly ("Eryngium maritmum") .. 2·50 1·50
E1182 30 pf. "Dactylorchis latifolia" .. 25 10

See also Nos. E1284/9.

E **368**. Plantation of Young Conifers. E **369**. Symbols of the Societies.

**1969.** Forest Fires Prevention. Mult.

E 1183. 5 pf. Type E **368** .. 10 10
E 1184. 10 pf. Lumber, and resin extraction .. 20 10
E 1185. 20 pf. Forest stream .. 20 10
E 1186. 25 pf. Woodland camp 1·00 45

**1969.** 50th Anniv. of League of Red Cross Societies. Multicoloured.

E1187 10 pf. Type E **369** .. 20 10
E1188 15 pf. Similar design with symbols in oblong .. .. 65 20

E **370**. Erythrite (Schneeberg). E **371**. Women and Symbols.

**1969.** East German Minerals. Multicoloured.

E 1189. 5 pf. Type E **370** .. 10 10
E 1190. 10 pf. Fluorite (Halsbrucke) .. 10 10
E 1191. 15 pf. Galena (Neudorf) 10 10
E 1192. 20 pf. Smoky Quartz (Lichtenberg) .. 10 10
E 1193. 25 pf. Calcite (Niederrabenstein) .. .. 1·10 1·10
E 1194. 50 pf. Silver (Freiberg) 15 10

**1969.** 2nd DDR Women's Congress.

E 1195. E **371**. 20 pf., red & blue 10 10
E 1196. – 25 pf. blue & red 50 25

DESIGN: 25 pf. Woman and Symbols (different).

**1969.** As Nos. E 586/7 (Ulbricht), but with face values expressed in "M" (Mark).

E 1197. 1 M green .. .. 35 20
E 1198. 2 M. brown .. .. 65 50

E **372**. Badge of DDR Philatelists' Association. E **373**. Armed Volunteers.

**1969.** 20th Anniv. of DDR Stamp Exhibition, Magdeburg (1st issue).

E 1199. E **372**. 10 pf. gold, blue and red .. 15 10

See also Nos. E 1233/4.

**1969.** Aid for Vietnam.

E 1200. E **373**. 10 pf. + 5 pf. mult. 15 10

E 374. "Development of Youth". E 375. Inaugural Ceremony.

**1969.** Int. Peace Meeting, East Berlin. Multicoloured.

E 1201. 10 pf. Type E **374** .. 45 45
E 1202. 20 pf. + 5 pf. Berlin landmarks (50 × 28 mm.) 45 45
E 1203. 25 pf. "Workers of the World" .. .. 45 45

**1969.** 5th Gymnastics and Athletic Meeting, Leipzig. Multicoloured.

E 1204. 5 pf. Type E **375** .. 10 10
E 1205. 10 pf. + 5 pf. Gymnastics 10 10
E 1206. 15 pf. Athletes' parade 10 10
E 1207. 20 pf. + 5 pf. "Sport" Art Exhibition .. 10 10
E 1208. 25 pf. Athletic events .. 1·00 50
E 1209. 30 pf. Presentation of colours .. 10 10

E 376. Pierre de Coubertin (from bust by W. Forster). E **377**. Knight.

**1969.** 75th Anniv. of Pierre de Coubertin's Revival of Olympic Games' Movement.

E 1210. E **376**. 10 pf. sepia, black and blue .. 10 10
E 1211. – 25 pf. sepia, black and red .. 70 50

DESIGN: 25 pf. Coubertin monument, Olympia.

**1969.** World Sports Championships. Mult.

E 1212. E **377**. 20 pf. gold, red and purple .. 30 15
E 1213. – 20 pf. mult. .. 15 15
E 1214. – 20 pf. mult. .. 15 15

DESIGNS AND EVENTS: No. E1212, 16th World Students' Team Championship, Dresden. No. E1213, Cycle Wheel (World Covered Court Cycling Championships, Erfurt). No. E1214, Ball and net (2nd World Volleyball Cup-ties).

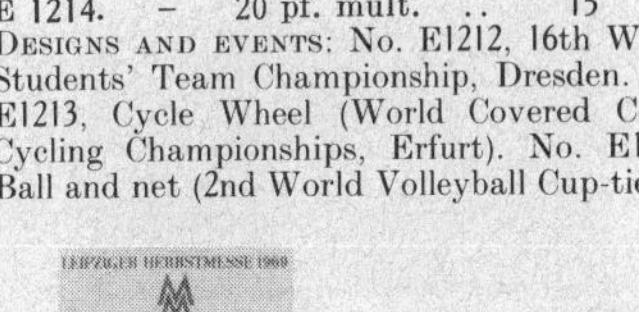

E 378. Fair Display Samples. E 381. TV Tower, East Berlin.

E 379. Rostock.

**1969.** Leipzig Autumn Fair.

E 1215. E **378**. 10 pf. mult. .. 15 15

**1969.** 20th Anniv. of German Democratic Republic. Multicoloured.

(a) 1st Issue. As Type E **379**.

E 1216. 10 pf. Type E **379** .. 10 10
E 1217. 10 pf. Neubrandenburg 10 10
E 1218. 10 pf. Potsdam .. 10 10
E 1219. 10 pf. Eisenhuttenstadt 10 10
E 1220. 10 pf. Hoyerswerda .. 10 10
E 1221. 10 pf. Magdeburg .. 10 10
E 1222. 10 pf. Halle-Neustadt 10 10
E 1223. 10 pf. Suhl .. .. 10 10
E 1224. 10 pf. Dresden .. 10 10
E 1225. 10 pf. Leipzig .. 10 10
E 1226. 10 pf. Karl-Marx Stadt 10 10
E 1227. 10 pf. East Berlin .. 10 10

(b) 2nd Issue. As Type E **381**.

E 1230. 10 pf. Type E **381** .. 10 10
E 1231. 20 pf. "Globe" of Tower with TV Screen .. 20 15

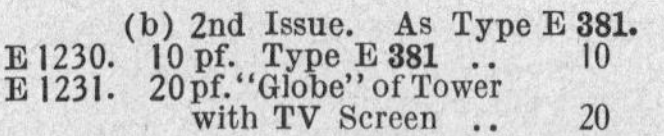

E 382. O. von Guericke Memorial, Cathedral and Hotel International, Magdeburg.

**1969.** 20th Anniv. of D.D.R. Stamp Exhibition, Magdeburg (2nd issue). Mult.

E 1233. 20 pf. Type E **382** .. 10 10
E 1234. 40 pf. + 10 pf. Von Guericke's vacuum experiment .. .. .. 55 40

E 383. Ryvangen Memorial. E 384. U.F.I. Emblem.

**1969.** War Victims' Memorial, Ryvangen (Copenhagen).

E 1235. E **383**. 25 pf. mult. .. 30 10

**1969.** 36th Int. Fairs Union (U.F.I.) Congress, Leipzig.

E 1236. E **384**. 10 pf. mult. .. 20 10
E 1237. 15 pf. mult. .. 1·00 25

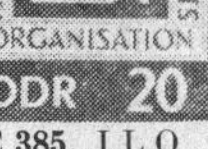

E 385. I.L.O. Emblem. E 386. University Seal and Building.

**1969.** 50th Anniv. of I.L.O.

E 1238. E **385**. 20 pf. silver & grn. 15 10
E 1239. 25 pf. silv. & mve. 80 30

**1969.** 550th Anniv. of Rostock University. Multicoloured.

E 1240. 10 pf. Type E **386** .. 20 10
E 1241. 15 pf. Steam-turbine rotor and curve (University emblem) 65 20

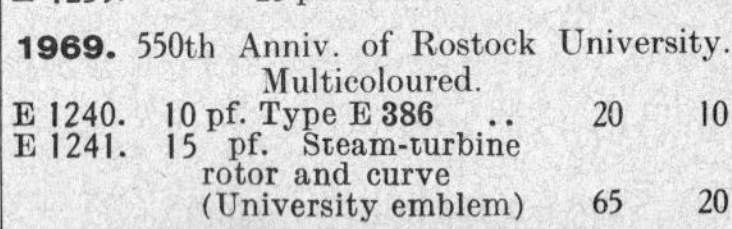

E 387. "Horseman" Pastry-mould. E 388. Antonov An-24B.

**1969.** Lausitz Folk Art.

E 1242. E **387** 10 pf. brown, black and flesh 1·00 90
E 1243. – 20 pf. + 5 pf. multicoloured 15 15
E 1244. – 50 pf. mult. .. 1·50 1·25

DESIGNS: 20 pf. Plate. 50 pf. Pastry in form of Negro couple.

**1969.** Interflug Aircraft. Multicoloured.

E1245 20 pf. Type E **388** .. 10 10
E1246 25 pf. Ilyushin Il-18 .. 1·25 1·25
E1247 30 pf. Tupolev Tu-134 .. 15 15
E1248 50 pf. Mil Mi-8 helicopter 15 15

E 389. "Siberian Teacher" (Svechnikov).

**1969.** Dresden Gallery Paintings (3rd series). Multicoloured.

E 1249. 5 pf. Type E **389** .. 10 10
E 1250. 10 pf. "Steel-worker" (Serov) .. 10 10
E 1251. 20 pf. "Still Life" (Aslamasjan) .. 10 10
E 1252. 25 pf. "A Warm Day" (Romas) .. 1·00 1·25
E 1253. 40 pf. "Springtime Again" (Kabatchek) 15 10
E 1254. 50 pf. "Man by the River" (Makovsky) 20 10

**1970.** Coil Stamp. As Nos. E 577 etc., but value expressed in "M".

E 1255. E **196**. 1 m. olive .. 45 10

**1970.** Celebrities Annivs. (3rd series). As Type E **352**.

E 1256. 5 pf. blue .. .. 10 10
E 1257. 10 pf. brown .. .. 10 10
E 1258. 15 pf. blue .. .. 10 10
E 1259. 20 pf. purple .. .. 15 10
E 1260. 25 pf. blue .. .. 2·10 60
E 1261. 40 pf. red .. .. 30 10

DESIGNS: 5 pf. E. Barlach (sculptor and playwright; birth cent.). 10 pf. J. Gutenberg (printer; 500th death anniv.) (1968). 15 pf. K. Tucholsky (author; 80th birth anniv.). 20 pf. Beethoven (birth bicent.). 25 pf. F. Holderlin (poet; birth bicent.). 40 pf G. W. F. Hegel (philosopher; birth bicent.).

E 390. Red fox.

**1970.** Int. Fur Auction, Leipzig. Mult.

E 1262. 10 pf. Rabbit .. .. 20 10
E 1263. 20 pf. Type E **390** .. 20 10
E 1264. 25 pf. European mink 3·00 2·25
E 1265. 40 pf. Common hamster .. .. 40 10

**E 391.** "Little Brother and Little Sister".

**1970.** Fairy Tales (5th series). "Little Brother and Little Sister". As Type **E 391.** showing different scenes.

E 1266. 5 pf. multicoloured .. 25 25
E 1267. 10 pf. multicoloured .. 25 25
E 1268. 15 pf. multicoloured .. 25 25
E 1269. 20 pf. multicoloured .. 25 25
E 1270. 25 pf. multicoloured .. 25 25
E 1271. 30 pf. multicoloured .. 25 25

**E 392.** Telephone and Electrical Switchgear.

**1970. Leipzig Spring Fair. Multicoloured.**

E 1272. 10 pf. Type E 392 .. 10 10
E 1273. 15 pf. High-voltage transformer (vert.) 30 10

**E 393.** Horseman's Gravestone (A.D. 700).

**1970.** Archaeological Discoveries.

E 1274. E **393.** 10 pf. ol., blk. & grn. 10 10
E 1275. – 20 pf. blk., yell. & red 10 10
E 1276. – 25 pf. green, black and yellow .. 80 80
E 1277. – 40 pf. chestnut, black & brown 15 15

DESIGNS: 20 pf. Helmet (A.D. 500). 25 pf. Bronze basin (1000 B.C.). 40 pf. Clay drum (2500 B.C.).

**E 394.** Lenin and "Iskra" (=the Spark) press.

**1970.** Birth Cent. Lenin. Multicoloured.

E 1278. 10 pf. Type E **394** .. 10 10
E 1279. 20 pf. Lenin and Clara Zetkin .. .. 10 10
E 1280. 25 pf. Lenin and "State & Revolution" (book) 1·60 90
E 1281. 40 pf. Lenin Monument, Eisleben .. .. 10 10
E 1282. 70 pf. Lenin Square, East Berlin .. 20 15

**1970.** Protected Plants (3rd series). Vert designs as Type E **367.** Multicoloured.

E1284 10 pf. Sea kale ("Crambe maritima") .. .. 10 10
E1285 20 pf. Pasque flower ("Pulsatilla vulgaris") 15 10
E1286 25 pf. Fringed gentian ("Gentiana ciliata") 1·60 1·75
E1287 30 pf. Military orchid ("Orchis militaris") .. 15 10
E1288 40 pf. Labrador tea ("Ledum palustre") 15 15
E1289 70 pf. Round-leaved wintergreen ("Pyrola rotundifolia") .. 30 10

**E 395.** Capture of the Reichstag, 1945. **E 396.** Shortwave Aerial.

**1970.** 25th Anniv. of "Liberation from Fascism". Multicoloured.

E 1290. 10 pf. Type E **395** .. 10 10
E 1291. 20 pf. Newspaper headline, Kremlin and State Building, East Berlin .. .. 10 10
E 1292. 25 pf. C.M.E.A. Building, Moscow and flags .. .. 75 45

**1970.** 25th Anniv. of D.D.R. Broadcasting Service. Multicoloured.

E 1294. 10 pf. Type E **396** .. 40 40
E 1295. 15 pf. Radio Station, East Berlin .. 60 60

No. E 1295 is a horiz. design, size 50 × 28 mm.

**E 397.** Globe and Ear of Corn. **E 398.** Fritz Heckert Medal.

**1970.** 5th World Corn and Bread Congress, Dresden. Multicoloured.

E 1296. 20 pf. Type E **397** .. 80 80
E 1297. 25 pf. Palace of Culture and ear of corn .. 80 80

**1970.** 25th Annivs. of German Confederation of Trade Unions and World Trade Union Federation ("Federation Syndicale Mondiale"). Multicoloured.

E 1298. 20 pf. Type E **398** .. 10 10
E 1299. 25 pf. F.S.M. Emblem 50 40

**E 399.** Gods Amon, Shu and Tefnut.

**1970.** Sudanese Archaeological Excavations by Humboldt University Expedition. Multicoloured.

E 1300. 10 pf. Type E **399** .. 10 10
E 1301. 15 pf. King Arnekhamani 10 10
E 1302. 20 pf. Cattle frieze .. 10 10
E 1303. 25 pf. Prince Arka 1·10 65
E 1304. 30 pf. God Arensnuphis (vert.) .. .. .. 10 10
E 1305. 40 pf. War elephants and prisoners .. 15 10
E 1306. 50 pf. God Apedemak .. 15 10

The above designs reproduce carvings unearthed at the Lions' Temple, Musawwarat, Sudan.

**E 400.** Road Patrol. **E 401.** D.K.B. Emblem.

**1970.** 25th Anniv. of "Deutsche Volkspolizei" (police force). Multicoloured.

E1307 5 pf. Type E **400** .. 10 10
E1308 10 pf. Policeman with children .. .. 10 10
E1309 15 pf. Radio patrol car 15 10
E1310 20 pf. Railway policeman .. .. .. 15 10
E1311 25 pf. River police in patrol boat .. 1·25 55

**1970.** 25th Anniv. of "Deutscher Kulturbund" (cultural assn.).

E 1312. E **401.** 10 pf. brn., silver and blue .. 1·60 2·00
E 1313. – 25 pf. brown, gold and blue .. 1·60 2·00

DESIGN: 25 pf. Johannes Becher medal.

**E 402.** Arms of D.D.R. and Poland.

**1970.** 20th Anniv. of Gorlitz Agreement on Oder-Neisse Border.

E 1314. E **402.** 20 pf. mult. .. 25 10

**1970.** 3rd Children and Young People's Sports Days. Multicoloured.

E1315 10 pf. Type E **403** .. 10 10
E1316 20 pf. + 5 pf. Hurdling .. 20 15

**1970.** 6th Young Pioneers Meeting. Cottbus. Multicoloured.

E 1317. 10 pf. + 5 pf. Type E **404** 20 20
E 1318. 25 pf. + 5 pf. Girl pioneer with neckerchief .. 20 20

Nos. E1317/18 were issued together, se-tenant, forming a composite design.

**1970.** 25th Anniv. of Potsdam Agreement.

E 1319. E **405.** 10 pf. yellow, red and black .. 15 15
E 1320. – 20 pf. black, red and yellow .. 15 15
E 1321. – 25 pf. black & red 15 15

DESIGNS—VERT. 20 pf. "Potsdam Agreement" in four languages. HORIZ. (77 × 28 mm.): 25 pf. Conference delegates around the table.

**E 406.** Pocket-watch and Wristwatch. **E 407.** T. Neubauer and M. Poser.

**1970.** Leipzig Autumn Fair.

E 1322. E **406.** 10 pf. mult. .. 20 10

**1970.** "Anti-Fascist Resistance".

E 1323. E **407.** 20 pf. purple, red and blue .. 15 10
E 1324. – 25 pf. olive & red 25 20

DESIGN—VERT. 25 pf. "Motherland"—detail from Soviet War Memorial, Treptow, Berlin.

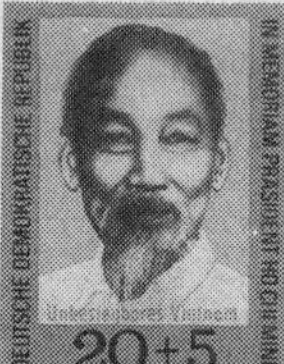

**E 408.** Pres. Ho-Chi-Minh. **E 409.** Compass and Map.

**1970.** Aid for Vietnam and Ho-Chi-Minh. Commemoration.

E 1325. E **408.** 20 pf. + 5 pf. blk., red and pink .. 20 10

**1970.** World "Orienteering" Championships. East Germany. Mult.

E 1326. 10 pf. Type E **409** .. 10 10
E 1327. 25 pf. Runner and three map sections .. 60 30

**E 410.** "Forester Scharf's Birthday" (Nagel).

**1970.** "The Art of Otto Nagel, Kathe Kollwitz and Ernst Barlach".

E 1328. E **410.** 10 pf. multicoloured 10 10
E 1329. – 20 pf. multicoloured 10 10
E 1330. – 25 pf. brown & mauve 1·10 1·10
E 1331. – 30 pf. black & pink 10 10
E 1332. – 40 pf. black & yell. 15 10
E 1333. – 50 pf. black & yell. 15 10

DESIGNS: 20 pf. "Portrait of a Young Girl" (Nagel). 25 pf. "No More War" (Kollwitz). 30 pf. "Mother and Child" (Kollwitz). 40 pf. Sculptured head from Gustrow Cenotaph (Barlach). 50 pf. "The Flute-player" (Barlach).

**E 412.** Flags Emblem.

**1970.** 2nd National Youth Stamp Exhibition, Karl-Marx-Stadt. Multicoloured.

E 1334. 10 pf. Type E **411** .. 15 10
E 1335. 15 pf. + 5 pf. East German 25 pf. stamp of 1959 .. .. 20 20

**1970.** "Comrades-in-Arms". Warsaw Pact Military Manoeuvres.

E 1336. E **412.** 10 pf. multicoloured 10 10
E 1337. 20 pf. multicoloured 15 10

**1970.** Animals in East Berlin "Tierpark" (Zoo). Multicoloured.

E 1338. 10 pf. Type E **413** .. 30 10
E 1339. 15 pf. Whale-headed Stork .. .. 90 10
E 1340. 20 pf. Addax .. .. 1·00 30
E 1341. 25 pf. Sun bear .. 4·00 3·50

**E 414.** U.N. Emblem and Headquarters, New York. **E 415.** Engels.

**1970.** 25th Anniv. of United Nations.

E 1342. E **414.** 20 pf. multicoloured 45 15

**1970.** 150th Birth Anniv. of Friedrich Engels.

E 1343. E **415.** 10 pf. black, grey and orange .. 20 10
E 1344. – 20 pf. black, grn. and orange .. 20 10
E 1345. – 25 pf. black, red and orange .. 1·00 55

DESIGNS: 20 pf. Engels, Marx and "Communist Manifesto". 25 pf. Engels and "Anti Duhring".

**E 416.** "Epiphyllum hybr.". **E 417.** Dancer's Mask, Bismarck Archipelago.

**1970.** Cacti Cultivation in D.D.R. Mult.

E 1346. 5 pf. Type E **416** .. 10 10
E 1347. 10 pf. "Astrophytum myriostigma" .. 10 10
E 1348. 15 pf. "Echinocereus salm-dyckianus" .. 10 10
E 1349. 20 pf. "Selenicereus grandiflorus" .. 10 10
E 1350. 25 pf. "Hamatoc setispinus" .. .. 1·60 1·40
E 1351. 30 pf. "Mamillaria boolii" .. .. 20 10

**1971.** Exhibits from the Ethnological Museum, Leipzig.

E 1353. E **417.** 10 pf. multicoloured 10 10
E 1354. – 20 pf. brn. & orge. 10 10
E 1355. – 25 pf. multicoloured 80 80
E 1356. – 40 pf. brown & red 10 10

DESIGNS: 20 pf. Bronze head, Benin. 25 pf. Tea-pot, Thailand. 40 pf. Zapotec earthenware Jaguar-god, Mexico.

**E 418.** "Venus 5".

**1971.** Soviet Space Research. Multicoloured.

E1357 20 pf. Type E **418** .. 30 30
E1358 20 pf. Orbital space station .. .. 30 30
E1359 20 pf. "Luna 10" and "Luna 16" .. .. 30 30
E1360 20 pf. Various "Soyuz" spacecraft .. .. 30 30
E1361 20 pf. "Proton 1" satellite and "Vostok" rocket .. .. 30 30
E1362 20 pf. "Molniya 1" communications satellite 30 30
E1363 20 pf. Gagarin and "Vostok 1" .. .. 30 30
E1364 20 pf. Leonov in space 30 30

**E 411.** "The Little Trumpeter" (Weineck Memorial, Halle). **E 413.** Musk Ox.

**E 403.** Vaulting. **E 405.** Cecilienhof Castle.

**E 404.** Boy Pioneer with Neckerchief.

E 419. K. Liebknecht. E 420. J. R. Becher (poet).

**1971.** Birth Centenaries of Karl Liebknecht and Rosa Luxemburg (revolutionaries).
E1365 E 419 20 pf. mauve, gold and black .. 40 40
E1366 – 25 pf. mauve, gold and black .. 40 40
DESIGN: 25 pf. Rosa Luxemburg.

**1971.** Celebrities' Birth Anniversaries.
E 1367. E 420. 5 pf. brown .. 10 10
E 1368. – 10 pf. blue .. 10 10
E 1369. – 15 pf. black .. 10 10
E 1370. – 20 pf. purple .. 10 10
E 1371. – 25 pf. green .. 80 65
E 1372. – 50 pf. blue .. 10 10
DESIGNS: 5 pf. (80th birth anniv). 10 pf. H. Mann (writer—birth cent). 15 pf. J. Heartfield (artist—80th birth anniv). 20 pf. W. Bredel (70th birth anniv). 25 pf. F. Mehring (politician—125th birth anniv). 50 pf. J. Kepler (astronomer—400th birth anniv).
See also Nos. E1427 and E1451/5.

E 421. Soldier and Army Badge.

**1971.** 15th Anniv. of National People's Army.
E 1373. E 421. 20 pf. multicoloured 20 10

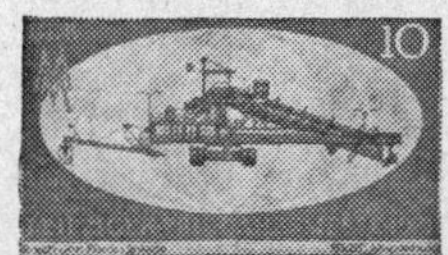

E 422. "Sket" Mobile Ore-crusher.

**1971.** Leipzig Spring Fair. Multicoloured.
E1374 10 pf. Type E 422 .. 10 10
E1375 15 pf. Dredger "Takraf" 15 10

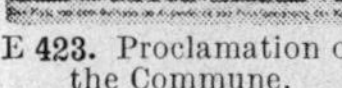

E 423. Proclamation of the Commune. E 425. St. Mary's Church.

E 424. "Lunokhod 1" on Moon's Surface.

**1971.** Centenary of Paris Commune.
E 1376. E 423. 10 pf. black, brown and red .. 10 10
E 1377. – 20 pf. black, brown and red .. 10 10
E 1378. – 25 pf. black, brown and red .. 65 65
E 1379. – 30 pf. black, grey and red .. 15 10
DESIGNS: 20 pf. Women at the Place Blanche barricade. 25 pf. Cover of "L'Internationale". 30 pf. Title page of Karl Marx's "The Civil War in France".

**1971.** Moon Mission of "Lunokhod 1".
E 1380. E 424. 20 pf. turquoise, blue and red .. 40 20

**1971.** Berlin Buildings. Multicoloured.
E 1381. 10 pf. Type E 425 .. 10 10
E 1382. 15 pf. Kopenick Castle (horiz.) .. 10 10
E 1383. 20 pf. Old Library (horiz.) 10 10
E 1384. 25 pf. Ermeler House .. 2·50 2·00
E 1385. 50 pf. New Guardhouse (horiz.) .. 25 10
E 1386. 70 pf. National Gallery (horiz.) .. .. 30 15

E 426. "The Discus-thrower".

**1971.** 20th Anniv. of D.D.R. National Olympics Committee.
E 1387. E 426. 20 pf. mult. .. 45 15

E 427. Handclasp and XXV Emblem. E 428. Schleife Costume.

**1971.** 25th Anniv of Socialist Unity Party.
E1388 E 427 20 pf. black, red and gold .. 20 10

**1971.** Sorbian Dance Costumes. Mult.
E 1389. 10 pf. Type E 428 .. 10 10
E 1390. 20 pf. Hoyerswerda .. 15 10
E 1391. 25 pf. Cottbus .. .. 1·10 75
E 1392. 40 pf. Kamenz .. .. 25 10
For 10 pf. and 20 pf. in smaller size, see Nos. E 1443/4.

E 429. Self-portrait, c. 1500. E 432. "Internees".

E 430. Construction Worker. E 433. Cherry stone with 180 Carved Heads.

**1971.** 500th Birth Anniv. of Albrecht Durer. Paintings. Multicoloured.
E 1393. 10 pf. Type E 429 .. 10 10
E 1394. 40 pf. "The Three Peasants" .. .. 25 10
E 1395. 70 pf. "Philipp Melanchthon" .. 1·25 1·00

**1971.** 8th S.E.D. Party Conference.
E 1396. E 430. 5 pf. multicoloured 10 10
E 1397. – 10 pf. multicoloured 10 10
E 1398. – 20 pf. multicoloured 10 10
E 1400. – 20 pf. gold, red & mauve .. 20 10
E 1399. – 25 pf. multicoloured 40 40
DESIGNS: 10 pf. Technician. 20 pf. (No. E 1398) Farm girl. 20 pf. (No. E 1400) Conference emblem (smaller, 23×29 mm.). 25 pf. Soldier.

**1971.** 20th Anniv of International Resistance Federation (F.I.R.). Lithographs from Fritz Cremer's "Buchenwaldzyklus".
E 1401. E 432. 20 pf. blk. & yell. 50 55
E 1402. – 25 pf. blk. & blue 50 55
DESIGN: 25 pf. "Attack on Guard".

**1971.** Art Treasures of Dresden's Green Vaults. Multicoloured.
E 1403. 5 pf. Type E 433 .. 10 10
E 1404. 10 pf. Insignia of the Golden Fleece, c. 1730 10 10
E 1405. 15 pf. Nuremberg jug, c. 1530 .. .. 10 10
E 1406. 20 pf. Mounted Moorish drummer figurine, c. 1720 .. .. 15 10
E 1407. 25 pf. Writing-case, 1562 90 90
E 1408. 30 pf. St. George medallion, c. 1570 .. .. 15 10

E 434. Mongolian Arms. E 435. Child's Face.

**1971.** 50th Anniv. of Mongolian People's Republic.
E 1409. E 434. 20 pf. multicoloured 20 10

**1971.** 25th Anniv. of U.N.I.C.E.F.
E 1410. E 435. 20 pf. multicoloured 20 10

E 436. Servicemen. E 438. Vietnamese Woman and Child.

E 437. Liner "Ivan Franko".

**1971.** 10th Anniv. of Berlin Wall. Mult.
E 1411. 20 pf. Type E 436 .. 65 30
E 1412. 35 pf. Brandenburg Gate 1·25 80

**1971.** East German Shipbuilding Industry.
E 1413. E 437. 10 pf. brown .. 15 10
E 1414. – 15 pf. bl. & brn. 15 10
E 1415. – 20 pf. green .. 20 10
E 1416. – 25 pf. blue .. 2·25 1·25
E 1417. – 40 pf. brown .. 20 10
E 1418. – 50 pf. blue .. 25 10
DESIGNS: 15 pf. "Type 17" freighter. 20 pf. Freighter "Rostock". 25 pf. Fish-factory ship "Junge Welt". 40 pf. Container ship "Hansel". 50 pf. Research ship "Akademik Kurchatov".

**1971.** Aid for Vietnam.
E 1419. E 438. 10 pf.+5 pf. mult. 20 10

E 439. MAG-Butadien Plant. E 440. Upraised Arms (motif by J. Heartfield).

**1971.** Leipzig Autumn Fair.
E 1420. E 439. 10 pf. violet, mauve and green 10 10
E 1421. – 25 pf. violet, grn. and blue .. 20 15
DESIGN: 25 pf. SKL reactor plant.

**1971.** Racial Equality Year.
E 1422. E 440. 35 pf. black, silver and blue .. 25 10

E 441. Tupolev Tu-134 Mail Plane at Airport.

**1971.** Philatelists' Day.
E 1423. E 441. 10 pf.+5 pf. blue, red and green 20 10
E 1424. – 25 pf. red, green and blue .. 40 35
DESIGN: 25 pf. Milestone and Zurner's measuring cart.

E 442. Wiltz Memorial, Luxembourg. E 443. German Violin.

**1971.** Monuments. Multicoloured.
E 1425. 25 pf. Type E 442 .. 20 10
E 1426. 35 pf. Karl Marx monument, Karl-Marx-Stadt 30 10

**1971.** 150th Birth Anniv. of R. Virchow (physician). As Type E 420.
E 1427. 40 pf. plum .. .. 30 10

**1971.** Musical Instruments in Markneukirchen Museum. Multicoloured.
E1428 10 pf. North African "darbuka" .. .. 10 10
E1429 15 pf. Mongolian "morin chuur" .. .. 10 10
E1430 20 pf. Type E 443 .. 15 10
E1431 25 pf. Italian mandolin 15 10
E1432 40 pf. Bohemian bagpies 15 10
E1433 50 pf. Sudanese "kasso" 1·10 1·10

E 444. "Dahlta 0 10 A" Theodolite. E 445. Donkey and Windmill.

**1971.** 125th Anniv. of Carl Zeiss Optical Works, Jena.
E 1434. E 444. 10 pf. black, red and blue .. 40 40
E 1435. – 20 pf. black, red and blue .. 40 40
E 1436. – 25 pf. blue, yellow and ultram. .. 40 40
DESIGNS—VERT. 20 pf. "Ergaval" microscope. HORIZ. (52×29 mm.) 25 pf. Planetarium.

**1971.** Fairy Tales (6th series). As Type E 445. "The Town Musicians of Bremen".
E 1437. 5 pf. multicoloured .. 30 30
E 1438. 10 pf. multicoloured .. 30 30
E 1439. 15 pf. multicoloured .. 30 30
E 1440. 20 pf. multicoloured .. 30 30
E 1441. 25 pf. multicoloured .. 30 30
E 1442. 30 pf. multicoloured .. 30 30

**1971.** Sorbian Dance Costumes. As Nos. E1389/90 but smaller, size 23×28 mm.
E1443 E 428 10 pf. mult .. 10 10
E1444 – 20 pf. mult .. 55 35

E 446. Tobogganing.

**1971.** Winter Olympic Games, Sapporo, Japan (1972).
E1445 5 pf. black, green & mve 10 10
E1446 10 pf.+5 pf. black, blue and mauve .. .. 10 10
E1447 15 pf.+5 pf. black, green and blue .. .. 10 10
E1448 20 pf. black, mve & vio 15 10
E1449 25 pf. black, vio & mve 1·75 1·00
E1450 70 pf. black, blue & vio 30 15
DESIGNS: 5 pf. Type E 446. 10 pf. Figure skating. 15 pf. Speed skating. 20 pf. Cross-country skiing. 25 pf. Biathlon. 70 pf. Ski jumping.

**1972.** German Celebrities. As Type E 420.
E 1451. 10 pf. green .. .. 10 10
E 1452. 20 pf. mauve .. .. 10 10
E 1453. 25 pf. blue .. .. 10 10
E 1454. 35 pf. brown .. .. 10 10
E 1455. 50 pf. lilac .. .. 1·25 1·25
CELEBRITIES: 10 pf. J. Tralow (writer). 20 pf. L. Frank (writer). 25 pf. K. A. Kocor (composer). 35 pf. H. Schliemann (archaeologist). 50 pf. Caroline Neuber (actress).

E 447. Gypsum from Eisleben.

**1972.** Minerals. Multicoloured.
E 1456. 5 pf. Type E 447 .. 10 10
E 1457. 10 pf. Zinnwaldite, Zinnwald .. .. 10 10
E 1458. 20 pf. Malachite, Ullersreuth .. .. 15 10
E 1459. 25 pf. Amethyst, Wiesenbad .. .. 15 10
E 1460. 35 pf. Halite, Merkers 20 10
E 1461. 50 pf. Proustite, Schneeberg .. .. 1·25 80

E 448. Vietnamese Woman. E 449. Soviet Exhibition Hall.

**1972.** Aid for Vietnam.
E 1462. E 448. 10 pf.+5 pf. mult. 20 10

**1972.** Leipzig Spring Fair. Multicoloured.
E 1463. 10 pf. Type E 449 .. 10 10
E 1464. 25 pf. East German and Soviet flags .. .. 20 15

E 451. W.H.O. Emblem.

**1972.** World Health Day.
E 1466. E 451. 35 pf. ultram., silver & blue.. 25 10

E 452. Kamov Ka-26 Helicopter.

**1972.** East German Aircraft. Multicoloured.
E1467 5 pf. Type E 452 .. 20 10
E1468 10 pf. Letov Z-37 Cmelak crop-sprayer 20 10
E1469 35 pf. Ilyushin Il-62M .. 30 10
E1470 1 m. Ilyushin Il-62M .. 2·25 1·75

E 453. Wrestling.

**1972.** Olympic Games, Munich. Mult.
E 1471. 5 pf. Type E 453 .. 10 10
E 1472. 10 pf.+5 pf. High-diving .. 20 10
E 1473. 20 pf. Pole-vaulting .. 20 10
E 1474. 25 pf.+10 pf. Rowing 20 10
E 1475. 35 pf. Handball .. 30 10
E 1476. 70 pf. Gymnastics .. 2·75 1·50

E 454. Soviet and East German Flags.

**1972.** 25th Anniv. of German-Soviet Friendship Society. Multicoloured.
E 1477. 10 pf. Type E 454 .. 30 20
E 1478. 20 pf. Brezhnev (U.S.S.R.) and Honecker (D.D.R.) 50 30

E 455. Steel Workers. E 456. "Karneol" Rose.

**1972.** Trade Unions Federation Congress.
E 1479. E 455. 10 pf. purple, orange & brown 15 15
E 1480. – 35 pf. blue & brn. 15 15
DESIGNS: 35 pf. Students.

**1972.** Int. Rose Exhib. German Species. Multicoloured.
E 1481. 5 pf. Type E 456 .. 10 10
E 1482. 10 pf. "Berger's Rose" 10 10
E 1497. 10 pf. "Berger's Rose" 15 10
E 1483. 15 pf. "Charme" .. 1·60 1·40
E 1484. 20 pf. "Izetka Spreeathen" .. 10 10
E 1485. 25 pf. "Kopernicker Sommer" .. 10 10
E 1498. 25 pf. "Kopernicker Sommer" .. 70 35
E 1486. 35 pf. "Professor Knoll" 15 10
E 1499. 35 pf. "Professor Knoll" 70 35
Nos. E 1497/9 are smaller, size 24×28 mm.

E 457. "Portrait of Young Man".

**1972.** 500th Birth Anniv. of Lucas Cranach the Elder. Multicoloured.
E 1487. 5 pf. Type E 457 .. 10 10
E 1488. 20 pf. "Mother and Child" .. .. 10 10
E 1489. 25 pf. "Margarete Luther" .. 15 10
E 1490. 70 pf. "Nymph" (horiz.) 2·00 2·10

E 458. Compass and Motor Cyclist. E 460. Overhead Projector.

E 459. "Young Worker Reading" (J. Damme).

**1972.** Sports and Technical Sciences Association. Multicoloured.
E1491 5 pf. Type E 458 .. 10 10
E1492 10 pf. Light airplane and parachute .. 10 10
E1493 20 pf. Target and obstacle race .. 15 10
E1494 25 pf. Radio set and Morse key .. .. 1·25 80
E1495 35 pf. Brigantine "Wilhelm Pieck" and propeller .. .. 20 10

**1972.** Int. Book Year.
E 1496. E 459. 50 pf. mult. .. 45 15

**1972.** Leipzig Autumn Fair.
E 1500. E 460. 10 pf. blk. & red 10 10
E 1501. – 25 pf. blk. & grn. 20 15
DESIGN—HORIZ. 25 pf. Slide projector.

E 461. G. Dimitrov. E 462. "Catching Birds" (Egyptian relief painting, c. 2400 B.C.).

**1972.** 90th Birth Anniv. of Georgi Dimitrov (Bulgarian statesman).
E 1502. E 461. 20 pf. blk. & red 25 10

**1972.** "Interartes" Stamp Exhib. East Berlin. Multicoloured.
E 1503. 10 pf. Type E 462 .. 10 10
E 1504. 15 pf.+5 pf. "Persian Spearman" (glazed tile, c. 500 B.C.) .. 1·00 90
E 1505. 20 pf. Anatolian tapestry c. 1400 B.C. 10 10
E 1506. 35 pf.+5 pf. "The Grapesellers" (Max Lingner, 1949) (horiz.) .. .. 10 10

E 463. Red Cross Team and Patient. E 464. Terrestrial Globe (J. Praetorius, 1568).

**1972.** East German Red Cross.
E 1507. E 463. 10 pf. ultram., blue and red .. 25 25
E 1508. – 15 pf. ultram., blue and red .. 25 25
E 1509. – 35 pf. red, blue and ultram. .. 25 25
DESIGNS—VERT. 15 pf. Sea-rescue launch. HORIZ. (50½×28 mm.). 35 pf. World map on cross, and transport.

**1972.** Terrestrial and Celestial Globes. Multicoloured.
E 1510. 5 pf. Arab celestial globe, 1279 .. 10 10
E 1511. 10 pf. Type E 464 .. 10 10
E 1512. 15 pf. Globe clock (J. Reinhold and G. Roll, 1586) .. .. 2·00 2·00
E 1513. 20 pf. Globe clock (J Burgi, 1590) .. 15 15
E 1514. 25 pf. Armillary sphere (J. Moeller, 1687) .. 20 15
E 1515. 35 pf. Heraldic celestial globe, 1690 .. .. 30 20

E 465. Monument. E 467. "Mauz and Hoppel" (Cat and Hare).

E 466. Educating Juveniles.

**1972.** German-Polish Resistance Memorial. Berlin. Inauguration.
E 1516. E 465. 25 pf. mult. .. 25 15

**1972.** Juvenile Inventions Exhib. Mult.
E1517 10 pf. Type E 466 .. 15 15
E1518 25 pf. Youths with welding machine .. 15 15

**1972.** Children's T.V. Characters. Mult.
E1519 5 pf. Type E 467 .. 30 30
E1520 10 pf. "Fuchs and Elster" (Fox and Magpie) .. .. 30 30
E1521 15 pf. "Herr Uhu" (Eagle Owl) .. .. 30 30
E1522 20 pf. "Frau Igel and Borstel" (Hedgehogs) 30 30
E1523 25 pf. "Schuffel and Pieps" (Dog and Mouse) .. .. 30 30
E1524 35 pf. "Paulchen" (Paul from the children's library) .. .. 30 30

E 468. "The Snow Queen". E 470. Arms of U.S.S.R.

**1972.** Fairy Tales (7th series). As Type E 468. "The Snow Queen" (Hans Christian Andersen).
E 1525. 5 pf. multicoloured .. 30 30
E 1526. 10 pf. multicoloured .. 30 30
E 1527. 15 pf. multicoloured .. 30 30
E 1528. 20 pf. multicoloured .. 30 30
E 1529. 25 pf. multicoloured .. 30 30
E 1530. 35 pf. multicoloured .. 30 30

**1972.** 50th Anniv. of U.S.S.R.
E 1532. E 470. 20 pf. mult. .. 30 10

E 471. Leninplatz, East Berlin. E 472. M. da Caravaggio.

**1973.**
(a) Size 29×24 mm.
E 1533. – 5 pf. green .. 50 10
E 1534. – 10 pf. green .. 35 10
E 1535. – 15 pf. mauve .. 25 10
E 1536. E 471. 20 pf. mauve .. 45 10
E 1537. – 25 pf. green .. 70 10
E 1538. – 30 pf. orange .. 60 10
E 1539. – 35 pf. blue .. 80 10
E 1540. – 40 pf. violet .. 35 10
E 1541. – 50 pf. blue .. 50 10
E 1542. – 60 pf. purple .. 80 10
E 1543. – 70 pf. brown .. 75 10
E 1544. – 80 pf. blue .. 1·00 10
E 1545. – 1 m. green .. 1·25 10
E 1546. – 2 m. red .. 1·75 10
E 1546a. – 3 m. mauve .. 2·75 40

(b) Size 22×18 mm.
E2197 – 5 pf. green .. 40 10
E1548 – 10 pf. green .. 30 10
E2198 – 10 pf. green .. 15 10
E2199 – 15 pf. mauve .. 30 10
E2200 E 471 20 pf. mauve .. 60 10
E1549a – 25 pf. green .. 35 15
E2202 – 30 pf. orange .. 40 15
E2203 – 35 pf. blue .. 45 15
E2204 – 40 pf. violet .. 65 15
E2205 – 50 pf. blue .. 50 15
E2206 – 60 pf. purple .. 50 15
E2207 – 70 pf. brown .. 50 25
E2208 – 80 pf. blue .. 85 20
E2209 – 1 m. green .. 85 35
E2210 – 2 m. red .. 1·40 50
E2211 – 3 m. mauve .. 2·40 65

DESIGNS: 5 pf. Eastern white pelican and Alfred Brehm House, Tierpark, Berlin. 10 pf. (Nos. E1534, E1548) Neptune Fountain and Rathausstrasse, Berlin. 10 pf. (No. E2198) Palace of the Republic, Berlin. 15 pf. Apartment Blocks, Fishers' Island, Berlin. 25 pf. TV Tower, Alexander Square, Berlin. 30 pf, Workers' Memorial, Halle. 35 pf. Karl-Marx-Stadt. 40 pf. Brandenburg Gate Berlin. 50 pf. New Guardhouse, Berlin. 60 pf. Crown Gate and Zwinger, Dresden. 70 pf. Old Town Hall, Leipzig. 80 pf. Rostock-Warnemunde 1 m. Soviet War Memorial, Treptow. 2, 3 m. Arms of East Germany.

**1973.** Cultural Anniversaries.
E 1551. E 472. 5 pf. brown .. 1·00 80
E 1552. – 10 pf. green .. 10 10
E 1553. – 20 pf. purple .. 15 10
E 1554. – 25 pf. blue .. 15 10
E 1555. – 35 pf. red .. 15 10

PORTRAITS AND ANNIVERSARIES: 5 pf. (painter, 400th birth anniv.). 10 pf. Friedrich Wolf (dramatist, 85th birth anniv.). 20 pf. Max Reger (composer, birth cent.). 25 pf. Max Reinhardt (impressario, birth cent.).35 pf. Johannes Dieckmann (politician, 80th birth anniv.).

E 473. "Lebachia speciosa".

**1973.** Fossils in Palaeontological Collection, Berlin Natural History Museum. Mult.
E 1556. 10 pf. Type E 473 .. 10 10
E 1557. 15 pf. "Spheronopteris hollandica" .. 10 10
E 1558. 20 pf. "Pterodactylus kochi" .. .. 10 10
E 1559. 25 pf. "Botryopteris" 15 10
E 1560. 35 pf. "Archaeopteryx lithographica" .. 30 10
E 1561. 70 pf. "Odontopleura ovata" .. .. 1·75 1·60

E 474. Copernicus.
(Illustration reduced. Actual size 77½×29 mm.)

**1973.** 500th Birth Anniv. of Copernicus.
E 1562. E 474. 70 pf. multicoloured 65 25

E 475. National Flags.

E 476. Bobsleigh Course.

**1973.** 10th World Youth Festival, Berlin (1st issue). Multicoloured.
E 1563. 10 pf.+5 pf. Type E **475** .. 15 10
E 1564. 25 pf.+5pf. Youths and peace dove .. .. 25 15
See also Nos. E 1592/6.

**1973.** 15th World Bobsleigh Championships, Oberhof.
E 1565. E **476.** 35 pf. multicoloured 30 20

E 477. Combine Harvester.

**1973.** Leipzig Spring Fair. Multicoloured.
E 1566. 10 pf. Type E **477** .. 10 10
E 1567. 25 pf. Automatic lathe 20 15

E 478. Firecrests.

**1973.** Songbirds. Multicoloured.
E 1568. 5 pf. Type E **478** .. 20 10
E 1569. 10 pf. White-winged crossbill .. .. 25 10
E 1570. 15 pf. Bohemian wax-wing .. .. .. 25 10
E 1571. 20 pf. Bluethroats .. 25 10
E 1572. 25 pf. Goldfinch .. 30 10
E 1573. 35 pf. Golden oriole .. 30 10
E 1574. 40 pf. Grey wagtail .. 35 15
E 1575. 60 pf. Wallcreeper .. 4·75 2·50

E 479. Electric Locomotive.

**1973.** Railway Rolling Stock. Multicoloured.
E 1576. 5 pf. Type E **479** .. 20 10
E 1577. 10 pf. Refrigerator wagon .. .. 20 10
E 1578. 20 pf. Long-distance coach .. .. 20 10
E 1579. 25 pf. Tank wagon .. 20 10
E 1580. 35 pf. Double-deck coach 30 15
E 1581. 85 pf. Tourist coach .. 3·50 2·50

E 480. "King Lear" (directed by W. Langhoff). E 481. H. Matern.

**1973.** Famous Theatrical Productions. Mult.
E 1582. 10 pf. Type E **480** .. 10 10
E 1583. 25 pf. "A Midsummer Night's Dream" (opera) (Benjamin Britten) (directed by Walter Felsenstein) 10 10
E 1584. 35 pf. "Mother Courage" (directed by Berthold Brecht) 75 75

**1973.** 80th Birth Anniv. of Hermann Matern (politician).
E 1585. E **481.** 40 pf. red .. 40 10

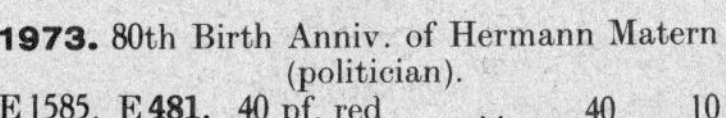

E 482. Goethe and House.

E 483. Firework Display.

**1973.** Cultural Celebrities and Houses in Weimar. Multicoloured.
E 1586. 10 pf. Type E **482** .. 10 10
E 1587. 15 pf. C. M. Wieland (writer) .. .. 10 10
E 1588. 20 pf. F. Schiller (writer) 10 10
E 1589. 25 pf. J. G. Herder (writer) .. .. 10 10
E 1590. 35 pf. Lucas Cranach the Elder (painter) .. 15 10
E 1591. 50 pf. Franz Liszt (composer) .. .. 1·60 85

**1973.** World Festival of Youth and Students, East Berlin (2nd issue). Multicoloured.
E 1592. 5 pf. Type E **483** .. 10 10
E 1593. 15 pf. Students ("Int. Solidarity") .. 10 10
E 1594. 20 pf. Young workers ("Economic Integration") .. .. 10 10
E 1595. 30 pf. Students ("Aid for Young Nations") 90 35
E 1596. 35 pf. Youth and Students' Emblems .. 10 10

E 484. W. Ulbricht. E 485. Power Network.

**1973.** Death of Walter Ulbricht.
E 1598. E **484.** 20 pf. black .. 25 15

**1973.** 10th Anniv. of "Peace" United Energy Supply System.
E 1599. E **485.** 35 pf. orge., pur. and blue .. 30 20

E 486. "Leisure Activities".

**1973.** Leipzig Autumn Fair. Multicoloured.
E 1600. 10 pf. Type E **486** .. 10 10
E 1601. 25 pf. Yacht, guitar and power drill .. .. 20 15

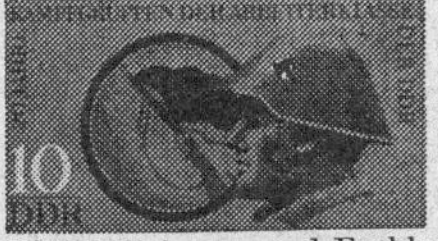

E 487. Militiaman and Emblem.

**1973.** 20th Anniv. of Workers Militia. Mult.
E 1602. 10 pf. Type E **487** .. 10 10
E 1603. 20 pf. Militia guard .. 25 20

E 488. Red Flag encircling Globe. E 489. Langenstein-Zwieberge Memorial.

**1973.** 15th Anniv. of "Problems of Peace and Socialism".
E 1605. E **488.** 20 pf. red & gold 25 10

**1973.** Langenstein-Zwieberge Monument.
E 1606. E **489.** 25 pf. multicoloured 25 15

E 490. U.N. H.Q. and Emblems.

E 491. "Young Couple" (G. Glombitza).

**1973.** Admission of German Democratic Republic to United Nations Organization.
E 1607. E **490.** 35 pf. mult. .. 30 15

**1973.** Philatelists' Day and 3rd Young Philatelists' Stamp Exhibition, Halle.
E 1608. E **491.** 20 pf.+5 pf. mult. 25 15

E 492. Congress Emblem. E 493. Vietnamese Child.

**1973.** 8th World Trade Union Congress, Varna, Bulgaria.
E 1609. E **492.** 35 pf. mult. .. 30 20

**1973.** "Solidarity with Vietnam".
E 1610. E **493.** 10 pf.+5 pf. mult. 20 15

E 494. Launching Rocket.

**1973.** Soviet Science and Technology Days. Multicoloured.
E 1611. 10 pf. Type E **494** .. 15 10
E 1612. 20 pf. Soviet map and emblem (horiz.) .. 20 10
E 1612. 25 pf. Oil refinery .. 1·25 55

E 495. L. Corvalan. E 496. "Child with Doll" (C. L. Vogel).

**1973.** Solidarity with the Chilean People. Multicoloured.
E 1614. 10 pf.+5 pf. Type E **495** 10 10
E 1615. 25 pf.+5 pf. Pres. Allende 30 30

**1973.** Paintings by Old Masters. Mult.
E 1616. 10 pf. Type E **496** .. 10 10
E 1617. 15 pf. "Madonna with Rose" (Parmigianino) 10 10
E 1618. 20 pf. "Woman with Fair Hair" (Rubens) 10 10
E 1619. 25 pf. "Lady in White" (Titian) .. .. 10 10
E 1620. 35 pf. "Archimedes" (D. Fetti) .. .. 15 10
E 1621. 70 pf. "Flower Arrangement" (Jan D. de Heem) .. .. 2·00 1·50

E 497. Flame Emblem.

E 498. "Catching the Pike".

**1973.** 25th Anniv. of Declaration of Human Rights.
E 1622. E **497.** 35 pf. multicoloured 30 15

**1973.** Fairy Tales (8th series). As Type E **498.** "At the Bidding of the Pike".
E 1623. 5 pf. multicoloured .. 30 30
E 1624. 10 pf. multicoloured .. 30 30
E 1625. 15 pf. multicoloured .. 30 30
E 1626. 20 pf. molticoloured .. 30 30
E 1627. 25 pf. multicoloured .. 30 30
E 1628. 35 pf. multicoloured .. 30 30

E 499. E. Hoernle. E 500. Pablo Neruda.

**1974.** Socialist Personalities.
E 1629. E **499.** 10 pf. grey .. 10 10
E 1630. – 10 pf. lilac .. 10 10
E 1631. – 10 pf. blue .. 10 10
E 1632. – 10 pf. brown .. 10 10
E 1633. – 10 pf. green .. 10 10
E 1634. – 10 pf. brown .. 10 10
E 1635. – 10 pf. blue .. 10 10
E 1636. – 10 pf. brown .. 10 10

PERSONALITIES: No. E1630, Etkar Andre. E1631, Paul Merker. E1632, Hermann Duncker. E1633, Fritz Heckert. E1634, Otto Grotewohl. E1635, Wilhelm Florin. E1636, Georg Handke.
See also Nos. E1682/4.

**1974.** Pablo Neruda (Chilean poet) Commem.
E 1637. E **500.** 20 pf. multicoloured 20 15

E 501. "Comecon" Emblem. E 502. "Echinopsis multiplex".

**1974.** 25th Anniv. of Council for Mutual Economic Aid.
E 1638. E **501.** 20 pf. mult. .. 40 10

**1974.** Cacti. Multicoloured.
E 1639. 5 pf. Type E **502** .. 10 10
E 1640. 10 pf. "Lobivia haageana" 10 10
E 1641. 15 pf. "Parodia sanguiniflora" .. 3·00 2·00
E 1642. 20 pf. "Gymnocal. monvillei" .. 15 10
E 1643. 25 pf. "Neoporteria rapifera" .. 25 10
E 1644. 35 pf. "Notocactus concinnus" .. .. 30 15

E 503. Handball Players. E 504. High-tension Testing Plant.

**1974.** Eighth Men's World Indoor Handball Championships.
E 1645. E **503.** 5 pf. multicoloured 25 25
E 1646. – 10 pf. multicoloured 25 25
E 1647. – 35 pf. multicoloured 25 25
Nos. E1645/7 were issued together, se-tenant, forming a composite design of a handball match.

**1974.** Leipzig Spring Fair. Multicoloured.
E 1648. 10 pf. Type E **504** .. 10 10
E 1649. 25 pf. "Robotron" computer (horiz.) .. 20 15

E 505. Leaden Entoloma. E 506. Gustav Kirchhoff.

**1974.** Poisonous Fungi. Multicoloured.
E1650 5 pf. Type E **505** .. 10 10
E1651 10 pf. Devil's boletus .. 15 10
E1652 15 pf. False blusher .. 20 10
E1653 20 pf. Fly agaric .. 30 10
E1654 25 pf. Beefsteak morel 35 10
E1655 30 pf. Red-staining inocybe .. .. 40 15
E1656 35 pf. Death cap .. 50 15
E1657 40 pf. "Clitocybe dealbata" .. .. 2·75 1·10

**1974.** Celebrities. Birth Anniversaries.

E 1658. E **506.** 5 pf. blk., & grey 10 10
E 1659. – 10 pf. ultram. & bl. 10 10
E 1660. – 20 pf. red & pink 10 10
E 1661. – 25 pf. grn. & turq. 15 10
E 1662. – 35 pf. choc. & brn. 75 50

PORTRAITS AND ANNIVERSARIES: 5 pf. (physicist, 150th). 10 pf. Immanuel Kant (philosopher, 250th). 20 pf. Elm Welk (writer, 90th). 25 pf. Johann Herder (author, 230th). 35 pf. Lion Feuchtwanger (novelist, 90th).

E **507.** Globe and "PEACE".

**1974.** 25th Anniv of 1st World Peace Congress.

E1663 E **507** 35 pf. mult .. 30 20

E **508.** Tractor Driver.

E **509.** Buk Lighthouse, 1878.

**1974.** 25th Anniv. of German Democratic Republic. Multicoloured.

E 1664. 10 pf. Type E **508** .. 10 10
E 1665. 20 pf. Students .. 10 10
E 1666. 25 pf. Woman worker 15 10
E 1667. 35 pf. East German family 90 90

**1974.** Lighthouses (1st series). Multicoloured.

E 1668. 10 pf. Type E **509** .. 10 10
E 1669. 15 pf. Warnemunde lighthouse, 1898 .. 10 10
E 1670. 20 pf. Darsser Ort lighthouse, 1848 .. 10 10
E 1671. 35 pf. Arkona lighthouse in 1827 and 1902 .. 15 10
E 1672. 40 pf. Greifswalder Oie lighthouse, 1855 .. 1·00 65

See also Nos. E 1760/4.

E **510.** "Man and Woman looking at the Moon".

**1974.** Birth Bicentary of Caspar Friedrich (painter). Multicoloured.

E 1673. 10 pf. Type E **510** .. 10 10
E 1674. 20 pf. "The Stages of Life" (seaside scene) .. 15 10
E 1675. 25 pf. "Heath near Dresden" .. 1·10 1·25
E 1676. 35 pf. "Trees in the Elbe Valley" .. 30 10

E **512.** Lace Pattern. E **513.** Show Jumping.

**1974.** Plauen Lace.

E1678 E **512** 10 pf. black & vio 10 10
E1679 – 20 pf. brown, black and bistre 10 10
E1680 – 25 pf. black, blue and turquoise 1·10 1·00
E1681 – 35 pf. black, mauve and pink 25 10

DESIGNS: Nos. E1679/81, Lace patterns similar to Type E **512**.

**1974.** Socialist Personalities. As Type E **499**.

E 1682. 10 pf. blue .. .. 10 10
E 1683. 10 pf. violet .. .. 10 10
E 1684. 10 pf. brown .. .. 10 10

DESIGNS: No. E 1682, R. Breitscheid. No. E 1683, K. Burger. No. E 1684, C. Moltmann.

**1974.** Int. Horse-breeders' Congress, Berlin. Multicoloured.

E 1685. 10 pf. Type E **513** .. 10 10
E 1686. 20 pf. Horse & trap (horiz.) .. .. 10 10
E 1687. 25 pf. Haflinger draught horses (horiz.) .. .. 1·60 1·40
E 1688. 35 pf. Horse-racing (horiz.) .. .. 15 15

E **514.** Mobile Railway Crane.

**1974.** Leipzig Autumn Fair. Multicoloured.

E 1689. 10 pf. Type E **514** .. 15 10
E 1690. 25 pf. Agricultural machine .. .. 25 15

E **515.** "The Porcelain Shop".

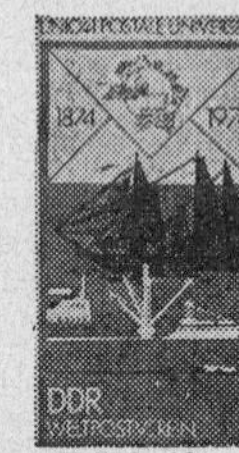


E **518.** 19th-century Paddle-steamer and Modern Freighter

E **516.** Ardeatine Caves Memorial, Rome.

**1974.** "Mon Plaisir". Exhibits in Dolls' Village, Castle Museum, Arnstadt. Mult.

E 1691. 5 pf. Type E **515** .. 10 10
E 1692. 10 pf. "Fairground Crier" 10 10
E 1693. 15 pf. "Wine-tasting in Cellar" .. .. 10 10
E 1694. 20 pf. "Cooper and Apprentice" .. 10 10
E 1695. 25 pf. "Bagpiper playing for Dancing Bear" 2·25 1·25
E 1696. 35 pf. "Butcher's Wife and Crone" .. 30 15

**1974.** International War Memorials.

E 1697. E **516.** 35 pf. blk., grn. & red 25 20
E 1698. – 35 pf. blk., bl. & red 25 20

DESIGN: No. E 1698, Resistance Memorial, Chateaubriant, France.

**1974.** Centenary of U.P.U. Multicoloured.

E1700 10 pf. Type E **518** .. 10 10
E1701 20 pf. Old and modern railway locomotives 30 15
E1702 25 pf. Early and Tupolev Tu-134 airliners .. 20 10
E1703 35 pf. Early mail coach and modern truck .. 1·25 70

E **519.** "The Revolutionaries" (E. Rossdeutscher).

E **520.** "The Sun shines for all" (G. Milosch).

**1974.** "DDR 74" Stamp Exhibition. Sculptures in Karl-Marx-Stadt. Each black, bistre and green.

E 1704. 10 pf.+5 pf. Type E **519** 15 15
E 1705. 20 pf. "The Dialectics" 15 15
E 1706. 25 pf. "The Party" .. 15 15

**1974.** Children's Paintings. Mult.

E 1707. 20 pf. Type E **520** .. 25 20
E 1708. 20 pf. "My Friend Sascha" (B. Ozminski) .. 25 20
E 1709. 20 pf. "Carsten the Best Swimmer" (M. Kluge) .. 25 20
E 1710. 20 pf. "Me and the Blackboard (P. Westphal) .. 25 20

E **521.** "The Woodchopper".

E **523.** Banded Jasper.

E **522.** "Still Life" (R. Paris).

**1974.** Fairy Tales (9th series). "Twittering To and Fro" by A. Tolstoi.

E 1711. E **521.** 10 pf. mult. .. 30 30
E 1712. – 15 pf. mult. .. 30 30
E 1713. – 20 pf. mult. .. 30 30
E 1714. – 30 pf. mult. .. 30 30
E 1715. – 35 pf. mult .. 30 30
E 1716. – 40 pf. mult. .. 30 30

DESIGNS: Nos. E 1712/6, Scenes from "Twittering To and Fro" fairy tale, similar to Type E **521**.

**1974.** Paintings from Berlin Museums. Mult.

E1717 10 pf. Type E **522** .. 10 10
E1718 15 pf. "Girl in Meditation" (W. Lachnit) (vert) .. .. 10 10
E1719 20 pf. "Fisherman's House" (H. Hakenbeck) (vert) .. .. 10 10
E1720 35 pf. "Girl in Red" (R. Bergander) .. .. 15 10
E1721 70 pf. "Parents" (W. Sitte) (vert) .. 1·50 1·50

**1974.** Gem-stones in Freiberg Mining Academy Collection. Multicoloured.

E 1722. 10 pf. Type E **523** .. 10 10
E 1723. 15 pf. Smoky quartz .. 10 10
E 1724. 20 pf. Topaz .. .. 10 10
E 1725. 25 pf. Amethyst .. 10 10
E 1726. 35 pf. Aquamarine .. 15 15
E 1727. 70 pf. Agate .. .. 1·25 1·25

E **524.** Martha Arendsee.

E **525.** Peasants doing Forced Labour.

**1975.** 90th Birth Anniv. of Martha Arendsee (Socialist).

E 1728. E **524.** 10 pf. red .. 15 10

**1975.** 450th Anniv. of Peasants' War.

E 1729. E **525.** 5 pf. black, green and grey .. 30 30
E 1730. – 10 pf. black, brown and grey 30 30
E 1731. – 20 pf. black, blue and grey .. 30 30
E 1732. – 25 pf. black, yellow and grey 50 50
E 1733. – 35 pf. black, lilac and grey .. 50 50
E 1734. – 50 pf. black, grey and light grey 30 30

DESIGNS: 10 pf. "Paying Tithe". 20 pf. Thomas Muntzer (leader). 25 pf. "Armed Peasants". 35 pf. "Liberty" flag. 50 pf. Peasants on trial.

E **526.** Women and Emblem.

E **527.** Pentakta "A-100" (microfilm camera).

**1975.** International Women's Year.

E 1735. E **526.** 10 pf. mult. .. 20 20
E 1736. – 20 pf. mult. .. 20 20
E 1737. – 25 pf. mult. .. 20 20

DESIGNS: 20 pf., 25 pf. Similar to Type E **526**.

**1975.** Leipzig Spring Fair. Multicoloured.

E 1738. 10 pf. Type E **527** .. 10 10
E 1739. 25 pf. "SKET" (cement works) .. 20 15

E **528.** Hans Otto (actor). (1900–1933).

E **529.** Blue and Yellow Macaws.

**1975.** Celebrities' Birth Anniversaries.

E 1740. E **528.** 5 pf. blue .. 10 10
E 1741. – 10 pf. red .. 10 10
E 1742. – 20 pf. green .. 10 10
E 1743. – 25 pf. brown .. 15 10
E 1744. – 35 pf. blue .. 75 60

PORTRAITS AND ANNIVERSARIES: 10 pf. Thomas Mann, author (1875–1955). 20 pf. Dr. A. Schweitzer (1875–1965). 25 pf. Michelangelo (1475–1564). 35 pf. Andre-Marie Ampere, scientist (1775–1836).

**1975.** Zoo Animals. Multicoloured.

E 1745. 5 pf. Type E **529** .. 40 10
E 1746. 10 pf Orang-utans .. 10 10
E 1747. 15 pf. Ibex .. .. 10 10
E 1748. 20 pf. Indian rhinoceros (horiz.) .. .. 20 10
E 1749. 25 pf. Pygmy hippopotamus (horiz.) .. 20 10
E 1750. 30 pf. Grey seals (horiz.) .. .. 20 10
E 1751. 35 pf. Tiger (horiz.) .. 35 15
E 1752. 50 pf. Common zebra 1·90 1·75

E **530.** Soldiers, "Industry" and "Agriculture".

**1975.** 20th Anniv. of Warsaw Treaty.

E 1753. E **530.** 20 pf. multicoloured 45 10

E **531.** Soviet Memorial, Berlin-Treptow.

E **532.** Ribbons with "Komsomol" and "F.D.J." Badges.

**1975.** 30th Anniv. of Liberation. Mult.

E 1754. 10 pf. Type E **531** .. 10 10
E 1755. 20 pf. Detail of Buchenwald memorial .. .. 10 10
E 1756. 25 pf. Woman voluntary worker .. .. 10 10
E 1757. 55 pf. "Socialist economic integration .. 65 60

**1975.** 3rd Youth Friendship Festival, Halle.

E 1759. E **532.** 10 pf. mult. .. 20 10

**1975.** Lighthouses (2nd series). As Type E **509.** Multicoloured.

E 1760. 5 pf. Trimmendorf lighthouse .. .. 10 10
E 1761. 10 pf. Gellen lighthouse 10 10
E 1762. 20 pf. Sassnitz lighthouse .. .. 15 10
E 1763. 25 pf. Dornbusch lighthouse .. .. 15 10
E 1764. 35 pf. Peenemunde lighthouse .. .. 80 50

E 533. Wilhelm Leibknecht and August Bebel.

E 534. Dove and "Scientific Co-operation between Socialist Countries".

**1975.** Centenary of Marx's "Programmkritik" and Gotha Unity Congress.

E1765 E 533 10 pf. deep brown, brown and red 15 15
E1766 – 20 pf. mult .. 15 15
E1767 – 25 pf. deep brown, brown and red 15 15

DESIGNS: 20 pf. Tivoli (meeting place at Gotha) and title-page of Minutes of Unity Congress. 25 pf. Karl Marx and Friedrich Engels.

**1975.** 25th Anniv. of Eisenhuettenstadt.

E 1768. E 534. 20 pf. mult. .. 15 10

E 535. Construction Workers.

E 536. Automatic Clock, 1585.

**1975.** 30th Anniv. of Free-German Trade Union Association.

E 1769. E 535. 20 pf. mult. .. 15 10

**1975.** Ancient Clocks. Multicoloured.

E 1770. 5 pf. Type E 536 .. 10 10
E 1771. 10 pf. Astronomical Mantlepiece clock, 1560 10 10
E 1772. 15 pf. Automatic clock, 1600 .. .. .. 1·25 1·60
E 1773. 20 pf. Mantlepiece Clock, 1720 .. .. .. 10 10
E 1774. 25 pf. Mantlepiece Clock, 1700 .. .. .. 10 10
E 1775. 35 pf. Astronomical Clock, 1738 .. .. .. 15 15

E 537. Jacob and Wilhelm Grimm's German Dictionary.

**1975.** 275th Anniv. of Academy of Science.

E 1776. E 537. 10 pf. black, green and red .. 10 10
E 1777. – 20 pf. black & bl. 10 10
E 1778. – 25 pf. black, yellow & green 10 10
E 1779. – 35 pf. mult. .. 1·00 65

DESIGNS: 20 pf. Karl Schwarzschildt observatory, Tautenberg. 25 pf. Electron microscope and chemical plant. 35 pf. Intercosmic satellite.

E 538. Runner with Torch.

E 539. Map of Europe.

**1975.** 5th National Youth Sports Day.

E 1780. E 538. 10 pf. blk. & pink 10 10
E 1781. – 20 pf. blk. & yell. 10 10
E 1782. – 25 pf. blk. & blue 15 10
E 1783. – 35 pf. blk. & green 80 65

DESIGNS: 20 pf. Hurdling. 25 pf. Swimming. 35 pf. Gymnastics.

**1975.** European Security and Co-operation Conference, Helsinki.

E 1784. E 539. 20 pf. multicoloured 20 10

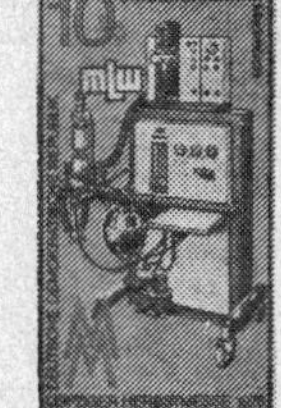

E 540. Asters.

E 541. "Medimorph" (Anaesthetizing machine).

**1975.** Flowers. Multicoloured.

E 1785. 5 pf. Type E 540 .. 10 10
E 1786. 10 pf. Pelargoniums .. 10 10
E 1787. 20 pf. Gerberas .. 10 10
E 1788. 25 pf. Carnation .. 10 10
E 1789. 35 pf. Chrysanthemum 20 15
E 1790. 70 pf. Pansies .. 2·25 1·75

**1975.** Leipzig Autumn Fair. Multicoloured.

E 1791. 10 pf. Type E 541 .. 15 10
E 1792. 25 pf. Zschopau "TS-250" motor-cycle (horiz.) .. .. 25 20

E 542. School Crossing.

**1975.** Road Safety. Multicoloured.

E 1793. 10 pf. Type E 542 .. 10 10
E 1794. 15 pf. Policewoman controlling traffic .. 1·00 50
E 1795. 20 pf. Policeman assisting motorist .. 10 10
E 1796. 25 pf. Car having check-up .. .. .. 10 10
E 1797. 35 pf. Road safety instruction .. .. 20 15

E 543. Launch of "Soyuz".

E 544. Clenched Fist and Red Star.

**1975.** "Apollo"–"Soyuz" Space Link. Mult.

E1798 10 pf. Type E 543 .. 10 10
E1799 20 pf. Spaceships in linking manoeuvre .. 15 10
E1800 70 pf. The completed link (88 × 33 mm) .. 1·90 1·00

**1975.** "International Solidarity".

E 1801. E 544. 10 pf. + 5 pf. black, red and olive .. .. 20 10

E 545. "Weimar in 1650" (Merian).

**1975.** Millenary of Weimar.

E 1802. E 545. 10 pf. brown, light green and green 10 10
E 1803. – 20 pf. mult. .. 10 10
E 1804. – 35 pf. mult. .. 50 40

DESIGNS:—VERT. 20 pf. Buchenwald memorial. HORIZ. 35 pf. Weimar buildings (975–1975).

E 546. Vienna Memorial. (F. Cremer).

E 547. Louis Braille.

**1975.** Austrian Patriots Monument, Vienna.

E 1805. E 546. 35 pf. mult. .. 30 10

**1975.** International Braille Year. Mult.

E 1806. 20 pf. Type E 547 .. 10 10
E 1807. 35 pf. Hands reading braille .. .. 15 10
E 1808. 50 pf. An eye-ball, eye shade and safety goggles .. .. 80 70

E 548. Post Office Gate, Wurzen.

**1975.** National Philatelists' Day. Mult.

E 1809. 10 pf. + 5 pf. Type E 548 50 30
E 1810. 20 pf. Post Office, Barenfels 10 10

E 549. Hans Christian Andersen and scene from "The Emperor's New Clothes". (Actual size 70 × 25 mm.)

**1975.** Fairy Tales (10th series). "The Emperor's New Clothes".

E 1811. E 549. 20 pf. multicoloured 30 30
E 1812. – 35 pf. multicoloured 40 40
E 1813. – 50 pf. multicoloured 40 40

DESIGNS: 35, 50 pf. Different scenes.

E 550. Tobogganing.

**1975.** Winter Olympic Games, Innsbruck (1976). Multicoloured.

E 1814. 5 pf. Type E 550 .. 10 10
E 1815. 10 pf. + 5 pf. Bobsleigh track .. .. 10 10
E 1816. 20 pf. Speed-skating rink 10 10
E 1817. 25 pf. + 5 pf. Ski-jump 15 10
E 1818. 35 pf. Skating-rink .. 15 10
E 1819. 70 pf. Skiing .. .. 1·60 1·25

E 551. W. Pieck.

E 552. Organ, Rotha.

**1975.** Birth Cent. of President Pieck (statesman).

E 1821. E 551. 10 pf. brn. & blue 15 10

**1976.** Members of German Workers' Movement. As Type E 551.

E 1822. 10 pf. brown and red .. 10 10
E 1823. 10 pf. brown and green 10 10
E 1824. 10 pf. brown & orge. 10 10
E 1825. 10 pf. brown and violet 10 10

PORTRAITS: No. E1822, Ernst Thalmann. E1823, Georg Schumann. E1824, Wilhelm Koenen. E1825, John Schehr.

**1976.** Gottfried Silbermann (organ builder) Commemoration. Multicoloured.

E 1826. 10 pf. Type E 552 .. 10 10
E 1827. 20 pf. Organ, Freiberg 10 10
E 1828. 35 pf. Organ, Fraureuth 15 15
E 1829. 50 pf. Organ, Dresden 1·25 55

E 554. Servicemen and Emblem.

**1976.** 20th Anniv. of National Forces (NVA). Multicoloured.

E 1831. 10 pf. Type E 554 .. 15 10
E 1832. 20 pf. N.V.A. equipment 30 15

E 555. Telephone and Inscription.

E 556. Block of Flats, Leipzig.

**1976.** Centenary of Telephone.

E 1833. E 555. 20 pf. blue .. 20 10

**1976.** Leipzig Spring Fair. Multicoloured.

E 1834. 10 pf. Type E 556 .. 15 10
E 1835. 25 pf. "Prometey" deep sea trawler (horiz.) .. 30 15

E 557. Palace of the Republic, Berlin.

**1976.** Opening of Palace of Republic, Berlin.

E 1836. E 557. 10 pf. mult. .. 50 10

E 558. Telecommunications Satellite Tracking Radar.

E 559. Marx, Engels, Lenin and Socialist Party Emblem.

**1976.** "Intersputnik".

E 1837. E 558. 20 pf. mult. .. 25 10

**1976.** 9th East German Socialist Party Congress.

E1838 E 559 10 pf. red, gold and deep red .. 20 10
E1839 – 20 pf. mult .. 30 10

DESIGN—HORIZ. 20 pf. Industrial site, housing complex and emblem.

E 560. Cycling.

**1976.** Olympic Games, Montreal. Mult.

E 1841. 5 pf. Type E 560 .. 10 10
E 1842. 10 pf. + 5 pf. Modern swimming pool .. 10 10
E 1843. 20 pf. Modern sports hall 10 10
E 1844. 25 pf. Regatta course .. 15 10
E 1845. 35 pf. + 10 pf. Rifle-range .. .. 20 15
E 1846. 70 pf. Athletics .. 1·75 1·10

E 561. Intertwined Ribbon and Emblem.

**1976.** 10th Youth Parliament Conference, Berlin. Multicoloured.

E 1848. 10 pf. Type E 561 .. 15 10
E 1849. 20 pf. Members of Youth Parliament and stylised industrial plant .. 30 15

E **562.** "Himantoglossum bircinum".

E **564.** Marx, Engels, Lenin and Red Flag.

E **563.** "Shetland Pony" (H. Drake).

**1976.** Flowers. Multicoloured.

E 1850. 10 pf. Type E **562** .. 10 10
E 1851. 20 pf. "Dactylorhiza incarnata" .. .. 10 10
E 1852. 25 pf. "Anacamptis pyramidalis" .. 15 10
E 1853. 35 pf. "Dactylorhiza sambucina" .. 25 15
E 1854. 40 pf. "Orchis coriophora" .. .. 30 15
E 1855. 50 pf. "Cypripedium calceolus" .. .. 2·75 2·25

**1976.** Statuettes from Berlin Museums.

E 1856. E **563.** 10 pf. blk. & blue 10 10
E 1857. – 20 pf. blk. & brn. 10 10
E 1858. – 25 pf. blk. & orge. 10 10
E 1859. – 35 pf. blk. & grn. 15 15
E 1860. – 50 pf. blk. & pink 1·25 1·00

STATUETTES—VERT. 20 pf. "Tanzpause" (W. Arnold); 25 pf. "Am Strand" (L. Englehardt); 35 pf. "Herman Duncker" (W. Howard); 50 pf. "Das Gesprach" (G. Weidanz).

**1976.** European Communist Parties' Conference.

E 1861. E **564.** 20 pf. blue, deep red and red .. 25 10

E **565.** State Carriage, 1790.

**1976.** 19th Century Horse-drawn Vehicles. Multicoloured.

E 1862. 10 pf. Type E **565** .. 10 10
E 1863. 20 pf. Russian trap, 1800 10 10
E 1864. 25 pf. Carriage, 1840 .. 10 10
E 1865. 35 pf. State carriage, 1860 10 10
E 1866. 40 pf. Stagecoach, 1850 15 15
E 1867. 50 pf. Carriage, 1889 .. 1·75 1·75

E **566.** Gera, circa 1652.

**1976.** National Philatelists' Day. Gera. Multicoloured.

E 1868. 10 pf. + 5 pf. Type E **566** 15 15
E 1869. 20 pf. Gera buildings .. 15 15

E **567.** Boxer.

**1976.** Domestic Dogs. Multicoloured.

E 1870. 5 pf. Type E **567** .. 10 10
E 1871. 10 pf. Airedale Terrier 10 10
E 1872. 20 pf. Alsatian .. 10 10
E 1873. 25 pf. Collie .. .. 10 10
E 1874. 35 pf. Schnauzer .. 15 10
E 1875. 70 pf. Great Dane .. 2·00 2·00

E **568.** Oil Refinery.

**1976.** Autumn Fair, Leipzig. Multicoloured.

E 1876. 10 pf. Type E **568** .. 15 10
E 1877. 25 pf. Library, Leipzig 25 10

E **569.** Templin Lake Bridge.

**1976.** East German Bridges. Multicoloured.

E 1878. 10 pf Type E **569** .. 15 10
E 1879. 15 pf. Adlergestell Bridge, Berlin .. 15 10
E 1880. 20 pf. Elbe River Bridge, Rosslau .. 20 10
E 1881. 25 pf. Goltzschtal Viaduct .. .. 20 10
E 1882. 35 pf. Elbe River Bridge, Magdeburg 30 15
E 1883. 50 pf. Grosser Dreesch Bridge, Scherwin .. 2·75 2·25

E **570.** Memorial Figures.

**1976.** Patriot's Memorial, Budapest.

E 1884. E **570.** 35 pf. mult. .. 30 10

E **571.** Brass Jug, c. 1500.

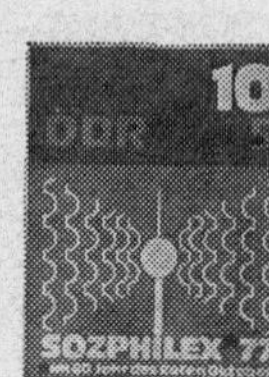


E **572.** Berlin T.V. Tower.

**1976.** Exhibits from Applied Arts Museum, Kopenick Castle, Berlin. Multicoloured.

E 1885. 10 pf. Type E **571** .. 10 10
E 1886. 20 pf. Faience covered vase, c. 1710 .. 10 10
E 1887. 25 pf. Porcelain "fruit-seller" table centre, c. 1768 .. .. 10 10
E 1888. 35 pf. Silver "basket-carrier" statuette, c. 1700 .. .. 10 10
E 1889. 70 pf. Coloured glass vase, c. 1900 .. 1·60 2·00

**1976.** "Sozphilex 77" Stamp Exhibition. East Berlin (1st issue).

E 1890. E **572.** 10 pf. + 5 pf. blue, black and red .. 20 10

See also Nos. E 1962/3.

E **573.** Pointed-tail Guppy.

E **575.** The Miller and the King.

E **574.** Clay Pots C. 3000 B.C.

**1976.** Aquarium Fishes – Guppies. Mult.

E 1891. 10 pf. Type E **573** .. 10 10
E 1892. 15 pf. Double-sword .. 10 10
E 1893. 20 pf. Flagtail .. 10 10
E 1894. 25 pf. Swordtail .. 10 10
E 1895. 35 pf. Triangle .. 15 10
E 1896. 70 pf. Roundtail .. 1·75 1·10

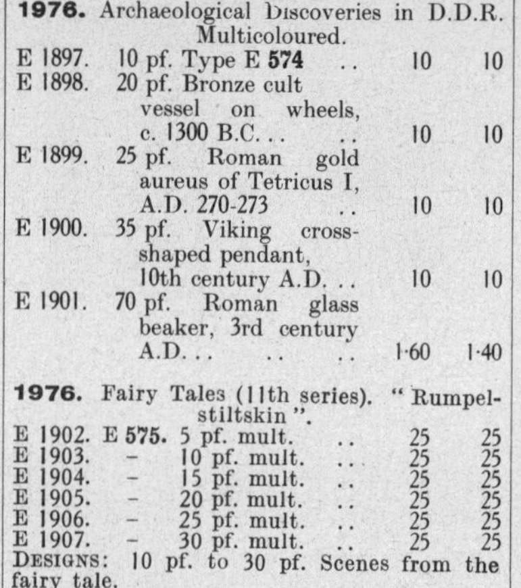

**1976.** Archaeological Discoveries in D.D.R. Multicoloured.

E 1897. 10 pf. Type E **574** .. 10 10
E 1898. 20 pf. Bronze cult vessel on wheels, c. 1300 B.C. .. .. 10 10
E 1899. 25 pf. Roman gold aureus of Tetricus I, A.D. 270-273 .. 10 10
E 1900. 35 pf. Viking cross-shaped pendant, 10th century A.D. .. 10 10
E 1901. 70 pf. Roman glass beaker, 3rd century A.D. .. .. .. 1·60 1·40

**1976.** Fairy Tales (11th series). "Rumpelstiltskin".

E 1902. E **575.** 5 pf. mult. .. 25 25
E 1903. – 10 pf. mult. .. 25 25
E 1904. – 15 pf. mult. .. 25 25
E 1905. – 20 pf. mult. .. 25 25
E 1906. – 25 pf. mult. .. 25 25
E 1907. – 30 pf. mult. .. 25 25

DESIGNS: 10 pf. to 30 pf. Scenes from the fairy tale.

E **576.** "The Air" (R. Carriera).

E **577.** Arnold Zweig (author).

**1976.** Paintings by Old Masters from the National Art Collection, Dresden. Mult.

E 1908. 10 pf. Type E **576** .. 10 10
E 1909. 15 pf. "Madonna and Child" (Murillo) .. 10 10
E 1910. 20 pf. "Viola Player" (B. Strozzi) .. .. 10 10
E 1911. 25 pf. "Ariadne Forsaken" (A. Kauffman) .. .. 10 10
E 1912. 35 pf. "Old Man in Black Cap" (B. Nazzari) .. 15 10
E 1913. 70 pf. "Officer reading a Letter" (G. Terborch) .. .. 1·50 95

**1977.** German Celebrities.

E1914 E **577** 10 pf. blk & pink 10 10
E1915 – 20 pf. blk & grey 10 10
E1916 – 35 pf. black & grn 10 10
E1917 – 40 pf. black & blue 75 50

DESIGNS: 20 pf. Otto von Guericke (scientist). 35 pf. Albrecht D. Thaer (agriculturalist). 40 pf. Gustav Hertz (physicist).

E **578.** Spring near Plaue, Thuringia.

E **579.** Book Fair Building.

**1977.** Natural Phenomena. Multicoloured.

E 1918. 10 pf. Type E **578** .. 10 10
E 1919. 20 pf. Rock face near Jonsdorf .. .. 10 10
E 1920. 25 pf. Oaks near Reuterstadt Stavenhagen 10 10
E 1921. 35 pf. Rocky ledge near Saalburg .. .. 10 10
E 1922. 50 pf. Erratic boulder near Furstenwalde/Spree .. .. 1·00 85

**1977.** Leipzig Spring Fair. Multicoloured.

E 1923. 10 pf. Type E **579** .. 10 10
E 1924. 25 pf. Aluminium casting machine .. 25 15

E **580.** Senftenberg Costume, Zly Komorrow.

E **581.** Carl Friedrich Gauss.

**1977.** Sorbian Historical Costumes. Mult.

E1925 10 pf. Type E **580** .. 10 10
E1926 20 pf. Bautzen, Budysin 10 10
E1927 25 pf. Klitten, Kletno 10 10
E1928 35 pf. Nochten, Wochozy 15 10
E1929 70 pf. Muskau, Muzakow 1·60 1·25

**1977.** Birth Bicentenary of Carl Friedrich Gauss (mathematician).

E 1930. E **581** 20 pf. black & blue 30 10

E **582.** Start of Race.

E **583.** Three Flags.

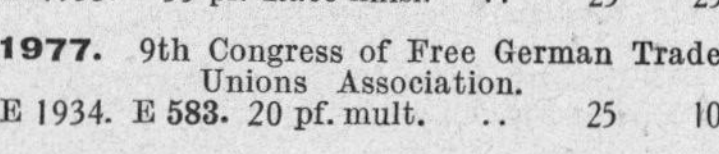

**1977.** 30th International Peace Cycle Race. Multicoloured.

E 1931. 10 pf. Type E **582** .. 25 25
E 1932. 20 pf. Spurt .. .. 25 25
E 1933. 35 pf. Race finish .. 25 25

**1977.** 9th Congress of Free German Trade Unions Association.

E 1934. E **583.** 20 pf. mult. .. 25 10

E **584.** VKM Channel Converter and Filters.

E **585.** Shooting.

**1977.** World Telecommunications Day.

E 1935. E **584.** 20 pf. black, blue and red .. 20 10

**1977.** 25th Anniv of Sports and Technical Sciences Association.

E 1936. E **585.** 10 pf. black, green and red .. 10 10
E 1937. – 20 pf. black, blue and mauve .. 10 10
E 1938. – 35 pf. black, pink and green .. 1·00 1·00

DESIGNS: 20 pf. Skin diving. 25 pf. Radio-controlled model boat.

E **586.** Accordion, 1900.

E **587.** "Bathsheba at the Fountain".

**1977.** Old Musical Instruments from Vogtland. Multicoloured.

E 1939. 10 pf. Type E **586** .. 10 10
E 1940. 20 pf. Treble viola da gamba, 1747 .. 10 10
E 1941. 25 pf. Oboe, 1785, Clarinet, 1830, Flute, 1817 .. .. .. 10 10
E 1942. 35 pf. Concert zither, 1891 .. .. .. 10 10
E 1943. 70 pf. Trumpet, 1860 .. 1·75 1·60

**1977.** 400th Birth Anniv of Peter Paul Rubens. Dresden Gallery Paintings. Mult.

E 1944. 10 pf. Type E **587** .. 10 10
E 1945. 15 pf. "Mercury and Argus" (horiz.) .. 10 10
E 1946. 20 pf. "The Drunk Hercules" .. .. 15 10
E 1947. 25 pf. "Diana's Return from Hunting" (horiz.) .. .. 15 10
E 1948. 35 pf. "The Old Woman with the Brazier" .. 30 10
E 1949. 50 pf. "Leda with the Swan" (horiz.) .. 2·50 2·10

E **589.** Tractor and Plough.

**1977.** Modern Agricultural Techniques. Multicoloured.

E 1951. 10 pf. Type E **589** .. 10 10
E 1952. 20 pf. Fertilizer spreader on truck .. .. 15 10
E 1953. 25 pf. Potato digger and loader .. .. 15 10
E 1954. 35 pf. High pressure collecting press .. 25 10
E 1955. 50 pf. Milking machine 2·50 1·75

E **590.** High Jump. E **591.** " Bread for Everybody " (Wolfram Schubert).

**1977.** 6th Gymnastics and Athletic Meeting and 6th Children and Young People's Sports Days, Leipzig. Multicoloured.

E 1956. 5 pf. Type E **590** .. 15 10
E 1957. 10 pf. + 5 pf. Running 15 10
E 1958. 20 pf. Hurdling .. 15 10
E 1959. 25 pf. + 5 pf. Gymnastics 15 10
E 1960. 35 pf. Dancing .. 20 10
E 1961. 40 pf. Torch bearer and flags .. .. .. 2·25 1·50

**1977.** " Sozphilex 77 " Stamp Exhibition, East Berlin (2nd issue). Multicoloured.

E 1962. 10 pf. Type E **591** .. 15 10
E 1963. 25 pf. "... when Communists are Dreaming " (Walter Womacka) 30 25

E **592.** " Konsument " Department Store, Leipzig.

**1977.** Leipzig Autumn Fair. Multicoloured.

E 1966. 10 pf. Type E **592** .. 10 10
E 1967. 25 pf. Carved bowl and Thuringian blown-glass vases .. .. 30 20

E **594.** Steam Locomotive " Muldenthal ", 1861.

**1977.** Transport Museum, Dresden. Mult.

E1969 5 pf. Type E **594** .. 20 10
E1970 10 pf. Dresden tram, 1896 .. .. .. 20 10
E1971 20 pf. Hans Grade's monoplane, 1909 .. 20 10
E1972 25 pf. Phanomobil tricar, 1924 .. .. 30 10
E1973 35 pf. River Elbe passenger steamer, 1837 .. .. .. 3·00 2·00

E **595.** Cruiser "Aurora".

**1977.** 60th Anniv. of October Revolution. Multicoloured.

E 1974 10 pf. Type E **595** .. 20 20
E 1975 25 pf. Assault on Winter Palace .. 30 20

E **596.** Soviet Memorial. E **597.** Flaming Torch.

**1977.** Soviet Memorial, Berlin-Schoenholz.

E 1977. E **596.** 35 pf. mult. 25 10

**1977.** " Solidarity ".

E 1978. E **597.** 10 pf. + 5 pf. mult. 20 10

E **598.** Ernst Meyer. E **600.** Rocket pointing Right.

**1977.** Socialist Personalities.

E 1979. E **598.** 10 pf. brown .. 10 10
E 1980. – 10 pf. red .. 10 10
E 1981. – 10 pf. blue .. 10 10

PERSONALITIES: No. E 1980, A. Frolich. No. E 1981, G. Eisler.

**1977.** 20th " Masters of Tomorrow " Fair, Leipzig.

E 1983. E **600.** 10 pf. red, silver and black .. 15 15
E 1984. – 20 pf. blue, gold and black .. 15 15

DESIGN: 20 pf. Rocket pointing left.

E **601.** Mouflon. E **602.** Firemen with Scaling Ladders.

**1977.** Hunting. Multicoloured.

E 1985. 10 pf. Type E **601** .. 10 10
E 1986. 15 pf. Red deer .. 3·00 2·50
E 1987. 20 pf. Shooting ring-necked pheasant .. 40 10
E 1988. 25 pf. Red fox and mallard .. .. 30 10
E 1989. 35 pf. Tractor driver with roe deer fawn 30 15
E 1990. 70 pf. Wild boars .. 50 20

**1977.** Fire Brigade. Multicoloured.

E1991 10 pf. Type E **602** .. 10 10
E1992 20 pf. Children visiting fire brigade (vert) .. 15 10
E1993 25 pf. Fire engines in countryside .. 15 10
E1994 35 pf. Artificial respiration (vert) .. 20 15
E1995 50 pf. Fire-fighting tug 2·50 2·00

E **603.** Traveller and King. E **605.** Amilcar Cabral.

E **604.** Rosehips.

**1977.** Fairy Tales (12th series). " Six World Travellers " (Brothers Grimm).

E 1996. E **603.** 5 pf. mult. .. 30 30
E 1997. – 10 pf. mult. .. 30 30
E 1998. – 20 pf. mult. .. 30 30
E 1999. – 25 pf. mult. .. 30 30
E 2000. – 35 pf. mult. .. 30 30
E 2001. – 60 pf. mult. .. 30 30

DESIGNS: 10 pf. to 60 pf. Scenes from the fairy tale.

**1978.** Medicinal Plants. Multicoloured.

E 2002. 10 pf. Type E **604** .. 10 10
E 2003. 15 pf. Birch leaves .. 10 10
E 2004. 20 pf. Camomile flowers .. .. 10 10
E 2005. 25 pf. Coltsfoot .. 10 10
E 2006. 35 pf. Lime flowers .. 15 10
E 2007. 50 pf. Elder flowers .. 1·60 1·50

**1978.** Amilcar Cabral (nationalist leader of Guinea-Bissau) Commemoration.

E 2008. E **605.** 20 pf. mult. .. 20 10

E **606.** Town Hall, Suhl-Heinrichs. E **608.** Ear-pendant, 11th century.

E **607.** Post Office Van, 1921.

**1978.** Half-timbered Buildings. Multicoloured.

E 2009. 10 pf. Type E **606** .. 10 10
E 2010. 20 pf. Farmhouse, Niederoderwitz .. 10 10
E 2011. 25 pf. Farmhouse, Strassen .. .. 10 10
E 2012. 35 pf. House, Quedlinburg .. .. .. 15 10
E 2013. 40 pf. House, Eisenach 1·40 1·25

**1978.** Postal Transport. Multicoloured.

E 2014. 10 pf. Type E **607** .. 15 15
E 2015. 20 pf. Postal truck, 1978 30 30
E 2016. 25 pf. Railway mail carriage, 1896 .. 60 60
E 2017. 35 pf. Railway mail carriage, 1978 .. 80 80

**1978.** Slavonic Treasures. Multicoloured.

E 2018. 10 pf. Type E **608** .. 10 10
E 2019. 20 pf. Ear-ring, 10th century .. .. 10 10
E 2020. 25 pf. Bronze tag, 10th century .. .. 10 10
E 2021. 35 pf. Bronze horse, 12th century .. .. 10 10
E 2022. 70 pf. Arabian coin, 8th century .. .. 1·40 1·25

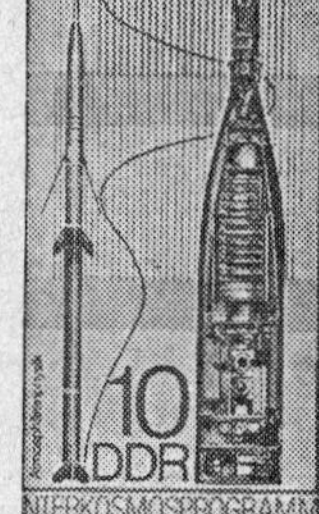


E **609.** " Royal House " Market Square, Leipzig. E **610.** "M-100" Meteorological Rocket.

**1978.** Leipzig Spring Fair.

E 2023. E **609.** 10 pf. yellow, black & red .. 15 10
E 2024. – 25 pf. green, blk. and red .. 30 20

DESIGN: 25 pf. Universal measuring instrument, UMK 10/1318.

**1978.** " Interkosmos " Space Programme. Multicoloured.

E 2025. 10 pf. Type E **610** .. 15 10
E 2026. 20 pf. " Interkosmos 1 " satellite .. 20 10
E 2027. 35 pf. " Meteor " satellite with Fourier spectrometer .. .. 1·00 65

E **611.** Samuel Heinicke (founder).

**1978.** Bicentenary of First National Deaf and Dumb Educational Institution.

E 2029. 20 pf. Type E **611** .. 10 10
E 2030. 25 pf. Child learning alphabet .. .. 70 70

E **612.** Radio-range Tower, Dequede, and Television Transmission Van. E **613.** Saxon miner in Gala Uniform.

**1978.** World Telecommunications Day. Mult.

E 2031. 10 pf. Type E **612** .. 10 10
E 2032. 20 pf. Equipment in Berlin television tower and Dresden television tower .. 25 20

**1978.** 19th-Century Gala Uniforms of Mining and Metallurgical Industries. Mult.

E 2033. 10 pf. Type E **613** .. 10 10
E 2034. 20 pf. Freiberg foundry worker .. .. 10 10
E 2035. 25 pf. School of Mining academician .. 10 10
E 2036. 35 pf. Chief Inspector of Mines .. .. 1·50 80

E **614.** Lion Cub. E **615.** Loading Container.

**1978.** Leipzig Zoo. Cent. Multicoloured.

E 2037. 10 pf. Type E **614** .. 10 10
E 2038. 20 pf. Leopard cub .. 15 10
E 2039. 35 pf. Tiger cub .. 20 10
E 2040. 50 pf. Snow leopard cub .. .. 1·60 95

**1978.** Container Goods Traffic. Multicoloured.

E 2041. 10 pf. Type E **615** .. 10 10
E 2042. 20 pf. Placing container on truck .. .. 10 10
E 2043. 35 pf. Container sidings 35 15
E 2044. 70 pf. Placing containers on "Boltenhagen" .. 1·90 1·90

E **616.** Clay Ox (Egyptian Museum, Leipzig).

**1978.** Ancient African Works of Art in Egyptian Museums at Leipzig and Berlin. Multicoloured.

E 2045. 5 pf. Type E **616** .. 10 10
E 2046. 10 pf. Clay head of woman (Leipzig) .. 10 10
E 2047. 20 pf. Gold bangle (Berlin) (horiz.) .. 10 10
E 2048. 25 pf. Gold ring plate (Berlin) .. 10 10
E 2049. 35 pf. Gold signet-ring plate (Berlin) .. 10 10
E 2050. 40 pf. Necklace (Berlin) (horiz.) .. .. 1·10 1·10

E **617.** Justus von Liebig (agricultural chemist, 175th birth anniv.)

**1978.** Celebrities' Birth Anniversaries.

E 2051. E **617.** 5 pf. black & ochre 10 10
E 2052. – 10 pf. blk. & blue 10 10
E 2053. – 15 pf. blk. & grn. 10 10
E 2054. – 20 pf. blk. & blue 10 10
E 2055. – 25 pf. blk. & red 10 10
E 2056. – 35 pf. blk. & grn. 10 10
E 2057. – 70 pf. blk. & drab 1·40 1·10

DESIGNS: 10 pf. Joseph Dietzgen (writer, 150th). 15 pf. Alfred Doblin (novelist, 100th). 20 pf. Hans Loch (politician, 80th). 25 pf. Theodor Brugsch (scientist, 100th). 35 pf. Friedrich Ludwig Jahn (gymnast, 200th). 70 pf. Albrecht von Graefe (ophthalmotician, 150th).

E 618. Cottbus, 1730.

**1978.** 5th National Youth Stamp Exhibition, Cottbus. Multicoloured.

E 2058. 10 pf.+5 pf. Type E 618 25 10
E 2059. 20 pf. Modern Cottbus 25 10

E 619. Havana Buildings and Festival Emblem.

**1978.** 11th World Youth and Students' Festival, Havana. Multicoloured.

E 2060. 20 pf. Type E 619 .. 30 30
E 2061. 35 pf. Festival emblem and East Berlin buildings .. .. 30 30

E 621. " Multicar 25 " Truck.

**1978.** Leipzig Autumn Fair. Multicoloured.

E2063 10 pf. Type E 621 .. 10 10
E2064 25 pf. "Three Kings" Fair building, Petersstrasse .. .. 25 20

E 622. "Soyuz" Spaceship and Emblems.

**1978.** Soviet–East German Space Flight (1st issue).

E 2065. E 622. 20 pf. mult. .. 40 10

See also Nos. E 2069/72

E 623. Mauthausen Memorial.

**1978.** War Victims' Memorial, Mauthausen, Austria.

E 2066. E 623. 35 pf. mult. .. 30 10

E 624. W.M.S.Unit on the March

**1978.** 25th Anniv. of Workers' Militia Squads.

E 2067. 20 pf. Type E 624 .. 40 40
E 2068. 35 pf. Members of Red Army, National People's Army and W.M.S. .. 40 40

E 625. "Soyuz" "MKF 6M" Camera and Space Station.

E 626. Human Pyramid.

**1978.** Soviet–East German Space Flight (2nd issue). Multicoloured.

E2069 5 pf. Type E 625 .. 10 10
E2070 10 pf. Albert Einstein and "Soyuz" .. 15 10
E2071 20 pf. Sigmund Jahn (first East German cosmonaut) (vert) .. 20 10
E2072 35 pf. "Salyut", "Soyuz" and Otto Lilienthal monoplane glider .. .. 1·25 1·10

**1978.** The Circus. Multicoloured.

E 2074. 5 pf. Type E 626 .. 15 30
E 2075. 10 pf. Elephant on tricycle .. .. .. 50 65
E 2076. 20 pf. Performing horse 70 85
E 2077. 35 pf. Polar bear kissing girl .. .. 1·50 1·60

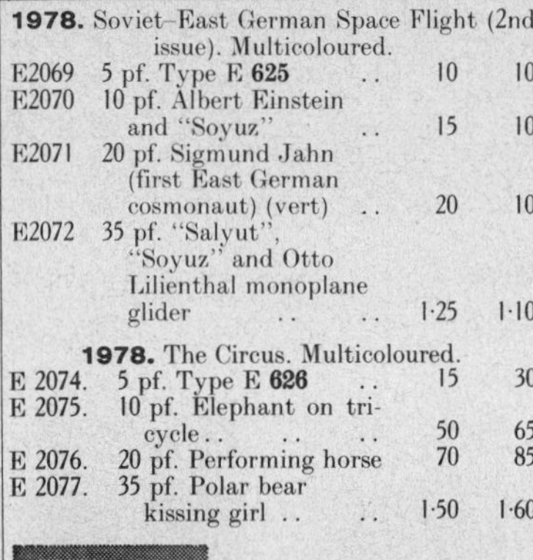


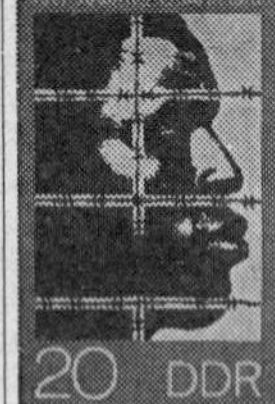

E 627. African behind Barbed Wire.

E 628. Construction of Natural Gas Pipe Line.

**1978.** International Anti-Apartheid Year.

E 2078. E 627. 20 pf. mult. .. 20 10

**1978.** Construction of " Friendship Line " (Drushba-Trasse) by East German Youth.

E 2079. E 628. 20 pf. mult. .. 30 10

E 629. "Papilio hahneli".

E 631. Old Woman and Youth.

E 630. Wheel-lock Gun, 1630.

**1978.** 250th Anniv. of Dresden Scientific Museums. Multicoloured.

E 2080. 10 pf. Type E 629 .. 20 10
E 2081. 20 pf. " Agama lehmanni " 20 10
E 2082. 25 pf. Agate .. .. 25 10
E 2083. 35 pf. " Palaeobatrachus diluvianus " .. 30 10
E 2084. 40 pf. Mantlepiece clock, c. 1720 .. .. 30 10
E 2085. 50 pf. Table telescope, c. 1750 .. .. 3·00 2·40

**1978.** Sporting Guns from Suhl. Multicoloured.

E 2086. 5 pf. Type E 630 .. 10 10
E 2087. 10 pf. Double-barrelled gun, 1978 .. .. 15 15
E 2088. 20 pf. Spring-cock gun, 1780.. .. .. 25 25
E 2089. 25 pf. Superimposed double-barrelled gun, 1978.. .. .. 40 40
E 2090. 35 pf. Percussion gun, 1850.. .. .. 50 50
E 2091. 70 pf. Three-barrelled gun, 1978 .. .. 1·10 1·10

**1978.** Fairy Tales. "Rapunzel". Multicoloured.

E 2092. 10 pf. Type E 631 .. 40 40
E 2093. 15 pf. Old Woman climbing tower on Rapunzel's hair .. .. .. 40 40
E 2094. 20 pf. Prince calling to Rapunzel .. .. 40 40
E 2095. 25 pf. Prince climbing through window .. 40 40
E 2096. 35 pf. Old woman about to cut Rapunzel's hair 40 40
E 2097. 50 pf. " Happy ever after " .. .. 40 40

E 632. Chaffinches.

E 633. Chabo.

**1979.** Songbirds. Multicoloured.

E2098 5 pf. Type E 632 .. 15 10
E2099 10 pf. European nuthatch .. .. 15 10
E2100 20 pf. European robin .. 20 10
E2101 25 pf. Common rosefinch 30 10
E2102 35 pf. Blue tit .. .. 45 15
E2103 50 pf. Linnet .. .. 3·75 2·25

**1979.** Poultry. Multicoloured.

E 2104. 10 pf. Type E 633 .. 15 10
E 2105. 15 pf. Crows head .. 15 10
E 2106. 20 pf. Porcelain-colour Feather-footed dwarf .. .. 15 10
E 2107. 25 pf. Saxonian .. 20 10
E 2108. 35 pf. Phoenix .. 25 10
E 2109. 50 pf. Striped Italian .. 2·50 2·10

E 634. Telephone Exchanges in 1900 and 1979.

**1979.** Telephone and Telegraphs Communications. Multicoloured.

E 2110. 20 pf. Type E 634 .. 10 10
E 2111. 35 pf. Transmitting telegrams in 1800 and 1979 .. .. 75 45

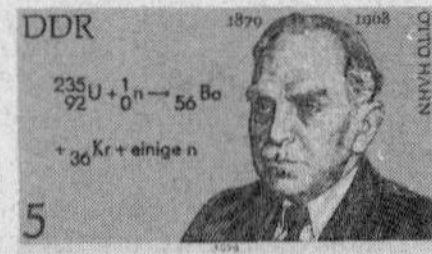


E 636. Max Klinger Exhibition House, Leipzig.

E 637. Otto Hahn (physicist, centenary).

**1979.** Leipzig Spring Fair. Multicoloured.

E 2113. 10 pf. Type E 636 .. 15 10
E 2114. 25 pf. Horizontal drill and milling machine 30 20

**1979.** Celebrities' Birth Anniversaries.

E 2115. E 637. 5 pf. blk. & pink 10 10
E 2116. – 10 pf. blk. & blue 10 10
E 2117. – 20 pf. blk. & yell. 10 10
E 2118. – 25 pf. blk. & grn. 10 10
E 2119. – 35 pf. blk. & blue 25 15
E 2120. – 70 pf. blk. & pink 1·25 1·10

DESIGNS: 10 pf. Max von Laue (physicist, centenary). 20 pf. Arthur Scheunert (physiologist, centenary). 25 pf. Friedrich August Kekule (chemist, 150th). 35 pf. Georg Forster (explorer and writer, 225th). 70 pf. Gotth Ephraim Lessing (playwright and essayist, 250th).

E 638. "Radebeul" (container ship), Tug and Shipping Route Map.

**1979.** World Navigation Day.

E 2121. E 638. 20 pf. multicoloured 40 25

E 639. Horch " 8 ", 1911.

**1979.** Zwickau Motor Industry. Multicoloured.

E 2122. 20 pf. Type E 639 .. 50 30
E 2123. 35 pf. Trabant " 601 S de luxe ", 1978 .. 80 60

E 640. " MXA " Electric Locomotive.

**1979.** East German Locomotives and Wagons. Multicoloured.

E 2124. 5 pf. Type E 640 .. 10 10
E 2125. 10 pf. Self-discharging wagon .. .. 10 10
E 2126. 20 pf. Diesel locomotive " BR 110 " .. .. 20 10
E 2127. 35 pf. Railway car transporter .. 2·40 2·00

E 641. Durga (18th century).

E 642. Children Playing.

**1979.** Indian Miniatures. Multicoloured.

E 2128. 20 pf. Type E 641 .. 10 10
E 2129. 35 pf. Mahavira (15th/16th century) .. 15 10
E 2130. 50 pf. Todi Ragini (17th century) .. .. 20 15
E 2131. 70 pf. Asavari Ragini (17th century) .. 1·90 1·50

**1979.** International Year of the Child. Multicoloured.

E 2132. 10 pf. Type E 642 .. 10 10
E 2133. 20 pf. Overseas aid for children .. .. 55 35

E 643. Construction Work on Leipziger Strasse Complex.

**1979.** " Berlin Project " of Free German Youth Organization. Multicoloured.

E 2134. 10 pf. Type E 643 .. 10 10
E 2135. 20 pf. Berlin-Marzahn building site .. 40 25

E 644. Torch-light Procession of Free German Youth, 1949.

**1979.** National Youth Festival. Mult.

E 2136. 10 pf.+5 pf. Type E 644 25 20
E 2137. 20 pf. Youth rally .. 25 20

E 645. Exhibition Symbol.

**1979.** " agra 79 " Agricultural Exhibition, Markkleeberg.

E 2138. E 645. 10 pf. mult. .. 20 10

E 646. Train Ferry " Rostock ".

**1979.** 70th Anniv. of Sassnitz–Trelleborg Railway Ferry. Multicoloured.

E 2139. 20 pf. Type E 646 .. 65 65
E 2140. 35 pf. Train ferry "Rugen" .. .. 65 65

E 647. Hospital Classroom.

**1979.** Rehabilitation. Multicoloured.

E 2141. 10 pf. Type E 647 .. 10 10
E 2142. 35 pf. Wheelchair-bound factory worker 50 35

E 648. Cycling.

**1979.** 7th Children's and Young People's Sports Day, Berlin. Multicoloured.
E 2143. 10 pf. Type E 648 .. 15 10
E 2144. 20 pf. Roller-skating .. 50 40

E 649. Dahlia "Rubens". E 650. Goose-thief Fountain, Dresden.

**1979.** "iga" International Garden Exhibition, Erfurt. Dahlias. Multicoloured.
E 2145. 10 pf. Type E 649 .. 10 10
E 2146. 20 pf. "Rosalie" .. 10 10
E 2147. 25 pf. "Corinna" .. 10 10
E 2148. 35 pf. "Enzett-Dolli" 15 10
E 2149. 50 pf. "Enzett-Carola" 25 15
E 2150. 70 pf. "Don Lorenzo" 2·75 2·10

**1979.** National Stamp Exhibition, Dresden. Multicoloured.
E 2151. 10 pf.+5 pf. Type E 650 50 30
E 2152. 20 pf. Dandelion fountain, Dresden .. 10 10

E 651. World Map and Russian Alphabet.

**1979.** 4th International Congress of Russian Language and Literature Teachers, Berlin.
E 2154. E 651. 20 pf. multicoloured 15 10

E 652. Italian Lira de Gamba, 1592.

**1979.** Musical Instruments in Leipzig Museum. Multicoloured.
E 2155. 20 pf. Type E 652 .. 15 10
E 2156. 25 pf. French serpent, 17th/18th century .. 20 10
E 2157. 40 pf. French barrel-lyre, 1750 .. .. 25 10
E 2158. 85 pf. German tenor flugelhorn, 1850 .. 3·00 1·50

E 653. Horseracing.

**1979.** 30th International Congress on Horse-breeding in Socialist Countries, Berlin. Multicoloured.
E 2159. 10 pf. Type E 653 .. 15 10
E 2160. 25 pf. Dressage (pas de deux) .. .. 1·00 50

## MINIMUM PRICE

The minimum price quoted is 10p which represents a handling charge rather than a basis for valuing common stamps. For further notes about prices see introductory pages.

E 654. Mittelbau-Dora Memorial. E 655. Teddy Bear.

**1979.** Mittelbau-Dora Memorial. Nordhausen.
E 2161. E 654. 35 pf. blk. & vio. 30 10

**1979.** Leipzig Autumn Fair. Multicoloured.
E 2162. 10 pf. Type E 655 .. 10 10
E 2163. 25 pf. Grosser Blumenberg building, Richard Wagner Square .. 35 10

E 656. Philipp Dengel. E 657. Building Worker and Flats.

**1979.** Socialist Personalities.
E2164 E 656 10 pf. black, green and deep green 15 10
E2165 – 10 pf. black, blue and indigo .. 15 10
E2166 – 10 pf. black, stone and bistre .. 15 10
E2167 – 10 pf. black, red and brown .. 15 10
DESIGNS: No. E2165, Otto Buchwitz. No. E2166, Bernard Koenen. No. E2167, Heinrich Rau.

**1979.** 30th Anniv. of German Democratic Republic. Multicoloured.
E 2168. 5 pf. Type E 657 .. 10 10
E 2169. 10 pf. Boy and girl .. 10 10
E 2170. 15 pf. Soldiers .. 50 35
E 2171. 20 pf. Miner and Soviet soldier .. .. 10 10

E 658. Girl applying Lipstick (1966/7). E 659. Vietnamese Soldier, Mother and Child.

**1979.** Meissen Porcelain. Multicoloured.
E 2173. 5 pf. Type E 658 .. 10 10
E 2174. 10 pf. "Altozier" coffee pot (18th cent.) .. 10 10
E 2175. 15 pf. "Gosser Ausschnitt" coffee pot (1973/4) 25 20
E 2176. 20 pf. Vase with lid (18th century) .. 30 25
E 2177. 25 pf. Parrot with cherry (18th century) .. 40 25
E 2178. 35 pf. Harlequin with tankard (18th century) 50 50
E 2179. 50 pf. Flower girl (18th century) .. .. 80 70
E 2180. 70 pf. Sake bottle (18th century) .. .. 1·25 1·00

**1979.** "Invincible Vietnam".
E 2181. E 659. 10 pf.+5 pf. black and red .. 20 10

E 660. Rag-doll, 1800. E 661. "Balance on Ice" (Johanna Starke).

**1979.** Dolls. Multicoloured.
E 2182. 10 pf. Type E 660 .. 35 35
E 2183. 15 pf. Ceramic doll, 1960 35 35
E 2184. 20 pf. Wooden doll, 1780 35 35
E 2185. 35 pf. Straw puppet, 1900.. .. .. 35 35
E 2186. 50 pf. Jointed doll, 1800 35 35
E 2187. 70 pf. Tumbler-doll, 1820.. .. .. 35 35

**1980.** Winter Olympic Games, Lake Placid. Multicoloured.
E 2188. 10 pf. "Bobsleigh Start" (Gunter Rechn) (horiz.) .. 10 10
E 2189. 20 pf. Type E 661 .. 10 10
E 2190. 25 pf.+10 pf. "Ski jumpers" (plastic sculpture, Gunter Schultz) .. .. 15 10
E 2191. 35 pf. "Speed Skaters at the Start" (Axel Wunsch) .. .. 1·00 70

E 662. Stille Musik Rock Garden, Grosssedlitz.

**1980.** Baroque Gardens. Multicoloured.
E 2193. 10 pf. Type E 662 .. 10 10
E 2194. 20 pf. Belvedere Orangery, Weimar .. 10 10
E 2195. 50 pf. Flower garden, Dornburg Castle .. 20 15
E 2196. 70 pf. Park, Rheinsberg Castle .. .. 1·25 1·25

E 663. Cable-laying Machine and Dish Aerial.

**1980.** Post Office Activities. Multicoloured.
E 2212. 10 pf. Type E 663 .. 10 10
E 2213. 20 pf. T.V. Tower, Berlin, and television .. 20 15

E 664. Johann Wolfgang Dobereiner (chemist, Bicent).

**1980.** Celebrities. Birth Anniversaries.
E 2214. E 664. 5 pf. blk. & bistre 15 10
E 2215. – 10 pf. blk. & red 25 10
E 2216. – 20 pf. blk. & grn. 60 10
E 2217. – 25 pf. blk. & blue 20 10
E 2218. – 35 pf. blk. & blue 25 15
E 2219. – 70 pf. blk. & red 1·75 1·00
DESIGNS: 10 pf. Frederic Joliot-Curie (physicist, and chemist, 80th anniv.). 20 pf. Johann Friedrich Naumann (zoologist, bicent.) 25 pf. Alfred Wegener (explorer and geophysicist, cent.). 35 pf. Carl von Clausewitz (Prussian general, bicent.). 70 pf. Helene Weigel (actress, 80th anniv.).

E 665. Karl Marx University, Leipzig. E 666. Werner Eggerath.

**1980.** Leipzig Spring Fair. Multicoloured.
E 2220. 10 pf. Type E 665 .. 10 10
E 2221. 25 pf. "ZT 303" tractor 25 20

**1980.** 80th Birth Anniv. of Werner Eggerath (socialist).
E 2222. E 666. 10 pf. brown and red .. .. 30 10

E 668. "On the Horizontal Beam" (sculpture, Erich Wurzer).

**1980.** Olympic Games, Moscow (1st issue). Multicoloured.
E 2224. 10 pf. Type E 668 .. 10 10
E 2225. 20 pf.+5 pf. "Runners before the Winning Post" (Lothar Zitzmann) .. .. 10 10
E 2226. 50 pf. "Coxless Four" (Wilfred Falkenthal). 95 65
See also Nos. 2247/9.

E 669. Flags of Member States. E 670. Co-operative Society Building (W. Gropius).

**1980.** 25th Anniv. of Warsaw Pact.
E 2227. E 669. 20 pf. multicoloured 30 10

**1980.** Bauhaus Architecture. Multicoloured.
E 2228. 5 pf. Type E 670 .. 10 10
E 2229. 10 pf. Socialists' Memorial Place (M. v. d. Rhode) (horiz.) .. 10 10
E 2230. 15 pf. Monument to the Fallen of March 1922 (W. Gropius) .. 10 10
E 2231. 20 pf. Steel Building 1926 (G. Muche and R. Paulick) (horiz.) 10 10
E 2232. 50 pf. Trade Union school (H. Meyer) .. 20 15
E 2233. 70 pf. Bauhaus building (W. Gropius) (horiz.) .. 1·75 1·10

E 671. Rostock Buildings.

**1980.** 18th Workers' Festival, Rostock. Multicoloured.
E 2234. 10 pf. Type E 671 .. 10 10
E 2235. 20 pf. Costumed dancers 20 10

E 672. Radar Complex, Berlin-Schoenefeld Airport.

**1980.** "Aerosozphilex 1980" International Airmail Exhibition, Berlin. Multicoloured.
E2236 20 pf. Type E 672 .. 40 40
E2237 25 pf. Ilyushin Il-62M at Schonfeld Airport .. 50 50
E2238 35 pf. PZL-106A Kruk crop-spraying airplane 60 60
E2239 70 pf. Antonov An-2 aerial photography biplane and multispectrum camera 1·25 1·25

E 673. Okapi.

**1980.** Endangered Animals. Multicoloured.
E2241 5 pf. Type E 673 .. 15 10
E2242 10 pf. Lesser pandas .. 15 10
E2243 15 pf. Maned wolf .. 20 10
E2244 20 pf. Arabian oryx .. 25 10
E2245 25 pf. White-eared pheasant .. .. 60 15
E2246 35 pf. Musk oxen .. 2·75 1·75

**1980.** Olympic Games, Moscow (2nd issue). As Type E **668**. Multicoloured.

| | | | |
|---|---|---|---|
| E 2247. | 10 pf. "Judo" (Erhard Schmidt) .. .. | 10 | 10 |
| E 2248. | 20 pf. + 10 pf. "Swimmer" (Willi Sitte) (vert.) .. | 15 | 10 |
| E 2249. | 50 pf. "Spurt" (sculpture, Siegfried Schreiber) .. .. | 1·25 | 75 |

E **674**. Suhl, 1700.

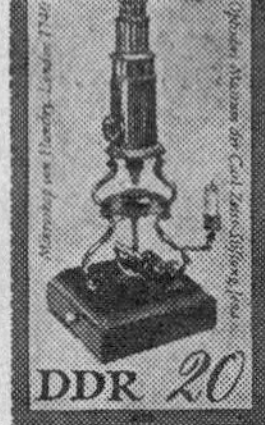
E **675**. Huntley Microscope.

**1980.** Sixth National Youth Stamp Exhibition, Suhl. Multicoloured.

| | | | |
|---|---|---|---|
| E 2251. | 10 pf. + 5 pf. Type E **674** | 25 | 25 |
| E 2252. | 20 pf. Modern Suhl .. | 25 | 25 |

**1980.** Carl Zeiss Optical Museum, Jena. Mult.

| | | | |
|---|---|---|---|
| E2253 | 20 pf. Type E **675** .. | 30 | 15 |
| E2254 | 25 pf. Magny microscope, 1751 .. .. | 30 | 30 |
| E2255 | 35 pf. Amici microscope, 1845 .. .. .. | 65 | 30 |
| E2256 | 70 pf. Zeiss microscope, 1873 .. .. .. | 65 | 65 |

E **676**. Majdanek Memorial.

**1980.** War Victims' Memorial, Majdanek, Poland.

| | | | |
|---|---|---|---|
| E 2257. | E **676**. 35 pf. multicoloured | 40 | 15 |

E **677**. Information Centre, Leipzig.

**1980.** Leipzig Autumn Fair. Multicoloured.

| | | | |
|---|---|---|---|
| E 2258. | 10 pf. Type E **677** .. | 10 | 10 |
| E 2259. | 25 pf. Carpet-knitting machine .. | 30 | 10 |

E **678**. Palace of Republic, Berlin.

**1980.** 67th Interparliamentary Conference, Berlin.

| | | | |
|---|---|---|---|
| E2260 | E **678** 20 pf. mult .. | 60 | 10 |

E **679**. " Laughing Boy with Flute ".

E **680**. Clenched Fist and Star.

**1980.** 400th Anniv. of Frans Hals (artist). Multicoloured.

| | | | |
|---|---|---|---|
| E 2261. | 10 pf. Type E **679** .. | 10 | 10 |
| E 2262. | 20 pf. "Portrait of Young Man in Drab Coat" .. .. | 10 | 10 |
| E 2263. | 25 pf. "The Mulatto" | 10 | 10 |
| E 2264. | 35 pf. "Portrait of Young Man in Black Coat" .. .. | 80 | 60 |

**1980.** " Solidarity ".

| | | | |
|---|---|---|---|
| E 2266. | E **680**. 10 pf. + 5 pf. turquoise and red | 20 | 10 |

E **681**. Red Cap.

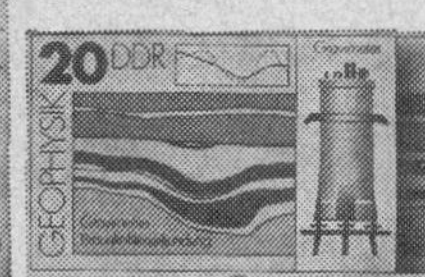
E **682**. Gravimetry.

**1980.** Edible Mushrooms. Multicoloured.

| | | | |
|---|---|---|---|
| E2267 | 5 pf. Type E **681** .. | 10 | 10 |
| E2268 | 10 pf. Flaky-stemmed witches' mushroom .. | 10 | 10 |
| E2269 | 15 pf. Field mushroom | 45 | 15 |
| E2270 | 20 pf. Chestnut mushroom .. .. | 15 | 10 |
| E2271 | 35 pf. Cep .. .. | 20 | 10 |
| E2272 | 70 pf. Chanterelle .. | 2·50 | 1·50 |

**1980.** Geophysics. Multicoloured.

| | | | |
|---|---|---|---|
| E 2273. | 20 pf. Type E **682** .. | 25 | 25 |
| E 2274. | 25 pf. Bore-hole measuring .. .. .. | 30 | 30 |
| E 2275. | 35 pf. Seismic prospecting .. .. .. | 50 | 50 |
| E 2276. | 50 pf. Seismology .. | 65 | 65 |

E **683**. Radebeul-Radeburg Locomotive.

E **684**. Toy Steam Locomotive, 1850.

**1980.** Narrow-gauge Railways (1st series). Multicoloured.

| | | | |
|---|---|---|---|
| E 2277. | 20 pf. Type E **683** .. | 1·00 | 60 |
| E 2278. | 20 pf. Bad Doberan-Ostseebad Kuhlungsborn locomotive .. | 1·00 | 60 |
| E 2279. | 25 pf. Radebeul-Radeburg passenger carriage | 1·00 | 60 |
| E 2280. | 35 pf. Bad Doberan-Ostseebad Kuhlungsborn passenger carriage | 1·00 | 60 |

See also Nos. E2342/5, E2509/12 and E2576/9.

**1980.** Historical Toys. Multicoloured.

| | | | |
|---|---|---|---|
| E 2281. | 10 pf. Type E **684** .. | 45 | 45 |
| E 2282. | 20 pf. Aeroplane, 1914 | 45 | 45 |
| E 2283. | 25 pf. Steam-roller, 1920 | 45 | 45 |
| E 2284. | 35 pf. Sailing ship, 1825 | 45 | 45 |
| E 2285. | 40 pf. Car, 1900 .. | 45 | 45 |
| E 2286. | 50 pf. Balloon, 1920 .. | 45 | 45 |

E **686**. " Malus pumila ".

E **687**. Heinrich von Stephan.

**1981.** Rare Plants in Berlin Arboretum. Multicoloured.

| | | | |
|---|---|---|---|
| E 2288. | 5 pf. Type E **686** .. | 10 | 10 |
| E 2289. | 10 pf. "Halesia carolina" (horiz.) .. | 10 | 10 |
| E 2290. | 20 pf. "Colutea arborescens" .. .. | 10 | 10 |
| E 2291. | 25 pf. "Paulownia tomentosa" .. .. | 10 | 10 |
| E 2292. | 35 pf. "Lonicera periclymenum" (horiz.) .. .. | 20 | 10 |
| E 2293. | 50 pf. "Calycanthus floridus" .. .. | 1·75 | 1·60 |

**1981.** 150th Birth Anniv. of Heinrich von Stephan (founder of U.P.U.).

| | | | |
|---|---|---|---|
| E 2294. | E **687**. 10 pf. blk. & yell. | 25 | 10 |

E **688**. Soldiers on Parade.

**1981.** 25th Anniv. of National People's Army. Multicoloured.

| | | | |
|---|---|---|---|
| E 2295. | 10 pf. Type E **688** .. | 15 | 10 |
| E 2296. | 20 pf. Marching soldiers | 20 | 15 |

E **689**. Marx and Lenin.

**1981.** 10th East German Socialist Party Congress (1st series).

| | | | |
|---|---|---|---|
| E 2297. | E **689**. 10 pf. mult. .. | 15 | 10 |

See Nos. 2309/12.

E **690**. Counter Clerks.

**1981.** Post Office Training. Multicoloured.

| | | | |
|---|---|---|---|
| E 2298. | 5 pf. Type E **690** .. | 10 | 10 |
| E 2299. | 10 pf. Telephone engineers .. .. | 10 | 10 |
| E 2300. | 15 pf. Radio communications .. | 10 | 10 |
| E 2301. | 20 pf. Rosa Luxemburg Engineering School, Leipzig .. .. | 10 | 10 |
| E 2302. | 25 pf. Friedrich List Communications School, Dresden | 1·10 | 65 |

E **691**. Erich Baron.

E **692**. Hotel Merkur Leipzig.

**1981.** Socialist Personalities.

| | | | |
|---|---|---|---|
| E 2303. | E **691**. 10 pf. blk. & grn. | 10 | 10 |
| E 2304. | – 10 pf. blk. & yell. | 10 | 10 |
| E 2305. | – 10 pf. blk. & blue | 10 | 10 |
| E 2306. | – 10 pf. blk. & brn. | 10 | 10 |

DESIGNS: No. E 2304, Conrad Blenkle. No. 2305, Arthur Ewert. No. 2306, Walter Stoecker.

**1981.** Leipzig Spring Fair. Multicoloured.

| | | | |
|---|---|---|---|
| E 2307. | 10 pf. Type E **692** .. | 15 | 10 |
| E 2308. | 25 pf. Open-cast mining machine .. .. | 35 | 20 |

E **693**. " Ernst Thalmann " (Willi Sitte).

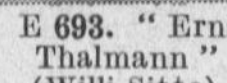
E **695**. Plugs and Socket.

**1981.** 10th East German Socialist Party Congress (2nd series). Multicoloured.

| | | | |
|---|---|---|---|
| E 2309. | 10 pf. Type E **693** .. | 10 | 10 |
| E 2310. | 20 pf. " Brigadier " (Bernhard Heisig) .. | 10 | 10 |
| E 2311. | 25 pf. " Festival Day " (Rudolf Bergander) | 75 | 60 |
| E 2312. | 35 pf. " Comrades in Arms " (Paul Michaelis) | 15 | 10 |

**1981.** Conservation of Energy.

| | | | |
|---|---|---|---|
| E 2315. | E **695**. 10 pf. blk. & orge. | 15 | 10 |

E **696**. Heinrich Barkhausen.

**1981.** Celebrities' Birth Anniversaries.

| | | | |
|---|---|---|---|
| E 2316. | E **696**. 10 pf. blk. & blue | 10 | 10 |
| E 2317. | – 20 pf. blk. & red | 10 | 10 |
| E 2318. | – 25 pf. blk. & brn. | 2·00 | 1·10 |
| E 2319. | – 35 pf. blk. & vio. | 15 | 10 |
| E 2320. | – 50 pf. blk. & grn. | 20 | 10 |
| E 2321. | – 70 pf. blk. & brn. | 20 | 15 |

DESIGNS: 10 pf. Type E **696** (physicist, birth centenary). 20 pf. Johannes R. Becher (writer, 90th birth anniv.). 25 pf. Richard Dedekind (mathematician, 150th birth anniv.). 35 pf. Georg Philipp Telemann (composer, 300th anniv.). 50 pf. Adelbert V. Chamisso (poet and naturalist, bicentenary). 70 pf. Wilhelm Raabe (novelist, 150th birth anniv.).

E **697**. Free German Youth Members and Banner.

E **698**. Worlitz Park.

**1981.** 11th Free German Youth Parliament. Multicoloured.

| | | | |
|---|---|---|---|
| E 2322. | 10 pf. Type E **697** .. | 15 | 15 |
| E 2323. | 20 pf. Free German Youth members instructing foreign students | 15 | 15 |

**1981.** Landscaped Parks. Multicoloured.

| | | | |
|---|---|---|---|
| E 2324. | 5 pf. Type E **698** .. | 10 | 10 |
| E 2325. | 10 pf. Tiefurt Park, Weimar .. .. | 10 | 10 |
| E 2326. | 15 pf. Marxwalde .. | 10 | 10 |
| E 2327. | 20 pf. Branitz Park .. | 10 | 10 |
| E 2328. | 25 pf. Treptow Park, Berlin .. .. | 1·50 | 1·00 |
| E 2329. | 35 pf. Wiesenburg Park | 20 | 15 |

E **699**. Children at Play and Sport.

**1981.** 8th Children's and Young People's Sports Days, Berlin. Multicoloured.

| | | | |
|---|---|---|---|
| E 2330. | 10 pf. + 5 pf. Type E **699** | 55 | 35 |
| E 2331. | 20 pf. Artistic gymnastics | 10 | 10 |

E **700**. Berlin Theatre.

**1981.** Birth Bicentenary of Karl Friedrich Schinkel (architect).

| | | | |
|---|---|---|---|
| E 2332. | E **700**. 10 pf. stone & blk. | 65 | 15 |
| E 2333. | – 25 pf. stone & blk. | 1·60 | 65 |

DESIGN: 25 pf. Old Museum, Berlin.

E **701**. Throwing the Javelin from a Wheel chair.

E **702**. House, Zaulsdorf.

**1981.** International Year of Disabled Persons. Multicoloured.

| | | | |
|---|---|---|---|
| E 2334. | 5 pf. Type E **701** | 15 | 15 |
| E 2335. | 15 pf. Disabled people in art gallery .. | 15 | 15 |

**1981.** Half-timbered Buildings. Mult.

| | | | |
|---|---|---|---|
| E 2336. | 10 pf. Type E **702** .. | 10 | 10 |
| E 2337. | 20 pf. "Sugar-loaf" cottage, Gross Zicker (horiz.) .. .. | 15 | 10 |
| E 2338. | 25 pf. Farmhouse, Weckersdorf .. | 20 | 10 |
| E 2339. | 35 pf. House, Pillgram (horiz.) .. .. | 25 | 15 |
| E 2340. | 50 pf. House, Eschenbach .. .. | 30 | 15 |
| E 2341. | 70 pf. House, Ludersdorf (horiz.) .. | 3·50 | 2·25 |

**1981.** Narrow-Gauge Railways (2nd series). As Type E **683**. Multicoloured.

| | | | |
|---|---|---|---|
| E2342 | 5 pf. black and red .. | 45 | 45 |
| E2343 | 5 pf. black and red .. | 45 | 45 |
| E2344 | 15 pf. multicoloured .. | 45 | 45 |
| E2345 | 20 pf. multicoloured .. | 45 | 45 |

DESIGNS: Nos. E2342, Freital–Kurort Kipsdorf locomotive. E2343, Putbus–Gohren locomotive. E2344, Freital–Kurort Kipsdorf luggage van. E2345, Putbus–Gohren passenger carriage.

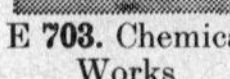
E 703. Chemical Works.

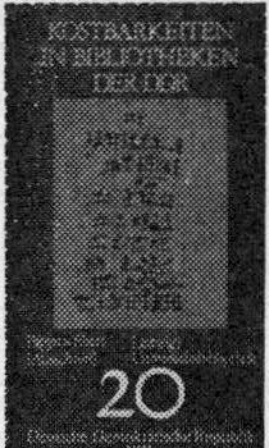
E 704. Ebers Papyrus (Leipzig University Library).

**1981.** Leipzig Autumn Fair. Multicoloured.
E2346 10 pf. Type E 703 .. 10 10
E2347 25 pf. New Draper's Hall (horiz) .. .. 35 25

**1981.** Precious Books from East German Libraries. Multicoloured.
E 2348. 20 pf. Type E 704 .. 10 10
E 2349. 35 pf. Maya manuscript (Dresden Library) .. 20 10
E 2350. 50 pf. Miniature from "Les six visions Messire Francoys Petrarque" (Berlin State Library) .. .. 1·25 80

E 705. Sassnitz Memorial.

E 706. Henbane and Incense Burner.

**1981.** Resistance Fighters' Memorial, Sassnitz.
E 2351. E 705. 35 pf. multicoloured 40 10

**1981.** Early Medical Equipment in the Karl-Sudhoff Institute, Leipzig. Mult.
E 2352. 10 pf. Type E 706 .. 10 10
E 2353. 20 pf. Dental instruments .. .. 10 10
E 2354. 25 pf. Forceps .. .. 10 10
E 2355. 35 pf. Bladder knife and hernia shears .. 20 10
E 2356. 50 pf. Speculum and gynaecological forceps (vert.) .. 2·10 1·50
E 2357. 85 pf. Triploid elevators (vert.) .. 35 15

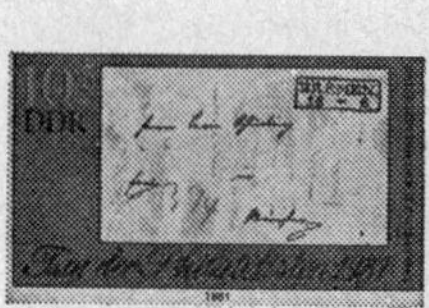
E 707. Letter from Friedrich Engels, 1840.

E 708. African breaking Chains.

**1981.** Stamp Day. Multicoloured.
E 2358. 10 pf. + 5 pf. Type E 707 65 40
E 2359. 20 pf. Postcard from Karl Marx, 1878 .. 15 10

**1981.** "Solidarity".
E2360 E 708 10 pf. + 5 pf. mult 20 10

E 709. Tug.

E 710. Windmill, Dabel.

**1981.** Inland Shipping. Multicoloured.
E2361 10 pf. Type E 709 .. 10 10
E2362 20 pf. Tug and barges .. 10 10
E2363 25 pf. Diesel-electric paddle-ferry on the Elbe .. .. 15 10
E2364 35 pf. Ice-breaker in the Oder estuary .. 20 10
E2365 50 pf. Motor barge "Schonewalde" .. 25 20
E2366 85 pf. Dredger .. .. 3·00 2·75

**1981.** Windmills. Multicoloured.
E 2367. 10 pf. Type E 710 .. 10 10
E 2368. 20 pf. Pahrenz .. 10 10
E 2369. 25 pf. Dresden-Gohlis 10 10
E 2370. 70 pf. Ballstadt .. 1·40 1·10

E 711. Snake, 1850.

E 712. Coffee Pot, 1715.

**1981.** Historical Toys. Multicoloured.
E2371 10 pf. Type E 711 .. 50 50
E2372 20 pf. Teddy bear, 1910 50 50
E2373 25 pf. Goldfish, 1935 .. 50 50
E2374 35 pf. Hobby-horse, 1850 50 50
E2375 40 pf. Pull-along duck, 1800 .. .. .. 50 50
E2376 70 pf. Clockwork frog, 1930 .. .. .. 50 50

**1982.** 300th Birth Anniv. of Johann Friedrich Bottger (founder of Meissen China Works). Multicoloured.
E 2377. 10 pf. Type E 712 .. 15 15
E 2378. 20 pf. Vase decorated with flowers, 1715 .. 30 30
E 2379. 25 pf. "Oberon" (figurine), 1969 .. 40 40
E 2380. 35 pf. Vase "Day and Night", 1979 .. 60 60

E 713. Post Office, Bad Liebenstein.

**1982.** Post Office Building. Multicoloured.
E 2382. 20 pf. Type E 713 .. 10 10
E 2383. 25 pf. Telecommunications Centre, Berlin 10 10
E 2384. 35 pf. Head Post Office, Erfurt .. 20 10
E 2385. 50 pf. Head Post Office, Dresden 6 .. 1·25 1·00

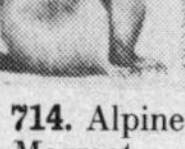
E 714. Alpine Marmot.

E 718. Max Fechner.

E 716. West Entrance to Fairground.

**1982.** International Fur Auction, Leipzig. Multicoloured.
E 2386. 10 pf. Type E 714 .. 15 10
E 2387. 20 pf. Polecat .. .. 20 10
E 2388. 25 pf. European mink 25 10
E 2389. 35 pf. Beech marten .. 1·60 1·10

**1982.** Leipzig Spring Fair. Multicoloured.
E 2391. 10 pf. Type E 716 .. 15 10
E 2392. 25 pf. Seamless steel tube plant, Riesa Zeithain .. .. 30 15

**1982.** Socialist Personalities.
E 2394. E 718. 10 pf. brown .. 10 10
E 2395. – 10 pf. green .. 10 10
E 2396. – 10 pf. lilac .. 10 10
E 2397. – 10 pf. blue .. 10 10
E 2398. – 10 pf. green .. 10 10
DESIGNS: No. E 2395, Ottomar Geschke. No. E 2396, Helmut Lehmann. No. E 2397, Herbert Warnke. No. E 2398, Otto Winzer.

E 719. Meadow Saffron.

E 720. Decorative Initial "I".

**1982.** Poisonous Plants. Multicoloured.
E 2399. 10 pf. Type E 719 .. 15 10
E 2400. 15 pf. Bog arum .. 15 10
E 2401. 20 pf. Labrador tea .. 20 10
E 2402. 25 pf. Bryony .. .. 25 10
E 2403. 35 pf. Monkshood .. 30 10
E 2404. 50 pf. Henbane .. 2·25 1·40

**1982.** International "Art of the Book" Exhibition, Leipzig.
E 2405. E 720. 15 pf. multicoloured 40 40
E 2406. – 35 pf. brown, red and black .. 40 40
DESIGN: 35 pf. Exhibition emblem.

E 721. "Mother with Child" (W. Womacka).

E 722. Osprey.

**1982.** 10th Free German Trade Unions Association Congress, Berlin.
E 2407. E 721. 10 pf. black, red and yellow .. 10 10
E 2408. – 20 pf. multicoloured 10 10
E 2409. – 25 pf. multicoloured 65 55
DESIGNS—HORIZ. 20 pf. "Discussion by Collective of Innovators" (Willi Neubert). VERT. 25 pf. "Young Couple" (Karl-Heinz Jakob).

**1982.** Protected Birds. Multicoloured.
E 2410. 10 pf. Type E 722 .. 25 10
E 2411. 20 pf. White-tailed sea eagle (horiz.) .. 35 10
E 2412. 25 pf. Little owl .. 40 15
E 2413. 35 pf. Eagle owl .. 4·00 1·60

E 723. Old and Modern Buildings.

**1982.** 19th Workers' Festival, Neubrandenburg. Multicoloured.
E 2414. 10 pf. Type E 723. .. 15 10
E 2415. 20 pf. Couple in traditional costume .. 30 20

E 725. Freighter "Frieden".

**1982.** Ocean-going Ships. Multicoloured.
E2417 5 pf. Type E 725 .. 10 10
E2418 10 pf. Roll-on roll-off freighter "Fichtelberg" .. .. 10 10
E2419 15 pf. Heavy cargo carrier "Brocken" .. 15 10
E2420 20 pf. Container ship "Weimar" .. 20 10
E2421 25 pf. First DSR freighter "Vorwarts" 20 10
E2422 35 pf. Container ship "Berlin" .. .. 2·00 1·90

E 726. Members' Activities.

**1982.** 30th Anniv. of Sports and Science Association.
E 2423. E 726. 20 pf. multicoloured 40 10

E 727. Bird Wedding.

**1982.** Sorbian Folk Customs. Multicoloured.
E 2424. 10 pf. Type E 727 .. 15 15
E 2425. 20 pf. Shrove Tuesday procession .. .. 30 30
E 2426. 25 pf. Egg rolling .. 40 40
E 2427. 35 pf. Painted Easter eggs .. .. 50 50
E 2428. 40 pf. St. John's Day riders .. .. 55 55
E 2429. 50 pf. Distribution of Christmas gifts to hard-working children .. .. 65 65

E 728. Schwerin, 1640.

**1982.** 7th National Youth Stamp Exhibition, Schwerin. Multicoloured.
E 2430. 10 pf. + 5 pf. Type E 728 .. .. 25 25
E 2431. 20 pf. Modern Schwerin 25 25

E 729. Flag and Pioneers.

**1982.** 7th Pioneers Meeting, Dresden. Mult.
E 2432. 10 pf. + 5 pf. Type E 729 .. .. 50 25
E 2433. 20 pf. Trumpet and drum .. .. 10 10

E 730. "Stormy Sea" (Ludolf Backhuysen).

**1982.** Paintings in Schwerin State Museum. Multicoloured.
E 2434. 5 pf. Type E 730 .. 15 10
E 2435. 10 pf. "Music making at Home" (Frans van Mieris) (vert.) .. 15 10
E 2436. 20 pf. "The Watchman" (Carel Fabritius) (vert.) .. .. 20 10
E 2437. 25 pf. "Company of Peasants" (Adriaen Brouwer) .. .. 20 15
E 2438. 35 pf. "Breakfast Table with Ham" (Willem Claesz Heda) .. .. 30 15
E 2439. 70 pf. "River Landscape" (Jan van Goyen) .. .. 2·50 2·00

E 731. Karl-Marx-Stadt.

**1982.** 13th Socialist Countries' Postal Ministers Conference, Karl-Marx-Stadt.
E 2440. E 731. 10 pf. mult. .. 15 10

E 732. Stentzlers Hof.

**1982.** Leipzig Autumn Fair. Multicoloured.

E 2441. 10 pf. Type E 732 .. 10 10
E 2442. 25 pf. Amber box, ring and pendant .. 25 10

E 733. Auschwitz-Birkenau Memorial. E 734. Federation Badge.

**1982.** War Victims' Memorial, Auschwitz-Birkenau.

E 2443. E 733. 35 pf. blue, blk., and red .. 25 10

**1982.** 9th International Federation of Resistance Fighters Congress, Berlin.

E 2444. E 734. 10 pf. multicoloured 25 10

E 735. "Anemone hupehensis". E 736. Palestinian Family.

**1982.** Autumn Flowers. Multicoloured.

E 2445. 5 pf. Type E 735 .. 15 10
E 2446. 10 pf. French marigolds .. .. 15 10
E 2447. 15 pf. Gazania .. 20 10
E 2448. 20 pf. Sunflower .. 25 10
E 2449. 25 pf. Annual chrysanthemum .. 30 10
E 2450. 35 pf. Cosmea .. .. 2·75 1·25

**1982.** Solidarity with Palestinian People.

E 2451. E 736. 10 pf.+5 pf. multicoloured .. 30 10

E 737. "B 1000" Ambulance. E 738. Fair Emblem.

**1982.** IFA Vehicles. Multicoloured.

E 2452. 5 pf. Type E 737 .. 10 10
E 2453. 10 pf. Road cleaner .. 15 10
E 2454. 20 pf. "LD 3000" omnibus .. .. 20 10
E 2455. 25 pf. "LD 3000" lorry 25 10
E 2456. 35 pf. "W 50" lorry .. 30 10
E 2457. 85 pf. "W 50" milk tanker .. .. 2·75 1·75

**1982.** 25th "Masters of Tomorrow" Fair, Leipzig.

E 2458. E 738. 20 pf. mult. 20 10

E 739. Aircraft and Envelope E 740. Seal of Eisleben, 1500.

**1982.** Air.

E2459 E 739 5 pf. black & blue 15 10
E2460 15 pf. black & mve 20 10
E2461 20 pf. black & orge 20 15
E2462 25 pf. blk & bistre 30 15
E2463 30 pf. black & grn 20 10
E2464 40 pf. black & grn 25 10
E2465 1 m. black & blue 65 25
E2466 3 m. black & brn 3·50 1·25
E2467 5 m. black and red 5·50 90

**1982.** 500th Birth Anniv of Martin Luther (Protestant reformer).

E2471 10 pf. Type E 740 .. 10 10
E2472 20 pf. Luther as Junker Jog, 1521 .. .. 20 10
E2473 35 pf. Seal of Wittenberg, 1500 .. .. 30 10
E2474 85 pf. Luther (after Cranach) .. .. 2·50 1·75

E 741. Carpenter.

**1982.** Mechanical Toys. Multicoloured.

E 2475. 10 pf. Type E 741 .. 40 40
E 2476. 20 pf. Shoemaker .. 40 40
E 2477. 25 pf. Baker .. 40 40
E 2478. 35 pf. Cooper .. .. 40 40
E 2479. 40 pf. Tanner .. .. 40 40
E 2480. 70 pf. Wheelwright .. 40 40

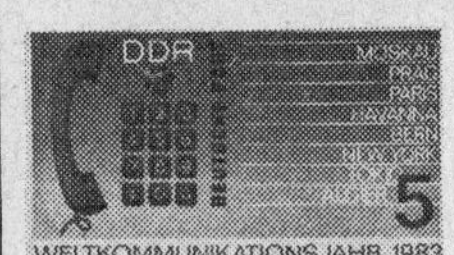


E 743. Franz Dahlem. E 744. Telephone Handset and Push-buttons.

**1983.** Socialist Personalities.

E 2482. E 743. 10 pf. brown .. 10 10
E 2483. – 10 pf. green .. 10 10
E 2484. – 10 pf. green .. 10 10
E 2485. – 10 pf. lilac .. 10 10
E 2486. – 10 pf. blue .. 10 10

DESIGN: No. E 2483, Karl Maron, E 2484, Josef Miller, E 2485, Fred Oelssner, E 2486, Siegfried Radel.

**1983.** World Communications Year.

E 2487. E 744. 5 pf. brown, black & deep brown .. 10 10
E 2488. – 10 pf. blue, turq. & deep blue .. 15 10
E 2489. – 20 pf. green, deep green & black .. 20 10
E 2490. – 35 pf. mult .. 1·10 75

DESIGNS: 10 pf. Aerials and tankers (Rugen Radio). 20 pf. Aircraft, container ship, letter and parcel. 35 pf. Optical fibre cables.

E 745. Otto Nuschke. E 746. Stolberg Town Hall.

**1983.** Birth Cent. of Otto Nuschke (politician).

E 2491. E 745. 20 pf. light brown, black and brown 20 10

**1983.** Historic Town Halls. Multicoloured.

E 2492. 10 pf. Type E 746 .. 10 10
E 2493. 20 pf. Gera (vert.) .. 10 10
E 2494. 25 pf. Possneck (vert.) 10 10
E 2495. 35 pf. Berlin .. .. 1·40 1·00

E 747. Petershof.

**1983.** Leipzig Spring Fair. Multicoloured.

E 2496. 10 pf. Type E 747 .. 10 10
E 2497. 25 pf. Robotron micro-electronic calculator 25 10

E 748. Paul Robeson.

**1983.** 85th Birth Anniv. of Paul Robeson (singer).

E 2498. E 748. 20 pf. multicoloured 25 10

E 750. Karl Marx and Newspaper Mastheads.

**1983.** Death Cent. of Karl Marx. Mult.

E 2500. 10 pf. Type E 750 .. 10 10
E 2501. 20 pf. Marx, Lyons silk weavers and title page of "Deutsche-Franzosische Jahrbucher" .. .. 10 10
E 2502. 35 pf. Marx, Engels and "Communist Manifesto" .. .. 20 10
E 2503. 50 pf. Marx and German, Russian and French versions of "Das Kapital" .. 20 10
E 2504. 70 pf. Marx and part of letter to Wilhelm Bracke containing commentary on German Workers' Party Programme .. 25 20
E 2505. 85 pf. Globe and banner portraying Marx, Engels, Lenin 2·50 2·40

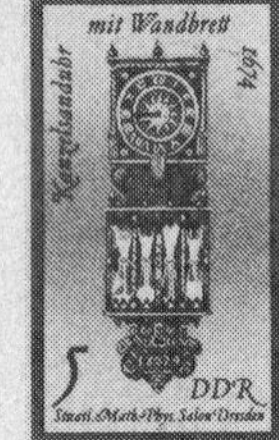


E 751. "Athene". E 752. Chancery Hourglass with Wallmount, 1674.

**1983.** Sculptures in State Museum, Berlin.

E 2507. E 751. 10 pf. brn., light brn. and blue 10 10
E 2508. – 20 pf. brn., light brn. and grn. 25 10

DESIGN: 20 pf. "Amazon".

**1983.** Narrow-gauge Railways (3rd series). As Type E 683.

E 2509. 15 pf. grey, blk. & red 90 90
E 2510. 20 pf. multicoloured .. 90 90
E 2511. 20 pf. grey, blk. and red 90 90
E 2512. 50 pf. brown, black & grey .. .. .. 90 90

DESIGNS: No. E 2509. Wernigerode-Nordhausen locomotive. E 2510, Wernigerode-Nordhausen passenger carriage. E 2511, Zittau-Kurort Oybib/Kurort Jonsdorf locomotive. E 2512, Zittau-Kurort Oybib/Kurort Jonsdorf luggage van.

**1983.** Hourglasses and Sundials. Mult.

E 2513. 5 pf. Type E 752 .. 10 10
E 2514. 10 pf. Chancery hourglass, 1700 .. .. 10 10
E 2515. 20 pf. Horizontal table sundial, 1611 .. 10 10
E 2516. 30 pf. Equatorial sundial, 1750 .. .. 15 10
E 2517. 50 pf. Equatorial sundial, 1760 .. .. 25 20
E 2518. 85 pf. "Noon Gun" table sundial, 1800 .. 2·50 1·75

E 753. "Coryphantha elephantidens". E 755. "Glasewaldt and Zinna defending the Barricade, Berlin, 1848" (Theodor Hosemann).

E 754. Thimo and Wilhelm.

**1983.** Cultivated Cacti. Multicoloured.

E 2519. 5 pf. Type E 753 .. 10 10
E 2520. 10 pf. "Thelocactus schwarzii" .. .. 10 10
E 2521. 20 pf. "Leuchtenbergia principis" .. .. 10 10
E 2522. 25 pf. "Submatucana madisoniorum" .. 10 10
E 2523. 35 pf. "Oroya peruviana" 15 10
E 2524. 50 pf. "Copiapoa cinerea" .. .. 2·00 1·25

**1983.** Founders of Naumberg Cathedral. Statues in the West Choir. Multicoloured.

E 2525. 20 pf. Type E 754 .. 35 35
E 2526. 25 pf. Gepa and Gerburg 35 35
E 2527. 35 pf. Hermann and Reglindis .. .. 35 35
E 2528. 85 pf. Eckehard and Uta 1·25 1·25

**1983.** "Junior Sozphilex 1983" Stamp Exhibition, Berlin.

E 2529. E 755. 10 pf.+5 pf. brown, black & red .. 60 55
E 2350. – 20 pf. multicoloured 10 10

DESIGN—HORIZ. 20 pf. "Instruction at Polytechnic" (Harald Metzkes).

E 756. Simon Bolivar and Alexander von Humboldt.

**1983.** Birth Bicent. of Simon Bolivar.

E 2531. E 756. 35 pf. black, brown & deep brown .. 40 15

E 757. Exercise with Balls. E 758. Arms of Cottbus.

**1983.** 7th Gymnastics and Sports Festival and 9th Children and Young People's Sports Days, Leipzig. Multicoloured.

E 2532. 10 pf.+5 pf. Type E 757 .. .. 75 35
E 2533. 20 pf. Volleyball .. 10 10

**1983.** Town Arms (1st series).

E2532 E 758 50 pf. mult .. 65 60
E2535 – 50 pf. mult .. 65 60
E2536 – 50 pf. red, black and silver .. 65 60
E2537 – 50 pf. mult .. 65 60
E2568 – 50 pf. black, red and silver .. 65 60

DESIGNS: No. E 2535, Dresden. E 2536, Erfurt. E 2537, Frankfurt-on-Oder. (21 × 39 mm.) No. E 2538, Berlin.

See also Nos. E 2569/73 and E 2644/8.

E 759. Central Fair Palace.

**1983.** Leipzig Autumn Fair. Multicoloured.
E 2539. 10 pf. Type E **759** .. 15 10
E 2540. 25 pf. Microchip .. 30 10

E **761.** Euler, Formula and Model.

**1983.** Death Bicentenary of Leonhard Euler (mathematician).
E 2542. E **761.** 20 pf. blue and black .. .. 30 15

E **762.** Sanssouci Castle.

**1983.** Public Palaces and Gardens of Potsdam-Sanssouci. Multicoloured.
E 2543. 10 pf. Type E **762** .. 10 10
E 2544. 20 pf. Chinese tea house .. .. .. 10 10
E 2545. 40 pf. Charlottenhof Palace .. .. .. 30 15
E 2546. 50 pf. Film museum (former stables) .. 2·50 1·90

E **763.** "Mother Homeland" (Yevgeni Vuzhetich).

E **765.** Learning to Read and Write.

**1983.** Volograd War Memorial.
E 2547. E **763.** 35 pf. blue, black and green .. 40 15

**1983.** "Solidarity with Nicaragua".
E 2549. E **765.** 10 pf.+5 pf. multicoloured. 30 10

E **766.** Cockerel.

**1983.** Thuringian Glass. Multicoloured.
E 2550. 10 pf. Type E **766** .. 10 10
E 2551. 20 pf. Beaker .. .. 10 10
E 2552. 25 pf. Vase .. .. 10 10
E 2553. 70 pf. Goblet .. .. 1·75 1·40

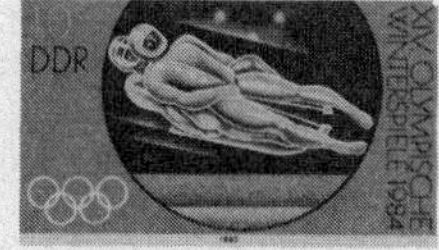

E **767.** Luge.

**1983.** Winter Olympic Games, Sarajevo (1984). Multicoloured.
E 2554. 10 pf.+5 pf. Type E **767** .. .. 15 10
E 2555. 20 pf.+10 pf. Cross-country skiing and ski jumping .. .. 20 10
E 2556. 25 pf. Cross-country skiing .. .. 20 10
E 2557. 35 pf. Biathlon .. 1·75 1·25

**INDEX**
Countries can be quickly located by referring to the index at the end of this volume.

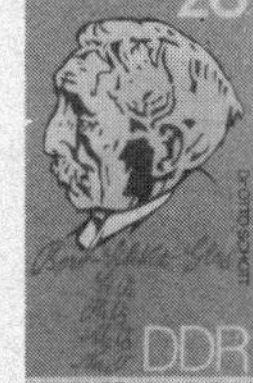

E **769.** Dr. Otto Schott (chemist).

E **770.** Friedrich Ebert.

**1984.** Centenary of Jena Glass.
E2560 E **769** 20 pf. mult .. 20 10

**1984.** Socialist Personalities.
E 2561. E **770.** 10 pf. black .. 10 10
E 2562. – 10 pf. green .. 10 10
E 2563. – 10 pf. black .. 10 10
DESIGNS: No. E 2562, Fritz Grosse. E 2563, Albert Norden.

E **772.** Milestones, Muhlau and Oederan.

E **773.** Old Town Hall, Leipzig.

**1984.** Postal Milestones. Multicoloured.
E 2565. 10 pf. Type E **772** .. 10 10
E 2566. 20 pf. Milestones, Johanngeorgenstadt and Schonbrunn .. 20 20
E 2567. 35 pf. Distance column, Freiberg .. .. 30 30
E 2568. 85 pf. Distance column, Pegau .. .. .. 80 50

**1984.** Town Arms (2nd series). As Type E **758**.
E 2569. 50 pf. multicoloured .. 40 40
E 2570. 50 pf. red, black and silver .. .. 40 40
E 2571. 50 pf. multicoloured .. 40 40
E 2572. 50 pf. multicoloured .. 40 40
E 2573. 50 pf. multicoloured .. 40 40
DESIGNS: No. E2569, Gera. E2570, Halle. E2571, Karl-Marx-Stadt. E2572, Leipzig. E2573, Magdeburg.

**1984.** Leipzig Spring Fair. Multicoloured.
E 2574. 10 pf. Type E **773** .. 10 10
E 2575. 25 pf. Body stamping press .. .. .. 20 10

**1984.** Narrow-gauge Railways (4th series). As Type E **683**.
E 2576. 30 pf. grey, black and red .. .. .. 30 30
E 2577. 40 pf. grey, black and red .. .. .. 30 30
E 2578. 60 pf. multicoloured .. 30 30
E 2579. 80 pf. multicoloured .. 30 30
DESIGNS: 30 pf. Cranzahl–Kurort Oberwiesenthal locomotive. 40 pf. Selketalbahn locomotive. 60 pf. Selketalbahn passenger coach. 80 pf. Cranzahl–Kurort Oberwiesenthal passenger coach.

E **774.** Town Hall, Rostock.

E **775.** Telephone, Letter, Pencil and Headquarters.

**1984.** 7th International Society for Preservation of Monuments General Assembly, Rostock and Dresden. Multicoloured.
E 2580. 10 pf. Type E **774** .. 10 10
E 2581. 15 pf. Albrecht Castle, Meissen .. .. 10 10
E 2582. 40 pf. Gateway, Rostock (vert.) .. .. 30 30
E 2583. 85 pf. Stables, Dresden 75 75

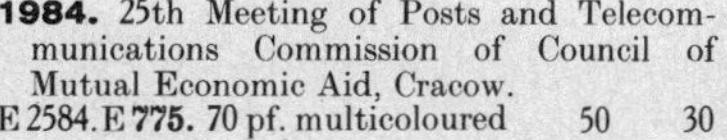
**1984.** 25th Meeting of Posts and Telecommunications Commission of Council of Mutual Economic Aid, Cracow.
E 2584. E **775.** 70 pf. multicoloured 50 30

E **776.** Cast Iron Bowl.

E **777.** String Puppet.

**1984.** Cast Iron from Lauchhammer. Multicoloured.
E 2585. 20 pf. Type E **776** .. 30 30
E 2586. 85 pf. "Climber" (Fritz Cremer) .. .. 50 50

**1984.** Puppets. Multicoloured.
E 2587. 50 pf. Type E **777** .. 40 40
E 2588. 80 pf. Hand puppet .. 70 70

E **778.** Marchers with Flags.

**1984.** National Youth Festival, Berlin. Multicoloured.
E 2589. 10 pf.+5 pf. Type E **778** 10 10
E 2590. 20 pf. Young construction workers .. 10 10

E **779.** Gera Buildings.

**1984.** 20th Workers' Festival, Gera. Multicoloured.
E 2591. 10 pf. Type E **779** .. 10 10
E 2592. 20 pf. Couple in traditional costume .. 15 15

E **780.** Salt Carrier.

E **781.** Bakers' Seal, Berlin.

**1984.** National Stamp Exhibition, Halle. Multicoloured.
E 2593. 10 pf.+5 pf. Type E **780** 15 10
E 2594. 20 pf. Citizen of Halle with his bride .. 20 10

**1984.** Historical Seals of 1442. Multicoloured.
E2595 5 pf. Type E **781** .. 50 15
E2596 10 pf. Wool weavers, Berlin .. .. 70 20
E2597 20 pf. Wool weavers, Colln on Spree .. 1·00 35
E2598 35 pf. Shoemakers, Colln on Spree .. .. 2·00 1·25

E **782.** New Flats and Restored Terrace.

E **783.** Frege House, Katherine Street.

**1984.** 35th Anniv. of German Democratic Republic (1st issue). Multicoloured.
E 2599. 10 pf. Type E **782** .. 10 10
E 2600. 20 pf. Surface mining 20 15
See also Nos. E 2604/6 and 2609/12.

**1984.** Leipzig Autumn Fair. Multicoloured.
E 2602. 10 pf. Type E **783** .. 10 10
E 2603. 25 pf. Crystal jar from Olbernhau .. .. 25 10

E **784.** East Ironworks.

**1984.** 35th Anniv of German Democratic Republic (2nd issue). Multicoloured.
E2604 10 pf. Type E **784** .. 10 10
E2605 20 pf. Soldiers, Mil Mi-8 helicopter, tank and warship .. .. 20 20
E2606 25 pf. Petro-chemical complex, Schwedt .. 30 30

E **785.** "Members of the Resistance" (Arno Wittig).

**1984.** Resistance Memorial, Georg-Schumann Building, Technical University of Dresden.
E 2608. E **785.** 35 pf. multicoloured 50 10

E **786.** Construction Workers.

**1984.** 35th Anniv. of German Democratic Republic (3rd issue). Multicoloured.
E 2609. 10 pf. Type E **786** .. 10 10
E 2610. 20 pf. Soldiers .. .. 15 10
E 2611. 25 pf. Industrial workers 20 20
E 2612. 35 pf. Agricultural workers 35 30

E **787.** Magdeburg, 1551.

**1984.** Eighth National Youth Exhibition, Magdeburg. Multicoloured.
E 2614. 10 pf.+5 pf. Type E **787** 10 10
E 2615. 20 pf. Modern Magdeburg .. .. .. 15 15

E **788.** "Spring".

E **789.** Entwined Cable and Red Star.

**1984.** Statuettes by Balthasar Permoser in Green Vault, Dresden. Multicoloured.
E 2616. 10 pf. Type E **788** .. 15 15
E 2617. 20 pf. "Summer" .. 20 20
E 2618. 35 pf. "Autumn" .. 40 40
E 2619. 70 pf. "Winter" .. 65 65

**1984.** "Solidarity".
E2621 E **789** 10 pf.+5 pf. mult 30 10

E **790.** Falkenstein Castle.

**1984.** Castles (1st series). Multicoloured.
E2622 10 pf. Type E **790** .. 10 10
E2623 20 pf. Kriebstein Castle 20 20
E2624 35 pf. Ranis Castle .. 50 30
E2625 80 pf. Neuenburg .. 65 50
See also Nos. E 2686/9 and E 2742/5.

E 791. Queen and Princess.

**1984.** Fairy Tales. "Dead Tsar's Daughter and the Seven Warriors" by Pushkin. Mult.

| | | | |
|---|---|---|---|
| E2626 | 5 pf. Type E **791** .. | 60 | 15 |
| E2627 | 10 pf. Princess and dog outside cottage .. | 70 | 25 |
| E2628 | 15 pf. Princess and seven warriors .. .. | 1·00 | 40 |
| E2629 | 20 pf. Princess holding poisoned apple .. | 1·40 | 50 |
| E2630 | 35 pf. Princess awakened by Prince .. .. | 1·75 | 90 |
| E2631 | 50 pf. Prince and Princess on horse .. | 2·25 | 1·10 |

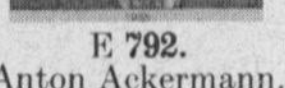

E **792.** Anton Ackermann. E **794.** Letter-box, 1850.

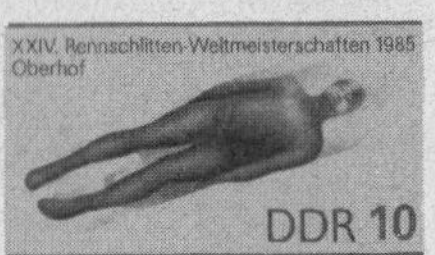


E **793.** Luge.

**1985.** Socialist Personalities.

| | | | |
|---|---|---|---|
| E 2632. | E **792.** 10 pf. black .. | 10 | 10 |
| E 2633. | – 10 pf. brown .. | 10 | 10 |
| E 2634. | – 10 pf. purple .. | 10 | 10 |

DESIGNS: No. E 2633, Alfred Kurella. E 2634, Otto Schon.

**1985.** 24th World Luge Championships, Oberhof.

| | | | |
|---|---|---|---|
| E 2635. | E **793.** 10 pf. multicoloured | 30 | 10 |

**1984.** Letter-boxes.

| | | | |
|---|---|---|---|
| E 2636. | E **794.** 10 pf. brn. & blk. | 10 | 10 |
| E 2637. | – 20 pf. black, brn. & red .. | 20 | 20 |
| E 2638. | – 35 pf. mult. .. | 30 | 30 |
| E 2639. | – 50 pf. brown, black and grey | 40 | 40 |

DESIGNS: 20 pf. Letter-box, 1860. 35 pf. Letter-box, 1900. 50 pf. Letter-box, 1920.

E **796.** Bach Statue, Leipzig. E **798.** Liberation Monument.

**1985.** Leipzig Spring Fair. Multicoloured.

| | | | |
|---|---|---|---|
| E 2641. | 10 pf. Type E **796** | 10 | 10 |
| E 2642. | 25 pf. Meissen porcelain pot .. .. .. | 20 | 10 |

**1985.** Town Arms (3rd series). As Type E **758.** Multicoloured.

| | | | |
|---|---|---|---|
| E 2644. | 50 pf. Neubrandenburg | 40 | 30 |
| E 2645. | 50 pf. Potsdam .. | 40 | 30 |
| E 2646. | 50 pf. Rostock .. .. | 40 | 30 |
| E 2647. | 50 pf. Schwerin .. | 40 | 30 |
| E 2648. | 50 pf. Suhl .. | 40 | 30 |

**1985.** Liberation Monument, Seelow Heights.

| | | | |
|---|---|---|---|
| E2649 | E **798** 35 pf. mult .. | 30 | 15 |

E **799.** Egon Erwin Kisch.

**1985.** Birth Centenary of Egon Erwin Kisch (journalist).

| | | | |
|---|---|---|---|
| E 2650. | E **799.** 35pf. multicoloured | 40 | 25 |

E **800.** Sigmund Jahn and Valeri Bykovski.

**1985.** 40th Anniv. of Defeat of Fascism. Multicoloured.

| | | | |
|---|---|---|---|
| E 2651. | 10 pf. Type E **800** .. | 10 | 10 |
| E 2652. | 20 pf. Adolf Hennecke as miner .. .. | 15 | 15 |
| E 2653. | 25 pf. Agricultural workers reading paper .. .. | 20 | 20 |
| E 2654. | 50 pf. Laboratory technicians .. | 45 | 45 |

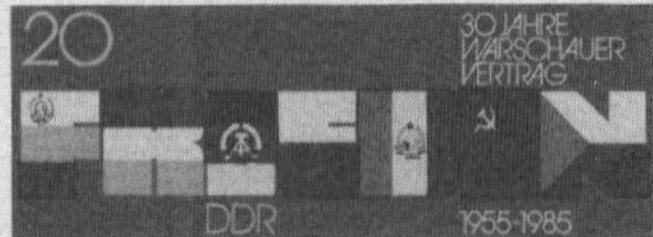


E **801.** Flags forming "Frieden" (Peace).

**1985.** 30th Anniv. of Warsaw Pact.

| | | | |
|---|---|---|---|
| E 2656. | E **801.** 20pf. multicoloured | 20 | 10 |

E **802.** Emblem and Berlin Buildings.

**1985.** 12th Free German Youth Parliament, Berlin. Multicoloured.

| | | | |
|---|---|---|---|
| E 2657. | 10 pf. +5 pf. Type E **802** .. .. | 10 | 10 |
| E 2658. | 20 pf. Flags, Ernst Thalmann and emblem .. .. | 20 | 20 |

E **803.** "Solidarity" and Dove on Globe. E **804.** Olympic Flag.

**1985.** "Solidarity".

| | | | |
|---|---|---|---|
| E 2659. | E **803.** 10 pf+5 pf. mult. | 15 | 10 |

**1985.** 90th International Olympic Committee Meeting, Berlin.

| | | | |
|---|---|---|---|
| E 2660. | E **804.** 35 pf. multicoloured | 40 | 30 |

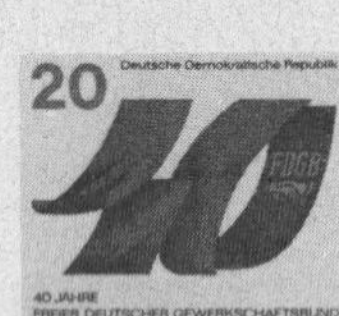


E **805.** "40" and Emblem. E **806.** Harpy Eagle.

**1985.** 40th Anniv. of Free German Trade Unions Federation.

| | | | |
|---|---|---|---|
| E 2661. | E **805.** 20 pf. multicoloured | 20 | 10 |

**1985.** Protected Animals. Multicoloured.

| | | | |
|---|---|---|---|
| E2662 | 5 pf. Type E **806** .. | 55 | 10 |
| E2663 | 10 pf. Red-breasted geese (horiz) .. | 80 | 30 |
| E2664 | 20 pf. Spectacled bear (horiz) .. .. | 30 | 25 |
| E2665 | 50 pf. Bantengs (horiz) | 60 | 60 |
| E2666 | 85 pf. Sunda gavial (horiz) .. .. | 1·50 | 1·00 |

E **807.** Support Steam-engine, Gera, 1833. E **808.** Students reading.

**1985.** Steam Engines. Multicoloured.

| | | | |
|---|---|---|---|
| E 2667. | 10 pf. Type E **807** .. | 10 | 10 |
| E 2668. | 85 pf. Balance steam-engine, Frieberg, 1848 .. .. .. | 75 | 75 |

**1985.** 12th World Youth and Students' Festival, Moscow. Multicoloured.

| | | | |
|---|---|---|---|
| E 2669. | 20 pf. +5 pf. Type E **808** .. .. | 20 | 20 |
| E 2670. | 50 pf. Students with raised arms .. .. | 40 | 40 |

E **809.** Diver at Turning Post.

**1985.** Second World Orienteering Diving Championship, Neuglobsow. Multicoloured.

| | | | |
|---|---|---|---|
| E 2671. | 10 pf. Type E **809** .. | 10 | 10 |
| E 2672. | 70 pf. Divers .. .. | 65 | 65 |

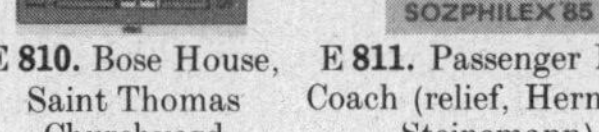

E **810.** Bose House, Saint Thomas Churchyard. E **811.** Passenger Mail Coach (relief, Hermann Steinemann).

**1985.** Leipzig Autumn Fair. Multicoloured.

| | | | |
|---|---|---|---|
| E 2673. | 10 pf. Type E **810** .. | 10 | 10 |
| E 2674. | 25 pf. J. Scherzer Bach-trumpet .. | 30 | 10 |

**1985.** "Sozphilex '85" Stamp Exhibition, Berlin. Multicoloured.

| | | | |
|---|---|---|---|
| E 2675. | 5 pf. Type E **811** .. | 10 | 10 |
| E 2676. | 20 pf. +5 pf. Team of horses .. .. | 25 | 25 |

Nos. E2675/6 were printed together, se-tenant, forming a composite design.

E **812.** Electrification of Railway. E **813.** Gertrauden Bridge.

**1985.** Railways. Multicoloured.

| | | | |
|---|---|---|---|
| E 2677. | 20 pf. Signal box .. | 40 | 20 |
| E 2678. | 25 pf. A. Schubert (engineer), "Saxonia", 1838 and electric locomotive "BR 250" | 50 | 30 |
| E 2679. | 50 pf. Type E **812** .. | 75 | 65 |
| E 2680. | 85 pf. Leipzig Central Station | 1·50 | 65 |

**1985.** Berlin Bridges. Multicoloured.

| | | | |
|---|---|---|---|
| E 2681. | 10 pf. Type E **813** .. | 10 | 10 |
| E 2682. | 20 pf. Jungfern Bridge | 15 | 15 |
| E 2683. | 35 pf. Weidendammer Bridge .. .. | 50 | 50 |
| E 2684. | 70 pf. Marx-Engels Bridge .. .. | 95 | 95 |

**1985.** Castles (2nd series). As Type E **790.** Multicoloured.

| | | | |
|---|---|---|---|
| E 2686. | 10 pf. Hohnstein Castle | 10 | 10 |
| E 2687. | 20 pf. Rochsburg .. | 15 | 15 |
| E 2688. | 35 pf. Schwarzenberg Castle .. .. | 30 | 30 |
| E 2689. | 80 pf. Stein Castle .. | 80 | 80 |

E **814.** Humboldt University. E **815.** Cecilienhof Castle and U.N. Emblem.

**1985.** Anniversaries. Multicoloured.

| | | | |
|---|---|---|---|
| E 2690. | 20 pf. Type E **814** (175th anniv. of Humboldt University, Berlin) | 30 | 15 |
| E 2691. | 85 pf. New and old Charite buildings (275th anniv. of Berlin Charite (training clinic)) .. .. | 65 | 65 |

**1985.** 40th Anniv of U.N.O.

| | | | |
|---|---|---|---|
| E2692 | E **815** 85 pf. mult .. | 85 | 40 |

E **816.** Elephants on Balls. E **817.** Grimm Brothers.

**1985.** Circus. Multicoloured.

| | | | |
|---|---|---|---|
| E 2693. | 10 pf. Type E **816** .. | 20 | 20 |
| E 2694. | 20 pf. Trapeze artiste | 30 | 30 |
| E 2695. | 35 pf. Acrobats on monocycles .. .. | 1·00 | 1·00 |
| E 2696. | 50 pf. Tigers and trainer .. .. | 1·25 | 1·25 |

**1985.** Birth Bicentenaries of Jacob and Wilhelm Grimm (folklorists). Multicoloured.

| | | | |
|---|---|---|---|
| E 2697. | 5 pf. Type E **817** .. | 10 | 10 |
| E 2698. | 10 pf. "The Valiant Tailor" | 10 | 10 |
| E 2699. | 20 pf. "Lucky John" .. | 20 | 20 |
| E 2700. | 25 pf. "Puss in Boots" | 30 | 30 |
| E 2701. | 35 pf. "The Seven Ravens" .. .. | 35 | 35 |
| E 2702. | 85 pf. "The Sweet Pap" .. .. | 65 | 65 |

E **818.** Water Pump, Berlin, 1900. E **819.** Saxon Postilion.

**1986.** Water Supply.

| | | | |
|---|---|---|---|
| E 2703. | E **818.** 10 pf. green and red .. .. | 10 | 10 |
| E 2704. | – 35 pf. deep brown, brown & green | 20 | 20 |
| E 2705. | – 50 pf. pur. & grn. | 30 | 30 |
| E 2706. | – 70 pf. blue & brn. | 65 | 65 |

DESIGNS: 35 pf. Water tower, Berlin-Altglienicke, 1906. 50 pf. Waterworks, Berlin-Friedrichshagen, 1893. 70 pf. Rappbode dam, 1959.

**1986.** Postal Uniforms of 1850. Multicoloured.

| | | | |
|---|---|---|---|
| E 2707. | 10 pf. Type E **819** .. | 15 | 15 |
| E 2708. | 20 pf. Prussian postman .. .. .. | 50 | 30 |
| E 2709. | 85 pf. Prussian postal official .. .. | 1·00 | 1·00 |
| E 2710. | 1 m. Postal official from Mecklenburg region .. .. | 1·25 | 1·25 |

E 820. Flag.

**1986.** 40th Anniv. of Free German Youth.
E 2711. E 820. 20 pf. yellow, blue and black 20 10

E 821. Flag.

**1986.** 30th Anniv. of National People's Army.
E 2712. E 821. 20 pf. multicoloured 30 10

E 822. Exhibition Hall.

**1986.** Leipzig Spring Fair. Multicoloured.
E2713 35 pf. Type E 822 .. 30 15
E2714 50 pf. Factory trawler "Atlantik 488" .. 45 35

E 823. Yury Gagarin and "Vostok".

**1986.** 25th Anniv. of Manned Space Flight. Multicoloured.
E 2715. 40 pf. Type E 823 (first man in space) .. 15 15
E 2716. 50 pf. Cosmonauts Valeri Bykovski and Sigmund Jahn, space station and "Interkosmos" emblem .. 30 30
E 2717. 70 pf. Space probe "Venera", orbit around Venus and spectrometer .. 40 40
E 2718. 85 pf. Reconnaissance camera MKF-6, photo, "Soyuz 22" spaceship, airplane and ship .. .. 65 65

E 824. Marx, Engels and Lenin.
E 825. Memorial.

**1986.** 11th Socialist Unity Party of Germany Day.
E 2719. E 824. 10 pf. black, red and silver .. 10 10
E 2720. – 20 pf. red, black and silver .. 20 20
E 2721. – 50 pf. mult. .. 30 30
E 2722. – 85 pf. black, red and silver .. 65 65
DESIGNS: 20 pf. Ernst Thalmann (birth centenary). 50 pf. Wilhelm Pieck and Otto Grotewohl, April 1946. 85 pf. Family.

**1986.** Opening of Ernst Thalmann Park, Berlin.
E 2724. E 825. 20 pf. multicoloured 20 10

E 826. Horse-drawn Tram, Dresden, 1886.

**1986.** Trams. Multicoloured.
E 2725. 10 pf. Type E 826 .. 20 15
E 2726. 20 pf. Leipzig, 1896 .. 30 25
E 2727. 40 pf. Berlin, 1919 .. 60 50
E 2728. 70 pf. Halle, 1928 .. 1·00 90

E 827. Orang-utang.
E 828. City Seal, 1253.

**1986.** 125th Anniv. of Dresden Zoo. Multicoloured.
E 2729. 10 pf. Type E 827 .. 15 10
E 2730. 20 pf. Eastern black-and-white colobus .. 30 20
E 2731. 50 pf. Mandrill .. 65 30
E 2732. 70 pf. Ring-tailed lemurs .. .. 80 65

**1986.** 750th Anniv. of Berlin (1st issue).
E2733 E 828 10 pf. dp. brown, bistre & brown 15 10
E2734 – 20 pf. olive, green and brown .. 30 20
E2735 – 50 pf. black, brown and red 85 50
E2736 – 70 pf. green and brown .. 1·60 85
Designs—HORIZ. 20 pf. City map, 1648. 50 pf. Oldest City arms. VERT. 70 pf. St. Nicholas's Church, 1832.
See also Nos. E2780/3.

E 829. Couple, Tractor and House.

**1986.** 21st Workers' Festival, Magdeburg. Multicoloured.
E 2738. 20 pf. Type E 829 .. 20 20
E 2739. 50 pf. Port and town of Magdeburg .. .. 65 65

E 830. Berlin, 1652.

**1986.** 9th Youth Stamp Exhibition, Berlin. Multicoloured.
E 2740. 10 pf. + 5 pf. Type E 830 .. .. 10 10
E 2741. 20 pf. Historic and modern Berlin buildings .. .. 15 15

E 831. Schwerin Castle.

**1986.** Castles (3rd series). Multicoloured.
E 2742. 10 pf. Type E 831 .. 15 15
E 2743. 20 pf. Gustrow castle .. 30 30
E 2744. 85 pf. Rheinsberg castle .. .. 85 85
E 2745. 1 m. Ludwigslust castle 1·00 1·00

E 832. Soldiers and Girl before Brandenburg Gate.

**1986.** 25th Anniv. of Berlin Wall.
E 2746. E 832. 20 pf. multicoloured 40 20

E 833. Doves flying from Emblem.

**1986.** International Peace Year.
E 2747. E 833. 35pf. multicoloured 40 20

E 835. Rostock, 1637.
E 836. Man with Rifle.

**1986.** Coins.
E 2749. E 835. 10 pf. black, silver and red 15 10
E 2750. – 35 pf. black, silver and blue 30 30
E 2751. – 50 pf. mult. .. 50 40
E 2752. – 85 pf. black, silver and blue 65 50
E 2753. – 1 m. black, silver and green .. 1·00 1·00
DESIGNS: 35 pf. Nordhausen, 1660. 50 pf. Erfurt, 1633. 85 pf. Magdeburg, 1638. 1 m. Stralsund, 1622.

**1986.** 44th World Sports Shooting Championships, Suhl.
E 2754. E 836. 20 pf. black, green and grey 15 15
E 2755. – 70 pf. black, red and grey .. 65 65
E 2756. – 85 pf. black, blue and grey .. 85 85
DESIGNS: 70 pf. Woman with pistol. 85 pf. Man with double-barrelled shotgun.

E 837. Guard and Boundary Post.
E 838. Hemispheres and Red Banner.

**1986.** 40th Anniv. of Border Guards.
E 2757. E 837. 20 pf. multicoloured 20 15

**1986.** 11th World Trade Unions Congress, Berlin.
E 2758. E 838. 70 pf. multicoloured 80 60

E 839. German Members Memorial, Friedrichshain.
E 840. Memorial.

**1986.** 50th Anniv. of Formation of International Brigades in Spain.
E 2759. E 839. 20 pf. brown, black and red 25 10

**1986.** 25th Anniv. of Sachsenhausen Memorial.
E 2760. E 840. 35 pf. black, green and blue 30 15

E 841. Double-deck Loading Ramps.

**1986.** Opening of Mukran–Klaipeda Railway Ferry Service. Multicoloured.
E2761 50 pf. Type E 841 .. 65 65
E2762 50 pf. Two deck ferry .. 65 65
Nos. E2761/2 were printed together, se-tenant, forming a composite design.

E 842. "Help for Developing Countries".

**1986.** "Solidarity".
E 2763. E 842. 10 pf. + 5 pf. mult. 20 15

E 844. Indira Gandhi.
E 845. Candle Holder, 1778.

**1986.** 2nd Death Anniv. of Indira Gandhi (Indian Prime Minister).
E 2765. E 844. 10 pf. stone and brown .. 15 10

**1986.** Candle Holders from the Erzgebirge. Multicoloured.
E 2766. 10 pf. Type E 845 .. 10 10
E 2767. 20 pf. Candle holder, 1796 .. .. .. 15 15
E 2768. 25 pf. Candle holder, 1810 .. .. .. 15 15
E 2769. 35 pf. Candle holder, 1821 .. .. .. 25 25
E 2770. 40 pf. Candle holder, 1830 .. .. .. 30 30
E 2771. 85 pf. Candle holder, 1925 .. .. .. 65 65

E 846. Roland Statue, Stendal.
E 847. Post Office, Freiberg.

**1987.** Statues of Roland (1st series).
E2772 10 pf. light brown, brown and yellow .. 10 10
E2773 20 pf. light brown, brown and blue .. 20 10
E2774 35 pf. light brown, brown and orange .. 35 30
E2775 50 pf. light brown, brown and green .. 50 45
DESIGNS: Statues at—10 pf. Type E 846. 20 pf. Halle. 35 pf. Brandenburg. 50 pf. Quedlinburg.
See also Nos. E2984/7.

**1987.** Post Offices.
E 2776. E 847. 10 pf. black, red and blue 15 15
E 2777. – 20 pf. mult. .. 30 25
E 2778. – 70 pf. mult. .. 80 75
E 2779. – 1 m. 20 mult. .. 95 85
DESIGNS: 20 pf. Perleberg. 70 pf. Weimar. 1 m. 20 Kirschau.

**1987.** 750th Anniv of Berlin (2nd issue). As Type E 828.
E 2780 20 pf. brown and green 15 15
E 2781 35 pf. green and red .. 30 25
E 2782 70 pf. blue and red .. 65 55
E 2783 85 pf. olive and green 85 70
DESIGNS:—VERT. 20 pf. Ephraim Palace. HORIZ. 35 pf. New buildings, Alt Marzahn; 70 pf. Marx-Engels Forum. 85 pf. Friedrichstadtpalast.

E **848.** Woman with Flower in Hair.

E **850.** Clara Zetkin.

E **849.** Fair Hall 20.

**1987.** 40th Anniv and 12th Congress (Berlin) of German Democratic Women's Federation.
E2785 E **848** 10 pf. bl, red & sil 15 10

**1987.** Leipzig Spring Fair. Multicoloured.
E 2786. 35 pf. Type E **849** .. 30 30
E 2787. 50 pf. "Traders at Weighbridge, 1804" (Christian Geissler) 50 50

**1987.** Socialist Personalities. Multicoloured.
E 2788. E **850.** 10 pf. purple .. 10 10
E 2789. – 10 pf. black .. 10 10
E 2790. – 10 pf. black .. 10 10
E 2791. – 10 pf. green .. 10 10
DESIGNS: No. E 2789, Fritz Gabler. E 2790, Walter Vesper. E 2791, Robert Siewert.

E **851.** Construction Industry.

**1987.** 11th Federation of Free German Trade Unions Congress, Berlin. Multicoloured.
E 2792. 20 pf. Type E **851** .. 15 15
E 2793. 50 pf. Communications industry .. .. 40 40

E **852.** Flag, World Map and Doves.

**1987.** 10th German Red Cross Congress, Dresden.
E2794 E **852** 35 pf. mult .. 40 10

E **853.** Museum and Karl August Lingner (founder) (after Robert Sterl).

**1987.** 75th Anniv of German Hygiene Museum, Dresden.
E2795 E **853** 85 pf. mult .. 65 40

E **854.** Old and New Farming Methods.

**1987.** 35th Anniv. of Agricultural Co-operatives.
E 2796. E **854.** 20 pf. mult. .. 20 10



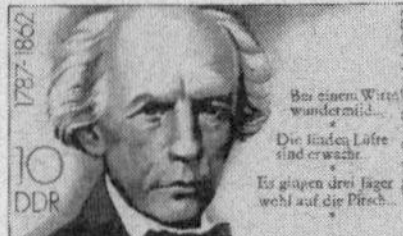

E **855.** Ludwig Uhland (poet).

**1987.** Birth Anniversaries. Multicoloured.
E 2797. 10 pf. Type E **855** (bicentenary) .. 10 10
E 2798. 20 pf. Arnold Zweig (writer, centenary) .. 25 20
E 2799. 35 pf. Gerhart Hauptmann (writer, 125th anniv.) .. 30 25
E 2800. 50 pf. Gustav Hertz (physicist, centenary) .. .. 60 45

E **856.** Bream.

**1987.** Freshwater Fishes. Multicoloured.
E2801 5 pf. Type E **856** .. 10 10
E2802 10 pf. Brook trout .. 10 10
E2803 20 pf. Catfish .. .. 20 20
E2804 35 pf. Grayling .. 30 30
E2805 50 pf. Barbel .. .. 50 50
E2806 70 pf. Pike .. .. 75 75

E **857.** Woman holding Baby.

**1987.** "Solidarity" Anti-apartheid Campaign.
E2807 E **857** 10 pf.+5 pf. mult 15 10

E **858.** Horse-drawn Hand-pumped Fire Engine, 1756.

**1987.** Fire Engines. Multicoloured.
E 2808. 10 pf. Type E **858** .. 15 15
E 2809. 25 pf. Steam engine, 1903 .. .. 30 30
E 2810. 40 pf. Model "LF 15", 1919 .. .. 30 30
E 2811. 70 pf. Model "LF 16-TS 8", 1971 .. .. 65 50

E **860.** Otters.

**1987.** Endangered Animals. European Otter. Multicoloured.
E 2813. 10 pf. Type E **860** .. 10 10
E 2814. 25 pf. Otter swimming 15 15
E 2815. 35 pf. Otter .. .. 40 40
E 2816. 60 pf. Otter's head .. 65 65

E **861.** Tug-of-War.

**1987.** 8th Gymnastics and Sports Festival and 11th Children and Young People's Sports Days, Leipzig. Multicoloured.
E 2817. 5 pf. Type E **861** .. 10 10
E 2818. 10 pf. Handball .. 15 15
E 2819. 20 pf.+5 pf. Long jumping .. .. 20 20
E 2820. 35 pf. Table tennis .. 30 30
E 2821. 40 pf. Bowling .. 30 40
E 2822. 70 pf. Running .. 75 75

E **862.** Association Activities.

**1987.** 35th Anniv. of Association of Sports and Technical Sciences.
E 2823. E **862.** 10 pf. mult. .. 15 10

E **863.** Head Post Office, Berlin, 1760.

**1987.** Stamp Day. Multicoloured.
E 2824. 10 pf.+5 pf. Type E **863** .. .. 10 10
E 2825. 20 pf. Wartenberg Palace .. .. 15 15

E **865.** Memorial Statue (Jozsef Somogyi).

E **867.** "Weidendamm Bridge" (Arno Mohr).

**1987.** War Victims' Memorial, Budapest.
E2827 E **865** 35 pf. mult .. 30 15

**1987.** 10th Art Exhibition, Dresden. Mult.
E 2829. 10 pf. Type E **867** .. 10 10
E 2830. 50 pf. "They only wanted to learn Reading and Writing (Nicaragua)" (Willi Sitte) .. .. 50 50
E 2831. 70 pf. "Big Mourning Man" (Wieland Forster) .. .. 65 65
E 2832. 1 m. Vase (Gerd Lucke) (horiz.) .. 85 85

E **868.** Red Flag, Smolny Building (Leningrad), "Aurora" and Lenin.

**1987.** 70th Anniv. of Russian Revolution. Multicoloured.
E 2833. 10 pf. Type E **868** .. 10 10
E 2834. 20 pf. Moscow Kremlin towers .. .. 20 10

E **869.** Youth using Personal Computer.

E **870.** Annaberg, 1810.

**1987.** 39th "Masters of Tomorrow" Fair, Leipzig. Multicoloured.
E2835 10 pf. Type E **869** .. 10 10
E2836 20 pf. "ZIM 10-S" robot-welder .. .. 20 10

**1987.** Christmas Pyramids from Erzgebirge. Multicoloured.
E 2837. 10 pf. Type E **870** .. 10 10
E 2838. 20 pf. Freiberg, 1830 .. 15 15
E 2839. 25 pf. Neustadtel, 1870 20 20
E 2840. 35 pf. Schneeberg, 1870 25 25
E 2841. 40 pf. Lossnitz, 1880 .. 30 30
E 2842. 85 pf. Seiffen, 1910 .. 65 65

E **871.** Ski Jumping.

E **874.** "Tillandsia macrochlamys".

E **872.** Berlin-Buch Post Office.

**1988.** Winter Olympic Games, Calgary. Multicoloured.
E 2843. 5 pf. Type E **871** .. 10 10
E 2844. 10 pf. Speed skating .. 15 10
E 2845. 20 pf.+10 pf. Four-man bobsleigh .. 30 25
E 2846. 35 pf. Biathlon .. 50 30

**1988.** Postal Buildings. Multicoloured.
E2848 15 pf. Type E **872** .. 15 15
E2849 20 pf. Postal museum .. 30 20
E2850 50 pf. Berlin-Marzahn general post office .. 65 50

**1988.** Bromeliads. Multicoloured.
E 2852. 10 pf. Type E **874** .. 10 10
E 2853. 25 pf. "Tillandsia bulbosa" .. .. 25 25
E 2854. 40 pf. "Tillandsia kalmbacheri" .. 40 30
E 2855. 70 pf. "Guzmania blassii" .. .. 65 50

E **875.** Madler-passage Entrance.

E **877.** Saddler, Muhlhausen, 1565.

**1988.** Leipzig Spring Fair. 75th Anniv of Madler-passage (fair building). Each brown, orange and pink.
E2856 20 pf. Type E **875** .. 15 15
E2857 70 pf. "Faust and Mephistopheles" (bronze statue, Matthieu Molitor) .. 65 50

**1988.** Historic Seals. Multicoloured.
E 2859. 10 pf. Type E **877** .. 10 10
E 2860. 25 pf. Butcher, Dresden, 1564 .. 20 15
E 2861. 35 pf. Smith, Nauen, 16th-century .. 25 20
E 2862. 50 pf. Clothier, Frankfurt on Oder, 16th-century .. .. 40 35

E **878.** Georg Forster Antarctic Research Station.

**1988.** 12th Anniv. of Georg Forster Antarctic Research Station.
E 2863. E **878.** 35 pf. mult. .. 30 15

E **879.** Wismar.

**1988.** Northern Towns of the Democratic Republic.

E 2864. 5 pf. black, green and turquoise .. .. 10 10
E 2865. 10 pf. black, ochre and brown .. .. .. 10 10
E 2866. 25 pf. black, light blue and blue .. .. 20 15
E 2867. 60 pf. black, pink and red 50 40
E 2868. 90 pf. black, light green and green .. .. 75 60
E 2869. 1 m. 20 black, brown and red .. .. .. 1·10 1·00

DESIGNS: 5 pf. Type E **879.** 10 pf. Anklam. 25 pf. Ribnitz-Damgarten. 60 pf. Stralsund. 90 pf. Bergen. 1 m. 20, Greifswald.

E **881.** Chorin and Neuzelle Monasteries, Industrial and Agricultural Symbols.

**1988.** 22nd Workers' Arts Festival, Frankfurt-on-Oder. Multicoloured.

E2871 20 pf. Type E **881** .. 15 15
E2872 50 pf. Buildings of Frankfurt .. .. 45 45

E **882.** Cosmonauts Sigmund Jahn and Valery Bykovski.

**1988.** 10th Anniv. of U.S.S.R.–East German Manned Space Flight (1st issue). Mult.

E2873 5 pf. Type E **882** .. 10 10
E2874 10 pf. "MKS-M" multi-channel spectrometer 10 10
E2875 20 pf. "Mir"–"Soyuz" space complex .. 15 15

See also Nos. E2894/6.

E **883.** Erfurt, 1520.

**1988.** 10th Youth Stamp Exhibition, Erfurt and Karl-Marx-Stadt. Multicoloured.

E2876 10 pf.+5 pf. Type E **883** 10 10
E2877 20 pf.+5 pf. Chemnitz, 1620 .. .. .. 20 20
E2878 25 pf. Modern view of Erfurt .. .. 20 20
E2879 50 pf. Modern view of Karl-Marx-Stadt (formerly Chemnitz) 45 45

E **884.** Swearing-in Ceremony.

**1988.** 35th Anniv of Workers' Militia Squads. Multicoloured.

E 2880. 5 pf. Type E **884** .. 10 10
E 2881. 10 pf. Tribute to Ernst Thalmann .. .. 10 10
E 2882. 15 pf. Parade .. .. 15 15
E 2883. 20 pf. Arms distribution .. .. 20 20

E **885.** Balloons and Doves over Karl-Marx-Stadt.

**1988.** 8th Pioneers Meeting, Karl-Marx-Stadt. Multicoloured.

E 2884. 10 pf. Type E **885** .. 10 10
E 2885. 10 pf.+5 pf. Doves, balloons and Pioneers .. .. 15 15

E **886.** Swimming.

**1988.** Olympic Games, Seoul. Multicoloured.

E 2886. 5 pf. Type E **886** .. 10 10
E 2887. 10 pf. Handball .. .. 15 15
E 2888. 20 pf.+10 pf. Hurdling 30 30
E 2889. 25 pf. Rowing .. .. 30 30
E 2890. 35 pf. Boxing .. .. 45 45
E 2891. 50 pf.+20 pf. Cycling .. 65 65

**1988.** 10th Anniv. of U.S.S.R.–East German Manned space Flight (2nd issue). As Nos. E 2873/5 but values changed. Multicoloured.

E 2894. 10 pf. Type E **882** .. 10 10
E 2895. 20 pf. As No. E 2874 .. 25 25
E 2896. 35 pf. As No. E 2875 .. 35 35

E **888.** Buchenwald Memorial (Fritz Cremer).

**1988.** War Memorials.

E 2897. E **888.** 10 pf. green, black and brown .. 10 10
E 2898. – 35 pf. mult. .. 30 15

DESIGN: 35 pf. Resistance Monument, Lake Como, Italy (Gianni Colombo)

E **889.** " 'Adolph Friedrich' at Stralsund: Captain C. Leplow" (E. Laschke).

**1988.** 500th Anniv of Stralsund Shipping Company. Captains' Paintings. Multicoloured.

E2899 5 pf. Type E **889** .. 15 15
E2900 10 pf. " 'Gartenlaube' of Stralsund: Captain J. F. Kruger" (A. Luschky) .. .. 30 30
E2901 70 pf. "Brigantina 'Auguste Mathilde' of Stralsund: Captain I. C. Grunwaldt" (Johnsen-Seby Bergen) 90 90
E2902 1 m. 20 "Brig 'Hoffnung' of Cologne-on-Rhine: Captain G. A. Luther" (anon) .. .. 1·60 1·60

E **890.** Medical Scene and African Child.

**1988.** "Solidarity".

E2903 E **890** 10 pf.+5 pf. mult 40 30

E **891.** Bridge, Magdeburg. E **892.** Menorah.

**1988.** Drawbridges and Ship Lifts. Mult.

E 2904. 5 pf. Type E **891** .. 10 10
E 2905. 10 pf. Lift, Magdeburg-Rothensee Canal .. 10 10
E 2906. 35 pf. Lift, Niederfinow 20 20
E 2907. 70 pf. Bridge and lock, Altfriesack .. .. 50 30
E 2908. 90 pf. Drawbridge, Rugendamm .. .. 80 80

**1988.** 50th Anniv. of "Kristallnacht" (Nazi pogrom).

E 2909. E **892.** 35 pf. purple, yellow & black .. 40 10

E **893.** "In the Boat". E **894.** Lace (Regine Wengler).

**1988.** Birth Centenary of Max Lingner (artist). Multicoloured.

E 2910. 5 pf. Type E **893** .. 10 10
E 2911. 10 pf. "Mademoiselle Yvonne" .. .. 15 10
E 2912. 20 pf. "Free, Strong and Happy" .. .. 20 15
E 2913. 85 pf. "New Harvest" .. 85 30

**1988.** Bobbin Lace from Erzgebirge. Pieces by lacemakers named. Each black, brown and yellow.

E 2914. 20 pf. Type E **894** .. 10 10
E 2915. 25 pf. Wally Tilp .. 10 10
E 2916. 35 pf. Elisabeth Mehnert-Pfabe .. .. .. 25 25
E 2917. 40 pf. Ute Siewert .. 30 30
E 2918. 50 pf. Regine Siebdraht 50 50
E 2919. 85 pf. Elise Schubert .. 65 65

E **895.** W.H.O. Emblem. E **897** Members' Flags

**1988.** 40th Anniv of W.H.O.

E2920 E **895** 85 pf. sil, bl & grey 65 30

**1989.** 40th Anniv of Council of Mutual Economic Aid.

E2922 E **897** 20 pf. mult .. 20 10

E **898** Edith Baumann E **899** Philipp Reis Telephone, 1861

**1989.** Socialist Personalities.

E2923 E **898** 10 pf. brown .. 10 10
E2924 – 10 pf. green .. 10 10
E2925 – 10 pf. brown .. 10 10
E2926 – 10 pf. blue .. 10 10

DESIGNS: No. E2924, Otto Meier; E2925, Alfred Oelssner; E2926, Fritz Selbmann.

**1989.** Telephones. Multicoloured.

E2927 10 pf. Type E **899** .. 10 10
E2928 20 pf. Siemens & Halske wall telephone, 1882 .. 20 20
E2929 50 pf. "OB 03" wall telephone, 1903 .. 60 60
E2930 85 pf. "OB 05" desk telephone, 1905 .. 90 90

E **900** Johann Beckmann (technologist, 250th anniv)

**1989.** Birth Anniversaries. Multicoloured.

E2931 10 pf. Type E **900** .. 10 10
E2932 10 pf. Rudolf Mauersberger and church choir (musician, cent) 10 10
E2933 10 pf. Carl von Ossietzky and masthead of "Die Weltbuhne" (journalist and peace activist, centenary) .. .. 10 10
E2934 10 pf. Ludwig Renn and International Brigades flag (writer, centenary) .. .. 10 10
E2935 10 pf. Adam Scharrer and cover of "Stateless People" (novelist, centenary) 10 10

E **901** Handelshof Fair Building

**1989.** Leipzig Spring Fair. Mult.

E2936 70 pf. Type E **901** (80th anniv) .. .. 50 50
E2937 85 pf. Naschmarkt bake-house and bread shop, 1690 .. 85 85

E **903** Friedrich List (economist and promoter of railway system)

**1989.** 150th Anniv of Leipzig–Dresden Railway (first German long-distance service).

E2939 E **903** 15 pf. brown, pale brown & green 15 15
E2940 – 20 pf. black, green and red .. 20 20
E2941 – 50 pf. black, brown and deep brown 65 65

DESIGNS: 20 pf. Dresdner Station, Leipzig, 1839; 50 pf. Leipziger Station, Dresden, 1839.

E **904** Tea Caddy E **905** Renaissance Initial "I"

**1989.** Meissen Porcelain. 250th Anniv of Onion Design. Each brown, blue and ultramarine.

E2942 10 pf. Type E **904** .. 10 10
E2943 20 pf. Vase .. .. 25 10
E2944 35 pf. Bread board .. 40 25
E2945 70 pf. Coffee pot .. 75 50

**1989.** 7th International Typography Exhibition, Leipzig.

E2946 E **905** 20 pf. mult .. 15 15
E2947 – 50 pf. black, yellow and green .. 65 50
E2948 – 1 m. 35 red, black and grey .. 1·00 1·00

DESIGNS: 50 pf. Art Nouveau initial "B"; 1 m. 35, Modern initial "A"s.

E **906** Chollima Statue, Pyongyang E **907** "Princess Louise"

**1989.** 13th World Youth and Students' Festival, Pyongyang (E2949) and Free German Youth Whitsun Festival, Berlin (E2950). Multicoloured.

| | | | |
|---|---|---|---|
| E2949 | 20 pf. Type E **906** .. | 20 | 20 |
| E2950 | 20 pf.+5 pf. Berlin buildings .. .. | 20 | 20 |

**1989.** 225th Birth Anniv of Johann Gottfried Schadow (sculptor). Details of "Princesses". Multicoloured.

| | | | |
|---|---|---|---|
| E2951 | 50 pf. Type E **907** .. | 60 | 40 |
| E2952 | 85 pf. "Princess Friederike" .. .. | 90 | 75 |

E **908** JENEVAL Interference Microscope

E **909** Front Page of Address

**1989.** Centenary of Carl Zeiss Foundation, Jena. Multicoloured.

| | | | |
|---|---|---|---|
| E2953 | 50 pf. Type E **908** .. | 50 | 50 |
| E2954 | 85 pf. "ZKM 01-250 C" bi-coordinate measuring instrument | 65 | 65 |

**1989.** Bicentenary of Inaugural Address to Jena University by Friedrich Schiller (writer and philosopher). Each brown, black & grey.

| | | | |
|---|---|---|---|
| E2955 | 25 pf. Type E **909** .. | 30 | 30 |
| E2956 | 85 pf. Part of address | 65 | 65 |

E **911** Storming the Bastille

**1989.** Bicent of French Revolution. Mult.

| | | | |
|---|---|---|---|
| E2958 | 5 pf. Type E **911** .. | 10 | 10 |
| E2959 | 20 pf. Sans-culottes .. | 25 | 25 |
| E2960 | 90 pf. Invading the Tuileries .. .. | 90 | 90 |

E **912** Haflingers

**1989.** 40th International Horse Breeding in Socialist States Congress, Berlin. Mult.

| | | | |
|---|---|---|---|
| E2961 | 10 pf. Type E **912** .. | 10 | 10 |
| E2962 | 20 pf. English thoroughbreds (racehorses) .. | 20 | 20 |
| E2963 | 70 pf. Heavy horses (plough team) .. | 50 | 50 |
| E2964 | 110 pf. Thoroughbreds (dressage) .. .. | 1·00 | 1·00 |

E **913** Till Eulenspiegel Fountain

**1989.** National Stamp Exn, Magdeburg. Fountains by Heinrich Apel. Mult.

| | | | |
|---|---|---|---|
| E2965 | 20 pf. Type E **913** .. | 25 | 25 |
| E2966 | 70 pf.+5 pf. Devil's fountain .. .. | 70 | 70 |

E **914** "Annunciation to the Peasants"

E **916** African Children

**1989.** 500th Birth Anniv of Thomas Muntzer (Protestant reformer) (2nd issue). Details of "Early Bourgeois Revolution in Germany" by Werner Tubke. Multicoloured.

| | | | |
|---|---|---|---|
| E2967 | 5 pf. Type E **914** .. | 10 | 10 |
| E2968 | 10 pf. "Fountain of Life" .. .. | 10 | 10 |
| E2969 | 20 pf. "Muntzer in the Battle" .. .. | 25 | 25 |
| E2970 | 50 pf. "Lutheran Cat Battle" .. .. | 45 | 45 |
| E2971 | 85 pf. "Justice, Jester" | 90 | 90 |

**1989.** "Solidarity".

| | | | |
|---|---|---|---|
| E2974 | E **916** 10 pf.+5 pf. mult | 15 | 10 |

E **917** "Mother Group" (Fritz Cremer)

E **918** "Adriana"

**1989.** 30th Anniv of Ravensbruck War Victims' Memorial.

| | | | |
|---|---|---|---|
| E2975 | E **917** 35 pf. mult .. | 30 | 15 |

**1989.** Epiphyllums. Multicoloured.

| | | | |
|---|---|---|---|
| E2976 | 10 pf. Type E **918** .. | 10 | 10 |
| E2977 | 35 pf. "Fire Magic" .. | 25 | 25 |
| E2978 | 50 pf. "Franzisko" .. | 45 | 45 |

E **919** Dove, Flag and Schoolchildren

**1989.** 40th Anniv of German Democratic Republic. Multicoloured.

| | | | |
|---|---|---|---|
| E2979 | 5 pf. Type E **919** .. | 10 | 10 |
| E2980 | 10 pf. Combine harvester and agricultural workers | 10 | 10 |
| E2981 | 20 pf. Political activists working together .. | 20 | 20 |
| E2982 | 25 pf. Industrial workers .. .. | 25 | 25 |

**1989.** Statues of Roland (2nd series). As Type E **846**. Multicoloured.

| | | | |
|---|---|---|---|
| E2984 | 5 pf. Zerbst .. .. | 10 | 10 |
| E2985 | 10 pf. Halberstadt .. | 15 | 15 |
| E2986 | 20 pf. Buch-Altmark .. | 20 | 20 |
| E2987 | 50 pf. Perleberg .. | 50 | 50 |

E **920** Nehru

E **921** Schneeberg, 1860

**1989.** Birth Centenary of Jawaharlal Nehru (Indian statesman).

| | | | |
|---|---|---|---|
| E2988 | E **920** 35 pf. brown & blk | 40 | 25 |

**1989.** Chandeliers from the Erzgebirge. Mult.

| | | | |
|---|---|---|---|
| E2989 | 10 pf. Type E **921** .. | 10 | 10 |
| E2990 | 20 pf. Schwarzenberg, 1850 .. .. | 15 | 15 |
| E2991 | 25 pf. Annaberg, 1880 | 20 | 20 |
| E2992 | 35 pf. Seiffen, 1900 .. | 30 | 30 |
| E2993 | 50 pf. Seiffen, 1930 .. | 40 | 40 |
| E2994 | 70 pf. Annaberg, 1925 | 75 | 75 |

E **922** Bee on Apple Blossom

E **923** "Courier" (Albrecht Durer)

**1990.** The Honey Bee. Multicoloured.

| | | | |
|---|---|---|---|
| E2995 | 5 pf. Type E **922** .. | 10 | 10 |
| E2996 | 10 pf. Bee on heather | 10 | 10 |
| E2997 | 20 pf. Bee on rape .. | 15 | 15 |
| E2998 | 50 pf. Bee on clover .. | 65 | 50 |

**1990.** 500th Anniv of Regular European Postal Services.

| | | | |
|---|---|---|---|
| E2999 | E **923** 35 pf. chocolate, lt brown & brown | 50 | 30 |

E **924** Erich Weinert

E **925** 19th-century Sign, Blankenburg

**1990.** Socialist Personalities.

| | | | |
|---|---|---|---|
| E3000 | E **924** 10 pf. blue .. | 25 | 10 |
| E3001 | – 10 pf. brown .. | 25 | 10 |

DESIGN: No. E3001, Bruno Leuschner.

**1990.** Posthouse Signs. Multicoloured.

| | | | |
|---|---|---|---|
| E3002 | 10 pf. Type E **925** .. | 15 | 15 |
| E3003 | 20 pf. Royal Saxony sign (19th century) | 20 | 20 |
| E3004 | 50 pf. German Empire sign (1870s) .. | 65 | 65 |
| E3005 | 110 pf. German Empire auxiliary station sign (1900s) .. .. | 85 | 85 |

E **926** Bebel

E **927** Drawings by Leonardo da Vinci

**1990.** 150th Birth Anniv of August Bebel (politician).

| | | | |
|---|---|---|---|
| E3006 | E **926** 20 pf. black, grey and red .. | 30 | 20 |

**1990.** "Lilienthal '91" European Airmail Exhibition. Historic Flying Machine Designs. Multicoloured.

| | | | |
|---|---|---|---|
| E3007 | 20 pf. Type E **927** .. | 35 | 35 |
| E3008 | 35 pf.+5 pf. Melchior Bauer's man-powered airplane design, 1764 | 60 | 60 |
| E3009 | 50 pf. Albrecht-Ludwig Berblinger's man-powered flying machine, 1811 .. | 75 | 75 |
| E3010 | 90 pf. Otto Lilienthal's design for monoplane glider .. .. | 1·25 | 1·25 |

E **928** St. Nicholas's Church, Leipzig, and Demonstrators

E **929** Warrior's Head

**1990.** "We Are The People".

| | | | |
|---|---|---|---|
| E3011 | E **928** 35 pf.+15 pf. mult | 65 | 50 |

**1990.** Museum of German History, Berlin. Stone Reliefs by Andreas Schluter.

| | | | |
|---|---|---|---|
| E3012 | E **929** 40 pf. yellow, green and black | 30 | 30 |
| E3013 | – 70 pf. mult .. | 65 | 65 |

DESIGN: 70 pf. Warrior's head (different).

E **930** Fair Seal, 1268

E **931** Kurt Tucholsky (writer, centenary)

**1990.** Leipzig Spring Fair and 825th Anniv of Leipzig. Multicoloured.

| | | | |
|---|---|---|---|
| E3014 | 70 pf. Type E **930** .. | 80 | 65 |
| E3015 | 85 pf. Fair seal, 1497 .. | 1·00 | 65 |

**1990.** Birth Anniversaries.

| | | | |
|---|---|---|---|
| E3016 | E **931** 10 pf. black, green and deep green | 20 | 15 |
| E3017 | – 10 pf. black, brown and red | 20 | 15 |

DESIGN: No. E3017, Friedrich Adolph Wilhelm Diesterweg (educationist, bicent).

E **932** "Solidarity of Labour" (Walter Crane)

E **933** Dicraeosaurus

**1990.** Centenary of Labour Day.

| | | | |
|---|---|---|---|
| E3018 | E **932** 10 pf. grey, black and red .. | 30 | 25 |
| E3019 | – 20 pf. red, grey and black .. | 65 | 40 |

DESIGN: 20 pf. Red carnation.

**1990.** Centenary of Natural Science Museum, Berlin. Dinosaur Skeletons. Multicoloured.

| | | | |
|---|---|---|---|
| E3020 | 10 pf. Type E **933** .. | 10 | 10 |
| E3021 | 25 pf. Kentrurosaurus | 20 | 20 |
| E3022 | 35 pf. Dysalotosaurus | 30 | 30 |
| E3023 | 50 pf. Brachiosaurus (vert) .. .. | 50 | 50 |
| E3024 | 85 pf. Skull of brachiosaurus (vert) | 75 | 75 |

E **934** Penny Black

E **935** Edward Hughes and 1855 Printing Telegraph

**1990.** 150th Anniv of the Penny Black.

| | | | |
|---|---|---|---|
| E3025 | E **934** 20 pf. black, mve & magenta .. | 30 | 30 |
| E3026 | – 35 pf.+15 pf. red, lilac and black | 65 | 65 |
| E3027 | – 110 pf. mult .. | 1·60 | 1·60 |

DESIGNS: 35 pf. Saxony 1850 3 pf. stamp; 110 pf. First East Germany stamp, 1949.

**1990.** 125th Anniv of I.T.U. Multicoloured.

| | | | |
|---|---|---|---|
| E3028 | 10 pf. Type E **935** .. | 10 | 10 |
| E3029 | 20 pf. Distribution rods from Berlin-Kopenick post office | 30 | 30 |
| E3030 | 25 pf. Transmitting tower and radio control desk .. | 40 | 40 |
| E3031 | 50 pf. "Molniya" communications satellite and globe .. | 50 | 50 |

E 936 Pope John Paul II

**1990.** Pope's 70th Birthday.
E3033 E **936** 35 pf. mult .. 40 30

E 937 Halle (18th-century)

**1990.** 11th National Youth Stamp Exhibition, Halle. Multicoloured.
E3034 10 pf.+5 pf. Type E **937** .. .. 20 20
E3035 20 pf. Modern Halle .. 25 25

E 938 Rules of Order of Teutonic Knights, 1264
E 939 Albrechts Castle and Cathedral, Meissen

**1990.** Exhibits in German State Library, Berlin. Multicoloured.
E3036 20 pf. Type E **938** .. 30 30
E3037 25 pf. World map from "Rudimentum Novitiorum", 1475 .. 40 30
E3038 40 pf. "Chosrou and Schirin" by Nizami (18-th century Persian manuscript) .. .. 80 65
E3039 110 pf. Book cover from Amalia musical library .. .. 1·50 1·00

WEST GERMAN CURRENCY

On 1 July 1990 the Ostmark was abolished and replaced by the West German Deutsche Mark.

**1990.** Tourist Sights.
E3040 E **939** 10 pf. blue .. 10 10
E3041 – 30 pf. green .. 25 15
E3042 – 50 pf. green .. 40 25
E3043 – 60 pf. brown .. 60 30
E3044 – 70 pf. brown .. 60 30
E3045 – 80 pf. red .. 65 40
E3046 – 100 pf. red .. 1·00 50
E3047 – 200 pf. violet .. 2·00 1·60
E3048 – 500 pf. green .. 3·00 3·00

DESIGNS: 30 pf. Goethe-Schiller Monument, Weimar; 50 pf. Brandenburg Gate, Berlin; 60 pf. Kyffhauser Monument; 70 pf. Semper Opera House, Dresden; 80 pf. Sanssouci Palace, Potsdam; 100 pf. Wartburg Castle, Eisenach; 200 pf. Magdeburg Cathedral; 500 pf. Schwerin Castle.

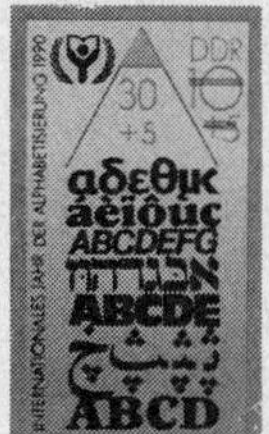

E 940 Different Alphabets

E 942 Louis Lewandowski (choir conductor)

E 941 Letter-carrier (from playing card) and Messenger, 1486

**1990.** International Literacy Year.
E3049 E **940** 30 pf.+5 pf. on 10 pf.+5 pf. multicoloured .. 1·00 1·00

No. E3049 was not issued without surcharge.

**1990.** 500th Anniv of Regular European Postal Services.
E3050 E **941** 30 pf. black, brown & green 30 15
E3051 – 50 pf. black, red and blue .. 65 65
E3052 – 70 pf. black, brown and red 65 65
E3053 – 100 pf. black, green and blue 1·00 85

DESIGNS: 50 pf. "Courier" (Albrecht Durer) and post rider, 1590; 70 pf. Open wagon, 1595, and mail carriage, 1750; 100 pf. Travelling post offices, 1842 and 1900.

**1990.** Reconstruction of New Synagogue, Berlin. Multicoloured.
E3054 30 pf. Type E **942** .. 30 30
E3055 50 pf.+15 pf. New Synagogue .. .. 65 50

E 943 Schliemann and Two-handled Vessel

E 944 Dresden

**1990.** Death Cent of Heinrich Schliemann (archaeologist). Multicoloured.
E3056 30 pf. Type E **943** .. 45 45
E3057 50 pf. Schliemann and double pot (horiz) .. 80 80

**1990.** 41st International Astronautics Federation Congress, Dresden.
E3058 E **944** 30 pf. blk & grey 30 30
E3059 – 50 pf. mult .. 50 30
E3060 – 70 pf. deep blue, green and blue 65 50
E3061 – 100 pf. mult .. 85 85

DESIGNS: 50 pf. Earth; 70 pf. Moon; 100 pf. Mars.

On 3 October 1990 the territory of the Democratic Republic was absorbed into the Federal Republic of Germany, whose stamps have been used since then.

OFFICIAL STAMPS

EO 58. (Cross-piece projects to left).

EO 59. (Cross-piece projects to right).

EO 84.

**1954.** (a) Design in minute dots.
EO 185. EO **58.** 5 pf. green .. — 15
EO 186. 6 pf. violet .. — 1·40
EO 187. 8 pf. brown .. — 10
EO 188. 10 pf. turquoise — 10
EO 189. 12 pf. blue .. — 10
EO 190. 15 pf. violet .. — 10
EO 191. 16 pf. violet .. — 1·25
EO 192. 20 pf. olive .. — 10
EO 193. 24 pf. red .. — 50
EO 194. 25 pf. turquoise — 40
EO 195. 30 pf. red .. — 35
EO 196. 40 pf. red .. — 20
EO 197. 48 pf. lilac .. — 7·00
EO 198. 50 pf. lilac .. — 50
EO 199. 60 pf. blue .. — 65
EO 200. 70 pf. brown .. — 50
EO 201. 84 pf. brown .. — 18·00

(b) Design in lines.
EO295 EO **59.** 5 pf. green .. — 10
EO296 10 pf. turquoise — 10
EO204 12 pf. turquoise — 15
EO297 15 pf. violet .. — 10
EO298 20 pf. olive .. — 10
EO212 EO **58.** 20 pf. olive .. — 20
EO207 EO **59.** 25 pf. green .. — 1·60
EO299 30 pf. red .. — 10
EO300 40 pf. red .. — 10
EO301 50 pf. lilac .. — 10
EO302 70 pf. brown .. — 10

**1956.** For internal use. Postally used. Cto.
EO 257. EO **84.** 5 pf. black .. 2·50 10
EO 258. 10 pf. black .. 40 10
EO 259. 20 pf. black .. 25 10
EO 260. 40 pf. black .. 2·40 10
EO 261. 70 pf. black .. £120 10

**Nos. EO 257/61 were not on sale to the public in unused condition, although specimens of all values are available on the market. Therefore, the prices listed above refer to postally used stamps (Col. 1) and cancelled-to-order stamps (Col. 2).**

OFFICIAL CENTRAL COURIER SERVICE STAMPS

These were for use on special postal services for confidential mail between Government officials and state-owned enterprises.

EO 95

**1956.** With or without control figures.
EO303 EO **95** 10 pf. blk & pur 10 30
EO304 20 pf. blk & pur 60 30
EO305 40 pf. blk & pur 10 25
EO306 70 pf. blk & pur 1·00 1·90

EO 123

**1958.** With various control figures.
(a) With one bar (thick or thin) each side of figure
EO357 EO **123** (10 pf.) red and yellow .. 4·00 3·75
EO373 (10 pf.) brown and blue .. 3·50 5·00
EO375 (10 pf.) violet and orange 4·00 5·00
EO377 (10 pf.) red and green .. 7·00 4·50
(b) With two bars (thick or thin) each side of figure
EO358 EO **123** (20 pf.) red and yellow .. 10·00 1·50
EO374 (20 pf.) brown and blue .. 25·00 1·75
EO376 (20 pf.) violet and orange 17·00 1·75
EO378 (20 pf.) red and green .. 12·00 1·00

EO 149

**1959.** With various control figures.
(a) With one bar each side of figure
EO414 EO **149** (10 pf.) red, violet & green 10·00 3·50
EO416 (10 pf.) black and blue .. 6·50 15·00
EO418 (10 pf.) black, brown & blue 14·00 13·00
(b) With two bars each side of figure
EO415 EO **149** (20 pf.) blue, brown & yell 15·00 1·75
EO417 (20 pf.) green, blue and red 15·00 1·75
EO419 (20 pf.) violet, black & brn 17·00 1·25

REGISTRATION STAMPS

SELF-SERVICE POST OFFICE

**These registration labels embody a face value to cover the registration fee and have franking value to this extent. They are issued in pairs from automatic machines together with a certificate of posting against a 50 pf. coin. The stamps are serially numbered in pairs and inscribed with the name of the town of issue.**

**The procedure is to affix one label to the letter (already franked with stamps for carriage of the letter) and complete page 1 of the certificate of posting which is then placed in the box provided together with the letter. The duplicate label is affixed to the second page of the certificate and retained for production as evidence in the event of a claim.**

They are not obtainable over the post office counter.

Unused prices are for pairs.

ER 318.

**1967.**
ER 992. ER **318.** 50 pf. red & black 2·25

ER **319.**

**1968.**
ER 993. ER **319.** 50 pf. red .. 65

ER **345.**

**1968.** For Parcel Post.
ER 1089. ER **345.** 50 pf. black 5·00

## GHADAMES Pt. 6

A caravan halting place in the Libyan desert, under French administration from 1943 until 1951 when the area reverted to Libya. From 1943 to 1948 stamps of Fezzan were used.

100 centimes = 1 franc.

**1.** Cross of Agadem.

**1949.**
1 **1** 4 f. chestnut & brn (post) 1·50 3·00
2 5 f. green and blue .. 1·50 3·00
3 8 f. chestnut and brown .. 2·50 4·00
4 10 f. blue and black .. 2·50 4·00
5 12 f. mauve and purple .. 5·00 7·75
6 15 f. chestnut and brown 5·00 7·00
7 20 f. green and brown .. 5·00 7·00
8 25 f. blue and brown .. 5·00 7·00
9 50 f. cerise and purple (air) 5·00 7·00
10 100 f. purple and brown .. 5·00 7·00

## GREAT COMORO Pt. 6

A French island north west of Madagascar. From 1914 to 1950 the stamps of Madagascar were used. In 1950 it became part of the Comoro Islands.

100 centimes = 1 franc.

**1897.** "Tablet" key-type inscr "GRANDE COMORE" in red or blue.
1 D 1 c. black on blue .. 35 60
2 2 c. brown on buff .. 45 65
3 4 c. brown on grey .. 95 90
4 5 c. green on light green 1·25 1·25
5 10 c. black on lilac .. 2·50 3·00
14 10 c. red .. .. 5·50 6·00
6 15 c. blue .. .. 7·50 4·00
15 15 c. grey .. .. 5·50 5·50
7 20 c. red on green .. 4·50 6·50
8 25 c. black on pink .. 4·00 3·50
16 25 c. blue .. .. 9·50 5·50
9 30 c. brown on drab .. 9·00 8·25
17 35 c. black on yellow .. 9·50 8·00
10 40 c. red on yellow .. 8·00 7·50
18 45 c. black on green .. 50·00 40·00
11 50 c. red on pink .. 19·00 10·00
19 50 c. brown on blue .. 23·00 20·00
12 75 c. brown on orange .. 35·00 20·00
13 1 f. green .. 18·00 15·00

**1912.** Surch.
20 D 05 on 2 c. brown on buff 20 55
21 05 on 4 c. brown on grey 40 40
22 05 on 15 c. blue .. 50 50
23 05 on 20 c. red on green 30 70
24 05 on 25 c. black on pink 30 50
25 05 on 30 c. brn on drab 40 40
26 10 on 40 c. red on yellow 40 75
27 10 on 45 c. black on grn 30 55
28 10 on 50 c. red on pink 40 40
29 10 on 75 c. brn on orge 45 80

## GREECE Pt. 3

**A country in the S.E. of Europe, under Turkish rule till 1830, when it became a kingdom. A republic was established from 1924 to 1935 when the monarchy was restored. The country was under German occupation from April, 1941 to Oct. 1944.**

**The monarchy was once again abolished during 1973 and a republic set up.**

100 lepta = 1 drachma.

1. Hermes. 2.

**1861.** Imperf or perf.

| | | | | |
|---|---|---|---|---|
| 62 | 1 | 1 l. brown | 4·00 | 3·25 |
| 33 | | 2 l. buff | 6·00 | 8·00 |
| 55 | | 5 l. green | 16·00 | 2·00 |
| 19 | | 10 l. orange on blue | £200 | 24·00 |
| 56 | | 10 l. orange | 16·00 | 2·00 |
| 20 | | 20 l. blue | £160 | 4·00 |
| 59a | | 20 l. red | 2·40 | 1·10 |
| 53 | | 30 l. brown | 32·00 | 2·00 |
| 60 | | 30 l. blue | £140 | 5·00 |
| 28 | | 40 l. mauve on blue | £180 | 14·00 |
| 37 | | 40 l. orange on green | £300 | 90·00 |
| 43d | | 40 l. bistre on blue | 16·00 | 24·00 |
| 43f | | 40 l. green on blue | 48·00 | 35·00 |
| 50 | | 40 l. buff | 14·00 | 32·00 |
| 61 | | 40 l. mauve | 40·00 | 5·00 |
| 52 | | 60 l. green | 24·00 | 60·00 |
| 22 | | 80 l. red | 40·00 | 6·00 |

**1886.** Imperf.

| | | | | |
|---|---|---|---|---|
| 85. | 2. | 1 l. brown | 1·25 | 60 |
| 86. | | 2 l. buff | 1·25 | 1·25 |
| 87. | | 5 l. green | 2·00 | 40 |
| 88. | | 10 l. orange | 7·00 | 40 |
| 89c. | | 20 l. red | 2·40 | 60 |
| 90d. | | 25 l. blue | 30·00 | 1·00 |
| 91a. | | 25 l. purple | 2·40 | 60 |
| 79. | | 40 l. purple | 40·00 | 12·00 |
| 93. | | 40 l. blue | 6·00 | 2·00 |
| 80. | | 50 l. green | 3·00 | 1·00 |
| 81. | | 1 d. grey | 40·00 | 1·00 |

**1886.** Perf.

| | | | | |
|---|---|---|---|---|
| 100. | 2. | 1 l. brown | 1·60 | 80 |
| 96. | | 2 l. buff | 1·25 | 1·25 |
| 102. | | 5 l. green | 3·00 | 75 |
| 103. | | 10 l. orange | 15·00 | 70 |
| 104a. | | 20 l. red | 4·00 | 2·00 |
| 105. | | 25 l. blue | 45·00 | 2·00 |
| 106. | | 25 l. purple | 4·00 | 1·90 |
| 107. | | 40 l. purple | 48·00 | 28·00 |
| 108. | | 40 l. blue | 10·00 | 2·00 |
| 83. | | 50 l. green | 12·00 | 2·40 |
| 84. | | 1 d. grey | 90·00 | 2·40 |

3. Wrestlers. 4. Discus thrower.

5. Vase depicting Pallas Athene. 6. Quadriga of Chariot driving.

**1896.** First Int. Olympic Games. Perf.

| | | | | |
|---|---|---|---|---|
| 110. | 3. | 1 l. yellow | 40 | 20 |
| 111. | | 2 l. red | 40 | 20 |
| 112. | 4. | 5 l. mauve | 60 | 40 |
| 113. | | 10 l. grey | 80 | 40 |
| 114. | 5. | 20 l. brown | 6·50 | 20 |
| 115. | 6. | 25 l. red | 8·00 | 60 |
| 116. | 5. | 40 l. violet | 5·50 | 2·00 |
| 117. | 6. | 60 l. black | 14·00 | 8·00 |
| 118. | – | 1 d. blue | 28·00 | 8·00 |
| 119. | – | 2 d. olive | £100 | 24·00 |
| 120. | – | 5 d. green | £140 | £140 |
| 121. | – | 10 d. brown | £140 | £140 |

DESIGNS—As Type **6**—HORIZ. 1 d. Acropolis and Stadium. 10 d. Acropolis with Parthenon. VERT. 2 d. "Hermes" (after statue by Praxiteles) 5 d. "Victory" (after statue by Paeonius).

**1900.** Surch. Imperf.

| | | | | |
|---|---|---|---|---|
| 122. | 2. | 20 l. on 25 l. blue | 1·25 | 80 |
| 130. | 1. | 30 l. on 40 l. purple | 3·00 | 2·75 |
| 131. | | 40 l. on 2 l. buff | 4·00 | 3·00 |
| 132. | | 50 l. on 40 l. buff | 5·00 | 3·00 |
| 123. | 2. | 1 d. on 40 l. purple | 9·00 | 5·25 |
| 124. | | 2 d. on 40 l. purple | £200 | |
| 133. | 1. | 3 d. on 10 l. orange | 32·00 | 19·00 |
| 134. | | 5 d. on 40 l. purple on blue | 80·00 | 70·00 |

**1900.** Surch. Perf.

| | | | | |
|---|---|---|---|---|
| 125. | 2. | 20 l. on 25 l. blue | 1·25 | 80 |
| 135. | 1. | 30 l. on 40 l. purple | 4·00 | 3·00 |
| 136. | | 40 l. on 2 l. buff | 6·00 | 3·00 |
| 137. | | 50 l. on 40 l. buff | 6·00 | 3·25 |
| 126. | 2. | 1 d. on 40 l. purple | 11·00 | 9·50 |
| 127a. | | 2 d. on 40 l. purple | 6·00 | 6·00 |
| 138. | 1. | 3 d. on 10 l. orange | 40·00 | 19·00 |
| 139. | | 5 d. on 40 l. pur. on blue | 95·00 | 70·00 |

**1900.** Surch. **AM** and value.

| | | | | |
|---|---|---|---|---|
| 140. | 2. | 25 l. on 40 l. pur. (No. 79) | 4·00 | 4·00 |
| 141. | | 25 l. on 40 l. pur. (No. 107) | 10·00 | 10·00 |
| 142. | | 50 l. on 25 l. blue (No. 90d) | 20·00 | 20·00 |
| 143. | | 50 l. on 25 l. blue (No. 105) | 35·00 | 35·00 |
| 144. | 1. | 1 d. on 40 l. brown on blue (No. 43d) | 95·00 | 95·00 |
| 146. | | 1 d. on 40 l. brown on blue (Perf.) | £120 | £120 |
| 145. | | 2 d. on 5 l. green (No. 55) | 12·00 | 12·00 |
| 147. | | 2 d. on 5 l. green (No. 102) | 14·00 | 14·00 |

**1900.** Olympic Games stamps surch. **AM** and value.

| | | | | |
|---|---|---|---|---|
| 148. | 5 | 5 l. on 1 d. blue | 8·00 | 8·00 |
| 149. | 5. | 25 l. on 40 l. violet | 48·00 | 40·00 |
| 150. | – | 50 l. on 2 d. olive | 35·00 | 32·00 |
| 151. | – | 1 d. on 5 d. green | £180 | £110 |
| 152. | – | 2 d. on 10 d. brown | 28·00 | 28·00 |

15. 16. Hermes after the "Mercury" of Giovanni da Bologna. 17.

**1901.**

| | | | | |
|---|---|---|---|---|
| 153. | 15. | 1 l. brown | 30 | 10 |
| 154. | | 2 l. grey | 30 | 20 |
| 155. | | 3 l. orange | 20 | 25 |
| 170. | 16. | 5 l. green | 20 | 10 |
| 171. | | 10 l. red | 50 | 10 |
| 172. | 15. | 20 l. mauve | 65 | 10 |
| 173. | 16. | 25 l. blue | 70 | 15 |
| 174. | 15. | 30 l. purple | 6·00 | 95 |
| 161. | | 40 l. brown | 1·60 | 1·25 |
| 176. | | 50 l. lake | 12·00 | 35 |
| 163. | 17. | 1 d. black | 28·00 | 80 |
| 164. | | 2 d. bronze | 4·00 | 3·50 |
| 165. | | 3 d. silver | 4·00 | 3·50 |
| 166. | | 5 d. gold | 4·00 | 4·00 |

19. Head of Hermes. 20. Athlete throwing Discus. 21. Jumper.

23. Atlas offering the Apples of Hesperides to Hercules.

**1902.**

| | | | | |
|---|---|---|---|---|
| 178. | 19. | 5 l. orange | 1·60 | 65 |
| 179. | | 25 l. green | 21·00 | 2·00 |
| 180. | | 50 l. blue | 21·00 | 2·00 |
| 181. | | 1 d. red | 21·00 | 5·25 |
| 182. | | 2 d. brown | 28·00 | 28·00 |

**1906.** Olympic Games. Dated "1906".

| | | | | |
|---|---|---|---|---|
| 183. | 20. | 1 l. brown | 40 | 25 |
| 184. | | 2 l. black | 40 | 25 |
| 185. | 21. | 3 l. orange | 40 | 25 |
| 186. | | 5 l. green | 80 | 15 |
| 187. | – | 10 l. red | 1·60 | 15 |
| 188. | 23. | 20 l. red | 2·40 | 15 |
| 189. | – | 25 l. blue | 3·25 | 30 |
| 190. | – | 30 l. purple | 2·40 | 1·60 |
| 191. | – | 40 l. brown | 2·40 | 1·60 |
| 192. | 23. | 50 l. purple | 4·00 | 1·60 |
| 193. | – | 1 d. black | 35·00 | 6·00 |
| 194. | – | 2 d. red | 48·00 | 16·00 |
| 195. | – | 3 d. yellow | 70·00 | 70·00 |
| 196. | – | 5 d. blue | 75·00 | 75·00 |

DESIGNS—As Type **20**: 10 l. Victory. 20 l. Wrestlers. 40 l. "Daemon" or God of the Games. As Type **23**: 25 l. Hercules and Antaeus. 1 d., 2 d., 3d. Race, Ancient Greeks. 5 d. Olympic Offerings.

29. Head of Hermes. 30. Iris. 31. Hermes.

32. Hermes and Arcas. (34.) "Greek Administration".

ΕΛΛΗΝΙΚΗ ΔΙΟΙΚΗΣΙΣ

**1911.** Roul.

| | | | | |
|---|---|---|---|---|
| 213. | 29. | 1 l. green | 15 | 10 |
| 214. | 30. | 2 l. red | 15 | 10 |
| 215. | 29. | 3 l. red | 15 | 10 |
| 216. | 31. | 5 l. green | 15 | 10 |
| 217. | 29. | 10 l. red | 15 | 10 |
| 218. | 30. | 15 l. blue | 25 | 10 |
| 219. | | 20 l. lilac | 25 | 10 |
| 220. | | 25 l. blue | 2·40 | 40 |
| 221. | 31. | 30 l. red | 30 | 15 |
| 222. | 30. | 40 l. blue | 1·25 | 65 |
| 223. | 31. | 50 l. purple | 2·40 | 10 |
| 224. | | 80 l. purple | 3·00 | 1·00 |
| 225. | 32. | 1 d. blue | 3·25 | 15 |
| 226. | | 2 d. red | 5·00 | 25 |
| 227. | | 3 d. red (20 × 26½ mm.) | 5·00 | 25 |
| 209. | – | 3 d. red (20¼ × 25½ mm.) | 16·00 | 60 |
| 228 | – | 5 d. blue (20 × 26½ mm.) | 8·00 | 60 |
| 210. | – | 5 d. blue (20¼ × 25½ mm.) | 28·00 | 2·40 |
| 229. | – | 10 b. blue (20 × 26½ mm.) | 5·75 | 60 |
| 211b. | – | 10 d. blue (20¼ × 25½ mm.) | 24·00 | 24·00 |
| 212. | – | 25 d. blue | 32·00 | 32·00 |
| 230. | – | 25 d. slate | 5·75 | 2·00 |

The 25 d. is as Type **29** but larger (24 × 31 mm.).

**1912.** Optd. with T **34.**

| | | | | |
|---|---|---|---|---|
| 248. | 29. | 1 l. green | 60 | 25 |
| 233. | 30. | 2 l. red | 60 | 25 |
| 234. | 29. | 3 l. red | 60 | 25 |
| 249. | 31. | 5 l. green | 60 | 25 |
| 236. | 29. | 10 l. red | 80 | 35 |
| 237. | 30. | 20 l. lilac | 1·25 | 60 |
| 231. | 15. | 20 l. mauve | 2·00 | 2·00 |
| 251. | 30. | 25 l. blue | 1·60 | 80 |
| 239. | 31. | 30 l. red | 1·60 | 1·60 |
| 240. | 30. | 40 l. blue | 2·00 | 2·00 |
| 241. | 31. | 50 l. purple | 2·75 | 1·75 |
| 242. | 32. | 1 d. blue | 5·25 | 1·60 |
| 243. | | 2 d. red | 28·00 | 20·00 |
| 244. | | 3 d. red | 20·00 | 18·00 |
| 245. | | 5 d. blue | 10·00 | 10·00 |
| 246. | | 10 d. blue | 20·00 | 16·00 |
| 247a. | – | 25 d. blue (No. 212) | 40·00 | 40·00 |

35. Vision of Constantine over Athens and Salamis. 36. Victorious Eagle over Mt. Olympus.

**1913.** Occupation of Macedonia, Epirus and the Aegean Is. Rouletted.

| | | | | |
|---|---|---|---|---|
| 252. | 35. | 1 l. brown | 25 | 15 |
| 253. | 36. | 2 l. red | 25 | 15 |
| 254. | | 3 l. orange | 25 | 30 |
| 255. | 35. | 5 l. green | 80 | 10 |
| 256. | | 10 l. red | 1·90 | 10 |
| 257. | | 20 l. violet | 10·00 | 2·00 |
| 258. | 36. | 25 l. blue | 1·60 | 40 |
| 259. | 35. | 30 l. green | 35·00 | 1·25 |
| 260. | 36. | 40 l. blue | 4·00 | 2·00 |
| 261. | 35. | 50 l. blue | 2·00 | 2·00 |
| 262. | 36. | 1 d. purple | 2·75 | 1·60 |
| 263. | 35. | 2 d. brown | 32·00 | 4·00 |
| 264. | 36. | 3 d. blue | 90·00 | 15·00 |
| 265. | 35. | 5 d. grey | 90·00 | 22·00 |
| 266. | 36. | 10 d. red | 95·00 | £150 |
| 267. | 35. | 25 d. black | 95·00 | £160 |

37. Hoisting the Greek Flag at Suda Bay, 1 May 1913. (38.)

**1913.** Union of Crete with Greece.

| | | | | |
|---|---|---|---|---|
| 268. | 37. | 25 l. black and blue | 5·00 | 4·00 |

**1916.** Stamps of 1911 optd. with T **38.**

| | | | | |
|---|---|---|---|---|
| 269. | 29. | 1 l. green | 30 | 20 |
| 270 | 30. | 2 l. red | 40 | 20 |
| 271. | 29. | 3 l. red | 40 | 35 |
| 272. | 31. | 5 l. green | 45 | 60 |
| 273. | 29. | 10 l. red | 80 | 30 |
| 274. | 30. | 20 l. lilac | 1·25 | 20 |
| 275. | | 25 l. blue | 1·25 | 20 |
| 276. | 31. | 30 l. red | 1·40 | 1·25 |
| 277. | 30. | 40 l. blue | 8·00 | 2·40 |
| 278. | 31. | 50 l. purple | 24·00 | 1·60 |
| 281. | 32. | 1 d. blue | 20·00 | 60 |
| 282. | | 2 d. red | 20·00 | 2·00 |
| 283. | | 3 d. red | 12·00 | 2·00 |
| 284. | | 5 d. blue | 32·00 | 5·75 |
| 285. | | 10 d. blue | 16·00 | 16·00 |

ΕΠΑΝΑΣΤΑΣΙΣ 1922 ΛΕΠΤΑ 10

39. Iris. (46.) "Revolution, 1922".

**1917.** Perf. or imperf.

| | | | | |
|---|---|---|---|---|
| 286. | 39. | 1 l. green | 35 | 20 |
| 287. | | 5 l. green | 35 | 20 |
| 288. | | 10 l. red | 40 | 20 |
| 289. | | 25 l. blue | 60 | 35 |
| 290. | | 50 l. purple | 5·00 | 2·50 |
| 291. | | 1 d. blue | 80 | 50 |
| 292. | | 2 d. red | 2·40 | 80 |
| 293. | | 3 d. red | 11·00 | 6·00 |
| 294. | | 5 d. blue | 2·75 | 2·40 |
| 295. | | 10 d. blue | 45·00 | 14·00 |
| 296. | | 25 d. grey | 60·00 | 60·00 |

**1923.** Revolution of 1922. Stamps of 1913, surch. as T **46.**

| | | | | |
|---|---|---|---|---|
| 340. | 36. | 5 l. on 3 l. orange | 15 | 15 |
| 341. | 35. | 10 l. on 20 l. violet | 60 | 50 |
| 342. | 36. | 10 l. on 25 l. blue | 25 | 20 |
| 343. | 35. | 10 l. on 30 l. green | 25 | 30 |
| 344. | 36. | 10 l. on 40 l. blue | 30 | 30 |
| 345. | 35. | 50 l. on 50 l. blue | 30 | 30 |
| 346. | | 2 d. on 2 d. brown | 35·00 | 35·00 |
| 347. | 36. | 3 d. on 3 d. blue | 2·00 | 2·00 |
| 348. | 35. | 5 d. on 5 d. grey | 2·25 | 2·25 |
| 349. | 36. | 10 d. on 1 d. purple | 6·00 | 6·00 |
| 350. | | 10 d. on 10 d. red | £550 | |

**1923.** Stamps of 1916 surch. as T **46.**

| | | | | |
|---|---|---|---|---|
| 351. | 39. | 5 l. on 10 l. red | 10 | 10 |
| 352. | | 50 l. on 50 l. purple | 15 | 10 |
| 353. | | 1 d. on 1 d. blue | 15 | 10 |
| 354. | | 2 d. on 2 d. red | 25 | 15 |
| 355. | | 3 d. on 3 d. red | 85 | 85 |
| 356. | | 5 d. on 5 d. blue | 80 | 80 |
| 357. | | 25 d. on 25 d. blue | 18·00 | 18·00 |

**1923.** Cretan stamps of 1900 surch. as T **46.**

| | | | | |
|---|---|---|---|---|
| 358. | 1. | 5 l. on 1 l. brown | 22·00 | |
| 359. | 3. | 10 l. on 10 l. red | 25 | 20 |
| 361. | | 10 l. on 25 l. blue | 25 | 25 |
| 362. | 1. | 50 l. on 50 l. lilac | 30 | 25 |
| 363. | | 50 l. on 50 l. blue | 2·40 | 2·40 |
| 364. | 4. | 50 l. on 1 d. violet | 80 | 80 |
| 365. | – | 50 l. on 5 d. (No. 19) | 22·00 | |

**1923.** Cretan stamps of 1905 surch. as T **46.**

| | | | | |
|---|---|---|---|---|
| 366. | – | 10 l. on 20 l. (No. 24) | 90·00 | 90·00 |
| 367. | – | 10 l. on 25 l. (No. 25) | 20 | 20 |
| 368. | – | 50 l. on 50 l. (No. 26) | 20 | 20 |
| 369. | 16. | 50 l. on 1 d. (No. 27) | 1·40 | 1·40 |
| 370. | – | 3 d. on 3 d. (No. 28) | 3·25 | 3·25 |
| 371. | – | 5 d. on 5 d. (No. 29) | 3·25 | 3·25 |

**1923.** Cretan stamps of 1907/8 surch. as T **46.**

| | | | | |
|---|---|---|---|---|
| 372. | 21. | 10 l. on 10 l. red | 20 | 10 |
| 373. | 19. | 10 l. on 25 l. blk. & blue | 50 | 50 |
| 374. | | 50 l. on 1 d. (No. 31) | 2·00 | 2·00 |

No. 372 is as Crete No. 36 but without "HELLAS" optd. No. 377 is the optd. stamp.

**1923.** Optd. stamps of Crete surch. as T **46.**

| | | | | |
|---|---|---|---|---|
| 375. | 1. | 5 l. on 1 l. brn. (No. 32) | 10 | 10 |
| 376. | – | 5 l. on 5 l. grn. (No. 34) | 20 | 20 |
| 377. | 21. | 10 l. on 10 l. red (No. 36) | 20 | 20 |
| 378. | – | 10 l. on 20 l. (No. 37) | 25 | 20 |
| 379. | – | 10 l. on 25 l. (No. 30) | 30 | 30 |
| 381. | – | 50 l. on 50 l. (No. 39) | 40 | 30 |
| 382. | 16. | 50 l. on 1 d. (No. 40) | 1·90 | 1·90 |
| 384. | – | 3 d. on 3 d. (No. 42) | 8·00 | 8·00 |
| 385. | – | 5 d. on 5 d. (No. 43) | £100 | £100 |

**1923.** Postage Due stamps of Crete of 1900 surch. as T **38.**

| | | | | |
|---|---|---|---|---|
| 386. | D 8. | 5 l. on 5 l. red | 15 | 15 |
| 387. | | 5 l. on 10 l. red | 15 | 15 |
| 388. | | 10 l. on 20 l. red | 6·00 | 6·00 |
| 389. | | 10 l. on 40 l. red | 25 | 30 |
| 390. | | 50 l. on 50 l. red | 25 | 20 |
| 391. | | 50 l. on 1 d. red | 40 | 40 |
| 392. | | 50 l. on 1 d. on 1 d. red | 3·50 | 3·50 |
| 393. | | 2 d. on 2 d. red | 75 | 60 |

**1923.** Postage Due stamps of Crete of 1908 with opt. surch. as T **46.**

| | | | | |
|---|---|---|---|---|
| 397. | D 8. | 5 l. on 5 l. red | 25 | 15 |
| 398. | | 5 l. on 10 l. red | 25 | 25 |
| 399. | | 10 l. on 20 l. red | 25 | 20 |
| 400. | | 50 l. on 50 l. red | 35 | 20 |
| 401. | | 50 l. on 1 d. red | 1·00 | 1·00 |
| 402. | | 2 d. on 2 d red | 3·50 | 3·50 |

47. Lord Byron. 49. Grave of Marco Botzaris.

**1924.** Byron Cent.

| | | | | |
|---|---|---|---|---|
| 403. | 47. | 80 l. blue | 45 | 15 |
| 404. | – | 2d. black and violet | 95 | 45 |

DESIGN—HORIZ. (45 × 30 mm.): 2 d. **Byron at Missolonghi.**

**1926.** Cent. of Fall of Missolonghi. Roul.

| | | | | |
|---|---|---|---|---|
| 405. | 49. | 25 l. mauve | 85 | 35 |

50. Savoia Marchetti S-55C Flying Boat.

**1926.** Air. As T **50.**

| | | | | |
|---|---|---|---|---|
| 406. | | 2 d. multicoloured | 1·25 | 45 |
| 407. | | 3 d. multicoloured | 11·00 | 6·50 |
| 408. | | 5 d. blue, lilac and red | 1·25 | 80 |
| 409. | | 10 d. multicoloured | 11·00 | 6·50 |

51. Corinth Canal. 52. Dodecanese Costume.

53. Temple of Theseus, Athens. 54. Acropolis.

**1927.**

410. **51.** 5 l. green .. .. 35 10
411. **52.** 10 l. red .. .. .. 40 10
412. – 20 l. violet .. .. 50 10
413. – 25 l. green .. .. 60 10
414. – 40 l. green .. .. 85 10
415. **51.** 50 l. violet .. .. 1·40 10
416. 80 l. black and blue .. 1·25 30
417. **53.** 1 d. brown and blue .. 1·25 10
418b. – 2 d. black and green .. 7·25 10
419d. – 3 d. black and violet .. 9·25 15
419e. – 4 d. brown .. .. 24·00 80
420. – 5 d. black and orange .. 18·00 1·00
421. – 10 d. black and red .. 60·00 4·00
422. – 15 d. black and green .. 60·00 8·00
423a. **54.** 25 d. black and green .. 32·00 12·00

DESIGNS—As Type **52**: 20 l. Macedonian costume. 25 l. Monastery of Simon Peter. **40 l.** White Tower, Salonika. As Type **53**: 2 d. Acropolis. 3 d. Cruiser " Averoff ". 4 d. Mistra Cathedral. As Type **54**: 5 d., 15 d. The Academy of Sciences, Athens. 10 d. Temple of Theseus.

**55.** General Favier and Acropolis.

**1927.** Cent. of Liberation of Athens.

424. **55.** 1 d. red .. .. .. 40 25
425. 3 d. blue .. .. 3·50 40
426. 6 d. green .. .. 10·00 7·25

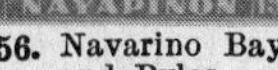

**56.** Navarino Bay and Pylos. **58.** Sir Edward Codrington.

**1927.** Centenary of Battle of Navarino.

427. **56.** 1 d. 50 green .. .. 2·00 15
428. – 4 d. blue .. .. 8·00 55
429. **58.** 5 d. black & brown (A) 8·00 2·75
430. – 5 d. black & brown (B) 35·00 6·00
431. – 5 d. black and blue .. 35·00 6·00
432. – 5 d. black and red .. 14·00 6·00

DESIGNS: 4 d. Battle of Navarino. 5 d. (No. 429) " Sir Codrington " (A). 5 d. (No. 430) " Sir Edward Codrington " (B). 5 d. (No. 431) De Rigny. 5 d. (No. 432) Van der Heyden.

**59.** Rhigas Ferreo. **64.** Monastery of Arkadi, Crete, and Abbott Gabriel.

**1930.** Independence Cent.

433. **59.** 10 l. brown .. .. 15 10
434. – 20 l. black .. .. 15 10
435. – 40 l. green .. .. 40 40
436. – 50 l. red .. .. .. 40 40
437. – 50 l. blue .. .. 40 40
438. – 1 d. red .. .. .. 40 40
439. – 1 d. orange .. .. 35 15
440. – 1 d. 50 blue .. .. 55 10
441. – 1 d. 50 red .. .. 70 10
442. – 2 d. orange .. .. 80 15
443. – 3 d. brown .. .. 1·25 45
444. – 4 d. blue .. .. 4·00 80
445. – 5 d. purple .. .. 2·00 1·25
446. – 10 d. black .. .. 12·00 4·75
447. – 15 d. green .. .. 14·50 8·00
448. – 20 d. blue .. .. 18·00 8·00
449. – 25 d. black .. .. 16·00 10·00
450. – 50 d. brown .. .. 40·00 35·00

DESIGNS as Type **59**: 20 l. Patriarch Gregory V. 40 l. A. Ypsilanti. 50 l. (No. 436) L. Boubou-lina. 50 l. (437), Ath. Diakos. 1 d. (438), Th. Colocotroni. 1 d. (439), C. Kanaris. 1 d. 50, (440), Karaiskakes. 1 d. 50 (441), M. Botzaris. 2 d. A. Miaoulis. 3 d. L. Kondouriotis. 5 d. Capo d'Istria. 10 d. P. Mavromichalis. 15 d. Solomos. 20 d. Corais. (27½ × 40 mm.): 4 d. Map of Greece. (27 × 44 mm.): 50 d. Sortie from Missolonghi. (43 × 28½ mm.): 25 d. Declaration of Independence.

**1930.**

451. **64.** 8 d. violet .. .. 20·00 80

**1932.** Stamps of 1927 surch.

452. – 1 d. 50 l. on 5 d. black and blue (No. 431) .. 3·00 15
453. – 1 d. 50 l. on 5 d. black and red (No. 432) .. 3·00 15
454. **55.** 2 d. on 3 d. blue .. 4·00 25
455. **58.** 2 d. on 5 d. black and brown (No. 429) .. 4·00 25
456. – 2 d. on 5 d. black and brown (No. 430) .. 10·00 25
457. **55.** 4 d. on 6 d. green .. 4·00 80

**66.** "Graf Zeppelin" and Acropolis.

**1933.** Air.

458. **66.** 30 d. red .. .. 16·00 8·00
459. 100 d. blue .. .. 90·00 40·00
460. 120 d. brown .. .. 90·00 40·00

**67.** Swinging the Propeller. **68.** " Flight ".

**1933.** Air. Aeroespresso Company issue.

461 **67** 50 l. orange and green 60 25
462 – 1 d. orange and blue .. 60 40
463 – 3 d. brown and purple 1·00 60
464 **68** 5 d. blue and orange .. 10·00 3·25
465 – 10 d. black and red 1·75 1·40
466 – 20 d. green and black .. 10·00 4·00
467 – 50 d. blue and brown .. 70·00 45·00

DESIGNS—HORIZ. 1 d. Temple of Neptune, Corinth. 3 d. Marina Fiat MF.5 flying boat over Hermoupolis. 10 d. Map of Italy–Greece–Rhodes–Turkey air routes. VERT. 20 d. Hermes and Marina Fiat MF.5 flying boat. 50 d. Woman and Marina Fiat MF.5 flying boat.

**71.** Greece.

**1933.** Air. Government issue.

468. **71.** 50 l. green .. .. 60 20
469. 1 d. red .. .. .. 1·00 60
470. – 2 d. violet .. .. 1·60 1·00
471. – 5 d. blue .. .. 7·25 2·75
472. – 10 d. red .. .. 9·75 5·25
473. **71.** 25 d. blue .. .. 48·00 16·00
474. – 50 d. brown .. .. 50·00 42·00

DESIGNS—VERT. 2, 10 d. Ikarian Islands. HORIZ. 5, 50 d. Junkers G.24 airplane and Acropolis.

**74.** Admiral Kondouriotis and Cruiser " Averoff ". **75.** " Greece ".

**1933.**

475. **74.** 50 d. blue and black .. 60·00 2·00
476. **75.** 75 d. purple and black .. £100 £100
477. – 100 d. green and brown £550 18·00

DESIGN—VERT. 100 d. Statue (Youth of Marathon).

**78.** Athens Stadium, Entrance.

**1934.**

479. **78.** 8 d. blue .. .. £110 2·40

**79.** Sun Chariot. **83.** King Constantine.

**1935.** Air. Mythological designs.

488a. **79.** 1 d. red .. .. .. 15 15
488b. – 2 d. blue .. .. 15 15
488c. – 5 d. mauve .. .. 15 20
488d. – 7 d. blue .. .. 15 20
484. – 10 d. brown .. .. 2·25 2·00
488e. – 10 d. orange .. .. 1·40 1·40
485. – 25 d. red .. .. 2·40 2·40
486. – 30 d. green .. .. 70 80
487. – 50 d. mauve .. .. 3·50 3·50
488. – 100 d. brown .. .. 1·00 1·00

DESIGNS—HORIZ. 2 d. Iris. 30 d. Triptolemus. 100 d. Phrixus and Helle. VERT. **5 d. Daedalus** and Icarus. 7 d. Minerva. 10 d. Hermes. 25 d. Zeus and Ganymede. 50 d. Bellerophon on Pegasus.

**1935.** Restoration of Greek Monarchy. Surch. **3 November 1935** in Greek, with crown or arms, and value.

489. D **20.** 50 l. on 40 l. blue .. 30 40
490. 3 d. on 3 d. red .. 80 80
492. – 5 d. on 100 d. green & brown (No. 477) .. 2·00 80
493. **75.** 15 d. on 75 d. purple and black .. .. 9·75 5·00

**1936.** Re-burial of King and Queen.

494. **83.** 3 d. brown and black .. 80 30
495. 8 d. blue and black .. 1·40 1·00

**85.** Pallas Athene (Minerva). **86.** Bull-leaping.

**89.** King George II. **89a.** Statue of King Constantine.

**1937.** Cent. of Athens University.

496. **85.** 3 d. brown .. .. 80 40

**1937.**

497. **86.** 5 l. blue and brown .. 10 10
498. – 10 l. brown and blue .. 10 10
499. – 20 l. green and black .. 10 10
500. – 40 l. black and green .. 10 10
501. – 50 l. black and brown 10 10
502. – 80 l. brown and violet 10 10
503. **89.** 1 d. green .. .. 30 10
515. **89a.** 1 d. 50 green .. .. 25 10
504. – 2 d. blue .. .. 10 10
505. **89.** 3 d. brown .. .. 40 10
506. – 5 d. red .. .. 10 10
507. – 6 d. olive .. .. 10 10
508. – 7 d. brown .. .. 40 35
509. **89.** 8 d. blue .. .. 40 15
510. – 10 d. brown .. .. 10 10
511. – 15 d. green .. .. 15 10
512. – 25 d. blue .. .. 15 10
516. **89a.** 30 d. red .. .. 2·75 2·25
513. **89.** 100 d. red .. .. 12·00 7·75

DESIGNS—(Size as Type **89a**). VERT. 10 l. Court Lady of Tiryns. 20 l. Zeus and Thunderbolt. 80 l. Venus of Milo. 25 d. " Glory " of Psara. HORIZ. 40 l. Amphictyonic Coin. 50 l. Chairing Diagoras of Rhodes. 2 d. Battle of Salamis. 5 d. Panathenaic chariot. 6 d. Alexander the Great at Battle of Issus. 7 d. St. Paul on Mt. Areopagus. 10 d. Temple of St. Demetrius, Salonica. 15 d. Leo III (the Isaurian) destroying Saracens.

**93.** Prince Paul and Princess Frederika Louise.

**1938.** Royal Wedding.

517. **93.** 1 d. green .. .. 25 15
518. 3 d. brown .. .. 25 15
519. 8 d. blue .. .. 1·25 60

**94.** Arms of Greece, Rumania, Turkey and Yugoslavia.

**1938.** Balkan Entente.

520. **94.** 6 d. blue .. .. 8·00 1·60

**1938.** Air. Postage Due stamp optd with Junkers G.24 airplane. Perf or rouletted.

521 D **20** 50 l. brown .. .. 10 10

**96.** Arms of Ionian Islands. **97.** Corfu Bay and Citadel.

**1939.** 75th Anniv. of Cession of Ionian Islands.

523. **96.** 1 d. blue .. .. 1·25 40
524. **97.** 4 d. green .. .. 6·75 1·25
525. – 20 d. orange .. .. 24·00 13·00
526. – 20 d. blue .. .. 24·00 13·00
527. – 20 d. red .. .. 24·00 13·00

DESIGN—HORIZ. 20 d. As Type 1 of Ionian Is. but with portraits of George I of Greece and Queen Victoria.

**99.** Javelin Thrower. **100.** Arms of Greece, Rumania, Turkey and Yugoslavia.

**1939.** 10th Pan-Balkan Games, Athens. Inscr. " 'I' BALKANIAS 1939 ".

528. – 50 l. green .. .. 30 15
529. **99.** 3 d. red .. .. .. 60 15
530. – 6 d. brown on orange .. 3·50 1·90
531. – 8 d. blue on grey .. 3·50 1·90

DESIGNS: 50 l. Runner. 6 d. Discus-thrower. 8 d. Jumper.

**1940.** Balkan Entente.

532. **100.** 6 d. blue .. .. 6·00 1·60
533. 8 d. slate .. .. 6·00 2·00

**101.** Greek Youth Badge. **103.** Meteora Monasteries.

**1940.** 4th Anniv. of Greek Youth Organization.

(a) Postage.

534. **101.** 3 d. blue, red and silver 40 40
535. – 5 d. black and blue .. 6·50 3·50
536. – 10 d. black and orange 11·00 6·00
537. – 15 d. black and green .. 40·00 35·00
538. – 20 d. black and red .. 35·00 24·00
539. – 25 d. black and blue .. 35·00 24·00
540. – 30 d. black and purple .. 40·00 24·00
541. – 50 d. black and red .. 40·00 28·00
542. – 75 d. gold, brown & blue 40·00 28·00
543. **101.** 100 d. blue. red & silver 50·00 45·00

DESIGNS—VERT. 5 d. Boy member. 10 d. Girl member. 15 d. Javelin thrower. 20 d. Youths in column formation. 25 d. Standard bearer and buglers. 30 d. Three youths in uniform. 50 d. Youths on parade. 75 d. Coat of arms.

(b) Air.

544. **103.** 2 d. black and orange .. 80 30
545. – 4 d. black and green .. 2·40 1·60
546. – 6 d. black and red .. 4·75 3·25
547. – 8 d. black and blue .. 8·00 4·75
548. – 16 d. black and violet .. 20·00 14·00
549. – 32 d. black and orange 45·00 35·00
550. – 45 d. black and green .. 45·00 35·00
551. – 55 d. black and red .. 45·00 35·00
552. – 65 d. black and blue .. 45·00 35·00
553. – 100 d. black and violet 48·00 38·00

DESIGNS (views and aircraft): 4 d. Simon Peter Monastery, Mt. Athos. 6, 16 d. Isle of Santorin. 8 d. Church at Pantanassa. 32 d. Ponticonissi, Corfu. 45 d. Acropolis. 55 d. Erechtheum. 65 d. Temple of Nike. 100 d. Temple of Zeus.

**1941.** Postage Due stamps optd with Junkers G.24 airplane, No. 556 also surch. Perf (558/60), perf or rouletted (556/7).

556 D **20** 1 d. on 2 d. red .. 10 10
557 5 d. blue .. .. 20 20
558 10 d. green .. .. 10 10
559 25 d. red .. .. 40 40
560 50 d. orange .. .. 50 50

105. "Boreas" (North Wind). 106. Windmills on Mykonos Is.

**1942.** Air. Designs symbolical of winds.

| No. | Type | Description | Unused | Used |
|---|---|---|---|---|
| 561. | 105. | 2 d. green | 15 | 15 |
| 562. | – | 5 d. red | 15 | 15 |
| 563. | – | 10 d. brown | 20 | 20 |
| 567 | – | 10 d. red | 10 | 10 |
| 564. | – | 20 d. blue | 40 | 40 |
| 565. | – | 25 d. orange | 15 | 15 |
| 568. | – | 25 d. green | 10 | 10 |
| 566. | – | 50 d. black | 60 | 60 |
| 569. | – | 50 d. blue | 10 | 10 |
| 570. | 105. | 100 d. black | 10 | 10 |
| 571. | – | 200 d. red | 10 | 10 |
| 572. | – | 400 d. grey | 10 | 10 |

DESIGNS: 5 d. "Notos" (South). 10 d. "Apiliotis" (East). 20 d. "Lips" (South-west). 25 d. "Zephyr" (West). 50 d. "Kekias" (North-east). 200 d. "Evros" (South-east). 400 d. "Skiron" (North-west).

**1942.**

| No. | Type | Description | Unused | Used |
|---|---|---|---|---|
| 573. | 106. | 2 d. brown | 20 | 20 |
| 574. | – | 5 d. green | 15 | 10 |
| 575. | – | 10 d. blue | 15 | 10 |
| 576. | – | 15 d. purple | 15 | 10 |
| 577. | – | 25 d. orange | 15 | 10 |
| 578. | – | 50 d. blue | 15 | 10 |
| 579. | – | 75 d. red | 15 | 10 |
| 580. | – | 100 d. black | 15 | 10 |
| 581. | – | 200 d. blue | 15 | 10 |
| 582. | – | 500 d. brown | 15 | 10 |
| 583. | – | 1000 d. brown | 15 | 10 |
| 584. | – | 2000 d. blue | 15 | 10 |
| 585. | – | 5000 d. red | 15 | 15 |
| 586. | – | 15,000 d. purple | 15 | 15 |
| 587. | – | 25,000 d. green | 15 | 15 |
| 588. | – | 500,000 d. blue | 20 | 15 |
| 589. | 106. | 2,000,000 d. green | 20 | 15 |
| 590. | – | 5,000,000 d. red | 20 | 15 |

DESIGNS: 5 d., 5,000,000 d. Burzi Fortress, Nauplion. 10 d., 500,000 d. Katokhi on Aspropotamos River. 15 d. Heraklion, Crete. 25 d. Houses on Hydra Is. 50 d., Meteora Monastery. 75 d. Edessa. 100 d., 200 d. Monastery on Mt. Athos. 500 d., 5000 d. Konitza Bridge. 1000 d., 15,000 d. Ekatontapiliani Church. 2000 d., 25,000 d. Kerkyra (Corfu) Is.

110. Child.

**1943.** Children's Welfare Fund.

| No. | Type | Description | Unused | Used |
|---|---|---|---|---|
| 592. | 110. | 25 d.+25 d. green | 10 | 15 |
| 593. | – | 100 d.+50 d. purple | 10 | 15 |
| 594. | – | 200 d.+100 d. brown | 10 | 15 |

DESIGN: 100 d. Mother and child. 200 d. Madonna and child.

(112.)

**1944.** Children's Convalescent Camp Fund. Surch. as T **112**. (a) Postage.

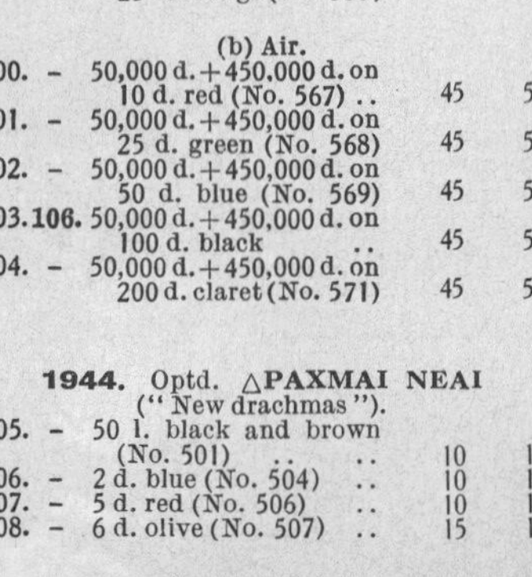

| No. | Type | Description | Unused | Used |
|---|---|---|---|---|
| 595. | 106. | 50,000 d.+450,000 d. on 2 d. brown | 45 | 50 |
| 596. | – | 50,000 d.+450,000 d. on 5 d. green (No. 574) | 45 | 50 |
| 597. | – | 50,000 d.+450,000 d. on 10 d. blue (No. 575) | 45 | 50 |
| 598. | – | 50,000 d.+450,000 d. on 15 d. purple (No. 576) | 45 | 50 |
| 599. | – | 50,000 d.+450,000 d. on 25 d. orange (No. 577) | 45 | 50 |

(b) Air.

| No. | Type | Description | Unused | Used |
|---|---|---|---|---|
| 600. | – | 50,000 d.+450,000 d. on 10 d. red (No. 567) | 45 | 50 |
| 601. | – | 50,000 d.+450,000 d. on 25 d. green (No. 568) | 45 | 50 |
| 602. | – | 50,000 d.+450,000 d. on 50 d. blue (No. 569) | 45 | 50 |
| 603. | 106. | 50,000 d.+450,000 d. on 100 d. black | 45 | 50 |
| 604. | – | 50,000 d.+450,000 d. on 200 d. claret (No. 571) | 45 | 50 |

**1944.** Optd. ΔΡΑΧΜΑΙ ΝΕΑΙ ("New drachmas").

| No. | Type | Description | Unused | Used |
|---|---|---|---|---|
| 605. | – | 50 l. black and brown (No. 501) | 10 | 10 |
| 606. | – | 2 d. blue (No. 504) | 10 | 10 |
| 607. | – | 5 d. red (No. 506) | 10 | 10 |
| 608. | – | 6 d. olive (No. 507) | 15 | 15 |

92. "Glory" of Psara. 114. "ΟΧΙ" = No.

**1945.**

| No. | Type | Description | Unused | Used |
|---|---|---|---|---|
| 609 | 92 | 1 d. purple | 15 | 10 |
| 610 | | 3 d. red | 20 | 10 |
| 611 | | 5 d. blue | 20 | 10 |
| 612 | | 10 d. brown | 20 | 10 |
| 613 | | 20 d. violet | 40 | 10 |
| 614 | | 50 d. green | 60 | 30 |
| 615 | | 100 d. blue | 4·00 | 3·25 |
| 616 | | 200 d. green | 1·60 | 1·10 |

For 25 d. in Type **92** but larger, see No. 512.

**1945.** Resistance to Italian Ultimatum.

| No. | Type | Description | Unused | Used |
|---|---|---|---|---|
| 617. | 114. | 20 d. orange | 15 | 15 |
| 618. | | 40 d. blue | 15 | 15 |

115. President Roosevelt. 117. E. Venizelos.

**1945.** Roosevelt Mourning Issue. Black borders.

| No. | Type | Description | Unused | Used |
|---|---|---|---|---|
| 619. | 115. | 30 d. purple | 10 | 10 |
| 620. | | 60 d. grey | 15 | 15 |
| 621. | | 200 d. violet | 15 | 15 |

**1946.** Surch. Δ **PX** and new value in ornamental rectangle.

| No. | Type | Description | Unused | Used |
|---|---|---|---|---|
| 622. | – | 10 d. on 10 d. (No. 567) | 15 | 10 |
| 623. | – | 10 d. on 2000 d. (No. 584) | 15 | 15 |
| 624. | – | 20 d. on 50 d. (No. 569) | 15 | 15 |
| 625. | – | 20 d. on 500 d. (No. 582) | 15 | 15 |
| 626. | – | 20 d. on 1000 d. (No. 583) | 20 | 20 |
| 627. | – | 30 d. on 5 d. (No. 574) | 30 | 15 |
| 628. | – | 50 d. on 50 d. (No. 578) | 30 | 15 |
| 629. | – | 50 d. on 25,000 d. (No. 587) | 30 | 15 |
| 630. | – | 100 d. on 10 d. (No. 575) | 1·00 | 20 |
| 631. | 106. | 100 d. on 2,000,000 d. | 80 | 20 |
| 632. | – | 130 d. on 20 l. (No. 499) | 80 | 20 |
| 633. | – | 250 d. on 20 l. (No. 499) | 80 | 20 |
| 634. | – | 300 d. on 80 l. (No. 502) | 80 | 25 |
| 635. | – | 450 d. on 75 d. (No. 579) | 1·25 | 30 |
| 636. | – | 500 d. on 5,000,000 d. (No. 590) | 2·00 | 60 |
| 637. | – | 1000 d. on 500,000 d. (No. 588) | 9·00 | 1·60 |
| 638. | – | 2000 d. on 5,000 d. (No. 585) | 22·00 | 2·75 |
| 639. | – | 5000 d. on 15,000 d. (No. 586) | 80·00 | 20·00 |

**1946.** Tenth Anniversary of Death of Venizelos (statesman).

| No. | Type | Description | Unused | Used |
|---|---|---|---|---|
| 640. | 117. | 130 d. green | 25 | 20 |
| 641. | | 300 d. brown | 15 | 10 |

**1946.** Restoration of Monarchy. Surch. with value in circle and date **1-9-1946.**

| No. | Type | Description | Unused | Used |
|---|---|---|---|---|
| 642. | 89. | 50 d. on 1 d. green | 20 | 10 |
| 643. | | 250 d. on 3 d. brown | 40 | 15 |
| 644. | | 600 d. on 8 d. blue | 3·25 | 1·00 |
| 645. | | 3000 d. on 100 d. red | 4·50 | 80 |

119. Women carrying Munitions, Pindos Mountains. 121. Panayiotis Tsaldaris.

**1946.** Victory. War Scenes.

| No. | Type | Description | Unused | Used |
|---|---|---|---|---|
| 646. | – | 50 d. green | 40 | 10 |
| 647. | – | 100 d. blue | 20 | 10 |
| 648. | 119. | 250 d. green | 25 | 10 |
| 649. | – | 500 d. brown | 40 | 20 |
| 650. | – | 600 d. brown | 60 | 40 |
| 651. | – | 1000 d. violet | 1·75 | 25 |
| 682. | – | 1000 d. green | 2·40 | 30 |
| 652. | – | 2000 d. blue | 8·75 | 1·40 |
| 653. | – | 5000 d. red | 11·00 | 80 |

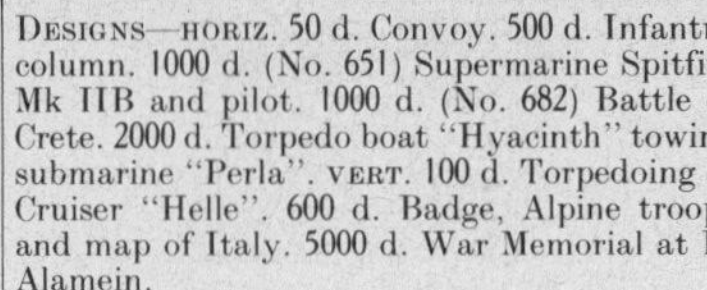

DESIGNS—HORIZ. 50 d. Convoy. 500 d. Infantry column. 1000 d. (No. 651) Supermarine Spitfire Mk IIB and pilot. 1000 d. (No. 682) Battle of Crete. 2000 d. Torpedo boat "Hyacinth" towing submarine "Perla". VERT. 100 d. Torpedoing of Cruiser "Helle". 600 d. Badge, Alpine troops and map of Italy. 5000 d. War Memorial at El Alamein.

**1946.** 10th Death Anniv. of P. Tsaldaris.

| No. | Type | Description | Unused | Used |
|---|---|---|---|---|
| 654. | 121. | 250 d. brown and pink | 1·25 | 30 |
| 655. | | 600 d. blue | 1·40 | 40 |

**1947.** King George II Mourning issue. Surch. with value in circle in corner and black border.

| No. | Type | Description | Unused | Used |
|---|---|---|---|---|
| 656. | 89. | 50 d. on 1 d. green | 15 | 15 |
| 657. | | 250 d. on 3 d. brown | 30 | 15 |
| 658. | | 600 d. on 8 d. blue | 80 | 30 |

124. Castelrosso Fortress. 126. Apollo (T1 of Aegean Is.)

**1947.** Restoration of Dodecanese Is. to Greece.

| No. | Type | Description | Unused | Used |
|---|---|---|---|---|
| 659. | 124. | 20 d. blue | 25 | 10 |
| 660. | – | 30 d. pink and black | 25 | 10 |
| 661. | – | 50 d. blue | 30 | 10 |
| 662. | – | 100 d. green and olive | 30 | 10 |
| 663. | – | 200 d. orange | 25 | 10 |
| 664. | – | 250 d. grey | 40 | 10 |
| 665. | – | 300 d. orange | 30 | 10 |
| 666. | – | 400 d. blue | 35 | 10 |
| 667. | 126. | 450 d. blue | 50 | 10 |
| 668. | – | 450 d. blue | 75 | 10 |
| 669. | 126. | 500 d. red | 35 | 10 |
| 670. | – | 600 d. purple | 35 | 20 |
| 671. | – | 700 d. mauve | 65 | 15 |
| 672. | – | 700 d. green | 4·75 | 20 |
| 673. | – | 800 d. green and violet | 1·25 | 20 |
| 674. | – | 1000 d. olive | 40 | 10 |
| 675. | 126. | 1300 d. red | 2·40 | 25 |
| 676. | 124. | 1500 d. brown | 20·00 | 60 |
| 677. | – | 1600 d. blue | 2·75 | 25 |
| 678. | – | 2000 d. red and brown | 20·00 | 20 |
| 679. | – | 2600 d. green | 2·75 | 1·25 |
| 680. | – | 5000 d. violet | 24·00 | 40 |
| 681. | – | 10,000 d. blue | 26·00 | 40 |

DESIGNS—HORIZ. 100 d., 400 d. St. John's Convent, Patmos. VERT. 30 d., 1600 d., 2000 d. Dodecanese vase. 50 d., 300 d. Woman in national costume. 200 d., 250 d. E. Xanthos. 450 d. (No. 668), 800 d. Casos Is. and frigate. 600 d., 700 d. (2), 5000 d. Statue of Hippocrates. 1000 d., 2600 d., 10000 d. Colossus of Rhodes.

DESIGNS — VERT. 1000 d. Captive children and map of Greece. 1800 d. Hand menacing woman and child.

129. Column of Women and Children.

**1949.** Abduction of Greek Children to other Countries.

| No. | Type | Description | Unused | Used |
|---|---|---|---|---|
| 683. | 129. | 450 d. violet | 1·00 | 40 |
| 684. | – | 1000 d. brown | 2·50 | 35 |
| 685. | – | 1800 d. red | 3·50 | 40 |

130. Maps and Flags.

**1950.** Battle of Crete.

| No. | Type | Description | Unused | Used |
|---|---|---|---|---|
| 686. | 130. | 1000 d. blue | 2·00 | 25 |

131. "Youth of Marathon".

**1950.** 75th Anniv. of U.P.U. Inscr. "1874–1949" in white figures at top.

| No. | Type | Description | Unused | Used |
|---|---|---|---|---|
| 687. | 131. | 1000 d. green on buff | 55 | 25 |

133. St. Paul. 134.

**1951.** 19th Cent. of St. Paul's Travels in Greece.

| No. | Type | Description | Unused | Used |
|---|---|---|---|---|
| 688. | – | 700 d. purple | 80 | 25 |
| 689. | 133. | 1600 d. blue | 2·75 | 60 |
| 690. | 134. | 2600 d. brown | 4·25 | 1·25 |
| 691. | – | 10,000 d. brown | 55·00 | 38·00 |

DESIGNS—As Type **134**: 700 d. Sword and altar (horiz.). 10,000 d. St. Paul preaching to Athenians (vert.).

135. "Industry". 136. Blessing before Battle.

**1951.** Reconstruction Issue.

| No. | Type | Description | Unused | Used |
|---|---|---|---|---|
| 692. | 135. | 700 d. orange | 2·00 | 10 |
| 693. | – | 800 d. green | 4·00 | 40 |
| 694. | – | 1300 d. blue | 6·00 | 15 |
| 695. | – | 1600 d. olive | 20·00 | 20 |
| 696. | – | 2600 d. violet | 55·00 | 1·10 |
| 697. | – | 5000 d. purple | 55·00 | 35 |

DESIGNS—VERT. 800 d. Fish and trident. 1300 d. Workmen and column. 1600 d. Ceres and tractors. 2600 d. Women and loom. 5000 d. Map and stars ("Electrification").

**1952.** Air. Anti-Communist Campaign.

| No. | Type | Description | Unused | Used |
|---|---|---|---|---|
| 698. | 136. | 1,000 d. blue | 80 | 20 |
| 699. | – | 1,700 d. turquoise | 2·40 | 1·00 |
| 700. | – | 2,700 d. brown | 6·75 | 3·25 |
| 701. | – | 7,000 d. green | 20·00 | 9·50 |

DESIGNS—VERT. 1,700 d. "Victory" over mountains. 2,700 d. Infantry attack. 7,000 d. "Victory" and soldiers.

137. King Paul. 138. "Spirit of Greece".

**1952.** 50th Birthday of King Paul.

| No. | Type | Description | Unused | Used |
|---|---|---|---|---|
| 702. | 137. | 200 d. green | 40 | 20 |
| 703. | – | 1,000 d. red | 60 | 20 |
| 704. | 138. | 1,400 d. blue | 4·75 | 1·25 |
| 705. | 137. | 10,000 d. purple | 28·00 | 8·00 |

139. "Oranges".

**1953.** National Products.

| No. | Type | Description | Unused | Used |
|---|---|---|---|---|
| 706. | 139. | 500 d. orange and red | 80 | 15 |
| 707. | – | 700 d. yellow and brown | 1·25 | 10 |
| 708. | – | 1,000 d. green and blue | 1·60 | 15 |
| 709. | – | 1,300 c. buff & purple | 2·75 | 15 |
| 710. | – | 2,000 d. green & brown | 8·50 | 25 |
| 711. | – | 2,600 d. bistre & violet | 6·75 | 1·00 |
| 712. | – | 5,000 d. green & brown | 14·50 | 40 |

DESIGNS—VERT. 700 d. "Tobacco" (tobacco plant). 1,300 d. "Wine" (wineglass and vase). 2,000 d. "Figs" (basket of figs). 2,600 d. "Dried Fruit" (grapes and currant bread). 5,000 d. "Grapes" (male figure holding grapes). HORIZ. 1,000 d. "Olive Oil" (Pallas Athene and olive branch).

**MORE DETAILED LISTS**

are given in the Stanley Gibbons Catalogues referred to in the country headings.

For lists of current volumes see Introduction.

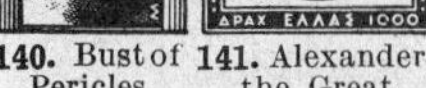

140. Bust of Pericles. 141. Alexander the Great. 143. Athlete Bearing Torch.

**1954.** Ancient Greek Art. Sculptures, etc.
713. 140. 100 d. brown .. .. 35 10
714. – 200 d. black .. .. 45 10
715. – 300 d. violet .. .. 45 10
716. – 500 d. green .. .. 45 10
717. – 600 d. red .. .. 45 15
718. 141. 1,000 d. black and blue 80 10
719. – 1,200 d. olive .. .. 80 10
720. – 2,000 d. brown .. 3·25 15
721. – 2,400 d. blue .. .. 3·25 45
722. – 2,500 d. green .. 3·50 35
723. – 4,000 d. red .. .. 6·50 30
724. – 20,000 d. purple .. 80·00 1·25
DESIGNS—As Type 140: VERT. 200 d. Mycenaean oxhead vase. 1,200 d. Head of charioteer of Delphi. 2,000 d. Vase of Dipylon. 2,500 d. Man carrying calf. 20,000 d. Two pitcher bearers. HORIZ. 2,400 d. Hunting wild boar. As Type 141: VERT. 300 d. Bust of Homer. 500 d. Zeus of Istiaca. 600 d. Youth's head. 4,000 d. Dish depicting voyage of Dionysus.
See also Nos. 733a/41.

**1954.** Air. 5th Anniv. of N.A.T.O. Inscr. "NATO".
725. 143. 1,200 d. orange .. 2·75 15
726. – 2,400 d. green .. 23·00 1·10
727. – 4,000 d. blue .. 48·00 2·00
DESIGNS—VERT. 2,400 d. Amphictyonic coin. 4,000 d. Pallas Athene.

Currency revalued. 1000 old drachma = one new drachma.

144. Extracts from "Hansard" (Parliamentary Debates). 145. Samian Coin Depicting Pythagoras.

**1954.** "Enosis" (Union of Cyprus with Greece).
728. 144. 1.20 d. black & yellow 1·60 40
729. 2 d. black and salmon 5·50 1·40
730. 2 d. black and blue .. 5·50 1·40
731. 2.40 d. blk. & lavender 5·50 80
732. 2.50 d. black and pink 5·50 1·00
733. 4 d. black and lemon .. 20·00 2·75
On No. 728 the text is in Greek, on Nos. 730/1 in French and on the remainder in English.

**1955.** As Nos. 713/24 but new colours and values.
733a. 140. 10 l. green .. .. 20 10
734. – 20 l. myrtle (No. 714) 20 10
734a. – 20 l. purple (No. 714) 15 25
735. 140. 30 l. brown .. .. 30 10
736. – 50 l. lake (No. 716) .. 50 10
736a. – 50 l. green (No. 716) .. 50 10
736b. – 70 l. orange (No. 719) 15 20
737. – 1 d. green (No. 717) .. 80 10
737a. – 1 d. brown (No. 717) 1·25 10
737b. – 1 d. 50 blue (No. 724) 5·50 30
738. 141. 2 d. black and brown 3·00 10
738a. 2 d. 50 black & mauve 5·25 10
739. – 3 d. orange (No. 721) 5·50 20
739a. – 3 d. blue (No. 722) .. 1·00 25
740. – 3 d. 50 red (No. 715) 5·50 50
741. – 4 d. blue (No. 723) .. 40·00 35

**1955.** Pythagorean Congress.
742. 145. 2 d. green .. .. 2·00 25
743. – 3 d. 50 black .. .. 6·00 1·75
744. 145. 5 d. purple .. .. 20·00 1·25
745. – 6 d. blue .. .. 16·00 16·00
DESIGNS—VERT. 3 d. 50, Representation of Pythagoras theorem. HORIZ. 6 d. Map of Samos.

146. Rotary Emblem and Globe. 147. King George I.

**1956.** 50th Anniv. of Rotary Int.
746. 146. 2 d. blue .. .. 4·50 30

**1956.** Royal Family.
747. – 10 l. violet .. .. 20 10
748. – 20 l. purple .. .. 20 10
749. 147. 30 l. sepia .. .. 25 10
750. – 50 l. brown .. .. 25 10
751. – 70 l. blue .. .. 25 15
752. – 1 d. turquoise .. 40 10
753. – 1 d. 50 slate .. .. 1·25 25
754. – 2 d. black .. .. 1·40 10
755. – 3 d. brown .. .. 80 15
756. – 3 d. 50 brown .. 4·75 25
757. – 4 d. green .. .. 3·50 15
758. – 5 d. red .. .. 1·40 10
759. – 7 d. 50 blue .. .. 3·50 1·25
760. – 10 d. blue .. .. 9·25 25
PORTRAITS—HORIZ. 10 l. King Alexander. 5 d. King Paul and Queen Frederica. 10 d. King and Queen and Crown Prince Constantine. VERT. 20 l. Crown Prince Constantine. 50 l. Queen Olga. 70 l. King Otto. 1 d. Queen Amalia. 1 d. 50, King Constantine. 2 d. King Paul. 3 d. King George II. 3 d. 50, Queen Sophia. 4d. Queen Frederica. 7 d. 50, King Paul.
See also Nos. 764/77.

148. Dionysios Solomos. 149. "Argo" (5th Century B.C.).

**1957.** Death Centenary of D. Solomos (national poet).
761. – 2 d. yellow and brown 3·00 20
762 148. 3 d. 50 grey and blue .. 3·00 1·90
763. – 5 d. bistre and green .. 4·00 4·00
DESIGNS—HORIZ. 2 d. Solomos and K. Mantzaros (composer). 5 d. Zante landscape and Solomos.

**1957.** As Nos. 747/60. Colours changed.
764. – 10 l. red .. .. 15 10
765. – 20 l. orange .. .. 15 10
766. 147. 30 l. black .. .. 15 10
767. – 50 l. green .. .. 20 10
768. – 70 l. purple .. .. 25 15
769. – 1 d. red .. .. 45 10
770. – 1 d. 50 l. green .. 55 10
771. – 2 d. red .. .. 1·25 10
772. – 3 d. blue .. .. 1·75 10
773. – 3 d. 50 l. purple .. 3·50 25
774. – 4 d. brown .. .. 4·00 15
775. – 5 d. blue .. .. 5·25 20
776. – 7 d. 50 l. yellow .. 60 80
777. – 10 d. green .. .. 24·00 60

**1958.** Greek Merchant Marine Commemoration. Ship designs.
778. – 50 l. multicoloured .. 25 10
779. – 1 d. ochre, blk. & blue 35 10
780. – 1 d. 50 l. red, blk. & blue 1·75 1·40
781. – 2 d. multicoloured .. 70 15
782. – 3 d. 50 l. blk., red & bl. 1·75 40
783. 149. 5 d. multicoloured .. 7·25 5·75
SHIPS: 50 l. "Michael Carras" (tanker). 1 d. "Queen Frederika" (liner). 1 d. 50, Full-rigged sailing ship, 1821. 2 d. Byzantine galley. 3 d. 50, 6th-century B.C. galley.

150. The Piraeus (Port of Athens). 151. "Narcissus" and Flower.

**1958.** Air. Greek Ports.
784. 150. 10 d. multicoloured .. 5·50 15
785. – 15 d. multicoloured .. 1·40 20
786. – 20 d. multicoloured .. 5·50 15
787. – 25 d. multicoloured .. 1·40 25
788. – 30 d. multicoloured .. 1·40 25
789. – 50 d. blue, blk. & brn. 2·50 25
790. – 100 d. blue, blk. & brn. 12·00 1·75
PORTS: 15 d. Salonika. 20 d. Patras. 25 d. Hermoupolis (Syra). 30 d. Volos (Thessaly). 50 d. Kavalla. 100 d. Heraklion (Crete).

**1958.** Int. Congress for Protection of Nature, Athens. Mythological and Floral designs. Multicoloured.
791. 20 l. Type 151 .. .. 15 15
792. 30 l. "Daphne and Apollo" 15 15
793. 50 l. "Venus and Adonis" (Venus and hibiscus) .. 15 15
794. 70 l. "Pan and the Nymph" (Pan and pine cones) .. 25 15
795. 1 d. Crocus .. .. 30 15
796. 2 d. Iris .. .. 35 15
797. 3 d. 50 Tulip .. .. 15 15
798. 5 d. Cyclamen .. .. 1·25 1·25
SIZES—As Type 151: 30 l. to 70 l. 21½ × 26 mm. 1d.): 22×32 mm. (2 d., 3 d., 50 l. and 5 d.)

152. Jupiter's Head and Eagle (Olympia 4th-century B.C. coin).

**1959.** Ancient Greek Coins. Designs as T 152 showing both sides of each coin. Inscriptions in black.
799. 152. 10 l. green & brown .. 15 20
800. – 20 l. grey and blue .. 15 10
801. – 50 l. grey and purple .. 15 10
802. – 70 l. grey and blue .. 25 25
803. – 1 d. drab and red .. 30 10
804. – 1 d. 50 grey and ochre 50 10
805. – 2 d. 50 drab & mauve .. 85 10
806. – 4 d. 50 grey and green 1·75 35
807. – 6 d. blue and olive .. 7·25 10
808. – 8 d. 50 drab and red .. 80 80
COINS—HORIZ. 20 l. Athene's head and owl (Athens 5th cent. B.C.). 50 l. Nymph Arethusa and chariot (Syracuse 5th cent. B.C.). 70 l. Hercules and Jupiter (Alexander the Great 4th cent. B.C.). 1 d. 50, Griffin and squares (Abdera, Thrace 5th cent. B.C.). 2 d. 50, Apollo and lyre (Chalcidice, Macedonia 4th cent. B.C.). VERT. 1 d. Helios and rose (Rhodes 4th cent. B.C.). 4 d. 50, Apollo and labyrinth (Crete 3rd cent. B.C.). 6 d. Venus and Apollo (Paphos, Cyprus 4th cent. B.C.). 8 d. 50, Ram's heads and incised squares (Delphi 5th cent. B.C.).
See also Nos. 909/17.

153. Amphitheatre, Delphi. 154. "Victory" and Greek Soldiers through the Ages.

156. Imre Nagy (formerly Prime Minister of Hungary). 155. "The Good Samaritan".

**1959.** Ancient Greek Theatre.
809. – 20 l. multicoloured .. 20 20
810. – 50 l. brown and olive .. 35 20
811. – 1 d. multicoloured .. 35 30
812. – 2 d. 50 brown and blue 55 10
813. 153. 3 d. 50 multicoloured .. 4·75 4·75
814. – 4 d. 50 brown & black 80 50
815. – 6 d. brn., grey & blk. 80 45
DESIGNS—VERT. 20 l. Ancient theatre audience (after a Pharsala Thessaly, vase of 580 B.C.). 50 l. Clay mask of 3rd century B.C. 1 d. Flute, drum and lyre. 2 d. 50, Actor (3rd century statuette). 6 d. Performance of a satirical play (after a mixing-bowl of 410 B.C.). HORIZ. 4 d. 50, Performance of Euripides' "Andromeda" (after a vase of 4th century B.C.).

**1959.** 10th Anniv. of Greek Anti-Communist Victory.
816. 154. 2 d. 50 blue, black and brown .. .. 1·25 25

**1959.** Red Cross Commem. Cross in red.
817. – 20 l. multicoloured .. 15 15
818. – 50 l. grey, red and blue 25 15
819. – 70 l. blk., brn., bis. & bl. 45 40
820. – 2 d. 50 blk., brn., gry. & red .. .. .. 50 10
821. – 3 d. multicoloured .. 4·00 4·00
822. – 4 d. 50 orange and red 1·00 1·00
823. 155. 6 d. multicoloured .. 60 30
DESIGNS—HORIZ. 20 l. Hippocrates Tree, Cos. VERT. 50 l. Bust of Aesculapius. 70 l. St. Basil (after mosaic in Hosios Loukas Monastery, Boeotia). 2 d. 50, Achilles and Patroclus (from vase of 6th cent., B.C.). 3 d. (32×47½ mm.) Red Cross, globe, infirm people and nurses. 4 d. 50, J. H. Dunant.

**1959.** 3rd Anniv. of Hungarian Revolt.
824. 156. 4 d. 50 sepia, brn. & red 40 40
825. 6 d. blk., blue & ultram. 40 40

157. Kostes Palamas. 158. Brig in Storm.

160. Sprinting. 159. Scout emulating St. George.

**1960.** Birth Cent. of Palamas (poet).
826. 157. 2 d. 50 multicoloured 1·25 25

**1960.** World Refugee Year. Multicoloured.
827. 2 d. 50 Type 158 .. .. 50 10
828. 4 d. 50 Brig in calm waters 1·25 60

**1960.** 50th Anniv. of Greek Boy Scout Movement. Multicoloured.
829. 20 l. Type 159 .. .. 15 15
830. 30 l. Ephebi Oath and Scout Promise .. .. 15 15
831. 40 l. Fire rescue work .. 15 15
832. 50 l. Planting tree .. 25 15
833. 70 l. Map reading .. 15 15
834. 1 d. Scouts on beach .. 20 15
835. 2 d. 50 Crown Prince Constantine in uniform .. 60 15
836. 6 d. Greek Scout Flag and Medal .. .. .. 60 60
Nos. 829/30 and 835 are vert. and the rest horiz.

**1960.** Olympic Games.
837. – 20 l. brn., blk. and blue 15 10
838. – 50 l. brown and black 15 10
839. – 70 l. brn., blk. & green 15 15
840. – 80 l. multicoloured .. 15 15
841. – 1 d. multicoloured .. 20 15
842. – 1 d. 50 brn., blk. & orge. 30 10
843. – 2 d. 50 brn., blk. & blue 40 20
844. 160. 4 d. 50 multicoloured .. 80 40
845. – 5 d. multicoloured .. 80 60
846. – 6 d. brn., black & violet 80 60
847. – 12 d. 50 multicoloured 3·50 3·50
DESIGNS—VERT. 20 l. "Armistice" (official holding plaque). 70 l. Athlete taking oath. 2 d. 50, Discus-throwing. 5 d. Javelin-throwing. HORIZ. 50 l. Olympic flame. 80 l. Cutting branches from crown-bearing olive tree. 1 d. Entrance of chief judges. 1 d. 50 Long jumping. 6 d. Crowning the victor. 12 d. 50, Quadriga or chariot-driving (entrance of the victor).

**1960.** 1st Anniv. of European Postal and Telecommunications Conference. As T 373 of Belgium.
848. 4 d. 50 blue .. .. 2·25 1·25

162. Crown Prince Constantine and "Nirefs".

**1961.** Victory of Crown Prince Constantine in Dragon-class Yacht Race, Olympic Games.
849 162 2 d. 50 multicoloured .. 50 25

163. Kastoria.

164. Lilies Vase of Knossos. 165. Reactor Building.

**1961.** Tourist Publicity Issue.
850. 163. 10 l. blue .. .. 15 10
851. – 20 l. plum .. .. 15 10
852. – 50 l. blue .. .. 20 10
853. – 70 l. purple .. .. 20 10
854. – 80 l. blue .. .. 30 20
855. – 1 d. brown .. .. 35 10
856. – 1 d. 50 green .. .. 80 10
857. – 2 d. 50 red .. .. 1·40 10
858. – 3 d. 50 violet .. .. 40 40
859. – 4 d. green .. .. 3·25 10
860. – 4 d. 50 blue .. .. 50 10
861. – 5 d. lake .. .. 3·50 10
862. – 6 d. myrtle .. .. 70 10
863. – 7 d. 50 black .. .. 30 25
864. – 8 d. blue .. .. 2·00 15
865. – 8 d. 50 orange .. 2·40 55
866. – 12 d. 50 sepia .. .. 80 30
DESIGNS—HORIZ. 20 l. The Meteora (Monasteries). 50 l. Hydra. 70 l. Acropolis, Athens. 80 l. Mykonos. 1 d. Salonika. 1 d. 50, Olympia. 2 d. 50, Knossos. 3 d. 50, Rhodes. 4 d. Epidavros. 4 d. 50, Sounion. 5 d. Temple of Zeus, Athens. 7 d. 50, Yannina. 8 d. 50, Delos. VERT. 6 d. Delphi. 8 d. Mount Athos. 8 d. 50, Santorini (Thira).

**1961.** Minoan Art.
867. 164. 20 l. multicoloured .. 20 10
868. – 50 l. multicoloured .. 15 10
869. – 1 d. multicoloured .. 20 10
870. – 1 d. 50 multicoloured 40 15
871. – 2 d. 50 multicoloured 2·75 10
872. – 4 d. 50 multicoloured 1·40 1·40
873. – 6 d. multicoloured .. 2·50 50
874. – 10 d. multicoloured .. 4·50 4·50
DESIGNS—VERT. 1 d. 50, Knossos rhyton-bearer. 4 d. 50, Part of Hagia trias sarcophagus. HORIZ. 50 l. Partridges and fig-pecker (Knossos frieze). 1 l. Kamares fruit dish. 2 d. 50, Ladies of Knossos Palace (painting). 6 d. Knossos dancer (painting). 10 d. Kamares prochus and pithos with spout.

**1961.** Inaug. of "Democritus" Nuclear Research Centre, Aghia Paraskevi.
875. **165.** 2 d. 50 purple & mauve 15 15
876. – 4 d. 50 blue and grey .. 35 35
DESIGN: 4 d. 50, Democritus and atomic symbol.

**166.** Doves. **167.** Emperor Nicephorus Phocas.

**1961.** Europa.
877. **166.** 2 d. 50 red and pink .. 10 10
878. 4 d. 50 ultram. & blue 15 15

**1961.** Millenary of Liberation of Crete from the Saracens.
879. **167.** 2 d. 50 multicoloured .. 40 40

**168.** "Hermes" 1 l. Stamp of 1861. **169.** Ptolemais Steam Plant.

**1961.** Cent. of First Greek Postage Stamps. "Hermes" stamps of 1861. Multicoloured.
880. 20 l. Type **168** .. .. 10 10
881. 50 l. "2 l" .. .. 10 10
882. 1 d. 50 "5 l" .. .. 15 10
883. 2 d. 50 "10 l" .. .. 25 10
884. 4 d. 50 "20 l" .. .. 20 15
885. 6 d. "40 l" .. .. 20 15
886. 10 d. "80 l" .. .. 50 50

**1962.** Electrification Project. Multicoloured.
887. 20 l. Tauropos dam (vert.) 15 10
888. 50 l. Ladhon River hydro-electric plant (vert.) .. 20 10
889. 1 d. Type **169** .. .. 25 25
890. 1 d. 50 Louros River dam 30 15
891. 2 d. 50 Aliverion steam plant .. .. 45 10
892 4 d. 50 Salonika hydro-electric sub-station .. 55 70
893. 6 d. Agra River power station .. .. 1·60 1·60

**170.** Zappion Building. **171.** Europa "Tree".

**1962.** N.A.T.O. Ministers' Conference, Athens.
894. **170.** 2 d. 50 multicoloured .. 20 10
895. – 3 d. sepia, brown & buff 10 10
896. – 4 d. 50 black and blue 30 30
897. – 6 d. black and red .. 25 25
DESIGNS—VERT. 3 d. Ancient Greek warrior with shield. 4 d. 50, Soldier kneeling (after Marathon tomb). 6 d. (21×37 mm.), Soldier (statue in Temple of Aphea, Aegina).

**1962.** Europa.
898. **171.** 2 d. 50 red and black .. 25 10
899. 4 d. 50 blue and black 65 65

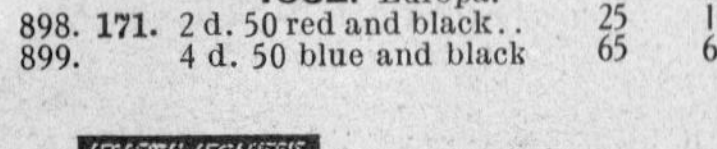
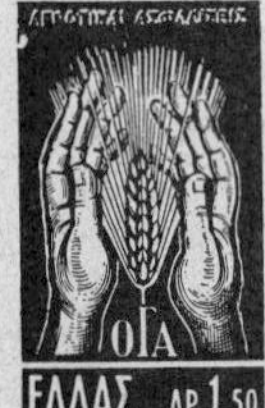

**172.** "Protection". **173.** Demeter, Goddess of Corn.

**1962.** Greek Farmers' Social Insurance Scheme.
900. **172.** 1 d. 50 blk., brn. & red 25 15
901. 2 d. 50 blk., brn. & grn. 30 25

**1963.** Freedom from Hunger. Multicoloured.
902 2 d. 50 Type **173** .. .. 20 15
903 4 d. 50 Wheat ears and globe .. .. 40 40

**174.** Kings of the Greek Dynasty.

**1963.** Cent. of Greek Royal Dynasty.
904 **174** 50 l. red .. .. 30 10
905 1 d. 50 green .. .. 35 15
906 2 d. 50 brown .. 60 10
907 4 d. 50 blue .. .. 1·25 70
908 6 d. violet .. .. 1·40 20

**1963.** Ancient Greek Coins. As Nos. 799/808 but colours changed and some designs rearranged. Inscr. in black; coins in black and drab or grey; background colours given.
909. 50 l. blue (As No. 801) .. 20 10
910. 80 l. purple (As 802) .. 25 25
911. 1 d. green (As 803) .. 35 10
912 1 d. 50 red (As 804) .. 40 10
913. 3 d. olive (As 799) .. 20 10
914. 3 d. 50 red (As 800) .. 20 20
915. 4 d. 50 brown (As 806) .. 20 10
916. 6 d. turquoise (As 807) .. 20 10
917. 8 d. 50 blue (As 808) .. 90 60

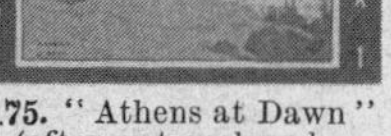

**175.** "Athens at Dawn" (after watercolour by Lord Baden-Powell). **176.** Delphi.

**1963.** 11th World Scout Jamboree, Marathon.
918. **175.** 1 d. multicoloured .. 15 10
919. – 1 d. 50 orge., blk. & blue 15 10
920. – 2 d. 50 multicoloured 30 10
921. – 3 d. blk., brn. and grn. 15 15
922. – 4 d. 50 multicoloured 40 30
DESIGNS—HORIZ: 3 d. A. Lefkadites (founder of Greek Scout Movement) and Lord Baden-Powell. VERT: 1 d. 50, Jamboree Badge. 2 d. 50, Crown Prince Constantine, Chief Scout of Greece. 4 d. 50, Scout bugling with Atlantic trumpet triton shell.

**1963.** Red Cross Cent. Multicoloured.
923. 1 d. Type **176** .. .. 30 15
924. 2 d. Centenary emblem .. 10 10
925. 2 d. 50 Queen Olga .. 10 10
926. 4 d. 50 Henri Dunant .. 30 30

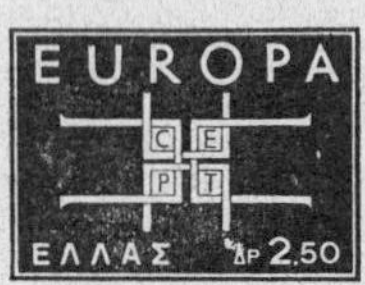

**177.** "Co-operation".

**1963.** Europa.
927. **177.** 2 d. 50 green .. .. 1·75 20
928. 4 d. 50 purple .. 2·25 2·25

**178.** Great Lavra Church. **179.** King Paul.

**1963.** Millenary of Mt. Athos Monastic Community.
929. 30 l. Vatopediou Monastery 15 10
930. 80 l. Dionysion Monastery 20 20
931. 1 d. Protaton Church, Karyae 30 10
932. 2 d. Stavronikita Monastery 40 10
933. 2 d. 50 Cover of Nicephorus Phocas Gospel, Great Lavra Church .. .. 1·25 10
934. 3 d. 50 St. Athanasius the Anthonite (fresco) .. 40 40
935. 4 d. 50 11th-century papyrus, Iviron Monastery 30 30
936. 6 d. Type **178** .. .. 35 40
The 1 d. and 6 d. are horiz., the rest vert.

**1964.** Death of Paul I.
937. **179.** 30 l. brown .. .. 15 10
938. 50 l. violet .. .. 20 10
939. 1 d. green .. .. 55 10
940. 1 d. 50 orange .. 25 10
941. 2 d. blue .. .. 40 10
942. 2 d. 50 sepia .. .. 25 10
943. 3 d. 50 purple .. .. 60 10
944. 4 d. blue .. .. 60 10
945. 4 d. 50 blue .. .. 60 50
946. 6 d. red .. .. 1·25 10

**180.** Gold Coin. **181.** Trident of Paxi.

**182.** Greek Child. **183.** Europa "Flower".

**1964.** Byzantine Art Exn., Athens. Mult.
947. 1 d. Type **180** .. .. 20 10
948. 1 d. 50 "Two Saints" .. 20 10
949. 2 d. "Archangel Michael" 20 10
950. 2 d. 50 "Young Lady" .. 35 10
951. 4 d. 50 "Angel" .. .. 50 50
DESIGN origins: 1 d. reign of Emperor Basil II (976-1025). 1 d. 50, from Harbaville's 10th-cent. ivory triptych (Louvre). 2 d. 14th cent. Constantinople icon (Byzantine Museum, Athens). 2 d. 50, from 14th cent. fresco "The Birth of the Holy Virgin" by Panselinos (Protaton Church, Mt. Athos). 4 d. 50, from 11th cent. mosaic (Daphne Church, Athens).

**1964.** Union of Ionian Islands with Greece. Cent. Inscr. "1864–1964".
952. **181.** 20 l. grey, slate & green 10 10
953. – 30 l. multicoloured .. 10 10
954. – 1 d. light brown, brown and red-brown .. 10 10
955. – 2 d. multicoloured .. 15 10
956. – 2 d. 50 pale green, deep green and green .. 25 10
957. – 4 d. 50 multicoloured 75 65
958. 6 d. multicoloured .. 40 35
DESIGNS: 30 l. Venus of Cythera. 1 d. Ulysses of Ithaca. 2 d. St. George of Levkas. 2 d. 50, Zakynthos of Zante. 4 d. 50, Cephalus of Cephalonia. 6 d. Trireme emblem of Corfu.

**1964.** 50th Anniv. of National Institution of Social Welfare (P.I.K.P.A.).
959. **182.** 2 d. 50 multicoloured .. 40 20

**1964.** Europa.
960. **183.** 2 d. 50 red and green .. 25 15
961. 4 d. 50 brown & drab .. 80 80

**184.** King Constantine II and Queen Anne-Marie. **185.** Peleus and Atalanta (amphora).

**1964.** Royal Wedding.
962. **184.** 1 d. 50 green .. .. 15 15
963. 2 d. 50 red .. .. 30 10
964. 4 d. 50 blue .. .. 20 20

**1964.** Olympic Games, Tokyo. Multicoloured.
965. 10 l. Type **185** .. .. 10 10
966. 1 d. Running (bowl) .. 10 10
967. 2 d. Jumping (pot) .. 15 10
968. 2 d. 50 Throwing the discus 25 10
969. 4 d. 50 Chariot-racing (sculpture) .. .. 45 45
970. 6 d. Boxing (vase) .. .. 15 15
971. 10 d. Apollo (part of frieze, Zeus Temple, Olympia) 40 35
The 1 d., 2 d., 4 d. 50, and 6 d. are horiz.

**186.** "Christ stripping off His garments". **187.** Aesculapius Theatre, Epidavros.

**1965.** 350th Death Anniv. of El Greco.
972. 50 l. Type **186** .. .. 15 10
973. 1 d. "Angels' Concert" .. 15 10
974. 1 d. 50 El Greco's signature 15 10
975. 2 d. 50 Self-portrait .. 15 10
976. 4 d. 50 "Storm-lashed Toledo" .. .. 40 35
The 1 d. 50, is horiz.

**1965.** Greek Artistic Festivals. Mult.
977. 1 d. 50 Type **187** .. .. 15 10
978. 4 d. 50 Herod Atticus Theatre, Athens .. 40 30

**188.** I.T.U. Emblem and Symbols.

**1965.** Centenary of I.T.U.
979. **188.** 2 d. 50 red, blue & grey .. .. 30 15

**189.** "New member making affirmation" (after Tsokos).

**1965.** 150th Anniv. of "Philiki Hetaeria" ("Friends Society"). Multicoloured.
980. 1 d. 50 Type **189** .. .. 10 10
981. 4 d. 50 Society flag .. 30 25

**190.** AHEPA Emblem. **191.** Venizelos as Revolutionary.

**1965.** American Hellenic Educational Progressive Assn. (AHEPA) Congress, Athens.
982. **190.** 6 d. blk., olive & blue 40 25

**1965.** Birth Cent. of E. Venizelos (statesman).
983. **191.** 1 d. 50 green .. .. 10 10
984. – 2 d. blue .. .. 30 40
985. – 2 d. 50 brown .. .. 20 10
DESIGNS: 2 d. Venizelos signing Treaty of Sevres (1920). 2 d. 50, Venizelos.

**192.** Games' Flag. **193.** Symbols of the Planets.

**1965.** Balkan Games, Athens. Multicoloured.
986. 1 d. Type **192** .. .. 10 10
987. 2 d. Victor's medal (vert.) 10 10
988. 6 d. Karaiskakis Stadium, Athens .. .. 25 30

**1965.** Int. Astronautic Conf., Athens. Mult.
989. 50 l. Type **193** .. .. 15 10
990. 2 d. 50 Astronaut in space 15 10
991. 6 d. Rocket and space-ship 30 30

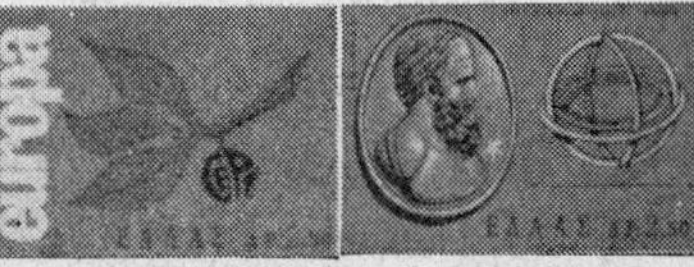

**194.** Europa "Sprig". **195.** Hipparchus (astronomer) and Astrolabe.

**1965.** Europa.
992. **194.** 2 d. 50 blue, blk. & grey 25 15
993. 4 d. 50 grn., blk. & ol. 60 45

**1965.** Opening of Evghenides Planetarium, Athens.
994. **195.** 2 d. 50 blk., red & grn. 30 15

**196.** Carpenter Ants. **197.** St. Andrew's Church, Patras.

**1965.** 50th Anniv. of P.O. Savings Bank. Multicoloured.
995. 10 l. Type **196** .. .. 10 10
996. 2 d. 50 Savings Bank and book .. .. 35 15

**1965.** Restoration of St. Andrew's Head to Greece. Multicoloured.
997. 1 d. Type **197** .. .. 10 10
998. 5 d. St. Andrew, after 11th-cent mosaic, Hosios Loukas Monastry, Boeotia .. .. .. 25 15

**198.** T. Brysakes.

**200.** Geannares (revolutionary leader).

**199.** Greek 25 d. Banknote of 1867.

**1966.** Modern Greek Painters. Mult.

| | | | |
|---|---|---|---|
| 999. | 80 l. Type **198** .. .. | 10 | 10 |
| 1000. | 1 d. N. Lytras .. .. | 10 | 10 |
| 1001. | 2 d. 50 C. Volonakes .. | 10 | 10 |
| 1002. | 4 d. N. Gyses .. .. | 10 | 10 |
| 1003. | 5 d. G. Jacobides .. | 20 | 15 |

**1966.** 125th Anniv. of Greek National Bank.

| | | | |
|---|---|---|---|
| 1004. – | 1 d. 50 green .. | 10 | 10 |
| 1005. – | 2 d. 50 brown .. | 10 | 10 |
| 1006. – | 4 d. blue .. .. | 15 | 10 |
| 1007. **199.** | 6 d. black .. .. | 25 | 20 |

DESIGNS—VERT. (23 × 33½ mm.): 1 d. 50, J.-G. Eynard. 2 d. 50, G. Stavros (founders). HORIZ. (As Type **199**): 4 d. National Bank Headquarters, Athens.

**1966.** Cent. of Cretan Revolt. Mult.

| | | | |
|---|---|---|---|
| 1008. | 2 d. Type **200** .. .. | 15 | 10 |
| 1009. | 2 d. 50 Magazine explosion, Arkadi Monastery (horiz.) | 15 | 10 |
| 1010. | 4 d. 50 Map of Crete (horiz.) | 30 | 25 |

**201.** "Movement of Water" (Decade of World Hydrology).

**202.** Tragedian's Mask of 4th Century, B.C.

**1966.** U.N.O. Events.

| | | | |
|---|---|---|---|
| 1011. **201.** | 1 d. brown, black & blue | 10 | 10 |
| 1012. – | 3 d. multicoloured .. | 10 | 10 |
| 1013. – | 5 d. black, red and blue | 25 | 25 |

DESIGNS—VERT. 3 d. U.N.E.S.C.O. emblem (20th anniv.). 5 d. W.H.O. Building (inauguration of H.Q., Geneva).

**1966.** 2,500th Anniv. of Greek Theatre.

| | | | |
|---|---|---|---|
| 1014. **202.** | 1 d. multicoloured .. | 10 | 10 |
| 1015. – | 1 d. 50 blk., red & brn. | 10 | 10 |
| 1016. – | 2 d. 50 black, green and light green .. | 10 | 10 |
| 1017. – | 4 d. 50 multicoloured | 25 | 25 |

DESIGNS—HORIZ. 1 d. 50, Dionysus in a Thespian ship-chariot (vase painting, 500–480 B.C.). 2 d. 50, Theatre of Dionysus, Athens. VERT. 4 d. 50, Dionysus dancing (after vase painting by Kleophredes, circa 500 B.C.).

**203.** Boeing 707 crossing Atlantic Ocean.

**204.** Tending Plants.

**205.** Europa "Ship". **206.** Horseman (embroidery).

**1966.** Inauguration of Greek Airways Transatlantic Flights.

| | | | |
|---|---|---|---|
| 1018. **203.** | 6 d. indigo and blue | 30 | 15 |

**1966.** Greek Tobacco. Multicoloured.

| | | | |
|---|---|---|---|
| 1019. | 1 d. Type **204** .. | 15 | 10 |
| 1020. | 5 d. Sorting leaf .. | 30 | 25 |

**1966.** Europa.

| | | | |
|---|---|---|---|
| 1021. **205.** | 1 d. 50 olive .. | 20 | 10 |
| 1022. | 4 d. 50 brown .. | 45 | 40 |

**1966.** Greek "Popular" Art. Multicoloured.

| | | | |
|---|---|---|---|
| 1023. | 10 l. Knitting-needle boxes | 10 | 10 |
| 1024. | 30 l. Type **206** .. .. | 10 | 10 |
| 1025. | 50 l. Cretan lyre .. .. | 10 | 10 |
| 1026. | 1 d. "Massa" (Musical instrument) .. .. | 15 | 10 |
| 1027. | 1 d. 50 "Cross and Angels" (bas-relief after Melios) | 15 | 10 |
| 1028. | 2 d. "Sts. Constantine and Helen" (icon) .. | 60 | 10 |
| 1029. | 2 d. 50 Carved altar screen, St. Nicholas' Church, Galaxidion .. .. | 25 | 10 |
| 1030. | 3 d. 19th-century ship of Skyros (embroidery) .. | 25 | 10 |
| 1031. | 4 d. "Psiki" (wedding procession) (embroidery) | 40 | 10 |
| 1032. | 4 d. 50 Distaff .. .. | 30 | 10 |
| 1033. | 5 d. Ear-rings and necklace | 35 | 10 |
| 1034. | 20 d. Detail of handwoven cloth .. .. | 35 | 15 |

The 10 l., 50 l., 1 d., 1 d. 50, 2 d., 2 d. 50, 4 d. 50, and 5 d. designs are vert.

**207.** Princess Alexia. **208.** "Woodcutter" (after D. Filippotes).

**1966.** Princess Alexia's First Birthday.

| | | | |
|---|---|---|---|
| 1035. **207.** | 2 d. green .. .. | 15 | 10 |
| 1036. – | 2 d. 50 brown .. | 20 | 15 |
| 1037. – | 3 d. 50 blue .. .. | 35 | 25 |

PORTRAITS: 2 d. 50, Royal Family. 3 d. 50, Queen Anne-Marie with Princess Alexia.

**1967.** Greek Sculpture. Multicoloured.

| | | | |
|---|---|---|---|
| 1038. | 20 l. "Night" (I. Cossos) | 10 | 10 |
| 1039. | 50 l. "Penelope" (L. Drossos) .. .. | 10 | 10 |
| 1040. | 80 l. "Shepherd" (G. Phitalis) .. .. | 10 | 10 |
| 1041. | 2 d. "Woman's Torso" (K. Demetriades) .. | 25 | 10 |
| 1042. | 2 d. 50 "Kolokotronis" (L. Sochos) .. .. | 15 | 10 |
| 1043. | 3 d. "Girl Sleeping" (I. Halepas) .. .. | 35 | 20 |
| 1044. | 10 d. Type **208** .. .. | 30 | 20 |

Nos. 1038/42 are vert.

**209.** Olympic Rings ("Olympic Day"). **210.** Cogwheels.

**1967.** Sports Events. Multicoloured.

| | | | |
|---|---|---|---|
| 1045. | 1 d. Type **209** .. .. | 15 | 10 |
| 1046. | 1 d. 50 Marathon Cup, first Olympics (1896) .. | 15 | 10 |
| 1047. | 2 d. 50 Hurdling .. .. | 15 | 10 |
| 1048. | 5 d. "The Discus-thrower" after C. Demetriades .. | 30 | 25 |
| 1049. | 6 d. Ancient Olympic stadium .. .. | 35 | 15 |

The 2 d. 50, commemorates the European Athletics Cup, 1967. 5 d. (vert.), The European Highest Award Championships, 1968. 6 d. The Inaug. of "International Academy" buildings, Olympia.

**1967.** Europa.

| | | | |
|---|---|---|---|
| 1050. **210.** | 2 d. 50 multicoloured | 20 | 10 |
| 1051. | 4 d. 50 multicoloured | 50 | 50 |

211 "Lonchi" (Destroyer) and Sailor. **212.** The Plaka, Athens.

**1967.** Nautical Week.

| | | | |
|---|---|---|---|
| 1052. **211.** | 20 l. multicoloured .. | 10 | 10 |
| 1053. – | 1 d. multicoloured .. | 10 | 10 |
| 1054. – | 2 d. 50 multicoloured | 10 | 10 |
| 1055. – | 3 d. multicoloured .. | 30 | 25 |
| 1056. – | 6 d. multicoloured .. | 40 | 15 |

DESIGNS—VERT. 1 d. "Eugene Eugenides" (cadet ship) HORIZ. 2 d. 50, Merchant Marine Academy, Aspropyrgos, Attica. 3 d. Cruiser "Averoff" and Naval School Poros. 6 d. "Australis" (liner) and figure-head.

**1967.** Int. Tourist Year.

| | | | |
|---|---|---|---|
| 1057. – | 2 d. 50 multicoloured | 15 | 10 |
| 1058. – | 4 d. 50 multicoloured | 30 | 25 |
| 1059. **212.** | 6 d. multicoloured .. | 40 | 10 |

DESIGNS—HORIZ. 2 d. 50, Island of Skopelos. 4 d. 50, Apollo's Temple, Bassai, Peleponnese.

**213.** Soldier and Phoenix. **214.** Industrial Skyline.

**1967.** National Revolution of April 21st (1967).

| | | | |
|---|---|---|---|
| 1060. **213.** | 2 d. 50 multicoloured | 15 | 10 |
| 1061. | 3 d. multicoloured .. | 20 | 10 |
| 1062 | 4 d. 50 multicoloured | 45 | 30 |

**1967.** 1st Convention of U.N. Industrial Development Organisation, Athens.

| | | | |
|---|---|---|---|
| 1063. **214.** | 4 d. 50 ultramarine, black and blue .. | 40 | 30 |

**215.** "Seaside Scene" (A. Pelaletos).

**1967.** Children's Drawings. Multicoloured.

| | | | |
|---|---|---|---|
| 1064. | 20 l. Type **215** .. .. | 10 | 10 |
| 1065. | 1 d. 50 "Steamer and Island" (L. Tsirikas) .. | 15 | 10 |
| 1066. | 3 d. 50 "Country Cottage" (K. Ambeliotis) .. | 50 | 40 |
| 1067. | 6 d. "The Church on the Hill" (N. Frangos) .. | 20 | 15 |

**216.** Throwing the Javelin. **217.** F.I.A. and E.L.P.A. Emblems.

**1968.** Sports Events, 1968.

| | | | |
|---|---|---|---|
| 1068. **216.** | 50 l. multicoloured .. | 10 | 10 |
| 1069. – | 1 d. multicoloured .. | 10 | 10 |
| 1070. – | 1 d. 50 multicoloured | 15 | 10 |
| 1071. – | 2 d. 50 multicoloured | 15 | 10 |
| 1072. – | 4 d. multicoloured .. | 35 | 25 |
| 1073. – | 4 d. 50 multicoloured | 30 | 30 |
| 1074. – | 6 d. multicoloured .. | 10 | 10 |

DESIGNS—HORIZ. 1 d. Long-jumping. 4 d. Olympic rings (Olympic Day). VERT. 1 d. 50, "Apollo's Head", Temple of Zeus. 2d. 50, Olympic scene on Attic vase. 4 d. 50, "Throwing the Discus", sculpture by Demetriades (European Athletic Championships, 1969). 6 d. Long-distance running. The 50 l., 1 d. and 6 d. represent the Balkan Games, and the 1 d. 50, and 2 d. 50, the Olympic Academy Meeting.

**1968.** General Assembly of Int. Automobile Federation (F.I.A.), Athens.

| | | | |
|---|---|---|---|
| 1075. **217.** | 5 d. blue and brown .. | 20 | 15 |

**218.** Europa "Key".

**1968.** Europa.

| | | | |
|---|---|---|---|
| 1076. **218.** | 2 d. 50 multicoloured | 15 | 15 |
| 1077. | 4 d. 50 multicoloured | 50 | 50 |

**219.** "Athene defeats Alkyoneus" (from frieze, Altar of Zeus, Pergamos).

**1968.** "Hellenic Fight for Civilization" Exn., Athens.

| | | | |
|---|---|---|---|
| 1078. **219.** | 10 l. multicoloured .. | 10 | 10 |
| 1079. – | 20 l. multicoloured .. | 10 | 10 |
| 1080. – | 50 l. multicoloured .. | 10 | 10 |
| 1081. – | 1 d. 50 multicoloured | 10 | 10 |
| 1082. – | 2 d. 50 multicoloured | 20 | 10 |
| 1083. – | 3 d. multicoloured .. | 25 | 10 |
| 1084. – | 4 d. 50 multicoloured | 15 | 15 |
| 1085. – | 6 d. multicoloured .. | 20 | 20 |

DESIGNS—VERT. (24×37 mm.). 20 l. Athene attired for battle (bronze from Piraeus). 50 l. Alexander the Great (from sarcophagus of Alexander of Sidon.) 2 d. 50, Emperor Constantine Paleologos (lithograph by D. Tsokos). (28×40 mm.). 3 d. "Greece in Missolonghi" (painting by Delacroix). 4 d. 50, "Evzone" (Greek soldier, painting by G. B. Scott). 6 d. "Victory of Samothrace" (statue). HORIZ. (40×28 mm.). 1 d. 50, Emperors Constantine and Justinian making offerings to the Holy Mother (Byzantine mosaic).

**220.** "The Unknown Priest and Teacher" (Rhodes monument). **221.** Congress Emblem.

**1968.** 20th Anniv. of Dodecanese Union with Greece. Multicoloured.

| | | | |
|---|---|---|---|
| 1086. | 2 d. Type **220** .. .. | 15 | 10 |
| 1087. | 5 d. Greek-flag on map (vert.) .. .. .. | 50 | 45 |

**1968.** 19th Biennial Congress of Greek Orthodox Arch-diocese of North and South America.

| | | | |
|---|---|---|---|
| 1088. **221.** | 6 d. multicoloured .. | 20 | 10 |

**222.** GAPA Emblem. **223.** "Hand of Aesculapius" (fragment of bas-relief from Asclepios' Temple, Athens).

**1968.** Regional Congress of Greek-American Progressive Assn. (GAPA).

| | | | |
|---|---|---|---|
| 1089. **222.** | 6 d. multicoloured .. | 20 | 10 |

**1968.** 5th European Cardiological Congress. Athens.

| | | | |
|---|---|---|---|
| 1090. **223.** | 4 d. 50 blk., yell. & lake | 70 | 50 |

**224.** Panathenaic Stadium. **226.** Goddess "Hygeia".

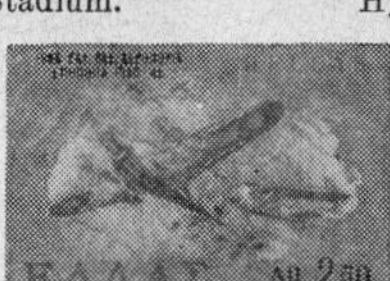


**225.** Westland Lysander Mk 1 ramming Savoia Marchetti Sparviero.

**1968.** Olympic Games, Mexico. Multicoloured.

| | | | |
|---|---|---|---|
| 1091. | 2 d. 50 Type **224** .. | 15 | 10 |
| 1092. | 5 d. Ancient Olympia .. | 35 | 15 |
| 1093. | 10 d. One of Pindar's odes | 55 | 50 |

The 10 d. is 28×40 mm.

**1968.** Royal Hellenic Air Force. Mult.

| | | | |
|---|---|---|---|
| 1094 | 2 d. 50 Type **225** .. | 15 | 10 |
| 1095 | 3 d. 50 Mediterranean Flight in Breguet 19, 1928 .. .. | 35 | 15 |
| 1096 | 8 d. Farman H.F.III biplane and Lockheed Super Starfighter (vert) | 50 | 35 |

**1968.** 20th Anniv. of World Health Organization.

| | | | |
|---|---|---|---|
| 1097. **226.** | 5 d. multicoloured .. | 20 | 10 |

**227.** St. Zeno, the Letter-carrier. **228.** "Workers' Festival Parade" (detail from Minoan vase).

**1969.** Greek Post Office Festival.

| | | | |
|---|---|---|---|
| 1098. **227.** | 2 d. 50 multicoloured | 35 | 15 |

**1969.** 50th Anniv. of Int. Labour Organization.

| | | | |
|---|---|---|---|
| 1099. – | 1 d. 50 multicoloured | 15 | 10 |
| 1100. **228.** | 10 d. multicoloured .. | 50 | 50 |

DESIGN: 1 d. 50 "Hephaestus and Cyclops" (detail from ancient bas-relief).

229. Yacht Harbour, Vouliagmeni.

230. Ancient Coin of Kamarina.

**1969.** Tourism. Multicoloured.

| | | | |
|---|---|---|---|
| 1101. | 1 d. Type **229** .. .. | 15 | 10 |
| 1102. | 5 d. "Chorus of Elders" (Ancient drama) (vert.) | 45 | 45 |
| 1103. | 6 d. View of Astypalia .. | 30 | 10 |

**1969.** 20th Anniv. of N.A.T.O. Multicoloured.

| | | | |
|---|---|---|---|
| 1104. | 2 d. 50 Type **230** .. | 40 | 10 |
| 1105. | 4 d. 50 "Going into Battle" (from Corinthian vase) | 70 | 65 |

No. 1105 is horiz.

231. Colonnade.

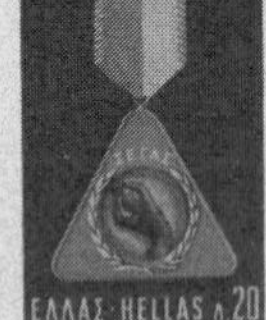

232. Gold Medal.

**1969.** Europa.

| | | | |
|---|---|---|---|
| 1106. **231.** | 2 d. 50 multicoloured | 15 | 15 |
| 1107. | 4 d. 50 multicoloured | 80 | 90 |

**1969.** 9th European Athletic Championships, Athens. Multicoloured.

| | | | |
|---|---|---|---|
| 1108. | 20 l. Type **232** .. .. | 15 | 10 |
| 1109. | 3 d. Pole-vaulting, and ancient pentathlon contest .. .. .. | 20 | 10 |
| 1110. | 5 d. Relay-racing, and Olympic race c. 525 B.C. (horiz.) .. .. | 30 | 10 |
| 1111. | 8 d. Throwing the discus modern and c. 480 B.C. | 50 | 50 |

233. "19th-century Brig and Steamship" (I. Poulakas).

234. Raising the Flag on Mt. Grammos.

**1969.** Navy Week and Merchant Marine Year. Multicoloured.

| | | | |
|---|---|---|---|
| 1112. | 80 l. Type **233** .. .. | 25 | 25 |
| 1113. | 2 d. "Olympic Garland" (tanker) .. .. | 25 | 10 |
| 1114. | 2 d. 50 "Naval and Merchant Ships. War of Independence, 1821" (Anon.) .. .. | 65 | 10 |
| 1115. | 4 d. 50 "Velos" (destroyer) .. .. | 1·10 | 40 |
| 1116. | 6 d. "The Battle of Salamis" (C. Volonakis) | 1·25 | 65 |

**1969.** 20th Anniv. of Communists' Defeat on Mounts Grammos and Vitsi.

| | | | |
|---|---|---|---|
| 1117. **234.** | 2 d. 50 multicoloured | 60 | 20 |

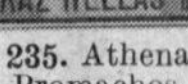

235. Athena Promachos.

236. Demetrius Karatasios (statue by G. Demetriades).

**1969.** 25th Anniv. of Liberation. Mult.

| | | | |
|---|---|---|---|
| 1118. | 4 d. Type **235** .. .. | 20 | 10 |
| 1119. | 5 d. "Resistance" (21 × 37 mm) .. .. | 40 | 40 |
| 1120. | 6 d. Map of Eastern Mediterranean theatre .. | 25 | 10 |

**1969.** Heroes of Macedonia's Fight for Freedom. Multicoloured.

| | | | |
|---|---|---|---|
| 1121. | 1 d. 50 Type **236** .. .. | 15 | 10 |
| 1122. | 2 d. 50 Emmanuel Pappas (statue by N. Perantinos) .. .. | 25 | 10 |
| 1123. | 3 d. 50 Pavlos Melas (from painting by P. Mathiopoulos) .. .. | 30 | 15 |
| 1124. | 4 d. 50 Capetan Kotas .. | 35 | 35 |

237. Dolphin Mosaic, Delos.

**1970.** Greek Mosaics. Multicoloured.

| | | | |
|---|---|---|---|
| 1125. | 20 l. "Angel of the Annunciation", Daphne (11th-century) .. | 15 | 10 |
| 1126. | 1 d. Type **237** .. .. | 20 | 10 |
| 1127. | 1 d. 50 "The Holy Ghost". Hosios Loukas Monastery (11th-century) .. | 25 | 10 |
| 1128. | 2 d. "Hunter", Pella (4th-century B.C.) .. | 25 | 10 |
| 1129. | 5 d. "Bird", St. George's Church, Salonika (5th-century) .. .. | 30 | 20 |
| 1130. | 6 d. "Christ", Nea Moni Church, Khios (5th century) .. .. | 35 | 30 |

SIZES—VERT. Nos. 1125, 1127/9, 23 × 34 mm. No. 1130 as Type **237**.

238. Overwhelming the Cretan Bull (sculpture).

239. "Flaming Sun".

**1970.** "The Labours of Hercules".

| | | | |
|---|---|---|---|
| 1131. **238.** | 20 l. multicoloured .. | 15 | 10 |
| 1132. – | 30 l. multicoloured .. | 15 | 10 |
| 1133. – | 1 d. blk., blue & slate | 20 | 10 |
| 1134. – | 1 d. 50 brn., green & ochre .. .. | 20 | 10 |
| 1135. – | 2 d. multicoloured .. | 1·25 | 10 |
| 1136. – | 2 d. 50 brn., red & buff | 15 | 10 |
| 1137. – | 3 d. multicoloured .. | 1·25 | 10 |
| 1138. – | 4 d. 50 multicoloured | 15 | 20 |
| 1139. – | 5 d. multicoloured .. | 15 | 10 |
| 1140. – | 6 d. multicoloured .. | 15 | 10 |
| 1141. – | 20 d. multicoloured | 35 | 30 |

DESIGNS—HORIZ. 30 l. Hercules and Cerberus (from decorated pitcher). 1 d. 50, The Lernean Hydra (from stamnos). 2 d. Hercules and Geryon (from amphora). 4 d. 50, Combat with the River-god Achelous (from pitcher). 5 d. Overwhelming the Nemean Lion (from amphora). 6 d. The Stymphalian Birds (from vase). 20 d. Wrestling with Antaeus (from bowl). VERT: 1 d. Golden Apples of the Hesperides (sculpture). 2 d. 50, The Erymanthine Boar (from amphora). 3 d. The Centaur Nessus (from vase).

**1970.** Europa.

| | | | |
|---|---|---|---|
| 1142. **239.** | 2 d. 50 yellow & red | 1·25 | 15 |
| 1143. – | 3 d. blue & new blue | 40 | 10 |
| 1144. **239.** | 4 d. 50 yellow & blue | 1·25 | 1·25 |

DESIGN—VERT. 3 d. "Owl" and CEPT emblem.

240. Satellite and Dish Aerial.

241. Saints Cyril and Methodius with Emperor Michael III, (from 12th-cent. wall-painting).

**1970.** Satellite Earth Telecommunications Station, Thermopylae.

| | | | |
|---|---|---|---|
| 1145. **240.** | 2 d. 50 multicoloured | 15 | 10 |
| 1146. | 4 d. 50 multicoloured | 45 | 45 |

**1970.** Saints Cyril and Methodius Commemoration. Multicoloured.

| | | | |
|---|---|---|---|
| 1147. | 50 l. Saints Demetrius, Cyril and Methodius (mosaic) .. .. | 10 | 10 |
| 1148. | 2 d. St. Cyril (Russian miniature) .. .. | 30 | 30 |
| 1149. | 5 d. Type **241** .. .. | 30 | 20 |
| 1150. | 10 d. St. Methodius (Russian miniature) .. | 30 | 30 |

SIZES (all stamps are vert.): 50 l. 21 × 37 mm. 2 d. and 10 d. 26 × 37 mm. 5 d. $28\frac{1}{2}$ × 41 mm.

Nos. 1148 and 1150 were issued together se-tenant in the sheet forming a composite design.

242. Cephalonian Fir.

244. New U.P.U. Headquarters Building, Berne (Opening).

243. "Cultural Links".

**1970.** Nature Conservation Year. Mult.

| | | | |
|---|---|---|---|
| 1151. | 80 l. Type **242** .. .. | 35 | 30 |
| 1152. | 2 d. 50 "Jankaea heldreichii" (plant) .. | 80 | 15 |
| 1153. | 6 d. Rock Partridge (horiz.) .. .. | 3·50 | 50 |
| 1154. | 8 d. Wild goat .. .. | 1·75 | 1·75 |

SIZES: 2 d. 50, is smaller, 23 × 34 mm.

**1970.** American-Hellenic Education Progressive Association Congress, Athens.

| | | | |
|---|---|---|---|
| 1155. **243.** | 6 d. multicoloured .. | 40 | 10 |

**1970.** Anniversaries. Multicoloured.

| | | | |
|---|---|---|---|
| 1156. | 50 l. Type **244** .. .. | 15 | 10 |
| 1157. | 2 d. 50 Emblem (Int. Education Year) (vert.) .. | 25 | 10 |
| 1158. | 3 d. 50 Mahatma Gandhi (birth cent.) (vert.) .. | 25 | 20 |
| 1159. | 4 d. "25" (25th Anniv. of United Nations) (vert.) | 30 | 15 |
| 1160. | 4 d. 50 Beethoven (birth bicent.) (vert.) .. | 65 | 65 |

Nos. 1157 and 1160 are larger, $28\frac{1}{2}$ × 41 mm.

245. "The Nativity".

**1970.** Christmas. Scenes from "The Mosaic of the Nativity", Hosios Loukas Monastery. Multicoloured.

| | | | |
|---|---|---|---|
| 1161. | 2 d. "The Shepherds" (vert.) .. .. .. | 15 | 10 |
| 1162. | 4 d. 50 "The Magi" (vert.) .. .. | 35 | 25 |
| 1163. | 6 d. Type **245** .. .. | 40 | 40 |

246. "Death of Bishop of Salona in Battle, Alamana" (lithograph).

**1971.** 150th Anniv. of War of Independence. (1st issue). The Church. Multicoloured.

| | | | |
|---|---|---|---|
| 1164. | 50 l. Warriors taking the oath (medal) (vert.) .. | 15 | 10 |
| 1165. | 2 d. Patriarch Gregory V (statue by Phitalis) (vert.) .. .. | 30 | 10 |
| 1166. | 4 d. Type **246** .. .. | 10 | 10 |
| 1167. | 10 d. "Bishop Germanos blessing the Standard" (Vryzakis) .. | 40 | 40 |

See also Nos. 1168/73, 1178/80, 1181/6 and 1187/89.

**1971.** 150th Anniv. of War of Independence (2nd issue). The War at Sea. Designs as T **246**. Multicoloured.

| | | | |
|---|---|---|---|
| 1168. | 20 l. "Leonidas" .. | 15 | 10 |
| 1169. | 1 d. "Pericles" .. .. | 25 | 10 |
| 1170. | 1 d. 50 "Terpsichore" (from painting by Roux) | 30 | 10 |
| 1171. | 2 d. 50 "Karteria" (from painting by Hastings) | 40 | 10 |
| 1172. | 3 d. "Battle of Samos" (contemporary painting) | 80 | 15 |
| 1173. | 6 d. "Turkish Frigate ablaze, Battle of Yeronda" (Michalis) .. | 1·40 | 90 |

SIZES: Nos. 1168/71, 37 × 24 mm. Nos. 1172/3. 40 × 28 mm.

247. Spyridon Louis winning Marathon, Athens, 1896.

**1971.** 75th Anniv. of Olympic Games Revival. Multicoloured.

| | | | |
|---|---|---|---|
| 1174. | 3 d. Type **247** .. .. | 20 | 10 |
| 1175. | 8 d. P. de Coubertin and Memorial, Olympia (vert.) | 35 | 30 |

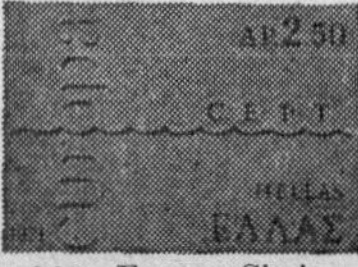

248. Europa Chain.

**1971.** Europa.

| | | | |
|---|---|---|---|
| 1176. **248.** | 2 d. 50 yell., grn. & blk. | 25 | 10 |
| 1177. | 5 d. yell., orge. & blk. | 1·25 | 1·10 |

**1971.** 150th Anniv. of War of Independence (3rd issue). "Teaching the People", Designs as T **246**. Multicoloured.

| | | | |
|---|---|---|---|
| 1178. | 50 l. Eugenius Voulgaris (vert.) .. .. .. | 10 | 10 |
| 1179. | 2 d. 50 Dr. Adamantios Korais (vert.) .. .. | 10 | 10 |
| 1180. | 15 d. "The Secret School" (N. Ghyzis) (horiz.) .. | 45 | 40 |

SIZES: 50 l., 2 d. 50, 23 × 34 mm. 15 d. as Type **246**.

**1971.** 150th Anniv. of War of Independence (4th issue). The War on Land. Designs as T **246**. Multicoloured.

| | | | |
|---|---|---|---|
| 1181. | 50 l. "Battle of Corinth" (Krazeisen) (vert). .. | 10 | 10 |
| 1182. | 1 d. "Sacrifice of Kapsalia" (Vryzakis) (vert.) .. | 20 | 10 |
| 1183. | 2 d. "Suliot Women in Battle" (Deneuville) (horiz.) .. .. .. | 25 | 10 |
| 1184. | 5 d. "Battle of Athens" (Zographos) (vert.) .. | 30 | 30 |
| 1185. | 6 d. 50 Battle of Maniaki" (lithograph) (horiz.) .. | 25 | 15 |
| 1186. | 9 d. "Death of Markos Botsaris at Karpenisi" (Vryzakis) (horiz.) .. | 40 | 40 |

SIZES: 50 l., 1 d., 5 d. 25 × 40 mm. 2 d. 40 × 25 mm. 6 d. 50, 9 d. as Type **246**.

249. Kaltetsi Monastery and Seal of Peloponnesian Senate.

**1971.** 150th Anniv. of War of Independence. (5th issue). Government.

| | | | |
|---|---|---|---|
| 1187. **249.** | 2 d. blk., green & brn. | 25 | 10 |
| 1188. – | 2 d. 50 black, light bl. and blue .. .. | 30 | 10 |
| 1189. – | 20 d. blk., yell. & brn. | 70 | 65 |

DESIGNS: 2 d. 50, National Assembly Memorial, Epidavros, and Seal of Provincial Administration. 20 d. Signature and seal of John Capodistria, first President of Greece.

250. Hosios Loukas Monastery, Boeotia.

**1972.** Greek Monasteries and Churches. Multicoloured.

| | | | |
|---|---|---|---|
| 1190. | 50 l. Type **250** .. .. | 10 | 10 |
| 1191. | 1 d. Daphni Church, Attica | 15 | 10 |
| 1192. | 2 d. St. John the Divine Monastery, Patmos .. | 20 | 10 |
| 1193. | 2 d. 50 Panaghia Koumbelidiki Church, Castoria | 25 | 10 |
| 1194. | 4 d. 50 Panaghia ton Chalkeon, Thessaloniki | 25 | 15 |
| 1195. | 6 d. 50 Panaghia Paregoritissa Church, Arta | 30 | 15 |
| 1196. | 8 d. 50 St. Paul's Monastery, Mt. Athos .. .. | 60 | 60 |

251. Cretan Costume.

252. Flag and Map.

**1972.** Greek Costumes (1st series). Mult.

| | | | |
|---|---|---|---|
| 1197. | 50 l. Type **251** .. .. | 10 | 10 |
| 1198. | 1 d. Pindus bride .. | 15 | 10 |
| 1199. | 2 d. Warrior-chief Missolonghi .. .. | 25 | 10 |
| 1200. | 2 d. 50 Sarakatsana woman. Attica .. .. | 10 | 10 |
| 1201. | 3 d. Nisiros woman .. | 10 | 10 |
| 1202. | 4 d. 50 Megara woman .. | 15 | 15 |
| 1203. | 6 d. 50 Trikeri (rural) .. | 20 | 10 |
| 1204. | 10 d. Pylaia woman, Macedonia .. .. | 80 | 50 |

See also Nos. 1232/48 and 1282/96.

**1972.** 5th Anniv. of 1967 Revolution. Mult.

| | | | |
|---|---|---|---|
| 1205. | 2 d. 50 Commemorative medal (horiz.) .. | 15 | 10 |
| 1206. | 4 d. 50 Type **252** .. | 15 | 15 |
| 1207. | 5 d. Facets of modern development .. .. | 15 | 15 |

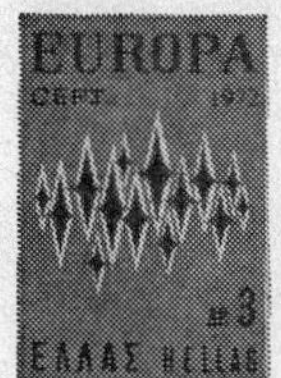

253. "Communications". 254. Acropolis, Athens.

**1972.** Europa.

1208. 253. 3 d. multicoloured .. 40 10
1209. 4 d. 50 multicoloured 1·00 90

**1972.** 20th Anniv. of Acropolis Motor Rally. Multicoloured.

1210. 4 d. 50 Type 254 .. 20 15
1211. 5 d. Emblem and map .. 25 25

255. "Gaia delivering Erecthonius to Athene . . .".

**1972.** Greek Mythology. Museum Pieces (1st series).

1212. 255. 1 d. 50 black and green 10 10
1213. – 2 d. black and blue .. 10 10
1214. – 2 d. 50 black & brn. 10 10
1215. – 5 d. black and brown 15 15

DESIGNS: 2 d. "Uranus" (altar piece). 2 d. 50, "The Gods repulsing the Giants". 5 d. "Zeus".

See also Nos. 1252/5.

256. "Young Athlete" (statue).

**1972.** Olympic Games, Munich. Ancient Olympics. Multicoloured.

1216. 256. 50 l. grey, blk. & brn. 10 10
1217. – 1 d. 50 grey, blk. & brn. 10 10
1218. – 3 d. 50 grey, blk. & orge. 15 15
1219. – 4 d. 50 brn., grey & grn 20 15
1220. – 10 d. red, pink & brn. 25 25

DESIGNS—VERT. 3 d. 50, "Female Athlete" (statuette). HORIZ. 1 d. 50, "Wrestlers" (bas-relief). 4 d. 50, "Ball game" (bas-relief). 10 d. "Runners" (Amphora).

257. "Young Stamp Collector". 258. "The Birth of Christ".

**1972.** Stamp Day.

1221. 257. 2 d. 50 multicoloured 15 15

**1972.** Christmas. Multicoloured.

1222. 2 d. 50 "Pilgrimage of the Magi" .. .. 10 10
1223. 4 d. 50 Type 258 .. 15 15

259. University Buildings.

**1973.** Centenary of Nat. Polytechnic University, Athens.

1224. 259. 2 d. 50 multicoloured 25 15

260. "Spring" (wall fresco).

**1973.** Archaeological Discoveries, Island of Thera. Multicoloured.

1225. 10 l. Type 260 .. 15 10
1226. 20 l. "Barley" jug .. 15 10
1227. 30 l. "Blue Apes" fresco (horiz.) .. .. 15 10
1228. 1 d. 50 "Bird" (jug) .. 20 10
1229. 2 d. 50 "Swallows" (detail, "Spring" fresco) (horiz.) 20 10
1230. 5 d. "Wild Goats" fresco (horiz.) .. .. 20 15
1231. 6 d. 50 "Wrestlers" (detail, fresco) (horiz.) .. 45 45

**1973.** Greek Regional Costumes (2nd series). As Type 251. Multicoloured.

1232. 10 l. Peloponnese .. 10 10
1233. 20 l. Central Greece .. 10 10
1234. 30 l. Locris (Livanates) .. 10 10
1235. 50 l. Skyros (male) .. 10 10
1236. 1 d. Spetsai .. 10 10
1237. 1 d. 50 Almyros .. 10 10
1238. 2 d. 50 Macedonia (Roumlouki) .. .. 15 10
1239. 3 d. 50 Salamis .. 25 10
1240. 4 d. 50 Epirus (Souli) .. 25 10
1241. 5 d. Lefkas (Santa Maura) 30 10
1242. 6 d. 50 Skyros (female) .. 30 10
1243. 8 d. 50 Corinth .. 30 15
1244. 10 d. Corfu (Garitsa) .. 30 10
1245. 15 d. Epirus .. 30 10
1246. 20 d. Thessaly (Karagouniko) .. .. 30 10
1247. 30 p. Macedonia (Episkopi) 65 10
1248. 50 d. Thrace (Makra Gefyra) .. .. 1·25 45

261. Europa "Posthorn".

**1973.** Europa.

1249. 261. 2 d. 50 blue & new blue 20 15
1250. 3 d. red, orge. & lake 25 15
1251. 4 d. 50 brn., bronze and green .. .. 35 30

262. "Olympus" (from photograph by Boissonnas).

**1973.** Greek Mythology (2nd series).

1252. 262. 1 d. grey and black .. 15 10
1253. – 2 d. multicoloured .. 15 15
1254. – 2 d. 50 grey, yell. & blk. 20 15
1255. – 4 d. 50 multicoloured 30 30

DESIGNS: 2 d. "Zeus in combat with Typhoeus" (amphora). 2 d. 50, "Zeus at Battle of Giants" (altar relief). 4 d. 50, The "Punishment of Atlas and Prometheus" (vase).

263. Dr. G. Papanicolaou. 264. "Our Lady of the Annunciation".

**1973.** Honouring Dr. George Papanicolaou (cancer specialist).

1256. 263. 2 d. 50 multicoloured 10 10
1257. 6 d. 50 multicoloured 15 15

**1973.** 150th Anniv. of Discovery of Miraculous Icon of our Lady of the Annunciation, Tinos.

1258. 264. 2 d. 50 multicoloured 25 15

265. "Triptolemus in a Chariot" (vase). 267. G. Averof.

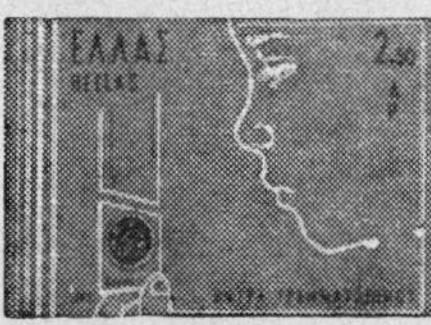

266. Child examining Stamp.

**1973.** European Transport Ministers Conf., Athens.

1259. 265. 4 d. 50 multicoloured 10 25

**1973.** Stamp Day.

1260. 266. 2 d. 50 multicoloured 20 15

**1973.** National Benefactors (1st series).

1261. 267. 1 d. 50 brown .. 10 10
1262. – 2 d. red .. 10 10
1263. – 2 d. 50 green .. 10 10
1264. – 4 d. lilac .. 15 10
1265. – 6 d. 50 black .. 10 10

DESIGNS: 2 d. A. Arsakis. 2 d. 50, C. Zappas. 4 d. A. Syngros. 6 d. 50, I. Varvakis.

See also Nos. 1315/18.

268. "Lord Byron in Suliot costume" (by Thomas Phillips). 269. "Harpist of Keros".

**1974.** 150th Death Anniv. of Lord Byron. Multicoloured.

1266. 2 d. 50 Type 268 .. 10 10
1267. 4 d. 50 "Byron taking the Oath at Grave of Markos Botsaris" (lithograph) 20 20

**1974.** Europa. Ancient Greek Sculptures. Multicoloured.

1268. 3 d. Type 269 .. .. 15 10
1269. 4 d. 50 "Athenian Maiden" 20 10
1270. 6 d. 50 "Charioteer of Delphi" (bronze) .. 30 35

270. "Theocracy of Zeus" (vase). 271. U.P.U. Emblem within Mycenaean Vase Design.

**1974.** Greek Mythology (3rd series).

1271. 270. 1 d. 50 blk. & orange 10 10
1272. – 2 d. brn., red & orge. 10 10
1273. – 2 d. 50 blk., brn. & orge. 15 10
1274. – 10 d. brn., red & orge. 15 15

DESIGNS—HORIZ. 2 d. "Athena's Birth" (vase). 2 d. 50, "Artemis, Apollo and Lito" (vase). VERT. 10 d. "Hermes" (vase).

**1974.** Cent. of Universal Postal Union. Each black, violet and blue.

1275. 2 d. Type 271 .. 10 10
1276. 4 d. 50 "Hermes" (horiz.) 15 15
1277. 6 d. 50 "Woman reading letter" .. .. 20 25

272. Crete 1 d. Stamp of 1905.

**1974.** Stamp Day.

1278. 272. 2 d. 50 blk. red & vio. 20 15

273. Joseph. 274. Secret Assembly, Vostitsa.

**1974.** Christmas. "The Flight into Egypt" (from Codex No. 587, Dionysos Monastery, Mt. Athos). Multicoloured.

1279. 2 d. Type 273 .. .. 10 10
1280. 4 d. 50 "Virgin and Child on donkey" .. .. 10 10
1281. 8 d. 50 "Jacob leading donkey" .. .. 15 15

Nos. 1279/81 were issued together in the form of a triptych making a composite design.

**1974.** Greek Costumes (3rd series). As T 251. Multicoloured.

1282. 20 l. Megara .. .. 10 10
1283. 30 l. Salamis .. .. 10 10
1284. 50 l. Edipsos .. .. 10 10
1285. 1 d. Kymi .. .. 10 10
1286. 1 d. 50 Sterea Hellas .. 10 10
1287. 2 d. Desfina .. .. 10 10
1288. 3 d. Iaonnina (Epirus) .. 15 10
1289. 3 d. 50 Naousa .. .. 15 10
1290. 4 d. Hasia .. .. 25 10
1291. 4 d. 50 Thasos .. .. 25 10
1292. 5 d. Skopelos .. .. 25 10
1293. 6 d. 50 Grammenochoria (Epirus) .. .. 30 10
1294. 10 d. Pelion .. .. 30 10
1295. 25 d. Lefkimmi (Kerkyra) 15 10
1296. 30 d. Tanagra (Boeotia) 20 15

**1975.** 150th Death Anniv. of Girgorios Dikeos Papaflessas (Soldier). Multicoloured.

1297. 4 d. Type 274 .. .. 15 10
1298. 7 d. Papaflessas in uniform (vert.) .. .. 20 10
1299. 11 d. Aghioi Apostoli (chapel) Kalamata .. 35 30

275. Roses in Vase. 277. Neolithic Goddess.

276. Mansion, Kastoria.

**1975.** Europa. Paintings by Theophilus Hatzimicheal. Multicoloured.

1300. 4 d. Type 275 .. .. 15 10
1301. 7 d. "Erotokritos and Aretussa" .. .. 25 15
1302. 11 d. Girl and sheep .. 30 30

**1975.** Greek Folk Architecture.

1303. 276. 10 l. black and blue 10 10
1304. – 40 l. black and red .. 10 10
1305. – 4 d. black and brown 15 10
1306. – 6 d. black and blue .. 30 15
1307. – 11 d. black & orange 20 20

DESIGNS: 40 l. House, Arnea, Halkidiki. 4 d. House, Veria. 6 d. Mansion, Siatista. 11 d. Mansion, Amelakia, Thessaly.

**1975.** International Women's Year. Mult.

1308. 1 d. 50 Type 277 .. 10 10
1309. 8 d. 50 Confrontation between Antigone and Creon .. .. 20 10
1310. 11 d. Modern women .. 30 30

278. Alexandros Papanastasiou (founder) and University Buildings.

**1975.** 50th Anniv. of Thessaloniki University. Multicoloured.

1311. 1 d. 50 Type 278 .. 10 10
1312. 4 d. Original University Building .. .. 10 10
1313. 11 d. Plan of "University City" .. .. 10 10

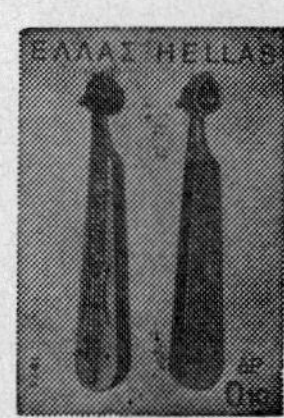

279. Greek 100 d. Stamp of 1933. 281. Pontos Lyre.

280. Evangelos Zappas and Zappeion Building.

**1975.** Stamp Day.
1314. 279. 11 d. green and brown 10 10

**1975.** National Benefactors (2nd series).
1315. 280. 1 d. blk,. grey & grn. 10 10
1316. – 4 d. blk., grey & brn. 10 10
1317. – 6 d. blk., brn. & orge. 15 10
1318. – 11 d. blk., lilac & red 25 30
DESIGNS: 4 d. Georgios Rizaris and Rizarios Ecclesiastical School. 6 d. Michael Tositsas and Metsovion Technical University. 11 d. Nicolaos Zosimas and Zosimea Academy.

**1975.** Musical Instruments. Mult.
1319 10 l. Type **281** .. .. 10 10
1320 20 l. Musicians (Byzantine mural) .. .. 10 10
1321 1 d. Cretan lyre .. .. 10 10
1322 1 d. 50 Tambourine .. 10 10
1323 4 d. Cithern player (from amphora) (horiz) .. 15 10
1324 6 d. Bagpipes .. .. 15 10
1325 7 d. Lute .. .. 15 10
1326 10 d. Barrel-organ .. 20 10
1327 11 d. Pipes and zournades 25 10
1328 20 d. "Praise God" (Byzantine mural) (horiz) .. .. 30 20
1329 25 d. Drums .. .. 35 20
1330 30 d. Kanonaki (horiz) .. 45 15

**282.** Early telephone.

**1976.** Cent. of First Telephone Transmission. Multicoloured.
1331. 7 d. Type **282** .. .. 20 20
1332. 11 d. Modern Telephone.. 25 25

**283.** Battle of Missolonghi.

**1976.** 150th Anniv. of Fall of Missolonghi.
1333. **283.** 4 d. multicoloured .. 15 15

**284.** Florina Jug. **285.** "Lion attacking Bull".

**1976.** Europa. Multicoloured.
1334. 7 d. Type **284** .. .. 15 10
1335. 8 d. 50 Plate with birds.. 20 10
1336. 11 d. Egina pitcher .. 30 30
No. 1335 is larger, 24 × 28 mm.

**1976.** Ancient Sealing stones. Multicoloured.
1337. 2 d. Type **285** .. .. 10 10
1338. 4 d. 50 " Water Birds " 15 10
1339. 7 d. " Wounded Bull ".. 20 10
1340. 8 d. 50 " Head of Silenus " 25 15
1341. 11 d. " Cow feeding Calf " 30 30
SIZES: 8 d. 50, 24 × 37 mm. 11 d. 37 × 24 mm. (horiz.).

**286.** Long-jumping. **287.** Lemnos

**1976.** Olympic Games, Montreal. Mult.
1342. 50 l. Type **286** .. .. 10 10
1343. 2 d. Handball .. .. 10 10
1344. 3 d. 50 Wrestling .. 15 10
1345. 4 d. Swimming .. .. 15 10
1346. 11 d. Athens and Montreal stadiums .. .. 30 15
1347. 25 d. " Lighting of Olympic Flame " and Olympic Torch, Montreal .. 15 15
No. 1346 is larger, 49 × 34 mm.

**1976.** Tourism. Aegean Landscapes. Mult.
1348. 30 d. Type **287** .. .. 20 15
1349. 50 d. Lesbos (horiz.) .. 40 25
1350. 75 d. Chios (horiz.) .. 60 15
1351. 100 d. Samos (horiz.) .. 80 50

**288.** " The Magi speaking to the Jews " **289.** Lascaris Book of Grammar, 1476.

**1976.** Christmas. Multicoloured.
1352. 4 d. Type **288** .. .. 15 10
1353. 7 d. " The Adoration of the Magi " .. .. 25 25

**1976.** 500th Anniv. of Printing of First Greek Book.
1354. **289.** 4 d. multicoloured .. 15 15

**290.** Heinrich Schliemann. **291.** "Patients visiting Aesculapius" (relief).

**1976.** Schliemann (archaeologist) Commemoration. Multicoloured.
1355. 2 d. Type **290** .. .. 10 10
1356. 4 d. Gold bracelet (horiz.) 10 10
1357. 5 d. Silver brooch .. 10 10
1358. 7 d. Gold diadem (horiz.) 10 10
1359. 11 d. Gold mask .. 15 15

**1977.** International Rheumatism Year. Mult.
1360. 50 l. type **291** .. .. 10 10
1361. 1 d. Ancient clinic .. 10 10
1362. 1 d. 50 "Aesculapius curing young man" (relief) .. .. .. 10 10
1363. 2 d. Hercules and nurse 15 10
1364. 20 d. Cured patient offering model of leg (relief) .. .. .. 20 20
Nos. 1361/3 are smaller. 22 × 27 m.

**292.** Fortresses of Mani.

**1977.** Europa. Multicoloured.
1365. 5 d. Type **292** .. .. 15 10
1366. 7 d. Santorin (vert.) .. 20 10
1367. 15 d. Lassithi Plain, Crete 35 35

**293.** Emblem and Transport.

**1977.** 45th European Conference of Ministers of Transport.
1368. **293.** 7 d. multicoloured.. 30 25

**294.** Alexandria Lighthouse (Roman coin).

**1977.** "The Civilizing Influence of Alexander the Great". Multicoloured.
1369. 50 l. Type **294** .. .. 10 10
1370. 1 d. "Placing the Works of Homer in Achilles' tomb" (fresco, Raphael) 10 10
1371. 1 d. 50 Descending to sea bed in special ship (Flemish miniature) .. 10 10
1372. 3 d. In search of the water of life (Hindu plate) .. .. .. 10 10
1373. 7 d. Alexander the Great on horseback (Coptic carpet) .. .. 15 10
1374. 11 d. Listening to oracle (Byzantine manuscript) .. .. 30 20
1375. 30 d. Death of Alexander the Great (Persian miniature) .. .. 35 30

**295.** Wreath in Front of University. **296.** Archbishop Makarios.

**1977.** Restoration of Democracy.
1376. **295.** 4 d. blue, gold & black 10 10
1377. – 7 d. multicoloured .. 15 10
1378. – 20 d. multicoloured .. 30 35
DESIGNS—HORIZ. (26 × 22 mm.) 7 d. Demonstrators at University. VERT. (22 × 26 mm.) 20 d. Hand with olive branch, University and flags.

**1977.** Archbishop Makarios Commemoration.
1379. **296.** 4 d. black and grey .. 10 10
1380. – 7 d. blk., brn. & cream 15 15
DESIGN: 7 d. Archbishop Makarios and map of Cyprus.

**297.** Melas Building, Athens (former post office).

**1977.** 19th-century Hellenic Architecture.
1381. **297.** 50 l. blk., stone & brn. 10 10
1382. – 1 d. blk., stone & grn. 10 10
1383. – 1 d. 50 black, stone and blue .. .. 10 10
1384. – 2 d. blk., stone & olive 10 10
1385. – 5 d. blk., stone & yell. 15 10
1386. – 50 d. black, stone and orange .. .. 30 25
DESIGNS: 1 d. Institution for the Blind, Thessalonika. 1 d. 50, Town Hall of Hermoupolis, Syros. 2 d. Branch Office of National Bank, Piraeus. 5 d. Ilissia (Palace of Duchess of Plakentia), Athens. 50 d. Municipal Theatre, Patras.

**298.** The Battle of Navarino. **299.** Parthenon and Industrial Complex.

**1977.** 150th Anniv. of Battle of Navarino.
1387. **298.** 4 d. yell., blk. & brn. 20 10
1388. – 7 d. multicoloured .. 20 15
DESIGN: 7 d. Admirals Van der Heyden, Sir Edward Codrington and Comte de Rigny.

**1977.** Environmental Protection. Mult.
1389. 3 d. Type **299** .. .. 10 10
1390. 4 d. Birds and fish (horiz.) 15 10
1391. 7 d. Living and dead trees (horiz.) .. .. 15 15
1392. 30 d. Head of Erechtheum caryatid and chimneys 25 20

**300.** Map of Greece and Ships.

**1977.** " Greeks Abroad ". Multicoloured.
1393. 4 d. Type **300** .. .. 10 10
1394. 5 d. Globe and Greek flag 10 10
1395. 7 d. Globe and swallows 10 10
1396. 11 d. Envelope with flags 20 20
1397. 13 d. Map of the World.. 35 30

**301.** " The Port of Kalamata " (C. Parthenis).

**1977.** Greek Paintings. Multicoloured.
1398. 1 d. 50 Type **301** .. 15 10
1399. 2 d. 50 " Arsanas " (S. Papaloucas) (vert.) .. 10 10
1400. 4 d. " Santorin " (C. Maleas) .. .. 15 10
1401. 7 d. " The Engagement " (N. Gyzis) .. .. 20 10
1402. 11 d. " The Straw Hat " (N. Lytras) (vert.) .. 20 10
1403. 15 d. " Spring " (G. Iacovidis) .. .. 30 40

**302.** " Ebenus cretica ". **303.** Horse Postman and Pre-stamp Cancel.

**1978.** Greek Flora. Multicoloured.
1404. 1 d. 50 Type **302** .. .. 10 10
1405. 2 d. 50 " Fritillaria rhodokanakis " .. 10 10
1406. 3 d. " Campanula oreadum " .. .. 15 10
1407. 4 d. " Lilium heldreichii " 15 10
1408. 7 d. " Viola delphinantha " 25 15
1409. 25 d. " Paeonia rhodia " 35 20

**1978.** 150th Anniv of Postal Service. Mult.
1410 4 d. Type **303** .. .. 15 10
1411 5 d. "Maximilianos" (passenger steamer) and Greek "Hermes" stamp 20 10
1412 7 d. Mail train and 1896 Olympic Games stamp 35 25
1413 30 d. Postmen on motor cycles and 1972 "Stamp Day" commemorative 25 25

**304.** Lighting the Olympic Flame. **305.** St. Sophia, Salonika.

**1978.** 80th International Olympic Committee Session, Athens. Multicoloured.
1415. 7 d. Type **304** .. .. 10 10
1416. 13 d. Start of 100 m. race 10 10

**1978.** Europa. Multicoloured.
1417 4 d. Type **305** .. .. 15 10
1418 7 d. Lysicrates' Monument, Athens .. 25 15

**306.** Bust of Aristotle. **307.** Rotary Emblem (50th anniv.).

**1978.** 2300th Death Anniv. of Aristotle. Multicoloured.
1419. 2 d. Type **306** .. .. 10 10
1420. 4 d. " The School of Athens " (detail Raphael) .. 15 10
1421. 7 d. Map of Chalkidiki and statue plinth .. 25 15
1422. 20 d. " Aristotle the Wise " (Byzantine fresco) (21 × 37 mm.) .. .. 25 25

**1978.** Anniversaries and Events. Mult.
1423 1 d. Type **307** .. .. 10 10
1424 1 d. 50 Surgery (11th Greek Surgery Congress) (vert) .. 10 10
1425 2 d. 50 Ugo Foscolo (poet, birth bicentenary) .. 10 10
1426 5 d. Bronze head (25th anniv of European Convention on Human Rights) .. .. 15 10
1427 7 d. Hand with reins (Conference of Ministers of Culture of Council of Europe countries) (vert) 20 15
1428 13 d. Wright Flyer I with Daedalus and Icarus (75th anniv of first powered flight) (vert) 35 35

**308.** The Poor Woman with Five Children.

**309.** Grafted Plant and Circulation Diagram.

**1978.** " The Twelve Months " (Greek fairy tale). Multicoloured.

1429. 2 d. Type **308** .. .. 10 10
1430. 3 d. The poor woman and the twelve months .. 10 10
1431. 4 d. The poor woman and the gold coins .. 15 10
1432. 20 d. The poor woman with her children and the rich woman with the snakes .. .. 30 15

**1978.** Transplant Surgery. Multicoloured.

1433. 4 d. Type **309** .. .. 15 10
1434. 10 d. " Miracle of Sts. Cosmas and Damian " (Alonso de Sedano) .. 25 30

**310.** " Virgin and Child  ". **311.** First Academy, Nauplion, and Cadet.

**1978.** Christmas. Icons from Stavronikita Monastery. Multicoloured.

1435. 4 d. Type **310** .. .. 10 10
1436. 7 d. " The Baptism of Christ " .. .. 20 20

**1978.** 150th Anniv. of Military Academy. Multicoloured.

1437. 1 d. 50 Type **311** .. 10 10
1438. 2 d. Academy coat of arms (vert.) .. .. 10 10
1439. 10 d. Modern Academy, Athens, and cadet .. 25 25

**312.** Destroyer.

**1978.** Greek Naval Ships. Multicoloured.

1440 50 l. Type **312** .. .. 10 10
1441 1 d. "Andromeda" (motor torpedo-boat) .. .. 10 10
1442 2 d. 50 "Papanicolis" (submarine) .. .. 10 10
1443 4 d. "Psara" (cruiser) 15 10
1444 5 d. "Madonna of Hydra" (armed sailing caique) 15 10
1445 7 d. Byzantine dromon .. 30 10
1446 50 d. Athenian trireme .. 1·50 85

**313.** Map of Greece.  **314.** Kitsos Tsavellas.

**1978.** The Greek State.

1447. **313.** 7 d. multicoloured .. 20 10
1448. 11 d. multicoloured.. 25 10
1449. 13 d. multicoloured.. 30 30

**1979.** " The Struggle of the Souliots ".

1450. **314.** 1 d. 50 light brown, black and brown .. 10 10
1451. – 3 d. multicoloured .. 10 10
1452. – 10 d. multicoloured.. 20 15
1453. – 20 d. ochre, black and brown .. .. 40 40

DESIGNS—HORIZ. 3 d. Souli Castle. 10 d. Fighting Souliots. VERT. 20 d. The dance of Zalongo.

**315.** Figurine found at Amorgos.  **316.** Cretan Postmen.

**1979.** Art of the Aegean.

1454. **315.** 20 d. multicoloured.. 20 15

**1979.** Europa. Multicoloured.

1455. 4 d. Type **316** .. .. 10 10
1456. 7 d. Mounted postman.. 15 15

Nos. 1454/5 were issued in se-tenant pairs, forming a composite design.

**317.** Nicolas Skoufas.  **318.** Flags of Member States forming Ear of Wheat.

**1979.** Anniversaries and Events. Mult.

1457. 1 d. 50 Type **317** (founder of Friendly Society, birth bi-cent.) .. .. 10 10
1458. 2 d. Locomotive (75th anniv. of railway) (horiz.).. .. .. 30 10
1459. 3 d. Basketball (European Basketball Championship) .. .. .. 10 10
1460. 4 d. Fossil fish " Mene psarianos " (7th International Congress of Mediterranean Neogene) (horiz.) .. .. 10 10
1461. 10 d. Greek church (Balkan Tourist Year).. .. 15 15
1462. 20 d. Victory of Paeonius and flags (50th anniv. of Balkan Sports) .. 35 15

**1979.** Entry into European Community. Multicoloured.

1463. 7 d. Type **318** .. .. 10 10
1464. 30 d. European Parliament (horiz.) .. .. 15 15

**319.** " Girl with Dove " (classic statue).  **320.** Head of Philip of Macedonia.

**1979.** International Year of the Child. Multicoloured.

1465. 5 d. Type **319** .. .. 10 10
1466. 8 d. Girl with doves .. 15 10
1467. 20 d. " Mother and Children " (detail, Iacovides) .. .. 30 15

**1979.** Archaeological Discoveries from Vergina. Multicoloured.

1468. 6 d. Type **320** .. 15 10
1469. 8 d. Gold Wreath .. 20 10
1470. 10 d. Copper vessel .. 25 10
1471. 14 d. Golden casket (horiz.) 30 15
1472. 18 d. Silver ewer .. 10 10
1473. 20 d. Gold quiver .. 15 15
1474. 30 d. Iron cuirass .. 25 25

**321.** Purple Heron.  **322.** Agricultural Bank of Greece (50th anniv.).

**1979.** Endangered Birds. Multicoloured.

1475. 6 d. Type **321** .. 35 10
1476. 8 d. Audouin's gull .. 50 15
1477. 10 d. Eleonora's falcon (horiz.) .. 55 20
1478. 14 d. Common kingfisher (horiz.) .. 75 30
1479. 20 d. Eastern white pelican.. .. .. 1·25 45
1480. 25 d. White-tailed sea eagle .. .. .. 1·40 90

**1979.** Anniversaries and Events.

1481. **322.** 3 d. blk., yell. & olive 10 10
1482. – 4 d. multicoloured .. 10 10
1483. – 6 d. multicoloured .. 15 10
1484. – 8 d. multicoloured .. 20 10
1485. – 10 d. multicoloured.. 25 10
1486. – 12 d. multicoloured.. 30 15
1487. – 14 d. multicoloured.. 30 10
1488. – 18 d. multicoloured.. 10 10
1489. – 25 d. multicoloured.. 20 20

DESIGNS—HORIZ. 10 d. Ionic capital and map of Balkans (" Balkanfila '79 " Stamp Exhibition). 25 d. Parliamentary Meeting (104th anniv. of Greek Parliament). VERT. 4 d. Cosmas the Aetolian (monk and martyr) (death bicent.). 6 d. Basil the Great (1600th death anniv.). 8 d. Magnifying glass and map of Balkan countries (" Balkanfila '79 " Stamp Exhibition). 12 d. Aristolelis Valaoritis (poet) (death centenary). 14 d. Golfer (World Golfing Championship). 18 d. Bust of Hippocrates (International Hippocratic Foundation, Kos).

**323.** Parnassos.  **324.** Gate of Galerius.

**1979.** Landscapes. Multicoloured.

1490. 50 l. Type **323** .. 10 10
1491. 1 d. Tempi (horiz.) 10 10
1492. 2 d. " Glaronisia ", Milos 10 10
1493. 4 d. Vikos Gorge .. 15 10
1494. 5 d. Salt Lake, Misolonghi (horiz.) .. .. 15 10
1495. 6 d. Louros Aqueduct .. 20 10
1496. 7 d. Samothraki.. .. 25 10
1497. 8 d. Sithonia, Halkidiki (horiz.) .. .. 25 10
1498. 10 d. Samaria Gorge .. 30 10
1499. 12 d. Sifnos .. 30 10
1500. 14 d. Kymi (horiz.) .. 30 10
1501. 18 d. Ios .. .. 10 10
1502. 20 d. Thasos .. 10 10
1503. 30 d. " Kolybithres " Paros (horiz.) .. 20 15
1504. 50 d. Cephalonia .. 35 30

**1980.** First Hellenic Nephrology Congress, Thessalonika.

1505. **324.** 8 d. blue, blk. and red 25 20

**325.** Aegosthena Castle.  **326.** Aristarchus' Theorem and Temple of Hera.

**1980.** Castles, Caves and Bridges. Mult.

1506. 4 d. Type **325** .. .. 10 10
1507. 6 d. Byzantine castle, Thessalonika (horiz.).. 15 10
1508. 8 d. Perama cave, Ioannina .. .. .. 20 10
1509. 10 d. Dyros cave, Mani.. 25 10
1510. 14 d. Arta bridge (horiz.) 10 10
1511. 20 d. Kalogiros bridge, Epirus (horiz.) .. 15 15

**1980.** 2300th Birth Anniv. of Aristarchus of Samos (astronomer).

1512. **326.** 10 d. pink, blk. & brn. 25 10
1513. – 20 d. multicoloured.. 30 35

DESIGN: 20 d. Heliocentric system.

**327.** George Seferis (writer).

**1980.** Europa.

1514. **327.** 8 d. brown, blue & black 25 15
1515. – 14 d. brn., blk. and cream 20 20

DESIGN: 14 d. Maria Callas (opera singer).

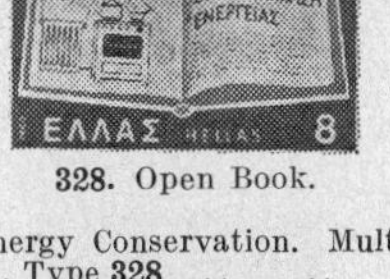

**328.** Open Book.

**1980.** Energy Conservation. Multicoloured.

1516. 8 d. Type **328** .. .. 20 10
1517. 20 d. Lightbulb and candle (vert.) .. .. 15 35

**329.** Fire-fighting.

**1980.** Anniversaries and Events. Mult.

1518. 4 d. Type **329** (50th anniv. of fire brigade) .. 15 10
1519. 6 d. St. Demetrius (mosaic) (1700th birth anniv.) (vert.) .. .. 15 10
1520. 8 d. Revolutionaries (Theriso revolution, 75th anniv.) 20 10
1521. 10 d. Ancient vase and olive branch (World Olive Oil Year) (vert.) 25 10
1522. 14 d. International press emblem (15th International Journalists Federation Congress) (vert.) .. .. .. 10 10
1523. 20 d. Constantinos Ikonomos (cleric and scholar), (birth bicent.) (vert.).. 15 15

**330.** Olympia and Coin of Elia.

**1980.** Olympic Games, Moscow. Designs showing Greek stadia. Multicoloured.

1524. 8 d. Type **330** .. .. 20 10
1525. 14 d. Delphi and Delphic coin .. .. .. 30 10
1526. 18 d. Epidaurus and coin of Olympia .. .. 10 10
1527. 20 d. Rhodes and coin of Kos .. .. .. 15 10
1528. 50 d. Panathenaik stadium and First Olympic Games medal 50 40

**331.** Asbestos.

**1980.** Minerals. Multicoloured.

1529. 6 d. Type **331** .. .. 10 10
1530. 8 d. Gypsum (vert.) .. 10 10
1531. 10 d. Copper .. .. 10 10
1532. 14 d. Barite (vert.) .. 20 10
1533. 18 d. Chromite .. .. 10 10
1534. 20 d. Mixed sulphides (vert.) .. .. .. 10 10
1535. 30 d. Bauxite (vert.) .. 30 20

**332.** Dassault Mirage III Jet Fighter.  **333.** Left Detail of Poulakis' Painting.

**1980.** Anniversaries and Events. Mult.

1536 6 d. Breakdown truck (20th anniv of Automobile and Touring Club of Greece road assistance service) (horiz) .. .. 15 10
1537 8 d. Type **332** (50th anniv of Air Force) .. .. 20 10
1538 12 d. Piper Super Cub airplane outside hangar (50th anniv of Thessalonika Flying Club) (horiz) .. .. 30 15
1539 20 d. Harbour scene (50th anniv of Piraeus Port Organization) .. .. 55 20
1540 25 d. Association for Macedonian Studies Headquarters (40th anniv) .. .. 20 20

**1980.** Christmas. Multicoloured designs showing details from " He is Happy Thanks to You " by T. Poulakis (in St. John's Monastery, Pataros).

1541. 6 d. Type **333** .. .. 15 10
1542. 14 d. Virgin and Child (centre) .. .. 25 20
1543. 20 d. Right detail .. 35 30

**334.** Fresh and Canned Vegetables.  **335.** " Kira Maria " (Alexandrian folk dance).

**1981.** Exports. Multicoloured.

1544. 9 d. Type **334** .. .. 10 10
1545. 17 d. Fruit .. .. 20 15
1546. 20 d. Cotton .. .. 10 10
1547. 25 d. Marble .. .. 20 20

**1981.** Europa. Multicoloured.

1548. 12 d. Type **335** .. .. 30 10
1549. 17 d. " Sousta " (Cretan dance) .. .. .. 45 40

**336.** Olympic Statium, Kalogreza.  **337.** Human Figure showing Kidneys.

**1981.** European Athletic Championships, Athens (1982) (1st issue).
1550. **336.** 12 d. blue, blk. & light blue 30 10
1551. 17 d. multicoloured .. 40 40
DESIGN: 17 d. Athletes converging on Greece.
See also Nos. 1586/8.

**1981.** Anniversaries and Events.
1552. 2 d. multicoloured .. 10 10
1553. 3 d. multicoloured .. 20 10
1554. 6 d. multicoloured .. 20 10
1555. 9 d. yell., blk. and brn.. 30 10
1556. 12 d. multicoloured .. 50 10
1557. 21 d. multicoloured .. 15 15
1558. 40 d. red, light blue and dark blue .. .. 30 35
DESIGNS AND EVENTS—VERT: 2 d. Type **337** (8th World Nephrology Conference, Athens). 3 d. Parachutist, glider, Potez 25 biplane and boy with model glider (50th anniv of Greek National Air Club). 6 d. Meteora Monasteries, Thessaly, and Konitsa Bridge, Epirus (International Historical Symposium, Volos, and centenary of incorporation of Thessaly and Epirus into Greece). 12 d. Oil rig (first Greek oil production). 40 d. Heart (15th World Cardiovascular Surgery Conference, Athens). HORIZ: 9 d. Bowl with "eye" decoration (50th anniv of Greek Ophthalmological Society). 21 d. Globes, plant and coin (Foundation in Athens of World Association for International Relations).

**338.** Variable Scallops.
**339.** Aegean Island Bell Tower.

**1981.** Shells, Fishes and Butterflies. Mult.
1559 4 d. Type **338** .. .. 25 10
1560 5 d. Painted comber (fish) 15 10
1561 12 d. Parrot-fishes .. 15 10
1562 15 d. Common dentex (fish) .. .. 20 25
1563 17 d. "Parnassius apollo" (butterfly) .. .. 30 25
1564 50 d. "Colias hyale" (butterfly) .. .. 60 30

**1981.** Bell Towers and Altar Screens. Mult.
1565. 4 d. Type **339** .. .. 15 10
1566. 6 d. Altar gate, St. Paraskevi Church, Metsovo 20 10
1567. 9 d. Altar gate, Pelion (horiz.).. .. .. 30 10
1568. 12 d. Bell tower, Saints Constantine and Helen Church, Halkiades, Epirus .. .. .. 10 10
1569. 17 d. Altar screen, St. Nicholas Church, Velvendos (horiz.) .. 10 15
1570. 30 d. Icon of St. Jacob and stand, Alexandroupolis Church Museum .. 25 10
1571. 40 d. Upper section of altar gate, St. Nicholas Church, Makrinitsa .. 30 30

**340.** Town Scene.

**1981.** Anniversaries and Events. Mult.
1572. 3 d. Type **340** (Council of Europe Urban Renaissance campaign) .. 10 10
1573. 9 d. St. Simeon, Archbishop of Thessalonika (Canonization by Greek Orthodox Church) (vert.) 30 10
1574. 12 d. Child Jesus (detail from Byzantine icon) (Breast feeding campaign) (vert.).. .. 10 10
1575. 17 d. Gina Bachauer (pianist, 5th death anniv.) (vert.) .. 10 20
1576. 21 d. Constantine Broumidis (artist, 175th birth anniv.) (vert.) .. .. 15 15
1577. 50 d. " Phoenix " banknotes 1831 (first banknotes, 150th anniv.).. 45 45

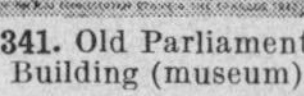
**341.** Old Parliament Building (museum).

**342.** " Flight from Missolonghi ".

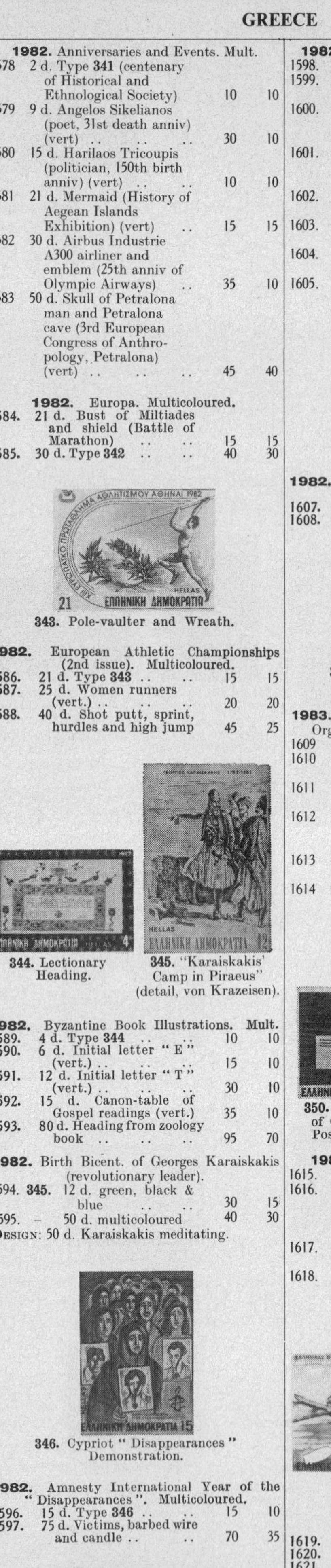

**1982.** Anniversaries and Events. Mult.
1578 2 d. Type **341** (centenary of Historical and Ethnological Society) 10 10
1579 9 d. Angelos Sikelianos (poet, 31st death anniv) (vert) .. .. .. 30 10
1580 15 d. Harilaos Tricoupis (politician, 150th birth anniv) (vert) .. 10 10
1581 21 d. Mermaid (History of Aegean Islands Exhibition) (vert) .. 15 15
1582 30 d. Airbus Industrie A300 airliner and emblem (25th anniv of Olympic Airways) .. 35 10
1583 50 d. Skull of Petralona man and Petralona cave (3rd European Congress of Anthropology, Petralona) (vert) .. .. .. 45 40

**1982.** Europa. Multicoloured.
1584. 21 d. Bust of Miltiades and shield (Battle of Marathon) .. .. 15 15
1585. 30 d. Type **342** .. .. 40 30

**343.** Pole-vaulter and Wreath.

**1982.** European Athletic Championships (2nd issue). Multicoloured.
1586. 21 d. Type **343** .. .. 15 15
1587. 25 d. Women runners (vert.) .. .. .. 20 20
1588. 40 d. Shot putt, sprint, hurdles and high jump 45 25

**344.** Lectionary Heading.
**345.** "Karaiskakis' Camp in Piraeus" (detail, von Krazeisen).

**1982.** Byzantine Book Illustrations. Mult.
1589. 4 d. Type **344** .. .. 10 10
1590. 6 d. Initial letter " E " (vert.) .. .. 15 10
1591. 12 d. Initial letter " T " (vert.) .. .. 30 10
1592. 15 d. Canon-table of Gospel readings (vert.) 35 10
1593. 80 d. Heading from zoology book .. .. .. 95 70

**1982.** Birth Bicent. of Georges Karaiskakis (revolutionary leader).
1594. **345.** 12 d. green, black & blue .. .. 30 15
1595. – 50 d. multicoloured 40 30
DESIGN: 50 d. Karaiskakis meditating.

**346.** Cypriot " Disappearances " Demonstration.

**1982.** Amnesty International Year of the " Disappearances ". Multicoloured.
1596. 15 d. Type **346** .. .. 15 10
1597. 75 d. Victims, barbed wire and candle .. .. 70 35

**347.** " Demonstration in Athens, 25 March 1942 ". (P. Zachariou.)

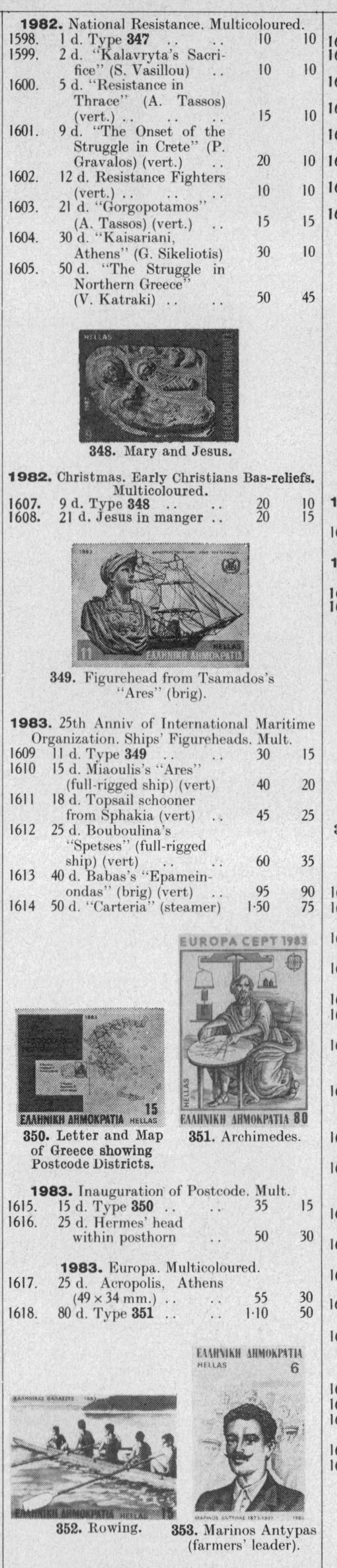

**1982.** National Resistance. Multicoloured.
1598. 1 d. Type **347** .. .. 10 10
1599. 2 d. "Kalavryta's Sacrifice" (S. Vasillou) .. 10 10
1600. 5 d. "Resistance in Thrace" (A. Tassos) (vert.) .. .. 15 10
1601. 9 d. "The Onset of the Struggle in Crete" (P. Gravalos) (vert.) .. 20 10
1602. 12 d. Resistance Fighters (vert.) .. .. 10 10
1603. 21 d. "Gorgopotamos" (A. Tassos) (vert.) .. 15 15
1604. 30 d. "Kaisariani, Athens" (G. Sikeliotis) 30 10
1605. 50 d. "The Struggle in Northern Greece" (V. Katraki) .. 50 45

**348.** Mary and Jesus.

**1982.** Christmas. Early Christians Bas-reliefs. Multicoloured.
1607. 9 d. Type **348** .. .. 20 10
1608. 21 d. Jesus in manger .. 20 15

**349.** Figurehead from Tsamados's "Ares" (brig).

**1983.** 25th Anniv of International Maritime Organization. Ships' Figureheads. Mult.
1609 11 d. Type **349** .. .. 30 15
1610 15 d. Miaoulis's "Ares" (full-rigged ship) (vert) 40 20
1611 18 d. Topsail schooner from Sphakia (vert) .. 45 25
1612 25 d. Bouboulina's "Spetses" (full-rigged ship) (vert) .. .. 60 35
1613 40 d. Babas's "Epameinondas" (brig) (vert) .. 95 90
1614 50 d. "Carteria" (steamer) 1·50 75

**350.** Letter and Map of Greece showing Postcode Districts.
**351.** Archimedes.

**1983.** Inauguration of Postcode. Mult.
1615. 15 d. Type **350** .. .. 35 15
1616. 25 d. Hermes' head within posthorn .. 50 30

**1983.** Europa. Multicoloured.
1617. 25 d. Acropolis, Athens (49 × 34 mm.) .. .. 55 30
1618. 80 d. Type **351** .. .. 1·10 50

**352.** Rowing.
**353.** Marinos Antypas (farmers' leader).

**1983.** Sports. Multicoloured.
1619. 15 d. Type **352** .. .. 10 10
1620. 18 d. Water skiing (vert.) 40 20
1621. 27 d. Windsurfing (vert.) 55 30
1622. 50 d. Ski lift (vert.) .. 40 10
1623. 80 d. Skiing .. .. 80 40

**1983.** Personalities. Multicoloured.
1624. 6 d. Type **353** .. .. 10 10
1625. 9 d. Nicholas Plastiras (soldier and statesman) 15 15
1626. 15 d. George Papandreou (statesman) .. .. 20 15
1627. 20 d. Constantine Cavafy (poet) .. .. 30 20
1628. 27 d. Nikos Kazantzakis (author and poet) .. 40 30
1629. 32 d. Manolis Calomiris (composer) .. .. 45 10
1630. 40 d. George Papanicolaou (physician) .. .. 55 10
1631. 50 d. Despina Achladioti (patriot) .. .. 60 45

**354.** Democritus.

**355.** Poster by V. Katraki.

**1983.** First International Democritus Congress, Xanthe.
1632. **354.** 50 d. multicoloured 40 20

**1983.** 10th Anniv. of Polytechnic School Uprising. Multicoloured.
1633. 15 d. Type **355** .. .. 10 10
1634. 30 d. Students leaving Polytechnic .. .. 40 40

**356.** The Deification of Homer.

**357.** Horse's Head, Chariot of Seline.

**1983.** Homeric Odes. Multicoloured.
1635. 2 d. Type **356** .. .. 10 10
1636. 3 d. The Abduction of Helen by Paris (horiz.) 10 10
1637. 4 d. The Wooden Horse (horiz.) .. .. 10 10
1638. 5 d. Achilles throwing Dice with Ajax (horiz.) 10 10
1639. 6 d. Achilles .. .. 10 10
1640. 10 d. Hector receiving his Arms from his Parents 15 15
1641. 14 d. Battle between Ajax and Hector (horiz.) .. .. 20 20
1642. 15 d. Priam requesting the Body of Hector (horiz.) .. .. 20 20
1643. 20 d. The Blinding of Polyphemus .. .. 30 25
1644. 27 d. Ulysses escaping from Polyphemus' Cave (horiz.) .. 40 10
1645. 30 d. Ulysses meeting with Nausicaa .. 40 10
1646. 32 d. Ulysses and Sirens (horiz.) .. .. 60 10
1647. 50 d. Ulysses slaying the suitors (horiz.) .. 45 10
1648. 75 d. Heroes of the Iliad (horiz.) .. .. 45 10
1649. 100 d. Bust of Homer .. 80 35

**1984.** Parthenon Marbles. Multicoloured.
1650. 14 d. Type **357** .. .. 30 15
1651. 15 d. Dionysus .. .. 35 20
1652. 20 d. Hestia, Dione and Aphrodite .. .. 45 25
1653. 27 d. Ilissus .. .. 55 30
1654. 32 d. Lapith and Centaur 45 40

**358.** Bridge.

**359.** Ancient Stadium, Olympia.

**1984.** Europa. 25th Anniv. of C.E.P.T.
1656 **358** 15 d. multicoloured .. 35 15
1657 27 d. multicoloured .. 60 60

**1984.** Olympic Games, Los Angeles. Multicoloured.

1658. 14 d. Type **359** .. .. 30 15
1659. 15 d. Athletes preparing for training .. .. 35 15
1660. 20 d. Flute player, discus thrower and long jumper .. .. 45 25
1661. 32 d. Athletes training .. 50 30
1662. 80 d. K. Vikelas and Panathenaic Stadium 1·25 40

**360.** Tank on Map of Cyprus. **361.** Pelion Train.

**1984.** 10th Anniv. of Turkish Invasion of Cyprus. Multicoloured.

1663. 20 d. Type **360** .. .. 35 15
1664. 32 d. Hand grasping barbed wire and map of Cyprus .. .. 60 30

**1984.** Railway Centenary. Multicoloured.

1665. 15 d. Type **361** .. .. 30 15
1666. 20 d. Train on Papadia Bridge (vert.) .. .. 40 25
1667. 30 d. Piraeus-Peloponnese train .. .. 55 10
1668. 50 d. Cogwheel railway, Kalavryta (vert.) .. 1·00 60

**362.** Athens 5th Cent. B.C. Silver Coin on Plan of City. **363.** "10" enclosing Arms.

**1984.** 150th Anniv. of Athens as Capital. Multicoloured.

1669. 15 d. Type **362** .. .. 30 15
1670. 100 d. Symbols of ancient Athens and skyline of modern Athens .. 1·10 25

**1984.** 10th Anniv. of Revolution.

1671. **363.** 95 d. multicoloured 80 15

**364.** "Annunciation". **365.** Running.

**1984.** Christmas. Multicoloured.

1672. 14 d. Type **364** .. .. 30 15
1673. 20 d. "Nativity" .. 40 20
1674. 25 d. "Presentation in the Temple" .. 50 25
1675. 32 d. "Baptism of Christ" 55 25

Nos. 1672/5 show scenes from Hagion Panton icon by Athanasios Tountas.

**1985.** 16th European Indoor Athletics Championships, New Phaleron. Multicoloured.

1676. 12 d. Type **365** .. .. 25 15
1677. 15 d. Putting the shot .. 30 15
1678. 20 d. Sports stadium (37×24 mm.) .. .. 40 20
1679. 25 d. Hurdling .. .. 25 25
1680. 80 d. High jumping .. 65 30

**366.** Catacomb Niche.

**1985.** Catacombs of Melos. Multicoloured.

1681. 15 d. Type **366** .. .. 30 15
1682. 20 d. 'Martyrs' altars and niches central passageway .. .. 40 20
1683. 100 d. Catacomb niches 70 30

**367.** Apollo and Marsyas.

**1985.** Europa. Multicoloured.

1684. 27 d. Type **367** .. .. 55 30
1685. 80 d. Dimitris Mitropoulos and Nikos Skalkotas (composers) 60 40

**368.** Coin (315 B.C.) and "Salonika" (relief).

**1985.** 2300th Anniv. of Salonika. Mult.

1686. 1 d. Type **368** .. .. 10 10
1687. 5 d. Saints Demetrius and Methodius (mosaics) (49×34 mm.) 10 10
1688. 15 d. Galerius's Arch (detail) (Roman period) 30 10
1689. 20 d. Salonika's eastern walls (Byzantine period) .. .. .. 15 15
1690. 32 d. Upper City, Salonika .. .. 25 20
1691. 50 d. Greek army liberating Salonika, 1912 .. .. 35 10
1692. 80 d. Soldier's legs and Salonika (German occupation 1941–44) .. 60 35
1693. 95 d. Contemporary views of Salonika (60th anniv. of Aristotelian University and International Trade Fair) (49×34 mm.) .. .. 80 45

**369.** Urn on Map of Cyprus. **370.** "Democracy crowning the City" (relief).

**1985.** 25th Anniv. of Republic of Cyprus.

1694. **369.** 32 d. multicoloured 25 20

**1985.** Athens, "Cultural Capital of Europe".

1695. **370.** 15 d. multicoloured 30 10
1696. – 20 d. black, grey and blue .. .. 35 15
1697. – 32 d. multicoloured 25 20
1698. – 80 d. multicoloured 65 30

DESIGNS—HORIZ. 20 d. Tritons and dolphins (mosaic floor, Roman baths, Hieratis). 80 d. Capodistrian University, Athens. VERT. 32 d. Angel (fresco, Pentelis Cave).

**371.** Children of different Races. **373.** Folk Dance.

**1985.** International Youth Year (15, 25 d.) and 40th Anniv. of United Nations Organization. (27,100 d.). Multicoloured.

1699. 15 d. Type **371** .. .. 30 10
1700. 25 d. Doves and youths 20 20
1701. 27 d. Interior of U.N. General Assembly .. 25 25
1702. 100 d. U.N. Building, New York, and U.N. emblem .. .. 70 35

**1985.** Pontic Culture. Multicoloured.

1704. 12 d. Type **373** .. .. 20 10
1705. 15 d. Monastery of Our Lady of Soumela .. 25 10
1706. 27 d. Women's costumes (vert) .. .. .. 40 15
1707. 32 d. Trapezus High School .. .. 45 20
1708. 80 d. Sinope Castle .. 60 45

**374.** Hestia. **375.** "Ephebos of Antikythera".

**1986.** Gods of Olympus.

1709. **374.** 5 d. orange, black and brown .. 10 10
1710. – 18 d. orange, black and brown .. 25 10
1711. – 27 d. orange, black and blue .. .. 35 15
1712. – 32 d. orange, black and red .. .. 40 15
1713. – 35 d. orange, black and brown .. 40 15
1714. – 40 d. orange, black and red .. .. 50 25
1715. – 50 d. orange, black and grey .. .. 60 25
1716. – 110 d. orange, black and brown .. 80 30
1717. – 150 d. orange, black and grey .. .. 95 10
1718. – 200 d. orange, black and blue .. .. 1·25 10
1719. – 300 d. orange, black and blue .. 1·90 10
1720. – 500 d. orange, black and blue .. .. 3·25 1·90

DESIGNS: 18 d. Hermes. 27 d. Aphrodite. 32 d. Ares. 35 d. Athene. 40 d. Hephaestus. 50 d. Artemis. 110 d. Apollo. 150 d. Demeter. 200 d. Poseidon. 300 d. Hera. 500 d. Zeus.

**1986.** Sports Events and Anniversaries.

1721. **375.** 18 d. green, black and grey .. .. 25 10
1722. – 27 d. yellow, black and red .. .. 35 15
1723. – 32 d. multicoloured 40 20
1724. – 35 d. green, black and bistre .. 45 25
1725. – 40 d. multicoloured 50 25
1726. – 50 d. multicoloured 60 30
1727. – 110 d. multicoloured 1·40 4·00

DESIGNS—VERT. 18 d. Type **375** (1st World Junior Athletics Championships). 32 d. Footballers (Pan-European Junior Football Finals). 35 d. "Wrestlers" (sculpture) (Pan-European Freestyle and Greco-Roman Wrestling Championships). 50 d. Cyclists (6th International Round Europe Cycling Meet.). HORIZ. 27 d. "Diadoumenos" (sculpture by Polycleitus) (1st World Junior Athletics Championships). 40 d. Volleyball players (Men's World Volleyball Championships). 110 d. "Victory" (unadopted design by Nikephoros Lytras for first Olympic Games commemoratives, 1896) (90th anniv. of modern Olympic Games).

**376.** Fastening Seat Belt. **377.** Intelpost.

**1986.** European Road Safety Year. Mult.

1728. 18 d. Type **376** .. .. 25 10
1729. 27 d. Motorcyclist in traffic .. .. .. 35 15
1730. 110 d. Child strapped in back seat of car and speed limit signs .. 80 25

**1986.** New Postal Services. Multicoloured.

1731. 18 d. Type **377** .. .. 25 10
1732. 110 d. "Express Mail" banner around globe .. 80 20

**378.** Sapling between Hands and burning Forest. **379.** Victims' Memorial and Workers.

**1986.** Europa.

1733. **378.** 35 d. green, black and orange .. 1·25 25
1734. – 110 d. blue, black and green .. .. 2·25 1·10

DESIGN: 110 d. Dalmatian pelicans on Prespa Lake.

**1986.** Centenary of Chicago May Day Strike.

1735. **379.** 40 d. multicoloured 50 25

**380.** Swearing-in of Venizelos Government. **381.** Dove and Sun.

**1986.** 50th Death Anniv. of Eleftherios Venizelos (politician) (18 d.) and 6th International Crete Conference, Hania (110 d.). Multicoloured.

1736. 18 d. Type **380** .. .. 25 10
1737. 110 d. Hania harbour .. 75 30

**1986.** International Peace Year. Mult.

1738. 18 d. Type **381** .. .. 25 10
1739. 35 d. Dove holding olive branch with flags as leaves .. .. .. 45 25
1740. 110 d. Dove with olive branch flying out of globe (horiz.) .. .. 65 30

**382.** "Madonna and Child". **383.** "The Fox and the Grapes".

**1986.** Christmas. Designs showing icons. Multicoloured.

1741. 22 d. Type **382** .. .. 30 15
1742. 46 d. "Adoration of the Magi" (24×32 mm.) .. 30 25
1743. 130 d. "Christ enthroned with St. John the Evangelist" .. .. 90 30

**1987.** Aesop's Fables. Multicoloured.

1744. 2 d. Type **383** .. .. 10 10
1745. 5 d. "The North Wind and the Sun" .. .. 10 10
1746. 10 d. "The Stag at the Spring and the Lion" 10 10
1747. 22 d. "Zeus and the Snake" .. .. 20 10
1748. 32 d. "The Crow and the Fox" .. .. .. 25 10
1749. 40 d. "The Woodcutter and Hermes" .. .. 35 15
1750. 46 d. "The Ass in a Lion's Skin and the Fox" .. .. 40 20
1751. 130 d. "The Hare and the Tortoise" .. .. 1·25 25

**384.** "Composition". (Archilleas Apergis). **385.** Player shooting Goal and Indoor Court.

**1987.** Europa. Sculptures. Multicoloured.

1752. 40 d. Type **384** .. 1·25 40
1753. 130 d. "Delphic Light" (Gerassimos Sklavos) 1·60 60

**1987.** 25th European Men's Basketball Championships, Athens. Multicoloured.

1754. 22 d. Type **385** .. .. 20 10
1755. 25 d. Emblem and spectators (32×24 mm.) .. 25 10
1756. 130 d. Players .. 1·00 25

**386.** Banner and Students.

**1987.** 150th Annivs. of Athens University (3, 23 d.) and National Metsovio Polytechnic Institute (others). Multicoloured.
1758. 3 d. Type **386** . . . . 10 10
1759. 23 d. Medal and owl . . 20 10
1760. 40 d. Building facade, measuring instruments and computer terminal (vert.) . . . . . . 35 15
1761. 60 d. Students outside building (vert.) . . 55 25

**387.** Ionic and Corinthian Capitals, Temple of Apollo, Phigaleia-Bassae.

**1987.** Classical Architecture Capitals. Mult.
1762. 2 d. Type **387** . . . . 10 10
1763. 26 d. Doric capital, Parthenon . . . . 25 10
1764. 40 d. Ionic capital, The Erechtheum . . . . 35 15
1765. 60 d. Corinthian capital, The Tholos, Epidaurus 55 25

**388.** Hands holding Cup Aloft. **389.** Brush and Picture in Frame.

**1987.** Greek Victory in European Basketball Championship.
1766. **388.** 40 d. multicoloured 35 15

**1987.** 150th Anniv. of Fine Arts High School (1767) and 60th Anniv. of Panteios Political Science High School (1768). Multicoloured.
1767. 26 d. Type **389** . . . . 25 10
1768. 60 d. School campus . . 55 25

**390.** Angel and (left). **391.** Eleni Papadaki in "Hecuba" (Euripides) and Philippi Amphitheatre.

**1987.** Christmas.
1769. 26 d. Type **390** . . . . 25 10
1770. 26 d. Angel and Christmas tree (right) 25 10
Nos. 1769/70 were printed together, se-tenant, forming a composite design.

**1987.** Greek Theatre. Multicoloured.
1771. 2 d. Type **391** . . . . 10 10
1772. 4 d. Christopher Nezer in "The Wasps" (Aristophanes) and Dodona amphitheatre 10 10
1773. 7 d. Emilios Veakis in "Oedipus Rex" (Sophocles) and Delphi amphitheatre . . . . 10 10
1774. 26 d. Marika Cotopouli in "The Shepherdess's Love" (Dimitris Koromilas) . . . . 25 10
1775. 40 d. Katina Paxinou in "Abraham's Sacrifice" (Vitzentzos Cornaros) 35 15
1776. 50 d. Kyveli in "Countess Valeraina's Secret" (Gregory Xenopoulos) . . . . 45 20
1777. 60 d. Carolos Koun and stage set . . . . 55 25
1778. 100 d. Dimitris Rontiris teaching National Theatre dancers an ancient dance . . . . 90 40

**392.** "Codonellina sp". **394.** Satellite and Fax Machine.

**393.** Ancient Olympia.

**1988.** Marine Life. Multicoloured.
1779. 30 d. Type **392** . . . . 25 10
1780. 40 d. "Diaperoecia major" . . . . 35 15
1781. 50 d. "Artemia" (marine animal) . . . . 45 20
1782. 60 d. "Posidonia oceanica" (plant) . . 55 50
1783. 100 d. "Padina pavonica" (plant) . . 1·25 40

**1988.** Olympic Games, Seoul. Multicoloured.
1784. 4 d. Type **393** . . . . 10 10
1785. 20 d. Ancient athletes in Gymnasium . . . . 15 10
1786. 30 d. Modern Olympics centenary emblem . . 80 10
1787. 60 d. Ancient athletes training . . . . 1·25 80
1788. 170 d. Runner with Olympic flame . . 2·40 40

**1988.** Europa. Transport and Communications. Multicoloured.
1789. 60 d. Type **394** . . . . 3·25 80
1790. 150 d. Trains . . . . 4·00 20

**395.** Catarractis Falls. **396.** Emblems.

**1988.** European Campaign for Rural Areas. Waterfalls. Multicoloured.
1791. 10 d. Type **395** . . . . 10 10
1792. 60 d. Edessa waterfalls . . 1·00 1·00
1793. 100 d. River Edessaios cascades . . . . 1·60 35

**1988.** 20th European Postal Workers Trade Unions Congress.
1794. **396.** 60 d. multicoloured 1·40 60

**397.** "Mytilene Harbour, Lesbos" (painting by Theophilos). **398.** Eleftherios Venizelos, Map and Flag.

**1988.** Prefecture Capitals. Multicoloured.
1795. 2 d. Type **397** . . . . 10 10
1796. 3 d. Alexandroupolis lighthouse, Evros (vert.) . . . . 10 10
1797. 4 d. St. Nicholas's bell-tower, Kozani (vert.) 10 10
1798. 5 d. Workmen's centre, Hermoupolis, Cyclades (vert.) . . . . 10 10
1799. 7 d. Sparta Town Hall, Lakonia . . . . 10 10
1800. 8 d. Pegasus, Leukas . . 10 10
1801. 10 d. Castle of the Knights, Rhodes, Dodecanese (vert.) . . 10 10
1802. 20 d. Acropolis, Athens (vert.) . . . . 15 10
1803. 25 d. Aqueduct, Kavala 20 10
1804. 30 d. Castle and statue of Athanasios Diakos, Lamia, Phthiotis (vert.) . . . . 25 10
1805. 50 d. Preveza Cathedral bell-tower and clock (vert.) . . . . 40 20
1806. 60 d. Esplanade, Corfu . . 45 20
1807. 70 d. Aghios Nicholaos, Lassithi . . 55 25
1808. 100 d. Six Springheads, Poligiros, Khalkidiki 80 10
1809. 200 d. Church of Paul the Apostle, Corinth, Corinthia . . . . 1·50 10

**1988.** 75th Annivs. of Union of Crete and Greece (30 d.) and Liberation of Epirus and Macedonia (70 d.). Multicoloured.
1810. 30 d. Type **398** . . . . 25 10
1811. 70 d. Flags, map and "Liberty" . . . . 80 25

**399.** "Adoration of the Magi" (El Greco). **400.** Map of E.E.C. and Castle of Knights, Rhodes.

**1988.** Christmas. Multicoloured.
1812 30 d. Type **399** . . . . 25 10
1813 70 d. "The Annunciation" (Konstantine Parthenis (horiz) . . . . 55 25

**1988.** European Economic Community Meeting of Heads of State, Rhodes. Mult.
1814. 60 d. Type **400** . . . . 80 80
1815. 100 d. Coin and members' flags . . 1·25 35

**401** Ancient Olympia and High Jumper **402** Flags

**1989.** Centenary (1996) of Modern Olympic Games (1st issue). Multicoloured.
1816 30 d. Type **401** . . . . 25 10
1817 60 d. Delphi and wrestlers 80 20
1818 70 d. Acropolis, Athens, and swimmers . . 1·25 25
1819 170 d. Stadium and Golden Olympics emblem . . . . 2·00 70
See also Nos. 1863/7.

**1989.** International Anniversaries. Mult.
1820 30 d. Type **402** (5th anniv of Six-nation Initiative for Peace and Disarmament) . . . . 20 10
1821 50 d. Flag and "Liberty" (bicentenary of French Revolution) . . 35 15
1822 60 d. Flag and ballot box (third direct European Parliament elections) . . 45 60
1823 70 d. Coins (cent of Inter-parliamentary Union) 50 60
1824 200 d. Flag (40th anniv of Council of Europe) . . 2·00 30

**403** Whistling Bird **404** Magnifying Glass and Bird

**1989.** Europa. Children's Toys. Multicoloured.
1825 60 d. Type **403** . . . . 1·40 80
1826 170 d. Butterfly . . . . 1·75 60

**1989.** "Balkanfila XII" International Stamp Exhibition, Salonica. Multicoloured.
1827 60 d. Type **404** . . . . 45 20
1828 70 d. Eye looking through magnifying glass . . 50 25

**405** Wild Roses

**1989.** Wild Flowers. Multicoloured.
1830 8 d. Type **405** . . . . 10 10
1831 10 d. Common myrtle . . 10 10
1832 20 d. Field poppies . . 15 10
1833 30 d. Anenomes . . . . 20 10
1834 60 d. Dandelions and chicory . . . . 45 20
1835 70 d. Mallow . . . . 50 25
1836 200 d. Thistles . . . . 1·50 15

**406** Brown Bear **407** Gregoris Lambrakis

**1990.** Endangered Animals. Multicoloured.
1837 40 d. Type **406** . . . . 30 15
1838 70 d. Loggerhead turtle . . 75 30
1839 90 d. Mediterranean monk seal . . . . . . 60 30
1840 100 d. Lynx . . . . 75 35

**1990.** Politicians' Death Anniversaries. Mult.
1841 40 d. Type **407** (27th anniv) . . . . 30 15
1842 40 d. Pavlos Bakoyiannis (first anniv) . . 30 15

**408** Clasped Hands, Roses and Flag **409** Old Central Post Office Interior

**1990.** National Reconciliation. Multicoloured.
1843 40 d. Type **408** . . . . 30 15
1844 70 d. Dove with banner . . 50 25
1845 100 d. Map and hands holding roses . . 70 35

**1990.** Europa. Post Office Buildings. Mult.
1846 70 d. Type **409** . . . . 50 25
1847 210 d. Present Central Post Office exterior . . 1·40 70

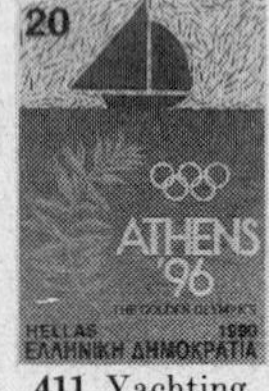

**410** "Animal Fair"(D. Gioldassi) (Karditsa) **411** Yachting

**1990.** Prefecture Capitals. Multicoloured.
1848 2 d. Type **410** . . . . 10 10
1849 5 d. Fort, Trikala (horiz) 10 10
1850 8 d. Street, Veroia (Imathia) . . . . 10 10
1851 10 d. Monument to Fallen heroes, Missolonghi (Aetolia) (horiz) . . 10 10
1852 15 d. Harbour, Chios (horiz) . . . . 10 10
1853 20 d. Street, Tripolis (Arcadia) (horiz) . . 15 10
1854 25 d. "City and Town Hall" (woodcut, A. Tassos) (Volos, Magnessia) (horiz) . . 20 10
1855 40 d. Town Hall, Kalamata (Messenia) (horiz) . . . . 30 15
1856 50 d. Market, Pyrgos (Elia) (horiz) . . 35 20
1857 70 d. Lake and island, Yannina (horiz) . . 50 25

1858 80 d. Harbour sculpture, Rethymnon .. .. 55 25
1859 90 d. Argostolion (Kefallenia) (horiz) .. 60 55
1860 100 d. Citadel and islet, Nauplion (Argolis) (horiz) .. .. 70 10
1861 200 d. Lighthouse, Patras (Akhaia) .. .. 1·40 10
1862 250 d. Street, Florina (horiz) .. .. 2·00 10

**1990.** Centenary (1996) of Modern Olympic Games (2nd issue). Multicoloured.
1863 20 d. Type **411** .. .. 15 10
1864 50 d. Wrestling .. 35 20
1865 80 d. Running .. 55 25
1866 100 d. Handball .. 70 35
1867 250 d. Football .. 2·00 85

**412** Schliemann and Lion Gate, Mycenae

**413** "Woman knitting" (lithograph, Vasso Katraki)

**1990.** Death Cent of Heinrich Schliemann (archaeologist).
1868 **412** 80 d. multicoloured .. 55 25

**1990.** 50th Anniv of Greek–Italian War. Mult.
1869 50 d. Type **413** .. .. 35 25
1870 80 d. "Virgin Mary protecting Army" (lithograph, George Gounaropoulou) .. 55 25
1871 100 d. "Women's War Work" (lithograph, Kosta Grammatopoulou) .. .. 70 35

**415** Calliope, Euterpe and Erato

**1991.** The Nine Muses. Multicoloured.
1873 50 d. Type **415** .. .. 35 20
1874 80 d. Terpsichore, Polyhymnia and Melpomene .. .. 55 30
1875 250 d. Thalia, Clio and Urania .. .. 2·00 85

**416** "Battle Scene" (Ioannis Anousakis)

**1991.** 50th Anniv of Battle for Crete. Mult.
1876 60 d. Type **416** .. .. 80 60
1877 300 d. Map and flags of allied nations (32 × 24 mm) .. .. 1·90 40

**417** Icarus pushing Satellite

**418** Swimming

**1991.** Europa. Europe in Space. Mult.
1878 80 d. Type **417** .. .. 50 25
1879 300 d. Chariot of the Sun 2·40 95

**1991.** 11th Mediterranean Games, Athens. Multicoloured.
1880 10 d. Type **418** .. .. 10 10
1881 60 d. Basketball .. .. 35 15
1882 90 d. Gymnastics .. 55 30
1883 130 d. Weightlifting .. 80 40
1884 300 d. Throwing the hammer .. .. 2·40 1·40

**419** Pillar of Democracy

**421** Pres. Konstantinos Karamanlis signing Treaty of Athens

**1991.** 2500th Anniv of Birth of Democracy.
1885 **419** 100 d. blk, stone & bl 60 80

**1991.** 10th Anniv of Greek Admission to European Community. Multicoloured.
1887 50 d. Type **421** .. .. 30 15
1888 80 d. Map of Europe and Pres. Karamanlis .. 50 25

**422** Emblem and Skaters

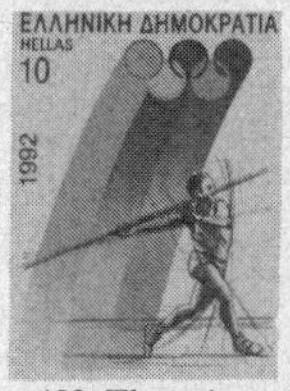

**423** Throwing the Javelin

**1991.** Winter Olympic Games, Albertville. Multicoloured.
1889 80 d. Type **422** .. .. 50 25
1890 300 d. Slalom skier .. 2·40 95

**1992.** Olympic Games, Barcelona. Mult.
1891 10 d. Type **423** .. .. 10 10
1892 60 d. Show jumping .. 35 15
1893 90 d. Runner (37 × 24 mm) 80 25
1894 120 d. Gymnastics .. 1·00 35
1895 340 d. Runners' heads forming Olympic rings (37 × 24 mm) .. .. 2·75 1·00

**424** Couple beneath Umbrella

**425** "Santa Maria", Map and Columbus

**1992.** Health. Multicoloured.
1896 60 d. Type **424** (anti-AIDS campaign) .. .. 35 15
1897 80 d. Doctor examining child (1st European Gastroenterology Week) 50 25
1898 90 d. Crab killing flower on healthy plant (anti-cancer campaign) .. 55 25
1899 120 d. Hephaestus's forge (from 6th-century B.C. urn) (European Year of Social Security, Hygiene and Health in the Workplace) .. 75 35
1900 280 d. Alexandros Onassis Cardiosurgical Centre 1·75 85

**1992.** Europa. 500th Anniv of Discovery of America by Columbus. Multicoloured.
1901 90 d. Type **425** .. .. 55 25
1902 340 d. Chios in late 15th century .. .. 2·40 1·25

## MORE DETAILED LISTS

are given in the Stanley Gibbons Catalogues referred to in the country headings.
For lists of current volumes see Introduction.

**427** Head of Hercules with Lion Skin (relief)

**428** Piraeus

**1992.** Macedonia. Multicoloured.
1904 10 d. Type **427** .. .. 10 10
1905 20 d. Map of Macedonia and bust of Aristotle (horiz) .. .. 10 10
1906 60 d. Alexander the Great at Battle of Issus (mural) (horiz) .. 35 15
1907 80 d. Tomb of Philip II, Vergina, and Manolis Andronikos (archaeologist) .. .. 50 25
1908 90 d. Deer hunt (mosaic, Pella) .. .. .. 55 25
1909 120 d. Macedonian coin .. 75 35
1910 340 d. 4th-century Church, Philippi, and Apostle Paul .. .. .. 2·10 1·00

**1992.** Prefecture Capitals. Multicoloured.
1911 10 d. Type **428** .. .. 10 10
1912 20 d. Amphissa (Phocis) 10 10
1913 30 d. The Heraion, Samos 20 10
1914 40 d. Canea .. .. 25 10
1915 50 d. Zakynthos .. .. 30 15
1916 60 d. Karpenissi (Evrytania) .. .. 35 15
1917 70 d. Cave, Kilkis (vert) 40 20
1918 80 d. Door of Town Hall, Xanthi (vert) .. .. 50 25
1919 90 d. Macedonian Struggle Museum, Thessaloniki 55 25
1920 120 d. Tsanakleous School, Comotini (Rhodope) .. 75 35
1921 340 d. Spring, Drama .. 2·10 1·00
1922 400 d. Pinios Bridge, Larissa .. .. 2·40 1·10

**429** Column, Map, Flags and European Community Emblem

**1992.** Single European Market.
1923 **429** 90 d. multicoloured .. 55 25

**430** Headstone

**431** Georgakis Olympios at Sekkou Monastery, 1821

**1993.** 2400th Anniv of Rhodes. Multicoloured.
1924 60 d. Type **430** .. .. 35 15
1925 90 d. "Aphrodite bathing" (statue) .. .. 55 25
1926 120 d. "St. Irene" (from St. Catherine's church) 75 35
1927 250 d. St. Paul's Gate, Naillac Mole .. .. 1·50 75

**1993.** Historical Events. Multicoloured.
1928 10 d. Type **431** (War of Independence) .. 10 10
1929 30 d. Theodore Kolokotronis (War of Independence) .. 15 10
1930 60 d. Pavlos Melas (military hero) .. 30 15
1931 90 d. "Glory crowns the Casualties" (Balkan Wars, 1912–13) .. 50 25
1932 120 d. Soldiers of Sacred Company, El Alamein, 1942 (horiz) .. .. 65 30
1933 150 d. Sacred Company on Aegean Islands, 1943–45 (horiz) .. .. 80 40
1934 200 d. Victims' Monument, Kalavryta (destruction of village, 1943) .. .. .. 1·10 55

**432** "The Benefits of Transportation" (Constantinus Parthenis) (left half)

**1993.** Europa. Contemporary Art. Mult.
1935 90 d. Type **432** .. .. 50 25
1936 350 d. "The Benefits of Transportation" (right half) .. .. .. 1·90 95

Nos. 1935/6 were issued together, se-tenant, forming a composite design.

**433** Athens Concert Hall

**1993.** Modern Athens. Multicoloured.
1937 30 d. Type **433** .. .. 15 10
1938 60 d. Iliou Melathron (former house of Heinrich Schliemann (archaeologist), now Numismatic Museum) 30 15
1939 90 d. National Library .. 50 25
1940 200 d. Athens Eye Hospital .. .. 1·10 55

**435** "Hermes driving Chariot" (Boeotian vase)

**436** "Last Supper" (icon by Michael Damaskinou, St. Catherine's Church, Heraklion, Crete)

**1994.** 2nd Pan-European Transport Conf.
1942 **435** 200 d. multicoloured .. 1·10 55

**1994.** Easter. Multicoloured.
1943 30 d. Type **436** .. .. 15 10
1944 60 d. "Crucifixion" (detail of wall painting, Great Meteoron) .. .. 30 15
1945 90 d. "Burial of Christ" (icon, Church of the Presentation of the Lord, Patmos) (horiz) 50 25
1946 150 d. "Resurrection" (detail, illuminated manuscript from Mt. Athos) (horiz) .. 80 40

**437** Thalesof Miletus (philosopher)

**438** Demetrios Vikelas (first president of I.O.C.) (after G. Roilos)

**1994.** Europa. Discoveries. Multicoloured.
1947 90 d. Type **437** .. .. 50 25
1948 350 d. Konstantinos Karatheodoris (mathematician) and equations .. .. 1·90 95

**1994.** Sports Events and Anniversary. Mult.
1949 60 d. Type **438** (centenary of International Olympic Committee) .. 30 15
1950 90 d. Modern footballer and ancient relief (World Cup Football Championship, U.S.A.) (horiz) .. .. 50 25
1951 120 d. Ball, net and laurel (World Volleyball Championship, Piraeus and Salonika) .. .. 65 30

**439** "Greece" driving E.U. Chariot

**1994.** Greek Presidency of European Union. Multicoloured.
1953 90 d. Type **439** .. .. 50 25
1954 120 d. Doric columns and E.U. flag .. .. 65 30

**440** Parigoritissas Byzantine Church, Arta

**441** "Declaration of Constitution" (detail, Carl Howpt)

**1994.** Prefecture Capitals. Multicoloured.
1955 10 d. Tsalopoulou mansion house, Katerini (Pieria) (vert) .. .. .. 10 10
1956 20 d. Type **440** .. .. 10 10
1957 30 d. Bridge and tower, Levadia (Boeotia) (vert) 15 10
1958 40 d. Koumbelidikis church, Kastoria .. 20 10
1959 50 d. Outdoor theatre, Grevena .. .. 25 10
1960 60 d. Waterfall, Edessa (Pella) .. .. 30 15
1961 80 d. Red House, Chalcis (Euboea) .. .. 40 20
1962 90 d. Government House, Serres .. .. .. 50 25
1963 120 d. Town Hall, Heraklion .. .. 65 30
1964 150 d. Church of Our Lady of the Annunciation, Igoumenitsa (Thesprotia) (vert) .. 80 40

**1994.** 150th Anniv of Constitution. Mult.
1965 60 d. Type **441** .. .. 30 15
1966 150 d. Ioannis Makrygiannis, Andreas Metaxas and Dimitrios Kallergis (horiz) .. 80 40
1967 200 d. "The Night of 3rd September, 1843" (anon) (horiz) .. .. 1·10 55
1968 340 d. Article 107 of 1844 Constitution and Parliament Seal (horiz) 1·90 95

**442** Mercouri and Demonstrators (fighter for Democracy)

**1995.** Melina Mercouri (actress and Minister of Culture) Commemoration. Multicoloured.
1969 60 d. Type **442** .. .. 35 15
1970 90 d. Mercouri and Acropolis (politician) .. 50 25
1971 100 d. Mercouri in three roles (actress) .. .. 55 25
1972 340 d. Mercouri with flowers (vert) .. .. 1·90 95

**443** Prisoners behind Barbed Wire

**444** Emblem

**1995.** Europa. Peace and Freedom. Mult.
1973 90 d. Type **443** .. .. 50 25
1974 340 d. Doves flying from crushed barbed wire 1·90 95
Nos. 1973/4 were issued together, se-tenant, forming a composite design.

**1995.** Anniversaries and Events. Mult.
1975 10 d. Type **444** (5th World Junior Basketball Championship) .. 10 10
1976 70 d. Agriculture University, Athens (75th anniv) (horiz) .. 40 20
1977 90 d. Delphi (50th anniv of U.N.O.) .. .. 50 25
1978 100 d. Greek flag and returning soldier (50th anniv of end of Second World War) .. .. 55 25
1979 120 d. "Peace" (statue by Kifissodotos) (50th anniv of U.N.O.) .. 65 30
1980 150 d. Dolphins (European Nature Conservation Year) (horiz) .. 80 40
1981 200 d. Old telephone and modern key-pad (cent of telephone in Greece) 1·10 55
1982 300 d. Owl sitting on ball (29th European Basketball Championship) .. 1·60 80

**445** "The First Vision of the Apocalypse" (icon, Thomas Bathas)

**1995.** 1900th Anniv of the Apocalypse of St. John. Multicoloured.
1983 80 d. Type **445** .. .. 45 20
1984 110 d. St. John and the Cave of the Apocalypse (miniature from the Four Gospels) .. 60 30
1985 300 d. Trumpet of the First Angel (gilded Gospel cover) (horiz) .. 1·60 80

**446** Goddess Athene with Argonauts

**447** Psyttaleia

**1995.** Jason and the Argonauts. Mult.
1986 80 d. Type **446** .. .. 45 20
1987 120 d. Phineas (blind seer), god Hermes and the Voreadae persuing Harpies .. .. 65 30
1988 150 d. Medea, Nike and Jason taming bull .. 80 40
1989 200 d. Jason and Medea killing snake and taking the Golden Fleece .. 1·10 55
1990 300 d. Jason presenting Golden Fleece to Pelias 1·60 80

**1995.** Lighthouses. Multicoloured.
1991 80 d. Type **447** .. .. 45 20
1992 120 d. Sapienza .. .. 65 30
1993 150 d. Kastri, Othonoi .. 80 40
1994 500 d. Zourva, Hydra .. 2·75 1·25

**449** Sappho (poet)

**450** Running

**1996.** Europa. Famous Women.
1996 **449** 120 d. multicoloured 65 30
1997 – 430 d. brown, blk & bl 2·25 1·10
DESIGN: 430 d. Amalia Fleming.

**1996.** Cent of Modern Olympic Games. Mult.
1998 10 d. Type **450** .. .. 10 10
1999 80 d. Throwing the discus 40 20
2000 120 d. Weightlifting .. 65 30
2001 200 d. Wrestling (horiz) .. 1·00 50

**451** Hippocrates

**452** Mytilene

**1996.** 1st Int Medical Olympiad, Athens.
2002 **451** 80 d. brn, pink & blk 40 20
2003 – 120 d. brn, grn & blk 65 30
DESIGN: 120 d. Galen.

**1996.** Castles. Multicoloured.
2004 10 d. Type **452** .. .. 10 10
2005 20 d. Lindos .. .. 10 10
2006 30 d. Rethymnon .. .. 15 10
2007 70 d. Assos Cephalonia .. 35 15
2008 80 d. Castle of the Serbs 40 20
2009 120 d. Monemvasia .. 65 30
2010 200 d. Didimotihon .. 1·00 50
2011 430 d. Vonitsas .. .. 2·25 1·10
2012 1000 d. Nikopolis .. 5·25 2·50

## CHARITY TAX STAMPS

**C 38.** Dying Soldier, Widow and Child.

**C 39.** Red Cross, Nurses, Wounded and Bearers.

**1914.** Roul.
C 269. C **38.** 2 l. red .. .. 15 15
C 270. 5 l. blue .. .. 30 25

**1915.** Red Cross. Roul.
C 271. C **39.** (5 l.) red and blue 10·00 60

**C 40.** Greek Women's Patriotic League Badge.

**1915.** Greek Women's Patriotic League.
C 272. C **40.** (5 l.) red and blue .. 30 30

K. Π.
λεπτοῦ
1
(C 42.)

C 43.

*K. Π.*
λεπτοῦ
1
(C 44.)

K.Π.
10 ΛΕΠΤΑ 10
(C 46.)

**1917.** Surch. as Type C **42.**
C 297. **15.** 1 on 1 l. brown .. 1·40 1·40
C 303. 1 on 3 l. orange .. 30 30
C 299. 5 on 1 l. brown .. 1·40 1·40
C 300. 5 on 20 l. mauve .. 55 55
C 307. **36.** 5 on 25 l. blue .. 25 25
C 304. **15.** 5 on 40 l. brown .. 20 20
C 308. **36.** 5 on 40 l. blue .. 25 25
C 305. **15.** 5 on 50 l. lake .. 20 20
C 309. **35.** 5 on 50 l. blue .. 25 25
C 306. **17.** 5 on 1 d. black .. 60 60
C 301. **15.** 10 on 30 l. purple .. 50 50
C 302. 30 on 30 l. purple .. 50 50

**1917.** Fiscal stamps surch. as Type C **44.** Roul.
C 310. C **43.** 1 l. on 10 l. blue .. 40 40
C 328. 1 l. on 50 l. purple .. 40 35
C 311. 1 l. on 80 l. blue .. 40 60
C 330. 5 l. on 10 l. purple .. 60 35
C 329. 5 l. on 10 l. blue .. 60 35
C 312. 5 l. on 60 l. blue .. 1·60 1·25
C 313. 5 l. on 80 l. blue .. 1·25 1·25
C 331. 10 l. on 50 l. purple 1·25 65
C 326. 10 l. on 70 l. blue .. 2·00 2·00
C 327. 10 l. on 90 l. blue .. 4·00 2·00
C 316. 20 l. on 20 l. blue .. £475 £350
C 317. 20 l. on 30 l. blue .. 2·40 2·25
C 318. 20 l. on 40 l. blue .. 6·75 5·00
C 319. 20 l. on 50 l. blue .. 3·00 2·40
C 320. 20 l. on 60 l. blue .. £190 £120
C 321. 20 l. on 80 l. blue .. 24·00 20·00
C 322. 20 l. on 90 l. blue .. 1·90 1·40
C 333. 20 l. on 2 d. blue .. 3·50 2·00

**1917.** Fiscal stamps surch. as Type C **46.** Roul.
C 334. C **43.** 1 l. on 10 l. blue .. 40 40
C 341. 5 l. on 10 l. pur. & red 4·75 95
C 335. 5 l. on 50 l. blue .. 24·00 16·00
C 338. 10 l. on 50 l. blue .. 3·50 2·00
C 339. 20 l. on 50 l. blue .. 9·00 4·75
C 340. 30 l. on 50 l. blue .. 5·50 5·00

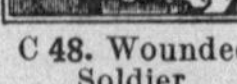

**C 48.** Wounded Soldier.

**C 77.** St Demetrius.

C 49.

**1918.** Red Cross. Roul.
C 342. C **48.** 5 l. red, blue & yell. 4·00 1·25

**1918.** Optd. II.Ι.II.
C 343. C **48.** 5 l. red, blue & yell. 5·00 1·25

**1922.** Greek Women's Patriotic League. Surch. as in Type C **49.**
C 344. C **49.** 5 l. on 10 l. red & bl. £200 2·75
C 345. 5 l. on 20 l. red & bl. 32·00 20·00
C 346. 5 l. on 50 l. red & bl. £180 48·00
C 347. 5 l. on 1 d. red & bl. 2·00 32·00
Nos. C 344/7 were not issued without surcharge.

**1924.** Red Cross. As Type C **48** but wounded soldier and family.
C 405. 10 l. red, blue and yellow 25 15

**1934.** Salonika Int. Exn. Fund.
C 478. C **77.** 20 l. brown .. .. 10 10

C **78.** Allegory of Health.

ΠΡΟΝΟΙΑ (C **85.**).

**1934.** Postal Staff. Anti-Tuberculosis Fund.
C 480. C **78.** 10 l. orange & green 10 10
C 481. 20 l. orange & blue 30 20
C 482. 50 l. orange & green 60 45

**1935.** As Type C **78** but inscr. "ΕΛΛΑΣ" at top.
C 494. 10 l. orange & green 10 10
C 495. 20 l. orange & blue 10 10
C 496. 50 l. orange & green 50 25
C 497. 50 l. orange & brown 25 20

**1937.** Nos. D 273 and 415 optd. with Type C **85.**
C 498. D **20.** 10 l. red .. .. 40 10
C 500. **51.** 50 l. violet .. .. 40 10

Λ.50 ΠΡΟΝΟΙΑ (C **95.**) C **96.** Queens Olga and Sophia.

**1938.** Surch. with Type C **95.**
C 521. D **20.** 50 l. on 5 l. green .. 60 20
C 522. 50 l. on 20 l. slate .. 80 40
C 523. **52.** 50 l. on 20 l. violet 60 40

**1939.**
C 524. C **96.** 10 l. red .. .. 10 10
C 525. 50 l. green .. .. 10 10
C 526. 1 d. blue .. .. 15 15

ΠΡΟΣΤΑΣΙΑ ΦΥΜΑΤΙΚΩΝ ΤΤΤ (C **104.**)

**1940.** Postal staff Anti-Tuberculosis Fund. Optd. with Type C **104.**
C 554. C **96.** 50 l. green .. .. 20 20

Κ.Π. λεπτῶν 50 (C **105.**)

ΥΠΕΡ ΤΩΝ ΦΥΜΑΤΙΚΩΝ Τ.Τ.Τ. ΔΡΧ. 25.000 (C **113.**)

**1941.** Surch. with Type C **105.**
C 561. **51.** 50 l. on 5 l. green .. 15 15

**1941.** Postal Staff Anti-Tuberculosis Fund. Surch. **50** and bars.
C 562. C **78.** 50 l. on 10 l. .. 1·00 1·00
C 563. – 50 l. on 10 l. (No. C 494) 15 15

**1942.** Sample Fair, Salonika. Surch. Δ **P. 1.**
C 573. C **77.** 1 d. on 20 l. brown .. 15 15

**1942.** Postal Staff Anti-Tuberculosis Fund. Surch. **ΦΥΜ. T.T.T. 10** ΔP and Cross of Lorraine.
C 591. **51.** 10 d. on 5 l. green .. 10 10
C 592. 10 l. on 25 l. green .. 10 10

**1944.** Postal Staff Anti-Tuberculosis Fund. Optd. **ΦΥΜ. T.T.T.** and Cross of Lorraine.
C 599. 100 d. black (No. 580) 10 10

**1944.** Postal Staff Anti-Tuberculosis Fund. Surch. **ΦΥΜ. T.T.T.** Δ**P.5000.**
C 600. 5000 d. on 75 d. (No. 579) .. .. .. 10 10

**1944.** Postal Staff Anti-Tuberculosis Fund. Surch. as Type C **113.**
C 619. – 1 d. on 40 l. (No. 500) 10 10
C 620. – 2 d. on 40 l. (No. 500) 10 10
C 605. **106.** 25,000 d. on 2 d. .. 10 15

ΠΡΟΝΟΙΑ ΠΡΟΣΩΠΙΚΟΥ Τ.Τ.Τ. ΔΡΑΧΜΑΙ 50 (C **117.**)

ΠΡΟΝΟΙΑ ΤΑΧ. ΥΠΑΛΛΗΛΩΝ ΔΡΑΧΜΑΙ 50 (C **136.**)

**1946.** Postal Staff Anti-Tuberculosis Fund. Surch. as Type C **117.**
C 640 C **117** 20 d. on 5 l. .. 25 20
C 641 20 d. on 40 l. (No. 500) .. .. 15 10

**1946.** Red Cross. Surch as Type C **117.**
C 642. C **96.** 50 d. on 50 l. (No. C 525) 15 15

**1946.** Social Funds. Surch. as Type C **117.**
C 643. C **96.** 50 d. on 1 d. (No. C 526) 15 10

**1947.** Postal Staff Anti-Tuberculosis Fund. Surch.
C 659. C **96.** 50 d. on 50 l. (C 525) 20·00 20·00
C 660. 50 l. on 50 d. (C 554) 25 20

C **127.** St. Demetrius. C **140.** Argostoli, Cephalonia.

**1948.** Church Restoration Fund.
C 682. C **127.** 50 d. brown .. 10 10

**1950.** Postal Staff Anti-Tuberculosis Fund. Surch. with Type C **117.**
C 686. 50 d. on 10 l. (No. 498) 15 10

**1951.** Postal Staff Welfare Fund. Surch. with Type C **136.**
C 698. **86.** 50 d. on 5 l. blue & brn. 15 15

**1951.** Postal Staff Anti-Tuberculosis Fund. Surch. with Cross of Lorraine and **50.**
C 699. **89.** 50 d. on 3 d. brown .. 15 15

**1952.** State Welfare Fund. Surch. *ΠΡΟΣΘΕΤΟΝ* and value.
C 706. **89.** 100 d. on 8 d. blue .. 15 15

**1953.** Ionian Is. Earthquake Fund.
C 713. – 300 d. slate .. 35 15
C 714. C **140.** 500 d. brown & yell. 75 55
DESIGN: 300 d. Church of Faneromeni, Zante.

C **148.** Zeus (Macedonian Coin of Philip II).

**1956.** Macedonian Cultural Fund.
C 761. C **148.** 50 l. red .. .. 35 10
C 762. – 1 d. blue (Aristotle) 90 65

POSTAGE DUE STAMPS

D **2.** D **20.**

**1875.**
D 73. D **2.** 1 l. green and black 1·00 50
D 74. 2 l. green and black 1·00 50
D 75. 5 l. green and black 1·25 80
D 88. 10 l. green and black 1·25 80
D 89. 20 l. green and black 2·40 1·60
D 78. 40 l. green and black 8·00 4·00
D 91a. 60 l. green and black 12·00 12·00
D 80. 70 l. green and black 6·00 6·00
D 81. 80 l. green and black 10·00 10·00
D 82. 90 l. green and black 8·00 8·00
D 95. 100 l. green and black 8·00 8·00
D 96. 200 l. green and black 10·00 8·00
D 83. 1 d. green and black 9·50 8·00
D 84. 2 d. green and black 9·50 8·00

**1902.**
D 183. D **20.** 1 l. brown .. 15 10
D 184. 2 l. grey .. 15 10
D 185. 3 l. orange .. 15 10
D 186. 5 l. green .. 15 10
D 273. 10 l. red .. 15 10
D 188. 20 l. mauve .. 25 25
D 275. 25 l. blue .. 4·00 2·40
D 190. 30 l. purple .. 20 20
D 191. 40 l. brown .. 25 25
D 451. 50 l. brown .. 15 15
D 193. 1 d. black .. 40 40
D 194. 2 d. bronze .. 65 65
D 195. 3 d. silver .. 1·25 1·25
D 196. 5 d. gold .. 4·00 4·00

**1912.** Optd. with T **34.**
D 252. D **20.** 1 l. brown .. .. 30 30
D 253. 2 l. grey .. .. 30 30
D 254. 3 l. orange .. 30 30
D 255. 5 l. green .. .. 45 45
D 256. 10 l. red .. .. 45 45
D 257. 20 l. mauve .. 80 45
D 258. 30 l. purple .. .. 1·60 1·60
D 259. 40 l. brown .. 75 75
D 260. 50 l. brown .. 65 65
D 261. 1 d. black .. .. 2·75 2·00
D 262. 2 d. bronze .. 6·00 6·00
D 263. 3 d. silver .. .. 12·00 12·00
D 264. 5 d. gold .. .. 24·00 24·00

**1913.** Perf. or roul.
D 269. D **20.** 1 l. green .. .. 10 10
D 270. 2 l. red .. .. 10 10
D 271. 3 l. red .. .. 10 10
D 274. 20 l. slate .. .. 20 20
D 276. 30 l. red .. .. 15 15
D 277. 40 l. blue .. .. 20 20
D 279. 80 l. purple .. .. 50 30
D 452. 1 d. blue .. .. 35 25
D 453. 2 d. red .. .. 15 15
D 282. 3 d. red .. .. 4·25 1·40
D 455. 5 d. blue .. .. 15 15
D 456. 10 d. green .. .. 15 10
D 595. 10 d. orange .. 15 10
D 457. 15 d. brown .. 15 10
D 458. 25 d. red .. .. 45 50
D 596. 25 d. blue .. .. 10 15
D 480. 50 d. orange .. 25 25
D 481. 100 d. green .. 25 25
D 597. 100 d. brown .. 10 10
D 598. 200 d. violet .. 10 10

**1942.** Surch. **50.**
D 564. D **20.** 50 l. on 30 l. red .. 60 60

GREEK WAR ISSUES, 1912–1913

For provisional issues used in territories occupied by Greece during the Balkan War, see Stanley Gibbons Part 3 (Balkans) Catalogue.

## GREEK OCCUPATION OF ALBANIA Pt. 3

100 lepta = 1 drachma.

Stamps of Greece optd. with T **1.**

ΕΛΛΗΝΙΚΗ ΔΙΟΙΚΗΣΙΣ (**1.**)

**1940.** Stamps of 1937.
1 86 5 l. blue and brown 15 15
2 – 10 l. brn. & blue (No. 498) 15 15
3 – 20 l. grn. & blk. (No. 499) 15 15
4 – 40 l. blk. & grn. (No. 500) 15 15
5 – 50 l. blk. & brn. (No. 501) 20 20
6 – 80 l. brn. & vio. (No. 502) 20 25
7 89 1 d. green .. .. 20 15
8 – 2 d. blue (No. 504) .. 20 25
9 89 3 d. brown .. .. 20 40
10 – 5 d. red (No. 506) .. 40 45
11 – 6 d. olive (No. 507) .. 40 45
12 – 7 d. brown (No. 508) .. 50 60
13 89 8 d. blue .. .. 40 60
14 – 10 d. brown (No. 510) .. 70 1·00
15 – 15 d. green (No. 511) .. 80 80
16 – 25 d. blue (No. 512) .. 2·25 2·25
17 89a 30 d. red .. .. 4·00 4·00

**1940.** Charity Tax stamps of 1939.
18. C **96.** 10 l. red .. .. 15 15
19. 50 l. green .. .. 15 15
20. 1 d. blue .. .. 30 35

**1940.** Nos. 534/53 (Youth Organization).
26. **101.** 3 d. bl., red & sil. (post.) 40 40
27. – 5 d. black and blue .. 2·75 2·75
28. – 10 d. black and orange .. 4·00 4·00
29. – 15 d. black and green .. 14·00 14·00
30. – 20 d. black and red .. 5·25 5·25
31. – 25 d. black and blue .. 5·25 5·25
32. – 30 d. black and violet 6·50 6·50
33. – 50 d. black and red .. 10·00 10·00
34. – 75 d. gold, blue & brown 10·00 10·00
35. **101.** 100 d. blue, red and silver 14·00 14·00
36. **103.** 2 d. black & orange (air) 40 40
37. – 4 d. black and green .. 40 40
38. – 6 d. black and red .. 2·00 2·00
39. – 8 d. black and blue .. 3·25 3·25
40. – 16 d. black and violet .. 4·00 4·00
41. – 32 d. black and orange .. 8·00 8·00
42. – 45 d. black and green .. 8·75 8·75
43. – 55 d. black and red .. 9·75 9·75
44. – 65 d. black and blue .. 9·75 9·75
45. – 100 d. black and violet .. 13·00 13·00

POSTAGE DUE STAMPS

**1940.** Postage Due stamps of 1913.
D 21. D **20.** 2 d. red .. .. 40 40
D 22. 5 d. blue .. .. 40 45
D 23. 10 d. green .. .. 40 55
D 24. 15 d. brown .. .. 60 75

**1940.** Postage Due stamp surch. also.
D 25. D **20.** 50 l. on 25 d. red .. 35 30

### MINIMUM PRICE

The minimum price quoted is 10p which represents a handling charge rather than a basis for valuing common stamps. For further notes about prices see introductory pages.

## GREEK OCCUPATION OF THE DODECANESE ISLANDS Pt. 3

The Dodecanese Islands, formerly Italian, were transferred to Greece in **1947.** Now use Greek stamps.

100 lepta = 1 drachma.

**1947.** Stamps of Greece optd. Σ Δ Δ.
1. – 10 d. on 2000 d. blue (No. 623) .. .. .. 45 45
3. **89.** 50 d. on 1 d. grn. (No. 642) 80 80
4. 250 d. on 3 d. brn (No. 643) 80 80

(**1.**)

**1947.** Stamps of Greece surch. as T **1.**
5. – 20 d. on 500 d. brown (No. 582) .. .. 30 40
6. – 30 d. on 5 d. green (No. 574) .. .. .. 30 40
7. **106.** 50 d. on 2 d. brown .. 60 60
8. – 250 d. on 10 d. brown (No. 510) .. .. 80 80
9. – 400 d. on 15 d. green (No. 511) .. .. 1·25 1·25
10. – 1000 d. on 200 d. blue (No. 581) .. .. 75 75

## GREENLAND Pt. 11

A Danish possession N.E. of Canada. On 5 June 1963, Greenland became an integral part of the Danish Kingdom.

100 ore = 1 krone

**1.** Christian X.

**2.** Polar Bear.

**1938.**
1. **1.** 1 ore green .. .. .. 10 20
2. 5 ore red .. .. .. 1·50 1·00
3. 7 ore green .. .. .. 2·00 2·40
4. 10 ore violet .. .. .. 60 55
5. 15 ore red .. .. .. 60 60
5a. 20 ore red .. .. .. 1·50 85
6. **2.** 30 ore blue .. .. .. 5·50 6·00
6a. 40 ore blue .. .. .. 32·00 6·50
7. 1 k. brown .. .. .. 7·00 6·00

**3.** Harp Seal.

**4.** King Christian X.

**5.** Eskimo Kayak.

DESIGNS—HORIZ. As Type **5**: 30 ore Dog team. 1 k. Polar bear. 5 k. Eider.

**1945.**
8. **3.** 1 ore violet and black .. 35·00 27·00
9. 5 ore buff and violet .. 35·00 27·00
10. 7 ore black and green .. 35·00 27·00
11. **4.** 10 ore olive and purple .. 30·00 27·00
12. 15 ore blue and red .. 30·00 27·00
13. – 30 ore brown and blue .. 30·00 27·00
14. – 1 k. grey and brown .. 35·00 27·00
15. **5.** 2 k. green and brown .. 50·00 35·00
16. – 5 k. brown and purple .. 60·00 35·00

**1945.** Liberation of Denmark. Nos. 8/16 optd. **DANMARK BEFRIET 5 MAJ 1945.**
17. **3.** 1 ore violet and black .. 60·00 27·00
18. 5 ore buff and violet .. 60·00 27·00
19. 7 ore black and green .. 60·00 27·00
20. **4.** 10 ore olive and purple .. 60·00 40·00
21. 15 ore blue and red .. 60·00 40·00
22. – 30 ore brown and blue .. 60·00 40·00
23. – 1 k. grey and brown .. 60·00 40·00
24. **5.** 2 k. green and brown .. 60·00 40·00
25. – 5 k. brown and purple .. 85·00 45·00

**7.** King Frederik IX.

**8.** Polar Ship "Gustav Holm".

**1950.**

26. 7 1 ore green .. .. 10 10
27. 5 ore red .. .. .. 30 20
28. 10 ore green .. .. 45 20
29. 15 ore violet .. .. 80 40
30. 25 ore red .. .. 2·00 90
31. 30 ore blue .. .. 24·00 1·75
32. 30 ore red .. .. 70 30
33. 8. 50 ore blue .. .. 40·00 18·00
34. 1 k. brown .. .. 18·00 2·25
35. 2 k. red .. .. .. 8·00 2·25
36. 5 k. grey .. .. .. 4·00 1·00

**1956.** Nos. 6a and 7 surch **60 ore.**

37 2 60 ore on 40 ore blue .. 8·00 1·00
38 60 ore on 1 k. brown .. 48·00 5·75

10. "Mother of the Sea". 12. Hans Egede (after J. Horner) 14. Knud Rasmussen (founder of Thule).

**1957.** Greenland Legends.

39. 10. 60 ore blue .. .. 3·00 85

**1958.** Royal Tuberculosis Relief Fund. No. 33 surch with Cross of Lorraine and **30 + 10.**

40 8 30 ore + 10 ore on 50 ore blue .. .. .. 3·50 1·75

**1958.** Death Bicent. of Hans Egede (missionary).

41. 12. 30 ore red .. .. 7·25 1·00

**1959.** Greenland Fund. Surch. **Grønlands-fonden 30 + 10** and bars.

42. 7. 30 ore + 10 ore on 25 ore red 3·50 3·50

The note below No. 413 of Denmark also applies here.

**1960.** 50th Anniv. of Thule Settlement.

43. 14. 30 ore red .. .. 1·10 50

15. Drum Dance. 16. Northern Lights.

17. Frederik IX. 18. Polar Bear. 19. S. Kleinschmidt.

**1961.** Greenland Legends.

44. 15. 35 ore green .. .. 1·00 60

**1963.**

45. 16. 1 ore green .. .. 10 10
46. 5 ore red .. .. 10 10
47. 10 ore green .. .. 40 30
48. 12 ore green .. .. 40 25
49. 15 ore purple .. .. 80 65
50. 17. 20 ore blue .. .. 2·50 2·50
51. 25 ore brown .. .. 45 20
51a. 30 ore green .. .. 30 15
52. 35 ore red .. .. 35 10
53. 40 ore grey .. .. 40 25
54. 50 ore blue .. .. 5·75 5·25
54a. 50 ore red .. .. 40 20
54b. 60 ore red .. .. 40 20
55. 80 ore orange .. .. 80 60
56. 18. 1 k. brown .. .. 1·00 20
57. 2 k. red .. .. 3·50 60
58. 5 k. blue .. .. 3·00 85
59. 10 k. green .. .. 3·00 70

**1963.** 50th Anniv. of Bohr's Atomic Theory. As Nos. 455/6 of Denmark but inscr. "GRONLAND".

60. 127. 35 ore red .. .. 50 30
61. 60 ore blue .. .. 3·50 3·50

**1964.** 150th Birth Anniv. of S. Kleinschmidt (philologist).

62. 19. 35 ore brown .. .. 60 60

20. "The Boy and the Fox". 21. "Great Northern Diver and Raven".

**1966.** Greenland Legends.

63. 20. 50 ore red .. .. 1·10 80

**1967.** Royal Wedding. As No. 487 of Denmark, but inscr. "GRONLAND".

64. 50 ore red .. .. .. 3·25 3·00

**1967.** Greenland Legends.

65. 21. 90 ore blue .. .. 3·50 3·25

**1968.** Child Welfare. As No. 493 of Denmark, but inscr. "GRONLAND".

66 60 ore + 10 ore red .. .. 60 60

22. King Frederik IX and Map of Greenland. 23. "The Girl and the Eagle".

**1969.** King Frederik's 70th Birthday.

67. 22. 60 ore red .. .. 1·50 1·10

**1969.** Greenland Legends.

68 23 80 ore brown .. .. 2·75 2·00

24. Musk Ox. 25. Celebrations at Jakobshavn.

**1969.**

69. – 1 k. blue .. .. .. 55 20
70. – 2 k. green .. .. 70 45
71. – 5 k. blue .. .. .. 1·40 70
72. – 10 k. brown .. .. 2·50 1·00
73. 24. 25 k. olive .. .. 7·00 2·00

DESIGN—HORIZ. 1 k. Bowhead whale and coastline. 2 k. Narwhal. 5 k. Polar bear. 10 k. Walruses.

**1970.** 25th Anniv. of Denmark's Liberation.

74. 25. 60 ore red .. .. 1·50 1·50

26. Hans Egede and Gertrud Rask aboard the "Haabet". 27. Mail Kayaks.

**1971.** 250th Anniv. of Hans Egede's Arrival in Greenland.

75. 26. 60 ore red .. .. 1·25 1·00
76. – 60 ore + 10 ore red .. 1·50 1·75

DESIGN: No. 76, Hans Egede and Gertrud Rask meeting Greenlanders.

The premium on No. 76 was for the Greenland Church Building Fund.

**1971.** Greenland Mail Transport.

77. 27. 50 ore green .. .. 25 20
78. – 70 ore red .. .. 50 25
79. – 80 ore black .. .. 50 25
80. – 90 ore blue .. .. 40 20
81. – 1 k. red .. .. 70 60
82. – 1 k. 30 blue .. .. 40 40
83. – 1 k. 50 green .. .. 50 40
84. – 2 k. deep blue .. .. 60 45

DESIGNS: 70 ore Umiak (women's boat). 80 ore Consolidated Catalina amphibian. 90 ore Mail dog-sledge. 1 k. Coaster "Kununguak" and tug "Dlik". 1 k. 30, Schooner "Sokongen". 1 k. 50, Sailing longboat "Karen". 2 k. Sikorsky S-61N helicopter.

28. King Frederik IX and Royal Yacht "Dannebrog". 29. Queen Margrethe.

**1972.** King Frederik IX's and Queen Ingrid's Fund.

85. 28. 60 + 10 ore red .. .. 1·25 1·50

**1973.**

86. 29. 10 ore green .. .. 10 10
87. 60 ore brown .. .. 30 20
88. 90 ore brown .. .. 70 35
88a. 100 ore red .. .. 30 15
89. 120 ore blue .. .. 80 60
89a. 130 ore blue .. .. 50 50

For values inscribed "KALAALLIT NUNAAT" at top, see Nos. 99/104.

**1973.** Aid for Victims of Heimaey (Iceland) Eruption. As T **204** of Denmark.

90. 70 ore + 20 ore blue and red 1·25 1·25

31. "Carl Egede" (trawler) and Kayaks. 32. Gyrfalcon and Radio Aerial.

**1974.** Bicentenary of Royal Greenland Trade Department.

91. 31. 1 k. brown .. .. 70 45
92. – 2 k. brown .. .. 70 45

DESIGN—VERT: 2 k. Trade Department Headquarters, Trangraven, Copenhagen.

**1975.** 50th Anniv of Greenland's Telecommunications Service.

93 32 90 ore red .. .. 65 40

33. Sirius Sledge Patrol.

**1975.** 25th Anniv. of Sirius Sledge Patrol.

94. 33. 1 k. 20 brown .. .. 50 35

34. Arm-wrestling (after H. Egede). 35. Inuit Carved Mask.

**1976.** Greenland Sports Publicity.

95 34 100 ore + 20 ore brown and green on cream .. 55 70

**1977.** Eskimo Mask.

96. 35. 9 k. grey .. .. .. 2·40 2·00

36. Bronlund and Disko Bay, Jakobshavn. 37. Cape York Meteorite and "Ulo" (woman's knife).

**1977.** Birth Centenary of Jorgen Bronlund (explorer).

97. 36. 1 k. brown .. .. 30 25

**1978.** Centenary of Commission for Scientific Researches in Greenland.

98 37 1 k. 20 brown .. .. 40 25

38. Queen Margrethe.

**1978.**

99. 38. 5 ore red .. .. 10 10
100. 80 ore brown .. .. 20 20
101. 120 ore brown .. .. 30 20
102. 130 ore red .. .. 30 20
103. 160 ore blue .. .. 45 40
104. 180 ore green .. .. 50 45

39. Sun rising over Mountains.

**1978.** 25th Anniv of Constitution.

105 39 1 k. 50 blue .. .. 40 35

40. Foundation Ceremony. 41. Tupilak (imaginary animal).

**1978.** 250th Anniv. of Godthab.

106. 40. 2 k. 50 brown .. .. 50 40

**1978.** Folk Art.

107. 41. 6 k. red .. .. 1·50 1·25

42. Helmsman. 43. Rasmussen with Eskimos.

**1979.** Internal Autonomy.

108. 42. 1 k. 10 brown .. .. 30 30

**1979.** Birth Centenary of Knud Rasmussen (polar explorer).

109. 43. 1 k. 30 + 20 ore red .. 30 45

44. Soapstone Figure (Simon Kristoffersen). 45. Eskimo Child.

**1979.** Folk Art.

110. 44. 7 k. green .. .. 2·00 1·50

**1979.** International Year of the Child.

111. 45. 2 k. green .. .. 30 30

46. "Eskimo Family" (driftwood sculpture). 47. Queen Margrethe and Map of Greenland.

**1980.** Folk Art.

112. 46. 8 k. blue .. .. 2·10 1·60

**1980.**

113 47 50 ore violet .. .. 20 15
114 80 ore brown .. .. 40 30
115 1 k. 30 red .. .. 40 30
116 1 k. 50 blue .. .. 65 55
117 1 k. 60 blue .. .. 70 55
118 1 k. 80 red .. .. 85 75
119 2 k. 30 green .. .. 60 50
120 2 k. 50 red .. .. 60 40
121 2 k. 80 brown .. .. 1·25 50
122 3 k. red .. .. 1·40 60
122a 3 k. 20 red .. .. 1·50 65
123 3 k. 80 black .. .. 1·40 1·40
124 4 k. 10 blue .. .. 1·50 1·50
124a 4 k. 40 blue .. .. 1·90 1·90

48. Eskimos and Rasmus Berthelsen in Library. 49. "Foot Race between Quloqutsuk and Aqigssiaq".

**1980.** 150th Anniv. of Greenland Public Libraries.

125. 48. 2 k. brown on yellow .. 50 40

**1980.** Woodcut by Aron from Kangeq.

126. 49. 3 k. black .. .. 70 60

50. Mikkelsen and Eskimo. 51. "Reindeer Sledge and the Larva" (engraving, Jons Kreutzmann).

**1980.** Birth Centenary of Ejnar Mikkelsen (Inspector of East Greenland).

127. 50. 4 k. green .. .. 95 80

**1981.** Greenland Legends.

128. 51. 1 k. 60 red .. .. 50 30

52. Codfish. 53. Stone Tent Ring, Wolf and King Eiders.

**1981.**

129. 52. 25 k. brown and blue .. 6·25 2·75

**1981.** Peary Land Expeditions.

130. 53. 1 k. 60 + 20 ore. brown 1·00 1·00

54. Reindeer and Hunter (Saqqaq culture, 2000 B.C.). 55. Shrimps.

**1981.** Greenland History.

131. 54. 3 k. 50 blue .. .. 1·00 1·00
132. – 5 k. brown .. .. 1·40 1·40

DESIGN: 5 k. Hunters dragging walrus (Tunit-Dorset culture, 50 B.C.).

**1982.**

133. 55. 10 k. blue and red .. 2·75 1·40

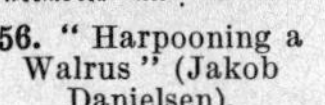

**56.** " Harpooning a Walrus " (Jakob Danielsen).

**57.** Eric the Red discovering Greenland, 982.

**1982.**

134. **56.** 2 k. 70 violet .. .. 80 60

**1982.** Greenland History.

135. **57.** 2 k.+40 ore, brown .. 1·50 1·50

**58.** Eskimos hunting Bowhead Whale.

**1982.** Greenland History.

136 **58** 2 k. red .. .. 40 40
137 – 2 k. 70 blue .. .. 60 45

DESIGN: 2 k. 70, Bishop Joen Smyrill's staff and house at Gardar (1100–1200).

**59.** Salmon.

**60.** Blind Person, Armband, Cassette and White Stick.

**1983.**

138. **59.** 50 k. black and blue .. 13·00 7·00

**1983.** Welfare of the Blind.

139. **60.** 2 k. 50+40 ore, red .. 75 85

**61.** Eskimos and Northerners bartering (1200–1300).

**62.** Herrnhut Bandsmen.

**1983.** Greenland History.

140. **61.** 2 k. 50 brown .. .. 65 65
141. – 3 k. 50 brown .. .. 95 95
142. – 4 k. 50 blue .. .. 1·10 1·10

DESIGNS: 3 k. 50, Mummy of Eskimo boy (1300–1400); 4 k. 50, Hans Pothorst's expedition to America (1400–1500).

**1983.** 250th Anniv of Herrnhut Moravian Brethren Settlement.

143 **62** 2 k. 50 brown .. .. 60 70

**63.** "Polar Bear killing Seal Hunter".

**64.** Bowhead Whales and Glass Beads (trading goods) (1500–1600).

**1984.** 50th Death Anniv. of Karale Andreassen (writer and artist).

144. **63.** 3 k. 70 black .. .. 90 90

**1984.** Greenland History.

145. **64.** 2 k. 70 brown .. .. 90 75
146. – 3 k. 70 blue .. .. 90 90
147. – 5 k. 50 brown .. .. 1·50 1·50

DESIGNS: 3 k. 70 Greenlanders in European dress and apostle spoons (1600–1700). 5 k. 50, Hans Egede's mission station, Godthab, and key (1700–1800).

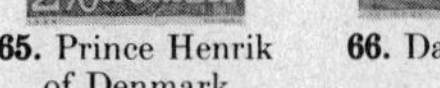

**65.** Prince Henrik of Denmark.

**66.** Danish Grenadier, 1734.

**1984.** Prince Henrik's 50th Birthday.

148. **65.** 2 k. 70 brown .. .. 1·50 1·40

**1984.** 250th Anniv of Christianshab.

149 **66** 3 k. 70 brown .. .. 90 1·25

**67.** Lund.

**68.** Catfish.

**1984.** 36th Death Anniv. of Henrik Lund (composer).

150. **67.** 5 k. green .. .. 2·10 2·00

**1984.**

151. **68.** 10 k. black and blue .. 4·50 3·00

**69.** "Hvalfisken" (1800–1900).

**70.** Queen Ingrid and "Chrysanthemum frutescens" "Sofiero".

**1985.** Greenland History.

152. **69.** 2 k. 80 purple .. .. 1·25 1·10
153. – 6 k. black .. .. 1·75 2·00

DESIGN: 6 k. Communications satellite and globe (1900–2000).

**1985.** 50th Anniv. of Queen Ingrid's Arrival in Denmark.

154. **70.** 2 k. 80 multicoloured .. 60 70

**71.** Nesting Birds and I.Y.Y. Emblem.

**72.** "Hare Hunt".

**1985.** International Youth Year.

155. **71.** 3 k. 80 multicoloured .. 75 85

**1985.** 130th Birth Anniv of Gerhard Kleist (artist).

156 **72** 9 k. green .. .. 2·75 2·25

**73.** Halibut.

**74.** Post Office Flags.

**1985.**

157. **73.** 10 k. brown and blue .. 2·75 2·75

**1986.** Postal Independence.

158. **74.** 2 k. 80 red .. .. 65 65

**75.** Towing Man on Bladder.

**76.** Ulos (knives for working sealskin).

**1986.** Traditional Sport.

159. **75.** 2 k. 80+50 ore mult... 90 1·25

**1986.**

160. **76.** 3 k. black and blue .. 1·00 1·00
161. – 6 k. 50 brown and green 1·50 1·50

DESIGN: 6 k. 50, Lard lamps.

**77.** "Daily Life in Thule" (Aninaaq).

**78.** Capelin.

**1986.**

162. **77.** 2 k. 80 brown .. .. 70 80

**1986.**

163. **78.** 10 k. brown and green 2·75 2·75

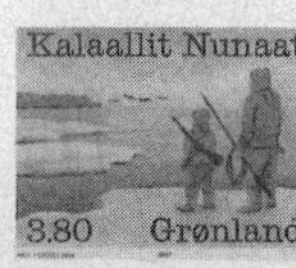


**80.** "Ammassalik Fjord" (Peter Rosing).

**81.** Father and Son on Ice-floe.

**1987.**

165 **80** 2 k. 80 brown .. .. 95 65

**1987.** Fishing, Sealing and Whaling Industries Year.

166. **81.** 3 k. 80 multicoloured .. 1·10 1·00

**82.** Needle Case and Combs.

**83.** Rock Ptarmigans.

**1987.** Craftwork.

167. **82.** 2 k. 80 brown and red 55 55
168. – 3 k. 80 purple and blue 85 1·10

DESIGN: 3 k. 80, Eye masks.

**1988.** Birds. Multicoloured.

169 3 k. Gyrfalcons .. .. 1·00 1·00
170 3 k. 20 Long-tailed ducks 1·00 1·00
171 4 k. Snow geese .. .. 1·00 80
172 4 k. 10 Ravens .. .. 1·40 1·40
173 4 k. 40 Snow buntings .. 1·50 1·50
174 5 k. Type **83** .. .. 1·40 1·00
175 5 k. 50 White-tailed sea eagles .. .. .. 2·40 2·40
176 5 k. 50 Black guillemots .. 2·40 2·40
177 6 k. 50 Brunnich's guillemots .. .. 2·00 2·00
178 7 k. Great northern divers 2·40 2·40
179 7 k. 50 Long-tailed skuas 2·00 2·00
180 10 k. Snowy owl .. .. 2·75 2·00

**85.** Telefax, Sledge and De Havilland Dash Seven.

**1988.** 50 Years of Post Office Communication.

191. **85.** 3 k.+50 ore mult. .. 1·40 1·40

**86** Tubs

**87** National Flag

**1988.** Craftwork.

192 **86** 3 k. violet and red .. 60 60
193 – 5 k. brown and green 1·25 1·00
194 – 10 k. brown and purple 2·50 2·00

DESIGNS: 5 k. Harpoon heads; 10 k. Masks.

**1989.** 10th Anniv of Internal Autonomy. Mult.

195 3 k. 20 Type **87** .. .. 65 65
196 4 k. 40 National arms .. 90 90

**88** Cotton Grass

**89** Queen Margrethe

**1989.** Flowers. Multicoloured.

197 4 k. Bellflower (vert) .. 80 80
198 4 k. Hairy lousewort (vert) 80 80
199 5 k. Type **88** .. .. 1·40 1·40
200 5 k. 50 Labrador tea .. 1·10 1·10
201 6 k. 50 Arctic white heather .. .. 1·60 1·60
202 7 k. 25 Purple saxifrage .. 2·00 2·00
203 10 k. Arctic poppy (vert) 2·50 2·50

**1990.**

210 **89** 25 ore green .. .. 10 10
213 1 k. brown .. .. 20 20
218 4 k. red .. .. 80 80
219 4 k. 25 red .. .. 90 90
221 6 k. 50 blue .. .. 1·75 1·25
222 7 k. violet .. .. 1·75 1·40

**90** Chained Sledge Dog and nesting Eiders

**91** Frederik Lynge

**1990.** Greenland Environmental Foundation.

225 **90** 400 ore+50 ore mult .. 1·60 1·60

**1990.** Augo and Frederik Lynge (Greenland Members of Danish Folketing).

226 **91** 10 k. red and blue .. 2·50 2·00
227 – 25 k. purple and blue .. 6·25 4·75

DESIGN: 25 k. Augo Lynge.

**92** Ringed Seal ("Phoca hispida")

**93** Dogs and Fisherman

**1991.** Marine Mammals. Multicoloured.

228 4 k. Type **92** .. .. 80 80
229 4 k. Harp seals ("Pagophilus groenlandicus") 80 80
230 7 k. 25 Hooded seals ("Cystophora cristata") 1·90 1·90
231 7 k. 25 Walrus ("Odobenus rosmarus") .. .. 1·90 1·90
232 8 k. 50 Bearded seal ("Erignatus barbatus") 2·10 2·10
233 8 k. 50 Common seal ("Phoca vitulina") .. 2·10 2·10

**1991.** 250th Anniv of Ilulissat (Jakobshavn).

235 **93** 4 k. multicoloured .. 80 80

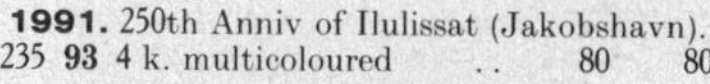

**94** Iceberg and Summer Flowers

**1991.** Nordic Countries' Postal Co-operation. Tourism. Multicoloured.

236 4 k. Type **94** .. .. 80 80
237 8 k. 50 Ski party and dog sled in winter .. .. 2·25 2·25

**95** Birds

**96** Jonathan Petersen (composer, 110th anniv)

**1991.** 75th Anniv of Blue Cross (health education organization)

238 **95** 4 k.+50 ore mult .. 8·00 8·00

**1991.** Birth Anniversaries.

239 **96** 10 k. black and blue .. 2·40 2·00
240 – 50 k. brown and blue .. 12·00 10·00

DESIGN: 50 k. Hans Lynge (writer and artist, 85th anniv).

**97** Arms and Paamiut

**1992.** Bicentenary of Paamiut.

241 **97** 7 k. 25 brown and blue 1·90 1·90

**98** Royal Couple in 1992 and in Official Wedding Photograph

**1992.** Silver Wedding of Queen Margrethe and Prince Henrik.
242 **98** 4 k. multicoloured .. 80 80

**99** Moller and Drawing of Godthab Church
**100** Rainbow and Landscape

**1992.** 150th Birth Anniv of Lars Moller (editor and printer).
243 **99** 100 k. red and blue .. 22·00 21·00

**1992.** Neriuffik Cancer Research Organization.
244 **100** 4 k.+50 ore mult .. 1·40 1·40

**101** Mother and Child with Father Christmas
**102** Flame and Laurel Wreath framed by Dance Drum

**1992.** Christmas.
245 **101** 4 k. multicoloured .. 1·10 1·10

**1993.** Int Year of Indigenous Peoples.
246 **102** 4 k. multicoloured .. 80 80

**103** Flat Crab

**1993.** Crabs.
247 **103** 4 k. red, yellow & grn 80 80
248 – 7 k. 25 brown and blue 2·00 2·00
249 – 8 k. 50 multicoloured 2·10 2·10
DESIGNS: 7 k. 25, Sand crab; 8 k. 50, Stone crabs.

**104** Ummannaq Church

**1993.** Nordic Countries' Postal Co-operation. Churches. Multicoloured.
250 4 k. Type **104** .. .. 80 80
251 8 k. 50 Hvalso church ruins 2·10 2·10

**105** Children in Tent

**1993.** Anniversaries.
252 **105** 4 k.+50 ore mult .. 90 90
253 – 4 k.+50 ore red & vio 90 90
DESIGNS: No. 252 Type, **105** (50th anniv of scouts in Greenland); 253, Birds, crosses and landscape (70th anniv of Red Cross in Greenland).

**106** Corpuscles and "AIDS"

**1993.** Anti-AIDS Campaign.
255 **106** 4 k. multicoloured .. 80 80

**107** Wolf
**108** Dog Sled

**1993.** Animals. Multicoloured.
255a 4 k. Polar bear .. .. 95 95
256 5 k. Type **107** .. .. 1·00 1·00
257 5 k. 50 Ermine .. .. 1·40 1·40
258 7 k. 25 Arctic lemmings 1·90 1·90
258a 7 k. 25 Wolverine .. 1·75 1·75
258b 7 k. 50 Musk ox .. .. 1·75 1·75
259 8 k. 50 Arctic fox .. 2·25 2·25
260 9 k. Mountain hare .. 2·40 2·40
261 10 k. Reindeer .. .. 2·50 2·50

**1993.** Christmas.
265 **108** 4 k. multicoloured .. 80 80

**109** Skiers
**111** First Church

**110** Transmission Line

**1994.** Winter Olympic Games, Lillehammer, Norway.
266 **109** 4 k.+50 ore mult .. 90 90

**1994.** Inauguration of Buksefjorden Hydro-electric Power Station.
268 **110** 4 k. multicoloured .. 80 80

**1994.** Centenary of Ammassalik.
269 **111** 7 k. 25 blue, brn & grn 1·90 1·90

**112** "Danmark" (steam barque)

**1994.** Europa. Discoveries. "Danmark" Expedition to North-east Coast, 1906–08. Mult.
270 4 k. Type **112** .. .. 85 85
271 7 k. 25 "Danmark" and dogs following ELG Mobil car .. .. 1·90 1·90

**113** "Ceres" (William Moen)

**1994.** Figureheads from Greenlandic Ships (1st series). Multicoloured.
272 4 k. Type **113** .. .. 85 85
273 8 k. 50 "Nordlyset" (carved Johan Heldt) .. 2·10 2·10
See also Nos. 290/1 and 309/10.

**114** Visiting

**1994.** Christmas. Multicoloured.
274 4 k. Type **114** .. .. 85 85
275 5 k. Santa Claus outside igloo .. .. .. 1·10 1·10

**115** "Listera cordata"
**116** Teacher and Student

**1995.** Orchids. Multicoloured.
276 4 k. Type **115** .. .. 85 85
277 7 k. 25 "Leucorchis albida" 1·50 1·50

**1995.** 150th Anniv of Ilinniarfissuaq (teacher training college) (4 k.) and 50th Anniv of United Nations Organization (7 k. 25).
278 **116** 4 k. multicoloured .. 85 85
279 – 7 k. 25 blue, grn & red 1·50 1·50
DESIGN—VERT: 7 k. 25, U.N. emblem and "50".

**117** Iceberg and Meadow

**1995.** Nordic Countries' Postal Co-operation. Tourism.
280 4 k. Type **117** .. .. 95 95
281 8 k. 50 Mountains and valleys .. .. 2·00 2·00

**118** Airmail Envelope

**1995.** Europa. Peace and Freedom. Mult.
282 4 k. Type **118** .. .. 95 95
283 8 k. 50 Doves and seascape 2·00 2·00

**120** Children with Flag
**121** Boy running with Lamps

**1995.** 10th Anniv of National Flag.
285 **120** 4 k.+50 ore mult .. 1·00 1·00
The premium was for the benefit of the Greenland Flag Society.

**1995.** Figureheads from Greenlandic Ships (2nd series). As T **113**. Multicoloured.
290 4 k. "Hvalfisken" (H. J. Moen) (vert) .. .. 95 95
291 8 k. 50 "Tjalfe" .. .. 2·00 2·00

**1995.** Christmas. Multicoloured.
292 4 k. Type **121** .. .. 95 95
293 5 k. Boy running with lamp and moon .. 1·10 1·10

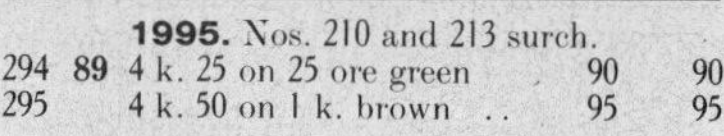
**1995.** Nos. 210 and 213 surch.
294 **89** 4 k. 25 on 25 ore green .. 90 90
295 4 k. 50 on 1 k. brown .. 95 95

**123** Early Coral-root
**124** Killer Whale

**1996.** Arctic Orchids. Multicoloured.
296 4 k. 25 Type **123** .. .. 90 90
297 4 k. 50 Round-leaved orchid .. .. .. 95 95
298 7 k. 50 Northern green orchid .. .. .. 1·60 1·60

**1996.** Whales. Each black, red and blue.
299 25 ore Type **124** .. .. 10 10
300 50 ore Humpback whale .. 10 10
301 1 k. Beluga .. .. 20 20
302 4 k. 50 Sperm whale .. 95 95
303 6 k. 50 Bowhead whale .. 1·40 1·40
304 9 k. 50 Minke whale .. 2·00 2·00

**125** Arnarulunnguaq (Eskimo traveller)

**1996.** Europa. Famous Women.
306 **125** 4 k. 50 blue .. .. 95 95

**126** Man in Wheelchair at Sea Shore

**1996.** Regional Society of Handicapped and Disabled in Greenland.
307 **126** 4 k. 25+50 ore mult .. 1·00 1·00

**1996.** Figureheads from Greenlandic Ships (3rd series). As T **113**. Multicoloured.
309 15 k. "Blaa Hejren" .. 3·25 3·25
310 20 k. "Gertrud Rask" (horiz) .. .. .. 4·25 4·25

**127** Child and Angels

**1996.** Christmas. Multicoloured.
311 4 k. 25 Type **127** .. .. 90 90
312 4 k. 50 Star and children .. 95 95

PARCEL POST

**P 1.** Arms of Greenland.

**1905.**
P4 **P 1** 1 ore green .. 24·00 29·00
P5 2 ore yellow .. £150 65·00
P6 5 ore brown .. 60·00 65·00
P7 10 ore blue .. 19·00 38·00
P8 15 ore violet .. 95·00 £110
P9 20 ore red .. 3·75 4·75
P13 70 ore violet .. 19·00 95·00
P14 1 k. yellow .. 24·00 38·00
P12 3 k. brown .. 60·00 £110

**Prices for used stamps are for rubber stamp cancellations applied in Copenhagen, the various Greenland cancellations being worth much more. Stamps with numeral cancellations have been used as saving stamps.**

## GUADELOUPE Pt. 6

An overseas department of France, formerly a Fr. colony in the W. Indies, consisting of a group of islands between Antigua and Dominica. Now uses the stamps of France.

100 centimes = 1 franc.

**1894.** French Colonies, "Peace and Commerce" type, surch **G. P. E.** and new value in frame.
6 H 20 on 30 c. brown .. 38·00 30·00
7 25 on 35 c. black on orge 35·00 30·00

**1889.** French Colonies, "Commerce" type, surch **GUADELOUPE** and value in figures and words in plain frame.
8 J 3 c. on 20 c. red & green 2·25 2·25
9 15 c. on 20 c. red on green 19·00 17·00
10 25 c. on 20 c. red on green 18·00 17·00

**1889.** Fr. Colonies, "Commerce" type, surch **GUADELOUPE** and value in figures and words in ornamental frame.
11 J 5 c. on 1 c. black on blue 7·50 7·25
12 10 c. on 40 c. red on yell 19·00 17·00
13 15 c. on 20 c. red on green 18·00 13·50
14 25 c. on 30 c. brn on drab 27·00 23·00

**1890.** French Colonies, "Commerce" type, surch **5 C. G. P. E.**
15 J 5 c. on 10 c. black on lilac 8·25 6·75
16 5 c. on 1 f. olive on green 8·75 6·75

**1891.** French Colonies, "Ceres" and "Commerce" types, optd **GUADELOUPE**.
21 J 1 c. black on blue 75 75
22 2 c. brown on buff .. 1·25 80
23 4 c. brown on grey .. 2·75 2·50
24 5 c. green on light green 3·75 3·50
25 10 c. black on lilac .. 8·00 6·75
26 15 c. blue on light blue 20·00 2·25
27 20 c. red on green .. 23·00 16·00
28 25 c. black on pink .. 22·50 2·50
19 F 30 c. brown .. .. £225 £225
29 J 30 c. brown on drab .. 24·00 19·00
30 35 c. black on orange .. 48·00 40·00
31 40 c. red on yellow .. 29·00 26·00
32 75 c. red on pink .. 90·00 80·00
20 F 80 c. red .. .. £550 £550
33 J 1 f. green .. .. 50·00 48·00

**1892.** "Tablet" key-type inscr "GUADELOUPE ET DEPENDANCES" in red (1, 5, 15, 25, 50 (No. 52), 75 c., 1 f.) or blue (others).
34 D 1 c. black on blue 75 65
36 2 c. brown on buff .. 65 60
37 4 c. brown on grey .. 65 70
38 5 c. green on light green 1·75 50
39 10 c. black on lilac .. 6·25 1·60
49 10 c. red .. .. 3·75 1·25
40 15 c. blue .. .. 5·75 45
50 15 c. grey .. .. 5·50 80
41 20 c. red on green .. 4·50 2·00
42 25 c. black on pink .. 4·75 75
51 25 c. blue .. .. 65·00 60·00
43 30 c. brown on drab .. 11·50 7·25
44 40 c. red on yellow .. 11·50 6·25
45 50 c. red on pink .. 21·00 10·00
52 50 c. brown on blue .. 24·00 17·00
46 75 c. brown on yellow .. 16·00 12·50
47 1 f. green .. .. 22·00 20·00

**1903.** "Tablet" key-type surch **G & D** (5, 15 c., 1 f.) or **G et D** (10, 40 c.) and new value.
53b D 5 on 30 c. brown on buff 2·50 2·25
54b 10 on 40 c. red on yellow 3·50 3·75
55 15 on 50 c. red .. 4·75 4·75
56 40 on 1 f. green .. 5·75 5·75
57 1 f. on 75 c. brn on yell 23·00 23·00

**1904.** Nos. 56/7 further optd **1903** in frame.
59c D 40 on 1 f. green .. 23·00 25·00
60 1 f. on 75 c. brn on yell 40·00 40·00

**49.** Mount Houllemont, Basse-Terre.

**50.** La Soufriere.

**51.** Pointe-a-Pitre, Grande Terre.

**1905.**
61. 49. 1 c. black on blue .. 10 10
62. 2 c. brown on yellow .. 15 15
63. 4 c. brown on grey .. 20 20
64. 5 c. green .. .. 60 25
83. 5 c. blue .. .. 15 20
65. 10 c. red .. .. 60 15
84. 10 c. green .. .. 30 35
85. 10 c. red on blue .. .. 15 25
66. 15 c. lilac .. .. 25 15
67. 50. 20 c. red on green .. 15 15
86. 20 c. green .. .. 15 25
68. 25 c. blue .. .. 25 25
87. 25 c. green .. .. 15 15
69. 30 c. black .. .. 2·25 1·75
88. 30 c. red .. .. 25 30
89. 30 c. olive on lilac .. 25 30
70. 35 c. black on yellow .. 30 25
71. 40 c. red on yellow .. 40 50
72. 45 c. brown on lilac .. 35 40
90. 45 c. red .. .. 40 55
73. 50 c. green on yellow .. 3·00 1·50
91. 50 c. blue .. .. 45 60
92. 50 c. mauve .. .. 30 25
93. 65 c. blue .. .. 45 55
74. 75 c. red on blue .. 50 45
75. 51. 1 f. black on green .. 80 85
94. 1 f. blue .. .. 60 75
76. 2 f. red on orange .. 90 90
77. 5 f. blue on orange .. 3·75 4·25

**1912.** Nos. 37 and 43/4 surch in figures.
78 D 05 on 4 c. brown on grey 25 45
79 05 on 30 c. brown on drab 40 60
80 10 on 40 c. red on yellow 70 1·00

**1915.** Surch **5c** and red cross.
81 49 10 c.+5 c. red .. .. 2·00 1·75
82 15 c.+5 c. lilac .. .. 1·25 1·75

**1924.** Surch. in figures and bars.
95. 51. 25 c. on 5 f. blue on orge. 35 45
96. 65 on 1 f. green.. .. 60 60
97. 85 on 1 f. green.. .. 60 65
98. 50. 90 c. on 75 c. red .. 60 60
99. 51. 1 f. 05 on 2 f. red .. 30 45
100. 1 f. 25 on 1 f. blue .. 15 30
101. 1 f. 50 on 1 f. blue .. 45 60
102. 3 f. on 5 f. brown .. 55 70
103. 10 f. on 5 f. red on yellow 5·25 5·75
104. 20 f. on 5 f. mauve on red 6·00 6·50

**53.** Sugar Refinery.

**54.** Saints Harbour.

**55.** Pointe-a-Pitre Harbour.

**1928.**
105 53 1 c. mauve and yellow 10 25
106 2 c. red and black .. 10 20
107 3 c. mauve and yellow 10 25
108 4 c. brown and green .. 10 25
109 5 c. green and red .. 15 20
110 10 c. blue and brown .. 15 25
111 15 c. black and red .. 15 25
112 20 c. brown and mauve 15 20
113 54 25 c. olive and blue .. 15 15
114 30 c. green & deep green 15 15
115 35 c. green .. .. 30 40
116 40 c. mauve and yellow 20 20
117 45 c. grey and purple .. 40 50
118 45 c. deep green & green 50 65
119 50 c. red and green .. 20 20
120 55 c. red and blue .. 40 50
121 60 c. red and blue .. 35 50
122 65 c. red and black .. 20 30
123 70 c. red and black .. 25 35
124 75 c. green and red .. 30 35
125 80 c. brown and red .. 30 45
126 90 c. red .. .. 85 1·25
127 90 c. blue and red .. 50 60
128 55 1 f. blue and red .. 2·75 1·75
129 1 f. orange and red .. 75 75
130 1 f. brown and blue .. 30 45
131 1 f. 05 red and blue .. 70 80
132 1 f. 10 green and orange 1·75 1·90
133 1 f. 25 brown and blue 35 50
134 1 f. 25 orange and red .. 45 60
135 1 f. 40 mauve and blue 45 60
136 1 f. 50 light blue & blue 20 25
137 1 f. 60 orange & mauve 40 60
138 1 f. 75 brown and mauve 2·25 1·75
139 1 f. 75 blue .. .. 3·50 3·00
140 2 f. brown and green .. 25 25
141 2 f. 25 blue .. .. 45 55
142 2 f. 50 green and orange 60 75
143 3 f. black and brown .. 25 30
144 5 f. red and blue .. 40 40
145 10 f. brown and mauve 50 60
146 20 f. red and green .. 65 65

**1931.** "Colonial Exhibition" key-types inscr. "**GUADELOUPE**".
147. E. 40 c. black and green .. 1·50 1·60
148. F. 50 c. black and mauve 1·60 1·75
149. G. 90 c. black and red .. 3·25 3·50
150. H. 1 f. 50 black and blue .. 2·50 2·50

**57.** Richelieu founding W. India Co., 1635.

**58.** Victor Hughes and Corsairs 1793.

**1935.** West Indies Tercent.
151. 57. 40 c. brown .. .. 5·25 5·50
152. 50 c. red .. .. .. 5·25 5·00
153. 1 f. 50 blue .. .. 5·25 5·00
154. 58. 1 f. 75 mauve .. .. 5·25 5·00
155. 5 f. brown .. .. 5·25 5·25
156. 10 f. green .. .. 5·25 5·25

**1937.** International Exhibition, Paris. As Nos. 110/15 of Cameroun.
157. 20 c. violet .. .. 65 70
158. 30 c. green .. .. 65 65
159. 40 c. red .. .. 95 1·00
160. 50 c. brown .. .. 95 1·00
161. 90 c. red .. .. 95 1·00
162. 1 f. 50 blue .. .. 95 1·00

**1938.** Int. Anti-Cancer Fund. As T **19** of Cameroun.
163. 1 f. 75+50 c. blue .. 5·25 6·75

**1939.** New York World's Fair. As T **20** of Cameroun.
164. 1 f. 25 red .. .. 60 60
165. 2 f. 25 blue .. .. 60 60

**1939.** 150th Anniv. of French Revolution. As T **25** of Cameroun.
166. 45 c.+25 c. green & black 4·75 4·75
167. 70 c.+30 c. brown & black 5·00 5·00
168. 90 c.+35 c. orge. & black 5·00 5·00
169. 1 f. 25+1 f. red & black.. 5·00 5·00
170. 2 f. 25+2 f. blue & black 5·00 5·00

**1944.** Surch **UN FRANC** (No. 177) or in figures (others). (a) On Nos. 164/5.
178 40 c. on 1 f. 25 red .. 45 40
179 40 c. on 2 f. 25 blue .. 90 80

(b) On Issue of 1928.
172 54 40 c. on 35 c. green .. 40 45
173 50 c. on 25 c. olive & bl 20 30
174 50 c. on 65 c. red & blk 60 60
175 1 f. on 90 c. red .. 85 90
176 1 f. on 90 c. blue and red 55 55
177 1 f. on 65 c. red & black 60 55

(c) On No. 99.
171 51 4 f. on 1 f. 05 on 2 f. red 1·25 1·10

**1944.** Mutual Aid and Red Cross Funds. As T **33** of Cameroun.
180. 5 f.+20 f. blue .. .. 60 70

**1945.** Eboue. As T **34** of Cameroun.
181. 2 f. black .. .. 25 30
182. 25 f. green .. .. 65 70

**63.**

**1945.**
183. 63. 10 c. blue and orange .. 15 30
184. 30 c. green and orange.. 15 30
185. 40 c. blue and red .. 35 35
186. 50 c. orange and green.. 15 20
187. 60 c. grey and blue .. 15 30
188. 70 c. grey and green .. 35 45
189. 80 c. green and yellow.. 40 40
190. 1 f. purple and green .. 20 20
191. 1 f. 20 mauve and green 20 25
192. 1 f. 50 brown and red .. 35 25
193. 2 f. red and blue .. 35 35
194. 2 f. 40 red and green .. 70 80
195. 3 f. brown and blue .. 25 25
196. 4 f. blue and orange .. 20 20
197. 4 f. 50 orange and green 25 15
198. 5 f. violet and green .. 30 25
199. 10 f. green and mauve.. 30 25
200. 15 f. grey and orange .. 60 50
201. 20 f. grey and orange .. 1·00 75

**1945.** Air. As T **32** of Cameroun.
202. 50 f. green .. .. 65 65
203. 100 f. red .. .. 90 90

**1946.** Air. Victory. As T **35** of Cameroun.
204. 8 f. brown .. .. 65 75

**1946.** Air. From Chad to the Rhine. As Nos. 226/31 of Cameroun.
205. 5 f. olive .. .. .. 85 95
206. 10 f. blue.. .. .. 85 95
207. 15 f. purple .. .. 85 85
208. 20 f. red .. .. .. 90 95
209. 25 f. black .. .. 85 85
210. 50 f. brown .. .. 85 85

**64.** Woman and Port Basse Terre.

**65.** Cutting Sugar Cane.

**66.** Guadeloupe Woman.

**67.** Sud Ouest Bretagne over Guadeloupe, Woman and Fishing Boats.

**1947.**
211. 64. 10 c. lake (postage) .. 15 25
212. 30 c. brown .. .. 15 25
213. 50 c. green .. .. 15 30
214. 65. 60 c. brown .. .. 15 25
215. 1 f. red .. .. .. 25 40
216. 1 f. 50 blue .. .. 55 55
217. – 2 f. green .. .. 65 70
218. – 2 f. 50 red .. .. 65 65
219. – 3 f. blue .. .. 70 75
220. – 4 f. violet .. .. 70 75
221. – 5 f. green .. .. 70 75
222. – 6 f. red .. .. .. 70 75
223. – 10 f. blue .. .. 70 75
224. – 15 f. purple .. .. 1·10 1·00
225. – 20 f. red .. .. 1·40 1·25
226. 66. 25 f. green .. .. 2·00 1·75
227. 40 f. orange .. .. 2·25 1·75
228. – 50 f. purple (air) .. 4·00 3·25
229 – 100 f. blue .. .. 4·50 3·50
230. 67. 200 f. red .. .. 6·25 4·75

DESIGNS—As Type **66**: 2 f. to 3 f. Women carrying pineapples. 4 f. to 6 f. Woman in kerchief facing left. 10 f. to 20 f. Picking coffee. As Type **67**: 50 f. Latecoere 631 flying boat over village. 100 f. Short Hythe flying boat landing in bay.

POSTAGE DUE STAMPS.

D 1. D 3.

**1876.**
D 1. D 1. 15 c. black on blue .. 25·00 20·00
D 2. 25 c. black on white .. £575 £500
D 3. 30 c. black on white .. 60·00 40·00
D 4. 40 c. black on blue .. — £18000
D 5. 40 c. black on white .. £575 £575

**1884.** Imperf.
D 8. D 3. 5 c. black on white .. 13·50 13·50
D 9. 10 c. black on blue .. 35·00 20·00
D 10. 15 c. black on lilac .. 60·00 38·00
D 11. 20 c. black on red .. 90·00 60·00
D 12. 30 c. black on yellow 85·00 80·00
D 13. 35 c. black on grey .. 26·00 23·00
D 14. 50 c. black on green 13·00 11·50

**1903.** Postage Due stamps of French Colonies surch **G & D 30** in frame.
D59b U 30 on 60 c. brn on buff £150 £150
D61c 30 on 1 f. red on yellow £200 £200

**D 48.** Gustavia Bay, Island of St. Bartholomew.

**D 56.** Allee Dumanoir, Capesterre.

**D 68.** Palms and Houses.

**1905.**
D 63. D 48. 5 c. blue .. .. 15 20
D 64. 10 c. brown .. .. 20 20
D 65. 15 c. green .. .. 20 40
D 66. 20 c. brown on yellow 35 40
D 67. 30 c. red .. .. 30 45
D 68. 50 c. black .. .. 1·00 1·75
D 69. 60 c. orange .. .. 70 85
D 70. 1 f. lilac .. .. 1·75 1·90

**1926.** Surch. in figures and words and **a percevoir.**
D 105. D 48. 2 f. on 1 f. grey .. 90 1·00
D 106. 3 f. on 1 f. blue .. 1·25 1·40

**1928.**
D 147. D 56. 2 c. mauve & brown 15 25
D 148. 4 c. brown and blue 15 25
D 149. 5 c. brown and green 15 25
D 150. 10 c. yellow & mauve 15 25
D 151. 15 c. olive and red.. 15 30
D 152. 20 c. olive and orange 15 30
D 153. 25 c. green and red.. 25 35
D 154. 30 c. yellow and blue 25 35
D 155. 50 c. red and brown 30 45
D 156. 60 c. black and blue 50 60
D 157. 1 f. red and green .. 1·00 1·75
D 158. 2 f. red and brown.. 1·00 1·25
D 159. 3 f. blue and mauve 55 60

**1947.**

D 231. D 68. 10 c. black .. .. 15 25
D 232. 30 c. green .. .. 15 25
D 233. 50 c. blue .. .. 15 30
D 234. 1 f. green .. .. 20 30
D 235. 2 f. blue .. .. 40 30
D 236. 3 f. brown .. .. 55 60
D 237. 4 f. purple .. .. 65 70
D 238. 5 f. violet .. .. 85 90
D 239. 10 f. red .. .. 1·00 1·25
D 240. 20 f. purple .. .. 1·25 1·40

## GUAM Pt. 22

An island in the Pacific Ocean belonging to the United States. Now uses U.S. stamps.

100 cents = 1 dollar.

**1899.** Stamps of U.S.A. optd **GUAM**.

1 1 c. green (No. 283) .. 17·00 28·00
2 2 c. red (No. 270) .. .. 14·00 24·00
4 3 c. violet (No. 271) .. 90·00 £130
5 4 c. brown (No. 285) .. 90·00 £130
6 5 c. blue (No. 286) .. 22·00 32·00
7 6 c. purple (No. 287a) .. 90·00 £140
8 8 c. brown (No. 275) .. 85·00 £120
9 10 c. brown (No. 289) .. 40·00 50·00
11 15 c. green (No. 290) .. £100 £130
12 50 c. orange (No. 278) .. £170 £225
13 $1 black (No. 279) .. £275 £400

SPECIAL DELIVERY STAMP

**1899.** Special Delivery stamp of U.S.A. optd **GUAM**.

E 15 E 46 10 c. blue (No. E 283) £100 £150

## GUANACASTE Pt. 15

A province of Costa Rica whose stamps it now uses.

100 centavos = 1 peso.

Stamps of Costa Rica optd.

**1885.** Stamps of 1883 optd. **Guanacaste** or **GUANACASTE.**

G 1. 8. 1 c. green .. .. 2·00 2·00
G 36. 2 c. red .. .. 2·00 2·00
G 3. 5 c. violet .. .. 8·00 3·00
G 4. 10 c. orange .. .. 8·00 8·00
G 5. 40 c. blue .. .. 15·00 15·00

**1887.** Stamps of 1887 optd. **Guanacaste**

G 37. 14. 5 c. violet .. .. 10·00 4·00
G 39. 10 c. orange .. .. 2·00 2·00

**1887.** Fiscal stamps optd. **Guanacaste** or **GUANACASTE.**

G 44. 1 c. red .. .. £150 £150
G 41. 2 c. blue .. .. 25·00 25·00

**1889.** Stamps of 1889 optd. **GUANACASTE.**

G 62. 17. 1 c. brown .. .. 75 75
G 63. 2 c. blue .. .. 75 75
G 64. 5 c. orange .. .. 75 75
G 65. 10 c. lake .. .. 75 75
G 56. 20 c. green .. .. 80 70
G 57. 50 c. red .. .. 2·00 2·00
G 59. 1 p. blue .. .. 4·00 4·00
G 60. 2 p. violet .. .. 6·00 6·00
G 61. 5 p. olive .. .. 20·00 20·00

## GUATEMALA Pt. 15

A republic of Central America; independent since 1847.

1871. 100 centavos = 8 reales = 1 peso.
1927. 100 centavos de quetzal = 1 quetzal

1. Arms. 2. 3. Liberty.

**1871.**

1. 1. 1 c. bistre .. .. .. 50 6·50
2. 5 c. brown .. .. .. 3·00 5·00
3. 10 c. blue .. .. .. 3·50 5·75
4. 20 c. red .. .. .. 2·75 5·00

**1873.**

5. 2. 4 r. mauve .. .. .. £200 50·00
6. 1 p. yellow .. .. .. £100 70·00

**1875.** Various frames

7. 3. ¼ r. black .. .. .. 90 2·25
8. ½ r. green .. .. .. 90 2·00
9. 1 r. blue .. .. .. 90 2·00
10. 2 r. red .. .. .. 90 2·00

4. Native Indian. 5. Resplendent Quetzal.

**1878.**

11. 4. ½ r. green .. .. .. 50 2·00
12. 2 r. red .. .. .. 85 2·75
13. 4 r. mauve .. .. .. 85 3·00
14. 1 p. yellow .. .. .. 1·40 6·00

**1879.**

15. 5. ¼ r. green and brown .. 6·00 8·00
16. 1 r. green and black .. 9·00 12·00

For similar stamps, but inscr. differently, see Nos. 21/25.

**1881.** Surch.

17. 5. 1 c. on ¼ r. green & brown 11·00 16·00
18. 4. 5 c. on ½ r. green .. .. 3·50 5·00
19. 5. 10 c. on 1 r. green & black 15·00 22·00
20. 4. 20 c. on 2 r. red .. .. 24·00 27·00

**1881.** As T 5 inscr. "UNION POSTAL UNIVERSAL—GUATEMALA". Centres in green.

21. 5. 1 c. black .. .. .. 3·50 2·00
22. 2 c. brown .. .. .. 3·50 2·00
23. 5 c. red .. .. .. 6·50 2·50
24. 10 c. lilac .. .. .. 3·25 2·00
25. 20 c. yellow .. .. .. 3·25 2·40

7. President. J. Rufino Barios.

Correos Nacionales
150 c. 150 c.
Guatemala.
150 c. 150 c.
150 Ctavos.

(8.)

**1886.** Railway stamp various surch. as T 8.

26. 7. 25 c. on 1 p. red .. .. 60 60
27. 50 c. on 1 p. red .. .. 60 60
28. 75 c. on 1 p. red .. .. 60 60
29. 100 c. on 1 p. red .. .. 1·00 1·25
30. 150 c. on 1 p. red .. .. 1·00 1·00

9. Arms of Guatemala.

16. Steamship, arms, portrait of Pres. J. M. Reyna Barrios and locomotive in centre, Arms of El Salvador, Honduras, Nicaragua and Costa Rica in corners.

**1886.**

43a. 9. 1 c. blue .. .. .. 1·40 40
44. 2 c. brown .. .. .. 2·50 40
46. 5 c. violet .. .. .. 3·25 40
47. 6 c. mauve .. .. .. 3·00 40
48. 10 c. red .. .. .. 3·00 40
49. 20 c. green .. .. .. 6·00 1·00
50. 25 c. orange .. .. .. 10·00 1·50
37. 50 c. olive .. .. .. 20·00 6·50
38. 75 c. red .. .. .. 20·00 5·00
39. 100 c. brown .. .. .. 20·00 15·00
40. 150 c. blue .. .. .. 25·00 20·00
41. 200 c. yellow .. .. .. 25·00 20·00

See also Nos. 101/9.

**1886.** Surch. **PROVISIONAL 1886 1 UN CENTAVO.**

42. 9. 1 c. on 2 c. brown .. 4·50 7·00

**1894.** Surch. **1894** and bar and value.

55. 9. 1 c. on 2 c. brown .. 1·25 1·00
51. 2 c. on 100 c. brown .. 5·75 5·75
57. 6 c. on 150 c. blue .. 8·50 5·75
53. 10 c. on 75 c. red .. 9·00 6·25
54. 10 c. on 200 c. yellow .. 5·75 4·00

**1895.** Surch. **1895 1 CENTAVO** and bar.

59. 9. 1 c. on 5 c. violet .. 75 60

**1897.** Central American Exhibition.

62. 16. 1 c. black on grey .. 45 45
63. 2 c. black on green .. 45 45
64. 6 c. black on orange .. 45 45
65. 10 c. black on blue .. 45 45
66. 12 c. black on red .. 80 80
67. 18 c. black on white .. 7·00 7·00
68. 20 c. black on red .. 1·00 1·00
69. 25 c. black on brown .. 1·00 1·00
70. 50 c. black on brown .. 1·00 1·00
71. 75 c. black on blue .. 60·00 60·00
72. 100 c. black on green .. 1·00 1·00
73. 150 c. black on pink .. £100 £100
74. 200 c. black on mauve .. 1·00 1·00
75. 500 c. black on green .. 1·00 1·00

**1897.** Surch. **1898** and value in words.

76. 16. 1 c. on 12 c. black on red 1·10 1·10

**1898.** Surch. **1898** and bar and value.

77. 9. 1 c. on 5 c. violet .. 1·50 15
78. 1 c. on 25 c. orange .. 3·50 3·25
79. 1 c. on 50 c. olive .. 3·00 2·75
80. 1 c. on 75 c. red .. 3·00 2·75
81. 6 c. on 5 c. violet .. 3·50 85
82. 6 c. on 10 c. red .. 13·50 13·00
83. 6 c. on 20 c. green .. 5·50 5·50
84. 6 c. on 100 c. brown .. 5·50 5·50
85. 6 c. on 150 c. blue .. 5·50 5·50
86. 6 c. on 200 c. yellow .. 5·50 5·50
87. 10 c. on 20 c. green .. 5·50 5·50

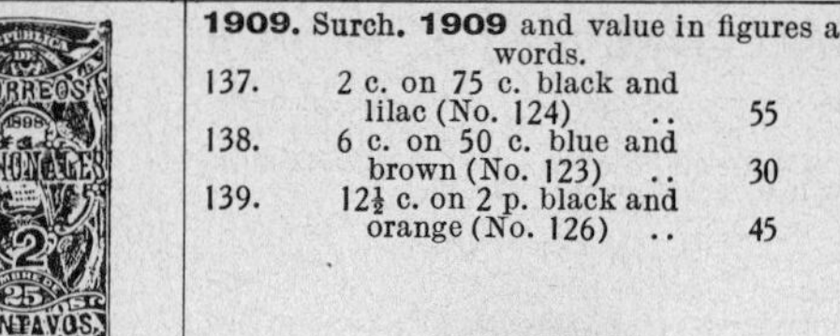

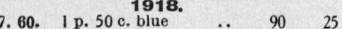

20. 22.

**1898.** Fiscal stamps as T 20 optd. **CORREOS NACIONALES** or surch. **2 CENTAVOS** also.

88. 20. 1 c. blue .. .. 1·50 1·50
89. 2 c. on 1 c. blue .. .. 2·50 2·50

**1898.** Fiscal stamps dated "1898" as T 22 surch. **CORREOS NACIONALES** and value.

90. 22. 1 c. on 10 c. blue .. 50 50
91. 2 c. on 1 c. red .. 2·40 1·75
92. 2 c. on 5 c. violet .. 85 70
93. 2 c. on 10 c. blue .. 4·50 4·75
94. 2 c. on 25 c. red .. 5·00 5·50
95. 2 c. on 50 c. blue .. 5·50 6·00
96. 6 c. on 1 p. violet .. 2·75 3·00
97. 6 c. on 5 p. blue .. 5·00 5·00
98. 6 c. on 10 p. green .. 5·00 5·00

**1899.** Surch. **Un 1 Centavo 1899.**

99. 9. 1 c. on 5 c. violet .. 60 50

**1900.** Surch. **1900 1 CENTAVO.**

100. 9. 1 c. on 10 c. red .. .. 70 70

**1900.**

101. 9. 1 c. green .. .. 50 30
102. 2 c. red .. .. 50 30
103. 5 c. blue .. .. 2·00 90
104. 6 c. green .. .. 50 30
105. 10 c. brown .. .. 2·00 40
106. 20 c. mauve .. .. 5·50 8·50
107. 20 c. brown .. .. 8·50 17·50
108. 25 c. yellow .. .. 5·50 8·50
109. 25 c. green .. .. 8·50 17·50

**1901.** Surch. **1901** and value.

110. 9. 1 c. on 20 c. green .. 85 85
111. 1 c. on 25 c. orange .. 85 85
112. 2 c. on 20 c. green .. 2·25 2·25

**1902.** Fiscal stamp surch. **CORREOS NACIONALES 1902** and value in figures and words.

113. 20. 1 c. on 1 c. blue .. 1·50 1·50
114. 2 c. on 1 c. blue .. 1·50 1·50

**1902.** Fiscal stamp, dated "1898", surch. **CORREOS 1902 Seis 6 Cts.**

115. 22. 6 c. on 25 c. red .. 1·40 1·75

30. Arms. 31. J. Rufino Barrios Statue.

35. Statesmen discussing Independence (after painting by E. Bravo). 47. President Manuel Estrada Cabrera.

**1902.** Inscr. "U.P.U. 1902".

116. 30. 1 c. purple and green .. 15 15
117. 31. 2 c. black and red .. 15 15
118a. – 5 c. black and blue .. 20 15
119. – 6 c. green and yellow .. 20 15
120. – 10 c. blue and orange .. 15 15
121. 35. 12½ c. black and blue .. 15 15
122. – 20 c. black and red .. 45 20
141. – 25 c. black and blue .. 55 20
123a. – 50 c. blue and brown .. 30 15
124. – 75 c. black and lilac .. 35 20
125. – 1 p. black and brown .. 45 20
126. – 2 p. black and orange .. 55 35
142. 47. 5 p. black and red .. 70 70

DESIGNS—HORIZ. 5 c. La Reforma Palace, 6 c. Temple of Minerva. 10 c. Lake Amatitlan. 20 c. Cathedral. 25 c. G.P.O. 50 c. Columbus Theatre. 75 c. Artillery Barracks. 1 p. Columbus Monument. 2 p. Indian Institute.

**1903.** Surch. **1903. 25 CENTAVOS.**

127. 9. 25 c. on 1 c. green .. 1·50 55
128. 25 c. on 2 c. red .. 1·90 55
129. 25 c. on 6 c. green .. 3·00 2·10
130. 25 c. on 10 c. brown .. 12·50 4·50
131. 25 c. on 75 c. red .. 16·00 11·00
132. 25 c. on 150 c. blue .. 16·00 11·00
133. 25 c. on 200 c. yellow .. 18·00 13·00

**1908.** Surch. **1908** and value in figures and words.

134. – 1 c. on 10 c. blue and orange (No. 120) .. 35 35
135. 35. 2 c. on 12½ c. blk. & blue 35 35
136. – 6 c. on 20 c. black and red (No. 122) .. 30 30

**1909.** Surch. **1909** and value in figures and words.

137. 2 c. on 75 c. black and lilac (No. 124) .. 55 55
138. 6 c. on 50 c. blue and brown (No. 123) .. 30 30
139. 12½ c. on 2 p. black and orange (No. 126) .. 45 45

45. M. Garcia Granados.

**1910.** Granados Cent.

140. 45. 6 c. black and bistre .. 55 35

**1911.** Surch. **1911 Un Centavo.**

143. 45. 1 c. on 6 c. black & bis. 13·00 5·00

**1911.** Surch. **Correos de Guatemala 1911** and value.

144. 2 c. on 5 c. (No. 118a) .. 1·00 50
145. 6 c. on 10 c. (No. 120) .. 85 85

**1912.** Surch. **1912** and value.

146. 1 c. on 20 c. (No. 122) .. 35 35
147. 2 c. on 50 c. (No. 123) .. 35 35
148. 5 c. on 75 c. (No. 124) .. 90 90

**1913.** Surch. **1913** and value.

149. 1 c. on 50 c. (No. 123) .. 30 30
150. 6 c. on 1 p. (No. 125) .. 45 45
151. 12½ c. on 2 p. (No. 126) 45 45

**1916.** Surch. with value only.

156 30. 2 c. on 1 c. pur. & grn. 30 30
152. 6 c. on 1 c. pur. & grn. 30 30
153. 12½ c. on 1 c. pur. & grn. 30 30
154. 31. 25 c. on 2 c. blk. & red 20 20

59. Pres. Manuel Estrada Cabrera. 60.

**1917.** Re-election of President Cabrera.

155. 59. 25 c. brown and blue .. 35 20

**1918.**

157. 60. 1 p. 50 c. blue .. 90 25

61. Arms. 64. Technical School.

**1919.** Buildings and Obligatory Tax G.P.O. Rebuilding Fund. (No. 158.)

158. 61. 12½ c. red .. .. 20 15
159. – 30 c. black & red (postage) 1·00 75
160. – 60 c. black and olive .. 90 45
161. 64. 90 c. black and brown .. 70 70
169. – 1 p. 50 orange and blue .. 50 30
162. – 3 p. black and green .. 1·75 45
170. – 5 p. green and sepia .. 1·25 40
171. – 15 p. red and black .. 20·00 12·50

DESIGNS—Dated 1918: 30 c. Radio station. 60 c. Maternity hospital. 3 p. Arms. Dated 1921: 1 p. 50, Monolith at Quirigua. 5 p. Garcia Granados Monument. 15 p. Railway bridge, Guatemala City.

**1920.** Nos. 159/60 surch. **1920 2 centavos.**

163. 2 c. on 30 c. black and red 45 45
164. 2 c. on 60 c. black & olive 25 25

**1920.** No. 126 surch. **25 Centavos** and bars.

165. 25 c. on 2 p. black & orange 35 30

68.

**1920.** Telegraph stamp as T 68 optd. **CORREOS.**

166. 68. 25 c. green .. .. 25 15

**1921.** Optd. **1921. CORREOS.**

173. 68. 25 c. green .. .. 35 20

**1921.** Surch. **1921. CORREOS** and value in words.

172. 68. 12½ c. on 25 c. green .. 30 20

**1921.** Surch. **1921** and value in words.
167. 12½ c. on 20 c. black and red (No. 122) .. 35 20
168. 50 c. on 75 c. black and lilac (No. 124) .. 45 35

**1922.** Surch. **1922** and values.
174. – 12½ c. on 20 c. (No. 122) 30 30
175. – 12½ c. on 60 c. (No. 160) 70 70
176. **64.** 12½ c. on 90 c. (No. 161) 70 70
179. – 12½ c. on 3 p. (No. 162) 30 25
180. – 12½ c. on 5 p. (No. 170) 70 65
181. – 12½ c. on 15 p. (No. 171) 75 65
185. – 25 c. on 30 c. (No. 159) 55 55
186. – 25 c. on 60 c. (No. 160) 1·40 1·40
187. – 25 c. on 75 c. (No. 124) 45 45
188. **64.** 25 c. on 90 c. (No. 161) 1·40 1·40
189. – 25 c. on 1 p. (No. 125) 35 35
190. – 25 c. on 1 p. 50 (No. 169) 35 35
191. – 25 c. on 2 p. (No. 126) 55 55
192. – 25 c. on 3 p. (No. 162) 45 45
193. – 25 c. on 5 p. (No. 170) 1·10 1·10
194. – 25 c. on 15 p. (No. 171) 1·40 1·40

**80.** Independence Centenary Palace. **81.** National Palace, Antigua.

**1922.**
195. **80.** 12½ c. green .. .. 20 15
196. **81.** 25 c. brown .. .. 20 15

**82.** Columbus Theatre. **83.** Resplendent Quetzal. **84.** Garcia Granados Monument.

**1923.**
197. **82.** 50 c. red .. .. 45 30
198. **83.** 1 p. green .. .. 90 30
199. **84.** 5 p. orange .. .. 1·40 55

**1924.** Surch. **1924** and value.
200. – 1 p. on 1 p. 50 (No. 169) 35 30
201. **84.** 1 p. 25 on 5 p. orange 55 45

**87.** Pres. J. R. Barrios. **88.** Dr. L. Montufar.

**1924.**
202. – 6 c. olive (as No. 119) 20 15
203. **81.** 25 c. brown .. .. 20 15
204. – 50 c. red (as No. 123a.) 20 15
205. – 1 p. brown (as No. 125) 20 15
206. **87.** 1 p. 25 blue .. .. 50 15
207. – 2 p. orange (as No. 126) 35 25
208. **88.** 2 p. 50 purple .. .. 55 30
209. – 3 p. green (as No. 162) 2·40 55
210. – 15 p. black (as No. 171) 5·50 3·50
These all have imprint "PERKINS BACON & CO. LD. LONDRES" at foot.

**1925.** No. 201 with two bars obliterating "25 cents" of surch. making it "UN PESO".
211. **84.** 1 p. on 5 p. orange .. 55 45

**89.** Aurora Park. **90.** General Post Office.

**91.** National Observatory. **92.** Proposed new G.P.O.

**1926.** Dated "1926".
212. – 6 c. bistre (as No. 119) 15 15
213. **89.** 12½ c. green .. .. 15 15
214. **81.** 25 c. brown .. .. 15 15
215. **90.** 50 c. red .. .. 20 15
216. – 1 p. brown (as No. 125) 20 20
217. **87.** 1 p. 50 blue .. .. 20 20
218. **91.** 2 p. orange .. .. 85 70
219. **88.** 2 p. 50 purple .. .. 1·75 70
220. – 3 p. green (as No. 162) 55 30
221. – 5 p. lilac (as No. 170) .. 70 45
222. – 15 p. black (as No. 171) 4·75 2·75
These all have imprint "WATERLOW & SONS LIMITED. LONDRES" at foot.

**1927.** Obligatory Tax. G.P.O. Rebuilding Fund.
223. **92.** 1 c. olive .. .. 15 15

**1928.** Surch. **1928** and value.
224. **91.** ½ c. de q. on 2 p. orange 70 55
225. – ½ c. de q. on 5 p. lilac (No. 221) .. .. 35 30
226. **88.** 1 c. de q. on 2 p. 50 purple (No. 219) .. 35 30

**95.** Pres. J. R. Barrios. **96.** Dr. L. Montufar. **97.** Garcia Granados.

**98.** General Orellana. **99.** City Arms, Guatemala.

**1929.**
227. **91.** ½ c. green .. .. 70 15
228. **81.** 1 c. sepia .. .. 20 15
229. **95.** 2 c. blue .. .. 20 15
230. **96.** 3 c. lilac .. .. 20 15
231. **97.** 4 c. yellow .. .. 20 20
232. **98.** 5 c. red .. .. 30 15
233. – 10 c. brown (as No. 119) 45 15
234. – 15 c. blue (as No. 125) 55 15
235. **31.** 25 c. brown .. .. 90 20
236. **89.** 30 c. green .. .. 1·10 35
237. – 50 c. red (as No. 120) .. 1·75 45
238. **99.** 1 q. black .. .. 3·00 55
These all have imprint "T. DE LA RUE & CO. Ld., LONDRES" at foot.

**1929.** Air. Nos. 210 and 222 surch. **SERVICIO POSTAL AEREO ANO DE 1928** and new value.
239. Q 0.03 on 15 p. black (222) 1·75 2·10
240. Q 0.05 on 15 p. black (222) 80 60
240a. Q 0.05 on 15 p. black (210) 3·25 4·25
241. Q 0.15 on 15 p. black (222) 2·00 1·10
242. Q 0.20 on 15 p. black (222) 3·25 4·25

**1929.** Air. Surch. **SERVICIO POSTAL AEREO ANO DE 1929 Q0.03.**
243. **88.** Q 0.03 on 2 p. 50 purple (No. 208) .. .. 1·00 1·00

**1929.** Opening of Guatemala–Salvador Railway. No. 220 surch. **FERROCARRIL ORIENTAL 1929** and new value.
244. Q 0.03 on 3 p. green .. 1·75 2·25
245. Q 0.05 on 3 p. green .. 1·75 2·25

**1930.** Opening of Los Altos Railway. No. 222 surch. **FERROCARRIL DE LOS ALTOS,** etc. and new value.
246. 1 c. on 15 p. black .. 1·00 1·10
247. 2 c. on 15 p. black .. 1·00 1·10
248. 3 c. on 15 p. black .. 1·00 1·10
249. 5 c. on 15 p. black .. 1·00 1·10
250. 15 c. on 15 p. black .. 1·00 1·10

**104.** Bridge and Permanent Way.

DESIGNS: 2 c. Embankment. 5 c. Station.

**1930.** Opening of Los Altos Railway.
251. – 2 c. black and purple .. 1·25 1·25
252. **104.** 3 c. black and red .. 2·50 2·50
253. – 5 c. blue and orange .. 2·50 2·50

**105.** Fokker Super Trimotor over Mt. Agua.

**1930.** Air.
254. **105.** 6 c. red .. .. 75 55

**1930.** Air. Surch. **SERVICIO AEREO INTERIOR 1930** and value.
255. 1 c. on 3 p. grn. (No. 220) 20 20
256. 2 c. on 3 p. green .. 50 90
257. 3 c. on 3 p. green .. 50 90
258. 4 c. on 3 p. green .. 70 70
259. 10 c. on 15 p. blk. (No. 222) 3·00 3·00

**1931.** Air. Optd. **EXTERIOR—1931.**
260. **105.** 6 c. red .. .. 70 70

**1931.** Air. Optd. **AEREO EXTERIOR 1931.**
261. **97.** 4 c. yellow .. .. 35 30

**1931.** Air. Optd. **AEREO INTERNACIONAL 1931.**
262. – 15 c. blue (No. 234) 1·00 35
263. **89.** 30 c. green (No. 236) 1·75 60

**1931.** Air. Optd. **Primer Vuelo Posta BARRIOS—MIAMI 1931.**
264. **95.** 2 c. blue .. .. 1·75 2·00
265. **96.** 3 c. lilac .. .. 1·75 2·00
266. – 15 c. blue (No. 234) .. 1·75 2·00

**1932.** Air. Surch. **SERVICIO AEREO INTERIOR 1932** and value.
267. **87.** 2 c. on 1 p. 50 blue (217) 75 60
268. – 3 c. on 3 p. green (220) .. 70 20
270. – 10 c. on 15 p. blk. (222) 12·00 8·00
271. – 15 c. on 15 p. blk. (222) 17·00 12·00

**114.** Monolith of Quirigua. **116.** Flag of the Race, Columbus and Tecum Uman.

**1932.**
272. **114.** 3 c. red .. .. .. 50 15
See also Nos. 416a/b.

**1933.** Air. Optd. **AEREO INTERIOR 1933.**
273. **97.** 4 c. yellow .. .. 35 20

**1933.** 441st Anniv. of Departure of Columbus from Palos.
274. **116.** ½ c. green .. .. 35 70
275. 1 c. brown .. .. 70 85
276. 2 c. blue .. .. 70 85
277. 3 c. mauve .. .. 70 50
278. 5 c. red .. .. 70 70

**1934.** Air. (a) Optd. **AERO EXTERIOR 1934.**
280. **98.** 5 c. red .. .. 1·75 15
281. – 15 c. blue (No. 234) .. 1·75 35

(b) Optd. **AEREO INTERIOR 1934.**
279. **95.** 2 c. blue .. .. 55 20

**117.** Barrios' Birthplace.

**118.** Barrios and "Agamemnon" (freighter).

**1935.** Birth Cent. of J. R. Barrios.
282. **117.** ½ c. pink & grn. (post.) 35 40
283. – 1 c. blue and orange .. 35 40
284. – 2 c. black and orange 35 45
285. – 3 c. blue and red .. 2·00 1·50
286. – 4 c. red and blue .. 3·50 9·00
287. – 5 c. brown and green .. 2·75 3·50
288. – 10 c. red and green .. 4·00 4·50
289. – 15 c. brown and green 3·50 4·00
290. – 25 c. black and red .. 3·50 4·00
291. **118.** 10 c. blue & brown (air) 4·25 3·25
292. – 15 c. brown and grey .. 1·40 1·50
293. – 30 c. violet and red .. 1·40 1·00
DESIGNS—POSTAGE—HORIZ. 1 c. San Lorenzo. 2 c. Barrios and Official Decree. 3 c. Arms and locomotive. 5 c. Telegraph office and Barrios. 10 c. Polytechnic School. 15 c. Police H.Q. 25 c. Pres. Ubico, arms and Barrios. VERT. 4 c. G.P.O. AIR—HORIZ. Barrios and (15 c.) tomb, (30 c.) statue.

**120.** Lake Atitlan. **121.** Resplendent Quetzal.

**122.** Arms and Map of Guatemala.

**1935.**
293a. – ½ c. blue and green .. 15 15
294. **120.** 1 c. red and brown .. 20 15
295. **121.** 3 c. green and orange .. 1·10 25
296. 3 c. green and red .. 1·10 25
297. – 4 c. red and blue .. 45 20
297a. **122.** 5 c. brown and blue .. 55 20
DESIGNS—As Type **120:** ½ c. Govt. Printing Works. 4 c. National Assembly.

**123.** Lake Amatitlan.

**1935.** Air.
(a) Inscr. "INTERIOR" (37 × 17 mm.).
298. **123.** 2 c. brown .. .. 15 15
299. – 3 c. blue .. .. 40 20
300. – 4 c. black .. .. 35 10
300a. – 4 c. blue .. .. 30 10
301. **123.** 6 c. green .. .. 35 15
301a. 6 c. violet .. .. 2·75 10
302. – 10 c. red .. .. 35 35
303. – 15 c. orange .. .. 45 55
303a. – 15 c. green .. .. 45 65
304. – 30 c. olive .. .. 4·00 4·50
304a. – 30 c. brown .. .. 50 35
305. – 50 c. purple .. .. 12·00 10·00
305a. – 50 c. blue .. .. 2·75 2·00
306. **123.** 1 q. orange .. .. 12·00 13·00
306a. 1 q. red .. .. 3·00 2·00
DESIGNS: 3 c. Puerto Barrios. 4 c. San Felipe. 10 c. Livingston. 15 c. San Jose. 30 c. Atitlan. 50 c. La Aurora Airport.

(b) Inscr. "EXTERIOR" (34 × 15 mm.) (except Nos. 319/20 which are 46 × 20 mm.).
307. 1 c. brown .. .. 10 10
308. 2 c. red .. .. 20 20
309. 3 c. mauve .. .. 35 35
309a. 4 c. yellow .. .. 1·25 1·00
309b. 4 c. red .. .. 70 50
310. 5 c. blue .. .. 35 15
310a. 5 c. orange .. .. 20 15
311. 10 c. brown .. .. 35 25
311a. 10 c. green .. .. 35 25
312. 15 c. red .. .. 35 10
312a. 15 c. orange .. .. 30 10
313. 20 c. blue .. .. 1·60 2·00
313a. 20 c. red .. .. 35 25
314. 25 c. black .. .. 2·00 2·40
314a. 25 c. green .. .. 65 35
315. 30 c. green .. .. 5·00 3·50
315a. 30 c. red .. .. 1·50 20
316. 50 c. red .. .. 13·00 13·00
316a. 50 c. violet .. .. 10·00 10·00
317. 1 q. blue .. .. 15·00 17·00
318. 1 q. green .. .. 5·00 5·00
319. 2 q. 50 olive and red .. 3·50 2·00
320. 5 q. blue and orange .. 4·75 2·75
DESIGNS: 1 c. Guatemala City. 2 c., 15 c. (No. 312) Views of Central Park. 3 c. Cerrito del Carmen. 4 c. Estuary of R. Dulce. 5 c. Plaza J. R. Barrios. 10 c. National Liberators' Monument. 15 c. (No. 312a) R. Dulce. 20 c. Quezaltenango. 25 c. Antigua. 30 c. Puerto Barrios. 50 c. San Jose. 1 q. Aurora Airport. 2 q. 50, Islet. 5 q. Rocks on Atlantic Coast.

**1936.** Obligatory Tax. 65th Anniv of Liberal Revolution. Optd 1871 **30 DE JUNIO 1936**.
321 **92** 1 c. green .. .. 35 35

**1936.** Obligatory Tax. 115th Anniv of Independence. Optd **1821 15 de SEPTIEMBRE 1936**.
322 **92** 1 c. green .. .. 45 25

**1936.** Obligatory Tax. National Fair. Optd. **FERIA NACIONAL 1936.**
323. **92.** 1 c. olive .. .. 55 55

**1937.** Philatelic Exhibition Fund. Optd. **EXPOSICION FILATELICA 1937** or surch. also.
325. **120.** 1 c. + 1 c. red & brown 90 70
326. **121.** 3 c. + 1 c. green & orge. 90 70
327. 3 c. + 1 c. green & red 90 70
329. – 4 c. + 1 c. (No. 300a) .. 75 75
328. **122.** 5 c. + 1 c. brown & blue 90 70
330. – 6 c. + 1 c. (No. 301a) .. 75 75
331. – 10 c. + 1 c. (No. 311a) 75 75
332. – 15 c. + 1 c. (No. 312a) .. 75 75
324. **92.** 1 c. olive .. .. 40 40

**128.** Resplendent Quetzal. **129.** General Ubico on horseback.

**130.** Quezaltenango.

**1937.** Second Term of Pres. Ubico. (a) Postage.
333. **128.** ½ c. red and blue .. 80 50
334. – 1 c. brown and grey .. 45 45
335. – 2 c. red and violet .. 45 45
336. – 3 c. blue and purple .. 35 35
337. – 4 c. olive and yellow .. 1·40 1·25
338. – 5 c. purple and red .. 1·40 1·25
339. – 10 c. black and purple 2·00 2·40
340. – 15 c. red and blue .. 1·60 2·40
341. – 25 c. violet and orange 2·00 2·50
342. – 50 c. orange and green 3·00 3·75
343. **129.** 1 q. purple and brown .. 15·00 17·00
344. – 1 q. 50 brown and olive 15·00 17·00

DESIGNS: As Type **128**—VERT. 1 c. Tower of the Reformer. 5 c. National Congress entrance. 10 c. Customs House. HORIZ. 2 c. Union Park, Quezaltenango. 3 c. G.P.O. 4 c. Government Building, Retalhuleu. 15 c. Aurora Airport. 25 c. National Fair. 50 c. Presidential Guards' Barracks. As Type **129**: 1 q. 50, Gen. Ubico.

(b) Air. As T **130**, inscr. "INTERIOR" and optd. with aeroplane.

| | | | | |
|---|---|---|---|---|
| 345. | **130.** | 2 c. black and red | 20 | 15 |
| 346. | – | 3 c. black and blue | 70 | 85 |
| 347. | – | 4 c. black and yellow | 20 | 15 |
| 348. | – | 6 c. black and green | 50 | 35 |
| 349. | – | 10 c. black, and purple | 1·40 | 1·50 |
| 350. | – | 15 c. black and orange | 1·00 | 70 |
| 351. | – | 30 c. black and olive | 2·50 | 2·00 |
| 352. | – | 50 c. black and blue | 3·50 | 3·00 |
| 353. | – | 75 c. black and violet | 7·00 | 7·50 |
| 354. | – | 1 q. black and red | 7·50 | 8·00 |

DESIGNS: 3 c. Lake Atitlan. 4 c. Progressive colony on Lake Amatitlan. 6 c. Carmen Hill. 10 c. Relief map. 15 c. National University. 30 c. Plaza Espana. 50 c. Aurora Police Station. 75 c. Aurora Amphitheatre. 1 q. Aurora Airport.

(c) Air. As T **130** inscr. "EXTERIOR" and optd. with aeroplane.

| | | | | |
|---|---|---|---|---|
| 355. | – | 1 c. blue and orange | 15 | 15 |
| 356. | – | 2 c. violet and red | 25 | 20 |
| 357. | – | 3 c. brown and purple | 70 | 70 |
| 358. | – | 5 c. red and green | 2·75 | 2·00 |
| 359. | – | 10 c. green and red | 85 | 70 |
| 360. | – | 15 c. olive and pink | 55 | 35 |
| 361. | – | 20 c. black and blue | 1·75 | 1·10 |
| 362. | – | 25 c. red and grey | 1·75 | 1·75 |
| 363. | – | 30 c. violet and green | 85 | 85 |
| 364. | – | 50 c. blue and purple | 14·00 | 14·00 |
| 365. | – | 1 q. purple and olive | 7·00 | 8·00 |
| 366. | – | 1 q. 50 c. brown and red | 7·00 | 8·00 |

DESIGNS: 1 c. Seventh Avenue. 2 c. Liberators' Monument. 3 c. National Printing Offices. 5 c. National Museum. 10 c. Central Park. 15 c. Escuintla Park. 20 c. Mobile Police. 25 c. Slaughter-house, Escuintla. 30 c. Campo de Marte Stadium. 50 c. Plaza Barrios. 1 q. Polytechnic. 1 q. 50 c. Aurora Airport.

**1938.** 150th Anniv. of U.S. Constitution. Optd. **1787-1789 CL ANIVERSARIO DE LA CONSTITUCION**, etc.

| | | | | |
|---|---|---|---|---|
| 367. | **92.** | 1 c. olive | 25 | 20 |

**1938.** Obligatory Tax. Optd. **1938.**

| | | | | |
|---|---|---|---|---|
| 368a. | **92.** | 1 c. olive | 25 | 15 |

134.

**1938.** 1st Central American Philatelic Exn.

(a) Air. As T **134** inscr. "PRIMERA EXPOSICION FILATELICA CENTRO AMERICANA".

| | | | | |
|---|---|---|---|---|
| 369. | **134.** | 1 c. brown and orange | 25 | 25 |
| 370. | – | 2 c. brown and red | 25 | 25 |
| 371. | – | 3 c. brown, buff & green | 40 | 40 |
| 372. | – | 4 c. brown and purple | 55 | 55 |
| 373. | – | 5 c. brown and grey | 35 | 40 |
| 374. | – | 10 c. brown and blue | 70 | 1·00 |

(b) Postage. Optd. **Primera Exposicion Filatelica Centroamericana 1938.**

| | | | | |
|---|---|---|---|---|
| 375. | **92.** | 1 c. olive | 25 | 15 |

137. La Merced Church.

**1939.** Optd. with flying quetzal.

(a) Inland Air Mail. As T **137** inscr. "CORREO AEREO INTERIOR".

| | | | | |
|---|---|---|---|---|
| 376. | **137.** | 1 c. brown and olive | 15 | 10 |
| 377. | – | 2 c. green and red | 20 | 15 |
| 378. | – | 3 c. olive and blue | 20 | 20 |
| 379. | – | 4 c. green and pink | 20 | 10 |
| 380. | – | 5 c. blue and purple | 25 | 20 |
| 381. | – | 6 c. grey and orange | 35 | 25 |
| 382. | – | 10 c. grey and brown | 55 | 30 |
| 383. | – | 15 c. black and purple | 70 | 20 |
| 384. | – | 30 c. red and blue | 75 | 35 |
| 385. | – | 50 c. violet and orange | 1·00 | 55 |
| 386. | – | 1 q. blue and green | 1·40 | 1·00 |

DESIGNS: 2 c. Christ's Church Ruins, Antigua. 3 c. Aurora Airport. 4 c. Campo de Marte Stadium. 5 c. Cavalry Barracks. 6 c. Palace of Justice. 10 c. Customs House, San Jose. 15 c. Post Office, Retalhuleu. 30 c. Municipal Theatre, Quezaltenango. 50 c. Customs House, Retalhuleu. 1 q. Departmental Palace, Retalhuleu.

(b) Foreign Air Mail. As T **137** inscr. "AEREO EXTERIOR" (10 c. and 25 c.) or "AEREO INTERNACIONAL".

| | | | | |
|---|---|---|---|---|
| 387. | – | 1 c. brown and sepia | 15 | 10 |
| 388. | – | 2 c. black and green | 25 | 25 |
| 389. | – | 3 c. green and blue | 20 | 15 |
| 390. | – | 4 c. green and brown | 20 | 15 |
| 391. | – | 5 c. red and green | 35 | 10 |
| 392. | – | 10 c. slate and red | 1·10 | 10 |
| 393. | – | 15 c. red and blue | 1·40 | 10 |
| 394. | – | 20 c. yellow and green | 55 | 25 |
| 395. | – | 25 c. olive and purple | 60 | 35 |
| 396. | – | 30 c. grey and red | 70 | 15 |
| 397. | – | 50 c. orange and red | 1·00 | 20 |
| 398. | – | 1 q. green and orange | 1·60 | 35 |

DESIGNS: 1 c. Mayan Altar, Aurora Park. 2 c. Ministry of Health. 3 c. Lake Amatitlan. 4 c. Lake Atitlan. 5 c. Bridge over Tamazulapa. 10 c. National Liberators' Monument. 15 c. Palace of the Captains General. 20 c. Carmen Hill. 25 c. Barrios Square. 30 c. Mayan Altar, Archaeological Museum. 50 c. Carlos III Fountain. 1 q. Antigua.

**1939.** Obligatory Tax. As No. 368a, but optd. **1939.**

| | | | | |
|---|---|---|---|---|
| 399. | **92.** | 1 c. olive | 25 | 15 |

140. National Flower (White Nun).

142. Arms and Map of Guatemala.

**1939.**

| | | | | |
|---|---|---|---|---|
| 400. | | ½ c. brown and green | 20 | 20 |
| 401. | **140.** | 2 c. black and blue | 1·00 | 35 |
| 402. | – | 3 c. green and brown | 1·50 | 75 |
| 403. | – | 3 c. green and red | 1·50 | 75 |
| 404. | **142.** | 5 c. red and blue | 1·25 | 1·25 |

DESIGNS—As Type **142**: ½ c. Mayan Calendar. 3 c. Resplendent Quetzal.

**1939.** No. 229 surch. **UN CENTAVO.**

| | | | | |
|---|---|---|---|---|
| 405. | **95.** | 1 c. on 2 c. blue | 30 | 20 |

**1940.** As No. 223, but optd. **1940.**

| | | | | |
|---|---|---|---|---|
| 406. | **92.** | 1 c. olive | 25 | 15 |

**1940.** 50th Anniv. of Pan-American Union.

(a) Optd. **Commemorative Union Panamericana 1890-1940.**

| | | | | |
|---|---|---|---|---|
| 407. | **92.** | 1 c. olive | 25 | 15 |

(b) Air. Optd. **UNION PANAMERICANA 1890-1940. CORREO AEREO.**

| | | | | |
|---|---|---|---|---|
| 408. | – | 15 c. blue (No. 234) | 35 | 20 |

**1940.** Surch. with new values.

| | | | | |
|---|---|---|---|---|
| 409. | **31.** | 1 c. on 25 c brown | 25 | 15 |
| 410. | – | 5 c. on 50 c. red (No. 237) | 35 | 30 |

**1941.** Obligatory Tax. Optd. **1941.**

| | | | | |
|---|---|---|---|---|
| 411. | **92.** | 1 c. olive | 25 | 15 |

**1941.** Obligatory Tax. Surch. **CONSTRUCCION** (twice) and **UN CENTAVO.**

| | | | | |
|---|---|---|---|---|
| 412. | **95.** | 1 c. on 2 c. blue | 25 | 15 |

**1941.** Air. 2nd Pan-American Health Day. Optd. **DICIEMBRE 2 1941 SEGUNDO DIA PAN-AMERICANO**, etc.

| | | | | |
|---|---|---|---|---|
| 414. | – | 2 c. blk. & grn. (No. 388) | 55 | 30 |

**1941.** Surch. **½ MEDIO CENTAVO ½.**

| | | | | |
|---|---|---|---|---|
| 415. | **31.** | ½ c. on 25 c. brown | 20 | 20 |

**1942.** Obligatory Tax. Surch. **CONSTRUCCION/1942/UN CENTAVO.**

| | | | | |
|---|---|---|---|---|
| 416. | **95.** | 1 c. on 2 c. blue | 25 | 15 |

**1942.** As T **114**, but tablet dated "1942".

| | | | | |
|---|---|---|---|---|
| 416a. | – | 3 c. green | 35 | 20 |
| 416b. | – | 3 c. blue | 35 | 20 |

153. Archway between wings of new G.P.O.

154. Guastatoya Vase.

**1942.** Obligatory Tax.

| | | | | |
|---|---|---|---|---|
| 417a. | **153.** | 1 c. brown | 25 | 15 |

**1942.**

| | | | | |
|---|---|---|---|---|
| 418. | **154.** | ½ c. brown | 20 | 15 |
| 419. | – | 1 c. red | 25 | 15 |

DESIGN—HORIZ. 1 c. Old peoples' home.

156. Ruins of Zakuleu.

157. National Printing Works.

158. National Police H.Q.

159. San Carlos Borromeo University, Antigua, Guatemala.

**1943.**

| | | | | |
|---|---|---|---|---|
| 420. | **156.** | ½ c. brown (postage) | 15 | 10 |
| 421. | **157.** | 2 c. red | 20 | 15 |
| 422. | **158.** | 10 c. mauve (air) | 50 | 15 |
| 423. | **159.** | 15 c. brown | 55 | 15 |

160. Don Pedro de Alvarado.

161. Archway between wings of G.P.O.

**1943.** Air. 400th Anniv. of Founding of Antigua.

| | | | | |
|---|---|---|---|---|
| 424. | **160.** | 15 c. blue | 55 | 15 |

**1943.** Obligatory Tax.

| | | | | |
|---|---|---|---|---|
| 425. | **161.** | 1 c. orange | 25 | 15 |

162. Rafael Maria Landivar.

163. National Palace.

**1943.** 150th Death Anniv. of R. M. Landivar (poet).

| | | | | |
|---|---|---|---|---|
| 426. | **162.** | 5 c. blue | 35 | 20 |

**1944.** Inauguration of National Palace.

| | | | | |
|---|---|---|---|---|
| 427. | **163.** | 3 c. green (postage) | 20 | 15 |
| 444. | | 5 c. red (air) | 35 | 15 |
| 445. | | 10 c. lilac | 35 | 15 |
| 446. | | 15 c. blue | 35 | 30 |

**1945.** Optd. **25 de junio de 1944 PALACIO NACIONAL** and bar.

| | | | | |
|---|---|---|---|---|
| 428. | **163.** | 3 c. blue | 35 | 15 |

**1945.** Air. Optd. **PALACIO NACIONAL** and bar.

| | | | | |
|---|---|---|---|---|
| 429. | **163.** | 5 c. red | 30 | 20 |

165. Archway between Wings of G.P.O.

166. Allegory of the Revolution.

**1945.** Obligatory Tax.

| | | | | |
|---|---|---|---|---|
| 430. | **165.** | 1 c. orange | 25 | 15 |
| 479. | | 1 c. blue | 25 | 15 |

**1945.** Revolution of 20 October 1944.

| | | | | |
|---|---|---|---|---|
| 431. | **166.** | 3 c. blue (postage) | 15 | 15 |
| 432. | | 5 c. red (air) | 45 | 30 |
| 433. | | 6 c. green | 45 | 30 |
| 434. | | 10 c. violet | 45 | 30 |
| 435. | | 15 c. blue | 45 | 30 |

**1945.** Air. Book Fair. No. 389 surch. **1945 FERIA DEL LIBRO 2½ CENTAVOS.**

| | | | | |
|---|---|---|---|---|
| 436. | | 2½ c. on 3 c. grn.&.blue | 1·40 | 1·40 |

168. Jose Milla y Vidaurre (author).

169. Archbishop Pavo Enriquez de Rivera.

170. Torch.

**1945.**

| | | | | |
|---|---|---|---|---|
| 437. | **168.** | 1 c. green (postage) | 15 | 15 |
| 438. | **169.** | 2 c. violet | 15 | 15 |
| 439. | | 5 c. red (air) | 35 | 20 |
| 678. | | 5 c. olive | 20 | 10 |
| 679. | | 5 c. blue | 20 | 10 |
| 680. | | 5 c. green | 20 | 10 |
| 681. | | 5 c. orange | 20 | 10 |
| 682. | | 5 c. violet | 20 | 10 |
| 683. | | 5 c. grey | 20 | 10 |
| 440. | **168.** | 7½ c. purple | 50 | 90 |
| 441. | | 7½ c. blue | 30 | 30 |

For stamps as Type **169** but dated " 1660 1951 " see Nos. 523/27.

**1945.** 1st Anniv. of Revolution of 20 October 1944.

| | | | | |
|---|---|---|---|---|
| 442. | **170.** | 3 c. blue (postage) | 20 | 15 |
| 443. | | 5 c. mauve (air) | 45 | 30 |

171. Jose Batres y Montufar (military leader and writer).

174. Rowland Hill.

**1945.**

| | | | | |
|---|---|---|---|---|
| 447. | **171.** | ½ c. brown (postage) | 20 | 15 |
| 448. | | 3 c. blue | 25 | 15 |
| 449. | | 3 c. green | 30 | 25 |
| 450. | | 10 c. green (air) | 45 | 20 |

DESIGN—HORIZ. 10 c. Montufar.

**1946.** Cent. of First Postage Stamps.

| | | | | |
|---|---|---|---|---|
| 451. | – | 1 c. ol. & vio. (post.) | 30 | 25 |
| 452. | **174.** | 5 c. brown & grey (air) | 25 | 20 |
| 453. | – | 15 c. blue, green & red | 35 | 35 |

DESIGNS: 1 c. U.P.U. Monument, Berne. 15 c. Hemispheres and quetzal.

175. Signing the Declaration of Independence.

176. Franklin D. Roosevelt.

**1946.** Air. 125th Anniv. of Independence.

| | | | | |
|---|---|---|---|---|
| 454. | **175.** | 5 c. red | 15 | 10 |
| 455. | | 6 c. brown | 20 | 15 |
| 456. | | 10 c. violet | 25 | 20 |
| 457. | | 20 c. blue | 50 | 45 |

**1947.** Air. 2nd Anniv. of Revolution of 20 October 1944. As T **170** but inscr. "1944–1946" instead of "1944–1945" and "II" for "I".

| | | | | |
|---|---|---|---|---|
| 458. | | 1 c. green | 20 | 15 |
| 459. | | 2 c. red | 20 | 15 |
| 460. | | 3 c. violet | 20 | 15 |
| 461. | | 5 c. blue | 25 | 15 |

**1947.** Air.

| | | | | |
|---|---|---|---|---|
| 462. | **176.** | 5 c. red | 20 | 15 |
| 463. | | 6 c. blue | 25 | 15 |
| 464. | | 10 c. blue | 55 | 20 |
| 465. | | 30 c. black | 1·75 | 1·40 |
| 466. | | 50 c. violet | 1·75 | 1·75 |
| 467. | | 1 q. green | 2·75 | 2·75 |

177. " Labour ".

180. Football Match.

**1948.** Labour Day and 1st Anniv of Adoption of Labour Code.

| | | | | |
|---|---|---|---|---|
| 468. | **177.** | 1 c. green | 20 | 15 |
| 469. | | 2 c. purple | 20 | 15 |
| 470. | | 3 c. blue | 20 | 15 |
| 471. | | 5 c. red | 20 | 15 |

**1948.** Optd. **1948.**

| | | | | |
|---|---|---|---|---|
| 472. | **142.** | 5 c. red and blue | 20 | 15 |

**1948.** Air. Optd. **1948.** AEREO.

| | | | | |
|---|---|---|---|---|
| 473. | **142.** | 5 c. red and blue | 25 | 20 |

**1948.** Air. 4th Central American and Caribbean Football Championship Games.

| | | | | |
|---|---|---|---|---|
| 474. | **180.** | 3 c. black and red | 40 | 20 |
| 475. | | 5 c. black and green | 50 | 30 |
| 476. | | 10 c. black and mauve | 60 | 70 |
| 477. | | 30 c. black and blue | 2·00 | 2·40 |
| 478. | | 50 c. black and yellow | 2·75 | 2·75 |

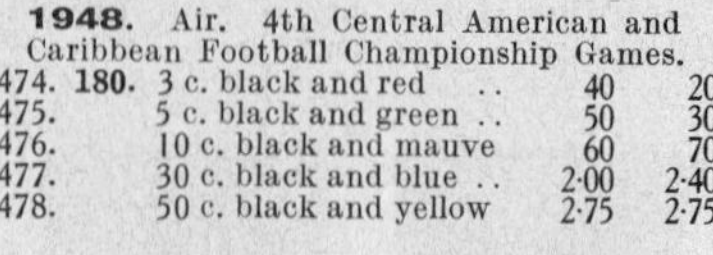

181. Fray Bartolome de Las Casas and Indian.

182. Seal of University of Guatemala.

**1949.** Fray Bartolome de Las Casas ("Apostle of the Indians").

| | | | | |
|---|---|---|---|---|
| 480. | **181.** | ½ c. red | 20 | 15 |
| 661. | | ½ c. blue | 15 | 10 |
| 481. | | 1 c. brown | 20 | 15 |
| 662. | | 1 c. violet | 15 | 10 |
| 663. | | 2 c. green | 15 | 10 |
| 664. | | 3 c. red | 15 | 10 |
| 484. | | 4 c. blue | 30 | 20 |
| 665a. | | 4 c. brown | 10 | 10 |

**1949.** Air. Latin-American Universities' Congress.

| | | | | |
|---|---|---|---|---|
| 485. | **182.** | 3 c. blue and red | 35 | 35 |
| 486. | | 10 c. blue and green | 75 | 55 |
| 487. | | 50 c. blue and yellow | 1·90 | 2·10 |

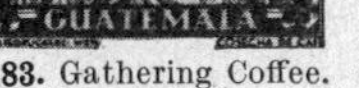

**183.** Gathering Coffee. **184.** Tecum Uman Monument.

**1950.** Tourist Propaganda. (a) Postage.

488. **183.** ½ c. olive, blue & pink 30 15
489. – ½ c. blue and brown .. 20 15
490. – 1 c. olive, brn. & yell. 30 15
491. – 1 c. green & orange .. 20 15
492. – 2 c. blue, green & red 30 15
493. – 2 c. brown and red .. 20 15
494. – 3 c. brn., blue & violet 30 15
495. – 6 c. violet, orge. & grn. 55 15

DESIGNS—As Type **183**: ½ c. (No. 489). 3 c. Cutting sugar canes. 1 c. (No. 490), 2 c. (No. 493), Agricultural colony. 1 c. (No. 491), 2 c. (No. 492), Banana trees. 6 c. International Bridge.

(b) Air. Multicoloured centres.

496. – 3 c. red .. .. 55 15
497. **184.** 5 c. lake .. .. 55 15
498. – 8 c. black .. .. 30 20
499. – 13 c. brown .. .. 60 35
500. – 35 c. violet .. .. 1·50 1·75

DESIGNS—As Type **184**—HORIZ. 3 c. Lake Atitlan. 8 c. San Cristobal Church. 35 c. Momostenango Cliffs. VERT. 13 c. Weaver.

**185.** Footballers

DESIGNS—HORIZ. 4 c. Pole vaulting. 35 c. Diving. 65 c. Stadium. VERT. 3 c. Runners. 8 c. Tennis.

**1950.** Air. 6th Central American and Caribbean Games. Inscr. "VI JUEGOS DEPORTIVOS . . . 1950".

501. **185.** 1 c. black and violet .. 35 15
502. – 3 c. black and red .. 40 15
503. – 4 c. black and brown .. 50 20
504. – 8 c. black and purple 60 20
505. – 35 c. black and blue .. 1·40 1·90
506. – 65 c. green .. .. 3·00 3·00

**186.** Ministry of Health Badge. **187.** Nursing School.

**1950.** Social Assistance and Public Health Fund.

507. **186.** 1 c. blue & red (post.) 20 15
508. – 3 c. red & grn. (Nurse) 35 20
509. – 5 c. brn. & blue (Map) 55 35
511. – 5 c. red, grn. & vio. (air) 25 20
512. **187.** 10 c. green and brown 40 35
513. – 50 c. purple, green & red 1·40 1·60
514. – 1 q. olive, grn. & yellow 1·60 1·75

DESIGNS—As Type **187**: 5 c. Nurse. 50 c., 1 q. Zacapa and Roosevelt Hospitals.

**1951.** No. E 479 without surcharge for use as ordinary postage.

517. E **181.** 4 c. black & green .. 35 30

**188.** School. **189.** Ceremonial Axe-head.

**1951.** Aerial views of schools as T **188.**

519. **188.** ½ c. brown and violet 20 15
520. – 1 c. green and lake .. 20 15
521. **188.** 2 c. brown and blue .. 20 15
522. – 4 c. purple and black 30 20

**1952.** As No. 438 but dated "1660 1951" below portrait.

523. **169.** ½ c. violet .. .. 15 10
524. 1 c. red .. .. 15 10
525. 2 c. green .. .. 15 10
526. 4 c. orange .. .. 20 15
527. 4 c. blue .. .. 15 10

**1953.** Air.

528. **189.** 3 c. drab and blue .. 20 20
529. 5 c. brown and slate .. 20 20
530. 10 c. slate and violet .. 45 35

**190.** Flag and Constitution. **191.** R. Alvarez Ovalle (music), J. J. Palma (words).

**1953.** Air. Presidential Succession, 1951.

531. **190.** 1 c. multicoloured .. 30 20
532. 2 c. multicoloured .. 35 30
533. 4 c. multicoloured .. 45 35

**1953.** National Anthem.

534. **191.** ½ c. grey and violet .. 35 20
535. 1 c. brown and grey .. 45 20
536. 2 c. olive and brown .. 45 25
537. 3 c. olive and blue .. 45 25

**192.** "Work and Play". **193.** Horse Racing.

**1953.** Air. National Fair. Inscr. "FERIA NACIONAL".

538. – 1 c. red and blue .. 20 15
539. – 4 c. green and orange .. 90 25
540. **192.** 5 c. brown and green .. 55 30
541. **193.** 15 c. lilac and brown .. 85 75
542. – 20 c. blue and red .. 75 70
543. – 30 c. blue and sepia .. 85 1·00
544. – 50 c. black and violet .. 1·00 1·00
545. – 65 c. green and blue .. 1·75 1·90
546. – 1 q. green and red .. 17·00 11·00

DESIGNS—VERT. 1 c. National dance. 4 c. National flower (White Nun). 30 c. Picture and corn cob. 1 q. Resplendent Quetzal. HORIZ. 20 c. Ruins of Zakuleu. 50 c. Champion bull. 65 c. Cycle-racing.

**194.** Indian Warrior. **196.** Flags of Guatemala and O.D.E.C.A.

**1954.** Air. National Revolutionary Army Commemoration.

547. **194.** 1 c. red .. .. 35 35
548. 2 c. blue .. .. 35 35
549. 4 c. green .. .. 35 35
550. 5 c. turquoise .. .. 55 45
551. 6 c. orange .. .. 55 45
552. 10 c. violet .. .. 70 55
553. 20 c. sepia .. .. 1·90 2·00

**1954.** As T **5** but inscr. "UNION POSTAL UNIVERSAL GUATEMALA" around oval.

554. 1 c. blue .. .. 90 25
1222. 1 c. green .. .. 25 10
555. 2 c. violet .. .. 45 20
556. 2 c. brown .. .. 60 20
1222a. 2 c. blue .. .. 25 10
557. 3 c. red .. .. 60 20
558. 3 c. blue .. .. 60 20
1225. 3 c. brown .. .. 25 10
1226. 3 c. green .. .. 25 10
1227. 3 c. orange .. .. 25 10
559. 4 c. orange .. .. 1·00 20
560. 4 c. violet .. .. 90 20
1228. 4 c. brown .. .. 25 10
561. 5 c. brown .. .. 1·40 25
562. 5 c. red .. .. 1·40 25
563. 5 c. green .. .. 1·00 25
564. 5 c. grey .. .. 1·75 25
1228a. 5 c. mauve .. .. 25 10
565. 6 c. green .. .. 1·40 45
1229. 6 c. blue .. .. 25 10

**1954.** Air. 3rd Anniv. of Organization of Central American States.

566. **196.** 1 c. multicoloured .. 20 15
567. 2 c. multicoloured .. 20 15
568. 4 c. multicoloured .. 30 20

**HAVE YOU READ THE NOTES AT THE BEGINNING OF THIS CATALOGUE?**
These often provide answers to the enquiries we receive.

**197.** Goal-keeper. **198.** Red Cross and Globe.

**1955.** Golden Jubilee of Football in Guatemala. Inscr. "1902—1952".

569. – 4 c. violet (Camposeco) 70 45
570. – 4 c. red (Camposeco) 70 45
571. – 4 c. green (Camposeco) 70 45
572. – 10 c. green (Matheu) .. 2·00 55
573. **197.** 15 c. blue .. .. 2·00 1·50

**1956.** Red Cross. Inscr. "CONMEMORATIVAS CRUZ ROJA".

574. **198.** 1 c. red & brn. (post.) 20 20
575. – 3 c. red and green .. 20 20
576. – 4 c. red and black .. 25 20
577. – 5 c.+15 c. red & blue 60 90
578. – 15 c.+50 c. red & lilac 1·40 1·75
579. **198.** 25 c.+50 c. red and blue .. .. .. 1·40 1·75
580. – 35 c.+1 q. green and red (air) .. .. 3·50 3·75
581. – 50 c.+1 q. red & blue 3·50 3·75
582. – 1 q.+1 q. red & green 3·50 3·75

DESIGNS: 3 c. 15 c., Telephone and red cross. 4 c., 5 c. Nurse, patient and red cross. 35 c. Red Cross ambulance. 50 c. Nurse and hospital. 1 q. Red Cross nurse.

**199.** Road Map of Guatemala. **200.** Maya Warrior.

**1956.** Revolution of 1954-55. Inscr. "LIBERACION 1954-55".

583. – ½ c. violet (postage) .. 15 10
584. **199.** 1c. green .. .. 15 10
585. – 3 c. sepia .. .. 15 10
586. **200.** 2 c. multicoloured (air) 20 15
587. – 4 c. black and red .. 20 15
588. – 5 c. brown and blue .. 30 30
589. – 6 c. blue and sepia .. 20 20
590. – 20 c. brn., blue & violet 1·00 1·00
591. – 30 c. olive and blue .. 1·50 1·00
592. – 65 c. green and brown 1·50 1·75
593. – 1 q. multicoloured .. 2·25 2·40
594. – 5 q. brn., blue & green 9·00 9·50

DESIGNS: ½ c. Liberation dagger symbol. 3 c. Oil production. 4 c. Family. 5 c. Sword smashing Communist emblems. 6 c. Hands holding map and cogwheel. 20 c. Martyrs' Monument. 30 c. Champerico Port. 65 c. Telecommunications symbols. 1 q. Flags of ODECA countries. 5 q. Pres. Armas.

**201.** Rotary Emblem and Road Map. **203.** Esquipulas Cathedral and "Black Christ".

**1956.** Air. 50th Anniv. of Rotary International.

595. **201.** 4 c. bistre and blue .. 35 30
596. 6 c. bistre and green .. 35 30
597. 35 c. bistre and violet 1·00 1·40

**1957.** Air. Red Cross Fund. Nos. 577/9 optd. **AEREO-1957** and ornaments.

598. – 5 c.+15 c. red & blue 4·00 4·50
599. – 15 c.+50 c. red & lilac 4·00 4·50
600. **198.** 25 c.+50 c. red & blue 4·00 4·50

**1957.** Esquipulas Highway Fund. Inscr. "PRO-CARRETERA ESQUIPULAS JUNIO 1957".

601. **203.** 1½ c.+½ c. violet and brown (postage) .. 70 45
602. – 10 c.+1 q. brown and green (air) .. .. 4·00 4·50
603. – 15 c.+1 q. grn. & sepia 4·00 4·50
604. – 20 c.+1 q. slate & brn. 4·00 4·50
605. – 25 c.+1 q. red & lilac 4·00 4·50

DESIGNS—HORIZ. 10 c. Esquipulas Cathedral. VERT. 15 c. Cathedral and "Black Christ". 20 c. Map of Guatemala and "Black Christ". 25 c. Bishop of Esquipulas.

**204.** Red Cross, Map and Resplendent Quetzal. **207.** Caravel of 1532 and freighter "Quetzaltenango".

**1958.** Air. Red Cross.

606. **204.** 1 c. multicoloured .. 50 25
607. – 2 c. red, brown & blue 35 15
608. – 3 c. brown, red & blue 35 15
609. – 4 c. red, green & brown 35 15

DESIGNS—VERT. 2 c. J. R. Angulo; Mother and Child. HORIZ. 3 c. P. de Bethancourt and Invalid. 4 c. R. Ayau and Red Cross.

**1959.** Birth Centenary of R. A. Ovalle (composer of National Anthem). Optd **1858 1958 CENTENARIO.**

610 **191** ½ c. grey and violet .. 30 30

**1959.** Air. Pres. Castillo Armas Commem. As No. 594 but inscr. "LIBERACION 3 DE JULIO DE 1954", etc. Centre in blue and yellow. Frame colours given.

615. 1 c. black .. .. 15 15
616. 2 c. red .. .. 15 15
617. 4 c. brown .. .. 15 15
618. 6 c. green .. .. 20 15
619. 10 c. violet .. .. 35 25
620. 20 c. green .. .. 1·00 65
621. 35 c. grey .. .. 1·75 95

**1959.** Air United Nations. Optd. **HOMENAJE A LAS NACIONES UNIDAS.**

622. **168.** 7½ c. blue .. .. 1·10 1·10

**1959.** Air. Central American Merchant Marine Commemoration.

623. **207.** 6 c. blue and red .. 60 15

**1959.** Air. Guatemala's Claim to Belize (British Honduras). As No. 509 optd. **BELICE ES NUESTRO AEREO** ("Belize is Ours").

624. 5 c. brown and blue .. 35 20

**1959.** Air Cent. of First Export of Coffee. No. 589 optd. **1859 CENTENARIO PRIMERA EXPORTACION DE CAFE 1959.**

625. 6 c. blue and sepia .. 55 20

**210.** Pres. and Senora Morales.

**1959.** Air. Visit of President of Honduras.

626. **210.** 6 c. brown .. .. 20 15

**211.** Red Cross Shield. **213.** Abraham Lincoln.

**1960.** Red Cross Commem. Cross in red.

627. **211.** 1 c.+1 c. blue and brown (postage) .. 30 20
628. – 3 c.+3 c. blue and lilac 30 20
629. **211.** 4 c.+4 c. blue & black 30 25
630. – 5 c.+5 c. blue, pink and red (air) 1·40 1·50
631. – 6 c.+6 c. green and brown-red .. 1·40 1·50
632. – 10 c.+10 c. pink, blue and deep blue 1·40 1·50
633. – 15 c.+15 c. red, blue and brown .. 1·40 1·50
634. – 20 c.+20 c. green, pink and purple .. 1·40 1·50
635. – 25 c.+25 c. pink, blue and grey .. 1·40 1·50
636. – 30 c.+30 c. mult. .. 1·40 1·50

**DESIGNS—3 c., 5 c. Wounded soldier at Solferino. 6 c., 20 c. Houses and debris afloat on flood waters. 10 c., 25 c. Earth, Moon and planets. 15 c., 30 c. Red Cross H.Q., Guatemala City.**

**1960.** Air. World Refugee Year. Nos. 606/9 optd. **ANO MUNDIAL DE REFUGIADOS** or **Ano Mundial de Refugiados** or surch. also.
637. 1 c. multicoloured .. 1·75 1·00
638. 2 c. red, brown and blue .. 90 70
639. 3 c. brown, red and blue .. 90 70
640. 4 c. red, green and brown 90 70
641. 6 c on 1 c. multicoloured 3·50 2·10
642. 7 c. on 2 c. red, brn. & blue 1·50 1·25
643. 10 c.. on 3 c. brn., red & bl. 2·50 2·75
644. 20 c. on 4 c. red, grn. & brn. 2·75 2·75

**1960.** Air. Founding of City of Melchor de Mencos. No. 589 optd. **Fundacion de la cuidad Melchor de Mencos 30-IV-1960.**
645. 6 c. blue and sepia .. 1·10 1·10

**1980.** Air. 150th Birth Anniv. of Abraham Lincoln.
646. **213.** 5 c. blue .. .. 30 20
647. 30 c. violet .. .. 70 1·00
648. 50 c. slate .. .. 3·50 4·00

**214.** U.N.E.S.C.O. Headquarters, Paris.

**1960.** Air. Inaug. of U.N.E.S.C.O. Headquarters Building, Paris (1958).
649. **214.** 5 c. violet and mauve 15 15
650. 6 c. sepia and blue .. 20 15
651. 8 c. red and green .. 35 20
652. 20 c. blue and brown .. 85 90

**1961.** Air. Red Cross. Nos. 606/9 optd. **MAYO DE 1960.**
653. 1 c. multicoloured .. 75 40
654. 2 c. red, brown and blue .. 45 40
655. 3 c. brown, red and blue .. 45 40
656. 4 c. red, green and brown .. 45 40

**216.** Romulus, Remus and Wolf. **217.** Independence Ceremony.

**1961.** Plaza Italia Inauguration.
657. **216.** 3 c. blue .. .. 15 15

**1962.** Air. 140th Anniv. of Independence.
658. **217.** 4 c. sepia .. .. 15 15
659. 5 c. blue .. .. 20 15
660. 15 c. violet .. .. 70 35

**1962.** Air. Malaria Eradication. Optd. **1962. EL MUNDO UNIDO CONTRA LA MALARIA.**
666. **214.** 6 c. sepia and blue .. 55 85

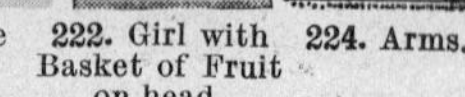
**219.** Dr. Jose Luna. **222.** Girl with Basket of Fruit on head. **224.** Arms.

**1962.** Air. Guatemalan Doctors.
667. **219.** 1 c. violet and olive .. 35 15
668. – 4 c. green and yellow .. 35 15
669. – 5 c. brown and blue .. 35 15
670. – 6 c. black and salmon 35 15
671. – 10 c. brown and green 55 20
672. – 20 c. blue and mauve .. 70 45
DOCTORS: 4 c. R. Robles. 5 c. N. Esparragoza. 6 c. J. Ortega. 10 c. D. Gonzalez. 20 c. J. Flores.

**1962.** Air. Pres. Ydigoras's Tour of Central America. No. 589 optd. **PRESIDENTE YDIGORAS FUENTES RE-CORRE POR TIERRA CENTRO AMERICA 14 A 20 DIC. 1962.**
673. 6 c. blue and sepia .. 60 55

**1963.** Air New ODECA Charter Commem. Optd. **CONMEMORACION FIRMA NUEVA CARTA ODECA.—1962.**
674. **214.** 6 c. sepia and blue .. 30 15
675. 8 c. red and green .. 35 15

**1963.** Air. National Fair, 1960.
676. **222.** 1 c. multicoloured .. 15 10

**1963.** Air. Presidents' Reunion No. 589 with H-line opt. starting "**REUNION PRESIDENTES: KENNEDY ...**"
677. 6 c. blue and sepia .. 2·40 1·60

**1963.**
684. **224.** 10 c. red .. .. 35 15
685. 10 c. black .. .. 30 15
686. 10 c. brown .. .. 30 15
687. 20 c. violet .. .. 55 20
688. 20 c. blue .. .. 55 20

**225.** Harvester. (after " The Reaper ", Mathieson). **226.** Ceiba (national tree).

**1963.** Air. Freedom from Hunger.
689. **225.** 5 c. turquoise .. .. 20 15
690. 10 c. blue .. .. 35 20

**1963.** Air.
691. **226.** 4 c. green and sepia .. 15 15

**227.** Pedro Bethancourt. tending sick man. **228.** Patzun Palace.

**1964.** Campaign for Canonization of Pedro Bethancourt.
692. **227.** $2\frac{1}{2}$ c. brown (postage) 15 10
693. $2\frac{1}{2}$ c. blue (air) .. 10 10
694. 3 c. orange .. .. 10 10
695. 4 c. violet .. .. 15 10
696. 5 c. green .. .. 20 10

**1964.** Air. Guatemalan Palaces.
697. **228.** 1 c. brown and red .. 15 10
698. – 3 c. green and mauve .. 20 10
699. – 4 c. lake and blue .. 20 15
700. – 5 c. blue and brown .. 25 15
701. – 6 c. blue and green .. 25 15
PALACES: 3 c. Coban. 4 c. Retalhuleu. 5 c. San Marcos. 6 c. Los Capitanes Generales.

**229.** Municipal Building. **234.** Pres. Kennedy.

**1964.** Air. New Buildings. (a) As T **229.**
702. **229.** 3 c. brown and blue .. 15 15
703. – 4 c. blue and brown .. 20 15
DESIGN: 4 c. Social Security Building.

(b) Designs as Nos. 702/3 but different style frame and inscr., and new designs.
704. – 3 c. green (As No. 703) 20 10
705. – 4 c. slate .. .. 20 10
706. **229.** 7 c. blue .. .. 25 15
707. – 7 c. bistre .. .. 25 15
DESIGNS: 4 c. University Rectory. 7 c. (No. 707), Engineering Faculty.

**1964.** Air. Olympic Games, Tokyo. Optd. with Olympic rings and **OLIMPIADAS TOKIO-1964.**
708. **204.** 1 c. .. .. .. 1·25 1·00
709. – 2 c. (No. 607) .. 75 75
710. – 3 c. (No. 608) .. 75 75
711. – 4 c. (No. 609) .. 75 75

**1964.** Air. New York World's Fair. Optd. **FERIA MUNDIAL DE NEW YORK.**
712. **204.** 1 c. .. .. .. 1·25 90
713. – 2 c. (No. 607) .. 50 50
714. – 3 c. (No. 608) .. 50 50
715. – 4 c. (No. 609) .. 50 50

**1964.** Air. Surch. **HABILITADA-1964** and value.
716. **204.** 7 c. on 1 c. .. .. 40 25
717. – 9 c. on 2 c. (No. 607) 40 35
718. – 13 c. on 3 c. (No. 608) 45 45
719. – 21 c. on 4 c. (No. 609) 75 75

**1964.** Air. 8th Cycle Race. Optd. **VIII VUELTA CICLISTICA.**
720. **204.** 1 c. .. .. .. 2·50 1·40
721. – 2 c. (No. 607) .. 70 70
722. – 3 c. (No. 608) .. 70 70
723. – 4 c. (No. 609) .. 70 1·00

**1964.** Air. Pres. Kennedy Commem.
724. **234.** 1 c. violet .. .. 70 55
725. 2 c. green .. .. 70 55
726. 3 c. brown .. .. 70 55
727. 7 c. blue .. .. 70 55
728. 50 c. green .. .. 4·00 4·25

**235.** Centenary Emblem. **237.** Bishop F. Marroquin.

**1964.** Air. Red Cross Cent. Emblem in silver and red.
730. **235.** 7 c. blue .. .. 55 35
731. 9 c. orange .. .. 55 35
732. 13 c. violet .. .. 85 35
733. 21 c. green .. .. 50 70
734. 35 c. brown .. .. 1·00 1·00
735. 1 q. bistre .. .. 1·60 2·00

**1964.** 15th Anniv. (1963) of International Society of Guatemala Collectors. No. 559 optd. **HOMENAJE A LA "I.S.G.C." 1948–1963.**
736. 4 c. orange .. .. 50 25

**1985.** Air. 400th Death Anniv. of Bishop Maroquin.
737. **237.** 4 c. brown and purple 15 10
738. 7 c. sepia and grey .. 25 15
739. 9 c. black and blue .. 30 15

**1965.** Air. Optd. **AYUDENOS MAYO 1965.** Emblem in silver and red.
740. **235.** 7 c. blue .. .. 35 30
741. 9 c. orange .. .. 45 35
742. 13 c. violet .. .. 55 45
743. 21 c. green .. .. 70 60
744. 35 c. brown .. .. 70 95

**239.** Scout Badge. **240.** Flags.

**1966.** Air. 5th Regional Scout Training Conference, Guatemala City. Multicoloured.
745. 5 c. Type **239** .. .. 35 15
746. 9 c. Scouts by campfire .. 45 25
747. 10 c. Scout carrying torch and flag .. .. .. 55 35
748. 15 c. Scout saluting .. 70 55
749. 20 c. Lord Baden-Powell .. 90 90

**1966.** Air. "Centro America". 145th Anniv. of Central American Independence.
750. **240.** 6 c. multicoloured .. 25 15

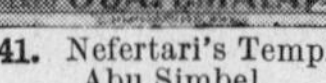

**241.** Nefertari's Temple, Abu Simbel. **242.** Arms.

**1966.** Air. Nubian Monuments Preservation.
751. **241.** 21 c. violet and bistre 55 35

**1966.** Air.
752. **242.** 5 c. orange .. .. 20 10
753. 5 c. green .. .. 20 10
754. 5 c. grey .. .. 20 10
755. 5 c. violet .. .. 20 10
756. 5 c. blue .. .. 20 10
757. 5 c. deep blue .. .. 20 10
758. 5 c. violet .. .. 20 10
759. 5 c. green .. .. 15 10
760. 5 c. lake .. .. 15 10
761. 5 c. green on yellow .. 15 10

**243.** Mgr. M. Rossell y Arellano. **244.** Mario M. Montenegro (revolutionary).

**1966.** Air. Monseigneur Rossell Commem.
765. **243.** 1 c. violet .. .. 20 15
766. 2 c. green .. .. 25 10
767. 3 c. sepia .. .. 25 15
768. 7 c. blue .. .. 35 25
769. 50 c. slate .. .. 95 1·10

**1966.** Air. Montenegro. Commem.
770. **244.** 2 c. red .. .. 15 10
771. 3 c. orange .. .. 20 15
772. 4 c. red .. .. 25 15
773. 5 c. grey .. .. 35 15
774. 5 c. blue .. .. 35 15
775. 5 c. green .. .. 35 15
776. 5 c. black .. .. 35 15

**245.** Morning Glory. **246.** Institute Emblem.

**1967.** Air. Flowers. Multicoloured.
777. 4 c. Type **245** .. .. 25 15
778. 8 c. "Bird of Paradise" .. 25 15
779. 10 c. "White Nun" orchid (national flower) .. 35 25
780. 20 c. " Nymphs of Amatitlan " .. .. 60 35
Nos. 778/9 are horiz.

**1967.** Air. 8th General Assembly of Pan-American Geographical and Historical Institute (1965).
781. **246.** 4 c. purple, black & brn. 20 15
782. 5 c. blue, black & bistre 35 15
783. 7 c. blue, black & yellow 55 15

**247.** Map of Guatemala and British Honduras.

**1967.** Guatemala's Claim to British Honduras.
784. **247.** 4 c. blue, red and green 15 10
785. 5 c. blue, red & yellow 20 10
786. 6 c. blue, grey & orge. 20 15

**1967.** Air. Guatemalan Victory in "Norceca" Football Games. No. 704 optd. **GUATEMALA CAMPEON III Norceca Foot-Ball** and football motif.
787. 3 c. green .. .. 35 30

**1967.** Air. American Heads of State Meeting, Punta del Este. No. 705 optd. **REUNION JEFES DE ESTADO AMERICANO, PUNTA DEL ESTE,** etc.
788. 4 c. slate .. .. 70 55

**250.** "Peace and Progress". **251.** Yurrita Church.

**1967.** Air. Int. Co-operation.
789. **250.** 7 c. multicoloured .. 35 15
790. 21 c. multicoloured .. 55 35

**1967.** Air. Religion in Guatemala.
791. **251.** 1 c. brown, grn. & blue 20 10
792. – 2 c. brn., pur. & salmon 25 10
793. – 3 c. indigo, red & blue 25 10
794. – 4 c. grn., pur. & salmon 25 10
795. – 5 c. brn., pur. and grn. 25 10
796. – 7 c. black, blue & mauve 35 15
797. – 10 c. blue, violet & yell. 55 20
DESIGNS—HORIZ. 2 c. Santo Domingo Church. 3 c. San Francisco Church. 7 c. Mercy Church. Antigua. 10 c. Metropolitan Cathedral. VERT. 4 c. Antonio Jose de Irisarri. 5 c. Church of the Recollection.

**252.** Lincoln.

**1967.** Air. Death Centenary (1965) of Abraham Lincoln.
798. **252.** 7 c. red and blue .. 35 20
799. 9 c. black and green .. 45 25
800. 11 c. black and brown 45 25
801. 15 c. red and blue .. 45 35
802. 30 c. green and purple 1·00 1·10

**1967.** Air. 8th Central American Scout Camporee. Nos. 745/9 optd. **VIII Camporee Scout Centroamericano Diciembre 1-8/1967.**
803. 5 c. Type **239** .. .. 35 35
804. 9 c. Scouts by campfire .. 55 55
805. 10 c. Scout carrying torch and flag .. .. .. 70 70
806. 15 c. Scout saluting .. 70 70
807. 20 c. Lord Baden Powell .. 90 90

**1967.** Air. Award of Nobel Prize for Literature to Miguel Angel Asturias (1st issue). Nos. 694/5 optd. **" Premio Nobel de Literatura – 10 diciembre 1967 – Miguel Angel Asturias ".**
808. **227.** 3 c. orange .. .. 35 30
809. – 4 c. violet .. .. 35 30
See also No. 838.

**255.** U.N.E.S.C.O. Emblem and Children.
**256.** Institute Emblem.

**1967.** Air. 20th Anniv. (1966) of U.N.E.S.C.O.
810. **255.** 4 c. green .. .. 15 10
811. 5 c. blue .. .. 20 15
812. 7 c. grey .. .. 25 15
813. 21 c. purple .. .. 60 60

**1967.** Air. 25th Anniv. of Inter-American Institute of Agricultural Sciences.
814. **256.** 9 c. black and green .. 45 45
815. 25 c. red and brown .. 95 95
816. 1 q. ultramarine & blue 2·40 2·40

**1968.** Air. 3rd Meeting of Central American Presidents. Optd. **III REUNION DE PRESIDENTES Nov. 15-18, 1967.**
817. **204.** 1 c. (No. 606) .. .. 1·25 90
819. – 2 c. (No. 607) .. .. 70 70
821. – 3 c. (No. 608) .. .. 70 70
823. **235.** 7 c. (No. 730) .. .. 70 70
824. 9 c. (No. 731) .. .. 70 90
825. 13 c. (No. 732) .. 95 90
826. 21 c. (No. 733) .. 1·40 70
827. 35 c. (No. 734) .. 1·10 1·10

**258.** " Madonna of the Choir ".
**260.** Miguel Angel Asturias.

**1968.** Air. 400th Anniv. of "Madonna of the Choir".
828a. **258.** 4 c. blue .. .. 10 10
829. 7 c. slate .. .. 35 15
830. 9 c. green .. .. 55 15
830a. 9 c. lilac .. .. 25 10
831. 10 c. red .. .. 70 15
832. 10 c. grey .. .. 45 15
832a. 10 c. blue .. .. 25 10
833. 1 q. purple .. .. 2·40 2·00
834. 1 q. yellow .. .. 2·40 2·00

**1968.** Air. 11th Cycle Race. Nos. 784/6 optd. **AEREO XI VUELTA CICLISTICA 1967.**
835. **247.** 4 c. blue, red and green 55 55
836. 5 c. blue, red & yellow 55 55
837. 6 c. blue, grey & orge. 45 45

**1968.** Air. Award of Nobel Prize for Literature to Miguel Angel Asturias.
838. **260.** 20 c. blue .. .. 70 35

**1968.** Air. Campaign for Conservation of the Forests. No. 789 optd **AYUDA A CONSERVAR LOS BOSQUES.—2968.**
839. **250.** 7 c. multicoloured .. 35 15

**1968.** Air. Human Rights Year. No. 626 optd. **1968.—ANO INTERNACIONAL DERECHOS HUMANOS.—ONU.**
840. **210.** 6 c. brown .. .. 55 30

**1968.** Air. Nahakin Scientific Expedition. No. 589 optd. **Expedicion Cientifica etc.**
841. 6 c. blue and sepia .. 30 20

**264.** " Visit Guatemala".
**265.** Mayan Ball Game Ring and Resplendent Quetzal.

**1968.** Air. Tourism.
842. **264.** 10 c. red and green .. 30 15
843. 20 c. red and black .. 55 35
844. 50 c. blue and red .. 85 85

**1968.** Olympic Games, Mexico. Quetzal in green and red.
845. **265.** 1 c. black .. .. 50 10
850. 1 c. slate .. .. 50 10
846. 5 c. yellow .. .. 65 15
851. 5 c. pink .. .. 40 15
852. 5 c. brown .. .. 40 15
853. 5 c. blue .. .. 40 15
847. 8 c. orange .. .. 80 20
848. 15 c. blue .. .. 1·40 30
849. 30 c. violet .. .. 2·40 85

**1968.** Air. 20th Anniv. of Federation of Central American Universities. No. 705 optd. **CONFEDERACION DE UNIVERSIDADES CENTRO AMERICANAS 1948 1968.**
854. 4 c. slate .. .. .. 30 15

**267.** Presidents Gustavo Diaz Ordaz and Julio Cesar Mendez Montenegro.

**1968.** Air. Exchange Visits of Mexican and Guatemalan Presidents.
855. **267.** 5 c. multicoloured .. 15 15
856. 10 c. blue and ochre .. 35 20
857. 25 c. blue and ochre .. 55 50

**268.** I.T.U. Emblem and Symbols.
**269.** Young Girl and Poinsettia.

**1968.** Air. Centenary (1965) of I.T.U.
858. **268.** 7 c. blue .. .. 20 15
859. 15 c. black and green .. 35 15
859a. 15 c. brown and orange 55 15
860. 21 c. purple .. .. 55 35
861. 35 c. red and green .. 70 35
862. 75 c. green and red .. 1·40 1·40
863. 3 q. brown and red .. 4·50 4·50

**1969.** Help for Abandoned Children.
864. **269.** $2\frac{1}{2}$ c. ochre, red & green 20 10
865. $2\frac{1}{2}$ c. orge., red & green 20 10
866. 5 c. black, red and grn. 30 10
867. 21 c. violet, red & green 65 55

**1969.** Air. Nos. 845/9 optd. **AEREO** and motif. Quetzal in green and red.
868. **265.** 1 c. black .. .. 75 25
869. 5 c. yellow .. .. 95 35
870. 8 c. orange .. .. 80 60
871. 15 c. blue .. .. 95 70
872. 30 c. violet .. .. 1·25 70

**271.** Dante.
**273.** "Apollo 11" and Moon Landing.

**272.** Map of Central and South America.

**1969.** Air. 700th Birth Anniv. (1965) of Dante.
873. **271.** 7 c. blue and plum .. 20 10
874. 10 c. blue .. .. 25 10
875. 20 c. green .. .. 35 15
876. 21 c. slate and brown 70 25
877. 35 c. violet and green 1·00 55

**1969.** Air. 20th Anniv. of Latin-American Universities Union.
878. **272.** 2 c. mauve and black .. 15 10
879. – 9 c. black and grey .. 25 15
DESIGN: (26×27 mm.) 9 c. University seal.

**1969.** Air. 1st Man on the Moon.
881. **273.** 50 c. black and purple 1·40 1·40
882. 1 q. black and blue .. 2·40 2·50

**1970.** 50th Anniv. of Int. Labour Organization. Nos. 847/8 optd. **Cincuentenario O.I.T.** in two lines.
884. **265.** 8 c. orge., grn. & red .. 50 15
886. 15 c. blue, green & red 75 20

**275.** Lake Atitlan.
**276.** Dr. V. M. Calderon.

**1970.** Air. Conservation of Atitlan Grebes. Multicoloured.
888. 4 c. Type **275** .. .. 15 15
889. 9 c. Family of Atitlan Grebes 2·50 50
890. 20 c. Young grebe in nest (vert.) .. .. .. 4·50 1·25

**1970.** Air. 1st Death Anniv of Dr. Victor M. Calderon (medical scientist).
892. **276.** 1 c. black and blue .. 15 10
893. 2 c. black and green .. 15 10
894. 9 c. black and yellow .. 30 15

**277.** Hand holding Bible.
**280.** Maya Indians and C.A.R.E. Package.

**279.** Arms and Newspaper.

**1970.** Air. 400th Anniv. of Spanish Bible.
895. **277.** 5 c. multicoloured .. 15 10

**1971.** Air. Surch **VALE QO. 50.**
896. **268.** 50 c. on 3 q. brn. & red 1·25 1·25

**1971.** Air. Stamp Centenary (1st issue) and Centenary of Newspaper "Gaceta de Guatemala".
897. **279.** 2 c. blue and red .. 10 10
899b. 5 c. brown and red .. 10 10
899. 25 c. blue and red .. 55 35
899c. 50 c. mauve and brown 90 35
See also Nos. 988/9d.

**1971.** 25th Anniv. of C.A.R.E. (Co-operative for American Relief Everywhere). Mult.
900. 1 c. Type **280** (black inscr.) (postage) .. .. 15 10
901. 1 c. Type **280** (brown inscr.) .. .. .. 15 10
902. 1 c. Type **280** (violet inscr.) 15 10
903. 2 c. Maya porter and C.A.R.E. parcel (air) .. 15 15
904. 5 c. Two Maya warriors & parcel .. .. .. 20 20
905. 10 c. C.A.R.E. parcel within Maya border .. 35 20
SIZES: 2 c. (36×30mm.). 50 c. (46×27mm.). 10 c. (28×31mm.).

**282.** J. Rufino Barrios, M. Garcia Granados and Emblems.

**1971.** Air. Cent. of Liberal Reforms.
909. **282.** 2 c. multicoloured .. 65 15
910. 10 c. multicoloured .. 1·25 30
911. 50 c. multicoloured .. 4·75 2·75
912. 1 q. multicoloured .. 9·25 5·75

**283.** J. A. Chavarry Arrue (stamp engraver) and Leon Bilak (philatelist).

**1971.** Air. " Homage to Philately ".
913. **283.** 1 c. black and green .. 10 10
914. 2 c. black and brown 15 10
915. 5 c. black and orange 15 15

**1971.** Air. "INTERFER 71" Int. Fair, Guatemala. Optd. **FERIA INTERNACIONAL "INTERFER-71" 30 Oct. al 21 Nov.**
916. **207.** 6 c. blue and red .. 20 15

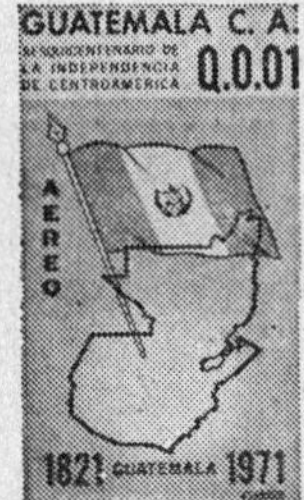

**285.** Flag and Map.
**286.** Maya Statue and U.N.I.C.E.F. Emblem.

**1971.** Air. 150th Anniv. of Central American Independence.
917. **285.** 1 c. blue, black & lilac 10 10
918. 3 c. bl., brown & pink 10 10
919. 5 c. bl., brown & orange 15 10
920. 9 c. bl., black & green 25 15

**1971.** Air. 25th Anniv. of U.N.I.C.E.F.
921. **286.** 1 c. green .. .. 10 10
921a. 2 c. purple .. .. 15 10
922. 50 c. purple .. .. 1·10 1·10
923. 1 q. blue .. .. 2·00 2·00

**287.** Boeing "Peashooter" and North American P-51 Mustang.

**1972.** Air. 50th Anniv. of Guatemala Air Force.
924. **287.** 5 c. blue and brown .. 20 10
925. – 10 c. blue .. .. 50 20
DESIGN—56×32 mm: 10 c. Bleriot XI airplane.

**289.** Ruins of Capuchin Monastery.

**1972.** Air. Tourism. Ruins of Antigua.
927. **289.** 1 c. blue and light blue 20 10
928. A. 1 c. blue and light blue 20 10
929. B. 1 c. blue and light blue 20 10
930. C. 1 c. blue and light blue 20 10
931. D. 1 c. blue and light blue 20 10
932. E. 1 c. blue and light blue 20 10
933. **289.** 2 c. black and brown .. 15 10
934. A. 2 c. black and brown .. 15 10
935. B. 2 c. black and brown .. 15 10
936. C. 2 c. black and brown .. 15 10
937. D. 2 c. black and brown .. 15 10
938. E. 2 c. black and brown .. 15 10
939. **289.** $2\frac{1}{2}$ c. blk., mve. & silver 35 10
940. A. $2\frac{1}{2}$ c. blk., mve. & silver 35 10
941. B. $2\frac{1}{2}$ c. blk., mve. & silver 35 10
942. C. $2\frac{1}{2}$ c. blk., mve. & silver 35 10
943. D. $2\frac{1}{2}$ c. blk., mve. & silver 35 10
944. E. $2\frac{1}{2}$ c. blk., mve. & silver 35 10
945. **289.** 5 c. blk., blue & orange 70 15
946. A. 5 c. blk., blue & orange 70 15
947. B. 5 c. blk., blue & orange 70 15
948. C. 5 c. blk., blue & orange 70 15
949. D. 5 c. blk., blue & orange 70 15
950. E. 5 c. blk., blue & orange 70 15

951. **289.** 20 c. black and yellow 55 35
952. **A.** 20 c. black and yellow 55 35
953. **B.** 20 c. black and yellow 55 35
954. **C.** 20 c. black and yellow 55 35
955. **D.** 20 c. black and yellow 55 35
956. **E.** 20 c. black and yellow 55 35
957. **289.** 1 q. light bl., red & blue 2·40 1·75
958. **A.** 1 q. light bl., red & blue 2·40 1·75
959. **B.** 1 q. light bl., red & blue 2·40 1·75
960. **C.** 1 q. light bl., red & blue 2·40 1·75
961. **D.** 1 q. light bl., red & blue 2·40 1·75
962. **E.** 1 q. light bl., red & blue 2·40 1·75

DESIGNS: A, "La Recoleccion" archways. B, Cathedral ruins. C, Santa Clara courtyard, D, San Francisco gateway. E, Fountain, Central Park.

See also Nos. 1230/41.

**290.** Pres. Carlos Arana Osorio.

**1973.** National Census.
963 **290** 2 c. black and blue .. 10 10
964 – 3 c. brown, pink & orge 15 10
965 **290** 5 c. purple, mve & blk 20 10
966 – 8 c. green, blk & emer 35 10

DESIGNS—VERT. 3 c. Pres. Osorio seated. 8 c. Pres. Osorio standing.

**291.** Francisco Ximenez.

**1973.** International Book Year (1972).
967. **291.** 2 c. black and green .. 10 10
968. 3 c. brown and orange 10 10
969a. 3 c. black and yellow 10 10
969. 6 c. black and blue .. 20 10

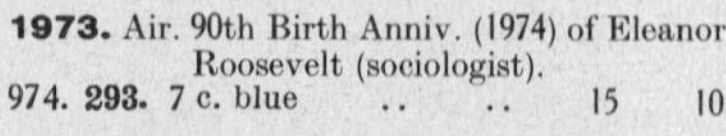
**292.** Simon Bolivar and Map.
**293.** Eleanor Roosevelt.

**1973.** Air. Simon Bolivar "The Liberator".
970. **292.** 3 c. black and red .. 10 10
971. 3 c. blue and orange .. 10 10
972. 5 c. black and yellow .. 15 10
973. 5 c. black and green .. 15 10

**1973.** Air. 90th Birth Anniv. (1974) of Eleanor Roosevelt (sociologist).
974. **293.** 7 c. blue .. .. 15 10

**294.** Star Emblem.

**1973.** Air. Cent. of Polytechnic School.
975. **294.** 5 c. yell., brn. & blue 10 10
See also Nos. 1000/1.

**1973.** Air. Nos. 927/32 optd. **"II Feria Internacional" INTERFER/73 31 Octubre-Noviembre 18 1973 GUATEMALA.**
976. **289.** 1 c. blue and light blue 20 10
977. **A.** 1 c. blue and light blue 20 10
978. **B.** 1 c. blue and light blue 20 10
979. **C.** 1 c. blue and light blue 20 10
980. **D.** 1 c. blue and light blue 20 10
981. **E.** 1 c. blue and light blue 20 10

**296.** 1 c. Stamp of 1871.

**1973.** Air. Stamp Centenary (1971). (2nd issue).
988. **296.** 1 c. brown .. .. 15 10
988a. 6 c. orange .. .. 15 10
988b. 6 c. green .. .. 15 10
988c. 6 c. blue .. .. 15 10
988d. 6 c. grey .. .. 15 10
989. 1 q. red .. .. 1·75 1·75

**297.** School Building.

**1973.** Air. Centenary of Instituto Varones, Chiquimula.
990. **297.** 3 c. multicoloured .. 10 10
991. 5 c. red and black .. 15 10

**1974.** No. 863 surch. **Desvalorizadas, a** value and leaves.
992. **268.** 50 c. on 3 q. brn. & red 85 70

**1974.** Air. Centenary of Universal Postal Union Nos. 927/32 opt. **UPU. HOMENAJE CENTENARIO 1874 1974** and U.P.U. emblem.
993. **289.** 1 c. blue and light blue 25 20
994. **A.** 1 c. blue and light blue 25 20
995. **B.** 1 c. blue and light blue 25 20
996. **C.** 1 c. blue and light blue 25 20
997. **D.** 1 c. blue and light blue 25 20
998. **E.** 1 c. blue and light blue 25 20

**300.** Barrios and Granados.
**302.** Costume of San Martin Sacatepequez.

**1974.** Air. Centenary (1973) of Polytechnic School (2nd issue).
1000. **300.** 6 c. red, grey and blue 15 10
1001. – 25 c. multicoloured .. 45 20
DESIGN—VERT. 25 c. School building.

**1974.** Air. "Protection of the Resplendent Quetzal" (Guatemala's national bird). No. 800 surch. **VALE 10 c. Proteccion del Ave Nacional el Quetzal** and bird.
1002. **252.** 10 c. on 11 c. black and brown .. .. 75 25

**1974.** Air. Guatemalan Costumes. Mult.
1003. 2 c. Solola costume .. 10 10
1004. $2\frac{1}{2}$ c. Type **302** .. .. 10 10
1005. 9 c. Coban costume .. 20 10
1006. 20 c. Chichicastenango costume .. .. 35 15

**303.** Mayan Girl and Resplendent Quetzals.

**1975.** Air. International Women's Year.
1007. **303.** 8 c. multicoloured .. 25 10
1008. 20 c. multicoloured .. 65 25

**304.** Rotary Emblem.

**1975.** Air. 50th Anniv. of Guatemala City Rotary Club.
1009. **304.** 10 c. multicoloured .. 15 10
1010. 15 c. multicoloured .. 30 15

**305.** IWY Emblem and Orchid.

**1975.** Air. International Women's Year (2nd series).
1011. **305.** 1 c. multicoloured .. 10 10
1012. 8 c. multicoloured .. 15 10
1013. 26 c. multicoloured .. 45 20

**306.** Ruined Village.

**1976.** Air. Earthquake of 4 February 1976. Multicoloured.
1014. 1 c. Type **306.** .. .. 10 10
1015. 3 c. Food queue .. .. 10 10
1016. 5 c. Jaguar Temple, Tikal 15 10
1017. 10 c. Broken bridge .. 20 10
1018. 15 c. Open-air casualty station .. .. .. 35 15
1019. 20 c. Harvesting sugar-cane .. .. .. 35 15
1020. 25 c. Ruined house .. 55 20
1021. 30 c. Reconstruction, Tecpan .. .. 70 20
1022. 50 c. Ruined church, Cerrodel Carmen .. 90 35
1023. 75 c. Clearing debris .. 1·40 55
1024. 1 q. Military aid .. 1·75 70
1025. 2 q. Lake Atitlan .. 3·50 1·40

Text in panels expresses gratitude for foreign aid.

**307.** Eagle and Resplendent Quetzal Emblems.

**1976.** Air. Bicentenary of American Revolution. Multicoloured.
1029. 1 c. Type **307** .. .. 25 10
1030. 2 c. Boston Tea Party .. 10 10
1031. 3 c. Thomas Jefferson (after G. Stuart) (vert.) 10 10
1032. 4 c. Eagle & Resplendent Quetzal emblems (vert.) .. .. .. 25 10
1033. 5 c. "Death of Gen. Warren at Bunker Hill". (detail, Trumbull) 10 10
1034. 10 c. "Washington reviewing his Ragged Army" (detail, Trego) 20 10
1035. 15 c. "Washington rallying the Troops at Monmouth" (detail, Leutze) 20 15
1036. 20 c. Eagle & Resplendent Quetzal emblems (diff.) .. .. .. 40 20
1037. 25 c. "Meeting of Generals at Yorktown after the Surrender" (detail, Peale) .. .. 55 20
1038. 30 c. "Washington crossing the Delaware" (detail, Leutze) .. .. 70 20
1039. 35 c. Eagle & Resplendent Quetzal emblems (diff.) .. .. .. 75 30
1040. 40 c. "Declaration of Independence" (detail, Trimbull) .. .. 60 30
1041. 45 c. "Patrick Henry before Virginia House of Burgesses" (detail, Rothermel) (vert.) .. 90 35
1042. 50 c. "Congress voting Independence" (detail, Savage) .. .. 1·00 35
1043. 1 q. George Washington (after G. Stuart). (vert.) .. .. .. 1·75 1·50
1044. 2 q. Abraham Lincoln (after D. D. Eisenhower). (vert.) .. 2·75 2·75
1045. 3 q. Benjamin Franklin (after C. W. Peale). (vert.) .. .. 4·00 4·00
1046. 5 q. John F. Kennedy (35 × 55mm.) .. .. 7·00 2·50

**308.** Quetzal Coin.

**1976.** Air. 50th Anniv. of Quetzal Currency.
1051. **308.** 8 c. blk., orge. & blue 20 10
1052. 20 c. blk., mve. & blue 45 20

**309.** " The Engineers " (sculpture).

**1976.** Air. Centenary of Engineering School, Guatemala City.
1053. **309.** 9 c. blue .. .. 20 10
1054. 10 c. green .. .. 20 10

**310.** Sculpture of Christ (Pedro de Mendoza).

**1977.** Holy Week. Multicoloured.
1055. 6 c. Type **310** (postage) .. 10 10
1056. 8 c. Sculpture of Christ (Lanuza Brothers) .. 15 10
1057. 3 c. Statue of Christ (air) 10 10
1058. 4 c. Statue of Christ (vert.) 10 10
1059. 7 c. Statue of Christ (vert.) 20 10
1060. 9 c. Statue of Christ (vert.) 25 10
1061. 20 c. Statue of Christ and Virgin (vert.) .. 55 15
1062. 26 c. Statue of Christ .. 70 55

**311.** Deed to Site of Guatemala City.
**312.** Arms of Quetzaltenango.

**1977.** Air. Bicentenary of Nueva Guatemala de la Asuncion (Guatemala City). Mult.
1064 6 c. Type **311** .. .. 10 10
1065 7 c. City Hall and Bank of Guatemala (horiz) .. 10 10
1066 8 c. Site of first legislative assembly (horiz) .. 10 10
1067 9 c. Archbishop's arms (horiz) .. .. 10 10
1068 22 c. Arms of Guatemala City .. .. .. 30 15

**1977.** Air. 150th Anniv. of Founding of Quetzaltenango.
1071. **312.** 7 c. black and silver .. 15 10
1072. – 30 c. orange and blue 55 20
DESIGN: 30 c. City Hall and torch.

**313.** " Interfer 77 " Emblem.
**315.** " The Holy Family ".

**314.** Mayan Bas-relief.

**1977.** 4th International Fair, Guatemala City.
1073. **313.** 7 c. multicoloured .. 10 10

**1977.** Air. 14th Congress of Latin Notaries.
1074. **314.** 10 c. black and red .. 20 10

**1977.** Air. Christmas. Multicoloured.
1075. 1 c. Type **315** .. .. 10 10
1076. 2 c. Boy and girl with animals, and Jesus in crib .. .. .. 10 10
1077. 4 c. Boy and girl with Mary and Jesus .. 15 10

**316.** Man from Almolongo. **317.** Virgin of Sorrows, Antigua.

**1978.** Air. Guatemalan Costumes. Mult.
1078. 1 c. Type **316** .. .. 10 10
1079. 2 c. Woman from Nebaj 10 10
1080. 5 c. Couple from San Juan Cotzal .. .. 15 10
1081. 6 c. Couple from Todos Santos .. .. .. 20 10
1082. 20 c. Couple from Regidores .. .. 70 15
1083. 30 c. Woman from San Cristobal .. .. 70 20

**1978.** Air. Holy Week. Multicoloured.
1085. 2 c. Type **317** .. .. 10 10
1086. 4 c. Virgin of Mercy, Antigua .. .. 15 10
1087. 5 c. Virgin of Anguish, Yurrita .. .. 15 10
1088. 6 c. Virgin of the Rosary, Santo Domingo .. 15 10
1089. 8 c. Virgin of Sorrows, Santo Domingo .. 20 10
1090. 9 c. Virgin of the Rosary, Quetzaltenango .. 20 15
1091. 10 c. Virgin of the Immaculate Conception, Church of St. Francis 25 15
1092. 20 c. Virgin of the Immaculate Conception, Cathedral Church .. 55 20

**318.** Footballer. **319.** Gymnastics.

**1978.** Air. World Cup Football Championship, Argentina.
1094. **318.** 10 c. multicoloured .. 20 15

**1978.** Air. 13th Central American and Caribbean Games, Medellin, Colombia.
1095. **319.** 6 c. mve., blue & blk. 10 10
1096. – 6 c. bright blue, blue & black .. .. 15 10
1097. – 6 c. blue, bright blue and black .. .. 15 10
1098. – 6 c. blue, mve. & blk. 15 10
1099. – 8 c. mve., blue & blk. 15 10
DESIGNS: No 1096, Volleyball. No. 1097, Target Shooting. No. 1098, Weightlifing. No. 1099, Running.

**320.** "Cattleya pachecoi". **321.** University Seal.

**1978.** Air. Orchids. Multicoloured.
1100. 1 c. Type **320** .. .. 10 10
1101. 1 c. "Sobralia xantholeuca" .. .. .. 10 10
1102. 1 c. "Cypripedium irapeanum" .. .. 10 10
1103. 1 c. "Oncidium splendidum" .. .. .. 10 10
1104. 3 c. "Cattleya bowringiana" .. .. .. 10 10
1105. 3 c. "Encyclia cordigera" 10 10
1106. 3 c. "Epidendrum imatophyllum" .. .. 10 10
1107. 3 c. "Barkeria skinneri" 10 10
1108. 8 c. "Spiranthes speciosa" 20 10
1109. 20 c. "Lycaste skinneri" 55 15

**1978.** Air. 300th Anniv. of San Carlos University of Guatemala. Multicoloured.
1110. 6 c. Type **321** .. .. 15 10
1111. 7 c Students from different faculties (26×46 mm.) .. .. .. 15 10
1112. 12 c. 17th-century student 20 10
1113. 14 c. Student and molecular model .. .. 30 10

**322.** Brown and White Children. **323.** Planting Seedling.

**1978.** Air. Guatemalan Children's Year (1977). Multicoloured.
1114. 6 c. Type **322** .. .. 15 10
1115. 7 c. Child skipping .. 15 10
1116. 12 c. "Helping Hand" 20 10
1117. 14 c. Hands protecting Indian girl .. .. 30 10

**1979.** Air. Forestry. Multicoloured.
1118. 6 c. Type **323** .. .. 10 10
1119. 8 c. Burnt forest .. 15 10
1120. 9 c. Woodland scene .. 15 10
1121. 10 c. Sawmill .. .. 15 10
1122. 26 c. Forest conservation 35 15

**324.** Ocellated Turkey. **325.** Clay Jar.

**1979.** Air. Wildlife Conservation. Mult.
1124. 1 c. Type **324** .. .. 40 15
1125. 3 c. White-tailed deer (horiz.) .. .. 25 10
1126. 5 c. King Vulture .. 1·25 15
1127. 7 c. Great Horned Owl .. 2·50 55
1128. 9 c. Ocelot .. .. 55 10

**1979.** Air. Archaeological Treasures from Tikal. Multicoloured.
1130. 2 c. Type **325** .. .. 10 10
1131. 3 c. Ceramic head of Mayan woman .. .. 10 10
1132. 4 c. Earring .. .. 10 10
1133. 5 c. Vase .. .. .. 10 10
1134. 6 c. Ceramic figure .. 10 10
1135. 7 c. Carved bone .. 10 10
1136. 8 c. Striped vase .. 15 10
1137. 10 c. Tripod vase with lid 15 10

**326.** Presidential Guard Headquarters. **327.** National Coat of Arms.

**1979.** 30th Anniv. of Presidential Guard. Multicoloured.
1138. 10 c. Type **326** (postage) 15 10
1139. 8 c. Presidential Guard insignia (air) .. 15 10

**1979.** Air. Municipal Arms. Multicoloured.
1140. 8 c. Type **327** .. .. 15 10
1141. 8 c. Alta Verapaz .. 15 10
1142. 8 c. Baja Verapaz .. 15 10
1143. 8 c. Chimal Tenango .. 15 10
1144. 8 c. Chiquimula .. .. 15 10
1145. 8 c. Escuintla .. .. 15 10
1146. 8 c. Flores (Peten) .. 15 10
1147. 8 c. Guatemala .. .. 15 10
1148. 8 c. Huehuetenango .. 15 10
1149. 8 c. Izabal .. .. 15 10
1150. 8 c. Jalapa .. .. 15 10
1151. 8 c. Jutiapa .. .. 15 10
1152. 8 c. Mazatenango .. 15 10
1153. 8 c. El Progreso .. .. 15 10
1154. 8 c. Quezaltenango .. 15 10
1155. 8 c. Quiche .. .. 15 10
1156. 8 c. Retalhuleu .. .. 15 10
1157. 8 c. Sacatepequez .. 15 10
1158. 8 c. San Marcos .. .. 15 10
1159. 8 c. Santa Rosa .. .. 15 10
1160. 8 c. Solola .. .. 15 10
1161. 8 c. Totonicapan .. 15 10
1162. 8 c. Zacapa .. .. 15 10

**328.** Rotary Emblem and Girl with Flowers. **329.** The Creation of the World.

**1980.** 75th Anniv. of Rotary International. Multicoloured.
1164. 4 c. Type **328** .. .. 10 10
1165. 6 c. Diamond, emblem and Resplendent Quetzal .. .. 50 10
1166. 10 c. Paul P. Harris (founder), emblem and Resplendent Quetzal .. .. 90 40

**1981.** Air. "Popol Vuh". Designs showing medallic illustrations of Guatemalan history and legends from the Sacred Book of the Ancient Quiches of Guatemala.

(a) The Creation.
1167. **329.** 1 c. black and mauve 10 10
1168. – 2 c. black and green 10 10
1169. – 4 c. black and blue .. 10 10
1170. – 8 c. black and yellow 15 10
1171. – 10 c. black and pink 15 10
1172. – 22 c. black and brown 30 10

(b) The Adventures of Hun Ahpu and Xbalanque.
1173. – 1 c. black and mauve 10 10
1174. – 4 c. black and violet 10 10
1175. – 6 c. black and brown 10 10
1176. – 8 c. black and green .. 15 10
1177. – 10 c. black and yellow 15 10
1178. – 26 c. black and green 35 10

(c) The Founding of the Quiche Race.
1179. – 2 c. black and mauve 10 10
1180. – 4 c. black and blue .. 10 10
1181. – 6 c. black and pink .. 10 10
1182. – 8 c. black and yellow 15 10
1183. – 10 c. black and green 15 10
1184. – 30 c. black and green 45 15

(d) The Territorial Expansion of the Quiches.
1185. – 3 c. black and blue .. 10 10
1186. – 4 c. black and violet 10 10
1187. – 6 c. black and pink .. 10 10
1188. – 8 c. black and grey .. 15 10
1189. – 10 c. black and green 15 10
1190. – 50 c. black and mauve 70 20
DESIGNS: No. 1168, Populating the earth. No. 1169, Birth of the stick-men. No. 1170, Destruction of the stick-men. No. 1171, Creation of the men of corn. No. 1172, "Thanks to the creator". No. 1173, Origin of the twin semi-gods. No. 1174, Punishment of the Princess Xquic. No. 1175, Odyssey of Hun Ahpu and Xbalanque. No. 1176, The test in Xibalba. No. 1177, Multiplication of the prodigies. No. 1178, The deification of Hun Ahpu and Xbalanque. No. 1179, Balam Quitze, father of Caviquib. No. 1180, Caha Paluma, wife of Balam Quitze. No. 1181, Balam Acab, father of Nihaibab. No. 1182, Chomiia, wife of Balam Acab. No. 1183, Mahucutah, father of Ahau Quiche. No. 1184, Tzununiha, wife of Mahucutah. No. 1185, Cotuha, Quiche monarch. No. 1186, The invincible Cotuha and Iztayul. No. 1187, Cucumatz, the prodigious king. No. 1188, Warrior with captive. No. 1189, "None can conquer or kill the king". No. 1190, "This was the greatness of the Quiches".

**330.** Early and Modern Telephones (cent.) **331.** Roderico Toledo and German Chupina (first and present Police Chiefs).

**1981.** Air. Anniversaries.
1191. – 3 c. red and black .. 10 10
1192. – 5 c. blue and black .. 10 10
1193. **330.** 6 c. multicoloured .. 10 10
1194. – 7 c. multicoloured .. 10 10
1195. – 12 c. multicoloured .. 15 10
1196. – 25 c. multicoloured .. 35 10
DESIGNS—26×46 mm: 3 c. Thomas Edison (centenary of gramophone). 29×39 mm: 7 c. Charles Lindbergh (50th anniv of solo Atlantic flight). 12 c. Jose Cecilio del Valle (patriot, birth bicentenary). 25 c. Jesues Castillo (composer, birth centenary). 46×26 mm: 5 c. Spool of film (50th anniv of sound film).

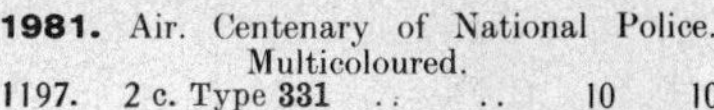
**1981.** Air. Centenary of National Police. Multicoloured.
1197. 2 c. Type **331** .. .. 10 10
1198. 4 c. Police Headquarters 10 10

**332.** Mayan Sun Calendar.

**1981.** Air. Seventh Latin American Aviculture Congress.
1199. **332.** 1 c. grn., yell. and blk. 10 10

**333.** Bernardo O'Higgins (Chile).

**1982.** Air. Liberators of the Americas.
1200. **333.** 2 c. multicoloured .. 10 10
1201. – 3 c. multicoloured .. 10 10
1202. – 4 c. multicoloured .. 10 10
1203. – 10 c. grey and black 15 10
DESIGNS—(31×45 mm.). 4 c. Jose de San Martin (Argentine). 10 c. Miguel Garcia Granados (Guatemala). (26×35 mm.) 3 c. Jose Artigas (Uruguay).

**334.** General Barrios and Bank.

**1982.** Air. Cent. of Banco de Occidente.
1204. **334.** 1 c. multicoloured .. 10 10
1205. – 2 c. black, red & blue 10 10
1206. – 3 c. multicoloured .. 10 10
1207. – 4 c. multicoloured .. 10 10
DESIGNS—HORIZ. 2 c. Bank building. VERT. 3 c. Centenary emblem. 4 c. Centenary medals.

**335.** Old and New Bank Buildings, Guatemala City.

**1982.** Air. 50th Anniv. of National Mortgage Bank.
1208. **335.** 1 c. multicoloured .. 10 10
1209. – 2 c. blk., yell. & grn. 10 10
1210. – 5 c. multicoloured .. 10 10
1211. – 10 c. blk., yell. & grn. 15 10
DESIGNS—HORIZ. 2 c. Bank emblem. 10 c. Bank and Anniversary emblems. VERT. 5 c. Bronze anniversary medallion.

**336.** Brother Pedro. **337.** I.T.U. and W.H.O. Emblems with Ribbons forming Caduceus.

**1983.** Air. Blessed Brother Pedro. Mult.
1212. 1 c. Type **336** .. .. 10 10
1213. 20 c. Apparition of Virgin Mary .. .. 30 10

**1983.** Air. World Communications and Health Day.
1214. **337.** 10 c. yell., red & blk. 15 10

**338.** Hands holding Bible.

**340.** F.A.O. Emblem and Starving Children.

**339.** Train crossing Puente de las Vacas Bridge.

**1983.** Air. Centenary (1982) of Evangelical Church in Guatemala. Multicoloured.

1215. 3 c. Type **338** .. .. 10 10
1216. 5 c. Central Evangelical Church .. .. 10 10

**1983.** Air. Centenary (1980) of Guatemalan Railways. Multicoloured.

1217. 10 c. Type **339** .. .. 45 40
1218. 25 c. General Barrios and trains at station .. 1·25 85
1219. 30 c. Train crossing Lake Amatitlan Dam .. 1·40 95

**1983.** Air. World Food Day (1981). Mult.

1220. 8 c. Maize and Globe .. 10 10
1221. 1 q. Type **340** .. .. 95 70

**1984.** Air. As Nos. 927/32 and 945/50 but colours changed. Values inscribed in black.

1230. **289.** 1 c. black and green 10 10
1231. A. 1 c. black and green 10 10
1232. B. 1 c. black and green 10 10
1233. C. 1 c. black and green 10 10
1234. D. 1 c. black and green 10 10
1235. E. 1 c. black and green 10 10
1236. **289.** 5 c. black and orange 10 10
1237. A. 5 c. black and orange 10 10
1238. B. 5 c. black and orange 10 10
1239. C. 5 c. black and orange 10 10
1240. D. 5 c. black and orange 10 10
1241. E. 5 c. black and orange 10 10

**341.** Pope John Paul II.

**342.** Rafael Landivar.

**1984.** Air. Papal Visit. Multicoloured.

1242. 4 c. Type **341** .. .. 10 10
1243. 8 c. Woman kneeling before Pope .. .. 15 10

**1984.** Air. 250th Birth Anniv. of Rafael Landivar (poet). Multicoloured.

1244. 2 c. Type **342** .. .. 10 10
1245. 4 c. Landivar's tomb, Antigua Guatemala (horiz.) .. .. 10 10

**343.** Casariego y Acevedo.

**344.** Bank's Emblem.

**1984.** Air. 1st Death Anniv. of Cardinal Mario Casariego y Acevedo, Archbishop of Guatemala.

1246. **343.** 10 c. multicoloured .. 15 10

**1984.** Air. 20th Anniv. of Central American Bank for Economic Integration.

1247. **344.** 30 c. multicoloured .. 50 15

**345.** Planting Coffee, 1870.

**346.** "Beaver" Cub and Tikal Pyramid.

**1984.** Air. Coffee.

1248. **345.** 1 c. black and brown 10 10
1249. – 2 c. black and flesh 10 10
1250. – 3 c. black and stone 10 10
1251. – 4 c. black and buff .. 20 10
1252. – 5 c. multicoloured .. 10 10
1253. – 10 c. multicoloured .. 15 10
1254. – 12 c. multicoloured .. 15 10
1255. – 25 c. multicoloured .. 1·10 30
1256. – 25 c. black & brown 35 10
1257. – 30 c. multicoloured .. 40 10

DESIGNS: As T **345.** 2 c. Harvesting coffee, 1870. 3 c. Drying coffee beans, 1870. 4 c. Exporting coffee, 1870. 5 c. Grafting seedlings. 10 c. Instant coffee. 12 c. Harvesting and processing coffee. 25 c. (1255), Exporting coffee (different). (81 × 108 mm.). 25 c. (1256) Women picking coffee. (100 × 81 mm.). 30 c. Globe and coffee beans.

**1985.** Air. 75th Anniv. of Boy Scout Movement. Multicoloured.

1258. 5 c. Type **346** .. .. 10 10
1259. 6 c. "Wolf" cub and Captains Palace, Old Guatemala .. 10 10
1260. 8 c. Scout, xylophone player and countryside 15 10
1261. 10 c. Rover scout and dancers .. .. 15 10
1262. 20 c. Lord Baden-Powell (founder) and Carlos Cipriani (founder of Guatemalan scouts) .. 30 10

**347.** Family.

**348.** Emblem.

**1985.** Air. Inter-American Family Year.

1263. **347.** 10 c. multicoloured .. 15 10

**1985.** Air. 25th Anniv. of Central American Air Navigation Services Association.

1264. **348.** 10 c. multicoloured .. 15 10

**349.** Morse Key, Samuel Morse, J. Rufino Barrios and Telegraph Aerial.

**1985.** Air. National Telegraph Service.

1265. **349.** 4 c. black and brown 10 10

**350.** Olympic Rings and Maya Pelota Player.

**351.** Rescue Team with Person in Cradle.

**1986.** Air. 90th Anniv. of First Modern Olympic Games and Foundation of International Olympic Committee. Mult.

1266. 8 c. Type **350** .. .. 15 10
1267. 10 c. Rings and Baron Pierre de Coubertin .. 15 10

**1986.** Air. Volunteer Fireman (1st series).

1268. **351.** 6 c. multicoloured .. 10 10

See also Nos. 1271/2.

**352.** Temple of Minerva, Quetzaltenango.

**1986.** Air. Centenary (1984) of Independence Fair, Quetzaltenango. Multicoloured.

1269. 8 c. Type **352** .. .. 15 10
1270. 10 c. City arms in courtyard of Quetzaltenango Municipal Palace 15 10

**353.** Fire behind Fireman carrying Child.

**354.** Arms.

**1986.** Air. Volunteer Firemen (2nd series). Multicoloured.

1271 8 c. Type **353** .. .. 15 10
1272 10 c. Searching rubble after explosion (33 × 24 mm) .. .. 15 10

**1986.** Air. 25th Anniv. (1976) of Association of Telegraphists and Radio-Telegraph Operators.

1273. **354.** 6 c. multicoloured .. 25 10

**355.** Architect with Plans looking at Building.

**1987.** Air. 25th Anniv. of San Carlos University Architecture Faculty.

1274. **355.** 10 c. multicoloured .. 15 10

**356.** Emblem and Boeing 727.

**1987.** Air. 40th Anniv of I.C.A.O. Mult.

1275 8 c Type **356** .. .. 15 10
1276 10 c. Boeing 727 airplane on runway (vert) .. 15 10

**357.** Aerial View of Site.

**1987.** Air. Chixoy Hydro-electric Plant.

1277. **357.** 2 c. multicoloured .. 10 10

**358.** Dr. Cayetano Francos y Monroy, Archbishop of Guatemala (founder).

**360.** Girls in Traditional Costumes.

**359.** Column beside Man studying Book.

**1987.** Air. Bicentenary (1981) of St. Joseph Children's College. Multicoloured.

1278. 8 c. Type **358** .. .. 10 10
1279. 10 c. College emblem .. 15 10

**1987.** Air. Regional Book Promotion Centre for Latin America and Caribbean.

1280. **359.** 12 c. multicoloured .. 15 10

**1987.** Coban Folklore Festival. Mult.

1281. 50 c. Girl weaving .. 55 15
1282. 1 q. Type **360** .. .. 1·25 30

**361.** Cesar Branas.

**362.** Footballer.

**1987.** Air. Writers (1st series).

1283. **361.** 6 c. orange and black 10 10
1284. – 8 c. red and black .. 10 10
1285. – 9 c. purple and black 15 10

DESIGNS: 8 c. Rafael Arevalo Martinez. 9 c. Jose Milla y Vidaurre.

See also Nos. 1297/8 and 1307/11.

**1987.** Air. Pan-American Games National Football Selection.

1286. **362.** 10 c. blue and black 15 10

**363.** Miguel Angel Asturias Cultural Centre.

**364.** Stylized Dove.

**1987.**

1287 **363** 2 c. brown .. .. 10 10
1288 3 c. blue .. .. 10 10
1289 4 c. mauve .. .. 10 10
1290 5 c. orange .. .. 10 10
1291 6 c. green .. .. 10 10
1292 7 c. red .. .. 10 10
1293 8 c. mauve .. .. 10 10
1294 9 c. black .. .. 10 10
1295 10 c. green .. .. 15 10

**1988.** Air. Writers (2nd series). As T **361.**

1297. 4 c. red and black .. 10 10
1298. 5 c. brown and black .. 10 10

DESIGNS: 4 c. Enrique A. Hidalgo. 5 c. Enrique Gomez Carrillo.

**1988.** Air. "Esquipulas II—A Firm Step towards Peace".

1299. **364.** 10 c. green .. .. 15 10
1300. – 40 c. red .. .. 45 10
1301. – 60 c. blue .. .. 65 20

DESIGNS—HORIZ. 40 c. Three stylized doves. VERT. 60 c. Stylized dove.

**366** St. John and Boys

**1989.** Death Centenary of St. John Bosco (founder of Salesian Brothers).
1303 **366** 40 c. black and gold .. 55 15

**367** Birds

**368** Madrid Codex (detail)

**1989.** Air. Bicentenary of French Revolution.
1304 **367** 1 q. red, blue & black 90 35

**1990.** Air. America. Pre-Columbian Culture. Multicoloured.
1305 10 c. Type **368** .. .. 10 10
1306 20 c. Tikal Pyramid .. 10 10

**1990.** Air. Writers (3rd series). As T **361**.
1307 1 c. mauve and black .. 10 10
1308 2 c. orange and black .. 10 10
1309 3 c. blue and black .. 10 10
1310 7 c. black and green .. 10 10
1311 10 c. black and yellow .. 10 10
DESIGNS: 1 c. Flavio Herrera; 2 c. Rosendo Santa Cruz; 3 c. Werner Ovalle Lopez; 7 c. Clemente Marroquin Rojas; 10 c. Miguel Angel Asturias.

**369** Games Emblem

**1990.** 6th Central American and Caribbean University Games. Multicoloured.
1312 15 c. Type **369** .. .. 10 10
1313 20 c. Mascot holding flame (vert) .. .. .. 10 10
1314 25 c. Mascot playing volleyball .. .. 10 10
1315 30 c. Mascot playing football .. .. 10 10
1316 45 c. Mascot performing judo movement .. 10 10
1317 1 q. Mascot playing baseball .. .. 25 10
1318 2 q. Mascot playing basketball .. .. 45 10
1319 3 q. Mascot hurdling .. 70 20

**370** Family, Cereal and Emblem

**1990.** Air. 40th Anniv of Central America and Panama Nutrition Institute.
1320 **370** 20 c. multicoloured .. 10 10

**371** Palais de l'Athenee, Geneva (venue of founding meeting)

**1990.** Air. 125th Anniv (1988) of International Red Cross.
1321 **371** 50 c. multicoloured .. 15 10

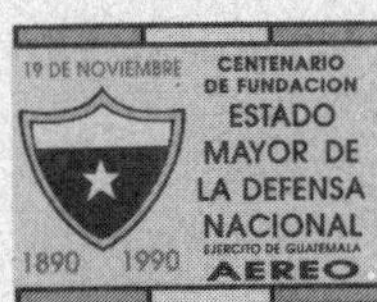

**372** Arms

**1991.** Air. Cent of National Defence Staff.
1322 **372** 20 c. multicoloured .. 10 10

**373** Atitlan Lake

**1991.** America. Natural World. Multicoloured.
1323 10 c. Pacaya Volcano in eruption .. .. 10 10
1324 60 c. Type **373** .. .. 15 10

**374** Martin and Vicente Pinzon

**375** Crops

**1992.** Air. America. 500th Anniv of Discovery of America by Columbus. Each black and green.
1325 40 c. Type **374** .. .. 20 10
1326 60 c. Christopher Columbus and "Santa Maria" (vert) .. .. 25 10

**1992.** Air. 50th Anniv of International Institute for Agricultural Co-operation.
1327 **375** 10 c. multicoloured .. 10 10

**376** Emblem

**377** "Encyclia cochleata"

**1992.** International Anti-AIDS Campaign.
1328 **376** 1 q. multicoloured .. 25 10

**1994.** Air. Orchids. Multicoloured.
1329 50 c. Type **377** .. .. 10 10
1330 1 q. "Encyclia vitellina" 20 10
1331 2 q. "Odontoglossum uroskinneri" .. .. 45 10

**378** Family around Tree

**1994.** 50th Anniv of 20 October Revolution. Multicoloured.
1332 40 c. Type **378** .. .. 10 10
1333 60 c. Dove on hand (horiz) 15 10
1334 1 q. Man holding book and rifle .. .. 20 10
1335 2 q. Representations of social developments since 1944 .. .. 45 10
1336 3 q. Three youths supporting torch ("Revolution, Liberty, Justice and Peace") .. 65 15

**379** City Buildings

**1995.** Air. Tourism. Multicoloured.
1337 20 c. White water rafting 10 10
1338 60 c. Pleasure boat on Lake Atitlan .. .. 15 10
1339 1 q. Erupting volcano .. 20 10
1340 2 q. Type **379** .. .. 45 10
1341 3 q. Parrots on perch (vert) .. .. .. 65 15
1342 4 q. Mayan ruins (vert) .. 90 20
1343 5 q. Ceremony (vert) .. 1·10 25

**380** Greeting Crowd

**1996.** Air. Papal Visit. Pope John Paul II. Multicoloured.
1344 10 c. Type **380** .. .. 10 10
1345 1 q. Holding child .. 20 10
1346 1 q. 75 Holding crucifix and wearing mitre .. 35 10
1347 1 q. 90 Wearing cross and red cloak .. .. 40 10
1348 2 q. 90 Wearing red hat .. 60 15

EXPRESS LETTER STAMPS.

**1940.** No. 231 optd. **EXPRESO.**
E 411. **97.** 4 c. yellow .. .. 85 35

**E 181.** Motor cyclist.

**1948.** Surch.
E 479. **E 181.** 10 c. on 4 c. blk. and green .. 1·00 60

OFFICIAL STAMPS

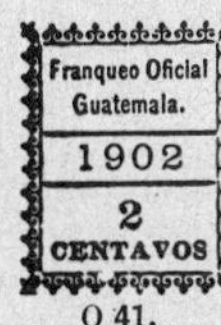

O **41.** O **100.**

**1902.**
O 127. O **41.** 1 c. green .. .. 2·50 1·25
O 128. 2 c. red .. .. 2·50 1·25
O 129. 5 c. blue .. .. 3·00 1·00
O 130. 10 c. purple .. 3·50 1·00
O 131. 25 c. orange .. 3·50 1·00

**1929.**
O 239. O **100.** 1 c. blue .. .. 30 30
O 240. 2 c. sepia .. 30 30
O 241. 3 c. green .. 30 30
O 242. 4 c. purple .. 35 35
O 243. 5 c. lake .. .. 35 35
O 244. 10 c. brown .. 40 40
O 245. 25 c. blue .. 85 70

**1939.** Air. Nos. 369/74 optd. **OFICIAL OFICIAL.**
O 400. **134.** 1 c. brown and orange 50 75
O 401. – 2 c. brown and red .. 50 75
O 402. – 3 c. brn., buff & grn. 50 75
O 403. – 4 c. brn. and purple 50 75
O 404. – 5 c. brown and grey 50 75
O 405. – 10 c. brown and blue 50 75



## GUINEA Pt. 13

The former French Colony on the W. coast of Africa which became fully independent in 1958.

1959. 100 centimes = 1 franc.
1973. 100 caury = 1 syli.
1986. 100 centimes = 1 franc.

**1959.** Stamps of Fr. West Africa optd. **REPUBLIQUE DE GUINEA** or surch. also.
188. – 10 f. multicoloured (No. 118) .. .. 2·00 2·50
189. **20.** 45 f. on 20 f. purple, grn. and olive .. .. 2·00 2·50

**10.** Pres. Sekou Toure.

**1959.** Proclamation of Independence.
190. **10.** 5 f. red .. .. .. 20 10
191. 10 f. blue .. .. 30 20
192. 20 f. orange .. .. 50 35
193. 65 f. green .. .. 1·60 1·00
194. 100 f. violet .. .. 2·50 1·90

**12.** Tamara Lighthouse and Fishing Boats. **13.** Flying Doves.

**1959.**
201. **12.** 1 f. red (postage) .. 10 10
202. 2 f. green .. .. 10 10
203. 3 f. brown .. .. 10 10
204. – 5 f. blue .. .. .. 15 15
205. – 10 f. purple .. .. 15 10
206. – 15 f. brown .. .. 85 25
207. – 20 f. purple .. .. 60 30
208. – 25 f. brown .. .. 1·50 30
209. **13.** 40 f. blue (air) .. .. 35 25
210. 50 f. green .. .. 55 40
211. 100 f. lake .. .. 1·25 65
212. 200 f. red .. .. 2·25 1·25
213. 500 f. red .. .. 6·00 3·25
DESIGNS—VERT. 5 f. Palms and dhow. 20 f. Pres. Sekou Toure. HORIZ. 10 f. Pirogue being launched. 15 f. African Elephant (front view). 25 f. African Elephant (side view).

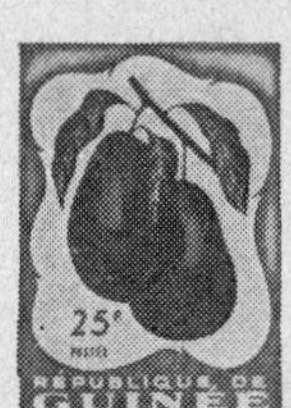

**14.** Mangoes.  **16.** "Raising the Flag".

**15.** Lockheed Super Constellation Airliner.

**1959.** Fruits in natural colours. Frame colours given.
214. – 10 f. red (Bananas) .. 15 15
215. – 15 f. green (Grapefruit) 25 15
216. – 20 f. brown (Lemons) .. 45 20
217. **14.** 25 f. blue .. .. 55 30
218. – 50 f. violet (Pineapple).. 1·00 35

**1959.** Air.
219. **15.** 100 f. blue, brn. & mauve 1·75 95
220. 200 f. mauve, brn. & grn. 5·00 1·25
221. – 500 f. multicoloured .. 8·00 2·50
DESIGN: 500 f. Lockheed Super Constellation airliner on ground.

**1959.** 1st Anniv. of Independence.
222. **16.** 50 f. multicoloured .. 55 25
223. 100 f. multicoloured .. 1·25 65

**18.** Africans acclaiming U.N. Headquarters Building.

**1959.** U.N.O.

230. **18.** 1 f. blue and orange (post.) 15 10
231. 2 f. purple and green .. 15 10
232. 3 f. brown and red .. 15 10
233. 5 f. brown and turquoise 15 10
234. 50 f. grn., blue and brn. (air) .. .. 65 50
235. 100 f. green, red and blue 90 70

Nos. 234/5 are larger (45×26 mm.).

**19.** Eye-testing. **20.** "Uprooted Tree".

**1960.** National Health. Inscr. "POUR NOTRE SANTE NATIONALE".

236. **19.** 20 f.+10 f. red and blue 75 70
237. – 30 f.+20 f. vio. and orge. 75 70
238. – 40 f.+20 f. blue and red 1·10 95
239. – 50 f.+50 f. brown & green 2·00 1·60
240. – 100 f.+100 f. green & pur. 2·75 2·10

DESIGNS—HORIZ. 30 f. Laboratory assistant. 40 f. Spraying trees. VERT. (28½×40 mm.): 50 f. Research with microscope. 100 f. Operating theatre.

**1960.** World Refugee Year.

241. **20.** 25 f. multicoloured .. 50 35
242. 50 f. multicoloured .. 70 45

**21.** U.P.U. Monument, Berne. **23.** Flag and Map.

**1960.** 1st Anniv. of Admission to U.P.U. Background differs for each value.

243. **21.** 10 f. black and brown.. 15 10
244. 15 f. lilac and mauve .. 25 15
245. 20 f. indigo and blue .. 40 15
246. – 25 f. myrtle and green.. 55 15
247. – 50 f. sepia and orange.. 65 25

DESIGN: 25 f., 50 f. As Type **10** but vert.

**1960.** Olympic Games. Optd. **Jeux Olympiques Rome 1960** and Olympic rings.

248. **16.** 50 f. multicoloured (post.) 5·00 5·00
249. 100 f. multicoloured .. 7·50 7·50
250. **15.** 100 f. blue, green and mauve (air) .. .. 6·50 4·50
251. 200 f. mauve, brn. & grn. 13·00 6·50
252. – 500 f. multicoloured (No. 221) .. .. .. 32·00 32·00

**1960.** 2nd Anniv. of Independence.

253. **23.** 25 f. multicoloured .. 30 25
254. 30 f. multicoloured .. 40 35

**1960.** 15th Anniv. of U.N.O. Optd. **XVEME ANNIVERSAIRE DES NATIONS UNIES.** (a) Nos. 214/18 Fruits in natural colours.

255. – 10 f. red .. .. .. 20 20
256. – 15 f. green .. .. 30 25
257. – 20 f. brown .. .. 35 30
258. **14.** 25 f. blue .. .. 45 35
259. – 50 f. violet .. .. 75 60

(b) Nos. 230/35.

260. **18.** 1 f. blue & orange (post.) 10 10
261. 2 f. purple and green .. 10 10
262. 3 f. brown and red .. 10 10
263. 5 f. brown and turquoise 10 10
264. 50 f. green, blue & brown (air) .. .. .. 65 50
265. 100 f. green, red and blue 90 70

**1961.** World Refugee Year stamps surch. **1961+10 FRS.** (or **20 FRS.**).

266. **20.** 25 f.+10 f. multicoloured 4·75 4·75
267. 50 f.+20 f. multicoloured 4·75 4·75

**27.** Bohar Reedbuck.

**1961.** Centres in brown, green and blue. Inscriptions and value tablets in colours given.

268. **27.** 5 f. turquoise .. .. 15 10
269. 10 f. green .. .. 15 10
270. 25 f. violet .. .. 40 15
271. 40 f. orange .. .. 55 20
272. 50 f. red .. .. 1·25 25
273. 75 f. blue .. .. 1·75 45

**28.** Guinea Flag and Exhibition Hall, Conakry.

**1961.** First Three-Year Plan. Flag in red, yellow and green.

274. **28.** 5 f. blue and red .. 15 15
275. 10 f. brown and red .. 15 15
276. 25 f. green and red .. 25 25

**29.** Helmet Guineafowl.

**1961.** Guineafowl in purple and blue.

277. **29.** 5 f. mauve and blue .. 70 30
278. 10 f. red and blue .. 75 30
279. 25 f. red and blue .. 75 45
280. 40 f. brown and blue .. 1·10 50
281. 50 f. bistre and blue .. 1·25 70
282. 75 f. olive and blue .. 3·25 85

**1961.** Protection of Animals. Surch **POUR LA PROTECTION DE NOS ANIMAUX + 5 FRS.**

283. **27.** 5 f.+5 f. turquoise .. 15 15
284. 10 f.+5 f. green .. 25 15
285. 25 f.+5 f. violet .. 55 30
286. 40 f.+5 f. orange .. 70 40
287. 50 f.+5 f. red .. .. 95 55
288. 75 f.+5 f. blue.. .. 1·50 70

**31.** Patrice Lumumba.

**1962.** 1st Death Anniv. of Lumumba (Congo leader).

289. **31.** 10 f. multicoloured .. 30 25
290. 25 f. multicoloured .. 40 25
291. 50 f. multicoloured .. 60 30

**1962.** Malaria Eradication (1st issue). Nos. 236/40 opt. with Malaria Eradication emblem and **ERADICATION DE LA MALARIA.**

292. **19.** 20 f.+10 f. red and blue 35 35
293. – 30 f.+20 f. violet & orge. 50 50
294. – 40 f.+20 f. blue and red 60 60
295. – 50 f.+50 f. brown & green 1·25 1·25
296. – 100 f.+100 f. grn. & pur. 2·50 2·50

**33.** King Mohammed V and Map. **34.** Mosquito and Emblem.

**1962.** 1st Anniv. of Casablanca Conf.

297. **33.** 25 f. multicoloured .. 95 25
298. 75 f. multicoloured .. 1·90 45

**1962.** Air. Malaria Eradication (2nd issue).

299. **34.** 25 f. black and orange.. 40 20
300. 50 f. black and red .. 50 35
301. 100 f. black and green.. 1·00 60

**1962.** African Postal Union Commem. As T **233** of Egypt.

303. 25 f. green, brown & orge. 65 15
304. 100 f. orange and brown.. 1·60 40

**1962.** Guinea-fowl stamps surch. **POUR LA PROTECTION DE NOS OISEAUX +5 FRS.**

305. **29.** 5 f.+5 f. .. .. 60 35
306. 10 f.+5 f. .. .. 60 45
307. 25 f.+5 f. .. .. 80 55
308. 40 f.+5 f. .. .. 95 70
309. 50 f.+5 f. .. .. 2·10 90
310. 75 f.+5 f. .. .. 3·75 1·90

**36.** Bote-player. **37.** Hippopotamus.

## INDEX

Countries can be quickly located by referring to the index at the end of this volume.

**1962.** Native Musicians.

311. **36.** 30 c. red, grn. & bl. (post.) 15 10
312. A. 50 c. grn., brn. & salmon 15 10
313. B. 1 f. purple and green .. 15 10
314. C. 1 f. 50 turq., red & yell. 15 10
315. D. 2 f. green, red and mauve 15 10
316. C. 3 f. violet, green & turq. 15 10
317. B. 10 f. blue, brn. & orge. 25 10
318. D. 20 f. red, sepia and olive 30 20
319. **36.** 25 f. violet, sepia & olive 45 25
320. A. 40 f. mauve, grn. & bl. 45 35
321. **36.** 50 f. blue, red and rose 60 40
322. A. 75 f. blue, brown & ochre 2·50 55
323. D. 100 f. bl., red & pink (air) 1·10 50
324. D. 200 f. red and blue .. 2·50 75
325. E. 500 f. blue, vio. & brown 6·50 2·50

DESIGNS—(Musicians playing). HORIZ. A, Bolon. C, Koni. D, Kora. E, Balafon. VERT. B, Flute.

**1962.** Wild Game.

326. **37.** 10 f. sepia, grn. & orge. 30 10
327. – 25 f. brown, sepia & grn. 60 20
328. – 30 f. sepia, yell. & olive 70 20
329. **37.** 50 f. sepia, green & blue 1·00 35
330. – 75 f. brown, pur. & lilac 1·50 60
331. – 100 f. sepia, yell. & turq. 2·00 80

DESIGNS: 25 f., 75 f. Lion. 30 f., 100 f. Leopard.

**38.** Boy at Blackboard.

**43.** Crowned Crane. **39.** Alfa Yaya.

**1962.** Campaign Against Illiteracy.

332. **38.** 5 f. sepia, yellow & red 10 10
333. – 10 f. sepia, orge. & purple 10 10
334. **38.** 15 f. sepia, green & red 20 10
335. – 20 f. sepia, turq. & pur. 30 20

DESIGN: 10 f., 20 f. Teacher at blackboard.

**1962.** African Heroes and Martyrs.

336. **39.** 25 f. sepia, turq. & gold 30 15
337. – 30 f. sepia, ochre & gold 40 20
338. – 50 f. sepia, pur. & gold 55 25
339. – 75 f. sepia, green & gold 1·10 40
340. – 100 f. sepia, red & gold 1·40 60

PORTRAITS: 30 f. King Behanzin. 50 f. King Ba Bemba of Sikasso. 75 f. Almamy Samory. 100 f. Chief Tierno Aliou of the Goumba.

**1962.** Algerian Refugees Fund. Surch. **Aide aux Refugies Algeriens** and premium.

341. **33.** 25 f.+15 f. multicoloured 65 65
342. 75 f.+25 f. multicoloured 1·25 1·25

**1962.** Air. "The Conquest of Space". Optd. with capsule and **La Conquete De L'Espace.**

343. **13.** 40 f. blue .. .. 50 25
344. 50 f. green .. .. 60 30
345. 100 f. lake .. .. 1·00 50
348. 200 f. red .. .. 1·75 95

**1962.** Birds. Multicoloured.

349. 30 c. Type **43** (postage) .. 1·10 25
350. 50 c. Grey Parrot .. .. 1·10 25
351. 1 f. Abyssinian Ground Hornbill .. .. 1·25 25
352. 1 f. 50 White Spoonbill .. 1·25 45
353. 2 f. Bateleur .. .. 1·25 45
354. 3 f. Type **43** .. .. 1·50 45
355. 10 f. As 50 d. .. .. 1·50 45
356. 20 f. As 1 f. .. .. 2·00 95
357. 25 f. As 1 f. 50 .. .. 2·50 1·10
358. 40 f. As 2 f. .. .. 2·50 1·10
359. 50 f. Type **43** .. .. 2·75 1·40
360. 75 f. As 50 c. .. .. 5·75 1·50
361. 100 f. As 1 f. (air) .. .. 6·75 1·90
362. 200 f. As 1 f. 50 .. .. 11·50 3·50
363. 500 f. As 2 f. .. .. 24·00 9·00

All except T **43** are horiz.

**44.** Handball.

**1963.** Sports.

364. **44.** 30 c. purple, red & green (postage) .. .. 10 10
365. A. 50 c. violet, lilac & blue 10 10
366. B. 1 f. sepia, orange & green 10 10
367. C. 1 f. 50 blue, orange and purple .. .. 10 10
368. D. 2 f. blue, turq. & purple 10 10
369. **44.** 3 f. purple, olive & blue 10 10
370. A. 4 f. violet, mauve & blue 10 10
371. B. 5 f. sepia green & purple 15 10
372. C. 10 f. blue & bright purple 20 10
373. D. 20 f. blue, orge. & red.. 30 15
374. **44.** 25 f. purple, green and black .. .. .. 40 15
375. A. 30 f. violet, black & blue 45 25
376. B. 100 f. sepia, lake & green (air) .. .. .. 1·10 40
377. C. 200 f. blue, brn. & pur. 2·25 90
378. D. 500 f. blue, brn. & purple 5·00 2·25

DESIGNS: A, Boxing. B, Running. C, Cycling. D, Canoeing.

**45.** Campaign Emblem. **47.** "African Unity".

**46.** "Amauris niavius".

**1963.** Freedom from Hunger.

379. **45.** 5 f. yellow and red .. 10 10
380. 10 f. yellow and green.. 10 10
381. 15 f. yellow and brown 15 10
382. 25 f. yellow and olive.. 25 15

**1963.** Butterflies. Multicoloured.

383. 10 c. Type **46** (postage) .. 10 10
384. 30 c. "Papilio demodocus" 10 10
385. 40 c. As 30 c. .. .. 10 10
386. 50 c. "Graphum policenes" 10 10
387. 1 f. "Papilio nireus" .. 15 10
388. 1 f. 50 Type **46** .. .. 20 10
389. 2 f. "Papilio menestheus" 20 10
390. 3 f. As 30 c. .. .. 20 10
391. 10 f. As 50 c. .. .. 35 10
392. 20 f. As 1 f. .. .. 60 15
393. 25 f. Type **46** .. .. 1·00 20
394. 40 f. As 2 f. .. .. 1·40 30
395. 50 f. As 30 c. .. .. 1·90 35
396. 75 f. As 1 f. .. .. 2·75 60
397. 100 f. Type **46** (air) .. 1·75 35
398. 200 f. As 50 c. .. .. 4·00 80
399. 500 f. As 2 f. .. .. 8·00 2·50

**1963.** Conference of African Heads of State, Addis Ababa.

400. **47.** 5 f. sepia, black and turquoise on green .. 10 10
401. 10 f. sepia, black and yellow on yellow .. 10 10
402. 15 f. sepia, black and olive on olive .. 15 10
403. 25 f. sepia, black and brown on cinnamon.. 25 15

**48.** Capsule encircling Globe.

**1963.** Centenary of Red Cross.

404. **48.** 5 f. red & green (post.) 10 10
405. 10 f. red and blue .. 15 10
406. 15 f. red and yellow .. 20 15
407. 25 f. red & black (air).. 45 20

**1963.** Air. 1st Pan-American Conakry–New York Direct Air Service. Optd **PREMIER SERVICE DIRECT CONAKRY–NEW YORK PAN AMERICAN 30 JUILLET 1963.**

409. **15.** 100 f. blue, grn. & mauve 1·90 75
410. 200 f. mauve, brn. & grn. 3·25 1·25

**1963.** Olympic Games Preparatory Commission, Conakry. Nos. 364/6 surch. **COMMISSION PREPARATOIRE AUX JEUX OLYMPIQUES A CONAKRY,** rings and new value.

411. 40 f. on 30 c. purple, red and green .. .. 1·00 80
412. 50 f. on 50 c. violet, lilac and blue .. .. 1·40 1·10
413. 75 f. on 1 f. sepia, orange and green .. .. 2·40 1·90

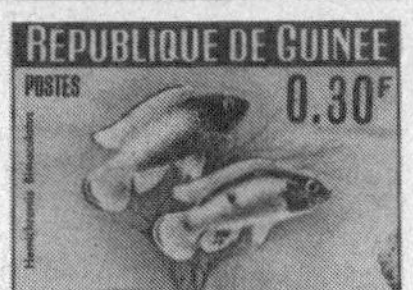

51. "Hemichromis bimaculatus".

**1964.** Guinea Fishes. Multicoloured.
414. 30 c. Type 51 (postage) .. 10 10
415. 40 c. "Golden Pheasant" carp .. .. .. 10 10
416. 50 c. "Aphyosemion coeruleum" .. .. 10 10
417. 1 f. Red cichlid and "Hemichromis fasciatus" 10 10
418. 1 f. 50 "Yellow Pride" carp 10 10
419. 2 f. Senegal herring .. 20 10
420. 5 f. Type 51 .. .. 20 10
421. 30 f. As 40 c. .. .. 50 20
422. 40 f. As 50 c. .. .. 1·00 35
423. 75 f. As 1 f. .. .. 1·75 55
424. 100 f. As 1 f. 50 (air) .. 1·75 55
425. 300 f. As 2 f. .. .. 5·00 1·60

52. President Kennedy. 53. Pipeline under Construction.

**1964.** Pres. Kennedy Memorial Issue. Flag in red and blue.
426. 52. 5 f. violet & black (post.) 10 10
427. 25 f. violet and green .. 25 20
428. 50 f. violet and brown .. 60 30
429. 100 f. blk. & violet (air) 1·00 85

**1964.** Inaug. of Piped Water Supply, Conakry.
430. 53. 5 f. red .. .. .. 10 10
431. – 10 f. violet .. .. 10 10
432. – 20 f. brown .. .. 15 10
433. – 30 f. blue .. .. 30 15
434. – 50 f. green .. .. 55 30
DESIGNS—HORIZ. 10 f. Reservoir. 20 f. Joining pipes. 30 f. Transporting pipes. 50 f. Laying pipes.

54. Ice hockey. 56. Eleanor Roosevelt with Children.

**1964.** Winter Olympic Games, Innsbruck. Rings, frame and tablet in gold.
435. 54. 10 f. olive & green (post.) 15 10
436. – 25 f. slate and violet .. 40 20
437. – 50 f. black and blue .. 75 40
438. – 100 f. black & brn. (air) 1·10 55
DESIGNS: 25 f. Ski-jumping. 50 f. Skiing. 100 f. Figure-skating.

**1964.** Air. Olympic Games, Tokyo (1st issue). Nos. 376/8 optd. **JEUX OLYMPIQUES TOKYO 1964** and Olympic rings.
439. 100 f. sepia, lake and green 1·50 1·00
440. 200 f. blue, brown & purple 2·25 1·50
441. 500 f. blue, brown & purple 5·00 3·50

**1964.** 15th Anniv. of Declaration of Human Rights.
442. 56. 5 f. green (postage) .. 10 10
443. 10 f. orange .. .. 10 10
444. 15 f. blue .. .. 15 10
445. 25 f. red .. .. 30 15
446. 50 f. violet (air) .. 70 30

57. Striped Hyena.

**1964.** Animals.
447. 57. 5 f. sepia and yellow .. 20 10
448. 30 f. sepia and blue .. 40 20
449. – 40 f. black and mauve 55 25
450. – 75 f. sepia and green .. 1·50 30
451. – 100 f. sepia and ochre 2·00 50
452. – 300 f. deep vio. & orge. 4·00 1·75
ANIMALS: 40 f., 300 f. African Buffalo. 75 f., 100 f. African Elephant.

58. Guinea Pavilion. 60. Nefertari, Isis and Hathor.

**1964.** New York World's Fair.
453. 58. 30 f. green and lilac .. 25 15
454. 40 f. green and purple .. 40 15
455. 50 f. green and brown .. 50 15
456. 75 f. blue and red .. 75 25
See also Nos. 484/87.

**1964.** Nubian Monuments Preservation. Multicoloured.
458. 10 f. Type 60 (postage) .. 20 15
459. 25 f. Pharaoh in battle .. 25 15
460. 50 f. The Nile—partly submerged sphinxes .. 45 20
461. 100 f. Rameses II, entrance hall of Great Temple, Abu Simbel .. .. 1·10 45
462. 200 f. Lower part of Colossi, Abu Simbel .. 2·00 80
463. 300 f. Nefertari (air) .. 3·75 1·60

61. Athlete with Torch. 62. Doudou (Boke) Mask.

**1965.** Olympic Games, Tokyo (2nd issue). Multicoloured.
464 5 f. Weightlifter and children (postage) .. 15 10
465 10 f. Type 61 .. .. 15 10
466 25 f. Pole vaulting .. 25 20
467 40 f. Running .. .. 30 20
468 50 f. Judo .. .. 50 30
469 75 f. Japanese hostess .. 1·00 45
470 100 f. Air hostess and Convair Coronado airliner (horiz) (air) .. 1·50 55

**1965.** Native Masks and Dancers. Mult.
472. 20 c. Type 62 (postage) .. 10 10
473. 40 c. Niamou (Nzerekore) mask .. .. .. 10 10
474. 60 c. "Yoki" (Boke) statuette .. .. 10 10
475. 80 c. Guekedou dancer .. 10 10
476. 1 f. Niamou (Nzerekore) mask .. .. .. 10 10
477. 2 f. Macenta dancer .. 15 10
478. 15 f. Niamou (Nzerekore) mask .. .. .. 25 15
479. 20 f. Tom-tom beater (forest region) .. 45 15
480. 60 f. Macenta "Bird-man" dancer .. .. .. 95 45
481. 80 f. Bassari (Koundara) dancer .. .. .. 1·10 55
482. 100 f. Karana sword dancer 1·60 70
483. 300 f. Niamou (Nzerekore) mask (air) .. .. 4·50 1·50
The 40 c., 1 f., 15 f. and 300 f. each show different masks.

**1965.** New York World's Fair. As Nos. 453/6 but additionally inscr "1965".
484. 58. 30 f. orange and green .. 20 15
485. 40 f. green and red .. 30 15
486. 50 f. violet and blue .. 45 25
487. 75 f. violet and brown .. 65 35

63. Metal-work.

**1965.** Native Handicrafts. Multicoloured.
489. 15 f. Type 63 (postage) .. 15 10
490. 20 f. Pottery .. .. 20 15
491. 60 f. Dyeing .. .. 60 35
492. 80 f. Basket-making .. 85 45
493. 100 f. Ebony-work (air) .. 1·25 45
494. 300 f. Ivory-work .. .. 4·50 1·25

64. I.T.U. Emblem and Symbols.

**1965.** I.T.U. Cent.
495. 64. 25 f. mult. (postage) .. 30 15
496. 50 f. multicoloured .. 60 25
497. 100 f. multicoloured (air) 1·10 40
498. 200 f. multicoloured .. 2·00 65

67. U.N. Headquarters and I.C.Y. Emblem.

**1965.** I.C.Y.
501. 67. 25 f. red and green (post.) 25 15
502. 45 f. red and violet .. 35 20
503. 75 f. red and brown .. 70 30
504. 100 f. orange & blue (air) 1·25 45

68. Polytechnic Institute, Conakry.

**1965.** 7th Anniv. of Independence. Mult.
505. 25 f. Type 68 (postage) .. 15 15
506. 30 f. Camayenne Hotel .. 20 15
507. 40 f. Gbessia Airport .. 60 30
508. 75 f. "28 Septembre" Stadium .. .. 55 35
509. 200 f. Polytechnic Institute, North facade (air) .. 1·40 1·00
510. 500 f. Ditto, West facade .. 4·25 2·50
Nos. 509/10 are larger, 53 × 23 mm.

69. Moon, Globe and Satellite. 70. Sabre Dance, Karana.

**1965.** "To the Moon". Multicoloured.
511. 5 f. Type 69 (postage) .. 15 10
512. 10 f. Trajectory of "Ranger 7" .. .. .. 20 10
513. 25 f. "Relay" satellite .. 30 20
514. 45 f. "Vostok 1, 2" and Globe .. .. .. 55 25
515. 100 f. "Ranger 7" approaching Moon (air) .. 85 40
516. 200 f. Launching of "Ranger 7" .. .. .. 2·00 75
Nos. 512/9 are larger, 36 × 25½ mm.; Nos. 515/6 are vert., 25 × 36 mm.

**1966.** Guinean Dances. Multicoloured.
519. 10 c. Type 70 (postage) .. 10 10
520. 30 c. Young girls' dance, Lower Guinea .. .. 10 10
521. 50 c. Tiekere musicians, "Eyora" (bamboo) dance Bandjinguene .. .. 10 10
522. 5 f. Doundouba dance, Kouroussa .. .. 10 10
523. 40 f. Bird-man's dance, Macenta .. .. .. 85 30
524. 100 f. Kouyate Kandia, national singer (air) .. 1·25 45
The 50 c. and 100 f. are horiz., 36 × 29 mm. See also Nos. 561/6.

**1966.** Stamp Cent. Exn., Cairo. Nos. 460 and 463 optd. **CENTENAIRE DU TIMBRE CAIRE 1966.**
525. 50 f. multicoloured (post.) 55 40
526. 300 f. multicoloured (air) 2·25 1·50

**1966.** Pan Arab Games, Cairo (1965). Nos. 464/5, 467/9 optd. **JEUX PANARABES CAIRE 1965** and pyramid motif.
527. – 5 f. multicoloured (post.) 20 15
528. 61. 10 f. multicoloured .. 20 15
529. – 40 f. multicoloured .. 55 35
530. – 50 f. multicoloured .. 70 45
531. – 75 f. multicoloured .. 1·25 75
532. – 100 f. multicoloured (air) 1·25 40

HAVE YOU READ THE NOTES AT THE BEGINNING OF THIS CATALOGUE?
These often provide answers to the enquiries we receive.

73. Vonkou Rocks, Telimele. 74. U.N.E.S.C.O. Emblem.

**1966.** Landscapes (1st series). Multicoloured.
534. 20 f. Type 73 (postage) .. 15 10
535. 25 f. Artificial lake, Coyah 20 10
536. 40 f. Waterfalls, Kate .. 35 15
537. 50 f. Bridge, Forecariah .. 45 20
538. 75 f. Liana bridge .. .. 70 35
539. 100 f. Lighthouse and bay, Boulbinet (air) .. .. 1·50 45
See also Nos. 603/608.

**1966.** 20th Anniv. of U.N.E.S.C.O. (a) Postage.
540. 74. 25 f. multicoloured .. 40 20
(b) Air. Nos. 509/10 optd. **vingtans 1946-1966** and UNESCO Emblem.
541. 200 f. multicoloured .. 2·00 1·25
542. 500 f. multicoloured .. 4·50 2·75

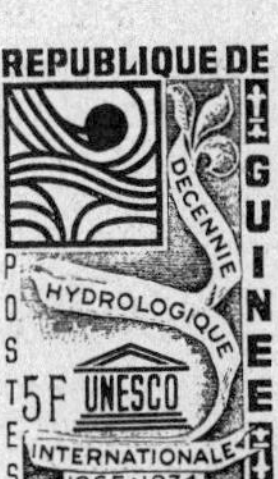

76. 78. Decade and U.N.E.S.C.O. Symbols.

**1966.** Guinean Flora and Female Headdresses. Similar designs.
543. 76. 10 c. multicoloured (post.) 10 10
544. – 20 c. multicoloured .. 10 10
545. – 30 c. multicoloured .. 10 10
546. – 40 c. multicoloured .. 10 10
547. – 3 f. multicoloured .. 10 10
548. – 4 f. multicoloured .. 10 10
549. – 10 f. multicoloured .. 15 10
550. – 25 f. multicoloured .. 55 10
551. – 30 f. multicoloured .. 70 15
552. – 50 f. multicoloured .. 1·10 30
553. 76. 80 f. multicoloured .. 1·40 40
554. – 200 f. multicoloured (air) 2·75 75
555. – 300 f. multicoloured .. 4·50 1·50
Nos. 551/555 are 29 × 42 mm.

**1966.** Int. Hydrological Decade.
558. 78. 5 f. red and blue .. 10 10
559. 25 f. red and green .. 20 10
560. 100 f. red and purple .. 1·00 50

**1966.** Guinean National Ballet. Designs show various dances as T 70.
561. 60 c. multicoloured .. 10 10
562. 1 f. multicoloured .. .. 10 10
563. 1 f. 50 multicoloured .. 15 10
564. 25 f. multicoloured .. 35 20
565. 50 f. multicoloured .. 85 30
566. 75 f. multicoloured .. 1·40 50
SIZES—VERT. (26 × 36 mm.): 60 c., 1 f., 1 f. 50, 50 f. HORIZ. (36 × 29 mm.): 25 f., 75 f.

79. "Village".

**1966.** 20th Anniv. of U.N.I.C.E.F. Multicoloured designs showing children's drawings.
567. 2 f. "Elephant" .. .. 10 10
568. 3 f. "Doll" .. .. 10 10
569. 10 f. "Girl" .. .. 10 10
570. 20 f. Type 79 .. .. 15 10
571. 25 f. "Footballer" .. 35 15
572. 40 f. "Still Life" .. .. 55 20
573. 50 f. "Bird in Tree" .. 70 25

80. Dispensing Medicine.

**1967.** Inauguration of W.H.O. Headquarters, Geneva. Multicoloured.
574. 30 f. Type 80 .. .. 25 10
575. 50 f. Doctor examining child 35 20
576. 75 f. Nurse weighing baby 60 30
577. 80 f. W.H.O. Building & flag 75 45

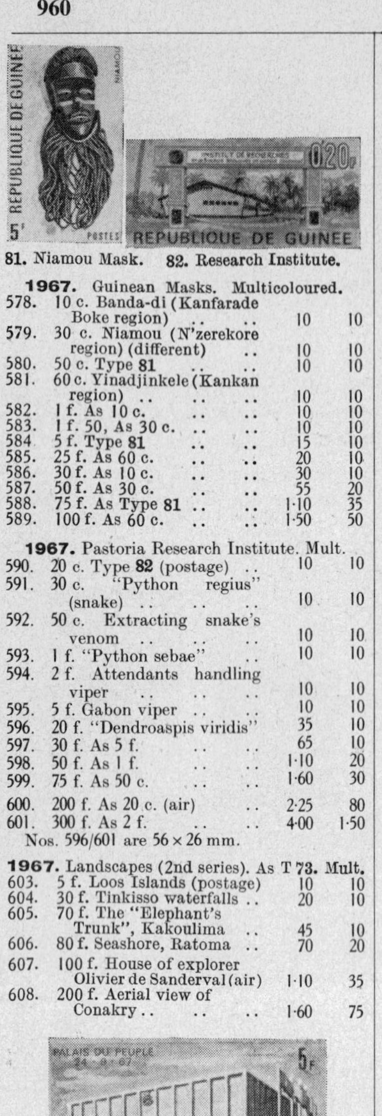

81. Niamou Mask. 82. Research Institute.

**1967.** Guinean Masks. Multicoloured.

578. 10 c. Banda-di (Kanfarade Boke region) .. .. 10 10
579. 30 c. Niamou (N'zerekore region) (different) .. 10 10
580. 50 c. Type **81** .. .. 10 10
581. 60 c. Yinadjinkele (Kankan region) .. .. .. 10 10
582. 1 f. As 10 c. .. .. 10 10
583. 1 f. 50, As 30 c. .. .. 10 10
584. 5 f. Type **81** .. .. 15 10
585. 25 f. As 60 c. .. .. 20 10
586. 30 f. As 10 c. .. .. 30 10
587. 50 f. As 30 c. .. .. 55 20
588. 75 f. As Type **81** .. .. 1·10 35
589. 100 f. As 60 c. .. .. 1·50 50

**1967.** Pastoria Research Institute. Mult.

590. 20 c. Type **82** (postage) .. 10 10
591. 30 c. "Python regius" (snake) .. .. .. 10 10
592. 50 c. Extracting snake's venom .. .. .. 10 10
593. 1 f. "Python sebae" .. 10 10
594. 2 f. Attendants handling viper .. .. .. 10 10
595. 5 f. Gabon viper .. .. 10 10
596. 20 f. "Dendroaspis viridis" 35 10
597. 30 f. As 5 f. .. .. 65 10
598. 50 f. As 1 f. .. .. 1·10 20
599. 75 f. As 50 c. .. .. 1·60 30
600. 200 f. As 20 c. (air) .. 2·25 80
601. 300 f. As 2 f. .. .. 4·00 1·50

Nos. 596/601 are 56 × 26 mm.

**1967.** Landscapes (2nd series). As T **73.** Mult.

603. 5 f. Loos Islands (postage) 10 10
604. 30 f. Tinkisso waterfalls .. 20 10
605. 70 f. The "Elephant's Trunk", Kakoulima .. 45 10
606. 80 f. Seashore, Ratoma .. 70 20
607. 100 f. House of explorer Olivier de Sanderval (air) 1·10 35
608. 200 f. Aerial view of Conakry .. .. .. 1·60 75

83. People's Palace, Conakry.

**1967.** 20th Anniv. of Guinean Democratic Party and Inaug. of People's Palace. Multicoloured.

609. 5 f. Type **83** (postage) .. 10 10
610. 30 f. African elephant's head .. .. .. 50 50
611. 55 f. Type **83** .. .. 40 25
612. 200 f. As 30 f. (air) .. 1·75 1·00

**1967.** 50th Anniv. of Lions Int. Landscape series optd. **AMITE DES PEUPLES GRACE AU TOURISME 1917-1967** and Lions Emblem.

613 5 f. (No. 603) (postage) .. 15 10
614. 30 f. (No. 604) .. .. 30 20
615. 40 f. (No. 536) .. .. 35 20
616. 50 f. (No. 537) .. .. 45 25
617. 70 f. (No. 605) .. .. 60 35
618. 75 f. (No. 538) .. .. 85 45
619. 80 f. (No. 606) .. .. 1·00 45
620. 100 f. (No. 539) (air) .. 1·10 60
621. 100 f. (No. 607) .. .. 1·10 60
622. 200 f. (No. 608) .. .. 2·00 1·10

85. Section of Mural. 86. W.H.O. Building, Brazzaville.

**1967.** Air. "World of Tomorrow". Jose Vanetti's Mural, Conf. Building, U.N. Headquarters. Designs showing various sections of mural.

623. – 30 f. multicoloured .. 20 15
624. – 50 f. multicoloured .. 30 20
625. **85.** 100 f. multicoloured .. 80 40
626. – 200 f. multicoloured .. 1·60 60

**1967.** Inaug. of W.H.O. Building, Brazzaville.

628. **86.** 30 f. olive, ochre & blue 30 15
629. 75 f. red, ochre and blue 60 25

87. Human Rights Emblem. 88. Coyah, Oubreka Region.

**1968.** Human Rights Year.

630. **87.** 30 f. red, green & ochre 25 15
631. 40 f. red, blue & violet 30 15

**1968.** Regional Costumes and Habitations. Multicoloured.

632. 20 c. Type **88** (postage) .. 10 10
633. 30 c. Kankan Region .. 10 10
634. 40 c. Kankan, Upper Guinea 10 10
635. 50 c. Forest region .. 10 10
636. 60 c. Foulamory, Gaoual Region .. .. .. 10 10
637. 5 f. Cognagui, Koundara Region .. .. .. 10 10
638. 15 f. As 50 c. .. .. 15 10
639 20 f. As 20 c. .. .. 30 15
640. 30 f. As 30 c. .. .. 45 20
641. 40 f. Fouta-Djallon, Middle Guinea .. .. .. 70 25
642. 100 f. Labe, Middle Guinea 1·50 40
643. 300 f. Bassari, Koundara Region (air) .. .. 3·25 1·00

The 60 c. to 300 f. are larger (60 × 39 mm.).

89. "The Village Story-teller."

**1968.** Paintings of African Legends (1st series). Multicoloured.

644. 25 f. Type **89** (postage) .. 15 10
645. 30 f. "The Moon and the Stars" .. .. .. 15 10
646. 75 f. "Leuk the Hare sells his Sister" .. .. 60 35
647. 80 f. "The Hunter and the Female Antelope" .. 1·00 35
648. 100 f. "Old Faya's Inheritance" (air) .. .. 1·00 30
649. 200 f. "Soumangourou Kante killed by Djegue" .. 2·00 45

The 75 f. and 100 f. are vert. designs.

**1968.** Paintings of African Legends (2nd series). As T **89.** Multicoloured.

651. 15 f. "Little Demons of Mount Nimba" (postage) 10 10
652. 30 f. "Lan, the Baby Buffalo" .. .. .. 20 10
653. 40 f. "The Nianablas and the Crocodiles" .. .. 30 20
654. 50 f. "Leuk the Hare and the Drum" .. .. 50 20
655. 70 f. "Malissadio—the Young Girl and the Hippopotamus" (air) .. .. 75 20
656. 300 f. "Little Goune, Son of the Lion" .. .. 3·25 1·10

The 30, 50 and 300 f. are vert.

90. Olive Baboon.

**1968.** African Fauna. Multicoloured.

658. 5 f. Type **90** (postage) .. 15 10
659. 10 f. Leopards .. .. 20 10
660. 15 f. Hippopotami .. 30 15
661. 20 f. Crocodile .. .. 55 20
662. 30 f. Warthog .. .. 70 20
663. 50 f. Kob .. .. .. 85 25
664. 75 f. African buffalo .. 1·60 45
665. 100 f. Lions (air) .. .. 1·75 40
666. 200 f. African elephant .. 4·00 1·00

Nos 665/6 are 50 × 35 mm.

91. Robert F. Kennedy.

**1968.** "Martyrs of Liberty". Multicoloured.

668 30 f. Type **91** (postage) .. 20 10
669 75 f. Martin Luther King 50 20
670 100 f. John F. Kennedy .. 65 35
671 50 f. Type **91** (air) .. 45 15
672 100 f. Martin Luther King 80 25
673 200 f. John F. Kennedy .. 1·75 60

92. Running.

**1969.** Olympic Games, Mexico (1968). Multicoloured.

674. 5 f. Type **92** (postage) .. 10 10
675. 10 f. Boxing .. .. 10 10
676. 15 f. Throwing the javelin 15 10
677. 25 f. Football .. .. 25 10
678. 30 f. Hurdling .. .. 30 10
679. 50 f. Throwing the hammer 50 25
680. 75 f. Cycling .. .. 70 25
681. 100 f. Gymnastics (air) .. 70 30
682. 200 f. Exercising on rings 1·25 50
683. 300 f. Pole-vaulting .. 2·50 95

The 25, 100, 200 and 300 f. are larger, 57 × 30 mm.

Each design also shows one of three different sculptured figures.

**1969.** Moon Flight of "Apollo 8". Nos. 514/16 optd. **APOLLO 8 DEC. 1968** and earth and moon motifs or surch.

684. 30 f. on 45 f. mult. (postage) 35 35
685. 45 f. multicoloured .. 35 35
686. 25 f. on 200 f. mult. (air) 35 15
687. 100 f. multicoloured .. 1·10 65
688. 200 f. multicoloured .. 2·00 1·00

95. "Tarzan". 97. "Apollo" Launch.

96. Pioneers lighting Fire.

**1969.** "Tarzan" (famous Guinea Chimpanzee). Multicoloured.

689. 25 f. Type **95** .. .. 25 15
690. 30 f. "Tarzan" in front of Pastoria Institute .. 30 20
691. 75 f. "Tarzan" and family 65 25
692. 100 f. "Tarzan" squatting on branch .. .. 1·25 40

**1969.** Guinean Pioneer Youth Organization. Multicoloured.

693. 5 f. Type **96** .. .. 10 10
694. 25 f. Pioneer and village .. 20 10
695. 30 f. Pioneers squad .. 25 10
696. 40 f. Playing basketball .. 35 20
697. 45 f. Two pioneers .. 40 20
698. 50 f. Pioneers emblem .. 50 25

**1969.** 1st Man on the Moon. Multicoloured.

700. 25 f. Type **97** .. .. 15 10
701. 30 f. View of Earth .. 20 10
702. 50 f. Modules descent to the Moon .. .. .. 35 10
703. 60 f. Astronauts on Moon .. 45 20
704. 75 f. Landing module on Moon .. .. .. 50 25
705. 100 f. Take-off from Moon 1·00 40
706. 200 f. "Splashdown" .. 2·00 1·00

No. 705 is size 35 × 71 mm.

The above stamps were issued with English and French inscriptions.

98. Pylon and Heavy Industry.

**1969.** 50th Anniv. of I.L.O. Mult.

707. 25 f. Type **98** .. .. 20 10
708. 30 f. Broadcasting studio .. 20 10
709. 75 f. Harvesting .. .. 50 20
710. 200 f. Making pottery .. 1·40 65

99. Child suffering from Smallpox. 100. O.E.R.S. Countries on Map of Africa.

**1970.** Campaign Against Measles and Smallpox. Multicoloured.

711. 25 f. Type **99** .. .. 15 10
712. 30 f. Mother and child with measles .. .. .. 20 15
713. 40 f. Inoculating girl .. 30 15
714. 50 f. Inoculating boy .. 50 25
715. 60 f. Inoculating family .. 60 25
716. 200 f. Dr. Edward Jenner 2·25 1·00

**1970.** Meeting of Senegal River Riparian States Organization (Organisation des Etats Riverains du fleuve Senegal).

717. **100.** 30 f. multicoloured .. 20 15
718. 200 f. multicoloured .. 1·50 95

NOTE: The Riparian States are Guinea, Mali, Mauritania and Senegal.

101. Dish Aerial and Open book.

**1970.** World Telecommunications Day.

719. **101.** 5 f. black and blue .. 15 15
720. 10 f. black and red .. 15 15
721. 50 f. black and yellow .. 45 15
722. 200 f. black and lilac .. 2·00 95

102. Lenin.

**1970.** Birth Cent. of Lenin. Multicoloured.

723. 5 f. Type **102** .. .. 10 10
724. 20 f. "Lenin in the Smolny" (Serov) .. 20 10
725. 30 f. "Lenin addressing Workers" (Serov) .. 25 15
726. 40 f. "Lenin speaking to Servicemen" (Vasiliev) 40 15
727. 100 f. "Lenin with Crowd" (Vasilev) .. .. 1·00 35
728. 200 f. Type **102** .. .. 1·75 1·00

103. Congo Tetra.

**1971.** Fishes. Multicoloured.
729. 5 f. Type **103**. .. .. 10 10
730. 10 f. Blue gularis .. .. 15 10
731. 15 f. Fire mouth panchax 15 10
732. 20 f. Six-lined distichodus 20 15
733. 25 f. Jewel cichlid .. 25 20
734. 30 f. Dwarf rainbow cichlid 40 20
735. 40 f. Red lyretail .. .. 50 20
736. 45 f. Banded jewel fish .. 70 25
737. 50 f. Gunther's killy .. 80 35
738. 75 f. Butterfly fish .. 1·40 40
739. 100 f. Kingfish .. .. 1·75 45
740. 200 f. African mouth-breeder .. .. .. 3·50 1·10

**104.** Violet-crested Turaco.

**1971.** Wild Birds. Multicoloured.
741. 5 f. Type **104** (postage) .. 1·10 55
742. 20 f. Golden Oriole .. 1·50 75
743. 30 f. Blue headed Coucal .. 1·75 90
744. 40 f. Great Grey Shrike .. 1·90 1·00
745. 75 f. Vulturine Guineafowl 3·75 1·25
746. 100 f. Southern Ground Hornbill .. .. 5·50 1·60
747. 50 f. Type **104** (air) .. 2·25 1·10
748. 100 f. As 20 f. .. .. 2·75 1·40
749. 200 f. As 75 f. .. .. 8·25 2·00

**105.** U.N.I.C.E.F. Emblem on Map of Africa.

**1971.** 25th Anniv. of U.N.I.C.E.F.
750.**105.** 25 f. multicoloured .. 15 10
751. 30 f. multicoloured .. 20 10
752. 50 f. multicoloured .. 35 15
753. 60 f. multicoloured .. 50 20
754. 100 f. multicoloured .. 80 35

**106.** John and Robert Kennedy and Martin Luther King.

**1972.** Air. Martyrs for Peace. Embossed on silver or gold foil.
755.**106.** 300 f. silver .. .. 3·25
756. 1500 f. gold, cream and green .. .. .. 16·00

**107.** Jules Verne and Moon Rocket.

**1972.** Air. Moon Exploration. Embossed on silver or gold foil.
757.**107.** 300 f. silver .. .. 3·25
758. 1200 f. gold .. .. 13·00

**108.** Pres. Richard Nixon.

**1972.** Air. Pres. Nixon's Visit to Peking. Embossed on gold or silver foil.
759 **108** 90 f. silver .. .. 75
760 – 90 f. silver .. .. 75
761 – 90 f. silver .. .. 75
762 – 90 f. silver .. .. 75
763 **108** 290 f. gold .. .. 2·50
764 – 290 f. gold .. .. 2·50
765 – 290 f. gold .. .. 2·50
766 – 290 f. gold .. .. 2·50
767 – 1200 f. gold and red .. 13·00
DESIGNS—VERT. Nos. 760, 764 Chinese table-tennis player. Nos. 761, 765, American table-tennis player. Nos. 762, 766, Mao Tse-tung. HORIZ. (45 × 35 mm). No. 767, Pres. Nixon and Mao Tae-tung.

**109.** "Flying Flatfish".

**1972.** Imaginary Space Creatures. Mult.
768. 5 f. Type **109**. .. .. 10 10
769. 20 f. "Radioactive crab" 20 10
770. 30 f. "Space octopus" .. 25 10
771. 40 f. "Rocket-powered serpent" .. .. 45 10
772. 100 f. "Winged eel" .. 1·10 40
773. 200 f. "Flying dragon" .. 2·00 70

**110.** African Child.

**1972.** Racial Equality Year. Multicoloured.
774. 15 f. Type **110**. (postage) 10 10
775. 20 f. Asiatic child .. 15 10
776. 30 f. Indian youth .. 20 10
777. 50 f. European girl .. 45 20
778. 100 f. Heads of four races 85 35
779. 100 f. As No. 778 (air) .. 90 40

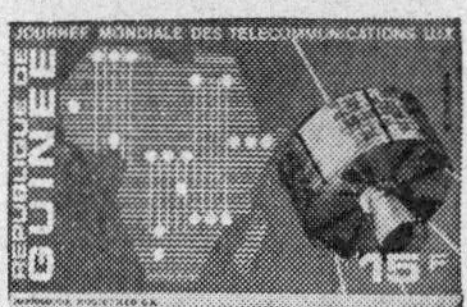

**111.** "Syncom" and African Map.

**1972.** World Telecommunications Day. Mult.
780. 15 f. Type **111**. (postage) .. 15 10
781. 30 f. "Relay" .. .. 25 10
782. 75 f. "Early Bird" .. 60 30
783. 80 f. "Telstar" .. .. 1·00 40
784. 100 f. As 30 f. (air) .. 1·00 35
785. 200 f. As 75 f. .. .. 1·90 65

**112.** APU Emblem and Dove with Letter.

**1972.** 10th Anniv. of African Postal Union.
786.**112.** 15 f. mult. (postage) .. 10 10
787. 30 f. multicoloured .. 20 10
788. 75 f. multicoloured .. 50 25
789. 80 f. multicoloured .. 65 40
790. – 100 f. multicoloured (air) 85 40
791. – 200 f. multicoloured .. 1·75 75
DESIGNS: 100 f. to 200 f. APU emblem and airmail envelope.

**113.** Child reading Book. **114.** Throwing the Javelin.

**1972.** Int. Book Year. Multicoloured.
792. 5 f. Type **113** .. .. 10 10
793. 15 f. Book with sails .. 15 10
794. 40 f. Girl with book and plant .. .. .. 30 15
795. 50 f. "Key of Knowledge" and open book .. .. 50 20
796. 75 f. "Man" reading book and globe .. .. 75 40
797. 200 f. Open book and laurel sprigs .. .. .. 1·75 70

**1972.** Olympic Games, Munich. Mult.
798. 5 f. Type **114** (postage) .. 10 10
799. 10 f. Pole-vaulting .. 10 10
800. 25 f. Hurdling .. .. 25 10
801. 30 f. Throwing the hammer 35 10
802. 40 f. Boxing .. .. 50 15
803. 50 f. Gymnastics (horse) .. 65 25
804. 75 f. Running .. .. 90 35
805. 100 f. Gymnastics (rings) (air) .. .. .. 1·50 45
806. 200 f. Cycling .. .. 2·75 85

**1972.** U.N. Environmental Conservation Conf., Stockholm. Nos. 750/4 optd. **UNE SEULE TERRE** and emblem.
808.**105.** 25 f. multicoloured .. 20 10
809. 30 f. multicoloured .. 20 10
810. 50 f. multicoloured .. 45 15
811. 60 f. multicoloured .. 70 25
812. 100 f. multicoloured .. 1·00 50

**116.** Dimitrov addressing "Reichstag Fire" Court.

**1972.** 90th Birth Anniv. of George Dimitrov (Bulgarian statesman).
813.**116.** 5 f. blue, gold and green 10 10
814. – 25 f. blue, gold & green 15 10
815. – 40 f. blue, gold and green 30 20
816. – 100 f. blue, gold & green 80 35
DESIGNS: 25 f. In Moabit Prison, Berlin, 1933. 40 f. Writing memoirs. 100 f. G. Dimitrov.

**117.** Emperor Haile Selassie. **118.** "Syntomeida epilais".

**1972.** Emperor Haile Selassie of Ethiopia's 80th Birthday. Multicoloured.
817. 40 f. Type **117** .. .. 35 20
818. 200 f. Emperor Haile Selassie in military uniform .. 1·60 80

**1973.** Guinean Insects. Multicoloured.
819. 5 f. Type **118** .. .. 10 10
820. 15 f. "Hippodamia californica" .. .. 25 10
821. 30 f. "Tettigonia viridissima" .. .. 50 15
822. 40 f. "Apis mellifica" .. 60 25
823. 50 f. "Photinus pyralis" .. 85 30
824. 200 f. "Ancyluris formosissima" .. .. .. 3·50 1·25

**119.** Dr. Kwame Nkrumah.

**1973.** 10th Anniv. of Organization of African Unity.
825.**119.** 1 s. 50 blk., gold & green 15 10
826. – 2 s. 50 blk., gold & green 25 10
827. – 5 s. black, gold & green 50 25
828. – 10 s. violet and gold .. 1·00 45
DESIGNS: Nos. 826/8, different portraits of Dr. Kwame Nkrumah similar to Type **119**.

**120.** Institute of Applied Biology, Kindia.

**1973.** 25th Anniv. of W.H.O. Multicoloured.
829. 1 s. Type **120** .. .. 10 10
830. 2 s. 50 Preparing vaccine from an egg .. .. 25 10
831. 3 s. Filling ampoules with vaccine .. .. .. 30 20
832. 4 s. Sterilization of vaccine 40 20
833. 5 s. Packing vaccines .. 60 25
834. 10 s. Preparation of vaccine base .. .. .. 1·25 40
835. 20 s. Inoculating patient .. 2·50 75
Nos. 833/35 are size 48 × 31 mm.

**121.** Volcanic Landscape.

**1973.** 500th Birth Anniv. of Copernicus. Multicoloured.
836. 50 c. Type **121** .. .. 10 10
837. 2 s. Sun over desert .. 20 10
838. 4 s. Earth and Moon .. 35 10
839. 5 s. Lunar landscape .. 60 15
840. 10 s. Jupiter .. .. 1·25 35
841. 20 s. Saturn .. .. 2·25 70

**122.** Loading Bauxite at Quayside.

**1974.** Air. Bauxite Industry, Bok. Mult.
843. 4 s. Type **122** .. .. 50 15
844. 6 s. Bauxite train .. .. 85 25
845. 10 s. Bauxite mining .. 1·50 40

**123.** "Clappertonia ficifolia". **125.** Pioneers testing Rope-bridge.

**124.** Drummers and Pigeon.

**1974.** Flowers of Guinea. Multicoloured.
846. 50 c. Type **123** (postage) .. 10 10
847. 1 s. "Rothmannia longiflora" 10 10
848. 2 s. "Oncoba spinosa" .. 20 10
849. 3 s. "Venidium fastuosum" 30 15
850. 4 s. "Bombax costatum" 50 15
851. 5 s. "Clerodendrum splendens" 75 20
852. 7 s. 50 "Combretuni grandiflorum" .. .. 1·25 25
853. 10 s. "Mussaendra erythrophylla" .. .. 1·50 40
854. 12 s. "Argemone mexicana" 1·75 60
855. 20 s. "Thunbergia alata" (air) .. .. .. 2·50 80
856. 25 s. "Diascia barberae" 3·50 80
857. 50 s. "Kigelia africana" 7·00 1·90
SIZES—VERT. Nos. 847/9, As Type **123**. Nos. 850/3, 36 × 47 mm. DIAMOND, Nos. 854/7, 61 × 61 mm.
No. 855 is wrongly inscribed "Thunbegia alata".

**1974.** Centenary of U.P.U. Multicoloured.
858 5 s. Type **124** .. .. 40 20
859 6 s. Runner and pigeon .. 55 25
860 7 s. Monorail train, lorry and pigeon .. .. 75 35
861 10 s. Boeing 707, liner and pigeon .. .. 1·25 60

**1974.** National Pioneers (Scouting) Movement. Multicoloured.

| | | | |
|---|---|---|---|
| 863. | 50 c. Type **125** .. .. | 15 | 10 |
| 864. | 2 s. " On safari " .. .. | 25 | 10 |
| 865. | 4 s. Using field-telephone | 35 | 15 |
| 866. | 5 s. Cooking on camp-fire .. | 60 | 15 |
| 867. | 7 s. 50 Saluting .. .. | 85 | 35 |
| 868. | 10 s. Playing basketball .. | 1·75 | 55 |

**127.** Chimpanzee.

**1975.** Wild Animals. Multicoloured.

| | | | |
|---|---|---|---|
| 871. | 1 s. Type **127** .. .. | 10 | 10 |
| 872. | 2 s. Impala .. .. .. | 20 | 10 |
| 873. | 3 s. Warthog .. .. | 35 | 10 |
| 874. | 4 s. Waterbuck .. .. | 40 | 20 |
| 875. | 5 s. Leopard .. .. | 60 | 20 |
| 876. | 6 s. Greater kudu .. .. | 60 | 25 |
| 877. | 6 s. 50 Common zebra .. | 75 | 35 |
| 878. | 7 s. 50 African buffalo .. | 75 | 35 |
| 879. | 8 s. Hippopotamus .. | 1·25 | 35 |
| 880. | 10 s. Lion .. .. .. | 1·50 | 40 |
| 881. | 12 s. Black rhinoceros .. | 1·90 | 45 |
| 882. | 15 s. African elephant .. | 2·75 | 80 |

**128.** Lion and Lioness beside Pipeline.

**1975.** 10th Anniv. of African Development Bank.

| | | | |
|---|---|---|---|
| 884. | 5 s. Type **128** .. .. | 70 | 20 |
| 885. | 7 s. African elephants beside pipeline .. .. | 1·00 | 30 |
| 886. | 10 s. Lions beside pipeline (horiz.) .. .. .. | 1·25 | 35 |
| 887. | 20 s. African elephant and calf beside pipeline (horiz.) .. .. .. | 2·25 | 80 |

**129.** Women playing Saxophones.

**1976.** Int. Women's Year (1975) Mult.

| | | | |
|---|---|---|---|
| 888. | 5 s. Type **129** .. .. | 40 | 20 |
| 889. | 7 s. Women playing guitars | 60 | 30 |
| 890. | 9 s. Woman railway shunter | 1·50 | 30 |
| 891. | 15 s. Woman doctor .. | 1·75 | 65 |
| 892. | 20 s. Genetics emblems .. | 2·25 | 90 |

**130.** Gymnastics.

**1976.** Olympic Games, Montreal. Mult.

| | | | |
|---|---|---|---|
| 894. | 3 s. Type **130** .. .. | 25 | 10 |
| 895. | 4 s. Long jump .. .. | 35 | 15 |
| 896. | 5 s. Throwing the hammer | 40 | 20 |
| 897. | 6 s. Throwing the discus .. | 45 | 25 |
| 898. | 6 s. 50 Hurdling .. .. | 50 | 25 |
| 899. | 7 s. Throwing the javelin | 50 | 30 |
| 900. | 8 s. Running .. .. | 60 | 30 |
| 901. | 8 s. 50 Cycling .. .. | 95 | 35 |
| 902 | 10 s. High-jumping .. | 1·10 | 35 |
| 903. | 15 s. Putting the shot .. | 1·60 | 60 |
| 904. | 20 s. Pole vaulting .. | 2·25 | 65 |
| 905. | 25 s. Football .. .. | 2·75 | 90 |

**131.** Bell and Early Telephone.

**1976.** Telephone Centenary. Multicoloured.

| | | | |
|---|---|---|---|
| 907. | 5 s. Type **131** .. .. | 50 | 20 |
| 908. | 7 s. Bell and wall telephone | 75 | 25 |
| 909. | 12 s. Bell and satellite "Syncom" .. .. | 1·40 | 50 |
| 910. | 15 s. Bell and satellite "Telstar" .. .. | 1·75 | 60 |

**132.** "Collybia fusipes".

**1977.** Mushrooms. Multicoloured.

| | | | |
|---|---|---|---|
| 912 | 5 s. Type **132** (postage) .. | 1·50 | 20 |
| 913 | 7 s. "Lycoperdon perlatum" .. .. .. | 2·25 | 25 |
| 914 | 9 s. "Boletus edulis" .. | 3·00 | 35 |
| 915 | 9 s. 50 "Lactarius deliciosus" .. .. .. | 3·00 | 45 |
| 916 | 11 s. 50 "Agaricus campestris" .. .. | 4·75 | 80 |
| 917 | 10 s. "Morchella esculenta" (air) .. .. .. | 3·50 | 40 |
| 918 | 12 s. "Lepiota procera" .. | 4·50 | 60 |
| 919 | 15 s. "Cantharellus cibarius" .. .. .. | 6·50 | 1·10 |

**133.** Duplex Murex.

**1977.** Sea Shells. Multicoloured.

| | | | |
|---|---|---|---|
| 921 | 1 s. Type **133** .. .. | 10 | 10 |
| 922 | 2 s. Wavy-leaved turrid .. | 25 | 10 |
| 923 | 4 s. Queen marginella .. | 60 | 15 |
| 924 | 5 s. "Tympanotonos radula" .. .. | 90 | 20 |
| 925 | 7 s. Striped marginella .. | 1·00 | 25 |
| 926 | 8 s. Doris harp .. | 1·40 | 30 |
| 927 | 10 s. Obtuse demoulia .. | 1·75 | 45 |
| 928 | 20 s. Pitted frog shell .. | 3·25 | 80 |
| 929 | 25 s. Adanson's marginella | 4·00 | 1·00 |

Nos. 927/9 are 50 × 34 mm in size.

**134.** President Sekou Toure.

**1977.** 30th Anniv. of Guinean Democratic Party (PDG). Multicoloured.

| | | | |
|---|---|---|---|
| 930. | 5 s. Type **134** .. .. | 35 | 25 |
| 931. | 10 s. Labourers and oxen | 95 | 45 |
| 932. | 20 s. Soldier driving tractor | 2·10 | 95 |
| 933. | 25 s. Pres. Toure addressing U.N. General Assembly | 2·50 | 1·25 |
| 934. | 30 s. Pres. Toure (vert.) .. | 3·00 | 1·50 |
| 935. | 40 s. As 30 s. .. .. | 3·75 | 1·60 |

**135.** "Varanus niloticus".

**1977.** Reptiles. Multicoloured.

| | | | |
|---|---|---|---|
| 937. | 3 s. Type (postage) **135** | 35 | 10 |
| 938. | 4 s. "Hyperolius quinquevittatus" .. .. | 40 | 15 |
| 939. | 5 s. "Uromastix" .. | 50 | 15 |
| 940. | 6 s. "Scincus scincus" .. | 75 | 15 |
| 941. | 6 s. 50 "Agama agama" | 95 | 20 |
| 942. | 7 s. "Naja melanoleuca" | 1·10 | 20 |
| 943. | 8 s. 50 "Python regius" | 1·40 | 25 |
| 944. | 20 s. "Bufo mauritanicus" | 3·00 | 60 |
| 945. | 10 s. "Chamaeleo diepis" (air) .. .. .. | 2·00 | 30 |
| 946. | 15 s. "Crocodylus niloticus" .. .. | 2·75 | 50 |
| 947. | 25 s. "Testudo elegans" | 4·25 | 75 |

**136.** Eland (male.)

**1977.** Endangered Animals. Multicoloured.

| | | | |
|---|---|---|---|
| 948. | 1 s. Type **136** (postage) .. | 15 | 10 |
| 949. | 1 s. Eland (female) .. | 15 | 10 |
| 950. | 1 s. Eland (young) .. | 15 | 10 |
| 951. | 2 s. Chimpanzee (young) .. | 20 | 10 |
| 952. | 2 s. Chimpanzee .. .. | 20 | 10 |
| 953. | 2 s. Chimpanzee sitting .. | 20 | 10 |
| 954. | 2 s. 50 African elephant .. | 30 | 10 |
| 955. | 2 s. 50 African elephant .. | 30 | 10 |
| 956. | 2 s. 50 African elephant .. | 30 | 10 |
| 957. | 3 s. Lion .. .. .. | 50 | 10 |
| 958. | 3 s. Lioness .. .. | 50 | 10 |
| 959. | 3 s. Lion Cub .. .. | 50 | 10 |
| 960. | 4 s. Indian Palm squirrel | 60 | 15 |
| 961. | 4 s. Indian Palm squirrel | 60 | 15 |
| 962. | 4 s. Indian Palm squirrel | 60 | 15 |
| 963. | 5 s. Hippopotamus .. | 80 | 20 |
| 964. | 5 s. Hippopotamus .. | 80 | 20 |
| 965. | 5 s. Hippopotamus .. | 80 | 20 |
| 966. | 5 s. Type **136** (air) .. | 60 | 20 |
| 967. | 5 s. As No. 949. | 60 | 20 |
| 968. | 5 s. As No. 950 .. .. | 60 | 20 |
| 969. | 8 s. As No. 954 .. .. | 1·50 | 25 |
| 970. | 8 s. As No. 955 .. .. | 1·50 | 25 |
| 971. | 8 s. As No. 956 .. .. | 1·50 | 25 |
| 972. | 9 s. As No. 963 .. .. | 1·50 | 25 |
| 973. | 9 s. As No. 964. .. .. | 1·50 | 25 |
| 974. | 9 s. As No. 965 .. .. | 1·50 | 25 |
| 975. | 10 s. As No. 951 .. .. | 1·75 | 30 |
| 976. | 10 s. As No. 952 .. .. | 1·75 | 30 |
| 977. | 10 s. As No. 953 .. .. | 1·75 | 30 |
| 978. | 12 s. As No. 960 .. .. | 1·75 | 40 |
| 979. | 12 s. As No. 961 .. .. | 1·75 | 40 |
| 980. | 12 s. As No. 962 .. .. | 1·75 | 40 |
| 981. | 13 s. As No. 957 .. .. | 2·00 | 50 |
| 982. | 13 s. As No. 958 .. .. | 2·00 | 50 |
| 983. | 13 s. As No. 959 .. .. | 2·00 | 50 |

Issued se-tenant in strips of three within the sheet, each strip showing different views of the same animal.

REPUBLIQUE de GUINEE

**137.** Lenin taking Parade in Red Square, Moscow.

**1976.** 60th Anniv of Russian Revolution. Multicoloured.

| | | | |
|---|---|---|---|
| 984 | 2 s. 50 Lenin's first speach in Moscow (postage) .. | 25 | 10 |
| 985 | 5 s. Lenin addressing revolutionary crowd .. | 45 | 15 |
| 986 | 7 s. 50 Lenin with militiamen .. .. .. | 85 | 20 |
| 987 | 8 s. Type **137** .. .. | 1·10 | 20 |
| 988 | 10 s. Russian ballet (air) .. | 2·00 | 30 |
| 989 | 30 s. Pushkin Monument | 3·75 | 75 |

**138.** Pres. Giscard d'Estaing at Microphones.

**1979.** Visit of President Giscard d'Estaing of France.

| | | | |
|---|---|---|---|
| 990. **138.** | 3 s. brn. and yell-brn. (postage) .. .. | 30 | 10 |
| 991. – | 5 s. brown, pale green and deep green .. | 55 | 15 |
| 992. – | 6 s. 50 brown, pale mauve and deep mauve .. | 80 | 20 |
| 993. – | 7 s. brown, pale blue and blue .. .. | 85 | 20 |
| 994. – | 8 s. 50 brown, rose and carmine .. .. | 1·25 | 30 |
| 995. – | 10 s. brown, pale violet and violet .. .. | 1·60 | 40 |
| 996. – | 20 s. brown, pale green and deep green .. | 3·50 | 65 |
| 997. – | 25 s. multicoloured (air) | 4·00 | 1·25 |

DESIGNS—HORIZ. 5 s. President Giscard d'Estaing and Sekou Toure in conference. 6 s. 50, Presidents signing agreement. 7 s. Presidents at official meeting. 8 s. 50, Presidents with their wives. 10 s. Presidents in conference. 20 s. Toasting the agreement. VERT. 25 s. President Giscard d'Estaing.

**139.** "20,000 Leagues Under the Sea".

**1979.** 150th Birth Anniv. (1978) of Jules Verne. Multicoloured.

| | | | |
|---|---|---|---|
| 998. | 1 s. Type **139** (postage) .. | 10 | 10 |
| 999. | 3 s. "The Children of Captain Grant" .. | 30 | 10 |
| 1000. | 5 s. "The Mysterious Island" .. .. | 60 | 15 |
| 1001. | 7 s. "A Captain of Fifteen Years" .. .. | 1·25 | 35 |
| 1002. | 10 s. "The Amazing Adventure of Barsac" | 1·75 | 50 |
| 1003. | 20 s. "Five Weeks in a Balloon" (air) .. | 2·25 | 40 |
| 1004. | 25 s. "Robur the Conqueror" .. .. | 3·00 | 60 |

**140.** William Henson's "Aerial Steam Carriage", 1842.

**1979.** Aviation History. Multicoloured.

| | | | |
|---|---|---|---|
| 1005 | 3 s. Type **140** .. .. | 30 | 10 |
| 1006 | 5 s. Wright Type A (inscr "Flyer I"), 1903 .. | 55 | 15 |
| 1007 | 6 s. 50 Caudron C-460, 1934 .. .. .. | 75 | 20 |
| 1008 | 7 s. Charles Lindbergh's "Spirit of St. Louis", 1927 .. .. .. | 95 | 20 |
| 1009 | 8 s. 50 Bristol Beaufighter, 1940 .. | 1·25 | 20 |
| 1010 | 10 s. Bleriot XI, 1909 .. | 1·50 | 25 |
| 1011 | 20 s. Boeing 727-100, 1963 | 2·75 | 55 |
| 1012 | 20 s. Concorde .. .. | 3·50 | 70 |

**141.** Hafia Football Team.

**1979.** Hafia Football Club's Victories. Multicoloured.

| | | | |
|---|---|---|---|
| 1013. | 1 s. Type **141** .. .. | 10 | 10 |
| 1014. | 2 s. Team members with cup (vert.) .. .. | 20 | 20 |
| 1015. | 5 s. President Toure presenting medals .. .. | 60 | 15 |
| 1016. | 7 s. President Toure presenting cup (vert.) .. | 85 | 20 |
| 1017. | 8 s. Ahmed Sekou Toure Cup (vert.) .. | 95 | 25 |
| 1018. | 10 s. Team captains shaking hands (vert.) | 1·25 | 30 |
| 1019. | 20 s. The winning goal .. | 2·40 | 75 |

**142.** Children dancing round Tree.

**1980.** International Year of the Child. Multicoloured.

| | | | |
|---|---|---|---|
| 1020. | 2 s. Type **142** .. .. | 15 | 10 |
| 1021. | 4 s. "Heureuse Enfance" | 40 | 15 |
| 1022. | 5 s. Train (horiz.) .. | 60 | 15 |
| 1023. | 7 s. Village (horiz.) .. | 85 | 20 |
| 1024. | 10 s. Boy climbing tree (horiz.) .. .. | 1·25 | 25 |
| 1025. | 25 s. Children of different races (horiz.) .. .. | 3·00 | 70 |

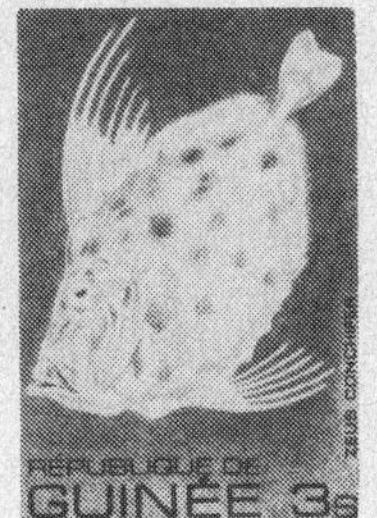


143. " Zeus conchifer ".

**1980.** Fishes. Multicoloured.

1026. 1 s. " Chaetodon luciae " (horiz.) .. .. 10 10
1027. 2 s. " Pagrus enhrenbergi " (horiz.) .. .. 20 10
1028. 3 s. Type **143** .. .. 30 10
1029. 4 s. " Epinephelus taeniops " (horiz.) .. .. 40 15
1030. 5 s. " Hippocampus puntulatus " .. .. 50 15
1031. 6 s. " Argyropelecus sp ". (horiz.) .. .. 80 20
1032. 7 s. " Pisodonophis semicinctus " (horiz.) .. 1·25 20
1033. 8 s. " Cephalacenthus volitans " .. .. 1·40 25
1034. 9 s. " Holocentrus hastatus " (horiz.) .. .. 1·50 25
1035. 10 s. " Psettus sebae " .. 1·60 25
1036. 12 s. " Abudefduf hoeffleri " (horiz.) .. .. 2·00 40
1037. 15 s. " Balistes forcipatus " (horiz.) .. .. 2·75 50

144. Rocket on Launch Pad.

**1980.** 10th Anniv. of 1st Moon Landing. Multicoloured.

1038. 1 s. Type **144** .. .. 10 10
1039. 2 s. Earth from the Moon 20 10
1040. 4 s. Armstrong descending from lunar module .. 35 15
1041. 5 s. Armstrong on the Moon 50 15
1042. 7 s. Astronaut collecting samples .. .. 75 20
1043. 8 s. Parachute descent .. 95 25
1044. 12 s. Winching capsule aboard recovery vessel 1·60 35
1045. 20 s. Astronauts .. 3·00 70

145. Dome of the Rock.

**1981.** Palestinian Solidarity.

1046. **145.** 8 s. multicoloured .. 1·40 55
1047. 11 s. multicoloured .. 1·90 70

146. Map of Member States and Agricultural Produce.

**1982.** 5th Anniv. of Economic Community of West African States. Multicoloured.

1048. 6 s. Type **146** .. .. 85 30
1049. 7 s. Transport .. 1·25 35
1050. 9 s. Heavy Industry .. 1·40 45

**HAVE YOU READ THE NOTES AT THE BEGINNING OF THIS CATALOGUE?**
These often provide answers to the enquiries we receive.

147. Ataturk as Soldier.

**1982.** Birth Centenary of Kemal Ataturk (Turkish statesman). Multicoloured.

1051. 7 s. Type **147** (postage) .. 95 40
1052. 10 s. Ataturk as statesman 1·25 50
1053. 25 s. Equestrian statue (horiz.) .. .. .. 3·50 85
1054. 25 s. As No. 1053 (air) .. 4·00 85

148. Football.

**1982.** Olympic Games, Moscow. Mult.

1055. 1 s. Type **148** (postage) .. 10 10
1056. 2 s. Basketball .. .. 20 15
1057. 3 s. Diving .. .. 25 15
1058. 4 s. Gymnastics .. .. 30 15
1059. 5 s. Boxing .. .. 55 20
1060. 6 s. High jumping .. 75 25
1061. 7 s. Running .. .. 95 35
1062. 8 s. Long jumping .. 1·10 40
1063. 9 s. Fencing (air) .. 1·10 20
1064. 10 s. Football (vert.) .. 1·25 30
1065. 11 s. Basketball (vert.) .. 1·40 45
1066. 20 s. Diving (vert.) .. 3·00 55
1067. 25 s. Boxing (vert.) .. 3·50 65

149. Balaidos Stadium, Vigo.

**1982.** World Cup Football Championship, Spain. Football Stadia. Multicoloured.

1068. 6 s. Type **149** (postage) .. 90 15
1069. 8 s. El Molinon, Gijon .. 1·10 25
1070. 9 s. San Mames, Bilbao .. 1·60 30
1071. 10 s. Sanchez Pizjuan, Seville .. .. .. 1·75 35
1072. 10 s. Luis Casanova, Valencia (air) .. .. 1·75 35
1073. 20 s. Nou Camps, Barcelona .. .. 3·50 45
1074. 25 s. Santiago Bernabeu, Madrid .. .. .. 4·50 65

150. Wrestling.

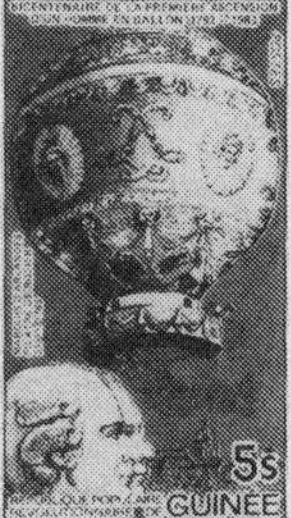


151. Marquis d'Arlandes, Pilatre de Rozier and Montgolfier Balloon, 1783.

**1983.** Olympic Games, Los Angeles (1st issue). Multicoloured.

1075. 5 s. Type **150** (postage) .. 40 15
1076. 7 s. Weightlifting .. 65 25
1077. 10 s. Gymnastics .. 95 35
1078. 15 s. Discus .. .. 1·60 60
1079. 20 s. Kayak (air) .. 1·60 50
1080. 25 s. Equestrian .. 2·25 80

See also Nos. 843/9.

**1983.** Bicent of Manned Flight. Mult.

1082 5 s. Type **151** (postage) .. 55 15
1083 7 s. Jean-Francois Pilatre de Rozier and Montgolfier balloon "Marie Antoinette", 1784 .. 65 25
1084 10 s. Henri Dupuy de Lome and airship, 1872 (horiz) .. .. 95 35
1085 15 s. Major A. Parseval and "Airship No. 1", 1906 (horiz) .. .. 1·60 60
1086 20 s. Count Zeppelin and airship "Bodensee", 1919 (horiz) (air) .. 1·60 50
1087 25 s. Balloon "Double Eagle II" and crew, 1978 .. .. .. 2·25 80

152. Lungs and Monkey.

**1983.** Cent. of Discovery of Tubercle Bacillus. Multicoloured.

1089. 6 s. Type **152** .. .. 75 20
1090. 10 s. Cow .. .. 1·25 30
1091. 11 s. Robert Koch and microscope .. .. 1·50 35
1092. 12 s. Koch using microscope .. .. .. 1·75 50
1093. 15 s. Laboratory .. 2·25 55
1094. 20 s. Scientist with test tube and monkey .. 3·00 70
1095. 25 s. Doctor examining young boy .. .. 3·50 95

153. Disabled and Emblem.

**1983.** International Year of Disabled Persons.

1096. **153.** 10 s. multicoloured .. 1·25 55
1097. 20 s. multicoloured .. 2·50 1·00

154. Mosque, Conakry.

**1983.** 25th Anniv. of Independence.

1098. **154.** 1 s. multicoloured .. 10 10
1099. 2 s. multicoloured .. 20 10
1100. 5 s. multicoloured .. 40 15
1101. 10 s. multicoloured .. 90 40

155. Citizens with Scrolls.

**1983.** 10th Anniv. of Mano River Union. Multicoloured.

1103. 2 s. Type **155** .. 20 10
1104. 7 s. Union emblem .. 50 25
1105. 8 s. Map and presidents of Guinea, Sierra Leone and Liberia .. .. 60 25
1106. 10 s. Signing the Declaration of Union .. .. 85 35

156. Biathlon.

**1983.** Winter Olympic Games, Sarajevo. Multicoloured.

1108. 5 s. Type **156** (postage) .. 50 15
1109. 7 s. Luge .. .. .. 60 25
1110. 10 s. Slalom .. .. 1·25 40
1111. 15 s. Speed skating .. 1·60 60
1112. 20 s. Ski jump (air) .. 1·90 55
1113. 25 s. Ice dancing .. .. 2·50 80

157. Raphael and "Virgin with the Blue Diadem".

**1984.** Anniversaries (1983). Multicoloured.

1115. 5 s. Type **157** .. .. 40 20
1116. 7 s. Rubens and "Holy Family" .. .. 60 25
1117. 10 s. Rembrandt and "Portrait of Saskia" .. 95 40
1118. 15 s. Goethe and scene from "The Young Werther" .. .. 1·40 60
1119. 20 s. Lord Baden-Powell and scout camp .. 1·75 55
1120. 25 s. P. P. Harris and speaker at Rotary meeting .. .. 2·50 80

158. Abraham Lincoln.

**1984.** Personalities. Multicoloured.

1122. 5 s. Type **158** (postage) 40 20
1123. 7 s. Jean-Henri Dunant (founder of Red Cross) 65 25
1124. 10 s. Gottlieb Daimler (automobile designer) 1·25 40
1125. 15 s. Louis Bleriot (pilot) 1·75 55
1126. 20 s. Paul P. Harris (founder of Rotary Club) (air) .. .. 1·75 65
1127. 25 s. Auguste Piccard (ocean explorer) .. 2·50 85

159. "The Mystic Marriage of Sts. Catherine and Sebastian" (detail, Correggio).

**1984.** Paintings. Multicoloured.

1129. 5 s. Type **159** (postage) 40 20
1130. 7 s. "The Holy Family" (A. Durer) .. .. 60 25
1131. 10 s. "The Veiled Lady" (Raphael) .. .. 1·00 40
1132. 15 s. "Portrait of a Young Man" (A. Durer) .. 1·25 55
1133. 20 s. "Portrait of Soutine" (A. Modigliani) (air) .. 1·75 65
1134. 25 s. "The Esterhazy Madonna" (Raphael) 2·50 85

**160.** Congo River Steamer and Canoe.

**1984.** Transport. Multicoloured.

1136 5 s. Type **160** (postage) .. 60 20
1137 7 s. Airship "Graf Zeppelin" .. .. 70 25
1138 10 s. Daimler car, 1886 .. 1·50 40
1139 15 s. Beyer-Garratt locomotive .. .. 2·00 65
1140 20 s. Latecoere seaplane "Comte de la Vaulx" (air) .. .. .. 1·75 55
1141 25 s. Savoia Marchetti S-73 airplane .. .. 2·50 80

**161.** W. Hoppe and D. Schauerhammer (bobsleigh).

**1984.** Winter Olympic Gold Medal Winners. Multicoloured.

1143. 5 s. Type **161** (postage) 40 20
1144. 7 s. T. L. Wassberg (cross-country skiing) .. 60 25
1145. 10 s. G. Boucher (speed skating) .. .. 1·00 40
1146. 15 s. K. Witt (ladies figure skating) .. 1·50 65
1147. 20 s. W. D. Johnson (downhill skiing) (air) 2·00 85
1148. 25 s. U.S.S.R. (ice hockey) .. .. 2·75 90

**162.** T. Ruiz and C. Costie (Synchronized Swimming Duet).

**1985.** Olympic Games Gold Medal Winners. Multicoloured.

1150. 5 s. Type **162** (postage) 40 20
1151. 7 s. R. Klimke, H. Krug and U. Sauer, West Germany (team dressage) .. .. 85 25
1152. 10 s. McKee and Buchan, U.S.A. (yachting, "Flying Dutchman" class) .. .. .. .. 95 40
1153. 15 s. Mark Todd (equestrian three-day event) 1·25 65
1154. 20 s. Daley Thompson (decathlon) (air) .. 2·00 75
1155. 25 s. M. Smith, C. Homfeld, L. Burr and J. Fargis, U.S.A. (equestrian team jumping) .. .. 2·25 85

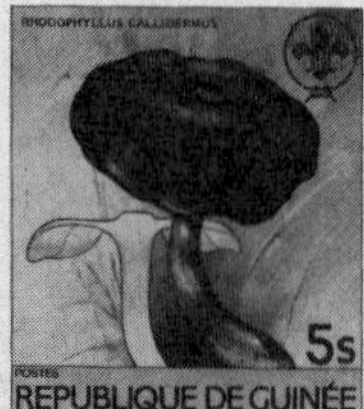


**163.** "Rhodophyllus callidermus".

**1985.** Fungi. Multicoloured.

1157. 5 s. Type **163** (postage) 80 35
1158. 7 s. "Agaricus niger" .. 1·00 45
1159. 10 s. "Thermitomyces globulus" .. .. 1·90 70
1160. 15 s. "Amanita robusta" 2·50 1·10
1161. 20 s. "Lepiota subradicans" (air) .. .. 3·50 1·00
1162. 25 s. "Cantharellus rhodophylus" .. .. 3·75 1·10

**164.** Hermann Oberth and 2-Stage Conical Motor Rocket.

**1985.** Space Achievements. Multicoloured.

1164. 7 s. Type **164** (postage) 50 25
1165. 10 s. "Lunik 1" .. .. 95 40
1166. 15 s. "Lunik 2" on Moon, 1959 .. .. .. 1·25 55
1167. 20 s. "Lunik 3" photographing hidden face of Moon .. .. 1·90 75
1168. 30 s. Armstrong, Aldrin and Collins (first manned landing on Moon) (air) .. .. 2·50 75
1169. 35 s. Sally Ride (first American woman in space) .. .. .. 3·25 80

**165.** Maimonides in Jewish Quarter (850th Birth Anniv.).

**1985.** Anniversaries and Events. Mult.

1171. 7 s. Type **165** (postage) 80 35
1172. 10 s. Christopher Columbus departing from Palos, 1492 .. .. 1·25 40
1173. 15 s. Frederic Bartholdi and Statue of Liberty (centenary) .. .. 1·50 55
1174. 20 s. Queen Mother with Duke of York and Princess Elizabeth (85th birthday) .. 1·75 75
1175. 30 s. Ulf Merbold and space shuttle "Columbia" (air) .. 2·50 75
1176. 35 s. Prince Charles and Lady Diana Spencer (Royal Wedding) .. 3·00 85

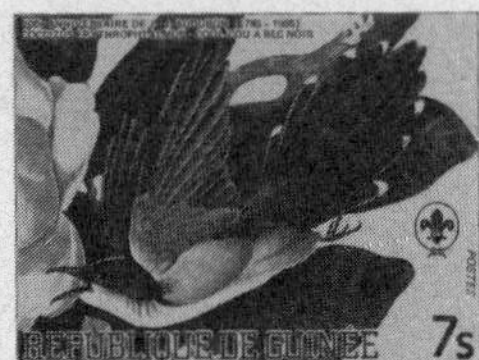


**166.** Black-billed Cuckoo.

**1995.** Birth Bicentenary of John J. Audubon (ornithologist). Multicoloured.

1178. 7 s. Type **166** (postage) 65 50
1179. 10 s. Carolina parakeet .. 1·00 75
1180. 15 s. American anhinga (vert.) .. .. .. 1·50 1·10
1181. 20 s. Red-shouldered hawk .. .. .. 3·25 1·60
1182. 30 s. Screech owl (air) .. 4·00 1·90
1183. 35 s. Brown thrasher (vert.) .. .. .. 5·00 2·40

**167.** Blue-point Siamese.

**1985.** Cats and Dogs. Multicoloured.

1185. 7 s. Type **167** (postage) .. 60 25
1186. 10 s. Cocker spaniel .. 1·25 40
1187. 15 s. Poodles .. .. 1·50 55
1188. 20 s. Persian blue cat .. 2·00 70
1189. 25 s. European tortoise-shell cat .. .. 2·40 85
1190. 30 s. German shepherd dog (air) .. .. 2·75 85
1191. 35 s. Abyssinian cats .. 3·25 95
1192. 40 s. Boxer dog .. .. 3·75 1·25

**168.** Bebeto and Footballers.

**1985.** World Cup Football Championship, Mexico (1986) (1st issue). Multicoloured.

1194. 7 s. Type **168** (postage) .. 60 25
1195. 10 s. Rinat Dassaev .. 1·25 40
1196. 15 s. Phil Neal .. .. 1·50 55
1197. 20 s. Jean Tigana .. 2·40 70
1198. 30 s. Fernando Chalana (air) .. .. .. .. 3·00 75
1199. 35 s. Michel Platini .. 3·50 85

See also Nos. 1268/71.

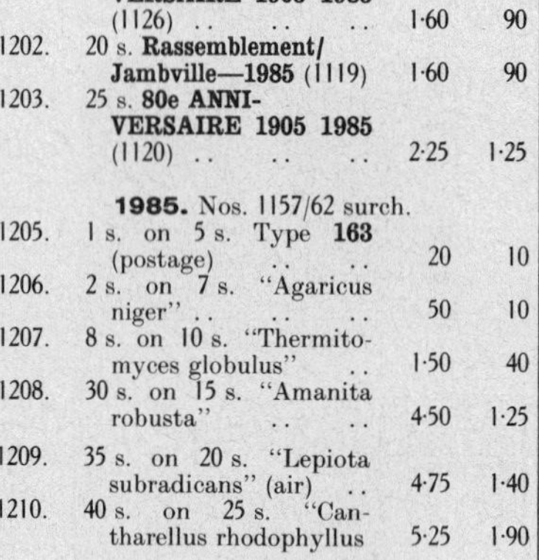

**1985.** Air. Nos. 1126 and 1119/20 optd.

1201. 20 s. **80e ANNIVERSAIRE 1905 1985** (1126) .. .. .. 1·60 90
1202. 20 s. **Rassemblement/ Jambville—1985** (1119) 1·60 90
1203. 25 s. **80e ANNIVERSAIRE 1905 1985** (1120) .. .. .. 2·25 1·25

**1985.** Nos. 1157/62 surch.

1205. 1 s. on 5 s. Type **163** (postage) .. .. 20 10
1206. 2 s. on 7 s. "Agaricus niger" .. .. .. 50 10
1207. 8 s. on 10 s. "Thermitomyces globulus" .. 1·50 40
1208. 30 s. on 15 s. "Amanita robusta" .. .. 4·50 1·25
1209. 35 s. on 20 s. "Lepiota subradicans" (air) .. 4·75 1·40
1210. 40 s. on 25 s. "Cantharellus rhodophyllus 5·25 1·90

**171.** Class 8 F Locomotive.

**1985.** Trains (1st series). Multicoloured.

1212. 7 s. Type **171** (postage) 65 25
1213. 15 s. Locomotive "BO'BO'/550 CH" series III .. .. 1·50 55
1214. 25 s. Pacific A Mazout No. 270 .. .. 2·50 80
1215. 35 s. Series 420 Reseaux "S-Bahn" (air) .. 3·25 1·25

Nos. 1213 and 1215 commemorate 150th anniv. of German railways.

See also Nos. 1252/5.

**172.** Columbus and "Pinta".

**1985.** 480th Death Anniv. of Christopher Columbus (explorer) (1st issue). Multicoloured.

1217. 10 s. Type **172** (postage) 1·25 40
1218. 20 s. "Santa Maria" .. 2·50 80
1219. 30 s. "Nina" (air) .. 3·00 90
1220. 40 s. "Santa Maria" and crow's nest .. .. 4·00 1·40

See also Nos. 1257/60.

**173.** Chopin, aged Eight, playing Piano.

**1986.** International Youth Year. Mult.

1222. 10 s. Type **173** (postage) 1·10 45
1223. 20 s. Sandro Botticelli and "Birth of Venus" 1·75 65
1224. 35 s. Gioachino Antonio Rossini, aged 15, conducting orchestra .. 3·50 90
1225. 25 s. Pablo Picasso and "Paul as Harlequin" (air) .. .. .. 2·25 85

**174.** Bayeux Tapestry.

**1986.** Appearance of Halley's Comet. Multicoloured.

1227. 5 f. Type **174** (postage) .. 10 10
1228. 30 f. Comet as seen by the Arabs .. .. 20 10
1229. 40 f. Comet as seen by Montezuma II .. 30 15
1230. 50 f. Edmond Halley and trajectory diagram .. 40 15
1231. 300 f. Halley and Sir Isaac Newton (air) .. 2·25 55
1232. 500 f. Comet, Earth, sun, "Giotto", Soviet and N.A.S.A. space probes 4·00 1·10

**175.** "Challenger" Space Shuttle Memorial Roll.

**1986.** Air. "Challenger" Astronauts Comm. Multicoloured.

1234. 100 f. Type **175** .. .. 70 30
1235. 170 f. Shuttle diagram and Christa McAuliffe holding model .. 1·25 55

**1986.** Various stamps surch.

(a) Nos. 1212/5 (Trains).

1237 2 f. on 7 s. multicoloured 15 10
1238 25 f. on 15 s. mult .. 20 10
1239 50 f. on 25 s. mult .. 35 15
1240 90 f. on 35 s. mult .. 70 25

(b) Nos. 1217/20 (Columbus).

1242. 5 f. on 10 s. multicoloured 15 10
1243. 35 f. on 20 s. multicoloured 25 15
1244. 70 f. on 30 s. multicoloured 55 20
1245. 200 f. on 40 s. mult. .. 1·50 65

(c) Nos. 1222/5 (International Youth Year).

1247. 5 f. on 10 s. mult. (post.) .. 15 10
1248. 35 f. on 20 s. multicoloured 25 15
1249. 90 f. on 35 s. multicoloured 60 25
1250. 50 f. on 25 s. mult. (air) .. 30 15

**177.** Dietrich Autorail Car.

**1986.** Trains (2nd series). Multicoloured.

1252. 20 f. Type **177** (postage) 20 10
1253. 100 f. Steam engine T 13 7906 .. .. .. 75 25
1254. 300 f. Steam locomotive 01220 .. .. .. 2·25 80
1255. 400 f. Autorail train ABH 3 type "5020" (air) .. .. .. 3·00 95

Nos. 1253/4 commemorate 150th anniv. of German Railways.

**178.** Building Fort Navidad and Map of First Voyage, 1492–93.

**1986.** 480th. Death Anniv. of Christopher Columbus (explorer) (2nd issue). Mult.

1257. 40 f. Type **178** (postage) 30 15
1258. 70 f. Disembarking at Hispaniola and map of second voyage, 1493–96 55 20
1259. 200 f. Columbus on deck with natives and map of third voyage, 1498–1500 .. .. 1·50 50
1260. 500 f. Columbus and crew with natives and map of fourth voyage, 1502–04 (air) .. .. 3·50 1·40

**179.** Prince and Princess of Wales and Prince William.

**1986.** Celebrities. Multicoloured.

1262. 30 f. Type **179** (postage) 20 10
1263. 40 f. Alain Prost (1985 Formula 1 world champion) .. .. 25 10
1264. 100 f. Duke and Duchess of York .. .. 60 20
1265. 300 f. Elvis Presley (entertainer) .. .. 2·75 75
1266. 500 f. Michael Jackson (entertainer) (air) .. 3·50 1·00

**180.** Pfaff, Trophy and Satellite.

**1986.** World Cup Football Championship, Mexico (2nd issue). Multicoloured.

1268. 100 f. Type **180** (postage) 75 20
1269. 300 f. Michel Platini .. 2·25 60
1270. 400 f. Matthaus .. .. 3·00 80
1271. 500 f. Diego Maradona (air) .. .. .. 3·75 1·00

**181.** Judo.

**1987.** Olympic Games, Seoul (1988). Mult.

1273. 20 f. Type **181** (postage) 15 10
1274. 30 f. High jumping .. 20 10
1275. 40 f. Handball .. .. 25 10
1276. 100 f. Gymnastics .. 60 20
1277. 300 f. Javelin throwing (air) .. .. .. 1·75 55
1278. 500 f. Showjumping .. 3·00 80

**182.** Rifle shooting.

**1987.** Winter Olympic Games, Calgary (1988) (1st issue). Multicoloured.

1280. 50 f. on 40 f. Type **182** (postage) .. .. 30 10
1281. 100 f. Cross-country skiing .. .. 65 20
1282. 400 f. Ski jumping (air) 2·75 75
1283. 500 f. Two-man bobsleigh 3·25 85

**183.** Skiing.

**1987.** Winter Olympic Games, Calgary (1988) (2nd issue). Multicoloured.

1285. 25 f. Type **183** (postage) 20 10
1286. 50 f. Ice hockey .. .. 40 15
1287. 100 f. Men's figure skating .. .. 70 20
1288. 150 f. Slalom .. .. 1·25 35
1289. 300 f. Speed skating (air) 2·00 70
1290. 500 f. Four-man bobsleigh .. .. 3·25 1·10

**184.** S. K. Doe, Gen. Lansana Conte, Gen. J. Momoh and National Flags.

**185.** Dimetrodon.

**1987.** 10th Anniv of River Mano Reconciliation.

1292. **184.** 40 f. multicoloured .. 25 15
1293. 50 f. multicoloured .. 30 15
1294. 75 f. multicoloured .. 50 25
1295. 100 f. multicoloured 70 35
1296. 150 f. multicoloured 90 45

**1987.** Pre-historic Animals. Multicoloured.

1297. 50 f. Type **185** (postage) 45 15
1298. 100 f. Iguanodon .. 80 25
1299. 200 f. Tylosaurus .. 1·50 55
1300. 300 f. Cave bear .. .. 2·50 75
1301. 400 f. Sabre-tooth tiger (air) .. .. 3·25 85
1302. 500 f. Stegosaurus .. 4·25 1·10

**186.** Statue and Portrait of Marquis de Lafayette (revolutionary).

**188.** Tennis Player and Emblem.

**1987.** Celebrities. Multicoloured.

1304 50 f. Type **186** (230th birth anniv) (postage) .. 35 15
1305 100 f. Ettore Bugatti (motor manufacturer) (40th death anniv) and "White Elephant" .. 70 25
1306 200 f. Gary Kasparov (world chess champion) and game diagram of Kasparov v. Karpov, 1986 .. .. .. 2·00 65
1307 300 f. Flag and George Washington (first U.S. President) (bicent of American constitution) 2·00 75
1308 400 f. Boris Becker (tennis player) (air) .. 3·50 85
1309 500 f. Winston Churchill (statesman) .. .. 4·00 1·10

**1987.** Olympic Games, Seoul (1988). Tennis.

1311. **188.** 50 f. mult. (postage) 40 10
1312. – 100 f. multicoloured 70 25
1313. – 150 f. multicoloured 1·10 35
1314. – 200 f. multicoloured 1·50 55
1315. – 300 f. mult. (air) .. 2·00 75
1316. – 500 f. multicoloured 3·50 1·10

Designs: 100 f. to 500 f. Various tennis players.

**189.** Discus thrower and Courtyard of Hospital of the Holy Cross and St. Paul.

**1987.** Olympic Games, Barcelona (1992). Multicoloured.

1318. 50 f. Type **189** (postage) 30 10
1319. 100 f. Statue of Pablo Casals (cellist) and pole vaulter .. .. 60 25
1320. 150 f. Long jumper and Labyrinth of Horta .. 90 35
1321. 170 f. Lizard in Guell Park and javelin thrower .. .. 1·00 40
1322. 400 f. Gymnast and Church of Mercy (air) 2·50 75
1323. 500 f. Tennis player and Picasso Museum .. 3·00 95

**190.** African Wild Dogs.

**1987.** Endangered Wildlife. Multicoloured.

1325 50 f. Type **190** (postage) 35 10
1326 70 f. African wild dog .. 55 20
1327 100 f. African wild dogs stalking prey .. 75 25
1328 170 f. African wild dog chasing prey .. .. 1·25 40
1329 400 f. South African crowned cranes (air) .. 4·00 2·25
1330 500 f. Giant eland .. 3·50 1·40

**191.** "Galaxy"-"Grasp".

**1988.** Space Exploration. Multicoloured.

1332. 50 f. Type **191** (postage) 30 10
1333. 150 f. "Energia"-"Mir" link-up .. .. 1·00 25
1334. 200 f. NASA space station .. .. .. 1·40 40
1335. 300 f. "Ariane-5" rocket depositing satellite payload .. .. .. 2·00 70
1336. 400 f. Mars "Rover" space vehicle (air) .. 2·75 85
1337. 450 f. Venus "Vega" space probe .. .. 3·00 95

**192.** Red-headed Bluebill.

**193.** Queen Elizabeth II and Prince Philip.

**1988.** Scouts, Birds and Butterflies. Designs showing scouts studying featured animals. Multicoloured.

1339. 50 f. Type **192** (postage) 75 20
1340. 100 f. "Medon nymphalidae" (butterfly) .. 65 25
1341. 150 f. Red bishop .. 1·50 45
1342. 300 f. Beautiful sunbird 2·75 1·50
1343. 400 f. "Sophia numphalidae" (butterfly) (air) .. .. .. 3·00 1·00
1344. 450 f. "Rumia nymphalidae" (butterfly) .. 3·00 1·10

**1988.** Celebrities. Multicoloured.

1346. 200 f. Type **193** (40th wedding anniv. (1987)) (postage) .. .. 1·25 40
1347. 250 f. Fritz von Opel (car designer) and "Rak 2 Opel", 1928 .. .. 1·75 55
1348. 300 f. Wolfgang Amadeus Mozart (composer) .. 2·25 55
1349. 400 f. Steffi Graf (tennis player) .. .. .. 3·00 70
1350. 450 f. Edwin "Buzz" Aldrin (astronaut) (air) 3·25 80
1351. 500 f. Paul Harris (founder of Rotary International) .. 3·50 95

**194.** Vreni Schneider (Women's Slalom and Giant Slalom).

**195** Scientist using Microscope

**1988.** Calgary Winter Olympic Games Gold Medal Winners. Multicoloured.

1353. 50 f. Type **194** (postage) 30 10
1354. 150 f. Matti Nykaenen (Ski jumping) .. .. 1·10 25
1355. 250 f. Marina Kiehl (Women's downhill) .. 1·75 40
1356. 400 f. Frank Piccard (Men's super giant slalom) .. .. 2·50 75
1357. 100 f. Frank-Peter Roetsch (Biathlon) (air) .. .. .. 70 25
1358. 450 f. Katarina Witt (Women's figure skating) .. .. 2·75 95

**1988.** World Health Day. Multicoloured.

1360 50 f. Type **195** .. .. 20 10
1361 150 f. Nurse vaccinating boy .. .. .. 55 15
1362 500 f. Dental check .. 1·90 50

**196** Baron Pierre de Coubertin (founder of modern Olympics)

**1988.** International Olympic Committee.

1363 **196** 50 f. multicoloured .. 20 10
1364 100 f. multicoloured .. 40 10
1365 150 f. multicoloured .. 55 15
1366 500 f. multicoloured .. 1·90 50

**197** Hands exchanging Letter

**198** Earth Communications Station

**1988.** 25th Anniv of Pan-African Postal Union.

1367 **197** 50 f. multicoloured .. 20 10
1368 75 f. multicoloured .. 30 10
1369 100 f. multicoloured .. 40 10
1370 150 f. multicoloured .. 55 15

**1988.** Inauguration of MT 20 International Transmission Centre.

| No. | Type | Description | Unused | Used |
|---|---|---|---|---|
| 1371 | 198 | 50 f. multicoloured .. | 20 | 10 |
| 1372 | | 100 f. multicoloured .. | 40 | 10 |
| 1373 | | 150 f. multicoloured .. | 55 | 15 |

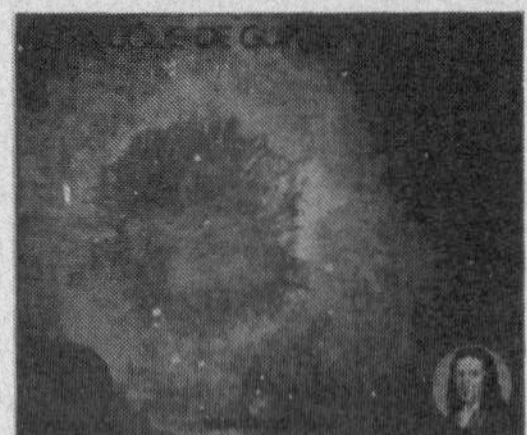

199 "Helix Nebular"

**1989.** Appearance of Halley's Comet. Nebulae. Multicoloured.

| No. | Description | Unused | Used |
|---|---|---|---|
| 1374 | 100 f. + 25 f. Type **199** (postage) .. .. | 50 | 15 |
| 1375 | 150 f. + 25 f. Orion | 70 | 20 |
| 1376 | 200 f. + 25 f. "The Eagle" | 90 | 25 |
| 1377 | 250 f. + 25 f. "Triffid" .. | 1·10 | 30 |
| 1378 | 300 f. + 25 f. Eta-Carinae (air) .. .. .. | 1·25 | 30 |
| 1379 | 500 f. + 25 f. NGC 2264 .. | 2·00 | 50 |

200 Diving

**1989.** Olympic Games, Barcelona (1992) (1st issue). Multicoloured.

| No. | Description | Unused | Used |
|---|---|---|---|
| 1381 | 50 f. Type **200** (postage) | 20 | 10 |
| 1382 | 100 f. Running (vert) .. | 40 | 10 |
| 1383 | 150 f. Shooting .. | 60 | 15 |
| 1384 | 250 f. Tennis (vert) .. | 1·00 | 25 |
| 1385 | 400 f. Football (air) .. | 1·60 | 40 |
| 1386 | 500 f. Equestrian (dressage) (vert) .. | 2·00 | 50 |

201 Oath of the Tennis Court and Jean Sylvain Bailly (President of National Assembly)

**1989.** "Philexfrance 89" Stamp Exhibition and Bicent of French Revolution. Mult.

| No. | Description | Unused | Used |
|---|---|---|---|
| 1388 | 250 f. Type **201** (postage) | 1·00 | 25 |
| 1389 | 300 f. King addressing the Three Estates and Comte de Mirabeau .. | 1·25 | 30 |
| 1390 | 400 f. 18th July 1790 celebrations and Marquis de La Fayette | 1·60 | 40 |
| 1391 | 450 f. The King's arrest at Varennes and Jerome Petion (first President of the Convention) (air) | 1·75 | 45 |

202 Girl carrying Plants

**1989.** 10th Anniv (1987) of International Fund for Agricultural Development. Campaign for Self-sufficiency. Multicoloured.

| No. | Description | Unused | Used |
|---|---|---|---|
| 1393 | 25 f. Type **202** .. .. | 10 | 10 |
| 1394 | 50 f. Men irrigating crops | 20 | 10 |
| 1395 | 75 f. Family with cattle .. | 30 | 10 |
| 1396 | 100 f. Fishermen .. | 40 | 10 |
| 1397 | 150 f. Harvesting crops .. | 60 | 15 |
| 1398 | 300 f. Pumping water .. | 1·25 | 30 |

203 Buildings, Vehicles and Envelopes on Map

**1989.** 15th Anniv of Mano River Union. Mult.

| No. | Description | Unused | Used |
|---|---|---|---|
| 1399 | 150 f. Type **203** .. .. | 60 | 15 |
| 1400 | 300 f. Map and Presidents of member countries .. | 1·25 | 30 |

204 Emblem, Banknotes and Produce

**1989.** 25th Anniv of African Development Bank.

| No. | Type | Description | Unused | Used |
|---|---|---|---|---|
| 1401 | 204 | 300 f. multicoloured .. | 1·25 | 30 |

205 Skiing and Super-Tignes

**1990.** Winter Olympic Games, Albertville (1992). Multicoloured.

| No. | Description | Unused | Used |
|---|---|---|---|
| 1402 | 150 f. Type **205** (postage) | 55 | 15 |
| 1403 | 250 f. Cross-country skiing and Le Lavachet .. | 90 | 25 |
| 1404 | 400 f. Bobsleighing and Val-Claret .. .. | 1·40 | 35 |
| 1405 | 500 f. Speed skating and Meribel (air) .. .. | 1·75 | 45 |

206 Presidents Bush and Gorbachev (1989 Summit, Malta)

**1990.** Multicoloured.

| No. | Description | Unused | Used |
|---|---|---|---|
| 1407 | 200 f. Type **206** (postage) | 70 | 20 |
| 1408 | 250 f. De Gaulle's appeal to resist, June 1940 .. | 90 | 25 |
| 1409 | 300 f. Pope Jean-Paul II, President Gorbachev and dove (1989 meeting) | 1·10 | 30 |
| 1410 | 400 f. Concorde and "TGV Atlantique" express .. | 1·60 | 45 |
| 1411 | 450 f. Robin Yount (cent of Baseball) (air) .. | 1·60 | 40 |
| 1412 | 500 f. "Galileo" space probe .. .. .. | 1·75 | 45 |

207 St. Dominic's, Naples

208 View of Exhibition

**1990.** World Cup Football Championship, Italy. Multicoloured.

| No. | Description | Unused | Used |
|---|---|---|---|
| 1414 | 200 f. Type **207** (postage) | 70 | 20 |
| 1415 | 250 f. Piazza San Carlo, Turin .. .. | 90 | 25 |
| 1416 | 300 f. San Cataldo church | 1·10 | 30 |
| 1417 | 450 f. St. Francis's Church, Udine (air) .. | 1·60 | 40 |

**1991.** "Telecom 91" International Telecommunications Exhibition. Multicoloured.

| No. | Description | Unused | Used |
|---|---|---|---|
| 1419 | 150 f. Type **208** .. .. | 55 | 10 |
| 1420 | 300 f. Emblem (horiz) .. | 1·10 | 30 |

209 Health Centre

**1991.** Medecins sans Frontieres.

| No. | Type | Description | Unused | Used |
|---|---|---|---|---|
| 1421 | 209 | 300 f. multicoloured .. | 1·10 | 30 |

210 "Madonna della Tenda"

**1991.** Christmas (1990). Paintings by Raphael. Multicoloured.

| No. | Description | Unused | Used |
|---|---|---|---|
| 1422 | 50 f. Type **210** (postage) | 20 | 10 |
| 1423 | 100 f. Small Cowper Madonna .. .. | 40 | 10 |
| 1424 | 150 f. Tempi Madonna | 55 | 15 |
| 1425 | 250 f. Niccolini Madonna | 95 | 25 |
| 1426 | 300 f. Orleans Madonna (air) .. .. .. | 1·10 | 30 |
| 1427 | 500 f. Solly Madonna .. | 1·90 | 50 |

211 Rudi Voller

**1991.** West Germany, 1990 World Cup Football Champion. West German Players and Goals Scored. Multicoloured.

| No. | Description | Unused | Used |
|---|---|---|---|
| 1429 | 200 f. Type **211** (postage) | 75 | 20 |
| 1430 | 250 f. Uwe Bein .. | 95 | 25 |
| 1431 | 300 f. Pierre Littbarski .. | 1·10 | 30 |
| 1432 | 400 f. Jurgen Klinsmann | 1·50 | 35 |
| 1433 | 450 f. Lothar Matthaus (air) .. .. .. | 1·75 | 45 |
| 1434 | 500 f. Andreas Brehme .. | 1·90 | 50 |

212 Fairey Swordfish sinking "Bismarck" (German battleship) and Admirals Raeder and Tovey

**1991.** Battles of Second World War. Mult.

| No. | Description | Unused | Used |
|---|---|---|---|
| 1436 | 100 f. Type **212** (postage) | 40 | 10 |
| 1437 | 150 f. Aichi D3A "Val" bombers sinking U.S.S. "Yorktown" (aircraft carrier) and Admirals Yamamoto and Nimitz (Battle of Midway) .. | 55 | 15 |
| 1438 | 200 f. American torpedo boat and Admirals Kondo and Halsey (Guadalcanal) .. | 75 | 20 |
| 1439 | 250 f. "Crusader III" tanks, Hawker Hurricane Mk II aircraft, Rommel and Montgomery (El Alamein) .. | 95 | 25 |
| 1440 | 300 f. "Tiger II" tanks and Generals Guderian and Patton (Ardennes) (air) .. .. .. | 1·10 | 30 |
| 1441 | 450 f. Grumman TBF Avenger aircraft sinking "Yamato" (Japanese battleship) and Admiral Kogo and General MacArthur .. .. | 1·75 | 45 |

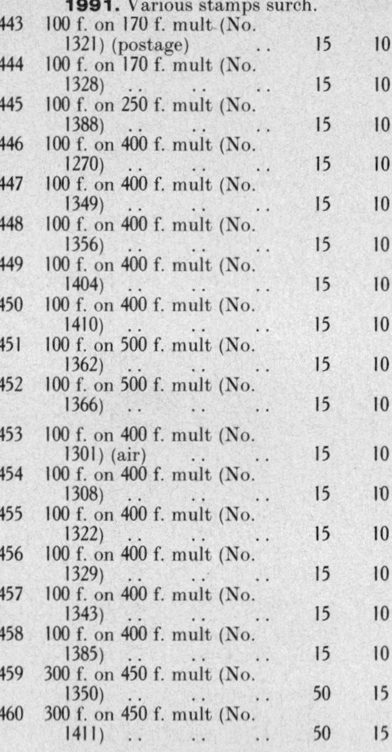

**1991.** Various stamps surch.

| No. | Description | Unused | Used |
|---|---|---|---|
| 1443 | 100 f. on 170 f. mult (No. 1321) (postage) .. | 15 | 10 |
| 1444 | 100 f. on 170 f. mult (No. 1328) .. .. .. | 15 | 10 |
| 1445 | 100 f. on 250 f. mult (No. 1388) .. .. .. | 15 | 10 |
| 1446 | 100 f. on 400 f. mult (No. 1270) .. .. .. | 15 | 10 |
| 1447 | 100 f. on 400 f. mult (No. 1349) .. .. .. | 15 | 10 |
| 1448 | 100 f. on 400 f. mult (No. 1356) .. .. .. | 15 | 10 |
| 1449 | 100 f. on 400 f. mult (No. 1404) .. .. .. | 15 | 10 |
| 1450 | 100 f. on 400 f. mult (No. 1410) .. .. .. | 15 | 10 |
| 1451 | 100 f. on 500 f. mult (No. 1362) .. .. .. | 15 | 10 |
| 1452 | 100 f. on 500 f. mult (No. 1366) .. .. .. | 15 | 10 |
| 1453 | 100 f. on 400 f. mult (No. 1301) (air) .. | 15 | 10 |
| 1454 | 100 f. on 400 f. mult (No. 1308) .. .. .. | 15 | 10 |
| 1455 | 100 f. on 400 f. mult (No. 1322) .. .. .. | 15 | 10 |
| 1456 | 100 f. on 400 f. mult (No. 1329) .. .. .. | 15 | 10 |
| 1457 | 100 f. on 400 f. mult (No. 1343) .. .. .. | 15 | 10 |
| 1458 | 100 f. on 400 f. mult (No. 1385) .. .. .. | 15 | 10 |
| 1459 | 300 f. on 450 f. mult (No. 1350) .. .. .. | 50 | 15 |
| 1460 | 300 f. on 450 f. mult (No. 1411) .. .. .. | 50 | 15 |

214 Nat King Cole Trio

**1991.** Music and Films. Multicoloured.

| No. | Description | Unused | Used |
|---|---|---|---|
| 1461 | 100 f. Type **214** (postage) | 15 | 10 |
| 1462 | 150 f. Yul Brynner and scene from "The Magnificent Seven" .. | 25 | 10 |
| 1463 | 250 f. Judy Garland and scene from "The Wizard of Oz" .. | 40 | 10 |
| 1464 | 300 f. Steve McQueen and scene from "Papillon" | 50 | 15 |
| 1465 | 500 f. Gary Cooper and scene from "Sergeant York" (air) .. | 80 | 20 |
| 1466 | 600 f. Bing Crosby and scene from "High Society" .. .. | 1·00 | 25 |

215 Dancer

216 Doves, Map and Pope John Paul II

**1991.** African Tourism Year. Multicoloured.

| No. | Description | Unused | Used |
|---|---|---|---|
| 1468 | 100 f. Type **215** .. .. | 15 | 10 |
| 1469 | 150 f. Baskets (horiz) .. | 25 | 10 |
| 1470 | 250 f. Drum (horiz) .. | 40 | 10 |
| 1471 | 300 f. Flautist .. .. | 50 | 15 |

**1991.** Papal Visit. Litho.

| No. | Type | Description | Unused | Used |
|---|---|---|---|---|
| 1472 | 216 | 150 f. multicoloured .. | 25 | 10 |

217 "ERS-1" Observation Satellite and Earth

218 Care-a-Lot and Care Bears around Globe

**1991.** Anniversaries and Events. Mult.
1473 100 f. Type **217** (postage) 15 10
1474 150 f. "Sunflowers" (Vincent van Gogh, 1888) .. .. .. 25 10
1475 200 f. Napoleon I (170th death anniv) .. .. 35 15
1476 250 f. Henri Dunant (founder of Red Cross) and Red Cross volunteers .. .. 40 10
1477 300 f. Bicentenary of Brandenburg Gate and second anniversary of fall of Berlin Wall .. 50 15
1478 400 f. Pope John Paul II's tour of Africa, 1989 .. 65 15
1479 450 f. Garry Kasparov and Anatoli Karpov (World Chess Championship, 1990) (air) .. 75 20
1480 500 f. Boy feeding dove and Rotary International and Lions International emblems 80 20

**1991.** Ecology. Care Bear cartoon characters. Multicoloured.
1481 50 f. Type **218** .. .. 10 10
1482 100 f. Care Bears around sink ("Save Water!") .. 15 10
1483 200 f. Care Bears in tree ("Recycle!") .. .. 35 15
1484 300 f. Traffic jam and Care Bear ("Control Noise") .. .. 50 15
1485 400 f. Elephant and Care Bear ("Protect Our Wild Life") (horiz) .. 65 15

**219** Player, Trophy and Little Five Points

**220** Emblem

**1992.** World Cup Football Championship, U.S.A. (1994) (1st issue). Multicoloured.
1487 100 f. Type **219** (postage) 15 10
1488 300 f. Germany player and Fulton Stadium, Atlanta .. .. 40 10
1489 400 f. Player and Inman Park .. .. .. 50 15
1490 500 f. Player and Museum of Fine Art (air) .. 65 15
See also Nos. 1565/8.

**1992.** 75th Anniv of Lions International.
1492 **220** 150 f. multicoloured .. 25 10
1493 400 f. multicoloured .. 65 15

**221** Emblem

**1992.** International Nutrition Conference, Rome.
1494 **221** 150 f. multicoloured (postage) .. .. 25 10
1495 400 f. multicoloured .. 65 15
1496 500 f. multicoloured (air) .. .. 80 20

## MINIMUM PRICE

The minimum price quoted is 10p which represents a handling charge rather than a basis for valuing common stamps. For further notes about prices see introductory pages.

**222** Scene from "The Devil and Catherine" and Antonin Dvorak (composer)

**1992.** Anniversaries and Events. Mult.
1497 200 f. Type **222** (150th birth (1991)) (postage) 25 10
1498 300 f. Antonio Vivaldi (composer) (250th death (1991)) and as choirmaster to the Hospital of the Pieta, Venice .. .. 40 10
1499 350 f. Meeting of airship "Graf Zeppelin" and Santos-Dumont's flying boat and Count Ferdinand von Zeppelin (airship pioneer) .. 45 10
1500 400 f. Projected locomotive emerging from Channel Tunnel (construction) .. 50 15
1501 450 f. Konrad Adenauer (German statesman) and Brandenburg Gate, Berlin (bicentenary of Gate) (air) .. .. 60 15
1502 500 f. Emperor Hirohito of Japan (third death anniv) .. .. 65 15

**223** Charlie Chaplin (actor) and Scene from "Modern Times"

**1992.** Anniversaries and Events. Mult.
1504 50 f. Type **223** (15th death anniv) (postage) .. 10 10
1505 100 f. Pavilion and Christopher Columbus ("Expo '92" World's Fair, Seville) .. .. 15 10
1506 150 f. St. Peter's Square, Rome .. .. .. 20 10
1507 200 f. Marlene Dietrich (actress, death) in scene from "Shanghai Express" .. .. 25 10
1508 250 f. Michael Schumacher and Formula 1 racing car .. .. .. 35 10
1509 300 f. Rocket launch and John Glenn (30th anniv of Glenn's three-orbit flight in "Mercury" space capsule) .. 40 10
1510 400 f. Bill Koch (skipper) and "America 3" (yacht) (winner of Americas Cup) (air) .. 50 15
1511 450 f. Victory of Washington Redskins in 26th American Superbowl baseball championships .. 60 15
1512 500 f. Recovery of "Intelsat VI" satellite by "Endeavour" space shuttle .. .. 65 15

**1993.** 50th Death Anniv (1991) of Robert Baden-Powell (founder of Scouting Movement). Nos. 1339/44 optd **50eme ANNIVERSAIRE DE LA MORT DE BADEN POWEL.**
1515 **192** 50 f. mult (postage) .. 10 10
1516 – 100 f. multicoloured .. 15 10
1517 – 150 f. multicoloured .. 20 10
1518 – 300 f. multicoloured .. 40 10
1519 – 400 f. mult (air) .. 50 15
1520 – 450 f. multicoloured .. 60 15

**1993.** Bicentenary of Year One of First Republic of France. Nos. 1388/91 optd **BICENTENAIRE DE L'AN I DE LA REPUBLIQUE FRANCAISE.**
1522 **201** 250 f. mult (postage) 35 10
1523 – 300 f. multicoloured .. 40 10
1524 – 400 f. multicoloured .. 50 15
1525 – 450 f. mult (air) .. 60 15

**1993.** Winter Olympic Games, Albertville, Gold Medal Winners. Nos. 1402/5 variously optd.
1527 150 f. **SLALOM GEANT Alberto Tomba, Italie** (postage) .. 20 10
1528 250 f. **SKI NORDIQUE Vegard Ulvang, Norvege** .. .. 35 15
1529 400 f. **BOB A DEUX G. Weder/D. Acklin, Suisse** .. .. 50 15
1530 500 f. **PATINAGE DE VITESSE Olaf Zinke 1000 m., Allemagne** (air) .. .. .. 65 15

**1993.** World Cup Football Championship, Italy, Results. Nos. 1414/17 optd **1. ALLEMAGNE 2. ARGENTINE 3. ITALIE.**
1532 **207** 200 f. mult (postage) 25 10
1533 – 250 f. multicoloured .. 35 15
1534 – 300 f. multicoloured .. 40 15
1535 – 450 f. mult (air) .. 60 15

**1993.** Air. Bobby Fischer–Boris Spassky Chess Match (1537) and 75th Anniv of Lions International (1538). Nos. 1479/80 optd.
1537 450 f. **RENCONTRE FISCHER - SPASSKY 3 SEPT au 5 NOV 1992 AU MONTENEGRO** .. 60 15
1538 500 f. **75eme ANNIVERSAIRE LIONS** .. .. 65 15

**230** West Germany Footballer and Little White House

**1993.** Olympic Games, Atlanta (1996) (1st issue). Multicoloured.
1539 150 f. Type **230** (postage) 20 10
1540 250 f. Cyclist and Georgia World Congress Center 35 10
1541 400 f. Basketball player and underground station .. .. 50 15
1542 500 f. Baseball player and steam train, Georgia Railroad (air) .. .. 65 15
See also Nos. 1623/7.

**231** Ice Hockey and "Whale Hunt" (sculpture)

**232** "Luna 3" and Dark Side of Moon

**1993.** Winter Olympic Games, Lillehammer, Norway (1994). Multicoloured.
1544 150 f. Type **231** (postage) 20 10
1545 250 f. Two-man bobsleigh and Edvard Grieg's house .. .. .. 35 10
1546 400 f. Biathlon and Fredrikstad Park (air) 50 15
1547 450 f. Ski jumping and Eidsvoll Manor 60 15

**1993.** 25th Anniv (1994) of First Manned Moon Landing. Multicoloured.
1549 150 f. Type **232** .. .. 20 10
1550 150 f. "Ranger 7" .. .. 10 10
1551 150 f. "Luna 9" .. .. 20 10
1552 150 f. "Surveyor 1" (first lunar probe) .. .. 20 10
1553 150 f. Lunar "Orbiter 1" and moon .. .. 20 10
1554 150 f. Launch of "Saturn 5" (rocket) carrying "Apollo 11" .. .. 20 10
1555 150 f. "Apollo 11" command module in lunar orbit .. .. 20 10

1556 150 f. Astronaut climbing from "Apollo 11" .. 20 10
1557 150 f. "Apollo 12" astronaut recovering "Surveyor 1" camera .. 20 10
1558 150 f. Explosion of "Apollo 13" .. .. 20 10
1559 150 f. "Luna 16" probe (first collection of lunar samples by automatic probe) .. .. 20 10
1560 150 f. Lunokhod of "Luna 17" (first lunar vehicle) 20 10
1561 150 f. Alan Sheppard playing golf on moon .. 20 10
1562 150 f. First lunar jeep from "Apollo 15" mission .. .. 20 10
1563 150 f. First lunar telescope from "Apollo 16" mission .. .. 20 10
1564 150 f. Astronaut from "Apollo 17" (last "Apollo" mission) .. 20 10

**233** San Francisco

**1993.** World Cup Football Championship, U.S.A. (1994) (2nd issue). Multicoloured.
1565 100 f. Type **233** (postage) 15 10
1566 300 f. Washington D.C. .. 40 10
1567 400 f. Renaissance Center, Detroit .. .. 50 15
1568 500 f. Dallas (air) .. 65 15

**234** Euparkeria

**1993.** Prehistoric Animals. Multicoloured.
1570 50 f. Type **234** .. .. 10 10
1571 50 f. Plateosaurus .. 10 10
1572 50 f. Anchisaurus .. 10 10
1573 50 f. Ornithosuchus .. 10 10
1574 100 f. Megalosaurus .. 15 10
1575 100 f. Scelidosaurus .. 15 10
1576 100 f. Camptosaurus .. 15 10
1577 100 f. Ceratosaurus .. 15 10
1578 250 f. Ouranosaurus .. 35 10
1579 250 f. Dicraeosaurus .. 35 10
1580 250 f. Tarbosaurus .. 35 10
1581 250 f. Gorgosaurus .. 35 10
1582 250 f. Polacanthus .. 35 10
1583 250 f. Deinonychus .. 35 10
1584 250 f. Corythosaurus .. 35 10
1585 250 f. Spinosaurus .. 35 10

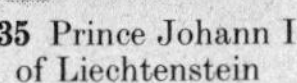
**235** Prince Johann I of Liechtenstein

**236** Johann Kepler and "Pluto" Space Probe

**1994.** Mult. (a) Battle of Austerlitz, 1805.
1587 150 f. Type **235** .. .. 20 10
1588 150 f. Marshal Joachim Murat .. .. .. 20 10
1589 600 f. Napoleon (59 × 47 mm) .. .. .. 80 20
Nos. 1587/9 were issued together, se-tenant, forming a composite design of a battle scene.

(b) Battle of the Moskva, 1912

| No. | Description | Unused | Used |
|---|---|---|---|
| 1590 | 150 f. Marshal Michel Ney | 20 | 10 |
| 1591 | 150 f. Prince Pyotr Ivanovich Bagration .. | 20 | 10 |
| 1592 | 600 f. Napoleon on horseback (59 × 47 mm) | 80 | 20 |

Nos. 1590/2 were issued together, se-tenant, forming a composite design of a battle scene.

(c) Normandy Landings, 1944

| No. | Description | Unused | Used |
|---|---|---|---|
| 1593 | 150 f. Field-Marshal Erwin Rommel (wrongly inscr "Romel") .. .. | 20 | 10 |
| 1594 | 150 f. Gen. George Patton | 20 | 10 |
| 1595 | 600 f. Gen. Dwight David Eisenhower (59 × 47 mm) .. .. .. | 80 | 20 |

Nos. 1593/5 were issued together, se-tenant, forming a composite design of a battle scene.

(d) Battle of the Ardennes, 1944

| No. | Description | Unused | Used |
|---|---|---|---|
| 1596 | 150 f. Lt.-Gen. William H. Simpson .. .. | 20 | 10 |
| 1597 | 150 f. Gen. Heinz Guderian .. .. | 20 | 10 |
| 1598 | 600 f. Tank battle scene (59 × 47 mm) .. .. | 80 | 20 |

Nos. 1596/8 were issued togther, se-tenant, forming a composite design of a battle scene.

**1994.** Astronomers. Multicoloured.

| No. | Description | Unused | Used |
|---|---|---|---|
| 1599 | 300 f. Type **236** .. .. | 40 | 10 |
| 1600 | 300 f. Sir Isaac Newton and "Voyager" space probe .. .. .. | 40 | 10 |
| 1601 | 500 f. Nicolas Copernicus and "Galileo" space probe (59 × 47 mm) .. | 65 | 15 |

Nos. 1599/1601 were issued together, se-tenant, forming a composite design.

**1994.** Winter Olympic Games, Laillehammer, Gold Medal Winners. Nos. 1544/7 variously optd.

| No. | Description | Unused | Used |
|---|---|---|---|
| 1602 | 150 f. **MEDAILLE D'OR SUEDE** (postage) .. | 20 | 10 |
| 1603 | 250 f. **G. WEDER D. ACKLIN SUISSE** .. | 35 | 10 |
| 1604 | 400 f. **F.B. LUNDBERG NORVEGE** (air) .. | 50 | 15 |
| 1605 | 450 f. **J. WEISSFLOG ALLEMAGNE** .. | 60 | 15 |

**1994.** World Cup Football Championship, U.S.A., Winners. Nos. 1565/8 optd **1. BRESIL 2. ITALIE 3. SUEDE.**

| No. | Type | Description | Unused | Used |
|---|---|---|---|---|
| 1607 | 233 | 100 f. mult (post) .. | 15 | 10 |
| 1608 | – | 300 f. multicoloured .. | 40 | 10 |
| 1609 | – | 400 f. multicoloured .. | 50 | 15 |
| 1610 | – | 500 f. mult (air) .. | 65 | 15 |

239 Banea Dam

**1995.** Garafiri Water Management. Mult.

| No. | Description | Unused | Used |
|---|---|---|---|
| 1612 | 100 f. Type **239** .. .. | 10 | 10 |
| 1613 | 150 f. Donkea .. .. | 20 | 10 |
| 1614 | 200 f. Tinkisso overflow (vert) .. .. .. | 25 | 10 |
| 1615 | 250 f. Waterfalls .. | 30 | 10 |
| 1616 | 500 f. Water works, Kinkon .. .. | 60 | 15 |

240 Red and White Persian

**1995.** Cats. Multicoloured.

| No. | Description | Unused | Used |
|---|---|---|---|
| 1617 | 150 f. Type **240** (inscr "Tortoiseshell") .. | 20 | 10 |
| 1618 | 250 f. Tabby and white .. | 30 | 10 |
| 1619 | 500 f. Black smoke persian ("Smoke long-haired") | 60 | 15 |
| 1620 | 500 f. Red tabby .. | 60 | 15 |
| 1621 | 500 f. Tortoiseshell and white persian ("longhair") .. .. | 60 | 15 |

## INDEX

Countries can be quickly located by referring to the index at the end of this volume.

241 Throwing the Javelin

242 Goldfinch

**1995.** Olympic Games, Atlanta (1996) (2nd issue). Multicoloured.

| No. | Description | Unused | Used |
|---|---|---|---|
| 1623 | 150 f. Type **241** .. .. | 20 | 10 |
| 1624 | 250 f. Boxing .. .. | 30 | 10 |
| 1625 | 500 f. Football .. .. | 60 | 15 |
| 1626 | 500 f. Basketball .. | 60 | 15 |
| 1627 | 500 f. Weightlifting .. | 60 | 15 |

**1995.** Birds. Multicoloured.

| No. | Description | Unused | Used |
|---|---|---|---|
| 1629 | 150 f. Type **242** .. .. | 20 | 10 |
| 1630 | 250 f. Nightingale ("Luscinia megarhynchos") .. | 30 | 10 |
| 1631 | 500 f. Canary ("Serinus canaria") .. .. | 60 | 15 |
| 1632 | 500 f. Chaffinch ("Fringilla coelebs") .. | 60 | 15 |
| 1633 | 500 f. Greenfinch ("Carduelis chloris") .. | 60 | 15 |

POSTAGE DUE STAMPS

D 11.

D 17.

**1959.**

| No. | Type | Description | Unused | Used |
|---|---|---|---|---|
| D 195. | D 11. | 1 f. green .. .. | 15 | 15 |
| D 196. | | 2 f. red .. .. | 15 | 15 |
| D 197. | | 3 f. brown .. .. | 30 | 20 |
| D 198. | | 5 f. blue .. .. | 90 | 45 |
| D 199. | | 10 f. orange .. .. | 1·60 | 70 |
| D 200. | | 20 f. mauve .. .. | 3·25 | 1·60 |

**1959.**

| No. | Type | Description | Unused | Used |
|---|---|---|---|---|
| D 224. | D 17. | 1 f. red .. .. | 10 | 15 |
| D 225. | | 2 f. orange .. .. | 15 | 15 |
| D 226. | | 3 f. lake .. .. | 15 | 15 |
| D 227. | | 5 f. green .. .. | 40 | 30 |
| D 228. | | 10 f. sepia .. .. | 1·00 | 90 |
| D 229. | | 20 f. blue .. .. | 1·90 | 1·60 |

**APPENDIX**

The following stamps have either been issued in excess of postal needs or have not been available to the public in reasonable quantities at face value. Such stamps may later be given full listing if there is evidence of regular postal use.

**1982.**
World Cup Winners. Nos. 1068/74 optd.

**1983.**
Olympic Games, Los Angeles. 100 s.
Bicentenary of Manned Flight. 100 s.
Winter Olympic Games, Sarajevo. 100 s.

**1984.**
Winter Olympic Gold Medal Winners. 100 s.

**1985.**
Space Achievements. 200 s.
Anniversaries and Events. 85th Birthday of Queen Elizabeth the Queen Mother. 100 s.

**1986.**
Appearance of Halley's Comet. 1500 f.

**1987.**
Winter Olympic Games, Seoul. 1500 f.

**1989.** Embossed on gold foil.
Scout and Butterfly. Air 1500 f.
Bicentenary of French Revolution. Air 1500 f.

**1990.** Embossed on gold foil.
World Cup Football Championship, Italy. Air 1500 f.
Winter Olympic Games, Albertville (1992). Air 1500 f.
De Gaulle and Free French Forces. Air 1500 f.

**1992.** Embosed on gold foil.
Olympic Games, Barcelona. Air 1500 f.
World Cup Football Championship, U.S.A. (1994) (1st issue). Air 1500 f. (vert design).
Elvis Presley. Air 1500 f.
Pope John Paul II's African Tour. Air 1500 f.

**1993.** Embossed on gold foil.
Bicentenary of Year One of First Republic of France. Air. Optd on 1989 French Revolution issue. 1500 f.
Olympic Games, Atlanta. Air 1500 f.
Winter Olympic Games, Lillehammer, Norway. Air 1500 f.
World Cup Football Championship, U.S.A. (1994) (2nd issue). Air 1500 f. (square design).

**1995.** Embossed on gold foil.
Normandy Landing, 1944. Air. Optd on 1990 De Gaulle Appendix. 1500 f.

# GUINEA - BISSAU Pt. 13

Following an armed rebellion against Colonial rule, the independence of former Portuguese Guinea was recognised on September 10th 1974.

1974. 100 centavos = 1 escudo.
1976. 100 centavos = 1 peso.

77. Amilcar Cabral, Map and Flag.

**1974.** 1st Anniv. of Proclamation of Republic. Country name inscr. in white.

| No. | Type | Description | Unused | Used |
|---|---|---|---|---|
| 426. | 77. | 1 p. multicoloured .. | 50 | 40 |
| 427. | | 2.5 p. multicoloured .. | 75 | 65 |
| 428. | | 5 p. multicoloured .. | 15·00 | 8·50 |
| 429. | | 10 p. multicoloured .. | 2·50 | 2·00 |

**1975.** No. 425 of Port. Guinea optd. **REP. DA BISSAU.**

| No. | Description | Unused | Used |
|---|---|---|---|
| 430. | 2 e. multicoloured .. .. | 60 | 60 |

79. Amilcar Cabral, Map and Flag.

**1975.** 2nd Anniv. of Proclamation of Republic (1st issue). Country name inscr. in black.

| No. | Type | Description | Unused | Used |
|---|---|---|---|---|
| 431. | 79. | 1 p. multicoloured .. | 45 | 30 |
| 432 | | 2.5 p. multicoloured .. | 60 | 45 |
| 433. | | 5 p. multicoloured .. | 2·50 | 1·40 |
| 434. | | 10 p. multicoloured .. | 2·50 | 2·25 |

See also Nos. 439/440.

80. Amilcar Cabral, Arms and Flag.

**1975.** 51st Birth Anniv. of Amilcar Cabral (founder of P.A.I.G.C.).

| No. | Type | Description | Unused | Used |
|---|---|---|---|---|
| 435. | 80. | 1 e. multicoloured .. | 20 | 10 |
| 436. | | 10 e. multicoloured .. | 80 | 40 |

81. Family, Arms and Flag.

**1975.** 19th Anniv. of P.A.I.G.C. (Partido Africano da Independencia da Guine e do Cabo Verde).

| No. | Type | Description | Unused | Used |
|---|---|---|---|---|
| 437. | 81. | 2 e. multicoloured .. | 50 | 20 |
| 438. | | 10 e. multicoloured .. | 2·00 | 75 |

82. Pres. Luis Cabral, Arms and Flag.

**1975.** 2nd Anniv. of Proclamation of Republic (2nd issue).

| No. | Type | Description | Unused | Used |
|---|---|---|---|---|
| 439. | 82. | 3 e. multicoloured .. | 40 | 20 |
| 440. | | 5 e. multicoloured .. | 85 | 30 |

83. General Henry Knox (after Stuart) and Cannons of Ticonderoga (after Lovell).

**1976.** Bicent. of American Independence (1st issue). Multicoloured.

| | | | |
|---|---|---|---|
| 441. | 5 e. Type **83** (postage) .. | 25 | 15 |
| 442. | 10 e. General Putnam and Battle of Bunker Hill .. | 55 | 30 |
| 443. | 15 e. Washington and Crossing of the Delaware | 80 | 35 |
| 444. | 20 e. General Kosciuszko and Battle of Saratoga | 1·25 | 50 |
| 445. | 30 e. General von Steuben and Valley Forge (air) .. | 1·75 | 90 |
| 446. | 40 e. Lafayette and Monmouth Court House .. | 2·00 | 1·00 |

See also Nos. 503/6.

**84.** Masked Dancer.

**1976.** Dancers. Multicoloured

| | | | |
|---|---|---|---|
| 448. | 2 p. Type **84** (postage) .. | 30 | 10 |
| 449. | 3 p. Dancer and drummer | 35 | 15 |
| 450. | 5 p. Dancers on stilts .. | 60 | 20 |
| 451. | 10 p. Dancers with spears and bows (air) .. .. | 65 | 40 |
| 452. | 15 p. Masked dancer .. | 1·00 | 50 |
| 453. | 20 p. "Devil" dancer .. | 1·50 | 65 |

**1976.** Cent. of Universal Postal Union (1st issue). Nos. 448/53 optd. **CENTENARIO DA U.P.U. 1874. MEMBRO DA U.P.U. 1974** and Emblem.

| | | | | |
|---|---|---|---|---|
| 455. | **84.** | 2 p. multicoloured (post.) | 10 | 10 |
| 456. | – | 3 p. multicoloured .. | 20 | 10 |
| 457. | – | 5 p. multicoloured .. | 25 | 15 |
| 458. | – | 10 p. multicoloured (air) | 50 | 25 |
| 459. | – | 15 p. multicoloured .. | 65 | 40 |
| 460. | – | 20 p. multicoloured .. | 90 | 50 |

See also Nos 518/23.

**1976.** Nos. 435/40 surch. in new currency.

| | | | |
|---|---|---|---|
| 462. | 1 p. on 1 e. multicoloured | 10 | 10 |
| 463. | 2 p. on 2 e. multicoloured | 10 | 10 |
| 464. | 3 p. on 3 e. multicoloured | 15 | 10 |
| 465. | 5 p. on 5 e. multicoloured | 25 | 15 |
| 466. | 10 p. on 10 e. multicoloured | 50 | 30 |
| 467. | 10 p. on 10 e. multicoloured | 50 | 30 |

**87.** Amilcar Cabral and Funeral.

**1976.** 3rd Anniv. of Amilcar Cabral Assassination.

| | | | | |
|---|---|---|---|---|
| 468. | **87.** | 3 p. multicoloured .. | 15 | 10 |
| 469. | | 5 p. multicoloured .. | 20 | 15 |
| 470. | | 6 p. multicoloured .. | 25 | 20 |
| 471. | | 10 p. multicoloured .. | 40 | 25 |

**88.** Party Emblem.


**89.** Launch of "Soyuz" Spacecraft.

**1976.** 20th Anniv. of P.A.I.G.C.

| | | | | |
|---|---|---|---|---|
| 472. | **88.** | 3 p. multicoloured .. | 15 | 15 |
| 473. | | 15 p. multicoloured .. | 65 | 50 |
| 474. | | 50 p. multicoloured .. | 1·60 | 1·25 |

**1976.** Air. "Apollo-Soyuz" Space Link. Multicoloured.

| | | | |
|---|---|---|---|
| 475. | 5 p. Type **89** .. .. | 25 | 15 |
| 476. | 10 p. Launch of "Apollo" spacecraft .. .. | 45 | 30 |
| 477. | 15 p. Leonov, Stafford and meeting in Space .. | 80 | 45 |
| 478. | 20 p. Eclipse of the Sun .. | 1·25 | 55 |
| 479. | 30 p. Infra-red photograph of Earth .. .. | 1·75 | 85 |
| 480. | 40 p. Return of Spacecraft to Earth .. .. | 2·25 | 95 |

**90.** Bell Telephone of 1876 and Laying First Atlantic Cable.

**1976.** Telephone Centenary. Multicoloured.

| | | | |
|---|---|---|---|
| 482. | 2 p. Type **90** (postage) .. | 15 | 10 |
| 483. | 3 p. French telephone of 1890 and first telephone box, 1893 .. .. | 20 | 10 |
| 484. | 5 p. German automatic telephone of 1908 and automatic telephone, 1898 .. .. .. | 25 | 15 |
| 485. | 10 p. English telephone of 1910 and trans-horizon link, 1963 (air) .. .. | 55 | 25 |
| 486. | 15 p. French telephone of 1924 and communications satellite .. .. .. | 85 | 45 |
| 487. | 20 p. Modern telephone and "Molnya" satellite | 1·25 | 50 |

**91.** Women's Figure Skating.

**1976.** Winter Olympic Games, Innsbruck. Multicoloured.

| | | | |
|---|---|---|---|
| 489. | 1 p. Type **91** (postage) .. | 15 | 10 |
| 490. | 3 p. Ice-hockey .. .. | 30 | 10 |
| 491. | 5 p. Bobsleighing .. .. | 30 | 15 |
| 492. | 10 p. Pairs figure-skating (air) .. .. .. | 55 | 30 |
| 493. | 20 p. Cross-country skiing | 1·25 | 45 |
| 494. | 30 p. Speed skating .. | 1·75 | 85 |

**92.** Footballers and Montreal Skyline.

**1976.** Olympic Games, Montreal. Mult.

| | | | |
|---|---|---|---|
| 496. | 1 p. Type **92** .. .. | 10 | 10 |
| 497. | 3 p. Pole vaulting .. | 15 | 10 |
| 498. | 5 p. Hurdling .. .. | 25 | 15 |
| 499. | 10 p. Discus throwing .. | 45 | 25 |
| 500. | 20 p. Running .. .. | 90 | 50 |
| 501. | 30 p. Wrestling .. .. | 1·40 | 75 |

**93.** "Viking" orbiting Mars.

**1976.** Bicentenary of American Revolution (2nd issue). Multicoloured.

(a) Postage. Horiz. designs as T **83**.

| | | | |
|---|---|---|---|
| 503. | 3 p. 50 Crispus Attuck and Boston Massacre .. | 30 | 10 |
| 504. | 5 p. Martin Luther King and Capitol .. .. | 40 | 20 |

(b) Air. Success of "Viking" Mission. Vert.

| | | | |
|---|---|---|---|
| 505. | 25 p. Type **93** .. .. | 1·25 | 65 |
| 506. | 35 p. Lander scooping samples from surface of Mars .. .. .. | 1·75 | 90 |

**94.** Amilcar Cabral.

**1977.** 4th Death Anniv. of Amilcar Cabral. Multicoloured.

| | | | |
|---|---|---|---|
| 507. | 50 c. Type **94** (postage) .. | 15 | 10 |
| 508. | 3 p. 50 Luis Cabral addressing U.N. Assembly .. | 35 | 10 |
| 509. | 15 p. Type **94** (air) .. | 55 | 30 |
| 510. | 30 p. As No. 508 .. .. | 1·25 | 50 |

**95.** Henri Dunant (Peace, 1901).

**1977.** 75th Anniv. of 1st Nobel Prizes. Mult.

| | | | |
|---|---|---|---|
| 511. | 3 p. 50 Type **95** (postage) .. | 30 | 10 |
| 512. | 5 p. Albert Einstein (Physics, 1921) .. .. .. | 35 | 20 |
| 513. | 6 p. Irene and Jean-Frederic Joliot-Curie (Chemistry, 1935) .. .. .. | 75 | 20 |
| 514. | 30 p. Alexander Fleming (Medicine, 1945) .. | 1·75 | 90 |
| 515. | 35 p. Ernest Hemingway (Literature, 1954) (air) .. | 2·00 | 90 |
| 516. | 40 p. J. Tinbergen (Economic Sciences, 1969) .. .. | 2·25 | 1·00 |

**96.** Postal Runner and "Telstar" Satellite.

**1977.** Cent. (1974) of Universal Postal Union (2nd issue). Multicoloured.

| | | | |
|---|---|---|---|
| 518 | 3 p. 50 Type **96** (postage) | 25 | 15 |
| 519 | 5 p. A.E.G. J-II biplane, and satellites circling globe .. .. .. | 35 | 15 |
| 520 | 6 p. Mail van and satellite control room .. .. | 55 | 15 |
| 521 | 30 p. Stage-coach and astronaut cancelling letters on Moon .. .. | 1·75 | 50 |
| 522 | 35 p. German Locomotive "Der Adler" and "Intelsat 4" satellite (air) .. .. .. .. | 2·50 | 80 |
| 523 | 40 p. Aircraft and "Apollo"–"Soyuz" link | 2·50 | 90 |

**97.** Coronation Coach.

**1977.** Silver Jubliee of Queen Elizabeth II. Multicoloured.

| | | | |
|---|---|---|---|
| 525. | 3 p. 50 Type **97** (postage) .. | 20 | 10 |
| 526. | 5 p. Coronation ceremony | 25 | 15 |
| 527. | 10 p. Yeoman of the Guard and Crown Jewels .. | 45 | 25 |
| 528. | 20 p. Trumpeter sounding fanfare .. .. .. | 90 | 45 |
| 529. | 25 p. Royal Horse Guard (air) .. .. .. | 1·25 | 50 |
| 530. | 30 p. Royal Family on balcony .. .. .. | 1·50 | 70 |

**98.** Congress Emblem. **99.** "Massacre of the Innocents" (detail).

**1977.** Third P.A.I.G.C. Congress, Bissau.

| | | | | |
|---|---|---|---|---|
| 532. | **98.** | 3 p. 50 multicoloured .. | 25 | 15 |

**1977.** 400th Birth Anniv. of Peter Paul Rubens (artist). Multicoloured.

| | | | |
|---|---|---|---|
| 533. | 3 p. 50 Type **99** (postage) .. | 20 | 10 |
| 534. | 5 p. "Rape of the Daughters of Leukippos" .. | 25 | 15 |
| 535. | 6 p. "Lamentation of Christ" (horiz.) .. | 35 | 15 |
| 536. | 30 p. "Francisco IV Gonzaga, Prince of Mantua" | 1·60 | 50 |
| 537. | 35 p. "The Four Continents" (detail) (horiz.) (air) .. .. .. | 1·75 | 50 |
| 538. | 40 p. "Marquise Brigida Spinola Doria" .. | 2·25 | 60 |

**100.** Santos-Dumont's Airship "Ballon No. 6".

**1978.** Airships. Multicoloured.

| | | | |
|---|---|---|---|
| 540 | 3 p. 50 Type **100** (postage) | 25 | 15 |
| 541 | 5 p. Beardmore airship R-34 crossing Atlantic .. | 35 | 15 |
| 542 | 10 p. "Norge" over North Pole .. .. .. | 55 | 20 |
| 543 | 20 p. "Graf Zeppelin" over Abu Simbel .. .. | 1·40 | 50 |
| 544 | 25 p. "Hindenburg" over New York (air) .. | 1·75 | 70 |
| 545 | 30 p. "Graf Zeppelin", Concorde airliner and space shuttle .. .. | 2·25 | 75 |

**101.** Footballers, Cup and Poster (Uruguay, 1930).

**1978.** World Cup Football Championship, Argentina. Multicoloured.

| | | | |
|---|---|---|---|
| 547 | 3 p. 50 Type **101** (postage) | 20 | 10 |
| 548 | 5 p. "Coupe du Monde, 1938" .. .. .. | 25 | 15 |
| 549 | 10 p. Brazil, 1950 .. .. | 55 | 25 |
| 550 | 20 p. Chile, 1962 .. .. | 1·10 | 45 |
| 551 | 25 p. Mexico, 1970 (air) .. | 1·40 | 50 |
| 552 | 30 p. "FIFA World Cup 1974" (Germany) .. | 1·60 | 65 |

DESIGNS: showing match scenes and posters from previous championships.

**102.** Black Antelope.

**1978.** Endangered Animals. Multicoloured.

| | | | |
|---|---|---|---|
| 554. | 3 p. 50 Type **102** (postage) | 30 | 10 |
| 555. | 5 p. Fennec .. .. | 1·75 | 55 |
| 556. | 6 p. Secretary bird .. | 2·00 | 70 |
| 557. | 30 p. Hippopotamuses .. | 2·00 | 65 |
| 558. | 35 p. Cheetahs (air) .. | 2·25 | 65 |
| 559. | 40 p. Gorillas .. .. | 2·50 | 75 |

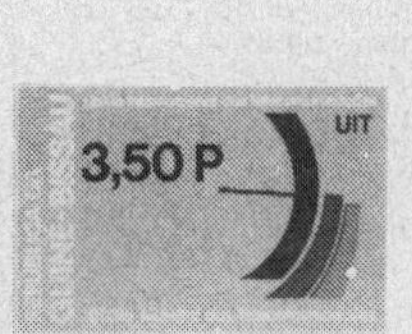

**103.** Microwave-antenna. **104.** Child.

**1978.** Telecommunications Day.

| | | | | |
|---|---|---|---|---|
| 561. | **103.** | 3 p. 50 multicoloured | 20 | 15 |
| 562. | | 10 p. multicoloured .. | 55 | 30 |

**1978.** Children's Day.

| | | | | |
|---|---|---|---|---|
| 563. | **104.** | 50 c. blue and green .. | 10 | 10 |
| 564. | – | 3 p. bright red and red | 15 | 10 |
| 565. | – | 5 p. light brown and brn. | 25 | 15 |
| 566. | – | 30 p. brown and red .. | 1·40 | 1·00 |

DESIGNS: 3 p. Amilcar Cabral and child. 5 p. Children. 30 p. Two children playing.

**105.** Reading the Proclamation.

**1978.** 25th Anniv. of Coronation of Queen Elizabeth II. Multicoloured.

567. 3 p. Type **105** (postage) .. 20 10
568. 5 p. Queen and Prince Philip in Coronation Coach 25 15
569. 10 p. Queen and Prince Philip .. .. 45 25
570. 20 p. Mounted drummer .. 90 45
571. 25 p. Imperial State Crown and St. Edward's Crown (air) .. .. .. 1·25 50
572. 30 p. Queen holding orb and sceptre .. .. 1·25 65
573. 100 p. Queen, stained glass window and Imperial State Crown (55 × 38 mm.) .. .. .. 4·50 1·50

**106.** Wright Brothers and Wright Flyer I.

**1978.** History of Aviation. Multicoloured.

575. 3 p. 50 Type **106** (postage) 20 10
576. 10 p. Alberto Santos-Dumont 45 20
577. 15 p. Louis Bleriot .. 75 35
578. 20 p. Charles Lindbergh (air) 90 40
579. 25 p. Moon landing .. 1·25 50
580. 30 p. Space shuttle .. 1·50 65

**1978.** World Cup Football Championship Results. Nos. 547/52 optd. **1o ARGENTINA 2o HOLANDA 3o BRAZIL**

582. 3 p. 50 mult. (postage) .. 20 10
583. 5 p. multicoloured .. 25 15
584. 10 p. multicoloured .. 45 25
585. 20 p. multicoloured .. 1·10 55
586. 25 p. multicoloured (air) .. 1·25 55
587. 30 p. multicoloured .. 1·50 70

**108.** " Virgin and Child ", 1497.

**109.** Rowland Hill and Wurttemberg 70 k. Stamp, 1873.

**1978.** 450th Death Anniv. of Albrecht Durer (artist). Multicoloured.

589. 3 p. 50 Type **108** (postage) 20 10
590. 5 p. " Virgin and Child ", 1507 .. .. .. 25 15
591. 6 p. " Virgin and Child ", 1512 .. .. .. 30 15
592. 30 p. " Virgin ", 1518 .. 1·40 70
593. 35 p. " Virgin and Child with St. Anne ", 1519 (air) .. .. .. 1·75 50
594. 40 p. " Virgin of the Pear ", 1526 .. .. .. 2·00 75

**1978.** Death Centenary of Rowland Hill.

596. 3 p. 50 Type **109** (postage) 15 10
597. 5 p. Belgian 10 c. stamp, 1849 .. .. .. 25 15
598. 6 p. Monaco 5 f. stamp, 1885 .. .. .. 30 20
599. 30 p. Spanish 10 r. stamp, 1851 .. .. .. 1·50 70
600. 35 p. Swiss 5 r. stamp, 1851 (air) .. .. .. 1·75 50
601. 40 p. Naples ½ t. stamp, 1860 .. .. .. 2·00 75

DESIGNS: 5 p. to 40 p. show Rowland Hill and stamp.

**110.** Nurse immunising Child.

**1979.** International Year of the Child (1st issue). Multicoloured.

603. 3 p. 50 Type **110** (postage) 20 10
604. 10 p. Children drinking .. 55 25
605. 15 p. Children with book .. 1·00 35
606. 20 p. Space shuttle (air) .. 1·00 40
607. 25 p. " Skylab " space station .. .. 1·40 50
608. 30 p. Children playing chess 2·00 75

See also Nos. 616/19.

**111.** Family.

**1979.** National Census.

610. **111.** 50 c. brn., bl. & pink 10 10
611. 2 p. brn., bl. & lt. blue 15 10
612. 4 p. brn., bl. & yellow 25 15

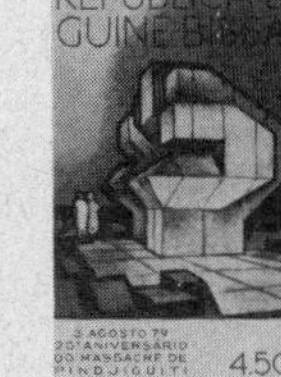


**112.** Wave Pattern and Human Figures.

**113.** Monument.

**1979.** World Telecommunications Day. Multicoloured.

613. 50 c. Type **112** .. .. 10 10
614. 4 p. Wave pattern and human figures (different) 20 15

**1979.** 20th Anniv. of Pindjiuouiti Massacre.

615. **113.** 4 p. 50 multicoloured .. 30 15

**114.** Classroom Scene.

**1980.** International Year of the Child (2nd issue). Multicoloured.

616. 6 p. Type **114** (postage) .. 30 25
617. 10 p. Jules Verne and child reading novel (vert.) .. 45 30
618. 25 p. Early and modern locomotives and child with toy train (vert.) .. 1·40 50
619. 35 p. Man and child with bows and arrows (vert.) 1·60 75

**115.** Amilcar Cabral, Workers and Children reading Books.

**1980.** Literacy Campaign. Multicoloured.

621. 3 p. 50 Type **115** (postage) 20 10
622. 5 p. Luis Cabral displaying school textbooks .. 30 15
623. 15 p. Type **115** (air) .. 80 50
624. 25 p. As No. 622 .. .. 1·40 75

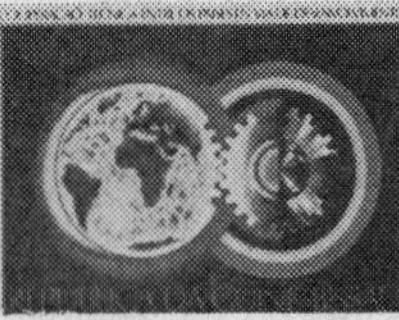

**116.** Globe and Cogwheel.

**1980.** Technical Co-operation among Developing Countries.

625. **116.** 3 p. 50 multicoloured 20 10
626. 6 p. multicoloured .. 30 20
627. 10 p. multicoloured .. 45 30

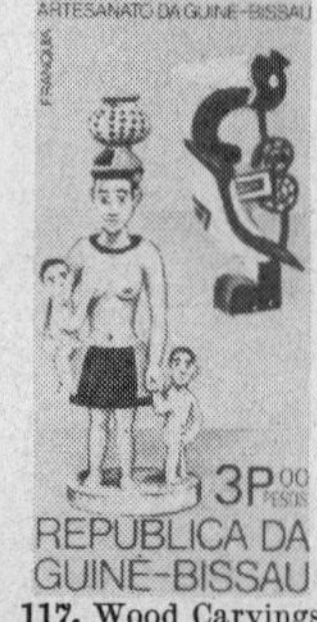

**117.** Wood Carvings.

**118.** Ernst Udet.

**1980.** Handicrafts. Multicoloured.

628 3 p. Type **117** .. .. 20 10
629 6 p. Weaving (horiz) .. 30 20
630 20 p. Bust and statuette (horiz) .. .. .. 1·00 50

**1980.** History of Aviation. Air Aces of 1st World War. Multicoloured.

631. 3 p. 50 Type **118** (postage) 25 15
632. 5 p. Charles Nungesser .. 35 25
633. 6 p. Manfred von Richthofen 55 25
634. 30 p. Francesco Baracca .. 1·75 70
635. 35 p. Willy Coppens de Houthulst (air) .. .. 2·10 75
636. 40 p. Charles Guynemer .. 2·50 90

**119.** Speed Skating.

**1980.** Winter Olympic Games, Lake Placid. Multicoloured.

638. 3 p. 50 Type **119** (postage) 20 10
639. 5 p. Ski jumping .. .. 30 20
640. 6 p. Luge .. .. .. 40 25
641. 30 p. Cross country skiing 1·75 70
642. 35 p. Downhill skiing (air) 2·00 75
643. 40 p. Figure skating .. 2·40 90

**120.** Putting the Shot.

**1980.** Olympic Games, Moscow. Mult.

645. 3 p. 50 Type **120** (postage) 20 15
646. 5 p. Gymnastics (ring exercise) .. .. .. 25 20
647. 6 p. Long jump .. .. 35 25
648. 30 p. Fencing .. .. 1·50 70
649. 35 p. Gymnastics (backward somersault) (air) .. 1·75 75
650. 40 p. Running .. .. 2·00 90

**121.** Congress Meeting.

**1980.** 16th Anniv. of Cassaca Congress.

652. **121.** 3 p. 50 multicoloured .. 15 10
653. 6 p. 50 multicoloured .. 30 20
654. 10 p. multicoloured .. 40 30

**122.** Satellites.

**1981.** Space Achievements. Multicoloured.

655. 3 p. 50 Type **122** (postage) 20 10
656. 5 p. Satellite .. .. 25 15
657. 6 p. Rocket .. .. 30 15
658. 30 p. Space Shuttle "Columbia" .. .. 1·75 95
659. 35 p. "Viking I" (air) .. 1·75 75
660. 40 p. U.S.–Soviet space link .. .. .. 2·00 90

**123.** Platini (France) and Football Scene.

**1981.** World Cup Football Championship, Spain. Multicoloured.

662. 3 p. 50 Type **123** (postage) 30 10
663. 5 p. Bettega (Italy) .. 35 15
664. 6 p. Rensenbrink (Netherlands) .. .. .. 40 15
665. 30 p. Rivelino (Brazil) .. 1·90 80
666. 35 p. Rummenigge (West Germany) (air) .. .. 1·90 80
667. 40 p. Kempes (Argentina) 2·00 90

**124.** Lady Diana Spencer with Horse.

**1981.** Wedding of Prince of Wales. Multicoloured.

669. 3 p. 50 Type **124** (postage) 20 15
670. 5 p. Investiture of Prince of Wales .. .. .. 25 15
671. 6 p. Lady Diana Spencer with children .. .. 30 15
672. 30 p. St. Paul's Cathedral 1·25 95
673. 35 p. Althorp House (air) 1·40 1·00
674. 40 p. Arms of Prince of Wales .. .. .. 1·50 1·25

**125.** Eric the Red and Viking Ship.

**1981.** Navigators. Multicoloured.

676 3 p. 50 Type **125** (postage) 25 15
677 5 p. Vasco da Gama and "Sao Gabriel" .. .. 30 15
678 6 p. Magellan and "Vitoria" .. .. 35 20
679 30 p. Cartier and "Emerillon" .. .. 2·00 1·00
680 35 p. Drake and "Golden Hind" (air) .. .. 2·50 1·25
681 40 p. Cook and H.M.S. "Endeavour" .. .. 2·75 1·60

**126.** "Girl with Bare Feet".

**1981.** Birth Centenary of Pablo Picasso. Multicoloured.

683. 3 p. 50 Type **126** (postage) 20 15
684. 5 p. "Acrobat on Ball" .. 25 15
685. 6 p. "Pierrot" .. .. 30 15
686. 30 p. "Girl in front of a Mirror" .. .. 1·50 95
687. 35 p. "The First Steps" (air) .. .. .. 2·00 1·00
688. 40 p. "Woman in Turkish Dress" .. .. .. 2·25 1·25

**127.** "Retable of St. Zeno" (Mantegna).

**1981.** Christmas. Multicoloured.

| | | | |
|---|---|---|---|
| 690. | 3 p. 50 Type **127** (postage) | 20 | 15 |
| 691. | 5 p. "Virgin with Child" (Bellini) .. .. .. | 25 | 15 |
| 692. | 6 p. "Virgin and Child with Cherubs" (Mantegna) .. | 30 | 15 |
| 693. | 25 p. "Madonna Campori" (Correggio) .. .. | 1·50 | 1·00 |
| 694. | 30 p. "Virgin and Child" (Memling) (air) .. .. | 2·00 | 1·10 |
| 695. | 35 p. "Virgin and Child" (Bellini) .. .. .. | 2·25 | 1·25 |

**128.** Archery.

**1982.** 75th Anniv. of Boy Scout Movement. Multicoloured.

| | | | |
|---|---|---|---|
| 697. | 3 p. 50 Type **128** (postage) | 15 | 10 |
| 698. | 5 p. First aid .. .. .. | 20 | 15 |
| 699. | 6 p. Bugler .. .. .. | 25 | 15 |
| 700. | 30 p. Cub scouts .. .. | 1·60 | 80 |
| 701. | 35 p. Girl scout in canoe (air) .. .. .. | 2·25 | 90 |
| 702. | 40 p. Scouts with model aircraft .. .. .. | 2·40 | 1·25 |

**129.** Keegan.

**1982.** World Cup Football Championship, Spain. Multicoloured.

| | | | |
|---|---|---|---|
| 704. | 3 p. 50 Type **129** (postage) | 20 | 10 |
| 705. | 5 p. Rossi .. .. .. | 20 | 15 |
| 706. | 6 p. Zico .. .. .. | 25 | 15 |
| 707. | 30 p. Arconada .. .. | 1·60 | 80 |
| 708. | 35 p. Kempes (air) .. | 2·25 | 1·00 |
| 709. | 40 p. Kaltz .. .. .. | 2·50 | 1·10 |

**130.** Lady Diana Spencer.

**1982.** 21st Birthday of Princess of Wales. Multicoloured.

| | | | |
|---|---|---|---|
| 711. | 3 p. 50 Type **130** (postage) | 15 | 10 |
| 712. | 5 p. Playing croquet .. | 25 | 15 |
| 713. | 6 p. Lady Diana with pony | 30 | 15 |
| 714. | 30 p. Fishing .. .. | 1·75 | 80 |
| 715. | 35 p. Engagement picture (air) .. .. .. | 1·90 | 90 |
| 716. | 40 p. Honeymoon picture | 2·00 | 1·10 |

**1982.** Birth of Prince William of Wales, Nos. 711/16 optd. **21 DE JULHO 1982. GUILHERMO ARTHUR FILIPE LUIS PRINCIPE DE GALES.**

| | | | |
|---|---|---|---|
| 718. | 3 p. 50 multicoloured (postage) .. .. .. | 20 | 10 |
| 719. | 5 p. multicoloured .. | 25 | 15 |
| 720. | 6 p. multicoloured .. | 30 | 15 |
| 721. | 30 p. multicoloured .. | 1·60 | 95 |
| 722. | 35 p. multicoloured (air) .. | 1·90 | 1·10 |
| 723. | 40 p. multicoloured .. | 2·00 | 1·25 |

**132.** National Colours.

**133.** Montgolfier Balloon.

**1982.** Visit of President Eanes of Portugal. Multicoloured.

| | | | |
|---|---|---|---|
| 725. | 4 p. 50 Type **132** .. .. | 10 | 10 |
| 726. | 20 p. Doves on national colours .. .. .. | 20 | 10 |

**1983.** Bicent of Manned Flight. Mult.

| | | | |
|---|---|---|---|
| 727 | 50 c. Type **133** .. .. | 10 | 10 |
| 728 | 2 p. 50 Charles's hydrogen balloon .. .. | 15 | 10 |
| 729 | 3 p. 50 Charles Green's balloon "Royal Vauxhall" .. .. | 20 | 10 |
| 730 | 5 p. Gaston Tissandier's balloon "Zenith" .. | 30 | 10 |
| 731 | 10 p. Salomon Andree's balloon "Ornen" over Arctic .. .. .. | 60 | 20 |
| 732 | 20 p. Stratosphere balloon "Explorer II" .. .. | 1·25 | 40 |
| 733 | 30 p. Modern hot-air balloons .. .. | 2·00 | 60 |

**134.** Hamadryas Baboon.

**136.** Satellite.

**1983.** African Primates. Multicoloured.

| | | | |
|---|---|---|---|
| 735. | 1 p. Type **134** .. .. | 10 | 10 |
| 736. | 1 p. 50 Gorilla .. .. | 20 | 10 |
| 737. | 3 p. 50 Gelada .. .. | 30 | 10 |
| 738. | 5 p. Mandrill .. .. | 40 | 15 |
| 739. | 8 p. Chimpanzee .. .. | 80 | 20 |
| 740. | 20 p. Eastern black-and-white colobus .. .. | 1·50 | 50 |
| 741. | 30 p. Diana monkey .. | 2·40 | 85 |

**1983.** Cosmonautics Day. Multicoloured.

| | | | |
|---|---|---|---|
| 743. | 1 p. Type **136** .. .. | 10 | 10 |
| 744. | 1 p. 50 Satellite (different) | 15 | 10 |
| 745. | 3 p. 50 Rocket carrying space shuttle .. .. | 20 | 10 |
| 746. | 5 p. Satellite (different) .. | 30 | 15 |
| 747. | 8 p. Satellite (different) .. | 60 | 20 |
| 748. | 20 p. Satellite (different) .. | 1·25 | 45 |
| 749. | 30 p. "Soyuz" docking with "Salyut" .. .. | 2·00 | 70 |

**137.** Woodcut from Caxton's "Game and Playe of Chesse", Arabian Pawn and Rook.

**1983.** Chess. Multicoloured.

| | | | |
|---|---|---|---|
| 751 | 1 p. Type **137** .. .. | 15 | 10 |
| 752 | 1 p. 50 12th-century European king and knight | 15 | 10 |
| 753 | 3 p. 50 Mid 18th-century German rook, queen and king .. .. .. | 25 | 10 |
| 754 | 5 p. Late 12th/early 13th-century Danish bishop and knight .. | 40 | 10 |
| 755 | 10 p. 18th-century French king and queen .. | 80 | 25 |
| 756 | 20 p. 18th-century Venetian king, knight and queen .. .. | 1·75 | 55 |
| 757 | 40 p. 19th-century faience knight, queen and rook | 3·00 | 1·10 |

**138.** "Vision of Ezekiel".

**1983.** 500th Birth Anniv. of Raphael (artist). Multicoloured.

| | | | |
|---|---|---|---|
| 759. | 1 p. Type **138** .. .. | 10 | 10 |
| 760. | 1 p. 50 "Tempi Madonna" | 10 | 10 |
| 761. | 3 p. 50 "Della Tenda Madonna" .. .. .. | 20 | 10 |
| 762. | 5 p. "Orleans Madonna" .. | 25 | 10 |
| 763. | 8 p. "La Belle Jardiniere" | 45 | 20 |
| 764. | 15 p. "Small Cowper Madonna" .. .. .. | 90 | 35 |
| 765. | 30 p. "St. George and the Dragon" .. .. .. | 2·00 | 60 |

**139.** Swimming.

**1983.** Olympic Games, Los Angeles (1932 and 1984) (1st issue). Multicoloured.

| | | | |
|---|---|---|---|
| 767. | 1 p. Type **139** .. .. | 10 | 10 |
| 768. | 1 p. 50 Hurdling .. .. | 15 | 10 |
| 769. | 3 p. 50 Fencing .. .. | 20 | 10 |
| 770. | 5 p. Weightlifting .. .. | 30 | 10 |
| 771. | 10 p. Marathon .. .. | 60 | 15 |
| 772. | 20 p. Show jumping .. | 1·10 | 35 |
| 773. | 40 p. Cycling .. .. | 2·40 | 65 |

See also Nos. 843/9.

**141.** Rowland Hill and Penny Black.

**1983.** World Communications Year. Mult.

| | | | |
|---|---|---|---|
| 776. | 50 c. Type **141** .. .. | 10 | 10 |
| 777. | 2 p. 50 Samuel Morse and morse machine .. .. | 15 | 10 |
| 778. | 3 p. 50 Heinrich Rudolf Hertz and electro-magnetic wave diagrams | 20 | 10 |
| 779. | 5 p. Lord Kelvin and cable ship .. .. .. | 40 | 10 |
| 780. | 10 p. Alexander Graham Bell and telephones .. | 60 | 15 |
| 781. | 20 p. Guglielmo Marconi and wireless apparatus | 1·10 | 40 |
| 782. | 30 p. Vladimir Kosma Zworykin and television | 1·60 | 55 |

**142.** JAAC Emblem.

**1983.** First JAAC Congress. Multicoloured.

| | | | |
|---|---|---|---|
| 784. | 4 p. Crowd and emblem .. | 25 | 15 |
| 785. | 5 p. Type **142** .. .. | 30 | 15 |

**143.** Speed Skating.

**145.** U.D.E.M.U. Emblem.

**144.** Hoeing Vegetable Patch.

**1983.** Winter Olympic Games, Sarajevo (1st issue). Multicoloured.

| | | | |
|---|---|---|---|
| 786. | 1 p. Type **143** .. .. | 10 | 10 |
| 787. | 1 p. 50 Ski jumping .. | 15 | 10 |
| 788. | 3 p. Cross-country skiing .. | 20 | 10 |
| 789. | 5 p. Bobsleigh .. .. | 25 | 10 |
| 790. | 10 p. Ice hockey .. .. | 70 | 25 |
| 791. | 15 p. Ice skating .. .. | 1·10 | 30 |
| 792. | 20 p. Luge .. .. .. | 1·25 | 35 |

See also Nos. 816/22.

**1983.** World Food Day.

| | | | |
|---|---|---|---|
| 794. | **144.** 1 p. 50 multicoloured .. | 10 | 10 |
| 795. | 2 p. multicoloured .. | 15 | 10 |
| 796. | 4 p. multicoloured .. | 30 | 15 |

**1983.** Democratic Union of Women. Multicoloured.

| | | | |
|---|---|---|---|
| 798. | 4 p. 50 Type **145** .. .. | 30 | 15 |
| 799. | 7 p. 50 Flag and woman .. | 50 | 20 |
| 800. | 9 p. Woman sewing .. | 70 | 30 |
| 801. | 12 p. Women working on plantation .. .. | 1·00 | 45 |

**146.** "Canna coccinea".

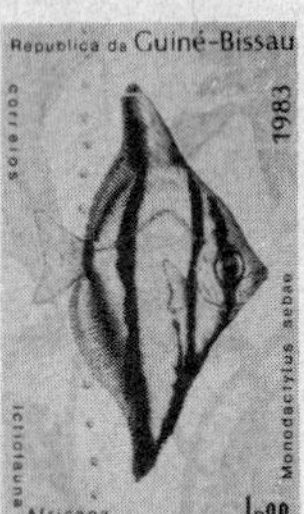

**147.** "Mondactylus sebae".

**1983.** Flowers. Multicoloured.

| | | | |
|---|---|---|---|
| 802. | 1 p. Type **146** .. .. | 15 | 10 |
| 803. | 1 p. 50 "Bouganville litoralis" .. .. .. | 20 | 10 |
| 804. | 3 p. 50 "Euphorbia milii" | 25 | 10 |
| 805. | 5 p. "Delonix regia" .. | 30 | 10 |
| 806. | 8 p. "Bauhinia variegata" | 50 | 15 |
| 807. | 10 p. "Spathodea campanulata" .. .. .. | 70 | 20 |
| 808. | 30 p. "Hibiscus rosa sinensis" .. .. .. | 2·00 | 60 |

**1983.** Fishes. Multicoloured.

| | | | |
|---|---|---|---|
| 809. | 1 p. Type **147** .. .. | 15 | 10 |
| 810. | 1 p. 50 "Botia macracanthus" .. .. .. | 20 | 10 |
| 811. | 3 p. 50 "Ctenopoma acutirostre" .. .. .. | 25 | 10 |
| 812. | 5 p. "Roloffia bertholdi" .. | 35 | 10 |
| 813. | 8 p. "Aphyosemion bualanum" .. .. .. | 55 | 15 |
| 814. | 10 p. "Aphyosemion bivittatum" .. .. .. | 75 | 20 |
| 815. | 30 p. "Aphyosemion australe" .. .. .. | 2·50 | 60 |

**148.** Ski Jumping.

**1984.** Winter Olympic Games, Sarajevo (2nd issue). Multicoloured.

| | | | |
|---|---|---|---|
| 816. | 50 c. Type **148** .. .. | 10 | 10 |
| 817. | 2 p. 50 Speed skating .. | 15 | 10 |
| 818. | 3 p. 50 Ice hockey .. .. | 30 | 10 |
| 819. | 5 p. Cross-country skiing .. | 35 | 10 |
| 820. | 6 p. Downhill skiing .. | 60 | 15 |
| 821. | 20 p. Ice skating .. .. | 1·25 | 40 |
| 822. | 30 p. Two-man bobsleigh | 2·00 | 60 |

**149.** Duesenberg, 1928.

**1984.** 150th Birth Anniv. of Gottlieb Daimler (automobile designer). Multicoloured.

824. 5 p. Type **149** .. .. 15 10
825. 8 p. MG "Midget", 1932 .. 25 10
826. 15 p. Mercedes, 1928 .. 50 20
827. 20 p. Bentley, 1928 .. 60 30
828. 24 p. Alfa Romeo, 1929 .. 85 30
829. 30 p. Datsun, 1932 .. 1·25 35
830. 35 p. Lincoln, 1932 .. 1·75 40

**150.** Sud Aviation Caravelle.

**1984.** 40th Anniv of I.C.A.O. Mult.

832 8 p. Type **150** .. .. 25 10
833 22 p. Douglas DC-6B .. 80 30
834 80 p. Ilyushin Il-76 .. 2·25 90

**151.** "Dona Tadea Arias de Enriquez" (Goya).

**153.** Fabric Headdress.

**152.** Football.

**1984.** "Espana 84" International Stamp Exhibition, Madrid. Multicoloured.

835. 3 p. "Virgin and Child" (Morales) .. .. 15 10
836. 6 p. Type **151** .. .. 20 10
837. 10 p. "Saint Cassilda" (Zurbaran) .. .. 30 10
838. 12 p. "Saints Andrew and Francis" (El Greco) .. 35 15
839. 15 p. "Infanta Isabel Clara Eugenia" (Coello) .. 55 15
840. 35 p. "Queen Maria of Austria" (Velazquez) .. 1·40 45
841. 40 p. "The Trinity" (El Greco) .. .. .. 1·75 55

**1984.** Olympic Games, Los Angeles (2nd issue). Multicoloured.

843. 6 p. Type **152** .. .. 15 10
844. 8 p. Show jumping .. 25 10
845. 15 p. Yachting .. .. 50 15
846. 20 p. Hockey .. .. 70 20
847. 22 p. Handball .. .. 75 20
848. 30 p. Canoeing .. .. 1·10 35
849. 40 p. Boxing .. .. 1·75 60

**1984.** "Lubrapex 84" Portuguese–Brazilian Stamp Exhibition, Lisbon. Multicoloured.

851. 7 p. 50 Type **153** .. .. 25 15
852. 7 p. 50 Headdress .. .. 25 15
853. 7 p. 50 Carved bird head-dress .. .. .. 25 15
854. 7 p. 50 Wooden mask .. 25 15
855. 7 p. 50 Carving of horse .. 25 15
856. 7 p. 50 Statuette .. .. 25 15

**155.** Pearl Throne, Cameroun.

**156.** Amilcar Cabral making Speech.

**1984.** World Heritage. Multicoloured.

864. 3 p. Type **155** .. .. 10 10
865. 6 p. Antelope (carving), West Sudan .. .. 20 10
866. 10 p. Setial, East Africa .. 30 15
867. 12 p. Mask, West African coast .. .. .. 40 20
868. 15 p. Leopard (statuette), Guinea coast .. .. 60 25
869. 35 p. Carved statuette of woman, Zaire .. .. 1·25 50
870. 40 p. Funeral figures, South-east Africa and Madagascar .. .. 1·25 55

**1984.** 60th Birth Anniv. of Amilcar Cabral. Multicoloured.

871. 5 p. Type **156** .. .. 15 10
872. 12 p. Amilcar Cabral in combat dress .. .. 35 15
873. 20 p. Amilcar Cabral memorial .. .. 60 25
874. 50 p. Amilcar Cabral mausoleum .. .. 1·50 60

**157.** Mechanic working on Engine.

**1984.** 11th Anniv. of Independence. Mult.

875. 3 p. Type **157** .. .. 10 10
876. 6 p. Children in school .. 20 10
877. 10 p. Laying bricks .. 30 10
878. 12 p. Doctor tending child (vert.) .. .. .. 35 20
879. 15 p. Sewing (vert.) .. 40 20
880. 35 p. Telephonist and switchboard .. .. 1·25 50
881. 40 p. P.A.I.G.C. head-quarters .. .. 1·25 55

**158.** Grey Whales.

**1984.** Whales. Multicoloured.

882. 5 p. Type **158** .. .. 25 10
883. 8 p. Blue whales .. .. 30 15
884. 15 p. Bottle-nosed dolphins 60 25
885. 20 p. Sperm whale .. 70 25
886. 24 p. Killer whale .. .. 85 35
887. 30 p. Bowhead whale .. 1·50 40
888. 35 p. Sei whale .. .. 1·75 45

**159.** "Hypolimnas dexithea".



**1984.** Butterflies and Moths. Multicoloured.

889 3 p. Type **159** .. .. 15 15
890 6 p. "Papilio arcturus" .. 20 15
891 10 p. "Morpho menelaus terrestris" .. .. 35 15
892 12 p. "Apaturina erminea" 45 20
893 15 p. "Prepona praeneste" 70 25
894 35 p. "Ornithoptera paradisea" .. .. 1·60 55
895 40 p. "Morpho hecuba obidona" .. .. 1·60 60

**160.** Carl Lewis (400 metres relay).

**1984.** Olympic Gold Medallists, Los Angeles. Multicoloured.

896. 6 p. Type **160** .. .. 15 10
897. 8 p. Koji Gushiken (men's gymnastics) .. .. 15 10
898. 15 p. Dr. Reiner Klimke (individual dressage) .. 45 20
899. 20 p. Tracie Ruiz (synchronized swimming) .. 55 20
900. 22 p. May Lou Retton (women's gymnastics) .. 65 25
901. 30 p. Michael Gross (100 m. freestyle and 100 m. butterfly) .. .. 90 35
902. 40 p. Edwin Moses (400 metres hurdles) .. .. 1·25 50

**161.** White Mountain Central Railroad Engine, 1926.

**1984.** Locomotives. Multicoloured.

904. 5 p. Type **161** .. .. 20 15
905. 8 p. Portuguese engine, 1886 .. .. .. 25 15
906. 15 p. Single-rail suspended railcar, 1901 .. .. 50 20
907. 20 p. Peruvian mountain rack-railway locomotive 60 25
908. 24 p. Rack-railway engine, Achensee, Austria .. 80 30
909. 30 p. Vitznau-Rigi railway steam locomotive .. 1·10 40
910. 35 p. Vitznau-Rigi railway locomotive, 1873 .. 1·60 60

**162.** Harley Davidson Motor Cycle.

**1985.** Centenary of Motor Cycle. Mult.

912. 5 p. Type **162** .. .. 20 15
913. 8 p. Kawasaki .. .. 25 15
914. 15 p. Honda .. .. 45 20
915. 20 p. Yamaha .. .. 70 30
916. 25 p. Suzuki .. .. 1·00 35
917. 30 p. BMW .. .. 1·40 45
918. 35 p. Moto Guzzi .. .. 1·50 50

**163.** Brown Pelican.

**164.** "Clitocybe gibba".

**1985.** Air. Birth Bicentenary of John J. Audubon (ornithologist). Multicoloured.

920. 5 p. Type **163** .. .. 35 15
921. 10 p. American white pelican .. .. .. 65 25
922. 20 p. Great blue heron .. 1·00 30
923. 40 p. Greater flamingo .. 2·40 65

**1985.** Fungi. Multicoloured.

924. 7 p. Type **164** .. .. 35 15
925. 9 p. "Morchella elata" .. 50 20
926. 12 p. "Lepista nuda" .. 75 25
927. 20 p. "Lactarius deliciosus" .. .. 90 30
928. 30 p. "Russula virescens" 1·25 35
929. 35 p. "Chroogomphus rutilus" .. .. .. 1·75 50

**165.** Dunant, Piper Twin Commanche and Volunteers attending Patient.

**1985.** 75th Death Anniv. of Henri Dunant (Red Cross founder). Multicoloured.

930. 20 p. Type **165** .. .. 40 15
931. 25 p. Doctor and volunteer putting patient in ambulance .. .. 50 15
932. 40 p. Helicopter team attending wounded soldier .. .. .. 75 35
933. 80 p. Volunteers in boat rescuing man from water 1·40 55

**166.** Long-haired White Cat.

**167.** Vincenzo Bellini, 1820 Harp and 16th-century Descant Viol.

**1985.** Cats. Multicoloured.

934. 7 p. Type **166** .. .. 20 15
935. 10 p. Siamese cat .. .. 25 15
936. 12 p. Grey cat .. .. 30 15
937. 15 p. Tortoiseshell cat .. 40 15
938. 20 p. Ginger cat .. .. 55 20
939. 40 p. Tabby cat .. .. 1·00 35
940. 45 p. Short-haired white cat .. .. .. 1·40 35

**1985.** International Music Year. Composers. Multicoloured.

942. 4 p. Type **167** (150th death anniv. of Bellini) .. 15 15
943. 5 p. Robert Schumann (175th birth anniv.) and pyramid piano, 1829 .. 15 15
944. 7 p. Frederic Chopin (175th birth anniv.) and piano, 1817 .. .. .. 15 15
945. 12 p. Luigi Cherubini (225th birth anniv.), 1720 baryton and 18th-century quinton .. 20 15
946. 20 p. Giovanni Battista Pergolesi (275th birth anniv.) and harpsichord, 1734 .. .. .. 45 15
947. 30 p. Georg Friedrich Handel (300th birth anniv.), 1825 valve trumpet and 18th-century timpani .. 65 20
948. 50 p. Heinrich Schutz (400th birth anniv.), 17th-century bass viol and 1680 oboe .. .. 1·00 45

**168.** "Santa Maria".

**169.** U.N. Emblem, Rainbow and Peace Doves.

**1985.** Sailing Ships. Multicoloured.

950 8 p. Type **168** .. .. 20 15
951 15 p. 16th-century Dutch carrack .. .. 30 15
952 20 p. "Mayflower" .. 40 15
953 30 p. "St. Louis" (French galleon) .. .. 65 20
954 35 p. "Royal Sovereign" (galleon), 1660 .. .. 75 20
955 45 p. "Soleil Royal" (17th-century French warship) .. .. 1·10 35
956 80 p. 18th-century British naval brig .. .. 1·75 60

**1985.** 40th Anniv. of U.N.O.

957. **169.** 10 p. multicoloured .. 25 15
958. – 20 p. blue and brown 50 35

DESIGN: 20 p. U.N. emblem in "40".

**170.** "Madonna of the Rose Garden" (detail).

**1985.** "Italia '85" International Stamp Exhibition, Rome. Paintings by Botticelli. Multicoloured.

959. 7 p. Type **170** .. .. 15 10
960. 10 p. "Venus and Mars" (detail) .. .. 15 10
961. 12 p. "St. Augustine in his Study" (detail) .. .. 20 15
962. 15 p. "Spring" (detail) .. 25 15
963. 20 p. "Virgin and Child" (detail) .. .. .. 35 15
964. 40 p. "Virgin and Child with St. John" (detail) 1·00 30
965. 45 p. "Birth of Venus" (detail) .. .. .. 1·10 35

**171.** Youths dancing.

**1985.** International Youth Year. Mult.

967. 7 p. Type **171** .. .. 10 10
968. 13 p. Windsurfing .. .. 20 15
969. 15 p. Roller skating .. 20 15
970. 25 p. Hang-gliding .. 35 15
971. 40 p. Surfing .. .. 55 25
972. 50 p. Skateboarding .. 75 40
973. 80 p. Free-falling from air-plane .. .. .. 1·50 60

**172.** Alfa Touring Car.

**1986.** Anniversaries and Events. Mult.

975. 15 p. Tail of comet .. 1·25 50
976. 15 p. Head of comet .. 1·25 50
977. 15 p. Type **172** .. 1·25 50
978. 15 p. Frankfurt am Main railway station, 1914 .. 1·25 50
979. 15 p. Top of trophy .. 2·50 1·00
980. 15 f. Base of trophy .. 2·50 1·00
981. 15 p. Olympic rings .. 3·00 1·00
982. 15 p. View of Barcelona .. 3·00 1·00
983. 15 p. Part of space station 1·25 50
984. 15 p. Deflectors .. .. 1·25 50
985. 15 p. Space station and Shuttle .. .. 1·25 50
986. 15 p. Part of space station and Earth .. .. 1·25 50
987. 15 p. Boris Becker's head and arm .. .. 1·50 75
988. 15 p. Becker's body .. 1·50 75
989. 15 p. Javier's head and arms .. .. 1·50 75
990. 15 p. Javier's body and legs .. .. .. 1·50 75

ANNIVERSARIES: Nos. 975/6, Appearance of Halley's Comet. 977, Centenary of motor car. 978, 150th anniv. of German railways. 979/80, World Cup Football Championship, Mexico. 981, Olympic Games, Seoul (1988). 982, "500th anniv. of discovery of America by Columbus" Exhibition and Olympic Games, Barcelona (1992). 983/6, 25 years of manned space flights. 987/8, Wimbledon Men's Singles champion, 1986. 989/90, Ivan Lendl, winner of U.S. Masters Tournament, 1986.

Nos. 975/90 were printed together in se-tenant sheetlets of 16 stamps, stamps for the same event forming a composite design.

**173.** "Santa Maria".

**1987.** 500th Anniv. (1992) of Discovery of America by Columbus. Multicoloured.

992. 50 p. Type **173** .. .. 2·00 60
993. 50 p. View of Seville .. 2·00 60
994. 50 p. Pedro Alvares Cabral disembarking at Bahia 2·00 60
995. 50 p. View of Seville (different) .. .. 2·00 60

**1987.** Nos. 352/5, 359 and 362/3 of Portuguese Guinea surch. **DA BISSAU** and new value.

997. 100 p. on 20 c. Type **51** .. 35 15
998. 200 p. on 35 c. African rock python .. .. 70 25
999. 300 p. on 70 c. Boomslang .. .. 1·10 35
1000. 400 p. on 80 c. West African mamba .. 1·25 40
1001. 500 p. on 3 e. 50 Brown house snake .. .. 1·50 50
1002. 1000 p. on 15 e. Striped beauty snake .. .. 3·00 1·00
1003. 2000 p. on 20 e. African egg-eating snake (horiz.) .. .. 6·00 3·00

**1987.** No. 430 surch. **2 500,00.**

1004. **76.** 2500 p. on 2 e. mult. 7·00 3·25

**176.** Ice Dancing.

**1988.** Winter Olympic Games, Calgary. Mult.

1005. 5 p. Type **176** .. .. 10 10
1006. 10 p. Luge .. .. 10 10
1007. 50 p. Skiing .. .. 30 15
1008. 200 p. Downhill skiing .. 75 30
1009. 300 p. Slalom .. .. 1·25 40
1010. 500 p. Ski jumping (vert.) 2·00 55
1011. 800 p. Speed skating (vert.) .. .. .. 3·00 1·10

**177.** Yachting.

**178.** Football.

**1988.** Olympic Games, Seoul. Multicoloured.

1013. 5 p. Type **177** .. .. 10 10
1014. 10 p. Equestrian events (horiz.) .. .. 10 10
1015. 50 p. High jumping (horiz.) .. .. 15 10
1016. 200 p. Rifle shooting (horiz.) .. .. 70 30
1017. 300 p. Triple jumping .. 1·10 40
1018. 500 p. Tennis .. .. 2·00 50
1019. 800 p. Archery .. .. 2·75 1·00

**1988.** "Essen 88" Stamp Fair and European Football Championship, Germany.

1021. **178.** 5 p. multicoloured .. 10 10
1022. – 10 p. multicoloured 10 10
1023. – 50 p. multicoloured 15 10
1024. – 200 p. multicoloured 70 30
1025. – 300 p. multicoloured 1·10 40
1026. – 500 p. multicoloured 2·00 50
1027. – 800 p. multicoloured 2·75 1·10

DESIGNS: 10 to 800 p. Various footballing scenes.

**179** Lioness

**1988.** Animals. Multicoloured.

1029 5 p. Type **179** .. .. 10 10
1030 10 p. Ferruginous pygmy owl .. .. .. 10 10
1031 50 p. Hoopoe (horiz) .. 10 10
1032 200 p. Common zebra (horiz) .. .. 30 10
1033 300 p. African elephant .. 50 20
1034 500 p. Vulturine guinea-fowl .. .. .. 80 30
1035 800 p. Black rhinoceros .. 1·25 50

**180** Machel

**1988.** 2nd Death Anniv of Pres. Samora Machel of Mozambique. Multicoloured.

1036 10 p. Type **180** .. .. 10 10
1037 50 p. With arm raised .. 10 10
1038 200 p. With soldier .. 30 10
1039 300 p. Wearing suit .. 50 20

**181** Henry Dunant (founder)

**1988.** 125th Anniv of Int Red Cross. Mult.

1040 10 p. Type **181** .. .. 10 10
1041 50 p. Dr T. Maunoir .. 10 10
1042 200 p. Dr Louis Appia .. 30 10
1043 800 p. Gustave Moynier 1·25 50

**182** Basset Hound

**1988.** Dogs. Multicoloured.

1044 5 p. Type **182** .. .. 10 10
1045 10 p. Grand bleu de Gascogne .. .. 10 10
1046 50 p. Italian spinone .. 10 10
1047 200 p. Yorkshire terrier .. 30 10
1048 300 p. Munsterlander .. 50 20
1049 500 p. Pointer .. .. 80 30
1050 800 p. German shorthaired pointer .. .. 1·25 50

**183** Egyptian Ship, 3300 B.C.

**1988.** Sailing Ships. Multicoloured.

1052 5 p. Type **183** .. .. 10 10
1053 10 p. Ship of Sahu Re, 2500 B.C. (wrongly inscr "2700 B.C.") .. .. 10 10
1054 50 p. Ship of Hatsheps-hut, 1500 B.C. .. 10 10
1055 200 p. Ship of Rameses III, 1200 B.C. .. .. 35 10
1056 300 p. Greek trireme, 480 B.C. .. .. 60 25
1057 500 p. Etruscan bireme, 600 B.C. .. .. 1·00 40
1058 800 p. 12th-century Venetian galley .. 1·50 65

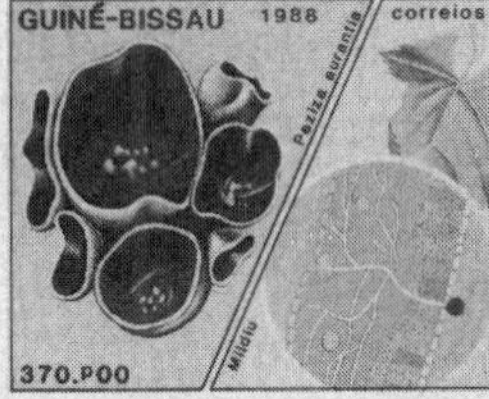


**184** "Peziza aurantia"

**1988.** Fungi. Multicoloured.

1059 370 p. Type **184** .. .. 75 30
1060 470 p. Morel .. .. 1·00 35
1061 600 p. Caesar's mushroom 1·25 45
1062 780 p. Fly agaric .. 1·60 55
1063 800 p. Deadly amanite .. 1·60 55
1064 900 p. Cultivated mush-room .. .. .. 1·90 70
1065 945 p. Pixie stool .. 2·10 75

**185** Francois-Andre Philidor and Rook

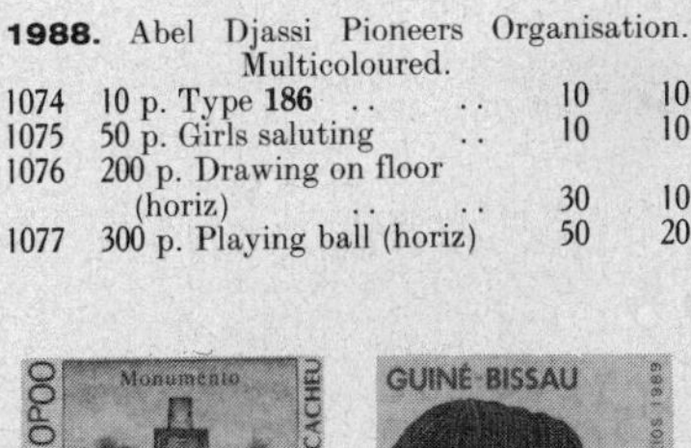


**186** Trumpeter, Flag Bearer and Drummer

**1988.** "Finlandia 88" International Stamp Exhibition, Helsinki. Chess. Multicoloured.

1066 5 p. Type **185** .. .. 10 10
1067 10 p. Howard Staunton and chessmen .. .. 10 10
1068 50 p. Adolf Anderssen and queen .. .. 10 10
1069 200 p. Paul Morphy and pawn .. .. .. 30 10
1070 300 p. Wilhelm Steinitz and knight .. .. 50 20
1071 500 p. Emanuel Lasker and bishop .. .. 80 30
1072 800 p. Jose Capablanca and king .. .. 1·25 50

**1988.** Abel Djassi Pioneers Organisation. Multicoloured.

1074 10 p. Type **186** .. .. 10 10
1075 50 p. Girls saluting .. 10 10
1076 200 p. Drawing on floor (horiz) .. .. 30 10
1077 300 p. Playing ball (horiz) 50 20

**187** Monument

**188** Woman with Long Hair

**1988.** 400th Anniv of Cacheu. Multicoloured.

1078 10 p. Type **187** .. .. 10 10
1079 50 p. Fort (horiz) .. 10 10
1080 200 p. Early building (horiz) .. .. 35 10
1081 300 p. Church (horiz) .. 50 20

**1989.** Traditional Hairstyles.

1082 **188** 50 p. multicoloured .. 10 10
1083 – 100 p. multicoloured 15 10
1084 – 200 p. multicoloured 30 10
1085 – 350 p. multicoloured 60 25
1086 – 500 p. multicoloured 80 30
1087 – 800 p. multicoloured 1·25 50
1088 – 1000 p. multicoloured 1·60 65

DESIGNS: 100 p. to 1000 p. Different hairstyles.

**189** Bombalon

**1989.** Traditional Musical Instruments. Mult.

1089 50 p. Type **189** .. .. 10 10
1090 100 p. Flute .. .. 15 10
1091 200 p. Tambor .. .. 35 15
1092 350 p. Dondon .. .. 65 25
1093 500 p. Balafon .. .. 90 35
1094 800 p. Kora .. .. 1·50 60
1095 1000 p. Nhanhero .. 1·75 70

**190** Seychelles Blue Pigeon **191** Pimento

**1989.** Birds. Multicoloured.

1096 50 p. Type **190** .. .. 10 10
1097 100 p. Laughing dove .. 15 10
1098 200 p. Namaqua dove .. 35 15
1099 350 p. Purple-breasted ground dove .. .. 65 25
1100 500 p. African collared dove .. .. .. 90 35
1101 800 p. Pheasant pigeon .. 1·50 60
1102 1000 p. Emerald dove .. 1·75 70

**1989.** Plants.

1104 **191** 50 p. blue .. .. 10 10
1105 – 100 p. violet .. .. 15 10
1106 – 200 p. green .. .. 35 15
1107 – 350 p. red .. .. 65 25
1108 – 500 p. brown .. 90 35
1109 – 800 p. brown .. 1·50 60
1110 – 1000 p. green .. 1·75 70

DESIGNS: 100 p. Solanum; 200 p. "Curcumis peco"; 350 p. Tomato; 500 p. "Solanum itiopium"; 800 p. "Hibiscus esculentus"; 1000 p. Baguiche.

**192** Electric Train

**1989.** Trains. Multicoloured.

1111 50 p. Type **192** .. .. 10 10
1112 100 p. "TEM 2" locomotive .. .. 15 10
1113 200 p. Locomotive .. 35 15
1114 350 p. F.G.V. train .. 65 25
1115 500 p. Skoda "55-E" locomotive .. .. 90 35
1116 800 p. "Tu 7 E" locomotive .. .. 1·50 60
1117 1000 p. Electric train (68 × 27 mm) .. .. 1·75 70

## INDEX

Countries can be quickly located by referring to the index at the end of this volume.

**193** Hurdling

**1989.** Olympic Games, Barcelona (1992) (1st issue). Multicoloured.

1119 50 p. Type **193** .. .. 10 10
1120 100 p. Boxing .. .. 20 10
1121 200 p. High jumping .. 35 15
1122 350 p. Sprinters in starting blocks .. 60 25
1123 500 p. Runner leaving starting block .. 90 35
1124 800 p. Gymnastics .. 1·50 60
1125 1000 p. Pole vaulting .. 1·75 70

See also Nos. 1245/8.

**194** "Limelight" **196** Teotihuacan Pot

**195** "La Marseillaise" (relief by Rude from Arc de Triomphe)

**1989.** Lilies. Multicoloured.

1127 50 p. Type **194** .. .. 10 10
1128 100 p. "Lilium candidum" 20 10
1129 200 p. "Lilium pardalinum" .. .. .. 35 15
1130 350 p. "Lilium auratum" 65 25
1131 500 p. "Lilium canadense" 90 35
1132 800 p. "Enchantment" .. 1·50 60
1133 1000 p. "Black Dragon" 1·75 70

**1989.** "PhilexFrance 89" International Stamp Exhibition, Paris. Multicoloured.

1135 50 p. Type **195** .. .. 10 10
1136 100 p. Champ de Mars .. 20 10
1137 200 p. Storming of the Bastille .. .. 35 15
1138 350 p. Fete (27 × 44 mm) 65 25
1139 500 p. Dancing round Tree of Liberty .. .. 90 35
1140 800 p. Rouget de Lisle singing "The Marseillaise" .. .. 1·50 60
1141 1000 p. Storming of the Bastille (different) .. 1·75 70

**1989.** "Brasiliana 89' International Stamp Exhibition, Rio de Janeiro. Multicoloured.

1143 50 p. Type **196** .. .. 10 10
1144 100 p. Mochica jar .. 20 10
1145 200 p. Jaina statuette .. 35 15
1146 350 p. Nayarit anthrozoomorphic jug .. 65 25
1147 500 p. Inca vase .. .. 90 35
1148 800 p. Hopewell statuette of mother and child .. 1·50 60
1149 1000 p. Taina mask .. 1·75 70

**197** Players Tackling

**1989.** World Cup Football Championship, Italy (1990). Multicoloured.

1151 50 p. Type **197** .. .. 10 10
1152 100 p. Players and ball .. 20 10
1153 200 p. Players and ball (different) .. .. 35 15
1154 350 p. "Scissors" kick .. 65 25
1155 500 p. Goalkeeper .. 90 35
1156 800 p. Foul .. .. 1·50 60
1157 1000 p. Player scoring goal 1·75 70

**198** Trachodon

**1989.** Prehistoric Animals. Multicoloured.

1159 50 p. Type **198** .. .. 10 10
1160 100 p. Edaphosaurus (68 × 22 mm) .. .. 20 10
1161 200 p. Mesosaurus .. 35 15
1162 350 p. "Elephius primigenius" .. .. 65 25
1163 500 p. Tyrannosaurus (horiz) .. .. 90 35
1164 800 p. Stegosaurus (horiz) 1·50 60
1165 1000 p. "Cervus megaceros" .. .. .. 1·75 70

**199** Speed Skating

**1989.** Winter Olympic Games, Albertville (1992). Multicoloured.

1166 50 p. Type **199** .. .. 10 10
1167 100 p. Figure skating .. 20 10
1168 200 p. Ski jumping .. 35 15
1169 350 p. Skiing .. 65 25
1170 500 p. Skiing (different) .. 90 35
1171 800 p. Bobsleighing .. 1·50 60
1172 1000 p. Ice hockey .. 1·75 70

**200** African Buffalo **201** "Adoration of Baby Jesus" (Fra Filippo Lippi)

**1989.** Animals.

1174 **200** 50 p. brown and red 10 10
1175 – 100 p. ultram & blue 20 10
1176 – 200 p. green & lt green 35 15
1177 – 350 p. purple and lilac 65 25
1178 – 500 p. chestnut & brn 90 35
1179 – 800 p. violet & dp vio 1·50 60
1180 – 1000 p. deep red & red 1·75 70
1181 – 1500 p. red and yellow 2·75 1·10

DESIGNS: 100 p. Steppe zebra; 200 p. Black rhinoceros; 350 p. Okapi; 500 p. Rhesus macacque; 800 p. Hippopotamus; 1000 p. Cheetah; 1500 p. Lion.

**1989.** Christmas. Multicoloured.

1182 50 p. Type **201** .. .. 10 10
1183 100 p. "Adoration of the Kings" (Pieter Brueghel) .. .. 20 10
1184 200 p. "Adoration of the Kings" (Jan Mostaert) 35 15
1185 350 p. "Nativity" (Albert Durer) .. .. 65 25
1186 500 p. "Adoration of the Kings" (Peter Paul Rubens) .. .. 90 35
1187 800 p. "Adoration of the Kings" (Roger van der Weyden) .. .. 1·50 60
1188 1000 p. "Adoration of the Kings" (Francesco Francia) (horiz) .. 1·75 70

**202** Pope John-Paul II and Map **204** Cockerel and Hen

**1990.** Papal Visit. Multicoloured.

1189 500 p. Type **202** .. .. 80 20
1190 1000 p. Pope and couple 1·60 40

**1990.** "Lubrapex 90" Brazilian–Portuguese Stamp Exhibition, Brasilia. Coop Fowls. Multicoloured.

1193 500 p. Type **204** .. .. 80 30
1194 800 p. Turkey .. .. 1·25 50
1195 1000 p. Duck and ducklings .. .. 1·60 65

**205** Radar Rainfall Map

**1990.** World Meteorology Day. Multicoloured.

1197 1000 p. Type **205** .. 1·60 65
1198 3000 p. Campbell-Stokes heliograph .. .. 5·00 2·00

**206** Crying Man and Baby in Womb **207** Cotton Plant

**1990.** 40th Anniv of United Nations Development Programme.

1199 **206** 1000 p. multicoloured 1·60 65

**1991.** Traditional Cotton Weaving. Mult.

1200 400 p. Type **207** .. .. 60 25
1201 500 p. Weaver .. .. 75 30
1202 600 p. Traditional cloth pattern .. .. 95 40

**208** Mickey Mouse

**1991.** Carnival Masks. Multicoloured.

1204 200 p. Type **208** .. .. 30 10
1205 300 p. Hippopotamus .. 45 20
1206 600 p. Buffalo .. 75 30
1207 1200 p. Buffalo (different) 95 40

**209** Royal Barb

**1991.** Fishes. Multicoloured.

1208 300 p. Type **209** .. .. 30 10
1209 400 p. Axe fish .. .. 60 25
1210 500 p. Shovel fish .. 1·00 40
1211 600 p. Painted mermaid 1·25 40

210 Fire Engine with Water Cannons

211 Lizard Buzzard

**1991.** Fire and First Aid Service. Mult.

| | | | |
|---|---|---|---|
| 1212 | 200 p. Type **210** .. .. | 30 | 10 |
| 1213 | 500 p. Fire engine with ladders .. .. | 75 | 30 |
| 1214 | 800 p. Emergency vehicle with ladders .. .. | 1·25 | 50 |
| 1215 | 1500 p. Ambulance .. | 2·25 | 90 |

**1991.** Birds. Multicoloured.

| | | | |
|---|---|---|---|
| 1216 | 100 p. Type **211** .. .. | 15 | 10 |
| 1217 | 250 p. Crowned crane .. | 40 | 10 |
| 1218 | 350 p. Abyssinian ground hornbill .. .. | 55 | 20 |
| 1219 | 500 p. Saddle-bill stork .. | 75 | 30 |

212 "Best Wishes"

213 Fula

**1991.** Greetings Stamps. Multicoloured.

| | | | |
|---|---|---|---|
| 1221 | 250 p. Type **212** .. .. | 40 | 10 |
| 1222 | 400 p. Couple embracing ("With love") .. | 65 | 25 |
| 1223 | 800 p. Horn-blower and map of Africa ("Congratulations") .. | 1·25 | 50 |
| 1224 | 1000 p. Doves ("Season's greetings") .. .. | 1·50 | 60 |

**1992.** Traditional Costume. Multicoloured.

| | | | |
|---|---|---|---|
| 1225 | 400 p. Type **213** .. .. | 10 | 10 |
| 1226 | 600 p. Balanta .. .. | 15 | 10 |
| 1227 | 1000 p. Fula (different) .. | 25 | 10 |
| 1228 | 1500 p. Manjaco .. | 40 | 15 |

214 "Landolfia owariensis"

215 Cigarette and Fruit "Hearts"

**1992.** Fruits. Multicoloured.

| | | | |
|---|---|---|---|
| 1229 | 500 p. Type **214** .. .. | 15 | 10 |
| 1230 | 1500 p. "Dialium guineensis" .. .. | 40 | 15 |
| 1231 | 2000 p. "Adansonia digitata" .. .. | 50 | 20 |
| 1232 | 3000 p. "Parkia biglobosa" .. .. .. | 75 | 30 |

**1992.** World Health Day. "Health in Rhythm with the Heart". Multicoloured.

| | | | |
|---|---|---|---|
| 1233 | 1500 p. Type **215** .. | 40 | 15 |
| 1234 | 4000 p. "Heart" running over food .. .. | 1·00 | 40 |

216 "Cassia alata"

**1992.** "Lubrapex 92" Brazilian–Portuguese Stamp Exhibition, Lisbon. Plants. Mult.

| | | | |
|---|---|---|---|
| 1235 | 100 p. Type **216** .. .. | 10 | 10 |
| 1236 | 400 p. "Perlebia purpurea" .. .. | 10 | 10 |
| 1237 | 1000 p. "Caesalpinia pulcherrima" .. .. | 25 | 15 |
| 1238 | 1500 p. "Adenanthera pavonina" .. .. | 40 | 15 |

Nos. 1235/8 were issued together, se-tenant, forming a composite design.

217 Canoe

**1992.** Canoes. Multicoloured.

| | | | |
|---|---|---|---|
| 1240 | 750 p. Type **217** .. .. | 25 | 10 |
| 1241 | 800 p. Pirogue .. .. | 25 | 10 |
| 1242 | 1000 p. Pirogue (different) | 35 | 10 |
| 1243 | 1300 p. Skiff .. .. | 50 | 20 |

218 Volleyball

**1992.** Olympic Games, Barcelona (2nd issue). Multicoloured.

| | | | |
|---|---|---|---|
| 1245 | 600 p. Basketball .. | 15 | 10 |
| 1246 | 1000 p. Type **218** .. | 25 | 10 |
| 1247 | 1500 p. Handball .. | 40 | 15 |
| 1248 | 2000 p. Football .. | 50 | 20 |

219 "Afzelia africana"

221 Colobus

**1992.** Forest Preservation. Multicoloured.

| | | | |
|---|---|---|---|
| 1249 | 1000 p. Type **219** .. | 25 | 10 |
| 1250 | 1500 p. African mahogany | 40 | 15 |
| 1251 | 2000 p. Iroko .. .. | 50 | 20 |
| 1252 | 3000 p. Ambila .. .. | 75 | 30 |

**1992.** The Red Colobus. Multicoloured.

| | | | |
|---|---|---|---|
| 1254 | 2000 p. Type **221** .. | 50 | 20 |
| 1255 | 2000 p. Colobus sitting in tree fork .. .. | 50 | 20 |
| 1256 | 2000 p. Mother and young | 50 | 20 |
| 1257 | 2000 p. Two colobus on tree branch .. .. | 50 | 20 |

222 Puff Adder

**1993.** Reptiles. Multicoloured.

| | | | |
|---|---|---|---|
| 1258 | 1500 p. Type **222** .. | 40 | 15 |
| 1259 | 3000 p. African dwarf crocodile .. .. | 80 | 30 |
| 1260 | 4000 p. Nile monitor .. | 1·10 | 45 |
| 1261 | 5000 p. Rainbow lizard .. | 1·40 | 55 |

224 Waterside Village

**1993.** Tourism. Multicoloured.

| | | | |
|---|---|---|---|
| 1264 | 1000 p. Type **224** .. | 25 | 10 |
| 1265 | 2000 p. Masked villagers on shore and crops .. | 55 | 20 |
| 1266 | 4000 p. Villages on offshore islands .. | 1·10 | 45 |
| 1267 | 5000 p. Crops on island .. | 1·40 | 55 |

Nos. 1264/7 were issued together, se-tenant, forming a composite design.

225 Bracelet

**1994.** Jewellery. Multicoloured.

| | | | |
|---|---|---|---|
| 1268 | 1500 p. Type **225** .. | 40 | 15 |
| 1269 | 3000 p. Tribal mask pendant .. .. | 80 | 30 |
| 1270 | 4000 p. Circles pendant .. | 1·10 | 45 |
| 1271 | 5000 p. Filigree pendant | 1·40 | 55 |

226 "Erythrina senegalensis"

**1994.** Medicinal Plants. Multicoloured.

| | | | |
|---|---|---|---|
| 1273 | 2000 p. Type **226** .. | 20 | 10 |
| 1274 | 3000 p. "Cassia occidentalis" .. | 30 | 10 |
| 1275 | 4000 p. "Gardenia ternifolia" .. .. | 45 | 20 |
| 1276 | 6000 p. "Cochlospermum tinctorium" .. .. | 65 | 25 |

227 Player kicking Ball

**1994.** World Cup Football Championship, U.S.A. Multicoloured.

| | | | |
|---|---|---|---|
| 1277 | 4000 p. Type **227** .. | 40 | 15 |
| 1278 | 5000 p. Goalkeeper making save .. .. | 55 | 20 |
| 1279 | 5500 p. Heading the ball | 60 | 25 |
| 1280 | 6500 p. Dribbling the ball | 70 | 30 |

228 Common Egg-eater (Dasypeltis scabra)

**1994.** "Philakorea 1994" International and "Singpex '94" Stamp Exhibitions. Snakes. Multicoloured.

| | | | |
|---|---|---|---|
| 1281 | 5000 p. Type **228** .. | 45 | 20 |
| 1282 | 5000 p. Green snake ("Philothamnus sp.") | 45 | 20 |
| 1283 | 5000 p. Black-lipped cobra ("Naja melanoleuca") | 45 | 20 |
| 1284 | 5000 p. African python ("Python sebae") .. | 45 | 20 |

229 Collecting Fruits

**1995.** Palm Oil. Multicoloured.

| | | | |
|---|---|---|---|
| 1286 | 3000 p. Type **229** .. | 20 | 10 |
| 1287 | 6500 p. Crushing fruit .. | 45 | 20 |
| 1288 | 7500 p. Palm oil production .. .. | 55 | 20 |
| 1289 | 8000 p. Animals and pot of palm oil .. .. | 60 | 25 |



## HAITI Pt. 15

The W. portion of the island of San Domingo in the West Indies. A republic, independent from 1804.

100 centimes = 1 gourde or piastre.

1. Liberty

2. Pres. Salomon.

**1881.** Imperf.

| | | | | |
|---|---|---|---|---|
| 1. | 1. | 1 c. red .. .. .. | 5·00 | 3·00 |
| 2. | | 2 c. purple .. .. | 6·50 | 3·25 |
| 3. | | 3 c. bistre .. .. .. | 11·00 | 4·00 |
| 4. | | 5 c. green .. .. .. | 18·00 | 7·00 |
| 5. | | 7 c. blue .. .. .. | 12·50 | 2·50 |
| 6. | | 20 c. brown .. .. | 45·00 | 16·00 |

**1882.** Perf.

| | | | | |
|---|---|---|---|---|
| 7. | 1. | 1 c. red .. .. .. | 3·25 | 1·00 |
| 9. | | 2 c. purple .. .. | 5·00 | 1·50 |
| 12. | | 3 c. bistre .. .. .. | 6·50 | 2·25 |
| 15. | | 5 c. green .. .. .. | 3·75 | 75 |
| 17. | | 7 c. blue .. .. .. | 5·00 | 1·25 |
| 20. | | 20 c. brown .. .. | 4·50 | 1·00 |

**1887.**

| | | | | |
|---|---|---|---|---|
| 24. | 2. | 1 c. lake .. .. .. | 30 | 30 |
| 25. | | 2 c. mauve .. .. | 55 | 50 |
| 26. | | 3 c. blue .. .. .. | 50 | 40 |
| 27. | | 5 c. green .. .. .. | 2·10 | 40 |

**1890.** Surch. **DEUX 2 CENT.**

| | | | | |
|---|---|---|---|---|
| 28. | 2. | 2 c. on 3 c. blue .. .. | 40 | 35 |

4. Tree with Leaves Upright.

5. Tree with Leaves Drooping.

6.

**1891.** Tree with leaves upright.

| | | | | |
|---|---|---|---|---|
| 29. | 4. | 1 c. mauve .. .. | 40 | 15 |
| 30. | | 2 c. blue .. .. .. | 60 | 20 |
| 31. | | 3 c. lilac .. .. .. | 60 | 40 |
| 31a. | | 3 c. grey .. .. .. | 80 | 50 |
| 32. | | 5 c. orange .. .. | 2·25 | 40 |
| 33. | | 7 c. red .. .. .. | 4·75 | 1·75 |

**1892.** Surch. **DEUX 2 CENT.**

| | | | | |
|---|---|---|---|---|
| 34. | 4. | 2 c. on 3 c. lilac .. .. | 85 | 70 |
| 34a. | | 2 c. on 3 c. grey .. .. | 85 | 70 |

**1893.** Tree with leaves drooping.

| | | | | |
|---|---|---|---|---|
| 35a. | 5. | 1 c. purple .. .. | 15 | 10 |
| 41. | | 1 c. blue .. .. .. | 20 | 20 |
| 36. | | 2 c. blue .. .. .. | 20 | 10 |
| 42. | | 2 c. red .. .. .. | 40 | 25 |
| 37. | | 3 c. lilac .. .. .. | 60 | 40 |
| 43. | | 3 c. brown .. .. | 20 | 15 |
| 38. | | 5 c. orange .. .. | 2·25 | 20 |
| 44. | | 5 c. green .. .. .. | 20 | 15 |
| 39. | | 7 c. red .. .. .. | 40 | 35 |
| 45. | | 7 c. grey .. .. .. | 30 | 20 |
| 40. | | 20 c. brown .. .. | 80 | 60 |
| 46. | | 20 c. orange .. .. | 40 | 40 |

**1898.** Surch. **DEUX 2 CENT.**

| | | | | |
|---|---|---|---|---|
| 47. | 5. | 2 c. on 20 c. brown .. | 85 | 25 |
| 48. | | 2 c. on 20 c. orange .. | 35 | 25 |

**1898.**

| | | | | |
|---|---|---|---|---|
| 49a. | 6. | 2 c. red .. .. .. | 20 | 15 |
| 50a. | | 5 c. green .. .. | 20 | 15 |

8. Pres. Simon Sam.

9.

**1898.**

| | | | | |
|---|---|---|---|---|
| 51. | 8. | 1 c. blue .. .. .. | 10 | 10 |
| 67. | 9. | 1 c. green .. .. .. | 10 | 10 |
| 52. | 8. | 2 c. orange .. .. | 15 | 15 |
| 68. | 9. | 2 c. red .. .. .. | 15 | 15 |
| 53. | 8. | 3 c. green .. .. .. | 15 | 15 |
| 54. | 9. | 4 c. red .. .. .. | 15 | 15 |
| 55. | 8. | 5 c. brown .. .. | 15 | 15 |
| 69. | 9. | 5 c. blue .. .. .. | 10 | 10 |
| 56. | 8. | 7 c. grey .. .. .. | 15 | 15 |
| 57. | 9. | 8 c. red .. .. .. | 20 | 15 |
| 58. | | 10 c. orange .. .. | 15 | 15 |
| 59. | | 15 c. olive .. .. | 35 | 25 |
| 60. | 8. | 20 c. black .. .. | 30 | 25 |
| 61. | | 50 c. lake .. .. | 35 | 25 |
| 62. | | 1 g. mauve .. .. | 1·40 | 1·25 |

**1902.** Optd. **MAI Gt. Pre 1902** in frame.

| | | | |
|---|---|---|---|
| 70. **8.** | 1 c. blue .. .. .. | 45 | 45 |
| 71. **9.** | 1 c. green .. .. .. | 35 | 15 |
| 72. **8.** | 2 c. orange .. .. .. | 45 | 45 |
| 73. **9.** | 2 c. red .. .. .. | 35 | 15 |
| 74. **8.** | 3 c. green .. .. .. | 35 | 35 |
| 75. **9.** | 4 c. red .. .. .. | 45 | 45 |
| 76. **8.** | 5 c. brown .. .. .. | 90 | 90 |
| 77. **9.** | 5 c. blue .. .. .. | 35 | 35 |
| 78. **8.** | 7 c. grey .. .. .. | 45 | 45 |
| 79. **9.** | 8 c. red .. .. .. | 45 | 45 |
| 80. | 10 c. orange .. .. | 45 | 45 |
| 81. | 15 c. olive .. .. | 2·10 | 1·50 |
| 82. **8.** | 20 c. black .. .. | 3·25 | 1·75 |
| 83. | 50 c. lake .. .. | 7·50 | 3·75 |
| 84. | 1 g. mauve .. .. | 9·50 | 7·75 |

12. Arms. 13. J.-J. Dessalines. 15. Pres. Nord Alexis.

**1904.** Cent. of Independence. Optd. **1804 POSTE PAYE 1904** in frame. T **12** and portraits as T **13**.

| | | | |
|---|---|---|---|
| 89. **12.** | 1 c. green .. .. .. | 25 | 25 |
| 90. – | 2 c. black and red .. | 30 | 30 |
| 91. – | 5 c. black and blue .. | 30 | 30 |
| 92. **13.** | 7 c. black and red .. | 30 | 30 |
| 93. – | 10 c. black and yellow .. | 30 | 30 |
| 94. – | 20 c. black and grey .. | 30 | 30 |
| 95. – | 50 c. black and olive .. | 30 | 30 |

DESIGNS: 2 c., 5 c. Toussaint l'Ouverture. 20 c., 50 c. Petion.

**1904.** Nos. 89/95 but without opt.

| | | | |
|---|---|---|---|
| 96. | 1 c. green .. .. .. | 20 | 15 |
| 97. | 2 c. black and red .. | 20 | 15 |
| 98. | 5 c. black and blue .. | 20 | 15 |
| 99. | 7 c. black and red .. | 20 | 15 |
| 100. | 10 c. black and yellow .. | 20 | 15 |
| 101. | 20 c. black and grey .. | 20 | 15 |
| 102. | 50 c. black and olive .. | 20 | 15 |

**1904.** External Mail. Optd. **1804 POSTE PAYE 1904** in frame.

| | | | |
|---|---|---|---|
| 103. **15.** | 1 c. green .. .. | 45 | 35 |
| 104. | 2 c. red .. .. .. | 45 | 35 |
| 105. | 5 c. blue .. .. | 45 | 35 |
| 106. | 10 c. brown .. .. | 45 | 35 |
| 107. | 20 c. orange .. .. | 45 | 35 |
| 108. | 50 c. plum .. .. | 45 | 35 |

**1904.** Nos. 103/108, but without opt.

| | | | |
|---|---|---|---|
| 109. **15.** | 1 c. green .. .. | 10 | 10 |
| 110. | 2 c. red .. .. .. | 10 | 10 |
| 111. | 5 c. blue .. .. | 10 | 10 |
| 112. | 10 c. brown .. .. | 10 | 10 |
| 113. | 20 c. orange .. .. | 10 | 10 |
| 114. | 50 c. plum .. .. | 10 | 10 |

**1906.** Optd. **SERVICE EXTERIEUR PROVISOIRE**, etc., in oval.

| | | | |
|---|---|---|---|
| 117. **8.** | 1 c. blue .. .. .. | 55 | 45 |
| 118. **9.** | 1 c. green .. .. .. | 55 | 55 |
| 119. **8.** | 2 c. orange .. .. | 1·10 | 1·10 |
| 120. **9.** | 2 c. red .. .. .. | 90 | 90 |
| 121. **8.** | 3 c. green .. .. | 90 | 90 |
| 122. **9.** | 4 c. red .. .. .. | 3·75 | 3·00 |
| 123. **8.** | 5 c. brown .. .. | 3·75 | 3·00 |
| 124. **9.** | 5 c. blue .. .. .. | 45 | 45 |
| 125. **8.** | 7 c. grey .. .. .. | 3·00 | 3·00 |
| 126. **9.** | 8 c. red .. .. .. | 45 | 45 |
| 127. | 10 c. orange .. .. | 85 | 55 |
| 128. | 15 c. olive .. .. | 1·10 | 60 |
| 129. **8.** | 20 c. black .. .. | 3·75 | 3·00 |
| 130. | 50 c. lake .. .. | 3·75 | 1·75 |
| 131. | 1 g. mauve .. .. | 6·25 | 4·75 |

19. Pres. Nord Alexis. 20. Arms.

**1906.**

| | | | |
|---|---|---|---|
| 132. **19.** | 1 c. de g. blue .. .. | 20 | 10 |
| 133. **20.** | 2 c. de g. orange .. | 35 | 15 |
| 134. | 2 c. de g. yellow .. | 55 | 15 |
| 135. **19.** | 3 c. de g. grey .. .. | 30 | 10 |
| 136. **20.** | 7 c. de g. green .. | 55 | 35 |

21. Iron Market, Port-au-Prince. 24. Pres. A. T. Simon.

**1906.** Currency changed from "gourdes" to "piastres".

| | | | |
|---|---|---|---|
| 137. **20.** | 1 c. de p. green .. | 20 | 15 |
| 138. **19.** | 2 c. de p. red .. .. | 35 | 20 |
| 139. **21.** | 3 c. de p. sepia .. | 1·00 | 20 |
| 140. | 3 c. de p. orange .. | 3·50 | 3·50 |
| 141. – | 4 c. de p. red .. .. | 55 | 30 |
| 167. – | 4 c. de p. olive .. .. | 5·50 | 4·25 |
| 142. **19.** | 5 c. de p. blue .. .. | 1·10 | 20 |
| 143. – | 7 c. de p. grey .. .. | 85 | 45 |
| 168. – | 7 c. de p. red .. .. | 12·50 | 8·25 |
| 144. – | 8 c. de p. red .. .. | 2·50 | 85 |
| 169. – | 8 c. de p. olive .. .. | 13·00 | 8·50 |
| 145. – | 10 c. de p. orange .. | 55 | 20 |
| 170. – | 10 c. de p. brown .. | 7·25 | 7·50 |
| 146. – | 15 c. de p. olive .. | 1·10 | 45 |
| 171. – | 15 c. de p. yellow .. | 3·25 | 1·75 |
| 147. **19.** | 20 c. de p. blue .. | 1·10 | 45 |
| 148. **20.** | 50 c. de p. red .. .. | 1·75 | 1·25 |
| 172. | 50 c. de p. yellow .. | 3·75 | 2·50 |
| 149. – | 1 pi. red .. .. .. | 3·25 | 2·10 |
| 173. – | 1 pi. red .. .. .. | 3·75 | 3·00 |

DESIGNS—As Type **21**: 4 c. Palace of Sans Souci-Milot. 7 c. Independence Palace, Gonaives. 8 c. Entrance to Catholic College, Port-au-Prince. 10 c. Catholic Monastery and Church, Port-au-Prince. 15 c. Government Offices, Port-au-Prince. 1 p. President's Palace, Port-au-Prince.

**1906.** Surch. with value in double-lined frame Without opt.

| | | | |
|---|---|---|---|
| 154. **15.** | 1 c. on 5 c. blue .. | 30 | 20 |
| 155. | 1 c. on 10 c. brown .. | 25 | 10 |
| 156. | 1 c. on 20 c. orange .. | 20 | 15 |
| 157. | 2 c. on 10 c. brown .. | 25 | 20 |
| 158. | 2 c. on 20 c. orange .. | 20 | 20 |
| 159. | 2 c. on 50 c. plum .. | 35 | 20 |

**1910.**

| | | | |
|---|---|---|---|
| 160. **24.** | 1 c. de g. black and lake | 15 | 15 |
| 161. | 2 c. de p. black and red | 55 | 35 |
| 162. | 5 c. de p. black & blue | 7·75 | 55 |
| 163. | 20 c. de p. blk. & green | 6·25 | 4·75 |

25. Pres. C. Leconte. 38.

**1912.** Various frames.

| | | | |
|---|---|---|---|
| 164. **25.** | 1 c. de g. lake .. .. | 20 | 20 |
| 165. | 2 c. de g. orange .. | 25 | 20 |
| 166. | 5 c. de p. blue .. .. | 55 | 20 |

**1914.** Optd. **GL O.Z. 7 FEV. 1914** in frame. A. On 1898 issue.

| | | | |
|---|---|---|---|
| 174. **9.** | 8 c. red .. .. .. | 7·75 | 6·25 |

B. On 1904 issue, without opt.

| | | | |
|---|---|---|---|
| 175. **15.** | 1 c. green (No. 109) .. | 22·00 | 19·00 |
| 176. | 2 c. red .. .. .. | 22·00 | 19·00 |
| 177. | 5 c. blue .. .. .. | 45 | 15 |
| 178. | 10 c. brown .. .. | 45 | 15 |
| 179. | 20 c. orange .. .. | 45 | 35 |
| 180. | 50 c. plum .. .. | 1·75 | 55 |

C. On pictorial stamps of 1906.

| | | | |
|---|---|---|---|
| 181. **20.** | 2 c. de g. yellow .. | 35 | 15 |
| 182. **19.** | 3 c. de g. grey .. .. | 35 | 20 |

D. On pictorial stamps of 1906.

| | | | |
|---|---|---|---|
| 183. **20.** | 1 c. de p. green (No. 137) | 35 | 25 |
| 184. **19.** | 2 c. de p. red (No. 138) | 55 | 25 |
| 185. **21.** | 3 c. de p. sepia (No. 139) | 1·60 | 55 |
| 186. | 3 c. de p. orge. (No. 140) | 35 | 15 |
| 187. – | 4 c. de p. red (No. 141) | 45 | 60 |
| 198. – | 4 c. de p. olive (No. 167) | 75 | 40 |
| 188. – | 7 c. de p. grey (No. 143) | 1·75 | 1·75 |
| 200. – | 7 c. de p. red (No. 168) | 1·75 | 1·75 |
| 189. – | 8 c. de p. red (No. 144) | 3·50 | 2·25 |
| 201. – | 8 c. de p. olive (No. 169) | 4·50 | 4·50 |
| 190. – | 10 c. de p. orge. (No. 145) | 55 | 55 |
| 202. – | 10 c. de p. brn. (No. 170) | 85 | 55 |
| 191. – | 15 c. de p. ol. (No. 146) | 1·75 | 1·75 |
| 203. – | 15 c. de p. yell. (No. 171) | 75 | 45 |
| 192. **19.** | 20 c. de p. bl. (No. 147) | 2·25 | 55 |
| 194. **20.** | 50 c. de p. red (No. 148) | 3·75 | 3·75 |
| 204. | 50 c. de p. yell. (No. 172) | 3·75 | 3·75 |
| 195. – | 1 pi. red (No. 149) .. | 3·75 | 3·75 |
| 205. – | 1 pi. red (No. 173) .. | 3·75 | 3·75 |

E. On stamp of 1910.

| | | | |
|---|---|---|---|
| 193. **24.** | 20 c. de p. black & grn. | 2·40 | 2·40 |

F. On stamps of 1912.

| | | | |
|---|---|---|---|
| 196. **25.** | 1 c. de g. lake .. .. | 25 | 20 |
| 197. | 2 c. de g. orange .. | 45 | 30 |
| 199. | 5 c. de p. blue .. .. | 70 | 20 |

**1914.** Stamps of 1904, without the opt., surch. **GL O.Z 7 FEV 1914 7 CENT** in diamond frame.

| | | | |
|---|---|---|---|
| 213. **15.** | 7 c. on 20 c. orange (No. 113) .. .. | 45 | 20 |
| 214. | 7 c. on 50 c. plum (No. 114) .. .. | 35 | 20 |

**1914.** Pictorial stamps of 1906 (Nos. 148/73), surch. **GL OZ 1 CENT DE PIASTRE 7 FEV. 1914** in frame.

| | | | |
|---|---|---|---|
| 215. **20.** | 1 c. de p. on 50 c. red .. | 30 | 20 |
| 216. | 1 c. de p. on 50 c. yellow | 45 | 35 |
| 217. – | 1 c. de p. on 1 p. red .. | 45 | 35 |
| 218. – | 1 c. de p. on 1 p. red .. | 55 | 45 |

**1915.**

| | | | |
|---|---|---|---|
| 219. – | 2 c. de g. black & yellow | 45 | |
| 220. **38.** | 5 c. de g. black & green | 45 | |
| 221. – | 7 c. de g. black and red | 45 | |

PORTRAIT: 2 c., 7 c. O. Zamor.

**1915.** As T **24**, inscr. "EMISSION 1914".

| | | | |
|---|---|---|---|
| 222. | 1 c. de p. black & green | 85 | |
| 223. | 3 c. de p. black and olive | 15 | |
| 224. | 5 c. de p. black and blue | 25 | |
| 225. | 7 c. de p. black and orge. | 60 | |
| 226. | 10 c. de p. black & brn. | 20 | |
| 227. | 15 c. de p. blk. and olive | 25 | |
| 228. | 20 c. de p. black & brn. | 55 | |

DESIGNS: 1 c., 5 c., 10 c., 15 c. O. Zamor. 3 c., 20 c. Arms. 7 c. T. Auguste.

**1915.** Surch. with figure in frame.

| | | | |
|---|---|---|---|
| 229. | 1 on 5 c. blue (No. 111) .. | 85 | 85 |
| 230. | 1 on 7 c. grey (No. 143) .. | 10 | 10 |
| 231. | 1 on 10 c. brown (No. 112) | 15 | 15 |
| 232. | 1 on 20 c. orange (No. 107) | 45 | 35 |
| 233. | 1 on 20 c. orange (No. 113) | 55 | 70 |
| 234. | 1 on 50 c. plum (No. 108) | 1·10 | 55 |
| 235. | 1 on 50 c. plum (No. 114) | 15 | 10 |
| 236. | 2 on 1 pi. red (No. 172) .. | 20 | 15 |

**1917.** Surch. **GOURDE** and value in frame.

A. On provisional stamps of 1906.

| | | | |
|---|---|---|---|
| 237. **8.** | 1 c. on 50 c. lake (No. 130) .. .. | 16·00 | 11·00 |
| 238. | 1 c. on 1 g. mauve (No. 131) .. .. | 19·00 | 14·00 |

B. On pictorial stamps of 1906.

| | | | |
|---|---|---|---|
| 239. – | 1 c. on 4 c. de p. red (No. 141) .. .. | 15 | 15 |
| 240. – | 1 c. on 4 c. de p. olive (No. 167) .. .. | 30 | 30 |
| 241. – | 1 c. on 7 c. de p. red (No. 168) .. .. | 45 | 45 |
| 242. – | 1 c. on 10 c. de p. orange (No. 145) .. .. | 10 | 10 |
| 243. – | 1 c. on 15 c. de p. yellow (No. 171) .. .. | 45 | 30 |
| 244. **19.** | 1 c. on 20 c. de p. blue (No. 147) .. .. | 20 | 15 |
| 246. **24.** | 1 c. on 20 c. de p. black and green (No. 163) .. | 2·50 | 2·50 |
| 247. **20.** | 1 c. on 50 c. de p. red (No. 148) .. .. | 20 | 15 |
| 249. – | 1 c. on 50 c. de p. yellow (No. 172) .. .. | 85 | 85 |
| 250. – | 1 c. on 1 p. red (No. 173) | 85 | 85 |
| 251. **21.** | 2 c. on 3 c. de p. sepia (No. 139) .. .. | 60 | 50 |
| 252. | 2 c. on 3 c. de p. orange (No. 140) .. .. | 75 | 60 |
| 253. – | 2 c. on 8 c. de p. red (No. 144) .. .. | 50 | 35 |
| 255. – | 2 c. on 8 c. de p. olive (No. 169) .. .. | 90 | 90 |
| 256. – | 2 c. de p. on 10 c. brown (No. 170) .. .. | 35 | 45 |
| 257. – | 2 c. on 15 c. de p. olive (No. 146) .. .. | 20 | 10 |
| 258. – | 2 c. on 15 c. de p. yellow (No. 171) .. .. | 45 | 45 |
| 259. **19.** | 2 c. on 20 c. de p. blue (No. 147) .. .. | 25 | 15 |
| 260. – | 5 c. on 10 c. de p. brown (No. 170) .. .. | 45 | 45 |
| 261. – | 5 c. on 15 c. de p. yellow (No. 171) .. .. | 3·25 | 3·25 |

**1919.** For inland use. Provisionals of 1914.

(a) Surch. with new value without frame.

| | | | |
|---|---|---|---|
| 262. – | 1 c. on 15 c. de p. olive (No. 191) .. .. | 20 | 20 |
| 263. **19.** | 1 c. on 20 c. de p. blue (No. 192) .. .. | 20 | 20 |
| 264. **24.** | 1 c. on 20 c. de p. black and green (No. 193) .. | 35 | 35 |
| 265. – | 1 c. on 1 p. red (No. 195) .. .. | 20 | 15 |
| 267. – | 1 c. on 1 p. red (No. 205) | 35 | 35 |

(b) Surch with new value in frame.

| | | | |
|---|---|---|---|
| 268. – | 2 c. on 4 c. de p. red (No. 187) .. .. | 35 | 35 |
| 269. – | 2 c. on 8 c. de p. red (No. 189) .. .. | 60 | 40 |
| 270. – | 2 c. on 8 c. de p. olive (No. 201) .. .. | 60 | 40 |
| 271. **24.** | 2 c. on 20 c. de p. black and green .. .. | 30 | 15 |
| 272. **20.** | 2 c. on 50 c. de p. red (No. 194) .. .. | 15 | 10 |
| 274. | 2 c. on 50 c. de p. yellow (No. 204) .. .. | 15 | 35 |
| 275. – | 2 c. on 1 p. red (No. 195) .. .. | 1·75 | 1·75 |
| 276. – | 2 c. on 1 p. red (No. 205) | 90 | 90 |
| 277. **21.** | 3 c. on 3 c. de p. sepia (No. 185) .. .. | 35 | 25 |
| 278. – | 3 c. on 7 c. de p. red (No. 200) .. .. | 35 | 20 |
| 279. **21.** | 5 c. on 3 c. de p. sepia (No. 185) .. .. | 70 | 40 |
| 280. | 5 c. on 3 c. de p. orange (No. 186) .. .. | 1·40 | 1·75 |
| 281. – | 5 c. on 4 c. de p. red (No. 187) .. .. | 45 | 45 |
| 282. – | 5 c. on 4 c. de p. olive (No. 198) .. .. | 25 | 25 |
| 283. – | 5 c. on 7 c. de p. grey (No. 188) .. .. | 30 | 30 |
| 284. – | 5 c. on 7 c. de p. red (No. 200) .. .. | 35 | 35 |
| 285. **15.** | 5 c. on 7 c. on 20 c. orge. (No. 213) .. .. | 35 | 35 |
| 286. | 5 c. on 7 c. on 50 c. plum (No. 214) .. .. | 2·40 | 2·40 |
| 287. **19.** | 5 c. on 10 c. de p. orange (No. 190) .. .. | 25 | 25 |
| 289. – | 5 c. on 10 c. de p. orange (No. 190) .. .. | 45 | 45 |
| 288. – | 5 c. on 15 c. de p. yellow (No. 203) .. .. | 35 | 35 |

No. 289 has the word "PIASTRE" in the surcharge.

**1919.** Postage Due stamps surch. **POSTES** and new value in frame.

| | | | |
|---|---|---|---|
| 290. D **23.** | 5 c. de g. on 10 c. de p. purple (No. D 211) | 35 | 35 |
| 291. | 5 c. de g. on 50 c. de p. olive (No. D 153) | 9·25 | 7·75 |
| 292. | 5 c. de g. on 50 c. de p. olive (No. D 212) .. | 45 | 45 |

HAVE YOU READ THE NOTES AT THE BEGINNING OF THIS CATALOGUE?
These often provide answers to the enquiries we receive.

48. " Agriculture ".

DESIGN: 10 c., 15 c., 25 c. " Commerce ".

**1920.**

| | | | |
|---|---|---|---|
| 294. **48.** | 3 c. de g. orange .. | 3·00 | 2·00 |
| 295. | 5 c. de g. green .. | 1·00 | 10 |
| 296. – | 10 c. de g. red .. .. | 55 | 30 |
| 297. – | 15 c. de g. violet .. | 45 | 15 |
| 298. – | 25 c. de g. blue .. | 55 | 15 |

50. Pres. L. J. Borno.

51. Christophe's Citadel.

54. Coffee.

DESIGNS—VERT. 20 c. Map of W. Indies. HORIZ. 1 g. National Palace.

**1924.**

| | | | |
|---|---|---|---|
| 299. **50.** | 5 c. green .. .. | 20 | 10 |
| 300. **51.** | 10 c. red .. .. | 35 | 10 |
| 301. – | 20 c. blue .. .. | 40 | 15 |
| 304. **54.** | 35 c. green .. .. | 1·75 | 25 |
| 302. **50.** | 50 c. black and orange | 40 | 20 |
| 303. – | 1 g. olive .. .. | 1·10 | 25 |

55. Pres. Borno.

**1929.** Frontier Agreement between Haiti and Dominican Republic.

| | | | |
|---|---|---|---|
| 305. **55.** | 10 c. red .. .. .. | 30 | 20 |

56. Fokker Super Trimotor over Port-au-Prince.

**1929.** Air.

| | | | |
|---|---|---|---|
| 306. **56.** | 25 c. green .. .. | 35 | 30 |
| 307. | 50 c. violet .. .. | 55 | 20 |
| 308. | 75 c. red .. .. | 1·10 | 90 |
| 309. | 1 g. blue .. .. | 1·50 | 1·10 |

57. Salomon and S. Vincent.

**1931.** 50th Anniv. of U.P.U. Membership.

| | | | |
|---|---|---|---|
| 310. **57.** | 5 c. green .. .. | 85 | 45 |
| 311. – | 10 c. red (S. Vincent) .. | 85 | 45 |

**1933.** Air. "Columbia" New York–Haiti Flight. Surch. **COLUMBIA VOL-DIRECT N.-Y.-P.AU-P. BOYD-LYON 60 CTS.**

| | | | |
|---|---|---|---|
| 311a. | 60 c. on 20 c. blue (No. 301) | 42·00 | 42·00 |

59. Pres. S. Vincent.

60. Prince's Aqueduct.

**1933.** T **59** and designs as T **60**.

| | | | |
|---|---|---|---|
| 312. **59.** | 3 c. orange .. .. | 10 | 10 |
| 313. | 3 c. green .. .. | 15 | 10 |
| 316. **60.** | 5 c. green .. .. | 15 | 10 |
| 317. | 5 c. olive .. .. | 45 | 10 |
| 318. – | 10 c. red .. .. | 35 | 10 |
| 320. – | 10 c. brown .. .. | 35 | 10 |
| 321. – | 25 c. blue .. .. | 40 | 20 |
| 322. – | 50 c. brown .. .. | 1·75 | 20 |
| 323. – | 1 g. green .. .. | 1·75 | 20 |
| 324. – | 2 g. 50 olive .. .. | 2·75 | 35 |

DESIGNS: 10 c. Fort National. 25 c. Palace of Sans Souci. 50 c. Christophe's Chapel, Milot. 1 g. King's Gallery, Citadel. 2 g. 50, Vallieres Battery.

**62.** Fokker Super Trimotor over Christophe's Citadel.

**1933.** Air.

| | | | | |
|---|---|---|---|---|
| 325. | **62.** | 50 c. orange .. .. | 3·25 | 40 |
| 326. | | 50 c. olive .. .. | 3·00 | 40 |
| 327. | | 50 c. red .. .. | 1·75 | 1·10 |
| 328. | | 50 c. black .. .. | 1·40 | 40 |
| 329. | | 60 c. brown .. .. | 40 | 10 |
| 330. | | 1 g. blue .. .. | 1·10 | 35 |

**63.** Alexandre Dumas and his father and son.

**1935.** Visit of French Delegation to West Indies.

| | | | | |
|---|---|---|---|---|
| 331. | **63.** | 10 c. brown & red (post.) | 40 | 30 |
| 332. | | 25 c. brown and blue .. | 1·10 | 35 |
| 333. | | 60 c. brn. & violet (air) | 3·00 | 1·75 |

**64.** Arms of Haiti, and George Washington.

**1938.** Air. 150th Anniv. of U.S. Constitution.

| | | | | |
|---|---|---|---|---|
| 334. | **64.** | 60 c. blue .. .. | 25 | 25 |

**1939.** Surch. **25 c** between bars.

| | | | | |
|---|---|---|---|---|
| 335. | **54.** | 25 c. on 35 c. green .. | 45 | 30 |

**66.** Pierre de Coubertin. **67.**

**1939.** Port-au-Prince Athletic Stadium Fund.

| | | | | |
|---|---|---|---|---|
| 336. | **66.** | 10 c.+10 c. red (postage) | 18·00 | 18·00 |
| 337. | | 60 c.+40 c. violet (air) | 12·00 | 12·00 |
| 338. | | 1 g. 25+60 c. black .. | 12·00 | 12·00 |

**1941.** 3rd Caribbean Conf.

| | | | | |
|---|---|---|---|---|
| 339. | **67.** | 10 c. red (postage) .. | 65 | 35 |
| 340. | | 25 c. blue .. .. | 40 | 25 |
| 341. | | 60 c. olive (air) .. | 2·25 | 40 |
| 342. | | 1 g. 25 violet .. .. | 2·10 | 25 |

**68.** Our Lady of Perpetual Succour.

**1942.** Our Lady of Perpetual Succour (National Patroness).

| | | | | |
|---|---|---|---|---|
| 343. | **68.** | 3 c. purple (postage) .. | 35 | 30 |
| 344. | | 5 c. green .. .. | 35 | 30 |
| 345. | | 10 c. red .. .. | 35 | 30 |
| 346. | | 15 c. orange .. .. | 40 | 30 |
| 347. | | 20 c. brown .. .. | 40 | 30 |
| 348. | | 25 c. blue .. .. | 1·10 | 30 |
| 349. | | 50 c. red .. .. | 1·60 | 65 |
| 350. | | 2 g. 50 brown .. .. | 5·50 | 1·45 |
| 351. | | 5 g. violet .. .. | 11·50 | 2·75 |

The 5 g. is larger (32½ × 47 mm.).

| | | | | |
|---|---|---|---|---|
| 352. | **68.** | 10 c. olive (air) .. | 35 | 15 |
| 353. | | 25 c. blue .. .. | 35 | 35 |
| 354. | | 50 c. green .. .. | 45 | 30 |
| 355. | | 60 c. red .. .. | 90 | 25 |
| 356. | | 1 g. 25 black .. .. | 1·90 | 25 |

69. Admiral Killick and Flagship "Crete a Pierrot".

**1943.** 41st Death Anniv. of Admiral Killick.

| | | | | |
|---|---|---|---|---|
| 358. | **69.** | 3 c. orange (postage) .. | 15 | 50 |
| 359. | | 5 c. green .. .. | 55 | 25 |
| 360. | | 10 c. red .. .. | 55 | 15 |
| 361. | | 25 c. blue .. .. | 70 | 25 |
| 362. | | 50 c. olive .. .. | 1·40 | 35 |
| 363. | | 5 g. brown .. .. | 5·50 | 3·75 |
| 364. | | 60 c. violet (air) .. | 95 | 35 |
| 365. | | 1 g. 25 black .. .. | 3·75 | 1·90 |

**1944.** Surch. (a) Postage.

| | | | | |
|---|---|---|---|---|
| 366. | **59.** | 0.02 on 3 c. green .. | 15 | 15 |
| 367. | | 0.05 on 3 c. green .. | 20 | 20 |
| 368. | **68.** | 0.10 on 15 c. orange .. | 35 | 30 |
| 369. | **69.** | 0.10 on 25 c. blue .. | 35 | 30 |
| 370. | – | 0.10 on 1 g. olive (No. 303) .. .. | 35 | 15 |
| 371. | – | 0.20 on 2 g. 50 olive (No. 324) .. .. | 35 | 30 |

(b) Air.

| | | | | |
|---|---|---|---|---|
| 372. | **62.** | 0.10 on 60 c. brown .. | 55 | 30 |

**71.** **72.** Nurse and Wounded Soldier.

**1944.** Obligatory Tax. United Nations Relief Fund.

| | | | | |
|---|---|---|---|---|
| 373. | **71.** | 5 c. blue .. .. | 90 | 35 |
| 374. | | 5 c. black .. .. | 90 | 35 |
| 375. | | 5 c. olive .. .. | 90 | 35 |
| 376. | | 5 c. violet .. .. | 90 | 35 |
| 377. | | 5 c. brown .. .. | 90 | 35 |
| 378. | | 5 c. green .. .. | 90 | 35 |
| 379. | | 5 c. red .. .. | 90 | 35 |

**1945.** Red Cross stamps. Cross in red.

| | | | | |
|---|---|---|---|---|
| 381. | **72.** | 3 c. black (postage) .. | 10 | 10 |
| 382. | | 5 c. green .. .. | 15 | 10 |
| 383. | | 10 c. orange .. .. | 20 | 10 |
| 384. | | 20 c. brown .. .. | 15 | 10 |
| 385. | | 25 c. blue .. .. | 30 | 10 |
| 386. | | 35 c. orange .. .. | 30 | 20 |
| 387. | | 50 c. red .. .. | 35 | 25 |
| 388. | | 1 g. olive .. .. | 40 | 30 |
| 389. | | 2½ g. violet .. .. | 1·75 | 25 |
| 390. | | 20 c. orange (air) .. | 15 | 10 |
| 391. | | 25 c. blue .. .. | 15 | 10 |
| 392. | | 50 c. brown .. .. | 20 | 10 |
| 393. | | 60 c. purple .. .. | 25 | 10 |
| 394. | | 1 g. yellow .. .. | 90 | 15 |
| 395. | | 1 g. 25 c. red .. .. | 70 | 30 |
| 396. | | 1 g. 35 c. green .. .. | 70 | 30 |
| 397. | | 5 g. black .. .. | 4·50 | 1·75 |

**73.** Franklin D. Roosevelt. **74.** Capois-la-Mort.

**1946.** Air.

| | | | | |
|---|---|---|---|---|
| 398. | **73.** | 20 c. black .. .. | 15 | 15 |
| 399. | | 60 c. black .. .. | 20 | 10 |

**1946.**

| | | | | |
|---|---|---|---|---|
| 400. | **74.** | 3 c. orange (postage) .. | 10 | 10 |
| 401. | | 5 c. green .. .. | 10 | 10 |
| 402. | | 10 c. red .. .. | 10 | 10 |
| 403. | | 20 c. black .. .. | 10 | 10 |
| 404. | | 25 c. blue .. .. | 10 | 10 |
| 405. | | 35 c. orange .. .. | 20 | 15 |
| 406. | | 50 c. brown .. .. | 25 | 20 |
| 407. | | 1 g. olive .. .. | 35 | 10 |
| 408. | | 2 g. 50 grey .. .. | 90 | 35 |
| 409. | | 20 c. red (air) .. .. | 10 | 10 |
| 410. | | 25 c. green .. .. | 10 | 10 |
| 411. | | 50 c. orange .. .. | 15 | 10 |
| 412. | | 60 c. purple .. .. | 20 | 10 |
| 413. | | 1 g. slate .. .. | 35 | 10 |
| 414. | | 1 g. 25 violet .. .. | 40 | 35 |
| 415. | | 1 g. 35 black .. .. | 45 | 30 |
| 416. | | 5 g. red .. .. | 1·40 | 90 |

**75.** J.-J. Dessalines.

**1947.** 141st Death Anniv. of Emperor Jean-Jacques Dessalines, founder of National Independence.

| | | | | |
|---|---|---|---|---|
| 417. | **75.** | 3 c. orange (postage) .. | 10 | 10 |
| 418. | | 5 c. green .. .. | 10 | 10 |
| 419. | | 5 c. violet .. .. | 45 | 10 |
| 420. | | 10 c. red .. .. | 10 | 10 |
| 421. | | 25 c. blue .. .. | 20 | 10 |
| 422. | | 20 c. brown (air) .. | 20 | 10 |

**1947.** Surch.

| | | | | |
|---|---|---|---|---|
| 423. | **74.** | 10 c. on 35 c. orge. (post.) | 20 | 10 |
| 424. | | 5 c. on 1 g. 35 black (air) | 55 | 20 |
| 425. | | 30 c. on 50 c. orange .. | 45 | 30 |
| 426. | | 30 c. on 1 g. 35 black .. | 45 | 40 |

**77.** Sanatorium and Mosquito.

**1949.** Air. Anti-T.B. and Malaria Fund. Cross in red.

| | | | | |
|---|---|---|---|---|
| 427. | **77.** | 20 c.+20 c. sepia .. | 6·25 | 4·50 |
| 428. | | 30 c.+30 c. green .. | 6·25 | 4·50 |
| 429. | | 45 c.+45 c. brown .. | 6·25 | 4·50 |
| 430. | | 80 c.+80 c. violet .. | 6·25 | 4·50 |
| 431. | | 1 g. 25+1 g. 25 red .. | 6·25 | 4·50 |
| 432. | | 1 g. 75+1 g. 75 blue .. | 6·25 | 4·50 |

**78.** Washington, Dessalines and Bolivar.

**1949.** Obligatory Tax. Bicent. of Port-au-Prince.

| | | | | |
|---|---|---|---|---|
| 434. | **78.** | 5 c. red .. .. | 20 | 15 |
| 435. | | 5 c. brown .. .. | 20 | 15 |
| 436. | | 5 c. orange .. .. | 20 | 15 |
| 437. | | 5 c. grey .. .. | 20 | 15 |
| 438. | | 5 c. violet .. .. | 20 | 15 |
| 439. | | 5 c. blue .. .. | 20 | 15 |
| 440. | | 5 c. green .. .. | 20 | 15 |
| 441. | | 5 c. black .. .. | 20 | 15 |

**79.** Arms of Port-au-Prince.

**80.** Columbus and "Santa Maria". **83.** Cocoa.

**1950.** Bicent. of Port-au-Prince. Exn.

(a) Postage. Multicoloured arms.

| | | | | |
|---|---|---|---|---|
| 442. | **79.** | 10 c. red .. .. | 15 | 10 |

(b) Air.

| | | | | |
|---|---|---|---|---|
| 443. | **80.** | 30 c. blue and grey .. | 2·25 | 55 |
| 444. | – | 1 g. black (Pres. D. Estime) .. .. | 45 | 30 |

**1950.** 75th Anniv. of U.P.U. Optd. **UPU 1874 1949** or surch. also.

| | | | | |
|---|---|---|---|---|
| 445. | **78.** | 3 on 5 c. grey (postage) | 10 | 10 |
| 446. | | 5 c. green .. .. | 25 | 20 |
| 447. | | 10 on 5 c. red .. | 25 | 20 |
| 448. | | 20 on 5 c. blue .. | 35 | 35 |
| 449. | **74.** | 30 on 25 c. green (air) | 30 | 30 |
| 450. | | 1 g. slate .. .. | 35 | 30 |
| 451. | | 1.50 on 1 g. 35 black .. | 60 | 40 |

**1951.** National Products.

| | | | | |
|---|---|---|---|---|
| 456. | **83.** | 5 c. green (postage) .. | 25 | 10 |
| 457. | – | 30 c. orange (Bananas) (air) .. .. | 30 | 20 |
| 458. | – | 80 c. pink and green (Coffee) .. .. | 85 | 35 |
| 459. | – | 5 g. grey (Sisal) .. | 3·00 | 2·50 |

**84.** Isabella the Catholic. **85.** Pres. Magloire and Nursery, La Saline.

**1951.** Air. 5th Birth Cent. of Isabella the Catholic.

| | | | | |
|---|---|---|---|---|
| 460. | **84.** | 15 c. brown .. .. | 25 | 15 |
| 461. | | 30 c. blue .. .. | 45 | 45 |

**1953.** Projects realized by Pres. Magloire. Designs with medallion of president.

| | | | | |
|---|---|---|---|---|
| 462. | **85.** | 5 c. green (postage) .. | 10 | 10 |
| 463. | – | 10 c. red .. .. | 15 | 10 |
| 464. | – | 20 c. blue (air) .. .. | 15 | 10 |
| 465. | – | 30 c. brown .. .. | 30 | 15 |
| 466. | – | 1.50 g. black .. .. | 45 | 45 |
| 467. | – | 2.50 g. violet .. .. | 90 | 65 |

DESIGNS—HORIZ. 10 c. Road-making. 20 c. Anchorage, Cap-Haitien. 30 c. Workers' estate, St. Martin. 1.50 g. Old Cathedral restoration. 2.50 g. School canteen.

**1953.** 150th Death Anniv. of Toussaint l'Ouverture. No. 405 surch. **7 AVRIL 1803-1953 50.**

| | | | | |
|---|---|---|---|---|
| 469. | **74.** | 50 c. on 35 c. orange .. | 35 | 20 |

**1953.** Air. 150th Anniv. of National Flag. Surch. **18 MAI 1803-1953 50.**

| | | | | |
|---|---|---|---|---|
| 470. | **74.** | 50 c. on 60 c. purple .. | 35 | 15 |
| 471. | | 50 c. on 1 g. 35 black .. | 35 | 15 |

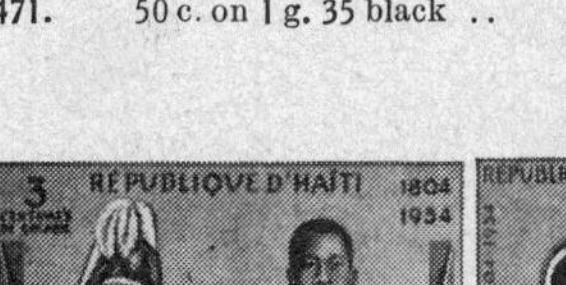

**87.** J.-J. Dessalines and Pres. Magloire. **88.** Toussaint l'Ouverture.

**89.** Marie-Jeanne and Lamartiniere on La Crete-a-Pierrot. **90.** Mme. Magloire.

**1954.** 150th Anniv. of Independence.

(a) As T **87/8**.

| | | | | |
|---|---|---|---|---|
| 472. | **87.** | 3 c. blk. & blue (post.) .. | 10 | 10 |
| 473. | **88.** | 5 c. black and green .. | 20 | 10 |
| 474. | – | 5 c. black and green .. | 15 | 10 |
| 475. | – | 5 c. black and green .. | 20 | 10 |
| 476. | – | 5 c. black and green .. | 15 | 10 |
| 477. | **87.** | 10 c. black and red .. | 15 | 10 |
| 478. | – | 15 c. black and lilac .. | 20 | 10 |
| 479. | **88.** | 50 c. black & green (air) | 35 | 20 |
| 480. | – | 50 c. black and green .. | 35 | 20 |
| 481. | – | 50 c. black and red .. | 35 | 20 |
| 482. | – | 50 c. black and brown .. | 35 | 20 |
| 483. | – | 50 c. black and blue .. | 35 | 20 |
| 484. | – | 1 g. black and grey .. | 45 | 25 |
| 485. | – | 1 g. 50 black and mauve | 90 | 60 |
| 486. | **87.** | 7 g. 50 black and orange | 3·00 | 3·00 |

PORTRAITS—As Type **88.** Nos. 474, 482, Lamartiniere. Nos. 475, 482, Boisrond-Tonnerre. Nos. 476, 483, 485, A. Petion. No. 478, Capois-La-Mort. No. 480, J. J. Dessalines. No. 481, H. Christophe.

For stamps as No. 480 without dates see Nos. 533/4.

(b) As T **89.**

| | | | | |
|---|---|---|---|---|
| 487. | **89.** | 25 c. orange (postage) .. | 20 | 10 |
| 488. | – | 25 c. slate .. .. | 20 | 10 |
| 489. | **89.** | 50 c. red (air) .. .. | 25 | 10 |
| 490. | | 50 c. black .. .. | 25 | 10 |
| 491. | – | 50 c. pink .. .. | 25 | 15 |
| 492. | – | 50 c. blue .. .. | 25 | 15 |

DESIGN—HORIZ. Nos. 488, 491, 492, Battle of Vertieres. Nos. 489/92 are larger (31½ × 26 mm.).

**1954.**

| | | | | |
|---|---|---|---|---|
| 493. | **90.** | 10 c. orange (postage) .. | 15 | 10 |
| 494. | | 10 c. blue .. .. | 15 | 10 |
| 495. | | 20 c. red (air) .. .. | 10 | 10 |
| 496. | | 50 c. brown .. .. | 20 | 20 |
| 497. | | 1 g. green .. .. | 45 | 35 |
| 498. | | 1 g. 50 red .. .. | 45 | 40 |
| 499. | | 2 g. 50 green .. .. | 65 | 60 |
| 500. | | 5 g. blue .. .. | 1·90 | 1·40 |

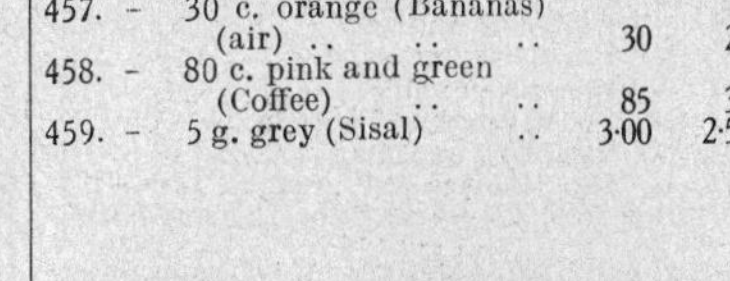

**91.** Tomb and Arms of King Henri Christophe. **92.** Christophe, Citadel and Pres. Magloire.

**1954.** Restoration of Christophe's Citadel.

(a) T **91.** Flag in black and red.

| | | | | |
|---|---|---|---|---|
| 501. | **91.** | 10 c. red (postage) .. | 15 | 10 |
| 502. | | 50 c. orange (air) .. | 35 | 15 |
| 503. | | 1 g. blue .. .. | 40 | 30 |
| 504. | | 1 g. 50 green .. .. | 60 | 50 |
| 505. | | 2 g. 50 grey .. .. | 1·10 | 65 |
| 506. | | 5 g. red .. .. | 1·75 | 1·25 |

(b) T **92.**

| | | | | |
|---|---|---|---|---|
| 507. | **92.** | 10 c. red (postage) .. | 15 | 10 |
| 508. | | 50 c. black & orge. (air) | 35 | 15 |
| 509. | | 1 g. black and blue .. | 40 | 30 |
| 510. | | 1 g. 50 black and green | 60 | 50 |
| 511. | | 2 g. 50 black and grey | 1·10 | 65 |
| 512. | | 5 g. black and red .. | 1·75 | 1·25 |

**93.** Columbus's Drawing of Fort de la Nativite.

**1954.** Air.

513. **93.** 50 c. red .. .. 35 30
514. 50 c. slate .. .. 35 30

**94.** Sikorsky S-55 Helicopter over Ruins.
**95.** Sikorsky S-55 Helicopter.

**1955.** Obligatory Tax. Cyclone "Hazel" Relief Fund (1st issue).

515 **94** 10 c. blue .. .. 10 10
516 10 c. green .. .. 10 10
517 10 c. orange .. .. 10 10
518 10 c. black .. .. 15 10
519 20 c. red .. .. 10 10
520 20 c. green .. .. 15 10

**1955.** Obligatory Tax. Cyclone "Hazel" Relief Fund (2nd issue).

521 **95** 10 c. black and grey (postage) .. .. 10 10
522 20 c. deep blue and blue 15 10
523 10 c. red and brown (air) 15 10
524 20 c. red and pink .. 15 10

**96.** J.-J. Dessalines.
**97.** Pres. Magloire and Monument.

**1955.** Dessalines Comm.

525. **96.** 3 c. black & brown (post.) 10 10
526. 5 c. black and lilac .. 10 10
527. 10 c. black and red .. 10 10
528. 10 c. black and pink .. 10 10
529. 25 c. black and blue .. 20 10
530. 25 c. black and light blue 20 10
531. 20 c. black & green (air) 10 10
532. 20 c. black and orange .. 10 10

**1955.** Air. As No. 480 but without dates and colours changed.

533. 50 c. black and blue .. 30 10
534. 50 c. black and grey .. 30 15

**1955.** 21st Anniv. of Haitian Army.

535. **97.** 10 c. blue & black (post.) 30 25
536. 10 c. red and black .. 30 25
537. 1 g. 50 grn. & blk. (air) 35 20
538. 1 g. 50 blue and black .. 45 20

**98.** Mallard.
**99.** Douglas DC-4, Liner and Map.

**1955.**

539. – 10 c. blue (postage) .. 3·00 40
540. **98.** 25 c. green & turquoise 4·00 65
541. **99.** 50 c. black & grey (air) 70 15
542. – 50 c. red and grey .. 30 15
543. **99.** 75 c. green & turquoise 90 45
544. – 1 g. olive and blue .. 55 30
545. – 2 g. 50 orange .. .. 16·00 3·00
546. **98.** 5 g. red and buff .. 26·00 5·50

**Designs—Vert.** 10 c., 2 g. 50, Greater Flamingo. **Horiz.** 50 c. (No. 542), 1 g. Car on coast road.

**100.** Immanuel Kant.
**101.** Zim Basin and Waterfall.

**1956.** 10th Anniv. of 1st Int. Philosophical Congress.

547. **100.** 10 c. blue (postage) .. 15 10
548. 50 c. brown (air) .. 25 15
549. 75 c. green .. .. 35 20
550. 1 g. 50 mauve .. .. 85 45

**1957.**

552. **101.** 10 c. orge. & blue (post.) 15 10
553. 50 c. green & turq. (air) 20 15
554. 1 g. 50 olive and blue .. 35 30
555. 2 g. 50 blue & light blue 60 45
556. 5 g. violet and blue .. 1·40 1·10

**102.** J.-J. Dessalines and Monument.
**103.** The "Atomium".

**1958.** Birth Bicent. of J. J. Dessalines.

557. **102.** 5 c. green & black (post.) 10 10
558. 10 c. red and black .. 10 10
559. 25 c. blue and black .. 20 10
560. 20 c. grey and black (air) 10 10
561. 50 c. orange and black .. 25 15

**1958.** Brussels Int. Exn.

562. **103.** 50 c. brown (postage) .. 30 15
563. – 75 c. green .. .. 30 20
564. **103.** 1 g. violet .. .. 35 25
565. – 1 g. 50 orange .. .. 30 25
566. **103.** 2 g. 50 red (air) .. 60 35
567. – 5 g. blue .. .. 85 60

**Design—Horiz.** 75 c., 1 g. 50, 5 g. Exhibition view.

**104.** Sylvio Cator making Long Jump.
**106.** Head of U.S. Satellite.

**1958.** Sylvio Cator (athlete) Commem.

569. **104.** 5 c. green (postage) .. 10 10
570. 10 c. brown .. .. 10 10
571. 20 c. purple and mauve 15 10
572. – 50 c. black (air) .. 20 10
573. – 50 c. green .. .. 20 10
574. – 1 g. brown .. .. 35 15
575. – 5 g. black and grey .. 1·40 70

**Design—Horiz.** Nos. 572/75, Sylvio Cator making long jump (head-on view).

**1958.** Red Cross. Nos. 564/66 surch. with red cross and **+50 CENTIMES.**

576. **103.** 1 g. + 50 c. violet (post.) 2·50 2·50
577. – 1 g. 50+50 c. orange .. 2·50 2·50
578. **103.** 2 g. 50+50 c. red (air) 2·75 2·75

**1958.** I.G.Y. Inscr. as in T **106.**

579. **106.** 10 c. lake & turq. (post.) 15 10
580. – 20 c. black and orange 3·25 90
581. – 50 c. red and green .. 35 25
582. – 1 g. black and blue .. 60 20
583. **106.** 50 c. lake and blue (air) 20 20
584. – 1 g. 50 brown and red .. 7·00 1·50
585. – 2 g. red and blue .. 1·10 35

**Designs:** 20 c., 1 g. 50 King Penguins on ice-floe. 50 c., 2 g. Giant radio telescope. 1 g. Ocean-bed exploration.

**107.** Duvalier.
**108.** Map of Haiti.

**1958.** 1st Anniv of Installation of President Francois Duvalier. Commemorative inscr in blue.

587. **107.** 10 c. blk. & pink (post.) 10 10
588. 50 c. black and green .. 35 15
589. 1 g. black and red .. 55 30
590. 5 g. black and salmon .. 1·60 1·10
591. – 50 c. black and red (air) 60 20
592. – 2 g. 50 black and orange 80 55
593. – 5 g. black and mauve .. 1·10 90
594. – 7 g. 50 black and green 1·60 1·25

**Design:** Nos. 591/94 as Type **107** but horiz.

**1958.** As T **107** but without commem. inscr.
(a) Postage. Vert. portrait.

596. 5 c. black and blue .. 10 10
597. 10 c. black and pink .. 10 10
598. 20 c. black and yellow .. 10 10
599. 50 c. black and green .. 20 15
600. 1 g. black and red .. 30 20
601. 1 g. 50 c. black and pink .. 45 35
602. 2 g. 50 c. black & lavender 70 60
603. 5 g. black and salmon .. 1·10 85

(b) Air. Horiz. portrait.

604. 50 c. black and red .. 25 15
605. 1 g. black and violet .. 30 25
606. 1 g. 50 c. black and brown 50 35
607. 2 g. black and pink .. 60 35
608. 2 g. 50 c. black and orange 60 35
609. 5 g. black and mauve .. 1·10 85
610. 7 g. 50 c. black and green .. 1·90 1·10

**1958.** United Nations.

611. **108.** 10 c. red (postage) .. 10 10
612. 25 c. green .. .. 15 10
613. – 50 c. red and blue (air) 20 10
614. **108.** 75 c. blue .. .. 30 15
615. – 1 g. brown .. .. 45 20

**Design:** 50 c. Flags of Haiti and U.N.

**1959.** 10th Anniv. of Declaration of Human Rights. Nos. 611/5 optd. **10TH ANNIVERSARY OF THE UNIVERSAL DECLARATION OF HUMAN RIGHTS.** (E), In English. (F), In French. (P), In Portuguese. (S), In Spanish. (a) Postage.

| | | E. | | F. | |
|---|---|---|---|---|---|
| 617. **108.** 10 c. red | .. | 10 | 10 | 10 | 10 |
| 618. 25 c. green | .. | 25 | 15 | 25 | 15 |
| | | P. | | S. | |
| 617. **108.** 10 c. red.. | .. | 10 | 10 | 10 | 10 |
| 618. 25 c. green | .. | 25 | 15 | 25 | 15 |

(b) Air.

| | | E. | | F. | |
|---|---|---|---|---|---|
| 619. – 50 c. red & bl. | .. | 30 | 30 | 30 | 30 |
| 620. **108.** 75 c. blue | .. | 40 | 40 | 40 | 40 |
| 621. 1 g. brown | .. | 90 | 90 | 90 | 90 |
| | | P. | | S. | |
| 619. – 50 c. red & bl. | .. | 30 | 30 | 30 | 30 |
| 620. **108.** 75 c. blue | .. | 40 | 40 | 40 | 40 |
| 621. 1 g. brown | .. | 90 | 90 | 90 | 90 |

Overprinted alternately in different languages through the sheet of 25.

**110.** Pope Pius XII with Children.

**Designs:** 50 c. (No. 623), 1 g. 50, Pope at prayer. 2 g., 2 g. 50, Pope giving blessing.

**1959.** Pope Pius XII Commem. Inscr. "PIE XII PAPE DE LA PAIX".

622. **110.** 10 c. olive & blue (post.) 10 10
623. – 50 c. brown and green .. 25 15
624. – 2 g. sepia and lake .. 40 35
625. **110.** 50 c. violet & green (air) 20 10
626. – 1 g. 50 brown and olive 35 15
627. – 2 g. 50 blue and purple 60 30

**1959.** Red Cross. (a) United Nations stamps surch. with red cross and **+25 CENTIMES.**

628. **108.** 10 c.+25 c. (post) .. 25 20
629. 25 c.+25 c. .. .. 35 30
630. – 50 c.+25 c. (air .. 35 35
631. **108.** 75 c.+25 c. .. .. 45 35
632. 1 g.+25 c. .. .. 65 70

(b) Pope Pius XII stamps surch. with red cross and **+50 CENTIMES.**

633. **110.** 10 c.+50 c. (postage) .. 45 20
634. – 50 c.+50 c. .. .. 45 30
635. – 2 g.+50 c. .. .. 65 90
636. **110.** 50 c.+50 c. (air) .. 60 60
637. – 1 g. 50+50 c. .. .. 60 60
638. – 2 g. 50+50 c. .. .. 65 65

**111.** Abraham Lincoln when a young man.

**1959.** 150th Birth Anniv. of Abraham Lincoln.

639. **111.** 50 c. pur. & blue (post.) 30 15
640. – 1 g. brown & green (air) 30 20
641. – 2 g. myrtle and green .. 35 20
642 – 2 g. 50 c. blue and buff .. 40 35

**Portraits** of Lincoln (bearded): 1 g. Looking right. 2 g., 2 g. 50, Looking left. The designs include various buildings associated with Lincoln.

**1959.** World Refugee Year (1st issue). Nos. 639/42 surch. **Nations Unies ANNEE DES REFUGIES 1959-1960 + 20 Centimes.**

644. **111.** 50 c.+20 c. purple & blue (postage) .. .. 45 45
645. – 1 g.+20 c. brn. & grn. (air) 60 60
646. – 2 g.+20 c. myrtle & green 60 60
647. – 2 g. 50+20 c. blue and buff 70 70

**113.** Chicago's First House and Modern Skyline.

**Designs—Horiz.** 50 c., 1 g. 50 Discus-thrower and Haitian flag. **Vert** 50 c. (air), 75 c. J. B. Paul Dessables (founder of Chicago) and map.

**1959.** 3rd Pan-American Games, Chicago.

649. **113.** 25 c. sepia & blue (post.) 30 15
650. – 50 c. multicoloured .. 30 20
651. – 75 c. sepia and blue .. 45 25
652. – 50 c. brown & turq. (air) 35 20
653. **113.** 1 g. turquoise & purple 60 35
654. – 1 g. 50 multicoloured .. 65 45

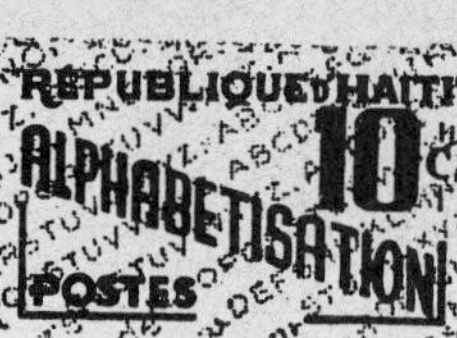

**114.**
**118.** "Uprooted Tree".

**1959.** Obligatory Tax. Literacy Fund.
(a) Postage. (i) Size 40 × 23 mm.

655. **114.** 5 c. green .. .. 10 10
656. 10 c. black .. .. 10 10
657. 10 c. red .. .. 10 10

(ii) Size 29 × 17 mm.

658. **114.** 5 c. green .. .. 10 10
659. 5 c. red .. .. 10 10
660. 10 c. blue .. .. 10 10

(b) Air. Size 29 × 17 mm.

661. **114.** 5 c. yellow .. .. 10 10
662. 10 c. blue .. .. 10 10
663. 10 c. orange .. .. 10 10

**1959.** Sports Fund. Nos. 649/54 surch. **POUR LE SPORT + 0.75 CENTIMES.**

664. 25 c.+75 c. sepia and blue (postage) .. .. 45 45
665. 50 c.+75 c. multicoloured 60 45
666. 75 c.+75 c. sepia and blue 60 45
667. 50 c.+75 c. brown and turquoise (air) .. .. 60 45
668. 1 g.+75 c. turq. & purple 60 45
669. 1 g. 50+75 c. multicoloured 60 60

**1960.** UNICEF Commem. Nos. 600 and 607/8 surch. **Hommage a l'UNICEF +G.0.50.**

670. 1 g.+50 c. blk. & red (post.) 60 60
671. 2 g.+50 c. blk. & pink (air) 65 65
672. 2 g. 50+50 c. blk. & orge. 1·10 1·10

**1960.** Winter Olympic Games. Nos. 650 and 652/4 optd. with Olympic rings and **VIIIEME JEUX OLYMPIQUES D'HIVER CALIFORNIE USA 1960.**

673. 50 c. multicoloured (post.) 1·10 90
674. 50 c. brown and turq. (air) 70 70
675. 1 g. turquoise and purple 1·10 1·10
676. 1 g. 50 multicoloured .. 1·25 1·25

**1960.** World Refugee Year (2nd issue).

677. **118.** 10 c. green & orge. (post.) .. 10 10
678. 50 c. purple and violet 20 15
679. 50 c. brn and bl. (air) 20 15
680. 1 g. red and green .. 45 30

**1960.** Surch. in figures.

682. **96.** 5 c. on 3 c. blk. & brown 10 10
683. 10 c. on 3 c. blk. & brn. 15 10

**1960.** 28th Anniv. of Haitian Red Cross. 1945 Red Cross stamps optd. **"28 eme ANNIVERSAIRE"** or surch. also.

684. **72.** 1 g. on 2½ g. vio. (post.) 45 35
685. 2½ g. violet .. .. 85 65
686. 20 c. on 1 g. 35 grn. (air) 20 10
687. 50 c. on 60 c. purple .. 25 15
688. 50 c. on 1 g. 35 green .. 25 20
689. 50 c. on 2½ g. violet .. 25 20
690. 60 c. purple .. .. 30 20
691. 1 g. on 1 g. 35 green .. 35 35
692. 1 g. 35 green .. .. 60 55
693. 2 g. on 1 g. 35 green .. 95 85

No. 689 is also optd. **Avion.**

**121.** "Sugar Queen, 1960" and Beach.

**1960.** Election of Miss Claudinette Fouchard ("Miss Haiti") as World "Sugar Queen, 1960".

694. – 10 c. vio. & brn. (post.) 15 10
695. – 20 c. black and brown .. 20 10
696. **121.** 50 c. brown and blue .. 45 10
697. – 1 g. brown and green .. 45 20
698. – 50 c. brn. and mve. (air) 35 15
699. **121.** 2 g. 50 brown and blue 55 35

**Designs:** Sugar Queen and—10 c., 1 g. Plantation (different views); 20 c, 50 c. Harvesting.

**1960.** Education Campaign. Surch. **ALPHABETISATION** + and value.

700. **118.** 10 c.+20 c. green and orange (postage) .. 25 15
701. 10 c.+30 c. grn. & orge. 30 25
702. 50 c.+20 c. pur. & vio. 30 35
703. 50 c.+30 c. pur. & vio. 40 35
704. 50 c.+20 c. black and blue (air) .. .. 25 15
705. 50 c.+30 c. blk. & blue 35 25
706. 1 g.+20 c. red & green 60 35
707. 1 g.+30 c. red & green 60 45

123. Olympic Torch, Victory Parade at Athens, 1896, and Melbourne Stadium.

**1960.** Olympic Games, Rome.
708.123. 10 c. blk. & orge. (post) 10 10
709. – 20 c. blue and red .. 10 10
710. – 50 c. green and brown 20 10
711. – 1 g. blue and black .. 45 15
712. – 50 c. pur. & bistre (air) 15 15
713. – 1 g. 50 mauve & green 35 25
714. – 2 g. 50 slate, pur. & blk. 60 35
DESIGNS: 20 c. and 1 g. 50, "The Discus-thrower" and Rome Stadium. 50 c. (No. 710), Pierre de Coubertin (founder) and Athletes Parade, Melbourne. 50 c. (No. 712), As Type **123** but P. de Coubertin inset. 1 g. Athens Stadium, 1896. 2 g. 50, Victory Parade, Athens, 1896, and Athletes Parade, Melbourne.

**1960.** Nos. 710/3 surch. **+25 CENTIMES.**
716. 50 c.+25 c. grn.& brn.(post.) 35 25
717. 1 g.+25 c. blue and black 45 30
718. 50 c.+25 c. pur. & bis. (air) 25 20
719. 1 g. 50+25 c. mve. & green 30 25

125. Occide Jeanty. 126. U.N., New York.

**1960.** Birth Cent. of Occide Jeanty (composer).
720.125. 10 c. pur. & orge. (post.) 15 10
721. – 20 c. purple and blue .. 30 10
722.125. 50 c. sepia and green .. 40 20
723. 50 c. blue & yellow (air) 20 10
724. – 1 g. 50 slate and mauve 45 25
DESIGN: 20 c., 1 g. 50, Jeanty and Capitol, Port-au-Prince.

**1960.** 15th Anniv. of U.N.O.
731.126. 1 g. black & grn. (post.) 35 20
732. 50 c. black and red (air) 20 10
733. 1 g. 50 black and blue.. 45 25

127. Sud Aviation Caravelle.

**1960.** Air. Aviation Week.
735.127. 20 c. blue and red .. 10 10
736. – 50 c. brown and green 30 20
737. – 50 c. blue and green .. 30 20
738. – 50 c. black and green .. 30 20
739.127. 1 g. green and red .. 45 25
740. – 1 g. 50 pink and blue .. 50 35
DESIGNS: 50 c. (3) Boeing 707 airliner and Wright Flyer I. 1 g. 50, Boeing 707 and 60 c. "Columbia" stamp of 1933.

**1961.** U.N.I.C.E.F. Child Welfare Fund. Surch. **UNICEF + 25 centimes.**
748.126. 1 g.+25 c. black and green (postage) .. 45 30
749. 50c.+25 c. blk.&red(air) 30 25
750. 1g. 50+25 c. blk. & blue 55 35

129. Alexandre Dumas (father and son).

**1961.** Alexandre Dumas Commem.
751. – 5 c. brn. and blue (post.) 10 10
752. – 10 c. black, purple & red 10 10
753.129. 50 c. blue and red .. 30 20
754. – 50 c. black & blue (air) 30 15
755. – 1 g. red and black .. 35 20
756. – 1 g. 50 black and green 55 35
DESIGNS—HORIZ. 5 c. Dumas' House. 50 c. (No. 754), A. Dumas and "The Three Musketeers". VERT. 10 c. A. Dumas and horseman in "Twenty Years After". 1 g. A. Dumas (son) and "The Lady of the Camellias" (Marguerite Gauthier). 1 g. 50, A. Dumas, and "The Count of Monte Cristo".

130. Pirates.

**1961.** Tourist Publicity.
761. – 5 c. yell. & blue (post.).. 10 10
762.130. 10 c. yellow and mauve 10 10
763. – 15 c. orange and green.. 10 10
764. – 20 c. orange and brown 30 10
765. – 50 c. yellow and blue .. 60 20
766. – 20 c. yell. and blue (air) 30 10
767. – 50 c. orange and violet 60 20
768. – 1 g. yellow and green .. 35 25
DESIGNS: Nos. 761, 768, Map of Tortuga. No. 763, Two pirates on beach. Nos. 764, 766, Pirate ships attacking galleon. Nos. 765, 767, Pirate in rigging.

**1961.** Re-election of Pres. Duvalier. Optd. **Dr. F. Duvalier President 22 Mai 1961.**
769.102. 5 c. grn. & black (post.) 10 10
770. 10 c. red and black .. 10 10
771. 25 c. blue and black .. 20 15
772. 74. 2 g. 50 grey .. .. 65 45
773.102. 20 c. grey & black (air) 10 10
774. 50 c. orange and black 20 15
775. 99. 75 c. green & turquoise 35 30

**1961.** Air. 18th World Scout Conference, Lisbon. Nos. 735 and 739/40 surch **18e CONFERENCE INTERNATIONALE DU SCOUTISME MONDIAL. LISBONNE SEPTEMBRE 1961 +0,25** and scout emblem.
776. 20 c.+25 c. blue and red.. 30 20
777. 1 g.+25 c. green and red.. 45 35
778. 1 g. 50+25 c. pink & blue.. 55 55

**1961.** U.N. and Haitian Malaria Eradication Campaign. Surch. **OMS SNEM +20 CENTIMES.**
780.126. 1 g.+20 c. black and green (postage) .. 45 35
781.126. 50 c.+20 c. black & red (air) .. .. .. 85 85
782. 1 g. 50+20 c. blk. & bl. 1·10 1·10

**1961.** Duvalier-Ville Reconstruction Fund Nos. 598, 600, 602, 604/5 and 608/10 surch. with U.N.I.C.E.F. emblem, **Duvalier-Ville** and premium.
783. 20 c.+25 c. black & yellow (postage) .. .. 30 25
787. 1 g.+50 c. black and red.. 60 45
788. 2 g. 50+50 c. black & blue 65 50
784. 50 c.+25 c. blk. & red (air) 25 25
785. 1 g.+50 c. black and violet 25 25
789. 2 g. 50+50 c. blk. & orge. 40 30
786. 5 g.+50 c. black & mauve 85 60
790. 7 g. 50+50 c. blk. & green 90 85

**1962.** Colonel Glenn's Space Flight. Nos. 761, 768 optd. **EXPLORATION SPATIALE JOHN GLENN** and outline of capsule or surch. also.
795. 50 c. on 5 c. yell. & bl. (post.) 45 30
796. 1 g. 50 on 5 c. yell. & blue 90 65
797. 1 g. yellow and green (air) 30 30
798. 2 g. on 1 g. yellow & green 85 70

136. Campaign Emblem.

**1962.** Malaria Eradication.
799. 136. 5 c. blue & red (postage) 10 10
800. – 10 c. green and brown.. 10 10
801. 136. 50 c. red and blue .. 30 15
802. – 20 c. red and violet (air) 10 10
803. 136. 50 c. red and green .. 20 15
804. – 1 g. blue and orange .. 35 25
DESIGN: 10 c., 20 c., 1 g. As Type **136** but with long side of triangle at top.

**1962.** World Refugee Year (3rd issue). As T **118** but additionally inscr. "1962" and colours changed.
806. 118. 10 c. orange & bl. (post.) 10 10
807. 50 c. green and mauve 25 20
808. 50 c. brown & blue (air) 15 15
809. 1 g. black and buff .. 25 25

137. Scout Badge.

DESIGNS—VERT. 5 c., 20 c., 50 c. (post.) Scout and camp. HORIZ. 10 c., 1 g. 50, Lord and Lady Baden-Powell.

**1962.** 22nd Anniv. of Haitian Boy Scout Movement.
811.137. 3 c. orange, black and violet (postage) .. 10 10
812. – 5 c. brown, olive & black 10 10
813. – 10 c. brown, black & grn. 10 10
814.137. 25 c. black, lake & olive 15 10
815. – 50 c. green, violet & red 30 15
816. – 20 c. slate, green and purple (air) .. .. 10 10
817.137. 50 c. brown, green & red 25 15
818. – 1 g. 50 turq., sepia & brn 45 35

**1962.** Surch. with premium.
(a) Nos. 799/804.
820.136. 5 c.+25 c. (postage) .. 20 15
821. – 10 c.+25 c. .. .. 25 20
822.136. 50 c.+25 c. .. .. 30 20
823. – 20 c.+25 c. (air) .. 20 20
824.136. 50 c.+25 c. .. .. 25 25
825. – 1 g. +25c. .. .. 35 30
(b) Nos. 806/9.
827.118. 10 c.+20 c. (postage).. 15 15
828. 50 c.+20 c. .. .. 25 15
829. 50 c.+20 c. (air) .. 25 15
830. 1 g.+20 c. .. .. 35 30

**1962.** Air. Port-au-Prince Airport Construction Fund. Optd. **AEROPORT INTERNATIONAL 1962** with No. 848 additionally optd. **Poste Aerienne.**
831. – 20 c. No. 816 .. .. 15 10
832. – 50 c. No. 815 .. .. 25 15
833.137. 50 c. No. 817 .. .. 25 15
834. – 1 g. 50 No. 818 .. 45 35

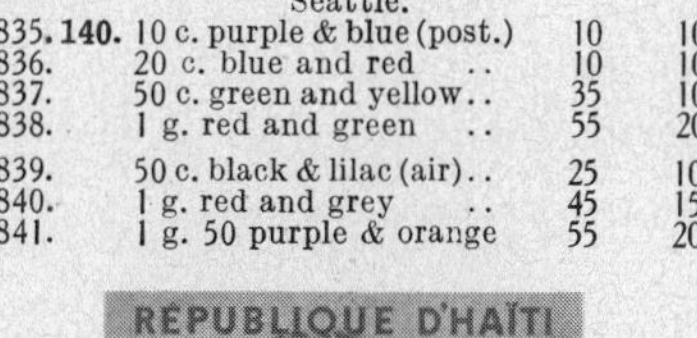

140. Tower, World's Fair.

**1962.** "Century 21" Exn. (World's Fair), Seattle.
835.140. 10 c. purple & blue (post.) 10 10
836. 20 c. blue and red .. 10 10
837. 50 c. green and yellow.. 35 10
838. 1 g. red and green .. 55 20
839. 50 c. black & lilac (air).. 25 10
840. 1 g. red and grey .. 45 15
841. 1 g. 50 purple & orange 55 20

141. Town plan and 1904 10 c. stamp.

**1963.** Duvalier-ville Commem.
843.141. 5 c. black, yellow and violet (postage) .. 10 10
844. 10 c. black, yellow & red 10 10
845 25 c. blk., yellow & grey 20 15
846. – 50 c. brn. and orge. (air) 20 15
847. – 1 g. brown and blue .. 35 30
848. – 1 g. 50 brown and green 55 45
DESIGN: Nos. 846/8 Houses and 1881 2 c. stamp.

**1963.** "Peaceful Uses of Outer Space". Nos. 837/38 and 841/2 optd. **UTILISATIONS PACIFIQUES DE L'ESPACE** and space capsule.
853.140. 50 c. green and yellow (post.) 20 15
854. 1 g. red and green .. 45 30
855. 1 g. red and grey (air) 45 35
856. 1 g. 50 purple and orge. 65 65

**1963.** Literacy Campaign. Surch. **ALPHABETISATION+0, 10.**
857.141. 25 c.+10 c. (postage).. 15 10
858. – 50 c.+10 c. (No. 846)(air) 25 15
859. – 1 g. 50+10 c. (No. 848) 35 35

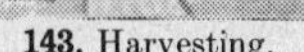

143. Harvesting. 145. Dessalines Statue.

144. Dag Hammarskjold and U.N. Emblem. 146. "Alphabetisation".

**1963.** Freedom from Hunger.
860. 143. 10 c. orange and black (post.) .. .. 10 10
861. 20 c. turq. & black .. 10 10
862. 50 c. mve. & blk. (air.) 15 10
863. 1 g. green and black 30 20

**1963.** Air. Dag Hammarskjold Commemoration. Portrait in blue.
864.144. 20 c. brown and bistre.. 10 10
865. 50 c. red and blue .. 20 20
866. 1 g. blue and mauve .. 30 30
867. 1 g. 50 green and grey.. 55 45
Nos. 864/67 were printed in sheets of 25 (5×5) with a map of Sweden in the background covering most stamps in the second and third vertical rows.

**1963.** Dessalines Commemoration.
869.145. 5 c. red & brown (post.) 10 10
870. 10 c. blue, grn. & ochre 10 10
871. 50 c. grn. & brown (air) 20 10
872. 50 c. pur., violet & blue 20 10

**1963.** Obligatory Tax. Education Fund.
873.146. 10 c. red (postage) .. 10 10
874. 10 c. blue .. .. 10 10
875. 10 c. olive .. .. 10 10
876. 10 c. brown (air) .. 10 10
877. 10 c. violet .. .. 10 10
878. 10 c. violet .. .. 10 10
See also Nos. 974/78, 1157/63 and 1260/1.

**1964.** Mothers' Festival. Optd. **FETE DES MERES 1964,** or surch. also.
879.145. 10 c. blue, green & ochre (postage) .. .. 10 10
880. 50 c. grn. & brown (air) 25 15
881. 50 c. purple, vio. & blue 25 15
882. – 1 g. 50 on 80 c. pink and green (No. 458) .. 35 25

**1964.** Winter Olympic Games, Innsbruck. Surch. **JEUX OLYMPIQUES D'HIVER INNSBRUCK 1964 0.50+0.10,** Olympic rings and games emblem.
883.137. 50 c.+10 c. on 3 c. (post.) 45 30
884. 50 c+10 c. on 5 c. (No. 812) .. .. .. 45 30
885. – 50 c.+10 c. on 10 c. (No. 813) .. .. .. 45 30
886.137. 50 c.+10 c. on 25 c. .. 45 30
887.101. 50 c.+10 c. on 2 g. 50 (air) 70 65

**1964.** Air. Red Cross Cent. (1963). Optd. **1863, 1963** and Centenary Emblem, on surch. also. Portrait in blue.
888.144. 20 c. brown and bistre.. 30 10
889. 50 c. red and blue .. 30 15
890. 1 g. blue and mauve .. 45 30
891. 1 g. 50 green and grey.. 55 35
892. 2 g. 50+1 g. 25 on 1 g. 50 green and grey .. 85 60

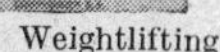

150. Weightlifting. 151. Our Lady of Perpetual Succour, and Airport.

**1964.** Olympic Games, Tokyo (1st issue).
893.150. 10 c. sepia and blue (post.) 10 10
894. 25 c. sepia and salmon.. 10 10
895. – 50 c. sepia and mauve.. 20 15
896.150. 50 c. sep. & purple (air) 15 15
897. – 50 c. sepia and green .. 15 15
898. – 75 c. sepia and yellow.. 20 20
899. – 1 g. 50 sepia and grey .. 35 35
DESIGN: Nos. 895, 897/99, Hurdling.
Nos. 893/09 were printed in sheets of 50 (10×5) with a large map of Japan in the background.

**1964.** Int. Airport.
901.151. 10 c. blk. & ochre (post.) 15 10
902. 25 c. black & turquoise 25 10
903. 50 c. black and green .. 35 15
904. 1 g. black and red .. 55 35
905. 50 c. blk. & orange (air) 30 15
906. 1 g. 50 black & mauve.. 40 20
907. 2 g. 50 black and violet 1·10 55

**1965.** Int. Airport Opening. Optd. **1965.**
908.151. 10 c. blk. & ochre (post.) 10 10
909. 25 c. black & turquoise 25 15
910. 50 c. black and green .. 35 15
911. 1 g. black and red .. 55 30
912. 50 c. black & orge (air) 30 10
913. 1 g. 50 black and mauve 50 25
914. 2 g. 50 black and violet 75 40

**1965.** Olympic Games, Tokyo (2nd issue). Nos. 893/9 surch.**+5 c.**
915.150. 10 c.+5 c. (postage) .. 10 10
916. – 25 c.+5 c. .. .. 15 15
917. – 50 c.+5 c. .. .. 30 25
918.150. 50 c.+5 c. (air) .. 25 25
919. – 50 c.+5 c. .. .. 25 25
920. – 75 c.+5 c. .. .. 35 35
921. – 1 g. 50+5 c. .. .. 45 45

154. Unisphere. 157. I.T.U. Emblem and Symbols.

155. "Likala" (freighter) in Port.

**1965.** New York World's Fair.
923. **154.** 10 c. mult. (postage) .. 10 10
924. – 20 c. purple and yellow 15 10
925. **154.** 50 c. multicoloured .. 30 20
926. – 50 c. blue & yellow (air) 25 10
927. – 1 g. 50 black and yellow 45 30
928. **154.** 5 g. multicoloured .. 1·60 1·40
DESIGN: 20 c., 50 c. (No. 926), 1 g. 50, "Reaching for the Stars" (statue).

**1965.** Haitian Merchant Marine Commem.
929. **155.** 10 c. mult. (postage) .. 15 10
930. 50 c. multicoloured .. 45 15
931. 50 c. multicoloured (air) 35 10
932. 1 g. 50 multicoloured .. 1·00 45

**1965.** Air. 20th Anniv. of U.N. Optd. **O.N.U. 1945-1965.** Portrait in blue.
933. **144.** 20 c. brown and bistre .. 10 10
934. 50 c. red and blue .. 15 10
935. 1 g. blue and mauve .. 25 20
936. 1 g. 50 green and grey .. 20 30

**1965.** Cent. of I.T.U.
937. **157.** 10 c. multicoloured (post.) 10 10
938. 25 c. multicoloured .. 15 10
939. 50 c. multicoloured .. 20 15
940. 50 c. multicoloured (air) 15 10
941. 1 g. multicoloured .. 30 25
942. 1 g. 50 multicoloured .. 45 35
943. 2 g. multicoloured .. 65 50

**1965.** 25th Anniv. of U.N.E.S.C.O. Nos. 937/41 optd. **20e Anniversaire UNESCO.**
945. **157.** 10 c. multicoloured (post.) 20 20
946. 25 c. multicoloured .. 55 55
947. 50 c. multicoloured .. 75 75
948. 50 c. multicoloured (air) 90 35
949. 1 g. multicoloured 1·75 70

158. Cathedral Facade. 159. "Passiflora quadrangularis".

**1965.** Bicent. of Cathedral of Our Lady of the Assumption, Port-au-Prince. Mult.
951. 5 c. Type **158** (postage) .. 10 10
952. 10 c. High Altar (vert.) .. 10 10
953. 25 c. "Our Lady of the Assumption" (painting) (vert.) .. .. 10 10
954. 50 c. Type **158** (air) .. 20 10
955. 1 g. High Altar (vert.) .. 30 20
956. 7 g. 50, as 25 c., but larger 38×51 mm. .. .. 1·75 1·25

**1965.** Haitian Flowers. Multicoloured.
957. 3 c. Type **159** (postage) .. 10 10
958. 5 c. "Sambucus canadensis" 10 10
959. 10 c. "Hibiscus esculentus" 10 10
960. 15 c. As 5 c. .. .. 10 10
961. 50 c. Type **159** .. .. 30 15
962. 50 c. Type **159** (air) .. 15 10
963. 50 c. As 5 c. .. .. 15 10
964. 50 c. As 10 c. .. .. 15 10
965. 1 g. 50, As 5 c. .. .. 45 35
966. 1 g. 50, As 10 c. .. .. 45 35
967. 5 g. Type **159** .. .. 1·10 75

160. Amulet. 162. Astronauts and "Gemini" Capsules.

**1966.** "Culture". Multicoloured.
968. 5 c. Type **160** (postage) .. 10 10
969. 10 c. Carved stool and Veve decoration (horiz.) .. 10 10
970. 50 c. Type **160** .. .. 20 15
971. 50 c. Carved stool and Veve decoration (horiz.) (air) 20 15
972. 1 g. 50 Type **160** .. .. 55 45
973. 2 g. 50 Modern abstract painting (52×37 mm.) 60 50

**1966.** Obligatory Tax. Education Fund. As T **146** but larger (17×25½ mm.).
974. **146.** 10 c. green (postage) .. 10 10
975. 10 c. violet .. .. 10 10
977. 10 c. orange (air) .. 10 10
978. 10 c. blue .. .. 10 10

**1966.** State Visit of Emperor Haile Selassie of Ethiopia. Nos. 969 and 971/3 optd. **Hommage Haile Selassie 1er 24-25 Avril 1966.**
979. – 10 c. multicoloured (post.) 15 15
980. – 50 c. multicoloured (air) 20 15
981. **160.** 1 g. 50 multicoloured .. 55 45
982. – 2 g. 50 multicoloured .. 60 50

**1966.** Space Rendezvous. Astronauts and capsules in brown.
983. **162.** 5 c. indigo & blue (post.) 10 10
984. 10 c. violet and blue .. 10 10
985. 25 c. green and blue .. 15 10
986. 50 c. red and blue .. 25 15
987. – 50 c. indigo & blue (air) 20 15
988. – 1 g. green and blue .. 35 30
989. – 1 g. 50 red and blue .. 55 45
DESIGN: Nos. 987/9, Astronauts and "Gemini" capsules (different arrangement).

163. Football and Pres. Duvalier.

**1966.** Caribbean Football Championships. Portrait in black.
(i) Inscr. "CHAMPIONNAT DE FOOTBALL DES CARAIBES".
990. **163.** 5 c. grn. & flesh (post.) 10 10
991. – 10 c. green and blue .. 10 10
992. **163.** 15 c. green and apple .. 10 10
993. – 50 c. green and lilac .. 25 15
994. **163.** 50 c. purple & sage (air) 15 15
995. – 1 g. 50 purple and pink 55 45
(ii) As Nos. 990/5 but additionally inscr. "COUPE DR. FRANCOIS DUVALIER 22 JUIN".
996. **163.** 5 c. grn. & flesh (post.) 10 10
997. – 10 c. green and blue .. 10 10
998. **163.** 15 c. green and apple 10 10
999. – 50 c. green and lilac .. 25 15
1000. **163.** 50 c. pur. & sage (air) 15 15
1001. – 1 g. 50 purple & pink 55 45
DESIGN: 10 c., 50 c. (No. 991, 993), 1 g. 50, Footballer and Pres. Duvalier.

164. Audio-visual Aids.

**1966.** National Education.
1002. – 5 c. purple, green and pink (postage) .. 10 10
1003. – 10 c. sepia, lake & brn. 10 10
1004. **164.** 25 c. violet, blue & grn. 10 10
1005. – 50 c. purple, green and yellow (air) .. 15 15
1006. – 1 g. sepia, brn. & orge. 30 30
1007. **164.** 1 g. 50 bl., turq. & grn. 45 45
DESIGNS—VERT. 5 c., 50 c. Young Haitians walking towards ABC "sun". 10 c., 1 g. Scouting—hat, knot and saluting hand.

165. Dr. Albert Schweitzer and Maps of Alsace and Gabon.

**1967.** Schweitzer Commem. Multicoloured.
1008. 5 c. Type **165** (postage) 10 10
1009. 10 c. Dr. Schweitzer and organ pipes .. .. 10 10
1010. 20 c. Dr. Schweitzer and Hospital Deschapelles, Haiti .. .. .. 15 10
1011. 50 c. As 20 c. (air) .. 20 15
1012. 1 g. As 20 c. .. .. 35 30
1013. 1 g. 50 Type **165** .. 50 45
1014. 2 g. As 10 c. .. .. 65 55

166. J.-J. Dessalines and Melon.

**1967.** Dessalines Commem. With Portrait of Dessalines. Multicoloured.
1015. 5 c. Type **166** (postage) .. 10 10
1016. 10 c. Chou (cabbage) .. 10 10
1017. 20 c. Mandarine (orange) 10 10
1018. 50 c. Mirliton (gourd) .. 15 15
1019. 50 c. Type **166** (air) .. 15 10
1020. 1 g. As 20 c. .. .. 30 20
1021. 1 g. 50 As 20 c. .. .. 45 35

**1967.** World Scout Jamboree, Idaho. Nos. 957/8, 960/1, 963 and 965 surch. **12e Jamboree Mondial 1967.** or with additional premium only.
1022. 10 c.+10 c. on 5 c. (post.) 10 10
1023. 15 c.+10 c. .. .. 10 10
1024. 50 c. on 3 c. .. .. 20 15
1025. 50 c.+10 c. .. .. 20 20
1026. 50 c.+10 c. (air) .. .. 20 20
1027. 1 g. 50+50 c. .. .. 60 50

**1967.** World Fair, Montreal. Nos. 968/70 and 972 optd. **EXPO CANADA 1967** and emblem, also surch. with new values (1 g. and 2 g.).
1028. **160.** 5 c. mult. (postage) .. 10 10
1029. – 10 c. multicoloured .. 10 10
1030. **160.** 50 c. multicoloured .. 15 15
1031. 1 g. on 5 c. mult. .. 35 30
1032. 1 g. 50 mult. (air) .. 55 45
1033. 2 g. on 1 g. 50 mult. .. 70 55

169. Head of Duvalier and Guineafowl Emblem.

**1967.** 10th Anniv. of Duvalierists Revolution.
1034. **169.** 5 c. gold & red (post.) 10 10
1035. 10 c. gold and blue .. 10 10
1036. 25 c. gold and brown 15 10
1037. 50 c. gold and purple 25 15
1038. 1 g. gold & green (air) 45 30
1039. 1 g. 50 gold and violet 70 45
1040. 2 g. gold and red .. 90 55

170. "Literacy".

**1967.** National Education. Multicoloured.
1041. 5 c. Type **170** (postage) .. 10 10
1042. 10 c. "Scouting" (Scout badge) (vert.) .. .. 10 10
1043. 25 c. "Visual Aids" (slide projection) .. .. 15 10
1044. 50 c. Type **170** (air) .. 15 10
1045. 1 g. As 10 c. (vert.) .. 30 25
1046. 1 g. 50 As 25 c. .. .. 45 35

**1968.** Olympic Games, Mexico. Nos. 990, 992 and 995 surch. **MEXICO 1968.** with Olympic rings and value or optd. only (1 g. 50).
1047. **163.** 50 c. on 15 c. (post.) .. 20 15
1048. 1 g. on 5 c. .. .. 30 25
1049. – 1 g. 50 (air) .. .. 55 45
1050. – 2 g. 50+1 g. 25 on 1 g. 50 1·25 1·00

**1968.** Winter Olympic Games, Grenoble. Nos. 986/9 optd. **Xeme JEUX OLYMPIQUES D'HIVER-GRENOBLE 1968** and Games' emblem.
1051. **162.** 50 c. red & blue (post.) 60 60
1052. – 50 c. indigo & blue (air) 45 30
1053. – 1 g. green and blue .. 60 35
1054. – 1 g. 50 red and blue .. 1·10 75

173. Bois Caiman Ceremony. 174. "The Unknown Slave".

**1968.** Slaves' Revolt, Commem.
1055. **173.** 5 c. mult. (postage) .. 10 10
1056. 10 c. multicoloured .. 10 10
1057. 25 c. multicoloured .. 10 10
1058. 50 c. multicoloured .. 20 15
1059. 50 c. multicoloured (air) 15 10
1060. 50 c. multicoloured .. 15 10
1061. 1 g. multicoloured .. 30 30
1062. 1 g. multicoloured .. 30 25
1063. 1 g. 50 multicoloured 45 45
1064. 2 g. multicoloured .. 45 55
1065. 5 g. multicoloured .. 85 60
Nos. 1060 and 1062/4 are in a larger size—49½×36 mm.

**1968.** Inaug. of Slavery Freedom Monument.
1066. **174.** 5 c. black & blue (post.) 10 10
1067. 10 c. black and brown 10 10
1068. 20 c. black and violet 15 10
1069. 25 c. black and blue .. 15 10
1070. 50 c. black and green 30 15
1071. 50 c. black & ochre (air) 20 15
1072. 1 g. black and red .. 35 25
1073. 1 g. 50 black & orange 55 35

**1968.** Air. Nos. 1044/6 surch. **CULTURE +0.10.**
1074. **170.** 50 c.+10 c. mult. .. 20 20
1075. – 1 g.+10 c. mult. .. 30 30
1076. – 1 g. 50+10 c. mult. .. 45 45

176. Various Arms and Palm.

**1968.** Consecration of Haitian Bishopric.
1077. **176.** 5 c. mult. (postage) .. 10 10
1078. – 10 c. multicoloured .. 10 10
1079. – 25 c. multicoloured .. 20 10
1080. **176.** 50 c. mult. (air) .. 15 10
1081. – 1 g. multicoloured .. 30 25
1082. – 1 g. 50 multicoloured 45 35
1083. – 2 g. 50 multicoloured 70 65
DESIGNS—HORIZ. (50×30 mm.): 10 c., 1 g., 2 g. 50, Virgin Mary. 25 c., 1 g. 50, Cathedral, Port-au-Prince.

177. Boeing 727-100 over Control Tower.

**1968.** Inauguration of Duvalier Airport, Port-au-Prince. Portrait in black.
1084. **177.** 5 c. brown & blue (post.) 10 10
1085. 10 c. brown and blue 10 10
1086. 25 c. brown and lilac 10 10
1087. – 50 c. pur. & violet (air) 20 15
1088. – 1 g. 50 purple & blue 55 35
1089. – 2 g. 50 purple & turq. 70 45
DESIGN: 50 c., 1 g. 50, 2 g. 50, Boeing 727-100 over airport entrance.

178. President Duvalier, Emblems and Map.

**1968.** Air. 4th Anniv. of Francois Duvalier's "Life Presidency". Die-stamped in gold.
1090. **178.** 30 g. gold, black & red .. .. 16·00

179. Slave breaking Chains.

**1968.** "Revolt of the Slaves" (1791).
1091. **179.** 5 c. purple, purple and blue (postage) .. 10 10
1092. 10 c. mve., pur. & orge. 10 10
1093. 25 c. mve., pur. & ochre 10 10
1094. 50 c. mauve, purple and lilac (air) .. 15 10
1095. 1 g. mve., pur. & grn. 35 25
1096. 1 g. 50 mve., pur. & bl. 50 35
1097. 2 g. mve., pur. & turq. 60 45

180. "Learning the Alphabet".

**1968.** "National Education". Mult.
1098. 5 c. Type **180** (postage) .. 10 10
1099. 10 c. Children watching TV screen ("Education by Audio-visual Methods") 10 10
1100. 50 c. Hands with ball ("Education Through Sport") .. .. 15 10
1101. 50 c. As No. 1099 (air) .. 15 10
1102. 1 g. As No. 1100 .. 30 25
1103. 1 g. 50 As No. 1099 .. 55 35

**181.** Boesman and Balloon. **182.** Airmail Cachet of 1925.

**1968.** Air. Boesman's Balloon Flight.
1104. **181.** 70 c. brown and green 40 30
1105. 1 g. 75 brown and blue 1·00 70

**1968.** Air. Galiffet's Balloon Flight of 1784. Each black and purple on mauve.
1106 70 c. Airplane and "AVION" ("2 May 1925") 35 35
1107 70 c. Type **182** .. .. 35 35
1108 70 c. "AVION" and airplane ("28 March 1927") .. .. .. 35 35
1109 70 c. "HAITI POSTE AVION" and airplane ("12 July 1927") .. .. .. 35 35
1110 70 c. Airplane and "AVION" within ring ("13 Sept. 1927") .. 35 35
1111 70 c. "LINDBERGH" and airplane ("6th February 1928") .. .. .. 35 35

Nos. 1106/11 were issued together se-tenant within a small sheet containing two blocks of six (3 × 2) with an overall background design representing Galiffet's balloon.

**183.** Churchill as Elder Brother of Trinity House. **185.** Blue-hooded Euphonia.

**1968.** Churchill Commemoration. Mult.
1112 3 c. Type **183** (postage) .. 10 10
1113 5 c. Churchill painting .. 10 10
1114 10 c. As Knight of the Garter .. .. 10 10
1115 15 c. 79th birthday portrait and troops .. 10 10
1116 20 c. Churchill and Farman M.F.7 floatplane .. .. 10 10
1117 25 c. Karsh portrait and taking leave of the Queen .. .. .. 10 10
1118 50 c. Giving "V"-sign and Houses of Parliament 15 10
1119 50 c. As No. 1116 (air) .. 15 10
1120 75 c. As No. 1115 .. 25 15
1121 1 g. As No. 1117 .. .. 30 25
1122 1 g. 50 As No. 1118 .. 45 35

**1969.** Nos. 1070/2 surch.
1124. **174.** 70 c. on 50 c. (postage) 45 20
1125. 70 c. on 50 c. (air) .. 35 25
1126. 1 g. 75 on 1 g. .. 85 55

**1969.** Birds. Multicoloured.
1127. 5 c. Type **185** (postage) 1·40 30
1128. 10 c. Hispaniolan trogon 1·40 30
1129. 20 c. Palm chat .. .. 1·60 30
1130. 25 c. Stripe-headed tanager .. .. 1·90 40
1131. 50 c. Type **185** .. 2·40 45
1132. 50 c. As 10 c. (air) 2·25 60
1133. 1 g. Black-cowled oriole 2·50 1·10
1134. 1 g. 50 As 25 c. .. 3·00 1·40
1135. 2 g. Hispaniolan woodpecker .. .. .. 3·50 1·75

**186.** "Theato, Paris-1900".

**1969.** Winners of Olympic Marathon showing commemorative inscr. and stamp of "host" country. Multicoloured.
1136. 5 c. "Louis, Athens-1896" (postage) .. .. 10 10
1137. 10 c. Type **186** .. 15 15
1138. 15 c. "Hicks, St. Louis-1904" .. .. 15 15
1139. 20 c. "Hayes, London-1908" .. .. 25 25
1140. 20 c. "McArthur, Stockholm-1912" .. .. 25 25
1141. 25 c. Kolehmainen, Antwerp-1920" .. .. 40 40
1142. 25 c. "Steenroos, Paris-1924" .. .. 40 40
1143. 25 c. "El Quafi, Amsterdam-1928" .. .. 40 40
1144. 30 c. "Zabala, Los Angeles-1932" (air) .. 45 45
1145. 50 c. "Son, Berlin-1936" 70 70
1146. 60 c. "Cabrera, London-1948" .. .. 90 90
1147. 75 c. "Zatopek, Helsinki-1952" .. 1·25 1·25
1148. 75 c. "Mimoun, Melbourne-1956" .. .. 1·25 1·25
1149. 90 c. "Bikila, Rome-1960" 1·50 1·50
1150. 1 g. "Bikila, Tokyo-1964" 1·75 1·75
1151. 1 g. 25 "Wolde, Mexico-1968" .. .. 2·50 2·50

Nos. 1136, 1139, 1142 and 1149 are larger, size 66 × 36 mm.

**187.** Pylons and Electric Light Bulb. **189.** Practising the Alphabet.

**1969.** Construction of Duvalier Hydro-electric Scheme.
1153. **187.** 20 c. violet & blue (post.) 10 10
1154. 20 c. blue and violet (air) 10 10
1155. 25 c. green and red .. 10 10
1156. 25 c. red and green .. 15 10

**1969.** Obligatory Tax. Education Fund. As Nos. 974/8.
1157. **146.** 10 c. brown (postage) 10 10
1158. 10 c. blue .. .. 10 10
1159. 10 c. purple (air) .. 10 10
1160. 10 c. red .. .. 10 10
1161. 10 c. yellow .. .. 10 10
1162. 10 c. green .. .. 10 10
1163. 10 c. maroon .. .. 10 10

**1969.** League of Red Cross Societies. 50th Anniv. Various stamps surch. **50 eme. Anniversaire de la Ligue des Societes de la Croix Rouge.**
1164. 10 c. + 10 c. (No. 1099) (postage) .. .. 10 10
1165. 50 c. + 20 c. (No. 1100) .. 20 20
1166. 50 c. + 20 c. (No. 1101) (air) 30 20
1167. 1 g. 50 + 25 c. (No. 1103) 70 50

**1969.** "National Education". Multicoloured.
1168. 5 c. Type **189** (postage) .. 10 10
1169. 10 c. Children at play .. 10 10
1170. 50 c. Audio-visual education 15 10
1171. 50 c. As No. 1170 (air) .. 15 10
1172. 1 g. Type **189** .. 35 20
1173. 1 g. 50 As No. 1169 .. 55 35

Nos. 1169/71 and 1173 are vert.

**190.** I.L.O. Emblem. **191.** "Papilio zonaria".

**1969.** 50th Anniv. of I.L.O.
1174. **190.** 5 c. grn. & blk. (post.) 10 10
1175. 10 c. brown and black 10 10
1176. 20 c. blue and black .. 10 10
1177. 25 c. red & black (air) 15 10
1178. 70 c. orange and black 25 15
1179. 1 g. 75 violet & black 40 45

**1969.** Haitian Butterflies. Multicoloured.
1180 10 c. Type **191** (postage) 15 10
1181 20 c. "Zerene cesonia" .. 30 10
1182 25 c. "Papilio machaonides" .. .. 35 10
1183 50 c. "Danaus eresimus" (air) .. .. 45 10
1184 1 g. 50 "Anaea marthesia" 1·40 60
1185 2 g. "Prepona antimache" 1·75 85

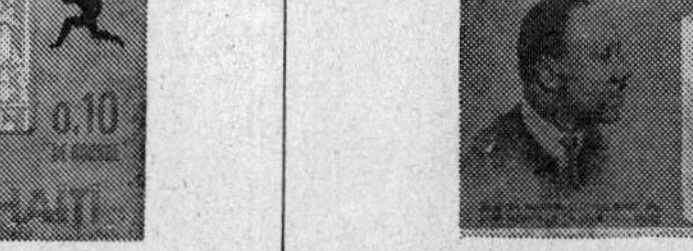

**192.** Dr. Martin Luther King.

**1970.** Dr. Martin Luther King (American Civil Rights leader). Commemoration.
1186. **192.** 10 c. brown, red and ochre (postage) .. 10 10
1187. 20 c. blk., red & new bl. 10 10
1188. 25 c. blk., red & pink 10 10
1189. 50 c. black, red and green (air) .. 20 10
1190. 1 g. blk., red & orange 35 25
1191. 1 g. 50 blk., red & blue 55 35

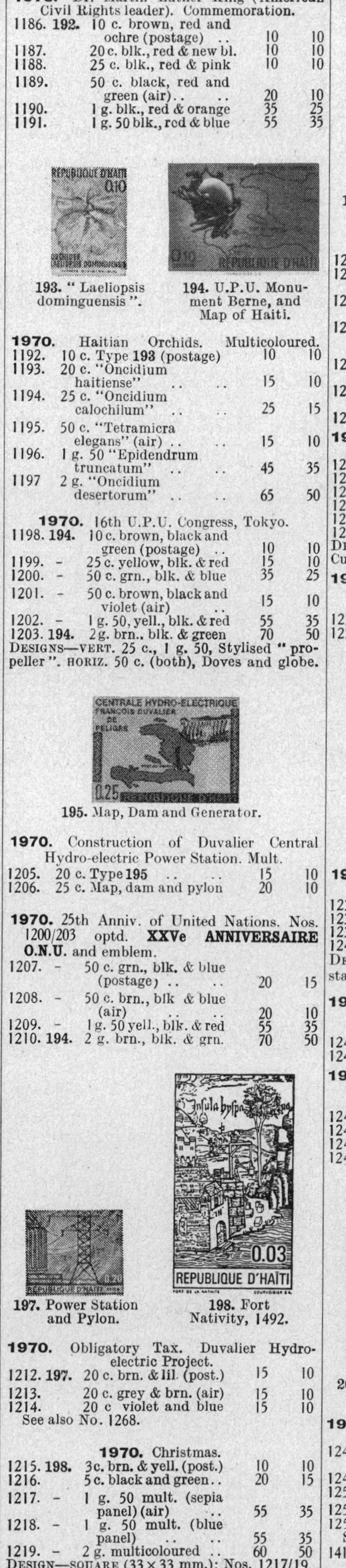

**193.** "Laeliopsis dominguensis". **194.** U.P.U. Monument Berne, and Map of Haiti.

**1970.** Haitian Orchids. Multicoloured.
1192. 10 c. Type **193** (postage) 10 10
1193. 20 c. "Oncidium haitiense" .. .. 15 10
1194. 25 c. "Oncidium calochilum" .. .. 25 15
1195. 50 c. "Tetramicra elegans" (air) .. 15 10
1196. 1 g. 50 "Epidendrum truncatum" .. 45 35
1197 2 g. "Oncidium desertorum" .. 65 50

**1970.** 16th U.P.U. Congress, Tokyo.
1198. **194.** 10 c. brown, black and green (postage) .. 10 10
1199. – 25 c. yellow, blk. & red 15 10
1200. – 50 c. grn., blk. & blue 35 25
1201. – 50 c. brown, black and violet (air) 15 10
1202. – 1 g. 50, yell., blk. & red 55 35
1203. **194.** 2 g. brn., blk. & green 70 50

DESIGNS—VERT. 25 c., 1 g. 50, Stylised "propeller". HORIZ. 50 c. (both), Doves and globe.

**195.** Map, Dam and Generator.

**1970.** Construction of Duvalier Central Hydro-electric Power Station. Mult.
1205. 20 c. Type **195** .. .. 15 10
1206. 25 c. Map, dam and pylon 20 10

**1970.** 25th Anniv. of United Nations. Nos. 1200/203 optd. **XXVe ANNIVERSAIRE O.N.U.** and emblem.
1207. – 50 c. grn., blk. & blue (postage) .. .. 20 15
1208. – 50 c. brn., blk. & blue (air) .. .. 20 10
1209. – 1 g. 50 yell., blk. & red 55 35
1210. **194.** 2 g. brn., blk. & grn. 70 50

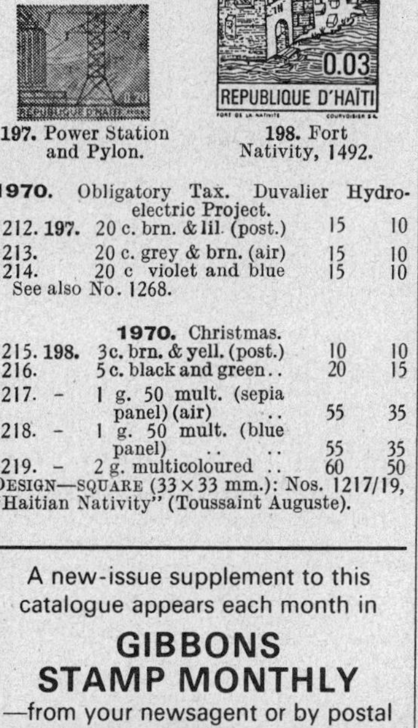

**197.** Power Station and Pylon. **198.** Fort Nativity, 1492.

**1970.** Obligatory Tax. Duvalier Hydro-electric Project.
1212. **197.** 20 c. brn. & lil. (post.) 15 10
1213. 20 c. grey & brn. (air) 15 10
1214. 20 c. violet and blue 15 10

See also No. 1268.

**1970.** Christmas.
1215. **198.** 3 c. brn. & yell. (post.) 10 10
1216. 5 c. black and green .. 20 15
1217. – 1 g. 50 mult. (sepia panel) (air) .. 55 35
1218. – 1 g. 50 mult. (blue panel) .. .. 55 35
1219. – 2 g. multicoloured .. 60 50

DESIGN—SQUARE (33 × 33 mm.): Nos. 1217/19, "Haitian Nativity" (Toussaint Auguste).



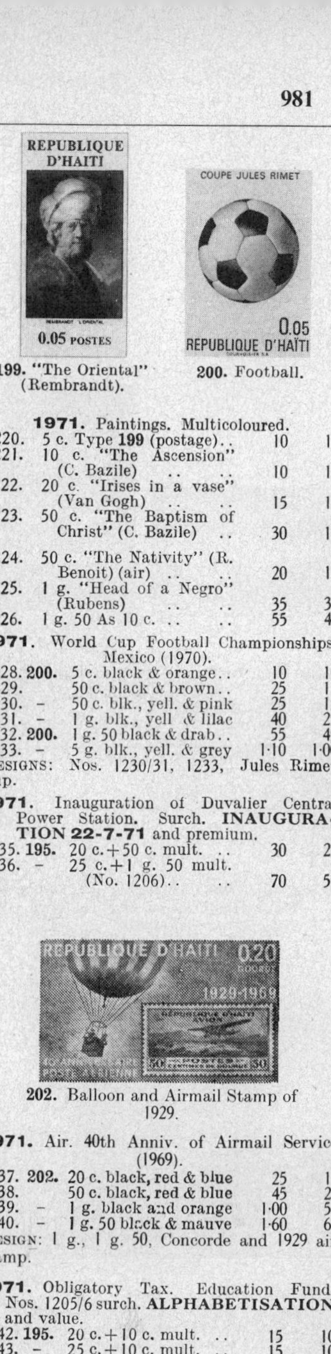

**199.** "The Oriental" (Rembrandt). **200.** Football.

**1971.** Paintings. Multicoloured.
1220. 5 c. Type **199** (postage) .. 10 10
1221. 10 c. "The Ascension" (C. Bazile) .. .. 10 10
1222. 20 c. "Irises in a vase" (Van Gogh) .. .. 15 10
1223. 50 c. "The Baptism of Christ" (C. Bazile) .. 30 15
1224. 50 c. "The Nativity" (R. Benoit) (air) .. .. 20 15
1225. 1 g. "Head of a Negro" (Rubens) .. .. 35 30
1226. 1 g. 50 As 10 c. .. .. 55 45

**1971.** World Cup Football Championships, Mexico (1970).
1228. **200.** 5 c. black & orange .. 10 10
1229. 50 c. black & brown .. 25 15
1230. – 50 c. blk., yell. & pink 25 15
1231. – 1 g. blk., yell & lilac 40 25
1232. **200.** 1 g. 50 black & drab .. 55 45
1233. – 5 g. blk., yell. & grey 1·10 1·00

DESIGNS: Nos. 1230/31, 1233, Jules Rimet Cup.

**1971.** Inauguration of Duvalier Central Power Station. Surch. **INAUGURATION 22-7-71** and premium.
1235. **195.** 20 c. + 50 c. mult. .. 30 25
1236. – 25 c. + 1 g. 50 mult. (No. 1206) .. .. 70 55

**202.** Balloon and Airmail Stamp of 1929.

**1971.** Air. 40th Anniv. of Airmail Service (1969).
1237. **202.** 20 c. black, red & blue 25 10
1238. 50 c. black, red & blue 45 20
1239. – 1 g. black and orange 1·00 50
1240. – 1 g. 50 black & mauve 1·40 60

DESIGN: 1 g., 1 g. 50, Concorde and 1929 air stamp.

**1971.** Obligatory Tax. Education Fund. Nos. 1205/6 surch. **ALPHABETISATION** and value.
1242. **195.** 20 c. + 10 c. mult. .. 15 10
1243. – 25 c. + 10 c. mult. .. 15 10

**1972.** Air. "INTERPEX" Int. Stamp Exhib., New York Nos. 1237/40 optd. **INTERPEX 72** and emblem.
1244. **202.** 20 c. black, red & blue 15 10
1245. 50 c. black, red & blue 55 20
1246. – 1 g. black and orange 95 50
1247. – 1 g. 50 black & mauve 1·40 75

**205.** J.-J. Dessalines and Emblem. **208.** "Sun" and "EXPO" Emblem.

**1972.** Jean-Jacques Dessalines ("founder of Haiti") (1st issue). Commem.
1248. **205.** 5 c. black and green (postage) .. .. 10 10
1249. 10 c. black and blue .. 10 10
1250. 25 c. black and orange 10 10
1251. 50 c. blk. & grn. (air) 20 10
1252. 2 g. 50 black and lilac 55 20

See also Nos. 1304/10, 1343/52, 1357/60, 1413/17 and 1451/2.

**1972.** Air. Fifth "Haipex" Congress. Nos. 1237/40 optd. **HAIPEX 5eme. CONGRES** and emblem.
1253. **202.** 20 c. blk. red & blue 15 10
1254. – 50 c. blk., red and blue 55 20
1255. – 1 g. black & orange .. 95 45
1256. – 1 g. 50 black & mauve 1·40 65

**1972.** Air. "Belgica 72" Stamp Exhibition, Brussels. Nos. 1238/40 optd. **BELGICA 72** and emblem.
1257. 50 c. blk., red and blue .. 55 20
1258. 1 g. black and orange .. 90 55
1259. 1 g. 50 black & mauve .. 1·60 65

**1972.** Obligatory Tax. As Nos. 974/8.
1260. **146.** 5 c. red .. .. 10 10
1261. 5 c. blue .. .. 10 10

**1972.** "EXPO 70" World Fair, Osaka, Japan (1970).

1262. **208.** 10 c. mult. (postage) 10 10
1263. 25 c. multicoloured .. 10 10
1264. – 50 c. multicoloured .. 15 10
1265. – 1 g. multicoloured .. 35 25
1266. – 1 g. 50 multicoloured 45 30
1267. – 2 g. 50 multicoloured 90 55

DESIGNS—HORIZ. Nos. 1264/7, Sun Tower and emblem.

**1972.** Obligatory Tax. Duvalier Hydro-electric Project. As Nos. 1212/14.

1268. **197.** 20 c. brown and blue 10 10

**209.** Basket Vendors. **210.** Headquarters and Map.

**1973.** 20th Anniv. of Caribbean Travel Assn. Multicoloured.

1269. 50 c. Type **209** .. .. 20 10
1270. 80 c. Postal bus service .. 30 20
1271. 1 g. 50 Type **209** .. 55 30
1272. 2 g. 50 As 80 c. .. .. 75 55

**1973.** Air. Education Fund. As Nos. 977/8 but larger size 17 × 25 mm.

1273. **146.** 10 c. brown and blue .. 10 10
1274. 10 c. brown and green 10 10
1275. 10 c. brown and orange 10 10

**1973.** Air. 70th Anniv. of Pan-American Health Organization. Multicoloured.

1276. **210.** 50 c. multicoloured .. 15 10
1277. 80 c. multicoloured .. 25 20
1278. 1 g. 50 multicoloured 45 30
1279. 2 g. multicoloured .. 55 45

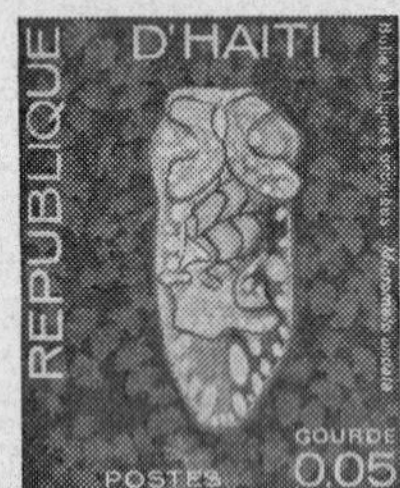

**211.** Miniature Melo.

**1973.** Marine Life. Multicoloured.

1280. 5 c. Type **211** postage).. 15 10
1281. 10 c. "Nemaster rubiginosa" 10 10
1282. 25 c. "Cyerce cristallina" 30 10
1283. 50 c. "Desmophyllum riisei" 15 10
1284. 50 c. "Platypodia spectabilis" (air) .. .. .. 15 10
1285. 85 c. "Goniaster tessellatus" 25 20
1286. 1 g. 50 "Stephanocyathus diadema" .. .. 45 30
1287. 2 g. "Phyllangia americana" 55 35

**211a.** 'Gramma loreto'.

**1973.** Fishes. Multicoloured.

1288. 10 c. Type **211a** (postage) 10 10
1289. 50 c. "Acanthrus coeruleus 15 10
1290. 50 c. "Gramma melacara" (air) .. .. .. 15 10
1291. 85 c. "Holacanthus tricolor" 25 20
1292. 1 g. 50 "Liopropoma rubre" 45 30
1293. 5 g. "Clepticus parrai" .. 85 60

**212.** Haitian Flag.

**1973.** Air.

1294. **212.** 80 c. black and red .. 25 20
1295. – 80 c. black and red .. 25 20
1296. – 1 g. 85 black and red 55 30
1297. – 1 g. 85 black and red 55 30

DESIGNS—As Type **212**. No. 1295, Flag and arms (framed). (47 × 29 mm.). No. 1296, Flag and arms. No. 1297, Flag and Pres. Jean-Claude Duvalier.

**213.** Football Stadium. **214.** J.-J. Dessalines.

**1973.** World Cup Football Championships. Preliminary Games between Caribbean Countries.

1298. **213.** 10 c. grn., blk. & brn. (postage) .. .. 10 10
1299. – 20 c. mve., blk. & brn. 10 10
1300. **213.** 50 c. grn., blk. & red (air) 15 10
1301. 80 c. grn., blk. & blue 25 20
1302. – 1 g. 75 grn., blk. & brn. 50 35
1303. – 10 g. grn., blk. & brn. 1·75 1·25

DESIGNS: 20 c., 1 g. 75, 10 g. World Cup stamp of 1971.

**1974.** Jean-Jacques Dessalines Commemoration (2nd issue).

1304. **214.** 10 c. green & blue (post.) 10 10
1305. 20 c. black and red .. 10 10
1306. 25 c. violet and brown 10 10
1307. 50 c. blue & brn. (air) 15 10
1308. 80 c. brown and grey 20 20
1309. 1 g. purple and green 30 20
1310. 1 g. 75 green & mauve 50 35

**215.** Symbol of Solar System. **216.** Pres. Jean-Claude Duvalier.

**1974.** 500th Birth Anniv (1973) of Nicolas Copernicus (astronomer). Multicoloured.

1311. 10 c. Type **215** (postage) 10 10
1312. 25 c. Copernicus .. .. 10 10
1313. 50 c. Type **215** (air) .. 15 10
1314. 50 c. As 25 c. .. .. 15 10
1315. 80 c. Type **215** .. .. 25 20
1316. 1 g. As 25 c. .. .. 30 20
1317. 1 g. 75 Type **215** .. .. 50 35

**1974.**

1319. **216.** 10 c. grn. & gold (post.) 10 10
1320. 20 c. purple and gold 10 10
1321. 50 c. blue and gold .. 15 10
1322. 50 c. pur. & gold (air) 15 15
1323. 80 c. red and gold .. 25 20
1324. 1 g. purple and gold .. 30 20
1325. 1 g. 50 blue and gold 45 30
1326. 1 g. 75 violet and gold 55 35
1327. 5 g. grey and gold .. 85 60

**1975.** Air. Nos. 1296/7 surch.

1328. 80 c. on 1 g. 85 blk. & red 25 20
1329. 80 c. on 1 g. 85 blk. & red 25 20

**1975.** Air. Centenary of U.P.U. Nos. 1296/7 optd. **1874 UPU 1974 100 ANS.**

1330. 1 g. 85 black and red .. 55 30
1331. 1 g. 85 black and red .. 55 30

**219.** Haiti 60 c. Stamp of 1937.

**1976.** Bicent. of American Revolution.

1332. **219.** 10 c. multicoloured (postage) .. .. 10 10
1333. – 50 c. multicoloured (air) .. .. 15 10
1334. – 80 c. multicoloured .. 25 15
1335. – 1 g. 50 multicoloured 45 30
1336. – 7 g. 50 multicoloured 1·75 1·25

DESIGN: 50 c. to 7 g. 50, text with names of Haitians at Siege of Savannah.

**1976.** Surch.

1337. **205.** 80 c. on 25 c. black and pink (postage) 35 20
1338. – 80 c. on 10 c. multicoloured (No. 1288) 35 20
1339. **214.** 80 c. on 25 c. violet and brown .. 35 20
1340. **215.** 80 c. on 10 c. mult. 35 20
1341. – 80 c. on 85 c. multicoloured (No. 1285) (air) .. .. 25 20
1342. – 80 c. on 85 c. multicoloured (No. 1291) 25 20

**1977.** Jean-Jacques Dessalines Commem. (3rd issue).

1343. **205.** 20 c. black and brown (postage) .. .. 10 10
1344. 50 c. black and mauve 15 10
1345. 75 c. blk. & yell (air) 20 20
1346. 1 g. black and blue .. 30 15
1347. 1 g. 25 blk. & olive .. 35 30
1348. 1 g. 50 blk & grey .. 45 30
1349. 1 g. 75 blk. and red 50 35
1350. 2 g. black and yellow 55 45
1351. 5 g. black and blue .. 85 60
1352. 10 g. black and brown 1·75 1·25

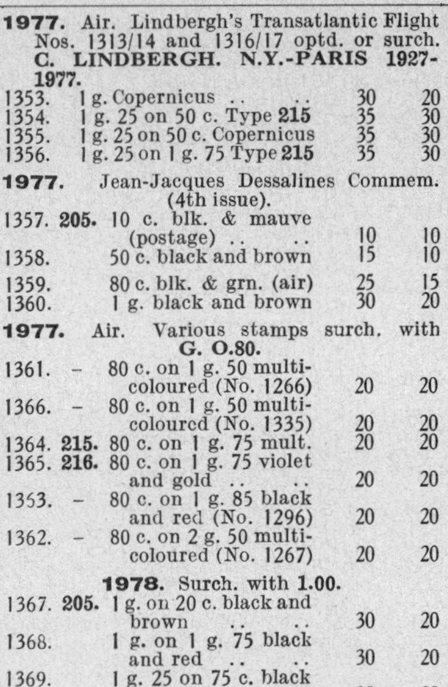

**1977.** Air. Lindbergh's Transatlantic Flight Nos. 1313/14 and 1316/17 optd. or surch. **C. LINDBERGH. N.Y.-PARIS 1927-1977.**

1353. 1 g. Copernicus .. .. 30 20
1354. 1 g. 25 on 50 c. Type **215** 35 30
1355. 1 g. 25 on 50 c. Copernicus 35 30
1356. 1 g. 25 on 1 g. 75 Type **215** 35 30

**1977.** Jean-Jacques Dessalines Commem. (4th issue).

1357. **205.** 10 c. blk. & mauve (postage) .. .. 10 10
1358. 50 c. black and brown 15 10
1359. 80 c. blk. & grn. (air) 25 15
1360. 1 g. black and brown 30 20

**1977.** Air. Various stamps surch. with **G. O.80.**

1361. – 80 c. on 1 g. 50 multicoloured (No. 1266) 20 20
1366. – 80 c. on 1 g. 50 multicoloured (No. 1335) 20 20
1364. **215.** 80 c. on 1 g. 75 mult. 20 20
1365. **216.** 80 c. on 1 g. 75 violet and gold .. .. 20 20
1363. – 80 c. on 1 g. 85 black and red (No. 1296) 20 20
1362. – 80 c. on 2 g. 50 multicoloured (No. 1267) 20 20

**1978.** Surch. with **1.00.**

1367. **205.** 1 g. on 20 c. black and brown .. .. 30 20
1368. 1 g. on 1 g. 75 black and red .. .. 30 20
1369. 1 g. 25 on 75 c. black and yellow .. 35 25
1370. 1 g. 25 on 1 g. 50 blk. and green .. .. 35 25

Nos. 1368/70 have the inscription "AVION" obliterated by the surcharge.

**224.** J.-C. Duvalier Telecommunications Stations. **225.** Flag-raising Ceremony.

**1978.** Telephone Centenary (1976). Mult.

1372. 10 c. Type **224** (postage) 10 10
1373. 20 c. Video telephone .. 10 10
1374. 50 c. Alexander Graham Bell (vert.) .. .. 15 10
1375. 1 g. Satellite over Earth (air) .. .. .. 30 15
1376. 1 g. 25 Type **224** .. 35 25
1377. 2 g. Wall telephone, 1890 (vert.) .. .. .. 55 45

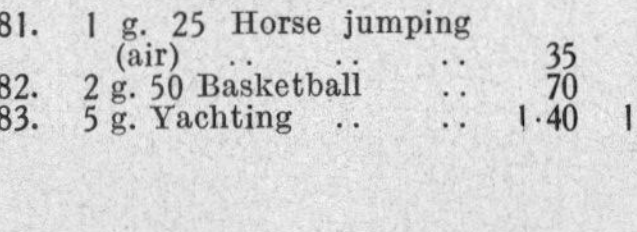

**1978.** Olympic Games, Montreal (1976). Multicoloured.

1378. 5 c. Type **225** (postage).. 10 10
1379. 25 c. Cycling .. .. 10 10
1380. 50 c. High jump .. 15 10
1381. 1 g. 25 Horse jumping (air) .. .. .. 35 25
1382. 2 g. 50 Basketball .. 70 55
1383. 5 g. Yachting .. .. 1·40 1·10

**226.** Mother feeding Baby. **227.** Mother feeding Child.

**1979.** 50th Anniv. of Inter-American Child Institute. Multicoloured.

1384. 25 c. Type **226** (postage) 10 10
1385. 1 g. 25 Type **226** (air) .. 35 25
1386. 2 g. Nurse vaccinating child 55 45

**1979.** 30th Anniv. of Co-operative for American Relief Everywhere (CARE). Mult.

1387. 25 c. Type **227** (postage) 10 10
1388. 50 c. Type **227** .. .. 15 15
1389. 1 g. Spinning cotton (air) 30 20
1390. 1 g. 25 As No. 1389 .. 35 25
1391. 2 g. As No. 1389 .. 55 45

**228.** Human Rights Emblem. **229.** Anteor Firmin and Book.

**1979.** 30th Anniv. of Declaration of Human Rights.

1392. **228.** 25 c. multicoloured (postage) .. .. 10 10
1393. 1 g. multicoloured (air) 30 20
1394. 1 g. 25 multicoloured 35 25
1395. 2 g. multicoloured .. 55 45

**1979.** International Anti-Apartheid Year.

1396. **229.** 50 c. pink and brown (postage) .. .. 15 15
1397. 1 g. green & brown (air) 30 20
1398. 1 g. 25 blue and brown 35 25
1399. 2 g. olive and brown 55 45

**230.** Children playing.

**1979.** International Year of the Child.

1400. **230.** 10 c. multicoloured (postage) .. .. 10 10
1401. 25 c. multicoloured.. 10 10
1402. 50 c. multicoloured.. 15 10
1403. 1 g. multicoloured (air) 30 20
1404. 1 g. 25 multicoloured 35 25
1405. 2 g. 50 multicoloured 45 55
1406. 5 g. multicoloured .. 85 60

**1980.** Air. Wedding of President Duvalier. Nos. 1322 and 1325/6 optd. **27 5 80 JOUR FASTE.**

1407. **216.** 50 c. purple and gold 15 10
1408. 1 g. 50 blue and gold 45 30
1409. 1 g. 75 violet and gold 50 40

**1980.** Nos. 1252, 1357 and 1359 surch. **TIMBRE POSTE** with value changed.

1410. **205.** 1 g. on 2 g. 50 black and lilac .. .. 30 20
1411. **205.** 1 g. 25 on 10 c. black and mauve .. 35 35
1412. 1 g. 25 on 80 c. black and green.. .. 35 55

**1980.** Jean-Jacques Dessalines Commemoration (5th issue).

1413. **205.** 25 c. black and orange (postage) .. .. 10 10
1414. 1 g. black and grey (air) 30 20
1415. 1 g. 25 black and pink 35 25
1416. 2 g. black and green.. 55 45
1417. 5 g. black and blue .. 85 60

**233.** Henri Christophe Citadel.

**1981.** World Tourism Conference, Manila. Multicoloured.

1418. 5 c. Type **233** (postage).. 10 10
1419. 25 c. Sans-Souci Palace.. 10 10
1420. 50 c. Vallieres market .. 15 10
1421. 1 g. Type **233** (air) .. 30 20
1422. 1 g. 25 As No. 1419 .. 35 25
1423. 1 g. 50 Carnival dancers 45 30
1424. 2 g. Women with flowers 55 45
1425. 2 g. 50 As No. 1424 .. 70 50

**234.** Players and Flag of Uruguay (1930).

**1981.** 50th Anniv. of First World Cup Football Championship. Multicoloured.

1426. 10 c. Type **234** (postage) 10 10
1427. 20 c. Italy (1934) .. 10 10
1428. 25 c. Italy (1938) .. 10 10
1429. 50 c. Uruguay (air) .. 15 10
1430. 75 c. West Germany (1954) 20 20
1431. 1 g. Brazil (1958) .. 30 20
1432. 1 g. 25 Brazil (1962) .. 35 25
1433. 1 g. 50 England (1966).. 45 30
1434. 1 g. 75 Brazil (1970) .. 50 40
1435. 2 g. West Germany (1974) 55 45
1436. 5 g. Argentina (1978) .. 85 60

**235.** " Woman with Birds and Flowers " (Hector Hyppolite).

**237.** President Duvalier, Dish Aerial and Freighter at Quayside.

**1981.** Paintings. Multicoloured.

1437. 5 c. Type **235** (postage) 10 10
1438. 10 c. "Going to Church" (Gregoire Etienne) .. 10 10
1439. 20 c. "Street Market" (Petion Savain) .. 10 10
1440. 25 c. "Market Sellers" (Michele Manual) .. 10 10
1441. 50 c. Type **235** (air) .. 15 10
1442. 1 g. 25 As No. 1438 .. 35 25
1443. 2 g. As No. 1439 .. .. 55 45
1444. 5 g. As No. 1440 .. .. 85 60

**1981.** Various stamps surch. **1.25.**

1445. **233.** 1 g. 25 on 5 c. multicoloured (postage) 35 30
1446. **235.** 1 g. 25 on 5 c. multicoloured .. .. 35 30
1447. – 1 g. 25 on 10 c. multicoloured (No. 1438) 35 30
1448. – 1 g. 25 on 20 c. multicoloured (No. 1427) 35 30
1449. – 1 g. 25 on 1 g. 50 multicoloured (No. 1423) (air) .. .. 35 30
1450. **205.** 2 g. on 5 g. black and blue (No. 1417) .. 55 45

The surcharge on No. 1446 is inverted.

**1982.** Jean-Jacques Dessalines ("founder of Haiti"). Commemoration (6th issue).

1451. **205.** 1 g. 25 black & brown 35 30
1452. 2 g. black and violet 55 45

**1982.** 10th Anniv of Duvalier Reforms ("Jean-Claudisme").

1453. **237.** 25 c. green and black 15 10
1454. 50 c. green and black 25 10
1455. 1 g. purple and black 50 20
1456. 1 g. 25 blue and black 55 30
1457. 2 g. orange and black 75 45
1458. 5 g. orange and black 2·25 1·10

**1982.** Nos. 1453 and 1455/7 optd. **1957–1982 25 ANS DE REVOLUTION.**

1459. **237.** 25 c. green and black 10 10
1460. 1 g. purple and black 35 30
1461. 1 g. 25 blue and black 45 40
1462. 2 g. orange and black 65 60

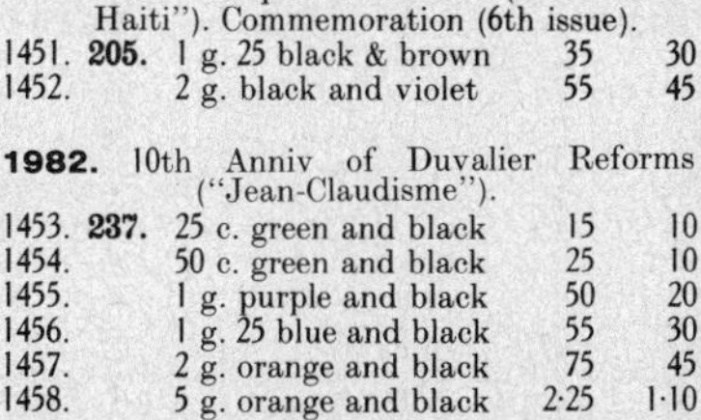


**239.** Scouts planting Trees.

**1983.** 75th Anniv. of Boy Scout Movement. Multicoloured.

1463. 5 c. Type **239** (postage) 10 10
1464. 10 c. Lord Baden-Powell (vert.) .. .. .. 10 10
1465. 25 c. Scout teaching villagers to read .. 25 10
1466. 50 c. As No. 1464 .. 15 10
1467. 75 c. As No. 1465 (air) .. 65 20
1468. 1 g. Type **239** .. .. 30 20
1469. 1 g. 25 As No. 1465 .. 90 30
1470. 2 g. As No. 1464 .. .. 55 45

**240.** Our Lady of Perpetual Succour.

**1983.** Centenary of Miracle of Our Lady of Perpetual Succour.

1471. **240.** 10 c. multicoloured (postage) .. .. 10 10
1472. 20 c. multicoloured .. 10 10
1473. 25 c. multicoloured .. 10 10
1474. 50 c. multicoloured .. 15 10
1475. **240.** 75 c. multicoloured (air) 20 20
1476. 1 g. multicoloured .. 30 20
1477. 1 g. 25 multicoloured 35 30
1478. 1 g. 50 multicoloured 45 30
1479. 1 g. 75 multicoloured 50 45
1480. – 2 g. multicoloured .. 55 45
1481. – 5 g. multicoloured .. 85 60

Nos. 1480/1 differ slightly in design of the frame.

**241.** Arms of Haiti and U.P.U. Monument, Berne.

**1983.** Centenary (1981) of U.P.U. Membership.

1483. **241.** 5 c. brown, red and black (postage) .. 10 10
1484. – 10 c. brown, blk. & bl. 10 10
1485. – 25 c. grn., blk. & red 10 10
1486. – 50 c. grn., red & blk. 15 10
1487. – 75 c. lilac, black and blue (air) .. .. 20 20
1488. – 1 g. blue, red & blk. 30 20
1489. – 1 g. 25 blue, blk. & red 35 30
1490. – 2 g. blue, black and red 55 45

DESIGNS: 50 c., 1 g. Type **241**; 10, 75 c. L.F. Salomon and J. C. Duvalier; 25 c., 1 g. 25, 2 g. First Haitian stamp and U.P.U. Monument, Berne.

**242.** Argentine and Belgian Footballers.

**1983.** World Cup Football Championship, Spain.

1491. **242.** 5 c. blk. & bl. (postage) 10 10
1492. – 10 c. black & brown 10 10
1493. – 20 c. black & green .. 10 10
1494. – 25 c. black & green .. 10 10
1495. – 50 c. black & yellow 15 10
1496. – 1 g. mult. (air) 30 20
1497. – 1 g. 25 multicoloured 35 30
1498. – 1 g. 50 multicoloured 45 30
1499. – 2 g. multicoloured .. 55 45
1500. – 2 g. 50 multicoloured 65 55

DESIGNS—VERT. 10 c. Northern Ireland and Yugoslavia. 20 c. England and France. 25 c. Spain and Northern Ireland. 50 c. Italian player with Cup. HORIZ. 1 g. Brazil and Scotland. 1 g. 25, Northern Ireland and France. 1 g. 50, Poland and Cameroun. 2 g. Italy and West Germany. 2 g. 50, Argentine and Brazil.

**243.** 1 c. Stamp of 1881.

**1984.** Stamp Centenary (1981).

1501. **243.** 5 c. mult (post.) .. 10 10
1502. – 10 c. multicoloured .. 10 10
1503. – 25 c. multicoloured .. 10 10
1504. – 50 c. multicoloured .. 20 15
1505. – 75 c. yellow, brown and silver (air) .. 25 20
1506. – 1 g. blue, red and gold .. .. 35 30
1507. – 1 g. 25 multicoloured 45 40
1508. – 2 g. gold, brown and green .. .. 70 60

DESIGNS: 10 c. 1881 2 c. stamp. 25 c., 1881 3 c. stamp. 50 c., 1881 7 c. stamp. 75 c., 1 g., Pres. Salomon. 1 g. 25, 2 g. Pres. Duvalier.

**244.** Modern Communications Equipment.

**1984.** World Communications Year.

1509. **244.** 25 c. blue and purple 10 10
1510. 50 c. blue and olive 20 15
1511. – 1 g. orange, brown and green .. .. 35 30
1512. – 1 g. 25 orange, brown and blue .. .. 45 40
1513. – 2 g. blue, orange and black .. .. 70 60
1514. – 2 g. 50 blue, bistre and black .. .. 1·00 80

DESIGNS—VERT. 1 g., 1 g. 25 Pres. Petion's drum. 2 g., 2 g. 50, W.C.Y. emblem as satellite over globe.

**245.** Javelin-thrower, Runner and Polevaulter.

**1984.** Olympic Games, Los Angeles.

1515. **245.** 5 c. black, green and red .. .. .. 10 10
1516. 10 c. black, olive and red .. .. .. 10 10
1517. – 25 c. black, green and red .. .. .. 10 10
1518. – 50 c. black, ochre and red .. .. .. 20 15
1519. – 1 g. black, blue and red .. .. .. 35 30
1520. – 1 g. 25 black, blue and orange .. 45 40
1521. – 2 g. black, violet and red .. .. .. 70 60

DESIGNS—HORIZ. 25 c., 50 c. Hurdler. VERT. 1 g. to 2 g. 50 Long jumper.

**246.** Head of "The Unknown Indian", Toussaint Square, Louverture.

**1984.** 500th Anniv. of Arrival of Europeans in America (1st issue).

1523. **246.** 5 c. mult. (post.) .. 10 10
1524. 10 c. multicoloured .. 10 10
1525. 25 c. multicoloured .. 10 10
1526. 50 c. multicoloured .. 15 10
1527. – 1 g. mult. (air) .. 25 20
1528. – 1 g. 25 multicoloured 35 30
1529. – 2 g. multicoloured .. 55 50

DESIGN: 1 to 2 g. "The Unknown Indian".

See also Nos. 1539/44.

**247.** Simon Bolivar and Alexandre Petion.

**1985.** Birth Bicent. of Simon Bolivar. Mult.

1531. 5 c. Type **247** (postage) 10 10
1532. 25 c. Bolivar and Alexandre Petion (different) .. .. 10 10
1533. 50 c. Bolivar and flags of members of Grand Colombian Confederation 15 10
1534. 1 g. Type **247** (air) .. 25 20
1535. 1 g. 25, As No. 1532 .. 30 25
1536. 2 g. Type **247** .. .. 50 45
1537. 7 g. 50, As No. 1532 .. 1·60 1·25

**248.** Chief Henri. **250.** Planting Saplings.

**1986.** 500th Anniv. of Arrival of Europeans in America (2nd issue).

1539. **248.** 10 c. mult. (post) .. 10 10
1540. 25 c. multicoloured .. 10 10
1541. 50 c. multicoloured .. 15 10
1542. – 1 g. mult. (air) .. 25 15
1543. – 1 g. 25 multicoloured 30 20
1544. – 2 g. multicoloured .. 35 25

DESIGN: 1 to 2 g. Chief Henri hunting.

**1986.** Various stamps surch.

1546. **241.** 25 c. on 5 c. brown, red & blk. (post) .. 10 10
1547. **242.** 25 c. on 5 c. black and blue .. .. 10 10
1548. **243.** 25 c. on 5 c. mult. .. 10 10
1549. – 25 c. on 75 c. mult. (1430) (air) .. 10 10
1550. – 25 c. on 75 c. mult. (1467) .. .. 10 10
1551. – 25 c. on 1 g. 50 mult. (1122) .. .. 10 10

**1986.** International Youth Year (1985). Multicoloured.

1552. 10 c. Type **250** (postage) 10 10
1553. 25 c. I.Y.Y. emblem .. 10 10
1554. 50 c. Boy and girl scouts and flag .. .. 15 10
1555. 1 g. Type **250** (air) .. 25 15
1556. 1 g. 25 As No. 1553 .. 30 20
1557. 2 g. As No. 1554 .. .. 50 40

**251.** Dove above Peace Year Emblem on Globe.

**1987.** International Peace Year (1986) and 40th Anniv. of United Nations Educational, Scientific and Cultural Organization.

1559. **251.** 10 c. mult. (post.) .. 10 10
1560. 25 c. multicoloured .. 10 10
1561. 50 c. multicoloured .. 15 10
1562. 1 g. mult. (air) .. 25 15
1563. 1 g. 25 multicoloured 30 25
1564. 2 g. 50 multicoloured 60 50

**252** Peralte and Flag

**1989.** Charlemagne Peralte Commemoration.

1566 **252** 25 c. mult (postage) 10 10
1567 50 c. multicoloured .. 15 10
1568 1 g. mult (air) .. 25 15
1569 2 g. multicoloured .. 50 40
1570 3 g. multicoloured .. 80 70

**253** Slaves and Tree forming Fist

**1991.** Bicentenary of Uprising of Slaves. Mult.

1572 25 c. Type **253** (postage) 10 10
1573 50 c. Type **253** .. .. 10 10
1574 1 g. Gathering of slaves around fire (air) .. 10 10
1575 2 g. As No. 1574 .. .. 25 20
1576 3 g. As No. 1574 .. .. 35 30

**254** Amerindian watching Europeans landing

**1993.** America. 500th Anniv (1992) of Discovery of America by Columbus. Mult.

1578 25 c. Type **254** (postage) 10 10
1579 50 c. Type **254** .. .. 10 10
1580 1 g. Columbus's fleet at anchor and rowing boats on shore (vert) (air) .. .. 10 10
1581 2 g. As No. 1580 .. .. 20 15
1582 3 g. As No. 1580 .. .. 35 30

**255** Map of Haiti and Emblem

**1995.** 25th General Assembly of Organization of American States. Multicoloured.

| No. | Description | Unused | Used |
|---|---|---|---|
| 1584 | 50 c. Type **255** | 10 | 10 |
| 1585 | 75 c. Type **255** | 10 | 10 |
| 1586 | 1 g. Map of Americas and emblems (vert) | 10 | 10 |
| 1587 | 2 g. As No. 1586 | 15 | 10 |
| 1588 | 3 g. As No. 1586 | 25 | 20 |
| 1589 | 5 g. As No. 1586 | 40 | 35 |

**256** Dove holding Flags in Beak

**1995.** 50th Anniv of U.N.O. Multicoloured.

| No. | Description | Unused | Used |
|---|---|---|---|
| 1591 | 50 c. Type **256** (postage) | 10 | 10 |
| 1592 | 75 c. Type **256** | 10 | 10 |
| 1593 | 1 g. Dove with olive branch flying over flags (air) | 10 | 10 |
| 1594 | 2 g. As No. 1593 | 15 | 10 |
| 1595 | 3 g. As No. 1593 | 25 | 20 |
| 1596 | 5 g. As No. 1593 | 40 | 35 |

OFFICIAL STAMPS

**1960.** Nos. 736/40 optd. **OFFICIEL.**

| No. | Type | Description | Price |
|---|---|---|---|
| O 742. | – | 50 c. brown and grn. | 25 |
| O 743. | – | 50 c. blue and green | 25 |
| O 744. | – | 50 c. black and green | 25 |
| O 745. | 127. | 1 g. green and red | 35 |
| O 746. | – | 1 g. 50 pink and blue | 55 |
| Set of 5 precancelled | | | 1·50 |

The above were only issued precancelled.

O 135. Dessalines' Statue.

**1962.** Air (a) Size 20½×37½ mm.

| No. | Type | Description | Unused | Used |
|---|---|---|---|---|
| O 791. | O 135. | 50 c. sepia and bl. | 20 | 15 |
| O 792. | | 1 g. red and blue | 35 | 30 |
| O 793. | | 1 g. 50 blue and bistre | 55 | 45 |
| | | (b) Size 30½×40 mm. | | |
| O 794. | O 135. | 5 g. green and red | 1·10 | 1·00 |

PARCEL POST STAMPS

**1960.** Optd. **COLIS POSTAUX.**

| No. | Type | Description | Unused | Used |
|---|---|---|---|---|
| P 725. | 102. | 5 c. green & blk. (post.) | 10 | 10 |
| P 726. | | 10 c. red and black | 10 | 10 |
| P 727. | | 25 c. blue and black | 15 | 15 |
| P 728. | 74. | 2 g. 50 grey | 1·10 | 1·10 |
| P 729. | 102. | 50 c. orge. & blk. (air) | 25 | 20 |
| P 730. | 101. | 5 g. violet and blue | 2·10 | 1·75 |

P 130. Arms.

**1961.**

| No. | Type | Description | Unused | Used |
|---|---|---|---|---|
| P 757. | P 130. | 50 c. vio. & bistre (postage) | 35 | 15 |
| P 758. | | 1 g. blue and red | 55 | 30 |
| P 759. | | 2 g. 50 lake & grn. (air) | 90 | 70 |
| P 760. | | 5 g. grn. & orge. | 1·50 | 1·10 |

POSTAGE DUE STAMPS

D 10.

D 23.

**1898.**

| No. | Type | Description | Unused | Used |
|---|---|---|---|---|
| D 63. | D 10. | 2 c. blue | 20 | 25 |
| D 64. | | 5 c. brown | 35 | 40 |
| D 65. | | 10 c. orange | 50 | 50 |
| D 66. | | 50 c. grey | 1·00 | 1·00 |

**1902.** Optd. **MAI Gt Pre 1902** in frame.

| No. | Type | Description | Unused | Used |
|---|---|---|---|---|
| D 85. | D 10. | 2 c. blue | 45 | 50 |
| D 86. | | 5 c. brown | 45 | 50 |
| D 87. | | 10 c. orange | 50 | 50 |
| D 88. | | 50 c. grey | 3·75 | 2·10 |

**1906.**

| No. | Type | Description | Unused | Used |
|---|---|---|---|---|
| D 150. | D 23. | 2 c. red | 45 | 35 |
| D 151. | | 5 c. blue | 1·50 | 1·50 |
| D 152. | | 10 c. purple | 1·50 | 1·50 |
| D 153. | | 50 c. olive | 6·75 | 3·75 |

**1914.** Optd. **GL O. Z. 7 FEV. 1914** in frame.

| No. | Type | Description | Unused | Used |
|---|---|---|---|---|
| D 206. | D 10. | 5 c. brown | 45 | 35 |
| D 207. | | 10 c. orange | 40 | 40 |
| D 208. | | 50 c. grey | 3·25 | 2·25 |

**1914.** optd. **GL. O. Z 7 FEV, 1914** in frame.

| No. | Type | Description | Unused | Used |
|---|---|---|---|---|
| D 209. | D 23. | 2 c. red | 55 | 35 |
| D 210. | | 5 c. blue | 90 | 55 |
| D 211. | | 10 c. purple | 2·60 | 2·25 |
| D 212. | | 50 c. olive | 4·75 | 3·00 |

D 83.

**1951.**

| No. | Type | Description | Unused | Used |
|---|---|---|---|---|
| D 452. | D 83. | 10 c. red | 10 | 10 |
| D 453. | | 20 c. brown | 15 | 15 |
| D 454. | | 40 c. green | 20 | 20 |
| D 455. | | 50 c. yellow | 30 | 30 |

SPECIAL DELIVERY STAMP

S 86. G.P.O.

**1953.**

| No. | Type | Description | Unused | Used |
|---|---|---|---|---|
| E 468. | S 86. | 25 c. red | 30 | 30 |

## APPENDIX

The following stamps have either been issued in excess of postal needs or have not been available to the public in reasonable quantities at face value. Such stamps may later be given full listing if there is evidence of regular postal use.

**1968.**

Medal Winners, Winter Olympic Games, Grenoble. Postage 5, 10, 20, 25, 50 c., 1 g. 50; Air 2 g.

**1969.**

Moon Landing of "Apollo 11". Optd. on 1969 Birds issue. Nos. 1132/5. Air 50 c., 1 g.50, 2 g.

Space Flights of "Apollo 7" and "Apollo 8". Postage 10, 15, 20, 25 c.; Air 70 c., 1 g. 25, 1 g. 50.

**1970.**

Moon Mission of "Apollo 12". Postage 5, 10, 15, 20, 25, 30, 40, 50 c.; Air 25, 30, 40, 50, 75 c., 1 g., 1 g., 1 g. 25, 1 g. 50.

**1971.**

Safe Return of "Apollo 13". Optd. on 1970 "Apollo 12" issue. Postage 5, 10, 15, 20, 25, 30, 40, 50 c.; Air 25, 30, 40, 50, 75 c., 1 g. 1 g. 25. 1 g. 50.

**1972.**

Gold Medal Winners Olympic Games, Munich. Air 50, 75 c., 1 g. 50, 2 g. 50, 5 g.

**1973.**

American and Russian Space Exploration. Postage 5, 10, 20, 25, 50 c., 2 g. 50, 5 g.; Air 50, 75 c., 1 g. 50, 2 g. 50, 5 g.

Moon Mission of "Apollo 17". Optd. on 1973 Space Exploration issue. 50 c., 2 g. 50, 5 g.



## HAMBURG — Pt. 7

A port in north-west Germany, formerly a Free City. In 1867 it joined the North German Confederation.

**16 schillinge = 1 mark.**

1. 3. 4

**1859.** Imperf.

| No. | Type | Description | Unused | Used |
|---|---|---|---|---|
| 1 | 1 | ½ s. black | 90·00 | £700 |
| 2 | | 1 s. brown | 90·00 | 75·00 |
| 3 | | 2 s. red | 90·00 | £100 |
| 4 | | 3 s. blue | 95·00 | £120 |
| 6 | | 4 s. green | £100 | £1100 |
| 7 | | 7 s. orange | 70·00 | 27·00 |
| 10 | | 9 s. yellow | £200 | £1800 |

**1864.** Imperf.

| No. | Type | Description | Unused | Used |
|---|---|---|---|---|
| 11 | 3 | 1¼ s. lilac | £120 | 70·00 |
| 15 | | 1¼ s. grey | 80·00 | 65·00 |
| 17 | | 1¼ s. blue | £325 | £800 |
| 18 | 4 | 2½ s. green | £120 | £120 |

**1864.** Perf.

| No. | Type | Description | Unused | Used |
|---|---|---|---|---|
| 19 | 1 | ½ s. black | 5·00 | 12·00 |
| 20 | | 1 s. brown | 12·00 | 16·00 |
| 21 | 3 | 1¼ s. mauve | 70·00 | 7·50 |
| 25 | 1 | 2 s. red | 13·00 | 22·00 |
| 27 | 4 | 2½ s. green | £120 | 28·00 |
| 30 | 1 | 3 s. blue | 35·00 | 32·00 |
| 33 | | 4 s. green | 7·50 | 18·00 |
| 34 | | 7 s. orange | £140 | £120 |
| 37 | | 7 s. mauve | 9·00 | 20·00 |
| 38 | | 9 s. yellow | 30·00 | £1800 |

5

**1866.** Roul.

| No. | Type | Description | Unused | Used |
|---|---|---|---|---|
| 44 | 5 | 1¼ s. mauve | 32·00 | 35·00 |
| 45 | | 1¼ s. pink | 6·50 | £130 |

**1867.** Perf.

| No. | Type | Description | Unused | Used |
|---|---|---|---|---|
| 46 | 1 | 2½ s. green | 7·50 | 65·00 |

## HANOVER — Pt. 7

In north-east Germany. An independent kingdom until 1866, when it was annexed by Prussia.

1850. 12 pfennige = 1 gutegroschen; 24 gutengroschen = 1 thaler.
1858. 10 (new) pfennige = 1 (new) groschen; 30 (new) groschen = 1 thaler.

2.

4.

**1850.** On coloured paper. Imperf.

| No. | Type | Description | Unused | Used |
|---|---|---|---|---|
| 1 | 2 | 1 ggr. black on blue | £2500 | 42·00 |
| 2 | | 1 ggr. black on green | 20·00 | 5·00 |
| 3 | | 1/30 th. black on orange | 60·00 | 40·00 |
| 4 | | 1/30 th. black on red | 60·00 | 40·00 |
| 5 | | 1/15 th. black on blue | 85·00 | 60·00 |
| 6 | | 1/10 th. black on orange | 95·00 | 50·00 |

**1853.** Imperf.

| No. | Type | Description | Unused | Used |
|---|---|---|---|---|
| 18 | 4 | 3 pf. pink | 50·00 | 85·00 |

**1855.** With coloured network. Imperf.

| No. | Type | Description | Unused | Used |
|---|---|---|---|---|
| 12 | 4 | 3 pf. pink and black | £200 | £300 |
| 14 | 2 | 1 ggr. black and green | 24·00 | 7·50 |
| 15 | | 1/30 th. black and pink | 80·00 | 30·00 |
| 16 | | 1/15 th. black and blue | 55·00 | 70·00 |
| 10 | | 1/10 th. black and orange | £150 | £140 |

5. King George V. 6.

**1859.** Imperf.

| No. | Type | Description | Unused | Used |
|---|---|---|---|---|
| 23 | 5 | 1 gr. pink | 2·50 | 1·40 |
| 25a | | 2 gr. blue | 14·00 | 30·00 |
| 28 | | 3 gr. yellow | £140 | 55·00 |
| 29 | | 3 gr. brown | 20·00 | 50·00 |
| 31 | | 10 gr. green | £250 | £750 |

**1860.** Imperf.

| No. | Type | Description | Unused | Used |
|---|---|---|---|---|
| 33 | 6 | ½ gr. black | 60·00 | £200 |

**1863.** Imperf.

| No. | Type | Description | Unused | Used |
|---|---|---|---|---|
| 34 | 4 | 3 pf. green | £275 | £900 |

**1864.** Roul.

| No. | Type | Description | Unused | Used |
|---|---|---|---|---|
| 35 | 4 | 3 pf. green | 22·00 | 55·00 |
| 36 | 6 | ½ gr. black | £160 | £225 |
| 37 | 5 | 1 gr. pink | 5·00 | 1·75 |
| 38 | | 2 gr. blue | 65·00 | 45·00 |
| 39 | | 3 gr. brown | 65·00 | 65·00 |

## HATAY — Pt. 16

The territory of Alexandretta. Autonomous under French control from 1923 to Sept. 1938. Hatay was returned to Turkey in June 1939.

1938. 100 centiemes = 1 piastre.
1939. 100 santims = 40 paras = 1 kurus.

**1938.** Stamps of Syria of 1930/31 optd **Sandjak d'Alexandrette** (Nos. 1, 4, 7 and 11) or **SANDJAK D'ALEXANDRETTE** (others), Nos. 7 and 11 surch also.

| No. | Description | Unused | Used |
|---|---|---|---|
| 1 | 0p. 10 purple | 30 | 30 |
| 2 | 0p. 20 red | 30 | 30 |
| 3 | 0p. 50 violet | 30 | 30 |
| 4 | 0p. 75 red | 35 | 35 |
| 5 | 1 p. brown | 35 | 35 |
| 6 | 2 p. violet | 40 | 40 |
| 7 | 2 p. 50 on 4 p. orange | 65 | 65 |
| 8 | 3 p. green | 90 | 90 |
| 9 | 4 p. orange | 1·00 | 1·00 |
| 10 | 6 p. black | 1·50 | 1·50 |
| 11 | 12 p. 50 on 15 p. red (No. 267) | 2·25 | 2·25 |
| 12 | 25 p. purple | 5·50 | 5·50 |

**1938.** Air. Stamps of Syria of 1937 (Nos. 322 etc) optd **SANDJAK D'ALEXANDRETTE.**

| No. | Description | Unused | Used |
|---|---|---|---|
| 13 | ½ p. violet | 35 | 35 |
| 14 | 1 p. black | 35 | 35 |
| 15 | 2 p. green | 1·10 | 1·10 |
| 16 | 3 p. blue | 1·60 | 1·60 |
| 17 | 5 p. mauve | 3·25 | 3·25 |
| 18 | 10 p. brown | 4·50 | 4·50 |
| 19 | 15 p. brown | 5·50 | 5·50 |
| 20 | 25 p. blue | 6·50 | 6·50 |

**1938.** Death of Kemal Ataturk. Nos. 4, 5, 7, 9 and 11 optd **10-11-1938** in frame.

| No. | Description | Unused | Used |
|---|---|---|---|
| 27 | 0p. 75 red | 19·00 | 17·00 |
| 28 | 1 p. brown | 14·00 | 12·00 |
| 29 | 2 p. 50 on 4 p. orange | 8·00 | 7·00 |
| 30 | 4 p. orange | 12·00 | 8·50 |
| 31 | 12 p. 50 on 15 p. red | 20·00 | 19·00 |

**1939.** Stamps of Turkey surch **HATAY DEVLETI** and value.

| No. | Type | Description | Unused | Used |
|---|---|---|---|---|
| 32 | 112 | 10 s. on 20 pa. orange | 20 | 20 |
| 33 | | 25 s. on 1 k. green | 20 | 20 |
| 34 | | 50 s. on 2 k. violet | 20 | 20 |
| 35 | | 75 s. on 2½ k. green | 20 | 20 |
| 36 | | 1 k. on 4 k. grey | 20 | 20 |
| 37 | | 1 k. on 5 k. red | 25 | 25 |
| 38 | | 1½ k. on 3 k. brown | 40 | 40 |
| 39 | | 2½ k. on 4 k. grey | 40 | 40 |
| 40 | | 5 k. on 8 k. blue | 1·25 | 1·25 |
| 41 | | 12½ k. on 20 k. green | 2·00 | 2·25 |
| 42 | | 20 k. on 25 k. blue | 2·25 | 2·50 |

9. Map of Hatay.

10. Flag of Hatay.

**1939.**

| No. | Type | Description | Unused | Used |
|---|---|---|---|---|
| 48. | 9. | 10 pa. orange and blue | 15 | 15 |
| 49. | | 30 pa. violet and blue | 20 | 20 |
| 50. | | 1½ k. olive and blue | 25 | 25 |
| 51. | – | 2½ k. green | 25 | 25 |
| 52. | – | 3 k. blue | 35 | 35 |
| 53. | – | 5 k. red | 35 | 35 |
| 54. | 10. | 6 k. red and blue | 40 | 40 |
| 55. | | 7½ k. red and green | 35 | 35 |
| 56. | | 12 k. red and violet | 50 | 50 |
| 57. | | 12½ k. red and blue | 55 | 55 |
| 58. | – | 17½ k. red | 1·25 | 1·25 |
| 59. | – | 25 k. olive | 1·60 | 1·60 |
| 60. | – | 50 k. blue | 3·50 | 3·50 |

DESIGNS—HORIZ. 2½ k., 3 k., 5 k. Lions of Antioch. 17½ k., 25 k., 50 k. Parliament House, Antioch.

**1939.** Commemorating Turkish Annexation. Optd. **T.C. ilhak tarihi 30-6-1939.**

| No. | Type | Description | Unused | Used |
|---|---|---|---|---|
| 65. | 9. | 10 pa. orange and blue | 20 | 20 |
| 66. | | 30 pa. violet and blue | 20 | 20 |
| 67. | | 1½ k. olive and blue | 25 | 25 |
| 68. | – | 2½ k. green (No. 51) | 25 | 25 |
| 69. | – | 3 k. blue (No. 52) | 35 | 35 |
| 70. | – | 5 k. red (No. 53) | 35 | 35 |
| 71. | 10. | 6 k. red and blue | 40 | 40 |
| 72. | | 7½ k. red and green | 40 | 40 |
| 73. | | 12 k. red and violet | 45 | 45 |
| 74. | | 12½ k. red and blue | 60 | 60 |
| 75. | – | 17½ k. red (No. 58) | 1·25 | 1·25 |
| 76. | – | 25 k. olive (No. 59) | 1·90 | 1·90 |
| 77. | – | 50 k. blue (No. 60) | 3·75 | 3·75 |

POSTAGE DUE STAMPS

**1938.** Postage Due stamps of Syria of 1925 optd **SANDJAK D'ALEXANDRETTE.**

| No. | Type | Description | Unused | Used |
|---|---|---|---|---|
| D21 | D 20 | 0p. 50 brown on yell | 75 | 75 |
| D22 | – | 1 p. purple on pink | 1·00 | 1·00 |
| D23 | – | 2 p. black on blue | 1·50 | 1·50 |
| D24 | – | 3 p. black on red | 2·00 | 2·00 |
| D25 | – | 5 p. black on green | 5·00 | 5·00 |
| D26 | – | 8 p. black on blue | 5·00 | 5·00 |

**1939.** Postage Due stamps of Turkey optd **HATAY DEVLETI** or surch also.

| No. | Type | Description | | |
|---|---|---|---|---|
| D43 | D 121 | 1 k. on 2 k. blue .. | 30 | 30 |
| D44 | | 3 k. violet .. | 45 | 45 |
| D45 | | 4 k. on 5 k. green .. | 60 | 60 |
| D46 | | 5 k. on 12 k. red .. | 90 | 1·10 |
| D47 | | 12 k. red .. .. | 7·50 | 6·50 |

D 11 Castle at Antioch

**1939.**

| No. | Type | Description | | |
|---|---|---|---|---|
| D61 | D 11 | 1 k. red .. .. | 30 | 30 |
| D62 | | 3 k. brown .. .. | 45 | 45 |
| D63 | | 4 k. green .. .. | 50 | 50 |
| D64 | | 5 k. grey .. .. | 70 | 70 |

**1939.** Nos. D61/4 optd **T.C. ilhak tarihi 30-6-1939**.

| No. | Type | Description | | |
|---|---|---|---|---|
| D73 | D 11 | 1 k. red .. .. | 75 | 75 |
| D74 | | 3 k. brown .. .. | 85 | 85 |
| D75 | | 4 k. green .. .. | 1·00 | 1·00 |
| D76 | | 5 k. grey .. .. | 1·10 | 1·10 |

## HAWAII Pt. 22

**A group of islands in the central Pacific, an independent kingdom till 1893 when a provisional government was set up. Annexed in 1898 by the United States. Now a State of the U.S.A.**

100 cents = 1 dollar.

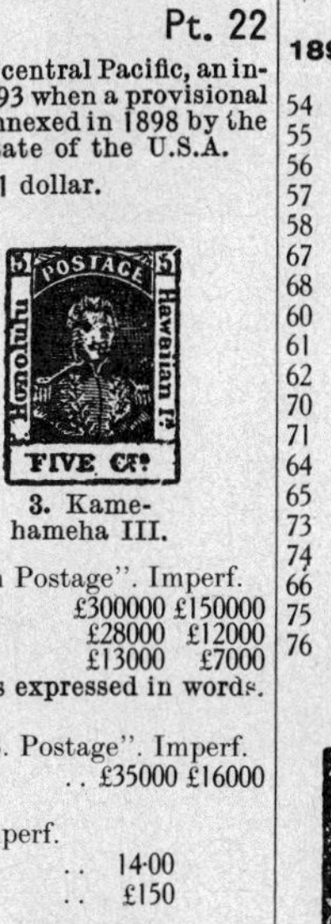

1. 3. Kamehameha III.

**1851.** Inscr "Hawaiian Postage". Imperf.

| No. | Type | Description | | |
|---|---|---|---|---|
| 1. | 1. | 2 c. blue .. .. | £300000 | £150000 |
| 2. | | 5 c. blue .. .. | £28000 | £12000 |
| 3. | | 13 c. blue .. .. | £13000 | £7000 |

On Nos. 1/2 the value is expressed in words.

**1852.** Inscr "H.I. & US. Postage". Imperf.

| No. | Type | Description | | |
|---|---|---|---|---|
| 4 | 1 | 13 c. blue .. .. .. | £35000 | £16000 |

**1853.** Imperf.

| No. | Type | Description | | |
|---|---|---|---|---|
| 18 | 3 | 5 c. blue .. .. .. | 14·00 | |
| 19 | | 13 c. red .. .. .. | £150 | |

5. 6. Kamehameha IV.

**1859.** Inter-island post.

| No. | Type | Description | | |
|---|---|---|---|---|
| 9 | 5 | 1 c. blue .. .. .. | £1700 | £850 |
| 12 | | 1 c. black .. .. | £190 | £325 |
| 14 | | 2 c. black .. .. | £275 | £225 |

**1862.** Imperf.

| No. | Type | Description | | |
|---|---|---|---|---|
| 22. | 6. | 2 c. red .. .. .. | 30·00 | £100 |

7. Princess Victoria Kamamalu. 12.

**1864.** Perf.

| No. | Type | Description | | |
|---|---|---|---|---|
| 27 | 7 | 1 c. mauve .. .. | 6·00 | 5·00 |
| 41 | – | 2 c. red .. .. | 5·00 | 3·50 |
| 42 | – | 5 c. blue .. .. | 10·00 | 1·75 |
| 30 | – | 6 c. green .. .. | 13·00 | 4·50 |
| 31 | – | 18 c. red .. .. | 65·00 | 13·00 |

DESIGNS: 2 c. Kamehameha IV. 5 c., 6 c. Portraits of Kamehameha V. 18 c. H.E. Mataio Kekuanaoa.

**1865.** Inter-island post.

| No. | Type | Description | | |
|---|---|---|---|---|
| 32 | 12 | 1 c. blue .. .. | £110 | |
| 33 | | 2 c. blue .. .. | £110 | |
| 34 | | 5 c. blue on blue | £190 | £225 |
| 35 | – | 5 c. blue on blue | £190 | £190 |

DESIGN: No. 35, As Type 12 but inscr "HAWAIIAN POSTAGE" on left side of frame.

16. Princess Likelike.

22. Princess (later Queen) Liliuokalani.

**1875.**

| No. | Type | Description | | |
|---|---|---|---|---|
| 38 | 16 | 1 c. blue .. .. | 3·00 | 5·00 |
| 39 | | 1 c. green .. .. | 1·50 | 1·00 |
| 36 | – | 2 c. brown .. .. | 4·00 | 1·75 |
| 40b | – | 2 c. red .. .. | 2·75 | 70 |
| 44 | – | 10 c. black .. .. | 17·00 | 13·00 |
| 45 | – | 10 c. red .. .. | 17·00 | 9·00 |
| 46 | – | 10 c. brown .. .. | 15·00 | 4·50 |
| 37 | – | 12 c. black .. .. | 30·00 | 15·00 |
| 47 | – | 12 c. lilac .. .. | 45·00 | 22·00 |
| 48 | – | 15 c. brown .. .. | 32·00 | 18·00 |
| 49 | – | 25 c. purple .. .. | 65·00 | 32·00 |
| 50 | – | 50 c. red .. .. | £110 | 55·00 |
| 51 | – | $1 red .. .. | £160 | 60·00 |

DESIGNS: 2 c. King Kalakaua. 10 c. Same in uniform. 12 c. Prince Leleiohoku. 15 c. Queen Kapiolani. 25 c. Statute of Kamehameha I. 50 c. King Lunalilo. $1, Queen Emma Kaleleonalani.

**1890.**

| No. | Type | Description | | |
|---|---|---|---|---|
| 53. | 22. | 2 c. violet .. .. | 3·50 | 75 |

**1893.** Stamps of 1864, 1875 and 1889, optd. **Provisional GOVT. 1893.**

| No. | Type | Description | | |
|---|---|---|---|---|
| 54 | 7 | 1 c. mauve .. .. | 3·00 | 3·50 |
| 55 | 16 | 1 c. blue .. .. | 3·00 | 5·00 |
| 56 | | 1 c. green .. .. | 1·00 | 2·00 |
| 57 | – | 2 c. brown .. .. | 3·75 | 7·50 |
| 58 | 22 | 2 c. violet .. .. | 1·25 | 80 |
| 67 | – | 2 c. red (No. 41) .. | 35·00 | 40·00 |
| 68 | – | 2 c. red (No. 40b) .. | 1·00 | 1·60 |
| 60 | – | 5 c. blue .. .. | 3·75 | 2·50 |
| 61 | – | 6 c. green .. .. | 7·50 | 14·00 |
| 62 | – | 10 c. black .. .. | 5·50 | 6·00 |
| 70 | – | 10 c. red .. .. | 8·50 | 15·00 |
| 71 | – | 10 c. brown .. .. | 4·25 | 6·50 |
| 64 | – | 12 c. black .. .. | 5·50 | 8·50 |
| 65 | – | 12 c. lilac .. .. | £110 | £120 |
| 73 | – | 15 c. brown .. .. | 13·00 | 22·00 |
| 74 | – | 18 c. red .. .. | 16·00 | 24·00 |
| 66 | – | 25 c. purple .. .. | 15·00 | 18·00 |
| 75 | – | 50 c. red .. .. | 42·00 | 65·00 |
| 76 | – | $1 red .. .. | 75·00 | £100 |

24. Arms.

26. Statue of King Kamehameha I.

**1894.**

| No. | Type | Description | | |
|---|---|---|---|---|
| 77 | 24 | 1 c. orange .. .. | 1·75 | 1·00 |
| 89 | | 1 c. green .. .. | 1·25 | 90 |
| 78 | – | 2 c. brown .. .. | 1·75 | 40 |
| 90a | – | 2 c. pink .. .. | 1·10 | 60 |
| 79 | 26 | 5 c. red .. .. | 3·50 | 1·25 |
| 91 | | 5 c. blue .. .. | 3·25 | 2·00 |
| 80 | – | 10 c. green .. .. | 4·00 | 3·25 |
| 81 | – | 12 c. blue .. .. | 9·00 | 9·00 |
| 82 | – | 25 c. blue .. .. | 9·00 | 9·00 |

DESIGNS—HORIZ. 2 c. Honolulu. 12 c. "Arawa" (steamer). VERT. 10 c. Star and palms. 25 c. President S. B. Dole.

### OFFICIAL STAMPS

O 30. Secretary L. A. Thurston.

**1896.**

| No. | Type | Description | | |
|---|---|---|---|---|
| O 83. | O 30. | 2 c. green .. .. | 30·00 | 13·00 |
| O 84. | | 5 c. brown .. .. | 30·00 | 13·00 |
| O 85. | | 6 c. blue .. .. | 35·00 | 13·00 |
| O 86. | | 10 c. red .. .. | 30·00 | 13·00 |
| O 87. | | 12 c. orange .. .. | 45·00 | 13·00 |
| O 88. | | 25 c. violet .. .. | 50·00 | 13·00 |

## HOI-HAO (HOIHOW) Pt. 17

An Indo-Chinese post office in China, closed in 1922.

1901. 100 centimes = 1 franc.
1918. 100 cents = 1 piastre.

HOI HAO
州 瓊
(1.)

**1902.** Stamps of Indo-China "Tablet" key-type, optd. with T 1. Chinese characters read "HOI-HAO" and are the same on every value.

| No. | Type | Description | | |
|---|---|---|---|---|
| 1. | D. | 1 c. black on blue .. | 1·50 | 1·60 |
| 2. | | 2 c. brown on yellow .. | 1·90 | 1·75 |
| 3. | | 4 c. red on grey .. | 1·75 | 1·75 |
| 4. | | 5 c. green .. .. | 1·75 | 1·75 |
| 5. | | 10 c. black on lilac .. | 3·25 | 3·00 |
| 6. | | 15 c. blue .. .. | £1100 | £550 |
| 7. | | 15 c. grey .. .. | 1·40 | 1·40 |
| 8. | | 20 c. red on green .. | 10·00 | 9·50 |
| 9. | | 25 c. black on red .. | 5·50 | 3·25 |
| 10. | | 30 c. brown .. .. | 18·00 | 17·00 |
| 11. | | 40 c. red on yellow .. | 18·00 | 13·50 |
| 12. | | 50 c. red on rose .. | 24·00 | 19·00 |
| 13. | | 75 c. brown on orange | £150 | £140 |
| 14. | | 1 f. olive .. .. | £525 | £450 |
| 15. | | 5 f. mauve on lilac .. | £425 | £375 |

**1903.** Stamps of Indo-China, "Tablet" key-type, surch. as T 1. Chinese characters indicate the value and differ for each denomination.

| No. | Type | Description | | |
|---|---|---|---|---|
| 16. | D. | 1 c. black on blue .. | 60 | 60 |
| 17. | | 2 c. brown on yellow .. | 60 | 60 |
| 18. | | 4 c. red on grey .. | 1·40 | 1·40 |
| 19. | | 5 c. green .. .. | 1·40 | 1·40 |
| 20. | D. | 10 c. red .. .. | 1·40 | 1·40 |
| 21. | | 15 c. grey .. .. | 1·40 | 1·40 |
| 22. | | 20 c. red on green .. | 3·75 | 3·75 |
| 23. | | 25 c. blue .. .. | 1·50 | 1·50 |
| 24. | | 25 c. black on red .. | 1·60 | 1·60 |
| 25. | | 30 c. brown .. .. | 1·90 | 1·90 |
| 26. | | 40 c. red on yellow .. | 20·00 | 21·00 |
| 27. | | 50 c. red on rose .. | 20·00 | 21·00 |
| 28. | | 50 c. brown on blue .. | 70·00 | 70·00 |
| 29. | | 75 c. brown on orange | 27·00 | 27·00 |
| 30. | | 1 f. olive .. .. | 30·00 | 30·00 |
| 31. | | 5 f. mauve on lilac .. | £140 | £140 |

**1906.** Stamps of Indo-China surch. **HOI-HAO** and with value in Chinese.

| No. | Type | Description | | |
|---|---|---|---|---|
| 32. | 8. | 1 c. olive .. .. | 1·10 | 1·10 |
| 33. | | 2 c. red on yellow .. | 1·10 | 1·10 |
| 34. | | 4 c. mauve on blue .. | 1·60 | 1·60 |
| 35. | | 5 c. green .. .. | 2·00 | 2·00 |
| 36. | | 10 c red .. .. | 2·00 | 2·00 |
| 37. | | 15 c. brown on blue .. | 2·25 | 2·25 |
| 38. | | 20 c. red on green .. | 3·25 | 3·00 |
| 39. | | 25 c. blue .. .. | 4·50 | 4·50 |
| 40. | | 30 c. brown on cream .. | 4·50 | 4·50 |
| 41. | | 35 c. black on yellow .. | 7·25 | 7·50 |
| 42. | | 40 c. black on grey .. | 8·00 | 8·00 |
| 43. | | 50 c. brown .. .. | 8·25 | 8·25 |
| 44. | D. | 75 c. brown on orange | 21·00 | 21·00 |
| 45. | 8. | 1 f. green .. .. | 21·00 | 21·00 |
| 46. | | 2 f. brown on yellow .. | 21·00 | 21·00 |
| 47. | D. | 5 f. mauve on lilac .. | 80·00 | 80·00 |
| 48. | 8. | 10 f. red on green .. | £100 | £100 |

**1908.** Native types of Indo-China surch **HOI HAO** (1 to 50 c.) or **HOI-HAO** (others) and with value in Chinese.

| No. | Type | Description | | |
|---|---|---|---|---|
| 49. | 10. | 1 c. black and olive .. | 45 | 45 |
| 50. | | 2 c. black and brown .. | 50 | 50 |
| 51. | | 4 c. black and blue .. | 80 | 75 |
| 52. | | 5 c. black and green .. | 1·00 | 1·00 |
| 53. | | 10 c. black and red .. | 1·40 | 1·40 |
| 54. | | 15 c. black and violet .. | 2·50 | 2·75 |
| 55. | 11. | 20 c. black and violet .. | 3·00 | 3·25 |
| 56. | | 25 c. black and blue .. | 3·25 | 3·00 |
| 57. | | 30 c. black & brown .. | 3·25 | 3·25 |
| 58. | | 35 c. black and green .. | 3·25 | 3·00 |
| 59. | | 40 c. black and brown .. | 2·75 | 3·00 |
| 60 | | 50 c. black and red .. | 4·00 | 4·00 |
| 61. | 12. | 75 c. black and orange .. | 4·50 | 4·50 |
| 62. | | 1 f. black and red .. | 9·50 | 9·50 |
| 63. | | 2 f. black and green .. | 23·00 | 23·00 |
| 64. | | 5 f. black and blue .. | 40·00 | 40·00 |
| 65. | | 10 f. black and violet .. | 60·00 | 60·00 |

**1919.** Stamps as last surch. in addition with value in figures and words.

| No. | Type | Description | | |
|---|---|---|---|---|
| 66. | 10. | ⅖ c. on 1 c. blk. & olive .. | 55 | 55 |
| 67. | | ⅘ c. on 2 c. blk. & brn. .. | 55 | 55 |
| 68. | | 1⅗ c. on 4 c. blk. & blue .. | 75 | 70 |
| 69. | | 2 c. on 5 c. blk. & grn. .. | 55 | 55 |
| 70. | | 4 c. on 10 c. blk. & red .. | 75 | 75 |
| 71. | | 6 c. on 15 c. blk. & violet | 75 | 70 |
| 72. | 11. | 8 c. on 20 c. blk. & violet | 1·10 | 1·10 |
| 73. | | 10 c. on 25 c. blk. & blue | 2·75 | 2·75 |
| 74. | | 12 c. on 30 c. blk. & brn. | 85 | 85 |
| 75. | | 14 c. on 35 c. blk. & grn. | 85 | 90 |
| 76. | | 16 c. on 40 c. blk. & brn. | 1·00 | 1·00 |
| 77. | | 20 c. on 50 c. blk. & red | 1·10 | 1·10 |
| 78. | 12. | 30 c. on 75 c. blk. & orge. | 1·60 | 1·60 |
| 79. | – | 40 c. on 1 f. blk. & red .. | 4·25 | 4·25 |
| 80. | – | 80 c. on 2 f. blk. & grn. .. | 11·00 | 11·00 |
| 81. | – | 2 p. on 5 f. blk. & blue .. | 35·00 | 35·00 |
| 82. | – | 4 p. on 10 f. blk. & violet | £110 | £120 |

## HONDURAS Pt. 15

A republic of C. America, independent since 1838.

1866. 8 reales = 1 peso.
1878. 100 centavos = 1 peso.
1933. 100 centavos = 1 lempira.

1. Seal of Honduras. 5. Pres. F. Morazan. 6.

**1866.** Imperf.

| No. | Type | Description | | |
|---|---|---|---|---|
| 1. | 1. | 2 r. black on green .. | 60 | |
| 2. | | 2 r. black on red .. | 60 | |

**1878.** Perf.

| No. | Type | Description | | |
|---|---|---|---|---|
| 31. | 5. | 1 c. violet .. .. .. | 40 | 60 |
| 32. | | 2 c. brown .. .. .. | 40 | 70 |
| 33. | | ½ r. black .. .. .. | 40 | 70 |
| 34. | | 1 r. green .. .. .. | 1·25 | 1·25 |
| 35. | | 2 r. blue .. .. .. | 1·75 | 1·75 |
| 36. | | 4 r. red .. .. .. | 2·75 | 2·00 |
| 37. | | 1 p. orange .. .. .. | 3·00 | 3·00 |

**1890.**

| No. | Type | Description | | |
|---|---|---|---|---|
| 45. | 6. | 1 c. green .. .. .. | 25 | 30 |
| 46. | | 2 c. red .. .. .. | 25 | 30 |
| 47. | | 5 c. blue .. .. .. | 25 | 30 |
| 48. | | 10 c. orange .. .. .. | 25 | 30 |
| 49. | | 20 c. bistre .. .. .. | 25 | 30 |
| 50. | | 25 c. red .. .. .. | 25 | 35 |
| 51. | | 30 c. violet .. .. .. | 25 | 70 |
| 52. | | 40 c. blue .. .. .. | 25 | 60 |
| 53. | | 50 c. brown .. .. .. | 25 | 60 |
| 54. | | 75 c. green .. .. .. | 25 | 1·50 |
| 55. | | 1 p. lake .. .. .. | 25 | 1·75 |

8. President Bogran.

10.

**1891.**

| No. | Type | Description | | |
|---|---|---|---|---|
| 56. | 8. | 1 c. blue .. .. .. | 15 | 20 |
| 57. | | 2 c. brown .. .. .. | 15 | 20 |
| 58. | | 5 c. green .. .. .. | 15 | 20 |
| 59. | | 10 c. red .. .. .. | 15 | 20 |
| 60. | | 20 c. lake .. .. .. | 15 | 25 |
| 61. | | 25 c. red .. .. .. | 20 | 30 |
| 62. | | 30 c. grey .. .. .. | 20 | 60 |
| 63. | | 40 c. green .. .. .. | 15 | 60 |
| 64. | | 50 c. sepia .. .. .. | 15 | 60 |
| 65. | | 75 c. violet .. .. .. | 15 | 90 |
| 66. | | 1 p. brown .. .. .. | 15 | 1·25 |
| 67. | – | 2 p. black and brown .. | 60 | 3·50 |
| 68. | – | 5 p. black and violet .. | 60 | 4·00 |
| 69. | – | 10 p. black and green .. | 60 | 4·00 |

DESIGN (LARGER): 2, 5, 10 p. Pres. Bogran facing left.

**1892.** 400th Anniv. of Discovery of America.

| No. | Type | Description | | |
|---|---|---|---|---|
| 70. | 10. | 1 c. grey .. .. .. | 20 | 25 |
| 71. | | 2 c. blue .. .. .. | 20 | 25 |
| 72. | | 5 c. green .. .. .. | 20 | 25 |
| 73. | | 10 c. green .. .. .. | 20 | 30 |
| 74. | | 20 c. red .. .. .. | 20 | 30 |
| 75. | | 25 c. brown .. .. .. | 20 | 50 |
| 76. | | 30 c. blue .. .. .. | 20 | 50 |
| 77. | | 40 c. orange .. .. .. | 20 | 80 |
| 78. | | 50 c. brown .. .. .. | 20 | 65 |
| 79. | | 75 c. lake .. .. .. | 20 | 1·00 |
| 80. | | 1 p. violet .. .. .. | 20 | 1·25 |

11. Gen. Cabanas.

12.

**1893.**

| No. | Type | Description | | |
|---|---|---|---|---|
| 81. | 11. | 1 c. green .. .. .. | 20 | 30 |
| 82. | | 2 c. red .. .. .. | 20 | 30 |
| 83. | | 5 c. blue .. .. .. | 20 | 30 |
| 84. | | 10 c. brown .. .. .. | 20 | 30 |
| 85. | | 20 c. brown .. .. .. | 20 | 40 |
| 86. | | 25 c. blue .. .. .. | 20 | 50 |
| 87. | | 30 c. orange .. .. .. | 20 | 70 |
| 88. | | 40 c. black .. .. .. | 20 | 90 |
| 89. | | 50 c. sepia .. .. .. | 20 | 1·00 |
| 90. | | 75 c. violet .. .. .. | 20 | 1·40 |
| 91. | | 1 p. brown .. .. .. | 20 | 1·60 |

**1895.**

| No. | Type | Description | | |
|---|---|---|---|---|
| 92. | 12. | 1 c. red .. .. .. | 20 | 20 |
| 93. | | 2 c. blue .. .. .. | 20 | 20 |
| 94. | | 5 c. grey .. .. .. | 20 | 30 |
| 95. | | 10 c. lake .. .. .. | 20 | 30 |
| 96. | | 20 c. lilac .. .. .. | 20 | 60 |
| 97. | | 30 c. lilac .. .. .. | 20 | 90 |
| 98. | | 50 c. brown .. .. .. | 20 | 1·25 |
| 99. | | 1 p. green .. .. .. | 20 | 1·60 |

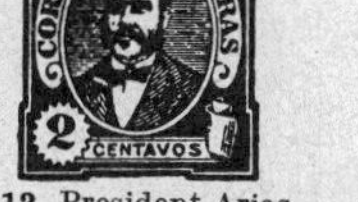

13. President Arias.

14.

**1896.**

| No. | Type | Description | | |
|---|---|---|---|---|
| 100. | 13. | 1 c. blue .. .. .. | 30 | 30 |
| 101. | | 2 c. brown .. .. .. | 30 | 30 |
| 102. | | 5 c. purple .. .. .. | 90 | 30 |
| 103. | | 10 c. red .. .. .. | 30 | 30 |
| 104. | | 20 c. green .. .. .. | 75 | 40 |
| 105. | | 30 c. blue .. .. .. | 50 | 60 |
| 106. | | 50 c. lake .. .. .. | 70 | 1·00 |
| 107. | | 1 p. sepia .. .. .. | 1·25 | 1·75 |

**1898.**

108. 14. 1 c. brown 15 10
109. 2 c. red 20 15
110. 5 c. blue 20 15
111. 6 c. purple 30 20
112. 10 c. blue 30 25
113. 20 c. bistre 70 70
114. 50 c. orange 1·50 2·50
115. 1 p. green 1·75 3·00

**16.** General Santos Guardiola.

**17.** President Medina.

**1903.**

118. 16. 1 c. green 25 20
119. 2 c. red 25 25
120. 5 c. blue 25 25
121. 6 c. lilac 30 25
122. 10 c. brown 30 30
123. 20 c. blue 35 35
124. 50 c. red 70 70
125. 1 p. orange 70 70

**1907.** Perf. or imperf.

127. 17. 1 c. green 25 25
136. 1 c. black 10·00 7·50
128a. 2 c. red 30 25
129. 5 c. blue 35 30
130. 6 c. violet 35 30
131. 10 c. sepia 35 35
132. 20 c. blue 60 55
133. 50 c. red 70 70
134. 1 p. orange 90 65

**1910.** Surch. in figures.

137. 17. 1 on 20 c. blue 4·00 3·50
138. 5 on 20 c. blue 4·00 3·50
139. 10 on 20 c. blue 4·00 3·50

**20.**  **23.**

**1911.**

140. 20. 1 c. violet 15 15
141. 2 c. green 15 15
142. 5 c. red 15 15
143. 6 c. blue 30 30
144. 10 c. blue 35 35
145. 20 c. yellow 45 45
146. 50 c. brown 1·10 1·10
147. 1 p. olive 1·60 1·25

**1911.** Optd. **XC Aniversario de la Independencia.**

157. 20. 2 c. green 8·00 7·50

**1912.** Election of President Manuel Bonilla.

158. 23. 1 c. red 9·25 9·25

**1913.** 90th Anniv. of Independence. Surch. **2 CENTAVOS.**

159. 20. 2 c. on 1 c. violet 65 50

**1913.** Surch. in figures and cts.

161. 20. 2 c. on 1 c. violet 4·50 4·00
162. 2 c. on 10 c. blue 1·10 90
163. 2 c. on 20 c. yellow 3·00 3·00
164. 5 c. on 1 c. violet 1·10 50
165. 5 c. on 10 c. blue 1·40 90
166. 6 c. on 1 c. violet 1·40 90

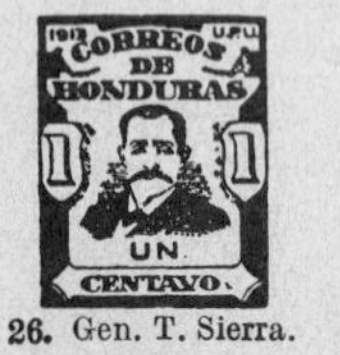

**26.** Gen. T. Sierra.

**27.** Gen. M. Bonilla.

**1913.**

167. 26. 1 c. brown 20 15
168. 2 c. red 25 20
169. 27. 5 c. blue 30 20
170. 5 c. blue 30 20
171. 6 c. violet 40 30
172. 6 c. mauve 45 35
173. 26. 10 c. blue 50 50
174. 10 c. brown 1·10 50
175. 20 c. brown 70 55
176. 27. 50 c. red 1·40 1·25
177. 1 p. green 1·60 1·25

**1914.** Surch.

178. 26. 1 c. on 2 c. red 50 50
179. 5 c. on 2 c. red 90 90
180. 27. 5 c. on 6 c. violet 1·60 1·60
181. 26. 5 c. on 10 c. brown 1·75 1·25
182. 10 c. on 2 c. red 1·60 1·60
184. 27. 10 c. on 6 c. violet 1·60 1·60
185. 10 c. on 50 c. red 4·00 3·00

**32.** Ulua Bridge.

**34.** Pres. Francisco Bertrand.

**1915.** Dated " 1915 ".

186. 32. 1 c. brown 20 10
187. 2 c. red 30 10
188. – 5 c. blue 25 10
189. – 6 c. violet 25 20
190. 32. 10 c. blue 60 30
191. 20 c. brown 1·75 1·75
192. – 50 c. red 70 70
193. – 1 p. green 1·40 1·25

DESIGN: 5 c., 6 c., 50 c., 1 p. Bonilla Theatre.

**1916.**

194. 34. 1 c. orange 1·75 1·90

**1918.** No. O 206 optd. **CORRIENTE** and bar.

195. 5 c. blue 1·75 1·40

**36.** Statue of Francisco Morazan.

**36a.**

**1919.** Dated "1919" at top.

196. 36. 1 c. brown 10 10
197. 2 c. red 20 10
198. 5 c. red 20 10
199. 6 c. mauve 25 10
200. 10 c. blue 25 20
201 15 c. blue 55 25
202. 15 c. violet 45 25
203. 20 c. brown 50 25
204. 50 c. brown 1·10 70
205 1 p. green 2·75 1·50

**1920.** Assumption of Power by Gen. R. L. Gutierrez.

206. 36a. 2 c. red 1·90 1·75
207. 2 c. gold 5·75 5·25
208. 2 c. silver 5·75 5·25
209. 2 c red 5·25 4·75

Nos. 207/9 are larger (51 × 40 mm.).

**1921.** As T **36**, but dated "1920" at top.

210. 36. 6 c. purple 3·00 1·75

**1922.** Surch. **VALE SEIS CTS.**

211. 36. 6 c. on 2 c. red 30 25

**1923.** Surch. **HABILITADO VALE** and value in words and figures.

212. 36. $0.10 on 1 c. brown 1·10 75
213. $0.50 on 2 c. red 1·10 1·10
214. 1 p. on 5 c. red 2·00 2·00

**39.** Dionisio de Herrera.

**40.** M. Paz Baraona.

**1923.**

215. 39. 1 c. olive 20 10
216. 2 c. red 20 10
217. 6 c. purple 30 10
218. 10 c. blue 30 15
219. 20 c. brown 60 25
220. 50 c. red 1·25 55
221. 1 p. green 2·25 70

**1925.** Inauguration of President Baraona. Imperf or perf.

222. 40. 1 c. blue 1·75 1·75
224. 1 c. red 4·50 4·50
225. 1 c. brown 7·25 7·25

**1925.** Air. Nos. 186/93 optd. **AERO CORREO** or surch. also.

227. 5 c. blue 65·00 65·00
229. 10 c. blue £225 £225
231. 20 c. brown £160 £160
235. 25 c. on 1 c. brown £110 £110
236. 25 c. on 5 c. blue £200 £200
236c. 25 c. on 10 c. blue £43000
237. 25 c. on 20 c. brown £225 £225
233. 50 c. red £300 £300
234. 1 p. green £900 £900

**1926.** Optd. **Acuerdo Mayo 3 de 1926 HABILITADO.**

238. 36. 6 c. mauve 95 70

**1926.** Optd. **HABILITADO 1926.**

242. 32. 2 c. red 50 75
243. 36. 2 c. red 20 20

**1926.** Optd. **1926.**

239. – 6 c. violet (No. 189) 1·75 1·75
240. 36. 6 c. violet 2·10 2·10

**1926.** Surch. **Vale 6 Cts. 1926** and bar.

243d. 36. 6 c. on 10 c. blue 35 20

**1927.** Surch. **vale 6 cts. 1927** and bar.

244. 36. 6 c. on 15 c. violet 70 70
245. 32. 6 c. on 20 c. brown 1·50 1·50
246. 36. 6 c. on 20 c. brown 65 55

**47.** Copan Ruins.

**50.** President Colindres and Vice-President Chavez.

**1927.** Various designs as T **47.**

247. – 1 c. blue (Road) 20 15
248. 47. 2 c. red 20 10
249. – 5 c. purple (Pine Tree) 20 10
250. – 5 c. blue (Pine Tree) 2·75 1·60
251. – 6 c. black (Palace) 60 55
252. – 6 c. blue (Palace) 25 15
253. – 10 c. blue (P. Leiva) 45 20
254. – 15 c. blue (Pres. Soto) 60 25
255. – 20 c. blue (Lempira) 75 35
256 – 30 c. brown (Map) 1·25 70
257. – 50 c. green (Pres. Lindo) 1·60 90
258. – 1 p. red (Columbus) 3·25 1·40

**1929.** Installation of President Colindres.

259. 50. 1 c. lake 2·40 2·40
260. – 2 c. green 2·40 2·40

DESIGN—VERT. 2 c. Pres. Colindres.

**1929.** Air. (a) Surch. **Servicio aereo Vale,** value and **1929.**

262. 39. 5 c. on 20 c. brown 1·40 1·40
263. 10 c. on 50 c. red 1·90 1·60
264. 15 c. on 1 p. green 3·25 3·25
261. 25 c. on 50 c. red 3·75 3·75

(b) Surch. **Servicio Aereo Internacional Vale,** value and **1929.**

265. 39. 5 c. on 10 c. blue 50 50
266. 20 c. on 50 c. red 95 95

**1929.** Herrera Monument type, dated 1924-1928. Surch. **Vale 1 cts. XI 1929.**

267. – 1 c. on 6 c. mauve 70 70

**1929.** Nos. 247/58 optd. **1929 a 1930.**

268. – 1 c. blue 15 10
269. 47. 2 c. red 20 20
270. – 5 c. purple 30 20
271. – 5 c blue 70 55
272. – 6 c. black 1·75 1·40
273. – 6 c. blue 30 15
274. – 10 c. blue 30 15
275. – 15 c. blue 30 15
276. – 20 c. blue 30 20
277. – 30 c. brown 55 45
278. – 50 c. green 70 55
279. – 1 p. red 1·90 1·90

**1930.** Air. No. O 264 optd. **HABILITADO Servicio Aereo Inter nacional 1930.**

281. – 50 c. green and yellow 1·40 1·40

**1930.** Air. Surch. **Servicio Aereo Internacional Vale,** value and **1930.**

282. 39. 5 c. on 10 c. blue 55 55
284. 5 c. on 20 c. brown £100 £100
285. 10 c. on 20 c. brown 70 70
287. – 25 c. on 50 c. red (No. 192) 95 95

**1930.** Air. Surch. **Vale** and value in addition in large letters and figures.

290. 39. 10 c. on 5 c. on 20 c. brown (No. 284) 90 90
291. 10 c. on 10 c. on 20 c. brown (No. 285) 75·00 75·00
292. – 50 c. on 25 c. on 1 p. green (No. 193) 3·50 3·50

**1930.** Air. Surch. **Servicio aereo Vale,** value and **Marzo—1930.**

293. 39. 5 c. on 10 c. blue 50 50
294. 15 c. on 20 c. brown 55 55
295. – 20 c. on 50 c. red (No. 192) 95 95

**1930.** Surch. **Vale,** value and **1930.**

297. 39. 1 c. on 10 c. blue 35 30
298. 2 c. on 10 c. blue 35 30

**1930.** Nos. O 259/60 optd. **Habilitado para el servicio publi-co 1930.**

299. – 1 c. blue 50 50
300. O 50. 2 c. red 90 90

**1930.** Air. Surch. **Servicio aereo Vale 5 centavos oro Mayo.**

301. 39. 5 c. on 20 c. brown 1·10 1·10

**1930.** Air. Nos. O 264/5 ptd. **HABILITADO Servicio Aereo MAYO, 1930.**

302. 20 c. blue 1·10 1·10
303. 50 c. green and yellow 1·10 90
304. 1 p. red 1·25 1·25

**1930.** Optd. **Habilitado julio—1930.**

305. 32. 1 c. brown 75 75
306. 36. 1 c. brown 8·50 8·50
309. 39. 1 c. olive 20 15
310. 2 c. red 25 25
307. 36. 20 c. brown 8·50 8·50
308. $0.50 on 2 c. red (No. 213) 60·00 60·00

**66.** Title Page, First Issue Government Gazette.

**67.** National Palace, Tegucigalpa.

**1930.** Newspaper Cent.

311. 66. 2 c. blue 45 45
312. 2 c. orange 45 45
313. 2 c. red 45 45

**1930.** Air.

314. 67. 5 c. yellow 55 30
315. 10 c. red 75 55
316. 15 c. green 1·10 70
317. 20 c. violet 1·40 70
318. 1 p. brown 3·50 2·75

**68.** Pres. Baraona.

**69.** Amapala.

**1931.**

319. 68. 1 c. sepia 15 10
320. – 2 c. red 15 10
321. – 5 c. violet 55 10
322. – 6 c. green 25 10
323. 69. 10 c. brown 35 15
324. – 15 c. blue 35 15
325. – 20 c. black 55 20
326. – 50 c. olive 1·40 60
327. – 1 p. slate 2·40 1·10

DESIGNS—As Type **68**: 2 c. Bonilla 15 c. Copan Ruins. 20 c. Columbia. As Type **69**: 5 c. Lake Yojoa. 6 c. Tegucigalpa Palace. 50 c. Discovery of America. 1 p. Loarq Bridge at Loarq.

**1931.** Nos. 319/27 and 314/18 opt. **T.S.de.C.**

328. 68. 1 c. sepia (postage) 20 15
329. – 2 c. red 25 15
330. – 5 c. violet 50 25
331. – 6 c. green 25 15
332. 69. 10 c. brown 35 30
333. – 15 c. blue 35 25
334. – 20 c. black 45 25
335. – 50 c. olive 2·75 2·50
336. – 1 p. slate 3·50 3·25
337. 67. 5 c. yellow (air) 1·10 1·10
338. 10 c. red 2·50 2·50
339. 15 c. green 3·50 3·50
339a. 20 c. violet 4·25 4·25
339b. 1 p. brown 9·25 9·25

**1931** Air. Surch **Servicio aereo interior Vale 15 cts Octubre 1931.**

340 39 15 c. on 20 c. 3·50 3·50
344a 32 15 c. on 20 c. (No. O 209) 4·50 4·50
342 36 15 c. on 20 c. (No. O 218) 4·25 4·25
344c 39 15 c. on 20 c. (No.O 226) 1·00 1·00
343 – 15 c. on 50 c. (No. O 210) 4·25 4·25
346 36 15 c. on 50 c. (No. O 219) 3·25 3·25
341 – 15 c. on 1 p. (No. O 265) 4·25 4·25

Nos. 342/3 come with or without the original OFICIAL overprint obliterated.

**1932.** Air. Surch. **S.—Aereo VI. 15 cts. XI 1931.**

347. 39. 15 c. on 20 c. brown 3·00 3·00
348. 36. 15 c. on 50 c. (No. O 219) 3·00 3·00
349. – 15 c. on 50 c. (No. O 264) 3·00 3·00
350. – 15 c. on 1 p. (No. O 265) 2·40 2·40

**1932.** Air. Nos. O 328/36 optd. **Servicio Aereo Exterior. Habilitado X. 1931.**

350c. O 70. 1 c. blue 35 35
350d. 2 c. purple 90 90
350e. 5 c. olive 1·10 1·10
350f. 6 c. red 1·10 1·10
350g. 10 c. green 1·25 1·25
350h. 15 c. brown 1·75 1·75
350i. 20 c. brown 1·75 1·75
350j. 50 c. violet 1·40 1·40
350k. 1 p. orange 1·75 1·75

**1932.** Nos. O 223/25 surch. **Aereo interiro VALE 15 Cts. 1932.**

351. 39. 15 c. on 2 c. red 45 45
352. 15 c. on 6 c. purple 45 45
353. 15 c. on 10 c. blue 45 45

**78.** Pres. Carias and Vice-Pres. Williams.

**1933.** Inaug. of Pres. Carias.
355. **78.** 2 c. red .. .. 30 25
356. 6 c. green .. .. 35 25
357. 10 c. blue .. .. 45 30
358. 15 c. orange .. .. 55 35

**79.** Flag of the Race.

**1933.** 441st Anniv. of Departure of Columbus from Palos.
359. **79.** 2 c. blue .. .. 35 30
360. 6 c. yellow .. .. 45 35
361. 10 c. yellow .. .. 55 45
362. 15 c. violet .. .. 70 60
363. 50 c. red .. .. 3·00 2·40
364. 1 l. green .. .. 4·75 4·75

**80.** Pres. T. Carias.

**1935.** Inscr. as in T **80**.
365. – 1 c. green .. .. 20 15
366. **80.** 2 c. red .. .. 20 20
367. – 5 c. blue .. .. 25 25
368. – 6 c. brown .. .. 35 35
DESIGNS: 1 c. Masonic Temple, Tegucigalpa. 5 c. National Flag. 6 c. Pres. T. E. Palma.

**82.** Tegucigalpa.

**1935.** Air. Inscr. as in T **82**.
369. – 8 c. blue .. .. 10 10
370. **82.** 10 c. grey .. .. 20 10
371. – 15 c. olive .. .. 30 15
372. – 20 c. green .. .. 80 40
373. – 40 c. brown .. .. 55 20
374. – 50 c. yellow .. .. 18·00 4·50
375. – 1 l. green .. .. 1·75 1·40
DESIGNS: 8 c. G.P.O. and Congress Building. 15 c. Map of Honduras. 20 c. Presidential Palace and Mayol Railway Bridge 40 c. Different view of Tegucigalpa. 50 c. Great Horned Owl. 1 l. National Arms.

**84.** President Carias and Carias Bridge.

**1937.** Re-election of President Carias.
376. **84.** 6 c. red and olive .. 1·60 55
377. 21 c. green and violet .. 1·60 70
378. 46 c. orange and brown 2·75 85
379. 55 c. blue and black .. 3·75 1·75

**85.** Book of the Constitution and Flags of U.S. and Honduras.

**1937.** Air. 150th Anniv. of U.S. Constitution.
380. **85.** 46 c. multicoloured .. 1·40 1·25

**86.** Comayagua Cathedral.

DESIGNS: 8 c. Founding of Comayagua. 15 c. Portraits of Caceres and Carias. 50 c. Lintel of Royal Palace.

**1937.** Air. 400th Anniv. of Comayagua.
381. **86.** 2 c. red .. .. .. 20 10
382. – 8 c. blue .. .. 25 15
383. – 15 c. black .. .. 45 35
384. – 50 c. brown .. .. 1·75 1·10

**90.** Arms of Honduras. **91.** Copan Ruins.

**1939.** Dated "1939 1942".
385. **90.** 1 c. yellow (postage) .. 10 10
386. – 2 c. red .. .. .. 10 10
387. – 3 c. red .. .. 15 10
388. – 5 c. orange .. .. 20 15
389. – 8 c. blue .. .. 25 20
DESIGNS: 2 c. Central District Palace. 3 c. Map of Honduras. 5 c. Choluteca Bridge. 8 c. National flag.

390. **91.** 10 c. brown (air) .. 15 10
391. – 15 c. blue .. .. 20 10
392. – 21 c. slate .. .. 35 10
393. – 30 c. green .. .. 45 10
394. – 40 c. violet .. .. 70 15
395. – 46 c. brown .. .. 70 45
396. – 55 c. green .. .. 90 60
397. – 66 c. black .. .. 1·40 80
398. – 1 l. olive .. .. 2·10 55
399. – 2 l. red .. .. 3·00 1·75
DESIGNS: 15 c. Pres. Carias. 21 c. Mayan Temple. 30 c. J. C. del Valle. 40 c. The Presidency. 46 c. Statue of Lempira. 55 c. Suyapa Church. 66 c. J. T. Reyes. 1 l. Choluteca Hospital. 2 l. R. Rosa.

**1940.** Air. Dedication of Columbus Memorial Lighthouse. Type O 4 optd. **Correo Aereo/Habilitado para Servicio Publico/Pro-Faro Colon—1940.**
400. O **92.** 2 c. blue and green .. 20 15
401. 5 c. blue and orange .. 25 25
402. 8 c. blue and brown .. 25 25
403. 15 c. blue and red .. 35 35
404. 46 c. blue and olive .. 70 70
405. 50 c. blue and violet .. 70 70
406. 1 l. blue and brown .. 3·00 2·00
407. 2 l. blue and red .. 5·75 4·50

**97.** Francisco Morazan. **98.** Red Cross.

**1941.** Obligatory Tax. Death Centenary of Gen. Morazan.
408. **97.** 1 c. brown .. .. 15 10

**1941.** Obligatory Tax. Red Cross.
409. **98.** 1 c. blue and red .. 15 10

**1941.** Air. Official stamps optd. **Habilitada para el Servicio Publico 1941.**
410. O **92.** 5 c. blue and orange .. 2·50 25
411. 8 c. blue and brown .. 4·00 25

**1941.** Air. Official stamps surch. **Rehabilitada para/el Servicio Publico/1941/Vale tres (or ocho) cts.**
412. O **92.** 3 c. on 2 c. blue & green 30 20
413. 8 c. on 2 c. blue & green 35 30
414. 8 c. on 15 c. blue & red 35 25
415. 8 c. on 46 c. blue & olive 55 45
416. 8 c. on 50 c. blue & violet 70 55
417. 8 c. on 1 l. blue & brown 1·10 70
418. 8 c. on 2 l. blue and red 1·40 1·10

**1942.** Air. Surch. **Correo Aereo** and value.
419. 8 c. on 15 c. blue (No. 391) 60 20
420. 16 c. on 46 c. brn. (No. 395) 60 20

**102.** Morazan's Birthplace. **103.** Tomb.

**1942.** Air. Death Cent. of Gen. Morazan.
421. – 2 c. orange .. .. 10 10
422. – 5 c. blue .. .. 10 10
423. **102.** 8 c. purple .. .. 15 10
424. **103.** 14 c. black .. .. 30 30
425. – 16 c. olive .. .. 20 20
426. – 21 c. blue .. .. 90 70
427. – 1 l. blue .. .. 2·75 1·75
428. – 2 l. brown .. .. 7·25 5·75
DESIGNS—HORIZ. 2 c. Commemoration plate. 5 c. Battle of La Trinidad. 16 c. Morazan's monument (as in Type **36**). 21 c. Church where Morazan was baptised. 1 l. Arms of C. American Federation. VERT. 2 l. Morazan.

**105.** Coat of Arms. **106.** Western Hemisphere.

**1943.** Air.
429. **105.** 1 c. green .. .. 10 10
430. – 2 c. blue .. .. 10 10
431. – 5 c. green .. .. 20 10
432. – 6 c. green .. .. 20 10
433. – 8 c. purple .. .. 25 10
434. – 10 c. brown .. .. 25 10
435. – 15 c. red .. .. 25 10
436. – 16 c. red .. .. 30 10
437. – 21 c. blue .. .. 40 10
438. – 30 c. brown .. .. 45 10
439. – 40 c. red .. .. 45 10
440. – 55 c. black .. .. 70 55
441. – 1 l. green .. .. 1·25 1·10
442. **106.** 2 l. lake .. .. 3·50 3·00
443. – 5 l. orange .. .. 8·75 8·75
DESIGNS—HORIZ. 2 c. National flag. 5 c. Cattle. 8 c. Rosario. 15 c. Tobacco plant. 21 c. Orchid. 30 c. Oranges. 40 c. Wheat. 5 l. Map of Honduras. VERT. 6 c. Banana Tree 10 c. Pine tree. 16 c. Sugar cane. 55 c. Coconut palms. 1 l. Maize.

**114.** Agricultural College. **117.** Flag, Mother and Child.

**1944.** Air. Inauguration of Pan-American Agricultural College.
444. **114.** 21 c. green .. .. 30 20

**1944.** Optd. **HABILITADO 1944-45.**
445. **90.** 1 c. yellow .. .. 30 30
446. – 2 c. red (No. 386) .. 45 45

**1945.** Air. Surch. **Correo Aereo HABILITADO Acd. No. 798-1945** and value.
447. – 1 c. on 50 c. (No 384) 10 10
448. **86.** 2 c. on 2 c. red .. .. 15 10
449. – 8 c. on 15 c. (No. 383) 20 20
450. **91.** 10 c. on 10 c. brown .. 35 30
451. – 15 c. on 15 c. (No. 391) 20 20
452. – 30 c. on 21 c. (No. 392) 3·00 3·00
453. – 40 c. on 40 c. (No. 394) 1·75 1·40
454. – 1 l. on 46 c. (No. 395) .. 1·75 1·40
455. – 2 l. on 66 c. (No. 397) .. 3·00 3·00

**1945.** Obligatory Tax. Red Cross.
456. **117.** 1 c. brown and red .. 15 10
456a. – 1 c. red and brown .. 15 10
DESIGN: No. 456a, Red Cross.

**118.** Arms of Honduras. **119.** Broken Column and F. D. Roosevelt.

**1946.** Air. Coats of Arms.
457. **118.** 1 c. red .. .. .. 10 10
458. – 2 c. orange .. .. 10 10
459. – 5 c. violet .. .. 20 10
461. – 15 c. purple .. .. 35 20
462. – 21 c. blue .. .. 35 30
463. – 1 l. green .. .. 1·40 90
464. – 2 l. grey .. .. 2·10 1·60
ARMS: 2 c. Von Gracias and Trujillo. 5 c. Comayagua and S. J. de Olancho. 15 c. Honduras Province and S. J. de Puerto Caballos. 21 c. Comayagua and Tencoa. 1 l. Jerez de la Frontera de Choluteca and San Pedro de Zula. 2 l. San Miguel de Heredia de Tegucigalpa.

**1946.** Air. Allied Victory over Japan and Death of Pres. Roosevelt.

(a) Inscribed "F.D.R."
460. **119.** 8 c. brown .. .. 70 55

(b) "FRANKLIN D. ROOSEVELT".
465. **119.** 8 c. brown .. .. 45 30

**120.** Honduras and Copan Antiquities.

**1947.** Air. 1st Int. Conference of Caribbean. Archaeologists. Various frames.
466. **120.** 16 c. green .. .. 35 15
467. 22 c. yellow .. .. 25 15
468. 40 c. orange .. .. 55 35
469. 1 l. blue .. .. 90 90
470. 2 l. mauve .. .. 3·00 3·00
471. 5 l. brown .. .. 7·25 6·50

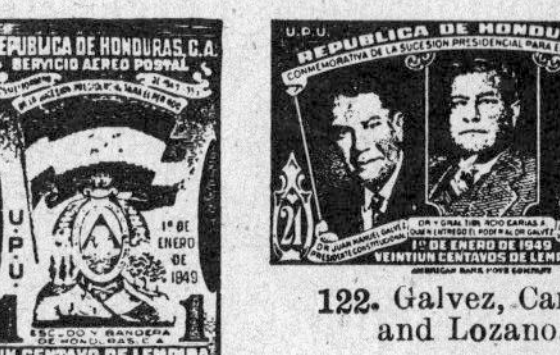

**121.** Flag and Arms of Honduras. **122.** Galvez, Carias and Lozano.

**123.** National Stadium. **124.** President Galvez.

**1949.** Air. Inauguration of President Juan Manuel Galvez. Inscr. "CONMEMORATIVA DE LA SUCESION PRESIDENCIAL", etc.
472. **121.** 1 c. blue .. .. 10 10
473. **124.** 2 c. red .. .. 10 10
474. – 5 c. blue .. .. 10 10
475. – 9 c. brown .. .. 10 10
476. – 15 c. brown .. .. 20 10
477. **122.** 21 c. black .. .. 35 10
478. **123.** 30 c. olive .. .. 45 15
479. – 40 c. grey .. .. 70 20
480. – 1 l. brown .. .. 1·10 35
481. – 2 l. violet .. .. 2·00 1·75
482. – 5 l. red .. .. 5·75 5·25
DESIGNS—HORIZ. 40 c. Toncontin Customs House. 5 l. Galvez and Lozano. VERT. 5 c., 15 c. Lozano (different frames). 9 c. Galvez. 1 l. Palace of Tegucigalpa. 2 l. Carias.

**1951.** Air. 75th Anniv. of U.P.U. Optd. **U.P.U. 75 Aniversario 1874-1949.**
483. **120.** 16 c. green .. .. 55 55
484. – 22 c. yellow .. .. 70 70
485. – 40 c. orange .. .. 70 70
486. – 1 l. blue .. .. 2·40 2·40
487. – 2 l. mauve .. .. 3·50 3·50
488. – 5 l. brown .. .. 26·00 26·00

**1951.** Air. Founding of Central Bank. Nos. 472/81 optd. **Conmemorativa Fundacion Banco Central Administracion Galvez-Lozano Julio 1°. de 1950.**
489. 1 c. blue .. .. 10 10
490. 2 c. red .. .. 10 10
491. 5 c. blue .. .. 10 10
492. 9 c. brown .. .. 15 10
493. 15 c. brown .. .. 15 10
494. 21 c. black .. .. 25 25
495. 30 c. olive .. .. 45 35
496. 40 c. grey .. .. 70 65
497. 1 l. brown .. .. 1·75 1·25
498. 2 l. violet .. .. 4·50 3·25

**127.** Discovery of America. **128.** Isabella the Catholic.

**1952.** Air. 500th Anniv. of Birth of Isabella the Catholic.
499. **127.** 1 c. slate and orange .. 10 10
500. – 2 c. brown and blue .. 10 10
501. – 8 c. sepia and green .. 20 10
502. **128.** 16 c. black and blue .. 30 20
503. – 30 c. green and violet .. 55 55
504. – 1 l. black and red .. 1·40 1·10
505. **127.** 2 l. violet and brown .. 2·75 2·75
506. **128.** 5 l. olive and purple .. 7·00 7·00
DESIGNS—HORIZ. 2 c. 1 l. King Ferdinand and Queen Isabella receive Columbus. 8 c. Surrender of Granada. 30 c. Queen Isabella pledging her jewels.

**1953.** Air. Surch **HABILITADO 1953** and value.
507. **122.** 5 c. on 21 c. black .. 10 10
508. 8 c. on 21 c. black .. 20 10
509. 16 c. on 21 c. black .. 35 20

**1953.** Air. Nos. O 507/509 and O 512/14 surch. **HABILITADO 1953** and value or optd. only.

510. **127.** 10 c. on 1 c. olive & pur. .. 10 10
511. 12 c. on 1 c. olive & pur. 10 10
512. – 15 c. on 2 c. vio. & brn. 15 15
513. – 20 c. on 2 c. vio. & brn. 25 25
514. – 24 c. on 2 c. vio. & brn. 25 25
515. – 25 c. on 2 c. vio. & brn. 25 25
516. – 30 c. on 8 c. black & red 25 25
517. – 35 c. on 8 c. black & red 30 30
518. – 50 c. on 8 c. black & red 45 45
519. – 60 c. on 8 c. black & red 55 55
520. – 1 l. sepia and green .. 1·40 1·25
521. **127.** 2 l. brown and blue .. 3·50 2·75
522. **128.** 5 l. slate and orange .. 9·00 9·00

**130.** U.N. Emblem.

**1953.** Air. United Nations. Inscr. as in T **130.**

523. – 1 c. blue and black .. 10 10
524. **130.** 2 c. blue and black .. 15 10
525. – 3 c. violet and black .. 20 15
526. – 5 c. green and black .. 15 15
527. – 15 c. brown and black .. 35 30
528. – 30 c. brown and black .. 90 75
529. – 1 l. red and black .. 6·00 5·25
530. – 2 l. orange and black .. 7·25 6·00
531. – 5 l. green and black .. 18·00 16·00

DESIGNS: 1 c. U.N. and Honduras flags. 3 c. U.N. Building, New York. 5 c. Arms of U.S.A. 15 c. Pres. J. M. Galvez. 30 c. Indian girl (U.N.I.C.E.F.). 1 l. Refugee mother and child (U.N.R.R.A.). 2 l. Torch and open book (U.N.E.S.C.O.). 5 l. Cornucopia (F.A.O.).

**1955.** Air. 50th Anniv. of Rotary International. Nos. O 532/38 optd. with rotary emblem, **1905 1955,** clasped hands and laurel sprigs or surch. also.

532. 1 c. blue and black .. 15 15
533. 2 c. green and black .. 15 15
534. 3 c. orange and black .. 20 20
535. 5 c. red and black .. 25 25
536. 8 c. on 1 c. blue and black 15 15
537. 10 c. on 2 c. green and black 20 20
538. 12 c. on 3 c. orange & black 25 25
539. 15 c. sepia and black .. 35 35
540. 30 c. purple and black .. 1·10 1·10
541. 1 l. olive and black .. 18·00 18·00

**1956.** Air. 10th Anniv. of U.N.O. Nos. O 523/5 and 527/31 optd. **O N U X ANIVERSARIO 1945-1955.**

542. 1 c. blue and black .. 20 20
543. 2 c. green and black .. 20 20
544. 3 c. orange and black .. 25 25
545. 5 c. red and black .. 30 30
546. 15 c. brown and black .. 35 35
547. 30 c. brown and black .. 55 55
548. 1 l. red and black .. 3·50 3·00
549. 2 l. orange and black .. 5·25 4·00
550. 5 l. green and black .. 13·00 11·00

**133.** J. Lozano Diaz. **134.** Southern Highway.

**1956.** Air.

551. – 1 c. blue and black .. 10 10
552. **133.** 2 c. blue and black .. 10 10
553. **134.** 3 c. sepia and black .. 10 10
554. – 4 c. purple and black 10 10
555. – 5 c. red and black .. 10 10
556. – 8 c. multicoloured .. 10 10
557. – 10 c. green and black .. 15 10
558. – 12 c. green and black .. 15 10
559. – 15 c. black and red .. 20 15
560. – 20 c. blue and black .. 20 15
561. **133.** 24 c. purple and black .. 25 20
562. – 25 c. green and black .. 30 25
563. – 30 c. red and black .. 30 25
564. – 40 c. brown and black .. 35 30
565. – 50 c. turquoise and black 45 40
566. – 60 c. orange and black .. 55 45
567. – 1 l. purple and black .. 1·40 1·10
568. – 2 l. red and black .. 2·75 1·75
569. – 5 l. lake and black .. 5·25 3·50

DESIGNS—HORIZ. 1 c. Suyapa Basilica. 8 c. Landscape and cornucopia. 10 c. National Stadium. 12 c. United States School. 15 c. Projected Central Bank of Honduras. 20 c. Legislative Building. 25 c. Projected Development Bank. 30 c. Toncontin Airport. 40 c. J. R. Molina Bridge. 60 c. Treasury Building. 1 l. Blood Bank. VERT. 4 c. Dona de Estrada Palma. 5 c. Dona de Morazan. 50 c. Peace Memorial. 2 l. Electrical Communications Building. 5 l. Presidential Palace.

**135.** Revolutionary Flag. **136.** Flags of Honduras and the U.S.A. and Book.

**1957.** Air. Revolution of October 21, 1956. Frames in black.

570. **135.** 1 c. blue and yellow .. 10 10
571. – 2 c. purple green & orge. 10 10
572. **135.** 5 c. blue and pink .. 15 10
573. – 8 c. violet, olive & orge. 20 10
574. – 10 c. brown and violet 20 15
575. **135.** 12 c. blue and turquoise 25 20
576. – 15 c. brown and green .. 30 25
577. – 30 c. grey and pink .. 45 25
578. – 1 l. brown and blue .. 1·40 1·25
579. – 2 l. grey and green .. 2·75 1·75

DESIGNS: 2 c., 8 c. Obelisk and mountains. 10 c., 15 c., 1 l. Indian with bow and arrow. 30 c., 2 l. Arms of 1821.

**NOTE.** In July 1958 after stocks of current issues had been looted, eighteen different facsimile signatures validated the remaining stamps for use.

**1958.** Air. Bi-national Centre Commem. (Institute of American Culture). Flags in national colours.

580. **136.** 1 c. blue .. .. 10 10
581. 2 c. red .. .. 10 10
582. 5 c. green .. .. 10 10
583. 10 c. brown .. .. 20 20
584. 20 c. orange .. .. 35 20
585. 30 c. red .. .. 35 30
586. 50 c. grey .. .. 45 35
587. 1 l. yellow .. .. 1·10 95
588. 2 l. olive .. .. 3·00 1·90
589. 5 l. blue .. .. 4·50 4·50

**137.** Abraham Lincoln. **138.** Henri Dunant.

**1959.** Air. 150th Birth Anniv. of Abraham Lincoln. Flags in blue and red

590. **137.** 1 c. green .. .. 15 15
591. – 2 c. blue .. .. 15 15
592. – 3 c. violet .. .. 20 20
593. – 5 c. red .. .. 20 20
594. – 10 c. slate .. .. 25 20
595. – 12 c. sepia .. .. 25 20
596. **137.** 15 c. orange .. .. 35 20
597. – 25 c. purple .. .. 55 30
598. – 50 c. blue .. .. 70 55
599. – 1 l. brown .. .. 1·40 1·25
600. – 2 l. olive .. .. 1·90 1·40
601. – 5 l. yellow .. .. 4·00 3·25

DESIGNS—HORIZ. 2 c., 25 c. Lincoln's birthplace. 3 c., 50 c. Gettysburg Address. 5 c. 1 l. Lincoln at conference to free slaves. 10 c., 2 l. Assassination of Lincoln. 12 c., 5 l. Lincoln Memorial, Washington.

**1959.** Obligatory Tax. Red Cross.

602. **138.** 1 c. red and blue .. 15 10
647. 1 c. red and green .. 15 10
648. 1 c. red and brown .. 20 10

Nos. 647/8 have no frame around portrait and values are at left.

**139.** Constitution of 21 December 1957. **140.** King Alfonso XIII of Spain and Map.

**1959.** Air. 2nd Anniv. of New Constitution. Inscr. "21 DE DICIEMBRE DE 1957".

603. **139.** 1 c. red, blue and brown 10 10
604. – 2 c. brown .. 10 10
605. – 3 c. blue .. 10 10
606. – 5 c. orange .. 20 10
607. **139.** 10 c. red, blue and green 25 10
608. – 12 c. red .. 35 20
609. – 25 c. violet .. 70 25
610. – 50 c. grey blue .. 1·10 35

DESIGNS—HORIZ. 2 c., 12 c. Inaug. of Pres. R. V. Morales. VERT. 3 c., 25 c. Pres. R. V. Morales. 5 c., 50 c. Flaming torch.

**1961.** Air. Settlement of Boundary Dispute with Nicaragua.

611. **140.** 1 c. blue .. .. 10 10
612. – 2 c. pink .. .. 10 10
613. – 5 c. green .. .. 10 10
614. – 10 c. brown .. .. 15 10
615. – 20 c. red .. .. 30 20
616. – 50 c. brown .. .. 70 55
617. – 1 l. slate .. .. 1·10 90

DESIGNS: 2 c. 1906 award (document). 5 c. Arbitration commission, 1907. 10 c. International Court of Justice, The Hague. 20 c. 1960 award (document). 50 c Pres. Morales Foreign Minister Puerto and map. 1 l. Presidents Davila and Morales.

**1964.** Air. Freedom from Hunger. Flags in National colours. Optd. **F A O Luncha Contra el Hambre.**

621. **136.** 1 c. blue .. .. 20 20
622. 2 c. red .. .. 20 20
623. 5 c. green .. .. 25 25
624. 30 c. red .. .. 1·10 70
625. 2 l. olive .. .. 5·25 4·00

**1964.** Air. Olympic Games, Tokyo. Optd. with Olympic Rings and **1964.**

626. – 1 c. blue & black (No. 523) 15 15
627. **130.** 2 c. blue and black .. 25 25
628. – 3 c. violet & blk. (No. 525) 30 30
629. – 15 c. brn. & blk. (No. 527) 55 55

See also No. O 646.

**144.** Ancient Stadium.

**1964.** Air. "Homage to Sport" and Olympic Games, Tokyo.

630. **144.** 1 c. black and green .. 10 10
631. – 2 c. black and mauve .. 10 10
632. – 5 c. black and blue .. 15 15
633. – 8 c. black & grey green 25 25
634. **144.** 10 c. black & bistre .. 35 30
635. – 12 c. black and yellow 55 35
636. – 1 l. black and buff .. 1·40 90
637. – 2 l. black and olive .. 3·00 1·75
638. **144.** 3 l. black and red .. 4·50 2·75

DESIGNS: 2 c., 12 c. Boundary stones. 5 c., 1 l. Mayan ball player. 8 c., 2 l. Olympic Stadium, Tokyo.

**1964.** Air. Surch.

639. – 4 c. on 5 c. (No. 593) .. 15 10
618. **137.** 6 c. on 15 c. .. .. 20 10
619. – 8 c. on 25 c. (No. 597) 20 10
640. – 10 c. on 15 c. (No. 476) 15 10
620. – 10 c. on 50 c. (No. 598) 30 20
641. – 12 c. on 16 c. (No. 425) 15 10
642. – 12 c. on 21 c. (No. 426) 25 10
643. **120.** 12 c. on 22 c. .. .. 25 10
644. 30 c. on 1 l. .. .. 45 25
645. – 40 c. on 1 l. (No. 480) .. 65 30
646. **120.** 40 c. on 2 l. .. .. 65 30

See also Nos. 716/8 and O 647/9.

**1965.** Air. Presidential Investiture of General Lopez. Optd. **Toma de Posesion General Oswaldo Lopez A. Junio 6, 1965.** Flags in blue and red.

649. **137.** 1 c. green .. .. 10 10
650. – 2 c. green .. .. 10 10
651. – 3 c. violet (No. 592) .. 10 10
652. – 5 c. red (No. 593) .. 10 10
653. **137.** 15 c. orange .. .. 20 15
654. – 25 c. purple (No. 597) .. 30 20
655. – 50 c. red .. .. 50 35
656. – 2 l. olive (No. 600) .. 1·75 1·40
657. – 5 l. yellow (No. 601) .. 5·25 3·50

**147.** Ambulance and Clinic.

**1965.** Air. Order of Malta Campaign Against Leprosy.

658. **147.** 1 c. blue .. .. 25 25
659. – 5 c. green .. .. 35 35
660. – 12 c. black .. .. 55 55
661. – 1 l. brown .. .. 1·75 1·75

DESIGNS: 5 c. Hospital. 12 c. Patients receiving treatment. 1 l. Map of Honduras.

**148.** Father Subirana. **151.** 2 r. Stamp of 1866.

**1965.** Air. Death Cent. of Father Manuel de Jesus Subirana. Centres in black and gold; inscr. in black.

662. – 1 c. violet .. .. 10 10
663. – 2 c. flesh .. .. 10 10
664. **148.** 8 c. pink .. .. 10 10
665. – 10 c. purple .. .. 10 10
666. – 12 c. brown .. .. 20 15
667. – 20 c. green .. .. 35 30
668. – 1 l. sage .. .. 1·75 70
669. – 2 l. blue .. .. 3·00 1·75

DESIGNS: 1 c. Abraham, Jicaque Indian. 2 c. Allegory of Catechism. 10 c. Msgr. Juan de Jesus Zepeda. 12 c. Pope Pius IX. 20 c. Subirana's Tomb, Yoro. 1 l. Hermitage. 2 l. Jicaque Indian woman and child.

**1965.** Air. Churchill Commem. Nos. 499/500 and 470 optd. **IN MEMORIAM Sir Winston Churchill 1874-1965.**

671. **127.** 1 c. black and orange .. 35 35
672. – 2 c. brown and blue .. 70 70
673. – 2 l. mauve .. .. 5·75 5·00

See also No. O 674.

**1966.** Air. Pope Paul's Visit to U.N. Organisation. Nos. 662/68 optd. **CONMEMORATIVA Visita S. S. Pablo VI a la ONU. 4-X-1965.**

675. – 1 c. violet .. .. 15 10
676. – 2 c. flesh .. .. 15 10
677. **148.** 8 c. pink .. .. 25 15
678. – 10 c. purple .. .. 25 15
679. – 12 c. brown .. .. 30 15
680. – 20 c. green .. .. 35 20
681. – 1 l. sage .. .. 2·40 90

**1966.** Air. Stamp Cent. Inscriptions in black (1 c., 2 c.) or in gold (others).

682. **151.** 1 c. black, green & gold 10 10
683. – 2 c. blue black & orge. 10 10
684. – 3 c. purple and red .. 10 10
685. – 4 c. indigo and blue .. 10 10
686. – 5 c. purple and mauve 2·50 75
687. – 6 c. violet and lilac .. 10 10
688. – 7 c. slate & turquoise .. 10 10
689. – 8 c. indigo and blue .. 15 15
690. – 9 c. blue and cobalt .. 15 15
691. – 10 c. black and olive .. 15 15
692. – 12 c. yellow, blk. & grn. 15 15
693. – 15 c. purple and mauve 25 25
694. – 20 c. black and orange 30 30
695. – 30 c. blue and yellow .. 35 35
696. – 40 c. multicoloured .. 55 55
697. – 1 l. green and emerald 1·25 1·10
698. – 2 l. black and grey .. 2·25 1·75

DESIGNS—VERT: 2 c. Honduras 5 c. air stamp of 1925. 3 c. T. Estrada Palma, 1st Director of Posts. 8 c. Sir Rowland Hill. 10 c. Pres. Arellano. 12 c. Postal emblem. 15 c. H. von Stephan. 30 c. Honduras flag. 40 c. Honduras arms. 1 l. U.P.U. Monument, Berne. 2 l. J. M. Medina (statesman). HORIZ: 4 c. Post Office, Tegucigalpa. 5 c. Steam locomotive. 6 c. 19th-century mule transport. 7 c. 19th-century sorting office. 9 c. Mail van. 20 c. Curtiss C-46 Commando mail plane.

See also No. E700.

**1966.** Air. World Cup Football Championships, Final Match between England and Germany. Optd. **CAMPEONATO DE FOOTBALL Copa Mundial 1966 Inglaterra-Alemania Wembley, Julio 30.**

701. – 2 c. violet and brown (No. O 508) 20 20
702. **128.** 16 c. black and blue .. 35 35
703. **127.** 2 l. violet and brown .. 7·25 5·75

**1967.** Air. 20th Anniv. of U.N.O. Nos. 662/4 and 666/9 optd. **CONMEMORATIVA del XX Aniversario ONU 1966.**

704. – 1 c. violet .. .. 20 20
705. – 2 c. flesh .. .. 25 25
706. **148.** 8 c. pink .. .. 35 35
707. – 12 c. brown .. .. 55 45
708. – 20 c. green .. .. 70 60
709. – 1 l. sage .. .. 1·75 1·40
710. – 2 l. blue .. .. 3·00 2·75

**1967.** Birth Bicent. of Simeon Canas y Villacorta (slave liberator). Nos. 551, 553, 559, 552 and 568. Optd. **Simeon Canas y Villacorta Libertador de los esclavos en Centro America 1767-1967.**

711. 1 c. blue and black .. 15 15
712. 3 c. sepia and black .. 25 25
713. 15 c. black and red .. 35 35
714. 25 c. green and black .. 70 55
715. 2 l. red and black .. 2·00 1·75

**1967.** Air. Nos. E 570 and 480/1 surch.

716. **E 135.** 10 c. on 20 c. grey, black and red .. 20 10
717. – 10 c. on 1 l. brown .. 20 10
718. – 10 c. on 2 l. violet .. 20 10

**156.** J. C. del Valle (Honduras).

**1967.** Air. Founding of Central-American Journalists' Federation.
719.**156.** 11 c. black, blue & gold 10 10
720. – 12 c. black, yellow & blue 10 10
721. – 14 c. black, grn. & silver 15 10
722. – 20 c. black, grn. & mve. 20 15
723. – 30 c. black, yell. & lilac 25 25
724. – 40 c. gold, blue & violet 70 70
725. – 50 c. green, red & olive 70 70
DESIGNS: 12 c. Ruben Dario (Nicaragua). 14 c. J. B. Montufar (Guatemala). 20 c. F. Gavidia (El Salvador). 30 c. J. M. Fernandez (Costa Rica). 40 c. Federation emblem. 50 c. Central American map.

**157.** Olympic Rings and Flags of Mexico and Honduras.

**1968.** Air. Olympic Games, Mexico. Mult.
726. 1 c. Type **157** .. .. 15 15
727. 2 c. Type **157** .. .. 25 25
728. 5 c. Italian flag and boxing 30 30
729. 10 c. French flag and skiing 35 35
730. 12 c. West German flag and show-jumping .. .. 55 55
731. 50 c. British flag and athletics .. .. .. 1·75 1·75
732. 1 l. U.S. flag and running .. 5·75 5·75

**158.** J. F. Kennedy and Rocket Launch.

**1968.** Air. International Telecommunications Union. Centenary. Multicoloured.
734. 1 c. Type **158** .. .. 15 15
735. 2 c. Dish aerial and telephone .. .. .. 20 20
736. 3 c. Dish aerial and television .. .. .. 20 20
737. 5 c. Dish aerial, globe and I.T.U. emblem as satellite .. .. .. 35 35
738. 8 c. "Early Bird" satellite 50 50
739. 10 c. Type **158** .. .. 55 55
740. 20 c. Type **158** .. .. 75 75

**1969.** Air. Robert F. Kennedy Commemoration. Nos. 734 and 739/40 optd. **In-Memoriam Robert F. Kennedy 1925-1968.**
741. 1 c. multicoloured .. .. 40 40
742. 10 c. multicoloured .. .. 40 40
743. 20 c. multicoloured .. .. 40 40

**1969.** Air. Gold Medal Winners, Olympic Games. Nos. 735/8 optd. **Medallas de Oro Mexico 1968.**
744. 2 c. multicoloured .. .. 25 25
745. 3 c. multicoloured .. .. 25 25
746. 5 c. multicoloured .. .. 40 40
747. 8 c. multicoloured .. .. 75 75

**161.** Patient and Nurse.

**1968.** Obligatory Tax. Red Cross.
748.**161.** 1 c. red and blue .. 15 10

**162.** Rocket Launch.

**1969.** Air. First Man on the Moon. Mult.
749. 5 c. Type **162** .. .. 10 10
750. 10 c. Moon .. .. .. 10 10
751. 12 c. Lunar landing module leaving space-ship (horiz.) .. .. .. 15 10
752. 20 c. Astronaut on Moon (horiz.) .. .. .. 15 15
753. 24 c. Lunar landing module taking off from Moon .. 20 15
754. 30 c. Capsule re-entering Earth's atmosphere (horiz.) .. .. .. 30 20

**1970.** No. E 700 optd. with **HABILITADO** from use as ordinary postage stamp.
755. 20 c. brn., orge. & gold .. 35 25

**1970.** Air. Various stamps surch. in figures.
756.**151.** 4 c.+1 c. (No. 682) .. 10 10
757. – 4 c.+3 c. (No. 525) .. 10 10
758. – 5 c.+1 c. (No. 662) .. 10 10
759. – 5 c.+7 c. (No. 688) .. 10 10
760. – 8 c.+2 c. (No. 663) .. 20 20
761. – 10 c.+2 c. (No. 500) .. 25 25
762.**133.** 10 c.+2 c. (No. 552) .. 25 25
763. – 10 c.+3 c. (No. 525) .. 25 25
764.**134.** 10 c.+3 c. (No. 553) .. 25 25
765. – 10 c.+3 c. (No. 684) .. 25 25
766. – 10 c.+9 c. (No. 690) .. 10 10
767.**156.** 10 c.+11 c. (No. 719) .. 10 10
768. – 12 c.+14 c. (No. 721) .. 15 15
769.**E135** 12 c.+20 c. (No. E570) 15 15
770. – 12 c.+1 l. (No. 480) .. 15 15
771. – 15 c.+12 c. (No. 783) .. 35 35
772. – 30 c.+12 c. (No. 783) .. 70 70
773. – 40 c.+24 c. (No. 753) .. 90 90
774. – 40 c.+50 c. (No. 731) .. 90 90

**1970.** Air. Safe Return of "Apollo 13". Nos. 749/54 optd. **Admiracion al Rescate del Apolo XIII, James A. Lovell, Fred W. Haise Jr., John L. Swigert Jr.**
775. 5 c. multicoloured .. .. 10 10
776. 10 c. multicoloured .. 15 15
777. 12 c. multicoloured .. 20 20
778. 20 c. multicoloured .. 30 30
779. 24 c. multicoloured .. 35 35
780. 30 c. multicoloured .. 45 45

**165.** J. A. Sanhueza (firefighter).

**166.** Hotel Honduras Maya.

**1970.** Air. Campaign Against Forest Fires. Multicoloured.
781. 5 c. Type **165** .. .. 10 10
782. 8 c. R. Ordonez Rodriguez (firefighter) .. .. 15 10
783. 12 c. Fire Brigade emblems (horiz.) .. .. .. 15 15
784. 20 c. Flag, map and emblems .. .. .. 30 25
785. 1 l. Emblems, and flags of Honduras, U.N. and U.S.A. .. .. .. 70 65

**1970.** Air. Opening of Hotel Honduras Maya, Tegucigalpa.
787.**166.** 12 c. 12 c. black and blue .. .. .. 25 25

**1972.** Air. 50th Anniv. of Honduras Masonic Grand Lodge. Nos. 749 and 751/3. optd. **Anniversario Gran Logia de Honduras 1922-1972.** or surch. also.
791. 5 c. multicoloured .. .. 25 30
792. 12 c. multicoloured .. 55 45
793. 1 l. on 20 c. multicoloured 1·10 70
794. 2 l. on 24 c. multicoloured 1·75 1·40

**168.** Soldiers' Bay, Guanaja.

**1972.** Air. 150th Anniv. of Independence (1970). Multicoloured.
795. 4 c. Type **168** .. .. 10 10
796. 5 c. Bugler sounding "Last Post" (vert.) .. .. 10 10
797. 6 c. Lake Yojoa .. .. 10 10
798. 7 c. "The Banana Carrier" (R. Aguilar) (vert.) .. 10 10
799. 8 c. Soldiers marching and fly-past .. .. .. 15 10
800. 9 c. "Brassavola digbyana" (national flower) (vert.) 15 10
801. 10 c. As 9 c. .. .. 20 10
802. 12 c. Machine-gunner .. 20 10
803. 15 c. Tela beach at sunset 25 10
804. 20 c. Stretcher-bearers .. 25 10
805. 30 c. "San Antonio de Oriente" (A. Velasquez) 35 25
806. 40 c. Ruins of Copan .. 55 30
807. 50 c. "Woman from Huacal" (P. Zelaya Sierra) .. 55 35
808. 1 l. Trujillo Bay .. .. 1·75 90
809. 2 l. As 9 c. .. .. .. 1·75 1·40

**169.** Sister Maria Rosa and Child.

**170.** Map of Honduras.

**1972.** Air. "S.O.S." Children's Villages in Honduras, each brown, green and gold.
812. 10 c. Type **169** .. .. 20 10
813. 15 c. "S.O.S. Villages" emblem (horiz.) .. .. 25 10
814. 30 c. Father J. T. Reyes (educationalist) .. .. 45 15
815. 40 c. First Central American "S.O.S." village (horiz.) 45 20
816. 1 l. "Future Citizen" (boy) 1·40 70

**1973.** Air. 25th Annivs. of Nat. Cartographic Service (10 c.) and Joint Cartographic Work (12 c.).
817.**170.** 10 c. multicoloured .. 35 25
818. – 12 c. multicoloured .. 45 25
DESIGN: 12 c. Similar to Type **170** but with two badges and inscr. "25 Anos de Labor Cartografica Conjunta".

**171.** Illustration from "Habitante de la Osa".

**1973.** Air. 25th Anniv. of U.N.E.S.C.O. and Juan Ramon Molina (poet) Commem. Multicoloured.
819. 8 c. Type **171** .. .. 20 10
820. 20 c. Juan Ramon Molina 70 30
821. 1 l. Illustration from "Tierras Mares y Cielos" 1·40 70
822. 2 l. U.N.E.S.C.O. emblem 2·40 1·60

**1973.** Air. Census and World Population Year. Various stamps optd. **Censos de Poblacion y Vivienda, marzo 1974 1974 Ano Mundial de Poblacion.**
824.**169.** 10 c. brn., grn. & gold 10 10
828.**170.** 10 c. multicoloured .. 10 10
829. – 12 c. mult. (No. 818) .. 30 15
825. – 15 c. brn., grn. & gold (No. 813) .. .. 35 20
826. – 30 c. brn., grn. & gold (No. 814) .. .. 10 10
827. – 40 c. brn., grn. & gold (No. 815) .. .. 10 10



**1974.** Air. Various stamps surch.
830. – 2 c. on 1 c. bl. and blk. (No. 551) .. .. 10 10
831.**137.** 2 c. on 1 c. green .. 10 10
832. – 3 c. on 1 c. bl. & blk. (No. 551) .. .. 10 10
833.**137.** 3 c. on 1 c. green .. 10 10
834. – 16 c. on 1 c. bl. & blk. (551) .. .. .. 15 15
835.**135.** 16 c. on 1 c. bl., yell. & blk. .. .. .. 15 15
836.**137.** 16 c. on 1 c. green .. 15 15
837. – 16 c. on 1 c. mult. (O 602) .. .. .. 15 15
838. – 16 c. on 1 c. violet (662) 15 15
839.**170.** 18 c. on 10 c. mult .. 20 15
840. – 18 c. on 12 c. mult. (818) .. .. .. 20 15
841.**171.** 18 c. on 8 c. mult. .. 20 15
842.**169.** 18 c. on 10 c. mult. .. 20 15
843. – 50 c. on 30 c. mult. (814) .. .. .. 55 45
844.**137.** 1 l. on 2 l. mauve .. 1·40 1·00
845. – 1 l. on 2 l. violet (No. 481) .. .. .. 1·40 1·00
846. – 1 l. on 50 c. blue (610) 1·40 1·00
847. – 1 l. on 30 c. mult. (814) 90 70

**1974.** Air. Honduras' Children's Villages. 25th Anniv. Nos. 786/9 optd. **1949-1974 SOS Kinderdorfer International Honduras-Austria.**
851.**169.** 10 c. multicoloured .. 15 10
852. – 15 c. multicoloured .. 20 15
853. – 30 c. multicoloured .. 25 15
854. – 40 c. multicoloured .. 35 25

**175.** Flags of West Germany and Austria.

**1975.** Air. Cent. (1974) of U.P.U. Mult.
855. 1 c. Type **175** .. .. 10 10
856. 2 c. Belgium and Denmark 10 10
857. 3 c. Spain and France .. 10 10
858. 4 c. Hungary and Russia 10 10
859. 5 c. Great Britain and Italy .. .. .. 10 10
860. 10 c. Norway and Sweden 20 10
861. 12 c. Honduras .. .. 25 15
862. 15 c. United States and Switzerland .. .. 35 20
863. 20 c. Greece and Portugal 35 20
864. 30 c. Rumania and Yugoslavia .. .. .. 55 25
865. 1 l. Egypt and Netherlands 1·75 1·50
866. 2 l. Luxembourg and Turkey .. .. .. 3·00 3·00

**176.** Jalteva Youth Centre.

**1976.** Air. Int. Women's Year (1975). Multicoloured.
868. 8 c. Humuya Youth Centre 10 10
869. 16 c. Type **176.** .. .. 20 10
870. 18 c. Sra Arellano and I.W.Y. emblem .. .. 20 15
871. 30 c. El Carmen Youth Centre, San Pedro Sula 35 20
872. 55 c. Flag of National Social Welfare Organization (vert.) .. .. 55 35
873. 1 l. Sports and recreation grounds, La Isla .. 1·10 65
874. 2 l. Women's Social Centre 1·75 1·75

**177.** "CARE" Package.

**1976.** Air. 20th Anniv. of "CARE" (Co-operative for American Relief Everywhere) in Honduras.

875.177. 1 c. blue and black .. 10 10
876. 5 c. mauve and black .. 10 10
877.177. 16 c. red and black .. 20 10
878. 18 c. green and black .. 25 10
879.177. 30 c. blue and black .. 35 20
880. 50 c. green and black .. 55 30
881.177. 55 c. brown and black .. 55 30
882. 70 c. purple and black 70 45
883.177. 1 l. blue and black .. 1·10 65
884. 2 l. orange and black .. 1·75 1·75

DESIGN—HORIZ. 5 c., 18 c., 50 c., 70 c., 2 l., "CARE" on globe.

Each of the above stamps has a different inscription detailing "CARE's" various fields of activities in Honduras.

**178.** White-tailed Deer in Burnt Forest. **179.** Boston Tea Party and "Liberty" Flag.

**1976.** Air. Forest Protection. Multicoloured.

885. 10 c. Type **178** .. .. 15 10
886. 16 c. COHDEFOR emblem 15 10
887. 18 c. Forest stream (horiz.) 15 15
888. 30 c. Live and burning trees 35 20
889. 50 c. Type **178** .. .. 80 30
890. 70 c. Protection emblem .. 70 45
891. 1 l. Forest of young trees (horiz.) .. .. .. 1·10 65
892. 2 l. As 30 c. .. .. 1·75 1·75

COHDEFOR = Corporation Hondurena de Desarollo Forestal.

**1976.** Air. Bicentenary of American Revolution. Multicoloured.

894 1 c. Type **179** .. .. 10 10
895 2 c. Hoisting the "Liberty and Union" flag .. 10 10
896 3 c. Battle of Bunker Hill and Pine Tree flag .. 10 10
897 4 c. Loading stores aboard "Washington" and "An Appeal to Heaven" flag 10 10
898 5 c. First naval ensign and navy warship .. .. 30 15
899 6 c. Presidential Palace, Tegucigalpa, and Honduras flag .. .. 10 10
900 18 c. Capitol, Washington and U.S. flag .. .. 35 30
901 55 c. Washington at Valley Forge and Grand Union flag .. .. .. 70 40
902 2 l. Battle scene and Bennington flag .. .. 1·75 1·50
903 3 l. Betsy Ross flag .. 3·00 3·00

**180.** Queen Sophia of Spain. **181.** Mayan Stelae.

**1977.** Air. Visit of King and Queen of Spain. Multicoloured

905. 16 c. Type **180** .. .. 15 10
906. 18 c. King Juan Carlos .. 15 10
907. 30 c. Queen Sophia and King Juan Carlos .. 25 20
908. 2 l. Arms of Honduras and Spain (horiz.) .. .. 1·40 1·40

**1978.** Air. "Honduras 78". Stamp Exhibition. Multicoloured.

909. 15 c. Type **181** .. .. 20 10
910. 18 c. Giant head .. .. 25 15
911. 30 c. Kneeling figure .. 35 20
912. 55 c. Sun God .. .. 70 60

**182.** Del Valle's Birthplace.

**1978.** Air. Birth Bicentenary of Jose Cecelio del Valle. Multicoloured.

914. 8 c. Type **182** .. .. 10 10
915. 14 c. La Merced Church, Choluteca .. .. 15 10
916. 15 c. Baptismal font (vert.) 15 10
917. 20 c. Reading Independence Act .. .. 25 15
918. 25 c. Portrait, documents and map of Central America .. .. .. 30 15
919. 40 c. Portrait (vert.) .. 45 35
920. 1 l. Monument, Choluteca (vert.) .. .. .. 1·10 90
921. 3 l. Bust (vert.) .. .. 3·00 3·00

**183.** Rural Heath Centre.

**1978.** Air. 75th Anniv. (1977) of Panamerican Health Organization. Multicoloured.

922. 5 c. Type **183** .. .. 10 10
923. 6 c. Child at water tap .. 10 10
924. 10 c. Los Laureles Dam, Tegucigalpa .. .. 10 10
925. 20 c. Rural aqueduct .. 25 10
926. 40 c. Teaching hospital, Tegucigalpa .. .. 55 30
927. 2 l. Parents and child .. 1·75 1·75
928. 3 l. Vaccination of child .. 3·00 3·00
929. 5 l. Panamerican Health Organization Building, Washington .. .. 4·50 4·50

**184.** Luis Landa and "Botanica".

**1978.** Air. Birth Centenary of Professor Luis Landa (botanist). Multicoloured.

930. 14 c. Type **184** .. .. 20 15
931. 16 c. Map of Honduras .. 20 15
932. 18 c. Medals received by Landa .. .. .. 20 15
933. 30 c. Birthplace, San Ignacio .. .. .. 20 15
934. 2 l. "Brassavola" (national flower) .. .. 2·00 1·75
935. 3 l. Women's normal school .. .. .. 3·00 3·00

**1978.** Air. Argentina's Victory in World Cup Football Championship. Nos. 909/12 optd. with **Argentina Campeon Holanda sub-Campeon, XI Campeonato Mundial de Foot-ball** and emblem.

936.181. 15 c. multicoloured .. 10 10
937. – 18 c. multicoloured .. 15 15
938. – 30 c. multicoloured .. 30 20
939. – 55 c. multicoloured .. 55 30

**186.** Central University.

**1978.** Air. 400th Anniv. of Founding of Tegucigalpa.

941.186. 6 c. brown and black .. 10 10
942. – 6 c. multicoloured .. 10 10
943. – 8 c. brown and black .. 10 10
944. – 8 c. multicoloured .. 10 10
945. – 10 c. brown and black .. 10 10
946. – 10 c. multicoloured .. 10 10
947. – 16 c. brown and black .. 20 10
948. – 16 c. multicoloured .. 20 10
949. – 20 c. brown and black .. 20 15
950. – 20 c. multicoloured .. 20 15
951. – 40 c. brown and black .. 45 25
952. – 40 c. multicoloured .. 45 25
953. – 50 c. brown and black .. 55 35
954. – 50 c. multicoloured .. 55 35
955. – 5 l. brown and black .. 4·50 4·50
956. – 5 l. multicoloured .. 4·50 4·50

DESIGNS—HORIZ. No. 942, University City. No. 943, Manuel Bonilla Theatre. No. 944, Present Manuel Bonilla Theatre. No. 947, National Palace. No. 948, Presidential House. No. 949. General San Felipe Hospital. No. 950, Teaching Hospital. No. 951, Parish Church and Convent of San Francisco. No. 952, Metropolitan Cathedral. No. 953, Old view of Tegucigalpa. No. 954, Modern view of Tegucigalpa. VERT. No. 945, Court House. No. 946, North Boulevard highway intersection. No. 955, Arms of San Miguel de Tegucigalpa. No. 956, President Marco Aurelio Soto.

**187.** Footballers jumping for Ball.

**1978.** Air. 7th Youth Football Championship of Central American Football League. Multicoloured.

958. 15 c. Type **187** .. .. 20 10
959. 30 c. Goalkeeper (horiz.) .. 35 15
960. 55 c. Tackling .. .. 55 30
961. 1 l. Goalkeeper and players (horiz.) .. .. .. 1·10 90
962. 2 l. Players at goalmouth (horiz.) .. .. .. 1·75 1·75

**188.** National Postal Emblem.

**1979.** Air. Centenary of Honduras's U.P.U. Membership (1st issue). Multicoloured.

963. 2 c. Type **188** .. .. 10 10
964. 15 c. U.P.U. emblem .. 15 10
965. 25 c. Roman Rosa (vert.) 20 15
966. 50 c. Marco Aurelio Soto (vert.) .. .. .. 35 30

See also Nos. 975/6.

**189.** Rotary Emblem and "50".

**1979.** Air. 50th Anniv. of Tegucigalpa Rotary Club.

967.189. 3 c. orge., turq. & bistre 10 10
968. 5 c. grn., emer. & bistre 10 10
969. 50 c. ochre, mauve and bistre .. .. 35 30
970. 2 l. blue, violet & bistre 1·40 1·00

**190.** Map of Caratasca Lagoon.

**1979.** Air. 50th Anniv. of Pan-American Institute of History and Geography. Mult.

971. 5 c. Type **190** .. .. 10 10
972. 10 c. Aerial view of Fort San Fernando de Omoa 10 10
973. 24 c. Institute anniversary emblem (vert.) .. .. 20 15
974. 5 l. Map of Santanilla Islands .. .. .. 3·00 3·00

**191.** Model of New General Post Office Building.

**1980.** Air. Centenary (1979) of U.P.U. Membership (2nd issue).

975.191. 24 c. multicoloured .. 20 15
976. – 3 l. brn., yell. and blk. 1·75 1·75

DESIGN: 3 l. 19th century Post Office.

**192.** "Landscape" (Roman E. Cooper).

**1980.** Air. International Year of the Child (1979). Multicoloured.

977. 1 c. "Workers in a Field (J. E. Mejia) (horiz.) .. 10 10
978. 5 c. Type **192** .. .. 10 10
979. 15 c. "Sitting boy" (D. M. Zavala) .. .. .. 20 10
980. 20 c. I.Y.C. emblem .. 35 15
981. 30 c. "Beach scene" (M. A. Hernandez) (horiz.) .. 45 20

**193.** Hill and "Maltese Cross" Cancellations.

**1980.** Air. Death Centenary (1979) of Sir Rowland Hill. Multicoloured.

983. 1 c. Type **193** .. .. 10 10
984. 2 c. Great Britain "Penny Black" .. .. .. 10 10
985. 5 c. 1866 Honduras 2 r. green .. .. .. 15 10
986. 10 c. 1866. Honduras 2 r. rose .. .. .. 20 15
987. 15 c. Honduras postal emblem .. .. .. 35 15
988. 20 c. Flags of Honduras and United Kingdom .. 75 40

Nos. 987/8 are 46 × 34 mm.

**194.** Visitacion Padilla (founder of Honduras section). **195.** "O'Higgins during the Liberation of Chile". (Cosmo San Martin).

**1981.** Air. 50th Anniv. of Inter-American Women's Commission. Multicoloured.

990. 2 c. Type **194** .. .. 10 10
991. 10 c. Maria Trinidad del Cid (founder of Honduras section) .. 15 10
992. 40 c. Intubucana Indian mother and child .. 50 30
993. 1 l. Emblem (horiz.) .. 65 65

**1981.** Air. Bernardo O'Higgins Commemoration. Multicoloured.

994. 16 c. Type **195** .. .. 15 10
995. 20 c. Don Ambrosio O'Higgins (father) (vert.) .. .. 20 15
996. 30 c. "Bernardo O'Higgins" (Jose Gil de Castro) (vert.) 35 20
997. 1 l. "Bernardo O'Higgins laying-down Office" (M. Antonio Caro) .. .. 70 70

**196.** National Sports Emblem.

**1981.** Air. World Cup Football Championship Preliminary Round. Multicoloured.

998 20 c. Type **196** .. .. 15 15
999 50 c. Footballer and map of Honduras .. .. 30 30
1000 70 c. Flags of Honduras, CONCACAF and FIFA 40 40
1001 1 l. National stadium .. 60 60

**197.** Curtiss Condor II Biplane.

**1983.** Air. 50th Anniv of Honduras Air Force. Multicoloured.

1003 3 c. Type **197** .. .. 10 10
1004 15 c. North America Texan .. .. .. 35 15
1005 25 c. Chance Vought F4U-5 Corsair .. 40 25
1006 65 c. Douglas C-47 Skytrain .. .. 85 65
1007 1 l. Cessna Dragonfly .. 90 65
1008 2 l. Dassault Super Mystere SMB-11 .. 1·90 1·25

**198.** U.P.U. Monument, Berne..

**1983.** Air. Election to U.P.U. Executive Council (1979). Multicoloured.

1010. 16 c. Type **198** .. .. 20 15
1011. 18 c. 18th U.P.U. Congress emblem .. .. 25 15
1012. 30 c. Honduras's postal emblem .. .. 20 20
1013. 55 c. View of Rio de Janeiro .. .. 45 45
1014. 2 l. "Stamp" showing pigeon on globe (vert.) 1·25 1·25

**199.** I.Y.D.P. Emblem.

**1983.** Air. International Year of Disabled Persons.

1016. **199.** 25 c. multicoloured .. 40 25

**200.** National Library, Tegucigalpa.

**1983.** Air. Centenary (1980) of National Library and Archives. Multicoloured.

1017 9 c. Type **200** .. .. 10 10
1018 1 l. Books .. .. 60 60

**1983.** Air. Papal Visit. Nos. 951/2 optd. **CONMEMORATIVA DE LA VISITA DE SS. JUAN PABLO II 8 de marzo de 1983.**

1019. 40 c. brown and black .. 35 35
1020. 40 c. multicoloured .. 35 35

**202.** Agricultural Produce. **203.** Hands reaching for Open Book.

**1983.** Air. World Food Day (1981).

1021. **202.** 65 c. multicoloured .. 40 40

**1983.** Air. Literacy Campaign (1980). Mult.

1022. 40 c. Type **203** .. .. 25 20
1023. 1 l. 50 Family with books 90 90

## MINIMUM PRICE

The minimum price quoted is 10p which represents a handling charge rather than a basis for valuing common stamps. For further notes about prices see introductory pages.

**204.** Motorway Bridge over River Comayagua.

**1983.** 20th Anniv. of Inter-American Development Bank. Multicoloured.

1024. 1 l. Type **204** .. .. 60 55
1025. 2 l. Luis Borgran Technical Institute .. 1·25 1·00

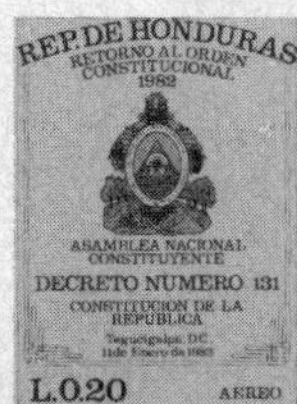

**205.** Arms. **206.** Hand, Dove and Map on Globe.

**1984.** Air. 2nd Anniv. of Return of Constitutional Government. Multicoloured.

1026. 20 c. Type **205** .. .. 40 20
1027. 20 c. President Roberto Suazo Cordova .. 40 20

**1984.** "Internationalization of Peace".

1028. **206.** 78 c. blk., bl. & green 75 45
1029. 85 c. black, orange and green .. .. 80 50
1030. 95 c. black, orange and green .. .. 90 55
1031. 1 l. 50 black, red and green .. .. 1·25 75
1032. 2 l. black, light green and green .. .. 1·50 1·00
1033. 5 l. blk., pur. & grn. 3·25 2·40

**207.** Front Page of "La Gaceta".

**1984.** Air. 150th Anniv. of "La Gaceta".

1034. **207.** 10 c. brn., blk. & grn. 10 10
1035. 20 c. brn., blk. & sepia .. .. 20 15

**1986.** Various stamps surch.

1036. **184.** 60 c. on 14 c. mult. (postage) .. .. 40 25
1037. **177.** 5 c. on 1 c. blue and black (air) .. 10 10
1038. – 10 c. on 8 c. mult. (No. 868) .. .. 10 10
1039. **176.** 20 c. on 16 c. mult. .. 15 10
1040. – 50 c. on 14 c. mult. (No. 915) .. .. 35 15
1041. – 85 c. on 6 c. mult. (No. 942) .. .. 50 30
1042. **186.** 85 c. on 6 c. brown and black .. .. 50 30
1043. – 95 c. on 6 c. brown and black .. .. 70 40
1044. – 95 c. on 6 c. mult. (No. 942) .. .. 70 40
1045. **171.** 1 l. on 1 c. blue and black .. .. 70 40

**1986.** Air. "Exfilhon '86" Stamp Exhibition and World Cup Winners. Nos. 951/2 optd.

1046. 40 c. **"EXFILHON '86"/ ARGENTINA CAMPEON/ MEXICO'86** (951) .. 25 15
1047. 40 c. **"EXFILHON '86"/ ALEMANIA FEDERAL Sub Campeon/ MEXICO'86** (952) .. .. .. 25 15
1048. 40 c. **"EXFILHON '86"/ "FRANCIA TERCER LUGAR"/ MEXICO'86** (952) .. .. .. 25 15
1049. 40 c. **"EXFILHON '86"/ "BELGICA— CUARTO LUGAR"/ MEXICO'86** (951) .. 25 15

**210.** Phulapanzak. **211.** Pres. Jose Azcona and Flag.

**1986.** Air. Tourism. Multicoloured.

1050. 20 c. Type **210** .. .. 15 10
1051. 78 c. Aerial view of Bahia Island beach and jetty (horiz.) .. .. 45 25
1052. 85 c. Yacht off Bahia Islands (horiz.) .. 1·50 60
1053. 95 c. Yojoa lake .. .. 60 35
1054. 1 l. Woman painting pottery .. .. 60 35

**1987.** Air. 1st Anniv. of Democratic Government.

1056. **211.** 20 c. multicoloured .. 15 10
1057. 85 c. multicoloured .. 50 30

**212.** Edward Warner Award Medal. **213.** "Eupatorium cyrilli-nelsonii".

**1987.** 25th Anniv. (1985) of Central American Air Navigation Services Association. Mult.

1058. 2 c. Type **212** .. .. 10 10
1059. 5 c. Flags of member countries (horiz.) .. 10 10
1060. 60 c. Transmission mast, arrows and airplane (horiz.) .. .. 50 20
1061. 75 c. Emblem .. .. 45 25
1062. 1 l. Members' flags and emblem (horiz.) .. 60 35

**1987.** Air. Flowering Plants. Multicoloured.

1064. 10 c. Type **213** .. .. 10 10
1065. 20 c. "Salvia ernesti-vargasii" .. .. 15 10
1066. 95 c. "Robinsonella erasmi-sosae" .. .. 60 35

**214.** Turquoise-browed Motmot. **216.** Emblem.

**215.** Family and House on Emblem.

**1987.** Air. Birds. Multicoloured.

1067 50 c. Type **214** .. .. 1·25 50
1068 60 c. Keel-billed toucan .. 1·50 55
1069 85 c. Red-crowned amazon .. .. 2·25 85

**1987.** 30th Anniv. of Housing Institute.

1070. **215.** 5 c. multicoloured .. 10 10
1071. – 95 c. black, brown and blue .. .. 60 35

Design: 95 c. Emblem.

**1987.** Air. 30th Anniv. of Honduras National Autonomous University.

1072. **216.** 1 l. red, black and yellow .. .. 60 35

**217.** Emblem. **218.** Emblem of President.

**1987.** Air. 50th Anniv. of Honduras Red Cross.

1073. **217.** 20 c. red and blue .. 15 10

**1988.** Air. 17th Lions International Latin-American and Caribbean Forum, Honduras.

1074. **218.** 95 c. blue and yellow 60 35

**219.** 1913 Headquarters Building, La Ceiba.

**1988.** Air. 75th Anniv. of Banco Atlantida.

1075. 10 c. Type **219** .. .. 10 10
1076. 85 c. Present headquarters building, Tegucigalpa .. .. 50 30

**1988.** Nos. 941/4 surch.

1078. 5 c. on 6 c. brn. & blk. .. 10 10
1079. 5 c. on 6 c. multicoloured 10 10
1080. 20 c. on 8 c. brn. & blk. 10 10
1081. 20 c. on 8 c. mult. .. 10 10

**221.** Postal Messenger. **222.** Athletes.

**1988.** Air. "Exfilhon 88" Stamp Exhibition, Honduras.

1082. **221.** 85 c. brown .. .. 50 30
1083. – 2 l. brown and red .. 1·10 60

Design: 2 l. Handstamp on cover.

**1988.** Air. Olympic Games, Seoul.

1085. **222.** 85 c. black, yellow and mauve .. 50 30
1086. – 1 l. yellow, black and orange .. .. 60 35

Design: 1 l. Ball games equipment.

**223** Three-legged Tub **228** Monkey swinging through Trees

**1988.** Air. 500th Anniv (1992) of Discovery of America by Christopher Columbus. Mult.

1088 10 c. Type **223** .. .. 10 10
1089 25 c. Bowl (horiz) .. 15 10
1090 30 c. Dish with legs shaped as animal heads (horiz) .. .. 20 15
1091 50 c. Jug .. .. 35 20

**1989.** Air. Various stamps surch.

1093 – 10 c. on 16 c. brown and black (No. 947) 10 10
1094 – 10 c. on 16 c. mult (No. 948) .. .. 10 10
1095 – 15 c. on 6 c. mult (No. 923) .. .. 10 10
1096 **195** 20 c. on 16 c. mult .. 10 10
1097 **176** 50 c. on 16 c. mult .. 10 10
1098 – 95 c. on 18 c. mult (No. 910) .. .. 20 15
1099 – 1 l. on 16 c. mult (No. 886) .. .. 20 15

**1990.** Air. 4th Central American Games. Nos. 887and 878 surch **IV Juegos Olimpicos Centroamericanos** and value.

1101 75 c. on 18 c. mult .. 15 10
1102 85 c. on 18 c. green & blk 20 15

**1990.** Air. Nos. 915 and 870 surch **L. 0.20**.

1103 20 c. on 14 c. mult .. 10 10
1104 20 c. on 18 c. mult .. 10 10

**1990.** Air. 50th Anniv (1989) of I.H.C.I. Nos. 930 and 915 surch **"50 Aniversario IHCI" 1939–1989** and new value.

1105 **184** 20 c. on 14 c. mult .. 10 10
1106 – 1 l. on 14 c. mult .. 20 15

**1990.** Air. The Black-handed Spider Monkey. Multicoloured.

1107 10 c. Type **228** .. .. 10 10
1108 10 c. Mother and baby .. 10 10
1109 20 c. Monkey swinging through trees (different) 10 10
1110 20 c. Mother and baby (different) .. 10 10

**1990.** Air. World Cup Football Championship, Italy. No. 960 surch **ITALIA '90 L.1.00**.

1111 1 l. on 55 c. multicoloured 20 15

**230** Institute Building

**1990.** Air Centenary of Luis Bogran Technical Institute, Tegucigalpa.

1113 **230** 20 c. red, black & grn 10 10
1114 – 85 c. multicoloured .. 20 15

DESIGN: 85 c. Cogwheel, globe and Institute emblem.

**231** Emblem

**232** "Santa Maria", Shoreline, Fish and Fruit

**1990.** Air. 45th Anniv of F.A.O.

1116 **231** 95 c. multicoloured .. 20 15

**1990.** America. The Natural World. Mult.

1117 20 c. Type **232** .. .. 20 10
1118 1 l. Maize, fish, fruit and palm (horiz) .. .. 20 15

**233** Congress Emblem

**1990.** Air. 30th Anniv and 17th Congress of Inter-American Construction Industry Federation.

1119 **233** 20 c. black and green 10 10
1120 – 1 l. black and blue .. 20 15

DESIGN—HORIZ. 1 l. Jose Cecilio del Valle Palace, Tegucigalpa (Ministry of Foreign Relations).

**234** Virgin and Child with Apostles

**1990.** Air. Christmas. Multicoloured.

1121 20 c. Type **234** .. .. 10 10
1122 95 c. Virgin and Child (vert) .. .. .. 20 15

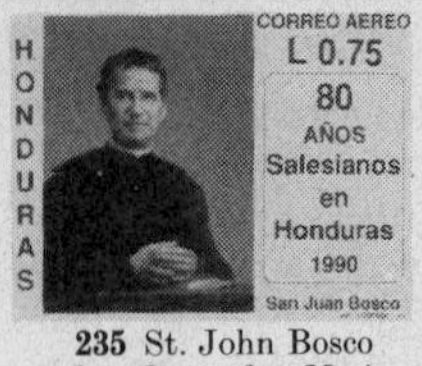

**235** St. John Bosco (founder) (after Mario Caffaro Roke)

**1990.** Air. 80th Anniv of Salesian Brothers in Honduras. Multicoloured.

1124 75 c. Type **235** .. .. 15 10
1125 1 l. Bosco and National Youth Sanctuary, Tegucigalpa .. .. 20 15

**236** Pres. Callejas

**1991.** Air. 1st Anniv of Presidency of Rafael Leonardo Callejas. Multicoloured.

1126 30 c. Type **236** .. .. 10 10
1127 2 l. Pres. Callejas wearing sash .. .. .. 45 25

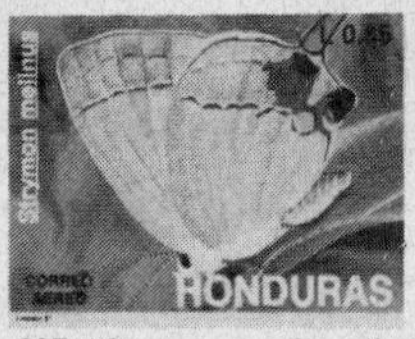

**237** "Strymon melinus"

**1991.** Air. Butterflies. Multicoloured.

1128 85 c. Type **237** .. .. 15 10
1129 90 c. "Diorina sp." .. .. 20 15
1130 1 l. 50 "Hyalophora cecropia" .. .. 30 20

**238** "Rhyncholaelia glauca"

**1991.** Air. Orchids. Multicoloured.

1132 30 c. Type **238** .. .. 10 10
1133 50 c. "Oncidium splendidum" (vert) .. .. 10 10
1134 95 c. "Laelia anceps (vert) 20 10
1135 1 l. 50 "Cattleya skinneri" 30 20

**239** International Latin Lawyers Union Emblem and Flags

**1991.** Air. 6th Caribbean and North and Central American Lawyers' Day.

1136 **239** 50 c. multicoloured .. 10 10

**241** Emblem, Flags and Carving

**1991.** Air. 25th Anniv of Italian–Latin American Institute.

1138 **241** 1 l. multicoloured .. 20 10

**242** Meeting of Old and New Worlds

**1991.** Air. "Espamer '91" Spain–Latin America Stamp Exhibition, Buenos Aires.

1139 **242** 2 l. multicoloured .. 45 30

**243** Valle

**1991.** Air. Birth Centenary of Rafael Heliodoro Valle.

1141 **243** 2 l. black and red .. 45 30

**244** Show Jumping

**1991.** Air. 11th Pan-American Games, Havana. Multicoloured.

1142 30 c. Type **244** .. .. 10 10
1143 85 c. Judo .. .. 20 10
1144 95 c. Swimming .. .. 20 10

**245** St. Manuel de Colohete's Church, Gracias, Lempira

**1991.** Air. Churches. Multicoloured.

1146 30 c. Type **245** .. .. 10 10
1147 95 c. Church of Mercy, Gracias, Lempira .. 20 10
1148 1 l. Comayagua Cathedral 20 10

**246** Stone Carving and Cobs of Corn

**1991.** Air. America. Pre-Columbian Civilisations. Multicoloured.

1149 25 c. Type **246** .. .. 10 10
1150 40 c. Stone carving, dried corn and map .. 10 10
1151 1 l. 50 Stone carving and map of Honduras .. 30 20

**247** Means of Control

**248** Poinsettias in Basket

**1991.** Air. 4th International Congress on Pest Control. Multicoloured.

1152 30 c. Type **247** .. .. 10 10
1153 75 c. Hoeing crop (scientific co-operation) 15 10
1154 1 l. Co-operation of scientists and producers 20 10

**1991.** Christmas. Multicoloured.

1156 1 l. Type **248** .. .. 20 10
1157 2 l. Poinsettia in chicken-shaped pot .. .. 45 30

**249** "Taking Possession of the New Continent" (Enrique Escher)

**1992.** Air. 75th Anniv of Savings Bank of Honduras. Multicoloured.

1158 85 c. Type **249** .. .. 15 10
1159 1 l. "First Celebration of Mass in the Americas" (Maury Flores) .. 20 10

**250** Presidents Callejas and Cossiga of Italy

**1992.** Air. 2nd Year in Office of President Rafael Leonardo Callejas. Multicoloured.

1161 20 c. Type **250** .. .. 10 10
1162 2 l. Callejas with Pope .. 40 25

**251** View From Crow's Nest

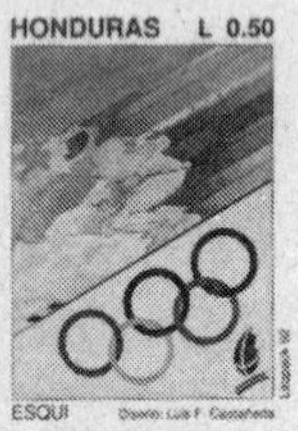

**252** Skiing

**1992.** Air. America 1991. 500th Anniv of Discovery of America. Multicoloured.

1163 90 c. Type **251** .. .. 15 10
1164 1 l. Fleet .. .. 20 10
1165 2 l. Ship approaching island .. .. .. 40 25

**1992.** Winter Olympic Games, Albertville. Multicoloured.

1166 50 c. Type **252** .. .. 10 10
1167 3 l. Jenny Palacios de Stillo (cross-country skier) .. .. .. 60 40

**253** Athletics

**254** "Seller" (Manuel Rodriguez)

**1992.** Olympic Games, Barcelona. Mult.

1168 20 c. Type **253** .. .. 10 10
1169 50 c. Tennis .. .. 10 10
1170 85 c. Football .. .. 15 10

**1992.** Mother's Day. Paintings. Multicoloured.

1171 20 c. Type **254** .. .. 10 10
1172 50 c. "Grandmother and Baby" (Manuel Rodriguez) .. .. 10 10
1173 5 l. "Sellers" (Maury Flores) .. .. 95 60

**255** "Chlosyne janais"

**1992.** Butterflies. Multicoloured.

| | | | | |
|---|---|---|---|---|
| 1174 | | 25 c. Type **255** .. .. | 10 | 10 |
| 1175 | | 85 c. "Agrilus vanillae" .. | 15 | 10 |
| 1176 | | 3 l. "Morpho granadensis" | 60 | 40 |

**256** "Bougainvillea glabra" "Napoleon"

**1992.** Air. Flowers. Multicoloured.

| | | | | |
|---|---|---|---|---|
| 1178 | | 20 c. Type **256** .. .. | 10 | 10 |
| 1179 | | 30 c. "Canna indica" .. | 10 | 10 |
| 1180 | | 75 c. "Epiphyllum sp." .. | 15 | 10 |
| 1181 | | 95 c. "Sobralia macrantha" .. .. | 20 | 10 |

**257** Dam **258** Crops

**1992.** Air. General Francisco Morazan Hydro-electric Project. Multicoloured.

| | | | | |
|---|---|---|---|---|
| 1182 | | 85 c. Type **257** .. .. | 15 | 10 |
| 1183 | | 4 l. Inner view of dam (horiz) .. .. | 75 | 45 |

**1992.** Air. 50th Anniv of Inter-American Institute for Agricultural Co-operation.

| | | | | |
|---|---|---|---|---|
| 1184 | **258** | 95 c. multicoloured (white background) | 20 | 10 |
| 1185 | | 95 c. multicoloured (black background) | 20 | 10 |

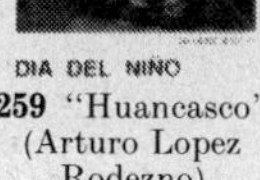

**259** "Huancasco" (Arturo Lopez Rodezno) **260** Morazan on Horseback (after Francisco Cisneros)

**1992.** Air. Children's Day. Multicoloured.

| | | | | |
|---|---|---|---|---|
| 1186 | | 25 c. Type **259** .. .. | 10 | 10 |
| 1187 | | 95 c. "Bougainvillea" (Enrique Escher) .. | 20 | 10 |
| 1188 | | 2 l. "Melissa" (Cesar Ordonez) .. .. | 40 | 25 |

**1992.** Air. Birth Bicentenary of General Francisco Morazan. Multicoloured

| | | | | |
|---|---|---|---|---|
| 1189 | | 5 c. Type **260** .. .. | 10 | 10 |
| 1190 | | 10 c. Statue of Morazan, Ampala .. .. | 10 | 10 |
| 1191 | | 50 c. Morazan's watch and sword (horiz) .. .. | 10 | 10 |
| 1192 | | 95 c. Josefa Lastiri de Morazan (wife) .. | 20 | 10 |

**261** Globe as Pot filled with Food

**1992.** Air. International Nutrition Conference, Rome.

| | | | | |
|---|---|---|---|---|
| 1194 | **261** | 1 l. 05 multicoloured .. | 20 | 10 |

**262** Cinnamon Hummingbird

**1992.** Air. "Exfilhon'92" National Stamp Exhibition, Tegucigalpa. Multiciloured.

| | | | | |
|---|---|---|---|---|
| 1195 | | 1 l. 50 Type **262** .. .. | 30 | 20 |
| 1196 | | 2 l. 45 Scarlet macaw .. | 50 | 30 |

**263** Bee-keeping

**1992.** Air. 50th Anniv of Pan-American School of Agriculture. Multicoloured.

| | | | | |
|---|---|---|---|---|
| 1198 | | 20 c. Type **263** .. .. | 10 | 10 |
| 1199 | | 85 c. Tending goats .. | 15 | 10 |
| 1200 | | 1 l. Ploughing with oxen | 20 | 10 |
| 1201 | | 2 l. Hoeing (vert) .. | 40 | 25 |

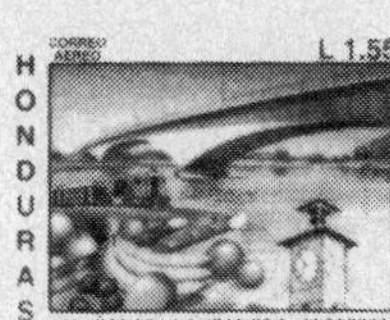

**264** Fruit, Locomotive, Clock and Bridge

**1992.** Air. Centenary of El Progreso (City).

| | | | | |
|---|---|---|---|---|
| 1202 | **264** | 1 l. 55 multicoloured .. | 30 | 20 |

**265** Amerindian Village **266** Columbus's Fleet and Landing Craft

**1992.** Air. America. 500th Anniv of Discovery of America by Columbus. Multicoloured.

| | | | | |
|---|---|---|---|---|
| 1203 | | 35 c. Type **265** .. .. | 10 | 10 |
| 1204 | | 5 l. Columbus's landing party meeting Amer-indians .. .. | 95 | 60 |

**1992.** Air. 500th Anniv of Discovery of America by Columbus. Details of "The First Mass" by Roque Zelaya. Multicoloured.

| | | | | |
|---|---|---|---|---|
| 1205 | | 95 c. Type **266** .. .. | 20 | 10 |
| 1206 | | 1 l. Mass (horiz) .. .. | 20 | 10 |
| 1207 | | 2 l. View of village (horiz) | 40 | 25 |

**267** Road and Bridge

**1992.** Air. 1st Central America–Panama Highway Maintenance Congress, San Pedro Sula. Multicoloured.

| | | | | |
|---|---|---|---|---|
| 1208 | | 20 c. Type **267** .. .. | 10 | 10 |
| 1209 | | 85 c. Bulldozer .. .. | 15 | 10 |

**268** The Greasy Pole

**1992.** Air. Christmas. Multicoloured.

| | | | | |
|---|---|---|---|---|
| 1210 | | 20 c. Type **268** .. .. | 10 | 10 |
| 1211 | | 85 c. Crib, San Antonio de Flores (horiz) .. .. | 15 | 10 |

**269** Globes, Children and Emblem

**1992.** Air. 90th Anniv of Pan-American Health Organization.

| | | | | |
|---|---|---|---|---|
| 1212 | **269** | 3 l. 95 multicoloured .. | 75 | 45 |

**1992.** Air. Nos. 894 and 899/900 surch.

| | | | | |
|---|---|---|---|---|
| 1213 | **179** | 20 c. on 1 c. mult .. | 10 | 10 |
| 1214 | – | 20 c. on 6 c. mult .. | 10 | 10 |
| 1215 | – | 85 c. on 18 c. mult .. | 15 | 10 |

**271** Pres. Callejas at Ceremony **272** Mother and Child

**1993.** Air. 3rd Year of Rafael L. Callejas's Presidential Term and International Court of Justice's Decision on Border with El Salvador. Multicoloured.

| | | | | |
|---|---|---|---|---|
| 1216 | | 90 c. Type **271** .. .. | 15 | 10 |
| 1217 | | 1 l. 05 Map (horiz) .. | 20 | 10 |

**1993.** Air. Mother's Day. Multicoloured.

| | | | | |
|---|---|---|---|---|
| 1218 | | 50 c. Type **272** .. .. | 10 | 10 |
| 1219 | | 95 c. Mother and child (different) .. .. | 20 | 10 |

**273** American Manatee

**1993.** Air. Endangered Mammals. Mult.

| | | | | |
|---|---|---|---|---|
| 1220 | | 85 c. Type **273** .. .. | 15 | 10 |
| 1221 | | 2 l. 45 Puma .. .. | 50 | 30 |
| 1222 | | 10 l. Jaguar (vert) .. | 1·90 | 1·25 |

**274** Scarlet Macaws

**1993.** Air. National Symbols. Multicoloured.

| | | | | |
|---|---|---|---|---|
| 1223 | | 25 c. Type **274** .. .. | 10 | 10 |
| 1224 | | 95 c. White-tailed deer .. | 15 | 10 |

**1993.** Air. Various stamps surch.

| | | | | |
|---|---|---|---|---|
| 1225 | – | 20 c. on 3 c. mult (No. 896) .. .. | 10 | 10 |
| 1226 | **189** | 20 c. on 3 c. orange, blue and bistre .. | 10 | 10 |
| 1227 | **197** | 20 c. on 3 c. mult .. | 10 | 10 |
| 1228 | – | 20 c. on 8 c. mult (No. 868) .. .. | 10 | 10 |
| 1229 | **182** | 20 c. on 8 c. mult .. | 10 | 10 |
| 1230 | **176** | 50 c. on 16 c. mult .. | 10 | 10 |
| 1231 | **177** | 50 c. on 16 c. red and black .. .. | 10 | 10 |
| 1232 | – | 50 c. on 16 c. mult (No. 886) .. .. | 10 | 10 |
| 1233 | **180** | 50 c. on 16 c. mult .. | 10 | 10 |
| 1234 | – | 50 c. on 16 c. mult (No. 931) .. .. | 10 | 10 |
| 1235 | **195** | 50 c. on 16 c. mult .. | 10 | 10 |
| 1236 | – | 50 c. on 18 c. mult (No. 870) .. .. | 10 | 10 |
| 1237 | – | 50 c. on 18 c. mult (No. 910) .. .. | 10 | 10 |
| 1238 | – | 50 c. on 18 c. mauve and black (No. 1011) | 10 | 10 |
| 1239 | – | 85 c. on 18 c. green and black (No. 878) | 10 | 10 |
| 1240 | – | 85 c. on 18 c. mult (No. 906) .. .. | 10 | 10 |
| 1241 | – | 85 c. on 18 c. mult (No. 932) .. .. | 10 | 10 |
| 1242 | – | 85 c. on 18 c. mult (No. 937) .. .. | 10 | 10 |
| 1243 | – | 85 c. on 24 c. mult (No. 973) .. .. | 10 | 10 |
| 1244 | **191** | 85 c. on 24 c. mult .. | 10 | 10 |

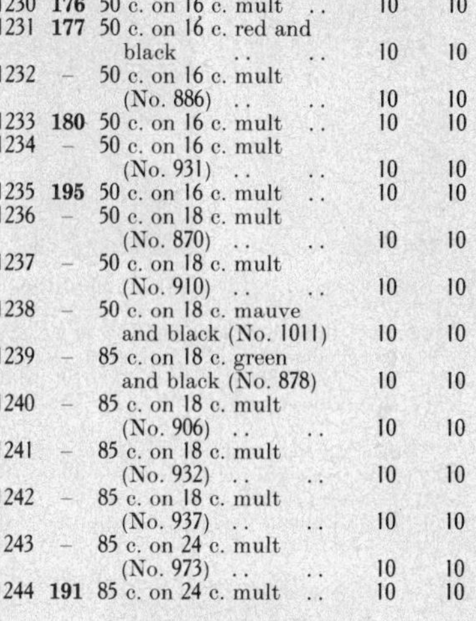

**276** 30 r. "Bull's Eye" Stamp

**1993.** Air. 150th Anniv of 1st Brazilian Stamps. Multicoloured.

| | | | | |
|---|---|---|---|---|
| 1245 | | 20 c. Type **276** .. .. | 10 | 10 |
| 1246 | | 50 c. 60 r. "Bull's eye" stamp .. .. .. | 10 | 10 |
| 1247 | | 95 c. 90 r. "Bull's eye" stamp .. .. .. | 15 | 10 |

**277** Atlantida

**1993.** Air. Departments. Multicoloured.

| | | | | |
|---|---|---|---|---|
| 1248 | | 20 c. Type **277** .. .. | 10 | 10 |
| 1249 | | 20 c. Colon .. .. | 10 | 10 |
| 1250 | | 20 c. Cortes .. .. | 10 | 10 |
| 1251 | | 20 c. Choluteca .. .. | 10 | 10 |
| 1252 | | 20 c. El Paraiso .. .. | 10 | 10 |
| 1253 | | 20 c. Francisco Morazan | 10 | 10 |
| 1254 | | 50 c. Comayagua (vert) .. | 10 | 10 |
| 1255 | | 50 c. Copan (vert) .. | 10 | 10 |
| 1256 | | 50 c. Intibuca (vert) .. | 10 | 10 |
| 1257 | | 50 c. Bahia Islands (vert) | 10 | 10 |
| 1258 | | 50 c. Lempira (vert) .. | 10 | 10 |
| 1259 | | 50 c. Ocotepeque (vert) .. | 10 | 10 |
| 1260 | | 1 l. 50 La Paz .. .. | 20 | 10 |
| 1261 | | 1 l. 50 Olancho .. .. | 20 | 10 |
| 1262 | | 1 l. 50 Santa Barbara .. | 20 | 10 |
| 1263 | | 1 l. 50 Valle .. .. | 20 | 10 |
| 1264 | | 1 l. 50 Yoro .. .. | 20 | 10 |
| 1265 | | 1 l. 50 Gracias a Dios .. | 20 | 10 |

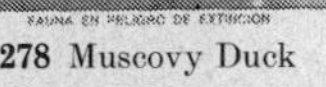

**278** Muscovy Duck **279** Painting by Julia Padilla

**1993.** Air. America. Endangered Birds. Mult.

| | | | | |
|---|---|---|---|---|
| 1266 | | 20 c. Ornate hawk eagle (vert) .. .. .. | 10 | 10 |
| 1267 | | 80 c. Type **278** .. .. | 10 | 10 |
| 1268 | | 2 l. Harpy eagle .. .. | 25 | 15 |

**1993.** Air. 40th Anniv of United Nations Development Programme.

| | | | | |
|---|---|---|---|---|
| 1269 | **279** | 95 c. multicoloured .. | 15 | 10 |

280 Church

281 Ramon Rosa

**1993.** Air. Christmas. Paintings by Aida Lara de Pedemonte. Multicoloured.

1270 20 c. Type **280** .. .. 10 10
1271 85 c. Flower vendor .. .. 10 10

**1993.** Air. Personalities. Multicoloured.

1272 25 c. Type **281** .. .. 10 10
1273 65 c. Jesus Aguilar Paz .. 10 10
1274 85 c. Augusto Coello .. 10 10

282 Black Angel Fish

**1993.** Air. Fishes. Multicoloured.

1275 20 c. Type **282** .. .. 10 10
1276 85 c. Queen angel fish .. 10 10
1277 3 l. Banded butterfly fish 40 25

283 Norma Callejas planting Tree

284 Family with Rushes (Aida Lara de Pedemonte)

**1994.** Air. 4th Year of Rafael L. Callejas's Presidential Term. Multicoloured.

1278 95 c. Type **283** .. .. 15 10
1279 1 l. Pres. Callejas and Government House (horiz) .. .. 15 10

**1994.** International Year of the Family.

1280 **284** 1 l. multicoloured .. 15 10

285 Dove and Maps on Globe

286 "Madonna and Child"

**1994.** Air. Int Peace and Development in Central America Conf, Tegucigalpa.

1281 **285** 1 l. multicoloured .. 15 10

**1994.** Air. Christmas. Paintings by Gelasio Gimenez. Multicoloured.

1282 95 c. Type **286** .. .. 10 10
1283 1 l. "Holy Family" .. 15 10

287 "Family Scene" (Delmer Mejia)

288 Pres. Reina

**1995.** Air. 50th Anniv of U.N.O. Mult.

1284 1 l. "The Sowing: Ecological Family" (Elisa Dulcey) .. 15 10
1285 2 l. Type **287** .. .. 25 15
1286 3 l. Anniversary emblem 40 25

**1995.** Air. 1st Anniv of Presidency of Carlos Roberto Reina. Multicoloured.

1287 80 c. Type **288** .. .. 10 10
1288 95 c. Pres. Reina with arms raised (horiz) .. 10 10
1289 1 l. Pres. Reina at summit conference (horiz) .. 15 10

289 Postman loading Mail Van

**1995.** Air. America. Postal Transport. Paintings by Ramiro Rodriguez Zelaya. Multicoloured.

1290 1 l. 50 Type **289** .. .. 20 10
1291 2 l. Postman on motor cycle .. .. .. 25 15

290 "Boletellus russelli"

292 Family and Farm over Globe

**1995.** Air. Fungi. Multicoloured.

1292 1 l. "Marasmius cohaerens" (horiz) 45 15
1293 1 l. Blue leg ("Lepista nuda") (horiz) .. 45 15
1294 1 l. "Polyporus pargamenus" (horiz) .. 45 15
1295 1 l. "Fomes sp." (horiz) .. 45 15
1296 1 l. "Paneolus sphinctrinus" (horiz) .. 45 15
1297 1 l. "Hygrophorus aurantiaca" (horiz) .. 45 15
1298 1 l. 50 The blusher ("Amanita rubescens") 65 20
1299 1 l. 50 "Boletus frostii" .. 65 20
1300 1 l. 50 "Fomes annosus" 65 20
1301 1 l. 50 "Psathyrella sp." 65 20
1302 1 l. 50 Type **290** .. 65 20
1303 1 l. 50 "Marasmius spegazzinii" .. 65 20
1304 2 l. "Amanita sp." .. 80 25
1305 2 l. Golden tops ("Psilocybe cubensis") 80 25
1306 2 l. Royal boletus ("Boletus regius") 80 25
1307 2 l. Black trumpet ("Craterellus cornucopioides") .. 80 25
1308 2 l. "Auricularia delicata" 80 25
1309 2 l. "Clavariadelphus pistilaris" .. 80 25
1310 2 l. 50 "Scleroderma aurantium" (horiz) .. 95 35
1311 2 l. 50 "Amanita praegraveolens" (horiz) 95 35
1312 2 l. 50 Chanterelle ("Cantharellus cibarius") (horiz) .. 95 35
1313 2 l. 50 "Geastrum triplex" (horiz) .. .. 95 35
1314 2 l. 50 "Russula emetica" (horiz) .. .. 95 35
1315 2 l. 50 "Boletus pinicola" (horiz) .. .. 95 35
1316 3 l. "Fomes versicolor" (horiz) .. .. 1·25 40
1317 3 l. "Cantharellus purpurascens" (horiz) 1·25 40
1318 3 l. "Lyophyllum decastes" (horiz) .. 1·25 40
1319 3 l. Oyster fungus ("Pleurotus ostreatus") (horiz) .. .. 1·25 40
1320 3 l. "Boletus ananas" (horiz) .. .. 1·25 40
1321 3 l. Caesar's mushroom ("Amanita caesarea") (horiz) .. .. 1·25 40

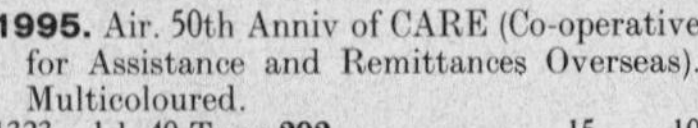

**1995.** Air. 50th Anniv of CARE (Co-operative for Assistance and Remittances Overseas). Multicoloured.

1323 1 l. 40 Type **292** .. .. 15 10
1324 5 l. 40 Crop farming .. 55 35
1325 5 l. 40 Toucan, orchid, planting tree and animals at waterfall .. 55 35

294 People around Japanese Character

**1995.** 20th Anniv of Japanese Overseas Co-operation Voluntary Workers in Honduras. Mlticoloured.

1327 1 l. 40 Type **294** (postage) 15 10
1328 4 l. 30 Amerindian-style figures on pages of leaflet (horiz) (air) .. 40 25
1329 5 l. 40 Volunteer and people in traditional costumes (horiz) .. 55 35

295 Scorpion Mud Turtle

**1995.** Air. America. Environmental Protection. Multicoloured.

1330 1 l. 40 Type **295** .. .. 15 10
1331 4 l. 54 Alpinia purpurata (flower) (vert) .. 45 30
1332 10 l. Common caracara (vert) .. .. .. 1·00 65

296 "Agalychnis sp."

**1995.** Air. Reptiles and Amphibians. Mult.

1333 5 l. 40 Type **296** .. .. 55 35
1334 5 l. 40 Iguana .. .. 55 35

297 Bell

**1995.** Air. Christmas. Multicoloured.

1335 1 l. 40 Type **297** .. .. 15 10
1336 5 l. 40 Crib figures (horiz) 55 35
1337 6 l. 90 Deer (carving) .. 70 45

298 "SICA" over Map

**1996.** Air. 3rd Anniv of Central American Integration System. Multicoloured.

1338 1 l. 40 Type **298** (signing of Protocol, 1991) .. 15 10
1339 4 l. 30 Emblem .. .. 40 25
1340 5 l. 40 Presidents of Central American countries at 17th Summit .. .. 55 35

299 Allegorical Design

**1996.** Air. United Nations Decade against Drug Abuse and Drug Trafficking. Mult.

1341 1 l. 40 Type **299** .. .. 15 10
1342 5 l. 40 Woman's head with butterfly as hat (vert) 55 35
1343 10 l. Guitar and bar of music .. .. .. 1·00 65

300 Traditional Headdress

**1996.** Air. Bicentenary of Arrival of Garifunas Tribe in Honduras. Multicoloured.

1344 1 l. 40 Type **300** .. .. 15 10
1345 5 l. 40 Tribesmen dancing to music (horiz) .. 55 35
1346 10 l. Drums (horiz) .. 1·00 60

301 Steam Locomotive "San Jose"

**1996.** Air. "Exfilhon 96" National Stamp Exn, Tegucigalpa. Railway Locomotives. Mult.

1347 5 l. 40 Type **301** .. .. 55 35
1348 5 l. 40 Modern railcar .. 55 35

302 Football

**1996.** Air. 6th Central American Games, San Pedro Sula (1997). Multicoloured.

1350 4 l. 30 Type **302** .. .. 40 25
1351 4 l. 54 Volleyball and games emblem .. 45 30
1352 5 l. 40 Games mascot (vert) .. .. .. 55 35

## EXPRESS LETTER STAMPS

**1953.** No. O 507 surch. **ENTREGA INMEDIATA 1953 L O.20.**
E523.**127.** 20 c. on 1 c. olive & purple .. .. 1·60 1·60

E 135. Lockheed Constellation.

**1956.** Air. Optd **ENTREGA INMEDIATA** as in Type **E 135**.
E570 **E 135** 20 c. grey and black 60 50

**1966.** Stamp Cent. Design similar to **T 144**.
E 700. 20 c. brn., gold and brn. 45 45
DESIGN—HORIZ. 20 c. Motor cyclist.

**1972.** As **T 168**, but inscr. "ENTREGA INMEDIATA". Multicoloured.
E811 20 c. Chance Vought F4U-5 Corsair fighter aircraft .. .. 45 25

**1975.** No. E 811 surch.
E 848. 60 c. on 20 c. mult. .. 75 55

**1976.** As **T 178**.
E 893. 60 c. Deer in forest .. 70 40

## OFFICIAL STAMPS

Various stamps overprinted **OFICIAL.**

**1890.** Stamps of 1890.
O 56. **6.** 1 c. yellow .. .. 15
O 57. 2 c. yellow .. .. 15
O 58. 5 c. yellow .. .. 15
O 59. 10 c. yellow .. .. 15
O 60. 20 c. yellow .. .. 15
O 61. 25 c. yellow .. .. 15
O 62. 30 c. yellow .. .. 15
O 63. 40 c. yellow .. .. 15
O 64. 50 c. yellow .. .. 15
O 65. 75 c. yellow .. .. 15
O 66. 1 p. yellow .. .. 15

**1891.** Stamps of 1891.
O 70. **8.** 1 c. yellow .. .. 15
O 71. 2 c. yellow .. .. 15
O 72. 5 c. yellow .. .. 15
O 73. 10 c. yellow .. .. 15
O 74. 20 c. yellow .. .. 15
O 75. 25 c. yellow .. .. 15
O 76. 30 c. yellow .. .. 15
O 77. 40 c. yellow .. .. 15
O 78. 50 c. yellow .. .. 15
O 79. 75 c. yellow .. .. 15
O 80. 1 p. yellow .. .. 15

**1898.** Stamps of 1898.
O 116. **14.** 5 c. blue .. .. 20
O 117. 10 c. blue .. .. 20
O 118. 20 c. bistre .. .. 20
O 119. 50 c. orange .. .. 40
O 120. 1 p. green .. .. 85

**1911.** Stamps of 1911.
O 148. **20.** 1 c. violet .. .. 90 35
O 149. 2 c. green .. .. 55 55
O 150. 5 c. red .. .. 90 90
O 151. 6 c. blue .. .. 1·60 1·25
O 152. 10 c. blue .. .. 90 70
O 153. 20 c. yellow .. .. 90 90
O 154. 50 c. brown .. .. 3·25 2·50
O 155. 1 p. olive .. .. 7·00 5·75

**1914.** No. O 150 and O 148 surch.
O 186. **20.** 1 c. on 5 c. red .. 1·10 90
O 187. 2 c. on 5 c. red .. 1·25 90
O 188. 10 c. on 1 c. violet .. 2·25 2·25
O 189. 10 c. on 5 c. red .. 8·75 8·75
O 190. 20 c. on 1 c. violet .. 1·60 1·60

**1914.** No. O 190 and O 146 surch. **OFICIAL** and value.
O 191. **20.** 10 c. on 20 c. on 1 c. vio. 3·50 3·50
O 193. 20 c. on 50 c. brown.. 3·25 3·25

**1915.** Stamps of 1913.
O 194. **26.** 1 c. brown .. .. 25 25
O 195. 2 c. red .. .. 25 25
O 197. **27.** 5 c. blue .. .. 25 25
O 198. 6 c. violet .. .. 85 85
O 199. **26.** 10 c. brown .. .. 70 70
O 200. 20 c. brown .. .. 1·75 1·75
O 202. **27.** 50 c. red .. .. 3·50 3·50

**1915.** No. 168 surch. **OFICIAL $001.**
O 203. **26.** 1 c. on 2 c. red .. 1·75 1·75

**1915.** Stamps of 1915.
O 204. **32.** 1 c. brown .. .. 50 50
O 205. 2 c. red .. .. 50 50
O 206. – 5 c. blue .. .. 20 20
O 207. – 6 c. violet .. .. 30 30
O 208. **32.** 10 c. blue .. .. 1·25 1·25
O 209. 20 c. brown .. .. 1·25 1·25
O 210. – 50 c. red .. .. 1·25 1·25
O 211. – 1 p. green .. .. 2·25 2·25

**1921.** Stamps of 1919.
O 212. **36.** 1 c. brown .. .. 1·60 1·60
O 213. 2 c. red .. .. 3·75 3·75
O 214. 5 c. red .. .. 3·75 3·75
O 215. 6 c. mauve .. .. 35 35
O 216. 10 c. blue .. .. 45 45
O 217. 15 c. blue .. .. 50 50
O 218. 20 c. brown .. .. 70 70
O 219. 50 c. brown .. .. 1·10 1·10
O 220. 1 p. green .. .. 1·60 1·60

**1925.** Stamps of 1923.
O 222. **39.** 1 c. olive .. .. 10 10
O 223. 2 c. red .. .. 15 15
O 224. 6 c. purple .. .. 25 25
O 225. 10 c. blue .. .. 35 35
O 226. 20 c. brown .. .. 45 45
O 227. 50 c. red .. .. 95 95
O 228. 1 p. green .. .. 1·40 1·40

O 50. J. R. Molina.

**1929.**
O 259. – 1 c. blue .. .. 15 15
O 260. **O 50.** 2 c. red .. .. 20 20
O 261. – 5 c. violet .. .. 30 30
O 262. – 10 c. green .. .. 35 35
O 263. – 20 c. blue .. .. 45 45
O 264. – 50 c. green & yellow 90 90
O 265. – 1 p. brown .. .. 1·60 1·60
DESIGNS: J. C. Valle. 5 c. Coffee Tree. 10 c. J. T. Reyes. 20 c. Tegucigalpa Cathedral. 50 c. Lake Yojoa. 1 p. Wireless Station.

**1930.** Air. Nos. O 224/8 surch. **Servicio aereo Vale 5 centavos VI—1930** or optd. **Servicio aereo Habilitado VI—1930.**
O 319. **39.** 5 c. on 6 c. purple .. 1·10 1·10
O 320. 6 c. purple .. .. 50·00 50·00
O 321. 10 c. blue .. .. 1·00 1·00
O 322. 20 c. brown .. .. 1·00 1·00
O 323. 50 c. red .. .. 1·50 1·50
O 324. 1 p. green .. .. 1·00 1·00

O 70. Tegucigalpa. O 92. Coat of Arms and National Flag.

**1931.**
O 328. **O 70.** 1 c. blue .. .. 20 20
O 329. 2 c. purple .. .. 75 75
O 330. 5 c. olive .. .. 90 90
O 331. 6 c. red .. .. 90 90
O 332. 10 c. green .. .. 1·00 1·00
O 333. 15 c. brown .. .. 1·75 1·75
O 334. 20 c. brown .. .. 1·75 1·75
O 335. 50 c. violet .. .. 1·25 1·25
O 336. 1 p. orange .. .. 1·75 1·75

**1933.** Air. Various stamps surch **Aereo Oficial Vale 1933** and new value.
O 354 **66** 20 c. on 2 c. blue .. 3·50 3·50
O 355 20 c. on 2 c. orange .. 3·50 3·50
O 356 20 c. on 2 c. red .. 3·50 3·50
O 357 40 c. on 2 c. orange .. 2·10 2·10
O 358 40 c. on 2 c. red .. 4·25 4·25
O 360 – 40 c. on 5 c. purple (249) .. 4·25 4·25
O 361 – 40 c. on 5 c. blue (250) 7·00 7·00
O 362 – 40 c. on 5 c. purple (270) .. 4·25 4·25
O 363 – 40 c. on 5 c. blue (271) 9·50 9·50
O 370 – 40 c. on 5 c. vio (O 261) 95 95
O 372 **39** 60 c. on 6 c. purple (O 224) .. 70 70
O 365 – 70 c. on 5 c. blue (188) 3·00 3·00
O 374 – 70 c. on 5 c. bl (O 206) 5·50 5·50
O 366 **39** 70 c. on 10 c. blue 3·50 3·50
O 375 **32** 70 c. on 10 c. bl (O 208) 8·00 8·00
O 377 **36** 70 c. on 10 c. bl (O 216) 4·75 4·75
O 378 **39** 70 c. on 10 c. bl (O 225) 3·50 3·50
O 380 **36** 70 c. on 15 c. bl (O 217) 90·00 90·00
O 381 90 c. on 10 c. bl (O 216) 5·50 5·50
O 382 90 c. on 15 c. bl (O 217) 4·00 4·00
O 383 **39** 1 l. on 2 c. red .. 1·40 1·40
O 367 **36** 1 l. on 20 c. brown .. 3·50 3·50
O 384 1 l. on 20 c. brn (O 218) 2·50 2·50
O 385 **39** 1 l. on 20 c. brn (O 226) 4·00 4·00
O 368 **39** 1 l. on 50 c. red .. 14·00 14·00
O 386 **36** 1 l. on 50 c. brn (O 219) 1·90 1·90
O 387 **39** 1 l. on 50 c. red (O 227) 4·25 4·25
O 369 **36** 120 l. on 1 p. green .. 1·10 1·10
O 388 – 1. 20 l. on 1 p. green (O 211) .. 9·50 9·50
O 389 **39** 1. 20 l. on 1 p. green (O 288) .. 1·60 1·60

**1935.** Stamps of 1931 optd. **HABILITADO 1935-1938.**, between thick lines.
O 390. **O 70.** 1 c. blue .. .. 20 20
O 391. 2 c. purple .. .. 20 20
O 392. 5 c. olive .. .. 25 25
O 393. 6 c. red .. .. 35 35
O 394. 10 c. green .. .. 40 40
O 395. 15 c. brown .. .. 45 45
O 396. 20 c. brown .. .. 55 55
O 397. 50 c. violet .. .. 1·25 1·25

**1939.** Air.
O 400. **O 92.** 2 c. blue and green .. 10 10
O 401. 5 c. blue and orange 10 10
O 402. 8 c. blue and brown 15 15
O 403. 15 c. blue and red .. 35 30
O 404. 46 c. blue and olive 35 45
O 405. 50 c. blue and violet 60 45
O 406. 1 l. blue and brown 1·75 1·75
O 407. 2 l. blue and red .. 3·00 3·00

**1952.** Air. 500th Birth Anniv. of Isabella the Catholic. As Nos. 499/506 but colours changed, optd. **OFICIAL.**
O 507. **127.** 1 c. olive and purple 10 10
O 508. – 2 c. violet and brown 10 10
O 509. – 8 c. black and red .. 15 15
O 510. **128.** 16 c. green and violet 25 25
O 511. – 30 c. black and blue .. 30 30
O 512. – 1 l. sepia and green .. 1·50 1·25
O 513. **127.** 2 l. brown and blue .. 3·00 3·00
O 514. **128.** 5 l. slate and orange .. 7·00 7·00

**1953.** Air. United Nations. As Nos. 523/31 but colours changed (except 1 c.), optd. **OFICIAL.**
O 532. – 1 c. blue and black .. 10 10
O 533. **130.** 2 c. green and black .. 10 10
O 534. – 3 c. orange and black 20 20
O 535. – 5 c. red and black .. 20 20
O 536. – 15 c. sepia and black 30 30
O 537. – 30 c. purple and black 55 55
O 538. – 1 l. olive and black .. 4·00 2·75
O 539. – 2 l. purple and black 5·00 3·25
O 540. – 5 l. blue and black .. 11·50 11·00

**1956.** Air. As Nos. 551/69 but colours changed, optd. **OFICIAL.**
O 570. 1 c. lake and black .. 10 10
O 571. 2 c. red and black .. 10 10
O 572. 3 c. purple and black .. 10 10
O 573. 4 c. orange and black .. 10 10
O 574. 5 c. turquoise and black 10 10
O 575. 8 c. multicoloured .. 15 15
O 576. 10 c. brown and black.. 15 15
O 577. 12 c. red and black .. 15 15
O 578. 15 c. black and red .. 15 15
O 579. 20 c. olive and black .. 15 15
O 580. 24 c. blue and black .. 20 20
O 581. 25 c. purple and black.. 25 25
O 582. 30 c. green and black .. 25 25
O 583. 40 c. orange and black.. 35 35
O 584. 50 c. red and black .. 35 35
O 585. 60 c. purple and black.. 45 45
O 586. 1 l. sepia and black .. 1·75 1·40
O 587. 2 l. blue and black .. 3·00 2·40
O 588. 5 f. blue and black .. 5·75 5·25

**1957.** Air. Revolution of October 21, 1956. Nos. 570/9 optd. **OFICIAL.** Frames in black.
O 589. 1 c. blue and yellow .. 10 10
O 590. 2 c. pur., green & orange 10 10
O 591. 5 c. blue and pink .. 10 10
O 592. 8 c. violet, olive & orange 10 10
O 593. 10 c. brown and violet.. 15 15
O 594. 12 c. blue and turquoise 15 15
O 595. 15 c. brown & green .. 20 15
O 596. 30 c. grey and pink .. 35 35
O 597. 1 l. brown and blue .. 1·75 1·40
O 598. 2 l. grey and green .. 3·00 2·40

**1959.** Air. Abraham Lincoln. 150th Birth Anniv. No. 590/601 but colours changed and optd. **OFICIAL.** Flags in blue and red.
O 602. 1 c. yellow .. .. 10 10
O 603. 2 c. olive .. .. 10 10
O 604. 3 c. brown .. .. 10 10
O 605. 5 c. blue .. .. 10 10
O 606. 10 c. purple .. .. 15 15
O 607. 12 c. orange .. .. 15 15
O 608. 15 c. sepia .. .. 20 20
O 609. 25 c. slate .. .. 30 30
O 610. 50 c. red .. .. 45 45
O 611. 1 l. violet .. .. 1·10 1·10
O 612. 2 l. blue.. .. 1·75 1·75
O 613. 5 l. green .. .. 5·25 5·25

**1964.** Air. Pres. Kennedy Memorial Issue. Optd. **IN MEMORIAM JOHN F. KENNEDY 22 NOVIEMBRE 1963.**
O 626. 1 c. yellow (No. O 602) 15 15
O 627. 2 c. olive (No. O 603) .. 20 20
O 628. 3 c. brown (No. O 604) 25 25
O 629. 5 c. blue (No. O 605) .. 30 30
O 630. 15 c. sepia (No. O 608).. 1·40 1·10
O 631. 50 c. red (No. O 610) .. 5·75 4·75

**1964.** Air. Nos. O 611/4 surch.
O 647. 10 c. on 50 c. red .. 15 10
O 648. 12 c. on 15 c. sepia .. 25 10
O 649. 12 c. on 25 c. slate .. 25 10
O 621. 20 c. on 25 c. slate .. 45 35

**1964.** Air. Olympic Games, Tokyo. Optd. with Olympic Rings and **1964.**
O 632. 2 l. purple and black (No. O 539) .. .. 5·75 4·75

**1965.** Air. Nos. 630/38 optd. **OFICIAL.**
O 650. **144.** 1 c. black and green.. 10 10
O 651. – 2 c. black and mauve 10 10
O 652. – 5 c. black and blue .. 15 15
O 653. – 8 c. black and green.. 15 15
O 654. **144.** 10 c. black and bistre 25 25
O 655. – 12 c. black and yellow 30 30
O 656. – 1 l. black and buff .. 3·00 2·75
O 657. – 2 l. black and olive .. 6·50 5·75
O 658. **144.** 3 l. black and red .. 7·50 7·00

**1965.** Air. Churchill Commem. Optd. **IN MEMORIAM, Sir Winston Churchill 1874-1965.**
O 674. **128.** 16 c. green and violet 70 70

**1971.** Air. Various official stamps surch. in figures.
O 788. **134.** 10 c. on 3 c. (O 572) 25 10
O 789. – 10 c. on 2 c. (O 603) 25 10
O 790. – 10 c. on 3 c. (O 604) 25 10

**1974.** Air. Nos. O 570 and O 602 surch.
O 849. 2 c. on 1 c. lake & black 10 10
O 850. 2 c. on 1 c. yellow .. 10 10

## HORTA Pt. 9

A district of the Azores for which separate issues were used from 1892 to 1905.

1865. 1000 reis = 1 milreis.

**1892.** As T **4** of Funchal, but inscr. "HORTA".

| No. | Description | Unused | Used |
|---|---|---|---|
| 4 | 5 r. yellow | 2·25 | 1·60 |
| 5 | 10 r. mauve | 2·25 | 2·00 |
| 6 | 15 r. brown | 2·25 | 2·10 |
| 7 | 20 r. lilac | 2·50 | 2·50 |
| 2 | 25 r. green | 4·00 | 1·00 |
| 8 | 50 r. blue | 6·25 | 3·00 |
| 22 | 75 r. red | 7·00 | 4·50 |
| 10 | 80 r. green | 9·25 | 8·75 |
| 23 | 100 r. brown on yellow | 40·00 | 19·00 |
| 24 | 150 r. red on rose | 45·00 | 40·00 |
| 25 | 200 r. blue on blue | 45·00 | 40·00 |
| 26 | 300 r. blue on brown | 45·00 | 40·00 |

**1897.** "King Carlos" key-type inscr "HORTA". Name and value in red (Nos. 46 and 41) or black (others).

| No. | Description | Unused | Used |
|---|---|---|---|
| 28. S. | 2½ r. grey | 45 | 30 |
| 29. | 5 r. orange | 45 | 30 |
| 30. | 10 r green | 45 | 30 |
| 31. | 15 r. brown | 6·25 | 4·75 |
| 42. | 15 r. green | 1·25 | 1·00 |
| 32. | 20 r. lilac | 1·25 | 1·00 |
| 33. | 25 r. green | 2·10 | 90 |
| 43. | 25 r. red | 1·25 | 60 |
| 34. | 50 r. blue | 2·40 | 80 |
| 45. | 65 r. blue | 90 | 65 |
| 35. | 75 r. red | 2·25 | 1·00 |
| 46. | 75 r. brown on yellow | 9·50 | 8·25 |
| 36. | 80 r. mauve | 1·25 | 85 |
| 37. | 100 r. blue on blue | 2·40 | 85 |
| 47. | 115 r. red on pink | 1·60 | 1·25 |
| 48. | 130 r. brown on yellow | 1·60 | 1·25 |
| 38. | 150 r. brown on yellow | 1·60 | 1·10 |
| 49. | 180 r. black on pink | 1·60 | 1·25 |
| 39. | 200 r. purple on pink | 4·50 | 3·75 |
| 40. | 300 r. blue on pink | 8·00 | 6·00 |
| 41. | 500 r. black on blue | 10·00 | 9·50 |

## HUNGARY Pt. 2

A country in central Europe. A Kingdom ruled by the Emperor of Austria until 1918. A Republic was then proclaimed, and later a Soviet style constitution was adopted. In 1919 parts of the country were occupied by France, Serbia and Rumania, including Budapest. Following the withdrawal of the Rumanians a National Republic was instituted, and in 1920 Hungary was declared a Monarchy with Admiral Nicholas Horthy as Regent. In 1946 Hungary became a Republic again.

1858. 100 krajczar = 1 forint.
1900. 100 filler (heller) = 1 korona (krone).
1926. 100 filler = 1 pengo.
1946. 100 filler = 1 forint.

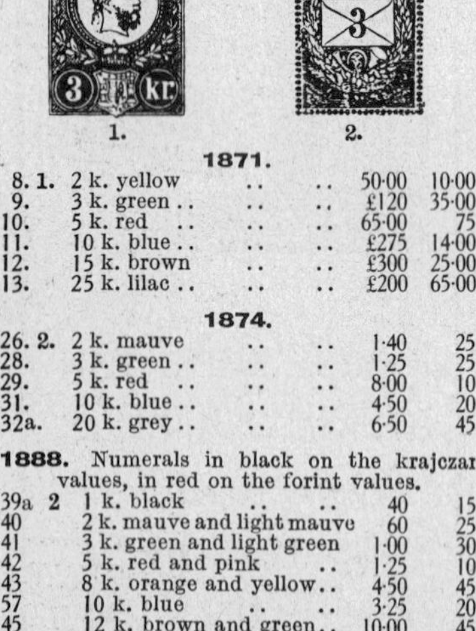

1. 2.

**1871.**

| No. | Description | Unused | Used |
|---|---|---|---|
| 8. 1. | 2 k. yellow | 50·00 | 10·00 |
| 9. | 3 k. green | £120 | 35·00 |
| 10. | 5 k. red | 65·00 | 75 |
| 11. | 10 k. blue | £275 | 14·00 |
| 12. | 15 k. brown | £300 | 25·00 |
| 13. | 25 k. lilac | £200 | 65·00 |

**1874.**

| No. | Description | Unused | Used |
|---|---|---|---|
| 26. 2. | 2 k. mauve | 1·40 | 25 |
| 28. | 3 k. green | 1·25 | 25 |
| 29. | 5 k. red | 8·00 | 10 |
| 31. | 10 k. blue | 4·50 | 20 |
| 32a. | 20 k. grey | 6·50 | 45 |

**1888.** Numerals in black on the krajczar values, in red on the forint values.

| No. | Description | Unused | Used |
|---|---|---|---|
| 39a 2 | 1 k. black | 40 | 15 |
| 40 | 2 k. mauve and light mauve | 60 | 25 |
| 41 | 3 k. green and light green | 1·00 | 30 |
| 42 | 5 k. red and pink | 1·25 | 10 |
| 43 | 8 k. orange and yellow | 4·50 | 45 |
| 57 | 10 k. blue | 3·25 | 20 |
| 45 | 12 k. brown and green | 10·00 | 45 |
| 59 | 15 k. red and blue | 3·25 | 25 |
| 60 | 20 k. grey | 4·00 | 2·00 |
| 61 | 24 k. purple and red | 5·00 | 1·40 |
| 62 | 30 k. olive and brown | 4·00 | 2·00 |
| 63 | 50 k. red and orange | 11·00 | 12·00 |
| 51 | 1 fo. grey and silver | £130 | 1·50 |
| 38i | 3 fo. brown and gold | 14·00 | 4·75 |

7. "Turul" (mythical bird of the Magyars).

8. King Francis Joseph wearing Hungarian Crown.

12.

**1900.** Figures of value in black.

| No. | Description | Unused | Used |
|---|---|---|---|
| 99 7 | 1 f. grey | 15 | 10 |
| 100 | 2 f. yellow | 10 | 10 |
| 118 | 3 f. orange | 10 | 10 |
| 67 | 4 f. mauve | 50 | 10 |
| 102 | 5 f. green | 10 | 10 |
| 69a | 6 f. purple | 45 | 10 |
| 103 | 6 f. drab | 25 | 10 |
| 120 | 6 f. green | 10 | 10 |
| 121 | 10 f. red | 10 | 10 |
| 105 | 12 f. lilac | 35 | 10 |
| 122 | 12 f. lilac on yellow | 15 | 10 |
| 123 | 16 f. green | 15 | 15 |
| 124 | 20 f. brown | 15 | 10 |
| 125 | 25 f. blue | 15 | 10 |
| 126 | 30 f. brown | 15 | 10 |
| 127 | 35 f. purple | 15 | 10 |
| 111 | 50 f. red | 65 | 10 |
| 128 | 50 f. red on blue | 15 | 10 |
| 129 | 60 f. green | 1·60 | 1·60 |
| 130 | 60 f. green on pink | 50 | 10 |
| 131 | 70 f. brown and green | 25 | 10 |
| 132 | 80 f. violet | 25 | 10 |
| 133 8 | 1 k. red | 2·00 | 10 |
| 134 | 2 k. blue | 5·50 | 10 |
| 81 | 3 k. blue | 65·00 | 1·40 |
| 135 | 5 k. red | 10·00 | 1·25 |

**1913.** Flood Charity stamps. As T **7/8**, but with label as T **12**.

| No. | Description | Unused | Used |
|---|---|---|---|
| 136. 12. | 1 f.+2 f. grey | 65 | 60 |
| 137. | 2 f.+2 f. yellow | 35 | 35 |
| 138. | 3 f.+2 f. orange | 35 | 35 |
| 139. | 5 f.+2 f. green | 30 | 30 |
| 140. | 6 f.+2 f. drab | 65 | 60 |
| 141. | 10 f.+2 f. red | 20 | 15 |
| 142. | 12 f.+2 f. lilac on yellow | 1·00 | 85 |
| 143. | 16 f.+2 f. green | 70 | 70 |
| 144. | 20 f.+2 f. brown | 2·25 | 1·50 |
| 145. | 25 f.+2 f. blue | 70 | 50 |
| 146. | 30 f.+2 f. brown | 1·00 | 65 |
| 147. | 35 f.+2 f. purple | 90 | 40 |
| 148. | 50 f.+2 f. lake on blue | 5·00 | 2·25 |
| 149. | 60 f.+2 f. green on red | 6·50 | 1·00 |
| 150. 8. | 1 k.+2 f. red | 24·00 | 9·00 |
| 151. | 2 k.+2 f. blue | 55·00 | 42·00 |
| 152. | 5 k.+2 f. red | 18·00 | 17·00 |

**1914.** War Charity. Nos. 136/52 (with labels) surch **Hadi segely Ozvegyeknek es arvaknak ket (2) filler**.

| No. | Description | Unused | Used |
|---|---|---|---|
| 153. 12. | 1 f.+2 f. grey | 55 | 40 |
| 154. | 2 f.+2 f. yellow | 55 | 50 |
| 155. | 3 f.+2 f. orange | 55 | 50 |
| 156. | 5 f.+2 f. green | 30 | 15 |
| 157. | 6 f.+2 f. drab | 65 | 50 |
| 158. | 10 f.+2 f. red | 30 | 15 |
| 159. | 12 f.+2 f. lilac on yellow | 55 | 35 |
| 160. 12. | 16 f.+2 f. green | 55 | 25 |
| 161. | 20 f.+2 f. brown | 55 | 30 |
| 162. | 25 f.+2 f. blue | 1·00 | 35 |
| 163. | 30 f.+2 f. brown | 1·25 | 35 |
| 164. | 35 f.+2 f. purple | 3·25 | 1·25 |
| 165. | 50 f.+2 f. lake on blue | 2·00 | 60 |
| 166. | 60 f.+2 f. green on red | 5·50 | 1·25 |
| 167. 8. | 1 k.+2 f. red (No. 150) | 60·00 | 35·00 |
| 168. | 2 k.+2 f. blue (No. 151) | 20·00 | 16·00 |
| 169. | 5 k.+2 f. red (No. 153) | 21·00 | 15·00 |

**1915.** War Charity. Stamps of 1900 (without labels) surch as last round the stamp.

| No. | Description | Unused | Used |
|---|---|---|---|
| 170. 7. | 1 f.+2 f. grey | 10 | 10 |
| 171. | 2 f.+2 f. yellow | 10 | 10 |
| 172. | 3 f.+2 f. orange | 10 | 10 |
| 173. | 5 f.+2 f. green | 10 | 10 |
| 174. | 6 f.+2 f. drab | 10 | 10 |
| 175. | 10 f.+2 f. red | 10 | 10 |
| 176. | 12 f.+2 f. lilac on yellow | 10 | 10 |
| 177. | 16 f.+2 f. green | 30 | 30 |
| 178. | 20 f.+2 f. brown | 30 | 30 |
| 179. | 25 f.+2 f. blue | 10 | 10 |
| 180. | 30 f.+2 f. brown | 10 | 10 |
| 181. | 35 f.+2 f. purple | 15 | 10 |
| 182. | 50 f.+2 f. lake on blue | 30 | 15 |
| 183. | 60 f.+2 f. green on red | 55 | 20 |
| 185. 8. | 1 k.+2 f. red (No. 133) | 1·50 | 70 |
| 186. | 2 k.+2 f. blue (No. 134) | 2·00 | 90 |
| 187. | 5 k.+2 f. red (No. 135) | 6·00 | 4·50 |

18. Harvesters.

19. Parliament Buildings, Budapest.

**1916.** As T **18** but with white figures in top corners.

| No. | Description | Unused | Used |
|---|---|---|---|
| 243 18 | 10 f. red | 35 | 10 |
| 244 | 15 f. purple | 15 | 10 |

**1916.** Inscr. "MAGYAR KIR POSTA".

| No. | Description | Unused | Used |
|---|---|---|---|
| 245. 18. | 2 f. brown | 10 | 10 |
| 246. | 3 f. red | 10 | 10 |
| 247. | 4 f. slate | 10 | 10 |
| 248. | 5 f. green | 10 | 10 |
| 249. | 6 f. blue | 10 | 10 |
| 250. | 10 f. red | 30 | 10 |
| 251. | 15 f. violet | 10 | 10 |
| 252. | 20 f. brown | 10 | 10 |
| 253. | 25 f. blue | 10 | 10 |
| 254. | 35 f. brown | 10 | 10 |
| 255. | 40 f. olive | 10 | 10 |
| 256. 19. | 50 f. purple | 10 | 10 |
| 257. | 75 f. blue | 10 | 10 |
| 258. | 80 f. green | 20 | 10 |
| 259. | 1 k. lake | 10 | 10 |
| 260. | 2 k. brown | 20 | 10 |
| 261. | 3 k. grey and violet | 50 | 10 |
| 262. | 5 k. brown | 70 | 15 |
| 263. | 10 k. lilac and brown | 1·00 | 40 |

In Type **19** the colours of the centres differ slightly from those of the frames.

For later issues in Types **18** and **19**, see Nos. 372/86 and 404/11.

20. In Trenches.

22. "Turul" at bay.

23. Queen Zita.

**1916.** War Charity.

| No. | Description | Unused | Used |
|---|---|---|---|
| 264. 20. | 10+2 f. red | 15 | 15 |
| 265. – | 15+2 f. violet | 15 | 15 |
| 266. 22. | 40+2 f. lake | 20 | 20 |

DESIGN: 15 f. Hand to hand combat.

**1916.** Coronation.

| No. | Description | Unused | Used |
|---|---|---|---|
| 267 23 | 10 f. mauve | 25 | 20 |
| 268 – | 15 f. red (Emperor Charles IV) | 25 | 20 |

**1917.** War Charity Exhibition. Nos. 243/4 surch **Jozsef foherczeg vezerezredes hadi kiallitasa 1 korona** (= "Archduke Joseph Colonel General War Exhibition").

| No. | Description | Unused | Used |
|---|---|---|---|
| 269 18 | 10 f.+1 k. red | 30 | 45 |
| 270 | 15 f.+1 k. violet | 30 | 45 |

**1918.** Air. Surch. **REPULO POSTA** and value.

| No. | Description | Unused | Used |
|---|---|---|---|
| 271. 19. | 1 k. 50 on 75 f. blue | 16·00 | 18·00 |
| 272. | 4 k. 50 on 2 k. brown | 14·00 | 17·00 |

27. Charles IV.

28. Zita.

**1918.**

| No. | Description | Unused | Used |
|---|---|---|---|
| 273. 27. | 10 f. red | 10 | 10 |
| 274. | 15 f. violet | 15 | 15 |
| 275. | 20 f. brown | 10 | 10 |
| 276. | 25 f. blue | 10 | 10 |
| 277. 28. | 40 f. olive | 10 | 40 |
| 278. | 50 f. purple | 10 | 10 |

**1918.** Optd **KOZTARSASAG**.

(a) War Charity Stamps (Nos. 264/6).

| No. | Description | Unused | Used |
|---|---|---|---|
| 279 20 | 10+2 f. red | 15 | 15 |
| 280 – | 15+2 f. violet | 15 | 15 |
| 281 22 | 40+2 f. red | 15 | 15 |

(b) Harvesters and Parliament

| No. | Description | Unused | Used |
|---|---|---|---|
| 282 18 | 2 f. brown | 10 | 10 |
| 283 | 3 f. red | 10 | 10 |
| 284 | 4 f. grey | 10 | 10 |
| 285 | 5 f. green | 10 | 10 |
| 286 | 6 f. blue | 10 | 10 |
| 287 | 10 f. red | 10 | 10 |
| 288 | 20 f. brown | 20 | 20 |
| 289 | 40 f. green | 10 | 10 |
| 290 19 | 1 k. red | 10 | 10 |
| 291 | 2 k. brown | 10 | 10 |
| 292 | 3 k. grey and violet | 15 | 15 |
| 293 | 5 k. brown | 60 | 60 |
| 294 | 10 k. mauve and brown | 80 | 80 |

(c) Charles and Zita

| No. | Description | Unused | Used |
|---|---|---|---|
| 295 27 | 10 f. pink | 10 | 10 |
| 296 | 15 f. purple | 10 | 10 |
| 297 | 20 f. brown | 10 | 10 |
| 298 | 25 f. blue | 15 | 15 |
| 299 28 | 40 f. green | 15 | 15 |
| 300 | 50 f. purple | 15 | 15 |

**1919.** As T **18/19**, but inscr "MAGYAR POSTA".

| No. | Description | Unused | Used |
|---|---|---|---|
| 301 18 | 2 f. brown | 10 | 10 |
| 302 | 4 f. grey | 10 | 10 |
| 303 | 5 f. green | 10 | 10 |
| 304 | 6 f. blue | 10 | 10 |
| 305 | 10 f. red | 10 | 10 |
| 306 | 15 f. violet | 10 | 10 |
| 307 | 20 f. brown | 10 | 10 |
| 308 | 20 f. green | 10 | 10 |
| 309 | 25 f. blue | 10 | 10 |
| 310 | 40 f. green | 10 | 10 |
| 311 | 40 f. red | 10 | 10 |
| 312 | 45 f. orange | 10 | 10 |
| 313 19 | 50 f. purple | 10 | 10 |
| 314 | 60 f. blue and brown | 10 | 10 |
| 315 | 95 f. blue | 10 | 10 |
| 316 | 1 k. red | 10 | 10 |
| 317 | 1 k. blue and indigo | 10 | 10 |
| 318 | 1 k. 20 green | 10 | 10 |
| 319 | 1 k. 40 green | 10 | 10 |
| 320 | 2 k. brown | 10 | 10 |
| 321 | 3 k. grey and violet | 10 | 10 |
| 322 | 5 k. brown | 10 | 10 |
| 323 | 10 k. mauve and brown | 60 | 25 |

32. Karl Marx.

PORTRAITS: 45 f. S. Petofi. 60 f. Ignacs Martinovics. 75 f. G. Dozsa. 80 f. F. Engels.

**1919.**

| No. | Description | Unused | Used |
|---|---|---|---|
| 324. 32. | 20 f. red and brown | 30 | 30 |
| 325. – | 45 f. green and orange | 35 | 35 |
| 326. – | 60 f. brown and grey | 2·75 | 2·75 |
| 327. – | 75 f. brown and red | 3·00 | 3·00 |
| 328. – | 80 f. brown and olive | 3·00 | 3·00 |

**1919.** Nos. 301 etc optd **MAGYAR TANACSKOZTARSASAG.** (second word hyphenated on 2 to 45 f.) (= "Hungarian Soviet Republic").

| No. | Description | Unused | Used |
|---|---|---|---|
| 329 18 | 2 f. brown | 15 | 15 |
| 330 | 3 f. purple | 15 | 15 |
| 331 | 4 f. grey | 15 | 15 |
| 332 | 5 f. green | 15 | 15 |
| 333 | 6 f. blue | 15 | 15 |
| 334 | 10 f. red | 15 | 15 |
| 335 | 15 f. violet | 15 | 15 |
| 336 | 20 f. brown | 15 | 15 |
| 337 | 25 f. blue | 15 | 15 |
| 338 | 40 f. green | 15 | 15 |
| 339 | 45 f. orange | 15 | 15 |
| 340 19 | 50 f. purple | 15 | 15 |
| 341 | 95 f. blue | 15 | 15 |
| 342 | 1 k. red | 15 | 15 |
| 343 | 1 k. 20 green | 15 | 15 |
| 344 | 1 k. 40 green | 15 | 15 |
| 345 | 2 k. brown | 40 | 40 |
| 346 | 3 k. grey and violet | 40 | 40 |
| 347 | 5 k. brown | 40 | 40 |
| 348 | 10 k. mauve and brown | 40 | 40 |

**1919.** Entry of National Army into Budapest. Nos. 303 etc optd **A nemzeti hadsereg bevonulasa. 1919. XI/16.**

| No. | Description | Unused | Used |
|---|---|---|---|
| 348a. 18. | 5 f. green | 40 | 40 |
| 348b. | 10 f. red | 40 | 40 |
| 348c. | 15 f. violet | 40 | 40 |
| 348d. | 20 f. brown | 40 | 40 |
| 348e. | 25 f. blue | 40 | 40 |

(36.)

(37.)

**1920.** Nos. 329/48 optd with T **36** (2 to 45 f.) or **37** (others).

| No. | Description | Unused | Used |
|---|---|---|---|
| 349 18 | 2 f. brown | 40 | 40 |
| 350 | 3 f. purple | 10 | 10 |
| 351 | 4 f. grey | 40 | 40 |
| 352 | 5 f. green | 10 | 10 |
| 353 | 6 f. blue | 10 | 10 |
| 354 | 10 f. red | 10 | 10 |
| 355 | 15 f. violet | 10 | 10 |
| 356 | 20 f. brown | 10 | 10 |
| 357 | 25 f. blue | 10 | 10 |
| 358 | 40 f. green | 75 | 75 |
| 359 | 45 f. orange | 75 | 75 |
| 360 19 | 50 f. purple | 75 | 75 |
| 361 | 95 f. blue | 75 | 75 |
| 362 | 1 k. red | 80 | 80 |
| 363 | 1 k. 20 green | 1·25 | 1·25 |
| 364 | 1 k. 40 green | 1·25 | 1·25 |
| 365 | 2 k. brown | 1·60 | 1·60 |
| 366 | 3 k. grey and violet | 1·60 | 1·60 |
| 367 | 5 k. brown | 30 | 30 |
| 368 | 10 k. mauve and brown | 2·50 | 2·50 |

38. Returning P.O.W.

42. Madonna and Child.

**1920.** Returned Prisoners-of-War Fund.

| No. | Description | Unused | Used |
|---|---|---|---|
| 369. 38. | 40 f.+1 k. lake | 35 | 40 |
| 370. – | 60 f.+2 k. brown | 30 | 40 |
| 371. – | 1 k.+5 k. blue | 30 | 40 |

DESIGNS—HORIZ. 60 f. Prison Camp. VERT. 1 k. Family Reunion.

**1920.** Re-issue of T **18** inscr. "MAGYAR KIR. POSTA".

| No. | Description | Unused | Used |
|---|---|---|---|
| 372 18 | 5 f. brown | 10 | 10 |
| 373 | 10 f. purple | 10 | 10 |
| 374 | 40 f. red | 10 | 10 |
| 375 | 50 f. green | 10 | 10 |
| 376 | 50 f. blue | 10 | 10 |
| 377 | 60 f. black | 10 | 10 |
| 378 | 1 k. green | 15 | 10 |
| 379 | 1½ k. purple | 15 | 10 |
| 380 | 2 k. blue | 15 | 10 |
| 381 | 2½ k. green | 15 | 10 |
| 382 | 3 k. brown | 15 | 10 |
| 383 | 4 k. red | 15 | 10 |
| 384 | 4½ k. violet | 15 | 10 |
| 385 | 5 k. brown | 15 | 10 |
| 386 | 6 k. blue | 15 | 10 |
| 387 | 10 k. brown | 15 | 10 |
| 388 | 15 k. black | 15 | 10 |
| 389 | 20 k. red | 15 | 10 |
| 390 | 25 k. orange | 15 | 10 |
| 391 | 40 k. green | 15 | 10 |
| 392 | 50 k. blue | 15 | 10 |
| 393 | 100 k. purple | 15 | 10 |
| 394 | 150 k. green | 15 | 10 |
| 395 | 200 k. green | 15 | 10 |
| 442 | 300 k. red | 15 | 10 |
| 397 | 350 k. violet | 20 | 20 |
| 443 | 400 k. blue | 15 | 10 |
| 444 | 500 k. black | 15 | 10 |
| 445 | 600 k. bistre | 15 | 10 |
| 446 | 800 k. yellow | 25 | 15 |

**1920.** Air. No. 263 surch. **LEGI POSTA** and value.

| No. | Description | Unused | Used |
|---|---|---|---|
| 401. 19. | 3 k. on 10 k. lilac & brn. | 75 | 1·40 |
| 402. | 8 k. on 10 k. lilac & brn. | 75 | 1·40 |
| 403. | 12 k. on 10 k. lilac & brn. | 75 | 1·40 |

**1920.** Re-issue of T **19** inscr. "MAGYAR KIR. POSTA".
404 **19** 2 k. 50 blue .. .. 10 10
405 3 k. 50 grey .. .. 10 10
406 10 k. brown .. .. 10 10
407 15 k. grey .. .. 10 10
408 20 k. red .. .. 10 10
409 25 k. orange .. .. 10 10
410 30 k. lake .. .. 15 10
411 40 k. green .. .. 15 10
412 50 k. blue .. .. 15 10
413 100 k. brown .. .. 15 10
414 400 k. green .. .. 20 15
415 500 k. violet .. .. 15 10
416 1000 k. red .. .. 30 10
448 2000 k. red .. .. 45 15

**1921.**
418 **42** 50 k. blue and brown .. 25 10
419 100 k. brown and bistre 40 10
420 200 k. ultramarine & bl 40 10
421 500 k. mauve and purple 40 15
422 1000 k. purple & mauve 40 15
423 2000 k. mauve and green 50 25
424 2500 k. brown and bistre 40 10
425 3000 k. mauve and red 70 10
426 5000 k. lt green & green 70 10
427 10000 k. blue and violet 1·40 45

**44.** Statue of Petofi in National Dress. **45.** John, the hero, on flying dragon.

DESIGNS—VERT. As Type **45**: 25 k. Petofi. 50 k. Petofi addressing the people.

**47.** Death of Petofi.

**1923.** Birth Cent. of Petofi (poet).
428. **44.** 10 k. (+10 k.) blue .. 30 30
429. **45.** 15 k. (+15 k.) blue .. 90 90
430. – 25 k. (+25 k.) brown .. 30 30
431. **47.** 40 k. (+40 k.) red .. 1·25 1·50
432. – 50 k. (+50 k.) purple .. 1·00 1·50

**49.** Icarus over Budapest. **50.**

**1924.** Air.
433 **49** 100 k. pink and brown 60 1·00
434 500 k. lt green & green 60 1·00
435 1000 k. brown & bistre 60 1·00
436 2000 k. blue & dp blue 60 1·00
436a 5000 k. mauve & purple 1·40 1·40
436b 10000 k. purple and red 1·40 1·40

**1924.** Tuberculosis Relief Fund.
437. **50.** 300 k. (+300 k.) blue 1·25 1·40
438. – 500 k. (+500 k.) brown 1·25 1·40
439. – 1000 k. (+1000 k.) grn. 1·25 1·40
DESIGNS: 500 k. Mother and child. 1000 k. Bowman.

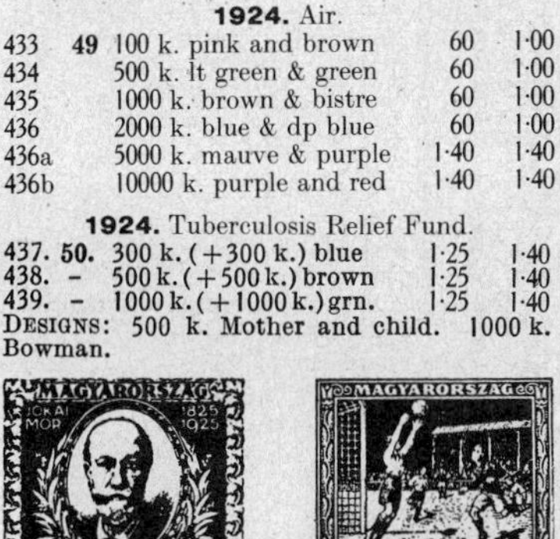

**53.** M. Jokai. **55.**

**1925.** Birth Cent. of Maurus Jokai (novelist).
449. **53.** 1000 k. brown and green 1·75 1·50
450. 2000 k. brown .. .. 1·40 50
451. 2500 k. brown and blue 1·75 1·50

**1925.** Sports Association Fund.
452. – 100 k. (+100 k.) brown and green .. 2·50 1·75
453. – 200 k. (+200 k.) green and brown .. 2·50 2·00
454. – 300 k. (+300 k) blue 4·00 2·50
455. – 400 k. (+400 k.) green and blue .. 4·00 3·50
456. – 500 k. (+500 k.) pur. 5·00 5·00
457. – 1000 k. (+1000 k.) red 6·50 6·00
458. **55.** 2000 k. (+2000 k.) pur. 8·50 7·00
459. – 2500 k. (+2500 k.) sep. 10·00 8·00
DESIGNS—HORIZ. 100 k. Athletes. 500 k. Fencing. VERT. 200 k. Skiing. 300 k. Skating. 400 k. Diving. 1000 k. Scouts. 2500 k. Hurdles.

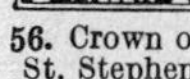

**56.** Crown of St. Stephen. **57.** Matthias Church and Fisher's Bastion. **60.** Madonna and Child.

**58.** Royal Palace, Budapest. **59.**

**1926.** T **59** is without boat.
460 **56** 1 f. black .. .. 20 10
461 2 f. blue .. .. 20 10
462 3 f. orange .. .. 20 10
463 4 f. mauve .. .. 20 10
464 6 f. green .. .. 25 10
465 8 f. mauve .. .. 35 10
466 **57** 10 f. blue .. .. 35 10
467 16 f. violet .. .. 35 10
468 20 f. red .. .. 35 10
469 25 f. brown .. .. 35 10
470 **59** 30 f. green .. .. 1·00 10
471 **58** 32 f. violet .. .. 3·25 15
472 40 f. blue and deep blue 5·00 15
473 **59** 46 f. blue .. .. 2·25 10
474 50 f. black .. .. 2·25 10
475 70 f. red .. .. 3·25 10
476 **60** 1 p. violet .. .. 22·00 40
477 2 p. red .. .. 11·00 70
478 5 p. blue .. .. 22·00 3·00
See also Nos. 502/6.

**61.** The fabulous "Turul". **62.** Mercury astride a "Turul".

**1927.** Air.
478a. **61.** 4 f. orange .. .. 60 25
479. 12 f. green .. .. 55 20
480. 16 f. brown .. .. 65 25
481. 20 f. red .. .. 65 35
482. 32 f. purple .. .. 1·75 1·50
483. 40 f. blue .. .. 1·75 30
484. **62.** 50 f. red .. .. 1·75 1·25
485. 72 f. olive .. .. 1·75 80
486. 80 f. violet .. .. 1·75 85
487. 1 p. green .. .. 3·50 90
488. 2 p. red .. .. 5·00 3·75
489. 5 p. blue .. .. 9·50 12·00

**66.** Royal Palace, Budapest. **67.** St. Stephen.

**1928.** T **66** has the boat in a different place and a redrawn frame.
502. **66.** 30 f. green .. .. 2·25 15
503. 32 f. purple .. .. 2·40 15
504. 40 f. blue .. .. 2·00 15
505. 46 f. green .. .. 2·00 15
506. 50 f. brown .. .. 1·50 15

**1928.** 890th Death Anniv. of St. Stephen of Hungary.
507. **67.** 8 f. green .. .. 30 20
508. 16 f. red .. .. 40 20
509. 32 f. blue .. .. 1·00 90

**1929.** Colours changed.
510. **67.** 8 f. red .. .. 30 15
511. 16 f. violet .. .. 40 20
512. 32 f. bistre .. .. 1·25 90

**68.** Admiral Horthy. **69.** St. Emeric.

**1930.** 10th Anniv. of Regency.
513. **68.** 8 f. green .. .. 80 15
514. 16 f. violet .. .. 80 20
515. 20 f. red .. .. 2·50 70
516. 32 f. brown .. .. 2·25 4·00
517. 40 f. blue .. .. 3·50 1·00

**1930.** 900th Death Anniv. of St. Emeric.
518. **69.** 8 f.+2 f. green .. 40 60
519. – 16 f.+4 f. purple .. 50 80
520. – 20 f.+4 f. red .. 1·75 2·00
521. – 32 f.+8 f. blue .. 2·00 2·25
DESIGNS—VERT: 16 f. St. Stephen and Queen Gisela. 20 f. St. Ladislas. HORIZ: 32 f. Sts. Gellert and Emeric.

**1931.** Surch.
526 **56** 2 on 3 f. orange .. 50 15
527 6 on 8 f. mauve .. 50 10
528 **57** 10 on 16 f. violet .. 50 10
525 20 on 25 f. brown .. 80 60

**1931.** Air. Optd. **Zeppelin 1931.**
529. **62.** 1 p. orange .. .. 25·00 45·00
530. 2 p. purple .. .. 25·00 45·00

**73.** St. Elizabeth. **75.** Madonna and Child. **77.**

**1932.** 700th Death Anniv. of St. Elizabeth of Hungary.
531. **73.** 10 f. blue .. .. 30 10
532. 20 f. red .. .. 30 10
533. – 32 f. purple .. .. 1·25 80
534. – 40 f. blue .. .. 80 35
DESIGN—18×28 mm: 32, 40 f. St. Elizabeth giving cloak to the poor.

**1932.**
535. **75.** 1 p. green .. .. 11·00 10
536. 2 p. red .. .. 11·00 25
537. 5 p. blue .. .. 50·00 2·25
538. 10 p. brown .. .. 70·00 28·00

**1932.** No. 527 further surch **2.**
540 **56** 2 on 6 on 8 f. mauve .. 80 10

**1932.** Famous Hungarians.
541 – 1 f. grey .. .. 15 10
542 – 2 f. orange .. .. 15 10
543 – 4 f. blue .. .. 15 10
543a **77** 5 f. brown .. .. 15 10
544 – 6 f. green .. .. 15 10
545 – 10 f. green .. .. 15 10
546 – 16 f. violet .. .. 15 10
547 – 20 f. red .. .. 45 10
547a – 25 f. green .. .. 30 10
548 – 30 f. brown .. .. 60 10
549 – 32 f. purple .. .. 60 15
550 – 40 f. blue .. .. 60 10
551 – 50 f. green .. .. 80 10
552 – 70 f. red .. .. 1·25 10
DESIGNS: 1 f. I. Madach (poet). 2 f. J Arany (poet). 4 f. I. Semmelweis (physician). 5 f. F. Kolcsey (poet). 6 f. L. Eotvos (physicist). 10 f. I. Szechenyi (statesman). 16 f. F. Deak (statesman). 20 f. F. Liszt (composer). 25 f. M. Vorosmarty (poet). 30 f. L. Kossuth (statesman). 32 f. I. Tisza (statesman). 40 f. M. Munkacsy (painter). 50 f. S. Korosi Csoma (explorer). 70 f. F. Bolyai (mathematician).

**1933.** Surch **10.**
553 **59** 10 on 70 f. red .. .. 60 20

**79.** "Justice for Hungary" over Danube. **80.** Gift Plane from Mussolini. **83.** "The Stag of Hungary".

**1933.** Air.
554. **79.** 10 f. green .. .. 2·00 25
555. 16 f. violet .. .. 2·00 40
556. **80.** 20 f. red .. .. 2·50 30
557. 40 f. blue .. .. 3·00 90
558. – 48 f. black .. .. 17·00 2·00
559. – 72 f. brown .. .. 42·00 3·00
560. – 1 p. green .. .. 18·00 1·50
561. – 2 p. red .. .. 27·00 9·00
562. – 5 p. grey .. .. 70·00 £120
DESIGNS—VERT. As Type **80**: 48, 72 f. "Spirit of Flight" on wing of Lockheed Model 8A Sirius. 1, 2, 5 p. Mercury and propeller.

**1933.** Int. Scout Jamboree, Godollo.
563. **83.** 10 f. green .. .. 90 20
564. 16 f. red .. .. 2·50 1·75
565. 20 f. red .. .. 1·25 40
566. 32 f. yellow .. .. 4·00 2·25
567. 40 f. blue .. .. 4·75 1·75

**84.** Ferenc Rakoczi II. **85.** Cardinal Peter Pazmany.

**1935.** Death Bicentenary of Prince Rakoczi.
569. **84.** 10 f. green .. .. 75 20
570. 16 f. violet .. .. 2·25 2·75
571. 20 f. red .. .. 75 20
572. 32 f. red .. .. 5·50 3·25
573. 40 f. blue .. .. 4·50 3·25

**1935.** Tercent. of Budapest University.
574. **85.** 6 f. green .. .. 75 70
575. – 10 f. green .. .. 30 15
576. **85.** 16 f. violet .. .. 1·40 95
577. 20 f. mauve .. .. 30 15
578. – 32 f. red .. .. 1·75 1·00
579. – 40 f. blue .. .. 1·50 1·00
DESIGN—HORIZ. (35×25 mm.): 10 f., 32 f., 40 f. Pazmany signing deed.

**87.** Fokker F.VIIb/3m.

**1936.** Air.
580. **87.** 10 f. green .. .. 30 10
581. 20 f. red .. .. 30 10
582. 36 f. brown .. .. 45 15
583. – 40 f. blue .. .. 50 15
584. – 52 f. orange .. .. 80 65
585. – 60 f. violet .. .. 22·00 2·25
586. – 80 f. green .. .. 3·00 60
587. – 1 p. green .. .. 3·00 50
588. – 2 p. lake .. .. 7·00 2·25
589. – 5 p. blue .. .. 29·00 32·00
DESIGNS: 40 f. to 80 f. Fokker F.VIIb/3m over Parliament Buildings. 1 p. to 5 p. Fokker F.VIIb/3m (different).

**88.** Ancient Buda.

DESIGNS: 16 f. Angel of Peace over Buda. 20 f. Arms of Buda. 32 f. Colour bearer and bugler.

**1936.** 250th Anniv. of Recapture of Buda from Turks.
590. **88.** 10 f. green .. .. 35 15
591. – 16 f. mauve .. .. 1·40 80
592. – 20 f. red .. .. 35 15
593. – 32 f. brown .. .. 1·40 90
594 **88.** 40 f. blue .. .. 1·40 90

**89.** "Commerce", "May Fair, 1937" and R. Danube. **90.** St. Stephen, the Church Builder.

**1937.** Budapest Int. Fair.
595. **89.** 2 f. orange .. .. 10 10
596. 6 f. green .. .. 20 10
597. 10 f. green .. .. 20 10
598. 20 f. red .. .. 20 10
599. 32 f. violet .. .. 45 25
600. 40 f. blue .. .. 45 20

**1938.** 900th Death Anniv. of St. Stephen. (1st issue).
601. – 1 f. violet .. .. 15 10
602. **90.** 2 f. sepia .. .. 15 10
603. – 4 f. blue .. .. 20 10
604. – 5 f. mauve .. .. 20 10
605. – 6 f. green .. .. 25 10
606. – 10 f. red .. .. 25 10
607. **90.** 16 f. violet .. .. 30 25
608. – 20 f. red .. .. 40 10
609. – 25 f. green .. .. 40 20
610. – 30 f. bistre .. .. 70 10
611. – 32 f. red on yellow .. 70 70
612. – 40 f. blue .. .. 80 10
613. – 50 f. purple on green .. 85 10
614. – 70 f. green on blue .. 1·25 10
DESIGNS: 1 f., 10 f. Abbot Astrik receiving Crown from Pope. 4 f., 20 f. St. Stephen enthroned. 5 f., 25, St. Gellert, St. Emeric and St. Stephen. 6 f., 30 f. St. Stephen offering Crown to Virgin Mary. 32 f., 50 f., St. Stephen. 40 f. Madonna and Child. 70 f. Crown of St. Stephen.
See also Nos. 620/1.

**92.** Admiral Horthy. **93.** Eucharistic Symbols.

**1938.**
615. **92.** 1 p. green .. .. 75 10
616. 2 p. sepia .. .. 1·00 10
617. 5 p. blue .. .. 2·25 70

**1938.** 34th Int. Eucharistic Congress.
618. – 16 f.+16 f. blue .. 1·75 3·00
619. **93.** 20 f.+20 f. red .. 1·75 3·00
DESIGN: 16 f. St. Ladislas.

**94.** St. Stephen the Victorious.

**1938.** 900th Death Anniv. of St. Stephen. (2nd issue).
620. **94.** 10 f.+10 f. purple .. 1·75 3·00
621 – 20 f.+20 f. red .. 1·75 3·00
DESIGN: 20 f. Differing crown to Virgin Mary.

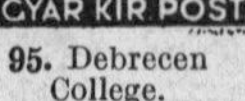

**95.** Debrecen College. **100.** Statue representing Northern Provinces.

**1938.** 400th Anniv. of Debrecen College.
622. **95.** 6 f. green .. .. 15 10
623. – 10 f. brown .. .. 10 10
624. – 16 f. red .. .. 15 10
625. – 20 f. red .. .. 10 10
626. – 32 f. green .. .. 30 20
627. – 40 f. blue .. .. 30 15
DESIGNS—HORIZ. 10 f., 20 f. 18th and 19th-cent. views of College. VERT. 16 f. 18th-century students as firemen. 32 f. Prof. Marothi. 40 f. Dr. Hatvani.

**1938.** Acquisition of Czech Territory. As Nos. 608 and 614 optd **HAZATERES 1938.**
628 20 f. red .. .. .. 60 10
629 70 f. brown on blue .. 60 10

**1939.** "Hungary for Hungarians" Patriotic Fund.
630. **100.** 6 f.+3 f. green.. .. 25 25
631. – 10 f.+5 f. green .. 25 25
632. – 20 f.+10 f. red .. 25 25
633. – 30 f.+15 f. green .. 40 40
634. – 40 f.+20 f. blue .. 40 40
DESIGNS: 10 f. Fort at Munkacs. 20 f. Admiral Horthy leading troops into Komarom. 30 f. Catherdral of St. Elizabeth of Hungary, Kassa. 40 f. Girls offering flowers to soldiers.

**101.** Crown of St. Stephen. **102.** Esztergom Basilica.

**1939.**
635 **101** 1 f. purple .. .. 10 10
636 2 f. green .. .. 10 10
690 3 f. brown .. .. 10 10
637 4 f. brown .. .. 10 10
638 5 f. violet .. .. 10 10
639 6 f. green .. .. 10 10
693 8 f. green .. .. 10 10
640 10 f. brown .. .. 10 10
695 12 f. red .. .. 10 10
641 16 f. violet .. .. 10 10
642 – 20 f. red .. .. 10 10
697 – 24 f. red .. .. 10 10
643 – 25 f. blue .. .. 10 10
699 – 30 f. mauve .. .. 10 10
645 – 32 f. brown .. .. 20 10
700 **102** 40 f. green .. .. 10 10
701 – 50 f. green .. .. 10 10
702 – 70 f. red .. .. 15 10
698 – 80 f. brown .. .. 15 10
DESIGNS—As T **101**: 20, 24 f. St. Stephen. 25, 80 f. Madonna and Child. As T **102**: 30 f. Buda Cathedral. 32 f. Debrecen Reformed Church. 50 f. Budapest Evangelical Church. 70 f. Kassa Cathedral.

For further issues in these designs, see Nos. 751/5.

**103.** Guides' Salute. **104.** Memorial Tablets.

**1939.** Girl Guides' Rally, Godollo. Inscr. "I. PAX-TING".
649. **103.** 2 f. orange .. .. 20 15
650. – 6 f. green .. .. 35 15
651. – 10 f. brown .. .. 35 10
652. – 20 f. pink .. .. 1·00 25
DESIGNS: 6 f. Lily symbol and Hungarian arms. 10 f. Guide and girl in national costume. 20 f. Dove of peace.

**1939.** National Protestant Day and Int. Protestant Cultural Fund.
653. **104.** 6 f.+3 f. green.. .. 40 20
654. – 10 f.+5 f. purple .. 40 20
655. – 20 f.+10 f. red .. 40 20
656. – 32 f.+16 f. brown .. 50 35
657. – 40 f.+20 f. blue .. 50 40
DESIGNS—HORIZ. 10 f., 20 f. G. Karoli and A. Molnar di Szenci (translators of the Bible and the Psalms). VERT. 32 f. Prince Gabriel Bethlen. 40 f. Zsuzsanna Lorantffy.

**106.** Boy Scout with Kite. **107.** Regent and Szeged Cathedral.

**1940.** Admiral Horthy Aviation Fund.
658. **106.** 6 f.+6 f. green.. .. 15 25
659. – 10 f.+10 f. brown .. 85 85
660. – 20 f.+20 f. red .. 1·25 1·25
DESIGNS: 10 f. "Spirit of Flight". 20 f. St. Elizabeth carrying Crown and Cross of St. Stephen.

**1940.** 20th Anniv. of Regency.
661. **107.** 6 f. green .. .. 10 10
662. – 10 f. brown and olive .. 10 10
663. – 20 f. red .. .. 20 10
DESIGNS: 10 f. Admiral Horthy. **20 f. Kassa** Cathedral and Angelic bellringer.

**108.** Stemming the Flood.

**1940.** Flood Relief Fund.
664. **108.** 10 f.+2 f. purple .. 15 10
665. 20 f.+4 f. orange .. 15 10
666. 20 f.+50 f. brown .. 45 40

**109.** Hunyadi Family Arms. **110.** Hunyadi Castle.

**1940.** 500th Birth Anniv. of King Matthias Hunyadi and Cultural Institutes Fund.
667. **109.** 6 f.+3 f. green.. .. 20 20
668. **110.** 10 f.+5 f. brown .. 20 20
669. – 16 f.+8 f. olive .. 25 25
670. – 20 f.+10 f. red .. 30 30
671. – 32 f.+16 f. grey .. 30 30
DESIGNS—VERT. 16 f. Bust of King Matthias (dated "1440-1490"). 32 f. Corvin Codex (dated "1473"). HORIZ. 20 f. Equestrian Statue of King Matthias.

**111.** Crown of St. Stephen. **112.** Madonna and Martyr.

**1940.** Recovery from Rumania of North-Eastern Transylvania.
672. **111.** 10 f. green and yellow 15 10

**1940.** Transylvanian Relief Fund. Various designs dated "1940".
673. – 10 f.+50 f. green .. 40 40
674. **112.** 20 f.+50 f. red .. 40 40
675. – 32 f.+50 f. brown .. 50 50
DESIGNS: 10 f. Prince Csaba and soldier. 32 f. Mother offering child to Fatherland.

DESIGNS—VERT. 10 f. Sculpture. 16 f. Painting. HORIZ. 20 f. Poetry (Pegasus).

**113.** Spirit of Music.

**1940.** Artists' Relief Fund. Inscr. "MAGYAR MUVESZETERT".
676. **113.** 6 f.+6 f. green .. 35 35
677. – 10 f.+10 f. brown .. 35 35
678. – 16 f.+16 f. violet .. 35 35
679. – 20 f.+20 f. red .. 35 35

**114.** Pilot.

**1941.** Air stamps. Horthy Aviation Fund. Various allegorical designs inscribed "HORTHY MIKLOS NEMZETI REPULO ALAP".
680. **114.** 6 f.+6 f. olive.. .. 30 40
681. – 10 f.+10 f. brown .. 60 40
682. – 20 f.+20 f. red .. 60 40
683. – 32 f.+32 f. blue .. 60 85
DESIGNS: 10 f. Youth releasing model glider. 20 f. Glider. 32 f. Madonna.

**1941.** Acquisition of Yugoslav Territory. Overprinted **DEL-UISSZATER** ("The South comes home").
684. **101.** 10 f. brown .. .. 15 10
685. – 20 f. red (No. 642) .. 15 10

**116.** Admiral Horthy.

**1941.**
686. **116.** 1 p. green and yellow .. 15 10
687. 2 p. brown and yellow 15 10
688. 5 p. purple and yellow 25 15

**118.** Count Szechenyi. **119.** Giant opening Straits of Kazan.

**1941.** 150th Birth Anniv. of Count Szechenyi.
703. **118.** 10 f. olive .. .. 10 10
704. – 16 f. brown .. .. 15 10
705. **119.** 20 f. red .. .. 15 10
706. – 32 f. orange .. .. 25 15
707. – 40 f. blue .. .. 45 15
DESIGNS: 16 f. Count Szechenyi and Academy of Science. 32 f. Budapest Chain Bridge. 40 f. Mercury, Locomotive and river steamer.

**120.** Infantry in Action. **121.** Pilot and Airplane.

**1941.** Soldiers' Gifts Fund. Inscr. "HONVEDEINK KARACSONYARA 1941".
(a) First issue.
708. **120.** 8 f.+12 f. green .. 25 15
709. – 12 f.+18 f. brown .. 25 15
710. – 20 f.+30 f. blue .. 30 25
711. – 40 f.+60 f. brown .. 30 25
DESIGNS: 12 f. Artillery. 20 f. Tanks. 40 f. Cavalryman and cyclist.
(b) 2nd issue (for Christmas Gifts).
712. – 20 f.+40 f. red.. .. 1·00 85
DESIGN: Soldier in helmet; cross and sword.

**1942.** Air. Horthy Aviation Fund. Inscr "HORTHY MIKLOS NEMZETI REPULO ALAP".
713. **121.** 8 f.+8 f. green.. .. 35 30
714. – 12 f.+12 f. blue .. 70 50
715. – 20 f.+20 f. brown .. 70 50
716. – 30 f.+30 f. red.. .. 35 30
DESIGNS—VERT. 30 f. Airmen and Turul. HORIZ 12 f. Aircraft and horsemen. 20 f. Airplane and archer.

**122.** Blood Transfusion. **123.** Vice-regent Stephen Horthy.

**1942.** Red Cross Fund. Cross in red.
717 **122** 3 f.+18 f. green .. 65 60
718 – 8 f.+32 f. brown .. 65 60
719 – 12 f.+50 f. purple .. 65 60
720 – 20 f.+1 p. blue .. 65 60
DESIGNS: 8 f. First Aid ("APOLAS"). 12 f. Wireless and carrier-pigeon service ("GONDOZAS"). 20 f. Bereaved parents and orphans ("GYAMOLITAS").

**1942.** Air. Mourning for Stephen Horthy and Horthy Aviation Fund.
721. – 20 f. black .. .. 25 10
722. **123.** 30 f.+20 f. violet .. 30 15
No. 721 is squarer in shape than No. 722 and is dated "1904-1942".

**124.** Stephen Horthy's Widow. **125.** King Ladislas.

**1942.** Red Cross Fund. Cross and Crown in red.
723. **124.** 6 f.+1 p. blue .. 1·75 2·25
724. – 8 f.+1 p. green .. 1·75 2·25
725. – 20 f.+1 p. brown .. 1·75 2·25
DESIGNS—HORIZ. 8 f. Nurse and wounded soldier. VERT. 20 f. Stephen Horthy's mother.

**1942.** Cultural Funds.
726 **125** 6 f.+6 f. brown .. 30 40
727 – 8 f.+8 f. green .. 30 40
728 – 12 f.+12 f. brown .. 30 40
729 – 20 f.+20 f. green .. 30 40
730 – 24 f.+24 f. brown .. 30 40
731 – 30 f.+30 f. red .. 30 40
DESIGNS—Statuettes: 8 f. Ladislas on horseback. 20 f. Bela IV with architect. 30 f. Lajos the Great enthroned. King's heads: 12 f. Bela IV. 24 f. Lajos the Great.

**126.** Prince Arpad. **127.** St. Stephen's Crown.

**1943.**
732. **126.** 1 f. grey .. .. 10 10
733. – 2 f. orange .. .. 10 10
734. – 3 f. blue.. .. .. 10 10
735. – 4 f. brown .. .. 10 10
736. – 5 f. red .. .. .. 10 10
737. – 6 f. blue.. .. .. 10 10
738. – 8 f. green .. .. 10 10
739. – 10 f. brown .. .. 10 10
740. – 12 f. green .. .. 10 10
741. – 18 f. black .. .. 10 10
742. **127.** 20 f. brown .. .. 10 10
743. – 24 f. purple .. .. 10 10
744. **127.** 30 f. red .. .. 10 10
745. – 30 f. red .. .. 10 10
746. **127.** 50 f. blue .. .. 10 10
747. 80 f. brown .. .. 10 10
748. 1 p. green .. .. 10 10
749. 2 p. brown .. .. 20 10
750. 5 p. purple .. .. 30 15
DESIGNS: 2 f. King Ladislas. 3 f. Miklos Toldi. 4 f. Janos Hunyadi. 5 f. Pal Kinizsi. 6 f. Miklos Zrinyi. 8 f. Ferenc Rakoczi II. 10 f. Andre Hadik. 12 f. Artur Gorgey. 18 f. and 24 f. Madonna. 30 f. (No. 745), St. Margaret.

**1943.** As T **102** (designs and colours changed).
751 – 30 f. red .. .. 10 10
752 – 40 f. grey .. .. 10 10
753 **102** 50 f. blue .. .. 10 10
754 – 70 f. green .. .. 10 10
755 – 80 f. brown .. .. 10 10
DESIGNS: 30 f. Kassa Cathedral. 40 f. Debrecen Reformed Church. 70 f. Budapest Evangelical Church. 80 f. Buda Cathedral.

**128.** Mounted Archer. **129.** Model Glider.

**1943.** Wounded Soldiers' Relief Fund. Inscr. as in T **128.**
756. **128.** 1 f.+1 f. grey .. 10 10
757. – 3 f.+1 f. lilac .. 20 30
758. – 4 f.+1 f. brown .. 15 10
759. – 8 f.+2 f. green .. 15 10
760. – 12 f.+2 f. brown .. 15 10
761. – 20 f.+2 f. brown .. 15 10
762. – 40 f.+4 f. grey .. 15 10
763. – 50 f.+6 f. brown .. 15 10
764. – 70 f.+8 f. blue .. 15 10
DESIGNS—VERT. 3 f., 4 f. Magyar soldier with battle-axe and buckler. 8 f. Warrior with shield and sword. 20 f. Musketeer. 50 f. Artilleryman. 70 f. Magyar Arms. HORIZ. 12 f. Lancer. 40 f. Hussar.

**1943.** Air. Horthy Aviation Fund. Inscr. "HORTHY MIKLOS NEMZETI REPULO ALAP".
765. **129.** 8 f.+8 f. green .. 50 45
766. – 12 f.+12 f. blue .. 50 45
767. – 20 f.+20 f. brown .. 1·50 55
768. – 30 f.+30 f. red .. 50 45
DESIGNS: 12 f. Gliders in flight. 20 f. White-tailed sea eagle and aircraft. 30 f. Cant Z.1007 bis Alcione bomber and gliders.

130. Shepherds and Angels.

131. Nurse and Soldier.

**1943.** Christmas.

769. **130.** 4 f. green .. .. 15 10
770. – 20 f. blue .. .. 15 10
771. – 30 f. red .. .. 15 10

DESIGNS: 20 f. Nativity. 30 f. Adoration of the Wise Men.

**1944.** Red Cross Fund. Cross and Crown in red.

772. **131.** 20 f.+20 f. brown .. 30 25
773. – 30 f.+30 f. brown .. 30 25
774. – 50 f.+50 f. purple .. 30 25
775. – 70 f.+70 f. blue .. 30 25

DESIGNS: 30 f. Soldier, nurse, mother and child. 50 f. Nurse shielding a lamp over the Fallen. 70 f. Soldier with crutches, nurse and sapling.

132. Drummer and Flags.

133. St. Elizabeth.

**1944.** 50th Death Anniv. of Kossuth (statesman).

776. – 4 f. brown .. .. 10 10
777. **132.** 20 f. green .. .. 10 10
778. – 30 f. red .. .. 10 10
779. – 50 f. blue .. .. 10 10

DESIGNS—VERT. 4 f. Kossuth and family group. 50 f. Portrait. HORIZ. 30 f. Kossuth speaking before an assembly.

**1944.** Famous Women.

780 **133** 20 f. bistre .. .. 10 10
781 – 24 f. purple .. .. 10 10
782 – 30 f. red .. .. 10 10
783 – 50 f. blue .. .. 10 10
784 – 70 f. red .. .. 10 10
785 – 80 f. brown .. .. 10 10

PORTRAITS: 24 f. St. Margaret. 30 f. Elizabeth Szilagyi. 50 f. Dorothy Kanizsai. 70 f. Zsuzsanna Lorantffy. 80 f. Ilona Zrinyi.

**1945.** Stamps as Nos. 732/48, surch **FELSZABADULAS** (= Liberation) **1945 apr 4** and value. On yellow or blue surface-tinted paper (same price).

786. 10 f. on 1 f. grey .. 90 90
787. 20 f. on 3 f. blue .. .. 90 90
788. 30 f. on 4 f. brown .. 90 90
789. 40 f. on 6 f. blue .. 90 90
790. 50 f. on 8 f. green .. 90 90
791. 1 p. on 10 f. brown .. 90 90
792. 150 f. on 12 f. green .. 90 90
793. 2 p. on 18 f. black .. 90 90
794. 3 p. on 20 f. brown .. 90 90
795. 5 p. on 24 f. purple .. 90 90
796. 6 p. on 50 f. blue.. .. 90 90
797. 10 p. on 80 f. brown .. 90 90
798. 20 p. on 1 p. green .. 90 90

135. Bajcsy-Zsilinszky.

**1945.** Bajcsy-Zsilinszky (patriot).

799. **135.** 1 p.+1 p. purple .. 30 30

**1945.** Provisionals. 1st issue. Surch. **1945** and value. (a) On stamps of 1943, Nos. 732/50, surface-tinted paper.

800. 10 f. on 4 f. brown on blue 10 10
801. 10 f. on 10 f. brown on blue 20 20
802. 10 f. on 12 f. green on yell. 10 10
803. 20 f. on 1 f. grey on yellow 10 10
804. 20 f. on 18 f. black on yell. 10 10
805. 28 f. on 5 f. red on blue .. 10 10
806. 30 f. on 30 f. red on blue (No. 745) .. .. 10 10
807. 30 f. on 30 f. red on blue (No. 744) .. .. 10 10
808. 40 f. on 24 f. purple on yell. 10 10
809. 42 f. on 20 f. brown on yell. 10 10
810. 50 f. on 50 f. blue on yell. 10 10
811. 60 f. on 8 f. green on yell. 10 10
812. 1 p. on 80 f. brown on blue 10 10
813. 1 p. on 1 p. green on yellow 10 10
814. 150 f. on 6 f. blue on yellow 40 40
815. 2 p. on 2 p. brown on blue 10 10
816. 3 p. on 3 f. blue on yellow 15 15
817. 5 p. on 5 p. purple on yellow 15 15
818. 10 p. on 2 f. orange on blue 3·00 3·00

(b) On Famous Women Series of 1944 (Nos. 780/5), surface-tinted paper.

819 20 f. on 20 f. bistre on blue 10 10
820 30 f. on 30 f. red on blue .. 10 10
821 40 f. on 24 f. purple on yell 10 10
822 50 f. on 50 f. blue on yellow 10 10
823 80 f. on 80 f. brown on yell 10 10
824 1 p. on 70 f. red on blue .. 10 10

**1945.** Provisionals. 2nd issue. Surch. **1945** and value. (a) On stamps of 1943, Nos. 732/48, surface-tinted paper.

825. 40 f. on 10 f. brown on blue 10 10
826. 1 p. on 20 f. brown on yell. 10 10
827. 1.60 p. on 12 f. grn. on yell. 10 10
828. 2 p. on 4 f. brown on blue 10 10
829. 4 p. on 30 f. red on blue (No. 744) .. .. 10 10
830. 5 p. on 8 f. green on yellow 10 10
831. 6 p. on 50 f. blue on yellow 10 10
832. 7 p. on 1 p. green on yellow 10 10
833. 9 p. on 1 f. grey on yellow 10 10
834. 10 p. on 80 f. brown on blue 10 10

(b) On Famous Women Series of 1944. (Nos. 780/3), surface-tinted paper.

835 80 f. on 24 f. purple on yell 10 10
836 3 p. on 50 f. blue on yellow 10 10
837 8 p. on 20 f. bistre on blue 10 10
838 20 p. on 30 f. red on blue 10 10

**1945.** National High School Fund. Nos. 776/9, with coloured surfaces, surch **BEKE A NEPFOISKOLAKERT**, new value and premium.

839 **132** 3 p.+9 p. on 20 f. green on yellow .. .. 20 20
840 – 4 p.+12 p. on 4 f. brown on blue .. 20 20
841 – 8 p.+24 p. on 50 f. blue on yellow .. .. 20 20
842 – 10 p.+30 p. on 30 f. red on blue .. .. 20 20

138. Mining.

139. I. Sallai and S. Furst.

**1945.** Int. Trade Union Conference, Paris.

843. **138.** 40 f. grey .. .. 2·50 2·50
844. – 1 p. 60 brown.. .. 2·50 2·50
845. – 2 p. green .. .. 2·50 2·50
846. – 3 p. purple .. .. 2·50 2·50
847. – 5 p. red .. .. 2·50 2·50
848. – 8 p. brown .. .. 2·50 2·50
849. – 10 p. red .. .. 2·50 2·50
850. – 20 p. blue .. .. 2·50 2·50

DESIGNS: Trade Symbols—1 p. 60, Hammer and anvil (ironworking). 2 p. Winged wheel (railway workers). 3 p. Trowel and bricks (building). 5 p. Plough (agriculture). 8 p. Carrier pigeon (communications). 10 p. Compasses (engineering). 20 p. Winged pen and book (clerks).

**1945.** National Relief Fund.

851. **139.** 2 p.+2 p. brown .. 75 75
852. – 3 p.+3 p. red.. .. 75 75
853. – 4 p.+4 p. violet .. 75 75
854. – 6 p.+6 p. green .. 75 75
855. – 10 p.+10 p. red .. 75 75
856. – 15 p.+15 p. olive .. 75 75
857. – 20 p.+20 p. brown .. 75 75
858. – 40 p.+40 p. blue .. 75 75

PORTRAITS: 3 p. L. Kabok and I. Monus. 4 p. F. Rozsa and Z. Schonherz. 6 p. A. Koltoi and P. Knurr. 10 p. G. Sarkozi and I. Nagy. 15 p. V. Tartsay and J. Nagy. 20 p. J. Kiss and E. Bajcsy-Zsilinszky. 40 p. E. Sagvari and O. Hoffmann.

**1945.** Provisionals. 3rd issue. Nos. 738, 740/1 and 745 (coloured surfaces) surch **1945** and new value.

859 40 p. on 8 f. green on yell 10 10
860 60 p. on 18 f. black on yell 10 10
861 100 p. on 12 f. green on yell 10 10
862 300 p. on 30 f. red on blue 10 10

140. Reconstruction.

**1945.**

863. **140.** 12 p. olive .. .. 25 25
864. 20 p. green .. .. 10 10
865. 24 p. brown .. .. 25 25
866. 30 p. black .. .. 10 10
867. 40 p. green .. .. 10 10
868. 60 p. red .. .. 10 10
869. 100 p. orange .. .. 10 10
870. 120 p. blue .. .. 10 10
871. 140 p. red .. .. 30 30
872. 200 p. brown .. .. 10 10
873. 240 p. blue .. .. 10 10
874. 300 p. red .. .. 10 10
875. 500 p. green .. .. 10 10
876. 1000 p. purple .. .. 10 10
877. 3000 p. red .. .. 10 10

Owing to the collapse of the pengo, the following stamps were overprinted to show the postage rate for which they were valid, and they were sold at the appropriate rate for the day. **Any.** or **Nyomtatv** = Sample Post or Printed Matter. **Hlp** or **Helyi lev. lap** = Local Postcard. **Hl** or **Helyi level** = Local Letter. **Tlp** or **Tavolsagi lev.-lap** = Inland Postcard. **Tl** or **Tavolsagi level** = Inland Letter. **Ajl** or **Ajanlas** = Registered Letter. **Cs.** or **Csomag** = Parcel.

**1946.** Optd as above. (a) First Issue.

878 **126** "Any. 1" on 1 f. grey 10 10
879 – "Hlp. 1" on 8 p. on 20 f. bistre on blue (No. 837) .. .. 10 10
880 – "Hl. 1" on 50 f. blue (No. 783) .. .. 10 10
881 – "Tlp. 1" on 4 f. brown (No. 735) .. .. 10 10
882 – "Tl. 1" on 10 f. brown (No. 739) .. .. 10 10
883 **133** "Ajl. 1" on 20 f. bistre 10 10
883b **127** "Cs. 5–1" on 30 f. red (No. 744) .. .. 11·00 11·00
884 – "Cs. 5–1" on 70 f. red (No. 784) .. .. 10 10
885 – "Cs. 10–1" on 70 f. red (No. 784) .. .. 10 10
885a **127** "Cs. 10–1" on 80 f. brown (No.747) .. 11·00 11·00

(b) Second Issue.

886 **126** "Any. 2" on 1 f. grey 10 10
887 – "Hlp. 2" on 8 p. on 20 f. bistre on blue (No. 837) .. .. 10 10
888 – "Hl. 2" on 40 f. on 10 f. brn on bl (No. 825) 10 10
889 – "Tlp. 2" on 4 f. brown (No. 735) .. .. 10 10
890 – "Tl. 2" on 10 f. on 4 f. brn on bl (No. 800) 10 10
891 – "Ajl. 2" on 12 f. green (No. 740) .. .. 10 10
892 – "Cs. 5–2" on 24 f. purple (No. 743) .. 10 10
893 – "Cs. 10–2" on 80 f. brown (No. 785) .. 10 10

(c) Third Issue.

894 – "Nyomtatv. 20 gr." on 60 f. on 8 f. green on yellow (No. 811) .. 10 10
895 – "Helyi lev.-lap" on 2 f. bistre on blue (as No. 780) .. .. 10 10
896 – "Helyi level" on 10 f. brown on blue (as No. 739) .. .. 10 10
897 – "Tavolsagi lev.-lap" on 4 f. brown (No. 735) 10 10
898 – "Tavolsagi level" on 18 f. black (No. 741) 10 10
899 – "Ajanlas" on 24 f. purple (No. 781) .. 10 10
900 – "Csomag 5 kg" on 2 p. on 4 f. brown on blue (No. 828) .. .. 10 10
901 – "Csomag 10 kg." on 30 f. red on blue (as No. 782) .. .. 10 10

Abbreviations used in the following issues:
ez(er) p. = thousand pengos.
m(illio) p. = million pengos.
m.p. (milpengo) = million pengos.
md.p. (milliard. p) = thousand million pengos.
b.p. (billio. p) = million million pengos.
ez. ap (ezer adopengo) = thousand "tax" pengos.
m. ap. (millio adopengo) = million "tax" pengos.

143.

144.

**1946.** Foundation of Republic.

902. **143.** 3 ez. p. brown .. 10 10
903. 15 ez. p. blue .. .. 10 10

**1946.**

904. **144.** 4 ez. p. brown .. 10 10
905. 10 ez. p. red .. .. 10 10
906. 15 ez. p. blue .. .. 10 10
907. 20 ez. p. brown .. 10 10
908. 30 ez. p. purple .. 10 10
909. 50 ez. p. grey .. 10 10
910. 80 ez. p. blue .. .. 10 10
911. 100 ez. p. red .. 10 10
912. 160 ez. p. green .. 10 10
913. 200 ez. p. green .. 10 10
914. 500 ez. p. red .. 10 10
915. 640 ez. p. olive .. 10 10
916. 800 ez. p. violet .. 10 10

145.

146.

**1946.** 75th Anniv of First Hungarian Stamps.

917 **145** 500+500 ez. p. green .. 75 75
918 1+1 m. p. brown .. 75 75
919 1.5+1.5 m. p. red .. 75 75
920 2+2 m. p. blue .. 75 75

**1946.**

921 **146** 1 m. p. red .. .. 10 10
922 2 m. p. blue .. .. 10 10
923 3 m. p. brown .. 10 10
924 4 m. p. grey .. .. 10 10
925 5 m. p. violet .. 10 10
926 10 m. p. green .. 10 10
927 20 m. p. red .. .. 10 10
928 50 m. p. green .. 10 10

147. Posthorn and Arms.

148. Posthorn.

149. Dove and Letter.

**1946.**

929 **147** 100 m.p. red .. .. 10 10
930 200 m.p. red .. .. 10 10
931 500 m.p. red .. .. 10 10
932 1000 m.p. red .. .. 10 10
933 2000 m.p. red .. .. 10 10
934 3000 m.p. red .. .. 10 10
935 5000 m.p. red .. .. 10 10
936 10,000 m.p. red .. 10 10
937 20,000 m.p. red .. 10 10
938 30,000 m.p. red .. 10 10
939 50,000 m.p. red .. 10 10

**1946.**

940 **148** 100 md.p. green & red 10 10
941 200 md.p. green & red 10 10
942 500 md.p. green & red 10 10

**1946.**

943. **149.** 1 b.p. black and red .. 10 10
944. 2 b.p. black and red .. 10 10
945. 5 b.p. black and red .. 10 10
946. 10 b.p. black and red.. 10 10
947. 20 b.p. black and red.. 10 10
948. 50 b.p. black and red.. 10 10
949. 100 b.p. black and red 10 10
950. 200 b.p. black and red 10 10
951. 500 b.p. black and red 10 10
952. 1000 b.p. black and red 10 10
953. 10,000 b.p. black & red 10 10
954. 50,000 b.p. black & red 15 15
955. 100,000 b.p. black & red 15 15
956. 500,000 b.p. black & red 15 15

150. "Heves" Class Locomotive.

151. Posthorn.

**1946.** Centenary of Hungarian Railways.

957 **150** 10000 ap. brown .. 4·50 4·00
958 – 20000 ap. blue .. 4·50 4·00
959 – 30000 ap. green .. 4·50 4·00
960 – 40000 ap. red .. .. 4·50 4·00

DESIGNS: 20000 ap. Class "424" steam locomotive. 30000 ap. Electric locomotive. 40000 ap. Arpad railcar.

**1946.**

961. **151.** 5 ez. ap. green & black 10 10
962. 10 ez. ap. green & black 10 10
963. 20 ez. ap. green & black 10 10
964. 50 ez. ap. green & black 10 10
965. 80 ez. ap. green & black 10 10
966. 100 ez. ap. green & blk. 10 10
967. 200 ez. ap. green & blk. 10 10
968. 500 ez. ap. green & blk. 10 10
969. 1 m. ap. red and black 10 10
970. 5 m. ap. red and black 10 10

152. Industry.

153. Agriculture.

**1946.** Currency Reform.

971. **152.** 8 fi. brown .. .. 15 10
972. 10 fi. brown .. .. 15 10
973. 12 fi. brown .. .. 15 10
974. 20 fi. brown .. .. 15 10
975. 30 fi. brown .. .. 15 10
976. 40 fi. brown .. .. 15 10
977. 60 fi. brown .. .. 20 10
978. **153.** 1 fo. green .. .. 60 10
979. 1 fo. 40 green.. .. 60 10
980. 2 fo. green .. .. 65 10
981. 3 fo. green .. .. 5·00 10
982. 5 fo. green .. .. 1·50 10
983. 10 fo. green .. .. 2·50 20

154. Ceres.

155. Liberty Bridge.

**1946.** Agricultural Fair.
984. 154. 30 fi.+60 fi. green .. 1·50 1·50
985. 60 fi.+1 fo. 20 red .. 1·50 1·50
986. 1 fo.+2 fo. blue .. 2·25 2·25

**1947.** Air. Views.
987 – 10 fi. red .. .. 15 10
988 – 20 fi. grey .. .. 15 10
989 155 50 fi. brown .. .. 40 10
990 – 70 fi. green .. .. 40 10
991 – 1 fo. blue .. .. 80 10
992 – 1 fo. 40 brown .. 90 10
993 – 3 fo. green .. .. 2·75 25
994 – 5 fo. lilac .. .. 2·00 45
DESIGNS—: 10 fi. Loyalty Tower, Sopron. 20 fi. Esztergom Catherdral. 70 fi. Palace Hotel, Lillafured. 1 fo. Vajdahunyad Castle, Budapest. 1 fo. 40, Visegrad Fortress. 3 fo. "Falcone" (racing yacht) on Lake Balaton. 5 fo. Parliament Buildings and Kossuth Bridge.

156. Gyorgy Dozsa. 157. Doctor Examining X-Ray Photograph.

**1947.** Liberty issue.
995. 156. 8 fi. red .. .. 15 10
996. – 10 fi. blue .. .. 15 10
997. – 12 fi. brown .. .. 15 10
998. – 20 fi. green .. .. 30 10
999. – 30 fi. brown .. .. 30 10
1000. – 40 fi. purple .. .. 40 10
1001. – 60 fi. red .. .. 40 10
1002. – 1 fo. blue .. .. 50 10
1003. – 2 fo. violet .. .. 80 10
1004. – 4 fo. green .. 1·50 10
PORTRAITS: 10 fi. A. Budai Nagy. 12 fi. T. Esze. 20 fi. I. Martinovics. 30 fi. J. Batsanyi. 40 fi. L. Kossuth. 60 fi. M. Tancsics. 1 fo. S. Petofi. 2 fo. E. Ady. 4 fo. A. Jozsef.

**1947.** Welfare Organizations. Inscr. "SIESS! ADJ! SEGITS!" (trans. "Come! Give! Help! ').
1005. – 8 fi.+50 fi. blue .. 2·00 1·50
1006. 157. 12 fi.+50 fi. brown .. 2·00 1·50
1007. – 20 fi.+50 fi. green .. 2·00 1·50
1008. – 60 fi.+50 fi. red .. 20 30
DESIGNS: 8 fi. Doctor testing syringe. 20 fi. Nurse and child. 60 fi. Released prisoner-of-war.

158. Emblem of Peace. 159. Liberty Statue.

**1947.** Peace Treaty.
1009. 158. 60 fi. red .. .. 20 10

**1947.** 30th Anniv of Soviet Union and Hungarian-Soviet Cultural Society Fund.
1010. – 40 fi.+40 fi. brn. & grn. 2·00 1·75
1011. 159. 60 fi.+60 fi. grey & red 40 40
1012. – 1 fo.+1 fo. blk. & blue 2·00 1·75
PORTRAITS: 40 fi. Lenin. 1 fo. Stalin.

161. Savings Bank. 162. XVIth Century Mail Coach.

**1947.** Savings Day. Type **161** and design inscr. "TAKAREKOS JELENBOLDOG JOVO".
1013. – 40 fi. red (beehive).. 15 10
1014. 161. 60 fi. red .. .. 15 10

**1947.** Stamp Day.
1015. 162. 30 fi. (+50 fi.) brown 3·00 3·75

165. Arms of Hungary. 167. Johann Gutenberg.

**1948.** Centenary of Insurrection.
1016. – 8 fi. red .. .. 15 10
1017. – 10 fi. blue .. .. 15 10
1018. – 12 fi. brown .. .. 15 10
1019. – 20 fi. green .. .. 50 10
1020. – 30 fi. brown .. .. 20 10
1021. – 40 fi. purple .. .. 20 10
1022. – 60 fi. red .. .. 60 10
1023. 165. 1 fo. blue .. .. 60 10
1024. – 2 fo. brown .. .. 80 10
1025. – 3 fo. green .. .. 1·00 20
1026. – 4 fo. red .. .. 2·75 30
DESIGNS—HORIZ. 8 fi., 40 fi. Hungarian independence flag. 10 fi. Printing press. 12 fi. Latticed window. 20 fi. Shako, trumpet and sword. 30 fi., 60 fi. Slogan.

**1948.** Air. Explorers and Inventors.
1027. 167. 1 fi. red .. .. 15 15
1028. – 2 fi. mauve .. .. 20 15
1029. – 4 fi. blue .. .. 20 15
1030. – 5 fi. brown .. .. 25 20
1031. – 6 fi. green .. .. 25 20
1032. – 8 fi. purple .. .. 25 20
1033. – 10 fi. brown .. .. 45 25
1034. – 12 fi. green .. .. 1·00 30
1035. – 30 fi. red .. .. 1·25 60
1036. – 40 fi. violet .. .. 90 75
PORTRAITS: 2 fi. Christopher Columbus. 4 fi. Robert Fulton. 5 fi. George Stephenson. 6 fi. David Schwarz and Count Ferdinand von Zeppelin. 8 fi. Thomas Edison. 10 fi. Louis Bleriot. 12 fi. Roald Amundsen. 30 fi. Kalman Kando. 40 fi. Alexander Popov.

169. Lorand Eotvos.

**1948.** Birth Cent. of L. Eotvos (physicist).
1037. 169. 60 fi. red .. .. 45 10

170. William Shakespeare.

PORTRAITS: 2 fi. Voltaire. 4 fi. Goethe. 5 fi. Byron. 6 fi. Victor Hugo. 8 fi. Edgar Allan Poe. 10 fi. Petofi. 12 fi. Mark Twain. 30 fi. Tolstoy. 40 fi. Gorki.

**1948.** Air. Writers.
1038. 170. 1 fi. blue .. .. 15 15
1039. – 2 fi. red .. .. 20 15
1040. – 4 fi. green .. .. 20 15
1041. – 5 fi. mauve .. .. 25 20
1042. – 6 fi. blue .. .. 25 20
1043. – 8 fi. brown .. .. 25 20
1044. – 10 fi. red .. .. 30 25
1045. – 12 fi. violet .. .. 35 30
1046. – 30 fi. brown .. .. 75 60
1047. – 40 fi. brown .. .. 90 75

171. Globe and Pigeon. 172. Symbolizing Industry, Agriculture and Culture.

**1948.** 5th National Philatelic Exn.
1048. 171. 30 fi. blue .. .. 1·75 1·75
Sold at 1 fo. 30 (incl. 1 fo. entrance fee).

**1948.** 17th Trades' Union Congress.
1049. 172. 30 fi. red .. .. 20 10

173. Agricultural Worker. 174. Reproduction of T 32.

**1949.** Int. Women's Day.
1050. 173. 60 fi.+60 fi. mve. .. 70 85

**1949.** 30th Anniv. of Bolshevist Regime.
1051. 174. 40 fi. brown and red.. 25 15
1052. – 60 fi. olive and red .. 30 15
DESIGN: 60 fi. Reproduction of No. 325.

175. Pushkin holding Torch and Scroll. 176. Symbolising Workers of Five Continents.

**1949.** 150th Birth Anniv. of A.S. Pushkin (poet).
1053. 175. 1 fo.+1 fo. red .. 2·50 3·00

**1949.** 2nd World Federation of Trade Unions Congress, Milan. Flag in red.
1054. 176. 30 fi. brown .. .. 1·75 1·75
1055. 40 fi. purple .. .. 1·75 1·75
1056. 60 fi. red .. .. 1·75 1·75
1057. 1 fo. blue .. .. 1·75 1·75

177. Sandor Petofi. 178. Heads and Globe

**1949.** Death Centenary of Petofi (poet).
1058 177 40 fi. purple .. .. 30 15
1096 40 fi. brown .. .. 30 15
1059 60 fi. red .. .. 20 10
1060 1 fo. blue .. .. 15 10
1098 1 fo. green .. .. 20 10

**1949.** World Youth Festival, Budapest.
1061. 178. 20 fi. brown .. .. 35 25
1062. – 30 fi. green .. .. 35 25
1063. – 40 fi. bistre .. .. 40 30
1064. – 60 fi. red .. .. 40 30
1065. – 1 fo. blue .. .. 90 55
DESIGNS: 30 fi. Three clenched fists. 40 fi. Man breaking chains. 60 fi. Young people and banner. 1 fo. Workers and tractor.

179. Hungarian Coat-of-Arms.

**1949.** Ratification of Constitution. Arms in blue, brown, red and green.
1066. 179. 20 fi. green .. .. 50 30
1067. 60 fi. red .. .. 25 10
1068. 1 fo. blue .. .. 45 25

181. Globes & Posthorn. 182. Chain Bridge.

**1949.** 75th Anniv. of U.P.U.
1069. 181. 60 fi. red (postage) .. 20 15
1070. 1 fo. blue .. .. 30 15
1071. – 2 fo. brown (air) .. 55 25
DESIGN: 2 fo. Lisunov Li-2 airplane replaces posthorn.

**1949.** Centenary of Budapest Chain Bridge.
1073. 182. 40 fi. green (postage) 30 10
1074. 60 fi. brown .. .. 30 10
1075. 1 fo. blue .. .. 30 15
1076. 1 fo. 60 red (air) .. 50 40
1077. 2 fo. olive .. .. 50 30

183. Postman and Forms of Transport. 184. Joseph Stalin.

**1949.** Air. Stamp Day.
1078. 183. 50 fi. grey .. .. 5·00 5·00

**1949.** Stalin's 70th Birthday.
1079. 184. 60 fi. red .. .. 25 10
1080. 1 fo. blue .. .. 25 10
1081. 2 fo. brown .. .. 50 20

185. Miners.

**1950.** Five Year Plan.
1082 185 8 fi. grey .. .. 60 10
1083 – 10 fi. purple .. .. 40 10
1084 – 12 fi. red .. .. 60 10
1085 – 20 fi. green .. .. 40 10
1086 – 30 fi. purple .. .. 60 10
1087 – 40 fi. brown .. .. 60 10
1088 – 60 fi. red .. .. 70 10
1089 – 1 fo. violet and yellow 1·25 10
1090 – 1 fo. 70 green & yellow 1·50 10
1091 – 2 fo. red and orange 2·75 10
1092 – 3 fo. blue and buff .. 3·00 10
1093 – 4 fo. green & orange 3·00 20
1094 – 5 fo. purple & yellow 3·50 35
1095 – 10 fo. brown & yellow 9·00 2·25
DESIGNS: 10 fi. Iron foundry. 12 fi. Power station. 20 fi. Textiles. 30 fi. Factory workers' entertainment. 40 fi. Mechanical farming. 60 fi. Village co-operative office. 1 fo. Steam locomotive on bridge. 1 fo. 70, Family at health resort. 2 fo. Soldier and tank. 3 fo. Freighter and Lisunov Li-2 airplane. 4 fo. Cattle. 5 fo. Draughtsman and factory. 10 fo. Sportsman, woman and football match.

186. Philatelic Museum.

**1950.** 20th Anniv. of P.O. Philatelic Museum.
1099. 186. 60 fi. brown and black (postage) .. 4·50 5·50
1100. – 2 fo. red and yellow (air) .. .. 6·75 6·75
DESIGN—HORIZ. 2 fo. Globe, coach, Douglas DC-4 airliner and stamps.

188. Family Greeting Soviet Troops.

**1950.** 5th Anniv. of Liberation.
1101. 188. 40 fi. black .. .. 75 45
1102. 60 fi. lake .. .. 50 10
1103. 1 fo. blue .. .. 50 15
1104. 2 fo. brown .. .. 75 20

DESIGNS; 1 fo. Trade Union Building. 1 fo. 60, Map.
189. Chess Match.

**1950.** 1st International Candidates Chess Tournament, Budapest. Designs incorporate rook and chessboard.
1105. 189. 60 fi. mauve (postage) 1·75 40
1106. – 1 fo. blue .. .. 3·25 1·00
1107. – 1 fo. 60 brown (air).. 4·50 2·00

DESIGN: 60 fi. Two workers.
190. Workers and Star.

**1950.** May Day. Inscr as in T **190**.
1108. 190. 40 fi. brown .. .. 60 40
1109. – 60 fi. red .. .. 30 10
1110. 190. 1 fo. blue .. .. 40 20

DESIGNS: 40 fi. Statue, dove and globes. 1 fo. Globes, Chain Bridge and Parliament Bldgs.
191. Workers and Flag.

**1950.** World Federation of Trade Unions Congress, Budapest.
1111. – 40 fi. green (postage) 40 30
1112. 191. 60 fi. red .. .. 25 10
1113. – 1 fo. brown (air) .. 40 15

DESIGNS: 30 fi. Baby boy and holiday scene. 40 fi. Schoolgirl and classroom. 60 fi. Pioneer boy and camp. 1 fo. 70, Pioneer boy and girl and model glider class.
192. Baby and Nursery.

**1950.** Children's Day.
1114. 192. 20 fi. brown and grey 80 70
1115. – 30 fi. mauve & brn. 30 10
1116. – 40 fi. green and blue 30 10
1117. – 60 fi. red and brown £1100 £1100
1117a. – 60 fi. red and brown 30 10
1118. – 1 fo. 70 blue & green 1·10 85
No. 1117 is inscr. "UTANPOTLASUNK A JOVO HARCAIHOZ" and No. 1117a is incr. "SZABAD HAZABAN BOLDOG IFJUSAG".

193. Workers and Globe.

DESIGNS:—HORIZ. 30 fi. Foundry worker and cauldron. VERT. 40 fi. Man, woman and banner, 60 fi. Workers, banner and Liberty Statue. 1 fo. 70, Three workers and banner.

**1950.** 1st Congress of Young Workers, Budapest.

| | | | | |
|---|---|---|---|---|
| 1119 | 193 | 20 fi. green | 40 | 30 |
| 1120 | – | 30 fi. orange | 15 | 10 |
| 1121 | – | 40 fi. brown | 15 | 10 |
| 1122 | – | 60 fi. mauve | 20 | 10 |
| 1123 | – | 1 fo. 70 green | 55 | 20 |

194. Peonies.

195. Miner.

**1950.** Flowers.

| | | | | |
|---|---|---|---|---|
| 1124 | 194 | 30 fi. purple and green | 90 | 15 |
| 1125 | – | 40 fi. grn, yell & mve | 90 | 15 |
| 1126 | – | 60 fi. brn, yell & grn | 2·00 | 15 |
| 1127 | – | 1 fo. violet, red & grn | 3·25 | 60 |
| 1128 | – | 1 fo. 70 vio, grn & lilac | 4·00 | 90 |

DESIGNS: 40 fi. Pasque flowers; 60 fi. Yellow pheasant's-eye. 1 fo. Geranium. 1 fo. 70, Campanulas.

**1950.** 2nd National Inventions Exn.

| | | | | |
|---|---|---|---|---|
| 1129. | 195. | 40 fi. brown | 30 | 15 |
| 1130. | – | 60 fi. red | 25 | 10 |
| 1131. | – | 1 fo. blue | 35 | 15 |

DESIGNS: 60 fi. Turner. 1 fo. Building factory.

196. Liberty Statue.

**1950.** Air.

| | | | | |
|---|---|---|---|---|
| 1132. | 196. | 20 fi. red | 15 | 10 |
| 1133. | – | 30 fi. violet | 15 | 10 |
| 1134. | – | 70 fi. purple | 20 | 10 |
| 1135. | – | 1 fo. brown | 25 | 10 |
| 1136. | – | 1 fo. 60 blue | 75 | 10 |
| 1137. | – | 2 fo. red | 50 | 10 |
| 1138. | – | 3 fo. black | 2·50 | 40 |
| 1139. | – | 5 fo. blue | 1·25 | 45 |
| 1140. | – | 10 fo. brown | 4·00 | 80 |
| 1140a. | – | 20 fo. green | 11·00 | 4·00 |

DESIGNS—VERT. 30 fi. Crane and buildings. 70 fi. Diosgyor steelworks. 1 fo. "Stalinyec" tractor. 1 fo. 60, Freighter. 2 fo. Combine harvester. 3 fo. Steam train. 5 fo. Matyas Rakosi steel-mill. 10, 20 fo. Lisunov Li-2 airplane at Budaors airport.

For No. 1139 but on silver paper see No. 1437.

198. Worker signing Peace Petition.

**1950.** Peace Propaganda.

| | | | | |
|---|---|---|---|---|
| 1141. | 198. | 40 fi. brown and blue | 3·00 | 1·75 |
| 1142. | – | 60 fi. green & orange | 75 | 30 |
| 1143. | – | 1 fo. brown and green | 3·25 | 1·75 |

DESIGNS—VERT. 60 fi. Girl holding dove. HORIZ. 1 fo. Soldier mother and children.

199. Swimmers.

**1950.**

| | | | | |
|---|---|---|---|---|
| 1144 | 199 | 10 fi. blue and light blue (postage) | 10 | 10 |
| 1145 | – | 20 fi. brown & orange | 15 | 10 |
| 1146 | – | 1 fo. green and olive | 60 | 10 |
| 1147 | – | 1 fo. 70 red & verm | 1·50 | 20 |
| 1148 | – | 2 fo. violet and brown | 2·25 | 30 |
| 1149 | – | 30 fi. mve & vio (air) | 60 | 10 |
| 1150 | – | 40 fi. blue and green | 60 | 10 |
| 1151 | – | 60 fi. orge, brn & grn | 75 | 10 |
| 1152 | – | 70 fi. brown and grey | 1·25 | 35 |
| 1153 | – | 3 fo. chestnut & brn | 3·50 | 1·25 |

DESIGNS—POSTAGE: 20 fi. Vaulting. 1 fo. Mountaineering. 1 fo. 70, Basketball. 2 fo. Motor cycling. AIR: 30 fi. Volleyball. 40 fi. Throwing the javelin. 60 fi. Emblem of "Ready for work and action" movement. 70 fi. Football. 3 fo. Gliding.

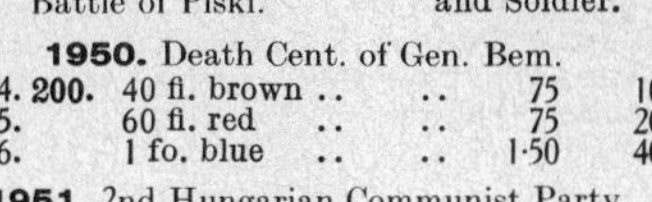
200. Jozef Bem and Battle of Piski.

201. Workers and Soldier.

**1950.** Death Cent. of Gen. Bem.

| | | | | |
|---|---|---|---|---|
| 1154. | 200. | 40 fi. brown | 75 | 10 |
| 1155. | | 60 fi. red | 75 | 20 |
| 1156. | | 1 fo. blue | 1·50 | 40 |

**1951.** 2nd Hungarian Communist Party Congress.

| | | | | |
|---|---|---|---|---|
| 1157. | 201. | 10 fi. green | 20 | 10 |
| 1158. | – | 30 fi. brown | 30 | 15 |
| 1159. | – | 60 fi. red | 40 | 15 |
| 1160. | – | 1 fo. blue | 75 | 15 |

DESIGNS—HORIZ. 30 fi. Workers, soldier and banner. 60 fi. Portrait and four workers with flags. VERT. 1 fo. Procession with banner.

202. Flags.

203. Mare and Foal.

**1951.** Hungarian-Soviet Amity. Inscr. "MAGYAR SZOVJET BARATSAG HONAPJA 1951".

| | | | | |
|---|---|---|---|---|
| 1161. | 202. | 60 fi. red | 25 | 10 |
| 1162. | – | 1 fo. violet | 30 | 20 |

DESIGN: 1 fo. Hungarian and Russian workers.

**1951.** Livestock Expansion Plan.

| | | | | |
|---|---|---|---|---|
| 1163 | 203 | 10 fi. brown & ochre (postage) | 15 | 10 |
| 1164 | – | 30 fi. brown and red | 40 | 25 |
| 1165 | – | 40 fi. brown and green | 45 | 25 |
| 1166 | – | 60 fi. brown & orange | 60 | 10 |
| 1167 | 203 | 20 fi. brn & grn (air) | 30 | 10 |
| 1168 | – | 70 fi. ochre and brown | 60 | 25 |
| 1169 | – | 1 fo. brown and blue | 1·50 | 40 |
| 1170 | – | 1 fo. 60 chestnut and brown | 2·75 | 80 |

DESIGNS: 30, 70 fi. Sow and litter. 40 fi., 1 fo. Ewe and lamb. 60 fi., 1 fo. 60, Cow and calf.

204. Worker.

DESIGNS — VERT. 60 fi. People with banners. HORIZ. 1 fo. Labour Day rally.

**1951.** May Day. Inscr. "1951 MAJUS".

| | | | | |
|---|---|---|---|---|
| 1171. | 204. | 40 fi. brown | 30 | 30 |
| 1172. | – | 60 fi. red | 25 | 10 |
| 1173. | – | 1 fo. blue | 25 | 10 |

205. Leo Frankel.

206. Street-fighting.

**1951.** 80th Anniv of Paris Commune.

| | | | | |
|---|---|---|---|---|
| 1174 | 205 | 60 fi. brown | 40 | 10 |
| 1175 | 206 | 1 fo. blue and red | 60 | 20 |

207. Children's Heads.

208. Ganz Wagon Works.

**1951.** Int. Children's Day. Inscr. "NEMZETKOZI GYERMEKNAP 1951".

| | | | | |
|---|---|---|---|---|
| 1176. | 207. | 30 fi. brown | 30 | 10 |
| 1177. | – | 40 fi. green | 40 | 10 |
| 1178. | – | 50 fi. brown | 45 | 20 |
| 1179. | – | 60 fi. mauve | 65 | 10 |
| 1180. | – | 1 fo. 70 fi. blue | 90 | 35 |

DESIGNS: 40 fi. Flying model airplane. 50 fi. Train on Budapest Pioneer Railway. 60 fi. Chemistry experiment. 1 fo. 70, Blowing bugle.

**1951.** Rebuilding Plan (1st series).

| | | | | |
|---|---|---|---|---|
| 1180a. | – | 8 fi. green | 50 | 10 |
| 1180b. | – | 10 fi. violet | 50 | 10 |
| 1180c. | – | 12 fi. red | 50 | 10 |
| 1181. | 208. | 20 fi. green | 50 | 10 |
| 1182. | – | 30 fi. orange | 65 | 10 |
| 1183. | – | 40 fi. brown | 70 | 10 |
| 1183a. | – | 50 fi. blue | 65 | 10 |
| 1184. | – | 60 fi. red | 90 | 10 |
| 1184a. | – | 70 fi. brown | 1·00 | 10 |
| 1184b. | – | 80 fi. purple | 1·40 | 10 |
| 1185. | – | 1 fo. blue | 1·25 | 10 |
| 1185a. | – | 1 fo. 20 red | 1·75 | 10 |
| 1185b. | – | 1 fo. 70 blue | 1·75 | 10 |
| 1185c. | – | 2 fo. green | 2·00 | 10 |
| 1186. | – | 3 fo. purple | 2·25 | 10 |
| 1186a. | – | 4 fo. olive | 2·50 | 10 |
| 1186b. | – | 5 fo. black | 3·75 | 15 |

BUILDINGS: 8 fi. Stalin School. 10 fi. Szekesfehervar railway station. 12 fi. Ujpest medical dispensary. 30 fi. Flats. 40 fi. Central Railway Station, Budapest. 50 fi. Inota power station. 60 fi. Matyas Rakosi Cultural Institute. 70 fi. Hajdunanas grain elevator. 80 fi. Tiszalok dam. 1 fo. Kilian Road School. 1 fo. 20, Mining Apprentices Institute, Ajkacsingervolgy. 1 fo. 70, Iron and Steel Apprentices Institute, Csepel. 2 fo. Cultural Centre, Hungarian Optical Works. 3 fo. Building Workers' Union Headquarters. 4 fo. Miners' Union Headquarters. 5 fo. Flats.

See also Nos. 1296/1304.

209. Gorky.

210. Engineers and Tractors.

**1951.** 15th Death Anniv. of Maksim Gorky (Russian writer).

| | | | | |
|---|---|---|---|---|
| 1187. | 209. | 60 fi. red | 15 | 10 |
| 1188. | | 1 fo. blue | 20 | 10 |
| 1189. | | 2 fo. purple | 50 | 25 |

**1951.** 1st Anniv. of Five Year Plan.

| | | | | |
|---|---|---|---|---|
| 1190. | 210. | 20 fi. sepia (postage) | 15 | 10 |
| 1191. | – | 30 fi. blue | 20 | 10 |
| 1192. | – | 40 fi. red | 20 | 10 |
| 1193. | – | 60 fi. brown | 25 | 10 |
| 1194. | – | 70 fi. brown (air) | 35 | 10 |
| 1195. | – | 1 fo. green | 35 | 10 |
| 1196. | – | 2 fo. purple | 1·25 | 50 |

DESIGNS: 30 fi. Doctor X-raying patient. 40 fi. Workman instructing apprentices. 60 fi. Girl driving tractor. 70 fi. Electrical engineers constructing pylon. 1 fo. Young people and recreation home. 2 fo. Lisunov Li-2 airplane over Stalin Bridge.

211. 1871 Stamp without portrait and Hungarian Arms.

212. Soldiers Parading.

**1951.** 80th Anniv. of 1st Hungarian Postage Stamp.

| | | | | |
|---|---|---|---|---|
| 1197. | 211. | 60 fi. green | 30 | 15 |
| 1198. | | 1 fo. + 1 fo. red | 7·00 | 3·00 |
| 1199. | | 2 fo. + 2 fo. blue | 9·00 | 5·00 |

**1951.** Army Day.

| | | | | |
|---|---|---|---|---|
| 1200. | 212. | 1 fo. brown (postage) | 60 | 15 |
| 1201. | – | 60 fi. blue (air) | 35 | 15 |

DESIGN—VERT. 60 fi. Tanks and Liberty Statue.

213. Lily of the Valley.

214. Revolutionaries and Flags.

**1951.** Flowers.

| | | | | |
|---|---|---|---|---|
| 1202. | – | 30 fi. violet, bl. & grn. | 35 | 10 |
| 1203. | 213. | 40 fi. myrtle & green | 75 | 45 |
| 1204. | – | 60 fi. red, pink & grn. | 50 | 10 |
| 1205. | – | 1 fo. blue, red & green | 1·25 | 15 |
| 1206. | – | 1 fo. 70 brown, yellow and green | 2·50 | 1·00 |

FLOWERS: 30 fi. Cornflowers. 60 fi. Tulips. 1 fo. Poppies. 1 fo. 70, Cowslips.

**1951.** 34th Anniv. of Russian Revolution.

| | | | | |
|---|---|---|---|---|
| 1207. | 214. | 40 fi. green | 40 | 20 |
| 1208. | – | 60 fi. blue | 40 | 10 |
| 1209. | – | 1 fo. red | 40 | 10 |

DESIGNS: 60 fi. Lenin addressing revolutionaries. 1 fo. Lenin and Stalin.

215. Parade before Stalin Statue.

**1951.** Stalin's 72nd Birthday.

| | | | | |
|---|---|---|---|---|
| 1210. | 215. | 60 fi. red | 25 | 10 |
| 1211. | | 1 fo. blue | 30 | 15 |

216. Bolshoi State Theatre, Moscow.

DESIGNS: 1 fo. Lenin Mausoleum. 1 fo. 60, Kremlin.

**1952.** Views of Moscow.

| | | | | |
|---|---|---|---|---|
| 1212. | 216. | 60 fi. lake and green | 25 | 10 |
| 1213. | – | 1 fo. brown and red | 25 | 10 |
| 1214. | – | 1 fo. 60 olive and lake | 35 | 25 |

217. Rakosi and Peasants.

218. Rakosi.

**1952.** 60th Birth Anniv. of Rakosi.

| | | | | |
|---|---|---|---|---|
| 1215. | 217. | 60 fi. purple | 40 | 10 |
| 1216. | 218. | 1 fo. brown | 40 | 15 |
| 1217. | – | 2 fo. blue | 70 | 30 |

DESIGN: 2 fo. Rakosi and foundry workers.

219. L. Kossuth.

**1952.** Heroes of 1848 Revolution.

| | | | | |
|---|---|---|---|---|
| 1218. | 219. | 20 fi. green | 10 | 10 |
| 1219. | – | 30 fi. purple (Petofi) | 15 | 10 |
| 1220. | – | 50 fi. black (Bem) | 30 | 15 |
| 1221. | – | 60 fi. lake (Tancsics) | 30 | 10 |
| 1222. | – | 1 fo. bl. (Damjanich) | 30 | 10 |
| 1223. | – | 1 fo. 50 brn. (Nagy) | 40 | 30 |

220. Avocet.

**1952.** Air. Birds.

| | | | | |
|---|---|---|---|---|
| 1224 | 220 | 20 fi. black and green | 15 | 10 |
| 1225 | – | 30 fi. black and green | 25 | 10 |
| 1226 | – | 40 fi. blk, yell & brn | 35 | 15 |
| 1227 | – | 50 fi. black and orange | 35 | 15 |
| 1228 | – | 60 fi. black and red | 40 | 15 |
| 1229 | – | 70 fi. blk, orge & red | 55 | 20 |
| 1230 | – | 80 fi. black, yell & grn | 80 | 30 |
| 1231 | – | 1 fo. black, red & blue | 1·10 | 35 |
| 1232 | – | 1 fo. 40 multicoloured | 1·25 | 40 |
| 1233 | – | 1 fo. 60 blk, grn & brn | 1·50 | 60 |
| 1234 | – | 2 fo. 50 black & purple | 2·75 | 1·00 |

DESIGNS: 30 fi. White stork. 40 fi. Golden oriole. 50 fi. Kentish plover. 60 fi. Black-winged stilt. 70 fi. Lesser grey strike. 80 fi. Great bustard. 1 fo. Red-footed falcon. 1 fo. 40, European bee eater. 1 fo. 60, Glossy ibis. 2 fo. 50, Great egret.

**1952.** Budapest Philatelic Exn. No. 1050 with bars obliterating inscription and premium.

| | | | | |
|---|---|---|---|---|
| 1235. | 173. | 60 fi. mauve | 20·00 | 27·00 |

222. Drummer and Flags.

DESIGNS: 60 fi. Workers. 1 fo. Workman and globe.

**1952.** May Day. Inscr. "1952 MAJUS I".

| | | | | |
|---|---|---|---|---|
| 1236. | 222. | 40 fi. red and green | 45 | 20 |
| 1237. | – | 60 fi. red and brown | 30 | 10 |
| 1238. | – | 1 fo. red and brown | 45 | 10 |

223. Running.

**1952.** 15th Olympic Games, Helsinki.
1239 **223** 30 fi. brown (postage) 25 10
1240 – 40 fi. green .. .. 25 10
1241 – 60 fi. red .. .. 40 10
1242 – 1 fo. blue .. .. 65 25
1243 – 1 fo. 70 orange (air) 1·00 50
1244 – 2 fo. brown .. .. 1·00 55
DESIGNS: 40 fi. Swimming. 60 fi. Fencing. 1 fo. Gymnastics. 1 fo. 70, Throwing the hammer. 2 fo. Stadium.

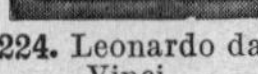

**224.** Leonardo da Vinci. **225.** Train and Railwayman.

**1952.** Air. 500th Birth Anniv of Leonardo da Vinci and 150th Birth Anniv of Victor Hugo.
1245 **224** 1 fo. 60 blue .. .. 45 15
1246 – 2 fo. purple (Victor Hugo) .. .. 45 25

**1952.** Railway Day. Inscr. "1952 VIII 10".
1247. **225.** 60 fi. brown .. .. 85 20
1248. – 1 fo. green .. .. 1·40 30
DESIGN: 1 fo. Railway tracks.

**226.** Mechanical Coal-cutter. **227.** L. Kossuth.

**1952.** Miners' Day. Inscr. as in T **226.**
1249. **226.** 60 fi. brown .. .. 60 15
1250. – 1 fo. green .. .. 80 20
DESIGN: 1 fo. Miners operating machinery.

**1952.** 150th Birth Anniv. of Kossuth (statesman).
1251. **227.** 40 fi. olive on pink .. 30 15
1252. – 60 fi. black on blue .. 20 10
1253. **227.** 1 fo. lilac on yellow .. 35 15
DESIGN: 60 fi. Statue of Kossuth.

**228.** Gy. Dozsa. **229.** Boy, Girl and Stamp Exhibition.

**1952.** Army Day. Inscr. as T **228.**
1254. 20 fi. lilac (J. Hunyadi) .. 15 10
1255. 30 fi. green (T **228**) .. 15 10
1256. 40 fi. blue (M. Zrinyi) .. 15 10
1257. 60 fi. purple (I. Zrinyi) .. 20 10
1258. 1 fo. turquoise (B. Vak) 30 10
1259. 1 fo. 50, brn. (A. Stromfeld) 50 30

**1952.** Air. Stamp Day. Inscr. "XXV. BELYEGNAP 1952".
1260. – 1 fo. + 1 fo. blue .. 3·00 3·75
1261. **229.** 2 fo. + 2 fo. red .. 3·00 3·75
DESIGN: 1 fo. Children examining stamps.

**230.** Lenin and Revolutionary Council. **231.** Harvester.

**1952.** 35th Anniv. of Russian Revolution.
1262. **230.** 40 fi. olive and purple 80 30
1263. – 60 fi. olive and black 40 10
1264. – 1 fo. olive and red .. 80 15
DESIGNS: 60 fi. Stalin and Cossacks. 1 fo. Marx, Engels, Lenin, Stalin and Spassky Tower.

**1952.** 3rd Hungarian Peace Congress. Inscr. as in T **231.**
1265. **231.** 60 fi. red on yellow .. 35 10
1266. – 1 fo. brown on green 35 20
DESIGN—HORIZ. 1 fo. Workers' discussion group.

DESIGN — HORIZ. 1 fo. Underground map and station.

**232.** Tunnel Construction.

**1953.** Budapest Underground Railway. Inscr. "BUDAPESTI FOLDALATTI GYORSVASUT".
1267. **232.** 60 fi. green .. .. 1·00 15
1268. – 1 fo. lake .. .. 1·00 25

**233.** Russian Flag and Tank. **234.** Eurasian Red Squirrel.

**1953.** 10th Anniv. of Battle of Stalingrad.
1269. **233.** 40 fi. red .. .. 70 15
1270. – 60 fi. brown .. .. 90 10
DESIGN: 60 fi. Soldier, map and flags.

**1953.** Air. Forest Animals.
1271. **234.** 20 fi. brown and olive 25 10
1272. – 30 fi. sepia and brown 30 10
1273. – 40 fi. sepia and green 35 10
1274. – 50 fi. sepia and brown 45 10
1275. – 60 fi. brown & turq. 55 10
1276. – 70 fi. brown and olive 60 15
1277. – 80 fi. brown and green 90 30
1278. – 1 fo. brown and green 1·10 30
1279. – 1 fo. 50, blk. & bistre 1·75 75
1280. – 2 fo. sepia and brown 2·75 90
DESIGNS—HORIZ. 30 fi. West European hedgehog. 40 fi. Brown hare. 60 fi. European otter. 70 fi. Red fox. 1 fo. Roe deer. 1 fo. 50, Wild boar. VERT. 50 fi. Beech marten. 80 fi. Fallow deer. 2 fo. Red deer.

**235.** Stalin. **236.** Rest Home, Galyateto.

**1953.** Death of Stalin.
1281. **235.** 60 fi. black .. .. 15 10

**1953.** Workers' Rest Homes.
1282. **236.** 30 fi. brown (postage) 15 10
1283. – 40 fi. blue .. .. 20 10
1284. – 50 fi. ochre .. .. 20 10
1285. – 60 fi. green .. .. 20 10
1286. – 70 fi. red .. .. 25 10
1287. – 1 fo. turquoise (air) .. 35 15
1288. – 1 fo. 50 purple .. 45 35
DESIGNS: 40 fi. Terrace, Mecsek. 50 fi. Parad Spa. 60 fi. Sports field, Kekes. 70 fi. Balatonfured Spa. 1 fo. Children paddling at Balaton. 1 fo. 50, Lillafured Rest Home.

**237.** Young People and Banners. **238.** Karl Marx.

**1953.** May Day.
1289. **237.** 60 fi. brn. & red on yell. 30 10

**1953.** 70th Death Anniv. of Karl Marx.
1290. **238.** 1 fo. black on pink .. 25 15
See also No. 2354.

**239.** Peasants and Flag.

**1953.** 250th Anniv of Rakoczi Rebellion.
1291 **239** 20 fi. orange and green on green .. .. 40 10
1292 – 30 fi. orange & purple 50 10
1293 – 40 fi. orange and blue on pink .. .. 55 20
1294 – 60 fi. orange and green on yellow .. .. 60 20
1295 – 1 fo. red & brn on yell 1·00 45
DESIGNS: 30 fi. Drummer and insurgents. 40 fi. Battle scene. 60 fi. Cavalryman attacking soldier. 1 fo. Ferenc Rakoczi II.

**1953.** Rebuilding Plan (2nd series). As T **208.**
1296. 8 fi. green .. .. 25 10
1297. 10 fi. lilac .. .. 35 10
1298. 12 fi. red .. .. 75 10
1299a. 20 fi. green .. .. 65 10
1300. 30 fi. orange .. .. 75 10
1301. 40 fi. brown .. .. 1·40 10
1302. 50 fi. blue .. .. 1·25 10
1303a. 60 fi. red .. .. 85 10
1304. 70 fi. brown .. .. 1·75 10
BUILDINGS: 8 fi. Day nursery, Ozd. 10 fi. Nursing school, Szombathely. 12 fi. Workers' houses, Komlo. 20 fi. Department store, Ujpest. 30 fi. Factory Maly. 40 fi. General Hospital, Fovaros. 50 fi. Gymnasium, Sztalinvaros. 60 fi. Post Office, Csepel. 70 fi. Blast-furnace, Diosgyor.

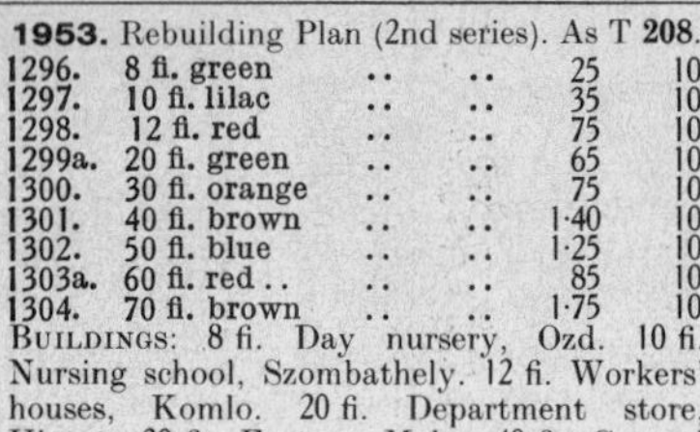

**240** Cycling

**1953.** Opening of People's Stadium. Budapest. Inscr. "1953 NEPSTADION".
1313. **240.** 20 fi. brown & orange (postage) .. .. 30 10
1314. – 30 fi. brown & green 15 10
1315. – 40 fi. brown and blue 20 10
1316. – 50 fi. brown and olive 30 10
1317. – 60 fi. brown & yellow 30 10
1318. – 80 fi. brn. & turq. (air) 45 10
1319. – 1 fo. brn. & purple .. 65 10
1320. – 2 fo. brn. & green .. 1·50 30
1321. – 3 fo. brn. and red .. 2·00 40
1322. – 5 fo. turq. & brn. .. 3·00 2·40
DESIGNS: 30 fi. Swimming. 40 fi. Gymnastics 50 fi. Throwing the discus. 60 fi. Wrestling. 80 fi. Water polo. 1 fo. Boxing. 2 fo. Football. 3 fo. Running. 5 fo. Stadium.

**241.** Kazar. **242.** Postwoman Delivering Letters.

**1953.** Provincial Costumes.
1323. **241.** 20 fi. green .. .. 1·00 10
1324. – 30 fi. brown .. .. 1·25 10
1325. – 40 fi. blue .. .. 1·50 15
1326. – 60 fi. red .. .. 2·00 20
1327. – 1 fo. turquoise .. 3·00 25
1328. – 1 fo. 70 green .. 4·50 75
1329. – 2 fo. red .. .. 7·50 90
1330. – 2 fo. 50 purple .. 11·00 3·50
PROVINCES: 30 fi. Ersekcsanad. 40 fi. Kalocsa. 60 fi. Sioagard. 1 fo. Sarkoz. 1 fo. 70, Boldog. 2 fo. Orhalom. 2 fo. 50, Hosszuheteny.

**1953.** Stamp Day.
1331. **242.** 1 fo. + 1 fo. turq. .. 2·00 2·00
1332. 2 fo. + 2 fo. lilac .. 2·00 2·00

**1953.** Air. Hungarian Football Team's Victory at Wembley. No. 1320 optd **LONDON-WEMBLEY 1953. XI 25. 6:3**
1333 2 fo. brown and green .. 11·00 1100

**244.** Bihari. **245.** Lenin.

**1953.** Air. Hungarian Composers.
1334 **244** 30 fi. grey and brown 30 10
1335 – 40 fi. orange and brown (Erkel) .. 35 10
1336 – 60 fi. grn & brn (Liszt) 40 10
1337 – 70 fi. red and brown (Mosonyi) .. .. 55 10
1338 – 80 fi. blue and brown (Goldmark) .. 65 15
1339 – 1 fo. bistre and brown (Bartok) .. .. 85 15
1340 – 2 fo. lilac and brown (Kodaly) .. .. 1·50 40

**1954.** 30th Death Anniv. of Lenin.
1341. **245.** 40 fi. green .. .. 65 60
1342. – 60 fi. brown .. .. 40 10
1343. – 1 fo. lake .. .. 60 30
DESIGNS: 60 fi. Lenin addressing meeting. 1 fo. Profile portrait of Lenin.

**246.** Turnip Beetle. **247.** Mother and Baby.

**1954.** Air. Insects.
1344 **246** 30 fi. brown & orange 30 15
1345 – 40 fi. brown and green 35 15
1346 – 50 fi. black and red .. 45 25
1347 – 60 fi. brn, yell & lilac 55 25
1348 – 80 fi. claret, purple and green .. .. 75 45
1349 – 1 fo. black and brown 85 45
1350 – 1 fo. 20 brown & green 1·00 60
1351 – 1 fo. 50 dp brn & brn 1·40 75
1352 – 2 fo. brn & chestnut 1·75 90
1353 – 3 fo. brown and green 2·50 1·25
INSECTS—HORIZ: 40 fi. Crawling cockchafer. 50 fi. Longhorn beetle. 60 fi. Hornet. 1 fo. 20, European field cricket. 1 fo. 50, European rhinoceros beetle. 2 fo. Stag beetle. VERT: 80 fi. Apple beetle. 1 fo. Corn beetle. 3 fo. Great silver water beetle.

**1954.** Child Welfare.
1354. – 30 fi. blue (postage) .. 15 10
1355. **247.** 40 fi. bistre .. .. 20 10
1356. – 60 fi. lilac .. .. 30 10
1357. – 1 fo. green (air) .. 50 10
1358. – 1 fo. 50 red .. .. 70 15
1359. – 2 fo. turquoise .. 95 45
DESIGNS: 30 fi. Woman having blood-test. 60 fi. Doctor examining child. 1 fo. Children in creche. 1 fo. 50, Doctor, mother and child. 2 fo. Children in nursery school.

**248.** Worker and Flag. **249.** Maypole.

**1954.** 35th Anniv. of Proclamation of Hungarian Soviet Republic.
1360. – 40 fi. blue and red .. 70 55
1361. **248.** 60 fi. brown and red .. 1·25 55
1362. – 1 fo. black and red .. 1·75 50
DESIGNS—HORIZ. 40 fi. Worker reading book. 1 fo. Soldier with rifle.

**1954.** May Day. Inscr. "1954-MAJUS I.".
1363. **249.** 40 fi. olive .. .. 15 10
1364. – 60 fi. red .. .. 20 10
DESIGN: 60 fi. Worker and flag.

**250.** Agricultural Worker.

**1954.** 3rd Hungarian Communist Party Congress, Budapest.
1365 **250** 60 fi. red on yellow .. 15 10

**251.** Boy Building Model Glider.

**1954.** Air.
1366 **251** 40 fi. grey and brown 20 10
1367 – 50 fi. brown and grey 30 10
1368 – 60 fi. grey and brown 25 10
1369 – 80 fi. brown and violet 30 10
1370 – 1 fo. grey and brown 30 10
1371 – 1 fo. 20 brown & green 45 30
1372 – 1 f. 50 grey and purple 1·40 50
1373 – 2 fo. brown and blue 1·75 1·10
DESIGNS—As Type **251**: 60 fi. Gliders. 1 fo. Parachutists. 1 fo. 50, Lisunov Li-2 airplane. 43×43 mm: 50 fi. Boy flying model airplane. 80 fi. Libis KB-6T Matajur aircraft and hangar. 1 fo. 20, Letov C-4 biplane. 2 fo. Mikoyan Gurevich MiG-15 jet fighters.

252. Hungarian National Museum.

253. Paprika.

**1954.** 5th Anniv. of Constitution.
1374. **252.** 40 fi. blue .. .. 30 20
1375. – 60 fi. brown .. .. 20 10
1376. – 1 fo. brown .. .. 40 15
DESIGNS: 60 fi. Hungarian Coat of Arms. 1 fo. Dome of Parliament Buildings, Budapest.

**1954.** Fruits. Multicoloured.
1377. 40 fi. Type **253** .. .. 30 10
1378. 50 fi. Tomatoes .. .. 30 10
1379. 60 fi. Grapes .. .. 30 10
1380. 80 fi. Apricots .. .. 35 20
1381. 1 fo. Apples .. .. 60 20
1382. 1 fo. 20 Plums .. .. 90 25
1383. 1 fo. 50 Cherries .. .. 1·75 80
1384. 2 fo. Peaches .. .. 2·00 65

254. M. Jokai.

255. C. J. Apacai.

**1954.** 50th Death Anniv of Jokai (novelist).
1385 **254** 60 fi. green .. .. 35 10
1386 1 fo. purple .. .. 50 40

**1954.** Hungarian Scientists.
1387. **255.** 8 fi. black on yellow .. 10 10
1388. – 10 fi. lake on pink .. 10 10
1389. – 12 fi. black on blue .. 10 10
1390. – 20 fi. brown on yellow 10 10
1391. – 30 fi. blue on pink .. 15 10
1392. – 40 fi. green on yellow 20 10
1393. – 50 fi. brown on green 20 10
1394. – 60 fi. blue on pink .. 30 10
1395. – 1 fo. olive .. .. 40 10
1396. – 1 fo. 70 red on yellow 70 20
1397. – 2 fo. turquoise .. 1·10 30
PORTRAITS: 10 fi. S. Korosi Csoma. 12 fi. A. Jedlik. 20 fi. I. Semmelweis. 30 fi. J. Irinyi. 40 fi. F. Koranyi. 50 fi. A. Vambery. 60 fi. K. Than. 1 fo. O. Herman. 1 fo. 70, T. Puskas. 2 fo. E. Hogyes.

256. Speed Skaters.

**1955.** Air. Winter Sports.
1398 – 40 fi. brown, bl & blk 60 15
1399 – 50 fi. red, green & brn 60 15
1400 – 60 fi. red, blue & brn 80 15
1401 – 80 fi. green, brn & blk 1·00 15
1402 – 1 fo. red, blue & brn 1·25 20
1403 **256** 1 fo. 20 red, grn & blk 1·50 40
1404 – 1 fo. 50 red, grn & brn 2·00 1·00
1405 – 2 fo. red, green & brn 2·25 80
DESIGNS—VERT. 40 fi. Boys on toboggan. 60 fi. Ice-yacht. 1 fo. Ski jumper. 1 fo. 50, Skier turning. HORIZ. 50 fi. Cross-country skier. 80 fi. Ice-hockey players. 2 fo. Figure skaters.

257. Blast Furnace.

258. " 1st May ".

**1955.** 10th Anniv of Liberation.
1406 – 40 fi. brown and red 15 15
1407 **257** 60 fi. red and green .. 30 10
1408 – 1 fo. green and brown 30 10
1409 – 2 fo. brown and green 40 15
DESIGNS—VERT: 40 fi. Reading room. 2 fo. Liberty statue. HORIZ: 1 fo. Combine harvester.

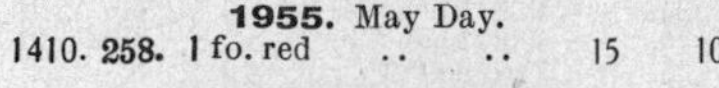

**1955.** May Day.
1410. **258.** 1 fo. red .. .. 15 10

259. State Printing Works.

**1955.** Cent. of Hungarian State Printing Office.
1411. **259.** 60 fi. brown and green 15 10

260. Young Workers and Flag.

**1955.** 2nd Congress of Young Workers' Federation.
1412 **260** 1 fo. brown .. .. 15 10

261. Postilion.

262. Radio Mechanic.

**1955.** Opening of P.O. Museum.
1413. **261.** 1 fo. purple .. .. 30 10

**1955.** Workers.
1414. – 8 fi. brown .. .. 10 10
1415. – 10 fi. turquoise .. 10 10
1416. – 12 fi. orange .. .. 10 10
1417. **262.** 20 fi. olive .. .. 10 10
1418. – 30 fi. red .. .. 10 10
1419. – 40 fi. brown .. .. 90 10
1420. – 50 fi. blue .. .. 15 10
1421. – 60 fi. red .. .. 15 10
1422. – 70 fi. olive .. .. 20 10
1423. – 80 fi. purple .. .. 25 10
1424. – 1 fo. blue .. .. 30 10
1425. – 1 fo. 20 bistre .. 40 10
1426. – 1 fo. 40 green .. 60 10
1427. – 1 fo. 70 lilac .. .. 60 10
1428. – 2 fo. lake .. .. 70 10
1429. – 2 fo. 60 red .. .. 90 10
1430. – 3 fo. green .. .. 1·40 10
1431. – 4 fo. blue .. .. 3·00 15
1432 – 5 fo. brown .. .. 2·00 15
1433. – 10 fo. violet .. .. 3·75 20
DESIGNS: 8 fi. Market gardener. 10 fi. Fisherman. 12 fi. Bricklayer. 30 fi. Potter. 40 fi. Railway guard. 50 fi. Shop assistant. 60 fi. Post Office worker. 70 fi. Herdsman. 80 fi. Mill-girl. 1 fo. Boat-builder. 1 fo. 20, Carpenter. 1 fo. 40, Tram conductor. 1 fo. 70, Swineherd. 2 fo. Welder. 2 fo. 60, Tractor-driver. 3 fo. Horse and groom. 4 fo. Bus driver. 5 fo. Telegraph lineman. 10 fo. Miner.

263. M. Csokonai Vitez.

**1955.** Hungarian Poets.
1434. **263.** 60 fi. black .. .. 45 15
1435. – 1 fo. blue .. .. 40 10
1436. – 2 fo. red .. .. 45 35
PORTRAITS: 1 fo. M. Vorosmarty. 2 fo. A. Jozsef.

**1955.** Air. Light Metal Industries Int. Congress, Budapest, As No. 1139.
1437. 5 fo. blue on silver .. 15·00 15·00

264. Bela Bartok

265. "Hargita" Diesel Multiple Unit.

**1955.** 10th Death Anniv. of Bartok (composer).
1438. **264.** 60 fi. brown (postage) 70 20
1439. 1 fo. green (air) .. 1·75 70
1440. 1 fo. brown .. .. 3·50 1·10

**1955.** Transport.
1441 **265** 40 fi. brown and green 40 10
1442 – 60 fi. bistre and green 35 10
1443 – 80 fi. brown and green 40 10
1444 – 1 fo. green and brown 55 10
1445 – 1 fo. 20 black & brown 1·40 50
1446 – 1 fo. 50 brown & black 85 25
1447 – 2 fo. brown and green 1·75 65
DESIGNS: 60 fi. Motor coach. 80 fi. Motor cyclist. 1 fo. Lorry. 1 fo. 20, Class "303" steam locomotive. 1 fo. 50, Tipper. 2 fo. "Beke" freighter.

266. Puli Sheepdog.

**1956.** Hungarian Dogs.
1448 **266** 40 fi. black, red & yell 30 10
1449 – 50 fi. black, buff & bl 30 10
1450 – 60 fi. black, red & grn 40 15
1451 – 80 fi. blk, orge & grey 50 15
1452 – 1 fo. black, orange and turquoise .. 70 25
1453 – 1 fo. 20 black, brown and orange .. 75 30
1454 – 1 fo. 50 black, buff and blue .. .. 1·25 45
1455 – 2 fo. black, brn & mve 1·75 80
DESIGNS—RECTANGULAR (36×26 mm.): 50 fi. Puli and cattle. 1 fo. 50, Kuvasz sheepdog and cottage. (27×35 mm.): 80 fi. Hungarian retriever. (27×38 mm.): 1 fo. Hungarian retriever carrying mallard. As Type **266**: 60 fi. Pumi. 1 fo. 20, Kuvasz sheepdog. 2 fo. Komondor sheepdog.

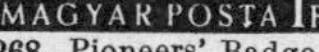

268. Pioneers' Badge.

269. Hunyadi on Horseback.

**1956.** 10th Anniv. of Pioneers Movement.
1456. **268.** 1 fo. red .. .. 20 10
1457. 1 fo. grey .. .. 20 10

**1956.** 500th Death Anniv. of Janos Hunyadi.
1458. **269.** 1 fo. brown on yellow 30 20

270. Miner.

271. Horse-jumping.

**1956.** Miners' Day.
1459. **270.** 1 fo. blue .. .. 40 10

**1956.** Olympic Games. Inscr. " 1956 ". Centres in brown.
1460. – 20 fi. blue (Canoeing) 15 10
1461. **271.** 30 fi. olive .. .. 15 10
1462. – 40 fi. brown (Fencing) 20 10
1463 – 60 fi. turq. (Hurdling) 20 10
1464. – 1 fo. red (Football) .. 25 10
1465. – 1 fo. 50 violet (Weight-lifting) .. .. 40 20
1466. – 2 fo. grn. (Gymnastics) 1·00 20
1467. – 3 fo. mauve (Basket-ball) .. .. 1·75 65

272. Chopin.

274. Dr. L. Zamenhof.

**1956.** Hungarian–Polish Philatelic Exn. Budapest.
1468. – 1 fo. blue (Liszt) .. 1·50 1·50
1469. **272.** 1 fo. mauve .. .. 1·50 1·50

**1957.** Hungarian Red Cross Fund Nos. 1417 etc., surch. with shield, cross and premium.
1470. **262.** 20 fi.+20 fi. olive .. 15 15
1471. – 30 fi.+30 fi. red .. 25 15
1472. – 40 fi.+40 fi. brown .. 40 15
1473. – 60 fi.+60 fi. red .. 25 15
1474. – 1 fo.+1 fo. blue .. 45 25
1475. – 2 fo.+2 fo. lake .. 90 75

**1957.** Air. 70th Anniv. of Esperanto.
1476. – 60 fi. brown .. .. 30 10
1477. **274.** 1 fo. green .. .. 35 15
DESIGN—HORIZ. 60 fi. Esperanto Star.

275. Letters, Letter-box and Globe.

276. Janos Arany.

**1957.** Air. Hungarian Red Cross Fund. Cross in red.
1478. **275.** 60 fi.+30 fi. brown .. 40 15
1479. – 1 fo.+50 fi. lilac .. 55 15
1480. – 2 fo.+1 fo. red .. 1·10 20
1481. – 3 fo.+1 fo. 50 blue .. 1·40 30
1482. – 5 fo.+2 fo. 50 grey .. 2·50 1·00
1483. – 10 fo.+5 fo. green .. 4·00 2·00
DESIGNS: 1 fo. Postal coach. 2 fo. Top of telegraph pole. 3 fo. Radio aerial mast. 5 fo. Desk telephone. 10 fo. (46×31 mm.) Posthorn.

**1957.** 75th Death Anniv. of Janos Arany (poet).
1484. **276.** 2 fo. blue .. .. 20 10

277. Arms.

278. Congress Emblem.

**1957.** Inaug. of National Emblem.
1485. **277.** 60 fi. red .. .. 20 10
1486. 1 fo. green .. .. 20 10

**1957.** 4th W.F.T.U. Congress, Leipzig.
1487. **278.** 1 fo. red .. .. 15 10

279. Courier.

**1957.** Air. Stamp Day.
1488. **279.** 1 fo. (+ 4 fo.) brn. & bistre on cream 70 70
1489. – 1 fo. (+ 4 fo.) brn. & bistre on cream 70 70
DESIGN: No. 1489, Tupolev Tu-104A airplane over Budapest.

280. Dove of Peace and Flags.

**1957.** 40th Anniv of Russian Revolution. Flags multicoloured.
1490 **280** 60 fi. black and grey 15 10
1491 – 1 fo. black and drab 20 10
DESIGN: 1 fo. Lenin.

281. Komarom Tumbler Pigeons.

282. Television Building.

**1957.** Int. Pigeon-fanciers' Exn., Budapest.
1492. **281.** 30 fi. brown, yell. and green (postage) .. 10 10
1493. – 40 fi. black and brown 15 10
1494. – 60 fi. grey and blue .. 20 10
1495. – 1 fo. brown and grey 40 10
1496. – 2 fo. grey and mauve 75 15
1497. – 3 fo. green, grey & red (air) .. .. 85 15
DESIGNS: 40 fi. Two short-beaked Budapest pigeons. 60 fi. Giant domestic pigeon. 1 fo. Three Szeged pigeons. 2 fo. Two Hungarian fantail pigeons. 3 fo. Two carrier pigeons.

**IMPERFORATE STAMPS.** Most modern Hungarian stamps issued up to the end of 1991 also exist imperforate.

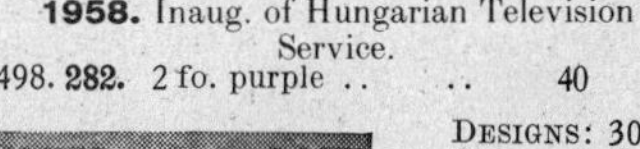

**1958.** Inaug. of Hungarian Television Service.
1498. **282.** 2 fo. purple .. .. 40 25

283. Mother and Child.

DESIGNS: 30 fi. Old man feeding pigeons. 40 fi. Schoolboys with savings stamps. 60 fi. "The Cricket and the Ant.". 1 fo. Bees on honeycomb. 2 fo. Hands holding banknotes.

**1958.** Savings Campaign.
1499 **283** 20 fi. deep green & grn 10 10
1500 – 30 fi. purple and green 10 10
1501 – 40 fi. brown and bistre 15 10
1502 – 60 fi. myrtle and red 20 10
1503 – 1 fo. brown and green 20 10
1504 – 2 fo. green and orange 55 25

**284.** Hungarian Pavilion.

**1958.** Air. Brussels Int. Exn. Inscr. "BRUXELLES 1958".

1505. **284.** 20 fi. brown and red .. 10 10
1506. – 40 fi. sepia and blue .. 15 10
1507. – 60 fi. sepia and red .. 15 10
1508. – 1 fo. brown and ochre 20 10
1509. – 1 fo. 40 multicoloured 25 10
1510. – 2 fo. sepia and brown 25 10
1511. – 3 fo. sepia and green 40 10
1512. – 5 fo. multicoloured .. 55 30

DESIGNS—HORIZ. 40 fi. Map of Hungary and exhibits. 60 fi. Parliament Buildings, Budapest. 1 fo. Chain Bridge, Budapest. 1 fo. 40, Arms of Belgium and Hungary and Exhibition emblem. 5 fo. Exhibition emblem. VERT. 2 fo. "Manneken Pis" statue, Brussels. 3 fo. Town Hall, Brussels.

**285.** Arms of Hungary. **286.** Youth with Book.

**1958.** 1st Anniv. of Amended Constitution. Arms multicoloured.

1513. **285.** 60 fi. red .. .. 10 10
1514. 1 fo. green .. .. 15 10
1515. 2 fo. drab .. .. 25 10

**1958.** 5th Youth Festival, Keszthely.

1516. **286.** 1 fo. brown .. .. 20 15

DESIGN: 1 fo. Prague Castle, telegraph pole and wires.

**287.** Town Hall, Prague, and Posthorn.

**1958.** Organization of Socialist Countries' Postal Administrations Conference, Prague.

1517. **287.** 60 fi. green (postage) 20 15
1518. – 1 fo. lake (air) .. 20 15

**288.** "Linum dolomiticum".

**1958.** Flowers.

1519 **288** 20 fi. yellow & purple 35 10
1520 – 30 fi. brown and blue 20 10
1521 – 40 fi. brn, buff & sepia 40 10
1522 – 60 fi. mauve and green 55 10
1523 – 1 fo. green and red .. 80 10
1524 – 2 fo. yellow and green 1·50 10
1525 – 2 fo. 50 pink and blue 1·75 30
1526 – 3 fo. pink, light green and green .. .. 2·25 50

FLOWERS—TRIANGULAR: 30 fi. "Kitaibelia vitifolia". 2 fo. 50, "Dianthus collinus". 3 fo. "Rosa sancti andreae". VERT. ($20\frac{1}{2} \times 31$ mm.): 40 fi. "Doronicum hungaricum". 60 fi. "Colchicum arenarium". 1 fo. "Helleborus purpuracens". 2 fo. "Hemerocallis lilio-asphodelus".

DESIGNS—VERT. 30 fi. Table-tennis player. 40 fi. Wrestlers. 1 fo. Water-polo player. 2 fo. 50, High-diver. HORIZ. 60 fi. Wrestlers. 3 fo. Swimmer.

**289.** Table-tennis Bat and Ball.

**1958.** European Table-tennis and Swimming Championships, and World Wrestling Championships, Budapest.

1527. **289.** 20 fi. red on pink .. 10 10
1528. – 30 fi. olive on green .. 15 10
1529. – 40 fi. purple on yellow 25 10
1530. – 60 fi. brown on blue .. 30 10
1531. – 1 fo. blue on blue .. 50 10
1532. – 2 fo. 50 red on yellow 95 20
1533. – 3 fo. blue on turquoise 1·40 40

**290.** **291.** Airliner over Millennium Monument Budapest.

**1958.** Air. (a) Int Correspondence Week.

1534 **290** 60 fi. bistre and purple 15 10
1535 – 1 fo. bistre and blue 35 20

(b) National Stamp Exhibition, Budapest.

1536 – 1 fo. (+2 fo.) bistre and red .. .. 35 45
1537 **290** 1 fo. (+2 fo.) bistre and green .. .. 35 45

DESIGNS: No. 1535, Posthorn, envelope and transport. No. 1536, Stamp and magnifier.

**1958.** Air. 40th Anniv. of 1st Hungarian Air Mail Stamp.

1538. **291.** 3 fo. pur., red & drab 75 20
1539. – 5 fo. blue, red & drab 1·00 35

DESIGN: 5 fo. Airliner over Sopron Tower.

For similar stamps but without commem. inscription see Nos. 1542/51.

DESIGN. 2 fo. Hand holding up the newspaper "Voros Ujsag" (Red Journal).

**292.** Red Flag.

**1958.** 40th Anniv. of Hungarian Communist Party and Founding of the "Red Journal".

1540. **292.** 1 fo. red and brown .. 15 10
1541. – 2 fo. red and blue .. 15 10

**1958.** Air. As T **291** but with "LEGIPOSTA" at top in place of commem. inscription. On cream paper.

1542. – 20 fi. green and red .. 10 10
1543. – 30 fi. violet and red .. 10 10
1544. – 70 fi. purple and red 15 10
1545. – 1 fo. blue and red .. 20 10
1546. – 1 fo. 60 pur. and red 30 10
1547. – 2 fo. green and red .. 50 10
1548. – 3 fo. brown and red (No. 1539) .. .. 50 10
1549. **291.** 5 fo. green and red .. 85 20
1550. – 10 fo. blue and red .. 2·25 55
1551. – 20 fo. sepia and red .. 5·00 1·25

DESIGNS: Airliner over: 20 fi. Town Hall, Szeged. 30 fi. Sarospatak Castle. 70 fi. Town Hall, Gyor. 1 fo. Opera House, Budapest. 1 fo. 60, Old City of Veszprem. 2 fo. Chain Bridge, Budapest. 10 fo. Danube Embankment, Budapest. 20 fo. Budapest Cathedral.

**293.** Rocket approaching the Moon.

**1959.** I.G.Y. Achievements.

1552 – 10 fi. brown and red 15 10
1553 – 20 fi. black and blue 55 10
1554 – 30 fi. buff and green 60 15
1555 – 40 fi. light blue & blue 1·40 25
1556 **293** 60 fi. green and blue 75 25
1557 – 1 fo. brown and red .. 1·25 35
1558 – 5 fo. brown & dp brn 2·00 50

DESIGNS—($31\frac{1}{2} \times 21$ mm.): 10 fi. Eotvos torsion balance (gravimetry). 20 fi. Ship using echo-sounder (oceanography). 30 fi. "Northern Lights" and polar scene. ($35\frac{1}{2} \times 26\frac{1}{2}$ mm.): 40 fi. Russian polar camp and Antarctic route map. 1 fo. Observatory and the sun. 5 fo. Russian "Sputnik" and American "Vanguard" (artificial satellites).

See also No. 1605.

**294.** Revolutionary. **296.** Early Steam Locomotive "Deru".

**295.** Rose.

**1959.** 40th Anniv. of Proclamation of Hungarian Soviet Republic.

1559. **294.** 20 fi. red and purple 10 10
1560. 60 fi. red and blue .. 10 10
1561. 1 fo. red and brown .. 15 10

**1959.** May Day.

1562. **295.** 60 fi. red, grn. & lilac 30 10
1563. 1 fo. red, grn. & brn. 40 10

**1959.** Transport Museum issue.

1564 **296** 20 fi. mult (postage) 35 10
1565 – 30 fi. green, blk & buff 35 10
1566 – 40 fi. multicoloured .. 45 10
1567 – 60 fi. multicoloured .. 35 10
1568 – 1 fo. multicoloured .. 45 10
1569 – 2 fo. multicoloured .. 70 15
1570 – 2 fo. 50 multicoloured (blue background) 85 15
1571 – 3 fo. mult (air) .. 2·00 40

DESIGNS—HORIZ. 30 fi. Ganz diesel railcar. 60 fi. Csonka motor car. 1 fo. Ikarusz rear-engine motor coach. 2 fo. First Lake Balaton steamer "Kisfaludy". 2 fo. 50, Stagecoach. 3 fo. Aladar Zselyi's monoplane. VERT. 40 fi. Early railway semaphore signal.

See also No. 1572.

**1959.** Int Philatelic Federation Congress, Hamburg. As No. 1570 but colours changed.

1572 2 fo. 50 multicoloured (yellow background) .. 80 1·00

**297.** Posthorn. **298.** Common Cormorant.

**1959.** Organization of Socialist Countries' Postal Administration Conf., Berlin.

1573. **297.** 1 fo. red .. .. 20 20

**1959.** Water Birds. Inscr. "1959".

1574. **298.** 10 fi. black & green. 20 10
1575. – 20 fi. green and blue 30 10
1576. – 30 fi. violet, myrtle and orange .. 45 15
1577. – 40 fi. grey and green 60 30
1578. – 60 fi. brown & pur. 65 30
1579. – 1 fo. black & turquoise 70 45
1580. – 2 fo. black and red .. 1·25 45
1581. – 3 fo. brown and bistre 2·25 1·00

DESIGNS: 20 fi. Little Egret. 30 fi. Purple Heron. 40 fi. Great Egret. 60 fi. White Spoonbill. 1 fo. Grey Heron. 2 fo. Squacco Heron. 3 fo. Glossy Ibis.

**299.** 10th-century Man-at-Arms. **300.** Bathers at Lake Balaton.

**1959.** 24th World Fencing Championships, Budapest. Inscr. as in T **299.**

1582. **299.** 10 fi. black and blue 10 10
1583. – 20 fi. black and lemon 10 10
1584. – 30 fi. black and violet 15 10
1585. – 40 fi. black and red .. 20 10
1586. – 60 fi. black and purple 25 10
1587. – 1 fo. black and turq. 35 10
1588. – 1 fo. 40, black & orge. 70 10
1589. – 3 fo. black and green 1·40 25

DESIGNS (Evolution of Hungarian swordsmanship). 20 fi. 15th-century man-at-arms. 30 fi. 18th-century soldier. 40 fi. 19th-century soldier. 60 fi. 19th-century cavalryman. Fencer: at the assault (1 fo.); on guard (1 fo. 40); saluting (3 fo.).

**1959.** Lake Balaton Summer Courses.

1590. – 30 fi. bl. on yell. (post.) 20 10
1591. – 40 fi. red on green .. 10 10
1592. **300.** 60 fi. brown on pink .. 20 10
1593. – 1 fo. 20 violet on pink 50 10
1594. – 2 fo. red on yellow .. 75 20
1595. – 20 fi. green (air) .. 10 10
1596. – 70 fi. blue .. 20 10
1597. – 1 fo. red and blue .. 30 10
1598. – 1 fo. 70 brn. on yell. 70 30

DESIGNS—VERT. 20 fi. Tihany (view). 30 fi. "Kek Madar" (yacht). 70 fi. "Tihany" (waterbus). 1 fo. Waterlily and view of Heviz. 1 fo. 20, Anglers. 1 fo. 70, "Saturnus" (yacht) and statue of fisherman (Balaton pier). 2 fo. Holidaymakers and "Beloiannis" (lake steamer). HORIZ. 40 fi. Vintner with grapes.

**301.** **302.** Shepherd with Letter.

**1959.** 150th Death Anniv. of Haydn (composer).

1599. **301.** 40 fi. yellow & purple 40 10
1600. – 60 fi. buff and slate .. 75 20
1601. – 1 fo. orange & violet 1·25 20

DESIGNS—HORIZ. 60 fi. Fertod Chateau. VERT. 1 fo. Haydn.

**1959.** Birth Bicentenary of Schiller (poet). As T **301** but inscr "F. SCHILLER" etc.

1602. 40 fi. yellow and olive .. 10 10
1603. 60 fi. pink and blue .. 10 10
1604. 1 fo. yellow and purple .. 20 10

DESIGNS—VERT. 40 fi. Stylized initials. "F" and "Sch" and Schiller's birthplace. 1 fo. Schiller. HORIZ. 60 fi. Pegasus.

**1959.** Landing of Russian Rocket on the Moon. As T **293** with addition of Russian Flag and "22 h 02' 34"" on Moon in red.

1605 **293** 60 fi. green and blue .. 35 10

**1959.** Stamp Day and National Stamp Exn.

1606. **302.** 2 fo. purple .. .. 75 1·00

**303.** "Taking delivery". **304.** Lenin and Szamuely.

**1959.** Int. Correspondence Week.

1607. **303.** 60 fi. multicoloured .. 15 10

**1959.** Russian Stamp Exn., Budapest.

1608. **304.** 20 fi. brown and red .. 10 10
1609. – 40 fi. lake & brn. on bl. 10 10
1610. – 60 fi. buff and blue .. 10 10
1611. – 1 fo. multicoloured .. 20 15

DESIGNS: 40 fi. Pushkin. 60 fi. Mayakovsky. 1 fo. Arms with hands clasping flag.

**305.** Swallowtail. **306.**

**1959.** Butterflies and Moths. Butterflies in natural colours, background colours given.

1612 **305** 20 fi. black and green (postage) .. .. 45 10
1613 – 30 fi. black and blue 45 10
1614 – 40 fi. black and brown 65 10
1615 – 60 fi. black and bistre 85 15
1616 – 1 fo. black & grn (air) 1·25 25
1617 – 2 fo. black and lilac 2·50 85
1618 – 3 fo. black and green 3·75 1·40

DESIGNS—HORIZ: 30 fi. Hebe tiger moth. 40 fi. Adonis blue. 2 fo. Death's-head hawk moth. VERT: 60 fi. Purple emperor. 1 fo. Scarce copper. 3 fo. Red emperor.

**1959.** 7th Socialist Workers' Party Congress. Flag in red and green.

1619. **306.** 60 fi. brown .. .. 10 10
1620. – 1 fo. red .. .. 10 10

DESIGN: 1 fo. Flag inscr. "MSZMP VII. KONGRESSZUSA".

**307.** "Fairy Tales". **308.** Sumeg Castle.

**1959.** Fairy Tales (1st series). Centres and inscr. in black.

1621. **307.** 20 fi. multicoloured .. 20 10
1622. – 30 fi. pink .. .. 20 10
1623. – 40 fi. turquoise .. 30 10
1624. – 60 fi. blue .. .. 50 10
1625. – 1 fo. yellow .. .. 65 10
1626. – 2 fo. green .. .. 85 10
1627. – 2 fo. 50 salmon .. 1·10 15
1628. – 3 fo. red .. .. 1·25 50

FAIRY TALE SCENES: 30 fi. "The Sleeping Beauty". 40 fi. "Mat the Goose" 60 fi. "The Cricket and the Ant". 1 fo. "Mashenka and the Bears". 2 fo. "The Babes in the Wood". 2 fo. 50, "The Pied Piper of Hamelin". 3 fo. "Little Red Riding Hood".

See also Nos. 1702/9 and 2133/41.

**1960.** Hungarian Castles. On white paper.
1629. **308.** 8 fi. purple .. .. 10 10
1630. – 10 fi. brown .. .. 10 10
1631. – 12 fi. blue .. .. 10 10
1632. – 20 fi. green .. .. 10 10
1633. – 30 fi. brown .. .. 10 10
1634. – 40 fi. turquoise .. 10 10
1635. – 50 fi. brown .. .. 10 10
1636. – 60 fi. red .. .. 25 10
1637. – 70 fi. green .. .. 25 10
1638. – 80 fi. purple .. .. 15 10
1639. – 1 fo. blue .. .. 20 10
1640. – 1 fo. 20 purple .. 30 10
1641. – 1 fo. 40 blue .. 30 10
1642. – 1 fo. 70 lilac ("SOMLO") .. 35 10
1642a. – 1 fo. 70 lilac ("SOMLYO") .. 70 10
1643. – 2 fo. bistre .. .. 60 10
1644. – 2 fo. 60 blue .. 75 10
1645. – 3 fo. brown .. .. 80 10
1646. – 4 fo. violet .. .. 1·00 10
1647. – 5 fo. green .. .. 1·50 10
1648. – 10 fo. red .. .. 2·25 10

CASTLES—As Type **308**: 10 fi. Kisvarda. 12 fi. Szigliget. 20 fi. Tata. 30 fi. Diosgyor. 40 fi. Simon Tornya. 50 fi. Fuzer. 60 fi. Sarospatak. 70 fi. Nagyvazsony. 80 fi. Egervar. 28½ × 21½ mm: 1 fo. Vitany. 1 fo. 20, Sirok. 1 fo. 40, Siklos. 1 fo. 70, Somlyo. 2 fo. Boldogko. 2 fo. 60, Holloko. 4 fo. Eger. 21½ x 28½ mm: 3 fo. Csesznek. 5 fo. Koszeg. 10 fo. Sarvar.

See also Nos. 1694/700.

**309.** Halas Lace. **310.** Cross-country Skiing.

**1960.** Halas Lace (1st series). Designs showing lace as T **309.** Inscriptions and values in orange.
1649. 20 fi. sepia .. .. 20 10
1650. 30 fi. violet .. .. 20 10
1651. 40 fi. turquoise .. .. 30 10
1652. 60 fi. brown .. .. 40 10
1653. 1 fo. green .. .. 75 10
1654. 1 fo. 50 green .. .. 90 10
1655. 2 fo. blue .. .. 1·50 10
1656. 3 fo. red .. .. .. 2·50 35

Nos. 1650/1, 1654/5 are larger 38 × 44 mm.
See also Nos. 1971/8.

**1960.** Winter Olympic Games.
1657. **310.** 30 fi. bistre and blue 10 10
1658. – 40 fi. bistre and green 15 10
1659. – 60 fi. bistre and red .. 25 10
1660. – 80 fi. bistre and violet 30 10
1661. – 1 fo. bistre & turquoise 50 10
1662. – 1 fo. 20 bistre & lake 60 25
1663. – 2 fo. + 1 fo. mult. .. 1·40 60

DESIGNS: 40 fi. Ice hockey. 60 fi. Ski jumping. 80 fi. Speed skating. 1 fo. Skiing. 1 fo. 20, Figure skating. 2 fo. Games emblem.

**311.** Kato Haman. **312.** Yellow Pheasant's-eye and Quill.

**1960.** Celebrities and Anniversaries. Portrait as T **311.**
1664 60 fi. purple (T **311**) .. 20 10
1665 60 fi. brown (Clara Zetkin) 20 10
1666 60 fi. violet (Garibaldi) .. 20 10
1667 60 fi. green (I. Turr) .. 20 10
1668 60 fi. red (I. Tukory) .. 20 10
1669 60 fi. deep blue and blue (O. Herman) .. .. 20 10
1670 60 fi. brown (Beethoven) 45 10
1671 60 fi. red (F. Mora) .. 20 10
1672 60 fi. black and grey (B. I. Toth) .. .. .. 20 10
1673 60 fi. purple and mauve (D. Banki) .. .. 20 10
1674 60 fi. deep green & green (A. G. Pattantyus) .. 20 10
1675 60 fi. blue and cobalt (I. P. Semmelweis) .. 25 10
1676 60 fi. brown (Joliot-Curie) 40 10
1677 60 fi. red (F. Erkel) .. 20 10
1678 60 fi. blue and light blue (J. Bolyai) .. .. 20 10
1679 60 fi. red (V. I. Lenin) .. 25 10

COMMEMORATIVE EVENTS: Nos. 1664/5, Int Women's Day; 1666, Centenary of Sicilian Expedition; 1669, 125th Birth Anniv; 1670, Martonvasar Beethoven Concerts; 1671, Szeged Festival; 1672, Miners' Day; 1677, 150th Birth Anniv; 1678, Birth Centenary; 1679, 90th Birth Anniv.

**1960.** Stamp Exhibition Budadpest.
1680 **312** 2 fo. (+4 fo.) yellow, green and brown .. 50 75

**313.** Soldier. **314.** Rowing.

**1960.** 15th Anniv. of Liberation.
1681. **313.** 40 fi. brown and red 10 10
1682. – 60 fi. red, grn. & brn. 10 10

DESIGN—HORIZ. 60 fi. Student with flag (inscr. "1945 FELSZABADULASUNK ... 1960".).

**1960.** Summer Olympic Games. Centres and inscr. in black (3 fo. multicoloured). Circular frames in bistre. Background colours given.
1683. 10 fi. blue (T **314**) .. 10 10
1684. 20 fi. brown (Boxing) .. 10 10
1685. 30 fi. lilac (Archery) .. 10 10
1686. 40 fi. ochre (Discus) .. 10 10
1687. 50 fi. red (Ball game) .. 10 10
1688. 60 fi. green (Javelin) .. 15 10
1689. 1 fo. pur. (Horse-riding) 30 10
1690. 1 fo. 40 blue (Wrestling) 35 10
1691. 1 fo. 70 brown (Swordplay) 40 10
1692. 2 fo. + 1 fo. red (Romulus, Remus and Wolf) .. 60 35
1693. 3 fo. grey (Olympic Rings and Arms of Hungary) 1·50 60

**1960.** Hungarian Castles. As Nos. 1629, 1632/3, 1636/7 and 1641/2 but printed on coloured paper.
1694. 8 fi. purple on blue .. 10 10
1695. 20 fi. bronze on green .. 25 10
1696. 30 fi. brown on yellow .. 25 10
1697. 60 fi. red on pink .. 30 10
1698. 70 fi. green on blue .. 40 10
1699. 1 fo. 40 blue on blue .. 65 10
1700. 1 fo. 70 lilac on blue ("SOMLO") .. .. 1·50 15

**315.** Girl in Mezokovesd Provincial Costume. **316.** "The Turnip".

**1960.** Stamp Day.
1701 **315** 2 fo. (+4 fo.) mult .. 75 75

**1960.** Fairy Tales (2nd series). Multicoloured.
1702. 20 fi. Type **316** .. .. 10 10
1703. 30 fi. "Snow White and the Seven Dwarfs" .. 15 10
1704. 40 fi. "The Miller, Son and Donkey" .. .. 15 10
1705. 60 fi. "Puss in Boots" .. 20 10
1706. 80 fi. "The Fox and the Raven" .. .. 45 10
1707. 1 fo. "The Maple-wood Pipe" .. .. .. 70 10
1708. 1 fo. 70 "The Stork and the Fox" .. .. 85 15
1709. 2 fo. "Momotaro" (Japanese tale) .. 1·40 30

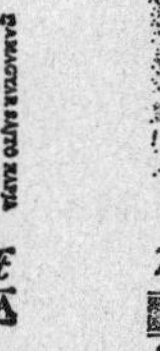

**317.** F. Rozsa. **318.** Eastern Grey Kangaroo with Young.

**1961.** Celebrities and Anniversaries. Portraits as T **317.**
1710. 1 fo. brown (T **317**) .. 15 10
1711. 1 fo. turq. (G. Kilian) .. 15 10
1712. 1 fo. red (J. Rippi-Ronai) 15 10
1713. 1 fo. olive (S. Latinka) .. 15 10
1714. 1 fo. green (M. Zalka) .. 15 10
1715. 1 fo. lake (J. Katona) .. 15 10

COMMEMORATIVE EVENTS: No. 1710, Press Day. No. 1711, Gyorgy Kilian Sports Movement. No. 1712, Birth Cent. No. 1713, 75th Birth Anniv. No. 1714, 65th Birth Anniv.

**1961.** Budapest Zoo Animals. Inscr. "ZOO 1961".
1716. **318.** 20 fi. black & orange 20 10
1717. – 30 fi. sepia and green 25 10
1718. – 40 fi. brown & chestnut 30 10
1719. – 60 fi. grey & mauve 50 10
1720. – 80 fi. yellow & black 65 10
1721. – 1 fo. brown & green 70 10
1722. – 1 fo. 40 sepia & turq. 90 10
1723. – 2 fo. black and red .. 1·75 50
1724. – 2 fo. 60 brown & violet 1·75 80
1725. – 3 fo. multicoloured .. 2·00 1·25

DESIGNS—HORIZ. 30 fi. American bison. 60 fi. Indian elephant and calf. 80 fi. Tiger and cubs. 1 fo. 40, Polar bear. 2 fo. Common zebra and foal. 2 fo. 60, European bison cow with calf. VERT. 40 fi. Brown bear. 1 fo. Ibex. 3 fo. Main entrance, Budapest Zoo.

**319.** Child chasing Butterfly. **320.** Launching of Rocket "Vostok".

**1961.** Health. Inscr. "1961". Cross in red.
1726. **319.** 30 fi. blk., pur. & brn. 20 10
1727. – 40 fi. sep., blue & turq. 30 10
1728. – 60 fi. yell., grey & vio. 35 10
1729. – 1 fo. multicoloured .. 40 10
1730. – 1 fo. 70 yellow, blue and green .. .. 65 10
1731. – 4 fo. green and grey .. 1·25 20

DESIGNS—As Type **319**: 40 fi. Patient on operating table. LARGE (29½ × 35 mm.): 60 fi. Ambulance and stretcher. 1 fo. Traffic lights and scooter. 1 fo. 70, Syringe and jars. 4 fo. Emblem of Health Department.

**1961.** World's First Manned Space Flight. Inscr. "1961.IV.12".
1732. **320.** 1 fo. brown and blue 40 15
1733. – 2 fo. brown and blue 1·75 90

DESIGN: 2 fo. Gagarin and "Vostok" in flight.

**321.** Roses. **322.** "Venus" Rocket.

**1961.** May Day.
1734. **321.** 1 fo. red and green .. 20 10
1735. – 2 fo. red and green .. 30 10

DESIGN: 2 fo. As Type **321** but roses and inscr. reversed.

**1961.** Launching of Soviet "Venus" Rocket. Inscr. "VENUSZ RAKETA 1961 II.12".
1736. 40 fi. black, bistre & blue 30 10
1737. 60 fi. black, bistre & blue 30 10
1738. 80 fi. black and blue .. 40 10
1739. 2 fo. bistre & violet-blue 1·00 75

DESIGNS: 40 fi. Type **322.** 60 fi. Separation of rocket capsule in flight. 80 fi. Capsule and orbit diagram. 2 fo. Allegory of flying woman and crescent moon.

**323.** Conference Emblem, Letter and Transport.

**1961.** Organization of Socialist Countries' Postal Administrations Conference.
1740. 40 fi. blk. & orge. (T **323**) 15 10
1741. 60 fi. black and mauve .. 15 10
1742. 1 fo. black and blue .. 15 10

DESIGNS: 60 fi. Television aerial. 1 fo. Radar receiving equipment.

**324.** Hungarian Flag. **325.** George Stephenson.

**1961.** Int. Stamp Exhibition, Budapest.
(a) 1st issue. Background in silver.
1743. 1 fo. red, green and black 25 25
1744. 1 fo. 70 multicoloured .. 25 25
1745. 2 fo. 60 multicoloured .. 1·00 75
1746. 3 fo. multicoloured .. 2·25 1·00

(b) 2nd issue. Background in gold. Inscriptions at left altered on 1 fo. and 3 fo.
1747. 1 fo. red, green and black 25 25
1748. 1 fo. 70 multicoloured .. 25 25
1749. 2 fo. 60 multicoloured .. 1·00 75
1750. 3 fo. multicoloured .. 2·25 1·00

DESIGNS: 1 fo. Type **324.** 1 fo. 70, Late spider orchids. 2 fo. 60, Small tortoiseshell. 3 fo. Goldfinch.

See also Nos. 1765/8.

**1961.** Communications Ministers' Conference, Budapest. Inscr. "KOZLEKEDESUGYI", etc.
1751. **325.** 60 fi. olive .. .. 15 10
1752. – 1 fo. bis., blk. & blue 20 10
1753. – 2 fo. brown .. .. 20 10

DESIGNS: 1 fo. Communications emblems. 2 fo. J. Landler (Minister of Communications).

**326.** Football and Club Badge.

**1961.** 50th Anniv. of VASAS Sports Club. Badge in gold, red and blue.
1754. 40 fi. orange, black & gold 10 10
1755. 60 fi. green, black & gold 10 10
1756. 1 fo. bistre, black & gold 10 10
1757. 2 fo. + 1 fo. bl., blk. & gold 65 60

DESIGNS: 40 fi. Type **326.** 60 fi. Wrestling. 1 fo. Vaulting. 2 fo. Sailing.

**327.** Three Racehorses.

**1961.** Racehorses.
1758. 30 fi. multicoloured .. 15 10
1759. 40 fi. multicoloured .. 25 10
1760. 60 fi. multicoloured .. 35 10
1761. 1 fo. black, green & orge. 40 10
1762. 1 fo. 70 sepia, black and green .. .. .. 85 15
1763. 2 fo. black, blue and brn. 1·00 15
1764. 3 fo. multicoloured .. 1·75 65

DESIGNS: 30 fi. Type **327.** 40 fi. Three hurdlers. 60 fi. Trotting race (two horses). 1 fo. Trotting race (three horses). 1 fo. 70, Two racehorses and two foals. 2 fo. Hungarian trotter "Baka". 3 fo. 19th century champion mare, "Kincsem".

**328.** Budapest.

**1961.** Stamp Day and Int. Stamp Exhibition, Budapest (3rd issue). Designs as T **328.**
1765. 2 fo. + 1 fo. bl., brn. & ol. 60 80
1766. 2 fo. + 1 fo. bl., brn. & ol. 60 80
1767. 2 fo. + 1 fo. bl., brn. & ol. 60 80
1768. 2 fo. + 1 fo. bl., brn. & ol. 60 80

Nos. 1765/8 are printed together in sheets of 40 (4 × 10) with one vertical row of each design. Horizontal strips of four form a composite panorama of Budapest.

**329.** Music, Keyboard and Silhouette. **330.** Lenin.

**1961.** 150th Birth and 75th Death Anniv. of Liszt (composer).
1769. **329.** 60 fi. black and gold 40 10
1770. – 1 fo. black .. .. 60 15
1771. – 2 fo. green and blue .. 1·40 30

DESIGNS—VERT. 1 fo. Statue. HORIZ. 2 fo. Music Academy.

**1961.** 22nd Soviet Communist Party Congress, Moscow.
1772. **330.** 1 fo. brown .. .. 10 10

**331.** Monk's Hood. **332.** Nightingale.

**1961.** Medicinal Plants. Multicoloured.
1773. 20 fi. Type **331** .. 10 10
1774. 30 fi. Centaury .. 15 10
1775. 40 fi. Blue iris .. 20 10
1776. 60 fi. Thorn-apple .. 25 10
1777. 1 fo. Purple hollyhock .. 50 10
1778. 1 fo. 70 Hop .. 65 10
1779. 2 fo. Poppy .. .. 1·00 15
1780. 3 fo. Mullein .. .. 1·40 40

**1961.** Birds of Woods and Fields. Multicoloured. Inscr. "1961".
1781. 30 fi. Type **332** .. .. 10 10
1782. 40 fi. Great tit .. .. 15 10
1783. 60 fi. Chaffinch (horiz.) .. 25 10
1784. 1 fo. Jay .. .. .. 35 10
1785. 1 fo. 20 Golden oriole (horiz.) .. .. 50 10
1786. 1 fo. 50 Blackbird (horiz.) 75 15
1787. 2 fo. Yellowhammer .. 90 20
1788. 3 fo. Lapwing (horiz.) .. 1·50 35

**333.** M. Karolyi. **334.** Railway Signals.

**1962.** Celebrities and Anniversaries. Inscr. "1962".

1789. **333.** 1 fo. sepia .. .. 15 10
1790. – 1 fo. brn. (F. Berkes) 15 10
1791. – 1 fo. blue (J. Pech).. 15 10
1792. – 1 fo. violet (A. Chazar) 15 10
1793. – 1 fo. blue (Dr. F. Hutyra) .. .. 15 10
1794. – 1 fo. red (G. Egressy) 15 10

ANNIVERSARIES: No. 1790, 5th Co-operative Movement Congress; 1791, 75th anniv of Hydrographic Institute; 1792, 50th anniv of Sports Club for the Deaf; 1793, 175th anniv of Hungarian Veterinary Service; 1794, 125th anniv of National Theatre.

**1962.** 14th Int. Railwaymen's Esperanto Congress.

1795. **334.** 1 fo. green .. .. 30 10

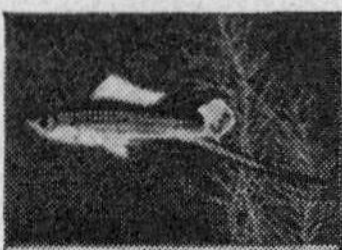

**335.** Swordtail.

**1962.** Ornamental Fishes. Inscr. "1962", Multicoloured.

1796. 20 fl. Type **335** .. .. 10 10
1797. 30 fl. Paradise fish .. 15 10
1798. 40 fl. Guppy .. .. 15 10
1799. 60 fl. Siamese Fighter .. 20 10
1800. 80 fl. Tiger Barb.. .. 25 10
1801. 1 fo. Angel fish .. .. 35 10
1802. 1 fo. 20 Sunfish .. .. 40 15
1803. 1 fo. 50 Lyretail .. 65 15
1804. 2 fo. Neon Tetra.. .. 75 20
1805. 3 fo. Pompadour.. .. 95 45

**336.** Flags of Argentina and Bulgaria.

**1962.** World Football Championships, 1962. Inscr. "CHILE 1962". Flags in national colours; ball, flagpole, value, etc., in bistre.

1806. – 30 fl. mauve .. .. 10 10
1807. – 40 fl. green .. .. 15 10
1808. – 60 fl. lilac .. .. 20 10
1809. – 1 fo. blue .. .. 30 10
1810. **336.** 1 fo. 70 orange .. 55 10
1811. – 2 fo. turquoise .. 65 10
1812. – 3 fo. red .. .. 90 20
1813. – 4 fo.+1 fo. green .. 1·25 60

FLAGS: 30 fl. Colombia and Uruguay 40 fl. U.S.S.R. and Yugoslavia. 60 fl. Switzerland and Chile. 1 fo. German Federal Republic and Italy. 2 fo. Hungary and Great Britain. 3 fo. Brazil and Mexico. 4 fo. Spain and Czechoslovakia. The two flags on each stamp represent the football teams playing against each other in the first round.

**337.** Gutenberg.

**338.** Campaign Emblem.

**1962.** Cent. of Hungarian Printing Union.

1814. **337.** 1 fo. blue .. .. 15 10
1815. – 1 fo. brown .. .. 15 10

PORTRAIT: No. 1815, Miklos Kis (first Hungarian printer).

**1962.** Malaria Eradication.

1816. **338.** 2 fo. 50 bistre & black 40 20

**339.** "Beating Swords into Ploughshares".

**340.** Festival Emblem.

**1962.** World Peace Congress, Moscow.

1817. **339.** 1 fo. brown .. .. 15 10

**1962.** World Youth Festival, Helsinki.

1818. **340.** 3 fo. multicoloured .. 20 10

**341.** Icarus.

**342.** Hybrid Tea.

**1962.** Air. Development of Flight.

1819. **341.** 30 fl. bistre and blue 15 10
1820. – 40 fl. blue and green 20 10
1821. – 60 fl. red and blue .. 30 10
1822. – 80 fl. silver, blue and turquoise .. .. 35 10
1823. – 1 fo. silver, bl. & pur. 40 10
1824. – 1 fo. 40 orge. & blue 45 15
1825. – 2 fo. brown and turq. 65 20
1826. – 3 fo. bl., silver & violet 75 25
1827. – 4 fo. silver, blk. & grn. 1·00 30

DESIGNS: 40 fl. Modern glider and Lilienthal monoplane glider. 60 fl. Zlin Trener 6 and Rakos's monoplane. 80 fl. Airship "Graf Zeppelin" and Montgolfier balloon. 1 fo. Ilyushin Il-18B and Wright Flyer I. 1 fo. 40, Nord 3202 sports airplane and Peter Nesterov's Nieuport biplane. 2 fo. Mil Mi-6 helicopter and Asboth's helicopter. 3 fo. Myasichev Mya-4 airliner and Zhukovsky's wind tunnel. 4 fo. Space rocket and Tsiolkovsky's rocket.

**1962.** Rose Culture. Roses in natural colours. Background colours given.

1828. – 20 fl. brown .. .. 20 10
1829. **342.** 40 fl. myrtle .. .. 30 10
1830. – 60 fl. violet .. .. 35 10
1831. – 80 fl. red .. .. 50 10
1832. – 1 fo. myrtle .. .. 60 10
1833. – 1 fo. 20 orange .. 80 10
1834. – 2 fo. turquoise .. 1·75 30

ROSES: 20 fl. Floribunda. 60 fl. to 2 fo. Various hybrid teas.

**343.** Globe, "Vostok 3" and "Vostok 4".

**1962.** Air. 1st "Team" Manned Space Flight.

1835. **343.** 1 fo. brown and blue 40 25
1836. – 2 fo. brown and blue 40 25

DESIGN: 2 fo. Cosmonauts Nikolaev and Popovich.

**344.** Weightlifting.

**345.** Austrian 2 kr. stamp of 1850.

**1962.** European Weightlifting Championships, Budapest.

1837. **344.** 1 fo. brown .. .. 20 10

**1962.** 35th Stamp Day.

1838. **345.** 2 fo.+1 fo. brown and yellow .. 30 45
1839. – 2 fo.+1 fo. brown and pink .. .. 30 45
1840. – 2 fo.+1 fo. brown and blue .. .. 30 45
1841. – 2 fo.+1 fo. brown and green .. .. 50 70

DESIGNS: Hungarian stamps of: No. 1839, 1919 (75 fi. Dozsa). No. 1840, 1955 (1 fo. 50 Skiing). No. 1841, 1959 (3 fo. "Vanessa atalanta").

**346.** Primitive and Modern Oilwells.

**347.** Gagarin.

**1962.** 25th Anniv. of Hungarian Oil Industry.

1842. **346.** 1 fo. green .. .. 30 10

**1962.** Air. Astronautical Congress, Paris.

1843. **347.** 40 fl. ochre & purple 20 10
1844. – 60 fl. ochre & green.. 25 10
1845. – 1 fo. ochre & turq. .. 40 10
1846. – 1 fo. 40 ochre & brown 60 10
1847. – 1 fo 70 ochre & blue.. 75 10
1848. – 2 fo. 60 ochre and violet 1·10 15
1849. – 3 fo. ochre and brown 1·40 25

ASTRONAUTS: 60 fl. Titov. 1 fo. Glenn. 1 fo. 40, Scott Carpenter. 1 fo. 70, Nikolaev. 2 fo. 60, Popovich. 3 fo. Schirra.

**348.** Cup and Football.

**349.** Osprey.

**1962.** "Budapest Vasas" Football Team's Victory in Central European Cup Competition.

1850. **348.** 2 fo.+1 fo. mult. .. 30 30

**1962.** Air. Birds of Prey. Multicoloured.

1851. 30 fl. Eagle owl .. .. 35 10
1852. 40 fl. Type **349** .. .. 40 15
1853. 60 fl. Marsh harrier .. 45 15
1854. 80 fl. Booted eagle .. 65 25
1855. 1 fo. African fish eagle .. 75 30
1856. 2 fo. Lammergeier .. 1·10 50
1857. 3 fo. Golden eagle .. 1·60 65
1858. 4 fo. Common kestrel .. 1·90 80

**350.** Racing Motor Cyclist.

**1962.** Motor Cycle and Car Sports. Mult.

1859. 20 fl. Type **350** .. .. 10 10
1860. 30 fl. Sidecar racing .. 10 10
1861. 40 fl. "Scrambling" (hill climb) .. .. 15 10
1862. 60 fl. Dirt-track racing .. 20 10
1863. 1 fo. Wearing "garland" 40 10
1864. 1 fo. 20 Speed trials .. 45 15
1865. 1 fo. 70 Sidecar trials .. 70 15
1866. 2 fo. "Go-kart" racing .. 80 15
1867. 3 fo. Car racing .. .. 1·25 65

**351.** Ice Skater.

**353.** Bulgarian 2 l. Rocket Stamp of 1959.

**352.** J. Batsanyi.

**1963.** European Figure Skating and Ice Dancing Championships, Budapest.

1868. **351.** 20 fl. grn., brn. & lilac 10 10
1869. – 40 fl. blk., brn. & salmon 15 10
1870. – 60 fl. multicoloured .. 30 10
1871. – 1 fo. multicoloured .. 45 10
1872. – 1 fo. 40 multicoloured 65 15
1873. – 2 fo. red, brn. and grn. 1·00 15
1874. – 3 fo. multicoloured .. 1·75 40

DESIGNS—VERT. 40 fl., 2 fo. Skater leaping. 60 fl., 1 fo. Pairs dancing. 1 fo. 40, Skater turning. HORIZ. 3 fo. Pair dancing.

**1963.** Celebrities and Anniversaries.

1875. 40 fl. lake (Type **352**) .. 10 10
1876. 40 fl. green (F. Entz) .. 15 10
1877. 40 fl. blue (I. Markovits) 15 10
1878. 40 fl. olive (L. Weiner) 35 10
1879. 60 fl. purple (Dr. F. Koranyi) .. .. 35 10
1880. 60 fl. bronze (G. Gardonyi) 15 10
1881. 60 fl. brown (P. de Coubertin) .. .. 25 10
1882. 60 fl. violet (J. Eotvos).. 15 10

ANNIVERSARIES: No. 1875, Revolutionary, Birth Bicent. No. 1876. Horticulture College founder, Horticulture Cent. No. 1877, Inventor, Hungarian Shorthand, Cent. No. 1878, Composer, Budapest Music Competitions. No. 1879, Tuberculosis researcher, 50th Death Anniv. No. 1880, Novelist, Birth Cent. No. 1881, Olympic Games reviver, Birth Cent. No. 1882, Author, 150th Birth Anniv.

**1963.** Organization of Socialist Countries' Postal Administrations Conference, Budapest.

1883. – 20 fl. red, yell. & grn. 10 10
1884. **353.** 30 fl. red, brn. & pur. 10 10
1885. – 40 fl. purple and blue 10 10
1886. – 50 fl. violet and blue 10 10
1887. – 60 fl. multicoloured .. 15 10
1888. – 80 fl. turq., blk. & blue 15 10
1889. – 1 fo. multicoloured .. 20 10
1890. – 1 fo. 20 yell., vio. & bl. 50 10
1891. – 1 fo. 40 blue, red & brn. 35 10
1892. – 1 fo. 70 brn., grn. & brn. 50 15
1893. – 2 fo. orge., blue & pur. 55 15
1894. – 2 fo. 60 vio, red & grn. 80 1·00

DESIGNS: Various "space" stamps—HORIZ. 20 fl. Albania 1 l. 50, (1962). 40 fl. Czechoslovakia 80 h. (1962). 50 fl. China 8 f. (1958). 60 fl. N. Korea 10 ch. (1961). 80 fl. Poland 40 g. (1959). 1 fo. Hungary 60 fl. (1961). 1 fo. 40, East Germany 25 pf. (1961). 1 fo. 70, Rumania 1 l. 20 (1957). 2 fo. 60, N. Vietnam 6 x. (1961). VERT. 1 fo. 20, Mongolia 30 m. (1959). 2 fo. Russia 6 k. (1961).

**354.** Fair Emblem.

**1963.** International Fair, Budapest.

1895. **354.** 1 fo. violet .. .. 20 10

**355.** Erkel (composer).

**1963.** Students' Erkel Memorial Festival Gyula.

1896. **355.** 60 fl. brown .. .. 40 10

**356.** Roses.

**1963.** 5th National Rose Show, Budapest.

1897. **356.** 2 fo. red, green & brn. 55 10

**357.** Helicon Monument.

**1963.** 10th Youth Festival, Keszthely.

1898. **357.** 40 fl. blue .. .. 10 10

358. Chain Bridge and "Snow White" (Danube steamer).

**1963.** Transport and Communications.

| No. | Type | Description | | |
|---|---|---|---|---|
| 1899 | 358 | 10 fi. blue | 10 | 10 |
| 1900 | – | 20 fi. green | 10 | 10 |
| 1901 | – | 30 fi. blue | 10 | 10 |
| 1902 | – | 40 fi. orange | 10 | 10 |
| 1902b | – | 40 fi. grey | 25 | 25 |
| 1903 | – | 50 fi. brown | 20 | 10 |
| 1904 | – | 60 fi. red | 10 | 10 |
| 1905 | – | 70 fi. olive | 25 | 10 |
| 1906 | – | 80 fi. brown | 20 | 10 |
| 1906a | – | 1 fo. brown | 15 | 10 |
| 1907 | – | 1 fo. purple | 20 | 10 |
| 1908 | – | 1 fo. 20 brown | 2·00 | 70 |
| 1909 | – | 1 fo. 20 violet | 20 | 10 |
| 1910 | – | 1 fo. 40 green | 30 | 10 |
| 1911 | – | 1 fo. 70 brown | 65 | 10 |
| 1912 | – | 2 fo. turquoise | 40 | 10 |
| 1913 | – | 2 fo. 50 purple | 60 | 10 |
| 1914 | – | 2 fo. 60 olive | 90 | 10 |
| 1915 | – | 3 fo. blue | 40 | 10 |
| 1916 | – | 4 fo. blue | 60 | 10 |
| 1917 | – | 5 fo. brown | 85 | 10 |
| 1918 | – | 6 fo. ochre | 90 | 10 |
| 1919 | – | 8 fo. mauve | 1·50 | 20 |
| 1920 | – | 10 fo. green | 1·50 | 75 |

DESIGNS—As Type **358**: HORIZ. 20 fi. Tramcar. 30 fi. Open-deck bus. 40 fi. (No. 1902), Articulated bus. 40 fi. (No. 1902b), Budapest 100 Post Office. 50 fi. Railway truck with gas cylinders. 60 fi. Trolley bus. 70 fi. Railway T.P.O. coach. 80 fi. Motor cyclist. VERT. 1 fo. (No. 1906a), Hotel Budapest. 28½ × 21 mm: 1 fo. (No. 1907) Articulated trolley bus. 1 fo. 40, Postal coach. 1 fo. 70, Diesel multiple-unit train. 2 fo. T.V. broadcast coach. 2 fo. 50, Tourist coach. 2 fo. 60, Signalbox and train. 3 fo. Parcels conveyor. 5 fo. Railway fork-lift truck. 6 fo. Telex operator. 8 fo. Telephonist and map. 10 fo. Postwoman. 21 × 28½ mm: 1 fo. 20 (No. 1908), Mail plane and trolley on tarmac. 1 fo. 20 (No. 1909), Control tower, Miskolc. 4 fo. Pylon, Pecs.

See also Nos. 2767/70.

359. Holidaymaker and "Beloiannis" (lake steamer).

**1963.** Cent. of Siofok Resort, Lake Balaton.

| No. | Type | Description | | |
|---|---|---|---|---|
| 1921. | – | 20 fi. blk., grn. and red | 50 | 10 |
| 1922. | 359. | 40 fi. multicoloured | 50 | 15 |
| 1923. | – | 60 fi. orge., brn. & blue | 90 | 20 |

DESIGNS—TRIANGULAR: 20 fi. Passenger launch. 60 fi. Yacht.

360. Mail Coach and Arc de Triomphe, Paris.

**1963.** Cent. of Paris Postal Conf.

| No. | Type | Description | | |
|---|---|---|---|---|
| 1924. | 360. | 1 fo. red | 20 | 10 |

361. Performance in front of Szeged Cathedral.

**1963.** Summer Drama Festival, Szeged.

| No. | Type | Description | | |
|---|---|---|---|---|
| 1925. | 361. | 40 fi. blue | 15 | 10 |

## INDEX

Countries can be quickly located by referring to the index at the end of this volume.

362. Child with towel.

364. Karancssag.

363. Pylon and Map.

**1963.** Red Cross Cent. Inscr. "1863-1963". Multicoloured.

| No. | Type | Description | | |
|---|---|---|---|---|
| 1926. | | 30 fi. Type **362** | 10 | 10 |
| 1927. | | 40 fi. Girl with medicine bottle and tablets | 10 | 10 |
| 1928. | | 60 fi. Girls of three races | 20 | 10 |
| 1929. | | 1 fo. Girl and "heart" | 25 | 10 |
| 1930. | | 1 fo. 40 Boys of three races | 35 | 10 |
| 1931. | | 2 fo. Child being medically examined | 45 | 10 |
| 1932. | | 3 fo. Hands tending plants | 1·10 | 25 |

**1963.** Village Electrification.

| No. | Type | Description | | |
|---|---|---|---|---|
| 1933. | 363. | 1 fo. black and grey | 25 | 10 |

**1963.** Provincial Costumes.

| No. | Type | Description | | |
|---|---|---|---|---|
| 1934. | 364. | 20 fi. lake | 20 | 10 |
| 1935. | – | 30 fi. green (Kapuvar) | 25 | 10 |
| 1936. | – | 40 fi. brown (Debrecen) | 25 | 10 |
| 1937. | – | 60 fi. blue (Hortobagy) | 35 | 10 |
| 1938. | – | 1 fo. red (Csokoly) | 50 | 10 |
| 1939. | – | 1 fo. 70 violet (Dunantul) | 60 | 10 |
| 1940. | – | 2 fo. turquoise (Bujak) | 70 | 10 |
| 1941. | – | 2 fo. 50 red (Alfold) | 85 | 15 |
| 1942. | – | 3 fo. blue (Mezokovesd) | 2·00 | 60 |

365. Hyacinth.

367. Calendar.

366. Skiing (slalom).

**1963.** Stamp Day. Flowers. Multicoloured.

| No. | Type | Description | | |
|---|---|---|---|---|
| 1943. | | 2 fo. + 1 fo. Type **365** | 45 | 55 |
| 1944. | | 2 fo. + 1 fo. Narcissus | 45 | 55 |
| 1945. | | 2 fo. + 1 fo. Chrysanthemum | 45 | 55 |
| 1946. | | 2 fo. + 1 fo. Tiger lily | 45 | 55 |

**1963.** Winter Olympic Games, Innsbruck, 1964. "MAGYAR" and emblems red and black; centres brown; background colours given.

| No. | Type | Description | | |
|---|---|---|---|---|
| 1947 | 366 | 40 fi. green | 10 | 10 |
| 1948 | – | 60 fi. violet | 10 | 10 |
| 1949 | – | 70 fi. blue | 15 | 10 |
| 1950 | – | 80 fi. green | 15 | 10 |
| 1951 | – | 1 fo. orange | 20 | 10 |
| 1952 | – | 2 fo. blue | 40 | 10 |
| 1953 | – | 2 fo. 60 purple | 1·00 | 40 |
| 1954 | – | 4 fo. + 1 fo. blue | 1·25 | 50 |

DESIGNS: 60 fi. Skiing (biathlon). 70 fi. Ski jumping. 80 fi. Rifle-shooting on skis. 1 fo. Figure skating (pairs). 2 fo. Ice hockey. 2 fo. 60 Speed skating. 4 fo. Bobsleighing.

**1963.** New Year Issue. Hungarian Postal and Philatelic Museum Fund. Mult.

| No. | Type | Description | | |
|---|---|---|---|---|
| 1955. | | 20 fi. Type **367** | 10 | 10 |
| 1956. | | 30 fi. Young chimney-sweep with glass of wine | 10 | 10 |
| 1957. | | 40 fi. Four-leafed clover | 15 | 10 |
| 1958. | | 60 fi. Piglet in top-hat | 15 | 10 |
| 1959. | | 1 fo. Young pierrot | 20 | 10 |
| 1960. | | 2 fo. Chinese lanterns and mask | 30 | 10 |
| 1961. | | 2 fo. 50 + 1 fo. 20 Holly, mistletoe, clover and horse-shoe | 50 | 20 |
| 1962. | | 3 fo. + 1 fo. 50 Piglets with balloon | 1·00 | 35 |

SIZES: As Type **367**—HORIZ. 20 fi., 1 fo., 3 fo. VERT. 40 fi. LARGER (28 × 38 mm.): 30 fi., 60 fi., 2 fo., 2 fo. 50.

368. Moon Rocket.

The 60 fi., 2 fo. and 3 fo. are horiz., the rest vert.

**1964.** Space Research. Multicoloured.

| No. | Type | Description | | |
|---|---|---|---|---|
| 1963. | | 30 fi. Type **368** | 15 | 10 |
| 1964. | | 40 fi. Venus rocket | 20 | 10 |
| 1965. | | 60 fi. "Vostok 1" | 20 | 10 |
| 1966. | | 1 fo. U.S. spaceship | 25 | 10 |
| 1967. | | 1 fo. 70 Soviet team space flights | 45 | 10 |
| 1968. | | 2 fo. "Telstar" | 50 | 10 |
| 1969. | | 2 fo. 60 Mars rocket | 75 | 15 |
| 1970. | | 3 fo. "Space Research" (rockets and tracking equipment) | 1·00 | 40 |

369. Swans.

**1964.** Halas Lace (2nd series). Lace patterns die-stamped in white on black; inscriptions black.

| No. | Type | Description | | |
|---|---|---|---|---|
| 1971. | 369. | 20 fi. green | 30 | 10 |
| 1972. | – | 30 fi. yellow | 45 | 10 |
| 1973. | – | 40 fi. red | 65 | 10 |
| 1974. | – | 60 fi. olive | 85 | 10 |
| 1975. | – | 1 fo. orange | 1·00 | 10 |
| 1976. | – | 1 fo. 40 blue | 1·25 | 15 |
| 1977. | – | 2 fo. turquoise | 1·40 | 15 |
| 1978. | – | 2 fo. 60 violet | 1·75 | 40 |

LACE PATTERNS—VERT. (38½ × 45 mm.): 30 fi. Peacocks. 40 fi. Pigeons. 60 fi. Peacock. 1 fo. Deer. 1 fo. 40, Fisherman. 2 fo. Pigeons. As Type **369**: 2 fo. 60, Butterfly.

370. Armour and Swords.

371. Basketball.

372. Dozsa and Kossuth.

373. Fair and Emblem.

374. "Breasting the Tape".

**1964.** Anniversaries and Events of 1964. Designs as T **325/9**, some showing portraits.

(a) As T **370**.

| No. | Type | Description | | |
|---|---|---|---|---|
| 1979. | | 60 fi. purple (I. Madach) | 15 | 10 |
| 1980. | | 60 fi. olive (E. Szabo) | 15 | 10 |
| 1981. | | 60 fi. olive (A. Fay) | 15 | 10 |
| 1982. | | 1 fo. red (Skittles) | 40 | 10 |
| 1983. | | 2 fo. brown (T **370**) | 35 | 10 |

ANNIV. OR EVENT: No. 1979, (author, death cent.). No. 1980, (founder of Municipal Libraries, 60th anniv.). No. 1981, (death cent.). No. 1982, (1st European Skittles Championships, Budapest). No. 1983, (50th anniv. of Hungarian Fencing Assn.).

(b) As T **371**.

| No. | Type | Description | | |
|---|---|---|---|---|
| 1984. | | 60 fi. turquoise (Stalactites and stalagmites) | 50 | 10 |
| 1985. | | 60 fi. blue (Bauxite excavator) | 75 | 10 |
| 1990. | | 60 fi. red (K. Marx) | 15 | 10 |
| 1986. | | 1 fo. green (Forest and waterfall) | 45 | 10 |
| 1987. | | 2 fo. brown (Galileo) | 55 | 10 |
| 1988. | | 2 fo. lake (Shakespeare) | 50 | 10 |
| 1989. | | 2 fo. blue (T **371**) | 1·40 | 10 |

ANNIV. OR EVENT—VERT. No. 1984, (Aggteleki Cave). No. 1985, (30th anniv. or Hungarian Aluminium Production). No. 1986, (National Forestry Federation Congress). No. 1987, (400th birth anniv.). No. 1988 (400th birth anniv.). No. 1989, (European Women's Basketball Championships). HORIZ. No. 1990, (cent. of "First International").

(c) As T **372**.

| No. | Type | Description | | |
|---|---|---|---|---|
| 1991. | | 1 fo. blue (T **372**) | 25 | 10 |
| 1992. | | 3 fo. + 1 fo. 50, black, grey and orange (Sports Museum, Budapest) | 70 | 30 |

ANNIV. OR EVENT: No. 1991, (60th Anniv. of City of Cegled). No. 1992, (Lawn Tennis Historical Exn., Budapest).

(d) T **373**.

| No. | Type | Description | | |
|---|---|---|---|---|
| 1993. | | 1 fo. green (Budapest Int. Fair) | 25 | 10 |

(e) As T **374**.

| No. | Type | Description | | |
|---|---|---|---|---|
| 1994. | | 60 fi. slate ("Alba Regia" statue) | 15 | 10 |
| 1995. | | 1 fo. brown (M. Ybl) | 25 | 10 |
| 1996. | | 2 fo. brown (T **374**) | 40 | 10 |
| 1997. | | 2 fo. dull purple (Michelangelo) | 50 | 10 |

ANNIV. OR EVENT: No. 1994, (Szekesfehervar Days). No. 1995, (architect, 150th birth anniv.). No. 1996, (50th anniv. of Hungarian-Swedish Athletic Meeting). No. 1997, (400th death anniv.).

375. Eleanor Roosevelt.

377. Peaches ("Magyar Kajszi").

376. Fencing.

**1964.** Eleanor Roosevelt Commemoration.

| No. | Type | Description | | |
|---|---|---|---|---|
| 1998 | 375 | 2 fo. ochre, deep brown and brown | 15 | 10 |

**1964.** Olympic Games, Tokyo. Multicoloured.

| No. | Type | Description | | |
|---|---|---|---|---|
| 1999. | | 30 fi. Type **376** | 10 | 10 |
| 2000. | | 40 fi. Gymnastics | 10 | 10 |
| 2001. | | 60 fi. Football | 10 | 10 |
| 2002. | | 80 fi. Horse-jumping | 15 | 10 |
| 2003. | | 1 fo. Running | 20 | 10 |
| 2004. | | 1 fo. 40 Weightlifting | 25 | 10 |
| 2005. | | 1 fo. 70 Gymnastics (trapeze) | 30 | 10 |
| 2006. | | 2 fo. Throwing the hammer, and javelin | 40 | 10 |
| 2007. | | 2 fo. 50 Boxing | 75 | 15 |
| 2008. | | 3 fo. + 1 fo. Water-polo | 80 | 30 |

**1964.** National Peaches and Apricots, Exn. Budapest. Designs of peaches or apricots. Multicoloured.

| No. | Type | Description | | |
|---|---|---|---|---|
| 2009. | | 40 fi. "J. H. Hale" | 15 | 10 |
| 2010. | | 60 fi. Type **377** | 15 | 10 |
| 2011. | | 1 fo. "Mandula Kajszi" | 30 | 10 |
| 2012. | | 1 fo. 50 "Borsi Rozsa" | 40 | 10 |
| 2013. | | 1 fo. 70 "Alexander" | 60 | 10 |
| 2014. | | 2 fo. "Champion" | 80 | 10 |
| 2015. | | 2 fo. 60 "Elberta" | 1·00 | 25 |
| 2016. | | 3 fo. "Mayflower" | 1·40 | 40 |

**378.** Lilac.

**1964.** Stamp Day. Multicoloured.
2017. 2 fo.+1 fo. Type **378** .. 40 55
2018. 2 fo.+1 fo. Mallard .. 1·25 1·25
2019. 2 fo.+1 fo. Gymnast .. 40 55
2020. 2 fo.+1 fo. Rocket and globe .. .. .. 40 55

**379.** Pedestrian Road Crossing.

**1964.** Road Safety. Multicoloured.
2021. 20 fi. Type **379** .. .. 30 10
2022. 60 fi. Child with ball running into road 45 10
2023. 1 fo. Woman and child waiting to cross road .. 70 20

**380.** Arpad Bridge, Budapest.

**1964.** Opening of Reconstructed Elizabeth Bridge, Budapest.
2024. **380.** 20 fi. grey, green and blue .. .. 10 10
2025. – 30 fi. green, blue and brown .. .. 10 10
2026. – 60 fi. brown, green and deep brown .. 30 10
2027. – 1 fo. brown, blue and deep brown .. 55 10
2028. – 1 fo. 50 grey, blue and brown .. 75 15
2029. – 2 fo. grey, green and brown .. .. 1·00 25
2030. – 2 fo. 50 grey, blue and brown .. 2·00 1·00
BUDAPEST BRIDGES: 30 fi. Margaret. 60 fi. Chain. 1 fo. Elizabeth. 1 fo. 50, Freedom. 2 fo. Petofi. 2 fo. 50, South.

**381.** Ring-necked Pheasant.

**1964.** "Hunting". Multicoloured.
2034. 20 fi. Type **381** .. .. 40 10
2035. 30 fi. Wild boar .. .. 15 10
2036. 40 fi. Grey partridges .. 60 10
2037. 60 fi. Brown hare .. 25 10
2038. 80 fi. Fallow deer .. 40 10
2039. 1 fo. Mouflon .. .. 60 10
2040. 1 fo. 70 Red deer .. 1·00 10
2041. 2 fo. Great bustard .. 3·00 40
2042. 2 fo. 50 Roe deer .. 1·25 30
2043. 3 fo. Emblem of Hunters' Federation .. .. 1·00 45

**382.** Horse-riding and Medals.

**1965.** Olympic Games, Tokyo—Hungarian Winners' Medals. Medals: Gold and brown (G); Silver and black (S); Bronze and brown (B).
2044. 20 fi. brn. & olive (G) 10 10
2045. 30 fi. brown and violet (S) 10 10
2046. 50 fi. brown and olive (G) 15 10
2047. 60 fi. brown & lt. blue (G) 15 10
2048. 70 fi. brn., slate & stone (B) 20 10
2049. 80 fi. brown & green (G) 25 10
2050. 1 fo. brn., vio. & mve. (S) 30 10
2051. 1 fo. 20 brown & blue (S) 40 10
2052. 1 fo. 40 brn. and grey (S) 55 10
2053. 1 fo. 50 brown & bistre (G) 65 10
2054. 1 fo. 70 brown & red (S) 85 10
2055. 3 fo. brown & turq. (G) .. 1·25 40
DESIGNS: 20 fi. Type **382**. 30 fi. Gymnastics. 50 fi. Rifle-shooting. 60 fi. Water-polo. 70 fi. Putting the shot. 80 fi. Football. 1 fo. Weight-lifting. 1 fo. 20, Canoeing. 1 fo. 40, Throwing the hammer. 1 fo. 50, Wrestling. 1 fo. 70, Throwing the javelin. 3 fo. Fencing.

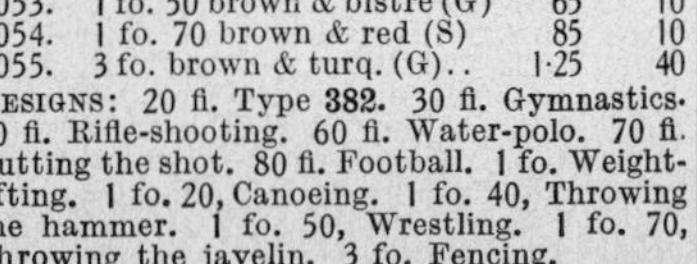

**383.** Mil Mi-4 Helicopter and Polar Station. **384.** Asters.

**1965.** Int. Quiet Sun Year.
2056. **383.** 20 fi. orge., blk. & blue 10 10
2057. – 30 fi. grn., blk. & grey 10 10
2058. – 60 fi. yell., blk. & mve. 15 10
2059. – 80 fi. yell., blk. & grn. 20 10
2060. – 1 fo. 50 multicoloured 25 10
2061. – 1 fo. 70 blk., mve. & bl. 30 10
2062. – 2 fo. red, black & blue 1·40 30
2063. – 2 fo. 50 yell., blk. & brn. 60 15
2064. – 3 fo. blk., blue & yell. 1·10 40
DESIGNS: 30 fi. Rocket and radar aerials. 60 fi. Rocket and diagram. 80 fi. Radio telescope. 1 fo. 50, Compass needle on Globe. 1 fo. 70, Weather balloon. 2 fo. Northern Lights and Adelie Penguins. 2 fo. 50, Space satellite. 3 fo. I.Q.S.Y. emblem and world map.

**1965.** 20th Anniv. of Liberation. Mult.
2066. 20 fi. Type **384** .. .. 10 10
2067. 30 fi. Peonies .. .. 10 10
2068. 50 fi. Carnations .. .. 10 10
2069. 60 fi. Roses .. .. 15 10
2070. 1 fo. 40 Lilies .. .. 30 10
2071. 1 fo. 70 Godetia .. .. 40 10
2072. 2 fo. Gladiolus .. .. 45 10
2073. 2 fo. 50 Parrot tulips .. 60 10
2074. 3 fo. Mixed bouquet .. 1·25 40

**385.** Leonov in Space. **386.** "Red Head" (after Leonardo da Vinci).

**1965.** Air. "Voskhod 2" Space Flight.
2075. **385.** 1 fo. grey and violet 15 10
2076. – 2 fo. brown & pur. .. 50 20
DESIGN: 2 fo. Belyaev and Leonov.

**1965.** Int. Renaissance Conf., Budapest.
2077. **386.** 60 fi. brown and ochre 20 10

**387.** Nikolaev, Tereshkova and View of Budapest. **388.** I.T.U. Emblem and Symbols.

**1965.** Visit of Astronauts Nikolaev and Tereshkova.
2078. **387.** 1 fo. brown and blue 25 10

**1965.** Centenary of I.T.U.
2079 **388** 60 fi. blue .. .. 20 10

**390.** French 13th-cent. Tennis. **391.** Marx and Lenin.

**1965.** "History of Tennis".
2081. **390.** 30 fi.+10 fi. lake on buff .. .. 20 10
2082. – 40 fi.+10 fi. blk. on lilac .. .. 25 10
2083. – 60 fi.+10 fi. green on bistre .. 30 10
2084. – 70 fi.+30 fi. purple on turquoise .. 35 10
2085. – 80 fi.+40 fi. bl. on lavender .. .. 40 15
2086. – 1 fo.+50 fi. green on yellow .. 70 15
2087. – 1 fo. 50+50 fi. brn. on green .. .. 75 35
2088. – 1 fo. 70+50 fi. black on blue .. .. 80 65
2089. – 2 fo.+1 fo. red on green .. .. 95 75

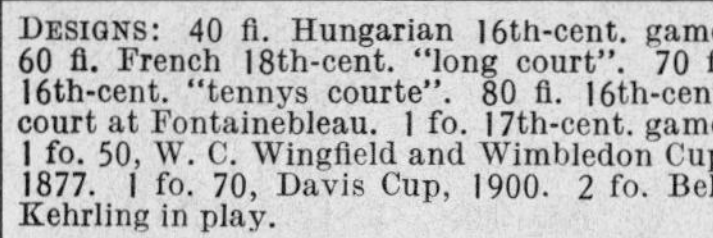
DESIGNS: 40 fi. Hungarian 16th-cent. game. 60 fi. French 18th-cent. "long court". 70 fi. 16th-cent. "tennys courte". 80 fi. 16th-cent. court at Fontainebleau. 1 fo. 17th-cent. game. 1 fo. 50, W. C. Wingfield and Wimbledon Cup, 1877. 1 fo. 70, Davis Cup, 1900. 2 fo. Bela Kehrling in play.

**1965.** Organization of Socialist Countries' Postal Administrations Congress, Peking.
2090. **391.** 60 fi. multicoloured .. 10 10

**392.** I.C.Y. Emblem and Pulleys. **393.** Equestrian Act.

**1965.** Int. Co-operation Year.
2091. **392.** 2 fo. red .. .. 30 10

**1965.** "Circus 1965". Multicoloured.
2093. 20 fi. Type **393** .. .. 15 10
2094. 30 fi. Musical clown .. 15 10
2095. 40 fi. Performing elephant 20 10
2096. 50 fi. Performing seal .. 25 10
2097. 60 fi. Lions .. .. 35 10
2098. 1 fo. Wild cat leaping through burning hoops 40 10
2099. 1 fo. 50 Black panthers .. 65 15
2100. 2 fo. 50 Acrobat with hoops 80 15
2101. 3 fo. Performing panther and dogs .. .. 1·10 15
2102. 4 fo. Bear on bicycle .. 1·50 40

**394.** Rescue Boat. **395.** Dr. I. Semmelweis.

**1965.** Danube Flood Relief.
2103. **394.** 1 fo.+50 fi. brn. & bl. 1·00 1·00

**1965.** Death Centenary of Ignac Semmelweis (physician).
2105. **395.** 60 fi. brown .. .. 30 10

**396.** Running.

**1965.** University Games, Budapest. Mult.
2106. 20 fi. Type **396** .. .. 10 10
2107. 30 fi. Start of swimming race .. .. .. 10 10
2108. 50 fi. Diving .. .. 10 10
2109. 60 fi. Gymnastics .. 15 10
2110. 80 fi. Tennis .. .. 20 10
2111. 1 fo. 70 Fencing .. .. 30 10
2112. 2 fo. Volleyball .. .. 45 10
2113. 2 fo. 50 Basketball .. 65 10
2114. 4 fo. Water-polo .. 90 35

**397.** Congress Emblem. **398.** "Phyllocactus hybridum".

**1965.** 6th W.F.T.U. Congress, Warsaw.
2116. **397.** 60 fi. blue .. .. 10 10

**1965.** Cacti and Orchids. Multicoloured.
2117. 20 fi. Type **398** .. .. 15 10
2118. 30 fi. "Cattleya warszewiczii" .. .. .. 20 10
2119. 60 fi. "Rebutia calliantha" 25 10
2120. 70 fi. "Paphiopedilum hybridum" .. .. 35 10
2121. 80 fi. "Opuntia rhodantha" 35 10
2122. 1 fo. "Laelia elegans" .. 60 10
2123. 1 fo. 50 "Zygocactus truncatus" .. .. 50 10
2124. 2 fo. "Strelitzia reginae" 75 10
2125. 2 fo. 50 "Lithops weberi" 80 10
2126. 3 fo. "Victoria amazonica" 1·60 40

**399.** Reproduction of No. 1127. **400.** F.I.R. Emblem.

**1965.** Stamp Day. Designs show reproductions of Hungarian stamps. Multicoloured.
2127. 2 fo.+1 fo. Type **399** .. 40 50
2128. 2 fo.+1 fo. No. 1280 .. 1·40 1·40
2129. 2 fo.+1 fo. No. 1873 .. 40 50
2130. 2 fo.+1 fo. No. 1733 .. 40 50

**1965.** 5th Int. Federation of Resistance Fighters Congress, Budapest.
2132. **400.** 2 fo. blue .. .. 15 10

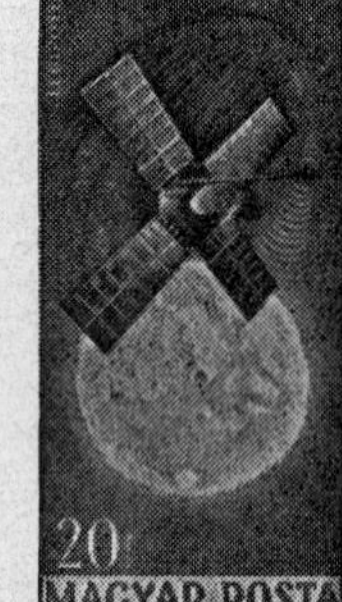

**401.** The Magic Horse. **402.** "Mariner 4".

**1965.** Fairy Tales (3rd series). Scenes from "The Arabian Nights Entertainments". Multicoloured.
2133. 20 fi. Type **401** .. .. 10 10
2134. 30 fi. Sultan Schahriah and Scheherazade .. .. 10 10
2135. 50 fi. Sinbad's 5th Voyage (ship) .. .. 10 10
2136. 60 fi. Aladdin and Genie of the Lamp .. .. 20 10
2137. 80 fi. Haroun al Rashid .. 30 10
2138. 1 fo. The Magic Carpet .. 50 10
2139. 1 fo. 70 The Fisherman and the Genie .. .. 70 10
2140. 2 fo. Ali Baba .. .. 85 10
2141. 3 fo. Sinbad's 2nd Voyage (roc—legendary bird) 1·40 35

**1965.** Air. Space Research.
2142. **402.** 20 fi. blk., yell. & blue 20 10
2143. – 30 fi. vio., yell. & brn. 25 10
2144. – 40 fi. brn., mve. & blue 30 10
2145. – 60 fi. multicoloured .. 45 10
2146. – 1 fo. multicoloured .. 65 10
2147. – 2 fo. 50 blk., grey & pur. 1·10 10
2148. – 3 fo. blk., grn. & brn. 1·25 35
DESIGNS: 30 fi. "San Marco" (Italian satellite). 40 fi. "Molnyija 1" (Polish satellite). 60 fi. Moon rocket. 1 fo. "Shapir" rocket. 2 fo. 50, "Szonda 3" satellite. 3 fo. "Syncom 3" satellite.

**403.** Scarlet Tiger Moth. **404.** Bela Kun.

**1966.** Butterflies and Moths. Multicoloured.
2150 20 fi. Type **403** .. .. 15 10
2151 60 fi. Orange tip .. 30 10
2152 70 fi. Meleager's blue .. 45 10
2153 80 fi. Scarce swallowtail 55 10
2154 1 fo. Common burnet .. 65 10
2155 1 fo. 50 Southern festoon 75 20
2156 2 fo. Camberwell beauty 85 20
2157 2 fo. 50 Nettle-tree butterfly .. .. 1·00 25
2158 3 fo. Clouded yellow 1·40 65

**1966.** Anniversaries of 1966.
2159. 60 fi. black and red (T **404**) 15 10
2160. 60 fi. blk. & blue (T. Esze) 15 10
2161. 1 fo. violet (Shastri) .. 50 10
2162. 2 fo. brown and ochre (I. Szechenyi) .. .. 30 10
2163. 2 fo. sepia and bistre (M. Zrinyi) .. .. 20 10
2164. 2 fo. sepia and green (S. Koranyi) .. .. 20 10
EVENTS: No. 2159, 80th Birth Anniv. (workers' leader). No. 2160, (after statue by M. Nemeth) 300th Birth Anniv. (war hero). No. 2161, Death commem. (Indian Prime Minister). No. 2162, 175th Birth Anniv. (statesman). No. 2163, 400th Death Anniv. (military commander). No. 2164, Birth Cent. (scientist).

**405.** "Luna 9" in Space. **406. Crocus.**

**1966.** Moon Landing of **"Luna 9".**
2165. **405.** 2 fo. blk. yell. & violet 20 10
2166. – 3 fo. blk., yellow & bl. 40 15
DESIGN—HORIZ. 3 fo. "Luna 9" on Moon.

**1966.** Flower Protection. Multicoloured.
2167. 20 fi. Type **406** .. .. 20 10
2168. 30 fi. European cyclamen 25 10
2169. 60 fi. Ligularia .. .. 40 10
2170. 1 fo. 40 Orange lily .. 60 10
2171. 1 fo. 50 Fritillary .. 70 10
2172. 3 fo. "Dracocephalum ruyschiana" .. .. 1·75 35

**407.** Order of Labour (bronze). **409.** Barn Swallows.

**408.** Early Transport and Budapest Railway Station, 1846.

**1966.** Hungarian Medals and Orders. Mult.
2173. 20 fi. Type **407** .. .. 10 10
2174. 30 fi. Order of Labour (silver) .. .. 10 10
2175. 50 fi. Banner Order of Republic, 3rd class ($21\frac{1}{2}\times28\frac{1}{2}$ mm.) .. 10 10
2176. 60 fi. Order of Labour (gold) 10 10
2177. 70 fi. Banner Order of Republic, 2nd class ($25\times30\frac{1}{2}$ mm.) .. 10 10
2178. 1 fo. Red Banner Order of Labour .. .. 20 10
2179. 1 fo. 20 Banner Order of Republic, 1st class ($28\frac{1}{2}\times38$ mm.) .. 25 10
2180. 2 fo. Order of Merit of Republic .. .. 55 10
2181. 2 fo. 50 Hero of Socialist Labour .. .. 75 15

**1966.** Re-opening of Transport Museum, Budapest.
2182. **408.** 1 fo. brn., grn. & yell. 50 15
2183. – 2 fo. blue, brn. & grn. 90 35
DESIGN: 2 fo. Modern transport and South Station, Budapest.

**1966.** Protection of Birds. Multicoloured.
2184. 20 fi. Type **409** .. .. 45 10
2185. 30 fi. Long-tailed tits .. 55 10
2186. 60 fi. Red crossbill .. 70 10
2187. 1 fo. 40 Middle spotted woodpecker .. .. 1·40 30
2188. 1 fo. 50 Hoopoe .. .. 1·50 50
2189. 3 fo. Forest and emblem of National Forestry Association .. .. 1·50 65

**410.** W.H.O. Building.

**1966.** Inaug. of W.H.O. Headquarters, Geneva.
2190. **410.** 2 fo. black and blue 20 10

**412.** Nuclear Research Institute.

**1966.** 10th Anniv. of United Nuclear Research Institute, Dubna (U.S.S.R.).
2192. **412.** 60 fi. black and green 15 10

**413.** Buda Fortress, after Schedel's "Chronicle" (1493).

**1966.** 20th Anniv. of UNESCO and 72nd Executive Board Session, Budapest.
2193. **413.** 2 fo. violet and blue 40 10

**414.** Jules Rimet, Football and Cup.

**1966.** World Cup Football Championships. Multicoloured.
2194. 20 fi. Type **414** .. .. 10 10
2195. 30 fi. Montevideo, 1930 .. 10 10
2196. 60 fi. Rome, 1934 .. 15 10
2197. 1 fo. Paris, 1938 .. 25 10
2198. 1 fo. 40 Rio de Janeiro, 1950 .. .. 30 10
2199. 1 fo. 70 Berne, 1954 .. 40 10
2200. 2 fo. Stockholm, 1958 .. 60 10
2201. 2 fo. 50 Santiago de Chile, 1962 .. .. 85 15
2202. 3 fo. + 1 fo. World Cup emblem on Union Jack, and map of England .. 1·10 40

**415.** Girl Pioneer and Emblem.

**1966.** 20th Anniv. of Hungarian Pioneers Movement.
2203. **415.** 60 fi. red and violet 15 10

**416.** Fire Engine.

**1966.** Cent. of Voluntary Fire Brigades.
2204. **416.** 2 fo. blk. & orge. .. 65 20

**417.** Red Fox. **418.** Throwing the Discus.

**1966.** Hunting Trophies. Multicoloured.
2205. 20 fi. Type **417** .. .. 10 10
2206. 60 fi. Wild boar .. .. 15 10
2207. 70 fi. Wild cat .. .. 25 10
2208. 80 fi. Roe deer .. .. 25 10
2209. 1 fo. 50 Red deer .. .. 55 10
2210. 2 fo. 50 Fallow deer .. 1·25 10
2211. 3 fo. Mouflon .. .. 1·40 30

**1966.** 8th European Athletic Championships, Budapest. Multicoloured.
2212. 20 fi. Type **418** .. .. 10 10
2213. 30 fi. High-jumping .. 10 10
2214. 40 fi. Throwing the javelin 15 10
2215. 50 fi. Throwing the hammer 20 10
2216. 60 fi. Long-jumping .. 30 10
2217. 1 fo. Putting the shot .. 50 10
2218. 2 fo. Pole-vaulting .. 75 10
2219. 3 fo. Running .. .. 1·00 30

**419.** Archery. **420.** Helsinki.

**1966.** Stamp Day. Multicoloured.
2221. 2 fo. + 50 fi Types **419** .. 40 55
2222. 2 fo. + 50 fi. Grapes .. 40 55
2223. 2 fo. + 50 fi. Poppies .. 40 55
2224. 2 fo. + 50 fi. Space dogs 40 55

**1966.** Air.
2226. **420.** 20 fi. red .. .. 10 10
2227. – 50 fi. brown .. .. 10 10
2228. – 1 fo. blue .. .. 15 10
2229. – 1 fo. 10 black .. 20 10
2230. – 1 fo. 20 orange .. 20 10
2231. – 1 fo. 50 green .. 30 10
2232. – 2 fo. blue .. .. 40 10
2233. – 2 fo. 50 red .. .. 45 10
2234. – 3 fo. green .. .. 60 15
2235. – 4 fo. brown .. .. 1·75 1·25
2236. – 5 fo. violet .. .. 75 20
2237. – 10 fo. blue .. .. 1·90 40
2238. – 20 fo. green .. .. 3·00 60
DESIGNS—Ilyushin Il-18 over: 50 fi. Athens. 1 fo. Beirut. 1 fo. 10, Frankfurt. 1 fo. 20, Cairo. 1 fo. 50, Copenhagen. 2 fo. London. 2 fo. 50, Moscow. 3 fo. Paris. 4 fo. Prague. 5 fo. Rome. 10 fo. Damascus. 20 fo. Budapest.
For 2 fo. 60 in similar design see No. 2369.

**421.** "Girl in the Woods" (after Barabas).

**1966.** Paintings in Hungarian National Gallery (1st series). Multicoloured.
2239. 60 fi. Type **421** .. .. 20 15
2240. 1 fo. "Mrs. Istvan Bitto" (Barabas) .. .. 25 15
2241. 1 fo. 50 "Laszlo Hunyadi" Farewell" (Benczur) .. .. 45 15
2242. 1 fo. 70 "Woman Reading" (Benczur) .. 50 15
2243. 2 fo. "The Faggot-carrier" (Munkacsy) .. 55 15
2244. 2 fo. 50 "The Yawning Apprentice" (Munkacsy) .. .. 75 25
2245. 3 fo. "Woman in Lilac" (Szinyei) .. .. 1·10 50
The 1 fo. 70 is horiz.
See also Nos. 2282/8, 2318/24, 2357/63, 2411/17, 2449/55 and 2525/2531.

**422.** "Vostok 3" and "Vostok 4" (Nikolaev and Popovich).

**1966.** Twin Space Flights. Multicoloured.
2247. 20 fi. Type **422** .. .. 10 10
2248. 60 fi. Borman and Lovell, Schirra and Stafford .. 15 10
2249. 80 fi. Bykovsky and Tereshkova .. .. 15 10
2250. 1 fo. Stafford and Cernan 25 10
2251. 1 fo. 50 Belyaev and Leonov (Leonov in space) .. .. .. 40 10
2252. 2 fo. McDivitt and White (White in space) .. 50 10
2253. 2 fo. 50 Komarov, Feoktistov and Yegorov .. 85 15
2254. 3 fo. Conrad and Gordon 1·10 35

**423.** Kitaibel and "Kitaibelia vitifolia". **424.** Militiaman.

**1967.** 150th Death Anniv. of Pal Kitaibel (botanist). Carpathian Flowers. Mult.
2255. 20 fi. Type **423** .. .. 10 10
2256. 60 fi. "Dentaria glandulosa" .. .. .. 20 10
2257. 1 fo. "Edraianthus tenuifolius" .. .. .. 30 10
2258. 1 fo. 50 "Althaea pallida" 45 10
2259. 2 fo. "Centaurea mollis" 60 10
2260. 2 fo. 50 "Sternbergia colchiciflora" .. .. 1·10 15
2261. 3 fo. "Iris hungarica" .. 1·25 40

**1967.** 10th Anniv. of Workers' Militia.
2262. **424.** 2 fo. blue .. .. 25 10

**425. Faustus Verancsics' Parachute Descent, 1617.**

**1967. Air. "Aerofila 67". Airmail Stamp Exn., Budapest.**
2263. 2 fo. + 1 fo. sepia & yell. 1·00 1·00
2264. 2 fo. + 1 fo. sepia & blue 1·00 1·00
2265. 2 fo. + 1 fo. sepia & green 1·00 1·00
2266. 2 fo. + 1 fo. sepia & pink 1·00 1·00
2268. 2 fo. + 1 fo. blue & green 1·00 1·00
2269. 2 fo. + 1 fo. blue & orge. 1·00 1·00
2270. 2 fo. + 1 fo. blue & yellow 1·00 1·00
2271. 2 fo. + 1 fo. blue & pink 1·00 1·00
DESIGNS: No. 2263, Type **425**. No. 2264, David Schwartz's aluminium airship, 1897. No. 2265, Erno Horvath's monoplane, 1911. No. 2266, PKZ-2 helicopter, 1918. No. 2268, Parachutist. No. 2269, Mil Mi-1 helicopter. No. 2270, Tupolev Tu-154 airliner. No. 2271, "Luna 12".

**426.** I.T.Y. Emblem and Transport.

**1967.** Int. Tourist Year.
2273. **426.** 1 fo. black and blue .. 25 10

**428.** "Ferenc Deak" (paddle-steamer), Schonbuchel Castle and Austrian Flag.

**1967.** 25th Session of Danube Commission. Vessels of Mahart Shipping Company.
2275. **428.** 30 fi. multicoloured .. 90 20
2276. – 60 fi. multicoloured .. 1·40 35
2277. – 1 fo. multicoloured .. 2·25 40
2278. – 1 fo. 50 multicoloured 3·75 65
2279. – 1 fo. 70 multicoloured 4·75 1·00
2280. – 2 fo. multicoloured .. 5·00 2·00
2281. – 2 fo. 50 multicoloured 5·50 3·00
DESIGNS (Vessels, backgrounds and flags): 60 fi. River-bus "Revfulop" Bratislava Castle, Czechoslovakia. 1 fo. Diesel passenger boat "Hunyadi", Buda Castle, Hungary. 1 fo. 50, Diesel tug "Szekszard", Golubac Castle, Yugoslavia. 1 fo. 70, Tug "Miscolc", Vidin Castle, Bulgaria. 2 fo. Motor-freighter "Tihany", Galati shipyard, Rumania. 2 fo. 50, Hydrofoil "Siraly I", port of Izmail, U.S.S.R.

**429.** "Szidonia Deak" (A. Gyorgyi).

**1967.** Paintings in National Gallery, Budapest (2nd series). Multicoloured.
2282. 60 fi. "Liszt" (M. Munkacsy) .. .. .. 20 15
2283. 1 fo. "Self-portrait" (S. Lanyi) .. .. .. 30 15
2284. 1 fo. 50 "Portrait of a Lady" (J. Borsos) .. 40 15
2285. 1 fo. 70 "The Lovers" (after P. Szinyei Merse) 60 15
2286. 2 fo. Type **429** .. .. 65 15
2287. 2 fo. 50 "National Guardsman" (J. Borsos) .. 70 15
2288. 3 fo. "Louis XV and Madame Dubarry" (G. Benczur) 85 30
The 1 fo. 70 is horiz.

430. Poodle.

**1967.** Dogs. Multicoloured.

| | | | |
|---|---|---|---|
| 2289. | 30 fi. Type **430** .. .. | 15 | 10 |
| 2290. | 60 fi. Collie .. .. | 25 | 10 |
| 2291. | 1 fo. Pointer .. .. | 35 | 10 |
| 2292. | 1 fo. 40 Fox terriers .. | 50 | 10 |
| 2293. | 2 fo. Pumi .. .. | 70 | 15 |
| 2294. | 3 fo. Alsatian .. .. | 85 | 45 |
| 2295. | 4 fo. Puli .. .. | 1·40 | 80 |

The 60 fi., 1 fo. 40 and 3 fo. are vert., size 23½ × 35 mm.

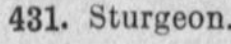
431. Sturgeon. 433. "Teaching" (14th-cent. class).

432. "Prince Igor" (Borodin).

**1967.** 14th Int. Anglers' Federation Congress, and World Angling Championships, Dunaujvaros. Multicoloured.

| | | | |
|---|---|---|---|
| 2296. | 20 fi. Type **431** .. .. | 10 | 10 |
| 2297. | 60 fi. Pikeperch .. .. | 20 | 10 |
| 2298. | 1 fo. Carp .. .. | 25 | 10 |
| 2299. | 1 fo. 70 European Wel .. | 60 | 10 |
| 2300. | 2 fo. Pike .. .. | 65 | 10 |
| 2301. | 2 fo. 50 Asp .. .. | 80 | 30 |
| 2302. | 3 fo.+1 fo. Anglers' and C.I.P.S. (Federation) emblem .. .. | 1·25 | 55 |

**1967.** Popular Operas. Designs showing scenes from various operas. Multicoloured.

| | | | |
|---|---|---|---|
| 2303. | 20 fi. Type **432** .. | 20 | 10 |
| 2304. | 30 fi. "Der Freischutz" (Weber) .. | 20 | 10 |
| 2305. | 40 fi. "The Magic Flute" (Mozart) .. | 35 | 10 |
| 2306. | 60 fi. "Bluebeard's Castle" (Bartok) .. | 50 | 10 |
| 2307. | 80 fi. "Carmen" (Bizet) | 65 | 10 |
| 2308. | 1 fo. "Don Carlos" (Verdi) | 85 | 10 |
| 2309. | 1 fo. 70 "Tannhauser" (Wagner) .. | 1·00 | 25 |
| 2310. | 3 fo. "Laszlo Hunyadi" (Erkel) .. .. .. | 1·40 | 90 |

Nos. 2307/10 are vert.

**1967.** 600th Anniv. of Higher Education in Hungary.

| | | | |
|---|---|---|---|
| 2311. | **433.** 2 fo. green and gold .. | 15 | 10 |

434. Faculty Building.

**1967.** 300th Anniv. of Political Law and Science Faculty, Lorand Eotvos University, Budapest.

| | | | |
|---|---|---|---|
| 2312. | **434.** 2 fo. green .. | 15 | 10 |

435. "Lenin as Teacher".

**1967.** 50th Anniv. of October Revolution. Multicoloured.

| | | | |
|---|---|---|---|
| 2313. | 60 fi. Type **435** .. .. | 10 | 10 |
| 2314. | 1 fo. "Lenin" .. .. | 10 | 10 |
| 2315. | 3 fo. "Lenin aboard the Aurora" .. .. | 30 | 15 |

436. "Venus 4".

**1967.** Landing of "Venus 4" on planet Venus.

| | | | |
|---|---|---|---|
| 2316 | **436** 5 fo. multicoloured .. | 75 | 25 |

437a. "Brother and Sister" (A. Fenyes).

**1967.** Paintings in National Gallery, Budapest (3rd series). As T **437a**. Multicoloured.

| | | | |
|---|---|---|---|
| 2318. | 60 fi. Type **437a** .. | 20 | 10 |
| 2319. | 1 fo. "Boys Wrestling on Beach" (O. Glatz) .. | 30 | 10 |
| 2320. | 1 fo. 50 "October" (K. Ferenczy) .. .. | 45 | 10 |
| 2321. | 1 fo. 70 "Women by the River" (I. Szonyi) .. | 50 | 15 |
| 2322. | 2 fo. "Godfather's Breakfast" (I. Csok) .. .. | 50 | 15 |
| 2323. | 2 fo. 50 "The Eviction Order" (G. Derkovits) | 55 | 20 |
| 2324. | 3 fo. "Self-Portrait" (T. Csontvary) .. .. | 65 | 35 |

The 1 fo. 70 is horiz.

"The Women by the River" (1 fo. 70) is in a private collection in Budapest.

438. Rifle-shooting on Skis.

**1967.** Winter Olympic Games, Grenoble. Multicoloured.

| | | | |
|---|---|---|---|
| 2326. | 30 fi. Type **438** .. .. | 10 | 10 |
| 2327. | 60 fi. Figure skating (pairs) .. .. .. | 15 | 10 |
| 2328. | 1 fo. Bobsleighing .. | 15 | 10 |
| 2329. | 1 fo. 40 Downhill skiing | 25 | 10 |
| 2330. | 1 fo. 70 Figure skating .. | 35 | 10 |
| 2331. | 2 fo. Speed skating .. | 45 | 10 |
| 2332. | 3 fo. Ski jumping .. | 55 | 25 |
| 2333. | 4 fo.+1 fo. Ice stadium, Grenoble .. .. | 90 | 45 |

439. Kalman Kando, Class "V43" Electric Locomotive and Map.

**1968.** Kando Commem.

| | | | |
|---|---|---|---|
| 2335. | **439.** 2 fo. blue .. .. | 60 | 10 |

440. Cat.

**1968.** Cats. Multicoloured.

| | | | |
|---|---|---|---|
| 2336. | 20 fi. Type **440** .. .. | 25 | 10 |
| 2337. | 60 fi. Cream angora .. | 30 | 10 |
| 2338. | 1 fo. Smoky angora .. | 40 | 10 |
| 2339. | 1 fo. 20 Domestic kitten | 50 | 10 |
| 2340. | 1 fo. 50 White angora .. | 70 | 10 |
| 2341. | 2 fo. Striped angora .. | 85 | 20 |
| 2342. | 2 fo. 50 Siamese .. .. | 1·25 | 20 |
| 2343. | 5 fo. Blue angora .. | 1·75 | 50 |

441. Zoltan Kodaly (composer). 442. City Hall, Arms, Grapes and Apricot.

**1968.** Kodaly Commem.

| | | | |
|---|---|---|---|
| 2344. | **441.** 5 fo. multicoloured .. | 1·10 | 40 |

**1968.** 600th Anniv. of Kecskemet.

| | | | |
|---|---|---|---|
| 2345. | **442.** 2 fo. brown .. .. | 35 | 10 |

443. White Stork. 444. Karl Marx.

**1968.** Int. Council for Bird Preservation Congress, Budapest. Protected Birds. Mult.

| | | | |
|---|---|---|---|
| 2346. | 20 f. Type **443** .. .. | 20 | 10 |
| 2347. | 50 fi. Golden orioles .. | 35 | 10 |
| 2348. | 60 fi. Imperial eagle .. | 40 | 15 |
| 2349. | 1 fo. Red-footed falcons | 45 | 15 |
| 2350. | 1 fo. 20 Scops owl .. | 60 | 20 |
| 2351. | 1 fo. 50 Great bustard .. | 75 | 25 |
| 2352. | 2 fo. European bee eaters | 1·60 | 30 |
| 2353. | 2 fo. 50 Greylag goose .. | 2·00 | 75 |

**1968.** 150th Birth Anniv. of Karl Marx.

| | | | |
|---|---|---|---|
| 2354. | **444.** 1 fo. purple .. .. | 15 | 10 |

See also No. 1290.

446. Student.

**1968.** 150th Anniv. of Mosonmagyarovar Agricultural College.

| | | | |
|---|---|---|---|
| 2356. | **446.** 2 fo. green .. .. | 15 | 10 |

**1968.** Paintings in National Gallery, Budapest (4th series). As T **437a**. Multicoloured.

| | | | |
|---|---|---|---|
| 2357. | 40 fi. "Girl with a Pitcher" (Goya) .. .. | 10 | 10 |
| 2358. | 60 fi. "Head of an Apostle" (El Greco) .. | 15 | 10 |
| 2359. | 1 fo. "Boy with Apples" (Nunez) .. .. | 20 | 10 |
| 2360. | 1 fo. 50 "The Repentant Magdalen" (El Greco) | 30 | 10 |
| 2361. | 2 fo. 50 "The Breakfast" (Velasquez) .. | 55 | 10 |
| 2362. | 4 fo. "St. Elizabeth" (detail from "The Holy Family"; El Greco) .. | 65 | 15 |
| 2363. | 5 fo. "The Knife-grinder" (Goya) .. .. | 80 | 30 |

The 1 fo. and 2 fo. 50 are horiz.

447. Lake Steamer, Flags and Badacsony Hills. 448. Ilyushin Il-18 over St. Stephen's Cathedral, Vienna.

**1968.** Lake Balaton Resorts. Mult.

| | | | |
|---|---|---|---|
| 2365 | 20 fi. Type **447** .. .. | 15 | 10 |
| 2365a | 40 fi. Type **447** .. .. | 15 | 10 |
| 2366 | 60 fi. Tihany peninsula, tower and feather .. | 15 | 10 |
| 2367 | 1 fo. Yachts and buoy, Balatonalmadi .. | 20 | 10 |
| 2368 | 2 fo. Szigliget bay, vineyard, wine and fish .. | 40 | 15 |

**1968.** Air. 50th Anniv. of Budapest-Vienna Airmail Service.

| | | | |
|---|---|---|---|
| 2369. | **448.** 2 fo. 60 violet .. | 50 | 15 |

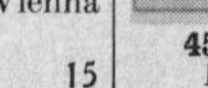

449. Steam Locomotive Type "424". 451. M. Tompa.

450. Grazing Stud.

**1968.** Cent. of Hungarian State Railways.

| | | | |
|---|---|---|---|
| 2370. | **449.** 2 fo. multicoloured .. | 1·25 | 25 |

**1968.** Horse-breeding on the Hortobagy "puszta" (Hungarian steppe). Multicoloured.

| | | | |
|---|---|---|---|
| 2371. | 30 fi. Type **450** .. .. | 15 | 10 |
| 2372. | 40 fi. Horses in storm .. | 15 | 10 |
| 2373. | 60 fi. Grooms horse-racing | 20 | 10 |
| 2374. | 80 fi. Horse-drawn sleigh | 30 | 10 |
| 2375. | 1 fo. Four-in-hand .. | 40 | 10 |
| 2376. | 1 fo. 40 Seven-in-hand .. | 55 | 10 |
| 2377. | 2 fo. Driving five horses .. | 60 | 10 |
| 2378. | 2 fo. 50 Groom preparing evening meal .. | 70 | 20 |
| 2379. | 4 fo. Five-in-hand .. | 1·25 | 45 |

**1968.** Death Cent. of Mihaly Tompa (poet).

| | | | |
|---|---|---|---|
| 2380. | **451.** 60 fi. violet .. .. | 15 | 10 |

452. Festival Emblem, Bulgarian and Hungarian Couples in National Costume.

**1968.** 9th World Youth Festival Sofia.

| | | | |
|---|---|---|---|
| 2381. | **452.** 60 fi. multicoloured .. | 20 | 10 |

454. Swimming.

**1968.** Air. Olympic Games, Mexico. Mult.

| | | | |
|---|---|---|---|
| 2383. | 20 fi. Type **454** .. | 10 | 10 |
| 2384. | 60 fi. Football .. .. | 10 | 10 |
| 2385. | 80 fi. Wrestling .. .. | 10 | 10 |
| 2386. | 1 fo. Canoeing .. .. | 10 | 10 |
| 2387. | 1 fo. 40 Gymnastics .. | 25 | 10 |
| 2388. | 2 fo.+1 fo. Horse-jumping | 80 | 30 |
| 2389. | 3 fo. Fencing .. .. | 70 | 20 |
| 2390. | 4 fo. Throwing the Javelin | 1·00 | 40 |

455. Baja Plate, 1870. 456. Society Emblem.

**1968.** Stamp Day. Hungarian Ceramics. Multicoloured.

| | | | |
|---|---|---|---|
| 2391. | 1 fo.+50 fi. Type **455** .. | 40 | 50 |
| 2392. | 1 fo.+50 fi. West Hungarian jug, 1618 .. | 40 | 50 |
| 2393. | 1 fo.+50 fi. Tiszafured flagon, 1847 .. .. | 40 | 50 |
| 2394. | 1 fo.+50 fi. Mezocsat flask, 1848 .. .. | 40 | 50 |

**1968.** "Hungarian Society for Popularisation of Scientific Knowledge".

| | | | |
|---|---|---|---|
| 2396. | **456.** 2 fo. black and blue | 20 | 10 |

457. Rocket Hesperus. 458. Two Girls waving Flags.

**1968.** Garden Flowers. Multicoloured.
2397. 20 fi. Type **457** .. .. 15 10
2398. 60 fi. Pansy .. .. 30 10
2399. 80 fi. Zinnias .. .. 45 10
2400. 1 fo. Morning Glory .. 65 10
2401. 1 fo. 40 Petunia .. .. 85 10
2402. 1 fo. 50 Purslane .. 90 15
2403. 2 fo. Michaelmas daisies 1·10 40
2404. 2 fo. 50 Dahlia .. .. 1·25 85

**1968.** Children's Stamp Designs for 50th Anniv. of Hungarian Communist Party. Multicoloured.
2405. 40 fi. Type **458** .. .. 20 10
2406. 60 fi. Children with flags and banner .. .. 25 10
2407. 1 fo. Pioneer bugler in camp 30 10

**459.** "Workers of the World Unite" (Bertalan Por's 1918 poster). **460.** Human Rights Emblem.

**1968.** 50th Anniv. of Hungarian Communist Party.
2408. **459.** 1 fo. blk., red & gold 10 10
2409. – 2 fo. multicoloured .. 10 10
DESIGN—HORIZ. 2 fo. "Martyrs" (statue by Zoltan Kiss).

**1968.** Human Rights Year.
2410. **460.** 1 fo. brown .. 10 10

**1968.** Paintings in National Gallery, Budapest (5th series). Italian Masters. Designs as T **437a.** Multicoloured.
2411. 40 fi. "Esterhazy Madonna" (Raphael) .. .. 10 10
2412. 60 fi. "The Annunciation" (Strozzi) .. .. 10 10
2413. 1 fo. "Portrait of a Young Man" (Raphael) .. 15 10
2414. 1 fo. 50 "The Three Graces" (Naldini) .. .. 30 10
2415. 2 fo. 50 "Portrait of a Man" (Sebastian del Piombo) 50 10
2416. 4 fo. "The Doge Marcantonio Trevisani" (Titian) .. 80 20
2417. 5 fo. "Venus, Cupid and Jealousy" (Bronzino) 1·10 40
Nos. 2411/17 are vert.

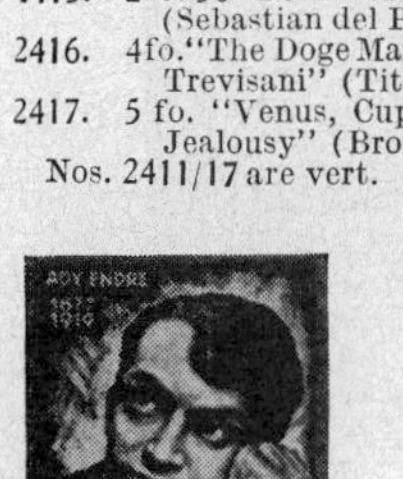

**461.** Endre Ady. **462.** Press Emblem.

**1969.** 50th Death Anniv. of Endre Ady (poet).
2419. **461.** 1 fo. blk., pur. & gold 10 10

**1969.** Centenary of Athenaeum Press.
2420 **462** 2 fo. multicoloured .. 10 10

**464.** Throwing the Javelin.

**1969.** Olympic Gold Medal Winners. Mult.
2422. 40 fi. Type **464** .. .. 10 10
2423. 60 fi. Canoeing .. .. 10 10
2424. 1 fo. Football .. .. 15 10
2425. 1 fo. 20 Throwing the Hammer .. .. 15 10
2426. 2 fo. Fencing .. .. 30 10
2427. 3 fo. Wrestling .. .. 50 10
2428. 4 fo. Kayak-canoeing .. 75 10
2429. 5 fo. Horse-jumping .. 1·00 35

**465.** Poster by O. Danko. **466.** Space Link-up of "Soyuz 4" and "Soyuz 5".

**1969.** 50th Anniv. of Proclamation of Hungarian Soviet Republic.
2431. **465.** 40 fi. blk., red & gold 10 10
2432. – 60 fi. black, red & gold 10 10
2433. – 1 fo. black, red & gold 10 10
2434. – 2 fo. multicoloured .. 15 10
2435. – 3 fo. multicoloured .. 30 10
DESIGNS: 60 fi. "Lenin" by unknown artist. 1 fo. "Young Man Breaking Chains" (R. Steiner). 2 fo. "Worker" (I. Foldes and G. Vegh). 3 fo. "Soldier" (unknown artist).

**1969.** Air. Space Flights of "Soyuz 4" and "Soyuz 5". Multicoloured.
2437. 2 fo. Type **466** .. .. 35 40
2438. 2 fo. Link-up and astronauts "walking" in Space .. .. 35 40

467. Jersey Tiger Moth.

**1969.** Butterflies and Moths. Multicoloured.
2439 40 fi. Type **467** .. .. 30 10
2440 60 fi. Eyed hawk moth .. 30 10
2441 80 fi. Painted lady .. 35 10
2442 1 fo. Foxy charaxes .. 40 10
2443 1 fo. 20 Lesser fiery copper .. .. 55 10
2444 2 fo. Large blue .. .. 1·00 15
2445 3 fo. Dark crimson underwing .. .. 1·40 40
2446 4 fo. Peacock .. .. 1·60 70

**468.** I.L.O. Emblem.

**1969.** 50th Anniv. of Int. Labour Organisation.
2447. **468.** 1 fo. brown and red 10 10

**469.** Chain Bridge, Budapest.

**1969.** "Budapest 71" Stamp Exn.
2448. **469.** 5 fo + 2 fo. mult. .. 80 1·00

**470.** "Black Pigs" (Gauguin).

**1969.** Paintings in National Gallery, Budapest (6th series). French Masters. Multicoloured.
2449. 40 fi. Type **470** .. .. 10 10
2450. 60 fi. "The Ladies" (Toulouse-Lautrec) (horiz.) 10 10
2451. 1 fo. "Venus on Clouds" (Vouet) .. .. 15 10
2452. 2 fo. "Lady with Fan" (Manet) (horiz.) .. 35 10
2453. 3 fo. "Petra Camara" (Chasseriau) .. .. 75 10
2454. 4 fo. "The Cowherd" (Troyon) (horiz.) .. 1·00 15
2455. 5 fo. "The Wrestlers" (Courbet) .. 1·40 40

**471.** Vac. **472.** "PAX".

**1969.** Danube Towns. Multicoloured.
2457. 40 fi. Type **471** .. .. 10 10
2458. 1 fo. Szentendre .. .. 20 10
2459. 1 fo. 20 Visegrad .. 25 10
2460. 3 fo. Esztergom .. .. 50 10

**1969.** 20th Anniv. of Int. Peace Movement.
2461. **472.** 1 fo. gold, deep blue and blue .. .. 10 10

**474.** Zelkova Leaf (fossil). **475.** Okorag Stirrup-cup, 1880.

**1969.** Cent of Hungarian Geological Institute. Minerals and Fossils. Multicoloured.
2463 40 fi. Type **474** .. .. 20 10
2464 60 fi. Greenockite calcite sphalerite crystals .. 25 10
2465 1 fo. "Clupea hungarica" (fossilized fish) .. 30 10
2466 1 fo. 20 Quartz crystals .. 30 10
2467 2 fo. "Reineckia crassicostata" (ammonite) .. .. 45 10
2468 3 fo. Copper ore .. 70 15
2469 4 fo. "Placochelys placodonta" (fossilized turtle) .. .. 1·50 50
2470 5 fo. Cuprite crystals .. 2·00 75

**1969.** Stamp Day. Hungarian Folk Art. Wood-carvings. Multicoloured.
2471. 1 fo. + 50 fi. Type **475** .. 40 55
2472. 1 fo. + 50 fi. Felsotizavidek jar, 1898 .. .. 40 55
2473. 1 fo. + 50 fi. Somogy-harsagy pot, 1935 .. 40 55
2474. 1 fo. + 50 fi. Alfold smoking-pipe, 1740 .. 40 55

**476.** "The Scientist at his Table" (Rembrandt). **477.** Horse-jumping.

**1969.** Int. "History of Art" Congress, Budapest.
2476. **476.** 1 fo. sepia .. 20 10

**1969.** World Pentathlon Championships, Budapest. Multicoloured.
2477. 40 fi. Type **477** .. .. 20 10
2478. 60 fi. Fencing .. .. 25 10
2479. 1 fo. Pistol-shooting .. 40 10
2480. 2 fo. Swimming .. 55 10
2481. 3 fo. Running .. 70 10
2482. 5 fo. All five sports .. 1·00 35

**478.** Postcard and Letterbox. **479.** Mahatma Gandhi.

**1969.** Cent. of 1st Hungarian Postcard.
2483. **478.** 60 fi. ochre and red .. 10 10

**1969.** Birth Cent. of Mahatma Gandhi.
2484. **479.** 5 fo. multicoloured .. 1·40 55

**480.** Hemispheres. **481.** "Janos Nagy" (self-portrait).

**1969.** World Trade Unions Federations Congress, Budapest.
2485. **480.** 2 fo. blue and brown 15 10

**1969.** 50th Death Anniv. of Janos Nagy (painter).
2486. **481.** 5 fo. multicoloured .. 40 20

**482.** "Flight to the Moon" (after Jules Verne).

**1969.** Air. 1st Man on the Moon. Mult.
2487 40 fi. Type **482** .. .. 10 10
2488 60 fi. Tsiolkovsky's "space station" .. .. 10 10
2489 1 fo. "Luna 1" .. .. 20 10
2490 1 fo. 50 "Ranger 7" .. 35 10
2491 2 fo. "Luna 9" .. .. 45 10
2492 2 fo. 50 "Apollo 8" .. 50 10
2493 3 fo. "Soyuz 4" and "5" .. 65 10
2494 4 fo. "Apollo 10" .. 1·00 35

**483.** "St. John the Evangelist" (Van Dyck). **484.** Kiskunfelegyhaza Pigeon.

**1969.** Dutch Paintings in Hungarian Museums. Multicoloured.
2495. 40 fi. Type **483** .. 10 10
2496. 60 fi. "Peasants" (P. de Molyn) .. .. 10 10
2497. 1 fo. "Boy lighting Pipe" (H. Terbruggen) .. 25 10
2498. 2 fo. "The Musicians" (detail, Jan Steen) .. 40 10
2499. 3 fo. "Woman reading Letter" (P. de Hooch) 70 10
2500. 4 fo. "The Fiddler" (Dirk Hals) .. .. 85 20
2501. 5 fo. "J. Asselyn" (Frans Hals) .. .. 1·10 35

**1969.** Int. Pigeon Exn., Budapest.
2503. **484.** 1 fo. multicoloured .. 30 10

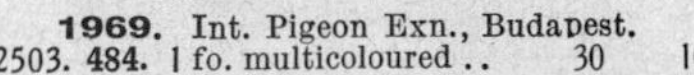

**485.** Daimler (1886).

**1970.** Air. Old Motor Cars. Multicoloured.
2504. 40 fi. Type **485** .. 20 10
2505. 60 fi. Peugeot (1894) .. 25 10
2506. 1 fo. Benz (1901) .. 30 10
2507. 1 fo. 50 Cudell (1902) .. 40 10
2508. 2 fo. Rolls-Royce (1908) .. 60 10
2509. 2 fo. 50 Ford "T" (1908) .. 80 10
2510. 3 fo. Vermorel (1912) .. 1·10 20
2511. 4 fo. Csonka (1912) .. 1·40 50

**486.** View of Budapest. **487.** "Soyuz 6, 7, 8".

**1970.** Budapest 71 Stamp Exn. and Cent. of Hungarian Stamps (1st series). Multicoloured. Background colours given.
2512. **486.** 2 fo. + 1 fo. brown .. 40 55
2513. – 2 fo. + 1 fo. lilac .. 40 55
2514. – 2 f. + 1 fo. blue .. 40 55
DESIGNS: Nos. 2513/4 show different views of Budapest, in style as Type **486.**
See also Nos. 2572/5 and 2604/7.

**1970.** Air. Space Exploration. Multicoloured.
2515. 3 fo. (× 4) Type **487** .. 2·00 2·50
2516. 3 fo. (× 4) Astronauts on Moon (Apollo 12) .. 2·00 2·50
Nos. 2515/6 were only available each in small sheets of four, and are priced thus.

488. Metro Train at Station.

**1970.** Opening of Budapest Metro.
2517. **488.** 1 fo. blue, turq. & blk. 40 10

490. Cloud Formation, Satellite and Globe.

491. Lenin.

**1970.** Cent. of Hungarian Meteorological Service.
2519. **490.** 1 fo. multicoloured .. 30 10

**1970.** Birth Cent. of Lenin. Mult.
2520. 1 fo. Lenin Statue, Budapest 10 10
2521. 2 fo. Type **491** .. .. 10 10

492. Lehar and Music.

**1970.** Birth Cent. of Franz Lehar (composer).
2522. **492.** 2 fo. multicoloured .. 60 20

493. Fujiyama and Hungarian Pavilion.

**1970.** Air. Expo 70. Multicoloured.
2523. 2 fo. Type **493** .. .. 30 30
2524. 3 fo. Tower of the Sun and Peace Bell .. 30 30

494. "Samson and Delilah" (M. Rocca).

**1970.** Paintings in National Gallery, Budapest (7th series). Multicoloured.
2525. 40 fi. Type **494** .. .. 10 10
2526. 60 fi. "Joseph's Dream" (G. B. Langetti) .. 15 10
2527. 1 fo. "Clio" (P. Mignard) 20 10
2528. 1 fo. 50 "Venus and Satyr" (S. Ricci) (horiz.) 25 10
2529. 2 fo. 50 "Andromeda" (F. Furini) .. .. 50 10
2530. 4 fo. "Venus, Adonis and Cupid" (L. Giordano) 80 20
2531. 5 fo. "Allegory" (woman) (C. Giaquinto) .. 1·00 40

496. Beethoven (from statue at Martonvasar).

497. Foundryman.

**1970.** Birth Bicentenary of Beethoven.
2534. **496.** 1 fo. grn., lilac & yell. 1·00 25

**1970.** Bicent. of Diosgyor Foundry, Miskolc.
2535. **497.** 1 fo. multicoloured .. 15 10

498. St. Stephen.

500. Illuminated Initial.

499. Rowing Four.

**1970.** 1,000th Birth Anniv. of St. Stephen (King Stephen I of Hungary).
2536. **498.** 3 fo. multicoloured 40 15

**1970.** 17th European Women's Rowing Championships, Lake Tata.
2537. **499.** 1 fo. multicoloured .. 30 10

**1970.** Stamp Day. Paintings and Illuminated Initials from Codices of King Matthias.
2538. 1 fo.+50 fi. Type **500** 40 55
2539. 1 fo. +50 fi. "N" and flowers .. .. 40 55
2540. 1 fo.+50 fi. "O" and ornamentation .. 40 55
2541. 1 fo.+50 fi. "King Matthias" .. .. 40 55

502. "Bread" (sculpture by I. Szabo) and F.A.O. Emblem.

**1970.** 7th F.A.O. European Regional Conference, Budapest.
2544. **502.** 1 fo. multicoloured.. 10 10

503. Boxing.

**1970.** 75th Anniv. of Hungarian Olympic Committee. Multicoloured.
2545. 40 fi. Type **503** .. .. 10 10
2546. 60 fi. Canoeing .. .. 10 10
2547. 1 fo. Fencing .. .. 10 10
2548. 1 fo. 50 Water-polo .. 20 10
2549. 2 fo. Gymnastics .. 40 10
2550. 2 fo. 50 Throwing the Hammer .. .. 45 10
2551. 3 fo. Wrestling .. .. 50 15
2552. 5 fo. Swimming .. 80 35

504. Family and "Flame of Knowledge".

**1970.** 5th Education Congress, Budapest.
2553 **504** 1 fo. blue, grn & orge 10 10

505. Chalice of Benedek Suky, c. 1400.

**1970.** Goldsmiths' Craft. Treasures from Budapest National Museum and Esztergom Treasury. Multicoloured.
2554. 40 fi. Type **505** .. 10 10
2555. 60 fi. Altar-cruet, c. 1500 10 10
2556. 1 fo. "Nadasdy" goblet, 16th-century .. .. 20 10
2557. 1 fo. 50 Coconut goblet with gold case, c. 1600 25 10
2558. 2 fo. Silver tankard of M. Toldalaghy, c. 1623 .. 40 10
2559. 2 fo. 50 Communion-cup of G.I. Rakoczi, c. 1670 60 10
2560. 3 fo. Tankard, c. 1690 .. 80 15
2561. 4 fo. "Bell-flower" cup, c. 1710 .. .. 1·25 45

506. "The Virgin and Child" ("Giampietrino", G. Pedrini).

**1970.** Paintings. Religious Art from Christian Museum, Esztergom. Multicoloured.
2562. 40 fi. Type **506** .. .. 10 10
2563. 60 fi. "Love" (G. Lazzarini) .. .. .. 10 10
2564. 1 fo. "Legend of St. Catherine of Alexandria" ("Master of Bat") .. 15 10
2565. 1 fo. 50 "Adoration of the Shepherds" (F. Fontebasso) (horiz.) .. 30 10
2566. 2 fo. 50 "Adoration of the Magi" ("Master of Aranyosmarot") .. 60 10
2567. 4 fo. "Temptation of St. Anthony the Hermit" (J. de Cock) .. .. 90 15
2568. 5 fo. "St. Sebastian" (Palmezzano) .. .. 1·00 35

507. Mauthausen Camp Memorial (A. Makrisz).

**1970.** 25th Anniv. of Liberation of Concentration Camps.
2570. **507.** 1 fo. brown and blue 25 10

509. Budapest, 1470.

**1971.** "Budapest 71" Stamp Exn., and Cent. of Hungarian Stamp (2nd series). "Budapest Through the Ages".
2572. **509.** 2 fo.+1 fo. blk. & yell. 35 45
2573. – 2 fo.+1 fo. blk. & mve. 35 45
2574. – 2 fo.+1 fo. blk. & grn. 35 45
2575. – 2 fo.+1 fo. blk. & orge. 35 45
DESIGNS: Budapest in: No. 2573, 1600. No. 2574, 1638. No. 2575, 1770.

511. "The Marseillaise" (sculpture by Rude).

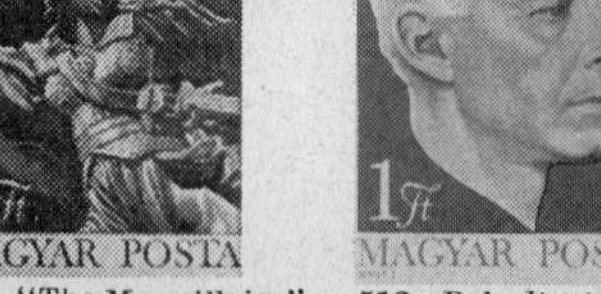

512. Bela Bartok.

**1971.** Cent. of Paris Commune.
2578. **511.** 3 fo. brown & green 35 10

**1971.** 90th Birth Anniv. of Bela Bartok (composer).
2579. **512.** 1 fo. black, grey & red 90 15

513. Gyor in 1594.

**1971.** 700th Anniv. of Gyor.
2580. **513.** 2 fo. multicoloured .. 30 10

**1971.** Birth Cent of Andras L. Achim (peasant leader). Portrait in similar style to T **512**.
2582. 1 fo. black, grey & green 10 10

516. Hunting European Bison.

**1971.** World Hunting Exhibition, Budapest. Multicoloured.
2583. 40 fi. Type **516** .. .. 15 10
2584. 60 fi. Hunting wild boar 15 10
2585. 80 fi. Deer-stalking .. 30 15
2586. 1 fo. Falconry .. .. 1·50 20
2587. 1 fo. 20 Stag-hunting .. 65 25
2588. 2 fo. Great Bustards with young .. .. .. 2·00 45
2589. 3 fo. Netting fish .. 1·10 50
2590. 4 fo. Angling .. .. 1·50 65

518. Emblem on Flower.

**1971.** 25th Anniv. of Hungarian Young Pioneers.
2593. **518.** 1 fo. multicoloured .. 20 10

519. F.I.R. Emblem.

**1971.** 20th Anniv. of International Federation of Resistance Fighters.
2594. **519.** 1 fo. multicoloured .. 20 10

520. "Walking in the Garden" (Toyokuni School).

**1971.** Japanese Colour Prints from Ferenc Hopp Collection, Budapest. Multicoloured.
2595. 40 fi. Type **520** .. 10 10
2596. 60 fi. "Geisha in boat" (Yeishi) .. .. 30 10
2597. 1 fo. "Woman with scroll-painting" (Yeishi) .. 20 10
2598. 1 fo. 50 "Oirans" (Kiyonaga) .. .. 35 10
2599. 2 fo. "Awabi Fishers" (Utamaro) .. .. 45 10
2600. 2 fo. 50 "Seated Oiran" (Harunobu) .. .. 60 10
2601. 3 fo. "Peasant Girl carrying Faggots" (Hokusai) 80 15
2602. 4 fo. "Women and Girls Walking" (Yeishi) .. 1·00 40

**521.** Locomotive "Bets" and Route Map (1846).

**1971.** 125th Anniv. of Hungarian Railways.
2603. **521.** 1 fo. multicoloured .. 65 10

**522.** Hungarian Newspaper Stamp of 1871.

**1971.** "Budapest 71" Stamp Exhib. and Cent. of Hungarian Stamp (3rd series). Multicoloured.
2604. 2 fo. + 1 fo. Type **522** .. 35 50
2605. 2 fo. + 1 fo. 45 f. "Petofi" stamp of 1919 35 50
2606. 2 fo. + 1 fo. 400 k. "Harvesters" stamp of 1920 35 50
2607. 2 fo. + 1 fo. 16 f. + 16 f. "Art" stamp of 1940 35 50

**523.** Griffin with Inking Balls.

**1971.** Cent. of State Printing Office, Budapest.
2609. **523.** 1 fo. multicoloured .. 30 30

**524.** O.I.J. Emblem and Page of "Magyar Sajto".

**1971.** 25th Anniv. of Int. Organisation of Journalists.
2610. **524.** 1 fo. gold and blue .. 15 10

**526.** J. Winterl (founder) and "Waldsteinia geoides".

**1971.** Bicentenary of Botanical Gardens, Budapest. Multicoloured.
2612. 40 fi. Type **526** .. .. 10 10
2613. 60 fi. "Bromeliaceae" .. 15 10
2614. 80 fi. "Titanopsis calcarea" 20 10
2615. 1 fo. "Vinca herbacea" .. 25 10
2616. 1 fo. 20 "Gymnocalycium mihanovichii" .. 25 10
2617. 2 fo. "Nymphaea gigantea" 50 10
2618. 3 fo. "Iris arenaria" .. 80 20
2619. 5 fo. "Paeonia banatica" 1·40 45

**527.** Horse-racing.

**1971.** Equestrian Sport. Multicoloured.
2620. 40 fi. Type **527** .. .. 15 10
2621. 60 fi. Trotting .. .. 20 10
2622. 80 fi. Cross-country riding 20 10
2623. 1 fo. Show-jumping .. 25 10
2624. 1 fo. 20 Start of race .. 30 10
2625. 2 fo. Polo .. .. 55 10
2626. 3 fo. Steeplechasing .. 85 15
2627. 5 fo. Dressage .. .. 1·40 45

**528.** "Execution of Koppany". **529.** Racial Equality Year Emblem.

**1971.** Miniatures from the "Illuminated Chronicle" of King Lajos I of Hungary. Multicoloured.
2628. 40 fi. Type **528** .. .. 15 10
2629. 60 fi. "The Pursuit of King Peter" .. .. 15 10
2630. 1 fo. "Bazarad's Victory over King Karoly I" 20 10
2631. 1 fo. 50 "The Strife between King Salamon and Prince Geza" .. 35 10
2632. 2 fo. 50 "The Founding of Obuda Monastery by King Stephen and Queen Gisela" .. 55 10
2633. 4 fo. "Reconciliation of King Kalman and his brother, Almos" .. 75 20
2634. 5 fo. "King Ladislas I supervising the construction of Nagyvarad Church" .. 1·10 40

**1971.** Racial Equality Year.
2636. **529.** 1 fo. multicoloured .. 15 10

**530.** Ice Hockey.

**1971.** Winter Olympic Games, Sapporo, Japan (1972). Multicoloured.
2637. 40 fi. Type **530** .. .. 10 10
2638. 60 fi. Downhill skiing .. 15 10
2639. 80 fi. Figure skating (female) .. .. 15 10
2640. 1 fo. Ski jumping .. 20 10
2641. 1 fo. 20 Cross-country skiing .. .. 30 10
2642. 2 fo. Figure skating (male) .. .. 40 10
2643. 3 fo. Bobsleighing .. 50 20
2644. 4 fo. Rifle-shooting (Biathlon) .. .. 85 45

**532.** Hungarian Class "303" (1950).

**1972.** Railway Steam Locomotives. Mult.
2647. 40 fi. Type **532** .. .. 30 10
2648. 60 fi. Prussia Class "P 6" (1902) .. .. 30 10
2649. 80 fi. Mediterranean Class "380" (Italy) (1894) .. 40 15
2650. 1 fo. Russia Class "P 36" (1950) .. .. 60 15
2651. 1 fo. 20 Heisler locomotive (Japan) .. 70 30
2652. 2 fo. Caledonian 0-4-4T (1873) .. .. 90 35
2653. 4 fo. Austria Class "166" (1882) .. .. 1·25 70
2654. 5 fo. Crampton "Le Continent" (France) (1852) .. .. 1·60 85

**533.** "J. Pannonius" (A. Mantegna). **535.** Doorway of Csempeszkopacs Church.

**534.** "Mariner 9".

**1972.** 500th Death Anniv. of Janus Pannonius (poet).
2655. **533.** 1 fo. multicoloured 15 10

**1972.** Exploration of Mars. Multicoloured.
2656. 2 fo. Type **534** .. .. 50 50
2657. 2 fo. "Mars 2 and 3" .. 50 50

**1972.** Protection of Monuments.
2658. **535.** 3 fo. green .. .. 40 10

**536.** Hungarian Greyhound.

**1972.** Dogs. Multicoloured.
2659. 40 fi. Type **536** .. 20 10
2660. 60 fi. Afghan hound (head) 25 10
2661. 80 fi. Irish wolfhound .. 25 10
2662. 1 fo. 20 Borzoi (head) .. 30 10
2663. 2 fo. Greyhound .. 65 20
2664. 4 fo. Whippet (head) .. 1·50 30
2665. 6 fo. Afghan hound .. 2·00 75

**537.** J. Imre, E. Grosz and L. Blaskovics.

**1972.** 1st. European Oculists' Congress, Budapest. Famous Oculists.
2666. **537.** 1 fo. brown and red 85 10
2667. – 2 fo. brown and blue 1·25 25
DESIGN: 2 fo. A. Gullstrand, V. P. Filatov and J. Gonin.

**538.** Footballers and Flag of Hungary.

**1972.** Air. European Football Championships. Footballers and Flags of participating countries. Multicoloured.
2668. 40 fi. Type **538** .. 10 10
2669. 60 fi. Rumania .. 15 10
2670. 80 fi. West Germany .. 20 10
2671. 1 fo. England .. 25 10
2672. 1 fo. 20 Yugoslavia .. 35 10
2673. 2 fo. Russia .. 50 10
2674. 4 fo. Italy .. 75 40
2675. 5 fo. Belgium .. 1·00 60

**539.** "V. Miskolcz" postmark, 1818-43.

**1972.** Stamp Day.
2676. **539.** 2 fo. + 1 fo. black & bl. 45 60
2677. – 2 fo. + 1 fo. blk. & yell. 45 60
2678. – 2 fo. + 1 fo. blk. & grn. 45 60
2679. – 2 fo. + 1 fo. mult. .. 45 60
DESIGNS: No. 2677, "Szegedin" postmark, 1827-48. No. 2678, "Esztergom" postmark, 1848-51. No. 2679, "Budapest 71" stamp cent., cancellation, 1971.

**540.** Girl reading Book. **541.** Roses.

**1972.** Int. Book Year.
2681. **540.** 1 fo. multicoloured .. 15 10

**1972.** National Rose Exhib.
2682. **541.** 1 fo. multicoloured .. 45 10

**543.** G. Dimitrov. **545.** Gy. Dozsa.

**1972.** 90th Birth Anniv. of Georgi Dimitrov (Bulgarian leader).
2684. **543.** 3 fo. multicoloured .. 15 10

**1972.** 500th Birth Anniv. of Gyorgy Dozsa (revolutionary).
2686. **545.** 1 fo. multicoloured .. 15 10

**546.** Football.

**1972.** Olympic Games, Munich. Mult
2687. 40 fi. Type **546** .. .. 10 10
2688. 60 fi. Water-polo .. .. 10 10
2689. 80 fi. Javelin-throwing .. 15 10
2690. 1 fo. Kayak-canoeing .. 20 10
2691. 1 fo. 20 Boxing .. .. 25 10
2692. 2 fo. Gymnastics .. .. 45 10
2693. 3 fo. + 1 fo. Wrestling .. 65 25
2694. 5 fo. Fencing .. .. 1·00 40

**547.** Prince Geza indicating Site of Szekesfehervar.

**1972.** Millenary of Szekesfehervar and 750th Anniv of "Aranybulla" (legislative document). Multicoloured.
2696. 40 fi. Type **547** .. .. 10 10
2697. 60 fi. King Stephen and shield .. .. 10 10
2698. 80 fi. Soldiers and cavalry .. .. 15 10
2699. 1 fo. 20 King Stephen drawing up legislation 30 10
2700. 2 fo. Mason sculpting column .. 40 10
2701. 4 fo. Merchant displaying wares to King Stephen 75 15
2702. 6 fo. Views of Szekesfehervar and Palace .. 1·00 30

**548.** Parliament Building, Budapest.

**1972.** Constitution Day. Multicoloured.
2704. 5 fo. Type **548** .. .. 20 10
2705. 6 fo. Parliament in session 30 15

**549.** Eger and "Bulls Blood".

**1972.** World Wines Competition, Budapest Multicoloured.
2706. 1 fo. Type **549** .. .. 25 10
2707. 2 fo. Tokay and "Tokay Aszu" .. .. 45 15

550. Ear of Wheat and Emblems on Open Book.

**1972.** 175th Anniv. of Georgikon Agricultural Academy, Keszthely.

2708. **550.** 1 fo. multicoloured .. 15 10

**551.** "Rothschild" Vase. **553.** Commemorative Emblem.

552. Diesel Train and U.I.C. Emblem.

**1972.** Herendi Porcelain. Multicoloured.

2709. 40 fi. Type **551** .. .. 15 10
2710. 60 fi. "Poisson" bonboniere .. .. 15 10
2711. 80 fi. "Victoria" vase .. 20 10
2712. 1 fo. "Miramare" dish .. 20 10
2713. 1 fo. 20 "Godollo" pot .. 25 10
2714. 2 fo. "Empire" tea-set .. 40 10
2715. 4 fo. "Apponyi" dish .. 80 20
2716. 5 fo. "Baroque" vase .. 1·40 45

The 60 fi., 1 fo., 1 fo. 20, and 4 fo. are size 34 × 36 mm.

**1972.** 50th Anniv. of Int. Railway Union.

2717. **552.** 1 fo. red .. .. 65 15

**1972.** 25th Anniv. of National Economy Plan.

2718 **553** 1 fo. yell, sepia & brn 15 10

**554.** River Steamer and Old Obuda.

**1972.** Centenary of Unification of Buda, Obuda and Pest as Budapest.

2719 **554** 1 fo. purple and blue 30 10
2720 – 1 fo. blue and purple 30 10
2721 – 2 fo. green and brown 30 10
2722 – 2 fo. brown and green 30 10
2723 – 3 fo. brown and green 40 15
2724 – 3 fo. green and brown 40 15

DESIGNS: No. 2720, River hydrofoil and modern Obuda; 2721, Buda, 1872; 2722, Budapest, 1972; 2723, Pest, 1872; 2724, Parliament Buildings, Budapest.

**555.** Congress Emblem within Ear. **558.** Miklos Radnoti (poet).

**557.** Postbox, Bell Telephone and Satellite "Molnya".

**1972.** Int. Audiological Congress, Budapest.

2725. **555.** 1 fo. multicoloured .. 35 10

**1972.** Reopening of Postal and Philatelic Museums, Budapest. Multicoloured.

2727 4 fo. + 2 fo. Type **557** .. 50 75
2728 4 fo. + 2 fo. Globe, posthorn and stamps .. 50 75

**1972.** Radnoti Commem.

2729. **558.** 1 fo. multicoloured .. 10 10

**559.** F. Martos. **560.** "The Muses" (J. Rippl-Ronai).

**1972.** 75th Birth Anniv. of Flora Martos (patriot).

2730. **559.** 1 fo. multicoloured .. 10 10

**1972.** Stained Glass Windows. Multicoloured.

2731 40 fi. Type **560** .. .. 15 10
2732 60 fi. "16th-century Scribe" (F. Sebestenyi) 15 10
2733 1 fo. "Exodus to Egypt" (K. Lotz and B. Szekely) .. .. 20 10
2734 1 fo. 50 "Prince Arpad's Messenger" (J. Percz) 35 10
2735 2 fo. 50 "The Nativity" (L. Sztehlo) .. 55 10
2736 4 fo. "Prince Arpad and Leaders" (K. Kernstock) .. .. 1·00 15
2737 5 fo. "King Matthias reprimands the Rich Aristocrats" (J. Haranghy) .. 1·50 40

**561.** "Textiles".

**1972.** Opening of Textile Technical Museum, Budapest.

2738. **561.** 1 fo. multicoloured .. 15 10

**562.** Main Square, Szarvas. **563.** S. Petofi.

**1972.** Views.

2739 **562** 40 fi. brown & orge 15 10
2739a – 40 fi. black and green 10 10
2740 – 1 fo. blue & lt blue 20 10
2741 – 1 fo. brown & yellow 15 10
2742 – 3 fo. green and blue 50 10
2743 – 4 fo. red and orange 80 10
2743a – 4 fo. brown and pink 70 10
2744 – 5 fo. blue and cobalt 1·00 10
2745 – 6 fo. brown and red 1·25 10
2746 – 7 fo. violet and lilac 85 10
2747 – 8 fo. dp green & grn 1·25 10
2748 – 10 fo. brown & yell 1·50 10
2749 – 20 fo. multicoloured 3·75 15
2750 – 50 fo. multicoloured 6·50 70

DESIGNS: 21 × 18 mm. 40 fi. (No. 2739a) Rotunda (public health centre), Vasvar. 1 fo. (No. 2740) Salgotarjan. 1 fo. (No. 2741) Nyirbator. 28 × 22 mm. 3 fo. Tokay. 4 fo. (No. 2743) Esztergom. 4 fo. (No. 2743a) Szentendre. 5 fo. Szolnok. 6 fo. Dunaujvaros. 7 fo. Kaposvar. 8 fo. Vac. 10 fo. Kiskunfelegyhaza. 20 fo. Veszprem. 50 ra. Pecs.

**1972.** 150th Birth Anniv. of Sandor Petofi (poet and patriot).

2762. – 1 fo. red .. .. 10 10
2763. **563.** 2 fo. lilac .. .. 15 10
2764. – 3 fo. green .. .. 30 15

DESIGNS: 1 fo. Petofi making speech in Cafe Pilvax. 3 fo. Petofi on horseback during War of Independence, 1848–49.

**564.** Arms of U.S.S.R.

**1972.** 50th Anniv. of U.S.S.R.

2765. **564.** 1 fo. multicoloured .. 10 10

**565.** Code Map and Crow Symbol.

**1973.** Introduction of Postal Codes.

2766 **565** 1 fo. black and red .. 15 10

**1973.** As Nos. 1912, 1915/16 and 1918 but smaller.

2767. 2 fo. blue .. .. .. 40 25
2768. 3 fo. blue .. .. .. 60 35
2769. 4 fo. green .. .. 80 50
2770. 6 fo. ochre .. .. 1·50 85

SIZES: Nos. 2767/8 and 2770, 22 × 19 mm. No. 2769 19 × 22 mm.

**567.** I. Madach. **568.** Carnival Mask.

**1973.** 150th Birth Anniv. of Imre Madach (writer).

2772. **567.** 1 fo. multicoloured .. 10 10

**1973.** Busho-Walking Ceremony, Mohacs. Carnival Masks.

2773. **568.** 40 fi. multicoloured .. 10 10
2774. – 60 fi. multicoloured .. 10 10
2775. – 80 fi. multicoloured .. 15 10
2776. – 1 fo. 20 multicoloured 25 10
2777. – 2 fo. multicoloured .. 40 10
2778. – 4 fo. multicoloured .. 70 15
2779. – 6 fo. multicoloured 1·25 40

**569.** Copernicus. **571.** Show-jumping (Pentathlon) and Gold Medal.

**1973.** 500th Birth Anniv. of Copernicus.

2780. **569.** 3 fo. blue .. .. 85 40

**1973.** Hungarian Medal Winners, Olympic Games, Munich. Multicoloured.

2782. 40 fi. Type **571** .. 15 10
2783. 60 fi. Weightlifting (Gold) 15 10
2784. 1 fo. Canoeing (Silver) .. 25 10
2785. 1 fo. 20 Swimming (Silver) 30 10
2786. 1 fo. 80 Boxing (Gold) .. 35 10
2787. 4 fo. Wrestling (Gold) .. 75 15
2788. 6 fo. Fencing (Gold) .. 1·10 50

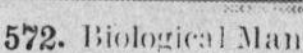

**572.** Biological Man. **573.** Winter Wrens.

**1973.** 25th Anniv. of W.H.O.

2790. **572.** 1 fo. brown and green 20 10

**1973.** Air. Hungarian Birds. Multicoloured.

2791. 40 fi. Type **573** .. .. 35 10
2792. 60 fi. Rock Thrush .. 40 10
2793. 80 fi. European Robins .. 45 10
2794. 1 fo. Firecrests .. .. 55 15
2795. 1 fo. 20 Linnets .. .. 80 15
2796. 2 fo. Blue Tits .. .. 85 25
2797. 4 fo. Bluethroat .. .. 1·40 40
2798. 5 fo. Grey Wagtails .. 1·90 45

**574.** Soldier and Weapons.

**1973.** Military Stamp Collectors' Exhibition, Budapest.

2799. **574.** 3 fo. multicoloured .. 40 20

**575.** "Budapest 61" 1 fo. Stamp.

**1973.** "IBRA 73" Stamp Exn, Munich, and "POLSKA '73", Poznan. Repoductions of Hungary Exhibition stamps. Multicoloured.

2800 40 fi. Type **575** .. .. 10 10
2801 60 fi. "Budapest 61" 1 fo. 70 stamp .. .. 10 10
2802 80 fi. "Budapest 61" 2 fo. 60 stamp .. .. 15 10
2803 1 fo. "Budapest 61" 3 fo. stamp .. .. .. 30 10
2804 1 fo. 20 "Budapaest 71" 2 fo. stamp .. .. 20 10
2805 2 fo. "Budapest 71" 2 fo. stamp .. .. .. 30 10
2806 4 fo. "Budapest 71" 2 fo. stamp .. .. .. 95 35
2807 5 fo. "Budapest 71" 2 fo. stamp .. .. .. 90 40

Nos. 2804/7 depict stamps from miniature sheets.

**576.** Setting Type and Preparing Ink. **578.** "Europa" Poster.

**577.** "Storm over Hortobagy Puszta".

**1973.** 500th Anniv. of Bookprinting in Hungary.

2809. **576.** 1 fo. black and gold 10 10
2810. – 3 fo. black and gold 35 10

DESIGN: 3 fo. Printer operating press.

**1973.** Paintings by Csontvary Kosztka Multicoloured.

2811. 40 fi. Type **577** .. .. 10 10
2812. 60 fi. "Mary's Well, Nazareth" .. .. 15 10
2813. 1 fo. "Carriage drive by Moonlight" .. .. 25 10
2814. 1 fo. 50 "Pilgrimage to the Lebanese Cedars" .. 30 10
2815. 2 fo. 50 "The Lone Cedar" 40 10
2816. 4 fo. "Waterfall at Jajce" 90 20
2817. 5 fo. "Ruins of Greek Theatre at Taormina" 1·10 50

Nos. 2813/14 are vert.

**1973.** European Security and Co-operation Conference, Helsinki.

2819. **578.** 2 fo. 50 brown & blk. 60 15

**579.** "Rosa gallica".

**580.** "Let's be friends...!".

**1973.** Wild Flowers. Multicoloured.

| | | | |
|---|---|---|---|
| 2820. | 40 fi. Type **579** .. .. | 15 | 10 |
| 2821. | 60 fi. "Cyclamen europaeum" .. .. | 20 | 10 |
| 2822. | 80 fi. "Pulmonaria mollissima" .. .. | 25 | 10 |
| 2823. | 1 fo. 20 "Bellis perennis" | 35 | 10 |
| 2824. | 2 fo. "Adonis vernalis" | 50 | 10 |
| 2825. | 4 fo. "Viola cyanea" .. | 85 | 15 |
| 2826. | 6 fo. "Papaver rhoeas" | 1·10 | 45 |

**1973.** Road Safety.

| | | | |
|---|---|---|---|
| 2827. **580.** | 40 fi. green and red | 15 | 10 |
| 2828. – | 60 fi. violet & orange | 20 | 10 |
| 2829. – | 1 fo. blue and red .. | 45 | 10 |

DESIGNS: 60 fi. "Not even a glass!" (hand reaching for tumbler). 1 fo. "Cyclist – use a lamp" (car running down cyclist).

**581.** Silver "Eagle" Disc.

**584.** Csokonai's Statue, Debrecen.

**583.** "The Three Kings" (Master of the High Altar, Szmrecsany).

**1973.** Jewelled Treasures, National Museum. Multicoloured.

| | | | |
|---|---|---|---|
| 2830. | 2 fo. + 50 fi. Type **581** .. | 50 | 60 |
| 2831. | 2 fo. + 50 fi. Serpent's head ring .. | 50 | 60 |
| 2832. | 2 fo. + 50 fi. "Loving couple" buckle .. | 50 | 60 |
| 2833. | 2 fo. + 50 fi. Silver "floral" buckle .. | 50 | 60 |

**1973.** Esztergom Millennium. "Old Master" Paintings in the Christian Museum. Mult.

| | | | |
|---|---|---|---|
| 2836. | 40 fi. Type **583** .. .. | 10 | 10 |
| 2837. | 60 fi. "Angels making Music" (Master "B.E.") | 10 | 10 |
| 2838. | 1 fo. "The Adoration of the Magi" (anon.) .. | 15 | 10 |
| 2839. | 1 fo. 50 "The Annunciation" (Szmrecsany Master) .. .. | 30 | 10 |
| 2840. | 2 fo. 50 "Angels making Music" (different Master "B.E.") .. | 45 | 10 |
| 2841. | 4 fo. "The Visitation of Mary and Elizabeth" (Szmrecsany Master) .. | 70 | 15 |
| 2842. | 5 fo. "The Legend of St. Catharine of Alexandria" (Master Bati) .. | 1·00 | 45 |

**1973.** Birth Bicentenary of M. Csokonai Vitez (poet).

| | | | |
|---|---|---|---|
| 2844. **584.** | 2 fo. multicoloured .. | 15 | 10 |

**585.** J. Marti.

**586.** B. Pesti.

**1973.** 120th Birth Anniv. of Jose Marti (Cuban patriot).

| | | | |
|---|---|---|---|
| 2845. **585.** | 1 fo. brn., red & blue | 10 | 10 |

**1973.** 30th Death Anniv. of Barnabas Pesti (patriot).

| | | | |
|---|---|---|---|
| 2846. **586.** | 1 fo. light brown, brown & blue .. | 10 | 10 |

**588.** Kayak-canoeing.

**1973.** World Aquatic Sports Championships, Belgrade and Tampere. Multicoloured.

| | | | |
|---|---|---|---|
| 2855. | 40 fi. Type **588** .. .. | 15 | 10 |
| 2856. | 60 fi. Water polo .. .. | 15 | 10 |
| 2857. | 80 fi. Men's solo kayak .. | 20 | 10 |
| 2858. | 1 fo. 20 Swimming .. | 30 | 10 |
| 2859. | 2 fo. Men's kayak fours | 45 | 10 |
| 2860. | 4 fo. Men's solo canoe .. | 75 | 15 |
| 2861. | 6 fo. Men's double canoe .. | 1·25 | 45 |

**590.** Lenin.

**1974.** 50th Death Anniv. of Lenin.

| | | | |
|---|---|---|---|
| 2863. **590.** | 2 fo. brn., blue & gold | 15 | 10 |

**591.** J. Boczor, I. Bekes and T. Elek.

**1974.** Hungarian Heroes of the French Resistance.

| | | | |
|---|---|---|---|
| 2864. **591.** | 3 fo. multicoloured .. | 20 | 10 |

**592.** "Comecon" Building, Moscow, and Flags.

**1974.** 25th Anniv. of Council for Mutual Economic Aid.

| | | | |
|---|---|---|---|
| 2865. **592.** | 1 fo. multicoloured .. | 10 | 10 |

**593.** Savings Bank Emblem, Note and Coins.

**595.** Pres. Salvador Allende.

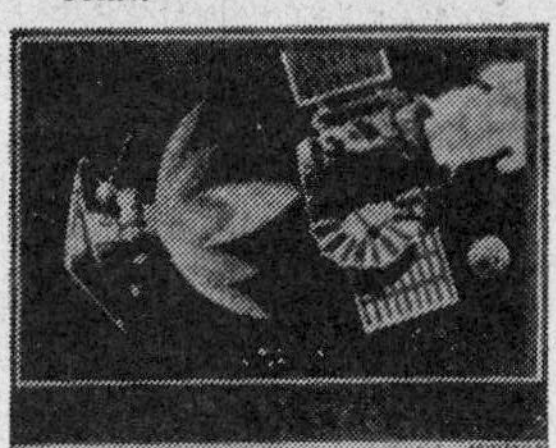

**594.** "Mariner 4" on course for Mars.

**1974.** 25th Anniv. of National Savings Bank.

| | | | |
|---|---|---|---|
| 2866. **593.** | 1 fo. multicoloured .. | 10 | 10 |

**1974.** Mars Research Projects. Mult.

| | | | |
|---|---|---|---|
| 2867. | 40 fi. Type **594** (postage) | 10 | 10 |
| 2868. | 60 fi. "Mars 2" approaching Mars .. | 15 | 10 |
| 2869. | 80 fi. "Mariner 4" space probe | 20 | 10 |
| 2870. | 1 fo. Mt. Palomar telescope and Mars photo | 35 | 10 |
| 2871. | 1 fo. 20 "Mars 3" on planet's surface .. .. .. | 45 | 10 |
| 2872. | 5 fo. "Mariner 9" approaching Mars and satellites .. | 1·25 | 15 |
| 2873. | 6 fo. G. Schiaparelli and Martian "canals" map (air) | 1·50 | 50 |

**1974.** Pres. Allende of Chile Commem.

| | | | |
|---|---|---|---|
| 2875. **595.** | 1 fo. multicoloured .. | 20 | 10 |

**596.** "Mona Lisa" (Leonardo da Vinci).

**1974.** Exhibition of "Mona Lisa" in Japan.

| | | | |
|---|---|---|---|
| 2876. **596.** | 4 fo. multicoloured .. | 3·50 | 4·00 |

**598.** Dove with Letter.

**1974.** Centenary of U.P.U. Multicoloured.

| | | | |
|---|---|---|---|
| 2878 | 40 fi. Type **598** .. .. | 10 | 10 |
| 2879 | 60 fi. Mail coach .. | 10 | 10 |
| 2880 | 80 fi. Early mail van and postbox .. .. | 15 | 10 |
| 2881 | 1 fo. 20 Balloon post .. | 20 | 10 |
| 2882 | 2 fo. Diesel mail train .. | 60 | 10 |
| 2883 | 4 fo. Post-bus .. .. | 75 | 15 |
| 2884 | 6 fo. Tupolev Tu-154 mail plane .. .. .. | 1·25 | 35 |

**599.** Swiss 2½ r. "Basle Dove" Stamp of 1845.

**1974.** "Internaba 1974" Stamp Exn., Basle.

| | | | |
|---|---|---|---|
| 2886. **599.** | 3 fo. multicoloured .. | 45 | 75 |

**600.** 13th-century miniature from King Alfonso X's "Book of Chess, Dice and Tablings" and Pawn.

**1974.** 50th Anniv of International Chess Federation and 21st Chess Olympiad, Nice.

| | | | |
|---|---|---|---|
| 2887 **600** | 40 fi. black, green & bl | 30 | 10 |
| 2888 – | 60 fi. blk, brn & lilac | 50 | 10 |
| 2889 – | 80 fi. blk, yell & grn | 75 | 10 |
| 2890 – | 1 fo. 20 black, yellow and lilac .. .. | 85 | 15 |
| 2891 – | 2 fo. black, stone & bl | 1·25 | 15 |
| 2892 – | 4 fo. blk, yell & pink | 1·75 | 65 |
| 2893 – | 6 fo. black, brn & grn | 1·90 | 85 |

DESIGNS: 60 fi. 15th-century woodcut from "The Game and Playe of Chesse" by William Caxton and knight; 80 fi. 15th-century illustration from Italian chess book and bishop; 1 fo. 20, "The Chess Players" (17th-century engraving by Jacob van der Heyden) and rook; 2 fo. Kempelen's chess playing machine (1769) and king; 4 fo. Geza Maroczy (Hungarian master) and queen; 6 fo. View of Nice and tournament emblem.

**602.** Congress Emblem.

**1974.** 4th International Economists' Congress, Budapest.

| | | | |
|---|---|---|---|
| 2895. **602.** | 2 fo. black, blue and silver .. .. | 20 | 10 |

**603.** "Woman Bathing" (K. Lotz).

**1974.** Nudes. Paintings. Multicoloured.

| | | | |
|---|---|---|---|
| 2896 | 40 fi. Type **603** .. .. | 15 | 10 |
| 2897 | 60 fi. "Awakening" (K. Brocky) .. .. | 15 | 10 |
| 2898 | 1 fo. "Venus and Cupid" (K. Brocky) (horiz) .. | 25 | 10 |
| 2899 | 1 f. 50 "After Bathing" (K. Lotz) .. .. | 40 | 10 |
| 2900 | 2 f. 50 "Honi soit qui mal y pense" (reclining nude) (I. Csok) (horiz) | 60 | 10 |
| 2901 | 4 fo. "After Bathing" (B. Szkely) .. .. | 80 | 15 |
| 2902 | 5 fo. "Devotion" (E. Korb) .. .. .. | 1·00 | 40 |

**604.** "Mimi" (Czobel).

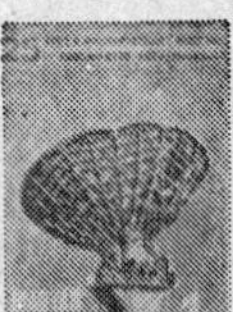

**605.** "Intersputnik" Satellite Tracking Radar.

**1974.** 91st Birth Anniv. of Bela Czobel (painter).

| | | | |
|---|---|---|---|
| 2904. **604.** | 1 fo. multicoloured .. | 40 | 15 |

**1974.** 25th Anniv. of Technical and Scientific Co-operation between Hungary and Soviet Union.

| | | | |
|---|---|---|---|
| 2905. **605.** | 1 fo. violet and blue | 15 | 10 |
| 2906. – | 3 fo. mauve & green | 30 | 10 |

DESIGN—HORIZ. 3 fo. Power installations.

**606.** Neruda.

**607.** Swedish 3 s. Stamp, 1855, and "Swedish Lion".

**1974.** Pablo Neruda (Chilean poet) Commemoration.

| | | | |
|---|---|---|---|
| 2907. **606.** | 1 fo. brown, deep brown and blue .. | 15 | 10 |

**1974.** "Stockholmia 74" International Stamp Exhibition.

| | | | |
|---|---|---|---|
| 2908. **607.** | 3 fo. green, blue and gold .. .. | 55 | 75 |

**608.** Tanks, and Infantry.

**1974.** Military Day.

| | | | |
|---|---|---|---|
| 2909. **608.** | 1 fo. black, red and gold (postage) .. | 30 | 10 |
| 2910. – | 2 fo. blk., grn. & gold (air) | 50 | 10 |
| 2911. – | 3 fo. blk. bl. & gold .. | 75 | 15 |

DESIGNS—VERT. 2 fo. Guided missile and radar. HORIZ. 3 fo. Parachutist, helicopter and jet fighter.

609. J. A. Segner and Moon.

**1974.** 270th Birth Anniv. of Janos Segner (scientist).
2912. 609. 3 fo. multicoloured .. 45 15

610 Hansa Brandenburg C-1 Biplane, 1918.

**1974.** Air. "Aerofila 1974" International Airmail Exhibition, Budapest, Mult.
2913 2 fo.+1 fo. Type **610** .. 1·25 1·10
2914 2 fo.+1 fo. Airship "Graf Zeppelin" .. .. 1·25 1·10
2915 2 fo.+1 fo. Hot air balloon 1·25 1·10
2916 2 fo.+1 fo. Mil Mi-1 helicopter .. .. 1·25 1·10

611. Purple Tiger Moth.

**1974.** Butterflies and Moths. Multicoloured.
2918 40 fi. Type **611** .. .. 40 10
2919 60 fi. Marbled white .. 50 10
2920 80 fi. Apollo .. .. 60 15
2921 1 fo. Spurge hawk moth 70 15
2922 1 fo. 20 Clifden's nonpareil 85 30
2923 5 fo. Purple emperor .. 1·60 45
2924 6 fo. Purple-edged copper 2·00 95

612. Istvan Pataki. 613. Mother and Child.

**1974.** Hungarian Antifascist Martyrs. Mult.
2925. 1 fo. Type **612** .. .. 10 10
2926. 1 fo. Robert Kreutz .. 10 10

**1974.** "Mothers".
2927 613 1 fo. black, yellow & bl 15 10

614. Puppy. 616. F. Bolyai.

615. Lambarene Hospital.

**1974.** Young Animals. (1st series). Mult.
2928. 40 fi. Type **614** .. .. 10 10
2929. 60 fi. Kittens (horiz.) .. 15 10
2930. 80 fi. Rabbit .. .. 20 10
2931. 1 fo. 20 Foal (horiz.) .. 30 10
2932. 2 fo. Lamb .. .. 55 10
2933. 4 fo. Calf (horiz.) .. 85 15
2934. 6 fo. Piglet .. .. 1·40 55
See also Nos. 3014/20.

**1975.** Birth Cent. of Dr. Albert Schweitzer (Nobel Peace Prize Winner). Multicoloured.
2935 40 fi. Type **615** .. .. 10 10
2936 60 fi. Casualty being treated .. .. 15 10
2937 80 fi. Casualty being transported by canoe .. 20 10
2938 1 fo. 20 Charitable goods arriving by freighter .. 30 10
2939 2 fo. View of Lambarene, doves, globe and Red Cross emblem .. .. 55 10
2940 4 fo. Schweitzer's Nobel Peace Prize medal and inscription .. .. 90 15
2941 6 fo. Schweitzer and organ-pipes .. .. 1·25 35

**1975.** Birth Bicentary of Farkas Bolyai (mathematician).
2942. 616. 1 fo. grey and red .. 10 10

617. Carrier-pigeon. 618. M. Karolyi.

**1975.** Air. Pigeon-racing Olympics, Budapest.
2943 617 3 fo. multicoloured .. 1·25 50

**1975.** Birth Centenary of Count Mihaly Karolyi (politician).
2944. 618. 1 fo. brown and blue 15 10

619. Woman's Head.

**1975.** International Woman's Year.
2945. 619. 1 fo. black and blue.. 15 10

620. " Railway Rebuilding ".

**1975.** 30th Anniv. of Liberation. Mult.
2946. 40 fi. Type **620** .. .. 25 10
2947. 60 fi. Hammer and sickle representing agriculture .. 10 10
2948. 2 fo. Blacksmith's hammer representing Communist party action .. .. 10 10
2949. 4 fo. Power hammer as "3" representing the "Three Year Heavy Industry Plan" .. 1·10 20
2950. 5 fo. Blocks of Flats representing "developed socialist society" 45 15

621. 1915 " Arrow ".

**1975.** 75th Anniv. of Hungarian Automobile Club. Vintage Motor Cars. Multicoloured.
2951. 40 fi. Type **621** .. 20 10
2952. 60 fi. 1911 "Swift" .. 20 10
2953. 80 fi. 1908 Ford "T" .. 25 10
2954. 1 fo. 1901 Mercedes .. 30 10
2955. 1 fo. 20 1912 Panhard Levassor .. .. 40 10
2956. 5 fo. 1906 Csonka .. 1·25 20
2957. 6 fo. Hungarian Automobile Club and international motoring organisations emblems 2·00 45

623. Academy Building.

**1975.** 150th Anniv. of National Academy of Sciences. Multicoloured.
2959 1 fo. Type **623** .. .. 10 10
2960 2 fo. Dates "1825" and "1975" .. .. 15 10
2961 3 fo. I. Szechenyi (statesman) .. .. 50 20

624. Olympic Stadium, Moscow.

**1975.** "Socphilex V" International Stamp Exhibition, Moscow.
2962. 624. 5 fo. multicoloured .. 70 90

625. French 1 f. Stamp, 1964.

**1975.** "Arphila 75" International Stamp Exhibition, Paris.
2963. 625. 5 fo. multicoloured .. 65 85

626. Electric Railway Locomotive and Transformer.

**1975.** 75th Anniv. of Hungarian Electrotechnical Assoc.
2964. 626. 1 fo. multicoloured .. 65 10

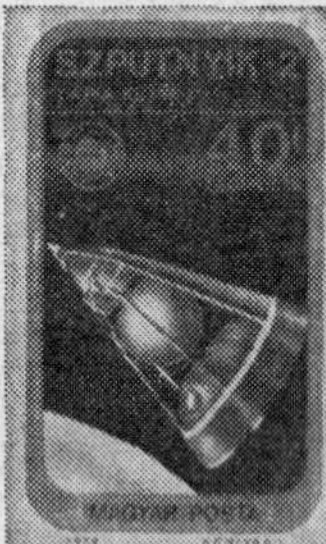

627. " Sputnik 2 ".

**1975.** Air. "Apollo-Soyuz" Space Link. Multicoloured.
2965. 40 fi. Type **627** .. .. 10 10
2966. 60 fi. "Mercury Atlas 5" 10 10
2967. 80 fi. "Lunokhod 1" (moon vehicle) .. 15 10
2968. 1 fo. 20 "Apollo 15" (moon vehicle) .. 25 10
2969. 2 fo. Launch of "Soyuz" from Baikonur .. 40 10
2970. 4 fo. Launch of "Apollo" 85 15
2971. 6 fo. "Apollo-Soyuz" link-up .. .. 1·25 45

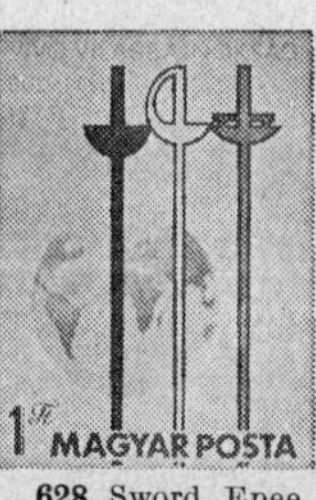

628. Sword, Epee, Rapier, and Globe. 631. A. Zimmermann.

**1975.** World Fencing Championships, Budapest.
2973. 628. 1 fo. multicoloured .. 25 10

**1975.** Birth Centenary of Dr. Agoston Zimmermann (veterinary surgeon).
2976 631 1 fo. dp brn, brn & bl 20 10

632. Branches of Tree symbolizing 14 Languages. 634. Anjou Wall Fountain.

**1975.** International Finno-Ugrian Congress, Budapest.
2977. 632. 1 fo. multicoloured .. 15 10

**1975.** Stamp Day. Preservation of Monuments. Monuments in Visegrad Palace. Multicoloured.
2979. 2 fo.+1 fo. Type **634** .. 75 1·25
2980. 2 fo.+1 fo. Anjou well house .. .. .. 75 1·25
2981. 2 fo.+1 fo. Hunyadi wall fountain .. .. 75 1·25
2982. 2 fo.+1 fo. Hercules fountain .. .. 75 1·25

635. Hungarian Arms and Map. 636. Ocean Pollution.

**1975.** 25th Anniv. of Hungarian Council System. Multicoloured.
2984. 1 fo. Type **635** .. .. 15 10
2985. 1 fo. Voters participating in council election .. 15 10

**1975.** International Exposition, Okinawa. Environmental Protection. Multicoloured.
2986. 40 fi. Type **636** .. .. 10 10
2987. 60 fi. Strangled rose (water pollution) .. 15 10
2988. 80 fi. Fish struggling for uncontaminated water (river pollution) .. 20 10
2989. 1 fo. Dead carnation (soil pollution) .. .. 30 10
2990. 1 fo. 20 Falling bird (air pollution) .. .. 40 10
2991. 5 fo. Infected lung (smoke pollution) .. 1·00 20
2992. 6 fo. Healthy and skeletal hands (life and death) .. .. .. 1·25 40

637. Mariska Gardos (writer) (1885–1973).

**1975.** Birth Annivs of Celebrities. Each black and red.
2993 1 fo. Type **637** .. .. 15 10
2994 1 fo. Imre Tarr (soldier) (1900–1937) .. .. 15 10
2995 1 fo. Imre Meso (Communist martyr) (1905–1956) .. .. 15 10

638. Treble Clef, Organ and Orchestra.

**1975.** Centenary of Ferenc Liszt Music Academy, Budapest.
2996 638 1 fo. multicoloured .. 40 10

**639.** 18th-century Icon of Szigetcsep.

**1975.** Hungarian Icons depicting the Virgin and Child. Multicoloured.

| | | | |
|---|---|---|---|
| 2997 | 40 fi. Type **639** .. .. | 10 | 10 |
| 2998 | 60 fi. 18th-century Icon of Graboc .. .. | 15 | 10 |
| 2999 | 1 fo. 18th-century Icon of Esztergom .. .. | 20 | 10 |
| 3000 | 1 fo. 50 18th-century Icon of Vatoped .. .. | 35 | 10 |
| 3001 | 2 fo. 50 17th-century Icon of Tottos .. .. | 50 | 10 |
| 3002 | 4 fo. 17th-century Icon of Gyor .. .. .. | 80 | 15 |
| 3003 | 5 fo. 18th-century Icon of Kazan .. .. | 1·00 | 45 |

**640.** Mother and Child, Flags and Radar Equipment.

**1975.** 20th Anniv. of Warsaw Treaty.

| | | | |
|---|---|---|---|
| 3004. **640.** | 1 fo. multicoloured .. | 15 | 10 |

**641.** Ice Hockey.

**1975.** Winter Olympic Games, Innsbruck. Multicoloured.

| | | | |
|---|---|---|---|
| 3005. | 40 fi. Type **641** .. .. | 25 | 10 |
| 3006. | 60 fi. Slalom skiing .. | 25 | 10 |
| 3007. | 80 fi. Slalom skiing (different) .. .. | 25 | 10 |
| 3008. | 1 fo. 20 Ski jumping .. | 35 | 10 |
| 3009. | 2 fo. Speed skating .. | 40 | 10 |
| 3010. | 4 fo. Cross-country skiing | 80 | 15 |
| 3011. | 6 fo. Bobsleighing .. | 1·00 | 45 |

**642.** Banknotes of 1925 and 1975.

**1976.** 50th Anniv of State Banknote Printing Office, Budapest.

| | | | |
|---|---|---|---|
| 3013 **642** | 1 fo. multicoloured .. | 35 | 10 |

**1976.** Young Animals (2nd series). As T **614**. Multicoloured.

| | | | |
|---|---|---|---|
| 3014 | 40 fi. Wild boars (horiz) | 10 | 10 |
| 3015 | 60 fi. Eurasian red squirrels .. .. | 10 | 10 |
| 3016 | 80 fi. Lynx (horiz) .. | 25 | 10 |
| 3017 | 1 fo. 20 Wolf cubs .. | 40 | 10 |
| 3018 | 2 fo. Red fox cubs (horiz) | 55 | 10 |
| 3019 | 4 fo. Brown bear cubs .. | 95 | 15 |
| 3020 | 6 fo. Lion cubs (horiz) .. | 1·40 | 45 |

**643.** Alexander Graham Bell, Telecommunications Satellite and Dish Aerial.

**1976.** Telephone Centenary.

| | | | |
|---|---|---|---|
| 3021. **643.** | 3 fo. multicoloured .. | 40 | 40 |

**645.** " Clash between Rakoczi's Kuruts and Hapsburg Soldiers ".

**1976.** 300th Birth Anniv. of Prince Ferenc Rakoczi II (soldier). Paintings. Multicoloured.

| | | | |
|---|---|---|---|
| 3023. | 40 fi. Type **645** .. .. | 10 | 10 |
| 3024. | 60 fi. "Meeting of Rakoczi and Tamas Esze" .. .. .. | 15 | 10 |
| 3025. | 1 fo. "The Parliament of Onod" (Mor Than) .. | 30 | 10 |
| 3026. | 2 fo. "Kuruts' Encampment" .. .. .. | 65 | 10 |
| 3027. | 3 fo. "Ilona Zrinyi" (Rakoczi's mother) (vert.) .. .. .. | 1·10 | 20 |
| 3028. | 4 fo. "Kuruts Officers" (vert.) .. .. .. | 1·50 | 25 |
| 3029. | 5 fo. "Prince Rakoczi II" (A. Manyoki) (vert.) .. | 2·00 | 55 |

**646.** Metric System Act, 1876. **647.** Knight.

**1976.** Centenary of Introduction of Metric System into Hungary. Multicoloured.

| | | | |
|---|---|---|---|
| 3030. | 1 fo. Type **646** .. .. | 10 | 10 |
| 3031. | 2 fo. Istvan Krusper (scientist) and vacuum balance .. .. | 15 | 10 |
| 3032. | 3 fo. Interferometer, space rocket and emblem .. .. | 35 | 10 |

**1976.** Stamp Day. Gothic Statues from Buda Castle.

| | | | |
|---|---|---|---|
| 3033. | 2 fo. 50+1 fo. Type **647** | 30 | 40 |
| 3034. | 2 fo. 50+1 fo. Armour bearer .. .. | 30 | 40 |
| 3035. | 2 fo. 50+1 fo. Apostle .. | 30 | 40 |
| 3036. | 2 fo. 50+1 fo. Bishop .. | 30 | 40 |

**648.** U.S. 6 c. Stamp, 1968.

**1976.** "Interphil '76". Int. Stamp Exn., Philadelphia.

| | | | |
|---|---|---|---|
| 3038. **648.** | 5 fo. multicoloured .. | 75 | 1·25 |

**649.** "Children Playing" (E. Gebora) within "30".

**1976.** 30th Anniv. of Hungarian Pioneers Movement.

| | | | |
|---|---|---|---|
| 3039. **649.** | 1 fo. multicoloured .. | 25 | 10 |

**650.** Truck, Tractor and Safety Headgear with Emblem.

**1976.** Industrial Safety.

| | | | |
|---|---|---|---|
| 3040. **650.** | 1 fo. multicoloured .. | 25 | 10 |

**651.** " Intelstar IV " Telecommunications Satellite.

**1976.** Olympic Games, Montreal. Mult.

| | | | |
|---|---|---|---|
| 3041. | 40 fi. Type **651** .. .. | 10 | 10 |
| 3042. | 60 fi. Horse-jumping .. | 10 | 10 |
| 3043. | 1 fo. Swimming .. .. | 15 | 10 |
| 3044. | 2 fo. Canoeing .. .. | 30 | 10 |
| 3045. | 3 fo. Fencing .. .. | 50 | 10 |
| 3046. | 4 fo. Javelin-throwing .. | 60 | 10 |
| 3047. | 5 fo. Gymnastics .. | 75 | 30 |

**652.** Danish 1851 4 R.B.S. Stamp and "Little Mermaid" Statue.

**1976.** " Hafnia '76 " International Stamp Exhibition, Copenhagen.

| | | | |
|---|---|---|---|
| 3049. **652.** | 3 fo. multicoloured .. | 60 | 85 |

**653.** " Flora " (Titian).

**1976.** 400th Death Anniv of Titian (painter).

| | | | |
|---|---|---|---|
| 3050 **653** | 4 fo. multicoloured .. | 50 | 15 |

**655.** Pal Gyulai (1826–1909). **656.** "Hussar" (Zs. Kisfaludy-Strobl).

**1976.** Writers' Anniversaries.

| | | | |
|---|---|---|---|
| 3052 **655** | 2 fo. black and red .. | 20 | 10 |
| 3053 – | 2 fo. black, yell & gold | 20 | 10 |

DESIGN: No. 3053, Daniel Berzsenyi (1776–1836).

**1976.** 150th Anniv. of Herend China Factory.

| | | | |
|---|---|---|---|
| 3054. **656.** | 4 fo. multicoloured .. | 75 | 15 |

**657.** Tuscany 1 q. Stamp, 1851 and Arms of Milan.

**1976.** "Italia '76" International Stamp Exhibition, Milan.

| | | | |
|---|---|---|---|
| 3055. **657.** | 5 fo. multicoloured .. | 1·75 | 2·25 |

**658.** Russian Dancer, Flags and Building.

**1976.** 2nd Anniv. of House of Soviet Culture and Science, Budapest.

| | | | |
|---|---|---|---|
| 3056. **658.** | 1 fo. multicoloured . | 20 | 10 |

**659.** Ignac Bogar.

**1976.** Hungarian Labour Movement Celebrities.

| | | | |
|---|---|---|---|
| 3057. **659.** | 1 fo. brown and red .. | 15 | 10 |
| 3058. – | 1 fo. brown and red .. | 15 | 10 |
| 3059. – | 1 fo. brown and red .. | 15 | 10 |

PORTRAITS: No. 3058, Rudolf Golub. No. 3059, Jozsef Madzsar.

**660.** Dr. F. Koranyi and Dispensary.

**1976.** 75th Anniv. of Koranyi T.B. Dispensary.

| | | | |
|---|---|---|---|
| 3060. **660.** | 2 fo. multicoloured .. | 50 | 10 |

**661.** Launch of " Viking " Mission.

**1976.** Air. Space Probes to Mars and Venus. Multicoloured.

| | | | |
|---|---|---|---|
| 3061 | 40 fi. Type **661** .. .. | 10 | 10 |
| 3062 | 60 fi. "Viking" in flight .. | 15 | 10 |
| 3063 | 1 fo. "Viking" on Mars .. | 20 | 10 |
| 3064 | 2 fo. Launch of "Venera" | 30 | 10 |
| 3065 | 3 fo. "Venera 9" in flight | 55 | 10 |
| 3066 | 4 fo. "Venera 10" descending to Venus .. | 85 | 10 |
| 3067 | 5 fo. "Venera" on Venus | 95 | 35 |

**662.** " Sigl " Locomotive, 1875.

**1976.** Centenary of Gyor–Sopron Railway.

| | | | |
|---|---|---|---|
| 3069 | 40 fi. Type **662** .. .. | 20 | 10 |
| 3070 | 60 fi. Locomotive No. 17, 1885 .. .. .. | 25 | 10 |
| 3071 | 1 fo. "Ganz" rail bus, 1925 | 30 | 10 |
| 3072 | 2 fo. "Hanomag" steam locomotive, 1920 .. | 55 | 10 |
| 3073 | 3 fo. "Ganz" railcar, 1926 | 75 | 10 |
| 3074 | 4 fo. "Ganz" express railcar, 1934 .. .. | 1·25 | 15 |
| 3075 | 5 fo. "Raba" railcar, 1971 | 2·00 | 50 |

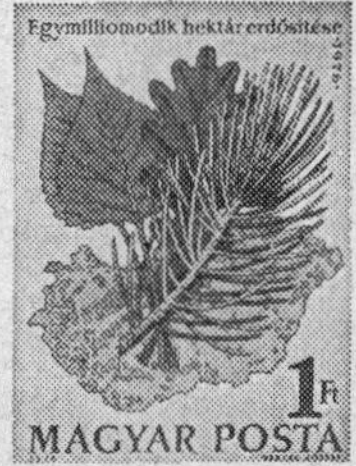


**663.** Tree Foliage and Map.

**1976.** "Afforestation of 1,000,000th Hectare".

| | | | |
|---|---|---|---|
| 3076. **663.** | 1 fo. multicoloured .. | 20 | 10 |

**664.** Weightlifting and Wrestling (silver medals).

**1976.** Olympic Games, Montreal. Hungarian Medal-winners. Multicoloured.

3077. 40 fi. Type **664** .. .. 10 10
3078. 60 fi. Men's solo kayak and Women's pairs kayak (silver medals) 15 10
3079. 1 fo. Men's gymnastics (horse) (gold medal) .. 20 10
3080. 4 fo. Women's rapier (gold medal) .. .. 85 15
3081. 6 fo. Men's javelin (gold medal) .. .. .. 1·25 45

**665.** White Spoonbill.

**1977.** Birds of Hortabagy National Park. Multicoloured.

3083. 40 fi. Type **665** .. .. 25 10
3084. 60 fi. White stork .. 35 10
3085. 1 fo. Purple heron .. 40 15
3086. 2 fo. Great bustard .. 50 20
3087. 3 fo. Common crane .. 80 30
3088. 4 fo. Pied wagtail .. 1·40 50
3089. 5 fo. Garganey .. .. 1·75 65

**666.** Imre Abonyi (champion driver) and Carriage, 1976.

**1977.** Historic Horse-drawn Vehicles. Mult.

3090. 40 fi. Type **666** .. 20 10
3091. 60 fi. Omnibus, 1870 .. 25 10
3092. 1 fo. Hackney-carriage, 1890 .. .. 30 10
3093. 2 fo. 19th-century mail coach .. .. .. 45 10
3094. 3 fo. 18th-century covered wagon .. 80 15
3095. 4 fo. Coach, 1568 .. 1·00 30
3096. 5 fo. Saint Elizabeth's carriage, 1430 .. .. 1·25 65

**667.** Common Peafowl.

**1977.** Peafowl and Pheasants. Multicoloured.

3097. 40 fi. Type **667** .. .. 25 10
3098. 60 fi. Green peafowl .. 30 10
3099. 1 fo. Congo peafowl .. 35 10
3100. 3 fo. Great Argus pheasant .. .. 1·00 15
3101. 4 fo. Himalayan monal pheasant .. .. 1·50 25
3102. 6 fo. Burmese peacock-pheasant .. 1·50 95

**668.** Front Page of "Nepszava" and Printing Works.

**670.** Isaac Newton and Lens.

**669.** Flower painting (Mihaly Munkacsy).

**1977.** Cent. of Newspaper "Nepszava".

3103. **668.** 1 fo. black, red & gold 10 10

**1977.** Flower Paintings by Hungarian Artists. Multicoloured.

3104. 40 fi. Type **669** .. .. 10 10
3105. 60 fi. Jakab Bogdany .. 10 10
3106. 1 fo. Istvan Csok (horiz.) 15 10
3107. 2 fo. Janos Halapy .. 30 10
3108. 3 fo. Jozsef Rippl-Ronai; (horiz.) .. .. 65 10
3109. 4 fo. Janos Tornyai .. 85 25
3110. 5 fo. Jozsef Koszta .. 1·00 55

**1977.** 250th Death Anniv of Isaac Newton (mathematician).

3111 **670** 3 fo. black, brn & red 60 60

**671.** Children Running.

**673.** Janos Vajda.

**672.** "Acrofila 74" 2 fo. + 1 fo. Stamp.

**1977.** Youth Sports.

3112. **671.** 3 fo. + 1 fo. 50 mult.. 50 60

**1977.** Stamp Exhibitions.

3113. **672.** 3 fo. multicoloured .. 1·00 1·50

**1977.** 150th Birth Anniv of Janos Vajda (poet).

3114 **673** 1 fo. stone, blk & grn 10 10

**674.** Netherlands 5 c. Stamp, 1852.

**1977.** "Amphilex 77" International Stamp Exhibition, Amsterdam.

3115 **674** 3 fo. multicoloured .. 60 80

**675.** "Wedding at Nagyrede" Dance.

**1977.** 25th Anniv. of State Folk Ensemble.

3116. **675.** 3 fo. multicoloured .. 95 15

**677.** View of Sopron (from medieval engraving), Arms and Fidelity Tower.

**679.** East German 10 pf. Stamp, 1957.

**678.** Kincsem (champion racehorse).

**1977.** 700th Anniv. of Sopron.

3118. **677.** 1 fo. multicoloured .. 70 90

**1977.** 150th Anniv. of Horse Racing in Hungary.

3119. **678.** 1 fo. multicoloured .. 1·25 1·25

**1977.** "Sozphilex 77" Stamp Exhibition, East Berlin.

3120. **679.** 3 fo. multicoloured .. 80 1·00

**680.** Scythian Iron Bell (6th century B.C.)

**681.** "Sputnik 1"

**1977.** Stamp Day and 175th Anniv. of Hungarian National Museum. Art Treasures.

3121. **680.** 2 fo. brown and blue 40 50
3122. – 2 fo. brown & violet 40 50
3123. – 2 fo. brn. & dp. brn. 40 50
3124. – 2 fo. gold & mauve.. 40 50

DESIGNS: No. 3122, Bronze candlestick, 12–13th century. 3123, Copper aquamanile, 13th century. 3124, Cast gold Christ (from crucifix), 11th century.

**1977.** Space Research. Multicoloured.

3126. 40 fi. Type **681** .. .. 10 10
3127. 60 fi. "Skylab" .. .. 15 10
3128. 1 fo. "Soyuz-Salyut 5" space station .. .. 20 10
3129. 3 fo. "Luna 24" .. .. 60 10
3130. 4 fo. "Mars 3" .. .. 1·25 15
3131. 6 fo. "Viking" .. .. 1·50 45

**683.** Tupolev Tu-154.

**1977.** Air.

3134. **683.** 60 fi. blk. & orange.. 15 10
3135. – 1 fo. 20 blk. & lilac .. 20 10
3136. – 2 fo. black & orange.. 30 10
3137. – 2 fo. 40 blk. & turq. 35 10
3138. – 4 fo. black and blue.. 50 10
3139. – 5 fo. black & mauve.. 70 10
3140. – 10 fo. black and blue 2·00 30
3141. – 20 fo. black & green 3·00 80

DESIGNS—As T **683**: 1 fo. 20, Douglas DC-8-62. 2 fo. Ilyushin Il-62M. 2 fo. 40, Airbus Industrie A300B4. 4 fo. Boeing 747. 5 fo. Tupolev Tu-144. 10 fo. Concorde. 38 × 28 mm: 20 fo. Ilyushin Il-86.

**684.** Montgolfier Brothers and Balloon.

**1977.** Air. Airships. Multicoloured.

3142 40 fi. Type **684** .. .. 10 10
3143 60 fi. David Schwarz and his aluminium airship 20 10
3144 1 fo. Alberto Santos-Dumont and airship "Ballon No. 5" over Paris .. .. .. 30 10
3145 2 fo. K. E. Tsiolkovsky and airship "Lebedi" over Kremlin .. .. 50 10
3146 3 fo. Roald Amundsen and airship "Norge" over North Pole .. 75 20
3147 4 fo. Hugo Eckener and airship "Graf Zeppelin" over Mount Fuji .. 1·10 30
3148 5 fo. Ferdinand Zeppelin and "Graf Zeppelin" over Chicago World Exhibition .. .. 1·60 55

**685.** Feet immersed in Water.

**686.** Ervin Szabo.

**1977.** World Rheumatism Year.

3150. **685** 1 fo. multicoloured .. 35 10

**1977.** Anniversaries.

3151. – 1 fo. black and red .. 10 10
3152. **686.** 1 fo. grey, blk. & red 10 10

DESIGNS: No 3151, Jamos Szanto Kovacs (agrarian socialist movement leader, 125th birth anniv); 3152, Type **686** (director of Municipal Libraries, journalist and labour movement leader, birth centenary.

**687.** Monument to Hungarian Participants, Omsk.

**1977.** 60th Anniv. of Russian Revolution.

3153. **687.** 1 fo. black and red .. 10 10

**688.** Endre Ady.

**689.** Lesser Panda.

**1977.** Birth Cent of Endre Ady (poet).

3154 **688** 1 fo. blue .. .. 20 20

**1977.** Bears. Multicoloured.

3155. 40 fi. Type **689** .. 15 10
3156. 60 fi. Giant Panda .. 25 10
3157. 1 fo. Asiatic black bear 40 10
3158. 4 fo. Polar bear .. .. 1·75 15
3159. 6 fo. Brown bear .. 2·50 50

**691.** Border-country Lancer, 17th-cent.

**1978.** Hussars. Multicoloured.

3161. 40 fi. Type **691** .. .. 15 10
3162. 60 fi. Kuruts horseman, 1710 .. .. .. 20 10
3163. 1 fo. Baranya hussar, 1762 .. .. 30 10
3164. 2 fo. Palatine Hussars officer, 1809 .. .. 50 10
3165. 4 fo. Alexander Hussar, 1848 .. .. .. 95 20
3166. 6 fo. Trumpeter, 5th Honved Regiment, 1900 1·40 55

**692.** Moon Station.

**1978.** Air. Science Fiction in Space Research. Multicoloured.

3167. 40 fi. Type **692** .. .. 10 10
3168. 60 fi. Moon settlement .. 15 10
3169. 1 fo. Phobos .. .. 25 10
3170. 2 fo. Exploring an asteroid .. .. 45 10
3171. 3 fo. Spacecraft in gravitational field of Mars 65 10
3172. 4 fo. One of Saturn's rings .. .. 95 15
3173. 5 fo. "Jupiter 3" .. 1·25 45

693. School of Arts and Crafts.

**1978.** Bicent. of School of Art and Crafts.
3174. **693.** 1 fo. multicoloured .. 10 10

**694.** Profile Heads.

**1978.** Youth Stamp Exhibition, Hatvan.
3175. **694.** 3 fo.+1 fo. 50 silver, red and black .. 70 1·00

**695.** " Generations " (Gyula Derkovits).

**1978.** "Socphilex '78" "Stamp Exhibition, Szombathely.
3176 **695** 3 fo.+1 fo. 50 mult .. 70 1·00

**696.** Louis Bleriot.

**1978.** Air. Famous Aviators and their Airplanes. Multicoloured.
3177 40 fi. Type **696** .. .. 15 10
3178 60 fi. John Alcock and Arthur Whitten Brown 20 10
3179 1 fo. Albert C. Read .. 25 10
3180 2 fo. Hermann Kohl, Gunther Hunefeld and James Fitzmaurice .. 55 10
3181 3 fo. Amy Johnson and Jim Mollison .. .. 75 15
3182 4 fo. Georgy Endresz and Sandor Magyar .. 95 20
3183 5 fo. Wolfgang von Gronau .. .. 1·00 70

**697.** Glass Vase and Glass-blowing Tube.

**1978.** Cent. of Ajka Glass Works.
3185. **697.** 1 fo. multicoloured .. 20 10

**698.** West Germany and Poland.

**1978.** World Cup Football Championship, Argentina. Multicoloured.
3186. 2 fo. Type **698** .. .. 50 20
3187. 2 fo. Hungary and Argentina .. .. .. 50 20
3188. 2 fo. France and Italy .. 50 20
3189. 2 fo. Tunisia and Mexico 50 20
3190. 2 fo. Sweden and Brazil .. 50 20
3191. 2 fo. Spain and Austria .. 50 20
3192. 2 fo. Peru and Scotland .. 50 20
3193. 2 fo. Iran and Netherlands 50 20

**699.** Canadian 3d. Stamp, 1851.

**1978.** " Capex 78 " International Stamp Exhibition, Toronto.
3195. **699.** 3 fo. multicoloured .. 1·00 1·25

**700.** Diesel MK 45 Locomotive. **702.** Festival Emblem.

**1978.** 30th Anniv. of Budapest Pioneer Railway.
3196. **700.** 1 fo. multicoloured .. 30 10

**1978.** 11th World Youth and Students' Festival, Havana. Multicoloured.
3198. 1 fo. Type **702** .. .. 10 10
3199. 1 fo. Map of Cuba and emblem .. .. 10 10

**703.** Human Torso and Heart. **705.** Dove and Fist holding Olive Branch.

**1978.** World Hypertension Year.
3200. **703.** 1 fo. red, blk. & blue 25 10

**1978.** 20th Anniv. of Communist Party Review "Peace and Socialism".
3202. **705.** 1 fo. red and black .. 10 10

**706.** Vladimir Remek cancelling Letters, " Salyut 6 " and " Soyuz 28 ".

**1978.** Air. "Praga 1978" International Stamp Exhibition, Prague.
3203. **706.** 3 fo. multicoloured .. 75 1·00

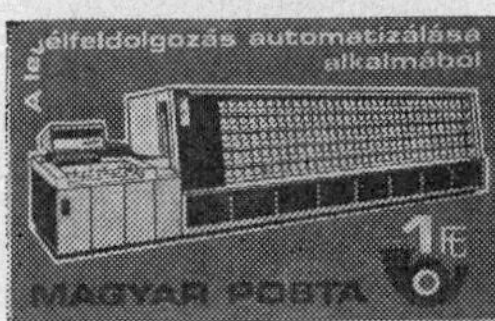


**707.** Toshiba Automatic Letter Sorting Equipment.

**1978.** Automation of Letter Sorting.
3204. **707.** 1 fo. multicoloured .. 20 20

**708.** Putto offering Grapes. **710.** Imre Thokoly.

**709.** Methods of Communication.

**1978.** Stamp Day. Mosaics. Multicoloured.
3205. 2 fo. Type **708** .. .. 90 1·25
3206. 2 fo. Tiger .. .. 90 1·25
3207. 2 fo. Bird .. .. 90 1·25
3208. 2 fo. Dolphin .. .. 90 1·25

**1978.** Organization of Socialist Countries' Postal Administrations Conference, Tbilisi.
3210. **709.** 1 fo. multicoloured .. 35 10

**1978.** 300th Anniv. of Thokoly's Revolt.
3211. **710.** 1 fo. black and yellow 35 10

**712.** " The Red Coach " (novel).

**1978.** Birth Cent. of Gyula Krudy (novelist).
3213. **712.** 3 fo. red and black .. 50 10

**713.** St. Ladislas (bust, Gyor Cathedral).

**1978.** 900th Anniv. of Accession of St. Ladislas.
3214. **713.** 1 fo. multicoloured .. 20 10

**714.** Buildings and Arms of Koszeg.

**1978.** 650th Anniv of Koszeg.
3215 **714** 1 fo. multicoloured .. 20 10

**715.** Samu Czaban and Gizella Berzeviczy.

**1978.** Birth Centenaries of Samu Czaban and Gizella Berzeviczy (teachers).
3216. **715.** 1 fo. multicoloured .. 20 10

**716.** Communist Party Emblem.

**1978.** 60th Anniv. of Hungarian Communist Party.
3217. **716.** 1 fo. red, grey and black .. .. 10 10

**717.** "Girl cutting Bread".

**1978.** Ceramics by Margit Kovacs. Mult.
3218. 1 fo. Type **717** .. .. 25 10
3219. 2 fo. " Girl with Pitcher " 40 20
3220. 3 fo. " Boy Potter" .. 70 25

**718.** " Self-portrait in Fur Coat ".

**1978.** 450th Death Anniv. of Albrecht Durer (artist). Multicoloured.
3221. 40 fi. " Madonna with Child " .. .. .. 10 10
3222. 60 fi. " Adoration of the Magi " (horiz.) .. 10 10
3223. 1 fo. Type **718** .. .. 20 10
3224. 2 fo. " St. George " .. 35 10
3225. 3 fo. " Nativity " (horiz.) 60 10
3226. 4 fo. " St. Eustace " .. 75 15
3227. 5 fo. " The Four Apostles " 90 45

**719.** Human Rights Emblem. **720.** Child with Dog.

**1979.** 30th Anniv. of Declaration of Human Rights.
3229. **719.** 1 fo. blue & light blue 65 80

**1979.** International Year of the Child (1st issue). Multicoloured.
3230. 1 fo. Type **720** .. .. 40 25
3231. 1 fo. Family group .. 40 25
3232. 1 fo. Children of different races .. .. .. 1·50 1·50
See also Nos. 3287/93.

**721.** " Soldiers of the Red Army, Forward! " (poster by Bela Uitz).

**1979.** 60th Anniv. of First Hungarian Soviet Republic.
3233. **721.** 1 fo. blk., red & grey 10 10

**722.** " Girl Reading " (Ferenc Kovacs).

**1979.** Youth Stamp Exhibition, Bekescsaba.
3234. **722.** 3 fo.+1 fo. 50 grey blue and black .. 30 45

**723.** Chessmen and Cup.

**1979.** 23rd Chess Olympiad, Buenos Aires (1978).

3235 723 3 fo. multicoloured .. 1·60 1·00

724. Alexander Nevski Cathedral, Sofia, and First Bulgarian Stamp.

**1979.** "Philaserdica 79" International Stamp Exhibition, Sofia.

3236. 724. 3 fo. multicoloured .. 65 75

725. Stephenson's "Rocket".

**1979.** International Transport Exhibition, Hamburg. Multicoloured designs depicting development of the railway.

3237 40 fi. Type 725 .. .. 25 10
3238 60 fi. Siemens and Halske electric locomotive, 1879 30 10
3239 1 fo. Early American locomotive "Pioneer" 40 10
3240 2 fo. Hungarian "MAV Ie" pulling "Orient Express" .. .. 55 15
3241 3 fo. "Trans-Siberian Express" .. .. 80 30
3242 4 fo. Japanese "Hikari Express" .. .. 1·10 40
3243 5 fo. German "Transrapid 05" .. .. .. 1·25 85

726. Soyuz Gas Pipe-line and Compressor Station.

727. Zsigmond Moricz (after J. Rippl-Ronai).

**1979.** 30th Anniv. of Council of Mutual Economic Aid. Multicoloured.

3245. 1 fo. Type 726 .. .. 10 10
3246. 2 fo. Pylon and dam, Lenin hydro-electric power station, Dnepropetrovsk 20 10
3247. 3 fo. Council building, Moscow .. .. 20 10

**1979.** Birth Centenary of Zsigmond Moricz (writer).

3248. 727. 1 fo. multicoloured .. 10 10

728. City Hall, Helsinki (1952 Games).

**1979.** Olympic Games, Moscow (1980) (1st issue). Multicoloured.

3249. 40 fi. Type 728 .. .. 10 10
3250. 60 fi. Colosseum, Rome (1960) .. .. 10 10
3251. 1 fo. Asakusa Temple, Tokyo (1964) .. .. 20 10
3252. 2 fo. Cathedral, Mexico City (1968) .. .. 30 10
3253. 3 fo. Frauenkirche, Munich (1972) .. .. 40 10
3254. 4 fo. Modern quarter, Montreal (1976) .. 60 10
3255. 5 fo. Lomonosov University, Moscow, and Misha the bear (mascot) (1980) 70 35

See also Nos. 3323/29.

729. "Child with Horse and Greyhounds" (Janos Vaszary).

**1979.** Animal Paintings. Multicoloured.

3256. 40 fi. Type 729 .. .. 20 10
3257. 60 fi. "Coach and Five" (Karoly Lotz) .. 25 10
3258. 1 fo. "Lads on Horseback" (Celesztin Pallya) .. 30 10
3259. 2 fo. "Farewell" (Karoly Lotz) .. .. 40 10
3260. 3 fo. "Horse Market" (Celeztin Pallya) .. 55 10
3261. 4 fo. "Wandering" (Bela Ivanyi-Grunwald) .. 65 20
3262. 5 fo. "Ready for Hunting" (Karoly Sterio) .. 1·00 45

730. Sturgeon, Cousteau's Ship "Calypso" and Black Sea.

**1979.** Sea and River Purity.

3263. 730. 3 fo. multicoloured .. 65 15

731. Globe and Five Pentathlon Sports.

**1979.** Pentathlon World Championship, Budapest.

3264. 731. 2 fo. multicoloured .. 20 10

732. Stephen I Denarius (reverse).

735. Flags and Globe filled with Coins.

**1979.** Ninth International Numismatic Congress, Berne. Designs showing old Hungarian coins. Multicoloured.

3265. 1 fo. Type 732 .. .. 25 10
3266. 2 fo. Bela III copper coin (obverse) .. .. 40 10
3267. 3 fo. Louis the Great groat (reverse) .. .. 50 15
3268. 4 fo. Matthias I gold forint (obverse) .. .. 65 40
3269. 5 fo. Wladislaw II gulden (reverse) .. .. 90 70

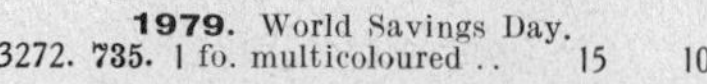

**1979.** World Savings Day.

3272. 735. 1 fo. multicoloured .. 15 10

736. "Vega-Chess" (Victor Vasarely).

737. European Otter.

**1979.** Modern Art.

3273. 736. 1 fo. multicoloured .. 20 10

**1979.** Protected Animals. Multicoloured.

3274. 40 fi. Type 737 .. .. 20 10
3275. 60 fi. Wild cat .. .. 25 10
3276. 1 fo. Pine marten .. 45 10
3277. 2 fo. Eurasian badger .. 65 10
3278. 4 fo. Steppe polecat .. 1·40 15
3279. 6 fo. Beech marten .. 2·00 50

738. Ski Jumping.

**1979.** Air. Winter Olympic Games, Lake Placid (1980). Multicoloured.

3280. 40 fi. Type 738 .. .. 25 10
3281. 60 fi. Figure skating .. 30 10
3282. 1 fo. Slalom .. .. 45 10
3283. 2 fo. Ice hockey .. .. 60 15
3284. 4 fo. Bobsleigh .. .. 1·00 15
3285. 6 fo. Cross-country skiing 1·25 45

739. "Tom Thumb".

**1979.** International Year of the Child (2nd issue). Designs depicting children's stories. Multicoloured.

3287. 40 fi. Type 739 .. .. 15 10
3288. 60 fi. "The Ugly Duckling" (Andersen) .. 25 10
3289. 1 fo. "The Fisher and the Goldfish" .. .. 35 10
3290. 2 fo. "Cinderella" .. 60 10
3291. 3 fo. "Gulliver's Travels" (Swift) .. .. 80 10
3292. 4 fo. "The Little Pig and the Wolves" .. .. 85 15
3293. 5 fo. "Gallant John" .. 1·10 85

740. Achillea and Bee-eating Beetles.

**1980.** Pollination. Multicoloured.

3295 40 fi. Type 740 .. .. 15 10
3296 60 fi. Gaillardia and bee 15 10
3297 1 fo. Rudbeckia and red admiral .. .. 20 10
3298 2 fo. Dog rose and rose chafer .. .. .. 40 10
3299 4 fo. "Petroselinum hortense" and striped bug 85 20
3300 6 fo. Achillea and longhorn beetle .. 1·25 50

741. Hanging Gardens of Babylon.

**1980.** Seven Wonders of the Ancient World. Multicoloured.

3301. 40 fi. Type 741 .. .. 15 10
3302. 60 fi. Temple of Artemis, Ephesus .. .. 15 10
3303. 1 fo. Statue of Zeus, Olympia .. .. 20 10
3304. 2 fo. Mausoleum of Halicarnassus .. .. 40 10
3305. 3 fo. Colossus of Rhodes 55 15
3306. 4 fo. Pharos, Alexandria 75 20
3307. 5 fo. Pyramids of Egypt 1·75 60

742. Gabor Bethlen (copperplate).

**1980.** 400th Birth Anniv. of Gabor Bethlen (Prince of Transylvania).

3308. 742. 1 fo. multicoloured .. 20 10

743. Tihany Abbey.

**1980.** 925th Anniv. of Foundation of Tihany Abbey.

3309. 743. 1 fo. multicoloured .. 10 10

744. Easter Sepulchre.

745. Bunch of Wild Flowers.

**1980.** Easter Sepulchre of Garamszentbenedek. Designs showing details of sepulchre. Multicoloured.

3310. 1 fo. Type 744 .. .. 15 10
3311. 2 fo. Three Marys .. 25 10
3312. 3 fo. Apostle Jacob .. 30 15
3313. 4 fo. Apostle Thaddeus .. 40 25
3314. 5 fo. Apostle Andrew .. 55 50

**1980.** 35th Anniv. of Liberation.

3315. 745. 1 fo. multicoloured .. 20 10

746. Watch symbolising Environmental Protection.

747. Attila Jozsef.

**1980.** Youth Stamp Exhibition, Dunaujvaros.

3316. 746. 3 fo. + 1 fo. 50 mult. 30 45

**1980.** 75th Birth Anniv. of Attila Jozsef (poet).

3317. 747. 1 fo. green and red .. 10 10

748. "Madonna and Child" Stamp of 1921 with Inverted Centre.

**1980.** 50th Anniv. of Hungarian Stamp Museum.

3318. 748. 1 fo. multicoloured .. 45 25

749. Great Britain 2d. Blue and Life Guard.

**1980.** "London 1980" International Stamp Exhibition.

3319. 749. 3 fo. multicoloured .. 65 75

750. Soviet and Hungarian Cosmonauts.

751. Margit Kaffka.

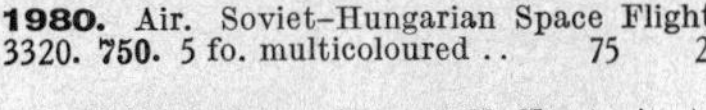

**1980.** Air. Soviet–Hungarian Space Flight.
3320. **750.** 5 fo. multicoloured .. 75 20

**1980.** Birth Cent. of Margit Kaffka (writer).
3321. **751.** 1 fo. yell., blk. & violet 10 10

**752.** Norwegian 1951 Olympic Stamp and Statue " Mother and Child " (Gustav Vigeland).

**1980.** " Norwex 80 " International Stamp Exhibition, Oslo.
3322. **752.** 3 fo. multicoloured .. 60 75

**753.** Handball.

**1980.** Air. Olympic Games, Moscow (2nd issue). Multicoloured.
3323. 40 fi. Type **753** .. .. 10 10
3324. 60 fi. Double kayak .. 10 10
3325. 1 fo. Running .. .. 15 10
3326. 2 fo. Gymnastics .. 30 10
3327. 3 fo. Show-jumping (modern pentathlon) .. 50 10
3328. 4 fo. Wrestling .. .. 60 40
3329. 5 fo. Water polo .. 80 75

**754.** Endre Hogyes (physician) and Congress Emblem.

**756.** Zoltan Schonherz.

**1980.** 28th International Congress of Physiological Sciences, Budapest.
3331. **754.** 1 fo. multicoloured .. 15 10

**1980.** 75th Birth Anniv. of Zoltan Schonherz (Workers' Movement member).
3333. **756.** 1 fo. multicoloured .. 10 10

**757.** Decanter.

**759.** Bertalan Por (self portrait).

**1980.** Stamp Day. Glassware. Multicoloured.
3334. 1 fo. Type **757** .. .. 20 10
3335. 2 fo. Wine glass, Budapest 40 10
3336. 3 fo. Drinking glass, Zay-Ugrocz .. .. .. 60 25

**1980.** Birth Cent. of Bertalan Por (artist).
3339. **759.** 1 fo. multicoloured .. 10 10

**760.** Greylag Goose.

**1980.** Protected Birds. Multicoloured.
3340 40 fi. Type **760** .. .. 20 10
3341 60 fi. Black-crowned night herons .. .. 30 10
3342 1 fo. Common shovelers 30 15
3343 2 fo. White-winged black tern .. .. .. 70 25
3344 4 fo. Great crested grebes 1·50 65
3345 6 fo. Black-winged stilts 2·25 1·10

**762.** Johannes Kepler.

**1980.** 350th Death Anniv. of Johannes Kepler (astronomer).
3348. **762.** 1 fo. multicoloured .. 30 15

**763.** Karoly Kisfaludy.

**1980.** 150th Death Anniv. of Karoly Kisfaludy (dramatist and poet).
3349. **763.** 1 fo. multicoloured .. 10 10

**764.** U.N. Building, New York.

**1980.** 25th Anniv. of United Nations Membership. Multicoloured.
3350. 40 fi. Type **764** .. .. 15 10
3351. 60 fi. U.N. building, Geneva 10 10
3352. 1 fo. International Centre, Vienna .. .. .. 20 10
3353. 2 fo. U.N. and Hungarian flags .. .. .. 35 10
3354. 4 fo. U.N. emblem and Hungarian arms .. 75 10
3355. 6 fo. World map .. 1·60 90

**765.** Ferenc Erdei.

**766.** Bela Szanto.

**1980.** 70th Birth Anniv. of Ferenc Erdei (agricultural economist and politician).
3356. **765.** 1 fo. multicoloured .. 10 10

**1981.** Birth Cent. of Bela Szanto (founder member of Hungarian Communist Party).
3357. **766.** 1 fo. multicoloured .. 10 10

**767.** Lajos Batthyany (after Miklos Barabas).

**1981.** 175th Birth Anniv. of Lajos Batthyany (politician).
3358. **767.** 1 fo. multicoloured .. 10 10

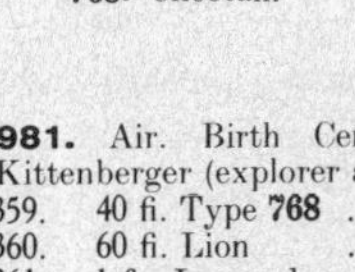

**768.** Cheetah.

**769.** "Graf Zeppelin" over Tokyo.

**1981.** Air. Birth Centenary of Kalman Kittenberger (explorer and zoologist). Mult.
3359. 40 fi. Type **768** .. .. 20 10
3360. 60 fi. Lion .. .. 20 10
3361. 1 fo. Leopard .. .. 30 10
3362. 2 fo. Black rhinoceros .. 60 15
3363. 3 fo. Greater kudu .. 65 20
3364. 4 fo. African elephant .. 1·10 25
3365. 5 fo. Kittenberger and Hungarian National Museum .. .. 2·50 1·10

**1981.** Air. "Luraba" International Exhibition of Aero- and Astro-philately, Lucerne. "Graf Zeppelin" Flights. Multicoloured.
3366 1 fo. Type **769** (first round-the-world flight, 1929) .. .. .. 15 10
3367 2 fo. Franz Josef Land and icebreaker "Malygin" (Polar flight, 1931) .. .. .. 45 10
3368 3 fo. Nine-arch Bridge, Hortobagy (Hungary flight, 1931) .. .. 45 15
3369 4 fo. Hostentor, Lubeck (Baltic flight, 1931) .. 60 15
3370 5 fo. Tower Bridge (England flight, 1931) 70 20
3371 6 fo. Federal Palace, Chicago (World Exhibition flight, 1933) 75 25
3372 7 fo. Lucerne (1st Swiss flight, 1929) .. .. 85 75

**771.** Flag of House of Arpad (11th century).

**1981.** Historical Hungarian Flags. Mult.
3374. 40 fi. Type **771** .. .. 20 10
3375. 60 fi. Hunyadi Family flag (15th century) .. 30 10
3376. 1 fo. Flag of Gabor Bethlen (1600) .. .. .. 45 10
3377. 2 fo. Flag of Ferenc Rakoczi II (1706) .. 65 10
3378. 4 fo. " Honved " (1848–49) 95 15
3379. 6 fo. Troop Flag (1919) .. 1·25 45

**772.** Red Deer seen through Binoculars.

**773.** First Hungarian Telephone Exchange.

**1981.** Centenary of Association of Hungarian Huntsmen.
3380. **772.** 2 fo. multicoloured .. 35 10

**1981.** Centenary of First Hungarian Telephone Exchange, Budapest.
3381. **773.** 2 fo. multicoloured .. 40 10

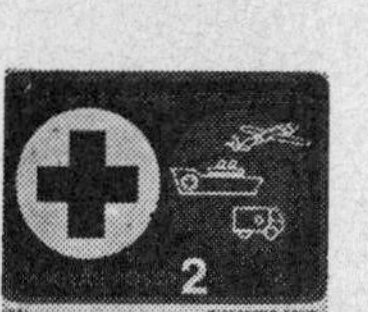

**775.** Red Cross, Transport and Globe.

**777.** I.Y.D.P. Emblem and Person pushing Wheelchair.

**1981.** Cent. of Hungarian Red Cross.
3383. **775.** 2 fo. orange and red .. 40 10

**1981.** International Year of Disabled Persons.
3385 **777** 2 fo.+1 fo. grn & yell 70 70

**778.** Young People and Factory.

**779.** Stephenson and " Locomotion ".

**1981.** 10th Young Communist League Congress, Budapest.
3386. **778.** 4 fo.+2 fo. mult. .. 70 75

**1981.** Birth Bicentenary of George Stephenson (railway pioneer).
3387. **779.** 2 fo. yell., grey & brn. 80 25

**780.** Bela Vago.

**1981.** Birth Centenary of Bela Vago (founder member of Hungarian Communist Party).
3388. **780.** 2 fo. green and brown 20 10

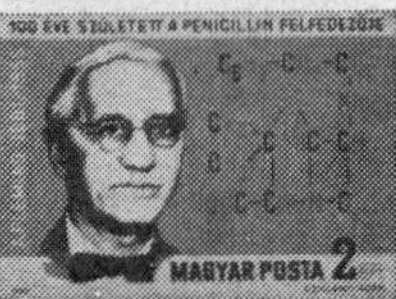


**781.** Alexander Fleming.

**1981.** Birth Centenary of Alexander Fleming (discoverer of penicillin).
3389. **781.** 2 fo. multicoloured .. 65 15

**782.** Bridal Chest from Szentgal.

**1981.** Stamp Day. Bridal Chests. Mult.
3390. 1 fo. Type **782** .. .. 15 10
3391. 2 fo. Chest from Hodmezovasarhely .. 35 30

**783.** Calvinist College.

**784.** Hands holding F.A.O. Emblem.

**1981.** 450th Anniv. of Calvinist College, Papa.
3393. **783.** 2 fo. multicoloured .. 20 10

**1981.** World Food Day.
3394. **784.** 2 fo. multicoloured .. 45 10

**785.** German Costume.

**786.** " Franz I " (1830) and 30 fi. stamp.

**1981.** National Costumes of Hungarian Ethnic Minorities. Multicoloured.
3395. 1 fo. Slovakian costume 1·50 1·75
3396. 2 fo. Type **785** .. .. 1·50 1·75
3397. 3 fo. Croatian costume .. 1·50 1·75
3398. 4 fo. Rumanian costume 1·50 1·75

**1981.** 125th Anniv of Danube Commission. Paddle-steamers and Danube Commission stamps issued in 1967. Multicoloured.
3399. 1 fo. Type **786** .. .. 35 20
3400. 1 fo. " Arpad " (1834) and 60 fi. stamp .. .. 35 20
3401. 2 fo. " Szechenyi " (1853) and 1 fo. stamp .. 50 35
3402. 2 fo. " Grof Szechenyi Istvan " (1896) and 1 fo. 50 stamp .. .. 50 35
3403. 4 fo. " Zsofia " (1914) and 1 fo. 70 stamp .. .. 85 60
3404. 6 fo. " Felszabadulas " (1917) and 2 fo. stamp 1·50 1·25
3405. 8 fo. " Rakoczi " (1964) and 2 fo. 50 stamp .. 2·00 2·00

787. " Mother Breast-feeding " (pottery, Margit Kovacs).

788. " Pen Pals " (Rockwell).

**1981.** Christmas. Multicoloured.

3407. 1 fo. Type **787** .. .. 10 10
3408. 2 fo. " Madonna of Csurgo " (bronze Amerigo Tot) 35 10

**1981.** Illustrations by Norman Rockwell and Anna Lesznai. Multicoloured.

3409. 1 fo. Type **788** .. .. 15 10
3410. 2 fo. " Courting under the Clock at Midnight " (Rockwell) .. .. 30 10
3411. 2 fo. " Maiden Voyage " (Rockwell) .. .. 30 10
3412. 4 fo. " Threading the Needle " (Rockwell) .. 70 40
3413. 4 fo. " At the End of the Village " (detail) (Lesznai) 70 40
3414. 5 fo. " Dance " (detail) (Lesznai) .. .. 1·00 55
3415. 6 fo. " Sunday " (detail) (Lesznai) .. .. 1·25 90

**790.** Militiaman at Shooting Practice.

**791.** Congress Emblem and Havana.

**1982.** 25th Anniv. of Workers' Militia. Mult.

3417. 1 fo. Type **790** .. .. 15 10
3418. 4 fo. Three generations of militiamen .. .. 60 10

**1982.** 10th World Trade Unions Federation Congress, Havana.

3419 **791** 2 fo. multicoloured .. 20 10

**792.** Gyula Alpari. **793.** Dr. Robert Koch.

**1982.** Birth Centenary of Gyula Alpari (journalist).

3420 **792** 2 fo. yellow, pur & brn 20 10

**1982.** Cent. of Discovery of Tubercle Bacillus.

3421. **793.** 2 fo. multicoloured .. 45 15

**794.** Tennis Racket and Ball.

**796.** Table Tennis Player and Map of Europe.

**795.** Hungary v. Egypt, 1934.

**1982.** Youth Stamp. European Junior Tennis Cup.

3422. **794.** 4 fo.+2 fo. mult. .. 1·10 1·10

**1982.** World Cup Football Championship, Spain. Multicoloured.

3423. 1 fo. Type **795** .. .. 20 10
3424. 1 fo. Italy v. Hungary, 1938 20 10
3425. 2 fo. West Germany v. Hungary, 1954 .. 40 10
3426. 2 fo. Hungary v. Mexico, 1958 .. .. 40 10
3427. 4 fo. Hungary v. England, 1962 .. .. 80 10
3428. 6 fo. Hungary v. Brazil, 1966 .. .. 1·25 15
3429. 8 fo. Argentine v. Hungary, 1978 .. .. 1·60 50

**1982.** European Table Tennis Championship, Budapest.

3431. **796.** 2 fo. multicoloured .. 45 10

**797.** " Pascali ". **798.** Georgi Dimitrov.

**1982.** Roses. Multicoloured.

3432. 1 fo. Type **797** .. .. 25 10
3433. 1 fo. " Michele Meilland " 25 10
3434. 2 fo. " Diorama " .. 45 10
3435. 2 fo. " Wendy Cussons " 45 10
3436. 3 fo. " Blue Moon " .. 75 15
3437. 3 fo. " Invitation " .. 75 15
3438. 4 fo. " Tropicana " .. 1·25 40

**1982.** Birth Centenary of Georgi Dimitrov (Bulgarian statesman).

3440. **798.** 2 fo. grey, grn. & brn. 25 25

**799.** " Columbia ". Space Shuttle.

**800.** Watermark.

**1982.** Space Research. Multicoloured.

3441. 1 fo. Type **799** .. .. 20 10
3442. 1 fo. Neil Armstrong (first man on Moon) .. 20 10
3443. 2 fo. A. Leonov (first space-walker) .. .. 35 10
3444. 2 fo. Yuri Gagarin (first man in space) .. .. 35 10
3445. 4 fo. Laika (first dog in space) .. .. 75 20
3446. 4 fo. "Sputnik I" (first artificial satellite) .. 75 20
3447. 6 fo. K. E. Tsiolkovsky (Russian scientist) .. 1·25 40

**1982.** Bicentenary of Diosgyor Paper-mill.

3448. **800.** 2 fo. multicoloured .. 30 10

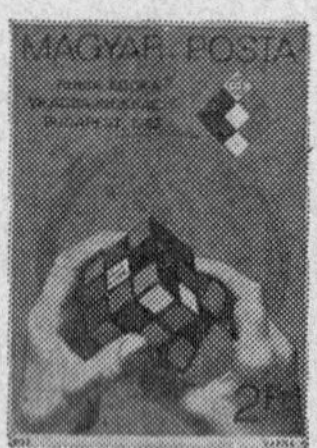

**801.** Rubik Cube. **804.** Blood Drop.

**1982.** World Rubik Cube Championship, Budapest.

3449. **801.** 2 fo. multicoloured .. 40 10

**1982.** World Haematology Congress, Budapest.

3452. **804.** 2 fo. multicoloured .. 40 10

**805.** Zirc Abbey and Seal of King Bela III.

**806.** Fishermen's Bastion, Budapest.

**1982.** 800th Anniv. of Zirc Abbey.

3453. **805.** 2 fo. multicoloured .. 30 10

**1982.** Stamp Day. Multicoloured.

3454 4 fo.+2 fo. Type **806** .. 75 90
3455 4 fo.+2 fo. Cupola of Parliament, Budapest 75 90

**808.** Kner Emblem.

**1982.** Cent. of Kner Printing Office, Gyoma.

3457. **808.** 2 fo. yell., blk. and red 30 10

**809.** Agricultural Symbols on Map of Hungary.

**1982.** " Agrofila '82 " Stamp Exhibition, Godollo.

3458. **809.** 5 fo. multicoloured .. 1·00 1·00

**810.** Horse-drawn Bus and Underground Train.

**1982.** 150th Anniv. of Public Transport in Budapest.

3459. **810.** 2 fo. multicoloured .. 60 20

**811.** Budapest Polytechnic University.

**812.** Gyorgy Boloni.

**1982.** Bicentenary of University Engineering Education.

3460 **811** 2 fo. brown, stone & bl 30 10

**1982.** Birth Centenary of Gyorgy Boloni (journalist).

3461. **812.** 2 fo. yellow, brown and deep brown .. 30 10

**813.** Lenin.

**1982.** 65th Anniv. of Russian Revolution.

3462. **813.** 5 fo. multicoloured .. 70 10

**814.** Vuk and Bird.

**1982.** Vuk the Fox Cub (cartoon character). Multicoloured.

3463. 1 fo. Type **814** .. .. 20 10
3464. 1 fo. Two dogs .. .. 20 10
3465. 2 fo. Vuk and cock .. 40 10
3466. 2 fo. Vuk and owl .. 40 10
3467. 4 fo. Vuk and geese .. 75 10
3468. 6 fo. Vuk and frog .. 1·25 35
3469. 8 fo. Vuk, old fox and butterflies .. .. 1·60 60

**815.** St. Stephen (sculpture, Imre Varga).

**816.** Dog and Cat crossing road.

**1982.** Works of Art in Hungarian Chapel, Vatican. Multicoloured.

3470. 2 fo. Type **815** .. .. 35 40
3471. 2 fo. "Pope Silvester II making donation to St. Stephen" (37×18 mm.) 35 40
3472. 2 fo. "St. John of Capistrano ringing Angelus to commemorate Hungarian victory over Turks" (37×18 mm.) .. 35 40
3473. 2 fo. "Pope Paul VI showing Cardinal Lekai site of Hungarian Chapel" (37×18 mm.) .. .. 35 40
3474. 2 fo. "Pope John Paul II consecrating chapel" (37×18 mm.) .. .. 35 40
3475. 2 fo. "Madonna" (sculpture, Imre Varga) .. 35 40

Nos. 3470/5 were printed together, se-tenant, Nos. 3471/4 forming a composite design of a relief by Amerigo Tot.

**1982.** New Year.

3476. **816.** 2 fo. multicoloured .. 50 10

**819.** Raven and Envelope Address Marks.

**821.** Student at School Door.

**820.** " Ship of Peace " (Endre Szasz).

**1983.** 10th Anniv. of Postal Codes.

3479. **819.** 2 fo. blk., grey & red 30 10

**1983.** Budapest Spring Festival.

3480 **820** 2 fo. grey, gold & blk 30 10

**1983.** Youth Stamp Exhibition, Baja.

3481. **821.** 4 fo.+2 fo. mult. .. 85 85

**822.** Gyula Juhasz. **823.** Menner's Balloon, 1811.

**1983.** Birth Cent of Gyula Juhasz (writer).

3482 **822** 2 fo. dp brn, brn & blk 30 10

**1983.** Air. Bicent of Manned Flight. Mult.

3483 1 fo. Type **823** (1st manned flight in Hungary) .. .. 20 10
3484 1 fo. Captive observation balloon at Budapest Exhibition, 1896 20 10
3485 2 fo. Pursuit race, 1904 .. 50 25
3486 2 fo. Hot-air balloon "Pannonia", 1977 .. 50 25
3487 4 fo. Hot-air balloon "Malev", 1981 .. 90 50
3488 4 fo. Hungarian National Defence Union balloon, 1982 .. .. 90 50
3489 5 fo. Non-rigid airship over Mecsek television tower, 1981 .. .. 1·25 75

**824. Szentgotthard Monastery and Seal.**

**1983.** 800th Anniv. of Szentgotthard.

3491. **824.** 2 fo. multicoloured .. 30 10

**825. Watermill, Tapolca.**

**1983.** "Tembal 83" Thematic Stamps Exhibition, Basel.

3492. **825.** 5 fo. multicoloured .. 90 90

**827.** Jeno Hamburger. **828.** "Giovanna d'Aragona".

**1983.** Birth Centenary of Jeno Hamburger (doctor and revolutionary).

3494. **827.** 2 fo. brn., bl. and red 30 10

**1983.** 500th Birth Anniv of Raphael (artist). Multicoloured.

3495 1 fo. Type **828** .. .. 15 10
3496 1 fo. "Lady with Unicorn" .. .. 15 10
3497 2 fo. "Madonna of the Chair" .. .. 30 10
3498 2 fo. "Madonna of the Grand Duke" .. .. 30 10
3499 4 fo. "La Muta" .. 60 10
3500 6 fo. "Lady with a Veil" 1·00 30
3501 8 fo. "La Fornaria" .. 1·25 45

**829.** Vagi and Newspapers. **830.** Bolivar and Map of Americas.

**1983.** Birth Cent. of Istvan Vagi (secretary of Socialist Workers' Party).

3503. **829.** 2 fo. multicoloured .. 30 10

**1983.** Birth Bicent. of Simon Bolivar.

3504. **830.** 2 fo. multicoloured .. 30 10

**831.** Globe and Congress Emblem. **833.** Lesser Spotted Eagle.

**1983.** 68th Universal Esperanto Congress, Budapest.

3505. **831.** 2 fo. multicoloured .. 30 10

**1983.** Birds of Prey. Multicoloured.

3507. 1 fo. Type **833** .. .. 25 15
3508. 1 fo. Imperial eagle .. 25 15
3509. 2 fo. White-tailed sea eagle .. .. .. 50 20
3510. 2 fo. Red-footed falcon 50 20
3511. 4 fo. Saker falcon .. 80 45
3512. 6 fo. Rough-legged buzzard .. .. 1·50 65
3513. 8 fo. Common buzzard .. 1·75 1·00

**834.** Bee collecting Pollen. **835.** Old National Theatre (after R. Alt).

**1983.** 29th Apimondia (Bee Keeping) Congress, Budapest.

3514. **834.** 1 fo. multicoloured .. 25 10

**1983.** Stamp Day. Engravings of Budapest Buildings.

3515. **835.** 4 fo.+2 fo. yellow, brown and black .. 1·25 1·25
3516. – 4 fo.+2 fo. yellow, brown and black .. 1·25 1·25

DESIGN—HORIZ. No. 3516, Municipal concert hall, Pest (after H. Luders).

**836.** "Fruit-piece".

**1983.** Birth Centenary of Bela Czobel (artist).

3518. **836.** 2 fo. multicoloured .. 30 10

**837.** "Molnya" Satellite and Kekes T.V. Tower. **838.** Flags encircling Globe.

**1983.** World Communications Year. Mult.

3519. 1 fo. Type **837** .. .. 15 10
3520. 1 fo. Dish aerials and rockets .. .. 15 10
3521. 2 fo. Manual telephone exchange and modern "TMM-81" telephone 35 10
3522. 3 fo. Computer terminal 50 10
3523. 5 fo. Automatic letter-sorting equipment .. 85 15
3524. 8 fo. Teletext and newspaper mastheads .. 1·50 35

**1983.** 34th International Astronautical Federation Congress, Budapest.

3526. **838.** 2 fo. multicoloured .. 30 10

**839.** Kremlin, Moscow.

**1983.** "Sozphilex '83" Stamp Exhibition Moscow.

3527. **839.** 2 fo. multicoloured .. 35 35

**841.** Babits (after Jozsef Rippl-Ronai). **842.** "Madonna with Rose".

**1983.** Birth Cent. of Mihaly Babits (writer).

3529. **841.** 2 fo. multicoloured .. 30 10

**1983.** Christmas. Multicoloured.

3530. 1 fo. Type **842** .. .. 10 10
3531. 2 fo. Altar painting, Csikmenasag .. .. 20 10

**843.** Zanka. **844.** Ice Dancing.

**1983.** Hungarian Resorts. Multicoloured.

3532. 1 fo. Type **843** .. .. 30 10
3533. 2 fo. Hajduszoboszlo .. 30 10
3534. 5 fo. Heviz .. .. 40 10

**1983.** Winter Olympic Games, Sarajevo.

3535 **844** 1 fo. multicoloured .. 25 10
3536 – 1 fo. multicoloured .. 25 10
3537 – 2 fo. multicoloured (man lifting girl) .. 45 10
3538 – 2 fo. multicoloured .. 45 10
3539 – 4 fo. multicoloured (man with both arms bent) .. 75 15
3540 – 4 fo. multicoloured (man with one arm outstretched) .. 75 15
3541 – 6 fo. multicoloured .. 1·00 45

DESIGNS: Nos. 3536/41, Differenr ice dancing designs.

**846.** Csoma (statue) and Sepulchre, Darjeeling. **847.** "Energy" and Sun.

**1984.** Birth Bicentenary of Sandor Korosi Csoma (traveller and philologist).

3544. **846.** 2 fo. multicoloured .. 30 10

**1984.** Save Energy Campaign.

3545. **847.** 1 fo. red and black .. 10 10

**848.** Parent and Child. **850.** Hair Ornaments from Rakamaz.

**1984.** Youth Stamp.

3546. **848.** 4 fo.+2 fo. mult. .. 60 70

**1984.** Archaeological Funds.

3548. **850.** 1 fo. stone and brown 20 10
3549. – 1 fo. stone and brown 20 10
3550. – 2 fo. stone and brown 35 10
3551. – 2 fo. stone and brown 35 10
3552. – 4 fo. stone and brown 60 10
3553. – 6 fo. stone and brown 95 15
3554. – 8 fo. stone and brown 1·40 40

DESIGNS: No. 3549, Purse plates from Szolnok-Strazsahalom and Galgocz. 3550, Hair ornaments from Sarospatak. 3551, St. Stephen's sword (Prague) and Attila's sword (Aachen). 3552, Bowl from Ketpo. 3553, Stick handles from Hajdudorog and Szabadattyan. 3554, Saddle-bow from Izsak and bit and stirrups from Muszka.

**851.** Cracow and Emblem. **852.** "Epiphile dilecta".

**1984.** 25th Session of Permanent Committee of Posts and Telecommunications, Cracow, Poland.

3555 **851** 2 fo. multicoloured .. 30 10

**1984.** Butterflies. Multicoloured.

3556 1 fo. Type **852** .. .. 40 10
3557 1 fo. "Agrias sara" .. 40 10
3558 2 fo. Blue morpho ("Morpho cypris") .. 65 20
3559 2 fo. "Ancyluris formosissima" .. 65 20
3560 4 fo. African monarch .. 1·00 30
3561 6 fo. "Catagramma cynosura" .. .. 1·50 70
3562 8 fo. Paradise birdwing .. 1·90 85

No. 3557 is inscribed "Agra sara".

**853.** "Archer". **854.** Hevesi.

**1984.** Birth Centenary of Zsigmond Kisfaludy Strobl (sculptor).

3563. **853.** 2 fo. brown & yellow 30 10

**1984.** Birth Cent. of Akos Hevesi (activist in working-class movement).

3564. **854.** 2 fo. multicoloured .. 30 10

**855.** Doves around Map of Hungary. **856.** World Map and Airplane.

**1984.** Peace Festival, Pusztavacs.

3565. **855.** 2 fo. multicoloured .. 30 10

**1984.** World Aerobatics Championship, Bekescsaba.

3566. **856.** 2 fo. multicoloured .. 50 20

**857.** Four-in-hand. **858.** Conference Emblem.

**1984.** World Team-driving Championships, Szilvasvarad.

3567. **857.** 2 fo. multicoloured .. 50 15

**1984.** 14th Organization of Socialist Countries' Postal Administrations Conference, Budapest.

3568. **858.** 2 fo. multicoloured .. 30 10

**859.** Four-handled Vase.

**1984.** Stamp Day. Multicoloured.

3569. 1 fo. Type **859** .. .. 25 10
3570. 2 fo. Platter with flower decoration .. .. 40 20

**860.** "Music crowned by Fame" (fresco, Mor Than).

**1984.** Reopening of Budapest Opera House. Multicoloured.

3572. 1 fo. Type **860** .. .. 25 10
3573. 2 fo. Central staircase .. 50 20
3574. 5 fo. Auditorium .. 1·00 55

**861.** Atrium Hyatt Hotel.

**1984.** Budapest Hotels along the Danube. Multicoloured.

3576. 1 fo. Type **861** .. .. 20 10
3577. 2 fo. Duna Intercontinental .. .. 40 20
3578. 4 fo. Forum .. .. 60 30
3579. 4 fo. Thermal Hotel, Margaret Island .. 60 30
3580. 5 fo. Hilton .. .. 75 35
3581. 8 fo. Gellert .. .. 1·25 50

**862.** Cep ("Boletus edulis").

**863.** Kato Haman (Labour Movement leader).

**1984.** Edible Mushrooms. Multicoloured.

3583 1 fo. Type **862** .. .. 50 15
3584 1 fo. Scotch bonnet ("Marasmius oreades") 50 15
3585 2 fo. Common morel ("Morchella esculenta") 75 15
3586 2 fo. Field mushroom ("Agaricus campester") 75 15
3587 3 fo. Chanterelle ("Cantharellus cibarius") .. .. 90 25
3588 3 fo. Parasol mushroom ("Macrolepiota procera") .. .. 90 25
3589 4 fo. Boot-lace fungus .. 1·25 60

**1984.** Birth Centenaries.

3590. **863.** 2 fo. brown, gold and black .. .. 30 10
3591. – 2 fo. brown, gold and black .. .. 30 10

DESIGN: No. 3591, Bela Balazs (writer).

**864.** "Virgin and Child" (small altar, Trencseny).

**865.** Torah Crown (Buda).

**1984.** Christmas

3592. **864.** 1 fo. multicoloured .. 20 10

**1984.** Reopening of Jewish Museum, Budapest. Multicoloured.

3593. 1 fo. Type **865** .. .. 25 10
3594. 1 fo. Chalice (Moscow) .. 25 10
3595. 2 fo. Torah shield (Vienna) .. .. 40 10
3596. 2 fo. Elias chalice (Warsaw) .. .. 40 10
3597. 4 fo. Esrog holder (Augsburg) .. .. 70 10
3598. 6 fo. Candle holder (Warsaw) .. .. 95 20
3599. 8 fo. Urn (Pest) .. .. 1·25 45

**866.** Barn Owl.

**868.** Novi Sad Bridge, Yugoslavia.

**1984.** Owls. Multicoloured.

3600. 1 fo. Type **866** .. .. 65 20
3601. 1 fo. Little owl .. .. 65 20
3602. 2 fo. Tawny owl .. .. 1·10 20
3603. 2 fo. Long-eared owl .. 1·10 20
3604. 4 fo. Snowy owl .. .. 1·75 45
3605. 6 fo. Ural owl .. .. 2·25 75
3606. 8 fo. Eagle owl .. .. 2·50 1·00

**1985.** Danube Bridges. Multicoloured.

3608. 1 fo. Type **868** .. .. 20 10
3609. 1 fo. Baja, Hungary .. 20 10
3610. 2 fo. Arpad bridge, Budapest .. .. 40 15
3611. 2 fo. Bratislava, Czechoslovakia .. 40 15
3612. 4 fo. Reichsbrucke bridge, Vienna .. 70 30
3613. 6 fo. Linz, Austria .. 95 50
3614. 8 fo. Regensburg, West Germany .. .. 1·25 70

**869.** Laszlo Rudas.

**870.** Woman and Flowers.

**1985.** Birth Centenary of Laszlo Rudas (philosopher and socialist).

3616. **869.** 2 fo. brown, gold and black .. .. 30 10

**1985.** International Women's Day.

3617. **870.** 2 fo. multicoloured .. 30 10

**871.** 1925 200 k. Skiing Stamp.

**873.** "Little Red Riding Hood".

**1985.** "Olymphilex '85" International Olympic Stamps Exhibition, Lausanne.

3618. **871.** 4 fo. green, gold and blue .. .. 40 15
3619. – 5 fo. blue, brown and gold .. .. 50 15

DESIGN: 5 fo. 1925 300 k. Skating stamp.

**1985.** Birth Centenary of Jacob Grimm (folklorist).

3621. **873.** 4 fo. + 2 fo. mult. .. 1·25 85

**874.** Gyorgy Lukacs.

**875.** Title Page.

**1985.** Birth Centenary of Gyorgy Lukacs (philosopher).

3622. **874.** 2 fo. multicoloured .. 30 10

**1985.** 300th Anniv. of Totfalusi Bible.

3623. **875.** 2 fo. black and gold 30 10

**876.** Peter Pazmany (founder).

**877.** Boxing.

**1985.** 350th Anniv. of Lorand Eotvos University.

3624. **876.** 2 fo. grey and red .. 30 30

**1985.** 26th European Boxing Championships, Budapest.

3625. **877.** 2 fo. multicoloured .. 30 10

**878.** Women Footballers.

**1985.** International Youth Year. Mult.

3626. 1 fo. Type **878** .. .. 20 10
3627. 2 fo. Windsurfing .. 40 10
3628. 2 fo. Women exercising 40 10
3629. 4 fo. Karate .. .. 70 10
3630. 4 fo. Go-karting .. .. 70 10
3631. 5 fo. Hang gliding .. 1·00 35
3632. 6 fo. Skate-boarding .. 95 40

**879.** High Speed Railway.

**1985.** "Expo '85" World's Fair, Tsukuba. Multicoloured.

3633. 2 fo. Type **879** .. .. 50 20
3634. 4 fo. Fuyo Theatre .. 55 20

**880.** Common Flicker.

**1985.** Birth Bicentenary of John J. Audubon (ornithologist). Multicoloured.

3635. 2 fo. Type **880** (postage) 50 20
3636. 2 fo. Bohemian waxwing 50 20
3637. 2 fo. Pileated woodpecker .. .. .. 50 20
3638. 4 fo. Northern oriole .. 95 35
3639. 4 fo. Common flicker (air) 95 35
3640. 6 fo. Common cardinal .. 1·60 65

**881.** Nonius XXXVI.

**1985.** Bicentenary of Horsebreeding at Mezohegyes. Multicoloured.

3641 1 fo. Type **881** .. .. 30 10
3642 2 fo. Furioso XXIII .. 50 10
3643 4 fo. Gidran I .. .. 90 15
3644 4 fo. Ramses III .. 90 15
3645 6 fo. Krozus I .. .. 1·40 40

**882.** Hand pointing to Cracked Earth (Imre Varga).

**883.** Handel, Kettledrum and Horn.

**1985.** Fifth Congress of International Association of Physicians against Nuclear War, Budapest.

3646. **882.** 2 fo. multicoloured .. 30 10

**1985.** Music Year. Multicoloured.

3647 1 fo. Type **883** (300th birth anniv) .. .. 30 10
3648 2 fo. Bach and Thomas Church organ, Leipzig (300th birth anniv) .. 55 10
3649 4 fo. Luigi Cherubini, harp, bass violin and baryton (225th anniv) 90 10
3650 4 fo. Chopin and piano (175th birth anniv) .. 90 10
3651 5 fo. Mahler, viola, double horn and kettledrum (125th birth anniv) .. 1·25 25
3652 6 fo. Ferenc Erkel, viola and bass tuba (175th birth anniv) .. .. 1·40 45

**886.** Key with Globe as Head.

**887.** Flags on Computer Keyboards.

**1985.** World Tourism Day.

3655. **886.** 2 fo. multicoloured .. 30 10

**1985.** "COMNET '85" Computer Networks Conference, Budapest.

3656. **887.** 4 fo. multicoloured .. 30 10

**889.** Water Holder.

**890.** Italian 1960 5 l. Stamp.

**1985.** Stamp Day. Haban Ceramics. Mult.

3658. 1 fo. Type **889** .. .. 15 10
3659. 2 fo. Tankard with cover 40 30

**1985.** "Italia '85" International Stamp Exhibition, Rome.

3661. **890.** 5 fo. multicoloured .. 90 90

**891.** Dove and U.N. Emblem.

**892.** Red Lily.

**1985.** 40th Anniv. of United Nations Organization.

3662. **891.** 4 fo. turquoise, blue and deep blue .. 35 10

**1985.** Lily Family. Multicoloured.

3663. 1 fo. Type **892** .. .. 25 10
3664. 2 fo. Turk's-cap lily .. 35 10
3665. 2 fo. Dog's tooth violet 35 10
3666. 4 fo. Tiger lily .. .. 65 10
3667. 4 fo. Snake's-head fritillary .. .. 65 10
3668. 5 fo. Day lily .. .. 85 30
3669. 6 fo. "Bulbocodium vernum" .. .. 1·10 40

**893.** Carol Singers.

**1985.** Christmas.
3670. **893.** 2 fo. multicoloured . . 30 10

**894.** Istvan Ries.

**895.** Three Houses under One Roof.

**1985.** Birth Centenary of Istvan Ries (Minister of Justice).
3671. **894.** 2 fo. multicoloured . . 30 10

**1985.** SOS Childrens' Village.
3672. **895.** 4 fo. + 2 fo. mult. . . 80 80

**896.** Fantic "Sprinter", 1984.

**1985.** Centenary of Motor Cycle.
3673. **896.** 1 fo. blk., orge. & bl. 25 10
3674. – 2 fo. blk., yell. & bl. 40 10
3675. – 2 fo. blk., grn. & grey 40 10
3676. – 4 fo. multicoloured . . 65 10
3677. – 4 fo. blk., grn. & grey 65 10
3678. – 5 fo. multicoloured . . 90 20
3679. – 6 fo. multicoloured . . 1·10 45

DESIGNS: No. 3674, Harley-Davidson "Duo-Glide", 1960. 3675, Suzuki "Katana GSX", 1983. 3676, BMW "R47", 1927. 3677, Rudge-Whitworth, 1935. 3678, NSU, 1910. 3679, Daimler, 1885.

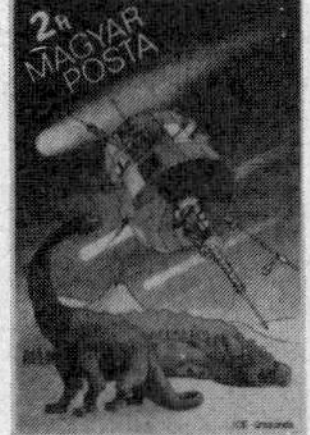

**897.** "Ice" Satellite and Dinosaurs.

**898.** Bela Kun.

**1986.** Air. Appearance of Halley's Comet. Multicoloured.
3680. 2 fo. Type **897** . . . . 45 10
3681. 2 fo. "Vega" satellite and detail of Bayeux Tapestry showing comet . . . . . . 45 10
3682. 2 fo. "Suisei" satellite and German engraving of 1507 . . . . . . 45 10
3683. 4 fo. "Giotto" satellite and "The Magi" (tapestry after Giotto) 75 10
3684. 4 fo. "Astron" satellite and Virgo, Leo, Corvus, Crater and Hydra constellations 75 10
3685. 6 fo. Space shuttle and Edmond Halley (wrongly inscr. "Edmund") . . . . 1·25 40

**1986.** Birth Centenary of Bela Kun. (Communist Party leader).
3686. **898.** 4 fo. multicoloured . . 35 10

**HAVE YOU READ THE NOTES AT THE BEGINNING OF THIS CATALOGUE?**
These often provide answers to the enquiries we receive.

**900.** Guide Dog.

**901.** Running for Ball.

**1986.** The Blind.
3688. **900.** 4 fo. multicoloured . . 75 10

**1986.** World Cup Football Championship, Mexico. Multicoloured.
3689. 2 fo. Type **901** . . . . 45 10
3690. 2 fo. Heading ball . . 45 10
3691. 4 fo. Tackling . . . . 1·00 10
3692. 4 fo. Goalkeeper diving for ball . . . . 1·00 10
3693. 4 fo. Goalkeeper catching ball . . . . . . 1·00 10
3694. 6 fo. Tackling (different) 1·40 45

**902.** Cable Railway.

**904.** Japanese and Hungarian Dolls.

**1986.** Re-opening of Buda Castle Cable Railway.
3696. **902.** 2 fo. brown, yellow and orange . . 50 25

**1986.** Hungarian Days in Tokyo.
3698. **904.** 4 fo. multicoloured . . 75 10

**905.** Fay.

**906.** Flag and "40".

**1986.** Birth Bicentenary of Andras Fay (writer, politician and founder of First Hungarian Savings Bank Union).
3699. **905.** 4 fo. brown and pale brown . . . . 60 20

**1986.** Youth Stamp. 40th Anniv. of Young Pioneers Movement.
3700. **906.** 4 fo. + 2 fo. mult. . . 1·00 1·00

**907.** Ferrari Racing Cars, 1961 and 1985.

**1986.** Centenary of Motor Car. Multicoloured.
3701. 2 fo. Type **907** . . . . 50 10
3702. 2 fo. Alfa Romeo racing cars, 1932 and 1984 . . 50 10
3703. 2 fo. Volkswagen "Beetle", 1936, and Porsche "959", 1986 . . 50 10
3704. 4 fo. Renault "14 CV", 1902, and "5 GT Turbo", 1985 . . . . 1·00 15
3705. 4 fo. Fiat "3 1/2", 1899, and "Ritmo", 1985 . . 1·00 15
3706. 6 fo. Daimler, 1886, and Mercedes-Benz "230 SE", 1986 . . . . 1·50 50

**908.** "Wasa" (Swedish ship of the line), 1628.

**1986.** "Stockholmia '86" International Stamp Exhibition.
3707. **908.** 2 fo. multicoloured . . 2·00 1·50

**909.** Moritz Kaposi (cancer specialist).

**911.** "Tranquillity".

**910.** "Recapture of Buda Castle" (Gyula Benczur). (Illustration half-size)

**1986.** 14th International Cancer Congress, Budapest.
3708. **909.** 4 fo. multicoloured . . 75 10

**1986.** 300th Anniv. of Recapture of Buda from Turks.
3709. **910.** 4 fo. multicoloured . . 60 10

**1986.** Stamp Day. Multicoloured.
3710. 2 fo. Type **911** . . . . 40 30
3711. 2 fo. "Confidence" . . 40 30

**912.** Fragment of 15th-cent. Carpet from Anatolia.

**1986.** 5th International Oriental Carpets and Tapestry Conference, Vienna and Budapest.
3713. **912.** 4 fo. multicoloured . . 60 10

**914.** Piano and Liszt.

**915.** Dove.

**1986.** 175th Birth Anniv. of Franz Liszt (pianist and composer).
3715. **914.** 4 fo. deep green and green . . . . 75 15

**1986.** International Peace Year.
3716. **915.** 4 fo. multicoloured . . 50 35

**917.** Pogany.

**918.** Munnich.

**1986.** Birth Centenary of Jozsef Pogany (writer and journalist).
3718. **917.** 4 fo. multicoloured . . 50 10

**1986.** Birth Centenary of Ferenc Munnich (former Prime Minister).
3719. **918.** 4 fo. multicoloured . . 50 10

**919.** Heads.

**1986.** 12th General Assembly of World Federation of Democratic Youth, Budapest.
3720. **919.** 4 fo. multicoloured . . 50 10

**920.** Apricots ("Kajszi" C.235).

**1986.** Fruits. Multicoloured.
3721. 2 fo. Type **920** . . . . 50 10
3722. 2 fo. Cherries ("Good bearer of Erd") . . 50 10
3723. 4 fo. Apples ("Jonathan" M.14) . . . . . . 1·00 15
3724. 4 fo. Raspberries ("Nagymaros") . . 1·00 15
3725. 4 fo. Peaches ("Piroska") 1·00 15
3726. 6 fo. Grapes ("Zalagyongye") . . 1·25 40

**921.** Forgach Castle, Szecseny.

**922.** Wild Cat.

**1986.** Castles. Inscr "MAGYAR POSTA".
3727 **921** 2 fo. bistre and yellow 15 10
3728 – 3 fo. green & lt green 15 10
3729 – 4 fo. blue & light blue 20 10
3730 – 5 fo. red and pink . . 25 10
3731 – 6 fo. brown & orange 30 10
3732 – 8 fo. red and orange 35 10
3733 – 10 fo. brown & ochre 35 10
3734 – 20 fo. green & yellow 65 10
3735 – 30 fo. lt green & green 85 10
3736 – 40 fo. blue & lt blue 90 10
3737 – 50 fo. deep red & red 1·10 10
3738 – 70 fo. dp grey & grey 1·50 15
3739 – 100 fo. violet and lilac 2·50 75

DESIGNS: 3 fo. Savoya Castle, Rackeve. 4 fo. Batthyany Castle, Kormend. 5 fo. Szechenyi Castle, Nagycenk. 6 fo. Rudnyanszky Castle, Nagyteteny. 8 fo. Szapary Castle, Buk. 10 fo. Festetics Castle, Keszthely. 20 fo. Brunswick Castle, Martonvasar. 30 fo. De La Motte Castle, Noszvaj. 40 fo. L'Huillier-Coburg Castle, Edeleny. 50 fo. Teleki-Degenfeld Castle, Szirak. 70 fo. Magochy Castle, Pacin. 100 fo. Esterhazy Castle, Fertod.

See also Nos. 3888 and 4045/9.

**1986.** Protected Animals. Multicoloured.
3740. 2 fo. Type **922** . . . . 50 10
3741. 2 fo. European otter . . 50 10
3742. 2 fo. Stoat . . . . 50 10
3743. 4 fo. Eurasian red squirrel . . . . 1·00 15
3744. 4 fo. East European hedgehog . . . . 1·00 15
3745. 6 fo. European pond turtle . . . . 1·50 40

**923.** St. Stephen I (coronation cloak, 1030).

**924.** Death Cap ("Amanita phalloides").

**1986.** Kings (1st series).

3746. **923.** 2 fo. brn., bl. & red 40 10
3747. – 2 fo. brn., grey & red 40 10
3748. – 4 fo. brn., grn. & red 75 10
3749. – 4 fo. brn., grey & red 75 10
3750. – 6 fo. brn., bl. & red 1·25 35

DESIGNS: No. 3747, Geza I (enamel portrait on Hungarian crown, 1070); 3748, St. Ladislas I (Gyor Cathedral, 1400); 3749, Bela III (Kalocsa Cathedral statue, 1200); 3750, Bela IV (Jak church statue, 1230).

See also Nos. 3835/7.

**1986.** Fungi. Multicoloured.

3751 2 fo. Type **924** .. .. 70 25
3752 2 fo. Fly agaric ("Amanita muscaria") 70 25
3753 2 fo. Red-staining inocybe ("Inocybe patouillardi") .. .. 70 25
3754 4 fo. Olive-wood pleurotus ("Omphalotus olearius") .. .. 1·50 60
3755 4 fo. Panther cap ("Amanita pantherina") .. .. 1·50 60
3756 6 fo. Beefsteak morel .. 2·10 1·00

**925.** "Colisa fasciata".

**926.** "Sitting Woman".

**1987.** Fishes. Multicoloured.

3757. 2 fo. Type **925** .. .. 50 10
3758. 2 fo. "Iriatherina werneri" .. .. 50 10
3759. 2 fo. "Pseudotropheus zebra" .. .. 50 10
3760. 4 fo. "Papiliochromis ramirezi" .. .. 1·00 15
3761. 4 fo. "Aphyosemion multicolor" .. .. 1·00 15
3762. 6 fo. "Hyphessobrycon erythrostigma" .. 1·50 40

**1987.** Birth Centenary of Bela Uitz (painter).

3763 **926** 4 fo. multicoloured .. 50 10

**927.** Abstract.

**928.** Flag, Books, Torch and Dove.

**1987.** Birth Centenary of Lajos Kassak (writer and painter).

3764. **927.** 4 fo. black and red .. 50 10

**1987.** 30th Anniv. of Young Communist League.

3765. **928.** 4 fo. + 2 fo. mult. .. 75 85

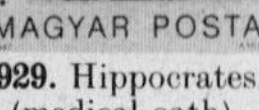


**929.** Hippocrates (medical oath).

**930.** Food Jar, Hodmezovasarhely.

**1987.** Pioneers of Medicine (1st series).

3766. **929.** 2 fo. brown & blue .. 50 10
3767. – 4 fo. green and black 1·00 10
3768. – 4 fo. blue and black 1·00 10
3769. – 4 fo. brown & black 1·00 10
3770. – 6 fo. brown & black 1·50 35

DESIGNS: No. 3767, Avicenna ("Kanun" book of medical rules). 3768, Ambroise Pare (improved treatment of wounds). 3769, William Harvey (circulation of blood). 3770, Ignac Semmelweis (aseptic treatment of wounds).

See also Nos. 3939/43.

**1987.** Neolithic and Copper Age Art. Multicoloured.

3771. **930.** 2 fo. brown & green 60 10
3772. – 4 fo. brown and flesh 1·00 10
3773. – 4 fo. brown and pink 1·00 10
3774. – 5 fo. brown & green 1·40 25

DESIGNS: No. 3772, Altar, Szeged. 3773, Statue with sickle, Szegvar-Tuzkoves. 3774, Vase with face, Center.

**932.** Old and Modern Ambulances.

**1987.** Centenary of Hungarian First Aid Association.

3776. **932.** 4 fo. multicoloured .. 65 10

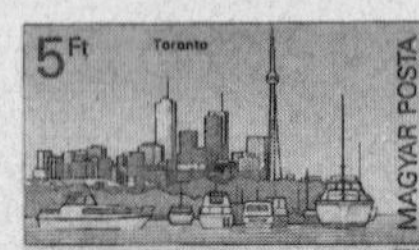


**933.** Toronto ("Capex '87").

**1987.** International Stamp Exhibitions. Multicoloured.

3777. 5 fo. Type **933** .. .. 1·25 1·00
3778. 5 fo. "Olymphilex 87" building, Rome .. 75 60
3779. 5 fo. "Hafnia 87" building, Copenhagen 75 60

**934.** Jozsef Marek.

**1987.** Bicentenary of University of Veterinary Sciences, Budapest.

3780 **934** 4 fo. sliver, blue & blk 50 10

**935.** Teleki, Route Map and Porters.

**1987.** Centenary of Samuel Teleki's African Expedition.

3781. **935.** 4 fo. multicoloured .. 50 10

**936.** Printing Shop (17th-century wood-print, Abraham von Werdt).

**937.** James Cook and H.M.S. "Resolution".

**1987.** 125th Anniv of Hungarian Printing, Paper and Press Workers' Union.

3782 **936** 4 fo. brown and stone 50 10

**1987.** Antarctic Exploration. Multicoloured.

3783 2 fo. Type **937** .. .. 90 30
3784 2 fo. Fabian von Bellingshausen and seals 60 20
3785 2 fo. Ernest Shackleton and emperor penguins 90 20
3786 4 fo. Roald Amundsen and huskies .. .. 1·10 45
3787 4 fo. Robert F. Scott and "Terra Nova" .. 1·10 45
3788 6 fo. Richard Byrd and Ford Trimotor "Floyd Bennett" .. .. 1·75 70

**938.** Old and New Railways Emblems and Institute.

**939.** Flowers and Dolphin.

**1987.** Centenary of Railway Officers Training Institute.

3790. **938.** 4 fo. black and blue 50 25

**1987.** Stamp Day. Carvings from Buda Castle.

3791 **939** 2 fo. indigo, blue and azure .. .. 30 10
3792 – 4 fo. olive, green and turquoise .. .. 60 40

DESIGN: 4 fo. King Matthias's arms.

**940.** Jesse Altar.

**941.** "Orchis purpurea".

**1987.** Gyongyospata Church.

3794. **940.** 4 fo. multicoloured .. 75 85

**1987.** Orchids. Multicoloured.

3795. 2 fo. Type **941** .. .. 50 10
3796. 2 fo. "Cypripedium calceolus" .. .. 50 10
3797. 4 fo. "Ophrys scolopax" 90 10
3798. 4 fo. "Himantoglossum hircinum" .. .. 90 10
3799. 5 fo. "Cephalanthera rubra" .. .. 1·25 20
3800. 6 fo. "Epipactis atrorubens" .. 1·50 40

**942.** Speed Skating.

**945.** "The White Crane" (Japanese folk tale).

**1987.** Winter Olympic Games, Calgary. Multicoloured.

3802 2 fo. Type **942** .. .. 40 10
3803 2 fo. Cross-country skiing 40 10
3804 4 fo. Biathlon .. .. 80 10
3805 4 fo. Ice hockey .. .. 80 10
3806 4 fo. Four-man bobsleigh 80 10
3807 6 fo. Ski jumping .. 1·25 30

**1987.** Fairy Tales. Multicoloured.

3816. 2 fo. Type **945** .. .. 45 10
3817. 2 fo. "The Fox and the Raven" (Aesop) .. 45 10
3818. 4 fo. "The Hare and The Tortoise" (Aesop) .. 90 20
3819. 4 fo. "The Ugly Duckling" (Hans Christian Andersen) .. 90 20
3820. 6 fo. "The Brave Little Lead Soldier" (Hans Christian Andersen) .. 1·40 40

**946.** Zeppelin and Airship LZ-2.

**1988.** 150th Birth Anniv. of Ferdinand von Zeppelin (airship pioneer).

3821. **946.** 2 fo. black and blue 50 20
3822. – 4 fo. dp. brn. & brn. 90 50
3823. – 4 fo. purple and lilac 90 50
3824. – 8 fo. olive and green 1·60 80

DESIGNS: No. 3822, LZ-4. 3823, "Schwaben". 3824, "Graf Zeppelin".

**947.** Skater. **949.** Monus.

**1988.** World Figure Skating Championships, Budapest. Skaters from 19th-century to date. Multicoloured.

3825. 2 fo. Type **947** .. .. 40 10
3826. 2 fo. Man wearing hat .. 40 10
3827. 4 fo. Woman .. .. 80 10
3828. 4 fo. Man in hat and coat 80 10
3829. 5 fo. Woman in modern skating dress .. .. 1·00 10
3830. 6 fo. Pair .. .. .. 1·25 35

**1988.** Birth Centenary of Illes Monus (newspaper editor).

3833. **949.** 4 fo. bl., red & blk. 40 10

**1988.** Kings (2nd series). As T **923**.

3835. 2 fo. brown, grn. & red .. 30 10
3836. 4 fo. brown, blue and red 55 10
3837. 6 fo. brown, vio. & red .. 90 10

DESIGNS: 2 fo. Karoly I (Charles Robert) (detail of decorated initial from "Illuminated Chronicle", 1358). 4 fo. Lajos the Great (relief, St. Simeon's reliquary, Zara, 1380). 6 fo. Zsigmond (Sigismund of Luxembourg) (after great seal, 1433).

**951.** Rowing.

**952.** Computer Drawing of Head.

**1988.** Olympic Games, Seoul. Multicoloured.

3838. 2 fo. Type **951** .. .. 30 10
3839. 4 fo. Hurdling .. .. 50 10
3840. 4 fo. Fencing .. .. 50 10
3841. 6 fo. Boxing .. .. 80 30

**1988.** 6th Anniv. of "Dilemma" (first computer-animated film).

3843. **952.** 4 fo. multicoloured .. 50 10

**953.** Card and Emblem.

**1988.** Eurocheque Congress, Budapest.

3844 **953** 4 fo. multicoloured .. 50 10

**954.** "Santa Maria", 1492.

**955.** Damaged Head.

**1988.** Ships. Multicoloured.

3845 2 fo. Type **954** .. .. 60 40
3846 2 fo. "Mayflower", 1620 .. 60 40
3847 2 fo. "Sovereign of the Seas", 1637 .. .. 60 40
3848 4 fo. "Jylland" (steam warship), 1860 .. 1·25 55
3849 6 fo. "St. Jupat" (yacht), 1985 .. .. .. 1·90 75

**1988.** Anti-Drugs Campaign.

3850. **955.** 4 fo. multicoloured .. 50 10

**956.** Green-winged Teal ("Anas crecca").

**957.** Train.

**1988.** Wild Ducks. Multicoloured.

3851 2 fo. Type **956** .. .. 75 40
3852 2 fo. Goldeneye ("Bucephula clangula") 75 40
3853 4 fo. European wigeon ("Anas penelope") .. 1·40 60
3854 4 fo. Red-crested pochard ("Netta rufina") .. 1·40 60
3855 6 fo. Gadwell .. .. 1·75 80

**1988.** Exhibits in Toy Museum, Kecskemet. Multicoloured.

3857. 2 fo. Type **957** .. .. 55 30
3858. 2 fo. See-saw .. .. 35 10
3859. 4 fo.+2 fo. Pecking chicks .. .. .. 1·00 20
3860. 5 fo. Johnny Hussar .. 85 15

**958.** Facade.

**959.** Congress Emblem.

**1988.** 450th Anniv. of Debrecen Calvinist College.

3861. **958.** 4 fo. multicoloured .. 50 10

**1988.** 58th American Society of Travel Agents Congress, Budapest.

3862. **959.** 4 fo. multicoloured .. 50 10

**960.** Lloyd C.II Biplane.

**961.** Post Official's Collar and Badge.

**1988.** Air. Hungarian Biplanes.

3863 **960** 1 fo. green .. .. 15 10
3864 – 2 fo. purple .. .. 35 10
3865 – 4 fo. bistre .. .. 60 25
3866 – 10 fo. blue .. .. 1·50 75
3867 – 12 fo. red .. .. 1·90 75

DESIGNS: 2 fo. Hansa Brandenburg C-1. 4 fo. UFAG C-1. 10 fo. Gerte 13 scout plane. 12 fo. WM 13 trainer.

**1988.** Centenary of Post Office Training School.

3868. **961.** 4 fo. red, bl. & brn. 50 10

**962.** Baross and Postal Savings Bank, Budapest.

**1988.** Stamp Day. 140th Birth Anniv. of Gabor Baross (politician). Multicoloured.

3869. 2 fo. Type **962** .. .. 40 40
3870. 4 fo. Baross with telephone and telegraph equipment .. .. 75 75

**963** Lengyel

**964** Christmas Tree

**1988.** Birth Centenary of Gyula Lengyel (labour movement activist).

3872 **963** 4 fo. multicoloured .. 50 10

**1988.** Christmas.

3873 **964** 2 fo. multicoloured .. 35 10

**965** Richard Adolf Zsigmondy (chemistry, 1925)

**966** Szakasits

**1988.** Noble Prize Winners.

3874 **965** 2 fo. dp brown & brn 35 10
3875 – 2 fo. dp green & green 35 10
3876 – 2 fo. dp brown & brn 35 10
3877 – 4 fo. dp mauve & mve 70 10
3878 – 4 fo. green and grey 70 10
3879 – 6 fo. brown & lt brn 1·10 20

DESIGNS: No. 3875, Robert Barany (medicine, 1914.); 3876, Gyorgy Hevesy (chemistry, 1943); 3877, Albert Szent-Gyorgyi (chemistry, 1937); 3878, Gyorgy Bekesy (medicine, 1961); 3879, Denes Gabor (physics, 1971).

**1988.** Birth Centenary of Arpad Szakasits (President, 1948–50).

3880 **966** 4 fo. multicoloured .. 50 10

**968** Silver Teapot from Pest, 1846

**1988.** Metal Work.

3882 **968** 2 fo. blue and brown 40 10
3883 – 2 fo. dp brown & brn 40 10
3884 – 4 fo. lilac and brown 80 15
3885 – 5 fo. green and brown 1·00 20

DESIGNS: No. 3883, 18th-century silver pot, Buda; 3884, Silver sugar basin from Pest, 1822; 3885, Pierced cast iron plate from Resicabanya, 1850.

**969** Emblem

**970** Wallisch

**1989.** Foundation of Post and Savings Bank Company.

3886 **969** 5 fo. blue, silver & blk 50 10

**1989.** Birth Centenary of Kalman Wallisch (workers' movement activist).

3887 **970** 3 fo. blue and red .. 35 10

**971** Festetics Castle, Keszthely

**1989.**

3888 **971** 10 fo. brown & bistre 60 10

**972** Athletes

**974** Gyetvai

**1989.** 2nd International Indoor Athletics Championships, Budapest.

3889 **972** 3 fo. multicoloured .. 35 10

**1989.** Birth Centenary of Janos Gyetvai (journalist).

3891 **974** 3 fo. green and red .. 35 10

**975** "Sky-high Tree" (detail, carpet)

**1989.** 27th National Youth Stamp Exhibition, Veszprem.

3892 **975** 5 fo.+2 fo. mult .. 1·10 1·10

**976** O Bajan

**1989.** Bicent of Babolina Stud Farm. Mult.

3893 3 fo. Type **976** .. .. 50 50
3894 3 fo. Stud officer .. 50 50
3895 3 fo. Gazal II .. .. 50 50

**977** Disabled People and "ART '89"

**978** Arrangement of Narcissi, Crocuses and Violets

**1989.** "Art '89" International Festival of Disabled People and their Artist Friends.

3896 **977** 5 fo. multicoloured .. 50 10

**1989.** Flower Arrangements. Multicoloured.

3897 2 fo. Type **978** .. .. 30 10
3898 3 fo. Irises, tulips and lilies (horiz) .. .. 45 10
3899 3 fo. Roses and chrysanthemums .. .. 45 10
3900 5 fo. Dahlias and lilies (horiz) .. .. 75 15
3901 10 fo. Roses, Chinese lanterns and holly .. 1·40 30

**979** Birds

**1989.** Bicentenary of French Revolution.

3902 **979** 5 fo. black, red & blue 50 10

**980** Model of Veszto Church

**981** Photographer with Camera

**1989.** Veszto Church Excavation.

3904 **980** 3 fo. multicoloured .. 35 10

**1989.** 150th Anniv of Photography.

3905 **981** 5 fo. lt brn, blk & brn 50 10

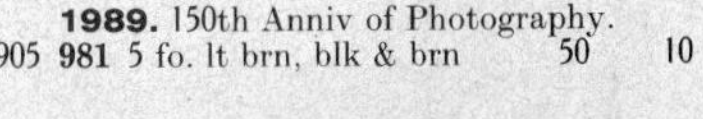

**982** Turistvandi Water-mill

**1989.** Mills. Multicoloured.

3906 2 fo. Type **982** .. .. 25 10
3907 3 fo. Szarvas horse-driven mill .. .. .. 40 10
3908 5 fo. Kiskunhalas windmill .. .. .. 65 15
3909 10 fo. Shipmill, River Drava .. .. .. 1·25 25

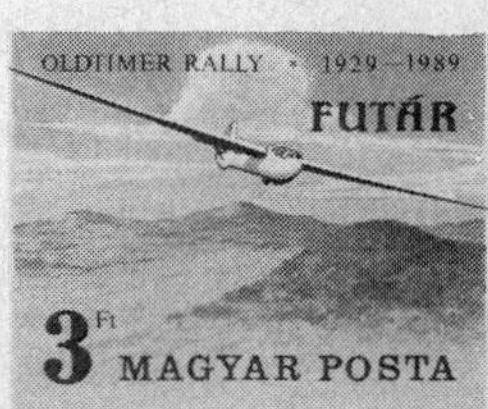


**984** Messenger Glider

**1989.** "Old Timer" Rally, Budakeszi Airport, and 60th Anniv of Gliding in Hungary. Multicoloured.

3911 3 fo. Type **984** .. .. 65 35
3912 5 fo. Pal glider .. .. 1·10 50

**985** Sand Lizard

**1989.** Endangered Reptiles. Multicoloured.

3913 2 fo. Type **985** .. .. 25 10
3914 3 fo. Green lizard .. 40 10
3915 5 fo. Grass snake ("Natrix natrix") .. 65 15
3916 5 fo. Orsinis's viper ("Vipera rakosiensis") 65 15
3917 10 fo. European pond terrapin .. .. 1·40 25

**986** Competitors

**1989.** 31st World Modern Pentathlon Championships, Budapest.

3918 **986** 5 fo. multicoloured .. 50 10

**1989.** Nos. 3851 and 3853 surch.

3919 3 fo. on 2 fo. mult .. 55 30
3920 5 fo. on 4 fo. mult .. 85 50

**988** Baradla Cave, Aggtelek

**989** Carriage

**1989.** 10th World Speleology Congress, Budapest. Multicoloured.

3921 3 fo. Type **988** .. 30 10
3922 5 fo. Szemlohegy cave, Budapest .. .. 50 10
3923 10 fo. Anna Cave, Lillafured .. .. 1·10 20
3924 12 fo. Tapolca cave lake, Miskolctapolca .. 1·25 25

**1989.** World Two-in-Hand Carriage Driving Championship, Balatonfenyves.

3925 **989** 5 fo. multicoloured .. 50 10

**990** Zsuzsa Kossuth (War of Independence nurse)

**993** Flowers and Broken Barbed Wire

**1989.** Stamp Day. 125th Anniv of Red Cross Movement.

3926 **990** 5 fo. black, blue & red 50 50
3927 – 10 fo. multicoloured 1·10 1·10

DESIGN: 10 fo. Florence Nightingale (nursing pioneer) and decoration.

**1989.** Dismantling of Electrified Fence on Western Border.

3931 **993** 5 fo. multicoloured .. 50 10

**994** "Conquest of Hungary" (Mor Than)

**1989.** 1100th Anniv of Arpad as Prince of the Magyars.

3932 **994** 5 fo. multicoloured .. 50 10

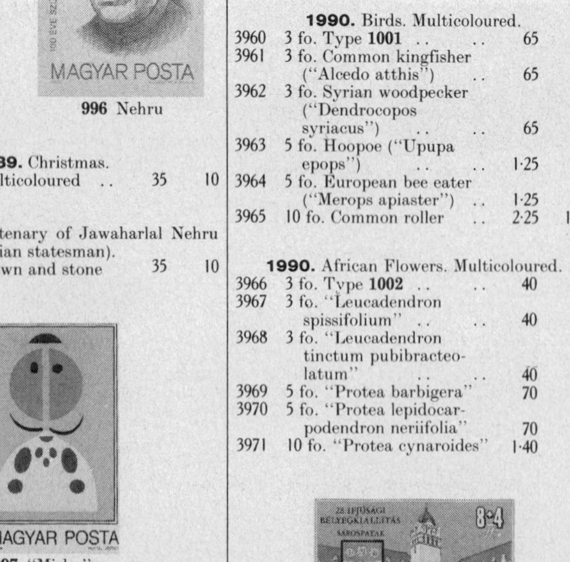

**995** Flight into Egypt

**996** Nehru

**1989.** Christmas.

3933 **995** 3 fo. multicoloured .. 35 10

**1989.** Birth Centenary of Jawaharlal Nehru (Indian statesman).

3934 **996** 3 fo. brown and stone 35 10

**997** "Miska" (Dezso Korniss)

**1990.** Modern Hungarian Paintings. Mult.

3935 3 fo. Type **997** .. .. 40 10
3936 5 fo. "Sunrise" (Lajos Kassak) .. .. 65 10
3937 10 fo. "Grotesque Burial" (Endre Balint) .. 1·40 20
3938 12 fo. "Remembered Toys" (Tihamer Gyarmathy) .. .. 1·60 25

**1989.** Pioneers of Medicine (2nd series). As T **929**.

3939 3 fo. green .. .. 40 10
3940 3 fo. brown .. .. 40 10
3941 4 fo. black .. .. 55 10
3942 6 fo. grey .. .. 80 15
3943 10 fo. purple .. .. 1·40 30

DESIGNS: No. 3939, Claudius Galenus (anatomist and physiologist); 3940, Paracelsus (pharmacy); 3941, Andreas Vesalius (dissection); 3942, Rudolf Virchow (pathology of cells); 3943, Ivan Petrovich Pavlov (blood circulation, digestion and nervous system).

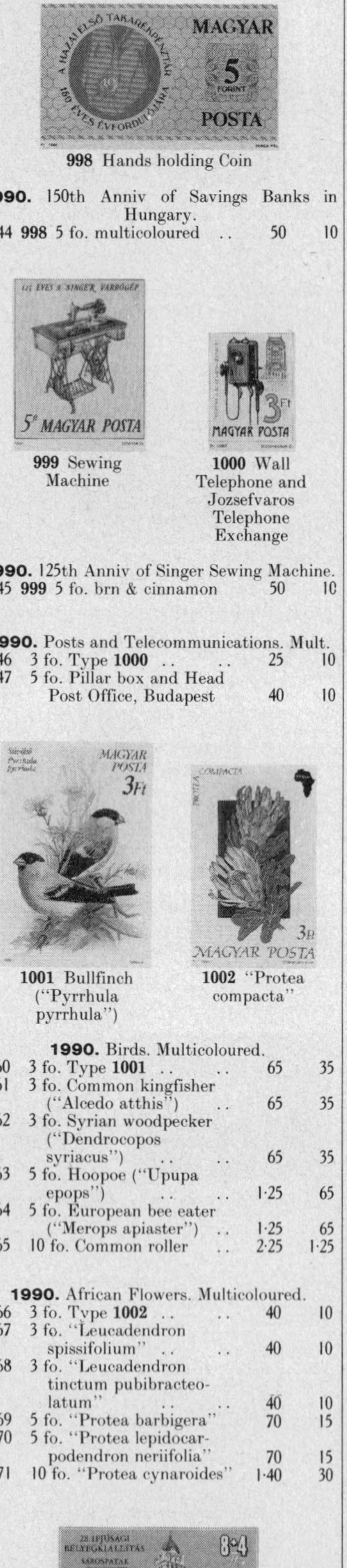

**998** Hands holding Coin

**1990.** 150th Anniv of Savings Banks in Hungary.

3944 **998** 5 fo. multicoloured .. 50 10

**999** Sewing Machine

**1000** Wall Telephone and Jozsefvaros Telephone Exchange

**1990.** 125th Anniv of Singer Sewing Machine.

3945 **999** 5 fo. brn & cinnamon 50 10

**1990.** Posts and Telecommunications. Mult.

3946 3 fo. Type **1000** .. .. 25 10
3947 5 fo. Pillar box and Head Post Office, Budapest 40 10

**1001** Bullfinch ("Pyrrhula pyrrhula")

**1002** "Protea compacta"

**1990.** Birds. Multicoloured.

3960 3 fo. Type **1001** .. .. 65 35
3961 3 fo. Common kingfisher ("Alcedo atthis") .. 65 35
3962 3 fo. Syrian woodpecker ("Dendrocopos syriacus") .. .. 65 35
3963 5 fo. Hoopoe ("Upupa epops") .. .. 1·25 65
3964 5 fo. European bee eater ("Merops apiaster") .. 1·25 65
3965 10 fo. Common roller .. 2·25 1·25

**1990.** African Flowers. Multicoloured.

3966 3 fo. Type **1002** .. .. 40 10
3967 3 fo. "Leucadendron spissifolium" .. .. 40 10
3968 3 fo. "Leucadendron tinctum pubibracteolatum" .. .. 40 10
3969 5 fo. "Protea barbigera" 70 15
3970 5 fo. "Protea lepidocarpodendron neriifolia" 70 15
3971 10 fo. "Protea cynaroides" 1·40 30

**1003** Sarospatak Teachers' Training School

**1990.** 28th National Youth Stamp Exhibition, Sarospatak.

3973 **1003** 8 fo. + 4 fo. mult .. 1·40 1·40

**1004** Janos Hunyadi (regent)

**1006** Gaspar Karoli (statue)

**1990.** The Hunyadis. Multicoloured.

3974 5 fo. Type **1004** .. .. 50 15
3975 5 fo. King Matthias I Corvinus .. .. 50 15

**1990.** 400th Anniv of Publication of Karoli Bible (first Hungarian translation).

3977 **1006** 8 fo. cream, grn & red 75 75

**1007** Footballers

**1990.** World Cup Football Championship, Italy.

3978 **1007** 3 fo. multicoloured 35 10
3979 – 5 fo. multicoloured (ball on ground) 60 10
3980 – 5 fo. multicoloured (ball in air) 60 10
3981 – 8 fo. multicoloured (dribbling) .. 95 15
3982 – 8 fo. mult (heading ball into goal) .. 95 15
3983 – 10 fo. multicoloured 1·25 20

DESIGNS: Nos. 3979/83, Various footballing scenes.

**1008** Hand writing with Quill Pen

**1990.** 300th Birth Anniv of Kelemen Mikes (writer).

3985 **1008** 8 fo. black and gold 65 10

**1009** "Weaver" (Noemi Ferenczy)

**1010** Kazinczy

**1990.** Birth Centenaries of Noemi and Beni Ferenczy (artists).

3986 **1009** 3 fo. multicoloured 35 10
3987 – 5 fo. black & brown 55 10

DESIGN: 5 fo. Bronze figure (Beni Ferenczy).

**1990.** 159th Death Anniv of Ferenc Kazinczy (writer and language reformer).

3988 **1010** 8 fo. multicoloured .. 65 10

**1011** Kolcsey (after Anton Einsle)

**1013** Cabernet Franc Grapes, Hajos

**1012** "St. Stephen" (carving in Parliament Hall) and Arms

**1990.** Birth Bicentenary of Ferenc Kolcsey (composer of national anthem).

3989 **1011** 8 fo. multicoloured .. 65 10

**1990.** New State Arms.

3990 **1012** 8 fo. multicoloured .. 65 10

**1990.** Wine Grapes and Regions. Mult.

3992 3 fo. Type **1013** .. .. 30 10
3993 5 fo. Cabernet Sauvignon, Villany .. .. 45 10
3994 8 fo. Riesling, Badacsony 75 15
3995 8 fo. Kadarka, Szekszard 75 15
3996 8 fo. Leanyka, Eger .. 75 15
3997 10 fo. Furmint, Tokaj-Hegyalja .. .. 1·00 15

**1014** "Feast"

**1990.** Stamp Day. Paintings by Ender Szasz. Multicoloured.

3998 8 fo. Type **1014** .. .. 80 80
3999 12 fo. "Message" .. 1·25 1·25

**1015** Tarbosaurus

**1990.** Prehistoric Animals. Multicoloured.

4001 3 fo. Type **1015** .. .. 30 10
4002 5 fo. Brontosaurus .. 45 10
4003 5 fo. Dimorphodon .. 45 10
4004 5 fo. Stegosaurus .. 45 10
4005 8 fo. Platybelodon .. 75 15
4006 10 fo. Mammoth .. 1·00 20

**1016** Dinosaurs reading

**1990.** International Literacy Year.

4007 **1016** 10 fo. multicoloured 65 10

1017 Bird holding Letter

**1990.** 60th Anniv of Stamp Museum, Budapest.
4008 **1017** 5 fo. red and green .. 50 10

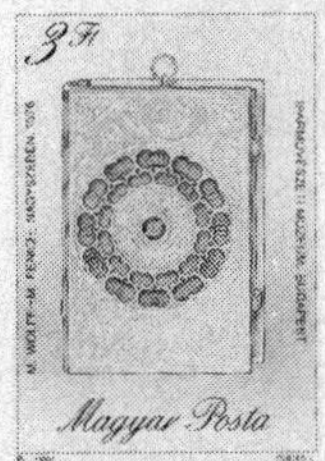

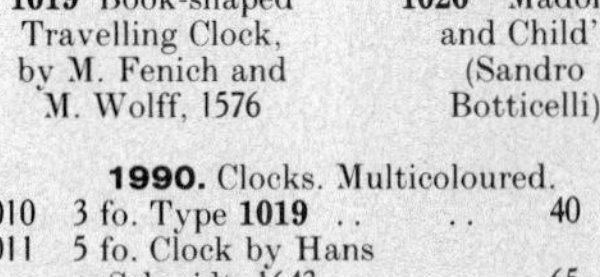

1019 Book-shaped Travelling Clock, by M. Fenich and M. Wolff, 1576

1020 "Madonna and Child" (Sandro Botticelli)

**1990.** Clocks. Multicoloured.
4010 3 fo. Type **1019** .. .. 40 10
4011 5 fo. Clock by Hans Schmidt, 1643 .. .. 65 10
4012 5 fo. Rococo style clock by J. M. Welz, 1790 .. 65 10
4013 10 fo. Clock by Johann Hillrich, 1814 .. .. 1·40 25

**1990.** Christmas.
4014 **1020** 5 fo. multicoloured .. 50 10

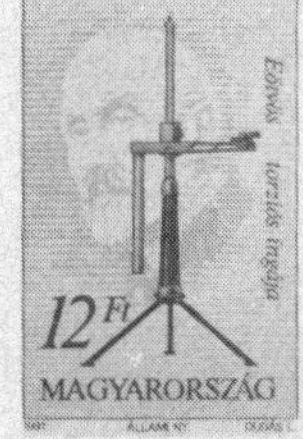

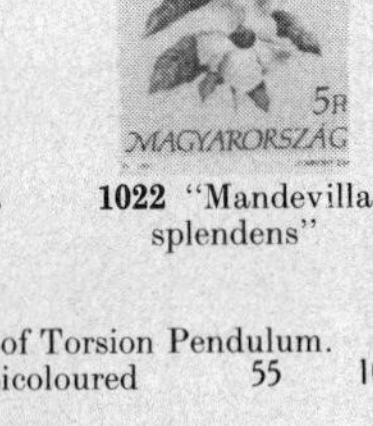


1021 Lorand Eotvos (inventor) and Torsion Pendulum

1022 "Mandevilla splendens"

**1991.** Centenary of Torsion Pendulum.
4015 **1021** 12 fo. multicoloured 55 10

**1991.** Flowers of the Americas. Mult.
4016 5 fo. Type **1022** .. .. 25 10
4017 7 fo. "Lobelia cardinalis" 35 10
4018 7 fo. Cup and saucer flower .. .. .. 35 10
4019 12 fo. "Steriphoma paradoxa" .. .. .. 60 15
4020 15 fo. Shrimp plant .. 75 20

1023 Post Office, Budapest

1024 "Ulysses" Jupiter Probe

**1991.** Hungarian Full Membership of Council of Europe and Entry into C.E.P.T. (European Posts and Telecommunications Conference). Multicoloured.
4022 5 fo. Type **1023** .. .. 1·50 75
4023 7 fo. Post Office, Pecs .. 2·25 1·25

**1991.** Europa. Europe in Space. Mult.
4024 12 fo. Type **1024** .. 85 45
4025 30 fo. "Cassini" and "Huygens" (wrongly inscr "Hughes") Saturn probes .. .. 1·90 95

**INDEX**
Countries can be quickly located by referring to the index at the end of this volume.

1025 "Peter and the Wolf" (tapestry, Gabriella Hajnal)

**1991.** Youth Stamp.
4026 **1025** 12 fo.+6 fo. mult .. 85 85

1026 Gorilla

**1991.** 125th Anniv of Budapest Zoological and Botanic Gardens. Multicoloured.
4027 7 fo. Type **1026** .. .. 35 20
4028 12 fo. Polar bear .. 75 40
4029 12 fo. Rhinoceros .. 75 40
4030 12 fo. Keel-billed toucan 75 40
4031 20 fo. Orchid and glasshouse .. .. .. 95 55

1027 Teleki

1028 Map, Emblem and Fencers

**1991.** 50th Death Anniv of Count Pal Teleki (Prime Minister, 1920–21 and 1939–41).
4032 **1027** 12 fo. brown, cinnamon & black 55 30

**1991.** 44th World Fencing Championships, Budapest.
4033 **1028** 12 fo. multicoloured 55 30

1029 Mariapocs

**1991.** Visit of Pope John Paul II (1st issue). Shrines to Virgin Mary. Multicoloured.
4034 7 fo. Type **1029** .. .. 35 20
4035 12 fo. Mariagyud .. 55 30
4036 12 fo. Celldomolk .. 55 30
4037 12 fo. Mariaremete .. 55 30
4038 20 fo. Esztergom .. 95 55

1030 "Appeggi Landscape" and Marko

**1991.** Birth Bicent of Karoly Marko (painter).
4039 **1030** 12 fo. multicoloured 55 30

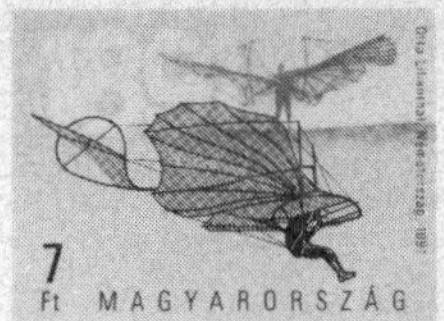


1031 Lilienthal and Monoplane Gliders, 1891

**1991.** Centenary of First Heavier-than-Air Manned Flight by Otto Lilienthal.
4040 **1031** 7 fo. blk, ochre & brn 55 30
4041 – 12 fo. black, drab and bistre .. 1·00 50
4042 – 20 fo. deep blue, azure and blue .. 1·60 80
4043 – 30 fo. blk, lilac & vio 2·40 1·25
DESIGNS: 12 fo. Wright brothers' Flyer 1, 1903; 20 fo. Santos-Dumont's "14 bis", 1906; 30 fo. Aladar Zselyi's monoplane, 1910.

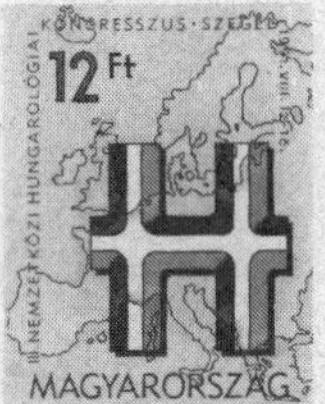


1032 Players

1034 Map of Europe and Congress Emblem

**1991.** Centenary of Basketball.
4044 **1032** 12 fo. multicoloured 55 30

**1991.** Castles. Inscr "MAGYARORSZAG". As T **921**.
4045 7 fo. brown and sepia .. 35 20
4047 12 fo. ultramarine & blue 55 30
4049 15 fo. brown and green .. 55 30
DESIGNS—32 × 25mm. 7 fo. Esterhazy Castle, Papa; 12 fo. Dory Castle, Mihaly. 35 × 26 mm. 15 fo. Festetics Castle, Keszthely.

**1991.** 3rd International Hungarian Philological Society Congress, Szeged.
4056 **1034** 12 fo. multicoloured 55 30

1035 Szechenyi

1036 Mozart as Child

**1991.** Birth Bicentenary of Count Istvan Szechenyi (social reformer).
4057 **1035** 12 fo. red .. .. 55 30

**1991.** Stamp Day. Death Bicentenary of Wolfgang Amadeus Mozart (composer). Mult.
4058 12 fo. Type **1036** .. 55 30
4059 20 fo. Mozart as youth .. 95 50

1037 "Telecom 91"

**1991.** "Telecom 91" International Telecommunications Exhibition, Geneva.
4061 **1037** 12 fo. multicoloured 55 30

**1991.** 35th Anniv of 1956 Uprising. No. 4047 optd **A FORRADALOM EMLEKERE 1956 1991.**
4062 12 fo. ultramarine & blue 55 30

1039 Sebastian Cabot

1040 Arms of Order

**1991.** 500th Anniv (1992) of Discovery of America by Columbus. Multicoloured.
4063 7 fo. Type **1039** .. .. 60 30
4064 12 fo. Amerigo Vespucci 90 45
4065 12 fo. Hernan Cortes .. 90 45
4066 15 fo. Ferdinand Magellan 1·25 65
4067 20 f. Francisco Pizarro .. 1·60 80

**1991.** Postal Convention with Sovereign Military Order of Malta.
4069 **1040** 12 fo. multicoloured 55 30

1041 "Virgin of Mariapocs"

1042 Flower

**1991.** Christmas. Multicoloured.
4070 7 fo. Type **1041** .. .. 55 30
4071 12 fo. "Virgin of Mariaremete" .. .. 70 35

**1991.** Human Rights.
4072 **1042** 12 fo. multicoloured 55 30

1043 Biathlon

1045 Arms

**1991.** Winter Olympic Games, Albertville (1992). Multicoloured.
4073 7 fo. Type **1043** .. .. 35 20
4074 12 fo. Slalom .. .. 55 30
4075 15 fo. Four-man bobsleigh 70 35
4076 20 fo. Ski jumping .. 95 40
4077 30 fo. Ice hockey .. 1·40 70

**1992.** 350th Anniv of Piarist Order in Hungary.
4080 **1045** 10 fo. gold, blue and ultramarine .. 40 20

1046 Holloko

**1992.** U.N.E.S.C.O. World Heritage Site.
4081 **1046** 15 fo. multicoloured 75 40

1047 Swimming

**1992.** Olympic Games, Barcelona. Mult.
4082 7 fo. Type **1047** .. .. 35 20
4083 9 fo. Cycling .. .. 40 20
4084 10 fo. Gymnastics .. 40 20
4085 15 fo. Running .. .. 65 35

1048 "Indian's Head" Map

1049 Comenius

**1992.** "Expo '92" World's Fair, Seville. Fantasy Maps. Multicoloured.

4086 10 fo. Type **1048** .. 75 30
4087 10 fo. Islands, sea monsters and "Santa Maria" forming face .. 75 30
4088 15 fo. "Conquistador's head" map .. .. 1·25 55
4089 15 fo. Navigation instruments and map forming face .. .. .. 1·25 55

**1992.** 400th Birth Anniv of Jan Komensky (Comenius) (educationist).

4090 **1049** 15 fo. multicoloured 55 30

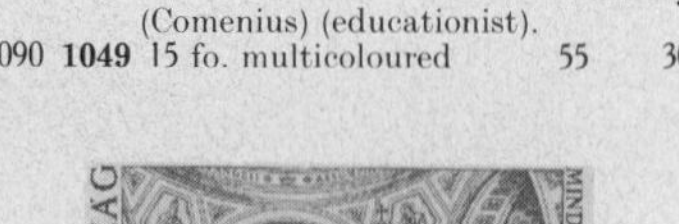

1050 Mindszenty

**1992.** Birth Centenary of Cardinal Jozsef Mindszenty, Archbishop of Esztergom.

4091 **1050** 15 fo. brown, cream and red .. .. 55 30

1051 Statue of Mayan Man

1052 "Self-portrait" (Renata Toth)

**1992.** Europa. 500th Anniv of Discovery of America by Columbus. Multicoloured.

4092 15 fo. Type **1051** .. 55 30
4093 40 fo. Statue of Mayan woman .. .. 1·50 75

**1992.** Youth Stamps. Children's Drawings. Multicoloured.

4094 9 fo. + 4 fo. Type **1052** .. 50 50
4095 10 fo. + 4 fo. "The Sun Shines for Me" (Sandor Pusoma) (horiz) .. 50 50
4096 15 fo. + 4 fo. "I will be a Beauty King" (Endre Knipf) .. .. 70 70

1053 Gymnasts and Emblem

**1992.** European Gymnastics Championships, Budapest.

4097 **1053** 15 fo. multicoloured 55 30

1054 St. Margaret (after J. S. Scott)

1055 Saker Falcon

**1992.** 750th Birth Anniv of St. Margaret.

4098 **1054** 15 fo. turquoise, light blue and blue .. 55 30

**1992.** Birds of Prey. Multicoloured.

4099 9 fo. Type **1055** .. .. 35 20
4100 10 fo. Booted eagle .. 35 20
4101 15 fo. Short-toed eagle .. 55 30
4102 40 fo. Red kite .. 1·40 70

1056 Wallenberg

1057 Millennium Monument, Budapest

**1992.** 80th Birth Anniv of Raoul Wallenberg (Swedish diplomat).

4103 **1056** 15 fo. grey, red & grn 55 30

**1992.** 3rd World Federation of Hungarians Congress, Budapest.

4104 **1057** 15 fo. multicoloured 55 30

1058 Theodore von Karman (space pioneer, birth centenary (1991))

**1992.** Anniversaries.

4105 **1058** 15 fo. grey, black and deep grey .. 55 30
4106 – 40 fo. grey, blk & brn 1·40 70

DESIGN: 40 fo. Neumann Janos (mathematician, 35th death anniv).

1059 Current Hungarian Post Emblem

1061 Entwined Cables

**1992.** Stamp Day. "Eurofilex '92" International Postal History Exhibition, Budapest. Multicoloured.

4107 10 fo. + 5 fo. Hungarian Royal Post emblem, 1867 (vert) .. 50 50
4108 15 fo. + 5 fo. Type **1059** .. 70 70

**1992.** As No. 4108 but without premium and commemorative inscription.

4111 15 fo. multicoloured .. 50 25

**1992.** "Europa Telecom '92" Telecommunications Exhibition, Budapest.

4112 **1061** 15 fo. multicoloured 50 25

1062 Istvan Bathory (King Stefan I of Poland)

1063 Pieces on Board

**1992.** Princes of Transylvania. Mult.

4113 10 fo. Type **1062** .. 35 20
4114 15 fo. Istvan Bocskai .. 50 25
4115 40 fo. Gabor Bethlen .. 1·40 70

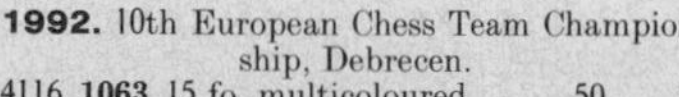
**1992.** 10th European Chess Team Championship, Debrecen.

4116 **1063** 15 fo. multicoloured 50 25

1064 "Clianthus formosus"

1065 Postal Rider of Prince Ferenc Rakoczi II, 1703–11

**1992.** Australian Flowers. Multicoloured.

4117 9 fo. Type **1064** .. .. 35 20
4118 10 fo. "Leschenaultia biloba" .. .. 35 20
4119 15 fo. "Anigosanthos manglesii" .. .. 55 30
4120 40 fo. "Comesperma ericinum" .. .. 1·40 70

**1992.** Post Office Uniforms. Multicoloured.

4122 10 fo. Type **1065** .. 20 10
4123 15 fo. Postmen, 1874 .. 30 15

1066 "Holy Family" (iron relief, 1850)

1067 "Arachnis flos-aeris"

**1992.** Christmas.

4124 **1066** 15 fo. black and blue 35 20

**1993.** Asian Flowers. Multicoloured.

4125 10 fo. Type **1067** .. 35 20
4126 10 fo. "Dendrobium densiflorium" .. .. 35 20
4127 15 fo. "Lilium speciosum" 50 25
4128 15 fo. "Meconopsis aculeata" .. .. 50 25

1068 Shield Decoration of Deer

**1993.** Scythian Remains in Hungary. Mult.

4130 10 fo. Type **1068** .. 35 20
4131 17 fo. Gilt-silver embossed deer .. .. .. 60 30

1069 Single Sculls

**1993.** Centenary of Rowing Association.

4132 **1069** 17 fo. multicoloured 60 30

1070 Queen Beatrix and King Matthias I Corvinus (detail of Missal) (⅔ size illustration)

**1993.** King Matthias I Corvinus's "Missale Romanum".

4133 **1070** 15 fo. multicoloured 50 25

1071 Animals in Wood

1072 Competitors and Globe

**1993.** Youth Stamps. Tapestries by Erzsebet Szekeres. Multicoloured.

4135 10 fo. + 5 fo. Type **1071** .. 50 50
4136 17 fo. + 8 fo. Animals in tree hiding from dragons .. .. 85 85

**1993.** World Motocross Championships, Cserenfa.

4137 **1072** 17 fo. multicoloured 55 30

1073 Diagram of Solar System and Copernicus

**1993.** "Polska'93" International Stamp Exn.

4138 **1073** 17 fo. multicoloured 55 30

1074 Paks Catholic Church

1075 Cauliflower Clavaria

**1993.** Europa. Contemporary Art. Architecture by Imre Makovecz. Multicoloured.

4139 17 fo. Type **1074** .. 55 30
4140 45 fo. Hungarian pavilion at "Expo '92" World's Fair, Seville .. .. 1·00 50

**1993.** Fungi. Multicoloured.

4141 10 fo. Type **1075** .. 35 15
4142 17 fo. Death trumpet .. 70 30
4143 45 fo. Caesar's mushroom 1·40 55

1076 "St. Christopher" (Albrecht Durer)

**1993.** European Year of the Aged.

4144 **1076** 17 fo. black, cream and silver .. 55 30

1077 Steam Locomotives

1078 Rowing Boat approaching Town

**1993.** 125th Anniv of Hungarian Railways.

4145 **1077** 17 fo. blue and cobalt 55 20

**1993.** 900th Anniv of Mohacs.

4146 **1078** 17 fo. brown, cinnamon and red 55 30

1079 Poplar Admiral

1080 Kalman Latabar

**1993.** Butterflies. Multicoloured.
4147 10 fo. Type **1079** .. 25 15
4148 17 fo. "Aricia artaxerxes" 55 30
4149 30 fo. "Plebejides pylaon" 75 40

**1993.** Great Humourists. Multicoloured.
4150 17 fo. Type **1080** .. 55 30
4151 30 fo. Charlie Chaplin .. 75 40

**1082** Solar Panel absorbing Sun's Rays

**1083** Laszlo Nemeth

**1993.** International Solar Energy Society Congress, Budapest.
4153 **1082** 17 fo. multicoloured 55 30

**1993.** Writers. Each blue and azure.
4154 17 fo. Type **1083** .. 55 30
4155 17 fo. Dezso Szabo .. 55 30
4156 17 fo. Antal Szerb .. 55 30

**1084** Zoltan Nagy and 1953 20 fi. Stamp

**1085** Arms

**1993.** Stamp Day. Designers. Multicoloured.
4157 10 fo.+5 fo. Type **1084** .. 50 50
4158 17 fo.+5 fo. Sandor Legrady and 1938 50 f. stamp .. .. .. 75 75

**1993.** 175th Anniv of Faculty of Agronomics, Pannon Agricultural University, Magyarovar.
4160 **1085** 17 fo. multicoloured 55 30

**1086** "Szent Istvan", 1892

**1087** Prehistoric Man and Skull (Vertesszolos)

**1993.** Hungarian Ships. Multicoloured.
4161 10 fo. Type **1086** .. 25 15
4162 30 fo. "Szent Istvan" (battleship), 1915 .. 85 45

**1993.** Palaeolithic Remains in Hungary. Multicoloured.
4163 17 fo. Type **1087** .. 55 30
4164 30 fo. Men round fire and stone tool (Szeleta Cave, Lillafured) .. 85 45

**1089** "Madonna and Child" (altarpiece by F. A. Hillebrant, Szekestehervar Cathedral)

**1091** Antall

**1090** Szechenyi Chain Bridge (½-size illustration)

**1993.** Christmas.
4166 **1089** 10 fo. multicoloured 35 20

**1993.** "Expo '96" World's Fair, Budapest (1st issue).
4167 **1090** 17 fo. dp green & grn 55 30
4168 – 30 fo. purple & claret 75 40
4169 – 45 fo. dp brn & brn 1·10 55
DESIGNS—HORIZ: 30 fo. Opera House. VERT: 45 fo. Matthias Church.
See also Nos. 4236/8 and 4268/9.

**1993.** Jozsef Antall (Prime Minister since 1990) Commemoration.
4170 **1091** 19 fo. multicoloured 55 30

**1092** Skiing

**1994.** Winter Olympic Games, Lillehammer, Norway. Multicoloured.
4172 12 fo. Type **1092** .. 30 15
4173 19 fo. Ice hockey .. 55 30

**1093** Douglas DC-3

**1994.** 50th Anniv of I.C.A.O.
4174 **1093** 56 fo. multicoloured 1·40 70

**1094** "Golgotha" (detail, Mihaly Munkacsy)

**1095** Mihaly Munkacsy (self-portrait)

**1994.** Easter.
4175 **1094** 12 fo. multicoloured 35 20

**1994.** Artists' 150th Birth Anniversaries. Multicoloured.
4176 12 fo. Gyula Benczur (self-portrait) .. .. 35 20
4177 19 fo. Type **1095** .. 60 30

**1096** Kossuth

**1097** Hen with Chicks

**1994.** Death Centenary of Lajos Kossuth (Governor of 1849 Republic).
4178 **1096** 19 fo. multicoloured 60 30

**1994.** The Great Bustard. Multicoloured.
4179 10 fo. Type **1097** .. 30 15
4180 10 fo. Bustards taking off 30 15
4181 10 fo. Cock in mating display .. .. 30 15
4182 10 fo. Hen with chicks (different) .. .. 30 15



**1098** Bem

**1099** Discovery of Franz Josef Land (120th anniv)

**1994.** Birth Bicentenary of Jozsef Bem (revolutionary).
4183 **1098** 19 fo. multicoloured 60 30

**1994.** Europa. Discoveries. Multicoloured.
4184 19 fo. Type **1099** .. 60 30
4185 50 fo. Mark Aurel Stein and Buddha (expeditions in Asia) .. 1·40 70

**1100** "The Little Prince"

**1101** Balint Balassi (poet, 400th death)

**1994.** Youth Stamp. 50th Anniv of Disappearance of Antoine de Saint-Exupery (writer and pilot).
4186 **1100** 19 fo.+5 fo. mult .. 70 70

**1994.** Writers' Anniversaries.
4187 **1101** 19 ft. pink and brown 50 25
4188 – 19 ft. stone and grey 50 25
DESIGN: No. 4188, Miklos Josika (novelist, birth bicentenary).

**1102** Horsemen

**1104** Elvis Presley and Players

**1103** Athens Stadium, 1896

**1994.** 1100th Anniv (1996) of Magyar Conquest (1st issue). Multicoloured.
4189 19 ft. Type **1102** .. 45 20
4190 19 ft. Arpad and standard bearers (58×39 mm) .. 45 20
4191 19 ft. Mounted archer .. 45 20
Nos. 4189/91 were issued together, se-tenant, forming a composite design of a detail of the painting "in the round" commissioned to celebrate the millenary of the Conquest.
See also Nos. 4240/2 and 4275/7.

**1994.** Centenary of International Olympic Committee. Multicoloured.
4192 12 ft. Olympic medals of 1896 and 1992 .. .. 25 10
4193 19 ft. Type **1103** .. 40 20
4194 19 ft. Ancient Greek athletes, Olympic flag and flame .. .. 40 20
4195 35 ft. Pierre de Coubertin (founder) .. .. 75 35

**1994.** World Cup Football Championship, U.S.A. American Entertainers. Mult.
4196 19 ft. Type **1104** .. 55 25
4197 19 ft. Marilyn Monroe and players .. .. 55 25
4198 35 ft. John Wayne and players .. .. 1·10 55

**1105** Family

**1994.** International Year of the Family.
4199 **1105** 19 fo. multicoloured 60 30

**1106** Summer Snowflake

**1994.** European Flowers. Multicoloured.
4200 12 fo. Type **1106** .. 25 10
4201 19 fo. Common rock-rose 30 15
4202 35 fo. "Eryngium alpinum" .. .. 40 20
4203 50 fo. Pennycress .. 85 40

**1107** Heinrich von Stephan (founder) and Emblem

**1108** Csik Megye

**1994.** 120th Anniv of Universal Postal Union.
4205 **1107** 19 fo. grey, brn & blk 30 15
4206 – 35 fo. blue, brn & blk 55 25
DESIGN: 35 fo. Gervay Mihaly (first Director General of Posts) and U.P.U. emblem.

**1994.** Traditional Patterns.
4208 – 1 fo. violet and black 10 10
4209 – 2 fo. multicoloured 10 10
4210 – 3 fo. multicoloured 10 10
4211 – 9 fo. multicoloured 15 10
4212 **1108** 11 fo. multicoloured 20 10
4213 – 12 fo. multicoloured 25 10
4214 – 13 fo. multicoloured 25 10
4215 – 14 fo. multicoloured 25 10
4216 – 16 fo. multicoloured 30 15
4217 – 17 fo. blk, grey & red 30 15
4218 – 19 fo. multicoloured 35 15
4219 – 22 fo. multicoloured 40 30
4220 – 24 fo. multicoloured 60 30
4221 – 32 fo. multicoloured 70 35
4222 – 35 fo. multicoloured 75 30
4223 – 38 fo. multicoloured 80 40
4224 – 40 fo. multicoloured 1·10 55
4225 – 50 fo. multicoloured 1·25 60
4226 – 75 fo. multicoloured 1·40 70
4227 – 80 fo. multicoloured 1·50 75
4230 – 300 fo. multicoloured 2·75 1·25
4231 – 500 fo. multicoloured 3·75 1·50
DESIGNS: 1 fo. Torocko; 2 fo. Buzsak; 3 fo. Vas megye (flowers); 9, 24 fo. Felfold; 12 fo. Vas megye (birds); 13, 32 fo. Debrecen; 14, 80 fo. Sarkoz; 16 fo. Csiki-Medence; 17, 35 fo. Dunantul; 19, 300 fo. Kalocsa; 22 fo. Heves megye; 38, 75 fo. Oroshaza; 40 fo. Kalotaszeg; 50 fo. Szentgal; 500 fo. Szolnok megye.

**1110** Hebrew Tombstone

**1111** "Nativity"

**1994.** Holocaust Victims' Commemoration.
4233 **1110** 19 fo. multicoloured 40 20

**1994.** Christmas. Paintings by Pal Molnar. Multicoloured.
4234 12 fo. Type **1111** .. 35 15
4235 35 fo. "Flight into Egypt" (31×29 mm) .. .. 95 45

**1112** National Museum

**1994.** "Expo '96" World's Fair, Budapest (2nd issue). Budapest landmarks.
4236 1112 19 fo. green .. 40 20
4237 – 19 fo. brown .. 40 20
4238 – 19 fo. violet .. 40 20
DESIGNS: No. 4237, University of Technical Sciences; 4238, Vajdahunyad Castle.

1113 "Ferencz Jozsef I" (paddle-steamer) and "Baross" (container ship)

**1995.** Cent of Hungarian Shipping Company.
4239 1113 22 fo. multicoloured 40 20

**1995.** 1100th Anniv (1996) of Magyar Conquest (2nd issue). As T 1102. Multicoloured.
4240 22 fo. Ox cart .. .. 40 20
4241 22 fo. Arpad's consort in ox cart (59 × 39 mm) .. 40 20
4242 22 fo. Men and pack ox .. 40 20
Nos. 4240/2 were issued together, se-tenant, forming a composite design of a detail of the painting "in the round" commissioned to celebrate the millenary of the Conquest.

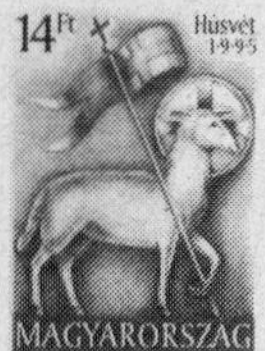

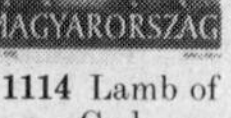


1114 Lamb of God

1116 Weather Map and Barometer

1115 Paddle-steamer

**1995.** Easter.
4243 1114 14 fo. purple & black 25 10

**1995.** 150th Anniv of Steamer Service on River Tisza (14 fo.) and Birth Bicentenary of Pal Vasarhelyi (engineer) (60 fo.). Multicoloured.
4244 14 fo. Type 1115 .. 25 10
4245 60 fo. Vasarhelyi (after Miklos Barabas) and survey ship .. .. 1·25 60

**1995.** Anniversaries. Multicoloured.
4246 22 fo. Type 1116 (125th anniv of Hungarian Meteorological Service) 45 20
4247 22 fo. Emblem (50th anniv of F.A.O) (25 × 41 mm) 45 20
4248 22 fo. + 10 fo. John the Hero (150th anniv of poem by Petofi) (37 × 45mm) .. .. 65 65
No. 4248 is the 1995 Youth Stamp.

1117 White Stork and Frog

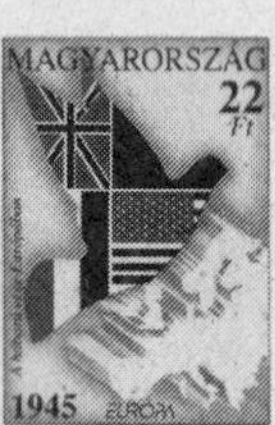


1118 Allied Flags forming Dove over Map of Europe

**1995.** European Nature Conservation Year. Multicoloured.
4249 14 fo. Type 1117 .. 25 10
4250 14 fo. Red squirrel .. 25 10
4251 14 fo. Blue tit .. .. 25 10
4252 14 fo. Butterfly and hedgehog .. .. 25 10
Nos. 4249/52 were issued together, se-tenant, forming a composite design.

**1995.** Europa. Peace and Freedom.
4253 1118 22 fo. multicoloured 35 15

1119 Gymnastics and Ferenc Kemeny (founder)

**1995.** Centenary of Hungarian Olympic Committee. Multicoloured.
4254 22 fo. Type 1119 .. 35 15
4255 60 fo. Throwing the javelin .. .. 1·00 50
4256 100 fo. Fencing .. .. 1·60 80

1120 Exhibition Emblem

**1995.** "Olympiafila '95" International Olympic and Sports Stamps Exn, Budapest.
4257 1120 22 fo. + 11 fo. mult (rings in yellow) .. 55 55
4258 22 fo. + 11 fo. mult (rings in purple) .. 55 55

1121 Saint Ladislas (detail of fresco, Szekelyderzs Castle Chapel)

1122 Almasy

**1995.** 900th Death Anniv of St. Ladislas, King of Hungary.
4259 1121 22 fo. multicoloured 35 15

**1995.** Birth Centenary of Laszlo Almasy (explorer).
4260 1122 22 fo. multicoloured 35 15

1123 Museum of Applied Arts, Budapest, and Lechner

**1995.** 150th Birth Anniv of Odon Lechner (architect).
4261 1123 22 fo. multicoloured 45 20

1124 "K XVIII. 1923" (Laszlo Moholy-Nagy)

1125 College Building and Jozsef Eotvos (founder).

**1995.** Artists' Birth Centenaries. Mult.
4262 22 fo. Type 1124 .. 45 20
4263 22 fo. "The Fiddler" (Aurel Bernath) .. 45 20

**1995.** Centenary of Eotvos College.
4264 1125 60 fo. multicoloured 1·25 60

1126 Postal Carriage and Map of Postal Routes

**1995.** Stamp Day. Multicoloured.
4265 22 fo. Type 1126 .. 40 20
4266 40 fo. Airplane and route map .. .. .. 85 40

**1995.** "Expo '96" World's Fair, Budapest (3rd issue). As T 1112 showing Budapest landmarks.
4268 22 fo. grey .. .. 45 20
4269 22 fo. purple .. .. 45 20
DESIGNS: No. 4268, Rail Station; 4269, Music Hall.

1127 Anniversary Emblem

1128 Sparklers

**1995.** 50th Anniv of U.N.O.
4270 1127 60 fo. multicoloured 1·25 60

**1995.** Christmas. Multicoloured.
4271 14 fo. Type 1128 .. 30 15
4272 60 fo. Three wise men in stable .. .. .. 1·25 60

1129 St. Elizabeth bathing Leper

**1995.** Saint Elizabeth of Hungary.
4273 1129 22 fo. multicoloured 45 20

1130 Nobel Medals

**1995.** Centenary of Nobel Trust Fund.
4274 1130 100 fo. multicoloured 2·00 1·00

**1996.** 1100th Anniv of Magyar Conquest (3rd issue). As T 1102. Multicoloured.
4275 24 fo. Rejoicing crowd .. 35 15
4276 24 fo. Shaman presenting sacrificial white horse (59 × 39 mm) .. 35 15
4277 24 fo. Bards .. .. 35 15
Nos. 4275/7 were issued together, se-tenant, forming a composite design.

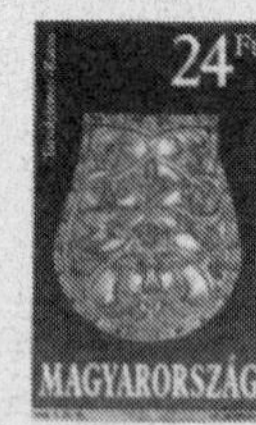


1131 Leather Purse

1133 Headquarters

**1996.** 9th-century Relics from Kares Cemeteries. Multicoloured.
4278 24 fo. Type 1131 .. 35 15
4279 24 fo. Gold and silver sabre hilt .. .. 35 15

**1996.** Centenary of Journalists' Association.
4281 1133 50 fo. multicoloured 65 30

1134 Emblem

1135 Swimming

**1996.** Promotion of Hungarian Production.
4282 1134 24 fo. blk, red & grn 35 15

**1996.** Centenary of Modern Olympic Games and Olympic Games, Atlanta. Mult.
4283 24 fo. Type 1135 .. 35 15
4284 50 fo. Tennis (Csilla Orosz) 65 30
4285 75 fo. Canoeing .. .. 95 45

1136 First Carriage

**1996.** Centenary of Budapest Underground Railway.
4287 1136 24 fo. multicoloured 35 15

1137 Queen Gizella (wife of St. Stephen)

**1996.** Europa. Famous Women. Hungarian Queens. Multicoloured.
4288 24 fo. Type 1137 .. 40 20
4289 75 fo. Queen Elisabeth (wife of Francis Joseph I) .. .. 85 40

1138 Triumphal Arch (entrance to Cathedral)

1139 Bird and "DRUG"

**1996.** Millenary of Pannonhalma Monastery.
4290 1138 17 fo. brown .. 20 10
4291 – 24 fo. blue .. .. 35 15
DESIGN: 24 fo. Monks gathered in cloisters.
See also Nos. 4305/6.

**1996.** International Day against Drug Abuse.
4292 1139 24 fo. multicoloured 35 15

1140 Denes Mihaly (television pioneer)

**1996.** Inventors. Multicoloured.
4293 24 fo. Type 1140 .. 35 15
4294 50 fo. Laszlo Biro and ballpoint pen .. 65 30
4295 75 fo. Zoltan Bay and Moon radar .. 95 45

**1141** Laszlo Vitez (puppet)

**1143** Pyramid

**1142** "Pest"

**1996.** Youth Stamp. Puppet Festival, Budapest.
4296 **1141** 24 fo. + 10 fo. mult .. 45 45

**1996.** 150th Anniv of Hungarian Railways. Steam Locomotives. Multicoloured.
4297 17 fo. Class "303" .. 20 10
4298 24 fo. Class "325" .. 35 15
4299 24 fo. Type **1142** .. 35 15

**1996.** 2nd European Mathematics Congress, Budapest.
4300 **1143** 24 fo. multicoloured 35 15

**1144** Hungarian Long-horned Wood Beetle ("Ropalopus ungaricus")

**1996.** "NATUREXPO '96" International Nature Conservation Exhibition, Budapest. Multicoloured.
4301 13 fo. Type **1144** .. 15 10
4302 13 fo. Lynx ("Lynx lynx") .. .. 15 10
4303 13 fo. Siberian iris ("Iris sibirica") .. .. 15 10
4304 13 fo. Great egret ("Egretta alba") .. 15 10

**1996.** Millenary of Pannonhalma Monastery. As T **1138**.
4305 17 fo. brown .. .. 20 10
4306 24 fo. green .. .. 35 15
DESIGNS: 17 fo. Refectory; 24 fo. Main library.

**1145** Homage to Prince Arpad (from "Vienna Picture Chronicle")

**1146** 1871 10 k. Engraved Stamp

**1996.** Stamp Day. "Budapest '96" International Stamp Exn, Budapest. Mult.
4307 17 fo. Type **1145** .. 20 10
4308 24 fo. Prince Arpad on horseback and soldiers (from "Vienna Picture Chronicle") .. .. 35 15

**1996.** World Convention of Hungarian Stamps and Postal History.
4310 **1146** 24 fo. multicoloured 35 15

**1147** Map and Paddle-steamer "Kisfaludy"

**1996.** 150th Anniv of Steamer Service on Lake Balaton.
4311 **1147** 17 fo. multicoloured 20 10

**1148** Mastheads and Demonstration

**1996.** 40th Anniv of 23rd October Uprising. Multicoloured.
4312 13 fo. Type **1148** .. 15 10
4313 16 fo. Newspaper, burning flag and motor vehicle 20 10
4314 17 fo. Men with rifles and newspaper .. .. 20 10
4315 24 fo. Newspaper and Imre Nagy (Prime Minister, Oct–Nov 1956) 35 15

## EXPRESS LETTER STAMPS

E 36.

**1916.** Inscr "MAGYAR KIR POSTA".
E245 **E 36** 2 f. olive and red .. 20 20

**1916.** Optd **KOZTARSASAG**.
E301 **E 36** 2 f. olive and red .. 20 30

**1919.** Inscr "MAGYAR POSTA".
E349 **E 36** 2 f. olive and red .. 15 15

## IMPERIAL JOURNAL STAMPS

J 1.

J 2.

**1868.** Imperf.
J52 **J 1** 1 k. blue .. .. 1·00 30
J3 **J 2** 1 k. blue .. .. £12000 £7500
J53 2 k. brown .. .. 3·75 4·50
No. J3 has the arms at the foot as in Type **J 2** but the corner designs differ.

## NEWSPAPER STAMPS

**N 2.** St. Stephen's Crown and Posthorn

N 4.

N 9.

**1871.** Posthorn turned to left. Imperf.
N 8. **N 2.** 1 k. red .. .. 65·00 20·00

**1872.** As Type **N 2** but with posthorn turned to right. Imperf.
N14 1 k. red .. .. .. 13·00 1·75

**1874.** Imperf.
N64 **N 4** 1 k. orange .. .. 45 10

**1900.** Imperf.
N 136. **N 9.** (2 f.) orange .. 10 10
N 401. (10 f.) blue .. .. 10 10
N 402. (20 f.) purple .. 10 10

## OFFICIAL STAMPS

O 44.

**1921.**
O428 **O 44** 10 f. black & purple 10 15
O429 20 f. black & brown 10 15
O430 60 f. black and grey 10 15
O431 100 f. black and red 10 15
O432 250 f. black and blue 10 15
O433 350 f. black and blue 10 15
O434 500 f. black & brown 10 15
O435 1000 f. black & brn 10 15

**1922.** Nos. O429/33 surch (No. O439 optd **KORONA** only).
O436 **O 44** 15 k. on 20 f. black and brown .. 10 15
O437 25 k. on 60 f. black and grey .. 10 15
O438 150 k. on 100 f. black and pink .. 15 15
O439 (350) k. on 350 f. black and blue .. 35 30
O440 2000 k. on 250 f. black and blue .. 35 40

**1922.**
O 441. **O 44.** 5 k. brown .. .. 10 15
O 442. 10 k. brown .. 10 15
O 443. 15 k. grey .. .. 10 15
O 444. 25 k. orange .. 10 15
O 445. 50 k. red and brown 10 15
O 446. 100 k. red and bistre 10 15
O 447. 150 k. red and green 10 15
O 448. 300 k. red .. .. 10 15
O 449. 350 k. red and violet 10 15
O 450a. 500 k. red and orange 15 15
O 451. 600 k. red and bistre 25 50
O 452. 1000 k. red and blue 15 15
O 453. 3000 k. red and violet 45 25
O 454. 5000 k. red and blue 50 50

## PARCEL POST STAMPS

**1954.** No. 979 surch. in figures and **Ft**.
P 1398. **153.** 1 fo. 70 on 1 fo. 40 grn. 75 35
P 1399. 2 fo. on 1 fo. 40 green 1·25 45
P 1400. 3 fo. on 1 fo. 40 green 1·75 60

## POSTAGE DUE STAMPS

D 9.

**1903.** Inscr "MAGYAR KIR. POSTA". Figures in centre in black.
D 170. **D 9.** 1 f. green .. .. 10 15
D 171. 2 f. green .. .. 10 10
D 172. 5 f. green .. .. 25 20
D 119. 6 f. green .. .. 35 30
D 174. 10 f. green .. .. 40 40
D 175. 12 f. green .. .. 10 10
D 176. 20 f. green .. .. 10 10
D 177. 50 f. green .. .. 20 25
D 91. 100 f. green .. 50 65

**1915.** Surch **20**.
D188 **D 9** 20 on 100 f. blk & grn 30 30

**1915.** As Type **D 9**, but figures in red.
D 190. **D 9.** 1 f. green .. .. 10 10
D 191. 2 f. green .. .. 10 10
D 192. 5 f. green .. .. 40 15
D 193. 6 f. green .. .. 15 15
D 194. 10 f. green .. .. 10 10
D 195. 12 f. green .. .. 10 10
D 196. 15 f. green .. .. 15 10
D 197. 20 f. green .. .. 10 10
D 198. 30 f. green .. .. 10 10
D 349. 40 f. green .. .. 15 15
D 350. 50 f. green .. .. 15 15
D 351. 120 f. green .. .. 15 15
D 352. 200 f. green .. .. 15 15
D 430. 2 k. green .. .. 10 15
D 431. 5 k. green .. .. 10 15
D 432. 50 k. green .. .. 10 15

**1919.** Overprinted **KOZTARSASAG**.
D325 **D 9** 2 f. red and green .. 10 10
D326 3 f. red and green .. 10 10
D327 10 f. red and green .. 10 10
D328 20 f. red and green .. 10 10
D329 40 f. red and green .. 10 10
D324 50 f. black and green 1·00 1·25
D330 50 f. red and green .. 10 10

**1919.** As Type **D 9** but inscr "MAGYAR POSTA" and optd with T **37** and **MAGYAR TANACS KOZTARSASAG**. Figures in black.
D 369. **D 9.** 2 f. green .. .. 35 35
D 370. 3 f. green .. .. 35 35
D 371. 10 f. green .. .. 3·25 3·25
D 372. 20 f. green .. .. 35 35
D 373. 40 f. green .. .. 35 35
D 374. 50 f. green .. .. 35 35

**1919.** As Type **D 9**, but inscribed. "MAGYAR POSTA". Figures in Black.
D 375. **D 9.** 2 f. green .. .. 10 10
D 376. 3 f. green .. .. 10 10
D 377. 20 f. green .. .. 10 15
D 378. 40 f. green .. .. 10 15
D 379. 50 f. green .. .. 10 15

**1921.** Surch. **PORTO** and value. Inscr. "MAGYAR KIR POSTA".
D 428. **18.** 100 f. on 15 f. purple 10 10
D 429. 500 f. on 15 f. purple 10 10
D 433. 2½ k. on 10 f. purple 10 10
D 434. 3 k. on 15 f. purple 10 10
D 437. 6 k. on 1½ k. purple 10 10
D 435. 9 k. on 40 f. green .. 10 10
D 438. 10 k. on 2½ k. green 10 10
D 436. 12 k. on 60 f. black 10 10
D 439. 15 k. on 1½ k. purple 10 10
D 440. 20 k. on 2½ k. green 10 10
D 441. 25 k. on 1½ k. purple 10 10
D 442. 30 k. on 1½ k. purple 10 10
D 443. 40 k. on 2½ k. green 10 10
D 444. 50 k. on 1½ k. purple 10 10
D 445. 100 k. on 4½ k. pur. 10 10
D 446. 200 k. on 4½ k. pur. 10 10
D 447. 300 k. on 4½ k. pur. 15 10
D 448. 500 k. on 2 k. blue 15 10
D 449. 500 k. on 3 k. brown 15 10
D 450. 1000 k. on 2 k. blue 15 10
D 451. 1000 k. on 3 k. brn. 30 10
D 452. 2000 k. on 2 k. blue 30 10
D 453. 2000 k. on 3 k. brn. 50 15
D 454. 5000 k. on 5 k. brn. 75 40

D 61.

D 84.

D 115.

**1926.**
D479 **D 61** 1 f. red .. .. 10 10
D480 2 f. red .. .. 10 10
D481 3 f. red .. .. 10 10
D482 4 f. red .. .. 10 10
D483 5 f. red .. .. 1·00 70
D509 8 f. red .. .. 10 10
D510 10 f. red .. .. 10 10

D486 D 61 16 f. red .. .. 15 10
D512 20 f. red .. .. 20 10
D487 32 f. red .. .. 30 15
D513 40 f. red .. .. 30 10
D489 50 f. red .. .. 50 15
D490 80 f. red .. .. 70 35

**1927.** Nos. 434/36b surch **PORTO** and value.
D491 49 1 f. on 500 k. light green and green .. 15 10
D492 2 f. on 1000 k. brown and bistre .. .. 15 10
D493 3 f. on 2000 k. blue and deep blue .. .. 15 35
D494 5 f. on 5000 k. mauve and purple .. .. 60 50
D495 10 f. on 10000 k. purple and red .. .. 50 25

**1931.** Surch.
D 529. D 61. 4 f. on 5 red .. 15 10
D 534. 10 f. on 16 f. red .. 50 25
D 531. 10 f. on 80 f. red .. 20 10
D 532. 12 f. on 50 f. red .. 30 10
D 533. 20 f. on 32 f. red .. 35 15

**1934.**
D 569. D 84. 2 f. blue .. .. 10 10
D 570. 4 f. blue .. .. 10 10
D 571. 6 f. blue .. .. 10 10
D 572. 8 f. blue .. .. 10 10
D 573. 10 f. blue .. .. 10 10
D 574. 12 f. blue .. .. 10 10
D 575. 16 f. blue .. .. 10 10
D 576. 20 f. blue .. .. 15 10
D 577. 40 f. blue .. .. 20 10
D 578. 80 f. blue .. .. 50 20

**1941.**
D 684. D 115. 2 f. brown .. .. 10 10
D 685. 3 f. brown .. .. 10 10
D 686. 4 f. brown .. .. 10 10
D 687. 6 f. brown .. .. 10 10
D 688. 8 f. brown .. .. 10 10
D 689. 10 f. brown .. .. 10 10
D 690. 12 f. brown .. .. 10 10
D 691. 16 f. brown .. .. 10 10
D 692. 18 f. brown .. .. 10 10
D 693. 20 f. brown .. .. 10 10
D 694. 24 f. brown .. .. 10 10
D 695. 30 f. brown .. .. 10 10
D 696. 36 f. brown .. .. 10 10
D 697. 40 f. brown .. .. 10 10
D 698. 50 f. brown .. .. 10 10
D 699. 60 f. brown .. .. 15 10

**1945.** Surch **1945** and value. Blue surface-tinted paper.
D 825. D 115. 10 f. on 2 f. brown 10 10
D 826. 10 f. on 3 f. brown 10 10
D 827. 20 f. on 4 f. brown 10 10
D 828. 20 f. on 6 f. brown 3·00 3·00
D 829. 20 f. on 8 f. brown 10 10
D 830. 40 f. on 12 f. brown 10 10
D 831. 40 f. on 16 f. brown 10 10
D 832. 40 f. on 18 f. brown 10 10
D 833. 60 f. on 24 f. brown 10 10
D 834. 80 f. on 30 f. brown 10 10
D 835. 90 f. on 36 f. brown 10 10
D 836. 1 p. on 10 f. brown 10 10
D 837. 1 p. on 40 f. brown 10 10
D 838. 2 p. on 20 f. brown 10 10
D 839. 2 p. on 50 f. brown 10 10
D 840. 2 p. on 60 f. brown 10 10
D 841. 10 p. on 3 f. brown 10 10
D 842. 12 p. on 8 f. brown 10 10
D 843. 20 p. on 24 f. brown 10 10

D 154. Numeral. D 201. D 215.

**1946.**
D 984. D 154. 4 f. red and brown 20 10
D 985. 10 f. red and brown 50 10
D 986. 20 f. red and brown 20 10
D 987. 30 f. red and brown 20 10
D 988. 40 f. red and brown 30 10
D 989. 50 f. red and brown 1·00 15
D 990. 60 f. red and brown 35 10
D 991. 1 fo. 20 red & brn. 80 10
D 992. 2 fo. red and brown 90 10

**1950.**
D1114 D 154 4 fi. purple .. 10 10
D1115 10 fi. purple .. 10 10
D1116 20 fi. purple .. 10 10
D1117 30 fi. purple .. 10 10
D1118 40 fi. purple .. 30 10
D1119 50 fi. purple .. 65 10
D1120 60 fi. purple .. 55 10
D1121 1 fo. 20 purple .. 85 10
D1122 2 fo. purple .. 1·75 10

**1951.** Fiscal stamps surch. with Arms. **MAGYAR POSTA PORTO** and value.
D 1157. D 201. 8 fi. brown .. 15 15
D 1158. 10 fi. brown .. 15 15
D 1159. 12 fi. brown .. 25 25

**1951.**
D 1210. D 215. 4 fi. brown .. 10 10
D 1211. 6 fi. brown .. 10 10
D 1212. 8 fi. brown .. 10 10
D 1213. 10 fi. brown .. 10 10
D 1214. 14 fi. brown .. 10 10
D 1215. 20 fi. brown .. 10 10
D 1216. 30 fi. brown .. 10 10
D 1217. 40 fi. brown .. 10 10
D 1218. 50 fi. brown .. 20 10
D 1219. 60 fi. brown .. 25 10
D 1220. 1 fo. 20 brown .. 35 10
D 1221. 2 fo. brown .. 60 10

D 240. D 282.

**1953.** 50th Anniv. of 1st Hungarian Postage Due Stamps.
D 1305. D 240. 4 fi. blk. & grn... 10 10
D 1306. 6 fi. blk. & grn... 10 10
D 1307. 8 fi. blk. & grn... 10 10
D 1308. 10 fi. blk. & grn. 10 10
D 1309. 12 fi. blk. & grn. 10 10
D 1310. 14 fi. blk. & grn. 10 10
D 1311. 16 fi. blk. & grn. 10 10
D 1312. 20 fi. blk. & grn. 10 10
D 1313. 24 fi. blk. & grn. 10 10
D 1314. 30 fi. blk. & grn. 10 10
D 1315. 36 fi. blk. & grn. 10 10
D 1316. 40 fi. blk. & grn. 15 10
D 1317. 50 fi. blk. & grn. 20 10
D 1318. 60 fi. blk. & grn. 20 10
D 1319. 70 fi. blk. & grn. 25 10
D 1320. 80 fi. blk. & grn. 30 10
D 1321. 1 fo. 20 blk. & grn. 40 10
D 1322. 2 fo. blk. & grn. 70 10

**1958.** Forint values are larger (31 × 22 mm.).
D 1498. D 282. 4 fi. blk. & red.. 10 10
D 1499. 6 fi. blk. & red.. 10 10
D 1500. 8 fi. blk. & red.. 10 10
D 1501. 10 fi. blk. & red.. 10 10
D 1502. 12 fi. blk. & red.. 10 10
D 1503. 14 fi. blk. & red.. 10 10
D 1504. 16 fi. blk. & red.. 10 10
D 1505. 20 fi. blk. & red.. 10 10
D 1506. 24 fi. blk. & red.. 10 10
D 1507. 30 fi. blk. & red.. 10 10
D 1508. 36 fi. blk. & red.. 10 10
D 1509. 40 fi. blk. & red.. 10 10
D 1510. 50 fi. blk. & red.. 10 10
D 1511. 60 fi. blk. & red.. 15 10
D 1512. 70 fi. blk. & red.. 20 10
D 1513. 80 fi. blk. & red.. 25 10
D 1514. – 1 fo. brown .. 15 10
D 1515. – 1 fo. 20 brown .. 35 10
D 1516. – 2 fo. brown .. 60 10
D 1517. – 4 fo. brown .. 60 10

D 587. Money-order Cancelling Machine. D 944. Foot Messenger.

**1973.** Postal Operations.
D2847 D 587 20 fi. brown & red 10 10
D2848 – 40 fi. blue and red 10 10
D2849 – 80 fi. violet & red 20 10
D2850 – 1 fo. green & red 25 10
D2851 – 1 fo. 20 grn & red 30 10
D2852 – 2 fo. violet, & red 1·10 15
D2853 – 3 fo. blue and red 65 10
D2854 – 4 fo. brown & red 70 10
D2855 – 8 fo. purple & red 80 10
D2856 – 10 fo. green & red 1·00 10

DESIGNS—As Type D 587: 40 fi. Parcel scales, self-service post office; 80 fi. Automatic parcels-registration machine; 1 fo. Data-recording machine. 28 × 22 mm: 1 fo. 20, Ilyushin Il-18 mail plane and van; 2 fo. Diesel mail train; 3 fo. Postman on motor cycle; 4 fo. Postman at mail-boxes; 8 fo. Toshiba automatic sorting machine; 10 f. Postman on motor cycle (different)

**1987.** Postal History. Multicoloured.
D 3810. 1 fo. Type D 944 .. 10 10
D 3811. 4 fo. Post rider .. 10 10
D 3812. 6 fo. Horse-drawn mail coach .. .. 10 10
D 3813. 8 fo. Railway mail carriage .. 15 10
D 3814. 10 fo. Mail van .. 20 10
D 3815. 20 fo. Mail plane .. 40 10

SAVINGS BANK STAMP

B 17.

**1916.**
B 199. B 17. 10 f. purple .. 15 15



## SZEGED

The following issues were made by the Hungarian National Government led by Admiral Horthy, which was set up in Szeged in 1919, then under French occupation, and which later replaced the Communist regime established by Bela Kun.

100 filler = 1 korona.

**1919.** Stamps of Hungary optd. **MAGYAR NEMZETI KORMÁNY Szeged, 1919.** or surch.

(a) War Charity stamps of 1916.
1. 20. 10 f. (+2 f.) red .. 1·25 1·25
2. – 15 f. (+2 f.) violet .. 50 50
3. 22. 40 f. (+2 f.) lake .. 3·00 3·00

(b) Harvesters and Parliament Types.
4. 18. 2 f. brown .. .. 15 15
5. 3 f. red .. .. 15 15
6. 5 f. green .. .. 15 15
7. 6 f. blue .. .. 8·00 8·00
8. 15 f. violet .. .. 30 30
9. 20 f. brown (No. 307) .. 20·00 20·00
10. 25 f. blue (No. 309) .. 15 15
11. 19. 50 f. purple .. .. 3·75 3·75
12. 75 f. blue .. .. 30 30
13. 80 f. green .. .. 3·00 3·00
14. 1 k. lake .. .. 20 20
15. 2 k. brown .. .. 35 35
16. 3 k. grey and violet .. 45 45
17. 5 k. brown .. .. 28·00 28·00
18. 10 k. lilac and brown 28·00 28·00

(c) Nos. 5 and 14 further surch.
19. 18. 45 on 3 f. red .. 40 40
20. 19. 10 on 1 k. lake .. 2·50 2·50

(d) Karl and Zita stamps.
21. 27. 10 f. red .. .. 20 20
22. 20 f. brown .. .. 15 15
23. 25 f. blue .. .. 11·00 11·00
24. 28. 40 f. olive .. .. 70 70

The following (Nos. 25/39) are also optd. **KOZTARSASAG.**

(e) War Charity stamp.
25. 22. 40 f. (+2 f.) lake .. 3·25 3·25

(f) Harvesters and Parliament Types.
26. 18. 3 f. red .. .. 8·50 8·50
27. 4 f. slate .. .. 45 45
28. 5 f. green .. .. 4·50 4·50
29. 6 f. blue .. .. 2·00 2·00
30. 10 f. red .. .. 5·00 5·00
31. 20 f. brown .. .. 21·00 21·00
32. 20 (f) on 2 f. bistre .. 15 15
33. 40 f. olive .. .. 20 20
34. 19. 3 k. grey and violet .. 20·00 20·00

(g) Karl and Zita stamps.
35. 27. 10 f. red .. .. 3·00 3·00
36. 15 f. violet .. .. 70 70
37. 20 f. brown .. .. 21·00 21·00
38. 25 f. blue .. .. 5·00 5·00
39. 28. 50 f. purple .. .. 15 15

EXPRESS LETTER STAMP

**1919.** No. E 245 optd. as above.
E 41. E 18. 2 f. olive and red .. 2·00 2·00

NEWSPAPER STAMP

**1919.** No. N 136 optd. **MAGYAR NEMZETI KORMANY Szeged, 1919.**
N 40. N 9. (2 f.) orange .. 15 15

POSTAGE DUE STAMPS

**1919.** Nos. D 191, etc.
(a) Optd. as above, in red.
D 42. D 9. 2 f. red and green .. 60 60
D 43. 6 f. red and green .. 1·40 1·40
D 44. 10 f. red and green 1·00 1·00
D 45. 12 f. red and green .. 1·00 1·00
D 46. 20 f. red and green 80 80
D 47. 30 f. red and green 1·00 1·00

(b) No. E 41 surch. **PORTO** and new value in red.
D 48. E 18. 50 f. on 2 f. olive & red 60 60
D 49. 100 f. on 2 f. olive & red 1·25 1·25

# ICELAND

Pt. 11

An island lying S.E. of Greenland. An independent state formerly under the Danish sovereign, now a republic.

1873. 96 skilling = 1 riksdaler.
1876. 100 aurar = 1 krona.

1. þrír (6.)

**1873.**
1. 1. 2 s. blue .. .. .. £750 £1600
5. 3 s. grey .. .. .. £300 £950
2. 4 s. red .. .. .. £120 £750
3. 8 s. brown .. .. .. £200 £850
7. 16 s. yellow .. .. .. 85·00 £500

**1876.**
42 1. 3 a. yellow .. .. 3·25 18·00
27 4 a. grey and red .. 14·00 17·00
13 5 a. blue .. .. £225 £500
28 5 a. green .. .. 2·50 2·10
29a 6 a. grey .. .. 13·50 11·50
30 10 a. red .. .. 6·25 2·10
31 16 a. brown .. .. 50·00 75·00
18 20 a. mauve .. .. £850 £375
32a 20 a. blue .. .. 35·00 26·00
33 25 a. blue and brown.. 15·00 24·00
19 40 a. green .. .. 75·00 £160
23b 40 a. mauve .. .. 28·00 32·00
24 50 a. red and blue .. 60·00 70·00
25 100 a. purple and brown 60·00 90·00

**1897.** Surch as T 6 with figure 3 under word.
38 1 3 on 5 a. green .. .. £325 £300

**1897.** Surch. as **T 6.**
40. 1. 3 on 5 a. green .. .. £500 £475

**1902.** Optd **I GILDI '02—'03.**
54. 1. 3 a. yellow .. .. 60 1·40
55. 4 a. grey and red .. 26·00 42·00
56. 5 a. green .. .. 30 6·25
58. 6 a. grey .. .. 30 6·25
60. 10 a. red .. .. 85 7·75
61. 16 a. brown .. .. 19·00 38·00
62. 20 a. blue .. .. 70 8·00
64. 25 a. blue and brown .. 50 13·00
66. 40 a. mauve .. .. 70 42·00
67. 50 a. red and blue .. 2·25 50·00
52. 100 a. purple and brown.. 38·00 60·00

11. King Christian IX. 12. Kings. Christian IX and Frederik VIII. 13. Jon Sigurdsson.

**1902.**
68. 11. 3 a. orange .. .. 4·75 2·50
69. 4 a. red and grey .. 2·75 1·10
70. 5 a. green .. .. 19·00 85
71. 6 a. brown .. .. 14·50 7·75
72. 10 a. red .. .. 4·75 85
73. 16 a. brown .. .. 5·75 7·75
74. 20 a. blue .. .. 2·40 3·00
75. 25 a. green and brown .. 2·25 5·25
76. 40 a. mauve .. .. 2·75 4·75
77. 50 a. black and grey .. 4·75 21·00
78. 1 k. brown and blue .. 5·75 8·50
79. 2 k. blue and brown .. 19·00 60·00
80. 5 k. grey and brown .. £120 £190

**1907.**
81. 12. 1 e. red and green .. 1·10 95
82. 3 a. brown .. .. 2·75 1·10
83. 4 a. red and grey .. 1·40 75
84. 5 a. green .. .. 55·00 85
85. 6 a. grey .. .. 24·00 2·50
114. 10 a. red .. .. 2·40 85
87. 15 a. green and red .. 4·75 1·00
88. 16 a. brown .. .. 6·50 28·00
89. 20 a. blue .. .. 5·75 3·75
90. 25 a. green and brown .. 3·75 9·50
91. 40 a. red .. .. 4·25 11·50
92. 50 a. red and grey .. 4·75 9·50
93. 1 k. brown and blue .. 19·00 50·00
94. 2 k. green and brown .. 19·00 55·00
95. 5 k. blue and brown .. £140 £275

**1911.** Birth Cent. of Jon Sigurdsson (historian and Althing member).
96. 13. 1 e. green .. .. 1·75 1·10
97. 3 a. brown .. .. 2·75 10·50
98. 4 a. blue .. .. 1·00 1·25
99. 6 a. grey .. .. 9·50 21·00
100. 15 a. violet .. .. 11·50 1·25
101. 25 a. orange .. .. 21·00 38·00

**1912.** As T 13, but portrait of King Frederik VIII and "JON SIGURDSSON" omitted.
102. 5 a. green .. .. 24·00 10·50
103. 10 a. red .. .. 24·00 10·50
104. 20 a. blue .. .. 35·00 14·50
105. 50 a. red .. .. 9·50 28·00
106. 1 k. yellow .. .. 24·00 55·00
107. 2 k. red .. .. 19·00 45·00
108. 5 k. brown .. .. £110 £180

15. King Christian X. 22. Landing Mails at Vik.

**1920.**
116 15. 1 e. red and green .. 65 95
117 3 a. brown .. .. 3·25 11·50
184 4 a. red and grey .. 1·40 1·60
132 5 a. green .. .. 2·75 1·00
185 6 a. grey .. .. 1·40 2·75
186 7 a. green .. .. 45 1·25
121 8 a. brown .. .. 4·75 1·90
122 10 a. red .. .. 1·40 8·00
133 10 a. green .. .. 2·40 1·10
187 10 a. brown .. .. 85·00 75
123 15 a. violet .. .. 28·00 1·10
124 20 a. blue .. .. 1·40 13·50
134 20 a. brown .. .. 42·00 1·10
125 25 a. green and brown 11·50 1·25
135 25 a. red .. .. 8·50 30·00
189 30 a. green and red .. 21·00 4·25
127 40 a. red .. .. 35·00 2·50
136 40 a. blue .. .. 50·00 11·50
128 50 a. red and grey .. £120 8·50
191 1 k. brown and blue .. 35·00 6·25
130 2 k. green and brown £170 24·00
131 5 k. blue and brown .. 48·00 10·50
193 10 k. black and green £225 £130

**1921.** Various types surch.
137. 11. 5 a. on 16 a. brown .. 2·75 23·00
138. 12. 5 a. on 16 a. brown .. 2·75 6·25
139. 15. 10 a. on 5 a. green .. 4·75 1·90
140. 11. 20 a. on 25 a. green & brown .. .. 5·75 5·75

141. **12.** 20 a. on 25 a. green & brown .. 3·25 6·25
142. **11.** 20 a. on 40 a. mauve .. 6·25 15·00
143. **12.** 20 a. on 40 a. red .. 7·25 13·50
144. **11.** 30 a. on 50 a. grey .. 21·00 13·50
145. 50 a. on 5 k. grey & brn. 48·00 28·00
146. **15.** 1 k. on 40 a. blue .. £100 28·00
147. **13.** 2 k. on 25 a. orange .. 85·00 £100
148. – 10 k. on 50 a. red (No. 105) .. .. £200 £350
149. – 10 k. on 1 k. yellow (No. 106) .. .. £250 £475
150. **11.** 10 k. on 2 k. bl. & brn. 48·00 24·00
150a. **12.** 10 k. on 5 k. bl. & brn. £350 £475

**1925.**

151. **22.** 7 a. green .. .. 32·00 6·25
152. – 10 a. brown and blue .. 32·00 45
153. – 20 a. red .. .. 32·00 45
154. – 35 a. blue .. .. 55·00 7·75
155. **22.** 50 a. brown and green .. 55·00 95

DESIGNS: 10 a., 35 a. Reykjavik and Esjaberg (mountain). 20 a. National Museum, Reykjavik.

**1928.** Air. Optd with airplane.

156 **15** 10 a. red .. .. 50 9·00
157 **12** 50 a. purple and grey .. 42·00 90·00

**24.** Discovery of Iceland.

**25.** Gyrfalcon.

**1930.** Parliament Millenary Celebration.

158. – 3 a. violet (postage) .. 2·40 7·00
159. **24.** 5 a. blue and grey .. 2·40 7·00
160. – 7 a. green .. .. 2·40 7·00
161. – 10 a. purple .. .. 7·75 12·00
162. – 15 a. blue .. .. 2·40 7·00
163. – 20 a. red .. .. 32·00 60·00
164. – 25 a. brown .. .. 5·75 9·50
165. – 30 a. green .. .. 3·75 9·50
166. – 35 a. blue .. .. 4·75 9·50
167. – 40 a. red, blue and grey .. 3·75 9·50
168. – 50 a. brown .. .. 48·00 £100
169. – 1 k. green .. .. 48·00 £100
170. – 2 k. blue and green .. 65·00 £120
171. – 5 k. orange and yellow .. 38·00 90·00
172. – 10 k. lake .. .. 38·00 90·00
173. **25.** 10 a. blue (air) .. 19·00 50·00

DESIGNS—HORIZ. 3 a. Parliament House, Reykjavik. 7 a. Encampment at Thingvellir. 10 a. Arrival of Ingolf Arnarsson. 15 a. Naming the Island. 20 a. The Dash for "Althing" (Parliament). 25 a. Discovery of Arnarsson's pillar. 30 a. Lake Thingvellir. 35 a. Queen Aud. 40 a. National flag. 50 a. First "Althing" (Parliament), A.D. 930. 1 k. Map of Iceland. 2 k. Winter-bound farmstead. 5 k. Woman spinning. 10 k. Viking sacrifice to Thor.

**26.** Snaefellsjokull.

DESIGNS: 20 a. Old Icelandic fishing boat. 35 a. Icelandic Pony. 50 a. The Gullfoss Falls. 1 k. Statue of Arnarsson, Reykjavik.

**1930.** Air. Parliamentary Millenary.

174. **26.** 15 a. blue and brown .. 24·00 45·00
175. – 20 a. blue and brown .. 24·00 45·00
176. – 35 a. brown and green 45·00 90·00
177. – 50 a. blue and green .. 45·00 90·00
178. – 1 k. red and green .. 45·00 90·00

**1931.** Air. Optd. **Zeppelin 1931.**

179. **15.** 30 a. green and red .. 29·00 £110
180. 1 k. brown and blue .. 10·50 £110
181. 2 k. green and brown 48·00 £110

**29.** Gulfoss Falls.

**30.** Shipwreck and Breeches-buoy.

**1931.**

195. **29.** 5 a. grey .. .. 10·50 75
196. 20 a. red .. .. 8·50 10
197. 35 a. blue .. .. 19·00 11·50
198. 60 a. mauve .. .. 8·50 1·10
199. 65 a. brown .. .. 1·50 95
200. 75 a. blue .. .. 75·00 26·00

**1933.** Charity.

201. **30.** 10 a.+10 a. brown 1·60 4·75
202. – 20 a.+20 a. red 1·60 4·75
203. **30.** 35 a.+25 a. blue 1·60 4·75
204. – 50 a.+25 a. green 1·60 4·75

DESIGNS: 20 a. Children gathering flowers. 50 a. Aged fisherman and rowing boat.

**1933.** Air. Balbo Transatlantic Mass Formation Flight. Optd. **Hopflug Itala 1933.**

205. **15.** 1 k. brown and blue £100 £500
206. 5 k. blue and brown £325 £1300
207. 10 k. black and green £650 £2500

**32.** Avro 504K Biplane over Thingvellir.

DESIGNS: 25 a., 50 a. Monoplane and Aurora Borealis, 1 k., 2 k. Monoplane over map of Iceland.

**1934.** Air.

208 **32** 10 a. blue .. .. 1·10 1·90
209 20 a. green .. .. 2·75 3·75
210a – 25 a. violet .. .. 9·00 14·50
211 – 50 a. purple .. .. 2·75 5·75
212 – 1 k. brown .. .. 19·00 28·00
213 – 2 k. red .. .. 7·00 11·50

**33.** Dynjandi falls.

**35.** Matthias Jochumsson.

**36.** King Christian X.

**1935.**

214. **33.** 10 a. blue .. .. 17·00 10
215. – 1 k. green .. .. 28·00 10

DESIGN—HORIZ. 1 k. Mt. Hekla.

**1935.** Birth Centenary of Matthias Jochumsson (poet).

216. **35.** 3 a. green .. .. 50 3·25
217. 5 a. grey .. .. 11·50 1·10
218. 7 a. green .. .. 15·00 1·25
219. 35 a. blue .. .. 40 1·10

**1937.** Silver Jubilee of King Christian X.

220. **36.** 10 a. green .. .. 2·00 19·00
221. 30 a. brown .. .. 2·00 8·25
222. 40 a. red .. .. 2·00 8·25

**37.** The Great Geyser.

**38.** Reykjavik University.

**1938.**

226. **37.** 15 a. purple .. .. 4·75 9·50
227. 20 a. red .. .. 19·00 10
228. 35 a. blue .. .. 40 50
229. – 40 a. brown .. .. 9·50 24·00
230. – 45 a. blue .. .. 80 75
231. – 50 a. green .. .. 17·00 75
232a. – 60 a. blue .. .. 5·25 1·00
233. – 1 k. blue .. .. 1·50 10

The frames of the 40 a. to 1 k. differ from Type 37.

**1938.** 20th Anniv. of Independence.

234. **38.** 25 a. green .. .. 6·25 13·50
235. 30 a. brown .. .. 6·25 13·50
236. 40 a. purple .. .. 6·25 13·50

**1939.** Surch. with bold figure **5.**

237. **35.** 5 on 35 a. blue .. .. 45 90

**40.** Trylon and Perisphere.

**41.** Codfish.

**42.** Icelandic Flag.

**1939.** New York World's Fair

238. **40.** 20 a. red .. .. 2·75 5·75
239. – 35 a. blue .. .. 3·25 7·00
240 – 45 a. green .. .. 3·50 8·50
241. – 2 k. black .. .. 42·00 £120

DESIGNS: 35 a. Viking longship and route to America. 45 a., 2 k. Statue of Thorfinn Karlsefni, Reykjavik.

**1939.**

242. **41.** 1 e. blue .. .. 10 3·25
243. – 3 a. violet .. .. 15 40
244. **41.** 5 a. brown .. .. 15 10
245. – 7 a. green .. .. 4·25 7·50
246. **42.** 10 a. red and blue .. 2·00 95
247. – 10 a. green .. .. 26·00 10
248. – 10 a. black .. .. 15 10
249. – 12 a. green .. .. 30 10
250. **41.** 25 a. red .. .. 17·00 10
251. 25 a. brown .. .. 20 10
252. – 35 a. red .. .. 45 10
253. **41.** 50 a. green .. .. 45 10

DESIGN: 3 a., 7 a., 10 a. (Nos. 247/8), 12 a., 35 a. Herring.

**43.** Statue of Thorfinn Karlsefni.

**46.** Statue of Snorri Sturluson (O. Vigeland).

**1939.**

254. **43.** 2 k. grey .. .. 2·40 10
255. 5 k. brown .. .. 19·00 20
256. 10 k. brown .. .. 9·50 1·40

**1940.** New York World's Fair. Optd. **1940.**

257. **40.** 20 a. red .. .. 11·50 28·00
258. – 35 a. blue (No. 239) .. 11·50 28·00
259. – 45 a green (No. 240) .. 11·50 28·00
260. – 2 k. black (No. 241) .. 80·00 £325

**1941.** Surch. **25.**

261. **35.** 25 a. on 3 a. olive .. 65 1·25

**1941.** 700th Death Anniv. of Snorri Sturluson (historian).

262. **46.** 25 a. red .. .. 75 1·90
263. 50 a. blue .. .. 1·00 3·75
264. 1 k. olive .. .. 1·00 3·75

**47.** Jon Sigurdsson (historian and Althing member).

**48.** Grumman Goose Amphibian over Thingvellir.

**1944.** Proclamation of Republic.

265. **47.** 10 a. grey .. .. 15 75
266. 25 a. brown .. .. 30 75
267. 50 a. green .. .. 30 75
268. 1 k. black .. .. 65 75
269. 5 k. brown .. .. 2·40 9·50
270. 10 k. brown .. .. 28·00 80·00

**1947.** Air.

271. **48.** 15 a. orange .. .. 60 1·00
272. – 30 a. black .. .. 60 1·00
273. – 75 a. red .. .. 50 75
274. – 1 k. blue .. .. 50 75
275. – 1 k. 80 blue .. .. 12·00 14·50
276. – 2 k. brown .. .. 1·10 1·75
277. – 2 k. 50 green .. .. 24·00 85
278. – 3 k. green .. .. 1·10 1·75
279. – 3 k. 30 blue .. .. 9·50 5·75

DESIGNS—HORIZ: 30 a. Catalina flying boat over Isafjordur. 75 a. Douglas DC-3 over Eyjafjord. 1 k. 80, Douglas DC-3 over Snaefellsjokull. 2 k. 50, Catalina over Eiriksjokull. 3 k. Douglas DC-3 over Reykjavik. 3 k. 30, Douglas DC-3 over Oraefajokull. VERT: 1 k. Grumman Goose over Sethisfjordur, Strandatindur. 2 k. Catalina over Hvalfjordur, Thyrill.

For stamps as Type **48** but without airplane, see Nos. 346/8.

**50.** Mt. Hekla in Eruption.

**53.** Hospital and Child.

**1948.** Inscr. "HEKLA 1947".

280. **50.** 12 a. purple .. .. 15 10
281. – 25 a. green .. .. 1·50 10
282. – 35 a. red .. .. 35 10
283. **50.** 50 a. brown .. .. 1·75 10
284. – 60 a. blue .. .. 6·50 3·75
285. – 1 k. brown .. .. 12·50 10
286. – 10 k. violet .. .. 48·00 20

DESIGNS—VERT. 35 a., 60 a. Mt. Hekla in Eruption (different view). HORIZ. 25 a., 1 k., 10 k. Mt. Hekla.

**1949.** Red Cross Fund.

287. **53.** 10 a.+10 a. green .. 40 80
288. – 35 a.+15 a. red .. 40 80
289. – 50 a.+25 a. brown .. 40 80
290. – 60 a.+25 a. blue .. 50 80
291. – 75 a.+25 a. blue .. 90 1·10

DESIGNS: 35 a. Nurse and patient. 50 a. Nurse arranging patient's bed. 60 a. Aged couple. 75 a. Freighter and ship's lifeboat.

**54.** Pony Pack-train.

**1949.** 75th Anniv. of U.P.U.

292. **54.** 25 a. green .. .. 30 40
293. – 35 a. red .. .. 30 40
294. – 60 a. blue .. .. 40 80
295. – 2 k. orange .. .. 1·25 90

DESIGNS: 35 a. Reykjavik. 60 a. Map of Iceland. 2 k. Almannagja Gorge.

**55.** Trawler "Ingolfur Arnarson".

**56.** Bishop Jon Arason.

**1950.**

296. – 5 a. brown .. .. 10 10
297. **55.** 10 a. grey .. .. 20 10
298. – 20 a. brown .. .. 10 10
299. **55.** 25 a. red .. .. 30 10
300. – 60 a. green .. .. 13·00 19·00
301. – 75 a. orange .. .. 40 10
302. – 90 a. red .. .. 40 10
303. – 1 k. brown .. .. 5·75 10
304. **55.** 1 k. 25 purple .. .. 19·00 10
305. 1 k. 50 blue .. .. 13·50 20
306. – 2 k. violet .. .. 23·00 10
307. – 5 k. green .. .. 32·00 1·00
308. – 25 k. black .. .. £150 14·50

DESIGNS—As T **55**: 5, 90 a., 2 k. Vestmannaeyjar harbour. 20, 75 a., 1 k. Tractor. 60 a., 5 k. Flock of sheep. 29×33 mm: 25 k. Parliament Building, Reykjavik.

**1950.** 400th Death Anniv. of Bishop Arason.

309. **56.** 1 k. 80 red .. .. 2·75 3·00
310. 3 k. 30 green .. .. 1·25 2·25

**57.** Postman, 1776.

**58.** President Bjornsson.

**1951.** 175th Anniv. of Icelandic Postal Service.

311. **57.** 2 k. blue .. .. 1·90 2·00
312. – 3 k. purple .. .. 2·40 2·75

DESIGN: 3 k. as 2 k. but aeroplane replaces man.

**1952.** Death of S. Bjornsson (First President of Iceland).

313. **58.** 1 k. 25 blue .. .. 2·25 10
314. 2 k. 20 green .. .. 50 3·75
315. 5 k. blue .. .. 8·25 60
316. 10 k. brown .. .. 35·00 25·00

**1953.** Netherlands Flood Relief Fund. Surch. **Hollandshjalp 1953+25.**

317. – 75 a.+25 a. orange (No. 301) .. .. 1·00 3·75
318. **55.** 1 k. 25+25 a. purple .. 1·60 3·75

**60.** "Reykjabok" (Saga of Burnt Njal).

**62.** Hannes Hafstein.

**1953.**

319. **60.** 10 a. black .. .. 10 10
320. – 70 a. green .. .. 30 10
321. – 1 k. red .. .. 40 10
322. – 1 k. 75 blue .. .. 24·00 1·40
323. – 10 k. brown .. .. 9·50 95

DESIGNS: 70 a. Hand writing on manuscript. 1 k. "Stjorn" (15th century manuscript). 1 k. 75, Books and candle. 10 k. Page from "Skardsbok" (14th century law manuscript).

**1954.** No. 282 surch. **5 AURAR** and bars.

324. 5 a. on 35 a. red .. 10 10

**1954.** 50th Anniv. of Appointment of Hannes Hafstein as first native Minister of Iceland. Portraits of Hafstein.

325. **62.** 1 k. 25 blue .. .. 3·75 45
326. – 2 k. 45 green .. .. 19·00 28·00
327. – 5 k. red .. .. 19·00 2·40

**63.** Icelandic Wrestling.

**64.** St. Thorlacas.

**1955.** Icelandic National Sports.

328. **63.** 75 a. brown .. .. 15 15
329. – 1 k. 25 blue (Diving) .. 30 15
330. **63.** 1 k. 50 red .. .. 95 10
331. – 1 k. 75 blue (Diving) .. 30 10

**1956.** 9th Cent. of Consecration of First Icelandic Bishop and Skalholt Rebuilding Fund. Inscr. as in T **64**.
332. **64.** 75 a.+25 a. red .. 15 30
333. – 1 k. 25+75 a. brown .. 15 30
334. – 1 k. 75+1 k. 25 black .. 55 85
DESIGNS—HORIZ. 1 k. 25, Skalholt Cathedral, 1772. VERT. 1 k. 75, J. P. Vidalin, Bishop of Skalholt, 1698–1720.

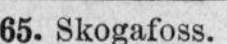

**65.** Skogafoss. **67.** Map of Iceland.

**1956.** Power Plants and Waterfalls.
335. **65.** 15 a. blue .. .. 15 10
336. – 50 a. green .. .. 25 10
337. – 60 a. brown .. .. 2·50 3·75
338. – 1 k. 50 violet .. 24·00 10
339. – 2 k. brown .. .. 1·50 10
340. – 2 k. 45 black .. .. 5·75 7·50
341. – 3 k. blue .. .. 3·75 55
342. – 5 k. green .. .. 11·50 1·40
DESIGNS—HORIZ. 50 a. Ellidaarvirkjun. 60 a. Godafoss. 1 k. 50, Sogsvirkjun. 2 k. Dettifoss. 2 k. 45, Andakilsarvirkjun. 3 k. Laxarvirkjun. VERT. 5 k. Gullfoss.

**1956.** 50th Anniv. of Icelandic Telegraph System.
343. **67.** 2 k. 30 blue .. .. 30 75

**1956.** Northern Countries' Day. As T **100** of Denmark.
344. 1 k. 50 red .. .. .. 1·00 75
345. 1 k. 75 blue .. .. 12·00 9·25

**1957.** Designs as T 48 but airplane omitted.
346. 2 k. green .. .. 2·75 10
347. 3 k. blue .. .. 2·75 10
348. 10 k. brown .. .. 5·75 20
DESIGNS—HORIZ. 2 k. Snaefellsjokull. 3 k. Eiriksjokull. 10 k. Oraefajokull.

**68.** Presidential Residence, Bessastadir. **69.** Norwegian Spruce.

**1957.**
349. **68.** 25 k. black .. .. 19·00 3·75

**1957.** Reafforestation Campaign.
350. **69.** 35 a. green .. .. 20 10
351. – 70 a. green .. .. 20 10
DESIGN: 70 a. Icelandic birch and saplings.

**70.** Jonas Hallgrimsson. **71.** River Beauty. **72.** Icelandic Pony.

**1957.** 150th Birth Anniv. of Hallgrimsson (poet).
352. **70.** 5 k. black and green .. 1·40 40

**1958.** Flowers. Multicoloured.
353. 1 k. Type **71** .. .. 15 10
354. 2 k. 50 Wild pansy .. 20 15

**1958.**
355. **72.** 10 a. black .. .. 15 10
356. 1 k. red .. .. 35 10
357. 2 k. 25 brown .. .. 75 10

**73.** Icelandic Flag. **74.** Old Government House.

**1958.** 40th Anniv. of Icelandic Flag.
358. **73.** 3 k. 50, red and blue .. 1·40 40
359. 50 k. red and blue .. 5·75 5·75
No. 359 is $23\frac{1}{2}\times26\frac{1}{2}$ mm.

**1958.**
360. **74.** 1 k. 50 blue .. .. 40 10
361. 2 k. green .. .. 50 10
362. 3 k. red .. .. 40 10
363. 4 k. brown .. .. 70 15

**75.** Jon Porkelsson with Children. **76.** Vickers Viscount and 1919 Avro 504K Biplane.

**1959.** Death Bicent. of Jon Porkelsson (Johannes Thorkillius, Rector of Skalholt).
364. **75.** 2 k. turquoise .. .. 35 40
365. 3 k. purple .. .. 35 65

**1959.** Air. 40th Anniv. of Iceland Civil Aviation.
366. **76.** 3 k. 50 blue .. .. 70 50
367. – 4 k. 05 green .. .. 55 40
DESIGN: 4 k. 05, Douglas DC-4 and Avro 504K aircraft.

**77.** Salmon. **78.** "The Outcast" (after Jonsson).

**1959.**
368. **77.** 25 a. blue .. .. 15 10
369. – 90 a. black and brown .. 55 10
370. – 2 k. black and green .. 70 10
371. **77.** 5 k. green .. .. 8·00 95
372. – 25 k. violet and yellow 14·00 13·00
DESIGNS—VERT. 90 a., 2 k. Eiders. 25 k. Gyrfalcon.

**1960.** World Refugee Year.
373. **78.** 2 k. 50 brown .. .. 10 10
374. 4 k. 50 blue .. .. 40 60

**1960.** Europa. As T **373** of Belgium, but size 33 × $22\frac{1}{2}$ mm.
375. 3 k. green .. .. 60 30
376. 5 k. 50 blue .. .. 50 1·10

**79.** Dandelions. **80.** Sigurdsson.

**1960.** Wild Flowers.
377. – 50 a. violet, green and myrtle (Campanulas) 10 10
378. – 1 k. 20 violet, green & brown (Geraniums) 20 10
379. **79.** 2 k. 50 yell., grn. & brn. 25 10
380. – 3 k. 50 yellow, green and blue (Buttercup) 70 10
See also Nos. 412/5 and 446/7.

**1961.** 150th Birth Anniv. of Jon Sigurdsson (historian and Althing member).
381. **80.** 50 a. red .. .. 10 15
382. 3 k. blue .. .. 1·25 90
383. 5 k. purple .. .. 30 45

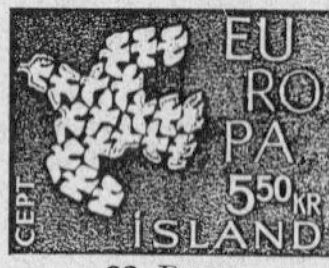

**81.** Reykjavik Harbour. **82.** Doves.

**1961.** 175th Anniv. of Reykjavik.
384. **81.** 2 k. 50 blue and green .. 50 10
385. 4 k. 50 blue and violet .. 75 15

**1961.** Europa.
386. **82.** 5 k. 50 multicoloured .. 30 50
387. 6 k. multicoloured .. 30 50

**83.** B. Sveinsson. **84.** Productivity Institute.

**1961.** 50th Anniv. of Iceland University.
388. **83.** 1 k. brown .. .. 10 10
389. – 1 k. 40 blue .. .. 10 10
390. – 10 k. green .. .. 1·00 30
DESIGNS—VERT. 1 k. 40, B. M. Olsen (first Vice-chancellor). HORIZ. 10 k. University building.

**1962.** Icelandic Buildings.
392. **84.** 2 k. 50 blue .. .. 30 10
393. – 4 k. green .. .. 40 15
394. – 6 k. brown .. .. 50 15
DESIGNS: 4 k. Fishing Research Institute. 6 k. Agricultural Society's Headquarters.

**85.** Europa "Tree". **86.** Cable Map.

**1962.** Europa.
395. **85.** 5 k. 50 brn., grn. & yell. 15 15
396. 6 k. 50 brn., grn. & yell. 30 45

**1962.** Opening of North Atlantic Submarine Telephone Communications.
397. **86.** 5 k. green, red and lavender .. .. 1·00 25
398. 7 k. green, red and blue 50 15

**87.** S. Gudmundsson (scholar and curator). **88.** Herring Catch.

**1963.** Centenary of National Museum.
399. **87.** 4 k. brown and bistre .. 50 15
400. – 5 k. 50 brown and olive 40 15
DESIGN: 5 k. 50, Detail from carving on church door, Valthjofsstad.

**1963.** Freedom from Hunger.
401. **88.** 5 k. multicoloured .. 80 20
402. 7 k. 50 multicoloured 30 20

**89.** View of Akureyri. **90.** "Co-operation".

**1963.**
403. **89.** 3 k. green .. .. 20 10

**1963.** Europa.
404. **90.** 6 k. yell., ochre & brn. 30 30
405. 7 k. yellow, green & blue 30 30

**91.** Ambulance.

**1963.** Red Cross Cent.
406. **91.** 3 k.+50 a. mult. .. 20 30
407. 3 k. 50+50 a. mult. .. 20 30

**92.** "Gullfoss" (cargo liner). **93.** Scout Emblem.

**1964.** 50th Anniv. of Iceland Steamship Co.
408. **92.** 10 k. blk., purple & blue 1·50 1·25

**1964.** Icelandic Boy Scouts Commemoration.
409. **93.** 3 k. 50 multicoloured .. 70 10
410. 4 k. 50 multicoloured .. 70 20

**94.** Arms of Iceland. **95.** Europa "Flower".

**1964.** 20th Anniv. of Icelandic Republic.
411. **94.** 25 k. multicoloured .. 2·25 1·75

**1964.** Wild Flowers. As T **79**. Multicoloured.
412. 50 a. Mountain avens .. 10 10
413. 1 k. Glacier buttercup .. 15 10
414. 1 k. 50 Boybean .. .. 20 10
415. 2 k. White clover .. .. 25 10

**1964.** Europa.
416. **95.** 4 k. 50 turquoise, cream and brown .. .. 65 30
417. 9 k. sepia, cream & blue 75 50

**96.** Running. **97.** Rock Ptarmigan (Summer Plumage).

**1964.** Olympic Games, Tokyo.
418. **96.** 10 k. black and green .. 75 45

**1965.** Charity.
419. **97.** 3 k. 50+50 a. mult. 1·00 1·00
420. – 4 k. 50+50 a. mult. 1·25 1·25
DESIGN: 4 k. 50, Rock Ptarmigan in winter plumage.

**98.** "Sound Waves". **99.** Eruption, Nov., 1963.

**1965.** Centenary of I.T.U.
421. **98.** 4 k. 50 green .. .. 70 40
422. 7 k. 50 blue .. .. 20 15

**1965.** Birth of Surtsey Island. Multicoloured.
423. 1 k. 50 Type **99** .. .. 60 40
424. 2 k. Surtsey in April 1964 .. 60 45
425. 3 k. 50 Surtsey in Sept. '64 90 45
Nos. 424/5 are horiz.

**100.** Europa "Sprig". **101.** E. Benediktsson.

**1965.** Europa.
426. **100.** 5 k. grn, brown & ochre 1·00 90
427. 8 k. green, brown & turq. 90 90

**1965.** 25th Death Anniv. of Einar Benediktsson (poet).
428. **101.** 10 k. brn., blk., & blue 2·75 3·75

**102.** Girl in National Costume. **103.** White-tailed Sea Eagle.

**1965.**
429. **102.** 100 k. multicoloured .. 6·75 3·75

**1966.** Multicoloured.
430. 20 k. Great Northern Diver 5·00 4·75
431. 50 k. Type **103** .. .. 10·00 8·00

**104.** Londrangar. **105.** Europa "Ship".

**1966.** Landscapes (1st series). Multicoloured.
432. 2 k. 50 Type **104** .. .. 25 20
433. 4 k. Myvatn .. .. 35 15
434. 5 k. Bulandstindur .. 45 15
435. 6 k. 50 Dyrholaey .. 55 15
See also Nos. 465/8.

**1966.** Europa.
436. **105.** 7 k. turquoise blue & red 1·40 1·40
437. 8 k. brown, cream & red 1·40 1·40

106. Society Emblem. 107. Cogwheels.

**1966.** 150th Anniv. of Icelandic Literary Society.
438. **106.** 4 k. blue .. .. 20 10
439. 10 k. red .. .. 45 30

**1967.** Europa.
440. **107.** 7 k. blue, brown & yellow 1·10 85
441. 8 k. blue, grey and green 1·10 85

108. Old and New Maps of Iceland. 109. Trade Symbols.

**1967.** World Fair, Montreal.
442. **108.** 10 k. multicoloured .. 20 25

**1967.** 50th Anniv. of Icelandic Chamber of Commerce.
443. **109.** 5 k. multicoloured .. 15 15

110. Nest and Eggs of Ringed Plover.

**1967.** Charity.
444. **110.** 4 k. + 50 a. multicoloured 65 1·00
445. – 5 k. + 50 a. multicoloured 65 1·00
DESIGN: 5 k. Nest and eggs of Rock Ptarmigan.

**1968.** Wild Flowers. As T **79**. Multicoloured.
446. 50 a. Saxifrage .. .. 10 10
447. 2 k. 50 Orchid .. .. 20 10

111. Europa "Key". 112. Right-hand Traffic.

**1968.** Europa.
448. **111.** 9 k. 50 mve., blk. & yell. 95 95
449. 10 k. yell., sepia & green 95 95

**1968.** Adoption of Changed Rule of the Road.
450. **112.** 4 k. brown and yellow 15 10
451. 5 k. brown .. .. 15 10

113. "Fridriksson and Boy" (statue by S. Olafsson). 114. Library Interior.

**1968.** Birth Cent. of Pastor Fridrik Fridriksson (founder of Icelandic Y.M.C.A. and Y.W.C.A.).
452. **113.** 10 k. black and blue 20 20

**1968.** 150th Anniv. of National Library.
453. **114.** 5 k. brown and buff .. 10 10
454. 20 k. ultram. and blue 45 65

115. Jon Magnusson (former Prime Minister). 117. Colonnade.

**1968.** 50th Anniv. of Independence.
455. **115.** 4 k. lake .. .. 15 10
456. 50 k. sepia .. .. 2·75 3·50

**1969.** 50th Anniv. of Northern Countries' Union. Similar to T **159** of Denmark.
457. 6 k. 50 red .. .. 20 30
458. 10 k. blue .. .. 20 40

**1969.** Europa.
459. **117.** 13 k. multicoloured .. 2·40 1·90
460. 14 k. 50 multicoloured 30 40

118. Republican Emblem (after S. Jonsson). 119. Boeing 727 Airliner.

**1969.** 25th Anniv. of Republic.
461. **118.** 25 k. multicoloured .. 75 40
462. 100 k. multicoloured .. 4·75 4·75

**1969.** 50th Anniv. of Icelandic Aviation.
463. **119.** 9 k. 50 ultram. and blue 30 40
464. – 12 k. ultram. and blue .. 30 40
DESIGN: 12 k. Canadair CL-44-D4 (inscr "Rolls-Royce 400").

120. Snaefellsjokull.

**1970.** Landscapes (2nd series). Multicoloured.
465. 1 k. Type **120** .. .. 10 10
466. 4 k. Laxfoss and Baula .. 10 10
467. 5 k. Hattver (vert.) .. 10 10
468. 20 k. Fjardagil (vert.) .. 95 30

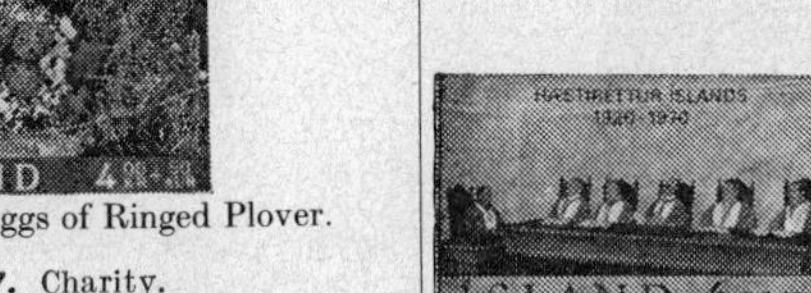

121. First Court Session. 122. Part of "Skardsbok" (14th-cent. law manuscript).

**1970.** 50th Anniv. of Icelandic Supreme Court.
469. **121.** 6 k. 50 multicoloured 15 10

**1970.** Icelandic Manuscripts. Multicoloured.
470. 5 k. Type **122** .. .. 10 10
471. 15 k. Part of preface to "Flateyjarbok" .. 35 50
472. 30 k. Illuminated initial from "Flateyjarbok" .. 65 80

123. "Flaming Sun". 124. Nurse tending Patient.

**1970.** Europa.
473. **123.** 9 k. yellow and brown 90 90
474. 25 k. brown and green 3·50 2·40

**1970.** 50th Anniv. of Icelandic Nurses Assn.
475. **124.** 7 k. ultramarine and blue 30 15

125. G. Thomsen. 126. "The Halt" (T. B. Thorlaksson).

**1970.** 150th Birth Anniv. of Grimur Thomsen (poet).
476. **125.** 10 k. indigo and blue .. 20 25

**1970.** Int. Arts Festival, Reykjavik.
477. **126.** 50 k. multicoloured .. 1·60 1·25

127. Purple Saxifrage. 128. U.N. Emblem and Map.

**1970.** Nature Conservation Year. Mult.
478. 3 k. Type **127** .. .. 20 25
479. 15 k. Lakagigar (view) .. 75 65

**1970.** 25th Anniv. of United Nations.
480. **128.** 12 k. multicoloured .. 20 30

129. "Flight" (A. Jonsson). 130. Europa Chain.

**1971.** "Help for Refugees".
481. **129.** 10 k. multicoloured .. 30 50

**1971.** Europa.
482. **130.** 7 k. yell., red and black 2·10 1·60
483. 15 k. yellow, blue & blk. 2·10 1·60

131. Postgiro Emblem. 132. Society Emblem.

**1971.** Inaug. of Postal Giro Service.
484. **131.** 5 k. blue & light blue 10 10
485. 7 k. green & light green 10 15

**1971.** Cent. of Icelandic Patriotic Society.
486. **132.** 30 k. blue and cobalt 1·10 75
487. – 100 k. grey and black 4·75 5·75
DESIGN: 100 k. T. Gunnarsson (President and editor).

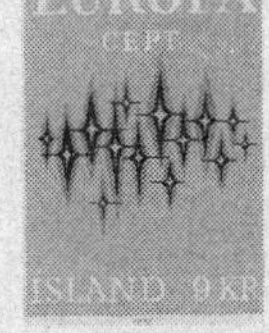

133. Freezing Plant and "Melanogrammus aeglefinus". 135. "Communications".

134. Mt. Herdubreid.

**1971.** Icelandic Fishing Industry. Mult.
488. 5 k. Type **133** .. .. 15 10
489. 7 k. Landing catch and "Gadus morhua" .. 10 10
490. 20 k. Canning shrimps and "Pandalus borealis" .. 40 40

**1972.**
491. **134.** 250 k. multicoloured .. 35 10

**1972.** Europa.
492. **135.** 9 k. multicoloured .. 1·40 75
493. 13 k. multicoloured .. 1·40 1·50

136. "Municipalities".

**1972.** Cent. of Icelandic Municipal Laws.
494. **136.** 16 k. multicoloured .. 10 15

137. World Map on Chessboard.

**1972.** World Chess Championship, Reykjavik.
495 **137** 15 k. multicoloured .. 60 20

138. Tomatoes.

**1972.** Hot-house Plant Cultivation. Mult.
496. 8 k. Type **138** .. .. 10 10
497. 12 k. Steam source and valve .. .. 10 10
498. 40 k. Rose cultivation .. 1·10 60

139. Contour Map and Continental Shelf.

**1972.** Iceland's Offshore Claims.
499. **139.** 9 k. multicoloured .. 10 10

140. Arctic Tern feeding Young. 141. Europa "Posthorn".

**1972.** Charity Stamps.
500. **140.** 7 k. + 1 k. multicoloured 60 60
501. 9 k. + 1 k. multicoloured 65 65

**1973.** Europa.
502. **141.** 13 k. multicoloured .. 2·75 2·25
503. 25 k. multicoloured .. 40 20

142. Postman and 2 s. stamp of 1873. 144. Pres. Asgeirsson.

**1973.** Stamp Centenary. Multicoloured.
504 10 k. Type **142** .. .. 20 20
505 15 k. Pony train .. .. 10 10
506 20 k. "Esja" (mail steamer) 10 10
507 40 k. Mail van .. .. 10 10
508 80 k. Beech Model 18 mail plane .. .. .. 1·10 70

**1973.** Nordic Countries' Postal Co-operation. As T **201** of Denmark.
509. 9 k. multicoloured .. 20 10
510. 10 k. multicoloured .. 1·10 95

**1973.** 5th Death Anniv. of Asgeir Asgeirsson (politician).
511. **144.** 13 k. red .. .. 15 15
512. 15 k. blue .. .. 15 15

145. Exhibition Emblem. 146. "The Elements".

**1973.** "Islandia 73" Stamp Exhibition. Multicoloured.
513. 17 k. Type **145** .. .. 20 30
514. 20 k. Exhibition emblem (different) .. .. 20 25

**1973.** Centenary of I.M.O.
515. **146.** 50 k. multicoloured .. 50 40

147. "Ingolfur and High-Seat Pillar" (tapestry, J. Briem). 148. "Horseman" (17th-century wood-carving).

**1974.** 1100th Anniv. of Icelandic Settlement. Multicoloured.
516. 10 k. Type **147** .. .. 15 10
517. 13 k. "Grimur Geitskor at Thingvellir" (painting) (horiz.) .. .. 15 10
518. 15 k. Bishop G. Thorlaksson of Holar .. .. 10 10
519. 17 k. "Snorri Sturluson slaying the King's messenger" (T. Skulason) 20 15
520. 20 k. Stained glass window from Hallgrimskirkja, Saurbaer .. .. 20 15
521. 25 k. Illuminated "I" from "Flateyjarbok" (manuscript) .. .. 10 10

522. 30 k. "Christ the King" (mosaic altar-piece, Skalholt Cathedral) .. 35 50
523. 40 k. 18th-century wood-carving .. .. .. 45 60
524. 60 k. "Curing the Catch" (concrete relief by S. Olafsson) .. .. 95 90
525. 70 k. "Saemunder smiting the Devil Seal" (bronze) 95 85
526. 100 k. Altar-cloth, Church of Stafafell (horiz.) .. 1·25 50

**1974.** Europa. Sculptures. Multicoloured.
527. 13 k. Type **148** .. .. 10 10
528. 20 k. "Through the Sound Barrier" (bronze, A. Sveinsson) .. .. 95 65

**149.** Purchasing Stamps.
**150.** Village with Erupting Volcano in distance. 

**1974.** Cent. of Universal Postal Union.
529. **149.** 17 k. brown, blue and yellow .. .. 15 20
530. – 20 k. brown, blue and green .. .. 20 25
DESIGN: 20 k. Postman sorting mail.

**1975.** Volcanic Eruption, Heimaey (1973).
531. **150.** 20 k. multicoloured .. 40 30
532. 25 k. multicoloured .. 20 10

**151.** "Autumn Bird" (T. Skullason).
**152.** Stephan G. Stephansson (poet). 

**1975.** Europa. Paintings. Multicoloured.
533. 18 k. Type **151** .. .. 20 10
534. 23 k. "Sun Queen" (J. S. Kjarval) (vert.) .. .. 60 30

**1975.** Centenary of Icelandic Settlements in North America.
535. **152.** 27 k. brown and green 30 25

**153.** Hallgrimur Petursson (religious poet).
**154.** Red Cross Flag on Map of Iceland. 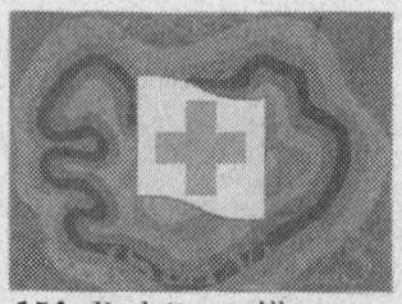

**1975.** Celebrities.
536. **153.** 18 k. black and green 10 10
537. – 23 k. blue .. .. 10 10
538. – 30 k. red .. .. 10 10
539. – 50 k. blue .. .. 10 10
PORTRAITS: 23 k. Arni Magnusson (historian). 30 k. Jon Eiriksson (statesman). 50 k. Einar Jonsson (painter and sculptor).

**1975.** 50th Anniv. of Icelandic Red Cross.
540. **154.** 23 k. multicoloured .. 15 15

**155.** "Abstract" (N. Tryggvadottir).
**156.** "Bertel Thorvaldsen" (self-statue). 

**1975.** International Women's Year.
541. **155.** 100 k. multicoloured .. 80 60

**1975.** Cent. of Thorvaldsen Society (Charity organization).
542. **156.** 27 k. multicoloured .. 40 15

**157.** "Forestry".
**158.** "Landscape" (Asgrimur Jonsson). 

**1975.** Reafforestation.
543. **157.** 35 k. multicoloured .. 35 25

**1976.** Birth Cent. of Asgrimur Jonsson (painter).
544. **158.** 150 k. multicoloured .. 1·40 1·00

**159.** Wooden Bowl.

**1976.** Europa. Old Wooden Crafts. Mult.
545. 35 k. Type **159** .. .. 95 75
546. 45 k. Spinning-wheel (vert.) 95 95

**160.** Title page of Postal Services Order.
**161.** Iceland 5 a. Stamp with Reykjavik Postmark, 1876. 

**1976.** Bicent. of Icelandic Postal Services.
547. **160.** 35 k. brown .. .. 25 25
548. – 45 k. blue .. .. 30 25
DESIGN: 45 k. Signature appended to Postal Services Order.

**1976.** Cent. of Icelandic Aurar-currency Stamps.
549. **161.** 30 k. multicoloured .. 15 10

**162.** "Workers" and Federation Emblem.
**164.** Ofaerufoss, Eldgja. 

**1976.** 60th Anniv. of Icelandic Labour Federation.
550. **162.** 100 k. multicoloured .. 60 40

**1977.** Nordic Countries' Co-operation in Nature Conservation and Environment Protection. As T **229** of Denmark.
551. 35 k. multicoloured .. 35 40
552. 45 k. multicoloured .. 35 40

**1977.** Europa. Multicoloured.
553. 45 k. Type **164** .. .. 1·50 50
554. 85 k. Kirkufell from Grundarfjord .. .. 25 20

**165.** Harlequin Duck.
**166.** Co-operative Emblem. 

**1977.** European Wetlands Campaign.
555. **165.** 40 k. multicoloured .. 50 10

**1977.** 75th Anniv. of Federation of Icelandic Co-operative Societies.
556. **166.** 60 k. blue & bright blue 40 30

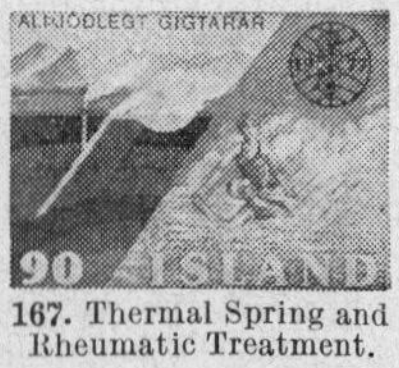

**167.** Thermal Spring and Rheumatic Treatment.

**1977.** World Rheumatism Year.
557. **167.** 90 k. multicoloured .. 45 30

**168.** Cairn and Glacier.
**169.** Thorvaldur Thoroddsen (geologist). 

**1977.** 50th Anniv. of Icelandic Touring Club.
558. **168.** 45 k. blue .. .. 55 40

**1978.** Famous Icelanders.
559. **169.** 50 k. green and brown 15 10
560. – 60 k. brown and green 40 30
DESIGN: 60 k. Briet Bjarnhedinsdottir (suffragette).

**170.** Videy Mansion.

**1978.** Europa. Multicoloured.
561. 80 k. Type **170** .. .. 75 45
562. 120 k. Husavik Church (vert.) .. .. .. 95 45

**171.** Dr. A. Johannesson and Junkers Seaplanes.

**1978.** 50th Anniv. of Domestic Flights.
563. **171.** 60 k. black and blue .. 20 15
564. – 100 k. multicoloured .. 30 15
DESIGN: 100 k. Fokker Friendship.

**172.** Skeidara Bridge.

**1978.** Skeidara Bridge.
565. **172.** 70 k. multicoloured .. 15 10

**173.** "Lava Scene near Mt. Hekla" (J. Stefansson).

**1978.**
566. **173.** 1000 k. multicoloured 3·25 2·75

**174.** Wreck of "Sargon" and Breeches-buoy.

**1978.** 50th Anniv. of National Life-Saving Association of Iceland.
567. **174.** 60 k. black .. .. 30 15

**175.** "Reykjanesviti" Lighthouse.
**176.** Halldor Hermannsson. 

**1978.** Cent. of Lighthouses in Iceland.
568. **175.** 90 k. multicoloured .. 65 20

**1978.** Birth Centenary of Halldor Hermannsson (scholar and librarian).
569. **176.** 150 k. blue .. .. 30 25

**177.** Old Telephone.
**178.** Bjarni Thorsteinsson (clergyman and composer). 

**1979.** Europa. Multicoloured.
570. 110 k. Type **177** .. .. 65 15
571. 190 k. Posthorn and mail-bag .. .. .. 75 45

**1979.** Famous Icelanders.
572. – 80 k. purple .. .. 10 10
573. **178.** 100 k. black .. .. 10 10
574. – 120 k. red .. .. 10 10
575. – 130 k. brown .. .. 20 20
576. – 170 k. red .. .. 30 25
DESIGNS: 80 k. Ingibjorg H. Bjarnason (headmistress and first female member of Althing). 120 k. Petur Gudjohnsen (organist). 130 k. Sveinbjorn Sveinbjornson (composer). 170 k. Torfhildur Holm (poetess and novelist).

**179.** Children with Flowers.
**180.** Icelandic Arms to 1904 and 1904–19. 

**1979.** International Year of the Child.
577. **179.** 140 k. multicoloured .. 40 30

**1979.** 75th Anniv. of Ministry of Iceland.
578. **180.** 500 k. multicoloured .. 1·00 80

**181.** Sigurdsson and I. Einarsdottir.

**1979.** Death Centenaries of Jon and Ingibjorg Sigurdsson (historians and Althing members).
579. **181.** 150 k. black .. .. 30 30

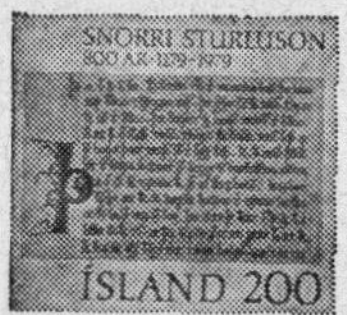

**182.** Part of Kringla Leaf (MS of Heimskringla).
**183.** Icelandic Dog 

**1979.** 800th Birth Anniv. of Snorri Sturluson (saga writer).
580. **182.** 200 k. multicoloured .. 45 40

**1980.** Fauna.
581. **183.** 10 k. black .. .. 10 10
582. – 90 k. brown .. .. 20 10
583. – 160 k. purple .. .. 70 10
584. – 170 k. black .. .. 90 35
585. – 190 k. brown .. .. 45 15
DESIGNS: 90 k. Arctic Fox. 160 k. Ocean perch. 170 k. Atlantic Puffins. 190 k. Common seal.
See also Nos. 611/13.

**184.** Jon Sveinsson "alias" Nonni (writer).
**185.** Rowan Berries. 

**1980.** Europa.
586. **184.** 140 k. pink and black 35 30
587. – 250 k. pink and black 45 50
DESIGN: 250 k. Gunnar Gunnarsson (writer).

**1980.** Year of the Tree.
588. **185.** 120 k. multicoloured .. 20 15

**186.** Sports Complex, Reykjavik.
**187.** Embroidered Cushion. 

**1980.** Olympic Games, Moscow.
589. **186.** 300 k. turquoise .. 45 40

**1980.** Nordic Countries' Postal Co-operation. Multicoloured.
590. 150 k. Carved and painted cabinet door .. .. 35 30
591. 180 k. Type **187** .. .. 40 40

**188.** University Hospital. **189.** Loudspeaker.

**1980.** 50th Anniv. of University Hospital.
592. **188.** 200 k. multicoloured .. 30 25

**1980.** 50th Anniv. of State Broadcasting Service.
593. **189.** 400 k. multicoloured .. 85 30
(New currency. 100 (old) Kronur = 1 (new) Krona).

**190.** Magnus Stephensen (Chief Justice and publisher). **191.** Loftur the Sorcerer.

**1981.** Famous Icelanders.
594. **190.** 170 a. blue .. .. 40 25
595. – 190 a. green .. .. 40 25
DESIGN: 190 a. Finnur Magnusson (writer and Keeper of Privy Archives).

**1981.** Europa. Multicoloured. Designs showing illustrations of Icelandic legends.
596. 180 a. Type **191** .. .. 95 50
597. 220 a. Witch wading the deeps off Iceland .. 95 50

**192.** Winter Wren. **193.** Human Jigsaw.

**1981.** Birds.
598. **192.** 50 a. brown .. .. 25 25
599. – 100 a. blue .. .. 50 50
600. – 200 a. black .. .. 1·00 1·00
DESIGNS: 100 a. Golden Plover. 200 a. Raven

**1981.** International Year for Disabled Persons.
601. **193.** 200 a. multicoloured .. 25 20

**194.** Skyggnir Dish Aerial. **195.** "Hauling the Line" (Gunnlaugur Scheving).

**1981.** 75th Anniv. of Icelandic Telephone Service.
602. **194.** 500 a. multicoloured .. 95 40

**1981.**
603. **195.** 5000 a. multicoloured 5·25 3·25

**196.** Medieval Driftwood crucifix from Alftamyri. **197.** Leaf-bread (star pattern).

**1981.** Millenary of Missionary Work in Iceland.
604. **196.** 200 a. lilac .. 20 15

**1981.** Christmas. Multicoloured.
605. 200 a. Type **197** .. .. 50 50
606. 250 a. Leaf-bread (tree pattern) .. .. .. 50 50

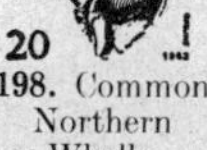

**198.** Common Northern Whelk. **199.** Casting Dais Post into Sea (first Iceland settlement, 874).

**1982.** Shells.
607. **198.** 20 a. red .. .. 10 10
608. – 600 a. brown .. .. 75 30
DESIGN: 600 a. Iceland scallop.

**1982.** Europa. Multicoloured.
609. 350 a. Type **199** .. .. 1·25 60
610. 450 a. Discovery of Vinland (America), 1000 .. 1·25 60

**200.** Sheep. **201.** Co-operative Trading House, Husavik.

**1982.** Domestic Animals.
611. **200.** 300 a. brown .. .. 65 30
612. – 400 a. red .. .. 30 15
613. – 500 a. grey .. .. 30 15
DESIGNS: 400 a. Cow. 500 a. Cat.

**1982.** Centenary of Thingeyjar Co-operative Society.
614 **201** 1000 a. black & brown 50 40

**202.** Horseman.

**1982.** Iceland Ponies and Horsemanship.
615. **202.** 700 a. multicoloured 45 25

**203.** Holar.

**1982.** Cent. of Holar Agricultural College.
616. **203.** 1500 a. multicoloured 80 80

**204.** "Mount Herdubreid" (Isleifur Konradsson). **205.** Thorbjorg Sveinsdottir.

**1982.** Year of the Aged.
617. **204.** 800 a. multicoloured 60 50

**1982.** Famous Icelanders. Thorbjorg Sveindsdottir (midwife and founder of Icelandic Women's Association).
618 **205** 900 a. brown .. 40 40

**207.** Doves and Opening of "The Night was such a Splendid One".

**1982.** Christmas. Multicoloured.
620. 300 a. Type **207** .. .. 70 30
621. 350 a. Bells and close of "The Night was such a Splendid One" (composed by Sigvaldi Kaldalons from poem by E. Sigurdsson) .. .. 80 40

**208.** Marsh Marigold. **209.** Mount Sulur.

**1983.** Flowers. Multicoloured.
622 7 k. 50 Type **208** .. .. 30 30
623 8 k. Alpine catchfly .. 60 30
624 10 k. Marsh cinquefoil .. 95 30
625 20 k. Water forgetmenot .. 2·00 1·25

**1983.** Nordic Countries' Postal Co-operation. "Visit the North". Multicoloured.
626 4 k. 50 Type **209** .. .. 75 50
627 5 k. Urridafossar Falls .. 75 50

**210.** Thermal Area and Heat-exchange Plant. **211.** Stern Trawler.

**1983.** Europa. Multicoloured.
628 5 k. Type **210** .. .. 1·90 90
629 5 k. 50 Thermal area heating houses .. .. 8·50 1·40

**1983.** Fishing Industry.
630 **211** 11 k. blue .. .. 1·50 1·50
631 – 13 k. blue .. .. 1·40 60
DESIGN: 13 k. Line fishing.

**212.** "Laki Craters" (Finnur Jonsson).

**1983.** Bicentenary of Skafta Eruption.
632 **212** 15 k. multicoloured .. 75 35

**213.** Skiing. **214.** Aircraft and W.C.Y. Emblem.

**1983.** Outdoor Sports. Multicoloured.
633 12 k. Type **213** .. .. 80 40
634 14 k. Jogging .. .. 80 50

**1983.** World Communications Year.
635 **214** 30 k. multicoloured .. 2·00 1·00

**216.** Virgin Mary and Child. **217.** Pres. Eldjarn.

**1983.** Christmas. Multicoloured.
637. 600 a. Type **216** .. .. 50 40
638. 650 a. Visitation of the Angel .. .. 50 40

**1983.** 1st Death Anniv. (September) of Kristjan Eldjarn (President, 1968–80).
639 **217** 6 k. 50 red .. .. 85 50
640 7 k. blue .. .. 40 20

**218.** Burnet Rose. **219.** Bridge.

**1984.** Flowers. Multicoloured.
641 6 k. Type **218** .. .. 75 35
642 25 k. Silverweed .. .. 1·00 65
See also Nos. 648/9, 657/60 and 717/18.

**1984.** Europa. 25th Anniv of European Post and Telecommunications Conference.
643 **219** 6 k. 50 dp blue & blue 1·25 40
644 7 k. 50 dp purple & pur 50 30

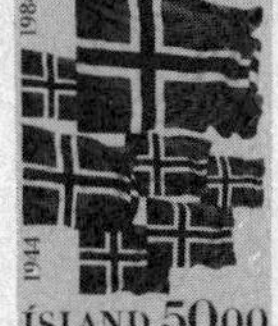


**221.** Icelandic Flags. **222.** I.O.G.T. Lodge, Akureyri.

**1984.** 40th Anniv of Republic.
646 **221** 50 k. multicoloured .. 3·75 2·50

**1984.** Centenary of International Order of Good Templars in Iceland.
647 **222** 10 k. green .. .. 50 40

**1984.** Flowers. As T **218**. Multicoloured.
648. 6 k. 50 Wild azalea .. 35 30
649. 7 k. 50 Alpine bearberry .. 35 30

**223.** Basalt symbolising Industries. **224.** Bjorn Bjarnarson (founder) (after J. P. Wildenradt).

**1984.** 50th Anniv. of Confederation of Icelandic Employers.
650. **223.** 30 k. multicoloured .. 1·25 80

**1984.** Centenary of National Gallery.
651. **224.** 12 k. black, brown and green .. .. 50 40
652. – 40 k. black, green and red .. .. 1·60 1·00
DESIGN: 40 k. New gallery building.

**225.** Virgin and Child. **226.** Text from Bible.

**1984.** Christmas.
653. **225.** 600 a. blue, light blue and gold .. .. 40 15
654. – 650 a. red and gold .. 50 25
DESIGN: 650 a. Angel with Christmas rose.

**1984.** 400th Anniv of Gudbrand's Bible.
655 **226** 6 k. 50 red .. .. 40 25
656 – 7 k. 50 purple .. 30 25
DESIGN: 7 k. 50, Illustration from Bible.

**1985.** Flowers. As T **218**. Multicoloured.
657 8 k. Stone bramble .. 40 25
658 9 k. Rock speedwell .. 50 25
659 16 k. Sea pea .. 1·40 60
660 17 k. Alpine whitlow-grass 70 40

**227.** Lady playing Langspil. **228.** Swedish Whitebeam.

**1985.** Europa. Music Year. Multicoloured.
661 6 k. 50 Type **227** .. .. 80 40
661 7 k. 50 Man playing Icelandic violin .. 80 40

**1985.** Centenary of Iceland Horticultural Society.
663. **228.** 20 k. multicoloured .. 90 50

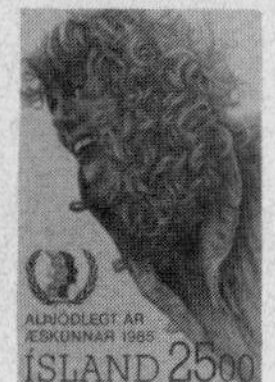

**229.** Girl and I.Y.Y. Emblem. **230.** Common Squid.

**1985.** International Youth Year.
664. **229.** 25 k. multicoloured .. 1·10 75

**1985.** Marine Life.
665. **230.** 7 k. purple .. .. 35 15
666. – 8 k. brown .. .. 30 10
667. – 9 k. red .. .. 40 30
DESIGNS: 8 k. Common spider crab. 9 k. Sea anemone.

**231.** Rev. Hannes Stephensen (politician).

**1985.** Famous Icelanders.
668. **231.** 13 k. red .. .. 50 40
669. – 30 k. violet .. .. 1·00 80
DESIGN: 30 k. Jon Gudmundsson (editor and politician).

**232.** "Flight Yearning". **233.** Snow Scene.

**1985.** Birth Centenary of Johannes Sveinsson Kjarval (artist).
670. **232.** 100 k. multicoloured 4·25 3·75

**1985.** Christmas. Multicoloured.
671. 8 k. Type **233** .. .. 50 10
672. 9 k. Snow scene (different) 50 30

**234.** Pied Wagtail.

**1986.** Birds. Multicoloured.
673. 6 k. Type **234** .. .. 65 35
674. 10 k. Pintail .. .. 1·60 95
675. 12 k. Merlin .. .. 1·40 95
676. 15 k. Razorbill .. .. 1·25 75
See also Nos. 697/700, 720/1, 726/7, 741/2 and 763/4.

**235.** Skaftafell National Park.

**1986.** Europa. Multicoloured.
677. 10 k. Type **235** .. .. 5·75 1·10
678. 12 k. Jokulsargljufur National Park .. .. 2·40 1·10

**236.** Stykkisholmur.

**1986.** Nordic Countries' Postal Co-operation. Twinned Towns. Multicoloured.
679. 10 k. Type **236** .. .. 75 60
680. 12 k. Seydisfjordur .. 75 40

**237.** Head Office, Reykjavik.

**1986.** Centenary of National Bank. Mult.
681. **237.** 13 k. green .. .. 50 40
682. – 250 k. brown .. .. 8·75 8·50
DESIGN: 250 k. Reverse of first National Bank 5 k. note.

**238.** First Official Seal. **239.** Early Telephone Equipment.

**1986.** Bicentenary of Reykjavik.
683. **238.** 10 k. red .. .. 45 25
684. – 12 k. brown .. .. 70 40
685. – 13 k. green .. .. 50 45
686. – 40 k. blue .. .. 1·25 90
DESIGNS: 12 k. "Reykjavik pond, 1856" (illustration from "Journey in the Northern Seas" by Charles Edmond). 13 k. Women washing clothes in natural hot water brook, Laugardalur. 40 k. City Theatre.

**1986.** 80th Anniv. of Icelandic Telephone and Telegraph Service. Multicoloured.
687. 10 k. Type **239** .. .. 50 20
688. 20 k. Modern digital telephone system .. .. 1·00 65

**241.** "Christmas at Peace".

**1986.** Christmas. Multicoloured.
690. 10 k. Type **241** .. .. 60 15
691. 12 k. "Christmas Night" .. 40 25

**242.** "Svanur" (ketch) anchored off Olafsvik.

**1987.** 300th Anniv. of Olafsvik Trading Station.
692. **242.** 50 k. purple .. .. 3·00 1·75

**243.** Terminal and Boeing 727 Tail.

**1987.** Opening of Leif Eiriksson Terminal, Keflavik Airport.
693. **243.** 100 k. multicoloured 2·50 1·90

**244.** Christ carrying Cross. **245.** Rask.

**1987.** Europa. Stained Glass Windows by Leifur Breidfoerd, Fossvogur Cemetery Chapel. Multicoloured.
694. 12 k. Type **244** .. .. 75 50
695. 15 k. Soldiers and peace dove .. .. 75 40

**1987.** Birth Bicentenary of Rasmus Kristjan Rask (philologist).
696. **245.** 20 k. black .. .. 80 60

**1987.** Birds. As T **234**. Multicoloured.
697. 13 k. Short-eared owl .. 65 55
698. 40 k. Redwing .. .. 1·75 1·50
699. 70 k. Oystercatcher .. 3·00 2·40
700. 90 k. Mallard .. .. 4·00 3·25

**246.** Girl Brushing Teeth. **247.** Vulture.

**1987.** Dental Protection.
701. **246.** 12 k. multicoloured 40 25

**1987.** National Guardian Spirits. Each red.
702. 13 k. Type **247** .. .. 40 40
703. 13 k. Dragon .. .. 40 40
704. 13 k. Bull .. .. 40 40
705. 13 k. Giant .. .. 40 40
See also Nos. 713/16, 732 and 743/50.

**249.** Christmas Tree. **250.** Steinn Steinarr (poet).

**1987.** Christmas. Multicoloured.
707. 13 k. Type **249** .. .. 65 20
708. 17 k. "Christmas Light" .. 65 35

**1988.** Famous Icelanders. Multicoloured.
709. 16 k. Type **250** .. .. 55 25
710. 21 k. David Stefansson (writer) .. .. .. 60 60

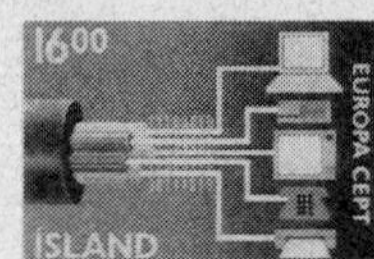


**251.** Transmission of Messages by Modern Data System.

**1988.** Europa. Communications. Mult.
711. 16 k. Type **251** .. .. 55 25
712. 21 k. Phone pad and globe within envelope (transmission of letters by facsimile machine) .. 1·25 1·00

**1988.** National Guardian Spirit. As Nos. 702/5 but values and colour changed.
713. 16 k. black (Type **247**) .. 35 35
714. 16 k. black (Dragon) .. 35 35
715. 16 k. black (Bull) .. 35 35
716. 16 k. black (Giant) .. 35 35

**1988.** Flowers. As T **218**. Multicoloured.
717. 10 k. Tufted vetch .. 25 25
718. 50 k. Wild thyme .. .. 1·10 75

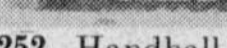

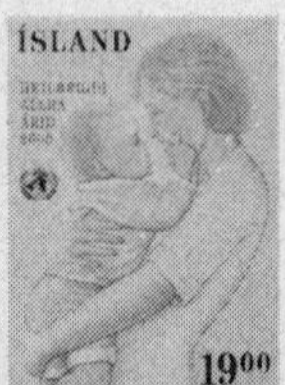


**252.** Handball. **254.** Mother and Baby.

**1988.** Olympic Games, Seoul.
719. **252.** 18 k. multicoloured .. 45 45

**1988.** Birds. As T **234**. Multicoloured.
720. 5 k. Black-tailed godwit .. 25 15
721. 30 k. Long-tailed duck .. 1·75 1·40

**1988.** 40th Anniv. of W.H.O. "Health for All in 2000".
723. **254.** 19 k. multicoloured .. 45 35

**255.** Fisherman with Haul of Fish.

**1988.** Christmas. Multicoloured.
724. 19 k. Type **255** .. .. 50 25
725. 24 k. Trawler and buoy .. 90 90

**1989.** Birds. As T **234**. Multicoloured.
726 19 k. Red-necked phalarope .. .. .. 75 50
727 100 k. Snow buntings .. 2·75 2·25

**256** Peysufot (dress costume) **257** Children at Seaside

**1989.** Nordic Countries' Postal Co-operation. Traditional Costumes. Multicoloured.
728 21 k. Type **256** .. .. 70 35
729 26 k. Upphlutur (everyday wear) .. .. .. 70 50

**1989.** Europa. Childrens' Toys and Games. Multicoloured.
730 21 k. Type **257** .. .. 2·40 60
731 26 k. Girl with hoop and boy with hobby-horse .. 2·40 70

**1989.** National Guardian Spirits. As No. 703 but colour and value changed.
732 500 k. brown (Dragon) .. 10·50 6·75

**258** Mount Skeggi, Arnarfjord

**1989.** Landscapes. Multicoloured.
733 35 k. Type **258** .. .. 75 50
734 45 k. Namaskard thermal spring .. .. .. 95 70
See also Nos. 757/8 and 765/6.

**259** College

**1989.** Cent of Hvanneyri Agricultural College.
735 **259** 50 k. multicoloured .. 1·00 85

**261** Stefan Stefansson (co-founder) and Flowers **262** "Virgin and Child"

**1989.** Centenary of Icelandic Natural History Society. Multicoloured.
737 21 k. Type **261** .. .. 50 45
738 26 k. Fishes and Bjarni Saemundsson (first Chairman) .. .. 60 45

**1989.** Christmas. Multicoloured.
739 21 k. Type **262** .. .. 50 35
740 26 k. "Three Wise Men" .. 60 50

**1990.** Birds. As T **234**. Multicoloured.
741 21 k. European wigeons .. 60 50
742 80 k. Pink-footed goose and goslings .. .. 2·00 1·40

**1990.** National Guardian Spirits. As Nos. 702/5 but value and colours changed.
743 5 k. green (Type **247**) .. 10 10
744 5 k. green (Dragon) .. 10 10
745 5 k. green (Bull) .. .. 10 10
746 5 k. green (Giant) .. 10 10
747 21 k. blue (Type **247**) .. 45 45
748 21 k. blue (Dragon) .. 45 45
749 21 k. blue (Bull) .. .. 45 45
750 21 k. blue (Giant) .. 45 45

**263** Gudrun Larusdottir (writer and politician) (after Halldor Petursson)

**264** Posthouse Street, Reykjavik, Post Office and Old Scales

**1990.** 110th Birth Anniversaries. Mult.
751 21 k. Type **263** .. .. 50 35
752 21 k. Ragnhildur Petursdottir (women's educationist) (after Asgrimur Jonsson) .. 50 35

**1990.** Europa. Post Office Buildings. Mult.
753 21 k. Type **264** .. .. 1·40 45
754 40 k. Thoenglabakki 4, Reykjavik, Post Office and modern scales .. 1·40 70

**265** Archery

**1990.** Sport. Multicoloured.
755 21 k. Type **265** .. .. 50 45
756 21 k. Football .. .. 50 45

**1990.** Landscapes. As T **258**. Multicoloured.
757 25 k. Hvitserkur, Hunafjord .. .. 55 55
758 200 k. Lomagnupur .. 4·25 2·75

**266** Bird, Stars and Map

**1990.** European Tourism Year.
759 **266** 30 k. multicoloured .. 65 65

**268** Children around Christmas Tree

**1990.** Christmas. Multicoloured.
761 25 k. Type **268** .. .. 50 50
762 30 k. Carol singers .. 60 60

**1991.** Birds. As T **234**. Multicoloured.
763 25 k. Slavonian grebes .. 75 75
764 100 k. Northern gannets .. 2·75 2·75

**1991.** Landscapes. As T **258**. Multicoloured.
765 10 k. Mt. Vestrahorn .. 20 10
766 300 k. Kverkfjoll range .. 6·25 4·25

**269** Meteorological Information

**1991.** Europa. Europe in Space. Mult.
767 26 k. Type **269** .. .. 2·50 45
768 47 k. Telecommunications satellite .. .. 1·40 75

**270** Joekulsarlon

**1991.** Nordic Countries' Postal Co-operation. Tourism. Multicoloured.
769 26 k. Type **270** .. .. 60 50
770 31 k. Strokkur hot spring 70 60

**272** Golf

**273** Pall Isolfsson (composer) (after Hans Muller)

**1991.** Sports. Multicoloured.
772 26 k. Type **272** .. .. 50 45
773 26 k. Glima (wrestling) .. 50 45

**1991.** Famous Icelanders. Multicoloured.
774 60 k. Ragnar Jonsson (founder of Reykjavik College of Music) (after Joannes Kjarval) (horiz) 1·25 1·00
775 70 k. Type **273** .. .. 1·50 1·25

**274** College Building

**1991.** Centenary of College of Navigation, Reykjavik.
776 **274** 50 k. multicoloured .. 1·00 85

**275** "Soloven" (mail brigantine)

**276** "Light of Christmas"

**1991.** Stamp Day. Ships. Multicoloured.
777 30 k. Type **275** .. .. 1·60 75
778 30 k. "Arcturus" (cargo liner) .. .. 1·60 75
779 30 k. "Gullfoss I" (cargo liner) .. .. 1·60 75
780 30 k. "Esja II" (cargo liner) .. .. 1·60 75

**1991.** Christmas. Multicoloured.
781 30 k. Type **276** .. .. 60 50
782 35 k. Star .. .. 70 60

**277** Skiing

**1992.** Sport. Multicoloured.
783 30 k. Type **277** .. .. 60 50
784 30 k. Volleyball .. .. 60 50

**278** Map and "Santa Maria"

**1992.** Europa. 500th Anniv of Discovery of America by Columbus. Multicoloured.
785 55 k. Map and Viking ship (Leif Eriksson) .. 1·60 1·50
786 55 k. Type **278** .. .. 1·60 1·50

**279** Agricultural and Industrial Symbols

**1992.** 75th Anniv of Iceland Chamber of Commerce (30 k.) and 50th Anniv of Icelandic Freezing Plants Corporation (35 k.). Mult.
788 30 k. Type **279** .. .. 60 60
789 35 k. Trawler and fish .. 85 75

**280** River Fnjoska Bridge, Skogar

**1992.** Bridges. Multicoloured.
790 5 k. Type **280** .. .. 10 10
791 250 k. River Olfusa bridge, Selfoss .. .. 5·00 4·50
See also Nos. 804/5.

**281** Ford "TT", 1920–26

**282** Face and Candle reflected in Window

**1992.** Postal Vehicles. Multicoloured.
792 30 k. Type **281** .. .. 1·10 55
793 30 k. Citroen snowmobile, 1929 .. .. 1·10 55
794 30 k. Mail/passenger transport car "RE 231", 1933 1·10 55
795 30 k. Ford bus, 1946 .. 1·10 55

**1992.** Christmas. Multicoloured.
796 30 k. Type **282** .. .. 55 45
797 35 k. Full moon .. .. 65 55

**283** Gyrfalcon with Chicks

**284** Handball

**1992.** The Gyrfalcon. Multicoloured.
798 5 k. Type **283** .. .. 10 10
799 10 k. Beating wings .. 20 15
800 20 k. Eating .. .. 75 30
801 35 k. On ground .. 1·10 55

**1993.** Sport. Multicoloured.
802 30 k. Type **284** .. .. 55 45
803 30 k. Running .. .. 55 45

**1993.** Bridges. As T **280**. Multicoloured.
804 90 k. River Hvita bridge, Ferjukot .. .. 1·90 1·40
805 150 k. River Jokulsa a Fjollum bridge, Grimsstadir .. .. 3·25 2·40

**285** The Blue Lagoon, Svartsengi

**286** "Sailing" (Jon Gunnar Arnason)

**1993.** Nordic Countries' Postal Co-operation. Tourism. Multicoloured.
806 30 k. Type **285** .. .. 55 45
807 35 k. Perlan (The Pearl), Reykjavik .. .. 95 55

**1993.** Europa. Contemporary Art. Mult.
808 35 k. Type **286** .. .. 1·10 55
809 55 k. "Hatching of the Jet" (Magnus Tomasson) 1·60 85

**288** Junkers "F-13" Seaplane "Sulan"

**1993.** 65th Anniv of 1st Icelandic Postal Flight. Multicoloured.
811 30 k. Type **288** .. .. 1·40 55
812 30 k. Waco YKS-7 seaplane .. .. 1·40 55
813 30 k. Grumman Goose amphibian ("RVK") .. 1·40 55
814 30 k. Consolidated PBY-5 Catalina flying boat "Old Peter" ("TF-ISP") 1·40 55

**289** Three Wise Men adoring Child

**290** Swimming

**1993.** Christmas. Multicoloured.
815 30 k. Type **289** .. .. 55 45
816 35 k. Madonna and Child 65 55

**1994.** Sport. Multicoloured.
817 30 k. Type **290** .. .. 55 45
818 30 k. Weightlifting .. 55 45

**291** Finger Puppets

**1994.** International Year of the Family.
819 **291** 40 k. multicoloured .. 75 65

**292** St. Brendan visiting Iceland

**1994.** Europa. Discoveries. St. Brendan's Voyages. Multicoloured.
820 35 k. Type **292** .. .. 1·10 55
821 55 k. St. Brendan discovering Faroe Islands .. .. 1·25 1·25

**293** Conductor and Instruments

**1994.** 50th Anniv of Independence. Art and Culture. Multicoloured.

823 30 k. Type **293** (44th anniv of Icelandic Symphony Orchestra) .. .. 55 45
824 30 k. Pottery (55th anniv of College of Arts and Crafts) .. .. .. 55 45
825 30 k. Cameraman and actors (16th anniv of National Film Fund) .. 55 45
826 30 k. Ballerina and modern dancers (21st anniv of Icelandic Dance Company) .. .. 55 45
827 30 k. Theatre masks (44th anniv of Icelandic National Theatre) .. 55 45

**294** Gisli Sveinsson (President of United Althing, 1944)

**1994.** 50th Anniv of New Constitution.
828 **294** 30 k. multicoloured .. 80 45

**297** Woman and Stars

**1994.** Christmas. Multicoloured.
831 30 k.Type **297** .. .. 55 45
832 35 k. Man and stars .. 65 55

**298** Emblem and Airplane

**1994.** 50th Anniv of I.C.A.O.
833 **298** 100 k. multicoloured .. 2·40 1·75

**299** Flag and Salvation Army Soldiers  **300** Geyser

**1995.** Anniversaries. Multicoloured.
834 35 k. Type **299** (centenary of Salvation Army in Iceland) .. .. 70 60
835 90 k. Map of fjord (centenary of Seydisfjordur) .. .. 1·75 1·50

**1995.** 14th World Men's Handball Championship. Multicoloured.
836 35 k. Type **300** .. .. 70 60
837 35 k. Stadium .. .. 70 60
838 35 k. Volcano .. .. 70 60
839 35 k. Entrance to fjord .. 70 60

**301** Laufas  **302** "Spell-broken" (Einar Jonsson)

**1995.** Nordic Countries' Postal Co-operation. Tourism. Multicoloured.
840 30 k. Type **301** .. .. 60 50
841 35 k. Fjallsjokull Glacier .. 70 60

**1995.** Europa. Peace and Freedom.
842 **302** 35 k. multicoloured .. 70 60
843 55 k. multicoloured .. 1·10 95

**303** "Laura"

**1995.** Post Boats. Multicoloured.
844 30 k. Type **303** .. .. 60 50
845 30 k. "Dronning Alexandrine" .. .. 60 50
846 30 k. "Laxfoss" .. .. 60 50
847 30 k. "Godafoss III" .. 60 50

**304** Common Redpoll

**1995.** European Nature Conservation Year. Birds. Multicoloured.
848 25 k. Type **304** .. .. 50 45
849 250 k. Common snipe .. 5·25 5·25

**305** Boeing 757

**1995.** 40th Anniv of Iceland–Luxembourg Air Link.
850 **305** 35 k. multicoloured .. 70 60

**307** Snowman and Snowwoman  **308** Anniversary Emblem

**1995.** Christmas. Multicoloured.
852 30 k. Type **307** .. .. 60 50
853 35 k. Coloured fir trees .. 70 60

**1995.** 50th Anniv of U.N.O.
854 **308** 100 k. multicoloured 2·00 2·00

**309** Common Cormorant

**1996.** Birds. Multicoloured.
855 20 k. Type **309** .. .. 35 30
856 40 k. Barrow's goldeneye 75 65

**310** "Seamen in a Boat" (Gunnlaugur Scheving)

**1996.** Paintings. Multicoloured.
857 100 k. Type **310** .. .. 1·90 1·60
858 200 k. "At the Washing Springs" (Kristin Jonsdottir) .. .. 3·75 3·25

**311** Halldora Bjarnadottir (founder of women's societies)

**1996.** Europa. Famous Women. Mult.
859 35 k. Type **311** .. .. 65 55
860 55 k. Olafia Johannsdottir (women's rights campaigner and temperance worker) .. 1·00 85

**312** 1931 Buick

**1996.** Post Buses. Multicoloured.
861 35 k. Type **312** .. .. 65 55
862 35 k. 1933 Studebaker .. 65 55
863 35 k. 1937 Ford .. .. 65 55
864 35 k. 1946 Reo .. .. 65 55

**313** Running

**1996.** Olympic Games, Atlanta. Mult.
865 5 k. Type **313** .. .. 10 10
866 25 k. Throwing the javelin 45 40
867 45 k. Long jumping .. 85 70
868 65 k. Putting the shot .. 1·25 1·10

**314** Hospital Ward

**1996.** Centenary of Order of the Sisters of St. Joseph in Iceland.
869 **314** 65 k. blk, stone & pur 1·25 1·10

**315** School

**1996.** 150th Anniv of Reykjavik School.
870 **315** 150 k. multicoloured .. 2·75 2·40

**317** Reykjavik Cathedral  **318** "Virgin Mary holding Child Jesus" (ivory figurine)

**1996.** Bicentenary of Reykjavik Cathedral.
872 **317** 45 k. multicoloured .. 85 70

**1996.** Christmas. Exhibits from National Museum of Iceland. Multicoloured.
873 35 k. Type **318** .. .. 65 55
874 45 k. Pax depicting nativity .. .. 85 70

## OFFICIAL STAMPS

**1873.** As T 1. but inscr. "PJON. FRIM". at foot.
O 8. 4 s. green .. .. 48·00 £250
O 10. 8 s. mauve .. .. £350 £475

O **4**.

**1876.**
O 36. O **4.** 3 a. yellow .. .. 8·50 19·00
O 37. 4 a. grey .. .. 24·00 26·00
O 21a. 5 a. brown .. .. 5·75 12·50
O 22a. 10 a. blue .. .. 50·00 10·50
O 23a. 16 a. red .. .. 14·00 32·00
O 24a. 20 a. green .. .. 10·50 19·00
O 25. 50 a. mauve .. .. 45·00 55·00

**1902.** Optd. **1 GILDI '02-'03.**
O 87. O **4.** 3 a. yellow .. .. 60 1·90
O 88. 4 a. grey .. .. 40 1·90
O 89. 5 a. brown .. .. 55 1·90
O 90. 10 a. blue .. .. 55 1·90
O 84. 16 a. red .. .. 8·50 48·00
O 91. 20 a. green .. .. 30 19·00
O 86. 50 a. mauve .. .. 4·25 48·00

**1902.** As T **11,** but inscr. "PJONUSTA".
O 92. 3 a. sepia and yellow .. 2·40 2·10
O 93. 4 a. sepia and green .. 3·25 1·50
O 94. 5 a. sepia and brown .. 2·40 2·50
O 95. 10 a. sepia and blue .. 2·75 2·50
O 96. 16 a. sepia and red .. 2·40 12·50
O 97. 20 a. sepia and green .. 11·50 6·25
O 98. 50 a. sepia and mauve .. 5·75 9·50

**1907** As T **12,** but inscr." PJONUSTU".
O 99. 3 a. grey and yellow .. 3·75 5·25
O 100. 4 a. grey and green .. 2·40 5·25
O 101. 5 a. grey and brown .. 6·75 3·25
O 102. 10 a. grey and blue .. 1·50 2·50
O 103. 15 a grey and blue .. 2·75 6·25
O 104. 16 a. grey and red .. 3·25 18·00
O 105. 20 a. grey and green .. 8·50 3·75
O 106 50 a. grey and mauve .. 4·75 8·50

**1920.** As T **15,** but inscr. "PJONUSTU".
O 132. 3 a. black and yellow .. 2·40 2·40
O 133. 4 a. black and green .. 65 2·40
O 134. 5 a. black and orange .. 65 95
O 135. 10 a. black and blue .. 1·90 75
O 136. 15 a. black and blue .. 40 75
O 137. 20 a. black and green 32·00 1·60
O 138. 50 a. black and violet 28·00 1·25
O 139. 1 k. black and red .. 28·00 2·10
O 140. 2 k. black and blue .. 5·75 14·00
O 141. 5 k. black and brown 28·00 32·00

**1922.** Optd. **Pjonusta.**
O 153. **15.** 20 a. on 10 a. red .. 12·50 1·90
O 151a. **13.** 2 k. red (No. 107) .. 21·00 48·00
O 152. 5 k. brown (No. 108) £160 £190

**1930.** Parliamentary Commemoratives of 1930 optd. **Pjonustumerki.**
O 174. **24.** 3 a. violet (postage) .. 9·50 28·00
O 175. – 5 a. blue and grey .. 9·50 28·00
O 176. – 7 a. green .. .. 9·50 28·00
O 177. – 10 a. purple .. .. 9·50 28·00
O 178. – 15 a. blue .. .. 9·50 28·00
O 179. – 20 a. red .. .. 9·50 28·00
O 180. – 25 a. brown .. .. 9·50 28·00
O 181. – 30 a. green .. .. 9·50 28·00
O 182. – 35 a. blue .. .. 9·50 28·00
O 183. – 40 a. red, blue & grey 9·50 28·00
O 184. – 50 a. brown .. .. £120 £190
O 185. – 1 k. green .. .. £120 £190
O 186. – 2 k. blue and green .. £130 £200
O 187. – 5 k. orange & yellow £120 £190
O 188. – 10 k. lake .. .. £120 £190
O 189. **25.** 10 a. blue (air) .. 19·00 95·00

**1936.** Optd. **Pjonusta.**
O 220. **15.** 7 a. green .. .. 2·40 32·00
O 221. 10 a. red .. .. 3·25 1·60
O 222. **12.** 50 a. red and grey .. 15·00 21·00

## IFNI Pt. 9

Spanish enclave on the Atlantic coast of Northern Morocco ceded in 1860.
By an agreement, made effective on 30th June, 1969, Ifni was surrendered by Spain to Morocco.

100 centimos = 1 peseta.

**1941.** Stamps of Spain optd. **TERRITORIO DE IFNI.**
1. **181.** 1 c. green (imperf.) .. 4·75 4·25
2. **182.** 2 c. brown .. .. 4·75 4·25
3. **183.** 5 c. brown .. .. 70 40
4. 10 c. red .. .. 2·75 1·50
5. 15 c. green .. .. 60 40
6. **196.** 20 c. violet .. .. 60 40
7. 25 c. red .. .. 60 40
8. 30 c. blue .. .. 60 60
9. 40 c. slate .. .. 95 40
10. 50 c. slate .. .. 5·50 1·40
11. 70 c. blue .. .. 5·50 3·75
12. 1 PTA. black .. .. 5·50 3·75
13. 2 PTAS. brown .. 65·00 23·00
14. 4 PTAS. red .. .. £200 £110
15. 10 PTS. brown .. .. £650 £275

3. El Santuario. 4. Nomad Family.

**1943.**
16 A 1 c. mve & brn (postage) 10 10
17 B 2 c. blue and green .. 10 10
18 C 5 c. blue and purple .. 10 10
19 A 15 c. green & deep green 15 15
20 B 20 c. brown and violet .. 15 15
21 A 40 c. violet and purple .. 15 15
22 B 45 c. red and brown .. 20 20
35 4 50 c. black and brown .. 6·00 55
23 C 75 c. blue and indigo .. 20 20
24 A 1 p. brown and red .. 1·25 1·10
25 B 3 p. green and blue .. 1·40 1·25
26 C 10 p. black and brown .. 15·00 14·00

27 **3** 5 c. brown & purple (air) 15 15
28 D 25 c. brown and green .. 15 15
29 **3** 50 c. blue and indigo .. 20 20
30 D 1 p. blue and violet .. 20 20
31 **3** 1 p. 40 blue and green .. 20 20
32 D 2 p. brown and purple .. 85 70
33 **3** 5 p. violet and brown .. 1·25 1·10
34 D 6 p. green and blue .. 17·00 15·00
DESIGNS: A, Nomadic shepherds; B, Arab rifleman; C, La Alcazaba; D, Airplane over oasis.

**1947.** Air. Autogyro type of Spain optd. **IFNI.**
36. **195.** 5 c. yellow .. .. 2·00 50
37. 10 c. green .. .. 2·00 50

**1948.** Stamps of Spain optd **Territorio de Ifni.**
45 **182** 2 c. brown (postage) .. 10 10
46 **183** 5 c. brown .. .. 10 10
47 10 c. red .. .. 10 10
48 15 c. green .. .. 10 10
39 **229** 15 c. green .. .. 1·90 45
49 **196** 25 c. purple .. .. 15 10
50 30 c. blue .. .. 15 15
51 **232** 40 c. brown .. .. 15 15
52 45 c. red .. .. 20 20
53 **196** 50 c. grey .. .. 20 15
54 **232** 75 c. blue .. .. 25 20
55 **201** 90 c. green .. .. 25 20
41 **196** 1 PTA. black .. .. 20 15
56 **201** 1 p. 35 violet .. .. 2·50 2·40
57 **196** 2 PTAS. brown .. 1·90 1·60
58 4 PTAS. pink .. .. 7·00 4·25
59 10 PTAS. brown .. 16·00 13·00

60 **195** 25 c. red (air) .. .. 25 10
61 50 c. brown .. .. 30 15
62 1 p. blue .. .. 30 15
63 2 p. green .. .. 1·75 45
64 4 p. blue .. .. 5·00 2·75
65 10 p. violet .. .. 7·00 6·00

**1949.** Stamp Day and 75th Anniv. of U.P.U. Spanish stamps optd. **Territorio de Ifni.**
42. **240.** 50 c. brown (postage) .. 1·50 75
43. 75 c. blue .. .. 1·50 75
44. 4 p. olive (air) .. .. 1·60 75

8. General Franco. 9. Lope Sancho de Valenzuela.

**1950.** Child Welfare.
66. **8.** 50 c. + 10 c. sepia .. 35 25
67. 1 p. + 25 c. blue .. .. 13·00 5·00
68. 6 p. 50 + 1 p. 65 green .. 4·50 2·40

**1950.** Air. Colonial Stamp Day.
69 **9** 5 p. green .. .. 1·75 55

10. Woman and Dove. 11. General Franco.

**1951.** Air. 500th Birth Anniv. of Isabella the Catholic.
70. **10.** 5 p. red .. .. .. 19·00 5·50

**1951.** Gen. Franco's Visit to Ifni.
71. **11.** 50 c. orange .. .. 25 10
72. 1 p. brown .. .. 3·50 80
73. 5 p. green .. .. 27·00 8·00

12. Fennec Fox. 13. Mother and Child.

**1951.** Colonial Stamp Day.
74. **12.** 5 c. + 5 c. brown .. 10 10
75. 10 c. + 5 c. orange .. 10 10
76. 60 c. + 15 c. olive .. 20 10

**1952.** Child Welfare.
77. **13.** 5 c. + 5 c. brown .. 10 10
78. 50 c. + 10 c. black .. 10 10
79. 2 p. + 30 c. blue .. .. 95 35

14. Ferdinand the Catholic. 15. Shag.

**1952.** Air. 500th Birth Anniv. of Ferdinand the Catholic.
80. **14.** 5 p. brown .. .. 25·00 5·50

**1952.** Colonial Stamp Day.
81. **15.** 5 c. + 5 c. brown .. 15 10
82. 10 c. + 5 c. red .. .. 25 10
83. 60 c. + 15 c. green .. 1·25 25

16. 17. Addra Gazelle and Douglas DC-4 Airliner.

**1952.** 400th Death Anniv of Leo Africanus (geographer).
84 **16** 5 c. orange .. .. 10 10
85 35 c. green .. .. 10 10
86 60 c. brown .. .. 15 10

**1953.** Air.
87. **17.** 60 c. green .. .. 10 10
88. 1 p. 20 lake .. .. 15 10
89. 1 p. 60 brown .. .. 25 10
90. 2 p. blue .. .. 1·75 20
91. 4 p. myrtle .. .. 95 20
92. 10 p. purple .. .. 5·75 1·25

DESIGN: 10 c., 60 c. Two native musicians.

18. Musician.

**1953.** Child Welfare. Inscr. "PRO INFANCIA 1953".
93. **18.** 5 c. + 5 c. lake .. .. 10 10
94. – 10 c. + 5 c. purple .. 10 10
95. **18.** 15 c. olive .. .. 10 10
96. – 60 c. brown .. .. 10 10

DESIGN: 10 c., 60 c. Fish and seaweed.

19. Fish and Jellyfish.

**1953.** Colonial Stamp Day. Inscr. "DIA DEL SELLO COLONIAL 1953".
97. **19.** 5 c. + 5 c. blue .. .. 15 10
98. – 10 c. + 5 c. mauve .. 15 10
99. **19.** 15 c. green .. .. 15 10
100. – 60 c. brown .. .. 25 10

20. Mediterranean Gull. 21. Asclepiad.

**1954.**
101 **20** 5 c. orange .. .. 45 10
102 **21** 10 c. green .. .. 10 10
103 – 25 c. red .. .. 10 10
104 **20** 35 c. green .. .. 30 10
105 **21** 40 c. purple .. .. 10 10
106 – 60 c. brown .. .. 10 10
107 **20** 1 p. brown .. .. 14·00 50
108 **21** 1 p. 25 red .. .. 10 10
109 – 2 p. blue .. .. 10 10
110 **21** 4 p. 50 green .. .. 20 40
111 – 5 p. black .. .. 32·00 9·75
DESIGN—VERT: 25, 60 c., 2, 5 p. Cactus.

22. Woman and child 23. Lobster.

**1954.** Child Welfare. Inscr. "PRO-INFANCIA 1954".
112. **22.** 5 c. + 5 c. orange .. 10 10
113. – 10 c. + 5 c. mauve .. 10 10
114. **22.** 15 c. green .. .. 10 10
115. – 60 c. brown .. .. 10 10
DESIGN: 10 c., 60 c. Woman and girl.

**1954.** Colonial Stamp Day. Inscr. "DIA DEL SELLO COLONIAL 1954".
116. **23.** 5 c. + 5 c. brown .. 10 10
117. – 10 c. + 5 c. violet .. 10 10
118. **23.** 15 c. green .. .. 10 10
119. – 60 c. lake .. .. 10 10
DESIGN: 10 c., 60 c. Hammer-headed shark.

DESIGN: 25 c. Camel caravan and "Spain".

24. Ploughman and "Justice".

**1955.** Native Welfare. Inscr. "PRO-INDIGENAS 1955".
120. **24.** 10 c. + 5 c. purple .. 10 10
121. – 25 c. + 10 c. lilac .. 10 10
122. **24.** 50 c. olive .. .. 10 10



25. Eurasian Red Squirrel. 26. "Senecio antheuphorbium".

**1955.** Colonial Stamp Day.
123 **25** 5 c. + 5 c. brown .. 10 10
124 – 15 c. + 5 c. bistre .. 10 10
125 **25** 70 c. green .. .. 15 10
DESIGN: 15 c. Eurasian red squirrel holding nut.

**1956.** Child Welfare. Inscr. "PRO-INFANCIA 1956".
126. **26.** 5 c. + 5 c. green .. 10 10
127. – 15 c. + 5 c. brown .. 10 10
128. **26.** 20 c. green .. .. 10 10
129. – 50 c. sepia .. .. 15 10
DESIGN: 15 c., 50 c. "Limoniastrum ifniensis".

27. Arms of Sidi-Ifni and Drummer. 28. Rock Doves.

**1956.** Colonial Stamp Day. Inscr. "DIA DEL SELLO 1956".
130. – 5 c. + 5 c. sepia .. 10 10
131. **27.** 15 c. + 5 c. brown .. 10 10
132. – 70 c. green .. .. 10 10
DESIGNS—VERT. 5 c. Arms of Spain and Bohar reedbucks. HORIZ. 70 c. Arms of Sidi-Ifni, shepherd and sheep.

**1957.** Child Welfare Fund.
133 **28** 5 c. + 5 c. green & brown 15 10
134 – 15 c. + 5 c. brn & ochre 30 10
135 **28** 70 c. brown and green .. 95 25
DESIGN: 15 c. Stock doves in flight.

29. Golden Jackal.

**1957.** Colonial Stamp Day. Inscr. "DIA DEL SELLO 1957".
136. **29.** 10 c. + 5 c. brn. & pur. 10 10
137. – 15 c. + 5 c. grn. & brn. 10 10
138. **29.** 20 c. brown & green .. 10 10
139. – 70 c. brown & green .. 15 10
DESIGN—VERT. 15 c., 70 c., Head of Golden jackal.

30. Barn Swallows and Arms of Valencia and Sidi-Ifni. 31. Basketball.

**1958.** "Aid for Valencia".
140 **30** 10 c. + 5 c. brown .. 10 10
141 15 c. + 10 c. brown .. 15 10
142 50 c. + 10 c. brown .. 35 25

**1958.** Child Welfare Fund.
143 **31** 10 c. + 5 c. brown .. 10 10
144 – 15 c. + 5 c. brown .. 10 10
145 **31** 20 c. green .. .. 10 10
146 – 70 c. green .. .. 15 10
DESIGN: 15, 70 c. Cycling.

32.

**1959.** Colonial Stamp Day.

| | | | | |
|---|---|---|---|---|
| 147 | 32 | 10 c.+5 c. red | 10 | 10 |
| 148 | – | 25 c.+10 c. purple | 10 | 10 |
| 149 | – | 50 c.+10 c. brown | 15 | 10 |

DESIGNS—VERT: 25 c. Ray. HORIZ: 50 c. Fishing boats.

33. Ewe and Lamb. 34. Footballer.

**1959.** Child Welfare Fund.

| | | | | |
|---|---|---|---|---|
| 150. | 33. | 10 c.+5 c. brown | 10 | 10 |
| 151. | – | 15 c.+5 c. brown | 10 | 10 |
| 152. | – | 20 c. turquoise | 10 | 10 |
| 153. | 33. | 70 c. green | 10 | 10 |

DESIGNS—VERT. 15 c. Native trader with mule. 20 c. Mountain goat.

**1959.** Colonial Stamp Day. Inscr. "DIA DEL SELLO 1959".

| | | | | |
|---|---|---|---|---|
| 154. | 34. | 10 c.+5 c. brown | 10 | 10 |
| 155. | – | 20 c.+5 c. myrtle | 10 | 10 |
| 156. | – | 50 c.+20 c. olive | 15 | 10 |

DESIGNS: 20 c. Footballers. 50 c. Javelin-thrower.

35. Dromedaries. 36. White Stork.

**1960.** Child Welfare.

| | | | | |
|---|---|---|---|---|
| 157 | 35 | 10 c.+5 c. purple | 10 | 10 |
| 158 | – | 15 c.+5 c. brown | 10 | 10 |
| 159 | – | 35 c. green | 50 | 10 |
| 160 | 35 | 80 c. green | 10 | 10 |

DESIGNS: 15 c. Wild boar. 35 c. Red-legged partridges.

**1960.** Birds.

| | | | | |
|---|---|---|---|---|
| 161 | 36 | 25 c. violet | 10 | 10 |
| 162 | – | 50 c. brown | 20 | 10 |
| 163 | – | 75 c. purple | 25 | 10 |
| 164 | 36 | 1 p. red | 30 | 10 |
| 165 | – | 1 p. 50 turquoise | 35 | 15 |
| 166 | – | 2 p. purple | 40 | 20 |
| 167 | 36 | 3 p. blue | 1·50 | 25 |
| 168 | – | 5 p. brown | 2·50 | 50 |
| 169 | – | 10 p. green | 6·50 | 1·40 |

BIRDS—HORIZ: 50 c., 1 p. 50, 5 p. Goldfinches. VERT: 75 c., 2, 10 p. Sky larks.

37. Church of Santa Cruze del Mar.

38. High Jump.

**1960.** Stamp Day. Inscr. "DIA DEL SELLO 1960".

| | | | | |
|---|---|---|---|---|
| 170. | 37. | 10 c.+5 c. brown | 10 | 10 |
| 171. | – | 20 c.+5 c. green | 10 | 10 |
| 172. | 37. | 30 c.+10 c. brown | 10 | 10 |
| 173. | – | 50 c.+50 c. brown | 10 | 10 |

DESIGN—HORIZ. 20 c., 50 c., School building.

**1961.** Child Welfare. Inscr. "PRO-INFANCIA 1961".

| | | | | |
|---|---|---|---|---|
| 174. | 38. | 10 c.+5 c. red | 10 | 10 |
| 175. | – | 25 c.+10 c. violet | 10 | 10 |
| 176. | 38. | 80 c.+20 c. turquoise | 10 | 10 |

DESIGN—VERT. 25 c. Football.

39.

**1961.** 25th Anniv of General Franco as Head of State.

| | | | | |
|---|---|---|---|---|
| 177 | – | 25 c. grey | 10 | 10 |
| 178 | 39 | 50 c. brown | 10 | 10 |
| 179 | – | 70 c. green | 10 | 10 |
| 180 | 39 | 1 p. red | 10 | 10 |

DESIGNS—VERT: 25 c. Map. HORIZ: 70 c. Government Building.

40. Camel and Motor Lorry. 41. Admiral Jofre Tenorio.

**1961.** Stamp Day. Inscr. "DIA DEL SELLO 1961".

| | | | | |
|---|---|---|---|---|
| 181. | 40. | 10 c.+5 c. lake | 10 | 10 |
| 182. | – | 25 c.+10 c. plum | 10 | 10 |
| 183. | 40. | 30 c.+10 c. brown | 10 | 10 |
| 184. | – | 1 p.+10 c. orange | 15 | 10 |

DESIGN: 25 c., 1 p. Freighter at wharf.

**1962.** Child Welfare. Inscr. "PRO-INFANCIA 1962".

| | | | | |
|---|---|---|---|---|
| 185. | 41. | 25 c. violet | 10 | 10 |
| 186. | – | 50 c. turquoise | 10 | 10 |
| 187. | 41. | 1 p. brown | 10 | 10 |

DESIGN: 50 c. C. Fernandez-Duro (historian).

42. Desert Postman. 43. "Golden Tower", Seville.

**1962.** Stamp Day.

| | | | | |
|---|---|---|---|---|
| 188 | 42 | 15 c. blue | 10 | 10 |
| 189 | – | 35 c. mauve | 10 | 10 |
| 190 | 42 | 1 p. purple | 10 | 10 |

DESIGN: 35 c. Winged letter on hands.

**1963.** Seville Flood Relief.

| | | | | |
|---|---|---|---|---|
| 191. | 43. | 50 c. green | 10 | 10 |
| 192. | | 1 p. brown | 10 | 10 |

44. Moroccan Copper and Flower. 45. Child and Flowers.

**1963.** Child Welfare. Inscr. "PRO-INFANCIA 1963".

| | | | | |
|---|---|---|---|---|
| 193. | – | 25 c. blue | 20 | 10 |
| 194. | 44. | 50 c. green | 30 | 10 |
| 195. | – | 1 p. red | 50 | 10 |

DESIGN: 25 c., 1 p. Moroccan orange-tips.

**1963.** "For Barcelona".

| | | | | |
|---|---|---|---|---|
| 196. | 45. | 50 c. green | 10 | 10 |
| 197. | | 1 p. brown | 10 | 10 |

46. Beetle ("Steraspis speciosa"). 47. Edmi Gazelle.

**1964.** Stamp Day. Inscr. "DIA DEL SELLO 1963".

| | | | | |
|---|---|---|---|---|
| 198. | 46. | 25 c. blue | 10 | 10 |
| 199. | – | 50 c. olive | 10 | 10 |
| 200. | 46. | 1 p. brown | 10 | 10 |

DESIGN: 50 c. Desert locust.

**1964.** Child Welfare.

| | | | | |
|---|---|---|---|---|
| 201 | 47 | 25 c. violet | 10 | 10 |
| 202 | – | 50 c. grey | 10 | 10 |
| 203 | 47 | 1 p. red | 10 | 10 |

DESIGN: 50 c. Head of roe deer.

48. Cyclists Racing.

**1964.** Stamp Day.

| | | | | |
|---|---|---|---|---|
| 204 | 48 | 50 c. brown | 10 | 10 |
| 205 | – | 1 p. red | 10 | 10 |
| 206 | 48 | 1 p. 50 green | 10 | 10 |

DESIGN: 1 p. Motor cycle racing.

49. Port Installation, Sidi Ifni.

**1965.** 25th Anniv. of End of Spanish Civil War.

| | | | | |
|---|---|---|---|---|
| 207. | – | 50 c. green | 10 | 10 |
| 208. | – | 1 p. red | 10 | 10 |
| 209. | 49. | 1 p. 50 blue | 10 | 10 |

DESIGNS—VERT. 50 c. Ifnian. 1 p. "Education" (children in class).

50. "Eugaster fernandezi".

**1965.** Child Welfare.

| | | | | |
|---|---|---|---|---|
| 210. | 50. | 50 c. purple | 10 | 10 |
| 211. | – | 1 p. red ("Halter halteratus") | 10 | 10 |
| 212. | 50. | 1 p. 50 blue | 15 | 10 |

51. Arms of Ifni.

**1965.** Stamp Day.

| | | | | |
|---|---|---|---|---|
| 213. | – | 50 c. brown | 60 | 20 |
| 214. | 51. | 1 p. red | 10 | 10 |
| 215. | – | 1 p. 50 blue | 90 | 20 |

DESIGN—VERT. 50 c., 1 p. 50, Golden Eagle.

52. De Havilland D.H.9C Biplanes.

**1966.** Child Welfare.

| | | | | |
|---|---|---|---|---|
| 216. | – | 1 p. brown | 15 | 10 |
| 217. | – | 1 p. 50 blue | 25 | 15 |
| 218. | 52. | 2 p. 50 violet | 1·50 | 90 |

DESIGN—VERT. 1 p., 1 p. 50, Douglas DC-8 jetliner over Sidi Ifni.

53. Maid Alice Moth. 54. Coconut Palm.

**1966.** Stamp Day. Insects.

| | | | | |
|---|---|---|---|---|
| 219 | 53 | 10 c. green and red | 10 | 10 |
| 220 | – | 40 c. brown & dp brown | 15 | 10 |
| 221 | 53 | 1 p. 50 violet & yellow | 50 | 10 |
| 222 | – | 4 p. blue and purple | 70 | 10 |

DESIGN: 40 c., 4 p. African monarch (butterfly).

**1967.** Child Welfare.

| | | | | |
|---|---|---|---|---|
| 223. | 54. | 10 c. green and brown | 10 | 10 |
| 224. | – | 40 c. green and brown | 10 | 10 |
| 225. | 54. | 1 p. 50 turquoise & sepia | 15 | 10 |
| 226. | – | 4 p. sepia and brown | 30 | 20 |

DESIGN: 40 c., 4 p. Cactus.

55. Bulk Carrier and Floating Crane.

**1967.** Inauguration of Port Ifni.

| | | | | |
|---|---|---|---|---|
| 227. | 55. | 1 p. 50 brown and green | 20 | 10 |

56. Saury Pike.

**1967.** Stamp Day.

| | | | | |
|---|---|---|---|---|
| 228. | 56. | 1 p. green and blue | 10 | 10 |
| 229. | – | 1 p. 50 purple & yellow | 10 | 10 |
| 230. | – | 3 p. 50 red and blue | 15 | 10 |

FISH—VERT. 1 p. 50, John Dory. HORIZ. 3 p. 50, Gurnard.

**1968.** Child Welfare. Signs of the Zodiac. As T 47 of Fernando Poo.

| | | | | |
|---|---|---|---|---|
| 231. | | 1 p. mauve on yellow | 10 | 10 |
| 232. | | 1 p. 50 brown on pink | 10 | 10 |
| 233. | | 2 p. 50 violet on yellow | 20 | 10 |

DESIGNS: 1 p., Fishes (Pisces). 1 p. 50, Ram (Aries). 2 p. 50, Archer (Sagattarius).

57. Posting Letter.

**1968.** Stamp Day.

| | | | | |
|---|---|---|---|---|
| 234 | 57 | 1 p. black and yellow | 10 | 10 |
| 235 | – | 1 p. 50 black, plum & bl | 10 | 10 |
| 236 | – | 2 p. 50 black, blue & grn | 15 | 10 |

DESIGNS: 1 p. 50, Dove with letter. 2 p. 50, Magnifying-glass and stamp.

EXPRESS LETTER STAMPS

**1943.** As T 4, but view of La Alcazaba inscr. "URGENTE".

| | | | | |
|---|---|---|---|---|
| E 35. | | 25 c. red and green | 90 | 65 |

**1949.** Express Letter stamp of Spain optd **Territorio de Ifni**.

| | | | | |
|---|---|---|---|---|
| E66 | E 198 | 25 c. red | 15 | 10 |

## INDO-CHINA Pt. 6

A French territory in south-east Asia. In 1949 it was split up into the three states of Vietnam, Cambodia and Laos.

1889. 100 centimes = 1 franc.
1918. 100 cents = 1 piastre.

**1889.** Stamp of French Colonies, "Commerce" type, surch. (a) **INDO-CHINE 1889 5 R-D.**

| | | | | |
|---|---|---|---|---|
| 1 | J | 5 on 35 c. black on orange | 60·00 | 40·00 |

(b) **INDO-CHINE 89 5 R D.**

| | | | | |
|---|---|---|---|---|
| 2 | J | 5 on 35 c. black on orange | 5·25 | 4·50 |

**1892.** "Tablet" key-type inscr "INDO-CHINE" in red (1, 5, 15, 25, 50 (No. 27), 75 c., 1 f.) or blue (others).

| | | | | |
|---|---|---|---|---|
| 6 | D | 1 c. black on blue | 55 | 40 |
| 7 | | 2 c. brown on buff | 60 | 50 |
| 8 | | 4 c. brown on grey | 60 | 50 |
| 23 | | 5 c. green | 55 | 25 |
| 10 | | 10 c. black on lilac | 1·75 | 50 |
| 24 | | 10 c. red | 1·25 | 45 |
| 11 | | 15 c. blue | 20·00 | 55 |
| 25 | | 15 c. grey | 3·50 | 40 |
| 12 | | 20 c. red on green | 4·25 | 2·25 |
| 13a | | 25 c. black on pink | 6·75 | 1·40 |
| 26 | | 25 c. blue | 9·75 | 85 |
| 14 | | 30 c. brown on drab | 11·00 | 3·25 |
| 15 | | 40 c. red on yellow | 12·00 | 3·25 |
| 16 | | 50 c. red on pink | 26·00 | 7·00 |
| 27 | | 50 c. brown on blue | 11·00 | 2·75 |
| 17 | | 75 c. brown on orange | 16·00 | 8·50 |
| 18 | | 1 f. green | 27·00 | 11·00 |
| 19 | | 5 f. mauve on lilac | 80·00 | 55·00 |

**1903.** Surch.

| | | | | |
|---|---|---|---|---|
| 28. | D. | 5 on 15 c. grey | 45 | 50 |
| 29. | | 15 on 25 c. blue | 70 | 65 |

**8.** " Grasset " type.

**1904.**

| No. | Type | Description | Unused | Used |
|---|---|---|---|---|
| 30 | 8 | 1 c. green .. .. | 25 | 15 |
| 31 | | 2 c. purple on yellow .. | 40 | 15 |
| 32 | | 4 c. mauve on blue .. | 25 | 15 |
| 33 | | 5 c. green .. .. | 30 | 15 |
| 34 | | 10 c. pink .. .. | 70 | 15 |
| 35 | | 15 c. brown on blue .. | 55 | 20 |
| 36 | | 20 c. red on green .. | 1·40 | 40 |
| 37 | | 25 c. blue .. .. | 7·25 | 60 |
| 38 | | 30 c. brown on cream .. | 3·25 | 1·00 |
| 39 | | 35 c. black on yellow .. | 9·00 | 80 |
| 40 | | 40 c. black on grey .. | 2·50 | 65 |
| 41 | | 50 c. brown .. .. | 4·00 | 1·00 |
| 42 | | 75 c. red on orange .. | 29·00 | 15·00 |
| 43 | | 1 f. green .. .. | 11·50 | 2·75 |
| 44 | | 2 f. brown on yellow .. | 28·00 | 22·00 |
| 45 | | 5 f. violet .. .. | £150 | £110 |
| 46 | | 10 f. red on green .. | £140 | £110 |

**10.** Annamite. **11.** Cambodian. **12.** Cambodian.

**1907.**

| No. | Type | Description | Unused | Used |
|---|---|---|---|---|
| 51. | 10. | 1 c. black and sepia .. | 20 | 15 |
| 52. | | 2 c. black and brown .. | 15 | 15 |
| 53. | | 4 c. black and blue .. | 40 | 45 |
| 54. | | 5 c. black and green .. | 30 | 20 |
| 55. | | 10 c. black and red .. | 30 | 15 |
| 56. | | 15 c. black and violet .. | 70 | 50 |
| 57. | 11. | 20 c. black and violet .. | 1·25 | 65 |
| 58. | | 25 c. black and blue .. | 3·00 | 30 |
| 59. | | 30 c. black and brown .. | 4·50 | 3·00 |
| 60. | | 35 c. black and green .. | 85 | 45 |
| 61. | | 40 c. black and brown .. | 2·25 | 1·00 |
| 62. | | 45 c. black and orange .. | 5·50 | 3·25 |
| 63. | | 50 c. black and red .. | 7·75 | 3·00 |
| 64. | 12. | 75 c. black and orange .. | 5·50 | 3·75 |
| 65. | – | 1 f. black and red .. | 26·00 | 6·50 |
| 66. | – | 2 f. black and green .. | 7·75 | 6·50 |
| 67. | – | 5 f. black and blue .. | 29·00 | 15·50 |
| 68. | – | 10 f. black and violet .. | 55·00 | 50·00 |

DESIGNS—As Type **12**: 1 f. Annamites. 2 f. Muong. 5 f. Laotian. 10 f. Cambodian.

**1912.** Surch in figures.

| No. | Type | Description | Unused | Used |
|---|---|---|---|---|
| 69 | 8 | 05 on 4 c. mauve on blue | 3·50 | 2·75 |
| 70 | | 05 on 15 c. brown on blue | 40 | 40 |
| 71 | | 05 on 30 c. brn on cream | 45 | 50 |
| 72 | | 10 on 40 c. black on grey | 50 | 60 |
| 73 | | 10 on 50 c. brown .. | 50 | 45 |
| 74 | | 10 on 75 c. red on orange | 2·75 | 2·75 |

**1914.** Red Cross. Surch **5c** and red cross.

| No. | Type | Description | Unused | Used |
|---|---|---|---|---|
| 76 | 10 | 5 c.+5 c. black & green | 35 | 60 |
| 75 | | 10 c.+5 c. black and red | 50 | 35 |
| 78 | | 15 c.+5 c. black & vio | 80 | 80 |

**1918.** Nos. 75/6 and 78 further surch in figures and words.

| No. | Type | Description | Unused | Used |
|---|---|---|---|---|
| 79 | 10 | 4 c. on 5 c.+5 c. black and green .. .. | 2·25 | 2·25 |
| 80 | | 6 c. on 10 c.+5 c. black and red .. .. | 2·25 | 2·00 |
| 81 | | 8 c. on 15 c.+5 c. black and violet .. .. | 8·00 | 6·50 |

**1919.** French stamps of " War Orphans " issue surch. **INDOCHINE** and value in figures and words.

| No. | Type | Description | Unused | Used |
|---|---|---|---|---|
| 82. | 23. | 10 c. on 15 c.+10 c. grey | 90 | 95 |
| 83. | | 16 c. on 25 c.+15 c. blue | 3·00 | 3·00 |
| 84. | – | 24 c. on 35 c.+25 c. violet and grey .. .. | 4·25 | 4·75 |
| 85. | – | 40 c. on 50 c.+50 c. brn. | 8·75 | 8·75 |
| 86. | 26. | 80 c. on 1 f.+1 f. red .. | 17·00 | 17·00 |
| 87. | | 4 p. on 5 f.+5 f. bl. & blk. | £170 | £170 |

**1919.** Surch. in figures and words.

| No. | Type | Description | Unused | Used |
|---|---|---|---|---|
| 88. | 10. | 2/5 c. on 1 c. black and sepia | 30 | 20 |
| 89. | | 4/5 c. on 2 c. black & brown | 55 | 45 |
| 90. | | 1 3/5 c. on 4 c. black and blue | 95 | 40 |
| 91. | | 2 c. on 5 c. black & green | 40 | 20 |
| 92. | | 4 c. on 10 c. black and red | 40 | 15 |
| 93. | | 6 c. on 15 c. black & violet | 1·10 | 40 |
| 94. | 11. | 8 c. on 20 c. black & violet | 1·25 | 1·25 |
| 95. | | 10 c. on 25 c. black & blue | 1·25 | 30 |
| 96. | | 12 c. on 30 c. black & brn. | 3·25 | 45 |
| 97. | | 14 c. on 35 c. black & grn | 70 | 30 |
| 98. | | 16 c. on 40 c. black & brn. | 3·25 | 70 |
| 99. | | 18 c. on 45 c. black & orge. | 3·25 | 1·25 |
| 100. | | 20 c. on 50 c. black & red | 4·75 | 50 |
| 101. | 12. | 30 c. on 75 c. blk. & orge. | 5·50 | 1·10 |
| 102. | – | 40 c. on 1 f. black and red | 9·75 | 1·00 |
| 103. | – | 80 c. on 2 f. black & green | 11·50 | 3·00 |
| 104. | – | 2 p. on 5 f. black and blue | 55·00 | 48·00 |
| 105. | – | 4 p. on 10 f. black & violet | 90·00 | 80·00 |

**1922.** As T **10** and **11** but value in cents or piastres.

| No. | Type | Description | Unused | Used |
|---|---|---|---|---|
| 115 | 10 | 1/10 c. red and grey .. | 15 | 25 |
| 116 | | 1/5 c. black and blue .. | 15 | 15 |
| 117 | | 2/5 c. black and brown | 20 | 20 |
| 118 | | 4/5 c. black and mauve | 25 | 25 |
| 119 | | 1 c. black and brown .. | 20 | 15 |
| 120 | | 2 c. black and green .. | 40 | 15 |
| 121 | | 3 c. black and violet .. | 25 | 20 |
| 122 | | 4 c. black and orange .. | 20 | 15 |
| 123 | | 5 c. black and red .. | 20 | 15 |
| 124 | 11 | 6 c. black and red .. | 25 | 20 |
| 125 | | 7 c. black and green .. | 25 | 25 |
| 126 | | 8 c. black on lilac .. | 65 | 50 |
| 127 | | 9 c. black and yellow .. | 65 | 50 |
| 128 | | 10 c. black and blue .. | 20 | 20 |
| 129 | | 11 c. black and violet .. | 25 | 20 |
| 130 | | 12 c. black and brown .. | 25 | 25 |
| 131 | | 15 c. black and orange | 40 | 25 |
| 132 | | 20 c. black and blue .. | 50 | 30 |
| 133 | | 40 c. black and red .. | 1·10 | 65 |
| 134 | | 1 p. black and green .. | 3·25 | 3·00 |
| 135 | | 2 p. black and purple on pink .. .. .. | 5·75 | 4·50 |

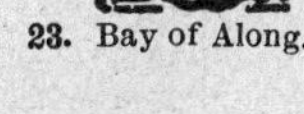

**22.** Ploughman and Tower of Confucius. **23.** Bay of Along.

**24.** Ruins of Angkor.

**1927.**

| No. | Type | Description | Unused | Used |
|---|---|---|---|---|
| 136. | 22. | 1/10 c. olive .. .. | 15 | 30 |
| 137. | | 1/5 c. yellow .. .. | 15 | 30 |
| 138. | | 2/5 c. blue .. .. .. | 20 | 30 |
| 139. | | 4/5 c. brown .. .. | 30 | 30 |
| 140. | | 1 c. orange .. .. | 30 | 15 |
| 141. | | 2 c. green .. .. | 50 | 20 |
| 142. | | 3 c. blue .. .. .. | 40 | 20 |
| 143. | | 4 c. mauve .. .. | 75 | 55 |
| 144. | | 5 c. violet .. .. | 35 | 15 |
| 145. | 23. | 6 c. red .. .. | 1·10 | 20 |
| 146. | | 7 c. brown .. .. | 70 | 40 |
| 147. | | 8 c. olive .. .. .. | 65 | 65 |
| 148. | | 9 c. purple .. .. | 75 | 60 |
| 149. | | 10 c. blue .. .. | 80 | 45 |
| 150. | | 11 c. orange .. .. | 80 | 60 |
| 151. | | 12 c. grey .. .. | 55 | 30 |
| 152. | 24. | 15 c. brown and red | 5·00 | 4·00 |
| 153. | | 20 c. grey and violet | 2·00 | 80 |
| 154. | – | 25 c. mauve and brown | 4·75 | 3·50 |
| 155. | – | 30 c. olive and blue | 2·50 | 1·75 |
| 156. | – | 40 c. blue and red | 3·50 | 2·00 |
| 157. | – | 50 c. grey and green | 4·75 | 1·40 |
| 158. | – | 1 p. black, yellow & blue | 8·50 | 6·00 |
| 159. | – | 2 p. blue, orange and red | 11·00 | 8·00 |

DESIGNS—As T **24**. 25, 30 c. Wood-carver. 40, 50 c. Temple, Thuat-Luong. 1, 2 p. Founding of Saigon.

**1931.** "Colonial Exn" key-types inscr "INDOCHINE" and surch with new value.

| No. | Type | Description | Unused | Used |
|---|---|---|---|---|
| 160. | F. | 4 c. on 50 c. mauve .. | 1·40 | 1·10 |
| 161. | G. | 6 c. on 90 c. red .. | 1·60 | 1·60 |
| 162. | H. | 10 c. on 1 f. 50 blue .. | 2·50 | 1·40 |

**33.** Junk. **36.** "Apsara", or dancing Nymph.

**1931.**

| No. | Type | Description | Unused | Used |
|---|---|---|---|---|
| 163 | 33 | 1/10 c. blue .. .. | 15 | 25 |
| 164 | | 1/5 c. red .. .. | 15 | 20 |
| 165 | | 2/5 c. orange .. .. | 15 | 30 |
| 166 | | 1/2 c. brown .. .. | 20 | 25 |
| 167 | | 4/5 c. violet .. .. | 20 | 30 |
| 168 | | 1 c. brown .. .. | 20 | 15 |
| 169 | | 2 c. green .. .. | 25 | 15 |
| 170 | – | 3 c. brown .. .. | 20 | 15 |
| 171 | – | 3 c. green .. .. | 2·75 | 85 |
| 172 | – | 4 c. blue .. .. | 25 | 20 |
| 173 | – | 4 c. green .. .. | 40 | 50 |
| 174 | – | 4 c. yellow .. .. | 30 | 30 |
| 175 | – | 5 c. purple .. .. | 30 | 15 |
| 176 | – | 5 c. green .. .. | 30 | 30 |
| 177 | – | 6 c. red .. .. | 30 | 20 |
| 178 | – | 7 c. black .. .. | 25 | 30 |
| 179 | – | 8 c. red .. .. | 25 | 30 |
| 180 | – | 9 c. black on yellow | 30 | 35 |
| 181 | – | 10 c. blue .. .. | 40 | 25 |
| 182 | – | 10 c. blue on pink .. | 30 | 25 |
| 183 | – | 15 c. brown .. .. | 3·50 | 60 |
| 184 | – | 15 c. blue .. .. | 25 | 15 |
| 185 | – | 18 c. blue .. .. | 25 | 30 |
| 186 | – | 20 c. red .. .. | 20 | 15 |
| 187 | – | 21 c. green .. .. | 25 | 25 |
| 188 | – | 22 c. green .. .. | 25 | 30 |
| 189 | – | 25 c. purple .. .. | 1·50 | 85 |
| 190 | – | 25 c. blue .. .. | 30 | 40 |
| 191 | – | 30 c. brown .. .. | 30 | 20 |
| 192 | 36 | 50 c. brown .. .. | 30 | 15 |
| 193 | | 60 c. purple .. .. | 30 | 20 |
| 194 | | 70 c. blue .. .. | 35 | 30 |
| 195 | | 1 p. green .. .. | 50 | 35 |
| 196 | | 2 p. red .. .. | 55 | 35 |

DESIGNS—As Type **33**. 3 c. to 9 c. Ruins at Angkor. 10 c. to 30 c. Worker in rice field.

**42.** Farman F.190 Mail Plane. **44.** Emperor Bao Dai of Annam.

**1933.** Air.

| No. | Type | Description | Unused | Used |
|---|---|---|---|---|
| 197 | 42 | 1 c. brown .. .. | 20 | 30 |
| 198 | | 2 c. green .. .. | 15 | 25 |
| 199 | | 5 c. green .. .. | 30 | 40 |
| 200 | | 10 c. brown .. .. | 35 | 20 |
| 201 | | 11 c. red .. .. | 30 | 35 |
| 202 | | 15 c. blue .. .. | 40 | 40 |
| 203 | | 16 c. mauve .. .. | 40 | 40 |
| 204 | | 20 c. green .. .. | 40 | 35 |
| 205 | | 30 c. brown .. .. | 20 | 25 |
| 206 | | 36 c. red .. .. | 1·00 | 30 |
| 207 | | 37 c. green .. .. | 20 | 25 |
| 208 | | 39 c. green .. .. | 40 | 50 |
| 209 | | 60 c. purple .. .. | 30 | 30 |
| 210 | | 66 c. green .. .. | 40 | 30 |
| 211 | | 67 c. blue .. .. | 65 | 65 |
| 212 | | 69 c. blue .. .. | 40 | 40 |
| 213 | | 1 p. black .. .. | 35 | 15 |
| 214 | | 2 p. orange .. .. | 70 | 20 |
| 215 | | 5 p. violet .. .. | 1·00 | 50 |
| 216 | | 10 p. red .. .. | 2·25 | 80 |
| 217 | | 20 p. green .. .. | 6·75 | 3·00 |
| 218 | | 30 p. brown .. .. | 7·50 | 3·00 |

**1936.** Issue for Annam.

| No. | Type | Description | Unused | Used |
|---|---|---|---|---|
| 219. | 44. | 1 c. brown .. .. | 50 | 55 |
| 220. | | 2 c. green .. .. | 50 | 55 |
| 221. | | 4 c. violet .. .. | 60 | 65 |
| 222. | | 5 c. lake .. .. | 60 | 70 |
| 223. | | 10 c. red .. .. | 95 | 90 |
| 224. | | 15 c. blue .. .. | 1·10 | 1·00 |
| 225. | | 20 c. red .. .. | 1·25 | 1·40 |
| 226. | | 30 c. purple .. .. | 1·50 | 1·60 |
| 227. | | 50 c. green .. .. | 1·90 | 1·60 |
| 228. | | 1 p. mauve .. .. | 3·00 | 3·00 |
| 229. | | 2 p. black .. .. | 3·50 | 3·25 |

**45.** King Sisowath Monivong of Cambodia. **46.** Pres. Doumer.

**1936.** Issue for Cambodia.

| No. | Type | Description | Unused | Used |
|---|---|---|---|---|
| 230. | 45. | 1 c. brown .. .. | 50 | 55 |
| 231. | | 2 c. green .. .. | 50 | 50 |
| 232. | | 4 c. violet .. .. | 65 | 65 |
| 233. | | 5 c. lake .. .. | 65 | 70 |
| 234. | | 10 c. red .. .. | 1·60 | 1·60 |
| 235. | | 15 c. blue .. .. | 1·90 | 1·90 |
| 236. | | 20 c. red .. .. | 1·40 | 1·40 |
| 237. | | 30 c. purple .. .. | 1·40 | 1·40 |
| 238. | | 50 c. green .. .. | 1·50 | 1·50 |
| 239. | | 1 p. mauve .. .. | 1·90 | 1·60 |
| 240. | | 2 p. black .. .. | 3·00 | 3·00 |

**1937.** Int. Exn., Paris. As Nos. 110/5 of Cameroun.

| No. | Description | Unused | Used |
|---|---|---|---|
| 241. | 2 c. violet .. .. .. | 45 | 65 |
| 242. | 3 c. green .. .. .. | 45 | 60 |
| 243. | 4 c. red .. .. .. | 40 | 55 |
| 244. | 6 c. brown .. .. .. | 40 | 50 |
| 245. | 9 c. red .. .. .. | 45 | 60 |
| 246. | 15 c. blue .. .. .. | 40 | 55 |

**1938.** Opening of Trans-Indo-China Railway.

| No. | Type | Description | Unused | Used |
|---|---|---|---|---|
| 247. | 46. | 5 c. red (postage) .. | 1·40 | 45 |
| 248. | | 6 c. brown .. .. | 1·40 | 35 |
| 249. | | 18 c. blue .. .. | 1·40 | 45 |
| 250. | | 37 c. orange (air) .. | 1·40 | 20 |

**1938.** Int. Anti-Cancer Fund. As T**19** of Cameroun.

| No. | Description | Unused | Used |
|---|---|---|---|
| 251. | 18 c.+5 c. blue .. .. | 5·50 | 6·75 |

**1939.** New York World's Fair. As T **20** of Cameroun.

| No. | Description | Unused | Used |
|---|---|---|---|
| 252. | 13 c. red .. .. .. | 30 | 35 |
| 253. | 23 c. blue .. .. .. | 35 | 45 |

**47.** Mot Cot Pagoda, Hanoi. **48.** King Sihanouk of Cambodia.

**1939.** San Francisco Exn.

| No. | Type | Description | Unused | Used |
|---|---|---|---|---|
| 254. | 47. | 6 c. sepia .. .. | 50 | 50 |
| 255. | | 9 c. red .. .. | 50 | 50 |
| 256. | | 23 c. blue .. .. | 35 | 40 |
| 257. | | 39 c. purple .. .. | 50 | 55 |

**1939.** 150th Anniv. of French Revolution. As T **25** of Cameroun.

| No. | Description | Unused | Used |
|---|---|---|---|
| 258. | 6 c.+2 c. green and black (postage) .. .. | 5·00 | 5·50 |
| 259. | 7 c.+3 c. brown and black | 5·00 | 5·50 |
| 260. | 9 c.+4 c. orange and black | 5·00 | 5·50 |
| 261. | 13 c.+10 c. red and black | 5·00 | 5·50 |
| 262. | 23 c.+20 c. blue and black | 5·00 | 5·50 |
| 263. | 39 c.+40 c. black and orge. (air) .. .. .. | 12·00 | 13·50 |

**1941.** Coronation of King of Cambodia. No gum.

| No. | Type | Description | Unused | Used |
|---|---|---|---|---|
| 264 | 48 | 1 c. orange .. .. | 50 | 50 |
| 265 | | 6 c. violet .. .. | 1·00 | 1·00 |
| 266 | | 25 c. blue .. .. | 11·50 | 11·50 |

**49.** Processional Elephant. **51.** Hanoi University.

**1942.** Fetes of Nam-Giao. No gum.

| No. | Type | Description | Unused | Used |
|---|---|---|---|---|
| 267 | 49 | 3 c. brown .. .. | 90 | 70 |
| 268 | | 6 c. red .. .. | 90 | 70 |

**1942.** No. 189 surch. **10 cents** and bars.

| No. | Description | Unused | Used |
|---|---|---|---|
| 269. | 10 c. on 25 c. purple .. | 40 | 30 |

**1942.** University Fund. No gum.

| No. | Type | Description | Unused | Used |
|---|---|---|---|---|
| 270 | 51 | 6 c.+2 c. red .. .. | 35 | 40 |
| 271 | | 15 c.+5 c. purple .. | 55 | 55 |

Surch **10c +2 c.**

| No. | Type | Description | Unused | Used |
|---|---|---|---|---|
| 271 | 51 | 10 c.+2 c. on 6 c.+2 c. red .. .. .. | 30 | 40 |

**53.** Marshal Petain. **54.** Shield and Sword.

**1942.** No gum.

| No. | Type | Description | Unused | Used |
|---|---|---|---|---|
| 273. | 53. | 1 c. brown .. .. | 15 | 25 |
| 274. | | 3 c. brown .. .. | 30 | 25 |
| 275. | | 6 c. red .. .. | 20 | 30 |
| 276. | | 10 c. green .. .. | 30 | 30 |
| 277. | | 40 c. blue .. .. | 25 | 35 |
| 278. | | 40 c. grey .. .. | 65 | 65 |

**1942.** National Relief Fund. No gum.

| No. | Type | Description | Unused | Used |
|---|---|---|---|---|
| 279 | 54 | 6 c.+2 c. red and blue | 25 | 35 |
| 280 | | 15 c.+5 c. blk, red & bl | 40 | 45 |

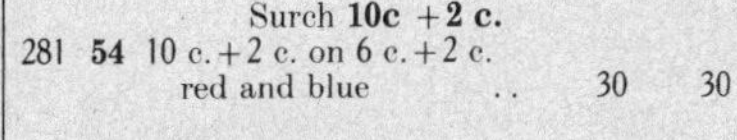

Surch **10c +2 c.**

| No. | Type | Description | Unused | Used |
|---|---|---|---|---|
| 281 | 54 | 10 c.+2 c. on 6 c.+2 c. red and blue .. .. | 30 | 30 |

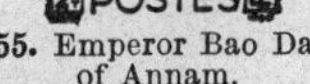

**55.** Emperor Bao Dai of Annam. **56.** King Sihanouk of Cambodia.

57. Empress Nam-Phaong of Annam.
58. King Sisavang-Vong of Laos.

**1942.** No gum.

| No. | Type | Description | | |
|---|---|---|---|---|
| 282. | 55. | ½ c. purple .. .. | 35 | 30 |
| 283. | 56. | 1 c. purple .. .. | 50 | 40 |
| 284. | 58. | 1 c. brown .. .. | 25 | 30 |
| 285. | 55. | 6 c. red .. .. | 70 | 40 |
| 286. | 56. | 6 c. red .. .. | 40 | 30 |
| 287. | 57. | 6 c. red .. .. | 55 | 35 |
| 288. | 58. | 6 c. red .. .. | 35 | 30 |

59. Saigon Fair.
60. Alexandre Yersin.

**1942.** Saigon Fair. No gum.

| No. | Type | Description | | |
|---|---|---|---|---|
| 289 | 59 | 6 c. red .. .. .. | 30 | 35 |

**1943.** No gum.

| No. | Type | Description | | |
|---|---|---|---|---|
| 290 | 60 | 6 c. red .. .. | 70 | 75 |
| 291 | | 15 c. purple .. .. | 25 | 30 |
| 292 | – | 15 c. purple .. .. | 20 | 25 |
| 293 | – | 20 c. red .. .. | 65 | 70 |
| 294 | – | 30 c. brown .. .. | 25 | 35 |
| 295 | 60 | $1 green .. .. | 40 | 40 |

DESIGNS—HORIZ. Nos. 292, 294, Alexandre de Rhodes. No. 293, Pigneau de Behaire, Bishop of Adran.

63. Do Huu-Vi.

**1943.** Airmen. No gum.

| No. | Type | Description | | |
|---|---|---|---|---|
| 296 | 63 | 6 c.+2 c. red .. .. | 35 | 40 |
| 297 | – | 6 c.+2 c. red .. .. | 30 | 30 |

Surch **10c +2 c**.

| No. | Type | Description | | |
|---|---|---|---|---|
| 298 | 63 | 10 c.+2 c. on 6 c.+2 c. red .. .. .. | 20 | 30 |
| 299 | – | 10 c.+2 c. on 6 c.+2 c. red .. .. .. | 20 | 30 |

DESIGN—VERT. Nos. 297, 299, Roland Garros.

64. Doudart de Lagree.
66. "Family, Homeland and Labour".

**1943.** Sailors. No gum.

| No. | Type | Description | | |
|---|---|---|---|---|
| 300 | 64 | 1 c. brown .. .. | 15 | 30 |
| 301 | A | 1 c. brown .. .. | 60 | 40 |
| 302 | B | 1 c. brown .. .. | 20 | 30 |
| 303 | | 5 c. brown .. .. | 25 | 30 |
| 304 | C | 6 c. red .. .. | 45 | 30 |
| 305 | D | 6 c. red .. .. | 25 | 30 |
| 306 | E | 6 c. red .. .. | 25 | 30 |
| 307 | F | 10 c. green .. .. | 20 | 30 |
| 308 | 64 | 15 c. purple .. .. | 25 | 35 |
| 309 | F | 20 c. red .. .. | 25 | 30 |
| 310 | 64 | 40 c. blue .. .. | 25 | 30 |
| 311 | F | 1 p. green .. .. | 50 | 45 |

DESIGNS—HORIZ. A, Francis Garnier. B, La Grandiere. C, Courbet. D, Rigault de Genouilly. VERT. E, Chasseloup Laubat. F, Charner.

**1943.** 3rd Anniv of National Revolution. No gum.

| No. | Type | Description | | |
|---|---|---|---|---|
| 312 | 66 | 6 c. red .. .. .. | 30 | 30 |

67. De Lanessan.

**1944.** Governors. No gum.

| No. | Type | Description | | |
|---|---|---|---|---|
| 313 | G | 1 c. brown .. .. | 25 | 30 |
| 314 | 67 | 1 c. brown .. .. | 30 | 50 |
| 315 | H | 2 c. mauve .. .. | 25 | 30 |
| 316 | J | 4 c. orange .. .. | 20 | 30 |
| 317 | H | 4 c. brown .. .. | 30 | 30 |
| 318 | K | 5 c. purple .. .. | 45 | 40 |
| 319 | J | 10 c. green .. .. | 30 | 30 |
| 320 | H | 10 c. green .. .. | 30 | 30 |
| 321 | K | 10 c. green .. .. | 30 | 30 |
| 322 | G | 10 c. green .. .. | 45 | 40 |
| 323 | 67 | 15 c. purple .. .. | 50 | 50 |

DESIGNS—HORIZ. G, Van Vollenhoven. J, Auguste Pavie. VERT. H, Paul Doumer. K, Pierre Pasquier.

69. Athlete.

**1944.** Juvenile Sports. No gum.

| No. | Type | Description | | |
|---|---|---|---|---|
| 324 | 69 | 10 c. purple and yellow | 1·75 | 1·90 |
| 325 | | 50 c. red .. .. | 1·75 | 1·90 |

70. Orleans Cathedral.

**1944.** Martyr Cities. No gum.

| No. | Type | Description | | |
|---|---|---|---|---|
| 326. | 70. | 15 c.+60 c. purple .. | 70 | 60 |
| 327. | | 40 c.+1 p. 10 blue .. | 85 | 75 |

**1945.** As T 149 of France surch. **INDOCHINE** and values.

| No. | Description | | |
|---|---|---|---|
| 328. | 50 c.+50 c. on 2 f. olive .. | 35 | 40 |
| 329. | 1 p.+1 p. on 2 f. brown .. | 35 | 40 |
| 330. | 2 p.+2 p. on 2 f. grey .. | 65 | 70 |

**1946.** Air. Victory. As T **35** of Cameroun.

| No. | Description | | |
|---|---|---|---|
| 331. | 80 c. orange .. .. | 50 | 50 |

**1946.** Air. From Chad to the Rhine. As Nos. 226/31 of Cameroun.

| No. | Description | | |
|---|---|---|---|
| 332. | 50 c. green .. .. | 50 | 60 |
| 333. | 1 p. mauve .. .. | 50 | 60 |
| 334. | 1 p. 50 red .. .. | 50 | 60 |
| 335. | 2 p. purple.. .. | 50 | 60 |
| 336. | 2 p. 50 blue .. .. | 70 | 80 |
| 337. | 5 p. red .. .. | 90 | 1·00 |

**1946.** Unissued stamps similar to T **24** with portrait of Marshal Petain optd. with R F monogram.

| No. | Description | | |
|---|---|---|---|
| 338. | 10 c. red .. .. | 50 | 50 |
| 339. | 25 c. blue .. .. | 70 | 70 |

**1949.** Air. 75th Anniv of U.P.U. As T **46** of Cameroun.

| No. | Description | | |
|---|---|---|---|
| 340 | 3 p. multicoloured .. | 1·60 | 1·60 |

OFFICIAL STAMPS

**1933.** Stamps of 1931 (Nos. 168, etc.) optd. **SERVICE.**

| No. | Description | | |
|---|---|---|---|
| O 197. | 1 c. sepia .. .. | 50 | 30 |
| O 198. | 2 c. green .. .. | 50 | 35 |
| O 199. | 3 c. brown .. .. | 60 | 45 |
| O 200. | 4 c. blue .. .. | 60 | 50 |
| O 201. | 5 c. purple .. .. | 1·10 | 25 |
| O 202. | 6 c. red .. .. | 1·10 | 35 |
| O 203. | 10 c. blue .. .. | 55 | 40 |
| O 204. | 15 c. sepia .. .. | 1·75 | 85 |
| O 205. | 20 c. red .. .. | 1·25 | 30 |
| O 206. | 21 c. green .. .. | 1·60 | 85 |
| O 207. | 25 c. purple .. .. | 55 | 35 |
| O 208. | 30 c. brown .. .. | 1·25 | 50 |
| O 209. | 50 c. sepia .. .. | 8·00 | 1·90 |
| O 210. | 60 c. purple .. .. | 1·25 | 90 |
| O 211. | 1 p. green .. .. | 17·00 | 5·75 |
| O 212. | 2 p. red .. .. | 6·25 | 5·25 |

**1934.** As T 11 but value in "CENTS" or "PIASTRES" and optd **SERVICE**.

| No. | Description | | |
|---|---|---|---|
| O219 | 1 c. brown .. .. | 55 | 40 |
| O220 | 2 c. brown .. .. | 60 | 40 |
| O221 | 3 c. green .. .. | 55 | 30 |
| O222 | 4 c. red .. .. | 90 | 75 |
| O223 | 5 c. orange .. .. | 45 | 30 |
| O224 | 6 c. red .. .. | 3·50 | 2·75 |
| O225 | 10 c. green .. .. | 1·60 | 1·40 |
| O226 | 15 c. blue .. .. | 1·40 | 95 |
| O227 | 20 c. green .. .. | 95 | 75 |
| O228 | 21 c. violet .. .. | 5·25 | 4·25 |
| O229 | 25 c. purple .. .. | 6·25 | 3·50 |
| O230 | 30 c. violet .. .. | 90 | 60 |
| O231 | 50 c. mauve .. .. | 4·00 | 4·25 |
| O232 | 60 c. grey .. .. | 7·00 | 5·25 |
| O233 | 1 p. blue .. .. | 16·00 | 8·25 |
| O234 | 2 p. red .. .. | 24·00 | 17·00 |

PARCEL POST STAMPS

**1891.** Stamp of French Colonies, "Commerce" type, optd. **INDO-CHINE TIMBRE COLIS POSTAUX.**

| No. | Type | Description | | |
|---|---|---|---|---|
| P 4. | J | 10 c. black on lilac .. | 8·75 | 2·00 |

**1898.** No. 10 optd **Colis Postaux**.

| No. | Type | Description | | |
|---|---|---|---|---|
| P20 | D | 10 c. black on lilac .. | 10·00 | 10·00 |

**1899.** Nos. 10 and 24 optd **TIMBRE COLIS POSTAUX**.

| No. | Type | Description | | |
|---|---|---|---|---|
| P21 | D | 10 c. black on lilac .. | 27·00 | 12·00 |
| P22 | | 10 c. red .. .. | 24·00 | 9·75 |

POSTAGE DUE STAMPS.

**1904.** Postage Due stamps of French Colonies optd. with value in figures.

| No. | Type | Description | | |
|---|---|---|---|---|
| D 48. | U | 5 on 40 c. black .. | 17·00 | 6·00 |
| D 47. | | 5 on 60 c. brn. on yell. | 6·25 | 4·75 |
| D 49. | | 10 on 60 c. black .. | 17·00 | 8·00 |
| D 50. | | 30 on 60 c. black .. | 17·00 | 8·75 |

D 13. Annamite Dragon.
D 28. Mot Cot Pagoda, Hanoi.
D 29. Annamite Dragon.

**1908.**

| No. | Type | Description | | |
|---|---|---|---|---|
| D 69. | D 13. | 2 c. black .. .. | 60 | 45 |
| D 70. | | 4 c. blue .. .. | 50 | 45 |
| D 71. | | 5 c. green .. .. | 50 | 45 |
| D 72. | | 10 c. red .. .. | 1·50 | 45 |
| D 73. | | 15 c. violet .. .. | 1·50 | 1·25 |
| D 74. | | 20 c. brown .. .. | 60 | 50 |
| D 75. | | 30 c. olive .. .. | 65 | 50 |
| D 76. | | 40 c. purple .. .. | 5·00 | 4·00 |
| D 77. | | 50 c. blue .. .. | 2·50 | 75 |
| D 78. | | 60 c. yellow .. .. | 5·50 | 5·00 |
| D 79. | | 1 f. grey .. .. | 10·00 | 9·00 |
| D 80. | | 2 f. brown .. .. | 9·25 | 7·00 |
| D 81. | | 5 f. red .. .. | 17·00 | 12·00 |

**1919.** Surch in figures and words.

| No. | Type | Description | | |
|---|---|---|---|---|
| D106 | D 13 | ⅘ c. on 2 c. black | 1·10 | 55 |
| D107 | | 1⅗ c. on 4 c. blue | 95 | 60 |
| D108 | | 2 c. on 5 c. green .. | 1·60 | 85 |
| D109 | | 4 c. on 10 c. red .. | 1·10 | 50 |
| D110 | | 6 c. on 15 c. violet | 3·50 | 1·60 |
| D111 | | 8 c. on 20 c. brown | 3·50 | 85 |
| D112 | | 12 c. on 30 c. green | 3·50 | 1·00 |
| D113 | | 16 c. on 40 c. brown | 3·50 | 85 |
| D114 | | 20 c. on 50 c. blue .. | 6·00 | 3·75 |
| D115 | | 24 c. on 60 c. yellow | 1·50 | 1·10 |
| D116 | | 40 c. on 1 f. grey .. | 2·00 | 1·10 |
| D117 | | 80 c. on 2 f. brown | 16·00 | 12·50 |
| D118 | | 2 p. on 5 f. red .. | 28·00 | 15·00 |

**1922.** Type D **13**, but values in cents. or piastres.

| No. | Type | Description | | |
|---|---|---|---|---|
| D 136. | D 13. | ⅖ c. black .. .. | 15 | 25 |
| D 137. | | ⅘ c. black and red | 20 | 25 |
| D 138. | | 1 c. black and yellow | 30 | 25 |
| D 139. | | 2 c. black and green | 40 | 40 |
| D 140. | | 3 c. black and violet | 40 | 40 |
| D 141. | | 4 c. black and orange | 35 | 30 |
| D 142. | | 6 c. black and olive.. | 50 | 50 |
| D 143. | | 8 c. black on lilac .. | 50 | 45 |
| D 144. | | 10 c. black and blue | 65 | 30 |
| D 145. | | 12 c. black and orange on green .. .. | 70 | 55 |
| D 146. | | 20 c. blk. & bl. on yell. | 90 | 50 |
| D 147. | | 40 c. blk. & red on grey | 90 | 50 |
| D 148. | | 1 p. black and purple on pink .. | 3·00 | 1·60 |

**1927.**

| No. | Type | Description | | |
|---|---|---|---|---|
| D160 | D 28 | ⅖ c. orange & pur | 15 | 30 |
| D161 | | ⅘ c. black & violet | 15 | 30 |
| D162 | | 1 c. grey and red .. | 30 | 50 |
| D163 | | 2 c. olive and green | 50 | 55 |
| D164 | | 3 c. blue and purple | 50 | 55 |
| D165 | | 4 c. brown and blue | 50 | 55 |
| D166 | | 6 c. red and scarlet | 65 | 60 |
| D167 | | 8 c. violet & brown | 65 | 55 |
| D168 | D 29 | 10 c. blue .. | 60 | 35 |
| D169 | | 12 c. brown .. | 2·50 | 1·90 |
| D170 | | 20 c. red .. | 1·40 | 75 |
| D171 | | 40 c. green .. | 1·75 | 1·25 |
| D172 | | 1 p. red .. | 9·75 | 7·25 |

D 37.
D 62.

**1931.**

All values from ⅕ c. to 50 c. are in the same colours).

| No. | Type | Description | | |
|---|---|---|---|---|
| D 197. | D 37. | ⅕ c. blk. & red on yell. | 15 | 30 |
| D 198. | | ⅖ c. .. .. | 15 | 30 |
| D 199. | | ⅘ c. .. .. | 20 | 30 |
| D 200. | | 1 c. .. .. | 15 | 30 |
| D 201. | | 2 c. .. .. | 20 | 25 |
| D 202. | | 2,5 c. .. .. | 20 | 30 |
| D 203. | | 3 c. .. .. | 20 | 30 |
| D 204. | | 4 c. .. .. | 20 | 30 |
| D 205. | | 5 c. .. .. | 20 | 30 |
| D 206. | | 6 c. .. .. | 20 | 30 |
| D 207. | | 10 c. .. .. | 20 | 30 |
| D 208. | | 12 c. .. .. | 20 | 30 |
| D 209. | | 14 c... .. | 20 | 30 |
| D 210. | | 18 c... .. | 30 | 35 |
| D 211. | | 20 c... .. | 25 | 35 |
| D 212. | | 50 c... .. | 25 | 35 |
| D 213. | | 1 p. blue and red on yellow .. .. | 1·10 | 90 |

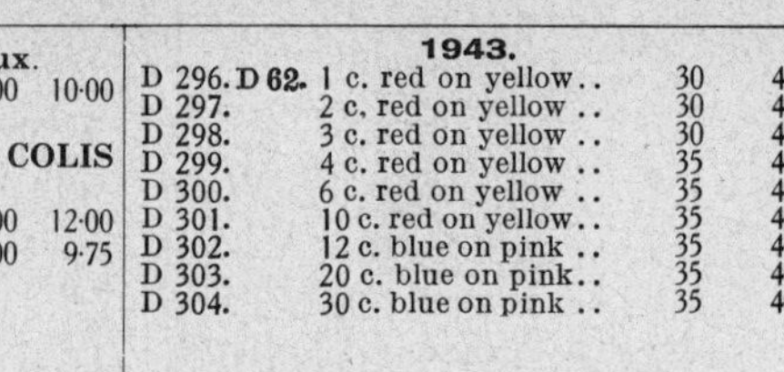

**1943.**

| No. | Type | Description | | |
|---|---|---|---|---|
| D 296. | D 62. | 1 c. red on yellow.. | 30 | 40 |
| D 297. | | 2 c. red on yellow .. | 30 | 40 |
| D 298. | | 3 c. red on yellow .. | 30 | 40 |
| D 299. | | 4 c. red on yellow .. | 35 | 40 |
| D 300. | | 6 c. red on yellow .. | 35 | 40 |
| D 301. | | 10 c. red on yellow.. | 35 | 40 |
| D 302. | | 12 c. blue on pink .. | 35 | 40 |
| D 303. | | 20 c. blue on pink.. | 35 | 40 |
| D 304. | | 30 c. blue on pink .. | 35 | 40 |

## INDO-CHINESE POST OFFICES IN CHINA Pts. 6 & 17

### General Issues.

100 centimes = 1 franc.

**1902.** Stamps of Indo-China, "Tablet" key-type, surch **CHINE** and value in Chinese.

| No. | Type | Description | | |
|---|---|---|---|---|
| 15 | D | 1 c. black on blue .. | 1·00 | 85 |
| 2 | | 2 c. brown on buff .. | 1·75 | 1·60 |
| 17 | | 4 c. brown on grey .. | 1·25 | 1·00 |
| 18 | | 5 c. green .. .. | 1·25 | 1·25 |
| 5 | | 10 c. red .. .. | 1·75 | 1·60 |
| 6 | | 15 c. grey .. .. | 2·75 | 2·75 |
| 20 | | 20 c. red on green .. | 3·50 | 3·00 |
| 21 | | 25 c. black on pink .. | 5·00 | 4·25 |
| 22 | | 25 c. blue .. .. | 4·00 | 3·50 |
| 23 | | 30 c. brown on drab .. | 2·50 | 2·50 |
| 24 | | 40 c. red on yellow .. | 11·50 | 10·00 |
| 11 | | 50 c. red on pink .. | 40·00 | 35·00 |
| 25 | | 50 c. brown on blue .. | 6·25 | 5·00 |
| 26 | | 75 c. brown on orange | 18·00 | 15·00 |
| 27 | | 1 f. green .. .. | 22·00 | 22·00 |
| 28 | | 5 f. mauve on lilac .. | 55·00 | 48·00 |

**1904.** Stamps of Indo-China surch. **CHINE** and value in Chinese.

| No. | Type | Description | | |
|---|---|---|---|---|
| 29 | 8 | 1 c. olive .. .. | 65 | 65 |
| 30 | | 2 c. red on yellow .. | 65 | 70 |
| 31 | | 4 c. brown on grey .. | £625 | £425 |
| 32 | | 5 c. green .. .. | 80 | 80 |
| 33 | | 10 c. red .. .. | 80 | 80 |
| 34 | | 15 c. brown on blue .. | 80 | 75 |
| 36 | | 20 c. red on green .. | 5·75 | 5·50 |
| 37 | | 25 c. blue .. .. | 2·75 | 1·60 |
| 38 | | 40 c. black on grey .. | 2·50 | 1·75 |
| 39 | | 1 f green .. .. | £225 | £170 |
| 40 | | 2 f. brown on yellow .. | 15·00 | 13·50 |
| 41 | | 10 f. red on green .. | 90·00 | 80·00 |

## INDONESIA Pt. 4; Pt. 21

An independent republic was proclaimed in Java and Sumatra on 17 August 1945 and lasted until the end of 1948. During this period the Dutch controlled the rest of the Netherlands Indies, renamed "Indonesia" in September 1948. On 27 December 1949 all Indonesia except New Guinea became independent as the United States of Indonesia which, during 1950, amalgamated with the original Indonesian Republic (Java and Sumatra), a single state being proclaimed on 15 August 1950 as the Indonesian Republic. This was within the Netherlands–Indonesian Union which was abolished on 10 August 1954.

100 cents (or sen) = 1 gulden (or rupiah).

### A. DUTCH ADMINISTRATION

**1948.** Stamps of Netherlands Indies optd. **INDONESIA** and bar or bars.

| No. | Type | Description | | |
|---|---|---|---|---|
| 541. | 81. | 15 c. orange .. .. | 50 | 10 |
| 533. | | 20 c. blue .. .. | 15 | 10 |
| 543. | | 25 c. green .. .. | 15 | 10 |
| 535. | | 40 c. green .. .. | 20 | 10 |
| 544. | | 45 c. mauve .. .. | 75 | 50 |
| 545. | | 50 c. lake .. .. | 20 | 10 |
| 536. | | 80 c. red .. .. | 65 | 10 |
| 537a. | | 1 g. violet .. .. | 55 | 10 |
| 538. | – | 2½ g. orange (No. 479).. | 12·00 | 5·00 |
| 539. | 81. | 10 g. green .. .. | 48·00 | 8·00 |
| 540. | | 25 g. orange .. .. | 60·00 | 40·00 |

86.
87. Portal to Tjandi Poentadewa Temple.
89. Globe and Arms of Berne.

**1949.** New Currency.

| No. | Type | Description | | |
|---|---|---|---|---|
| 548. | 86. | 1 s. grey .. .. | 15 | 10 |
| 549. | | 2 s. purple .. .. | 20 | 10 |
| 550. | | 2½ s. brown .. .. | 15 | 10 |
| 551. | | 3 s. red .. .. | 20 | 10 |
| 552. | | 4 s. green .. .. | 25 | 30 |
| 553. | | 5 s. blue .. .. | 10 | 10 |
| 554. | | 7½ s. green .. .. | 30 | 10 |
| 555. | | 10 s. mauve .. .. | 15 | 10 |
| 556. | | 12½ s. red .. .. | 25 | 10 |
| 557. | 87. | 15 s. red .. .. | 25 | 10 |
| 558. | | 20 s. black .. .. | 25 | 10 |
| 559. | | 25 s. blue .. .. | 25 | 10 |
| 560. | – | 30 s. red .. .. | 25 | 10 |
| 561. | – | 40 s. green .. .. | 25 | 10 |
| 562. | – | 45 s. purple .. .. | 25 | 20 |
| 563. | – | 50 s. brown .. .. | 25 | 10 |

564. – 60 s. brown .. .. 30 10
565. – 80 s. red .. .. 25 10
566. – 1 r. violet .. .. 20 10
567. – 2 r. green .. .. 1·75 10
568. – 3 r. purple .. .. 22·00 10
569. – 5 r. brown .. .. 17·00 10
570. – 10 r. black .. .. 35·00 20
571. – 25 r. brown .. .. 20 20

DESIGNS—As Type **87**: 30 to 45 s. Sculpture from Temple at Bedjoening, Bali. 50 to 80 s. Minangkabau house, Sumatra. 21 × 26 mm: 1 to 3 r. Toradja house. 5 to 25 r. Detail of Temple of Panahan.

**1949.** 75th Anniv. of U.P.U.

572. **89.** 15 s. red .. .. 55 30
573. 25 s. blue .. .. 55 20

## B. REPUBLIC 1945–48
### Issues for JAVA and MADURA

**1945.** Stamps of Netherlands Indies optd. **REPOEBLIK INDONESIA.**

J 1. **46.** 1 c. violet .. .. 50 80
J 2 2 c. purple .. .. 1·90 4·25
J 19. – 2 c. red (No. 461) .. 95 1·25
J 4. – 2½ c. red (No. 462) .. 1·90 2·75
J 5. – 3 c. green (No. 463) 80 1·25
J 3. **46.** 3½ c. grey .. .. 32·00 40·00
J 6. **71.** 4 c. olive .. .. 65 1·10
J 7. 5 c. blue (No. 465) .. 40·00 48·00

**1945.** Stamps of Japanese Occupation of Netherlands Indies optd. as above.

J 8. – 3½ s. red (No. 2) .. 65·00 95·00
J 10. – 3½ c. red (No. 5) .. 12·50 19·00
J 9. – 5 s. green (No. 3) .. 4·00 5·75
J 11. **2.** 5 s. green .. .. 35 40
J 12. – 10 c. blue (No. 7) .. 35 40
J 13. – 20 c. olive (No. 8) .. 35 50
J 14. – 40 c. purple (No. 9) .. 95 1·25
J 15. **4.** 60 c. orange .. .. 1·25 1·40
J 16. – 80 s. brown (No. 11) .. 9·25 16·00

J 5. Bull.

DESIGN—VERT. 20 s. Bull and Indonesian flag.

**1945.** Declaration of Independence. Inscr. "17 AGOESTOES 1945". Perf. or imperf.

J 23. **J 5.** 10 s. (+10 s.) brown .. 95 2·40
J 24. – 20 s. (+10 s.) brown & red 95 2·40

J 9. Boat in Storm. J 10. Wayang Puppet.

**1946.**

J49 – 5 s. blue .. .. 25 10
J50 – 20 s. brown .. .. 35 35
J51 J 9 30 s. red .. .. 60 65

DESIGNS: 5 s. Road and mountains. 20 s. Soldier on waterfront.

**1946.**

J52 J 10 50 s. blue .. .. 4·75 7·75
J53 – 60 s. red .. .. 4·75 32·00
J54 – 80 s. violet .. .. 48·00 £110

DESIGNS: 60 s. Kris and flag. 80 s. Temple.

J 13. Buffalo breaking Chains. J 14. Bandung, March, 1946.

**1946.** Perf or imperf.

J55 J 13 3 s. red .. .. 10 20
J56 J 14 5 s. blue .. .. 20 25
J57 – 10 s. black .. 4·75 4·75
J58 – 15 s. purple .. 25 35
J59 – 30 s. green .. 30 35
J60 – 40 s. blue .. 40 50
J61a J 13 50 s. black .. 35 40
J62 J 14 60 s. lilac .. 25 35
J63 – 80 s. red .. 95 3·25
J64 – 100 s. red .. 50 40
J65 – 200 s. lilac .. 65 1·90
J66 – 500 s. red .. 2·40 4·75
J67 – 1000 s. green .. 2·00 3·75

DESIGNS—HORIZ: 10, 15 s. Soerabaya, November 1945. 30 s. Anti-aircraft gunners. 100 s. Ambarawa, November 1945. 200 s. Wonokromo Dam, Soerabaya. 1000 s. Cavalryman. VERT: 40 s. Quay at Tandjong Priok. 80 s. Airman. 500 s. Mass meeting with flags, Djakarta.

**1948.** Postage Due Stamps of Netherlands Indies surch **SEGEL 25 sen PORTO.**

J68 D 7 25 s. on 7½ c. orange 11·00 19·00
J69 25 s. on 15 c. orange 6·25 14·00

Although surcharged for use as postage due stamps the above were employed for ordinary postal use.

J 16. "Labour and Transport". J 18. Flag over Waves.

**1948.** 3rd Anniv. of Independence. Imperf.

J 70. **J 16.** 50 s. blue .. .. 8·00 10·00
J 71. 100 s. red .. .. 8·00 10·00

**1949.** Government's Return to Jogjakarta. Perf. or Imperf.

J 77. **J 18.** 100 s. red .. .. 1·90 4·75
J 78. 150 s. red .. .. 2·40 7·75

POSTAGE DUE STAMPS

**1948.** Nos. J67 and J70/1 optd. **DENDA**, or surch. also.

JD 72. **J 16.** 50 s. blue .. .. — 13·50
JD 73. – 100 s. red .. .. — 13·50
JD 74. – 1 r. on 50 s. blue .. — 13·50
JD 76. – 1 r. on 1000 s. green — 13·50

### Issues for SUMATRA

**1946.** Stamps of Netherlands Indies surch. **Repoeblik Indonesia** and value.

S1 – 15 s. on 5 c. bl. (No. 465) 1·40 2·50
S2 46 20 s. on 3½ c. grey .. 5·50 5·50
S3 30 s. on 1 c. violet .. 6·25 6·25
S4 40 s. on 2 c. purple .. 25 65
S7 – 50 s. on 17½ c. orange (No. 431) .. .. 5·50 6·25
S9 46 60 s. on 2½ c. bistre .. 4·75 6·25
S10 80 s. on 3 c. green .. 6·25 6·25
S11 – 1 r. on 10 c. red (No. 429) 1·40 2·00

S 9. Ploughing. S 10. Pres. Sukarno. S 12.

**1946.** Freedom Fund.

S 17. **S 9.** 5 s. (+25 s.) green .. 30 95
S 18. 5 s. (+25 s.) blue .. 30 95
S 19. – 15 s. (+35 s.) red .. 2·75 2·75
S 20. – 15 s. (+35 s.) blue .. 30 95
S 21. – 40 s. (+60 s.) orange 50 95
S 22. – 40 s. (+60 s.) red .. 95 2·40
S 23. – 40 s. (+60 s.) purple 9·25 32·00
S 24. – 40 s. (+60 s.) brown 4·50 16·00

DESIGNS—VERT. 15 s. Soldier and flag. 40 s. Oil well and factories, Palembang.

**1946.**

S 25. **S 10.** 40 s. (+60 s.) red .. 65 1·40

**1946.** "FONDS KEMERDEKAAN" obliterated by one or two bars.

S 27. **S 9.** 5 s. blue .. .. 32·00 48·00
S 28. – 40 s. red (No. S 22) .. 32·00 48·00

**1946.** As Type S 9 but without "FONDS KEMERDEKAAN". Perf or imperf.

S29 2 s. red .. .. 65 1·90
S30 2 s. brown .. .. 6·00 12·00
S31 3 s. green .. .. 65 1·90
S32 3 s. red .. .. 7·75 18·00
S33 3 s. blue .. .. £130
S34 5 s. blue .. .. 50 1·60
S35 15 s. blue .. .. 30 75
S36 15 s. green .. .. 3·00 9·25
S37 40 s. brown .. .. 30 75
S38 40 s. blue .. .. 14·00 40·00

DESIGNS: 2, 3, 5 s. As Type S 9. 15 s. Soldier and flag. 40 s. Oil well and factories, Palembang.

**1947.** Fund for Palembang War Victims. Nos. S18, S20 and S23 optd **BPKPP** over triple circle.

S39 S 9 5 s. blue .. .. 38·00 38·00
S40 – 15 s. blue .. .. 38·00 48·00
S41 – 40 s. brown .. .. 38·00 48·00

**1947.** Fiscal stamps of Japanese Occupation with blank panels optd in black with **prangko N.R.I.** and value as in Tyre S 12.

S42 S 12 0 f. 50 orange .. 19·00 23·00
S43 1 f. orange .. 12·50 16·00
S44 2 f. orange .. 23·00 23·00
S45 2 f. 50 orange .. 9·50 12·50

**1947.** No. S25 surch with new value and bars.

S 46. 50 s. on 40 s. red .. 6·25 7·25
S 47. 1 f. on 40 s. red .. 7·75 7·75
S 48. 1 f. 50 on 40 s. red .. 6·25 7·75
S 49. 2 f. 50 on 40 s. red .. 95 3·25
S 50. 3 f. 50 on 40 s. red .. 95 3·25
S 51. 5 f. on 40 s. red .. 95 3·25

**1947.** Surch. with ornament and new value.

S 63. 1 s. on 15 s. (No. S 35) .. 60 2·25
S 64. 5 s. on 3 s. (No. S 33) .. 60 2·25
S 65. 10 s. on 15 s. red (as Nos. S 35/6) .. .. 60 2·25
S 52. 30 s. on 40 s. (No. S 28) .. 1·10 2·25
S 66. 50 s. on 3 s. (No. S 32) .. 14·00 18·00
S 53. 50 s. on 5 s. (No. S 34) .. 5·50 5·50
S 59. 50 s. on 40 s. (No. S 28) 12·00 18·00
S 54. 1 f. on 5 s. (No. S 34) .. 7·00 8·50
S 60. 1 f. on 40 s. (No. S 28) .. 60 2·10
S 55. 1 f. 50 on 5 s. (No. S 34) .. 5·50 5·50
S 61. 1 f. 50 on 40 s. (No. S 28) 1·90 2·50
S 62. 2 f. 50 on 40 s. (No. S 28) 60 2·10
S 56. 1 r. on 40 s. (No. S 37) .. 60 1·25
S 57. 2 r. on 5 s. (No. S 34) .. 60 1·25

**1947.** No. S 56 surch. **50.**

S 58. 50 (r.) on 1 r. on 40 s. .. 32·00 45·00

**1947.** Air. Surch **Pos Udara** with ornament and new value.

S67 10 r. on 40 s. (No. S22) .. 5·50 5·50
S68 20 r. on 5 s. (No. S34) .. 1·75 5·50

**1947.** Stamps of 1946 (Nos. S 29/37) surch.

S 69. 10 s. on 15 s. blue .. 9·25 9·25
S 70. 20 s. on 15 s. blue .. 9·25 9·25
S 71. 30 s. on 15 s. blue .. 9·25 9·25
S 75. 50 s. on 5 s. blue .. £100 £100
S 76. 50 s. on 15 s. blue .. 90·00 90·00
S 77. 0 f. 50 on 15 s. blue .. 90·00 90·00
S 78. 1 f. on 5 s. blue .. 90·00 90·00
S 79. 1 f. on 15 s. blue .. 60·00 60·00
S 72. 1 r. on 2 s. red .. 30·00 15·00
S 88. 2 r. on 3 s. green .. 12·00 18·00
S 80. 2 f. 50 on 5 s. blue .. 90·00 90·00
S 73. 2 f. 50 on 15 s. blue .. 10·00 11·00
S 82. 2 f. 50 on 40 s. brown £120 £120
S 85. 2 r. 50 on 3 s. green .. 7·75 11·00
S 83. 5 f. on 15 s. blue .. 90·00 £120
S 74. 5 f. on 40 s. brown .. 60·00 65·00
S 89. 5 r. on 15 s. blue .. 3·25 11·00
S 87. 10 r. on 3 s. green .. 11·00 20·00
S 91. 20 r. on 2 s. red .. £225 £225
S 92. 50 r. on 15 s. blue .. £180 £180
S 93. 100 r. on 15 s. blue .. 65·00 45·00
S 94. 150 r. on 40 s. red .. 80·00 80·00

No. S94 is surcharged on No. S22 with a pen-stroke through "FONDS KEMERDEKAAN".

(S 23.)
"O.R.I." = "Oeang Repoeblik Indonesia". (Indonesian Republican Money).

**1947.** Change of Currency. Various stamps optd. with Type S 23.

(a) On stamps of Netherlands Indies.

S 99. D **7.** 1 c. red (No. D 226) 6·50 7·00
S 96. **46.** 3 c. green (No. 338) 4·00 5·00
S 97. **71.** 4 c. olive (No. 464) 6·00 6·50
S 98. – 5 c. blue (No. 465) 3·00 4·50
S 100. D **7.** 15 c. red (No. D 448) 5·00 6·00

(b) On stamps of Japanese Occupation of Netherlands Indies.

S 101. – 1 c. green (No. 15) .. 90 1·25
S 102. – 2 c. green (No. 16) .. 90 1·25
S 103. – 3 c. blue (No. 17) .. 90 1·25
S 104. – 3½ c. red (No. 18) .. 1·25 1·60
S 105. – 4 c. blue (No. 19) .. 2·00 3·00
S 106. – 5 c. orange (No. 20) .. 1·25 1·60
S 107. – 10 c. blue (No. 21) .. 5·00 5·50
S 111. – 10 c. red (No. 57) .. 70 90
S 108. – 20 c. brown (No. 22) .. 5·00 5·50
S 113. – 25 c. green (No. 62) .. 8·00 10·00
S 109. **6.** 30 c. purple (No. 23) .. 90 90
S 114. – 30 c. brown (No. 63) .. 6·50 7·50
S 110. – 50 c. brown (No. 25) .. 4·50 4·50
S 115. – 50 c. red (No. 66) .. 8·50 10·50
S 116. – 60 c. blue (No. 67) .. 4·50 5·00
S 117. – 80 c. red (No. 68) .. 4·50 6·00
S 118. – 1 g. violet (No. 69) .. 8·50 10·00

(c) On stamps of Japan.

S119 – 1 s. brown (No. 317) 80 1·25
S120 – 3 s. green (No. 319) .. 80 1·25
S121 – 4 s. green (No. 320) .. 4·00 4·50
S122 – 6 s. orange (No. 322) 1·25 1·60
S123 – 25 s. brown and chocolate (No. 329) 80 1·25
S124 – 30 s. green (No. 330) 2·00 2·75
S125 – 50 s. green and bistre (No. 331) .. .. 80 1·25
S126 – 1 y. brown and chocolate (No. 332) 2·00 2·75

(d) On stamps of Indonesia-Sumatra.

S 149. – 1 s. on 15 s. blue (No. S 63) .. 50 1·00
S 136. – 2 s. red (No. S 29) .. 2·00 2·50
S 137. – 3 s. green (No. S 31) .. 80 1·40
S 138. – 3 s. red (No. S 32) .. 80 1·40
S 132. **S 9.** 5 s. grn. (No. S 17) .. 2·00 3·00
S 133. – 5 s. blue (No. S 18) .. 70 1·00
S 139. – 5 s. blue (No. S 34) .. 60 90
S 150. – 10 s. on 15 s. red (No. S 65) .. 2·00 3·00
S 134. – 15 s. blue (No. S 20) .. 2·00 2·50
S 140. – 15 s. blue (No. S 35) .. 60 90
S 141. – 15 s. grn. (No. S 36) .. 3·00 4·50
S 127. **46.** 20 s. on 3½ c. grey (No. S 2) .. 5·00 6·00
S 128. – 30 s. on 1 c. violet (No. S 3) .. 5·00 6·50
S 146. – 30 s. on 40 s. red (No. S 52) .. 5·00 6·00
S 129. **46.** 40 s. on 2 c. purple (No. S 4) .. 2·50 4·00
S 135. – 40 s. red (No. S 22) .. 2·25 2·75
S 142. – 40 s. brn. (No. S 37) .. 50 80
S 151. – 50 s. on 5 s. blue (No. S 53) .. 1·50 2·00
S 143. – 1 f. 50 on 40 s. red (No. S 48) .. 5·00 6·00
S 147. – 1 f. 50 on 40 s. red (No. S 61) .. 5·00 6·00
S 152. – 1 f. 50 on 5 s. blue (No. S 55) .. 4·50 6·00
S 153. – 2 r. on 5 s. blue (No. S 57) .. 1·40 2·00
S 144. – 2 f. 50 on 40 s. red (No. S 49) .. 5·00 6·00
S 148. – 2 f. 50 on 40 s. red (No. S 62) .. 5·00 6·00
S 145. – 3 f. 50 on 40 s. red (No. S 50) .. 5·00 6·00
S 154. – 10 r. on 40 s. red (No. S 67) .. 6·00 8·00

## C. UNITED STATES OF INDONESIA

90. Indonesian Flag.

**1950.** Inauguration of United States of Indonesia.

574. **90.** 15 s. red (20½ × 26 mm.) 50 10
575. 15 s. red (18 × 23 mm.) 3·50 45

**1950.** Stamps of 1949 optd. **RIS.**

579. **86.** 1 s. grey .. .. 20 35
580. 2 s. purple .. .. 25 20
581. 2½ s. brown .. .. 20 10
582. 3 s. red .. .. 20 10
583. 4 s. green .. .. 20 10
584. 5 s. blue .. .. 20 10
585. 7½ s. green .. .. 20 10
586. 10 s. mauve .. .. 20 10
587. 12½ s. red .. .. 25 10
588. **87.** 20 s. black .. .. 7·75 14·00
589. 25 s. blue .. .. 20 10
590. – 30 s. red .. .. 2·40 9·25
591. – 40 s. green .. .. 25 15
592. – 45 s. purple .. .. 35 10
593. – 50 s. brown .. .. 35 10
594. – 60 s. brown .. .. 1·60 6·25
595. – 80 s. red .. .. 1·25 35
596. – 1 r. violet .. .. 35 10
597. – 2 r. green .. .. £110 38·00
598. – 3 r. purple .. .. 65·00 28·00
599. – 5 r. brown .. .. 23·00 7·75
600. – 10 r. black .. .. 32·00 9·25
601. – 25 r. brown .. .. 9·25 3·25

## D. INDONESIAN REPUBLIC

94. Indonesian Arms. 95. Map and Torch.

**1950.** 5th Anniv. of Proclamation of Independence.

602. **94.** 15 s. red .. .. 65 10
603. 25 s. green .. .. 1·60 35
604. 1 r. sepia .. .. 7·25 70

**1951.** Asiatic Olympic Games, New Delhi.

605. **95.** 5 s. + 3 s. green .. 15 10
606. 10 s. + 5 s. blue .. 15 10
607. 20 s. + 5 s. red .. 15 10
608. 30 s. + 10 s. brown .. 35 20
609. 35 s. + 10 s. blue .. 1·40 1·00

96. 97. General Post-Office, Bandung.

98. "Spirit of Indonesia". 99. President Sukarno.

**1951.**

610. **96.** 1 s. grey .. .. 35 35
611. 2 s. mauve .. .. 35 30
612. 2½ s. brown .. .. 3·75 15
613. 5 s. red .. .. 35 15
614. 7½ s. green .. .. 35 15
615. 10 s. blue .. .. 35 10
616. 15 s. violet .. .. 35 10
618. 20 s. red .. .. 35 10
619. 25 s. green .. .. 35 10
620. **97.** 30 s. red .. .. 15 10
621. 35 s. violet .. .. 40 10
622. 40 s. green .. .. 15 10
623. 45 s. purple .. .. 15 10
624. 50 s. brown .. .. 3·25 10
625. **98.** 60 s. brown .. .. 15 10
626. 70 s. grey .. .. 15 10
627. 75 s. blue .. .. 15 10
628. 80 s. purple .. .. 15 10
629. 90 s. green .. .. 15 10

**1951.**

630 **99** 1 r. violet .. .. 10 10
631 1 r. 25 orange .. .. 45 10
632 1 r. 50 brown .. .. 10 10
633 2 r. green .. .. 10 10
634 2 r. 50 brown .. .. 10 10
635 3 r. blue .. .. 10 10
636 4 r. green .. .. 10 10
637 5 r. brown .. .. 10 10
638 6 r. mauve .. .. 10 10
639 10 r. grey .. .. 10 10
640 15 r. stone .. .. 10 10
641 20 r. purple .. .. 10 10
642 25 r. red .. .. 20 10
643 40 r. green .. .. 20 40
644 50 r. violet .. .. 20 10

101. Sports Emblem. 102. Doves.

**1951.** National Sports Festival.
655. 101. 5 a.+3 s. green .. 15 10
656. 10 s.+5 s. blue .. 15 10
657. 20 s.+5 s. orange .. 15 10
658. 30 s.+10 s. sepia .. 15 10
659. 35 s.+10 s. blue .. 15 25

**1951.** U.N. Day.
660. 102. 7½ s. green .. .. 3·25 20
661. 10 s. violet .. .. 65 20
662. 20 s. orange .. .. 65 20
663. 30 s. red .. .. 65 20
664. 35 s. blue .. .. 65 65
665. 1 r. sepia .. .. 9·25 1·50

**1953.** Natural Disasters Relief Fund. Surch **19 53 BENTJANA ALAM + 10s.**
666 97 35 s.+10 s. violet .. 25 10

104. Melati Flowers. 105. Merapi Volcano in Eruption.

**1953.** Mothers' Day and 25th Anniv of Indonesian Women's Congress.
667 104 50 s. green .. .. 4·75 2·40

**1954.** Natural Disasters Relief Fund.
668 105 15 s.+10 s. green .. 50 65
669 35 s.+15 s. violet .. 50 75
670 50 s.+25 s. red .. 50 75
671 75 s.+25 s. blue .. 50 75
672 1 r.+25 s. red .. 50 75
673 2 r.+50 s. brown .. 1·10 75
674a 3 r.+1 r. green .. 4·75 3·25
675a 5 r.+2 r. 50 brown .. 6·25 7·75

106. Girls with Musical Instruments. 107 Globe and Doves.

**1954.** Child Welfare.
676 106 10 s.+10 s. purple .. 10 10
677 – 15 s.+10 s. green .. 10 10
678 – 35 s.+15 s. mauve .. 10 10
679 – 50 s.+15 s. purple .. 25 10
680 – 75 s.+25 s. blue .. 15 15
681 – 1 r.+25 s. red .. 20 20
DESIGNS: 15 s. Menangkabau boy and girl performing Umbrella Dance. 35 s. Girls playing "Tjongkak". 50 s. Boy on bamboo stilts. 75 s. Ambonese boys playing flutes. 1 r. Srimpi dancing girl.

**1955.** Asian-African Conf., Bandung.
682. 107. 15 s. black .. .. 50 25
683. 35 s. brown .. .. 50 25
684. 50 s. red .. .. 1·40 10
685. 75 s. turquoise .. 80 10

108. Semaphore Signaller. 109. Proclamation of Independence.

**1955.** National Scout Jamboree.
686. – 15 s.+10 s. green .. 20 20
687. 108. 35 s.+15 s. blue .. 20 20
688. – 50 s.+25 s. red .. 20 20
689. – 75 s.+25 s. brown .. 20 20
690. – 1 r.+50 s. violet .. 20 20
DESIGNS: 15 s. Indonesian scout badge. 50 s. Scouts round campfire. 75 s. Scout feeding baby sika deer. 1 r. Scout saluting.

**1955.** 10th Anniv. of Independence.
691. 109. 15 s. green .. .. 65 35
692. 35 s. blue .. .. 65 35
693. 50 s. brown .. .. 4·00 35
694. 75 s. purple .. .. 95 35

110. Postmaster Sukarto. 111. Electors.

**1955.** 10th Anniv. of Indonesian Post Office.
695. 110. 15 s. brown .. .. 75 20
696. 35 s. red .. .. 75 20
697. 50 s. blue .. .. 4·75 65
698. 75 s. green .. .. 95 20

**1955.** First General Indonesian Elections.
699. 111. 15 s. purple .. .. 35 20
700. 35 s. green .. .. 35 20
701. 50 s. red .. .. 1·90 20
702. 75 s. blue .. .. 65 20

112. Memorial Column, Wreath and Helmet. 113. Weaving.

**1955.** Heroes' Day.
703. 112. 25 s. green .. .. 80 35
704. 50 s. blue .. .. 80 20
705. 1 r. red .. .. .. 6·25 20

**1956.** Blind Relief Fund.
706. 113. 15 s.+10 s. green .. 40 25
707. – 35 s.+15 s. brown .. 40 25
708. – 50 s.+25 s. red .. 75 40
709. – 75 s.+50 s. blue .. 40 25
DESIGNS—VERT. 35 s. Basketwork. 50 s. Map reading. 75 s. Reading.

114. Torch and Book. 115. Lesser Malay Chevrotain.

**1956.** Asian and African Students' Conf., Bandung.
710. 114. 25 s. blue .. .. 85 25
711. 50 s. red .. .. 4·50 20
712. 1 r. green .. .. 85 20

**1956.**
713. 115. 5 s. blue .. .. 10 10
714. 10 s. brown .. .. 10 10
715. 15 s. purple .. .. 10 10
716. – 20 s. green .. .. 10 10
717. – 25 s. purple .. .. 10 10
718. – 30 s. orange .. .. 10 10
719. – 35 s. blue .. .. 10 10
720. – 40 s. green .. .. 10 10
721. – 45 s. purple .. .. 40 10
722. – 50 s. bistre .. .. 10 10
723. – 60 s. blue .. .. 10 10
724. – 70 s. red .. .. 60 10
725. – 75 s. sepia .. .. 10 10
726. – 80 s. red .. .. 15 15
727. – 90 s. green .. .. 15 15
DESIGNS: 20 s. to 30 s. Hairy-nosed otter. 35 s. to 45 s. Malayan pangolin. 50 s. to 70 s. Banteng. 75 s. to 90 s. Sumatran rhinoceros.

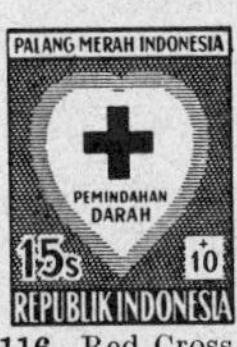

116. Red Cross. 117.

**1956.** Red Cross Fund.
728. 116. 10 s.+10 s. red and blue 20 10
729. 15 s.+10 s. red & carmine 20 10
730. – 35 s.+15 s. red & brown 20 10
731. – 50 s.+15 s. red & green 20 10
732. – 75 s.+25 s. red & orge. 25 20
733. – 1 r.+25 s. red & violet 25 20
DESIGNS: 35 s., 50 s. Blood transfusion bottle. 75 s., 1 r. Hands and drop of blood.

**1956.** Bicentenary of Djokjakarta.
734 117 15 s. green .. .. 50 10
735 35 s. brown .. .. 50 10
736 50 s. blue .. .. 1·90 50
737 75 s. purple .. .. 95 20

118. Crippled Child. 119. Telegraph Key and Tape. 120. Two men with Savings-box.

**1957.** Cripples' Rehabilitation Fund. Inscr. "UNTUK PENDERITA TJATJAT".
738. – 10 s.+10 s. blue .. 15 10
739. – 15 s.+10 s. brown .. 15 10
740. – 35 s.+15 s. red .. 15 10
741. 118. 50 s.+15 s. violet .. 15 10
742. – 75 s.+25 s. green .. 20 25
743. – 1 r.+25 s. red .. 20 25
DESIGNS: 10 s. One-legged woman painting cloth. 15 s. One-handed artist. 35 s. One-handed machinist. 75 s. Doctor tending cripple. 1 r. Man writing with artificial arm.

**1957.** Cent of Telegraphs in Indonesia.
744 119 10 s. red .. .. 1·25 35
745 15 s. blue .. .. 25 20
746 25 s. black .. .. 25 15
747 50 s. red .. .. 35 20
748 75 s. green .. .. 40 15

**1957.** Co-operation Day. Inscr. "HARI KOOPERASI".
749. 120. 10 s. blue .. .. 25 20
750. – 15 s. red .. .. 40 20
751. 120. 50 s. green .. .. 65 35
752. – 1 r. violet .. .. 80 10
DESIGN: 15 s., 1 r. "Co-operative Prosperity" (hands holding ear of rice and cotton).

121. Kembodja ("Plumeria acuminata"). 122. Convair CV 340 Airliner.

**1957.** Various Charity Funds. Floral designs. Multicoloured.
753 10 s.+10 s. Type 121 .. 1·60 40
754 15 s.+10 s. Tjempaka-kuning (michelia) .. 1·10 40
755 35 s.+15 s. Matahari (sunflower) .. .. 55 35
756 50 s.+15 s. Melati (jasmine) .. .. 40 25
757 75 s.+50 s. Larat (orchid) 40 25

**1958.** National Aviation Day. Inscr. "HARI PENERBANGAN NASIONAL 9-4-1958".
758. 122. 10 s. brown .. .. 15 15
759. – 15 s. blue .. .. 15 15
760. – 35 s. orange .. .. 30 20
761. 122. 50 s. turquoise .. 65 30
762. – 75 s. slate .. .. 95 40
DESIGNS: 15 s. Hiller "Skeeter" helicopter. 35 s. Nurtiano Sikumbang trainer. 75 s. De Havilland Vampire jet fighter.

123. "Helping Hands". 124. Thomas Cup.

**1958.** Indonesian Orphans Welfare Fund Inscr. "ANAK PIATU".
763. 123. 10 s.+10 s. blue .. 10 15
764. – 15 s.+10 s. red .. 10 15
765. 123. 35 s.+15 s. green .. 10 15
766. – 50 s.+25 s. drab .. 10 15
767. 123. 75 s.+50 s. brown .. 10 15
768. – 1 r.+50 s. brown .. 10 15
DESIGN: 15 s., 50 s., 1 r. Girl and boy orphans.

**1958.** Indonesian Victory in Thomas Cup World Badminton Championships, Singapore.
769. 124. 25 s. red .. .. 15 10
770. 50 s. orange .. .. 15 10
771. 1 r. brown .. .. 15 10

125. Satellite encircling Globe. 126. Racing Cyclist.

**1958.** Int. Geophysical Year
785. 125. 10 s. pink, green & blue 50 10
786. 15 s. drab, violet & grey 20 10
787. 35 s. blue, sepia & pink 20 10
788. 50 s. brn., blue & drab 20 10
789. 75 s. lilac, blk. & yellow 20 10

**1958.** Tour of Java Cycle Race.
790. 126. 25 s. blue .. .. 15 15
791. 50 s. red .. .. 25 15
792. 1 r. grey .. .. 15 10

127. "Human Rights". 128. Babirusa. 129. Indonesian Scout Badge.

**1958.** 10th Anniv. of Declaration of Human Rights.
793. 127. 10 s. sepia .. .. 10 10
794. – 15 s. brown .. .. 10 10
795. – 35 s. blue .. .. 10 10
796. – 50 s. bistre .. .. 15 10
797. – 75 s. green .. .. 15 10
DESIGNS: 15 s. Hands grasping "Flame of Freedom". 35 s. Native holding candle. 50 s. Family acclaiming "Flame of Freedom". 75 s. "Flame" superimposed on figure "10".

**1959.** Animal Protection Campaign.
798. 128. 10 s. sepia and olive .. 10 10
799. – 15 s. sepia and brown .. 20 10
800. – 20 s. sepia and green .. 20 10
801. – 50 s. sepia and brown .. 25 10
802. – 75 s. sepia and red .. 25 15
803. – 1 r. black and turquoise 30 15
ANIMALS: 15 s. Anoa (buffalo). 20 s. Orang-utan. 50 s. Javan rhinoceros. 75 s. Komodo lizard. 1 r. Malayan tapir.

**1959.** 10th World Scout Jamboree, Manila. Inscr. as in T 129. Badges in red.
804. 129. 10 s.+5 s. bistre .. 10 10
805. – 15 s.+10 s. green .. 10 10
806. 129. 20 s.+10 s. violet .. 10 10
807. – 50 s.+25 s. olive .. 10 10
808. 129. 75 s.+35 s. brown .. 10 10
809. – 1 r.+50 s. slate .. 15 10
DESIGN: 15 s., 50 s., 1 r. Scout badge within compass.

130. 131. Factory and Girder.

**1959.** Re-adoption of 1945 Constitution.
810. 130. 20 s. red and blue .. 10 10
811. 50 s. black and red .. 10 10
812. 75 s. red and brown .. 10 10
813. 1 r. 50 black and green 10 10

**1959.** 11th Colombo Plan Conf., Djakarta.
814. 131. 15 s. black and green .. 10 10
815. – 20 s. black and orange .. 10 10
816. 131. 50 s. black and red .. 10 10
817. – 75 s. black and blue .. 10 10
818. – 1 r. 15 black and purple 15 15
DESIGNS: 20 s., 75 s. Cogwheel and diesel-train. 1 r. 15, Forms of transport and communications.

132. 133. Refugee Camp.

**1960.** Indonesian Youth Conf., Bandung. Inscr. "1960".
819. 132. 15 s.+5 s. sep. & bistre 10 10
820. – 20 s.+10 s. sep. & grn. 10 10
821. 132. 50 s.+25 s. pur. & blue 10 10
822. – 75 s.+35 s. grn. & bis. 10 10
823. – 1 r. 15+50 s. blk. & red 25 15
DESIGNS: 20 s., 75 s. Test-tubes in frame. 1 r. 15, Youth wielding manifesto.

**1960.** World Refugee Year. Centres in black.
824. 133. 10 s. purple .. .. 10 10
825. – 15 s. ochre .. .. 10 10
826. – 20 s. brown .. .. 10 10
827. 133. 50 s. green .. .. 10 10
828. – 75 s. blue .. .. 10 10
829. – 1 r. 15 red .. .. 20 20
DESIGNS: 15 s., 75 s. Outcast family. 20 s., 1 r. 15, "Care of refugees" (refugee with protecting hands).

134. Tea plants. 135. Mosquito.

**1960.** Agricultural Products.
830. – 5 s. grey .. .. 10 10
831. – 10 s. brown .. .. 10 10
832. – 15 s. purple .. .. 10 10
833. – 20 s. bistre .. .. 10 10
834. 134. 25 s. green .. .. 10 10
835. – 50 s. blue .. .. 10 10
836. – 75 s. red .. .. 10 10
837. – 1 r. 15 red .. .. 10 10
DESIGNS: 5 s. Oil palm. 10 s. Sugar cane. 15 s. Coffee plant. 20 s. Tobacco plant. 50 s. Coconut palm. 75 s. Rubber trees. 1 r. 15, Rice plants.

**1960.** World Health Day.
838. 135. 25 s. red .. .. 20 10
839. 50 s. brown .. .. 20 10
840. 75 s. green .. .. 20 10
841. 3 r. orange .. .. 20 10

136. Socialist Emblem. 137. Pres. Sukarno and Workers Hoeing.

**1960.** 3rd Socialist Day. Inscr. as in T 136.
842. 136. 10 s.+10 s. brn. & black 10 10
843. – 15 s.+15 s. pur. & black 10 10
844. – 20 s.+20 s. blue & black 10 10
845. – 50 s.+25 s. black & brn. 15 15
846. – 75 s.+25 s. black & grn. 15 20
847. – 3 r.+50 s. black & red .. 20 20
DESIGNS: 15 s. Emblem similar to Type 136 within plants. 20 s. Lotus flower. 50 s. Boy and girl. 75 s. Ceremonial watering of plant. 3 r. Mother with children.

**1961.** National Development Plan.
848. 137. 75 s. black .. .. 25 10

**1961.** Flood Relief Fund. Nos. 832/3 and 836 surch **BENTJANA ALAM 1961** and premium.
849 15 s.+10 s. purple .. 10 10
850 20 s.+15 s. brown .. 10 10
851 75 s.+25 s. red .. .. 10 10

139. Bull Race.

**1961.** Tourist Publicity.
852. – 10 s. purple .. .. 30 20
853. – 15 s. grey .. .. 30 20
854. 139. 20 s. orange .. .. 30 20
855. – 25 s. red .. .. 30 20
856. – 50 s. lake .. .. 30 20
857. – 75 s. brown .. .. 30 20
858. – 1 r. green .. .. 50 20
859. – 1 r. 50 bistre .. .. 50 20
860. – 2 r. blue .. .. 80 20
861. – 3 r. grey .. .. 80 20
DESIGNS: 10 s. Ambonese boat. 15 s. Tangkuban Perahu crater. 25 s. Daja dancer. 50 s. Toradja houses. 75 s. Balinese temple. 1 r. Lake Toba. 1 r. 50, Bali dancer. 2 r. "Buffalo Hole" (gorge). 3 r. Borobudur temple.

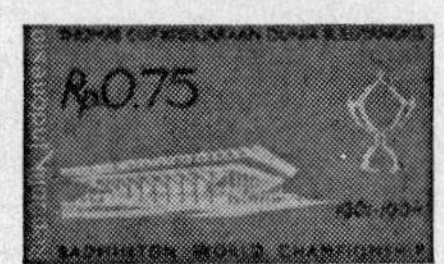

140. Stadium.

**1961.** Thomas Cup World Badminton Championships.
863. 140. 75 s. lilac and blue .. 10 10
864. 1 r. olive and green .. 10 10
865. 3 r. salmon and blue .. 15 10

141. "United Efforts".

**1961.** 16th Anniv. of Independence.
866. 141. 75 s. violet and blue .. 10 10
867. 1 r. 50 green and cream 10 10
868. 3 r. red and salmon .. 15 10

142. Sultan Hasanuddin.

**1961.** National Independence Heroes. Portraits in sepia; inscriptions in black.
869. – 20 s. olive .. .. 10 15
870. 142. 25 s. olive .. .. 10 15
871. – 30 s. violet .. .. 10 15
872. – 40 s. brown .. .. 10 15
873. – 50 s. myrtle .. .. 10 15
874. – 60 s. turquoise .. .. 10 15
875. – 75 s. brown .. .. 10 15
876. – 1 r. blue .. .. 60 15
877. – 1 r. 25 green .. .. 50 15
878. – 1 r. 50 green .. .. 60 15
879. – 2 r. red .. .. 40 15
880. – 2 r. 50 red .. .. 60 15
881. – 3 r. slate .. .. 50 15
882. – 4 r. green .. .. 35 15
883. – 4 r. 50 purple .. .. 20 15
884. – 5 r. red .. .. 50 15
885. – 6 r. ochre .. .. 60 15
886. – 7 r. 50 blue .. .. 65 15
887. – 10 r. green .. .. 95 15
888. – 15 r. orange .. .. 45 15
PORTRAITS: 20 s. Abdul Muis. 30 s. Surjopranoto. 40 s. Tengku Tjhik Di Tiro. 50 s. Teuku Umar. 60 s. K. H. Samanhudi. 75 s. Capt. Pattimura. 1 r. Raden Adjeng Kartini. 1 r. 25, K. H. Achmad Dahlan. 1 r. 50, Tuanku Imam Bondjol. 2 r. Si Singamangaradja XII. 2 r. 50, Mohammed Husni Thamrin. 3 r. Ki Hadjar Dewantoro. 4 r. Gen. Sudirman. 4 r. 50, Dr. G. S. S. J. Ratulangie. 5 r. Pangeran Diponegoro. 6 r. Dr. Setyabudi. 7 r. 50, H. O. S. Tjokroaminoto. 10 r. K. H. Agus Salim. 15 r. Dr. Soetomo.

143. Census Emblems.

144. Nenas (pineapples).

**1961.** 1st Indonesian Census.
889. 143. 75 s. purple .. .. 20 10

**1961.** Charity Fruits.
890. 144. 20 s.+10 s. yellow, red and blue .. .. 35 25
891. – 75 s.+25 s. purple, grn. and slate .. .. 40 25
892. – 3 r.+1 r. red, yell. & grn. 70 50
FRUITS: 75 s. Manggis. 3 r. Rambutan.

145. Djataju.

DANCERS: 40 s. Hanoman. 1 r. Dasamuka. 1 r. 50, Kidang Kentjana. 3 r. Dewi Sinta. 5 r. Rama.

**1962.** Ramayana Dancers.
893. 145. 30 s. brown and ochre .. 15 15
894. – 40 s. violet and purple 15 15
895. – 1 r. purple and green .. 25 15
896. – 1 r. 50 green and pink 25 15
897. – 3 r. blue and green .. 95 20
898. – 5 r. brown and buff .. 80 20

146. Aerial View of Mosque.

DESIGN: 40 s., 3 r. Ground-level view of Mosque.

**1962.** Construction of Istiqlal Mosque.
899. 146. 30 s.+20 s. blue & yell. 25 10
900. – 40 s.+20 s. red & yellow 25 10
901. 146. 1 r. 50+50 s. brn. & yell. 25 15
902. – 3 r.+1 r. green & yellow 25 20

147. Games Emblem.

148. Campaign Emblem.

**1962.** 4th Asian Games, Djakarta. Inscr as in T 147.
903 – 10 s. green and yellow 10 10
904 – 15 s. brown and ochre 10 10
905 – 20 s. lilac and green .. 10 10
906 – 25 s. red and green .. 10 10
907 – 30 s. green and buff .. 10 10
908 – 40 s. ultramarine & bl 10 15
909 – 50 s. brown and drab 10 15
910 – 60 s. mauve and grey 10 15
911 – 70 s. brown and red .. 10 10
912 – 75 s. brown and orange 10 15
913 – 1 r. violet and blue .. 10 15
914 147 1 r. 25 blue and mauve 10 15
915 – 1 r. 50 red and mauve 40 15
916 – 1 r. 75 red and pink .. 25 15
917 147 2 r. brown and green 25 15
918 – 2 r. 50 blue and green 25 15
919 147 3 r. black and red .. 25 15
920 – 4 r. 50 green and red .. 25 15
921 147 5 r. green and bistre .. 20 15
922 – 6 r. red and brown .. 20 15
923 – 7 r. 50 brown and pink 20 15
924 – 10 r. ultramarine & bl 35 25
925 – 15 r. violet & lt violet 50 50
926 – 20 r. green and bistre 95 65
DESIGNS—VERT: 10 s. Basketball. 20 s. Weightlifting. 40 s. Throwing the discus. 50 s. Diving. 60 s. Football. 70 s. Press building. 75 s. Boxing. 1 r. Volleyball. 1 r. 50, Badminton. 1 r. 75, Wrestling. 2 r. 50, Shooting. 4 r. 50, Hockey. 6 r. Water polo. 7 r. 50, Tennis. 10 r. Table tennis. 15 r. Cycling. 20 r. "Welcome" monument. HORIZ: 15 s. Main stadium. 25 s. Hotel Indonesia. 30 s. Road improvement.

**1962.** Malaria Eradication.
927. 148. 40 s. blue and violet .. 15 10
928. 1 r. 50 orange & brown 15 10
929. 3 r. green and blue .. 15 10
930. 6 r. violet and black .. 15 10
On the 1 r. 50 and 6 r. the inscription is at top.

149. National Monument. 150. Atomic Symbol.

**1962.** National Monument.
931. 149. 1 r.+50 c. brn. and blk. 20 20
932. – 1 r. 50+50 c. grn. & blue 20 20
933. 149. 3 r.+1 r. mauve & green 20 15
934. – 6 r.+1 r. 50 blue & red 20 15
DESIGN: 1 r. 50, 6 r. Aerial view of Monument.

**1962.** "Science for Development".
935. 150. 1 r. 50 blue and yellow .. 10 10
936. 4 r. 50 red and yellow .. 10 10
937. 6 r. green and yellow .. 15 10

151. "Phalaenopsis amabilis".

152. West Irian Monument, Djakarta.

**1962.** Charity. Orchids. Multicoloured.
938 1 r.+50 s. "Vanda tricolor" .. .. 25 15
939 1 r. 50+50 s. Type 151 .. 25 15
940 3 r.+1 r. "Dendrobium phalaenopsis" .. .. 25 15
941 6 r.+1 r. 50 "Paphiopedilum praestans" .. .. 25 15
Nos. 938 and 941 are horiz.

**1963.** Construction of West Irian Monument
942. 152. 1 r.+50 c. green and red 10 10
943. 1 r. 50+50 c. sepia, blk. and mauve .. .. 10 10
944. 3 r.+1 r. brown & blue 15 10
945. 6 r.+1 r. 50 bistre & grn. 15 10

153. Conference Emblem.

154. Rice Sheaves.

**1963.** 12th Pacific Area Travel Association Conference, Djakarta.
946. 153. 1 r. blue and green .. 15 15
947. – 1 r. 50 blue and olive .. 15 15
948. 153. 3 r. blue and brown .. 35 15
949. – 6 r. blue and orange .. 35 15
DESIGNS: 1 r. 50, Prambanan Temple and Mt. Merapi. 6 r. Balinese Meru in Pura Taman Ajun.

**1963.** Freedom from Hunger.
950. 154. 1 r. yellow and blue .. 10 10
951. – 1 r. 50 blue and green .. 10 10
952. 154. 3 r. yellow and red .. 10 10
953. – 6 r. orange and black .. 15 10
DESIGN—HORIZ. 1 r. 50, 6 r. Tractor. Nos. 950/1 are inscr. "CONTRE LA FAIM". Nos. 952/3, "FREEDOM FROM HUNGER".

155. Lobster.

**1963.** Marine Life. Multicoloured.
954. 1 r. Type 155 .. .. 20 10
955. 1 r. 50 Little tuna .. 20 10
956. 3 r. Red snapper .. 45 20
957. 6 r. Chinese pomfret .. 50 25

156. Conference Emblem.

**1963.** Asian-African Journalists' Conference.
958. 156. 1 r. red and blue .. 10 10
959. – 1 r. 50 brown & lavender 15 10
960. – 3 r. blue, black & olive 25 15
961. – 6 r. salmon and black .. 35 20
DESIGNS—HORIZ. 1 r. 50, Pen, emblem and map. VERT. 3 r. Pen. Globe and broken chain. 6 r. Pen severing chain around Globe.

157. Indonesia, from Atjeh to Merauke.

**1963.** Acquisition of West Irian (West New Guinea).
962. 157. 1 r. 50 orange, red and black .. .. .. 10 10
963. – 4 r. 50 blue, grn. & pur. 15 10
964. – 6 r. brown, yell. & green 30 15
DESIGNS: 4 r. 50, Parachutist. 6 r. Greater Bird of Paradise.

158. Centenary Emblem.

159. Volcano.

**1963.** Centenary of Red Cross.
965 158 1 r. green and red .. 20 10
966 – 1 r. 50 red and blue .. 20 10
967 158 3 r. grey and red .. 20 10
968 – 6 r. red and bistre .. 20 10
DESIGN: 1 r. 50, 6 r. Red Cross (inscribed in English).

**1963.** Bali Volcano Disaster Fund.
969. 159. 4 r. (+2 r.) red .. 10 10
970. 6 r. (+3 r.) green .. 10 10

160. Bank of Indonesia, Djakarta.

**1963.** National Banking Day.
971. 160. 1 r. 75 purple and blue 10 10
972. – 4 r. green and yellow .. 10 10
973. 160. 6 r. brown and green .. 10 10
974. – 12 r. purple and orange 10 10
DESIGN—VERT. 4 r., 12 r. Daneswara, God of Prosperity.

161. Athletes with Banners.

**1963.** Games of the New Emerging Forces, Djakarta.
975. 161. 1 r. 25 sepia and violet 10 10
976. – 1 r. 75 olive and buff .. 10 10
977. – 4 r. sepia and green .. 10 10
978. – 6 r. sepia and brown .. 15 10
979. – 10 r. sepia and green .. 15 10
980. – 12 r. olive and red .. 25 10
981. – 25 r. ultramarine & blue 35 20
982. – 50 r. sepia and red .. 45 25
DESIGNS: 1 r. 75, "Pendet" dance. 4 r. Conference Hall, Djakarta. 6 r. Archery. 10 r. Badminton. 12 r. Throwing the javelin. 25 r. Sailing. 50 r. "Ganefo" torch.

162. "Papilio blumei".

163. Pres. Sukarno.

**1963.** Social Day. Butterflies. Multicoloured.
983 1 r. 75+50 s. Type **162** .. 15 10
984 4 r.+1 r. "Charaxes dehaani" .. .. 15 10
985 6 r.+1 r. 50 Purple-spotted swallowtail .. .. 30 15
986 12 r.+3 r. "Troides amphrysus" .. .. 30 20

**1964.**
987. **163.** 6 r. blue and brown.. 10 10
988. 12 r. purple and bistre 10 10
989. 20 r. orange and blue.. 10 10
990. 30 r. blue and orange.. 10 10
991. 40 r. brown and green 10 10
992. 50 r. green and red .. 10 10
993. 75 r. red and violet .. 10 10
994. 100 r. brown and grey 10 10
995. 250 r. grey and blue .. 10 10
996. 500 r. gold and red .. 10 10

**164.** Lorry and Trailer. **165.** Rameses II, Abu Simbel.

**1964.**
997 – 1 r. purple .. .. 10 10
998 **164** 1 r. 25 brown .. 10 10
999 – 1 r. 75 blue .. .. 15 10
1000 – 2 r. red .. .. 10 10
1001 – 2 r. 50 blue .. .. 15 10
1002 – 4 r. green .. .. 10 10
1003 – 5 r. brown .. .. 10 10
1004 – 7 r. 50 green .. .. 10 10
1005 – 10 r. orange .. .. 10 10
1006 – 15 r. blue .. .. 25 10
1007 – 25 r. blue .. .. 15 10
1008 – 35 r. brown .. .. 15 10
DESIGNS—HORIZ. 1 r. Ox-cart. 1 r. 75, "Hadju Agus Salim" (freighter). 2 r. Lockheed Electra airliner. 4 r. Cycle-postman. 5 r. Douglas DC-3 airliner. 7 r. 50, Teletypist. 10 r. Diesel train. 15 r. "Sam Ratulangi" (freighter). 25 r. Convair Coronado airliner. 35 r. Telephone operator. VERT. 2 r. 50, Buginese sailing boat.

**1964.** Nubian Monuments Preservation. Monuments in brown.
1009. **165.** 4 r. drab .. .. 15 10
1010. – 6 r. blue .. .. 15 10
1011. **165.** 12 r. pink .. .. 15 10
1012. – 18 r. green .. .. 15 10
DESIGN: 6 r., 18 r., Trajan's Kiosk, Philae.

**166.** Various Stamps of Netherlands Indies and Indonesia.

**1964.** Stamp Centenary.
1013. **166.** 10 r. multicoloured .. 65 10

**167.** Indonesian Pavilion at Fair.

**1964.** New York World's Fair.
1014. **167.** 25 r. red, blue & silver 25 10
1015. 50 r. red, turq. & gold 40 10

**168.** Thomas Cup. **170.** Pied Fantail.

**169.** "Sandjaja" and "Siliwanghi" (destroyers).

**1964.** Thomas Cup World Badminton Championships.
1016. **168.** 25 r. gold, red and grn. 10 10
1017. 50 r. gold, red and blue 15 10
1018. 75 r. gold, red & violet 25 75

**1964.** Indonesian Navy.
1019. **169.** 20 r. brown & yellow 20 10
1020. – 30 r. black and red .. 25 10
1021. – 40 r. blue and green 40 75
DESIGNS: 30 r. "Nanggala" (submarine). 40 r. "Matjan Tutul" (torpedo-boat).

**1965.** Social Day. Birds.
1022. **170.** 4 r.+1 r. black, lilac and yellow .. 20 10
1023. – 6 r.+1 r. 50 black, buff and green .. 20 10
1024. – 12 r.+3 r. black, blue and olive .. .. 25 20
1025. – 20 r.+5 r. yellow, red and purple .. 30 20
1026. – 30 r.+7 r. 50 black, slate and mauve .. 40 20
BIRDS: 6 r. Zebra Dove. 12 r. Black Drongo. 20 r. Black-naped Oriole. 30 r. Java Sparrow.

**171.** Map and Mosque. **172.** Scroll in Hand.

**1965.** Afro-Asian Islamic Conf., Bandung.
1027. **171.** 10 r. blue and violet.. 15 10
1028. – 15 r. brown and orange 15 10
1029. **171.** 25 r. green and brown 25 10
1030. – 50 r. purple and red .. 25 75
DESIGN: 15 r., 50 r. Mosque and handclasp.

**1965.** 10th Anniv. of 1st Afro-Asian Conference, Bandung.
1031. **172.** 15 r. red and silver .. 20 10
1032. – 25 r. gold, red & turq. 20 10
1033. **172.** 50 r. blue and gold .. 25 10
1034. – 75 r. gold, red and lilac 35 80
DESIGN: 25 r., 75 r. Conference 10th-anniv. emblem.

**1965.** Conf. of "New Emerging Forces", Djakarta. T **163** additionally inscr. "Conefo". Value, "Conefo" and frame in red; portrait colour given.
1035 1 r.+1 r. brown .. .. 10 10
1036 1 r. 25+1 r. 25 red .. 10 10
1037 1 r. 75+1 r. 75 purple .. 10 10
1038 2 r.+ 2 r. green .. .. 10 10
1039 2 r. 50+2 r. 50 brown .. 10 10
1040 4 r.+3 r. 50 blue .. 10 10
1041 6 r.+4 r. green .. .. 10 10
1042 10 r.+5 r. brown .. 10 10
1043 12 r.+5 r. 50 orange .. 10 10
1044 15 r.+7 r. 50 turquoise .. 10 10
1045 20 r.+10 r. brown .. 10 10
1046 25 r.+10 r. violet .. 10 10
1047 40 r.+15 r. purple .. 10 10
1048 50 r.+15 r. violet .. 10 10
1049 100 r.+25 r. brown .. 10 10

**174.** Makara Mask and Rays. **175.** "Happy Family".

**1965.** Campaign against Cancer.
1050. **174.** 20 r.+10 r. red and blue 15 10
1051. 30 r. + 15 r. blue and red 15 10

**1965.** The State's Five Principles and 20th Anniv of Republic.
1052. **175.** 10 r.+5 r. yellow, black and brown .. .. 20 10
1053. – 20 r.+10 r. red, black and yellow .. .. 15 10
1054. – 25 r.+10 r. green, black and red .. .. 15 10
1055. – 40 r.+15 r. black, red and blue .. .. 20 10
1056. – 50 r.+15 r. yellow, black and mauve .. 20 10
DESIGNS ("State's Principles"): 20 r. "Humanitarianism" (globe and clasped hands). 25 r. "Nationalism" (map and garland). 40 r. "Democracy" (council meeting). 50 r. "Belief in God" (churches and mosques).

**177.** Samudra Beach Hotel.

**1965.** Tourist Hotels.
1060. **177.** 10 r.+5 r. blue & turq. 10 10
1061. – 25 r.+10 r. violet, black and green .. .. 15 10
1062. **177.** 40 r.+15 r. brn., blk. and blue .. .. 20 10
1063. – 80 r.+20 r. pur. & orge. 25 10
DESIGN: 25 r., 80 r. Ambarrukmo Palace Hotel.

**178.** "Gloriosa superba". **180.** Pres. Sukarno.

**1965.** Flowers. Multicoloured. Inscr. "1965" and with commas and dashes after figures of value.
1064. 30 r.+10 r. Type **178** .. 35 15
1065. 40 r.+15 r. "Hibiscus tiliaceus" .. .. 25 15
1066. 80 r.+20 r. "Impatiens balsamina" .. .. 35 15
1067. 100 r.+25 r. "Lagerstroemia indica" .. .. 45 15
See also Nos. 1108/1116.

**(Currency revalued. 100 (old) rupiahs = 1 (new) rupiah.)**

**1965.** Revalued Currency. Optd **'65 Sen.**
(a) On Nos. 989/94.
1068. **163.** (20) s. on 20 r... .. 10 10
1069. (30) s. on 30 r... .. 10 10
1070. (40) s. on 40r. .. 10 10
1071. (50) s. on 50 r... .. 10 10
1072. (75) s. on 75r. .. 10 35
1073. (100) s. on 100r. .. 15 10
(b) On Nos. 1005/7.
1074. – (10) s. on 10 r. .. 25 10
1075. – (15) s. on 15 r. .. 25 10
1076. – (25) s. on 25 r. .. 25 10

**1966.** Revalued Currency. Inscr. "1967" (12 r.) or "1966" (others). Values and frames turquoise (12 r., 25 r.) or chocolate (others); portrait and country name in colour given.
1077. **180.** 1 s. blue .. .. 10 20
1078. 3 s. olive .. .. 10 20
1079. 5 s. red .. .. 10 20
1080. 8 s. turquoise .. 10 20
1081. 10 s. blue .. 10 10
1082. 15 s. black .. 10 10
1083. 20 s. green .. 10 10
1084. 25 s. brown .. 10 10
1085. 30 s. blue .. 10 10
1086. 40 s. brown .. 10 10
1087. 50 s. violet .. 10 10
1088. 80 s. orange .. 10 10
1089. 1 r. green .. 10 10
1090. 1 r. 25 brown .. 10 10
1091. 1 r. 50 green.. .. 10 10
1092. 2 r. purple .. 10 10
1093. 2 r. 50 slate .. 10 10
1094. 5 r. orange .. 10 10
1095. 10 r. olive .. 10 10
1096. 12 r. orange .. 10 10
1097. 25 r. violet .. 10 10

**1966.** Flowers. As T **178** but inscr. "1966" and additionally inscr. "sen" instead of commas and dashes. Multicoloured.
1108. 10 s.+5 s. "Cassia alata" 25 15
1109. 20 s.+5 s. "Barleria cristata" .. .. 35 15
1110. 30 s.+10 s. "Ixora coccinea" .. .. 35 15
1111. 40 s.+10 s. "Hibiscus rosa sinensis" .. .. 35 15

**1966.** National Disaster Fund. Floral designs as T **178** additionally inscr. "BENTJANA ALAM NASIONAL 1966". Mult.
1113. 15 s.+5 s. "Gloriosa superba" .. .. 25 20
1114. 25 s.+5 s. "Hibiscus tiliaceus" .. .. 25 20
1115. 30 s.+10 s. "Impatiens balsamina" .. .. 25 20
1116. 80 s.+20 s. "Lagerstroemia indica" .. .. 40 20

**181.** Cleaning Ship's Rudder. **182.** Gen. A. Yani.

**1966.** Maritime Day.
1117. **181.** 20 s. green and blue.. 15 10
1118. – 40 s. blue and pink .. 15 10
1119. – 50 s. brown and green 15 10
1120. – 1 r. multicoloured .. 15 10
1121. – 1 r. 50 green and lilac 30 10
1122. – 2 r. red and grey .. 20 10
1123. – 2 r. 50 red and mauve 20 10
1124. – 3 r. black and green.. 60 15
DESIGNS: 40 s. Anyer Kidul lighthouse. 50 s. Fisherman. 1 r. Maritime emblem. 1 r. 50, Madurese sailing boat. 2 r. Quayside. 2 r. 50, Pearl-diving. 3 r. Liner in dry-dock.

**1966.** Victims of Attempted Communist Coup, 1965. Frames and date in blue.
1126. **182.** 5 r. brown .. .. 20 10
1127. A. 5 r. green .. .. 20 10
1128. B. 5 r. purple .. .. 20 10
1129. C. 5 r. olive .. .. 20 10
1130. D. 5 r. grey .. .. 20 10
1131. E. 5 r. violet .. .. 20 10
1132. F. 5 r. purple .. .. 20 10
1133. G. 5 r. green .. .. 20 10
1134. H. 5 r. purple .. .. 20 10
1135. I. 5 r. orange .. .. 20 10
PORTRAITS: A, Lt.-Gen. R. Soeprapto. B, Lt.-Gen. M. Harjono. C, Lt.-Gen. S. Parman. D, Maj.-Gen. D. Pandjaitan. E, Maj.-Gen. S. Siswomihardjo. F, Brig.-Gen. Katamso. G, Col. Soegijono. H, Capt. P. Tendean. I, Insp. K. S. Tubun.

**183.** Python. **184.** Tjlempung.

**1966.** Reptiles.
1136. **183.** 2 r.+25 s. brown, grn. and flesh .. .. 15 10
1137. – 3 r.+50 s. green, brn. and lilac .. .. 15 10
1138. – 4 r.+75 s. purple, buff and green .. .. 15 10
1139. – 6 r.+1 r. black, brn. and blue .. .. 15 10
REPTILES: 3 r. Chameleon. 4 r. Crocodile. 6 r. Green turtle.

**1967.** Musical Instruments.
1140. **184.** 50 s. red and black .. 15 10
1141. – 1 r. sepia and red .. 15 10
1142. – 1 r. 25 lake and blue .. 15 10
1143. – 1 r. 50 green and violet 15 10
1144. – 2 r. blue & ochre .. 15 10
1145. – 2 r. 50 green and red .. 15 10
1146. – 3 r. green and purple . 15 10
1147. – 4 r. blue and orange .. 25 10
1148. – 5 r. red and blue .. 25 10
1149. – 6 r. blue and mauve .. 15 15
1150. – 8 r. lake and green .. 15 15
1151. – 10 r. violet and red .. 20 10
1152. – 12 r. green and violet .. 35 10
1153. – 15 r. violet and olive 20 10
1154. – 20 r. black and sepia 20 10
1155. – 25 r. black and green 20 10
INSTRUMENTS: 1 r. Sasando. 1 r. 25, Foi doa. 1 r. 50, Kultjapi. 2 r. Arababu. 2 r. 50, Genderang. 3 r. Katjapi. 4 r. Hape. 5 r. Gangsa. 6 r. Serunai. 8 r. Rebab. 10 r. Trompet. 12 r. Totobuang. 15 r. Tamburn. 20 r. Kulintang. 25 r. Keledi.

**185.** Pilot and Mikoyan Gurevich MiG-21 Fighter. **186.** Thomas Cup and Silhouettes.

**1967.** Aviation Day. Multicoloured.
1156 2 r. 50 Type **185** .. .. 20 15
1157 4 r. Convair Coronado airliner and control tower 20 15
1158 5 r. Lockheed C-130 Hercules transport aircraft on tarmac .. 25 10

**1967.** Thomas Cup World Badminton Championships. Multicoloured.
1159. 5 r. Type **186** .. .. 20 10
1160. 12 r. Thomas Cup on Globe 35 10

187. Balinese Girl.

188. Heroes Monument.

**1967.** Int. Tourist Year.
1161. 187. 12 r. multicoloured .. 50 65

**1967.** "Heroes of the Revolution". Monument.
1163. 188. 2 r. 50, brown & green 10 10
1164. – 5 r. purple and drab .. 20 15
1165. – 7 r. 50 green and pink 20 15
DESIGNS—HORIZ. 5 r. Monument and shrine. VERT. 7 r. 50, Shrine.

190. "Forest Fire".

**1967.** Paintings by Raden Saleh.
1175. 190. 25 r. red and green .. 25 10
1176. – 50 r. purple and red .. 30 10
PAINTING: 50 r. "A Fight to the Death".

191. Flood Victims.

192. Human Rights Emblem.

**1967.** National Disaster Fund.
1178. 191. 1 r. 25+10 s. bl. & yell. 10 15
1179. – 2 r. 50+25 s. bl. & yell. 10 15
1180. – 4 r.+40 s. blk. & orge. 15 15
1181. – 5 r.+50 s. blk. & orge. 20 15
DESIGNS: 2 r. 50, Landslide. 4 r. Burning house. 5 r. Erupting volcano.

**1968.** Human Rights Year.
1183. 192. 5 r. red, green and blue 25 10
1184. 12 r. red, green & drab 25 15

193. Academy Badge.

197. W.H.O. Emblem and "20".

194. 195. 196.
"Sudhana and Manohara at Court of Druma" (relief on wall of Borobudur).

**1968.** Indonesian Military Academy.
1185. 193. 10 r. multicoloured .. 35 10

**1968.** "Save Borobudur Monument".
1186 194 2 r. 50+25 s. deep green and green .. 25 20
1187 195 2 r. 50+25 s. deep green and green .. 25 20
1188 196 2 r. 50+25 s. deep green and green .. 25 20
1189 – 7 r. 50+75 s. green and orange .. 35 20
DESIGN—VERT: 7 r. 50, Buddhist and statue of Buddha.

**1968.** 20th Anniv. of W.H.O.
1191. 197. 2 r. purple and yellow 25 15
1192. – 20 r. black and green .. 25 15
DESIGN: 20 r. W.H.O. emblem.

198. Trains of 1867 and 1967.

**1968.** Cent. (1967) of Indonesian Railways.
1193. 198. 20 r. multicoloured .. 75 40
1194. 30 r. multicoloured .. 75 40

199. Scout with Pick.

200. Butterfly Dancer.

**1968.** "Wirakarya" Scout Camp.
1195. 199. 5 r.+50 s. brn. & orge. 25 20
1196. – 10 r.+1 r. grey & brn. 35 30
1197. – 30 r.+3 r. brn. & grn. 40 20
DESIGNS—VERT. 10 r. Bugler on hillside. HORIZ. (69×29 mm.): 30 r. Scouts in camp.

**1968.** Tourism.
1198. 200. 30 r. multicoloured .. 65 35

202. Observatory and Stars.

**1968.** 40th Anniv. of Bosscha Observatory.
1207. 202. 15 r. blue, yell. & blk. 30 15
1208. – 30 r. violet & orange .. 35 15
DESIGN—VERT. 30 r. Observatory on Globe.

203. Yachting. 204.

**1968.** Olympic Games, Mexico.
1209 – 5 r. green, brn & blk 15 10
1210 203 7 r. 50 blue, yell & red 10 10
1211 204 7 r. 50 blue, yell & red 10 10
1212 – 12 r. red, blue & yell 20 10
1213 – 30 r. brn, grn & orge 35 15
DESIGNS—$28\frac{1}{2}\times44\frac{1}{2}$ mm. 5 r. Weightlifting. 12 r. Basketball. $44\frac{1}{2}\times28\frac{1}{2}$ mm: 30 r. Dove and Olympic flame.
Nos. 1210/11 were issued together, se-tenant, forming the composite design illustrated.

205. "Eugenia aquea".

**1968.** Fruits. Multicoloured.
1215. 7 r. 50 Type 205 .. 20 10
1216. 15 r. "Carica papaya" .. 35 15
1217. 30 r. "Durio zibethinus" (vert.) .. .. .. 45 15

206. I.L.O. Emblem and part of Globe.

207. R. Dewi Sartika.

**1969.** 50th Anniv. of I.L.O.
1219. 206. 5 r. red and green .. 15 10
1220. – 7 r. 50 green & orange 15 10
1221. 206. 15 r. red and violet .. 15 10
1222. – 25 r. red and turquoise 15 10
DESIGN: 7 r. 50, 25 r. I.L.O. emblem.

**1969.** National Independence Heroes.
1223. 207. 15 r. green and violet 25 15
1224. – 15 r. purple and green 25 15
1225. – 15 r. blue and red .. 25 15
1226. – 15 r. ochre and red .. 25 15
1227. – 15 r. sepia and blue .. 25 15
1228. – 15 r. lilac and blue .. 25 15
PORTRAITS: No. 1224, Tjut Nja Din. No. 1225, Tjut Nja Meuthia. No. 1226, Sutan Sjahrir. No. 1227, Dr. F. L. Tobing. No. 1228, General G. Subroto.

208. Woman with Flower.

209. Red Cross "Mosaic".

**1969.** Women's Emancipation Campaign.
1229. 208. 20 r.+2 r. red, yellow and green .. .. 35 10

**1969.** 50th Anniv. of League of Red Cross Societies.
1230. 209. 15 r. red and green .. 25 10
1231. – 20 r. red and yellow .. 25 15
DESIGN: 20 r. Hands encircling Red Cross.

210. "Planned" Family and Factory.

**1969.** South-East Asia and Oceania Family Planning Conf.
1232. 210. 10 r. orange and green 20 10
1233. – 20 r. mauve and green 30 15
DESIGN: 20 r. "Planned" family and "National Prosperity".

211. Balinese Mask.

**1969.** Tourism in Bali. Multicoloured.
1234. 12 r. Type 211 .. .. 30 20
1235. 15 r. Girl with offerings .. 40 25
1236. 30 r. Cremation rites .. 60 25

212. "Agriculture".

213. Dish Aerial.

**1969.** Five-year Development Plan.
1238. – 5 r. blue and green .. 15 10
1239. 212. 7 r. 50 yellow & pur. 15 10
1240. – 10 r. red and blue .. 15 10
1241. – 12 r. red and blue .. 75 35
1242. – 15 r. yellow & green 15 10
1243. – 20 r. yellow & violet 15 10
1244. – 25 r. red and black .. 15 10
1245. – 30 r. black and red .. 30 10
1246. – 40 r. orange & green 30 10
1247. – 50 r. brown & orange 50 10
DESIGNS: 5 r. Religious emblems ("Co-existence"). 10 r. Modern family ("Social Welfare"). 12 r. Crane and crate ("Overseas Trade"). 15 r. Bobbins ("Clothing Industry"). 20 r. Children in class ("Education"). 25 r. Research worker ("Scientific Research"). 30 r. Family and hypodermic syringe ("Health Care"). 40 r. Fish and net ("Fisheries"). 50 r. Graph ("Statistics").

**1969.** Satellite Communications and Inaug. of Djatiluhur Earth Station. Mult.
1248. 15 r. Type 213 .. .. 25 15
1249. 30 r. Communications satellite .. .. .. 40 20

214. Vickers Vimy Biplane over Borobudur Temple.

215. Noble Volute.

**1969.** 50th Anniv of 1st England–Australia Flight, by Ross and Keith Smith.
1253 214 75 r. purple and red .. 40 25
1254 – 100 r. green & yellow 50 25
DESIGN: 100 r. Vickers Vimy and map of Indonesia.

**1969.** Sea Shells. Multicoloured.
1255 5 r.+50 c. Type 215 .. 20 20
1256 7 r. 50+50 c. Common hairy triton .. .. 20 20
1257 10 r.+1 r. Common spider conch .. .. .. 35 35
1258 15 r.+1 r. 50 Bramble murex .. .. 35 35

216. Indonesian Pavilion.

217. Prisoner's Hands and Scales of Justice.

**1970.** "Expo 70" World Fair, Osaka, Japan.
1259. 216. 5 r. yell., grn. & brn. 35 15
1260. – 15 r. red, blue & green 50 20
1261. 216. 30 r. yell., blue & red 60 30
DESIGN: 15 r. Indonesian "Garuda" symbol.

**1970.** "Purification of Justice".
1262. 217. 10 r. purple and red .. 35 15
1263. 15 r. purple and green 50 15

218. U.P.U. Monument, Berne.

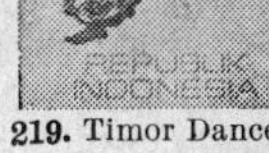
219. Timor Dancers.

**1970.** Inauguration of New U.P.U. Headquarters Building, Berne.
1264. 218. 15 r. red & green 50 25
1265. – 30 r. blue and ochre .. 65 30
DESIGN: 30 r. New Headquarters building.

**1970.** "Visit Indonesia Year". Traditional Dancers. Multicoloured.
1266. 20 r. Type 219 .. .. 65 25
1267. 45 r. Bali dancers .. .. 95 40

220. "Productivity" Symbol.

221. Independence Monument.

**1970.** Asian Productivity Year.
1269. 220. 5 r. red, yell. & green 40 10
1270. 30 r. red, yell. & violet 55 25

**1970.** 25th Anniv. of Independence.
1271. 221. 40 r. violet, purple & bl. 5·00 95

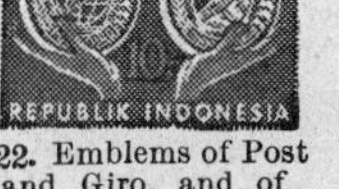
222. Emblems of Post and Giro, and of Telecommunications.

223. U.N. Emblem and Doves.

**1970.** 25th Anniv. of Indonesian Post and Telecommunications Services.
1272. 222. 10 r. brn., yell. & grn. 1·90 35
1273. – 25 r. blk., yell. & pink 2·75 20
DESIGN: 25 r. Telephone dial and P.T.T. worker.

**1970.** 25th Anniv. of United Nations.
1274. 223. 40 r. multicoloured .. 4·75 80

224. I.E.Y. Emblem on globe. 225. "Chrysocoris javanus" (shieldbug).

**1970.** Int. Education Year
1275. 224. 25 r. brn., red & yellow 3·75 80
1276. – 50 r. red, blk. and blue 5·75 1·40
DESIGNS: 50 r. I.E.Y. emblem.

**1970.** Insects. Multicoloured.
1277 7 r. 50+50 c. Type 225 .. 2·50 35
1278 15 r.+1 r. 50 "Orthetrum testaceum" (darter) .. 4·50 1·60
1279 20 r.+2 r. "Xylocopa flavonigrescens" (carpenter bee) .. 8·75 1·25

226. Batik handicrafts.

**1971.** "Visit ASEAN (South East Asian Nations Assn.) Year". Multicoloured.
1280. 20 r. Type 226 .. .. 1·10 35
1281. 50 r. Javanese girl playing angklung (musical instrument) (vert.) .. 1·60 95
1282. 75 r. Wedding group, Minangkabau .. .. 3·75 1·25

227. Restoration of Fatahillah Park.

**1971.** 444th Anniv. of Djakarta. Mult.
1284. 15 r. Type 277 .. .. 1·10 35
1285. 65 r. Performance at Lenong Theatre .. 1·60 1·25
1286. 80 r. Ismail Marzuki Cultural Centre .. .. 3·75 95

228. Sita and Rama. 229. Pigeon with Letter, and Workers.

**1971.** Int. Ramayana Festival.
1288. 228. 30 r. multicoloured .. 95 20
1289. – 100 r. black, blue & red 1·40 65
DESIGN: 100 r. Rama.

**1971.** 5th Asian Regional Telecommunications Conference.
1290 229 50 r. chocolate, brown and buff .. .. 80 25

230. U.P.U. Monument, Berne, and Hemispheres.

**1971.** U.P.U. Day.
1291. 230. 40 r. purple, blk. & blue 95 35

231. Schoolgirl. 233. Microwave Tower.

232. Lined Surgeon Fish.

**1971.** 25th Anniv. of U.N.I.C.E.F. Mult.
1292. 20 r. Type 231 .. .. 90 25
1293. 40 r. Boy with rice-stalks 1·25 35

**1971.** Fishes (1st series). Multicoloured.
1294 15 r. Type 232 .. .. 1·40 50
1295 30 r. Moorish idol ("Zanclus cornutus") 3·25 65
1296 40 r. Emperor angel fish ("Pomacanthus imperator") .. .. 4·75 1·60
See also Nos. 1318/20, 1343/5, 1390/2 and 1423/5.

**1972.** 25th Anniv. of E.C.A.F.E.
1297. 233. 40 r. blue & turquoise 95 35
1298. – 75 r. multicoloured .. 1·25 35
1299. – 100 r. multicoloured 1·75 65
DESIGNS—VERT: 40 r. E.C.A.F.E. emblem. HORIZ: 100 r. Irrigation and highways.

234. Human Heart. 235. Ancient and Modern Textile Production.

**1972.** World Heart Month.
1300. 234. 50 r. multicoloured .. 1·10 25

**1972.** 50th Anniv. of Textile Technological Institute.
1301. 235. 35 r. pur., yell. & orge. 80 25

236. Children reading Books. 237. "Essa 8" Weather Satellite.

**1972.** Int. Book Year.
1302. 236. 75 r. multicoloured .. 1·10 35

**1972.** Space Exploration.
1303. 237. 35 r. brn., violet & bl. 80 20
1304. – 50 r. bl., blk. & pink 1·25 1·10
1305. – 60 r. blk., grn. & brn. 2·25 35
DESIGNS: 50 r. Astronaut on Moon. 60 r. Indonesian "Kartika 1" rocket.

238. Hotel Indonesia.

**1972.** 10th Anniv. of Hotel Indonesia.
1306. 238. 50 r. grn., pale grn. & red 1·75 35

239. "Silat" (unarmed combat). 240. Family and Religious Buildings.

**1972.** Olympic Games, Munich.
1307 239 20 r. pur, cobalt & bl 70 10
1308 – 35 r. violet, brn & mve 70 15
1309 – 50 r. emerald, deep green and green .. 1·25 25
1310 – 75 r. rose, pur & pink 1·25 50
1311 – 100 r. brown, bl & grn 1·90 95
DESIGNS: 35 r. Running. 50 r. Diving. 75 r. Badminton. 100 r. Olympic stadium.

**1972.** Family Planning Campaign. Mult.
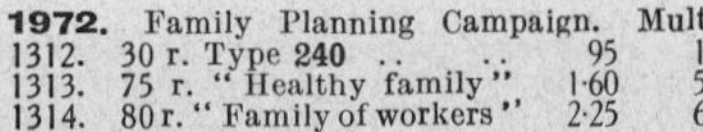
1312. 30 r. Type 240 .. .. 95 15
1313. 75 r. "Healthy family" 1·60 50
1314. 80 r. "Family of workers" 2·25 65

241. Moluccas Dancer. 242. Thomas Cup and Shuttlecock.

**1972.** "Art and Culture" (1st series).
1315 241 30 r. brn, pink & grn 1·10 20
1316 – 60 r. multicoloured .. 2·00 85
1317 – 100 r. blue, brown and cinnamon .. .. 3·25 75
DESIGNS—VERT: 60 r. Couple and Toraja traditional house. HORIZ: 100 r. West Irian traditional house.
See also 1336/8, 1373/5 and 1401/3.

**1972.** Fishes (2nd series). As T 232. Mult.
1318 30 r. Butterfly fish ("Chaetodon triangulum") .. .. 3·00 65
1319 50 r. Royal angel fish ("Pygoplites diacanthus") .. .. 3·75 95
1320 100 r. Clown trigger fish ("Balistoides conspicillum") .. 6·00 1·60

**1972.** Thomas Cup Badminton Championships, Djakarta.
1321. 242. 30 r. blue and green 30 15
1322. – 75 r. red and green .. 70 20
1323. – 80 r. brown and red .. 1·25 30
DESIGNS: 75 r. Thomas Cup and Sports Centre. 80 r. Thomas Cup and player.

243. Emblem Anemometer and "Gatotkaca".

**1973.** I.M.O. and W.M.O. Weather Organization Centenary.
1324. 243. 80 r. multicoloured .. 95 25

244. "Health begins at Home". 245. Java Mask.

**1973.** 25th Anniv of W.H.O.
1325 244 80 r. blue, orge & grn 95 25

**1973.** Tourism. Indonesian Folk Masks. Multicoloured.
1326. 30 r. Type 245 .. .. 50 20
1327. 60 r. Kalimantan mask .. 1·00 50
1328. 100 r. Bali mask .. .. 1·60 1·00

246. Savings Bank and Thrift Plant. 247. Chess.

**1973.** Two-Year National Savings Drive.
1329 246 25 r. black, yell & bis 45 20
1330 – 30 r. green, gold & yell 55 30
DESIGN—HORIZ: 30 r. Hand and "City" savings bank.

**1973.** National Sports Week. Multicoloured.
1331 30 r. Type 247 .. .. 65 40
1332 60 r. Karate .. .. 95 40
1333 75 r. Hurdling (horiz) .. 1·60 35

248. International Policemen.

**1973.** 50th Anniv. of Interpol.
1334. 248. 30 r. multicoloured .. 50 15
1335. – 50 r. yell., pur. & blk. 65 20
DESIGN—VERT. 50 r. Giant temple guard.

**1973.** "Art and Culture" (2nd series). Weaving and Fabrics. As T 241. Mult.
1336. 60 r. Parang Rusak pattern 95 50
1337. 80 r. Pagi Sore pattern .. 1·90 65
1338. 100 r. Merak Ngigel pattern 2·75 75

249. "Food Cultivation".

**1973.** 10th Anniv. of World Food Programme.
1339. 249. 30 r. multicoloured .. 1·10 25

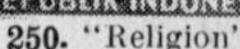
250. "Religion"

252. Bengkulu Costume.

251. Admiral Sudarso and Naval Battle of Arafuru.

**1973.** Family Planning.
1340. 250. 20 r. blue, light bl. & red 25 15
1341. – 30 r. blk., yell. & brn. 75 20
1342. – 60 r. blk., yell. & grn. 1·10 20
DESIGNS: 30 r. Teacher and class ("Population Education"). 60 r. Family and house ("Health").

**1973.** Fishes (3rd series). As T 232. Mult.
1343 40 r. Painted surgeon fish ("Acanthurus leucosternon") .. 55 35
1344 65 r. Lineated butterfly fish ("Chaetodon trifasciatus") .. .. 2·40 65
1345 100 r. Goldtail angel fish ("Pomacanthus annularis") .. .. 3·25 95

**1974.** Naval Day.
1346. 251. 40 r. multicoloured .. 1·40 50

**1974.** Pacific Area Travel Association Conference, Djakarta. Provincial Costumes. Multicoloured.
1347 5 r. Type 252 .. .. 6·25 50
1348 7 r. 50 Kalimantan, Timor 3·75 50
1349 10 r. Kalimantan, Tengah 2·50 35
1350 15 r. Jambi .. .. 65 35
1351 20 r. Sulawesi, Tenggara 65 35
1352 25 r. Nusatenggara, Timor 65 35
1353 27 r. 50 Maluku .. .. 65 1·90
1354 30 r. Lampung .. .. 65 65
1355 35 r. Sumatera, Barat .. 65 35
1356 40 r. Aceh .. .. 65 35
1357 45 r. Nusatenggara, Barat 1·90 35
1358 50 r. Riau .. .. 95 1·60
1359 55 r. Kalimantan, Barat 1·25 35
1360 60 r. Sulawesi, Utara 1·25 35
1361 65 r. Sulawesi, Tengah .. 1·25 35
1362 70 r. Sumatera, Selatan 1·40 35
1363 75 r. Java, Barat .. 1·40 35
1364 80 r. Sumatera, Utara .. 1·40 35
1365 90 r. Yogyakarta .. 1·40 3·25
1366 95 r. Kalimantan, Selatan 1·40 35
1367 100 r. Java, Timor .. 1·40 65
1368 120 r. Irian, Jaya .. 3·00 40
1369 130 r. Java, Tengah .. 3·00 35
1370 135 r. Sulawesi, Selatan .. 3·25 35
1371 150 r. Bali .. .. 3·25 35
1372 160 r. Djakarta .. .. 3·25 65

**1974.** "Art and Culture" (3rd series). Shadow Plays. As T 241. Mult.
1373. 40 r. Baladewa .. .. 1·60 65
1374. 80 r. Kresna .. .. 2·75 1·25
1375. 100 r. Bima .. .. 3·50 1·25

254. Pres. Suharto.

**1974.**

1376 **254** 40 r. brown, grn & blk 25 10
1377 50 r. brown, bl & blk 55 10
1378 65 r. brn, mve & blk 40 20
1379 75 r. brn, yell & blk 55 10
1380 100 r. brn, yell & blk 55 10
1381 150 r. brn, grn & blk 55 10

See also Nos. 1444/7.

**255.** "Improvement of Living Standards". **256.** "Welfare".

**1974.** World Population Year.

1382. **255.** 65 r. multicoloured .. 65 20

**1974.** Family Planning.

1383. **256.** 25 r. multicoloured .. 50 10
1384. – 40 r. blue, blk. & grn. 50 10
1385. – 65 r. ochre, brn. & yell. 1·10 10

DESIGNS: 40 r. Young couple ("Development"). 65 r. Arrows ("Religion").

**257.** Bicycle Postmen.

**1974.** Cent. of U.P.U.

1386. **257.** 20 r. brn., yell. & grn. 1·10 10
1387. – 40 r. brn., orge. & blue 1·10 35
1388. – 65 r. brn., yell. & blk. 1·10 35
1389. – 100 r. blk., blue & red 1·10 65

DESIGNS: 40 r. Mail-cart. 65 r. Mounted postman. 100 r. East Indies galley.

**1974.** Fishes (4th series). As T **232**. Mult.

1390 40 r. Sailfin surgeon fish ("Zebrasoma veliferum") .. .. 1·25 20
1391 80 r. ("Euxiphipops navarchus") .. .. 1·60 80
1392 100 r. Dragonet ("Synchiropus splendidus") .. .. 2·75 95

**258.** Drilling for Oil.

**1975.** 17th Anniv of Pertamina Oil Complex. Multicoloured.

1393 40 r. Type **258** .. .. 25 20
1394 75 r. Oil refinery .. 25 20
1395 95 r. Control centre (vert) 25 20
1396 100 r. Road tanker (vert) 25 20
1397 120 r. Fokker Fellowship airliner over storage tank farm (vert) .. 90 55
1398 130 r. Pipelines and tanker (vert) .. .. 1·00 55
1399 150 r. Petrochemical storage tanks .. .. 35 20
1400 200 r. Offshore oil rig .. 1·75 95

**1975.** "Art and Culture" (4th series). As T **241**.

1401. 50 r. silver, red & blk. .. 65 50
1402. 75 r. silver, grn. & blk. .. 95 50
1403. 100 r. yell., bl. & blk. .. 1·25 50

DESIGNS: 50 r. Sumatran spittoon. 75 r. Sumatran "sirh" dish. 100 r. Kalimantan "sirh" dish.

**260.** "Donorship".

**261.** Measures and Globe.

**1975.** Blood Donors' Campaign.

1404. **260.** 40 r. red, yell. & grn. 65 20

**1975.** Cent. of Metre Convention.

1405. **261.** 65 r. blue, red & yell. 95 25

**262.** Women in Public Service.

**1975.** International Women's Year. Mult.

1406. 40 r. Type **262** .. .. 80 35
1407. 100 r. I.W.Y. emblem (21 × 29 mm.) .. .. 1·10 35

**263.** "Dendrobium pakarena".

**264.** Stupas and Damaged Temple.

**1975.** Tourism. Indonesian Orchids. Mult.

1408 40 r. Type **263** .. .. 2·50 65
1409 70 r. "Aeridachnis bogor" 2·50 65
1410 85 r. "Vanda genta" .. 4·50 1·90

**1975.** U.N.E.S.C.O. "Save Borobudur Temple" Campaign. Multicoloured.

1411 25 r. Type **264** .. .. 1·50 35
1412 40 r. Buddhist shrines and broken wall .. .. 1·90 35
1413 65 r. Stupas and damaged building (horiz) .. 3·75 1·60
1414 100 r. Buddha and stupas (horiz) .. .. 5·25 1·60

**265.** Battle of Banjarmasin.

**1975.** 30th Anniv. of Independence.

1415. **265.** 25 r. black and yell. 35 20
1416. – 40 r. black and red .. 50 20
1417. – 75 r. black and red .. 80 50
1418. – 100 r. black and orange 80 50

DESIGNS: 40 r. Battle of Batua; 75 r. Battle of Margarana; 100 r. Battle of Palembang.

**266.** "Education".

**267.** Heroes' Monument, Surabaya.

**1975.** Family Planning. Multicoloured.

1419. 20 r. Type **266** .. .. 35 10
1420. 25 r. "Religion" .. 50 20
1421. 40 r. "Prosperity" .. 80 20

**1975.** 30th Anniv of Independence War.

1422 **267** 100 r. red and green .. 1·10 20

**1975.** Fishes (5th series). As Type **232**. Mult.

1423 40 r. "Coris angulata" .. 1·10 35
1424 75 r. Saddleback butterfly fish ("Chaetodon ephippium") .. .. 2·00 80
1425 150 r. Bat fish ("Platax pinnatus") (vert) .. 2·25 80

**269.** Thomas Cup.

**1976.** Indonesian Victory in World Badminton Championships. Multicoloured.

1428. 20 r. Type **269** .. .. 50 20
1429. 40 r. Uber cup .. .. 50 35
1430. 100 r. Thomas and Uber cups .. .. 95 35

**270.** Refugees and New Village.

**1976.** World Human Settlements Day. Multicoloured.

1431. 30 r. Type **270** .. .. 35 20
1432. 50 r. Old and restored villages .. .. 65 20
1433. 100 r. Derelict and rebuilt houses .. .. .. 65 20

**271.** Early and Modern Telephones.

**272.** Human Eye.

**1976.** Telephone Centenary.

1434. **271.** 100 r. brn., red & yell. 70 20

**1976.** World Health Day. Multicoloured.

1435. 20 r. Type **272** .. .. 25 10
1436. 40 r. Blind man with stick 55 20

**273.** Main Stadium, Montreal.

**1976.** Olympic Games, Montreal.

1437. **273.** 100 r. blue .. .. 85 35

**274.** Lake Tondano, Sulawesi.

**275.** "Light Traffic" Station.

**1976.** Tourism. Multicoloured.

1438. 35 r. Type **274** .. .. 50 20
1439. 40 r. Lake Kelimutu, Flores .. .. .. 50 20
1440. 75 r. Lake Maninjau, Sumatra .. .. 50 20

**1976.** Inaug of Domestic Satellite System.

1441 **275** 20 r. multicoloured .. 50 20
1442 – 50 r. black and green 50 20
1443 – 100 r. turq, bl & vio 80 35

DESIGNS: 50 r. "Master control" station; 100 r. "Palapa" satellite.

**1976.** Vert. designs as T **254** but with background of wavy lines.

1444. 200 r. brn., blue and grn. 1·60 10
1445. 300 r. brown, red & flesh 1·90 10
1446. 400 r. brn., grn and yell. 3·25 20
1447. 500 r. brown, red and lilac 4·50 65

**276.** "Vanda Putri Serang".

**1976.** Orchids. Multicoloured.

1448 25 r. "Arachnis flos-aeris" 1·40 50
1449 40 r. Type **276** .. .. 1·40 50
1450 100 r. "Coelogyne pandurata" .. .. 1·90 1·25

**277.** Stylised Tree.

**279.** Open Book.

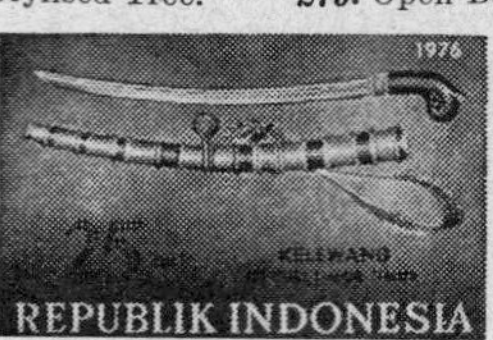


**278.** Kelewang Dagger and Sheath (Timor).

**1976.** Reafforestation Week.

1452 **277** 20 r. green, blue & brn 35 15

**1976.** Daggers and Sheaths.

1453 **278** 25 r. green, blk & brn 50 20
1454 – 40 r. brn, yell & orge 95 35
1455 – 100 r. brn, yell & grn 1·40 95

DESIGNS: 40 r. Mandau dagger and sheath (Borneo); 100 r. Rencong dagger and sheath (Aceh).

**1976.** Books for Children.

1457 **279** 20 r. green, orge & bl 50 10
1458 – 40 r. violet, red & yell 55 20

DESIGN: 40 r. Children reading book.

**280.** UNICEF Emblem.

**281.** Ballot Box.

**1976.** 30th Anniv of UNICEF.

1459 **280** 40 r. blue, turq & vio 40 20

**1977.** Elections.

1460 **281** 40 r. blue, yell & grey 1·40 20
1461 – 75 r. blue, yell & pink 1·75 20
1462 – 100 r. bistre, red & blk 2·50 80

DESIGNS: 75 r. Ballot box, factory and produce; 100 r. Indonesian arrow.

**282.** Scout Emblems and Camp.

**283.** Letter and A.O.P.U. Emblem.

**1977.** 11th National Scout Jamboree. Mult.

1463. 25 r. Type **282** .. .. 50 20
1464. 30 r. Emblems, tent and trees .. .. .. 50 20
1465. 40 r. Emblems, tent and flags .. .. .. 1·10 35

**1977.** 15th Anniv. of Asian–Oceanic Postal Union. Multicoloured.

1466. 65 r. Type **283** .. .. 50 20
1467. 100 r. Stylized carrier pigeon .. .. .. 65 45

**284.** Anniversary Emblem.

**285.** Rose.

**1977.** 450th Anniv of Jakarta.

1468 **284** 20 r. blue and red 40 25
1469 – 40 r. green and blue .. 40 25
1470 – 100 r. blue & turquoise 80 35

DESIGNS: 40, 100 r. Similar to Type **284** but with emblem and arms differently arranged.

**1977.** "Amphilex 77" International Stamp Exhibition, Amsterdam.

1472 **285** 100 r. red, green & blk 65 40
1473 – 100 r. red, green & blk 95 20

DESIGN: No. 1473, Envelope.

**286.** Sports Pictograms.

**287.** Trophy.

**1977.** Ninth National Sports Week.

1475. **286.** 40 r. silver, grn. & red 95 65
1476. – 50 r. silver, blue & red 1·25 65
1477. – 100 r. gold, blk. & red 1·60 1·60

DESIGNS: 50, 100 r. Similar to Type **286** but with different pictograms.

**1977.** 10th National Koran Reading Contest.

1478 **287** 40 r. brown, grn & yell 1·10 25
1479 – 100 r. black, yell & grn 1·25 35

DESIGN: 100 r. Emblem.

**288.** Carrier Pigeon and Map.

**289.** Government Officer, Djakarta Region.

**1977.** 10th Anniv. of Association of South East Asian Nations. Multicoloured.
1480. 25 r. Type **288** .. .. 20 10
1481. 35 r. Map of ASEAN members .. .. 95 35
1482. 50 r. Transport and flags of ASEAN members.. 95 35

**1977.** Economic and Cultural Co-operation with Pakistan.
1483. **289.** 25 r. brn., gold & grn. 20 10

**290.** " Taeniophyllum Sp. ". **291.** Child and Mosquito.

**1977.** Orchids. Multicoloured.
1484. 25 r. Type **290** .. .. 80 35
1485. 40 r. " Phalaenopsis violacea " .. .. 80 65
1486. 100 r. " Dendrobium spectabile " .. .. 1·60 95

**1977.** National Health Campaign.
1488 **291** 40 r. red, green & blk 20 10

**292.** Proboscis Monkey.

**1977.** Wildlife (1st series). Multicoloured.
1489. 20 r. Type **292** .. .. 65 25
1490. 40 r. Indian elephant .. 65 40
1491. 100 r. Tiger .. .. 1·60 1·25

**293.** Hands holding U.N. Emblem. **294.** Mother feeding Baby.

**1978.** U.N. Conference on Tenchincal Co-operation among Developing Countries.
1493 **293** 100 r. blue & ultram .. 50 15

**1978.** Campaign for the Promotion of Breast Feeding.
1494. **294.** 40 r. green and blue.. 30 10
1495. – 75 r. brown and red.. 40 15
DESIGN: 75 r. Stylised mother and child.

**295.** Dome of the Rock.

**1978.** Palestine Welfare.
1496 **295** 100 r. multicoloured .. 55 25

**296.** World Cup Emblem. **297.** Head and Blood Circulation Diagram.

**1978.** World Cup Football Competition, Argentina.
1497 **296** 40 r. green, blk & bl 35 15
1498 100 r. mauve, blk & bl 65 30

**1978.** World Health Day.
1499. **297.** 100 r. blue, black and red .. .. 40 15

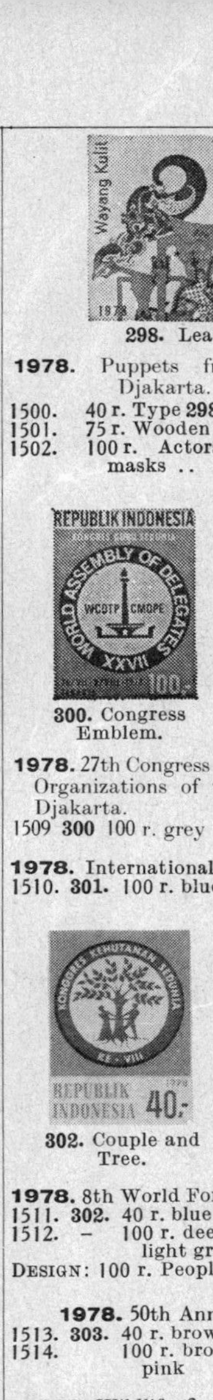

**298.** Leather Puppets.

**1978.** Puppets from Wayang Museum, Djakarta. Multicoloured.
1500. 40 r. Type **298** .. .. 80 25
1501. 75 r. Wooden puppets .. 95 75
1502. 100 r. Actors wearing masks .. .. .. 1·40 95

**300.** Congress Emblem. **301.** I.A.Y. Emblem.

**1978.** 27th Congress of World Confederation of Organizations of the Teaching Profession, Djakarta.
1509 **300** 100 r. grey .. .. 45 15

**1978.** International Anti-Apartheid Year.
1510. **301.** 100 r. blue and red .. 60 15

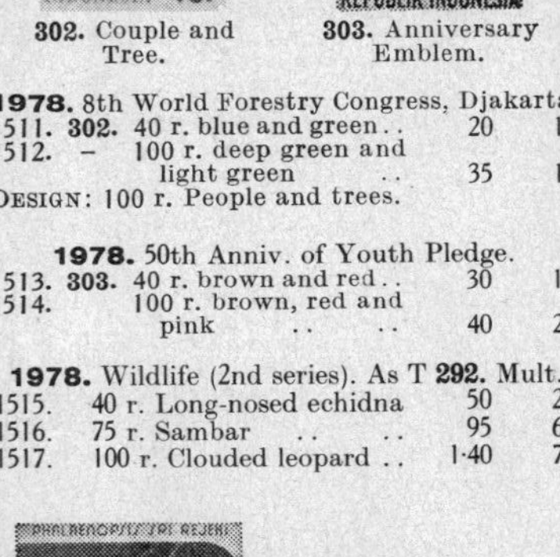

**302.** Couple and Tree. **303.** Anniversary Emblem.

**1978.** 8th World Forestry Congress, Djakarta.
1511. **302.** 40 r. blue and green.. 20 10
1512. – 100 r. deep green and light green .. 35 10
DESIGN: 100 r. People and trees.

**1978.** 50th Anniv. of Youth Pledge.
1513. **303.** 40 r. brown and red.. 30 10
1514. 100 r. brown, red and pink .. .. 40 20

**1978.** Wildlife (2nd series). As T **292.** Mult.
1515. 40 r. Long-nosed echidna 50 20
1516. 75 r. Sambar .. .. 95 60
1517. 100 r. Clouded leopard .. 1·40 70

**304.** " Phalaenopsis sri rejeki ". **307.** Thomas Cup and Badminton Player.

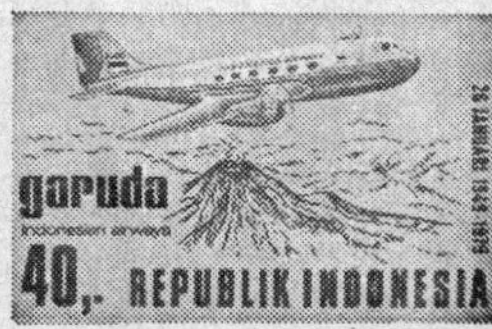

**306.** Douglas DC-3 over Volcano.

**1978.** Orchids. Multicoloured.
1519. 40 r. Type **304** .. .. 50 25
1520. 75 r. " Dendrobium macrophillum " .. .. 80 40
1521. 100 r. " Cymbidium fynlaysonianum " .. 1·25 50

**1979.** 30th Anniv of Garuda Indonesian Airways. Multicoloured.
1531 40 r. Type **306** .. .. 50 15
1532 75 r. Douglas DC-9-30 over village .. .. 60 30
1533 100 r. Douglas DC-10 over temple .. .. 80 50

**1979.** Thomas Cup Badminton Championships, Djakarta.
1534 **307** 40 r. pink & turquoise 25 20
1535 – 100 r. brown and pink 45 25
1536 – 100 r. brown and pink 45 25
DESIGNS: No. 1535, Player on left side of net hitting shuttlecock; 1536, Player on right side of net.

Nos. 1535/6 were issued together, se-tenant, forming a composite design.

**308.** " Paphiopedilum lowii ".

**309.** Family and Houses.

**1979.** Orchids. Multicoloured.
1537. 60 r. Type **308** .. .. 50 25
1538. 100 r. " Vanda limbata " 75 40
1539. 125 r. " Phalaenopsis gigantea " .. .. 1·00 65

**1979.** 3rd Five Year Development Plan.
1541 **309** 35 r. drab and green 10 10
1542 – 60 r. green and blue .. 15 10
1543 – 100 r. brown and blue 20 20
1544 – 125 r. brown & green 30 10
1545 – 150 r. yell, orge & red 30 10
DESIGNS: 60 r. Pylon, dam and fields; 100 r. School and clinic; 125 r. Loading produce at factory; 150 r. Delivering mail.

**310/311.** Mrs. R. A. Kartini.

**1979.** Birth Cent. of Mrs. R.A. Kartini (pioneer of women's rights).
1546 **310** 100 r. brown & green 35 20
1547 **311** 100 r. green & brown 35 20

**312.** Bureau Emblem.

**313.** Self Defence.

**1979.** 50th Anniv. of International Bureau of Education.
1549. **312.** 150 r. blue, light blue & lilac .. .. 65 20

**1979.** 10th South East Asia Games, Djakarta.
1550 **313** 60 r. yellow, blk & grn 25 15
1551 – 125 r. orge, grey & bl 40 30
1552 – 150 r. yell, blk & red 60 35
DESIGNS: 125 r. Games emblem; 150 r. Main stadium, Senayan.

**314.** Co-operation Emblem.

**315.** National I.Y.C. Emblem.

**1979.** Co-operation Day.
1553. **314.** 150 r. multicoloured 50 15

**1979.** International Year of the Child.
1554. **315.** 60 r. black and green 25 10
1555. – 150 r. blue and black 40 25
DESIGN: 150 r. International I.Y.C. emblem.

**316.** Exhibition Emblem.

**317.** Drug Addict.

**1979.** 3rd World Telecommunications Exhibition, Geneva
1556 **316** 150 r. grey, blue & orge 50 15

**1979.** "End Drug Abuse" Campaign.
1557 **317** 150 r. black and pink 50 15

**1979.** Wildlife (3rd series). As T **292.** Mult.
1558. 60 r. Bottle-nosed dolphin .. .. 50 40
1559. 125 r. Irrawaddy dolphin 95 50
1560. 150 r. Leatherback Turtle .. .. .. 1·25 55

**318.** Pinisi Sailing Ship.

**1980.** Djakarta–Amsterdam Spice Race.
1562. **318.** 60 r. blue .. .. 45 20
1563. – 125 r. brown .. .. 65 30
1564. – 150 r. purple .. 1·10 35
DESIGNS—HORIZ. 125 r. Schooner made of cloves. VERT. 150 r. Madurese sailing boat.

**319.** Riding the Rapids.

**1980.** Adventure Sports. Multicoloured.
1566. 60 r. Type **319** .. .. 25 10
1567. 125 r. Mountaineering (vert.) .. .. 35 25
1568. 150 r. Hang gliding .. 95 45

**320.** Cigarettes and Heart.

**321.** Artificial Flowers in Vase.

**1980.** Anti-smoking Campaign.
1570 **320** 150 r. flesh, blk & pink 50 20

**1980.** Second Flower Festival, Jakarta. Multicoloured.
1571. 125 r. Type **321** .. .. 50 25
1572. 150 r. Artificial bouquet 65 25

**322.** Conference Building and Globe.

**323.** Danau Poso Statue.

**1980.** 25th Anniv of First Asian–African Conference, Bandung.
1573 **322** 150 r. mauve and gold 65 20

**1980.** Prehistoric Monuments. Multicoloured.
1575 60 r. Type **323** .. .. 35 10
1576 125 r. Elephant stone, Pasemah Village, South Sumatra .. .. 40 25
1577 150 r. Taman Bali sarcophagus .. .. 55 30

**324.** Discus Thrower.

**325.** Draughtsman in Wheelchair.

**1980.** Olympics for the Disabled, Arnhem.
1580. **324.** 75 r. brown & orange 35 10

**1980.** 30th Anniv. of Disabled Veterans Corps.
1581. **325.** 100 r. yell., blue & blk. 35 10

**326.** President Suharto.

**327.** People and Map of Indonesia.

**1980.**

| | | | | |
|---|---|---|---|---|
| 1581a | 326 | 10 r. olive and green | 35 | 10 |
| 1582 | | 12 r. 50 grn & lt grn | 15 | 10 |
| 1582a | | 25 r. brown & orange | 20 | 10 |
| 1583 | | 50 r. blue and green | 15 | 10 |
| 1583a | | 55 r. red & vermilion | 20 | 10 |
| 1584 | | 75 r. brown & yellow | 25 | 10 |
| 1585a | | 100 r. bl, vio & mve | 20 | 20 |
| 1586 | | 200 r. brown & orge | 15 | 10 |
| 1586b | | 300 r. violet, lilac and gold .. | 50 | 15 |
| 1586c | | 400 r. grey, pink and gold .. .. | 50 | 15 |

Nos. 1585a and 1586 exist dated "1980" or "1981", and Nos. 1582a, 1583a and 1586b/c are dated "1983".

See also Nos. 1830/4.

**1980.** Population Census.

| | | | | |
|---|---|---|---|---|
| 1587. | 327. | 75 r. blue and pink .. | 35 | 10 |
| 1588. | | 200 r. blue and yellow | 55 | 20 |

**328.** Ship laying Cable.

**329.** Immigrants.

**1980.** Inauguration of Singapore–Indonesia Submarine Cable.

| | | | | |
|---|---|---|---|---|
| 1589. | 328. | 75 r. green, deep green and orange .. | 35 | 10 |
| 1590. | | 200 r. blue, deep blue and orange .. | 50 | 25 |

**1980.** Indonesian Immigration.

| | | | | |
|---|---|---|---|---|
| 1591. | 329. | 12 r. 50 red and green | 15 | 10 |

**330.** 1946 50 s. Stamp.

**331.** Map of A.O.P.U. Members.

**1980.** 35th Anniv. of Independence.

| | | | | |
|---|---|---|---|---|
| 1592. | 330. | 75 r. cream, blk. & brn. | 40 | 20 |
| 1593. | – | 100 r. cream, pur. & gold | 35 | 30 |
| 1594. | – | 200 r. cream, pink and silver .. .. | 75 | 35 |

DESIGNS—HORIZ. 100 r. 1946 15 s. stamp. VERT. 200 r. 1946 15 s. Freedom Fund stamp.

**1980.** 10th Anniv. of Asian–Oceanic Postal Union Training School, Bangkok.

| | | | | |
|---|---|---|---|---|
| 1595 | 331 | 200 r. bl, lt bl & turq | 65 | 20 |

**332.** O.P.E.C. Emblem on Globe.

**1980.** 20th Anniv. of Organization of Petroleum Exporting Countries.

| | | | | |
|---|---|---|---|---|
| 1596. | 332. | 200 r. turq., blue & red | 65 | 20 |

**333.** Service Members with Linked Arms.

**1980.** 35th Anniv. of Armed Forces. Mult.

| | | | |
|---|---|---|---|
| 1597. | 75 r. Indonesians hailing flag .. .. .. | 25 | 10 |
| 1598. | 200 r. Type **333** .. .. | 50 | 20 |

**334.** Pesquet's Parrot.

**335.** " Dendrobium insigne ".

**1980.** Parrots. Multicoloured.

| | | | |
|---|---|---|---|
| 1599. | 75 r. Type **334** .. .. | 1·10 | 35 |
| 1600. | 100 r. Chattering Lory .. | 1·25 | 65 |
| 1601. | 200 r. Rainbow Lory .. | 1·50 | 95 |

**1980.** Orchids. Multicoloured.

| | | | |
|---|---|---|---|
| 1603. | 75 r. Type **335** .. .. | 45 | 20 |
| 1604. | 100 r. " Dendrobium discolor " .. .. | 80 | 55 |
| 1605. | 200 r. " Dendrobium lasianthera " .. .. | 1·40 | 40 |

**336.** Von Stephan and U.P.U. Emblem.

**1981.** 150th Birth Anniv. of Heinrich von Stephan (U.P.U. founder).

| | | | | |
|---|---|---|---|---|
| 1607. | 336. | 200 r. blue & deep blue | 55 | 25 |

**337.** Jamboree and Scouting Emblems.

**1981.** 6th Asia-Pacific Scout Jamboree, Cibubur. Multicoloured.

| | | | |
|---|---|---|---|
| 1608. | 75 r. Type **337** .. .. | 25 | 15 |
| 1609. | 100 r. Scout and Guide map-reading (vert.) .. | 50 | 20 |
| 1610. | 200 r. Jamboree emblem and tents .. .. | 55 | 30 |

**338.** Ship (relief carving).

**339.** Child holding Blood Drop.

**1981.** 5th Asian-Oceanic Postal Union Congress, Yogyakarta.

| | | | | |
|---|---|---|---|---|
| 1612. | 338. | 200 r. blue, black and light blue .. .. | 55 | 20 |

**1981.** Blood Donors.

| | | | | |
|---|---|---|---|---|
| 1613. | 339. | 75 r. blue, blk. & red | 25 | 10 |
| 1614. | – | 100 r. red and grey .. | 40 | 15 |
| 1615. | – | 200 r. red, deep blue and blue .. .. | 50 | 25 |

DESIGNS: 100 r. Hands holding blood drop. 200 r. Hands and blood drop.

**340.** Monuments.

**1981.** International Family Planning Conference.

| | | | | |
|---|---|---|---|---|
| 1616. | 340. | 200 r. pale blue, brown and blue .. | 40 | 15 |

**341.** "Song of Sritanjung".

**1981.** Traditional Balinese Paintings. Mult.

| | | | |
|---|---|---|---|
| 1617. | 100 r. Type **341** .. .. | 50 | 15 |
| 1618. | 200 r. "Song of Sritanjung" (different) .. | 60 | 25 |

Nos. 1617/18 were issued together, se-tenant, forming a composite design.

**342.** Secretariat Building and Emblem.

**343.** Uber Cup.

**1981.** Inauguration of A.S.E.A.N. Secretariat, Djakarta.

| | | | | |
|---|---|---|---|---|
| 1620. | 342. | 200 r. yellow, orange and purple .. | 65 | 20 |

**1981.** International Ladies' Badminton Championships, Tokyo.

| | | | | |
|---|---|---|---|---|
| 1621. | 343. | 200 r. brown, yellow and orange .. | 95 | 25 |

**344.** "Tree of Life" (relief from Candi Mendut).

**346.** Blind Man.

**345.** Students reading Koran, Mosque and Emblem.

**1981.** World Environment Day.

| | | | | |
|---|---|---|---|---|
| 1622 | 344 | 75 r. bistre, grey & blk | 35 | 15 |
| 1623 | – | 200 r. bis, grey & blk | 40 | 15 |

DESIGN: 200 r. "Yaksha Apacaka".

**1981.** 12th National Koran Reading Contest, Banda Aceh.

| | | | | |
|---|---|---|---|---|
| 1624. | 345. | 200 r. blk., red & yell. | 50 | 25 |

**1981.** International Year of Disabled Persons.

| | | | | |
|---|---|---|---|---|
| 1625 | 346 | 75 r. brown, yell & bis | 25 | 10 |
| 1626 | – | 200 r. blue, brn & grn | 40 | 20 |

DESIGN: 200 r. Deaf and dumb person.

**347.** Soekarno-Hatta Monument, Djakarta.

**1981.** Independence Monument.

| | | | | |
|---|---|---|---|---|
| 1627. | 347. | 200 r. bl., yell. & gold | 55 | 20 |

**348.** Parachute Jumping.

**349.** Food Produce.

**1981.** National Sports Week, Djakarta.

| | | | | |
|---|---|---|---|---|
| 1628. | 348. | 75 r. red, black and blue .. .. | 20 | 15 |
| 1629. | – | 100 r. blk., blue & red | 35 | 20 |
| 1630. | – | 200 r. brn., grn. & red | 65 | 35 |

DESIGNS—HORIZ. 100 r. Scuba diving. VERT. 200 r. Horse riding.

**1981.** World Food Day.

| | | | | |
|---|---|---|---|---|
| 1631. | 349. | 200 r. multicoloured | 1·25 | 40 |

**350.** Arms of Aceh Special Territory.

**351.** Salmon-crested Cockatoo.

**1981.** Provincial Arms (1st series).

| | | | | |
|---|---|---|---|---|
| 1632. | 350. | 100 r. yell., grn. & gold | 1·10 | 35 |
| 1633. | – | 100 r. multicoloured | 1·10 | 35 |
| 1634. | – | 100 r. multicoloured | 1·10 | 35 |
| 1635. | – | 100 r. multicoloured | 1·40 | 1·10 |
| 1636. | – | 100 r. multicoloured | 4·00 | 50 |

DESIGNS: No. 1633, Bali. No. 1634, Bengkulu. No. 1635, Irian Jaya. No. 1636, Djakarta.

See also Nos. 1643/62 and 1710.

**1981.** Cockatoos. Multicoloured.

| | | | |
|---|---|---|---|
| 1637. | 75 r. Type **351**. .. .. | 1·75 | 35 |
| 1638. | 100 r. Sulphur-crested Cockatoo .. .. | 1·60 | 35 |
| 1639. | 200 r. Palm Cockatoo .. | 2·25 | 1·25 |

**1982.** Provincial Arms (2nd series). As T **350**. Multicoloured.

| | | | |
|---|---|---|---|
| 1641 | 100 r. Jambi .. .. | 50 | 10 |
| 1642 | 100 r. Java Barat (West) | 50 | 10 |
| 1643 | 100 r. Java Tengah (Cent) | 35 | 10 |
| 1644 | 100 r. Java Timur (East) | 35 | 10 |
| 1645 | 100 r. Kalimantan Barat (West) .. .. | 35 | 10 |
| 1646 | 100 r. Kalimantan Selatan (South) .. .. | 35 | 10 |
| 1647 | 100 r. Kalimantan Timur (East) .. .. | 35 | 10 |
| 1648 | 100 r. Kalimantan Tengah (Central) .. .. | 35 | 10 |
| 1649 | 100 r. Lampung .. .. | 35 | 10 |
| 1650 | 100 r. Moluccas .. .. | 25 | 10 |
| 1651 | 100 r. Nusa Tengarra Barat (West) .. .. | 25 | 10 |
| 1652 | 100 r. Nusa Tengarra Timur (East) .. .. | 25 | 10 |
| 1653 | 100 r. Riau .. .. | 35 | 10 |
| 1654 | 100 r. Sulawesi Tengah (Central Celebes) .. | 25 | 10 |
| 1655 | 100 r. Sulawesi Tenggara (South-east Celebes) .. | 25 | 10 |
| 1656 | 100 r. Sulawesi Selatan (South Celebes) .. | 25 | 10 |
| 1657 | 100 r. Sumatera Utara (North Celebes) .. | 25 | 10 |
| 1658 | 100 r. Sumatera Barat (West) .. .. | 35 | 10 |
| 1659 | 100 r. Sumatera Selatan (South) .. .. | 25 | 10 |
| 1660 | 100 r. Sumatera Utara (North) .. .. | 25 | 10 |
| 1661 | 100 r. Yogyakarta .. | 30 | 10 |
| 1662 | 250 r. Republic of Indonesia (45 × 29 mm) | 1·25 | 35 |

**352.** Hands enclosing Family.

**1982.** 70th Anniv of Bumiputera Mutual Life Insurance Company.

| | | | | |
|---|---|---|---|---|
| 1663 | 352 | 75 r. yellow, plum and purple .. .. | 20 | 10 |
| 1664 | – | 100 r. yellow, light green and green .. | 40 | 15 |
| 1665 | – | 200 r. multicoloured | 50 | 25 |

DESIGNS: 100 r. Family in countryside; 200 r. Hands supporting industrial activities.

**353.** Helicopter Rescue.

**354.** Houses and Ballot Boxes.

**1982.** 10th Anniv. of Search and Rescue Institute.

| | | | | |
|---|---|---|---|---|
| 1666. | 353. | 250 r. multicoloured | 1·75 | 70 |

**1982.** General Election. Multicoloured.

| | | | |
|---|---|---|---|
| 1667. | 75 r. Type **354** .. .. | 25 | 10 |
| 1668. | 100 r. Rural houses and ballot boxes .. .. | 25 | 10 |
| 1669. | 200 r. Houses and National arms .. | 50 | 25 |

**355.** Human Figures, Satellite and Dove.

**357.** Footballers.

**356.** Thomas Cup.

**1982.** 2nd U.N. Conference on Exploration and Peaceful Uses of Outer Space, Vienna.
1670 **355** 150 r. blue, vio & blk 35 10
1671 – 250 r. green, light green and dp green 45 15
DESIGN: 250 r. Peace dove and text.

**1982.** Thomas Cup Badminton Championship, London.
1672. **356.** 250 r. multicoloured 65 20

**1982.** World Cup Football Championship, Spain.
1674. **357.** 250 r. multicoloured 80 25

**358.** Taman Siswa Emblem.

**1982.** 60th Anniv. of Taman Siswa (educational organization).
1676. **358.** 250 r. yellow, green & red .. .. 40 15

**359.** Flags forming "15".

**1982.** 15th Anniv. of Association of South-East Asian Nations.
1677. **359.** 150 r. orange, red and blue .. .. 65 25

**360.** President Suharto.

**362.** Rothschild's Mynah.

**1982.**
1678. **360.** 110 r. red and orange 15 10
1679. 250 r. brn, & orange 20 10
1680. 275 r. green & yellow 25 10
Nos. 1678 and 1680 are inscribed "1983".

**1982.** Third World National Parks Congress, Bali. Multicoloured.
1682. 100 r. Type **362** .. .. 75 30
1683. 250 r. King Bird of Paradise .. .. .. 1·75 70

**363.** River Bridge.

**1982.** Five Year Plan.
1685. **363.** 17 r. 50 brown & grn. 10 10

**364.** Arfak Parotia.

**365.** Scouts and Anniversary Emblem.

**1982.** Birds of Paradise. Multicoloured.
1686. 100 r. Type **364** .. .. 75 30
1687. 150 r. Twelve-wired bird of paradise .. .. 1·10 40
1688. 250 r. Red bird of paradise .. .. 1·75 1·40

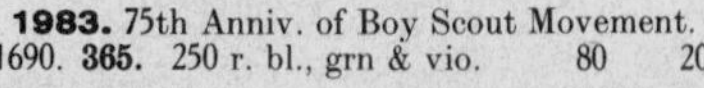
**1983.** 75th Anniv. of Boy Scout Movement.
1690. **365.** 250 r. bl., grn & vio. 80 20

**366.** Temple Restoration and Relief.

**1983.** Borobudur Temple.
1691. **366.** 100 r. grn., bl. & lt. bl. 50 20
1692. – 150 r. light green, green and brown.. 50 20
1693. – 250 r. black, deep brown and brown 1·10 50
DESIGNS—VERT. 150 r. Temple and statue. HORIZ. 250 r. Silhouette of temple and seated Buddha.

**367.** President Suharto.

**368.** Gas Storage Tanks.

**1983.**
1695. **367.** 500 r. brown .. 45 15

**1983.** Seventh International Liquefied Natural Gas Conference, Djarkarta.
1696. **368.** 275 r. multicoloured 50 20

**369.** Ships and Bird.

**370.** Man and Woman reading Koran.

**1983.** World Communications Year.
1697. **369.** 75 r. multicoloured.. 15 10
1698. – 110 r. multicoloured 25 15
1699. – 175 r. blue and red .. 30 20
1700. – 275 r. bl., dp. bl. & red 50 30
DESIGNS: 110 r. Satellite and receiving station. 175 r. Aircraft and dish aerial. 275 r. Globe and letter.

**1983.** 13th National Koran Reading Competition.
1701 **370** 275 r. yell, grn & blk 50 10

**371.** Eclipse and Map of Indonesia.

**1983.** Total Solar Eclipse.
1702. **371.** 110 r. brown, deep brown and black.. 25 15
1703. – 275 r. blue, vio. & pur. 55 20
DESIGN: 275 r. Map of Indonesia showing path of eclipse.

**372.** Satellite transmitting to Indonesia.

**373.** Patient receiving Radiation Treatment.

**1983.** Launching of "Palapa B" Communications Satellite.
1705. **372.** 275 r. green, blue & silver .. .. 40 20

**1983.** Anti-cancer Campaign.
1706. **373.** 55 r.+20 r. mult. .. 20 20
1707. 75 r.+25 r. mult. .. 25 20

**374.** Agricultural Produce.

**1983.** Agricultural Census.
1708 **374** 110 r. grey, grn & blk 30 15
1709 – 275 r. red, black & grn 75 35
DESIGN: 275 r. Farmer with produce.

**1983.** Provincial Arms (3rd series). As T **350**. Multicoloured.
1710. 100 r. Timor Timur .. 30 10

**375.** Traditional Weaving, Pakistan.

**1983.** Indonesia-Pakistan Economic and Cultural Co-operation. Multicoloured.
1711. 275 r. Type **375** .. .. 55 20
1712. 275 r. Traditional weaving, Indonesia .. .. 55 20

**376.** Eruption of Krakatoa.

**1983.** Centenary of Krakatoa Volcanic Eruption. Multicoloured.
1713. 110 r. Type **376** .. .. 20 15
1714. 275 r. Map showing position of Krakatoa .. .. 50 20

**377.** Casa-Nurtanio CN-235 Short-haul Passenger Aircraft.

**1983.** Indonesian Aircraft.
1715. **377.** 275 r. multicoloured 1·60 65

**378.** Sumatra Barb.

**1983.** Tropical Fishes. Multicoloured.
1717 110 r. Type **378** .. .. 50 20
1718 175 r. Brilliant rasbora .. 50 20
1719 275 r. Archer fish .. 1·40 65

**379.** Wilson's Bird of Paradise.

**1983.** Birds of Paradise, Multicoloured.
1721. 110 r. Type **379** .. .. 90 20
1722. 175 r. Black sicklebill .. 1·10 25
1723. 275 r. Black-billed sicklebill .. .. .. 1·60 40
1724. 500 r. As No. 1723 .. 2·50 1·10

**380.** Emblems of Peace and Co-operation.

**1983.** Palestinian Solidarity.
1726. **380.** 275 r. bl., brn. & sil. 35 10

**381.** "Stop" Emblem.

**382.** Agriculture.

**1984.** Anti-poliomyelitis Campaign.
1732. **381.** 110 r. red, pur. & bl. 10 10
1733. – 275 r. purple, orange and red .. .. 35 15
DESIGN: 275 r. Emblem of Save the Children Fund.

**1984.** Fourth Five Year Plan.
1734. **382.** 55 r. yellow and blue 10 10
1735. – 75 r. green & brown 30 15
1736. – 110 r. blue & orange 40 20
1737. – 275 r. multicoloured 25 10
DESIGNS: 75 r. Casa-Nurtiano CN-235 airliner (aircraft industry); 110 r. Shipbuilding; 275 r. Telephone (telecommunications).

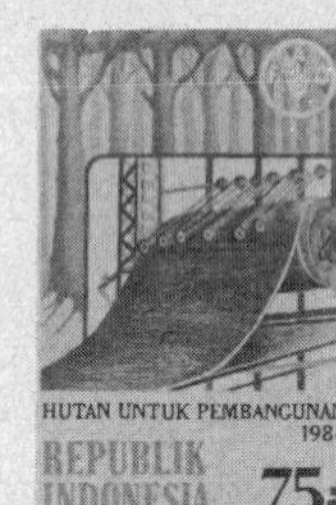

**383.** Manufacturing Plywood.

**1984.** Forestry. Multicoloured.
1738. 75 r. Type **383** .. .. 35 10
1739. 110 r. Seedling .. .. 35 10
1740. 175 r. Measuring tree trunk .. .. .. 35 20
1741. 275 r. Transporting trees 35 30

**384.** Children playing with Toys.

**1984.** Children's Day. Multicoloured.
1743. 75 r.+25 r. Type **384** .. 25 10
1744. 110 r.+25 r. Scout camp 20 15
1745. 175 r.+25 r. Children on farm .. .. .. 45 20
1746. 275 r.+25 r. Scouts and guides in camp .. 45 25

**385.** Flags of Member Nations.

**1984.** Association of South-East Asian Nations Meeting, Djakarta.
1747. **385.** 275 r. multicoloured 65 25

**HAVE YOU READ THE NOTES AT THE BEGINNING OF THIS CATALOGUE?**
These often provide answers to the enquiries we receive.

**386.** Pole Vaulting. **387.** Horse Dance.

**1984.** Olympic Games, Los Angeles. Multicoloured.
1748. 75 r. Type **386** .. .. 20 10
1749. 110 r. Archery .. .. 20 10
1750. 175 r. Boxing .. .. 20 10
1751. 250 r. Shooting .. .. 35 25
1752. 275 r. Weightlifting .. 50 25
1753. 325 r. Swimming .. 1·00 15

**1984.** Art and Culture. Multicoloured.
1754. 75 r. Type **387** .. .. 35 10
1755. 110 r. "Reog" mask .. 35 10
1756. 275 r. Lion dance .. 35 25
1757. 325 r. "Barong" mask .. 65 30

**388.** Thomas Cup (badminton).

**1984.** National Sports Day. Multicoloured.
1758. 110 r. Type **388** .. .. 20 10
1759. 275 r. Keep-fit exercise .. 35 20

**389.** Map and Post Code Zones. **390.** Lauterbach's Bowerbird.

**1984.** Introduction of New Post Code Zones.
1763. **389.** 110 r. blue, brown & orange .. .. 20 10
1764. 275 r. orange, blue & brown .. .. 35 15

**1984.** Birds. Multicoloured.
1765. 75 r. Type **390** .. .. 70 20
1766. 110 r. Flamed bowerbird 85 25
1767. 275 r. Arfak bird of paradise 1·75 95
1768. 325 r. Superb bird of paradise 1·75 60

**391.** Flag and Fists. **392.** Boeing 747-200.

**1984.** Youth Pledge.
1770. **391.** 275 r. black and red 35 10

**1984.** 40th Anniv. of I.C.A.O.
1771. **392.** 275 r. red, blk. & bl. 1·50 50

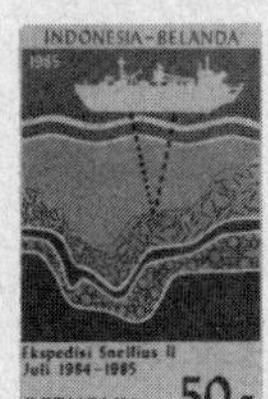

**393.** "Tyro" and Geological Structure of Seabed. **394.** Stylised Birds.

**1985.** Indonesia–Belanda Expedition.
1772. **393.** 50 r. blue and brown 20 10
1773. – 100 r. blue & purple 35 20
1774. – 275 r. blue and green 1·00 55
DESIGNS: 100 r. "Tyro" (oceanographic survey ship) and map. 275 r. "Tyro" and coral reef.

**1985.** International Women's Day.
1775. **394.** 100 r. mauve and red 65 15
1776. – 275 r. red and brown 1·25 1·40
DESIGN: 275 r. Profile silhouettes.

**395.** Jet Airliner and workers. **396.** Pres. Suharto.

**1985.** 4th Five Year Plan.
1777. **395.** 75 r. red and brown 25 15
1778. – 140 r. grey & brown 15 10
1779. – 350 r. green & brown 25 10
DESIGNS: 140 r. Children in classroom. 350 r. Industrial equipment and buildings.

**1985.**
1780 **396** 140 r. brown and red 20 10
1781 350 r. mauve and red 25 10

**397.** Conference Building.

**1985.** 30th Anniv. of First Asian–African Conference, Bandung.
1786. **397.** 350 r. multicoloured 50 15

**398.** Globe and Teenagers waving Palm Leaves. **399.** Profiles.

**1985.** International Youth Year.
1787. **398.** 75 r. yellow, brown and green .. 25 10
1788. – 140 r. blue, green and mauve .. .. 40 10
DESIGN: 140 r. Flower on globe supported by teenagers.

**1985.** United Nations Women's Decade.
1789. **399.** 55 r. brown & green 15 10
1790. – 140 r. black, green and brown .. 20 10
DESIGN: 140 r. Globe and decade emblems.

**400.** Housing and Hydro-electricity. **401.** Sky Diving.

**1985.** 40th Anniv of Indonesian Republic.
1791 **400** 140 r. green and red .. 25 10
1792 – 350 r. blue, mve & yell 45 20
DESIGN: 350 r. Tractor and industrial complex.

**1985.** National Sports Week, Djakarta. Multicoloured.
1793 55 r. Type **401** .. .. 15 10
1794 100 r. Unarmed combat .. 25 10
1795 140 r. High jumping .. 25 15
1796 350 r. Windsurfing (vert) 1·10 65

**402.** O.P.E.C. Emblem and Globe. **403.** Tanker.

**1985.** 25th Anniv. of Organization of Petroleum Exporting Countries.
1797 **402** 40 r. blue, mve & orge 35 10

**1985.** Centenary of Indonesian Oil Industry. Multicoloured.
1798. 140 r. Type **403** .. .. 45 20
1799. 250 r. Refinery .. .. 80 40
1800. 350 r. Derrick and rigs .. 1·00 65

**404.** Doves, "40" and U.N. Emblem.

**1985.** 40th Anniv. of U.N.O. Multicoloured.
1801. 140 r. Type **404** .. 15 10
1802. 300 r. Bombs and green leaves .. .. .. 35 15

**405.** Javan Rhinoceros. **406.** Emblem.

**1985.** Wildlife.
1803 **405** 75 r. brown, grn & bl 20 10
1804 – 150 r. brn, orge & grn 45 25
1805 – 300 r. brown, bl & red 65 30
DESIGNS: 150 r. Anoa; 300 r. Komodo dragon.

**1986.** Economic Census. Each orange and violet.
1806. 175 r. Type **406** .. .. 15 10
1807. 175 r. Symbols of economy .. .. 15 10

**407.** Baby feeding, Powdered Milk, Syringe and Graph. **408.** Industry.

**1986.** 40th Anniv of U.N.I.C.E.F.
1808 **407** 75 r. multicoloured .. 15 10
1809 – 140 r. flesh, brown and pink .. .. 20 10
DESIGN: 140 r. Vaccinating baby.

**1986.** 4th Five Year Plan.
1810 **408** 140 r. multicoloured 10 10
1811 – 500 r. yellow, brn & bl 30 10
DESIGN: 500 r. Agriculture.

**409.** Thomas Cup and Racket. **410.** Pinisi Sailing Ship.

**1986.** Thomas (men's) and Uber (women's) Cup Badminton Championships, Djakarta.
1812. **409.** 55 r. black, yellow and blue .. .. 25 10
1813. – 150 r. red, brown and gold .. .. 40 15
DESIGN: 150 r. Thomas and Uber Cups and shuttlecock.

**1986.** "Expo 86" World's Fair, Vancouver.
1814 **410** 75 r. black, red & yell 15 10
1815 – 150 r. multicoloured 35 15
1816 – 300 r. silver, red & pur 45 20
DESIGNS: 150 r. Kentongan village drum and "Palapa" satellite. 300 r. Indonesian pavilion emblem.

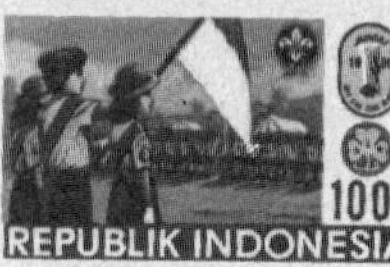

**411.** Guides on Parade.

**1986.** National Jamboree. Multicoloured.
1817. 100 r. Type **411** .. .. 15 10
1818. 140 r. Guides cooking over fire .. .. 45 15
1819. 210 r. Scouts consulting map (vert.) .. .. 65 25

**412.** "86"

**1986.** Indonesia Air Show.
1820. **412.** 350 r. multicoloured 40 15

**413.** Tari Legong Kraton.

**1986.** Traditional Dances. Multicoloured.
1821. 140 r. Type **413** .. .. 45 10
1822. 350 r. Tari Barong .. 65 20
1823. 500 r. Tari Kecak .. 95 35

**414.** Woman planting.

**1986.** 19th International Society of Sugar Cane Technologists Congress, Djakarta. Multicoloured.
1824. 150 r. Type **414** .. .. 25 10
1825. 300 r. Cane and sugar spilled from sack .. 35 10

**415.** Route Map of Cable.

**1986.** Opening of Sea-Me-We Communications Cable.
1826. **415.** 140 r. green, orange and violet .. 25 10
1827. – 350 r. green, yellow and blue .. 40 15
DESIGN: 350 r. Route map of cable (different).

**416.** Doves, Wheat and Globe. **417.** Party Emblems and Buildings.

**1986.** International Peace Year. Each brown, green and black.
1828. 350 r. Type **416** .. .. 35 10
1829. 500 r. Dove with olive twig flying around globe .. .. .. 50 15

**1986.**
1830 **326** 50 r. dp brown & brn 10 10
1831 55 r. red and pink .. 10 10
1833 100 r. ultram & bl .. 10 10
1834 300 r. turq, grn & gold 20 10
1835 400 r. grn, turq & gold 25 10

**1987.** General Election.
1840 417 75 r. blue, yell & brn 15 10
1841 – 140 r. grn, orge & yell 15 10
1842 – 350 r. blue, yell & blk 35 10
DESIGNS: 140 r. Party emblems and arms; 350 r. Party emblems, map, wheat and ballot box.

**418.** Satellite and Globe.

**419.** Boy carving Figures.

**1987.** Launch of "Palapa B2" Satellite.
1843. **418.** 350 r. yellow, green and brown .. 35 15
1844. – 500 r. multicoloured 50 20
DESIGN—VERT: 500 r. Rocket and satellite.

**1987.** 4th Five Year Plan.
1845. **419.** 140 r. brown, yellow and blue .. .. 15 10
1846. – 350 r. violet, green and orange .. 25 10
DESIGN: 350 r. Graph and cattle.

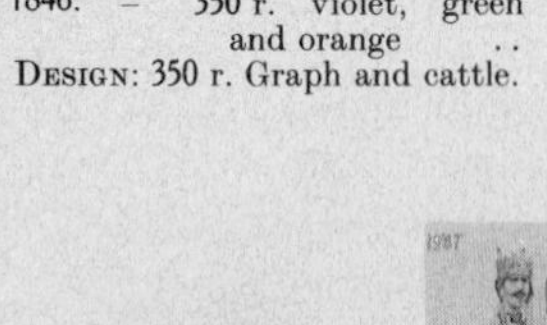

**420.** Crab and Scanner Unit.

**421.** East Kalimantan Couple.

**1987.** 10th Anniv of Indonesian Cancer Foundation.
1847 420 350 r.+25 r. yell & bl 35 15

**1987.** Wedding Costumes (1st series). Mult.
1848. 140 r. Type **421** .. .. 80 15
1849. 350 r. Aceh couple .. 3·75 4·00
1850. 400 r. East Timor couple 4·50 45
See also Nos. 1891/6, 1955/60, 1992/7 and 2010/15.

**422.** Weightlifting.

**423.** Emblems.

**1987.** 14th South-East Asia Games, Djakarta. Designs showing pictograms.
1851. **422.** 140 r. yellow, red and blue .. .. 15 10
1852. – 250 r. blue, yellow and red .. .. 35 20
1853. – 350 r. red, blue and brown .. .. 45 20
DESIGNS: 250 r. Swimming. 350 r. Running.

**1987.** 460th Anniv. of Djakarta and 20th Anniv. of Djakarta Fair.
1854. **423.** 75 r. blue, black and yellow .. .. 35 10
1855. – 100 r. blue, black and yellow .. .. 60 10
DESIGN—VERT. 100 r. Emblems (different).

**424.** Children reading.

**425.** Headquarters, Djakarta.

**1987.** Children's Day and National Family Planning Co-ordination Board.
1856. **424.** 100 r. mauve and orange .. .. 15 10
1857. – 250 r. yellow and blue .. .. 20 10
DESIGN—VERT. 250 r. Globe, baby in cupped hands and dropper.

**1987.** 20th Anniv. of Association of South-East Asian Nations.
1858. **425.** 350 r. multicoloured 40 15

**426.** Emblem.

**427.** Mount Bromo and Sand Craters.

**1987.** 30th Anniv. and 7th National Congress of Association of Specialists in Internal Diseases.
1859. **426.** 300 r. red and blue .. 35 10

**1987.** Tourism. Multicoloured.
1860. 140 r. Type **427** .. .. 15 10
1861. 350 r. Bedugul Lake, Bali 45 45
1862. 500 r. Sea gardens, Bunaken Island .. 65 20

**428.** Woman with Broken Chains, Helmet and Pennant flying from Pen.

**429.** Gourami.

**1987.** "Woman's Physical Revolution".
1863. **428.** 75 r. grn., red & yell. 10 10
1864. – 100 r. grn., yell. & red 15 10
DESIGN: 100 r. Women with rifles and barbed wire.

**1987.** Fishes.
1865 429 150 r. mauve, yell & bl 35 25
1866 – 200 r. mauve, yell & bl 35 20
1867 – 500 r. black, yell & bl 65 20
DESIGNS: 200 r. Carp; 300 r. Walking catfish.

**430.** Soldiers.

**432.** Carved Snake and Frog.

**431.** Welder.

**1988.** 31st Anniv of Veterans Legion.
1868 430 250 r. green and orange 25 10

**1988.** National Safety and Occupational Health Day.
1869. **431.** 350 r. blue and green 40 10

**1988.** 8th Anniv. of National Crafts Council.
1870. **432.** 120 r. blue and brown 15 10
1871. – 350 r. blue and brown 35 20
1872. – 500 r. brown & grn .. 50 20
DESIGN: 350 r. Cane rocking-chair. 500 r. Bamboo goods.

**433.** Industrial Symbols.

**434.** Indonesian Girls.

**1988.** 4th Five Year Plan.
1873 433 140 r. blue and green 15 15
1874 – 400 r. purple and red 50 25
DESIGN: 400 r. Fishing industry.

**1988.** "Expo 88" World's Fair, Brisbane. Multicoloured.
1875. 200 r. Type **434** .. .. 35 10
1876. 300 r. Indonesian girl .. 35 10
1877. 350 r. Indonesian girl and boy .. .. 50 15

**435.** Anniversary Emblem.

**436.** "Dendrobium none betawi".

**1988.** 125th Anniv of Red Cross.
1879 435 350 r. grey, blk & red 35 15

**1988.** Flowers. Multicoloured.
1880. 400 r. Type **436** .. .. 50 15
1881. 500 r. "Dendrobium abang betawi" .. 50 20

**437.** Running.

**438.** Figures around Emblem.

**1988.** Olympic Games, Seoul.
1882 437 75 r. black, brn & gold 15 10
1883 – 100 r. blk, red & gold 25 10
1884 – 200 r. blk, mve & gold 25 15
1885 – 300 r. blk, grn & gold 25 15
1886 – 400 r. black, bl & gold 25 15
1887 – 500 r. black, bl & gold 95 35
Designs: 100 r. Weightlifting. 200 r. Archery. 300 r. Table tennis. 400 r. Swimming. 500 r. Tennis.

**1988.** Centenary of International Women's Council.
1889. **438.** 140 r. black and blue 10 10

**439.** Family, Water and Ear of Wheat.

**440.** President Suharto.

**1988.** National Farmers' and Fishermen's Week.
1890 439 350 r. stone and red .. 15 10

**1988.** Wedding Costumes (2nd series). As T **421**. Multicoloured.
1891 55 r. Sumatera Barat (West) .. .. 10 10
1892 75 r. Jambi .. .. 10 10
1893 100 r. Bengkulu .. .. 20 10
1894 120 r. Lampung .. .. 35 10
1895 200 r. Moluccas .. .. 40 10
1896 250 r. Nusa Tenggara Timur (East) .. .. 85 35

**1988.**
1897 440 200 r. blue, pink & red 15 10
1898 700 r. mauve, light green and green .. 50 10
1899 1000 r. multicoloured 65 15

**441.** Emblem.

**442.** Doves and Envelopes.

**1988.** 13th Non-Aligned News Agencies Co-ordinating Committee Meeting, Djakarta.
1901 441 500 r. blue and red .. 40 10

**1988.** International Correspondence Week.
1902 442 140 r. blue and red .. 15 10

**443** Means of Transport and Communications

**1988.** Asian-Pacific Transport and Communications Decade.
1904 **443** 350 r. blue and black 40 20

**444** Al Mashun Mosque, Medan

**445** "Papilio gigon"

**1988.** Tourism. Multicoloured.
1905 250 r. Type **444** .. .. 15 10
1906 300 r. Pagaruyung Palace, Batusangkar .. .. 25 20
1907 500 r. Keong Emas Theatre, Djakarta .. 70 25

**1988.** Butterflies. Multicoloured.
1909 400 r. Type **445** .. .. 45 20
1910 500 r. "Graphium androcles" .. .. 80 25

**446** "Rafflesia sp."

**447** "40" and Boeing 747

**1989.** Flowers. Multicoloured.
1916 200 r. Type **446** .. .. 50 20
1917 1000 r. "Amorphophallus titanum" .. .. 80 65

**1989.** 40th Anniv of Garuda Airline.
1919 **447** 350 r. blue and green 35 15

**448** Mother and Baby

**449** Industrial Site

**1989.** Endangered Animals. The Orang-Utan. Multicoloured.
1920 75 r. Type **448** .. .. 65 15
1921 100 r. Orang-utan in tree 65 10
1922 140 r. Mother and baby in trees .. .. 65 15
1923 500 r. Orang-utan .. 2·00 1·25

**1989.** 5th Five Year Plan.
1925 **449** 55 r. violet and green 10 10
1926 – 150 r. blue and brown 15 10
1927 – 350 r. green & orange 20 15
DESIGNS: 150 r. Cement works; 350 r. Gas plant.

**450** Stamp and Map

**451** Ki Hadjar Dewantara and Graduate

**1989.** 125th Anniv of First Netherlands Indies Stamp.

1928 **450** 1000 r. green, purple and blue .. .. 65 35

**1989.** National Education Day.

1929 **451** 140 r. red and purple 15 10

1930 – 300 r. violet and green 25 10

DESIGN: 300 r. Dewantara (founder of Taman Siswa School), pencil and books.

**452** Emblem on Map

**453** Flag and Cup

**1989.** 10th Anniv of Asia-Pacific Telecommunity.

1931 **452** 350 r. purple and green 25 10

**1989.** Sudirman Cup.

1932 **453** 100 r. brown and red 15 10

**454** Students

**455** Headquarters

**1989.** Children's Day.

1933 **454** 100 r. brown & orange 15 10

1934 – 250 r. blue and green 20 10

DESIGN: 250 r. Youths exercising.

**1989.** 10th Anniv of Asia-Pacific Integrated Rural Development Centre.

1935 **455** 140 r. brown and blue 15 10

**456** Skull of "Sangiran 17" and Hunters

**457** Globe and People

**1989.** Centenary of Palaeoanthropology in Indonesia.

1936 **456** 100 r. black & brown 10 10

1937 – 150 r. green and red .. 15 10

1938 – 200 r. blue and brown 20 10

1939 – 250 r. violet & brown 35 10

1940 – 300 r. green and red .. 40 15

1941 – 350 r. blue and brown 45 15

DESIGNS—HORIZ: 150 r. Skull of "Perning 1" and cavemen; 200 r. Skull of "Sangiran 10" and hunter. VERT: 250 r. Skull of "Wajak 1"; 300 r. Skull of "Sambungmacan 1", 350 r. Skull of "Ngandong 7".

**1989.** Cent of Interparliamentary Union.

1942 **457** 350 r. green and blue 25 10

**458** Kung Fu

**1989.** 12th National Games, Djakarta. Mult.

1943 75 r. Type **458** .. .. 15 10

1944 100 r. Tennis .. .. 15 10

1945 140 r. Judo .. .. 15 10

1946 350 r. Volleyball .. 35 20

1947 500 r. Boxing .. .. 65 15

1948 1000 r. Archery .. .. 80 35

## MINIMUM PRICE

The minimum price quoted is 10p which represents a handling charge rather than a basis for valuing common stamps. For further notes about prices see introductory pages.

**459** Taman Burung

**460** Trophy

**1989.** Tourism. Multicoloured.

1949 120 r. Type **459** .. .. 15 10

1950 350 r. Prangko Museum .. 35 15

1951 500 r. Istana Anak-Anak (vert) .. .. .. 50 15

**1989.** Film Industry.

1953 **460** 150 r. ochre & brown 15 10

**1989.** Wedding Costumes (3rd series). As T **421**. Multicoloured.

1955 50 r. Sumatera Utara (North) .. .. 15 10

1956 75 r. Sumatera Selatan (South) .. .. 15 10

1957 100 r. Djakarta .. .. 15 10

1958 140 r. Sulawesi Utara (North Celebes) .. 35 10

1959 350 r. Sulawesi Tengah (Central Celebes) .. 45 25

1960 500 r. Sulawesi Selatan (South Celebes) .. 35 15

**461** Worker wearing Safety Belt and Flag

**1990.** Occupational Safety.

1962 **461** 200 r. brown and green 15 10

**462** Benteng Marlborough, Bengkulu

**1990.** Tourism. Multicoloured.

1963 200 r. Type **462** .. .. 15 10

1964 400 r. National Museum, Djakarta .. .. 35 10

1965 500 r. Baiturrahman Mosque, Banda Aceh .. 35 15

**463** "Mammilaria fragilis"

**1990.** Plants. Multicoloured.

1967 75 r. Type **463** .. .. 10 10

1968 1000 r. Bonsai of "Gmelina elliptica" .. 65 30

**464** Tree-felling Equipment

**1990.** 5th Five Year Plan.

1970 **464** 200 r. brown and blue 15 10

1971 – 1000 r. black and blue 90 40

DESIGN: 1000 r. Lighthouse and freighter.

**465** Arrow pointing to Indonesia

**467** Battle and Disabled Man using Soldering-iron

**1990.** Visit Indonesia Year (1991) (1st issue). Multicoloured.

1972 100 r. Type **465** .. .. 15 10

1973 500 r. Temple .. .. 35 15

See also Nos. 1998/2000.

**1990.** 40th Anniv of Disabled Veterans Corp.

1976 **467** 1000 r. orange & green 65 25

**468** Player and Goalkeeper

**469** U.N. Population Award

**1990.** World Cup Football Championship, Italy. Multicoloured.

1977 75 r. Type **468** .. .. 10 10

1978 150 r. Player tackling .. 15 10

1979 400 r. Players competing for high ball .. .. 40 15

**1990.** 20th Anniv of Family Planning Movement.

1981 **469** 60 r. brown and red .. 10 10

**470** Figure with Pencil and Open Book

**471** Children

**1990.** Population Census.

1982 **470** 90 r. green & turquoise 10 10

**1990.** Children's Day.

1983 **471** 500 r. purple and red 50 10

**472** Soldier planting Flag

**473** Buildings and Cultural Identities

**1990.** 45th Anniv of Independence. Mult.

1984 200 r. Type **472** .. .. 15 10

1985 500 r. Modern building and roads .. .. 45 15

**1990.** Indonesia–Pakistan Economic and Cultural Co-operation Organization. Mult.

1987 75 r. Type **473** .. .. 10 10

1988 400 r. Dancer (vert) .. 20 10

**474** Emblem

**475** Anniversary Emblem

**1990.** 20th Anniv of Asian-Pacific Postal Training Centre.

1989 **474** 500 r. blue & ultram .. 35 10

**1990.** 30th Anniv of Organization of Petroleum Exporting Countries.

1990 **475** 200 r. blk, grey & orge 15 10

**476** Houses

**477** Dancer and House

**1990.** Environmental Health.

1991 **476** 1000 r. multicoloured 65 15

**1990.** Wedding Costumes (4th series). As T **421**. Multicoloured.

1992 75 r. Java Barat (West) 15 10

1993 100 r. Java Tengah (Central) .. .. 15 10

1994 150 r. Yogyakarta .. 15 10

1995 200 r. Java Timur (East) 20 10

1996 400 r. Bali .. .. 30 15

1997 500 r. Nusa Tenggara Barat (West) .. .. 35 15

**1991.** Visit Indonesia Year (2nd issue). Dancers and Traditional Houses. Mult.

1998 200 r. Type **477** .. .. 20 10

1999 500 r. House and dancer with saucers .. .. 50 10

2000 1000 r. Dancer and house (different) .. .. 65 35

**478** Emblem

**479** Palace of Sultan Ternate, Moluccas

**1991.** 16th National Koran Reading Competition, Yogyakarta.

2002 **478** 200 r. green and yellow 15 10

**1991.** Tourism. Multicoloured.

2003 500 r. Type **479** .. .. 35 10

2004 1000 r. Bari House, Palembang .. .. 65 25

**480** Steel Mill

**481** Damaged Lungs and Cigarette Smoke forming Skull

**1991.** 5th Five Year Plan.

2006 **480** 75 r. red and blue .. 10 10

2007 – 200 r. blue and black 15 10

DESIGN—HORIZ. 200 r. Computer technology.

**1991.** Anti-smoking Campaign.

2008 **481** 90 r. red and black .. 10 10

**482** Hands

**483** Tents

**1991.** 24th Anniv of National Federation for the Welfare of the Mentally Handicapped.

2009 **482** 200 r. + 25 r. blk & red 15 10

**1991.** Wedding Costumes (5th series). As T **421**. Multicoloured.

2010 100 r. Kalimantan Barat (West) .. .. 15 10

2011 200 r. Kalimantan Tengah (Central) .. .. 20 10

2012 300 r. Kalimantan Selatan (South) .. .. 25 10

2013 400 r. Sulawesi Tenggara (South-east Celebes) .. 30 15

2014 500 r. Riau .. .. 35 15

2015 1000 r. Irian Jaya .. 65 25

**1991.** National Boy Scout Jamboree, Cibubur.

2016 **483** 200 r. blue, black & red 15 10

**484** Monument

**485** Temples and Family

**1991** 42nd Anniv of Return of Republican Government to Djokjakarta.
2017 **484** 200 r. green and brown 15 10

**1991.** Farmers' Week.
2018 **485** 500 r. yellow and blue 50 10

**486** Cells **487** Weightlifters

**1991.** "chemindo '91" Chemistry Congress, Surabaya.
2019 **486** 400 r. red and green .. 25 10

**1991.** 5th Junior Men's and Fourth Women's Asian Weightlifting Championships, Manado.
2020 **487** 300 r. red and black .. 20 10

**488** Parachutists **489** Red Cross and Hands

**1991.** World Parachuting Championships.
2021 **488** 500 r. mauve and blue 30 10

**1991.** 46th Anniv of Indonesian Red Cross.
2022 **489** 200 r. red and green .. 15 10

**490** Radio Mast **491** Script and Mosque

**1991.** 8th International Amateur Radio Union Region III Conference, Bandung.
2023 **490** 300 r. blue and yellow 20 10

**1991.** Istiqlal Festival, Djakarta.
2024 **491** 200 r. black and red .. 15 10

**492** Dancer and Inspectors

**1991.** International Convention on Quality Control Circles, Bali.
2025 **492** 500 r. multicoloured .. 30 10

**493** Orang-utan **494** Model of Jakarta Post Office

**1991.** International Conference on Great Apes of the World. The Orang-utan. Mult.
2026 200 r. Type **493** .. .. 15 10
2027 500 r. Orang-utan on forest path .. .. 30 15
2028 1000 r. Orang-utan sitting on ground .. .. 65 20

**1992.** Automation of Postal Service. Mult.
2030 200 r. Type **494** .. .. 15 10
2031 500 r. Sorting machine .. 30 10

**495** "Phalaenopsis ambilis"

**1992.** Flowers. Multicoloured.
2032 200 r. Type **495** .. .. 15 10
2033 500 r. "Rafflesia arnoldii" 30 10
2034 1000 r. "Jasminum sambac" .. .. 65 25

**496** Buildings, Ballot Boxes and State Arms

**1992.** Parliamentary Elections. Mult.
2036 75 r. Type **496** .. .. 10 10
2037 100 r. Ballot boxes and globe .. .. .. 10 10
2038 500 r. Ballot boxes and hands holding voting slips .. .. .. 30 10

**497** Lembah Baliem, Irian Jaya

**1992.** Visit ASEAN Year. Multicoloured.
2039 300 r. Type **497** .. .. 20 10
2040 500 r. Tanah Lot, Bali .. 30 10
2041 1000 r. Lembah Anai, Sumatra Barat .. 65 20

**498** Road-building **499** Emblem and Crab

**1992.** 5th Five Year Plan.
2043 **498** 150 r. purple & green 10 10
2044 – 300 r. blue and mauve 20 10
DESIGN: 300 r. Aircraft.

**1992.** 15th Anniv of Indonesian Cancer Foundation.
2045 **499** 200 r. + 25 r. red & brn 15 15
2046 500 r. + 50 r. red & bl 35 35

**500** Weightlifting **501** White-crested Laughing Thrush

**1992.** Olympic Games, Barcelona. Mult.
2047 75 r. Type **500** .. .. 10 10
2048 200 r. Badminton .. 15 10
2049 300 r. Sports pictograms 20 10
2050 500 r. Tennis .. .. 30 15
2051 1000 r. Archery .. .. 65 30

**1992.** Birds. Multicoloured.
2053 100 r. Type **501** .. .. 10 10
2054 200 r. Golden-backed three-toed woodpecker 15 10
2055 400 r. Rhinoceros hornbill 25 10
2056 500 r. Amboina king parrot .. .. .. 30 15

**502** Busy Street (Tammy Filia)

**1992.** National Children's Day. Children's paintings. Multicoloured.
2058 75 r. Type **502** .. .. 10 10
2059 100 r. Children with balloons (Cynthia Widiyana Halim) .. 10 10
2060 200 r. Native boats (Dandy Rahmad Adi Kurniawan) .. .. 15 10
2061 500 r. Girl and bird (Intan Sari Dewi Saputro) .. 30 15

**503** Anniversary Emblem **504** Earth and "Palapa B-4" (satellite)

**1992.** 25th Anniv of Association of South-East Asian Nations. Multicoloured.
2062 200 r. Type **503** .. .. 15 10
2063 500 r. Map and flags of member nations .. 30 10
2064 1000 r. "25" and flags .. 65 20

**1992.** Communications. Multicoloured.
2065 200 r. Type **504** .. .. 15 10
2066 500 r. "Palapa" satellite (16th anniv of launch) 30 10
2067 1000 r. Old and modern telephones (modernization of telephone system) .. .. 65 20

**505** Emblem **506** Ngremo Dance, East Java

**1992.** 10th Non-Aligned Countries Summit, Djakarta. Multicoloured.
2068 200 r. Type **505** .. .. 15 10
2069 500 r. Members' flags and emblem .. .. 30 15

**1992.** Traditional Dances (1st series). Mult.
2070 200 r. Type **506** .. .. 15 10
2071 500 r. Gending Sriwijaya dance, South Sumatra 30 15
See also Nos. 2122/4, 2168/72 and 2211/14.

**507** Anniversary Emblem **508** Antara Building, Djakarta

**1992.** 40th Anniv of International Planned Parenthood Federation.
2073 **507** 200 r. blue and green 15 10

**1992.** 55th Anniv of Antara News Agency.
2074 **508** 500 r. black and blue 30 15

**509** Planting Saplings

**1992.** National Afforestation.
2075 **509** 500 r. multicoloured .. 30 15

**1993.** No. 1831 surch **50r.**
2076 **326** 50 r. on 55 r. red and pink .. .. 10 10

**511** State Arms and Assembly Building

**1993.** 10th People's Consultative Assembly. Multicoloured.
2077 300 r. Type **511** .. .. 20 10
2078 700 r. Assembly hall .. 45 20

**512** Soldiers and Buildings

**1993.** 5th Five Year Plan. Multicoloured.
2079 300 r. Type **512** .. .. 20 10
2080 700 r. Workers and arrow 45 20
2081 1000 r. Runners .. .. 65 30

**513** Swarm of "Ornithoptera goliath"

**1993.**
2082 **513** 1000 r. multicoloured 65 30

**514** Peristiwa Hotel, Yamato, and Adipura Kencana Medal

**1993.** 700th Anniv of Surabaya (300, 700 r.) and "indo tourism 93" (1000 r.). Multicoloured.
2083 300 r. Type **514** .. .. 20 10
2084 700 r. Modern city and World Habitat Award, 1992 .. .. .. 45 20
2085 1000 r. Candi Bajang Ratu (temple) .. .. 65 30

**1993.** "indopex'93" Asian Stamp Exhibition, Surabaya. Nos. 2082/5 optd **indopex'93 surabaya**.
2086 **514** 300 r. multicoloured 20 10
2087 – 700 r. multicoloured 45 20
2088 **513** 1000 r. mult (No. 2082) 65 30
2089 – 1000 r. mult (No. 2085) 65 30

**517** "Jasminum sambac" **518** Scouts making Road

**1993.** Environmental Protection. Mult.
2091 300 r. Type **517** .. .. 20 10
2092 300 r. Moth orchid ("Phalaenopsis amabilis") .. .. 20 10
2093 300 r. "Rafflesia arnoldi" (flower) .. .. 20 10
2094 700 r. Komodo dragon .. 50 20
2095 700 r. Malayan bony-tongue .. .. 50 20
2096 700 r. Java hawk eagle .. 50 20
Stamps of the same value were issued together, se-tenant, in strips of three stamps, each strip forming a composite design.

**1993.** 1st World Community Development Camp, Lebakharjo. Multicoloured.
2098 300 r. Type **518** .. .. 15 10
2099 700 r. Pres. Suharto greeting girl scout .. 45 20

519 President Suharto

520 "Papilio blumei"

**1993.**

2100 519 150 r. multicoloured 10 10
2101 300 r. multicoloured 15 10
2102 700 r. multicoloured 45 20

On No. 2102 part of the background is a draped flag.

**1993.** International Butterfly Conference, Ujungpandang.

2103 520 700 r. multicoloured .. 45 20

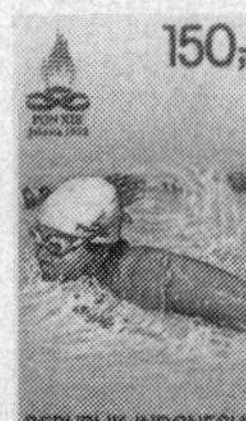

521 Swimming

522 Sigura-Gura Waterfall, North Sumatra

**1993.** "Pon XIII" Sports Week, Djakarta. Multicoloured.

2105 150 r. Type 521 .. .. 10 10
2106 300 r. Cycling .. .. 20 10
2107 700 r. Mascot .. .. 45 20
2108 1000 r. High jumping .. 60 30

**1993.** World Tourism Organization Meeting, Bali. Multicoloured.

2111 300 r. Type 522 .. .. 20 10
2112 700 r. Goa Petruk (cave), Central Java .. .. 45 20
2113 1000 r. Danau Segara Anak (cove), West Nusa Tenggara (horiz) 60 30

523 General Soedirman

524 "Michelia champaca"

**1993.** Armed Forces. Each brown, black and red.

2115 300 r. Type 523 .. .. 20 10
2116 300 r. Lt.-Gen. Oerip Soemohardjo .. .. 20 10

Nos. 2115/16 were issued together, se-tenant, forming a composite design.

**1993.** Flora and Fauna. Multicoloured.

2117 300 r. Type 524 .. .. 20 10
2118 300 r. "Cananga adorata" 20 10
2119 300 r. Orange-tailed shama ("Copsychus pyrrhopygus") .. 20 10
2120 300 r. Hill myna ("Gracula religiosa") .. 20 10

525 Plantation

526 South Sumatran Dancer

**1993.** Resettlement Programme.

2121 525 700 r. multicoloured .. 40 20

**1993.** Traditional Dances (2nd series). Mult.

2122 300 r. Type 526 .. .. 20 10
2123 700 r. West Kalimantan 40 20
2124 1000 r. Irian Jaya .. 60 30

527 Emblems

528 Working Women

**1994.** International Year of the Family.

2126 527 300 r. multicoloured .. 20 10

**1994.** 6th Five Year Plan. Multicoloured.

2127 100 r. Type 528 .. .. 10 10
2128 700 r. Graduate and school pupils .. .. 40 20
2129 2000 r. Doctor, nurse and children .. .. 1·10 55

529 Netherlands Indies, Japanese Occupation and Indonesia Stamps

**1994.** 130th Anniv of 1st Netherlands Indies Stamps.

2130 529 700 r. multicoloured .. 40 20

530 Celebes Sailfish

**1994.** Fishes. Multicoloured.

2131 300 r. Type 530 .. .. 15 10
2132 700 r. Rainbow fish .. 40 20

531 Emblem

532 Figure, Globe, and Anniversary Emblem

**1994.** National Kidney Foundation.

2134 531 300 r.+30 r. mult .. 20 10

**1994.** 75th Anniv of International Red Cross Red Crescent Organization.

2135 532 300 r. black, red & blue 20 10

533 Map and Emblem

534 Player

**1994.** Asia–Pacific Ministerial Conference on Women, Djakarta.

2136 533 700 r. multicoloured .. 40 20

**1994.** World Cup Football Championship, U.S.A.

2137 534 150 r. multicoloured 10 10
2138 – 300 r. multicoloured 20 10
2139 – 700 r. blue, red & blk 40 20
2140 – 1000 r. multicoloured 60 30

DESIGNS—VERT: 300 r. Striker (mascot). HORIZ: 700 r. Emblem; 1000 r. Ball in net.

535 Player and Uber Cup (Women's)

536 Hand holding Scales

**1994.** Indonesian Victories in World Team Badminton Championships. Multicoloured.

2142 300 r. Type 535 .. .. 20 10
2143 300 r. Thomas Cup (Men's) 20 10

Nos. 2142/3 were issued together, se-tenant, forming a composite design.

**1994.** National Commission on Human Rights.

2145 536 700 r. multicoloured .. 40 20

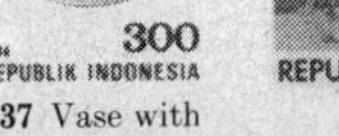

537 Vase with Bead Cover

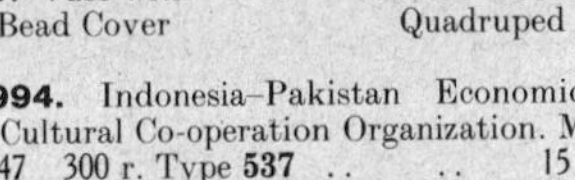

538 Skeleton of Quadruped

**1994.** Indonesia–Pakistan Economic and Cultural Co-operation Organization. Mult.

2147 300 r. Type 537 .. .. 15 10
2148 700 r. Blue and white vase 40 20

**1994.** Centenary of Bogoriense Zoological Museum. Multicoloured.

2149 700 r. Type 538 .. .. 40 20
2150 1000 r. Outline and skeleton of whale (80 × 22 mm) .. .. 55 25

539 Mascots

**1994.** 12th Asian Games, Hiroshima, Japan. Multicoloured.

2152 300 r. Type 539 .. .. 15 10
2153 700 r. Hurdling .. .. 40 20

540 Communications and Map

541 "Morus macroura"

**1994.** 25th Anniv of Bakosurtanal.

2154 540 700 r. multicoloured .. 40 20

**1994.** Flora and Fauna. Multicoloured.

2155 150 r. Type 541 .. .. 10 10
2156 150 r. "Oncosperma tiqillaria" .. .. 10 10
2157 150 r. "Eucalyptus urophylla" .. .. 10 10
2158 150 r. Moth orchid ("Phalaenopsis amabilis") .. .. 10 10
2159 150 r. "Pometia pinnata" 10 10
2160 150 r. Great argus pheasant ("Argusianus argus") .. .. 10 10
2161 150 r. Blue-crowned hanging parrot ("Loriculus pusillus") 10 10
2162 150 r. Timor helmeted friarbird ("Philemon buceroides") .. .. 10 10
2163 150 r. Amboina king parrot ("Alisterus amboinensis") .. 10 10
2164 150 r. Twelve-wired bird of paradise ("Seleucidis melanoleuca") .. 10 10

542 Venue

**1994.** Asia–Pacific Economic Co-operation Summit, Bogor.

2166 542 700 r. multicoloured .. 40 20

543 Airplane

**1994.** 50th Anniv of I.C.A.O.

2167 543 700 r. multicoloured .. 40 20

**1994.** Traditional Dances (3rd series). As T 506. Multicoloured.

2168 150 r. Mengaup, Jambi .. 10 10
2169 300 r. Topeng, West Java 15 10
2170 700 r. Anging Mamiri, South Sulawesi .. 40 20
2171 1000 r. Pisok, North Sulawesi .. .. 55 25
2172 2000 r. Bidu, East Nusa Tenggara .. .. 1·10 55

544 Yogyakarta Palace

**1995.** 20th Anniv of World Tourism Organization. Multicoloured.

2174 300 r. Type 544 .. .. 15 10
2175 700 r. Floating market, Banjarmasin .. .. 40 20
2176 1000 r. Pasola (equestrian tradition), Sumba .. 55 25

545 Children, President Suharto and First Lady

**1995.** "Dedication to the Nation".

2177 545 700 r. multicoloured .. 40 20

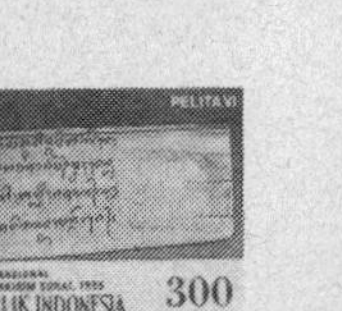

546 Letter from King of Klungkung, Bali

547 "Schizostachyum brachycladum"

**1995.** 6th Five Year Plan. National Letter Writing Campaign. Multicoloured.

2178 300 r. Type 546 .. .. 15 10
2179 700 r. Carrier pigeon (campaign mascot) and letters .. .. .. 40 20

**1995.** 4th International Bamboo Congress, Ubud, Bali. Multicoloured.

2180 300 r. Type 547 .. .. 15 10
2181 700 r. "Dendrocalamus asper" .. .. 40 20

548 N250 and National Flag

**1995.** Inaugural Flight of I.P.T.N. N250 Airliner.

2182 548 700 r. multicoloured .. 40 20

549 Anniversary Emblem

**1995.** 50th Anniv of Indonesian Republic. Multicoloured.
2183 300 r. Type **549** .. .. 15 10
2184 700 r. Boy with national flag .. .. .. 40 20

550 Kota Intan Drawbridge

**1995.** "Jakarta'95" Asian Stamp Exn. Mult.
2186 300 r. Type **550** .. .. 15 10
2187 700 r. Fatahillah Jakarta History Museum .. 40 20

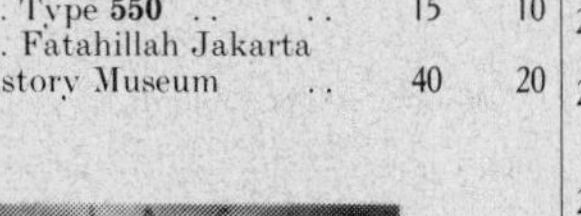
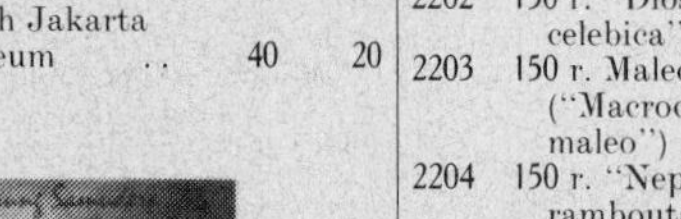
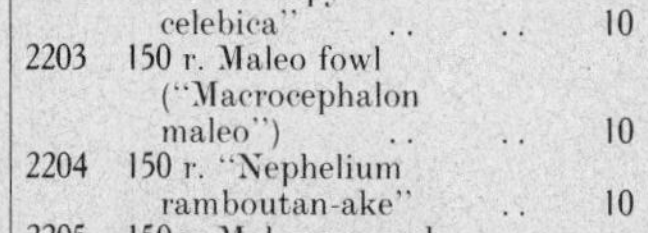

551 Barquentine and Flag

**1995.** "Sail Indonesia '95" Tall Ship Race and Fleet Review.
2188 **551** 700 r. multicoloured .. 40 20

552 "Mother Love" (Patricia Saerang)

553 Mushaf Istiqlal (illuminated Islamic text)

**1995.** 10th Asia and Pacific Regional Conference of Rehabilitation International, Indonesia.
2190 **552** 700 r.+100 r. mult .. 45 45

**1995.** Istiqlal Festival.
2191 **553** 700 r. multicoloured .. 40 20

554 PTT Monument

**1995.** 50th Anniv of Take-over of PTT Headquarters by Republicans.
2192 **554** 700 r. multicoloured .. 40 20

555 Rice

556 Flags and Emblem

**1995.** 50th Anniv of F.A.O.
2193 **555** 700 r. multicoloured .. 40 20

**1995.** 50th Anniv of U.N.O. Multicoloured.
2194 300 r. Type **556** .. .. 15 10
2195 700 r. Emblem, Earth and rainbow .. .. 40 20

557 "Cyrtostachys renda"

**1995.** Flora and Fauna. Multicoloured.
2196 150 r. Type **557** .. .. 10 10
2197 150 r. Tiger ("Panthera tigris") .. .. 10 10
2198 150 r. "Bouea macrophylla" .. .. 10 10
2199 150 r. Javan rhinoceros ("Rhinoceros sondaicus") .. .. 10 10
2200 150 r. "Santalum album" 10 10
2201 150 r. Komodo dragon ("Varanus komodoensis") .. 10 10
2202 150 r. "Diospyros celebica" .. .. 10 10
2203 150 r. Maleo fowl ("Macrocephalon maleo") .. .. 10 10
2204 150 r. "Nephelium ramboutan-ake" .. 10 10
2205 150 r. Malay peacock-pheasant ("Polyplectron schleiermacheri") 10 10

558 Yogyakarta Palace

**1995.** Award of Aga Khan Prize for Architecture to Indonesia. Multicoloured.
2207 300 r. Type **558** .. .. 15 10
2208 700 r. Surakarta Palace .. 40 20

559 Hill and Postal Carriers

560 Economic Sectors

**1995.** Birth Bicentenary of Sir Rowland Hill (instigator of postal stamps). Mult.
2209 300 r. Type **559** .. .. 15 10
2210 700 r. Hill and Indonesian Postal Service emblem 40 20

**1995.** Traditional Dances (4th series). As T **506**. Multicoloured.
2211 150 r. Nguri dance, West Nusa Tenggara .. 10 10
2212 300 r. Muli Betanggai dance, Lampung .. 15 10
2213 700 r. Mutiara dance, Moluccas .. .. 40 20
2214 1000 r. Gantar dance, East Kalimantan .. .. 55 25

**1996.** Economic Census.
2216 **560** 300 r. orange and blue 15 10
2217 – 700 r. turquoise & orge 40 20
DESIGN—HORIZ: 700 r. Graph of economic activity.

561 Satellite orbiting Earth

**1996.** Launch of "Palapa-C" Satellite. Multicoloured.
2218 300 r. Type **561** .. .. 15 10
2219 700 r. Satellite orbiting Earth (triangular) .. 40 20

562 Mixed Flowers

563 Soemanang Soeriowinoto (Association head, 1946–47 and 1949–50)

**1996.** Greetings Stamps. "Happy Holiday". Inscr "Selamat Hari Raya". Mult.
2220 150 r. Type **562** .. .. 10 10
2221 300 r. Mixed flowers (different) .. .. 15 10
2222 700 r. Mixed flowers (different) .. .. 40 20

**1996.** 50th Anniv of Indonesian Journalists' Association. Mult.
2223 300 r. Type **563** .. .. 15 10
2224 700 r. Djamaluddin Adinegoro (head of Indonesian Press Bureau Foundation and founder of Academy of Publicity and Publicity Faculty, Padjadjaran University) .. .. 40 20

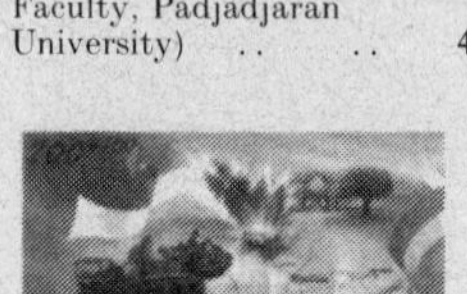

564 Tank firing and Map

**1996.** 47th Anniv of Return of Republican Government to Djokjakarta. Multicoloured.
2225 700 r.+100 r. Type **564** .. 45 45
2226 700 r.+100 r. Attack on Palace .. .. 45 45
Nos. 2225/6 were issued together, se-tenant, forming a composite design.

565 State House, Bandung

**1996.** "indonesia 96" International Youth Stamp Exhibition, Bandung. Multicoloured.
2227 300 r. Type **565** .. .. 15 10
2228 700 r. Painted parasols .. 40 20

566 Indonesian Bear Cuscus

567 Roses

**1996.** Cuscuses. Multicoloured.
2230 300 r. Australian spotted cuscus .. .. 15 10
2231 300 r. Type **566** .. .. 15 10
Nos. 2230/1 were issued together, se-tenant, forming a composite design.

**1996.** Greetings Stamps. "Congratulations and Best Wishes". Inscr "Selamat dan Sukses". Multicoloured.
2233 150 r. Type **567** .. .. 10 10
2234 300 r. Orchids .. .. 15 20
2235 700 r. Chrysanthemums .. 40 20

568 Students (Y. Edwin Purwanto)

**1996.** Compulsory Nine Year Education Programme. Winning Entries in Children's Stamp Design Competition. Multicoloured.
2236 150 r. Type **568** .. .. 10 10
2237 300 r. Children in playground (Andi Pradhana) .. .. 15 10
2238 700 r. Teacher and pupils (Intan Sari Dewi) .. 40 20

569 Archery

**1996.** Olympic Games, Atlanta. Mult.
2239 300 r. Type **569** .. .. 15 10
2240 700 r. Weightlifting .. 40 20
2241 1000 r. Badminton .. 55 25

571 Pres. Suharto and Procession

**1996.** National Youth Kirab. Multicoloured.
2244 300 r. Type **571** .. .. 15 10
2245 700 r. Pres. Suharto presenting national flag 40 20

572 Nusantara N-2130 Prototype over Soekarno-Hatta Airport

573 Scouts climbing over Rope Ladders

**1996.** Aviation and Maritime Year. Mult.
2246 300 r. Type **572** .. .. 15 10
2247 700 r. "Palindo Jaya" (inter-island ferry) .. 40 20

**1996.** National Scout Jamboree, Djakarta. Multicoloured.
2248 150 r. Type **573** .. .. 10 10
2249 150 r. Scouts on ladder and death slide .. 10 10
2250 150 r. Scouts at base of rope ladders .. .. 10 10
2251 150 r. Girl scouts constructing wooden apparatus .. .. 10 10
2252 150 r. Scouts on unicycle and climbing frame .. 10 10
2253 150 r. Girl scouts building frame on campsite .. 10 10
2254 150 r. Soldering metal .. 10 10
2255 150 r. Girl at radio taking notes .. .. .. 10 10
Nos. 2248/55 were issued together, se-tenant, Nos. 2248/51 and 2252/5 forming composite designs.

574 Prows and Wave

**1996.** 50th Anniv of Bank BNI. Multicoloured.
2256 300 r. Type **574** .. .. 15 10
2257 700 r. Pinisi sailing ship .. 40 20

575 Mother and Child reading (Salt Iodization Programme)

**1996.** 50th Anniv of U.N.I.C.E.F. Each brown, green and mauve.
2258 300 r. Type **575** .. .. 15 10
2259 700 r. Giving oral vaccine to children (elimination of polio) .. .. 40 20
2260 1000 r. Children (Children's Rights Convention) .. .. 55 25

## INDEX

Countries can be quickly located by referring to the index at the end of this volume.

EXPRESS LETTER STAMPS

E 189. " Garuda " Bird.

**1967.** Inscr. " 1967 ".

| | | | | |
|---|---|---|---|---|
| E 1166. | E 189. | 10 r. pur. & blue | 40 | 20 |
| E 1167. | | 15 r. pur. & orge. | 55 | 20 |

**1968.** As Nos. E1166/7 but dated "1968".

| | | | | |
|---|---|---|---|---|
| E1202 | E 189 | 10 r. purple & blue | 45 | 10 |
| E1203 | | 15 r. purple & orge | 55 | 10 |
| E1204 | | 20 r. purple & yell | 55 | 15 |
| E1205 | | 30 r. purple & grn | 75 | 25 |
| E1206 | | 40 r. pur & lt pur | 55 | 15 |

**1969.** As Nos. E1166/7 but dated "1969".

| | | | | |
|---|---|---|---|---|
| E1250 | E 189 | 20 r. purple & yell | 40 | 10 |
| E1251 | | 30 r. purple & grn | 40 | 10 |
| E1252 | | 40 r. pur & lt pur | 50 | 15 |

POSTAGE DUE STAMPS

**1950.** Postage Due stamps of Netherlands Indies surch. **BAJAR PORTO** and new value.

| | | | |
|---|---|---|---|
| D 576. | 2½ s. on 50 c. (No. D 499) | 65 | 50 |
| D 577. | 5 s. on 100c. (No. D 501) | 1·90 | 80 |
| D 578. | 10 s. on 75 c. (No. D 500) | 3·75 | 1·10 |

D 100. D 268. D 333a.

**1951.**

| | | | | |
|---|---|---|---|---|
| D 645. | D100. | 2½ s. orange .. | 10 | 50 |
| D 646. | | 5 s. orange .. | 10 | 10 |
| D 647. | | 10 s. orange | 10 | 10 |
| D 648. | | 15 s. red .. | 10 | 10 |
| D 773. | | 15 s. orange | 10 | 10 |
| D 649. | | 20 s. blue .. | 10 | 10 |
| D 774. | | 20 s. orange | 10 | 10 |
| D 650. | | 25 s. olive .. | 25 | 10 |
| D 775. | | 25 s. orange | 10 | 10 |
| D 651. | | 30 s. brown | 25 | 10 |
| D 776. | | 30 s. orange | 10 | 10 |
| D 652. | | 40 s. green .. | 25 | 20 |
| D 777. | | 50 s. orange | 55 | 15 |
| D 778. | | 50 s. green .. | 10 | 10 |
| D 779. | | 100 s. orange | 25 | 10 |
| D 780. | | 100 s. brown | 10 | 10 |
| D 781. | | 250 s. blue .. | 10 | 10 |
| D 782. | | 500 s. yellow | 10 | 10 |
| D 783. | | 750 s. lilac | 10 | 10 |
| D 784. | | 1000 s. salmon | 10 | 10 |
| D 654. | | 1 r. green .. | 1·40 | 1·25 |

P U S . B E A Rp. 25,-

D 176

**1965.** Provisional issue for use on parcels.

| | | | |
|---|---|---|---|
| D1057 | D 176 | 25 r. black on yell | 20 |

**1966.**

| | | | | |
|---|---|---|---|---|
| D 1058. | D100. | 50 r. red .. | 10 | 10 |
| D 1059. | | 100 r. lake | 10 | 10 |

**1966.** As Type D.100, but with coloured network background incorporating " 1966 ".

| | | | |
|---|---|---|---|
| D 1098. | 5 s. green and yellow.. | 15 | 20 |
| D 1099. | 10 s. red and blue .. | 15 | 20 |
| D 1100. | 20 s. blue and pink .. | 15 | 20 |
| D 1101. | 30 s. sepia and red .. | 15 | 20 |
| D 1102. | 40 s. violet and bistre | 15 | 20 |
| D 1103. | 50 s. olive and mauve | 15 | 10 |
| D 1104. | 100 s. lake and green | 15 | 10 |
| D 1105. | 200 s. green and pink | 15 | 10 |
| D 1106. | 500 s. yellow and blue | 15 | 10 |
| D 1107. | 1000 s. red and yellow | 15 | 15 |

**1967.** As Nos. 1098/1107 but dated " 1967 ".

| | | | |
|---|---|---|---|
| D 1168. | 50 s. green and lilac .. | 20 | 15 |
| D 1169. | 100 s. red and green .. | 20 | 15 |
| D 1170. | 200 s. green and pink | 20 | 15 |
| D 1171. | 500 s. brown and blue | 45 | 30 |
| D 1172. | 1000 s. mauve & yell. | 45 | 30 |
| D 1173. | 15 r. orange & grey .. | 80 | 40 |
| D 1174. | 25 r. violet and grey .. | 1·40 | 75 |

**1973.** As Type **D 100** but inscr "BAYAR PORTO" and dated "1973".

| | | | |
|---|---|---|---|
| D1320a | 25 r. violet and grey .. | 35 | 10 |

**1974.** As Type **D 100** but inscr "BAYAR PORTO" and dated "1974".

| | | | |
|---|---|---|---|
| D1346 | 65 r. green and yellow | 95 | 35 |
| D1347 | 125 r. purple and pink | 2·75 | 95 |

**1975.** As Type **D 100** but inscr "BAYAR PORTO" and dated "1975".

| | | | |
|---|---|---|---|
| D1401 | 25 r. violet and drab .. | 65 | 20 |

**1976.**

| | | | | |
|---|---|---|---|---|
| D1426 | D 268 | 25 r. vio & drab | 50 | 25 |
| D1427 | | 65 r. grn & stone | 50 | 25 |

**1978.** Various stamps surch. **BAYAR PORTO** and value.

| | | | |
|---|---|---|---|
| D 1503. | 25 r. on 1 r. sepia and red (No. 1141) .. | 25 | 25 |
| D 1504. | 50 r. on 2 r. blue and ochre (No. 1144) .. | 25 | 25 |
| D 1505. | 100 r. on 4 r. blue and orange (No. 1147) .. | 50 | 50 |
| D 1506. | 200r. on 5 r. red and blue (No. 1148) .. | 1·00 | 1·00 |
| D 1507. | 300 r. on 10 r. violet and red (No. 1151) .. | 1·40 | 1·40 |
| D 1508. | 400 r. on 15 r. violet and olive (No. 1153) | 1·60 | 1·60 |

**1978.** Nos. 1145 and 1152 surch. **BAYAR PORTO** and value.

| | | | |
|---|---|---|---|
| D 1523. | 40 r. on 2 r. 50 green and red .. .. | 65 | 65 |
| D 1524. | 40 r. on 12 r. green and violet .. .. | 65 | 65 |
| D 1525. | 65 r. on 2 r. 50 green and red .. .. | 1·25 | 1·25 |
| D 1526. | 65 r. on 12 r. green and violet .. .. | 2·25 | 2·25 |
| D 1527. | 125 r. on 2 r. 50 green and red .. .. | 65 | 65 |
| D 1528. | 125 r. on 12 r. green and violet .. .. | 65 | 65 |
| D 1529. | 150 r. on 2 r. 50 green and red .. .. | 1·25 | 1·25 |
| D 1530. | 150 r. on 12 r. green and violet .. .. | 2·25 | 2·25 |

**1980.** Dated "1980".

| | | | | |
|---|---|---|---|---|
| D1599 | D 268 | 25 r. mauve and drab .. | 10 | 10 |
| D1600 | D 333a | 50 r. grn & lilac | 20 | 10 |
| D1601 | | 75 r. pur & pink | 25 | 15 |
| D1062 | D 268 | 125 r. mauve and pink .. | 55 | 30 |

**1981.** Dated "1981".

| | | | | |
|---|---|---|---|---|
| D1641 | D 333a | 25 r. pur & stone | 10 | 10 |
| D1642 | | 50 r. grn & lilac | 10 | 10 |
| D1643 | | 75 r. pur & pink | 15 | 10 |
| D1644 | | 125 r. pur & grn | 30 | 15 |

**1992.** Dated "1982".

| | | | | |
|---|---|---|---|---|
| D1645 | D 333a | 125 r. pur & pink | 20 | 10 |

**1983.** Dated "1983".

| | | | | |
|---|---|---|---|---|
| D1728 | D 333a | 200 r. lilac & bl | 15 | 10 |
| D1729 | | 300 r. grn & yell | 25 | 15 |
| D1730 | | 400 r. grn & buff | 30 | 30 |
| D1731 | | 500 r. brown and pink .. | 40 | 25 |

**1984.** Dated "1984".

| | | | | |
|---|---|---|---|---|
| D1772 | D 333a | 25 r. pur & stone | 15 | 15 |
| D1773 | | 50 r. grn & lilac | 15 | 15 |
| D1774 | | 500 r. dp brown & brown .. | 45 | 40 |

**1988.** Dated "1988".

| | | | | |
|---|---|---|---|---|
| D1912 | D 333a | 1000 r. purple and grey .. | 65 | 45 |
| D1913 | | 2000 r. red and mauve .. | 1·25 | 95 |
| D1914 | | 3000 r. red & yell | 1·90 | 1·40 |
| D1915 | | 5000 r. grn & bl | 3·00 | 1·90 |

## INHAMBANE — Pt. 9

A district of Mozambique which used its own stamps from 1895 to 1920.

1895. 1000 reis = 1 milreis.
1913. 100 centavos = 1 escudo.

**1895.** 700th Birth Anniv of St. Anthony. Optd **CENTENARIO DE S. ANTONIO Inhambane MDCCCXCV** on (a) "Embossed" key-type inscr "PROVINCIA DE MOCAMBIQUE".

| No. | Type | Description | Unused | Used |
|---|---|---|---|---|
| 1. | Q. | 5 r. black .. .. | 11·00 | 9·50 |
| 2. | | 10 r. green .. .. | 10·00 | 7·50 |
| 3. | | 20 r. red .. .. .. | 19·00 | 15·00 |
| 5. | | 40 r. brown .. .. | 22·00 | 14·00 |
| 6. | | 50 r. blue .. .. | 22·00 | 14·00 |
| 8. | | 200 r. violet .. .. | 27·00 | 25·00 |
| 9. | | 300 r. orange .. .. | 27·00 | 25·00 |

(b) "Figures" key type inscr. "MOCAMBIQUE".

| No. | Type | Description | Unused | Used |
|---|---|---|---|---|
| 12. | R. | 50 r. blue .. .. | 17·00 | 15·00 |
| 16. | | 75 r. red .. .. .. | 19·00 | 16·00 |
| 13. | | 80 r. green .. .. | 19·00 | 16·00 |
| 14. | | 100 r. brown on yellow.. | 27·00 | 21·00 |
| 17. | | 150 r. red on rose .. | 24·00 | 19·00 |

**1903.** "King Carlos" key type inscr. "INHAMBANE".

| No. | Type | Description | Unused | Used |
|---|---|---|---|---|
| 18. | S. | 2½ r. grey .. .. | 20 | 20 |
| 19. | | 5 r. orange .. .. | 20 | 20 |
| 20. | | 10 r. green .. .. | 20 | 20 |
| 21. | | 15 r. green .. .. | 50 | 40 |
| 22. | | 20 r. lilac .. .. | 50 | 40 |
| 23. | | 25 r. red .. .. .. | 50 | 40 |
| 24. | | 50 r. brown .. .. | 80 | 55 |
| 25. | | 65 r. blue .. .. | 5·00 | 2·50 |
| 26. | | 75 r. purple .. .. | 75 | 70 |
| 27. | | 100 r. blue on blue .. | 75 | 70 |
| 28. | | 115 r. brown on pink .. | 2·10 | 2·10 |
| 29. | | 130 r. brown on yellow.. | 2·10 | 2·10 |
| 30. | | 200 r. purple on pink .. | 2·10 | 2·10 |
| 31. | | 400 r. blue on yellow .. | 3·75 | 3·00 |
| 32. | | 500 r. black on blue .. | 5·50 | 4·00 |
| 33. | | 700 r. grey on yellow .. | 6·25 | 5·50 |

**1905.** No. 25 surch. **50 REIS** and bar.

| No. | Type | Description | Unused | Used |
|---|---|---|---|---|
| 34. | S. | 50 r. on 65 r. blue .. | 1·00 | 90 |

**1911.** 1903 issue optd **REPUBLICA**.

| No. | Type | Description | Unused | Used |
|---|---|---|---|---|
| 35. | S. | 2½ r. grey .. .. | 15 | 15 |
| 36. | | 5 r. orange .. .. | 15 | 15 |
| 37. | | 10 r. green .. .. | 15 | 15 |
| 38. | | 15 r. green .. .. | 15 | 15 |
| 39. | | 20 r. lilac .. .. | 15 | 15 |
| 40. | | 25 r. red .. .. .. | 30 | 20 |
| 41. | | 50 r. brown .. .. | 20 | 15 |
| 42. | | 75 r. purple .. .. | 15 | 15 |
| 43. | | 100 r. blue on blue .. | 15 | 15 |
| 44. | | 115 r. brown on pink .. | 35 | 30 |
| 45. | | 130 r. brown on yellow.. | 35 | 30 |
| 46. | | 200 r. purple on pink .. | 45 | 30 |
| 47. | | 400 r. blue on yellow .. | 70 | 50 |
| 48. | | 500 r. black on blue .. | 70 | 50 |
| 49. | | 700 r. black on yellow .. | 90 | 75 |

**1913.** Surch. **REPUBLICA INHAMBANE** and value on "Vasco da Gama" stamps of (a) **Portuguese Colonies.**

| No. | Description | Unused | Used |
|---|---|---|---|
| 50. | ¼ c. on 2½ r. green .. | 35 | 25 |
| 51. | ½ c. on 5 r. red .. .. | 35 | 25 |
| 52. | 1 c. on 10 r. purple .. | 35 | 25 |
| 53. | 2½ c. on 25 r. green .. | 35 | 25 |
| 54. | 5 c. on 50 r. blue.. .. | 45 | 35 |
| 55. | 7½ c. on 75 r. brown .. | 75 | 65 |
| 56. | 10 c. on 100 r. brown .. | 75 | 65 |
| 57. | 15 c. on 150 r. bistre .. | 75 | 65 |

(b) **Macao.**

| No. | Description | Unused | Used |
|---|---|---|---|
| 58. | ¼ c. on ½ a. green.. .. | 55 | 45 |
| 59. | ½ c. on 1 a. red .. .. | 55 | 45 |
| 60. | 1 c. on 2 a. purple .. | 55 | 45 |
| 61. | 2½ c. on 4 a. green .. | 55 | 45 |
| 62. | 5 c. on 8 a. blue.. .. | 55 | 45 |
| 63. | 7½ c. on 12 a. brown .. | 95 | 80 |
| 64. | 10 c. on 16 a. brown .. | 70 | 45 |
| 65. | 15 c. on 24 a. bistre .. | 70 | 45 |

(c) **Timor.**

| No. | Description | Unused | Used |
|---|---|---|---|
| 66. | ¼ c. on ½ a. green.. .. | 55 | 45 |
| 67. | ½ c. on 1 a. red .. .. | 55 | 45 |
| 68. | 1 c. on 2 a. purple .. | 55 | 45 |
| 69. | 2½ c. on 4 a. green .. | 55 | 45 |
| 70. | 5 c. on 8 a. blue.. .. | 55 | 45 |
| 71. | 7½ c. on 12 a. brown .. | 1·00 | 75 |
| 72. | 10 c. on 16 a. brown .. | 70 | 45 |
| 73. | 15 c. on 24 a. bistre .. | 70 | 45 |

**1914.** No. 34 optd. **REPUBLICA.**

| No. | Type | Description | Unused | Used |
|---|---|---|---|---|
| 74. | S. | 50 r. on 65 r. blue .. | 95 | 70 |

**1914.** "Ceres" key type inscr. "INHAMBANE".

| No. | Type | Description | Unused | Used |
|---|---|---|---|---|
| 75. | U. | ¼ c. olive .. .. | 30 | 20 |
| 76a. | | ½ c. black .. .. | 35 | 30 |
| 77. | | 1 c. green .. .. | 30 | 20 |
| 78. | | 1½ c. brown .. .. | 30 | 20 |
| 79. | | 2 c. red .. .. .. | 30 | 20 |
| 80. | | 2½ c. violet .. .. | 10 | 10 |
| 81. | | 5 c. blue .. .. | 20 | 20 |
| 82. | | 7½ c. brown .. .. | 55 | 30 |
| 83. | | 8 c. grey .. .. | 55 | 30 |
| 84. | | 10 c. red .. .. | 55 | 40 |
| 85. | | 15 c. red.. .. .. | 65 | 50 |
| 86. | | 20 c. green .. .. | 65 | 50 |
| 87. | | 30 c. brown on green .. | 85 | 60 |
| 88. | | 40 c. brown on red .. | 85 | 60 |
| 89. | | 50 c. orange on pink .. | 1·50 | 1·00 |
| 90. | | 1 e. green on blue .. | 1·50 | 1·00 |

## ININI — Pt. 6

A territory in French Guiana, in the N.E. of S. America, separately administered from 1930 but reunited with Fr. Guiana in 1946.

100 centimes = 1 franc.

**1931.** Stamps of French Guiana optd **TERRITOIRE DE L'ININI** (Type **20**) or **Territoire de l'ININI** (others).

| No. | Type | Description | Unused | Used |
|---|---|---|---|---|
| 1 | 20 | 1 c. green and lilac .. | 40 | 60 |
| 2 | | 2 c. green and red .. | 50 | 75 |
| 3 | | 3 c. green and violet .. | 50 | 75 |
| 4 | | 4 c. mauve and brown .. | 50 | 75 |
| 5 | | 5 c. orange and blue .. | 50 | 75 |
| 6 | | 10 c. brown and mauve .. | 40 | 65 |
| 7 | | 15 c. orange and brown .. | 40 | 65 |
| 8 | | 20 c. green and blue .. | 50 | 75 |
| 9 | | 25 c. brown and red .. | 70 | 90 |
| 10 | 21 | 30 c. green & deep green | 1·00 | 1·40 |
| 11 | | 30 c. brown and green .. | 70 | 90 |
| 12 | | 35 c. green and blue .. | 80 | 1·00 |
| 13 | | 40 c. grey and brown .. | 70 | 90 |
| 14 | | 45 c. green and olive .. | 70 | 90 |
| 15 | | 50 c. grey and blue .. | 70 | 90 |
| 16 | | 55 c. red and blue .. | 2·25 | 3·00 |
| 17 | | 60 c. green and red .. | 70 | 90 |
| 18 | | 65 c. green and red .. | 1·10 | 1·50 |
| 19 | | 70 c. green and blue .. | 70 | 90 |
| 20 | | 75 c. blue & deep blue .. | 1·40 | 1·60 |
| 21 | | 80 c. blue and black .. | 75 | 1·00 |
| 22 | | 90 c. red and carmine .. | 1·00 | 1·40 |
| 23 | | 90 c. brown and mauve .. | 70 | 90 |
| 24 | | 1 f. brown and mauve .. | 7·50 | 8·00 |
| 25 | | 1 f. red .. .. | 75 | 1·00 |
| 26 | | 1 f. blue and black .. | 70 | 90 |
| 27 | 22 | 1 f. 25 green and brown .. | 80 | 1·10 |
| 28 | | 1 f. 25 red .. .. | 70 | 90 |
| 29 | | 1 f. 40 mauve and brown .. | 75 | 1·00 |
| 30 | | 1 f. 50 light blue & blue .. | 70 | 90 |
| 31 | | 1 f. 60 green and brown .. | 75 | 1·00 |
| 32 | | 1 f. 75 brown and red .. | 11·00 | 12·00 |
| 33 | | 1 f. 75 blue & deep blue .. | 85 | 1·25 |
| 34 | | 2 f. red and green .. | 80 | 1·10 |
| 35 | | 2 f. 25 blue .. .. | 80 | 1·10 |
| 36 | | 2 f. 50 brown and red .. | 80 | 1·10 |
| 37 | | 3 f. mauve and red .. | 80 | 1·10 |
| 38 | | 5 f. green and violet .. | 80 | 1·10 |
| 39 | | 10 f. blue and green .. | 80 | 1·10 |
| 40 | | 20 f. green and blue .. | 1·00 | 1·40 |

**1939.** New York World's Fair. As T **20** of Cameroun.

| No. | Description | Unused | Used |
|---|---|---|---|
| 51. | 1 f. 25 red.. .. | 2·50 | 3·00 |
| 52. | 2 f. 25 blue .. .. | 2·50 | 3·00 |

**1939.** 150th Anniv. of French Revolution. As T **25** of Cameroun.

| No. | Description | Unused | Used |
|---|---|---|---|
| 53. | 45 c.+25 c. green & black | 7·25 | 7·50 |
| 54. | 70 c.+30 c. brown & black | 7·50 | 7·50 |
| 55. | 90 c.+35 c. orange & black | 7·50 | 7·50 |
| 56. | 1 f. 25+1 f. red & black.. | 7·50 | 7·50 |
| 57. | 2 f. 25+2 f. blue & black.. | 7·50 | 7·50 |

POSTAGE DUE STAMPS

**1932.** Postage Due stamps of French Guiana optd **TERRITOIRE DE L'ININI**.

| No. | Type | Description | Unused | Used |
|---|---|---|---|---|
| D41 | D 23 | 5 c. blue & deep blue | 25 | 45 |
| D42 | | 10 c. blue and brown | 50 | 75 |
| D43 | | 20 c. red and green | 35 | 50 |
| D44 | | 30 c. red and brown | 35 | 50 |
| D45 | | 50 c. brown & mauve | 80 | 1·00 |
| D46 | | 60 c. brown and red | 80 | 1·00 |
| D47 | D 24 | 1 f. brown and blue | 1·25 | 1·75 |
| D48 | | 2 f. green and red | 1·50 | 2·00 |
| D49 | | 3 f. grey and mauve | 2·00 | 3·00 |

## IRAN — Pt. 16

A State of W. Asia.

1868. 20 shahis (or chahis) = 1 kran; 10 krans = 1 toman.
1932. 100 dinars = 1 rial.

NOTE.—The word "English" in the descriptive headings to various Persian issues is to be taken as referring to the lettering or figures and not to the language which is often French.

1. 3. Nasred-Din. 4. Nasred-Din.

**1868.** Imperf or roul.

| No. | Type | Description | Unused | Used |
|---|---|---|---|---|
| 1 | 1 | 1 (sh.) violet .. .. | 70·00 | |
| 1c | | 1 (sh.) grey .. .. | 80·00 | |
| 15 | | 1 (sh.) black .. .. | 10·00 | 15·00 |
| 2 | | 2 (sh.) green .. .. | 50·00 | |
| 16 | | 2 (sh.) blue .. .. | 80·00 | 40·00 |
| 35 | | 2 (sh.) black .. .. | £250 | £3000 |
| 3 | | 4 (sh.) blue .. .. | 70·00 | |
| 17 | | 4 (sh.) red .. .. | 70·00 | 35·00 |
| 4 | | 8 (sh.) red .. .. | 70·00 | |
| 8a | | 8 (sh.) green .. .. | 70·00 | 70·00 |
| 13 | | 1 (kr.) yellow .. .. | £1000 | |
| 18 | | 1 kr. red .. .. | £100 | 45·00 |
| 38 | | 1 kr. red on yellow .. | £1100 | 50·00 |
| 19 | | 4 kr. yellow .. .. | £300 | 45·00 |
| 36 | | 4 kr. blue .. .. | £120 | 70·00 |
| 40 | | 5 kr. violet .. .. | £225 | £180 |
| 41 | | 5 kr. gold .. .. | £750 | £200 |
| 39 | | 1 to. bronze on blue .. | £15000 | £2500 |

**1876.** Perf.

| No. | Type | Description | Unused | Used |
|---|---|---|---|---|
| 20 | 3 | 1 (sh.) black and mauve .. | 4·00 | 2·00 |
| 24 | | 2 (sh.) black and green .. | 5·00 | 1·50 |
| 25 | | 5 (sh.) black and pink .. | 4·50 | 75 |
| 30 | | 10 (sh.) black and blue .. | 6·00 | 3·00 |

**1879.** Perf.

| No. | Type | Description | Unused | Used |
|---|---|---|---|---|
| 45a | 4 | 1 (sh.) black and red .. | 11·00 | 1·00 |
| 46a | | 2 (sh.) black and yellow | 14·00 | 1·10 |
| 47 | | 5 (sh.) black and green .. | 13·00 | 60 |
| 48 | | 10 (sh.) black and mauve | £130 | 10·00 |
| 49 | | 1 (kr.) black and brown | 40·00 | 90 |
| 50c | | 5 (kr.) black and blue .. | 18·00 | 50 |

5. 6.

**1881.**

| No. | Type | Description | Unused | Used |
|---|---|---|---|---|
| 56. | 5. | 5 c. mauve .. .. | 5·00 | 2·00 |
| 57a. | | 10 c. red .. .. | 4·50 | 1·50 |
| 61. | | 25 c. green .. .. | £100 | 1·00 |
| 62. | 6. | 50 c. black, yell. & orge. | 75·00 | 6·00 |
| 69. | | 50 c. black .. .. | 20·00 | 3·00 |
| 63. | | 1 f. black and blue .. | 14·00 | 1·25 |
| 64. | | 5 f. black and red .. | 14·00 | 1·00 |
| 65. | | 10 f. black, yellow & red | 15·00 | 2·75 |

The 10 f. is larger (30½ × 36 mm.).

**1882.** As T **5** and **6.**

| No. | Type | Description | Unused | Used |
|---|---|---|---|---|
| 66. | – | 5 s. green .. .. | 5·00 | 20 |
| 68. | – | 10 s. black, yell. & orange | 15·00 | 90 |

10. 11. 13.

14. 15. 16.

**1885.**

| No. | Type | Description | Unused | Used |
|---|---|---|---|---|
| 70 | 10 | 1 c. green .. .. | 5·00 | 60 |
| 71 | | 2 c. red .. .. | 5·00 | 50 |
| 72 | | 5 c. blue .. .. | 5·00 | 10 |
| 73 | 11 | 10 c. brown .. .. | 6·50 | 20 |
| 74 | | 1 k. grey .. .. | 7·00 | 40 |
| 75 | | 5 k. purple .. .. | 70·00 | 5·50 |

**1885.** Surch. **OFFICIEL** and value in English and Persian.

| No. | Type | Description | Unused | Used |
|---|---|---|---|---|
| 81a | – | 3 on 5 s. green (No. 66) | 18·00 | 5·50 |
| 76 | – | 6 on 5 s. green (No. 66) | 40·00 | 6·00 |
| 83 | – | 6 on 10 s. (No. 68) | 32·00 | 5·50 |
| 84 | 6 | 8 on 50 c. black | 60·00 | 9·00 |
| 78 | | 12 on 50 c. black | 70·00 | 9·00 |
| 79 | – | 18 on 10 s. (No. 68) | 60·00 | 7·00 |
| 80 | 6 | 1 t. on 5 f. black and red | 60·00 | 4·00 |

**1889.**

| No. | Type | Description | Unused | Used |
|---|---|---|---|---|
| 85. | 13. | 1 c. pink .. .. | 25 | 10 |
| 86. | | 2 c. blue .. .. | 20 | 10 |
| 87. | | 5 c. mauve .. .. | 20 | 10 |
| 88. | | 7 c. brown .. .. | 1·00 | 30 |
| 89. | 14. | 10 c. black .. .. | 35 | 10 |
| 90. | | 1 k. orange .. .. | 45 | 10 |
| 91. | | 2 k. red .. .. | 3·00 | 90 |
| 92. | | 5 k. green .. .. | 2·25 | 1·00 |

**1891.**

| No. | Type | Description | Unused | Used |
|---|---|---|---|---|
| 93. | 15. | 1 c. black .. .. | 20 | 10 |
| 94. | | 2 c. brown .. .. | 30 | 10 |
| 95. | | 5 c. blue .. .. | 15 | 10 |
| 96. | | 7 c. grey .. .. | 65·00 | 2·00 |
| 97. | | 10 c. red .. .. | 55 | 10 |
| 98. | | 14 c. orange .. .. | 40 | 20 |
| 99. | 16. | 1 k. green .. .. | 7·00 | 15 |
| 100. | | 2 k. orange .. .. | £100 | 5·50 |
| 101. | | 5 k. orange .. .. | 80 | 40 |

17. 18. 21. Muzaffer-ed-Din.

**1894.**

| No. | Type | Description | Unused | Used |
|---|---|---|---|---|
| 102 | 17 | 1 c. mauve .. .. | 30 | 10 |
| 103 | | 2 c. green .. .. | 30 | 10 |
| 104 | | 5 c. blue .. .. | 30 | 10 |
| 105 | | 8 c. brown .. .. | 30 | 10 |
| 106 | 18 | 10 c. yellow .. .. | 50 | 15 |
| 107 | | 16 c. pink .. .. | 2·50 | 60 |
| 108 | | 1 k. pink and yellow .. | 2·00 | 15 |
| 109 | | 2 k. brown and blue .. | 2·00 | 15 |
| 110 | | 5 k. violet and silver .. | 2·25 | 30 |
| 111 | | 10 k. pink and gold .. | 10·00 | 2·50 |
| 112 | | 50 k. green and gold .. | 7·00 | 4·50 |

See also Nos. 116/24.

**1897.** Surch. in English and Persian in frame.

| No. | Type | Description | Unused | Used |
|---|---|---|---|---|
| 113. | 17. | 5 c. on 8 c. brown .. | 1·75 | 20 |
| 114. | 18. | 1 k. on 5 k. violet & silver | 5·50 | 1·50 |
| 115. | | 2 k. on 5 k. violet & silver | 5·50 | 2·00 |

**1898.** Chahi values on white or green paper.

| No. | Type | Description | Unused | Used |
|---|---|---|---|---|
| 116 | 17 | 1 c. grey .. .. | 20 | 10 |
| 117 | | 2 c. brown .. .. | 30 | 10 |
| 118 | | 3 c. purple .. .. | 30 | 10 |
| 119 | | 4 c. red .. .. | 30 | 10 |
| 120 | | 5 c. yellow .. .. | 30 | 10 |
| 121 | | 8 c. orange .. .. | 1·00 | 35 |
| 154 | | 10 c. blue .. .. | 60 | 10 |
| 123 | | 12 c. red .. .. | 90 | 10 |
| 124 | | 16 c. green .. .. | 1·50 | 35 |
| 125 | 21 | 1 k. blue .. .. | 2·00 | 10 |
| 157 | | 1 k. red .. .. | 1·75 | 20 |
| 126 | | 2 k. pink .. .. | 2·00 | 10 |
| 158 | | 2 k. green .. .. | 3·50 | 60 |
| 127 | | 3 k. yellow .. .. | 2·00 | 20 |
| 159 | | 3 k. brown .. .. | 5·00 | 1·00 |
| 128 | | 4 k. grey .. .. | 2·00 | 50 |
| 160 | | 4 k. red .. .. | 5·00 | 1·00 |
| 129 | | 5 k. green .. .. | 2·00 | 50 |
| 161 | | 5 k. brown .. .. | 7·50 | 1·00 |
| 130 | | 10 k. orange .. .. | 3·50 | 75 |
| 162 | | 10 k. blue .. .. | 17·00 | 3·50 |
| 131 | | 50 k. mauve .. .. | 9·50 | 4·00 |
| 163 | | 50 k. brown .. .. | 12·00 | 2·25 |

(21a.) (22.) (24.)

**1899.** Optd. with control mark of various scroll devices as T **21a.**

| No. | Type | Description | Unused | Used |
|---|---|---|---|---|
| 132. | 17. | 1 c. grey .. .. | 60 | 10 |
| 133. | | 2 c. brown .. .. | 60 | 10 |
| 134. | | 3 c. purple .. .. | 60 | 10 |
| 135. | | 4 c. red .. .. | 60 | 10 |
| 136. | | 5 c. yellow .. .. | 60 | 10 |
| 137. | | 8 c. orange .. .. | 1·50 | 15 |
| 138. | | 10 c. blue .. .. | 60 | 10 |
| 139. | | 12 c. red .. .. | 1·25 | 10 |
| 140. | | 16 c. green .. .. | 1·25 | 35 |
| 141. | 21. | 1 k. blue .. .. | 1·50 | 10 |
| 142. | | 2 k. pink .. .. | 2·75 | 45 |
| 143. | | 3 k. yellow .. .. | 8·50 | 1·50 |
| 144. | | 4 k. grey .. .. | 8·50 | 1·50 |
| 145. | | 5 k. green .. .. | 4·50 | 1·50 |
| 146. | | 10 k. orange .. .. | 12·00 | 1·50 |
| 147. | | 50 k. mauve .. .. | 10·00 | 4·00 |

**1900.** Optd. with T **22** across two stamps.

| No. | Type | Description | Unused | Used |
|---|---|---|---|---|
| 164. | 17. | 1 c. grey .. .. | 20·00 | 2·00 |
| 165. | | 2 c. brown .. .. | 20·00 | 2·00 |
| 166. | | 3 c. purple .. .. | 28·00 | 3·00 |
| 167. | | 4 c. red .. .. | 65·00 | 8·50 |
| 168. | | 5 c. yellow .. .. | 7·50 | 1·00 |
| 169. | | 10 c. blue .. .. | £275 | £110 |
| 170. | | 12 c. red .. .. | 28·00 | 2·00 |

Prices quoted in this issue are for pairs.

**1901.** Surch in various ways in English and Persian.

| No. | Type | Description | Unused | Used |
|---|---|---|---|---|
| 176. | 17. | 5 on 8 c. brown.. .. | 2·00 | 25 |
| 179. | 21. | 12 c. on 1 k. red .. | 10·00 | 4·00 |
| 180. | | 5 k. on 50 k. brown .. | 45·00 | 12·00 |

**1902.** Surch. with T **24.**

| No. | Type | Description | Unused | Used |
|---|---|---|---|---|
| 177. | 17. | 5 c. on 10 c. blue .. | 1·50 | 60 |
| 178. | 21. | 5 c. on 1 k. red.. .. | 1·50 | 80 |

**1902.** Optd. **PROVISOIRE 1319** in ornamental frame.

| No. | Type | Description | Unused | Used |
|---|---|---|---|---|
| 181. | 17. | 1 c. grey .. .. | 2·00 | 1·00 |
| 182. | | 2 c. brown .. .. | 3·50 | 2·50 |
| 183. | | 3 c. purple .. .. | 2·00 | 1·00 |
| 184. | | 4 c. red .. .. | 2·00 | 1·00 |
| 185. | | 5 c. yellow .. .. | 1·75 | 65 |
| 197. | | 5 on 8 c. brn (No. 176) | 5·00 | 40 |
| 186. | | 8 c. orange .. .. | 2·00 | 1·50 |
| 187. | | 10 c. blue .. .. | 2·00 | 1·00 |
| 188. | | 12 c. red .. .. | 3·50 | 1·00 |
| 198. | 21. | 12 c. on 1 k. (No. 179).. | 7·50 | 2·50 |
| 189. | 17. | 16 c. green .. .. | 7·00 | 3·00 |
| 190. | 21. | 1 k. red.. .. .. | 6·50 | 2·25 |
| 191. | | 2 k. green .. .. | — | 10·00 |
| 192. | | 3 k. brown .. .. | — | 25·00 |
| 193. | | 4 k. red .. .. | — | 28·00 |
| 194. | | 5 k. brown .. .. | — | 30·00 |
| 199. | | 5 k. on 50 k. (No. 180).. | 25·00 | 9·00 |
| 195. | | 10 k. blue .. .. | — | 30·00 |
| 196. | | 50 k. brown .. .. | — | 32·00 |

28. (29.)

**1902.** Inscr "CHAHIS" or "KRANS" in capital letters. Optd with T **29.**

| No. | Type | Description | Unused | Used |
|---|---|---|---|---|
| 200. | 28. | 1 c. grey .. .. | 1·25 | 10 |
| 201. | | 2 c. brown .. .. | 4·00 | 20 |
| 202. | | 3 c. green .. .. | 7·00 | 10 |
| 203. | | 5 c. red .. .. | 2·00 | 10 |
| 204. | | 10 c. yellow .. .. | 6·00 | 10 |
| 205. | | 12 c. blue .. .. | 9·00 | 40 |
| 206. | | 1 k. mauve .. .. | 22·00 | 50 |
| 207. | | 2 k. green .. .. | 25·00 | 2·00 |
| 208. | | 10 k. blue .. .. | 55·00 | 13·00 |
| 209. | | 50 k. red .. .. | £375 | £250 |

**1902.** Surch **5 KRANS** in English and Persian.
210 28 5 k. on 5 k. yellow .. 60·00 7·00

**1902.** Optd. **PROVISOIRE 1319** in ornamental frame.
211. 28. 1 c. grey .. .. 20·00 10·00
212. 2 c. brown .. .. 20·00 10·00
213. 3 c. green .. .. 20·00 10·00
214. 5 c. red .. .. 20·00 10·00
215. 12 c. blue .. .. 20·00 10·00

34.

**1902.** Inscr "Chahis" or "Krans" in lower case letters.
227 34 1 c. grey .. .. 11·00
228 2 c. brown .. .. 20·00
229 3 c. green .. .. 11·00
230 5 c. red .. .. 11·00 10
231 10 c. yellow .. .. 13·00 90
232 12 c. blue .. .. 16·00 1·10
233 1 k. mauve .. ..
234 2 k. green .. ..
235 10 k. blue .. ..
236 50 k. red .. .. £425

**1902.** Surch **5 KRANS** without T 29 opt.
237 34 5 k. on 5 k. yellow .. 30·00

**1903.** Optd. **PROVISOIRE 1903** and lion in frame, but without Arms opt. (T 29).
239. 28. 1 c. grey .. .. — 4·00
240. 2 c. brown .. .. — 4·00
241. 5 c. red .. .. — 4·00
242. 10 c. yellow .. .. — 6·00
243. 12 c. blue .. .. — 10·00
244. 1 k. mauve .. .. — 11·00

38. 39. Muzaffer ed-Din.

**1903.**
246. 38. 1 c. lilac .. .. 20 10
247. 2 c. grey .. .. 25 10
248. 3 c. green .. .. 30 10
249 5 c. red .. .. 35 10
250. 10 c. brown .. .. 40 10
251. 12 c. blue .. .. 40 10
252. 39. 1 k. purple .. .. 1·25 15
253. 2 k. blue .. .. 2·00 10
254. 5 k. brown .. .. 3·00 15
255. 10 k. red .. .. 7·50 30
256. 20 k. orange .. .. 12·00 60
257. 30 k. green .. .. 14·00 1·50
258. 50 k. green .. .. 55·00 14·00
See also Nos. 298/303.

**1903.** Surch. in both English and Persian except those marked * which are surch. in English only.
272. 38. "1 CHAHI" on 3 c. green 5·00 1·25
287. "1 CHAI" on 3 c. green 3·50 40
288. 39. 1 c. on 1 k. purple .. 12·00 3·50
273. 38. 2 c. on 3 c. green .. 10·00 4·25
289. 39. 2 c. on 5 k. brown .. 17·00 6·00
277. 38. 3 c. on 5 c. red .. 2·50 10
278. 6 c. on 10 c. brown .. 4·00 10
279. 39. 9 c. on 1 k. purple .. 5·00 15
274. 12 c. on 10 k. red .. 16·00 3·75
275. 2 t. on 50 k. green* .. 55·00 25·00
280. 2 t. on 50 k. green .. 55·00 25·00
276. 3 t. on 50 k. green* .. 55·00 25·00
281. 3 t. on 50 k. green .. 55·00 25·00

50. 52. Shah Muhammad Ali Mirza.

**1906.** Optd. **PROVISOIRE** and lion. Imperf. or perf.
292. 50. 1 c. violet .. .. 50 10
293. 2 c. grey .. .. 60 10
294. 3 c. green .. .. 60 10
295. 6 c. red .. .. 1·00 10
296. 10 c. brown .. .. 11·00 50
297. 13 c. blue .. .. 6·00 35

**1907.**
298 38 1 ch. violet on blue .. 15 10
299 2 ch. grey on blue .. 15 10
300 3 ch. green on blue .. 15 10
301 6 ch. red on blue .. 15 10
302 9 ch. yellow on blue .. 20 10
303 10 ch. sepia on blue .. 20 10
305 52 13 c. blue .. .. 50 10
306 26 c. brown .. .. 50 10
307 1 k. red .. .. 50 10
308 2 k. green .. .. 50 10
309 3 k. blue .. .. 60 10
311 4 k. brown .. .. 1·75 30
312 5 k. brown .. .. 1·25 15
313 10 k. pink .. .. 2·00 15
314 20 k. brown .. .. 4·75 25
315 30 k. purple .. .. 5·00 40
316 – 50 k. red and gold .. 20·00 17·00
The 50 k. is larger with the head facing the other way.

(54.) 56.

**1909.** Nos. 298/315 optd. as Type **54**. Imperf.
320. 38. 1 ch. on 1 ch. violet on bl. 30·00 20·00
321. 1 ch. on 2 ch. grey on bl. 30·00 20·00
322. 1 ch. on 3 ch. grn. on bl. 30·00 20·00
323. 1 ch. on 6 ch. red on blue 30·00 20·00
324. 1 ch. on 9 ch. yell. on bl. 30·00 20·00
325. 1 ch. on 10 ch. brn. on bl. 30·00 20·00
326. 52. 2 ch. on 13 ch. blue .. 32·00 22·00
327. 2 ch. on 26 ch. brown .. 32·00 22·00
328. 2 ch. on 1 kr. red .. 32·00 22·00
329. 2 ch. on 2 kr. green .. 32·00 22·00
330. 2 ch. on 3 kr. blue .. 32·00 22·00
331. 2 ch. on 4 kr. yellow .. 32·00 22·00
333. 2 ch. on 5 kr. brown .. 32·00 22·00
334. 2 ch. on 10 kr. pink .. 32·00 22·00
335. 2 ch. on 20 kr. black .. 35·00 24·00
336. 2 ch. on 30 kr. purple .. 35·00 24·00

**1909.**
337 56 1 c. purple and orange 35 10
338 2 c. purple and violet .. 35 10
339 3 c. purple and green .. 35 10
340 6 c. purple and red .. 35 10
341 9 c. purple and grey .. 40 10
342 10 c. maroon and purple 70 10
343 13 c. purple and blue .. 70 10
344 26 c. purple and green 3·00 10
345 1 k. brown, violet & sil 6·00 10
346 2 k. brown, green & sil 6·00 10
347 3 k. brown, grey & silver 7·00 15
348 4 k. brown, blue & silver 12·00 40
349 5 k. sepia, brown & gold 16·00 40
350 10 k. brown, orge & gold 30·00 70
351 20 k. brown, grn & gold 30·00 1·40
352 30 k. brown, red & gold 40·00 1·90
Stamps of this issue offered at very low prices are reprints.
For stamps as Type **56** but with curved inscriptions, see Nos. O836 etc.

57. Ahmed Mirza. ١٣٣٣ (65.)

**1911.**
361 57 1 c. orange and green .. 15 10
362 2 c. brown and red .. 15 10
363 3 c. green and grey .. 15 10
364 3 c. green and brown .. 15 10
365 5 c. red and brown .. 15 10
366 6 c. red and grey .. 15 10
367 6 c. red and green .. 15 10
368 9 c. lilac and brown .. 15 10
369 10 c. brown and red .. 15 10
370 12 c. blue and green .. 15 10
371 13 c. blue and violet .. 15 10
372 24 c. green and purple .. 15 10
373 26 c. green and blue .. 4·00 2·00
374 1 k. red and blue .. 10 10
375 2 k. purple and green .. 20 10
376 3 k. black and lilac .. 25 10
377 4 k. black and blue .. 4·00 2·00
378 5 k. blue and red .. 20 10
379 10 k. pink and brown .. 35 10
380 20 k. buff and brown .. 55 10
381 30 k. green and red .. 80 10

**1911.** Various stamps optd. **Relais** in English and Persian.
382. 56. 2 ch. purple and violet .. 13·00 3·00
383. 3 ch. purple and green .. 13·00 3·00
384. 6 ch. purple and red .. 13·00 3·00
385. 13 ch. purple and blue .. 13·00 3·00
386. 57. 2 ch. brown and red .. 13·00 3·00
387. 3 ch. green and grey .. 13·00 3·00
388. 6 ch. red and grey .. 13·00 3·00
388a. 13 ch. blue and violet .. 13·00 3·00

**1912.** Optd **Officiel** in English and Persian.
389 57 1 c. orange and green .. 40 10
390 2 c. brown and red .. 40 10
391 3 c. green and grey .. 40 10
392 6 c. red and grey .. 1·75 10
393 9 c. lilac and brown .. 85 15
394 10 c. brown and red .. 85 15
395 13 c. blue and violet .. 5·00 35
396 26 c. green and blue .. 13·00 70
397 1 k. red and blue .. 10·00 20
398 2 k. purple and green .. 11·00 20
399 3 k. black and lilac .. 15·00 20
400 5 k. blue and red .. 17·00 20
401 10 k. pink and brown .. 30·00 1·25
402 20 k. buff and brown .. 30·00 2·00
403 30 k. green and red .. 30·00 2·75

**1914.** Surch. with new value and **1914** in English and Persian.
412. 57. 1 c. on 13 c. bl. & violet 2·00 15
413. 3 c. on 26 c. grn. & blue 2·00 15

**1915.** Surch. with new value in frame and **1915** in English and Persian.
414. 57. 1 c. on 5 c. red & brown 1·75 10
415b. 2 c. on 5 c. red & brown 1·75 10
416. 6 c. on 12 c. bl. & green 2·50 10

**1915.** Surch. with new value in English and Persian.
417. 56. 5 c. on 1 k. (No. 345) .. 2·50 10
418. 12 c. on 13 c. (No. 343) 3·25 10

**1915.** Optd with T **65** ("1333").
419 56 1 c. purple and orange 40 10
420 2 c. purple and violet .. 70 10
421 3 c. purple and green .. 1·50 10
422 6 c. purple and red .. 1·75 10
423 9 c. purple and grey .. 3·50 10
424 10 c. purple and mauve 7·00 20
425 1 k. brown, violet & sil 7·50 15

66. The Imperial Crown. 67. King Darius on his Throne.

**1915.** Coronation of Shah Ahmed.
426 66 1 c. blue and red .. 10 10
427 2 c. red and blue .. 10 10
428 3 c. green .. .. 10 10
429 5 c. red .. .. 10 10
430 6 c. red and green .. 10 10
431 9 c. violet and brown .. 10 10
432 10 c. brown and green .. 15 10
433 12 c. blue .. .. 15 10
434 24 c. sepia and brown .. 45 10
435 67 1 k. black, brown & sil 45 10
436 2 k. red, blue and silver 45 10
437 3 k. brown, lilac & silver 45 15
438 5 k. grey, brown & silver 45 15
439 – 1 t. black, violet & gold 70 30
440 – 2 t. brown, green & gold 70 30
441 – 3 t. red, crimson & gold 1·00 30
442 – 5 t. grey, blue and gold 1·00 30
DESIGNS: 1 t. to 5 t. Gateway of the Palace of Persepolis.

١٣٣٤ (69.) ١٣٣٥ (73.)

**1915.** Optd with T **69** ("1334").
477 56 1 k. brown, violet & sil 5·50 40
478 10 k. brown, orge & gold 20·00 75
479 20 k. brown, grn & gold 90·00 8·50
480 30 k. brown, red & gold 35·00 2·75

**1917.** Surch. with value in English only.
481. 57. 12 c. on 1 k. red & blue £225 80·00
482. 24 c. on 1 k. red & blue £100 40·00

**1917.** Optd. with T **73** ("1335") or surch. also with new value in English and Persian.
483. 56. 1 c. purple and orange 35·00 9·00
484. 1 c. on 2 c. (No. 338) .. 4·00 10
485. 1 c. on 9 c. (No. 341) .. 4·00 10
486. 1 c. on 10 c. (No. 342) .. 4·00 10
490. 57. 1 c. on 10 c. brn. & red 4·00 10
487. 56. 3 c. on 9 c. pur. & grey 4·00 10
491. 57. 3 c. on 10 c. brn. & red 4·00 35
488. 56. 3 c. on 26 c. (No. 344) 4·50 10
489. 5 c. on 13 c. (No. 343) 4·25 10
492. 57. 5 c. on 1 k. red and blue 6·50 10
493. 6 c. on 10 c. brown & red 4·25 80
494. 6 c. on 12 c. blue & green 4·75 10

١٣٣٦ (78.) ١٣٣٧ (82.)

**1918.** Optd with T **78** ("1336").
507 56 2 k. brown, green & sil 12·00 55

**1918.** Surch. as T **78** and new value in English and Persian.
508. 56. 24 c. on 4 k. (No. 348) .. 13·00 50
509. 10 k. on 5 k. (No. 349) .. 14·00 1·25

**1918.** Coronation issue of 1915 optd **Novembre 1918** (date also in Persian).
510 67 2 k. red, blue and silver 2·00 1·50
511 3 k. brown, lilac & silver 2·00 1·50
512 5 k. grey, brown & silver 3·00 1·50
513 – 1 t. black, violet & gold 3·00 1·50
514 – 2 t. brown, green & gold 3·25 1·50
515 – 3 t. red, crimson & gold 4·00 1·50
516 – 5 t. grey, blue and gold 4·50 2·50

**1918.** Surch as T **82** and new value in English and Persian.
517 57 3 c. on 12 c. blue & grn 5·00 10
518 6 c. on 10 c. brown & red 5·00 10
519 6 c. on 1 k. red and blue 5·00 10

**1918.** Optd with T **82** ("1337").
520 56 2 k. brown, green & sil 28·00 1·50
521 3 k. brown, grey & silver 12·00 70
522 4 k. brown, blue & silver 65·00 2·75
523 5 k. sepia, brown & gold 35·00 1·50
524 10 k. brown, orge & gold 28·00 1·50
525 20 k. brown, grn & gold £150 18·00
526 30 k. brown, red & gold 48·00 3·25

84. Ahmed Mirza. 92. Ahmed Mirza.

**1919.** Type **84** surch **Provisoire 1919** and value in English and Persian.
527 84 1 c. yellow .. .. 70 10
528 3 c. green .. .. 1·00 10
529 5 c. purple .. .. 2·00 10
530 6 c. violet .. .. 4·00 10
531 12 c. blue .. .. 6·00 15

**1919.** Surch. **1919** and value in English and Persian.
532. 13. 2 k. on 5 c. mauve .. 1·60 70
533. 3 k. on 5 c. mauve .. 1·60 70
534. 4 k. on 5 c. mauve .. 1·60 70
535. 5 k. on 5 c. mauve .. 1·60 70
536. 15. 10 k. on 10 c. red .. 1·60 70
537. 20 k. on 10 c. red .. 2·25 1·10
538. 30 k. on 10 c. red .. 2·25 1·10
539. 50 k. on 14 c. orange .. 2·25 1·75

**1921.** Surch. **6-CHAHIS** in English and Persian.
539a. 57. 6 c. on 12 c. blue & green 17·00 15

**1921.** Coup d'Etat of Reza Khan. Coronation issue of 1915 optd. **21. FEV. 1921** in English and Persian.
540 66 3 c. green .. .. 4·00
541 5 c. red .. .. 4·00
542 6 c. red and green .. 4·00
543 10 c. brown and green .. 4·00
544 12 c. blue .. .. 4·00
545 67 1 k. black, brown & sil 4·00
546 2 k. red, blue and silver 5·00
547 5 k. grey, brown & silver 6·00
548 – 2 t. brown, green & gold 6·00
549 – 3 t. red, crimson & gold 6·00
550 – 5 t. grey, blue and gold 6·00

**1922.** Surch. with value in English only.
551. 57. 10 c. on 6 c. brn. & grn. 22·00 2·25
552. 1 k. on 12 c. blue & grn. 22·00 3·50

**1922.** Surcharged with value in English only over **BENADERS.**
553. 57. 10 c. on 6 c. brn. & grn. 15·00 2·25
554. 1 k. on 12 c. blue & grn. 15·00 2·75

**1922.** Optd. **CONTROLE 1922** in English and Persian.
555. 57. 1 c. orange and green .. 35 10
556. 2 c. brown and red .. 35 10
557. 3 c. green and grey .. 35 10
558. 3 c. green and brown .. 40 10
559. 3 c. red and brown .. 20·00 3·50
560. 6 c. brown and green .. 35 10
561. 9 c. lilac and brown .. 70 10
562. 10 c. brown and red .. 70 10
563. 57. 12 c. blue and green .. 1·10 10
564. 24 c. green and purple .. 3·50 10
565. 1 k. red and blue .. 9·00 10
566. 2 k. purple and green .. 13·00 10
567. 3 k. black and lilac .. 25·00 10
568. 4 k. blue and black .. 60·00 80
569. 5 k. blue and red .. 30·00 10
570. 10 k. red and brown .. 75·00 15
571. 20 k. yellow and brown 75·00 15
572. 30 k. green and red .. 85·00 15

**1922.** Surch in English and Persian.
573 57 3 c. on 12 c. (No. 563) .. 2·50 10
574 6 c. on 24 c. (No. 564) .. 3·25 10
575 10 c. on 20 k. (No. 571) 5·50 1·50
576 1 k. on 30 k. (No. 572) .. 14·00 3·00

**1924.**

577. **92.** 1 c. orange .. .. 20 10
578. 2 c. red .. .. 20 10
579. 3 c. brown .. .. 30 10
580. 6 c. sepia .. .. 30 10
581. 9 c. green .. .. 50 10
582. 10 c. violet .. .. 50 10
583. 12 c. red .. .. 50 10
584. 1 k. blue .. .. 1·00 10
585. 2 k. red and blue .. 2·00 10
586. 3 k. purple and violet .. 8·00 15
587. 5 k. sepia and red .. 12·00 30
588. 10 k. violet and sepia .. 25·00 1·25
589. 20 k. sepia and green .. 30·00 1·25
590. 30 k. black and orange .. 35·00 1·75

**1924.** Surch **p.re. 1924** and value in English and Persian.

591 **84** 1 c. brown .. .. 15 10
592 2 c. grey .. .. 15 10
593 3 c. red .. .. 20 10
594 6 c. orange .. .. 70 10

**1925.** Surch **p.re. 1925** and value in English and Persian.

595 **84** 2 c. green .. .. 15 10
596 3 c. red .. .. 20 10
597 6 c. blue .. .. 35 10
598 9 c. brown .. .. 1·50 10
599 10 c. grey .. .. 3·25 15
600 1 k. green .. .. 3·25 10
601 2 k. mauve .. .. 15·00 20

**94.**

(**95.** " Provisional Pahlavi Government, 31 Oct. 1925".)

**1925.** Deposition of Shah Ahmed and Provisional Government of Riza Khan Pahlavi. Fiscal stamps as T **94** (various frames) optd with T **95**.

602. **94.** 1 c. red .. .. 1·50 70
603. 2 c. yellow .. .. 1·50 70
604. 3 c. green .. .. 1·50 70
605. 5 c. grey .. .. 7·00 1·10
606. 10 c. red .. .. 1·50 1·60
607. 1 k. blue .. .. 3·00 70

(**96.**)

**1926.** Optd. with T **96.**

608. **92.** 1 c. orange .. .. 30 10
609. 2 c. red .. .. 35 10
610. 3 c. brown .. .. 70 15
611. 6 c. sepia .. .. 20·00 18·00

**1926.** Optd **Regne de Pahlavi 1926** in English and Persian.

612 **56** 1 c. purple and orange 20 10
613 2 c. purple and violet .. 20 10
614 3 c. purple and green .. 20 10
615 6 c. purple and red 30 10
616 9 c. purple and grey .. 65 10
617 10 c. maroon and purple 65 10
618 13 c. purple and blue .. 1·75 10
619 26 c. purple and green 5·50 10
620 1 k. brown, violet & sil 4·00 10
621 2 k. brown, green & sil 4·50 10
622 3 k. brown, grey & silver 4·50 15
623 4 k. brown, blue & silver 55·00 30
624 5 k. sepia, brown & gold 35·00 15
625 10 k. brown, orge & gold £200 15
626 20 k. brown, grn & gold £225 30
627 30 k. brown, red & gold £225 1·10

**98.** Riza Shah Pahlavi. **99.**

**1926.**

628 **98** 1 c. green .. .. 15 10
629 2 c. blue .. .. 30 10
630 3 c. green .. .. 55 10
631 6 c. red .. .. 65 10
632 9 c. red .. .. 7·50 10
633 10 c. brown .. 13·00 10
634 12 c. orange .. 17·00 10
635 15 c. blue .. .. 20·00 10
636 **99** 1 k. blue .. .. 32·00 65
637 2 k. mauve .. .. 70·00 10·00

**1927.** Air. Optd with airplane and **POSTE AERIENNE** in English and Persian.

642 **56** 1 c. purple and orange 30 20
643 2 c. purple and violet .. 70 35
644 3 c. purple and green .. 40 30
645 6 c. purple and red .. 55 30
646 9 c. purple and grey .. 55 30
647 10 c. maroon and purple 70 35
648 13 c. purple and blue .. 1·25 70
649 26 c. purple and green 1·40 70
650 1 k. brown, violet & sil 1·40 70
651 2 k. brown, green & sil 3·00 1·50
652 3 k. brown, grey & silver 4·50 1·75
653 4 k. brown, blue & silver 10·00 4·75
654 5 k. sepia, brown & gold 10·00 6·00
655 10 k. brown, orge & gold £400 £130
656 20 k. brown, grn & gold £275 £130
657 30 k. brown, red & gold £275 £130

**1928.** Air. Fiscal stamps surch with Junkers F-13 airplane, **Poste aerien** and new value in French and Persian.

657a **94** 3 k. brown .. .. 55·00 16·00
657b 5 k. brown .. .. 10·00 2·75
657c 1 t. violet .. .. 10·00 4·00
657d 2 t. green .. .. 16·00 7·00
657e 3 t. green .. .. 23·00 8·00

**102.** **104.** Riza Shah Pahlavi.

**1929.** Air. Fiscal stamps as T **102** (various frames) surch with Junkers F-13 airplane, **Poste aerienne** and value in French and Persian.

658 **102** 1 c. green .. .. 10 10
659 2 c. blue .. .. 20 10
660 3 c. red .. .. 10 10
661 5 c. brown .. .. 10 10
662 10 c. green .. .. 15 10
663 1 k. violet .. .. 35 10
664 2 k. orange .. .. 70 20
665 3 k. brn (22 × 30 mm) 50·00 8·00
666 5 k. brn (22 × 33 mm) 6·00 3·00
667 10 k. vio (21 × 31 mm) 15·00 5·50
668 20 k. grn (21 × 31 mm) 22·00 4·00
669 30 k. grn (21 × 31 mm) 27·00 8·00

**1929.**

670. **104.** 1 c. red and green .. 25 10
671. 2 c. blue and red .. 25 10
672. 3 c. green and red .. 25 10
673. 6 c. green and brown .. 25 10
674. 9 c. red and blue .. 50 10
675. 10 c. brown and green 85 10
676. 12 c. violet and black .. 1·10 10
677. 15 c. blue and yellow .. 2·00 10
678. 24 c. lake and olive .. 3·50 10
679. 1 k. black and blue .. 4·00 10
680. 2 k. violet and orange .. 8·00 10
681. 3 k. red and green .. 10·00 15
682. 5 k. green and brown .. 9·00 20
683. 1 t. red and blue .. 12·00 45
684. 2 t. black and red .. 25·00 2·00
685. – 3 t. violet and gold .. 30·00 3·25

DESIGN: 3 t. Shah enthroned (28½ × 39 mm.).

**106.** Riza Shah Pahlavi and Elburz Mts.

**1930.** Air.

686. **106.** 1 c. blue and yellow .. 10 10
687. 2 c. black and blue .. 15 10
688. 3 c. violet and olive .. 15 10
689. 4 c. blue and violet .. 15 10
690. 5 c. red and green .. 15 10
691. 6 c. green and red .. 15 10
692. 8 c. violet and grey .. 15 10
693. 10 c. red and blue .. 20 10
694. 12 c. orange and grey 25 10
695. 15 c. olive and brown .. 25 10
696. 1 k. red and blue .. 55 25
697. 2 k. blue and black .. 55 35
698. 3 k. green and brown .. 70 45
699. 5 k. black and red .. 1·75 55
700. 1 t. purple and orange 2·50 70
701. 2 t. brown and green .. 5·50 2·50
702. 3 t. green and purple .. 22·00 16·00

**107.** **108.** **109.**

Riza Shah Pahlavi.

**1931.**

703. **107.** 1 c. blue and brown .. 20 10
704. 2 c. black and red .. 30 10
705. 3 c. brown and mauve .. 25 10
706. 6 c. violet and red .. 35 10
707. 9 c. red and blue .. 2·00 10
708. 10 c. grey and red .. 5·00 10
709. 11 c. red and blue .. 7·00 10
710. 12 c. mauve and blue .. 6·00 10
711. 16 c. red and black .. 5·50 10
712. 27 c. blue and black .. 12·00 10
713. 1 k. blue and red .. 12·00 10

**1933.** New Currency.

714. **108.** 5 d. brown .. .. 15 10
715. 10 d. blue .. .. 15 10
716. 15 d. grey .. .. 30 10
717. 30 d. green .. .. 30 10
718. 45 d. blue .. .. 60 10
719. 50 d. mauve .. .. 60 10
720. 60 d. green .. .. 1·75 10
721. 75 d. brown .. .. 1·75 10
722. 90 d. red .. .. 1·75 10
723. **109.** 1 r. black and red .. 2·50 10
724. 1 r. 20 red and black .. 7·00 15
725. 1 r. 50 blue and yellow 12·00 15
726. 2 r. brown and blue .. 10·00 15
727. 3 r. green and mauve .. 25·00 35
728. 5 r. red and brown .. 32·00 7·00

**110.** " Justice ". **112.** Cement Works, Chah-Abdul-Azim.

**1935.** 10th Anniv of Riza Khan's Advent to Power.

729. **110.** 5 d. green and brown .. 20 10
730. – 10 d. grey and orange .. 20 10
731. – 15 d. blue and red .. 20 10
732. – 30 d. green and black .. 55 10
733. – 45 d. lake and olive .. 65 10
734. **112.** 75 d. brown and green .. 2·50 40
735. – 90 d. red and blue .. 4·00 70
736. – 1 r. violet and brown .. 14·00 2·75
737. – 1 r. 50 blue and purple .. 6·00 2·00

DESIGNS: 10 d. Ruins of Persepolis (40 × 26 mm). 15 d. "Education" (23 × 33 mm). 30 d. De Havilland Tiger Moth biplanes over Teheran Aerodrome (38 × 25 mm). 45 d. Sakhtessar Sanatorium, Mazanderan (40 × 27 mm). 90 d. Gunboat "Palang" (38 × 24 mm). 1 r. Railway bridge over R. Karun (42 × 29 mm). 1 r. 50, Post and Customs House, Teheran (42 × 27 mm).

**1935.** Optd. **POSTES IRANIENNES.**

(a) Stamps of 1929.

738 **104** 1 c. red and green .. 90·00 25·00
739 2 c. blue and red .. 32·00 12·00
740 3 c. green and red .. 16·00 8·50
741 6 c. green and brown .. 20·00 12·00
742 9 c. red and blue .. 9·00 6·50
743 1 t. red and blue .. 9·00 85
744 2 t. black and red .. 14·00 70
745 – 3 t. violet and gold .. 10·00 3·00

(b) Stamps of 1931.

746. **107.** 1 c. blue and brown .. 90·00 28·00
747. 2 c. black and red .. 9·00 3·25
748. 3 c. brown and mauve 4·50 4·00
749. 6 c. violet and red .. 20·00 12·00
750. 9 c. red and blue .. 20·00 12·00
751. 11 c. red and blue .. 90 10
752. 12 c. mauve and blue .. 60·00 22·00
753. 16 c. red and black .. 1·60 10
754. 27 c. blue and black .. 1·60 10

(c) Stamps of 1933.

755. **108.** 5 c. brown .. .. 15 10
756. 10 d. blue .. .. 20 10
757. 15 d. grey .. .. 20 10
758. 30 d. green .. .. 1·10 10
759. 45 d. blue .. .. 1·10 30
760. 50 d. mauve .. .. 70 10
761. 60 d. green .. .. 70 10
762. 75 d. brown .. .. 2·50 70
763. 90 d. red .. .. 3·25 3·25
764. **109.** 1 r. black and red .. 10·00 14·00
765. 1 r. 20 red and black .. 6·00 65
766. 1 r. 50 blue and green 4·00 20
767. 2 r. brown and blue .. 6·00 20
768. 3 r. green and mauve .. 7·00 20
769. 5 r. red and brown .. 45·00 23·00

**1935.** Air. Air stamps of 1930 optd. **IRAN.**

770. **106.** 1 c. blue and yellow .. 20 10
771. 2 c. black and blue .. 20 10
772. 3 c. violet and olive .. 20 10
773. 4 c. blue and violet .. 20 10
774. 5 c. red and green .. 20 10
775. 6 c. green and red .. 20 10
776. 8 c. violet and grey .. 20 10
777. 10 c. red and blue .. 20 10
778. 12 c. orange and blue .. 20 10
779. 15 c. olive and brown .. 55 20
780. 1 k. red and blue .. 1·75 70
781. 2 k. blue and black .. 2·25 70
782. 3 k. green and brown .. 2·75 2·25
783. 5 k. black and red .. 1·50 70
784. 1 t. purple and orange 35·00 17·00
785. 2 t. brown and green .. 4·50 1·75
786. 3 t. green and purple .. 6·50 2·00

**116.** **117.** **117a.**

Riza Shah Pahlavi.

**1935.** Rial values are larger, 22 × 31 mm.

787. **116.** 5 d. violet .. .. 20 10
788. 10 d. purple .. .. 20 10
789. 15 d. blue .. .. 20 10
790. 30 d. green .. .. 35 10
791. 45 d. orange .. .. 75 10
792. 50 d. brown .. .. 1·50 10
793. 60 d. blue .. .. 6·50 10
794. 75 d. red .. .. 4·50 10
795. 90 d. red .. .. 4·50 10
796. 1 r. purple .. .. 7·50 10
797. 1 r. 50 blue .. .. 13·00 35
798. 2 r. green .. .. 12·00 15
799. 3 r. brown .. .. 13·00 30
800. 5 r. grey .. .. 22·00 6·00

**1936.** Rial values are larger, 23 × 31 mm.

801. **117.** 5 d. violet .. .. 15 10
802. 10 d. mauve .. .. 15 10
803. 15 d. blue .. .. 30 10
804. 30 d. green .. .. 40 10
805. 45 d. red .. .. 55 10
806. 50 d. brown .. .. 80 10
807. 60 d. brown .. .. 55 10
808. 75 d. red .. .. 1·00 10
809. 90 d. red .. .. 1·60 10
810. 1 r. green .. .. 6·00 10
811. 1 r. 50 blue .. .. 3·00 10
812. 2 r. blue .. .. 11·00 10
813. 3 r. purple .. .. 15·00 10
814. 5 r. green .. .. 20·00 45
815. 10 r. blue and brown .. 35·00 5·50

**1938.** 60th Birthday of Shah. Perf or imperf.

815a. **117a.** 5 d. blue .. .. 15 10
815b. 10 d. red .. .. 15 10
815c. 30 d. blue .. .. 15 10
815d. 60 d. brown .. .. 20 10
815e. 90 d. red .. .. 30 15
815f. 1 r. violet .. .. 1·00
815g. 1 r. 50 blue .. .. 35 15
815h. 2 r. red .. .. 1·00
815i. 5 r. mauve .. .. 1·40 1·00
815j. 10 r. red .. .. 3·25 1·75

**118.** Riza Shah Pahlavi. **119.** Princess Fawzieh and Crown Prince.

**1938.** Rial values are larger, 23 × 31 mm.

816. **118.** 5 d. violet .. .. 15 10
817. 10 d. mauve .. .. 15 10
818. 15 d. blue .. .. 15 10
819. 30 d. green .. .. 20 10
820. 45 d. red .. .. 30 10
821. 50 d. brown .. .. 30 10
822. 60 d. orange .. .. 30 10
823. 75 d. red .. .. 35 10
824. 90 d. red .. .. 70 10
825. 1 r. green .. .. 1·25 10
826. 1 r. 50 blue .. .. 7·50 10
827. 2 r. blue .. .. 10·00 10
828. 3 r. purple .. .. 13·00 10
829. 5 r. green .. .. 20·00 25
830. 10 r. blue and brown .. 42·00 1·75

**1939.** Royal Wedding.

831. **119.** 5 d. brown .. .. 15 10
832. 10 d. violet .. .. 20 10
833. 30 d. green .. .. 70 20
834. 90 d. red .. .. 2·00 30
835. 1 r. 50 blue .. .. 3·00 1·10

**120.** Bridge over Karun River. **123.** Mohammed Riza Pahlavi.

**1942.**

850 **120** 5 d. violet .. .. 75 10
851 5 d. orange .. .. 15 10
852 – 10 d. mauve .. .. 75 10
853 – 10 d. green .. .. 15 10
854 – 20 d. violet .. .. 30 10
855 – 20 d. mauve .. .. 30 10
856 – 25 d. red .. .. 3·00 10
857 – 25 d. violet .. .. 45 10
858 – 35 d. green .. .. 25 10
859 – 50 d. blue .. .. 1·25 10
860 – 50 d. green .. .. 35 10
861 – 70 d. brown .. .. 50 10

| | | | | |
|---|---|---|---|---|
| 862 | – | 75 d. purple .. .. | 2·40 | 10 |
| 863 | – | 75 d. red .. .. | 6·00 | 10 |
| 864 | – | 1 r. red .. .. | 4·25 | 10 |
| 865 | – | 1 r. purple .. .. | 4·00 | 10 |
| 866 | – | 1 r. 50 red .. .. | 2·50 | 10 |
| 867 | **120** | 2 r. blue .. .. | 3·00 | 10 |
| 868 | – | 2 r. green .. .. | 4·00 | 10 |
| 869 | – | 2 r. 50 blue .. .. | 3·00 | 10 |
| 870 | – | 3 r. green .. .. | 40·00 | 10 |
| 871 | – | 3 r. purple .. .. | 15·00 | 10 |
| 872 | – | 5 r. green .. .. | 80·00 | 20 |
| 873 | – | 5 r. blue .. .. | 7·50 | 10 |
| 874 | **123** | 10 r. black and orange | 16·00 | 65 |
| 875 | | 10 r. black and brown | 12·00 | 10 |
| 876 | | 20 r. violet and brown | £200 | 8·00 |
| 877 | | 20 r. black and orange | 9·00 | 15 |
| 878 | | 30 r. green and black | £900 | 6·50 |
| 879 | | 30 r. black and green | 9·00 | 20 |
| 880 | | 50 r. red and blue .. | 35·00 | 17·00 |
| 881 | | 50 r. black and purple | 18·00 | 2·50 |
| 882 | | 100 r. black and red .. | £250 | 10·00 |
| 883 | | 200 r. black and blue | £170 | 12·00 |

DESIGNS—HORIZ. 10 d. Vereshk Bridge, N. Iran. 20 d. Granary, Ahwaz. 25 d. Steam train on Karj Bridge. 50 d. Ministry of Justice. 70 d. School building. VERT. 35 d. Museum. 75 d. Side view of museum. 1 to 5 r. Full-face portrait of Mohammed Riza Pahlavi.

**124.** Lion and Bull, Persepolis.

DESIGNS—VERT. 1 r. Persian Warrior, Persepolis. HORIZ. 2½ r. Palace of Darius, Persepolis. 5 r. Tomb of Cyrus, Pasargades. 10 r. King Darius enthroned.

**1948.** Fund to rebuild Avicenna's Tomb at Hamadan (1st issue).

| | | | | |
|---|---|---|---|---|
| 899. | **124.** | 50 d. +25 d. green .. | 20 | 35 |
| 900. | - | 1 r. +50 d. red .. .. | 40 | 50 |
| 901. | - | 2½ r. +1¼ r. blue .. | 80 | 70 |
| 902. | - | 5 r. +2½ r. violet .. | 1·75 | 1·50 |
| 903. | - | 10 r. +5 r. purple .. | 3·00 | 2·00 |

See also Nos. 909/13, 930/4, 939/43, and 1024/28.

**126.** National Flag.

**1949.** Iran's War Effort.

| | | | | |
|---|---|---|---|---|
| 904. | **126.** | 25 d. multicoloured .. | 50 | 15 |
| 905. | - | 50 d. violet .. .. | 1·60 | 30 |
| 906. | - | 1 r. 50 red .. .. | 3·50 | 70 |
| 907. | - | 2 r. 50 blue .. .. | 7·50 | 45 |
| 908. | - | 5 r. green .. .. | 7·50 | 1·00 |

DESIGNS: 50 d. Bandar Shahpur (port). 1 r. 50, Lorries on winding road. 2 r. 50, Vereshk Railway Bridge. 5 r. Mohammed Riza Pahlavi and map of Iran.

**127.** King Ardashir II. **128.** King Ardashir I and Ahura Mazda.

**1949.** Fund to rebuild Avicenna's Tomb (2nd issue).

| | | | | |
|---|---|---|---|---|
| 909. | **127.** | 50 d. +25 d. green .. | 20 | 20 |
| 910. | - | 1 r. +50 d. red .. .. | 30 | 20 |
| 911. | - | 2½ r. +1¼ r. blue .. | 60 | 35 |
| 912. | - | 5 r. +2½ r. plum .. | 1·10 | 1·00 |
| 913. | **128.** | 10 r. +5 r. green .. | 1·90 | 1·75 |

DESIGNS—VERT. 1 r. King Narses. HORIZ. 2½ r. King Shapur I and Emperor Valerian. 5 r. Arch of Ctesiphon.

**129.** Mohammed Riza Pahlavi and Post and Customs House, Teheran.

**130.** Old G.P.O., Teheran. **131.** Mohammed Riza Pahlavi.

**1949.**

| | | | | |
|---|---|---|---|---|
| 914. | – | 5 d. green and red .. | 10 | 10 |
| 915. | – | 10 d. brown and blue .. | 10 | 10 |
| 916. | – | 20 d. blue and violet .. | 20 | 10 |
| 917. | – | 25 d. blue and brown .. | 25 | 10 |
| 918. | – | 50 d. blue and green .. | 30 | 10 |
| 919. | – | 75 d. red and brown .. | 25 | 10 |
| 920. | – | 1 r. green and violet .. | 60 | 10 |
| 921. | – | 1 r. 50 red and green .. | 45 | 10 |
| 922. | **129.** | 2 r. brown and red .. | 60 | 10 |
| 923. | – | 2 r. 50 blue .. .. | 60 | 10 |
| 924. | – | 3 r. orange and blue .. | 1·40 | 10 |
| 925. | – | 5 r. violet and red .. | 1·60 | 10 |
| 926. | **130.** | 10 r. green and red .. | 6·00 | 15 |
| 927. | | 20 r. red and black .. | £300 | 8·50 |
| 928. | **131.** | 30 r. blue and brown .. | 18·00 | 2·25 |
| 929. | | 50 r. blue and red .. | 26·00 | 2·75 |

DESIGNS—HORIZ. All show buildings. In the dinar values, portrait is to right of stamp, and in rial values, to left. 5 d. Ramsar Hotel, Darband, Caspian Sea. 10 d. Zayende River Bridge. 20 d. Bank Melli Iran building. 25 d. Old Royal Palace, Isfahan. 50 d. Chaharbagh School, Isfahan. 75 d. Railway Square. 1 r. Justice Ministry. 1 r. 50, Shah Mosque, Teheran. 2 r. 50, Parliament Building. 3 r. The Great Gate, Isfahan. 5 r. Isfahan.

**132.** Tomb of Ali Abarquh. **134.** Allegory.

**1949.** Fund to rebuild Avicenna's Tomb (3rd issue).

| | | | | |
|---|---|---|---|---|
| 930. | **132.** | 50 d. +25 d. green .. | 20 | 20 |
| 931. | – | 1 r. +50 d. brown .. | 25 | 20 |
| 932. | – | 2½ r. +1¼ r. blue .. | 45 | 35 |
| 933. | – | 5 r. +2½ r. red .. .. | 85 | 85 |
| 934. | – | 10 r. +5 r. olive .. | 1·75 | 1·75 |

DESIGNS—VERT. 1 r. Jami Mosque, Isfahan. HORIZ. 2½ r. Tomb tower, Hamadan. 5 r. Jami Mosque, Ardistan. 10 r. Seljuk coin.

**1950.** 75th Anniv. of U.P.U.

| | | | | |
|---|---|---|---|---|
| 935. | – | 50 d. lake .. .. | 20·00 | 12·00 |
| 936. | **134.** | 2 r. 50 blue .. .. | 23·00 | 16·00 |

DESIGN—HORIZ. 50 d. Hemispheres and doves.

**135.** Riza Shah Pahlavi and Mausoleum.

**1950.** Interment of Riza Shah Pahlavi at Shah Abdul Azim.

| | | | | |
|---|---|---|---|---|
| 937. | **135.** | 50 d. brown .. .. | 5·50 | 1·75 |
| 938. | | 2 r. black .. .. | 12·00 | 2·50 |

**136.** Tomb of Baba Afzal, Kashan. **139.** Flag and Book.

**1950.** Fund to Rebuild Avicenna's Tomb (4th issue).

| | | | | |
|---|---|---|---|---|
| 939 | **136** | 50 d. +25 d. green .. | 15 | 15 |
| 940 | – | 1 r. +50 d. blue .. | 20 | 20 |
| 941 | – | 2½ r. +1¼ r. purple .. | 35 | 30 |
| 942 | – | 5 r. +2½ r. red .. | 85 | 75 |
| 943 | – | 10 r. +5 r. grey .. | 1·90 | 1·50 |

DESIGNS—VERT. 1 r. Gorgan vase. 2½ r. Ghazan Tower, Bistam. HORIZ. 5 r. Masjid-i Gawhar Shad Mosque, Meshed. 10 r. Niche in wall of Mosque at Rezaieh.

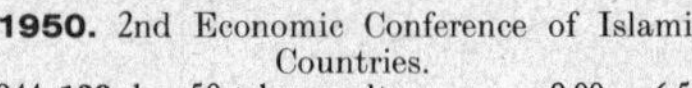

**1950.** 2nd Economic Conference of Islamic Countries.

| | | | | |
|---|---|---|---|---|
| 944 | **139** | 1 r. 50+1 r. mult .. | 9·00 | 6·50 |

**140.** Mohammed Riza Pahlavi in Military School Uniform. **142.** Memorial.

**1950.** Shah's 31st Birthday. Portraits of Shah at different ages, framed as T **140.**

| | | | | |
|---|---|---|---|---|
| 945. | **140.** | 25 d. black and red .. | 80 | 20 |
| 946. | – | 50 d. black and orange | 1·00 | 30 |
| 947. | – | 75 d. black and brown .. | 10·00 | 2·00 |
| 948. | – | 1 r. black and green .. | 7·00 | 80 |
| 949. | – | 2 r. 50 black and blue .. | 12·00 | 80 |
| 950. | – | 5 r. black and red .. | 17·00 | 1·40 |

PORTRAITS—Shah in uniform: 50 d. Naval cadet. 75 d. Boy scout. 1 r. Naval officer. 2 r. 50, Army officer-cadet. 5 r. Army general.

**1950.** 4th Anniv. of Re-establishment of Control in Azerbaijan.

| | | | | |
|---|---|---|---|---|
| 951 | – | 10 d. +5 d. brown .. | 7·00 | 1·25 |
| 952 | **142** | 50 d. +25 d. purple .. | 7·50 | 1·40 |
| 953 | – | 1 r. +50 d. purple .. | 15·00 | 1·75 |
| 954 | – | 1 r. 50+75 d. red & grn | 15·00 | 3·25 |
| 955 | – | 2 r. 50+1 r. 25 blue .. | 16·00 | 5·00 |
| 956 | – | 3 r. +1 r. 50 blue .. | 22·00 | 5·00 |

DESIGNS—VERT. 10 d. Shah and map. 1 r. 50, Map and battle scene. 2 r. 50, Shah and flags. HORIZ. 1 r. Troops marching. 3 r. Cavalry parade.

**143.** Shah and Queen Soraya. **144.** Farabi.

**1951.** Royal Wedding. T **143** and similar portraits.

| | | | | |
|---|---|---|---|---|
| 959. | **143.** | 5 d. purple .. .. | 85 | 35 |
| 960. | | 25 d. orange .. .. | 1·10 | 45 |
| 961. | | 50 d. green .. .. | 2·50 | 55 |
| 962. | – | 1 r. brown .. .. | 2·75 | 90 |
| 963. | – | 1.50 r. red .. .. | 4·00 | 1·10 |
| 964. | – | 2.50 r. blue .. .. | 5·50 | 1·75 |

DESIGNS: 1 r. to 2 r. 50, As T **143** but portraits centrally placed.

**1951.** Millenary of Death of Farabi (philosopher).

| | | | | |
|---|---|---|---|---|
| 965. | **144.** | 50 d. red .. .. | 2·00 | 60 |
| 966. | | 2 r. 50 blue .. .. | 9·00 | 1·75 |

**145.** Mohammed Riza Pahlavi. **146.**

**1951.**

| | | | | |
|---|---|---|---|---|
| 967. | **145.** | 5 d. red .. .. | 10 | 10 |
| 968. | | 10 d. violet .. .. | 10 | 10 |
| 969. | | 20 d. sepia .. .. | 10 | 10 |
| 970. | | 25 d. blue .. .. | 10 | 10 |
| 971. | | 50 d. green .. .. | 40 | 10 |
| 972. | | 50 d. deep green .. | 12·00 | 10 |
| 973. | | 75 d. red .. .. | 30 | 10 |
| 974. | **146.** | 1 r. green .. .. | 1·00 | 10 |
| 975. | | 1 r. turquoise .. .. | 1·00 | 10 |
| 976. | | 1 r. 50 red .. .. | 35 | 10 |
| 977. | | 2 r. brown .. .. | 3·25 | 10 |
| 978. | | 2 r. 50 blue .. .. | 70 | 10 |
| 979. | | 3 r. orange .. .. | 3·25 | 10 |
| 980. | | 5 r. green .. .. | 22·00 | 10 |
| 981. | | 10 r. olive .. .. | 32·00 | 20 |
| 982. | | 20 r. brown .. .. | 15·00 | 30 |
| 983. | | 30 r. blue .. .. | 7·00 | 40 |
| 984. | | 50 r. black .. .. | 30·00 | 1·25 |

**147.** Coran Gate, Shiraz.

**1951.** 600th Death Anniv of Saadi (Muslih-ad-Din) (poet).

| | | | | |
|---|---|---|---|---|
| 985 | **147** | 25 d. +25 d. green .. | 1·50 | 45 |
| 986 | – | 50 d. +50 d. green .. | 1·50 | 55 |
| 987 | – | 1 r. 50+50 d. blue .. | 7·00 | 1·25 |

DESIGNS—HORIZ. 50 d. Tomb of Saadi. VERT. (as T **144**). 1 r. 50, Saadi.

**150.** Shah and Lockheed Super Constellation over Mosque. **151.** Oil Well and Mosque.

**1952.** Air.

| | | | | |
|---|---|---|---|---|
| 988. | – | 50 d. green .. .. | 10 | 10 |
| 989. | **150.** | 1 r. red .. .. .. | 15 | 10 |
| 990. | | 2 r. blue .. .. | 20 | 10 |
| 991. | | 3 r. sepia .. .. | 30 | 10 |
| 992. | | 5 r. lilac .. .. | 45 | 10 |
| 993. | | 10 r. red .. .. | 65 | 10 |
| 994. | | 20 r. violet .. .. | 1·75 | 20 |
| 995. | | 30 r. olive .. .. | 2·25 | 30 |
| 996. | | 50 r. brown .. .. | 6·00 | 40 |
| 997. | | 100 r. sepia .. .. | 65·00 | 3·50 |
| 998. | | 200 r. green .. .. | 25·00 | 5·50 |

DESIGN: 50 d. Shah and Lockheed Super Constellation airplane over Mt. Demavend.

**1953.** Discovery of Oil at Qum. (a) Postage.

| | | | | |
|---|---|---|---|---|
| 999 | **151** | 50 d. bistre and green | 1·00 | 10 |
| 1000 | – | 1 r. bistre and mauve | 1·25 | 10 |
| 1001 | **151** | 2 r. 50 bistre and blue | 3·25 | 35 |
| 1002 | – | 5 r. bistre and brown | 6·00 | 80 |

(b) Air. With Lockheed Super Constellation airplane.

| | | | | |
|---|---|---|---|---|
| 1003 | **151** | 3 r. bistre and violet | 8·00 | 1·75 |
| 1004 | – | 5 r. bistre and brown | 22·00 | 2·75 |
| 1005 | **151** | 10 r. bistre and green | 50·00 | 7·00 |
| 1006 | – | 20 r. bistre and purple | 95·00 | 75·00 |

DESIGN: 1 r., 5 r. (2), 20 r. As Type **151** but horiz.

**153.** Power Station Boiler Plant.

DESIGNS—HORIZ. 1 r. Crude oil stabilizer. 5 r. Pipe-lines. 10 r. View of Abadan. VERT. 2 r. 50, Super fractionaters.

**1953.** 2nd Anniv. of Nationalization of Oil Industry.

| | | | | |
|---|---|---|---|---|
| 1007. | **153.** | 50 d. green .. .. | 1·25 | 15 |
| 1008. | – | 1 r. red .. .. | 1·75 | 15 |
| 1009. | – | 2 r. 50 blue .. .. | 7·00 | 40 |
| 1010. | – | 5 r. orange .. .. | 7·50 | 60 |
| 1011. | – | 10 r. lilac .. .. | 8·50 | 85 |

**154.** Family and U.N. Emblem. **155.** Gymnast.

**1953.** United Nations Day.

| | | | | |
|---|---|---|---|---|
| 1012. | **154.** | 1 r. green & turquoise | 50 | 20 |
| 1013. | | 2 r. 50 blue & light blue | 1·00 | 45 |

**1953.** Ancient Persian Sports.

| | | | | |
|---|---|---|---|---|
| 1014. | **155.** | 1 r. green .. .. | 1·40 | 85 |
| 1015. | – | 2 r. 50 blue .. .. | 6·00 | 1·10 |
| 1016. | – | 3 r. grey .. .. | 18·00 | 1·40 |
| 1017. | – | 5 r. ochre .. .. | 12·00 | 3·25 |
| 1018. | – | 10 r. violet .. .. | 24·00 | 4·50 |

DESIGNS—HORIZ. 2 r. 50, Archer. 3 r. Mountaineers. VERT. 5 r. Polo-player (Persian Sports Club Badge). 10 r. Lion-hunter.

**156.** Herring. **157.** Machinery.

**1954.** Nationalization of Fishing Industry.

| | | | | |
|---|---|---|---|---|
| 1019. | **156.** | 1 r. multicoloured .. | 2·00 | 55 |
| 1020. | – | 2 r. 50 multicoloured .. | 30·00 | 1·75 |
| 1021. | – | 3 r. red .. .. | 12·00 | 1·25 |
| 1022. | **157.** | 5 r. green .. .. | 11·00 | 2·25 |
| 1023. | – | 10 r. multicoloured .. | 20·00 | 5·50 |

DESIGNS—HORIZ. As Type **156:** 2 r. 50, Sardines. 10 r. Sturgeon. As Type **157:** 3 r. Refrigeration machinery.

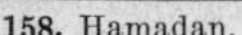

158. Hamadan. 159. Avicenna.

**1954.** Fund to Rebuild Avicenna's Tomb (5th issue).

1024. **158.** 50 d. + 25 d. green .. 15 15
1025. **159.** 1 r. + ½ r. brown .. 20 20
1026. – 2½ r. + 1¼ r. blue .. 45 30
1027. – 5 r. + 2½ r. red .. .. 70 50
1028. – 10 r. + 5 r. olive .. 1·40 1·25

DESIGNS—VERT. As Type **159**: 2½ r. Qabus tower, Gargan. HORIZ. As Type **158**: 5 r. Old tomb of Avicenna. 10 r. New tomb of Avicenna.

160. Shah in Military uniform. 161. Hands breaking Chain.

**1954.**

1029 **160** 5 d. brown .. .. 10 10
1062 5 d. violet .. .. 10 10
1030 10 d. violet .. .. 10 10
1063 10 d. red .. .. 10 10
1031 25 d. red .. .. 10 10
1064 25 d. brown .. .. 10 10
1032 50 d. brown .. .. 10 10
1065 50 d. red .. .. 10 10
1066 – 1 r. green .. .. 15 10
1034 – 1 r. 50 red .. .. 35 10
1067 – 1 r. 50 brown .. 15·00 10
1035 – 2 r. brown .. .. 45 10
1068 – 2 r. green .. .. 35 10
1069 – 2 r. 50 blue .. .. 20 10
1037 – 3 r. green .. .. 1·00 10
1070 – 3 r. brown .. .. 35 10
1038 – 5 r. green .. .. 1·40 10
1071 – 5 r. purple .. .. 80 10
1039 – 10 r. lilac .. .. 6·00 15
1072 – 10 r. blue .. .. 2·75 10
1040 – 20 r. blue .. .. 26·00 1·60
1073 – 20 r. green .. .. 11·00 10
1041 – 30 r. brown .. .. £160 4·50
1074 – 30 r. orange .. .. £130 5·00
1042 – 50 r. orange .. .. 13·00 2·25
1075 – 50 r. brown .. .. £110 6·00
1043 – 100 r. violet .. .. £400 24·00
1044 – 200 r. yellow .. £120 9·00

DESIGN: 1 r. to 200 r. Shah in naval uniform.

**1954.** 1st Anniv of Return of Shah. Mult.

1045. 2 r. Type **161** .. .. 3·25 45
1046. 3 r. Hand holding torch and Iranian flag .. 5·00 70
1047. 5 r. Man clasping Iranian flag .. .. 9·00 1·25

SIZES: 3 r. (19½ × 27½ mm.). 5 r. (20½ × 28½ mm.).

162. Nurse and Child. 163. Felling Trees.

**1954.** U.N. Day.

1048. **162.** 2 r. orange and purple 1·75 50
1049. 3 r. orange and violet 1·90 1·00

**1954.** 4th World Forestry Congress. Inscr. "4eme congres mondial forestier".

1050. **163.** 1 r. green and brown .. 16·00 3·50
1051. – 2 r. 50 blue and green 25·00 7·00
1052. – 5 r. brown and lavender 50·00 15·00
1053. – 10 r. lake and blue .. 60·00 28·00

DESIGNS: 2 r. 50, Man carrying logs. 5 r. Man operating circular saw. 10 r. Ancient Persian galley.

164. 165. Parliament Building.

**1955.** National Costumes.

1054. **164.** 1 r. multicoloured .. 1·25 45
1055. – 2 r. multicoloured .. 2·25 65
1056. – 2 r. 50 multicoloured 20·00 1·25
1057. – 3 r. multicoloured .. 8·00 1·25
1058. – 5 r. multicoloured .. 17·00 2·50

DESIGNS—2 r. Male costume. 2 r. 50, 3 r., 5 r. Female costumes.

**1955.** 50th Anniv. of Constitution.

1059. – 2 r. green and purple .. 2·00 40
1060. – 3 r. blue .. .. 4·00 60
1061. **165.** 5 r. orange and green .. 5·00 95

DESIGNS—HORIZ. 2 r. Gateway of Parliament Building. VERT. 3 r. Winged Statue.

167. U.N. Emblem and Hemispheres. 168. Wrestlers.

**1955.** United Nations Day.

1077 **167** 1 r. orange and red .. 65 30
1078 2 r. 50 lt blue & blue 1·10 35

**1955.** International Success of Iranian Wrestlers.

1079 **168** 2 r. 50 multicoloured 3·25 70

169. Hospital Buildings. 170.

**1956.** Opening of Nemazi Hospital, Shiraz. Multicoloured.

1080 – 50 d. (24 × 33½ mm) .. 1·00 40
1081 **169** 1 r. (36 × 24½ mm) .. 4·00 60
1082 – 2 r. 50 (24 × 33½ mm) 5·00 1·25
1083 – 5 r. (36 × 23 mm) .. 12·00 2·00
1084 – 10 r. (24 × 33½ mm) .. 20·00 5·00

DESIGNS: 50 d. Hospital garden. 2 r. 50, Spear thrower. 5 r. Koran gate, Shiraz. 10 r. Poet Hafiz and his tomb.

**1956.** 10th Anniv of National Olympic Committee.

1085 **170** 5 r. lilac .. .. 8·50 5·50

171. Tusi's Tomb, Maragheh. 172. Reveille.

**1956.** 700th Death Anniv. of Nasir ed-Din Tusi, 1201–74 (astronomer and scientist).

1086. **171.** 1 r. orange .. .. 2·50 40
1087. – 2 r. 50 blue (Astrolabe) 5·00 60
1088. – 5 r. lilac and sepia (Portrait) .. .. 8·00 1·00

**1956.** National Scout Jamboree.

1089. **172.** 2 r. 50 blue & ultram. 8·00 3·50
1090. – 5 r. mauve and lilac .. 15·00 4·00

DESIGN: 5 r. Shah in scout's uniform and badge.

173. 174. U.N. Emblem and Young People.

**1956.** World Health Organization.

1091. **173.** 6 r. mauve .. .. 2·00 70

**1956.** United Nations Day.

1092. **174.** 1 r. green .. .. 50 30
1093. – 2 r. 50 blue and green 1·25 50

DESIGN: 2 r. 50, U.N. emblem and scales of justice.

175. Telecommunications Centre, Teheran.

DESIGN: 6 r. Telegraph poles and mosque.

**1956.** Centenary of Persian Telegraphs.

1094 **175** 2 r. 50 green and blue 3·00 1·25
1095 – 6 r. mauve and pink 8·00 1·75

176. Shah and Pres. Mirza.

**1956.** Visit of President of Pakistan.

1096 **176** 1 r. multicoloured .. 1·00 20

177. Mohammed Riza Pahlavi. 178.

**1956.**

1097. **177.** 5 d. red and rose .. 10 10
1098. 10 d. violet and blue 10 10
1099. 25 d. brown and sepia 10 10
1100. 50 d. olive and sepia 10 10
1101. 1 r. green and brown 10 10
1102. 1 r. 50 brown & mauve 20 10
1103. 2 r. red and mauve .. 15 10
1104. 2 r. 50 blue & ultram. 30 10
1105. 3 r. bistre and brown 30 10
1106. 5 r. red .. .. 35 10
1132. 6 r. blue and light blue 70 10
1133. 10 r. turquoise & green 85 10
1134. 20 r. olive and green 2·50 10
1135. 30 r. sepia and blue .. 5·50 80
1136. 50 r. brown and sepia 6·50 1·50
1137. 100 r. red & brt. purple £150 7·50
1138. 200 r. bistre and violet 80·00 8·00

**1956.**

1122. **178.** 5 d. plum and violet .. 10 10
1123. 10 d. mauve & purple 10 10
1124. 25 d. orange and red 10 10
1125. 50 d. green and grey 10 10
1126. 1 r. turquoise & green 10 10
1127. 1 r. 50 pur. & mauve 10 10
1128. 2 r. turquoise and blue 30 10
1129. 2 r. 50 turq. and blue 30 10
1130. 3 r. red and rose .. 70 10
1131. 5 r. violet and blue .. 60 10
1107. 6 r. mauve and lilac .. 65 10
1108. 10 r. green and blue .. 90 10
1109. 20 r. blue and green .. 3·25 15
1110. 30 r. orange and red .. 14·00 1·75
1111. 50 r. sage and green .. 4·00 60
1112. 100 r. red and purple £190 22·00
1113. 200 r. violet & purple 70·00 15·00

179. Lord Baden-Powell. 180. Steam Express Train and Mosque.

**1957.** Birth Centenary of Lord Baden-Powell (founder of Boy Scout movement).

1114 **179** 10 r. brown and green 4·00 2·00

**1957.** Inauguration of Teheran–Meshed Railway. Multicoloured.

1115 2 r. 50 Track and signal .. 4·00 75
1116 5 r. Diesel train and map (horiz) .. .. 6·50 1·25
1117 10 r. Type **180** .. .. 15·00 8·00

181. President Gronchi and Shah.

**1957.** Visit of President of Italy.

1118 **181** 2 r. grey, green & red 1·00 50
1119 – 6 r. blue, green & red 2·50 1·10

DESIGN: 6 r., Plaque and flags between ruins of Persepolis and Colosseum.

183. Queen Soraya and Ramsar Hotel.

**1957.** 6th Medical Congress, Ramsar.

1120. **183.** 2 r. green and blue .. 1·50 20

184. Shah and King Faisal II of Iraq.

**1957.** Visit of King of Iraq.

1121. **184.** 2 r. blue, red & green 75 15

185. Globes within Laurel Sprays.

**1957.** Int. Cartographical Conf., Teheran.

1140. **185.** 10 r. multicoloured .. 4·00 65

186. "Flight". 187. "The Weight-lifter."

**1957.** Air. United Nations Day.

1141. **186.** 10 r. red and mauve .. 1·40 60
1142. 20 r. purple and violet 1·90 1·00

**1957.** Int. Weightlifting Championships.

1143. **187.** 10 r. blue, green & red 1·50 35

188. Radio Mast and Buildings. 189. Oil Derrick and "Bowl of Flames".

**1958.** 30th Anniv. of Iranian Broadcasting Service.

1144. **188.** 10 r. sepia, buff & blue .. .. 1·75 65

**1958.** 50th Anniv. of Iranian Oil Industry.

1145. **189.** 2 r. brn., yell. & grey 2·25 30
1146. 10 r. brn., yell. & blue 5·75 80

190. Exhibition Emblem. 191. Train on Viaduct.

**1958.** Brussels Int. Exn.

1147. **190.** 2 r. 50 red .. .. 45 10
1148. 6 r. red .. .. 80 20

**1958.** Inaug of Teheran–Tabriz Railway.

1149 **191** 6 r. lilac .. .. 10·00 2·50
1150 – 8 r. green .. .. 14·00 5·50

DESIGN: 8 r. Express train and route map.

192. Mohammed Riza Pahlavi.

193. U.N. Emblem and Map of Persia.

**1958.**

| | | | | |
|---|---|---|---|---|
| 1162 | **192** | 5 d. violet .. .. | 10 | 10 |
| 1163 | | 5 d. brown .. .. | 10 | 10 |
| 1164 | | 10 d. red .. .. | 10 | 10 |
| 1165 | | 10 d. green .. .. | 10 | 10 |
| 1166 | | 10 d. turquoise .. | 10 | 10 |
| 1167 | | 25 d. red .. .. | 10 | 10 |
| 1168 | | 25 d. orange .. .. | 20 | 10 |
| 1169 | | 50 d. blue .. .. | 20 | 10 |
| 1170 | | 50 d. red .. .. | 10 | 10 |
| 1171 | | 1 r. green .. .. | 35 | 10 |
| 1172 | | 1 r. violet .. .. | 35 | 10 |
| 1232 | | 2 r. brown .. .. | 3·50 | 10 |
| 1233 | | 3 r. brown .. .. | 2·50 | 10 |
| 1177 | | 6 r. blue .. .. | 1·25 | 10 |
| 1179 | | 8 r. purple .. .. | 1·00 | 10 |
| 1180 | | 8 r. brown .. .. | 2·10 | 10 |
| 1181 | | 10 r. black .. .. | 75 | 10 |
| 1182 | | 14 r. blue .. .. | 3·00 | 10 |
| 1183 | | 14 r. green .. .. | 95 | 10 |
| 1185 | | 20 r. green .. .. | 1·10 | 10 |
| 1186 | | 30 r. red .. .. | 6·00 | 20 |
| 1187 | | 30 r. brown .. .. | 1·50 | 10 |
| 1188 | | 50 r. purple .. .. | 60·00 | 25 |
| 1189 | | 50 r. blue .. .. | 2·75 | 10 |
| 1190 | | 100 r. orange .. | 6·50 | 50 |
| 1191 | | 100 r. green .. .. | 85·00 | 1·50 |
| 1192 | | 200 r. green .. .. | 40·00 | 1·75 |
| 1193 | | 200 r. mauve .. | £225 | 1·25 |

**1958.** United Nations Day.

| | | | | |
|---|---|---|---|---|
| 1194 | **193** | 6 r. blue & light blue | 75 | 60 |
| 1195 | | 10 r. violet and green | 95 | 80 |

194. Clasped Hands.

195. Rudagi playing Lyre.

**1958.** 10th Anniv. of Declaration of Human Rights.

| | | | | |
|---|---|---|---|---|
| 1196. | **194.** | 6 r. brown & chocolate | 35 | 20 |
| 1197. | | 8 r. olive and green .. | 90 | 35 |

**1958.** 1100th Birth Anniv. of Rudagi (poet and musician).

| | | | | |
|---|---|---|---|---|
| 1198. | **195.** | 2 r. 50 blue .. .. | 4·00 | 25 |
| 1199. | – | 5 r. violet .. .. | 8·50 | 45 |
| 1200. | **195.** | 10 r. sepia .. .. | 15·00 | 90 |

DESIGN: 5 r. Rudagi meditating.

196.

**1959.** Red Cross Commem.

| | | | | |
|---|---|---|---|---|
| 1201. | **196.** | 1 r. multicoloured .. | 85 | 20 |
| 1202. | | 6 r. multicoloured .. | 1·40 | 55 |

197. Wrestlers.

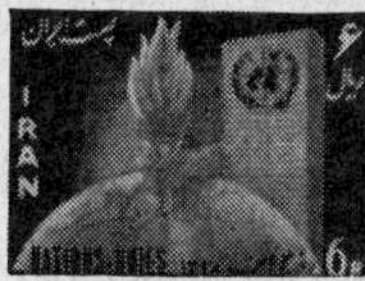

198. Torch of Freedom.

**1959.** World Wrestling Championships.

| | | | | |
|---|---|---|---|---|
| 1203. | **197.** | 6 r. multicoloured .. | 4·25 | 75 |

**1959.** United Nations Day.

| | | | | |
|---|---|---|---|---|
| 1204. | **198.** | 6 r. red, brn. & bistre | 65 | 25 |

**HAVE YOU READ THE NOTES AT THE BEGINNING OF THIS CATALOGUE?**
These often provide answers to the enquiries we receive.

199. Shah and President Khan.

**1959.** Visit of President of Pakistan.

| | | | | |
|---|---|---|---|---|
| 1205. | **199.** | 6 r. multicoloured .. | 2·50 | 45 |

200. I.L.O. Emblem.

201. Pahlavi Foundation Bridge, Khorramshahr.

**1959.** 40th Anniv of I.L.O.

| | | | | |
|---|---|---|---|---|
| 1206 | **200** | 1 r. blue & light blue | 50 | 20 |
| 1207 | | 5 r. brown & lt brown | 75 | 35 |

**1960.** Opening of Pahlavi Foundation Bridge, Khorramshahr.

| | | | | |
|---|---|---|---|---|
| 1208. | **201.** | 1 r. blue and brown .. | 1·00 | 10 |
| 1209. | – | 5 r. green and blue .. | 1·40 | 30 |

DESIGN: 5 r. Close-up view of bridge.

202. " Uprooted Tree ".

203. Insecticide Sprayer.

**1960.** World Refugee Year.

| | | | | |
|---|---|---|---|---|
| 1210 | – | 1 r. blue .. .. | 10 | 10 |
| 1211 | **202** | 6 r. black and green | 35 | 20 |

DESIGN: 1 r. "Uprooted tree" and columns.

**1960.** Anti-Malaria Campaign.

| | | | | |
|---|---|---|---|---|
| 1212. | – | 1 r. blk. & red on yell. | 30 | 15 |
| 1213. | **203.** | 2 r. blue, blk. & light-bl. | 80 | 20 |
| 1214. | – | 3 r. blk. & red on green | 1·40 | 50 |

DESIGNS (30×37 mm.): 1 r., 3 r. Different views of mosquito crossed out in red.

204. Polo Player.

206. Scout Emblem within Flower.

205. Shah and King Hussein.

**1960.** "Olympic Games Week".

| | | | | |
|---|---|---|---|---|
| 1215 | **204** | 1 r. purple .. .. | 50 | 20 |
| 1216 | – | 6 r. violet and blue .. | 1·10 | 50 |

DESIGN: 6 r. Archer.

**1960.** Visit of King of Jordan.

| | | | | |
|---|---|---|---|---|
| 1217. | **205.** | 6 r. multicoloured .. | 1·50 | 20 |

**1960.** 3rd National Scout Jamboree.

| | | | | |
|---|---|---|---|---|
| 1218. | **206.** | 1 r. green .. .. | 30 | 10 |
| 1219. | – | 6 r. ochre, sep. & blue | 60 | 20 |

DESIGN: 6 r. Scout camp Persepolis.

207. Shah and Queen Farah.

**1960.** Royal Wedding.

| | | | | |
|---|---|---|---|---|
| 1220. | **207.** | 1 r. green .. .. | 1·00 | 40 |
| 1221. | | 5 r. blue .. .. | 2·75 | 70 |

208. U.N. Emblem.

209. Shah and Queen Elizabeth II.

**1960.** 15th Anniv. of U.N.O.

| | | | | |
|---|---|---|---|---|
| 1222. | **208.** | 6 r. sepia, blue & bistre | 55 | 15 |

**1961.** Visit of Queen Elizabeth II.

| | | | | |
|---|---|---|---|---|
| 1223. | **209.** | 1 r. brown .. .. | 35 | 10 |
| 1224. | | 6 r. blue .. .. | 80 | 20 |

210. Girl playing Pan-pipes.

DESIGN — (24 × $39\frac{1}{2}$ mm.): 6 r. Safiaddin Anmavi (musician).

**1961.** Int. Music Congress, Teheran.

| | | | | |
|---|---|---|---|---|
| 1225. | **210.** | 1 r. stone and brown | 75 | 10 |
| 1226. | – | 6 r. slate .. .. | 1·25 | 15 |

211. Royal Family.

**1961.** Birth of Crown Prince.

| | | | | |
|---|---|---|---|---|
| 1227. | **211.** | 1 r. purple .. .. | 1·00 | 50 |
| 1228. | | 6 r. blue .. .. | 4·50 | 1·25 |

212. U.N. Emblem and Birds.

213. Tree-planting.

**1961.** United Nations Day.

| | | | | |
|---|---|---|---|---|
| 1236. | **212.** | 2 r. red and blue .. | 15 | 10 |
| 1237. | | 6 r. violet and blue | 45 | 20 |

**1962.** Afforestation Week.

| | | | | |
|---|---|---|---|---|
| 1238. | **213.** | 2 r. blue, cream & green | 25 | 10 |
| 1239. | | 6 r. grn., blue & ultram. | 55 | 20 |

214. Worker.

215. Family on Map.

**1962.** Workers' Day.

| | | | | |
|---|---|---|---|---|
| 1240. | **214.** | 2 r. multicoloured .. | 15 | 10 |
| 1241. | | 6 r. multicoloured .. | 45 | 30 |

**1962.** Social Insurance.

| | | | | |
|---|---|---|---|---|
| 1242. | **215.** | 2 r. vio., black & yell. | 15 | 10 |
| 1243. | | 6 r. blue, blk. & lt. blue | 45 | 30 |

216. Sugar Plantation.

217. Karaj Dam.

**1962.** Sugar Cane Production.

| | | | | |
|---|---|---|---|---|
| 1244. | **216.** | 2 r. grn., bl. & ultram. | 50 | 15 |
| 1245. | | 6 r. bl., cream & ultram. | 90 | 30 |

**1962.** Inaug. of Karaj Dam.

| | | | | |
|---|---|---|---|---|
| 1246. | **217.** | 2 r. green & brown .. | 1·00 | 10 |
| 1247. | | 6 r. bl. & ultramarine | 1·40 | 20 |

218. Sefid Rud Dam.

219. U.N. Emblem.

**1962.** Inaug. of Sefid Rud Dam.

| | | | | |
|---|---|---|---|---|
| 1248. | **218.** | 2 r. buff, bl. & myrtle | 1·00 | 15 |
| 1249. | – | 6 r. black, blue & brn. | 1·40 | 30 |

DESIGN: 6 r. Distant view of dam.

**1962.** 15th Anniv. of U.N.E.S.C.O.

| | | | | |
|---|---|---|---|---|
| 1250. | **219.** | 2 r. blk., green & red | 40 | 15 |
| 1251. | | 6 r. blue, green & red | 85 | 30 |

220. Arrow piercing Mosquito.

221. Mohammed Riza Pahlavi.

222. Shah and Palace of Darius, Persepolis.

223. Oil Pipelines.

**1962.** Malaria Eradication.

| | | | | |
|---|---|---|---|---|
| 1252. | **220.** | 2 r. black and green .. | 15 | 10 |
| 1253. | – | 6 r. blue and red .. | 50 | 20 |
| 1254. | – | 10 r. ultram. and blue | 90 | 25 |

DESIGNS—VERT. ($29\frac{1}{2}\times34\frac{1}{2}$ mm.): 6 r. Mosquito and insecticide-sprayer. HORIZ. (As Type 220)—10 r. Globe and campaign emblem.

**1962.**

| | | | | |
|---|---|---|---|---|
| 1255 | **221** | 5 d. green .. .. | 10 | 10 |
| 1256 | | 10 d. brown .. | 10 | 10 |
| 1257 | | 25 d. blue .. .. | 10 | 10 |
| 1336 | | 50 d. turquoise .. | 10 | 10 |
| 1337 | | 1 r. orange .. .. | 15 | 10 |
| 1338 | | 2 r. violet .. .. | 20 | 10 |
| 1339 | | 5 r. brown .. .. | 65 | 10 |
| 1340 | **222** | 6 r. blue .. .. | 2·75 | 10 |
| 1341 | | 8 r. green .. .. | 70 | 10 |
| 1342 | | 10 r. blue .. .. | 1·00 | 10 |
| 1265a | | 11 r. green .. .. | 60 | 10 |
| 1266a | | 14 r. violet .. .. | 1·00 | 10 |
| 1345 | | 20 r. brown .. | 2·00 | 20 |
| 1346 | | 50 r. red .. .. | 3·25 | 45 |

**1962.** 2nd Petroleum Symposium of Economic Commission for Asia and the Far East.

| | | | | |
|---|---|---|---|---|
| 1269 | **223** | 6 r. brown and blue .. | 65 | 15 |
| 1270 | | 14 r. brown and grey | 1·25 | 35 |

224. Hippocrates and Avicenna.

225. New Houses.

**1962.** W.H.O. Medical Congress, Teheran.

| | | | | |
|---|---|---|---|---|
| 1271. | **224.** | 2 r blue, brn. & cream | 1·00 | 15 |
| 1272. | | 6 r. blue, sage & green | 1·50 | 30 |

**1962.** United Nations Day.

| | | | | |
|---|---|---|---|---|
| 1273. | **225.** | 6 r. blue and indigo .. | 45 | 15 |
| 1274. | – | 14 r. green and blue .. | 95 | 20 |

DESIGN—HORIZ. 14 r. Laying foundation stone.

226. "Bouquet for the Crown Prince".

**1962.** Crown Prince's Birthday.

| | | | | |
|---|---|---|---|---|
| 1275 | **226** | 6 r. blue .. .. | 3·00 | 60 |
| 1276 | | 14 r. green .. .. | 6·00 | 1·40 |

**227.** Persian Gulf Map. **228.** Hilton Hotel, Teheran.

**1962.** Persian Gulf Seminar.
1277. **227.** 6 r. bl., pink & pale bl. 65 15
1278. 14 r. blue, flesh & pink 1·25 30

**1963.** Opening of Royal Teheran Hilton Hotel.
1279. **228.** 6 r. blue .. .. 1·40 20
1280. 14 r. brown .. .. 2·25 45

**229.** Refugees.

**1963.** Earthquake Relief Fund.
1281. **229.** 14 r.+6 r. blue, brown and green .. .. 90 60

**230.** Mohammed Riza Shah Dam.

**1963.** Inaug. of Mohammed Riza Shah Dam.
1282. **230.** 6 r. multicoloured .. 2·25 30
1283. 14 r. multicoloured .. 4·50 65

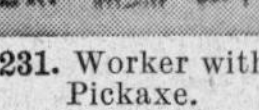

**231.** Worker with Pickaxe. **232.** Bird and Globe.

**1963.** Workers' Day.
1283a.**231.** 2 r. black & yellow .. 45 10
1283b. 6 r. black and blue .. 60 20

**1963.** Freedom from Hunger.
1284 **232** 2 r. ultramarine, blue and bistre .. 75 10
1285 – 6 r. black, bistre & bl 1·25 20
1286 – 14 r. bistre and green 3·00 45
DESIGNS: 6 r. Globe and ears of wheat (stylized). 14 r. Globe encircled by scroll, and campaign emblem.

**233.** Shah and Scroll.

**1963.** Agrarian Reform Act.
1287. **233.** 6 r. green and blue .. 1·25 20
1288. 14 r. green and yellow 2·50 55

**234.** Shah and King Frederick.

**1963.** Visit of King of Denmark.
1289. **234.** 6 r. blue and indigo .. 1·50 25
1290. 14 r. brown and sepia 3·50 50

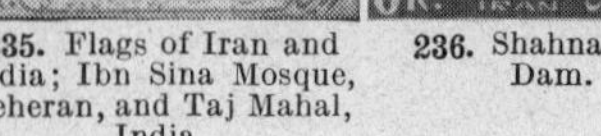

**235.** Flags of Iran and India; Ibn Sina Mosque, Teheran, and Taj Mahal, India. **236.** Shahnaz Dam.

**1963.** Visit of President Radhakrishnan of India.
1291. **235.** 6 r. multicoloured .. 2·00 25
1292. 14 r. multicoloured .. 4·50 50

**1963.** Inaug. of Shahnaz Dam.
1293. **236.** 6 r. ultram., bl. & grn. 2·00 25
1294. 14 r. green, blue & buff 3·00 50

**237.** Centenary Emblem. **238.** Shah and Queen Juliana.

**1963.** Red Cross Centenary.
1295. **237.** 6 r. multicoloured .. 2·50 30
1296. 14 r. grey, red & buff 4·50 60

**1963.** Visit of Queen of the Netherlands.
1304. **238.** 6 r. blue and ultram. 3·00 30
1305. 14 r. green & black .. 4·00 60

**240.** Students in Class.

**1963.** Formation of Literacy Teaching Corps.
1306. **240.** 6 r. multicoloured .. 1·75 15
1307. 14 r. multicoloured .. 3·00 30

**241.** Pres. De Gaulle and View of Teheran.

**1963.** Visit of President of France.
1308. **241.** 6 r. ultramarine & blue 2·00 30
1309. 14 r. brown and ochre 4·00 60

**242.** Plant, Route Map and Emblem. **243.** Pres. Lubke and Shah Mosque, Isfahan.

**1963.** Opening of Chemical Fertiliser Plant, Shiraz.
1310 **242** 6 r. black, yell & red 2·25 30
1311 – 14 r. black, blue & yell 4·25 60
DESIGN—HORIZ. 14 r. Fertiliser plant and emblem.

**1963.** Visit of President of German Federal Republic.
1312. **243.** 6 r. blue and violet .. 2·00 30
1313. 14 r. brown and grey 4·00 55

**244.** U.N. Emblem.

**1963.** United Nations Day.
1314. **244.** 8 r. multicoloured .. 1·25 20

**245.** Aircraft crossing U.N. Emblem. **246.** Crown Prince Riza.

**1963.** Iranian Air Force in Congo.
1315. **245.** 6 r. multicoloured .. 1·25 20

**1963.** Children's Day.
1316. **246.** 2 r. brown .. .. 1·00 15
1317. 6 r. blue .. .. 1·40 25

**247.** Chairman Brezhnev. **248.** Ataturk's Mausoleum.

**1963.** Visit of Chairman of Soviet Presidium.
1318. **247.** 5 r. multicoloured .. 2·25 30
1319. 11 r. multicoloured .. 3·50 50

**1963.** 25th Death Anniv. of Kemal Ataturk.
1320. **248.** 4 r. brown, grey & grn. 1·75 15
1321. – 5 r. black, red & yell. 2·00 20
DESIGN: 5 r. Kemal Ataturk.

**249.** Scales of Justice and Globe. **250.** Mother and Child.

**1963.** 15th Anniv. of Declaration of Human Rights.
1322. **249.** 6 r. black, blue & green 1·10 20
1323. 14 r. blk., cream & brn. 1·75 30

**1963.** Mothers Day.
1324. **250.** 2 r. multicoloured .. 1·00 15
1325. 4 r. multicoloured .. 2·00 20

**251.** Cogwheel and Map. **252.** Hand with Document (Profit-sharing).

**1963.** Industrial Development.
1326. **251.** 8 r. bl., cream & turq. 1·75 30

**1964.** Six-Point Reform Law.
1327. **252.** 2 r. brn., violet & blue 20 10
1328. – 4 r. brown and grey .. 1·10 15
1329. – 6 r. multicoloured .. 1·40 20
1330. – 8 r. multicoloured .. 1·50 25
1331. – 10 r. red, grn. & deep grn. 1·75 30
1332. – 12 r. brown and red .. 2·75 35
DESIGNS: 4 r. Factory and documents on scales (Sale of Shares to Workers). 6 r. Worker on Globe (Education Corps). 8 r. Tractor (Land reform). 10 r. Trees (Nationalization of forests). 12 r. Silhouettes within gateway (Votes for Women).

**253.** U.N. Emblem. **254.** Blossom.

**1964.** 20th Economic Commission for Asia and the Far East Session, Teheran.
1347. **253.** 14 r. black and green 1·50 30

**1964.** New Year Greetings.
1348. **254.** 50 d. orge., sepia & grn. 15 10
1349. 1 r. orge., black & blue 15 10

**255.** Weather Vane. **256.** "Tourism".

**1964.** World Meteorological Day.
1350. **255.** 6 r. violet and blue .. 1·25 20

**1964.** 1st Anniv. of Iranian Tourist Organization (INTO).
1351. **256.** 6 r. grn., vio. & black 90 20
1352. – 11 r. orge., brn. & blk. 1·60 45
DESIGN: 11 r. Winged beasts, column and INTO emblem.

**257.** Rudagi (blind poet). **258.** Sculptured Head.

**1964.** Opening of Blind Institute.
1353. **257.** 6 r. blue .. .. 90 20
1354. 8 r. brown .. .. 1·60 30

**1964.** "7000 Years of Persian Art" Exn.
1355. **258.** 2 r. blue and grey .. 1·00 10
1356. – 4 r. ultramarine & blue 4·00 20
1357. – 6 r. yellow and brown 1·50 30
1358. – 10 r. green and yellow 3·00 50
DESIGNS—HORIZ. 4 r. Sumerian war chariot on map. VERT. 6 r. Golden cup with lion decorations. 10 r. Sculptured head of man.

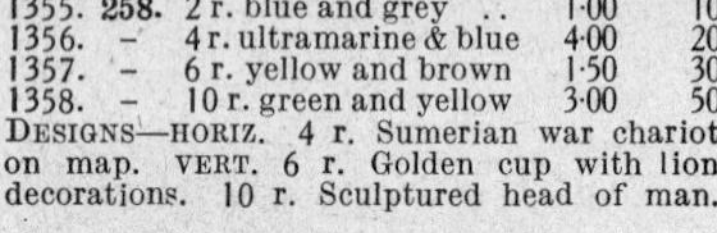

**259.** Shah and Emperor Haile Selassie.

**1964.** Visit of Emperor of Ethiopia.
1359. **259.** 6 r. ultramarine & blue 80 20

**260.** Congress Emblem. **261.** Bark Beetle under Lens.

**1964.** 2nd Iranian Dental Assn. Congress.
1360. **260.** 2 r. red, deep blue and blue .. .. 65 15
1361. – 4 r. multicoloured .. 1·25 30
DESIGN: 4 r. "2 IDA" in symbolic form.

**1964.** Inauguration of Plant Parasites and Diseases Research Institute.
1362 – 2 r. brown, red & buff 1·00 15
1363 **261** 6 r. indigo, brn & bl 1·75 30
DESIGN: 2 r. Microscope, plants and research centre.

**262.** Plaque. **263.** Eleanor Roosevelt.

**1964.** Mehregan Festival.
1364 **262** 8 r. red and yellow .. 1·25 15

**1964.** Eleanor Roosevelt Commem.
1365. **263.** 10 r. blue and violet .. 1·10 25

**264.** Clasped Hands and U.N. Emblem. **265.** Gymnast.

**1964.** United Nations Day.

1366 **264** 6 r. multicoloured .. 85 15
1367 – 14 r. red, blue & orge 1·40 30
DESIGN: 14 r. U.N. and "Bird" emblems.

**1964.** Olympic Games, Tokyo.

1368 **265** 4 r. sepia, turq & brn 70 15
1369 – 6 r. red and blue .. 1·00 25
DESIGN—Diamond (39 × 39 mm). 6 r. Polo.

**266.** Crown Prince Riza. **267.** Conference and U.N. Emblems.

**1964.** Children's Day.

1370. **266.** 1 r. green and brown 50 10
1371. 2 r. red and blue .. 1·00 15
1372. 6 r. blue and red .. 2·00 30

**1964.** Petro-Chemical Conf. and Gas Seminar.

1373. **267.** 6 r. multicoloured .. 75 15
1374. 8 r. multicoloured .. 1·50 25

**268.** Shah and King Baudouin.

**1964.** Visit of King of Belgium.

1375. **268.** 6 r. blk., orge. & yell. 40 15
1376. 8 r. blk., orge. & grn. 85 15

**269.** Rhazes.

**1964.** 1100th Birth Anniv of Rhazes (Zakariya Ar-Razi, alchemist).

1377 **269** 2 r. multicoloured .. 45 15
1378 6 r. multicoloured .. 50 20

**270.** Shah and King Olav.

**1965.** Visit of King of Norway.

1379 **270** 2 r. mauve and purple 50 15
1380 4 r. green and olive .. 90 20

**271.** Crown, Map and Star. **272.** Woman and U.N. Emblem.

**1965.** Six-Point Reform Law.

1381. **271.** 2 r. orge., blk. & blue 30 15

**1965.** 18th Session of United Nations Commission on Status of Women, Teheran.

1382 **272** 6 r. black, blue & lt bl 45 10
1383 8 r. blue, red & lt red 80 15

**273.** Festival Plant. **274.** Pres. Bourguiba and Minarets.

**1965.** New Year Festival.

1384. **273.** 50 d. multicoloured .. 10 10
1385. 1 r. multicoloured .. 20 10

**1965.** Visit of President of Tunisia.

1386. **274.** 4 r. multicoloured .. 75 15

**275.** Map of Oil Pipelines.

**1965.** 14th Anniv. of Nationalisation of Oil Industry.

1387. **275.** 6 r. multicoloured .. 1·40 20
1388. 14 r. multicoloured .. 2·75 40

**276.** I.T.U. Emblem and Symbols.

**1965.** Centenary of I.T.U.

1389. **276.** 14 r. red and grey .. 90 30

**277.** I.C.Y. Emblem.

**1965.** Int. Co-operation Year.

1390. **277.** 10 r. green and blue .. 2·00 20

**278.** Boeing 727-100 and Airline Emblem.

**1965.** Inaug. of Jet Services by Iranian National Airlines.

1391. **278.** 14 r. multicoloured .. 1·00 35

**279.** " Co-operation " (Hands holding Book).

**1965.** 1st Anniv. of Regional Development Co-operation Plan. Multicoloured.

1392. 2 r. Type **279** .. .. 20 10
1393. 4 r. Globe and flags of Turkey, Iran and Pakistan (40½ × 24½ mm.) .. 30 15

**280.** Moot Emblem and Arabesque Pattern.

**1965.** Middle East Rover (Scout) Moot.

1394. **280.** 2 r. multicoloured .. 40 15

**281.** Gateway of Parliament Building.

**1965.** 60th Anniv. of Iranian Constitution.

1397. **281.** 2 r. brown and mauve 30 10

**282.** Congress Emblem. **283.** Teacher and Class.

**1965.** Iranian Dental Congress.

1398. **282.** 6 r. blue, mve. & silver 35 15

**1965.** World Eradication of Illiteracy Congress, Teheran. Multicoloured.

1399. 2 r. Type **283** .. .. 10 10
1400. 5 r. Globe showing alphabets (25 × 30 mm.) .. 20 10
1401. 6 r. U.N.E.S.C.O. emblem and symbols (diamond, 36 × 36 mm.) .. .. 30 15
1402. 8 r. Various scripts (35 × 23 mm.) .. .. 30 15
1403. 14 r. Shah and multi-lingual inscriptions (41 × 52 mm.) .. .. .. 80 30

**284.** Shah Riza Pahlavi.

**1965.** 25th Anniv. (actually 24th) of Shah's Accession.

1404. **284.** 1 r. red and grey .. 10 10
1405. 2 r. red and yellow .. 30 10

**285.** Congress Emblem.

**1965.** 14th Medical Congress.

1406. **285.** 5 r. ultram., bl. & gold 40 10

**286.** President Jonas.

**1965.** Visit of President of Austria.

1407 **286** 6 r. blue and brown .. 85 20

**287.** Plaque.

**1965.** Mehregan Festival.

1408. **287.** 4 r. multicoloured .. 30 15
See also No. 1464.

**289.** U.N. Emblem and " Flowers ". **290.** Emblem and " Arches ".

**1965.** United Nations Day.

1409. **289.** 5 r. multicoloured .. 30 15

**1965.** Iranian Industrial Exn., Teheran.

1410. **290.** 3 r. multicoloured .. 20 10

**291.** Crown Prince Riza. **292.** "Weightlifting".

**1965.** Children's Day.

1411. **291.** 2r. choc., brn. & gold 40 10

**1965.** World Weightlifting Championships, Teheran.

1412. **292.** 10 r. mve., vio. & blue 45 15

**293.** Open Book. **295.** Scales of Justice.

**294.** Shah and King Faisal.

**1965.** Book Week.

1416 **293** 8 r. multicoloured .. 40 20

**1965.** Visit of King of Saudi Arabia.

1417 **294** 4 r. brown and bistre 70 15

**1965.** Human Rights Day.

1418 **295** 14 r. multicoloured .. 45 20

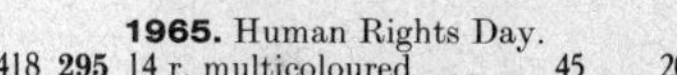
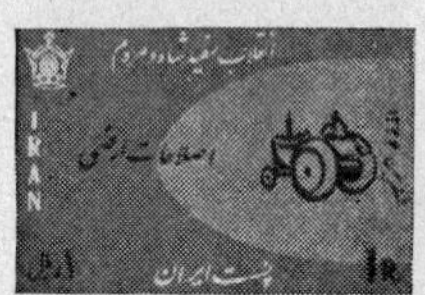

**296.** Tractor (Land Reform).

**1966.** 3rd Anniv of Shah's White Revolution (Parliamentary Assent to Shah's Reform Plan).

1419 **296** 1 r. brown and yellow 10 10
1420 – 2 r. green & lt green 15 10
1421 – 3 r. brown and silver 15 10
1422 – 4 r. violet & lt violet 15 10
1423 – 5 r. lake and red .. 15 10
1424 – 6 r. brown and bistre 20 10
1425 – 7 r. ultramarine & bl 30 15
1426 – 8 r. ultramarine & bl 30 15
1427 – 9 r. brown & lt brown 35 20
DESIGNS: 2 r. Trees (Nationalization of Forests). 3 r. Cogwheel emblem (Sale of shares to workers). 4 r. Cylinders (Profit-sharing). 5 r. Parliament gateway (Votes for Women). 6 r. Blackboard and pupils (Education Corps). 7 r. Staff of Aesculapius (Medical Corps). 8 r. Scales (Justice). 9 r. Girders (Construction Corps).

**297.** Mohammed Riza Pahlavi. **298.** Shah and Ruins of Persepolis.

**1966.**

1428. **297.** 5 d. green .. .. 10 10
1429. 10 d. brown .. .. 10 10
1430. 25 d. blue .. .. 10 10
1431. 50 d. turquoise .. 10 10
1432. 1 r. orange .. .. 10 10
1433. 2 r. violet .. .. 10 10
1434. 4 r. brown .. .. 3·00 10
1435. 5 r. sepia .. .. 15 10
1436. **298.** 6 r. blue .. .. 15 10
1437. 8 r. green .. .. 30 10
1438. 10 r. blue .. .. 20 10
1439. 11 r. green .. .. 70 10
1440. 14 r. violet .. .. 1·40 10
1441. 20 r. brown .. .. 15·00 10
1442. 50 r. red .. .. 3·50 10
1443. 100 r. blue .. .. 14·00 40
1444. 200 r. brown .. 7·00 75

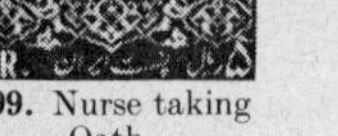

299. Nurse taking Oath.

300. Narcissus.

**1966.** Nurses' Day.
1445 **299** 5 r. blue & deep blue 25 15
1446 5 r. mauve and red .. 25 15

**1966.** New Year Festival.
1447. **300.** 50 d. multicoloured.. 15 10
1448. 1 r. multicoloured .. 15 10
See also Nos. 1530/3.

301. Oil Rigs.

**1966.** Inauguration of Six New Oil Companies in Persian Gulf.
1449. **301.** 14 r. black, pur. & blue 70 20

302. Radar Aerial.

**1966.** C.E.N.T.O. (Iran, Pakistan and Turkey) Telecommunications Organization.
1450. **302.** 2 r. green .. .. 15 10
1451. – 4 r. orange and blue.. 15 10
1452. – 6 r. grey and purple.. 25 10
1453. – 8 r. indigo and blue.. 35 10
1454. – 10 r. brown and ochre 45 30
DESIGNS—VERT. 4 r. Aerial and radio "waves". 6 r. "CENTO" and emblem. 8 r. Emblem and "waves". 10 r. Bowl aerial and "waves".

303. W.H.O. Building.

**1966.** Inaug. of W.H.O. Headquarters, Geneva.
1455. **303.** 10 r. black, blue & yell. 35 25

304. Globe Emblem and Motto.

**1966.** Conference of International Women's Council, Teheran.
1456 **304** 6 r. multicoloured .. 20 10
1457 8 r. multicoloured .. 30 15

305. U.N.E.S.C.O. Emblem.

**1966.** Air. 20th Anniv. of U.N.E.S.C.O.
1458. **305.** 14 r. multicoloured.. 75 30

306. Ruins of Persepolis, Map and Globe.

**1966.** Int. Iranology Congress, Teheran.
1459. **306.** 14 r. multicoloured.. 50 15

307. Medical Emblem.

**1966.** 15th Medical Congress, Teheran.
1460. **307.** 4 r. gold, blue & ultram. 30 10

308. Parliament Gateway.

**1966.** 55th Interparliamentary Union Conference, Teheran.
1461. **308.** 6 r. grn., blue and red 25 10
1462. – 8 r. grn., blue & mauve 25 15
DESIGN: 8 r. Senate Building.

309. President Sunay.

**1966.** Visit of President of Turkey.
1463 **309** 6 r. brown and violet 30 10

**1966.** Mehregan Festival. Plaque design similar to T 287 but vert. (30×40 mm.).
1464. 6 r. brown and bistre .. 25 10

310. Farmers.

**1966.** Rural Courts of Justice.
1465. **310.** 5 r. brown and bistre 35 25

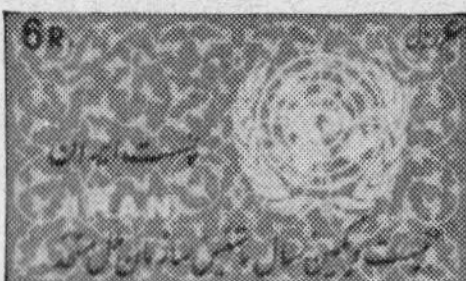


311. U.N. Emblem.

**1966.** U.N. Day and 21st Anniv. of U.N.O.
1466. **311.** 6 r. brown and black 20 10

312. Crown Prince. 313. I.W.O. Emblem.

**1966.** Children's Day.
1467. **312.** 1 r. blue .. .. 30 10
1468. 2 r. violet .. .. 30 10

**1966.** Iranian Women's Organization.
1469. **313.** 5 r. blue, black & gold 15 10

314. Strip of Film.

**1966.** 1st Children's Film Festival, Teheran.
1470. **314.** 4 r. blk., pur. & violet 30 10

315. Counting on the Fingers. 316. Cover of Book.

**1966.** National Census.
1471. **315.** 6 r. brown and grey 30 10

**1966.** Book Week.
1472. **316.** 8 r. brn., ochre & blue 20 15

317. Riza Shah Pahlavi.

Nos. 1475/6 show Riza Shah Pahlavi bare-headed.

**1966.** Riza Shah Pahlavi. Commem.
1473. **317.** 1 r. brown .. .. 30 10
1474. 1 r. blue .. .. 30 10
1475. – 2 r. blue .. .. 30 10
1476. – 2 r. green .. .. 30 10

318. E.R.O.P.A. Emblem and Map.

**1966.** 4th General Assembly of Public Administrators Organization (E.R.O.P.A.).
1477. **318.** 8 r. brown and green 30 15

319. Shah with Farmers.

**1967.** 5th Anniv. of Land Reform Laws.
1485. **319.** 6 r. brown, yellow and bistre .. 30 10

320. Torch and Stars.

**1967.** 4th Anniv. of Shah's White Revolution.
1486. **320.** 2 r. multicoloured .. 20 10
1487. – 6 r. multicoloured .. 35 15
DESIGN: 6 r. Shah acknowledging greetings.

321. Golden "Bull".

**1967.** Museum Week. Multicoloured.
1488. 3 r. Type **321** .. .. 20 10
1489. 5 r. Golden "leopard" 25 15
1490. 8 r. Capital with rams' heads .. .. .. 60 25

322. Planting a Tree.

323. Fishes.

**1967.** Tree-planting Week.
1491 **322** 8 r. green and brown 35 10

**1967.** New Year Festival.
1492 **323** 1 r. blue, red & brown 10 10
1493 – 8 r. ultram, bl & red 60 15
DESIGN—35×27 mm. 8 r. Barn swallows.

324. Microscope, Horses and Emblem.

**1967.** 2nd Veterinary Congress.
1494. **324.** 5 r. red, black & grey 20 10

325. Pres. Arif and Mosques.

**1967.** Visit of President of Iraq.
1495. **325.** 6 r. green and blue 30 10

326. U.N. Emblem and Fireworks.

**1967.** U.N. Stamp Day.
1496. **326.** 5 r. multicoloured .. 30 10

327. Map showing Pipeline Routes.

**1967.** Nationalization of Oil Industry.
1497. **327.** 6 r. multicoloured .. 60 15

328. Fencing.

**1967.** Int. Youth Fencing Championships, Teheran.
1498. **328.** 5 r. yellow and violet 30 10

329. Shah and King Bhumibol.

**1967.** Visit of King of Thailand.
1499. **329.** 6 r. brn. and light brn. 40 20

330. Emblem, Old and Young Couples.

**1967.** 15th Anniv. of Social Insurance Scheme.
1500. **330.** 5 r. blue and bistre .. 20 10

**331.** Skiing.

**1967.** Olympic Committee Meeting, Teheran.
1501. **331.** 3 r. brown and black 15 10
1502. – 6 r. multicoloured .. 15 10
1503. – 8 r. brown and blue 25 15
DESIGNS: 6 r. Olympic " shield ". 8 r. Wrestling.

**332.** "LIONS" and Lion's Head.

**1967.** 50th Anniv of Lions International. Mult.
1504 3 r. Type **332** .. .. 15 10
1505 7 r. Lion's emblem (36 × 42 mm) .. .. 40 15

**333.** President Stoica.

**1967.** Visit of Pres. of Rumania.
1506. **333.** 6 r. blue and orange .. 25 10

**334.** I.T.Y. Emblem. **335.** Iranian Pavilion.

**1967.** Int. Tourist Year
1507. **334.** 3 r. blue and red .. 10 10

**1967.** World Fair, Montreal.
1508. **335.** 4 r. red, gold & brown 10 10
1509. 10 r. brn., gold & red 20 10

**336.** First Persian Stamp. **337.** Globe and Schoolchildren.

**1967.** Stamp Cent.
1510. **336.** 6 r. pur., blue & light bl. 20 10
1511. 8 r. purple, myrtle and green .. .. 25 10

**1967.** Campaign Against Illiteracy.
1512. **337.** 3 r. violet and blue .. 15 10
1513. 5 r. brown and yellow 15 10

**338.** " Musician ". **339.** "Helping Hand ".

**1967.** Int. Musical Education in Oriental Countries Conf., Teheran.
1514. **338.** 14 r. purple and brown 45 20

**1967.** 1st "S.O.S." Children's Village in Iran.
1515 **339** 8 r. brown and yellow 1·00 60

**340.** Winged Ram. **341.** U.N. Emblem.

**1967.** 1st Shiraz Arts Festival, Persepolis.
1516 **340** 8 r. brown and bistre 35 10

**1967.** United Nations Day.
1517. **341.** 6 r. blue and bistre .. 20 10

**342.** Shah Mohammed Riza Pahlavi and Empress Farah. **343.** Crown Prince Riza.

**1967.** Coronation of Shah and Empress Farah.
1518 **342** 2 r. brown, blue & sil 10 10
1519 10 r. violet, blue & sil 35 25
1520 14 r. multicoloured .. 50 25

**1967.** Children's Day.
1521. **343.** 2 r. violet and silver 15 10
1522. 8 r. brown and silver 40 15

**344.** Pres. G. Traikov. **345.** Scout Emblem and Neckerchiefs.

**1967.** Visit of President of Bulgaria.
1523 **344** 10 r. brown and violet 20 10

**1967.** Boy Scouts Co-operation Week.
1524 **345** 8 r. brown and green 40 15

**346.** " Co-operation " (linked hands). **347.** Shaikh Sabah.

**1967.** Co-operation Year.
1525. **346.** 6 r. multicoloured .. 20 10

**1968.** Visit of Shaikh of Kuwait.
1526. **347.** 10 r. green and blue .. 25 10

**348.** Shah and Text of Reform Plan.

**1968.** 5th Anniv. of Shah's White Revolution.
1527. **348.** 2 r. grn., sepia & flesh 15 10
1528. 8 r. violet, grn. & blue 30 10
1529. 14 r. brn., blue & mve. 55 20

**1968.** New Year Festival. As T **300.** Mult.
1530. 1 r. Almond blossom .. 10 10
1531. 2 r. Red tulips .. 10 10
1532. 2 r. Yellow tulips .. 15 10
1533. 6 r. Festival dancer .. 65 10

## MINIMUM PRICE

The minimum price quoted is 10p which represents a handling charge rather than a basis for valuing common stamps. For further notes about prices see introductory pages.

**349.** Oil Technician and Rig. **350.** W.H.O. Emblem.

**1968.** Nat. Oil Industry.
1534. **349.** 14 r. blk., yellow & grn. 45 10

**1968.** 20th Anniv. of W.H.O.
1535. **350.** 14 r. orge., blue & pur. 40 10

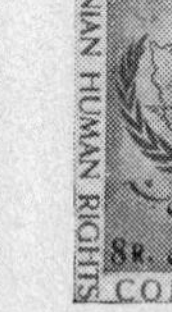

**351.** Ancient Chariot (sculpture). **353.** Human Rights Emblem.

**352.** Shah and King Hassan.

**1968.** 5th World Congress of Persian Archaeology and Art, Teheran.
1536. **351.** 8 r. multicoloured .. 25 10

**1968.** Visit of King of Morocco.
1537. **352.** 6 r. violet and flesh .. 30 15

**1968.** Human Rights Conference, Teheran.
1538. **353.** 8 r. red and green .. 15 10
1539. – 14 r. ultram. and blue 20 15
DESIGN: 14 r. As Type **353**, but rearranged, and inscr. "INTERNATIONAL CONFERENCE ON HUMAN RIGHTS—TEHERAN 1968".

**354.** Footballer. **355.** Oil Refinery.

**1968.** Asian Football Cup Finals, Teheran.
1540. **354.** 8 r. multicoloured .. 20 10
1541. 10 r. multicoloured .. 40 15

**1968.** Inaug. of Teheran Oil Refinery.
1542. **355.** 14 r. multicoloured .. 55 25

**356.** Empress Farah in Guides' Uniform. **357.** Mosquito Emblem.

**1968.** Iranian Girl Guides "Great Camp".
1543 **356** 4 r. blue and purple .. 50 15
1544 6 r. brown and red .. 75 25

**1968.** 8th Int. Tropical Medicine and Malaria Congresses, Teheran.
1545. **357.** 6 r. purple and black 20 10
1546. 14 r. green and purple 45 15

**358.** Allegory of Literacy. **359.** " Horseman " and " Flower ".

**1968.** World Illiteracy Eradication Campaign Day.
1547 **358** 6 r. blue, brn & lilac 15 10
1548 14 r. green, brn & yell 30 10

**1968.** 2nd Shiraz Arts Festival, Persepolis.
1549 **359** 14 r. multicoloured .. 45 15

**360.** Police Emblem on Map. **361.** Interpol Emblem.

**1968.** Police Day.
1550. **360.** 14 r. multicoloured .. 90 15

**1968.** 37th Interpol General Assembly.
1551. **361.** 10 r. pur., blk. & blue 50 15

**362.** U.N. Emblem and Dove.

**1968.** United Nations Day.
1552. **362.** 14 r. ultram. and blue 35 15

**363.** Empress Farah.

**1968.** 1st Anniv. of Coronation. Mult.
1553. **6 r. Type 363** .. .. 1·25 70
1554. **8 r. Shah Mohammed Riza Pahlavi** .. .. 1·25 70
1555. **10 r. Family group** .. 1·25 70

**364.** Imperial Crown and Bulls' Heads Capital (festival emblem). **365.** "Landscape".

**1968.** National Festival of Art and Culture, Teheran.
1556 **364** 14 r. multicoloured .. 45 15

**1968.** Children's Day. Children's Paintings. Multicoloured.
1557. 2 r. Type **365** .. .. 10 10
1558. 3 r. " Boat and House " (35×29 mm.) .. .. 15 10
1559. 5 r. " Flowers " (35× 29 mm.) .. .. 20 10

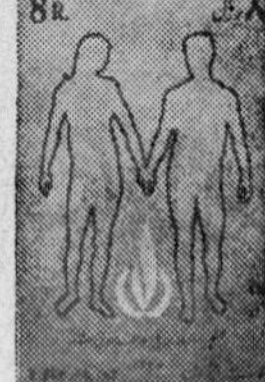

366. Hands supporting Globe. 367. Emblem and Human Figures.

**1968.** Insurance Day.

1560. 366. 4 r. blue and grey .. 10 10
1561. – 5 r. multicoloured .. 20 10
1562. – 8 r. multicoloured .. 15 10
1563. – 10 r. multicoloured .. 45 20

DESIGNS: 5 r. Factory aflame ("Fire risk"). 8 r. Urban workers ("Life"). 10 r. Insurance Institute emblem and transport ("Travel insurance").

**1968.** 20th Anniv. of Declaration of Human Rights.

1564. 367. 8 r. pur., ultram. & bl. 20 10

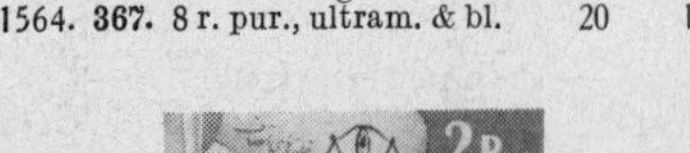

368. Justice, Construction Corps and Medical Corps.

**1969.** 6th Anniv of Shah's White Revolution. Each green, brown and lilac.

1565 2 r. Type **368** .. .. 30 10
1566 4 r. Working conditions, civil engineering and irrigation .. .. 40 15
1567 6 r. Land reform, nationalization of forests and sale of shares to workers .. 50 20
1568 8 r. Profit-sharing, votes for women and education corps .. 80 20

Nos. 1565/8, each showing symbols of three of the reforms, were issued, se-tenant, forming a composite design of a rosette.

369. Shah Mohammed Riza Pahlavi.

**1969.** 10,000th Day of Shah's Reign.

1569. 369. 6 r. brown, red & blue 30 15

370. Goldfinch.

**1969.** New Year Festival. Multicoloured.

1570. 1 r. Type **370** .. .. 30 10
1571. 2 r. Ring-necked Pheasant .. .. 30 10
1572. 8 r. Roses .. .. .. 70 15

371. Scales of Justice. and "Blindfold Globe". 372. Symbols of I.L.O.

**1969.** 15th FIDA (Female Jurists) Convention, Teheran.

1573. 371. 6 r. black and blue 30 10

**1969.** 50th Anniv. of I.L.O.

1574. 372. 10 r. violet and blue .. 30 10

373. Wrestling "Throw".

**1969.** 3rd Aryamehr Cup International Wrestling Championships.

1575 373 10 r. multicoloured .. 40 10

374. "Flower and Birds". 375. Mask and Cord.

**1969.** World Handicrafts Day.

1576. 374. 10 r. multicoloured 40 10

**1969.** "Philia 1969". Outdoor Course for Scout Patrol Leaders.

1577. 375. 6 r. multicoloured .. 40 15

376. Mughal Miniature (Pakistan).

**1969.** 5th Anniv. of Regional Co-operation for Development. Miniatures. Mult.

1578 25 r. Type **376** .. .. 1·10 50
1579 25 r. "Kneeling Figure" (Safavi, Iran) .. .. 1·10 50
1580 25 r. "Suleiman the Magnificent and Court" (Ottoman, Turkey) .. 1·10 50

377. Astronauts on Moon.

**1969.** 1st Man on the Moon.

1581. 377. 24 r. brown, blue & buff 1·50 85

378. "Education" (quotation from Shah's Declaration).

**1969.** Education Reform Conference.

1582. 378. 10 r. red, green & buff 40 20

379. Oil Rig.

**1969.** 10th Anniv. of Iranian/Italian Marine Drilling Project.

1583. 379. 8 r. multicoloured .. 70 15

380. Festival Emblem. 381. Thumb-print and Cross.

**1969.** Third Shiraz Arts Festival.

1584. 380. 6 r. multicoloured .. 15 10
1585. 8 r. multicoloured .. 25 10

**1969.** Int. Anti-Illiteracy Campaign.

1586. 381. 4 r. multicoloured .. 20 10

382. Shah, Persepolis and U.P.U. Emblem.

**1969.** 16th U.P.U. Congress, Tokyo.

1587. 382. 10 r. multicoloured 40 20
1588. 14 r. multicoloured 1·00 30

383. Fair Emblem. 384. "Justice".

**1969.** 2nd Int. Asian Trade Fair, Teheran. Multicoloured.

1589. 8 r. Type **383** .. .. 15 10
1590. 14 r. As T **383**, but inscr. "ASIA 69" .. 20 10
1591. 20 r. Emblem and sections of globe (horiz.) .. 50 20

**1969.** Rural Courts of Justice Day.

1592. 384. 8 r. brown and green 30 10

385. U.N. Emblem. 386. Festival Emblem.

**1969.** 25th Anniv. of United Nations Day.

1593. 385. 2 r. blue & pale blue .. 15 10

**1969.** National Festival of Art and Culture, Teheran.

1594 386 2 r. multicoloured .. 10 10

387. "In the Garden". 388. Global Emblem.

**1969.** Children's Week. Children's drawings. Multicoloured.

1595. 1 r. Type **387** .. 15 10
1596. 2 r. "Three Children" (horiz.) .. 20 10
1597. 5 r. "Mealtime" (horiz.) 50 15

**1969.** National Assn. of Parents and Teachers Congress, Teheran.

1598. 388. 8 r. brown and blue .. 20 10

389. Earth Station. 391. Mahatma Gandhi.

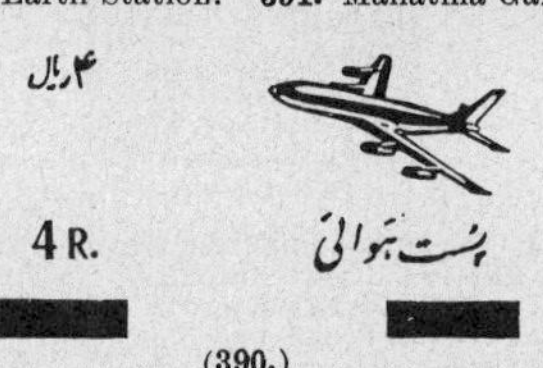

(390.)

**1969.** Opening of 1st Iranian Satellite Communications Earth Station.

1599. 389. 6 r. brown and ochre 20 10

**1969.** Air. 50th Anniv of 1st England–Australia Flight. No. 1281 surch as T **390**.

1600. 229. 4 r. on 14 r.+6 r. .. 1·10 45
1601. 10 r. on 14 r.+6 r. .. 1·10 45
1602. 14 r. on 14 r.+6 r. .. 1·10 45

**1969.** Birth Cent. of Mahatma Gandhi.

1603. 391. 14 r. brown and grey 2·25 70

392. Globe and Flags.

**1969.** 50th Anniv. of League of Red Cross Societies. Multicoloured.

1604. 2 r. Type **392** .. 30 10
1605. 6 r. Red Cross emblems on Globe .. .. .. 40 15

393. Shah and Reform Symbols.

**1970.** 7th Anniv. of Shah's White Revolution.

1606. 393. 1 r. multicoloured .. 30 15
1607. 2 r. multicoloured .. 40 15

394. Pansies. 396. "EXPO" Emblem.

395. Nationalization Decree.

**1970.** New Year Festival. Multicoloured.

1608. 1 r. Type **394** .. .. 15 10
1609. 8 r. New Year table (40 × 26 mm.) .. .. 80 20

**1970.** 20th Anniv. of Oil Industry Nationalization. Multicoloured.

1610. 2 r. Type **395** .. .. 50 15
1611. 4 r. Laying pipeline .. 70 15
1612. 6 r. Part of Kharg Island plant .. .. 75 15
1613. 8 r. Ocean terminal, Kharg Island (vert.) .. 80 30
1614. 10 r. Refinery, Teheran .. 1·10 35

**1970.** "EXPO 70" World Fair, Osaka Japan.

1615. 396. 4 r. blue and mauve 15 10
1616. 10 r. violet and blue 35 15

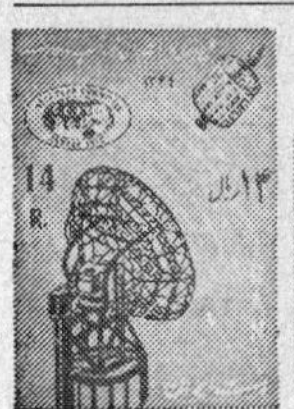

397. Dish Aerial and Satellite. 398. New U.P.U. H.Q.

**1970.** Asian Plan Communications Committee Meeting, Teheran.
1617. 397. 14 r. multicoloured .. 65 20

**1970.** New U.P.U. Headquarters Building, Berne.
1618. 398. 2 r. sepia, mve. & grn. 20 10
1619. 4 r. sepia, mve. & lilac 30 10

399. A.P.Y. Emblem. 400. Stork carrying Baby.

**1970.** Asian Productivity Year.
1620. 399. 8 r. multicoloured .. 20 10

**1970.** 50th Anniv. of Midwifery School.
1621. 400. 8 r. blue and brown.. 30 15

401. Tomb of Cyrus the Great.

**1970.** 2,500th Anniv. of Persian Empire (1st issue). Achaemenian Era.
1622. 401. 6 r. violet, red & grey 50 15
1623. – 8 r. grn., blk. and pink 55 15
1624. – 10 r. brn.,red & yell. 80 30
1625. – 14 r. brn., blk. & blue 1·40 70
DESIGNS—HORIZ. 10 r. Religious ceremony (Median bas-relief). 14 r. Achaemenian officers (bas-relief). VERT. 8 r. Columns, Palace of Apadana.
See also Nos. 1629/32, 1633/6, 1640/2, 1658/61, 1664/7, 1674/7 and 1679/82.

402. Saiful Malook Lake (Pakistan).

**1970.** 6th Anniv. of Regional Co-operation for Development. Multicoloured.
1626. 2 r. Type 402 .. .. 40 15
1627. 2 r. Seeyo-Se-Pol Bridge, Isfahan (Iran) (62×46 mm.) .. .. 40 15
1628. 2 r. View from Fethiye (Turkey) .. .. 40 15

**1970.** 2500th Anniv of Persian Empire (2nd issue). Achaemenian Era. Designs as T 401.
1629 2 r. gold, dp green & grn 50 15
1630 6 r. gold, violet and green 50 20
1631 8 r. gold, blue and orange 1·00 30
1632 14 r. red, black and blue 1·40 75
DESIGNS—VERT. 2 r. Eagle amulet. 6 r. "Lion" goblet. 8 r. Winged ibex statue. HORIZ. 14 r. Tapestry.

**1970.** 2500th Anniv. of Persian Empire (3rd issue). Coins of Sassanid and Parthian Eras. Designs as T 401. Multicoloured, frames in gold.
1633. 1 r. Queen Buran dirham 50 15
1634. 2 r. Mithridates I dirham 55 15
1635. 6 r. Shapur I dirham .. 1·00 20
1636. 8 r. Ardeshir I dirham .. 1·40 55

405. Candle and Globe Emblem.

**1970.** World Literacy Day.
1637. 405. 1 r. multicoloured .. 10 10
1638. 2 r. multicoloured .. 15 10

406. Isfahan Tile. 408. Councils Emblem.

**1970.** Int. Architects' Congress, Isfahan.
1639. 406. 6 r. multicoloured .. 20 15

**1970.** 2500th Anniv. of Persian Empire (4th issue). Achaemenian and Sassanid Eras. Designs as T **401**.
1640 2 r. multicoloured .. 50 15
1641 6 r. brown, blue and lilac 1·00 20
1642 8 r. green, red and lilac 1·25 30
DESIGNS—VERT. 2 r. Sassanid arch and art. HORIZ. 6 r. Achaemenian mounted courier. 8 r. Seal of Darius I.

**1970.** 1st Congress of Provincial Councils.
1643. 408. 2 r. violet and blue .. 10 10

409. Dove and U.N. Emblem. 411. Festival Emblem.

410. "1970" and I.A.T.A. Emblem.

**1970.** United Nations Day.
1644 409 2 r. ultram, pur & bl 10 10

**1970.** Air. 26th Int. Air Transport Assn. General Meeting, Teheran.
1645. 410. 14 r. multicoloured .. 2·25 40

**1970.** National Festival of Art and Culture, Teheran.
1646 411 2 r. multicoloured .. 15 10

412. "Goatherd and Goats".

**1970.** Children's Week. Children's Drawings. Multicoloured,.
1647. 50 d. Type 412 .. 15 10
1648. 1 r. "Family picnic" .. 20 10
1649. 2 r. "Mosque" .. 40 10

413. Shah Mohammed Riza Pahlavi.

**1971.** 8th Anniv. of Shah's White Revolution.
1650. 413. 2 r. multicoloured .. 20 20

414. Common Shelduck.

**1971.** Int. Wetland and Waterfowl Conf., Ramsar. Multicoloured.
1651. 1 r. Type 414 .. .. 50 10
1652. 2 r. Ruddy Shelduck .. 50 10
1653. 8 r. Greater Flamingo (vert.) 1·25 25

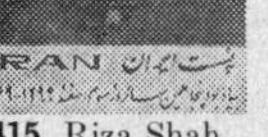

415. Riza Shah Pahlavi. 416. Red Junglefowl.

**1971.** 50th Anniv. of Rise of Pahlavi Dynasty.
1654. 415. 6 r. multicoloured .. 75 30

**1971.** New Year Festival. Birds. Mult.
1655. 1 r. Type 416 .. .. 40 10
1656. 2 r. Barn swallow at nest 1·00 10
1657. 6 r. Hoopoe .. .. 3·25 35

417. Stone Bull's Head, Persepolis.

**1971.** 2,500th Anniv. of Persian Empire (5th issue). Age of Cyrus the Great. Mult.
1658. 4 r. Type 417 .. .. 90 15
1659. 5 r. Winged lion ornament 1·25 15
1660. 6 r. Persian Archer (bas-relief) .. .. 1·25 20
1661. 8 r. Imperial audience (bas-relief) .. .. 1·50 30

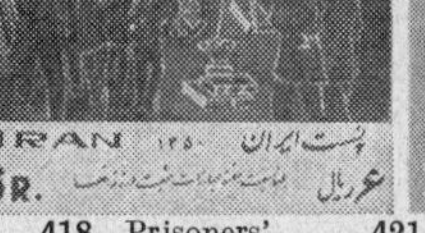


418. Prisoners' Rehabilitation. 421. "Shiraz Arts".

420. Badshahi Mosque, Lahore (Pakistan).

**1971.** Rehabilitation Week.
1662. 418. 6 r. multicoloured .. 1·00 15
1663. 8 r. multicoloured .. 1·50 15

**1971.** 2500th Anniv. of Persian Empire (6th issue). Art of Ancient Persia. As T **417**.
1664. 1 r. multicoloured .. 70 15
1665. 2 r. black and brown .. 70 15
1666. 2 r. brn. black and purple 70 15
1667. 10 r. black, blue & brown 90 30
DESIGNS—VERT. No. 1664, "Harpist" (mosaic). No. 1667, Bronze head of Parthian prince. HORIZ. No. 1665, "Shapur I hunting" (ornamental plate). No. 1666, "Investiture of Ardashir I" (bas-relief).

**1971.** 7th Anniv. of Regional Co-operation for Development. Multicoloured.
1668. 2 r. Type 420 .. .. 30 15
1669. 2 r. Selimiye Mosque, Edirne, Turkey (vert.) 30 15
1670. 2 r. Chaharbagh School, Isfahan (Iran) (vert.) 30 15

**1971.** 5th Shiraz Arts Festival, Persepolis.
1671 421 2 r. multicoloured .. 30 15

422. "Book-reading".

**1971.** World Literacy Day.
1672 422 2 r. multicoloured .. 20 10

423. Kings Abdullah and Hussein II.

**1971.** 50th Anniv. of Hashemite Kingdom of Jordan.
1673. 423. 2 r. multicoloured .. 20 10

424. National Steel Foundry.

**1971.** 2,500th Anniv. of Persian Empire (7th issue). Modern Iran. Multicoloured.
1674. 1 r. Type 424 .. .. 30 15
1675. 2 r. Shahyad Aryamehr Memorial .. .. 65 15
1676. 3 r. Senate Building, Teheran 65 20
1677. 11 r. Shah Abbas the Great Dam .. .. 1·25 40

425. Ghatur Rail Bridge.

**1971.** Inaug. of Iran–Turkey Railway Link.
1678. 425. 2 r. multicoloured .. 75 10

426. Shah Mohammed Riza Pahlavi.

**1971.** 2,500th Anniv. of Persian Empire (8th issue). Pahlavi Era. Multicoloured.
1679 1 r. Type 426 .. .. 70 15
1680 2 r. Riza Shah Pahlavi .. 75 15
1681 5 r. Proclamation tablet of Cyrus the Great (horiz) .. .. 80 15
1682 10 r. Pahlavi Crown .. 1·60 75

427. Racial Equality Year Emblem. 428. Shah Mohammed Riza Pahlavi.

**1971.** Racial Equality Year.
1683. 427. 2 r. multicoloured . 10 10

**1971.**
1684 428 5 d. purple .. .. 10 10
1685 10 d. red .. .. 10 10
1686 50 d. green .. .. 10 10
1687 1 r. green .. .. 10 10
1688 2 r. brown .. .. 10 10
1689 6 r. green .. .. 20 10
1690 8 r. violet .. .. 35 10
1691 10 r. purple .. .. 70 10
1692 11 r. green .. .. 2·00 10
1693 14 r. blue .. .. 7·50 10
1694 20 r. mauve .. .. 5·50 15
1695 50 r. ochre .. .. 3·25 50
Nos. 1689/95 are larger, 27×37 mm.
See also Nos. 1715/26b and 1846/50.

**429.** "Waiters at a Banquet".

**1971.** Children's Week. Children's Drawings. Multicoloured.
1696. 2 r. Type **429** .. .. 20 15
1697. 2 r. "Persepolis Ruins" (vert.) .. .. .. 20 15
1698. 2 r. "Persian Archer" (vert.) .. .. .. 20 15

**430.** U.N.E.S.C.O. Emblem.

**1971.** 25th Anniv of U.N.E.S.C.O.
1699 **430** 6 r. blue and purple .. 30 15

**431.** Congress Emblem and Livestock.

**1971.** 4th Iranian Veterinary Congress.
1700. **431.** 2 r. red, black & grey 30 10

**432.** I.L.O. Emblem and Globe.

**1971.** 7th Asian International Labour Organization Regional Conference, Teheran.
1701 **432** 2 r. orange, blue & blk 20 10

**433.** Bird feeding Young. **434.** Shah Mohammed Riza Pahlavi.

**1971.** 25th Anniv. of U.N.I.C.E.F.
1702. **433.** 2 r. multicoloured .. 20 10

**1972.** 9th Anniv. of Shah's White Revolution.
1703. **434.** 2 r. multicoloured .. 50 15

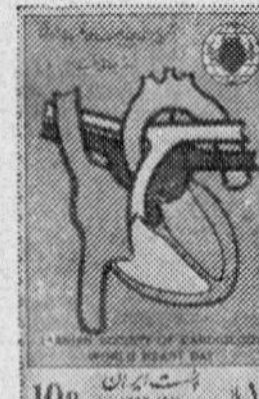
**435.** Chukar Partridge. **436.** Human Heart.

**1972.** New Year Festival. Birds. Mult.
1705. 1 r. Type **435** .. 30 15
1706. 1 r. Pin-tailed Sandgrouse 30 15
1707. 2 r. Yellow-bellied Waxbill & Red-cheeked Cordon-bleu .. .. .. 1·60 20

**1972.** World Heart Day.
1708. **436.** 10 r. multicoloured .. 1·10 20

**437.** Winged Ibex Symbol. **438.** Scarlet Roses.

**1972.** Int. Film Festival, Teheran.
1709. **437.** 6 r. gold and blue .. 70 15
1710. – 8 r. multicoloured .. 1·60 20
DESIGN: 8 r. Symbolic spectrum.

**1972.** Roses. Multicoloured.
1711. 1 r. Type **438** .. .. 20 10
1712. 2 r. Yellow roses .. 50 10
1713. 5 r. Red rose .. .. 75 15

**1972.** As Nos. 1684/95, but with bistre frames and inscriptions.
1715 **428** 5 d. purple .. .. 10 10
1716 10 d. brown .. 10 10
1717 50 d. green .. .. 10 10
1718 1 r. green .. .. 10 10
1719 2 r. brown .. .. 40 10
1720 6 r. green .. .. 30 10
1721 8 r. violet .. .. 35 15
1722 10 r. purple .. 55 10
1723 11 r. blue .. .. 70 15
1724 14 r. blue .. .. 3·50 20
1725 20 r. mauve .. 7·00 30
1726 50 r. blue .. .. 2·50 65
1726a 110 r. violet .. 3·50 75
1726b 200 r. black .. 7·50 3·50
Nos. 1720/26b are larger, 27 × 37 mm.

**439.** "U.I.T." Emblem.

**1972.** World Telecommunications Day.
1726c **439.** 14 r. multicoloured .. 1·50 30

**440.** "Fisherman" (Cevat Dereli, Turkey). **442.** Pens.

**441.** Floral Patterns.

**1972.** 8th Anniv. of Regional Co-operation for Development. Paintings. Mult.
1727. 5 r. Type **440** .. .. 90 25
1728. 5 r. "Iranian Woman" (Behzad, Iran) 90 25
1729. 5 r. "Will and Power" (A. R. Chughtai, Pakistan) 90 25

**1972.** 6th Shiraz Arts Festival.
1730 **441** 6 r. black, red & green 75 15
1731 8 r. black and purple 1·00 20

**1972.** World Literacy Day.
1732. **442.** 1 r. multicoloured .. 15 10
1733. 2 r. multicoloured .. 20 10

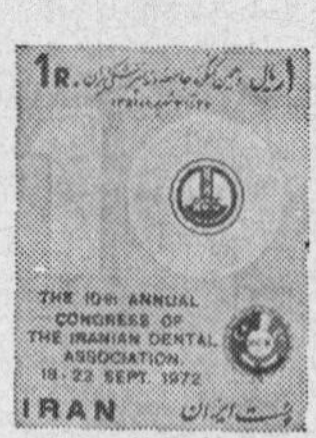
**443.** "10" and Dental Emblem. **444.** A.B.U. Emblem within "9".

**1972.** 10th Annual Congress of Iranian Dental Association.
1734. **443.** 1 r. multicoloured .. 20 10
1735. 2 r multicoloured .. 30 10

**1972.** 9th General Assembly of Asian Broadcasting Union, Teheran.
1736. **444.** 6 r. multicoloured .. 50 10
1737. 8 r. multicoloured .. 75 20

**445.** 3ch. stamp of 1910 on Cover. **447.** Communications Emblem.

**446.** Chess.

**1972.** World Stamp Day.
1738. **445.** 10 r. multicoloured .. 1·00 30

**1972.** Olympic Games, Munich. Iranian Sports. Mult.
1739. 1 r. Type **446** .. .. 1·00 20
1740. 2 r. Hunting .. .. 1·00 20
1741. 3 r. Archery .. .. 1·25 20
1742. 5 r. Horse-racing .. 1·25 20
1743. 6 r. Polo .. .. 1·25 20
1744. 8 r. Wrestling .. 1·40 25

**1972.** United Nations Day.
1746. **447.** 10 r. multicoloured 1·10 25

**448.** "Children in Garden". **449.** Festival Emblem.

**1972.** Children's Week. Children's Drawings. Multicoloured.
1747. 2 r. Type **448** .. 35 10
1748. 2 r. "At the Theatre" .. 55 10
1749 6 r. "Children at play" (horiz.) .. .. 1·25 20

**1972.** National Festival of Art and Culture, Teheran.
1750 **449** 10 r. multicoloured .. 2·75 30

**450.** Family Planning Emblem. **451.** Scouting Emblem.

**1972.** Family Planning Campaign.
1751. **450.** 1 r. multicoloured .. 15 10
1752. 2 r. multicoloured .. 20 10

**1972.** 20th Anniv. of Scouting in Iran.
1753. **451.** 2 r. multicoloured .. 40 10

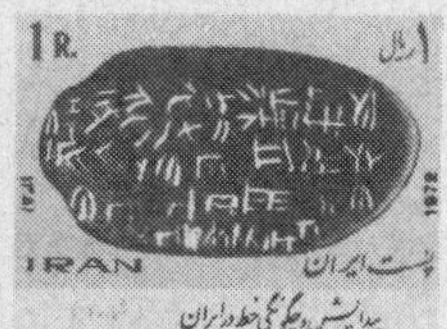
**452.** Cuneiform Seal.

**1973.** "Origins of Writing" (1st issue). Impressions from ancient seals. Multicoloured. Background colours given.
1754. **452.** 1 r. blue .. .. 40 15
1755. – 1 r. yellow .. .. 40 15
1756. – 1 r. mauve .. .. 40 15
1757. – 2 r. orange .. .. 45 15
1758. – 2 r. green .. .. 45 15
1759. – 2 r. buff .. .. 45 15
See also Nos. 1774/9 and 1822/7.

**453.** Open Books in Space. **454.** "Twelve Reforms".

**1973.** Int. Book Year. Multicoloured.
1760. 2 r. Type **453** .. .. 55 10
1761. 6 r. Illuminated manuscript 85 15

**1973.** 10th Anniv. of Shah's White Revolution. Multicoloured.
1762. 1 r. Type **454** .. .. 15 10
1763. 2 r. Pyramid of 12 balls.. 20 10
1764. 6 r. As Type **454** but size 71 × 92 mm. .. .. 1·00 45

**455.** Long-spined Red Bream ("Sparus spinifer"). **457.** "Footballers".

**456.** W.H.O. Emblem.

**1973.** New Year Festival. Fishes. Mult.
1766 1 r. Type **455** .. .. 35 10
1767 1 r. Surgeon fish ("Acanthurus sp.") .. 35 10
1768 2 r. Grunt ("Anisotremus sp.") .. .. .. 40 10
1769 2 r. Sergeant major ("Abdulef") .. .. 40 10
1770 2 r. Gold-flame snapper ("Lutyanus fulniflamma") .. .. 40 10

**1973.** 25th Anniv. of W.H.O.
1771. **456.** 10 r. multicoloured .. 80 20

**1973.** 15th Asian Youth Football Tournament, Teheran.
1772. **457.** 14 r. multicoloured 1·00 25

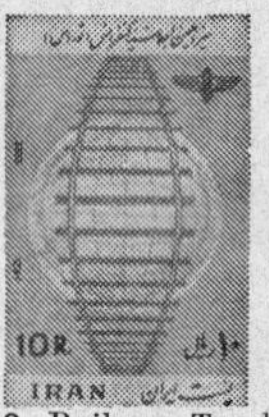

**458.** Railway Track encircling Globe. **459.** Ancient Aryan Script.

**1973.** International Railway Conference, Teheran
1773. **458.** 10 r. blue, blk. & mve. 1·25 20

**1973.** "Origins of Writing". Multicoloured.
1774. 1 r. Type **459** .. .. 25 15
1775. 1 r. Achaemenian priest and text .. .. 25 15
1776. 1 r. Kharochtani tablet.. 25 15
1777. 2 r. Parthian medallion (Arsacid) .. .. 45 15
1778. 2 r. Parthian coin (Mianeh) 45 15
1779. 2 r. Gachtak inscribed medallion (Dabireh) .. 45 15

**460.** Orchid. **461.** Carved Head, Tomb of Antiochus I (Turkey).

**1973** Flowers. Multicoloured.
1780. 1 r. Type **460** .. .. 20 10
1781. 2 r. Hyacinth .. .. 30 10
1782. 6 r. Wild rose .. .. 90 30

**1973.** 9th Anniv of Regional Co-operation for Development. Multicoloured.
1783. 2 r. Type **461** .. .. 30 15
1784. 2 r. Statue, Lut excavations (Iran) .. .. 30 15
1785. 2 r. Street in Moenjodaro (Pakistan) .. .. 30 15

**462.** Shah and Oil Installations. **463.** Soldiers and "Sun".

**1973.** Full Independence for Iranian Oil Industry.
1786. **462.** 5 r. black and blue .. 90 20

**1973.** 20th Anniv. of Gen. Zahedi's Uprising.
1787. **463.** 2 r. multicoloured .. 20 10

**464.** Sportswomen and Globe.

**1973.** 7th Int., Women's Congress on Physical Education and Sport, Teheran.

1788. **464.** 2 r. multicoloured (blue background) 20 10
1789. 2 r. multicoloured (green background) 20 10

**465.** Festival Poster. **467.** Wrestling.

**466.** Shahyad Monument and Rainbow.

**1973.** 7th Shiraz Arts Festival.

1790. **465.** 1 r. multicoloured .. 15 10
1791. 5 r. multicoloured .. 20 15

**1973.** Centenary of World Meteorological Organization.

1792. **466.** 5 r. multicoloured .. 60 15

**1973.** World Wrestling Championships, Teheran.

1793. **467.** 6 r. multicoloured .. 55 10

**468.** Alphabetic " Sun ". **469.** Globe wearing Earphones.

**1973.** World Literacy Day.

1794. **468.** 2 r. multicoloured .. 15 10

**1973.** Int., Audio-visual Exhibition, Teheran.

1795. **469.** 10 r. multicoloured.. 45 15

**470.** Al-Biruni. **472.** Crown Prince Cup.

**471.** C.I.S.M. Badge and Emblem.

**1973.** Birth Millenary of Abu al-Rayhan al-Biruni (mathematician and philosopher).

1796. **470.** 10 r. black and brown 80 20

**1973.** 25th Anniv. of International Military Sports Council (C.I.S.M.)

1797. **471.** 8 r. multicoloured .. 30 15

**1973.** Crown Prince Cup Football Championship.

1798. **472.** 2 r. brown, black & lilac 15 10

**473.** Interpol Emblem. **475.** U.P.U. Emblem, Post-horn and Letter.

**474.** Curves on Globe.

**1973.** 50th Anniv. of Int. Criminal Police Organization (Interpol).

1799. **473.** 2 r. multicoloured .. 30 10

**1973.** 25th Anniv. of World Mental Health Federation.

1800. **474.** 10 r. multicoloured .. 50 15

**1973.** World Post Day.

1801. **475.** 6 r. orange and blue.. 30 10

**476.** Emblems within Honeycomb. **477.** Festival Emblem and "People".

**1973.** 5th Anniv. of United Nations Volunteers.

1802. **476.** 2 r. multicoloured (brown background) 10 10
1803. 2 r. multicoloured (green background) 10 10

**1973.** National Festival of Art and Culture, Teheran.

1804 **477** 2 r. multicoloured .. 20 10

**478.** Bosphorus Bridge.

**1973.** 50th Anniv. of Turkish Republic. Mult.

1805. 2 r. Type **478** .. .. 50 10
1806. 8 r. Meeting of Kemal Ataturk and Reza Shah Pahlavi.. .. .. 60 20

**479.** "House and Garden". **481.** Cylinder of Cyrus and Red Cross Emblems.

**480.** Ear of Grain and Cow.

**1973.** Children's Week. Children's Drawings. Multicoloured.

1807. 2 r. Type **479** .. .. 25 15
1808. 2 r. " Collecting Fruit " 25 15
1809. 2 r. " Caravan " (horiz.) 25 15

**1973.** 10th Anniv. of World Food Programme.

1810. **480.** 10 r. multicoloured .. 75 15

**1973.** 22nd Int., Red Cross Conference, Teheran

1811. **481.** 6 r. multicoloured .. 35 10

**482.** IATA Emblem. **483.** Emblem, Film and Flags.

**1973.** Tourist Managers Congress, Teheran.

1812. **482.** 10 r. multicoloured.. 35 15

**1973.** International Film Festival, Teheran.

1813. **483.** 2 r. multicoloured. .. 20 10

**484.** Flame Emblem. **485.** Harp Emblem.

**1973.** 25th Anniv. of Declaration of Human Rights.

1814. **484.** 8 r. multicoloured .. 30 10

**1973.** " Art of Music " Festival.

1815. **485.** 10 r. red, grn. & blk. 40 15
1816. – 10 r. ultramarine, blue and purple .. 40 15

DESIGN: No. 1816, Musical symbols.

**486.** Reform Symbols.

**1974.** 11th Anniv of Shah's White Revolution. Multicoloured.

1817 1 r. Type **486** .. .. 20 15
1818 1 r. Tractor, factory in cogwheel, women and parliament gate .. 20 15
1819 2 r. Girders, hose and worker .. .. 20 15
1820 2 r. Rod of Aesculapius, scales and road passing house .. .. .. 20 15

**487.** Pir Amooz Ketabaty Script.

**1974.** " Origins of Writing " (3rd issue). Mult.

1822. 1 r. Din Dabireh Avesta 40 15
1823. 1 r. Mo Eghely Ketabaty 40 15
1824. 1 r. Type **487** .. .. 40 15
1825. 2 r. Pir Amooz, Naskh style 40 15
1826. 2 r. Pir Amooz, decorative 40 15
1827. 2 r. Pir Amooz, decorative and architectural .. 40 15

**488.** Chicken, Cow and Syringe.

**1974** Fifth Iranian Veterinary Congress.

1828. **488.** 6 r. multicoloured .. 40 15

**490.** Scarce Swallowtail. **491.** Mevlana.

**1974.** Nawrooz and Spring Festivals. Butterflies. Mult, background colours given.

1841 **490** 1 r. mauve .. .. 30 10
1842 – 1 r. purple .. .. 30 10
1843 – 2 r. green .. .. 35 10
1844 – 2 r. brown .. .. 35 10
1845 – 2 r. blue .. .. 35 10

DESIGNS: No. 1842, Swallowtail. 1843, Peacock. 1844, Painted lady. 1845, Cardinal.

**1974.** As Nos. 1684/95, but colours changed.

1846. **428.** 50 d. blue and orange 20 10
1847. 1 r. blue and green.. 25 10
1848. 2 r. blue and red .. 40 10
1849. 10 r. blue and green.. 5·00 10
1850. 20 r. blue and mauve 2·75 20

Nos. 1849/50 are larger, 27 × 37 mm.

**1974.** 700th Death Anniv. of Jalal-udin Mevlana (poet).

1851. **491.** 2 r. multicoloured .. 20 10

**492.** Palace of Forty Columns, Isfahan.

**1974.** 9th Near- and Middle-East Medical Congress, Isfahan.

1852 **492** 10 r. multicoloured .. 40 15

**493.** Asiatic Wild Ass. **494.** Gymnastics.

**1974.** International Game and Wild Life Protection Congress, Teheran. Mult.

1853. 1 r. Type **493** .. .. 20 15
1854. 2 r. Great Bustard .. 40 15
1855. 6 r. Fawn and Fallow deer .. .. .. 45 20
1856. 8 r. Georgian Black grouse .. .. .. 1·00 20

**1974.** 7th Asian Games, Teheran (1st series). Multicoloured.

1857 1 r. Type **494** .. .. 15 10
1858 1 r. Table tennis .. 20 10
1859 2 r. Boxing .. .. 50 10
1860 2 r. Hurdling .. .. 50 10
1861 6 r. Weightlifting .. 70 15
1862 8 r. Handball .. .. 1·25 15

See also Nos. 1874/9, 1890/3 and 1909.

**495.** Lion of St Mark's.

**1974.** U.N.E.S.C.O. "Save Venice" Campaign. Multicoloured.

1863. 6 r. Type **495** .. .. 30 10
1864. 8 r. Merchants at the Doge's court .. .. .. 65 15

**496.** Chain Link. **497.** Shah and Douglas DC-9-80 Super Eighty.

**1974.** Farm Co-operatives' Day.
1865. **496.** 2 r. multicoloured .. 15 10

**1974.** Air.

| | | | | |
|---|---|---|---|---|
| 1866. | **497.** | 4 r. black and orge... | 10 | 10 |
| 1867. | | 10 r. black & blue .. | 30 | 15 |
| 1868. | | 12 r. black & brown | 35 | 20 |
| 1869. | | 14 r. black & green .. | 55 | 20 |
| 1870. | | 20 r. black & mve. .. | 70 | 30 |
| 1871. | | 50 r. black & blue .. | 5·50 | 80 |

**498.** De Havilland D.H.9A, 1924.

**1974.** 50th Anniv of Imperial Iranian Air Force. Multicoloured.

| | | | |
|---|---|---|---|
| 1872 | 10 r. Type **498** .. .. | 80 | 15 |
| 1873 | 10 r. McDonnell Douglas F-4D Phantom II fighter of 1974 .. | 80 | 15 |

**499.** Tennis (men's doubles). **500.** Mazanderan Costume.

**1974.** 7th Asian Games, Teheran (2nd series). Multicoloured.

| | | | |
|---|---|---|---|
| 1874 | 1 r. Type **499** .. .. | 15 | 10 |
| 1875 | 1 r. Swimming .. .. | 15 | 10 |
| 1876 | 2 r. Wrestling .. .. | 20 | 10 |
| 1877 | 2 r. Hockey .. .. | 20 | 10 |
| 1878 | 4 r. Volleyball .. .. | 35 | 15 |
| 1879 | 10 r. Tennis (women's singles) .. .. | 70 | 15 |

**1974.** Regional Costumes. Multicoloured.

| | | | |
|---|---|---|---|
| 1880. | 2 r. Type **500** .. .. | 70 | 20 |
| 1881. | 2 r. Bakhtiari .. .. | 70 | 20 |
| 1882. | 2 r. Turkoman .. .. | 70 | 20 |
| 1883. | 2 r. Ghasgai .. .. | 70 | 20 |
| 1884. | 2 r. Kirmanshah (Kurdistan) | 70 | 20 |
| 1885. | 2 r. Sanandadj (Kurdistan) | 70 | 20 |

**501.** Gold Cup. **502.** Iranian Carpet.

**1974.** Iranian Football Championships.
1886. **501.** 2 r. yell., brn. and grn. 20 10

**1974.** 10th Anniv of Regional Co-operation for Development. Multicoloured.

| | | | |
|---|---|---|---|
| 1887. | 2 r. Pakistani carpet (diamond) centre .. .. | 35 | 15 |
| 1888. | 2 r. Turkish carpet (striped) | 35 | 15 |
| 1889. | 2 r. Type **502** .. .. | 35 | 15 |

**503.** Rifle-shooting. **504.** Persian King.

**1974.** Seventh Asian Games, Teheran (3rd series). Multicoloured.

| | | | |
|---|---|---|---|
| 1890. | 2 r. Type **503** .. .. | 30 | 15 |
| 1891. | 2 r. Fencing .. .. | 30 | 15 |
| 1892. | 2 r. Football .. .. | 30 | 15 |
| 1893. | 2 r. Cycling .. .. | 35 | 15 |

**1974.** 8th Shiraz Arts Festival, Persepolis.
1894. **504.** 2 r. multicoloured .. 15 10

**506.** Petrochemical Works, Khark.

**1974.**

| | | | | |
|---|---|---|---|---|
| 1896 | **506** | 5 d. green and brown | 10 | 10 |
| 1897 | – | 10 d. orange & brown | 10 | 10 |
| 1898 | – | 50 d. green and brown | 10 | 10 |
| 1899 | – | 1 r. blue and brown .. | 15 | 10 |
| 1900 | – | 2 r. purple and brown | 20 | 10 |
| 1901 | – | 6 r. brown and blue .. | 15 | 10 |
| 1902 | – | 8 r. turquoise and blue | 20 | 10 |
| 1903 | – | 10 r. purple and blue | 45 | 10 |
| 1904 | – | 14 r. green and blue | 1·00 | 10 |
| 1905 | – | 20 r. red and blue .. | 1·00 | 10 |
| 1906 | – | 50 r. violet and blue | 1·75 | 20 |

DESIGNS—As T **506**: 10 d. Railway bridge, Ghatur. 50 d. Dam, Farahnaz. 1 r. Oil Refinery. 2 r. Radio telescope. 37 × 27 mm: 6 r. Steelworks, Aryamehr. 8 r. Tabriz University. 10 r. Shah Abbas Kabir Dam. 14 r. Teheran Opera House. 20 r. Shahyad Square. 50 r. Aryamehr Stadium. See also Nos. 1939/49.

**507.** Family within Hands. **509.** Plan of Hasanlu.

**508.** Aryamehr Stadium, Teheran.

**1974.** State Education and Health Services. Multicoloured.

| | | | |
|---|---|---|---|
| 1907. | 2 r. Type **507** .. .. | 15 | 10 |
| 1908. | 2 r. Children, pen and book within hands .. | 15 | 10 |

**1974.** Seventh Asian Games, Teheran (4th series).
1909. **508.** 6 r. multicoloured .. 40 10

**1974.** 2nd International Architectural Congress, Shiraz.
1910. **509.** 8 r. multicoloured .. 30 10

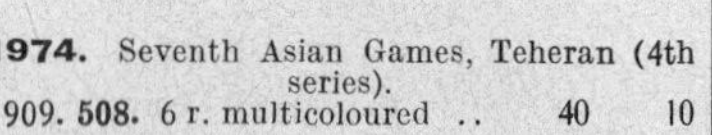
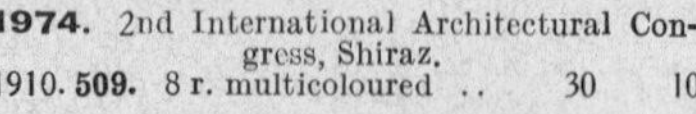

**510.** Charioteer.

**1974.** Centenary of U.P.U. Mult.

| | | | |
|---|---|---|---|
| 1911 | 6 r. Type **510** .. .. | 30 | 10 |
| 1912. | 14 r. U.P.U. emblem and letters .. .. .. | 50 | 20 |

**511.** Road through Park.

**1974.** Opening of Farahabad Park, Teheran. Multicoloured.

| | | | |
|---|---|---|---|
| 1913. | 1 r. Type **511** .. .. | 10 | 10 |
| 1914. | 2 r. Recreation pavilion | 15 | 10 |

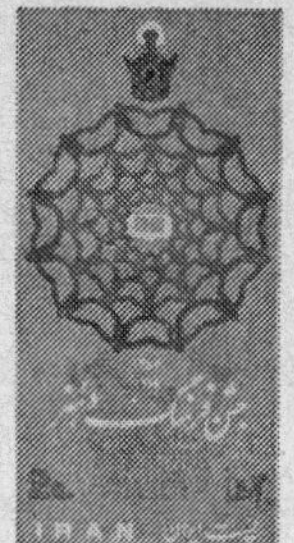


**512.** Festival Emblem.

**1974.** National Festival of Art and Culture, Teheran.
1915 **512** 2 r. multicoloured .. 15 10

**513.** Crown Prince in Aircraft.

**1974.** Air. Crown Prince's Birthday.
1916. **513.** 14 r. multicoloured .. 45 15

**514.** Destroyer "Palang".

**1974.** Navy Day.
1917. **514.** 10 r. multicoloured .. 65 20

**515.** Scarecrow. **516.** Winged Bull Emblem.

**1974.** Children's Week. Children's Drawings. Multicoloured.

| | | | |
|---|---|---|---|
| 1918. | 2 r. Type **515** .. .. | 15 | 10 |
| 1919. | 2 r. Girl at spinning wheel | 15 | 10 |
| 1920. | 2 r. New Year picnic .. | 15 | 10 |

Nos. 1919/20 are horiz.

**1974.** 3rd International Film Festival, Teheran.
1921. **516.** 2 r. multicoloured .. 15 10

**517.** W.P.Y. Emblem.

**1974.** World Population Year.
1922. **517.** 8 r. multicoloured .. 30 10

**518.** Gold Butterfly Brooch.

**1974.** 14th Wedding Anniv. of Shah and Empress Farah. Multicoloured.

| | | | |
|---|---|---|---|
| 1923. | 6 r. Type **518** .. .. | 15 | 10 |
| 1924. | 8 r. Gold diadem .. | 20 | 10 |

**519.** Angel with Banner.

**1975.** International Women's Year.
1925. **519.** 2 r. orge., blue & red 15 10

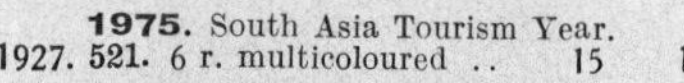

**520.** Emblems of Agriculture, Industry and the Arts. **521.** Tourism Year Emblem.

**1975.** 12th Anniv. of Shah's White Revolution.
1926. **520.** 2 r. multicoloured .. 15 10

**1975.** South Asia Tourism Year.
1927. **521.** 6 r. multicoloured .. 15 10

**522.** Farabi's Initial. **523.** Ornament.

**1975.** 1100th Birth Anniv of Abu-Nasr al-Farabi (philosopher).
1928 **522** 2 r. multicoloured .. 15 10

**1975.** New Year Festival. Multicoloured.

| | | | |
|---|---|---|---|
| 1929. | 1 r. Type **523** .. .. | 15 | 10 |
| 1930. | 1 r. Blossoms and tree .. | 15 | 10 |
| 1931. | 1 r. Arabesque and patterns | 15 | 10 |

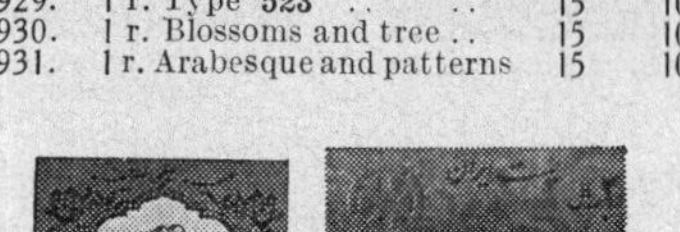

**524.** Nasser Khosrov. **525.** Persian Warriors.

**1975.** Birth Millenary of Nasser Khosrov (poet).
1932. **524.** 2 r. black, red & bistre 15 10

**1975.** 70th Anniv. of Rotary International. Multicoloured.

| | | | |
|---|---|---|---|
| 1933. | 2 r. Type **525** .. .. | 30 | 10 |
| 1934. | 10 r. Charioteer (horiz.) .. | 95 | 15 |

**526.** Biochemical Emblem. **527.** "Co-operative Peoples".

**1975.** Fifth Biochemical Symposium.
1935. **526.** 2 r. multicoloured .. 15 10

**1975.** Co-operatives Day.
1936. **527.** 2 r. multicoloured .. 10 10

**528.** Ancient Signal-beacons.

**1975.** World Telecommunications Day. Multicoloured.

| | | | |
|---|---|---|---|
| 1937. | 6 r. Type **528** .. .. | 20 | 10 |
| 1938. | 8 r. Telecommunications satellite .. .. | 30 | 15 |

**1975.** As Nos. 1896/1906 but colours changed.

| | | | | |
|---|---|---|---|---|
| 1939. | **506.** | 5 d. orange and turq. | 10 | 10 |
| 1940. | – | 10 d. purple and turq. | 10 | 10 |
| 1941. | – | 50 d. mauve and turq. | 10 | 10 |
| 1942. | – | 1 r. blue and turquoise | 20 | 10 |
| 1943. | – | 2 r. brown and turq. | 20 | 10 |
| 1944. | – | 6 r. violet and brown | 50 | 10 |
| 1945. | – | 8 r. red and brown .. | 70 | 10 |
| 1946. | – | 10 r. green and brown | 90 | 15 |
| 1947. | – | 14 r. mauve & brown | 6·00 | 25 |
| 1948. | – | 20 r. turq. and brown | 1·75 | 30 |
| 1949. | – | 50 r. blue and brown | 1·75 | 70 |

**529.** "Iran Air" Boeing 747SP.

**1975.** "Iran Air's" First Teheran–New York Flight.

1950. **529.** 10 r. multicoloured .. 35 15

**530.** Environmental Emblem. **532.** Party Emblem.

**531.** Dam and Reservoir.

**1975.** World Environment Day.

1951. **530.** 6 r. multicoloured .. 20 10

**1975.** 25th Anniv of International Commission on Irrigation and Drainage.

1952 **531** 10 r. multicoloured .. 25 15

**1975.** Formation of Resurgence Party.

1953. **532.** 2 r. multicoloured .. 10 10

**533.** Saluting Hand. **534.** Festival Motif.

**1975.** 2nd National Girl Scout Camp, Teheran.

1954. **533.** 2 r. multicoloured .. 20 10

**1975.** Festival of Tus (honouring poet Firdausi).

1955 **534** 2 r. multicoloured .. 10 10

**535.** Iranian Tile.

**1975.** 11th Anniv of Regional Co-operation for Development. Multicoloured.

| | | | |
|---|---|---|---|
| 1956. | 2 r. Type **535** .. .. | 15 | 10 |
| 1957. | 2 r. Pakistani camel-skin vase (vert.) .. .. | 15 | 10 |
| 1958. | 2 r. Turkish porcelain vase (vert.) .. .. .. | 15 | 10 |

**536.** Parliament Gateway.

**1975.** 70th Anniv. of Iranian Constitution.

1959. **536.** 10 r. multicoloured .. 25 15

**537.** Stylised Column. **538.** Flags over Globe.

**1975.** 9th Shiraz Arts Festival.

1960. **537.** 8 r. multicoloured .. 25 15

**1975.** International Literacy Symposium, Persepolis.

1961. **538.** 2 r. multicoloured .. 15 10

**539.** Stylised Globe. **541.** Festival Emblem.

**540.** Envelope on World Map.

**1975.** 3rd International Trade Fair, Teheran.

1962. **539.** 2 r. multicoloured .. 15 10

**1975.** World Post Day.

1963. **540.** 14 r. multicoloured .. 45 15

**1975.** National Festival of Art and Culture, Teheran.

1964 **541** 2 r. multicoloured .. 15 10

**542.** Face within Film. **543.** " Mother's Face ".

**1975.** International Festival of Children's Films, Teheran.

1965. **542.** 6 r. multicoloured .. 15 10

**1975.** Children's Week. Multicoloured.

| | | | |
|---|---|---|---|
| 1966. | 2 r. Type **543** .. .. | 15 | 10 |
| 1967. | 2 r. " Young Girl " .. | 15 | 10 |
| 1968. | 2 r. " Our House " (horiz.) | 15 | 10 |

**544.** " Sound Film ". **545.** Reform Symbols.

**1975.** 4th International Film Festival, Teheran.

1969. **544.** 8 r. multicoloured .. 20 15

**1976.** 13th Anniv. of Shah's White Revolution. Multicoloured.

| | | | |
|---|---|---|---|
| 1970. | 2 r. Type **545** .. .. | 10 | 10 |
| 1971. | 2 r. Symbols representing " People " .. .. | 10 | 10 |
| 1972. | 2 r. Five reform symbols | 10 | 10 |

**546.** Motor Cycle Patrol. **547.** Football Cup.

**1976.** Highway Police Day. Multicoloured.

| | | | |
|---|---|---|---|
| 1973 | 2 r. Type **546** .. .. | 40 | 15 |
| 1974 | 6 r. Bell Model 205 Iroquois police helicopter (horiz) .. | 85 | 20 |

**1976.** Third Int. Football Cup.

1975. **547.** 2 r. multicoloured .. 15 10

**548.** Candlestick. **549.** Early and Modern Telephones.

**1976.** New Year. Multicoloured.

| | | | |
|---|---|---|---|
| 1976. | 1 r. Type **548** .. .. | 15 | 10 |
| 1977. | 1 r. Incense burner .. | 15 | 10 |
| 1978. | 1 r. Rosewater jug .. | 15 | 10 |

**1976.** Telephone Centenary.

1979. **549.** 10 r. multicoloured .. 25 15

**550.** Human Eye.

**1976.** World Health Day.

1980. **550.** 6 r. multicoloured .. 30 10

**551.** Nurse holding Child.

**1976.** 30th Anniv. of Social Services Organization. Multicoloured.

| | | | |
|---|---|---|---|
| 1981 | 2 r. Type **551** .. .. | 15 | 10 |
| 1982 | 2 r. Workshop apprentices | 15 | 10 |
| 1983 | 2 r. Handclasp (help the aged) (vert) .. .. | 15 | 10 |

**552.** Linked Men on Map. **553.** Sound Waves and Headphones.

**1976.** 10th Anniv. of Iranian Co-operative Movement.

1984. **552.** 2 r. multicoloured .. 15 10

**1976.** World Telecommunications Day.

1985. **553.** 14 r. multicoloured .. 30 15

**554.** " Patriotism ". **555.** Nasser-Khosrow and Landmarks on Map.

**1976.** National Resistance Organization.

1986. **554.** 2 r. multicoloured .. 15 10

**1976.** Tourism Day and Birth Anniv. of Nasser-Khosrow "The Great Iranian Tourist".

1987. **555.** 6 r. multicoloured .. 15 10

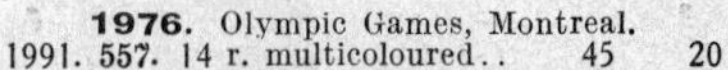

**556.** Riza Shah Pahlavi. **557.** Olympic Flame and Emblem.

**1976.** 12th Anniv. of Regional Co-operation for Development. Multicoloured.

| | | | |
|---|---|---|---|
| 1988 | 2 r. Type **556** .. .. | 15 | 10 |
| 1989 | 6 r. Mohammed Ali Jinnah (Pakistan) .. | 25 | 15 |
| 1990 | 8 r. Kemal Ataturk (Turkey) .. .. | 35 | 15 |

**1976.** Olympic Games, Montreal.

1991. **557.** 14 r. multicoloured .. 45 20

**558.** Riza Shah Pahlavi in Coronation Dress.

**1976.** 50th Anniv. of Pahlavi Dynasty. Multicoloured.

| | | | |
|---|---|---|---|
| 1992. | 2 r. Riza Shah Pahlavi and Mohammed Riza Pahlavi (horiz.) .. | 20 | 10 |
| 1993. | 6 r. Type **558** .. .. | 75 | 15 |
| 1994. | 14 r. Mohammed Riza Pahlavi in Coronation dress .. .. .. | 1·00 | 25 |

**559.** Festival Emblem. **560.** Conference Emblem.

**1976.** 10th Shiraz Arts Festival.

1995. **559.** 10 r. multicoloured .. 30 15

**1976.** 10th Asia–Pacific Scout Conference, Teheran.

1996 **560** 2 r. multicoloured .. 15 10

**561.** Radiation Treatment. **562.** Target and Presentation to Policewoman.

**1976.** Campaign against Cancer.

1997. **561.** 2 r. multicoloured .. 20 10

**1976.** Police Day.

1998. **562.** 2 r. multicoloured .. 30 10

**564.** U.P.U. Emblem and Iranian Stamp on Envelope.

**1976.** International Post Day.

2000. **564.** 10 r. multicoloured .. 30 15

**565.** Crown Prince presenting Cup.

**566.** Mohammed Riza Pahlavi, Riza Shah Pahlavi and Train.

**1976.** Society of Village Culture Houses.
2001. **565.** 6 r. multicoloured .. 20 10

**1976.** Railway Day.
2002. **566.** 8 r. multicoloured .. 90 50

**567.** Festival Emblem.

**568.** Census Symbols.

**1976.** National Festival of Art and Culture, Teheran.
2003 **567** 14 r. multicoloured .. 35 15

**1976.** National Census.
2004. **568.** 2 r. multicoloured .. 15 10

**569.** Flowers and Birds.

**570.** Mohammed Ali Jinnah (Quaid-i-Azam).

**1976.** Children's Week. Multicoloured.
2005. 2 r. Type **569** .. .. 15 10
2006. 2 r. Flowers and bird .. 15 10
2007. 2 r. Flowers and butterfly 15 10

**1976.** Birth Cent. of Mohammed Ali Jinnah (first Governor-General of Pakistan).
2008. **570.** 10 r. multicoloured .. 30 15

**571.** Tractor (Land reform).

**572.** Man in Guilan Costume.

**1977.** 14th Anniv of Shah's White Revolution. Shah's head and frame in gold.
2009 **571** 5 d. green and pink .. 10 10
2010 – 10 d. green and brown 10 10
2011 – 50 d. blue and orange 10 10
2012 – 1 r. blue and mauve 10 10
2013 – 2 r. green and orange 10 10
2014 – 3 r. red and blue .. 10 10
2015 – 5 r. lilac and green .. 20 10
2016 – 6 r. purple, brn & blk 30 10
2017 – 8 r. purple, blue & blk 30 10
2018 – 10 r. blue, green & blk 1·40 10
2019 – 12 r. brn, lilac & blk 70 10
2020 – 14 r. red, orange & blk 1·00 10
2021 – 20 r. orge, grey & blk 2·00 10
2022 – 30 r. green, blue & blk 1·75 10
2023 – 50 r. red, yellow & blk 3·50 10
2024 – 100 r. blue, mve & blk 3·25 55
2025 – 200 r. violet, grn & blk 6·50 1·50

DESIGNS—21 × 28 mm: 10 d. Trees (Nationalization of forests). 50 d. Bank notes (Profit-sharing). 1 r. Factory workers (Sale of shares to workers). 2 r. Parliament gate (Votes for women). 3 r. Teacher and pupils (Education corps). 5 r. Doctor examining patient (Medical corps). 36 × 27 mm: 6 r. Bulldozer (Civil engineering). 8 r. Scales (Justice). 10 r. Dam (Irrigation). 12 r. Building site (Construction corps). 14 r. Clock and receptionist (Working conditions). 20 r. Screen and students (Adult literacy). 30 r. Sound waves (Telecommunications). 50 r. Students and pupils (Education). 100 r. Baby in hands (Child care). 200 r. Elderly couple (Care of the aged).

**1977.** New Year Festival. Multicoloured.
2026. 1 r. Type **572** .. .. 10 10
2027. 2 r. Women in Guilan costume .. .. 15 10

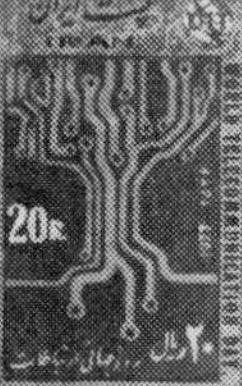

**573.** Circuit Diagram. **574.** Riza Shah Dam.

**1977.** World Telecommunications Day.
2028. **573.** 20 r. multicoloured .. 55 15

**1977.** Inauguration of Riza Shah Dam.
2029. **574.** 5 r. multicoloured .. 20 10

**575.** Olympic Rings.

**1977.** Olympic Day.
2030. **575.** 14 r. multicoloured .. 35 15

**576.** Turkish " Human Face " Vase.

**1977.** 13th Anniv. of Regional Co-operation for Development. Multicoloured.
2031. 5 r. Type **576** .. .. 20 10
2032. 5 r. Pakistani toy bullock cart .. .. .. 20 10
2033. 5 r. Iranian buff earthenware .. .. .. 20 10

**577.** Flowers on Map of Asia. **578.** Map and Emblem.

**1977.** 2nd Asia-Pacific Jamboree, Nishapur.
2034. **577.** 10 r. multicoloured .. 25 10

**1977.** 9th Asian Electronics Conference, Teheran.
2035. **578.** 3 r. multicoloured .. 15 10

**579.** " Tree " in Farsi Script. **580.** Globe and Envelope.

**1977.** Teachers' Day.
2036. **579.** 10 r. multicoloured .. 30 10

**1977.** Cent of Iran's Admission to U.P.U.
2037 **580** 14 r. multicoloured .. 30 10

**581.** " Tree and Lions ". **582.** Festival Emblem.

**1977.** Popular Arts Festival.
2038. **581.** 5 r. multicoloured .. 15 10

**1977.** National Festival of Art and Culture, Teheran.
2039 **582** 20 r. multicoloured .. 45 20

**583.** " Two Horsemen " (Persian miniature). **584.** Seminar Emblem.

**1977.** Children's Week. Multicoloured.
2040. 3 r. Type **583** .. .. 15 10
2041. 3 r. " Lover and his mistress " .. .. 15 10
2042. 3 r. " Five people round a bed " .. .. 15 10

**1977.** 1st Regional Seminar on Education and Welfare of the Deaf.
2043. **584.** 5 r. multicoloured .. 15 10

**585.** A. M. Iqbal. **586.** Bronze Head from Nigeria.

**1977.** Birth Cent. of Allama Mohammad Iqbal (Pakistani poet).
2044. **585.** 5 r. multicoloured .. 15 10

**1977.** " Art of Black Africa " Exhibition, Teheran.
2045. **586.** 20 r. multicoloured .. 1·25 30

**587.** Ruins at Persepolis. **588.** Mohammed Riza Pahlavi.

**1978.**
2059 **587** 1 r. brown and gold .. 10 10
2060 – 2 r. green and gold .. 20 10
2061 – 3 r. purple and gold 30 10
2062 – 5 r. green and gold .. 40 10
2063 – 9 r. brown and gold .. 85 30
2064 – 10 r. blue and gold .. 3·50 35
2065 – 20 r. red and gold .. 1·00 30
2066 – 25 r. blue and gold .. 17·00 2·75
2067 – 30 r. red and gold .. 1·75 35
2068 – 50 r. green and gold 2·75 1·75
2069 – 100 r. blue and gold .. 9·00 4·25
2070 – 200 r. violet and gold 12·00 9·00

DESIGNS: 30 × 23 mm. 2 r. Khajou Bridge, Isfahan. 3 r. Shah Mosque, Isfahan. 5 r. Imam Riza Shrine, Meshed. 35 × 26 mm. 9 r. Warrior frieze, Persepolis. 10 r. Djameh Mosque, Isfahan. 20 r. Bas-relief, Persepolis. 25 r. Shaikh Lotfollah Mosque. 30 r. Ruins, Persepolis (different). 50 r. Ali Ghapou Palace, Isfahan. 100 r. Stone relief, Tagh Bastan. 200 r. Relief, Naqsh Rostam.

**1978.** 15th Anniv. of Shah's White Revolution.
2071. **588.** 20 r. multicoloured .. 1·00 30

**589.** Animals (carpet). **590.** Costume of Mazandera Province.

**1978.** Inauguration of Persian Carpets Museum, Teheran. Multicoloured.
2072. 3 r. Type **589** .. .. 15 10
2073. 5 r. Court scene .. .. 20 10
2074. 10 r. Floral pattern .. 30 15

**1978.** New Year Festival. Multicoloured.
2075. 3 r. Type **590** .. .. 15 10
2076. 5 r. Woman in costume of Mazandera Province .. 25 10

**591.** Riza Shah Pahlavi and Crown Prince inspecting Girls' School.

**1978.** Birth Cent. of Riza Shah Pahlavi. Multicoloured.
2077. 3 r. Type **591** .. .. 15 10
2078. 5 r. Riza Shah Pahlavi and Crown Prince at inauguration of Trans-Iranian Railway 50 30
2079. 10 r. Riza Shah Pahlavi and Crown Prince at Palace of Persepolis .. 55 15
2080. 14 r. Shah handing Crown Prince officer's diploma 60 20

**592.** Satellite and Receiving Station.

**1978.** 10th Anniv. of Admission to International Telecommunications Union.
2081. **592.** 20 r. multicoloured .. 65 20

**593.** Microwave Antenna.

**1978.** World Telecommunications Day.
2082. **593.** 15 r. multicoloured .. 55 20

**594.** Welfare Legion Emblem. **595.** Pink Roses.

**1978.** 10th Anniv. of Universal Welfare Legion.
2083. **594.** 10 r. multicoloured .. 20 10

**1978.** 14th Anniv. of Regional Co-operation for Development. Roses. Multicoloured.
2084. 5 r. Type **595** .. .. 15 10
2085. 10 r. Salmon rose .. 35 10
2086. 15 r. Red roses .. .. 60 15

**596.** Rhazes and Pharmaceutical Equipment.

**1978.** Pharmacists' Day.
2087. **596.** 5 r. multicoloured .. 20 10

597. Girl Guides and Aryamehr Arch.

**1978.** 23rd World Girl Guides Conference, Teheran.
2088. 597. 5 r. multicoloured .. 20 10

598. Riza Shah Pahlavi.

**1978.** 50th Anniv. of Bank Melli Iran. Mult.
2089. 3 r. Type 598 .. .. 40 15
2090. 5 r. Mohammed Riza Pahlavi .. .. 60 15

599. Young Girl and Bird.

**1978.** Children's Week.
2091. 599. 3 r. multicoloured .. 20 10

600. U.P.U. Emblem over Map of Iran.

**1978.** World Post Day.
2092. 600. 14 r. multicoloured .. 50 10

601. Classroom and Communications Equipment.

**1978.** 50th Anniv. of Communications Faculty.
2093. 601. 10 r. multicoloured .. 60 10

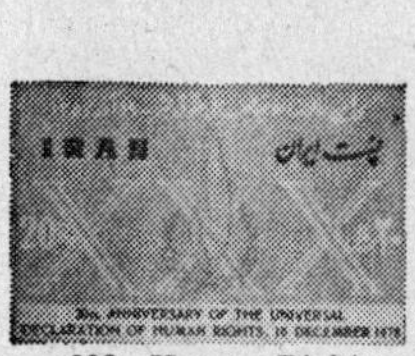
602. Human Rights Emblem.
603. Rose.

**1978.** 30th Anniv. of Human Rights Declaration.
2094. 602. 20 r. multicoloured .. 80 15

**1979.** New Year Festival. Multicoloured.
2095. 2 r. Type 603 .. .. 15 10
2096. 3 r. Man in Khurdistan costume .. 60 10
2097. 5 r. Woman in Khurdistan costume .. 90 15

604. Revolutionary Crowd.

**1979.** Islamic Revolution. Multicoloured.
2098. 3 r. Type 604 .. .. 80 15
2099. 5 r. Hands holding flower, gun and torch .. 60 15
2100. 10 r. Protest march .. 70 30
2101. 20 r. Bloodied hands releasing dove (vert.) .. 1·60 30

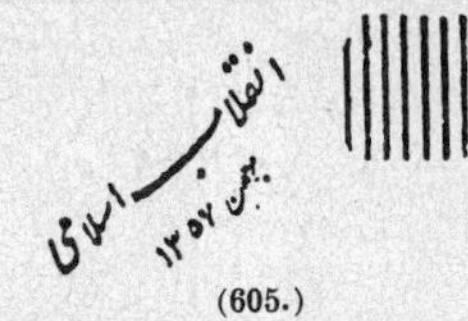
(605.)

**1979.** Designs as T 587 optd with T 605.
(a) Nos. 1945/6.
2102 8 r. red and brown .. 65 15
2103 10 r. green and brown .. 20·00 85
(b) Nos. 2063/4, 2068/70 and unissued 15 r. and 19 r. stamps.
2104. 9 r. brown and gold .. 1·00 15
2105. 10 r. turquoise and gold 30 15
2106. 15 r. mauve and gold .. 30 15
2107. 19 r. green and gold .. 65 15
2108. 50 r. green & gold .. 1·40 35
2109. 100 r. blue & gold .. 3·50 70
2110. 200 r. violet & gold .. 3·75 1·75
DESIGNS—HORIZ. (36 × 26 mm.). 15 r. Rock carvings, Naqsh Rostam. 19 r. Chehel Sotoon Palace, Isfahan.

606. Tulip formed from " Allah " and " Islamic Republic ".
607. " Iranian Goldsmith " (Kamal el Molk).

**1979.** Islamic Republic.
2111. 606. 5 r. multicoloured .. 1·25 15

**1979.** 15th Anniv. of Regional Co-operation for Development. Paintings. Mult.
2112. 5 r. Type 607 .. 1·50 15
2113. 5 r. " Turkish Harvest " (Namik Ismail) .. 1·50 15
2114. 5 r. " Pakistan Village Scene " (Allah Baksh) 1·50 15

608. " Telecom 79 ".

**1979.** Third World Telecommunications Exhibition, Geneva.
2115. 608. 20 r. gold, blk. & red 4·50 20

609. Tulip rising from Blood of Revolutionary.
610. Persian Rug.

**1979.** International Year of the Child. Children's Paintings. Multicoloured.
2116. 2 r. Type 609 .. .. 40 15
2117. 3 r. Children greeting the rising sun (vert.) .. 50 15
2118. 5 r. Children with banners 1·00 15

**1979.**
2119 610 50 d. brown & orange 10 10
2120 1 r. blue & light blue 10 10
2121 2 r. red and yellow .. 10 10
2122 3 r. blue and mauve 10 10
2123 5 r. olive and green .. 15 10
2124 10 r. black and pink 25 10
2125 20 r. brown and grey 35 10
2126 50 r. violet and grey 85 10
2127 100 r. black and green 4·00 70
2128 200 r. blue and stone 4·00 1·50
Nos. 2126/8 are larger, 27 × 37 mm.

611. Globe in Envelope.
612. Kashani and Astrolabe.

**1979.** World Post Day.
2134. 611. 10 r. multicoloured .. 2·50 15

**1979.** 550th Death Anniv of Ghyath-al-din Jamshid Kashani (mathematician and astronomer).
2135 612 5 r. black and brown 85 15

613. Kaaba, Mecca.

**1980.** 1400th Anniv. of Hegira (1st issue). Multicoloured.
2136. 3 r. Type 613 .. .. 10 10
2137. 5 r. Koran and globe (vert.) 15 10
2138. 10 r. Pilgrim and Kaaba 30 10
See also Nos. 2148/51.

614. Flag and Revolutionaries.
615. Dehkhoda.

**1980.** 1st Anniv of Islamic Revolution. Mult.
2139 1 r. Type 614 (28 × 40 mm) 10 10
2432 1 r. As No. 2139 but 24 × 35 mm .. .. 10 10
2140 3 r. Dagger and dripping blood (28 × 40 mm) .. 10 10
2433 3 r. As No. 2140 but 24 × 36 mm .. .. 15 15
2141 5 r. Open window and rising sun (28 × 40 mm) 15 10
2435 5 r. As No. 2141 but 24 × 36 mm .. .. 20 20

**1980.** Birth Centenary of Dehkhoda (compiler, Iranian encyclopedia).
2142. 615. 10 r. multicoloured .. 20 10

616. Female Costume of East Azerbaijan.
617. M. Mossadegh.

**1980.** New Year Festival. Multicoloured.
2143. 3 r. Type 616 .. .. 15 10
2144. 5 r. Male costume of East Azerbaijan .. .. 20 10

**1980.** Birth Centenary of Dr. Mohammed Mossadegh (statesman).
2145 617 20 r. multicoloured .. 45 20

618. Morteza Mottahari.
619. Telephone.

**1980.** 1st Death Anniv of Prof. Morteza Mottahari.
2146 618 10 r. black and red .. 20 10

**1980.** World Telecommunications Day.
2147. 619 20 r. blk., grn. & red 40 15

620. Mosque Interior.

**1980.** 1400th Anniv. of Hegira (2nd issue). Multicoloured.
2148. 50 d. Type 620 .. .. 10 10
2149. 1 r. Crowd with banner.. 10 10
2150. 3 r. Al-Biruni, Farabi and Avicenna .. .. 10 10
2151. 5 r. Mosque and Kaaba.. 15 10

621. Dr. Ali Shariati.
622. Kaaba and Banner.

**1980.** Dr. Ali Shariati (educator) Commemoration.
2152. 621. 5 r. multicoloured .. 20 10

**1980.** Birth Anniv. of Hazrat Mehdi (Shiite Imam).
2153. 622. 5 r. green, red & black 20 10

623. Ayatollah Teleghani.
624. O.P.E.C. Emblem and Globe.

**1980.** Ayatollah Teleghani Commemoration.
2154. 623. 5 r. multicoloured.. 35 10

**1980.** 20th Anniv. of Organization of Petroleum Exporting Countries. Mult.
2155. 5 r. Type 624 .. .. 20 10
2156. 10 r. Figures supporting O.P.E.C. emblem .. 35 10

625. Hands breaking Star of David around Dome of the Rock.
626. Tulip and Feizieh Theological College.

**1980.** " Let us Liberate Jerusalem ".
2157. 625. 5 r. multicoloured .. 20 10
2158. 20 r. multicoloured .. 45 20

**1981.** 2nd Anniv of Islamic Revolution. Mult.
2159 3 r. Type 626 (dated "1981" at right) .. 20 10
2434 3 r. As No. 2159 but dated at left .. .. 15 15
2160 5 r. Tulip (in red), drops of blood and "Martyr" in Persian script .. 25 10
2436 5 r. As No. 2160 but orange tulip .. .. 20 20
2161 20 r. Open tulip (in red) and crest of Republic 50 20
2441 20 r. As No. 2161 but orange tulip .. .. 50 50

627. Male Costume of Lorestan.
628. I.T.U. and W.H.O. Emblems with Ribbons forming Caduceus.

**1981.** New Year Festival. Multicoloured.
2162. 5 r. Type 627 .. .. 20 10
2163. 10 r. Female costume, Lorestan .. .. 40 10

**1981.** World Telecommunications Day.
2164 628 5 r. orange, blk & grn 20 10

630. Militia Training.
631. Ayatollah Kashani.

**1981.**

| | | | | |
|---|---|---|---|---|
| 2165 | 630 | 50 d. black and brown | 10 | 10 |
| 2166 | – | 1 r. purple and green | 10 | 10 |
| 2167 | – | 2 r. brown and blue .. | 10 | 10 |
| 2168 | – | 3 r. black and green | 10 | 10 |
| 2169 | – | 5 r. blue and brown .. | 15 | 10 |
| 2170 | – | 10 r. ultramarine & bl | 20 | 10 |
| 2171 | – | 20 r. black and red .. | 50 | 20 |
| 2172 | – | 50 r. black and mauve | 1·25 | 30 |
| 2173 | – | 100 r. black & brown | 2·50 | 55 |
| 2174 | – | 200 r. blue and black | 5·00 | 1·40 |

DESIGNS—As Type **630**: 1 r. Man and boy at school desk (Literacy campaign). 2 r. Digging irrigation ditch. 37 × 27 mm: 3 r. Massed prayers. 20 r. Woman with rifle. 50 r. Worker at lathe. 100 r. Pilgrims around Kaaba. 27 × 37 mm: 5 r. Revolutionary Guards emblem and crowd. 10 r. Arabic tapestry. 200 r. Niche in Mosque illuminated by sun.

**1981.** Birth Cent. of Ayatollah Kashani.
2175. **631.** 15 r. purple and green 35 15

**632.** Armed Forces.

**1981.** Islamic Iranian Army.
2176. **632.** 5 r. multicoloured .. 20 10

**633.** Carrier Pigeon flying over Gun Barrels.

**1981.** U.P.U. Day.
2177. **633.** 20 r. black and blue .. 55 15

**634.** Inscription.

**1981.** Millenary of "Nabj al-Blagah" (sacred book).
2178 **634** 25 r. green, blue & blk 50 15

**635.** Victims of Bomb at Islamic Party's Headquarters.

**1981.** Iranian Bomb and War Victims, Commemoration.

| | | | | |
|---|---|---|---|---|
| 2179. | **635.** | 3 r. black and red .. | 15 | 10 |
| 2180. | – | 5 r. brn. and deep brn. | 20 | 10 |
| 2181. | – | 10 r. multicoloured .. | 30 | 15 |

DESIGNS: 5 r. President Rajai and Prime Minister Bahomar (bomb victims). 10 r. Dr. Chamran (killed in Iran–Iraq War).

**636.** Ayatollah Tabatabaee. **637.** Hand writing on Board.

**1981.** Death Centenary of Ayatollah Ghazi Tabatabaee.
2182 **636** 5 r. brown, grn & gold 15 10

**1982.** Literacy Campaign.
2183. **637.** 5 r. blue and gold .. 15 10

**638.** Text "God is Great" over Map of Iran. **639.** Banner around Globe.

**1982.** 3rd Anniv. of Islamic Revolution. Multicoloured.

| | | | |
|---|---|---|---|
| 2184. | 5 r. Type **638** .. .. | 15 | 10 |
| 2185. | 10 r. Dove forming tulip | 25 | 15 |
| 2186. | 20 r. "God is Great" over Globe .. .. | 45 | 25 |

**1982.** Islamic Unity Week.
2187. **639.** 25 r. multicoloured .. 50 15

**640.** Manacled Hands reaching towards Christ.

**1982.** Glorification of Christ's Birth.
2188. **640.** 20 r. multicoloured .. 55 20

**641.** Male Costume of Khuzestan. **642.** National Flag.

**1982.** New Year Festival. Multicoloured.

| | | | |
|---|---|---|---|
| 2189. | 3 r. Type **641** .. .. | 10 | 10 |
| 2190. | 5 r. Female costume of Khuzestan .. .. | 15 | 10 |

**1982.** 3rd Anniv. of Islamic Republic.
2191. **642.** 30 r. blk., red and grn. 75 20

**643.** Ayatollah Sadr.

**1982.** 2nd Death Anniv. of Ayatollah Sadr.
2192. **643.** 50 r. multicoloured .. 1·25 30

**644.** Ayatollahs Madani and Dastghib.

**1982.** Ayatollahs Sayed Assadollah Madani and Sayed Abdolhossein Dastghib Commemoration.
2193 **644** 50 r. red, black & gold 1·25 30

**645.** Hand holding Cogwheels. **646.** Geometric Pattern.

**1982.** Labour Day.
2194. **645.** 100 r. multicoloured 2·25 50

**1982.** World Telecommunications Day.
2195 **646** 100 r. multicoloured .. 2·50 50

**647.** Symbolic Design. **648.** Rifles and Clenched Fist.

**1982.** Ma'bas Festival.
2196. **647.** 32 r. multicoloured .. 85 20

**1982.** 19th Anniv. of 1963 Islamic Rising.
2197. **648.** 20 r. blk., red & silver 60 20

**649.** Lieutenant Islambuli. **650.** Ayatollah Beheshti.

**1982.** Lieutenant Khaled Islambuli (assassin of Pres. Sadat of Egypt). Commemoration.
2198 **649** 2 r. multicoloured .. 20 10

**1982.** 1st Death Anniv of Ayatollah Mohammed Hossein Beheshti.
2199 **650** 10 r. multicoloured .. 30 15

**651.** Soldiers, Tanks and Hand holding Banner.

**1982.** Victims of War against Iraq. Commemoration.
2200. **651.** 5 r. multicoloured .. 20 10

**652.** Dome of the Rock.

**1982.** World Jerusalem Day.
2201. **652.** 1 r. multicoloured .. 20 10

**653.** Pilgrims around Kaaba. **654.** Globe and Letters.

**1982.** Pilgrimage to Mecca.
2202. **653.** 10 r. multicoloured .. 25 10

**1982.** World U.P.U. Day.
2203 **654** 30 r. multicoloured .. 65 20

**655.** Bloodied Hand releasing Dove. **656.** Casting Vote.

**1983.** 4th Anniv of Islamic Revolution.

| | | | | |
|---|---|---|---|---|
| 2204 | **655** | 30 r. multicoloured (crowd in brown) .. | 60 | 15 |
| 2445 | | 30 r. multicoloured (crowd in orange) | 75 | 75 |

**1983.** 4th Anniv. of Islamic Republic.
2205. **656.** 10 r. red, blk. & grn. 30 10

**657.** "Enlightenment". **658.** Microwave Antenna and "83".

**1983.** Teachers' Day.
2206. **657.** 5 r. multicoloured .. 15 10

**1983.** World Communications Year.
2207 **658** 20 r. blue, mve & brn 55 10

**659.** Assembly. **660.** Doves and Crowd.

**1983.** First Session of Islamic Consultative Assembly.
2208 **659** 5 r. multicoloured .. 15 10

**1983.** 20th Anniv. of 1963 Islamic Rising.
2209. **660.** 10 r. multicoloured .. 25 10

**661.** Map of Persian Gulf and burning Oil Wells at Nowruz.

**1983.** Ecology Week.
2210 **661** 5 r. black, red and blue 30 10

**662.** Sadooghi. **663.** Hands holding Rifle over Dome of the Rock.

**1983.** Ayatollah Mohammad Sadooghi Commemoration.
2211. **662.** 20 r. black and red .. 55 10

**1983.** World Jerusalem Day.
2212 **663** 5 r. yellow, brown & bl 20 10

**664.** Rajai and Bahomar.

**1983.** Government Week (death anniv of Pres. Rajai and Prime Minister Dr. Bahomar).
2213 **664** 3 r. orange and blue .. 20 10

665. **Cartridges and Text.**

666. Stamps and Map of Iran around Globe.

**1983.** War Week.
2214 **665** 5 r. green and red .. 20 10

**1983.** World U.P.U. Day.
2215 **666** 10 r. multicoloured .. 30 10

667. Esfahani.

668. Mirza Kuchik Khan.

**1983.** 4th Death Anniv of Ayatollah Ashrafi Esfahani.
2216 **667** 5 r. multicoloured .. 15 10

**1983.** Religious and Political Personalities.
2217 – 1 r. black and pink .. 10 10
2218 **668** 2 r. black and orange 10 10
2219 – 3 r. black and blue .. 10 10
2220 – 5 r. black and red .. 15 10
2221 – 10 r. black and green 30 10
2222 – 20 r. black and purple 55 20
2223 – 30 r. black and brown 75 30
2224 – 50 r. black and blue .. 1·25 50
2225 – 100 r. black and red .. 2·50 90
2226 – 200 r. black and green 5·00 2·00

DESIGNS: 1 r. Sheikh Mohammed Khiabani. 3 r. Seyd Modjtaba Navab Safavi. 5 r. Seyd Jamal-ed-Din Assadabadi. 10 r. Seyd Hassah Modaress. 20 r. Sheikh Fazel Assad Nouri. 30 r. Mirza Mohammed Hossein Naieni. 50 r. Sheikh Mohammed Hossein Kashef. 100 r. Seyd Hassan Shirazi. 200 r. Mirza Reza Kermani.

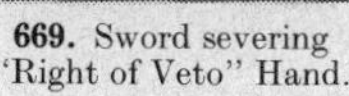


669. Sword severing "Right of Veto" Hand.

670. **Storming the U.S. Embassy, Hostage and burning American Flag.**

**1983.** United Nations Day.
2228. **669. 32 r. multicoloured ..** 85 30

**1983.** 4th Anniv of Storming of United States Embassy.
2229. **670. 28 r. multicoloured ..** 75 40

671. **Avicenna and Globe.**

**1983.** International Medical Seminar, Teheran.
2230 **671** 3 r. purple and blue .. 20 10

672. **Young and Old Soldiers.**

**1983.** Preparation Day.
2231 **672** 20 r. green, blk & red 55 20

673. **Fist with Gun and Dove.**

**1983.** Saddam's Crimes Conference.
2232 **673** 5 r. black and mauve 20 10

674. **Dr. Mohammad Mofatteh.**

675. **Light shining on Globe.**

**1983.** 4th Death Anniv of Dr. Mohammed Mofatteh.
2233 **674** 10 r. mve, blk & gold 30 10

**1983.** Mohammed's Birth Anniv.
2234 **675** 5 r. blue, brown & grn 20 10

676. Tulips and Flag.

677. Nurse tending Wounded Soldier.

**1984.** 5th Anniv of Islamic Revolution.
2235 **676** 10 r. multicoloured .. 30 10

**1984.** Nurses' Day.
2240 **677** 20 r. multicoloured .. 55 20

678. Soldier in Wheelchair.

679. "Lotus gebelia".

**1984.** Invalids' Day.
2241 **678** 5 r. multicoloured .. 20 10

**1984.** New Year Festival. Flowers. Mult.
2242 3 r. Type **679** .. .. 15 10
2243 5 r. "Tulipa chrysantha" 25 10
2244 10 r. "Glycyrrhiza glabra" 35 15
2245 20 r. "Matthiola alyssifolia" .. .. .. 60 25

680. Malcolm Little (founder of Union of Moslem Mosques and Organization for African–American Unity).

**1984.** Struggle Against Racial Discrimination.
2246 **680** 5 r. multicoloured .. 20 10

681. Flag around Globe.

683. Harb.

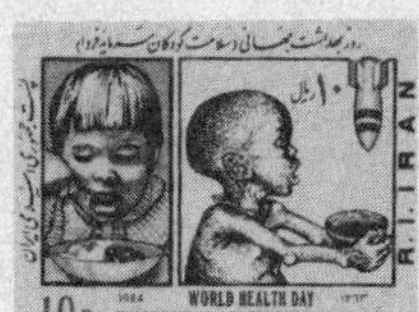


682. Well-fed and Starving Children.

**1984.** 5th Anniv of Islamic Republic.
2247 **681** 5 r. multicoloured .. 20 10

**1984.** World Health Day.
2248 **682** 10 r. multicoloured .. 30 15

**1984.** 22nd Death Anniv of Sheikh Ragheb Harb.
2249 **683** 5 r. black, red & green 20 10

684. Family holding Red Crescent Banner.

685. Transmitter.

**1984.** World Red Cross and Red Crescent Day.
2250 **684** 5 r. multicoloured .. 20 10

**1984.** World Telecommunications Day.
2251 **685** 20 r. black, blue & red 55 30

686. Ghotb.

688. Jerusalem, Map of Israel and Koran.

687. Kaaba and Destruction of Images.

**1984.** 19th Death Anniv of Seyyed Ghotb.
2252 **686** 10 r. black, gold & orge 25 15

**1984.** Conquest of Mecca.
2253 **687** 5 r. multicoloured .. 20 10

**1984.** World Jerusalem Day (5 r.) and Fetr Feast (10 r.). Multicoloured.
2254 5 r. Type **688** .. .. 20 10
2255 10 r. Crowd around Mosque .. .. 30 20

689. Choga Zanbil, Susa.

**1984.** Preservation of Cultural Heritage. Mult.
2256 5 r. Type **689** .. .. 20 10
2257 5 r. Emamzadeh Hossein shrine, Qazvin (Arabic date at left) .. .. 20 10
2258 5 r. Imam Mosque, Isfahan .. .. 20 10
2259 5 r. Ark Fortress, Tabriz 20 10
2260 5 r. Prophet Daniel's Mausoleum, Susa (with conical tower) .. 20 10

691. Crowd around Kaaba.

692. Spirit Nebula.

**1984.** Feast of Sacrifices.
2261. **691.** 10 r. multicoloured .. 25 15

**1984.** 10th International Trade Fair, Teheran.
2262 **692** 10 r. blue and red .. 25 15

693. Rifle and Cartridges on Flower.

694. Stylized Pigeon and U.P.U. Emblem.

**1984.** War Week.
2263. **693.** 5 r. multicoloured .. 20 10

**1984.** World Universal Postal Union Day.
2264 **694** 20 r. multicoloured .. 45 30

695. Khomeini.

696. Tabatabaie.

**1984.** 7th Death Anniv of Haj Seyyed Mostafa Khomeini.
2265 **695** 5 r. multicoloured .. 20 10

**1984.** Ghazi Tabatabaie Commemoration.
2266. **696.** 5 r. black, gold and red .. .. 20 10

697. Saadi.

698. Clasped Hands, Mosque and Koran.

**1984.** 800th Birth Anniv of Saadi (poet) Congress.
2267 **697** 10 r. multicoloured .. 25 15

**1984.** Mohammed's Birth Anniv. and Unity Week.
2268. **698.** 5 r. multicoloured .. 20 10

699. Doves as Petals.

700. Sapling and Forest.

**1985.** 6th Anniv of Islamic Revolution (1st issue).

2269 **699** 40 r. multicoloured (tulip emblem in red) . . . . 85 60
2446 40 r. multicoloured (tulip emblem in mauve) . . . . 1·00 1·00

See also No. 2277.

**1985.** Tree Planting Day. Multicoloured.

2270. 3 r. Type **700** . . . . 15 10
2271. 5 r. Sapling growing near forest . . . . . . 20 10

**701.** Crown Imperial ("Fritillaria imperialis".

**702.** Procession of Women with Flags.

**1985.** New Year Festival. Multicoloured.

2272 5 r. Type **701** . . . . 20 10
2273 5 r. Pilewort ("Ranunculus ficarioides") . . 20 10
2274 5 r. Saffron crocus ("Crocus sativus") . . 20 10
2275 5 r. "Primula heterochroma" . . . . 20 10

**1985.** Women's Day and Birth Anniv of Fatima.

2276 **702** 10 r. multicoloured . . 25 15

**703.** Tulip and Ballot Box.

**704.** Koran.

**1985.** 6th Anniv. of Islamic Republic (2nd issue).

2277. **703.** 20 r. multicoloured . . 50 30

**1985.** Mab'as Festival.

2278. **704.** 10 r. multicoloured . . 25 15

**705.** Globe, Chain, Banner, Kaaba and Scales.

**706.** I.T.U. Emblem and Telephone Handsets.

**1985.** World Day of the Oppressed.

2279. **705.** 5 r. multicoloured . . 20 10

**1985.** World Telecommunications Day.

2280. **706.** 20 r. multicoloured . . 50 30

**707.** Soldier saluting and Bridge.

**708.** Fist, Rifles and Qum Theological College.

**1985.** Liberation of Khorramshahr.

2281. **707.** 5 r. multicoloured . . 25 10

**1985.** 22nd Anniv. of 1963 Islamic Rising.

2282. **708.** 10 r. multicoloured . . 25 15

**709.** Decorated Plates and Vases.

**1985.** World Handicrafts Day.

2283. **709.** 20 r. multicoloured . . 50 30

**710.** Map of Israel and Dome of the Rock.

**711.** Arabic Script.

**1985.** World Jerusalem Day.

2284. **710.** 5 r. multicoloured . . 20 10

**1985.** Fetr Feast.

2285 **711** 5 r. blue, red and black 20 10

**712.** Organization Emblem.

**1985.** 4th Anniv of Islamic Propagation Organization.

2286 **712** 5 r. brown, green & blk 20 10

**713.** Abdolhossein Amini and the Koran.

**714.** Pilgrims around Holy Kaaba.

**1985.** Ayatollah Sheikh Abdolhossein Amini (theologian) Commemoration.

2287 **713** 5 r. multicoloured . . 20 10

**1985.** Pilgrimage to Mecca.

2288. **714.** 10 r. multicoloured . . 30 15

**715.** Two Swords Pattern.

**716.** Revolutionaries and Mosque.

**1985.** Preservation of Cultural History. Ancient Ceramic Plates from Nishabur. Multicoloured.

2289 5 r. Type **715** . . . . 20 10
2290 5 r. Plate with border of Farsi script . . 20 10
2291 5 r. Stylised bird pattern 20 10
2292 5 r. Four leaves and knot pattern . . . . 20 10

**1985.** 50th Anniv of Rising in Goharshad Mosque, Meshed.

2293 **716** 10 r. multicoloured . . 30 15

**717.** Health Services.

**718.** Red Tulips dripping Blood.

**1985.** Government and People Week. Multicoloured.

2294. 5 r. Envelope, crane and mechanical digger . . 20 10
2295. 5 r. Factory, cogwheel and ear of wheat . . 20 10
2296. 5 r. Type **717** . . 20 10
2297. 5 r. Literacy campaign emblem on book . . 20 10

**1985.** 7th Anniv of "Bloody Friday" Riots.

2298 **718** 10 r. multicoloured . . 30 15

**719.** O.P.E.C. Emblem and "25".

**720.** Dead Iranian.

**1985.** 25th Anniv. of Organization of Petroleum Exporting Countries.

2299. **719.** 5 r. yellow and brown 20 10
2300. – 5 r. blue and green . . 20 10

DESIGN: No. 2300, O.P.E.C. emblem and world map.

**1985.** 5th Anniv of Iran–Iraq War. Mult.

2301 5 r. Type **720** . . . . 20 10
2302 5 r. Dome of mosque and text "Ashura" . . 20 10
2303 5 r. White doves with map of Iran under a hail of bombs . . . . 20 10
2304 5 r. Oasis and exploding rifle . . . . . . 20 10

**721.** Symbolic Design.

**722.** Envelopes and Posthorn.

**1985.** Death Millenary of Ash-Sharif Ar-Radi (writer).

2305 **721** 20 r. bl, gold & ultram 50 30

**1985.** World U.P.U. Day.

2306 **722** 20 r. multicoloured . . 50 30

**723.** Emblem.

**724.** Seedling and Ear of Wheat in Hand.

**1985.** World Standards Day.

2307. **723.** 20 r. multicoloured . . 50 30

**1985.** Agricultural Training and Extension Year.

2308. **724.** 5 r. multicoloured . . 20 10

**725.** Seal of U.S. Embassy.

**726.** Kaaba, Mosque and Clasped Hands.

**1985.** 6th Anniv. of Storming of United States Embassy.

2309. **725.** 40 r. multicoloured . . 1·00 55

**1985.** Mohammed's Birth Anniv. and Unity Week.

2310. **726.** 10 r. multicoloured . . 30 15

**727.** Rose growing from Pen Nib and Tulip.

**728.** Profiles and Symbols of Learning.

**1985.** High Council of Cultural Revolution Anniv.

2311. **727.** 5 r. multicoloured . . 20 10

**1985.** International Youth Year. Mult.

2312. 5 r. Type **728** . . . . 20 10
2313. 5 r. Profiles and symbols of war . . . . . . 20 10
2314. 5 r. Profiles and symbols of industry and agriculture . . . . 20 10
2315. 5 r. Profiles and sports pictograms . . . . 20 10

**729.** Ezzeddin Al-Qassam.

**730.** Bayonets, Map and Clenched Fists.

**1985.** 50th Death Anniv. of Ezzeddin Al-Qassam.

2316. **729.** 20 r. brown, red and silver . . . . 50 30

**1985.** Afghan Resistance to Occupation.

2317. **730.** 40 r. multicoloured . . 1·10 70

**731.** Mirza Taqi Khan Amir Kabir.

**732.** Tulips and Crowd destroying Statue.

**1986.** 135th Death Anniv. of Mirza Taqi Khan Amir Kabir.

2318. **731.** 5 r. multicoloured . . 20 15

**1986.** 7th Anniv. of Islamic Revolution.

2319. **732.** 20 r. multicoloured . . 60 35

**MORE DETAILED LISTS**
are given in the Stanley Gibbons Catalogues referred to in the country headings.
For lists of current volumes see Introduction.

733. Sulayman Khater and Dome of the Rock.

**1986.** 40th Death Anniv. of Sulayman Khater.
2320. **733.** 10 r. blk., bl. & red 30 15

734. Woman, Child and Crowd.

735. "Papaver orientale".

**1986.** Women's Day and Birth Anniv of Fatima.
2321 **734** 10 r. multicoloured .. 30 15

**1986.** New Year Festival. Flowers. Mult.
2322. 5 r. Type **735** .. .. 20 10
2323. 5 r. "Anemone coronaria" .. .. 20 10
2324. 5 r. "Papaver bracteatum" .. .. 20 10
2325. 5 r. "Anemone biflora" 20 10

736. Fist and Text.

737. Rose, Globe and Coloured Bands.

**1986.** "2000th Day of Sacred Defence" (Iran–Iraq war).
2326 **736** 5 r. green and red .. 20 15

**1986.** Struggle against Racial Discrimination.
2327. **737.** 5 r. multicoloured .. 20 15

738. Iranian Flag and Map.

**1986.** 7th Anniv. of Islamic Republic.
2328. **738.** 10 r. multicoloured .. 30 15

739. Dome.

740. Insignia.

**1986.** Mab'as Festival.
2329. **739.** 40 r. multicoloured .. 1·10 70

**1986.** Army Day.
2330. **740.** 5 r. multicoloured .. 25 15

741. Dead Soldier and Wrecked Helicopter.

742. Text.

**1986.** 6th Anniv of United States Landing at Tabas.
2331 **741** 40 r. orange, grn & blk 1·50 70

**1986.** World Day of the Oppressed. Birth Anniv of Imam Mahdi.
2332 **742** 10 r. black, red & gold 30 20

743. Symbolic Design.

744. Antennae and Radio Waves.

**1986.** Teachers' Day.
2333. **743.** 5 r. multicoloured .. 20 15

**1986.** World Communications Day.
2334. **744.** 20 r. black, silver and blue .. .. 60 35

745. Soldier and Tanks.

**1986.** International Children's Day.
2335. **745.** 15 r. multicoloured .. 40 30
2336. – 15 r. black, blue and mauve .. .. 40 30
DESIGN: No. 2336, Boy and text.

746. Qum Theological College and Sun Rays.

747. Dome of the Rock, Map of Israel and Barbed Wire.

**1986.** 23rd Anniv. of 1963 Islamic Rising.
2337. **746.** 10 r. multicoloured .. 30 15

**1986.** World Jerusalem Day.
2338. **747.** 10 r. multicoloured .. 40 15

748. Crowd at Prayer.

**1986.** Fetr Festival.
2339. **748.** 10 r. multicoloured .. 30 15

749. Baluchi Needle Work.

**1986.** World Handicrafts Day. Multicoloured.
2340. 10 r. Type **749** .. 30 20
2341. 10 r. Master craftswomen at work .. .. 30 20
2342. 10 r. Carpet .. .. 30 20
2343. 10 r. Engraved copper vase .. .. .. 30 20

750. Linked Hands around Map on Globe.

751. Dr. Beheshti, Doves and Explosion.

**1986.** Solidarity with South African People.
2344. **750.** 10 r. multicoloured .. 30 15

**1986.** 5th Anniv of Bomb Explosion at Islamic Party Headquarters, Teheran.
2345 **751** 10 r. multicoloured .. 30 15

752. Ayatollah Mohammad Taqi Shirazi and Map.

753. Shrine, Meshed.

**1986.** Iraqi Muslim Rising.
2346. **752.** 20 r. multicoloured .. 50 30

**1986.** Birth Anniv of Imam Riza.
2347 **753** 10 r. multicoloured .. 30 15

754. Crowd around Kaaba, Flag and Clenched Fists.

755. Soltanieh Mosque.

**1986.** Feast of Sacrifices.
2348 **754** 10 r. multicoloured .. 30 15

**1986.** Preservation of Cultural Heritage. Multicoloured.
2349 5 r. Type **755** .. .. 20 10
2350 5 r. Mausoleum of Sohel Ben Ali, Astaneh .. 20 10
2351 5 r. Bam fortress .. 20 10
2352 5 r. Gateway of Blue Mosque, Tabriz .. 20 10

756. "Eid-ul-Ghadir" in Arabic.

757. Graph, Roof and People.

**1986.** Ghadir Festival.
2353. **756.** 20 r. light green, green and black .. 50 30

**1986.** Population and Housing Census.
2354. **757.** 20 r. multicoloured .. 50 30

758. Missle Boat "Paykan" in Fist below Bombs.

**1986.** 6th Anniv of Iran–Iraq War. Mult.
2355 **758** 10 r. blue, black & red 40 15
2356 – 10 r. red and black .. 30 15
2357 – 10 r. yellow, blk & red 30 15
2358 – 10 r. blue, black & red 30 15
2359 – 10 r. green, blk & red 30 15
DESIGNS: No. 2356, Khorramshar; 2357, Howeizah; 2358, Siege of Abadan; 2359, Susangard.

759. Wrestling.

**1986.** 10th Asian Games. Seoul. Mult.
2360 15 r. Type **759** .. .. 35 20
2361 15 r. Rifle shooting .. 35 20

760. Bird with Envelopes as Wings on Globe.

**1986.** World Universal Postal Union Day.
2362 **760** 20 r. multicoloured .. 50 30

761. Emblem.

762. Allameh Tabatabaie.

**1986.** 40th Anniv. of U.N.E.S.C.O.
2363. **761.** 45 r. blue, black and red .. .. 1·00 60

**1986.** 5th Death Anniv. of Allameh Tabatabaie.
2364. **762.** 10 r. green, gold and black .. .. 20 15

763. Sun behind Dome and Minaret.

764. Militiamen with Flags.

**1986.** Mohammed's Birth Anniv. and Unity Week.
2365. **763.** 10 r. multicoloured .. 20 15

**1986.** "Mobilization of the Oppressed" Week.
2366 **764** 5 r. multicoloured .. 20 15

765. Guerrilla Fighters.

**1986.** Afghan Resistance to Occupation.
2367. **765.** 40 r. multicoloured . . 90 55

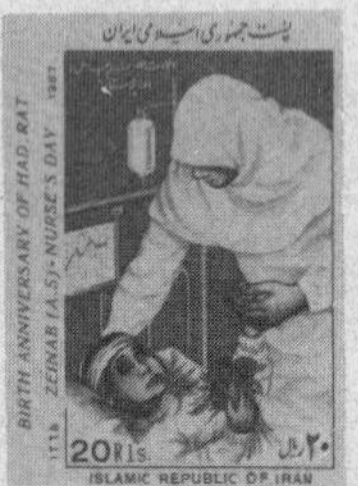

**766.** Nurse tending Boy. **767.** Emblem and Tulip on Globe.

**1987.** Nurses' Day.
2368. **766.** 20 r. multicoloured . . 50 30

**1987.** 5th Islamic Theology Conference, Teheran.
2369. **767.** 20 r. multicoloured . . 50 30

**768.** Emblems of Revolution.

**1987.** 8th Anniv of Islamic Revolution.
2370 **768** 20 r. multicoloured (38 × 58 mm) . . 50 30
2444 20 r. multicoloured (24 × 37 mm) . . 50 50

**769.** Emblem and Crowd. **770.** Woman and Soldiers.

**1987.** 8th Anniv. of Revolutionary Committees.
2371. **769.** 10 r. yell., bl. & red 30 15

**1987.** Women's Day and Birth Anniv of Fatima.
2372 **770** 10 r. multicoloured . . 30 15

**771.** Airbus Industrie A300 Aircraft and Banner around Globe.

**1987.** 25th Anniv of Iranair.
2373 **771** 30 r. multicoloured . . 1·25 45

**772.** Ayatollah Naeini. **773.** Flag Irises.

**1987.** 50th Death Anniv. of Ayatollah Mirza Mohammad Hossein Naeini.
2374. **772.** 10 r. multicoloured . . 30 15

**1987.** New Year Festival. Flowers. Mult.
2375. 5 r. Type **773** . . . . 20 10
2376. 5 r. Tulips . . . . 20 10
2377. 5 r. Dutch irises . . . . 20 10
2378. 5 r. Roses . . . . 20 10

**774.** Arabic Text and Arched Window. **775.** Flag as Star on Map.

**1987.** Mab'as Festival.
2379. **774.** 45 r. light green, green and gold . . 1·10 65

**1987.** 8th Anniv. of Islamic Republic.
2380. **775.** 20 r. multicoloured . . 45 30

**776.** Soldiers with Flag. **777.** Emblems on Map and Dome of the Rock.

**1987.** Revolutionary Guards' Day. Birth Anniv. of Imam Hossein.
2381. **776.** 5 r. multicoloured . . 20 15

**1987.** Commemoration of Lebanese Hizbollah Dead.
2382. **777.** 10 r. red, green and grey . . . . 30 15

**778.** Child and Vaccination Dropper. **779.** Stars around Holy Kaaba.

**1987.** World Health Day. Multicoloured.
2383 3 r. Syringe and children 15 10
2384 5 r. Type **778** . . . . 20 10

**1987.** World Day of the Oppressed. Birth Anniv of Imam Mahdi.
2385 **779** 20 r. multicoloured . . 50 30

## MINIMUM PRICE

The minimum price quoted is 10p which represents a handling charge rather than a basis for valuing common stamps. For further notes about prices see introductory pages.

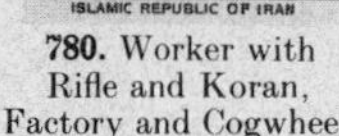

**780.** Worker with Rifle and Koran, Factory and Cogwheel. **781.** Ayatollah Mottahari, Candle and Book.

**1987.** International Labour Day.
2386. **780.** 5 r. multicoloured . . 20 15

**1987.** Teachers' Day.
2387. **781.** 5 r. red, yell. & bl. 20 15

**782.** Map in Telephone Dial. **783.** 12th-century Ceramic Lidded Pot, Rey.

**1987.** World Telecommunications Day.
2388. **782.** 20 r. violet and blue 50 30

**1987.** International Museums Day.
2389 **783** 20 r. chestnut, brown and grey . . . . 50 30
2390 – 20 r. brown, blk & grn 50 30
DESIGN: No. 2390, Sassanian silver-gilt flower vase.

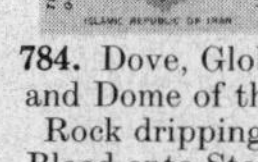

**784.** Dove, Globe and Dome of the Rock dripping Blood onto Star. **785.** Qum Theological College, Crown and Bayonets.

**1987.** World Jerusalem Day.
2391. **784.** 20 r. multicoloured . . 50 30

**1987.** 24th Anniv. of 1963 Islamic Rising.
2392. **785.** 20 r. multicoloured . . 50 30

**786.** Blown Glass.

**1987.** World Crafts Day. Multicoloured.
2393. 5 r. Type **786** . . . . 20 10
2394. 5 r. Khatam marquetry 20 10
2395. 5 r. Ceramic ware . . 20 10
2396. 5 r. Ceramic master-craftsman . . . . 20 10

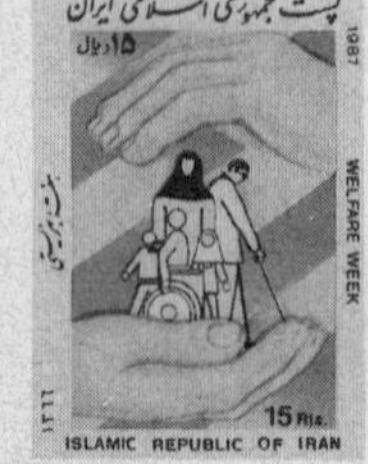

**787.** Factory, Freighter and Dam. **788.** Figures in Cupped Hand.

**1987.** Campaign against Tax Evasion.
2397. **787.** 10 r. gold, black and silver . . . . 30 15

**1987.** Welfare Week.
2398. **788.** 15 r. multicoloured . . 35 25

**789.** Crowd around Mosque.

**1987.** Feast of Sacrifices.
2399 **789** 12 r. turq, silver & blk 35 20

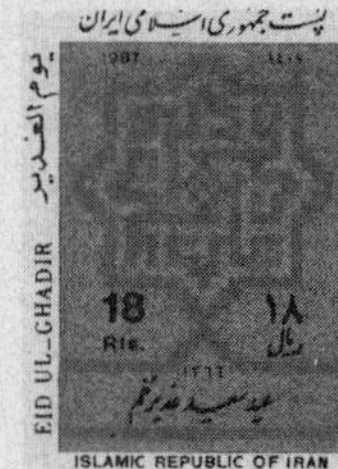

**790.** Design from Mosque Tile. **791.** Hands clasped over National Emblem.

**1987.** Ghadir Festival.
2400 **790** 18 r. gold, green & blk 45 30

**1987.** Islamic Banking Week.
2401. **791.** 15 r. brown, blue and gold . . . . 35 25

**792.** Typical Persian Calligraphy.

**1987.** 1st Iranian Calligraphers' Cultural and Artistic Congress.
2402. **792.** 20 r. multicoloured . . 50 30

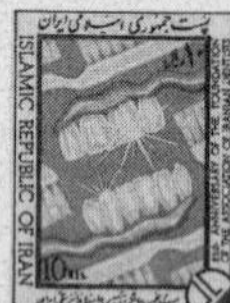

**793.** Blood running from Heart as Globe, Mosque and Kaaba. **794.** Toothbrushes as Mouths.

**1987.** Commemoration of Pilgrims killed at Mecca.
2403 **793** 8 r. multicoloured . . 30 15

**1987.** 25th Anniv. of Iranian Dentists Association.
2404. **794.** 10 r. multicoloured . . 35 15

**795.** Dove with Globe as Eye. **796.** Rifleman and Armed Launch.

**1987.** International Peace Day.
2405. **795.** 20 r. bronze and blue 50 30

**1987.** 7th Anniv of Iran–Iraq War.
2406 **796** 25 r. green, blue & blk 60 40
2407 – 25 r. red, black & blue 60 40
DESIGN: No. 2407, Rifleman and soldiers.

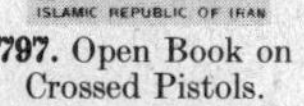
**797.** Open Book on Crossed Pistols.

**798.** People in Cupped Hands.

**1987.** Police Day.
2408. **797.** 10 r. multicoloured . . 50 20

**1987.** International Social Security Co-operation Week.
2409 **798** 15 r. black, blue & gold 35 25

**799.** Dove with Envelopes as Tail on Globe.

**800.** American Flag, Great Seal and Capitol.

**1987.** World Post Day. Multicoloured.
2410. 15 r. Type **799** . . . . 35 25
2411. 15 r. Dr. M. Ghandi (Postal Minister) commemoration . . 35 25

**1987.** 6th Anniv. of Storming of United States Embassy.
2412. **800.** 40 r. multicoloured . . 1·00 55

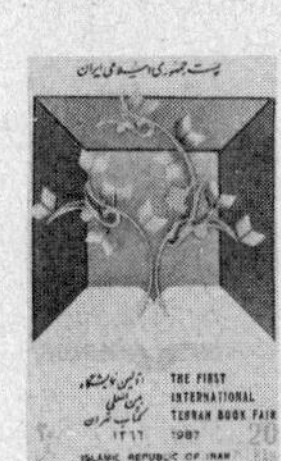
**801.** Tree growing from Open Book.

**802.** Clasped Hands.

**1987.** 1st Teheran Book Fair.
2413 **801** 20 r. multicoloured . . 50 30

**1987.** Mohammed's Birth Anniv. and Unity Week.
2414. **802.** 25 r. brown, flesh and green . . . . 55 35

**803.** Ayatollah Modarres.

**804.** Djameh Mosque, Urmia.

**1987.** 50th Death Anniv of Ayatollah Seyyed Hassan Modarres.
2415 **803** 10 r. brown and ochre 25 15

**1987.** Mosques.
2415a – 1 r. orange and silver 10 10
2416 **804** 2 r. mauve and silver 10 10
2416a – 3 r. green and silver 10 10
2417 – 5 r. red and silver . . 15 10
2594 – 10 r. blue and silver 15 10
2419 – 20 r. violet and silver 35 20
2420 – 30 r. red and silver 45 25
2421 – 40 r. blue and silver 55 30
2422 – 50 r. brown & silver 90 40
2423 – 100 r. green & silver 1·60 95
2424 – 200 r. black & silver 3·25 2·00
2604 – 500 r. green & silver 8·00 4·75
DESIGNS—HORIZ. 1 r. Djameh Mosque, Schuschter; 3 r. Djameh Mosque, Kerman; 5 r. Qazvin; 10 r. Veramin; 20 r. Saveh; 40 r. Shiraz; 100 r. Hamadan. VERT. 30 r. Natanz; 50 r. Isfahan; 200 r. Dizful; 500 r. Yezd.

**805.** Open Book, Profiles and Ear of Wheat.

**1987.** Agricultural Training and Extension Week.
2426 **805** 10 r. multicoloured . . 25 15

**806.** Guerrilla Fighters on Map.

**1987.** Afghan Resistance to Occupation.
2427 **806** 40 r. multicoloured . . 1·00 55

**807.** Crowd with Banners.

**1988.** 10th Anniv. of Qum Uprising.
2428. **807.** 20 r. multicoloured . . 50 30

**808.** Bombs and Pencils.

**809.** Takhti and Mountain.

**1988.** Iranian Schools Victims' Commemoration.
2429 **808** 10 r. multicoloured . . 25 15

**1988.** Victory of Gholamreza Takhti in World Freestyle Wrestling Championships.
2430. **809.** 15 r. multicoloured . . 35 25

**810.** Woman carrying armed Man.

**811.** Text.

**1988.** Women's Day and Birth Anniv. of Fatima.
2431. **810.** 20 r, multicoloured . . 50 30

**1988.** 9th Anniv of Islamic Revolution.
2447 **811** 40 r. multicoloured . . 1·00 1·00

**812.** Crowd burning Statue.

**1988.** 10th Anniv of Tabriz Uprising.
2448 **812** 25 r. multicoloured . . 60 35

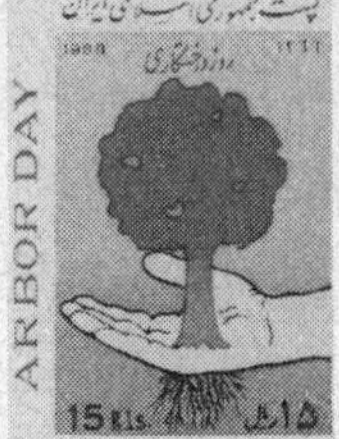

**813.** Tree in Hand.

**814.** "Anthemis hyalina".

**1988.** Tree Day.
2449 **813** 15 r. multicoloured . . 35 25

**1988.** New Year Festival. Flowers. Mult.
2450 10 r. Type **814** . . . . 25 15
2451 10 r. Common mallows . . 25 15
2452 10 r. Violets . . . . 25 15
2453 10 r. "Echium amaenum" 25 15

**815** Hand putting Ballot Paper into Box

**816** Calligraphy

**1988.** 9th Anniv of Islamic Republic.
2454 **815** 20 r. multicoloured . . 50 30

**1988.** World Day of the Oppressed. Birth Anniv of Imam Mahdi.
2455 **816** 20 r. brown and blue 50 30

**817** Shahid Mottahari Mosque and Theology School, Teheran

**818** Bomb, Gas Cloud and Victims

**1988.** Preservation of Cultural Heritage. Multicoloured.
2456 10 r. Type **817** . . . . 25 15
2457 10 r. Colonnade of Tarikhaneh Mosque, Damghan . . . . 25 15
2458 10 r. Gateway of Sepahdari Mosque and Theology School, Arak (horiz) . . . . 25 15
2459 10 r. Agha Bozorg Mosque and Theology School, Kashan (courtyard with pool) (horiz) . . 25 15

**1988.** Halabja Chemical Attack Victims' Commemoration.
2460 **818** 20 r. multicoloured . . 50 30

**819** Map, Dome of the Rock and Palestinian

**820** Satellite and Telephone Handset

**1988.** Palestinian "Intifida" Movement. Each brown, red and black.
2461 10 r. Type **819** . . . . 30 15
2462 10 r. Man with rounded beard . . . . 30 15
2463 10 r. Man wearing crew-necked jumper . . 30 15
2464 10 r. Man with long pointed beared . . 30 15
2465 10 r. Crowd and hand holding stone . . 30 15

**1988.** World Telecommunications Day.
2466 **820** 20 r. blue and green . . 50 30

**821** Ceramic Vase

**822** Miners pushing Coal Truck

**1988.** International Museum Day. Mult.
2467 10 t. Type **821** . . 25 15
2468 10 r. Iran Bastan Museum porch . . . . . . 25 15
2469 10 r. 14th-century Tabriz silk rug . . . . 25 15
2470 10 r. 7th-century B.C. gold ring, Arjan, Behbahan 25 15

**1988.** Mining Day.
2471 **822** 20 r. multicoloured . . 55 30

**823** Children playing by River

**824** Bleeding Dove and Broken Bayonets

**1988.** International Children's Day.
2472 **823** 10 r. multicoloured . . 30 15

**1988.** 25th Anniv of 1963 Islamic Rising.
2473 **824** 10 r. multicoloured . . 30 15

**825** Glim Weaving

**826** Child in Flower

**1988.** World Handicrafts Day. Multicoloured.
2474 10 r. Type **825** . . . . 25 15
2475 10 r. Miniature of horse-men . . . . . . 25 15
2476 10 r. Glim weaver (horiz) 25 15
2477 10 r. Straw basket (horiz) 25 15

**1988.** Child Health Campaign.
2478 **826** 20 r. blue, green & blk 35 20

**827** Symbols of Industry and Agriculture

**828** Balkhi

**1988.** Campaign Against Tax Evasion.
2479 **827** 20 r. gold, blue & silver 35 20

**1988.** Allameh Balkhi (Afghan revolutionary writer) Commemoration.
2480 **828** 20 r. black, red & sil 35 20

**829** Blood raining on Holy Kaaba

**830** Missile hitting Boeing 737 Airplane

**1988.** 1st Anniv of Death of Mecca Pilgrims. Multicoloured.
2481 10 r. Type **829** .. .. 20 15
2482 10 r. Holy Kaaba and blood-stained robe .. 20 15

**1988.** Destruction of Iranair Passenger Airplane.
2483 **830** 45 r. multicoloured .. 1·00 45

**831** Seyyed Ali Andarzgou

**832** Central Bank, Teheran

**1988.** 10th Death Anniv of Seyyed Ali Andarzgou (revolutionary).
2484 **831** 20 r. blue, black & brn 35 20

**1988.** Islamic Banking Week.
2485 **832** 20 r. grey, brn & gold 35 20

**833** Carrying away Victim

**834** Weightlifting

**1988.** 10th Anniv of "Bloody Friday" Riots.
2486 **833** 25 r. green, pur & red 45 25

**1988.** Olympic Games, Seoul. Multicoloured.
2487 10 r. Type **834** .. .. 20 15
2488 10 r. Men's gymnastics .. 20 15
2489 10 r. Judo .. .. 20 15
2490 10 r. Football .. .. 20 15
2491 10 r. Wrestling .. .. 20 15

**835** Plant

**836** Iranians and Rifle

**1988.** Agricultural Census.
2492 **835** 30 r. yellow, blk & grn 50 35

**1988.** 8th Anniv of Iran–Iraq War.
2493 **836** 20 r. multicoloured .. 35 20

**837** Envelopes around Globe

**1988.** World Post Day.
2494 **837** 20 r. green, black & bl 35 20

**838** Child's Face and Profiles

**839** Clasped Hands and Emblem

**1988.** Parents' and Teachers' Co-operation Week.
2495 **838** 20 r. multicoloured .. 35 20

**1988.** Mohammed's Birth Anniv and Unity Week.
2496 **839** 10 r. multicoloured .. 20 15

**840** Fist and Shattered Eagle

**841** Tree as Umbrella

**1988.** 7th Anniv of Storming of United States Embassy.
2497 **840** 45 r. multicoloured .. 75 45

**1988.** Insurance Day.
2498 **841** 10 r. multicoloured .. 20 15

**842** Tomb of Hafiz

**1988.** International Hafiz (writer) Congress, Shiraz.
2499 **842** 20 r. blue, gold & mve 35 20

**843** Agricultural Symbols on Open Book

**845** Map and Armed Afghan

**844** Parvin Etessami (writer)

**1988.** Agricultural Training and Extension Week.
2500 **843** 15 r. multicoloured .. 30 15

**1988.** Iranian Celebrities of Science, Art and Literature. Multicoloured.
2501 10 r. Type **844** .. .. 20 15
2502 10 r. Qaem Maqam Farahani (writer) .. 20 15
2503 10 r. Kamal al-Molk (artist) .. .. 20 15
2504 10 r. Jalal al-Ahmad (writer) .. .. 20 15
2505 10 r. Dr. Mohammad Mo'in (writer) .. 20 15

**1988.** Afghan Resistance to Occupation.
2506 **845** 40 r. multicoloured .. 75 45

**846** Satellite, Envelopes and Dish Aerial

**847** Tulips and Script

**1989.** Asian and Pacific Transport and Communications Decade. Multicoloured.
2507 20 r. Type **846** .. .. 45 30
2508 20 r. Air transport .. 45 30
2509 20 r. Road and rail transport .. .. 45 30
2510 20 r. Shipping .. .. 45 30

**1989.** Air. 10th Anniv of Islamic Revolution.
2511 **847** 40 r. mve, gold & blk 80 55
2512 50 r. violet, gold & blk 80 55

**848** Sun illuminating Koran

**849** Hands protecting Tree

**1989.** Mab'as Festival.
2513 **848** 20 r. multicoloured .. 35 25

**1989.** Tree Day.
2514 **849** 20 r. multicoloured .. 35 25

**850** "Cephalanthera kurdica"

**851** Wind Gauge and Wheat

**1989.** New Year Festival. Flowers. Mult.
2515 10 r. Type **850** .. .. 20 15
2516 10 r. "Dactylorhiza romana" .. .. 20 15
2517 10 r. "Comperia comperiana" .. .. .. 20 15
2518 10 r. "Orchis mascula" .. 20 15

**1989.** World Meteorological Day. Mult.
2519 20 r. Type **851** .. .. 40 25
2520 30 r. Wind gauge, airplane and weather ship .. 60 35

**852** State Arms

**853** Refinery

**1989.** 10th Anniv of Islamic Republic.
2521 **852** 20 r. multicoloured .. 35 25

**1989.** Commissioning of First Phase of Abadan Oil Refinery.
2522 **853** 20 r. multicoloured .. 40 25

**854** Mottahari

**855** Dome of the Rock and Barbed Wire

**1989.** Teachers' Day. 10th Death Anniv of Ayatollah Mottahari.
2523 **854** 20 r. multicoloured .. 35 25

**1989.** World Jerusalem Day.
2524 **855** 30 r. multicoloured .. 60 35

**856** Satellite, Globe and Dish Aerial

**857** Jar

**1989.** World Telecommunications Day.
2525 **856** 20 r. multicoloured .. 40 25

**1989.** International Museums Day. 6th-century Gurgan Artefacts.
2526 **857** 20 r. yellow, bl & blk 40 25
2527 – 20 r. blue, blk & mve 40 25
DESIGN: No. 2527, Flagon.

**858** Armed Men, Tent and Family with Sheep

**1989.** Nomads' Day.
2528 **858** 20 r. multicoloured .. 35 20

**859** Man engraving Vase

**1989.** World Crafts Day. Multicoloured.
2529 20 r. Type **859** .. .. 35 25
2530 20 r. Engraved copper vase .. .. .. 35 25
2531 20 r. Engraved copper plate (vert) .. .. 35 25
2532 20 r. Engraved copper wall-hanging (vert) .. 35 25

860 Khomeini and Crowd

861 Pasteur, Avicenna and Hand holding Quill

**1989.** Ayatollah Khomeini Commemoration.
2533 **860** 20 r. orange, black and blue (postage) 40 20
2534 – 70 r. black, violet and gold (air) .. .. 1·10 70
DESIGN—HORIZ. 70 r. Ayatollah Khomeini.

**1989.** "Philexfrance 89" International Stamp Exhibition, Paris. Each black, blue and brown, background colour given.
2535 **861** 30 r. blue .. .. 50 35
2536 50 r. brown .. .. 75 55

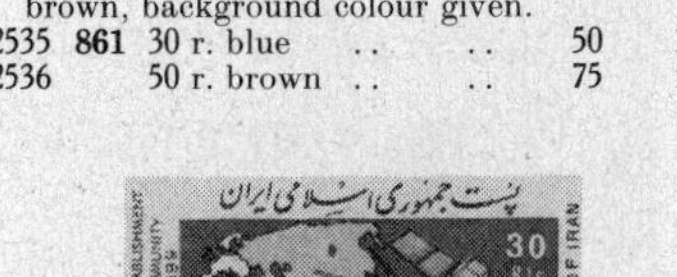
862 Map and Satellite

**1989.** 10th Anniv of Asia-Pacific Telecommunity.
2537 **862** 30 r. orange, blk & bl 50 30

863 Araghi

**1989.** 10th Death Anniv of Mehdi Araghi.
2538 **863** 20 r. orange and purple 35 20

864 Shahryar and Monument

**1989.** Mohammed Hossein Shahryar (poet) Commemoration.
2539 **864** 20 r. multicoloured .. 35 20

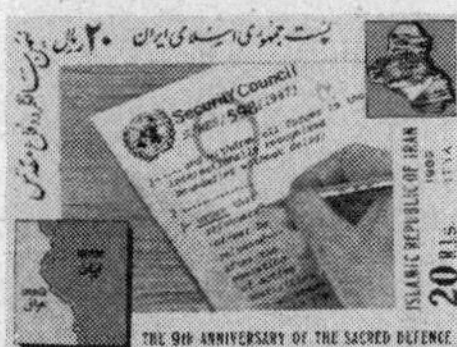
865 U.N. Security Council Document

**1989.** 9th Anniv of Iran–Iraq War.
2540 **865** 20 r. multicoloured .. 35 20

866 Khomeini addressing Crowd

**1989.** Ayatollah Khomeini.
2541 – 1 r. multicoloured .. 10 10
2542 – 2 r. multicoloured .. 10 10
2543 **866** 3 r. multicoloured .. 10 10
2544 – 5 r. multicoloured .. 25 10
2545 – 10 r. multicoloured .. 60 10
2546 – 20 r. multicoloured .. 35 10
2547 – 30 r. multicoloured .. 50 30
2548 – 40 r. multicoloured .. 65 50
2549 – 50 r. multicoloured .. 80 50
2550 – 70 r. multicoloured .. 1·10 65
2551 – 100 r. ultramarine, blue and green .. 1·60 95
2552 – 200 r. brn, yell & grn 3·25 1·90
2553 – 500 r. multicoloured 8·25 5·00
2554 – 1000 r. multicoloured 16·00 9·75
DESIGNS: 1 r. Rose and courtyard; 2 r. Khomeini as young man; 5 r. Khomeini going into exile; 10 r. Khomeini's return from exile; 20 r. Khomeini making speech; 30 r. Boy kissing Khomeini; 40 r. Ayatollahs; 50 r. Khomeini; 70 r. Meeting in house; 100 r. Arabic inscription; 200 r. Microphones and chair; 500 r. Qum Mosque and roses; 1000 r. Sun's rays.

867 Pigeon carrying Letter

**1989.** World Post Day.
2561 **867** 20 r. multicoloured .. 35 20

868 Multi-pointed Star in Window Arch

869 U.S. Emblem and Crowd in Dove

**1989.** Mohammed's Birth Anniv and Unity Week.
2562 **868** 10 r. multicoloured .. 15 10

**1989.** 8th Anniv of Storming of United States Embassy.
2563 **869** 40 r. orange, blk & bl 65 40

870 Iranian and Launch with Machine Gun

**1989.** 10th Anniv of People's Militia.
2564 **870** 10 r. multicoloured .. 30 15

871 Mehdi Elahi Ghomshei

**1989.** Iranian Celebrities of Science, Art and Literature.
2565 **871** 10 r. red, black & gold 15 10
2566 – 10 r. green, blk & gold 15 10
2567 – 10 r. yell, blk & gold 15 10
2568 – 10 r. green, blk & gold 15 10
2569 – 10 r. mve, blk & gold 15 10
DESIGNS: No. 2566, Grand Ayatollah Seyyed Hossein Boroujerdi; 2567, Grand Ayatollah Sheikh Abdulkarim Haeri; 2568, Dr. Abdulazim Gharib; 2569, Seyyed Hossein Mirkhani.

872 Guiding Child's Hand

873 Book as Profiles forming Flower

**1990.** International Literacy Year.
2570 **872** 20 r. multicoloured .. 35 20

**1990.** Identity Cards.
2571 **873** 10 r. multicoloured .. 15 10

874 Drinking Vessel

875 Crowd

**1990.** Cultural Heritage.
2572 **874** 20 r. black and orange 35 20
2573 – 20 r. black and green 35 20
DESIGN: No. 2563, Vase with stem.

**1990.** 11th Anniv of Islamic Revolution.
2574 **875** 50 r. multicoloured .. 80 50

876 Emblem

877 Soldier in Wheelchair

**1990.** Int Koran Recitation Competition.
2575 **876** 10 r. black, blue & grn 15 10

**1990.** Invalids' Day.
2576 **877** 10 r. multicoloured .. 15 10

878 Figures encircling Tree

879 "Coronilla varia"

**1990.** Tree Day.
2577 **878** 20 r. multicoloured .. 35 20

**1990.** New Year Festival. Flowers. Mult.
2578 10 r. Type **879** .. 15 10
2579 10 r. "Astragalus cornu-caprae" .. .. 15 10
2580 10 r. "Astragalus obtusifolius" .. .. 15 10
2581 10 r. "Astragalus straussii" .. .. 15 10

880 Crowd and Ballot Box

881 Flower growing from Globe

**1990.** 11th Anniv of Islamic Republic.
2582 **880** 30 r. multicoloured .. 50 30

**1990.** World Health Day.
2583 **881** 40 r. multicoloured .. 65 40

882 Khomeini

883 Turkoman Jewellery

**1990.** 1st Death Anniv of Ayatollah Khomeini.
2584 **882** 50 r. multicoloured .. 80 50

**1990.** World Handicrafts Day.
2585 20 r. Type **883** .. .. 35 20
2586 50 r. Gilded-steel bird .. 80 50

884 Crayons

885 Seismograph on Map and Red Crescent Camp

**1990.** International Children's Day.
2587 **884** 20 r. multicoloured .. 35 20

**1990.** Aid for Earthquake Victims.
2588 **885** 100 r. multicoloured .. 1·60 95

886 P.O.W. and Roses

887 Ayatollah Khomeini and Dome of the Rock

**1990.** Returned Prisoners of War.
2589 **886** 250 r. multicoloured .. 4·00 2·40

**1990.** World Jerusalem Day.
2590 **887** 100 r. multicoloured .. 1·60 95

**889** Flowers, Crowd and Khomeini

**1991.** 12th Anniv of Islamic Revolution.
2605 **889** 100 r. multicoloured .. 1·60 95

**890** 11th-century Gold Jug

**1991.** International Museum Day. Mult.
2606 50 r. Type **890** .. .. 80 50
2607 50 r. 14th-century silver-inlaid brass basin .. 80 50

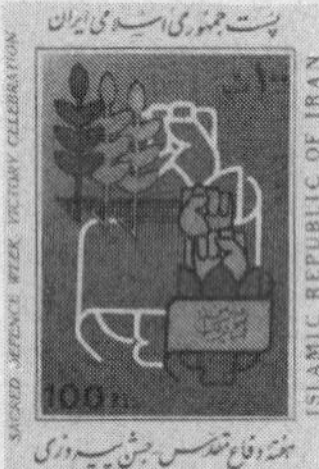

**891** Flowers and Fists

**892** Museum

**1991.** 11th Anniv of Iran–Iraq War.
2608 **891** 100 r. multicoloured .. 1·60 95

**1991.** Inauguration of Post Museum, Teheran.
2609 **892** 200 r. brown and black 3·25 2·00

**893** Headset on Globe

**894** "Iris spuria"

**1991.** World Telecommunications Day (1990).
2610 **893** 50 r. multicoloured .. 80 50

**1991.** New Year Festival. Irises. Mult.
2611 20 r. Type **894** .. .. 35 20
2612 20 r. "Iris lycotis" .. 35 20
2613 20 r. "Iris demawendica" 35 20
2614 20 r. "Iris meda" .. 35 20

**895** Map, Dome of the Rock and Hosseini

**897** Revolutionaries

**896** Light Beam on Mountains

**1991.** 10th Death Anniv of Saleh Hosseini.
2615 **895** 30 r. red and black .. 50 30

**1991.** Mab'as Festival.
2616 **896** 100 r. multicoloured .. 1·60 95

**1991.** 25th Death Anniv (1990) of Revolutionaries.
2617 **897** 50 r. brown and orange 80 50

**898** Arabic Script

**899** Crowd, Flag, and Ballot Box

**1991.** World Day of the Oppressed. Birth Anniv of Mahdi.
2618 **898** 50 r. multicoloured .. 80 50

**1991.** 12th Anniv of Islamic Republic.
2619 **899** 20 r. multicoloured .. 35 20

**900** Map and Bayonets

**901** Mother and Child

**1991.** World Jerusalem Day.
2620 **900** 100 r. multicoloured .. 1·60 95

**1991.** Women's Day and Birth Anniv of Fatima.
2621 **901** 50 r. multicoloured .. 80 50

**902** Boroujerdi

**903** Disasters

**1991.** 30th Death Anniv of Ayatollah Boroujerdi.
2622 **902** 200 r. black and green 3·25 2·00

**1991.** International Decade for Natural Disaster Reduction.
2623 **903** 100 r. multicoloured .. 2·00 1·10

**904** Book, Candle and Dr. Mottahari

**1991.** Teachers' Day.
2624 **904** 50 r. yellow, orge & blk 80 50

**905** Rays striking Globe

**906** Mausoleum, Meshed

**1991.** World Telecommunications Day. "Telecommunications and Safety of Human Life".
2625 **905** 100 r. multicoloured .. 1·60 95

**1991.** Birth Anniv of Imam Riza.
2626 10 r. Type **906** .. .. 15 10
2627 30 r. Tombstone .. 50 30

**907** Khomeini

**1991.** 2nd Death Anniv of Ayatollah Khomeini.
2628 **907** 100 r. multicoloured 1·60 95

**908** Karbala Shrine

**1991.** Iraqi Attack on Shi'ite Shrine, Karbala.
2629 **908** 70 r. multicoloured .. 1·10 65

**909** Nisami

**1991.** 900th Birth Anniv of Nisami (writer) International Congress, Tabris.
2630 **909** 50 r. multicoloured .. 80 50

**910** Archway

**1991.** 1330th Death Anniv of Ali ibn Ali Talib (Caliph).
2631 **910** 50 r. multicoloured .. 80 50

**911** Hands reaching through Parched Earth to Blood Drop

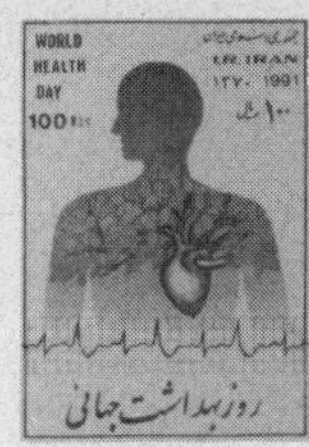

**912** Heart as Tree and Cardiograph

**1991.** Blood Donation.
2632 **911** 500 r. multicoloured .. 8·50 5·00

**1991.** World Health Day,
2633 **912** 100 r. multicoloured .. 1·60 95

**913** Nedjefi

**1991.** Marashi Nedjefi Commemoration.
2634 **913** 30 r. multicoloured .. 50 30

**914** Doves flying from Cage

**1991.** 1st Anniv of Return of Prisoners of War.
2635 **914** 100 r. multicoloured .. 1·60 95

**915** Engraved Brassware

**1991.** World Crafts Day. Multicoloured.
2636 40 r. Type **915** .. .. 65 40
2637 40 r. Gilded samovar .. 65 40

**916** Ayatollah Lari

**1991.**
2638 **916** 30 r. multicoloured .. 50 30

**917** Fist and Roses in Cartouche

**918** Islamic Symbols

**1991.** 11th Anniv of Iran–Iraq War.
2639 **917** 20 r. multicoloured .. 35 20

**1991.** Islamic Unity Week.
2640 **918** 30 r. multicoloured .. 50 30

**919** 13th-century Kashan Ewer

**920** Gharib

**1991.** International Museum Day. Mult.
2641 20 r. Type **919** .. .. 35 20
2642 40 r. 13th-century Kashan ewer with bird's head lip .. .. .. 65 40

**1991.** Dr. Mohammed Gharib.
2643 **920** 100 r. black and blue 1·60 95

**921** Banners

**922** Stamped Envelope

**1991.** Liberation of Khorramshahr.
2644 **921** 30 r. multicoloured .. 50 30

**1991.** World Post Day.
2645 **922** 70 r. multicoloured .. 1·10 65

**923** Khaju-Ye Kermani

**1991.** International Congress on Khaju-Ye Kermani (writer).
2646 **923** 30 r. multicoloured .. 50 30

**924** Globe and Seismograph

**925** Cogwheel, Grain, Tree, Figures and Globe

**1991.** 1st International Seismology and Earthquake Engineering Conference.
2647 **924** 100 r. multicoloured .. 1·60 95

**1991.** World Food Day.
2648 **925** 80 r. multicoloured .. 1·25 75

**926** Conference Emblem

**927** Green Woodpecker and Flower Decoration

**1991.** Palestinian Peoples Conference.
2649 **926** 40 r. gold and violet .. 65 40

**1991.** 1st Asian Biennial Exhibition of Children's Book Illustrations.
2650 **927** 100 r. multicoloured .. 2·00 95

**928** Script and Emblem

**929** Festival Award

**1991.** Children's Book Fair, Teheran.
2651 **928** 20 r. multicoloured .. 35 20

**1991.** Roshd International Educational Film Festival.
2652 **929** 50 r. multicoloured .. 80 50

**930** Meeting Emblem

**932** Child throwing Stone at Star of David

**931** Militia Members

**1991.** 7th Ministerial Meeting of Group of 77.
2653 **930** 30 r. green and violet 50 30

**1991.** People's Militia Week.
2654 **931** 30 r. multicoloured .. 50 30

**1991.** World Children's Day.
2655 **932** 50 r. multicoloured .. 80 50

**933** Globe and Doves

**1991.** World Tourism Day.
2656 **933** 200 r. black, mve & bl 3·25 2·00

**934** Emblems

**935** Trees, Hand, Water and Wheat

**1991.** World Standards Day.
2657 **934** 100 r. multicoloured .. 1·60 95

**1991.** Agricultural Training Week.
2658 **935** 70 r. multicoloured .. 1·10 65

**936** Araf Hosseini

**938** Revolutionary Scenes

**937** Sadegh Ghanji

**1992.**
2659 **936** 50 r. multicoloured .. 1·00 60

**1992.**
2660 **937** 50 r. multicoloured .. 1·00 60

**1992.** 13th Anniv of Islamic Revolution. Mult.
2661 30 r. Type **938** .. .. 60 35
2662 50 r. Revolutionary scenes (different) .. .. 1·00 60

**939** Members' Flags

**1992.** Economic Co-operation Organization Summit, Teheran.
2663 **939** 200 r. multicoloured .. 4·00 2·40

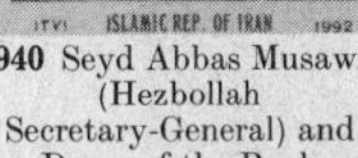

**940** Seyd Abbas Musawi (Hezbollah Secretary-General) and Dome of the Rock

**941** Planets, Satellite, Globe and Mobile Dish Aerial

**1992.** World Jerusalem Day.
2664 **940** 200 r. multicoloured .. 4·00 2·40

**1992.** World Meteorological Day.
2665 **941** 100 r. multicoloured .. 2·00 1·25

**942** Badshahi Mosque, Lahore, Pakistan

**943** Ayatollah Khomeini Voting

**1992.** South and West Asia Postal Union. Multicoloured.
2666 50 r. Type **942** .. .. 1·00 60
2667 50 r. Imam's Mosque, Isfahan .. .. 1·00 60
2668 50 r. St. Sophia's, Istanbul, Turkey .. 1·00 60

**1992.** 13th Anniv of Islamic Republic.
2669 **943** 50 r. multicoloured .. 1·00 60

**944** Embraer Bandeirante and Crates

**1992.** Establishment of Postal Air Service.
2670 **944** 60 r. multicoloured .. 1·25 75

**945** Hands holding Trees

**946** Tulips

**1992.** National Resources Week.
2671 **945** 100 r. multicoloured .. 2·00 1·25

**1992.** New Year Festival. Flowers. Mult.
2672 20 r. Type **946** .. .. 40 25
2673 20 r. Rose .. .. 40 25
2674 40 r. Orange blossom .. 80 50
2675 40 r. Yellow jasmine .. 80 50

**947** Members' Flags

**1992.** Economic Co-operation Organization.
2676 **947** 20 r. multicoloured .. 40 25

**948** Morse Apparatus

**1992.** World Telecommunications Day. Mult.
2677 20 r. Type **948** .. .. 40 25
2678 20 r. Telegraph poles and wires .. .. 40 25
2679 20 r. Old wall and candle-stick telephones .. 40 25
2680 40 r. Dish aerials .. 80 50
2681 40 r. Satellite and Earth 80 50

Nos. 2677/81 were issued together, se-tenant, forming a composite design.

**949** Sabzevari

**950** Emblem

**1992.** Science, Art and Literature. Mult.
2682 50 r. Type **949** .. .. 1·00 60
2683 50 r. Madjlessi (in turban) 1·00 60
2684 50 r. Arabic script by Mir Emad .. .. .. 1·00 60
2685 50 r. Samani (in fez) .. 1·00 60

**1992.** 21st Near East Regional Conference Session of F.A.O., Teheran.
2686 **950** 40 r. green, blue & blk 80 50

**951** Globe, Equipment and Charts

**952** Palm Trees

**1992.** Int Surveying and Mapping Conf.
2687 **951** 40 r. multicoloured .. 80 50

**1992.** 2nd Anniv of Unification of Yemen.
2688 **952** 50 r. multicoloured .. 1·00 60

**953** Dome of the Rock, Oasis and Child

**1992.** World Children's Day.
2689 **953** 50 r. multicoloured .. 90 55

**954** Khomeini

**955** Diagram of Wind Tunnel Test, Section of Spine and Robot Hand

**1992.** 3rd Death Anniv of Ayatollah Khomeini.
2690 **954** 100 r. multicoloured .. 1·75 1·00

**1992.** International Engineering Applications of Mechanics Conference, Teheran.
2691 **955** 50 r. multicoloured .. 90 55

**956** Building and Books

**1992.** Hajia Nosrat Baygom Amin Mo'in (lawyer) Commemoration.
2692 **956** 20 r. multicoloured .. 35 20

**957** Emblem and Iranian Flag

**958** ESCAP Emblem

**1992.** 6th Non-aligned News Agencies Pool Conference, Teheran.
2693 **957** 100 r. multicoloured .. 1·75 1·00

**1992.** Meeting of Economic and Social Commission for Asia and the Pacific Industry and Technology Minsters.
2694 **958** 100 r. green, gold & blk 1·75 1·00

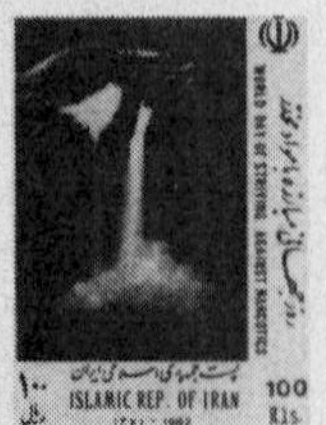
**959** Drugs in Hand

**961** Khomeini winding Turban

**960** Ceramic Bowl, Neyshabour City

**1992.** World Anti-drugs Day.
2695 **959** 100 r. multicoloured .. 1·25 75

**1992.** International Museum Day. Mult.
2696 40 r. Type **960** .. .. 70 40
2697 40 r. Ceramic vessel, Shahroud City .. 70 40

**1992.** Prayers of Ayatollah Khomeini (1st series). Multicoloured.
2698 50 r. Type **961** .. .. 90 55
2699 50 r. Mosque and Khomeini .. .. 90 55
2700 50 r. Khomeini .. .. 90 55
See also Nos. 2701/2 and 2703.

**962** Arabic Script

**1992.** Prayers of Ayatollah Khomeini (2nd series).
2701 **962** 50 r. turquoise & blue 90 55
2702 – 50 r. yellow and green 90 55
DESIGN: No. 2702, Arabic script (different).

**963** Kaaba

**965** Arabic Script

**964** Tanker

**1992.** Prayers of Ayatollah Khomeini (3rd series).
2703 **963** 50 r. multicoloured .. 90 55

**1992.** 25th Anniv of Iranian Shipping Lines.
2704 **964** 200 r. multicoloured .. 2·50 1·50

**1992.** Mohammed's Birth Anniv and Unity Week.
2705 **965** 40 r. multicoloured .. 65 40

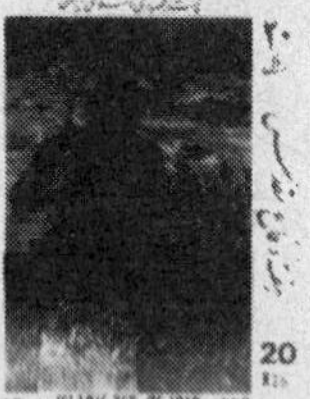
**966** Soldiers and Sun

**968** Foundry and Steel Products

**967** Patient and Doctor

**1992.** 12th Anniv of Iran–Iraq War. Mult.
2706 20 r. Type **966** .. .. 30 20
2707 40 r. Soldier on riverbank (horiz) .. .. 65 40

**1992.** International History of Medicine in Islam and Iran Congress. Multicoloured.
2708 20 r. Type **967** .. .. 30 20
2709 40 r. Medical instruments 65 40
Nos. 2708/9 were issued together, se-tenant, forming a composite design.

**1992.** Steel Industry. Multicoloured.
2710 20 r. Type **968** .. .. 30 20
2711 70 r. Steel products and steel works .. .. 1·00 60
Nos. 2710/11 were issued together, se-tenant, forming a composite design.

**969** Isfahan

**1992.** World Tourism Day. Multicoloured.
2712 20 r. Type **969** .. .. 30 20
2713 20 r. Mazandaran .. 30 20
2714 30 r. Bushehr .. .. 45 25
2715 30 r. Hormozgan .. 45 25

**970** Map and Flags

**1992.** International Trade Fair.
2716 **970** 200 r. multicoloured .. 2·50 1·50

**971** Early Post Office Service

**1992.** World Post Day.
2717 **971** 30 r. brown and violet 50 30

**972** Starving Child and Food Distribution

**1992.** World Food Day.
2718 **972** 100 r. multicoloured .. 1·25 75

**973** Child drawing

**974** Flames and Child's Face

**1992.** International Children's and Youth Photographic Festival.
2719 **973** 40 r. multicoloured .. 55 35

**1992.** Bosnia and Herzegovina.
2720 **974** 40 r. multicoloured .. 55 35

**975** Storming Embassy, Doves and Crow

**976** Emblem

**1992.** Multicoloured.
2721 100 r. Type **975** (11th anniv of storming of U.S. Embassy) .. 1·25 75
2722 100 r. Soldiers, crows and doves (Students' Day) 1·25 75
2723 100 r. Ayatollah Khomeini, crows and doves (13th anniv of Khomeini's return from exile) .. .. 1·25 75
Nos. 2721/3 were issued together, se-tenant, forming a composite design.

**1992.** 17th Annual Meeting of Islamic Development Bank Board of Governors.
2724 **976** 20 r. multicoloured .. 25 15

**977** Flags and Dish Aerials on Maps

**1992.** Azerbaijan–Iran Telecommunications Co-operation.
2725 **977** 40 r. multicoloured .. 55 35

**978** Star

**1992.** 10th Anniv of Islamic University.
2726 **978** 200 r. green & dp green 2·50 1·50

**979** Soldiers in Armed Motor Boat

**1992.** People's Militia Week.
2727 **979** 40 r. multicoloured .. 55 35

**980** Shahryar

**981** "Heaven and Hell"

**1992.** International Congress on Mohammed Hossein Shahryar (poet).
2728 **980** 80 r. multicoloured .. 1·00 60

**1992.** Women's Day and Birth Anniv of Fatima.
2729 **981** 70 r. multicoloured .. 90 55

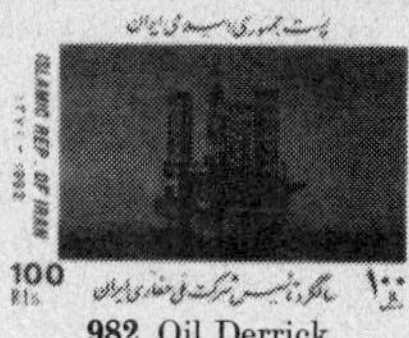
**982** Oil Derrick

**1992.** Oil Industry. Multicoloured.
2730 100 r. Type **982** .. .. 1·25 75
2731 100 r. Drilling .. .. 1·25 75

**983** Arabic Script and Hand holding Pen

**984** Ayatollah Mirza Abolhassan Sharani

**1992.** Literacy Campaign.
2732 **983** 80 r. multicoloured .. 1·00 60

**1993.** Celebrities. Multicoloured.
2733 20 r. Type **984** .. .. 25 15
2734 20 r. Prof. Mahmoud Hessabi and formula .. 25 15
2735 20 r. Mohit Tabatabaie and books .. .. 25 15
2736 20 r. Mehrdad Avesta and Arabic script .. .. 25 15

**985** Narcissi  **986** Wings and Koran

**1993.** Flowers. Multicoloured.
2737 20 r. Type **985** .. .. 25 15
2738 30 r. Blue and yellow irises .. .. 55 40
2738a 35 r. Tulips .. .. 40 25
2739 40 r. White irises .. 50 30
2740 50 r. White flowers .. 60 35
2741 60 r. Viburum berries .. 1·25 40
2742 70 r. Pansies .. .. 1·40 85
2743 75 r. Orchids .. .. 1·40 85
2745 100 r. Martagon lilies .. 1·25 75
2746 120 r. Petunias .. .. 1·90 1·00
2747 150 r. Hyacinths .. 1·60 95
2749 200 r. Roses .. .. 2·25 1·50
2750 500 r. Convolvulus .. 6·00 3·50
2751 1000 r. Poppies .. 12·00 7·25

**1993.** Mab'as Festival.
2752 **986** 200 r. multicoloured .. 2·50 1·50

**987** Rainbow and Emblem  **988** Man in Wheelchair tying Girl's Ribbon

**1993.** Programming Day.
2753 **987** 100 r. multicoloured .. 1·25 75

**1993.** Invalids' Day. Multicoloured.
2754 20 r. Type **988** .. .. 25 15
2755 40 r. Medal winner in wheelchair .. .. 50 30
Nos. 2754/5 were issued together, se-tenant, forming a composite design.

**989** Fatima Mosque, Qom

**1993.** Preservation of Cultural Heritage. Multicoloured.
2756 40 r. Type **989** .. .. 50 30
2757 40 r. Interior of mosque 50 30

**990** Hands reaching towards Sun

**1993.** World Day of the Oppressed. Birth Anniv of Mahdi.
2758 **990** 60 r. multicoloured .. 75 45

**991** National Flag

**1993.** 14th Anniv of Islamic Revolution. Multicoloured.
2759 20 r. Type **991** .. .. 25 15
2760 20 r. Flag and soldiers .. 25 15
2761 20 r. Guerrillas .. .. 25 15
2762 20 r. Oil derricks, harvesters and crowd 25 15
2763 20 r. Ayatollah Khomeini in motorcade and on arrival in Iran .. 25 15
Nos. 2759/63 were issued together, se-tenant, forming a composite design.

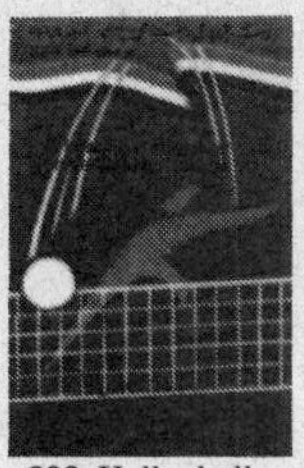

**992** Volleyball  **993** Ansari

**1993.** 1st Islamic Countries Women's Games. Multicoloured.
2764 40 r. Type **992** .. .. 50 30
2765 40 r. Basketball .. .. 50 30
2766 40 r. Gold medal .. 50 30
2767 40 r. Swimming .. .. 50 30
2768 40 r. Running .. .. 50 30
Nos. 2764/8 were issued together, se-tenant, forming a compostite design.

**1993.** Congress on Sheikh Morteza Ansari.
2769 **993** 40 r. multicoloured .. 50 30

**994** World Map as Tree Foliage and Rainbow

**1993.** Tree Day.
2770 **994** 70 r. multicoloured .. 90 55

**995** Burning Tank and Man with Sling  **996** Butterfly and Tulip

**1993.** World Jerusalem Day.
2771 **995** 20 r. multicoloured .. 25 15

**1993.** New Year Festival. Flowers and Butterflies. Multicolured.
2772 20 r. Type **996** .. .. 25 15
2773 20 r. Butterfly and narcissus .. .. 25 15
2774 40 r. Butterfly, tulips and rose .. .. .. 50 30
2775 40 r. Butterfly and roses 50 30

**997** Grass and Goldfish in Bowl

**1993.** Fetr Feast.
2776 **997** 100 r. multicoloured .. 2·00 1·25

## MINIMUM PRICE

The minimum price quoted is 10p which represents a handling charge rather than a basis for valuing common stamps. For further notes about prices see introductory pages.

**998** Open Music Book

**1993.** 14th Anniv of Islamic Republic.
2777 **998** 40 r. multicoloured .. 80 40

**999** Door and Landscape

**1993.** International Birth Millenary of Sheikh Mofeed Congress.
2778 **999** 80 r. multicoloured .. 1·50 90

**1000** Emblem  **1001** Globe

**1993.** 13th Asian and Pacific Labour Ministers' Conference, Teheran.
2779 **1000** 100 r. multicoloured 2·00 1·25

**1993.** Int Congress for Advancement of Science and Technology in Islamic World.
2780 **1001** 100 r. multicoloured 1·00 65

**1002** Mirror Box

**1993.** International Museum Day.
2781 **1002** 40 r. multicoloured .. 75 40

**1003** Khomeini  **1004** Girl on Swing

**1993.** 4th Death Anniv of Ayatollah Khomeini.
2782 **1003** 20 r. multicoloured .. 40 25

**1993.** World Children's Day.
2783 **1004** 50 r. multicoloured .. 1·00 60

**1005** Knitted Socks  **1006** Family at Window

**1993.** World Crafts Day.
2784 **1005** 70 r. multicoloured .. 1·25 75

**1993.** World Population Day.
2785 **1006** 30 r. multicoloured .. 55 40

**1007** Football

**1993.** Student Games. Multicoloured.
2786 20 r. Type **1007** .. .. 40 25
2787 40 r. Judo and wrestling 75 50
2788 40 r. Long jumping, weightlifting, badminton and basketball 75 50

**1008** Butterfly and Film Frame

**1993.** International Children's and Youths' Film Festival, Isfahan.
2789 **1008** 60 r. multicoloured 1·10 60

**1009** Postal Messenger  **1010** Stars and Birds

**1993.** World Post Day.
2790 **1009** 60 r. multicoloured 1·10 60

**1993.** 3rd International Biennial Children's Book Illustrations Exn, Teheran. Mult.
2791 30 r. Type **1010** .. .. 55 40
2792 30 r. Moon and girl in boat .. .. .. 55 40
2793 30 r. Cherub blowing trumpet .. .. 55 40
2794 30 r. Trees and clouds .. 55 40
Nos. 2791/4 were issued together, se-tenant, forming a composite design.

**1011** Khaje Nassireddin Tussy  **1013** Ayatollah Golpayegani

**1012** Militia Member

**1993.** 719th Death Anniv of Khaje Nassireddin Tussy (scientist).
2795 **1011** 30 r. multicoloured .. 60 40

**1993.** People's Militia Week. Multicoloured.
2796 50 r. Type **1012** .. .. 90 40
2797 50 r. Woman tying headband for Militia member .. .. 90 40

**1993.** Ayatollah Golpayegani Commem.
2798 **1013** 300 r. multicoloured 5·50 1·90

1014 Hopscotch Grid drawn in Blood

1015 Flags

**1993.** Support for Moslems of Bosnia and Herzegovina. Multicoloured.

2799 40 r. Type **1014** . . . . 75 40
2800 40 r. Youth giving "V" sign . . . . . . 75 40
2801 40 r. Woman and mosque 75 40

**1994.** Invalids' Day and Birthday of Abalfazil el Abbas.

2802 **1015** 80 r. multicoloured 1·50 75

1016 Trees and Ploughed Field in Book

**1994.** Agricultural Week.

2803 **1016** 60 r. multicoloured . . 1·10 65

1017 Electrification of Villages

1018 Dome of the Rock

**1994.** 15th Anniv of Islamic Revolution. Mult.

2804 40 r. Type **1017** . . 65 40
2805 40 r. Ayatollah Khomeini and workers with flag 65 40
2806 40 r. Fishing and new roads . . . . . . 65 40
2807 40 r. Harvesting wheat and weaving . . . . 65 40

Nos. 2804/7 were issued together, se-tenant, forming a composite design.

**1994.** Congress on Islamic Law.

2808 **1018** 60 r. multicoloured . . 95 60

1019 Doctor, Gymnast, Camera, Paintbrush, Book and Student

**1994.** Youth Welfare.

2809 **1019** 30 r. multicoloured . . 50 30

1020 Palestinian and Peaceful Scene

**1994.** World Jerusalem Day.

2810 **1020** 50 r. multicoloured . . 80 50

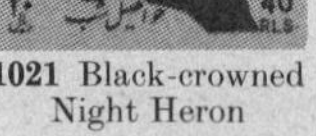

1021 Black-crowned Night Heron

1022 Ball and Rectangles

**1994.** New Year Festival. Birds. Mult.

2811 40 r. Type **1021** . . . . 65 40
2812 40 r. Eurasian bittern . . 65 40
2813 40 r. Chukar partridges (horiz) . . . . 65 40
2814 40 r. Ring-necked pheasants (horiz) . . 65 40

**1994.** 25th Annual Mathematics Conference.

2815 **1022** 30 r. multicoloured . . 50 30

1023 Book and Roses

**1994.** 15th Anniv of Islamic Republic.

2816 **1023** 40 r. multicoloured . . 60 35

1024 Child and Roses

**1994.** World Health Day.

2817 **1024** 100 r. multicoloured 1·50 90

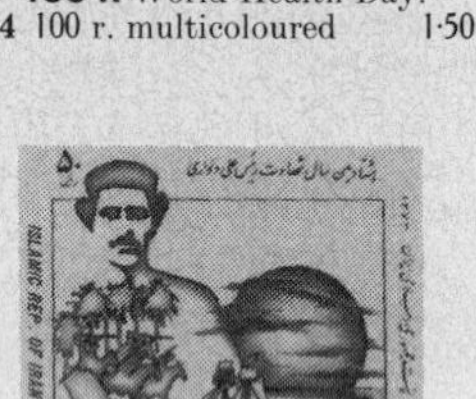

1025 Delvari, Cavalrymen and Ship

**1994.** 80th Death Anniv of Raiss Ali Delvari (revolutionary).

2818 **1025** 50 r. multicoloured . . 80 50

1026 I.Y.F. Emblem

**1994.** International Year of the Family.

2819 **1026** 50 r. multicoloured . . 80 50

1027 Old Telephone System and Computer Operator

**1994.** World Telecommunications Day.

2820 **1027** 50 r. multicoloured . . 80 50

1028 Marlik Gold Cup

1029 Kufic Enamelled Pot

**1994.** International Museum Day.

2821 **1028** 40 r. multicoloured . . 60 35

**1994.** Cultural Preservation.

2822 **1029** 40 r. multicoloured . . 60 35

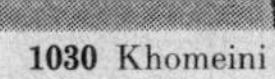

1030 Khomeini

1031 Motahhari

**1994.** 5th Death Anniv of Ayatollah Khomeini.

2823 **1030** 30 r. multicoloured . . 50 30

**1994.** 15th Death Anniv of Ayatollah Motahhari.

2824 **1031** 30 r. multicoloured . . 50 30

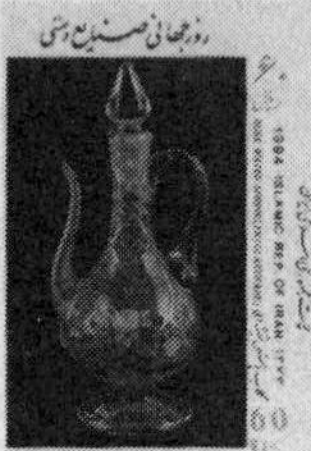

1032 Rose-water Sprinkler

1034 Mosaic and Rose

1033 Games Emblem

**1994.** World Crafts Day.

2825 60 r. Type **1032** . . . . 1·00 60
2826 60 r. Silk weaving, Khorassan . . . . 1·00 60

**1994.** Islamic Countries' University Student Games.

2827 **1033** 60 r. multicoloured . . 1·00 60

**1994.** Mohammed's Birth Anniv and Unity Week.

2828 **1034** 30 r. multicoloured . . 50 30

1035 Cameraman

**1994.** 14th Anniv of Iran–Iraq War.

2829 **1035** 70 r. multicoloured . . 1·10 65

1036 Envelope

**1994.** World Post Day.

2830 **1036** 50 r. multicoloured . . 80 50

1037 Allegory of Woman

1038 Soldier

**1994.** Women's Day and Birth Anniv of Fatima.

2831 **1037** 70 r. multicoloured . . 1·10 65

**1994.** People's Militia Week.

2832 **1038** 30 r. multicoloured . . 50 30

1039 Book

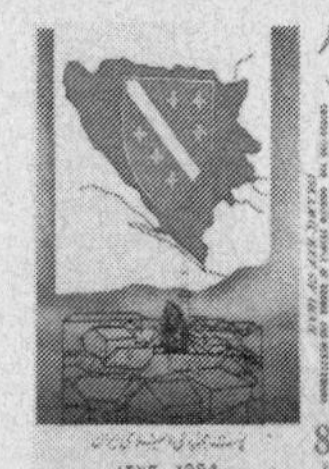

1040 Arms, Map and Town

**1994.** Book Week.

2833 **1039** 40 r. multicoloured . . 65 40

**1994.** Support for Moslems of Bosnia and Herzegovina. Multicoloured.

2834 80 r. Type **1040** . . . . 1·25 75
2835 80 r. Commander Adnan (deceased) and family 1·25 75

1041 Araki

1042 Arabic Script

**1995.** 2nd Death Anniv of Grand Ayatollah Mohammad Ali Araki (Shia leader).

2836 **1041** 100 r. multicoloured 1·60 95

**1995.** World Day of the Oppressed. Birth Anniv of Mahdi.

2837 **1042** 50 r. multicoloured . . 80 50

1043 Flag, Dome and Man

1044 Crowd, National Flag and Ayatollah Khomeini

**1995.** Revolutionaries. Multicoloured.

2838 50 r. Type **1043** . . . . 80 50
2839 50 r. Man in patterned shirt . . . . . . 80 50
2840 50 r. Man with full beard wearing grey shirt . . 80 50
2841 50 r. Man in jacket and sweater looking to right 80 50

**1995.** 16th Anniv of Islamic Revolution.

2842 **1044** 100 r. multicoloured 1·60 95

## MINIMUM PRICE

The minimum price quoted is 10p which represents a handling charge rather than a basis for valuing common stamps. For further notes about prices see introductory pages.

1045 Dome of the Rock

1046 Hand holding Tree

**1995.** World Jerusalem Day.
2843 **1045** 100 r. multicoloured 1·60 95

**1995.** Tree Day.
2844 **1046** 50 r. multicoloured .. 80 50

1047 Hyacinths

**1995.** New Year Festival. Multicoloured.

| | | | |
|---|---|---|---|
| 2845 | 50 r. Type **1047** .. .. | 80 | 50 |
| 2846 | 50 r. Pansies .. .. | 80 | 50 |
| 2847 | 50 r. Grass and bow .. | 80 | 50 |
| 2848 | 50 r. Tulips, bow and goldfish bowl .. .. | 80 | 50 |

1048 Train on Viaduct

**1995.** Inauguration of Bafq–Bandar Abbas Railway.
2849 **1048** 100 r. multicoloured 1·60 95

1049 Phoenix rising from Tulips

1050 Shapes

**1995.** 16th Anniv of Islamic Republic.
2850 **1049** 100 r. multicoloured 1·60 95

**1995.** Press Festival.
2851 **1050** 100 r. multicoloured 1·60 95

1051 Khomeini

1052 Arabic Script

**1995.** Ayatollah Ahmad Khomeini Commem.
2852 **1051** 50 r. multicoloured .. 80 50

**1995.** Invalids' Day.
2853 **1052** 80 r. multicoloured .. 1·25 75

1053 Yezd Mosque and Vaziri

**1995.** Ayatollah Ali Vaziri Commemoration.
2854 **1053** 100 r. multicoloured 1·60 95

1054 Telecommunications

**1995.** World Telecommunications Day.
2855 **1054** 100 r. multicoloured 1·50 90

1055 Khomeini

1056 Immunizing Baby

**1995.** 6th Death Anniv of Ayatollah Khomeini.
2856 **1055** 100 r. multicoloured 1·60 95

**1995.** 50th Anniv of U.N.O. Mult.

| | | | |
|---|---|---|---|
| 2857 | 100 r. Type **1056** .. | 1·60 | 95 |
| 2858 | 100 r. Child laughing .. | 1·60 | 95 |
| 2859 | 100 r. Cereals and world map .. .. .. | 1·60 | 95 |
| 2860 | 100 r. Woman reading .. | 1·60 | 95 |

1057 Ashtiany

1059 Man with Gun and Book

1058 Dam Workers

**1995.** Iqbal Ashtiany (historian) Commem.
2861 **1057** 100 r. multicoloured 1·50 90

**1995.** Government Week.
2862 **1058** 100 r. multicoloured 1·50 90

**1995.** People's Militia Week.
2863 **1059** 100 r. multicoloured 1·50 90

1060 Envelopes and Globe forming Flower

1061 Cypher

**1995.** World Post Day.
2864 **1060** 100 r. multicoloured 1·50 90

**1995.** Prophet Mohammed Commemoration.
2865 **1061** 100 r. multicoloured 1·50 90

1062 Tondgoyan

1063 Shaghaghi

**1995.** M. J. Tondgoyan (oil minister) Commemoration.
2866 **1062** 100 r. multicoloured 1·50 90

**1996.** Fathi Shaghaghi (Islamic Jihad Secretary-General) Commemoration.
2867 **1063** 100 r. multicoloured 1·50 90

1064 Crowd, Flowers and Ayatollah Khomeini

1065 Dome of the Rock

**1996.** 17th Anniv of Islamic Revolution.
2868 **1064** 100 r. multicoloured 1·50 90

**1996.** World Jerusalem Day.
2869 **1065** 100 r. multicoloured 1·50 90

1066 Crested Bird

**1996.** New Year Festival. Birds. Mult.

| | | | |
|---|---|---|---|
| 2870 | 100 r. Type **1066** .. | 1·50 | 90 |
| 2871 | 100 r. Budgerigar .. | 1·50 | 90 |
| 2872 | 100 r. Yellow-headed bird | 1·50 | 90 |
| 2873 | 100 r. Blue-headed bird .. | 1·50 | 90 |

NEWSPAPER POSTAGE DUE STAMPS

**1909.** Optd **Imprimes** in English and Persian.
N1319 **38** 2 ch. grey on blue .. 13·00 2·00

OFFICIAL STAMPS

**1902.** Stamp of 1898 surch. **Service** and value in English and Persian.

| | | | | |
|---|---|---|---|---|
| O 224. | **21.** | 5 c. on 1 k. red .. | 4·00 | 50 |
| O 225. | | 10 c. on 1 k. red .. | 3·00 | 60 |
| O 226. | | 12 c. on 1 k. red .. | 4·25 | 1·40 |

**1903.** Stamps of 1903 optd. **Service.**

| | | | | |
|---|---|---|---|---|
| O 259. | **38.** | 1 c. lilac .. .. | 15 | 10 |
| O 260. | | 2 c. grey .. .. | 15 | 10 |
| O 261. | | 3 c. green .. .. | 15 | 10 |
| O 262. | | 5 c. red .. .. | 15 | 10 |
| O 263. | | 10 c. brown .. | 15 | 10 |
| O 264. | | 12 c. blue .. .. | 20 | 10 |
| O 265. | **39.** | 1 k. purple .. .. | 40 | 10 |
| O 266. | | 2 k. blue .. .. | 80 | 10 |
| O 267. | | 5 k. brown .. .. | 6·00 | 20 |
| O 268. | | 10 k. red .. .. | 6·00 | 50 |
| O 269. | | 20 k. orange .. | 9·00 | 50 |
| O 270. | | 30 k. green .. .. | 12·00 | 1·00 |
| O 271. | | 50 k. green .. .. | 55·00 | 14·00 |

**1905.** Nos. 275/6 and 280/1 optd **Service**.

| | | | | |
|---|---|---|---|---|
| O283 | **39** | 2 t. on 50 k. green (275) | 45·00 | 22·00 |
| O285 | | 2 t. on 50 k. green (280) | 45·00 | 22·00 |
| O284 | | 3 t. on 50 k. green (276) | 45·00 | 25·00 |
| O286 | | 3 t. on 50 k. green (281) | 45·00 | 22·00 |

(O 57.)

O 120.

**1911.** Stamps of 1909 optd **Service** and with Type O **57**.

| | | | | |
|---|---|---|---|---|
| O353 | **56** | 1 c. purple and orange | 3·00 | 15 |
| O354 | | 2 c. purple and violet | 3·00 | 15 |
| O355 | | 3 c. purple and green | 3·00 | 20 |
| O356 | | 6 c. purple and red .. | 3·00 | 20 |
| O357 | | 9 c. purple and grey .. | 3·00 | 50 |
| O358 | | 10 c. purple and mauve | 6·00 | 60 |
| O359 | | 1 k. brown, violet & sil | 7·00 | 2·00 |
| O360 | | 2 k. brown, green & sil | 12·00 | 5·00 |

**1915.** Coronation stamps of 1915 optd. **SERVICE** in English and Persian.

| | | | | |
|---|---|---|---|---|
| O 460. | **66.** | 1 c. blue and red .. | 10 | 10 |
| O 461 | | 2 c. red and blue .. | 10 | 10 |
| O 462. | | 3 c. green .. .. | 10 | 10 |
| O 463. | | 5 c. red .. .. | 10 | 10 |
| O 464. | | 6 c. red and green .. | 20 | 10 |
| O 465. | | 9 c. violet and brown | 20 | 10 |
| O 466. | | 10 c. brown & green | 20 | 10 |
| O 467. | | 12 c. blue .. .. | 20 | 10 |
| O 468. | | 24 c. chocolate & brn. | 20 | 10 |
| O 469. | **67.** | 1 k. blk., brn. & silver | 80 | 15 |
| O 470. | | 2 k. red, blue & silver | 80 | 15 |
| O 471. | – | 3 k. sepia, lilac & silver | 80 | 20 |
| O 472. | **67.** | 5 k. grey, sepia & silver | 85 | 20 |
| O 473. | – | 1 t. black, vio. & gold | 85 | 35 |
| O 474. | – | 2 t. brown, grn. & gold | 90 | 35 |
| O 475. | – | 3 t. red, crimson & gold | 90 | 55 |
| O 476. | – | 5 t. grey, blue & gold | 1·25 | 60 |

**1941.** 55 10

| | | | | |
|---|---|---|---|---|
| O 836. | O **120.** | 5 d. violet .. | 55 | 10 |
| O 837. | | 10 d. mauve .. | 55 | 10 |
| O 838. | | 25 d. red .. .. | 55 | 10 |
| O 839. | | 50 d. black .. | 55 | 10 |
| O 840. | | 75 d. red .. .. | 80 | 10 |
| O 841. | | 1 r. green .. | 2·00 | 10 |
| O 842. | | 1 r. 50 blue .. | 2·25 | 10 |
| O 843. | | 2 r. blue .. .. | 4·25 | 10 |
| O 844. | | 3 r. purple .. | 8·50 | 10 |
| O 845. | | 5 r. green .. | 12·00 | 20 |
| O 846. | | 10 r. blue & brown | 35·00 | 40 |
| O 847. | | 20 r. mauve & bl. | £130 | 1·50 |
| O 848. | | 30 r. green & vio. | £250 | 2·75 |
| O 849. | | 50 r. brown & blue | £300 | 45·00 |

The rial values are larger (23 × 30 mm.).

O 489. Red Lion and Sun Emblem.

**1974.**

| | | | | |
|---|---|---|---|---|
| O1829 | O **489** | 5 d. violet & mve | 10 | 10 |
| O1830 | | 10 d. mauve & bl | 10 | 10 |
| O1831 | | 50 d. orange & grn | 10 | 10 |
| O1832 | | 1 r. blue and gold | 10 | 10 |
| O2046 | | 1 r. black & green | 10 | 10 |
| O1833 | | 2 r. green & orge | 10 | 10 |
| O2047 | | 2 r. brown & grey | 10 | 10 |
| O2048 | | 3 r. blue & orange | 10 | 10 |
| O2049 | | 5 r. green & pink | 15 | 15 |
| O1834 | | 6 r. green & yellow | 35 | 10 |
| O2050 | | 6 r. black and blue | 15 | 15 |
| O1835 | | 8 r. blue & yellow | 35 | 15 |
| O2051 | | 8 r. red and green | 20 | 15 |
| O1836 | | 10 r. blue & mve | 2·00 | 20 |
| O2052 | | 10 r. turq & green | 35 | 20 |
| O1837 | | 11 r. purple & blue | 70 | 20 |
| O2053 | | 11 r. blue & yellow | 70 | 25 |
| O1838 | | 14 r. red and blue | 70 | 50 |
| O2054 | | 14 r. green & grey | 75 | 30 |
| O2055 | | 15 r. blue & mve | 1·50 | 70 |
| O1839 | | 20 r blue & orange | 70 | 55 |
| O2056 | | 20 r. purple & yell | 1·75 | 30 |
| O2057 | | 30 r. brown & orge | 1·75 | 90 |
| O1840 | | 50 r. brown & grn | 3·50 | 1·40 |
| O2058 | | 50 r. black & gold | 3·50 | 1·00 |

The 6 r. to 50 r. are larger, 23 × 37 mm.

PARCEL POST STAMPS

**1915.** Coronation stamps of 1915 optd. **COLIS POSTAUX** in English and Persian.

| | | | | |
|---|---|---|---|---|
| P443 | **66** | 1 c. blue and red .. | 10 | 10 |
| P444 | | 2 c. red and blue .. | 10 | 10 |
| P445 | | 3 c. green .. .. | 10 | 10 |
| P446 | | 5 c. red .. .. | 10 | 10 |
| P447 | | 6 c. red and green .. | 20 | 10 |
| P448 | | 9 c. violet and brown | 20 | 10 |
| P449 | | 10 c. brown and green | 20 | 10 |
| P450 | | 12 c. blue .. .. | 20 | 10 |
| P451 | | 24 c. choc. & brown .. | 20 | 10 |
| P452 | **67** | 1 k. black, brn. & silver | 70 | 15 |
| P453 | | 2 k. red, blue & silver | 70 | 15 |
| P454 | | 3 k. sepia, lilac & silver | 70 | 20 |
| P455 | | 5 k. grey, sepia & silver | 70 | 20 |
| P456 | – | 1 t. blk., violet & gold | 75 | 35 |
| P457 | – | 2 t. brown, grn. & gold | 75 | 35 |
| P458 | – | 3 t. red and gold .. | 80 | 55 |
| P459 | – | 5 t. grey, blue & gold | 1·25 | 55 |

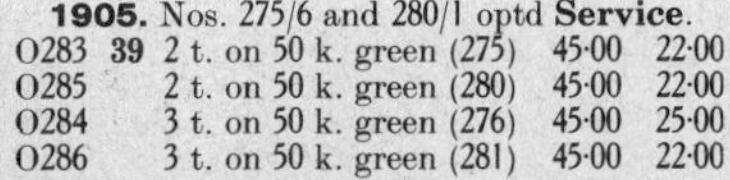

P 192.

**1958.**

| No. | Type | Description | Mint | Used |
|---|---|---|---|---|
| P 1151. | P 192. | 50 d. drab | 10 | 10 |
| P 1152. | | 1 r. red | 10 | 10 |
| P 1153. | | 2 r. blue | 20 | 10 |
| P 1154. | | 3 r. myrtle | 15 | 10 |
| P 1478. | | 5 r. violet | 15 | 10 |
| P 1479. | | 10 r. brown | 30 | 15 |
| P 1480. | | 20 r. orange | 50 | 35 |
| P 1481. | | 30 r. mauve | 1·00 | 15 |
| P 1482. | | 50 r. lake | 1·25 | 85 |
| P 1483. | | 100 r. yellow | 2·75 | 1·00 |
| P 1484. | | 200 r. green | 6·00 | 3·75 |

The word "IRAN" with a black frame is printed in reverse on the back of the above stamps and is intended to show through the stamps when attached to parcels.

POSTAL TAX STAMPS

T 142a. Red Lion and Sun Emblem (8 lines to each ray).

**1950.** Hospitals Fund.

| No. | Type | Description | Mint | Used |
|---|---|---|---|---|
| T1139 | T 142a. | 50 d. red & grn. | 50 | 15 |
| T1396 | | 2 r. red & lilac | 80 | 15 |

**1976.** As T **142a** but with five lines to each ray.

| No. | Type | Description | Mint | Used |
|---|---|---|---|---|
| T2007 | T142a | 50 d. red & green | 1·25 | 20 |
| T2008 | | 2 r. red & blue | 1·75 | 20 |

## IRAQ Pt. 19

A country W. of Persia, formerly under Turkish dominion, then under British mandate after the 1914-18 War. An independent kingdom since 1932 until 14 July, 1958, when the king was assassinated and a republic proclaimed.

1917. 16 annas = 1 rupee.
1931. 1000 fils = 1 dinar.

**1918.** Stamps of Turkey (Pictorial issue, Nos. 501/514) surch. **IRAQ IN BRITISH OCCUPATION,** and value in Indian currency.

| No. | Description | Mint | Used |
|---|---|---|---|
| 1 | ¼ a. on 5 pa. purple | 30 | 80 |
| 2 | ½ a. on 10 pa. green | 30 | 15 |
| 3 | 1 a. on 20 pa. red | 30 | 10 |
| 17 | 1½ a. on 5 pa. purple | 95 | 95 |
| 5 | 2½ a. on 1 pi. blue | 80 | 1·25 |
| 6 | 3 a. on 1½ pi. grey and red | 70 | 25 |
| 7 | 4 a. on 1¾ pi. brown & grey | 70 | 25 |
| 8 | 6 a. on 2 pi. black and green | 1·60 | 1·25 |
| 9 | 8 a. on 2½ pi. green & orge | 90 | 60 |
| 10 | 12 a. on 5 pi. lilac | 1·75 | 2·00 |
| 11 | 1 r. on 10 pi. brown | 2·25 | 1·40 |
| 12 | 2 r. on 25 pi. green | 7·50 | 2·50 |
| 13 | 5 r. on 50 pi. red | 20·00 | 19·00 |
| 14 | 10 r. on 100 pi. blue | 40·00 | 17·00 |

2. Sunni Mosque, Muadhdham.

3. Winged Cherub.

4. Allegory of Date Palm.

10. King Faisal I.

**1923.**

| No. | Type | Description | Mint | Used |
|---|---|---|---|---|
| 41 | 2 | ½ a. green | 40 | 10 |
| 42 | – | 1 a. brown | 50 | 10 |
| 43 | 3 | 1½ a. red | 40 | 10 |
| 44 | – | 2 a. buff | 40 | 15 |
| 45 | – | 3 a. blue | 85 | 15 |
| 46 | – | 4 a. violet | 1·25 | 30 |
| 47 | – | 6 a. blue | 1·00 | 30 |
| 48 | – | 8 a. bistre | 1·75 | 30 |
| 49 | 4 | 1 r. brown and green | 2·75 | 80 |
| 50 | 2 | 2 r. black | 12·00 | 7·00 |
| 51 | | 2 r. bistre | 28·00 | 3·25 |
| 52 | – | 5 r. orange | 26·00 | 13·00 |
| 53 | – | 10 r. red | 32·00 | 20·00 |

DESIGNS—30 × 24 mm: 1 a. Gufas on the Tigris; 2 a. Bull from Babylonian wall-sculpture; 6 a., 10 r. Shiah Mosque, Kadhimain. 34 × 24 mm: 3 a. Arch of Ctesiphon. 24 × 30 mm: 4, 8 a., 5 r. Tribal Standard, Dulaim Camel Corps.

**1927.**

| No. | Type | Description | Mint | Used |
|---|---|---|---|---|
| 78. | 10. | 1 r. brown | 6·00 | 50 |

11. King Faisal I. 12.

**1931.**

| No. | Type | Description | Mint | Used |
|---|---|---|---|---|
| 80 | 11 | ½ a. green | 50 | 10 |
| 81 | | 1 a. brown | 65 | 10 |
| 82 | | 1½ a. red | 60 | 30 |
| 83 | | 2 a. orange | 65 | 10 |
| 84 | | 3 a. blue | 60 | 10 |
| 85 | | 4 a. purple | 1·25 | 95 |
| 86 | | 6 a. blue | 1·25 | 60 |
| 87 | | 8 a. green | 1·25 | 1·50 |
| 88 | 12 | 1 r. brown | 3·00 | 1·25 |
| 89 | | 2 r. brown | 5·50 | 3·75 |
| 90 | | 5 r. orange | 18·00 | 30·00 |
| 91 | | 10 r. red | 50·00 | 70·00 |
| 92 | 10 | 25 r. violet | £500 | £650 |

**1932.** Nos. 80/92 and 46 surch in "Fils" or "Dinar".

| No. | Type | Description | Mint | Used |
|---|---|---|---|---|
| 106 | 11 | 2 f. on ½ a. green | 15 | 10 |
| 107 | | 3 f. on ½ a. green | 15 | 10 |
| 108 | | 4 f. on 1 a. brown | 1·00 | 25 |
| 109 | | 5 f. on 1 a. brown | 30 | 10 |
| 110 | | 8 f. on 1½ a. red | 35 | 30 |
| 111 | | 10 f. on 2 a. orange | 35 | 10 |
| 112 | | 15 f. on 3 a. blue | 65 | 1·00 |
| 113 | | 20 f. on 4 a. purple | 1·00 | 1·00 |
| 114 | – | 25 f. on 4 a. vio (No. 46) | 1·50 | 2·75 |
| 115 | 11 | 30 f. on 6 a. blue | 1·50 | 60 |
| 116 | | 40 f. on 8 a. green | 2·25 | 2·25 |
| 117 | 12 | 75 f. on 1 r. brown | 1·75 | 2·25 |
| 118 | | 100 f. on 2 r. brown | 5·50 | 3·75 |
| 119 | | 200 f. on 5 r. orange | 11·00 | 14·00 |
| 120 | | ½ d. on 10 r. red | 42·00 | 60·00 |
| 121 | 10 | 1 d. on 25 r. violet | 80·00 | £130 |

**1932.** As Types **10/12** but value in **FILS** or **DINAR.**

| No. | Type | Description | Mint | Used |
|---|---|---|---|---|
| 138. | 11. | 2 f. blue | 40 | 10 |
| 139. | | 3 f. green | 40 | 10 |
| 140. | | 4 f. purple | 40 | 10 |
| 141. | | 5 f. green | 40 | 10 |
| 142. | | 8 f. red | 70 | 10 |
| 143. | | 10 f. yellow | 70 | 10 |
| 144. | | 15 f. blue | 70 | 10 |
| 145. | | 20 f. orange | 70 | 40 |
| 146. | | 25 f. mauve | 70 | 30 |
| 147. | | 30 f. olive | 1·00 | 15 |
| 148. | | 40 f. violet | 90 | 70 |
| 149. | 12. | 50 f. brown | 90 | 20 |
| 150. | | 75 f. blue | 1·75 | 1·75 |
| 151. | | 100 f. green | 2·75 | 70 |
| 152. | | 200 f. red | 10·00 | 3·25 |
| 153. | 10. | ½ d. blue | 30·00 | 30·00 |
| 154. | | 1 d. purple | 65·00 | 65·00 |

16. King Ghazi.

17. King Ghazi.

**1934.**

| No. | Type | Description | Mint | Used |
|---|---|---|---|---|
| 172. | 16. | 1 f. violet | 45 | 30 |
| 173. | | 2 f. blue | 20 | 15 |
| 174. | | 3 f. green | 20 | 15 |
| 175. | | 4 f. purple | 25 | 15 |
| 176. | | 5 f. green | 25 | 15 |
| 177. | | 8 f. red | 35 | 15 |
| 178. | | 10 f. yellow | 45 | 15 |
| 179. | | 15 f. blue | 45 | 15 |
| 180. | | 20 f. orange | 45 | 15 |
| 181. | | 25 f. mauve | 85 | 20 |
| 182. | | 30 f. green | 65 | 20 |
| 183 | | 40 f. violet | 75 | 25 |
| 184. | 17. | 50 f. brown | 1·75 | 25 |
| 185. | | 75 f. blue | 1·50 | 30 |
| 186. | | 100 f. green | 1·90 | 45 |
| 187. | | 200 f. red | 3·50 | 75 |
| 188. | – | ½ d. blue | 5·50 | 2·40 |
| 189. | – | 1 d. red | 38·00 | 12·00 |

DESIGN—23 × 27½ mm: ½, 1 d. Portrait as in Types **16/17** but different frame.

19. Mausoleum of Sitt Zubaidah. 21. Lion of Babylon. 22. Spiral Tower of Samarra.

**1941.**

| No. | Type | Description | Mint | Used |
|---|---|---|---|---|
| 208 | 19 | 1 f. purple | 10 | 10 |
| 209 | | 2 f. brown | 10 | 10 |
| 210 | – | 3 f. green | 10 | 10 |
| 211 | – | 4 f. violet | 10 | 10 |
| 212 | – | 5 f. red | 20 | 10 |
| 213 | 21 | 8 f. red | 50 | 10 |
| 214 | | 8 f. yellow | 10 | 10 |
| 215 | | 10 f. yellow | 9·25 | 2·10 |
| 216 | | 10 f. red | 50 | 10 |
| 217 | | 15 f. blue | 85 | 20 |
| 218a | | 15 f. black | 85 | 30 |
| 219 | | 20 f. black | 1·25 | 40 |
| 220 | | 20 f. blue | 45 | 20 |
| 221 | 22 | 25 f. purple | 20 | 10 |
| 222 | | 30 f. orange | 25 | 15 |
| 223b | | 40 f. brown | 85 | 40 |
| 224b | – | 50 f. blue | 1·25 | 45 |
| 225a | – | 75 f. mauve | 85 | 45 |
| 226 | – | 100 f. olive | 1·25 | 75 |
| 227 | – | 200 f. orange | 2·10 | 75 |
| 228 | – | ½ d. blue | 10·00 | 3·50 |
| 229a | – | 1 d. green | 20·00 | 8·00 |

DESIGNS—HORIZ. 3 f., 4 f., 5 f. King Faisal's Mausoleum (24 × 20 mm.). ½ d., 1 d. Mosque of the Golden Dome, Samarra (24 × 21 mm.). VERT. 50 f., 75 f. as Type **22**, but larger (21 × 24 mm.). 100 f., 200 f. Oil Wells (20 × 22 mm.).

26. King Faisal II. 27.

**1942.**

| No. | Type | Description | Mint | Used |
|---|---|---|---|---|
| 255 | 26 | 1 f. brown and violet | 35 | 35 |
| 256 | | 2 f. brown and blue | 35 | 35 |
| 257 | | 3 f. brown and green | 35 | 35 |
| 258 | | 4 f. sepia and brown | 35 | 35 |
| 259 | | 5 f. brown and green | 35 | 35 |
| 260 | | 6 f. brown and red | 35 | 35 |
| 261 | | 10 f. brown and pink | 35 | 35 |
| 262 | | 12 f. brown and green | 35 | 35 |

**1948.**

| No. | Type | Description | Mint | Used |
|---|---|---|---|---|
| 271 | 27 | 1 f. blue | 30 | 10 |
| 272 | | 2 f. brown | 15 | 10 |
| 273 | | 3 f. green | 15 | 10 |
| 274 | | 3 f. red | 3·50 | 90 |
| 275 | | 4 f. lilac | 15 | 10 |
| 276 | | 5 f. red | 15 | 10 |
| 277 | | 5 f. green | 4·25 | 1·75 |
| 278 | | 6 f. mauve | 1·00 | 10 |
| 279 | | 8 f. brown | 2·50 | 45 |
| 280 | | 10 f. red | 25 | 10 |
| 281 | | 12 f. green | 20 | 10 |
| 282 | | 14 f. green | 1·40 | 10 |
| 283 | | 15 f. black | 4·25 | 85 |
| 284 | | 16 f. red | 65 | 25 |
| 285 | | 20 f. blue | 45 | 10 |
| 286 | | 25 f. purple | 50 | 10 |
| 287 | | 28 f. blue | 85 | 25 |
| 288 | | 30 f. orange | 50 | 10 |
| 289 | | 40 f. brown | 1·25 | 45 |
| 290 | | 50 f. blue | 4·25 | 85 |
| 291 | | 60 f. blue | 85 | 45 |
| 292 | | 75 f. mauve | 85 | 45 |
| 293 | | 100 f. green | 3·50 | 85 |
| 294 | | 200 f. orange | 2·75 | 85 |
| 295 | | ½ d. blue | 7·25 | 2·75 |
| 296 | | 1 d. green | 24·00 | 10·00 |

The 50 f. to 1 d. are larger (22½ × 27½ mm).

29. Vickers Viking "Al Mahfoutha" over Basrah Aerodrome.

31. King Faisal I and Equestrian Statue.

**1949.** Air.

| No. | Type | Description | Mint | Used |
|---|---|---|---|---|
| 330 | 29 | 3 f. green | 20 | 20 |
| 331 | – | 4 f. purple | 20 | 20 |
| 332 | – | 5 f. brown | 20 | 20 |
| 333 | 29 | 10 f. red | 2·50 | 85 |
| 334 | – | 20 f. blue | 85 | 45 |
| 335 | – | 35 f. orange | 75 | 45 |
| 336 | – | 50 f. green | 1·25 | 70 |
| 337 | – | 100 f. violet | 3·25 | 1·40 |

DESIGNS—As Type **29**: 4, 20 f. "Al Mahfoutha" over Kut Barrage; 5, 35 f. "Al Mahfoutha" over Faisal II Bridge. 31 × 22½ mm: 50, 100 f. "Al Mahfoutha" over Dhiyala Railway Bridge.

**1949.** 75th Anniversary of U.P.U.

| No. | Type | Description | Mint | Used |
|---|---|---|---|---|
| 339. | – | 20 f. blue | 1·75 | 1·25 |
| 340. | 31. | 40 f. orange | 2·50 | 1·25 |
| 341. | – | 50 f. violet | 5·50 | 4·50 |

DESIGNS: 20 f. King Ghazi and mounted postman. 50 f. King Faisal II, globe and wreath.

32. King Faisal II. 33. (35.)

**1953.** Coronation of King Faisal II.

| No. | Type | Description | Mint | Used |
|---|---|---|---|---|
| 342 | 32 | 3 f. red | 85 | 85 |
| 343 | | 14 f. brown | 1·75 | 85 |
| 344 | | 28 f. blue | 4·75 | 1·25 |

**1954.**

| No. | Type | Description | Mint | Used |
|---|---|---|---|---|
| 346. | 33. | 1 f. blue | 35 | 15 |
| 347. | | 2 f. brown | 15 | 10 |
| 348. | | 3 f. lake | 15 | 10 |
| 349. | | 4 f. violet | 15 | 10 |
| 350. | | 5 f. green | 20 | 10 |
| 351. | | 6 f. mauve | 20 | 10 |
| 352. | | 8 f. brown | 20 | 10 |
| 353. | | 10 f. blue | 20 | 10 |
| 354. | | 15 f. black | 1·10 | 75 |
| 355. | | 16 f. red | 1·75 | 1·50 |
| 356. | | 20 f. olive | 85 | 20 |
| 357. | | 25 f. purple | 85 | 10 |
| 358. | | 30 f. red | 85 | 10 |
| 359. | | 40 f. brown | 90 | 35 |
| 360. | | 50 f. blue | 1·25 | 50 |
| 361. | | 75 f. mauve | 2·10 | 60 |
| 362. | | 100 f. olive | 3·75 | 60 |
| 363. | | 200 f. salmon | 6·25 | 1·25 |

The 50 f. to 200 f. are larger (22 × 28 mm.)

**1955.** Abrogation of Anglo-Iraqi Treaty. Optd. with T **35.**

| No. | Type | Description | Mint | Used |
|---|---|---|---|---|
| 380. | 33. | 3 f. lake | 80 | 35 |
| 381. | | 10 f. blue | 80 | 35 |
| 382. | 27. | 28 f. blue | 1·25 | 60 |

36. King Faisal II.

**1955.** 6th Arab Engineers' Conference, Baghdad.

| | | | | |
|---|---|---|---|---|
| 383 | 36 | 3 f. red | 40 | 25 |
| 384 | | 10 f. blue | 95 | 45 |
| 385 | | 28 f. blue | 1·40 | 85 |

**37.** King Faisal II and Globe.

**1956.** 3rd Arab Postal Union Conference, Baghdad.

| | | | | |
|---|---|---|---|---|
| 386 | 37 | 3 f. red | 85 | 45 |
| 387 | | 10 f. blue | 90 | 45 |
| 388 | | 28 f. blue | 1·25 | 85 |

**38.** King Faisal II and Power Loom. **39.** King Faisal II and Exhibition Emblem.

**1957.** Development Week.

| | | | | |
|---|---|---|---|---|
| 389. | 38. | 1 f. blue and buff | 30 | 20 |
| 390. | – | 3 f. multicoloured | 35 | 20 |
| 391. | – | 5 f. multicoloured | 30 | 25 |
| 392. | – | 10 f. multicoloured | 55 | 25 |
| 393. | – | 40 f. multicoloured | 1·25 | 85 |

DESIGNS: 3 f. Irrigation dam. 5 f. Residential road, Baghdad. 10 f. Cement kiln. 40 f. Tigris Bridge.

**1957.** Agricultural and Industrial Exn., Baghdad.

| | | | | |
|---|---|---|---|---|
| 394. | 39. | 10 f. brown and cream | 60 | 50 |

C
١٩٥٧
(40.)

**1957.** Silver Jubilee of Iraqi Red Crescent Society. No. 388 optd. with T 40.

| | | | | |
|---|---|---|---|---|
| 395. | 37. | 28 f. blue | 3·00 | 1·25 |

**41.** King Faisal II. **42.** King Faisal II and Tanks.

**1957.**

| | | | | |
|---|---|---|---|---|
| 396 | 41 | 1 f. blue | 25 | 35 |
| 397 | | 2 f. brown | 25 | 35 |
| 398 | | 3 f. red | 25 | 35 |
| 399 | | 4 f. violet | 25 | 35 |
| 400 | | 5 f. green | 50 | 50 |
| 401 | | 6 f. red | 50 | 50 |
| 402 | | 8 f. brown | 1·00 | 75 |
| 403 | | 10 f. blue | 75 | 70 |

**1958.** Army Day.

| | | | | |
|---|---|---|---|---|
| 411. | 42. | 8 f. grey and green | 60 | 60 |
| 412. | – | 10 f. black and brown | 75 | 75 |
| 413. | – | 20 f. brown and blue | 75 | 75 |
| 414. | – | 30 f. violet and red | 1·25 | 85 |

DESIGNS—As T 42: King Faisal II and; 10 f. Platoon marching; 20 f. Mobile artillery unit and De Havilland D.H.112 Venom jet fighters. 22½ × 27½ mm: 30 f. King Faisal II (full-length portrait).

**1958.** Development Week. As T 38 inscr "1958".

| | | | |
|---|---|---|---|
| 415. | 3 f. green, drab and violet | 25 | 25 |
| 416. | 5 f. multicoloured | 35 | 35 |
| 417. | 10 f. multicoloured | 1·10 | 65 |

DESIGNS—VERT. 3 f. Sugar beet and refining plant. HORIZ. 5 f. Building and pastoral scene. 10 f. Irrigation dam.

الجمهورية العراقية
المؤتمر الرابع للمحامين العرب
بغداد ١٩٥٨

الجمهورية العراقية 10 FILS ١٠ فلوس

(43. "Iraqi Republic".) (44.)

**1958.** Optd with T 43. (a) On No. 189.

| | | | |
|---|---|---|---|
| 418 | 1 d. purple | 17·00 | 17·00 |

(b) On T 27.

| | | | |
|---|---|---|---|
| 418a. | 1 f. blue | 21·00 | 7·00 |
| 419. | 12 f. olive | 35 | 20 |
| 420. | 14 f. olive | 35 | 20 |
| 421. | 16 f. red | 6·50 | 2·10 |
| 422. | 28 f. blue | 35 | 35 |
| 423. | 60 f. blue | 85 | 1·25 |
| 424. | ½d. blue | 8·25 | 4·25 |
| 425. | 1 d. green | 21·00 | 8·25 |

(c) On T 33.

| | | | |
|---|---|---|---|
| 426. | 1 f. blue | 15 | 10 |
| 427. | 2 f. brown | 15 | 10 |
| 428. | 4 f. violet | 20 | 20 |
| 429. | 5 f. green | 20 | 20 |
| 430. | 6 f. mauve | 20 | 20 |
| 431. | 8 f. brown | 25 | 20 |
| 432. | 10 f. blue | 25 | 20 |
| 433. | 15 f. black | 45 | 20 |
| 434. | 16 f. red | 1·40 | 25 |
| 435. | 20 f. olive | 1·90 | 1·25 |
| 436. | 25 f. purple | 25 | 20 |
| 437. | 30 f. red | 35 | 20 |
| 438. | 40 f. brown | 45 | 35 |
| 439. | 50 f. blue | 5·50 | 3·00 |
| 440. | 75 f. mauve | 1·75 | 85 |
| 441. | 100 f. olive | 4·25 | 85 |
| 442. | 200 f. salmon | 6·75 | 4·25 |

Nos. 439/42 are larger (22 × 28 mm.).

(d) On T 41.

| | | | |
|---|---|---|---|
| 443 | 1 f. blue | 1·75 | 60 |
| 444 | 2 f. brown | 20 | 20 |
| 445 | 3 f. red | 20 | 20 |
| 446 | 4 f. violet | 35 | 20 |
| 447 | 5 f. green | 45 | 20 |
| 448 | 6 f. red | 45 | 20 |
| 449 | 8 f. brown | 45 | 20 |
| 450 | 10 f. blue | 45 | 20 |
| 451 | 20 f. green | 45 | 20 |
| 452 | 25 f. purple | 75 | 45 |
| 453 | 30 f. red | 65 | 45 |
| 454 | 40 f. brown | 2·50 | 1·25 |
| 455 | 50 f. purple | 1·25 | 85 |
| 456 | 75 f. green | 1·25 | 85 |
| 457 | 100 f. orange | 1·50 | 85 |
| 458 | 200 f. blue | 7·00 | 1·25 |

Nos. 455/8 are larger (22½ × 27½ mm).

**1958.** Arab Lawyers Conf., Baghdad. Surch. with T 44.

| | | | | |
|---|---|---|---|---|
| 506. | 36. | 10 f. on 28 f. blue | 1·25 | 85 |

**45.** Republican Soldier and Flag. **45a.** Orange Tree.

**1959.** Army Day.

| | | | | |
|---|---|---|---|---|
| 507. | 45. | 3 f. blue | 35 | 25 |
| 508. | | 10 f. olive | 50 | 40 |
| 509. | | 40 f. violet | 1·25 | 1·00 |

**1959.** Afforestation Day.

| | | | | |
|---|---|---|---|---|
| 510. | 45a. | 10 f. orange and green | 45 | 20 |

الجمهورية العراقية
يوم الطفل العالمي
١ حزيران ١٩٥٩
10 FILS ١٠ فلوس

(46.)

**1959.** Int. Children's Day. Surch. with T 46.

| | | | | |
|---|---|---|---|---|
| 511. | 37. | 10 f. on 28 f. blue | 95 | 50 |

**47.** Worker and Buildings. **48.** Harvesters.

**1959.** 1st Anniv. of Revolution. Inscr. "14TH JULY 1958".

| | | | | |
|---|---|---|---|---|
| 512. | 47. | 10 f. blue and ochre | 45 | 45 |
| 513. | – | 30 f. green and ochre | 85 | 45 |

DESIGN—HORIZ. 30 f. Revolutionaries brandishing weapons.

**1959.** Agricultural Reform.

| | | | | |
|---|---|---|---|---|
| 514. | 48. | 10 f. black and green | 45 | 25 |

**49.** Republican Emblem.

اسبوع
الصحة والنظافة

(50.)

**1959.**

| | | | | |
|---|---|---|---|---|
| 515. | 49. | 1 f. multicoloured | 15 | 10 |
| 516. | | 2 f. multicoloured | 15 | 10 |
| 517. | | 3 f. multicoloured | 15 | 10 |
| 518. | | 4 f. multicoloured | 15 | 10 |
| 519. | | 5 f. multicoloured | 15 | 10 |
| 520. | | 10 f. multicoloured | 15 | 10 |
| 521. | | 15 f. multicoloured | 45 | 20 |
| 522. | | 20 f. multicoloured | 45 | 20 |
| 523. | | 30 f. multicoloured | 45 | 25 |
| 524. | | 40 f. multicoloured | 70 | 25 |
| 525. | | 50 f. multicoloured | 3·00 | 75 |
| 526. | | 75 f. multicoloured | 85 | 20 |
| 527. | | 100 f. multicoloured | 1·50 | 45 |
| 528. | | 200 f. multicoloured | 2·50 | 45 |
| 529. | | 500 f. multicoloured | 4·25 | 1·90 |
| 530. | | 1 d. multicoloured | 10·50 | 5·50 |

**1959.** "Health and Hygiene". Optd. with T 50.

| | | | | |
|---|---|---|---|---|
| 531. | 49. | 10 f. multicoloured | 65 | 45 |

**51.** Gen. Kassem and Military Parade. **52.** Gen. Kassem.

**1960.** Army Day.

| | | | | |
|---|---|---|---|---|
| 532. | 51. | 10 f. lake and green | 45 | 45 |
| 533. | – | 16 f. red and blue | 70 | 45 |
| 534. | – | 30 f. olive, brown & buff | 70 | 45 |
| 535. | – | 40 f. violet and buff | 1·10 | 65 |
| 536. | – | 60 f. buff, choc. & brown | 1·40 | 85 |

DESIGNS—Gen. Kassem and: HORIZ. 16 f. Infantry on manoeuvres. 60 f. Partisans. VERT. 30 f. Anti-aircraft gun-crew. 40 f. Oilfield guards on parade.

**1960.** Gen. Kassem's Escape from Assassination.

| | | | | |
|---|---|---|---|---|
| 537. | 52. | 10 f. violet | 45 | 25 |
| 538. | | 30 f. green | 85 | 45 |

**53.** Al Rasafi (poet). **54.** Gen. Kassem at Tomb of Unknown Soldier.

**1960.** Al Rasafi Commem. Optd **1960** in English and Arabic.

| | | | | |
|---|---|---|---|---|
| 539 | 53 | 10 l. red | 2·10 | 1·25 |

See also No 732.

**1960.** 2nd Anniv. of Revolution.

| | | | | |
|---|---|---|---|---|
| 540. | – | 6 f. gold, olive & orange | 45 | 45 |
| 541. | 54. | 10 f. orge., grn. & blue | 45 | 45 |
| 542. | | 16 f. orange, vio. & blue | 65 | 65 |
| 543. | – | 18 f. gold, blue & orge. | 65 | 65 |
| 544. | – | 30 f. gold, brown & orge. | 85 | 85 |
| 545. | 54. | 60 f. orge., sep. & blue | 1·75 | 1·25 |

DESIGN—VERT. 6 f., 18 f., 30 f. Symbol of Republic.

**55.** Gen. Kassem, Flag and Troops. **56.** Gen. Kassem with Children.

**1961.** Army Day.

| | | | | |
|---|---|---|---|---|
| 546. | 55. | 3 f. multicoloured | 20 | 15 |
| 547. | | 6 f. multicoloured | 20 | 15 |
| 548. | | 10 f. multicoloured | 45 | 15 |
| 549. | – | 20 f. black, yell. & green | 45 | 40 |
| 550. | – | 30 f. blk., yell. and brn. | 45 | 40 |
| 551. | – | 40 f. black, yell. & blue | 85 | 55 |

DESIGN: 20 f., 30 f., 40 f. Kassem and triumphal arch.

**1961.** World Children's Day. Main design brown; background colours given.

| | | | | |
|---|---|---|---|---|
| 558. | 56. | 3 f. yellow | 55 | 40 |
| 559. | | 6 f. blue | 75 | 40 |
| 560. | | 10 f. pink | 1·00 | 40 |
| 561. | | 30 f. lemon | 1·00 | 40 |
| 562. | | 50 f. green | 1·75 | 40 |

**57.** Gen. Kassem saluting. **58.** Gen. Kassem and Army Emblem.

**1961.** 3rd Anniv. of Revolution.

| | | | | |
|---|---|---|---|---|
| 563. | – | 1 f. multicoloured | 15 | 10 |
| 564. | – | 3 f. multicoloured | 15 | 10 |
| 565. | 57. | 5 f. multicoloured | 15 | 10 |
| 566. | – | 6 f. multicoloured | 15 | 10 |
| 567. | – | 10 f. multicoloured | 25 | 20 |
| 568. | 57. | 30 f. multicoloured | 45 | 35 |
| 569. | | 40 f. multicoloured | 65 | 45 |
| 570. | – | 50 f. multicoloured | 1·25 | 90 |
| 571. | – | 100 f. multicoloured | 4·00 | 2·10 |

DESIGN: 1, 3, 6, 10, 50, 100 f. Gen. Kassem and Iraqi flag.

**1962.** Army Day.

| | | | | |
|---|---|---|---|---|
| 572. | – | 1 f. multicoloured | 15 | 10 |
| 573. | – | 3 f. multicoloured | 15 | 10 |
| 574. | – | 6 f. multicoloured | 20 | 10 |
| 575. | 58. | 10 f. black, gold & lilac | 40 | 20 |
| 576. | | 30 f. blk., gold & orange | 75 | 45 |
| 577. | | 50 f. blk., gold & green | 1·25 | 85 |

DESIGN—VERT: 1, 3, 6 f. Gen. Kassem saluting and part of speech.

مؤتمر
العالم الاسلامي
بغداد
١٣٨١هـ-١٩٦٢م

(59.) **60.** Gen. Kassem, Flag and Handclasp.

**1962.** 5th Islamic Congress. Optd with T 59.

| | | | | |
|---|---|---|---|---|
| 578 | 49 | 3 f. multicoloured | 25 | 25 |
| 579 | | 10 f. multicoloured | 25 | 25 |
| 580 | | 30 f. multicoloured | 65 | 60 |

**1962.** 4th Anniv. of Revolution. Flag in green and gold.

| | | | | |
|---|---|---|---|---|
| 581. | 60. | 1 f. orange and sepia | 10 | 10 |
| 582. | | 3 f. green and sepia | 10 | 10 |
| 583. | | 6 f. brown and black | 10 | 10 |
| 584. | | 10 f. lilac and sepia | 35 | 35 |
| 585. | | 30 f. red and sepia | 50 | 40 |
| 586. | | 50 f. grey and sepia | 1·00 | 70 |

**61.** Fanfare. **62.** Republican Emblem.

**1962.** Millenary of Baghdad. Multicoloured.

| | | | |
|---|---|---|---|
| 603. | 3 f. Type 61 | 15 | 15 |
| 604. | 6 f. Al Kindi (philosopher) | 25 | 15 |
| 605. | 10 f. Map of old "Round City" of Baghdad | 45 | 20 |
| 606. | 40 f. Gen. Kassem and flag | 1·25 | 85 |

**1962.** Aerogramme Stamps.

| | | | | |
|---|---|---|---|---|
| 607. | 62. | 14 f. black and green | 85 | 50 |
| 608. | | 35 f. black and red | 1·25 | 75 |

Nos. 607/8 were originally issued only attached to aerogramme forms covering the old imprinted King Faisal II stamps, but later appeared in sheets.

**63.** Campaign Emblem. **64.** Gen. Kassem and Tanks.

**1962.** Malaria Eradication.

| | | | | |
|---|---|---|---|---|
| 609. | 63. | 3 f. multicoloured | 20 | 20 |
| 610. | | 10 f. multicoloured | 50 | 20 |
| 611. | | 40 f. multicoloured | 85 | 50 |

**1963.** Army Day.

612. 64. 3 f. black and yellow .. 10 10
613. 5 f. sepia and purple .. 10 10
614. 6 f. black and green .. 10 10
615. 10 f. black and blue .. 25 20
616. 10 f. black and pink .. 25 20
617 20 f. black and blue .. 50 35
618. 40 f. black and mauve 85 45
619. 50 f. sepia and blue .. 1·25 70

65. Gufas on the Tigris.

66. Shepherd with Sheep.

**1963.**

620 65 1 f. green .. .. 25 15
621 – 2 f. violet .. .. 25 15
622 65 3 f. black .. .. 30 15
623 – 4 f. black and yellow .. 30 15
624 – 5 f. purple and green .. 40 15
625 – 10 f. red .. .. 65 20
626 – 15 f. brown and yellow 1·00 20
627 – 20 f. violet .. .. 1·25 20
628 – 30 f. orange .. .. 70 25
629 – 40 f. green .. .. 1·40 15
630 – 50 f. brown .. .. 5·25 45
631 – 75 f. black and green .. 1·50 25
632 – 100 f. purple .. .. 2·00 25
633 – 200 f. brown .. .. 3·00 35
634 – 500 f. blue .. .. 6·75 1·75
635 – 1 d. purple .. .. 10·00 3·25

DESIGNS: 2 f., 500 f. Spiral tower of Samarra. 4 f., 15 f. Sumerian Harp. 5 f., 75 f. Republican emblem. 10 f., 50 f. Lion of Babylon. 20 f., 40 f. Koranic school of Abbasid period. 30 f., 200 f. Mosque and minarets. 100 f., 1 d. Winged bull of Kharsabad.

**1963.** Freedom from Hunger.

636. 66. 3 f. black and green .. 35 15
637. – 10 f. mauve and brown 45 25
638. – 20 f. brown and blue .. 95 45

DESIGNS: 10 f. Harvester. 20 f. Trees.

67. Centenary Emblem.

68. Helmet, Rifle and Flag.

**1963.** Red Cross Centenary.

640. 67. 3 f. violet and red .. 25 20
641. 10 f. blue and red .. 40 35
642. – 30 f. blue and red .. 45 35

DESIGN—HORIZ. 30 f. Hospital.

**1964.** Army Day.

643. 68. 3 f. sepia, green & blue 20 15
644. 10 f. sepia, green & pink 45 25
645. 30 f. sepia, green & yell. 85 50

69. Revolutionaries and Flag.

**1964.** 1st Anniv. of 14th Ramadan Revolution. Flag in red, green and black.

646. 69. 10 f. violet .. .. 45 25
647. 30 f. brown .. .. 85 45

70. Shamash (Sun-God) and Hammurabi.

71. Soldier raising Flag on Map of Iraq.

**1964.** 15th Anniv. of Declaration of Human Rights.

649. 70. 6 f. olive and purple .. 45 35
650. – 10 f. violet and orange .. 85 40
651. 70. 30 f. green and blue .. 1·25 50

DESIGN: 10 f. U.N. Emblem and Scales of Justice.

**1964.** 6th Anniv. of Revolution.

652. – 3 f. orange, grey & black 15 20
653. 71. 10 f. red, black & green 25 20
654. 20 f. red, black & green 45 20
655. – 30 f. orange, grey & black 85 50

DESIGNS—HORIZ. 3. f., 30 f. Soldier "protecting" people and factories with outstretched arm.

72. Soldier, Civilians and Star Emblem.

73. Musician.

**1964.** 1st Anniv of Nov 18th Revolution.

656 72 5 f. orange and brown .. 35 20
657 10 f. orange and blue .. 45 20
658 50 f. orange and violet 95 65

**1964.** Int. Arab Music Conf., Baghdad.

659. 73. 3 f. multicoloured .. 40 25
660. 10 f. multicoloured .. 40 25
661. 30 f. multicoloured .. 1·10 55

74. Conference Emblem and Map.

75. A.P.U. Emblem.

**1964.** 9th Arab Engineer's Conf., Baghdad.

662. 74. 10 f. green and mauve .. 50 35

**1964.** 10th Anniv. of Arab Postal Union's Permanent Office.

663. 75. 3 f. blue and red .. 20 20
664. 10 f. slate and purple .. 30 20
665. 30 f. blue and orange .. 85 45

76. Soldier, Civilians and Flag.

77. Cogwheel and Factory.

**1965.** Army Day.

666. 76. 5 f. multicoloured .. 25 20
667. 15 f. multicoloured .. 30 20
668. 30 f. multicoloured .. 85 45

**1965.** 1st Arab Ministers of Labour Conf. Baghdad.

670. 77. 10 f. multicoloured .. 45 25

78. Oil Tanker.

79. Armed Soldier with Flag.

**1965.** Inauguration of Deep Sea Terminal for Tankers.

671 78 10 f. multicoloured .. 65 40

**1965.** 2nd Anniv of 14th Ramadan Revolution.

672 79 10 f. multicoloured .. 45 25

80. Tree.

81. Federation Emblem.

**1965.** Tree Week.

673. 80. 6 f. multicoloured .. 20 10
674. 20 f. multicoloured .. 65 35

**1965.** Arab Insurance Federation. Sun in gold.

675. 81. 3 f. ultram. and blue .. 25 20
676. 10 f. black and grey .. 25 20
677. 30 f. red and pink .. 80 45

82. Dagger of Deir Yassin, Palestine.

83. "Threat of Disease".

**1965.** Deir Yassin Massacre.

678. 82. 10 f. drab and black .. 35 25
679. 20 f. brown and blue .. 65 45

**1965.** World Health Day.

680. 83. 3 f. multicoloured .. 35 20
681. 10 f. multicoloured .. 50 25
682. 20 f. multicoloured .. 1·10 65

84. I.T.U. Emblem and Symbols.

**1965.** Cent. of I.T.U.

683. 84. 10 f. multicoloured .. 45 20
684. 20 f. multicoloured .. 1·10 45

85. Flag and Map.

86. Revolutionary and Flames.

**1965.** 1st Anniv. of Iraq U.A.R. Pact.

686. 85. 10 f. multicoloured .. 35 20

**1965.** Reconstitution of Algiers University Library. As T **294** of Egypt.

687. 5 f. red, green and black .. 20 20
688. 10 f. green, red and black .. 30 20

**1965.** 45th Anniv. of 1920 Rebellion.

689. 86. 5 f. multicoloured .. 30 20
690. 10 f. multicoloured .. 30 20

87. Mosque.

**1965.** Mohammed's Birthday.

691. 87. 10 f. multicoloured .. 50 50

88. Factory and Ear of Wheat.

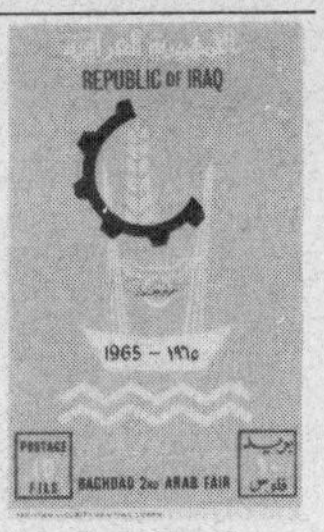

90. Fair Emblem.

89. I.C.Y. Emblem.

**1965.** 7th Anniv. of 14 July Revolution.

693. 88. 10 f. multicoloured .. 35 35

**1965.** Air. Int Co-operation Year.

694 89 5 f. black and brown .. 50 50
695 10 f. brown and green .. 75 60
696 30 f. black and blue .. 2·10 75

**1965.** Baghdad Fair.

697. 90. 10 f. multicoloured .. 25 20

91. Pres. Arif (photo. by Studio Jean).

**1965.** 2nd Anniv. of 18 November Revolution.

698. 91. 5 f. blue and orange .. 20 20
699. 10 f. sepia and blue .. 45 25
700. 50 f. blue and mauve .. 1·50 1·00

92. Census Graph.

**1965.** National Census.

701 92 3 f. black and purple .. 25 20
702 5 f. red and brown .. 25 20
703 15 f. bistre and blue .. 85 45

93. Hawker Siddeley Trident 1E Airliner.

**1965.** Air. Inauguration of Hawker Siddeley Trident 1E Aircraft by Iraqi Airways.

704. 93. 5 f. multicoloured .. 40 30
705. 10 f. multicoloured .. 50 35
706. 40 f. multicoloured .. 1·50 85

94. Date Palms.

95. Army Memorial.

**1965.** 2nd F.A.O. Dates Conf., Baghdad.

707. 94. 3 f. multicoloured .. 25 20
708. 10 f. multicoloured .. 55 20
709. 15 f. multicoloured .. 1·10 70

**1966.** 45th Anniv. of Army Day.

710. 95. 2 f. multicoloured .. 35 25
711. 5 f. multicoloured .. 35 25
712. 40 f. multicoloured .. 1·00 65

96. "Eagle" and Flag. 97. Footballers.

**1966.** 3rd Anniv. of 14th Ramadan Revolution.
713. **96.** 5 f. multicoloured .. 20 20
714. 10 f. multicoloured .. 25 20

**1966.** Arab Publicity Week. As T **309** of Egypt.
715. 5 f. green, brown & orange 25 25
716. 15 f. blue, purple and olive 40 25

**1966.** Arab Football Cup, Baghdad. Mult.
717. 2 f. Type **97** .. .. 25 25
718. 5 f. Goalkeeper with ball .. 25 25
719. 15 f. Type **97** .. .. 85 45

99. Excavator. 100. Queen Nefertari.

**1966.** Labour Day.
721. **99.** 15 f. multicoloured .. 25 15
722. 25 f. blk., silver & red .. 35 20

**1966.** Nubian Monuments Preservation.
723. **100.** 5 f. yell., black & olive 60 35
724. 15 f. yellow, brn. & blue 85 35
725. – 40 f. brown, chest. & red 1·50 1·00
DESIGN—HORIZ. (41 × 32 mm.): 40 f. Rock temples, Abu Simbel.

101. President Arif.

**1966.** 8th Anniv. of 14 July Revolution.
726. **101.** 5 f. multicoloured .. 25 20
727. 15 f. multicoloured .. 45 20
728. 50 f. multicoloured .. 1·25 70

102.

**1966.** Mohammed's Birthday.
729. **102.** 5 f. multicoloured .. 20 20
730. 15 f. multicoloured .. 25 20
731. 30 f. multicoloured .. 1·00 90

**1966.** As No. 539 but without opt "1960".
732 **53** 10 f. red .. .. 4·00 5·00

103. Iraqi Museum, Statue and Window. 104. Revolutionaries.

**1966.** Inauguration of Iraqi Museum, Baghdad. Multicoloured.
733. 15 f. Type **103** .. .. 40 40
734. 50 f. Gold head-dress .. 1·10 65
735. 80 f. Sumerian head (vert.) 1·90 1·10

**1966.** 3rd Anniv. of 18 November Revolution.
736. **104.** 15 f. multicoloured .. 45 25
737. 25 f. multicoloured .. 85 45

105. "Magic Carpet". 106. U.N.E.S.C.O. Emblem.

**1966.** Air. Meeting of Arab Int. Tourist Union, Baghdad. Multicoloured.
738 2 f. White stork emblem (27½ × 39 mm) .. .. 20 20
739 5 f. Type **105** .. .. 20 20
740 15 f. As 2 f. .. .. 95 25
741 50 f. Type **105** .. .. 1·75 70

**1966.** 20th Anniv. of U.N.E.S.C.O.
742. **106.** 5 f. brown, blk. & bl. 20 10
743. 15 f. green, black & red 45 25

107. Soldier and Rocket-launchers.

**1967.** Army Day.
744. **107.** 15 f. ochre, brn. & yell. 35 20
745. 20 f. ochre, brn. & lilac 50 25

108. Oil Refinery.

**1967.** 6th Arab Petroleum Congress, Baghdad. Multicoloured.
747. 5 f. Congress emblem (vert.) 20 20
748. 15 f. Type **108** .. .. 30 20
749. 40 f. Congress emblem (vert.) 55 45
750. 50 f. Type **108** .. .. 1·25 75

109. "Spider's Web" Emblem. 110. Worker holding Cogwheel.

**1967.** Hajeer Year (1967).
751. **109.** 5 f. multicoloured .. 25 15
752. 15 f. multicoloured .. 30 20

**1967.** Labour Day.
753. **110.** 10 f. multicoloured. .. 25 15
754. 15 f. multicoloured .. 30 15

111.

**1967.** Mohammed's Birthday.
755. **111.** 5 f. multicoloured .. 25 20
756. 15 f. multicoloured .. 50 25

112. Flag and Hands with Clubs.

**1967.** 47th Anniv. of 1920 Rebellion.
757. **112.** 5 f. multicoloured .. 20 10
758. 15 f. multicoloured .. 30 15

113. Um Qasr Port. 114. Costume.

**1967.** 9th Anniv. of 14 July Revolution and Inaug. of Um Qasr Port. Multicoloured.
759. 5 f. Type **113** .. .. 25 15
760. 10 f. Freighter at quayside 50 25
761. 15 f. As 10 f. .. .. 75 25
762. 40 f. Type **113** .. .. 1·25 70

**1967.** Iraqi Costumes. Designs showing different costumes.
765. **114.** 2 f. mult. (postage) .. 25 20
766. – 5 f. multicoloured .. 25 15
767. – 10 f. multicoloured .. 35 20
768. – 15 f. multicoloured .. 75 45
769. – 20 f. multicoloured .. 95 45
770. – 25 f. multicoloured .. 1·00 50
771. – 30 f. multicoloured .. 1·25 50
772. – 40 f. multicoloured (air) 85 65
773. – 50 f. multicoloured .. 1·50 85
774. – 80 f. multicoloured .. 1·90 1·00

115. Pres. Arif and Map.

**1967.** 4th Anniv. of November 18 Revolution. Multicoloured.
775. 5 f. President Arif .. 30 15
776. 15 f. Type **115** .. .. 45 20

116. Ziggurat of Ur.

**1967.** Int. Tourist Year. Multicoloured.
777. 2 f. Type **116** (postage) .. 25 15
778. 5 f. Statues of Nimroud .. 25 15
779. 10 f. Babylon (arch) .. 30 15
780. 15 f. Minaret of Mosul .. 35 15
781. 25 f. Arch of Ctesiphon .. 45 15
782. 50 f. Statue, Temple of Hatra (air) .. .. 1·75 25
783. 80 f. Spiral Minaret of Samarra .. .. .. 2·10 45
784. 100 f. Adam's Tree .. 1·75 60
785. 200 f. Aladdin ("Aladdin's Cave") .. .. 4·25 2·10
786. 500 f. Golden Mosque of Kadhimain .. .. 13·50 7·50
Nos. 780 and 782/785 are vert.

117. Guide Emblem and Saluting Hand.

**1967.** Iraqi Scouts and Guides. Multicoloured.
787. 2 f. Type **117** .. .. 40 35
788. 5 f. Guides by camp-fire .. 50 35
789. 10 f. Scout emblem and saluting hand .. .. 60 40
790. 15 f. Scouts setting up camp 1·00 45

118. Soldiers Drilling.

**1968.** Army Day.
792. **118.** 5 f. brown, grn. & blue 30 20
793. 15 f. indigo, olive & bl. 55 25

119. White-cheeked Bulbul.

**1968.** Iraqi Birds. Multicoloured.
794. 5 f. Type **119** .. .. 50 20
795. 10 f. Hoopoe .. .. 65 20
796. 15 f. Jay .. .. .. 95 25
797. 25 f. Peregrine Falcon .. 1·50 35
798. 30 f. White Stork .. .. 1·90 35
799. 40 f. Black Partridge .. 2·25 55
800. 50 f. Marbled Teal .. 2·75 75

120. Battle Scene.

**1968.** 5th Anniv. of 14th Ramadan Revolution.
801. **120.** 15 f. orange, blk. & blue 50 30

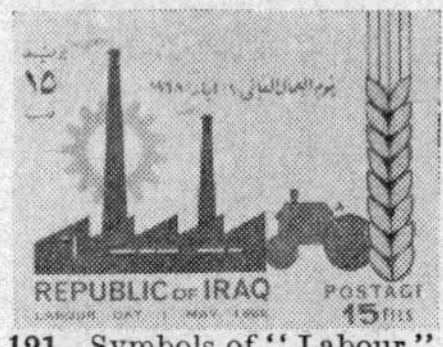

121. Symbols of "Labour".

**1968.** Labour Day.
802. **121.** 15 f. multicoloured .. 30 20
803. 25 f. multicoloured .. 50 25

122. Football. 123. Soldier with Iraqi Flag.

**1968.** 23rd International Military Sports Council Football Championship. Mult.
804. 2 f. Type **122** .. .. 30 20
805. 5 f. Goalkeeper in mid air 30 20
806. 15 f. Type **122** .. .. 55 20
807. 25 f. As 5 f. .. .. 75 45

**1968.** 10th Anniv. of 14 July Revolution.
809. **123.** 15 f. multicoloured .. 30 15

124. Anniversary and W.H.O. Emblems.

**1968.** 20th Anniv. of W.H.O.
810. – 5 f. multicoloured .. 25 20
811. – 10 f. multicoloured .. 25 20
812. **124.** 15 f. red, blue & black 30 25
813. 25 f. red, green and blk. 55 30
DESIGN—VERT. 5, 10 f. Combined anniversary and W.H.O. emblems.

125. Human Rights Emblem. 126. Mother and children.

**1968.** Human Rights Year.
814. **125.** 10 f. red, yellow and blue 25 20
815. 25 f. red, yellow & grn. 30 20

**1968.** U.N.I.C.E.F. Commem.
817. **126.** 15 f. multicoloured .. 25 20
818. 25 f. multicoloured .. 40 30

127. Army Tanks.

**1969.** Army Day.
820. **127.** 25 f. multicoloured .. 1·50 75

128. Agricultural Scene.

**1969.** 6th Anniv. of 14th Ramadan Revolution.
821. **128.** 15 f. multicoloured .. 45 25

**129.** Mosque and Worshippers.

**1969.** Hajeer Year.

822. **129.** 15 f. multicoloured .. 45 25

**130.** Emblem of Iraqi Veterinary Medical Association.

**1969.** 1st Arab Veterinary Union Conf. Baghdad.

823. **130.** 10 f. multicoloured .. 45 25
824. 15 f. multicoloured .. 60 35

**131.** "Barbus grypus".

**1969.** Multicoloured.

(a) Fishes.

825. 2 f. Type **131** (postage) .. 40 35
826. 3 f. "Barbus puntius" .. 40 35
827. 10 f. "Pampus argenteus" 50 35
828. 100 f. "Barbus esocinus" .. 2·10 1·25

(b) Fauna.

829. 2 f. Striped hyena (air) 20 15
830. 3 f. Leopard .. 20 15
831. 5 f. Mountain gazelle .. 20 15
832. 10 f. Head of Arab horse 75 50
833. 200 f. Arab horse .. 3·75 2·25

**132.** Kaaba, Mecca.

**1969.** Mohammed's Birthday.

834. **132.** 15 f. multicoloured .. 45 20

**133.** I.L.O. Emblem.  **134.** Weightlifting.

**1969.** 50th Anniv. of I.L.O.

835. **133.** 5 f. yell., blue & black 15 10
836. 15 f. yell., green & black 20 10
837. 50 f. yellow, red & black 1·10 85

**1969.** Olympic Games, Mexico (1968). Multicoloured.

839 3 f. Type **134** .. .. 50 35
840 5 f. High jumping .. 50 35
841 10 f. As Type **134** .. 50 35
842 35 f. As 5 f. .. .. 1·00 70

**135.** Arms of Iraq and "Industry." **136.** Rebuilding Roads.

**1969.** 11th Anniv. of 14 July Revolution.

844 **135.** 10 f. multicoloured 20 20
845. 15 f. multicoloured .. 25 20

**1969.** Anniv. of 17 July Revolution and Inaug. of Baghdad Int. Airport. Mult.

846. 10 f. Type **136** .. .. 20 20
847. 15 f. Type **136** .. .. 35 25
848. 20 f. Airport building .. 70 45
849. 200 f. President Bakr (vert.) 4·25 2·10

**137.** Ear of Wheat and Fair Emblem. **139.** Radio Beacon and Outline of Palestine.

**138.** Floating Crane " Antara ".

**1969.** 6th Int. Baghdad Fair.

850. **137.** 10 f. brown, gold & grn. 35 25
851. 15 f. red, gold and blue 50 30

**1969.** 50th Anniv of Port of Basra. Mult.

852 15 f. Type **138** .. .. 35 25
853 20 f. Harbour tender "Al-Walid" .. .. 45 25
854 30 f. Pilot boat "Al-Rashid" .. .. 75 25
855 35 f. Dredger "Hillah" .. 1·10 45
856 50 f. Survey ship "Al-Fao" 1·75 75

**1969.** 10th Anniv. of Iraqi News Agency.

857. **139.** 15 f. multicoloured .. 35 25
858. 50 f. multicoloured .. 75 45

**140.** Emblem, Book and Hands. **141.** Ross and Keith Smith's Vickers Vimy Biplane.

**1969.** Campaign Against Illiteracy.

859. **140.** 15 f. multicoloured .. 25 15
860. 20 f. multicoloured .. 40 30

**1969.** Air. 50th Anniv of 1st England–Australia Flight.

861 **141** 15 f. multicoloured .. 1·75 85
862 35 f. multicoloured .. 2·50 1·75

**142.** Newspaper Headline. **144.** Iraqis supporting Wall.

**143.** Soldier and Map.

**1969.** Cent. of Iraqi Press.

864. **142.** 15 f. blk., orge. & yell. 45 45

**1970.** Army Day.

865. **143.** 15 f. multicoloured .. 45 30
866. 20 f. multicoloured .. 65 55

**1970.** 7th Anniv. of 14th Ramadan Revolution.

867. **144.** 10 f. multicoloured .. 20 20
868. 15 f. multicoloured .. 25 20

عيدنوروز
1970
(145.)

مهرجان الربيع
الموصل
1970
(147.)

**146.** Map of Arab Countries, and Slogans.

**1970.** New Year (" Nawrooz "). Nos. 891/6 optd. with T **145.**

869. 2 f. multicoloured .. .. 25 25
870. 3 f. multicoloured .. .. 25 25
871. 5 f. multicoloured .. .. 25 25
872. 10 f. multicoloured .. 50 25
873. 15 f. multicoloured .. 65 25
874. 50 f. multicoloured .. 1·75 1·10

**1970.** 23rd Anniv. of Al-Baath Party. Mult.

875. 15 f. Type **146** .. .. 25 25
876. 35 f. Type **146** .. .. 45 45
877. 50 f. Iraqis acclaiming Party 1·25 55

**1970.** Mosul Spring Festival. Nos. 891/6 optd. with T **147.**

879. 2 f. multicoloured .. .. 60 60
880. 3 f. multicoloured .. .. 60 60
881. 5 f. multicoloured .. .. 60 60
882. 10 f. multicoloured .. 60 60
883. 15 f. multicoloured .. 80 70
884. 50 f. multicoloured .. 1·25 85

**148.** Iraqis celebrating Labour Day.

**1970.** Labour Day.

885. **148.** 10 f. multicoloured .. 15 15
886. 15 f. multicoloured .. 15 15
887. 35 f. multicoloured .. 1·00 85

**149.** Kaaba, Mecca, Broken Statues and Koran.

**1970.** Mohammed's Birthday.

888. **149.** 15 f. multicoloured .. 25 15
889. 20 f. multicoloured .. 30 25

**150.** Poppies.

1970 ١٩٧٠
عيد الصحافة
(151.)

**1970.** Spring Festival. Flowers. Mult.

891. 2 f. Type **150** .. .. 40 25
892. 3 f. Narcissi .. .. 40 25
893. 5 f. Tulip .. .. 40 25
894. 10 f. Carnations .. .. 45 30
895. 15 f. Roses .. .. 85 45
896. 50 f. As 10 f. .. .. 1·75 1·10

**1970.** Press Day. No. 864 optd. with T **151.**

896a. **142.** 15 f. blk., orge. & yell. 45 45

**152.** Revolutionaries.

**1970.** 50th Anniv. of Revolution of 1920.

897. **152.** 10 f. black and green .. 20 20
898. 15 f. black and gold .. 30 20
899. – 35 f. black and orange 70 35

DESIGN: 35 f. Revolutionary and rising sun.

**153.** Bomb-burst and Broken Chain.

**1970.** 12th Anniv. of 14 July Revolution.

901. **153.** 15 f. multicoloured .. 25 15
902. 20 f. multicoloured .. 30 20

**154.** Hands and Map of Iraq.

**1970.** 2nd Anniv. of 17 July Revolution.

903. **154.** 15 f. multicoloured .. 25 15
904. 25 f. multicoloured .. 45 25

**155.** Pomegranates.

**1970.** Fruits. Multicoloured.

905. 3 f. Type **155** .. .. 35 15
906. 5 f. Grapefruit .. .. 35 15
907. 10 f. Grapes .. .. 35 15
908. 15 f. Oranges .. .. 70 20
909. 35 f. Dates .. .. 1·75 1·50

The Latin inscriptions on Nos. 906/7 are transposed.

**156.** Kaaba, Mecca.

**1970.** Hajeer Year.

910. **156.** 15 f. multicoloured .. 25 15
911. 25 f. multicoloured .. 45 25

الدورة السابعة

970 – ٩٧٠
(157.)

**1970.** 7th Int. Baghdad Fair. Optd. with T **157.**

912. **137.** 10 f. brown, gold & grn. 2·10 1·25
913. 15 f. red, gold & blue .. 2·10 1·25

**158.** Arab League Flag and Map.

**1970.** 25th Anniv of Arab League.

914 **158** 15 f. purple, green & ol 20 15
915 35 f. red, green & grey 45 40

**159.** Euphrates Bridge.

**1970.** Air. National Development. Mult.

916 10 f. Type **159** .. .. 1·25 35
917 15 f. Type **159** .. .. 2·00 50
918 1 d. Pres. Bakr and banknotes (37 × 27 mm) 32·00 14·00

**160.** I.E.Y. Emblem.

**1970.** Int. Education Year.

919. **160.** 5 f. multicoloured .. 20 15
920. 15 f. multicoloured .. 40 25

**161.** Baghdad Hospital and Society Emblem.

**1970.** 50th Anniv. of Iraq Medical Society.

| | | | | |
|---|---|---|---|---|
| 922. | 161. | 15 f. multicoloured .. | 25 | 20 |
| 923. | | 40 f. multicoloured .. | 85 | 50 |

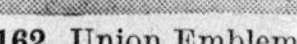

**162.** Union Emblem. **163.** Sugar Beet.

**1970.** Air. 10th Arab Telecommunications Union Conf., Baghdad.

| | | | | |
|---|---|---|---|---|
| 924. | 162. | 15 f. multicoloured .. | 25 | 15 |
| 925. | | 25 f. multicoloured .. | 45 | 35 |

**1970.** 12th Anniv. of Mosul Sugar Refinery. Multicoloured.

| | | | |
|---|---|---|---|
| 926. | 5 f. Type **163** .. .. | 20 | 10 |
| 927. | 15 f. Sugar refinery (horiz.) | 35 | 15 |
| 928. | 30 f. Type **163** .. .. | 1·25 | 60 |

**164.** O.P.E.C. Emblem.

**1970.** 10th Anniv of Organization of Petroleum Exporting Countries (O.P.E.C.).

| | | | | |
|---|---|---|---|---|
| 929 | 164 | 10 f. blue, bistre & pur | 45 | 25 |
| 930 | | 40 f. blue, bistre & grn | 1·50 | 1·00 |

**165.** Soldiers, Tank and Aircraft.

**1971.** 50th Anniv of Army Day.

| | | | | |
|---|---|---|---|---|
| 931 | 165 | 15 f. black, mve & gold | 50 | 20 |
| 932 | – | 40 f. multicoloured .. | 1·50 | 85 |

DESIGN—42×35 mm: 40 f. Soldiers and map of Middle East.

**166.** " Revolutionary Army ".

**1971.** 8th Anniv. of 14th Ramadan Revolution.

| | | | | |
|---|---|---|---|---|
| 934. | 166. | 15 f. multicoloured .. | 30 | 20 |
| 935. | | 40 f. multicoloured .. | 85 | 55 |

**167.** Pilgrims and Web.

**1971.** Hajeer Year.

| | | | | |
|---|---|---|---|---|
| 936. | 167. | 10 f. multicoloured .. | 15 | 10 |
| 937. | | 15 f. multicoloured .. | 35 | 25 |

**168.** Pres. Bakr with Torch.

**1971.** 1st Anniv. of 11th March Manifesto.

| | | | | |
|---|---|---|---|---|
| 938. | 168. | 15 f. multicoloured .. | 60 | 45 |
| 939. | | 100 f. multicoloured .. | 1·90 | 1·60 |

**169.** Boatman in Marshland.

**1971.** Tourism Week. Multicoloured.

| | | | |
|---|---|---|---|
| 940. | 5 f. Type **169** .. .. | 35 | 25 |
| 941. | 10 f. Stork over Baghdad | 55 | 25 |
| 942. | 15 f. Landscape (" Summer Resorts") .. .. | 60 | 35 |
| 943. | 100 f. " Return of Sinbad " | 2·75 | 1·75 |

**170.** Blacksmith taming Serpent.

**1971.** New Year ("Nawrooz").

| | | | | |
|---|---|---|---|---|
| 944 | 170 | 15 f. multicoloured .. | 45 | 25 |
| 945 | | 25 f. multicoloured .. | 55 | 35 |

**1971.** World Meteorological Day. Nos. 780 and 783 optd **W.M. DAY, 1971** in English and Arabic.

| | | | |
|---|---|---|---|
| 946 | 15 f. multicoloured (post) | 2·00 | 85 |
| 947 | 80 f. multicoloured (air) .. | 4·25 | 3·25 |

**172.** Emblem and Workers.

**1971.** 24th Anniv of Al-Baath Party. Mult.

| | | | |
|---|---|---|---|
| 948 | 15 f. Type **172** .. .. | 30 | 30 |
| 949 | 35 f. Type **172** .. .. | 50 | 50 |
| 950 | 250 f. As Type **172** but central portion of design only (42×42 mm) .. | 6·75 | 6·75 |

On No. 950 the circular centre is also perforated.

مهرجان الربيع

1971

(173.)

**174.** Worker and Farm-girl.

**1971.** Mosul Spring Festival. Nos. 765/6 and 770 optd. with T **173**.

| | | | | |
|---|---|---|---|---|
| 951. | 114. | 2 f. multicoloured | 40 | 25 |
| 952. | – | 5 f. multicoloured .. | 40 | 25 |
| 953. | – | 25 f. multicoloured .. | 1·25 | 75 |

**1971.** Labour Day.

| | | | | |
|---|---|---|---|---|
| 954. | 174. | 15 f. multicoloured .. | 35 | 25 |
| 955. | | 40 f. multicoloured .. | 60 | 50 |

**175.** Muslim at Prayer.

**1971.** Mohammed's Birthday.

| | | | | |
|---|---|---|---|---|
| 956. | 175. | 15 f. multicoloured .. | 35 | 25 |
| 957. | | 100 f. multicoloured .. | 1·40 | 1·10 |

**176.** Revolutionaries, and Hands with Broken Chains.

**1971.** 13th Anniv. of 14 July Revolution.

| | | | | |
|---|---|---|---|---|
| 958. | 176. | 25 f. multicoloured .. | 45 | 20 |
| 959. | | 50 f. multicoloured .. | 1·10 | 55 |

**177.** Rising Sun and "Prosperity".

**1971.** 3rd Anniv. of 17 July Revolution.

| | | | | |
|---|---|---|---|---|
| 960. | 177. | 25 f. multicoloured .. | 45 | 20 |
| 961. | | 70 f. multicoloured .. | 1·60 | 85 |

**182.** Bank Emblem.

**1971.** 30th Anniv of Rafidain Bank.

| | | | | |
|---|---|---|---|---|
| 989 | 182 | 10 f. multicoloured .. | 45 | 30 |
| 990 | | 15 f. multicoloured .. | 45 | 30 |
| 991 | | 25 f. multicoloured .. | 45 | 30 |
| 992 | | 65 f. multicoloured .. | 2·10 | 1·10 |
| 993 | | 250 f. multicoloured .. | 10·00 | 10·00 |

Nos. 992/3 are larger, 42×42 mm.

التعداد الزراعي العام

١٩٧١/١٠/١٥

(183.)

**1971.** Agricultural Census. Nos. 905, 908/9 optd. with T **183**.

| | | | |
|---|---|---|---|
| 994. | 3 f. multicoloured .. .. | 1·40 | 1·50 |
| 995. | 15 f. multicoloured .. | 1·40 | 1·50 |
| 996. | 35 f. multicoloured .. | 1·40 | 1·50 |

**184.** Football.

**1971.** 4th Pan-Arab Schoolboy Games, Baghdad. Multicoloured.

| | | | |
|---|---|---|---|
| 997 | 15 f. Type **184** .. .. | 35 | 25 |
| 998 | 25 f. Throwing the discus and running .. .. | 50 | 25 |
| 999 | 35 f. Table tennis .. | 85 | 50 |
| 1000 | 70 f. Gymnastics .. | 1·50 | 1·00 |
| 1001 | 95 f. Volleyball and basketball .. .. | 1·90 | 1·00 |

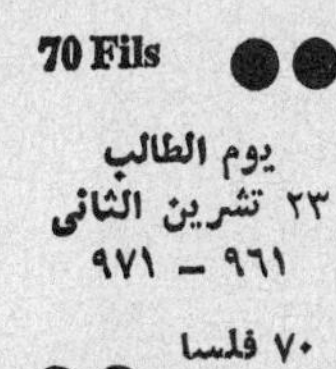

70 Fils ●●

يوم الطالب

٢٣ تشرين الثاني

٩٦١ – ٩٧١

٧٠ فلسا ●●

(185.)

**186.** Society Emblem.

**1971.** Students' Day. Nos. 892/3 surch and 895 optd as T **185**.

| | | | |
|---|---|---|---|
| 1003 | 15 f. multicoloured .. | 1·00 | 1·00 |
| 1004 | 25 f. on 5 f. multicoloured | 1·50 | 1·50 |
| 1005 | 70 f. on 3 f. multicoloured | 3·00 | 3·00 |

**1971.** Air. 20th Anniv. of Iraqi Philatelic Society.

| | | | | |
|---|---|---|---|---|
| 1006. | 186. | 25 f. multicoloured .. | 1·10 | 75 |
| 1007. | | 70 f. multicoloured .. | 1·50 | 1·40 |

**1971.** 25th Anniv of U.N.I.C.E.F. Nos. 817/18 optd **25th Anniversary 971**.

| | | | | |
|---|---|---|---|---|
| 1008. | 126. | 15 f. multicoloured .. | 2·25 | 2·10 |
| 1009. | | 25 f. multicoloured .. | 2·25 | 2·10 |

**188.** Schoolchildren on Zebra Crossing.

**1971.** 2nd Traffic Week.

| | | | | |
|---|---|---|---|---|
| 1010. | 188. | 15 f. multicoloured | 2·50 | 1·60 |
| 1011. | | 25 f. multicoloured .. | 2·50 | 1·60 |

**189.** A.P.U. Emblem. **190.** Racial Equality Year Symbol.

**1971.** 25th Anniv of Founding of Arab Postal Union at Sofar Conference.

| | | | | |
|---|---|---|---|---|
| 1012 | 189 | 25 f. brown, yell & grn | 25 | 15 |
| 1013 | | 70 f. red, yellow & bl | 1·10 | 70 |

**1971.** Racial Equality Year.

| | | | | |
|---|---|---|---|---|
| 1014. | 190. | 25 f. multicoloured | 20 | 20 |
| 1015. | | 70 f. multicoloured | 85 | 75 |

**191.** Soldiers with Flag and Torch. **192.** Workers.

**1972.** Army Day.

| | | | | |
|---|---|---|---|---|
| 1016. | 191. | 25 f. multicoloured .. | 1·10 | 35 |
| 1017. | | 70 f. multicoloured .. | 2·00 | 1·40 |

**1972.** 9th Anniv. of 14th Ramadan Revolution.

| | | | | |
|---|---|---|---|---|
| 1018. | 192. | 25 f. multicoloured .. | 1·40 | 45 |
| 1019. | | 95 f. multicoloured .. | 2·50 | 1·75 |

**193.** Mosque and Crescent.

**1972.** Hajeer Year.

| | | | | |
|---|---|---|---|---|
| 1020. | 193. | 25 f. multicoloured | 25 | 20 |
| 1021. | | 35 f. multicoloured | 65 | 45 |

المؤتمر التاسع للاتحاد الوطني

لطلبة العراق

٢٥ شباط – ٢ آذار / ١٩٧٢

(194.)

**1972.** Air. 9th Iraqi Students' Union Congress. Nos. 916/17 optd. with T **194**.

| | | | | |
|---|---|---|---|---|
| 1022. | 159. | 10 f. multicoloured.. | 1·75 | 1·75 |
| 1023. | | 15 f. multicoloured .. | 1·75 | 1·75 |

**195.** Dove, Olive Branch and Manifesto.

**1972.** 2nd Anniv of 11 March Manifesto.

| | | | | |
|---|---|---|---|---|
| 1024 | 195 | 25 f. blue, lt bl & blk | 55 | 20 |
| 1025 | | 70 f. pur, mve & blk | 2·00 | 1·10 |

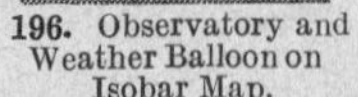

196. Observatory and Weather Balloon on Isobar Map.

197. Cogwheel Emblem.

**1972.** World Meteorological Day.
1026. **196.** 25 f. multicoloured .. 1·25 45
1027. 35 f. multicoloured .. 2·25 1·25

**1972.** Iraqi Chamber of Commerce.
1028. **197.** 25 f. multicoloured .. 35 20
1029. 35 f. multicoloured .. 60 35

198. Oil Rig and Flame.

**1972.** Inaug. of North Rumaila Oilfield.
1030. **198.** 25 f. multicoloured .. 1·00 25
1031. 35 f. multicoloured .. 1·10 85

199. Party Emblem.

**1972.** 25th Anniv. of Al Baath Party. Mult.
1032. 10 f. Type **199** .. .. 30 25
1033. 25 f. Emblem and inscription 50 35
1034. 35 f. Type **199** .. .. 65 45
1035. 70 f. As 25 f. .. .. 1·90 1·60
Sizes—Horiz. 25 f., 70 f. 51 × 27 mm.

200. Mountain Scene.

**1972.** New Year ("Nawrooz").
1036 **200** 25 f. mauve, yell & bl 90 35
1037 70 f. brown, yell & bl 2·10 1·60

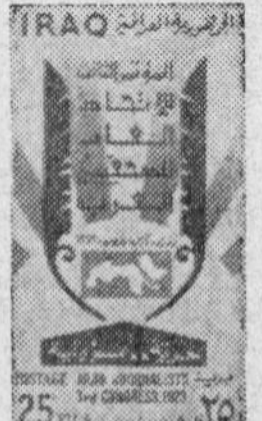

201. Congress "Quills" Emblem.

**1972.** 3rd Arab Journalists Congress.
1038 **201** 25 f. orange, blk & grn 45 35
1039 35 f. blue, black & grn 1·25 1·10

202. Federation Emblem.

204. Hand holding Spanner.

**1972.** 4th Anniv. of Iraqi Women's Federation.
1040. **202.** 25 f. multicoloured .. 45 25
1041. 35 f. multicoloured .. 1·25 1·10

**1972.** Labour Day.
1046. **204.** 25 f. multicoloured .. 35 15
1047. 35 f. multicoloured .. 65 20

205. Kaaba, Mecca.

**1972.** Mohammed's Birthday.
1048 **205** 25 f. black, gold & grn 45 25
1049 35 f. black, gold & vio 1·40 1·10

206. Shooting for Goal.

**1972.** Air. 25th International Military Sports Council Football Championship, Baghdad. Multicoloured.
1050. 10 f. Type **206** .. .. 55 25
1051. 20 f. Players in goalmouth 80 35
1052. 25 f. Type **206** .. .. 1·10 45
1053. 35 f. As 20 f. .. .. 1·60 65

207. Soldiers and Artillery.

**1972.** 14th Anniv. of 14 July Revolution.
1055. **207.** 35 f. multicoloured .. 1·10 65
1056. 70 f. multicoloured .. 2·40 1·60

208. "Spirit of Revolution".

**1972.** 4th Anniv. of 17 July Revolution.
1057. **208.** 25 f. multicoloured .. 90 50
1058. 95 f. multicoloured .. 2·50 2·00

209. Scout Badge and Camp Scene.

**1972.** 10th Jamboree and Conference of Arab Scouts, Mosul.
1059. **209.** 20 f. multicoloured .. 1·50 1·00
1060. 25 f. multicoloured .. 1·90 1·00

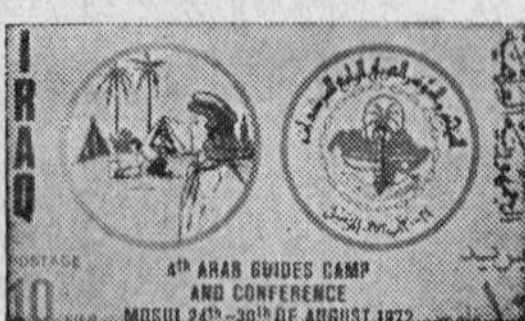

210. Guide Badge and Camp.

**1972.** 4th Conference and Camp of Arab Guides, Mosul.
1061. **210.** 10 f. multicoloured .. 90 60
1062. 45 f. multicoloured .. 3·00 1·50

(211.)

**1972.** 3rd Traffic Week. Nos. 1010/11 surch or optd as T **211**.
1063 **188** 25 f. multicoloured .. 3·00 2·10
1064 70 f. on 15 f. mult .. 4·75 4·25

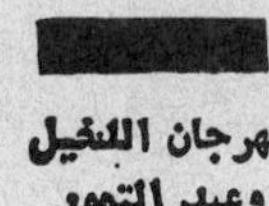


(212.)

213. "Strong Man" Statuette.

**1972.** Festival of Palm Trees and Feast of Dates. Nos. 707 and 709 surch as T **212**.
1065. **94.** 25 f. on 3 f. mult. .. 2·10 1·25
1066. 70 f. on 15 f. mult. .. 4·25 3·25

**1972.** Air. World Body-building Championships and Asian Congress, Baghdad. Multicoloured.
1067. 25 f. Type **213** .. .. 1·00 55
1068. 70 f. Ancient warriors and modern Strong Man .. 2·10 1·50

214. Bank Building.

**1972.** 25th Anniv. of Central Bank of Iraq.
1069. **214.** 25 f. multicoloured 95 35
1070. 70 f. multicoloured .. 1·90 1·90

216. International Railway Union Emblem.

**1972.** 50th Anniv. of Int. Railway Union.
1073. **216.** 25 f. multicoloured .. 1·10 35
1074. 45 f. multicoloured .. 2·75 1·90

**1973.** Various "Faisal" definitives with portrait obliterated with 3 bars.

(a) 1954 issue.
1075. **33.** 10 f. blue .. .. 2·25 85
1076. 15 f. black .. .. 2·25 85
1077. 25 f. purple .. .. 2·25 85

(b) 1957 issue.
1078. **41.** 10 f. blue .. .. 2·25 85
1079. 15 f. black .. .. 2·25 85
1080. 25 f. purple .. .. 2·25 85

المؤتمر الدولي
للتاريخ/١٩٧٢

(219.)

**1973.** Int. History Congress Nos 780, 783 and 786 optd. with T **219**.
1094. 15 f. mult. (postage) .. 2·50 2·50
1095. 80 f. multicoloured (air).. 4·25 4·25
1096. 500 f. multicoloured .. 38·00 38·00

220. Iraqi Oil Workers.

**1973.** 1st Anniv. of Nationalisation of Iraqi Oil Industry.
1097. **220.** 25 f. multicoloured .. 1·75 1·25
1098. 70 f. multicoloured .. 3·75 2·10

221. Harp.

225a. Iraqis and Flags.

**1973.**
1099 **221** 5 f. black and orange 15 10
1100 10 f. black and brown 15 10
1101 20 f. black and mauve 20 10
1102 – 25 f. black and blue 35 15
1103 – 35 f. black and green 40 20
1104 – 45 f. black and blue .. 40 25
1105 – 50 f. yellow and green 65 25
1106 – 70 f. yellow and violet 70 40
1107 – 95 f. yellow and brown 1·25 65
Designs: 25, 35, 45 f. Minaret of Mosul. 50, 70, 95 f. Statue of a Goddess.

**1973.** July Festivals.
1122. **225a.** 25 f. multicoloured .. 70 25
1123. 35 f. multicoloured .. 1·40 85

**1973.** Int. Journalists' Conference. Nos. 857/8 optd **I.O.J. SEPTEMBER 26-29, 1973.**
1124. **139.** 15 f. multicoloured .. 2·10 2·10
1125. 50 f. multicoloured .. 3·00 3·00

227. Interpol H.Q., Paris.

228. Flags and Fair Emblems.

**1973.** 50th Anniv. of Int. Criminal Police Organization (Interpol).
1126. **227.** 25 f. multicoloured .. 70 25
1127. 70 f. multicoloured .. 3·50 2·25

**1973.** 10th Baghdad International Fair.
1128. **228.** 10 f. multicoloured .. 30 15
1129. 20 f. multicoloured .. 70 30
1130. 55 f. multicoloured .. 1·40 75

229. W.M.O. Emblem.

230. Arab Flags and Map.

**1973.** Centenary of World Meteorological Organization.
1148. **229.** 25 f. blk., grn. & orge. 45 15
1149. 35 f. blk., grn. & mve. 1·40 95

**1973.** 11th Session of Arab States' Civil Aviation Council, Baghdad.
1150. **230.** 20 f. multicoloured .. 35 25
1151. 35 f. multicoloured .. 1·10 75

المجلس التنفيذي

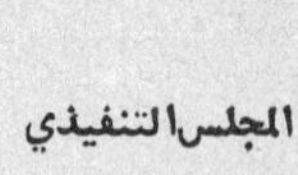


(232.)

233. Human Rights Emblem.

**1973.** Sixth Executive Council Meeting of Arab Postal Union, Baghdad. No. 665 optd. with Type **232**.
1153. **75.** 30 f. blue & orange .. 3·25 2·10

**1973.** 25th Anniv of Declaration of Human Rights.
1154. **233.** 25 f. multicoloured .. 35 15
1155. 70 f. multicoloured .. 1·40 85

234. Shield and Military Activities.

**1974.** 50th Anniv. of Military College.
1156. **234.** 25 f. multicoloured .. 35 25
1157. 35 f. multicoloured .. 1·25 85

236. U.P.U. Emblem.

**1974.** Cent. of Universal Postal Union.
1159. **236.** 25 f. multicoloured .. 60 20
1160. 35 f. multicoloured .. 65 35
1161. 70 f. multicoloured .. 1·75 1·10

**237.** Allegory of Nationalization.

**1974.** 2nd Anniv. of Nationalization of Iraqi Oil Industry.
1162. **237.** 10 f. multicoloured .. 25 15
1163. 25 f. multicoloured .. 65 25
1164. 70 f. multicoloured .. 1·75 1·75

**238.** Festival Theme. **240.** Cement Plant.

**239.** National Front Emblem and Heads.

**1975.** July Festivals.
1165. **238.** 20 f. multicoloured .. 30 15
1166. 35 f. multicoloured .. 85 45

**1975.** 1st Anniv. of Progressive National Front.
1167. **239.** 20 f. multicoloured .. 35 15
1168. 50 f. multicoloured .. 1·40 85

**1975.** 25th Anniv. of Iraqi Cement Industry.
1169. **240.** 20 f. multicoloured .. 40 25
1170. 25 f. multicoloured .. 40 30
1171. 70 f. multicoloured .. 1·25 95

**1975.** Surch.
1172. **155.** 10 f. on 3 f. mult. .. 2·50 1·10
1173. – 25 f. on 3 f. multicoloured (No. 892) .. 3·75 1·25

**242.** W.P.Y. Emblem.

**1975.** World Population Year (1974).
1174. **242.** 25 f. green and blue .. 40 20
1175. 35 f. blue and mauve 70 30
1176. 70 f. violet and olive 1·75 1·10

**243.** Festival Emblems.

**1975.** July Festivals.
1177. **243.** 5 f. multicoloured .. 20 15
1178. 10 f. multicoloured .. 25 20
1179. 35 f. multicoloured .. 1·10 65

**244.** Map and Emblems. **245.** "Equality, Development, Peace".

**1975.** 10th Anniv. of Arab Labour Organization.
1180. **244.** 25 f. multicoloured .. 40 15
1181. 35 f. multicoloured .. 65 55
1182. 45 f. multicoloured .. 70 55

**1975.** International Women's Year.
1183. **245.** 10 f. multicoloured .. 35 15
1184. 35 f. multicoloured .. 65 35
1185. 70 f. multicoloured .. 2·00 1·75

**246.** Diyala Barrage.

**1975.** 25th Anniv of International Commission on Irrigation and Drainage.
1187. **246.** 3 f. multicoloured .. 20 15
1188. 25 f. multicoloured .. 45 25
1189. 70 f. multicoloured .. 1·75 1·10

**247.** Company Seal.

**1975.** 25th Anniv. of National Insurance Company, Baghdad.
1190. **247.** 20 f. multicoloured .. 35 15
1191. 25 f. multicoloured .. 70 50

**248.** Court Musicians.

**1975.** Int. Music Conference, Baghdad.
1193. **248.** 25 f. multicoloured.. 55 25
1194. 45 f. multicoloured.. 1·25 75

**250.** Telecommunications Centre.

**1975.** Opening of Telecommunications Centre.
1203. **250.** 5 f. multicoloured .. 15 15
1204. 10 f. multicoloured .. 20 15
1205. 60 f. multicoloured .. 1·40 95

**251.** Diesel Train. **252.** Goddess (statue).

**1975.** 15th Taurus Railway Conf., Baghdad. Multicoloured.
1206 25 f. Type **251** .. .. 2·25 2·25
1207 30 f. Diesel locomotive .. 3·00 3·00
1208 35 f. Steam tank locomotive and train .. 4·50 4·50
1209 50 f. German steam locomotive .. .. 6·50 6·50

**1976.**
1210. **252.** 5 f. multicoloured .. 10 10
1211. 10 f. multicoloured .. 10 10
1212. 15 f. multicoloured .. 15 10
1213. – 20 f. multicoloured .. 20 10
1214. – 25 f. multicoloured .. 30 10
1215. – 30 f. multicoloured .. 40 10
1216. – 35 f. multicoloured .. 50 20
1217. – 50 f. multicoloured .. 70 20
1218. – 75 f. multicoloured .. 1·00 50

DESIGNS: 20, 25, 30 f. Two females forming column. 35, 50, 75 f. Head of bearded man.

**253.** Soldier and Symbols of Industry and Agriculture. **254.** Crossed-out Thumbprint.

**1976.** Arab Day.
1219. **253.** 5 f. multicoloured .. 20 15
1220. 25 f. multicoloured on silver .. .. 45 15
1221. 50 f. multicoloured on gold .. .. 1·25 50

**1976.** Arab Literacy Day.
1222. **254.** 5 f. multicoloured .. 15 10
1223. 15 f. multicoloured .. 20 15
1224. 35 f. multicoloured .. 1·25 45

**255.** Iraq Earth Station. **256.** Early and Modern Telephones.

**1976.** 13th Anniv. of Revolution of 14th Ramadan.
1225. **255.** 10 f. multicoloured .. 25 10
1226. 25 f. multicoloured on silver .. .. 60 30
1227. 75 f. multicoloured on gold .. .. 2·10 1·40

**1976.** Telephone Centenary.
1228. **256.** 35 f. multicoloured .. 55 25
1229. 50 f. multicoloured .. 1·10 60
1230. 75 f. multicoloured .. 1·60 1·10

**257.** Map and Emblem. **258.** Iraqi Family on Map.

**1976.** 20th Int. Arab Trade Unions Conf.
1231. **257.** 5 f. multicoloured (postage) .. .. 25 20
1232. 10 f. multicoloured .. 25 20
1233. 75 f. multicoloured (air) 2·10 1·10

**1976.** Police Day.
1234. **258.** 5 f. multicoloured .. 25 15
1235. 15 f. multicoloured .. 35 15
1236. 35 f. multicoloured .. 1·50 85

**259.** " Strategy " Pipeline. **260.** Human Eye.

**1976.** 4th Anniv. of Oil Nationalization.
1237. **259.** 25 f multicoloured .. 65 35
1238. 75 f. multicoloured .. 2·10 1·25

**1976.** Air. World Health Day. "Foresight Prevents Blindness".
1240 **260** 25 f. blue and black .. 25 15
1241 35 f. green and black 35 25
1242 50 f. orange & brown 70 45

**261.** " Agriculture, Industry and Construction ". **262.** Basketball.

**1976.** July Festivals.
1243. **261.** 15 f. multicoloured .. 25 15
1244. 35 f. multicoloured .. 70 30

**1976.** Olympic Games, Montreal. Mult.
1245. 25 f. Type **262** .. .. 35 35
1246. 35 f. Volleyball .. .. 50 40
1247. 50 f. Wrestling .. .. 75 50
1248. 75 f. Boxing .. .. 1·40 85

**263.** Bishop Capucci, Wounded Dove and Map of Palestine. **264.** Common Kingfisher.

**1976.** 2nd Anniv. of Bishop Capucci's Arrest.
1250. **263.** 25 f. multicoloured .. 40 20
1251. 35 f. multicoloured .. 50 30
1252. 75 f. multicoloured .. 1·60 1·10

**1976.** Birds. Multicoloured.
1253. 5 f. Type **264** .. .. 85 20
1254. 10 f. Turtle Dove .. 95 30
1255. 15 f. Pin-tailed Sandgrouse 1·10 35
1256. 25 f. Blue Rock Thrush.. 1·90 40
1257. 50 f. Purple Heron and Grey Heron .. .. 3·00 80

**265.** Emblem within " 15 ". **266.** Children with Banner.

**1976.** 15th Anniv. of Iraqi Students' Union.
1263. **265.** 30 f. multicoloured .. 35 10
1264. 70 f. multicoloured .. 1·60 75

**1976.** 30th Anniv. of U.N.E.S.C.O. "Children's Books". Multicoloured.
1265. 10 f. Type **266** .. .. 30 10
1266. 25 f. Children in garden 55 15
1267. 75 f. Children with Iraqi flag .. .. .. 1·90 1·40

**267.** Tanker " Rumaila " and Emblem.

**1976.** 4th Anniv. of First Iraqi Oil Tanker and 1st Anniv. of Basrah Petroleum Co. Nationalization. Multicoloured.
1268. 10 f. Type **267** .. .. 35 15
1269. 15 f. Type **267** .. .. 45 25
1270. 25 f. Oil jetty and installations .. .. .. 65 25
1271. 50 f. As 25 f. .. .. 1·75 1·00

**268.** Islamic Design with Inscriptions. **269.** Dove Emblem.

**1977.** Birthday of Prophet Mohammed.
1272. **268.** 25 f. multicoloured .. 35 15
1273. 35 f. multicoloured .. 70 65

**1977.** Peace Day.
1274. **269.** 25 f. multicoloured .. 30 20
1275. 30 f. multicoloured .. 45 30

**270.** Dahlia.

**1977.** Flowers. Multicoloured.
1276. 5 f. Type **270** .. .. 20 10
1277. 10 f. " Lathyrus odoratus " 20 10
1278. 35 f. " Chrysanthemum coronarium " .. .. 65 25
1279. 50 f. " Verbena hybrida " 1·00 90

271. " V " Emblem with Doves.

**1977.** 30th Anniv of Al-Baath Party. Mult.
1280. 25 f. Type 271 .. .. 35 15
1281. 75 f. Human figures as a flame .. .. .. 1·40 70

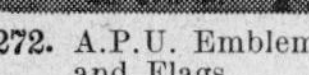

272. A.P.U. Emblem and Flags.

273. 1st May Emblem.

**1977.** 25th Anniv. of Arab Postal Union.
1283. 272. 25 f. multicoloured .. 35 15
1284. 35 f. multicoloured .. 55 40

**1977.** Labour Day.
1285. 273. 10 f. multicoloured .. 20 10
1286. 30 f. multicoloured .. 45 15
1287. 35 f. multicoloured .. 65 50

274. First Stage of Lift.

275. Dome of the Rock.

**1977.** 8th Asian Weightlifting Championships, Baghdad. Multicoloured.
1288. 25 f. Type 274 .. 60 45
1289. 75 f. Press-up stage of lift 1·60 1·00

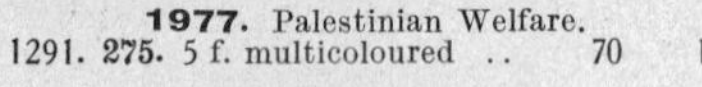

**1977.** Palestinian Welfare.
1291. 275. 5 f. multicoloured .. 70 15

276. Arabian Garden.

277. Dove and Ear of Wheat.

**1977.** Arab Tourism Year. Multicoloured.
1292. 5 f. Type 276 .. .. 15 10
1293. 10 f. Town view with Minarets (horiz.) .. 20 15
1294. 30 f. Country stream .. 50 25
1295. 50 f. Oasis (horiz.) .. 1·50 90

**1977.** July Festivals.
1296. 277. 25 f. multicoloured .. 45 20
1297. 30 f. multicoloured .. 70 30

278. Map of Middle East and North Africa.

279. Emblem.

**1977.** U.N. Conference on Desertification.
1298. 278. 30 f. multicoloured .. 50 35
1299. 70 f. multicoloured .. 1·40 70

**1977.** Census Day.
1300. 279. 20 f. multicoloured .. 20 15
1301. 30 f. multicoloured .. 50 15
1302. 70 f. multicoloured .. 90 60

280. Abstract Calligraphic Emblem.

281. Kamal Jumblatt and Political Caricatures.

**1977.** Al-Mutanabby Festival.
1303. 280. 25 f. multicoloured .. 20 15
1304. 50 f. multicoloured .. 55 35

**1977.** Kamal Jumblatt (Lebanese socialist). Commemoration.
1305. 281. 20 f. multicoloured .. 20 15
1306. 30 f. multicoloured .. 30 15
1307. 70 f. multicoloured .. 75 50

282. Hajeer Year Emblem.

283. Girl, Boy and National Flag Ribbon.

**1977.** Hajeer Year.
1308. 282. 30 f. multicoloured .. 35 15
1309. 35 f. multicoloured .. 40 15

**1978.** Youth Day.
1310. 283. 10 f. multicoloured .. 15 15
1311. 15 f. multicoloured .. 15 15
1312. 35 f. multicoloured .. 40 30

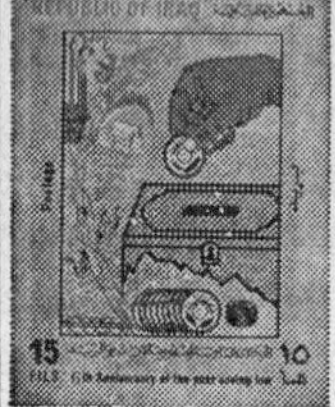

284. Hand placing Coin in Box.

285. Transmitting and Receiving Equipment.

**1978.** 6th Anniv. of Postal Savings Bank.
1313. 284. 15 f. multicoloured .. 25 15
1314. 25 f. multicoloured .. 35 15
1315. 35 f. multicoloured .. 70 35

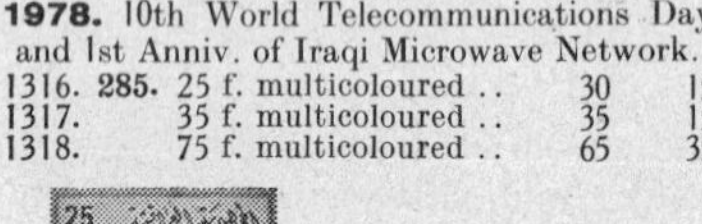

**1978.** 10th World Telecommunications Day and 1st Anniv. of Iraqi Microwave Network.
1316. 285. 25 f. multicoloured .. 30 15
1317. 35 f. multicoloured .. 35 15
1318. 75 f. multicoloured .. 65 35

286. Map and Flags.

287. Silver Coins.

**1978.** 1st Conference of Arabian Gulf Postal Ministers.
1319. 286. 25 f. multicoloured .. 45 15
1320. 35 f. multicoloured .. 65 40

**1978.** Ancient Iraqi Coins.
1321 287 1 f. black, silver & yell 15 10
1322 – 2 f. black, gold & blue 15 10
1323 – 3 f. black, sil & orge 15 10
1324 – 4 f. black, gold & grn 15 10
1325 – 75 f. black, gold & grn 1·50 1·50

DESIGNS—HORIZ. 2 f. Two gold coins. 3 f. Two silver coins. 4 f. Two gold coins. VERT. 75 f. Gold coin.

288. Flower Emblem.

**1978.** July Festivals.
1326. 288. 25 f. multicoloured .. 25 15
1327. 35 f. multicoloured .. 40 25

289. Nurse, Hospital and Sick Child.

**1978.** Global Eradication of Smallpox.
1329. 289. 25 f. multicoloured .. 25 15
1330. 35 f. multicoloured .. 50 25
1331. 75 f. multicoloured .. 1·40 75

290. Altharthar-Euphrates Canal.

**1978.**
1332. 290. 5 f. multicoloured .. 15 10
1333. 10 f. multicoloured .. 15 10
1334. 15 f. multicoloured .. 15 15
1335. 25 f. multicoloured .. 15 15
1336. 35 f. multicoloured .. 35 15
1337. 50 f. multicoloured .. 45 35

291. I.M.C.O. Emblem.

**1978.** World Maritime Day.
1342. 291. 25 f. multicoloured .. 45 15
1343. 75 f. multicoloured .. 75 65

292. Workers in the Countryside.

**1978.** 10th Anniv. of People's Work Groups.
1344. 292. 10 f. multicoloured .. 15 10
1345. 25 f. multicoloured .. 35 15
1346. 35 f. multicoloured .. 55 50

293. Fair Emblem.

294. Map, Rule and Emblem.

**1978.** Baghdad International Fair.
1347. 293. 25 f. multicoloured .. 15 15
1348. 35 f. multicoloured .. 25 15
1349. 75 f. multicoloured .. 1·40 60

**1978.** World Standards Day.
1350. 294. 25 f. multicoloured .. 15 15
1351. 35 f. multicoloured .. 25 15
1352. 75 f. multicoloured .. 1·10 65

295. Conference Chamber.

296. Congress Emblem.

**1978.** Ninth Arab Summit Conference, Baghdad.
1353. 295. 25 f. multicoloured .. 20 15
1354. 35 f. multicoloured .. 30 20
1355. 75 f. multicoloured .. 85 70

**1978.** 4th Congress of Association of Thoracic and Cardiovascular Surgeons of Asia.
1356. 296. 25 f. multicoloured .. 30 15
1357. 75 f. multicoloured .. 85 60

297. Pilgrims and Kaaba.

**1978.** Pilgrimage to Mecca.
1358. 297. 25 f. multicoloured .. 30 15
1359. 35 f. multicoloured .. 45 25

298. Map and Symbol.

**1978.** U.N. Conference for Technical Co-operation among Developing Countries.
1360. 298. 25 f. multicoloured .. 25 15
1361. 50 f. multicoloured .. 45 20
1362. 75 f. multicoloured .. 75 50

299. Hands holding Emblem.

300. Globe and Human Rights Emblem.

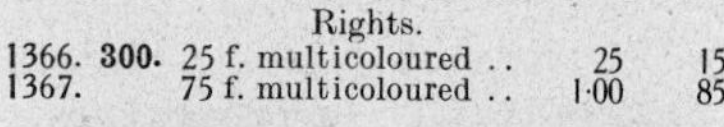

**1978.** International Year to Combat Racism.
1363. 299. 25 f. multicoloured .. 25 15
1364. 50 f. multicoloured .. 45 25
1365. 75 f. multicoloured .. 1·25 50

**1978.** 30th Anniv. of Declaration of Human Rights.
1366. 300. 25 f. multicoloured .. 25 15
1367. 75 f. multicoloured .. 1·00 85

301. Candle and Emblem.

302. Open Book, Pencil and Flame.

**1979.** Police Day.
1368. 301. 10 f. multicoloured .. 15 15
1369. 25 f. multicoloured .. 30 15
1370. 35 f. multicoloured .. 65 35

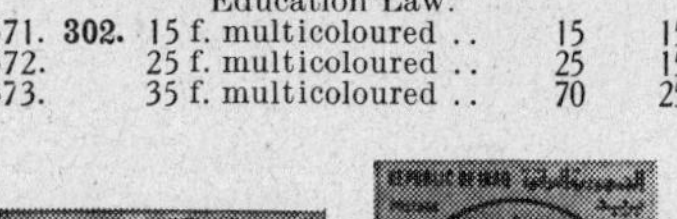

**1979.** Anniv of Application of Compulsory Education Law.
1371. 302. 15 f. multicoloured .. 15 15
1372. 25 f. multicoloured .. 25 15
1373. 35 f. multicoloured .. 70 25

303. School, Teacher and Assyrian Relief.

304. Clenched Fist, Pencil and Book.

**1979.** Teachers' Day.
1374. 303. 10 f. multicoloured .. 15 15
1375. 15 f. multicoloured .. 20 15
1376. 50 f. multicoloured .. 60 35

**1979.** National Literacy Campaign.
1377. 304. 15 f. multicoloured .. 15 15
1378. 25 f. multicoloured .. 30 15
1379. 35 f. multicoloured .. 55 25

305. World map, Koran and Symbols of Arab Achievements.

306. Girl playing Flute.

**1979.** The Arabs.
1380. 305. 35 f. multicoloured .. 45 20
1381. 75 f. multicoloured .. 1·25 65

**1979.** Mosul Spring Festival.
1382. 306. 15 f. multicoloured .. 25 15
1383. 25 f. multicoloured .. 40 20
1384. 35 f. multicoloured .. 85 35

307. Iraqi Map and Flag with U.P.U. Emblem.

308. Championship Emblem with Sea and Sky.

**1979.** 50th Anniv. of Admission to Universal Postal Union.
1385. 307. 25 f. multicoloured .. 40 15
1386. 35 f. multicoloured .. 55 25
1387. 75 f. multicoloured .. 1·00 45

**1979.** Fifth Arabian Gulf Football Championship.
1388. 308. 10 f. multicoloured .. 15 15
1389. 15 f. multicoloured .. 25 15
1390. 50 f. multicoloured .. 70 45

**309.** Child with Globe and Candle. **310.** Flower and Branch.

**1979.** International Year of the Child.

| | | | | |
|---|---|---|---|---|
| 1391. | **309.** | 25 f. multicoloured .. | 45 | 25 |
| 1392. | | 75 f. multicoloured .. | 1·10 | 75 |

**1979.** July Festivals.

| | | | | |
|---|---|---|---|---|
| 1394. | **310.** | 15 f. multicoloured .. | 15 | 10 |
| 1395. | | 25 f. multicoloured .. | 25 | 25 |
| 1396. | | 35 f. multicoloured .. | 45 | 25 |

**311.** Children supporting Globe. **312.** Jawad Selim (sculptor).

**1979.** 50th Anniv. of International Bureau of Education.

| | | | | |
|---|---|---|---|---|
| 1397. | **311.** | 25 f. multicoloured .. | 45 | 25 |
| 1398. | | 50 f. multicoloured .. | 75 | 40 |
| 1399. | | 100 f. multicoloured | 1·10 | 85 |

**1979.** Writers and Artists. Multicoloured.

| | | | |
|---|---|---|---|
| 1400. | 25 f. Type **312** .. .. | 35 | 15 |
| 1401. | 25 f. S. al-Hosari (philosopher) .. .. | 35 | 15 |
| 1402. | 25 f. Mustapha Jawad (historian) .. .. | 35 | 15 |

**313.** The Kaaba, Mecca. **314.** Figure "20" and Globe.

**1979.** Pilgrimage to Mecca.

| | | | | |
|---|---|---|---|---|
| 1403. | **313.** | 25 f. multicoloured .. | 30 | 15 |
| 1404. | | 50 f. multicoloured .. | 55 | 25 |

**1979.** 20th Anniv. of Iraqi News Agency.

| | | | | |
|---|---|---|---|---|
| 1405. | **314.** | 25 f. multicoloured .. | 30 | 15 |
| 1406. | | 50 f. multicoloured .. | 65 | 20 |
| 1407. | | 75 f. multicoloured .. | 1·00 | 35 |

**315.** Wave Pattern and Television Screen.

**1979.** World Telecommunications Exhibition and Radio Conference, Geneva.

| | | | | |
|---|---|---|---|---|
| 1408. | **315.** | 25 f. multicoloured .. | 35 | 15 |
| 1409. | | 50 f. multicoloured .. | 50 | 30 |
| 1410. | | 75 f. multicoloured .. | 85 | 50 |

**316.** Clenched Fists and Refugee.

**1979.** Palestinian Solidarity Day.

| | | | | |
|---|---|---|---|---|
| 1411. | **316.** | 25 f. multicoloured .. | 45 | 15 |
| 1412. | | 50 f. multicoloured .. | 65 | 35 |
| 1413. | | 75 f. multicoloured .. | 1·10 | 65 |

**317.** Ahmed Hassan Al-Bakir. **318.** Boy with Violin.

**1979.** Inauguration of President Saddam Hussain. Multicoloured.

| | | | |
|---|---|---|---|
| 1414. | 25 f. Type **317** .. .. | 25 | 15 |
| 1415. | 35 f. Pres. Hussain taking the oath .. .. | 45 | 20 |
| 1416. | 75 f. Type **317** .. .. | 75 | 45 |
| 1417. | 100 f. As No. 1415 .. | 1·10 | 85 |

**1979.** Activities of Vanguards (youth organization). Multicoloured.

| | | | |
|---|---|---|---|
| 1418 | 10 f. Type **318** .. .. | 10 | 10 |
| 1419 | 15 f. Boys on building site | 15 | 15 |
| 1420 | 25 f. Boys on assault course and in personal combat .. .. | 20 | 15 |
| 1421 | 35 f. Vanguards emblem | 45 | 20 |

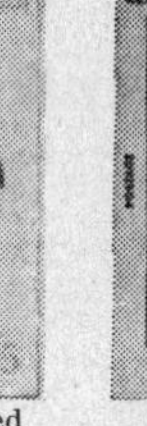

**319.** Wind-speed Indicator and Thermometer. **320.** Lighting Cigarette and Cancerous Lungs.

**1980.** World Meteorological Day.

| | | | | |
|---|---|---|---|---|
| 1422. | **319.** | 15 f. multicoloured .. | 15 | 15 |
| 1423. | | 25 f. multicoloured .. | 25 | 15 |
| 1424. | | 35 f. multicoloured .. | 45 | 25 |

**1980.** World Health Day. Anti-Smoking Campaign.

| | | | | |
|---|---|---|---|---|
| 1425. | **320.** | 25 f. multicoloured .. | 30 | 15 |
| 1426. | | 35 f. multicoloured .. | 45 | 15 |
| 1427. | | 75 f. multicoloured .. | 75 | 45 |

**321.** Festivals Emblem. **322.** Hurdling.

**1980.** July Festivals.

| | | | | |
|---|---|---|---|---|
| 1428. | **321.** | 25 f. multicoloured .. | 20 | 15 |
| 1429. | | 35 f. multicoloured .. | 25 | 15 |

**1980.** Olympic Games. Moscow. Multicoloured.

| | | | |
|---|---|---|---|
| 1431. | 15 f. Type **322** .. .. | 20 | 15 |
| 1432. | 20 f. Weightlifting (vert.) | 30 | 15 |
| 1433. | 30 f. Boxing .. .. | 45 | 25 |
| 1434. | 35 f. Football (vert.) .. | 50 | 35 |

**323.** "Rubus sanctus".

**1980.** Fruit. Multicoloured.

| | | | |
|---|---|---|---|
| 1436 | 5 f. Type **323** .. .. | 20 | 10 |
| 1437 | 15 f. Peaches .. .. | 35 | 15 |
| 1438 | 20 f. Pears .. .. | 50 | 15 |
| 1439 | 25 f. Apples .. .. | 60 | 15 |
| 1440 | 35 f. Plums .. .. | 80 | 30 |

**324.** Conference Emblem and Arabic Text. **325.** A.P.U. Emblem, Posthorn and Map.

**1980.** World Tourism Conference, Manila.

| | | | | |
|---|---|---|---|---|
| 1441. | **324.** | 25 f. multicoloured .. | 25 | 15 |
| 1442. | | 50 f. multicoloured .. | 50 | 25 |
| 1443. | | 100 f. multicoloured | 95 | 65 |

**1980.** 11th Congress of Arab Postal Union, Baghdad.

| | | | | |
|---|---|---|---|---|
| 1444. | **325.** | 10 f. multicoloured .. | 15 | 10 |
| 1445. | | 30 f. multicoloured .. | 25 | 15 |
| 1446. | | 35 f. multicoloured .. | 40 | 25 |

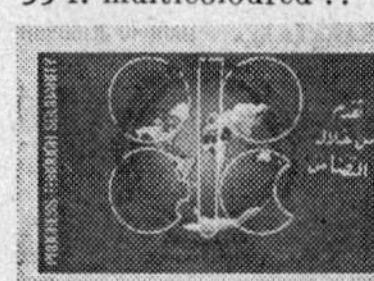

**326.** O.P.E.C. Emblem and Globe.

**1980.** 20th Anniv. of Organization of Petroleum Exporting Countries.

| | | | | |
|---|---|---|---|---|
| 1447. | **326.** | 30 f. multicoloured .. | 50 | 20 |
| 1448. | | 75 f. multicoloured .. | 1·00 | 65 |

**327.** African Monarch.

**1980.** Butterflies. Multicoloured.

| | | | |
|---|---|---|---|
| 1449 | 10 f. Swallowtail .. | 25 | 20 |
| 1450 | 15 f. Type **327** .. | 50 | 25 |
| 1451 | 20 f. Red admiral .. | 70 | 40 |
| 1452 | 30 f. Clouded yellow .. | 1·00 | 45 |

**328.** Mosque and Kaaba.

**1980.** 1400th Anniv. of Hegira.

| | | | | |
|---|---|---|---|---|
| 1453. | **328.** | 15 f. multicoloured .. | 20 | 15 |
| 1454. | | 25 f. multicoloured .. | 35 | 15 |
| 1455. | | 35 f. multicoloured .. | 45 | 20 |

**329.** Riflemen and Dome of the Rock on Map of Israel.

**1980.** Palestinian Solidarity Day.

| | | | | |
|---|---|---|---|---|
| 1456. | **329.** | 25 f. multicoloured .. | 30 | 15 |
| 1457. | | 35 f. multicoloured .. | 45 | 20 |
| 1458. | | 75 f. multicoloured .. | 1·00 | 50 |

**330.** Soldier and Rocket. **331.** "8" and Flags forming Torch.

**1981.** 60th Anniv. of Army Day.

| | | | | |
|---|---|---|---|---|
| 1459. | **330.** | 5 f. multicoloured .. | 15 | 10 |
| 1460. | | 30 f. multicoloured .. | 40 | 15 |
| 1461. | | 75 f. multicoloured .. | 90 | 50 |

**1981.** 18th Anniv. of 14th Ramadan Revolution.

| | | | | |
|---|---|---|---|---|
| 1462. | **331.** | 15 f. multicoloured .. | 15 | 10 |
| 1463. | | 30 f. multicoloured .. | 30 | 15 |
| 1464. | | 35 f. multicoloured .. | 40 | 20 |

**332.** Map of Arab States tied with Ribbon.

**1981.** The Arabs.

| | | | | |
|---|---|---|---|---|
| 1465. | **332.** | 5 f. multicoloured .. | 10 | 10 |
| 1466. | | 25 f. multicoloured .. | 30 | 15 |
| 1467. | | 35 f. multicoloured .. | 45 | 20 |

**333.** Pres. Hussain, Saddam and Modern Military Equipment. **334.** I.T.U. and W.H.O. Emblems and Ribbons forming Caduceus.

**1981.** Saddam's Battle of Qadisiya.

| | | | | |
|---|---|---|---|---|
| 1468. | **333.** | 30 f. multicoloured .. | 30 | 15 |
| 1469. | | 35 f. multicoloured .. | 40 | 15 |
| 1470. | | 75 f. multicoloured .. | 70 | 35 |

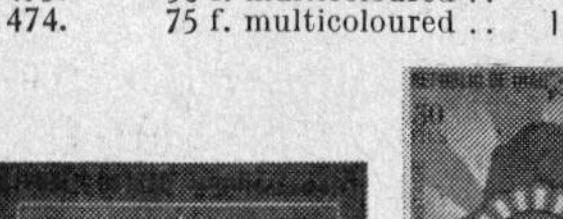

**1981.** World Telecommunications Day.

| | | | | |
|---|---|---|---|---|
| 1472. | **334.** | 25 f. multicoloured .. | 35 | 20 |
| 1473. | | 50 f. multicoloured .. | 70 | 30 |
| 1474. | | 75 f. multicoloured .. | 1·10 | 60 |

**335.** Mil Mi-24 Helicopters attacking Ground Forces. **336.** Map and Flower enclosing Ballot Box.

**1981.** 50th Anniv of Air Force. Mult.

| | | | |
|---|---|---|---|
| 1475 | 5 f. Type **335** (postage) .. | 15 | 15 |
| 1476 | 10 f. Antonov An-2 biplane trainer .. | 25 | 15 |
| 1477 | 15 f. "SAM-15" missile .. | 25 | 15 |
| 1478 | 120 f. De Havilland Dragon Rapide biplane and Mikoyan Gurevich MiG-21 jet fighters (vert) (air) .. .. | 2·50 | 1·50 |

**1981.** 1st Anniv. of National Assembly Election.

| | | | | |
|---|---|---|---|---|
| 1479. | **336.** | 30 f. multicoloured .. | 30 | 10 |
| 1480. | | 35 f. multicoloured .. | 45 | 15 |
| 1481. | | 45 f. multicoloured .. | 55 | 25 |

**337.** Festivals Emblem. **338.** Basket Weaver.

**1981.** July Festivals.

| | | | | |
|---|---|---|---|---|
| 1482. | **337.** | 15 f. multicoloured .. | 20 | 10 |
| 1483. | | 25 f. multicoloured .. | 30 | 15 |
| 1484. | | 35 f. multicoloured .. | 45 | 20 |

**1981.** Popular Industries. Multicoloured.

| | | | |
|---|---|---|---|
| 1485. | 5 f. Type **338** .. .. | 10 | 10 |
| 1486. | 30 f. Copper worker .. | 35 | 20 |
| 1487. | 35 f. Potter .. .. | 55 | 20 |
| 1488. | 50 f. Weaver (horiz.) .. | 70 | 30 |

**339.** Saddam Hussain Gymnasium.

**1981.** Modern Buildings. Multicoloured.

| | | | |
|---|---|---|---|
| 1489. | 45 f. Type **339** .. .. | 45 | 20 |
| 1490. | 50 f. Palace of Conferences .. .. .. | 45 | 20 |
| 1491. | 120 f. As 50 f. .. .. | 1·25 | 95 |
| 1492. | 150 f. Type **339** .. .. | 1·75 | 1·10 |

**340.** Pilgrims.

**1981.** Pilgrimage to Mecca.

| | | | | |
|---|---|---|---|---|
| 1493. | **340.** | 25 f. multicoloured .. | 40 | 15 |
| 1494. | | 45 f. multicoloured .. | 65 | 25 |
| 1495. | | 50 f. multicoloured .. | 65 | 25 |

**341.** Harvesting.

**1981.** World Food Day.

| | | | | |
|---|---|---|---|---|
| 1496. | **341.** | 30 f. multicoloured .. | 30 | 15 |
| 1497. | | 45 f. multicoloured .. | 60 | 30 |
| 1498. | | 75 f. multicoloured .. | 90 | 55 |

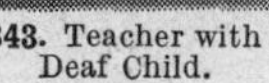

**343.** Teacher with Deaf Child. **344.** Medal and Map.

**1981.** International Year of Disabled Persons.

| | | | | |
|---|---|---|---|---|
| 1501. | **343.** | 30 f. multicoloured .. | 30 | 15 |
| 1502. | | 45 f. multicoloured .. | 70 | 25 |
| 1503. | | 75 f. multicoloured .. | 95 | 60 |

**1981.** Martyr's Day.

| | | | | |
|---|---|---|---|---|
| 1504. | **344.** | 45 f. multicoloured .. | 50 | 20 |
| 1505. | | 50 f. multicoloured .. | 50 | 20 |
| 1506. | | 120 f. multicoloured | 1·50 | 1·00 |

**345.** "Ibn Khaldoon" (freighter).

**1981.** 5th Anniv. of United Arab Shipping Company.

| | | | | |
|---|---|---|---|---|
| 1507. | **345.** | 50 f. multicoloured .. | 75 | 35 |
| 1508. | | 120 f. multicoloured | 2·00 | 1·10 |

**346.** Woman and Symbols of Technology. **347.** President Hussain, "7" and "Flowers".

**1982.** Iraqi Women's Day.

| | | | | |
|---|---|---|---|---|
| 1509. | **346.** | 25 f. multicoloured .. | 35 | 15 |
| 1510. | | 45 f. multicoloured .. | 60 | 30 |
| 1511. | | 50 f. multicoloured .. | 60 | 35 |

**1982.** 35th Anniv of Al-Baath Party. Mult.

| | | | |
|---|---|---|---|
| 1512 | 25 f. Type **347** .. .. | 35 | 15 |
| 1513 | 30 f. Rainbow and "7 7 7" | 35 | 15 |
| 1514 | 45 f. Type **347** .. .. | 55 | 35 |
| 1515 | 50 f. As 30 f. .. .. | 55 | 35 |

**348.** A.P.U. Emblem. and Globe. **349.** White Storks.

**1982.** 30th Anniv. of Arab Postal Union.

| | | | | |
|---|---|---|---|---|
| 1517. | **348.** | 25 f. multicoloured .. | 30 | 15 |
| 1518. | | 45 f. multicoloured .. | 50 | 25 |
| 1519. | | 50 f. multicoloured .. | 55 | 25 |

**1982.** Mosul Spring Festival. Multicoloured.

| | | | |
|---|---|---|---|
| 1520. | 25 f. Type **349** .. .. | 75 | 15 |
| 1521. | 30 f. Doll .. .. .. | 45 | 15 |
| 1522. | 45 f. Type **349** .. .. | 75 | 35 |
| 1523. | 50 f. As 30 f. .. .. | 65 | 30 |

**350.** World Map, Factories and "1".

**1982.** Labour Day.

| | | | | |
|---|---|---|---|---|
| 1524. | **350.** | 25 f. multicoloured .. | 30 | 10 |
| 1525. | | 45 f. multicoloured .. | 45 | 25 |
| 1526. | | 50 f. multicoloured .. | 50 | 30 |

**351.** Geometric Figure and I.T.U. Problem. **352.** Oil Gusher.

**1982.** World Telecommunications Day.

| | | | | |
|---|---|---|---|---|
| 1527. | **351.** | 5 f. multicoloured .. | 10 | 10 |
| 1528. | | 45 f. multicoloured .. | 50 | 25 |
| 1529. | | 100 f. multicoloured | 1·10 | 70 |

**1982.** 10th Anniv. of Oil Nationalization. Multicoloured.

| | | | |
|---|---|---|---|
| 1530 | 5 f. Type **352** .. .. | 10 | 10 |
| 1531 | 25 f. Type **352** .. .. | 45 | 15 |
| 1532 | 45 f. Bronze sculpture of bull and horse flanking couple holding model of oil rig .. .. | 75 | 35 |
| 1533 | 50 f. As 45 f. .. .. | 85 | 45 |

**353.** Nuclear Power Emblem and Lion. **354.** Footballers.

**1982.** 1st Anniv. of Attack on Iraqi Nuclear Reactor. Multicoloured.

| | | | |
|---|---|---|---|
| 1534. | 30 f. Type **353**. .. .. | 45 | 15 |
| 1535. | 45 f. Bomb aimed at egg | 70 | 25 |
| 1536. | 50 f. Type **353**. .. .. | 75 | 35 |
| 1537. | 120 f. As No. 1535 .. | 1·50 | 95 |

**1982.** World Cup Football Championship, Spain. Multicoloured.

| | | | |
|---|---|---|---|
| 1538. | 5 f. Type **354** .. .. | 15 | 10 |
| 1539. | 45 f. Three footballers .. | 50 | 30 |
| 1540. | 50 f. Type **354** .. .. | 50 | 30 |
| 1541. | 100 f. As 45 f. .. .. | 1·10 | 75 |

**355.** President Hussain and Fireworks. **356.** Green Lizard.

**1982.** July Festivals.

| | | | | |
|---|---|---|---|---|
| 1543. | **355.** | 25 f. multicoloured .. | 25 | 15 |
| 1544. | | 45 f. multicoloured .. | 45 | 25 |
| 1545. | | 50 f. multicoloured .. | 45 | 30 |

**1982.** Reptiles. Multicoloured.

| | | | |
|---|---|---|---|
| 1546 | 25 f. Type **356** .. .. | 1·40 | 60 |
| 1547 | 30 f. Asp .. .. .. | 1·50 | 60 |
| 1548 | 45 f. Two green lizards .. | 1·75 | 80 |
| 1549 | 50 f. "Natrix tessellata" | 2·00 | 1·10 |

**357.** Pandit Nehru (India).

**1982.** Seventh Non-Aligned Countries Conference, Baghdad. Multicoloured.

| | | | |
|---|---|---|---|
| 1550. | 50 f. Type **357** .. .. | 55 | 25 |
| 1551. | 50 f. Josef Tito (Yugoslavia) .. | 55 | 25 |
| 1552. | 50 f. Abdul Nasser (Egypt) .. .. | 55 | 25 |
| 1553. | 50 f. Kwame Nkrumah (Ghana) .. .. | 55 | 25 |
| 1554. | 100 f. President Hussain (Iraq) .. .. .. | 1·25 | 70 |

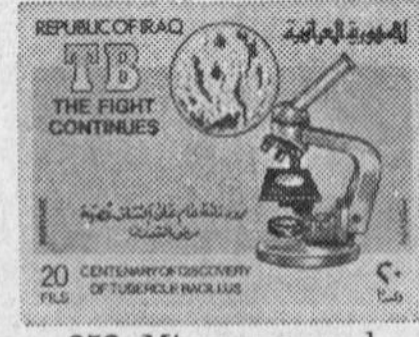

**358.** Microscope and Bacilli.

**1982.** Cent of Discovery of Tubercule Bacillus.

| | | | | |
|---|---|---|---|---|
| 1555. | **358.** | 20 f. multicoloured .. | 45 | 15 |
| 1556. | | 50 f. multicoloured .. | 80 | 25 |
| 1557. | | 100 f. multicoloured | 1·40 | 80 |

**359.** U.P.U. Building, Berne. **360.** Drums.

**1982.** U.P.U. Day.

| | | | | |
|---|---|---|---|---|
| 1561. | **359.** | 5 f. multicoloured .. | 15 | 10 |
| 1562. | | 45 f. multicoloured .. | 45 | 25 |
| 1563. | | 100 f. multicoloured | 1·10 | 70 |

**1982.** Musical Instruments. Multicoloured.

| | | | |
|---|---|---|---|
| 1564. | 5 f. Type **360** .. .. | 15 | 10 |
| 1565. | 10 f. Stringed board instrument .. .. | 20 | 10 |
| 1566. | 35 f. Bowed instruments | 55 | 20 |
| 1567. | 100 f. Mandolin .. .. | 1·75 | 75 |

**361.** Mosque and Minaret, Mecca.

**1982.** Prophet Mohammed's Birthday. Mult.

| | | | |
|---|---|---|---|
| 1568. | 25 f. Type **361** .. .. | 25 | 15 |
| 1569. | 30 f. Courtyard of mosque | 25 | 15 |
| 1570. | 45 f. Type **361** .. .. | 40 | 25 |
| 1571. | 50 f. As No. 1569 .. | 45 | 40 |

**362.** Flowers.

**1982.** Flowers. Multicoloured.

| | | | |
|---|---|---|---|
| 1572. | 10 f. Type **362** .. .. | 20 | 15 |
| 1573. | 20 f. Flowers (different) .. | 30 | 15 |
| 1574. | 30 f. Type **362** .. .. | 35 | 20 |
| 1575. | 40 f. As No. 1573 .. | 50 | 35 |
| 1576. | 50 f. Type **362** .. .. | 65 | 35 |
| 1577. | 100 f. As No. 1573 .. | 1·10 | 60 |

**1983.** Nos. 1489/51 surch.

| | | | |
|---|---|---|---|
| 1578. | 60 f. on 50 f. Palace of Conferences .. .. | 75 | 30 |
| 1579. | 70 f. on 45 f. Type **339** .. | 1·10 | 45 |
| 1580. | 160 f. on 120 f. Palace of Conferences .. .. | 2·50 | 1·50 |

**364.** President Hussain.

**1983.** July Festivals.

| | | | | |
|---|---|---|---|---|
| 1583. | **364.** | 30 f. multicoloured .. | 30 | 15 |
| 1584. | | 60 f. multicoloured .. | 70 | 35 |
| 1585. | | 70 f. multicoloured .. | 75 | 35 |

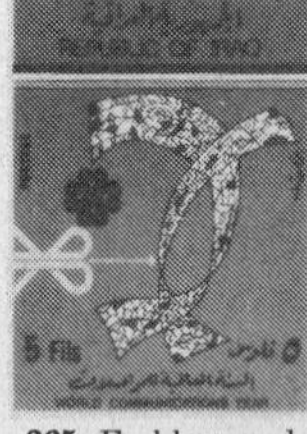

**365.** Emblem and Interlocked Bands. **366.** Horseman and Map.

**1983.** World Communications Year. Mult.

| | | | |
|---|---|---|---|
| 1586. | 5 f. Type **365** .. .. | 15 | 15 |
| 1587. | 25 f. Hexagons of primary colours .. .. | 25 | 15 |
| 1588. | 60 f. Type **365** .. .. | 75 | 45 |
| 1589. | 70 f. As No. 1587 .. | 85 | 50 |

**1983.** Battle of Thiqar. Multicoloured.

| | | | |
|---|---|---|---|
| 1591. | 20 f. Type **366** .. .. | 25 | 15 |
| 1592. | 50 f. Eagle swooping on pyre .. .. | 65 | 30 |
| 1593. | 60 f. Type **366** .. .. | 70 | 35 |
| 1594. | 70 f. As No. 1592 .. | 80 | 45 |

**367.** Fair Emblem and Silhouette of Baghdad. **368.** Pres. Hussain within Figure "9".

**1983.** Baghdad International Fair.

| | | | | |
|---|---|---|---|---|
| 1595. | **367.** | 60 f. multicoloured .. | 65 | 30 |
| 1596. | | 70 f. multicoloured .. | 70 | 45 |
| 1597. | | 160 f. multicoloured | 1·50 | 1·10 |

**1983.** Ninth Al-Baath Party Congress. Mult.

| | | | |
|---|---|---|---|
| 1598. | 30 f. Type **368** .. .. | 25 | 15 |
| 1599. | 60 f. Eagle, torch, map and book .. .. | 60 | 35 |
| 1600. | 70 f. Type **368** .. .. | 70 | 40 |
| 1601. | 100 f. As No. 1599 .. | 1·00 | 55 |

**369.** Fishermen hauling Boat.

**1983.** Paintings. Multicoloured.

| | | | |
|---|---|---|---|
| 1602. | 60 f. Type **369** .. .. | 65 | 45 |
| 1603. | 60 f. Festive crowd .. | 65 | 45 |
| 1604. | 60 f. Hanging decorations | 65 | 45 |
| 1605. | 70 f. Crowd .. .. | 75 | 55 |
| 1606. | 70 f. Bazaar .. .. | 75 | 55 |

**370.** Dove and Victim. **371.** Apartment Building.

**1983.** Massacre of Palestinians in Sabra and Shatila Refugee Camps, Lebanon. Mult.

| | | | |
|---|---|---|---|
| 1607. | 10 f. Type **370** .. .. | 20 | 10 |
| 1608. | 60 f. Type **370** .. .. | 70 | 35 |
| 1609. | 70 f. Dove and clasped fist shedding blood and victims .. .. | 75 | 45 |
| 1610. | 160 f. As No. 1609 .. | 1·60 | 1·10 |

**1983.** Buildings.

| | | | | |
|---|---|---|---|---|
| 1611 | **371** | 60 f. lt grn, blk & grn | 60 | 35 |
| 1612 | – | 70 f. pur, blk & grey | 65 | 45 |
| 1613 | – | 160 f. pur, blk & grey | 1·50 | 85 |
| 1614 | **371** | 200 f. green, blk & ol | 2·00 | 1·10 |

DESIGNS: 70, 160 f. Apartment building (different).

**372.** President Hussain.

**1983.** 4th Anniv. of President Hussain as Party and State Leader.

| | | | | |
|---|---|---|---|---|
| 1617. | **372.** | 60 f. multicoloured .. | 65 | 35 |
| 1618. | | 70 f. multicoloured .. | 75 | 45 |
| 1619. | | 250 f. multicoloured | 2·50 | 1·50 |

**373.** Congress Emblem.

**1984.** 25th International Military Medicine and Pharmacy Congress.

| | | | | |
|---|---|---|---|---|
| 1620. | **373.** | 60 f. multicoloured .. | 65 | 35 |
| 1621. | | 70 f. multicoloured .. | 75 | 45 |
| 1622. | | 200 f. multicoloured | 2·25 | 1·10 |

**374.** President Hussain and Flowers. **375.** Boxing.

**1984.** Pres. Saddam Hussain's 47th Birthday. Multicoloured.

| | | | |
|---|---|---|---|
| 1623. | 60 f. Type **374** .. .. | 45 | 25 |
| 1624. | 70 f. Pres. Hussain in army uniform .. | 55 | 35 |
| 1625. | 160 f. As No. 1623 .. | 1·60 | 1·25 |
| 1626. | 200 f. Type **374** .. .. | 1·90 | 1·25 |

**1984.** Olympic Games, Los Angeles. Multicoloured.

| | | | |
|---|---|---|---|
| 1628. | 50 f. Type **375** .. .. | 50 | 40 |
| 1629. | 60 f. Hurdling, weight-lifting and wrestling .. | 70 | 40 |
| 1630. | 70 f. Type **375** .. .. | 85 | 50 |
| 1631. | 100 f. As No. 1629 .. | 1·10 | 65 |

**376.** Pres. Hussain and Horses' Heads.

**377.** Flag as Ribbon and Two Domes.

**1984.** Battle of Qadisiya. Multicoloured.

| | | | |
|---|---|---|---|
| 1633. | 50 f. Type **376** .. .. | 45 | 30 |
| 1634. | 60 f. President Hussain and symbolic representation of battle .. | 65 | 35 |
| 1635. | 70 f. Type **376** .. .. | 75 | 55 |
| 1636. | 100 f. As No. 1634 .. | 1·10 | 60 |

**1984.** Martyr's Day. Multicoloured.

| | | | |
|---|---|---|---|
| 1638. | 50 f. Type **377** .. .. | 50 | 25 |
| 1639. | 60 f. Woman holding rifle and medal .. .. | 60 | 35 |
| 1640. | 70 f. Type **377** .. .. | 70 | 50 |
| 1641. | 100 f. As No. 1639 .. | 1·00 | 65 |

**378.** Text.

**1985.** 5th Anniv. of President Hussain's Visit to Al-Mustansiriyah University.

| | | | |
|---|---|---|---|
| 1646. | **378.** 60 f. red and blue .. | 60 | 40 |
| 1647. | 70 f. red and green .. | 70 | 45 |
| 1648. | 250 f. red and black | 2·40 | 85 |

**379.** Pres. Hussain and Jet Fighters.

**380.** Pres. Hussain within Flower.

**1985.** 54th Anniv of Iraqi Air Force. Mult.

| | | | |
|---|---|---|---|
| 1649. | 10 f. Type **379** .. .. | 25 | 10 |
| 1650. | 60 f. Fighter airplanes trailing flag and "54" (horiz.) .. .. | 1·00 | 55 |
| 1651. | 70 f. As No. 1650 .. | 1·10 | 60 |
| 1652. | 160 f. Type **379** .. .. | 2·75 | 1·40 |

**1985.** 48th Birthday of President Saddam Hussain. Multicoloured.

| | | | |
|---|---|---|---|
| 1654. | 30 f. Type **380** .. .. | 30 | 20 |
| 1655. | 60 f. Pres. Hussain, candle and flowers .. | 60 | 40 |
| 1656. | 70 f. Type **380** .. .. | 75 | 55 |
| 1657. | 100 f. As No. 1655 .. | 1·10 | 75 |

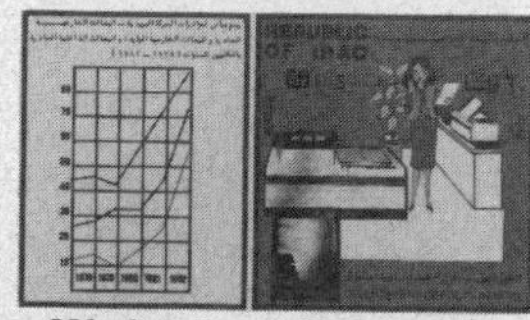
**381.** Graph and Modern Office.

**1985.** Posts and Telecommunications Development. Multicoloured.

| | | | |
|---|---|---|---|
| 1659. | 20 f. Type **381** .. .. | 20 | 15 |
| 1660. | 50 f. Dish aerial and graph .. .. | 60 | 30 |
| 1661. | 60 f. Type **381** .. .. | 65 | 30 |
| 1662. | 70 f. As No. 1660 .. | 75 | 45 |

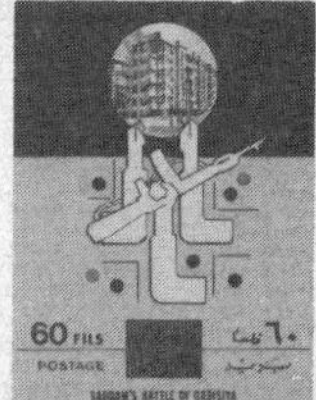

**382.** Arms at Crossroads, and Building.

**1985.** Saddam's Battle of Qadisiya. Multicoloured.

| | | | |
|---|---|---|---|
| 1663. | 10 f. Type **382** .. .. | 15 | 10 |
| 1664. | 20 f. Pres. Hussain and emblem of Al-Baath Party .. .. .. | 20 | 15 |
| 1665. | 60 f. Type **382** .. .. | 65 | 35 |
| 1666. | 70 f. As No. 1664 .. | 70 | 55 |

**383.** Solar Energy Research Centre.

**1985.**

| | | | |
|---|---|---|---|
| 1668. | **383.** 10 f. multicoloured .. | 15 | 10 |
| 1669. | 50 f. multicoloured .. | 60 | 30 |
| 1670. | 100 f. multicoloured | 1·10 | 70 |

**384.** Disabled Children.

**385.** Hand holding Quill.

**1985.** U.N.I.C.E.F. Child Survival Campaign. Multicoloured.

| | | | |
|---|---|---|---|
| 1671. | 10 f. Type **384** .. .. | 15 | 10 |
| 1672. | 15 f. Toddler and baby .. | 25 | 15 |
| 1673. | 50 f. Type **384** .. .. | 60 | 30 |
| 1674. | 100 f. As No. 1672 .. | 1·10 | 80 |

**1985.** Death Millenary of Al-Sharif Al-Radhi (poet).

| | | | |
|---|---|---|---|
| 1675. | **385.** 10 f. multicoloured .. | 15 | 10 |
| 1676. | 50 f. multicoloured .. | 45 | 30 |
| 1677. | 100 f. multicoloured | 95 | 65 |

**386.** U.N. Emblem.

**1985.** 40th Anniv. of U.N.O.

| | | | |
|---|---|---|---|
| 1678. | **386.** 10 f. multicoloured .. | 15 | 10 |
| 1679. | 40 f. blue, black and yellow .. .. | 45 | 25 |
| 1680. | 100 f. multicoloured | 1·10 | 65 |

**387.** World Map.

**1985.** Palestinian Solidarity Day.

| | | | |
|---|---|---|---|
| 1681. | **387.** 10 f. multicoloured .. | 15 | 10 |
| 1682. | 50 f. multicoloured .. | 55 | 30 |
| 1683. | 100 f. multicoloured | 1·40 | 70 |

## MINIMUM PRICE

The minimum price quoted is 10p which represents a handling charge rather than a basis for valuing common stamps. For further notes about prices see introductory pages.

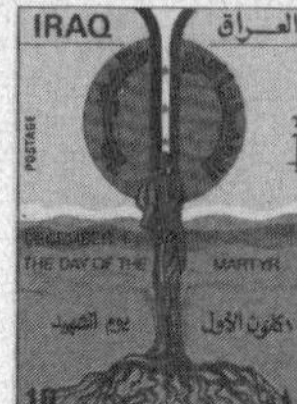

**388.** Flag, Man and Blood Vessels as Roots.

**389.** I.Y.Y. Emblem and Soldier with Flag.

**1985.** Martyr's Day.

| | | | |
|---|---|---|---|
| 1684. | **388.** 10 f. multicoloured .. | 15 | 10 |
| 1685. | 40 f. multicoloured .. | 45 | 30 |
| 1686. | 100 f. multicoloured | 95 | 60 |

**1985.** International Youth Year. Mult.

| | | | |
|---|---|---|---|
| 1687 | 40 f. Type **389** .. .. | 35 | 20 |
| 1688 | 50 f. Young couple, flag and I.Y.Y. emblem .. | 50 | 25 |
| 1689 | 100 f. Type **389** .. .. | 90 | 60 |
| 1690 | 200 f. As No. 1688 .. | 1·75 | 1·40 |

**390.** Pres. Hussain and Soldier in "6".

**391.** Pen as Knife in Sheet of Text.

**1986.** Army Day. Multicoloured.

| | | | |
|---|---|---|---|
| 1692. | 10 f. Type **390** .. .. | 15 | 15 |
| 1693. | 40 f. Pres. Hussain, cog-wheel, "6" and missiles (horiz.) .. .. | 45 | 20 |
| 1694. | 50 f. Type **390** .. .. | 55 | 30 |
| 1695. | 100 f. As No. 1693 .. | 1·25 | 70 |

**1986.** Iraqi Prisoners of War Commemoration. Multicoloured.

| | | | |
|---|---|---|---|
| 1697 | 30 f. Type **391** .. .. | 30 | 20 |
| 1698 | 70 f. Dove, cherub holding flag and three prisoners | 75 | 45 |
| 1699 | 100 f. Type **391** .. .. | 95 | 60 |
| 1700 | 200 f. As No. 1698 .. | 2·00 | 1·40 |

**392.** Pres. Hussain with Children.

**393.** Worker, Globe and Cogwheel.

**1986.** 49th Birthday of President Saddam Hussain. Multicoloured.

| | | | |
|---|---|---|---|
| 1702. | 30 f. Type **392** .. .. | 30 | 15 |
| 1703. | 50 f. Pres. Hussain and doves holding flag .. | 60 | 20 |
| 1704. | 100 f. Type **392** .. .. | 90 | 65 |
| 1705. | 150 f. As No. 1703 .. | 1·60 | 1·00 |

**1986.** Labour Day. Multicoloured.

| | | | |
|---|---|---|---|
| 1707. | 10 f. Type **393** .. .. | 10 | 10 |
| 1708. | 40 f. Candle in cogwheel | 35 | 15 |
| 1709. | 100 f. Type **393** .. .. | 90 | 65 |
| 1710. | 150 f. As No. 1708 .. | 1·25 | 90 |

**394.** Pres. Hussain and "30 July 17".

**1986.** July Festivals and 7th Anniv. of Pres. Hussain's State Leadership. Multicoloured.

| | | | |
|---|---|---|---|
| 1711 | 20 f. Type **394** .. .. | 15 | 10 |
| 1712 | 30 f. Pres. Hussain and "17 1986" .. .. | 25 | 15 |
| 1713 | 100 f. Type **394** .. .. | 90 | 60 |
| 1714 | 150 f. As No. 1712 .. | 1·40 | 95 |

**395.** Pres. Hussain and Jet Fighter.

**1986.** 55th Anniv. of Iraqi Air Force. Multicoloured.

| | | | |
|---|---|---|---|
| 1716 | 30 f. Type **395** .. .. | 55 | 20 |
| 1717 | 50 f. Pres. Hussain and jet fighters .. .. | 1·10 | 30 |
| 1718 | 100 f. Type **395** .. | 2·10 | 1·25 |
| 1719 | 150 f. As No. 1717 .. | 3·00 | 1·60 |

**396.** Refinery.

**397.** Arab Warrior.

**1986.** Oil Nationalization Day. Mult.

| | | | |
|---|---|---|---|
| 1721. | 10 f. Type **396** .. .. | 15 | 10 |
| 1722. | 40 f. Derrick and pipeline within flag (vert.) .. | 45 | 20 |
| 1723. | 100 f. Type **396** .. .. | 1·10 | 60 |
| 1724. | 150 f. As No. 1722 .. | 1·60 | 1·10 |

**1986.** 1st Battle of Qadisiya. Multicoloured.

| | | | |
|---|---|---|---|
| 1725. | 20 f. Type **397** .. .. | 30 | 15 |
| 1726. | 60 f. Pres. Hussain and battle scene .. .. | 60 | 35 |
| 1727. | 70 f. Type **397** .. .. | 65 | 45 |
| 1728. | 100 f. As No. 1726 .. | 95 | 60 |

**398.** Pres. Hussain, Battlefield and Cheering Soldiers.

**399.** Pres. Hussain.

**1986.** Saadam's Battle of Qadisiya. Mult.

| | | | |
|---|---|---|---|
| 1729 | 30 f. Type **398** .. .. | 65 | 25 |
| 1730 | 40 f. Pres. Hussain within flag "swords" and symbols of ancient and modern warfare (horiz) | 90 | 35 |
| 1731 | 100 f. Type **398** .. .. | 1·50 | 1·00 |
| 1732 | 150 f. As No. 1730 .. | 3·00 | 1·50 |

**1986.**

| | | | |
|---|---|---|---|
| 1734. | **399.** 30 f. multicoloured .. | 50 | 15 |
| 1735. | 50 f. multicoloured .. | 75 | 20 |
| 1736. | 100 f. multicoloured | 1·40 | 40 |
| 1737. | 150 f. multicoloured | 2·00 | 60 |
| 1738. | 250 f. multicoloured | 3·50 | 1·10 |
| 1739. | 350 f. multicoloured | 5·00 | 1·50 |

**401.** Women.

**402.** Flag and Treble Clef forming Dove.

**1986.** Iraqi Women's Day. Multicoloured.

| | | | |
|---|---|---|---|
| 1744 | 30 f. Type **401** .. .. | 30 | 15 |
| 1745 | 50 f. Woman and battle scenes (horiz) .. | 70 | 25 |
| 1746 | 100 f. Type **401** .. .. | 95 | 60 |
| 1747 | 150 f. As No. 1745 .. | 1·90 | 95 |

**1986.** International Peace Year. Mult.

| | | | |
|---|---|---|---|
| 1748 | 50 f. Type **402** .. .. | 45 | 15 |
| 1749 | 100 f. Globe, dove with flag and hand holding rifle and olive branch | 95 | 55 |
| 1750 | 150 f. Type **402** .. .. | 1·40 | 90 |
| 1751 | 250 f. As No. 1749 .. | 2·10 | 1·10 |

**403.** Freighter "Al Alwah" and Map.

**404.** Activities on Tree.

**1987.** 10th Anniv. of United Arab Shipping Company. Multicoloured.
1753. 50 f. Type **403** .. .. 40 20
1754. 100 f. Container ship "Khaled Ibn Al Waleed" .. .. 80 45
1755. 150 f. Type **403** .. .. 1·25 70
1756. 250 f. As No. 1754 .. 1·75 1·10

**1987.** 40th Anniv. of U.N.I.C.E.F. Mult.
1758 20 f. Type **404** .. .. 15 15
1759 40 f. Doves and "40" containing children and U.N.I.C.E.F. emblem (horiz) .. .. 25 20
1760 90 f. Type **404** .. .. 65 40
1761 100 f. As No. 1759 .. 70 50

**405.** Pres. Hussain in "6".

**406.** Torch, Cogwheel, Wheat and Map.

**1987.** Army Day. Multicoloured.
1762. 20 f. Type **405** .. .. 15 10
1763. 40 f. Pres. Hussain and military scenes .. 40 15
1764. 90 f. Type **405** .. .. 50 25
1765. 100 f. As No. 1763 .. 80 40

**1987.** 40th Anniv. of Al-Baath Party. Mult.
1766. 20 f. Type **406** .. .. 15 10
1767. 40 f. Pres. Hussain, map and flag as "7" .. 20 15
1768. 90 f. Type **406** .. .. 50 25
1769. 100 f. As No. 1767 .. 60 30

**407.** Pres. Hussain.

**408.** Pres. Hussain, Civilians, Soldiers and buried Soldier.

**1987.** 50th Birthday of President Saddam Hussain. Multicoloured.
1770 20 f. Type **407** .. .. 15 10
1771 40 f. Anniversary dates, flowers and Pres. Hussain .. .. 20 15
1772 90 f. Type **407** .. .. 50 30
1773 100 f. As No. 1771 .. 60 35

**1987.** July Festivals and 8th Anniv. of Pres. Hussain's State Leadership. Multicoloured.
1774 20 f. Pres. Hussain and flag (horiz) .. .. 15 10
1775 40 f. Type **408** .. .. 30 15
1776 90 f. As No. 1174 .. 55 35
1777 100 f. Type **408** .. 70 45

**409.** Symbolic Family on Graph.

**1987.** Census. Multicoloured.
1778. 20 f. Type **409** .. .. 20 10
1779. 30 f. People on graph .. 30 15
1780. 50 f. As No. 1779 .. 40 20
1781. 500 f. Type **409** .. .. 3·50 2·50

**410.** Pres. Hussain in "6" and Troops.

**412.** Flag as "V" and Lyre.

**411.** "8" and Pres. Hussain.

**1988.** Army Day. Multicoloured.
1782 20 f. Type **410** .. .. 20 10
1783 30 f. Soldier and medal (horiz) .. .. 20 15
1784 50 f. Type **410** .. .. 35 20
1785 150 f. As No. 1783 .. 85 50

**1988.** 18th Anniv of People's Army (1786, 1788) and 25th Anniv of 8th February Revolution (others). Multicoloured.
1786 20 f. Type **411** .. .. 20 10
1787 30 f. Pres. Hussain and eagle on "8" (vert) .. 25 15
1788 50 f. Type **411** .. .. 35 20
1789 150 f. As No. 1787 .. 1·00 60

**1988.** Art Day. Multicoloured.
1790. 20 f. Type **412** .. .. 20 10
1791. 30 f. Pres. Hussain, rifle as torch, clef and dove on film strip .. .. 25 15
1792. 50 f. Type **412** .. .. 35 25
1793. 100 f. As No. 1791 .. 70 45

**413.** Rally and Ears of Wheat.

**1988.** 41st Anniv. of Al-Baath Party. Mult.
1795. 20 f. Type **413** .. .. 15 10
1796. 30 f. Flowers and "7 April 1947–1988" .. 15 15
1797. 50 f. Type **413** .. .. 35 25
1798. 150 f. As No. 1796 .. 85 60

**414.** Emblem.

**415.** Pres. Hussain.

**1988.** Regional Marine Environment Day. Multicoloured.
1799 20 f. Type **414** .. .. 15 10
1800 40 f. Fishes (horiz) .. 25 15
1801 90 f. Type **414** .. .. 60 45
1802 100 f. As No. 1800 .. 80 50

**1988.** 51st Birthday of President Saddam Hussain. Multicoloured.
1803. 20 f. Type **415** .. .. 15 10
1804. 30 f. Pres. Hussain and hands holding flowers .. 20 15
1805. 50 f. Type **415** .. .. 35 20
1806. 100 f. As No. 1804 .. 65 45

**416.** Emblem.

**1988.** 40th Anniv. of W.H.O. Multicoloured.
1808 20 f. Type **416** .. .. 15 10
1809 40 f. Red crescent protecting line of people (vert) .. .. 20 15
1810 90 f. Type **416** .. .. 65 45
1811 100 f. As No. 1809 .. 75 55

**417.** Bomb and Open Book showing School, Child and Wreath.

**418** Hand holding Flash of Lightning

**1988.** Bilat Al-Shuhada School Bomb Victims. Multicoloured.
1812 20 f. Type **417** .. .. 15 10
1813 40 f. Explosion and girl (horiz) .. .. 25 15
1814 90 f. Type **417** .. .. 60 45
1815 100 f. As No. 1813 .. 70 50

**1988.** July Festivals and 9th Anniv of President Hussain's State Leadership. Mult.
1817 50 f. Type **418** .. .. 35 25
1818 90 f. Sun, map and Pres. Hussain .. .. 50 35
1819 100 f. Type **418** .. .. 65 45
1820 150 f. As No. 1818 .. 1·00 70

**419** Pres. Hussain and al-Sail al-Kabir Miqat.

**1988.** President Hussain's Pilgrimage to Mecca.
1822 **419** 90 f. multicoloured .. 60 40
1823 100 f. multicoloured .. 70 50
1824 150 f. multicoloured .. 1·00 70

**420** Mosul

**1988.** Tourism. Multicoloured.
1825 50 f. Type **420** .. .. 60 40
1826 100 f. Basrah .. .. 80 55
1827 150 f. Baghdad (vert) .. 1·50 1·00

**421** Pres. Hussain and Soldiers

**422** Emblem

**1988.** "Vctorious Iraq".
1828 **421** 50 f. multicoloured .. 2·00 2·00
1829 100 f. multicoloured .. 4·25 4·25
1830 150 f. multicoloured .. 6·25 6·25

**1988.** Navy Day. Multicoloured.
1831 50 f. Type **422** .. .. 40 30
1832 90 f. Missile boats .. 90 55
1833 100 f. Type **422** .. .. 85 60
1834 150 f. As No. 1832 .. 1·25 90

**423** Map and Hands holding Flag

**1988.** Liberation of Fao City.
1836 **423** 100 f. multicoloured .. 60 40
1837 150 f. multicoloured .. 1·25 90

**424** Missile Launch from Winged Map

**425** Boxer and Hodori (mascot)

**1988.** Iraq Missile Research.
1839 **424** 100 f. multicoloured .. 60 40
1840 150 f. multicoloured .. 85 60

**1988.** Olympic Games, Seoul. Multicoloured.
1842 100 f. Type **425** .. .. 85 60
1843 150 f. Games emblem .. 1·25 90

**426** Dancers and Golden Cow

**427** Crescent and Camel Train

**1988.** 2nd Babylon International Festival.
1845 **426** 100 f. multicoloured .. 50 35
1846 150 f. multicoloured .. 80 55

**1988.** Mohammed's Birth Anniv.
1848 **427** 100 f. multicoloured .. 50 35
1849 150 f. multicoloured .. 75 55
1850 1 d. multicoloured .. 5·50 4·00

**428** Hand holding Candle

انتصر العراق
١٩٨٨/٨/٨
(**429** "Victory")

**1988.** Martyr's Day.
1851 **428** 100 f. multicoloured .. 55 40
1852 150 f. multicoloured .. 80 55
1853 500 f. multicoloured .. 2·50 1·75

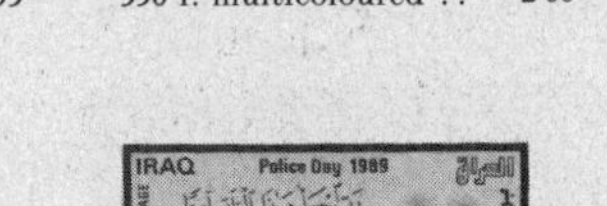

**1988.** Nos. 1738/9 optd with T **429**.
1854 **399** 250 f. multicoloured .. 1·40 1·00
1855 350 f. multicoloured .. 2·00 1·40

**430** Family on Pedestrian Crossing

**1989.** Police Day.
1856 **430** 50 f. multicoloured .. 30 20
1857 100 f. multicoloured .. 55 40
1858 150 f. multicoloured .. 85 60

431 Children and Money

**1989.** Postal Savings Bank.
(a) Size 32×32 mm.
1859 **431** 50 f. multicoloured .. 25 20

(b) Size 24×25 mm. With or without Arabic overprint.
1860 – 100 f. multicoloured .. 55 40
1861 – 150 f. multicoloured .. 80 55

DESIGN: 100, 150 f. Motif as Type **431** but with inscriptions differently arranged and inscr "REPUBLIC OF IRAQ".

Nos. 1860/1 were not issued without overprint.

432 Members' Flags and Leaders

**1989.** Formation of Arab Co-operation Council (Egypt, Iraq, Jordan and Yemen Arab Republic). Multicoloured.
1862 100 f. Type **432** .. .. 55 40
1863 150 f. Leaders in formal pose .. .. .. 80 55

433 Dates

**1989.** 1st Anniv of Liberation of Fao City.
1864 **433** 100 f. multicoloured .. 55 40
1865 150 f. multicoloured .. 80 55

434 Pres. Hussain

**1989.** 52nd Birthday of President Saddam Hussain.
1867 **434** 100 f. multicoloured ... 70 50
1868 150 f. multicoloured .. 1·10 75

435 Khairalla

436 Hussain laying Mortar

**1989.** General Adnan Khairalla Commem.
1870 **435** 50 f. multicoloured .. 35 25
1871 100 f. multicoloured .. 70 50
1872 150 f. multicoloured .. 1·00 70

**1989.** Completion of Basrah Reconstruction Project.
1873 **436** 100 f. multicoloured .. 70 50
1874 150 f. multicoloured .. 1·00 70

437 Crane and Buildings

438 "Women"

**1989.** Start of Reconstruction of Fao City.
1875 **437** 100 f. multicoloured .. 70 50
1876 150 f. multicoloured .. 1·00 70

**1989.**
1877 **438** 100 f. multicoloured .. 70 50
1878 150 f. multicoloured .. 1·10 75
1879 1 d. multicoloured .. 5·75 4·00
1880 5 d. multicoloured .. 25·00 17·00

439 Pres. Hussain

440 Flag and Victory Signs

**1989.** July Festivals and 10th Anniv of President Hussain's State Leadership.
1881 **439** 50 f. multicoloured .. 30 20
1882 100 f. multicoloured .. 55 40
1883 150 f. multicoloured .. 90 65

**1989.** Victory Day.
1884 **440** 100 f. multicoloured .. 55 40
1885 150 f. multicoloured .. 90 65

441 Children, Heart and Bride

**1989.** Iraqi Family.
1887 **441** 50 f. multicoloured .. 30 20
1888 100 f. multicoloured .. 60 40
1889 150 f. multicoloured .. 95 65

442 Najaf

**1989.** Tourism. Multicoloured.
1890 100 f. Type **442** .. .. 60 40
1891 100 f. Arbil .. .. 60 40
1892 100 f. Marsh Arab punter and Ziggurat of Ur .. 60 40

443 Map and Means of Transport

**1989.** 5th Session of Arab Ministers of Transport Council, Baghdad. Mult.
1893 50 f. Type **443** .. .. 30 20
1894 100 f. Sun, means of transport and map .. 60 40
1895 150 f. Means of transport, and members' flags (vert) .. .. 85 60

444 City and Pres. Hussain placing Final Stone

445 Anniversary Emblem

**1989.** Completion of Fao City Reconstruction.
1896 **444** 100 f. multicoloured .. 70 50
1897 150 f. multicoloured .. 1·00 70

**1989.** 30th Anniv of Iraqi News Agency.
1898 **445** 50 f. multicoloured .. 30 20
1899 100 f. multicoloured .. 60 40
1900 150 f. multicoloured .. 85 60

446 Emblem

447 Pansies

**1989.** 1st Anniv of Declaration of Palestinian State. Multicoloured.
1901 25 f. Type **446** .. .. 15 10
1902 50 f. Crowd of children .. 30 20
1903 100 f. Type **446** .. .. 60 40
1904 150 f. As No. 1902 .. 95 65

**1989.** Flowers. Multicoloured.
1905 25 f. Type **447** .. .. 15 10
1906 50 f. Antirrhinums .. 30 20
1907 100 f. "Hibiscus trionum" 60 40
1908 150 f. Mesembryanthemums .. .. 1·00 70

448 Map and Emblem

**1989.** Cent of Interparliamentary Union.
1910 **448** 25 f. multicoloured .. 20 10
1911 100 f. multicoloured .. 60 40
1912 150 f. multicoloured .. 90 60

449 Sun, Flag, Doves and Mosque Domes

450 Dove, Red Crescent and Pres. Hussain

**1989.** Martyr's Day.
1913 **449** 50 f. multicoloured .. 25 20
1914 100 f. multicoloured .. 55 40
1915 150 f. multicoloured .. 80 55

**1989.** Iraqi Red Crescent Society.
1916 **450** 100 f. multicoloured .. 50 35
1917 150 f. multicoloured .. 75 55
1918 500 f. multicoloured .. 2·50 1·75

451 Members' Flags on Map

**1990.** 1st Anniv of Arab Co-operation Council.
1919 **451** 50 f. multicoloured .. 60 40
1920 100 f. multicoloured .. 1·00 70

مؤتمر القمة العربي
الاستثنائي
بغداد ٢٨/أيار/١٩٩٠
(452)

**1990.** Arab League Summit Conference, Baghdad. Nos. 1906 and 1908 optd with T **452**.
1922 50 f. multicoloured .. 30 20
1923 150 f. multicoloured .. 85 60

453 Doves and Flag as Flame

**1990.** 2nd Anniv of Liberation of Fao City.
1924 **453** 50 f. multicoloured .. 30 20
1925 100 f. multicoloured .. 60 40

OBLIGATORY TAX

28a. King Faisal II.
28b. King Faisal II.

مالية
فلسان
انقاذ فلسطين
(28c. "Tax 2 Fils Save Palestine").

مالية
انقاذ فلسطين
(28d. "Tax Save Palestine").

انقاذ
فلسطين
(28e. "Save Palestine") (size varies).

١٠ فلوس
انقاذ فلسطين
(28g. "Tax 10 Fils Save Palestine") (size varies).

مالية
٥ فلوس
انقاذ فلسطين
(28h. "Tax 5 Fils Save Palistine").

**1949.** Aid for Palestine.
(a) Nos. O300 and 278 surch as T 28c.
T324 27 2 f. on 3 f. green .. 9·00 7·50
T325 2 f. on 6 f. mauve .. 8·50 6·75
(b) Nos. O299 and O303 optd as T 28d but smaller.
T326 27 2 f. brown .. .. 5·00 4·25
T327 5 f. red .. .. 12·50 10·00
(c) No. O234 optd with T 28d.
T328 20 5 f. red .. .. 3·00 4·25
(d) Revenue stamp surch in Arabic (="2 Fils Save Palestine") as bottom two lines of T 28c.
T329 28a 2 f. on 5 f. blue .. 4·00 2·50
(e) Revenue stamps optd with T 28e.
T330 28a 5 f. blue .. .. 1·90 35
T335 10 f. orange .. 6·75 3·00
T332 28b 10 f. orange .. — 13·50
(f) Revenue stamp surch as T 28g.
T336 28b 10 f. on 20 f. green .. 15·00 9·25
(h) No. 278 surch with T 28h.
T337 27 5 f. on 6 f. mauve .. 17·00 6·50

(113a.)

دفاع
وطني
(113b.)

**1968.** Flood Relief.
T 763. 113a. 5 f. brown.. .. 20 15

**1968.** Defence Fund. Optd. with Type 113b.
T 764. 113a. 5 f. brown .. 20 15

دفاع وطني
٥ فلوس
(164a.)

دفاع وطني
٥ فلوس
(215.)

**1970.** Obligatory Tax. Defence Fund. Nos. 620 and 625/9 surch. with Type T 164a.
T 931. 65. 5 f. on 1 f. green .. 2·50 2·75
T 932. – 5 f. on 10 f. red .. 2·50 2·75
T 933. – 5 f. on 15 f. brn. & yell. 2·50 2·75
T 934. – 5 f. on 20 f. violet .. 2·50 2·75
T 935. – 5 f. on 30 f. orange .. 2·50 2·75
T 936. – 5 f. on 40 f. green .. 2·50 2·75

**1973.** Obligatory Tax. Defence Fund. Nos. 607/8 surch. with Type 215.
T 1071. 62. 5 f. on 14 f. blk. & grn. 3·50 3·50
T 1072. 5 f. on 35 f. blk. & red 3·50 3·50

دفاع وطني
٥ فلوس
(223.)

دفاع
وطني
(231.)

**1973.** Nos. 738, 765, 777, 787 and 891 optd similar to Type 215 (No. T1119) or as Type 223 (others).
T 1117. – 5 f. on 2 f. mult. .. 2·75 3·00
T 1118. 114. 5 f. on 2 f. mult. .. 2·75 3·00
T 1119. 116. 5 f. on 2 f. mult. .. 2·75 3·00
T 1120. 117. 5 f. on 2 f. mult. .. 2·75 3·00
T 1121. 150. 5 f. on 2 f. mult. .. 2·75 3·00

**1973.** No. 1099 optd with Type 231.
T1152 221 5 f. black and orange 2·40 1·00

235 Soldier

**1974.** Defence Fund.
T1158 235 5 f. black, yell & brn 60 80

OFFICIAL STAMPS

**1920.** Issue of 1918 (surch Turkish stamps) optd On STATE SERVICE.
O33 ½ a. on 10 pa. green .. 50 60
O34 1 a. on 20 pa. red .. 1·25 60
O35 1½ a. on 5 pa. brown .. 1·25 45
O22 2½ a. on 1 pi. blue .. 1·40 2·25
O23 3 a. on 1½ pi. black & pink 5·00 80
O36 4 a. on 1¾ pi. brown & bl 2·00 90
O25 6 a. on 2 pi. black & green 9·50 4·75
O38 8 a. on 2½ pi. green & brn 3·00 2·00
O27 12 a. on 5 pi. purple .. 6·00 4·50
O28 1 r. on 10 pi. brown .. 6·50 4·25
O29 2 r. on 25 pi. green .. 15·00 10·00
O30 5 r. on 50 pi. red .. 30·00 23·00
O31 10 r. on 100 pi. blue .. 50·00 55·00

**1923.** Nos. 41/50 and 52/3 optd ON STATE SERVICE in English only.
O54 2 ½ a. green .. .. 70 30
O55 – 1 a. brown .. .. 70 10
O56 3 1½ a. red .. .. 1·75 45
O57 – 2 a. buff .. .. 1·50 20
O58 – 3 a. blue .. .. 2·50 85
O59 – 4 a. violet .. .. 2·50 40
O60 – 6 a. blue .. .. 3·50 1·25
O61 – 8 a. bistre .. .. 4·00 1·25
O62 4 1 r. brown and green .. 5·00 1·25
O63 2 2 r. black .. .. 18·00 8·00
O64 – 5 r. orange .. .. 48·00 24·00
O65 – 10 r. red .. .. 70·00 48·00

**1924.** Nos. 41/9 and 51/3 optd ON STATE SERVICE in English and Arabic.
O66 2 ½ a. green .. .. 60 10
O67 – 1 a. brown .. .. 40 10
O68 3 1½ a. red .. .. 70 10
O69 – 2 a. buff .. .. 90 10
O70 – 3 a. blue .. .. 90 10
O71 – 4 a. violet .. .. 2·50 30
O72 – 6 a. blue .. .. 1·75 20
O73 – 8 a. bistre .. .. 1·75 35
O74 4 1 r. brown and green .. 9·50 1·00
O75 2 2 r. bistre .. .. 24·00 3·75
O76 – 5 r. orange .. .. 45·00 40·00
O77 – 10 r. red .. .. 65·00 42·00

**1927.** Optd ON STATE SERVICE in English and Arabic.
O79 10 1 r. brown .. .. 5·50 1·50

**1931.** Optd ON STATE SERVICE in English and Arabic.
O93 11 ½ a. green .. .. 30 2·75
O94 1 a. brown .. .. 50 10
O95 1½ a. red .. .. 4·50 15·00
O96 2 a. orange .. .. 50 10
O97 3 a. blue .. .. 85 70
O98 4 a. purple .. .. 95 90
O99 6 a. blue .. .. 3·50 12·00
O100 8 a. green .. .. 3·50 12·00
O101 12 1 r. brown .. .. 9·50 11·00
O102 2 r. brown .. .. 16·00 42·00
O103 5 r. orange .. .. 35·00 75·00
O104 10 r. red .. .. 70·00 £130
O105 10 25 r. violet .. .. £550 £700

**1932.** Official stamps of 1924 and 1931 surch in "Fils" or "Dinar".
O122 11 3 f. on ½ a. green .. 2·50 2·75
O123 4 f. on 1 a. brown .. 2·25 10
O124 5 f. on 1 a. brown .. 2·00 10
O125 4 8 f. on 1½ a. red .. 2·75 50
O126 11 10 f. on 2 a. orange .. 2·50 10
O127 15 f. on 3 a. blue .. 3·00 85
O128 20 f. on 4 a. purple .. 3·00 1·10
O129 11 25 f. on 4 a. purple 3·50 1·25
O130 – 30 f. on 6 a. blue (No. O72) .. .. 3·50 1·75
O131 11 40 f. on 8 a. green .. 3·50 3·50
O132 12 50 f. 1 r. brown .. 3·50 3·50
O133 75 f. on 1 r. brown .. 5·00 6·00
O134 2 100 f. on 2 r. bistre .. 9·00 3·50
O135 – 200 f. on 5 r. orange (No. O76) .. .. 17·00 17·00
O136 – ½ d. on 10 r. red (No. 77) .. .. 50·00 70·00
O137 10 1 d. on 25 r. violet .. 85·00 £140

**1932.** Issue of 1932 optd. ON STATE SERVICE in English and Arabic.
O 155. 11. 2 f. blue .. .. 85 10
O 156. 3 f. green .. .. 85 10
O 157. 4 f. purple .. .. 1·00 10
O 158. 5 f. green .. .. 1·00 10
O 159. 8 f. red .. .. 1·00 10
O 160. 10 f. yellow .. .. 1·75 10
O 161. 15 f. blue .. .. 2·25 10
O 162. 20 f. orange .. .. 2·25 15
O 163. 25 f. mauve .. .. 2·00 15
O 164. 30 f. olive .. .. 3·25 20
O 165. 40 f. violet .. .. 4·25 20
O 166. 12. 50 f. brown .. .. 3·00 20
O 167. 75 f. blue .. .. 2·25 90
O 168. 100 f. green .. .. 8·00 85
O 169. 200 f. red .. .. 14·00 6·50
O 170. 10. ½ d. blue .. .. 11·00 20·00
O 171. 1 d. purple .. .. 50·00 70·00

**1934.** Issue of 1934 optd. ON STATE SERVICE in English and Arabic.
O 190. 16. 1 f. violet .. .. 1·10 40
O 191. 2 f. blue .. .. 90 15
O 192. 3 f. green .. .. 50 15
O 193. 4 f. purple .. .. 1·00 15
O 194. 5 f. green .. .. 90 15
O 195. 8 f. red .. .. 3·50 25
O 196. 10 f. yellow .. .. 35 15
O 197. 15 f. blue .. .. 8·00 1·25
O 198. 20 f. orange .. .. 75 15
O 199. 25 f. mauve .. .. 16·00 4·75
O 200. 30 f. green .. .. 3·50 25
O 201. 40 f. violet .. .. 4·50 25
O 202. 17. 50 f. brown .. .. 70 55
O 203. 75 f. blue .. .. 5·00 65
O 204. 100 f. green .. .. 1·40 85
O 205. 200 f. red .. .. 3·50 2·00
O 206. – ½ d. blue (No. 188) 10·00 15·00
O 207. – 1 d. red (No. 189) .. 38·00 45·00

**1941.** Issue of 1941 optd. ON STATE SERVICE in English and Arabic.
O230 19 1 f. purple .. 20 15
O231 2 f. brown .. 20 15
O232 – 3 f. green (No. 210) 20 15
O233 – 4 f. violet (No. 211) 20 15
O234 – 5 f. red (No. 212) 20 15
O235 21 8 f. red .. .. 65 15
O236b 8 f. yellow .. 15 15
O237 10 f. yellow .. 4·25 35
O238 10 f. red .. .. 50 15
O239 15 f. blue .. .. 4·25 65
O240 15 f. black .. 85 25
O241 20 f. black .. 1·25 25
O242 20 f. blue .. 40 15
O244 22 25 f. purple .. 65 25
O246a 30 f. orange .. 35 25
O248a 40 f. brown.. .. 45 25
O249c – 50 f. blue (No. 224) 75 50
O250 – 75 f. mauve (No. 225) 85 25
O251 – 100 f. olive (No. 226) 1·75 25
O252 – 200 f. orge. (No. 227) 2·00 70
O253 – ½ d. blue (No. 228) 9·00 4·25
O254 – 1 d. green (No. 229).. 14·00 7·50

**1942.** Issue of 1942 optd ON STATE SERVICE in English and Arabic.
O263 26 1 f. brown and violet 25 25
O264 2 f. brown and blue .. 25 25
O265 3 f. brown and green 25 25
O266 4 f. sepia and brown .. 25 25
O267 5 f. brown and green 35 35
O268 6 f. brown and red .. 35 35
O269 10 f. brown and pink 45 45
O270 12 f. brown and green 45 45

**1948.** Issue of 1948 optd ON STATE SERVICE in English and Arabic.
O298 27 1 f. blue .. .. 15 25
O299 2 f. brown .. .. 15 30
O300 3 f. green .. .. 15 30
O301 3 f. red .. .. 2·10 20
O302 4 f. lilac .. .. 15 25
O303 5 f. red .. .. 15 20
O304 5 f. green .. .. 2·50 20
O305 6 f. mauve .. .. 20 30
O306 8 f. brown .. .. 20 30
O307 10 f. red .. .. 20 25
O308 12 f. green .. .. 20 25
O309 14 f. green .. .. 90 25
O310 15 f. black .. .. 4·00 5·00
O311 16 f. red .. .. 2·00 30
O312 20 f. blue .. .. 20 15
O313 25 f. purple .. .. 20 15
O314 28 f. blue .. .. 65 30
O315 30 f. orange .. .. 20 20
O316 40 f. brown .. .. 45 35
O317 50 f. blue .. .. 50 30
O318 60 f. blue .. .. 45 20
O319 75 f. mauve .. .. 85 20
O320 100 f. green .. .. 85 85
O321 200 f. orange .. .. 1·40 85
O322 ½ d. blue .. .. 11·50 12·00
O323 1 d. green .. .. 17·00 25·00

**1955.** Issue of 1954 optd. ON STATE SERVICE in English and Arabic.
O 364. 33. 1 f. blue .. .. 20 20
O 365. 2 f. brown .. .. 20 20
O 366. 3 f. lake .. .. 20 20
O 367. 4 f. violet .. .. 20 20
O 368. 5 f. green .. .. 20 20
O 369. 6 f. mauve .. .. 20 20
O 370. 8 f. brown .. .. 20 20
O 371. 10 f. blue .. .. 20 20
O 372. 16 f. red .. .. 17·00 20·00
O 373. 20 f. olive .. .. 35 25
O 374. 25 f. purple .. .. 1·75 85
O 375. 30 f. red .. .. 75 25
O 376. 40 f. brown .. .. 35 25
O 377. – 50 f. blue .. .. 1·90 65
O 378. – 60 f. purple .. .. 10·00 4·50
O 379. – 100 f. olive .. .. 24·00 11·00
No. O 378 does not exist without opt.

**1958.** Issue of 1957 optd ON STATE SERVICE in English and Arabic.
O404 41 1 f. blue .. .. 1·50 1·50
O405 2 f. brown .. .. 2·10 2·10
O406 3 f. red .. .. 2·10 2·10
O407 4 f. violet .. .. 1·50 1·50
O408 5 f. green .. .. 1·50 1·50
O409 6 f. red .. .. 1·50 1·50
O410 10 f. blue .. .. 1·50 1·50

**1958.** Official stamps optd with T 43.
(a) Nos. O251/2.
O459 – 100 f. green .. ..
O459a – 200 f. orange .. 2·75 1·50
(b) Nos. O298 etc.
O460 27 1 f. blue .. .. 17·00 17·00
O461 2 f. brown .. .. 17·00 17·00
O462 3 f. green .. .. 17·00 17·00
O463 3 f. red .. .. 17·00 17·00
O464 4 f. lilac .. .. 17·00 17·00
O465 5 f. red .. .. 17·00 17·00
O466 5 f. green .. .. 17·00 17·00
O467 6 f. mauve .. .. 17·00 17·00
O468 8 f. brown .. .. 17·00 17·00
O470 12 f. green .. .. 50 45
O471 14 f. green .. .. 85 40
O472 15 f. black .. .. 85 45
O473 16 f. red .. .. 2·10 1·25
O474 25 f. purple .. .. 1·75 1·25
O475 28 f. blue .. .. 1·25 65
O476 40 f. brown .. .. 85 70
O477 60 f. blue .. .. 3·00 2·10
O478 75 f. mauve .. .. 1·25 1·50
O479 200 f. orange .. .. 2·10 1·50
O480 ½ d. blue .. .. 6·75 5·00
O481 1 d. green .. .. 12·50 10·00
(c) Nos. O364 etc.
O482 33 1 f. blue .. .. 45 20
O483 2 f. brown .. .. 45 20
O484 3 f. red .. .. 45 20
O485 4 f. violet .. .. 45 20
O486 5 f. green .. .. 50 20
O487 6 f. mauve .. .. 45 20
O488 8 f. brown .. .. 45 20
O489 10 f. blue .. .. 45 20
O490 16 f. red .. .. 4·25 4·75
O491 20 f. green .. .. 45 20
O492 25 f. purple .. .. 45 25
O493 30 f. red .. .. 45 35
O494 40 f. brown .. .. 65 35
O495 – 50 f. blue .. .. 65 45
O496 – 60 f. purple .. .. 65 50
O497 – 100 f. green .. .. 1·25 50
(d) On Nos. O404 etc.
O498 41 1 f. blue .. .. 20 20
O499 2 f. brown .. .. 20 20
O500 3 f. red .. .. 25 20
O501 4 f. violet .. .. 25 20
O502 5 f. green .. .. 25 20
O503 6 f. red .. .. 25 20
O504 8 f. brown .. .. 45 10
O505 10 f. blue .. .. 40 20
No. O504 does not exist without opt T 43.

**1961.** Nos. 515, etc., optd. On State Service in English and Arabic.
O 552. 49. 1 f. multicoloured .. 15 10
O 553. 2 f. multicoloured .. 15 10
O 554. 4 f. multicoloured .. 15 10
O 555. 5 f. multicoloured .. 35 10
O 556. 10 f. multicoloured .. 40 10
O 557. 50 f. multicoloured .. 5·00 3·00

**1962.** Nos. 515, etc., optd. ON STATE SERVICE in English and Arabic.
O 587. 49. 1 f. multicoloured .. 10 10
O 588. 2 f. multicoloured .. 10 10
O 589. 3 f. multicoloured .. 10 10
O 590. 4 f. multicoloured .. 10 10
O 591. 5 f. multicoloured .. 10 10
O 592. 10 f. multicoloured .. 10 10
O 593. 15 f. multicoloured .. 15 10
O 594. 20 f. multicoloured .. 20 10
O 595. 30 f. multicoloured .. 25 20
O 596. 40 f. multicoloured .. 30 20
O 597. 50 f. multicoloured .. 30 20
O 598. 75 f. multicoloured .. 55 30
O 599. 100 f. multicoloured.. 85 60
O 600. 200 f. multicoloured.. 2·10 1·25
O 601. 500 f. multicoloured.. 5·50 4·25
O 602. 1 d. multicoloured .. 11·00 8·50

**1971.** Various stamps optd. or surch Official in English and Arabic.
(a) Costumes. Nos. 768 and 770/4.
O 962. 15 f. multicoloured (post.) 1·25 40
O 963. 25 f. multicoloured .. 3·25 2·75
O 964. 30 f. multicoloured .. 3·25 2·75
O 965. 40 f. multicoloured (air) 2·10 85
O 966. 50 f. multicoloured .. 2·10 85
O 967. 80 f. multicoloured .. 3·50 1·75

(b) Int., Tourist Year. Nos. 778 and 780/2.
O 969. 5 f. mult. (postage) .. 1·90 30
O 970. 15 f. multicoloured .. 1·90 45
O 971. 25 f. multicoloured .. 1·90 90
O 972. 50 f. multicoloured (air) 2·10 1·10

(c) Birds. No. 798.
O1178 30 f. multicoloured .. 3·50 2·75

(d) 20th Anniv of W.H.O. Nos. 811/13.
O973 – 10 f. multicoloured .. 2·25 50
O974 124 15 f. red, blue & black 2·25 50
O975 25 f. red, green & blk 2·25 50

(e) Human Rights Year. Nos. 814/15.
O976 125 10 f. red, yellow & bl 3·25 40
O977 25 f. red, yell & grn 3·25 70

(f) U.N.I.C.E.F. Nos. 817/18.
O978 126 15 f. multicoloured .. 3·25 35
O979 25 f. multicoloured .. 3·25 35

(g) Army Day. No. 820.
O980 127 25 f. multicoloured .. 7·50 2·75

(h) Fish and Fauna. Nos. 825/7, 829/30 and 832.
O 981. 10 f. mult. (postage) .. 3·25 2·50
O 982. 15 f. on 3 f. mult. .. 3·25 2·50
O 983. 25 f. on 2 f. mult. .. 3·25 2·50
O 984. 10 f. mult. (air) .. 3·25 2·75
O 985. 15 f.+3 f. mult. .. 3·25 2·75
O 986. 25 f.+2 f. mult. .. 3·25 2·75

(i) Fruits. Nos. 906/9.
O 987 5 f. multicoloured .. 3·25 2·75
O 988 10 f. multicoloured .. 3·25 2·75
O 989. 15 f. multicoloured .. 3·25 2·75
O 990. 35 f. multicoloured .. 3·25 2·75

(j) Arab Football Cup, Baghdad. No. 717.
O991 97 2 f. multicoloured .. 3·25 2·75

(k) 50th Anniv of I.L.O. No. 836.
O992 133 15 f. yellow, grn & blk 3·25 2·75

**1972.** Nos. 625/8 optd. **Official** in English and Arabic.
O 1042. 10 f. red .. .. 4·50 4·50
O 1043. 15 f. brown and yellow 4·50 4·50
O 1044. 20 f. violet .. .. 4·50 4·50
O 1045. 30 f. orange .. .. 4·50 4·50

**1973.** Various stamps with portrait obliterated by 3 bars.
(i) 1948 issue.
O 1081. 27. 25 f. pur. (No. O 313) 2·50 60
O 1082. 50 f. blue (No. O 317) 2·50 2·25
(ii) 1955 issue.
O 1083. 33. 25 f. pur. (No. O 374) 2·50 60
O 1084. - 50 f. blue (No. O 377) 2·50 2·25
(iii) Similar to 1958 issue (T 41) but size 22½ × 27½ mm.
O1085 – 50 f. purple .. .. 2·50 2·25

Official

(O 218.) (size varies) (O 237a.)

**1973.** "Faisal" stamps with portrait obliterated.
(a) Optd with 3 bars and Type O 218.
O1086 33 10 f. blue .. .. 2·75 2·75
O1087 41 15 f. black .. .. 2·75 3·00
(b) Optd with Type O 218 only.
O1090 33 15 f. black .. .. 2·75 75
O1091 41 15 f. black .. .. 2·75 75
O1096 27 25 f. purple .. .. 11·00 11·50
O1092 33 25 f. purple .. .. 2·75 75
O1093 41 25 f. purple .. .. 2·75 75

**1973.** No. 1097 optd. **Official** in English and Arabic.
O 1099. 220. 25 f. multicoloured 35 15

**1973.** Nos. 1099/1107 optd **OFFICIAL** in English and Arabic.
O1108 221 5 f. black and orange 15 15
O1109 10 f. black & brown 15 10
O1110 20 f. black & mauve 25 15
O1111 – 25 f. black and blue 40 15
O1112 – 35 f. black and green 50 20
O1113 – 45 f. black and blue 50 30
O1114 – 50 f. yellow & green 80 30
O1115 – 70 f. yellow & violet 1·10 45
O1116 – 95 f. yellow & brown 1·75 90

**1973.** Various "Faisal" Officialstamps optd. **ON STATE SERVICE** in English and Arabic, with portrait obliterated by "leaf" motif similar to that used in Type O 218.
(a) 1948 issue.
O 1130a. 27. 12 f. olive .. .. 3·50 80
O 1131. 14 f. olive .. .. 3·50 1·00
O 1132. 15 f. black .. .. 3·50 1·00
O 1133. 16 f. red .. .. 7·00 6·50
O 1134. 28 f. blue .. .. 3·50 1·00
O 1134a. 30 f. orange .. 3·50 1·60
O 1134b. 40 f. brown.. .. 3·50 1·60
O 1135. 60 f. blue .. .. 4·25 1·60
O 1136. 100 f. green .. 16·00 6·50
O 1137. ½ d. blue .. .. 35·00 14·00
O 1138. 1 d. green .. .. 55·00 23·00
(b) 1955 issue.
O 1139. 33. 3 f. lake .. .. 3·50 80
O 1140. 6 f. mauve .. .. 4·25 1·40
O 1141. 8 f. brown .. .. 3·50 80
O 1142. 16 f. red .. .. 7·00 6·50
O 1142a. 20 f. green .. .. 3·50 80
O 1142b. 30 f. red .. .. 3·50 80
O 1142c. 40 f. brown.. .. 3·50 80
O 1143. – 60 f. purple.. .. 6·25 2·00
O 1144. – 100 f. green .. 14·00 3·25
(c) 1958 issue.
O 1145. 41. 3 f. lake .. .. 3·50 80
O 1146. 6 f. mauve .. .. 3·50 80
O 1147. 8 f. brown .. .. 3·50 80
O 1147a. 30 f. red .. .. 3·50 80

**1974.** No. T1168 optd with Type O 237a.
O1165 235 5 f. black, yell & brn 1·60 1·40

**O 249.** Eagle Emblem. **O 342.** Entrance to Baghdad University.

**1975.**
O 1195. O 249. 5 f. multicoloured 10 10
O 1196. 10 f. multicoloured 15 10
O 1197. 15 f. multicoloured 25 10
O 1198. 20 f. multicoloured 35 10
O 1199. 25 f. multicoloured 45 10
O 1200. 30 f. multicoloured 55 20
O 1201. 50 f. multicoloured 90 35
O 1202. 100f. multicoloured 2·00 85

**1976.** Nos. 1253/7 additionally inscr. "OFFICIAL" in English and Arabic.
O 1258. 264. 5 f. multicoloured 80 65
O 1259. – 10 f. multicoloured 85 70
O 1260. – 15 f. multicoloured 90 75
O 1261. – 25 f. multicoloured 2·50 1·10
O 1262. – 50 f. multicoloured 3·50 2·00

**1978.** As T 290, but additionally inscr "OFFICIAL" in English and Arabic.
O 1338. 5 f. multicoloured .. 15 10
O 1339. 10 f. multicoloured .. 15 15
O 1340. 15 f. multicoloured .. 25 15
O 1341. 25 f. multicoloured .. 45 15

**1981.**
O 1499. O 342. 45 f. multicoloured 45 20
O 1500. 50 f. multicoloured 45 20

**1982.** As Nos. 1504/6, additionally inscr. "OFFICIAL" in English and Arabic.
O 1507. 45 f. multicoloured .. 65 20
O 1508. 50 f. multicoloured .. 65 25
O 1509. 120 f. multicoloured .. 1·50 1·10

**1983.** Nos. O 1499/1500 surch.
O 1581. O 342. 60 f. on 45 f. mult. 90 35
O 1582. 70 f. on 50 f. mult. 1·25 50

**1983.** Design as T 371.
O1615 60 f. yellow, blk & pink 65 35
O1616 70 f. yellow, blk & pink 75 45
DESIGN: Nos. O1615/16, Aerial view of building.

**1984.** Multicoloured.
O 1642. 20 f. Type 377.. .. 15 15
O 1643. 30 f. Type 377.. .. 30 15
O 1644. 50 f. As No. 1639 .. 45 25
O 1645. 60 f. As No. 1639 .. 55 40

O 400. Pres Hussain

**1986.**
O1740 O 400 30 f. mult. .. 50 10
O1741 50 f. mult. .. 75 20
O1742 100 f. mult. .. 1·40 45
O1743 150 f. mult. .. 2·00 75
Nos. O 1740/3 are inscribed "POSTAGE".

# IRELAND (REPUBLIC) BC

The Republic of Ireland (Eire) is an independent state comprising Ireland, except the six counties of N. Ireland. It was formerly part of the United Kingdom of Great Britain and Ireland. For stamps issued before Independence in 1949, see Volume 3.

1949. 12 pence = 1 shilling. 20 shillings = 1 pound.
1971. 100 (new) pence = 1 pound (Punt).

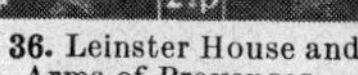
**36.** Leinster House and Arms of Provences.

**37.** J. C. Mangan.

**1949.** Int. Recognition of Republic.
146. 36. 2½d. brown .. .. 1·50 10
147. 3d. blue.. .. .. 5·50 3·75

**1949.** Death Centenary of James Clarence Mangan (poet).
148. 37. 1d. green .. .. 1·50 20

**38.** Statue of St. Peter, Rome.

**39.** Thomas Moore.

**40.** Irish Harp.

**1950.** Holy Year.
149. 38. 2½d. violet .. .. 1·00 40
150. 3d. blue.. .. .. 8·00 8·50
151. 9d. brown .. .. 8·00 10·00

**1952.** Death Cent. of Thomas Moore (poet).
152. 39. 2½d. purple .. .. 50 10
153. 3½d. olive .. .. 1·75 2·75

**1953.** "An Tostal" (Ireland at Home) Festival.
154. 40. 2½d. green .. .. 1·25 35
155. 1s. 4d. blue .. .. 15·00 24·00

**41.** Robert Emmet.

**42.** Madonna and Child (Della Robbia).

**1953.** 150th Death Anniv. of Emmet (patriot).
156. 41. 3d. green .. .. 3·25 15
157. 1s. 3d. red .. .. 42·00 9·50

**1954.** Marian Year.
158. 42. 3d. blue.. .. .. 2·00 10
159. 5d. green .. .. 3·50 5·50

**43.** Cardinal Newman (first Rector).

**44.** Statue of Commodore Barry.

**45.** John Redmond.

**1954.** Centenary of Founding of Catholic University of Ireland.
160. 43. 2d. purple .. .. 1·50 10
161. 1s. 3d. blue .. .. 16·00 6·00

**1956.** Barry Commem.
162. 44. 3d. lilac .. .. 2·00 10
163. 1s. 3d. blue .. .. 7·00 8·50

**1957.** Birth Centenary of John Redmond (politician).
164. 45. 3d. blue .. .. 1·25 10
165. 1s. 3d. purple .. .. 10·00 14·00

## INDEX

Countries can be quickly located by referring to the index at the end of this volume.

**46.** Thomas O'Crohan.

**47.** Admiral Brown.

**48.** "Father Wadding" (Ribera).

**1957.** Birth Cent. of Thomas O'Crohan (author).
166. 46. 2d. purple .. .. 2·00 15
167. 5d. violet .. .. 2·00 5·50

**1957.** Death Cent. of Admiral William Brown.
168. 47. 3d. blue .. .. 2·25 20
169. 1s. 3d. red .. .. 30·00 16·00

**1957.** Death Tercentenary of Father Luke Wadding (theologian).
170. 48. 3d. blue .. .. 2·00 10
171. 1s. 3d. lake .. .. 17·00 8·50

**49.** Tom Clarke.

**50.** Mother Mary Aikenhead.

**1958.** Birth Centenary of Thomas J. ("Tom") Clarke (patriot).
172. 49. 3d. green .. .. 2·50 10
173. 1s. 3d. brown .. .. 6·50 13·00

**1958.** Death Centenary of Mother Mary Aikenhead (foundress of Irish Sisters of Charity).
174. 50. 3d. blue .. .. 1·25 10
175. 1s. 3d. red .. .. 15·00 10·00

**1958.** 21st Anniv. of Irish Constitution.
176. 19. 3d. brown .. .. 1·25 10
177. 5d. green .. .. 2·25 4·50

**51.** Arthur Guinness.

**52.** "The Flight of the Holy Family".

**1959.** Bicentenary of Guinness Brewery.
178. 51. 3d. purple .. .. 4·00 10
179. 1s. 3d. blue .. .. 14·00 10·00

**1960.** World Refugee Year.
180. 52. 3d. purple .. .. 50 10
181. 1s. 3d. sepia .. .. 75 3·25

**1960.** 1st Anniv. of Europa. As T **373** of Belgium.
182. 6d. brown .. .. 4·00 2·50
183. 1s. 3d. violet .. .. 10·00 20·00

**54.** Dublin Airport, De Havilland Dragon Mk 2 "Iolar" and Boeing 720.

**55.** St. Patrick.

**1961.** Silver Jubilee of Aer Lingus Airlines.
184. 54. 6d. blue.. .. .. 1·50 3·25
185. 1s. 3d. green .. .. 2·00 4·75

**1961.** 15th Death Cent. of St. Patrick.
186. 55. 3d. blue.. .. .. 1·25 10
187. 8d. purple .. .. 2·25 5·00
188. 1s. 3d. green .. .. 2·50 1·50

**56.** John O'Donovan and Edugen O'Curry.

**1962.** Death Centenaries of O'Donovan and O'Curry (scholars).
189. 56. 3d. red .. .. 40 10
190. 1s. 3d. purple .. .. 2·00 2·50

57. Europa "Tree".

**1962.** Europa.

191. 57. 6d. red .. .. 50 1·00
192. 1s. 3d. turquoise .. 90 1·50

58. Campaign Emblem.

**1963.** Freedom from Hunger.

193. 58. 4d. violet .. .. 50 10
194. 1s. 3d. red .. .. 1·75 2·75

59. "Co-operation".

**1963.** Europa.

195. 59. 6d. red .. .. 75 75
196. 1s. 3d. blue .. .. 2·75 3·75

60. Centenary Emblem.

**1963.** Centenary of Red Cross.

197. 60. 4d. red and grey .. 50 10
198. 1s. 3d. red, grey & green 1·25 2·25

61. Wolfe Tone.

**1964.** Birth Bicentenary of Wolfe Tone (revolutionary).

199. 61. 4d. black .. .. 75 10
200. 1s. 3d. blue .. .. 2·25 1·75

62. Irish Pavilion at Fair. 63. Europa "Flower".

65. W. B. Yeats (poet). 64. "Waves of Communications".

**1964.** New York World's Fair.

201. 62. 5d. multicoloured .. 50 10
202. 1s. 5d. multicoloured .. 2·25 3·75

**1964.** Europa.

203. 63. 8d. green and blue .. 1·00 1·25
204. 1s. 5d. brown and orge. 3·00 2·75

**1965.** Centenary of I.T.U.

205. 64. 3d. blue and green .. 40 10
206. 8d. black and green .. 1·60 2·00

**1965.** Birth Centenary of Yeats.

207. 65. 5d. black, brown and green .. 50 10
208. 1s. 5d. black, green and brown .. 3·00 1·75

66. I.C.Y. Emblem.

**1965.** Int. Co-operation Year.

209. 66. 3d. blue.. .. .. 75 10
210. 10d. brown .. .. 1·25 3·50

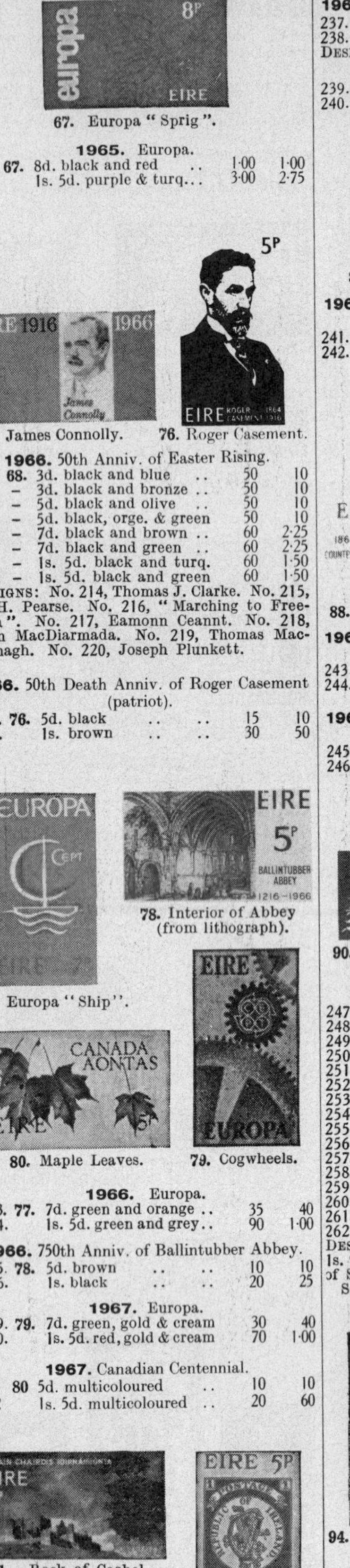

67. Europa "Sprig".

**1965.** Europa.

211. 67. 8d. black and red .. 1·00 1·00
212. 1s. 5d. purple & turq.. 3·00 2·75

68. James Connolly. 76. Roger Casement.

**1966.** 50th Anniv. of Easter Rising.

213. 68. 3d. black and blue .. 50 10
214. – 3d. black and bronze .. 50 10
215. – 5d. black and olive .. 50 10
216. – 5d. black, orge. & green 50 10
217. – 7d. black and brown .. 60 2·25
218. – 7d. black and green .. 60 2·25
219. – 1s. 5d. black and turq. 60 1·50
220. – 1s. 5d. black and green 60 1·50

DESIGNS: No. 214, Thomas J. Clarke. No. 215, P. H. Pearse. No. 216, "Marching to Freedom". No. 217, Eamonn Ceannt. No. 218, Sean MacDiarmada. No. 219, Thomas MacDonagh. No. 220, Joseph Plunkett.

**1966.** 50th Death Anniv. of Roger Casement (patriot).

221. 76. 5d. black .. .. 15 10
222. 1s. brown .. .. 30 50

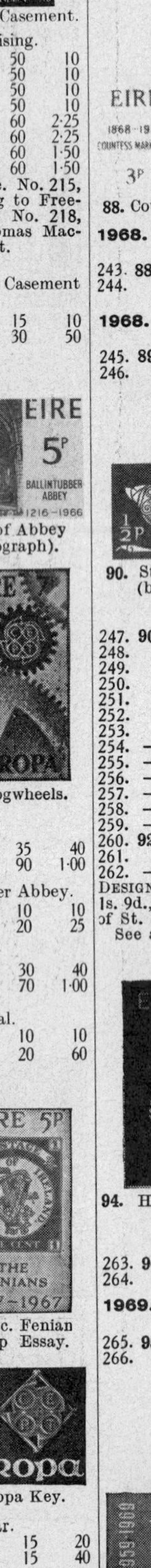

77. Europa "Ship". 78. Interior of Abbey (from lithograph).

80. Maple Leaves. 79. Cogwheels.

**1966.** Europa.

223. 77. 7d. green and orange .. 35 40
224. 1s. 5d. green and grey.. 90 1·00

**1966.** 750th Anniv. of Ballintubber Abbey.

225. 78. 5d. brown .. .. 10 10
226. 1s. black .. .. 20 25

**1967.** Europa.

229. 79. 7d. green, gold & cream 30 40
230. 1s. 5d. red, gold & cream 70 1·00

**1967.** Canadian Centennial.

231 80 5d. multicoloured .. 10 10
232 1s. 5d. multicoloured .. 20 60

81. Rock of Cashel (from photo by Edwin Smith). 82. 1 c. Fenian Stamp Essay.

84. Jonathan Swift. 86. Europa Key.

**1967.** Int. Tourist Year.

233. 81. 7d. sepia .. .. 15 20
234. 10d. blue .. .. 15 40

**1967.** Centenary of Fenian Rising.

235. 82. 5d. black and green .. 10 10
236. – 1s. black and pink .. 20 30

DESIGN: 1s. 24 c. Fenian Stamp Essay.

**1967.** 300th Birth Anniv. of Jonathan Swift.

237. 84. 3d. black and grey .. 10 10
238. – 1s. 5d. brown and blue.. 20 20

DESIGN: 1s. 5d. Gulliver and Lilliputians.

**1968.** Europa.

239. 86. 7d. red, gold and brown 25 50
240. 1s. 5d. blue, gold & brn. 40 1·00

87. St. Mary's Cathedral, Limerick.

**1968.** 800th Anniv. of St. Mary's Cathedral, Limerick.

241. 87. 5d. blue.. .. .. 10 10
242. 10d. green .. .. 20 60

88. Countess Markievicz. 89. James Connolly.

**1968.** Birth Centenary of Countess Markievicz (patriot).

243. 88. 3d. black .. .. 10 10
244. 1s. 5d. indigo and blue 20 20

**1968.** Birth Centenary of James Connolly (patriot).

245. 89. 6d. brown & chocolate.. 15 50
246. 1s. green, light green and myrtle .. .. 15 10

90. Stylised Dog (brooch). 92. Winged Ox (Symbol of St. Luke).

**1968.**

247. 90. ½d. orange .. .. 10 30
248. 1d. green .. .. 15 10
249. 2d. ochre .. .. 50 10
250. 3d. blue.. .. .. 35 10
251. 4d. red .. .. .. 30 10
252. 5d. green .. .. 40 35
253. 6d. brown .. .. 30 10
254. – 7d. brown and yellow.. 45 3·50
255. – 8d. brown and chestnut 45 1·00
256. – 9d. blue and green .. 50 10
257. – 10d. brown and violet.. 1·50 90
258. – 1s. chocolate and brown 40 10
259. – 1s. 9d. black & turquoise 4·00 90
260. 92. 2s. 6d. multicoloured .. 1·75 30
261. 5s. multicoloured .. 3·00 1·25
262. – 10s. multicoloured .. 4·50 3·50

DESIGNS—As Type 90: 7d., 8d., 9d., 10d., 1s., 1s. 9d., Stag. As Type 92: 10s Eagle (Symbol of St. John The Evangelist).

See also Nos. 287, etc.

94. Human Rights Emblem. 95. Dail Eireann Assembly.

**1968.** Human Rights Year.

263. 94. 5d. yell., gold & black.. 15 10
264. 7d. yellow, gold and red 15 40

**1969.** 50th Anniv. of Dail Eireann (1st National Parliament).

265. 95. 6d. green .. .. 15 10
266. 9d. blue.. .. .. 15 30

96. Colonnade. 97. Quadruple I.L.O. Emblems.

**1969.** Europa.

267. 96. 9d. grey, ochre and blue 40 1·10
268. 1s. 9d. grey, gold and red 70 1·40

**1969.** 50th Anniv. of I.L.O.

269. 97. 6d. black and grey .. 20 10
270. 9d. black and yellow .. 20 25

98. "The Last Supper and Crucifixion" (Evie Hone Window, Eton Chapel).

**1969.** Contemporary Irish Art (1st issue).

271 98 1s. multicoloured .. 30 1·50

See also Nos. 280, 306, 317, 329, 362, 375, 398, 408, 452, 470 and 498.

99. Mahatma Gandhi.

**1969.** Birth Cent. of Mahatma Gandhi.

272. 99. 6d. black and green .. 20 10
273. 1s. 9d. black and yellow 30 90

100. Symbolic Bird in Tree.

**1970.** European Conservation Year.

274. 100. 6d. bistre and black .. 35 10
275. 9d. violet and black .. 35 80

101. "Flaming Sun".

**1970.** Europa.

276. 101. 6d. violet and silver .. 35 10
277. 9d. brown and silver .. 75 1·25
278. 1s. 9d. grey and silver.. 1·10 2·00

102. "Sailing Boats" (Peter Monamy). 103. "Madonna of Eire" (Mainie Jellett).

**1970.** 250th Anniv. of Royal Cork Yacht Club.

279. 102. 4d. multicoloured .. 15 10

**1970.** Contemporary Irish Art (2nd issue).

280. 103. 1s. multicoloured .. 15 20

104. Thomas MacCurtain. 106. Kevin Barry.

**1970.** 50th Death Annivs. of Irish Patriots.

281. 104. 9d. black, violet & grey 50 25
282. – 9d. black, violet & grey 50 25
283. 104. 2s. 9d. black, blue & grey 1·75 1·50
284. – 2s. 9d. blk., blue & grey 1·75 1·50

DESIGN: Nos. 282 and 284, Terence MacSwiney.

**1970.** 50th Death Anniv. of Kevin Barry (patriot).

| | | | | |
|---|---|---|---|---|
| 285. | **106.** | 6d. green .. .. | 40 | 10 |
| 286. | | 1s. 2d. blue .. .. | 55 | 1·40 |

**1971.** Decimal Currency. As Nos. 247/62 but with face values in new currency, without "p", and some colours changed.

| | | | | |
|---|---|---|---|---|
| 287 | **90** | ½p. green .. .. | 10 | 10 |
| 340 | | 1p. blue .. .. | 10 | 10 |
| 289 | | 1½p. brown .. .. | 15 | 15 |
| 341 | | 2p. green .. .. | 10 | 10 |
| 291 | | 2½p. brown .. .. | 15 | 10 |
| 342 | | 3p. brown .. .. | 10 | 10 |
| 293 | | 3½p. brown .. .. | 15 | 10 |
| 294 | | 4p. violet .. .. | 15 | 10 |
| 295 | – | 5p. brown and olive .. | 70 | 20 |
| 344 | **90** | 5p. green .. .. | 60 | 10 |
| 296 | – | 6p. grey and brown .. | 3·50 | 30 |
| 346 | **90** | 6p. grey .. .. | 20 | 10 |
| 347 | – | 7p. blue and green .. | 1·75 | 35 |
| 348 | **90** | 7p. green .. .. | 35 | 10 |
| 297 | – | 7½p. mauve and brown | 50 | 85 |
| 349 | – | 8p. brn. and deep brn. | 1·00 | 50 |
| 350 | **90** | 8p. brown .. .. | 30 | 10 |
| 298 | – | 9p. black and green .. | 1·50 | 35 |
| 352 | **90** | 9p. green .. .. | 30 | 10 |
| 352a | | 9½p. red .. .. | 35 | 20 |
| 353 | **92** | 10p. multicoloured .. | 3·25 | 30 |
| 354 | – | 10p. black and lilac .. | 1·75 | 10 |
| 354a | **90** | 10p. mauve .. .. | 70 | 10 |
| 355 | – | 11p. black and red .. | 45 | 30 |
| 299b | **92** | 12p. multicoloured .. | 75 | 80 |
| 355a | – | 12p. black and green.. | 75 | 10 |
| 355b | **90** | 12p. green .. .. | 30 | 10 |
| 355c | – | 13p. brown .. .. | 40 | 1·25 |
| 356 | **92** | 15p. multicoloured .. | 75 | 40 |
| 356a | **90** | 15p. blue .. .. | 40 | 10 |
| 356b | – | 16p. black and green.. | 40 | 80 |
| 356c | **92** | 17p. multicoloured .. | 70 | 40 |
| 478 | **90** | 18p. red .. .. | 45 | 40 |
| 479 | | 19p. blue .. .. | 55 | 1·50 |
| 357 | **92** | 20p. multicoloured .. | 70 | 15 |
| 480 | **90** | 22p. blue .. .. | 65 | 10 |
| 481 | | 24p. brown .. .. | 75 | 95 |
| 482 | | 26p. green .. .. | 1·50 | 40 |
| 483 | | 29p. mauve .. .. | 1·75 | 2·00 |
| 358 | – | 50p. multicoloured .. | 90 | 30 |
| 359 | – | £1 multicoloured .. | 1·50 | 30 |

Designs—As Type **90**: 5p. (295), 6p. (296), 7p. (347), 7½p., 8p., 9p. (351) 10p. (354), 11p. 12p. (No. 355a), 13p., 16p. Stag. As Type **92**: 50p. £1, Eagle (symbol of St. John the Evangelist).

**107.** " Europa Chain ". **108.** J. M. Synge.

**1971.** Europa.

| | | | | |
|---|---|---|---|---|
| 302. | **107.** | 4p. brown and green | 50 | 10 |
| 303. | | 6p. black and blue .. | 1·75 | 2·25 |

**1971.** Birth Cent. of J. M. Synge (playwright).

| | | | | |
|---|---|---|---|---|
| 304. | **108.** | 4p. multicoloured .. | 15 | 10 |
| 305. | | 10p. multicoloured .. | 60 | 80 |

**109.** " An Island Man" (Jack B. Yeats). **110.** Racial Harmony Symbol.

**1971.** Contemporary Irish Art (3rd issue). Birth Centenary of J. B. Yeats (artist).

| | | | | |
|---|---|---|---|---|
| 306. | **109.** | 6p. multicoloured .. | 55 | 55 |

**1971.** Racial Equality Year.

| | | | | |
|---|---|---|---|---|
| 307. | **110.** | 4p. red .. .. .. | 20 | 10 |
| 308. | | 10p. black .. .. | 50 | 75 |

**111.** " Madonna and Child " (statue by J. Hughes). **112.** Heart.

**1971.** Christmas.

| | | | | |
|---|---|---|---|---|
| 309. | **111.** | 2½p. blk., gold & green | 10 | 10 |
| 310. | | 6p. blk., gold and blue | 55 | 65 |

**1972.** World Health Day.

| | | | | |
|---|---|---|---|---|
| 311 | **112.** | 2½ p. gold and brown | 30 | 15 |
| 312 | | 12 p. silver and grey | 1·10 | 1·75 |

**113.** "Communications". **114.** Dove and Moon.

**1972.** Europa.

| | | | | |
|---|---|---|---|---|
| 313 | **113.** | 4p. orge., blk. & silver.. | 1·25 | 25 |
| 314. | | 6p. blue, blk. & silver.. | 3·25 | 4·50 |

**1972.** Patriot Dead 1922–23.

| | | | | |
|---|---|---|---|---|
| 315. | **114.** | 4p. multicoloured .. | 15 | 10 |
| 316. | | 6p. yell., grn. & dull grn. | 60 | 40 |

**115.** " Black Lake" (Gerard Dillon). **116.** " Horseman" (Carved Slab).

**1972.** Contemporary Irish Art (4th issue).

| | | | | |
|---|---|---|---|---|
| 317. | **115.** | 3p. multicoloured .. | 50 | 35 |

**1972.** 50th Anniv. of Olympic Council of Ireland.

| | | | | |
|---|---|---|---|---|
| 318. | **116.** | 3p. yellow, black and gold .. .. | 15 | 10 |
| 319. | | 6p. pink, blk. and gold | 55 | 60 |

**117.** Madonna and Child (from Book of Kells). **118.** 2d. Stamp of 1922.

**1972.** Christmas.

| | | | | |
|---|---|---|---|---|
| 320. | **117.** | 2½p. multicoloured .. | 15 | 10 |
| 321. | | 4p. multicoloured .. | 30 | 10 |
| 322. | | 12p. multicoloured .. | 75 | 65 |

**1972.** 50th Anniv. of 1st Irish Postage Stamp.

| | | | | |
|---|---|---|---|---|
| 323. | **118.** | 6p. grey and green .. | 50 | 60 |

**119.** Celtic Head Motif.

**1973.** Entry into European Communities.

| | | | | |
|---|---|---|---|---|
| 325. | **119.** | 6p. multicoloured .. | 40 | 90 |
| 326. | | 12p. multicoloured .. | 60 | 1·10 |

**120.** Europa " Posthorn ".

**1973.** Europa.

| | | | | |
|---|---|---|---|---|
| 327. | **120.** | 4p. blue.. .. .. | 50 | 10 |
| 328. | | 6p. black .. .. | 1·75 | 2·25 |

**121.** " Berlin Blues II " (W. Scott).

**1973.** Contemporary Irish Art (5th issue).

| | | | | |
|---|---|---|---|---|
| 329. | **121.** | 5p. blue and black .. | 40 | 30 |

**122.** Weather Map. **123.** Tractor ploughing.

**1973.** Centenary of I.M.O./W.M.O.

| | | | | |
|---|---|---|---|---|
| 330. | **122.** | 3½p. multicoloured .. | 40 | 10 |
| 331. | | 12p. multicoloured .. | 1·10 | 2·25 |

**1973.** World Ploughing Championships, Wellington Bridge.

| | | | | |
|---|---|---|---|---|
| 332. | **123.** | 5p. multicoloured .. | 15 | 10 |
| 333. | | 7p. multicoloured .. | 75 | 50 |

**124.** " Flight into Egypt " (Jan de Cock). **125.** Daunt Island Lightship and Ballycotton Lifeboat, 1936.

**1973.** Christmas.

| | | | | |
|---|---|---|---|---|
| 334. | **124.** | 3½p. multicoloured .. | 15 | 10 |
| 335. | | 12p. multicoloured .. | 1·10 | 1·50 |

**1974.** 150th Anniv. of R.N.L.I.

| | | | | |
|---|---|---|---|---|
| 336. | **125.** | 5p. multicoloured .. | 30 | 30 |

**126.** "Edmund Burke" (statue by J. H. Foley). **127.** "Oliver Goldsmith" (Statue by J. H. Foley).

**1974.** Europa.

| | | | | |
|---|---|---|---|---|
| 337. | **126.** | 5p. black and blue .. | 75 | 10 |
| 338. | | 7p. black and green .. | 3·00 | 2·50 |

**1974.** Death Bicentenary of Oliver Goldsmith (writer).

| | | | | |
|---|---|---|---|---|
| 360. | **127.** | 3½p. black and yellow | 20 | 10 |
| 361. | | 12p. black and green | 90 | 1·00 |

**128.** "Kitchen Table" (Norah McGuiness). **129.** Rugby Players.

**1974.** Contemporary Irish Art (6th issue).

| | | | | |
|---|---|---|---|---|
| 362. | **128.** | 5p. multicoloured .. | 35 | 30 |

**1974.** Centenary of Irish Rugby Football.

| | | | | |
|---|---|---|---|---|
| 363. | **129.** | 3½p. green .. .. | 30 | 10 |
| 364. | | 12p. multicoloured .. | 2·25 | 2·50 |

**130.** U.P.U. "Postmark". **131.** "Madonna and Child" (Bellini).

**1974.** Cent. of Universal Postal Union.

| | | | | |
|---|---|---|---|---|
| 365. | **130.** | 5p. green and black .. | 30 | 10 |
| 366. | | 7p. blue and black .. | 50 | 80 |

**1974.** Christmas.

| | | | | |
|---|---|---|---|---|
| 367. | **131.** | 5p. multicoloured .. | 15 | 10 |
| 368. | | 15p. multicoloured .. | 1·00 | 90 |

**132.** " Peace ".

**1975.** International Women's Year.

| | | | | |
|---|---|---|---|---|
| 369. | **132.** | 8p. purple and blue .. | 25 | 75 |
| 370. | | 15p. blue and green .. | 50 | 1·25 |

**133.** " Castletown Hunt " (R. Healy).

**1975.** Europa.

| | | | | |
|---|---|---|---|---|
| 371. | **133.** | 7p. grey .. .. | 80 | 15 |
| 372. | | 9p. green .. .. | 1·60 | 2·50 |

**134.** Putting.

**1975.** Ninth European Amateur Golf Team Championship, Killarney.

| | | | | |
|---|---|---|---|---|
| 373. | **134.** | 6p. multicoloured .. | 1·00 | 45 |
| 374. | – | 9p. multicoloured .. | 1·75 | 1·50 |

No. 374 is similar to Type **134** but shows a different view of the putting green.

**135.** " Bird of Prey " (sculpture by Oisin Kelly).

**1975.** Contemporary Irish Art (7th issue).

| | | | | |
|---|---|---|---|---|
| 375. | **135.** | 15p. brown .. .. | 55 | 75 |

**136.** Nano Nagle (founder) and Waifs. **137.** Tower of St. Anne's Church, Shandon.

**1975.** Bicent. of Presentation Order of Nuns.

| | | | | |
|---|---|---|---|---|
| 376. | **136.** | 5p. black and blue .. | 20 | 10 |
| 377. | | 7p. black and brown | 30 | 30 |

**1975.** European Architectural Heritage Year.

| | | | | |
|---|---|---|---|---|
| 378. | **137.** | 5p. brown .. .. | 20 | 10 |
| 379. | | 6p. multicoloured .. | 40 | 85 |
| 380. | – | 7p. blue .. .. | 40 | 10 |
| 381. | – | 9p. multicoloured .. | 45 | 80 |

Design: Nos. 380/1, Interior of Holycross Abbey, Co. Tipperary.

**138.** St. Oliver Plunkett (commemorative medal by Imogen Stuart). **139.** " Madonna and Child " (Fra Filippo Lippi).

**1975.** Canonisation of Oliver Plunkett.

| | | | | |
|---|---|---|---|---|
| 382. | **138.** | 7p. black .. .. | 15 | 10 |
| 383. | | 15p. brown .. .. | 55 | 45 |

**1975.** Christmas.

| | | | | |
|---|---|---|---|---|
| 384. | **139.** | 5p. multicoloured .. | 15 | 10 |
| 385. | | 7p. multicoloured .. | 15 | 10 |
| 386. | | 10p. multicoloured .. | 45 | 30 |

**140.** James Larkin (from a drawing by Sean O'Sullivan). **141.** Alexander Graham Bell.

**1975.** Birth Centenary of James Larkin (Trade Union Leader).

| | | | | |
|---|---|---|---|---|
| 387. | **140.** | 7p. green and grey .. | 20 | 10 |
| 388. | | 11p. brown and yellow | 60 | 55 |

**1976.** Centenary of Telephone.
389. **141.** 9p. multicoloured .. 20 10
390. 15 p. multicoloured .. 45 50

**142.** 1847 Benjamin Franklin Essay.

**1976.** Bicent. of American Revolution.
391. – 7p. blue, red and silver 20 10
392. – 8p. blue, red and silver 30 1·10
393. **142.** 9p. blue, orge. & silver 30 10
394. 15p. red, grey & silver 50 75
DESIGNS: 7p. Thirteen Stars. 8p. Fifty Stars.

**143.** Spirit Barrel.

**1976.** Europa. Irish Delft. Multicoloured.
396. 9p. Type **143** .. .. 60 20
397. 11p. Dish .. .. .. 1·00 1·60

**144.** " The Lobster Pots, West of Ireland " (Paul Henry).

**1976.** Contemporary Irish Art (8th issue).
398. **144.** 15p. multicoloured .. 60 60

**145.** Radio Waves.

**1976.** 50th Anniv. of Irish Broadcasting Service.
399. **145.** 9 p. blue and green .. 20 10
400. – 11p. brn., red and blue 60 1·00
DESIGN—VERT. 11p. Transmitter, radio waves and globe.

**146.** "The Nativity" (Lorenzo Monaco).

**1976.** Christmas.
401. **146.** 7p. multicoloured .. 15 10
402. 9p. multicoloured .. 15 10
403. 15p. multicoloured .. 55 55

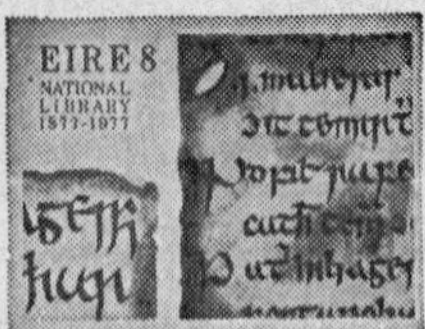

**147.** 16th Century Manuscript.

**1977.** Centenaries of National Library (8p.) and National Museum (10p.) Multicoloured
404. 8p. Type **147** .. .. 30 30
405. 10p. Prehistoric stone .. 40 35

**148.** Ballynahinch, Galway. **149.** " Head " (Louis le Brocquy).

**1977.** Europa. Multicoloured.
406. 10p. Type **148** .. .. 30 25
407. 12p. Lough Tay, Wicklow 90 1·50

**1977.** Contemporary Irish Art (9th issue).
408. **149.** 17p. multicoloured .. 55 75

**150.** Guide and Tents.

**1977.** Scouting and Guiding. Multicoloured.
409. 8p. Type **150** .. .. 40 10
410. 17p. Tent and Scout saluting .. .. .. 1·00 1·75

**151.** " The Shanachie " (drawing by Jack B. Yeats).

**1977.** Anniversaries.
411. **151.** 10p. black .. .. 30 15
412. – 12p. black .. .. 50 1·00
DESIGNS AND EVENTS: 10p. Type **151** (Golden Jubilee of Irish Folklore Society). 12p. The philosopher Eriugena (1100th death anniv.).

**152.** " Electricty " (Golden Jubilee of Electricity Supply Board).

**1977.** Golden Jubilees.
413. **152.** 10p. multicoloured .. 15 10
414. – 12p. multicoloured .. 45 1·40
415. – 17p. black and brown 50 85
DESIGNS: 12p. Bulls (from Irish coins) (Agricultural Credit Act). 17p. Greyhound (Greyhound Track Racing).

**153.** " The Holy Family " (Giorgione). **154.** Junkers W.33 "Bremen" in Flight.

**1977.** Christmas.
416. **153.** 8p. multicoloured .. 20 10
417. 10p. multicoloured .. 20 10
418. 17p. multicoloured .. 70 1·25

**1978.** 50th Anniv. of 1st East-West Transatlantic Flight.
419. **154.** 10p. black and blue .. 20 15
420. 17p. black and brown 55 1·10

**155.** Spring Gentian. **156.** Catherine McAuley.

**1978.** Wild Flowers. Multicoloured.
421. 8p. Type **155** .. .. 30 50
422. 10p. Strawberry tree .. 35 15
423. 11p. Large-flowered Butterwort .. 45 70
424. 17p. St. Dabeoc's Heath .. 70 2·00

**1978.** Anniversaries and Events. Mult.
425. 10p. Type **156** (founder of Sisters of Mercy) (Birth bicent.) .. .. .. 25 10
426. 11p. Doctor performing vaccination (Global Eradication of Smallpox) (horiz.) 40 80
427. 17p. " Self-portrait " (Sir William Orpen (painter) (birth cent.) .. .. 50 1·10

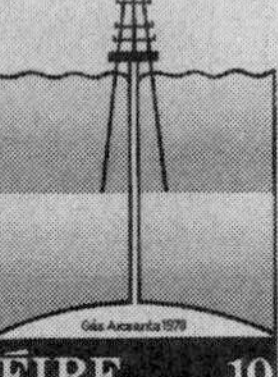

**157.** Diagram of Drilling Rig. **159.** " Virgin and Child " (Guercino).

**158.** Farthing.

**1978.** Arrival Onshore of Natural Gas.
428. **157.** 10p. multicoloured .. 30 30

**1978.** 50th Anniv. of Irish Currency.
429. **158.** 8p. blk., copper & grn. 20 20
430. – 10p. blk., silver & grn. 30 10
431. – 11p. blk., copper & brn. 35 50
432. – 17p. blk., silver & blue 60 1·00
DESIGNS: 10p. Florin. 11p. Penny. 17p. Half-crown.

**1978.** Christmas.
433. **159.** 8p. brown, blue & gold 20 10
434. 10p. brn , blue & purple 20 10
435. 17p. brn , blue & grn 60 1·40

**160.** Conolly Folly, Castletown.

**1978.** Europa.
436. **160.** 10p. brown .. .. 45 15
437. – 11p. green .. .. 45 1·00
DESIGN: 11p. Dromoland Belvedere.

**161.** Athletes in Cross-country Race.

**1979.** 7th World Cross-country Championships, Limerick. Multicoloured
438. **161.** 8p. multicoloured .. 20 30

**162.** " European Communities " (in languages of member nations). **163.** Sir Rowland Hill.

**1979.** 1st Direct Elections to European Assembly.
439. **162.** 10p. turquoise-green .. 15 15
440. 11p. violet .. 15 35

**1979.** Death Centenary of Sir Rowland Hill.
441. **163.** 17p. black, grey and red .. .. .. 30 60

**164.** Winter Wren.

**1979.** Birds. Multicoloured.
442. 8p. Type **164** .. .. 40 10
443. 10p. Great Crested Grebe 40 15
444. 11p. White-fronted Goose 45 10
445. 17p. Peregrine Falcon .. 70 2·00

**165.** " A Happy Flower " (David Gallagher).

**1979.** International Year of the Child. Paintings by Children. Multicoloured.
446. 10p. Type **165** .. .. 20 10
447. 11p. " Myself and My Skipping Rope " (Lucy Norman) (vert.) .. 25 60
448. 17p " Swans on a Lake " (Nicola O'Dwyer) .. 35 85

**166.** Pope John Paul II.

**1979.** Visit of Pope John Paul II.
449. **166.** 12p. multicoloured .. 30 20

**167.** Brother with Child.

**1979.** Anniversaries and Events.
450. **167.** 9½p. brown and mauve 20 10
451. – 11p. orge., black & blue 20 70
452. – 20p. multicoloured .. 40 1·40
DESIGNS—VERT. 11p. Windmill and sun (Int. Energy Conservation Month). HORIZ. 9½p. Type **167** (Cent of Hospitaller Order of St. John of God in Ireland). 20p. "Seated Figure" (sculpture F. E. McWilliam) (Contemporary Irish Art (10th issue)).

**168.** Patrick Pearse, "Liberty" and G.P.O., Dublin. **169.** " Madonna and Child" (panel painting from the Domnach Airgid Shrine).

**1979.** Birth Cent. of Patrick Pearse (patriot).
453. **168.** 12p. multicoloured .. 30 15

**1979.** Christmas.
454. **169.** 9½p. multicoloured .. 15 10
455. 20p. multicoloured .. 30 55

**170.** Bianconi Long Car, 1836.

**1979.** Europa. Multicoloured.
456. 12p. Type **170** .. .. 30 30
457. 13p. Transatlantic cable, Valentia, 1866 .. .. 45 1·40

**171.** John Baptist de la Salle (founder). **172.** George Bernard Shaw.

**1980.** Cent of Arrival of De La Salle Order.
458 171 12p. multicoloured .. 30 30

**1980.** Europa. Personalities. Multicoloured.
459 12p. Type **172** .. .. 40 50
460 13p. Oscar Wilde (28 × 38 mm) .. .. .. 40 1·00

**173.** Stoat.

**174.** Playing Bodhran and Whistle.

**1980.** Wildlife. Multicoloured.
461. 12p. Type **173** .. .. 25 40
462. 15p. Arctic hare .. .. 30 15
463. 16p. Red fox .. .. 35 50
464. 25p. Red deer .. .. 50 1·40

**1980.** Traditional Music and Dance. Mult.
466. 12p. Type **174** .. .. 15 10
467. 15p. Playing Uilleann pipes 20 15
468. 25p. Dancing .. .. 35 1·10

**175.** Sean O'Casey.

**176.** Nativity Scene (painting by Geraldine McNulty).

**1980.** Commemorations.
469. 12p. multicoloured .. 15 10
470. 25p. black, buff and brown 30 55
DESIGNS AND COMMEMORATIONS: 12p. Type **175** (playwright) (birth centenary). 25p. "Gold Painting No. 57" (P. Scott) (Contemporary Irish Art (11th issue)).

**1980.** Christmas.
471. **176.** 12p. multicoloured .. 20 10
472. 15p. multicoloured .. 20 10
473. 25p. multicoloured .. 55 1·25

**177.** Boyle Air-pump, 1659.

**178.** "The Legend of the Cock and the Pot".

**1981.** Irish Science and Technology. Mult.
474. 12p. Type **177** .. .. 30 10
475. 15p. Ferguson tractor, 1936 .. .. 30 10
476. 16p. Parsons turbine, 1884 30 90
477. 25p. Holland submarine, 1878 .. .. 45 1·25

**1981.** Europa. Folklore. Paintings by Maria Simonds-Gooding.
491. **178.** 18p. black, yellow & red 40 10
492. – 19p. blk., orge. & yell. 50 70
DESIGN: 19p. "The Angel with the Scales of Judgement".

**179.** Cycling.

**180.** Jeremiah O'Donovan Rossa.

**1981.** 50th Anniv. of "An Oige" (Irish Youth Hostel Association). Multicoloured.
493. 15p. Type **179** .. .. 30 40
494. 18p. Hill-walking (horiz.) 30 10
495. 19p. Mountaineering (horiz.) 30 95
496. 30p. Rock-climbing .. 50 95

**1981.** 150th Birth Anniv. of Jeremiah O'Donovan Rossa (politician).
497. **180.** 15p. multicoloured .. 30 30

**181.** "Railway Embankment" (W. J. Leech).

**1981.** Contemporary Irish Art (12th issue).
498. **181.** 30p. multicoloured .. 60 60

**182.** James Hoban and White House.

**1981.** 150th Death Anniv. of James Hoban (White House architect).
499. **182.** 18p. multicoloured .. 30 30

**183.** "Arkle" (steeplechaser).

**1981.** Famous Irish Horses. Multicoloured.
500. 18p. Type **183** .. .. 50 1·00
501. 18p. "Boomerang" (show-jumper) .. .. 50 1·00
502. 22p. "King of Diamonds" (Draught horse) .. 60 30
503. 24p. "Ballymoss" (flat-racer) .. .. 60 70
504. 36p. "Coosheen Finn" (Connemara pony) .. 75 1·00

**184.** "Nativity" (F. Barocci).

**185.** Eviction Scene.

**1981.** Christmas.
505. **184.** 18p. multicoloured .. 25 10
506. 22p. multicoloured .. 30 10
507. 36p. multicoloured .. 70 2·00

**1981.** Anniversaries. Multicoloured.
508. 18p. Type **185** .. .. 35 25
509. 22p. Royal Dublin Society emblem .. .. .. 40 30
ANNIVERSARIES: 18p. Centenary of Land Law (Ireland) Act. 22p. Royal Dublin Society (organization for the advancement of agriculture, industry, art and science). 250th Anniv.

**186.** Upper Lake, Killarney National Park.

**1982.** 50th Anniv. of Killarney National Park. Multicoloured.
510. 18p. Type **186** .. .. 35 20
511. 36p. Eagle's Nest .. .. 65 1·60

**187.** "The Stigmatization of St. Francis" (Sassetta).

**188.** The Great Famine, 1845–50.

**1982.** Religious Anniversaries.
512. **187.** 22p. multicoloured .. 85 15
513. – 24p. brown .. .. 40 80
DESIGNS AND ANNIVERSARIES: 22p. Type **187** (St. Francis of Assisi (founder of Franciscan order) (500th birth anniv). 24p. Francis Makemie (founder of American Presbyterianism) and old Presbyterian Church, Ramelton, Co. Donegal (300th anniv of ordination).

**1982.** Europa. Historic Events.
514 **188** 26p. black and stone .. 80 50
515 – 29p. multicoloured .. 80 2·00
DESIGN—HORIZ. 29p. The coming of Christianity to Ireland.

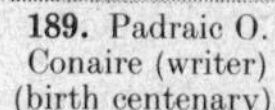
**189.** Padraic O. Conaire (writer) (birth centenary).

**191.** "St. Patrick" (Galway hooker).

**190.** Porbeagle Shark.

**1982.** Anniversaries of Cultural Figures.
516. **189.** 22p. black and blue .. 35 30
517. – 26p. black and brown 45 30
518. – 29p. black and blue .. 60 1·75
519. – 44p. black and grey .. 80 1·60
DESIGNS AND ANNIVERSARIES: 26p. James Joyce (writer) (birth centenary); 29p. John Field (musician) (birth centenary); 44p. Charles Kickham (writer) (death centenary).

**1982.** Marine Life. Multicoloured.
520 22p. Type **190** .. .. 55 1·25
521 22p. Common European oyster .. .. .. 55 1·25
522 26p. Salmon .. .. 70 30
523 29p. Dublin Bay prawn .. 70 2·25

**1982.** Irish Boats. Multicoloured.
524 22p. Type **191** .. .. 75 1·25
525 22p. Curragh (horiz) .. 75 1·25
526 26p. "Asgard II" (cadet brigantine) (horiz) .. 75 30
527 29p. Howth 17-foot yacht 75 2·25

**192.** "Irish House of Commons" (painting by Francis Wheatley).

**1982.** Bicentenary of Grattan's Parliament and Birth Centenary of Eamon de Valera. Multicoloured.
528 22p. Type **192** .. .. 45 1·25
529 26p. Eamon de Valera (vert) .. .. .. 50 40

**193.** "Madonna and Child" (sculpture).

**194.** Aughnanure Castle.

**1982.** Christmas.
530. **193.** 22p. multicoloured .. 40 90
531. 26p. multicoloured .. 40 35

**1983.** Irish Architecture.
532 – 1p. blue .. .. 10 10
533 – 2p. green .. .. 20 10
534 – 3p. black .. .. 20 10
535 – 4p. red .. .. 20 10
536 – 5p. brown .. .. 30 10
537 – 6p. blue .. .. 30 15
538 – 7p. green .. .. 30 15
539 – 10p. black .. .. 30 15
540 – 12p. brown .. .. 30 30
541 **194** 15p. green .. .. 45 35
542 20p. purple .. .. 50 45
543 22p. blue .. .. 50 10
544 – 23p. green .. .. 85 80
544a – 24p. brown .. .. 1·25 35
545 – 26p. brown .. .. 75 10
545c – 28p. red .. .. 75 45
546 – 29p. green .. .. 90 65
547 – 30p. black .. .. 70 30
547c – 32p. brown .. .. 1·75 2·00
547d – 37p. blue .. .. 90 1·25
547e – 39p. red .. .. 1·50 2·00
548 – 44p. black and grey .. 90 90
548b – 46p. green and grey .. 3·50 2·00
549 – 50p. blue and grey .. 1·00 65
550 – £1 brown and grey .. 4·50 3·00
550b – £1 blue and grey .. 3·25 1·25
550c – £2 green and black .. 4·00 4·50
551 – £5 red and grey .. 10·00 5·00
DESIGNS—HORIZ. (As T **194**). 1 to 5p. Central Pavilion, Dublin Botanic Gardens. 6 to 12p. Dr. Steevens' Hospital, Dublin. 28 to 37p. St. MacDara's Church. (37 × 21 mm). 46p., £1 (No. 550) Cahir Castle. 50p., £2 Casino Marino. £5 Central Bus Station, Dublin. VERT. (As T **194**). 23 to 26p., 39p. Cormac's Chapel. (21 × 37 mm). 44p., £1 (No. 550b) Killarney Cathedral.

**195.** Ouzel Gallery Goblet.

**196.** Padraig O. Siochfhradha (writer and teacher).

**1983.** Bicentenaries of Dublin Chamber of Commerce (22p.) and Bank of Ireland (26p.). Multicoloured.
552. 22p. Type **195** .. .. 30 65
553. 26p. Bank of Ireland building (horiz.) .. 35 35

**1983.** Anniversaries. Multicoloured.
554. 26p. Type **196** (Birth cent.) 60 75
555. 29p. Young Boys' Brigade member (Centenary) .. 80 1·50

**197.** Neolithic Carved Pattern, Newgrange Tomb.

**1983.** Europa.
556. **197.** 26p. black and yellow 1·75 50
557. – 29p. blk., brn. & yell. 4·00 4·50
DESIGN: 29p. Sir William Rowan Hamilton's formulae for the multiplication of quaternions.

**198.** Kerry Blue Terrier.

**1983.** Irish Dogs. Multicoloured.
558. 22p. Type **198** .. .. 65 35
559. 26p. Irish Wolfhound .. 75 45
560. 26p. Irish Water Spaniel .. 75 45
561. 29p. Irish Terrier .. .. 95 2·25
562. 44p. Irish Setters .. .. 1·40 2·50

**199.** Animals (Irish Society for the Prevention of Cruelty to Animals).

**1983.** Anniversaries and Commemorations.
564. **199.** 22p. multicoloured .. 60 1·00
565. – 22p. multicoloured .. 60 1·00
566. – 26p. multicoloured .. 70 60
567. – 26p. multicoloured .. 70 60
568. – 44p. blue and black .. 1·25 2·00
DESIGNS—VERT. No. 565, Sean Mac Diarmada (patriot) (birth cent.). No. 567, "St. Vincent de Paul in the Streets of Paris" (150th anniv. of Society of St. Vincent de Paul). No. 568, "Andrew Jackson" (Frank McKelvey) (President of the United States). HORIZ. No. 566, "100" (Centenary of Industrial Credit Company).

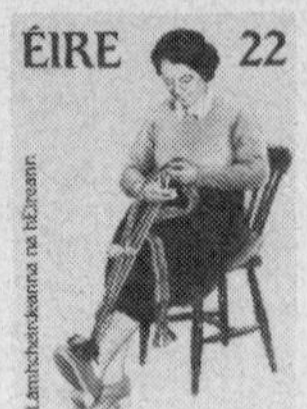


**200.** Postman with Bicycle. **201.** Weaving.

**1983.** World Communications Year. Multicoloured.

569. 22p. Type **200** .. .. 75 75
570. 29p. Dish antenna .. 1·25 2·00

**1983.** Irish Handicrafts. Multicoloured.

571. 22p. Type **201** .. .. 50 60
572. 26p. Basket making .. 60 45
573. 29p. Irish crochet .. 75 1·50
574. 44p. Harp making .. 1·25 2·25

**202.** " La Natividad " (R. van der Weyden).

**1983.** Christmas.

575. **202.** 22p. multicoloured .. 50 30
576. 26p. multicoloured .. 60 30

**203.** "Princess" (Dublin and Kingstown Railway).

**1984.** 150th Anniv. of Irish Railways. Multicoloured.

577. 23p. Type **203** .. .. 85 1·25
578. 26p. "Macha" (Great Southern Rly.) .. .. 85 35
579. 29p. "Kestrel" (Great Northern Rly.) .. .. 1·00 1·75
580. 44p. Two-car electric train (Coras Iompair Eireann) 1·40 2·25

**204.** " Sorbus hibernica ".

**1984.** Irish Trees. Multicoloured.

582. 22p. Type **204** .. .. 75 70
583. 26p. " Taxus baccata fastigiata " .. .. 80 40
584. 29p. " Salix hibernica " .. 1·00 2·00
585. 44p. " Betula pubescens " 1·40 2·75

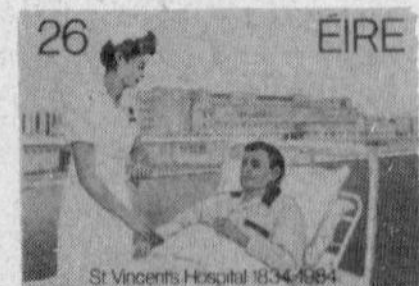


**205.** St. Vincent's Hospital, Dublin.

**1984.** 150th Anniv. of St. Vincent's Hospital and Bicentenary of Royal College of Surgeons. Multicoloured.

586. 26p. Type **205** .. .. 50 30
587. 44p. Royal College and logo .. .. .. 90 1·50

## INDEX

Countries can be quickly located by referring to the index at the end of this volume.

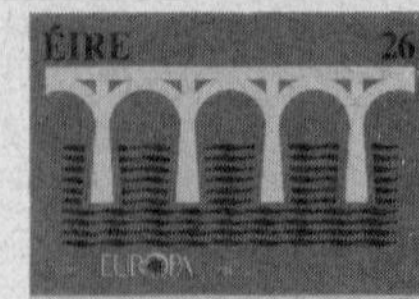


**206.** C.E.P.T. 25th Anniversary Logo.

**1984.** Europa.

588. **206.** 26 p. blue, deep blue and black .. .. 1·75 50
589. 29p. light green, green and black .. .. 2·25 2·50

**207.** Flags on Ballot Box. **208.** John McCormack.

**1984.** Second Direct Elections to European Assembly.

590. **207.** 26p. multicoloured .. 50 70

**1984.** Birth Cent. of John McCormack (tenor).

591. **208.** 22p. multicoloured .. 50 70

**209.** Hammer-throwing.

**1984.** Olympic Games, Los Angeles.

592. **209.** 22p. mve., blk. & gold 45 80
593. – 26p. vio., blk. & gold 60 65
594. – 29p. bl., blk. & gold .. 75 1·25

Designs: 26p. Hurdling. 29p. Running.

**210.** Hurling.

**1984.** Centenary of Gaelic Athletic Association. Multicoloured.

595. 22p. Type **210** .. .. 50 90
596. 26p. Irish football (vert.) .. 60 90

**211.** Galway Mayoral Chain. **212.** Hands passing Letter.

**1984.** Anniversaries. Multicoloured.

597. 26p. Type **211** (500th anniv. of mayoral charter) .. 60 50
598. 44p. St. Brendan (from 15th-cent Bodleian manuscript) (1500th birth anniv.) (horiz.) .. 1·25 1·50

**1984.** Bicentenary of Irish Post Office.

599. **212.** 26p. multicoloured .. 60 70

**213.** "Virgin and Child" (Sassoferrato). **214.** "Love" and Heart-shaped Balloon.

**1984.** Christmas. Multicoloured.

600. 17p. Christmas star (horiz.) 60 80
601. 22p. Type **213** .. .. 60 1·25
602. 26p. Type **213** .. .. 80 40

**1985.** Greetings Stamps. Multicoloured.

603. 22p. Type **214** .. .. 50 75
604. 26p. Bouquet of hearts and flowers (vert.) .. .. 60 75

**215.** Dunsink Observatory (Bicentenary). **216.** "Polyommatus icarus".

**1985.** Anniversaries. Multicoloured.

605. 22p. Type **215** .. .. 50 50
606. 26p. "A Landscape at Tivoli, Cork, with Boats" (Nathaniel Grogan) (800th anniv. of City of Cork) (horiz.) .. 60 30
607. 37p. Royal Irish Academy (Bicentenary) .. .. 90 1·75
608. 44p. Richard Crosbie's balloon flight (Bicentenary of first aeronautic flight by an Irishman) .. .. .. 1·10 1·75

**1985.** Butterflies. Multicoloured.

609 22p. Type **216** .. .. 1·25 1·00
610 26p. "Vanessa atalanta" .. 1·25 70
611 28p. "Gonepteryx rhamni" .. 1·50 2·75
612 44p. "Eurabyas aurinia" 2·00 3·00

**217.** Charles Villiers Stanford (composer).

**1985.** Europa. Irish Composers. Mult.

613. 26p. Type **217** .. .. 2·00 50
614. 37p. Turlough Carolan (composer and lyricist) 4·00 5·50

**218.** George Frederick Handel.

**1985.** European Music Year. Composers. Multicoloured.

615. 22p. Type **218** .. .. 1·25 2·25
616. 22p. Guiseppe Domenico Scarlatti .. .. .. 1·25 2·25
617. 26p. Johann Sebastian Bach .. .. .. 1·50 50

**219.** U.N. Patrol of Irish Soldiers, Congo, 1960.

**1985.** Anniversaries. Multicoloured.

618. 22 p. Type **219** (25th anniv. of Irish Participation in U.N. Peace-keeping Force) .. .. .. 95 80
619. 26p. Thomas Ashe (patriot) (birth cent.) (vert.) .. 1·00 60
620. 44p. "Bishop George Berkeley" (James Lathan) (philosopher, 300th birth anniv.) (vert.) .. .. .. 1·75 3·00

**220.** Group of Young People.

**1985.** International Youth Year. Mult.

621. 22p. Type **220** .. .. 75 50
622. 26p. Students and young workers (vert.) .. .. 75 50

**221.** Visual Display Unit.

**1985.** Industrial Innovation. Multicoloured.

623. 22p. Type **221** .. .. 65 75
624. 26p. Turf cutting with hand tool and with modern machinery .. 70 55
625. 44p. "The Key Man" (Sean Keating) (150th anniv. of Institution of Engineers of Ireland) .. .. 1·25 2·25

**222.** Lighted Candle and Holly. **224.** Stylised Love Bird with Letter.

**1985.** Christmas. Multicoloured.

626. 22p. Type **222** .. .. 75 65
627. 22p. "Virgin and Child in a Landscape" (Adrian van Ijsenbrandt) .. .. 90 2·25
628. 22p. "The Holy Family" (Murillo) .. .. 90 2·25
629. 26p. "The Adoration of the Shepherds" (Louis le Nain) (horiz.) .. 90 25

No. 626 was only issued in sheetlets of 16 sold at £3, providing a discount of 52p. off the face value of the stamps.

**1986.** Greetings Stamps. Multicoloured.

630. 22p. Type **224** .. .. 85 1·25
631. 26p. Heart-shaped pillar-box .. .. .. 90 1·25

**225.** Hart's Tongue Fern. **226.** "Harmony between Industry and Nature".

**1986.** Ferns. Multicoloured.

632. 24p. Type **225** .. .. 80 70
633. 28p. Rusty-back Fern .. 90 70
634. 46p. Killarney Fern .. 1·60 2·10

**1986.** Europa. Protection of the Environment. Multicoloured

635 28p. Type **226** .. .. 1·75 50
636 39p. "Vanessa atalanta" (butterfly) and tractor in field ("Preserve hedgerows") (horiz) .. .. 3·25 4·50

**227.** Boeing 747-200 over Globe showing Aer Lingus Routes.

**1986.** 50th Anniv. of Aer Lingus (airline). Multicoloured.

637 28p. Type **227** .. .. 1·40 75
638 46p. De Havilland Dragon Mk 2 "Iolar" (first airplane) .. .. 1·90 3·00

**228.** Grand Canal at Robertstown.

**1986.** Irish Waterways. Multicoloured.

639. 24p. Type **228** .. .. 1·00 1·00
640. 28p. Fishing in County Mayo (vert.) .. .. 1·25 1·00
641. 30p. Motor cruiser on Lough Derg .. .. 1·50 2·50

**229.** "Severn" (19th-century paddlesteamer).

**1986.** 150th Anniv. of British and Irish Steam Packet Company. Multicoloured.

642. 24p. Type **229** .. .. 75 1·00
643. 28p. "Leinster" (modern ferry) .. .. 85 60

**230.** Kish Lighthouse and Bell JetRanger III Helicopter.

**231.** J. P. Nannetti (first president) and Linotype Operator (Dublin Council of Trade Unions centenary).

**1986.** Irish Lighthouses. Multicoloured.

644. 24p. Type **230** .. .. 75 75
645. 30p. Fastnet Lighthouse .. 1·50 2·25

**1986.** Anniversaries and Commemorations.

646. **231.** 24p. multicoloured .. 70 90
647. – 28p. black and grey .. 80 80
648. – 28p. multicoloured .. 80 80
649. – 30p. multicoloured .. 85 1·00
650. – 46p. multicoloured .. 1·25 1·75

DESIGNS:—VERT. No. 647, Arthur Griffith (statesman). 649, Clasped hands (International Peace Year). HORIZ. No. 648, Woman surveyor (Women in Society). 650, Peace dove (International Peace Year).

**232.** William Mulready and his Design for 1840 Envelope.

**1986.** Birth Bicentenaries of William Mulready (artist) (24p.) and Charles Bianconi (originator of Irish mail coach service) (others). Multicoloured.

651. 24p. Type **232** .. .. 65 70
652. 28p. Bianconi car outside Hearns Hotel, Clonmel (vert.) .. .. 75 55
653. 39p. Bianconi car on the road .. .. .. 1·25 1·50

**233.** "Adoration of the Shepherds" (Francesco Pascucci).

**1986.** Christmas. Multicoloured.

654. 21p. Type **233** .. .. 1·10 1·40
655. 28p. "Adoration of the Magi" (Frans Francken III) (vert.) .. .. 65 60

**234.** "Butterfly and Flowers" (Tara Collins).

**1987.** Greetings Stamps. Children's Paintings. Multicoloured.

656. 24p. Type **234** .. .. 80 1·25
657. 28p. "Postman on Bicycle delivering Hearts" (Brigid Teehan) (vert.) 95 1·25

**235.** Cork Electric Tram.

**1987.** Irish Trams. Multicoloured.

658. 24p.Type **235** .. .. 70 65
659. 28p. Dublin Standard tram 80 55
660. 30p. Howth (G.N.R.) tram 90 2·00
661. 46p. Galway horse tram .. 1·50 4·50

**236.** Ships from Crest (Bicentenary of Waterford Chamber of Commerce).

**1987.** Anniversaries.

663. **236.** 24p. black., bl. & grn. 80 60
664. – 28p. multicoloured .. 90 60
665. – 30p. multicoloured .. 95 2·00
666. – 39p. multicoloured .. 1·25 1·75

DESIGNS—HORIZ. 28p. Canon John Hayes and symbols of agriculture and development (birth centenary and 50th anniv. of Muintir na Tire programme). 39p. Mother Mary Martin and International Missionary Training Hospital, Drogheda (50th anniv. of Medical Missionaries of Mary). VERT. 30p. "Calceolaria burbidgei" and College crest (300th anniv. of Trinity College Botanic Gardens, Dublin).

**237.** Bord na Mona Headquarters and "The Turf Cutter" (sculpture, John Behan), Dublin.

**1987.** Europa. Modern Architecture. Mult.

667. 28p. Type **237** .. .. 1·50 60
668. 39p. St. Mary's Church, Cong .. .. .. 3·50 4·50

**238.** Kerry Cow.

**1987.** Irish Cattle. Multicoloured.

669. 24p. Type **238** .. .. 75 75
670. 28p. Friesian cow and calf 90 60
671. 30p. Hereford bullock .. 1·10 2·25
672. 39p. Shorthorn bull .. 1·25 2·25

**239.** Fleadh Nua, Ennis.

**1987.** Festivals. Multicoloured.

673. 24p. Type **239** .. .. 75 70
674. 28p. Rose of Tralee International Festival .. 85 60
675. 30p. Wexford Opera Festival (horiz.) .. .. 1·10 2·00
676. 46p. Ballinasloe Horse Fair (horiz.) .. .. .. 1·40 2·00

**240.** Flagon (1637), Arms and Anniversary Ornament (1987) (350th anniv of Dublin Goldsmiths' Company).

**1987.** Anniversaries and Commemorations.

677. **240.** 24p. multicoloured .. 55 80
678. – 24p. grey and black .. 55 80
679. – 28p. multicoloured .. 65 60
680. – 46p. multicoloured .. 1·00 1·10

DESIGNS—VERT. 24p. (No. 678) Cathal Brugha (patriot). 46p. Woman chairing board meeting (Women in Society). HORIZ. 28p. Arms of Ireland and inscription (50th anniv. of Constitution).

**241.** Scenes from "The Twelve Days of Christmas"(carol).

**1987.** Christmas. Multicoloured.

681. 21p. Type **241** .. .. 60 1·00
682. 24p. The Nativity (detail, late 15th-century Waterford Vestments) (vert.) 75 1·00
683. 28p. Figures from Neapolitan crib, c. 1850 (vert.) .. .. .. 75 80

**242.** Acrobatic Clowns spelling "LOVE".

**1988.** Greetings Stamps. Multicoloured.

684. 24p. Type **242** .. .. 60 60
685. 28p. Pillar box and hearts (vert.) .. .. .. 65 65

**243.** "Robert Burke" (Sidney Nolan) and Map of Burke and Wills Expedition Route.

**1988.** Bicentenary of Australian Settlement. Multicoloured.

686. 24p. Type **243** .. .. 50 60
687. 46p. "Eureka Stockade" (mural detail, Sidney Nolan) .. .. .. 1·10 1·75

**244.** Past and Present Buildings of Dublin.

**1988.** Dublin Millennium.

688. **244.** 28p. multicoloured .. 60 55

**245.** Showjumping.

**1988.** Olympic Games, Seoul. Multicoloured.

689. 28p. Type **245** .. .. 1·00 1·40
690. 28p. Cycling .. .. 1·00 1·40

**246.** William T. Cosgrave (statesman).

**1988.** Anniversaries and Events.

691. **246.** 24p. grey and black .. 60 45
692. – 30p. multicoloured .. 1·00 1·00
693. – 50p. multicoloured .. 1·25 1·50

DESIGNS—HORIZ. 30p. Members with casualty and ambulance (50th anniv of Order of Malta Ambulance Corps). VERT. 50p. Barry Fitzgerald (actor) (birth centenary).

**247.** Air Traffic Controllers and Airbus Industrie A320.

**1988.** Europa. Transport and Communications. Multicoloured.

694. 28p. Type **247** .. .. 1·25 55
695. 39p. Globe with stream of letters from Ireland to Europe .. .. .. 1·75 1·75

**248.** "Sirius" (paddle-steamer).

**1988.** Transatlantic Transport Anniversaries. Multicoloured.

696 24p. Type **248** (150th anniv of regular transatlantic steamship services) .. 75 50
697 46p. Short S.20 seaplane "Mercury" and Short S.21 flying boat "Maia" (Short Mayo composite aircraft) in Foynes Harbour (50th anniv of first commercial transatlantic flight) .. 1·25 2·25

**249.** Cottonweed.

**251.** Computer and Abacus.

**250.** Garda on Duty.

**1988.** Endangered Flora of Ireland. Mult.
698. 24p. Type **249** .. .. 65 55
699. 28p. Hart's saxifrage .. 75 55
700. 46p. Purple milk-vetch .. 1·10 2·00

**1988.** Irish Security Forces. Multicoloured.
701 28p. Type **250** .. .. 75 1·00
702 28p. Army unit with personnel carrier .. 75 1·00
703 28p. Navy and Air Corps members with "Eithne" (helicopter patrol vessel) 75 1·00
704 28p. Army and Navy reservists .. .. 75 1·00

**1988.** Anniversaries. Multicoloured.
705. 24p. Type **251** (Institute of Chartered Accountants in Ireland centenary) .. 50 50
706. 46p. "Duquesa Santa Ana" off Donegal (400th anniv. of Spanish Armada) (horiz.) .. .. .. 1·50 1·50

**252.** "President Kennedy" (James Wyeth).
**253.** St. Kevin's Church, Glendalough.

**1988.** 25th Death Anniv. of John F. Kennedy (American statesman).
707. **252.** 28p. multicoloured .. 70 80

**1988.** Christmas. Multicoloured.
708. 21p. Type **253** .. .. 70 70
709. 24p. The Adoration of the Magi .. .. .. 60 60
710. 28p. The Flight into Egypt 70 55
711. 46p. The Holy Family .. 1·10 1·50
The designs of Nos. 709/11 are from a 15th-century French Book of Hours.

**254.** Spring Flowers spelling "Love" in Gaelic.

**1989.** Greetings Stamps. Multicoloured.
712. 24p. Type **254** .. .. 60 55
713. 28p. "The Sonnet" (William Mulready) (vert.) .. .. .. 65 55

**255** Italian Garden, Garinish Island

**1989.** National Parks and Gardens. Mult.
714 24p. Type **255** .. .. 80 55
715 28p. Lough Veagh, Glenveagh National Park .. .. .. 95 55
716 32p. Barnaderg Bay, Connemara National Park .. .. .. 1·00 1·25
717 50p. St. Stephen's Green, Dublin .. .. .. 1·50 1·75

**256** "Silver Stream", 1908

**1989.** Classic Irish Cars. Multicoloured.
718 24p. Type **256** .. .. 50 55
719 28p. Benz "Comfortable", 1898 .. .. .. 50 55
720 39p. "Thomond", 1929 .. 1·25 1·50
721 46p. Chambers' 8 h.p. model, 1905 .. .. 1·50 1·50

**257** Ring-a-ring-a-roses

**1989.** Europa. Children's Games. Mult.
722 28p. Type **257** .. .. 1·00 75
723 39p. Hopscotch .. .. 1·40 2·00

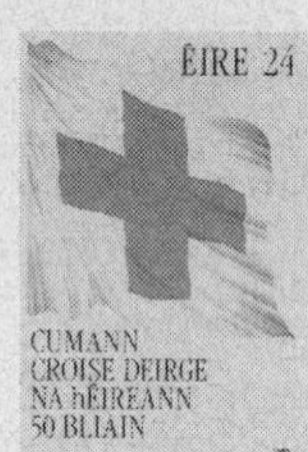

**258** Irish Red Cross Flag (50th anniv)

**1989.** Anniversaries and Events.
724 **258** 24p. red and black .. 55 60
725 – 28p. blue, black & yell 1·10 1·10
DESIGN: 28p. Circle of twelve stars (third direct elections to European Parliament).

**259** Saints Kilian, Totnan and Colman (from 12th-century German manuscript)

**1989.** 1300th Death Anniv of Saints Kilian, Totnan and Colman.
726 **259** 28p. multicoloured .. 80 1·10

**260** 19th-century Mail Coach passing Cashel

**1989.** Bicentenary of Irish Mail Coach Service.
727 **260** 28p. multicoloured .. 1·00 75

**261** Crest and 19th-century Dividers (150th anniv of Royal Institute of Architects of Ireland)

**1989.** Anniversaries and Commemorations.
728 – 24p. grey and black .. 65 55
729 **261** 28p. multicoloured .. 65 55
730 – 30p. multicoloured .. 1·40 1·75
731 – 46p. brown .. .. 1·60 1·75
DESIGNS—VERT. 24p. Sean T. O'Kelly (statesman) (drawing by Sean O'Sullivan); 46p. Jawaharlal Nehru (birth centenary). HORIZ. 30p. Margaret Burke-Sheridan (soprano) (portrait by De Gennaro) and scene from "La Boheme" (birth centenary).

**262** " 'NCB Ireland' rounding Cape Horn" (Des Fallon)

**1989.** First Irish Entry in Whitbread Round the World Yacht Race.
732 **262** 28p. multicoloured .. 1·25 1·25

**263** Willow/Red Grouse
**264** "The Annunciation"

**1989.** Game Birds. Multicoloured.
733 24p. Type **263** .. .. 1·00 55
734 28p. Lapwing .. .. 1·10 55
735 39p. Woodcock .. .. 1·40 1·75
736 46p. Ring-necked Pheasant 1·50 1·75

**1989.** Christmas. Multicoloured.
738 21p. Children decorating crib .. .. .. 75 75
739 24p. Type **264** .. .. 85 60
740 28p. "The Nativity" .. 90 55
741 46p. "The Adoration of the Magi" .. .. .. 1·75 2·50

**265** Logo (Ireland's Presidency of the European Communities)
**266** Dropping Messages from Balloon

**1990.** European Events. Multicoloured.
742 30p. Type **265** .. .. 75 60
743 50p. Logo and outline map of Ireland (European Tourism Year) .. .. 2·00 2·75

**1990.** Greetings Stamps.
744 **266** 26p. multicoloured .. 1·25 1·25
745 – 30p. red, buff & brown 1·25 1·25
DESIGN: 30p. Heart and "Love" drawn in lipstick.

**267** Silver Kite Brooch
**268** Posy of Flowers

**1990.** Irish Heritage.
746 **267** 1p. black and blue .. 10 10
747 2p. black and orange 10 10
748 – 4p. black and violet 10 10
749 – 5p. black and green .. 10 10
750 – 10p. black and orange 20 25
751 – 20p. black and yellow 40 45
752 – 26p. black and violet 50 55
753 – 28p. black and orange 55 60
754 – 30p. black and blue .. 65 65
755 – 32p. black and green 65 70
756 – 34p. black and yellow 70 75
757 – 37p. black and green 75 80
758 – 38p. black and violet 75 80
758a – 40p. black and blue .. 80 85
759 – 41p. black and orange 80 85
760 – 44p. brown and yellow 90 95
760a – 45p. black and violet 90 95
761a – 50p. black and yellow 1·00 1·10
762 – 52p. black and blue .. 1·00 1·10
763 – £1 black and yellow 2·00 2·10
764 – £2 black and green .. 4·00 4·25
765 – £5 black and blue .. 10·00 10·50
DESIGNS: 4, 5p. Dunamase food vessel; 26, 28p. Lismore crozier; 34, 37, 38, 40p. Gleninsheen collar; 41, 44p. Silver thistle brooch; 45, 50, 52p. Broighter boat. 22×38 mm: £5 St. Patrick's Bell Shrine. HORIZ. As T **267**: 10p. Derrinboy armlets; 20p. Gold dress fastener; 30p. Enamelled latchet brooch; 32p. Broighter collar. 38×22 mm: £1 Ardagh Chalice; £2 Tara brooch.
For 32p. value as No. 755 but larger, 27×20 mm, see No. 823.

**1990.** Greetings Stamps. Multicoloured.
766 26p. Type **268** .. .. 2·00 2·50
767 26p. Birthday presents .. 2·00 2·50
768 30p. Flowers, ribbon and horseshoe .. .. 2·00 2·50
769 30p. Balloons .. .. 2·00 2·50

**269** Player heading Ball
**271** 1990 Irish Heritage 30p. Stamp and 1840 Postmark

**270** Battle of the Boyne, 1690

**1990.** World Cup Football Championship, Italy. Multicoloured.
770 30p. Type **269** .. .. 1·50 2·00
771 30p. Tackling .. .. 1·50 2·00

**1990.** 300th Anniv of the Williamite Wars (1st issue). Multicoloured.
772 30p. Type **270** .. .. 1·00 1·40
773 30p. Siege of Limerick, 1690 1·00 1·40
See also Nos. 806/7.

**1990.** 150th Anniv of the Penny Black. Mult.
774 30p. Type **271** .. .. 90 90
775 50p. Definitive stamps of 1922, 1969, 1982 and 1990 1·50 2·00

**272** General Post Office, Dublin
**274** Narcissus "Foundling" and Japanese Gardens, Tully

**273** Medical Missionary giving Injection

**1990.** Europa. Post Office Buildings. Mult.
776 30p. Type **272** .. .. 1·00 60
777 41p. Westport Post Office, County Mayo .. .. 1·40 2·25

**1990.** Anniversaries and Events.
778 **273** 26p. multicoloured .. 90 55
779 – 30p. black .. .. 1·00 2·00
780 – 50p. multicoloured .. 1·50 1·50
DESIGNS—VERT. 30p. Michael Collins (statesman) (birth centenary). HORIZ. 50p. Missionaries working at water pump (Irish missionary service).

**1990.** Garden Flowers. Multicoloured.
781 26p. Type **274** .. .. 70 55
782 30p. "Rosa x hibernica" and Mulahide Castle gardens .. .. 85 80
783 41p. Primula "Rowallane Rose" and Rowallane garden .. .. 1·75 1·75
784 50p. "Erica erigena" "Irish Dusk" and Palm House, National Botanical Gardens .. .. 2·00 2·00

**275** "Playboy of the Western World" (John Synge)

**1990.** Irish Theatre. Multicoloured.
785 30p. Type **275** .. .. 1·25 1·50
786 30p. "Juno and the Paycock" (Sean O'Casey) .. 1·25 1·50
787 30p. "The Field" (John Keane) .. .. .. 1·25 1·50
788 30p. "Waiting for Godot" (Samuel Beckett) .. 1·25 1·50

**276** Nativity

**277** Hearts in Mail Sack and Postman's Cap

**1990.** Christmas. Multicoloured.
789 26p. Child praying by bed 70 80
790 26p. Type **276** .. .. 70 60
791 30p. Madonna and Child .. 90 90
792 50p. Adoration of the Magi 1·60 2·25

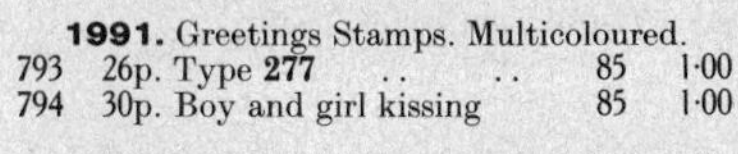
**1991.** Greetings Stamps. Multicoloured.
793 26p. Type **277** .. .. 85 1·00
794 30p. Boy and girl kissing 85 1·00

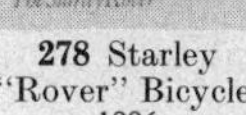

**278** Starley "Rover" Bicycle, 1886

**279** "Cuchulainn" (statue by Oliver Sheppard) and Proclamation

**1991.** Early Bicycles. Multicoloured.
795 26p. Type **278** .. .. 80 60
796 30p. Child's horse tricycle, 1875 .. .. .. 90 95
797 50p. "Penny Farthing", 1871 .. .. .. 1·60 1·75

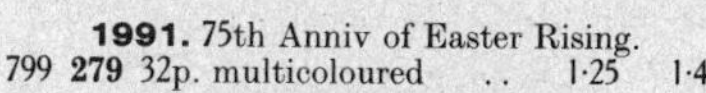
**1991.** 75th Anniv of Easter Rising.
799 **279** 32p. multicoloured .. 1·25 1·40

**280** Scene from "La Traviata" (50th anniv of Dublin Grand Opera Society)

**1991.** "Dublin 1991 European City of Culture". Multicoloured.
800 28p. Type **280** .. .. 65 75
801 32p. City Hall and European Community emblem 85 85
802 44p. St. Patrick's Cathedral (800th anniv) 1·25 1·25
803 52p. Custom House (bicent) (41 × 24 mm) .. .. 1·40 1·60

**281** "Giotto" Spacecraft approaching Halley's Comet

**1991.** Europa. Europe in Space. Mult.
804 32p. Type **281** .. .. 1·25 1·00
805 44p. Hubble Telescope orbiting Earth .. .. 1·75 2·50

**282** Siege of Athlone

**1991.** 300th Anniv of the Williamite Wars (2nd issue). Multicoloured.
806 28p. Type **282** .. .. 90 1·25
807 28p. Generals Ginkel and Sarsfield (signatories of Treaty of Limerick) .. 90 1·25

**283** John A. Costello (statesman)

**1991.** Anniversaries.
811 **283** 28p. black .. .. 70 70
812 – 32p. multicoloured .. 85 85
813 – 52p. multicoloured .. 1·40 2·00
DESIGNS—VERT. 28p. Type **283** (birth cent) (drawing by Sean O'Sullivan; 32p. "Charles Stewart Parnell" (Sydney Hall) (death cent); HORIZ. 52p. Meeting of United Irishmen.

**284** Player on 15th Green, Portmarnock (Walker Cup)

**1991.** Golf Commemorations. Multicoloured.
814 28p. Type **284** .. .. 1·00 75
815 32p. Logo and golfer of 1900 (cent of Golfing Union of Ireland) (vert) 1·25 1·00

**285** Wicklow Cheviot

**1991.** Irish Sheep. Multicoloured.
816 32p. Type **285** .. .. 1·00 80
817 38p. Donegal Blackface .. 1·40 1·50
818 52p. Galway (horiz) .. 2·00 3·25

**286** Boatyard

**1991.** Fishing Fleet. Multicoloured.
819 28p. Type **286** .. .. 60 65
820 32p. Traditional inshore trawlers .. .. 70 80
821 44p. Inshore lobster pot boat .. .. .. 1·60 2·00
822 52p. "Veronica" (fish factory ship) .. .. 2·00 2·25

**1991.** As No. 755, but larger, 27 × 20 mm. Self-adhesive.
823 32p. black and green .. 65 70

**287** The Annunciation

**289** Healthy Family on Apple

**288** Multicoloured Heart

**1991.** Christmas.
827 – 28p. multicoloured .. 75 80
828 **287** 28p. blue, green & blk 75 65
829 – 32p. red and black .. 85 75
830 – 52p. multicoloured .. 1·60 2·25
DESIGNS: No. 827, Three Kings; No. 829, The Nativity; No. 830, Adoration of the Kings.

**1992.** Greetings Stamps. Multicoloured.
831 28p. Type **288** .. .. 85 95
832 32p. "LOVE" at end of rainbow (vert) .. .. 95 1·10

**1992.** "Healthy Living" Campaign.
833 **289** 28p. multicoloured .. 85 85

**290** Boxing

**1992.** Olympic Games, Barcelona. Mult.
834 32p. Type **290** .. .. 90 90
835 44p. Sailing .. .. 1·40 1·90

**291** "Mari" (cog) and 14th-century Map

**1992.** Irish Maritime Heritage. Multicoloured.
837 32p. Type **291** .. .. 1·00 90
838 52p. "Ovoca" (trawler) and chart (vert) .. .. 1·50 2·10

**292** Chamber Logo and Commercial Symbols

**1992.** Bicentenary of Galway Chamber of Commerce and Industry.
839 **292** 28p. multicoloured .. 70 85

**293** Cliffs and Cove

**1992.** Greetings Stamps. Multicoloured.
840 28p. Type **293** .. .. 75 1·00
841 28p. Meadow .. .. 75 1·00
842 32p. Fuchsia and honeysuckle .. .. .. 75 1·00
843 32p. Lily pond and dragonfly .. .. .. 75 1·00

**294** Fleet of Columbus

**1992.** Europa. 500th Anniv of Discovery of America by Columbus. Multicoloured.
844 32p. Type **294** .. .. 1·25 90
845 44p. Columbus landing in the New World .. 1·75 1·75

**295** Irish Immigrants

**1992.** Irish Immigrants in the Americas. Multicoloured.
846 52p. Type **295** .. .. 1·60 1·60
847 52p. Irish soldiers, entertainers and politicians .. 1·60 1·60

**296** Pair of Pine Martens

**1992.** Endangered Species. Pine Marten. Mult.
848 28p. Type **296** .. .. 1·00 70
849 32p. Marten on branch .. 1·00 80
850 44p. Female with kittens 1·60 1·50
851 52p. Marten catching great tit .. .. .. 2·00 1·75

**297** "The Rotunda and New Rooms" (James Malton)

**1992.** Dublin Anniversaries. Multicoloured.
852 28p. Type **297** .. .. 80 65
853 32p. Trinity College Library (28 × 45 mm) .. 1·25 85
854 44p. "Charlemont House" 1·25 1·75
855 52p. Trinity College main gate (28 × 45 mm) .. 1·75 2·25
ANNIVERSARIES: 28, 44p. Bicentenary of Publication of Malton's "Views of Dublin"; 32, 52p. 400th anniv of Founding of Trinity College.

**298** European Star and Megalithic Dolmen

**1992.** Single European Market.
856 **298** 32p. multicoloured .. 70 80

**299** Farm Produce

**300** "The Annunciation" (from illuminated manuscript)

**1992.** Irish Agriculture. Multicoloured.

857 32p. Type **299** .. .. 1·00 1·25
858 32p. Dairy and beef herds .. 1·00 1·25
859 32p. Harvesting cereals .. 1·00 1·25
860 32p. Market gardening .. 1·00 1·25

Nos. 857/60 were printed together, se-tenant, forming a composite design.

**1992.** Christmas. Multicoloured.

861 28p. Congregation entering church .. .. .. 80 65
862 28p. Type **300** .. .. 80 65
863 32p. "Adoration of the Shepherds" (Da Empoli) 1·10 1·00
864 52p. "Adoration of the Magi" (Rottenhammer) 1·40 1·50

**301** Queen of Hearts

**303** Bee Orchid

**302** "Evening at Tangier" (Sir John Lavery)

**1993.** Greetings Stamps. Multicoloured.

865 28p. Type **301** .. 75 85
866 32p. Hot air balloon trailing hearts (horiz) .. 75 85

**1993.** Irish Impressionist Painters. Mult.

867 28p. Type **302** .. .. 75 60
868 32p. "The Goose Girl" (William Leech) .. 80 65
869 44p. "La Jeune Bretonne" (Roderic O'Conor) (vert) 1·25 1·60
870 52p. "Lustre Jug" (Walter Osborne) (vert) .. 1·75 1·90

**1993.** Irish Orchids. Multicoloured.

871 28p. Type **303** .. .. 90 60
872 32p. O'Kelly's orchid .. 1·10 70
873 38p. Dark red helleborine 1·60 2·00
874 52p. Irish lady's tresses .. 1·90 2·25

**304** "Pears in a Copper Pan" (Hilda van Stockum)

**1993.** Europa. Contemporary Art. Mult.

876 32p. Type **304** .. .. 75 75
877 44p. "Arrieta Orzola" (Tony O'Malley) .. 1·10 1·10

**305** Cultural Activities

**1993.** Centenary of Conradh Na Gaelige (cultural organization). Multicoloured.

878 32p. Type **305** .. .. 85 75
879 52p. Illuminated manuscript cover (vert) .. 1·50 1·50

**306** Diving

**1993.** Centenary of Irish Amateur Swimming Association. Multicoloured.

880 32p. Type **306** .. .. 1·00 1·25
881 32p. Swimming .. .. 1·00 1·25

**307** Nurse with Patient and Hospital Buildings

**1993.** Anniversaries and Events. Mult.

882 28p. Type **307** (250th anniv of Royal Hospital, Donnybrook) .. .. 80 60
883 32p. College building and crest (bicentenary of St. Patrick's College, Carlow) (vert) .. .. 80 65
884 44p. Map of Neolithic field system, Ceide (opening of interpretative centre) 1·25 1·40
885 52p. Edward Bunting (musicologist) (150th death anniv) (25 × 42 mm) .. .. .. 1·40 1·60

**308** Great Northern Railways Gardner at Drogheda

**1993.** Irish Buses. Multicoloured.

886 28p. Type **308** .. .. 60 65
887 32p. C.I.E. Leyland Titan at College Green, Dublin 65 70
888 52p. Horse-drawn omnibus at Old Baal's Bridge, Limerick .. .. 1·25 1·75
889 52p. Char-a-banc at Lady's View, Killarney .. 1·25 1·75

**309** The Annunciation

**1993.** Christmas. Multicoloured.

890 28p. The flight into Egypt (vert) .. .. .. 60 65
891 28p. Type **309** .. .. 60 55
892 32p. Holy Family .. 70 70
893 52p. Adoration of the shepherds .. .. 1·60 1·90

**310** Biplane skywriting "Love"

**1994.** Greetings Stamps. Multicoloured.

894 28p. Type **310** .. .. 75 75
895 32p. Couple within heart (vert) .. .. .. 85 85

**311** Smiling Sun

**1994.** Greetings Stamps. Multicoloured.

896 32p. Type **311** .. .. 70 75
897 32p. Smiling daisy .. 70 75
898 32p. Smiling heart .. 70 75
899 32p. Smiling rose .. .. 70 75

**312** Stylised Logo of Macra na Feirme (50th anniv)

**1994.** Anniversaries and Events.

901 **312** 28p. gold and blue .. 75 65
902 – 32p. multicoloured .. 1·25 75
903 – 38p. multicoloured .. 1·25 1·50
904 – 52p. black, cobalt & bl 1·40 1·75

DESIGNS—38 × 35 mm: 32p. "The Taking of Christ" (Caravaggio) (loan of painting to National Gallery). 37½ × 27 mm: 38p. Sir Horace Plunkett with 19th-century milk carts and modern tankers (centenary of Irish Co-operative Organisation Society); 52p. Congress emblem (centenary of Irish Congress of Trade Unions).

**313** St. Brendan visiting Iceland

**1994.** Europa. St. Brendan's Voyages. Mult.

905 32p. Type **313** .. .. 75 75
906 44p. Discovering Faroe Islands .. .. .. 1·50 1·75

**314** First Meeting of Dail, 1919

**1994.** Parliamentary Anniversaries. Mult.

908 32p. Type **314** (75th anniv) 90 75
909 32p. European Parliament (4th direct elections) .. 90 75

**315** Irish and Argentine Footballers

**317** Statue of Edmund Rice and Class



**316** "Arctia caja"

**1994.** Sporting Anniversaries and Events. Multicoloured.

910 32p. Type **315** .. .. 80 90
911 32p. Irish and German footballers .. .. 80 90
912 32p. Irish and Dutch women's hockey match (horiz) .. .. .. 1·25 90
913 52p. Irish and English women's hockey match (horiz) .. .. .. 1·50 1·75

ANNIVERSARIES AND EVENTS: Nos. 910/11, World Cup Football Championship, U.S.A.; 912, Women's Hockey World Cup, Dublin; 913, Centenary of Irish Ladies' Hockey Union.

**1994.** Moths. Mult. (a) Size 37 × 26 mm.

914 28p. Type **316** .. .. 65 60
915 32p. "Calamia tridens" .. 75 70
916 38p. "Saturnia pavonia" .. 90 90
917 52p. "Deilephila elpenor" 1·50 1·75

(b) Size 34 × 22 mm. Self-adhesive.

919 32p. "Calamia tridens" .. 85 90
920 32p. Type **316** .. .. 85 90
921 32p. "Deilephila elpenor" 85 90
922 32p. "Saturnia pavonia" .. 85 90

**1994.** Anniversaries and Events. Mult.

923 28p. St. Laurence Gate, Drogheda (41½ × 25 mm) 70 70
924 32p. Type **317** .. .. 75 85
925 32p. Edmund Burke (politician) .. .. 75 85
926 52p. Vickers FB-27 Vimy and map (horiz) .. 1·25 1·25
927 52p. Eamonn Andrews (broadcaster) .. .. 1·25 1·25

ANNIVERSARIES AND EVENTS: No. 923, 800th anniv of Drogheda; 924, 150th death anniv of Edmund Rice (founder of Irish Christian Brothers); 925, 927, The Irish abroad; 926, 75th anniv of Alcock and Brown's first transatlantic flight.

**318** George Bernard Shaw (author) and "Pygmalion" Poster

**1994.** Irish Nobel Prize Winners. Mult.

928 28p. Type **318** .. .. 60 60
929 28p. Samuel Beckett (author) and pair of boots .. .. .. 60 60
930 32p. Sean MacBride (human rights campaigner) and peace doves .. .. .. 70 75
931 52p. William Butler Yeats (poet) and poem .. 1·10 1·60

**319** "The Annunciation" (ivory plaque)

**320** Tree of Hearts

**1994.** Christmas. Multicoloured.

932 28p. Nativity .. .. 70 60
933 28p. Type **319** .. .. 70 60
934 32p. "Flight into Egypt" (wood carving) .. 80 70
935 52p. "Nativity" (ivory plaque) .. .. 1·10 1·75

**1995.** Greetings Stamps. Multicoloured.

936 32p. Type **320** .. .. 80 80
937 32p. Teddy bear holding balloon .. .. 80 80
938 32p. Clown juggling hearts 80 80
939 32p. Bouquet of flowers .. 80 80

**321** West Clare Railway Locomotive No. 1 "Kilkee" at Kilrush Station

**1995.** Transport. Narrow Gauge Railways. Multicoloured.
941 28p. Type **321** .. .. 75 60
942 32p. Co. Donegal Railway locomotive No. 2 "Blanche" at Donegal Station .. .. 90 80
943 38p. Cork and Muskerry Railway locomotive No. 1 "City of Cork" on Western Road, Cork .. 1·25 1·40
944 52p. Cavan and Leitrim Railway locomotive No. 3 "Lady Edith" on Arigna Tramway .. 1·75 2·00

**322** English and Irish Rugby Players

**1995.** World Cup Rugby Championship, South Africa. Multicoloured.
946 32p. Type **322** .. .. 75 70
947 52p. Australian and Irish players .. .. 1·25 1·40

**323** Peace Dove and Skyscrapers

**1995.** Europa. Peace and Freedom. Mult.
949 32p. Type **323** .. .. 80 70
952 32p. Peace dove and map of Europe and North Africa .. .. .. 80 80
950 44p. As No. 952 .. .. 1·10 1·25
No. 949 exists with ordinary or self-adhesive gum, No. 952 with self-adhesive gum only and No. 950 with ordinary gum only.

**324** Soldiers of the Irish Brigade and Memorial Cross

**325** Irish Brigade, French Army, 1745

**1995.** 250th Anniv of Battle of Fontenoy.
953 **324** 32p. multicoloured .. 80 80

**1995.** Military Uniforms. Multicoloured.
954 28p. Type **325** .. .. 70 60
955 32p. Tercio Irlanda, Spanish army in Flanders, 1605 .. .. 80 75
956 32p. Royal Dublin Fusiliers, 1914 .. .. 80 75
957 38p. St. Patrick's Battalion, Papal Army, 1860 .. .. .. 1·10 1·25
958 52p. 69th Regiment, New York State Militia, 1861 1·60 1·75

**326** Guglielmo Marconi and Original Radio Transmitter

**1995.** Centenary of Radio. Multicoloured.
959 32p. Type **326** .. .. 80 1·00
960 32p. Traditional radio dial 80 1·00

**327** Bartholomew Mosse (founder) and Hospital Building

**1995.** Anniversaries. Multicoloured.
961 28p. Type **327** (250th anniv of Rotunda Hospital) .. 70 70
962 32p. St. Patrick's House, Maynooth College (bicent) (25 × 41mm) .. 80 80
963 32p. Laurel wreath and map of Europe (50th anniv of end of Second World War) .. .. 80 80
964 52p. Geological map of Ireland (150th anniv of Geological Survey of Ireland) ($32\frac{1}{2} \times 32\frac{1}{2}$ mm) 1·25 1·50

**328** Natterjack Toad

**1995.** Reptiles and Amphibians. Mult.
965 32p. Type **328** .. .. 90 1·10
966 32p. Common lizards .. 90 1·10
967 32p. Smooth newts .. 90 1·10
968 32p. Common frog .. 90 1·10
Nos. 965/8 were printed together, se-tenant, with the backgrounds forming a composite design.
Nos. 965/8 also come self-adhesive.

**329** "Crinum moorei"

**1995.** Bicentenary of National Botanic Gardens, Glasnevin. Flowers. Mult.
973 32p. Type **329** .. .. 85 70
974 38p. "Sarracenia x moorei" 1·10 95
975 44p. "Solanum crispum" "Glasnevin" .. .. 1·50 1·75

**330** Anniversary Logo and Irish United Nations Soldier

**1995.** 50th Anniv of United Nations. Mult.
976 32p. Type **330** .. .. 80 70
977 52p. Emblem and "UN" .. 1·25 1·40

**331** "Adoration of the Shepherds" (illuminated manuscript) (Benedotto Bardone)

**1995.** Christmas. Multicoloured.
978 28p. Adoration of the Magi 70 65
979 28p. Type **331** .. .. 70 65
980 32p. "Adoration of the Magi" (illuminated manuscript) (Bardone) 80 70
981 52p. "The Holy Family" (illuminated manuscript) (Bardone) .. .. 1·40 1·60

**332** Zig and Zag on Heart

**333** Wheelchair Athlete

**1996.** Greetings Stamps. Multicoloured.
982 32p. Type **332** .. .. 80 80
983 32p. Zig and Zag waving 80 80
984 32p. Zig and Zag in space suits .. .. .. 80 80
985 32p. Zig and Zag wearing hats .. .. .. 80 80

**1996.** Olympic and Paralympic Games, Atlanta. Multicoloured.
987 28p. Type **333** .. .. 70 65
988 32p. Running .. .. 80 80
989 32p. Throwing the discus 80 80
990 32p. Single kayak .. 80 80

**334** Before the Start, Fairyhouse Race Course

**1996.** Irish Horse Racing. Multicoloured.
991 28p. Type **334** .. .. 70 65
992 32p. Steeplechase, Punchestown .. .. 80 80
993 32p. On the Flat, The Curragh .. .. 80 80
994 38p. Steeplechase, Galway 1·00 1·25
995 52p. After the race, Leopardstown .. .. 1·40 1·50

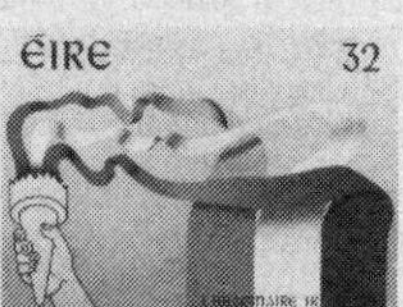

**335** Irish and French Coloured Ribbons merging

**1996.** "L'Imaginaire Irlandais" Festival of Contemporary Irish Arts, France.
996 **335** 32p. multicoloured .. 80 80

**336** Louie Bennett (suffragette)

**1996.** Europa. Famous Women. Ordinary or Self-adhesive gum.
997 **336** 32p. violet .. .. 80 70
998 – 44p. green .. .. 1·10 1·25
DESIGN: 44p. Lady Augusta Gregory (playwright).

**337** Newgrange Passage Tomb (Boyne Valley World Heritage Site)

**1996.** Anniversaries and Events.
1001 **337** 28p. brown and black 70 60
1002 – 32p. multicoloured .. 80 90
DESIGN: 32p. Children playing (50th anniv of U.N.I.C.E.F.).

**338** Stanley Woods

**1996.** Isle of Man Tourist Trophy Motor Cycle Races. Irish Winners. Multicoloured.
1004 32p. Type **338** .. .. 80 70
1005 44p. Artie Bell .. .. 1·25 1·40
1006 50p. Alec Bennett .. 1·50 1·60
1007 52p. Joey and Robert Dunlop .. .. 1·50 1·60

**339** Michael Davitt (founder of The Land League)

**1996.** Anniversaries and Events. Mult.
1009 28p. Type **339** (150th birth anniv) .. .. 70 60
1010 32p. Presidency logo (Ireland's Presidency of European Union) (horiz) .. .. 80 70
1011 38p. Thomas McLaughlin (hydro-electric engineer) and Ardnacrusha Power Station (birth centenary) (horiz) .. 1·00 1·10
1012 52p. Mechanical peat harvester (50th anniv of Bord na Mona) (horiz) 1·60 1·75

**340** Coastal Patrol Vessel

**1996.** 50th Anniv of Irish Naval Service. Multicoloured.
1013 32p. Type **340** .. .. 80 70
1014 44p. Corvette .. .. 1·40 1·50
1015 52p. Motor torpedo boat (vert) .. .. .. 1·50 1·60

**341** Blind Woman with Child

**1996.** People with Disabilities. Mult.
1016 28p. Type **341** .. .. 55 60
1017 28p. Man in wheelchair playing bowls .. .. 55 60

**342** Green-winged Teal

**1996.** Freshwater Ducks. Multicoloured.
1018 32p. Type **342** .. .. 65 70
1019 38p. Common shoveler .. 75 80
1020 44p. European wigeon .. 90 95
1021 52p. Mallard .. .. 1·10 1·25

343 "Man of Aran"

**1996.** Centenary of Irish Cinema. Mult.

| | | | | |
|---|---|---|---|---|
| 1023 | 32p. Type **343** .. | .. | 65 | 70 |
| 1024 | 32p. "My Left Foot" | .. | 65 | 70 |
| 1025 | 32p. "The Commitments" | .. | 65 | 70 |
| 1026 | 32p. "The Field" | .. | 65 | 70 |

344 Visit of the Magi

**1996.** Christmas. Designs from 16th-century "Book of Hours" (Nos.1028/30). Multicoloured.

| | | | | |
|---|---|---|---|---|
| 1027 | 28p. The Holy Family | .. | 55 | 60 |
| 1028 | 28p. Type **344** .. | .. | 55 | 60 |
| 1029 | 32p. The Annunciation | .. | 65 | 70 |
| 1030 | 52p. The Shepherds receiving news of Christ's birth .. | .. | 1·10 | 1·25 |

POSTAGE DUE STAMPS

**1971.** Decimal Currency. Colours changed.

| | | | | | |
|---|---|---|---|---|---|
| D 15. | **D 1.** | 1p. brown .. | .. | 30 | 60 |
| D 16. | | 1½p. green .. | .. | 50 | 1·50 |
| D 17. | | 3p. stone .. | .. | 90 | 1·50 |
| D 18. | | 4p. orange .. | .. | 90 | 1·25 |
| D 19. | | 5p. blue .. | .. | 95 | 2·50 |
| D 20. | | 7p. yellow .. | .. | 40 | 3·50 |
| D 21. | | 8p. red. .. | .. | 40 | 2·50 |

D 2.

D 3.

**1980.**

| | | | | | |
|---|---|---|---|---|---|
| D25 | D 2 | 1p. green .. | .. | 30 | 55 |
| D26 | | 2p. blue .. | .. | 30 | 55 |
| D27 | | 4p. green .. | .. | 40 | 55 |
| D28 | | 6p. flesh .. | .. | 40 | 70 |
| D29 | | 8p. blue .. | .. | 40 | 75 |
| D30 | | 18p. green .. | .. | 75 | 1·25 |
| D31 | | 20p. red .. | .. | 2·25 | 4·00 |
| D32 | | 24p. green .. | .. | 75 | 1·75 |
| D33 | | 30p. violet .. | .. | 3·00 | 5·00 |
| D34 | | 50p. pink .. | .. | 3·75 | 6·00 |

**1988.**

| | | | | |
|---|---|---|---|---|
| D 35. | **D 3.** 1p. black, red & yell. | | 10 | 10 |
| D 36. | 2p. black, red & brn. | | 10 | 10 |
| D 37. | 3p. black, red & pur. | | 10 | 10 |
| D 38. | 4p. black, red & vio. | | 10 | 10 |
| D 39. | 5p. black, red & blue | | 10 | 15 |
| D 40. | 17p. black, red & grn. | | 35 | 40 |
| D 41. | 20p. black, red & blue | | 40 | 45 |
| D 42. | 24p. black, red & grn. | | 50 | 55 |
| D 43. | 30p. blk., red & grey | | 60 | 65 |
| D 44. | 50p. blk., red & grey | | 1·00 | 1·10 |
| D 45. | £1 black, red & brown | | 2·00 | 2·10 |

# ISRAEL Pt. 19

**The former British Mandate over Palestine was ended by the partition plan approved by the United Nations General Assembly on 29 November, 1947, and on 14 May, 1948, the new state of Israel was proclaimed.**

**1948. 1000 prutot (mils) = 1 Israeli pound.**
**1960. 100 agorot = 1 Israeli pound.**
**1980. 100 agorot = 1 shekel.**

**"TABS".** All Israeli stamps (except the Postage Dues) exist with descriptive sheet margin attached. These so-called "Tabs" are popular and in some cases scarce.

Prices are for stamps without "tab". Separate prices for stamps with "tabs" are given in Stanley Gibbons Catalogue, Part 19 (Middle East).

**1.** Palm Tree and Baskets with Dates.

**2.** Silver Shekel and Pomegranates.

**1948.** Ancient Jewish Coins. Perf or roul.

| | | | | | |
|---|---|---|---|---|---|
| 1 | **1** | 3 m. orange .. | .. | 50 | 10 |
| 2 | – | 5 m. green .. | .. | 50 | 10 |
| 3a | – | 10 m. mauve .. | .. | 40 | 15 |
| 4 | – | 15 m. red .. | .. | 1·00 | 10 |
| 5 | – | 20 m. blue .. | .. | 2·50 | 10 |
| 6 | – | 50 m. brown .. | .. | 12·50 | 65 |
| 7 | **2** | 250 m. green .. | .. | 32·00 | 12·50 |
| 8 | | 500 m. red on buff | .. | £120 | 45·00 |
| 9 | | 1000 m. blue on blue (36 × 24 mm) .. | .. | £250 | £100 |

DESIGNS ON COINS: 5 m. Vine leaf; 10 m. Ritual jar; 15 m. Bunch of grapes; 20 m. Ritual cup; 50 m. Tied palm branches and lemon.

See also Nos. 21/6, 40/51 and 90/93.

**3.** "Flying Scroll" Emblem.

**1948.** Jewish New Year.

| | | | | | |
|---|---|---|---|---|---|
| 10 | **3** | 3 m. brown and blue | .. | 40 | 25 |
| 11 | | 5 m. green and blue | .. | 40 | 25 |
| 12 | | 10 m. red and blue | .. | 50 | 40 |
| 13 | | 20 m. blue and light blue | | 2·75 | 90 |
| 14 | | 65 m. brown and red | .. | 11·00 | 4·25 |

**4.** Road to Jerusalem.

**5.** National Flag.

**1949.** Inaug. of Constituent Assemby.

| | | | | |
|---|---|---|---|---|
| 15. | **4.** | 250 pr. brown and grey | 1·50 | 1·25 |

**1949.** Adoption of New National Flag.

| | | | | |
|---|---|---|---|---|
| 16. | **5.** | 20 pr. blue .. .. | 60 | 35 |

**6.** Petah Tiqwa Well.

**7.** Air Force Badge.

**1949.** 70th Anniv of Founding of Petah Tiqwa.

| | | | | |
|---|---|---|---|---|
| 17. | **6.** | 40 pr. brown and green | 9·50 | 75 |

**1949.** Jewish New Year.

| | | | | |
|---|---|---|---|---|
| 18. | **7.** | 5 pr. blue .. .. .. | 90 | 40 |
| 19. | – | 10 pr. green .. .. | 90 | 40 |
| 20. | – | 35 pr. brown .. .. | 7·25 | 4·25 |

BADGES: 10 pr. Navy. 35 pr. Army.

**8.** Ancient Jewish Coin.

**10.** Stag and Globe.

**1949.** 2nd Jewish Coins issue. Inscr at left of 6 or 8 characters.

| | | | | | |
|---|---|---|---|---|---|
| 21 | **8** | 3 pr. grey .. | .. | 10 | 10 |
| 22 | – | 5 pr. violet (as No. 2) | .. | 10 | 10 |
| 23 | – | 10 pr. green (as No. 3) | .. | 10 | 10 |
| 24 | – | 15 pr. red (as No. 4) | .. | 15 | 10 |
| 25 | – | 30 pr. blue .. | .. | 35 | 10 |
| 26 | – | 50 pr. brown (as No. 6) | .. | 1·25 | 15 |

DESIGN: 30 p.r. Ritual vessel.

For designs with larger inscription at left, see Nos. 40/51 and 90/93.

**1950.** Israel's Membership and 75th Anniv of U.P.U.

| | | | | |
|---|---|---|---|---|
| 27. | **10.** | 40 pr. violet .. .. | 90 | 65 |
| 28. | | 80 pr. red .. .. .. | 1·00 | 75 |

**11.** Landing of Immigrants.

**1950.** 2nd Anniv. of Independence.

| | | | | |
|---|---|---|---|---|
| 29. | **11.** | 20 pr. brown .. .. | 2·25 | 1·75 |
| 30. | – | 40 pr. green .. .. | 9·75 | 5·50 |

DESIGN: 40 pr. Line of immigrant ships.

**12.** Library and Book.

**1950.** 25th Anniv. of Founding of Hebrew University, Jerusalem.

| | | | | |
|---|---|---|---|---|
| 31. | **12.** | 100 pr. green .. .. | 40 | 25 |

**13.** Eagle.

**1950.** Air.

| | | | | | |
|---|---|---|---|---|---|
| 32. | – | 5 pr. blue .. | .. | 50 | 25 |
| 33. | – | 30 pr. grey .. | .. | 40 | 25 |
| 34. | – | 40 pr. green .. | .. | 40 | 25 |
| 35. | – | 50 pr. brown .. | .. | 40 | 25 |
| 36. | **13.** | 100 pr. red .. | .. | 15·00 | 11·00 |
| 37. | – | 250 pr. blue .. | .. | 2·25 | 90 |

DESIGNS—VERT. 5 pr. Doves pecking grapes. 30 pr. Eagle. 40 pr. Ostrich. 50 pr. Dove. HORIZ. 250 pr. Dove with olive branch.

**14.** Star of David and Fruit.

**16.** Runner and Track.

**1950.** Jewish New Year.

| | | | | |
|---|---|---|---|---|
| 38. | **14.** | 5 pr. violet and orange.. | 15 | 10 |
| 39. | | 15 pr. brown and green.. | 60 | 40 |

**1950.** 3rd Jewish Coins issue. Inscr at left of 13 characters.

| | | | | |
|---|---|---|---|---|
| 40 | 3 pr. grey .. | .. | 10 | 10 |
| 41 | 5 pr. violet | .. | 10 | 10 |
| 42 | 10 pr. green | .. | 10 | 10 |
| 43 | 15 pr. red .. | .. | 10 | 10 |
| 44 | 20 pr. orange | .. | 10 | 10 |
| 45 | 30 pr. blue | .. | 10 | 10 |
| 46 | 35 pr. green | .. | 30 | 10 |
| 47 | 40 pr. brown | .. | 10 | 10 |
| 48 | 45 pr. mauve | .. | 10 | 10 |
| 49 | 50 pr. brown | .. | 10 | 10 |
| 50 | 60 pr. red | .. | 10 | 10 |
| 51 | 85 pr. blue | .. | 10 | 10 |

DESIGNS ON COINS: 3, 20 pr. Palm tree and baskets with dates; 5, 35 pr. Vine leaf; 10, 40 pr. Ritual jar; 15, 45 pr. Bunch of grapes; 30, 60 pr. Ritual vessel; 50, 85 pr. Tied palm branches and lemon.

For further designs with value at right, see Nos. 90/93.

**1950.** 3rd Maccabiah (sports meeting).

| | | | | |
|---|---|---|---|---|
| 52 | **16** | 80 pr. green and olive .. | 1·90 | 1·25 |

**17.** "The Negev" (after R. Rubin).

**1950.** Opening of Post Office at Elat.

| | | | | |
|---|---|---|---|---|
| 53 | **17** | 500 pr. brown & lt brown | 9·50 | 4·50 |

**19.** Memorial Tablet.

**1951.** 40th Anniv of Founding of Tel Aviv.

| | | | | |
|---|---|---|---|---|
| 54. | **19.** | 40 pr. brown .. | 40 | 25 |

**20.** " Supporting Israel ".

**21.** Metsudat Yesha.

**1951.** Independence Bonds Campaign.

| | | | | |
|---|---|---|---|---|
| 55 | **20** | 80 pr. red .. .. | 25 | 15 |

**1951.** 3rd Anniv of State of Israel.

| | | | | |
|---|---|---|---|---|
| 56 | **21** | 15 pr. red .. .. | 20 | 15 |
| 57 | – | 40 pr. blue (Hakastel) .. | 50 | 40 |

**22.** Tractor.

**23.** Ploughing and Savings Stamp.

**1951.** 50th Anniv. of Jewish National Fund.

| | | | | | |
|---|---|---|---|---|---|
| 58. | **22.** | 15 pr. brown .. | .. | 10 | 10 |
| 59. | – | 25 pr. green .. | .. | 10 | 10 |
| 60. | **23.** | 80 pr. blue .. | .. | 1·00 | 70 |

DESIGN—As Type **22**: 25 pr. Stylised tree.

**24.** Dr. T. Herzl.

**25.** Carrier Pigeons.

**1951.** 23rd Zionist Congress.

| | | | | |
|---|---|---|---|---|
| 61. | **24.** | 80 pr. green .. .. | 25 | 20 |

**1951.** Jewish New Year. As T **25**.

| | | | | | |
|---|---|---|---|---|---|
| 62. | **25.** | 5 pr. blue .. | .. | 10 | 10 |
| 63. | – | 15 pr. red .. | .. | 10 | 10 |
| 64. | – | 40 pr. violet .. | .. | 25 | 20 |

DESIGNS: 15 pr. Woman and dove. 40 pr. Scroll of the Law.

**26.** Menora and Emblems.

**1952.**

| | | | | |
|---|---|---|---|---|
| 64a. | **26.** | 1000 pr. blk. and blue | 16·00 | 7·50 |

**26a.** Haifa Bay, Mt. Carmel and City Seal.

**1952.** Air. National Stamp Exn. ("TABA").

| | | | | |
|---|---|---|---|---|
| 64b. | – | 100 pr. blue & blk. .. | 40 | 30 |
| 64c. | **26a.** | 120 pr. pur & blk. .. | 40 | 30 |

DESIGN: 100 pr. Haifa Bay and City Seal.

**27.** Thistle and Yad Mordechai.

**1952.** 4th Anniv. of Independence.
65. **27.** 30 pr. brown and mauve 15 10
66. – 60 pr. slate and blue .. 20 10
67. – 110 pr. brown and red .. 45 30
DESIGNS: 60 pr. Cornflower and Deganya. 110 pr. Anemone and Safed.

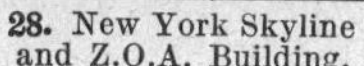

**28.** New York Skyline and Z.O.A. Building.

**29.** Figs.

**1952.** Opening of American Zionist Building, Tel Aviv.
68. **28.** 220 pr. grey and blue .. 45 30

**1952.** Jewish New Year.
69. **29.** 15 pr. yellow and green .. 20 10
70. – 40 pr. yell., blue & violet 25 15
71. – 110 pr. grey and red .. 40 30
72. – 220 pr. grn., brn. & orge. 50 35
FLOWERS: 40 pr. Lily (" Rose of Sharon"). 110 pr. Dove. 220 pr. Nuts.

**30.** Dr. C. Weizmann (from sketch by R. Errell).

**1952.** Death of First President.
73. **30.** 30 pr. blue .. .. 10 10
74. 110 pr. black .. .. 35 30

**31.**

**32.** Douglas DC-4 Airliner over Tel Aviv Yafo.

**1952.** 70th Anniv of Bet Yaakov Lechu Venelcha Immigration Organization.
75. **31.** 110 pr. buff, green & brn. 25 15

**1953.** Air.
76 – 10 pr. dp green & green 10 10
77 – 70 pr. violet and lilac .. 10 10
78 – 100 pr. dp green & green 10 10
79 – 150 pr. brown & orange 10 10
80 – 350 pr. red and pink .. 15 10
81 – 500 pr. deep blue & blue 20 10
81a – 750 pr. dp brown & brn 20 10
82 32 1000 pr. dp green & grn 3·75 95
82a – 3000 pr. purple .. ·50 45
DESIGNS—HORIZ. 10 pr. Olive tree. 70 pr. Sea of Galilee. 100 pr. Shaar Hogay on road to Jerusalem. 150 pr. Lion Rock, Negev. 350 pr. Bay of Elat. VERT. 500 pr. Tanour Falls, near Metoulla. 750 pr. Lake Hula. 3000 pr. Tomb of Meir Baal Haness.

**33.** Anemones and Arms.

**35.** Maimonides (philosopher).

**1953.** 5th Anniv of Independence.
83 33 110 pr. red, green & blue 25 20

**1953.** 7th Int. Congress of History of Science.
84. **35.** 110 pr. brown .. .. 95 60

**36.** Holy Ark, Petah-Tikvah.

**37.** Hand holding Globe/Football.

**1953.** Jewish New Year.
85. – 20 pr. blue .. .. 10 10
86. **36.** 45 pr. red .. .. 10 10
87. – 200 pr. violet .. .. 35 25
DESIGNS: 20 pr. Holy Ark, Jerusalem. 200 pr. Holy Ark, Zefat.

**1953.** 4th Maccabiah.
88. **37.** 110 pr. brown and blue .. 20 20

**38.** Exhibition Emblem.

**39.** Ancient Jewish Coin.

**1953.** "Conquest of the Desert" Exhibition.
89. **38.** 200 pr. multicoloured .. 20 15

**1954.** 4th Jewish Coins issue.
90 39 80 pr. bistre .. .. 10 10
91 – 95 pr. green .. .. 10 10
92 – 100 pr. brown .. .. 10 10
93 – 125 pr. blue .. .. 15 10
DESIGNS ON COINS: 95 pr. Wheat; 100 pr. Gate; 125 pr. Lyre.

**40.** Gesher and Narcissus.

**41.** Dr. T. Z. Herzl.

**1954.** 6th Anniv. of Independence.
94. – 60 pr. blue, red & grey .. 10 10
95. **40.** 350 pr. brown, yell. & grn. 20 15
DESIGN: 60 pr. Yehiam and helichrysum.

**1954.** 50th Death Anniv. of Herzl (founder of World Zionist Movement).
96. **41.** 160 pr. sepia, buff & blue 20 15

**43.**

**1954.** Jewish New Year.
97. **43.** 25 pr. sepia .. .. 15 10

**44.** 19th-century Mail Coach and P.O.

**1954.** National Stamp Exhibition.
98 44 60 pr. black, yellow & bl 10 10
99 – 200 pr. black, red & green 25 15
DESIGN: 200 pr. Mail van and G.P.O., 1954.

**45.** Baron Edmond de Rothschild.

**1954.** 20th Death Anniv. of De Rothschild (financier).
100. **45.** 300 pr. turquoise .. 20 10

**46.** Lamp of Knowledge.

**1955.** 50th Anniv. of Teachers' Association.
101. **46.** 250 pr. blue .. .. 15 10

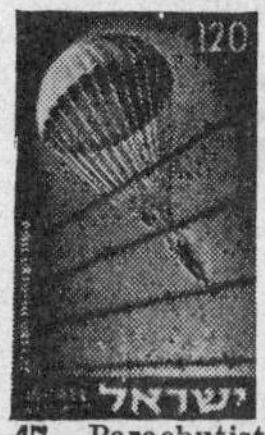

**47.** Parachutist and Barbed Wire.

**48.** Menora and Olive Branches.

**1955.** Jewish Mobilisation during 2nd World War.
102. **47.** 120 pr. black & turquoise 15 10

**1955.** 7th Anniv. of Independence.
103. **48.** 150 pr. orge., blk. & grn. 25 15

**49.** Immigrants and Ship.

**50.** Musicians playing Timbrel and Cymbals.

**1955.** 20th Anniv of Youth Immigration Scheme.
104 49 5 pr. black and blue .. 10 10
105 – 10 pr. black and red .. 10 10
106 – 25 pr. black and green 10 10
107 – 30 pr. black and orange 10 10
108 – 60 pr. black and violet 10 10
109 – 750 pr. black and brown 45 35
DESIGNS: 10 pr. Immigrants and Douglas DC-3 airplane. 25 pr. Boy and calf. 30 pr. Girl watering flowers. 60 pr. Boy making pottery. 750 pr. Boy using theodolite.

**1955.** Jewish New Year.
110 50 25 pr. green and orange 10 10
111 – 60 pr. grey and orange 10 10
112 – 120 pr. blue and yellow 10 10
113 – 250 pr. brown & orange 25 15
DESIGNS—Musicians playing: 60 pr. Ram's horn; 120 pr. Tuba; 250 pr. Harp.

**51.** Ambulance.

**52.** " Reuben".

**1955.** 25th Anniv. of Magen David Adom (Jewish Red Cross).
114. **51.** 160 pr. green, black & red 20 15

**1955.** Twelve Tribes of Israel.
115. **52.** 10 pr. green .. .. 10 10
116. – 20 pr. mauve .. .. 10 10
117. – 30 pr. blue .. .. 10 10
118. – 40 pr. brown .. .. 10 10
119. – 50 pr. blue .. .. 10 10
120. – 60 pr. bistre .. .. 10 10
121. – 80 pr. violet .. .. 10 10
122. – 100 pr. red .. .. 10 10
123. – 120 pr. olive .. .. 10 10
124. – 180 pr. mauve .. .. 15 10
125. – 200 pr. green .. .. 15 10
126. – 250 pr. grey .. .. 15 10
EMBLEMS: 20 pr. "Simeon" (castle). 30 pr. "Levi" (High Priest's breastplate). 40 pr. "Judah" (lion). 50 pr. "Dan" (scales). 60 pr. "Naphtali" (gazelle). 80 pr. "Gad" (tents). 100 pr. "Asher" (tree). 120 pr. "Issachar" (sun and stars). 180 pr. "Zebulun" (ship). 200 pr. "Joseph" (sheaf of wheat). 250 pr. "Benjamin" (wolf).

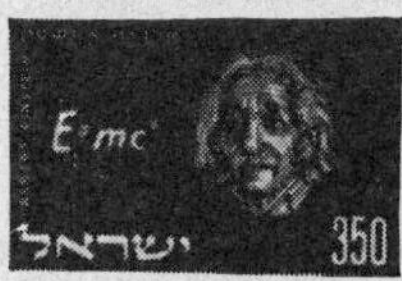

**53.** Professor Einstein.

**1956.** Einstein Commem.
127. **53.** 350 pr. brown .. 15 15

**54.** Technion.

**55.** " Eight Years of Independence".

**1956.** 30th Anniv. of Israel Institute of Technology, Haifa.
128. **54.** 350 pr. green and black 15 10

**1956.** 8th Anniv. of Independence.
129. **55.** 150 pr. multicoloured .. 15 10

**56.** Oranges.

**57.** Musican playing Lyre.

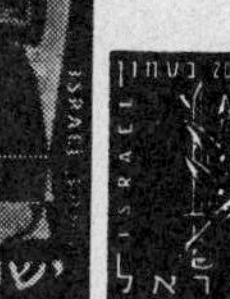

**58.** Insignia of "Haganah".

**1956.** 4th Int. Congress of Mediterranean Citrus Fruit Growers.
130 56 300 pr. multicoloured .. 20 15

**1956.** Jewish New Year. Musicians playing instruments.
131. **57.** 30 pr. brown and blue .. 10 10
132. – 50 pr. violet and orange 10 10
133. – 150 pr. turquoise & orge. 20 15
INSTRUMENTS—VERT. 50 pr. Sistrum. HORIZ. 150 pr. Double oboe.

**1957.** Defence Fund.
134. **58.** 80 pr. + 20 pr. green .. 10 10
135. 150 pr. + 50 pr. red .. 10 10
136. 350 pr. + 50 pr. blue .. 15 10

**59.** Airplane sky-writing Figure "9".

**60.** Bezalel Museum and Candelabrum.

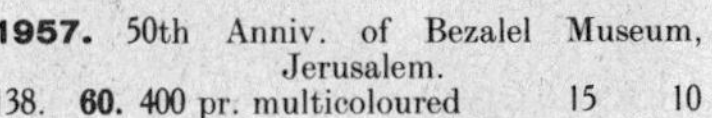

**1957.** 9th Anniv of Independence.
137 59 250 pr. black, blue & lt bl 15 10

**1957.** 50th Anniv. of Bezalel Museum, Jerusalem.
138. **60.** 400 pr. multicoloured 15 10

**61.** Seal of Tamach and Horse.

**62.** Throwing the Hammer.

**1957.** Jewish New Year. Ancient Hebrew Seals.
139. **61.** 50 pr. blk. & brn. on blue 10 10
140. – 160 pr. blk. & grn. on buff 10 10
141. – 300 pr. blk. & red on pink 15 10
DESIGNS: 160 pr. Seal of Shema and lion. 300 pr. Seal of Netanyahuv Ne'avadyahu and gazelle.

**1958.** 25th Anniv. of Maccabiah Games.
142. **62.** 500 pr. red and bistre 15 10

**63.** Ancient Hebrew Ship.

**1958.** Israel Merchant Marine Commem.
143 63 10 pr. red, blue & brown 10 10
144 – 20 pr. brown and green 10 10
145 – 30 pr. grey and red .. 10 10
146 – 1000 pr. green and blue 45 35
DESIGNS—As T 63: 10 pr. Immigration ship "Nirit"; 20 pr. Freighter "Shomron". $57 \times 22\frac{1}{2}$ mm: 1000 pr. Liner "Zion".

**64.** Menora and Olive Branch. **65.** Dancing Children forming "10".

**1958.** 10th Anniv. of Independence.
147. **64.** 400 pr. grn. blk. & gold 20 15

**1958.** 1st World Conference of Jewish Youth, Jerusalem.
148 **65** 200 pr. green and orange 20 15

**66.** Convention Centre, Jerusalem, and Exhibition Emblem.

**1958.** 10th Anniv. (of Israel) Exn., Jerusalem.
149. **66.** 400 pr. orange and lilac on cream .. .. 20 15

**67.** Wheat. **68.** Ancient Stone.

**1958.** Jewish New Year.
150. **67.** 50 pr. brown & ochre .. 10 10
151. – 60 pr. black and yellow 10 10
152. – 160 pr. purple & violet 15 10
153. – 300 pr. green and apple 20 15
DESIGNS: 60 pr. Barley. 160 pr. Grapes. 300 pr. Figs.
See also Nos. 166/8.

**1958.** 10th Anniv. of Declaration of Human Rights.
154. **68.** 750 pr. blk., yell. & blue 20 15

**69.** Post Office Emblem. **70.** Sholem Aleichem.

**1959.** 10th Anniv. of Israel Postal Services.
155. **69.** 60 pr. blk., red & olive 10 10
156. – 120 pr. blk., red & olive 10 10
157. – 250 pr. blk., red & olive 10 10
158. – 500 pr. blk., red & olive 20 15
DESIGNS—HORIZ. 120 pr. Mail van. VERT. 250 pr. Radio-telephone equipment. 500 pr. "Telex" dial and keyboard.

**1959.** Birth Cent. of Sholem Aleichem (writer).
159. **70.** 250 pr. brown and green 20 15

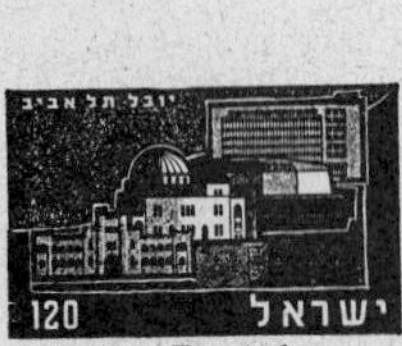
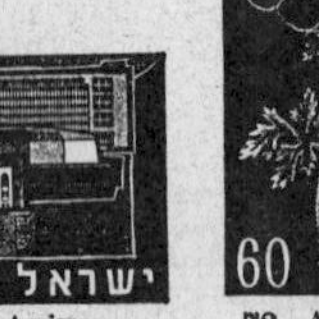

**71.** Tel Aviv. **72.** Anemone.

**1959.** 50th Anniv. of Tel Aviv.
160. **71.** 120 pr. multicoloured 20 15

**1959.** 11th Anniv. of Independence. Mult.
161. 60 pr. Type **72** .. .. 10 10
162. 120 pr. Cyclamen .. .. 10 10
163. 300 pr. Narcissus .. .. 20 15
See also Nos. 188/9, 211/3 and 257/9.

**73.** C. N. Bialik. **74.** Bristol 175 Britannia Airliner and Wind-sock.

**1959.** 25th Anniv of Chaim Bialik (poet).
164 **73** 250 pr. olive and orange 20 15

**1959.** 10th Anniv. of Civil Aviation in Israel.
165. **74.** 500 pr. multicoloured .. 20 15

**1959.** Jewish New Year. As T **67**.
166 60 pr. red and brown .. 10 10
167 200 pr. green & deep green 15 10
168 350 pr. orange and brown 25 15
DESIGNS: 60 pr. Pomegrantaes. 200 pr. Olives. 350 pr. Dates.

**76.** E. Ben-Yehuda. **77.** Merhavya Settlement

**1959.** Birth Centenary of Ben-Yehuda (pioneer of Hebrew language).
169 **76** 250 pr. deep blue & blue 25 50

**1959.** 50th Anniv of Merhavya and Deganya Settlements. 75th Anniv of Yesud Ha-Maala Settlement.
170 **77** 60 pr. green and yellow 10 10
171 – 120 pr. brown & lt brn 15 10
172 – 180 pr. green and blue 30 20
DESIGNS: 120 pr. Yesud Ha-Maala; 180 pr. Deganya.

**78.** Ancient Jewish Coin. **79.** Tiberias.

**1960.** New currency. Values in black.
173. **78.** 1 a. bistre on pink .. 10 10
174. 3 a. red on pink .. 10 10
175. 5 a. slate on pink .. 10 10
176. 6 a. green on blue .. 10 10
176a. 7 a. grey on blue .. 10 10
177. 8 a. mauve on blue .. 10 10
178. 12 a. blue on blue .. 10 10
179. 18 a. orange .. .. 10 10
180. 25 a. blue .. .. 15 10
181. 30 a. red .. .. 15 10
182. 50 a. lilac .. .. 15 10

**1960.** Air.
183. – 15 a. black and lilac .. 15 10
184. – 20 a. black and green .. 15 10
184a. – 25 a. black and orange 15 10
184b. – 30 a. black & turquoise 15 10
184c. – 35 a. black and green .. 15 10
184d. – 40 a. black and lilac .. 50 25
184e. – 50 a. black and olive .. 50 25
185. **79.** 65 a. black and blue .. 35 15
185a. – I£1 black and pink .. 75 35
DESIGNS—VERT. 15 a. Old town, Zefat. 20 a. Tower, Ashqelon. 25 a. Akko Tower and boats. 30 a. View of Haifa from Mt. Carmel. HORIZ. 35 a. Ancient synagogue, Capernaum. 40 a. Kefar Hittim—Tomb of Jethro. 50 a. City walls, Jerusalem. I£1, Old city, Yafo (Jaffa).

**80.** Operation "Magic Carpet".

**1960.** World Refugee Year.
186. **80.** 25 a. brown .. .. 15 10
187. – 50 a. green .. .. 20 15
DESIGN: 50 a. Resettled family.

**1960.** 12th Anniv of Independence. Flowers as T **72**.
188 12 a. multicoloured .. 15 10
189 32 a. yellow, green & brn 20 15
DESIGNS: 12 a. "Pancratium maritimum"; 32 a. "Oenothera drummondi".

**81.** Atomic Symbol and Reactor Building. **83.** King Saul.

**1960.** Inaug. of Atomic Reactor.
190. **81.** 50 a. red, black and blue 25 20

**1960.** Jewish New Year. Centres mult.
191. **83.** 7 a. green .. .. 10 10
192. – 25 a. brown .. .. 20 20
193. – 40 a. blue .. .. 30 20
DESIGNS: 25 a. King David. 40 a. King Solomon.

**84.** Dr. Theodor Herzl. **85.** Postal Courier, Prague, 1741.

**1960.** Birth Cent. of Dr. Theodor Herzl (founder of World Zionist Movement).
194. **84.** 25 a. sepia and cream 25 20

**1960.** "TAVIV" National Stamp Exhibition, Tel Aviv.
195 **85** 25 a. black and grey .. 30 25

**86.** Henrietta Szold.

**1960.** Birth Cent. of Henrietta Szold (founder of Youth Immigration Scheme).
196. **86.** 25 a. violet and blue .. 20 15

**87.** Badges of First Zionist Congress and Jerusalem.

**1960.** 25th Zionist Congress, Jerusalem.
197. **87.** 50 a. light and deep blue 25 20

**88.** Ram (Aries). **89.** The Twelve Signs.

**1961.** Signs of the Zodiac.
198. **88.** 1 a. green .. .. 10 10
199. – 2 a. red .. .. 10 10
200. – 6 a. blue .. .. 10 10
201. – 7 a. brown .. .. 10 10
202. – 8 a. myrtle .. .. 10 10
203. – 10 a. orange .. .. 10 10
204. – 12 a. violet .. .. 10 10
205. – 18 a. mauve .. .. 10 10
206. – 20 a. olive .. .. 10 10
207. – 25 a. purple .. .. 10 10
208. – 32 a. black .. .. 15 10
209. – 50 a. turquoise .. .. 15 10
210. **89.** I£1 blue, gold & indigo 40 35
DESIGNS—As Type **88**: 2 a. Bull (Taurus). 6 a. Twins (Gemini). 7 a. Crab (Cancer). 8 a. Lion (Leo). 10 a. Virgin (Virgo). 12 a. Scales (Libra). 18 a. Scorpion (Scorpio). 20 a. Archer (Sagittarius). 25 a. Goat (Capricorn). 32 a. Waterman (Aquarius). 50 a. Fishes (Pisces).

**1961.** 13th Anniv. of Independence. Flowers as T **72**.
211. 7 a. yell., brown & green 10 10
212. 12 a. grn., pur. and mve. 15 10
213. 32 a. red, green and blue 25 15
FLOWERS: 7 a. Myrtle. 12 a. Squill. 32 a. Oleander.

**91.** Throwing the Javelin. **92.** "A Decade of Israel Bonds".

**1961.** 7th "Hapoel" Sports Association Int. Congress, Ramat Gan.
214. **91.** 25 a. multicoloured .. 25 20

**1961.** 10th Anniv. of Israel Bond Issue.
215. **92.** 50 a. blue .. .. 25 20

**93.** Samson. **94.** Bet Hamidrash (synagogue), Medzibozh (Russia).

**1961.** Jewish New Year. Heroes of Israel. Centres multicoloured.
216 **93** 7 a. red .. .. 15 10
217 – 25 a. grey .. .. 20 15
218 – 40 a. lilac .. .. 30 20
HEROES: 25 a. Yehuda Maccabi; 40 a. Bar Kochba.

**1961.** Death Bicent. of Rabbi Baal Shem Tov (founder of Hassidism movement).
219. **94.** 25 a. sepia and yellow .. 25 20

**95.** Fir Cone. **96.** Musical Instruments.

**1961.** Afforestation Achievements.
220. **95.** 25 a. yellow, black & grn. 25 20
221. – 30 a. multicoloured .. 25 20
DESIGN: 30 a. Symbol of afforestation.

**1961.** 25th Anniv. of Israel Philharmonic Orchestra.
222. **96.** 50 a. multicoloured .. 55 45

**97.** Bay of Elat.

**1962.** Air.
223. **97.** I£3 multicoloured .. 2·00 1·25

**1962.** As Nos. 198, 201 and 208 but colours changed and surch.
224. **88.** 3 a. on 1 a. mauve .. 10 10
225. – 5 a. on 7 a. grey .. 10 10
226. – 30 a. on 32 a. green .. 15 10

**99.** Symbolic Flame. **100.** Sud Aviation Vatour IIA Bomber.

**1962.** Heroes and Martyrs Day.
227. **99.** 12 a. yellow, red & black 15 10
228. – 55 a. multicoloured .. 45 35
DESIGN: 55 a. Nazi "Yellow Star" and candles.

**1962.** 14th Anniv. of Independence.
229. **100.** 12 a. blue .. .. 20 15
230. – 30 a. green .. .. 40 25
DESIGN: 30 a. Flight of Vatour IIA bombers.

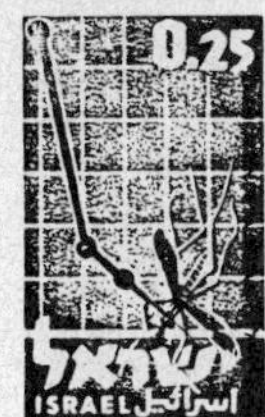
101. Mosquito and Malaria Graph.

102. Rosh Pinna.

**1962.** Malaria Eradication.
231.101. 25 a. bistre, red & black 25 20

**1962.** 80th Anniv. of Rosh Pinna.
232. 102. 20 a. green and yellow 25 20

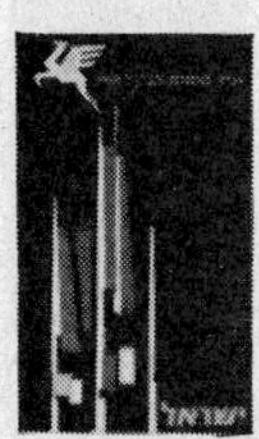
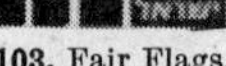
103. Fair Flags.

104. "The wolf also shall dwell with the lamb...".

**1962.** Near East Int. Fair, Tel Aviv.
233.103. 55 a. multicoloured .. 25 30

**1962.** Jewish New Year. Illustrating quotations from the Book of Isaiah.
234.104. 8 a. black, red and olive 10 10
235. – 28 a. black, purple & olive 25 20
236. – 43 a. black, orge. & olive 35 25
DESIGNS: 28 a. "And the leopard shall lie down with the kid . . . ". 43 a. "And the suckling child shall play on the hole of the asp . . . ".

105. Boeing 707 Jetliner.

**1962.** El Al Airline Commem.
237.105. 55 a. indigo, lilac & blue 45 30

106. Pennant Coralfish.

**1962.** Red Sea Fish (1st series). Mult.
238. 3 a. Type 106 .. .. 15 10
239. 6 a. Butterfly Fish .. 15 10
240. 8 a. Scorpion Fish .. 20 10
241. 12 a. Angelfish .. .. 20 15
See also Nos. 265/8.

107. Symbolic Cogwheels.

**1962.** 25th Anniv. of United Jewish Appeal.
242.107. 20 a. blue, silver and red 30 25

108. J. Korczak (child educator).

109. Houbara Bustard.

**1962.** Janusz Korczak Commemeration.
243 108 30 a. sepia and grey .. 40 30

**1963.** Air. Birds.
244 – 5 a. pink, brown & vio 10 10
245 – 20 a. turq, brn & red .. 20 15
246 – 28 a. black, brn & grn 25 15
247 – 30 a. multicoloured .. 25 15
248 – 40 a. multicoloured .. 30 20
249 – 45 a. multicoloured .. 50 40
250 109 55 a. orge, blk & turq 50 40
251 – 70 a. bistre, brn & blk 55 50
252 – I£1 orange, black & red 55 50
253 – I£3 multicoloured .. 1·90 1·90
DESIGNS—HORIZ: 5 a. Sinai rosefinch; 20 a. White-breasted kingfisher; 28 a. Mourning wheatear. VERT: 30 a. European bee eater; 40 a. Graceful prinia; 45 a. Palestine sunbird; 70 a. Scops owl; I£1, Purple heron; I£3, White-tailed sea eagle.

110. Bird in the Hand.

**1963.** Freedom from Hunger.
254.110. 55 a. grey and black .. 30 35

111. Construction at Daybreak.

112. Compositor.

**1963.** 25th Anniv. of Stockade and Tower Settlements.
255.111. 12 a. brown, blk. & yell. 15 10
256. – 30 a. purple, blk. & blue 25 25
DESIGN: 30 a. Settlement at night.

**1963.** 15th Anniv. of Independence. Flowers. As T 72.
257. 8 a. multicoloured .. 25 15
258. 30 a. yellow, rose and pink 40 25
259. 37 a. multicoloured .. 50 25
FLOWERS: 8 a. White lily. 30 a. Bristly hollyhock. 37 a. Sharon tulip.

**1963.** Centenary of Hebrew Press.
260. 112. 12 a. purple and buff 40 30
No. 260 comes in sheets of 16 (4×4) with overall background of replica of front page of first issue of Hebrew newspaper "Halbanon".

113. "And the sun beat upon the head of Jonah . . . "

114. Hoe clearing Thistles.

**1963.** Jewish New Year. Illustrating quotations from the Book of Jonah. Multicoloured.
261. 8 a. Type 113 .. .. 15 10
262. 30 a. "And there was a mighty tempest in the sea" .. .. 40 25
263. 55 a. "And Jonah was in the belly of the fish" .. 35 30
Nos. 262/3 are horiz.

**1963.** 80th Anniv. of Israeli Agricultural Settlements.
264. 114. 37 a. multicoloured .. 25 20

**1963.** Red Sea Fish (2nd series). As T 106. Multicoloured.
265. 2 a. Undulate triggerfish .. 15 10
266. 6 a. Scorpion fish .. .. 20 10
267. 8 a. Scad .. .. .. 25 20
268. 12 a. Angelfish .. .. 25 20

115. "Shalom".

**1963.** Maiden Voyage of Liner "Shalom".
269 115 I£1 blue, turq & pur .. 1·25 1·00

116. " Old Age and Survivors ".

117. Pres. Ben-Zvi.

**1964.** 10th Anniv. of National Insurance. Multicoloured.
270. 12 a. Type 116 .. .. 15 15
271. 25 a. Nurse and child within hands ("Maternity") 20 20
272. 37 a. Family within hand ("Large families") .. 30 25
273. 50 a. Hand with arm and crutch ("Employment injuries") .. .. 35 25

**1964.** 1st Death Anniv. of President Izhak Ben-Zvi.
274. 117. 12 a. brown .. .. 15 10

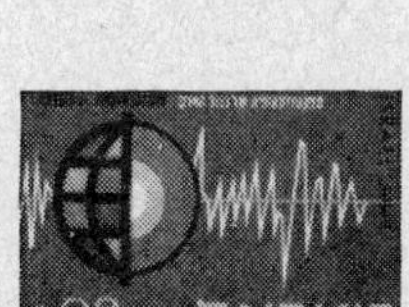
118. "Terrestrial Spectroscopy".

119. Running.

**1964.** 16th Anniv. of Independence. Israel's Contribution to Science. Multicoloured.
275. 8 a. Type 118 .. .. 15 10
276. 35 a. Macromolecules of living cell .. .. 35 25
277. 70 a. Electronic computer 40 30

**1964.** Olympic Games, Tokyo.
278. 119. 8 a. black and red .. 10 10
279. – 12 a. black and mauve 15 10
280. – 30 a. red, black & blue 20 15
281. – 50 a. red, purple & grn. 20 20
DESIGNS: 12 a. Throwing the discus. 30 a. Basketball. 50 a. Football.

120. 3rd Century Glass Vessel.

121. Congress Emblem.

**1964.** Jewish New Year. Showing glass vessels in Haaretz Museum, Tel Aviv. Multicoloured.
282. 8 a. Type 120 .. .. 15 10
283. 35 a. 1st-2nd century vessel 20 20
284. 70 a. 1st century vessel .. 30 20

**1964.** 6th Israel Medical Assn's. World Congress.
285. 121. I£1 multicoloured .. 40 30

122. Immigrant Ship.

123. Eleanor Roosevelt.

**1964.** "Year of the Blockade-Runners".
286. 122. 25 a. blk., blue & turq. 25 20

**1964.** 80th Birth Anniv of Eleanor Roosevelt.
287. 123. 70 a. purple .. .. 35 30

124. Olympics Symbols and Knight.

**1964.** 16th Chess Olympics.
288. 124. 12 a. brown .. .. 30 25
289. – 70 a. green .. .. 90 85
DESIGN: 70 a. Olympics symbol and rook.

125. "African-Israeli Friendship".

126. Masada.

**1964.** "TABAI" National Stamp Exn. Haifa.
290. 125. 57 a. multicoloured .. 45 30

**1965.** Masada.
291. 126. 25 a. green .. .. 25 20
292. – 36 a. blue .. .. 35 20
293. – I£1 brown .. .. 40 40
DESIGNS—HORIZ. 36 a. "Northern Palace", lower section. VERT. I£1, "Northern Palace" aerial view.

127. Ashdod.

128. Fair Emblem.

**1965.** Civic Arms (1st series).
294 – 1 a. brown (Lod) .. 10 10
295 – 2 a. mauve (Qiryat Shmona) .. .. 10 10
296 – 5 a. black (Petah Tiqwa) .. .. 10 10
297 – 6 a. violet (Nazareth) 10 10
298 – 8 a. orge (Beer Sheva) 10 10
299 – 10 a. grn (Bet Shean) 10 10
300 – 12 a. purple (Tiberias) 10 10
301 127 15 a. green .. .. 10 10
302 – 20 a. red (Elat) .. 10 10
303 – 25 a. blue (Akko) .. 10 10
304 – 35 a. purple (Dimona) 10 10
305 – 37 a. green (Zefat) .. 40 10
305a – 40 a. brown (Mizpe Ramon) .. .. 15 10
306 – 50 a. blue (Rishon Le Zion) .. .. 15 10
306a – 55 a. red (Ashqelon) 15 10
307 – 70 a. brn (Jerusalem) 20 15
307a – 80 a. red (Rosh Pinna) .. .. 40 25
308 – I£1 green (Tel Aviv-Yafo) .. .. 25 25
309 – I£3 mauve (Haifa) .. 40 30
Nos. 307, 308/9 are 22½ × 27 mm. in size. See also Nos. 413/24.

**1965.** 2nd Int. Book Fair, Jerusalem.
310. 128. 70 a. blk., blue & grn. 30 25

129. Hands reaching for barbed wire.

130. "National Water Supply".

**1965.** 20th Anniv. of Concentration Camps Liberation.
311. 129. 25 a. blk., yell. & grey 25 20

**1965.** 17th Anniv. of Independence.
312 130 37 a. brown, dp bl & bl 25 20

131. Potash Works, Sedom.

132. "Syncom" Satellite and Telegraph Pole.

**1965.** Dead Sea Industrial Development. Multicoloured.
313. 12 a. Potash Works, Sedom 15 10
314. 50 a. Type 131 .. .. 30 25
The two stamps form one composite design when placed side by side.

**1965.** I.T.U. Cent.
315 132 70 a. violet, black & bl 25 20

133. "Co-operation".

134. "Light".

**1965.** Int. Co-operation Year.
316. **133.** 36 a. multicoloured .. 25 20

**1965.** Jewish New Year. "The Creation". Multicoloured.
317. 6 a. Type **134** .. .. 10 10
318. 8 a. "Heaven" .. .. 10 10
319. 12 a. "Earth" .. .. 10 10
320. 25 a. "Stars" .. .. 25 20
321. 35 a. "Birds and Beasts" 35 25
322. 70 a. "Man" .. .. 45 30

135. Foxy Charaxes.

136. War of Independence Memorial.

137. Flags.

**1965.** Butterflies and Moths. Multicoloured.
323 2 a. Type **135** .. .. 10 10
324 6 a. Southern swallowtail 15 10
325 8 a. Oleander hawk moth 20 15
326 12 a. Sooty orange-tip .. 20 15

**1966.** Memorial Day.
327. **136.** 40 a. brown and black 20 15

**1966.** 18th Anniv of Independence. Mult.
328 12 a. Type **137** .. .. 10 10
329 30 a. Fireworks .. .. 15 15
330 80 a. Dassault Mirage IIICJ jet fighters and warships .. .. 25 20

138. Knesset Building.

**1966.** Inaug. of Knesset Building, Jerusalem.
331. **138.** I£1 blue .. .. 30 25

139. Scooter Rider.

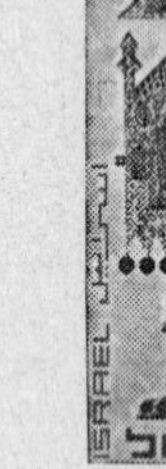
140. Spice Box.

**1966.** Road Safety. Multicoloured.
332. 2 a. Type **139** .. .. 10 10
333. 5 a. Cyclist .. .. 10 10
334. 10 a. Pedestrian on crossing 10 10
335. 12 a. Child with ball .. 10 10
336. 15 a. Motorist in car .. 10 10

**1966.** Jewish New Year. Religious Ceremonial Objects. Multicoloured.
337. 12 a. Type **140** .. .. 10 10
338. 15 a. Candlesticks .. 10 10
339. 35 a. Kiddush cup .. 20 15
340. 40 a. Torah pointer .. 20 15
341. 80 a. Hanging lamp .. 20 20

141. Panther (bronze).

**1966.** Israel Museum Exhibits. Multicoloured.
342. 15 a. Type **141** .. 35 15
343. 30 a. Synagogue menora (stone) .. 35 15
344. 40 a. Phoenician sphinx (ivory) .. 35 20
345. 55 a. Earring (gold) 45 25
346. 80 a. Miniature capital (gold) 70 35
347. I£1·15 Drinking horn (gold) 1·25 90
No. 347 is vert.

142. Levant Postman and Mail Coach.

143. "Fight Cancer and Save Life".

**1966.** Stamp Day.
348 **142** 12 a. green and brown 10 10
349 – 15 a. mauve, brn & grn 10 10
350 – 40 a. blue and mauve 25 10
351 – I£1 brown and blue .. 35 30
DESIGNS: 15 a. Turkish postman and camels. 40 a. Palestine postman and steam locomotive. I£1, Israeli postman and Boeing 707 jetliner.

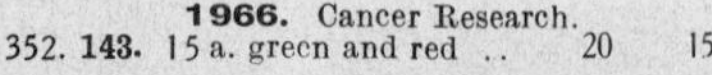

**1966.** Cancer Research.
352. **143.** 15 a. green and red .. 20 15

144. Akko (Acre).

145. Book and Crowns.

**1967.** Ancient Israeli Ports.
353. **144.** 15 a. purple .. .. 15 10
354. – 40 a. green .. .. 25 20
355. – 80 a. blue .. .. 35 30
PORTS: 40 a. Caesarea. 80 a. Yafo (Jaffa).

**1967.** Shulhan Arukh ("Book of Wisdom").
356. **145.** 40 a. multicoloured .. 25 20

146. War of Independence Memorial.

**1967.** Memorial Day.
357. **146.** 55 a. silver, blue & turq. 25 20

147. Taylorcraft Auster AOP.5 Reconnaissance Plane.

**1967.** Independence Day. Military Aircraft.
358. **147.** 15 a. blue and green .. 15 15
359. – 30 a. brown and orange 20 15
360. – 80 a. violet & turquoise 30 20
AIRCRAFT: 30 a. Dassault Mystere IVA jet fighter. 80 a. Dassault Mirage IIICJ jet fighters.

148. Freighter "Dolphin" in Straits of Tiran

149. Law Scroll.

**1967.** Victory in Arab-Israeli War.
361. – 15 a. black, yell. & red 10 10
362. **148.** 40 a. green .. .. 15 15
363. – 80 a. violet .. .. 20 20
DESIGNS—VERT. 15 a. Sword emblem of "Zahal" (Israeli Defence Forces). HORIZ. 80 a. "Wailing Wall", Jerusalem.

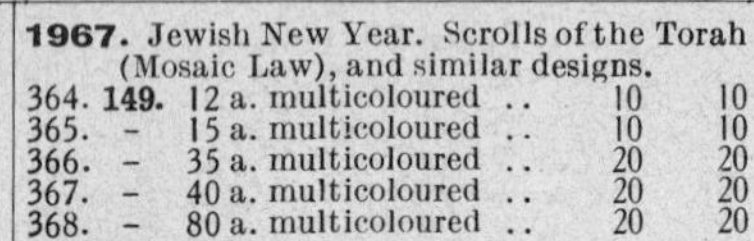

**1967.** Jewish New Year. Scrolls of the Torah (Mosaic Law), and similar designs.
364. **149.** 12 a. multicoloured .. 10 10
365. – 15 a. multicoloured .. 10 10
366. – 35 a. multicoloured .. 20 20
367. – 40 a. multicoloured .. 20 20
368. – 80 a. multicoloured .. 20 20

150. "Welcome to Israel".

151. Lord Balfour.

**1967.** Int. Tourist Year. Each with "Sun" emblem. Multicoloured.
369. 30 a. Type **150** .. .. 15 15
370. 40 a. "Air hostess" .. 15 15
371. 80 a. "Orange" child .. 20 20

**1967.** 50th Anniv. of Balfour Declaration.
372. – 15 a. green .. .. 10 10
373. **151.** 40 a. brown .. .. 25 15
DESIGN: 15 a. Dr. C. Weizmann.

152. Ibex.

153. Diamond.

**1967.** Israeli Nature Reserves. Multicoloured.
374. 12 a. Type **152** .. .. 15 15
375. 18 a. Caracal .. .. 20 15
376. 60 a. Dorcas gazelle .. 25 20

**1968.** Air. Israeli Exports.
377 – 10 a. multicoloured .. 10 10
378 – 30 a. multicoloured .. 10 10
379 – 40 a. multicoloured .. 15 10
380 – 50 a. multicoloured .. 15 10
381 – 55 a. multicoloured .. 15 10
382 – 60 a. multicoloured .. 20 20
383 – 80 a. multicoloured .. 20 20
384 – I£1 multicoloured .. 25 15
385 – I£1.50 multicoloured .. 35 20
386 **153** I£3 violet and green .. 55 30
DESIGNS: 10 a. Draped curtains ("Textiles"). 30 a. "Stamps". 40 a. Jar and necklace ("Arts and Crafts"). 50 a. Chick and egg ("Chicks"). 55 a. Melon, avocado and strawberries ("Fruits"). 60 a. Gladioli ("Flowers"). 80 a. Telecommunications equipment ("Electronics"). I£1, Atomic equipment ("Isotopes"). I£1.50, Models ("Fashion").

154. Beflagged Football.

155. "Immigration".

**1968.** Pre-Olympic Football Tournament.
387. **154.** 80 a. multicoloured .. 25 20

**1968.** Independence Day. Multicoloured.
388. 15 a. Type **155** .. .. 10 10
389. 80 a. "Settlement" .. 25 20

156. Rifles and Helmet.

157. Zahal Emblem.

**1968.** Memorial Day.
390. **156.** 55 a. multicoloured .. 20 15

**1968.** Independence Day (Zahal—Israel Defence Forces).
391. **157.** 40 a. multicoloured .. 20 15

158. Resistance Fighter (detail from Warsaw Monument).

159. Moshe Sharett.

**1968.** 25th Anniv. of Warsaw Ghetto Rising.
392. **158.** 60 a. bistre .. .. 25 20

**1968.** 27th Zionist Congress, Jerusalem.
393. **159.** I£1 sepia .. .. 35 25

160. Candle and Cell Bars.

161. Jerusalem.

**1968.** Fallen Freedom Fighters.
394. **160.** 80 a. black, grey & brn. 30 25

**1968.** Jewish New Year.
395. **161.** 12 a. multicoloured .. 10 10
396. – 15 a. multicoloured .. 10 10
397. – 35 a. multicoloured .. 20 20
398. – 40 a. multicoloured .. 20 15
399. – 60 a. multicoloured .. 20 20
DESIGNS: Jerusalem—views of the Old City (12, 15, 35 a.) and of the New City (40, 60 a.).

162. Scout Badge and Knot.

163. "Lions' Gate", Jerusalem (detail).

**1968.** 50th Anniv. of Jewish Scout Movement.
400. **162.** 30 a. multicoloured .. 20 15

**1968.** "Tabira" Stamp Exn., Jerusalem.
401. **163.** I£1 brown .. .. 20 15

164. A. Mapu.

165. Paralytics playing Basketball.

**1968.** Death Cent. of Abraham Mapu (writer).
403. **164.** 30 a. olive .. .. 20 15

**1968.** Int. Games for the Paralysed.
404. **165.** 40 a. green and lt. green 20 15

166. Elat.

**1969.** Israeli Ports.
405. **166.** 30 a. mauve .. .. 30 20
406. – 60 a. brown (Ashdod) 35 25
407. – I£1 green (Haifa) 45 30

167. "Worker" and ILO Emblem.

168. Israeli Flag at Half-mast.

**1969.** 50th Anniv. of I.L.O.
408. **167.** 80 a. green and lilac .. 20 15

**1969.** Memorial Day.
409. **168.** 55 a. gold, blue & violet 25 15

**169.** Army Tank. **170.** Flaming Torch.

**1969.** Independence Day. Multicoloured.
410. 15 a. Type **169** .. .. 15 10
411. 80 a. "Elat" (destroyer) .. 30 25

**1969.** 8th Maccabiah.
412. **170.** 60 a. multicoloured .. 25 20

**171.** Arms of Hadera. **172.** Building the Ark.

**1969.** Civic Arms (2nd series).
413 2 a. green (Type **171**) .. 10 10
414 3 a. purple (Herzliyya) .. 10 10
415 5 a. orange (Holon) .. 10 10
416 15 a. red (Bat Yam) .. 10 10
417 18 a. blue (Ramla) .. 15 10
418 20 a. brown (Kefar Sava) 15 10
419 25 a. blue (Giv'atayim) .. 15 10
420 30 a. mauve (Rehovot) .. 15 10
421 40 a. violet (Netanya) .. 25 10
422 50 a. blue (Bene Beraq) .. 25 10
423 60 a. green (Nahariyya) .. 25 10
424 80 a. green (Ramat Gan) 25 10

**1969.** Jewish New Year, showing scenes from "The Flood". Multicoloured.
425. 12 a. Type **172** .. .. 10 10
426. 15 a. Animals going aboard 10 10
427. 35 a. Ark afloat .. .. 20 20
428. 40 a. Dove with olive branch 20 15
429. 60 a. Ark on Mt. Ararat .. 20 15

**173.** "King David" (Chagall). **174.** Atomic "Plant".

**1969.** "King David".
430. **173.** I£3 multicoloured .. 1·10 75

**1969.** 25th Anniv. of Weizmann Institute of Science.
431. **174.** I£1.15 multicoloured 85 60

**175.** Dum Palms, Emeq He-Arava. **176.** Immigrant "Aircraft".

**1970.** Nature Reserves.
432. **175.** 2 a. olive .. .. 10 10
433. – 3 a. blue .. .. 10 10
434. – 5 a. red .. .. 10 10
435. – 6 a. green .. .. 10 10
436. – 30 a. violet .. .. 25 20
DESIGNS: 3 a. Tahana Waterfall, Nahal Iyon. 5 a. Nahal Baraq Canyon, Negev. 6 a. Ha-Masreq, Judean Hills. 30 a. Soreq Cave, Judean Hills.

**1970.** 20th Anniv. of Operation "Magic Carpet" (Immigration of Yemenite Jews).
437. **176.** 30 a. multicoloured .. 20 15

**177.** Joseph Trumpeldor. **178.** Prime Minister Levi Eshkol.

**1970.** 50th Anniv. of Defence of Tel Hay.
438. **177.** I£1 violet .. .. 40 35

**1970.** Levi Eshkol Commemoration.
439. **178.** 15 a. multicoloured .. 20 15

**179.** Ze'ev Jabotinsky (commander). **180.** Camel and Diesel Train.

**1970.** 50th Anniv. of Defence of Jerusalem.
440. **179.** 80 a. green and cream 45 30

**1970.** Opening of Dimona-Oron Railway.
441. **180.** 80 a. multicoloured .. 70 30

**181.** Mania Schochat (author). **183.** Memorial Flame. **184.** "Orchis laxifloris".

**182.** Scene from "The Dybbuk".

**1970.** 60th Anniv. of "Ha-Shomer".
442. **181.** 40 a. purple & cream 25 20

**1970.** 50th Anniv. of Habimah National Theatre.
443. **182.** I£1 multicoloured .. 45 30

**1970.** Memorial Day.
444. **183.** 55 a. blk., red & violet 30 25

**1970.** Independence Day. Israeli Wild Flowers. Multicoloured.
445. 12 a. Type **184** .. .. 20 15
446. 15 a. "Iris mariae" .. 20 20
447. 80 a. "Lupinus pilosus" .. 75 65

**185.** C. Netter (founder). **186.** I.A.I. Arava Transport Airplane.

**1970.** Cent. of Miqwe Yisrael Agricultural College. Multicoloured.
448. 40 a. Type **185** .. .. 30 25
449. 80 a. College building and gate 45 40

**1970.** Israeli Aircraft Industry.
450 **186** I£1 silver, violet & blue 30 25

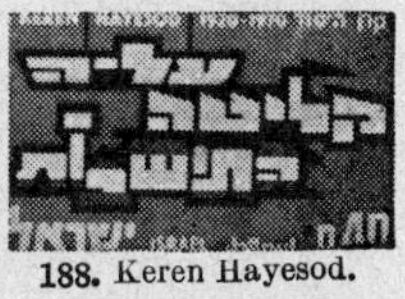

**187.** Yachts. **188.** Keren Hayesod.

**1970.** World "420" Class Sailing Championships. Multicoloured.
451. 15 a. Type **187** .. .. 25 20
452. 30 a. Yacht with spinnaker 25 25
453. 80 a. Yachts turning around buoy .. .. 45 35

**1970.** 50th Anniv. of Keren Hayesod.
454. **188.** 40 a. multicoloured .. 30 25

**189.** Old Synagogue, Cracow. **191.** Mother and Child.

**190.** Jewish "Bird" heading for Sun.

**1970.** Jewish New Year. Multicoloured.
455. 12 a. Type **189** .. .. 10 10
456. 15 a. Great Synagogue, Tunis .. .. .. 10 10
457. 35 a. Portuguese Synagogue, Amsterdam 15 15
458. 40 a. Great Synagogue, Moscow .. .. 20 15
459. 60 a. Shearith Israel Synagogue, New York 20 15

**1970.** "Operation Ezra and Nehemiah" (Exodus of Iraqi Jews to Israel).
460. **190.** 80 a. multicoloured .. 30 20

**1970.** 50th Anniv. of Women's International Zionist Organization (W.I.Z.O.).
461. **191.** 80 a. yell., grn. & silver 30 25

**192.** Tel Aviv Post Office, 1920. **193.** Histadrut Emblem.

**1970.** "Tabit" Stamp Exhibition, Tel Aviv, and 50th Anniv. of Tel Aviv Post Office.
462. **192.** I£1 multicoloured .. 30 25

**1970.** 50th Anniv. of "Histadrut" (General Federation of Labour).
464. **193.** 35 a. multicoloured .. 20 15

**194.** "Landscape with Bridge" (C. Pissaro).

**1970.** Paintings in Tel Aviv Museum. Mult.
465. 85 a. "Jewish Wedding" (J. Israels) .. .. 35 25
466. I£1 Type **194** .. .. 35 30
467. I£2 "Flowers in a Vase" (F. Leger) .. .. 45 40

**195.** "Inn of the Ghosts" (Cameri Theatre).

**1971.** Israeli Theatre. Multicoloured.
468. 50 a. Type **195** .. .. 25 25
469. 50 a. "Samson and Delilah" (National Opera Company) 25 25
470. 50 a. "A Psalm of David" (I.N.B.A.L. Dance Theatre) 25 25

**196.** Fallow Deer.

**1971.** Nature Reserves. Animals of Biblical Times. Multicoloured.
471. 2 a. Type **196** .. .. 10 10
472. 3 a. Asiatic wild ass .. 10 10
473. 5 a. Arabian oryx .. .. 10 10
474. 78 a. Cheetah .. .. 40 30

**197.** "Haganah" Emblem. **198.** Jaffa Gate.

**1971.** Memorial Day.
475. **197.** 78 a. multicoloured .. 30 20

**1971.** Independence Day. Gates of Jerusalem (1st series). Multicoloured.
476. 15 a. Type **198** .. .. 45 25
477. 18 a. New Gate .. .. 50 25
478. 35 a. Damascus Gate .. 50 35
479. 85 a. Herod's Gate .. 50 35
See also Nos. 527/30.

**199.** Gymnastics. **200.** "... and he wrote upon the tables ..."

**1971.** 9th "Hapoel" Games. Multicoloured.
481. 50 a. Type **199** .. .. 25 20
482. 50 a. Basketball .. .. 25 20
483. 50 a. Running .. .. 25 20

**1971.** Feast of Weeks ("Shavuot"). Illuminated verses from the Bible. Multicoloured.
484. 50 a. Type **200** .. .. 35 30
485. 85 a. "The first of the firstfruits ..." .. .. 45 40
486. I£1.50 "... and ye shall observe the feast ..." 60 45
See also Nos. 488/92.

**201.** "Sun over the Emeq".

**1971.** 50th Anniv of Settlements in the "Emeq" (Yezreel Valley).
487 **201** 40 a. multicoloured .. 25 20

**1971.** Jewish New Year. Feast of the Tabernacles ("Sukkot"). Illuminated Verses from the Bible. As Type **200**. Multicoloured.
488. 15 a. "You shall rejoice in your feast" .. .. 15 10
489. 18 a. "You shall dwell in booths ..." .. .. 15 10
490. 20 a. "That I made the people ..." .. .. 15 15
491. 40 a. "... gathered in the produce" .. .. 20 15
492. 65 a. "... I will give you your rains ..." .. 25 20

**202.** Kinneret. **203.** "Agricultural Research".

**1971.** Landscapes (1st series).
493 – 3 a. blue .. .. 20 10
494 – 5 a. green .. .. 10 10
495 – 15 a. orange .. 10 10
496 **202** 18 a. purple .. 65 10
497 – 20 a. green .. 10 10
498 – 22 a. blue .. .. 80 10
498a – 25 a. red .. .. 10 10
499 – 30 a. mauve .. 15 10
500 – 35 a. purple .. 10 10
501 – 45 a. blue .. .. 15 10
502 – 50 a. green .. 20 10
503 – 55 a. green .. 20 10
504 – 65 a. brown .. 15 10
505 – 70 a. red .. .. 20 10
505apa – 80 a. blue .. .. 25 25
506 – 88 a. blue .. .. 80 30
507 – 95 a. red .. .. 80 35
508 – I£1.10 brown .. 20 10
508a – I£1.30 blue .. 25 15
508b – I£1.70 brown .. 20 10

509pa – I£2 brown .. 15 15
510pa – I£3 violet .. 25 20
510a – I£10 blue .. .. 90 50

DESIGNS—As T **202**: 3 a. Judean desert; 5 a. Gan Ha-Shelosha; 15 a. Negev desert; 20 a. Tel Dan; 22 a. Yafo; 25 a. Arava; 30 a. En Avedat; 35 a. Brekhat Ram; 45 a. Mt. Hermon; 50 a. Rosh Pinna; 55 a. Natanya; 65 a. Plain of Zebulun; 70 a. Engedi; 80 a. Beach at Elat; 88 a. Akko (Acre); 95 a. Hamifratz Hane'Elam; I£1.10, Aqueduct near Acre; I£1.30, Zefat; I£1.70, Nazerat Illit; I£2, Coral Island; I£3, Haifa. 28×27 mm: I£10, Elat.

See also Nos. 682/4a.

**1971.** 50th Anniv. of Volcani Institute of Agricultural Research.
511. **203.** I£1 multicoloured .. 30 20

**204.** Hebrew Text. **205.** "The Scribe" (sculpture, B. Schatz).

**1971.** Educational Development. Multicoloured.
512. 15 a. Type **204** .. .. 10 10
513. 18 a. Mathematical formulae 10 10
514. 20 a. Engineering symbols 10 10
515. 40 a. University degree abbreviations .. .. 15 15

**1972.** Jewish Art.
516 **205** 40 a. brn, copper & blk 20 15
517 – 55 a. multicoloured .. 20 15
518 – 70 a. multicoloured .. 20 15
519 – 85 a. black and yellow 25 20
520 – I£1 multicoloured .. 25 20

DESIGNS—VERT: 55 a. "Sarah" (A. Pann); 85 a. "Old Jerusalem" (woodcut, J. Steinhardt); I£1, "Resurrection" (A. Kahana). HORIZ: 70 a. "Zefat" (M. Shemi).

**206.** The Flight from Egypt. **207.** "Let My People Go".

**1972.** Passover Feast ("Pesah"). Mult.
521. 18 a. Type **206** .. .. 25 20
522. 45 a. Baking unleavened bread .. .. 25 25
523. 95 a. "Seder" table .. 35 30

**1972.** Campaign for Jewish Immigration.
524. **207.** 55 a. multicoloured .. 85 60

**208.** Bouquet. **209.** Jethro's Tomb.

**1972.** Memorial Day.
525. **208.** 55 a. multicoloured .. 30 20

**1972.** "Nebi Shuaib" (Jethro's Tomb) (Druse shrine)
526. **209.** 55 a. multicoloured .. 25 20

**1972.** Independence Day. Gates of Jerusalem (2nd series). Designs as T **198.** Multicoloured.
527. 15 a. Lion's Gate .. .. 40 20
528. 18 a. Golden Gate .. 45 25
529. 45 a. Dung Gate .. 50 35
530. 55 a. Zion Gate .. .. 60 40

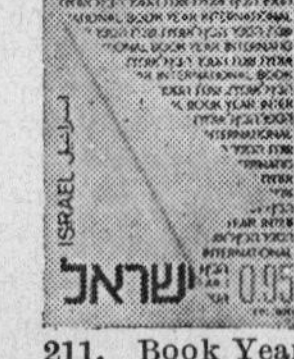

**210.** Ghetto Entrance. **211.** Book Year Texts.

**1972.** 400th Death Anniv. of Rabbi Yizhaq Luria ("Ari").
532. **210.** 70 a. multicoloured .. 1·00 70

**1972.** Int. Book Year.
533. **211.** 95 a. blk., red and blue 30 25

**212.** Dish Aerial. **213.** Ancona Ark.

**1972.** Opening of Satellite Earth Station.
534. **212.** I£1 multicoloured .. 30 25

**1972.** Jewish New Year. Holy Arks from Italy.
535 **213** 15 a. brown and yellow 15 10
536 – 45 a. grn, gold & lt grn 20 15
537 – 70 a. red, blue & yellow 25 20
538 – 95 a. purple and gold 40 30

DESIGNS: 45 a. Soragna Ark. 70 a. Padua Ark. 95 a. Reggio Emilia Ark.

**214.** Menora Emblem. **215.** Hanukka Lamp (Morocco, 18th-19th century).

**1972.** 25th Anniv of State of Israel.
539 **214** I£1 blue, purple & silver 30 25

**1972.** Festival of Lights ("Hanukka"). Ceremonial Lamps. Multicoloured.
540. 12 a. Type **215** .. .. 15 15
541. 25 a. 18th-century Polish lamp .. .. 20 15
542. 70 a. 17th-century German silver lamp .. .. 20 20

**216.** Pendant. **217.** "Horse and Rider".

**1973.** Immigration of North African Jews.
543. **216.** 18 a. multicoloured .. 20 15

**1973.** Children's Drawings. Multicoloured.
544 2 a. Type **217** .. .. 10 10
545 3 a. "Balloon ride" (17×48 mm) .. .. 10 10
546 55 a. "Party-time" .. 15 15

**218.** "Reuben" Window. **219.** Flame of Remembrance.

**1973.** "Tribes of Israel" Stained-glass Windows by Chagall, Hadassah Synagogue, Jerusalem. Multicoloured.
547. I£1 "Levi" .. .. 65 50
548. I£1 "Simeon" .. .. 65 50
549. I£1 Type **218** .. .. 65 50
550. I£1 "Issachar" .. .. 65 50
551. I£1 "Zebulun" .. .. 65 50
552. I£1 "Judah" .. .. 65 50
553. I£1 "Asher" .. .. 65 45
554. I£1 "Gad" .. .. 65 45
555. I£1 "Dan" .. .. 65 45
556. I£1 "Benjamin" .. .. 65 45
557. I£1 "Joseph" .. .. 65 45
558. I£1 "Naphtali" .. .. 65 45

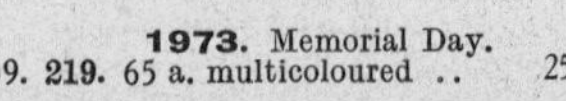

**1973.** Memorial Day.
559. **219.** 65 a. multicoloured .. 25 15

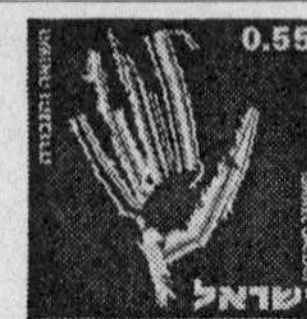

**220.** Skeletal Hand.

**1973.** Holocaust (Persecution of European Jews 1933–45) Memorial.
560. **220.** 55 a. blue .. .. 20 15

**221.** Signatures of Declaration of Independence.

**1973.** Independence Day.
561. **221.** I£1 multicoloured .. 25 20

**222.** Star of David and Runners. **223.** Isaiah.

**1973.** 9th Maccabiah.
563. **222.** I£1.10 multicoloured .. 25 15

**1973.** Jewish New Year. Prophets of Israel.
564. 18 a. Type **223** .. .. 10 10
565. 65 a. Jeremiah .. .. 10 10
566. I£1.10 Ezekiel .. .. 20 15

**224.** Jews in Boat, and Danish Flag. **225.** Institute Emblem and Cogwheel.

**1973.** 30th Anniv. of Rescue of Danish Jews.
567. **224.** I£5 black, red & brn. 60 45

**1973.** 50th Anniv. of "Technion" Israel Institute of Technology.
568. **225.** I£1.25 multicoloured 25 20

**226.** Collectors within "Stamp".  **227.** Soldier with Prayer Shawl.

**1973.** "Jerusalem 73" International Stamp Exhibition. Multicoloured.
569. 20 a. Type **226** .. .. 10 10
570. I£1 Collectors within "Stamp" (different) .. 20 20

**1974.** Memorial Day.
572. **227** I£1 black and blue .. 20 15

**228.** Quill and Bottle of Ink. **229.** "Woman in Blue" (M. Kisling).

**1974.** 50th Anniv. of Hebrew Writers' Association.
573. **228.** I£2 black and gold .. 20 15

**1974.** Jewish Art. Multicoloured.
574. I£1.25 Type **229** .. .. 15 15
575. I£2 "Mother and Child" (bronze, C. Orloff) .. 20 15
576. I£3 "Girl in Blue" (C. Soutine) .. .. .. 25 20

See also Nos. 604/6.

**230.** Spanner.

**1974.** 50th Anniv. of Young Workers' Movement.
577. **230.** 25 a. multicoloured .. 30 25

**231.** Lady Davis Technical Centre, Tel Aviv.

**1974.** "Architecture in Israel" (1st series).
578. **231.** 25 a. grey .. .. 10 10
579. – 60 a. blue .. .. 15 10
580. – I£1.45 brown .. .. 20 15

DESIGNS: 60 a. Elias Sourasky Library, Tel Aviv University. I£1.45, Mivtahim Rest-home, Zikhron Yaaqov.

See also Nos. 596/8.

**232.** Istanbuli Synagogue. **233.** Arrows on Globe.

**1974.** Jewish New Year. Rebuilt Synagogues in Jerusalem's Old City. Multicoloured.
581 25 a. Type **232** .. .. 10 10
582 70 a. Emtzai Synagogue .. 15 10
583 I£1 Raban Yohanan Ben Zakai Synagogue .. 15 15

**1974.** Cent. of U.P.U. Multicoloured.
584. 25 a. Type **233** .. .. 10 10
585. I£1.30 Dove "postman" (27×27 mm.) .. 25 20

**234.** David Ben Gurion (statesman).

**1974.** Ben Gurion Memorial.
586. **234.** 25 a. brown .. .. 10 10
587. I£1.30 green .. .. 20 20

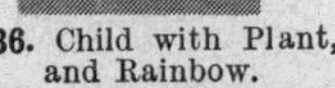

**236.** Child with Plant, and Rainbow. **238.** Welding.

237. Hebrew University, Jerusalem.

1975. Arbour Day. Multicoloured.
588. 1 a. Type 236 .. .. 10 10
589. 35 a. Bird in tree .. .. 10 10
590. I£2 Child with plant & sun 20 15

1975. 50th Anniv. of Hebrew University, Jerusalem.
591. 237. I£2.50 multicoloured 25 20

1975. "Occupational Safety". Mult.
592 30 a. Type 238 .. .. 10 10
593 80 a. Tractor-driving .. 10 10
594 I£1.20 Telegraph line maintenance .. .. 15 15

239. Harry S. Truman. 240. Memorial.

1975. Truman Commemoration.
595. 239. I£5 brown .. .. 25 20

1975. "Architecture in Israel" (2nd series). As Type 231.
596. 80 a. brown .. .. 15 10
597. I£1.30 green .. .. 15 10
598. I£1.70 brown .. .. 20 15
DESIGNS: 80 a. Hebrew University Synagogue, Jerusalem. I£1.30, Museum, Yad Mordechai. I£1.70, City Hotel, Bat Yam.

1975. Memorial Day.
599. 240. I£1 red, black & mauve 20 15

241. Text and Poppy. 242. Hurdling.

1975. Fallen Soldiers' Memorial.
600. 241. I£1.45 black, red & grey 20 15

1975. 10th Hapoel Games. Multicoloured.
601 25 a. Type 242 .. .. 10 10
602 I£1.70 Cycling .. .. 10 10
603 I£3 Volleyball .. .. 20 15

1975. Jewish Art. As T 229. Mult.
604. I£1 "Hanukka" (M. D. Oppenheim) .. .. 20 15
605. I£1.40 "The Purim Players" (J. Adler) (horiz.) .. .. 20 15
606. I£4 "Yom Kippur" (M. Gottlieb) .. .. 25 20

243. Old People. 244. Gideon.

1975. Gerontology.
607. 243. I£1.85 multicoloured .. 20 15

1975. Jewish New Year. Judges of Israel. Multicoloured.
608. 35 a. Type 244 .. .. 10 10
609. I£1 Deborah .. .. 15 10
610. I£1.40 Jephthah .. .. 20 15

245. Zalman Shazar. 246. Emblem of Pioneer Women.

1975. 1st Death Anniv of Zalman Shazar (President 1963–73).
611. 245. 35 a. black and silver 20 15

1975. 50th Anniv. of Pioneer Women's Organization.
612. 246. I£5 multicoloured .. 35 30

247. New Hospital Buildings.

1975. Return of Hadassah Hospital to Mt. Scopus.
613. 247. I£4 multicoloured .. 25 20

248. Pratincole. 249. "Air Pollution".

1975. Protected Wild Birds. Multicoloured.
614. I£1.10 Type 248 .. .. 30 30
615. I£1.70 Spur-winged plover 40 40
616. I£2 Black-winged stilt 50 50

1975. "Environmental Quality". Mult.
617. 50 a. Type 249 .. .. 15 10
618. 80 a. "Water pollution" 15 10
619. I£1.70 "Noise pollution" 15 15

250. Star of David. 251. Symbolic "Key".

1975.
620 250 75 a. blue and red .. 20 10
621 I£1.80 blue and grey 15 10
622 I£1.85 blue and brown 25 10
623 I£2.45 blue and green 25 10
623a I£2.70 blue & mauve 20 10
623b I£4.30 blue and red .. 20 10
624 I£5.40 blue and bistre 25 15
625 I£8 blue & turquoise 30 15

1976. 70th Anniv. of Bezalel Academy of Arts and Design, Jerusalem.
626. 251. I£1.85 multicoloured 20 15

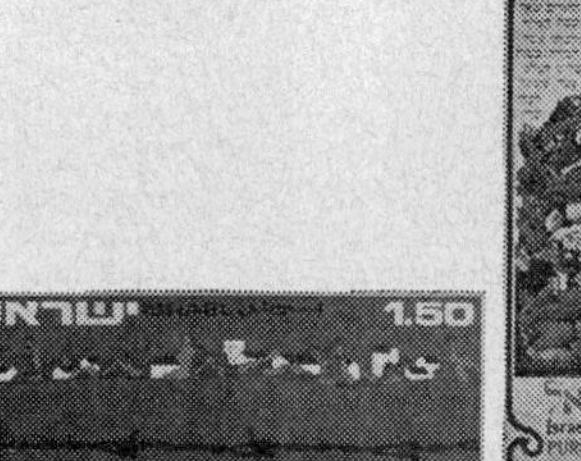
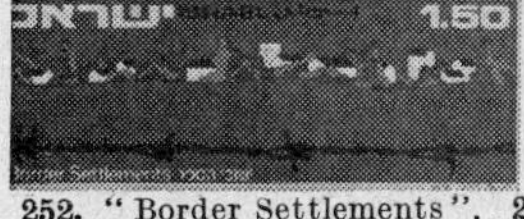
252. "Border Settlements". 253. "In the days of Ahasuerus ..".

1976. Jewish Border Settlements.
627 252 I£1.50 multicoloured .. 20 15

1976. "Purim" Festival. Multicoloured.
628 40 a. Type 253 .. .. 10 10
629 80 a. "He set the royal crown. . ." .. .. 15 10
630 I£1.60 "Thus shall it be done. . ." .. .. 15 15

254. Monument to the Fallen. 255. "Dancers of Meron" (R. Rubin).

1976. Memorial Day.
632 254 I£1.85 multicoloured .. 30 25

1976. Lag Ba-Omer Festival.
633 255 I£1.30 multicoloured .. 30 25

256. "200" Flag.

1976. Bicent. of American Revolution.
634. 256. I£4 multicoloured .. 40 30

258. High Jump.

1976. Olympic Games, Montreal.
636 258 I£1.60 black and red .. 20 15
637 – I£2.40 black and blue 20 15
638 – I£4.40 black & mauve 25 20
DESIGNS: I£2.40, Swimming. I£4.40, Gymnastics.

259. Multiple Tent Emblems. 260. "Truth".

1976. Camping.
639 259 I£1.60 multicoloured .. 25 20

1976. Jewish New Year. Multicoloured.
640 45 a. Type 260 .. .. 10 10
641 I£1.60 "Judgement" .. 15 15
642 I£1.90 "Peace" .. .. 20 20

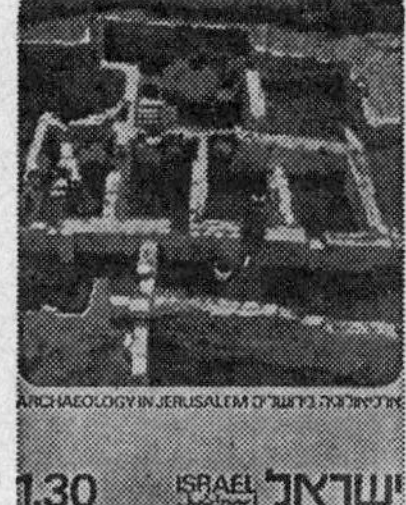
261. Excavated Byzantine House.

1976. Archaeology in Jerusalem (1st series). Multicoloured.
643 I£1.30 Type 261 .. .. 30 20
644 I£2.40 Arch of 2nd Temple 35 30
645 I£2.80 Staircase to 2nd Temple .. .. 35 30

262. Pawn. 263. Clearing Ground.

1976. 22nd Chess Olympiad, Haifa. Mult.
646 I£1.30 Type 262 .. .. 15 15
647 I£1.60 Rook .. .. 20 15

1976. Archaeology in Jerusalem (2nd series). Designs as T 261. Multicoloured.
648. 70 a. City Wall, First Temple period .. .. 25 10
649. I£5 Omayyad palace .. 45 40

1976. Pioneers.
650 263 5 a. brown and gold .. 10 10
651 – 10 a. lilac and gold .. 10 10
652 – 60 a. red and gold .. 10 10
653 – I£1.40 blue and gold .. 15 15
654 – I£1.80 green and gold 20 15
DESIGNS—HORIZ: 10 a. Building breakwater. I£1.40, Ploughing. I£1.80, Ditch-clearing. VERT: 60 a. Road construction.

264. "Grandfather's Carrot".

1977 Voluntary Service.
655. 264. I£2.60 multicoloured .. 25 20

265. "By the Rivers of Babylon".

1977. Drawings of E. M. Lilien.
656 265 I£1.70 brn, grey & blk 40 35
657 – I£1.80 blk, stone & brn 40 35
658 – I£2.10 grn, lt grn & blk 40 35
PAINTINGS—VERT: I£1.80, "Abraham". HORIZ: I£2.10, "May Our Eyes Behold".

266. Jew and Arab shaking Hands.

1977. Children's Drawings on Peace. Mult.
659. 50 a. Type 266 .. .. 15 10
660. I£1.40 Arab and Jew holding hands .. .. 25 20
661. I£2.70 Peace dove, Jew and Arab .. .. .. 35 25

267. Parachute Troops Memorial.

1977. Memorial Day.
662. 267. I£3.30 multicoloured .. 35 30

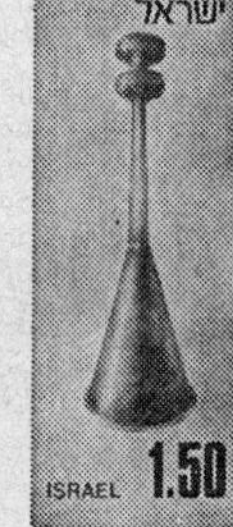
268. Embroidery showing Sabbath Loaves. 269. Trumpet.

1977. Sabbath.
663. 268. I£3 multicoloured .. 30 25

1977. Ancient Musical Instruments. Mult.
664. I£1.50 Type 269 .. .. 25 20
665. I£2 Lyre .. .. 25 20
666. I£5 "Jingle" (cymbals) .. 35 25

270. Fencing. 272. American Zionist Emblem.

271. Petah Tiqwa.

1977. 10th Maccabiah Games.
667 270 I£1 grey, blue & black 25 20
668 – I£2.50 grey, red & blk 25 25
669 – I£3.50 grey, grn & blk 30 30
DESIGNS: I£2.50, Putting the shot. I£3.50, Judo.

1977. Centenary of Petah Tiqwa.
670. 271. I£1.50 multicoloured 35 20

**1977.** Zionist Organization of America Convention.

671. 272. I£4 multicoloured .. 30 30

273. Page of 16th-cent. Book "Kohelet Yaakov".

274. Sarah.

**1977.** 400th Anniv of Hebrew Printing at Zefat.

672. 273. I£4 black, gold & red 30 25

**1977.** Jewish New Year. Matriarchs of Israel. Multicoloured.

673. 70 a. Type **274** .. .. 15 10

674. I£1.50 Rebekah .. .. 25 20

675. I£2 Rachel.. .. .. 35 30

676. I£3 Leah .. .. .. 35 35

See also Nos. 728/30.

275. Police.

276. Helmet and Model Settlement.

**1977.** National Police Force. Multicoloured.

677. I£1 Type **275** .. .. 25 20

678. I£1 Civil Guard .. .. 25 20

679. I£1 Frontier Guard .. 25 20

**1977.** "Nahal" Pioneering Fighting Youth.

680. 276. I£3.50 multicoloured.. 30 25

277. Accelerator building, Weizmann Institute.

278. Caesarea.

**1977.** Inauguration of Koffler Accelerator.

681. 277. I£8 blue and black .. 60 50

**1977.** Landscapes (2nd series).

682 278 10 a. blue .. .. 10 10

683b – I£1 bistre .. .. 15 15

684 – I£20 green and orange 75 30

684a – I£50 multicoloured .. 95 60

DESIGNS—As T 278: I£1, Arava. 29 × 27 mm: I£20, Rosh Pinna. 27½ × 36½ mm: I£50, Soreq Cave.

279. "Mogul" 2-6-0 Locomotive.

280. Blood-stained Scallop ("Gloripallium pallium").

**1977.** Railways in the Holy Land. Mult.

685 65 a. Type **279** .. .. 20 15

686 I£1.50 0-6-0 locomotive .. 25 25

687 I£2 4-6-0 "P" Class locomotive .. .. 30 25

688 I£2.50 Diesel locomotive .. 35 30

**1977.** Red Sea Shells. Multicoloured.

690 I£2 Type **280** .. .. 20 20

691 I£2 Pacific grinning tun ("Malea pomum") .. 20 20

692 I£2 Isabelle cowrie ("Cypraea isabella") .. 20 20

693 I£2 Camp Pitar venus ("Lioconcha castrensis") 20 20

281. "The Marriage Parties" (Dutch Ketubah).

**1978.** Illuminated Jewish Marriage Contracts (Ketubah). Multicoloured.

694 75 a. Type **281** .. .. 15 15

695 I£3.90 Moroccan Ketubah 25 20

696 I£6 Jerusalem Ketubah .. 40 30

282. "A Street in Jerusalem" (H. Gliksberg).

283. Eliyahu Golomb (leader of Hagana).

**1978.** Jewish Art.

697. 282. I£3 multicoloured .. 25 25

698. – I£3.80 blk., yell. & grey 30 25

699. – I£4.40 multicoloured.. 35 25

DESIGNS: I£3.80, "Thistles" (L. Krakauer). I£4.40, "An Alley in Zefat" (M. Levanon).

**1978.** Historical Personalities (1st series).

700 283 I£2 green and yellow 20 15

701 – I£2 blue and grey .. 20 15

702 – I£2 purple and stone .. 20 15

703 – I£2 brown and stone .. 20 15

704 – I£2 black and grey .. 20 15

DESIGNS: No. 701, David Raziel (Irgun commander). 702, Yitzhak Sadeh (nationalist and military commander). 703, Dr. Moshe Sneh (Zionist politician). 704, Abraham Stern (underground fighter).

See also Nos. 721/2, 725/6, 732/3, 738/40, 763/5, 809/11 and 831/3.

284. Children's Flower Paintings (from mural, Petah Tikvah Museum).

286. Y.M.C.A. Building Jerusalem.

**1978.** Memorial Day.

705. 284. I£1.50 multicoloured.. 20 10

706. – I£1.50 multicoloured.. 20 10

707. – I£1.50 multicoloured.. 20 10

708. – I£1.50 multicoloured.. 20 10

709. – I£1.50 multicoloured.. 20 10

710. – I£1.50 multicoloured.. 20 10

711. – I£1.50 multicoloured.. 20 10

712. – I£1.50 multicoloured.. 20 10

713. – I£1.50 multicoloured.. 20 10

714. – I£1.50 multicoloured.. 20 10

715. – I£1.50 multicoloured.. 20 10

716. – I£1.50 multicoloured.. 20 10

717. – I£1.50 multicoloured.. 20 10

718. – I£1.50 multicoloured.. 20 10

719. – I£1.50 multicoloured.. 20 10

**Nos. 705/19 issued together form a composite design, each showing a different portion of the Memorial Wall.**

**1978.** Historical Personalities (2nd series). As T 283.

721 I£2 blue and stone .. 20 15

722 I£2 brown and grey .. 20 15

DESIGNS: No. 721, Dr. Chaim Weizmann (first president of Israel). No. 722, Dr. Theodor Herzl (founder of Zionism).

**1978.** Cent. of Jerusalem Y.M.C.A.

723. 286. I£5.40 multicoloured 35 30

287. Verse of National Anthem.

288. Family Groups.

**1978.** Cent of Publication of "Hatiqwa" (Jewish National Anthem).

724. 287. I£8.40 silver, deep blue and blue .. .. 55 40

**1978.** Historical Personalities (3rd series). As T 283.

725 I£2 purple and cream .. 20 15

726 I£2 green and cream .. 20 15

DESIGNS: No. 725, Rabbi Ouziel. No. 726, Rabbi Kook.

**1978.** Social Welfare.

727. 288. I£5.10 multicoloured.. 35 30

**1978.** Jewish New Year, Patriarchs of Israel. As T 274. Multicoloured.

728. I£1.10 Abraham .. .. 20 15

729. I£5.20 Isaac .. .. 35 30

730. I£6.60 Jacob .. .. 40 35

289. Star of David, Young Tree and Globe showing U.S.A.

291. Indian Silver and Enamelled Vase.

290. Shaare Zedek Medical Centre. New and Old Buildings.

**1978.** United Jewish Appeal.

731. 289. I£8.40 multicoloured.. 65 60

**1978.** Historical Personalities (4th series). As T 283.

732 I£2 purple and stone .. 20 15

733 I£2 blue and grey .. 20 15

DESIGNS: No. 732, David Ben-Gurion (first Prime Minister). No. 733, Ze'ev Jabotinsky (Zionist leader).

**1978.** Opening of New Shaare Zedek Medical Centre, Jerusalem.

734. 290. I£5.40 multicoloured.. 40 30

**1978.** Institute for Islamic Art, Jerusalem. Multicoloured.

735 I£2.40 Type **291** .. .. 25 20

736 I£3 13th-century Persian pottery chess rook (elephant with howdah) 30 25

737 I£4 Syrian Mosque lamp 35 25

**1978.** Historical Personalities (5th series). As T 283.

738 I£2 black and stone .. 20 15

739 I£2 blue and grey .. 20 15

740 I£2 black and stone .. 20 15

DESIGNS: No. 738, Menahem Ussishkin (president of Jewish National Fund). No. 739, Berl Katzenelson (pioneer of Zionist socialism). No. 740, Dr. Max Nordau (journalist).

292. "Iris lortetii".

293. Agricultural Mechanization.

**1978.** Wild Irises. Multicoloured.

741. I£1.10 Type **292** .. .. 20 15

742. I£5.40 "Iris haynei" .. 40 30

743. I£8.40 "Iris nazarena" .. 50 45

**1979.** Technological Achievements. Mult.

744. I£1.10 Type **293** .. .. 15 10

745. I£2.40 Sea water desalination .. .. 20 15

746. I£4.30 Electronics .. .. 20 15

747. I£5 Chemical fertilizers .. 25 20

294. Jewish Brigade Flag.

295. "Good from Evil".

**1979.** Yishuv Volunteers serving in Second World War.

748. 294. I£5.10 yellow, blue and deep blue .. .. 45 40

**1979.** "Salute to the Righteous among Nations".

749. 295. I£5.40 multicoloured.. 45 40

296. Prayer for Peace in Western Wall.

297. Naval Memorial, Ashdod.

**1979.** Signing of Egyptian–Israeli Peace Treaty.

750 296 I£10 multicoloured .. 35 30

**1979.** Memorial Day.

752. 297. I£5.10 multicoloured.. 30 20

298. Weightlifting.

299. "50" and Rotary Emblem.

**1979.** 11th Hapoel Games. Multicoloured.

753. I£1.50 Type **298** .. .. 25 15

754. I£6 Tennis .. .. 35 35

755. I£11 Gymnastics.. .. 50 45

**1979.** 50th Anniv. of Rotary in Israel.

756. 299. I£7 multicoloured .. 45 40

300. Rabbi Joshua Ben Hananiah (blacksmith).

301. Tiberias Hot Springs.

**1979.** Jewish New Year. The "Hazal" (sages and craftsmen). Multicoloured.

757. I£1.80 Type **300** .. .. 25 20

758. I£8.50 Rabbi Meir Ba'al Ha-Nes (scribe) .. 45 40

759. I£13 Rabbi Johanan the Sandal-maker .. .. 60 55

**1979.** Health Resorts. Multicoloured.

760. I£8 Type **301** .. .. 30 25

761. I£12 Dead Sea Hot Spring 50 35

302. "Searchlight Beam".

303. Arab and Jew before Jerusalem

**1979.** 50th Anniv. of Jewish Agency.

762. 302. I£10 blue, grey & turq. 45 30

**1979.** Historical Personalities (6th series). As T 283.

763 I£7 purple and grey .. 30 25

764 I£9 blue .. .. 35 35

765 I£13 black and stone .. 45 40

DESIGNS: I£7, Dr. Arthur Ruppin ("father of Zionist settlement"). I£9, Joseph Trumpeldor (founder of Zion Mule Corps and Jewish Legion). I£13, Aaron Aaronsohn (botanist).

**1979.** Children Paint Jerusalem. Mult.

766. I£1.80 Type **303** .. .. 20 15

767. I£4 Jewish, Christian and Muslim citizens of Jerusalem (horiz.) .. 20 20

768. I£5 Worshippers at the Western Wall (horiz.).. 25 25

304. Boy sliding down Rainbow. 305. Cog with Star of David.

**1979.** International Year of the Child.
769. **304.** I£8.50 multicoloured .. 40 30

**1980.** Centenary of Organization for Rehabilitation through Training.
770. **305.** I£13 multicoloured .. 55 45

306. " Scolymus maculatus ". 307. " The Road of Courage " Monument.

**1980.** Thistles. Multicoloured.
771. 50 a. Type **306** .. .. 20 15
772. I£5.50 " Echinops viscosus " .. .. .. 35 25
773. I£8·50 " Cynara syriaca " 65 60

**1980.** Memorial Day.
774. **307.** I£12 multicoloured .. 40 30

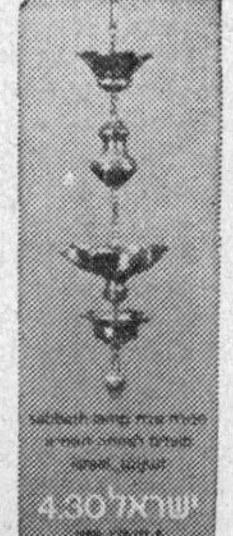

308. Symbolical Human Figure with Blood-drop. 309. Sabbath Lamp, Netherlands, 18th cent.

**1980.** 50th Anniv. of Magden David Adom (voluntary medical corps).
775. **308.** I£2.70 red, grey & blk. 15 15
776. – I£13 multicoloured .. 40 35
DESIGN: I£13, Mobile intensive care unit and graph.

**1980.** Jewish New Year. Sabbath Lamps. Multicoloured.
778. I£4.30 Type **309** .. .. 35 20
779. I£20 Germany, 18th cent. 50 45
780. I£30 Morocco, 19th cent. 65 50

310. Yizhak Gruenbrum. 311. Tree and Flowers.

**1980.** 10th Death Anniv of Yizhak Gruenbaum (Zionist and politician).
781. **310.** I£32 brown .. .. 1·25 1·10

**1980.** Renewal of Jewish Settlement in Gush Etzion.
782. **311.** I£19 multicoloured .. 70 60

New currency. 1 (new) Shekel = 10 (old) Israeli Pounds.

313. " Shekel ". 314. Golda Meir.

**1980.**

| | | | | |
|---|---|---|---|---|
| 784 | **313** | 5 a. green & emerald | 10 | 10 |
| 785 | | 10 a. red and mauve | 10 | 10 |
| 786 | | 20 a. turquoise & bl | 10 | 10 |
| 787 | | 30 a. violet & dp vio | 10 | 10 |
| 788 | | 50 a. orange and red | 10 | 10 |
| 789a | | 60 a. green & purple | 15 | 10 |
| 790 | | 70 a. blue and black | 15 | 10 |
| 791 | | 90 a. violet & brown | 15 | 10 |
| 792 | | 1 s. mauve and green | 15 | 10 |
| 793 | | 1 s. 10 green and red | 15 | 10 |
| 794 | | 1 s. 20 blue and red | 15 | 10 |
| 795 | | 2 s. green and purple | 20 | 10 |
| 796 | | 2 s. 80 brown & grn | 25 | 10 |
| 797a | | 3 s. red and blue .. | 20 | 15 |
| 798 | | 3 s. 20 grey and red | 40 | 30 |
| 799b | | 4 s. purple & mauve | 25 | 15 |
| 800 | | 4 s. 20 blue & violet | 25 | 10 |
| 801a | | 5 s. green and black | 25 | 10 |
| 802pa | | 10 s. brown & dp brn | 30 | 15 |

**1981.** Golda Meir (former Prime Minister). Commemoration.
803. **314.** 2 s. 60 purple .. .. 60 55

315. Landscape (Anna Ticho).

**1981.** Paintings of Jerusalem. Multicoloured.
804 50 a. Type **315** .. .. 20 15
805 1 s. 50 "View of City" (Joseph Zaritsky) (vert) 40 30
806 2 s. 50 Landscape (Mordechai Ardon) .. 50 45

316. Hand putting Coin into Light Bulb. 317. A. H. Silver (Zionist).

**1981.** Energy. Multicoloured.
807. 2 s. 60 Type **316** .. .. 50 40
808. 4 s. 20 Hand squeezing energy from the sun .. 60 50

**1981.** Historical Personalities (7th series).
809 – 2 s. blue .. .. 55 45
810 – 2 s. 80 green .. .. 55 45
811 **317** 3 s. 20 ochre and black 55 45
DESIGNS—As T **283**. 2 s. Shmuel Yosef Agnon (writer). 2 s. 80, Moses Montefiore (Zionist).

318. Biq'at Ha-yarden Memorial. 319. Board Sailing.

**1981.** Memorial Day.
812. **318.** 1 s. multicoloured .. 30 25

**1981.** 11th Maccabiah Games. Multicoloured.
813 80 a. Type **319** .. .. 45 30
814 4 s. Basketball .. .. 65 50
815 6 s. High jump .. .. 85 75

320. " Family Tree ". 321. Moses and the Burning Bush.

**1981.** The Jewish Family Heritage.
816. **320.** 3 s. multicoloured .. 55 45

**1981.** Jewish New Year. Moses. Multicoloured.
817. 70 a. Type **321** .. 25 10
818. 1 s. Moses and Aaron petitioning Pharoah for Israelites' freedom .. 30 20
819. 3 s. Israelites crossing the Red Sea .. 50 30
820. 4 s. Moses with the Tablets 55 50

322. " Rosa damascena ".

**1981.** Roses. Multicoloured.
821. 90 a. Type **322** .. .. 40 25
822. 3 s. 50 " Rosa phoenicia " 50 40
823. 4 s. 50 " Rosa hybrida " 65 50

323. Ha-Shiv'a Interchange.

**1981.** Ha-Shiv'a Motorway Interchange.
824. **323.** 8 s. multicoloured .. 1·25 1·10

324. Balonea Oak. 325. Elat Stone.

**1981.** Trees. Multicoloured.
825. 3 s. Type **324** .. .. 40 35
826. 3 s. Wild strawberry .. 40 35
827. 3 s. Judas tree .. .. 40 35

**1981.** Precious Stones. Multicoloured.
828. 2 s. 50 Type **325** .. 25 20
829. 5 s. 50 Star sapphire .. 60 40
830. 7 s. Emerald .. .. 70 50

**1982.** Historical Personalities (8th series). Vert designs as T **283**.
831 7 s. multicoloured .. 75 60
832 8 s. brown, stone and black 75 60
833 9 s. blue and grey .. 75 60
DESIGNS: 7 s. Perez Bernstein (politician). 8 s. Rabbi Arye Levin. 9 s. Joseph Gedaliah Klausner (writer, editor and President of Hebrew Language Academy).

327. Child crossing Road.

**1982.** Road Safety.
834. **327.** 7 s. multicoloured .. 75 60

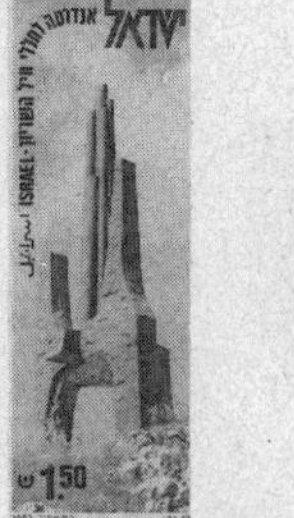

328. Armoured Brigade Memorial, En Zetim. 330. Emblem and Flowers.

329. Landscape (Aryeh Lubin).

**1982.** Memorial Day.
836. **328.** 1 s. 50 multicoloured .. 30 20

**1982.** Israeli Art. Multicoloured.
837. 7 s. Type **329** .. .. 85 70
838. 8 s. " Landscape " (Sionah Tagger) (vert.) .. 90 85
839. 15 s. " Pastorale " (Israel Paldi) .. .. 1·25 1·25

**1982.** 40th Anniv. of Gadna (Youth Corps).
840. **330.** 5 s. multicoloured .. 80 70

331. Agricultural Products. 332. Joshua and Israelites setting out for Canaan.

**1982.**

| | | | | |
|---|---|---|---|---|
| 841 | **331** | 40 a. blue and green | 10 | 10 |
| 842 | | 80 a. blue and mauve | 10 | 10 |
| 843 | | 1 s. 40 green and red | 20 | 15 |
| 844a | | 6 s. mauve and red | 30 | 20 |
| 845 | | 7 s. red and green | 15 | 10 |
| 846 | | 8 s. green and red .. | 20 | 15 |
| 847 | | 9 s. green and brown | 10 | 10 |
| 848a | | 15 s. red and green | 25 | 15 |
| 849 | | 30 s. purple and red | 20 | 15 |
| 850b | | 50 s. bistre and red | 50 | 20 |
| 851a | | 100 s. black & green | 70 | 50 |
| 852a | | 500 s. red and black | 70 | 60 |

**1982.** Jewish New Year. Joshua. Mult.
860. 1 s. 50 Type **332** .. .. 35 25
861. 5 s. 50 Priests carrying Ark of the Covenant over River Jordan .. 45 35
862. 7 s. 50 The fall of the walls of Jericho .. .. 50 40
863. 9 s. 50 The suspension of twilight during the battle against the five kings of Amorite .. 65 55

333. Rosh Pinna. 334. Symbolic Figures on Star of David.

**1982.** Centenaries of Rosh Pinna and Rishon Le Zion Settlements. Multicoloured.
864 2 s. 50 Type **333** .. .. 45 40
865 3 s. 50 Rishon Le Zion .. 45 40
See also Nos. 868/9, 905/6 and 967.

**1982.** 70th Anniv. of Hadassah (Women's Zionist Organization of America).
866. **334.** 12 s. multicoloured .. 1·10 90

335. Branch. 336. Flower.

**1982.** No value expressed.
867 **335** (–) brown and orange 55 20
No. 867 was initially sold at 1 s. 70 but this value was subsequently increased several times.

**1982.** Centenaries of Zikhron Yaaqov and Mazkeret Batya. As T **333.** Multicoloured.
868 6 s. Zikhron Yaaqov .. 45 40
869. 9 s. Mazkeret Batya .. 45 40

**1982.** Council for a Beautiful Israel.
870. **336.** 17 s. multicoloured .. 1·25 1·10

337. Eliahu Bet Tzuri. 338. Honey Bee, Honeycomb and Flowers.

**1982.** "Martyrs of the Struggle for Israel's Independence".

872. **337.** 3 s. grey, blk. & brn. 35 25
873. – 3 s. grey, blk. & olive 35 25
874. – 3 s. grey, blk. & blue 35 25
875. – 3 s. grey, blk. & olive 35 25
876. – 3 s. grey, blk. & brn. 35 25
877. – 3 s. grey, blk. & blue 35 25
878. – 3 s. grey, blk. & brn. 35 25
879. – 3 s. grey, blk. & olive 35 25
880. – 3 s. grey, blk. & blue 35 25
881. – 3 s. grey, blk. & olive 35 25
882. – 3 s. grey, blk. & brn. 35 25
883. – 3 s. grey, blk. & olive 35 25
884. – 3 s. grey, blk. & blue 35 25
885. – 3 s. grey, blk. & brn. 35 25
886. – 3 s. grey, blk. & blue 35 25
887. – 3 s. grey, blk. & olive 35 25
888. – 3 s. grey, blk. & blue 35 25
889. – 3 s. grey, blk. & brn. 35 25
890. – 3 s. grey, blk. & olive 35 25
891. – 3 s. grey, blk. & brn. 35 25

DESIGNS: No. 873, Hannah Szenes. 874, Shlomo Ben Yosef. 875, Yosef Lishanski. 876, Naaman Belkind. 877, Eliezer Kashani. 878, Yechiel Dresner. 879, Dov Gruner. 880, Mordechai Alkachi. 881, Eliahu Hakim. 882, Meir Nakar. 883, Avshalom Haviv. 884, Ya'akov Weiss. 885, Meir Feinstein. 886, Moshe Barazani. 887, Eli Cohen. 888, Samuel Azaar. 889, Dr. Moshe Marzouk. 890, Shalom Salih. 891, Yosef Basri.

**1983.** Bee-keeping.

892. **338.** 30 s. multicoloured .. 1·90 1·75

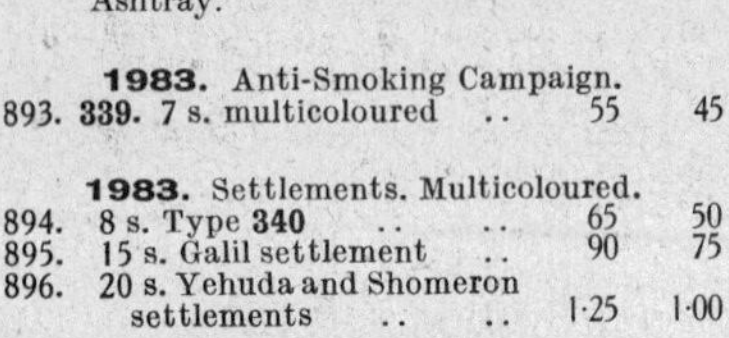

**339.** Sweets in Ashtray. **340.** Golan Settlement.

**1983.** Anti-Smoking Campaign.

893. **339.** 7 s. multicoloured .. 55 45

**1983.** Settlements. Multicoloured.

894. 8 s. Type **340** .. .. 65 50
895. 15 s. Galil settlement .. 90 75
896. 20 s. Yehuda and Shomeron settlements .. .. 1·25 1·00

**341.** 84th Division "of Steel" Memorial, Besor (Israel Godowitz).

**1983.** Memorial Day.

897. **341.** 3 s. multicoloured .. 30 25

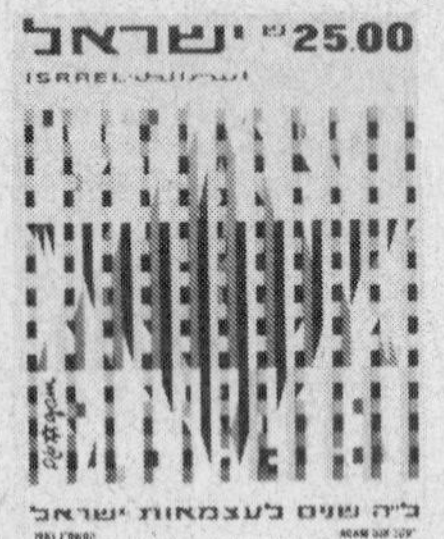

**342.** Star of David.

**1983.** 35th Anniv. of Independence.

898. **342.** 25 s. multicoloured .. 1·90 1·75

**343.** Running.

**1983.** 12th Hapoel Games.

900. **343.** 6 s. multicoloured .. 50 40

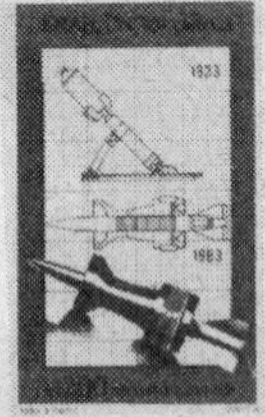

**344.** Missile and Blueprint.

**1983.** 50th Anniv. of Israel Military Industries.

901. **344.** 12 s. multicoloured .. 80 60

**345.** "The Last Way" (Iosef Kuzhovsky).

**1983.** Babi Yar Massacre.

902. **345.** 35 s. multicoloured .. 1·90 1·50

**347.** Raoul Wallenberg. **348.** Ohel Moed Synagogue, Tel Aviv.

**1983.** Raoul Wallenberg (Swedish diplomat) Commemoration.

904 **347** 14 s. stone and brown 1·10 90

**1983.** Centenary of Yesud Ha-Maala and Nes Ziyyona. As T **333**. Multicoloured.

905. 11 s. Yesud Ha-Maala .. 60 55
906. 13 s. Nes Ziyyona .. .. 65 60

**1983.** Jewish New Year. Synagogues. Mult.

907 3 s. Type **348** .. .. 35 25
908 12 s. Yeshurun Synagogue, Jerusalem .. .. 60 50
909 16 s. Ohel Aharon Synagogue, Haifa .. 85 70
910 20 s. Khalaschi Synagogue, Beer Sheva .. .. 95 85

**349.** Afula Landscape.

**1983.** Afula Urban Centre, Jezreel Valley.

911. **349.** 15 s. multicoloured .. 75 60

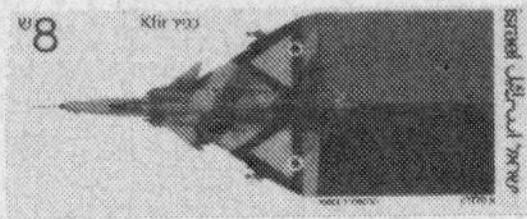

**351.** Israeli Aircraft Industry Kfir-C2 Jet Fighter.

**1983.** Military Equipment. Multicoloured.

913 8 s. Type **351** .. .. 25 20
914 18 s. "Reshef" (missile vessel) .. .. .. 45 40
915 30 s. "Merkava" battle tank .. .. .. 60 55

**352.** Rabbi Meir Bar-Ilan. **353.** "Aliya" ("immigration").

**1983.** 34th Death Anniv of Rabbi Meir Bar-Ilan (Zionist leader).

916. **352.** 9 s. blue and green .. 35 30

**1983.** 50th Anniv. of Jewish Immigration from Germany.

917. **353.** 14 s. red, gold and blue .. .. .. 45 35

**354.** Michael Halperin. **355.** Yigal Allon.

**1984.** 65th Death Anniv of Michael Halperin (nationalist).

918 **354** 7 s. brn, stone & dp brn 40 30

**1984.** 4th Death Anniv of Yigal Allon (politician).

919. **355.** 15 s. blue, grn. & blk. 40 30

**356.** Uri Zvi Grinberg. **357.** Hevel Ha-Besor.

**1984.** 3rd Death Anniv of Uri Zvi Grinberg (poet).

920 **356** 16 s. brown and red .. 40 30

**1984.** Settlements. Multicoloured.

921. 12 s. Type **357** .. .. 45 40
922. 17 s. Arava.. .. .. 60 50
923. 40 s. Hevel Azza .. .. 70 65

**358.** Alexander Zaid Monument (David Polus).

**1984.** Sculptures.

924 **358** 15 s. stone, black & bl 50 45
925 – 15 s. stone, black & brn 50 45
926 – 15 s. green, blk & grey 50 45

DESIGNS: No. 925, Tel Hay Memorial (Abraham Melnikov). 926, Dov Gruner monument (Chana Orloff).

**359.** Oliphant House, Dalyat Al Karmil (memorial to Druse Community). **360.** Worker with Flag.

**1984.** Memorial Day.

927. **359.** 10 s. multicoloured .. 30 25

**1984.** 50th Anniv. of National Labour Federation.

928. **360.** 35 s. multicoloured .. 75 70

**361.** Leon Pinsker. **362.** Stars and Hearts.

**1984.** 93rd Death Anniv of Leon Pinsker (Zionist leader).

929 **361** 20 s. lilac and purple .. 70 60

**1984.** 70th Anniv. of American Jewish Joint Distribution Committee.

930. **362.** 30 s. red, blue & black 70 60

**363.** Dove on Olympic Podium. **364.** General Charles Orde Wingate.

**1984.** Olympic Games, Los Angles.

931. **363.** 80 s. multicoloured .. 1·40 1·25

**1984.** 40th Death Anniv. of Charles Orde Wingate (British Soldier).

933. **364.** 20 s. grey, blk. & grn. 70 60

**365.** Hannah. **366.** Nahalal (first Moshav).

**1984.** Jewish New Year. Women in the Bible. Multicoloured.

934. 15 s. Type **365** .. .. 40 30
935. 70 s. Ruth .. .. .. 65 55
936. 100 s. Huldah the prophetess .. .. 90 80

**1984.** Moshavim (Co-operative Workers' Settlements).

937. **366.** 80 s. multicoloured .. 1·10 90

**367.** David Wolffsohn. **368.** "Apartment to Let" (Leah Goldberg, illus Shemuel Katz).

**1984.** 70th Death Anniv of David Wolffsohn (president of Zionist Organization).

938 **367** 150 s. brown, blue & blk 1·90 1·75

**1984.** Children's Books. Multicoloured.

939. 20 s. Type **368** .. .. 30 25
940. 30 s. "Why is the Zebra wearing pyjamas?" (O. Hillel, illus Alona Frankel) (28 × 28 mm.) .. 30 30
941. 50 s. "Across the Sea" (Haim Nahman Bialik, illus Nahum Gutman) .. 35 30

**369.** Bread and Wheat.

**1984.** World Food Day.

942. **369.** 200 s. multicoloured .. 1·50 1·25

**370.** Isaac Herzog.

**1984.** 25th Death Anniv. of Isaac Herzog (Israel's first Chief Rabbi).

943. **370.** 400 s. multicoloured .. 2·50 2·00

**371.** Lappet-faced Vulture.

**1985.** Biblical Birds of Prey (1st series). Multicoloured.
944. 100 s. Type **371** . . . . 90 90
945. 200 s. Bonelli's eagle . . 1·25 1·25
946. 300 s. Sooty falcon . . 1·50 1·25
947. 500 s. Griffon vulture . . 2·40 2·00
See also Nos. 1015/18.

**372.** Golani Brigade Monument and Museum.

**1985.** Memorial Day.
949. **372.** 50 s. multicoloured . . 30 25

**373.** Bleriot XI.

**1985.** Aviation in the Holy Land. Mult.
950 50 s. Type **373** (landing by Jules Vedrines, 1913) . . 45 35
951 150 s. Short S.17 Kent flying boat "Scipio" (Imperial Airways regular flights via Palestine, 1931–42) . . 60 45
952 250 s. De Havilland D.H.82A Tiger Moth (foundation of Palestine Flying Club, 1934) . . 75 70
953 300 s. Short S.16 Scion II (international flights by Palestine Airways, 1937–40) . . . . 90 85

**374.** Zivia and Yitzhak Zuckerman.

**1985.** Zivia and Yitzhak Zuckerman (Polish Jewish freedom fighters) Commemoration.
954 **374** 200 s. brown, grey & blk 95 85

**375.** Nurses tending Patients.

**1985.** 18th International Congress of Nurses.
955. **375.** 400 s. multicoloured . . 1·40 1·25

**377.** Ark of the Covenant. **378.** "Medals".

**1985.** Jewish New Year. Tabernacle Furnishings. Multicoloured.
957. 100 s. Type **377** . . . . 35 25
958. 150 s. The table . . . . 35 25
959. 200 s. Candlestick . . . . 40 40
960. 300 s. Incense altar . . 50 45

**1985.** International Youth Year.
961. **378.** 150 s. multicoloured . . 35 30

**379.** Basketball. **380.** Recanati.

**1985.** 12th Maccabiah Games. Multicoloured.
962. 400 s. Type **379** . . . . 90 75
963. 500 s. Tennis . . . . 1·00 90
964. 600 s. Windsurfing . . 1·25 1·00

**1985.** 40th Death Anniv. of Leon Yehuda Racanati (founder of Palestine Discount Bank).
965. **380.** 200 s. brown, grey and blue . . . . 45 40

**381.** Dizengoff (after J. Steinhardt and M. Sima).

**1985.** 49th Death Anniv of Meir Dizengoff (founder and Mayor of Tel Aviv).
966 **381** 500 s. black, brown & sil 1·00 75

**1985.** Cent of Gedera. As T **333**. Mult.
967 600 s. Gedera . . . . 1·10 95

**382.** Kibbutz Members.

**1985.** The Kibbutz.
968. **382.** 900 s. multicoloured . . 1·75 1·25

Currency Reform.
1000 (old) Shekalim = 1 (new) Shekel

**383.** Dr. Theodor Herzl. **384.** Corinthian Capital, 1st Century B.C.

**1986.**
969 **383** 1 a. blue and red . . 10 10
970 2 a. blue and green . . 10 10
971 3 a. blue and bistre . . 10 10
972 5 a. blue & turquoise 10 10
973 10 a. blue and orange 20 15
974a 20 a. blue and purple 25 20
975a 30 a. blue and yellow 40 25
976a 50 a. blue and violet 60 35

**1986.** Jerusalem Archaeology.
977 – 40 a. green, orge & blk 30 15
978 – 60 a. brown, vio & blk 45 15
979 – 70 a. green, brn & blk 50 15
980 – 80 a. purple, bis & blk 55 20
981 – 90 a. yell, lilac & blk 60 20
982 **384** 1 s. brown, grn & blk 60 20
983a – 2 s. blue, green & blk 1·25 35
984 – 3 s. mauve, blue & blk 1·75 55
987 – 10 s. green, blue & blk 2·00 55

Designs—As T **384**: 40 a. Relief, 1st century B.C. (Second Temple); 60 a. Byzantine captial, 6th century A.D.; 3 s. Archaic Ionic capital, 1st century B.C. (Second Temple). 32 × 23 mm: 70 a. Relief from palace of Umayyid Caliphs, 8th century A.D.; 80 a. Crusader capital from Church of Ascension, Mount of Olives, 12–13th centuries; 90 a. Relief from Suleiman's Wall, 16th century A.D.; 2 s. Insignia of Sayif addin Attaz from Mameluke Academy, 14th century A.D.; 10 s. Frieze from burial cave entrance, end of Second Temple period.

**HAVE YOU READ THE NOTES AT THE BEGINNING OF THIS CATALOGUE?**
These often provide answers to the enquiries we receive.

**385.** "Balanophyllia coccinea." **387.** Microphone and Map

**386.** Sketches of Rubinstein (Pablo Picasso).

**1986.** Red Sea Corals. Multicoloured.
991. 30 a. Type **385** . . . . 60 50
992. 40 a. "Goniopora" . . 60 50
993. 50 a. "Dendronephthya" . . 60 50

**1986.** Birth Cent (1987) of Arthur Rubinstein and 5th International Rubinstein Piano Competition.
994. **386.** 60 a. multicoloured . . 1·25 1·10

**1986.** 50th Anniv. of Broadcasting from Jerusalem.
995. **387.** 70 a. multicoloured . . 1·25 1·10

**388.** Negev Bridge Monument, Beer Sheva. **389.** El-Jazzar Mosque, Akko.

**1986.** Memorial Day.
996. **388.** 20 a. multicoloured . . 45 35

**1986.** Id Al-Fitr (end of Ramadan).
997 **389** 30 a. emerald, grn & ol 55 45

**390.** Hebrew Union College, Cincinnati.

**1986.** "Ameripex '86" International Stamp Exhibition, Chicago. Jewish Institutes of Higher Learning. Multicoloured.
998. 50 a. Type **390** . . . . 85 75
999. 50 a. Yeshiva University, New York . . . . 85 75
1000. 50 a. Jewish Theology Seminary, New York 85 75

**391.** Nabi Sabalan's Tomb, Hurfeish.

**1986.** Feast of Nabi Sabalan (Druse feast).
1002. **391.** 40 a. multicoloured 70 55

**392.** Graffiti on Wall.

**1986.** Anti-Racism Campaign.
1003. **392.** 60 a. multicoloured 1·25 95

**393.** Sprinzak. **395.** Gates of Heaven, with Jerusalem above, opening to Power of Prayer.

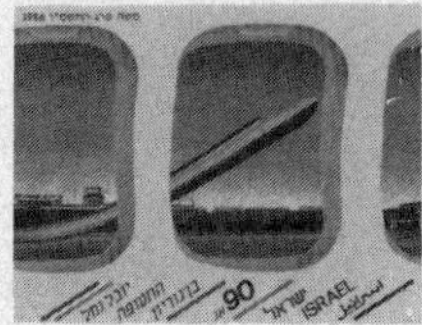

**394.** Airport through Cabin Windows.

**1986.** Birth Centenary (1985) of Joseph Sprinzak (first Speaker of Knesset).
1004 **393** 80 a. blue, green & blk 1·25 1·10

**1986.** 50th Anniv. of Ben Gurion Airport.
1005. **394.** 90 a. multicoloured 1·90 1·50

**1986.** Jewish New Year. Pages from Worms Mahzor (prayer book). Multicoloured.
1006. 20 a. Type **395** (prayers for Yom Kippur) . . 60 50
1007. 40 a. Man weighing shekel for Temple (prayer for Sheqalim, first special Sabbath) 65 65
1008. 90 a. Roses (illustration of liturgical poem) . . 85 75

**396.** David Ben Gurion.

**1986.** Birth Centenary of David Ben Gurion (Prime Minister, 1948–53 and 1955–63).
1009 **396** 1 s. bistre, brn & blk 1·75 1·50

**398.** Satellite and Isobars over Map. **399.** Basilica of the Annunciation, Nazareth.

**1986.** 50th Anniv. of Meteorological Service.
1011. **398.** 50 a. multicoloured 1·10 90

**1986.** Christmas.
1012. **399.** 70 a. multicoloured 1·40 1·25

**400.** Bronislaw Huberman (violinist and founder).

**1986.** 50th Anniv. of Israel Philharmonic Orchestra.
1013. **400.** 1 s. 50 brown, black and yellow . . 2·25 1·90
1014. – 1 s. 50 grey, black and yellow . . 2·25 1·90
Design: No. 1014, Arturo Toscanini (conductor of Orchestra's first concert, 1936).

**401.** Hume's Tawny Owl.

**1987.** Biblical Birds of Prey (2nd series). Owls. Multicoloured.

1015 30 a. Eagle owl . . . . 50 45
1016 40 a. Striated scops owl . . 65 60
1017 50 a. Barn owl . . . . 85 70
1018 80 a. Type **401** . . . . 1·50 95

**402.** Six-Day War Memorial, Ammunition Hill, Jerusalem.

**1987.** Memorial Day.

1020. **402.** 30 a. multicoloured 55 45

**403.** Emblem.

**1987.** 13th Hapoel Games.

1021. **403.** 90 a. multicoloured 1·25 1·10

**405.** Street Cleaner.

**406.** Saluki.

**1987.** "A Clean Environment".

1023. **405.** 40 a. multicoloured 55 40

**1987.** World Dog Show. Dogs of Israeli Origin. Multicoloured.

1024. 40 a. Type **406** . . . . 1·25 1·00
1025. 50 a. Sloughi . . . . 1·25 1·00
1026. 2 s. Canaan dog . . . . 2·75 2·50

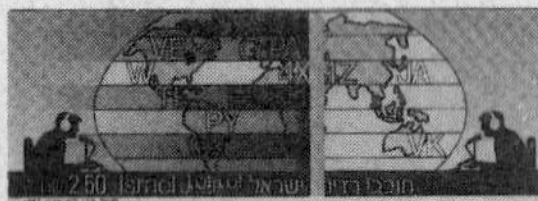
**407.** Radio Operators and Globe.

**1987.** Israel Radio Amateurs.

1027. **407.** 2 s. 50 multicoloured 3·75 3·00

**408.** Altneuschul Synagogue, Prague.

**409.** Rabbi Amiel.

**1987.** Jewish New Year. Synagogue Models in Museum of the Diaspora, Tel Aviv (1st issue). Multicoloured.

1028 30 a. Type **408** . . . . 45 45
1029 50 a. Main Synagogue, Aleppo, Syria . . 60 50
1030 60 a. Israelite Temple Florence . . . . 70 60

See also Nos. 1054/6.

**1987.** 104th Birth Anniv of Rabbi Moshe Avigdor Amiel (Chief Rabbi of Tel Aviv).

1031. **409.** 1 s. 40 multicoloured 1·75 1·25

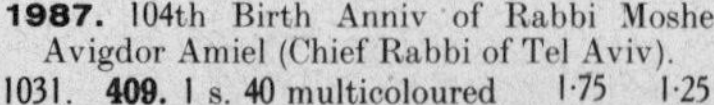

**410.** Family.

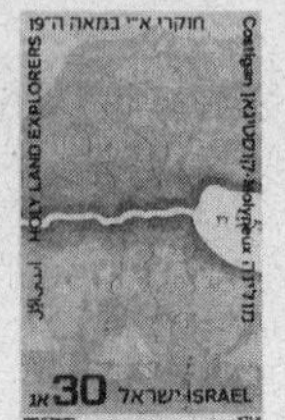
**411.** Camp (Christopher Costigan, 1835, and Thomas Howard Molyneux, 1847).

**1987.** 75th Anniv. of Kupat Holim Health Insurance Institution.

1032. **410.** 1 s. 50 multicoloured 1·75 1·50

**1987.** Holy Land Explorers. Multicoloured.

1033. 30 a. Type **411** . . . . 50 45
1034. 50 a. Map of River Jordan (William Francis Lynch, 1848) 60 50
1035. 60 a. Men in canoe (John MacGregor, 1868–9) . . 65 60

**412.** Rosen.

**413.** Computers in Industry.

**1987.** Birth Centenary of Pinhas Rosen (lawyer and politician).

1037. **412.** 80 a. multicoloured 1·00 95

**1988.** Centenary of Israeli Industry. Mult.

1038. 10 a. Type **413** . . . . 40 25
1039. 80 a. Genetic engineering 1·25 1·00
1040. 1 s. 40 Medical engineering . . . . 1·50 1·40

**414.** Corked Tap.

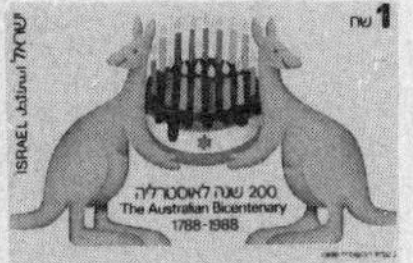
**415.** Kangaroos holding Birthday Cake.

**1988.** "Save Water".

1041. **414.** 40 a. multicoloured 70 55

**1988.** Bicentenary of Australian Settlement.

1042. **415.** 1 s. multicoloured . . 1·75 1·50

**416.** Sunflower.

**417.** Hebrew Year 5748.

**1988.** No value expressed.

1043. **416.** (30 a.) green & yell. 60 30

**1988.** Memorial Day.

1044. **417.** 40 a. multicoloured 45 40

**418.** Anne Frank and House, Amsterdam.

**419.** Jerusalem.

**1988.** 43rd Death Anniv. of Anne Frank (concentration camp victim).

1046. **418.** 60 a. multicoloured 85 70

**1988.** "Independence 40" National Stamp Exhibition, Jerusalem.

1047. **419.** 1 s. light brn. & brn. 1·40 1·25

**421.** Ein Zin Nature Reserve.

**422.** Jerusalem Lodge.

**1988.** Nature Reserves in the Negev. Mult.

1050. 40 a. Type **421** . . . . 55 50
1051. 60 a. She' zaf . . . . 70 60
1052. 70 a. Ramon . . . . 80 65

**1988.** Centenary of B'nai B'rith in Jerusalem.

1053. **422.** 70 a. multicoloured 95 85

**1988.** Jewish New Year. Synagogue Models in Museum of the Diaspora, Tel Aviv (2nd issue). As T **408**. Multicoloured.

1054. 35 a. 12th-century Kai-Feng Fu Synagogue, China . . . . . . 60 50
1055. 60 a. 17th-century Zabludow Synagogue, Poland . . . . . . 65 60
1056. 70 a. 18th-century Touro Synagogue, Newport, Rhode Island . . . . 70 65

**423.** Havivah Reik.

**1988.** Jewish World War II Underground Fighters. Multicoloured.

1057 **423** 40 a. multicoloured . . 55 50
1058 – 1s. 65 dp bl, bl & blk 2·25 1·90

DESIGN: 1 s. 65, Enzo Hayyim Sereni.

**424.** Dayan.

**425.** Burning Illustration of German Synagogue.

**1988.** 7th Death Anniv. of Moshe Dayan (soldier and politician).

1059. **424.** 40 a. multicoloured 60 50

**1988.** 50th Anniv. of "Kristallnacht" (Nazi pogrom).

1060. **425.** 80 a. multicoloured 1·25 95

**426.** Menorah and Soldiers.

**1988.** 74th Anniv. of Formation of Jewish Legion.

1061. **426.** 2 s. deep brown, brown and bistre 2·50 1·90

**427.** Avocado (fruit-growing).

**1988.** Agricultural Achievements in Israel. Multicoloured.

1062 50 a. Type **427** . . . . 75 65
1063 60 a. Easter lily (plant breeding) . . . . 90 75
1064 90 a. Plants and drip-pipe (irrigation systems) . . 1·00 90

**428** Red Sea

**429** Rabbi Maimon

**1989.** Tourism. Multicoloured.

1065 40 a. Type **428** . . . . 65 60
1066 60 a. Dead Sea . . . . 75 70
1067 70 a. Mediterranean . . 1·00 85
1068 1 s. 70 Sea of Galilee . . 1·40 1·40

**1989.** 114th Birth Anniv of Rabbi Judah Leib Maimon (writer).

1069 **429** 1 s. 70 multicoloured 2·25 2·00

**430** "Rashi" in Rashi Script

**431** Airforce Memorial, Har Tayassim

**1989.** 950th Birth Anniv of Rashi (Rabbi Solomon Ben Isaac of Troyes) (scholar).

1070 **430** 4 s. cream and brown 4·50 3·75

**1989.** Memorial Day.

1071 **431** 50 a. multicoloured . . 60 50

**432** Child

**433** Games Emblem

**1989.** 20th Anniv of Israel United Nations Children's Fund National Committee.

1072 **432** 90 a. multicoloured . . 1·25 1·00

**1989.** 13th Maccabiah Games.

1073 **433** 80 a. multicoloured . . 90 75

**434** Smoira

**436** Garganey

**1989.** Birth Centenary (1988) of Moshe Smoira (first President of Israel's Supreme Court).

1074 **434** 90 a. blue . . . . 1·25 1·00

**1989.** Ducks. Multicoloured.

1076 80 a. Type **436** . . . . 95 85
1077 80 a. Mallard . . . . 95 85
1078 80 a. Green-winged teal . . 95 85
1079 80 a. Common shelduck . . 95 85

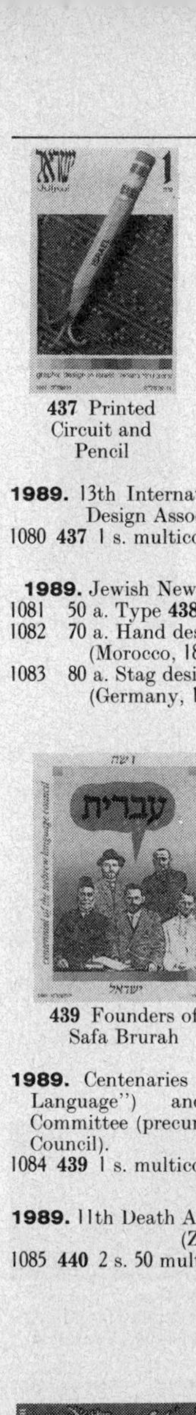

437 Printed Circuit and Pencil

438 Lion Design (Ukraine, 1921)

**1989.** 13th International Council of Graphic Design Associations Congress.
1080 **437** 1 s. multicoloured .. 1·10 1·10

**1989.** Jewish New Year. Paper-cuts. Mult.
1081 50 a. Type **438** .. .. 50 45
1082 70 a. Hand design (Morocco, 1800s) .. 65 50
1083 80 a. Stag design (Germany, 1818) .. 75 60

439 Founders of Safa Brurah

440 Rabbi Alkalai

**1989.** Centenaries of Safa Brurah ("Clear Language") and Hebrew Language Committee (precursors of Hebrew Language Council).
1084 **439** 1 s. multicoloured .. 1·10 1·10

**1989.** 11th Death Anniv of Rabbi Hai Alkalai (Zionist).
1085 **440** 2 s. 50 multicoloured 2·50 1·90

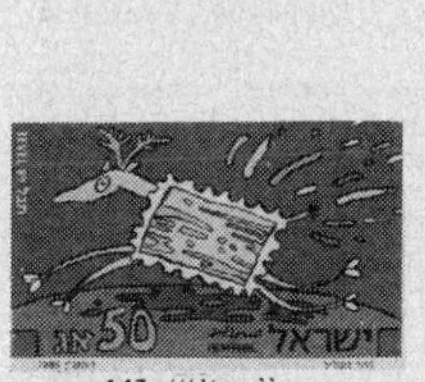

441 "Stag"

442 Postal Authority Emblem

**1989.** "Tevel 89" Youth Stamp Exhibition.
1086 **441** 50 a. multicoloured .. 55 50

**1989.** First Stamp Day.
1087 **442** 1 s. multicoloured .. 1·00 90

443 "See You Again"

444 Rebab and Carpet

**1989.** Greetings Stamps. No value expressed. Multicoloured.
1088 (–) Type **443** .. .. 40 35
1089 (–) Patched heart ("With Love") .. .. 40 35
1090 (–) Flower ("Good Luck") 40 35
See also Nos. 1111/13 and 1128/30.

**1990.** The Bedouin in Israel.
1092 **444** 1 s. 50 multicoloured 1·40 1·10

445 Traditional Dancing

446 Photograph Album and Orange

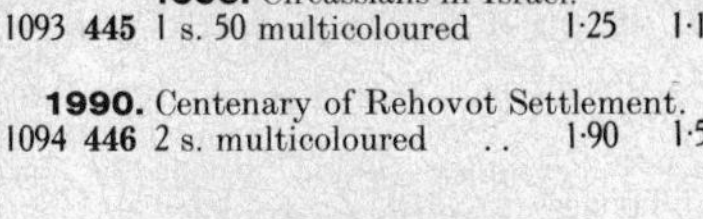

**1990.** Circassians in Israel.
1093 **445** 1 s. 50 multicoloured 1·25 1·10

**1990.** Centenary of Rehovot Settlement.
1094 **446** 2 s. multicoloured .. 1·90 1·50

447 Artillery Corps Monument, Zikhron Yaaqov

**1990.** Memorial Day.
1095 **447** 60 a. multicoloured .. 55 45

448 Ruins of Gamla, Yehudiyya

449 School, Deganya Kibbutz (Richrd Kauffmann)

**1990.** Nature Reserves (1st series). Mult.
1096 60 a. Type **448** .. .. 55 45
1097 80 a. Huleh .. .. 70 55
1098 90 a. Mt. Meron .. .. 80 70
See also Nos. 1200/2.

**1990.** Architecture.
1099b 75 a. Type **449** .. .. 30 25
1100 1 s. 10 Dining hall, Tel Yosef Kibbutz (Leopold Krahauer) .. 60 35
1101 1 s. 20 Engel House, Tel Aviv (Ze'ev Rechter) 70 45
1102 1 s. 40 Weizmann House, Rehovot (Erich Mendelsohn) .. 75 45
1103 1 s. 60 National Institutions Building, Jerusalem (Yohanan Ratner) .. .. 75 45

**1990.** Greetings Stamps. As Nos. 1088/90 but with value.
1111 55 a. As No. 1090 .. 50 35
1112a 80 a. Type **443** .. 35 25
1113a 1 s. As No. 1089 .. 55 35

451 Badges

452 Dancers

**1990.** 70th Anniv of Formation of Hagana (underground military organization).
1114 **451** 1 s. 50 multicoloured 1·40 1·10

**1990.** 8th International Folklore Festival, Haifa. Multicoloured.
1115 1 s. 90 Type **452** .. .. 1·90 1·75
1116 1 s. 90 Dancers and accordion player .. 1·90 1·75
Nos. 1115/16 were printed together, se-tenant, forming a composite design.

453 19th-century Austro-Hungarian Spice Box

454 People forming Star of David

**1990.** Jewish New Year. Silver Spice Boxes. Multicoloured.
1117 55 a. Type **453** .. .. 65 50
1118 80 a. 19th-century Italian box .. .. .. 75 65
1119 1 s. German painted and gilt box by Matheus Wolf, 1700 .. .. 90 75

**1990.** Absorption of Immigrants.
1120 **454** 1 s. 10 multicoloured 1·10 95

455 Ancient and Modern Means of Communication

457 Basketball

**1990.** Electronic Mail.
1121 **455** 1 s. 20 green, blk & yell 1·10 95

**1990.** Computer Games. Multicoloured.
1123 60 a. Type **457** .. .. 65 55
1124 60 a. Chess .. .. 65 55
1125 60 a. Racing cars .. 65 55

458 Tel Aviv-Yafo Post Office and 1948 20 m. Stamp

459 Jabotinsky

**1990.** Stamp Day.
1126 **458** 1 s. 20 multicoloured 1·10 1·00

**1990.** 50th Death Anniv of Ze'ev Jabotinsky (Zionist leader).
1127 **459** 1 s. 90 multicoloured 1·90 1·50

**1991.** Greetings Stamps. No value expressed. As T **443.** Multicoloured.
1128 (–) Birthday cake ("Happy Birthday") .. 40 30
1129 (–) Champagne bottle ("Greetings") .. 40 30
1130 (–) Envelopes ("Keep in Touch") .. .. 40 30
Nos. 1128/30 were sold at the current inland letter rate.

460 Sarah Aaronsohn (intelligence agent)

**1991.** Anniversaries. Multicoloured.
1131 1 s. 30 Type **460** (birth centenary (1990)) .. 1·00 75
1132 1 s. 30 Rahel Bluwstein (poet, 60th death anniv) 1·00 75
1133 1 s. 30 Lea Goldberg (writer and translator, 80th birth anniv) .. 1·00 75

461 Eucalyptus Tree and Hadera

**1991.** Centenary of Hadera.
1134 **461** 2 s. 50 multicoloured 2·00 1·75

462 Karate

**1991.** 14th Hapoel Games. Multicoloured.
1135 60 a. Type **462** .. .. 65 50
1136 90 a. Table tennis .. 75 65
1137 1 s. 10 Football .. 90 75

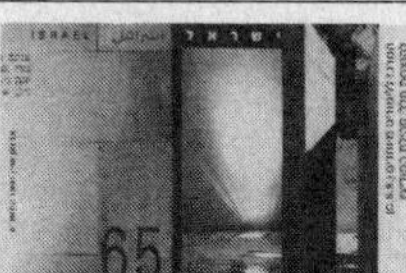

463 Intelligence Services Memorial, Centre for Special Studies, Tel Aviv

**1991.** Memorial Day.
1138 **463** 65 a. multicoloured .. 55 45

464 First (Diesel) Power Station, Tel Aviv

465 Rabbi Shimon Hakham (co-founder) and Armon Building

**1991.** Inauguration of Rutenberg Power Station. Multicoloured.
1139 70 a. Type **464** .. .. 65 45
1140 90 a. Yarden Hydro-electric Station, Naharayim .. .. 90 55
1141 1 s. 20 Rutenberg coal-fired power station, Ashqelon .. .. 1·00 70

**1991.** Centenary (1990) of Bukharim Quarter of Jerusalem.
1142 **465** 2 s. 10 multicoloured 1·50 1·25

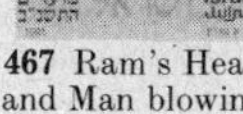

467 Ram's Head and Man blowing Shofar

468 Front Page of First Edition

**1991.** Festivals. Multicoloured.
1144 65 a. Type **467** (Jewish New Year) .. .. 65 50
1145 1 s. "Penitence Cock", father blessing children and men blowing shofars (Day of Atonement) .. .. 75 65
1146 1 s. 20 Family in booth (Festival of Tabernacles) .. .. 90 75

**1991.** 150th Anniv of "Jewish Chronicle" (weekly newspaper).
1147 **468** 1 s. 50 black, bl & red 1·40 1·10

469 Colonists and Baron Maurice de Hirsch (founder)

**1991.** Centenary of Jewish Colonization Association.
1148 **469** 1 s. 60 multicoloured 1·40 1·10

471 Cancelled 1948 5 m. Stamp

**1991.** Stamp Day.
1150 **471** 70 a. multicoloured .. 55 45

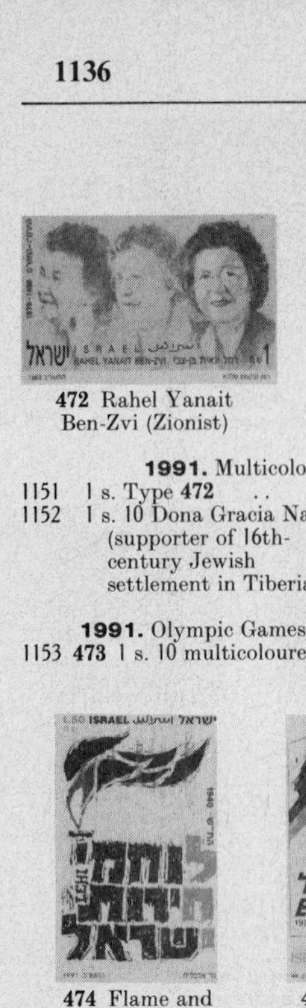

**472** Rahel Yanait Ben-Zvi (Zionist)

**473** Runner

**1991.** Multicoloured.
1151 1 s. Type **472** .. .. 75 70
1152 1 s. 10 Dona Gracia Nasi (supporter of 16th-century Jewish settlement in Tiberias) 80 75

**1991.** Olympic Games, Barcelona.
1153 **473** 1 s. 10 multicoloured 95 60

**474** Flame and Hebrew Script

**475** Southern Wing of Acre Prison

**1991.** 51st Anniv of Lehi (resistance organization).
1154 **474** 1 s. 50 multicoloured .. 1·25 1·10

**1991.** 60th Anniv of Etzel (resistance organization).
1155 **475** 1 s. 50 blk, red & grey 1·25 1·10

**476** Mozart and Score of "Don Giovanni"

**477** Anemone

**1991.** Death Bicentenary of Wolfgang Amadeus Mozart (composer).
1156 **476** 2 s. multicoloured .. 1·75 1·50

**1992.** No value expressed.
1157 **477** (–) red and green .. 30 15
No. 1157 was sold at the current inland letter rate, initially 75 a.

**478** Hanna Rovina (actress)

**479** Trees

**1992.** Multicoloured.
1158 80 a. Type **478** .. .. 50 45
1159 1 s. 30 Rivka Guber (teacher and writer) .. 65 55

**1992.** Sea of Galilee. Multicoloured.
1160 85 a. Type **479** .. .. 65 50
1161 85 a. Sailboard .. .. 65 50
1162 85 a. Fishes .. .. 65 50

**480** Palmah Emblem

**481** Samaritans praying on Mount Gerizim

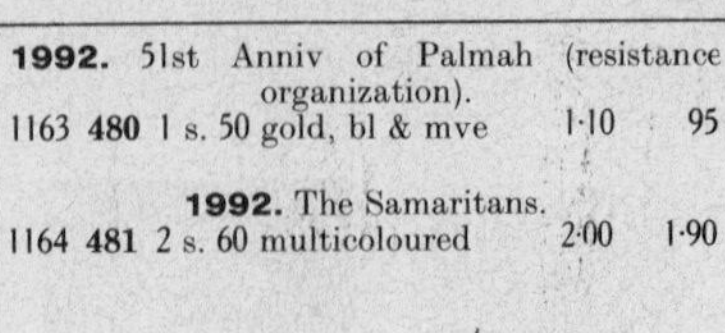

**1992.** 51st Anniv of Palmah (resistance organization).
1163 **480** 1 s. 50 gold, bl & mve 1·10 95

**1992.** The Samaritans.
1164 **481** 2 s. 60 multicoloured 2·00 1·90

**482** Border Guard Memorial, Eiron Junction (Yechiel Arad)

**1992.** Memorial Day.
1165 **482** 85 a. multicoloured .. 45 40

**483** Azulai

**484** Hayyim

**1992.** 186th Death Anniv of Rabbi Hayyim Joseph David Azulai (scholar).
1166 **483** 85 a. multicoloured .. 45 40

**1992.** 83rd Death Anniv of Rabbi Joseph Hayyim Ben Elijah.
1167 **484** 1 s. 20 multicoloured 60 45

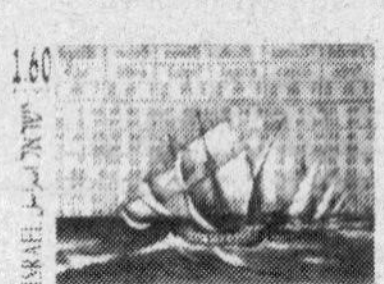

**485** "Almanach Perpetuum" and Models of Columbus's Ships

**1992.** 500th Anniv of Discovery of America by Columbus.
1168 **485** 1 s. 60 multicoloured 1·00 80

**487** Modern Locomotives, Greasing of Wheels and Blueprint of Baldwin Engine

**1992.** Cent of Jaffa–Jerusalem Railway. Mult.
1170 85 a. Type **487** .. .. 50 45
1171 1 s. Scottish locomotive, track plan at Lod, electric signalling board at Tel Aviv, semaphore arms and points at Lod 55 50
1172 1 s. 30 Diesel locomotive, interior and exterior of passenger carriages, Palestine Railways ticket and 1926 timetable .. .. 70 65
1173 1 s. 60 Motor-train, drawing of facade of Jerusalem station, platform at Lod, Jaffa station in 1900 and points at Bar-Giora station .. .. 90 70

**488** Cover of "Or-HaHayyim" ("Light of Life") (Rabbi Hayyim Benatar, 250th (1993) anniv)

**489** Leopard

**1992.** Death Anniversaries.
1175 **488** 1 s. 30 lilac, green and gold .. .. 75 65
1176 – 3 s. lilac, green & gold 1·75 1·60
DESIGN: 3 s. 19th-century drawing of Bet-El Yeshiva, Jerusalem (Rabbi Shalom Sharabi, 215th anniv).

**1992.** Zoo Animals. Multicoloured.
1177 50 a. Type **489** .. .. 35 30
1178 50 a. Indian elephant .. 35 30
1179 50 a. Chimpanzee .. 35 30
1180 50 a. Lion .. .. 35 30

**490** "Parables" (Yitzhak ben Shlomo ibn Sahula) (1st edition, Brescia, 1491)

**1992.** Jewish New Year. Centenary of Jewish National and University Library, Jerusalem. Multicoloured.
1181 85 a. Type **490** .. .. 50 45
1182 1 s. Mahzor (prayer book) (15th-century manuscript by Leon ben Yehoshua de Rossi) 65 55
1183 1 s. 20 Draft of translation by Martin Buber of Leviticus 25: 10–13 .. 75 70

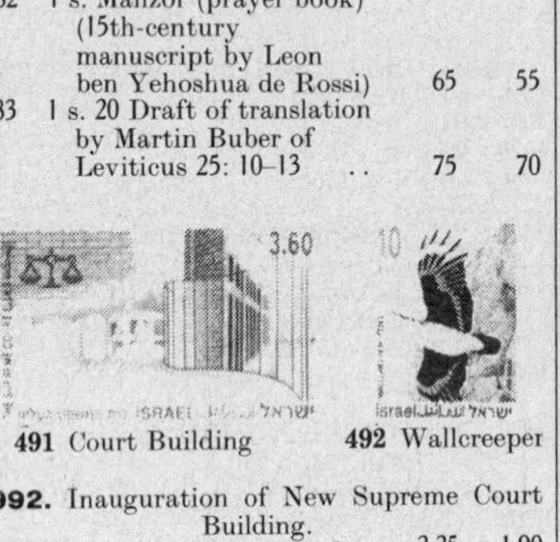

**491** Court Building

**492** Wallcreeper

**1992.** Inauguration of New Supreme Court Building.
1184 **491** 3 s. 60 multicoloured 2·25 1·90

**1992.** Songbirds. Multicoloured.
1185 10 a. Type **492** .. .. 10 10
1186 20 a. Tristram's grackle .. 10 10
1187 30 a. Pied ("White") wagtail .. .. 15 10
1188 50 a. Palestine sunbird .. 20 10
1189 85 a. Sinai rosefinch .. 35 20
1190 90 a. Barn swallows .. 40 25
1191 1 s. Trumpeter finches .. 40 25
1192 1 s. 30 Graceful prinia ("warbler") .. .. 55 35
1193 1 s. 50 Black-eared wheatear .. .. 65 40
1194 1 s. 70 Black-capped ("Common") bulbuls .. 70 45

**493** "Judah Released"

**494** European Community Emblem on Graph

**1992.** 75th Anniv of First All-Hebrew Film. Scenes from films. Multicoloured.
1195 80 a. Type **493** (first Hebrew film) .. .. 75 70
1196 2 s. 70 "Oded the Wanderer" (first Hebrew feature film) 1·50 1·40
1197 3 s. 50 "This is the Land" (first Hebrew talking film) .. .. .. 1·90 1·75

**1992.** Stamp Day. European Single Market.
1198 **494** 1 s. 50 multicoloured 85 75

**495** Begin

**496** Shrine of the Bab

**1993.** 1st Death Anniv of Menahem Begin (Prime Minister, 1977–83).
1199 **495** 80 a. multicoloured .. 45 40

**1993.** Nature Reserves (2nd series). As T **448**. Multicoloured.
1200 1 s. 20 Hof Dor .. .. 75 65
1201 1 s. 50 Nahal Ammud .. 90 75
1202 1 s. 70 Nahal Ayun .. 1·00 90

**1993.** Baha'i World Centre, Haifa.
1203 **496** 3 s. 50 multicoloured 1·90 1·75

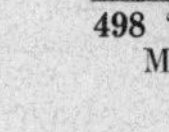

**497** Medical Corps Memorial, Carmel, Haifa (Akiva Lomnitz)

**498** "The Eye's Memory"

**1993.** Memorial Day.
1204 **497** 80 a. multicoloured .. 45 40

**1993.** Illustration of Scientific Concepts. Exhibits from the Israel National Museum of Science, Haifa (Nos. 1205/6) or the Bernard M. Bloomfield Science Museum, Jerusalem (others).
1205 80 a. Type **498** .. .. 45 40
1206 80 a. Colour mixing .. 45 40
1207 80 a. Waves .. .. 45 40
1208 80 a. Floating balls (principle of lift) .. 45 40

**499** Prisoner

**500** Hurbat Rabbi Yehuda Hassid Synagogue, Jerusalem

**1993.** 50th Anniv of Uprisings in the Ghettos and Concentration Camps.
1209 **499** 1 s. 20 black, yell & bl 70 55

**1993.** 45th Anniv of Independence.
1210 **500** 3 s. 60 multicoloured 2·10 1·90

**501** Giulio Racah

**502** Family using Crossing (Lior Abohovsky)

**1993.** Physicists. Multicoloured.
1211 80 a. Type **501** .. .. 45 40
1212 1 s. 20 Aharon Katchalsky-Katzir .. 65 55

**1993.** Road Safety. Children's Paintings. Multicoloured.
1213 80 a. Type **502** .. .. 55 50
1214 1 s. 20 Vehicles and road signs (Elinor Paz) .. 70 60
1215 1 s. 50 Road signals on "man" (Moran Dadush) 80 75

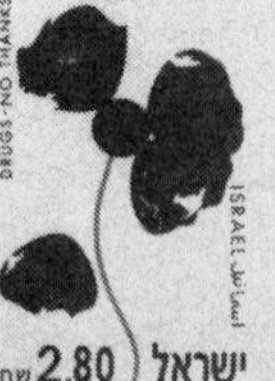

**503** Poppy

**504** Passing Baton

**1993.** Anti-drugs Campaign.
1216 **503** 2 s. 80 multicoloured 1·50 1·40

**1993.** 14th Maccabiah Games.
1217 **504** 3 s. 60 multicoloured 2·25 1·90

**505** Tree **506** Ear of Wheat

**1993.** International Day of the Elderly.
1218 **505** 80 a. multicoloured . . 40 30

**1993.** Jewish New Year. Multicoloured.
1219 80 a. Type **506** . . . . 40 30
1220 1 s. 20 Grapes . . . . 65 45
1221 1 s. 50 Olives . . . . 90 75

**507** Environmental Concerns

**1993.** Environment Year.
1222 **507** 1 s. 20 multicoloured 60 45

**508** Emblems

**1993.** 150th Anniv of B'nai B'rith (cultural and social organization).
1223 **508** 1 s. 50 multicoloured 60 45

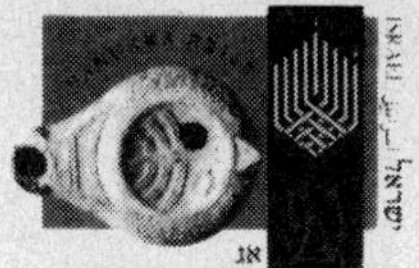

**510** Talmudic Oil Lamp

**1993.** Festival of Hanukka. Multicoloured.
1225 90 a. Type **510** . . . . 45 30
1226 1 s. 30 Hanukka lamp in shape of building . . 65 45
1227 2 s. "Lighting the Hanukka Lamp" (illustration from the "Rothschild Miscellany") . . . . 1·00 75

**511** Cover of First Issue

**1993.** Stamp Day. Centenary (1992) of "Miniature World" (children's magazine).
1228 **511** 1 s. 50 multicoloured 75 55

**512** Yellow-banded Borer ("Chlorophorus varius")

**1994.** Beetles. Multicoloured.
1229 85 a. Type **512** . . . . 40 30
1230 85 a. Copper beetle ("Potosia cuprea") . . 40 30
1231 85 a. Pied ground beetle ("Graphopterus serrator") . . . . 40 30
1232 85 a. Seven-spotted ladybird ("Coccinella septempunctata") . . 40 30

**513** Man carrying Car ("Exercise Regularly")

**1994.** Health and Well-being. Multicoloured.
1233 85 a. Type **513** . . . . 40 30
1234 1 s. 30 Blowing soap bubbles ("Don't Smoke") . . . . 65 45
1235 1 s. 60 Inspecting food through magnifying glass ("Eat Sensibly") 90 75

**514** Haffkine **515** Communications, Electronics and Computer Corps Memorial, Yehud (Claude Grundman)

**1994.** 64th Death Anniv of Dr. Mordecai Haffkine (bacteriologist).
1236 **514** 3 s. 85 multicoloured 1·90 1·50

**1994.** Memorial Day.
1237 **515** 85 a. multicoloured . . 40 30

**516** Assuta Private Hospital (Yosef Neufeld)

**1994.** International Style Architecture in Tel Aviv. Each grey, blue and green.
1238 85 a. Type **516** . . . . 40 30
1239 85 a. Co-operative workers' housing (flats with separate balconies) (Arieh Sharon) . . 40 30
1240 85 a. Citrus House (Karl Rubin) . . . . 40 30

**517** Battered Child

**1994.** "No to Violence" Campaign.
1241 **517** 3 s. 85 black and red 1·90 1·50

**518** Saul Adler

**1994.** Birth Centenary (1995) of Saul Adler (scientist).
1242 **518** 4 s. 50 multicoloured 2·25 1·75

**519** Inflating Balloon **521** Israeli Team at Munich Games, 1972, and National Committee Emblem

**520** Chemistry Class at Bialystok and Physical Education at Wolyn

**1994.** Ayalon Valley International Hot-Air Balloon Race. Multicoloured.
1243 85 a. Type **519** . . . . 40 30
1244 85 a. Balloons in air . . 40 30
1245 85 a. Balloon hovering over target (cross on ground) . . . . 40 30

**1994.** 75th Anniv of Tarbut Schools (Hebrew schools in Eastern Europe).
1246 **520** 1 s. 30 multicoloured 60 45

**1994.** Centenary of Int Olympic Committee.
1247 **521** 2 s. 25 multicoloured 1·10 85

**522** The Little Prince (book character) and Saint-Exupery

**1994.** 50th Death Anniv of Antoine de Saint-Exupery (writer and pilot).
1248 **522** 5 s. multicoloured . . 2·25 1·90

**523** "Adam and Eve" (Itai Cohen) **524** Jewish and Arab Houses merging

**1994.** Jewish New Year. Entries in the "Children and Young People draw the Bible" exhibition. Multicoloured.
1249 85 a. Type **523** . . . . 40 30
1250 1 s. 30 "Jacob's Dream" (Moran Sheinberg) . . 65 45
1251 1 s. 60 "Moses in the Bulrushes" (Carmit Crspi) . . . . . . 85 75

**1994.** Israeli–Palestinian Peace Process.
1253 **524** 90 a. multicoloured . . 45 35

**525** Silicat Brick Factory, Tel Aviv (Fourth Aliya, 1924–28) **526** Road to Peace

**1994.** Aliyot (immigration of Jews to Israel). Multicoloured.
1254 1 s. 40 Settlers and booklet distributed in Poland to encourage Jews to settle the Valley of Jezreel (Third Aliya, 1919–23) . . 60 50
1255 1 s. 70 Type **525** . . . . 85 60

**1994.** Signing of Israel–Jordan Peace Treaty.
1256 **526** 3 s. 50 multicoloured 1·50 1·10

**527** Ford Model "T" Converted Car, 1920s

**1994.** Public Transport. Multicoloured.
1257 90 a. Type **527** . . . . 40 30
1258 1 s. 40 "White Super" bus, 1940s . . . . 60 45
1259 1 s. 70 Leyland "Royal Tiger" bus, 1960s 70 55

**528** Hanukka Lamp from Mazagan, Morocco

**1994.** Festival of Hanukka.
1260 **528** 1 s. 50 multicoloured 65 50

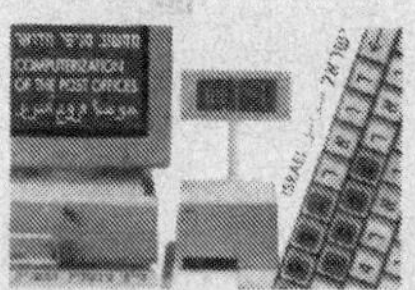

**529** Computerized Post Office Counter

**1994.** Stamp Day. Computerization of the Post Office.
1261 **529** 3 s. multicoloured . . 1·25 95

**530** Breaking Dreyfus's Sword

**1994** Centenary of "The Dreyfus Affair" (conviction for treason of French Army Captain Alfred Dreyfus).
1262 **530** 4 s. 10 multicoloured 1·75 1·25

**531** "Serpentine" (Itzhak Danziger), Yarkon Park, Tel Aviv

**1995.** Outdoor Sculptures. Multicoloured.
1263 90 a. Type **531** . . . . 40 30
1264 1 s. 40 "Stabile" (Alexander Calder), Mount Herzl, Jerusalem 60 45
1265 1 s. 70 Hall of Remembrance Gate (David Palombo), Yad Vashem, Jerusalem . . 70 55

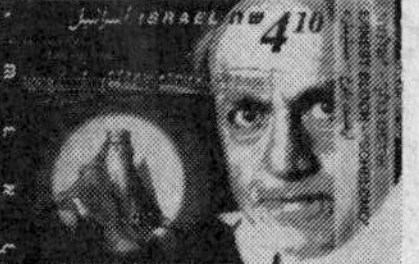

**532** Score from "Schelomo", Solomon (after Dore) and Ernest Bloch

**1995.** Composers (1st series). Multicoloured.
1266 4 s. 10 Type **532** .. .. 1·75 1·25
1267 4 s. 10 Score from "Jeremiah", Jeremiah (after Gustave Dore) and Leonard Bernstein 1·75 1·25
See also Nos. 1272/3, 1330 and 1338.

**533** Ordnance Corps Memorial, Netanya

**1995.** Memorial Day.
1268 **533** 1 s. multicoloured .. 40 30

**534** Liberation of Dachau Concentration Camp

**1995.** 50th Anniv of End of Second World War.
1269 **534** 1 s. multicoloured .. 40 30

**535** U.N. Projects

**1995.** 50th Anniv of U.N.O.
1271 **535** 1 s. 50 multicoloured 65 50

**1995.** Composers (2nd series). As T **532**. Multicoloured.
1272 2 s. 40 Arnold Schoenberg and scene from "Moses and Aaron" .. .. 1·00 75
1273 2 s. 40 Darius Milhaud and score and scene from opera "David" .. 1·00 75

**537** Canoeist

**1995.** 15th Hapoel Games.
1275 **537** 1 s. multicoloured .. 40 30

**538** Box Kite and Cody "War" Kite

**1995.** Kites. Multicoloured.
1276 1 s. Type **538** .. .. 40 30
1277 1 s. Bird-shaped, hexagonal "Tiara" and rhombic "Eddy" kites 40 30
1278 1 s. Multiple rhombic and triangular "Deltic" aerobatic kites .. 40 30
Nos. 1276/8 were printed together, se-tenant, forming a composite design.

**539** "Stars in a Bucket" (Anda Amir-Pinkerfeld, illus. Hava Nathan)

**1995.** Children's Books. Designs illustrating poems. Multicoloured.
1279 1 s. Type **539** .. .. 40 30
1280 1 s. 50 "Hurry, Run, Dwarfs" (Miriam Yallan-Stekelis, illus. Tirzah Tanny) .. 65 50
1281 1 s. 80 "Daddy's Big Umbrella" (Levin Kipnis, illus. Pazit Meller-Dushi) .. .. 75 55

**540** Container Ship

**1995.** 50th Anniv of Zim Navigation Company.
1282 **540** 4 s. 40 multicoloured 1·90 1·40

**541** Elijah's Chair (German, 1768)

**1995.** Jewish New Year. Multicoloured.
1283 1 s. Type **541** (circumcision) .. 40 30
1284 1 s. 50 Velvet bag for prayer shawl (Moroccan, 1906) (Bar-Mitzvah) .. 65 50
1285 1 s. 80 Marriage stone (from Bingen Synagogue, Germany, 1700) 75 55

**542** King David playing Harp (mosaic pavement, Gaza Synagogue)

**1995.** 3000th Anniv of City of David (Jerusalem). Multicoloured.
1286 1 s. Type **542** .. .. 40 30
1287 1 s. 50 Illustration of Jerusalem from 19th-century map by Rabbi Pinie .. .. 65 50
1288 1 s. 80 Aerial view of Knesset (parliament) .. 75 55

**543** "Sheep" (Menashe Kadishman)

**1995.** 75th Anniv of Veterinary Services.
1289 **543** 4 s. 40 multicoloured 1·90 1·40

**544** Rabin

**1995.** Yitzhak Rabin (Prime Minister) Commemoration.
1290 **544** 5 s. multicoloured .. 2·10 1·60

**545** Putting out Fire

**1995.** 70th Anniv of Fire and Rescue Service. Multicoloured.
1291 1 s. Type **545** .. .. 40 30
1292 1 s. Cutting crash victim out of car .. .. 40 30

**546** Miniature Silver Menorah (Zusia Ejbuszyc)

**1995.** Festival of Hanukka.
1293 **546** 1 s. 40 multicoloured 60 45

**547** Flying Model Plane

**1995.** Stamp Day.
1294 **547** 1 s. 80 multicoloured 75 55

**548** Film Stars

**550** Cycling

**1995.** Centenary of Motion Pictures.
1295 **548** 4 s. 40 multicoloured 1·90 1·40
The stars depicted are the Marx Brothers, Simone Signoret, Peter Sellers, Danny Kaye and Al Jolson.

**1996.** Sport. Multicoloured.
1301 1 s. 05 Type **550** .. .. 40 30
1304 1 s. 90 Paragliding .. 70 55
1305 2 s. Volleyball .. .. 75 55

**552** Cow and Computer

**553** Abraham Shlonsky (poet)

**1996.** 70th Anniv of Israel Dairy Cattle Breeders' Association.
1311 **552** 4 s. 65 multicoloured 1·75 1·25

**1996.** Modern Hebrew Writers. Mult.
1313 40 a. Type **553** .. .. 15 10
1314 40 a. Joseph Brenner (novelist and essayist) 15 10
1315 40 a. Judah Gordon (poet) 15 10
1316 40 a. Haim Hazaz (novelist) .. .. 15 10
1317 40 a. Devorah Baron (novelist) .. .. 15 10
1318 40 a. Yehuda Burla (novelist) .. .. 15 10
1319 40 a. Micha Berdyczewski (novelist and historian) 15 10
1320 40 a. Yaakov Shabtai (novelist) .. .. 15 10
1321 40 a. Isaac Peretz (novelist) .. .. 15 10
1322 40 a. Nathan Alterman (poet) .. .. 15 10
1323 40 a. Saul Tchernichowsky (poet) .. .. 15 10
1324 40 a. Amir Gilboa (poet) 15 10
1325 40 a. Yokheved Bat-Miriam (poet) .. 15 10
1326 40 a. Mendele Sefarim (novelist) .. .. 15 10

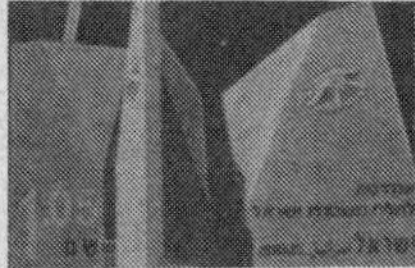

**554** Fallen Policemen Monument, National Police Academy, Kiryat Ata (Yosef Assa)

**1996.** Memorial Day.
1327 **554** 1 s. 05 multicoloured 40 30

**555** Circuit Boards

**556** Emblem and Old Photographs

**1996.** 75th Anniv of Manufacturers' Assn.
1328 **555** 1 s. 05 multicoloured 40 30

**1996.** Centenary of Metulla.
1329 **556** 1 s. 90 multicoloured 70 55

**1996.** Composers (3rd series). As T **532**. Multicoloured.
1330 4 s. 65 Gustav Mahler, score from "Resurrection Symphony" and creation of light .. 1·75 1·25

**557** Plant growing in Cracked Earth

**558** Fencing

**1996.** 50th Anniv of the 11 Negev Settlements.
1331 **557** 1 s. 05 multicoloured 40 30

**1996.** Olympic Games, Atlanta. Mult.
1332 1 s. 05 Type **558** .. .. 40 30
1333 1 s. 60 Pole vaulting .. 60 45
1334 1 s. 90 Wrestling .. 70 55

**559** Jaffa Orange Tree and Citrus Fruit

**1996.** Israeli Fruit Production. Mult.
1335 1 s. 05 Type **559** .. .. 40 30
1336 1 s. 60 Grape vine, avocado, date, sharon fruit and mango .. 60 45
1337 1 s. 90 Star fruit plant and exotic fruit .. .. 70 55

**1996.** Composers (4th series). As T **532**. Multicoloured.
1338 4 s. 65 Felix Mendelssohn, Prophet Elijah (after Albrecht Durer) and score from oratorio "Elijah" .. .. 1·75 1·25

**560** Road Systems

**1996.** 75th Anniv of Public Works Department.
1339 **560** 1 s. 05 multicoloured 40 30

**561** New Year

**1996.** Jewish Festivals. Paintings by Sahar Pick. Multicoloured.

| | | | |
|---|---|---|---|
| 1340 | 1 s. 05 Type **561** .. .. | 40 | 30 |
| 1341 | 1 s. 60 Booth decoration (Festival of Tabernacles) .. .. | 60 | 45 |
| 1342 | 1 s. 90 Pulpit (Simchat Torah Festival) .. | 70 | 55 |

**562** Herzl looking out at David's Tower (wall hanging)

**1996.** Centenary of 1st Zionist Congress, Basel, Switzerland.

| | | | |
|---|---|---|---|
| 1343 | **562** 4 s. 65 multicoloured | 1·75 | 1·25 |

**563** Lighted Candles

**1996.** Festival of Hanukkah. Self-adhesive.

| | | | |
|---|---|---|---|
| 1345 | **563** 2 s. 50 multicoloured | 95 | 70 |

OFFICIAL STAMPS

**בול שרות**

(O 18.)

**1951.** As Nos. 41 etc but colours changed. Optd with Type O 18.

| | | | |
|---|---|---|---|
| O54 | 5 pr. mauve .. .. | 10 | 10 |
| O55 | 15 pr. red .. .. | 10 | 10 |
| O56 | 30 pr. blue .. .. | 10 | 10 |
| O57 | 40 pr. brown .. .. | 20 | 15 |

POSTAGE DUE STAMPS

**דמי דאר**

(D **3.**)

**1948.** As T **1** optd. with Type D **3.**

| | | | |
|---|---|---|---|
| D 10. | **1.** 3 m. orange on yellow.. | 1·90 | 1·00 |
| D 11. | 5 m. green on yellow .. | 1·90 | 1·25 |
| D 12. | 10 m. mauve on yellow | 6·25 | 3·25 |
| D 13. | 20 m. blue on yellow .. | 19·00 | 10·50 |
| D 14. | 50 m. brown on yellow | 75·00 | 60·00 |

D **9.**

D **30.**

**1949.**

| | | | |
|---|---|---|---|
| D 27. | D **9.** 2 pr. orange .. .. | 15 | 10 |
| D 28. | 5 pr. violet .. .. | 35 | 15 |
| D 29. | 10 pr. green .. .. | 20 | 10 |
| D 30. | 20 pr. red .. .. | 25 | 10 |
| D 31. | 30 pr. blue .. .. | 40 | 25 |
| D 32. | 50 pr. brown .. | 65 | 55 |

**1952.**

| | | | |
|---|---|---|---|
| D 73. | D **30.** 5 pr. brown .. .. | 10 | 10 |
| D 74. | 10 pr. blue .. .. | 10 | 10 |
| D 75. | 20 pr. purple .. | 10 | 10 |
| D 76. | 30 pr. black .. .. | 10 | 10 |
| D 77. | 40 pr. green .. .. | 10 | 10 |
| D 78. | 50 pr. sepia .. | 10 | 10 |
| D 79. | 60 pr. violet .. | 10 | 10 |
| D 80. | 100 pr. red .. .. | 15 | 10 |
| D 81. | 250 pr. blue .. .. | 25 | 15 |

# ITALIAN COLONIES Pt. 8

GENERAL ISSUES

100 centesimi = 1 lira.

**1932.** As Garibaldi stamps of Italy, but inscr "POSTE COLONIALI ITALIANE".

| | | | | |
|---|---|---|---|---|
| 1 | – | 10 c. green (post.) .. | 1·40 | 3·75 |
| 2 | 128 | 20 c. red .. | 1·40 | 3·75 |
| 3 | – | 25 c. green .. | 1·40 | 3·75 |
| 4 | 128 | 30 c. green .. | 1·40 | 3·75 |
| 5 | – | 50 c. red .. | 1·40 | 3·75 |
| 6 | – | 75 c. red .. | 1·40 | 3·75 |
| 7 | – | 1 l. 25 c. blue .. | 1·40 | 3·75 |
| 8 | – | 1 l. 75 c.+25 c. blue .. | 2·75 | 8·00 |
| 9 | – | 2 l. 55 c.+50 c. sepia .. | 2·75 | 8·00 |
| 10 | – | 5 l.+1 l. blue .. | 2·75 | 8·00 |
| 11 | 130 | 50 c. red (air) .. | 1·40 | 4·25 |
| 12 | – | 80 c. green .. | 1·40 | 4·25 |
| 13 | 130 | 1 l.+25 c. sepia .. | 3·50 | 8·00 |
| 14 | – | 2 l.+50 c. sepia .. | 3·50 | 8·00 |
| 15 | – | 5 l.+1 l. sepia .. | 3·50 | 8·00 |

**1932.** Dante stamps of Italy (colours changed) optd **COLONIE ITALIANE**.

| | | | | |
|---|---|---|---|---|
| 18. | – | 10 c. slate (postage) .. | 20 | 45 |
| 19. | – | 15 c. sepia .. | 20 | 45 |
| 20. | – | 20 c. green .. | 20 | 35 |
| 21. | – | 25 c. green .. | 20 | 35 |
| 22. | – | 30 c. brown .. | 20 | 60 |
| 23. | – | 50 c. blue .. | 20 | 15 |
| 24. | – | 75 c. red .. | 50 | 80 |
| 25. | – | 1 l. 25 c. blue .. | 50 | 75 |
| 26. | – | 1 l. 75 c. violet .. | 60 | 1·40 |
| 27. | – | 2 l. 75 c. orange .. | 60 | 1·40 |
| 28. | – | 5 l.+2 l. olive .. | 60 | 1·40 |
| 29. | 124. | 10 l.+2 l. 50 c. blue .. | 60 | 1·40 |
| 30. | 125. | 50 c. slate (air) .. | 50 | 1·10 |
| 31. | – | 1 l. blue .. | 50 | 1·10 |
| 32. | – | 3 l. green .. | 90 | 1·90 |
| 33. | – | 5 l. sepia .. | 90 | 1·90 |
| 34. | 125. | 7 l. 70 c.+2 l. red .. | 90 | 1·90 |
| 35. | – | 10 l.+2 l. 50 c. orange .. | 90 | 1·90 |
| 36. | 127. | 100 l. sepia and green .. | 10·00 | 20·00 |

No. 36 is inscribed instead of overprinted.

9. Ploughing.

10. Savoia Marchetti S-55X Flying Boat.

**1933.** 50th Anniv of Foundation of Colony of Eritrea.

| | | | | |
|---|---|---|---|---|
| 37 | 9 | 10 c. brown (postage) .. | 2·25 | 3·50 |
| 38 | – | 20 c. purple .. | 2·25 | 3·50 |
| 39 | – | 25 c. green .. | 2·25 | 2·50 |
| 40 | 9 | 50 c. violet .. | 2·25 | 2·50 |
| 41 | – | 75 c. red .. | 2·25 | 5·50 |
| 42 | – | 1 l. 25 blue .. | 2·25 | 5·50 |
| 43 | 9 | 2 l. 75 red .. | 4·50 | 9·00 |
| 44 | – | 5 l.+2 l. green .. | 6·50 | 18·00 |
| 45 | – | 10 l.+2 l. brown .. | 6·50 | 18·00 |
| 46 | – | 50 c. brown (air) .. | 2·25 | 4·50 |
| 47 | – | 1 l. black .. | 2·25 | 4·50 |
| 48 | 10 | 3 l. red .. | 2·75 | 8·00 |
| 49 | | 5 l. brown .. | 2·75 | 8·00 |
| 50 | – | 7 l. 70+2 l. green .. | 6·50 | 16·00 |
| 51 | 10 | 10 l.+2 l. 50 blue .. | 6·50 | 16·00 |
| 52 | – | 50 l. violet .. | 6·50 | 16·00 |

DESIGNS—VERT: (Postage): 20, 75 c., 5 l. Camel transport. 25 c., 1 l. 25, 10 l. Lioness with star on left shoulder (Arms). HORIZ. (Air): 50 c., 1 l., 7 l. 70, Eagle. 50 l. Savoia Marchetti S-55X flying boat over map of Eritrea.

11. Agricultural Implements.

13. Macchi Castoldi MC-72 Seaplane.

**1933.** 10th Anniv. of Fascist March on Rome.

(a) Postage.

| | | | | |
|---|---|---|---|---|
| 53. | 11. | 5 c. orange .. | 2·50 | 3·75 |
| 54. | – | 25 c. green .. | 2·50 | 3·75 |
| 55. | – | 50 c. violet .. | 2·50 | 3·75 |
| 56. | 11. | 75 c. red .. | 2·50 | 5·00 |
| 57. | – | 1 l. 25 blue .. | 2·50 | 5·00 |
| 58. | – | 1 l. 75 red .. | 2·50 | 6·00 |
| 59. | 11. | 2 l. 75 blue .. | 2·50 | 7·50 |
| 60. | – | 5 l. black .. | 4·00 | 9·00 |
| 61. | – | 10 l. blue .. | 4·00 | 9·50 |
| 62. | – | 25 l. olive .. | 5·00 | 12·00 |

DESIGNS—HORIZ: 50 c., 1 l. 75, 10 l. Tractor. VERT: 25 c., 1 l. 25, 5 l. Arab and camel; 25 l. Soldier.

(b) Air.

| | | | | |
|---|---|---|---|---|
| 63. | 13. | 50 c. brown .. | 3·00 | 6·00 |
| 64. | – | 75 c. purple .. | 3·00 | 6·00 |
| 65. | 13. | 1 l. sepia .. | 3·00 | 6·00 |
| 66. | – | 3 l. green .. | 3·00 | 11·00 |
| 67. | 13. | 10 l. violet .. | 3·00 | 11·00 |
| 68. | – | 12 l. blue .. | 3·00 | 11·00 |
| 69. | – | 20 l. green .. | 5·00 | 15·00 |
| 70. | – | 50 l. blue .. | 7·00 | 17·00 |

DESIGNS—HORIZ: 75 c., 3, 12 l. Savoia Marchetti S-71 airplane. VERT: 20 l. Pilot swinging propeller. 50 l. Propeller.

15.

16. Hailing Marina Fiat MF.5 Flying Boat.

**1934.** 15th Milan Exhibition.

| | | | | |
|---|---|---|---|---|
| 71. | 15. | 20 c. red .. | 40 | 1·50 |
| 72. | | 30 c. green .. | 40 | 1·50 |
| 73. | | 50 c. black .. | 40 | 1·50 |
| 74. | | 1 l. 25 blue .. | 40 | 1·50 |

**1934.** Air. Honouring the Duke of the Abruzzi (explorer).

| | | | | |
|---|---|---|---|---|
| 75 | 16 | 25 l. black .. | 12·00 | 45·00 |

17. Scoring a Goal.

18. Marina Fiat MF.5 Flying Boat over Stadium.

**1934.** World Football Championship.

| | | | | |
|---|---|---|---|---|
| 76. | 17. | 10 c. green (postage) .. | 6·00 | 14·00 |
| 77. | | 50 c. violet .. | 15·00 | 10·00 |
| 78. | | 1 l. 25 blue .. | 15·00 | 35·00 |
| 79. | – | 5 l. brown .. | 19·00 | 60·00 |
| 80. | – | 10 l. blue .. | 19·00 | 60·00 |

DESIGN—VERT: 5, 10 l. Fascist salute before kick-off.

| | | | | |
|---|---|---|---|---|
| 81. | 18. | 50 c. brown (air) .. | 5·00 | 10·00 |
| 82. | | 75 c. purple .. | 5·00 | 10·00 |
| 83. | – | 5 l. black .. | 12·00 | 32·00 |
| 84. | – | 10 l. red .. | 12·00 | 32·00 |
| 85. | 18. | 15 l. red .. | 12·00 | 32·00 |
| 86. | – | 25 l. green .. | 12·00 | 32·00 |
| 87. | – | 50 l. green .. | 12·00 | 32·00 |

DESIGNS—VERT: 5, 10, 25 l. "Saving a goal". HORIZ: 50 l. Giant football and Marina Fiat MF.5 flying boat.

EXPRESS STAMPS

**1932.** Air. As Garibaldi stamps of Italy.

| | | | | |
|---|---|---|---|---|
| E16 | E 131 | 2 l. 25+1 l. black and violet .. | 3·50 | 8·00 |
| E17 | | 4 l. 50+1 l. 50 green and brown .. | 3·50 | 8·00 |

# ITALIAN EAST AFRICA Pt. 8

Italian Empire in East Africa comprising Eritrea, Ethiopia and It. Somaliland constituted by Royal Decree of 1 June 1936. Occupied by British Forces 1942–43 (see BRITISH OCCUPATION OF ITALIAN COLONIES (MIDDLE EAST FORCES) in Volume 3).

100 centesimi = 1 lira.

1. Grant's Gazelle.

2. R. Nile Statue and Lake Tsana.

**1938.**

| | | | | |
|---|---|---|---|---|
| 1 | 1 | 2 c. red .. | 20 | 70 |
| 2 | A | 5 c. brown .. | 25 | 20 |
| 3 | B | 7½ c. violet .. | 40 | 1·10 |
| 4 | 2 | 10 c. brown .. | 25 | 20 |
| 5 | C | 15 c. green .. | 25 | 35 |
| 6 | B | 20 c. red .. | 25 | 15 |
| 7 | D | 25 c. green .. | 25 | 15 |
| 8 | 1 | 30 c. brown .. | 35 | 60 |
| 9 | A | 35 c. blue .. | 70 | 1·60 |
| 10 | B | 50 c. violet .. | 25 | 10 |
| 11 | C | 75 c. red .. | 45 | 45 |
| 12 | D | 1 l. green .. | 30 | 10 |
| 13 | B | 1 l. 25 blue .. | 45 | 35 |
| 14 | 2 | 1 l. 75 orange .. | 9·00 | 10 |
| 15 | A | 2 l. red .. | 65 | 40 |
| 16 | D | 2 l. 55 brown .. | 3·50 | 6·50 |
| 17 | 1 | 3 l. 70 violet .. | 16·00 | 9·50 |
| 18 | C | 5 l. blue .. | 1·40 | 65 |
| 19 | A | 10 l. red .. | 5·50 | 3·25 |
| 20 | 2 | 20 l. green .. | 3·50 | 2·50 |

DESIGN—VERT: A, Italian eagle and Lion of Judah; B, Profile of King Emmanuel III; C, Soldier implanting Fascist emblem. HORIZ: D, Shadows on road.

5. Mussolini Monument and Mt. Amba Aradam.

**1938.** Air.

| | | | | |
|---|---|---|---|---|
| 21 | E | 25 c. green (air) .. | 70 | 1·75 |
| 22 | 5 | 50 c. brown .. | 22·00 | 10 |
| 23 | F | 60 c. red .. | 70 | 2·25 |
| 24 | E | 75 c. brown .. | 1·25 | 1·50 |
| 25 | G | 1 l. blue .. | 30 | 10 |
| 26 | 5 | 1 l. 50 violet .. | 35 | 20 |
| 27 | F | 2 l. blue .. | 35 | 40 |
| 28 | E | 3 l. red .. | 55 | 1·25 |
| 29 | G | 5 l. brown .. | 1·50 | 1·60 |
| 30 | 5 | 10 l. purple .. | 2·50 | 2·25 |
| 31 | E | 25 l. blue .. | 4·50 | 3·25 |

DESIGNS—HORIZ: E, Savoia Marchetti S-73 airplane, rock sculpture of eagle and Mt. Amba Aradam; F, Savoia Marchetti S-73 airplane over Lake Tsana. VERT: G, Bateleur.

9. Statue of Augustus.

10. Eagle and Serpent.

**1938.** Birth Bimillenary of Augustus the Great.

| | | | | |
|---|---|---|---|---|
| 36. | 9. | 5 c. brown (postage) .. | 10 | 60 |
| 37. | – | 10 c. red .. | 10 | 60 |
| 38. | 9. | 25 c. green .. | 40 | 40 |
| 39. | – | 50 c. violet .. | 40 | 20 |
| 40. | 9. | 75 c. red .. | 40 | 1·40 |
| 41. | – | 1 l. 25 blue .. | 40 | 1·40 |

DESIGN: 10 c., 50 c., 1 l. 25, Statue of Goddess of Abundance.

| | | | | |
|---|---|---|---|---|
| 42. | 10. | 50 c. brown (air) .. | 30 | 60 |
| 43. | | 1 l. violet .. | 40 | 1·60 |

11. Ethiopian Canoe.

**1940.** Naples Exn.

| | | | | |
|---|---|---|---|---|
| 44. | 11. | 5 c. brown (postage) .. | 10 | 35 |
| 45. | – | 10 c. orange .. | 10 | 35 |
| 46. | – | 25 c. green .. | 45 | 85 |
| 47. | 11. | 50 c. violet .. | 45 | 85 |
| 48. | – | 75 c. red .. | 45 | 1·40 |
| 49. | – | 1 l. 25 blue .. | 45 | 1·50 |
| 50 | – | 2 l.+75 c. red .. | 45 | 2·25 |

DESIGNS—VERT. 10 c., 75 c., 2 l. Soldier. 25 c., 1 l. 25, Allegory of Italian Conquest of Ethiopia.

| | | | | |
|---|---|---|---|---|
| 51. | | 50 c. grey (air) .. | 30 | 1·50 |
| 52. | | 1 l. violet .. | 30 | 1·50 |
| 53. | | 2 l.+75 c. blue .. | 55 | 2·25 |
| 54. | | 5 l.+2 l. brown .. | 55 | 2·25 |

DESIGNS—VERT. 50 c., 2 l. Savoia Marchetti S-66 flying boat over tractor. HORIZ: Savoia Marchetti S.M.83 airplane over city.

15. Hitler and Mussolini.

**1941.** Axis Commemoration.

| | | | |
|---|---|---|---|
| 55 | 15 | 5 c. yellow (postage) .. | 20 |
| 56 | | 10 c. brown .. | 20 |
| 57 | | 20 c. black .. | 45 |
| 58 | | 25 c. green .. | 45 |
| 59 | | 50 c. purple .. | 45 |
| 60 | | 75 c. red .. | 45 |
| 61 | | 1 l. 25 blue .. | 45 |
| 62 | | 1 l. blue (air) .. | 12·00 |
| 63 | | 1 l. blue .. | 1·10 |

In No. 62 the "1 lira" tablet is in the centre; in No. 63 it is in the lower left corner.

EXPRESS LETTER STAMPS

E 7. Plough and Native Huts.

**1938.** Air.

| | | | | |
|---|---|---|---|---|
| E32 | E 7 | 2 l. blue .. | 35 | 90 |
| E33 | | 2 l. 50 brown .. | 45 | 1·75 |

E 8. King Victor Emmanuel III.

**1938.**

| | | | | |
|---|---|---|---|---|
| E34 | E 8 | 1 l. 25 green .. | 35 | 45 |
| E35 | | 2 l. 50 red (inscr "EXPRES") .. | 55 | 3·75 |

POSTAGE DUE STAMPS

**1941.** Nos. D 395/407 of Italy optd. **A.O.I.**

| | | | |
|---|---|---|---|
| D 64. | D 141. | 5 c. brown .. | 35 |
| D 65. | | 10 c. blue .. | 35 |
| D 66. | | 20 c. red .. | 85 |
| D 67. | | 25 c. green .. | 85 |
| D 68. | | 30 c. orange .. | 1·90 |
| D 69. | | 40 c. brown .. | 2·25 |
| D 70. | | 50 c. violet .. | 2·25 |
| D 71. | | 60 c. blue .. | 4·00 |
| D 72. | D 142. | 1 l. orange .. | 16·00 |
| D 73. | | 2 l. green .. | 16·00 |
| D 74. | | 5 l. violet .. | 16·00 |
| D 75. | | 10 l. blue .. | 16·00 |
| D 76. | | 20 l. red .. | 16·00 |

# ITALIAN OCCUPATION OF CEPHALONIA AND ITHACA Pt. 3

Two of the Greek Ionian Islands off the W. coast of Greece, under Italian occupation in 1941.

100 lepta = 1 drachma.

**1941.** Stamps of Greece optd. **ITALIA Occupazione Militare Italiana isole Cefalonia e Itaca** across a pair of stamps

**PRICES.** Prices are for unsevered pairs. Single stamps from severed pairs are worth ⅓ unused and ½ used prices.

(a) On postage stamps of 1937.

| | | | | |
|---|---|---|---|---|
| 1. | 86. | 5 l. blue and brown .. | 35 | 65 |
| 2. | – | 10 l. brown and blue .. | 30 | 60 |
| 3. | – | 20 l. green and black .. | 30 | 60 |
| 4. | – | 40 l. black and green .. | 30 | 60 |
| 5. | – | 50 l. black and brown | 30 | 60 |
| 6. | – | 80 l. brown and violet | 60 | 1·10 |
| 7. | 89. | 1 d. green .. | 10·00 | 9·00 |
| 8. | 89a. | 1 d. 50 green .. | 11·00 | 7·50 |
| 9. | – | 2 d. blue .. | 30 | 60 |
| 10. | – | 5 d. red .. | 1·50 | 1·50 |
| 11. | – | 6 d. brown .. | 2·00 | 2·00 |
| 12. | | 7 d. brown .. | 2·75 | 2·75 |
| 13. | 89. | 8 d. blue .. | 12·00 | 10·00 |
| 14. | – | 10 d. brown .. | 5·50 | 4·00 |
| 15. | – | 15 d. green .. | 9·50 | 7·50 |
| 16. | – | 25 d. blue .. | 18·00 | 14·00 |
| 17. | 89a. | 30 d. red .. | 50·00 | 32·00 |

(b) On air stamps of 1938 and 1935.

| | | | | |
|---|---|---|---|---|
| 18. | D20. | 50 l. brown (No. 521) .. | 25·00 | 32·00 |
| 19. | 79. | 1 d. red .. | 4·50 | 4·50 |
| 20. | – | 2 d. blue .. | 2·50 | 2·50 |
| 21. | – | 5 d. mauve .. | 1·50 | 1·50 |
| 22. | – | 7 d. blue .. | 5·50 | 5·50 |
| 23. | – | 25 d. red .. | 35·00 | 30·00 |
| 24. | – | 30 d. green .. | 35·00 | 25·00 |
| 25. | – | 50 d. mauve .. | £275 | £150 |
| 26. | – | 100 d. brown .. | £150 | 75·00 |

(c) On Charity Tax stamps.

| | | | | |
|---|---|---|---|---|
| 27. | D20. | 10 l. red (No. C 498) .. | 2·00 | 2·00 |
| 28. | C96. | 10 l. red .. | 2·00 | 2·00 |
| 29. | | 50 l. green (No. C 525) | 55 | 55 |
| 30. | | 50 l. green (No. C 554) | 55 | |
| 31. | | 1 d. blue (No. C526) .. | 5·50 | 5·00 |

## ITALIAN OCCUPATION OF CORFU Pt. 3

One of the Greek Ionian Islands situated off the coast of Albania temporarily occupied by Italy during a dispute with Greece in 1923. For later Occupation Issues see Corfu & Paxos below.

100 centesimi = 1 lira.
100 lepta = 1 drachma.

**1923.** Stamps of Italy optd. **CORFU.**

1. **37.** 5 c. green .. .. .. 50 1·00
2. 10 c. red .. .. .. 50 1·00
3. 15 c. grey .. .. .. 50 1·00
4. **41.** 20 c. orange .. .. 50 1·00
5. **39.** 30 c. brown .. .. 50 1·00
6. 50 c. mauve .. .. 50 1·00
7. 60 c. blue .. .. .. 50 1·00
8. **34.** 1 l. brown and green .. 50 1·00

**1923.** Stamps of Italy surch. **CORFU** and value.

9. **37.** 25 l. on 10 c. red .. 7·25 3·50
10. **39.** 60 l. on 25 c. blue .. 2·25
11. 70 l. on 30 c. brown .. 2·25
12. 1 d. 20 on 50 c. mauve.. 5·25 3·50
13. **34.** 2 d. 40 on 1 l. brn. & grn. 5·25 3·50
14. 4 d. 75 on 2 l. grn. & orge. 2·25

## ITALIAN OCCUPATION OF CORFU AND PAXOS Pt. 3

Greek Ionian Islands occupied by Italy in 1941.

100 lepta = 1 drachma.

**1941.** Stamps of Greece optd. **CORFU.**
(a) On postage stamps of 1937.

1. **86.** 5 l. blue and brown .. 1·10 75
2. – 10 l. brown and blue .. 20 25
4. – 20 l. green and black .. 20 25
5. – 40 l. black and green .. 20 30
6. – 50 l. black and brown .. 20 20
7. – 80 l. brown and violet .. 25 30
8. **89.** 1 d. green .. .. 90 65
9. **89a.** 1 d. 50 green .. .. 2·75 1·40
10. – 2 d. blue .. .. .. 1·25 65
11. **89.** 3 d. brown .. .. 90 50
12. – 5 d. red .. .. .. 1·10 90
13. – 6 d. olive .. .. .. 1·25 1·00
14. – 7 d. brown .. .. 1·40 1·10
15. **89.** 8 d. blue .. .. .. 2·75 1·40
16. – 10 d. brown .. .. £100 38·00
17. – 15 d. green .. .. 4·50 4·00
18. – 25 d. blue .. .. 4·00 3·50
19. **89a.** 30 d. red .. .. .. 20·00 16·00
20. **89.** 100 d. red .. .. 50·00 22·00

(b) On air stamps of 1938 and 1935.

22. **D 20.** 50 l. brown (No. 521) .. 45 40
23. **79.** 1 d. red .. .. .. £110 29·00
24. 2 d. blue .. .. .. 1·00 55
25. 5 d. mauve .. .. 1·00 55
26. 7 d. blue .. .. .. 1·25 80
27. 10 d. brown .. .. £100 45·00
28. 10 d. orange .. .. 16·00 8·00
29. 25 d. red .. .. .. 18·00 10·00
30. 30 d. green .. .. 22·00 18·00
31. 50 d. mauve .. .. 20·00 16·00
32. 100 d. brown .. .. £375 £160

(c) On Charity Tax stamps of 1939.

33. **C 96.** 10 l. red .. .. .. 65 55
34. 50 l. green .. .. 75 65
35. 1 d. blue .. .. .. 4·00 2·75

POSTAGE DUE STAMPS

(d) On Postage Due stamps of 1902 and 1913.

D 36. **D 20.** 10 l. red .. .. 65 55
D 37. 25 l. blue .. .. 75 65
D 38. 80 l. purple .. .. £275 60·00
D 39. 1 d. blue .. .. £400 £130
D 40. 2 d. red .. .. .. 1·40 90
D 41. 5 d. blue .. .. 5·00 2·75
D 42. 10 d. green .. .. 3·00 2·25
D 43. 15 d. brown .. .. 3·75 2·25
D 44. 25 d. red .. .. 3·75 2·25
D 45. 50 d. orange .. .. 3·75 2·25
D 46. 100 d. green .. .. £160 £100

## ITALIAN OCCUPATION OF IONIAN ISLANDS Pt. 3

A group of islands off the W. coast of Greece, placed under the protection of Gt. Britain in 1815 and ceded to Greece in 1864. Under Italian occupation in 1941.

For use in all islands except Kithyra.
100 lepta = 1 drachma.

**1941.** Stamps of Italy optd. **ISOLE JONIE.**
(a) On postage stamps of 1929.

1. **98.** 5 c. brown .. .. 15 45
2. – 10 c. brown .. .. 15 45
3. **99.** 20 c. red .. .. .. 15 45
4. – 25 c. green .. .. 15 45
5. **103.** 30 c. brown .. .. 15 45
6. 50 c. violet .. .. 15 45
7. – 75 c. red .. .. .. 15 45
8. – 1 l. 25 blue .. .. 15 45

(b) On air stamp of 1930.

9. **110.** 50 c. brown .. .. 15 25

(c) On Postage Due stamps of 1934.

D 10. **D 141.** 10 c. blue .. .. 15 75
D 11. 20 c. red .. .. 15 75
D 12. 30 c. orange .. .. 15 75
D 13. **D 142.** 1 l. orange .. .. 15 75

## ITALIAN POST OFFICES IN CHINA Pt. 8

Italian Military Posts in China, including Peking and Tientsin, now closed.

100 centesimi = 1 lira. 100 cents = 1 dollar.

Stamps of Italy overprinted or surcharged.

### A. PEKING

**1917.** Surch **PECHINO** and value.

1 **37** 2 c. on 5 c. green .. 50·00 24·00
2 **33** 4 c. on 10 c. red .. £3000 £2500
3 **37** 4 c. on 10 c. pink .. 90·00 50·00
4 **41** 6 c. on 15 c. grey .. £225 £125
5 8 c. on 20 c. on 15 c. grey £1500 £650
6 8 c. on 20 c. orange .. £2500 £550
7 **33** 20 c. on 50 c. violet .. £14000 £7500
8 **34** 40 c. on 1 l. brown & grn £70000 £10000

**1917.** Optd **Pechino**.

9 **30** 1 c. brown .. .. 3·00 4·50
10 **31** 2 c. brown .. .. 3·00 4·50
11 **37** 5 c. green .. .. 1·00 2·00
12 10 c. pink .. .. 1·00 2·00
13 **41** 20 c. orange .. .. 24·00 26·00
14 **39** 25 c. blue .. .. 1·00 3·00
15 50 c. violet .. .. 1·50 3·50
16 **34** 1 l. brown and green .. 1·75 5·50
17 5 l. blue and pink .. 3·25 9·00
18 10 l. green and pink .. 35·00 60·00

**1918.** Surch **Pechino** and value.

19 **30** ½ c. on 1 c. brown .. 20·00 32·00
20 **31** 1 c. on 2 c. brown .. 1·25 2·75
21 **37** 2 c. on 5 c. green .. 1·00 2·50
22 4 c. on 10 c. pink .. 1·00 2·50
23 **41** 8 c. on 20 c. orange .. 3·00 5·00
28 **39** 10 c. on 25 c. blue .. 2·00 3·25
25 20 c. on 50 c. violet .. 2·50 5·00
26 **34** 40 c. on 1 l. brown & grn 30·00 40·00
27 2 dollari on 5 l. bl & pink £120 £140
30 2 DOLLARI on 5 l. blue and pink .. .. £20000 £22000

EXPRESS LETTER STAMPS

**1917.** Express Letter stamp optd **Pechino** or surch **12 CENTS** also.

E28 **E 41** 12 c. on 30 c. blue and pink .. .. 17·00 32·00
E19 30 c. blue and pink 4·00 10·00

POSTAGE DUE STAMPS

**1917.** Postage Due stamps optd **Pechino**.

D19 **D 12** 10 c. mauve & orange 1·25 3·00
D20 20 c. mauve & orange 1·25 3·00
D21 30 c. mauve & orange 1·25 4·00
D22 40 c. mauve & orange 1·25 4·00

**1918.** Surch **Pechino** and value.

D28 **D 12** 4 c. on 10 c. mauve and orange .. £20000 £16000
D29 8 c. on 20 c. mauve and orange .. 2·75 6·00
D30 12 c. on 30 c. mauve and orange .. 14·00 30·00
D31 16 c. on 40 c. mauve and orange .. 55·00 90·00

### B. TIENTSIN

**1917.** Surch **TIENTSIN** and value.

31a **37** 2 c. on 5 c. green .. 90·00 65·00
32a 4 c. on 10 c. pink .. £180 £110
33b **41** 6 c. on 15 c. grey .. £350 £225

Prices for the above are for stamps with surcharge inverted.

**1917.** Optd **Tientsin**.

34 **30** 1 c. brown .. .. 2·00 4·00
35 **31** 2 c. brown .. .. 2·00 4·50
36 **37** 5 c. green .. .. 75 1·50
37 10 c. pink .. .. 75 1·50
38 **41** 20 c. orange .. .. 25·00 32·00
39 **39** 25 c. blue .. .. 1·00 2·25
40 50 c. violet .. .. 1·00 3·25
41 **34** 1 l. brown and green .. 2·25 6·50
42 5 l. blue and pink .. 2·75 12·00
43 10 l. green and pink .. 40·00 75·00

**1918.** Surch **Tientsin** and value.

44 **30** ½ c. on 1 c. brown .. 18·00 32·00
45 **31** 1 c. on 2 c. brown .. 1·00 3·25
46 **37** 2 c. on 5 c. green .. 1·00 1·75
47 4 c. on 10 c. pink .. 1·00 1·75
48 **41** 8 c. on 20 c. orange .. 2·50 4·00
49 **39** 10 c. on 25 c. blue .. 2·00 4·00
50 20 c. on 50 c. violet .. 2·50 4·50
51 **34** 40 c. on 1 l. brown & grn 25·00 35·00
52 2 Dollari on 5 l. bl & pink £140 £150
53 2 dollari on 5 l. bl & pink £4000 £3500

EXPRESS LETTER STAMPS

**1917.** Express Letter stamp optd **Tientsin** or surch **12 CENTS** also.

E53 **E 41** 12 c. on 30 c. blue and pink .. .. 18·00 50·00
E44 30 c. blue and pink 3·75 12·00

POSTAGE DUE STAMPS

**1917.** Postage Due stamps optd **Tientsin**.

D44 **D 12** 10 c. mauve & orange 1·25 3·25
D45 20 c. mauve & orange 1·25 3·25
D46 30 c. mauve & orange 1·25 3·25
D47 40 c. mauve & orange 1·25 3·25

**1918.** Surch **Tientsin** and value.

D53 **D 12** 4 c. on 10 c. mauve and orange .. £650 £900
D54 8 c. on 20 c. mauve and orange .. 3·00 7·00
D55 12 c. on 30 c. mauve and orange .. 14·00 28·00
D56 16 c. on 40 c. mauve and orange .. 60·00 £110

## ITALIAN POST OFFICES IN CRETE Pt. 8

Italian P.O.s in Crete now closed.

1900. 40 paras = 1 piastre.
1906. 100 centesimi = 1 lira.

Stamps of Italy surcharged or overprinted.

**1900.** Surch. **1 PIASTRA 1.**

1. **27.** 1 pi. on 25 c. blue .. 2·40 16·00

**1901.** Surch. **LA CANEA 1 PIASTRA 1.**

2. **33.** 1 pi. on 25 c. blue .. 1·75 2·75

**1906.** 1901 stamps optd **LA CANEA**.

3 **30** 1 c. brown .. .. 40 70
4 **31** 2 c. brown .. .. 40 70
5 5 c. green .. .. 60 85
6 **33** 10 c. red .. .. 70·00 45·00
7 15 c. on 20 c. orange .. 1·00 1·25
8 25 c. blue .. .. 2·75 3·00
9 40 c. brown .. .. 2·75 3·00
10 45 c. green .. .. 2·75 3·00
11 50 c. mauve .. .. 2·75 3·25
12 **34** 1 l. brown and green .. 14·00 18·00
13 5 l. blue and pink .. 42·00 65·00

**1907.** 1906 stamps optd **LA CANEA**.

14 **37** 5 c. green .. .. 35 75
15 10 c. red .. .. 35 75
16 **41** 15 c. black .. .. 90 1·90
17 **39** 25 c. blue .. .. 1·10 2·25
18 40 c. brown .. .. 5·50 8·50
19 50 c. violet .. .. 90 2·25

EXPRESS LETTER STAMP

**1906.** Express Letter stamp optd. **LA CANEA.**

E 1. **E 35.** 25 c. red .. .. 2·00 4·00

## ITALIAN POST OFFICES IN THE TURKISH EMPIRE Pt. 8

Currency: Italian and Turkish.

Stamps of Italy overprinted and surcharged.

### A. GENERAL ISSUES.

The following were in use in P.O.s in Alexandria, Assab, La Goletta, Massawa, Susa, Tripoli and Tunis and also at Consular post offices at Buenos Aires and Montevideo.

**1874.** 1863 type, slightly altered, optd. **ESTERO.**

1. **4.** 1 c. green .. .. 60 4·50
2. **5.** 2 c. brown .. .. 70 6·00
3. **6.** 5 c. grey .. .. £100 5·00
4. 10 c. orange .. .. £400 12·00
10. 10 c. blue .. .. 65·00 3·50
5. **10.** 20 c. blue .. .. £300 6·00
11. 20 c. orange .. .. £900 3·00
6. **6.** 30 c. brown .. .. 70 3·25
7. 40 c. red .. .. 70 4·00
8. 60 c. mauve .. .. 70 20·00
9. **7.** 2 l. red .. .. .. 40·00 £200

**1881.** 1879 type, slightly altered, optd. **ESTERO.**

12. **12.** 5 c. green .. .. 3·00 3·00
13. 10 c. red .. .. 1·00 2·00
14. 20 c. orange .. .. 1·00 2·00
15. 25 c. blue .. .. 1·00 2·00
16. 50 c. mauve .. .. 1·25 20·00

### B. OFFICES IN TURKISH EMPIRE.

(a) **Albania.**

**1902.** Surch **ALBANIA** and value.

18. **31.** 10 pa. on 5 c. green .. 1·25 1·00
24. **37.** 10 pa. on 5 c. green .. 18·00 20·00
25. 20 pa. on 10 c. red .. 10·00 8·00
19. **33.** 35 pa. on 20 c. orange .. 2·00 1·75
20. 40 pa. on 25 c. blue .. 3·25 1·75
26. 80 pa. on 50 c. mauve .. 10·00 8·00

**1902.** Surch with figures of value repeated twice and currency in words thus, **20 Para 20**.

21. **31.** 10 pa. on 5 c. green .. 4·00 1·00
27. **37.** 10 pa. on 5 c. green .. 1·00 1·00
28. 20 pa. on 10 c. red .. 1·00 1·25
22. **33.** 35 pa. on 20 c. orange .. 1·50 1·50
23. 40 pa. on 25 c. blue .. 8·00 2·50
29. 80 pa. on 50 c. mauve .. 20·00 14·00

(b) **General Offices in Europe and Asia.**

**1908.** Surch. with figures of value repeated twice and currency in words thus, **30 Para 30.**

32 **41** 30 pa. on 15 c. grey .. 75 1·00
30 **39** 40 pa. on 25 c. blue .. 1·00 85
31 80 pa. on 50 c. mauve .. 1·25 1·00

EXPRESS LETTER STAMPS

**1908.** Express Letter stamps surch. **LEVANTE** and new value.

E 33. **E 35.** 1 pi. on 25 c. red .. 75 1·00
E 34. **E 41.** 60 pa. on 30 c. bl. & red 1·25 1·60

### C. INDIVIDUAL OFFICES IN EUROPE AND ASIA.

(a) **Constantinople.**

**1908.** Surch in one line with figure of value and currency in words.

40 **37** 10 pa. on 5 c. green .. 1·00 2·00
41 20 pa. on 10 c. pink .. 1·00 2·00
47 **41** 30 pa. on 15 c. grey .. 1·00 1·00
43 **39** 1 pi. on 25 c. blue .. 1·00 2·00
44 2 pi. on 50 c. mauve .. 16·00 16·00
45 **34** 4 pi. on 1 l. brown & grn £400 £300
46 20 pi. on 5 l. blue & pink £1400 £1000

**1908.** Surch in two lines with figures of value repeated twice and currency in words.

48 **34** 4 pi. on 1 l. brown & grn 20·00 24·00
51 20 pi. on 5 l. blue & pink 24·00 26·00

**1909.** Surch **Costantinopoli** (10 pa. to 2 pi.) or **COSTANTINOPOLI** (4 to 40 pi.) and value in figures twice repeated and currency in words.

52 **37** 10 pa. on 5 c. green .. 40 50
53 20 pa. on 10 c. pink .. 40 50
54 **41** 30 pa. on 15 c. grey .. 40 50
55 **39** 1 pi. on 25 c. blue .. 40 50
56 2 pi. on 50 c. mauve .. 1·00 1·50
57 **34** 4 pi. on 1 l. brown & grn 1·00 1·50
58 20 pi. on 5 l. blue & pink 18·00 20·00
59 40 pi. on 10 l. grn & pink 2·00 8·00

**1921.** Surch. with value in figures and currency in words thus, **4 PIASTRE.**

60. **37.** 1 pi. on 5 c. green .. 80·00 £160
61. 2 pi. on 15 c. grey .. 2·00 3·00
62. **41.** 4 pi. on 20 c. orange .. 12·00 20·00
63. **39.** 5 pi. on 25 c. blue .. 12·00 20·00
64. 10 pi. on 60 c. red .. 1·00 2·00

**1921.** Surch. with value in figures and currency in words thus, **PARA 20.**

65 **30** 10 pa. on 1 c. brown .. 60 2·00
66 **31** 20 pa. on 2 c. brown .. 60 2·00
67 **37** 30 pa. on 5 c. green .. 1·50 2·00
68 1 pi. 20 on 15 c. grey .. 1·60 1·50
69 **41** 3 pi. on 20 c. orange .. 2·50 5·00
70 **39** 3 pi. 30 on 25 c. blue .. 1·10 2·00
71 7 pi. 20 on 60 c. red .. 1·75 2·00
72 **34** 15 pi. on 1 l. brown & grn. 10·00 15·00

**1922.** Surch. **COSTANTINOPOLI** and value in figures once only after currency in words.

73. **37.** 20 pa. on 5 c. green .. 6·00 14·00
74. 1 pi. 20 on 15 c. grey 75 1·00
75. **39.** 3 pi. on 30 c. brown .. 75 1·50
76. 3 pi. 30 on 40 c. brown 75 1·00
77. **34.** 7 pi. 20 on 1 l. brown and green .. .. 75 1·00

**1922.** Surch **Piastre 3,75** in two lines.

78 **39** 3,75 pi. on 25 c. blue .. 1·25 1·00

**1922.** Para values surch. in one line thus **30 PARA** and piastre values with **PIASTRE** over new value except Nos. 81, 86, 98 and 99 where the figures of value are above.

79. **31.** 30 pa. on 2 c. brown .. 60 2·00
80. **37.** 30 pa. on 5 c. green .. 2·00 4·00
81. **41.** 1,50 pi. on 20 c. orange 60 2·00
82. **39.** 1,50 pi. on 25 c. blue .. 75 2·50
83. 3,75 pi. on 40 c. brown 1·00 2·50
84. 4,50 pi. on 50 c. mauve 3·00 5·00
85. 7,50 pi. on 60 c. red .. 3·00 4·75
86. 15 pi. on 85 c. brown .. 4·00 10·00
87. **34.** 18,75 pi. on 1 l. brown and green .. 2·00 6·50
98. 45 pi. on 5 l. blue and red 30·00 40·00
99. 90 pi. on 10 l. olive & red 30·00 45·00

**1922.** Para values surch. in two lines and piastre values with **PIASTRE** under new value.

90. **37.** 30 pa. on 5 c. green .. 60 1·25
91. 1½ pi. on 10 c. red .. 65 1·25
92. **39.** 3 pi. on 25 c. blue .. 4·50 3·00
93. 3¾ pi. on 40 c. brown .. 75 1·00
94. 4½ pi. on 50 c. mauve .. 18·00 15·00
95. 7½ pi. on 85 c. brown .. 2·00 4·00
96. **34.** 7½ pi. on 1 l. brn. & green 2·50 5·00
97. 15 pi. on 1 l. brn. & green 24·00 42·00

**1923.** Surch. **COSTANTINOPOLI** and value in figures once only after currency in words.

100 **37** 30 pa. on 5 c. green .. 1·50 1·50
101 **39** 1 pi. 20 on 25 c. blue .. 1·50 1·50
103 4 pi. 20 on 50 c. mauve 1·50 1·50
104 7 pi. 20 on 60 c. red .. 1·50 1·50
105 15 pi. on 85 c. brown .. 1·50 2·25
106 **34** 18 pi. 30 on 1 l. brown and green .. .. 1·75 2·25
107 45 pi. on 5 l. blue & pink 2·00 4·00
108 90 pi. on 10 l. grn & pink 2·00 5·00

EXPRESS LETTER STAMPS

**1922.** Express Letter stamps surch **15 PIASTRE**.

E 90. E **41.** 15 pi. on 1 l. 20 on 30 c. blue and red .. 6·00 16·00
E 100. 15 pi. on 30 c. blue and red .. .. £100 £200

**1923.** Express Letter stamp surch **COSTANTINOPOLI 15 PIASTRE**.

E109 E **41** 15 pi. on 1 l. 20 blue and red .. .. 3·00 10·00

POSTAGE DUE STAMPS

**1922.** Postage Due stamps optd **Costantinopoli**.

D100 D **12** 10 c. mauve & orge 2·00 5·00
D101 30 c. mauve & orge 2·00 5·00
D102 60 c. mauve & orge 2·00 5·00
D103 1 l. mauve and blue 2·00 5·00
D104 2 l. mauve and blue £425 £600
D105 5 l. mauve and blue £150 £250

Nos. D100/5 bear a control cachet applied over blocks of four so that a quarter of the circle falls on a corner of each stamp.

(b) **Durazzo.**

**1909.** Surch **Durazzo** (10 pa. to 2 pi.) or **DURAZZO** (4 to 40 pi.) and value.

109 **37** 10 pa. on 5 c. green .. 50 1·00
110 20 pa. on 10 c. pink .. 50 1·00
111 **41** 30 pa. on 15 c. grey .. 2·00 2·00
112 **39** 1 pi. on 25 c. blue .. 60 1·00
113 2 pi. on 50 c. mauve .. 60 1·25
114 **34** 4 pi. on 1 l. brown & grn 80 2·00
115 20 pi. on 5 l. blue & pink 75·00 80·00
116 40 pi. on 10 l. grn & pink 6·00 25·00

**1915.** No. 111 of Durazzo surch **CENT. 20**.

116a **41** 20 c. on 30 pa. on 15 c. grey .. .. 1·60 8·50

(c) **Janina.**

**1909.** Surch **Janina** (10 pa. to 2 pi.) or **JANINA** (4 to 40 pi.) and value.

117 **37** 10 pa. on 5 c. green .. 50 1·00
118 20 pa. on 10 c. pink .. 50 1·00
119 **41** 30 pa. on 15 c. grey .. 50 1·25
120 **39** 1 pi. on 25 c. blue .. 50 2·00
121 2 pi. on 50 c. mauve .. 50 2·00
122 **34** 4 pi. on 1 l. brown & grn 60 2·00
123 20 pi. on 5 l. blue & pink £100 £100
124 40 pi. on 10 l. grn & pink 8·00 30·00

(d) **Jerusalem.**

**1909.** Surch **Gerusalemme** (10 pa. to 2 pi.) or **GERUSALEMME** (4 to 40 pi.) and value.

125 **37** 10 pa. on 5 c. green .. 60 2·00
126 20 pa. on 10 c. pink .. 60 2·00
127 **41** 30 pa. on 15 c. grey .. 60 2·00
128 **39** 1 pi. on 25 c. blue .. 60 2·00
129 2 pi. on 50 c. mauve .. 2·50 5·00
130 **34** 4 pi. on 1 l. brown & grn 5·00 7·50
131 20 pi. on 5 l. blue & pink £180 £180
132 40 pi. on 10 l. grn & pink 20·00 60·00

(e) **Salonica.**

**1909.** Surch **Salonicco** (10 pa. to 2 pi.) or **SALONICCO** (4 to 40 pi.) and value.

133 **37** 10 pa. on 5 c. green .. 60 1·00
134 20 pa. on 10 c. pink .. 60 1·00
135 **41** 30 pa. on 15 c. grey .. 60 1·00
136 **39** 1 pi. on 25 c. blue .. 60 1·00
137 2 pi. on 50 c. mauve .. 60 1·25
138 **34** 4 pi. on 1 l. brown & grn 75 2·00
139 20 pi. on 5 l. blue & pink £140 £160
140 40 pi. on 10 l. grn & pink 10·00 28·00

(f) **Scutari.**

**1909.** Surch **Scutari di Albania** (4 pa. to 2 pi.) or **SCUTARI DI ALBANIA** (4 to 40 pi.) and value.

141 **31** 4 pa. on 2 c. brown .. 60 1·75
142 **37** 10 pa. on 35 c. green .. 60 1·00
143 20 pa. on 10 c. pink .. 60 1·00
144 **41** 30 pa. on 15 c. grey .. 5·00 5·00
145 **39** 1 pi. on 25 c. blue .. 60 1·00
146 2 pi. on 50 c. mauve .. 60 1·25
147 **34** 4 pi. on 1 l. brown & grn 75 1·50
148 20 pi. on 5 l. blue & pink 12·00 16·00
149 40 pi. on 10 l. grn & pink 40·00 50·00

**1916.** No. 144 of Scutari surch **CENT. 20**.

150 **41** 20 c. on 30 pa. on 15 c. grey .. .. .. 3·00 10·00

(g) **Smyrna.**

**1909.** Surch **Smirne** (10 pa. to 2 pi.) or **SMIRNE** (4 to 40 pi.) and value.

151 **37** 10 pa. on 5 c. green .. 50 1·00
152 20 pa. on 10 c. pink .. 50 1·00
153 **41** 30 pa. on 15 c. grey .. 50 1·00
154 **39** 1 pi. on 25 c. blue .. 50 1·25
155 2 pi. on 50 c. mauve .. 60 1·25
156 **34** 4 pi. on 1 l. brown & grn 1·00 2·00
157 20 pi. on 5 l. blue & pink 60·00 50·00
158 40 pi. on 10 l. grn & pink 14·00 28·00

(h) **Valona.**

**1909.** Surch **Valona** (10 pa. to 2 pi.) or **VALONA** (4 to 40 pi.) and value.

159 **37** 10 pa. on 5 c. green .. 50 1·00
160 20 pa. on 10 c. pink .. 50 1·00
161 **41** 30 pa. on 15 c. grey† .. 5·00 4·00
167 30 pa. on 15 c. grey† .. 2·25 5·00
162 **39** 1 pi. on 25 c. blue .. 50 1·25
163 2 pi. on 50 c. mauve .. 50 1·25
164 **34** 4 pi. on 1 l. brown & grn 60 1·75
165 20 pi. on 5 l. blue & pink 24·00 28·00
166 40 pi. on 10 l. grn & pink 32·00 55·00

† On No. 161 the surcharge is **Para**, on No. 167 **PARA**.

**1916.** No. 167 of Valona surch **CENT. 20**.

168 **41** 20 c. on 30 pa. on 15 c. grey .. .. .. 1·00 6·00

**D. OFFICES IN AFRICA.**

(a) **Benghazi.**

**1901.** Surch **BENGASI 1 PIASTRA 1**.

169 **33** 1 pi. on 25 c. blue .. 25·00 50·00
170 **39** 1 pi. on 25 c. blue .. 22·00 60·00

(b) **Tripoli.**

**1909.** Optd **Tripoli di Barberia** (1 to 50 c.) or **TRIPOLI DI BARBERIA** (1, 2 l.).

171 **30** 1 c. brown .. .. 1·40 2·00
173 **31** 2 c. brown .. .. 1·00 1·00
174 **37** 5 c. green .. .. 30·00 6·00
175 10 c. red .. .. 1·25 1·40
176 **41** 15 c. grey .. .. 2·00 2·25
177 **39** 25 c. blue .. .. 90 1·25
178 40 c. brown .. .. 3·00 3·25
179 50 c. violet .. .. 3·00 3·25
180 **34** 1 l. brown and green .. 55·00 35·00
181 5 l. blue and pink .. 20·00 75·00

EXPRESS LETTER STAMPS

**1909.** Express Letter stamps optd **TRIPOLI DI BARBERIA**.

E182 E **35** 25 c. pink .. .. 3·00 4·00
E183 E **41** 30 c. blue and pink 4·00 8·00

## ITALY Pt. 8

**A Republic in S. Europe on the Mediterranean and Adriatic Seas. Originally a kingdom formed by the union of various smaller kingdoms and duchies which issued their own stamps.**

100 centesimi = 1 lira.

1. King Victor Emmanuel II. 3.

**1862.** Head embossed. Imperf (15 c.) or perf (others).

1 **1** 10 c. bistre .. .. £4500 £130
5 15 c. blue .. .. 35·00 28·00
2a 20 c. blue .. .. 4·25 14·00
3 40 c. red .. .. £170 75·00
4 80 c. yellow .. .. 20·00 £1000

For stamps of this type imperf, see Sardinia Nos. 27 etc.

**1863.** Imperf.

**7. 3.** 15 c. blue .. .. .. 1·10 2·75

4. 5. 6.

7. 10.

**1863.** Perf.

**8. 4.** 1 c. green .. .. .. 1·40 20
**9. 5.** 2 c. brown .. .. 5·00 20
**10. 6.** 5 c. grey .. .. .. £800 40
11. 10 c. brown .. .. £1200 60
21. 10 c. blue .. .. .. £2750 1·25
12. 15 c. blue .. .. .. £1000 60
20a. **10.** 20 c. blue .. .. £500 55
22. 20 c. orange .. .. £2000 60
13. **6.** 30 c. brown .. .. 6·50 1·40
14. 40 c. red .. .. .. £2500 1·50
15. 60 c. mauve .. .. 5·00 7·00
16. **7.** 2 l. red .. .. .. 10·00 35·00

**1865.** Surch. **C 20 20 C** and curved bar.

**17. 6.** 20 c. on 15 c. blue .. £300 55

**1878.** Official stamps surch **2 C** and wavy bars.

**23. O 11.** 2 c. on 2 c. red .. .. 85·00 4·00
**24.** 2 c. on 5 c. red .. .. 85·00 5·00
**25.** 2 c. on 20 c. red .. £400 1·75
**26.** 2 c. on 30 c. red .. £250 2·00
**27.** 2 c. on 1 l. red .. .. £300 1·90
**28.** 2 c. on 2 l. red .. .. £300 2·75
**29.** 2 c. on 5 l. red .. .. £400 4·00
**30.** 2 c. on 10 l. red .. £275 4·75

12. King Umberto I. 13. Arms of Savoy. 14.

**1879.** Corners vary for each value.

**31. 12.** 5 c. green .. .. 5·00 20
**32.** 10 c. red .. .. £275 20
**33.** 20 c. orange .. .. £225 20
**34.** 25 c. blue .. .. £300 50
**35.** 30 c. brown .. .. 90·00 £1000
**36.** 50 c. mauve .. .. 7·50 3·25
**37.** 2 l. orange .. .. 30·00 £140

**1889.** Figures in four corners. Various frames.

**38. 13.** 5 c. green .. .. £300 90
**39. 14.** 40 c. brown .. .. 7·00 1·75
**40.** 45 c. green .. .. £1000 1·75
**41.** 60 c. mauve .. .. 7·00 7·00
**42.** 1 l. brown and orange .. 8·00 1·75
**43.** 5 l. red and green .. 9·00 £325

**1890.** Surch. thus **Cmi 2.**

**44. 12.** 2 c. on 5 c. green .. 10·00 30·00
**45.** 20 c. on 30 c. brown .. £200 3·00
**46.** 20 c. on 50 c. mauve .. £200 14·00

**1890.** Parcel Post stamps surch **Valevole per le stampe Cmi 2**.

47 P **13** 2 c. on 10 c. grey .. 2·50 2·75
48 2 c. on 20 c. blue .. 3·50 2·75
49 2 c. on 50 c. pink .. 22·00 12·00
50 2 c. on 75 c. green .. 2·25 2·25
51 2 c. on 1 l. 25 orange .. 24·00 10·00
52 2 c. on 1 l. 75 brown .. 11·00 20·00

21. 22. 23.

24. 25. 26.

27. 29.

**1891.**

**53. 21.** 1 c. brown .. .. 3·00 1·75
**54. 22.** 2 c. brown .. .. 3·00 30
**55. 23.** 5 c. green .. .. £275 75
**56. 24.** 5 c. green .. .. 8·00 25
**57. 25.** 10 c. red .. .. 4·00 30
**58. 26.** 20 c. orange .. .. 4·00 30
**59. 27.** 25 c. blue .. .. 4·00 55
**60.** 45 c. olive .. .. 4·00 1·00
**61. 29.** 5 l. red and blue .. 30·00 60·00

30. 31.

King Victor Emmanuel III.
33. 34.

**1901.** Designs vary.

62 **30** 1 c. brown .. .. 10 10
63 **31** 2 c. brown .. .. 10 10
64 5 c. green .. .. 24·00 10
65 **33** 10 c. red .. .. 26·00 10
66 20 c. orange .. .. 4·25 10
67 25 c. blue .. .. 30·00 10
68 40 c. brown .. .. £275 2·50
69 45 c. green .. .. 3·00 10
70 50 c. violet .. .. £300 4·00
71 **34** 1 l. brown and green .. 1·60 10
72 5 l. blue and pink .. 12·00 1·00
85 10 l. green and pink .. 30·00 5·50

See also Nos. 171s, 181, 185 and 186/7.

**1905.** Surch. **C. 15.**

**73. 33.** 15 c. on 20 c. orange .. 40·00 30·00

37. 39. 41.

**1906.**

75 **37** 5 c. green .. .. 15 10
76 10 c. red .. .. 15 10
90 **41** 15 c. grey .. .. 12·00 30
77 **39** 25 c. blue .. .. 55 10
78 40 c. brown .. .. 85 10
79 50 c. violet .. .. 70 10

See also Nos. 104 etc, 171d/h and 171j/r.

42. Garibaldi 43.

**1910.** 50th Anniv. of Plebiscite in Naples and Sicily.

81 **42** 5 c. (+5 c.) green .. 8·00 14·00
82 15 c. (+5 c.) red .. 16·00 30·00

**1910.** National Plebiscite of Southern States, 1860.

83 **43** 5 c. (+5 c.) pink .. 50·00 60·00
84 15 c. (+5 c.) green .. 85·00 85·00

45. 46. 50.

**1911.** Jubilee of Italian Kingdom.

86. **45.** 2 c. (+3 c.) brown .. 1·00 2·25
87. **46.** 5 c. (+5 c.) green .. 3·00 10·00
88. – 10 c. (+5 c.) red .. 3·00 10·00
89. – 15 c. (+5 c.) grey .. 3·00 10·00

DESIGNS: Symbolic of the Genius of Italy (10 c.) and the Glory of Rome (15 c.).

**1912.** Re-erection of Campanile of St. Mark, Venice.

91. **50.** 5 c. black .. .. 3·00 3·50
92. 15 c. brown .. .. 8·00 14·00

**1913.** Surch. **2 2.**

93. **46.** 2 on 5 c. green .. .. 40 1·10
94. – 2 on 10 c. red (No. 88) .. 40 1·10
95. – 2 on 15 c. grey No. 89) .. 40 1·10

53. Banner of United Italy.

54. Italian Eagle and Arms of Savoy.

**1915.** Red Cross Society. No. 98 is surch. **20.**

96. **53.** 10 c.+5 c. red .. .. 1·40 3·50
97. **54.** 15 c.+5 c. grey .. .. 1·40 4·75
98. 20 on 15 c.+5 c. grey .. 2·75 15·00
99. 20 c.+5 c. orange .. 2·00 12·00

**1916.** Surch **CENT. 20.**

100 **41** 20 c. on 15 c. grey .. 5·50 30

**1917.** Air. Express Letter stamp optd **ESPERIMENTO POSTA AEREA MAGGIO 1917 TORINO = ROMA ROMA = TORINO.**

102 E **35** 25 c. red .. .. 4·00 6·00

**1917.** Air. Express Letter stamp surch **IDROVOLANTE NAPOLI-PALERMO NAPOLI 25 CENT 25.**

103 E **59** 25 c. on 40 c. violet .. 5·00 11·00

**1917.**

104 **37** 15 c. grey .. .. 85 10
105 **41** 20 c. orange .. .. 85 10
178 **39** 20 c. orange .. .. 55 10
179 20 c. green .. .. 35 10
180 20 c. purple .. .. 1·10 10
181 **34** 25 c. green & light green 25 10
182 **39** 25 c. green .. .. 3·50 3·25
106 30 c. brown .. .. 1·10 25
183 30 c. grey .. .. 90 10
107 55 c. purple .. .. 3·75 3·25
108 60 c. red .. .. 90 10
109 60 c. blue .. .. 3·25 12·00
184 60 c. orange .. .. 2·25 10
185 **34** 75 c. red and carmine .. 1·60 15
110 **39** 85 c. brown .. .. 2·50 10
186 **34** 1 l. 25 blue & ultram .. 1·90 10
111 2 l. green and orange .. 9·00 1·00
187 2 l. 50 green and orange 20·00 1·10

See also Nos. 171a/c and 171i.

60.

59. Ancient Seal of Republic of Trieste.

**1921.** Union of Venezia Giulia with Italy.

112. **59.** 15 c. red and black .. 1·00 10·00
113. 25 c. red and blue .. 1·00 10·00
114. 40 c. red and brown .. 1·00 10·00

**1921.** 600th Death Anniv. of Dante.

115. **60.** 15 c. red .. .. 1·00 8·00
116. – 25 c. green .. .. 1·00 8·00
117. – 40 c. brown .. .. 1·00 8·00

DESIGNS: 25 c. Woman with book. 40 c. Dante.

62. " Victory ".

64.

**1921.** Victory of 1918.

118. **62.** 5 c. green .. .. 20 1·00
119. 10 c. red .. .. 35 1·40
120. 15 c. grey .. .. 60 4·25
121. 25 c. blue .. .. 35 3·00

**1922.** 9th Italian Philatelic Congress, Trieste. Optd **IX CONGRESSO FILATELICO ITALIANO TRIESTE 1922.**

122. **37.** 10 c. red .. .. £160 £100
123. 15 c. grey .. .. £120 £100
124. **39.** 25 c. blue .. .. £120 £100
125. 40 c. brown .. .. £160 £100

**1922.** 50th Death Anniv of Mazzini.

126 **64** 25 c. purple .. .. 2·00 11·00
127 – 40 c. purple .. .. 3·00 11·00
128 – 80 c. blue .. .. 2·00 11·00

DESIGNS—VERT: 40 c. Mazzini. HORIZ: 80 c. Tomb of Mazzini.

66.

**1923.** Tercent. of Propagation of the Faith.

129. **66.** 20 c. orange and green 1·00 26·00
130. 30 c. orange and red .. 1·00 26·00
131. 50 c. orange and violet 1·00 26·00
132. 1 l. orange and blue .. 1·00 26·00

The portraits and arms in the corners at right vary for each value.

**1923.** Surch. in words and figures. (15 c. surch. **DIECI** only).

133. **39.** 7½ c. on 85 c. brown .. 15 40
135. **30.** 10 c. on 1 c. brown .. 15 15
136. **31.** 10 c. on 2 c. brown .. 15 15
137. **37.** 10 c. on 15 c. grey .. 10 10
138. **39.** 20 c. on 25 c. blue .. 10 10
139. **33.** 25 c. on 45 c. olive .. 15 2·50
140. **39.** 25 c. on 60 c. blue .. 70 35
141. 30 c. on 50 c. mauve .. 10 10
142. 30 c. on 55 c. purple .. 25 20
143. 50 c. on 40 c. brown .. 35 15
144. 50 c. on 55 c. purple .. 15·00 4·50
145. **34.** 1 l. 75 on 10 l. ol. & red 5·50 9·50

73.

74.

75.

**1923.** 1st Anniv. of Fascist March on Rome.

146. **73.** 10 c. green .. .. 1·00 2·50
147. 30 c. violet .. .. 1·10 2·50
148. 50 c. red .. .. 1·25 3·75
149. **74.** 1 l. blue .. .. 1·00 2·50
150. 2 l. brown .. .. 1·10 4·50
151. **75.** 5 l. black and blue .. 3·25 17·00

76.

**1923.** Fascist "Black Shirt" Fund.

152. **76.** 30 c.+30 c. brown .. 15·00 40·00
153. 50 c.+50 c. mauve .. 17·00 40·00
154. 1 l.+1 l. grey .. 15·00 40·00

77.

DESIGNS: 10 c. to 50 c. Scenes from Manzoni's "I Promessi Sposi". 1 l. Manzoni's home, Milan. 5 l. Portrait of Manzoni.

**1923.** 50th Death Anniv. of A. Manzoni (writer).

155. **77.** 10 c. black and red .. 90 20·00
156. – 15 c. black and green .. 90 20·00
157. – 30 c. black .. .. 90 20·00
158. – 50 c. black and brown .. 90 20·00
159. – 1 l. black and blue .. 13·00 £100
160. – 5 l. black and purple .. £240 £1000

**1924.** Victory stamps surch. **LIRE UNA** between stars.

161 **62** 1 l. on 5 c. green .. 7·00 42·00
162 1 l. on 10 c. red .. 4·50 42·00
163 1 l. on 15 c. grey .. 7·00 42·00
164 1 l. on 25 c. blue .. 4·50 42·00

**1924.** Trade Propaganda. Optd **CROCIERA ITALIANA 1924.**

165 **37** 10 c. red .. .. 60 7·00
166 **39** 30 c. brown .. .. 60 7·00
167 50 c. violet .. .. 60 7·00
168 60 c. blue .. .. 4·75 28·00
169 85 c. brown .. .. 2·50 28·00
170 **34** 1 l. brown and green .. 21·00 £120
171 2 l. green and orange .. 17·00 £120

Used on an Italian cruiser which visited South America for trade propaganda.

**1924.** Previous issues with attached advertising labels (imperf between stamp and label). Colour of label given.

171a 15 c. (104) + Columbia (blue) .. .. 12·00 14·00
171b 15 c. (104) + Bitter Campari (blue) .. 1·00 5·00
171c 15 c. (104) + Cordial Campari (black) .. 1·00 5·00
171d 25 c. (77) + Coen (green) 75·00 12·00
171e 25 c. (77) + Piperno (brown) .. .. £650 £140
171f 25 c. (77) + Tagliacozzo (brown) .. .. £300 £140
171g 25 c. (77) + Abrador (blue) .. .. 40·00 30·00
171h 25 c. (77) + Reinach (green) .. .. 40·00 20·00
171i 30 c. (106) + Columbia (green) .. .. 12·00 12·00
171j 50 c. (79) + Coen (blue) .. £600 24·00
171k 50 c. (79) + Columbia (red) .. .. 6·00 2·00
171l 50 c. (79) + De Montel (blue) .. .. 1·00 4·00
171m 50 c. (79) + Piperno (green) .. .. £700 50·00
171n 50 c. (79) + Reinach (blue) 75·00 15·00
171o 50 c. (79) + Singer (red) .. 1·00 70
171p 50 c. (79) + Tagliacozzo (green) .. .. £900 £100
171q 50 c. (79) + Siero Casali (blue) .. .. 6·00 12·00
171r 50 c. (79) + Tantal (red) £100 35·00
171s 1 l. (71) + Columbia (blue) £300 £200

81. Church of St. John Lateran.

**1924.** Holy Year (1925).

172. – 20 c.+10 c. brn. & grn... 1·00 5·00
173. **81.** 30 c.+15 c. brn. & choc. 1·00 5·00
174. – 50 c.+25 c. brn. & vio... 1·00 5·00
175. – 60 c.+30 c. brn. & red .. 1·00 10·00
176. – 1 l.+50 c. pur. & blue .. 1·00 10·00
177. – 5 l.+2 l. 50 pur. & red .. 1·00 30·00

DESIGNS: 20 c. Church of St. Maria Maggiore. 50 c. Church of St. Paul. 60 c. St. Peter's. 1 l. Pope opening Holy Door. 5 l. Pope shutting Holy Door.

82.

83. Vision of St. Francis.

**1925.** Royal Jubilee.

188. **82.** 60 c. red .. .. .. 20 20
189. 1 l. blue .. .. .. 20 20
190. 1 l. 25 blue .. .. 1·75 70

**1926.** 700th Death Anniv of St. Francis of Assisi.

191 **83** 20 c. green .. .. 10 30
194 – 30 c. black .. .. 10 15
192 – 40 c. violet .. .. 10 20
193 – 60 c. red .. .. 15 20
195 – 1 l. 25 blue .. .. 10 20
196 – 5 l.+2 l. 50 brown .. 4·50 40·00

DESIGNS—HORIZ. 40 c. St. Damian's Church and Monastery, Assisi. 60 c. St. Francis's Monastery, Assisi. 1 l. 25, Death of St. Francis, from fresco in Church of the Holy Cross, Florence. VERT. 30 c., 5 l. St. Francis (after Luca della Robbia).

88.

**1926.** Air.

197 **88** 50 c. red .. .. 1·25 2·75
198 60 c. grey .. .. 1·10 2·25
199 80 c. brown and purple 7·00 21·00
200 1 l. blue .. .. 60 2·75
201 1 l. 20 brown .. .. 7·00 35·00
202 1 l. 50 orange .. .. 4·50 7·50
203 5 l. green .. .. 12·00 26·00

89. Castle of St. Angelo.

**1926.** 1st National Defence issue.

204. **89.** 40 c.+20 c. blk. & brn. .. 60 4·75
205. – 60 c.+30 c. brn. & red .. 60 4·75
206. – 1 l. 25+60 c. blk. & grn. .. 60 14·00
207. – 5 l.+2 l. 50 blk. & blue .. 90 45·00

DESIGNS: 60 c. Aqueduct of Claudius. 1 l. 25, Capitol. 5 l. Porta del Popolo.

See also Nos. 219/22 and 278/81.

90. Volta.

91.

92.

**1927.** Death Centenary of Volta.

208 **90** 20 c. red .. .. 20 25
209 50 c. green .. .. 65 10
210 60 c. purple .. .. 80 1·10
211 1 l. 25 blue .. .. 80 1·10

**1927.**

216 **91** 50 c. grey and brown .. 75 10
212 1 l. 75 brown .. .. 1·50 10
213 1 l. 85 black .. .. 40 30
214 2 l. 55 red .. .. 1·90 3·25
215 2 l. 65 purple .. .. 1·90 21·00

No. 216 is smaller (17½ × 21½ mm) than Type 91.

**1927.** Air. Surch.

217. **88.** 50 c. on 60 c. grey .. 2·00 15·00
218. 80 c. on 1 l. blue .. 10·00 60·00

**1928.** 2nd National Defence issue. As Nos. 204/7.

219 **89** 30 c.+10 c. black & vio. 2·00 9·50
220 – 50 c.+20 c. blk. & olive 2·00 6·50
221 – 1 l. 25+50 c. blk. & blue 5·00 21·00
222 – 5 l.+2 l. blk. & red .. 8·00 55·00

**1928.**

223 **92** 7½ c. brown .. .. 70 2·00
224 15 c. orange .. .. 70 15
225 35 c. grey .. .. 1·10 3·50
226 50 c. mauve .. .. 1·60 15

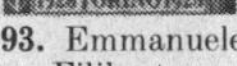
93. Emmanuele Filiberto.

94. Soldier of First World War and Statue.

95. Statue, Turin (Maroghetti).

96. King Victor Emmanuel II.

**1928.** 400th Birth Anniv of Emmanuele Filiberto, Duke of Savoy, and 10th Anniv of Victory in World War.

227a **93** 20 c. blue and brown .. 35 50
228a 25 c. green and red .. 35 50
229a 30 c. brown and green 45 70
230 **94** 50 c. red and blue .. 25 15
231 75 c. red and pink .. 35 25
232 **95** 1 l. 25 black and blue 55 30
233 **94** 1 l. 75 green and blue 1·10 1·25
234 **93** 5 l. green and mauve .. 3·50 35·00
235 **94** 10 l. black and pink .. 7·00 80·00
236 **95** 20 l. green and mauve 12·00 £250

**1929.** 50th Death Anniv of King Victor Emmanuel II. Veterans' Fund.

237 **96** 50 c.+10 c. green .. 1·10 3·00

97. Fascist Arms of Italy.

98. Romulus, Remus and Wolf.

99. Julius Caesar.

103. King Victor Emmanuel III.

**1929.** Imperial Series.

| No. | Type | Description | Mint | Used |
|---|---|---|---|---|
| 238. | 97. | 2 c. orange | 10 | 10 |
| 239. | 98. | 5 c. brown | 10 | 10 |
| 240. | 99. | 7½ c. violet | 10 | 10 |
| 241. | – | 10 c. brown | 10 | 10 |
| 242. | – | 15 c. green | 10 | 10 |
| 243. | 99. | 20 c. red | 10 | 10 |
| 244. | – | 25 c. green | 10 | 10 |
| 245. | 103. | 30 c. brown | 10 | 10 |
| 246. | – | 35 c. blue | 10 | 10 |
| 247. | 103. | 50 c. violet | 10 | 10 |
| 248. | – | 75 c. red | 10 | 10 |
| 249. | 99. | 1 l. violet | 10 | 10 |
| 250. | – | 1 l. 25 blue | 10 | 10 |
| 251. | – | 1 l. 75 orange | 10 | 10 |
| 252. | – | 2 l. red | 10 | 10 |
| 253. | 98. | 2 l. 55 green | 10 | 10 |
| 254. | | 3 l. 70 violet | 10 | 10 |
| 255. | | 5 l. red | 10 | 10 |
| 256. | – | 10 l. violet | 25 | 25 |
| 257. | 99. | 20 l. green | 85 | 3·75 |
| 258. | – | 25 l. black | 1·90 | 12·00 |
| 259. | – | 50 l. violet | 2·75 | 18·00 |

**Designs—As Type 99: 10 c., 1 l. 75, 25 l. Augustus the Great. 15 c., 35 c., 2 l., 10 l. Italia (Woman with castle on her head). 25 c., 75 c., 1 l. 25, 50 l. Profile of King Victor Emmanuel III.**

For stamps as above but without Fascist emblems, see Nos. 633 etc, and for stamps with integral label for armed forces see Nos. 563/74.

**104. Bramante Courtyard.**

**1929.** 1400th Anniv of Abbey of Montecassino.

| No. | Type | Description | Mint | Used |
|---|---|---|---|---|
| 260 | 104 | 20 c. orange | 30 | 25 |
| 261 | – | 25 c. green | 30 | 25 |
| 262 | – | 50 c.+10 c. brown | 1·25 | 6·00 |
| 263 | – | 75 c.+15 c. red | 1·40 | 8·50 |
| 264 | 104 | 1 l. 25+25 c. blue | 1·75 | 10·00 |
| 265 | – | 5 l.+1 l. purple | 1·75 | 32·00 |
| 266 | – | 10 l.+2 l. green | 2·75 | 55·00 |

Designs—horiz: 25 c. "Death of St. Benedict" (fresco). 50 c. Monks building Abbey. 75 c., 5 l. Abbey of Montecassino. vert: 10 l. St. Benedict.

**109.**

**1930.** Marriage of Prince Umberto and Princess Marie Jose.

| No. | Type | Description | Mint | Used |
|---|---|---|---|---|
| 267. | 109. | 20 c. orange | 25 | 25 |
| 268. | | 50 c.+10 c. brown | 65 | 1·60 |
| 269. | | 1 l. 25+25 c. blue | 1·10 | 5·00 |

**110.** Pegasus. **113.**

**1930.** Air.

| No. | Type | Description | Mint | Used |
|---|---|---|---|---|
| 270. | – | 25 c. green | 10 | 10 |
| 271. | 110. | 50 c. brown | 10 | 10 |
| 272. | – | 75 c. brown | 10 | 10 |
| 273. | – | 80 c. orange | 10 | 25 |
| 274. | – | 1 l. violet | 10 | 10 |
| 275. | 113. | 2 l. blue | 10 | 10 |
| 276. | 110. | 5 l. green | 10 | 25 |
| 277. | | 10 l. red | 15 | 55 |

**Designs—As Type 110: 25 c., 80 c. Wings. 75 c., 1 l. Angel.**

**1930.** 3rd National Defence issue. Designs as Nos. 204/7.

| No. | Type | Description | Mint | Used |
|---|---|---|---|---|
| 278 | 89 | 30 c.+10 c. violet & grn | 40 | 6·00 |
| 279 | – | 50 c.+10 c. blue & green | 40 | 3·50 |
| 280 | – | 1 l. 25+30 c. green & bl | 55 | 11·00 |
| 281 | – | 5 l.+1 l. 50 choc & brn | 2·75 | 42·00 |

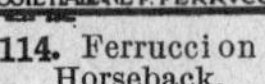

**114.** Ferrucci on Horseback. **117.** Francesco Ferrucci.

**1930.** 400th Death Anniv. of Francesco Ferrucci.

| No. | Type | Description | Mint | Used |
|---|---|---|---|---|
| 282. | 114. | 20 c. red (postage) | 20 | 35 |
| 283. | – | 25 c. green | 25 | 35 |
| 284. | – | 50 c. violet | 15 | 15 |
| 285. | – | 1 l. 25 blue | 1·00 | 70 |
| 286. | – | 5 l.+2 l. orange | 3·25 | 35·00 |
| 287. | 117. | 50 c. violet (air) | 80 | 4·00 |
| 288. | | 1 l. brown | 80 | 7·00 |
| 289. | | 5 l.+2 l. purple | 2·50 | 45·00 |

Designs—horiz. 25 c., 50 c., 1 l. 25, Ferrucci assassinated by Maramaldo. vert. 5 l. Ferrucci in helmet.

**119.** Jupiter sending forth Eagle.

**1930.** Birth Bimillenary of Virgil.

| No. | Type | Description | Mint | Used |
|---|---|---|---|---|
| 290. | – | 15 c. brown (postage) | 40 | 30 |
| 291. | – | 20 c. orange | 40 | 30 |
| 292. | – | 25 c. green | 50 | 20 |
| 293. | – | 30 c. purple | 55 | 30 |
| 294. | – | 50 c. violet | 40 | 15 |
| 295. | – | 75 c. red | 85 | 1·00 |
| 296. | – | 1 l. 25 blue | 85 | 70 |
| 297. | – | 5 l.+1 l. 50 brown | 23·00 | 70·00 |
| 298. | – | 10 l.+2 l. 50 olive | 23·00 | 80·00 |
| 299. | 119. | 50 c. brown (air) | 2·50 | 3·50 |
| 300. | | 1 l. orange | 3·50 | 5·50 |
| 301. | | 7 l. 70+1 l. 30 purple | 18·00 | 75·00 |
| 302. | | 9 l.+2 l. blue | 19·00 | 80·00 |

Designs (scenes from "Aeneid" or "Georgics"): 15 c. Helenus and Anchises. 20 c. The passing legions. 25 c. Landing of Aeneas. 30 c. Earth's bounties. 50 c. Harvesting. 75 c. Rural life. 1 l. 25, Aeneas sights Italy. 5 l. A shepherd's hut. 10 l. Turnus, King of the Rutuli.

**120.** Savoia Marchetti S-55A Flying Boats.

**1930.** Air. Transatlantic Mass Formation Flight.

| No. | Type | Description | Mint | Used |
|---|---|---|---|---|
| 303 | 120 | 7 l. 70 blue and brown | £120 | £375 |

**121.** St. Antony's Installation as a Franciscan. **123.** Tower of the Marzocco.

**1931.** 700th Death Anniv of St. Antony of Padua.

| No. | Type | Description | Mint | Used |
|---|---|---|---|---|
| 304. | 121. | 20 c. purple | 40 | 25 |
| 305. | – | 25 c. green | 45 | 25 |
| 306. | – | 30 c. brown | 75 | 40 |
| 307. | – | 50 c. violet | 40 | 15 |
| 308. | – | 75 c. lake | 3·50 | 1·40 |
| 309. | – | 1 l. 25 c. blue | 2·50 | 65 |
| 310. | – | 5 l.+2 l. 50 c. olive | 15·00 | 65·00 |

Designs—horiz: 25 c. Sermon to the Fishes. 30 c. Hermitage of Olivares. 50 c. Basilica of the Saint at Padua. 75 c. Death of St. Antony. 1 l. 25, St. Antony liberating prisoners. vert: 5 l. Vision of St. Antony.

**1931.** 50th Anniv. of Naval Academy, Leghorn.

| No. | Type | Description | Mint | Used |
|---|---|---|---|---|
| 311. | 123. | 20 c. red | 75 | 30 |
| 312. | – | 50 c. violet | 75 | 15 |
| 313. | – | 1 l. 25 blue | 3·25 | 85 |

Designs—horiz. 50 c. Cadet ship "Amerigo Vespucci". 1 l. 25 c. Cruiser "Trento".

**124.** Dante (1265–1321).

**125.** Leonardo da Vinci's Drawing "Flying Man". **127.** Leonardo da Vinci.

**1932.** Dante Alighieri Society. (a) Postage.

| No. | Type | Description | Mint | Used |
|---|---|---|---|---|
| 314. | – | 10 c. brown | 40 | 30 |
| 315. | – | 15 c. green | 45 | 30 |
| 316. | – | 20 c. red | 40 | 20 |
| 317. | – | 25 c. green | 45 | 25 |
| 318. | – | 30 c. brown | 75 | 35 |
| 319. | – | 50 c. violet | 35 | 15 |
| 320. | – | 75 c. red | 1·25 | 1·00 |
| 321. | – | 1 l. 25 blue | 1·00 | 70 |
| 322. | – | 1 l. 75 orange | 1·25 | 1·00 |
| 323. | – | 2 l. 75 green | 8·00 | 12·00 |
| 324. | – | 5 l.+2 l. red | 13·00 | 60·00 |
| 325. | 124. | 10 l.+2 l. 50 olive | 14·00 | 75·00 |

Designs: 10 c. Giovanni Boccaccio (writer). 15 c. Niccolo Machiavelli (statesman). 20 c. Fra Paolo Sarpi (philosopher). 25 c. Vittorio Alfieri (poet). 30 c. Ugo Foscolo (writer). 50 c. Giacomo Leopardi (poet). 75 c. Giosue Carducci (poet). 1 l. 25, Carlo Botta (historian). 1 l. 75, Torquato Tasso (poet). 2 l. 75, Francesco Petrarch (poet). 5 l. Ludovico Ariosto (poet).

(b) Air.

| No. | Type | Description | Mint | Used |
|---|---|---|---|---|
| 326 | 125 | 50 c. brown | 75 | 3·25 |
| 327 | – | 1 l. violet | 75 | 2·00 |
| 328 | – | 3 l. red | 2·00 | 8·00 |
| 329 | – | 5 l. green | 2·25 | 10·00 |
| 330 | 125 | 7 l. 70+2 l. blue | 3·50 | 42·00 |
| 331 | – | 10 l.+2 l. 50 grey | 4·00 | 42·00 |
| 332 | 127 | 100 l. green and blue | 20·00 | £140 |

Design—horiz: 1, 3, 5, 10 l. Leonardo da Vinci.

**128.** Garibaldi and Victor Emmanuel. **130.** Caprera.

**1932.** 50th Death Anniv. of Garibaldi.

| No. | Type | Description | Mint | Used |
|---|---|---|---|---|
| 333. | – | 10 c. blue (postage) | 40 | 30 |
| 334. | 128. | 20 c. brown | 45 | 20 |
| 335. | – | 25 c. green | 70 | 35 |
| 336. | 128. | 30 c. orange | 75 | 50 |
| 337. | – | 50 c. violet | 40 | 15 |
| 338. | – | 75 c. red | 2·50 | 1·50 |
| 339. | – | 1 l. 25 blue | 1·75 | 70 |
| 340. | – | 1 l. 75+25 c. blue | 9·00 | 38·00 |
| 341. | – | 2 l. 55+50 c. brown | 15·00 | 50·00 |
| 342. | – | 5 l.+1 l. lake | 15·00 | 55·00 |

Designs—horiz. 10 c. Garibaldi's birthplace, Nice. 25 c., 50 c. "Here we make Italy or die". 75 c. Death of Anita (Garibaldi's wife). 1 l. 25, Garibaldi's tomb. 1 l. 75, Quarto Rock. vert. 2 l. 55, Garibaldi's statue in Rome. 5 l. Garibaldi.

| No. | Type | Description | Mint | Used |
|---|---|---|---|---|
| 343. | 130. | 50 c. lake (air) | 65 | 2·25 |
| 344. | – | 80 c. green | 1·25 | 4·00 |
| 345. | 130. | 1 l.+25 c. brown | 1·75 | 12·00 |
| 346. | – | 2 l.+50 c. blue | 3·25 | 24·00 |
| 347. | – | 5 l.+1 l. green | 4·25 | 28·00 |

Designs—vert. 80 c. The Ravenna hut. 2 l. Anita. 5 l. Garibaldi.

**132.** Agriculture.

**1932.** 10th Anniv of Fascist March on Rome. (a) Postage).

| No. | Type | Description | Mint | Used |
|---|---|---|---|---|
| 350. | 132. | 5 c. sepia | 30 | 25 |
| 351. | – | 10 c. sepia | 40 | 25 |
| 352. | – | 15 c. green | 45 | 30 |
| 353. | – | 20 c. red | 40 | 20 |
| 354. | – | 25 c. green | 45 | 20 |
| 355. | – | 30 c. sepia | 60 | 90 |
| 356. | – | 35 c. blue | 2·00 | 3·00 |
| 357. | – | 50 c. violet | 30 | 15 |
| 358. | – | 60 c. brown | 2·00 | 2·00 |
| 359. | – | 75 c. red | 90 | 40 |
| 360. | – | 1 l. violet | 1·75 | 90 |
| 361. | – | 1 l. 25 blue | 90 | 30 |
| 362. | – | 1 l. 75 orange | 1·10 | 40 |
| 363. | – | 2 l. 55 green | 13·00 | 18·00 |
| 364. | – | 2 l. 75 green | 13·00 | 19·00 |
| 365. | – | 5 l.+2 l. 50 red | 25·00 | £110 |

**Designs: 10 c. Fascist soldier. 15 c. Fascist coastguard. 20 c. Italian youth. 25 c. Tools forming a shadow of the Fasces. 30 c. Religion. 35 c. Imperial highways. 50 c. Equestrian statue of Mussolini. 60 c. Land reclamation. 75 c. Colonial expansion. 1 l. Marine development. 1 l. 25, Italians abroad. 1 l. 75, Sport, 2 l. 55, Child Welfare. 2 l. 75, "O.N.D." Recreation. 5 l. Caesar's statue.**

(b) Air.

| No. | Type | Description | Mint | Used |
|---|---|---|---|---|
| 366 | | 50 c. brown | 1·50 | 3·75 |
| 367 | | 75 c. brown | 4·50 | 11·00 |

Designs: 50 c. Eagle (front of Air Ministry Building, Rome). 75 c. Aerial view of Italian cathedrals.

**134.** Airship "Graf Zeppelin".

**1933.** Air. " Graf Zeppelin " issue.

| No. | Type | Description | Mint | Used |
|---|---|---|---|---|
| 372. | 134. | 3 l. green and black | 6·00 | 22·00 |
| 373. | – | 5 l. brown and green | 6·00 | 22·00 |
| 374. | – | 10 l. blue and red | 6·00 | 50·00 |
| 375. | – | 12 l. orange and blue | 6·00 | 75·00 |
| 376. | – | 15 l. black and brown | 6·00 | 90·00 |
| 377. | – | 20 l. blue and brown | 6·00 | £100 |

**Designs (all with airship); 3 l. S. Paola Gate and tomb of Consul Caius Cestius. 5 l. Appian Way and tomb of Cecilia Metella. 10 l. Portion of Mussolini Stadium. 12 l. S. Angelo Castle. 15 l. Forum Romanum. 20 l. Empire Way, Colosseum and Baths of Domitian.**

Italian Flag. King Victor Emmanuel III. " Flight ".
**135.**

Italian Flag. King Victor Emmanuel III. Rome—Chicago.
**136.**

(½-size illustrations).

**1933.** Air. Balbo Transatlantic Mass Formation Flight by Savoia Marchetti S-55X Flying Boats.

| No. | Type | Description | Mint | Used |
|---|---|---|---|---|
| 378 | 135 | 5 l. 25+19 l. 75 red, green and blue | 42·00 | £850 |
| 379 | 136 | 5 l. 25+44 l. 75 red, green and blue | 42·00 | £850 |

The first part of the illustration in each group is of the Registered Air Express label and has an abbreviation of one of the pilots' names overprinted on it; the second part is the stamp for Ordinary Postage and the third is the actual Air Mail stamp.

**137.** Athlete.

**1933.** Int. University Games, Turin.

| No. | Type | Description | Mint | Used |
|---|---|---|---|---|
| 380. | 137. | 10 c. brown | 20 | 30 |
| 381. | | 20 c. red | 20 | 35 |
| 382. | | 50 c. violet | 35 | 15 |
| 383. | | 1 l. 25 blue | 85 | 1·60 |

**138.** Dome of St. Peter's. **139.** St. Peter's and Church of the Holy Sepulchre.

**1933.** "Holy Year". (a) Postage.

| No. | Type | Description | Mint | Used |
|---|---|---|---|---|
| 384 | 138 | 20 c. red | 40 | 30 |
| 385 | – | 25 c. green | 55 | 40 |
| 386 | – | 50 c. violet | 40 | 15 |
| 387 | 138 | 1 l. 25 blue | 75 | 65 |
| 388 | – | 2 l. 55+2 l. 50 black | 2·25 | 45·00 |

Designs: 25, 50 c. Angel with Cross. 2 l. 55, Cross with Doves of Peace.

(b) Air.

| No. | Type | Description | Mint | Used |
|---|---|---|---|---|
| 389 | 139 | 50 c.+25 c. brown | 60 | 6·00 |
| 390 | | 75 c.+50 c. purple | 1·10 | 8·00 |

**1934.** Air. Rome–Buenos Aires Flight. Surch with airplane, **1934 XII PRIMO VOLO DIRETTO ROMA=BUENOS-AYRES TRIMOTORE "LOMBARDI MAZZOTTI"**, value and fasces.

| No. | Type | Description | Mint | Used |
|---|---|---|---|---|
| 391. | 113. | 2 l. on 2 l. yellow | 1·50 | 28·00 |
| 392. | | 3 l. on 2 l. green | 1·50 | 35·00 |
| 393. | | 5 l. on 2 l. red | 1·50 | 42·00 |
| 394. | | 10 l. on 2 l. violet | 1·50 | 48·00 |

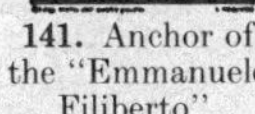

141. Anchor of the "Emmanuele Filiberto". 142. Antonio Pacinotti.

**1934.** 10th Anniv. of Annexation of Fiume.
395. **141.** 10 c. brown (postage) 1·60 40
396. 20 c. red 20 25
397. – 50 c. violet 20 15
398. – 1 l. 25 blue 20 75
399. – 1 l. 75+1 l. blue 35 21·00
400. – 2 l. 55+2 l. purple 45 24·00
401. – 2 l. 75+2 l. 50 olive 45 24·00
Designs: 50 c. Gabriele d'Annunzio. 1 l. 25, St. Vito's Tower barricaded. 1 l. 75, Hands supporting crown of historical monuments. 2 l. 55, Victor Emmanuel III's arrival in the "Brindisi". 2 l. 75, Galley, gondola and battleship.

402. 25 c. green (air) 20 1·00
403. 50 c. brown 20 55
404. 75 c. brown 20 1·25
405. 1 l.+50 c. purple 20 9·50
406. 2 l.+1 l. 50 blue 20 12·00
407. 3 l.+2 l. black 20 13·50
Designs—Marina Fiat MF.5 flying boat over: 25, 75 c. Fiume Harbour. 50 c., 1 l. War Memorial. 2 l. Three Venetian lions. 3 l. Roman Wall.

**1934.** 75th Anniv of Invention of Pacinotti's Dynamo.
411 142 50 c. violet 40 15
412 1 l. 25 blue 60 1·25

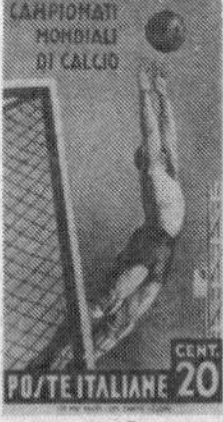

143. 145. Luigi Galvani.

**1934.** World Cup Football Championship, Italy.
413 143 20 c. red (postage) 2·25 2·75
414 – 25 c. green 2·25 80
415 – 50 c. violet 2·25 30
416 – 1 l. 25 blue 8·50 4·00
417 – 5 l.+2 l. 50 brown 40·00 £140
Designs—vert. 5 l. Players heading the ball. horiz. 25 c., 50 c., 1 l. 25, Two footballers.

418 50 c. red (air) 4·00 6·00
419 75 c. blue 7·00 7·50
420 5 l.+2 l. 50 olive 21·00 70·00
421 10 l.+5 l. brown 24·00 80·00
Designs—horiz. 50 c. Marina Fiat MF.5 flying boat over Mussolini Stadium, Turin. 5 l. Marina Fiat MF.5 flying boat over Stadium, Rome. vert. 75 c. Savoia Marchetti S-55X flying boat over footballer. 10 l. Marina Fiat MF.5 flying boat over Littoral Stadium, Bologna.

**1934.** 1st Int. Congress of Electro-Radio-Biology.
422. **145.** 30 c. brown on buff 50 40
423. 75 c. red on pink 75 1·75

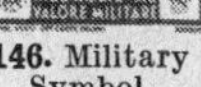

146. Military Symbol. 148. King Victor Emmanuel III.

**1934.** Military Medal Centenary.
424 146 10 c. brown (postage) 55 55
425 – 15 c. green 65 1·00
426 – 20 c. red 55 35
427 – 25 c. green 85 35
428 – 30 c. brown 1·40 1·40
429 – 50 c. violet 85 20
430 – 75 c. red 3·50 1·50
431 – 1 l. 25 blue 2·75 85
432 – 1 l. 75+1 l. red 9·50 32·00
433 – 2 l. 55+2 l. purple 10·00 35·00
434 – 2 l. 75+2 l. violet 11·00 35·00
Designs—vert: 25 c. Mountaineers. 1 l. 75, Cavalry. horiz: 15 c., 50 c. Barbed-wire cutter. 20 c. Throwing hand-grenade. 30 c. Cripple wielding crutch. 75 c. Artillery. 1 l. 25, Soldiers cheering. 2 l. 55, Sapper. 2 l. 75, First Aid.

435 25 c. green (air) 60 2·00
436 50 c. grey 60 2·25
437 75 c. brown 80 2·50
438 80 c. blue 1·10 3·00
439 1 l.+50 c. brown 2·25 15·00
440 2 l.+1 l. blue 3·50 17·00
441 3 l.+2 l. black 4·75 19·00
Designs—horiz: 25, 80 c. Italian "P" Type airship under fire. 50, 75 c. Naval launch. 1 l. Caproni Ca 101 airplane and troops in desert. 2 l. Pomilio PC type biplane and troops. vert: 3 l. Unknown soldier's tomb.

**1934.** Air. Rome—Mogadiscio Flight and King's visit to Italian Somaliland.
444. **148.** 1 l. violet 50 7·50
445. 2 l. blue 50 9·50
446. 4 l. brown 1·10 45·00
447. 5 l. green 1·10 55·00
448. 8 l. red 5·00 75·00
449. 10 l. brown 5·00 85·00

149. Man with Fasces. 150.

**1935.** University Contests. Inscr. "LITTORIALI".
450. **149.** 20 c. red 15 30
451. – 30 c. brown 90 2·25
452. – 50 c. violet 15 15
Designs: 30 c. Eagle and soldier. 50 c. Standard-bearer and bayonet attack.

**1935.** National Militia. Inscr. "PRO OPERA PREVID. MILIZIA".
453. **150.** 20 c.+10 c. red (post.) 2·75 4·75
454. – 25 c.+15 c. green 2·75 5·50
455. – 50 c.+30 c. violet 2·75 6·50
456. – 1 l. 25+75 c. blue 2·75 8·00
457. – 50 c.+50 c. brown (air) 3·75 11·00
Designs: 25 c. Roman standards. 50 c. Soldier and cross. 50 c.+50 c. Wing over Globe. 1 l. 25, Soldiers and arch.

152. Symbol of Flight. 153. Leonardo da Vinci.

**1935.** Int. Aeronautical Exn., Milan.
458. **152.** 20 c. red 2·25 55
459. 30 c. brown 5·50 1·90
460. **153.** 50 c. violet 11·00 20
461. 1 l. 25 blue 8·00 1·00

154. Vincenzo Bellini. 155. "Music".

**1935.** Death Cent. of Bellini (composer).
462. **154.** 20 c. red (postage) 75 45
463. 30 c. brown 1·00 95
464. 50 c. violet 75 20
465. 1 l. 25 blue 3·00 1·25
466. – 1 l. 75+1 l. orange 20·00 55·00
467. – 2 l. 75+2 l. olive 21·00 60·00
Designs—vert. 2 l. 75, Bellini's villa. horiz. 1 l. 75, Hands at piano.

468 155 25 c. brown (air) 1·10 2·00
469 50 c. brown 1·10 2·00
470 60 c. red 1·90 2·50
471 – 1 l.+1 l. violet 7·50 48·00
472 – 5 l.+2 l. green 11·00 60·00
Designs: 1 l. Angelic musicians. 5 l. Mountain landscape (Bellini's birthplace).

Design—horiz. 30 c., 50 c. Cogwheel and plough.

156. "Commerce" and Industrial Map of Italy.

**1936.** 17th Milan Fair. Inscr. as in T **156.**
473. **156.** 20 c. red 20 30
474. – 30 c. brown 25 45
475. – 50 c. violet 20 20
476. **156.** 1 l. 25 blue 50 70

157. "Fertility".

**1936.** 2000th Birth Anniv. of Horace.
477. **157.** 10 c. green (postage) 1·40 40
478. – 20 c. red 1·40 40
479. – 30 c. brown 1·40 70
480. – 50 c. violet 1·10 15
481. – 75 c. red 2·00 90
482. – 1 l. 25+1 l. blue 11·00 40·00
483. – 1 l. 75+1 l. red 13·00 50·00
484. – 2 l. 55+1 l. blue 15·00 55·00
Designs—horiz. 20 c., 1 l. 25, Landscape. 75 c. Capitol. 2 l. 55, Dying gladiator. vert. 30 c. Ajax defying lightning. 50 c. Horace. 1 l. 75, Pan.

485. – 25 c. green (air) 1·10 1·90
486. – 50 c. brown 1·60 1·90
487. – 60 c. red 1·90 3·50
488. – 1 l.+1 l. violet 7·00 50·00
489. – 5 l.+2 l. green 11·00 70·00
Designs—horiz. 25 c. Savoia Marchetti S-55A flying boat. 50 c., 1 l. Caproni Ca 101 airplane over lake. 60 c. Eagle and oak tree. 5 l. Rome.

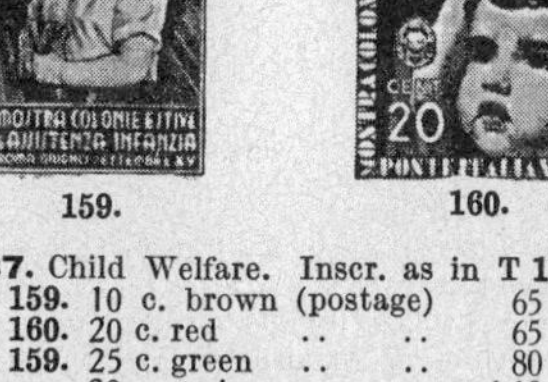

159. 160.

**1937.** Child Welfare. Inscr. as in T **159/60.**
490. **159.** 10 c. brown (postage) 65 40
491. **160.** 20 c. red 65 40
492. **159.** 25 c. green 80 45
493. – 30 c. sepia 1·10 85
494. **160.** 50 c. violet 65 20
495. – 75 c. red 3·50 1·25
496. **160.** 1 l. 25 blue 4·25 1·25
497. – 1 l. 75+75 c. orange 19·00 50·00
498. – 2 l. 75+1 l. 25 green 14·00 55·00
499. **160.** 5 l.+3 l. blue 16·00 60·00
Designs—As Type **159**: 30 c., 1 l. 75, Boy between Fasces. 75 c., 2 l. 75, "Bambino" (after della Robbia).

500. – 25 c. green (air) 2·00 3·50
501. – 50 c. brown 2·75 3·50
502. – 1 l. violet 2·00 4·50
503. – 2 l.+1 l. blue 8·50 50·00
504. – 3 l.+2 l. orange 10·00 55·00
505. – 5 l.+3 l. red 11·00 60·00
Designs—As Type **160**: 25 c., 1 l., 3 l. Little child with rifle. As Type **159**: 50 c., 2 l., 5 l. Children's heads.

163. Naval Memorial. 164. Augustus the Great.

**1937.** 2000th Birth Anniv. of Augustus the Great.
506. **163.** 10 c. green (postage) 40 40
507. – 15 c. brown 40 45
508. – 20 c. red 40 40
509. – 25 c. green 40 40
510. – 30 c. brown 70 50
511. – 50 c. violet 40 15
512. – 75 c. red 75 80
513. – 1 l. 25 blue 1·10 80
514. – 1 l. 75+1 l. purple 20·00 42·00
515. – 2 l. 55+2 l. black 21·00 45·00
Designs—vert. 15 c. Military trophies. 20 c. Reconstructing temples of Rome. 25 c. Census (with reference to birth of Jesus Christ). 30 c. Statue of Julius Caesar. 50 c. Election of Augustus as Emperor. 75 c. Head of Augustus (conquest of Ethiopia). 1 l. 25, Constructing new fleet. 1 l. 75, Building Altar of Peace. 2 l. 55, The Capitol.

516. – 25 c. purple (air) 1·75 2·75
517. – 50 c. brown 1·75 2·00
518. – 80 c. brown 3·75 4·25
519. – 1 l.+1 l. blue 10·00 32·00
520. **164.** 5 l.+1 l. violet 15·00 50·00
Designs—horiz. 25 c. "Agriculture". 50 c. Prosperity of the Romans. 80 c. Horses of the Sun Chariot. 1 l. Staff and map of ancient Roman Empire.

165. Gasparo Spontini (composer). 166. Marconi.

**1937.** Famous Italians.
521. **165.** 10 c. sepia 15 40
522. – 20 c. red 15 40
523. – 25 c. green 15 20
524. – 30 c. brown 15 60
525. – 50 c. violet 15 15
526. – 75 c. red 40 90
527. – 1 l. 25 blue 50 90
528. **165.** 1 l. 75 orange 50 90
529. – 2 l. 55+2 l. green 4·00 38·00
530. – 2 l. 75+2 l. brown 4·00 38·00
Designs: 20 c., 2 l. 55, Antonio Stradivarius (violin maker). 25, 50 c. Giacomo Leopardi (poet). 30, 75 c., Giovanni Battista Pergolesi (composer). 1 l. 25, 2 l. 75, Giotto di Bondone (painter and architect).

**1938.** Guglielmo Marconi (telegraphy pioneer) Commemoration.
531. **166.** 20 c. red 40 35
532. 50 c. violet 20 25
533. 1 l. 25 blue 25 1·10

167. Founding of Rome. 168. Victor Emmanuel III.

**1938.** 2nd Anniv of Proclamation of Italian Empire.
534 167 10 c. brown (postage) 35 20
535 – 20 c. red 35 20
536 – 25 c. green 35 20
537 – 30 c. brown 35 35
538 – 50 c. violet 35 15
539 – 75 c. red 45 35
540 – 1 l. 25 blue 70 35
541 – 1 l. 75 violet 80 45
542 – 2 l. 75 green 4·25 13·00
543 – 5 l. red 5·00 17·00
Designs—vert: 20 c. Emperor Augustus. 25 c. Dante. 30 c. Columbus. 50 c. Leonardo da Vinci. 75 c. Garibaldi and Victor Emmanuel II. 1 l. 25, Italian Unknown Warrior's Tomb. 1 l. 75, "March on Rome". 2 l. 75, Wedding ring on map of Ethiopia. 5 l. Victor Emmanuel III.

544 168 25 c. green (air) 70 1·10
545 – 50 c. brown 70 1·10
546 – 1 l. violet 85 1·25
547 – 2 l. blue 1·25 8·50
548 168 3 l. red 1·50 13·00
549 – 5 l. green 2·50 16·00
Designs—horiz: 50 c., 1 l. Dante; 2, 5 l. Leonardo da Vinci.

169. "Bayard" (steam locomotive), 1839, and 1939 Railcar. 170. Hitler and Mussolini.

171. Hitler and Mussolini. 172. Roman Cavalry.

**1939.** Cent. of Italian Railways.
550. **169.** 20 c. red 30 25
551. 50 c. violet 35 15
552. 1 l. 25 blue 60 1·10

**1941.** Italo-German Friendship.
553. **170.** 10 c. brown 40 30
554. 20 c. orange 40 30
555. 25 c. green 40 30
556. **171.** 50 c. violet 50 15
557. 75 c. red 60 60
558. 1 l. 25 blue 60 70

**1941.** 2000th Birth Anniv. of Livy (Latin historian).

| | | | | |
|---|---|---|---|---|
| 559. | 172. | 20 c.+10 c. red .. | 20 | 80 |
| 560. | | 30 c.+15 c. brown .. | 20 | 85 |
| 561. | – | 50 c.+25 c. violet .. | 25 | 1·00 |
| 562. | – | 1 l. 25+1 l. blue .. | 25 | 1·25 |

DESIGN: 50 c., 1 l. 25, Roman legionary.

**1942.** War Propaganda. Nos. 244/5 and 247 with attached labels (imperf between stamp and label) to encourage war effort.

| | | | |
|---|---|---|---|
| 563 | 25 c. green (Navy) .. | 10 | 60 |
| 564 | 25 c. green (Army) .. | 10 | 60 |
| 565 | 25 c. green (Air Force) .. | 10 | 60 |
| 566 | 25 c. green (Militia) .. | 10 | 60 |
| 567 | 30 c. brown (Navy) .. | 10 | 1·00 |
| 568 | 30 c. brown (Army) .. | 10 | 1·00 |
| 569 | 30 c. brown (Air Force) .. | 10 | 1·00 |
| 570 | 30 c. brown (Militia) .. | 10 | 1·00 |
| 571 | 50 c. violet (Navy) .. | 10 | 30 |
| 572 | 50 c. violet (Army) .. | 10 | 30 |
| 573 | 50 c. violet (Air Force) .. | 10 | 30 |
| 574 | 50 c. violet (Militia) .. | 10 | 30 |

**173.** Galileo teaching at Padua.

**174.** Rossini.

**1942.** Death Tercent. of Galileo.

| | | | | |
|---|---|---|---|---|
| 575. | 173. | 10 c. red and orange .. | 15 | 30 |
| 576. | – | 25 c. green and olive | 15 | 35 |
| 577. | – | 50 c. violet and purple | 15 | 15 |
| 578. | – | 1 l. 25 blue and grey.. | 20 | 70 |

DESIGNS: Galileo at Venice (25 c.) and at Arcetri, near Florence (1 l. 25), 50 c. Portrait of Galileo.

**1942.** 150th Birth Anniv. of Rossini (composer).

| | | | | |
|---|---|---|---|---|
| 579. | – | 25 c. green .. .. | 15 | 25 |
| 580. | – | 30 c. brown .. .. | 15 | 30 |
| 581. | 174. | 50 c. violet .. .. | 15 | 20 |
| 582. | | 1 l. blue .. .. | 15 | 55 |

DESIGN: 25 c., 30 c. Rossini Monument, Pescaro.

**175.**

**187.** Romulus, Remus and Wolf (after Pollaiuolo).

**1943.** Allied Military Government issue.

| | | | | |
|---|---|---|---|---|
| 583. | 175. | 15 c. orange .. .. | 25 | 60 |
| 584. | | 25 c. bistre .. .. | 25 | 60 |
| 585. | | 30 c. grey .. .. | 25 | 60 |
| 586. | | 50 c. violet .. .. | 25 | 60 |
| 587. | | 60 c. yellow .. .. | 25 | 80 |
| 588. | | 1 l. green .. .. | 25 | 1·00 |
| 589. | | 2 l. red .. .. | 25 | 1·00 |
| 590. | | 5 l. blue .. .. | 25 | 2·00 |
| 591. | | 10 l. brown .. .. | 25 | 3·00 |

**1943.** Allied Military Government issue Stamps of 1929 optd. **GOVERNO MILITARE ALLEATO.**

| | | | | |
|---|---|---|---|---|
| 592. | 99. | 20 c. red .. .. | 55 | 1·75 |
| 593. | | 35 c. blue .. .. | 4·50 | 15·00 |
| 594. | 103. | 50 c. violet .. .. | 10 | 1·00 |

**1944.**

| | | | | |
|---|---|---|---|---|
| 619 | 187 | 50 c. purple .. .. | 10 | 15 |

**1944.** As issue of 1929, but with Fascist emblems removed.

| | | | | |
|---|---|---|---|---|
| 633 | – | 10 c. brown (Augustus the Great) .. .. | 10 | 10 |
| 640 | 99 | 20 c. red .. .. | 10 | 10 |
| 620 | 103 | 30 c. brown .. .. | 30 | 20 |
| 635 | – | 50 c. violet (Italia) .. | 10 | 10 |
| 621 | 103 | 50 c. violet .. .. | 30 | 1·00 |
| 636 | – | 60 c. orange (Italia) .. | 10 | 10 |
| 641 | 103 | 60 c. green .. .. | 10 | 10 |
| 637 | 99 | 1 l. violet .. .. | 10 | 10 |
| 643 | – | 1 l. 20 brown (Italia).. | 10 | 10 |
| 638 | – | 2 l. red (Italia) .. | 10 | 10 |
| 645 | 98 | 5 l. red .. .. | 10 | 10 |
| 646 | – | 10 l. violet (Italia) .. | 1·00 | 2·50 |

**1945.** Stamps of Italy surch **L. 2,50** (No. 629) and stamps of Italian Social Republic surch **POSTE ITALIANE** and new value (Nos. 627/8).

| | | | |
|---|---|---|---|
| 627 | 1 l. 20 on 20 c. red (No. 102) | 10 | 10 |
| 628 | 2 l. on 25 c. green (No. 103) | 10 | 10 |
| 629 | 2 l. 50 on 1 l. 75 orange (No. 251) .. .. | 10 | 10 |

**193.** "Work, Justice and Family".

**195.** Planting a Sapling.

**196.** " Peace ".

**197.** " Work Justice and Family ".

**1945.**

| | | | | |
|---|---|---|---|---|
| 647 | – | 10 c. brown .. .. | 10 | 10 |
| 648 | 193 | 20 c. brown .. .. | 10 | 10 |
| 649 | – | 25 c. blue .. .. | 10 | 10 |
| 650 | 195 | 40 c. grey .. .. | 10 | 10 |
| 651 | – | 50 c. violet .. .. | 10 | 10 |
| 652 | – | 60 c. green .. .. | 10 | 15 |
| 653 | – | 80 c. red .. .. | 10 | 10 |
| 654 | 195 | 1 l. green .. .. | 10 | 10 |
| 655 | – | 1 l. 20 brown .. .. | 10 | 10 |
| 656 | – | 2 l. brown .. .. | 10 | 10 |
| 657 | – | 3 l. red .. .. | 10 | 10 |
| 658 | – | 4 l. red .. .. | 25 | 10 |
| 659 | 193 | 5 l. blue .. .. | 70 | 10 |
| 660 | 195 | 6 l. violet .. .. | 3·75 | 10 |
| 661 | – | 8 l. green .. .. | 1·75 | 10 |
| 662 | – | 10 l. grey .. .. | 70 | 10 |
| 663 | 193 | 10 l. red .. .. | 11·00 | 10 |
| 664 | 195 | 15 l. blue .. .. | 5·00 | 10 |
| 665 | – | 20 l. purple .. .. | 85 | 10 |
| 666 | 196 | 25 l. green .. .. | 10·00 | 10 |
| 667 | – | 30 l. blue .. .. | £225 | 10 |
| 668 | 196 | 50 l. purple .. .. | 4·00 | 10 |
| 669 | 197 | 100 l. red .. .. | £200 | 1·10 |

DESIGNS: 10, 50, 80 c., 8, 10 (662) l. Hammer breaking chain ("Freedom"). 25 c., 1 l. 20, 3, 4, 20, 30 l. Flaming torch ("Enlightenmemt"). 60 c., 2 l. Gardener tying sapling to stake.

**198.** Clasped Hands and Caproni Campini N-1 Jet.

**200.** Amalfi.

**1945.** Air.

| | | | | |
|---|---|---|---|---|
| 670 | 198 | 1 l. grey .. .. | 10 | 15 |
| 671 | – | 2 l. blue .. .. | 25 | 10 |
| 672 | 198 | 3 l. 20 red .. .. | 15 | 20 |
| 673 | – | 5 l. green .. .. | 15 | 10 |
| 674 | 198 | 10 l. red .. .. | 10 | 10 |
| 675 | – | 25 l. blue .. .. | 14·00 | 10·00 |
| 676 | – | 25 l. brown .. .. | 10 | 10 |
| 677 | 198 | 50 l. green .. .. | 19·00 | 11·00 |
| 678 | | 50 l. violet .. .. | 15 | 10 |

DESIGN: 2, 5, 25 l. Barn swallows in flight.

**1946.** Mediaeval Italian Republics.

| | | | | |
|---|---|---|---|---|
| 679. | 200. | 1 l. sepia .. .. | 10 | 10 |
| 680. | – | 2 l. blue .. .. | 10 | 10 |
| 681. | – | 3 l. green .. .. | 10 | 10 |
| 682. | – | 4 l. orange .. .. | 10 | 10 |
| 683. | – | 5 l. violet .. .. | 10 | 10 |
| 684. | – | 10 l. red .. .. | 10 | 10 |
| 685. | – | 15 l. blue .. .. | 35 | 25 |
| 686. | – | 20 l. brown .. .. | 20 | 15 |

DESIGNS—VERT. 2 l. Lucca. 3 l. Siena. 4 l. Florence. HORIZ. 5 l. Pisa. 10 l. Genoa. 15 l. Venice. 20 l. "The Oath of Pontida".

**1947.** Air. Surch **LIRE 6–.**

| | | | | |
|---|---|---|---|---|
| 687 | 198 | 6 l. on 3 l. 20 orange .. | 15 | 10 |

**202.** Wireless Mast.

**204.** Douglas DC-2 over Rome.

**1947.** Air. 50th Anniv of Radio.

| | | | | |
|---|---|---|---|---|
| 688 | 202 | 6 l. violet .. .. | 15 | 10 |
| 689 | – | 10 l. red .. .. | 15 | 10 |
| 690 | – | 20 l. orange .. .. | 85 | 85 |
| 691 | 202 | 25 l. blue .. .. | 1·00 | 1·00 |
| 692 | – | 35 l. blue .. .. | 1·25 | 1·25 |
| 693 | – | 50 l. purple .. .. | 2·25 | 2·25 |

DESIGNS: 10, 35 l. Ship's aerial. 20, 50 l. Heinkel He 70 Blitz wireless-equipped airplane.

**1948.** Air.

| | | | | |
|---|---|---|---|---|
| 911 | 204 | 100 l. green .. .. | 60 | 10 |
| 912 | | 300 l. mauve .. .. | 50 | 30 |
| 913 | | 500 l. blue .. .. | 70 | 55 |
| 914 | | 1000 l. brown .. .. | 1·50 | 1·25 |

For No. 911 in smaller size see No. 1297.

**205.** St. Catherine giving her Cloak to a Beggar.

**206.** St. Catherine carrying the Cross.

**1948.** 600th Birth Anniv of St. Catherine of Siena.

| | | | | |
|---|---|---|---|---|
| 698 | 205 | 3 l. bl & grn (postage) | 20 | 15 |
| 699 | – | 5 l. blue and violet .. | 20 | 20 |
| 700 | – | 10 l. violet and brown | 2·50 | 1·00 |
| 701 | – | 30 l. grey and bistre .. | 6·00 | 4·00 |
| 702 | 206 | 100 l. violet & brn (air) | 40·00 | 25·00 |
| 703 | – | 200 l. blue and bistre | 15·00 | 12·00 |

DESIGNS—All show St. Catherine. VERT: 5 l. Carrying the Cross. 10 l. Extending her arms to Italy. 30 l. Dictating "The Dialogue" to a Disciple. HORIZ: 200 l. Extending her arms to Italy.

**207.** "Proclamation of New Constitution".

**1948.** Proclamation of New Constitution.

| | | | | |
|---|---|---|---|---|
| 704. | 207. | 10 l. violet .. .. | 40 | 55 |
| 705. | | 30 l. blue .. .. | 2·00 | 1·25 |

**208.** Rising at Palermo.

**1948.** Centenary of Revolution of 1848.

| | | | | |
|---|---|---|---|---|
| 706. | 208. | 3 l. brown .. .. | 50 | 20 |
| 707. | – | 4 l. purple .. .. | 50 | 20 |
| 708. | – | 5 l. blue .. .. | 1·60 | 25 |
| 709. | – | 6 l. green .. .. | 85 | 75 |
| 710. | – | 8 l. brown .. .. | 95 | 50 |
| 711. | – | 10 l. red .. .. | 2·00 | 25 |
| 712. | – | 12 l. green .. .. | 4·75 | 1·75 |
| 713. | – | 15 l black .. .. | 13·00 | 70 |
| 714. | – | 20 l. red .. .. | 30·00 | 6·00 |
| 715. | – | 30 l. blue .. .. | 6·00 | 55 |
| 716. | – | 50 l. violet .. .. | 80·00 | 2·00 |
| 717. | – | 100 l. blue .. .. | £110 | 17·00 |

DESIGNS: 4 l. Rising at Padua. 5 l. Concession of Statute, Turin. 6 l. Storming Porta Tosa, Milan. 8 l. Proclamation of Venetian Republic. 10 l. Defence of Vicenza. 12 l. Hero of Curtatone. 15 l. Hero of Goito. 20 l. Austrian retreat from Bologna. 30 l. Fighting at Brescia. 50 l. Garibaldi. 100 l. Promotion of a wounded officer.

**209.** Alpinist and Bassano Bridge.

**210.** Gaetano Donizetti.

**1948.** Rebuilding of Bassano Bridge.

| | | | | |
|---|---|---|---|---|
| 718. | 209. | 15 l. green .. .. | 1·40 | 1·25 |

**1948.** Death Cent. of Donizetti (composer).

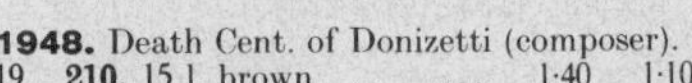

| | | | | |
|---|---|---|---|---|
| 719. | 210. | 15 l. brown .. .. | 1·40 | 1·10 |

**211.** Exhibition Grounds.

**212.**

**1949.** 27th Milan Fair.

| | | | | |
|---|---|---|---|---|
| 720 | 211 | 20 l. sepia .. .. | 6·25 | 1·60 |

**1949.** 25th Biennial Art Exhibition, Venice.

| | | | | |
|---|---|---|---|---|
| 721 | 212 | 5 l. red and flesh .. | 25 | 20 |
| 722 | – | 15 l. green and cream | 2·00 | 1·10 |
| 723 | – | 20 l. brown and buff .. | 8·00 | 20 |
| 724 | – | 50 l. blue and yellow .. | 30·00 | 1·10 |

DESIGNS: 15 l. Clock bell-ringers, St. Mark's Column and Campanile. 20 l. Emblem of Venice and "Bucentaur" (state galley). 50 l. Winged lion on St. Mark's Column.

**213.** Globes and Forms of Transport.

**1949.** 75th Anniv. of U.P.U.

| | | | | |
|---|---|---|---|---|
| 725. | 213. | 50 l. blue .. .. | 45·00 | 4·25 |

**214.** Vascello Castle.

**1949.** Centenary of Roman Republic.

| | | | | |
|---|---|---|---|---|
| 726. | 214. | 100 l. brown .. .. | £200 | 60·00 |

**215.** Worker and Ship.

**216.** Statue of Mazzini.

**1949.** European Recovery Plan.

| | | | | |
|---|---|---|---|---|
| 727. | 215. | 5 l. green .. .. | 4·00 | 3·75 |
| 728. | | 15 l. violet .. .. | 18·00 | 14·00 |
| 729. | | 20 l. brown .. .. | 85·00 | 15·00 |

**1949.** Honouring Giuseppe Mazzini (founder of " Young Italy ").

| | | | | |
|---|---|---|---|---|
| 730. | 216. | 20 l. black .. .. | 7·50 | 1·25 |

**217.** V. Alfieri.

**218.** San Giusto Cathedral.

**1949.** Birth Bicent. of Vittorio Alfieri (poet).

| | | | | |
|---|---|---|---|---|
| 731. | 217. | 20 l. brown .. .. | 7·00 | 1·25 |

**1949.** First Trieste Free Election.

| | | | | |
|---|---|---|---|---|
| 732. | 218. | 20 l. lake .. .. | 10·00 | 8·00 |

**219.** Staff of Aesculapius and Globe.

**220.** A. Palladio and Vicenza Basilica.

**1949.** 2nd World Health Congress, Rome.

| | | | | |
|---|---|---|---|---|
| 733. | 219. | 20 l. violet .. .. | 26·00 | 7·50 |

**1949.** 400th Anniv. of Completion of Palladio's Basilica at Vicenza.

| | | | | |
|---|---|---|---|---|
| 734. | 220. | 20 l. violet .. .. | 14·00 | 5·00 |

**221.** Lorenzo de Medici. **222.** Galleon and Exhibition Buildings.

**1949.** 500th Birth Anniv. of Lorenzo de Medici "The Magnificent".
735. **221.** 20 l. blue .. .. 10·00 1·25

**1949.** 13th Levant Fair, Bari.
736 **222** 20 l. red .. .. 6·00 1·25

**223.** Voltaic Pile. **224.** Count Alessandro Volta.

**1949.** 150th Anniv. of Volta's Discovery of the Electric Cell.
737. **223.** 20 l. red .. .. 4·00 1·25
738. **224.** 50 l. blue .. .. 50·00 12·00

**225.** Holy Trinity Bridge, Florence. **226.** Caius Valerius Catullus.

**1949.** Rebuilding of Holy Trinity Bridge Florence.
739. **225.** 20 l. green .. .. 12·00 1·25

**1949.** Death Bimillenary of Catullus (poet).
740. **226.** 20 l. blue .. .. 12·00 1·25

**227.** Domenico Cimarosa. **228.** Entrance to Exhibition.

**1949.** Birth Bicent of Cimarosa (composer).
741 **227** 20 l. violet .. .. 10·00 90

**1950.** 28th Milan Fair.
742. **228.** 20 l. brown .. .. 2·25 90

**229.** Car and Flags.

**1950.** 32nd Int. Automobile Exn., Turin.
743. **229.** 20 l. violet .. .. 10·00 90

**230.** Statue of Perseus. **231.** St. Peter's Basilica.

**1950.** 5th General U.N.E.S.C.O. Conference, Florence.
744. – 20 l. green .. .. 4·00 1·10
745. **230.** 55 l. blue .. .. 35·00 4·00
DESIGN—HORIZ. 20 l. Pitti Palace, Florence.

**1950.** Holy Year.
746. **231.** 20 l. violet .. .. 3·00 50
747. 55 l. blue .. .. 40·00 1·25

**232.** Gaudenzio Ferrari. **233.** Town Hall, Florence, Statue of Columbus and Wireless Mast. **234.** L. Muratori.

**1950.** Honouring Gaudenzio Ferrari (painter).
748 **232** 20 l. green .. .. 14·00 1·50

**1950.** Int. Radio Conf., Florence.
749. **233.** 20 l. violet .. .. 10·00 4·00
750. 55 l. blue .. .. £140 60·00

**1950.** Death Bicent. of Ludovico Muratori (historian).
751. **234.** 20 l. brown .. .. 7·00 1·25

**235.** Guido D'Arezzo. **236.** Galleon.

**1950.** 9th Death Cent. of D'Arezzo (musician).
752. **235.** 20 l. green .. .. 15·00 1·25

**1950.** 14th Levant Fair, Bari.
753. **236.** 20 l. brown .. .. 10·00 1·25

**237.** Marzotto and Rossi. **238.** Tobacco Plant and Factory.

**1950.** Pioneers of Wool Industry.
754. **237.** 20 l. blue .. .. 80 65

**1950.** European Tobacco Conf, Rome.
755 **238** 5 l. green and mauve 80 1·60
756 – 20 l. green and brown 2·25 65
757 – 55 l. brown and blue .. 45·00 10·00
DESIGNS: 20 l. Plant. 55 l. Girl and plant.

**239.** Seal of Academy. **240.** A. Righi. **241.** Blacksmith.

**1950.** Bicentenary of Academy of Fine Arts, Venice.
758 **239** 20 l. lt brown & brown 4·00 1·00

**1950.** Birth Centenary of Augusto Righi (physicist).
759. **240.** 20 l. black and buff .. 2·75 1·25

**1950.** Provincial Occupations. As T **241**.
760 **241** 50 c. blue .. .. 10 10
881 – 1 l. violet .. .. 10 10
762 – 2 l. brown .. .. 10 10
763 – 5 l. black .. .. 50 10
764 – 6 l. brown .. .. 25 10
765 – 10 l. green .. .. 4·75 10
766 – 12 l. green .. .. 2·00 10
883 – 15 l. blue .. .. 60 10
768 – 20 l. violet .. .. 10·00 10
769 – 25 l. brown .. .. 3·25 10
770 – 30 l. purple .. .. 1·90 10
771 – 35 l. red .. .. 8·50 35
772 – 40 l. brown .. .. 55 10
773 – 50 l. violet .. .. 14·00 10
774 – 55 l. blue .. .. 80 10
775 – 60 l. red .. .. 4·50 25
776 – 65 l. green .. .. 90 10
777 – 100 l. brown .. .. 30·00 10
778 – 200 l. brown .. .. 16·00 15

DESIGNS: 1 l. Motor mechanic. 2 l. Stonemason. 5 l. Potter. 6 l. Girls embroidering and water-carrying. 10 l. Weaver. 12 l. Fisherman at tiller. 15 l. Boat builder. 20 l. Fisherman trawling. 25 l. Girl packing oranges. 30 l. Girl carrying grapes. 35 l. Gathering olives. 40 l. Carter and wagon. 50 l. Shepherd. 55 l. Ploughman. 60 l. Ox-cart. 65 l. Girl harvester. 100 l. Women handling maize. 200 l. Woodcutter.

**242.** First Tuscan Stamp. **243.** Car and Flags.

**1951.** Centenary of First Tuscan Stamp.
779 **242** 20 l. red and purple .. 1·25 80
780 55 l. bl & ultramarine 20·00 14·00

**1951.** 33rd International Motor Show, Turin.
781 **243** 20 l. green .. .. 14·00 1·60

**244.** Peace Hall, Rome.

**1951.** Consecration of Hall of Peace, Rome.
782. **244.** 20 l. violet .. .. 8·75 1·60

**245.** Westland W.81 Helicopter over Fair. **246.** Fair Building.

**1951.** 29th Milan Fair.
783. **245.** 20 l. brown .. .. 10·00 1·10
784. **246.** 55 l. blue .. .. 30·00 20·00

**247.** Allegory. **248.** Columbus disembarking.

**1951.** 10th International Textile Art and Fashion Exhibition, Turin.
785 **247** 20 l. violet .. .. 16·00 1·75

**1951.** 500th Birth Anniv of Columbus.
786 **248** 20 l. green .. .. 20·00 2·25

**249.** Gymnastics Symbols. **250.** Montecassino Abbey restored.

**1951.** Int. Gymnastic Festival Florence.
787. **249.** 5 l. red and brown .. 18·00 £150
788. 10 l. red and green .. 18·00 £150
789. 15 l. red and blue .. 18·00 £150

**1951.** Restoration of Montecassino Abbey.
790. **250.** 20 l. violet .. .. 3·50 90
791. – 55 l. blue .. .. 40·00 16·00
DESIGN: 55 l. Abbey in ruins, 1944.

**251.** Perugino. **252.** Modern Art.

**1951.** 500th Birth Anniv. of Perugino (painter).
792. **251.** 20 l. brown and sepia 3·25 2·00

**1951.** Triennial Art Exn. Milan.
793. **252.** 20 l. black and green .. 4·75 1·75
794. – 55 l. pink and blue .. 20·00 16·00
DESIGN—HORIZ. 55 l. Jug and symbols.

**253.** Cyclist and Globe. **254.** Galleon and Hemispheres.

**1951.** World Cycling Championship.
795 **253** 25 l. black .. .. 3·00 1·60

**1951.** 15th Levant Fair, Bari.
796. **254.** 25 l. blue .. .. 5·50 1·25

**255.** "Jorio's Daughter".

**1951.** Birth Centenary of Francesco Paolo Michetti (painter).
797 **255** 25 l. brown .. .. 6·00 1·25

**256.** T 1 of Sardinia and Arms of Cagliari.

**1951.** Sardinian Postage Stamp Cent.
798. **256.** 10 l. black and sepia .. 1·00 1·75
799. – 25 l. green and red .. 1·50 1·00
800. – 60 l. red and blue .. 9·00 7·00
DESIGNS: 25 l. 20 c. stamp and arms of Genoa. 60 l. 40 c. stamp and arms of Turin.

**257.** "Industry and Commerce". **258.** Census in Ancient Rome.

**1951.** 3rd Industrial and Commercial Census.
801. **257.** 10 l. green .. .. 1·25 1·25

**1951.** 9th National Census.
802 **258** 25 l. black .. .. 1·75 1·00

**259.** G. Verdi and Roncole Church. **260.** Mountain Forest.

**1951.** 50th Death Anniv of Giuseppe Verdi (composer).
803. – 10 l. green and purple .. 1·50 1·00
804. **259.** 25 l. brown & choc. .. 6·00 1·00
805. – 60 l. blue and green .. 20·00 9·00
DESIGNS: 10 l. Verdi, Theatre Royal and Cathedral, Parma. 60 l. Verdi, La Scala Opera House and Cathedral, Milan.

**1951.** Forestry Festival. Inscr. "FESTA DEGLI ALBERI".
806. **260.** 10 l. green and olive .. 1·75 1·75
807. – 25 l. green .. 3·50 75
DESIGN—HORIZ. 25 l. Tree and wooded hills.

**261.** V. Bellini. **262.** Royal Palace, Caserta.

**1952.** 150th Birth Anniv. of Bellini (composer).
808. **261.** 25 l. black .. .. 2·50 50

**1952.** Bicentenary of Construction of Caserta Palace by Vanvitelli.
809. **262.** 25 l. bistre and green 2·75 50

**263.** **264.** Motor-boat Pavilion.

**1952.** 1st Int Sports Stamps Exn, Rome.
810 **263** 25 l. brown and black 90 65

**1952.** 30th Milan Fair.
811. **264.** 60 l. blue .. .. 8·00 6·00

**265.** Leonardo da Vinci. **267.** Campaniles and First Stamps.

**1952.** 500th Birth Anniv. of Leonardo da Vinci.
812. **265.** 25 l. orange .. .. 35 10
813. – 60 l. blue .. .. 3·00 3·75
814. **265.** 80 l. red .. .. 18·00 30
DESIGN—(inscr. "LEONARDO DA VINCI 1452–1952"): 60 l. "The Virgin of the Rocks".

**1952.** Modena and Parma Stamp Cent.
815. **267.** 25 l. black & brown 80 65
816. 60 l. indigo and blue 5·00 5·00

**268.** Hand, Torch and Globe. **269.** Lion of St. Mark.

**1952.** Overseas Fair, Naples.
817. **268.** 25 l. blue .. .. 1·40 50

**1952.** 26th Biennial Art Exhibition, Venice.
818 **269** 25 l. black and cream .. 1·40 50

**270.** Emblem of Fair. **271.** San Giusto Cathedral and Flag.

**1952.** 30th Padua Fair.
819. **270.** 25 l. red and blue .. 2·25 60

**1952.** 4th Trieste Fair.
820 **271** 25 l. green, red & brown 1·75 60

**272.** Caravel and Bari Fair. **273.** Girolamo Savonarola.

**1952.** 16th Levant Fair, Bari.
821. **272.** 25 l. green .. .. 1·60 60

**1952.** 5th Birth Cent. of Savonarola (reformer).
822. **273.** 25 l. violet .. .. 2·50 60

**274.** Savoia Marchetti S.M.95C over Colosseum. **275.** Alpine Climbing Equipment.

**1952.** 1st Civil Aeronautics Law Conf. Rome.
823. **274.** 60 l. bl. & ultramarine 16·00 14·00

**1952.** Alpine Troops National Exhibition.
824 **275** 25 l. black .. .. 1·00 40

**276.** Army, Navy and Air Force Symbols. **277.** Sailor, Soldier and Airman.

**1952.** Armed Forces Day.
825. **276.** 10 l. green .. .. 15 10
826. **277.** 25 l. sepia and brown .. 35 10
827. – 60 l. black and blue .. 3·00 2·50
DESIGN—As Type **277**: 60 l. Airplane, motor torpedo boat and tank.

**278.** Cardinal Massaia and Map. **279.** V. Gemito

**1952.** Cent. of Mission to Ethiopia.
828. **278.** 25 l. deep brn. & brn. 1·60 1·00

**1952.** Birth Cent. of Gemito (sculptor).
829. **279.** 25 l. brown .. .. 1·25 45

**280.** A. Mancini. **281.**

**1952.** Birth Cent. of Mancini (painter).
830. **280.** 25 l. myrtle .. .. 1·25 45

**1952.** Cent. of Martyrdom of Belfiore.
831. **281.** 25 l. blue and black .. 1·60 45

**282.** Antonello da Messina. **283.** Cars Racing.

**1953.** Antonello Exhibition, Messina.
832. **282.** 25 l. red .. .. 1·50 45

**1953.** 20th "Mille Miglia" Car Race.
833. **283.** 25 l. violet .. .. 1·25 50

**284.** Bee and Medals. **285.** Arcangelo Corelli. **286.** Coin of Syracuse.

**1953.** Creation of Orders of Meritorious Labour.
834. **284.** 25 l. violet .. .. 1·00 45

**1953.** Birth Tercent. of Corelli (composer).
835. **285.** 25 l. brown .. .. 1·50 45

**1953.** (a) Size 17 × 21 mm.
887 **286** 1 l. black .. .. 10 10
888 5 l. grey .. .. 10 10
889 6 l. brown .. .. 10 10
890 10 l. red .. .. 10 10
891 12 l. green .. .. 10 10
839 13 l. purple .. .. 15 10
893 15 l. grey .. .. 20 10
894 20 l. brown .. .. 10 10
895 25 l. violet .. .. 25 10
896 30 l. brown .. .. 25 10
897 35 l. red .. .. 30 10
898 40 l. mauve .. .. 70 10
899 50 l. green .. .. 30 10
900 60 l. blue .. .. 25 10
901 70 l. green .. .. 40 10
902 80 l. brown .. .. 25 10
903 90 l. brown .. .. 50 10
1008 100 l. brown .. .. 55 10
905 130 l. red and grey .. 25 10
1009 200 l. blue .. .. 55 10

(b) Size $22\frac{1}{2} \times 28$ mm.
904 **286** 100 l. brown .. .. 14·00 10
846 200 l. blue .. .. 5·00 30
See also Nos. 1202/19b.

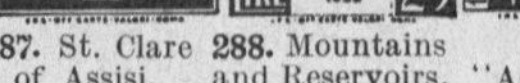

**287.** St. Clare of Assisi. **288.** Mountains and Reservoirs. **289.** "Agriculture".

**1953.** 700th Death Anniv of St. Clare.
847 **287** 25 l. red and brown .. 85 30

**1953.** Mountains Festival.
848. **288.** 25 l. green .. .. 2·50 30

**1953.** Int. Agricultural Exn., Rome.
849. **289.** 25 l. brown .. .. 1·25 10
850. 60 l. blue .. .. 4·00 1·50

**290.** Rainbow over Atlantic. **291.** L. Signorelli.

**1953.** 4th Anniv of Atlantic Pact.
851 **290** 25 l. turquoise & orge 4·00 20
852 60 l. blue and mauve 11·00 2·50

**1953.** 500th Birth Anniv. of Signorelli (painter).
853. **291.** 25 l. green & brown .. 55 20

**292.** A. Bassi. **293.** Capri.

**1953.** 6th Int Microbiological Congress, Rome.
854 **292** 25 l. brown and black 85 20

**1953.** Tourist Series.
855 – 10 l. brown and sepia 10 10
856 – 12 l. black and blue .. 15 15
857 – 20 l. brown and orange 40 10
858 – 25 l. green and blue .. 1·25 10
859 – 35 l. brown and buff .. 2·00 20
860 **293** 60 l. blue and green .. 3·00 50
DESIGNS—VERT. 10 l. Siena. 25 l. Cortina d'Ampezzo. HORIZ. 12 l. Rapallo. 20 l. Gardone. 35 l. Taormina.

**294.** Lateran Palace. **295.** Television Aerial and Screen.

**1954.** 25th Anniv. of Lateran Treaty.
861. **294.** 25 l. brown and sepia 65 15
862. 60 l. blue and bright bl. 2·25 1·50

**1954.** Introduction of Television in Italy.
863. **295.** 25 l. violet .. .. 1·00 15
864. 60 l. turquoise .. 4·50 2·00

**296.** "Everyone Must Contribute to the Public Expense". **297.** Vertical Flight Trophy.

**1954.** "Encouragement to Taxpayers".
865. **296.** 25 l. violet .. .. 2·50 15

**1954.** 1st Experimental Helicopter Mail Flight, Milan–Turin.
866 **297** 25 l. green .. .. 85 55

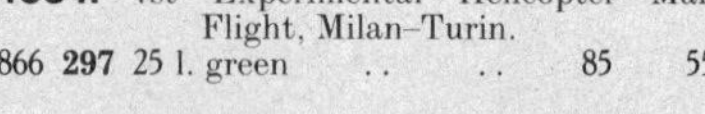

**298.** Golden Eagle and Campanile. **299.** A. Catalani.

**1954.** 10th Anniv. of Resistance Movement.
867. **298.** 25 l. black & brown .. 40 20

**1954.** Birth Cent. of Catalani (composer).
868. **299.** 25 l. green .. .. 50 20

**300.** Marco Polo, Lion of St. Mark, Venice, and Dragon Pillar, Peking.

**1954.** 7th Birth Cent. of Marco Polo.
869. **300.** 25 l. brown .. .. 50 20
870. 60 l. green .. .. 3·25 2·25

**301.** Cyclist, Car and Landscape.

**1954.** 60th Anniv. of Italian Touring Club.
871. **301.** 25 l. green and red .. 50 20

**302.** " St. Michael the Archangel" (after Guido Reni). **303.** " Pinocchio". **304.** Amerigo Vespucci.

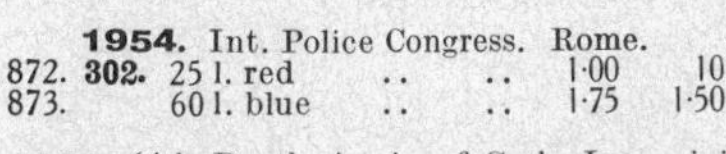

**1954.** Int. Police Congress. Rome.
872. **302.** 25 l. red .. .. 1·00 10
873. 60 l. blue .. .. 1·75 1·50

**1954.** 64th Death Anniv of Carlo Lorenzini (Collodi) (writer).
874 **303** 25 l. red .. .. 50 20

**1954.** 5th Birth Cent. of Vespucci (explorer).
875. **304.** 25 l. purple .. .. 45 10
876. 60 l. blue .. .. 2·50 1·25

**305.** " Madonna" (Perugino). **306.** Silvio Pellico. **308.** " The Nation Expects a Faithful Declaration of Your Income".

**1954.** Termination of Marian Year.
877. **305.** 25 l. brown and buff .. 30 15
878. – 60 l. black and cream 1·60 1·25
DESIGN: 60 l. Madonna's head (Michelangelo).

**1955.** Death Cent. of Pellico (dramatist).
879. **306.** 25 l. blue and violet .. 55 20

**1955.** "Encouragement to Taxpayers".
907. **308.** 25 l. lilac .. .. 2·25 10

**309.** **310.** A. Rosmini.

**1955.** 4th World Petroleum Congress.
908. **309.** 25 l. green .. .. 1·00 10
909. – 60 l. red .. .. 1·75 1·25
DESIGN: 60 l. Oil derricks and globe.

**1955.** Death Cent. of Rosmini (theologian).
910. **310.** 25 l. brown .. .. 65 15

**311.** Girolamo Fracastoro (physician) and Roman Arena, Verona.

**1955.** Int. Medical Conf., Verona.
915. **311.** 25 l. brown and black 65 15

# INDEX

Countries can be quickly located by referring to the index at the end of this volume.

**312.** Basilica of St. Francis. **313.** Scholar and Drawing-board.

**1955.** Bicentenary of Elevation of Basilica of St. Francis of Assisi to Papal Chapel.
916. **312.** 25 l. black & cream .. 35 15

**1955.** Cent. of "Montani" Institute, Fermo.
917. **313.** 25 l. green .. .. 30 15

**314.** " The Harvester". **315.** F.A.O. Building, Rome.

**1955.** 50th Anniv. of Int. Agricultural Institute.
918. **314.** 25 l. brown and red .. 30 15

**1955.** 10th Anniv of F.A.O.
919 **315** 60 l. violet and black .. 85 60

**316.** G. Matteotti. **317.** B. Grassi.

**1955.** 70th Birth Anniv of Giacomo Matteotti (politician).
920 **316** 25 l. red .. .. 70 15

**1955.** 30th Death Anniv. of Grassi (biologist).
921. **317.** 25 l. green .. .. 50 15

**318.** " St. Stephen giving Alms to the Poor". **319.** G. Pascoli.

**1955.** 5th Death Centenary of Fra Angelico (painter).
922 **318** 10 l. black and cream 20 10
923 – 25 l. blue and cream .. 35 10
DESIGN—HORIZ. 25 l. "St. Lawrence giving goods of the Church to the poor".

**1955.** Birth Cent. of Pascoli (poet).
924. **319.** 25 l. black .. .. 40 15

**320.** G. Mazzini. **321.** "Italia" Ski-jump.

**1955.** Air. 150th Birth Anniv. of Mazzini (founder of "Young Italy").
925. **320.** 100 l. green .. .. 2·25 1·00

**1956.** 7th Winter Olympic Games, Cortina d'Ampezzo.
926 **321** 10 l. green and orange 10 10
927 – 12 l. black and yellow 15 20
928 – 25 l. purple and orange 15 10
929 – 60 l. blue and orange 2·25 1·10
DESIGNS: 12 l. Snow Stadium. 25 l. Ice Stadium. 60 l. Skating Arena, Misurina.

**1956.** Air. Italian President's Visit to U.S.A. and Canada. Surch **1956 Visita del Presidente della Repubblica negli U.S.A. e nel Canada L. 120.**
930 **198** 120 l. on 50 l. mauve .. 1·25 1·90

**323.** Coach and Train.

**1956.** 50th Anniv. of Simplon Tunnel.
931. **323.** 25 l. green .. .. 5·00 20

**324.**

**1956.** 10th Anniv of Republic.
932 **324** 10 l. grey and blue .. 15 10
933 25 l. carmine and red 30 10
934 60 l. light blue and blue 3·00 2·25
935 80 l. orange and brown 6·00 15

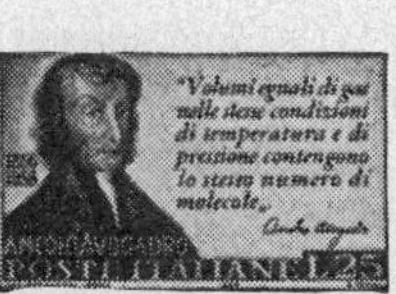

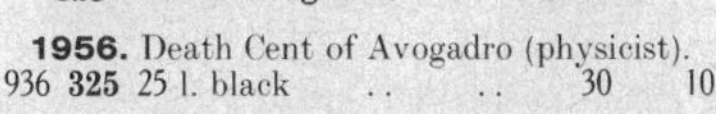

**325.** Count Avogadro. **326.**

**1956.** Death Cent of Avogadro (physicist).
936 **325** 25 l. black .. .. 30 10

**1956.** Europa.
937 **326** 25 l. dp green & green 80 10
938 60 l. deep blue and blue 8·00 35

**327.** **328.** The Globe.

**1956.** Int. Astronautical Congress, Rome.
939. **327.** 25 l. blue .. .. 30 10

**1956.** 1st Anniv. of Admission to U.N.
940. **328.** 25 l. red & green on pink 15 10
941. 60 l. grn. & red on green 30 10

**329.** Savings Bank, Books and Certificates. **330.** Ovid.

**1956.** 80th Anniv. of Post Office Savings Bank.
942. **329.** 25 l. blue and slate .. 20 10

**1957.** Birth Bimillenary of Ovid (poet).
943. **330.** 25 l. black and olive .. 30 10

**331.** St. George (after Donatello). **332.** Antonio Canova.

**1957.**
944 **331** 500 l. green .. .. 1·60 10
945a 1000 l. red .. .. 2·25 20

**1957.** Birth Bicent. of Canova (sculptor).
946. **332.** 25 l. brown .. .. 15 10
947. – 60 l. slate .. .. 25 30
948. – 80 l. blue .. .. 25 15
DESIGNS—VERT. 60 l. Hercules and Lica. HORIZ. 80 l. Pauline Borghese (bust).

**333.** Traffic Lights at Crossroads. **334.** "Europa" Flags.

**1957.** Road Safety Campaign.
949. **333.** 25 l. red, black & green 40 10

**1957.** Europa. Flags in National colours.
950. **334.** 25 l. blue .. .. 15 10
951. 60 l. blue .. .. 1·00 20

**335.** Giosue Carducci. **336.** Filippino Lippi (after self-portrait).

**1957.** 50th Death Anniv. of Carducci (poet).
954. **335.** 25 l. sepia .. .. 30 10

**1957.** 500th Birth Anniv. of Filippino Lippi (painter).
955. **336.** 25 l. brown .. .. 20 10

**337.** Cicero (bust). **338.** Garibaldi (after M. Lorusso).

**1957.** 2,000th Death Anniv. of Cicero (statesman).
956. **337.** 25 l. red .. .. 25 10

**1957.** 150th Birth Anniv. of Garibaldi.
957. **338.** 15 l. grey .. .. 10 10
958. – 110 l. lilac .. .. 45 25
DESIGN—HORIZ. 110 l. Statue of Garibaldi on horseback (after Romanelli).

**339.** St. Domenico Savio and Youths. **340.** St. Francis of Paola.

**1957.** Death Cent. of St. Domenico Savio.
959. **339.** 15 l. black and violet .. 10 10

**1957.** 450th Death Anniv. of St. Francis of Paola.
960. **340.** 25 l. black .. .. 30 10

**341.** Dams, Peasant and Map of Sardinia. **342.** Statue of the Holy Virgin and Lourdes Basilica.

**1958.** Inaug. of Flumendosa—Mulargia Irrigation Scheme, Sardinia.
961. **341.** 25 l. turquoise .. 10 10

**1958.** Centenary of Apparition of Virgin Mary at Lourdes.
962 **342** 15 l. purple .. .. 10 10
963 60 l. blue .. .. 15 10

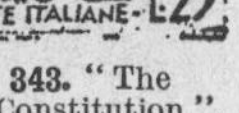


343. "The Constitution".

344. Exhibition Emblem and Ancient Roman Road.

**1958.** 10th Anniv. of Constitution.
964. **343.** 25 l. green & brown .. 10 10
965. – 60 l. sepia and blue .. 15 10
966. – 110 l. sepia & brown .. 40 15
DESIGNS—VERT. 60 l. Oak tree with new growth. HORIZ. 110 l. Montecitorio Palace, Rome.

**1958.** Brussels Int. Exn.
967. **344.** 60 l. yellow and blue .. 10 10

345. Rodolfo's Attic ("La Boheme").

346. The Prologue ("I Pagliacci").

**1958.** Birth Centenary of Puccini (operatic composer).
968. **345.** 25 l. blue .. .. 30 10

**1958.** Birth Cent. of Leoncavallo (operatic composer).
969. **346.** 25 l. red and indigo .. 40 10

347. "Ave Maria" (after Segantini).

348. "Fattori in his Studio" (self-portrait).

**1958.** Birth Centenary of Giovanni Segantini (painter).
970 **347** 110 l. green on cream .. 35 15

**1958.** 50th Death Anniv. of Giovanni Fattori (painter).
971. **348.** 110 l. brown .. .. 50 20

349. Federal Palace, Brasilia and Arch of Titus, Rome.

349a. "Europa".

**1958.** Visit of Pres. Gronchi to Brazil.
972 **349** 175 l. green .. .. 90 1·25

**1958.** Europa.
973 **349a** 25 l. blue and red .. 10 10
974 60 l. red and blue .. 30 10

350. Naples ½ grano stamp of 1858.

POSTE ITALIANE L.25
VISITA DI S.M.I. LO SCIAHINSCIAH DELL'IRAN
ROMA OTTOBRE 1958

351. "Winged Horse" (sculpture in Sorrento Cathedral).

**1958.** 1st Naples Postage Stamps Cent.
975. **350.** 25 l. brown .. .. 10 10
976. – 60 l. brown & sepia .. 20 10
DESIGN: 60 l. Naples 1 grano stamp of 1858.

**1958.** Visit of Shah of Iran.
977. **351.** 25 l. sepia & lavender 10 10
978. 60 l. blue & pale blue .. 35 50

352. E. Torricelli.

353. "Triumphs of Julius Caesar" (after fresco by Mantegna).

**1958.** 350th Birth Anniv. of Evangelista Torricelli (physicist).
979. **352.** 25 l. red .. .. 60 30

**1958.** 40th Anniv. of Victory in World War I.
980. **353.** 15 l. green .. .. 10 10
981. – 25 l. slate .. .. 10 10
982. – 60 l. red .. .. 15 15
DESIGNS—HORIZ. 25 l. Arms of Trieste, Rome and Trento. VERT. 60 l. Memorial bell of Rovereto.

354. Eleonora Duse.

355. "Drama".

**1958.** Birth Cent. of Eleonora Duse (actress).
983. **354.** 25 l. blue .. .. 15 10

**1958.** 10th Anniv. of "Premio Italia" (international contest for radio and television plays).
984. **355.** 25 l. black, blue & red 10 10
985. – 60 l. black and blue .. 15 10
DESIGN: 60 l. "Music" (radio mast and grand piano).

356. Sicily 5 gr. stamp of 1859.



357. Capitol, Quirinal Square Obelisk and Dome of St. Peter's.

**1959.** 1st Sicilian Postage Stamps Cent.
986. – 25 l. turquoise .. .. 10 10
987. **356.** 60 l. orange .. .. 20 10
DESIGN: 25 l. Sicily 2 gr. stamp of 1859.

**1959.** 30th Anniv. of Lateran Treaty.
988. **357.** 25 l. blue .. .. 10 10



358. N.A.T.O. Emblem and Map.

**1959.** 10th Anniv. of N.A.T.O.
989. **358.** 25 l. blue and yellow 10 10
990. 60 l. blue and green 20 15

359. Arms of Paris and Rome.

360. Olive Branch growing from shattered Tree.

**1959.** Rome–Paris Friendship.
991 **359** 15 l. red, brown & blue 15 10
992 25 l. red, brown & blue 15 10

**1959.** Int. War Veterans' Assn. Convention, Rome.
993. **360.** 25 l. green .. .. 10 10

361. Lord Byron Monument.

362. C. Prampolini.

**1959.** Unveiling of Lord Byron Monument, Rome.
994. **361.** 15 l. green .. .. 10 10

**1959.** Birth Centenary of Camillo Prampolini (politician).
995. **362.** 15 l. red .. .. 1·25 10

363. Quirinal Square Obelisk Rome.

364. Victor Emmanuel II, Garibaldi, Cavour and Mazzini.

**1959.** Olympic Games Propaganda. Roman Monuments and Ruins. Inscr. "ROMA MCMLX".
996. **363.** 15 l. sepia & orange 15 10
997. – 25 l. sepia & blue .. 15 10
998. – 35 l. sepia and buff 20 10
999. – 60 l. sepia & mauve 30 15
1000. – 110 l. sepia & yellow 40 15
DESIGNS—VERT. 25 l. Tower of City Hall, Quirinal Hill. HORIZ. 35 l. Baths of Caracalla. 60 l. Arch of Constantine (Colosseum). 110 l. Basilica of Massentius.

**1959.** Cent. of 2nd War of Independence.
1001. **364.** 15 l. black .. .. 10 10
1002. – 25 l. red and brown .. 15 10
1003. – 35 l. violet .. .. 15 15
1004. – 60 l. blue .. .. 15 15
1005. – 110 l. lake .. .. 20 15
DESIGNS—VERT. 25 l. Italian camp after the Battle of Magenta (after painting by Fattori). 110 l. Battle of Magenta (after painting by Induno). HORIZ. 35 l. Battle of San Fermo (after painting by Trezzini). 60 l. Battle of Palestro.
The 25 l. is also a Red Cross commemorative.

365. Workers' Monument and I.L.O. Building, Geneva.

366. Romagna 8 b. Stamp of 1859.

**1959.** 40th Anniv. of I.L.O.
1006. **365.** 25 l. violet .. .. 10 10
1007. 60 l. brown .. .. 10 10

**1959.** Romagna Postage Stamps Cent.
1010. **366.** 25 l. brown and black 10 10
1011. – 60 l. green and black 10 10
DESIGN: 60 l. Romagna 20 b. stamp of 1859.

366a. "Europa".

367.

**1959.** Europa.
1012 **366a** 25 l. green .. .. 10 10
1013 60 l. blue .. .. 10 10

**1959.** Stamp Day.
1014. **367.** 15 l. red, blk. & grey 10 10

368. "The Fire of Borgo" (after Raphael).

369. Garibaldi's Message to Sicilians.

**1960.** World Refugee Year.
1015. **368.** 25 l. red .. .. 10 10
1016. 60 l. purple .. .. 10 10

**1960.** Cent. of Garibaldi's Expedition to Sicily.
1017. **369.** 15 l. brown .. .. 10 10
1018. – 25 l. red .. .. 10 10
1019. 60 l. blue .. .. 20 20
DESIGNS—VERT. 25 l. Garibaldi meeting King Victor Emmanuel II near Naples (after Matania). HORIZ. 60 l. Embarkation of volunteers at Quarto, near Genoa (after T. van Elven).

370. "The Discus Thrower". (after Miron).

371. Vittorio Bottego (after Ettore Ximenes).

**1960.** Olympic Games. Inscr. as in T **370.**
1020. – 5 l. brown .. .. 10 10
1021. – 10 l. blue and orange 10 10
1022. – 15 l. blue .. .. 10 10
1023. – 25 l. sepia and lilac .. 10 10
1024. **370.** 35 l. red .. .. 10 10
1025. – 60 l. sepia and green 15 10
1026. – 110 l. purple .. .. 20 10
1027. – 150 l. brown and blue 1·40 1·10
1028. – 200 l. green .. .. 70 20
DESIGNS—VERT. 5 l. Games emblem. 15 l. "Starting the Race" (statue). 110 l. "Pugilist at rest" (after Apollonius). 200 l. "The Apoxiomenos" (after Lisippos). HORIZ. 10 l. Olympic Stadium, Rome. 25 l. Cycling Stadium, Rome. 60 l. Sports Palace, Rome. 150 l. Little Sports Palace.

**1960.** Birth Centenary of Vittorio Bottego (explorer).
1029. **371.** 30 l. brown .. .. 10 10

371a. Conference Emblem.

**1960.** Europa.
1030 **371a** 30 l. brown & green 10 10
1031 70 l. orange and blue 20 10

372. Caravaggio.



373. Coach and Posthorn.

**1960.** 350th Death Anniv. of Caravaggio (painter).
1032. **372.** 25 l. brown .. .. 10 10

**1960.** Stamp Day.
1033. **373.** 15 l. sepia and red .. 10 10

374. Michelangelo.

375. Douglas DC-8 Jetliner crossing Atlantic Ocean.

**1961.** Works of Michelangelo. Frescoes on ceiling of Sistine Chapel.
(a) Size 17 × 20½ mm.

1034 – 1 l. black .. .. 10 10
1035 – 5 l. orange .. .. 10 10
1036 – 10 l. red .. .. 10 10
1037 – 15 l. purple .. .. 10 10
1038 – 20 l. green .. .. 15 10
1039 – 25 l. brown .. .. 15 10
1040 – 30 l. purple .. .. 15 10
1041 – 40 l. red .. .. 15 10
1042 – 50 l. green .. .. 20 10
1043 – 55 l. brown .. .. 15 10
1044 – 70 l. blue .. .. 20 10
1045 – 85 l. green .. .. 20 10
1046 – 90 l. mauve .. .. 35 20
1047 – 100 l. violet .. .. 40 10
1048 – 115 l. blue .. .. 20 10
1049 – 150 l. brown .. .. 70 10
1050 374 200 l. blue .. .. 1·40 10

(b) Size 22 × 26½ mm.

1051 – 500 l. green .. .. 2·75 10
1052 – 1000 l. red .. .. 4·00 2·00

DESIGNS: 1, 5, 10, 115, 150 l. Ignudo (different versions). 15 l. Joel. 20 l. Libyan Sibyl. 25 l. Isaiah. 30 l. Erythraean Sibyl. 40 l. Daniel. 50 l. Delphic Sibyl. 55 l. Cumaean Sibyl. 70 l. Zachariah. 85 l. Jonah. 90 l. Jeremiah. 100 l. Ezekiel. 500 l. Adam. 1000 l. Eve.

**1961.** Visit of President Gronchi to S. America.

1053. **375.** 170 l. bl. (Argentina) 3·50 4·25
1054. 185 l. grn. (Uruguay) 3·50 4·25
1055. 205 l. violet (Peru) .. 9·50 10·00

The countries indicated are shown in deep colours on the map.

**376.** Pliny the Younger. **377.** Ippolito Nievo.

**1961.** 19th Birth Cent. of Pliny the Younger.

1056. **376.** 30 l. brown and buff 10 10

**1961.** Birth Cent. of Ippolito Nievo (poet).

1057. **377.** 30 l. blue and red .. 10 10

**378.** St. Paul in Ship (from 15th-century Bible of Borso d'Este).

**1961.** 19th Cent. of St. Paul's Arrival in Rome.

1058. **378.** 30 l. multicoloured .. 20 10
1059. 70 l. multicoloured .. 40 30

**379.** Cannon and Gaeta Fortress.

**1961.** Cent. of Italian Unification and Independence.

1060. **379.** 15 l. brown and blue 20 10
1061. – 30 l. brown and blue 20 10
1062. – 40 l. brown and blue 25 25
1063. – 70 l. mauve and brown 35 10
1064. – 115 l. blue and brown 1·25 10
1065. – 300 l. red, brn. & grn. 4·25 4·50

DESIGNS: 30 l. Carignano Palace, Turin. 40 l. Montecitorio Palace, Rome. 70 l. Vecchio Palace, Florence. 115 l. Madama Palace, Rome. 300 l. Capitals, "Palace of Work", Int. Exn. of Work Turin.

**380.** Doves. **381.** G. Romagnosi.

**1961.** Europa.

1066. **380.** 30 l. red .. .. 10 10
1067. 70 l. green .. .. 10 10

**1961.** Birth Bicent. of Romagnosi (philosopher).

1068. **381.** 30 l. green .. .. 10 10

**382.** Imprint of 50 c. Provisional Postal Franked Paper of Sardinia, 1819.

**1961.** Stamp Day.

1069. **382.** 15 l. mauve and black 10 10

**383.** "The Sweet-burning Lamp" from Pascoli's "La Poesia" (after wood-eng. by P. Morbiducci).

**1962.** 50th Death Anniv. of G. Pascoli (poet).

1070. **383.** 30 l. red .. .. 15 10
1071. 70 l. blue .. .. 30 40

**384.** Pacinotti's Dynamo (diagram). **385.** St. Catherine (after 15th-century woodcut).

**1962.** 50th Death Anniv. of Antonio Pacinotti (physicist).

1072. **384.** 30 l. black and red .. 15 10
1073. 70 l. black and blue .. 30 40

**1962.** 5th Cent. of Canonization of St. Catherine of Siena.

1074. – 30 l. violet .. .. 15 10
1075. **385.** 70 l. black and red .. 40 50

DESIGN: 30 l. St. Catherine (after A. Vanni).

**386.** Camera Lens. **387.** Cyclist being paced.

**1962.** 30th Anniv. of Int. Cinematograph Art Fair, Venice.

1076. **386.** 30 l. black and blue .. 25 10
1077. – 70 l. black and red .. 30 35

DESIGN: 70 l. Lion of St. Mark.

**1962.** World Cycling Championships.

1078. **387.** 30 l. black and green 20 10
1079. – 70 l. blue and black .. 20 10
1080. – 300 l. black and red 3·00 3·00

DESIGNS: 70 l. Cyclists road-racing. 300 l. Cyclists on track.

**388.** Europa "Tree".

**1962.** Europa.

1081 388 30 l. red and carmine 40 10
1082 70 l. ultramarine & bl 40 30

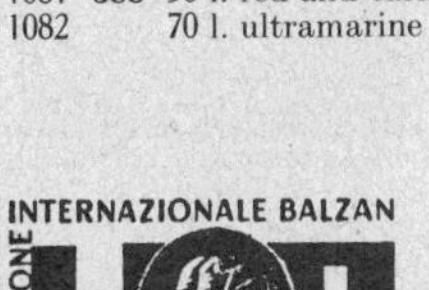

**389.** Balzan Medal. **390.** Campaign Emblem.

**1962.** Int. Balzan Foundation.

1083. **389.** 70 l. red and green .. 10 10

**1962.** Malaria Eradication.

1084. **390.** 30 l. violet .. .. 10 10
1085. 70 l. blue .. .. 25 25

**391.** 10 c. Stamp of 1862 and 30 l. Stamp of 1961. **392.** "The Pentecost" (from "Codex Syriacus").

**1962.** Stamp Day.

1086. **391.** 15 l. multicoloured .. 10 10

**1962.** Ecumenical Council, Vatican City.

1087 392 30 l. orange and blue on cream .. .. 10 10
1088 70 l. blue and orange on cream .. .. 15 15

**393.** Statue of Cavour (statesman). **394.** Pico della Mirandola (scholar). **395.** D'Annunzio.

**1962.** Cent. of Court of Accounts.

1089. **393.** 30 l. green .. .. 10 10

**1963.** 5th Birth Cent. of G. Pico della Mirandola.

1090. **394.** 30 l. violet .. .. 10 10

**1963.** Birth Cent. of Gabriele D'Annunzio (author and soldier).

1091. **395.** 30 l. green .. .. 10 10

**396.** "Sowing" (bas-relief after G. and N. Pisano). **397.** Monviso, Italian Alps, Ice-axe and Rope.

**1963.** Freedom from Hunger.

1092. **396.** 30 l. sepia and red .. 10 10
1093. – 70 l. sepia and blue .. 20 30

DESIGN: 70 l. "Harvesting" (bas-relief after G. and N. Pisano).

**1963.** Italian Alpine Club, Cent.

1094. **397.** 115 l. sepia and blue 10 10

**398.** "I.N.A." Lighthouse. **399.** Posthorn and Globe.

**1963.** 50th Anniv. of Italian National Insurance Corporation.

1095. **398.** 30 l. black and green 10 10

**1963.** Paris Postal Conference Cent.

1096. **399.** 70 l. blue and green 10 10

**400.** Three-dimensional Emblem. **401.** "World Tourism".

**1963.** Red Cross Cent.

1097. **400.** 30 l. red and purple .. 10 10
1098. 70 l. red and blue .. 25 30

**1963.** U.N. Tourism Conf., Rome.

1099. **401.** 15 l. blue and olive 10 10
1100. 70 l. brown and blue 15 20

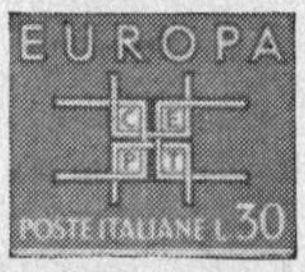

**402.** "Co-operation". **403.** "Naples".

**1963.** Europa.

1101. **402.** 30 l. brown and red .. 10 10
1102. 70 l. green and brown 20 10

**1963.** 4th Mediterranean Games, Naples. Inscr. "NAPOLI 1963".

1103. **403.** 15 l. ochre and blue 10 10
1104. – 70 l. orange & green .. 20 30

DESIGN: 70 l. Greek "Olympic" vase.

**404.** Mascagni and Costanzi Theatre. **405.** G. Belli.

**1963.** 150th Birth Anniv. of Verdi (1105) and Birth Centenary of Mascagni (1106) (composers).

1105 – 30 l. brown and green 15 10
1106 404 30 l. green and brown 15 10

DESIGN: No. 1105, Verdi and La Scala Opera House.

**1963.** Death Cent. of Giuseppei Belli (poet).

1107. **405.** 30 l. brown .. .. 10 10

**406.** Stamp "Flower". **407.** Galileo Galilei.

**1963.** Stamp Day.

1108. **406.** 15 l. red and blue .. 10 10

**1964.** 400th Birth Anniv. of Galileo Galilei.

1109. **407.** 30 l. brown .. .. 15 10
1110. 70 l. black .. .. 15 15

**408.** Nicodemus (from Michelangelo's "Pieta"). **410.** Carabinieri on Parade.

**1964.** 400th Death Anniv. of Michelangelo.

1111. **408.** 30 l. sepia (postage) .. 10 10
1112. – 185 l. black (air) .. 35 50

DESIGN: 185 l. Michelangelo's "Madonna of Bruges".

**1964.** 150th Anniv. of Carabinieri (military police).

1113. **410.** 30 l. red and blue .. 10 10
1114. – 70 l. brown .. .. 15 15

DESIGN: 70 l. "The Charge at Pastrengo (1848)" (De Albertis).

**411.** G. Bodoni. **412.** Europa "Flower".

**1964.** 150th Death Anniv. (1963) of Giambattista Bodoni (type-designer and printer).

1115. **411.** 30 l. red .. .. 10 10

**1964.** Europa.

1116. **412.** 30 l. purple .. .. 10 10
1117. 70 l. blue .. .. 10 10

**413.** European Buildings. **414.** Victor Emannuel Monument, Rome.

**1964.** 7th European Municipalities' Assembly.
1118. **413.** 30 l. brown and green 10 10
1119. 70 l. brown and blue 10 10
1120. 500 l. red .. .. 1·25 1·40

**1964.** War Veterans' Pilgrimage to Rome.
1121. **414.** 30 l. brown .. .. 10 10
1122. 70 l. blue .. .. 10 10

**415.** G. da Verrazzano and Verrazano Bridge.

**1964.** Opening of Verrazano Narrows Bridge, New York.
1123. **415.** 30 l. blk. & brn. (post.) 10 10
1124. 130 l. blk. & grn. (air) 20 35
This American bridge is designated " Verrazano " with one " z ".

**416.** Italian Stamps. **417.** Prisoners of War.

**1964.** Stamp Day.
1125. **416.** 15 l. brown and bistre 10 10

**1965.** 20th Anniv. of Resistance.
1126. **417.** 10 l. black .. .. 10 15
1127. – 15 l. blk., red & grn. 10 10
1128. – 30 l. purple .. .. 10 10
1129. – 70 l. blue .. .. 15 15
1130. – 115 l. red .. .. 15 15
1131. – 130 l. brn., grn. & red 15 15
DESIGNS—VERT. 15 l. Servicemen and casualty ("Liberation Army"). 70 l. Alpine soldiers ("Resistance in the mountains"). HORIZ. 30 l. Gaunt hands and arms on swastika ("Political and Racial Persecution"). 115 l. Patriots with banners ("Resistance in the Towns"). 130 l. Ruined building and torn flags ("Martyred Cities").

**418.** I.T.U. Emblem, Meucci and Marconi.

**1965.** I.T.U. Cent.
1132. **418.** 70 l. red and green .. 10 10

**419.** Yachts of "Flying Dutchman" Class.

**1965.** World Sailing Championships, Alassio and Naples.
1133. **419.** 30 l. black and red .. 15 10
1134. – 70 l. black and blue .. 15 10
1135. – 500 l. black & grey-bl. 50 60
DESIGNS—VERT. 70 l. "5.5 S.I" class yachts. HORIZ. 500 l. "Lightning" class yachts.

**420.** Mont Blanc and Tunnel. **421.** A. Tassoni and Episode from his " Secchia Rapita ".

**1965.** Opening of Mont Blanc Road Tunnel.
1136. **420.** 30 l. black .. .. 10 10

**1965.** 400th Birth Anniv. of Alessandro Tassoni (poet).
1137. **421.** 40 l. multicoloured .. 10 10

**422.** Europa " Sprig ". **423.** " Hell " (Codex, Vatican Library).

**1965.** Europa.
1138 422 40 l. green and orange 10 10
1139 90 l. green and blue .. 10 10

**1965.** 700th Birth Anniv. of Dante.
1140. **423.** 40 l. multicoloured .. 10 10
1141. – 90 l. multicoloured .. 15 15
1142. – 130 l. multicoloured .. 15 15
1143. – 500 l. green .. .. 40 45
DESIGNS—VERT. 90 l. " Purgatory " (codex, Marciana Library, Venice). 500 l. Head of Dante (bronze, Naples Museum), HORIZ. 130 l. " Paradise " (codex, British Museum.)

**424.** House and Savings-bank. **425.** Douglas DC-6B Airliner passing Control-tower.

**1965.** Savings Day.
1144. **424.** 40 l. multicoloured .. 10 10

**1965.** Night Airmail Service.
1145 425 40 l. red and blue .. 15 10
1146 – 90 l. multicoloured .. 15 10
DESIGN: 90 l. Sud Aviation Caravelle jetliner within airmail envelope "border".

**426.** Map of "Highway to the Sun ". **427.** Two-man Bobsleigh.

**1965.** Stamp Day.
1147. **426.** 20 l. multicoloured .. 10 10

**1966.** World Bobsleigh Championships, Cortina d'Ampezzo.
1148 427 40 l. red, blue & grey 15 10
1149 – 90 l. violet and blue .. 15 10
DESIGN: 90 l. Four-man bobsleigh.

**428.** Skier carrying Torch. **429.** B. Croce.

**1966.** University Winter Games, Turin.
1150. **428.** 40 l. black and red .. 15 10
1151. – 90 l. violet and red .. 15 10
1152. – 500 l. brown and red 35 45
DESIGNS—VERT. 90 l. Ice skating. 500 l. Ice hockey.

**1966.** Birth Centenary of Benedetto Croce (philosopher).
1153. **429.** 40 l. sepia .. .. 10 10

**430.** Arms of Cities of Venezia.

**1966.** Cent. of Union of Venezia and Italy.
1154. **430.** 40 l. multicoloured 10 10

**431.** Pine, Palatine Hill, Rome. **432.** " Visit Italy ".

**1966.** "Trees and Flowers". Multicoloured.
1155. 20 l. Type **431** .. .. 10 10
1156. 25 l. Apples .. .. 15 10
1157. 40 l. Carnations .. .. 15 10
1158. 50 l. Irises .. .. 15 10
1241. 55 l. Cypresses .. .. 20 10
1159. 90 l. Anthemis (Golden Marguerite) .. .. 15 15
1160. 170 l. Olive tree, Villa Adriana, Tivoli .. 20 15
1242. 180 l. Broom .. .. 40 20
Nos. 1241 and 1242 are 26 × 35½ mm.

**1966.** Tourist Propaganda.
1161. **432.** 20 l. multicoloured 10 10

**433.** Capital " I ". **434.** Battle Scene.

**1966.** 20th Anniv. of Republic.
1162. **433.** 40 l. multicoloured 10 10
1163. 90 l. multicoloured 10 10

**1966.** Cent. of Battle of Bezzecca.
1164. **434.** 90 l. olive .. 10 10

**435.** "Singing Angels" (from copper panel on altar of St. Antony's Basilica, Padua). **436.** Europa " Ship ".

**1966.** 5th Death Cent. of Donatello.
1165. **435.** 40 l. multicoloured 10 10

**1966.** Europa.
1166. **436.** 40 l. violet .. .. 10 10
1167. 90 l. blue .. .. 10 10

**437.** " Madonna in Maesta " (after Giotto). **438.** Filzi, Battisti, Chiesa and Sauro.

**1966.** Giotto's 700th Birth Anniv.
1168. **437.** 40 l. multicoloured .. 10 10

**1966.** 50th Death Annivs. of World War I Heroes.
1169. **438.** 40 l. green and slate .. 10 10

**439.** Postal Emblem. **440.** Compass and Globe.

**1966.** Stamp Day.
1170. **439.** 20 l. multicoloured .. 10 10

**1967.** Cent. of Italian Geographical Society.
1171. **440.** 40 l. blue and black .. 10 10

**441.** Toscanini.

**1967.** Birth Centenary of Arturo Toscanini (orchestral conductor).
1172. **441.** 40 l. buff and blue .. 30 10

**442.** Campidoglio, Rome.

**1967.** 10th Anniv. of Rome Treaties.
1173. **442.** 40 l. brown & black .. 10 10
1174. 90 l. purple and black 10 10

**443.** Cogwheels. **444.** Brown Bear (Abruzzo Park).

**1967.** Europa.
1175. **443.** 40 l. purple and pink 10 10
1176. 90 l. blue and cream 10 10

**1967.** Italian National Parks. Multicoloured.
1177. 20 l. Ibex (Gran Paradiso Park) (vert.) .. .. 10 10
1178. 40 l. Type **444** .. .. 10 10
1179. 90 l. Red deer stag (Stelvio Park) .. 20 15
1180. 170 l. Tree (Circeo Park) (vert.) .. .. .. 30 20

**445.** Monteverdi.

**1967.** 400th Death Anniv. of Claudio Monteverdi (composer).
1181. **445.** 40 l. brown & chest. 15 10

**446.** Racing Cyclists.

**1967.** 50th Tour of Italy Cycle Race. Designs showing cyclists.
1182. **446.** 40 l. multicoloured 10 10
1183. – 90 l. multicoloured 10 10
1184. – 500 l. multicoloured 65 80

**447.** Pirandello and Stage.

**1967.** Birth Centenary of Luigi Pirandello (dramatist).
1185. **447.** 40 l. multicoloured .. 10 10

**448.** Stylised Mask.

**1967.** Two Worlds Festival, Spoleto.
1186. **448.** 20 l. black and green 10 10
1187. 40 l. black and red 10 10

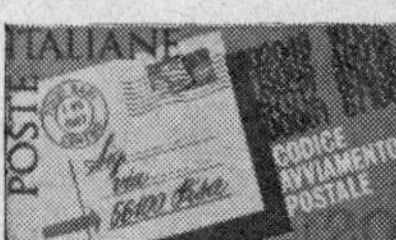

**449.** Coded Addresses.

**1967.** Introduction of Postal Codes.
1188 449 20 l. black, blue & yell 10 10
1189 25 l. black, red & yell 10 10
1190 40 l. black, pur & yell 10 10
1191 50 l. black, grn & yell 10 10

**450.** Pomilio PE Type Biplane and Postmark.

**451.** St. Ivo's Church, Rome.

**1967.** 50th Anniv. of 1st Airmail Stamp.

1192. **450.** 40 l. black and blue 10 10

**1967.** 300th Death Anniv. of Francesco Borromini (architect).

1193. **451.** 90 l. multicoloured .. 10 10

**452.** U. Giordano and Music from "Andrea Chenier".

**453.** "The Oath of Pontida" (from painting by Adolfo Cao).

**1967.** Birth Centenary of Umberto Giordano (composer).

1194. **452.** 20 l. brown & black .. 10 10

**1967.** 800th Anniv. of Oath of Pontida.

1195. **453.** 20 l. brown .. .. 10 10

**454.** I.T.Y. Emblem.

**455.** Lions Emblem.

**1967.** Int. Tourist Year.

1196. **454.** 20 l. blk., bl. & yell. 10 10
1197. 50 l. blk., bl. & orge. 10 10

**1967.** 50th Anniv. of Lions Int.

1198. **455.** 50 l. multicoloured .. 10 10

**456.** Sentry.

**457.** E. Fermi (scientist) and Reactor.

**1967.** 50th Anniv. of Stand on the Piave.

1199. **456.** 50 l. multicoloured .. 10 10

**1967.** 25th Anniv. of 1st Nuclear Chain Reaction.

1200. **457.** 50 l. black & brown 10 10

**458.** Stamp and Dove.

**1967.** Stamp Day.

1201. **458.** 25 l. multicoloured 10 10

**1968.** As Nos. 887, etc. (1952) size 16 × 20 mm.

1202. **286.** 1 l. black .. .. 10 10
1203. 5 l. slate .. .. 10 10
1204. 6 l. brown .. .. 10 10
1205. 10 l. red .. .. 10 10
1206. 15 l. violet .. .. 10 10
1207. 20 l. sepia .. .. 10 10
1208. 25 l. violet .. .. 10 10
1209. 30 l. brown .. .. 10 10
1210. 40 l. purple .. .. 10 10
1211. 50 l. olive .. .. 10 10
1212. 55 l. violet .. .. 20 10
1213. 60 l. blue .. .. 10 10
1214. 70 l. green .. .. 10 10
1215. 80 l. brown .. .. 10 10
1215a. 90 l. brown .. .. 10 10
1216. 100 l. brown .. .. 10 10
1216a. 120 l. blue and green 10 10

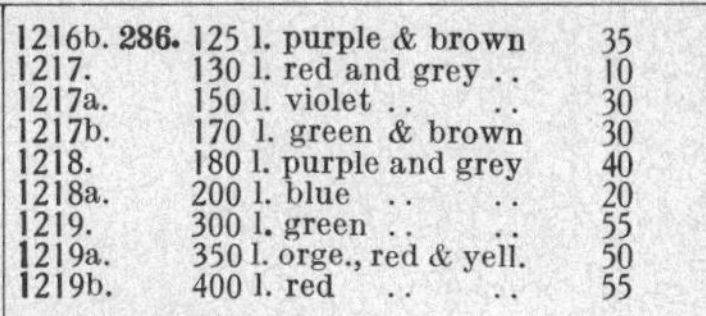

1216b. **286.** 125 l. purple & brown 35 10
1217. 130 l. red and grey .. 10 10
1217a. 150 l. violet .. .. 30 10
1217b. 170 l. green & brown 30 10
1218. 180 l. purple and grey 40 10
1218a. 200 l. blue .. .. 20 10
1219. 300 l. green .. .. 55 10
1219a. 350 l. orge., red & yell. 50 10
1219b. 400 l. red .. .. 55 20

**459.** Scouts around Campfire.

**460.** Europa "Key".

**1968.** Italian Boy Scouts.

1220. **459.** 50 l. multicoloured 10 10

**1968.** Europa.

1221. **460.** 50 l. green and pink 10 10
1222. 90 l. brown and blue 10 10

**461.** "Tending the Sick".

**462.** Boito and "Mephistopheles".

**1968.** 400th Birth Anniv. of Luigi Gonzaga (St. Aloysius).

1223. **461.** 25 l. violet and brown 10 10

**1968.** 50th Death Anniv. of Arrigo Boito (composer and librettist).

1224. **462.** 50 l. multicoloured .. 15 10

**463.** F. Baracca and "Aerial Combat" (abstract by G. Balla).

**464.** Giambattista Vico (300th Birth Anniv.).

**1968.** 500th Death Anniv. of Francesco Baracca (airman of World War I).

1225. **463.** 25 l. multicoloured 10 10

**1968.** Italian Philosophers' Birth Annivs.

1226. **464.** 50 l. blue .. .. 10 10
1227. – 50 l. black .. .. 10 10

DESIGN: No. 1227, Tommaso Campanella (400th birth anniv.).

**465.** Cycle Wheel and Stadium.

**467.** Rossini.

**466.** "St. Mark's Square, Venice" (Canaletto).

**1968.** World Road Cycling Championships.

1228. **465.** 25 l. blue, pink and brown .. .. 15 10
1229. – 90 l. indigo, red & blue 15 10

DESIGN: 90 l. Cyclists and Imola Castle.

**1968.** Death Bicent. of Canaletto (painter).

1230. **466.** 50 l. multicoloured 20 10

**1968.** Death Centenary of Gioacchino Rossini (composer).

1231. **467.** 50 l. red .. .. 15 10

**468.** Mobilization.

**469.** "Conti Correnti Postali".

**1968.** 50th Anniv. of Victory in World War I. Multicoloured.

1232. 20 l. Type **468** .. .. 10 10
1233. 25 l. Trench warfare .. 10 10
1234. 40 l. Naval forces .. 10 10
1235. 50 l. Air Force .. 10 10
1236. 90 l. Battle of Vittorio Veneto .. .. 15 15
1237. 180 l. Tomb of Unknown Soldier .. .. 20 20

**1968.** 50th Anniv. of Postal Cheque Service.

1238. **469.** 50 l. multicoloured .. 10 10

**470.** Tracking Equipment and Buildings.

**471.** "Postal Development".

**1968.** Space Telecommunications Centre, Fucino.

1239. **470.** 50 l. multicoloured 10 10

**1968.** Stamp Day.

1240. **471.** 25 l. red & yellow .. 10 10

**472.** Commemorative Medal.

**473.** Colonnade.

**1969.** Cent. of State Audit Department.

1243. **472.** 50 l. black and pink 10 10

**1969.** Europa.

1244. **473.** 50 l. multicoloured .. 15 10
1245. 90 l. multicoloured .. 15 15

**474.** Machiavelli.

**475.** I.L.O. Emblem.

**1969.** 500th Birth Anniv. of Niccolo Machiavelli (statesman).

1246. **474.** 50 l. multicoloured .. 10 10

**1969.** 50th Anniv. of I.L.O.

1247. **475.** 50 l. black and green 10 10
1248. 90 l. black and red .. 10 10

**476.** Postal Emblem.

**1969.** 50th Anniv. of Italian Philatelic Federation.

1249. **476.** 50 l. multicoloured .. 10 10

**477.** Sondrio-Tirano Mailcoach of 1903.

**1969.** Stamp Day.

1250. **477.** 25 l. blue .. .. 15 10

**478.** Skiing.

**479.** "Galatea" (detail of fresco by Raphael).

**1970.** World Skiing Championships, Val Gardena. Multicoloured.

1251. 50 l. Type **478** .. .. 15 10
1252. 90 l. Dolomites .. .. 15 10

**1970.** 450th Death Anniv. of Raphael. Mult.

1253. 20 l. Type **479** .. .. 15 10
1254. 50 l. "Madonna of the Goldfinch" .. .. 15 10

**480.** Symbols of Flight.

**1970.** 50th Anniv of Rome–Tokyo Flight by A. Ferrarin.

1255. **480.** 50 l. multicoloured .. 15 10
1256. 90 l. multicoloured .. 15 10

**481.** "Flaming Sun".

**482.** Erasmo da Narni (from statue by Donatello).

**1970.** Europa.

1257. **481.** 50 l. yellow and red .. 15 10
1258. 90 l. yellow and green 30 10

**1970.** 600th Birth Anniv. of Erasmo da Narni "Il Gattamelata" (Condottiere).

1259. **482.** 50 l. green .. .. 10 10

**483.** Running.

**1970.** World University Games, Turin. Multicoloured.

1260. 20 l. Type **483** .. .. 10 10
1261. 180 l. Swimming .. 20 20

**484.** Dr. Montessori and children.

**1970.** Birth Cent. of Dr. Maria Montessori (educationist).

1262. **484.** 50 l. multicoloured .. 15 10

**485.** Map and Cavour's Declaration.

**1970.** Centenary of Union of Rome and Papal States with Italy.

1263 485 50 l. multicoloured .. 15 10

**486.** Loggia of Campanile, St. Mark's Square, Venice.

**1970.** 400th Death Anniv of Jacopo Tatti, "Il Sansovino" (architect).

1264 486 50 l. brown .. .. 10 10

**487.** "Garibaldi at Dijon" (engraving).

**1970.** Centenary of Garibaldi's Participation in Franco-Prussian War.

1265. **487.** 20 l. grey and blue .. 20 15
1266. 50 l. purple and blue 20 15

488. U.N. Emblem within Tree. 489. Rotary Emblem.

**1970.** 25th Anniv. of United Nations.
1267. 488. 25 l. grn., blk. & brn. .. 10 10
1268. 90 l. yell., black & blue 20 15

**1970.** 65th Anniv of Rotary International.
1269 489 25 l. ultramarine, yellow and blue .. 15 10
1270 90 l. ultramarine, yellow and blue .. 25 10

490. Telephone Dial and " Network ". 491. Urban Complex and Tree.

**1970.** Completion of Telephone Trunk-dialling System.
1271 490 25 l. green and red .. 20 10
1272 90 l. blue and red .. 25 10

**1970.** Nature Conservation Year.
1273. 491. 20 l. red and green .. 15 10
1274. 25 l. grey and green 15 10

492. Electric Train. 493. "The Adoration" (F. Lippi).

**1970.** Stamp Day.
1275 492. 25 l. black .. .. 40 10

**1970.** Christmas. Multicoloured.
1276. 25 l. Type 493. (postage) 10 10
1277. 150 l. " The Adoration of the Magi " (Gentile da Fabriano). (air) .. 20 15
No. 1277 is horiz., size 44 × 35 mm.

494. Saverio Mercadante.

**1970.** Death Centenary of Saverio Mercadante (composer).
1278 494 25 l. violet and grey .. 15 10

495. " Mercury " (part of Cellini's " Perseus with the Head of Medusa "). 496. Bramante's " Little Temple ", St. Peter's Montorio, Rome.

**1971.** 400th Death Anniv. of Benvenuto Cellini (goldsmith and sculptor).
1279. 495. 50 l. blue .. .. 10 10

**1971.**
1280. 496. 50 l. black and brown 10 10

497. Adenauer, Schuman and De Gasperi.

**1971.** 20th Anniv. of European Coal and Steel Community.
1281. 497. 50 l. brn., blk. & grn. 15 10
1282. 90 l. brn., black & red 15 10

498. Europa Chain. 499. Mazzini.

**1971.** Europa.
1283. 498. 50 l. red .. .. 10 10
1284. 90 l. purple .. .. 20 10

**1971.** 25th Anniv. of Republic.
1285. 499. 50 l. multicoloured .. 15 10
1286. 90 l. multicoloured .. 15 10

500. Canoeist in Slalom.

**1971.** World Canoeing Slalom and Free Descent Championships. Merano. Mult.
1287. 25 l. Type 500 .. .. 10 10
1288. 90 l. Canoeist making free descent .. .. 20 15

501. Three Sports.

**1971.** Youth Games.
1289. 501. 20 l. blk., grn. & brn. 10 10
1290. – 50 l. blk., violet & orge. 10 10
DESIGN: 50 l. Four other sports.

502. Alitalia Emblem.

**1971.** 25th Anniv. of Alitalia State Airline. Multicoloured.
1291. 50 l. Type 502 .. .. 10 10
1292. 90 l. Emblem and Globe 15 15
1293. 150 l. Tailplane of Boeing 747 .. .. .. 25 20

503. Grazia Deledda. 504. Boy in " Savings " Barrel.

**1971.** Birth Cent. of Grazia Deledda (writer).
1294. 503. 50 l. black and brown 10 10

**1971.** Postal Savings Bank.
1295. 504. 25 l. multicoloured .. 10 10
1296. 50 l. multicoloured .. 10 10

**1971.** Air. As No. 911 but smaller, 20 × 36 mm.
1297 204 100 l. green .. .. 30 10

505. U.N.I.C.E.F. Emblem and Paper Dolls.

**1971.** 25th Anniv. of U.N.I.C.E.F. Mult.
1301. 25 l. Type 505 .. .. 10 10
1302. 90 l. Children acclaiming U.N.I.C.E.F. emblem 20 15

506. Liner "Tirrenia".

**1971.** Stamp Day.
1303. 506. 25 l. green .. .. 20 10

507. " The Nativity ".

**1971.** Christmas. Miniatures from " Matilda's Evangelarium ", Nonantola Abbey, Modena. Multicoloured.
1304. 25 l. Type 507 .. .. 10 10
1305. 90 l. " The Adoration of the Magi " .. .. 20 15

508. G. Verga and Sicilian Cart.

**1972.** 50th Death Anniv. of Giovanni Verga (writer).
1306. 508. 25 l. multicoloured .. 15 10
1307. 50 l. multicoloured .. 15 10

509. G. Mazzini. 510. Stylized Flags.

**1972.** Death Cent. of Giuseppe Mazzini (statesman).
1308. 509. 25 l. green and black 10 10
1309. 90 l. grey and black .. 15 15
1310. 150 l. red and black .. 20 20

**1972.** 50th Int. Fair, Milan.
1311. 510. 25 l. green and black 10 10
1312. – 50 l. red and black .. 10 10
1313. – 90 l. blue and black 15 15
DESIGNS: 50 l. " Windows, stand and pavilions " (abstract). 90 l. Abstract general view of Fair.

511. "Communications". 512. Alpine Soldier.

**1972.** Europa.
1314. 511. 50 l. multicoloured 15 10
1315. 90 l. multicoloured .. 25 15

**1972.** Cent. of Alpine Corps. Multicoloured
1316. 25 l. Type 512 .. .. 10 10
1317. 50 l. Soldier's hat .. 15 15
1318. 90 l. Soldier and mountains 20 20

513. Brenta Mountains.

**1972.** Centenary of Tridentine Alpinists Society. Multicoloured.
1319. 25 l. Type 513 .. .. 10 10
1320. 50 l. Alpinist .. .. 10 10
1321. 180 l. Mt. Crozzon .. 35 30

514. Diagram of Conference Hall.

**1972.** 60th Interparliamentary Union Conference, Rome.
1322. 514. 50 l. multicoloured .. 15 10
1323. 90 l. multicoloured .. 15 15

515. " St. Peter Damiani " (miniature, after G. di Paolo). 516. " The Three Graces " (Canova).

**1972.** 900th Death Anniv. of St Peter Damiani.
1324. 515. 50 l. multicoloured .. 10 10

**1972.** 150th Death Anniv of Antonio Canova (sculptor).
1325 516 50 l. green .. .. 15 10

517. Initial and First Verse (Foligno edition).

**1972.** 500th Anniv. of "The Divine Comedy". Multicoloured.
1326. 50 l. Type 517 .. .. 10 10
1327. 90 l. Initial and first verse (Mantua edition) (vert.) 15 10
1328. 180 l. Initial and first verse (" Jesino " edition) .. 35 20

518. " Angel ".

**1972.** Christmas. Multicoloured.
1329. 20 l. Type 518 .. .. 10 10
1330. 25 l. " Holy Child in Crib " (horiz.) .. .. .. 10 10
1331. 150 l. " Angel " (looking to left) .. .. 20 20

519. Postal Coach.

**1972.** Stamp Day.
1332. 519. 25 l. red .. .. 15 10

520. L. B. Alberti (from bronze by M. de Pasti, Louvre). 521. L. Perosi.

**1972.** 500th Death Anniv. of Leon B. Alberti (writer and savant).
1333. 520. 50 l. blue and yellow 15 10

**1972.** Birth Cent. of Lorenzo Perosi (composer and priest).
1334. 521. 50 l. brown & yellow 10 10
1335. 90 l. black and green 20 15

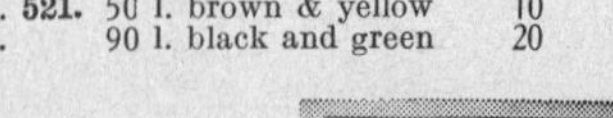

522. Don Orione. 523. Oceanic Survey.

**1972.** Birth Centenary of Don Orione (child-welfare pioneer).
1336. 522. 50 l. blue and turq... 10 10
1337. 90 l. green and yellow 20 15

**1973.** Centenary of Military Marine Institute of Hydrography.
1338. 523. 50 l. multicoloured .. 15 10

524. Grand Staircase, Royal Palace, Caserta.

**1973.** Death Bicentenary of Luigi Vanvitelli (architect).
1339. **524.** 25 l. green .. .. 15 10

525. Schiavoni Shore.

**1973.** "Save Venice" Campaign. Mult.
1340. 20 l. Type **525** .. .. 15 10
1341. 25 l. "The Tetrarchs" (sculpture) (vert.) .. 15 10
1342. 50 l. "The Triumph of Venice" (V. Carpaccio) 20 10
1343. 90 l. Bronze horses, St. Mark's Basilica (vert.) 20 15
1344. 300 l. Piazetta S. Marco .. 65 45

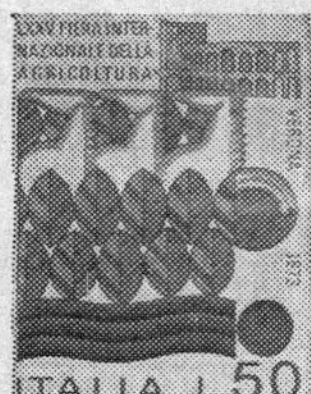

526. Fair Theme. 527. Title-page of "Diverse Figure".

**1973.** 75th Int. Agricultural Fair, Verona.
1345. **526.** 50 l. multicoloured .. 15 10

**1973.** 300th Death Anniv. of Salvator Rosa (painter and poet).
1346. **527.** 25 l. black & orange 10 10

528. Formation of Fiat PAN Acrobatic Jet Aircraft.

**1973.** 50th Anniv of Military Aviation. Mult.
1349 20 l. Type **528** (postage) 10 10
1350 25 l. Formation of Savoia Marchetti S-55X flying boats .. .. .. 10 10
1351 50 l. Fiat G-91Y jet fighters on patrol .. 10 10
1352 90 l. Fiat CR-32 biplanes performing aero[illegible] 15 10
1353 180 l. Cap[illegible] N-1 jet [illegible] 30 20
1354 150 l. Lockheed F-104S Starfighter over Aeronautical Academy, Pozzuoli (air) .. 30 20

529. Football and Pitch. 530. A. Manzoni (after F. Hayez).

**1973.** 75th Anniversary of Italian Football Association. Multicoloured.
1355. 25 l. Type **529** .. .. 20 10
1356. 90 l. Players in goal mouth 45 20

**1973.** Death Cent. of Alessandro Manzoni (writer and politician).
1357. **530.** 25 l. brown & black .. 10 10

531. Palladio's "Rotunda", Vicenza. 532. Spring and Cogwheels.

**1973.** Andrea Palladio Commem.
1358. **531.** 90 l. multicoloured .. 30 15

**1973.** 50th Anniv. of Italian State Supplies Office.
1359. **532.** 50 l. multicoloured .. 10 10

533. Europa "Posthorn".

**1973.** Europa.
1360. **533.** 50 l. gold, lilac & yell. 10 10
1361. 90 l. gold, grn. & yell. 30 20

534. "Catcher" and Baseball Field.

**1973.** 1st Intercontinental Baseball Cup. Multicoloured.
1362. 25 l. Type **534** .. .. 10 10
1363. 90 l. "Striker" and base-ball field .. .. 20 15

535. Carnival Setting. 536. "Argenta Episode".

**1973.** Viareggio Carnival.
1364. **535.** 25 l. multicoloured .. 10 10

**1973.** 50th Death Anniv. of Don Giovanni Minzoni (military chaplain).
1365. **536.** 50 l. multicoloured .. 15 10

537. G. Salvemini. 538. Farnese Palace, Caprorola.

**1973.** Birth Centenary of Gaetano Salvemini (political historian).
1366. **537.** 50 l. multicoloured .. 10 10

**1973.** 400th Birth Anniv. of "Vignola" (Jacopa Barozzi-architect).
1367. **538.** 90 l. purple and yellow 20 15

539. "St. John the Baptist". 540. Leaning Tower of Pisa.

**1973.** 400th Birth Anniv. of Caravaggio (painter).
1368. **539.** 25 l. black & yellow .. 20 10

**1973.** Tourism.
1369. **540.** 50 l. multicoloured .. 20 10

541. Botticelli. 542. Immacolatella Fountain, Naples.

**1973.** Italian Painters (1st series).
1370. **541.** 50 l. brown and red .. 10 10
1371. – 50 l. blue and brown 10 10
1372. – 50 l. green and emerald 10 10
1373. – 50 l. black and red .. 10 10
1374. – 50 l. brown and blue 10 10
PAINTERS: No. 1371, Piranesi. No. 1372, Veronese. No. 1373, Verrocchio. No. 1374, Tiepolo.
See also Nos. 1392/6, 1456/61, 1495/9 and 1518/22.

**1973.** Italian Fountains (1st series). Mult.
1375. 25 l. Type **542** .. .. 10 10
1376. 25 l. Trevi Fountain, Rome 10 10
1377. 25 l. Pretoria Fountain, Palermo .. .. 10 10
See also Nos. 1418/20, 1453/5, 1503/5, 1529/31, 1570/2 and 1618/20.

543. "Angels". 544. Map and Emblems.

**1973.** Christmas. Sculptures by A. di Duccio.
1378. **543.** 20 l. black and green 10 10
1379. – 25 l. black and blue .. 10 10
1380. – 150 l. black & yellow 15 20
DESIGNS: 25 l. "Virgin and Child". 150 l. "Angels" (different).

**1973.** 50th Anniv. of Italian Rotary.
1381. **544.** 50 l. blue, green & red 10 10

545. Sud Aviation Super Caravelle 12. 546. Military Medal for Valour.

**1973.** Stamp Day.
1382. **545.** 25 l. blue .. .. 25 10

**1973.** 150th Anniv. of Holders of the Gold Medal for Military Valour Organisation.
1383. **546.** 50 l. multicoloured .. 10 10

547. Caruso as Duke of Mantua in Verdi's "Rigoletto". 548. "Christ crowning King Roger" (Martorana Church, Palermo).

**1973.** Birth Centenary of Enrico Caruso (operatic tenor).
1384. **547.** 50 l. red .. .. 30 10

**1974.** Norman Art in Sicily, Mosaics.
1385. **548.** 20 l. blue and yellow 15 10
1386. – 50 l. red and green .. 15 10
DESIGN: 50 l. "King William offering Church to the Virgin Mary" (Monreale Cathedral).

549. Pres. L. Einaudi. 550. G. Marconi in Headphones.

**1974.** Birth Centenary of Luigi Einaudi (President 1948–55).
1387 **549** 50 l. green .. .. 10 10

**1974.** Birth Centenary of Guglielmo Marconi (radio pioneer).
1388. **550.** 50 l. brown and green 15 10
1389. – 90 l. multicoloured .. 15 15
DESIGN: 90 l. Marconi and world map.

551. "David" (Bernini). 552. Guards from Lombardy-Venetia (1848), Sardinian Marines (1815) and Tebro Battalion (1849).

**1974.** Europa. Sculptures. Multicoloured.
1390. 50 l. Type **551** .. .. 10 10
1391. 90 l. "Spirit of Victory" (Michelangelo) .. .. 20 15

**1974.** Italian Painters (2nd series). As T **541**.
1392. 50 l. blue and green .. 10 10
1393. 50 l. brown and blue .. 10 10
1394. 50 l. black and red .. 10 10
1395. 50 l. brown and yellow .. 10 10
1396. 50 l. blue and brown .. 10 10
PORTRAITS: No. 1392, Borromini. No. 1393, Carriera. No. 1394, Giambellino (Giovanni Bellini). No. 1395, Mantegna. No. 1396, Raphael.

**1974.** Bicentenary of Italian Excise Guards. Uniforms. Multicoloured.
1397 40 l. Sardinian chasseurs, 1774 and 1795, and Royal Fusilier of 1817 15 10
1398 50 l. Type **552** .. .. 15 10
1399 90 l. Lieutenant (1866), Sergeant-major of Marines (1892) and guard (1880) .. .. 20 15
1400 180 l. Helicopter pilot, naval and alpine guards of 1974 .. .. 35 20

553. Feather Headdress.

**1974.** 50th Anniv of National Bersaglieri Association. Multicoloured.
1401. 40 l. Type **553** .. .. 10 10
1402. 50 l. Bersaglieri emblem on rosette .. .. 10 10

554. Running. 555. Francesco Petrarch.

**1974.** European Athletics Championships, Rome. Multicoloured.
1403 40 l. Type **554** .. 15 10
1404 50 l. Pole vaulting .. 15 10

**1974.** 600th Death Anniv of Francesco Petrarch (poet and scholar).
1405 **555** 40 l. multicoloured .. 15 10
1406 – 50 l. blue, yell & brn 15 10
DESIGN: 50 l. Petrarch at work in his study.

556. Portofino.

**1974.** Tourist Publicity (1st series). Mult.
1407 40 l. Type **556** .. 20 10
1408 40 l. Gradara .. .. 20 10
See also Nos. 1442/4, 1473/5, 1513/14, 1515/17, 1543/5, 1596/9, 1642/5, 1722/5, 1762/5, 1806/9, 1845/8, 1877/80, 1917/20, 1963/6, 1992/5, 2031/4, 2088/91, 2115/18, 2165/8, 2212/15, 2248/51, 2315/16 and 2365/8.

**557.** Tommaseo's Statue, Sebenico.

**558.** Giacomo Puccini.

**1974.** Death Centenary of Niccolo Tommaseo (writer).

1409. **557.** 50 l. green and pink 15 10

**1974.** 50th Death Anniv. of Giacomo Puccini (composer).

1410. **558.** 40 l. multicoloured .. 30 15

**559.** Cover Engraving of Ariosto's "Orlando Furioso".

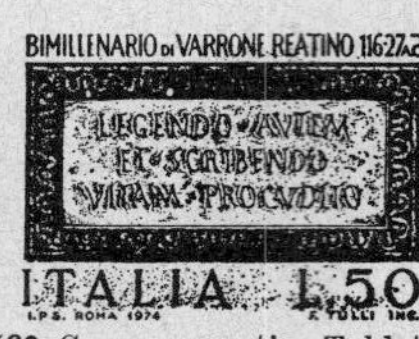


**560.** Commemoration Tablet (Quotation from Varrone's "Menippean Satire").

**1974.** 500th Birth Anniv. of Ludovico Ariosto (poet).

1411. **559.** 50 l. blue and red .. 15 10

**1974.** 2000th Death Anniv of Marco Varrone (Varrone Reatino) (author).

1412 **560** 50 l. lake, red & yellow 15 10

**561.** "The Month of October" (detail from 15th-century mural).

**1974.** 14th International Wine Congress.

1413. **561.** 50 l. multicoloured .. 15 15

**562.** "U.P.U." and Emblem.

**1974.** Cent. of Universal Postal Union. Mult.

1414. 50 l. Type **562** .. .. 15 10

1415. 90 l. "U.P.U." emblem and letters .. .. 15 15

**563.** "The Triumph of St. Thomas Aquinas" (detail—F. Traini). **564.** Detail of Bas-relief, Ara Pacis.

**1974.** 700th Death Anniv. of St. Thomas Aquinas.

1416. **563.** 50 l. multicoloured .. 15 10

**1974.** Cent of Italian Order of Advocates.

1417 **564** 50 l. black, grn & brn 15 10

**1974.** Italian Fountains (2nd series). As Type **542.** Multicoloured.

1418 40 l. Oceanus Fountain, Florence .. .. 15 15

1419 40 l. Neptune Fountain, Bologna .. .. 15 15

1420 40 l. Maggiore Fountain, Perugia .. .. 15 15

**565.** "The Adoration" (Presepe di Greccio).

**1974.** Christmas.

1421 **565** 40 l. multicoloured .. 15 10

**566.** Pulcinella.

**567.** "God admonishing Adam" (Jacopo della Quercia (sculptor) (1374–1438)).

**1974.** Children's Comic Characters. Mult.

1422 40 l. Type **566** .. .. 15 10

1423 50 l. Clowns .. .. 15 10

1424 90 l. Pantaloon from Bisognosi .. .. 15 15

**1974.** Italian Artists' Anniversaries (1st series).

1425. **567.** 90 l. violet .. .. 20 15

1426. – 90 l. multicoloured .. 20 15

DESIGN: No. 1426, Uffizi Gallery, Florence (Giorgio Vasari (architect and painter) (1511–1574)).

See also Nos. 1445/6, 1480/2, 1523/4, 1564/5, 1593/4, 1699/1700, 1731/2, 1774/5, 1824/5, 1885/6, 1949/50 and 1987.

**568.** "Angel with Tablet". **569.** "Pitti Madonna".

**1975.** Holy Year. Multicoloured.

1427. 40 l. Type **568** .. .. 10 10

1428. 50 l. Angel with column 10 10

1429. 90 l. Bridge of the Holy Angels, Rome (49×40mm.) 15 10

1430. 150 l. Angel with crown of thorns .. .. 25 25

1431. 180 l. Angel with cross .. 25 25

**1975.** 500th Birth Anniv. of Michelangelo.

1432. **569.** 40 l. green .. .. 10 10

1433. – 50 l. brown .. .. 10 10

1434. – 90 l. red .. .. 15 15

DESIGNS: 50 l. Sculptured niche, Vatican Palace. 90 l. Detail from fresco "Flood of the Universe" (Sistine Chapel).

**570.** "The Four Days of Naples" (M. Mazzacurati). **571.** "The Flagellation of Christ" (Caravaggio).

**1975.** 30th Anniv of Italian Resistance Movement. Resistance Monuments. Mult.

1435 70 l. Type **570** .. .. 15 15

1436 100 l. "Martyrs of the Ardeatine Caves" (F. Coccia) .. .. 15 15

1437 150 l. "The Resistance Fighters of Cuneo" (U. Mastroianni) .. .. 20 15

**1975.** Europa. Paintings. Multicoloured.

1438 100 l. Type **571** .. .. 20 10

1439 150 l. "The Appearance of the Angel to Agar and Ishmael in the Desert" (Tiepolo) .. .. 20 20

**572.** Globe and Emblems.

**1975.** International Women's Year.

1440. **572.** 70 l. multicoloured .. 15 10

**573.** "San Marco III" (satellite) and "Santa Rita" (marine launching pad).

**574.** Cover Engraving from Palestrina's "Primo Libro delle Messe".

**1975.** Italian Space Project.

1441. **573.** 70 l. multicoloured .. 15 10

**1975.** Tourist Publicity (2nd series). As T **556.** Multicoloured.

1442 150 l. Cefalu .. .. 25 15

1443 150 l. Isola Bella .. 25 15

1444 150 l. Montecatini Terme 25 15

**1975.** Italian Artists' Annivs. (2nd series). As T **567.** Multicoloured.

1445 90 l. "Flora" (Guido Reni (1575–1642)) .. .. 15 15

1446 90 l. "Artist and Model" (Armando Spadini (1883–1925)) .. .. 15 15

**1975.** 450th Birth Anniv of Giovanni Pierluigi da Palestrina (composer).

1447 **574** 100 l. purple & brown 20 10

**575.** Boat in Harbour.

**1975.** Italian Emigration.

1448. **575.** 70 l. multicoloured .. 15 10

**576.** Notoriat Emblem.

**1975.** Cent of Unification of Italian Laws.

1449 **576** 100 l. mve, stone & bl 15 10

**577.** Railway Steam Locomotive Driving-wheels.

**1975.** 21st International Railway Congress, Bologna.

1450. **577.** 70 l. multicoloured .. 30 10

**578.** "D'Acquisto's Sacrifice" (Vittorio Pisani). **579.** Symbolised Head representing Files.

**1975.** 32nd Death Anniv of Salvo d'Acquisto (carabiniere who sacrificed himself to save 22 hostages).

1451 **578** 100 l. multicoloured .. 20 10

**1975.** Cent. of State Archives Unification.

1452. **579.** 100 l. multicoloured 15 10

**1975.** Italian Fountains (3rd series). As T **542.** Multicoloured.

1453 70 l. Rosello Fountain, Sassari .. .. 20 15

1454 70 l. 99 Channel Fountain, L'Aquila .. .. 20 15

1455 70 l. Piazza Fountain, Milan .. .. .. 20 15

**1975.** Italian Composers. As T **541.**

1456 100 l. blue, pink and red 20 15

1457 100 l. blue, green & dp grn 20 15

1458 100 l. green, brn & dp brn 20 15

1459 100 l. brown, red and lake 20 15

1460 100 l. purple, grey & green 20 15

1461 100 l. black, lt yell & yell 20 15

DESIGNS: No. 1456, Ferruccio Busoni. 1457, Alessandro Scarlatti. 1458, Francesco Cilea. 1459, Antonio Vivaldi. 1460, Franco Alfano. 1461, Gaspare Spontini.

**581.** "Annunciation to the Shepherds".

**1975.** Christmas. Alatri Cathedral Carvings. Multicoloured.

1462. 70 l. Type **581** .. .. 15 10

1463. 100 l. "The Nativity" .. 15 10

1464. 150 l. "Annunciation to the Kings" .. .. 20 20

**582.** "Children on Horseback". **583.** "Boccaccio" (from fresco by A. del Castagno).

**1975.** Stamp Day. Children's Stories. Mult.

1465. 70 l. Type **582** .. .. 15 10

1466. 100 l. "The Magic Orchard" (vert.) .. 20 10

1467. 150 l. "Church Procession" .. .. .. 25 20

**1975.** 600th Death Anniv. of Giovanni Boccaccio. Multicoloured.

1468. 100 l. Type **583** .. .. 15 10

1469. 150 l. Cover engraving fro[illegible]ccio's [illegible] .. 20 20

**584.** Entrance to State Advocate's Office. **585.** "Italia 1976" Emblem.

**1976.** Cent. of State Advocate's Office.

1470. **584.** 150 l. multicoloured 20 15

**1976.** "Italia 76" International Stamp Exhibition, Milan (1st issue).

1471 **585** 150 l. red, green & blk 20 15

1472 – 180 l. multicoloured .. 20 15

DESIGN: 180 l. Exhibition Hall, Milan.

See also Nos. 1487/91.

**1976.** Tourist Publicity (3rd series). As T **556.** Multicoloured.

1473. 150 l. Fenis Castle, Aosta 25 15

1474. 150 l. Forio Ischia .. 25 15

1475. 150 l. Itria Valley .. 25 15

**HAVE YOU READ THE NOTES AT THE BEGINNING OF THIS CATALOGUE?**

These often provide answers to the enquiries we receive.

586. Majolica Plate.

587. Republican Flags.

**1976.** Europa. Italian Crafts. Multicoloured.
1476 150 l. Type **586** .. .. 20 15
1477 180 l. Vase in form of woman's head .. 25 15

**1976.** 30th Anniv of Republic. Multicoloured.
1478 100 l. Type **587** .. .. 15 10
1479 150 l. Statesmen .. 20 15

588. "Fortitude" (Giacomo Serpotta) (1656–1732).

**1976.** Italian Artists' Annivs. (3rd series).
1480. **588.** 150 l. blue .. .. 25 15
1481. – 150 l. multicoloured 25 15
1482. – 150 l. black and red .. 25 15
Designs: No. 1481, "Woman at Table" (Umberto Boccioni (1882–1916)). 1482, "Gunner's Letter from the Front" (Filippo Tommaso Marinetti (1876–1944)).

589. " The Dragon ".

**1976.** 450th Death Anniv of Vittore Carpaccio (painter).
1483 **589** 150 l. red .. .. 20 15
1484 – 150 l. red .. .. 20 15
Design: No. 1484, " St. George ".
Nos. 1483/4 form Carpaccio's " St. George and the Dragon ".

590. " Flora " (Titian).

**1976.** 400th Death Anniv. of Titian.
1485. **590.** 150 l. red .. .. 30 15

591. St. Francis (13th-century fresco).

592. " Cursus Publicus " Post Cart.

**1976.** 750th Death Anniv of St. Francis of Assisi.
1486 **591** 150 l. brown & lt brn 30 15

**1976.** "Italia 76" International Stamp Exhibition, Milan (2nd issue).
1487 **592** 70 l. black, grey & bl 10 10
1488 – 100 l. blk, grey & yell 15 10
1489 – 150 l. blk, grey & brn 20 10
1490 – 200 l. multicoloured .. 25 15
1491 – 400 l. multicoloured .. 55 20
Designs: 100 l. Emblem of Royal Sardinian Posts. 150 l. 19th-century "Lion's head" letter-box. 200 l. Early cancelling machine. 400 l. Modern letter-coding machine.

593. Girl with " Protective Umbrella " and Animals.

594. " The Visit " (S. Lega).

**1976.** Stamp Day. Nature Protection. Multicoloured.
1492. 40 l. Type **593** .. .. 10 10
1493. 100 l. "Protective scarf" 15 10
1494. 150 l. Doctor with bandaged tree .. 15 15

**1976.** Italian Painters (3rd series). As T **541**.
1495 170 l. green, yellow & red 25 15
1496 170 l. black, turq & grn .. 25 15
1497 170 l. black, purple & mve 25 15
1498 170 l. brown, lav & vio .. 25 15
1499 170 l. black and brown .. 25 15
Designs: No. 1495, Carlo Dolci. 1496, Lorenzo Ghiberti (sculptor). 1497, Domenico Ghirlandaio. 1498, Giovanni Piazzetta. 1499, "Sassoferrato" (Giovanni Salvi).

**1976.** 150th Birth Anniv of Silvestro Lega (painter).
1500 **594** 170 l. multicoloured .. 30 15

595. " Adoration of the Magi " (Bartolo di Fredi).

596. Net of Serpents obscuring the Sun.

**1976.** Christmas. Multicoloured.
1501 70 l. Type **595** .. .. 15 20
1502 120 l. "The Nativity" (Taddao Gaddi) .. 25 20

**1976.** Italian Fountains (4th series). As Type **542.** Multicoloured.
1503. 170 l. Antique Fountain, Gallipoli .. .. 30 15
1504. 170 l. Erbe Madonna Fountain, Verona .. 30 15
1505. 170 l. Fountain of Palazzo Doria, Gerona .. 30 15

**1977.** Campaign against Drug Abuse. Mult.
1506 120 l. Type **596** .. .. 20 15
1507 170 l. "Addict" and poppy 30 15

597. Igniting Explosives.

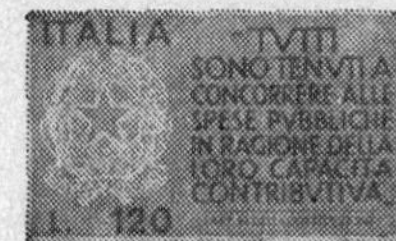


598. "Globe" and Cross.

**1977.** 300th Birth Anniv of Pietro Micca (national hero).
1508 **597** 170 l. multicoloured .. 20 15

**1977.** Salesian Missionaries. Multicoloured.
1509 70 l. Type **598** .. .. 15 10
1510 120 l. St. John Bosco and "United people" .. 15 20

599. Article 53 of the Italian Constitution.

**1977.** "Encouragement to Taxpayers".
1511 **599** 120 l. blk, brn & stone 25 10
1512 170 l. black, ol & grn 30 10

**1977.** Europa. As T **556**. but with C.E.P.T. emblem. Multicoloured.
1513 170 l. Mount Etna .. 40 15
1514 200 l. Castel del Monte .. 50 15

**1977.** Tourist Publicity (4th series). As T **556**. Multicoloured.
1515. 170 l. Canossa Castle .. 30 15
1516. 170 l. Castellana Grotto 30 15
1517. 170 l. Fermo .. .. 30 15

**1977.** Famous Italians. As T **541**.
1518 70 l. brown, grn & dp grn 20 15
1519 70 l. black, blue and green 20 15
1520 70 l. brown, yell & lt brn 20 15
1521 70 l. blue, pink and red .. 20 15
1522 70 l. black, brn & dp brn 20 15
Designs: No. 1518, Filippo Brunelleschi (architect). 1519, Pietro Aretino (satirist). 1520, Carlo Goldoni (dramatist). 1521, Luigi Cherubini (composer). 1522, Edoardo Bassini (surgeon).

**1977.** Italian Artists' Anniversaries (4th series). As Type **567**. Multicoloured.
1523 170 l. "Winter" (G. Arcimboldi (c. 1527–1593)) .. .. 30 15
1524 170 l. "Justice" (Andrea Delitio (15th century)) 25 15

601. Paddle-steamer "Ferdinando Primo".

**1977.** Italian Ship-building (1st series). Multicoloured.
1525 170 l. Type **601** .. .. 35 20
1526 170 l. Sail corvette "Carracciolo" .. .. 35 20
1527 170 l. Liner "Saturnia" .. 35 20
1528 170 l. Hydrofoil missile boat "Sparviero" .. 35 20
See also Nos. 1552/5, 1621/4 and 1691/4.

**1977.** Italian Fountains (5th series). As T **542.** Multicoloured.
1529. 120 l. Pacassi Fountain, Gorizia .. .. 30 15
1530. 120 l. Fraterna Fountain, Isernia .. .. .. 30 15
1531. 120 l. Palma Fountain, Palmi .. .. .. 30 15

602. Handball.

**1977.** Stamp Day. " Leisure Time ". Multicoloured.
1532. 120 l. Type **602** .. .. 15 15
1533. 120 l. Catching butterflies 15 15
1534. 120 l. Kites .. .. 15 15

603. " Pulse ".

604. Quintino Sella and 1863 1 l. Stamps.

**1977.** " Give Blood ". Multicoloured.
1535. 70 l. Type **603** .. .. 20 10
1536. 120 l. " Transfusion " .. 25 15

**1977.** 150th Birth Anniv. of Quintino Sella (statesman).
1537 **604** 170 l. green and brown 25 10

605. Dina Galli.

607. La Scala Opera House.

606. " Adoration of the Shepherds " (P. Testa).

**1977.** Birth Cent. of Dina Galli (actress).
1538. **605.** 170 l. multicoloured .. 20 10

**1977.** Christmas.
1539 **606** 70 l. black and green 10 10
1540 – 120 l. black and green 20 15
Design: 120 l. "The Adoration of the Shepherds" (J. Caraglio).

**1978.** Bicent. of La Scala Opera House.
1541. 170 l. Type **607** .. .. 30 15
1542. 200 l. Theatre interior .. 40 15

**1978.** Tourist Publicity (5th series). As T **556**. Multicoloured.
1543. 70 l. Gubbio .. .. 15 10
1544. 200 l. Udine .. .. 30 15
1545. 600 l. Paestum .. .. 75 45

608. Grouper.

**1978.** Environmental Protection. Mediterranean Fauna. Multicoloured.
1546. 170 l. Type **608** .. .. 70 30
1547. 170 l. Leathery turtle .. 70 30
1548. 170 l. Mediterranean monk seal .. .. 70 30
1549. 170 l. Audouin's gull .. 1·50 30

609. Maschio Angioino Castle, Naples.

**1978.** Europa. Multicoloured.
1550. 170 l. Type **609** .. .. 35 10
1551. 200 l. Pantheon, Rome .. 35 15

**1978.** Italian Ship-building (2nd series). As T **601.** Multicoloured.
1552. 170 l. Brigantine "Fortuna" .. .. 55 25
1553. 170 l. Cruiser "Benedetto Brin" .. .. 55 25
1554. 170 l. Frigate "Lupo" .. 55 25
1555. 170 l. Container ship "Africa" .. .. 55 25

610. Matilde Serao (writer).

611. First and Last Paragraphs of Constitution.

**1978.** Famous Italians.
1556. **610.** 170 l. black and red .. 20 15
1557. – 170 l. brown and blue 20 15
1558. – 170 l. blue & pale blue 20 15
1559. – 170 l. black and green 20 15
1560. – 170 l. brown and green 20 15
1561. – 170 l. blue and red .. 20 15
Designs: No. 1557, Vittorino da Feltre (scientist). No. 1558, Victor Emmanuel II. No. 1559, Pope Pius IX. No. 1560, Marcello Malpighi (biologist). No. 1561, Antonio Meucci (telephone pioneer).
See also Nos. 1600/4.

**1978.** 30th Anniv. of Constitution.
1562. **611.** 170 l. multicoloured 30 10

612. Telephone Wires and Lens.

**1978.** Photographic Information.
1563. **612.** 120 l. grey, blue & grn. 20 10

**1978.** Italian Artists' Annivs. (5th series). As T **567.** Multicoloured.
1564. 170 l. " The Ivy " (Tranquillo Cremona 1837–1878) .. .. 1·25 15
1565. 520 l. " The Cook " (Bernardo Strozzi 1581–1644) .. .. .. 2·00 1·25

613. The Holy Shroud of Turin.

**1978.** 400th Anniv. of Translation of the Holy Shroud from Savoy to Turin.
1566. **613.** 220 l. yell., blk. & red 40 15

614. Volleyball Players.

615. Detail from " St. Peter distributing Ananias's Silver ".

**1978.** World Volleyball Championships.
1567. **614.** 80 l. blk., red & blue 25 10
1568. – 120 l. blk., blue & orge. 40 15
DESIGN: 120 l. Players with ball.

**1978.** 550th Death Anniv. of Tommaso Guidi (Masaccio).
1569. **615.** 170 l. blue .. .. 30 10

**1978.** Italian Fountains (6th series). As T **542.** Multicoloured.
1570. 120 l. Neptune Fountain, Trento .. .. .. 25 15
1571. 120 l. Fountain of Fortune, Fano .. .. .. 25 15
1572. 120 l. Cavallina Fountain, Genzano di Lucania .. 25 15

616. " Madonna and Child " (Giorgione).

617. " Flowers ".

**1978.** Christmas.
1573. **616.** 80 l. red and brown .. 15 10
1574. – 120 l. multicoloured .. 15 15
DESIGN—HORIZ. (48×27 mm.): 120 l. " Adoration of the Magi " (Giorgione).

**1978.** Stamp Day. United Europe. Mult.
1575. 120 l. Type **617** .. .. 15 10
1576. 120 l. Flags and ribbon .. 15 10
1577. 120 l. Figures raising globe inscribed " E " .. 15 10

618.

619. State Polygraphic Institute.

**1978.**
1578. **618.** 1500 l. multicoloured 1·00 10
1579. 2000 l. multicoloured 1·40 10
1580. 3000 l. multicoloured 2·00 10
1581. 4000 l. multicoloured 2·50 10
1582. 5000 l. multicoloured 3·25 10
1583. 10000 l. mult. .. 7·00 60
1584. 20000 l. mult. .. 14·00 4·00

**1979.** 50th Anniv. of State Polygraphic Institute. Multicoloured.
1588. 170 l. Type **619** .. .. 50 15
1589. 220 l. Printing press .. 30 15

620. "St. Francis washing the Feet of a Leper" (Maestro di Francesco Bardi).

**1979.** Leprosy Relief.
1590. **620.** 80 l. multicoloured .. 15 10

621. Cyclist carrying Bicycle.

622. Albert Einstein.

**1979.** World Cyclo-cross Championships.
1591. **621.** 170 l. multicoloured 25 10
1592. 220 l. multicoloured 40 15

**1979.** Italian Artists' Annivs. (6th series). As T **567.** Multicoloured.
1593. 170 l. " Annunciation " (Antonella da Messina c. 1430–1479) .. .. 40 15
1594. 520 l. " Field with Haystack " (Ardengo Soffici 1879–1964) .. .. 85 85

**1979.** Birth Centenary of Albert Einstein (physicist).
1595. **622.** 120 l. pur., grey & bl. 20 15

**1979.** Tourist Publicity (6th series). As T **556.** Multicoloured.
1596. 70 l. Asiago .. .. 10 10
1597. 90 l. Castelsardo, Sardinia 15 15
1598. 170 l. Orvieto .. .. 30 15
1599. 220 l. Scilla .. .. 45 20

**1979.** Famous Italians. As T **610.**
1600 170 l. brown, blue & black 25 15
1601 170 l. green, yellow & vio 25 15
1602 170 l. blue and pink .. 25 15
1603 170 l. brown and ochre .. 25 15
1604 170 l. mauve, brown & grn 25 15
DESIGNS: No. 1600, Carlo Maderno (architect). No. 1601, Lazzaro Spallanzani (biologist). No. 1602, Ugo Foscolo (author). No. 1603, Massimo Bontempelli (writer). No. 1604, Francesco Severi (mathematician).

623. Morse Telegraph Apparatus.

**1979.** Europa. Multicoloured.
1605. 170 l. Type **623** .. .. 25 10
1606. 220 l. Carrier pigeon with message tube .. 35 10

624. Flags of Member States forming "E".

**1979.** First Direct Elections to European Parliament.
1607. **624.** 170 l. multicoloured 20 10
1608. 220 l. multicoloured 30 15

625. Head of Aeneas (bas-relief, Ara Pacis, Rome).

626. Ball in Basket (poster).

**1979.** 70th World Rotary Congress, Rome.
1609. **625.** 220 l. multicoloured .. 30 15

**1979.** 21st European Basketball Championships.
1610. **626.** 80 l. multicoloured .. 15 10
1611. – 120 l. lake, blk. & yell. 25 15
DESIGN: 120 l. Two players.

627. "Doctor examining Patient with Stomach Ailment" (woodcut from Giovanni da Cuba's "Hortus Sanitatus").

629. Ottorino Respighi and Appian Way, Rome.

628. Emblem, Ribbon "3" and Milan Cathedral.

**1979.** Prevention of Digestive Illnesses.
1612. **627.** 120 l. multicoloured 20 15

**1979.** Third World Machine Tool Exhibition, Milan.
1613. **628.** 170 l. multicoloured 15 10
1614. 220 l. multicoloured 30 15

**1979.** Birth Centenary of Ottorino Respighi (composer).
1615. **629.** 120 l. multicoloured 30 15

630. Woman with Telephone and Morse Key.

**1979.** 3rd World Telecommunications Exhibition, Geneva.
1616 **630** 170 l. black and red .. 25 15
1617 – 220 l. grey and green 35 20
DESIGN: 220 l. Woman with early telephone and communications satellite.

**1979.** Italian Fountains (7th series). As T **542.** Multicoloured.
1618. 120 l. Melograno Fountain, Issogne .. .. 35 15
1619. 120 l. Bollente Fountain, Acqui Terme .. .. 35 15
1620. 120 l. Grand Fountain, Viterbo .. .. 35 15

**1979.** Italian Ship-building (3rd series). As T **601.** Multicoloured.
1621 170 l. Full-rigged sailing ship "Cosmos" .. 40 15
1622 170 l. Cruiser "Dandolo" 40 15
1623 170 l. Ferry "Deledda" .. 40 15
1624 170 l. Submarine "Carlo Fecia di Cossato" .. 40 15

631. Sir Rowland Hill and Penny Black.

**1979.** Death Cent. of Sir Rowland Hill.
1625. **631.** 220 l. multicoloured 40 15

632. Christmas Landscape.

**1979.** Christmas.
1626. **632.** 120 l. multicoloured 20 10

633. Children under Umbrella (Group IIB, Varapodio School).

**1979.** Stamp Day. International Year of the Child. Drawings by Schoolchildren. Mult.
1627 70 l. Children of different races holding hands (L. Carra) (horiz) .. 15 15
1628 120 l. Type **633** .. .. 20 15
1629 150 l. Children with balloons (V. Fedon) (horiz) .. .. 20 15

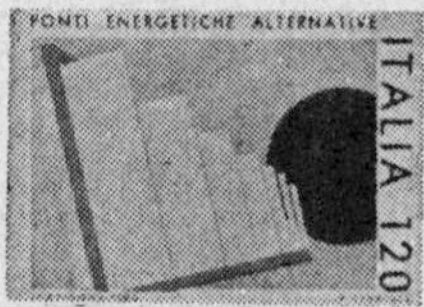

634. Solar Energy (alternative sources).

**1980.** Energy Conservation. Multicoloured.
1630. 120 l. Type **634** .. .. 15 10
1631. 170 l. Oil well (reduction of consumption) .. 25 20

635. "St Benedict" (detail, fresco by Sodoma in Monastery of Monteoliveto Maggiore).

636. Royal Palace, Naples.

**1980.** 1500th Birth Anniv. of St. Benedict of Nursia (Founder of Benedictine Order).
1632. **635.** 220 l. blue .. .. 30 15

**1980.** "Europa 80" International Stamp Exhibition, Naples.
1633 **636** 220 l. multicoloured .. 30 15

637. Antonio Pigafetta (navigator) and "Vitoria".

638. St. Catherine (reliquary bust.)

**1980.** Europa. Multicoloured.
1634 170 l. Type **637** .. .. 35 10
1635 220 l. Antonio lo Surdo (geophysicist) .. .. 40 15

**1980.** 600th Death Anniv. of St. Catherine of Siena.
1636. **638.** 170 l. multicoloured 25 15

639. Red Cross Flags.

**1980.** First International Exhibition of Red Cross Stamps in Italy.
1637. **639.** 70 l. multicoloured .. 20 10
1638. 80 l. multicoloured .. 20 10

640. Philae Temples.

**1980.** Italian Work for the World (1st series). Preservation of Philae Temples, Egypt. Multicoloured.

1639. 220 l. Type **640** .. .. 40 20
1640. 220 l. Right hand view of temples .. .. 40 20

**Nos. 1639/40 were issued together se-tenant, forming a composite design.**

See also Nos. 1720/1, 1758/9, 1780/1, 1830/1, 1865/6 and 1937/40.

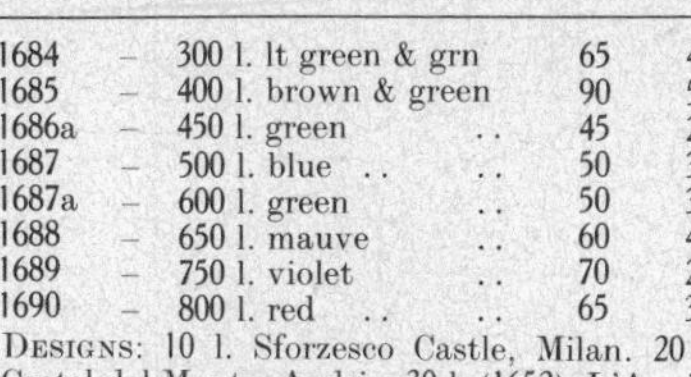

**641.** Footballer.

**1980.** European Football Championship, Italy.

1641 **641** 80 l. multicoloured .. 1·25 40

**1980.** Tourist Publicity (7th series). As T **556**. Multicoloured.

1642. 80 l. Erice .. .. 15 10
1643. 150 l. Ravello .. .. 30 15
1644. 200 l. Roseto degli Abruzzi 35 15
1645. 670 l. Salsomaggiore Terme 85 85

**642.** "Cosimo I with his Artists" (Vasari).

**643.** Fonte Avellana Monastery.

**1980.** "Florence and Tuscany of the Medicis in 16th Century Europe" Exhibition. Multicoloured.

1646 170 l. Type **642** (ceiling medallion, Palazzo Vecchio, Florence) .. 20 15
1647 170 l. Armillary sphere .. 20 15

**1980.** Millenary of Fonte Avellana Monastery.

1648. **643.** 200 l. deep grn., grn. and brown .. 40 15

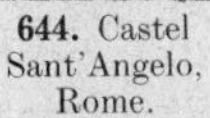

**644.** Castel Sant'Angelo, Rome.

**645.** Filippo Mazzei.

**1980.** Castles. (a) Size 22 × 27 mm.

1649 **644** 5 l. blue and red .. 20 10
1650 – 10 l. brown & ochre 10 10
1651 – 20 l. brown and blue 10 10
1652 – 30 l. orange and blue 20 10
1653 – 40 l. brown and blue 10 10
1654 – 50 l. multicoloured 10 10
1655 – 60 l. green & mauve 10 10
1656 – 70 l. multicoloured 20 10
1657 – 80 l. multicoloured 10 10
1658 – 90 l. multicoloured 10 10
1659 – 100 l. multicoloured 10 10
1660 – 120 l. blue and pink 15 10
1661 – 150 l. violet & brown 15 10
1662 – 170 l. black & yellow 20 10
1663 – 180 l. blue and pink 80 35
1664 – 200 l. multicoloured 20 10
1665 – 250 l. multicoloured 25 10
1666a – 300 l. multicoloured 20 10
1667 – 350 l. brn, bl & grn 35 10
1667a – 380 l. multicoloured 50 10
1668 – 400 l. blue, grn & brn 35 10
1669 – 450 l. multicoloured 40 10
1670 – 500 l. blue, brn & grn 45 10
1670a – 550 l. multicoloured 60 10
1671 – 600 l. black & green 50 10
1671a – 650 l. multicoloured 60 10
1672 – 700 l. multicoloured 60 10
1673 – 750 l. brn, green & bl 80 10
1674 – 800 l. brn, grn & mve 65 10
1675 – 850 l. multicoloured 90 10
1676 – 900 l. multicoloured 75 10
1677 – 1000 l. multicoloured 80 10
1678 – 1400 l. brown, bl & vio 1·10 10

(b) Size 16 × 21 mm.

1679 – 30 l. mauve .. 30 10
1680b – 50 l. blue .. .. 15 10
1680c – 100 l. brown .. 20 10
1681 – 120 l. brown .. 60 20
1682 – 170 l. violet .. 70 20
1683 – 200 l. violet and blue 3·75 4·00
1684 – 300 l. lt green & grn 65 40
1685 – 400 l. brown & green 90 55
1686a – 450 l. green .. 45 25
1687 – 500 l. blue .. .. 50 30
1687a – 600 l. green .. 50 30
1688 – 650 l. mauve .. 60 40
1689 – 750 l. violet .. 70 25
1690 – 800 l. red .. .. 65 35

DESIGNS: 10 l. Sforzesco Castle, Milan. 20 l. Castel del Monte, Andria. 30 l. (1652), L'Aquila Castle. 30 l. (1679), 100 l. (1680c), Santa Severa Castle. 40 l. Ursino Castle, Catania. 50 l. (1654), Rocca di Calascio, L'Aquila. 50 l. (1680b), Scilla. 60 l. Norman Tower, San Mauro. 70 l. Aragonese Castle, Reggio Calabria. 80 l. Sabbionara, Avio. 90 l. Isola Capo Rizzuto. 100 l. (1659), Aragonese Castle, Ischia. 120 l. (1660), Estense Castle, Ferrara. 120 l. (1681), Lombardia Enna. 150 l. Miramare, Trieste. 170 l. (1662), Ostia. 170 l. (1682), 650 l. (1688), Serralunga d'Alba. 180 l. Castel Gavone, Finale Ligure. 200 l. (1664), Cerro al Volturno. 200 l. (1683), Svevo Angioina Fortress, Lucera. 250 l. Rocca di Mondavio, Pesaro. 300 l. (1666a), Norman Castle, Svevo, Bari. 300 l. (1684), 500 l. (1687), Norman Castle, Melfi. 350 l. Mussomeli. 380 l. Rocca di Vignola, Modena. 400 l. (1668), Emperor's Castle, Prato. 400 l. (1685), 750 l. (1689), Venafro. 450 l. (1669), Bosa. 450 l. (1686a), Piobbico Castle, Pesaro. 500 l. (1670), Rovereto. 550 l. Rocca Sinibalda. 600 l. Scaligero Castle, Sirmione. 650 l. (1671a), Montecchio. 700 l. Ivrea. 750 l. (1673), Rocca di Urbisaglia. 800 l. Rocca Maggiore, Assisi. 850 l. Castello di Arechi, Salerno. 900 l. Castello di Saint-Pierre, Aosta. 1000 l. Montagnana, Padua. 1400 l. Caldoresco Castle, Vasto.

**1980.** Italian Ship-building (4th series). As T **601**. Multicoloured.

1691 200 l. Corvette "Gabbiano" .. .. 60 15
1692 200 l. Destroyer "Audace" .. .. 60 15
1693 200 l. Barque "Italia" .. 60 15
1694 200 l. Pipe-layer "Castoro Sei" .. .. 60 15

**1980.** 250th Birth Anniv of Filippo Mazzei (writer and American revolutionary).

1695 **645** 320 l. multicoloured .. 50 30

**646.** Villa Foscari Malcontenta, Venice.

**1980.** Italian Villas (1st series). Multicoloured.

1696. 80 l. Type **646** .. .. 25 25
1697. 150 l. Barbaro Maser, Treviso .. .. 45 15
1698. 170 l. Godi Valmarana, Vicenza .. .. 70 15

See also Nos. 1737/9, 1770/2, 1811/14, 1853/6, 1893/6 and 1943/7.

**1980.** Italian Artists Anniversaries (7th series). As T **567**. Multicoloured.

1699 520 l. "Saint Barbara" (Jacopo Palma, the Elder (1480–1528)) .. 75 55
1700 520 l. "Apollo and Daphne" (Gian Lorenzo Bernini (1598–1680)) .. 75 55

**647.** "Nativity" (Federico Brandani).

**1980.** Christmas.

1701. **647.** 120 l. green and brown 20 10

**648.** "My Town" (Treviso).

**1980.** Stamp Day. Paintings by Schoolchildren entitled "My Town". Mult.

1702 70 l. Type **648** .. 10 10
1703 120 l. Sansepolcro .. 15 15
1704 170 l. Sansepolcro (different) .. .. 20 15

**649.** Daniele Comboni and African Village.

**1981.** 150th Birth Anniv and Death Centenary of Daniele Comboni (missionary).

1705 **649** 80 l. brn, indigo & bl 15 10

**650.** Alcide de Gasperi.

**651.** Landscape outlined by Person in Wheelchair.

**1981.** Birth Centenary of Alcide de Gasperi (politician).

1706. **650.** 200 l. green .. .. 30 10

**1981.** International Year of Disabled Persons.

1707 **651** 300 l. multicoloured .. 45 15

**652.** Anemone.

**653.** Human Chess Game, Marostica.

**1981.** Flowers (1st series). Multicoloured.

1708. 200 l. Type **652** .. .. 35 15
1709. 200 l. Oleander .. .. 35 15
1710. 200 l. Rose .. .. 35 15

See also Nos. 1753/5 and 1797/9.

**1981.** Europa. Multicoloured.

1711. 300 l. Type **653** .. .. 60 15
1712. 300 l. "Il Palio" horse race, Siena .. .. 60 15

**654.** St. Rita of Cascia.

**655.** Ciro Menotti.

**1981.** 600th Birth Anniv. of St. Rita of Cascia.

1713. **654.** 600 l. multicoloured 90 35

**1981.** 150th Death Anniv. of Ciro Menotti (patriot).

1714. **655.** 80 l. black and brown 15 10

**656.** Agusta A.109 Helicopter.

**1981.** Italian Aircraft (1st series). Mult.

1715 200 l. Type **656** .. .. 40 20
1716 200 l. Partenavia P.68B Victor airplane .. 40 20
1717 200 l. Aeritalia G.222 transport .. .. 40 20
1718 200 l. Aermacchi MB 339 jet trainer .. .. 40 20

See also Nos. 1748/51 and 1792/5.

**657.** Fertile and Barren Soil.

**1981.** Water Conservation.

1719. **657.** 80 l. multicoloured .. 15 10

**1981.** Italian Work for the World (2nd series). As T **640**.

1720. 300 l. blue .. .. 35 20
1721. 300 l. red .. .. 35 20

DESIGNS: No. 1720, Sao Simao, Brazil. No. 1721, High Island, Hong Kong.

**1981.** Tourist Publicity (8th series). As T **556**. Multicoloured.

1722. 80 l. Matera .. .. 15 10
1723. 150 l. Riva del Garda .. 20 20
1724. 300 l. Santa Teresa di Gallura .. .. 55 15
1725. 900 l. Tarquinia .. .. 2·10 60

**658.** Naval Academy and Badge.

**1981.** Centenary of Naval Academy, Livorno. Multicoloured.

1726. 80 l. Type **658** .. .. 15 10
1727. 150 l. Aerial view of Academy .. .. 20 20
1728. 200 l. "Amerigo Vespucci" (cadet ship) and sailor using sextant .. .. 35 10

**659.** Spada Palace, Rome, and Decorative Motif from Grand Hall.

**1981.** 150th Anniv of Council of State.

1729 **659** 200 l. brn, grn & blue 30 15

**660.** Running.

**661.** Riace Bronze.

**1981.** World Cup Light Athletics Championships, Rome.

1730 **660** 300 l. multicoloured .. 40 15

**1981.** Italian Artists' Annivs. (8th series). Designs as T **567**. Multicoloured.

1731. 200 l. "Harbour" (Carlo Carra (1881–1966)) .. 35 30
1732. 200 l. "Nightfall" (Giuseppe Ugonia (1881–1944)) .. .. 35 30

**1981.** Riace Bronzes (ancient Greek statues). Multicoloured.

1733. 200 l. Type **661** .. .. 35 15
1734. 200 l. Riace bronze (different) .. .. .. 35 15

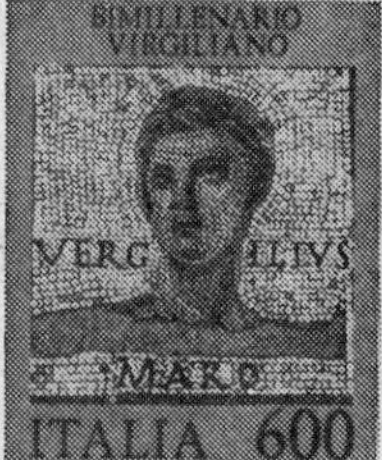



**662.** Virgil (Treviri mosaic).

**1981.** Death Bimillenary of Virgil (poet).

1735. **662.** 600 l. multicoloured 75 40

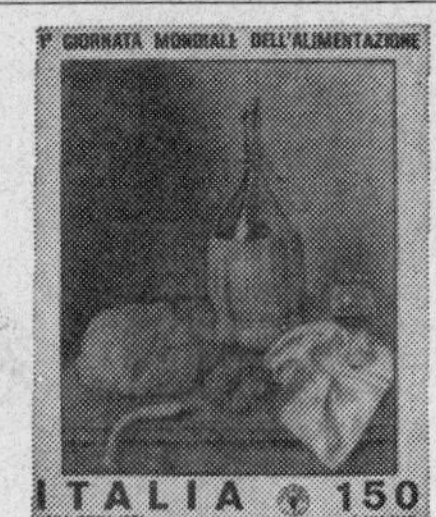


**663.** " Still-life " (Gregorio Sciltian).

**1981.** World Food Day.
1736. **663.** 150 l. multicoloured 30 25

**1981.** Italian Villas (2nd series). As T **646.** Multicoloured.
1737. 100 l. Villa Campolieto, Ercolano .. .. 15 10
1738. 200 l. Villa Cimbrone, Ravello .. .. 35 15
1739. 300 l. Villa Pignatelli, Naples .. .. .. 50 15

**664.** " Adoration of the Magi " (Giovanni da Campione d'Italia).

**1981.** Christmas.
1740. **664.** 200 l. deep blue, brown and blue .. .. 30 10

**665.** Pope John XXIII.
**666.** Envelopes forming Railway Track.

**1981.** Birth Cent. of Pope John XXIII.
1741. **665.** 200 l. multicoloured 40 10

**1981.** Stamp Day.
1742. **666.** 120 l. grn., red & blk. 50 20
1743. – 200 l. multicoloured 50 20
1744. – 300 l. multicoloured 60 15
DESIGNS—VERT. 200 l. Caduceus, chest, envelopes and cherub blowing posthorn. HORIZ. 300 l. Letter seal.

**667.** " St. Francis receiving the Stigmata " (Pietro Cavaro).
**668.** Paganini (after Ingres).

**1982.** 800th Birth Anniv. of St. Francis of Assisi.
1745. **667.** 300 l. brown and blue 40 15

**1982.** Birth Bicentenary of Niccolo Paganini (composer and violinist).
1746. **668.** 900 l. multicoloured 1·60 1·40

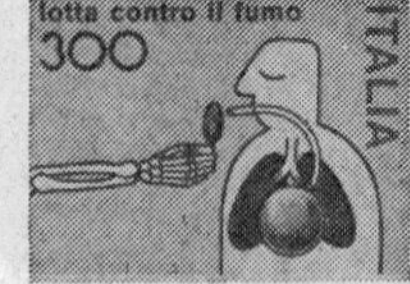


**669.** Skeletal Hand lighting Cigarette "Bomb".

**1982.** Anti-Smoking Campaign.
1747. **669.** 300 l. multicoloured 40 10

**1982.** Italian Aircraft (2nd series). As T **656.** Multicoloured.
1748 300 l. Panavia (inscr "Aeritalia") MRCA Tornado jet fighter .. 50 20
1749 300 l. Savoia SIAI 260 Turbo trainer .. .. 50 20
1750 300 l. Piaggio P-166 DL-3 Turbo .. .. .. 50 20
1751 300 l. Nardi NH 500 helicopter .. .. 50 20

**670.** Church of Santo Spirito o del Vespro, Palermo.
**671.** Coronation of Charlemagne, 799.

**1982.** 700th Anniv. of Sicilian Vespers (uprising).
1752. **670.** 120 l. red, blue & purple .. .. 20 10

**1982.** Flowers (2nd series). As T **652.** Mult.
1753. 300 l. Camellias .. .. 70 30
1754. 300 l. Carnations .. 70 30
1755. 300 l. Cyclamen .. .. 70 30

**1982.** Europa.
1756. **671.** 200 l. brn., blk. & blue 40 30
1757. – 450 l. multicoloured 70 30
DESIGN: 450 l. Stars and signatures to Treaty of Rome, 1957.

**1982.** Italian Work for the World (3rd series). As T **640.** Multicoloured.
1758. 450 l. Radio communication across Red Sea .. 50 25
1759. 450 l. Automatic letter sorting .. .. .. 50 25

**672.** Garibaldi.
**673.** Bridge Game, Pisa.

**1982.** Death Cent. of Giuseppe Garibaldi.
1760. **672.** 200 l. multicoloured 65 20

**1982.** Folk Customs (1st series).
1761. **673.** 200 l. multicoloured 45 35
See also Nos. 1804, 1850, 1875/6, 1914, 1972, 2004, 2028 and 2092.

**1982.** Tourist Publicity (9th series). As T **556.** Multicoloured.
1762. 200 l. Frasassi Grotto .. 40 35
1763. 200 l. Fai della Paganella 40 25
1764. 450 l. Rodi Garganico .. 70 30
1765. 450 l. Temples of Agrigento .. .. 70 30

**674.** Coxless Four.

**1982.** World Junior Rowing Championships.
1766. **674.** 200 l. multicoloured 45 40

**675.** Ducal Palace, Urbino, Montefeltro and Palazzo dei Consoli, Gubbio.

**1982.** 500th Death Anniv. of Federico da Montefeltro, Duke of Urbino.
1767. **675.** 200 l. multicoloured 30 20

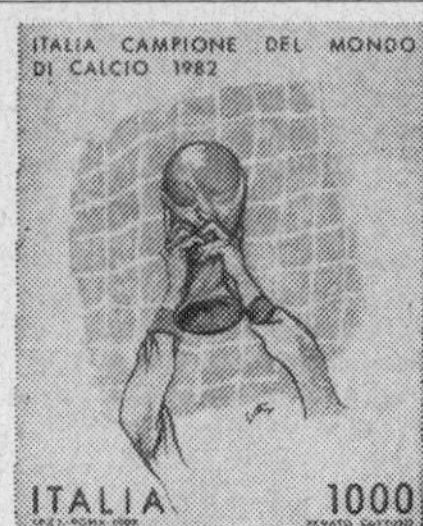


**676.** Footballer holding aloft World Cup.

**1982.** Italy's World Cup Football Victory.
1768. **676.** 1000 l. multicoloured 2·40 1·75

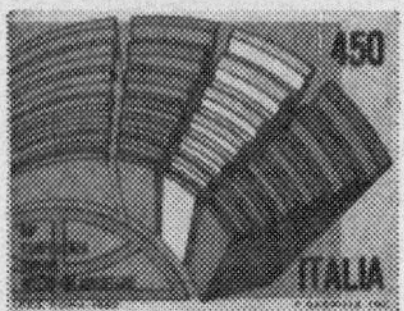


**677.** Seating Plan.

**1982.** 69th Interparliamentary Union Conference.
1769 **677** 450 l. multicoloured .. 50 25

**1982.** Italian Villas (3rd series). As T **646.** Multicoloured.
1770. 150 l. Temple of Aesculapius, Villa Borghese, Rome .. 50 20
1771. 250 l. Villa D'Este, Tivoli 95 15
1772. 350 l. Villa Lante, Bagnaia, Viterbo .. 1·60 35

**678.** Francis of Taxis.

**1982.** Commemoration of Establishment of First Public Postal System in Europe.
1773 **678** 300 l. red, blue & verm 35 20

**1982.** Italian Artists' Annivs. (9th series). As T **567.** Multicoloured.
1774. 300 l. " Portrait of Antonietta Negroni Prati Morosini as a Child " (Francesco Hayez (1791–1882)) .. .. 60 20
1775. 300 l. " The Fortune-teller " (Giovanni .. Piazzetta (1682–1754)) 60 20

**679.** Tree, Chair and Bed (Maria di Pastena).

**1983.** Stamp Day. Timber in Human Life. Drawings by Schoolchildren. Multicoloured.
1776 150 l. Type **679** .. .. 35 20
1777 250 l. Tree with timber products in branches (Lucia Andreoli) .. 55 20
1778 350 l. Forest (Marco Gallea) .. .. 80 25

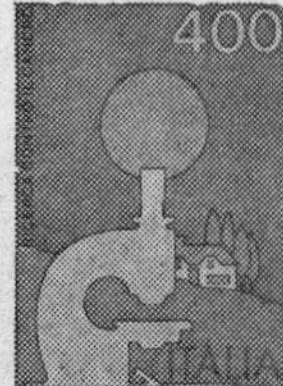


**680.** Microscope.

**1983.** Cancer Control.
1779. **680.** 400 l. multicoloured 70 15

**1983.** Italian Work for the World (4th series). Automobile Industry. As T **640.** Mult.
1780 400 l. Factories on globe 35 25
1781 400 l. Assembly line .. 35 25

**681.** Academy Emblem.
**682.** Shooting.

**1983.** 400th Anniv of Accademia della Crusca (Florentine Academy of Letters).
1782 **681** 400 l. red, brown & bl 70 15

**1983.** World Biathlon Championships, Antholz.
1783. **682.** 200 l. multicoloured 50 30

**683.** Gabriele Rossetti.
**684.** Guicciardini (after G. Bugiardini).

**1983.** Birth Cent. of Gabriele Rossetti (poet).
1784. **683.** 300 l. blue and brown 30 10

**1983.** 500th Birth Anniv. of Francesco Guicciardini (lawyer and diplomat).
1785. **684.** 450 l. brown .. .. 70 30

**685.** Saba and Trieste.
**686.** Pope Pius XII.

**1983.** Birth Cent. of Umberto Saba (poet).
1786. **685.** 600 l. multicoloured 1·00 35

**1983.** 25th Death Anniv. of Pope Pius XII.
1787. **686.** 1400 l. blue .. .. 2·40 60

**687.** Pope and St. Paul's Basilica.
**688.** Launch of Ship.

**1983.** Holy Year. Multicoloured.
1788. 250 l. Type **687** .. 40 30
1789. 300 l. Pope John Paul II and Basilica of Santa Maria Maggiore .. 50 15
1790. 400 l. Pope and St. John's Basilica .. 65 15
1791. 500 l. Pope and St. Peter's Cathedral. .. 85 25

**1983.** Italian Aircraft (3rd series). As T **656.** Multicoloured.
1792 400 l. Savoia SIAI 211 .. 75 25
1793 400 l. Agusta A.129 Mangusta helicopter .. 75 25
1794 400 l. Caproni C22J glider 75 25
1795 400 l. Aeritalia/Aermacchi AM-X jet fighter .. 75 25

**1983.** Labour Day.
1796. **688.** 1200 l. blue .. .. 2·00 60

**1983. Flowers (3rd series). As T 652. Mult.**
**1797. 200 l. Gladiolus .. .. 90 50**
**1798. 200 l. Mimosa .. .. 90 50**
**1799. 200 l. Rhododendron .. 90 50**

**689.** Galileo (after O. Leoni) and Telescope.

**1983.** Europa. Multicoloured.
1800 400 l. Type **689** .. .. 4·00 40
1801 500 l. Archimedes (marble bust) and screw .. 4·00 25

**690.** Moneta and Doves.

**1983.** 150th Birth Anniv. of Ernesto Teodoro Moneta (Nobel Peace Prize winner).
1802. **690.** 500 l. multicoloured 90 25

**691.** Quadriga, Globe and V.D.U.

**1983.** Third International Juridical Information Congress, Rome.
1803. **691.** 500 l. multicoloured 90 25

**1983.** Folk Customs (2nd issue). As T **673.** Multicoloured.
1804. 300 l. Ceri procession, Gubbio .. .. 65 20

**692.** Elevation of Host. **693.** Frescobaldi.

**1983.** 20th National Eucharistic Congress, Milan.
1805. **692.** 300 l. multicoloured 50 20

**1983.** Tourist Publicity (10th series). As T **556.** Multicoloured.
1806. 250 l. Alghero .. .. 1·00 90
1807. 300 l. Bardonecchia .. 95 25
1808. 400 l. Riccione .. .. 1·50 25
1809. 500 l. Taranto .. .. 2·25 25

**1983.** 400th Birth Anniv. of Girolamo Frescobaldi (composer).
1810. **693.** 400 l. grn., bl., & brn. 60 25

**1983.** Italian Villas (4th series). As T **646.** Multicoloured.
1811. 250 l. Villa Fidelia, Spello 95 65
1812. 300 l. Villa Imperiale, Pesaro .. .. 85 15
1813. 400 l. Michetti Convent, Francavilla al Mare .. 1·25 15
1814. 500 l. Villa di Riccia .. 1·50 25

**694.** Francesco de Sanctis. **695.** "Madonna of the Chair".

**1983.** Death Centenary of Francesco de Sanctis (writer).
1815. **694.** 300 l. multicoloured 50 15

**1983.** Christmas. 500th Birth Anniv. of Raphael (artist). Multicoloured.
1816. 250 l. Type **695** .. .. 60 20
1817. 400 l. "Sistine Madonna" 85 15
1818. 500 l. "Madonna of the Candles" .. .. 95 15

**696.** Chain of Letters. (Roberta Rizzi). **697.** Battered Road Sign.

**1983.** Stamp Day. Drawings by school-children. Multicoloured.
1819. 200 l. Type **696** .. .. 60 15
1820. 300 l. Space postman delivering letter (Maria Grazia Federico) (vert.) .. .. .. 85 15
1821. 400 l. Train leaving envelope and globe (Paolo Bucciarelli) .. 1·25 30

**1984.** Road Safety. Multicoloured.
1822. 300 l. Type **697** .. .. 70 15
1823. 400 l. Crashed car and policeman .. .. 80 15

**1984.** Italian Artists Anniversaries (10th series). As T **567.** Multicoloured.
1824. 300 l. Races at Bois de Boulogne" (Giuseppe de Nittis (1846–1884)) 60 20
1825. 400 l. "Paul Guillaume (Amedeo Modigliani (1884–1920)) .. .. 80 20

**698.** Maserati "Biturbo".

**1984.** Italian Motor Industry (1st series). Multicoloured.
1826. 450 l. Type **698** .. .. 1·40 25
1827. 450 l. Iveco "190.38 Special" lorry .. 1·40 25
1828. 450 l. Same Trattori "Galaxy" tractor .. 1·40 25
1829. 450 l. Alfa "33" .. .. 1·40 25
See also Nos. 1867/70 and 1933/6.

**699.** Glassblower, Glasses and Jug.

**1984.** Italian Work for the World (5th series). Ceramic and Glass Industries. Mult.
1830 300 l. Ceramic plaque and furnace .. .. 45 20
1831 300 l. Type **699** .. .. 45 20

**700.** European Parliament Building. Strasbourg.

**1984.** Second European Parliament Direct Elections.
1832. **700.** 400 l. multicoloured 70 30

**701.** State Forest Corps Helicopter.

**1984.** Nature Protection. Forests. Mult.
1833. 450 l. Type **701** .. .. 1·50 80
1834. 450 l. Forest animals and burning cigarette .. 1·10 80
1835. 450 l. River and litter .. 1·75 80
1836. 450 l. Wildlife and building construction 1·75 80

**702.** Ministry of Posts and Telecommunications, Rome.

**1984.** "Italia '85" International Stamp Exhibition, Rome (1st issue). Mult.
1837. 450 l. Type **702** .. .. 90 25
1838. 550 l. Appian Way .. 1·10 30
See also Nos. 1857/9, 1862/4, 1871/3 and 1898/1911.

**703.** G. di Vittorio, B. Buozzi and A. Grandi.

**1984.** 40th Anniv. of Rome Pact (foundation of Italian Trade Unions).
1839. **703.** 450 l. multicoloured 1·00 25

**704.** Bridge.

**1984.** Europa. 25th Anniv of European Post and Telecommunications Conference.
1840. **704.** 450 l. multicoloured 3·00 50
1841. 550 l. multicoloured 5·00 2·00

**705.** Symposium Emblem. **706.** Horse-race.

**1984.** International Telecommunications Symposium, Florence.
1842. **705.** 550 l. multicoloured 1·25 35

**1984.** Centenary of Italian Derby. Mult.
1843. 250 l. Type **706**.. .. 1·50 1·25
1844. 400 l. Horse-race (different) .. .. 2·00 40

**1984.** Tourist Publicity (11th series). As T **556.** Multicoloured.
1845 350 l. Campione d'Italia 1·10 85
1846 400 l. Chianciano Terme 1·10 15
1847 450 l. Padula .. .. 1·25 20
1848 550 l. Syracuse .. .. 1·25 40

**1984.** Folk Customs (3rd issue). As T **673.** Multicoloured.
1850. 400 l. Procession of Shrine of Santa Rosa, Viterbo 1·00 20

**708.** Harvester, Thresher and Medieval Fields Map.

**1984.** Peasant Farming. Multicoloured.
1851. 250 l. Type **708**.. .. 45 45
1852. 350 l. Hand oil press, cart and medieval fields map .. .. 75 20

**1984.** Italian Villas (5th series). As T **646.** Multicoloured.
1853. 250 l. Villa Caristo, Stignano .. .. 1·00 85
1854. 350 l. Villa Doria Pamphili, Genoa .. .. 1·10 70
1855. 400 l. Villa Reale, Stupinigi 1·25 20
1856. 450 l. Villa Mellone, Lecce 1·40 25

**709.** Etruscan Bronze of Warrior. **710.** Dish Aerial, Globe and Punched Tape.

**1984.** "Italia '85" International Stamp Exhibition, Rome (2nd issue). Mult.
1857. 550 l. Type **709** .. .. 70 30
1858. 550 l. Exhibition emblem 70 30
1859. 550 l. Etruscan silver-backed mirror .. 70 30

**1985.** Information Technology.
1860. **710.** 350 l. multicoloured 70 15

**711.** Man helping Old Woman. **712.** "Venus in her Chariot" (fresco, Raphael).

**1985.** Problems of Elderly People.
1861. **711.** 250 l. multicoloured 55 35

**1985.** "Italia '85" International Stamp Exhibition, Rome (3rd issue). Multicoloured.
1862 600 l. Type **712** .. .. 70 30
1863. 600 l. Exhibition emblem 70 30
1864. 600 l. Warriors (detail of fresco, Baldassare Peruzzi) .. .. 70 30

**713.** Plate, Vase and Pot.

**1985.** Italian World Aid (6th series). Ceramics. Multicoloured.
1865. 600 l. Type **713** .. .. 60 30
1866. 600 l. Decorated plate .. 60 30

**1985.** Italian Motor Industry (2nd series). As T **698.** Multicoloured.
1867 450 l. Fiat "Uno" .. 80 25
1868 450 l. Lamborghini "Countach LP500" .. 80 25
1869 450 l. Lancia "Thema" .. 80 25
1870 450 l. Fiat Abarth "100 Bialbero" .. .. 80 25

**714.** St. Mary of Peace Church, Rome. **715.** Pope Sixtus V.

**1985.** "Italia '85" International Stamp Exhibition, Rome (4th issue). Baroque Art. Multicoloured.
1871. 250 l. Type **714** .. .. 35 25
1872. 250 l. Exhibition emblem 35 25
1873. 250 l. Fountain, obelisk and Saint Agnes's Church, Rome .. 35 25

**1985.** 400th Anniv. of Election of Pope Sixtus V.
1874. **715.** 1500 l. multicoloured 3·00 1·00

**1985.** Folk Customs (4th series). As T **673.** Multicoloured.

1875. 250 l. March of the Turks, Potenza .. 90 30
1876. 350 l. Republican regatta, Amalfi .. 1·10 15

**1985.** Tourist Publicity (12th series). As T **556.** Multicoloured.

1877. 350 l. Bormio .. .. 85 70
1878. 400 l. Castellammare di Stabia .. .. 90 20
1879. 450 l. Stromboli .. .. 1·00 25
1880. 600 l. Termoli .. .. 1·90 35

**716.** European Otter. **717.** Aureliano Pertile and Giovanni Martinelli (singers).

**1985.** Nature Protection. Multicoloured.

1881. 500 l. Type **716** .. .. 65 30
1882. 500 l. Primulas .. .. 65 30
1883. 500 l. Fir tree .. .. 65 30
1884. 500 l. Black-winged stilts 2·00 50

**1985.** Anniversaries of Italian Artists (11th series). As T **567.** Multicoloured.

1885. 350 l. "Madonna" (Giambattista Salvi (1609–85)) .. .. 90 60
1886. 400 l. "The Pride of Work" (Mario Sironi (1885–1961) .. .. 1·10 15

**1985.** Europa. Music Year. Multicoloured.

1887. 500 l. Type **717** .. .. 3·00 25
1888. 600 l. Vicenzo Bellini and Johann Sebastian Bach (composers) .. 4·50 50

**718.** San Salvatore Abbey.

**1985.** 950th Anniv. of San Salvatore Abbey, Mt. Amiata.

1889. **718.** 450 l. multicoloured 1·25 20

**719.** Cyclists.

**1985.** World Cycling Championships, Bassano del Grappa.

1890. **719.** 400 l. multicoloured 1·25 15

**720.** U.N. and Congress Emblems and Globe.

**1985.** Seventh United Nations Crime Prevention Congress, Milan.

1891. **720.** 600 l. multicoloured 1·90 30

## INDEX

Countries can be quickly located by referring to the index at the end of this volume.

**721.** Profile and Emblem.

**1985.** International Youth Year.

1892. **721.** 600 l. multicoloured 1·90 30

**1985.** Villas (6th series). As T **646.** Mult.

1893. 300 l. Villa Nitti, Maratea .. .. 1·10 30
1894. 400 l. Villa Aldrovandi Mazzacorati, Bologna 1·50 20
1895. 500 l. Villa Santa Maria, Pula .. .. .. 2·00 30
1896. 600 l. Villa de Mersi, Villazzano .. .. 2·25 40

**722.** State Emblems of Italy and Vatican City and Medallion (Mario Soccorsi).

**1985.** Ratification of the Modification of 1929 Lateran Concordat.

1897. **722.** 400 l. multicoloured 1·10 15

**723.** Parma Town Hall and 1857 25 c. Stamp.

**724.** Basel 1845 2½ r. Stamp.

**1985.** "Italia '85" International Stamp Exhibition. Rome (5th issue). Multicoloured.

(a) As T **723.**

1898. 300 l. Type **723** .. .. 55 40
1899. 300 l. Naples New Castle and 1858 2 g. stamp .. 55 40
1900. 300 l. Palermo Cathedral and Sicily 1859 ½ g. stamp .. .. .. 55 40
1901. 300 l. Modena Cathedral and 1852 15 c. stamp .. 55 40
1902. 300 l. Piazzo Navona, Rome, and Papal States 1852 7 b. stamp 55 40
1903. 300 l. Palazzo Vecchio, Florence, and Tuscany 1851 2 c. stamp .. 55 40
1904. 300 l. Turin and Sardinia 1861 3 l. stamp .. 55 40
1905. 300 l. Bologna and Romagna 1859 6 b. stamp .. .. .. 55 40
1906. 300 l. Palazzo Litta, Milan, and Lombardy and Venetia 1850 15 c. stamp .. .. .. 55 40

(b) As T **724.**

1907. 500 l. Type **724** .. .. 1·00 35
1908. 500 l. Japan 1871 48 m. stamp .. .. .. 1·00 35
1909. 500 l. United States 1847 10 c. stamp .. .. 1·00 35
1910. 500 l. Western Australia 1854 1d. stamp .. 1·00 35
1911. 500 l. Mauritius 1848 2d. stamp .. .. .. 1·00 35

**725.** Skiers.

**1986.** Cross-country Skiing.

1913. **725.** 450 l. multicoloured 1·00 20

**1986.** Folk Customs (5th series). As T **673.** Multicoloured.

1914. 450 l. Le Candelore, Catania .. .. 90 20

**726.** Amilcare Ponchielli and Scene from "La Gioconda".

**1986.** Composers. Multicoloured.

1915. 2000 l. Type **726** (death centenary) .. .. 3·25 80
1916. 2000 l. Giovan Battista Pergolesi (250th death anniv.) .. .. .. 3·25 80

**727.** Acitrezza.

**1986.** Tourist Publicity (13th series). Mult.

1917 350 l. Type **727** .. .. 65 30
1918 450 l. Capri .. .. 85 20
1919 550 l. Merano .. .. 1·10 30
1920 650 l. San Benedetto del Tronto .. .. 1·25 40

**728.** Heart-shaped Tree (life). **729.** "Eyes".

**1986.** Europa. Multicoloured.

1921. 650 l. Type **728** .. .. 1·10 45
1922. 650 l. Star-shaped tree (poetry) .. .. 1·10 45
1923. 650 l. Butterfly-shaped tree (colour) .. .. 1·10 45
1924. 650 l. Sun-shaped tree (energy) .. .. 1·10 45

**1986.** 25th International Ophthalmology Congress, Rome.

1925. **729.** 550 l. multicoloured 1·25 30

**730.** Italian Police.

**1986.** European Police Meeting, Chianciano Terme.

1926. **730.** 550 l. multicoloured 75 25
1927. 650 l. multicoloured 1·00 35

**731.** Battle Scene.

**1986.** 120th Anniv. of Battle of Bezzecca.

1928. **731.** 550 l. multicoloured 1·10 25

**732.** Figure with Flag. **733.** Bersagliere and Helmets.

**1986.** National Independence Martyrs' Day.

1929. **732.** 2000 l. multicoloured 3·50 60

**1986.** 150th Anniv of Turin Bersaglieri Corps (alpine troops).

1930 **733** 450 l. multicoloured .. 1·40 15

**734.** Dish Aerial, Transmitter and "Messages".

**1986.** Telecommunications.

1931. **734.** 350 l. multicoloured 60 15

**735.** Varallo.

**1986.** Holy Mountain of Varallo.

1932 **735** 2000 l. green and blue 3·25 55

**1986.** Italian Motor Industry (3rd series). As T **698.** Multicoloured.

1933. 450 l. Alfa Romeo "AR 8 Turbo" .. .. 65 25
1934. 450 l. Innocenti "650 SE" 65 25
1935. 450 l. Ferrari "Testarossa" .. .. 65 25
1936. 450 l. Fiatallis "FR 10B" 65 25

**736.** Clothes and Woman (fashion).

**1986.** Italian World Aid (7th series). Mult.

1937 450 l. Type **736** .. .. 80 20
1938 450 l. Man and clothes (fashion) .. .. 80 20
1939 650 l. Olivetti personal computer, keyboard and screen .. .. 1·10 30
1940 650 l. Breda steam turbine 1·10 30

**737.** Airplane flying through "40". **738.** "Madonna and Child" (bronze sculpture by Donatello).

**1986.** 40th Anniv. of Alitalia (national airline). Multicoloured.

1941. 550 l. Type **737** .. .. 1·25 20
1942. 650 l. Airplane and landing lights .. 1·40 25

**1986.** Villas (7th series). As T **646.** Mult.

1943. 350 l. Villa Necker, Trieste .. .. .. 65 15
1944. 350 l. Villa Borromeo, Cassana d'Adda .. 65 15
1945. 450 l. Villa Palagonia, Bagheria .. .. 85 15
1946. 550 l. Villa Medicea, Poggio a Caiano .. 1·10 20
1947. 650 l. Issogne Castle .. 1·25 25

**1986.** Christmas.

1948 **738** 450 l. bistre .. .. 1·00 10

**1986.** Anniversaries of Italian Artists (12th series). As T **567.**

1949. 450 l. black and orange 1·25 20

1950. 550 l. multicoloured .. 1·50 20

DESIGNS: 450 l. Drawing of woman (Andrea del Sarto (1486–1531)). 550 l. "Daphne at Pavarola" (Felice Casorati (1883–1963)).

**739.** Lockheed Hercules Transport dropping Squares in National Colours onto Globe.

**740.** Engraving 1862 Stamp.

**1986.** International Peace Year. Mult.

1951 550 l. Type **739** .. 1·00 20

1952 650 l. Airplane, Cross and people (commemoration of Italian airmen killed on mission to Kindu, Congo) .. .. 1·25 20

**1986.** Stamp Day. Francesco Maria Matraire (engraver).

1953 **740** 550 l. multicoloured .. 1·25 15

**741.** Woven Threads (Marzotto Textile Industry).

**1987.** Italian Industry.

1954. **741.** 700 l. multicoloured 1·10 30

1955. – 700 l. blue & turq. .. 1·10 30

DESIGN: No. 1955, Clouds and flame (Italgas Gas Corporation).

**742.** River Volturno.

**743.** Gramsci.

**1987.** Nature Protection. Rivers and Lakes. Multicoloured.

1956. 500 l. Type **742** .. 85 30

1957. 500 l. Lake Garda .. 85 30

1958. 500 l. Lake Trasimeno .. 85 30

1959. 500 l. River Tirso .. 85 30

**1987.** 50th Death Anniv. of Antonio Gramsci (politician).

1960 **743** 600 l. grey, black & red 90 15

**744.** Church of the Motorway of the Sun, Florence (Giovanni Michelucci).

**745.** View of Naples on Football.

**1987.** Europa. Architecture. Multicoloured.

1961. 600 l. Type **744** .. 1·25 20

1962. 700 l. Termini station, Rome (Nervi) .. .. 1·60 35

**1987.** Tourist Publicity (14th series). As T **556.** Multicoloured.

1963. 380 l. Verbania Pallanza 85 30

1964. 400 l. Palmi .. .. 95 20

1965. 500 l. Vasto .. .. 1·10 20

1966. 600 l. Villacidro .. .. 1·40 30

**1987.** S.S.C. Naples, National Football Champion, 1986–87.

1967 **745** 500 l. multicoloured .. 2·75 40

**746.** "The Absinthe Drinker" (Edgar Degas).

**747.** Liguori and Gulf of Naples.

**1987.** Anti-alcoholism Campaign.

1968. **746.** 380 l. multicoloured 1·00 15

**1987.** Death Bicentenary of St. Alfonso Maria de Liguori (co-founder of Redemptorists).

1969. **747.** 400 l. multicoloured 80 15

**748.** Emblem and Olympic Stadium, Rome.

**1987.** World Light Athletics Championships, Rome (1970) and "Olymphilex '87" Stamp Exhibition, Rome (1971).

1970. 700 l. Type **748** .. .. 1·00 20

1971. 700 l. International Olympic Committee building, Foro Italico, Rome .. .. .. 1·00 20

**1987.** Folk Customs (6th series). As T **673.** Multicoloured.

1972. 380 l. Joust, Foligno .. 85 15

**749.** Piazza del Popolo, Ascoli Piceno.

**750.** "The Adoration in the Manger" (St. Francis's Basilica, Assisi).

**1987.** Piazzas (1st series). Multicoloured.

1973. 380 l. Type **749** .. .. 70 20

1974. 500 l. Piazza Giuseppe Verdi, Palermo .. 85 15

1975. 600 l. Piazza San Carlo, Turin .. .. 95 15

1976. 700 l. Piazza dei Signori, Verona .. 1·10 15

See also Nos. 2002/3 and 2023/4.

**1987.** Christmas. Frescoes by Giotto. Mult.

1977 500 l. Type **750** .. .. 1·00 15

1978 600 l. "Epiphany" (Scrovegni Chapel, Padua) .. .. 1·10 15

**751.** Battle Scene.

**1987.** 120th Anniv. of Battle of Mentana.

1979. **751.** 380 l. multicoloured 85 15

**752.** "Christ Pantocrator" (mosaic, Monreale Cathedral).

**1987.** Artistic Heritage. Multicoloured.

1980. 500 l. Type **752** .. .. 1·40 20

1981. 500 l. San Carlo Theatre, Naples (18th-century engraving) .. .. 1·40 20

**753.** College and 1787 and 1987 Uniforms.

**754.** Marco de Marchi (philatelist) and Milan Cathedral.

**1987.** Bicentenary of Nunziatella Military Academy, Naples.

1982 **753** 600 l. multicoloured .. 1·25 20

**1987.** Stamp Day.

1983. **754.** 500 l. multicoloured 1·25 15

**755.** Man chipping Flints.

**756.** Lyceum.

**1988.** "Homo aeserniensis".

1984. **755.** 500 l. multicoloured 85 15

**1988.** E.Q. Visconti Lyceum, Rome.

1985 **756** 500 l. multicoloured .. 85 15

See also Nos. 2019, 2109 and 2127.

**757.** Statue, Bosco and Boy.

**758.** 15th-Century Soncino Bible.

**1988.** Death Centenary of St. John Bosco (founder of Salesian Brothers).

1986 **757** 500 l. multicoloured .. 70 15

**1988.** Anniversaries of Italian Artists (13th series). As T **567.** Multicoloured.

1987 650 l. "Archaeologists" (Giorgio de Chirico (1888–1978)) .. .. 1·25 20

**1988.** 500th Anniv. of First Printing of Bible in Hebrew.

1988. **758.** 550 l. multicoloured 1·25 20

**759.** St. Valentine, Epileptics and Wave Patterns.

**1988.** Anti-epilepsy Campaign.

1989 **759** 500 l. multicoloured .. 90 15

**760.** "ETR 450" Electric Train in Station.

**761.** Golfer on Ball.

**1988.** Europa. Transport and Communications. Multicoloured.

1990. 650 l. Type **760** .. .. 1·25 40

1991. 750 l. Map and keyboard operator (electronic postal systems) .. 1·50 40

**1988.** Tourist Publicity (15th series). As T **556.** Multicoloured.

1992 400 l. Castiglione della Pescaia .. .. 65 30

1993 500 l. Lignano Sabbiadoro 80 30

1994 650 l. St. Domenico's Church, Noto .. .. 90 15

1995 750 l. Vieste .. .. 95 40

**1988.** Golf.

1996. **761.** 500 l. multicoloured 90 15

**762.** Stadium and Mascot.

**763.** Milan Cathedral on Football.

**1988.** World Cup Football Championship, Italy (1990) (1st series).

1997 **762** 3150 l. multicoloured 4·00 2·75

See also Nos. 2049 and 2052/87.

**1988.** A. C. Milan, National Football Champion, 1987–88.

1998 **763** 650 l. multicoloured .. 90 40

**764.** Horse's Head.

**1988.** Artistic Heritage. Pergola Bronzes. Multicoloured.

1999. 500 l. Type **764** .. .. 80 30

2000. 650 l. Bust of woman .. 1·00 40

**765.** Student (bas-relief).

**766.** Emblem and Appian Way.

**1988.** 900th Anniv. of Bologna University.

2001. **765.** 500 l. violet .. .. 70 15

**1988.** Piazzas (2nd series). As T **749.** Mult.

2002. 400 l. Piazza del Duomo, Pistoia .. .. 70 20

2003. 550 l. Piazza del Unita d'Italia, Trieste .. 80 20

**1988.** Folk Customs (7th series). As T **673.** Multicoloured.

2004. 550 l. Candle procession, Sassari .. .. .. 90 15

**1988.** "Roma 88" Int Gastroenterology and Digestive Endoscopy Congress.

2005 **766** 750 l. multicoloured .. 1·25 30

**767.** "Ossessione" (Luchino Visconti, 1942).

**769.** "Holy Family" (Pasquale Celommi).

**768.** Bird (aluminium).

**1988.** Italian Films. Scenes from and Advertising Posters of named Films. Multicoloured.
2006. 500 l. Type **767** .. .. 90 30
2007. 650 l. "Ladri di Biciclette" (Vittorio de Sica, 1948) .. .. 1·00 30
2008. 2400 l. "Roma Citta Aperta" (Roberto Rossellini, 1945) .. 3·25 70
2009. 3050 l. "Riso Amaro" (Giuseppe de Santis, 1949) .. .. .. 5·00 1·00

**1988.** Italian Industry. Multicoloured.
2010 750 l. Type **768** .. .. 80 25
2011 750 l. Oscilloscope display (electronics) .. .. 80 25
2012 750 l. Banknote engraving, 1986 tourism stamp and medals (60th anniv of State Polygraphic Institute) .. .. 80 25

**1988.** Christmas (1st issue).
2013. **769.** 650 l. multicoloured 1·25 10
See also No. 2015.

**770** Borromeo and Plague Victims

**1988.** 450th Birth Anniv of St. Carlo Borromeo, Archbishop of Milan.
2014 **770** 2400 l. multicoloured 2·75 75

**771** "Nativity" (bas-relief)

**772** Edoardo Chiossone (stamp designer) and Japanese 1879 2 s. "Koban" Stamp

**1988.** Christmas (2nd issue).
2015. **771.** 500 l. green & brown 1·10 10

**1988.** Stamp Day.
2016. **772.** 500 l. multicoloured 60 10

**773** AIDS Virus

**1989.** Anti-AIDS Campaign.
2017 **773** 650 l. multicoloured .. 1·00 15

**774** 1907 Itala Car and Route Map

**1989.** Re-enactment of 1907 Peking–Paris Car Rally.
2018 **774** 3150 l. multicoloured 4·00 3·00

**1989.** Giuseppe Parini Lyceum, Milan. As T **756**.
2019 650 l. multicoloured .. 1·10 20

**776** Fresco, Ragione Palace, Padua

**777** Stylized Yachts

**1989.** Artistic Heritage.
2020 **776** 500 l. multicoloured .. 90 30
2021 – 650 l. blue .. .. 1·00 20
DESIGN: 650 l. Crypt, Basilica of St. Nicolas, Bari.

**1989.** World Sailing Championships, Alassio, Naples and Porto Cervo.
2022 **777** 3050 l. multicoloured 3·75 60

**1989.** Piazzas (3rd series). As T **749**. Mult.
2023 400 l. Piazza di Spagna, Rome .. .. .. 50 30
2024 400 l. Piazza del Duomo, Catanzaro .. .. 50 30

**778** Leap-frog (Luca Rizzello)

**1989.** Europa. Children's Games. Mult.
2025 500 l. Type **778** .. .. 65 15
2026 650 l. Girl dressing up (Serena Forcuti) (vert) 80 15
2027 750 l. Sack race (Adelise Lahner) .. .. 1·25 30

**1989.** Folk Customs (8th series). As T **673**. Multicoloured.
2028 400 l. Spello flower paintings .. .. 55 35

**779** Cloisters

**1989.** Pisa University.
2029 **779** 500 l. violet .. .. 70 35

**780** Parliamentary Emblem as Tree on Map

**781** 1889 5 c. Savoy Arms Stamp

**1989.** 3rd Direct Elections to European Parliament.
2030 **780** 500 l. multicoloured .. 90 35
No. 2030 is also inscribed with the European Currency Unit rate of 0.31 ECU.

**1989.** Tourist Publicity (16th series). As T **556**. Multicoloured.
2031 500 l. Grottammare .. 85 35
2032 500 l. Spotorno .. .. 85 35
2033 500 l. Pompeii .. .. 85 35
2034 500 l. Giardini Naxos .. 85 35

**1989.** Centenary of Ministry of Posts and Telecommunications. Multicoloured.
2035 500 l. Type **781** .. .. 1·00 60
2036 2400 l. Globe within posthorn .. .. 3·25 75

**782** Ball and Club Emblem

**1989.** Inter Milan, National Football Champion, 1988–89.
2037 **782** 650 l. multicoloured .. 1·00 45

**783** Stylized Chamber

**1989.** Centenary of Interparliamentary Union.
2038 **783** 750 l. multicoloured .. 1·10 40

**784** Phrygian Cap

**1989.** Bicentenary of French Revolution.
2039 **784** 3150 l. multicoloured 3·50 3·00

**785** Corinaldo Wall

**1989.** Artistic Heritage. 550th Birth Anniv of Francesco di Giorgio Martini (architect).
2040 **785** 500 l. multicoloured 75 25

**786** Chaplin in Film Scenes

**1989.** Birth Centenary of Charlie Chaplin (film actor and director).
2041 **786** 750 l. black and brown 1·50 40

**787** "Inauguration of Naples–Portici Line" (left-hand detail, S. Fergola)

**1989.** 150th Anniv of Naples–Portici Railway. Multicoloured.
2042 550 l. Type **787** .. .. 90 25
2043 550 l. Right-hand detail 90 25
Nos. 2042/3 were printed together, se-tenant, forming a composite design.

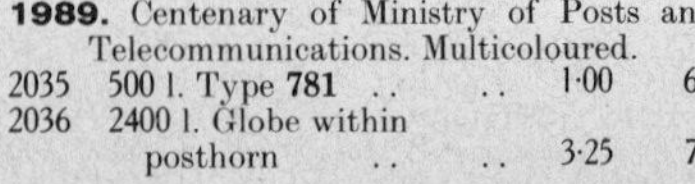

**788** Castelfidardo, Accordion and Stradella

**1989.** Italian Industry. Multicoloured.
2044 450 l. Type **788** .. .. 50 25
2045 450 l. Books (Arnoldo Mondadori Publishing House) .. .. 50 25

**789** Madonna and Child

**790** Emilio Diena (stamp dealer)

**1989.** Christmas. Details of "Adoration of the Magi" (Correggio). Multicoloured.
2046 500 l. Type **789** .. .. 80 25
2047 500 l. Magi .. .. 80 25
Nos. 2046/7 were printed together, se-tenant, forming a composite design.

**1989.** Stamp Day.
2048 **790** 500 l. black, brn & bl 70 15

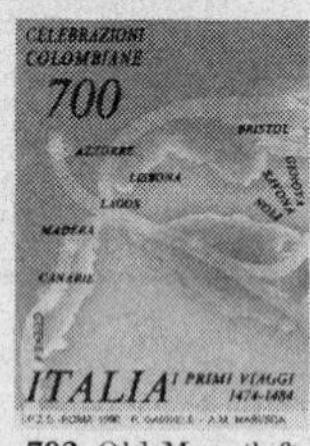

**791** Monument (Mario Ceroli) and Football Pitch

**792** Old Map (left half) with Route superimposed

**1989.** World Cup Football Championship, Italy (1990) (2nd issue).
2049 **791** 450 l. multicoloured .. 1·00 35

**1990.** Columbus's First Voyages, 1474–84. Multicoloured.
2050 700 l. Type **792** .. .. 85 35
2051 700 l. Right half of map 85 35
Nos. 2050/1 were printed together, se-tenant, forming a composite design.

**793** Italy

**1990.** World Cup Football Championship, Italy (3rd issue). Designs showing finalists' emblems or playing venues. Multicoloured.
2052 450 l. Type **793** .. .. 50 30
2053 450 l. U.S.A .. .. 50 30
2054 450 l. Olympic Stadium, Rome .. .. .. 50 30
2055 450 l. Comunale Stadium, Florence .. .. 50 30
2056 450 l. Austria .. .. 50 30
2057 450 l. Czechoslovakia .. 50 30
2058 600 l. Argentina .. .. 70 35
2059 600 l. U.S.S.R. .. .. 70 35
2060 600 l. San Paolo Stadium, Naples .. .. 70 35
2061 600 l. New Stadium, Bari 70 35
2062 600 l. Cameroun .. .. 70 35
2063 600 l. Rumania .. .. 70 35
2064 650 l. Brazil .. .. 75 40
2065 650 l. Costa Rica .. 75 40
2066 650 l. Delle Alpi Stadium, Turin .. .. .. 75 40
2067 650 l. Ferraris Stadium, Genoa .. .. .. 75 40
2068 650 l. Sweden .. .. 75 40
2069 650 l. Scotland .. .. 75 40
2070 700 l. United Arab Emirates .. .. 85 45
2071 700 l. West Germany .. 85 45

2072 700 l. Dall'Ara Stadium, Bologna .. .. 85 45
2073 700 l. Meazza Stadium, Milan .. .. .. 85 45
2074 700 l. Colombia .. .. 85 45
2075 700 l. Yugoslavia .. .. 85 45
2076 800 l. Belgium .. .. 90 50
2077 800 l. Uruguay .. .. 90 50
2078 800 l. Bentegodi Stadium, Verona .. .. .. 90 50
2079 800 l. Friuli Stadium, Udine .. .. .. 90 50
2080 800 l. South Korea .. .. 90 50
2081 800 l. Spain .. .. 90 50
2082 1200 l. England .. .. 1·50 75
2083 1200 l. Netherlands .. 1·50 75
2084 1200 l. Sant'Elia Stadium, Cagliari .. .. 1·50 75
2085 1200 l. La Favorita Stadium, Palermo .. 1·50 75
2086 1200 l. Ireland .. .. 1·50 75
2087 1200 l. Egypt .. .. 1·50 75
See also No. 2104.

**1990.** Tourist Publicity (17th series). As T **556**. Multicoloured.
2088 600 l. San Felice Circeo .. 75 30
2089 600 l. Castellammare del Golfo .. .. .. 75 30
2090 600 l. Montepulciano .. 75 30
2091 600 l. Sabbioneta .. 75 30

**1990.** Folk Customs (9th series). As T **673**. Multicoloured.
2092 600 l. Avelignesi horse race, Merano .. .. 75 30

**794** National Colours

**1990.** Death Centenary of Aurelio Saffi.
2093 **794** 700 l. multicoloured .. 85 35

**795** Giovanni Giorgi (inventor)

**796** Flags, Globe and Workers (after "The Four States" (Pellizza da Volpedo))

**1990.** 55th Anniv of Invention of Giorgi/MKSA System of Electrotechnical Units.
2094 **795** 600 l. multicoloured .. 75 30

**1990.** Centenary of Labour Day.
2095 **796** 600 l. multicoloured .. 75 30

**797** Ball on Map

**798** Piazza San Silvestro Post Office, Rome

**1990.** S. S. C. Naples, National Football Champion, 1989–90.
2096 **797** 700 l. multicoloured .. 1·00 35

**1990.** Europa. Post Office Buildings. Mult.
2097 700 l. Type **798** .. .. 85 35
2098 800 l. Fondaco Tedeschi post office, Venice .. 1·00 40

**799** Paisiello

**800** Globe, Open Book and Bust of Dante

**1990.** 250th Birth Anniv of Giovanni Paisiello (composer).
2099 **799** 450 l. multicoloured .. 60 20

**1990.** Centenary of Dante Alighieri Society.
2100 **800** 700 l. multicoloured .. 85 35

**801** Byzantine Mosaic, Ravenna

**802** Malatestiana Temple, Rimini

**1990.** Artistic Heritage. Multicoloured.
2101 450 l. Type **801** .. .. 55 20
2102 700 l. "Christ and Angels" (detail of Rachis altar, Friuli) (Lombard art) 85 35

**1990.** 40th Anniv of Malatestiana Religious Music Festival.
2103 **802** 600 l. multicoloured .. 75 30

**1990.** West Germany, Winner of World Cup Football Championship. As No. 2071 but value changed and additionally inscr "CAMPIONE DEL MONDO".
2104 600 l. multicoloured .. 1·50 1·00

**803** "Still Life"

**1990.** Birth Cent of Giorgio Morandi (painter).
2105 **803** 750 l. black .. .. 90 35

**804** Ancient and Modern Wrestlers

**1990.** World Greco-Roman Wrestling Championships, Rome.
2106 **804** 3200 l. multicoloured 3·50 1·50

**805** "New Life" (Emidio Vangelli)

**1990.** Christmas. Multicoloured.
2107 600 l. Type **805** .. .. 75 30
2108 750 l. "Adoration of the Shepherds" (fresco by Pellegrino in St. Daniel's Church, Friuli) 90 35

**806** Catania University

**1990.**
2109 – 600 l. multicoloured .. 80 30
2110 **806** 750 l. blue & ultra .. 1·00 35
DESIGN—As T **756**. 600 l. Bernardino Telesio High School, Cosenza.

**807** Corrado Mezzana (stamp designer, self-portrait)

**808** Holy Family

**1990.** Stamp Day.
2111 **807** 600 l. multicoloured .. 80 30

**1991.** "The Living Tableau", Rivisondoli.
2112 **808** 600 l. multicoloured .. 70 30

**809** Fair Emblem

**810** Emblem

**1991.** "EuroFlora '91" Fair, Genoa.
2113 **809** 750 l. multicoloured .. 90 30

**1991.** 750th Anniv of Siena University.
2114 **810** 750 l. gold, black & bl 80 30

**1991.** Tourist Publicity (18th series). As T **556**. Multicoloured.
2115 600 l. Cagli .. .. 70 30
2116 600 l. La Maddalena .. 70 30
2117 600 l. Roccaraso .. .. 70 30
2118 600 l. Sanremo .. .. 70 30

**811** European Community Flag

**812** City and Columbus's Fleet

**1991.** Europa Youth Meeting, Venice.
2119 **811** 750 l. multicoloured .. 80 30
No. 2119 is also valued in ECUs (European Currency Unit).

**1991.** 500th Anniv (1992) of Discovery of America by Christopher Columbus (1st issue). Multicoloured.
2120 750 l. Type **812** .. .. 1·25 40
2121 750 l. Map, Columbus, seal and King and Queen of Spain .. .. 80 30
Nos. 2120/1 were printed together, se-tenant, forming a composite design.
See also Nos. 2151/4.

**813** Belli and View of Rome

**1991.** Birth Bicentenary of Giuseppe Gioachino Belli (poet).
2122 **813** 600 l. brown and blue 60 25

**814** St. Gregory's Church, Rome

**1991.** Artistic Heritage.
2123 **814** 3200 l. multicoloured 3·25 1·25

**815** "DRS" Satellite

**1991.** Europa. Europe in Space. Mult.
2124 750 l. Type **815** .. .. 90 30
2125 800 l. "Hermes" spaceship and "Columbus" space station .. .. 90 30

**816** Sta. Maria Maggiore Church, Lanciano

**817** Football and Genoa Lantern

**1991.** Artistic Heritage.
2126 **816** 600 l. brown .. .. 60 25

**1991.** D. A. Azuni Lyceum, Sassari. As T **756**.
2127 600 l. multicoloured .. 60 25

**1991.** Sampdoria, National Football Champion, 1990–91.
2128 **817** 3000 l. multicoloured 3·00 1·25

**818** Hands and Ball

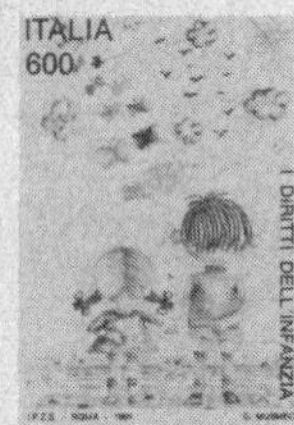

**819** Children and Butterflies

**1991.** Centenary of Basketball.
2129 **818** 500 l. multicoloured .. 50 20

**1991.** United Nations Conference on Rights of the Child. Multicoloured.
2130 600 l. Type **819** .. .. 60 25
2131 750 l. Child with balloon on man's shoulders .. 75 30

**820** "Youth and Gulls" (sculpture, Pericle Fazzini)

**821** Winged Sphinx

**1991.** Artistic Heritage. Multicoloured.
2132 **820** 600 l. yellow, bl & blk 60 25
2133 – 3200 l. multicoloured 3·25 1·25
DESIGN: 3200 l. Palazzo Esposizioni, Turin (Pier Luigi Nervi (birth centenary)).

**1991.** Egyptian Museum, Turin.
2134 **821** 750 l. gold, grn & yell 75 30

**822** Luigi Galvani (physiologist) and Experimental Equipment

**823** Mozart at Spinet

**1991.** 100 Years of Radio (1st issue).
2135 **822** 750 l. multicoloured .. 75 30
Galvani carried out experiments in electricity.
See also Nos. 2148, 2203, 2241 and 2321/2.

**1991.** Death Bicentenary of Wolfgang Amadeus Mozart (composer).
2136 **823** 800 l. multicoloured .. 80 30

**824** Bear

**825** "The Angel of Life" (Giovanni Segantini)

**1991.** Nature Protection. Multicoloured.
2137 500 l. Type **824** .. .. 60 25
2138 500 l. Peregrine falcon .. 70 25
2139 500 l. Deer .. .. 70 25
2140 500 l. Marine life .. 1·00 25

**1991.** Christmas.
2141 **825** 600 l. multicoloured .. 65 25

**826** Giulio and Alberto Bolaffi (stamp catalogue publishers)

**1991.** Stamp Day.
2142 **826** 750 l. multicoloured .. 80 30

**827** Signature and National Flag

**1991.** Birth Cent of Pietro Nenni (politician).
2143 **827** 750 l. multicoloured .. 80 30

**828** Runners

**1992.** 22nd European Indoor Light Athletics Championships, Genoa.
2144 **828** 600 l. multicoloured .. 75 25

**829** Neptune Fountain, Florence

**830** Statue of Marchese Alberto V of Este (founder) and University

**1992.** 400th Death Anniv of Bartolomeo Ammannati (architect and sculptor).
2145 **829** 750 l. multicoloured .. 80 30

**1992.** 600th Anniv (1991) of Ferrara University.
2146 **830** 750 l. multicoloured .. 80 30

**831** Pediment

**1992.** Naples University.
2147 **831** 750 l. multicoloured .. 80 30

**1992.** 100 Years of Radio (2nd issue). As T **822**. Multicoloured.
2148 750 l. Alessandro Volta (physicist) and Voltaic pile .. .. .. 80 30
Volta formulated the theory of current electricity and invented an electric battery.

**832** Emblem and Venue

**833** Medal of Lorenzo (Renato Beradi)

**1992.** "Genova '92" International Thematic Stamp Exhibition (1st issue).
2149 **832** 750 l. multicoloured .. 75 30
See also Nos. 2170/5.

**1992.** 500th Death Anniv of Lorenzo de Medici, "The Magnificent".
2150 **833** 750 l. multicoloured .. 75 30

**834** Columbus before Queen Isabella

**835** Scenes from Life of St. Maria Filippini (altar, Montefiascone Cathedral)

**1992.** 500th Anniv of Discovery of America by Columbus (2nd issue). Multicoloured.
2151 500 l. Type **834** .. .. 65 20
2152 500 l. Columbus's fleet .. 75 25
2153 500 l. Sighting land .. 65 20
2154 500 l. Landing in the New World .. .. 75 25

**1992.** 300th Anniv of Maestre Pie Filippini Institute.
2155 **835** 750 l. multicoloured .. 75 30

**836** Columbus Monument, Genoa (G. Giannetti)

**1992.** Europa. 500th Anniv of Discovery of America by Columbus. Multicoloured.
2156 750 l. Type **836** .. .. 1·00 30
2157 850 l. Emblem of "Colombo '92" exhibition, Genoa .. 1·25 35

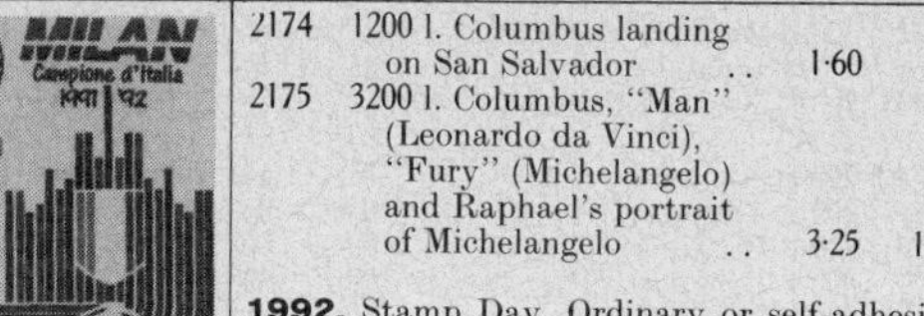


**838** Seascape and Cyclists

**839** Ball, Team Badge and Stylization of Milan Cathedral

**1992.** 75th "Tour of Italy" Cycle Race. Multicoloured.
2159 750 l. Type **838** .. .. 75 30
2160 750 l. Mountains and cyclists .. .. 75 30
Nos. 2159/60 were issued together, se-tenant, forming a composite design.

**1992.** A.C. Milan, National Football Champion, 1991–92.
2161 **839** 750 l. green, red & blk 75 30

**840** Viareggio

**1992.** Seaside Resorts. Multicoloured.
2162 750 l. Type **840** .. .. 75 30
2163 750 l. Rimini .. .. 75 30

**841** Nuvolari

**1992.** Birth Centenary of Tazio Nuvolari (racing driver).
2164 **841** 3200 l. multicoloured 3·25 1·25

**1992.** Tourist Publicity (19th series). As T **556**. Multicoloured.
2165 600 l. Arcevia .. .. 60 25
2166 600 l. Braies .. .. 60 25
2167 600 l. Maratea .. .. 60 25
2168 600 l. Pantelleria .. 60 25

**842** "Adoration of the Shepherds" (detail)

**1992.** 400th Death Anniv of Jacopo da Ponte (painter).
2169 **842** 750 l. multicoloured .. 75 30

**843** Columbus's House, Genoa

**844** Woman's Eyes and Mouth

**1992.** "Genova '92" International Thematic Stamp Exhibition (2nd issue). Mult.
2170 500 l. Type **843** .. .. 50 20
2171 600 l. Departure of Columbus's fleet from Palos, 1492 .. .. 80 25
2172 750 l. Route map of Columbus's first voyage 75 30
2173 850 l. Columbus sighting land .. .. .. 85 35
2174 1200 l. Columbus landing on San Salvador .. 1·60 70
2175 3200 l. Columbus, "Man" (Leonardo da Vinci), "Fury" (Michelangelo) and Raphael's portrait of Michelangelo .. 3·25 1·25

**1992.** Stamp Day. Ordinary or self-adhesive gum.
2176 **844** 750 l. multicoloured .. 75 30

**845** Map of Europe and Lions Emblem

**1992.** 75th Anniv of Lions International and 38th Europa Forum, Genoa.
2178 **845** 3000 l. multicoloured 3·00 1·25

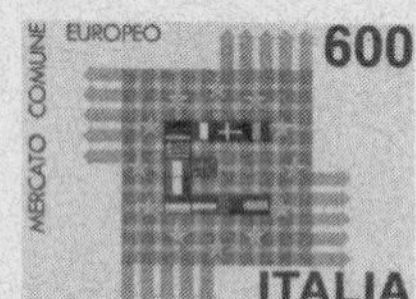


**846** European Community Emblem and Members' Flags

**1992.** European Single Market (1st issue).
2179 **846** 600 l. multicoloured .. 60 25
See also Nos. 2182/93.

**847** Woman with Food Bowl

**1992.** International Nutrition Conference, Rome.
2180 **847** 500 l. multicoloured .. 50 20

**848** Caltagirone Crib

**849** Buildings on Flag of Italy

**1992.** Christmas.
2181 **848** 600 l. muticoloured .. 60 25

**1993.** European Single Market (2nd issue). Designs differing in flag of country and language of inscription. Multicoloured.
2182 750 l. Type **849** .. .. 75 30
2183 750 l. Belgium .. .. 75 30
2184 750 l. Denmark .. .. 75 30
2185 750 l. France .. .. 75 30
2186 750 l. Germany .. .. 75 30
2187 750 l. Greece .. .. 75 30
2188 750 l. Ireland .. .. 75 30
2189 750 l. Luxembourg .. 75 30
2190 750 l. Netherlands .. 75 30
2191 750 l. Portugal .. .. 75 30
2192 750 l. United Kingdom .. 75 30
2193 750 l. Spain .. .. 75 30

**850** Russian and Italian Alpine Veterans

**851** Mezzettino, Colombina and Arlecchino

**1993.** 50th Anniversary Meeting of Veterans of Battle of Nikolayevka.
2194 **850** 600 l. multicoloured .. 60 25

**1993.** Death Bicentenary of Carlo Goldoni (dramatist). Multicoloured.
2195 500 l. Type **851** .. .. 40 20
2196 500 l. Arlecchino and portrait of Goldoni .. 40 20

**852** "Africa" (mosaic, Roman villa, Piazza Armerina)

**1993.** Artistic Heritage.
2197 **852** 750 l. multicoloured .. 80 25

**853** Wedge stopping Heart-shaped Cog

**1993.** National Health Day. Campaign against Heart Disease.
2198 **853** 750 l. multicoloured .. 70 20

**854** Tabby

**1993.** Domestic Cats. Multicoloured.
2199 600 l. Type **854** .. .. 50 30
2200 600 l. White Persian .. 50 30
2201 600 l. Devon rex (vert) .. 50 30
2202 600 l. Maine coon (vert) .. 50 30

**1993.** 100 Years of Radio (3rd issue). As T **822**. Multicoloured.
2203 750 l. Temistocle Calzecchi Onesti (physicist) and apparatus for detecting electromagnetic waves 80 20

**855** "The Piazza" **856** Horace

**1993.** Death Bicentenary of Francesco Guardi (artist).
2204 **855** 3200 l. multicoloured 3·25 1·60

**1993.** 2000th Death Anniv of Horace (Quintus Horatius Flaccus) (poet).
2205 **856** 600 l. multicoloured .. 55 30

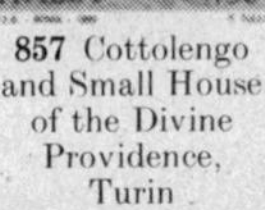

**857** Cottolengo and Small House of the Divine Providence, Turin

**858** "Carousel Horses" (Lino Bianchi Barriviera)

**1993.** St. Giuseppe Benedetto Cottolengo Commemoration.
2206 **857** 750 l. multicoloured .. 70 20

**1993.** Europa. Contemporary Art. Mult.
2207 750 l. Type **858** .. .. 80 20
2208 850 l. "Dynamism of Coloured Shapes" (Gino Severini) .. .. 90 30

**859** Medal (Giuseppe Romagnoli) **860** Emblem

**1993.** 400th Anniv of San Luca National Academy.
2209 **859** 750 l. multicoloured .. 70 20

**1993.** "Family Fest '93" International Conference, Rome.
2210 **860** 750 l. multicoloured .. 70 30

**861** Player and Club Badge **863** Canoeing

**862** Carloforte

**1993.** Milan, National Football Champion, 1992–93.
2211 **861** 750 l. multicoloured .. 80 30

**1993.** Tourist Publicity (20th series). Mult.
2212 600 l. Type **862** .. .. 50 30
2213 600 l. Palmanova .. 50 30
2214 600 l. Senigallia .. 50 30
2215 600 l. Sorrento .. 50 30
See also Nos. 2248/51 and 2315/18.

**1993.** World Canoeing Championships, Trentino.
2216 **863** 750 l. multicoloured .. 70 20

**864** Observatory **865** Staircase, St. Salome's Cathedral, Veroli

**1993.** Centenary of Regina Margherita Observatory.
2217 **864** 500 l. multicoloured .. 55 30

**1993.** Artistic Heritage.
2218 **865** 750 l. multicoloured .. 70 20

**866** Soldier, Boy with Rifle and German Helmet

**867** Carriage

**1993.** Second World War 50th Anniversaries (1st series). Multicoloured.
2219 750 l. Type **866** (the Four Days of Naples) .. 70 20
2220 750 l. Menorah, people in railway truck and Star of David (deportation of Roman Jews) .. 70 20
2221 750 l. Seven Cervi brothers (execution) .. .. 70 20
See also Nos. 2259/61.

**1993.** The Taxis Family in Postal History. Multicoloured.
2222 750 l. Type **867** .. .. 60 20
2223 750 l. Taxis arms .. 60 20
2224 750 l. Gig .. .. 60 20
2225 750 l. 17th-century postal messenger .. .. 60 20
2226 750 l. 18th-century postal messenger .. .. 60 20

**868** Head Office, Rome

**1993.** Centenary of Bank of Italy. Mult.
2227 750 l. Type **868** .. .. 80 20
2228 1000 l. 1000 lire banknote (first note issued by Bank) .. .. .. 1·25 40

**869** Colonies Express Letter Stamp Design

**1993.** Stamp Day. Centenary of First Italian Colonies Stamps.
2229 **869** 600 l. red and blue .. 55 25

**870** Tableau Vivant, Corchiano

**1993.** Christmas. Multicoloured.
2230 600 l. Type **870** .. .. 50 25
2231 750 l. "The Annunciation" (Piero della Francesca) 70 20

**871** 17th-century Map of Foggia

**1993.** Treasures from State Archives and Museums (1st series). Multicoloured.
2232 600 l. Type **871** (Foggia Archives) .. .. 55 25
2233 600 l. "Concert" (Bartolomeo Manfredi) (Uffizi Gallery, Florence) .. .. 55 25
2234 750 l. View of Siena from 15th-century illuminated manuscript (Siena Archives) (vert) .. 65 20
2235 850 l. "The Death of Adonis" (Sebastiano del Piombo) (Uffizi Gallery) 65 30
See also Nos. 2266/9, 2306/9 and 2346/9.

**872** Ringmaster and Bareback Riders

**873** Mother and Child inside House

**1994.** The Circus. Multicoloured.
2236 600 l. Type **872** .. .. 45 25
2237 750 l. Clowns .. .. 60 20

**1994.** "The Housewife, a Presence that Counts".
2238 **873** 750 l. multicoloured .. 60 20

**874** "Bread" (Dario Piazza) **876** "The Risen Christ" (statue)

**875** Boxer

**1994.** Paintings of Italian Food. Mult.
2239 500 l. Type **874** .. .. 40 25
2240 600 l. "Italian Pasta in the World" (Erminia Scaglione) .. .. 45 25

**1994.** 100 Years of Radio (4th issue). As T **822**. Multicoloured.
2241 750 l. Augusto Righi (physicist) and his Hertzian oscillator .. 60 20

**1994.** Dogs. Multicoloured.
2242 600 l. Type **875** .. .. 45 30
2243 600 l. Dalmatian .. 45 30
2244 600 l. Maremma sheepdog 45 30
2245 600 l. German shepherd .. 45 30

**1994.** Procession of "The Risen Christ", Tarquinia.
2246 **876** 750 l. multicoloured .. 60 20

**877** Pacioli in Study

**1994.** 500th Anniv of Publication of "Summary of Arithmetic, Geometry, Proportion and Proportionality" by Fra' Luca Pacioli.
2247 **877** 750 l. multicoloured .. 60 20

**1994.** Tourist Publicity (21st series). As T **862**. Multicoloured.
2248 600 l. Odescalchi Castle, Santa Marinella .. 45 30
2249 600 l. St. Michael's Abbey, Monticchio .. 45 30
2250 600 l. Orta San Giulio .. 45 30
2251 600 l. Cathedral, Messina 45 30

**878** Kossuth **879** Women's High-diving

**1994.** Death Centenary of Lajos Kossuth (Hungarian statesman).
2252 **878** 3750 l. multicoloured 3·00 1·50

**1994.** World Water Sports Championships. Multicoloured.
2253 600 l. Type **879** .. .. 45 25
2254 750 l. Water polo .. 60 20

880 Club Badge, Football and Colours

**1994.** Milan, National Football Champion, 1993–94.
2255 **880** 750 l. multicoloured .. 80 30

881 Camillo Golgi (cytologist) and Golgi Cells

882 "Goddess of Caldevigo" (bronze statuette, 5th century B.C.)

**1994.** Europa. Discoveries. Italian Nobel Prize winners. Multicoloured.
2256 750 l. Type **881** (medicine, 1906) .. .. .. 70 20
2257 850 l. Giulio Natta (chemist) and diagram of polymer structure (chemistry, 1963) .. 70 30

**1994.** "Ancient Peoples of Italy" Archaeological Exhibition, Rimini.
2258 **882** 750 l. multicoloured .. 60 20

883 Destruction of Montecassino

884 Washing of Feet

**1994.** Second World War 50th Anniversaries (2nd series). Multicoloured.
2259 750 l. Type **883** .. .. 60 20
2260 750 l. Bound prisoners (Ardeatine Caves Massacre) .. .. 60 20
2261 750 l. Family (Marzabotto Massacre) .. .. 60 20

**1994.** 22nd National Eucharistic Congress, Siena.
2262 **884** 600 l. multicoloured .. 45 25

885 "Ariadne, Venus and Bacchus"

**1994.** Artistic Heritage. 400th Death Anniv of Tintoretto (artist).
2263 **885** 750 l. multicoloured .. 60 20

886 "Piazza del Duomo during the Plague, 1630" (attr. Cigoli)

**1994.** 750th Anniv of Arciconfraternita della Misericordia, Florence.
2264 **886** 750 l. multicoloured .. 60 20

887 "E", European Union Emblem and Parliament

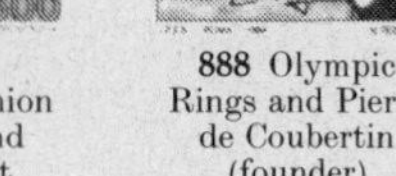

888 Olympic Rings and Pierre de Coubertin (founder)

**1994.** European Parliament Elections.
2265 **887** 600 l. multicoloured .. 45 25

**1994.** Treasures from State Archives and Museums (2nd series). As T **871**. Mult.
2266 600 l. Frontispiece of notary's register, 1623–24 (Catania Archives) (vert) .. 45 25
2267 600 l. "Death of Patroclus" (Attic vase, 5th century B.C.) (Agrigento Archaeological Museum) (vert) 45 25
2268 750 l. "Galata and his Wife" (statue) (National Roman Museum) (vert) .. 60 20
2269 850 l. Civic seal, 1745 (Campobasso Archives) (vert) .. .. .. 65 30

**1994.** Centenary of Int Olympic Committee.
2270 **888** 850 l. multicoloured .. 65 30

889 Vesuvius and "G 7"

890 Church of the Holy House and "Madonna and Child"

**1994.** Group of Seven (industrialized countries) Summit, Naples.
2271 **889** 600 l. bl, ultram & grn 45 25

**1994.** 700th Anniv of Shrine of the Nativity of the Virgin, Loreto.
2272 **890** 500 l. multicoloured .. 40 25

891 Pietro Miliani (papermaker) (after Francesco Rosaspina)

892 Frederick II (sculpture, Bitonto Cathedral)

**1994.** Stamp Day. Multicoloured.
2273 600 l. Type **891** .. .. 45 25
2274 750 l. Paper and Watermark Museum (former St. Dominic's Monastery), Fabriano 60 20

**1994.** 800th Birth Anniv of Frederick II, Holy Roman Emperor.
2275 **892** 750 l. multicoloured .. 60 20

893 St. Mark's Basilica

**1994.** 900th Anniv of Dedication of St. Mark's Basilica, Venice.
2276 **893** 750 l. multicoloured .. 70 60

894 "The Annunciation" (Melozzo da Forli)

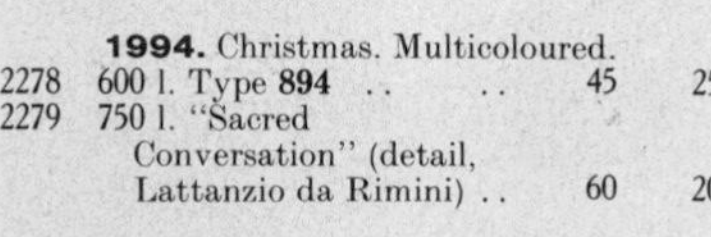


895 Club Emblem on Globe

**1994.** Christmas. Multicoloured.
2278 600 l. Type **894** .. .. 45 25
2279 750 l. "Sacred Conversation" (detail, Lattanzio da Rimini) .. 60 20

**1994.** Centenary of Italian Touring Club.
2280 **895** 600 l. multicoloured .. 45 25

896 Headquarters, Rome

897 New Emblem

**1994.** 75th Anniv of Credit for Businesses and Public Works.
2281 **896** 750 l. multicoloured .. 60 20

**1994.** Incorporation of Italian Post. Size 34 × 26 mm.
2282 – 600 l. red and silver .. 45 25
2283 **897** 750 l. black, grn & red 60 20
2284 – 750 l. red .. .. 60 20
DESIGN—VERT: 600 l. Palazzo Querini Dubois, Venice (restored with Post Office help).
For 750 and 850 l. values, size 26 × 17 mm, see Nos. 2343/4.

898 Gentile

899 Rainbow, Dove, Olive Tree and Flood

**1994.** 50th Death Anniv of Giovanni Gentile (philosopher).
2285 **898** 750 l. multicoloured .. 60 20

**1995.** For Flood Victims.
2286 **899** 750 l. + 2250 l. mult .. 4·00 3·00

900 Skater

**1995.** World Speed Skating Championships, Baselga di Pine.
2287 **900** 750 l. multicoloured .. 60 20

901 First Issue of "La Domenica del Corriere"

902 Rice

**1995.** 50th Death Anniv of Achille Beltrame (painter).
2288 **901** 500 l. multicoloured .. 40 25

**1995.** Italian Food. Multicoloured.
2289 500 l. Type **902** .. .. 40 25
2290 750 l. Olives and olive oil 60 20

903 Grey Herons

**1995.** Birds. Multicoloured.
2291 600 l. Type **903** .. .. 50 25
2292 600 l. Griffon vultures ("Grifone") .. .. 50 25
2293 600 l. Golden eagles ("Aquila Reale") .. 50 25
2294 600 l. Snow finches ("Fringuello Alpino") 50 25

904 Anniversary Emblem

**1995.** 50th Anniv of U.N.O.
2295 **904** 850 l. black, bl & gold 65 30

905 Detail of Monument (Giuseppe Grande)

**1995.** Centenary of Monument to the Fallen of the Five Days of Milan (1848 uprising).
2296 **905** 750 l. multicoloured .. 60 20

906 Princess Mafalda of Savoy and Concentration Camp

**1995.** 50th Anniv of End of Second World War. Multicoloured.
2297 750 l. Type **906** .. .. 60 20
2298 750 l. DUKW at Anzio .. 60 20
2299 750 l. Teresa Gullace and scene of her death .. 60 20
2300 750 l. Florence Town Hall and Military Medal .. 60 20
2301 750 l. Vittorio Veneto Town Hall and Military Medal .. .. .. 60 20
2302 750 l. Cagliari Town Hall and Military Medal .. 60 20
2303 750 l. Battle of Mount Lungo .. .. 60 20
2304 750 l. Parachuting supplies in the Balkans 60 20
2305 750 l. Light cruisers of the Eighth Division in Atlantic .. .. 60 20

**1995.** Treasures from State Archives and Museums (3rd series). As T **871**. Mult.
2306 500 l. Illuminated letter "P" from statute of Pope Innocent III (Rome Archives) (vert) 40 25
2307 500 l. "Port of Naples" (detail, Bernardo Strozzi) (St. Martin National Museum, Naples) .. .. 40 25
2308 750 l. Illuminated letter "I" showing the Risen Christ from 1481 document (Mantua Archives) (vert) .. 60 20
2309 850 l. "Sacred Love and Profane Love" (Titian) (Borghese Museum and Gallery, Rome) .. 65 30

**907** Emblem

**908** Santa Croce Basilica, Florence

**1995.** Centenary of Venice Biennale.

| | | | | |
|---|---|---|---|---|
| 2310 | **907** | 750 l. blue, gold & yell | 60 | 20 |

**1995.** Artistic Heritage.

| | | | | |
|---|---|---|---|---|
| 2311 | **908** | 750 l. brown .. .. | 60 | 20 |

**909** Soldiers and Civilians celebrating

**910** Players

**1995.** Europa. Peace and Freedom. Mult.

| | | | | |
|---|---|---|---|---|
| 2312 | | 750 l. Type **909** (50th anniv of end of Second World War in Europe) | 60 | 20 |
| 2313 | | 850 l. Mostar Bridge, (Bosnia) and Council of Europe emblem .. | 65 | 30 |

**1995.** Centenary of Volleyball.

| | | | | |
|---|---|---|---|---|
| 2314 | **910** | 750 l. blue, orge & grn | 60 | 20 |

**1995.** Tourist Publicity (22nd series). As T **862**. Multicoloured.

| | | | | |
|---|---|---|---|---|
| 2315 | | 750 l. Alatri .. .. | 60 | 20 |
| 2316 | | 750 l. Nuoro .. .. | 60 | 20 |
| 2317 | | 750 l. Susa .. .. | 60 | 20 |
| 2318 | | 750 l. Venosa .. .. | 60 | 20 |

**911** Experiment demonstrating X-rays

**1995.** Centenary of Discovery of X-rays by Wilhelm Rontgen.

| | | | | |
|---|---|---|---|---|
| 2319 | **911** | 750 l. multicoloured .. | 60 | 20 |

**912** Player and Club Badge

**1995.** Juventus, National Football Champion, 1994–95.

| | | | | |
|---|---|---|---|---|
| 2320 | **912** | 750 l. multicoloured .. | 60 | 25 |

**913** Villa Griffone (site of Marconi's early experiments)

**1995.** 100 Years of Radio (5th issue). Cent of First Radio Transmission. Mult.

| | | | | |
|---|---|---|---|---|
| 2321 | | 750 l. Type **913** .. .. | 60 | 20 |
| 2322 | | 850 l. Guglielmo Marconi and transmitter (36 × 21 mm) .. .. | 65 | 30 |

**914** St. Antony, Holy Basilica (Padua) and Page of Gospel

**916** Milan Cathedral and Eye (congress emblem)

**915** Durazzo Pallavicini, Pegli

**1995.** 800th Birth Anniv of St. Antony of Padua. Multicoloured.

| | | | | |
|---|---|---|---|---|
| 2323 | | 750 l. Type **914** .. .. | 60 | 20 |
| 2324 | | 850 l. St. Antony holding Child Jesus (painting, Vieira Lusitano) (horiz) | 65 | 30 |

**1995.** Public Gardens. Multicoloured.

| | | | | |
|---|---|---|---|---|
| 2325 | | 750 l. Type **915** .. .. | 60 | 20 |
| 2326 | | 750 l. Boboli, Florence .. | 60 | 20 |
| 2327 | | 750 l. Ninfa, Cisterna di Latina .. .. | 60 | 20 |
| 2328 | | 750 l. Parco della Reggia, Caserta .. .. | 60 | 20 |

**1995.** 10th European Ophthalmological Society Congress, Milan.

| | | | | |
|---|---|---|---|---|
| 2329 | **916** | 750 l. multicoloured .. | 60 | 20 |

**917** "Sailors' Wives"

**1995.** Birth Centenary of Massimo Campigli (painter).

| | | | | |
|---|---|---|---|---|
| 2330 | **917** | 750 l. multicoloured .. | 60 | 20 |

**918** Dome of Santa Maria del Fiore (Florence), Galileo and Albert Einstein

**1995.** 14th World Relative Physics Conference, Florence.

| | | | | |
|---|---|---|---|---|
| 2331 | **918** | 750 l. blue, brn & blk | 60 | 20 |

**919** Rudolph Valentino in "The Son of the Sheik"

**1995.** Centenary of Motion Pictures.

| | | | | |
|---|---|---|---|---|
| 2332 | **919** | 750 l. black, bl & red | 60 | 20 |
| 2333 | – | 750 l. multicoloured .. | 60 | 20 |
| 2334 | – | 750 l. multicoloured .. | 60 | 20 |
| 2335 | – | 750 l. multicoloured .. | 60 | 20 |

DESIGNS: No. 2333, Toto in "The Gold of Naples"; 2334, Frederico Fellini's "Cabiria Nights"; 2335, Poster (by Massimo Geleng) for "Cinecitta 95" film festival.

**920** Wheatfield and Anniversary Emblem

**1995.** 50th Anniv of F.A.O.

| | | | | |
|---|---|---|---|---|
| 2336 | **920** | 850 l. multicoloured .. | 65 | 30 |

**921** St. Albert's Stone Coffin (detail) and Basilica

**1995.** 900th Anniversaries of Pontida Basilica and Death of St. Albert of Prezzate.

| | | | | |
|---|---|---|---|---|
| 2337 | **921** | 1000 l. brown and blue | 80 | 40 |

**922** Athletes

**1995.** 1st World Military Games, Rome.

| | | | | |
|---|---|---|---|---|
| 2338 | **922** | 850 l. multicoloured .. | 65 | 30 |

**923** Globe and Means of Communication

**1995.** 50th Anniv of Ansa News Agency.

| | | | | |
|---|---|---|---|---|
| 2339 | **923** | 750 l. multicoloured .. | 60 | 20 |

**924** Crib (Stefano da Putignano), Polignano Cathedral

**1995.** Christmas. Multicoloured.

| | | | | |
|---|---|---|---|---|
| 2340 | | 750 l. Type **924** .. .. | 60 | 20 |
| 2341 | | 850 l. "Adoration of the Wise Men" (detail, Fra Angelico) .. .. | 65 | 30 |

**925** Renato Mondolfo (philatelist) and Trieste 1949 20 l. Stamp

**1995.** Stamp Day.

| | | | | |
|---|---|---|---|---|
| 2342 | **925** | 750 l. multicoloured .. | 60 | 20 |

**1995.** 1st Anniv of Incorporation of Italian Post. Size 26 × 17 mm.

| | | | | |
|---|---|---|---|---|
| 2343 | **897** | 750 l. red .. .. | 60 | 20 |
| 2344 | | 850 l. black, grn & red | 65 | 30 |

**926** Collage representing Marinetti's Works

**1996.** 120th Birth Anniv of Filippo Marinetti (writer and founder of Futurist movement).

| | | | | |
|---|---|---|---|---|
| 2345 | **926** | 750 l. multicoloured .. | 60 | 20 |

**1996.** Treasures from State Archives and Museums (4th series). As T **871**. Mult.

| | | | | |
|---|---|---|---|---|
| 2346 | | 750 l. Arms (Georgofili Academy, Florence) .. | 60 | 20 |
| 2347 | | 750 l. Illuminated letter showing St. Luke and his ox from Constitution of 1372 (Lucca Archives) (vert) | 60 | 20 |
| 2348 | | 850 l. Inkwells, pen and manuscript of Gabriele d'Annunzio (writer) (Il Vittoriale, Gardone Riviera) .. .. | 65 | 30 |
| 2349 | | 850 l. "Life of King Modus and Queen Racio" from 1486 miniature (Turin Archives) .. .. | 65 | 30 |

**927** "Sarah and the Angel" (fresco, Archbishop's Palace, Udine)

**1996.** 300th Birth Anniv of Giambattista Tiepolo (painter).

| | | | | |
|---|---|---|---|---|
| 2350 | **927** | 1000 l. multicoloured | 80 | 40 |

**928** White Wine

**1996.** Italian Wine Production. Mult.

| | | | | |
|---|---|---|---|---|
| 2351 | | 500 l. Type **928** .. .. | 40 | 25 |
| 2352 | | 750 l. Red wine .. .. | 60 | 20 |

**929** Marco Polo and Palace in the Forbidden City

**1996.** 700th Anniv (1995) of Marco Polo's Return from Asia and "China '96" International Stamp Exhibition, Peking.

| | | | | |
|---|---|---|---|---|
| 2353 | **929** | 1250 l. multicoloured | 1·00 | 50 |

**930** Milan Cathedral (left detail)

**931** Quill pen and Satellite (50th Anniv of National Federation of Italian Press)

**1996.** "Italia 98" International Stamp Exhibition, Milan (1st issue). Mult.
2354 750 l. Type **930** .. .. 60 20
2355 750 l. Cathedral (right detail) .. .. 60 20
Nos. 2354/5 were issued together, se-tenant, forming a composite design of the Cathedral.

**1996.** Anniversaries.
2356 **931** 750 l. multicoloured .. 60 20
2357 – 750 l. blue, pink & blk 60 20
DESIGN—HORIZ: No. 2357, Globe (centenary of "La Gazetta dello Sport" (newspaper)).

**932** Postman and Emblem

**933** Uniforms of Different Periods

**1996.** International Museum of Postal Images, Belvedere Ostrense.
2358 **932** 500 l. multicoloured .. 40 25

**1996.** Cent of Academy of Excise Guards.
2359 **933** 750 l. multicoloured .. 60 20

**934** Truck and Route Map

**935** Carina Negrone (pilot)

**1996.** Trans-continental Drive, Rome–New York.
2360 **934** 4650 l. multicoloured 3·75 1·75

**1996.** Europa. Famous Women. Mult.
2361 750 l. Type **935** .. .. 60 20
2362 850 l. Adelaide Ristori (actress) .. .. 65 30

**936** Fishes, Sea and Coastline from St. Raphael to Genoa

**1996.** 20th Anniv of Ramoge Agreement on Environmental Protection of the Mediterranean.
2363 **936** 750 l. multicoloured .. 60 20

**937** Celestino V and Town of Fumone

**1996.** 700th Death Anniv of Pope Celestino V.
2364 **937** 750 l. multicoloured .. 60 20

**938** St. Anthony's Church, Diano Marina

**1996.** Tourist Publicity (23rd series). Mult.
2365 750 l. Type **938** .. .. 60 20
2366 750 l. Pienza Cathedral .. 60 20
2367 750 l. Belltower of St. Michael the Archangel's Church, Monte Sant'Angelo .. .. 60 20
2368 750 l. Prehistoric stone dwelling, Lampedusa .. 60 20

**939** Abbey and Relief from 12th-century Ivory Reliquary

**1996.** 500th Anniv of Reconsecration of Farfa Abbey.
2369 **939** 1000 l. blk, yell & orge 80 40

**940** Fair Entrance and Mt. Pellegrino

**1996.** Mediterranean Fair, Palermo.
2370 **940** 750 l. multicoloured .. 60 20

**941** State Arms

**942** Rider and Emblem

**1996.** 50th Anniv of Italian Republic.
2371 **941** 750 l. multicoloured .. 60 20

**1996.** 50th Anniv of Production of Vespa Motor Scooters.
2372 **942** 750 l. multicoloured .. 60 20

**943** Views of Messina and Venice

**1996.** 40th Anniv of Founding Meetings of European Economic Community, Messina and Venice.
2373 **943** 750 l. multicoloured .. 60 20

**944** Athlete on Starting Block and 1896 Athletes

**1996.** Centenary of Modern Olympic Games and Olympic Games, Atlanta. Multicoloured.
2374 500 l. Type **944** .. .. 40 25
2375 750 l. Putting the shot and view of Atlanta (vert) .. .. 60 20
2376 850 l. Gymnast, stadium and basketball player 65 30
2377 1250 l. 1896 stadium, Athens, and 1996 stadium, Atlanta (vert) 1·00 50

**945** "Acanthobrahmaea europaea"

**1996.** Butterflies. Multicoloured.
2378 750 l. Type **945** .. .. 60 20
2379 750 l. "Melanargia arge" 60 20
2380 750 l. "Papilio hospiton" 60 20
2381 750 l. "Zygaena rubicundus" .. .. 60 20

**946** "Prima Comunione"

**1996.** Italian Films.
2382 **946** 750 l. black, red & bl 60 20
2383 – 750 l. multicoloured .. 60 20
2384 – 750 l. multicoloured .. 60 20
DESIGNS: No. 2383, Poster for "Cabiria"; 2384, "Scusate il Ritardo".

**947** Santa Maria del Fiore

**1996.** 700th Anniv of Cathedral of Santa Maria del Fiore, Florence.
2385 **947** 750 l. blue .. 60 20

**948** Player, Shield and Club Badge

**949** Choppy (congress mascot)

**1996.** Milan, National Football Champion, 1995–96.
2386 **948** 750 l. multicoloured .. 60 20

**1996.** 13th International Prehistoric and Protohistoric Sciences Congress.
2387 **949** 850 l. multicoloured .. 65 30

**950** Games Emblem and Pictograms

**952** Rejoicing Crowd and Club Badge

**951** Fair Entrance

**1996.** Mediterranean Games, Bari (1997).
2388 **950** 750 l. multicoloured .. 60 20

**1996.** Levant Fair, Bari.
2389 **951** 750 l. multicoloured .. 60 20

**1996.** Juventus, European Football Champion, 1995–96.
2390 **952** 750 l. multicoloured .. 60 20

**953** Pertini

**954** Montale and Hoopoe

**1996.** Birth Centenary of Alessandro Pertini (President 1978–85).
2391 **953** 750 l. multicoloured .. 60 20

**1996.** Birth Centenary of Eugenio Montale (poet).
2392 **954** 750 l. brown and blue 60 20

**955** "The Annunciation"

**1996.** 400th Birth Anniv of Pietro Berrettini da Cortona (artist).
2393 **955** 500 l. multicoloured .. 40 25

**956** Tex Willer (Galep)

**1996.** Stamp Collecting. Strip Cartoons. Multicoloured.
2394 750 l. Type **956** .. .. 60 20
2395 850 l. Corto Maltese (Hugo Pratt) .. .. .. 65 30

**957** Vortex and "Stamps"

**958** Bell Tower and Former Benedictine Abbey (seat of faculty)

**1996.** Stamp Day.
2396 **957** 750 l. multicoloured .. 60 20

**1996.** Universities.
2397 **958** 750 l. brown .. .. 60 20
2398 – 750 l. blue .. .. 60 20
2399 – 750 l. green .. .. 60 20
DESIGNS—VERT: No. 2397, Type **958** (centenary of Faculty of Agriculture, Perugia University); 2398, Former St. Matthew's Cathedral (seat of Medical School), Salerno University. HORIZ: No. 2399, Athenaeum, Sassari University.

## CONCESSIONAL LETTER POST

CL 93. Arms of Savoy and Fasces. CL 109. Arms and Fasces.

| No. | Type | Description | Unused | Used |
|---|---|---|---|---|
| **1928.** | | | | |
| CL 227. | CL 93. | 10 c. blue | 50 | 10 |
| **1930.** | | | | |
| CL 267. | CL 109. | 10 c. brown | 10 | 10 |

**1945.** No. CL 267, surch. Royal Arms (obliterating fasces) and new value.

| No. | Type | Description | Unused | Used |
|---|---|---|---|---|
| CL 647. | CL 109. | 40 c. on 10 c. brn. | 10 | 10 |

**1945.** As Type CL 109, but Arms redrawn without fasces.

| No. | Type | Description | Unused | Used |
|---|---|---|---|---|
| CL 648. | | 10 c. brown | 10 | 10 |
| CL 649. | | 1 l. brown | 2·00 | 2·00 |

CL 201. Italia. CL 220. Italia.

| No. | Type | Description | Unused | Used |
|---|---|---|---|---|
| **1947.** | | | | |
| CL 687. | CL 201. | 1 l. green | 15 | 10 |
| CL 688. | | 8 l. red | 12·00 | 20 |
| **1948.** | | | | |
| CL734 | CL 220 | 15 l. violet | 85·00 | 10 |
| CL916 | | 20 l. violet | 20 | 10 |
| CL917 | | 30 l. green | 15 | 10 |
| CL918 | | 35 l. brown | 15 | 10 |
| CL919 | | 110 l. blue | 15 | 10 |
| CL920 | | 270 l. mauve | 75 | 20 |
| CL921 | | 300 l. grn & pink | 40 | 15 |
| CL922 | | 370 l. brn & orge | 45 | 20 |

## CONCESSIONAL PARCEL POST

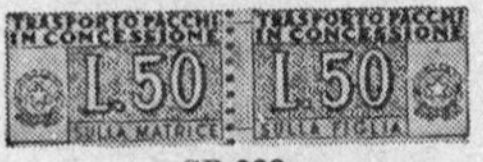


CP 288.

| No. | Type | Description | Unused | Used |
|---|---|---|---|---|
| **1953.** | | | | |
| CP918 | CP 288 | 40 l. orange | 75 | 15 |
| CP919 | | 50 l. blue | 1·75 | 15 |
| CP920 | | 60 l. violet | 5·00 | 75 |
| CP921 | | 70 l. green | 35·00 | 2·75 |
| CP850 | | 75 l. sepia | £100 | 2·00 |
| CP923 | | 80 l. brown | 25 | 10 |
| CP924 | | 90 l. lilac | 25 | 10 |
| CP851 | | 110 l. red | £100 | 2·50 |
| CP926 | | 110 l. yellow | 25 | 10 |
| CP927 | | 120 l. green | 25 | 10 |
| CP928 | | 140 l. black | 25 | 10 |
| CP929 | | 150 l. red | 25 | 10 |
| CP930 | | 180 l. red | 35 | 10 |
| CP931 | | 240 l. slate | 35 | 10 |
| CP932 | | 500 l. brown | 80 | 30 |
| CP933 | | 600 l. turquoise | 1·40 | 30 |
| CP934 | | 900 l. blue | 1·60 | 30 |

Unused prices are for the complete pair. Used prices are for the left half; right halves are worth more.

CP 707.

| No. | Type | Description | Unused | Used |
|---|---|---|---|---|
| **1984.** | | | | |
| CP 1849. | CP 707. | 3000 l. bl. & red | 3·50 | 2·50 |

## EXPRESS LETTER STAMPS

E 35.

| No. | Type | Description | Unused | Used |
|---|---|---|---|---|
| **1903.** For inland letters. | | | | |
| E 73. | E 35. | 25 c. red | 8·00 | 30 |
| E 113. | | 50 c. red | 65 | 35 |
| E 129. | | 60 c. red | 60 | 30 |
| E 178. | | 70 c. red | 15 | 20 |
| E 179. | | 1 l. 25 blue | 15 | 10 |

E 41. King Victor Emmanuel III.

| No. | Type | Description | Unused | Used |
|---|---|---|---|---|
| **1908.** For foreign letters. | | | | |
| E 80 | E 41 | 30 c. blue and pink | 40 | 1·00 |
| E180 | | 2 l. blue and pink | 40 | 20·00 |
| E181 | | 2 l. 50 blue and pink | 40 | 1·10 |

E 59.

| No. | Type | Description | Unused | Used |
|---|---|---|---|---|
| **1917.** Surch **25.** | | | | |
| E112 | E 59 | 25 c. on 40 c. violet | 8·00 | 20·00 |
| **1921.** Surch with new value. | | | | |
| E118 | E 41 | L. 1.20 on 30 c. blue and pink | 35 | 5·50 |
| E173 | | L. 1.60 on 1 l. 20 blue and pink | 40 | 23·00 |
| **1922.** Surch in words and figures. | | | | |
| E122 | E 35 | 60 c. on 50 c. red | 7·00 | 30 |
| E172 | | 70 c. on 60 c. red | 20 | 40 |

E 131. "Garibaldi" (statue), Savoia Marchetti S-55A Flying Boat and "Anita Garibaldi" (statue).

| No. | Type | Description | Unused | Used |
|---|---|---|---|---|
| **1932.** Air. 50th Death Anniv. of Garibaldi. | | | | |
| E 348. | E 131. | 2 l. 25+1 l. violet and red | 4·75 | 24·00 |
| E 349. | | 4 l. 50+1 l. 50 brn. and green | 5·50 | 26·00 |

E 132. King Victor Emmanuel III.

| No. | Type | Description | Unused | Used |
|---|---|---|---|---|
| **1932.** | | | | |
| E 350. | E 132. | 1 l. 25 green | 10 | 10 |
| E 351. | | 2 l. 50 orange | 10 | 1·00 |

**1932.** 10th Anniv. of March on Rome. As Type **132.**

(a) For inland letters. Inscribed "ESPRESSO".

| No. | Type | Description | Unused | Used |
|---|---|---|---|---|
| E 368. | | 1 l. 25 green | 40 | 80 |

(b) For foreign letters. Inscribed "EXPRES".

| No. | Type | Description | Unused | Used |
|---|---|---|---|---|
| E 369. | | 2 l. 50 orange | 2·25 | 70·00 |

DESIGNS: 1 l. 25, Roman road. 2 l. 50, Flags and head of Mussolini.

E 133. Savoia Marchetti S-55A Flying Boat.

| No. | Type | Description | Unused | Used |
|---|---|---|---|---|
| **1933.** Air. | | | | |
| E 370. | E 133. | 2 l. black | 10 | 75 |
| E 371. | | 2 l. 25 black | 1·75 | 60·00 |

**1934.** Air. 10th Anniv. of Annexation of Fiume. Inscr. as in T **141.**

| No. | Type | Description | Unused | Used |
|---|---|---|---|---|
| E 408. | | 2 l.+1 l. 25 blue | 50 | 17·00 |
| E 409. | | 2 l. 25+1 l. 25 green | 20 | 13·00 |
| E 410. | | 4 l. 50+2 l. red | 20 | 14·00 |

DESIGN: Foundation of Fiume.

**1934.** Air. Military Medal Centenary. Inscr as in T **146.**

| No. | Type | Description | Unused | Used |
|---|---|---|---|---|
| E 442. | | 2 l.+1 l. 25 brown | 3·50 | 15·00 |
| E 443. | | 4 l. 50+2 l. red | 5·50 | 17·00 |

DESIGN—HORIZ: 2 l., 4 l. 50, Caproni Ca 101 airplane over triumphal arch.

E 192. Italia.

| No. | Type | Description | Unused | Used |
|---|---|---|---|---|
| **1945.** | | | | |
| E 647. | E 192. | 5 l. red | 10 | 50 |

E 200. Winged Foot of Mercury.

| No. | Type | Description | Unused | Used |
|---|---|---|---|---|
| **1945.** | | | | |
| E679 | E 200 | 5 l. red | 10 | 10 |
| E680 | – | 10 l. blue | 10 | 10 |
| E681 | – | 15 l. red | 3·00 | 10 |
| E682 | E 200 | 25 l. orange | 30·00 | 10 |
| E683 | | 30 l. violet | 4·00 | 75 |
| E915 | | 50 l. purple | 5·00 | 10 |
| E685 | – | 60 l. red | 35·00 | 20 |

DESIGN: 10, 15, 60 l. Horse and torch bearer.

E 341. Etruscan Horses.

| No. | Type | Description | Unused | Used |
|---|---|---|---|---|
| **1958.** | | | | |
| E 961 | E 341 | 75 l. purple | 25 | 10 |
| E1220 | | 150 l. green | 20 | 10 |
| E1221 | | 250 l. blue & lt bl | 30 | 10 |
| E1222 | | 300 l. brn & lt brn | 35 | 10 |

E 209. Rising at Naples.

| No. | Type | Description | Unused | Used |
|---|---|---|---|---|
| **1948.** Centenary of 1848 Revolution. | | | | |
| E 718. | E 209. | 35 l. violet | 60·00 | 10·00 |

## MILITARY POST STAMPS

**1943.** Stamps of Italy optd. **P.M.**

(a) Postage stamps of 1929 (Nos. 239/56).

| No. | Type | Description | Unused | Used |
|---|---|---|---|---|
| M 583. | | 5 c. brown | 20 | 35 |
| M 584. | | 10 c. brown | 20 | 35 |
| M 585. | | 15 c. green | 20 | 35 |
| M 586. | | 20 c. red | 20 | 35 |
| M 587. | | 25 c. green | 20 | 35 |
| M 588. | | 30 c. brown | 20 | 35 |
| M 589. | | 50 c. violet | 20 | 20 |
| M 590. | | 1 l. violet | 20 | 5·00 |
| M 591. | | 1 l. 25 blue | 20 | 55 |
| M 592. | | 1 l. 75 orange | 20 | 35 |
| M 593. | | 2 l. red | 20 | 50 |
| M 594. | | 5 l. red | 20 | 2·25 |
| M 595. | | 10 l. violet | 20 | 7·00 |

(b) Air stamps of 1930 (Nos. 271/7).

| No. | Type | Description | Unused | Used |
|---|---|---|---|---|
| M 596. | | 50 c. brown | 20 | 35 |
| M 597. | | 1 l. violet | 20 | 55 |
| M 598. | | 2 l. blue | 20 | 4·00 |
| M 599. | | 5 l. green | 20 | 5·50 |
| M 600. | | 10 l. red | 20 | 11·00 |

(c) Air Express stamp of 1933 (No. E 370).

| No. | Type | Description | Unused | Used |
|---|---|---|---|---|
| M 601. | | 2 l. black | 20 | 8·50 |

(d) Express Letter stamp of 1932 (No. E 350).

| No. | Type | Description | Unused | Used |
|---|---|---|---|---|
| M 602. | | 1 l. 25 green | 20 | 80 |

## NEWSPAPER STAMPS

N 2.

| No. | Type | Description | Unused | Used |
|---|---|---|---|---|
| **1862.** Imperf. | | | | |
| N5 | N 2 | 2 c. yellow | 20·00 | 50·00 |

For similar stamps in black, see Sardinia.

## OFFICIAL STAMPS

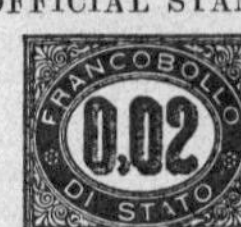


O 11.

| No. | Type | Description | Unused | Used |
|---|---|---|---|---|
| **1875.** | | | | |
| O 21. | O 11. | 2 c. red | 70 | 75 |
| O 22. | | 5 c. red | 70 | 75 |
| O 23. | | 20 c. red | 15 | 15 |
| O 24. | | 30 c. red | 25 | 25 |
| O 25. | | 1 l. red | 1·60 | 3·00 |
| O 26. | | 2 l. red | 8·00 | 10·00 |
| O 27. | | 5 l. red | 50·00 | 55·00 |
| O 28. | | 10 l. red | 85·00 | 30·00 |

**1934.** Air. Optd **SERVIZIO DI STATO.**

| No. | Type | Description | Unused | Used |
|---|---|---|---|---|
| O450 | 148 | 10 l. grey | £275 | £5000 |

## PARCEL POST STAMPS

P 13. King Umberto I.

| No. | Type | Description | Unused | Used |
|---|---|---|---|---|
| **1884.** Various frames. | | | | |
| P38 | P 13 | 10 c. grey | 65·00 | 16·00 |
| P39 | | 20 c. blue | £110 | 28·00 |
| P40 | | 50 c. pink | 5·00 | 3·50 |
| P41 | | 75 c. green | 5·00 | 3·50 |
| P42 | | 1 l. 25 orange | 12·00 | 10·00 |
| P43 | | 1 l. 75 brown | 14·00 | 26·00 |

The left-hand portion of the following parcel post stamps is affixed to the packet-card, the right-hand portion to the receipt. Unused prices are for the complete pair and used prices for the half-stamp. Unsevered stamps in used condition are usually from cancelled-to-order material and are worth more than the half-stamp.

P 53.

| No. | Type | Description | Unused | Used |
|---|---|---|---|---|
| **1914.** | | | | |
| P 96. | P 53. | 5 c. brown | 10 | 10 |
| P 97. | | 10 c. blue | 10 | 10 |
| P 98. | | 20 c. black | 20 | 10 |
| P 99. | | 25 c. red | 35 | 10 |
| P 100. | | 50 c. orange | 45 | 10 |
| P 101. | | 1 l. violet | 55 | 10 |
| P 102. | | 2 l. green | 75 | 10 |
| P 103. | | 3 l. yellow | 90 | 10 |
| P 104. | | 4 l. grey | 1·25 | 10 |
| P 105. | | 10 l. purple | 11·00 | 1·00 |
| P 106. | | 12 l. brown | 80·00 | 10·00 |
| P 107. | | 15 l. olive | 80·00 | 10·00 |
| P 108. | | 20 l. purple | 80·00 | 10·00 |

**1923.** Surch. with figures on left half and words and figures on right half.

| No. | Type | Description | Unused | Used |
|---|---|---|---|---|
| P 146. | P 53. | 30 c. on 5 c. brown | 30 | 10 |
| P 147. | | 60 c. on 5 c. brown | 55 | 10 |
| P 148. | | 1 l. 50 on 5 c. brown | 1·75 | 50 |
| P 149. | | 3 l. on 10 l. purple | 1·75 | 50 |

P 92.

| No. | Type | Description | Unused | Used |
|---|---|---|---|---|
| **1927.** | | | | |
| P217 | P 92 | 5 c. brown | 10 | 10 |
| P218 | | 10 c. blue | 10 | 10 |
| P219 | | 25 c. red | 10 | 10 |
| P220 | | 30 c. blue | 10 | 10 |
| P221 | | 50 c. orange | 10 | 10 |
| P222 | – | 60 c. red | 10 | 10 |
| P223 | P 92 | 1 l. violet | 10 | 10 |
| P224 | | 2 l. green | 10 | 10 |
| P225 | | 3 l. bistre | 10 | 10 |
| P226 | | 4 l. black | 10 | 10 |
| P227 | | 10 l. purple | 45 | 10 |
| P228 | | 20 l. purple | 70 | 10 |

The value in the right-hand portion of the 60 c. is in figures.

**1945.** Optd with ornamental device obliterating Fascist Emblems in centre.

| No. | Type | Description | Unused | Used |
|---|---|---|---|---|
| P647 | P 92 | 5 c. brown | 50 | 10 |
| P648 | | 10 c. blue | 50 | 10 |
| P649 | | 25 c. red | 50 | 10 |
| P650 | | 30 c. blue | 6·00 | 40 |
| P651 | | 50 c. orange | 50 | 10 |
| P652 | – | 60 c. red | 50 | 10 |
| P653 | P 92 | 1 l. violet | 50 | 10 |
| P654 | | 2 l. green | 50 | 10 |
| P655 | | 3 l. bistre | 50 | 10 |
| P656 | | 4 l. black | 50 | 10 |
| P657 | | 10 l. purple | 5·00 | 45 |
| P658 | | 20 l. purple | 12·00 | 1·00 |

**1946.** As Type **P 92**, but without fasces between stamps.

| No. | Type | Description | Unused | Used |
|---|---|---|---|---|
| P679 | P 92 | 1 l. mauve | 75 | 10 |
| P680 | | 2 l. green | 60 | 10 |
| P681 | | 3 l. orange | 1·25 | 10 |
| P682 | | 4 l. black | 2·00 | 10 |
| P683 | | 10 l. purple | 30·00 | 40 |
| P684 | | 20 l. purple | 35·00 | 90 |

P 201.

| No. | Type | Description | Unused | Used |
|---|---|---|---|---|
| **1946.** | | | | |
| P687 | P 201 | 25 c. blue | 10 | 10 |
| P688 | | 50 c. brown | 40 | 10 |
| P689 | | 1 l. brown | 40 | 10 |
| P690 | | 2 l. blue | 80 | 10 |
| P691 | | 3 l. orange | 30 | 10 |
| P692 | | 4 l. grey | 4·75 | 40 |
| P910 | | 5 l. purple | 10 | 10 |
| P911 | | 10 l. violet | 10 | 10 |
| P912 | | 20 l. purple | 10 | 15 |
| P1348 | | 30 l. purple | 15 | 10 |
| P914 | | 40 l. violet | 10 | 10 |
| P915 | | 50 l. red | 10 | 10 |
| P916 | | 60 l. violet | 10 | 10 |
| P917 | | 100 l. blue | 15 | 10 |
| P918 | | 140 l. red | 15 | 10 |
| P919 | | 150 l. brown | 25 | 10 |
| P920 | | 200 l. green | 25 | 10 |
| P921 | | 280 l. yellow | 35 | 10 |
| P922 | | 300 l. purple | 30 | 10 |
| P923 | | 400 l. black | 40 | 10 |
| P924 | | 500 l. brown | 75 | 10 |
| P925 | | 600 l. brown | 70 | 20 |
| P926 | | 700 l. blue | 85 | 15 |
| P927 | | 800 l. orange | 90 | 15 |

P 298.

**1954.**

| No. | Type | Description | Unused | Used |
|---|---|---|---|---|
| P928a | P 298 | 1000 l. blue | 1·10 | 10 |
| P929 | | 2000 l. red & brn | 3·00 | 15 |

## PNEUMATIC POST LETTERS

PE 53.

**1913.**

| No. | Type | Description | Unused | Used |
|---|---|---|---|---|
| PE 96 | PE 53 | 10 c. brown | 1·10 | 7·50 |
| PE 97 | | 15 c. lilac | 1·40 | 10·00 |
| PE191 | | 15 c. pink | 80 | 5·00 |
| PE192 | | 15 c. purple | 2·00 | 10·00 |
| PE193 | | 20 c. purple | 3·75 | 13·00 |
| PE 98 | | 30 c. blue | 2·50 | 25·00 |
| PE194 | | 35 c. red | 5·00 | 60·00 |
| PE195 | | 40 c. red | 7·00 | 65·00 |

**1924.** Surch.

| No. | Type | Description | Unused | Used |
|---|---|---|---|---|
| PE 165. | PE 53. | 15 c. on 10 c. brn. | 1·75 | 10·00 |
| PE 166. | | 15 c. on 20 c. pur. | 2·75 | 14·00 |
| PE 167. | | 20 c. on 10 c. brn. | 2·75 | 18·00 |
| PE 168. | | 20 c. on 15 c. lilac | 1·75 | 10·00 |
| PE 169. | | 35 c. on 40 c. red | 5·50 | 60·00 |
| PE 170. | | 40 c. on 30 c. bl. | 2·75 | 45·00 |

PE 134. Galileo Galilei. PE 204. Minerva.

**1933.**

| No. | Type | Description | Unused | Used |
|---|---|---|---|---|
| PE 372. | – | 15 c. purple | 10 | 45 |
| PE 373. | PE 134. | 35 c. red | 10 | 45 |

DESIGN: 15 c. Dante Alighieri.

**1945.** As Type PE 134, but inscr. "ITALIA" instead of "REGNO D'ITALIA".

| No. | Type | Description | Unused | Used |
|---|---|---|---|---|
| PE 679. | – | 60 c. brown (Dante) | 20 | 40 |
| PE 680. | PE 134. | 1 l. 40 blue | 20 | 40 |

**1947.**

| No. | Type | Description | Unused | Used |
|---|---|---|---|---|
| PE 694. | PE 204. | 3 l. purple | 8·00 | 12·00 |
| PE 695. | | 5 l. blue | 15 | 10 |
| PE 961. | | 10 l. red | 15 | 10 |
| PE 962. | | 20 l. blue | 15 | 10 |

## POSTAGE DUE STAMPS

D 3. D 11.

**1863.** Imperf.

| No. | Type | Description | Unused | Used |
|---|---|---|---|---|
| D 6. | D 3. | 10 c. yellow | 50·00 | 90·00 |

**1869.** Perf.

| No. | Type | Description | Unused | Used |
|---|---|---|---|---|
| D 21. | D 11. | 10 c. brown | £2500 | 10·00 |

D 12. D 13. (D 20.)

**1870.**

| No. | Type | Description | Unused | Used |
|---|---|---|---|---|
| D22 | D 12 | 1 c. mauve & orange | 1·25 | 2·50 |
| D23 | | 2 c. mauve & orange | 9·50 | 11·00 |
| D24 | | 5 c. mauve & orange | 20 | 10 |
| D25 | | 10 c. mauve & orange | 30 | 10 |
| D26 | | 20 c. mauve & orange | 50 | 10 |
| D27 | | 30 c. mauve & orange | 1·25 | 25 |
| D28 | | 40 c. mauve & orange | 1·40 | 35 |
| D29 | | 50 c. mauve & orange | 1·25 | 15 |
| D30 | | 60 c. mauve & orange | 50·00 | 60 |
| D31 | | 60 c. brown & orange | 9·50 | 2·25 |
| D32 | | 1 l. brown and blue | £2250 | 5·00 |
| D33 | | 1 l. mauve and blue | 50 | 15 |
| D34 | | 2 l. brown and blue | £2750 | 6·50 |
| D35 | | 2 l. mauve and blue | 15·00 | 60 |
| D36 | | 5 l. brown and blue | £150 | 4·75 |
| D37 | | 5 l. mauve and blue | 48·00 | 1·40 |
| D38 | | 10 l. brown and blue | £4000 | 7·50 |
| D39 | | 10 l. mauve and blue | 50·00 | 60 |

**1884.**

| No. | Type | Description | Unused | Used |
|---|---|---|---|---|
| D 40. | D 13. | 50 l. green | 20·00 | 10·00 |
| D 73. | | 50 l. yellow | 26·00 | 13·00 |
| D 41. | | 100 l. red | 25·00 | 5·00 |
| D 74. | | 100 l. blue | 20·00 | 5·00 |

**1890.** Surch. over numeral as Type D 20.

| No. | Type | Description | Unused | Used |
|---|---|---|---|---|
| D 47. | D 12. | 10 (c.) on 2 c. (D 23) | 50·00 | 10·00 |
| D 48. | | 20 (c.) on 1 c. (D 22) | £250 | 7·50 |
| D 49. | | 30 (c.) on 2 c. (D 23) | £900 | 3·75 |

D 141. D 142.

**1934.** With Fascist emblems.

| No. | Type | Description | Unused | Used |
|---|---|---|---|---|
| D 395. | D 141. | 5 c. brown | 10 | 10 |
| D 396. | | 10 c. blue | 10 | 10 |
| D 397. | | 20 c. red | 10 | 10 |
| D 398. | | 25 c. green | 10 | 10 |
| D 399. | | 30 c. orange | 10 | 10 |
| D 400. | | 40 c. brown | 10 | 20 |
| D 401. | | 50 c. violet | 10 | 10 |
| D 402. | | 60 c. blue | 15 | 45 |
| D 403. | D 142. | 1 l. orange | 10 | 10 |
| D 404. | | 2 l. green | 10 | 10 |
| D 405. | | 5 l. violet | 25 | 15 |
| D 406. | | 10 l. blue | 60 | 20 |
| D 407. | | 20 l. red | 70 | 25 |

D 191. D 192. D 201.

**1945.** Fascist emblems removed.

| No. | Type | Description | Unused | Used |
|---|---|---|---|---|
| D630 | D 191 | 5 c. brown | 15 | 10 |
| D631 | | 10 c. blue | 10 | 10 |
| D632 | | 20 c. red | 15 | 10 |
| D633 | | 25 c. green | 10 | 10 |
| D634 | | 30 c. orange | 10 | 10 |
| D635 | | 40 c. black | 10 | 15 |
| D636 | | 50 c. violet | 10 | 10 |
| D637 | | 60 c. blue | 10 | 15 |
| D685 | D 192 | 1 l. orange | 15 | 10 |
| D639 | | 2 l. green | 10 | 10 |
| D640 | | 5 l. violet | 15 | 10 |
| D641 | | 10 l. blue | 10 | 10 |
| D642 | | 20 l. red | 20 | 20 |

**1947.**

| No. | Type | Description | Unused | Used |
|---|---|---|---|---|
| D690 | D 201 | 1 l. orange | 10 | 10 |
| D691 | | 2 l. green | 25 | 10 |
| D692 | | 3 l. red | 1·25 | 85 |
| D693 | | 4 l. brown | 85 | 70 |
| D924 | | 5 l. violet | 15 | 10 |
| D695 | | 6 l. blue | 3·75 | 80 |
| D696 | | 8 l. mauve | 14·00 | 1·40 |
| D926 | | 10 l. blue | 15 | 10 |
| D698 | | 12 l. brown | 4·75 | 1·10 |
| D927 | | 20 l. purple | 15 | 10 |
| D928 | | 25 l. red | 15 | 10 |
| D929 | | 30 l. purple | 15 | 10 |
| D930 | | 40 l. brown | 15 | 10 |
| D931 | | 50 l. green | 15 | 10 |
| D932 | | 100 l. orange | 15 | 10 |
| D935 | | 500 l. red and blue | 70 | 15 |
| D936 | | 500 l. purple & blue | 60 | 20 |
| D937 | | 900 l. mauve, black and green | 1·25 | 55 |
| D938 | | 1500 l. orge & brn | 1·60 | 55 |

## PUBLICITY ENVELOPE STAMPS

**1921.** Optd **B.L.P.**

| No. | Type | Description | Unused | Used |
|---|---|---|---|---|
| B129 | 37 | 10 c. red | 35·00 | 6·50 |
| B137 | | 15 c. grey | £130 | 38·00 |
| B138 | 41 | 20 c. orange | £130 | 38·00 |
| B132 | 39 | 25 c. blue | 42·00 | 10·00 |
| B140 | | 30 c. brown | 85·00 | 20·00 |
| B115 | | 40 c. brown | 27·00 | 1·75 |
| B134 | | 50 c. violet | £325 | 65·00 |
| B135 | | 60 c. red | £1300 | £425 |
| B141 | | 85 c. brown | £130 | 38·00 |
| B136 | 34 | 1 l. brown and green | £2500 | £700 |

# ITALIAN SOCIAL REPUBLIC

**Following the surrender of Italy on 3 September 1943, and his rescue from imprisonment on 12 September, Mussolini proclaimed the Italian Social Republic at Salo on 23 September 1943. From this town on Lake Garda the Republican government administered those parts of Italy, north of the Gustav Line, which were under German occupation.**

**1944.** Stamps of Italy optd **G. N. R.**

(a) Postage. (i) Nos. 239 and 241/59.

| No. | Type | Description | Unused | Used |
|---|---|---|---|---|
| 1 | 98 | 5 c. brown | 1·00 | 2·00 |
| 2 | – | 10 c. brown | 1·00 | 2·00 |
| 3 | – | 15 c. green | 1·00 | 2·00 |
| 4 | 99 | 20 c. red | 1·00 | 2·00 |
| 5 | – | 25 c. green | 1·00 | 2·00 |
| 6 | 103 | 30 c. brown | 1·00 | 2·00 |
| 7 | – | 35 c. blue | 40·00 | 60·00 |
| 8 | 103 | 50 c. violet | 1·00 | 2·00 |
| 9 | – | 75 c. red | 1·00 | 2·00 |
| 10 | 99 | 1 l. violet | 1·00 | 2·00 |
| 11 | – | 1 l. 25 blue | 1·00 | 2·00 |
| 12 | – | 1 l. 75 red | 2·75 | 12·00 |
| 13 | – | 2 l. red | 3·00 | 14·00 |
| 14 | 98 | 2 l. 55 green | 20·00 | 80·00 |
| 15 | – | 3 l. 70 violet | 18·00 | 65·00 |
| 16 | – | 5 l. red | 3·00 | 12·00 |
| 17 | – | 10 l. violet | 30·00 | 40·00 |
| 18 | 99 | 20 l. green | £150 | £300 |
| 19 | – | 25 l. black | £350 | £800 |
| 20 | – | 50 l. violet | £300 | £800 |

(ii) War Propaganda issue. Nos. 563/74.

| No. | Description | Unused | Used |
|---|---|---|---|
| 21 | 25 c. green (Navy) | 1·25 | 5·00 |
| 22 | 25 c. green (Army) | 1·25 | 5·00 |
| 23 | 25 c. green (Air Force) | 1·25 | 5·00 |
| 24 | 25 c. green (Militia) | 1·25 | 5·00 |
| 25 | 30 c. brown (Navy) | 1·25 | 7·50 |
| 26 | 30 c. brown (Army) | 1·25 | 7·50 |
| 27 | 30 c. brown (Air Force) | 1·25 | 7·50 |
| 28 | 30 c. brown (Militia) | 1·25 | 7·50 |
| 29 | 50 c. violet (Navy) | 1·25 | 5·00 |
| 30 | 50 c. violet (Army) | 1·25 | 5·00 |
| 31 | 50 c. violet (Air Force) | 1·25 | 5·00 |
| 32 | 50 c. violet (Militia) | 1·25 | 5·00 |

(b) Air. Nos. 270/7.

| No. | Type | Description | Unused | Used |
|---|---|---|---|---|
| 33 | – | 25 c. green | 4·00 | 14·00 |
| 34 | 110 | 50 c. brown | 2·00 | 2·50 |
| 35 | – | 75 c. brown | 5·00 | 18·00 |
| 36 | – | 80 c. red | 18·00 | 70·00 |
| 37 | – | 1 l. violet | 2·00 | 8·50 |
| 38 | 113 | 2 l. blue | 18·00 | 70·00 |
| 39 | 110 | 5 l. green | 30·00 | £100 |
| 40 | | 10 l. red | £400 | £1000 |

(4.) (5.)

**1944.** Stamps of Italy. (a) Optd. with T 4.

| No. | Type | Description | Unused | Used |
|---|---|---|---|---|
| 57. | – | 25 c. green (No. 244) | 10 | 10 |
| 60. | – | 75 c. red (No. 248) | 10 | 10 |

(b) Optd. with T5.

| No. | Type | Description | Unused | Used |
|---|---|---|---|---|
| 58. | 103. | 30 c. brown | 10 | 10 |
| 61. | – | 1 l. 25 blue (No. 250) | 10 | 10 |
| 77. | – | 50 l. violet (No. 259) | £130 | £700 |

(c) Optd **REPUBBLICA SOCIALE ITALIANA.**

| No. | Type | Description | Unused | Used |
|---|---|---|---|---|
| 59. | 103. | 50 c. violet | 10 | 10 |

**1944.** War Propaganda stamps. Nos. 563/74 optd with T 4 (25 c.), T 5 (30 c.) or **REPUBBLICA SOCIALE ITALIANA** (50 c.).

| No. | Description | Unused | Used |
|---|---|---|---|
| 64 | 25 c. green (Navy) | 10 | 45 |
| 65 | 25 c. green (Army) | 10 | 45 |
| 66 | 25 c. green (Air Force) | 10 | 45 |
| 67 | 25 c. green (Militia) | 10 | 45 |
| 68 | 30 c. brown (Navy) | 15 | 60 |
| 69 | 30 c. brown (Army) | 15 | 60 |
| 70 | 30 c. brown (Air Force) | 15 | 60 |
| 71 | 30 c. brown (Militia) | 15 | 60 |
| 72 | 50 c. violet (Navy) | 10 | 45 |
| 73 | 50 c. violet (Army) | 10 | 45 |
| 74 | 50 c. violet (Air Force) | 10 | 45 |
| 75 | 50 c. violet (Militia) | 10 | 45 |

Prices are for examples overprinted on the stamp part only; items overprinted twice (on stamp and label) are worth more.

10. Loggia dei Mercanti, Bologna. 11.

12. Basilica de St. Lorenzo, Rome. 13.

**1944.** Inscr. "REPUBBLICA SOCIALE ITALIANA".

| No. | Type | Description | Unused | Used |
|---|---|---|---|---|
| 106. | – | 5 c. brown | 10 | 15 |
| 107. | – | 10 c. brown | 10 | 15 |
| 102. | 10. | 20 c. red | 10 | 15 |
| 108. | 11. | 20 c. red | 10 | 15 |
| 103. | 12. | 25 c. green | 10 | 15 |
| 109. | 13. | 25 c. green | 10 | 15 |
| 110. | – | 30 c. brown | 10 | 15 |
| 111. | – | 50 c. violet | 10 | 15 |
| 112. | – | 75 c. red | 10 | 15 |
| 113. | – | 1 l. violet | 10 | 15 |
| 114. | – | 1 l. 25 blue | 10 | 1·75 |
| 115. | – | 3 l. green | 10 | 9·50 |

DESIGN: 5 c. St. Ciriaco's Church, Ancona. 10 c., 1 l. Montecassino, Abbey. 30 c., 75 c. Drummer. 50 c. Fascist allegory. 1 l. 25, 3 l. St. Mary of Grace, Milan.

17. Bandiera Brothers.

**1944.** Death Centenary of Attilio and Emilio Bandiera (revolutionaries).

| No. | Type | Description | Unused | Used |
|---|---|---|---|---|
| 117. | 17. | 25 c. green | 10 | 15 |
| 118. | | 1 l. violet | 10 | 15 |
| 119. | | 2 l. 50 red | 10 | 2·00 |

## CONCESSIONAL LETTER POST

**1944.** Concessional Letter Post stamp of Italy optd. as T 5 but smaller.

| No. | Type | Description | Unused | Used |
|---|---|---|---|---|
| CL 76. | CL 109. | 10 c. brown | 10 | 10 |

## EXPRESS LETTER STAMPS

**1944.** Express stamps of Italy optd **G. N. R.**

| No. | Type | Description | Unused | Used |
|---|---|---|---|---|
| E 41. | E 132. | 1 l. 25 green (postage) | 2·00 | 10·00 |
| E 42. | | 2 l. 50 red | 70·00 | £180 |
| E 43. | E 133. | 2 l. black (air) | £325 | £750 |

REPUBBLICA
SOCIALE
ITALIANA

(E 7.)

**1944.** Express stamps of Italy optd with Type E 7.

| No. | Type | Description | Unused | Used |
|---|---|---|---|---|
| E 62. | E 132. | 1 l. 25 green | 10 | 10 |
| E 63. | | 2 l. 50 orange | 10 | 1·00 |

E 16. Palermo Cathedral.

**1944.**

| No. | Type | Description | Unused | Used |
|---|---|---|---|---|
| E 116. | E 16. | 1 l. 25 green | 10 | 40 |

## PARCEL POST STAMPS

**1944.** Parcel Post stamps of Italy optd **REP. SOC. ITALIANA** on left-hand side and Fascist Emblem on right.

| No. | Type | Description | Unused | Used |
|---|---|---|---|---|
| P77 | P 92 | 5 c. brown | 1·00 | 2·00 |
| P78 | | 10 c. blue | 1·00 | 2·00 |
| P79 | | 25 c. red | 1·00 | 2·00 |
| P80 | | 30 c. blue | 1·00 | 2·00 |
| P81 | | 50 c. orange | 1·00 | 2·00 |
| P82 | | 60 c. red | 1·00 | 2·00 |
| P83 | | 1 l. violet | 1·00 | 2·00 |
| P84 | | 2 l. green | £120 | £160 |
| P85 | | 3 l. bistre | 2·00 | 4·00 |
| P86 | | 4 l. black | 2·00 | 4·00 |
| P87 | | 10 l. purple | 70·00 | £100 |
| P88 | | 20 l. purple | £200 | £300 |

The unused and used prices are for unsevered stamps.

## POSTAGE DUE STAMPS

**1944.** Postage Due stamps of Italy optd **G. N. R.**

| No. | Type | Description | Unused | Used |
|---|---|---|---|---|
| D 44. | D 141. | 5 c. brown | 4·50 | 18·00 |
| D 45. | | 10 c. blue | 4·50 | 18·00 |
| D 46. | | 20 c. red | 2·00 | 10·00 |
| D 47. | | 25 c. green | 1·75 | 10·00 |
| D 48. | | 30 c. orange | 3·00 | 16·00 |
| D 49. | | 40 c. brown | 1·75 | 10·00 |
| D 50. | | 50 c. violet | 25·00 | 80·00 |
| D 51. | | 60 c. blue | £140 | £300 |
| D 52. | D 142. | 1 l. orange | 3·00 | 15·00 |
| D 53. | | 2 l. green | 5·00 | 18·00 |
| D 54. | | 5 l. violet | 70·00 | £140 |
| D 55. | | 10 l. blue | 35·00 | £100 |
| D 56. | | 20 l. red | 35·00 | £100 |

**1944. Postage Due stamps of Italy optd. with small Fascist emblems.**

| No. | Type | Description | Unused | Used |
|---|---|---|---|---|
| D 89. | D 141. | 5 c. brown | 20 | 80 |
| D 90. | | 10 c. blue | 20 | 60 |
| D 91. | | 20 c. red | 20 | 60 |
| D 92. | | 25 c. green | 20 | 60 |
| D 93. | | 30 c. orange | 20 | 1·40 |
| D 94. | | 40 c. brown | 20 | 1·60 |
| D 95. | | 50 c. violet | 20 | 35 |
| D 96. | | 60 c. blue | 55 | 5·00 |
| D 97. | D 142. | 1 l. orange | 20 | 35 |
| D 98. | | 2 l. green | 1·00 | 3·50 |
| D 99. | | 5 l. violet | 10·00 | 30·00 |
| D 100. | | 10 l. blue | 26·00 | 65·00 |
| D 101. | | 20 l. red | 26·00 | 65·00 |

## IVORY COAST Pt. 6; Pt. 13

A French colony in W. Africa on the Gulf of Guinea, incorporated in French West Africa in 1944. In 1958 it became an autonomous republic within the French Community, and in 1960 it became fully independent.

100 centimes = 1 franc.

**1892.** "Tablet" key-type inscr "COTE D'IVOIRE" in blue (Nos. 2, 3, 5, 14, 7, 9/11) or red (others).

1 D 1 c. black on blue .. 65 85
2 2 c. brown on buff .. 1·00 1·10
3 4 c. brown on grey .. 1·50 1·50
4a 5 c. green on green .. 5·75 3·75
5 10 c. black on lilac .. 5·00 5·25
14 10 c. red .. .. 70·00 45·00
6 15 c. blue .. .. 9·50 7·00
15 15 c. grey .. .. 5·00 1·75
7 20 c. red on green .. 9·50 8·75
8 25 c. black on pink .. 9·50 1·60
16 25 c. blue .. .. 17·00 12·50
9 30 c. brown on drab .. 16·00 12·50
10 40 c. red on yellow .. 11·00 4·50
11 50 c. red on pink .. 45·00 35·00
17 50 c. brown on blue .. 11·00 6·75
12 75 c. brown on yellow .. 8·00 12·50
13 1 f. green .. .. 28·00 20·00

**1904.** Surch. in figures and bars.

18. D. 0.05 on 30 c. brown .. 42·00 45·00
19. 0.10 on 75 c. brn. on yell. 2·50 8·25
20. 0.15 on 1 f. olive .. 9·00 9·50

**1906.** "Faidherbe", "Palms" and "Balay" key-types inscr "COTE D'IVOIRE" in blue (10 c., 5 f.) or red (others).

22 I 1 c. grey .. .. 70 50
23 2 c. brown .. .. 50 50
24 4 c. brown on blue .. 60 60
25 5 c. green .. .. 1·50 90
26 10 c. pink .. .. 3·50 2·00
27 J 20 c. black on blue .. 4·00 3·00
28 25 c. blue .. .. 3·50 1·75
29 30 c. brown on pink .. 5·75 5·00
30 35 c. black on yellow .. 4·00 2·25
32 45 c. brown on green .. 7·75 6·00
33 50 c. violet .. .. 7·25 6·00
34 75 c. green on orange .. 8·50 6·00
35 K 1 f. black on blue .. 20·00 19·00
36 2 f. blue on pink .. 32·00 27·00
37 5 f. red on yellow .. 50·00 50·00

**1912.** Surch in figures.

38 D 05 on 15 c. grey .. .. 25 40
39 05 on 30 c. brown on drab 70 80
40 10 on 40 c. red on yellow 50 75
41 10 on 50 c. brown on blue 60 1·10
42 10 on 75 c. brown on orge 2·00 3·50

7. River Scene.

**1913.**

43 7 1 c. violet and purple .. 10 10
44 2 c. black and brown .. 10 25
45 4 c. purple and violet .. 10 25
46 5 c. green and light green 50 50
61 5 c. brown and chocolate 25 40
47 10 c. pink and red .. 50 65
62 10 c. green and light green 25 40
63 10 c. pink on blue .. 15 20
48 15 c. red and orange .. 30 50
49 20 c. grey and black .. 40 60
50 25 c. blue and ultramarine 4·25 2·75
64 25 c. violet and black .. 30 30
51 30 c. brown and chocolate 65 80
65 30 c. pink and red .. 80 85
66 30 c. red and blue .. 20 30
67 30 c. green and olive .. 25 40
52 35 c. orange and violet .. 65 80
53 40 c. green and grey .. 60 80
54 45 c. brown and red .. 40 50
68 45 c. purple and red .. 3·00 4·00
55 50 c. violet and black .. 1·90 2·00
69 50 c. blue and ultramarine 50 65
70 50 c. blue and green .. 50 50
71 60 c. violet on pink .. 40 55
72 65 c. green and red .. 85 95
56 75 c. pink and brown .. 30 45
73 75 c. ultramarine and blue 1·90 2·00
74 85 c. black and purple .. 85 1·00
75 90 c. carmine and red .. 6·00 7·25
57 1 f. black and yellow .. 65 55
76 1 f. 10 brown and green .. 3·75 4·00
77 1 f. 50 blue and light blue 4·25 4·00
78 1 f. 75 mauve and blue .. 6·75 6·00
58 2 f. blue and brown .. 1·50 85
79 3 f. mauve on pink .. 4·25 2·50
59 5 f. brown and blue .. 3·00 3·00

**1915.** Surch **5c** and red cross.

60 7 10 c.+5 c. pink and red .. 40 65

**1934.** Surch with new value twice.

80 7 50 on 45 c. purple and red 1·60 1·60
81 50 on 75 c. ultram & blue 1·00 95
82 50 on 90 c. pink and red 1·00 95
83 60 on 75 c. violet on pink 50 50
84 65 on 15 c. red and orange 50 60
85 85 on 75 c. pink & brown 50 60

**1922.** Surch in figures and bars.

86 7 25 c. on 2 f. blue & brown 40 50
87 25 c. on 5 f. brown & blue 40 50
88 90 c. on 75 c. pink and red 50 65
89 1 f. 25 on 1 f. ultram & bl 35 50
90 1 f. 50 on 1 f. blue & lt bl 50 55
91 3 f. on 5 f. green and red 1·25 2·00
92 10 f. on 5 f. mauve and red 5·00 8·00
93 20 f. on 5 f. red and green 9·00 9·00

**1931.** "Colonial Exhibition" key-types inscr "COTE D'IVOIRE".

94 E 40 c. black and green .. 1·25 1·40
95 F 50 c. black and mauve .. 3·00 3·25
96 G 90 c. black and red .. 1·10 1·40
97 H 1 f. 50 black and blue .. 3·00 3·50

**1933.** Stamps of Upper Volta optd **Cote d'Ivoire** or surch also.

98 3 2 c. brown and violet .. 10 25
99 4 c. black and yellow .. 20 30
100 5 c. indigo and blue .. 30 40
101 10 c. blue and pink .. 35 40
102 15 c. brown and blue .. 40 50
103 20 c. brown and green .. 40 50
104 – 25 c. brown and yellow .. 50 1·00
105 – 30 c. deep green and green 50 1·00
106 – 45 c. brown and blue .. 5·00 4·00
107 – 65 c. indigo and blue .. 1·50 1·75
108 – 75 c. black and violet .. 60 1·40
109 – 90 c. red and mauve .. 85 1·50
110 6 1 f. brown and green .. 1·60 1·40
111 – 1 f. 25 on 40 c. blk & pink 65 75
112 6 1 f. 50 ultramarine & blue 1·60 1·00
113 – 1 f. 75 on 50 c. black & grn 1·60 90

12. Baoule Woman. 16. General Binger.

**1936.**

114. 12. 1 c. red .. .. .. 10 25
115. 2 c. blue .. .. .. 10 25
116. 3 c. green .. .. 10 25
117. 4 c. brown .. .. 10 30
118. 5 c. violet .. .. 10 25
119. 10 c. blue .. .. 10 20
120. 15 c. red .. .. 10 20
121. – 20 c. blue .. .. 10 25
122. – 25 c. red .. .. 10 20
123. – 30 c. green .. .. 10 25
124. – 30 c. brown .. .. 10 25
125. 12. 35 c. green .. .. 15 30
126. – 40 c. red .. .. 10 25
127. – 45 c. brown .. .. 25 45
128. – 45 c. green .. .. 40 60
129. – 50 c. purple .. .. 10 10
130. – 55 c. violet .. .. 45 60
131. – 60 c. red .. .. 45 60
132. – 65 c. brown .. .. 30 45
133. – 70 c. brown .. .. 35 45
134. – 75 c. violet .. .. 15 25
135. – 80 c. brown .. .. 20 35
136. – 90 c. red .. .. 2·00 3·25
137. – 90 c. green .. .. 75 90
138. – 1 f. green .. .. 70 75
139. – 1 f. red .. .. 30 50
140. – 1 f. violet .. .. 20 30
141. – 1 f. 25 red .. .. 15 20
142. – 1 f. 40 blue .. .. 60 75
143. – 1 f. 50 blue .. .. 20 20
144. – 1 f. 50 grey .. .. 60 60
145. – 1 f. 60 brown .. .. 45 60
146. – 1 f. 75 red .. .. 30 50
147. – 1 f. 75 blue .. .. 40 55
148. – 2 f. blue .. .. 30 30
149. – 2 f. 50 blue .. .. 50 65
150. – 2 f. 50 red .. .. 40 60
151. – 3 f. green .. .. 30 35
152. – 5 f. brown .. .. 30 40
153. – 10 f. violet .. .. 35 50
154. – 20 f. red .. .. 1·40 95

DESIGNS—HORIZ. 20 c. to 30 c. and 40 c. to 55 c. Mosque at Bobo-Dioulasso. 60 c. to 1 f. 60, Coastal scene. VERT. 1 f. 75, to 20 f. Comoe Rapids.

**1937.** International Exhibition, Paris. As Nos. 110/15 of Cameroun.

155 20 c. violet .. .. 35 60
156 30 c. green .. .. 35 60
157 40 c. red .. .. 35 75
158 50 c. brown and blue .. 35 75
159 90 c. red .. .. 35 60
160 1 f. 50 blue .. .. 45 80

**1937.** 50th Anniv. of Gen. Binger's Exploration.

161. 16. 65 c. brown .. .. 20 15

**1938.** Int. Anti-Cancer Fund. As T **19** of Cameroun.

162. 1 f. 75+50 c. blue .. 2·50 5·25

**1939.** Caillie Cent. As T **11** of Dahomey.

163. 90 c. orange .. .. 25 40
164. 2 f. violet .. .. 30 55
165. 2 f. 25 blue .. .. 55 65

**1939.** New York World's Fair. As T **20** of Cameroun.

166. 1 f. 25 red .. .. .. 60 65
167. 2 f. 25 blue .. .. 60 65

**1939.** 150th Anniv of French Revolution. As T **25** of Cameroun.

168 45 c.+25 c. green & black 3·50 4·25
169 70 c.+30 c. brown & black 3·50 4·25
170 90 c.+35 c. orange & black 3·50 4·25
171 1 f. 25+1 f. red and black 3·50 4·25
172 2 f. 25+2 f. blue and black 3·50 4·25

**1940.** Air. As T **12** of Dahomey.

173. 1 f. 90 blue .. .. 30 45
174. 2 f. 90 red .. .. .. 35 55
175. 4 f. 50 green .. .. 35 55
176. 4 f. 90 olive .. .. 35 55
177. 6 f. 90 orange .. .. 85 1·00

**1941.** National Defence Fund. Surch. **SECOURS NATIONAL** and value.

178. +1 f. on 50 c. (No. 129) .. 2·00 2·00
178a. +2 f. on 80 c. (No. 135) 6·50 6·75
178b. +2 f. on 1 f. 50 (No. 143) 6·50 6·75
178c. +3 f. on 2 f. (No. 148) .. 6·50 6·50

16a. Pirogue.

**1942.** Marshal Petain issue.

178d 16a 1 f. green .. .. 20 1·25
178e 2 f. 50 blue .. .. 20 1·25

**1942.** Air. Colonial Child Welfare Fund. As Nos. 143g/i of Dahomey.

178f 1 f. 50+3 f. 50 green .. 35
178g 2 f.+6 f. brown .. .. 30
178h 3 f.+9 f. red .. .. 30

**1942.** Air. Imperial Fortnight. As No. 143j of Dahomey.

178i 1 f. 20+1 f. 80 blue & red 30

**1942.** Air. As T **14e** of Dahomey.

179 50 f. olive and green .. 95 1·40

### REPUBLIC

17. African Elephant. 19. Pres. Houphouet-Boigny.

18. Place Lapalud, Abidjan.

**1959.**

180. 17. 10 f. black and green .. 40 20
181. 25 f. brown and bistre .. 75 30
182. 30 f. olive and turquoise 1·00 40

**1959.** Air.

183. 18. 100 f. brown, green and chocolate .. .. 2·50 60
184. – 200 f. brn., myrtle & turq. 5·00 2·00
185. – 500 f. turq., brn. & grn. 9·00 4·00

DESIGNS—As Type **18**: 200 f. Houphouet-Boigny railway bridge. 500 f. Ayame Barrage.

**1959.** 1st Anniv. of Republic.

186. 19. 25 f. brown .. .. 50 30



20. Bete Mask. 22. "Thoningia sanguinea".

21a. "World Peace".

**1960.** Native Masks.

187. 20. 50 c. chocolate & brown 10 10
188. – 1 f. violet and red .. 10 10
189. – 2 f. green and blue .. 10 10
190. – 4 f. red and green .. 15 15
191. – 5 f. brown and red .. 20 20
192. – 6 f. blue and purple .. 25 20
193. – 45 f. purple and green .. 1·25 50
194. – 50 f. blue and brown .. 2·00 75
195. – 85 f. green and red .. 3·25 1·50

DESIGNS—VERT. MASKS OF: 1 f. Guere. 2 f. Guere (different type). 45 f. Bete (different type). 50 f. Gouro. 85 f. Gouro (different type). HORIZ. 4 f. Baole. 5 f. Senoufo. 6 f. Senoufo (different type).

**1960.** 10th Anniv. of African Technical Co-operation Commission. As T **62** of Cameroun.

196. 25 f. violet and turquoise .. 50 40

**1960.** 1st Anniv. of Conseil de l'Entente. As T **16** of Dahomey.

197. 25 f. multicoloured .. 50 50

**1961.** 1st Anniv. of Independence.

198. 21a. 25 f. black, green & brown 55 35

**1961.**

199. – 5 f. red, yellow and green 20 15
200. – 10 f. yellow, red and blue 30 20
201. – 15 f. pur., grn. & orange 60 30
202. 22. 20 f. yellow, red & brown 90 30
203. – 25 f. yellow, red & green 70 30
204. – 30 f. red, green & black .. 90 50
205. – 70 f. yellow, red & green 2·50 1·00
206. – 85 f. multicoloured .. 3·25 1·40

FLOWERS: 5 f. "Plumeria rubra". 10 f. "Haemanthus cinnabarinus". 15 f. "Bougainvillea spectabilis". 25 f. "Eulophia cucullata". 30 f. "Newbouldia laevis". 70 f. "Mussaenda erythrophylla". 85 f. "Strophantus sarmentosus".

23. Mail-carriers.

**1961.** Stamp Day.

207. 23. 25 f. brn., blue and grn. 55 40

24. Ayame Dam.

25. Swimming. 26. Palms.

**1961.**

208. 24. 25 f. sepia, blue & green 55 30

**1961.** Abidjan Games. Inscr. as in T **25**.

209. 25. 5 f. sepia, green and blue (postage) .. .. 20 10
210. – 20 f. brn., green & grey 35 20
211. – 25 f. brn., green & blue 55 25
211a. – 100 f. black, red and blue (air) .. .. 2·75 1·60

DESIGNS: 20 f. Basketball. 25 f. Football. 100 f. High-jumping.

**1962.** 17th Session of African Technical Co-operation Commission, Abidjan.
212. **26.** 25 f. multicoloured .. 55 35

**1962.** Air. "Air Afrique" Airline. As T **69** of Cameroun.
213. 50 f. blue, brn. & chestnut 1·25 65

**1962.** Malaria Eradication. As T **70** of Cameroun.
214. 25 f.+5 f. green .. .. 65 65

**27.** Fort Assinie.

**1962.** Postal Cent.
215. **27.** 85 f. multicoloured .. 1·90 1·10

**28.** Village, Man Region.

**1962.** Air.
216. – 200 f. sepia, pur. & grn. 5·00 1·90
217. **28.** 500 f. grn., pur. and blk. 8·25 3·50
DESIGN—VERT. 200 f. Street Scene, Odienne.

**1962.** 1st Anniv. of Union of African and Malagasy States. As No. 328 of Cameroun.
218. **72.** 30 f. red .. .. 1·00 55

**29.** U.N. Headquarters and Emblem.

**1962.** Air. 2nd Anniv. of Admission to U.N.
219. **29.** 100 f. multicoloured .. 1·90 85

**30.** Bouake Arms and Cotton Exhibit.

**1963.** Bouake Fair.
220. **30.** 50 f. sepia, brown & grn. 65 35

**1963.** Freedom from Hunger. As T **76** of Cameroun.
221. 25 f.+5 f. vio., brn. & pur. 85 85

**31.** Map of Africa.

**1963.** Conf. of African Heads of State, Addis Ababa.
222. **31.** 30 f. green and blue .. 60 60

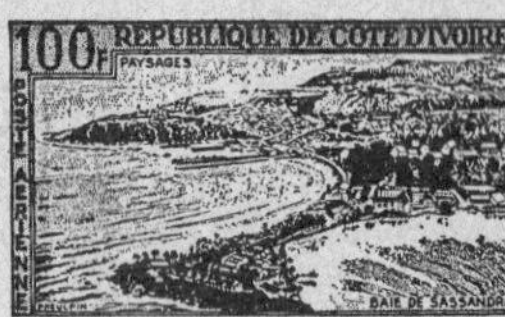

**32.** Sassandra Bay.

**1963.** Air.
223. – 50 f. green, brown & blue 1·25 45
224. **32.** 100 f. brn., bl. & myrtle 1·90 95
225. – 200 f. turq., grn. & brn. 3·50 1·60
DESIGNS: 50 f. Moosou Bridge. 200 f. River Comoe.

**1963.** Air. African and Malagasian Posts and Telecommunications Union. As T **18** of Central African Republic.
226. 85 f. multicoloured .. 1·40 85

**33.** Hartebeest.

**34.** Scales of Justice, Globe and U.N.E.S.C.O. Emblem.

**1963.** "Tourism and Hunting".
227. – 1 f. multicoloured .. 30 10
228. – 2 f. multicoloured .. 30 15
229. – 4 f. multicoloured .. 25 15
230. – 5 f. multicoloured .. 25 10
247. – 5 f. grn., yell. & brn. .. 45 20
231. **33.** 10 f. brn., green & grey 45 20
248. – 10 f. brn., green & pur. 1·00 20
232. – 15 f. black, grn. & brn. 60 30
249. – 15 f. brown, grn. & pur. 1·60 30
233. – 20 f. brown, grn. & red 85 30
234. – 25 f. brn., grn. and yell. 1·40 50
235. – 45 f. purple, green and turquoise .. .. 2·75 1·00
236. – 50 f. blk., grn. and brn. 3·50 1·40
DESIGNS—HORIZ. 1 f. Yellow-backed duiker. 4 f. Beecroft's hyrax. 5 f. (No. 247) African manatee. 10 f. (No. 248) Pygmy hippopotamus. 15 f. (No. 232) Giant forest hog. 20 f. Warthog. 45 f. Hunting dogs. VERT. 2 f. Potto. 5 f. (No. 230) Water chevrotain. 15 f. (No. 249) Royal antelope. 25 f. Bongo. 50 f. Western black and white colobus.

**1963.** Air. 1st Anniv. of "Air Afrique" and "DC-8" Service Inaug. As T **11** of Congo Republic.
237. 25 f. multicoloured .. 55 25

**1963.** 15th Anniv. of Declaration of Human Rights.
238. **34.** 85 f. black, blue & orge. 1·25 70

**35.** Rameses II and Nefertari, Abu Simbel.

**36.** Map of Africa.

**1964.** Air. Nubian Monuments Preservation.
239. **35.** 60 f. black, brown & red 1·60 85

**1964.** Inter-African National Education Ministers' Conference, Abidjan.
240. **36.** 30 f. red, green and blue 60 35

**37.** Weather Balloon.

**38.** Doctor tending Child.

**1964.** World Meteorological Day.
241. **37.** 25 f. multicoloured .. 60 40

**1964.** National Red Cross Society.
242. **38.** 50 f. multicoloured .. 95 50

**39.** Arms of the Ivory Coast.

**1964.** Air.
243. **39.** 200 f. gold, blue & green 3·00 1·40

**40.** Globe and Athletes.

**41.** Symbolic Tree.

**1964.** Olympic Games. Tokyo.
244. **40.** 35 f. brown, green & vio. 95 45
245. – 65 f. ochre, brown & blue 1·90 95
DESIGN—HORIZ. 65 f. Wrestling and Globe.

**1964.** 1st Anniv. of European-African Convention.
246. **41.** 30 f. multicoloured .. 65 35

**1964.** French, African and Malagasy Co-operation. As T **547** of France.
250. 25 f. brown, red and green 55 35

**42.** Pres. Kennedy.

**43.** Korhogo Mail-carriers, 1914.

**1964.** Air. Pres. Kennedy Commem.
251. **42.** 100 f. brown and grey 1·90 1·40

**1964.** Stamp Day.
252. **43.** 85 f. sepia, brown & blue 1·60 95

**44.** Pottery.

**1965.** Native Handicrafts.
253. **44.** 5 f. black, red and green 20 15
254. – 10 f. black, purple & grn. 25 15
255. – 20 f. blue, choc. & brown 50 20
256. – 25 f. brown, red & olive 55 30
DESIGNS: 10 f. Wood-carving. 20 f. Ivory-carving. 25 f. Weaving.

**45.** Mail coming ashore.

**1965.** Stamp Day.
257. **45.** 30 f. multicoloured .. 60 45

**46.** I.T.U. Emblem and Symbols.

**1965.** I.T.U. Cent.
258. **46.** 85 f. blue, red and green 1·40 85

**47.** Abidjan Railway Station.

**1965.**
259. **47.** 30 f. multicoloured .. 75 35

**48.** Pres. Houphouet-Boigny and Map.

**49.** Hammerkop.

**1965.** 5th Anniv. of Independence.
260. **48.** 30 f. multicoloured .. 55 35

**1965.** Birds.
261. – 1 f. green, yell. & violet 1·50 50
262. – 2 f. multicoloured .. 1·50 55
263. – 5 f. purple, red and olive 1·60 65
264. **49.** 10 f. brn., black & pur. 1·60 45
265. – 15 f. red, grey and green 1·90 65
266. – 30 f. brn., green & lake 2·75 65
267. – 50 f. blue, black & brn. 5·25 1·25
268. – 75 f. red, green & orange 5·25 1·50
269. – 90 f. multicoloured .. 7·50 3·25
BIRDS—HORIZ. 1 f. Yellow-bellied Green Pigeon. 2 f. Spur-winged Goose. 30 f. Namaqua Dove. 50 f. Lizard Buzzard. VERT. 5 f. Stone Partridge. 15 f. White-breasted Guineafowl. 75 f. Yellow-billed Stork. 90 f. Latham's Francolin.

**50.** Lieupleu Rope-bridge.

**1965.** Air.
270. **50.** 100 f. brn., grn. & lt. grn. 1·90 1·10
271. – 300 f. pur., flesh & blue 5·50 2·75
DESIGN: 300 f. Street in Kong.

**51.** Mail Train, 1906.

**52.** "Maternity".

**1966.** Stamp Day.
272. **51.** 30 f. green, black & pur. 1·90 1·25

**1966.** World Festival of Negro Arts, Dakar.
273. **52.** 5 f. black and green .. 20 15
274. – 10 f. black and violet .. 30 20
275. – 20 f. black and orange 90 45
276. – 30 f. black and red .. 1·10 65
DESIGNS—CARVED WORK: 10 f. Pomade box. 20 f. Drums. 30 f. "Ancestor".

**53.** Ivory Hotel.

**1966.** Inaug. of Ivory Hotel.
277. **53.** 15 f. multicoloured .. 45 25

**54.** Tractor Cultivation.

**1966.** 6th Anniv. of Independence.
278. **54.** 30 f. multicoloured .. 50 35

**1966.** Air. Inaug of Douglas DC-8F Air Services. As T **54** of Central African Republic.
279 30 f. grey, black and green 55 30

**55.** Open-air Class.

**1966.** National School of Administration.
280. **55.** 30 f. black, blue and lake 55 35

56. Inoculating Cattle.

57. U.N.E.S.C.O. "Waves" enveloping "Man".

**1966.** Campaign for Prevention of Cattle Plague.
281. 56. 30 f. brown, green & blue 65 40

**1966.** 20th Anniv. of U.N.E.S.C.O.
282. 57. 30 f. violet and blue .. 60 40
283. – 30 f. blk., brown & blue 55 35
DESIGN: No. 283, Distributing food parcels to children.

58. Bouake Hospital.

59. "Air Afrique" Headquarters.

**1966.**
284. 58. 30 f. multicoloured .. 55 35

**1966.** Air.
285. 59. 500 f. blue, ochre & grn. 8·25 3·25

60. Sikorsky S-43 Amphibian (30th anniv).

**1967.** Stamp Day.
286. 60. 30 f. blue, brown & turq. 1·25 80

61. Cutting Pineapples.

62. "African Mythology".

**1967.** Fruits.
287. 61. 20 f. purple, brn. & grn. 35 15
288. – 30 f. red, brown & green 45 30
289. – 100 f. brn., olive & blue 1·90 85
DESIGNS: 30 f. Cutting palm-nuts. 100 f. Cutting bananas.

**1967.** 35th Pen Club Int. Congress, Abidjan.
290. 62. 30 f. black, green & lake 60 40

63. "Improvement of Rural Housing".

**1967.** 7th Anniv. of Independence.
291. 63. 30 f. multicoloured .. 50 30

64. Lions Emblems.

65. African Man and Woman.

**1967.** 50th Anniv. of Lions Int.
292. 64. 30 f. multicoloured .. 80 45

**1967.** Air. 5th Anniv. of U.A.M.P.T. As T 123 of Cameroun.
293. 100 f. red, blue and violet 1·60 85

**1967.** 5th Anniv. of West African Monetary Union. As T 72 of Dahomey.
294. 30 f. black, green & mauve 50 30

**1967.** 20th Anniv. of Recognition Days.
295. 65. 90 f. multicoloured .. 1·10 65
See also No. 342.

66. Senoufo Village.

**1968.** Air.
296. 66. 100 f. brn., yell. & grn. 1·90 90
297. – 500 f. brown, blue and green.. .. .. 8·25 3·25
DESIGN: 500 f. Tiegba lake village.

68. Cotton Loom.

69. Canoeing.

67. Tabou Radio Station, 1912.

**1968.** Stamp Day.
298. 67. 30 f. grn., brn. & turq. 60 35

**1968.** Industries.
299. – 5 f. black, red and green 20 10
300. 68. 10 f. brn., grn. and slate 30 15
301. – 15 f. black, blue and red 70 45
302. – 20 f. blue and purple .. 50 30
303. – 30 f. brn., grn. and blue 60 35
304. – 50 f. blk., grn. & mauve 95 45
305. – 70 f. choc., blue & brn. 1·40 70
306. – 90 f. black, purple & blue 1·60 1·10
DESIGNS—HORIZ. 5 f. Palm-oil works. 30 f. Flour mills. 50 f. Cocoa-butter extraction machine. 90 f. Timber sawmill and logs. VERT. 15 f. Oil refinery, Abidjan. 20 f. Raw cotton and reeling machine. 70 f. Soluble-coffee plant.
See also Nos. 335/7.

**1968.** Olympic Games, Mexico.
307. 69. 30 f. brown, blue & grn. 60 30
308. – 100 f. purple, ult. & blue 1·60 65
DESIGN: 100 f. 100-metres sprint.

70. Sacrificial Offering.

**1968.** 8th Anniv. of Independence.
309. 70. 30 f. multicoloured .. 55 30

71. Doctor inoculating Patient.

72. Impala in Forest.

**1968.** 20th Anniv. of W.H.O.
310. 71. 30 f. choc., brown & bl. 55 30

**1968.** Fauna and Flora Protection.
311. 72. 30 f. brn., grn. & blue.. 1·10 55

73. Museum and Carved Screen.

**1968.** Opening of Abidjan Museum.
312. 73. 30 f. brown, red & blue 55 30

74. Human Rights Emblem and "Justice" Totems.

**1968.** Human Rights Year.
313. 74. 30 f. orge., purple & blue 55 30

**1969.** Air. "Philexafrique" stamp Exn., Abidjan, Ivory Coast (1st issue). As T 137 of Cameroun. Multicoloured.
314. 100 f. "Grand Bassam" (Achalme) .. .. 3·00 3·00

**1969.** Air. "Philexafrique" Stamp Exn., Abidjan, Ivory Coast (2nd issue). As T 138 of Cameroun.
315. 50 f. red, blue and green.. 1·90 1·90
316. 100 f. blue, brown & orge. 3·00 3·00
317. 200 f. slate, blue & brown 4·50 4·50
DESIGNS—HORIZ. 50 f. Aerial view of San Pedro village and stamp of 1936. 200 f. Chambers of Agriculture and Industry building, Abidjan, and 5 f. stamp of 1913. VERT. 100 f. Chief's costume and 5 f. stamp of 1936.

75. "Ville de Maranhao" (mail steamer) at Grand-Bassam.

**1969.** Stamp Day.
319. 75. 30 f. purple, blue & green 65 30

76. Ivory Hotel.

**1969.** Opening of Ivory Hotel.
320. 76. 30 f. blue, red and green 65 30

77. "Man on Horse-back" (statuette).

78. Hertzian-wave Radio Station, Man.

**1969.** Ivory Coast Art Exn., Vevey, Switzerland.
321. 77. 30 f. black, purple & red 65 45

**1969.** 9th Anniv. of Independence.
322. 78. 30 f. green, brn. & blue 60 35

**1969.** 5th Anniv. of African Development Bank. As T 146 of Cameroun.
323. 30 f. brown, green and lake 50 30

80. Arms of Bouake.

81. Game Fishing.

**1969.** Coats of Arms.
324. 80. 10 f. multicoloured .. 20 10
325. – 15 f. multicoloured .. 30 15
326. – 30 f. blk., gold & green 45 15
ARMS: 15 f. Abidjan. 30 f. Ivory Coast Republic.
See also Nos. 402/3 and 432/36.

**1969.** Int. SKAL Tourist Assn. Congress Abidjan.
327. 81. 30 f. blue, pur. & violet 1·10 40
328. – 100 f. multicoloured .. 1·90 1·00
DESIGN: 100 f. Assinie Holiday Village.

**1969.** 10th Anniv. of Aerial Navigation Security Agency for Africa and Madagascar (A.S.E.C.N.A.). As T 150 of Cameroun.
329. 30 f. red .. .. .. 55 35

82. Man Waterfall.

**1970.** Air.
330. 82. 100 f. blue, grn. & brn. 1·90 1·00
331. – 200 f. red, green & emer. 2·75 1·10
DESIGN: 200 f. Mt. Niangbo.

83. University Hospital Centre, Abidjan.

**1970.** "10 Years of Higher Education".
332. 83. 30 f. indigo, green & blue 55 35

84. Telegraphist and Gabriel Dadie (Postal administrator).

**1970.** Stamp Day.
333. 84. 30 f. black, green and red 50 30

85. Abidjan University.

**1970.** 3rd A.U.P.E.L.F. (Association of French Speaking Universities). General Assembly, Abidjan.
334. 85. 30 f. purple, grn. & bl. 55 35

86. Safety-match Manufacture.

88. Wild Life.

87. Dish Aerial and Television Class.

**1970.** Industrial Expansion.
335. 86. 5 f. brn., blue & choc. 20 15
336. – 20 f. red, green & grey 40 15
337. – 50 f. brn., blue & green 90 35
DESIGNS: 20 f. Textile-printing. 50 f. Ship-building.

**1970.** World Telecommunications Day.
338. 87. 40 f. green, drab and red 65 40

**1970.** New U.P.U. Headquarters Building Berne. As T 155 of Cameroun.
339. 30 f. brown, green & purple 65 35

**1970.** 25th Anniv. of United Nations.
340. 88. 30 f. brn., green & blue 90 55

89. Coffee Plant.

90. African Man and Woman.

**1970.** 10th Anniv. of Independence (1st issue).
341. 89. 30 f. grn., brn. & orge. 55 35
See also Nos. 344/9.

**1970.** Fifth P.D.C.I. (Ivory Coast Democratic Party) Congress.
342. 90. 40 f. multicoloured .. 65 35

91. Power Station.

**1970.** Thermal Power Plant, Vridi.
343. 91. 40 f. brn., blue and grn. 60 20

92. Pres. Houphouet-Boigny and De Gaulle.

**1970.** 10th Anniv. of Independence (2nd issue). Embossed on silver (300 f. values) or gold foil.
344. 300 f. Type 92 (postage) .. 8·25
345. 300 f. Ivory Coast Arms .. 7·25
346. 1000 f. Type 92 .. .. 30·00
347. 1000 f. As No. 345 .. .. 29·00
348. 300 f. Pres. Houphouet-Boigny and African elephants (air) .. .. 7·25
349. 1200 f. As No. 348 .. .. 29·00

93. Mail Bus, 1925.

**1971.** Stamp Day.
350. 93. 40 f. pur., grn. and brn. 70 30

94. Port of San Pedro.

**1971.** Air.
351. 94. 100 f. red, blue & green 1·50 55
352. – 500 f. grn., blue & brown 7·75 3·50
DESIGN: 500 f. African Riviera coastline.

95. Desjardin's Marginella.

**1971.** Marine Life.
353. – 1 f. brn., blue and green 15 10
354. – 5 f. red, lilac and blue.. 20 15
355. – 10 f. red, blue and green 45 20
356. 95. 15 f. brn., purple & blue 50 25
357. – 15 f. brown, violet & red 75 25
358. – 20 f. red and yellow .. 80 40
359. – 20 f. lake, purple & red 1·25 45
360. – 25 f. brn., black & lake 75 25
361. – 35 f. red, yellow & green 1·10 55
362. – 40 f. brn., blue and green 3·00 1·25
363. – 40 f. red, turq. and brn. 1·60 45
364. – 45 f. brn., grn. and emer. 2·75 1·25
365. – 50 f. green, red & violet 2·25 1·10
366. – 65 f. blue, grn. and brn. 3·25 2·25
DESIGNS—HORIZ: 1 f. African's pelican's-foot; 5 f. "Neptunus validus"; 20 f. (No. 359) Digitate carrier shell; 25 f. Butterfly cone; 40 f. (No. 362) Garter cone; 45 f. Bubonion conch; 65 f. Rat cowrie. VERT: 10 f. "Hermodice carunculata"; 15 f. (No. 357) Fanel moon; 20 f. (No. 358) "Goniaster cuspidatus"; 35 f. "Polycheles typhiops"; 40 f. (No. 363) African fan scallop; 50 f. "Enoplometopus callistas".

96. Telegraph Station, Grand Bassam, 1891.

**1971.** World Telecommunications Day.
367. 96. 100 f. brn., green and bl. 1·10 65

97. Treichville Swimming Pool.

**1971.** Air.
368. 97. 100 f. multicoloured .. 1·90 70

98. Tool-making.

99. African Telecommunications Map.

**1971.** Technical Training and Instruction.
369. 98. 35 f. blue, red and green 60 30

**1971.** Pan-African Telecommunications Network.
370. 99. 45 f. yellow, red & pur. 60 30

100. Bondoukou Market.

**1971.** 11th Anniv. of Independence.
371. 100. 35 f. brn., bl. & grey (postage) .. .. 60 35
372. – 200 f. blk. & bl. on gold (air) 2·50 1·60
No. 372 has a similar design to Type 100 but in smaller format, size 38 × 27 mm.

101. Children of Three Races.

**1971.** Racial Equality Year. Multicoloured.
373. 40 f. Type 101 .. .. 55 20
374. 45 f. Children around Globe 55 20

**1971.** 10th Anniv. of U.A.M.P.T. As T 184 of Cameroun. Multicoloured.
375. 100 f. H.Q. and Ivory Coast Arms .. .. 1·40 65
U.A.M.P.T. = African and Malagasy Posts and Telecommunications Union.

102. Gaming Table.

**1971.** National Lottery.
376. 102. 35 f. multicoloured .. 50 20

103. Technicians working on Power Cables.

105. Cogwheel and Students.

104. Lion of St. Mark's.

**1971.** Electricity Works Centre, Akovai-Santai.
377. 103. 35 f. multicoloured .. 70 35

**1972.** Air. U.N.E.S.C.O. "Save Venice" Campaign. Multicoloured.
378. 100 f. Type 104 .. .. 1·60 85
379. 200 f. St. Mark's Square 3·25 1·60

**1972.** Technical Instruction Week.
380. 105. 35 f. blue, brn. and red 50 35

106. Heart Emblem. 107. Child learning to write.

**1972.** World Heart Month.
381. 106. 40 f. blue, red & green 60 35

**1972.** Int. Book Year.
382. – 35 f. brn., orge. & grn. 40 20
383. 107. 40 f. blk., orge. & grn. 55 30
DESIGN—HORIZ. 35 f. Students and open book.

108. Gouessesso Tourist Village.

**1972.** Air.
384. 108. 100 f. brn., green & blue 1·90 85
385. – 200 f. grn., brown & blue 2·75 1·10
386. – 500 f. brn., bistre & blue 7·75 3·50
DESIGNS: 200 f. Jacqueville Lake. 500 f. Mosque of Kawara.

109. Regional Postal Training Centre, Abidjan. 110. Aerial Mast, Abobo Hertzian Centre.

**1972.** Stamp Day.
387. 109. 40 f. bistre, grn. & pur. 60 35

**1972.** World Telecommunications Day.
388. 110. 40 f. red, blue and green 70 35

112. Computer Operator.

**1972.** Development of Information Services.
393. 112. 40 f. blue, brn. & green 70 35

113. Odienne.

**1972.** 12th Anniv. of Independence.
394. 113. 35 f. brn., grn. & blue 55 35

**1972.** 10th Anniv. of West African Monetary Union. As Type 132 of Dahomey.
395. 40 f. grey, pur. & brown .. 60 35

115. Diamond and Mine.

**1972.** Development of the Diamond Industry.
396. 115. 40 f. blue, grey & brn. 1·60 85

116. Lake-dwellings, Bletankoro.

**1972.** Air.
397. 116. 200 f. pur., grn. & blue 2·50 1·10
398. – 500 f. brn., grn. & blue 7·75 3·50
DESIGN: 500 f. Kossou Dam.

117. Louis Pasteur and Institute.

**1972.** Inaug. of Pasteur Institute, Abidjan.
399. 177. 35 f. blue, grn. & brn. 60 35

118. Satellite Earth Station.

**1972.** Air. Opening of Satellite Earth Station Akakro.
400. 118. 200 f. brn., green & blue 2·75 1·10

119. Child pumping Water.

120. Dr. G. A. Hansen.

**1972.** "Conserve Water" Campaign.
401. 119. 35 f. blk., green & red 60 30
See also No. 414.

**1973.** Coats of Arms. As Type 80. Mult.
402. 5 f. Arms of Daloa .. 15 10
403. 10 f. Arms of Gagnoa .. 20 10
See also Nos. 432/36.

**1973.** Centenary of Hansen's Identification of Leprosy Bacillus.
404. 120. 35 f. brn., bl. & pur. 60 30

121. " Xyrichthys novacula "

**1973.** Fishes.
405. – 15 f. blue and green .. 45 35
406. – 20 f. red and brown .. 80 45
406a. – 25 f. red and green .. 1·10 35
406b. – 35 f. red and green .. 1·40 65
407. 121. 50 f. red, blue and black 2·00 1·00
FISHES: 15 f. " Balistes capriscus ". 20 f. " Pseudupeneus prayensis ". 25 f. " Cephalopholis taeniops ". 35 f. " Priacanthus arenatus ".

122. Child and Emblem.

**1973.** Establishment of first S.O.S. Children's Village in Africa.
408. 122. 40 f. blk., red & green 55 30

123. National Assembly Building.

**1973.** 112th Interparliamentary Council Session, Abidjan.
409. 123. 100 f. multicoloured .. 85 35

124. Classroom and Shop.

125. " Women's Work ".

**1973.** " Commercial Action " Programme.
410. 124. 40 f. multicoloured .. 45 15

**1973.** Technical Instruction for Women.
411. 125. 35 f. multicoloured .. 50 30

126. Scouts helping with Food Cultivation.

**1973.** 24th World Scouting Congress, Nairobi, Kenya.
412. 126. 40 f. multicoloured .. 65 35

127. Party Headquarters.

**1973.** New Party Headquarters Building, Yamoussokro.
413. 127. 35 f. multicoloured .. 45 25

128. Children at Dry Pump.

**1973.** Pan-African Drought Relief.
414. 128. 40 f. sepia, brown & red 60 30

129. " The Judgment of Solomon " (Nandjui Legue).

**1973.** Air. 6th World Peace and Justice Conf.
415. 129. 500 f. multicoloured .. 9·00 4·00

**1973.** U.A.M.P.T. As T 216. of Cameroun.
416. 100 f. black, red and violet 1·10 60

130. " Arrow-heads ".

132. Motorway Junction.

131. Ivory Coast 1 c. Stamp of 1892.

**1973.** Abidjan Museum.
417. 130. 5 f. black, red & brown 15 10

**1973.** Stamp and Post Day.
418. 131. 40 f. blk., orge. & green 65 35

**1973.** Motorway Projects. Indenie Interchange, Abidjan.
419. 132. 35 f. black, green & blue 55 30

133. Map of Africa and Emblem.

134. "Elephants" Ticket.

**1973.** 18th General Assembly of Int. Social Security Assn.
420. 133. 40 f. brown, ultramarine and blue .. .. 50 20

**1973.** Travel-Agents' Assns., 7th World Congress.
421. 134. 40 f. multicoloured .. 50 20

136. Kong Mosque.

**1974.**
426. 136. 35 f. brn., bl. & grn... 55 35

137. Grand-Lahou Post Office.

**1974.** Stamp Day.
427. 137. 35 f. brn., grn. & bl... 55 20

138. Converging Columns.

**1974.** "Formation Permanente".
428. 138. 35 f. multicoloured .. 40 20

139. Sassandra Bridge.

**1974.** Air.
429. 139. 100 f. brn. & green .. 1·10 50
430. 500 f. blk. & green .. 7·25 2·50

**1974.** 15th Anniv. of Conseil de l'Entente. As T 158 of Dahomey.
431. 40 f. multicoloured .. 45 20

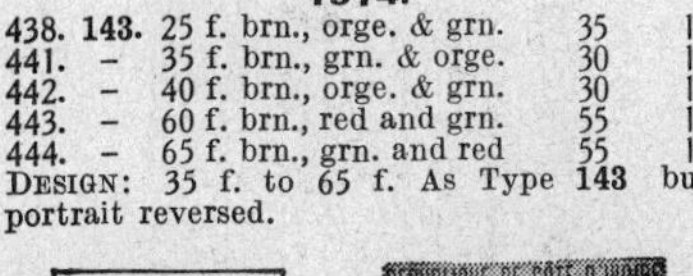
141. Arms of Ivory Coast.

143. Pres. Houphouet-Boigny.

142. View of Factory.

**1974.**
432. 141. 35 f. gold, grn. & brn. 35 10
433. 40 f. gold, grn. & blue 40 10
434. 60 f. gold, grn. & red .. 50 20
435. 65 f. gold, light grn. & green .. .. 55 20
436. 70 f. gold, grn. & blue 60 30

**1974.** Air. Vridi Soap Factory Abidjan.
437. 142. 200 f. multicoloured .. 2·25 1·10

**1974.**
438. 143. 25 f. brn., orge. & grn. 35 15
441. – 35 f. brn., grn. & orge. 30 10
442. – 40 f. brn., orge. & grn. 30 10
443. – 60 f. brn., red and grn. 55 15
444. – 65 f. brn., grn. and red 55 10
DESIGN: 35 f. to 65 f. As Type 143 but portrait reversed.


144. W.P.Y. Emblem.

145. Cotton-Picking.

**1974.** World Population Year.
439. 144. 40 f. blue and green .. 55 20

**1974.** Cotton Production (1st series).
440. 145. 50 f. multicoloured .. 60 30
See also Nos. 456/7.


147. U.P.U. Emblem.


148. Flag and U.P.U. Emblems.

**1974.** Cent. of U.P.U.
445. 147. 40 f. grn., bl. & brn. (post.) 60 30
446. 148. 200 f. multicoloured (air) 3·00 1·60
447. 300 f. multicoloured .. 4·00 2·25


149. Raoul Follereau.


150. Civic Service Emblem.

**1974.** Follereau (leprosy pioneer). Commem.
448. 149. 35 f. red, yell. & grn. 50 30

**1974.** 14th Anniv. of Independence.
449. 150. 35 f. multicoloured .. 50 20

151. Library Building and Students.

**1975.** 1st Anniv. of Inauguration of National Library.
450. 151. 40 f. multicoloured .. 50 20

152. Congress Emblem.

153. Coffee Flower.

**1975.** 52nd International Seedcrushers Association Congress, Abidjan.
451. 152. 40 f. black and green .. 45 20

**1975.** Coffee Production. Multicoloured.
452. 5 f. Type 153 .. .. 20 10
453. 10 f. Coffee-berries .. 30 15

154. Sassandra Wharf.

**1975.**
454. 154. 100 f. brn., grn. & bl... 1·10 65

155. Postal Sorters.

**1975.** Stamp Day.
455. 155. 40 f. multicoloured .. 60 30

156. Cotton Flower.

**1975.** Cotton Production (2nd series). Multicoloured.
456. 5 f. Type 156 .. .. 20 15
457. 10 f. Cotton bolls .. 35 15

157. Marie Kore and I.W.Y. Emblem.

**1975.** International Women's Year.
458. 157. 45 f. brn., bl. & grn... 55 30

158. Dabou Fort.

**1975.**
459. 158. 50 f. vio., bl. & grn. .. 55 30

159. Abidjan Harbour.

**1975.** 25th Anniv. of Abidjan Port.
460. **159.** 35 f. multicoloured .. 65 30

160. Cocoa Tree.

**1975.**
462. **160.** 35 f. multicoloured .. 80 35

161. Rural Activities.

**1975.** Promotion of Rural Development.
463. **161.** 50 f. mauve, violet & black .. .. 55 35

162. Railway Bridge over the N'Zi, Dimbokro.

**1975.** 15th Anniv. of Independence.
464. **162.** 60 f. multicoloured .. 85 35

163. "Mother" (statue). 164. Baoule Mask.

**1976.** Mothers' Day.
465. **163.** 65 f. multicoloured .. 85 45

**1976.** Ivory Coast Art. Multicoloured.
466. 20 f. Type **164** (postage).. 30 15
467. 25 f. Senoufo statuette .. 35 20
468. 150 f. Chief Abron's chair 1·75 85
469. 200 f. Akans royal symbols: fly swatter and panga (air) .. .. .. 3·25 1·40

165. Early and Modern Telephones. 166. Effigy, Map and Carrier Pigeon.

**1976.** Telephone Centenary.
470. **165.** 70 f. blue, brn. & blk. 65 40

**1976.** 20th Anniv. of Stamp Day and Ivory Coast Philatelic Club.
471. **166.** 65 f. multicoloured .. 55 35

167. "Smiling Trees" and Cat. 168. Children Reading.

**1976.** Nature Protection.
472. **167.** 65 f. multicoloured .. 65 35

**1976.** Literature for Children.
473. **168.** 65 f. multicoloured .. 60 35

169. Throwing the Javelin.

**1976.** Olympic Games, Montreal. Mult.
474. 60 f. Type **169** .. .. 55 30
475. 65 f. Running (horiz.) .. 55 30

170. Mohammed Ali Jinnah.

**1976.** Birth Centenary of Mohammed Ali Jinnah (first Governor-General of Pakistan).
476. **170.** 50 f. multicoloured .. 28·00 5·50

171. Cashew-nut.

**1976.**
477. **171.** 65 f. multicoloured .. 1·10 45

172. Motorway Bridge.

**1976.** 3rd African Roads Conference, Abidjan.
478. **172.** 60 f. multicoloured .. 55 30

173. John Paul Jones (after Peale) and detail of "First Salute to the Stars and Stripes" (E. Moran).

**1976.** Bicentenary of American Revolution. Multicoloured.
479 100 f. Type **173** .. .. 90 35
480 125 f. Comte de Rochambeau, grenadier and flag 1·10 30
481 150 f. Admiral D'Estaing, French marine and French warships .. 1·40 55
482 175 f. Marquis de Lafayette (after Peale), grenadier and flag .. .. 1·40 40
483 200 f. Thomas Jefferson (after Peale), militiaman and Declaration of Independence .. .. 1·60 45

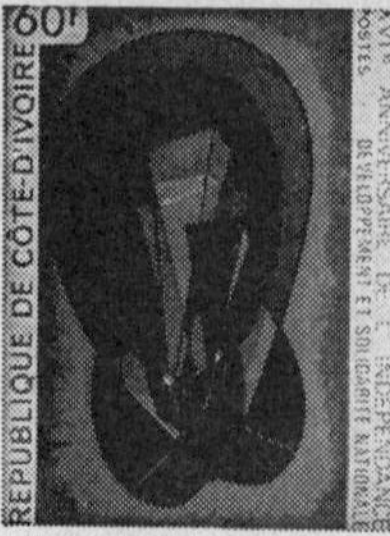
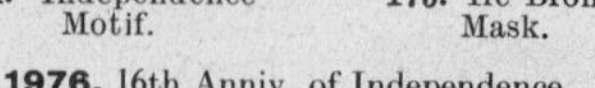
174. Independence Motif. 175. Ife Bronze Mask.

**1976.** 16th Anniv. of Independence.
485. **174.** 60 f. multicoloured .. 60 35

**1977.** 2nd World Festival of Negro Arts. Lagos.
486. **175.** 65 f. multicoloured .. 65 45

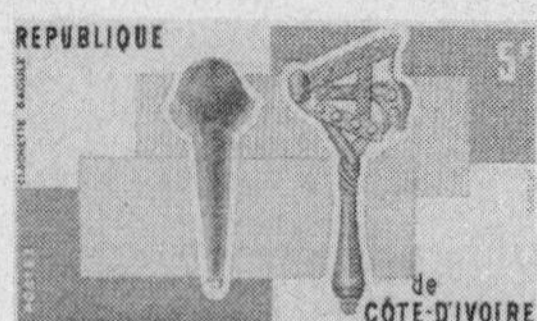

176. Baoule Handbells.

**1977.** Musical Instruments (1st series).
487. **176.** 5 f. brown and green.. 15 15
488. – 10 f. black and red .. 20 15
489. – 20 f. black and violet.. 35 15
DESIGNS: 10 f. Senoufo xylophone. 20 f. Dida tom-tom.
See also Nos. 603/4.

177. Unloading Mail from Douglas DC-8.

**1977.** Stamp Day.
490. **177.** 60 f. multicoloured .. 60 30

178. "Charaxes jasius epijasius".

**1977.** Butterflies (1st series). Multicoloured.
491. 30 f. "Epiphora rectifascia boolana" .. .. 1·60 55
492. 60 f. Type **178** .. .. 10·00 5·00
493. 65 f. "Imbrasia arata".. 2·25 1·10
494. 100 f. "Palla decius" .. 2·75 1·10
See also Nos. 546/9 and 585/7.

179. Tingrela Mosque.

**1977.** Air.
495. **179.** 500 f. brn., grn. & blue 5·00 2·75

**1977.** 10th Anniv. of International French Language Council. As T **204** of Benin.
496. 100 f. multicoloured .. 80 40

181. Wright Brothers and Wright Type A Biplane.

**1977.** History of Flying. Multicoloured.
497 60 f. Type **181** .. .. 45 15
498 75 f. Louis Bleriot crossing English Channel .. 65 20
499 100 f. Ross Smith and Vickers Vimy aircraft .. 90 20
500 200 f. Charles Lindbergh and "Spirit of St. Louis" 1·75 45
501 300 f. Concorde .. .. 2·75 85

182. Santos Dumont's "Ville de Paris".

**1977.** History of the Airship. Multicoloured.
503 60 f. Type **182** .. .. 55 15
504 65 f. Launch of LZ-1 .. 55 15
505 150 f. "Schwaben" .. 1·25 35
506 200 f. "Bodensee" .. 1·90 55
507 300 f. "Graf Zeppelin" over Egypt .. .. .. 2·50 85

183. Congress Emblem.

**1977.** 17th International Congress of Administrative Sciences in Africa.
509. **183.** 60 f. green and emerald 50 30

184. Pres. Houphouet-Boigny. 185. Container Ship "Yamoussoukro".

**1977.**
510. **184.** 35 f. blk., mauve & brn. 20 10
511. 40 f. blk., orge. & grn. 65 30
512. 45 f. blk., grn. & orge. 80 30
513. 60 f. blk., pur. & brn. 1·00 35
514. 65 f. blk., orge. & grn. 1·40 45

**1977.** Yamoussoukro Container Port.
515. **185.** 65 f. multicoloured .. 85 45

186. Hand holding Symbols of Development. 187. "Strophanthus hispidus".

**1977.** 17th Anniv. of Independence.
516. **186.** 60 f. blk., orge. & grn. 55 30

**1977.** Flowers (1st series). Multicoloured.
517. 5 f. Type **187** .. .. 15 10
518. 20 f. "Anthurium cultorum" 30 20
519. 60 f. "Arachnis flos-aeris" 50 30
520. 65 f. "Renanthera storiei" 55 35
See also Nos. 571/3, 622/5, 678/80, 791c/e, 827a/b and 873e/f.

188. Presidents Giscard d'Estaing and Houphouet-Boigny.

**1978.** Visit of President Giscard d'Estaing of France.
521. **188.** 60 f. multicoloured .. 70 30
522. 65 f. multicoloured .. 70 30
523. 100 f. multicoloured .. 1·10 55

189. "St. George and the Dragon".

**1978.** 400th Birth Anniv. of Peter Paul Rubens (artist).

525. 65 f. Type **189** .. .. 50 15
526. 150 f. "Head of a Child" 1·25 45
527. 250 f. "The Annunciation" 1·90 65
528. 300 f. "The Birth of Louis XIII" .. .. .. 2·75 95

**190.** Members of the Royal Guard.

**1978.** Images of History.

530. **190.** 60 f. red, black & blue 80 35
531. – 65 f. black, blue & red 80 35
DESIGN: 65 f. Figures of traditional cosmology.

**191.** Rural Post Office.

**1978.** Stamp Day.

532. **191.** 60 f. multicoloured .. 55 30

**192.** Microwave Antenna.

**1978.** Telecommunications Day.

533. **192.** 60 f. multicoloured .. 60 35

**193.** S. A. Arrhenius and Equipment (Chemistry, 1903).

**1978.** Nobel Prize Winners. Multicoloured.

534 60 f. Type **193** .. .. 45 10
535. 75 f. Jules Bordet (Medicine, 1920) .. .. .. 55 15
536. 100 f. Andre Gide (Literature, 1947) .. .. 80 20
537. 200 f. John Steinbeck (Literature, 1962) .. .. 1·40 45
538. 300 f. U.N.I.C.E.F. (Peace, 1965) .. .. .. 2·40 70

**194.** Player kicking Ball.

**1978.** World Cup Football Championship, Argentina. Multicoloured.

540. 60 f. Football and player (horiz.) .. .. .. 45 15
541. 65 f. Type **194** .. .. 50 20
542. 100 f. Football and player (different) (horiz.) .. 70 35
543. 150 f. Goalkeeper (horiz.) .. 1·10 35
544. 300 f. Football "sun" and player .. .. .. 2·25 65

**1978.** Butterflies (2nd series). As T **178**. Multicoloured.

546. 60 f. "Miniodes discolor" 90 45
547. 65 f. "Charaxes lactetinctus" .. .. .. 90 45
548. 100 f. "Papilio zalmoxis" 1·40 80
549. 200 f. "Papilio antimachus" .. .. .. 3·00 1·60

**195.** Banded Cricket.

**1978.** Insects (1st series). Multicoloured.

550 10 f. Type **195** .. .. 20 15
551 20 f. "Nepa cinerea" (water scorpion) .. .. 30 15
552 60 f. Horned tree-hopper 70 35
553 65 f. "Goliathus cassicus" (beetle) .. .. 1·00 45
See also Nos. 600/2.

**196.** Passengers in Train.

**1978.** Educational Television. Multicoloured.

554. 60 f. Figures emerging from television screen .. 45 20
555. 65 f. Type **196** .. .. 45 20

**197.** "Astragale" (oil exploration ship).

**1978.** 1st Anniv. of Discovery of Oil in Ivory Coast. Multicoloured.

556. 60 f. Type **197** .. .. 85 35
557. 65 f. Ram, map of Ivory Coast and gold goblets .. 85 35

**1978.** Air. "Philexafrique" Stamp Exhibition, Gabon (1st issue) and Int. Stamp Fair, Essen, West Germany. As T **262** of Gabon. Multicoloured.

559. 100 f. Ring-necked pheasant and Bavaria 1849 1 k. stamp .. .. 2·10 1·60
560. 100 f. African elephant and Ivory Coast 1965 90 f. stamp .. .. .. 2·10 1·60
See also Nos. 588/9.

**198.** National Assembly Building, Paris. **199.** African with Ballot Box.

**1978.** Centenary of Paris U.P.U. Congress.

561. **198.** 200 f. multicoloured .. 1·40 55

**1978.** 18th Anniv. of Independence.

562. **199.** 60 f. multicoloured .. 55 30

**200.** Ribbon of Flags.

**1978.** Technical Co-operation among Developing Countries. Multicoloured.

563. 60 f. Type **200** .. .. 50 20
564. 65 f. Ribbon of flags forming arrows .. .. 50 20

**201.** Ploughing.

**1979.** Agriculture.

565. **201.** 100 f. multicoloured .. 90 35

**202.** King Hassan and Pres. Houphouet-Boigny.

**1979.** Visit of King Hassan of Morocco.

566. **202.** 60 f. multicoloured .. 1·60 35
567. 65 f. multicoloured .. 2·25 35
568. 500 f. multicoloured .. 10·00 2·50

**203.** Isis.

**1979.** U.N.E.S.C.O. Campaign for Preservation of Nubian Monuments.

569. **203.** 200 f. silver, green and turquoise .. .. 1·60 85
570. – 500 f. gold, brown and salmon .. .. 4·00 2·25
DESIGN: 500 f. Gold medal.

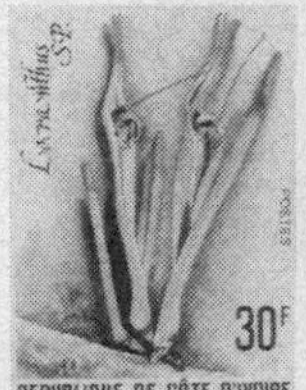

**204.** "Loranthus sp.". **205.** Sable Antelopes.

**1979.** Flowers (2nd series). Multicoloured.

571. 30 f. Type **204** .. .. 45 35
572. 60 f. "Vanda josephine" 90 45
573. 65 f. "Renanthera storiei" .. .. .. 90 55

**1979.** Endangered Animals (1st series). Multicoloured.

574. 5 f. Type **205** .. .. 20 15
575. 20 f. Yellow-backed duiker 35 20
576. 50 f. Pygmy hippopotamus 55 20
577. 60 f. Aardvark .. .. 1·10 55
See also Nos. 613/18.

**206.** Children and Globe. **207.** Travelling Post Office.

**1979.** International Year of the Child. Multicoloured.

578. 60 f. Type **206** .. .. 45 30
579. 65 f. Child on dove .. 50 30
580. 100 f. Type **206** .. .. 95 55
581. 500 f. As 65 f. .. .. 3·75 2·25

**1979.** Stamp Day.

582. **207.** 60 f. multicoloured .. 55 20

**208.** Korhogo Cathedral.

**1979.** 75th Anniv. of Arrival of Holy Fathers.

583. **208.** 60 f. multicoloured .. 55 30

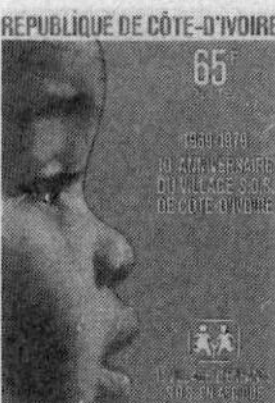

**209.** Crying Child. **210.** "Euphaedra xypete".

**1979.** 10th Anniv. of S.O.S Children's Village.

584. **209.** 65 f. multicoloured .. 55 30

**1979.** Butterflies (3rd series). Multicoloured.

585. 60 f. Type **210** .. .. 80 35
586. 65 f. "Pseudacraea boisduvali" .. .. .. 90 35
587. 70 f. "Auchenisa schausi" 1·40 55

**211.** Carved Figure and Antelope. **212.** Astronaut Greeting Boy.

**1979.** "Philexafrique", Stamp Exhibition, Gabon (2nd issue).

588. **211.** 70 f. multicoloured .. 1·40 1·10
589. – 70 f. green, turq. & red 1·40 1·10
DESIGN: No. 589, U.P.U. emblem antenna, ship and truck.

**1979.** 10th Anniv. of Moon Landing. Mult.

590. 60 f. Type **212** .. .. 65 45
591. 65 f. Trajectory between Earth and Moon (horiz.) 65 45
592. 70 f. Type **212** .. .. 1·10 55
593. 150 f. As 65 f. .. .. 2·00 1·40

**213.** "Flying Scotsman" and Great Britain £1 stamp, 1878.

**1979.** Death Centenary of Sir Rowland Hill. Multicoloured

594. 60 f. Type **213** .. .. 45 15
595. 75 f. Narrow-gauge locomotive and Ivory Coast 45 c. stamp, 1936 60 20
596. 100 f. Diesel locomotive and Hawaiian 13 c. "missionary" stamp, 1852 .. .. 80 30
597. 150 f. Steam locomotive and Japanese 20 s. stamp, 1872 .. .. .. 1·10 40
598. 300 f. Electric locomotive and French 15 c. stamp, 1850 .. .. .. 2·10 60

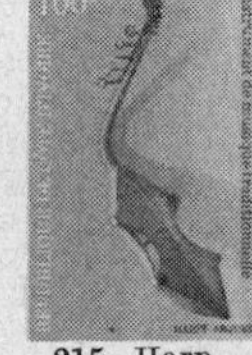

**214.** "Delta sp." **215.** Harp.

**1979.** Insects (2nd series). Multicoloured.

600 30 f. Type **214** .. .. 2·25 1·10
601 60 f. "Mantis religiosa" (vert) .. .. .. 3·25 1·60
602 65 f. "Locusta migratorius" .. .. 4·00 1·60

**1979.** Musical Instruments (2nd series). Multicoloured.

603. 100 f. Type **215** .. .. 11·00 4·50
604. 150 f. Senoufo funeral horns 17·00 6·75

**216.** "Telecom 79". **217.** Carved Head.

**1979.** Third World Telecommunications Exhibition, Geneva.
605. **216.** 60 f. grey, orge. & blue 55 30

**1979.** Culture Days.
606. **217.** 65 f. multicoloured .. 55 20

218. Boxing.

**1979.** Pre-Olympic Year. Multicoloured.

| | | | |
|---|---|---|---|
| 607. | 60 f. Type **218** .. .. | 45 | 15 |
| 608. | 65 f. Running .. .. | 45 | 15 |
| 609. | 100 f. Football .. .. | 70 | 30 |
| 610. | 150 f. Cycling .. .. | 1·10 | 45 |
| 611. | 300 f. Wrestling .. .. | 2·25 | 80 |

See also Nos. 642/5.

219. Jentink's Duiker.

**1979.** Endangered Animals (2nd series). Multicoloured.

| | | | |
|---|---|---|---|
| 613. | 40 f. Type **219** .. .. | 45 | 20 |
| 614. | 60 f. Olive colobus .. .. | 50 | 20 |
| 615. | 75 f. African manatees .. | 70 | 25 |
| 616. | 100 f. Temminck's Giant squirrel .. .. .. | 1·00 | 35 |
| 617. | 150 f. Pygmy hippopotamus .. .. .. | 1·40 | 45 |
| 618. | 300 f. Chimpanzee .. .. | 5·00 | 1·75 |

220. Raoul Follereau and Institute.

**1979.** Raoul Follereau d'Adzope Institute.
619. **220.** 60 f. multicoloured .. 60 35

221. Post, Adze and Plant.

222. Concorde and Map of Africa.

**1979.** 19th Anniv. of Independence.
620. **221.** 60 f. multicoloured .. 55 15

**1979.** 20th Anniv. of ASECNA (African Air Safety Organization).
621. **222.** 60 f. multicoloured .. 75 30

222a. Coelancanth.

**1979.** Fishes (1st series). Multicoloured.
621a. 60 f. "Pterois volitans" ..
621b. 65 f. Type **222a** .. ..
See also Nos. 629/31 and 666/8.

223. "Clerodendron thomsonae".

224. Elephant, Map and Rotary Emblem.

**1980.** Flowers (3rd series). Multicoloured.

| | | | |
|---|---|---|---|
| 622. | 5 f. Type **223** .. .. | 10 | 10 |
| 623. | 10 f. "La Boule de Feu" (horiz.) .. .. .. | 15 | 10 |
| 624. | 50 f. "Costus incanusiamus" | 55 | 15 |
| 625. | 60 f. "Ficus elastica" .. | 55 | 20 |

**1980.** 75th Anniv. of Rotary International.
626. **224.** 65 f. multicoloured .. 55 30

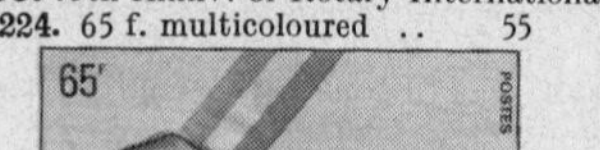

225. Seal.

**1980.** International Archives Day.
627. **225.** 65 f. multicoloured .. 55 35

226. Boys with Stamp Album.

**1980.** Stamp Day.
628. **226.** 65 f. brn. & turquoise 60 20

**1980.** Fishes (2nd series). As T **222a**.

| | | | |
|---|---|---|---|
| 629. | 60 f. "Lutjanus sebae" .. | 80 | 35 |
| 630. | 65 f. "Monodactylus sebae" (vert.) .. .. | 80 | 35 |
| 631. | 100 f. "Colisa fasciata" .. | 1·25 | 55 |

228. Missionary and Church, Aboisso.

**1980.** 75th Anniv. of Settlement of Holy Fathers at Aboisso.
632. **228.** 60 f. multicoloured .. 60 35

229. Hands protecting Child from Cigarettes.

**1980.** Anti-Smoking Campaign.
633. **229.** 60 f. multicoloured .. 60 20

230. Pope John-Paul II and President Houphouet-Boigny.

**1980.** Papal Visit.
634. **230.** 65 f. yell., brn. & dp. brn. 1·00 45

231. "Le Belier" (Abidjan–Niger Line).

232. Headquarters Building, Dakar.

**1980.** Railways. Multicoloured.

| | | | |
|---|---|---|---|
| 635. | 60 f. Type **231** .. .. | 55 | 35 |
| 636. | 65 f. Abidjan Station, 1904 | 55 | 35 |
| 637. | 100 f. Passenger coach, 1908 .. .. .. | 95 | 40 |
| 638. | 150 f. Steam locomotive, 1940 .. .. .. | 1·40 | 70 |

**1980.** West African Central Bank. First Anniv.
639. **232.** 60 f. multicoloured .. 60 30

233. Cobra.

**1980.** Animals. Multicoloured.

| | | | |
|---|---|---|---|
| 640. | 60 f. Type **233** .. .. | 55 | 20 |
| 641. | 150 f. Toad .. .. .. | 1·50 | 65 |

234. Gymnastics.

235. World Tourism Conference Emblem.

**1980.** Air. Olympic Games, Moscow. Multicoloured.

| | | | |
|---|---|---|---|
| 642. | 75 f. Type **234** .. .. | 65 | 15 |
| 643. | 150 f. Ring exercise .. | 1·10 | 30 |
| 644. | 250 f. Vaulting horse (horiz.) | 2·00 | 55 |
| 645. | 350 f. Bar exercise .. | 3·00 | 85 |

**1980.** Tourism. Multicoloured.

| | | | |
|---|---|---|---|
| 647. | 60 f. Village scene .. | 45 | 15 |
| 648. | 65 f. Type **235** .. .. | 45 | 15 |

**1980.** Insects (3rd series). As Type **214**. Multicoloured.

| | | | |
|---|---|---|---|
| 649 | 60 f. "Ugada limbata" (25 × 35 mm) .. .. | 85 | 55 |
| 650 | 60 f. "Forticula auricularia" (36 × 26 mm) .. | 1·60 | 95 |
| 651 | 65 f. "Mantis religiosa" (26 × 32 mm) .. .. | 1·60 | 85 |
| 652 | 200 f. Grasshopper (35 × 25 mm) .. .. .. | 2·25 | 1·40 |

236. Hands breaking Chains, Map and President.

**1980.** President Houphouet-Boigny's 75th Birthday.

| | | | | |
|---|---|---|---|---|
| 653. | **236.** | 60 f. multicoloured (postage) .. .. | 55 | 30 |
| 654. | – | 65 f. multicoloured .. | 55 | 30 |
| 655. | – | 70 f. multicoloured .. | 70 | 45 |
| 656. | **236.** | 150 f. multicoloured .. | 1·75 | 1·10 |
| 657. | – | 300 f. multicoloured .. | 3·25 | 1·75 |
| 658. | – | 2000 f. silver (air) .. | 15·00 | 15·00 |
| 659. | – | 3000 f. gold .. .. | 22·00 | 22·00 |

DESIGNS: SQUARE. 70 f. Presidential speech on map in national colours. HORIZ. (44 × 29 mm.) 65 f., 300 f. President and symbols of progress. VERT. (35 × 45 mm.) 2000 f., 3000 f. President Houphouet-Boigny.

237. Map of Ivory Coast.

**1980.** Seventh P.D.C.I.–R.D.A. Congress.
660. **237.** 60 f. grn., orge. & blk. 45 15
661. 65 f. grn., orge. & blk. 45 15

238. "Sotra" (ferry).

**1980.** New Lagoon Transport.
662 **238** 60 f. multicoloured .. 55 30

239. Abidjan.

**1980.** 20th Anniv. of Independence.
663. **239.** 60 f. multicoloured .. 45 20

240. Conference Emblem.

241. Map of Africa and Posthorn.

**1980.** 5th General Conference of African Universities Association, Yamoussoukro.
664. **240.** 60 f. multicoloured .. 55 30

**1980.** 5th Anniv. of African Posts and Telecommunications Union.
665. **241.** 150 f. multicoloured .. 1·10 35

241a. Red-billed Dwarf Hornbill.

242. "Herichtys cyanoguttatum".

**1980.** Birds. Multicoloured.

| | | | |
|---|---|---|---|
| 665a | 60 f. Superb starling .. | 13·50 | 8·50 |
| 665b | 65 f. Type **241a** .. | 13·50 | 8·50 |
| 665c | 65 f. South African crowned crane .. | 14·00 | 9·00 |
| 665d | 100 f. Saddle-bill stork | 38·00 | 24·00 |

**1981.** Fishes (3rd series). Multicoloured.

| | | | |
|---|---|---|---|
| 666. | 60 f. Type **242** .. .. | 55 | 35 |
| 667. | 65 f. "Labeo bicolor" .. | 55 | 35 |
| 668. | 200 f. "Tetraodon fluviatilis" | 1·60 | 1·00 |

243. Post Office, Grand Lahou.

**1981.** Stamp Day.
669. **243.** 60 f. multicoloured .. 55 20

244. Mask.

**1981.** 25th Anniv. of Ivory Coast Philatelic Club.
670. **244.** 65 f. blk., lt. brn. & brn. 45 20

245. Red Cross Aircraft, Satellite and Globe (Telecommunications and Health).

**1981.** World Telecommunications Day.
671. **245.** 30 f. multicoloured .. 20 10
672. 60 f. multicoloured .. 45 20

246. " Viking " landing on Mars.

**1981.** Conquest of Space. Multicoloured.
673. 60 f. Type **246** .. .. 45 15
674. 75 f. Space Shuttle on launch pad .. .. .. 55 20
675. 125 f. Space Shuttle erecting experiment .. .. 85 40
676. 300 f. Space Shuttle performing experiment .. 2·10 90

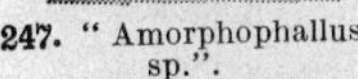

**247.** " Amorphophallus sp.". **249.** Map formed of Flag.

**248.** Prince Charles, Lady Diana Spencer and Coach.

**1981.** Flowers (4th series). Multicoloured.
678. 50 f. Type **247** .. .. 55 20
679. 60 f. Sugar cane flowers .. 65 35
680. 100 f. "Heliconia ivoirea" 1·25 55
See also Nos. 791c/e, 827a/b and 873e/f.

**1981.** Royal Wedding.
681. **248.** 80 f. multicoloured .. 55 20
682. – 100 f. multicoloured .. 65 35
683. – 125 f. multicoloured .. 85 40
DESIGNS: 100 f., 125 f. Similar designs showing portraits and coaches.

**1981.**
684a. **249.** 5 f. multicoloured .. 10 10
684aa. 10 f. multicoloured .. 15 10
684ab. 20 f. multicoloured .. 15 10
684b. 25 f. multicoloured .. 15 10
684c. 30 f. multicoloured .. 20 10
684ca. 35 f. multicoloured .. 20 10
684d. 40 f. multicoloured .. 30 10
684e. 50 f. multicoloured .. 35 10
685. 80 f. multicoloured .. 50 20
686. 100 f. multicoloured 60 35
687. 125 f. multicoloured 85 40

**250.** Goalkeeper.

**1981.** World Cup Football Championships, Spain (1982). Multicoloured.
688. 70 f. Type **250** .. .. 45 30
689. 80 f. Saving a goal .. 55 35
690. 100 f. Diving for ball (vert.) 65 40
691. 150 f. Goalmouth scene .. 1·00 60
692. 350 f. Fighting for ball (vert.) 2·40 1·10

**251.** Association Emblem.

**1981.** West Africa Rice Development Association.
694. **251.** 80 f. multicoloured .. 60 30

**252.** Post Office.

**1981.** Stamp Day.
695. **252.** 70 f. multicoloured .. 45 20
696. 80 f. multicoloured .. 55 35
697. 100 f. multicoloured .. 65 35

**253.** Hands with and without Fruit, and F.A.O. Emblem.

**1981.** World Food Day.
698. **253.** 100 f. multicoloured .. 65 35

**254.** Felice Nazarro.

**1981.** 75th Anniv. of French Grand Prix Motor Race. Multicoloured.
699. 15 f. Type **254** .. .. 15 10
700. 40 f. Jim Clark .. .. 35 15
701. 80 f. Fiat, 1907 .. .. 65 40
702. 100 f. Auto Union, 1936 .. 80 45
703. 125 f. Ferrari, 1961 .. 1·10 55

**255.** Symbols of Economic Growth.

**1981.** 21st Anniv. of Independence.
705. **255.** 50 f. multicoloured .. 35 15
706. 80 f. multicoloured .. 55 30

**256.** " Queue de Cheval ". **258.** Rotary Emblem on Map of Africa.

**257.** Bingerville Post Office, 1902.

**1982.** Hairstyles. Multicoloured.
707. 80 f. Type **256** .. .. 55 30
708. 100 f. " Belier " .. .. 1·10 45
709. 125 f. " Cheri regarde mon visage " .. .. .. 1·40 55

**1982.** Stamp Day.
710. **257.** 100 f. multicoloured .. 65 35

**1982.** Rotary International Conference, Abidjan.
711. **258.** 100 f. blue and gold .. 70 40

**259.** George Washington.

**1982.** Celebrities' Anniversaries. Mult.
712. 80 f. Type **259** (250th birth anniv.) .. .. 55 20
713. 100 f. Auguste Picard (20th death anniv.) .. .. 65 30
714. 350 f. Goethe (150th death anniv.) .. .. .. 2·25 85
715. 450 f. Princess of Wales (21st birthday) .. 3·00 1·25

**260.** Hexagonal Pattern and Telephone.

**1982.** World Telecommunications Day.
717. **260.** 80 f. multicoloured .. 55 20

**261.** Presidents Mitterand and Houphouet-Boigny.

**1982.** Visit of President Mitterand of France.
718. **261.** 100 f. multicoloured .. 90 45

**262.** Dr. Koch, Bacillus and Microscope. **263.** Scouts in Dinghy.

**1982.** Cent. of Discovery of Tubercle Bacillus.
719. **262.** 30 f. multicoloured .. 30 20
720. 80 f. multicoloured .. 85 45

**1982.** 75th Anniv. of Boy Scout Movement. Multicoloured.
721. 80 f. Type **263** .. .. 60 40
722. 100 f. Yacht (horiz.) .. 70 50
723. 150 f. Leaning into wind 1·00 65
724. 350 f. Hauling sail .. 2·50 80

**264.** Aerial View of Coastline. **265.** Congress Emblem.

**1982.** 10th Anniv. of U.N. Environmental Programme.
726. **264.** 40 f. multicoloured .. 35 15
727. 80 f. multicoloured .. 55 30

**1982.** First League of Ivory Coast Secretaries Congress, Abidjan.
728. **265.** 80 f. multicoloured .. 55 20
729. 100 f. multicoloured .. 65 35

**1982.** Birth of Prince William of Wales. Nos. 681/3 optd. **NAISSANCE ROYALE 1982.**
730. **247.** 80 f. multicoloured .. 55 30
731. – 100 f. multicoloured .. 65 35
732. – 125 f. multicoloured .. 85 40

**267.** " Child with Dove ".

**1982.** Picasso Paintings. Multicoloured.
734. 80 f. Type **267** .. .. 55 20
735. 100 f. " Self-portrait " .. 65 20
736. 185 f. " Les Demoiselles d'Avignon " .. .. 1·60 40
737. 350 f. " The Dream " .. 2·75 85
738. 500 f. " La Colombe de l'Avenir " (horiz.) .. 4·00 1·10

**268.** Post Office Counter, Abidjan 17.

**1982.** World U.P.U. Day. Multicoloured.
739. 80 f. Type **268** .. .. 55 30
740. 100 f. Postel 2001 Building, Abidjan (vert.) .. .. 85 35
741. 350 f. Counter clerks at Abidjan 17 Post Office 2·50 95
742. 500 f. Exterior and interior views of Postel 2001 (48 × 36 mm.) .. .. 3·50 1·50

**1982.** World Cup Football Championship Results. Nos. 688/92 optd.
743. 70 f. Type **249** .. .. 45 25
744. 80 f. Saving a goal .. 55 25
745. 100 f. Diving for ball (vert.) 60 35
746. 150 f. Goalmouth scene .. 90 55
747. 350 f. Fighting for ball (vert.) .. .. .. 2·25 1·10
OVERPRINTS: 70 f. **1966 VAINQUEUR GRANDE-BRETAGNE.** 80 f. **1970 VAINQUEUR BRESIL.** 100 f. **1974 VAINQUEUR ALLEMAGNE (RFA).** 150 f. **1978 VAINQUEUR ARGENTINE.** 350 f. **1982 VAINQUEUR ITALIE.**

**270.** President Houphouet-Boigny with Farming Implements and Agricultural Produce.

**1982.** 22nd Anniv. of Independence.
749. **270.** 100 f. multicoloured .. 70 35

**271.** Emblem and Map of Member Countries.

**1982.** 20th Anniv. of West African Monetary Union.
750. **271.** 100 f. brown, blue and deep blue .. .. 65 35

**272.** Man Waterfall.

**1982.** Landscapes. Multicoloured.
751. 80 f. Type **272** .. .. 1·10 55
752. 80 f. Wooded savanna .. 70 35
753. 500 f. Type **272** .. .. 7·75 2·75

**273.** Child and S.O.S. Village. **274.** Long-tailed Pangolin.

**1983.** S.O.S. Children's Village.
754. **273.** 125 f. multicoloured . . 90 40

**1983.** Animals. Multicoloured.
755. 35 f. Type **274** . . . . 30 15
756. 90 f. Bush pig (horiz) . . 65 35
757. 100 f. Eastern black-and-white colobus . . . . 70 40
758. 125 f. African buffalo (horiz) . . . . . . 95 50

**275.** Post Office, Grand Bassam, 1903.

**1983.** Stamp Day.
759. **275.** 100 f. multicoloured . . 70 35

**276.** Montgolfier Balloon, 1783.

**1983.** Bicent of Manned Flight. Mult.
760 100 f. Type **276** . . . . 70 25
761 125 f. Charles's hydrogen balloon, 1783 . . . . 95 30
762 150 f. Balloon "Armand Barbes" (Paris siege post, 1870) (horiz) . . 1·10 35
763 350 f. Balloon "Double Eagle II" over Atlantic 2·50 80
764 500 f. Advertising airship (horiz) . . . . . . 4·00 1·10

**277.** " Descent from the Cross ".

**1983.** Easter. Multicoloured.
765. 100 f. Type **277** . . . . 65 20
766. 125 f. " The Resurrection of Christ " (horiz.) . . 85 30
767. 350 f. " The Raising of the Cross " (horiz.) . . 2·25 85
768. 400 f. " The Piercing of the Lance " . . . . 2·75 90
769. 500 f. " Descent from the Cross " . . . . . . 3·25 1·10

**278.** Safe containing U.N. Emblem.

**1983.** 25th Anniv. of U.N. Economic Commission for Africa.
770. **278.** 100 f. multicoloured . . 65 30

**279.** African Fish Eagle.

**1983.** Birds. Multicoloured.
771. 100 f. Type **279** . . . . 2·00 85
772. 125 f. Grey Parrot (horiz.) 2·50 65
773. 150 f. Violet Turaco (horiz.) 3·75 1·00

**280.** Swimming.

**1983.** Air. Pre-Olympic Year. Multicoloured.
774. 100 f. Type **280** . . . . 65 20
775. 125 f. Diving . . . . 90 30
776. 350 f. Backstroke . . . . 2·40 80
777. 400 f. Butterfly stroke . . 2·75 95

**281.** Forest destroyed by Fire.

**1983.** Ecology in Action. Multicoloured.
779. 25 f. Type **281** . . . . 35 20
780. 100 f. Animals running from fire . . . . . . 1·10 45
781. 125 f. Protected animals . . 1·40 65

**282.** Flali Dance.

**1983.** Traditional Dances. Multicoloured.
782. 50 f. Type **282** . . . . 35 15
783. 100 f. Mask dance . . 65 30
784. 125 f. Stilt dance . . . . 95 40

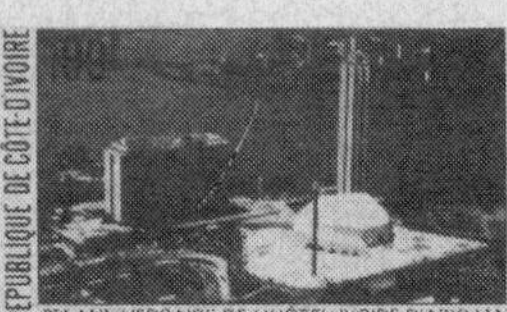


**283.** Hotel Ivoire.

**1983.** 20th Anniv. of Hotel Ivoire, Abidjan.
785. **283.** 100 f. multicoloured . . 65 35

**284.** Rally Car and Route.

**1983.** World and African Car Rally Championships.
786. **284.** 100 f. multicoloured . . 90 45

**285.** " Christ and St. Peter ".

**1983.** Christmas. Paintings by Raphael. Multicoloured.
787. 100 f. Type **285** . . . . 65 30
788. 125 f. Study for St. Joseph 90 35
789. 350 f. " Virgin of the House of Orleans " . . . . 2·40 80
790. 500 f. " Virgin of the Blue Diadem " . . . . 3·25 1·10

**286.** President Houphouet-Boigny.

**1983.** 23rd Anniv. of Independence.
791. **286.** 100 f. multicoloured . . 65 30

**286a.** Telegraphist, Dish Aerial and National Postal Sorting Centre.

**1983.** World Communications Year. Mult.
791a. 100 f. Cable-laying, Postel 2001 building, Abidjan, and telephonists . .
791b. 125 f. Type **286a** . . . .

**1983.** Flowers (5th series). As T **247**. Multicoloured.
791c. 100 f. Pineapple flowers . . 40 35
791d. 125 f. "Heliconia rostrata" 1·90 85
791e. 150 f. "Rose de Porcelaine" 2·50 1·40

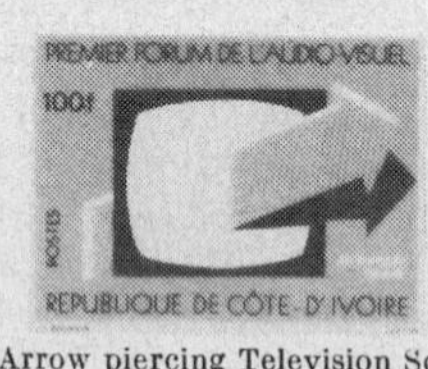


**287.** Arrow piercing Television Screen.

**1984.** First Audio-Visual Forum.
792. **287.** 100 f. black & green . . 65 30

**288.** Competition Emblem.

**290.** Abidjan Post Office, 1934.

**289.** Spider.

**1984.** Africa Cup Football Competition.
793. **288.** 100 f. multicoloured . . 65 30
794. – 200 f. orange, green and black . . . . 1·40 55
DESIGN: 200 f. Maps of Africa and Ivory Coast shaking hands.

**1984.** Multicoloured.
795 100 f. Type **289** . . . . 1·00 55
796 125 f. "Polistes gallicus" (wasp) . . . . . . 1·25 65

**1984.** Stamp Day.
797. **290.** 100 f. multicoloured . . 65 30

**291.** Swimming.

**1984.** Air. Olympic Games, Los Angeles. Multicoloured.
798. 100 f. Type **291** . . . . 65 30
799. 125 f. Cross-country . . 80 30
800. 185 f. Pistol shooting . . 1·25 45
801. 350 f. Fencing . . . . 2·40 65

**292.** Lions Club Badge.

**1984.** Third Lions Multi District 403 Convention. Multicoloured.
803. 100 f. Type **292** . . . . 85 35
804. 125 f. As T **292** but with badge at right . . . . 1·00 55

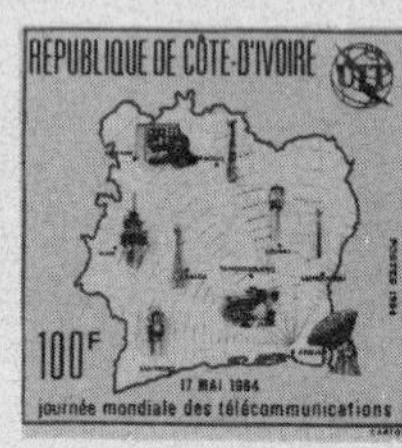


**293.** Telecommunications Stations on Map of Ivory Coast.

**1984.** World Telecommunications Day.
805. **293.** 100 f. multicoloured . . 65 30

**294.** Flags, Agriculture and Symbols of Unity and Growth.

**1984.** 25th Anniv. of Council of Unity.
806. **294.** 100 f. multicoloured . . 65 30
807. 125 f. multicoloured . . 85 35

**295.** First Government House, Grand-Bassam.

**1984.** Old Buildings (1st series). Mult.
808. 100 f. Type **295** . . . . 65 30
809. 125 f. Palace of Justice, Grand-Bassam . . . . 85 35
See also Nos. 873a/c.

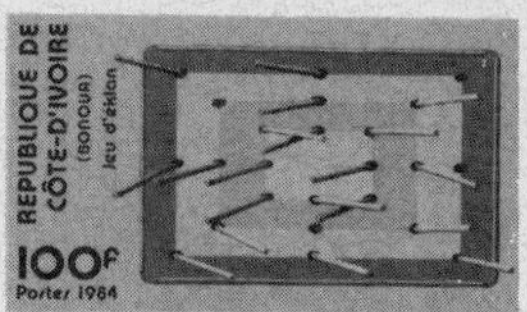


**296.** Eklan Board.

**1984.** Eklan. Multicoloured.
810. 100 f. Type **296** . . . . 65 35
811. 125 f. Two Eklan players . . 85 45

**297.** "La Gazelle".

**1984.** Transport. Multicoloured.
(a) Locomotives.

812. 100 f. Type **297** .. .. 65 30
813. 125 f. "Superpacific" 31251–31290 .. .. 90 40
814. 350 f. "Pacific Type 10" .. 2·40 1·25
815. 500 f. "Mallet" class .. 3·50 1·75

(b) Ships.

816. 100 f. Container Ship .. 65 40
817. 125 f. Cargo liner .. .. 90 50
818. 350 f. "Queen Mary" (liner) 2·40 1·60
819. 500 f. "France" (liner) .. 4·25 2·50

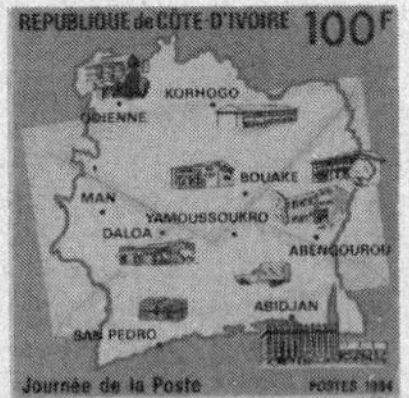


**298.** Envelope, Map and Symbols of Postal Service.

**1984.** Stamp Day.

820. **298.** 100 f. multicoloured .. 85 45

**299.** Emblem.

**1984.** 10th Anniv. of West African Economic Community.

821. **299.** 100 f. multicoloured .. 65 30

**300.** Book Cover.

**1984.** 90th Anniv. (1982) of Ivory Coast Postage Stamps.

822. **300.** 125 f. multicoloured .. 95 65

**301.** Map Outline, People and Flag.

**1984.** 24th Anniv. of Independence.

823. **301.** 100 f. multicoloured .. 65 30

**302.** G. Tiacoh (400 metres silver).

**302a.** Serval.

**1984.** Air. Olympic Games Medallists. Multicoloured.

824. 100 f. Type **302** .. .. 65 20
825. 150 f. C. Lewis (100 and 200 metres gold) .. .. 1·00 35
826. 200 f. A. Babers (400 metres gold) .. .. 1·40 45
827. 500 f. J. Cruz (800 metres gold) .. .. .. 3·00 1·00

**1984.** Flowers (6th series). As T **247**. Mult.

827a. 100 f. "Allamanda cathartica" .. .. 22·00 8·25
827b. 125 f. Baobab flowers .. 22·00 8·25

**1984.** Animals. Multicoloured.

827c. 100 f. Bushbuck .. .. 22·00 8·25
827d. 150 f. Type **302a** .. .. 22·00 8·25

**302b.** Valtur Club, Assouinde.

**1984.**

827e. 50 f. Type **302b** .. .. 19·00 3·25
827f. 100 f. Azagni Canal .. 19·00 5·00

**303.** "Virgin and Child" (Correggio).

**1985.** Air. Christmas. Multicoloured.

828. 100 f. Type **303** .. .. 80 30
829. 200 f. "Virgin and Child" (Andrea del Sarto) .. 1·40 55
830. 400 f. "Virgin and Child" (Jacopo Bellini) .. .. 2·75 1·10

Nos. 829/30 are wrongly inscribed "Le Correge" (Correggio).

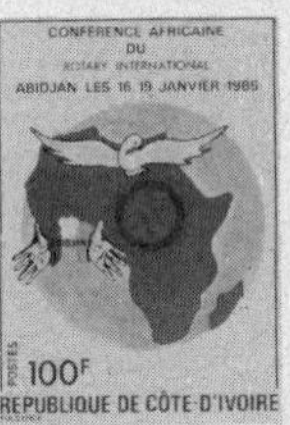

**304.** Map, Hands, Emblem and Dove.

**305.** "Le Babou" (Dan costume).

**1985.** African Conference of Rotary International, Abidijan.

831. **304.** 100 f. multicoloured .. 65 30
832. 125 f. multicoloured .. 85 35

**1985.** Traditional Costumes. Multicoloured.

833. 90 f. Type **305** .. .. 70 35
834. 100 f. Avikam post-natal dress .. .. .. 95 45

**305a.** Hadada Ibis.

**308.** Emblem.

**306.** River Steamer "Adjame".

**1985.** Birds. Multicoloured.

834a 25 f. Marabou stork
834b 100 f. African jacana
834c 350 f. Type **305a**

**1985.** Stamp Day.

835. **306.** 100 f. multicoloured .. 1·00 55

**1985.** 7th Conference of District 18 of Zonta International, Abidjan.

836. **308.** 125 f. multicoloured .. 85 30

**309.** Airplane, Van and Industrial Landscape.

**1985.** "Philexafrique" Stamp Exhibition, Lome, Togo (1st issue). Multicoloured.

837. 200 f. Type **309** .. .. 1·60 1·25
838. 200 f. Sports and agriculture .. .. 1·60 1·25

See also Nos. 864/5.

**310.** Red-breasted Mergansers.

**1985.** Air. Birth Bicentenary of John J. Audubon (ornithologist). Multicoloured.

839. 100 f. Type **310** .. .. 95 75
840. 150 f. American white pelican (vert.) .. .. 1·50 80
841. 200 f. American wood stork (vert.) .. .. .. 3·00 90
842. 350 f. Velvet scoters .. 4·50 1·10

**311.** Chemical Plant, Senegal.

**1985.** 20th Anniv. of African Development Bank.

843. 100 f. Type **311** .. .. 65 20
844. 125 f. Tree seedlings, Gambia .. .. .. 85 35

**312.** Profiles within Map and I.Y.Y. Emblem.

**1985.** International Youth Year.

845. **312.** 125 f. multicoloured .. 85 35

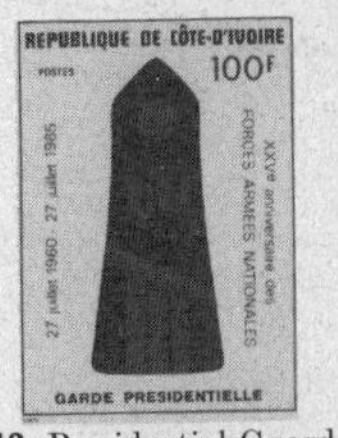


**313.** Presidential Guard Shoulder Flash.

**314.** Ivory Coast Arms.

**1985.** 25th Anniv. of National Armed Forces.

846. **313.** 100 f. gold and purple 65 20
847. – 100 f. gold and blue .. 65 20
848. – 125 f. gold and black 95 30
849. – 200 f. gold and brown 1·50 45
850. – 350 f. silver and blue 2·40 80

DESIGNS: Shoulder flashes of—No. 847, F.A.N.C.I. (army). 848, Air Force. 849, Navy. 850, Gendarmerie.

**1985.** Postal Convention with Sovereign Military Order of Malta. Multicoloured.

851. 125 f. Type **314** .. .. 85 35
852. 350 f. Sovereign Military Order of Malta arms .. 2·50 1·40

**315.** Footballers.

**1985.** World Cup Football Championship, Mexico. Multicoloured.

853. 100 f. Type **315** .. .. 65 20
854. 150 f. Footballers (different) .. .. 1·00 35
855. 200 f. Footballers (different) .. .. 1·10 40
856. 350 f. Footballers (different) .. .. 2·50 70

**316.** Pope and Abidjan Cathedral.

**1985.** Visit of Pope John Paul II.

858. **316.** 100 f. multicoloured .. 1·00 55

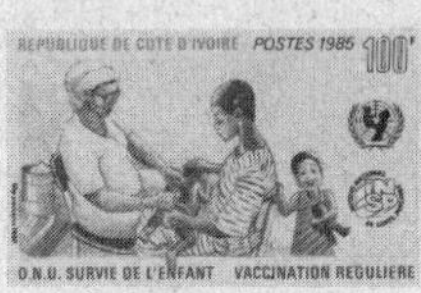

**317.** Vaccinating Baby.

**1985.** U.N.I.C.E.F. Child Survival Campaign. Multicoloured.

859. 100 f. Type **317** .. .. 65 30
860. 100 f. Mother breast-feeding baby while child plays .. .. .. 65 30
861. 100 f. Mother spoon-feeding child .. .. 65 30
862. 100 f. Mother giving child a drink (oral rehydration) 65 30

**318.** Rainbow, U.N. Emblem and Joined Hands.

**1985.** 40th Anniv. of U.N.O. and 25th Anniv. of Ivory Coast Membership.

863. **318.** 100 f. multicoloured .. 65 20

**319.** Footballers and Children with Injured Animal.

**1985.** Air. "Philexafrique" International Stamp Exhibition, Lome, Togo (2nd issue). Multicoloured.

864. 250 f. Type **319** .. .. 2·00 1·40
865. 250 f. Dish aerial, rocket and container ship .. 2·00 1·40

**320.** City Skyline.

**1985.** "Expo 85" World's Fair, Tsukuba, Japan.
866. **320.** 125 f. multicoloured .. 85 30

**321.** Young Duiker.

**1985.** World Wildlife Fund. Banded Duiker. Multicoloured.
867. 50 f. Type **321** .. .. 45 20
868. 60 f. Duiker in front of bushes .. .. .. 55 20
869. 75 f. Two duikers .. .. 65 35
870. 100 f. Duiker (different) .. 95 45

**322.** Children on Open Ground. **323.** Woman spinning Cotton.

**1985.** "Return to the Earth".
871. **322.** 125 f. multicoloured .. 85 35

**1985.** Rural Handicrafts. Multicoloured.
872. 125 f. Type **323** .. .. 85 35
873. 155 f. Man painting on cotton cloth .. .. 1·10 45

**323a.** Samatiguila Mosque.

**1985.** Old Buildings (2nd series). Mult.
873a. 100 f. Bondoukou Market 17·00 5·50
873b. 125 f. Type **323a** .. .. 17·00 5·50
873c. 200 f. Samory House, Bondoukou .. .. 17·00 5·50

**1985.** Flowers (7th series). As T **247**. Mult.
873d. 100 f. "Amorphophallus staudtii" .. .. .. 22·00 5·50
873e. 125 f. Crinum .. .. 22·00 5·50
873f. 200 f. "Triphyophyllum peltotum" .. .. 22·00 5·50

**324.** Edmond Halley and Computer Picture of Comet.

**1986.** Air. Appearance of Halley's Comet. Multicoloured.
874. 125 f. Type **324** .. .. 85 25
875. 155 f. Sir William Herschel and Uranus .. .. 1·00 30
876. 190 f. Space telescope and comet .. .. .. 1·25 40
877. 350 f. "MS T-5" space probe and comet .. 2·50 85
878. 440 f. "Skylab" and Kohoutek's comet .. 2·75 1·00

**325.** "Millettia takou". **326.** Vase from We.

**1986.** Plants. Multicoloured.
879. 40 f. "Omphalocarpum elatum" .. .. .. 30 15
880. 50 f. "Momordica charantia" .. .. 35 15
881. 125 f. Type **325** .. .. 85 40
882. 200 f. "Costus afer" .. 1·40 65

**1986.** Traditional Kitchenware and Tools. Multicoloured.
883. 20 f. Type **326** .. .. 15 10
884. 30 f. Baoule vase .. .. 20 10
885. 90 f. Baoule dish .. .. 60 20
886. 125 f. Dan knife (vert.) .. 90 30
887. 440 f. Baoule pottery jug (vert.) .. .. .. 3·25 1·25

**327.** Institute Building. **328.** Pres. Houphouet-Boigny.

**1986.** 10th Anniv. of Institute for Higher Technical and Professional Education.
888. **327.** 125 f. multicoloured .. 85 30

**1986.**
889. **328.** 5 f. brown, mve. & red 10 10
890. 10 f. brown, bl. & grn. 10 10
891. 20 f. light brown, brown and red .. 15 10
892. 25 f. brown, mauve & blue .. .. 15 10
893. 30 f. light brown, brown and red .. 20 10
894. 40 f. brn., orge. & grn. 25 10
895. 60 f. brn., pur. & red 30 15
896. 90 f. brown, red and purple .. .. 55 15
897. 125 f. brown, red and purple .. .. 65 20
898. 155 f. brown, blue and lilac .. .. .. 85 35

**329.** Cable Ship "Stephan", 1910.

**1986.** Stamp Day.
899. **329.** 125 f. multicoloured .. 1·00 55

**330.** Footballers.

**1986.** Air. World Cup Football Championship, Mexico.
900. **330.** 90 f. multicoloured .. 60 20
901. – 125 f. multicoloured .. 85 25
902. – 155 f. multicoloured .. 1·10 35
903. – 440 f. multicoloured .. 3·00 90
904. – 500 f. multicoloured .. 3·25 1·10
DESIGNS: 125 f. to 500 f. Different football scenes.

**331.** Emblem. **333.** Sacred Tom-tom.

**332.** "Polypterus endlicheri".

**1986.** 25th Anniv. of National Youth and Sports Institute.
906. **331.** 125 f. green and orge. 85 30

**1986.** Fishes. Multicoloured.
907. 5 f. Type **332** .. .. 10 10
908. 125 f. "Synodontis punctifer" .. .. 90 45
909. 150 f. "Protopterus annectens" .. .. 1·10 55
910. 155 f. "Synodontis koensis" .. .. .. 1·25 55
911. 440 f. "Malapterurus electricus" .. .. 3·25 1·60

**1986.** Enthronement of King of the Agni. Multicoloured.
912. 50 f. Type **333** .. .. 35 20
913. 350 f. King being carried .. 2·25 1·40
914. 440 f. King and his Court 3·00 1·90

**334.** Baoule Village, Aoulo.

**1986.** Rural Dwellings (1st series). Mult.
915. 125 f. Type **334** .. .. 85 45
916. 155 f. Avikam village, Eva 1·10 65
917. 350 f. Lobi village, Soukala 2·50 1·40
See also Nos. 938/9, 990 and 1012.

**335.** Ivory Coast Arms. **336.** Rocky Coastline.

**1986.**
921. **335.** 50 f. red .. .. 30 10
924. 125 f. green .. .. 70 15
926. 155 f. red .. .. 95 20
927. 195 f. blue .. .. 1·10 30

**1986.** Coastal Landscapes. Multicoloured.
930. 125 f. Type **336** .. .. 1·00 55
931. 155 f. Sandy beach .. 1·40 85

**337.** Fishery Lake. **338.** Pres. Houphouet-Boigny, Rainbow and Dove.

**1986.** Oceanographic Research Centre. Multicoloured.
932. 125 f. Type **337** .. .. 85 45
933. 155 f. Fishermen hauling in net .. .. .. 1·10 65

**1986.** International Peace Year.
934. **338.** 155 f. multicoloured .. 1·00 55

**339.** Bull.

**1986.** Research and Development. Mult.
935. 125 f. Type **339** .. .. 1·10 65
936. 155 f. Rice (IDSA 6) .. 1·10 65

**340.** Pres. Houphouet-Boigny and Symbols of Development.

**1986.** 26th Anniv. of Independence.
937. **340.** 155 f. multicoloured .. 1·10 55

**341.** Guesseple Dan Village.

**1987.** Rural Dwellings (2nd series). Mult.
938. 190 f. Type **341** .. .. 1·40 90
939. 550 f. M'Bagui Senoufo village .. .. .. 4·00 2·25

**342.** Postman, 1918. **343.** Elephant and Cockerel.

**1987.** Stamp Day.
940. **342.** 155 f. multicoloured .. 1·10 65

**1987.** 25th Anniv. of French–Ivory Coast Cultural Friendship. Jean Mermoz College. Multicoloured.
941. 40 f. Type **343** .. .. 30 15
942. 155 f. Children's faces in dove .. .. .. 1·10 55

**344.** Child running to Adult.

**1987.** World Red Cross Day.
943. **344.** 195 f. + 5 f. mult. .. 1·50 1·40

**345.** "Soling" Class Yachts.

**1987.** Air. Olympic Games, Seoul (1988) (1st issue). Sailing Multicoloured.
944. 155 f. Type **345** .. .. 1·10 50
945. 195 f. Windsurfers .. .. 1·40 45
946. 250 f. "470" class yachts .. 1·60 55
947. 550 f. Windsurfer .. .. 4·00 1·25
See also Nos. 959/62.

**346.** "Excavations" (Krah N'Guessan). **347.** Airplane and Van.

**1987.** Paintings. Multicoloured.
949. 195 f. Type **346** .. .. 1·40 90
950. 500 f. "Ceremonial Cortege" (Santoni Gerard) .. .. .. 3·25 2·25

**1987.** World Post Day. International Express Post.
951. **347.** 155 f. multicoloured .. 1·10 80
952. 195 f. multicoloured .. 1·40 90

**348.** Map and Forms of Communication.

**1987.** 100 Years of International Mail and Communications Exchanges.
953. **348.** 155 f. multicoloured .. 1·10 65

**349.** Tower Block reflecting Symbols of Progress **350.** Baby in Aloe Plant on Map.

**1987.** 27th Anniv. of Independence.
954. **349.** 155 f. multicoloured .. 1·10 65

**1988.** Lions International. "For the Life of a Child".
955. **350.** 155 f. multicoloured .. 1·10 65

**351.** Bereby Post Office, 1900 **352.** Heart.

**1988.** Stamp Day.
956. **351.** 155 f. multicoloured .. 1·00 55

**1988.** 15th Francophone Cardiological Congress, Abidjan.
957. **352.** 195 f. red and black .. 1·60 1·10

**353.** Man working Soil.

**1988.** 10th Anniv. of International Agricultural Development Fund.
958. **353.** 195 f. multicoloured .. 1·40 80

**354.** Gymnastics (rings).

**1988.** Air. Olympic Games, Seoul (2nd issue). Multicoloured.
959. 100 f. Type **354** .. .. 65 35
960. 155 f. Women's handball .. 1·00 45
961. 195 f. Boxing .. .. 1·40 45
962. 500 f. Gymnastics (parallel bar) .. .. .. 3·25 1·25

**355.** Stone Sculpture with Deep Nostrils. **356.** Healthy Youth and Drug Addict.

**1988.** Archaeological Research. Stone Sculptures from Niangoran-Bouah Collection.
964. **355.** 5 f. brown and flesh .. 10 10
965. – 10 f. brown and green 10 10
966. – 30 f. brown and green 20 10
967. – 155 f. brown & yell. .. 1·00 55
968. – 195 f. brown and green 1·40 80
DESIGNS: 10 f. Sculpture with full lips. 30 f. Sculpture with large nose. 155 f. Sculpture with triangular mouth. 195 f. Sculpture with sunken eyes.

**1988.** 1st International Drug Abuse and Illegal Trafficking Day.
969. **356.** 155 f. multicoloured .. 1·10 80

**357.** "The Couple" (K. J. Houra).

**1988.** Paintings by Local Artists. Mult.
970. 20 f. Type **357** .. .. 15 10
971. 30 f. "The Canary of Gentleness" (Monne Bou) (horiz.) .. .. 20 10
972. 150 f. "The Eternal Dancer" (Monne Bou) .. 1·00 55
973. 155 f. "The Termite Hill" (Mathilde Moro) .. 1·00 55
974. 195 f. "The Sun of Independence" (Michel Kodjo) .. .. .. 1·25 70

**358.** Emblem.

**1988.** 25th Anniv. of Organization of African Unity.
975. **358.** 195 f.+5 f. mult. .. 1·40 1·25

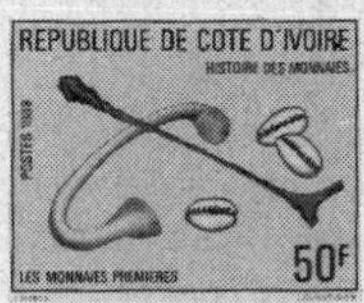


**360** Emblem **361** Marie Therese Houphouet Boigny and Emblem

**1988.** 28th Anniv of Independence. Forestry Year. Multicoloured.
977 40 f. Type **360** .. .. 30 20
978 155 f. "To each his tree" .. 1·10 65
979 155 f. "Stop fires" .. 1·10 65

**1988.** 1st Anniv of N'Daya International.
980 **361** 195 f.+5 f. mult .. 1·40 1·25

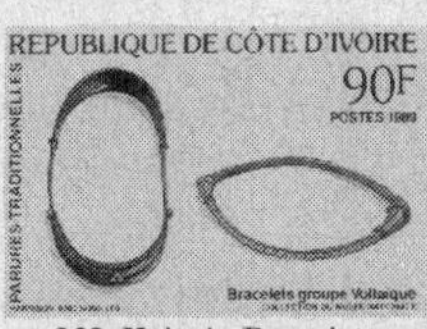


**362** Money Cowries and Bones.

**1989.** History of Money (1st series).
981 **362** 50 f. multicoloured .. 70 30
982 – 195 f. black, grey & bl 1·50 90
DESIGN: 195 f. Bank of Senegal notes.
See also Nos. 1004/5, 1019/21 and 1053.

**363** Voltaic Bracelets

**1989.** Traditional Jewellery. Multicoloured.
983 90 f. Type **363** .. .. 70 45
984 155 f. Dan ankle bracelets 1·25 90

**364** Stamp used as Money **365** "Old Man and Child"

**1989.** Stamp Day.
985 **364** 155 f. multicoloured .. 1·25 85

**1989.** Carvings by Christian Lattier. Mult.
986 40 f. Type **365** .. .. 30 20
987 155 f. "Saxophone Player" 1·10 55
988 550 f. "Panther" (horiz) .. 3·50 2·00

**366** Map and Tractor

**1989.** 30th Anniv of Council of Unity.
989 **366** 75 f. multicoloured .. 50 30

**367** Sirikukube Dan

**1989.** Rural Dwellings (3rd series).
990 **367** 155 f. multicoloured .. 1·10 65

**368** Congress Venue and Pres. Houphouet-Boigny

**1989.** International Peace Congress, Yamoussoukro.
991 **368** 195 f. multicoloured .. 1·40 80

**369** Map and King holding Court

**1989.** Anniversaries. Multicoloured.
992 200 f. Type **369** (279th anniv of accession of King Sekou Watara of Kong) .. .. .. 1·50 1·00
993 200 f. Bastille and detail of Declaration of Rights of Man (bicentenary of French Revolution) .. 1·50 1·00

**370** Nile Monitor

**1989.** Reptiles. Multicoloured.
994 25 f. Type **370** .. .. 15 10
995 100 f. Nile crocodile .. 70 50

**371** Globe and Emblem

**1989.** World Post Day.
996 **371** 195 f. multicoloured .. 1·40 65

**372** Telephone Kiosks and Mail Boxes

**1989.** 30th Anniv of West African Posts and Telecommunications Association.
997 **372** 155 f. multicoloured .. 1·10 65

**373** Milan **374** Crowd and Handclasp

**1989.** Air. World Cup Football Championship (1990) Preliminary Rounds. Multicoloured.

998 195 f. Type **373** .. .. 1·40 45
999 300 f. Genoa .. .. 2·00 65
1000 450 f. Turin .. .. 2·75 1·00
1001 550 f. Bologna .. .. 3·50 1·25

**1989.** 29th Anniv of Independence.

1002 **374** 155 f. multicoloured .. 1·00 55

**375** Emblem

**376** West African Bank 25 f. Banknote

**1990.** 10th Anniv of Pan-African Postal Union.

1003 **375** 155 f. multicoloured .. 1·00 55

**1990.** History of Money (2nd series).

1004 **376** 155 f. black and green 1·00 55
1005 – 195 f. black & orange 1·50 85

DESIGN: 195 f. Banknotes, 1917–44.

See also Nos. 1019/21 and 1053.

**377** "Afrique" (steam packet)

**1990.** Stamp Day.

1006 **377** 155 f. multicoloured .. 1·50 75

**378** Envelopes on Map

**1990.** 20th Anniv of Multinational Postal Training School, Abidjan.

1007 **378** 155 f. multicoloured .. 1·10 55

**379** Footballers

**1990.** Air. World Cup Football Championship, Italy. Designs showing match scenes. Mult.

1008 155 f. Type **379** .. .. 1·00 35
1009 195 f. Brazil v. West Germany .. .. 1·25 45
1010 500 f. England v. Russia 3·25 1·10
1011 600 f. England v. Netherlands .. 4·25 1·40

**1990.** Rural Dwellings (4th series). As T **367**. Multicoloured.

1012 155 f. Malinke village .. 1·00 45

**380** Teacher writing Letters on Blackboard

**1990.** International Literacy Year.

1013 **380** 195 f. multicoloured .. 1·40 65

**381** Cathedral

**1990.** Consecration of Our Lady of Peace Cathedral, Yamoussoukro. Multicoloured.

1014 155 f. Type **381** .. 1·00 55
1015 195 f. Aerial view .. 1·40 80

**382** Pres. Houphouet-Boigny and Pope

**1990.** 3rd Visit of Pope John Paul II.

1016 **382** 500 f. multicoloured .. 3·25 1·90

**383** Postman delivering to Village

**385** Communications

**384** Modern Building and Road Network

**1990.** World Stamp Day.

1017 **383** 195 f. multicoloured .. 1·40 80

**1990.** 30th Anniv of Independence.

1018 **384** 155 f. multicoloured .. 1·00 55

**1991.** History of Money (3rd series). As T **376**.

1019 40 f. black and yellow .. 30 15
1020 155 f. black and green .. 1·00 65
1021 195 f. black and mauve .. 1·25 85

DESIGNS: 40, 155 f. West African Bank 100 f. and 5 f. notes, 1942; 195 f. Issuing Institute for French West Africa and Togo 50 f. and 500 f. notes.

**1991.** Stamp Day.

1022 **385** 150 f. multicoloured .. 1·00 35

**386** Suzanne Lenglen

**1991.** Centenary of French Open Tennis Championships. Tennis players. Mult.

1023 200 f. Type **386** .. .. 1·40 1·10
1024 200 f. Helen Wills Moody 1·40 1·10
1025 200 f. Simone Mathieu .. 1·40 1·10
1026 200 f. Maureen Connolly 1·40 1·10
1027 200 f. Francoise Durr .. 1·40 1·10
1028 200 f. Margaret Court .. 1·40 1·10
1029 200 f. Chris Evert .. 1·40 1·10
1030 200 f. Martina Navratilova 1·40 1·10
1031 200 f. Steffi Graf .. 1·40 1·10
1032 200 f. Henri Cochet .. 1·40 1·10
1033 200 f. Rene Lacoste .. 1·40 1·10
1034 200 f. Jean Borotra .. 1·40 1·10
1035 200 f. Donald Budge .. 1·40 1·10
1036 200 f. Marcel Bernard .. 1·40 1·10
1037 200 f. Ken Rosewall .. 1·40 1·10
1038 200 f. Rod Laver .. 1·40 1·10
1039 200 f. Bjorn Borg .. 1·40 1·10
1040 200 f. Yannick Noah .. 1·40 1·10

**387** "Europe"

**1991.** Steam Packets. Multicoloured.

1041 50 f. Type **387** .. .. 35 20
1042 550 f. "Asie" .. .. 3·50 2·25

**1991.** Various stamps surch.

1043 – 150 f. on 155 f. mult (987) .. 1·00 35
1044 **367** 150 f. on 155 f. multicoloured .. 1·00 35
1045 – 150 f. on 155 f. blk and green (1020) 1·10 45
1046 – 200 f. on 195 f. blk & mauve (1021) 1·40 55

**389** Post and Savings Society's Emblem and Letter-box

**390** We Drum

**1991.** World Post Day. Multicoloured.

1047 50 f. Type **389** .. .. 35 20
1048 100 f. S.I.P.E. emblem and globe .. .. 65 35

**1991.** Drums.

1049 **390** 5 f. purple and lilac .. 10 10
1050 – 25 f. red and pink .. 15 10
1051 – 150 f. green & turq .. 1·10 80
1052 – 200 f. green and brown 1·40 1·00

DESIGNS: 25 f. Krou drum, Soubre; 150 f. Nafana drum, Sinematiau; 200 f. Akye drum, Alepe.

**1991.** History of Money (4th series). As T **376**.

1053 100 f. black and mauve .. 65 45

DESIGN: 100 f. French West Africa and Togo banknotes.

**391** Government Buildings

**1991.** 31st Anniv of Independence.

1054 **391** 150 f. multicoloured .. 1·00 45

**392** Orchid

**394** African Civet

**393** Footballer and Cup

**1991.** Orchids.

1055 **392** 150 f. mve, grn & blk 1·00 35
1056 – 200 f. red, emerald and green .. .. 1·25 45

DESIGNS—HORIZ. 200 f. Different orchid.

**1992.** Ivory Coast Victory in African Nations Football Cup Championship, Senegal. Mult.

1057 20 f. Type **393** .. .. 20 15
1058 150 f. Elephants supporting cup with their trunks (vert) .. .. 1·10 95

**1992.** Animals in Abidjan Zoo.

1059 **394** 5 f. brown, red & grn 10 10
1060 – 40 f. brn, grn & orge 30 15
1061 – 150 f. brn, grn & red 1·00 55
1062 – 500 f. brn, grn & ochre 3·25 2·25

DESIGNS: 40 f. African palm civet; 150 f. Bongo; 500 f. Leopard.

**395** World Map

**1992.** World Post Day.

1063 **395** 150 f. blue and black 1·00 55

**396** 1892 "Tablet" and 1962 Postal Centenary Stamps

**1992.** Stamp Day. Centenary of First Ivory Coast Stamps. Multicoloured.

1064 150 f. Type **396** .. .. 1·00 65
1065 150 f. 1961 Independence and 1991 World Post Day stamps .. .. 1·00 65

**397** Tomb Entrance

**1992.** Tourism. Funerary Monuments.

1067 **397** 5 f. red, green & blue 10 10
1068 – 50 f. brown, grn & bl 25 15
1069 – 150 f. brown, bl & grn 70 35
1070 – 400 f. green, bl & red 1·90 95

DESIGNS (tombs): 50 f. Angels, lions and figures; 150 f. Drummer, angel, sentry and animals; 400 f. Angels, figures and tree.

**398** Dove, Flag and Head of Statue of Liberty

**400** Emblem and Map

**399** Runners and Flags

**1992.** 32nd Anniv of Independence. Mult.

1071 30 f. Type **398** .. .. 20 10
1072 150 f. Crowd waving flags, Statue of Liberty and map .. .. .. 70 35

**1992.** International Marathon. Multicoloured.
1073 150 f. Type **399** .. .. 70 35
1074 200 f. Runners and landmarks .. .. 1·00 50

**1992.** 1st Anniv of Ity Gold Mine.
1075 **400** 200 f. multicoloured .. 1·00 50

**401** Girl with Stockbook and Collectors swapping Stamp

**402** "Argemone mexicana"

**1993.** Stamp Day. Youth Philately. Mult.
1076 50 f. Type **401** .. .. 25 15
1077 50 f. Girl pointing at stamps .. .. 25 15
1078 150 f. Boy perusing album and girls viewing exhibition display .. 70 35

**1993.** Medicinal Plants. Multicoloured.
1079 5 f. Type **402** .. .. 10 10
1080 20 f. "Hibiscus esculentus" .. 10 10
1081 200 f. "Cassia alata" .. 90 45

**403** Presidential Decree establishing Colony

**404** "Calyptrochilum emarginatum"

**1993.** Centenary of Ivory Coast.
1082 **403** 25 f. black and green 10 10
1083 – 100 f. blue and black 45 25
1084 – 500 f. black and brown 2·25 1·25
DESIGNS: 100 f. Louis Binger (first Governor) and Felix Houphouet-Boigny (President); 500 f. Factory.

**1993.** Orchids. Multicoloured.
1085 10 f. Type **404** .. .. 10 10
1086 50 f. "Plectrelminthus caudathus" .. .. 25 15
1087 150 f. "Eulophia guineensis" .. .. 70 35

**405** Heading Ball

**407** Abstract Design

**406** 19th-century Map of Ivory Coast

**1993.** World Cup Football Championship, U.S.A. (1994). Multicoloured.
1088 150 f. Type **405** .. .. 70 35
1089 200 f. Players jumping .. 95 50
1090 300 f. Player dribbling ball past opponent .. 1·40 70
1091 400 f. Ball ricocheting off players .. .. 1·90 95

**1993.** World Post Day.
1092 **406** 30 f. red, black & blue 15 10
1093 – 200 f. multicoloured .. 95 50
DESIGN: 200 f. Bouake post office.

**1993.** African Plastic Arts Biennale, Abidjan.
1094 **407** 200 f. multicoloured .. 90 45

**408** Map of Mining Centre

**1993.** 33rd Anniv of Independence.
1095 **408** 200 f. multicoloured .. 90 45

**409** Boigny and Modern Developments

**1994.** Felix Houphouet Boigny (President, 1960–93) Commemoration. Multicoloured.
1096 150 f. Type **409** .. .. 35 20
1097 150 f. Boigny, tractor, ploughing with oxen and container ship .. 35 20
1098 150 f. Boigny and Our Lady of the Peace Cathedral, Yamoussoukro .. 35 20
1099 200 f. Type **409** .. .. 50 25
1100 200 f. As No. 1097 .. 50 25
1101 200 f. As No. 1098 .. 50 25

**410** Raoul Follereau and Globe

**1994.** 50th Anniv (1992) of World Anti-leprosy Campaign.
1103 **410** 150 f. multicoloured .. 35 20

**411** Globe, Satellites and Flags

**412** Country-woman with Basket on Back

**1994.** 1st Meeting of Regional African Satellite Communications Organization Board of Directors, Abidjan.
1104 **411** 150 f. multicoloured .. 35 20

**1994.** Multicoloured, colour of frame given.
1105 **412** 5 f. orange .. .. 10 10
1106 25 f. blue .. .. 10 10
1107 30 f. bistre .. .. 10 10
1108 40 f. green .. .. 10 10
1109 50 f. brown .. .. 15 10
1110 75 f. purple .. .. 20 10
1111 150 f. green .. .. 40 20
1112 180 f. purple .. .. 45 25
1115 280 f. grey .. .. 75 40
1116 300 f. violet .. .. 80 40

**413** "Christ"

**414** Modern Developments

**1994.** Stained Glass Windows by Pierre Fakhoury from Our Lady of Peace Cathedral, Yamoussoukro. Multicoloured.
1120 25 f. Type **413** .. .. 10 10
1121 150 f. "The Fisher of Men" .. .. .. 40 20
1122 200 f. "Madonna and Child" .. .. 50 25

**1994.** 34th Anniv of Independence. The Family.
1124 **414** 150 f. multicoloured .. 40 20

**415** Green Mamba

**1995.** Snakes. Multicoloured.
1125 10 f. Royal python .. 10 10
1126 20 f. Green bush snake .. 10 10
1127 100 f. Type **415** .. .. 25 15
1128 180 f. Common puff adder 45 25
1129 500 f. Rhinoceros viper .. 1·25 65

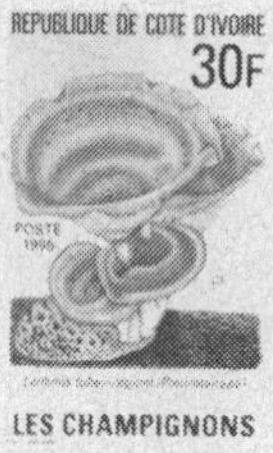

**416** Women collecting Water

**417** "Lentinus tuber-regium"

**1995.** 50th Anniversaries. Multicoloured.
1130 100 f. Type **416** (F.A.O.) 25 15
1131 280 f. Dove on globe (U.N.O.) .. .. 75 40

**1995.** Fungi. Multicoloured.
1132 30 f. Type **417** .. .. 20 10
1133 50 f. Chinese mushroom .. 30 15
1134 180 f. "Dictyophora indusiata" .. .. 90 45
1135 250 f. Termite mushroom 1·25 60

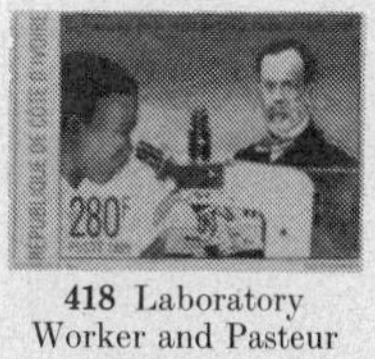

**418** Laboratory Worker and Pasteur

**1995.** Death Centenary of Louis Pasteur (chemist).
1136 **418** 280 f. multicoloured .. 70 35

**419** GSR Emblem on Butterfly Wing

**1995.** School Philatelic Clubs. Multicoloured.
1137 50 f. Type **419** .. .. 10 10
1138 180 f. LBP emblem on butterfly wing .. 45 25

**420** Palla

**1995.** Butterflies. Multicoloured.
1139 180 f. Type **420** .. .. 45 25
1140 280 f. Mocker swallowtail 70 35
1141 550 f. Emperor swallowtail 1·40 70

**421** Motor Vehicles and Handcart

**1996.** Abidjan Transport. Multicoloured.
1142 180 f. Type **421** .. .. 45 25
1143 280 f. Catching bus .. 70 35

**422** "Heterotis niloticus"

**1996.** Fishes. Multicoloured.
1144 50 f. Type **422** .. .. 10 10
1145 180 f. Western grunter .. 45 25
1146 700 f. "Schilbe mandibularis" .. 1·75 90

**423** "Cyrtorchis arcuata"

**424** Boxing

**1996.** Flowers. Multicoloured.
1147 40 f. Type **423** .. .. 10 10
1148 100 f. "Eulophia horsfalii" 25 15
1149 180 f. "Eulophidium maculatum" .. .. 45 25
1150 200 f. "Ansellia africana" 50 25

**1996.** Centenary of Modern Olympic Games and Olympic Games, Atlanta. Mult.
1151 200 f. Type **424** .. .. 50 25
1152 280 f. Running .. .. 70 35
1153 400 f. Long jumping .. 95 50
1154 500 f. National Olympic Committee arms and pictograms .. .. 1·25 65

## MILITARY FRANK STAMP

**MF 59.**

**1967.** No value indicated.
MF 1. **MF 59.** (–) multicoloured 1·90 1·90

## OFFICIAL STAMPS

**O 135.** Arms of Ivory Coast.

**1973.** No value indicated. Multicoloured. Background colours given.
O 422. **O 135.** (–) grn. & turq... 45 20
O 423. (–) yell. & orge. 75 35
O 424. (–) pink & mve. 1·00 55
O 425. (–) vio. & blue .. 2·75 1·10
Nos. O 422/25 represent the following face values. No. O 422, 35 f. No. O 423, 75 f. No. O 424, 100 f. No. O 425, 250 f.

PARCEL POST STAMPS

**1903.** Postage Due stamps of French Colonies optd.

(a) **Cote d'Ivoire COLIS Postaux.**

| | | | | |
|---|---|---|---|---|
| P18 | U | 50 c. purple | 22·00 | 22·00 |
| P20 | | 1 f. pink on buff | 22·00 | 22·00 |

(b) **Colis Postaux.**

| | | | | |
|---|---|---|---|---|
| P19 | U | 50 c. purple | £2000 | £2000 |
| P21 | | 1 f. pink on buff | £2000 | £2000 |

(c) **Cote d'Ivoire Colis Postaux.**

| | | | | |
|---|---|---|---|---|
| P22 | U | 50 c. purple | 75·00 | 75·00 |
| P23 | | 1 f. pink on buff | 42·00 | 42·00 |

**1903.** Postage Due stamps of French Colonies surch.

(a) **Cote d'Ivoire Colis Postaux** and new value.

| | | | | |
|---|---|---|---|---|
| P24 | U | 50 c. on 15 c. green | 6·50 | 6·50 |
| P25 | | 50 c. on 60 c. brown on buff | 27·00 | 23·00 |
| P26 | | 1 f. on 5 c. blue | 8·25 | 6·25 |
| P27 | | 1 f. on 10 c. brown | 11·00 | 11·00 |
| P30 | | 4 f. on 60 c. brown on buff | 85·00 | 55·00 |

(b) **Colis Postaux Cote d'Ivoire** and new value.

| | | | | |
|---|---|---|---|---|
| P35 | U | 4 f. on 5 c. blue | £140 | £160 |
| P28 | | 4 f. on 15 c. green | 85·00 | 55·00 |
| P29 | | 4 f. on 30 c. pink | 85·00 | 55·00 |
| P36 | | 8 f. on 15 c. green | £160 | £160 |

**1904.** Postage Due stamps of French Colonies optd.

(a) **C. P. Cote d'Ivoire.**

| | | | | |
|---|---|---|---|---|
| P31 | U | 50 c. purple | 22·00 | 22·00 |
| P32 | | 1 f. pink on buff | 20·00 | 22·00 |

(b) **Cote d'Ivoire C. P.**

| | | | | |
|---|---|---|---|---|
| P33 | U | 50 c. purple | 22·00 | 19·00 |
| P34 | | 1 f. pink on buff | 28·00 | 27·00 |

**1905.** Postage Due stamps of French Colonies surch **Cote d'Ivoire C. P.** and new value.

| | | | | |
|---|---|---|---|---|
| P39 | U | 2 f. on 1 f. pink on buff | £160 | £160 |
| P40 | | 4 f. on 1 f. pink on buff | £180 | £180 |
| P41 | | 8 f. on 1 f. pink on buff | £400 | £400 |

POSTAGE DUE STAMPS

**1906.** "Natives" key-type inscr. "COTE D'IVOIRE".

| | | | | |
|---|---|---|---|---|
| D38 | L | 5 c. green | 75 | 75 |
| D39 | | 10 c. purple | 75 | 60 |
| D40 | | 15 c. blue on blue | 75 | 75 |
| D41 | | 20 c. black on yellow | 75 | 75 |
| D42 | | 30 c. red on cream | 2·50 | 4·00 |
| D43 | | 50 c. violet | 2·00 | 3·00 |
| D44 | | 60 c. black on buff | 5·50 | 12·00 |
| D45 | | 1 f. black on pink | 19·00 | 22·00 |

**1915.** "Figure" key-type inscr. "COTE D'IVOIRE".

| | | | | |
|---|---|---|---|---|
| D 60. | M. | 5 c. green | 10 | 25 |
| D 61. | | 10 c. red | 10 | 25 |
| D 62. | | 15 c. grey | 10 | 25 |
| D 63. | | 20 c. brown | 15 | 25 |
| D 64. | | 30 c. blue | 20 | 35 |
| D 65. | | 50 c. black | 20 | 40 |
| D 66. | | 60 c. orange | 50 | 55 |
| D 67. | | 1 f. violet | 50 | 75 |

**1927.** Surch. in figures.

| | | | | |
|---|---|---|---|---|
| D 94. | M. | "2 F." on 1 f. purple | 40 | 85 |
| D 95. | | "3 F." on 1 f. brown | 40 | 85 |

D 21. Guere Mask.

D 30. Mask.

D 70 Baoule Weight.

**1960.** Values in black.

| | | | | |
|---|---|---|---|---|
| D 196. | D 21. | 1 f. violet | 15 | 15 |
| D 197. | | 2 f. green | 15 | 15 |
| D 198. | | 5 f. yellow | 30 | 30 |
| D 199. | | 10 f. blue | 55 | 55 |
| D 200. | | 20 f. mauve | 95 | 95 |

**1962.**

| | | | | |
|---|---|---|---|---|
| D 220. | D 30. | 1 f. blue and orange | 15 | 15 |
| D 221. | – | 2 f. red and black | 20 | 20 |
| D 222. | – | 5 f. green and red | 30 | 30 |
| D 223. | – | 10 f. purple and green | 55 | 55 |
| D 224. | – | 20 f. black and violet | 90 | 90 |

DESIGNS: 2 f. to 20 f. Various native masks from Bingerville Art School.

**1968.** Designs showing different types of weights.

| | | | | |
|---|---|---|---|---|
| D 309. | D 70. | 5 f. multicoloured | 15 | 15 |
| D 310. | – | 10 f. multicoloured | 20 | 20 |
| D 311. | – | 15 f. multicoloured | 50 | 50 |
| D 312. | – | 20 f. multicoloured | 80 | 80 |
| D 313. | – | 30 f. multicoloured | 1·10 | 1·10 |

D 111. "Animal" Weight.

**1972.** Gold Weights and Measures.

| | | | | |
|---|---|---|---|---|
| D 389. | D 111. | 20 f. brn. & vio. | 65 | 65 |
| D 390. | – | 40 f. brn. & red | 1·00 | 1·00 |
| D 391. | – | 50 f. pur. & orge. | 1·50 | 1·50 |
| D 392. | – | 100 f. brn. & grn. | 3·00 | 3·00 |

DESIGNS: 40 f. "Dagger". 50 f. "Bird". 100 f. "Triangle".

## JAPAN Pt. 18

An empire of E. Asia, consisting of numerous islands.

1871. 100 mon = 1 sen.
1872. 10 rin = 1 sen. 100 sen = 1 yen.

1. (48 mon.)

**1871.** Imperf.

| | | | | |
|---|---|---|---|---|
| 1 | 1 | 48 m. brown | £180 | £225 |
| 3 | | 100 m. blue | £200 | £180 |
| 5 | | 200 m. red | £350 | £225 |
| 15b | | 500 m. green | £400 | £400 |

**1872.** Perf.

| | | | | |
|---|---|---|---|---|
| 17. | 1. | ½ s. brown | 80·00 | £125 |
| 19. | | 1 s. blue | £170 | £160 |
| 21. | | 2 s. red | £350 | £275 |
| 22. | | 5 s. green | £375 | £425 |

5. 12. 13. Bean Goose.

**1872.** Various sizes. Design details differ.

| | | | | |
|---|---|---|---|---|
| 34 | 5 | ½ s. brown | 18·00 | 24·00 |
| 66 | | ½ s. grey | 16·00 | 15·00 |
| 35 | | 1 s. blue | 70·00 | 28·00 |
| 67 | | 1 s. brown | 30·00 | 13·00 |
| 36 | | 2 s. red | £110 | 30·00 |
| 74 | | 2 s. yellow | 70·00 | 12·00 |
| 46 | | 4 s. red | £100 | 30·00 |
| 68 | | 4 s. green | £110 | 18·00 |
| 75 | 12 | 5 s. green | £200 | 85·00 |
| 57 | | 6 s. brown | £110 | 40·00 |
| 69 | | 6 s. orange | 75·00 | 15·00 |
| 58 | 5 | 10 s. green | £110 | 45·00 |
| 70 | | 10 s. blue | £125 | 17·00 |
| 59 | | 20 s. violet | £200 | 70·00 |
| 71 | | 20 s. red | £100 | 12·00 |
| 60 | | 30 s. black | £250 | 70·00 |
| 72 | | 30 s. violet | £125 | 35·00 |

**1875.**

| | | | | |
|---|---|---|---|---|
| 61. | 13. | 12 s. red | £400 | £190 |
| 62. | – | 15 s. lilac (Pied Wagtail) | £325 | £160 |
| 63. | – | 45 s. red (Northern Goshawk) | £500 | £250 |

20. 21. 22. 23. 24.

**1876.**

| | | | | |
|---|---|---|---|---|
| 116 | 20 | 5 r. grey | 3·50 | 30 |
| 77 | | 1 s. black | 25·00 | 3·00 |
| 78 | | 1 s. brown | 12·00 | 1·00 |
| 113 | | 1 s. green | 5·50 | 25 |
| 79 | | 2 s. grey | 50·00 | 2·00 |
| 102 | | 2 s. violet | 24·00 | 1·50 |
| 114 | | 2 s. red | 7·50 | 10 |
| 95 | | 3 s. orange | 50·00 | 24·00 |
| 117 | | 3 s. red | 12·00 | 25 |
| 82a | | 4 s. blue | 32·00 | 2·75 |
| 103 | | 4 s. green | 40·00 | 1·75 |
| 118 | | 4 s. bistre | 8·50 | 30 |
| 83 | 21 | 5 s. brown | 50·00 | 18·00 |
| 115 | | 5 s. blue | 14·00 | 15 |
| 104 | | 6 s. orange | £150 | 70·00 |
| 105 | | 8 s. brown | 45·00 | 2·75 |
| 119 | | 8 s. violet | 15·00 | 90 |
| 86 | | 10 s. blue | 40·00 | 1·50 |
| 120 | | 10 s. brown | 16·00 | 30 |
| 87 | | 12 s. red | £200 | £160 |
| 88 | 22 | 15 s. green | £125 | 6·50 |
| 121 | | 15 s. violet | 45·00 | 40·00 |
| 89 | | 20 s. blue | £150 | 12·00 |
| 122 | | 20 s. orange | 55·00 | 1·40 |
| 123 | 23 | 25 s. green | 90·00 | 1·25 |
| 90 | 22 | 30 s. mauve | £200 | 75·00 |
| 111 | | 45 s. red | £500 | £500 |
| 112 | | 50 s. red | £160 | 10·00 |
| 124 | | 50 s. brown | 85·00 | 3·00 |
| 125 | 24 | 1 y. red | £120 | 2·50 |

25. Imperial Crest and Cranes.

**1894.** Emperor's Silver Wedding.

| | | | | |
|---|---|---|---|---|
| 126. | 25. | 2 s. red | 20·00 | 30 |
| 127. | | 5 s. blue | 25·00 | 4·00 |

26. Prince Kitashirakawa. 27. Prince Arisugawa.

**1896.** China War.

| | | | | |
|---|---|---|---|---|
| 128. | 26. | 2 s. red | 14·00 | 75 |
| 129. | 27. | 2 s. red | 14·00 | 75 |
| 130. | 26. | 5 s. blue | 35·00 | 2·00 |
| 131. | 27. | 5 s. blue | 35·00 | 2·00 |

Both 2 s. have an oval medallion, and both 5 s. a circular one.

28. 29. 30.

31. 32. Empress Jingu.

**1899.**

| | | | | |
|---|---|---|---|---|
| 132. | 28. | 5 r. grey | 5·50 | 1·00 |
| 133. | | ½ s. grey | 3·50 | 10 |
| 134. | | 1 s. brown | 4·50 | 10 |
| 135. | | 1½ s. blue | 15·00 | 85 |
| 136. | | 1½ s. violet | 8·00 | 15 |
| 137. | | 2 s. green | 6·00 | 10 |
| 138. | | 3 s. purple | 6·50 | 10 |
| 139. | | 3 s. red | 6·00 | 10 |
| 140. | | 4 s. red | 6·00 | 1·00 |
| 141. | | 5 s. yellow | 14·00 | 10 |
| 142. | 29. | 6 s. red | 30·00 | 3·00 |
| 143. | | 8 s. olive | 35·00 | 4·00 |
| 144. | | 10 s. blue | 10·00 | 15 |
| 145. | | 15 s. violet | 40·00 | 1·00 |
| 146. | | 20 s. orange | 32·00 | 10 |
| 147. | 30. | 25 s. green | 70·00 | 75 |
| 148. | | 50 s. brown | 65·00 | 80 |
| 149. | 31. | 1 y. red | 80·00 | 1·00 |
| 183. | 32. | 5 y. green | £475 | 4·50 |
| 184. | | 10 y. violet | £650 | 6·50 |

33. Rice Cakes used at Japanese Weddings.

**1900.** Prince Imperial Wedding.

| | | | | |
|---|---|---|---|---|
| 152. | 33. | 3 s. red | 25·00 | 30 |

34. Symbols of Korea and Japan 35. Gun and Japanese Flag.

**1905.** Amalgamation of Japanese and Korean Postal Services.

| | | | | |
|---|---|---|---|---|
| 153. | 34. | 3 s. red | 90·00 | 20·00 |

**1906.** Triumphal Military Review of Russo-Japanese War.

| | | | | |
|---|---|---|---|---|
| 154. | 35. | 1½ s. blue | 40·00 | 3·50 |
| 155. | | 3 s. red | 70·00 | 14·00 |

36. 37. 38.

**1914.**

| | | | | |
|---|---|---|---|---|
| 167 | 36 | ½ s. brown | 2·25 | 10 |
| 168 | | 1 s. orange | 3·25 | 10 |
| 232 | | 1½ s. blue | 3·00 | 10 |
| 170 | | 2 s. green | 5·50 | 10 |
| 298 | | 3 s. red | 1·50 | 20 |
| 172 | 37 | 4 s. red | 16·00 | 1·50 |
| 300 | | 5 s. violet | 7·50 | 10 |
| 174 | | 6 s. brown | 24·00 | 4·00 |
| 302 | | 7 s. orange | 12·00 | 15 |
| 175 | | 8 s. grey | 18·00 | 15·00 |
| 176 | | 10 s. blue | 12·00 | 10 |
| 236 | | 13 s. brown | 10·00 | 10 |
| 178 | | 20 s. red | 60·00 | 15 |
| 179 | | 25 s. olive | 18·00 | 50 |
| 180 | 38 | 30 s. brown | 22·00 | 45 |
| 238 | | 30 s. orange and green | 25·00 | 25 |
| 181 | | 50 s. brown | 30·00 | 25 |
| 239 | | 50 s. brown and blue | 15·00 | 30 |
| 309 | | 1 y. green and brown | 80·00 | 75 |

40. Ceremonial Cap. 42. Hall of Ceremony.

**1915.** Emperor's Coronation.

| | | | | |
|---|---|---|---|---|
| 185 | 40 | 1½ s. grey and red | 3·00 | 50 |
| 186 | – | 3 s. violet and brown | 3·50 | 65 |
| 187 | 42 | 4 s. red | 16·00 | 7·50 |
| 188 | | 10 s. blue | 38·00 | 15·00 |

DESIGN—As T 40: 3 s. Imperial throne.

43. Mandarin Duck. 44. "Kammuri" (ceremonial headband).

**1916.** Ivestiture of Prince Hirohito as Heir Apparent.

| | | | | |
|---|---|---|---|---|
| 189. | 43. | 1½ s. green, red & yellow | 4·00 | 85 |
| 190. | | 3 s. red and yellow | 5·00 | 1·00 |
| 191. | 44. | 10 s. blue | £800 | £300 |

45. Dove of Peace. 46. Dove of Peace.

**1919.** Restoration of Peace.

| | | | | |
|---|---|---|---|---|
| 192. | 45. | 1½ s. brown | 2·50 | 1·00 |
| 193. | 46. | 3 s. green | 3·50 | 1·25 |
| 194. | 45. | 4 s. red | 7·00 | 3·50 |
| 195. | 46. | 10 s. blue | 22·00 | 8·00 |

**1919.** Air. 1st Tokyo–Osaka Airmail Service. Optd with airplane.

| | | | | |
|---|---|---|---|---|
| 196 | 36 | 1½ s. blue | £275 | £100 |
| 197 | | 3 s. red | £425 | £250 |

48. 7th Century Censor. 49. Meiji Shrine.

**1920.** First Census.

| | | | | |
|---|---|---|---|---|
| 198. | 48. | 1½ s. purple | 8·00 | 4·25 |
| 199. | | 3 s. red | 9·00 | 4·25 |

**1920.** Dedication of Meiji (Emperor Mutsuhito) Shrine.

| | | | | |
|---|---|---|---|---|
| 200. | 49. | 1½ s. violet | 3·00 | 1·50 |
| 201. | | 3 s. red | 3·00 | 1·50 |

50. Postal and National Flags. 51. Dept. of Communications, Tokyo.

**1921.** 50th Anniv of Japanese Post.

| | | | | |
|---|---|---|---|---|
| 202 | 50 | 1½ s. red and green | 3·00 | 1·50 |
| 203 | 51 | 3 s. brown | 3·50 | 1·75 |
| 204 | 50 | 4 s. red and pink | 50·00 | 25·00 |
| 205 | 51 | 10 s. blue | £250 | 90·00 |

52. Warships "Katori" and "Kashima". 53. Mt. Fuji and Sika Deer.

**1921.** Return of Crown Prince from European Tour.

| | | | | |
|---|---|---|---|---|
| 206. | 52. | 1½ s. violet | 3·00 | 2·10 |
| 207. | | 3 s. olive | 3·50 | 2·25 |
| 208. | | 4 s. red | 42·00 | 35·00 |
| 209. | | 10 s. blue | 60·00 | 35·00 |

**1922.**

| | | | | |
|---|---|---|---|---|
| 293 | 53 | 4 s. green | 3·25 | 20 |
| 266 | | 4 s. orange | 12·00 | 30 |
| 211 | | 8 s. red | 20·00 | 8·00 |
| 267 | | 8 s. green | 20·00 | 15 |
| 303 | | 8 s. bistre | 14·00 | 75 |
| 305 | | 20 s. blue | 16·00 | 60 |
| 268 | | 20 s. purple | 65·00 | 30 |

54. Mt. Niitaka. 55.

56. 58. Empress Jingu.

**1923.** Crown Prince's visit to Taiwan.

| | | | | |
|---|---|---|---|---|
| 213. | 54. | 1½ s. yellow | 20·00 | 18·00 |
| 214. | | 3 s. violet | 25·00 | 8·00 |

**1923.** Imperf.

| | | | | |
|---|---|---|---|---|
| 215. | 55. | ½ s. grey | 3·00 | 2·75 |
| 216. | | 1½ s. blue | 5·00 | 60 |
| 217. | | 2 s. brown | 5·00 | 60 |
| 218. | | 3 s. red | 2·50 | 50 |
| 219. | | 4 s. green | 30·00 | 15·00 |
| 220. | | 5 s. violet | 14·00 | 60 |
| 221. | | 8 s. red | 45·00 | 35·00 |
| 222. | 56. | 10 s. brown | 24·00 | 50 |
| 223. | | 20 s. blue | 30·00 | 1·00 |

**1924.**

| | | | | |
|---|---|---|---|---|
| 224. | 58. | 5 y. green | £225 | 3·50 |
| 225. | | 10 y. violet | £425 | 2·75 |

59. Cranes. 60. Phoenix.

**1925.** Imperial Silver Wedding.

| | | | | |
|---|---|---|---|---|
| 226 | 59 | 1½ s. purple | 2·25 | 1·40 |
| 227a | 60 | 3 s. brown and silver | 3·00 | 3·00 |
| 228 | 59 | 8 s. red | 25·00 | 15·00 |
| 229b | 60 | 20 s. green and silver | 65·00 | 50·00 |

61a. Yomei Gate, Tosho Shrine, Nikko.

**1926.**

| | | | | |
|---|---|---|---|---|
| 241. | – | 2 s. green | 2·40 | 10 |
| 242. | 61a. | 6 s. red | 12·00 | 25 |
| 243. | – | 10 s. blue | 10·00 | 10 |
| 304. | – | 10 s. red | 10·00 | 15 |

DESIGNS: 2 s. Mt. Fuji. 10 s. Nagoya Castle.

62. Baron Maeshima. 63. Globe.

**1927.** 50th Anniv of Membership of U.P.U.

| | | | | |
|---|---|---|---|---|
| 244. | 62. | 1½ s. purple | 2·75 | 1·75 |
| 245. | | 3 s. olive | 2·75 | 1·75 |
| 246. | 63. | 6 s. red | 85·00 | 60·00 |
| 247. | | 10 s. blue | 95·00 | 50·00 |

64. Phoenix. 65. Ceremonial Shrines.

**1928.** Emperor's Enthronement.

| | | | | |
|---|---|---|---|---|
| 248. | 64. | 1½ s. green on yellow | 1·00 | 50 |
| 249. | 65. | 3 s. purple on yellow | 1·00 | 50 |
| 250. | 64. | 6 s. red on yellow | 3·75 | 3·00 |
| 251. | 65. | 10 s. blue on yellow | 5·00 | 3·75 |

66. Shrine of Ise. 67. Nakajima-built Fokker F.VIIb/3m over Lake Ashi, Hakone.

**1929.** 58th Vicennial Removal of Shrine of Ise.

| | | | | |
|---|---|---|---|---|
| 255 | 66 | 1½ s. violet | 2·00 | 1·50 |
| 256 | | 3 s. red | 2·75 | 1·50 |

**1929.** Air.

| No. | Type | Description | Unused | Used |
|---|---|---|---|---|
| 257 | **67** | 8½ s. brown | 50·00 | 40·00 |
| 258 | | 9½ s. red | 15·00 | 12·00 |
| 259 | | 16½ s. green | 15·00 | 14·00 |
| 260 | | 18 s. blue | 16·00 | 8·00 |
| 261 | | 33 s. black | 35·00 | 5·00 |

**68.** Map of Japan. **69.** Meiji Shrine.

**1930.** 3rd Census.

| No. | Type | Description | Unused | Used |
|---|---|---|---|---|
| 262. | **68.** | 1½ s. purple | 2·75 | 1·25 |
| 263. | | 3 s. red | 3·00 | 1·25 |

Although Type **68** is inscr. "Second Census", this was actually the third census.

**1930.** 10th Anniv. of Meiji Shrine Dedication.

| No. | Type | Description | Unused | Used |
|---|---|---|---|---|
| 264. | **69.** | 1½ s. green | 2·00 | 1·50 |
| 265. | | 3 s. orange | 2·75 | 1·50 |

**70.** Insignia of Red Cross Society.

Design—horiz. 3 s., 10 s. Red Cross Society Buildings, Tokyo.

**1934.** 15th Int. Red Cross Conf., Tokyo.

| No. | Type | Description | Unused | Used |
|---|---|---|---|---|
| 272. | **70.** | 1½ s. green | 2·50 | 1·40 |
| 273. | – | 3 s. violet | 2·75 | 1·90 |
| 274. | **70.** | 6 s. red | 10·00 | 7·00 |
| 275. | – | 10 s. blue | 14·00 | 10·00 |

**72.** Cruiser "Hiyei" and Pagoda, Liaoyang.

**73.** Akasaka Palace, Tokyo.

**1935.** Visit of Emperor of Manchukuo.

| No. | Type | Description | Unused | Used |
|---|---|---|---|---|
| 276. | **72.** | 1½ s. green | 2·50 | 1·60 |
| 277. | **73.** | 3 s. brown | 2·00 | 1·00 |
| 278. | **72.** | 6 s. red | 14·00 | 7·50 |
| 279. | **73.** | 10 s. blue | 10·00 | 7·00 |

**74.** Mt. Fuji (after Kazan Watanabe).

**75c.** Mt. Fuji from Mishima.

**1935.** New Year's Greetings.

| No. | Type | Description | Unused | Used |
|---|---|---|---|---|
| 280. | **74.** | 1½ s. red | 15·00 | 10 |

**1936.** Fuji-Hakone National Park.

| No. | Type | Description | Unused | Used |
|---|---|---|---|---|
| 281. | – | 1½ s. brown | 5·00 | 4·00 |
| 282. | – | 3 s. green | 7·00 | 6·00 |
| 283. | – | 6 s. red | 16·00 | 14·00 |
| 284. | **75c.** | 10 s. blue | 22·00 | 15·00 |

Designs: Mt. Fuji (1½ s.), from Lake Ashi (3 s.), from Lake Kawaguchi (6 s.).

**76.** Dove of Peace.

**77.** Shinto Shrine Port Arthur.

**1936.** 30 years Occupation of Kwantung.

| No. | Type | Description | Unused | Used |
|---|---|---|---|---|
| 285. | **76.** | 1½ s. violet | 12·00 | 12·00 |
| 286. | **77.** | 3 s. brown | 15·00 | 16·00 |
| 287. | – | 10 s. green | £180 | £225 |

Design—horiz. 10 s. Govt. House, Kwantung.

**78.** Imperial Diet.

**80.** Wedded Rocks, Futami Bay.

**1936.** Inauguration of New Houses of the Imperial Diet, Tokyo.

| No. | Type | Description | Unused | Used |
|---|---|---|---|---|
| 288. | **78.** | 1½ s. green | 1·50 | 1·25 |
| 289. | – | 3 s. purple | 1·50 | 1·50 |
| 290. | – | 6 s. red | 5·50 | 5·00 |
| 291. | **78.** | 10 s. blue | 12·00 | 4·50 |

Design: 3, 6 s. Grand Staircase.

**1936.** New Year's Greetings.

| No. | Type | Description | Unused | Used |
|---|---|---|---|---|
| 292 | **80** | 1½ s. red | 6·00 | 10 |

**82.** Goshuin-sen (16th-cent trading ship).

**83.** General Nogi.

**84.** Lake Taisho, Kamikochi.

**85.** Mitsubishi B5N1 and Map.

**86.** Kamatari Fujiwara.

**87.** Plum Tree.

**1937.** Imperf or perf (424), perf (others). Without gum (424), with or without gum (392, 394, 396), with gum (others).

| No. | Type | Description | Unused | Used |
|---|---|---|---|---|
| 313 | **82** | ½ s. violet | 1·50 | 80 |
| 314 | – | 1 s. brown | 2·00 | 50 |
| 392b | **83** | 2 s. red | 15 | 10 |
| 316 | – | 3 s. green | 75 | 10 |
| 394 | **83** | 3 s. brown | 75 | 20 |
| 317 | – | 4 s. green | 1·00 | 10 |
| 318 | **84** | 5 s. blue | 2·00 | 10 |
| 396 | – | 5 s. purple | 30 | 10 |
| 319 | – | 6 s. orange | 4·00 | 2·00 |
| 320 | – | 7 s. green | 75 | 20 |
| 398 | – | 7 s. red | 25 | 15 |
| 321 | – | 8 s. violet | 1·00 | 50 |
| 322 | – | 10 s. red | 6·00 | 10 |
| 323 | **85** | 12 s. blue | 60 | 60 |
| 324 | – | 14 s. red and brown | 1·00 | 30 |
| 325 | – | 20 s. blue | 1·00 | 10 |
| 326 | – | 25 s. lt brown & brown | 80 | 10 |
| 327 | – | 30 s. blue | 3·00 | 10 |
| 328 | – | 50 s. green and bistre | 2·00 | 10 |
| 329 | – | 1 y. lt brown & brown | 6·00 | 75 |
| 424 | **86** | 5 y. green | 5·50 | 60 |
| 331 | **87** | 10 y. purple | 20·00 | 1·50 |

Designs: 1 s. Rice harvesting. 3 s. Hydro-electric Power Station. 4, 5 s. (No. 396), 7 s. (No. 398), Admiral Togo. 6 s. Garambi Lighthouse, Taiwan. 7 s. (No. 320), Diamond Mountains, Korea. 8 s. Meiji Shrine. 10 s. Yomei Gate, Tosho Shrine, Nikko. 14 s. Inner Gate, Kasuga Shrine. 20 s. Mt. Fuji and cherry blossom. 25 s. Horyu Temple. 30 s. Torii, Itsukushima Shrine at Miyajima. 50 s. Temple of Golden Pavilion, Kyoto. 1 y. Great Buddha, Kamakura.

**88.** Nakajima-built Douglas DC-2 Airliner.

**89.** New Year's Emblem.

**1937.** Aerodrome Fund.

| No. | Type | Description | Unused | Used |
|---|---|---|---|---|
| 336 | **88** | 2 s.+2 s. red | 2·25 | 1·25 |
| 337 | | 3 s.+2 s. violet | 2·25 | 1·50 |
| 338 | | 4 s.+2 s. green | 3·25 | 1·25 |

**1937.** New Year's Greetings.

| No. | Type | Description | Unused | Used |
|---|---|---|---|---|
| 339. | **89.** | 2 s. red | 12·00 | 10 |

**90.** Nantai Volcano.

**92.** Shinkyo Bridge.

**93.** Hiuchi Volcano.

**91.** Kegon Falls

**1938.** Nikko National Park.

| No. | Type | Description | Unused | Used |
|---|---|---|---|---|
| 340 | **90** | 2 s. orange | 75 | 55 |
| 341 | **91** | 4 s. green | 75 | 55 |
| 342 | **92** | 10 s. red | 7·00 | 4·00 |
| 343 | **93** | 20 s. blue | 8·00 | 5·00 |

**94.** Daisen Volcano and Meadow.

**95.** Yashima Plateau and Estuary.

**96.** Abuto Kwannon Shrine.

**97.** Tomo Bay.

**1939.** Daisen and Setonaikai National Parks.

| No. | Type | Description | Unused | Used |
|---|---|---|---|---|
| 345. | **94.** | 2 s. brown | 50 | 60 |
| 346. | **95.** | 4 s. green | 2·25 | 2·00 |
| 347. | **96.** | 10 s. red | 8·00 | 7·00 |
| 348. | **97.** | 20 s. blue | 8·00 | 6·00 |

**98.** Mt. Kuju and Village.

**99.** Naka Volcano.

**100.** Naka Crater.

**101.** Volcanic Cones of Mt. Aso.

**1939.** Aso National Park.

| No. | Type | Description | Unused | Used |
|---|---|---|---|---|
| 350. | **98.** | 2 s. brown | 60 | 70 |
| 351. | **99.** | 4 s. green | 3·25 | 3·25 |
| 352. | **100.** | 10 s. red | 26·00 | 18·00 |
| 353. | **101.** | 20 s. blue | 30·00 | 20·00 |

**102.** Globe.

Design: 4 s., 20 s. Count Tsunetami Sano.

**1939.** 75th Anniv. of Membership of International Red Cross Union.

| No. | Type | Description | Unused | Used |
|---|---|---|---|---|
| 355. | **102.** | 2 s. brown | 2·00 | 1·25 |
| 356. | – | 4 s. green | 2·25 | 1·40 |
| 357. | **102.** | 10 s. red | 12·00 | 8·50 |
| 358. | – | 20 s. blue | 14·00 | 8·50 |

**INDEX**

Countries can be quickly located by referring to the index at the end of this volume.

**104.** Golden Bird.

**105.** Mt. Takachiho.

**106.** Sake Jar and Trout.

**107.** Kashiwara Shrine.

**1940.** 2600th Anniv of Japanese Empire.

| No. | Type | Description | Unused | Used |
|---|---|---|---|---|
| 359 | **104** | 2 s. orange | 90 | 85 |
| 360 | **105** | 4 s. green | 45 | 40 |
| 361 | **106** | 10 s. red | 4·00 | 4·25 |
| 362 | **107** | 20 s. blue | 1·00 | 75 |

**108.** Mt. Hokuchin.

**109.** Mt. Asahi.

**110.** Sounkyo Gorge, Kobako.

**111.** Tokachi Range.

**1940.** Daisetsu-zan National Park.

| No. | Type | Description | Unused | Used |
|---|---|---|---|---|
| 363. | **108.** | 2 s. brown | 60 | 60 |
| 364. | **109.** | 4 s. green | 2·50 | 2·50 |
| 365. | **110.** | 10 s. red | 8·50 | 6·50 |
| 366. | **111.** | 20 s. blue | 11·00 | 5·00 |

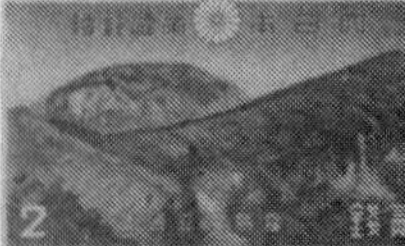

**112.** Mt. Shimmoe.

**113.** Takachiho Peak.

**114.** Kirishima Shrine.

**115.** Lake Roku-Kwannon.

**1940.** Kirishima National Park, Kyushu.

| No. | Type | Description | Unused | Used |
|---|---|---|---|---|
| 368. | **112.** | 2 s. brown | 60 | 60 |
| 369. | **113.** | 4 s. green | 1·00 | 1·00 |
| 370. | **114.** | 10 s. red | 7·50 | 5·00 |
| 371. | **115.** | 20 s. blue | 10·00 | 5·00 |

**116.** Ceremonial Shrine (after Y. Araka).

**117.** " Loyalty and Filial Piety ".

**1940.** 50th Anniv of Promulgation of Imperial Re-script on Education.
373. **116.** 2 s. violet .. .. 85 1·00
374. **117.** 4 s. green .. .. 1·25 1·40

**118.** Mt. Daiton.

**119.** Central Peak, Mt. Niitaka.

**120.** Buddhist Temple, Mt. Kwannon.

**121.** View of Mt. Niitaka.

**1941.** Daiton and Niitaka-Arisan National Parks.
375. **118.** 2 s. brown .. .. 80 60
376. **119.** 4 s. green .. .. 1·25 1·00
377. **120.** 10 s. red .. .. 5·00 3·00
378. **121.** 20 s. blue .. .. 6·00 2·75

**122.** Seisui Precipice, East Taiwan Coast.

**124.** Taroko Gorge, Taiwan.

**123.** Mt. Tsugitaka.

**125.** Mt. Taroko, Source of R. Takkiri.

**1941.** Tsugitaka and Taroko National Parks.
380. **122.** 2 s. brown .. .. 75 60
381. **123.** 4 s. green .. .. 1·25 1·00
382. **124.** 10 s. red .. .. 4·00 4·25
383. **125.** 20 s. blue .. .. 5·50 4·00

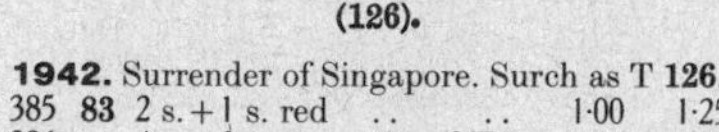

**+1**
**(126).**

**1942.** Surrender of Singapore. Surch as T **126**.
385 **83** 2 s.+1 s. red .. .. 1·00 1·25
386 – 4 s.+2 s. green (No. 317) 1·00 1·25

**127.** Kenkoku Shrine.

**129.** Orchids and Crest of Manchukuo.

**1942.** 10th Anniv. of Establishment of Manchukuo.
387. **127.** 2 s. brown .. .. 40 50
388. – 5 s. olive .. .. 60 90
389. **127.** 10 s. red .. .. 85 1·25
390. **129.** 20 s. blue .. .. 3·00 2·75
DESIGN—VERT. 5 s. Boys of Japan and Manchukuo.

**130.** Girl War-worker.

**135.** "The Enemy will Surrender".

**140.** Garambi Lighthouse, Taiwan.

**141.** Garambi Lighthouse, Taiwan.

**1942.** Imperf (418/19, 421), imperf or perf (400, 420), perf (others). With or without gum (398, 420), without gum (400, 418/19, 421), with gum (others).
391 **130** 1 s. brown .. .. 10 10
393 – 2 s. green .. .. 80 45
395 – 4 s. green .. .. 20 10
397 – 6 s. blue .. .. 60 60
399 – 10 s. red and pink .. 85 10
400 **135** 10 s. grey .. .. 7·50 8·00
418 10 s. blue .. .. 25·00
419 – 10 s. orange .. .. 30 10
401 – 15 s. blue .. .. 2·00 50
402 – 17 s. violet .. .. 60 25
420 – 20 s. blue .. .. 30 10
404 – 27 s. red .. .. 65 80
405 – 30 s. green .. .. 3·00 1·00
421 – 30 s. blue .. .. 2·00 40
406 **140** 40 s. purple .. .. 90 10
407 **141** 40 s. purple .. .. 2·00 1·00
DESIGNS: 2 s. Shipbuilding. 4 s. Hyuga Monument and Mt. Fuji. 6 s. War-worker, 10 s. (No. 399) Palms and map of Greater East Asia. 10 s. (No. 419), 20 s. Mt. Fuji. 15 s. Airman. 17 s., 27 s. Yasukuni Shrine. 30 s. 2) Myajima Shrine.

**142.** Steam Locomotive.

**143.** Tanks in action at Bataan.

**1942.** 70th Anniv. of First National Railway.
408. **142.** 5 s. green .. .. 4·00 6·00

**1942.** 1st Anniv. of Declaration of War.
409. **143.** 2 s.+1 s. brown .. 2·00 2·75
410. – 5 s.+2 s. blue .. 2·25 3·25
DESIGN: 5 s. Attack on Pearl Harbour.

**144.** Yasukuni Shrine.

**145.** Kwantung Shrine and Map of Kwantung Peninsula.

**1944.** 75th Anniv. of Yasukuni Shrine.
411. **144.** 7 s. green .. .. 85 1·00

**1944.** Dedication of Kwantung Shrine.
412. **145.** 3 s. brown .. .. 3·00 10·00
413. 7 s. grey .. .. 3·00 10·00

**146.** Sun and Cherry Blossom.

**149.** Torii of Yasukuni Shrine.

**1945.** Imperf or perf and with or without gum (422), imperf without gum (others).
415 **146** 3 s. red .. .. 35 40
416 – 5 s. green .. .. 40 20
422 – 50 s. brown .. .. 60 10
423 **149** 1 y. olive .. .. 1·50 85
DESIGNS: 5 s. Sunrise and Kawasaki Ki-61 Hien fighter. 50 s. Coal miners.

**150.** Pagoda of Horyu Temple, Nara.

**153.** Kiyomizu Temple, Kyoto.

**154.** Noh Mask.

**1946.** Imperf or perf (30 s., 50, 100 y.), imperf (others). With or without gum (30 s., 5, 50, 100 y.), without gum (others).
426 – 15 s. green .. .. 45 45
427 **150** 30 s. violet .. .. 75 10
428a – 1 y. blue .. .. 1·00 10
429 – 1 y. 30 bistre .. 5·00 1·60
430 – 1 y. 50 grey .. .. 3·00 50
431 **153** 2 y. red .. .. 2·50 10
432 – 5 y. mauve .. .. 7·50 25
433b **154** 50 y. brown .. .. 80·00 30
434a – 100 y. purple .. 80·00 40
DESIGNS: 15 s. Baron H. Maeshima. 1 y. Mt. Fuji, after Hokusai. 1 y. 30, Snow and white-fronted geese (after Hokusai). 1 y. 50, Kintai Bridge, Iwakuni. 5 y. Goldfish. 100 y. Plum tree.
For 30 s., 1 y. 20, 4 y. and 10 y. as Nos. 427, 429 and 434a but with Japanese characters reading in reverse order, see Nos. 441, 445/6 and 449.

**156.** Mediaeval Postman's Bell.

**157.** Baron Maeshima.

**1946.** 75th Anniv. of Govt. Postal Service.
436. **156.** 15 s. orange .. .. 4·00 3·00
437. **157.** 30 s. green .. .. 6·00 5·00
438. – 50 s. red .. .. 3·25 2·50
439. – 1 y. blue .. .. 4·50 4·50
DESIGNS—As Type **156**: 50 s. First Japanese Postage Stamp. 1 y. Symbols of communication.

**160.**

**161.** Baron Maeshima.

**163.** National Art.

**1947.** As issues of 1946 but with Japanese characters in reverse order and new designs. Imperf without gum (449), perf with gum (others).
441 **150** 30 s. violet .. .. 3·00 2·00
442 **160** 35 s. green .. .. 75 30
443 – 45 s. mauve .. .. 85 50
444 **161** 1 y. brown .. .. 3·25 40
445 **150** 1 y. 20 green .. .. 2·00 30
446 – 4 y. blue (as No. 429) 6·00 30
447 – 5 y. blue .. .. 8·00 10
448 **163** 10 y. violet .. .. 14·00 10
449 – 10 y. purple (as No. 434a) .. .. 28·00 70
DESIGNS—VERT. 45 s. Numeral. 5 y. Whaling.
For similar designs, but without the chrysanthemum emblem, see Nos. 467/70.

**MINIMUM PRICE**
The minimum price quoted is 10p which represents a handling charge rather than a basis for valuing common stamps. For further notes about prices see introductory pages.

**164.** Mother and Child.

**165.** Roses and Wistaria.

**1947.** Inaug. of New Constitution.
451. **164.** 50 s. red .. .. 60 40
452. **165.** 1 y. blue .. .. 70 40

**166.** National Products.

**167.** Lily of the Valley.

**1947.** Re-opening of Private Foreign Trade.
455. **166.** 1 y. 20 brown .. 3·00 1·25
456. 4 y. blue .. .. 5·00 1·50

**1947.** Relief of Ex-convicts Day.
458. **167.** 2 y. green .. .. 4·00 1·75

**169.** Hurdling.

**170.**

**1947.** 2nd National Athletic Meeting, Kanazawa. Each mauve.
460 1 y. 20 Type **169** .. .. 10·00 6·00
461 1 y. 20 Diving .. .. 10·00 6·00
462 1 y. 20 Throwing the discus 10·00 6·00
463 1 y. 20 Volleyball .. 10·00 6·00

**1947.** Community Chest.
465. **170.** 1 y. 20+80 s. red .. 75 85

**172.** Kiyomizu Temple, Kyoto.

**173.** National Art.

**1948.** Designs without chrysanthemum.
467. – 1 y. 50 blue .. .. 2·50 50
468. **172.** 2 y. red .. .. 8·00 10
469. – 3 y. 80 brown .. 8·00 6·50
470. **173.** 10 y. violet .. 12·00 10
DESIGNS: 1 y. 50, 3 y. 80, Numeral types.

**174.** Stylised Tree.

**176.** Boy and Girl reading.

**1948.** Encouragement of Afforestation.
474. **174.** 1 y. 20 green .. .. 80 60

**1948.** Re-organization of Educational System.
480. **176.** 1 y. 20 red .. .. 65 65

**177.** Horse Race.

**178.** Swimmer.

**1948.** 25th Anniv. of Japanese Horse Racing Laws.
481. **177.** 5 y. brown .. .. 2·25 85

**1948.** 3rd National Athletic Meeting, Yawata.
482. **178.** 5 y. blue .. .. 3·00 1·25

**179.** Distillery Towers.

**1948.** 10th Anniv. of Govt. Alcohol Monopoly.

483 **179** 5 y. brown .. .. 3·75 2·25

**180.** Nurse.  **181.** Varied Tit Feeding Young.

**1948.** Red Cross and Community Chest.

485. **180.** 5 y.+2 y. 50 red .. 8·00 5·00
486. **181.** 5 y.+2 y. 50 green 16·00 14·50

**182.** Farm Girl. **183.** Harpooning. **184.** Miner.

**185.** Girl plucking Tea. **186.** Girl Printer. **187.** Mill Girl.

**188.** Mt. Hodaka. **189.** Tree Planting.

**190.** Postman. **191.** Blast-Furnace. **192.** Locomotive Construction.

**1948.**

488 **182** 2 y. green & light green 2·00 10
489 **183** 3 y. turquoise .. 5·00 10
490 **184** 5 y. bistre .. .. 16·00 10
491 **185** 5 y. green .. .. 40·00 7·00
492 **186** 6 y. orange .. .. 7·00 10
493 **184** 8 y. brown .. .. 8·00 10
494 **187** 15 y. blue .. .. 3·00 10
495 **188** 16 y. blue .. .. 8·00 5·00
496 **189** 20 y. green .. .. 32·00 10
497 **190** 30 y. blue .. .. 36·00 10
506 **191** 100 y. red .. .. £400 40
507 **192** 500 y. blue .. .. £375 3·00

**193.** Baseball.

**1948.** 3rd National Athletic Meeting, Fukuoke.

509. **193.** 5 y. green .. .. 12·00 5·00
510. – 5 y green (bicycle race) 12·00 5·00
511. – 5 y. green (sprinter) .. 12·00 5·00
512. – 5 y. green (high jumper) 12·00 5·00

**194.** "Beauty Looking Back" (Moronobu Hishikawa). **195.** Girl playing with Shuttlecock.

**1948.** Philatelic Week.

514. **194.** 5 y. brown .. .. 60·00 40·00

**1948.** New Year's Greetings.

516. **195.** 2 y. red .. .. 3·75 2·25

**196.** Skater.  **197.** Ski Jumper.

**1949.** 4th National Athletic Meeting.

(a) Suwa City.

517. **196.** 5 y. violet .. .. 3·50 2·00

(b) Sapporo, Hokkaido.

518. **197.** 5 y. blue .. .. 4·00 2·00

**198.** "Koan Maru" (ferry) in Beppu Harbour. **199.** Exhibition Grounds.

**1949.**

519. **198.** 2 y. blue and red .. 2·00 1·25
520. 5 y. blue and green .. 5·50 1·50

**1949.** Foreign Trade Fair, Yokohama. Perf. or imperf.

521. **199.** 5 y. red .. .. 2·50 1·00

**200.** Seto Inland Sea.  **201.** Stylised Trees.

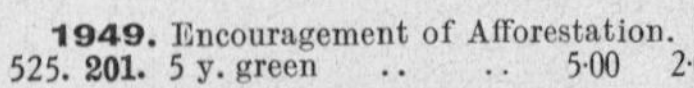

**1949.** Matsuyama, Okayama and Takamatsu Exhibitions.

522. **200.** 10 y. red (Matsuyama) 30·00 15·00
523. 10 y. pink (Okayama) 35·00 20·00
524. 10 y. clar. (Takamatsu) 50·00 25·00

**1949.** Encouragement of Afforestation.

525. **201.** 5 y. green .. .. 5·00 2·00

**202.** Shishi-Iwa (Lion Rock).

**203.** Mt. Omine.

**204.** Doro-Hatcho River Pool.

**205.** Hashikui-Iwa.

**1949.** Yoshino-Kumano National Park.

526. **202.** 2 y. brown .. .. 1·00 60
527. **203.** 5 y. green .. .. 3·25 1·00
528. **204.** 10 y. red .. .. 14·00 8·00
529. **205.** 16 y. blue .. .. 7·50 2·25

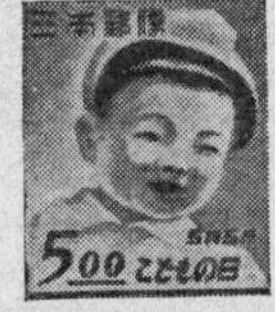

**206.** Boy.

**1949.** Children's Day.

531. **206.** 5 y. purple and buff .. 5·00 1·50

**208.** Observatory Tower.  **209.** Radio Mast, Pigeon and Globe.

**1949.** 75th Anniv. of Central Meteorological Observatory, Tokyo.

534. **208.** 8 y. green .. .. 3·50 1·40

**1949.** Establishment of Joint Ministries of Postal and Electrical Communications.

535. **209.** 8 y. blue .. .. 3·50 1·25

**210.** Park in Autumn.

**211.** Park in Spring.

**212.** Park in Summer.

**213.** Park in Winter.

**1949.** Fuji-Hakone National Park.

536. **210.** 2 y. brown .. .. 2·50 60
537. **211.** 8 y. green .. .. 3·00 1·00
538. **212.** 14 y. red .. .. 1·75 30
539. **213.** 24 y. blue .. .. 3·25 40

**214.** Woman holding Rose. **215.** Doves.

**1949.** Establishment of Memorial City at Hiroshima.

541. **214.** 8 y. brown .. .. 6·00 2·00

**1949.** Establishment of Int. Cultural City at Nagasaki.

542. **215.** 8 y. green .. .. 5·00 2·00

**216.** Swimmer.

**1949.** 4th National Athletic Meeting, Yokohama.

543 **216** 8 y. blue .. .. 4·00 1·25

**217.** Boy Scout. **218.** Symbolical of Writing and Printing.

**1949.** 1st National Scout Jamboree, Tokyo.

544. **217.** 8 y. brown .. .. 7·50 2·00

**1949.** Press Week.

545. **218.** 8 y. blue .. .. 4·50 2·00

**219.** Map of Japan and Letters. **220.** Globe and Forms of Transport.

**1949.** 75th Anniv. of U.P.U.

546. **219.** 2 y. green .. .. 2·75 1·50
547. **220.** 8 y. red .. .. 4·25 1·60
548. **219.** 14 y. red .. .. 9·50 4·00
549. **220.** 24 y. blue .. .. 16·00 9·25

**221.** Throwing the Javelin. **222.** Telescope.

**1949.** 4th National Athletic Meeting, Tokyo. Each brown.

551 8 y. Type **221** .. .. 4·00 1·50
552 8 y. Yachting .. .. 4·00 1·50
553 8 y. Relay racing .. 4·00 1·50
554 8 y. Tennis .. .. 4·00 1·50

**1949.** 50th Anniv. of Establishment of Latitude Observatory, Mizusawa.

555. **222.** 8 y. green .. .. 3·50 2·00

**223.** " Moon and Brent Geese " (after Hiroshige). **224.** Dr. H. Noguchi.

A B C D

E F G H I J K L M N O P Q R

**1949.** Postal Week.

| | | | | |
|---|---|---|---|---|
| 556. | **223.** | 8 y. violet .. .. | £130 | 60·00 |

**1949.** Various portraits as illustrated, in frame as T **224.**

| | | | | |
|---|---|---|---|---|
| 557 | A | 8 y. green .. .. | 10·00 | 1·00 |
| 558 | B | 8 y. green .. .. | 4·00 | 1·00 |
| 559 | C | 8 y. green .. .. | 4·00 | 1·00 |
| 560 | D | 8 y. green .. .. | 3·50 | 1·00 |
| 561 | E | 8 y. violet .. .. | 10·00 | 4·00 |
| 562 | F | 8 y. purple .. .. | 3·50 | 1·00 |
| 563 | G | 8 y. green .. .. | 8·00 | 2·00 |
| 564 | H | 8 y. violet .. .. | 8·00 | 2·00 |
| 565 | I | 8 y. red .. .. | 16·00 | 2·00 |
| 566 | J | 8 y. red .. .. | 30·00 | 2·50 |
| 567 | K | 8 y. brown .. .. | 15·00 | 2·25 |
| 568 | L | 8 y. blue .. .. | 9·00 | 2·25 |
| 569 | M | 10 y. green .. .. | 60·00 | 4·50 |
| 570 | N | 10 y. purple .. .. | 9·00 | 1·50 |
| 571 | O | 10 y. red .. .. | 4·00 | 1·40 |
| 572 | P | 10 y. grey .. .. | 7·00 | 1·40 |
| 573 | Q | 10 y. brown .. .. | 6·00 | 1·40 |
| 574 | R | 10 y. blue .. .. | 6·00 | 1·40 |

PORTRAITS: A, Hideyo Noguchi (bacteriologist). B, Y. Fukuzawa (educationist). C, Soseki Natsume (novelist). D, Shoyo Tsubouchi (dramatist). E, Danjuro Ichikawa (actor). F, Jo Niijima (religious leader). G, Hogai Kano (painter). H, Kanzo Uchimura (religious leader). I, Mme. Higuchi (author). J, Ogai Mori (doctor). K, S. Masaoka (poet). L, S. Hishida (painter). M, A. Nishi (scholar). N, K. Ume (lawyer). O, H. Kimura (astrophysicist). P, I. Nitobe (statesman). Q, T. Torada (physicist). R, Tenshin Okakura (writer).

**225.** Japanese Pheasant and Pampas Grass.

**226.** Tiger (after Maruyama Okyo).

**1950.** Air.

| | | | | |
|---|---|---|---|---|
| 575. | **225.** | 16 y. grey .. .. | 38·00 | 18·00 |
| 576. | | 34 y. purple .. | 70·00 | 23·00 |
| 577. | | 59 y. red .. .. | £100 | 18·00 |
| 578. | | 103 y. orange .. | 75·00 | 30·00 |
| 579. | | 144 y. olive .. | 75·00 | 30·00 |

**1950.** New Year's Greetings.

| | | | | |
|---|---|---|---|---|
| 580. | **226.** | 2 y. red .. .. | 8·00 | 1·00 |

**227.** Microphones of 1925 and 1950.

**228.** Dove.

**1950.** 25th Anniv. of Japanese Broadcasting System.

| | | | | |
|---|---|---|---|---|
| 582. | **227.** | 8 y. blue .. .. | 4·00 | 1·50 |

**1950.** 1st Anniv. of Joint Ministries of Postal and Electrical Communications.

| | | | | |
|---|---|---|---|---|
| 583. | **228.** | 8 y. green .. .. | 3·75 | 1·25 |

**229.** Lake Akan and Mt. O-Akani.

**230.** Lake Kutcharo.

**231.** Mt. Akan-Fuji.

**232.** Lake Mashu.

**1950.** Akan National Park.

| | | | | |
|---|---|---|---|---|
| 584. | **229.** | 2 y. brown .. .. | 1·10 | 50 |
| 585. | **230.** | 8 y. green .. .. | 1·75 | 75 |
| 586. | **231.** | 14 y. red .. .. | 8·50 | 2·25 |
| 587. | **232.** | 24 y. blue .. .. | 10·00 | 2·25 |

**233.** Gymnast on rings.

**1950.** 5th National Athletic Meeting.

| | | | | |
|---|---|---|---|---|
| 589 | **233** | 8 y. red .. .. | 30·00 | 12·00 |
| 590 | – | 8 y. red (Pole vaulting) | 30·00 | 12·00 |
| 591 | – | 8 y. red (Football) .. | 30·00 | 12·00 |
| 592 | – | 8 y. red (Horse jumping) .. .. | 30·00 | 12·00 |

**234.** Tahoto Pagoda, Ishiyama Temple.

**235.** Baron Maeshima.

**236.** Long-tailed Cock.

**237.** Kannon Bosatsu (detail of wall painting, Horyu Temple).

**238.** Himeji Castle.

**239.** Phoenix Temple, Uji. **240.** Buddhisattva Statue, Chugu Temple.

**1950.** With noughts for sen after value.

| | | | | |
|---|---|---|---|---|
| 593 | **234** | 80 s. red .. .. | 2·00 | 1·75 |
| 594 | **235** | 1 y. brown .. .. | 4·75 | 30 |
| 595 | **236** | 5 y. green and brown | 8·00 | 30 |
| 596 | **237** | 10 y. lake and mauve | 18·00 | 10 |
| 597 | **238** | 14 y. brown .. .. | 50·00 | 35·00 |
| 598 | **239** | 24 y. blue .. .. | 40·00 | 16·00 |
| 599 | **240** | 50 y. brown .. .. | £140 | 1·00 |

For designs without noughts see Nos. 653 etc and for designs additionally inscr "NIPPON" see Nos. 1041/59.

**241.** Girl and Rabbit.

**242.** Skiing, Mt. Zao.

**1951.** New Year's Greetings.

| | | | | |
|---|---|---|---|---|
| 604. | **241.** | 2 y. red .. .. | 7·00 | 1·00 |

**1951.** Tourist Issue. Mt. Zao.

| | | | | |
|---|---|---|---|---|
| 606. | **242.** | 8 y. olive .. .. | 14·00 | 3·00 |
| 607. | – | 24 y. blue .. .. | 15·00 | 5·00 |

DESIGN—HORIZ. 24 y. Two skiers on Mt. Zao.

**243.** Nihon Daira.

**244.** Mt. Fuji from Nihon Daira.

**1951.** Tourist Issue. Nihon-Daira.

| | | | | |
|---|---|---|---|---|
| 608 | **243** | 8 y. green .. .. | 14·00 | 3·00 |
| 609 | **244** | 24 y. blue .. .. | 70·00 | 18·00 |

**245.** Child's Head.

**1951.** Children's Charter.

| | | | | |
|---|---|---|---|---|
| 611. | **245.** | 8 y. brown .. .. | 25·00 | 3·00 |

**246.** Hot Springs, Owaki Valley.

**247.** Lake Ashi.

**1951.** Tourist Issue. Hakone Spa.

| | | | | |
|---|---|---|---|---|
| 612 | **246** | 8 y. brown .. .. | 10·00 | 2·00 |
| 613 | **247** | 24 y. blue .. .. | 8·00 | 3·00 |

**248.** Senju Waterfall. **249.** Ninai Waterfall.

**1951.** Tourist Issue. Akame Waterfalls.

| | | | | |
|---|---|---|---|---|
| 614 | **248** | 8 y. green .. .. | 10·00 | 2·00 |
| 615 | **249** | 24 y. blue .. .. | 10·00 | 3·00 |

**250.** Waka-no-Ura. **251.** Tomo-ga-Shima.

**1951.** Tourist Issue. Coastal Resorts.

| | | | | |
|---|---|---|---|---|
| 616 | **250** | 8 y. brown .. .. | 8·00 | 2·00 |
| 617 | **251** | 24 y. blue .. .. | 8·00 | 3·00 |

**252.** Oirase River.

**253.** Lake Towada.

**254.** View from Kankodai.

**255.** Hakkoda Mountains.

**1951.** Towada National Park.

| | | | | |
|---|---|---|---|---|
| 618. | **252.** | 2 y. brown .. .. | 1·25 | 30 |
| 619. | **253.** | 8 y. green .. .. | 6·50 | 70 |
| 620. | **254.** | 14 y. red .. .. | 5·50 | 4·00 |
| 621. | **255.** | 24 y. blue .. .. | 7·50 | 4·00 |

**256.** Uji River.

**257.** Uji Bridge.

**1951.** Tourist Issue. Uji River.

| | | | | |
|---|---|---|---|---|
| 623 | **256** | 8 y. brown .. .. | 9·00 | 2·00 |
| 624 | **257** | 24 y. blue .. .. | 8·00 | 3·00 |

**258.** Douglas DC-4 Airliner over Horyuji Pagoda.

**259.** Airplane and Mt. Tate.

**1951.** Air. With noughts for sen after numerals of value.

| | | | | |
|---|---|---|---|---|
| 625 | **258** | 15 y. violet .. .. | 4·00 | 3·25 |
| 626 | | 20 y. blue .. .. | 32·00 | 1·00 |
| 627 | | 25 y. green .. .. | 35·00 | 15 |
| 628 | | 30 y. red .. .. | 26·00 | 15 |
| 629 | | 40 y. black .. .. | 7·00 | 30 |
| 630 | **259** | 55 y. blue .. .. | £225 | 45·00 |
| 631 | | 75 y. red .. .. | £175 | 28·00 |
| 632 | | 80 y. mauve .. .. | 30·00 | 3·50 |
| 633 | | 85 y. black .. .. | 22·00 | 12·00 |
| 634 | | 125 y. brown .. .. | 18·00 | 3·25 |
| 635 | | 160 y. green .. .. | 40·00 | 5·50 |

For similar designs, but without noughts after numerals of value, see Nos. 671/81.

**260.** Chrysanthemum.

**261.** Japanese Flag.

**1951.** Peace Treaty.

| | | | | |
|---|---|---|---|---|
| 636. | **260.** | 2 y. brown .. .. | 2·50 | 1·00 |
| 637. | **261.** | 8 y. red and blue .. | 7·00 | 2·00 |
| 638. | **260.** | 24 y. green .. .. | 18·00 | 6·00 |

**262.** Oura Catholic Church, Nagasaki.

**263.** Gateway, Sofuku Temple.

**1951.** Tourist Issue. Nagasaki.

| | | | | |
|---|---|---|---|---|
| 639 | **262** | 8 y. red .. .. | 10·00 | 2·00 |
| 640 | **263** | 24 y. blue .. .. | 8·00 | 3·00 |

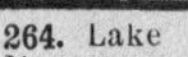

**264.** Lake Marunuma. **265.** Lake Sugenuma.

**1951.** Tourist Issue.

| | | | | |
|---|---|---|---|---|
| 641 | **264** | 8 y. purple .. .. | 10·00 | 2·00 |
| 642 | **265** | 24 y. green .. .. | 8·00 | 3·00 |

**266.** Shosenkyo Valley. **267.** Nagatoro Bridge.

**1951.** Tourist Issue. Shosenkyo.

| | | | | |
|---|---|---|---|---|
| 643 | **266** | 8 y. red .. .. | 9·50 | 2·00 |
| 644 | **267** | 24 y. blue .. .. | 9·00 | 3·00 |

**268.** Putting the Shot. **269.** Noh Mask.

**1951.** 6th National Athletic Meeting.

| | | | | |
|---|---|---|---|---|
| 645. | **268.** | 2 y. brown .. .. | 3·50 | 1·00 |
| 646. | – | 2 y. blue (hockey) .. | 3·50 | 1·00 |

**1952.** New Year's Greetings.

| | | | | |
|---|---|---|---|---|
| 647. | **269.** | 5 y. red .. | 10·00 | 90 |

**270.** Ship's Davit and Southern Cross. **271.** Red Cross and Lily.

**1952.** 75th Anniv. of U.P.U. Membership.

| | | | | |
|---|---|---|---|---|
| 649. | **270.** | 5 y. violet .. .. | 5·00 | 1·25 |
| 650. | – | 10 y. green .. .. | 16·00 | 3·00 |

DESIGN: 10 y. Earth and Ursa Major. Inscr. "1952".

**1952.** 75th Anniv. of Japanese Red Cross.

| | | | | |
|---|---|---|---|---|
| 651. | **271.** | 5 y. red .. .. | 5·00 | 1·00 |
| 652. | – | 10 y. grn. & red (Nurse) | 11·00 | 2·00 |

**272.** Akita Dog. **273.** Little Cuckoo. **274.** Tahoto Pagoda, Ishiyama Temple.

**275.** Mandarins. **276.** Japanese Serow. **277.** Chuson Temple.

**278.** Goldfish. **279.** Yomei Gate, Tosho Shrine, Nikko. **280.** "Marimo" (water plant) and Fish.

**281.** Great Purple. **282.** Fishing with Japanese Cormorants. **283.** "Bridge and Irises" (from lacquered box).

**1952.** Without noughts after numerals of value.

| | | | | |
|---|---|---|---|---|
| 653 | **235** | 1 y. brown .. .. | 30 | 10 |
| 654 | **272** | 2 y. black .. .. | 40 | 10 |
| 655 | **273** | 3 y. turquoise .. | 25 | 10 |
| 656 | **274** | 4 y. purple and red .. | 2·50 | 10 |
| 657 | **275** | 5 y. brown and blue .. | 25 | 10 |
| 658 | **276** | 8 y. brown & pale brn | 30 | 10 |
| 659 | **237** | 10 y. red and mauve .. | 6·00 | 10 |
| 660 | **238** | 14 y. green .. .. | 7·50 | 1·25 |
| 661 | **277** | 20 y. green .. .. | 1·00 | 10 |
| 662 | **239** | 24 y. violet .. .. | 16·00 | 2·00 |
| 663 | | 30 y. purple .. .. | 35·00 | 40 |
| 664 | **278** | 35 y. orange .. .. | 10·00 | 10 |
| 665 | **279** | 45 y. blue .. .. | 4·50 | 10 |
| 666 | **240** | 50 y. brown .. .. | 4·50 | 10 |
| 667 | **280** | 55 y. green, black & bl | 16·00 | 30 |
| 668 | **281** | 75 y. multicoloured .. | 14·00 | 90 |
| 669 | **282** | 100 y. red .. .. | 38·00 | 10 |
| 670 | **283** | 500 y. purple .. .. | 85·00 | 10 |

For 1, 2, 3, 50, 55 and 75 y. in same designs, but inscr "NIPPON", see Nos. 1041, 1582a, 1226, 1058/60, 1232 and 1064.

**1952.** Air. As Nos. 625/35 but without noughts after numerals of value.

| | | | | |
|---|---|---|---|---|
| 671 | **258** | 15 y. violet .. .. | 2·00 | 1·10 |
| 672 | | 20 y. blue .. .. | 50·00 | 70 |
| 673 | | 25 y. green .. .. | 1·00 | 10 |
| 674 | | 30 y. red .. .. | 3·50 | 10 |
| 675 | | 40 y. black .. .. | 4·00 | 10 |
| 676 | **259** | 55 y. blue .. .. | 75·00 | 4·50 |
| 677 | | 75 y. red .. .. | £140 | 10·00 |
| 678 | | 80 y. mauve .. .. | 95·00 | 3·00 |
| 679 | | 85 y. black .. .. | 5·00 | 1·25 |
| 680 | | 125 y. brown .. .. | 10·00 | 1·40 |
| 681 | | 160 y. green .. .. | 40·00 | 1·75 |

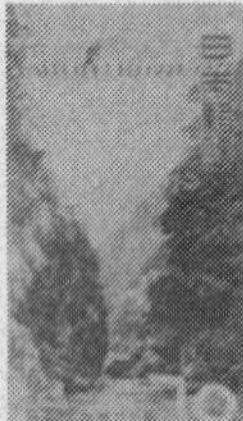

**284.** Mt. Yari. **285.** Kurobe Valley.

**286.** Mt. Shirouma.

**287.** Mt. Norikura.

**1952.** Chubu-Sangaku National Park.

| | | | | |
|---|---|---|---|---|
| 682. | **284.** | 5 y. brown .. .. | 2·75 | 40 |
| 683. | **285.** | 10 y. green .. .. | 18·00 | 2·00 |
| 684. | **286.** | 14 y. red .. .. | 5·50 | 2·00 |
| 685. | **287.** | 24 y. blue .. .. | 8·00 | 2·75 |

**288.** Central Hall. **289.** Wrestlers.

**1952.** 75th Anniv. of Tokyo University.

| | | | | |
|---|---|---|---|---|
| 687. | **288.** | 10 y. green .. .. | 11·00 | 2·00 |

**1952.** 7th National Athletic Meeting.

| | | | | |
|---|---|---|---|---|
| 688. | – | 5 y. blue (Mountaineer) | 6·00 | 1·00 |
| 689. | **289.** | 5 y. brown .. .. | 6·00 | 1·00 |

**290.** Mt. Azuma-Kofuji.

**291.** Mt. Asahi.

**292.** Mt. Bandai.

**293.** Mt. Gessan.

**1952.** Bandai-Asahi National Park.

| | | | | |
|---|---|---|---|---|
| 690. | **290.** | 5 y. brown .. .. | 2·00 | 40 |
| 691. | **291.** | 10 y. olive .. .. | 11·00 | 1·75 |
| 692. | **292.** | 14 y .red .. .. | 4·25 | 2·75 |
| 693. | **293.** | 24 y. blue .. .. | 8·00 | 4·00 |

**294.** "Kirin" and Chrysanthemums. **295.** Flag of Crown Prince.

**1952.** Investiture of Crown Prince Akihito.

| | | | | |
|---|---|---|---|---|
| 695. | **294.** | 5 y. orange and brown | 2·75 | 50 |
| 696. | | 10 y. orange and green | 3·00 | 75 |
| 697. | **295.** | 24 y. blue .. .. | 15·00 | 4·25 |

**296.** Dancing Doll. **297.** First Japanese Electric Lamp.

**1953.** New Year's Greetings.

| | | | | |
|---|---|---|---|---|
| 699. | **296.** | 5 y. red .. .. | 7·00 | 1·00 |

**1953.** 75th Anniv. of Electric Lamp in Japan.

| | | | | |
|---|---|---|---|---|
| 701. | **297.** | 10 y. brown .. .. | 7·50 | 2·00 |

**299.** Kintai Bridge. **302.** Great Buddha, Kamakura.

**300.** Lake Shikotsu. **301.** Mt. Yotei.

(Illustrations reduced: each 40×23 mm.)

**1953.** Tourist Issue. Kintai Bridge.

| | | | | |
|---|---|---|---|---|
| 702 | – | 10 y. brown .. .. | 7·50 | 2·00 |
| 703 | **299** | 24 y. blue .. .. | 7·50 | 3·00 |

DESIGN—VERT. 10 y. Kintai Bridge (after Hiroshige).

**1953.** Shikotsu-Toya National Park.

| | | | | |
|---|---|---|---|---|
| 704. | **300.** | 5 y. blue .. .. | 1·75 | 35 |
| 705. | **301.** | 10 y. green .. .. | 5·50 | 75 |

**1953.** Air.

| | | | | |
|---|---|---|---|---|
| 707. | **302.** | 70 y. brown .. .. | 3·50 | 10 |
| 708. | | 80 y. blue .. .. | 5·00 | 10 |
| 709. | | 115 y. olive .. .. | 2·75 | 30 |
| 710. | | 145 y. turquoise .. | 18·00 | 2·00 |

**303.** Wedded Rocks, Futami Bay. **304.** Nakiri Coast.

(Illustrations reduced: each 40×23 mm.)

**1953.** Ise Shima National Park.

| | | | | |
|---|---|---|---|---|
| 711 | **303** | 5 y. red .. .. | 1·75 | 30 |
| 712 | **304** | 10 y. blue .. .. | 4·00 | 70 |

**305.** "Ho-o" (Happy Phoenix).

**1953.** Return of Crown Prince from Overseas Tour.

| | | | | |
|---|---|---|---|---|
| 714. | **305.** | 5 y. lake .. .. | 3·00 | 1·50 |
| 715. | – | 10 y. blue .. .. | 8·75 | 3·25 |

DESIGN: 10 y. Manchurian crane in flight.

**306.** Judo. **307.** Tokyo Observatory.

**1953.** 8th National Athletic Meeting, Matsuyama.

| | | | | |
|---|---|---|---|---|
| 716. | **306.** | 5 y. green .. .. | 8·00 | 2·00 |
| 717. | – | 5 y. black .. .. | 8·00 | 2·00 |

DESIGN: 5 y. Rugby footballers.

**1953.** 75th Anniv. of Tokyo Observatory.

| | | | | |
|---|---|---|---|---|
| 718. | **307.** | 10 y. blue .. .. | 10·00 | 2·00 |

**308.** Mt. Unzen. **309.**

(Illustrations reduced: each 40×23 mm.)

**1953.** Unzen National Park.

| | | | | |
|---|---|---|---|---|
| 719. | **308.** | 5 y. red .. .. | 1·50 | 25 |
| 720. | **309.** | 10 y. blue .. .. | 4·00 | 65 |

**310.** Wooden Horse. **311.** Ice Skaters.

**1953.** New Year's Greetings.

| | | | | |
|---|---|---|---|---|
| 722. | **310.** | 5 y. red .. .. | 5·50 | 25 |

**1954.** World Speed Skating Championships, Sapporo.

| | | | | |
|---|---|---|---|---|
| 724. | **311.** | 10 y. blue .. .. | 4·00 | 1·10 |

**312.** **313.** Wrestlers.

**1954.** Int. Trade Fair, Osaka.

| | | | | |
|---|---|---|---|---|
| 725. | **312.** | 10 y. red .. .. | 4·25 | 1·10 |

**1954.** Int. Free-style Wrestling Championship.

| | | | | |
|---|---|---|---|---|
| 726. | **313.** | 10 y. green .. .. | 4·00 | 1·00 |

**314.** Mt. Asama. **315.** Tanigawa.

(Illustrations reduced: each 40×23 mm.)

**1954.** Jo-Shin-Etsu Kogen National Park.

| | | | | |
|---|---|---|---|---|
| 727. | **314.** | 5 y. sepia .. .. | 1·50 | 25 |
| 728. | **315.** | 10 y. turquoise .. | 3·75 | 65 |

**316.** Archery. **317.** Telegraph Table.

**1954.** 9th National Athletic Meeting, Sapporo.
730 **316** 5 y. green .. .. 5·00 1·50
731 – 5 y. brn (Table tennis) 5·00 1·50

**1954.** 75th Anniv. of Japan's Membership of I.T.U.
732. **317.** 5 y. purple .. .. 2·25 75
733. – 10 y. blue .. .. 6·00 1·00
DESIGN—HORIZ. 10 y. I.T.U. Monument.

**318.** Tumbler. **319.** Tama Gorge.

**320.** Chichibu Mountains.

**1954.** New Year's Greetings.
735. **318.** 5 y. red and black .. 7·00 80

**1955.** Chichibu-Tama National Park.
737. **319.** 5 y. blue .. .. 1·25 25
738. **320.** 10 y. lake .. .. 1·50 40

**321.** Paper Carp.

**1955.** 15th Int. Chamber of Commerce Congress, Tokyo.
740. **321.** 10 y. multicoloured .. 6·00 1·50

**322.** Bentenzaki Peninsula. **323.** Jodoga Beach.

**1955.** Rikuchu-Kaigan National Park.
741. **322.** 5 y. green .. .. 1·50 25
742. **323.** 10 y. red .. .. 2·00 40

**324.** Gymnastics. **325.** " Girl Playing Glass Flute" (Utamaro).

**1955.** 10th National Athletic Meeting, Kanagawa.
744 **324** 5 y. red .. .. 3·00 1·00
745 – 5 y. blue (Running) .. 3·00 1·00

**1955.** Philatelic Week.
746. **325.** 10 y. multicoloured .. 12·00 8·00

**326.** " Kokeshi" Dolls. **327.** Table Tennis.

**1955.** New Year's Greetings.
747. **326.** 5 y. green and red .. 3·00 20

**1956.** World Table Tennis Championships.
749 **327** 10 y. brown .. .. 1·10 35

**328.** Judo. **329.** Children and Paper Carps.

**1956.** World Judo Championships.
750. **328.** 10 y. purple and green 1·40 40

**1956.** Int. Children's Day.
751. **329.** 5 y. black and blue .. 1·00 30

**330.** Osezaki Lighthouse. **331.** Kujuku Island.

(Illustrations reduced: each 40 × 22 mm.)

**1956.** 25th Anniv. of National Park Law. Saikai National Park.
752. **330.** 5 y. brown .. .. 1·25 50
753. **331.** 10 y. indigo and blue.. 1·75 85

**332.** Imperial Palace, and Modern Buildings. **333.** Sakuma Dam.

**1956.** 5th Cent. of Tokyo.
755. **332.** 10 y. purple .. .. 3·25 50

**1956.** Completion of Sakuma Dam.
756. **333.** 10 y. blue .. .. 2·50 50

**334.** Basketball. **335.** Ebizo Ichikawa (actor), (after Sharaku).

**1956.** 11th National Athletic Meeting, Kobe.
757 **334** 5 y. green .. .. 1·50 30
758 – 5 y. purple (Long jumping) .. .. 1·50 30

**1956.** Philatelic Week.
759. **335.** 10 y. blk., orge. & grey 13·00 4·75

**336.** Mt. Manaslu and Mountaineer.

**1956.** Conquest of Mt. Manaslu.
760 **336** 10 y. multicoloured .. 4·50 1·25

**337.** View of Yui (after Hiroshige) and Electric Train.

**1956.** Electrification of Tokaido Railway Line.
761. **337.** 10 y. blk., grn. & brn. 10·00 3·00

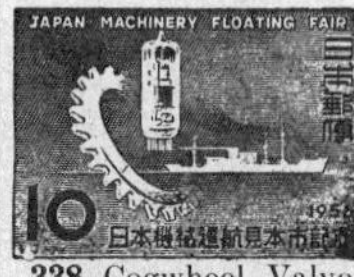


**338.** Cogwheel, Valve and Freighter "Nissyo Maru". **339.** Whale (float).

**1956.** Floating Machinery Fair.
762. **338.** 10 y. blue .. .. 1·60 70

**1956.** New Year's Greetings.
763. **339.** 5 y. multicoloured .. 2·00 15

**340.** U.N.O. Emblem. **341.** I.G.Y. Emblem, Emperor Penguin and Antarctic Research Vessel "Soya".

**1957.** 1st Anniv. of Japan's Admission into U.N.
765. **340.** 10 y. red and blue .. 1·00 95

**1957.** Int. Geophysical Year.
766. **341.** 10 y. blue, yell. & blk. 2·25 75

**342.** Atomic Reactor. **343.** Gymnast.

**1957.** Completion of Atomic Reactor at Tokai-Mura.
767. **342.** 10 y. violet .. .. 50 15

**1957.** 12th National Athletic Meeting, Shizuoka.
768 **343** 5 y. blue .. .. 60 15
769 – 5 y. red (Boxing) .. 60 15

**344.** " Girl Bouncing Ball" (after Harunobu). **345.** Ogochi Dam.

**1957.** Philatelic Week.
770. **344.** 10 y. multicoloured .. 4·00 1·50

**1957.** Completion of Ogochi Dam.
771. **345.** 10 y blue .. .. 45 15

**346.** Japan's First Blast Furnace and Modern Plant. **347.** " Inu-hariko" (toy dog).

**1957.** Cent. of Japanese Iron Industry.
772. **346.** 10 y. purple & orange 35 15

**1957.** New Year's Greetings.
773. **347.** 5 y. multicoloured .. 30 15



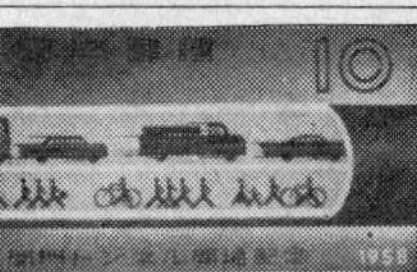

**348.** Kan-Mon Tunnel.

**1958.** Opening of Kan-Mon Undersea Tunnel.
775. **348.** 10 y. multicoloured .. 50 10

**349.** "Lady returning from Bath-house" (after Kiyonaga).

**1958.** Philatelic Week.
776. **349.** 10 y. multicoloured .. 1·00 15

**350.** Statue of Ii Naosuke, "Powhattan" (1858 paddle-steamer) and Modern Liner. **351.** National Stadium, Tokyo.

**1958.** Cent of Opening of Ports to Traders.
777 **350** 10 y. red and blue .. 30 10

**1958.** 3rd Asian Games, Tokyo. Inscr. as in T **351**. Multicoloured.
778. 5 y. Type **351** .. .. 30 10
779. 10 y. Flame and Games emblem .. .. 45 50
780. 14 y. Runner breasting tape 35 15
781. 24 y. High-diver.. .. 40 50

**352.** Emigration Ship "Kasato Maru" and South American Map.

**1958.** 50th Anniv. of Japanese Emigration to Brazil.
782. **352.** 10 y. multicoloured .. 40 10

**353.** Dado-Okesa Dancer on Sado Island. **354.** Mt. Yahiko and Echigo Plain.

**1958.** Sado-Yahiko Quasi-National Park.
783. **353.** 10 y. multicoloured .. 70 10
784. **354.** 10 y. multicoloured .. 40 10

**355.** Stethoscope.

**1958.** Int. Congresses of Chest Diseases and Bronchoesophagology, Tokyo.
785. **355.** 10 y. turquoise .. 60 10

**356.** "Old Kyoto Bridge" (after Hiroshige). **357.** Badminton Player.

**1958.** Int. Correspondence Week.
786. **356.** 24 y. multicoloured .. 4·50 50
The design is taken from the series of 53 woodcuts, showing stages of the Tokaido Road. Others from this series are shown on Nos. 810, 836, 878 and 908.

**1958.** 13th National Athletic Meeting, Toyama.
787 357 5 y. purple .. .. 75 10
788 – 5 y. blue (Weight-lifting) .. .. 75 10

**358.** Yukichi Fukuzawa (founder) and Keio University.

**359.** Children Skipping across Globe.

**1958.** Cent. of Keio University.
789. **358.** 10 y. red .. .. 30 10

**1958.** Int. Child and Social Welfare Conferences, Tokyo.
790. **359.** 10 y. green .. .. 30 10

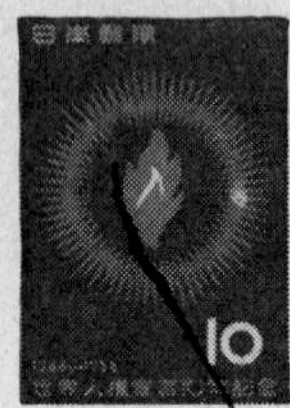
**360.** "Flame of Freedom".

**361.** Ebisu with Bream (toy).

**1958.** 10th Anniv. of Declaration of Human Rights.
791. **360.** 10 y. multicoloured .. 30 10

**1958.** New Year's Greetings.
792. **361.** 5 y. multicoloured .. 50 10

**362.** Map of Kojima Bay and Tractor.

**1959.** Completion of Kojima Bay Reclamation Project.
794. **362.** 10 y. purple and ochre 40 15

**363.** Karst Plateau.

**364.** Akiyoshi Cavern.

**1959.** Akiyoshidai Quasi-National Parks.
795. **363.** 10 y. multicoloured .. 1·75 10
796. **364.** 10 y. multicoloured .. 2·25 10

**365.** Map of Asia.

**366.** Crown Prince Akihito and Princess Michiko.

**1959.** Asian Congress Commem. of 2,500th Anniv. of Buddha's Death.
797. **365.** 10 y. red .. .. 40 10

**1959.** Imperial Wedding.
798 – 5 y. violet and purple 35 10
799 366 10 y. purple and brown 85 10
800 – 20 y. sepia and brown 1·00 15
801 366 30 y. dp green & green 2·00 15
DESIGN: 5, 20 y. Ceremonial fan.

**367.** "Ladies reading poems" (from "Ukiyo Genji" after Eishi).

**368.** Graduated Glass and Scales.

**1959.** Philatelic Week.
803. **367.** 10 y. multicoloured .. 2·50 1·25

**1959.** Ratification of Adoption of Metric System in Japan.
804. **368.** 10 y. sepia and blue .. 30 10

**369.** Stretcher-party with Casualty.

**370.** Mt. Fuji from Lake Motosu.

**1959.** Red Cross.
805. **369.** 10 y. red and green .. 40 10

**1959.** National Parks Day.
806. **370.** 10 y. grn., pur. & blue 60 10

**371.** Ao Caves. Yabakei.

**372.** Japanese Cormorant with Hita and Mt. Hiko background.

(Illustrations reduced: each 32×22 mm.)

**1959.** Yaba-Hita-Hikosan Quasi-National Parks.
807. **371.** 10 y. multicoloured .. 2·00 30
808. **372.** 10 y. multicoloured .. 3·75 30

**373.** Nagoya and Golden Dolphin.

**374.** "Kuwana" (after Hiroshige).

**1959.** 350th Anniv. of Nagoya.
809. **373.** 10 y. gold, blk. & blue 60 10

**1959.** Int. Correspondence Week.
810. **374.** 30 y. multicoloured .. 10·00 2·00

**375.** Flying Manchurian Crane and I.A.T.A. Emblem.

**376.** Throwing the Hammer.

**1959.** 15th Int. Air Transport Association Meeting, Tokyo
811. **375.** 10 y. blue .. .. 1·40 30

**1959.** 14th National Athletic Meeting, Tokyo.
812 376 5 y. blue .. .. 1·00 10
813 – 5 y. brown (Fencer) .. 1·00 10

**377.** Open Book showing portrait of Shoin Yoshida.

**378.** Halves of Globe.

**1959.** Death Centenary of Shoin Yoshida (educator) and Nat. Parents/Teachers Assoc. Convention.
814. **377.** 10 y. brown .. .. 40 10

**1959.** 15th Session of Contracting Parties to G.A.T.T.
815. **378.** 10 y. brown .. .. 60 10

**379.** Rice-eating Rat of Kanazawa (toy).

**380.** Yukio Ozaki and Clock Tower Memorial Hall.

**381.** Deer.

**1959.** New Year's Greetings.
816. **379.** 5 y. multicoloured .. 1·00 10

**1960.** Completion of Ozaki Memorial Hall, Tokyo.
818. **380.** 10 y. purple and brown 40 10

**1960.** 1250th Anniversary of Transfer of Capital to Nara.
819. **381.** 10 y. olive .. .. 70 10

**382.** Godaido Temple, Matsushima.

**383.** Bridge of Heaven (sandbank), Miyazu Bay.

**384.** Miyajima from the Sea.

**1960.** "Scenic Trio".
820. **382.** 10 y. turq. and brown 2·50 25
821. **383.** 10 y. green and blue .. 3·00 25
822. **384.** 10 y. green and violet 3·00 25

**385.** Takeshima-Gamagori Causeway.

**1960.** Mikawa Bay Quasi-National Park.
823. **385.** 10 y. multicoloured .. 1·25 20

**386.** "Ise" (from Satake picture scroll "Thirty-six Immortal Poets").

**1960.** Philatelic Week.
824 386 10 y. black, red & brn 3·75 2·00

**387.** "Kanrin Maru" (barque) crossing the Pacific.

**388.** Japanese Crested Ibis.

**1960.** Cent. of Japanese-American Treaty.
825. **387.** 10 y. sepia and green 1·75 30
826. – 30 y. blue-black & red 1·60 20
DESIGN: 30 y. Pres. Buchanan receiving Japanese mission.

**1960.** 12th Int. Bird Preservation Congress, Tokyo.
827. **388.** 10 y. red, pink and grey 1·75 50

**389.** Radio Waves around Globe.

**390.** Abashiri Flower Gardens.

**1960.** 25th Anniv. of Japanese Overseas Broadcasting Service, "Radio Japan".
828. **389.** 10 y. red .. .. 40 10

**1960.** Abashiri Quasi-National Park.
829. **390.** 10 y. multicoloured .. 1·50 25

**391.** Cape Ashizuri.

**392.** Rainbow linking Hawaii and Japan.

**1960.** Ashizuri Quasi-National Park.
830. **391.** 10 y. multicoloured .. 1·00 25

**1960.** 75th Anniv. of Japanese Emigration to Hawaii.
831. **392.** 10 y. multicoloured .. 1·00 20

**393.** Douglas DC-8 Jetliner and Farman H.F.III Biplane.

**394.** Seat Plan of the Diet.

**1960.** 50th Anniv. of Japanese Aviation.
832. **393.** 10 y. brown and grey .. 1·25 25

**1960.** 49th Inter-Parliamentary Union Conf. Inscr. "49TH INTER-PARLIAMENTARY CONFERENCE TOKYO 1960".
833. **394.** 5 y. orange and blue 70 10
834. – 10 y. brown and blue 1·60 20
DESIGN: 10 y. "Clear Day with Southern Breeze" (from "36 Views of Mt. Fuji" by Hokusai Katsushika).

**395.** "Kambara" (after Hiroshige).

**396.** Okayama Observatory.

**1960.** Int. Correspondence Week.
836. **395.** 30 y. multicoloured .. 18·00 4·00

**1960.** Opening of Okayama Astrophysical Observatory.
837 396 10 y. violet .. .. 90 25

**397.** "Kendo" (Japanese fencing).

**398.** Lieut. Shirase and Map of Antarctica.

**1960.** 15th National Athletic Meeting, Kumamoto.
838. **397.** 5 y. blue .. .. 1·00 15
839. – 5 y. purple (Vaulting) 1·00 15

**1960.** 50th Anniv. of 1st Japanese Antarctic Expedition.
840. **398.** 10 y. black and brown 1·00 15

**399.** Red Beko and Golden Bekokko (Japanese toys).

**400.** Diet Building and Stars.

**1960.** New Year's Greetings.
841. **399.** 5 y. multicoloured .. 50 10

**1960.** 70th Anniv. of Diet.
843. **400.** 5 y. violet and black .. 60 10
844. – 10 y. red .. .. 75 15
DESIGN: 10 y. Opening ceremony of first session of Diet.

401. Narcissus.

402. Pearl-divers at Shirahama.

**1961.** Japanese Flowers. Flowers in natural colours. Background colours given.

845. 10 y. purple (T **401**) .. 5·00 80
846. 10 y. brown (Plum blossom) 3·00 80
847 10 y. bistre (Camellia) .. 2·00 70
848. 10 y. grey (Cherry blossom) 2·00 70
849. 10 y. sepia (Peony) .. 1·90 55
850. 10 y. grey (Iris) .. 1·50 55
851. 10 y. turquoise (Lily) .. 1·00 30
852. 10 y. blue (Morning Glory) 1·00 30
853. 10 y. sage (Bellflower) .. 1·00 30
854. 10 y. orange (Gentian) .. 1·00 30
855. 10 y. blue (Chrysanthemum) 1·25 30
856. 10 y. slate (Camellia) .. 1·00 30

**1961.** Minami-Boso Quasi-National Park.
857. **402.** 10 y. multicoloured .. 1·00 10

403. Hirase's Slit Shell.

404. Nanten.

405. Cherry Blossoms.

406. Engaku Temple.

407. Yomei Gate, Tosho Shrine, Nikko.

408. Noh Mask.

409. Copper Pheasant.

410. " The Wind God ". 411. Manchurian Cranes.

412. "Kalavinka" (legendary bird).

**1961.**

858. **403.** 4 y. red and brown .. 35 10
859. **404.** 6 y. red and green .. 20 10
860. **405.** 10 y. mauve & purple 45 10
861. **406.** 30 y. violet .. .. 5·00 10
862. **407.** 40 y. red .. .. 6·00 10
863. **408.** 70 y. black and ochre 3·00 10
864. **409.** 80 y. brown and red .. 1·75 10
865. **410.** 90 y. green .. .. 35·00 15
866. **411.** 100 y. grey, blk. & pink 18·00 10
867. **412.** 120 y. violet .. .. 12·00 30

For 70, 80, 90, 100, and 120 y. in different colours and additionally inscr "NIPPON" see Nos. 1065/6, 1068, 1234/6 and 1238.

413. Baron Maeshima. 414. " Dancing Girl " (from 17th-century screen).

**1961.** 90th Anniv. of Japanese Postal Service.
868. **413.** 10 y. green and black .. 1·00 15

**1961.** Philatelic Week.
869. **414.** 10 y. multicoloured .. 1·75 90

415. Lake Biwa.

416. Rotary Emblem and " Peoples of the World ".

**1961.** Lake Biwa Quasi-National Park.
870. **415.** 10 y. multicoloured .. 80 20

**1961.** 52nd Rotary International Convention
871. **416.** 10 y. orange and black 45 10

417. " Benefits of Irrigation ".

418. Globe showing Longitude 135° E. and Sun.

**1961.** Inaug. of Aichi Irrigation Scheme.
872. **417.** 10 y. blue and purple .. 50 15

**1961.** 75th Anniv. of Japanese Standard Time.
873. **418.** 10 y. red, blk. & ochre 50 15

419. Parasol Dancer, Tottori Beach.

420. Komagatake Volcano.

**1961.** San'in Kaigan Quasi-National Park.
874. **419.** 10 y. multicoloured .. 80 20

**1961.** Onuma Quasi-National Park.
875. **420.** 10 y. multicoloured .. 80 20

421. Gymnast.

422. " Hakone " (after Hiroshige).

**1961.** 16th National Athletic Meeting, Akita.
876. **421.** 5 y. green .. .. 1·00 10
877. – 5 y. blue (Rowing) .. 1·00 10

**1961.** International Correspondence Week.
878. **422.** 30 y. multicoloured .. 9·00 4·00

423. Throwing the Javelin.

424. Library and Book.

**1961.** Olympic Games, Tokyo, 1964 (1st issue).
879. **423.** 5 y.+5 y. brown .. 1·50 70
880. – 5 y.+5 y. green .. 1·50 70
881. – 5 y.+5 y. red .. 1·50 70

DESIGNS: No. 880, Wrestling. No. 881, Diver (Woman).

See also Nos. 899/901, 909/11, 935/7, 949/52, 969/72 and 981/5.

**1961.** Opening of National Diet Library.
882. **424.** 10 y. blue and gold .. 60 15

425. Tiger. (Izumo toy).

**1961.** New Year's Greetings.
883. **425.** 5 y. multicoloured .. 75 10

426. Mt. Fuji from Lake Aishi.

427. Minokake-Iwa, Irozaki.

428. Mt. Fuji from Mitsutoge.

429. Mt. Fuji from Osezaki.

**1962.** Fuji-Hakone-Izu National Park.
885. **426.** 5 y. green .. .. 1·00 10
886. **427.** 5 y. blue .. .. 1·00 10
887. **428.** 10 y. brown .. .. 1·75 25
888. **429.** 10 y. black .. .. 1·25 25

430. Omishima Island.

431. Doll Festival.

**1962.** Kitanagato-Kaigan Quasi-National Park.
889. **430.** 10 y. multicoloured .. 60 20

**1962.** National Festivals. Multicoloured.
890 10 y. Type **431** .. .. 1·75 25
891 10 y. Children and decorated tree ("Star Festival") .. .. 75 20
892 10 y. Three children ("Seven-Five-Three Festival") .. .. 65 20
893 10 y. Children throwing beans ("Spring Festival") .. .. 55 15

432. " Dancer " (after N. Kano).

433. Sakurajima Volcano.

**1962.** Philatelic Week.
894. **432.** 10 y. multicoloured .. 1·50 1·00

**1962.** Kinkowan Quasi-National Park.
895. **433.** 10 y. multicoloured .. 60 20

434. Mount Kongo.

**1962.** Kongo-Ikoma Quasi-National Park.
896. **434.** 10 y. multicoloured .. 60 20

435. Suigo View.

436. Diesel Train emerging from Tunnel.

**1962.** Suigo Quasi-National Park.
897. **435.** 10 y. multicoloured .. 80 20

**1962.** Opening of Hokuriku Railway Tunnel.
898 **436** 10 y. brown .. .. 2·50 45

**1962.** Olympic Games, Tokyo, 1964 (2nd issue). Sports designs as T **423.**
899. 5 y.+5 y. red .. .. 75 35
900. 5 y.+5 y. green .. .. 75 35
901. 5 y.+5 y. purple .. .. 75 35

SPORTS: No. 899 Judo. 900, Water-polo. 901, Gymnastics (female).

437. Scout's Hat on Map.

**1962.** Asian Scout Jamboree, Mt. Fuji.
902. **437.** 10 y. black, bistre & red 40 10

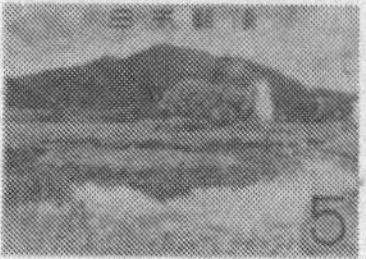

438. Mt. Shibutsu and Ozegahara Swamp.

439. Smoking Summit of Mt. Chausu, Nasu.

440. Lake Chuzenji and Mt. Nantai.

441. Senryu-kyo Narrows, Shiobara.

**1962.** Nikko National Park.
903. **438.** 5 y. turquoise .. 60 10
904. **439.** 5 y. lake .. 60 10
905. **440.** 10 y. purple .. .. 80 10
906. **441.** 10 y. olive .. .. 80 10

442. Wakato Suspension Bridge. 443. " Nihonbashi " (after Hiroshige).

**1962.** Opening of Wakato Suspension Bridge.
907. **442.** 10 y. red .. .. 1·50 35

**1962.** Int. Correspondence Week.
908. **443.** 40 y. multicoloured .. 7·50 3·00

**1962.** Olympic Games, Tokyo, 1964 (3rd issue). Sports designs as T **423.**
909. 5 y.+5 y. green .. .. 65 25
910. 5 y.+5 y. lilac .. .. 65 25
911. 5 y.+5 y. red .. .. 65 25

SPORTS: No. 909, Basketball. No. 910, Rowing. No. 911, Fencing.

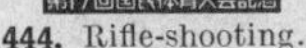

444. Rifle-shooting. 445. Hare-bell (Nogomi toy).

**1962.** 17th National Athletic Meeting, Okayama.

912. **444.** 5 y. purple .. .. 40 10
913. – 5 y. blue .. .. 40 10
DESIGN: No. 913, Softball.

**1962.** New Year's Greetings.

914. **445.** 5 y. multicoloured .. 40 10

446. Mt. Ishizuchi and Kamega Forest. 447. "Five Towns".

**1963.** Ishizuchi Quasi-National Park.

916. **446.** 10 y. multicoloured .. 30 10

**1963.** Amalgamation of Five Towns as Kita-Kyushu.

917. **447.** 10 y. brown .. .. 25 10

448. Frosted Foliage, Fugen Peak. 449. Amakusa Islands and Mt. Unzen.

(Illustrations reduced: each 33×22 mm.)

**1963.** Unzen-Amakusa National Park.

918 **448.** 5 y. blue .. .. 35 10
919. **449.** 10 y. red .. .. 65 10

450. Midorigaike (Green Pond). 451. Hakusan Mountains.

(Illustrations reduced: each 33×22 mm.)

**1963.** Hakusan National Park.

920. **450.** 5 y. brown .. .. 45 10
921. **451.** 10 y. green .. .. 75 10

452. Great Rocks, Keya. 453. Globe and Emblem.

**1963.** Genkai Quasi-National Park.

922. **452.** 10 y. multicoloured .. 25 10

**1963.** Freedom from Hunger.

923. **453.** 10 y. green .. .. 40 10

454. "Portrait of Heihachiro Honda" (anon-Yedo period). 455. Centenary Emblem and World Map.

**1963.** Philatelic Week.

924. **454.** 10 y. multicoloured .. 85 45

**1963.** Cent. of Red Cross.

925. **455.** 10 y. multicoloured .. 35 10

456. Globe and Leaf.

**1963.** 5th Int. Irrigation and Drainage Commission Congress, Toyko.

926. **456.** 10 y. blue .. .. 15 10

457. Mt. Ito, Asahi Range. 458. Mt. Bandai across Lake Hibara.

(Illustrations reduced: each 33×23 mm.)

**1963.** Bandai-Asahi National Park.

927. **457.** 5 y. green .. .. 45 10
928. **458.** 10 y. brown .. .. 75 10

459. Purple Jay.

**1963.** Japanese Birds. Multicoloured.

929. 10 y. Type **459** .. .. 2·00 65
930. 10 y. Rock Ptarmigan .. 60 15
931. 10 y. Eastern Turtle Dove 60 15
932. 10 y. White Stork .. .. 60 15
933. 10 y. Japanese Bush Warbler 60 15
934. 10 y. Siberian Meadow Bunting .. .. .. 60 15

**1963.** Olympic Games, Tokyo, 1964 (4th issue). Sports designs as T **423**.

935. 5 y.+5 y. blue .. .. 75 25
936. 5 y.+5 y. brown .. .. 75 25
937. 5 y.+5 y. brown .. .. 75 25
SPORTS: No. 935, Yachting. No. 936, Boxing. No. 937, Volleyball.

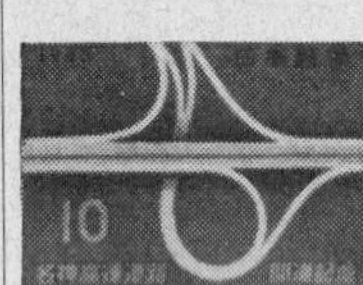

460. Road Junction, Ritto, Shiga. 461. Girl Scout and Flag.

**1963.** Opening of Nagoya-Kobe Expressway.

938. **460.** 10 y. green, blk. & orge. 35 10

**1963.** Asian Girl Scout Camp, Nagano.

939. **461.** 10 y. multicoloured .. 35 10

462. Mt. Washiu. 463. Whirlpool at Naruto.

(Illustrations reduced: each 33×23 mm.)

**1963.** Seto Inland Sea National Park.

940. **462.** 5 y. brown .. .. 25 10
941. **463.** 10 y. green .. .. 35 10

464. Lake Shikaribetsu. 465. Mt. Kurodake.

(Illustrations reduced: each 33×23 mm.)

**1963.** Daisetsuzan National Park.

942. **464.** 5 y. blue .. .. 25 10
943. **465.** 10 y. purple .. .. 35 10

466. Antennae. 467. "Great Wave off Kanagawa" (from "36 Views of Mt. Fuji" by Hokusai Katsushika).

**1963.** 14th Int. Scientific Radio Union Conference, Tokyo.

944. **466.** 10 y multicoloured .. 25 10

**1963.** Int. Correspondence Week.

945. **467.** 40 y. multicoloured .. 4·25 50

The design is taken from the series of 36 woodcuts showing Mt. Fuji. Others from this series are shown as Nos. 989, 1010, 1075, 1100, 1140 and 1185.

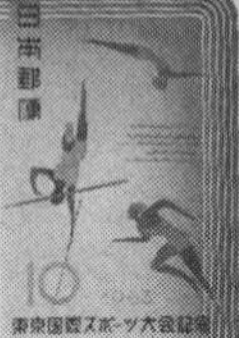

468. Athletes. 469. Wrestling.

**1963.** "Pre-Olympic" Athletic Meeting, Tokyo.

946. **468.** 10 y. multicoloured .. 15 10

**1963.** 18th National Athletic Meeting, Yamaguchi.

947. **469.** 5 y. brown .. .. 20 10
948. – 5 y. green .. .. 20 10
DESIGN: No. 948, Free-style gymnastics.

**1963.** Olympic Games, Tokyo, 1964 (5th issue). Sports designs as T **423**.

949. 5 y.+5 y. blue .. .. 35 10
950. 5 y.+5 y. olive .. .. 35 10
951. 5 y.+5 y. black .. .. 35 10
952. 5 y.+5 y. purple .. .. 35 10
SPORTS: No. 949, Cycling. 950, Show jumping. 951, Hockey. 952, Pistol-shooting.

470. Hachijo Island. 471. Kai and Iwai Dragon Toys.

**1963.** Izu Islands Quasi-National Park.

953. **470.** 10 y. multicoloured .. 25 10

**1963.** New Year's Greetings.

954. **471.** 5 y. multicoloured .. 35 10

472. Wakasa Bay. 473. View from Horikiri Pass and Agave Plant.

**1964.** Wakasa Bay Quasi-National Park.

956. **472.** 10 y. multicoloured .. 35 10

**1964.** Nichinan-Kaigan Quasi-National Park.

957. **473.** 10 y. multicoloured .. 15 10

474. Uji Bridge. 475. View of Toba.

(Illustrations reduced: each 33×23 mm.)

**1964.** Ise-Shima National Park.

958. **474.** 5 y. brown .. .. 15 10
959. **475.** 10 y. purple .. 20 10

476. Festival Float and Mt. Norikura (Tokayama Festival). 477. "Yamaboko" Shrine (Gion Festival).

478. Warriors on Horseback (Soma Horse Festival).

479. Festival Scene (Chichibu Festival).

**1964.** Regional Festivals.

960. **476.** 10 y. multicoloured .. 35 10
961. **477.** 10 y. multicoloured .. 35 10
962. **478.** 10 y. multicoloured .. 35 10
963. **479.** 10 y. multicoloured .. 35 10

480. Prince Niou playing for Lady Nakanokimi (detail of Takayoshi "Yadorigi" scroll illustrating "Tale of Genji" by Lady Murasaki).

**1964.** Philatelic Week.

964. **480.** 10 y. multicoloured .. 40 15

481. Himeji Castle. 482. Handball.

**1964.** Rebuilding of Himeji Castle.

965. **481.** 10 y. brown .. .. 15 10

**1964.** 19th National Athletic Meeting, Niigata.

966. **482.** 5 y. green .. .. 10 10
967. – 5 y. red (Gymnastics) 10 10

483. Cross-section of Cable.

**1964.** Opening of Japan–U.S. Submarine Telephone Cable.

968. **483.** 10 y. multicoloured .. 15 10

**1964.** Olympic Games, Tokyo (6th issue). Sports designs as T **423**.

969. 5 y.+5 y. violet .. .. 45 10
970. 5 y.+5 y. blue .. .. 45 10
971. 5 y.+5 y. lake .. .. 45 10
972. 5 y.+5 y. olive .. .. 45 10
SPORTS: No. 969, Modern pentathlon. 970, Canoeing. 971, Football. 972, Weightlifting.

484. Nihonbashi Bridge. 485. "Coins".

**1964.** Opening of Tokyo Expressway.

973. **484.** 10 y. grn., silver & blk. 25 10

**1964.** Int. Monetary Fund Convention, Tokyo.

980. **485.** 10 y. gold and red .. 25 10

486. Olympic Flame. 487. "Agriculture".

**1964.** Olympic Games, Tokyo (7th issue). Inscr. "1964". Multicoloured.

981. 5 y. Type **486** .. .. 20 15
982. 10 y. Main stadium .. 30 20
983. 30 y. Fencing hall .. 50 30
984. 40 y. Indoor stadium .. 70 30
985. 50 y. Komazawa hall .. 90 30
Nos. 982/5 are horiz.

**1964.** Reclamation of Hachirogata Lagoon.

987. **487.** 10 y. gold and purple .. 15 10

488. Electric Express Train.

**1964.** Inaug. of Tokyo-Osaka Railway.

988. **488.** 10y. blue and black .. 1·00 20

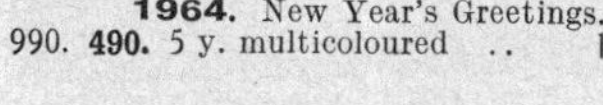

**489.** "Tokaido Highway" (from "36 Views of Mt. Fuji" by Hokusai Katsushika).

**490.** Straw Snake.

**1964.** Int. Correspondence Week.
989. **489.** 40 y. multicoloured .. 1·75 10

**1964.** New Year's Greetings.
990. **490.** 5 y. multicoloured .. 15 10

**491.** Mt. Daisen and Akamatsu Pond.

**492.** Jodo-ga-Ura (Paradise Islands) of Oki.

(Illustrations reduced: each 33×23 mm.)

**1965.** Daisen-Oki National Park.
992. **491.** 5 y. blue .. .. 25 10
993. **492.** 10 y. brown .. .. 35 10

**493.** Niseko-Annupuri Mountains.

**494.** Radar Station.

**1965.** Niseko Shakotan Otaru Quasi-National Park.
994. **493.** 10 y. multicoloured .. 30 10

**1965.** Completion of Meteorological Radar Station, Mt. Fuji.
995. **494.** 10 y. multicoloured .. 25 10

**495.** Kiyotsu Gorge.

**496.** Mt. Myoko across Lake Nojiri.

**1965.** Jo-Shin-Etsu Kogen National Park.
996. **495.** 5 y. brown .. .. 20 10
997. **496.** 10 y. purple .. .. 35 10

**497.** Postal Museum.

**1965.** Inaug. of Postal Museum, Ote-machi, Tokyo, and Stamp Exn.
998. **497.** 10 y. green .. .. 15 10

**498.** "The Prelude" (after Shoen Uyemura).

**499.** Children at Play.

**1965.** Philatelic Week.
999. **498.** 10 y. multicoloured .. 50 10

**1965.** Inaug. of National Children's Gardens.
1000. **499.** 10 y. multicoloured 20 10

## INDEX

Countries can be quickly located by referring to the index at the end of this volume.

**500.** Tree within "Leaf".

**501.** Globe and Symbols.

**1965.** Reafforestation.
1001. **500.** 10 y. multicoloured .. 20 10

**1965.** Cent. of I.T.U.
1002. **501.** 10 y. multicoloured 35 10

**502.** Mt. Naka Crater.

**503.** Aso Peaks.

(Illustrations reduced: each 33×23 mm.)

**1965.** Aso National Park.
1003. **502.** 5 y. red .. .. 25 10
1004. **503.** 10 y. green .. .. 35 10

**504.** I.C.Y. Emblem and Doves.

**1965.** Int. Co-operation Year.
1005. **504.** 40 y. multicoloured .. 75 10

**505.** "Meiji Maru" (cadet ship) and Japanese Gulls.

**506.** "Blood Donation".

**1965.** 25th Maritime Day.
1006. **505.** 10 y. multicoloured .. 1·00 10

**1965.** Campaign for Blood Donors.
1007. **506.** 10 y. multicoloured .. 25 10

**507.** Atomic Power Station, Tokyo.

**508.** "Population".

**1965.** 9th International Atomic Energy Authority Conference, Tokyo.
1008 **507** 10 y. multicoloured .. 35 10

**1965.** 10th National Census.
1009. **508.** 10 y. multicoloured .. 20 10

**509.** "Water at Misaka" (from "36 Views of Mt. Fuji" by Hokusai Katsushika).

**510.** Emblems and Plan of Diet.

**1965.** Int. Correspondence Week.
1010. **509.** 40 y. multicoloured .. 80 60

**1965.** 75th Anniv. of National Suffrage.
1011. **510.** 10 y. multicoloured .. 20 10

**511.** Walking.

**512.** Outline of Face, and Baby.

**1965.** 20th National Athletic Meeting, Gifu.
1012. **511.** 5 y. green .. 15 10
1013. – 5 y. brown (Gymnastics) 15 10

**1965.** Int. Conferences of Otology, Rhinology and Laryngology (ICORL) and Pediatrics (ICP), Tokyo.
1014. **512.** 30 y. multicoloured .. 40 10

**513.** Mt. Iwo.

**514.** Mt. Rausu.

**1965.** Shiretoko National Park.
1015. **513.** 5 y. turquoise .. 25 10
1016. **514.** 10 y. blue .. .. 35 10

**515.** Antarctic Map, Research Vessel "Fuji" and Aurora Australis.

**516.** "Straw Horse".

**1965.** Antarctic Expedition of 1965.
1017. **515.** 10 y. multicoloured 1·00 15

**1965.** New Year's Greetings.
1018. **516.** 5 y. multicoloured .. 15 10

**517.** Telephone Switch-board (1890) and Modern Dial.

**518.** Spiny Lobster.

**1965.** 75th Anniv. of Japanese Telephone Service.
1020. **517.** 10 y. multicoloured .. 15 10

**NIPPON.** From this point onwards all stamps are additionally inscribed "NIPPON".

**1966.** Fishery Products. Multicoloured.
1021. 10 y. Type **518** .. .. 30 15
1022. 10 y. Carp .. .. 30 15
1023. 10 y. Bream .. .. 30 15
1024. 10 y. Bonito .. .. 30 15
1025. 10 y. "Ayu" (trout) .. 30 15
1026. 15 y. Eel .. .. .. 40 15
1027. 15 y. Mackerel .. .. 40 15
1028. 15 y. Salmon .. .. 40 15
1029. 15 y. Buri .. .. 60 15
1030. 15 y. Globefish .. .. 60 20
1031. 15 y. Japanese common squid .. 75 30
1032. 15 y. Horned turban (shellfish) .. .. 85 30

**519.** Pleasure Garden, Mito.

**519a.** Pleasure Garden and Manchurian Cranes, Okayama.

**519b.** Kerokuen Garden, Kanazawa.

**1966.** Famous Japanese Gardens.
1033 **519** 10 y. grn, blk & gold 25 10
1034 **519a** 15 y. black, red & bl 1·25 10
1035 **519b** 15 y. black, grn & sil 35 10

**520.** Crater of Mt. Zao.

**1966.** Zao Quasi-National Park.
1036. **520.** 10 y. multicoloured .. 35 10

**521.** Muroto Cape.

**522.** Senba Cliffs, Anan.

**1966.** Muroto-Anan Kaigan Quasi-National Park.
1037. **521.** 10 y. multicoloured 25 10
1038. **522.** 10 y. multicoloured 30 10

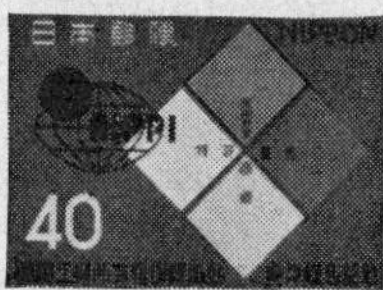

**523.** A.I.P.P.I. Emblem.

**1966.** General Assembly of Int. Assn. for Protection of Industrial Property (A.I.P.P.I.).
1039. **523.** 40 y. multicoloured .. 35 10

**524.** "Butterflies" (after T. Fujishima).

**1966.** Philatelic Week.
1040. **524.** 10 y. multicoloured .. 35 10

**525.** Goldfish.

**526.** Chrysanthemums.

**527.** Fuji (wisteria).

**528.** Hydrangea.

**529.** Golden Hall, Chuson Temple.

**530.** "Watasenia scintillans" (squid).

**531.** Yomei Gate, Tosho Shrine, Nikko.

**532.** Mizu-basho.

**533.** Konpon-chudo Hall, Enryaku Temple.

**534.** Ancient Clay Horse.

**535.** Garden of Katsura Palace.

**536.** Onjo Bosatsu (relief from bronze lantern, Todai Temple).

**537.** Kongo-Rikishi Statue, Todai Temple Nara.

**1966.** Inscr "NIPPON".

| | | | | |
|---|---|---|---|---|
| 1041 | **235** | 1 y. bistre .. .. | 10 | 10 |
| 1047 | **525** | 7 y. orange and green | 40 | 10 |
| 1049 | **526** | 15 y. yellow and blue | 1·25 | 10 |
| 1050 | | 15 y. yellow and blue | 25 | 10 |
| 1052 | **527** | 20 y. green and violet | 1·25 | 10 |
| 1053 | **528** | 25 y. blue and green | 60 | 10 |
| 1054 | **529** | 30 y. gold and blue .. | 40 | 10 |
| 1055 | **530** | 35 y. black, brn & bl | 3·25 | 10 |
| 1056 | **531** | 40 y. green and brown | 60 | 10 |
| 1057 | **532** | 45 y. multicoloured .. | 50 | 10 |
| 1058 | **240** | 50 y. red .. .. | 11·00 | 10 |
| 1059 | | 50 y. mauve .. .. | 80 | 10 |
| 1060 | **280** | 55 y. green, black & bl | 75 | 10 |
| 1061 | **533** | 60 y. green .. .. | 1·00 | 10 |
| 1062 | **534** | 65 y. brown .. .. | 16·00 | 10 |
| 1063 | | 65 y. orange .. .. | 1·00 | 10 |
| 1064 | **281** | 75 y. multicoloured .. | 1·40 | 10 |
| 1065 | **410** | 90 y. brown and gold | 2·00 | 10 |
| 1066 | **411** | 100 y. grey, blk & red | 1·75 | 10 |
| 1067 | **535** | 110 y. brown .. | 1·50 | 10 |
| 1068 | **412** | 120 y. red .. .. | 3·50 | 10 |
| 1069 | **536** | 200 y. green .. .. | 7·50 | 10 |
| 1070 | **537** | 500 y. purple .. | 8·50 | 10 |

No. 1050 is as T **526** but with white figures of value.

See also Nos. 1226/49.

**538.** U.N. and U.N.E.S.C.O. Emblems.

**539.** Pacific Ocean.

**1966.** 20th Anniv. of U.N.E.S.C.O.
1071. **538.** 15 y. multicoloured .. 15 10

**1966.** 11th Pacific Science Congress, Tokyo.
1072. **539.** 15 y. multicoloured .. 20 10

**540.** Amakusa Bridges.

**1966.** Completion of Amakusa Bridges.
1073. **540.** 15 y. multicoloured .. 20 10

**541.** Family and Emblem.

**542.** "Sekiya on the Sumida" (from "36 Views of Mt. Fuji" by Hokusai Katsushika).

**1966.** 50th Anniv. of Post Office Life Insurance Office.
1074. **541.** 15 y. multicoloured .. 15 10

**1966.** Int. Correspondence Week.
1075. **542.** 50 y. multicoloured .. 1·75 15

**543.** Rotary Cobalt Radiator.

**544.** Triple Jump.

**1966.** 9th. Int. Cancer Congress, Tokyo.
1076. **543.** 7 y.+3 y. blk. & orge. 25 15
1077. – 15 y.+5 y. mult. .. 35 15
DESIGN—VERT. 15 y. Detection by X-rays.

**1966.** 21st National Athletic Meeting, Oita.
1078. **544.** 7 y. red .. .. 30 10
1079. – 7 y. blue (clay-pigeon shooting) .. .. 30 10

**545.** National Theatre Building.

**546.** Rice Year Emblem.

**1966.** Inaug. of Japanese National Theatre. Multicoloured.
1080. 15 y. Type **545** .. .. 25 10
1081. 25 y. "Kabuki" performance (48×33½ mm.) .. 90 10
1082. 50 y. "Bunraku" puppet act (33½×48 mm.) 1·00 10

**1966.** Int. Rice Year.
1083. **546.** 15 y. black, ochre & red 15 10

**547.** Ittobori Sheep (sculpture).

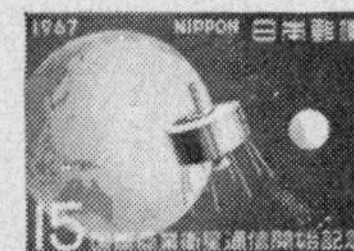


**548.** Satellite "Intelsat 2", Earth and Moon.

**1966.** New Year's Greetings.
1084. **547.** 7 y. multicoloured .. 15 10

**1967.** Inauguration of Int. Commercial Satellite Communications in Japan.
1086. **548.** 15 y. brown and blue 15 10

**549.** Douglas DC-8 and Flight Route.

**550.** Literature Museum.

**1967.** Inaug. of Round-the-World Air Service.
1087. **549.** 15 y. multicoloured 50 10

**1967.** Opening of Japanese Modern Literature Museum, Meguro-ku, Tokyo.
1088. **550.** 15 y. multicoloured .. 15 10

**551.** "Lakeside" (after S. Kuroda).

**1967.** Philatelic Week.
1089. **551.** 15 y. multicoloured .. 60 10

**552.** Port of Kobe.

**553.** Emblem of Welfare Service.

**1967.** 5th Int. Assn. of Ports and Harbours Congress, Tokyo.
1090. **552.** 50 y. multicoloured .. 80 10

**1967.** 50th Anniv. of Welfare Commissioner Service.
1091. **553.** 15 y. gold and agate 25 10

**554.** Pedestrian Road Crossing.

**1967.** 20th Anniv. of Road Safety Campaign.
1092. **554.** 15 y. multicoloured 15 10

**555.** Mts. Kita and Koma.

**556.** Mts. Akashi, Hijiri and Higashi.

(Illustrations reduced: each 33×23 mm.)

**1967.** Southern Alps National Park.
1093. **555.** 7 y. blue .. .. 25 10
1094. **556.** 15 y. purple .. .. 35 10

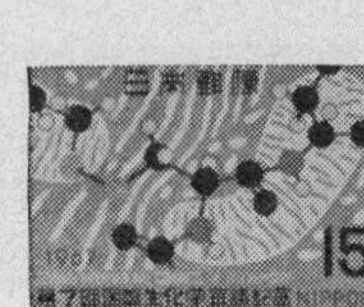


**557.** Protein Molecules.

**558.** Gymnast.

**1967.** 7th Int. Biochemistry Congress, Tokyo.
1095. **557.** 15 y. multicoloured .. 15 10

**1967.** "Universiade 1967" (Sports Meeting), Tokyo. T **558** and similar multicoloured design.
1096. 15 y. Type **558** .. .. 20 10
1097. 50 y. Universiade "U" emblem (25×35½ mm.) 90 10

**559.** Paper Lantern.

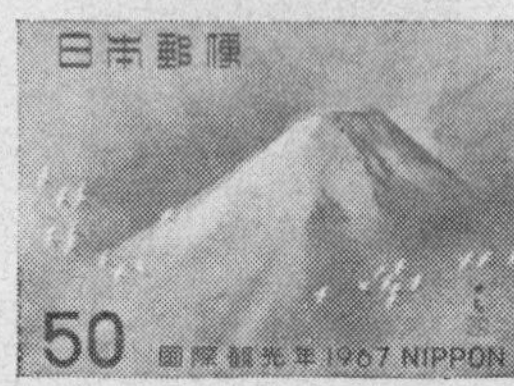


**560.** Mt. Fuji (after T. Yokoyama).

**1967.** Int. Tourist Year.
1098. **559.** 15 y. multicoloured .. 25 10
1099. **560.** 50 y. multicoloured .. 3·25 3·25

**561.** "Kajikazawa in Kai Province" (from "36 Views of Mt. Fuji" by Hokusai Katsushika).

**562.** Athlete.

**1967.** Int. Correspondence Week.
1100. **561.** 50 y. multicoloured .. 2·75 15

**1967.** 22nd National Athletic Meeting, Saitama.
1101 **562** 15 y. multicoloured .. 50 10

**563.** Buddha, Koryu Temple, Kyoto.

**564.** Kudara Kannon (Budda), Horyu Temple, Nara.

**565.** Horyu Temple, Nara.

**1967.** National Treasures. Asuka Period.
1102. **563.** 15 y. multicoloured .. 40 10
1103. **564.** 15 y. multicoloured .. 60 10
1104. **565.** 50 y. multicoloured .. 2·50 20
See also Nos. 1113/15, 1120/2, 1134/6, 1152/4, 1170/2 and 1177/80.

**566.** Motor Expressway.

**569.** "Noborizaru" (Miyazaki toy).

**567.** Mt. Kumotori.

**568.** Lake Chichibu.

**1967.** 13th World Road Congress, Tokyo.
1105. **566.** 50 y. multicoloured .. 75 10

**1967.** Chichibu-Tama National Park.
1106. **567.** 7 y. olive .. .. 35 10
1107. **568.** 15 y. violet .. .. 45 10

**1967.** New Year's Greetings.
1108. **569.** 7 y. multicoloured .. 35 10

**570.** Mt. Sobo.

**571.** Takachiho Gorge.

**1967.** Sobo-Katamuki Quasi-National Park.
1110. **570.** 15 y. multicoloured .. 35 10
1111. **571.** 15 y. multicoloured .. 35 10

**572.** Boy and Girl and Cruise Liner "Sakura Maru".

**573.** Asura Statue, Kofuku Temple, Nara.

**574.** Gakko Bosatsu, Todai Temple, Nara.

**575.** Srimaha devi (painting), Yakushi Temple, Nara.

**1968.** Youth Goodwill Cruise to mark Meiji Centenary.
1112 **572** 15 y. violet, yell & bl 15 10

**1968.** National Treasures. Nara Period (710–784).
1113 **573** 15 y. multicoloured .. 45 10
1114 **574** 15 y. multicoloured .. 70 10
1115 **575** 50 y. multicoloured .. 2·50 20

**576.** Mt. Yatsugatake and Cattle.

**577.** Mt. Tateshina and Lake.

**1968.** Yatsugatake-Chushin Kogen Quasi-National Park.
1116. **576.** 15 y. multicoloured .. 30 10
1117. **577.** 15 y. multicoloured .. 30 10

## MINIMUM PRICE

The minimum price quoted is 10p which represents a handling charge rather than a basis for valuing common stamps. For further notes about prices see introductory pages.

578. "Dancer in a Garden" (after Bakusen Tsuchida).

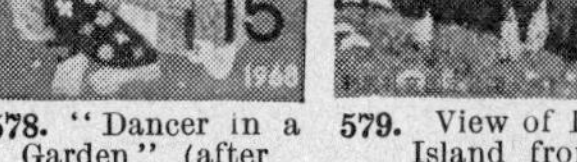

579. View of Rishiri Island from Rebun Island.

**1968.** Philatelic Week.
1118. **578.** 15 y. multicoloured .. 40 10

**1968.** Rishiri-Rebun Quasi-National Park.
1119. **579.** 15 y. multicoloured.. 15 10

580. Lacquer Casket

582. "Fugen Bosatsu" (painting of Bodishattva Samantabhadva).

581. "The Origin of Shigisan" (painting in Chogo-sonshi Temple).

**1968.** National Treasures. Heinan Period (794–1185).

| | | | | |
|---|---|---|---|---|
| 1120 | 580 | 15 y. multicoloured .. | 30 | 10 |
| 1121 | 581 | 15 y. multicoloured .. | 60 | 10 |
| 1122 | 582 | 50 y. multicoloured .. | 4·25 | 35 |

583. Centenary Tower and Star.

584. Biro Trees and Pacific Sunrise.

**1968.** Hokkaido Cent.
1123. **583.** 15 y. multicoloured .. 15 10

**1968.** Return of Ogasawara Islands to Japan.
1124. **584.** 15 y. multicoloured .. 15 10

585. "Map of Japan" in Figures.

**1968.** Postal Codes Campaign.

| | | | | |
|---|---|---|---|---|
| 1125. | 585. | 7 y. red, brn. & grn. (I) | 2·75 | 10 |
| 1126. | – | 7 y. red, brn. & grn. (II) | 2·75 | 10 |
| 1127. | 585. | 15 y. mve., vio. & bl. (I) | 1·00 | 10 |
| 1128. | – | 15 y. mve., vio. & bl. (II) | 1·00 | 10 |

(I) Inscr. as in Type **585** reading "Don't omit postal code on the address" measures 11 mm.

(II) Inscr. reading "Postal code also on your address" measures 12 mm.

586. River Kiso.

587. Inuyama Castle and View.

**1968.** Hida-Kisogawa Quasi-National Park.
1129. **586.** 15 y. multicoloured.. 25 10
1130. **587.** 15 y. multicoloured.. 25 10

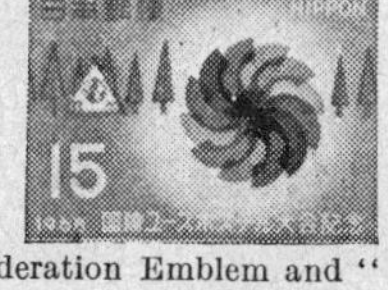

588. Federation Emblem and "Sun".

**1968.** Int. Youth Hostel Conf., Tokyo.
1131. **588.** 15 y. multicoloured .. 20 10

589. Humans forming Emblem.

590. Baseball "Pitcher".

**1968.** 50th All-Japan High School Baseball Championships, Koshi-en, Tokyo.
1132. **589.** 15 y. multicoloured .. 60 10
1133. **590.** 15 y. multicoloured .. 60 10

591. "Minamoto Yoritomo" (Jingo Temple Collection).

593. Red-braided Armour (Kasuga Grand Shrine Collection).

592. Emperor Nijo escaping from Black Palace (from "Tale of Heiji" picture scroll).

**1968.** National Treasures. Kamakura Period (1185–1334). Multicoloured.

| | | | |
|---|---|---|---|
| 1134. | 15 y. Type **591** .. .. | 40 | 10 |
| 1135. | 15 y. Type **592** .. .. | 40 | 10 |
| 1136. | 50 y. Type **593** .. .. | 3·00 | 30 |

594. Mount Iwate.

595. Lake Towada.

**1968.** Towada-Hachimantai National Park.
1137. **594.** 7 y. brown .. .. 25 10
1138. **595.** 15 y. green .. .. 45 10

596. Gymnastics.

597. "Fujimihara in Owari Province" (from "36 Views of Mt. Fuji" by Hokusai Katsushika).

**1968.** 23rd National Athletic Meeting.
1139. **596.** 15 y. multicoloured .. 40 10

**1968.** Int. Correspondence Week.
1140. **597.** 50 y. multicoloured .. 2·00 25

598. Centenary Emblem and Sail Warship "Shohei Maru", 1868.

599. "Arrival of the Imperial Carriage in Tokyo" (after Tomone Kobori).

**1968.** Cent. of Meiji Era.
1141. **598.** 15 y. multicoloured .. 15 10
1142. **599.** 15 y. multicoloured .. 15 10

600. Old and New Kannonzaki Lighthouses.

**1968.** Cent. of Japanese Lighthouses.
1143. **600.** 15 y. multicoloured .. 30 10

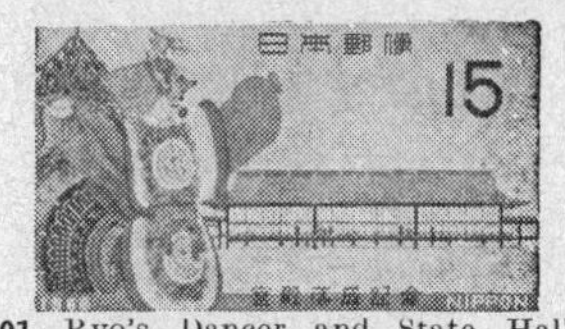

601. Ryo's Dancer and State Hall.

**1968.** Completion of Imperial Palace.
1144. **601.** 15 y. multicoloured .. 20 10

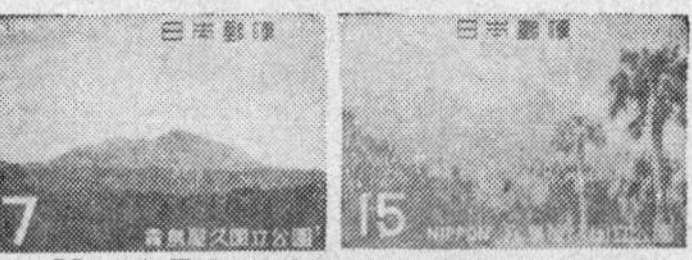

602. Mount Takachiho. 603. Mount Motobu, Yaku Island.

**1968.** Kirishima-Yaku National Park.
1145. **602.** 7 y. violet .. .. 20 10
1146. **603.** 15 y. orange .. .. 25 10

604. "Niwatori" (Yamagata toy).

605. Human Rights Emblem and Dancers.

**1968.** New Year's Greetings.
1147. **604.** 7 y. multicoloured .. 25 10

**1968.** Human Rights Year.
1149. **605.** 50 y. multicoloured .. 25 15

606. Siberian Chipmunk with Nuts.

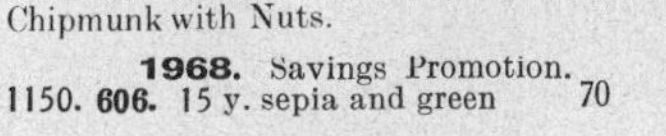

607. Coastal Scenery.

**1968.** Savings Promotion.
1150. **606.** 15 y. sepia and green 70 10

**1969.** Echizen-Kaga-Kaigan Quasi-National Park.
1151. **607.** 15 y. multicoloured .. 15 10

608. Silver Pavilion, Jisho Temple, Kyoto.

609. Pagoda, Anraku Temple, Nagano.

610. "Winter Landscape" (Sesshu).

**1969.** National Treasures. Muromachi Period. Multicoloured.

| | | | |
|---|---|---|---|
| 1152. | 15 y. Type **608** .. .. | 40 | 10 |
| 1153. | 15 y. Type **609** .. .. | 40 | 10 |
| 1154. | 50 y. Type **610** .. .. | 2·00 | 30 |

611. Mt. Chokai, from Tobishima.

**1969.** Chokai Quasi-National Park.
1155. **611.** 15 y. multicoloured.. 35 10

612. "Expo" Emblem and Globe.

613. "Cherry Blossom" (from mural Chichakuin Temple, Kyoto).

**1969.** "EXPO 70" World Fair, Osaka (1st issue).
1156. **612.** 15 y.+5 y. mult. 35 15
1157. **613.** 50 y.+10 y. mult. 85 50
See also Nos. 1193/5 and 1200/2.

614. Mt. Koya from Jinnogamine.

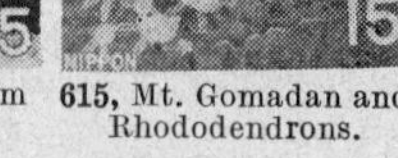

615. Mt. Gomadan and Rhododendrons.

**1969.** Koya-Ryujin Quasi-National Park.
1158. **614.** 15 y. multicoloured.. 15 10
1159. **615.** 15 y. multicoloured.. 15 10

616. "Hair" (Kokei Kobayashi).

617. Woman and Child crossing "Roads".

**1969.** Philatelic Week.
1160. **616.** 15 y. multicoloured.. 40 10

**1969.** Road Safety Campaign.
1161 **617** 15 y. green, blue & red 15 10

618. Sakawagawa Bridge.

**1969.** Completion of Tokyo-Nagoya Expressway.
1162. **618.** 15 y. multicoloured.. 15 10

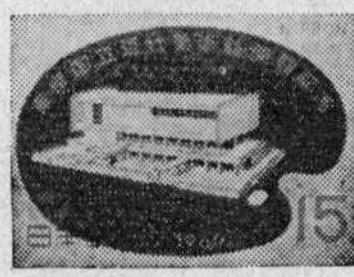

619. Museum Building.

**1969.** Opening of National Museum of Modern Art, Tokyo.
1163. **619.** 15 y. multicoloured.. 15 10

620. Nuclear-powered Freighter "Mutsu" and Atomic Symbol.

**1969.** Launching of Japan's 1st Nuclear Ship "Mutsu".
1164. **620.** 15 y. multicoloured.. 30 10

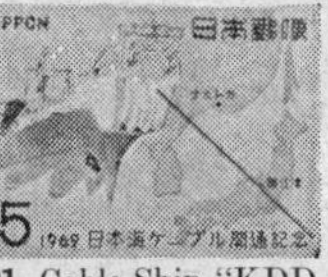

621. Cable Ship "KDD Maru" and Map.

622. Symbol and Cards.

**1969.** Opening of Japanese Ocean Cable.
1165. **621.** 15 y. multicoloured .. 15 10

**1969.** Postal Codes Campaign.
1166. **622.** 7 y. red and green .. 15 10
1167. – 15 y. red and blue .. 20 10
DESIGN: 15 y. Symbol, postbox and code numbers.

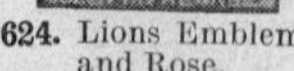

**624.** Lions Emblem and Rose.

**625.** Hotoke-ga-ura (coast).

**1969.** 52nd Lions Int. Convention Tokyo.
1168. **624.** 15 y. multicoloured .. 20 10

**1969.** Shimokita-Hanto Quasi-National Park.
1169. **625.** 15 y. multicoloured .. 15 10

**626.** Himeji Castle, Hyogo Prefecture.

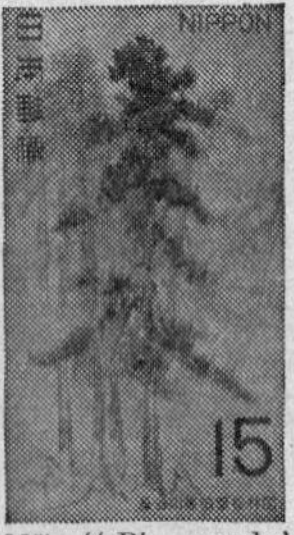

**627.** " Pinewoods" (T. Hasegawa).

**628.** " The Japanese Cypress " (artist unknown).

**1969.** National Treasures. Momoyama Period.
1170. **626.** 15 y. multicoloured .. 50 10
1171. **627.** 15 y. black and drab 50 10
1172. **628.** 50 y. multicoloured .. 1·00 10

**629.** Harano-fudo Waterfalls.

**630.** Mount Nagisan.

**1969.** Hyonosen-Ushiroyama-Nagisan Quasi-National Park.
1173. **629.** 15 y. multicoloured .. 25 10
1174. **630.** 15 y. multicoloured .. 25 10

**631.** Mount O-akan.

**632.** Mount Iwo.

**1969.** Akan National Park.
1175. **631.** 7 y. blue .. .. 25 10
1176. **632.** 15 y. sepia .. .. 25 10

**633.** " Choben " (T. Ikeno).

**634.** "The Red-plum Tree" (K. Ogata).

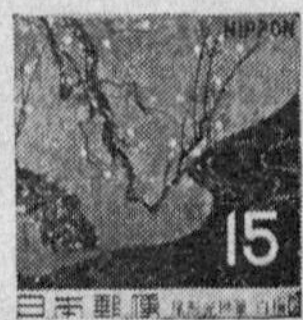

**635.** " The White-plum Tree" (K. Ogata).

**636.** "Japanese Pheasant" Incense-burner (after Ninsei).

**1969.** National Treasures. Edo Period.
1177. **633.** 15 y. multicoloured .. 40 10
1178. **634.** 15 y. multicoloured .. 50 10
1179. **635.** 15 y. multicoloured .. 50 10
1180. **636.** 50 y. multicoloured .. 1·25 95

**637.** Globe and Doves.

**638.** "Woman Reading a Letter" (Utamaro Kitagawa).

**639.** "Reading a Letter" (Harunobu Suzuki).

**640.** "Miyako Dennai" (Sharaku Toshusai).

**1969.** 16th U.P.U. Congress, Tokyo.
1181. **637.** 15 y. multicoloured .. 30 10
1182. **638.** 30 y. multicoloured .. 65 10
1183. **639.** 50 y. multicoloured .. 1·25 10
1184. **640.** 60 y. multicoloured .. 1·40 10

**641.** "Mishima Pass" (from "36 Views of Mt. Fuji" by Hokusai Katsushika).

**642.** Rugby Football.

**1969.** Int. Correspondence Week.
1185. **641.** 50 y. multicoloured .. 1·00 10

**1969.** 24th National Athletic Meeting.
1186. **642.** 15 y. multicoloured .. 50 10

**643.** Cape Kitayama.

**644.** Goishi Coast.

**1969.** Rikuchu-Kaigan National Park.
1187. **643.** 7 y. blue .. .. 15 10
1188. **644.** 15 y. red and salmon 20 10

**645.** Worker in Safety Helmet.

**646.** Guardian Dog, Hokkeji Temple.

**1969.** 50th Anniv. of I.L.O.
1189. **645.** 15 y. black, yellow, brown and blue .. 15 10

**1969.** New Year's Greetings.
1190. **646.** 7 y. multicoloured .. 35 10

**647.** Peasants, Tsushima Island.

**1970.** Iki-Tsushima Quasi-National Park.
1192. **647.** 15 y. multicoloured .. 20 10

**648.** View of Fair and Firework Display.

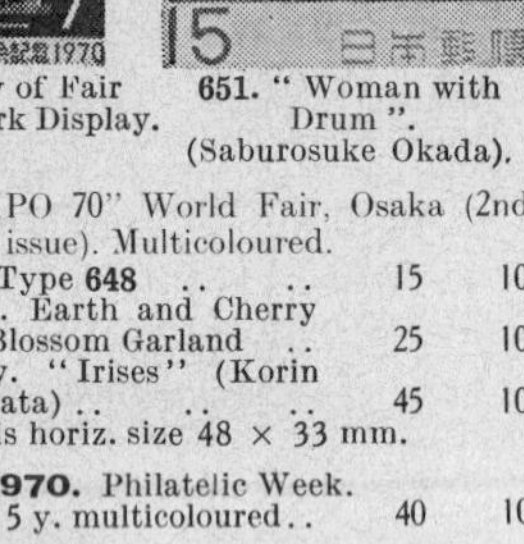

**651.** " Woman with Drum ". (Saburosuke Okada).

**1970.** "EXPO 70" World Fair, Osaka (2nd issue). Multicoloured.
1193. 7 y. Type **648** .. .. 15 10
1194. 15 y. Earth and Cherry Blossom Garland .. 25 10
1195. 50 y. " Irises" (Korin Ogata) .. .. .. 45 10
No. 1195 is horiz. size 48 × 33 mm.

**1970.** Philatelic Week.
1197. **651.** 15 y. multicoloured .. 40 10

**652.** Cherry Blossom, Mt. Yoshino.

**653.** Waterfall, Nachi.

**1970.** Yoshino-Kumano National Park.
1198 **652** 7 y. black and pink .. 30 10
1199 **653** 15 y. dp grn, grn & bl 45 10

**654.** Kanto (lantern) Festival.

**655.** Japanese Pavilions.

**656.** " Flowers of Autumn " (detail, Hoitsu Sakai).

**1970.** "EXPO 70" World Fair, Osaka (3rd issue).
1200. **654.** 7 y. multicoloured .. 20 10
1201. **655.** 15 y. multicoloured .. 30 10
1202. **656.** 50 y. multicoloured .. 45 10

**657.** Houses and Code Symbol.

**658.** Utaemon Nakamura VI as Hanako in "Musume Dojoji".

**659.** Danjuro Ichikawa XI as Sukeroku in "Sukeroku".

**661.** Girl Scout saluting.

**660.** " Kanjincho ".

**1970.** Postal Codes Campaign.
1204. **657.** 7 y. violet and green 25 10
1205. 15 y. purple and blue 35 10

**1970.** Japanese Theatre " Kabuki".
1206. **658.** 15 y. multicoloured .. 25 10
1207. **659.** 15 y. multicoloured .. 25 10
1208. **660.** 50 y. multicoloured .. 75 10
See also Nos. 1250/2, 1284/6 and 1300/2.

**1970.** 50th Anniv. of Japanese Girl Scouts.
1209. **661.** 15 y. multicoloured 35 10

**662.** Festival Drummer and Kinoura Coastline.

**663.** Mt. Tate from Himi Shore.

**1970.** Noto-Hanto Quasi-National Park.
1210. **662.** 15 y. multicoloured .. 25 10
1211. **663.** 15 y. multicoloured .. 25 10

**664.** " Sunflower " and U.N. Emblem.

**667.** "Tokyo Post Office" (woodcut, Hiroshige III).

**665.** Mt. Myogi **666.** Mt. Arafune.

**1970.** 4th U.N. Congress on Prevention of Crime and Treatment of Offenders, Kyoto.
1212. **664.** 15 y. multicoloured .. 25 10

**1970.** Myogi-Arafune-Sakukuogen Quasi-National Park.
1213. **665.** 15 y. multicoloured .. 20 10
1214. **666.** 15 y. multicoloured .. 20 10

**1970.** International Correspondence Week.
1215. **667.** 50 y. multicoloured .. 85 10

**668.** Show Jumping, Mt. Iwate and Paulownia Flowers.

**669.** "Hodogaya Stage" (print, Hiroshige III).

**1970.** 25th National Athletic Meeting, Iwate.
1216 **668** 15 y. multicoloured .. 50 10

**1970.** Cent. of Telegraph Service.
1217. **669.** 15 y. multicoloured 45 10

**670.** U.N. Emblem within "Tree".

**672.** Competition Emblem.

**1970.** 25th Anniv. of U.N.O. Mult.
1218. 15 y. Type **670** .. 15 10
1219. 50 y. U.N. emblem, New York H.Q. and flags .. 40 10

**1970.** 19th International Vocational Training Competition, Chiba City.
1220. **672.** 15 y. multicoloured.. 15 10

**673.** Diet Building and Doves.

**674.** "Wild Boar" (folk-handicraft).

**1970.** 80th Anniv. of Japanese Diet.
1221. **673.** 15 y. multicoloured 15 10

**1970.** New Year's Greetings.
1222. **674.** 7 y. multicoloured .. 20 10

675. Ski Jumping.

**1971.** Winter Olympic Games, Sapporo (1972) (1st issue). Multicoloured.
1224. 15 y. + 5 y. Type **675** 30 10
1225. 15 y. + 5 y. Ice-hockey (horiz.) .. .. 30 10
See also Nos. 1280/82

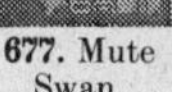

**677.** Mute Swan.

**678.** Sika Deer.

**679.** "Allomyrina dichotomus".

**680.** "Pine Tree" (T. Kano).

**682.** Golden Eagle.

**684.** "Ho-o" (Phoenix), Byodoin Temple, Uji.

**692.** Statue of Kissho, Joruri Temple.

**1971.** Inscribed "NIPPON".
1226 **273** 3 y. green .. .. 10 10
1227 **677** 5 y. blue .. .. 10 10
1228 **678** 10 y. brown & green 25 10
1229 **679** 12 y. brown .. 20 10
1230 **680** 20 y. brown & green 20 10
1231 **528** 25 y. blue and green 35 10
1232 **240** 50 y. green .. .. 35 10
1233 – 60 y. green & yellow 40 10
1234 **408** 70 y. black & orange 95 10
1235 **409** 80 y. brown and red 1·50 10
1236 **410** 90 y. brown & orange 1·40 10
1237 **682** 90 y. black and red 2·00 10
1238 **412** 120 y. brown & green 55 10
1239 – 140 y. purple & mve 75 10
1240 **684** 150 y. turq & green 1·75 10
1240a 150 y. brown and red 60 10
1241 – 200 y. red .. .. 3·00 10
1242 – 200 y. brown .. 3·50 10
1243 – 200 y. red .. .. 1·25 10
1244 – 250 y. blue .. .. 1·25 10
1245 – 300 y. blue .. .. 3·50 10
1246 – 350 y. brown .. 2·00 10
1247 – 400 y. red .. .. 2·40 10
1248 – 500 y. green .. 3·00 10
1249 **692** 1000 y. multicoloured 5·50 60

Designs: 60 y. Narcissi. 140 y. Noh mask of aged man. 200 y. (No. 1241), Onjo Bosatsu (relief), Todai Temple. 200 y. (Nos. 1242/3), Warrior (statuette). 250 y. Komainu (guardian dog), Katori Shrine. 300 y. Buddha, Kofuku Temple. 350 y. Goddess of Mercy, Yaluski Temple, Nara. 400 y. Tentoki (demon). 500 y. Buddhist deity.

No. 1231 is Type **528**, redrawn. The inscription and face value are smaller, but the main difference is in the position of the leaves, on No. 1053 they touch the left edge of the design, but on No. 1231 they are completely clear of it.

No. 1241 is as Type **536** but smaller, 18 × 22 mm.

For 210 y. as Nos. 1242/3 and 360 y. as No. 1246, see Nos. 1600 and 1604.

**693.** "Gen-jo-raku".

**694.** "Ko-cho".

**695.** "Tai-hei-raku".

**1971.** Japanese Theatre "Gagaku".
1250. **693.** 15 y. multicoloured.. 30 10
1251. **694.** 15 y. multicoloured.. 30 10
1252. **695.** 50 y. multicoloured.. 85 10

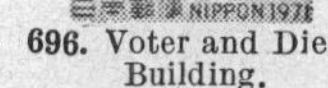

**696.** Voter and Diet Building.

**697.** Pine Trees and Maple Leaves.

**1971.** 25th Anniv. of Women's Suffrage.
1253. **696.** 15 y. multicoloured 15 10

**1971.** National Afforestation Campaign.
1254. **697.** 7 y. blk., violet & grn. 40 10

**698.** "Tsukiji-akashicho" (K. Kaburagi).

**699.** "Posting a Letter" (K. Dogishi).

**700.** "Postman" (K. Kasai).

**701.** "Railway Post Office". (S. Onozaki).

**1971.** Philatelic Week.
1255. **698.** 15 y. multicoloured.. 40 10

**1971.** Cent. of Japanese Postal Services.
1256. **699.** 15 y. multicoloured.. 20 10
1257. **700.** 15 y. black & brown.. 20 10
1258. **701.** 15 y. multicoloured.. 20 10

**702.** Great Tit.

**703.** Adelie Penguins.

**1971.** 25th Bird Week.
1259. **702.** 15 y. multicoloured.. 1·25 10

**1971.** 10th Anniv. of Antarctic Treaty.
1260. **703.** 15 y. multicoloured.. 1·50 20

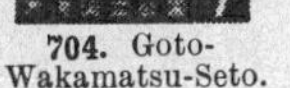

**704.** Goto-Wakamatsu-Seto.

**705.** Kuzyuku-shima.

**1971.** Saikai National Park.
1261. **704.** 7 y. green .. .. 25 10
1262. **705.** 15 y. brown .. .. 35 10

**706.** Postal Code Numerals.

**707.** Scout Bugler.

**1971.** Postal Code Campaign.
1263. **706.** 7 y. red and green .. 20 10
1264. 15 y. red and blue .. 30 10

**1971.** 13th World Scout Jamboree, Asagiri.
1265. **707.** 15 y. multicoloured.. 40 10

**708.** Rose Emblem.

**709.** "Tokyo Horse Tram" (Yoshimura).

**1971.** 50th Anniv. of Family Conciliation System.
1266. **708.** 15 y. multicoloured 25 10

**1971.** Int. Correspondence Week.
1267. **709.** 50 y. multicoloured.. 60 25

**710.** Emperor's Standard.

**712.** Tennis.

**1971.** European Tour by Emperor Hirohito and Empress Nagako. Multicoloured.
1268 15 y. Type **710** .. .. 15 10
1269 15 y. "Beyond the Sea" (drawing by Empress Nagako) .. .. 15 10

**1971.** 26th National Athletic Meeting.
1271. **712.** 15 y. multicoloured.. 30 10

**713.** Child's Face and "100".

**714.** "Dragon" (G. Hashimoto.)

**1971.** Centenary of National Family Registration System.
1272. **713.** 15 y. multicoloured 15 10

**1971.** Centenary of Government Printing Works, Tokyo. Multicoloured.
1273. 15 y. Type **714** .. 20 10
1274. 15 y. "Tiger" (from same drawing as above) 20 10

**716.** Mt. Yotei from Lake Toya.

**718.** Takarabune ("Treasure Ship").

**717.** Mt. Showa-Shinzan.

**1971.** Shikotsu-Toya National Park.
1275. **716.** 7 y. green and olive.. 25 10
1276. **717.** 15 y. blue and brown 40 10

**1971.** New Year's Greetings.
1277. **718.** 7 y. multicoloured .. 25 10
1278. 10 y. multicoloured.. 35 10

**719.** Skiing.

**1972.** Winter Olympic Games, Sapporo. (2nd issue). Multicoloured.
1280. 20 y. Type **719** .. 15 10
1281. 20 y. Bobsleighing .. 15 10
1282. 50 y. Figure skating (pair) (horiz. 52 × 36 mm.).. 45 10

**722.** "Kumagai-jinya".

**723.** "Nozaki-mura".

**724.** "Awa-no-Naruto".

**1972.** Japanese Theatre. "Banraku" Puppet Theatre.
1284. **722.** 20 y. multicoloured.. 30 10
1285. **723.** 20 y. multicoloured.. 30 10
1286. **724.** 50 y. multicoloured.. 70 10

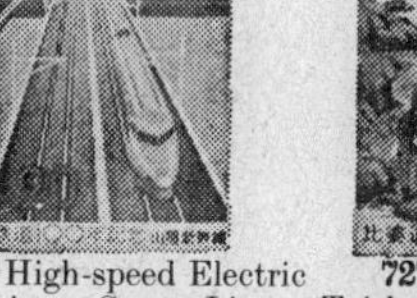

**725.** High-speed Electric Train on Sanyo Line.

**727.** Fishing, Taishakukyo Valley.

**726.** Hiba Mountains.

**1972.** Cent. of Japanese Railways (1st issue) and Opening of Sanyo Line.
1287. **725.** 20 y. multicoloured.. 25 10
See also Nos. 1305/6.

**1972.** Hiba-Dogo-Taishaku Quasi-National Park.
1288. **726.** 20 y. multicoloured.. 15 10
1289. **727.** 20 y. multicoloured.. 20 10

**728.** Adult with Human Heart.

**729.** "Rising Balloon" (Gakuryo Nakamura).

**1972.** World Heart Month.
1290. 728. 20 y. multicoloured . . 15 10

**1972.** Philatelic Week.
1291. 729. 20 y. multicoloured . . 15 10

730. Courtesy Gate, Shuri.

731. Japanese Camellia.

**1972.** Return of Ryukyu Islands to Japan.
1292. 730. 20 y. multicoloured . . 15 10

**1972.** National Afforrestation Campaign.
1293. 731. 20 y. yell., bl. & grn. 35 10

732. Mt. Kurikoma and Kokeshi Doll.

733. Naruko-kyo Gorge and Kokeshi Doll.

**1972.** Kurikoma Quasi-National Park.
1294. 732. 20 y. multicoloured . . 15 10
1295. 733. 20 y. multicoloured . . 15 10

734. Envelope and Code Symbol.

736. Mt. Hodaka.

737. Mt. Tate.

**1972.** Postal Codes Campaign (5th issue).
1296. 734. 10 y. blk., purple & blue 10 10
1297. – 20 y. red and green . . 15 10
DESIGN: 20 y. Mail-box and Code symbol.

**1972.** Chubu Sangaku National Park.
1298. 736. 10 y. violet & mauve 20 10
1299. 737. 20 y. blue & brown . . 30 10

738. " Tamura ".

739. " Aoi-no-ue ".

740. "Hagoromo".

**1972.** Japanese Theatre. "Noh".
1300. 738. 20 y. multicoloured . . 20 10
1301. 739. 20 y. multicoloured . . 20 10
1302. 740. 50 y. multicoloured . . 45 15

741. " Profiles of Schoolchildren ".

742. "Eitai Bridge" (Hiroshige III).

**1972.** Cent. of Japanese Educational System.
1303. 741. 20 y. multicoloured 15 10

**1972.** Int. Correspondence Week.
1304. 742. 50 y multicoloured . . 60 10

743. " Inauguration of Railway Service " (Hiroshige III).

745. Kendo (Japanese Fencing).

**1972.** Centenary of Japanese Railways (2nd issue). Multicoloured.
1305. 20 y. Type 743 . . . . 50 10
1306. 20 y. Steam locomotive, Class "C-62" . . . . 50 10

**1972.** 27th National Athletic Meeting, Kagoshima.
1307 745 10 y. multicoloured . . 35 10

746. Scout and Cub.

747. "Harbour and Bund, Yokohama" (Hiroshige III).

**1972.** 50th Anniv. of Japanese Boy Scouts.
1308. 746. 20 y. multicoloured 35 10

**1972.** Cent of Japanese Customs Service.
1309 747 20 y. multicolured . . 55 10

748. " Plum Blossoms " Plate (K. Ogata).

749. Mt. Tsurugi.

750. River Yoshino, Oboke Valley.

**1972.** New Year's Greetings.
1310. 748. 10 y. multicoloured . . 15 10

**1973.** Tsurugi-San Quasi-National Park.
1312. 749. 20 y. multicoloured . . 30 10
1313. 750. 20 y. multicoloured . . 30 10

751. Mt. Takao.

752. Minoo Falls and Japanese Macaques.

**1973.** Meiji-no-mori Quasi National Park.
1314. 751. 20 y. multicoloured . . 20 10
1315. 752. 20 y. multicoloured . . 20 10

753. "Dragon" (East Wall).

754. " Male Figures " (East Wall).

755. " Female Figures" (West Wall).

**1973.** Asuka Archaeological Conservation Fund. Takamatsuzuka Kofun Tomb Murals.
1316. 753. 20 y. + 5 y. mult. . . 30 10
1317. 754. 20 y. + 5 y. mult. . . 30 10
1318. 755. 50 y. + 10 y. mult. . . 80 35

756. Phoenix Tree.

757. " Sumiyoshi-mode " (R. Kishida).

**1973.** National Afforestation Campaign.
1319. 756. 20 y. multicoloured . . 35 10

**1973.** Philatelic Week.
1320. 757. 20 y. multicoloured . . 15 10

758. Mt. Kama.

759. Rock Outcrops. Mt. Haguro.

**1973.** Suzuka Quasi-National Park.
1321. 758. 20 y. multicoloured . . 25 10
1322. 759. 20 y. multicoloured . . 25 10

760. Chichi-jima Island Beach.

761. Coral Reef, Minami-jimi Island.

**1973.** Ogasawara Islands National Park.
1323. 760. 10 y. blue . . . . 25 10
1324. 761. 20 y. purple . . . . 35 10

762. Postal Code Symbol and Tree.

765. Waterfall, Sanden-kyo Gorge.

764. Mt. Shinnyu.

**1973.** Postal Codes Campaign.
1325. 762. 10 y. gold and green . . 10 10
1326. – 20 y. lilac, red & blue 15 10
DESIGN: 20 y. Postman and Symbol.

**1973.** Nishi-Chugoku-Sanchi Quasi-National Park.
1327. 764. 20 y. multicoloured . . 30 10
1328. 765. 20 y. multicoloured . . 30 10

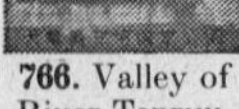
766. Valley of River Tenryu.

767. Scops Owl and Woodland Path, Mt. Horaiji.

**1973.** Tenryu-Okumikowa Quasi-National Park.
1329. 766. 20 y. multicoloured . . 25 10
1330. 767. 20 y. blue, grn. & sil. 1·25 20

768. " Cock " (J. Ito).

769. Sprinting.

**1973** International Correspondence Week.
1331 768. 50 y. multicoloured . . 65 10

**1973.** 28th National Athletic Meeting, Chiba.
1332 769 10 y. multicoloured . . 20 10

770. Kan-Mon Bridge.

**1973.** Opening of Kan-Mon Suspension Bridge.
1333. 770. 20 y. multicoloured 25 10

771. Hanasaka-jijii and his Dog.

772. Hanasaka-jijii finds the Gold.

773. Hanasaka-jijii and Tree in Blossom.

**1973.** Japanese Folk Tales (1st series). "Hanasaki-jijii"
1334. 771. 20 y. multicoloured . . 15 10
1335. 772. 20 y. multicoloured . . 15 10
1336. 773. 20 y. multicoloured . . 15 10
See also Nos. 1342/4, 1352/4, 1358/60, 1362/4, 1378/80 and 1387/9.

774. Lantern.

775. Niju-bashi Bridge.

**1973.** New Year's Greetings.
1337. 774. 10 y. multicoloured . . 10 10

**1974.** Imperial Golden Wedding. Mult.
1339. 20 y. Type 775 . . . . 15 10
1340. 20 y. Imperial Palace . . 15 10

777. " The Crane Damsel ".

**1974.** Japanese Folk Tales (2nd series). "Tsuru-Nyobo". Multicoloured.
1342. 20 y. Type 777 . . . . 15 10
1343. 20 y. Manchurian Crane " weaving " . . . . 50 10
1344. 20 y. Manchurian Cranes in flight . . 50 10

780. " A Reefy Coast " (Hyakusui Hirafuku).

**1974.** International Ocean Exposition, Okinawa (1975) (1st issue).
1345 780 20 y. + 5 y. mult . . 15 10
See also Nos. 1401/3.

781. Marudu Falls.

782. Seascape.

**1974.** Iriomote National Park.
1346. 781. 20 y. multicoloured . . 25 10
1347. 782. 20 y. multicoloured . . 25 10

**783.** Iriomote Cat.

**1974.** Nature Conservation (1st series).
1348 **783** 20 y. multicoloured .. 25 10
See also Nos. 1356, 1361, 1372, 1377, 1381, 1405, 1419, 1422, 1430, 1433/4, 1449, 1457, 1469, 1470, 1475, 1490, 1497 and 1502.

**784.** "Finger" (Shinsui Ito).

**1974.** Philatelic Week.
1349. **784.** 20 y. multicoloured .. 40 10

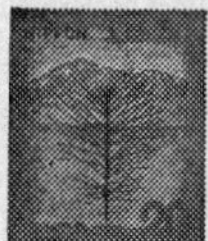

**785.** Nambu Red Pine. **786.** Supreme Court Building.

**1974.** National Afforestation Campaign.
1350. **785.** 20 y. multicoloured .. 20 10

**1974.** Completion of Supreme Court Building, Tokyo.
1351. **786.** 20 y. brown .. .. 15 10

**787.** "Sailing in a Wooden Bowl".

**788.** "Conquering the Goblins".

**789.** "Wielding the Little Magic Mallet".

**1974.** Japanese Folk Tales (3rd series). "The Dwarf".
1352. **787.** 20 y. multicoloured .. 15 10
1353. **788.** 20 y. multicoloured .. 15 10
1354. **789.** 20 y. multicoloured .. 15 10

**790.** "Uniform Rivalry" (detail after Kunimasa Baido). **792.** World Blood Donation.

**1974.** Centenary of Japanese Police System.
1355. **790.** 20 y. multicoloured 15 10

**1974.** Nature Conservation (2nd series). As T **783.** Multicoloured.
1356 20 y. European otter ("Lutra lutra") .. 25 10

**1974.** Int. Red Cross Day.
1357. **792.** 20 y. multicoloured 15 10

**793.** "Discovery of Kaguya Hime".

**794.** "Kaguya Hime as Young Woman".

**795.** "The Ascent to Heaven".

**1974.** Japanese Folk Tales (4th series). "Kaguya Hime".
1358. **793.** 20 y. multicoloured .. 25 10
1359. **794.** 20 y. multicoloured .. 25 10
1360. **795.** 20 y. multicoloured .. 25 10

**1974.** Nature Conservation (3rd series). As T **783.** Multicoloured.
1361 20 y. Ryukyu rabbit ("Pentalagus furnessi") 25 10

**797.** Old Men in front of Yahata Shrine.

**798.** Old Man dancing with Demons.

**799.** Old Man with Two Warts.

**1974.** Japanese Folk Tales (5th series). "Kobutori-Jiisan".
1362. **797.** 20 y. multicoloured .. 15 10
1363. **798.** 20 y. multicoloured .. 15 10
1364. **799.** 20 y. multicoloured .. 15 10

**800.** Map of World. **802.** "Pine and Northern Goshawk" (detail, Sesson).

**1974.** 61st Inter-Parliamentary Union Congress, Tokyo. Multicoloured.
1365 20 y. Type **800** .. .. 25 10
1366 50 y. "Aizen"–Mandarins in pond (Kawabata) (48 × 33 mm) .. .. 1·00 10

**1974.** International Correspondence Week.
1367. **802.** 50 y. brown & purple 90 15

**803.** U.P.U. Emblem. **805.** Footballers.

**1974.** Cent. of U.P.U. Mult.
1368. 20 y. Type **803** .. .. 10 10
1369. 50 y. "Tending a Cow" (fan-painting—Sotatsu Tawaraya) (50 × 29 mm.) 30 10

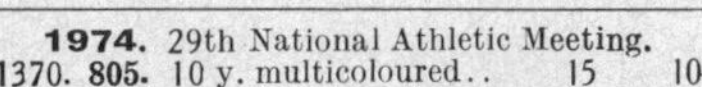

**1974.** 29th National Athletic Meeting.
1370. **805.** 10 y. multicoloured .. 15 10

**806.** Shii-take Mushrooms. **808.** Class "D-51" Locomotive.

**809.** Class "C-57" Locomotive.

**1974.** Ninth International Scientific Congress on Cultivation of Edible Fungi.
1371. **806.** 20 y. multicoloured .. 40 10

**1974.** Nature Conservation (4th series). As T **783.** Multicoloured.
1372 20 y. Bonin Islands flying fox ("Pteropus pselaphon") .. .. 15 10

**1974.** Railway Steam Locomotives (1st series).
1373. **808.** 20 y. multicoloured .. 65 10
1374. **809.** 20 y. multicoloured .. 65 10
See also Nos. 1382/3, 1385/6, 1395/6 and 1398/9.

**810.** "Kugikakushi" (ornamental nail-covering) in the form of a daffodil.

**1974.** New Year's Greetings.
1375. **810.** 10 y. multicoloured .. 15 10

**1975.** Nature Conservation (5th series). As T **783.** Multicoloured.
1377 20 y. Short-tailed albatrosses ("Diomedea albatrus") (vert) .. 65 10

**812.** Taro releasing Tortoise.

**813.** Sea-God's Palace.

**814.** Taro and Pandora's Box.

**1975.** Japanese Folk Tales (6th series). "Urashima Taro".
1378. **812.** 20 y. multicoloured .. 25 10
1379. **813.** 20 y. multicoloured .. 25 10
1380. **814.** 20 y. multicoloured .. 25 10

**1975.** Nature Conservation (6th series). As T **783.** Multicoloured.
1381 20 y. Manchurian cranes ("Grus japonensis") (vert) .. .. .. 75 10

**816.** Class "C-58" Locomotive.

**817.** Class "D-52" Locomotive.

**1975.** Railway Steam Locomotives (2nd series).
1382. **816.** 20 y. multicoloured .. 65 10
1383. **817.** 20 y. multicoloured .. 65 10

**818.** "Sight and Hearing". (Shiko Munakata).

**1975.** 50th Anniv. of Japanese Broadcasting Corporation.
1384. **818.** 20 y. multicoloured .. 15 10

**819.** Class "8620" Locomotive. **820.** Class "C-11" Locomotive.

**1975.** Railway Steam Locomotives (3rd series).
1385. **819.** 20 y. multicoloured .. 65 10
1386. **820.** 20 y. multicoloured .. 65 10

**821.** Old Man feeding Mouse.

**822.** Old Man holding Mouse's Tail.

**823.** Mice giving Feast to Old Man.

**1975.** Japanese Folk Tales (7th series). "Nezumi No Jodo".
1387. **821.** 20 y. multicoloured .. 25 10
1388. **822.** 20 y. multicoloured .. 25 10
1389. **823.** 20 y. multicoloured .. 25 10

**824.** Matsuura Screen. **825.**

**1975.** Philatelic Week.
1390. **824.** 20 y. multicoloured .. 30 10
1391. **825.** 20 y. multicoloured .. 30 10

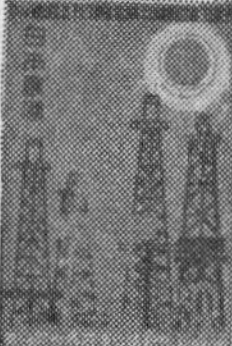

**827.** Oil Rigs.

**1975.** Ninth World Petroleum Congress, Tokyo.
1394. **827.** 20 y. multicoloured .. 15 10

**828.** Class "9600" Locomotive.

**829.** "Class "C-51" Locomotive.

**830.** Plantation.

**1975.** Railway Steam Locomotives (4th series).
1395. **828.** 20 y. multicoloured .. 65 10
1396. **829.** 20 y. multicoloured .. 65 10

**1975.** National Land Afforestation Campaign.
1397. **830.** 20 y. multicoloured .. 15 10

**831.** Class "7100" Locomotive.

**832.** Class "150" Locomotive.

**1975.** Railway Steam Locomotives (5th series).
1398. **831.** 20 y. black & buff .. 65 10
1399. **832.** 20 y. black & yellow 65 10

**833.** Woman's Head and I.W.Y. Emblem.

**834.** Okinawa Dance.

**1975.** International Women's Year.
1400. **833.** 20 y. multicoloured .. 15 10

**1975.** International Ocean Exposition, Okinawa (2nd issue). Multicoloured.
1401. 20 y. Type **834** .. .. 25 10
1402. 30 y. Bingata textile pattern 40 10
1403. 50 y. "Aquapolis and Globe" emblem (48 × 34 mm.) 55 10

**1975.** Nature Conservation (7th series). As T **783**. Multicoloured.
1405 20 y. Bonin Island honey-eater ("Apalopteron familiare") .. .. 70 10

**838.** Kentoshisen (7th–9th centuries).

**839.** Kenminsen (7th–9th centuries).

**1975.** Japanese Ships (1st series).
1406. **838.** 20 y. red .. .. 40 15
1407. **839.** 20 y. brown .. .. 40 15
See also Nos. 1409/10, 1420/1, 1423/4, 1428/9 and 1431/2.

**840.** Apple.

**843.** "Green Peafowl" (after K. Ogata).

**841.** Goshuin-sen (16th-century trading ship).

**842.** "Tenchi-maru" (state barge), 1630.

**1975.** Cent of Apple Cultivation in Japan.
1408 **840** 20 y. multicoloured .. 15 10

**1975.** Japanese Ships (2nd series).
1409. **841.** 20 y. green .. .. 40 15
1410. **842.** 20 y. blue .. .. 40 15

**1975.** International Correspondence Week.
1411. **843.** 50 y. multicoloured .. 1·00 15

**844.** United States Flag.

**1975.** American Tour by Emperor Hirohito and Empress Nagako. Multicoloured.
1412. 20 y. Type **844** .. .. 25 10
1413. 20 y. Japanese flag .. 25 10

**846.** Savings Box.

**847.** Weightlifting.

**1975.** Centenary of Japanese Post Office Savings Bank.
1415 **846** 20 y. multicoloured .. 15 10

**1975.** 30th National Athletic Meeting.
1416. **847.** 10 y. multicoloured .. 20 10

**848.** "Tatsu-guruma" (toy).

**850.** Sengoku-bune (fishing boat).

**851.** "Shohei Maru" (sail warship).

**1975.** New Year's Greetings.
1417. **848.** 10 y. multicoloured .. 35 10

**1976.** Nature Conservation (8th series). As T **783**. Multicoloured.
1419 50 y. Ryukyu robin ("Erithacus komadori") 60 25

**1976.** Japanese Ships (3rd series).
1420. **850.** 50 y. blue .. .. 65 15
1421. **851.** 50 y. violet .. .. 65 15

**1976.** Nature Conservation (9th series). As T **783**. Multicoloured.
1422 50 y. Tortoise ("Goemyda spengleri") .. .. 60 15

**853.** "Taisei Maru" (cadet ship).

**854.** "Tenyo Maru" (liner).

**1976.** Japanese Ships (4th series).
1423. **853.** 50 y. black .. .. 65 15
1424. **854.** 50 y. brown .. .. 65 15

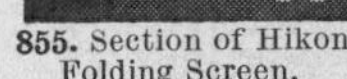

**855.** Section of Hikone Folding Screen.

**857.** Cedar Forest, Plum Blossom, and Mt. Tsukuba.

**1976.** Philatelic Week. Multicoloured.
1425. 50 y. Type **855** .. .. 45 10
1426. 50 y. Similar to Type **855** 45 10
NOTE: The two stamps form a composite design of the "Hikone Folding Screen".

**1976.** National Land Afforestation Campaign.
1427. **857.** 50 y. multicoloured .. 30 10

**858.** "Asama Maru" (liner).

**859.** "Kinai Maru" (cargo liner).

**1976.** Japanese Ships (5th series).
1428 **858** 50 y. green .. .. 65 15
1429 **859** 50 y. brown .. .. 65 15

**1976.** Nature Conservation (10th series). As T **783**. Multicoloured.
1430 50 y. Green tree frog ("Racophorus arboreus") (vert) .. 50 10

**861.** "Kamakura Maru" (container ship).

**862.** "Nissei Maru" (oil tanker).

**1976.** Japanese Ships (6th series).
1431. **861.** 50 y. blue .. .. 65 15
1432. **862.** 50 y. blue .. .. 65 15

**1976.** Nature Conservation (11th and 12th series). As T **783**. Multicoloured.
1433 50 y. Carps ("Tanakia tanago") .. .. 75 10
1434 50 y. Three-spined sticklebacks ("Gasterosteus aculeatus") .. .. 75 10

**865.** "Kite and Rooks" (detail, Yosa Buson).

**866.** Gymnastics.

**1976.** International Correspondence Week.
1435 **865** 100 y. multicoloured .. 1·25 25

**1976.** 31st National Athletic Meeting.
1436. **866.** 20 y. multicoloured .. 35 10

**867.** "KDD Maru" (cable ship) laying cable.

**1976.** Opening of Sino-Japanese Cable.
1437. **867.** 50 y. multicoloured .. 60 10

**868.** Man-zai-raku (classical dance)

**870.** Children at First Kindergarten.

**1976.** Golden Jubilee of Emperor's Accession.
1438 **868** 50 y. multicoloured .. 40 10
1439 – 50 y. red, gold & black 40 10
DESIGN: No. 1439, Coronation coach.

**1976.** Cent of First Kindergarten, Tokyo.
1441 **870** 50 y. multicoloured .. 50 10

**871.** Family Group.

**872.** Bamboo Snake.

**1976.** 50th Anniv (1977) of Health Insurance System.
1442 **871** 50 y. multicoloured .. 40 10

**1976.** New Year's Greetings.
1443. **872.** 20 y. multicoloured .. 20 10

**873.** East Pagoda, Yakushi Temple.

**1976.** National Treasures (1st series). Mult.
1445 50 y. Type **873** .. .. 50 10
1446 100 y. Deva King, Todai Temple (33 × 48 mm) .. 1·25 10
See also Nos. 1447/8, 1452/3, 1463/4, 1471/2, 1480/1 and 1486/9.

**875.** Golden Pavilion, Toshodai Temple.

**1977.** National Treasures (2nd series). Mult.
1447 50 y. Type **875** .. .. 50 10
1448 100 y. Illustration from "Heike Nokyo Sutra" (33 × 48 mm.) .. .. 1·25 10

**1977.** Nature Conservation (13th series). As T **783**. Multicoloured.
1449 50 y. Horseshoe crabs ("Tachypleus tridentatus") .. .. 45 10

**878.** Figure Skating. **879.**

**1977.** World Figure Skating Championships, Tokyo.
1450 **878** 50 y. multicoloured .. 55 10
1451 **879** 50 y. multicoloured .. 55 10

**880.** Detail of Picture Scroll (attr. Toba Sojo Kakuyu).

**881.** Wood Carving of Buddhist Saint, (attr. Jocho), Byodoin Temple, Uji.

**1977.** National Treasures (3rd series).
1452 **880** 50 y. multicoloured .. 50 10
1453 **881** 100 y. deep brown, brown and green .. 1·25 10

**882.** Forest in Sunshine.

**1977.** National Land Afforestation Campaign.
1454. **882.** 50 y. multicoloured .. 40 10

**883.** " Women Weavers " (part). **884.** " Women Weavers " (part).

**1977.** Philatelic Week.
1455. **883.** 50 y. multicoloured .. 50 10
1456. **884.** 50 y. multicoloured .. 50 10
Nos. 1455/6 were issued in se-tenant pairs, forming a composite design.

**1977.** Nature Conservation (14th series). As T **783.** Multicoloured.
1457 50 y. Mikado swallowtail ("Graphium doson") (vert) .. .. .. 60 10

**886.** Nurses. **887.** Central Part of Nuclear Reactor.

**1977.** 16th Congress of the International Council of Nurses.
1458. **886.** 50 y. multicoloured .. 40 10

**1977.** Reaching of Critical Mass by Joyo Fast-Breeder Reactor, Oarai Town.
1459 **887** 50 y. multicoloured .. 40 10

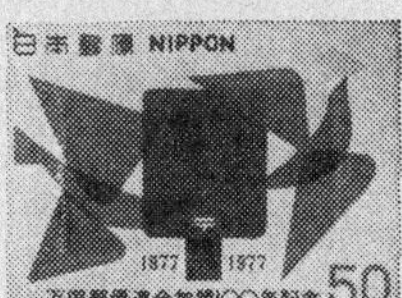

**888.** Carrier Pigeons and Mail Box with U.P.U. Emblem.

**889.** U.P.U. Emblem and World Map.

**1977.** Cent. of Japan's Admission to U.P.U.
1460. **888.** 50 y. multicoloured .. 40 10
1461. **889.** 100 y. multicoloured 1·40 10

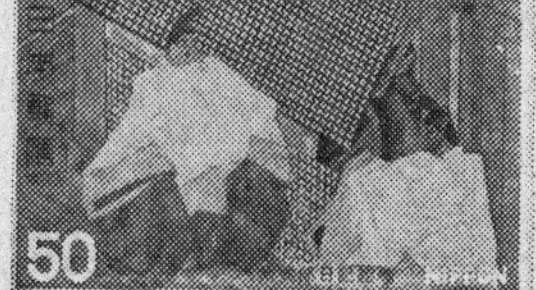

**890** Illustration from " Picture Scroll of Lady Murasaki's Diary ".

**891.** Statue of Seitaka Doji.

**892.** Green Cross (safety emblem) and Workmen.

**1977.** National Treasures (4th series).
1463 **890** 50 y. multicoloured .. 55 10
1464 **891** 100 y. brown, deep brown & lt brown 1·40 10

**1977.** National Safety Week. Multicoloured.
1465. 50 y. Type **892** .. .. 80 10
1466. 50 y. Worker and high-rise building .. .. 80 10
1467. 50 y. Unloading Freight 80 10
1468. 50 y. Machine-worker .. 80 10

**1977.** Nature Conservation (15th series). As T **783.** Multicoloured.
1469 50 y. Firefly ("Luciola cruciata") .. .. 50 10

**1977.** Nature Conservation (16th series). As T **783.** Multicoloured.
1470 50 y. Cicada ("Euterpnosia chibensis" .. 60 10

**898.** Drawing of Han Shan by Kao.

**899.** Matsumoto Castle.

**1977.** National Treasures (5th series).
1471. **898.** 50 y. multicoloured .. 60 10
1472. **899.** 100 y. multicoloured 1·40 10

**900.** Map and Child on Telephone.

**1977.** Opening of Okinawa–Luzon–Hong Kong Submarine Cable.
1473. **900.** 50 y. multicoloured .. 40 10

**901.** Surgeon.

**1977.** 27th Congress of International Society of Surgeons.
1474. **901.** 50 y. multicoloured .. 50 10

**1977.** Nature Conservation (17th series). As T **783.** Multicoloured.
1475 50 y. Dragonfly ("Boninthemis insularis") (vert) 60 10

**903.** Horn-shaped Speaker and Telegraph Key.

**904.** Racing Cyclist and Mt. Iwaki.

**1977.** 50th Anniv of Amateur Radio League.
1476 **903** 50 y. multicoloured .. 40 10

**1977.** 32nd National Athletic Meeting.
1477. **904.** 20 y. multicoloured .. 40 10

**905.** " Kacho-zu " (Nobuharu Hasegawa). **906.** Long-necked Dinosaur and Museum.

**1977.** International Correspondence Week.
1478. **905.** 100 y. multicoloured 1·40 25

**1977.** Centenary of National Science Museum.
1479. **906.** 50 y. multicoloured 75 10

**907.** Detail, Folding Screen, Chishakuin Temple, Kyoto.

**908.** Kiyomizu-dera Temple.

**1977.** National Treasures (6th series).
1480. **907.** 50 y. multicoloured .. 50 10
1481. **908.** 100 y. brown, green and blue .. .. 1·25 10

**909.** Toy Horse.

**1977.** New Year's Greetings.
1482. **909.** 20 y. multicoloured .. 25 10

**910.** Underground. Train, 1927.

**911.** Underground. Train, 1977.

**1977.** 50th Anniv. of Japanese Underground Railway.
1484. **910.** 50 y. multicoloured .. 90 10
1485. **911.** 50 y. multicoloured .. 90 10

**912.** Genji's Carriage at Sumiyoshi Shrine (scene on folding screen (Sotatsu Tawaraya) from "Tale of Genji" by Lady Murasaki).

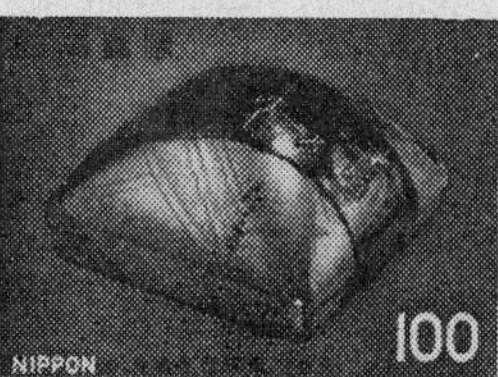

**913.** Inkstone Case (Koetsu Honami).

**1978.** National Treasures (7th series).
1486. **912.** 50 y. multicoloured .. 50 10
1487. **913.** 100 y. multicoloured 1·40 10

**914.** " Noryozu " (Morikage Kusumi).

**915.** Yomei Gate, Tosho Shrine, Nikko.

**1978.** National Treasures (8th series).
1488. **914.** 50 y. multicoloured .. 50 10
1489. **915.** 100 y. multicoloured 1·40 10

**916.** " Primula Sieboldi ".

**1978.** Nature Conservation (18th series).
1490. **916.** 50 y. multicoloured .. 50 10

**917.** Seated Woman with Flower. (hanging scroll). **918.** Dancing Woman (hanging scroll).

**1978.** Philatelic Week. " Kanbun Bijinzu " Genre Paintings.
1491. **917.** 50 y. multicoloured .. 40 10
1492. **918.** 50 y. multicoloured .. 40 10

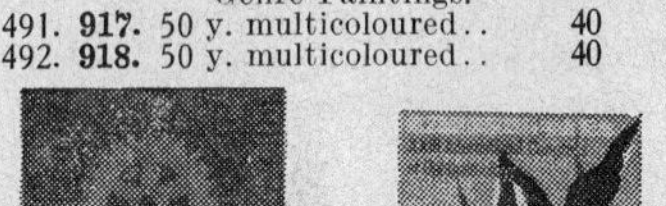

**919.** Rotary Emblem and Mt. Fuji (from "36 Views of Mt. Fuji" by Hokusai Katsushita). **920.** Congress Emblem.

**1978.** Rotary International Convention, Tokyo.
1493. **919.** 50 y. multicoloured .. 70 20

**1978.** 23rd International Ophthalmological Congress.
1494. **920.** 50 y. multicoloured .. 45 10

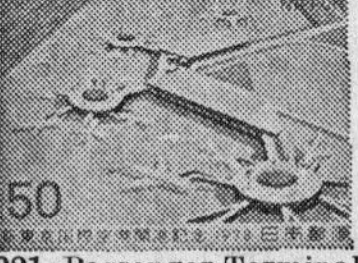

**921.** Passenger Terminal Buildings. **922.** Cape Ashizuri, Rainbow and Cedar Trees.

**1978.** Opening of Narita Airport, Tokyo.
1495 **921** 50 y. multicoloured .. 60 10

**1978.** National Afforestation Campaign.
1496. **922.** 50 y. multicoloured .. 50 10

**923.** " Pinguicula ramosa ".

**924.** " Karashishi " (attr. Sotatsu Tawaraya) and Lions Emblem.

**1978.** Nature Conservation. (19th series).
1497. **923.** 50 y. multicoloured . . 50 10

**1978.** 61st Lions International Convention, Tokyo.
1498. **924.** 50 y. multicoloured . . 55 10

**925.** "Grand Champion Raigoyo **926.** Hidenoyama in the Ring" (Toyokuni III).

**927.** "Drum Tower of Ekoin Temple, Ryogoku" (Hiroshige).

**928.** " Dicentra peregrina ".

**1978.** Sumo (Japanese Wrestling) Pictures (1st series).
1499. **925.** 50 y. multicoloured . . 50 10
1500. **926.** 50 y. multicoloured . . 50 10
1501. **927.** 50 y. multicoloured . . 60 10
Nos. 1499/500, were issued together se-tenant forming a composite design.
See also Nos. 1505/7, 1513/15, 1519/21 and 1523/5.

**1978.** Nature Conservation (20th series).
1502. **928.** 50 y. multicoloured . . 35 10

**929.** Keep Fit Exercise.

**930.** Chamber of Commerce and Industry Building and Centenary Emblem.

**1978.** 50th Anniv. of Radio Gymnastic Exercises.
1503. **929.** 50 y. multicoloured 1·25 10

**1978.** Centenary of 1st Chambers of Commerce, Tokyo and Osaka.
1504. **930.** 50 y. multicoloured 40 10

**931.** " Dohyoiri " wrestlers **932.** Tanikaze and Onogawa) (Shunsho Katsukawa).

**933.** " Jinmaku versus Raiden " (Shunnei Katsukawa).

**934.** Statues on Tokyo Securities Exchange Building.

**1978.** Sumo Pictures (2nd series).
1505. **931.** 50 y. multicoloured . . 50 10
1506. **932.** 50 y. multicoloured . . 50 10
1507. **933.** 50 y. multicoloured . . 60 10
Nos. 1505/6 were issued together se-tenant, forming a composite design.

**1978.** Centenary of Tokyo and Osaka Stock Exchanges.
1508. **934.** 50 y. brn., pur. & grn. 50 10

**935.** Copper Pheasant (detail of door painting attr. Sanraku Kano).

**936.** Mt. Yari and Softball Players.

**1978.** International Correspondence Week.
1509. **935.** 100 y. multicoloured 1·25 25

**1978.** 33rd National Athletic Meeting.
1510. **936.** 20 y. multicoloured . . 40 10

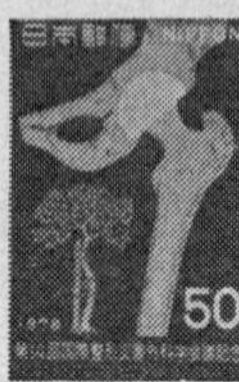

**937.** Artificial Joint. **938.** Refracting Telescope and Stars.

**1978.** 14th Congress of Int Society of Orthopaedic and Traumatic Surgeons, Kyoto.
1511 **937** 50 y. blue, ultramarine and silver . . . . 55 10

**1978.** Centenary of Tokyo Astronomical Observatory.
1512. **938.** 50 y. multicoloured 55 10

**939.** "The then Heroic Champion's **940.** Sumo Wrestling" (detail, Toyokuni III).

**941.** " Children's Charming Sumo Play " (Utamaro Kitagawa).

**942.** Sheep Bell (folk toy).

**1978.** Sumo Pictures (3rd series).
1513. **939.** 50 y. multicoloured . . 50 10
1514. **940.** 50 y. multicoloured . . 50 10
1515. **941.** 50 y. multicoloured . . 60 10
Nos. 1513/14 were issued together se-tenant, forming a composite design.

**1978.** New Year's Greetings.
1516. **942.** 20 y. multicoloured . . 35 10

**943.** Family and Human Rights Emblem.

**1978.** 30th Anniv. of Declaration of Human Rights.
1518. **943.** 50 y. multicoloured 45 10

**944/5.** "Great Sumo Wrestlers crossing Ryogoku Bridge" (Toyokuni III).

**946.** "Yumitori Ceremony at Grand Fund-raising Tournament" (Kunisada II).

**947.** Hands protecting Children.

**1979.** Sumo Pictures. (4th series).
1519. **944.** 50 y. multicoloured . . 50 10
1520. **945.** 50 y. multicoloured . . 50 10
1521. **946.** 50 y. multicoloured . . 60 10
Nos. 1519/20 were issued together se-tenant, forming a composite design.

**1979.** Education for the Handicapped.
1522. **947.** 50 y. multicoloured . . 45 10

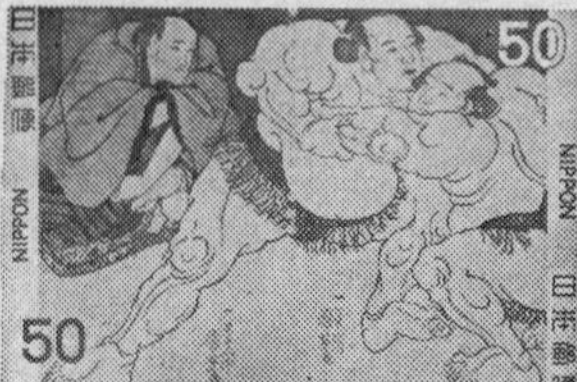

**948/9.** " Takekuma versus Iwamigata " (Kuniyoshi Utagawa).

**950.** " Daidozan's Dohyoiri " (Sharaku Toshusai).

**951.** Telephone Dial and Pushbuttons.

**1979.** Sumo Pictures (5th series).
1523. **948.** 50 y. multicoloured . . 50 10
1524. **949.** 50 y. multicoloured . . 50 10
1525. **950.** 50 y. multicoloured . . 60 10
Nos. 1523/4 were issued together se-tenant, forming a composite design.

**1979.** Telephone Automation Completion.
1526. **951.** 50 y. multicoloured . . 50 10

**952.** Drawing by Leonardo da Vinci.

**1979.** Centenary of Western Medicine in Japan.
1527. **952.** 50 y. multicoloured . . 55 10

**953.** " Standing Beauties " **954.** (Kaigetsudo School).

**1979.** Philatelic Week.
1528. **953.** 50 y. multicoloured . . 50 10
1529. **954.** 50 y. multicoloured . . 50 10

**955.** Mt. Horaiji and Maple Leaves.

**1979.** National Afforestation Campaign.
1530. **955.** 50 y. multicoloured . . 50 10

**956.** "Goddess of Maternal Mercy" (Kano Hogai).

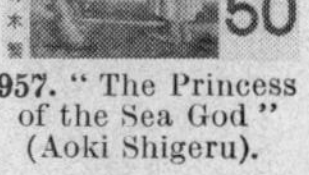

**957.** " The Princess of the Sea God " (Aoki Shigeru).

**1979.** Modern Japanese Art (1st series).
1531. **956.** 50 y. multicoloured . . 60 10
1532. **957.** 50 y. multicoloured . . 60 10
See also Nos. 1533/4, 1544/5, 1550/1, 1558/9, 1567/8, 1574/5, 1610/11, 1618/19, 1628/9, 1650/1, 1656/7, 1675/6, 1689/90, 1693/4 and 1697/8.

**958.** " Fire Dance " (Gyosha Hayami).

**959.** " Leaning Figure " (Tetsugoro Yorozu).

**1979.** Modern Japanese Art (2nd series).
1533. **958.** 50 y. multicoloured . . 60 10
1534. **959.** 50 y. multicoloured . . 60 10

**960.** Quarantine Officers.

**1979.** Centenary of Quarantine System.
1535. **960.** 50 y. multicoloured 75 10

**961.** Girl with Letter.

**962.** Hakata Doll.

**1979.** Letter writing Day.
1536. **961.** 20 y. multicoloured . . 30 10
1537. **962.** 50 y. multicoloured . . 45 10

**963.** Baseball Pitcher and Ball.

**1979.** 50th National Inter-City Amateur Baseball Tournament.
1538. **963.** 50 y. multicoloured . . 70 10

**964.** Girl collecting Stars.

**965.** Boy catching Toy Insects.

**1979.** International Year of the Child.
1539. **964.** 50 y. multicoloured . . 50 10
1540. **965.** 50 y. multicoloured . . 50 10

**966.** " The Moon over the Castle Ruins " (Bansui Doi and Rentaro Taki).

**967.** " Evening Glow " (Uko Nakamura and Shin Kusakawa).

**1979.** Japanese Songs (1st series).
1542. **966.** 50 y. multicoloured . . 70 10
1543. **967.** 50 y. multicoloured . . 70 10
See also Nos. 1552/3, 1556/7, 1561/2, 1565/6, 1572/3, 1580/1, 1616/17 and 1620/1.

**968.** " Black Cat " (Shunso Hishida). **969.** " Kinyo " (Sotaro Yasui).

**1979.** Modern Japanese Art (3rd series).
1544. **968.** 50 y. multicoloured . . 70 10
1545. **969.** 50 y. multicoloured . . 70 10

**970.** " Steep Mountains and the Dark Dale " (Okyo Maruyama). **971.** Long Distance Runner.

**1979.** International Correspondence Week.
1546. **970.** 100 y. multicoloured 1·75 30

**1979.** 34th National Athletic Meeting, Miyazaki.
1547. **971.** 20 y. multicoloured 60 10

**972.** " ITU " and Globe. **973.** Woman and Embryo.

**1979.** Centenary of Admission to International Telecommunications Union.
1548. **972.** 50 y. multicoloured . . 60 10

**1979.** Ninth International Obstetrics and Gynaecology Convention, Tokyo.
1549. **973.** 50 y. multicoloured 60 10

**974.** " Nude " (Kagaku Murakami).

**975.** " Harvest " (Asai Chu).

**1979.** Modern Japanese Art (4th series).
1550. **974.** 50 y. multicoloured . . 50 10
1551. **975.** 50 y. multicoloured . . 50 10

**976.** "Maple Leaves" (Tatsuyuki Takano and Teiichi Okano). **977.** "Birthplace" (Tatsuyuki Takano and Teiichi Okano).

**1979.** Japanese Songs (2nd series).
1552. **976.** 50 y. multicoloured . . 50 10
1553. **977.** 50 y. multicoloured . . 50 10

**978.** "Happy Monkeys" (folk toy). **979.** "Winter Scene" (anon.).

**980.** "Mount Fuji" (anon.).

**1979.** New Year's Greeting.
1554. **978.** 20 y. multicoloured . . 30 10

**1980.** Japanese Songs (3rd series).
1556. **979.** 50 y. multicoloured . . 50 20
1557. **980.** 50 y. multicoloured . . 50 10

**981.** "Salmon" (Yuichi Takahashi). **982.** "Hall of the Supreme Buddha" (Kokei Kobayashi).

**1980.** Modern Japanese Art (5th series).
1558. **981.** 50 y. multicoloured . . 55 10
1559. **982.** 50 y. multicoloured . . 55 10

**983.** Scales.

**1980.** Cent of Government Auditing Bureau.
1560 **983** 50 y. multicoloured . . 50 10

**984.** "Spring Brook" (Tatsuyuki Takano and Teiichi Okano).

**985.** "Cherry Blossoms" (anon.).

**1980.** Japanese Songs (4th series).
1561. **984.** 50 y. multicoloured . . 55 10
1562. **985.** 50 y. multicoloured . . 55 10

**986/7.** " Scenes of Outdoor Play in Spring " (Sukenobu Nishikawa).

**1980.** Philatelic Week.
1563. **986.** 50 y. multicoloured . . 30 10
1564. **987.** 50 y. multicoloured . . 50 10

**988.** "Sea" (Ryuha Hayashi and Takeshi Inoue).

**989.** "Misty Moonlight Night" (Tatsuyuki Takano and Teiichi Okano).

**1980.** Japanese Songs (5th series).
1565. **988.** 50 y. multicoloured . . 55 10
1566. **989.** 50 y. multicoloured . . 55 10

**990.** " Maiko Girls " (Seiki Kuroda). **991.** " Mother and Child " (Shoen Uemura).

**1980.** Modern Japanese Art (6th series).
1567. **990.** 50 y. multicoloured . . 55 10
1568. **991.** 50 y. multicoloured . . 55 10

**992.** "Nippon Maru I". **993.** Mount Gozaisho and Cedars.

**1980.** 50th Anniv of Training Cadet Ships "Nippon Maru I" and "Kaio Maru".
1569 **992** 50 y. multicoloured . . 75 20

**1980.** National Afforestation Campaign.
1570. **993.** 50 y. multicoloured . . 60 10

**994.** "Acrobatic Performances on a Ladder at New Year's Parade of Yayosu Fire Brigades" (Hiroshige III).

**1980.** Centenary of Fire Fighting System.
1571. **994.** 50 y. multicoloured . . 60 10

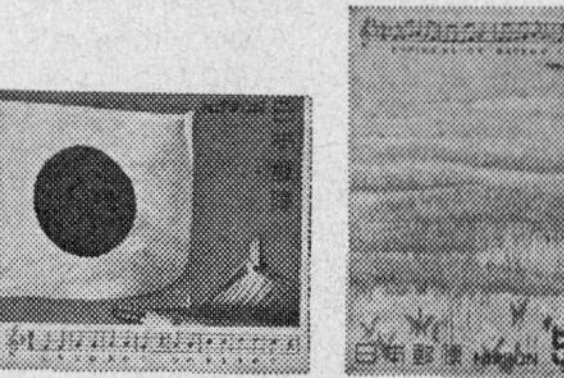

**995.** "The Sun" (Taksuyuki Takano and Teiichi Okano). **996.** "Memories of Summer" (Shoko Ema and Yoshinao Nakata).

**1980.** Japanese Songs (6th series).
1572. **995.** 50 y. multicoloured . . 60 10
1573. **996.** 50 y. multicoloured . . 60 10

**997.** " Black Fan " (Takeji Fujishima). **998.** " The Dance 'Are Yudachi ni' " (Seiho Takeuchi).

**1980.** Modern Japanese Art (7th series).
1574. **997.** 50 y. multicoloured . . 65 10
1575. **998.** 50 y. multicoloured . . 65 10

**999.** Teddy Bear holding Letter. **1000.** Knotted Letter.

**1980.** Letter Writing Day.
1576. **999.** 20 y. multicoloured 30 10
1577. **1000.** 50 y. multicoloured 50 10

**1001.** "Luehdorfia japonica".

**1980.** 16th International Congress of Entomology, Kyoto.
1578. **1001.** 50 y. multicoloured 90 10

**1002.** Map on Three-dimensional Graph.

**1980.** 24th International Geographical Congress and 10th International Cartographic Conference, Tokyo.
1579. **1002.** 50 y. multicoloured 40 10

**1003.** "Red Dragonfly" (Rofu Miki and Kosaku Yamada). **1004.** "Song by the Sea" (Kokui Hayashi and Tamezo Narita).

**1980.** Japanese Songs (7th series).
1580. **1003.** 50 y. multicoloured 70 10
1581. **1004.** 50 y. multicoloured 70 10

**1005.** Integrated Circuit.

**1980.** Eighth World Computer Congress and Third World Conference on Medical Informatics, Tokyo.
1582. **1005.** 50 y. multicoloured 60 10

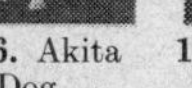

**1006.** Akita Dog. **1007.** Adonis. **1008.** Lily.

**1009.** Camellia. **1010.** Small Cabbage Whites on Rape Blossom. **1011.** Japanese Babylonia.

**1012.** Noble Scallops.

**1013.** Flowering Cherry.

**1014.** Hanging Bell, Byodoin Temple, Uji.

**1015.** Yoka Star Shell.

**1016.** Precious Wentletrap.

**1017.** Flautist, Horyu Temple.

**1018.** Deer (from lacquer writing box).

**1019.** Mirror with Figures.

**1020.** Heart-shaped Earthen Figurine.

**1021.** Silver Crane, Kasuga Taisha Shrine, Nara.

**1022.** Miroku Bosatsu, Horyu Temple.

**1023.** Dainichi Buddha, Chuson Temple.

**1024.** Keiki Doji, Kongobu Temple.

**1025.** Komoku Ten, Todai Temple, Nara.

**1026.** Lady Maya, Horyu Temple.

**1027.** Tea Jar with Wisteria Decoration (Ninsei Nonomura).

**1028.** Miroku Bosatsu.

**1980.** 41 y. and 62 y. perf or imperf (self-adhesive), others perf.

| | | | | |
|---|---|---|---|---|
| 1582a | **1006** | 2 y. blue .. .. | 10 | 10 |
| 1583 | **1007** | 10 y. yellow, green and brown .. | 10 | 10 |
| 1584 | **1008** | 20 y. yell, bl & grn | 15 | 10 |
| 1585 | **1009** | 30 y. multicoloured | 20 | 25 |
| 1586 | **1010** | 40 y. multicoloured | 40 | 10 |
| 1587 | **1011** | 40 y. multicoloured | 35 | 10 |
| 1588 | **1012** | 41 y. multicoloured | 35 | 10 |
| 1589 | **1013** | 50 y. multicoloured | 60 | 10 |
| 1590 | **1014** | 60 y. green & black | 70 | 10 |
| 1591 | **1015** | 60 y. multicoloured | 50 | 10 |
| 1592 | **1016** | 62 y. multicoloured | 50 | 10 |
| 1593 | **1017** | 70 y. blue & yellow | 90 | 10 |
| 1594 | **1018** | 70 y. yell, blk & bl | 60 | 10 |
| 1594a | | 72 y. yell, blk & bl | 60 | 10 |
| 1595 | **1019** | 80 y. green & black | 1·25 | 10 |
| 1596 | **1020** | 90 y. yell, blk & grn | 1·25 | 10 |
| 1597 | **1021** | 100 y. black, blue and ultramarine | 85 | 10 |
| 1598 | **1022** | 170 y. pur & bistre | 65 | 10 |
| 1599 | | 175 y. brn, grn & bis | 1·25 | 10 |
| 1600 | – | 210 y. orange and lilac (as No. 1242) | 1·25 | 10 |
| 1601 | **1023** | 260 y. brown & red | 2·00 | 10 |
| 1602 | **1024** | 300 y. brown .. | 2·00 | 10 |
| 1603 | **1025** | 310 y. brown & vio | 2·00 | 10 |
| 1604 | – | 360 y. purple and pink (as No. 1246) | 2·25 | 10 |
| 1605 | **1026** | 410 y. orange & blue | 5·50 | 10 |
| 1606 | **1027** | 410 y. multicoloured | 1·50 | 10 |
| 1607 | **1028** | 600 y. yellow, purple and lilac | 4·00 | 10 |

**1031** "Manchurian Cranes" (door painting, Motooki Watanabe).

**1032.** Archery and Mt. Nantai.

**1980.** International Correspondence Week.
1608. **1031.** 100 y. multicoloured 1·00 35

**1980.** 35th National Athletic Meeting, Tochigi.
1609. **1032.** 20 y. multicoloured 40 10

**1033.** "Woman" (sculpture, Morie Ogiwara).

**1034.** "Woman of the Kurofune-ya" (Yumeji Takehisa).

**1980.** Modern Japanese Art (8th series).
1610. **1033.** 50 y. multicoloured 65 10
1611. **1034.** 50 y. multicoloured 65 10

**1035.** "Energy".

**1036.** Diet Building and Doves.

**1980.** 35th World Congress of Junior Chambers of Commerce, Osaka.
1612. **1035.** 50 y. multicoloured 45 10

**1980.** 90th Anniv. of Japanese Diet.
1613. **1036.** 50 y. multicoloured 35 10

**1037.** Toy Rooster.

**1980.** New Year's Greetings.
1614. **1037.** 20 y. multicoloured 40 10

**1038.** "Komori-Uta" (nursery song).

**1039.** "Coconut" (Toson Shimazaki and Toraji Ohaka).

**1981.** Japanese Songs (8th series).
1616. **1038.** 60 y. multicoloured 55 10
1617. **1039.** 60 y. multicoloured 55 10

**1040.** "Power Station in the Snow" (Shiskanosuke Oka).

**1041.** "Nukada-no-Okimi of Asuka in Spring" (Yukihiko Yasuda).

**1981.** Modern Japanese Art (9th series).
1618. **1040.** 60 y. multicoloured 60 10
1619. **1041.** 60 y. multicoloured 60 10

**1042.** "Spring has Come" (Tatsuyuki Takano and Teiichi Okano).

**1043.** "Cherry Blossoms" (Hagoromo Takeshima and Rentaro Taki).

**1981.** Japanese Songs (9th series).
1620. **1042.** 60 y. multicoloured 60 10
1621. **1043.** 60 y. multicoloured 60 10

**1044.** Port Island and Exposition Emblem.

**1981.** Kobe Port Island Exposition. Kobe City.
1622. **1044.** 60 y. multicoloured 35 10

**1045.** Cereal, Tree and Fish on "100".

**1981.** Centenary of Agricultural, Forestry and Fishery Promotion.
1623. **1045.** 60 y. multicoloured 50 10

**1046.** "Yugao" (Lady of the Evening Roses).

**1047.** Genji.

**1981.** Philatelic Week. Details of Harunobu Suzuki's Illustrations of "Tale of Genji" by Lady Murasaki.
1624 **1046** 60 y. multicoloured 50 10
1625 **1047** 60 y. multicoloured 50 10
Nos. 1624/5 were issued together, se-tenant, forming a composite design.

**1048.** Pagodas at Nara and Double Cherry Blossom.

**1049.** Container Ship and Crane.

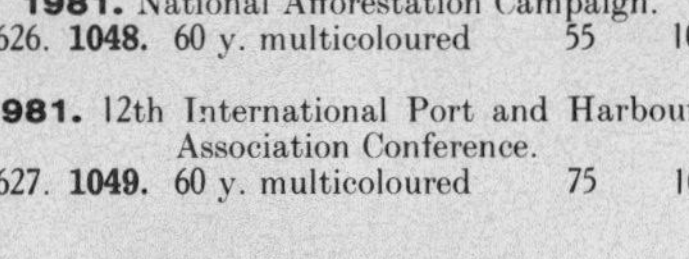

**1981.** National Afforestation Campaign.
1626. **1048.** 60 y. multicoloured 55 10

**1981.** 12th International Port and Harbour Association Conference.
1627. **1049.** 60 y. multicoloured 75 10

**1050.** "N's Family" (Narashinge Koide).

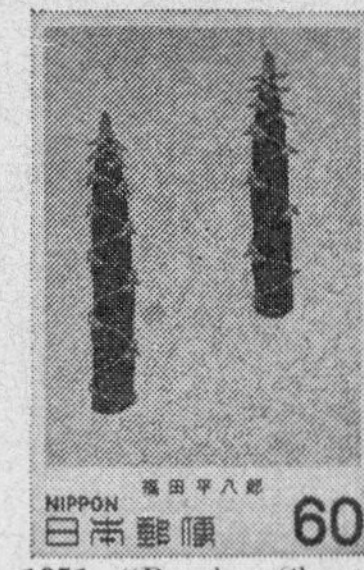

**1051.** "Bamboo Shoots" (Heihachiro Fukuda).

**1981.** Modern Japanese Art (10th series).
1628. **1050.** 60 y. multicoloured 65 10
1629. **1051.** 60 y. multicoloured 65 10

**1052.** Stylized Debris Barriers.

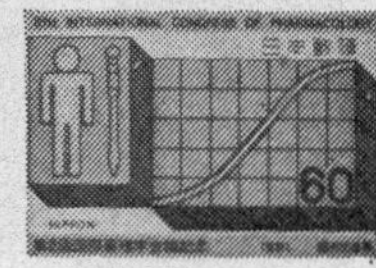

**1053.** Human Figure and Dose Response Chart.

**1981.** Centenary of Land Erosion Control.
1630. **1052.** 60 y. multicoloured 40 10

**1981.** 8th International Congress of Pharmacology, Tokyo.
1631. **1053.** 60 y. multicoloured 40 10

**1054.** Girl writing Letter.

**1055.** Boy with Pencil and Stamp.

**1981.** Letter Writing Day.
1632. **1054.** 40 y. multicoloured 40 10
1633. **1055.** 60 y. multicoloured 55 10

**1056.** Japanese Crested Ibis.

**1981.** 50th Anniv. of National Parks.
1634. **1056.** 60 y. multicoloured 1·25 30

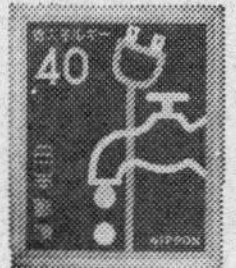

**1057.** Electric Plug and dripping Tap.

**1058.** Energy Recycling.

**1981.** Energy Conservation.
1635. **1057.** 40 y. deep blue, lilac & blue .. .. 40 10
1636. **1058.** 60 y. multicoloured 50 10

**1059.** Oura Cathedral, Nagasaki. **1060.** Hyokei Hall, Tokyo.

**1981.** Modern Western-style Architecture (1st series).

1637. **1059.** 60 y. multicoloured 55 10
1638. **1060.** 60 y. multicoloured 55 10

See also Nos. 1648/9, 1654/5, 1658/9, 1669/70, 1680/1, 1695/6, 1705/6, 1710/11 and 1732/3.

**1061.** Bluebird and I.Y.D.P. Emblem. **1062.** Globe in Brain.

**1981.** International Year of Disabled Persons.

1639 **1061** 60 y.+10 y. mult .. 45 10

**1981.** International Neurological Conferences, Kyoto.

1640 **1062** 60 y. multicoloured .. 35 10

**1063.** Convention Emblem. **1064.** "Eastern Turtle Doves", (Sanraku Kano).

**1981.** International Federation of Postal, Telegram and Telephone Workers' Unions World Convention, Tokyo.

1641 **1063** 60 y. multicoloured .. 45 10

**1981.** International Correspondence Week.

1642. **1064.** 130 y. multicoloured 2·25 75

**1065.** 48 m. Stamp, 1871. **1069.** Badminton and Lake Biwa.

**1981.** "Philatokyo '81" International Stamp Exhibition, Tokyo. Multicoloured, frame colour of stamp within design given.

1643 **1065** 60 y. brown .. 60 10
1644 – 60 y. blue .. .. 60 10
1645 – 60 y. red .. .. 60 10
1646 – 60 y. green .. .. 60 10

DESIGNS: No. 1644, 100 m. stamp, 1871; 1645, 200 m. stamp, 1871; 1646, 500 m. stamp, 1871.

**1981.** 36th National Athletic Meeting, Shiga.

1647. **1069.** 40 y. multicoloured 50 10

**1070.** Former Kaichi School, Matsumoto.

**1071.** Doshisha Chapel, Kyoto.

**1981.** Modern Western-style Architecture (2nd series).

1648. **1070.** 60 y. multicoloured 50 10
1649. **1071.** 60 y. multicoloured 50 10

**1072.** "Portrait of Reiko" (Ryusei Kishida). **1073.** "Ichiyo" (Kiyokata Kaburagi).

**1981.** Modern Japanese Art (11th series).

1650. **1072.** 60 y. multicoloured 55 10
1651. **1073.** 60 y. multicoloured 55 10

**1074.** Clay Dog (folk toy).

**1981.** New Year's Greetings.

1652. **1074.** 40 y. multicoloured 45 10

**1075.** St. John's Church, Inuyama. **1076.** Military Exercise Hall, Sapporo Agricultural School.

**1982.** Modern Western-style Architecture (3rd series).

1654. **1075.** 60 y. multicoloured 55 10
1655. **1076.** 60 y. multicoloured 55 10

**1077.** "Yoritomo in a Cave" (Seison Maeda).

**1078.** "Posters on a Terrace" (Yuzo Saeki).

**1982.** Modern Japanese Art (12th series).

1656. **1077.** 60 y. multicoloured 55 10
1657. **1078.** 60 y. multicoloured 55 10

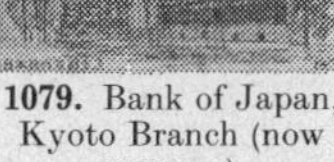

**1079.** Bank of Japan, Kyoto Branch (now museum). **1080.** Saiseikan Hospital, Yamagata.

**1982.** Modern Western-style Architecture (4th series).

1658. **1079.** 60 y. multicoloured 50 10
1659. **1080.** 60 y. multicoloured 50 10

**1081.** Gorilla and Greater Flamingo.

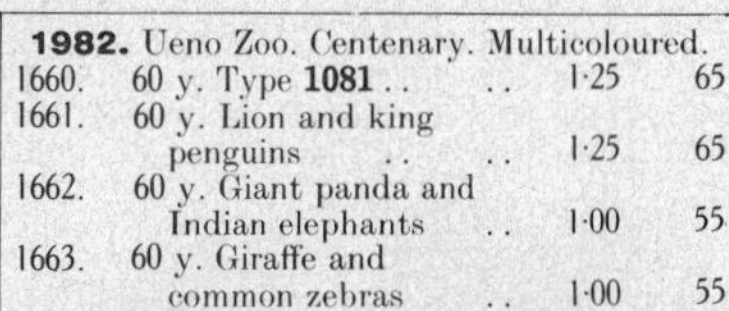

**1982.** Ueno Zoo. Centenary. Multicoloured.

1660. 60 y. Type **1081** .. .. 1·25 65
1661. 60 y. Lion and king penguins .. .. 1·25 65
1662. 60 y. Giant panda and Indian elephants .. 1·00 55
1663. 60 y. Giraffe and common zebras .. 1·00 55

**1085/6.** "Enjoying Snow Landscape of Matsuchi-yama" (Torii Kiyonaga).

**1982.** Philatelic Week.

1664. **1085.** 60 y. multicoloured 50 10
1665. **1086.** 60 y. multicoloured 50 10

Nos. 1664/5 were issued together se-tenant forming a composite design.

**1087.** Lion. **1088.** Arbor Festival Emblem and Blue and White Flycatcher.

**1982.** 10th Anniv. of Return of Okinawa (Ryukyu Islands).

1666. **1087.** 60 y. multicoloured 60 10

**1982.** National Afforestation Campaign.

1667. **1088.** 60 y. multicoloured 60 25

**1089.** Noh Mask.

**1982.** 16th World Dermatology Congress, Tokyo.

1668. **1089.** 60 y. multicoloured 65 10

**1090.** Divine Gate of Oyama Shrine, Kanazawa. **1091.** Former Iwasaki Mansion, Taito-ku, Tokyo (now Training Institute).

**1982.** Modern Western-style Architecture (5th series).

1669. **1090.** 60 y. multicoloured 50 10
1670. **1091.** 60 y. multicoloured 50 10

**1092.** "SL 1290" Steam Locomotive. **1093.** Super-Express Diesel.

**1982.** Opening of Tohoku-Shinkansen Railway Line.

1671. **1092.** 60 y. multicoloured 1·00 30
1672. **1093.** 60 y. multicoloured 1·00 30

**1094.** Gull and Balloon with Letter. **1095.** Bird carrying Letter to Fairy.

**1982.** Letter Writing Day.

1673. **1094.** 40 y. multicoloured 40 10
1674. **1095.** 60 y. multicoloured 55 10

**1096.** "Garment Patterned with Irises" (Saburosuke Okada). **1097.** "Buddhisattva Kannon on Potalaka Island" (Tessai Tomioka).

**1982.** Modern Japanese Art (13th series).

1675. **1096.** 60 y. multicoloured 65 10
1676. **1097.** 60 y. multicoloured 65 10

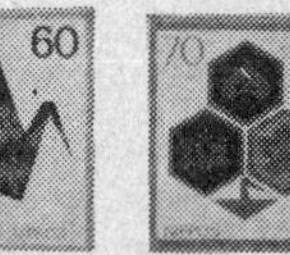

**1098.** Wreath (condolences). **1099.** Folded Paper Crane (congratulations). **1100.** Pine, Plum and Bamboo Blossom (congratulations).

**1982.** Special Correspondence Stamps.

1677. **1098.** 60 y. multicoloured 75 10
1678. **1099.** 60 y. multicoloured 75 10
1679. **1100.** 70 y. multicoloured 95 10

For other values see Nos. 1722/3, 2013/16 and 2289/92.

**1101.** Hokkaido Prefectural Building, Sapporo.

**1102.** Saigo Tsugumichi Mansion, Meguro (now in Inuyama).

**1982.** Modern Western-style Architecture (6th series).

1680. **1101.** 60 y. multicoloured 75 10
1681. **1102.** 60 y. multicoloured 75 10

**1103.** 16th-century Portuguese Galleon and World Map.

**1982.** 400th Anniv. of Christian Boys' Delegation to Europe.

1682. **1103.** 60 y. multicoloured 70 10

**1104.** "T'ien T'an in the Clouds" (Ryuzaburo Umehara).

**1982.** 10th Anniv. of Restoration of Diplomatic Relations with China.

1683. **1104.** 60 y. multicoloured 55 10

**1105.** Table Tennis and Monument of the Meet. **1106.** "Amusement" (wooden doll by Goyo Hirata).

**1982.** 37th National Athletic Meeting, Matsue.

1684. **1105.** 40 y. multicoloured 60 10

**1982.** International Correspondence Week.
1685. **1106.** 130 y. multicoloured 2·00 10

**1107.** "Bank of Japan near Eitaibashi in Snow" (Yasuji Inoue).

**1982.** Centenary of Central Bank System.
1686. **1107.** 60 y. multicoloured 45 10

**1108.** Joetsu Express Train.

**1109.** "ED 16" Electric Locomotive.

**1982.** Opening of Joetsu–Shinkansen Railway Line.
1687. **1108.** 60 y. multicoloured 1·00 25
1688. **1109.** 60 y. multicoloured 1·00 25

**1110.** "Srimhadevi" (Shiko Munakata).

**1111.** "Saltimbanque" (Seiji Togo).

**1982.** Modern Japanese Art (14th series).
1689. **1110.** 60 y. multicoloured 65 10
1690. **1111.** 60 y. multicoloured 65 10

**1112.** "Kintaro on a Wild Boar" (clay Tsutsumi doll).

**1982.** New Year Greetings.
1691. **1112.** 40 y. multicoloured 45 10

**1113.** "Snowstorm" (Shinsui Ito).

**1114.** "Spiraea and Calla in a Perrian Vase" (Zenzaburo Kojima).

**1983.** Modern Japanese Art (15th series).
1692. **1113.** 60 y. multicoloured 75 10
1693. **1114.** 60 y. multicoloured 75 10

**1115.** Fujimura Memorial Hall, Kofu (formerly Mutsuzawa School).

**1116.** Porch of Sakuranomiya Public Hall, Osaka.

**1983.** Modern Western-style Architecture (7th series).
1695. **1115.** 60 y. multicoloured 75 10
1696. **1116.** 60 y. multicoloured 75 10

**1117.** "Selflessness" (Taikan Yokoyama).

**1118.** "Aged Monkey" (wood carving, Koun Takamura).

**1983.** Modern Japanese Art (16 series).
1697. **1117.** 60 y. multicoloured 75 10
1698. **1118.** 60 y. multicoloured 75 10

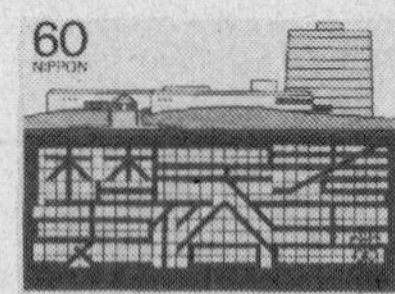

**1119.** Museum and Japanese Characters representing History, Folklore and Antiquity.

**1983.** Opening of National Museum of History and Folklore.
1699. **1119.** 60 y. multicoloured 40 10

**1120/1.** "Women working in the Kitchen" (Utamaro Kitagawa).

**1983.** Philatelic Week.
1700. **1120.** 60 y. multicoloured 75 10
1701. **1121.** 60 y. multicoloured 75 10
Nos. 1695/6 were issued together, se-tenant, forming a composite design.

**1122.** "Hiba arborvitae", Japanese Black Fritillary and Hakusan Mountains.

**1123.** Colt and Racehorse.

**1983.** National Afforestation Campaign.
1702. **1122.** 60 y. multicoloured 75 10

**1983.** 50th Nippon Derby.
1703. **1123.** 60 y. multicoloured 85 10

**1124.** Rabbit and Empty Can.

**1983.** Islands Clean-up Campaign.
1704. **1124.** 60 y. multicoloured 70 10

**1125.** Hohei-kan House (Wedding Hall), Sapporo.

**1126.** Glover House, Nagasaki.

**1983.** Modern Western-style Architecture (8th series).
1705. **1125.** 60 y. multicoloured 75 10
1706. **1126.** 60 y. multicoloured 75 10

**1127.** First Issue and Nihonbashi Bulletin Board.

**1983.** Centenary of "Government Journal".
1707. **1127.** 60 y. multicoloured 75 10

**1128.** Boy with Letter.

**1129.** Fairy with Letter.

**1983.** Letter Writing Day.
1708. **1128.** 40 y. multicoloured 35 10
1709. **1129.** 60 y. multicoloured 65 10

**1130.** 59th Bank, Hirosaki.

**1131.** Auditorium of Gakushuin Elementary School (now in Narita).

**1983.** Modern Western-style Architecture (9th series).
1710. **1130.** 60 y. multicoloured 75 10
1711. **1131.** 60 y. multicoloured 75 10

**1132.** Theatre and Noh Player.

**1983.** Opening of National Noh Theatre, Tokyo.
1712. **1132.** 60 y. multicoloured 75 10

**1133.** Okinawa Rail.

**1983.** Endangered Birds (1st series). Multicoloured.
1713 60 y. Type **1133** . . . . 1·10 80
1714 60 y. Blakiston's fish owl ("Ketupa blakistoni") (horiz) . . . . 1·10 80
See also Nos. 1724/5, 1729/30, 1735/6 and 1742/3.

**1135.** "Chi-kyu" (paper doll by Juzo Kagoshima).

**1136.** Naginata Player and Myogi Mountains.

**1983.** International Correspondence Week.
1715. **1135.** 130 y. multicoloured 1·75 25

**1983.** 38th National Athletic Meeting, Gumman.
1716. **1136.** 40 y. multicoloured 40 10

**1137.** Ferris Wheel.

**1138.** Children supporting Globe.

**1983.** World Communications Year.
1717. **1137.** 60 y. multicoloured 50 10
1718. **1138.** 60 y. multicoloured 50 10

**1139.** Park and Monument.

**1140.** Congress Emblem and Mouth Mirror.

**1983.** Opening of Showa Memorial National Park.
1719. **1139.** 60 y. multicoloured 60 10

**1983.** 71st World Dental Congress, Tokyo.
1720. **1140.** 60 y. multicoloured 60 10

**1141.** "Shirase".

**1983.** Maiden Voyage of Antarctic Research Ship "Shirase".
1721 1141 60 y. multicoloured . . 2·25 35

**1983.** Special Correspondence Stamps.
1722. **1098.** 40 y. multicoloured 45 10
1723. **1099.** 40 y. multicoloured 45 10

**1983.** Endangered Birds (2nd series). As T **1133**. Multicoloured.
1724. 60 y. Pryer's woodpecker ("Sapheopipo noguchii") 1·25 40
1725. 60 y. Canada goose ("Branta canadensis leucopareia") (horiz.) 1·25 40

**1144.** "Mouse riding a Small Hammer" (folk toy).

**1145.** Human Rights Emblem.

**1983.** New Year's Greetings.
1726. **1144.** 40 y. multicoloured 60 10

**1983.** 35th Anniv. of Declaration of Human Rights.
1728. **1145.** 60 y. multicoloured 45 10

**1984.** Endangered Birds (3rd series). As T **1133**. Multicoloured.
1729. 60 y. Japanese marsh warbler ("Megalurus pryeri pryeri") (horiz.) 1·25 30

1730. 60 y. Crested Serpent Eagle ("Spilornis cheela perplexus") .. .. 1·25 30

1148. Exhibition Emblem and Mascot.

**1984.** "Expo '85" International Science and Technology Exhibition, Tsukuba (1985).
1731. **1148.** 60 y. + 10 y. mult. .. 80 15

1149. Bank of Japan Head Office.

1150. Hunter House, Kobe.

**1984.** Modern Western-style Architecture (10th series).
1732 **1149** 60 y. multicoloured 75 10
1733 **1150** 60 y. multicoloured 75 10

1151. Japanese-style Cake and Bamboo Tea Whisk.

**1984.** 20th Confectionery Fair, Tokyo.
1734. **1151.** 60 y. multicoloured 55 10

**1984.** Endangered Birds (4th series). As T **1133.** Multicoloured.
1735. 60 y. Black wood pigeon ("Columba janthina nitens") .. .. 1·25 30
1736. 60 y. Spotted greenshank ("Tringa guttifer") (horiz.) .. .. 1·25 30

1154. Bunraku Puppet and Theatre.

**1984.** Opening of National Bunraku Theatre, Osaka.
1737. **1154.** 60 y. multicoloured 75 10

1155. "Otani Oniji as Edobeh" (Toshusai Sharaku). 1156. "Iwai Hanshiro IV as Shigenoi" (Toshusai Sharaku).

**1984.** Philatelic Week.
1738. **1155.** 60 y. multicoloured 75 10
1739. **1156.** 60 y. multicoloured 75 10

1157. Kaikozu Tree and Sakura Volcano. 1158. "Himawari" Weather Satellite and Chart.

**1984.** National Afforestation Campaign.
1740. **1157.** 60 y. multicoloured 75 10

**1984.** Cent. of National Weather Forecasts.
1741. **1158.** 60 y. multicoloured 75 10

**1984.** Endangered Birds (5th series). As T **1133.** Multicoloured.
1742 60 y. White-backed woodpecker ("Dendrocopos leucotos owstoni") (horiz) .. .. 1·25 30
1743 60 y. Peregrine falcon ("Falco peregrinus fruitii") .. .. 1·25 30

1161. Doves.

**1984.** Federation of U.N.E.S.C.O. Clubs and Associations World Congress, Sendai.
1744 **1161** 60 y. multicoloured .. 45 10

1162. Birds in Tree. 1163. Bird and Flowers.

**1984.** Letter Writing Day.
1745. **1162.** 40 y. multicoloured 35 10
1746. **1163.** 60 y. multicoloured 60 10

1164. "Fire and Wind" (Motomi Hagimoto). 1165. "Bonds" (Noboru Kanda).

**1984.** Disaster Prevention Week.
1747 **1164** 40 y. multicoloured 35 10
1748 **1165** 60 y. black & yellow 60 10

1166. "Leontopodium fauriei". 1168. Basho's Crossroads, Sendai.

**1984.** Alpine Plants (1st series). Mult.
1749 60 y. Type **1166** .. .. 70 10
1750 60 y. "Lagotis glauca" (horiz) .. .. 70 10
See also Nos. 1752/3, 1769/70, 1775/6, 1802/3, 1813/14 and 1827/8.

**1984.** 6th International Virology Congress, Sendai.
1751. **1168.** 60 y. multicoloured 55 10

**1984.** Alpine Plants (2nd series). As T **1166.** Multicoloured.
1752. 60 y. Globe Flower ("Trollius riederianus") 75 10
1753. 60 y. "Primula cuneifolia" 75 10

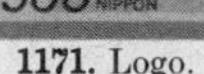

1171. Logo. 1172. "Serenity" (doll by Ryujo Hori)

**1984.** Electronic Mail.
1754. **1171.** 500 y. multicoloured 8·00 3·00

**1984.** International Correspondence Week.
1755. **1172.** 130 y. multicoloured 2·00 15

1173. Silver Pavilion, Jisho Temple. 1174. Hockey and East Pagoda of Yakushi Temple.

**1984.** 17th International Internal Medicine Congress, Kyoto Coty.
1756 **1173** 60 y. multicoloured .. 55 10

**1984.** 39th National Athletic Meeting, Nara.
1757. **1174.** 40 y. multicoloured 70 10

1175. Birds in Tree. 1176. Flowers.

1177. Chrysanthemums Design. 1178. Leaf and Bird Design.

**1984.** Traditional Crafts (1st series). Kutani Porcelain Plates and Nishijin Silk Weavings.
1758. **1175.** 60 y. multicoloured 80 10
1759. **1176.** 60 y. multicoloured 80 10
1760. **1177.** 60 y. multicoloured 80 10
1761. **1178.** 60 y. multicoloured 80 10
See also Nos. 1771/4, 1787/90, 1795/8, 1805/8, 1820/3 and 1829/32.

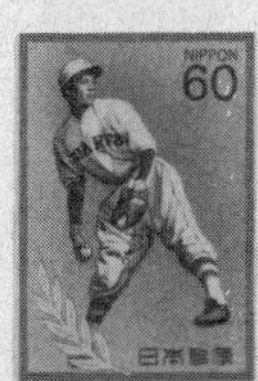
1179. Eiji Sawamura (pitcher).

**1984.** 50th Anniv of Japan Tokyo Baseball Club. Multicoloured.
1762 60 y. Type **1179** .. .. 60 10
1763 60 y. Masaru Kageura (striker) .. .. 60 10
1764 60 y. Ball, birds and Matsutaro Shoriki (founder) .. .. 60 10

1182. Workers' Profiles and Symbols. 1183. Bamboo Ox (Sakushu folk toy).

**1984.** Centenary of Technical Education.
1765 **1182** 60 y. multicoloured .. 45 10

**1984.** New Year's Greetings.
1766 **1183** 40 y. multicoloured .. 40 10

**1985.** Alpine Plants (3rd series). As T **1166.** Multicoloured.
1769 60 y. "Rhododendron aureum" .. .. 70 10
1770 60 y. "Oxytropis nigrescens" (horiz) .. 70 10

**HAVE YOU READ THE NOTES AT THE BEGINNING OF THIS CATALOGUE?**
These often provide answers to the enquiries we receive.

1186. Dolls. 1187. Doll with Cat.

1188. Bird and Flower Design. 1189. Birds and Chrysanthemums Design.

**1985.** Traditional Crafts (2nd series). Edo Kimekomi Dolls and Okinawa Bingata Cloth.
1771 **1186** 60 y. multicoloured .. 75 10
1772 **1187** 60 y. multicoloured .. 75 10
1773 **1188** 60 y. multicoloured .. 75 10
1774 **1189** 60 y. multicoloured .. 75 10

**1985.** Alpine Plants (4th Series). As T **1166.** Multicoloured.
1775 60 y. "Dryas octopetala" (horiz) .. .. 75 10
1776 60 y. "Draba japonica" .. 75 10

1192. Theme Pavilion and Symbol Tower. 1194. University Buildings, Chiba City, and Transmitter.

**1985.** "EXPO '85" World Fair, Tsukuba. Multicoloured.
1777. 40 y. Type **1192** .. .. 40 10
1778. 60 y. Geometric city .. 60 10

**1985.** Inauguration of University of the Air.
1780 **1194** 60 y. multicoloured .. 45 10

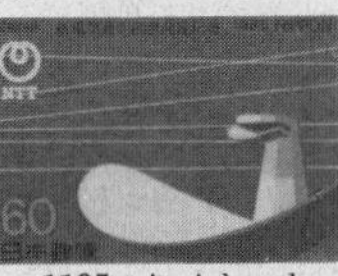
1195. Aerial and Communication Lines.

**1985.** Privatisation of Nippon Telegraph and Telephone Corporation.
1781 **1195** 60 y. multicoloured .. 45 10

1196. Map of Japan (after Teixeira's Map in Ortelius's "Atlas", 1595). 1197. Korekiyo Takahashi (proposer of Patent Laws).

**1985.** World Import Fair, Nagoya.
1782. **1196.** 60 y. multicoloured 60 10

**1985.** Cent. of Industrial Patents System.
1783. **1197.** 60 y. multicoloured 45 10

1198. "Winter in the North" (Yumeji Takehisa). 1199. "Toward the Morning Light" (Yumeji Takehisa).

**1985.** Philatelic Week.
1784. **1198.** 60 y. multicoloured 75 10
1785. **1199.** 60 y. multicoloured 75 10

**1200.** Mt. Aso and Gentian.

**1985.** National Afforestation Campaign.
1786. **1200.** 60 y. multicoloured 50 10

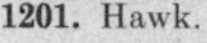

**1201.** Hawk. **1202.** Ducks.

**1203.** Bowl. **1204.** Plate.

**1985.** Traditional Crafts (3rd series). Yew Wood Carvings and Arita Porcelain.
1787. **1201.** 60 y. multicoloured 60 10
1788. **1202.** 60 y. multicoloured 60 10
1789. **1203.** 60 y. multicoloured 50 10
1790. **1204.** 60 y. multicoloured 50 10

**1205.** "Cherry Trees at Night" **1206.** (Taikan Yokoyama).

**1985.** 50th Anniv of Radio Japan (overseas broadcasting station).
1791. **1205.** 60 y. multicoloured 60 10
1792. **1206.** 60 y. multicoloured 60 10
Nos. 1791/2 were issued together, se-tenant, forming a composite design.

**1207.** Maeshima and "Tokyo Post Office" (Hiroshige III).

**1208.** Bridge.

**1985.** 150th Birth Anniv. of Baron Hisoka Maeshima (first Postmaster-General).
1793. **1207.** 60 y. multicoloured 55 10

**1985.** Opening of Great Naruto Bridge.
1794 **1208** 60 y. multicoloured .. 70 10

**1209.** Weaving. **1210.** Weaving.

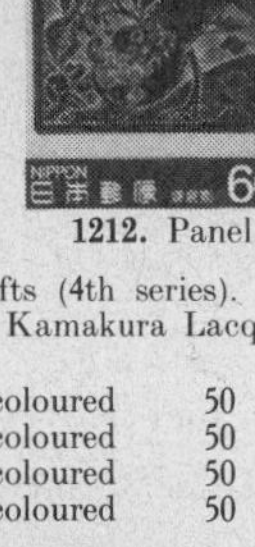

**1211.** Dish. **1212.** Panel.

**1985.** Traditional Crafts (4th series). Ojiya Linen Weavings and Kamakura Lacquered Wood Carvings.
1795. **1209.** 60 y. multicoloured 50 10
1796. **1210.** 60 y. multicoloured 50 10
1797. **1211.** 60 y. multicoloured 50 10
1798. **1212.** 60 y. multicoloured 50 10

**1213.** Silhouette of Laurel and Couple.

**1985.** International Youth Year.
1799. **1213.** 60 y. multicoloured 50 10

**1214.** Owl with Letter. **1215.** Girl holding Bird, Letter and Cat.

**1985.** Letter Writing Day.
1800. **1214.** 40 y. multicoloured 60 10
1801. **1215.** 60 y. multicoloured 60 10

**1985.** Alpine Plants (5th series). As T **1166.** Multicoloured.
1802 60 y. Gentian ("Gentiana nipponica") .. .. 70 10
1803 60 y. "Callianthemum insigne" .. .. 70 10

**1218.** Logo.

**1985.** Electronic Mail.
1804. **1218.** 500 y. multicoloured 5·00 30

**1219.** Noh Theatre Actor.

**1220.** Mother with Child.

**1221.** Tea Kettle with Fish Design.

**1222.** Tea Kettle.

**1985.** Traditional Crafts (5th series). Hakata Clay Figurines and Nambu Iron Ware.
1805. **1219.** 60 y. multicoloured 75 10
1806. **1220.** 60 y. multicoloured 75 10
1807. **1221.** 60 y. multicoloured 75 10
1808. **1222.** 60 y. multicoloured 75 10

**1223.** Hideki Yukawa (physicist) and Meson Field.

**1224.** Gymnasts.

**1985.** 50th Anniv. of Yukawa's Meson Theory.
1809. **1223.** 60 y. multicoloured 55 10

**1985.** University Games, Kobe.
1810. **1224.** 60 y. multicoloured 70 10

**1225.** Competitor filing Test Piece.

**1226.** "Hibiscus syriacus" (national flower of S. Korea).

**1985.** 28th International Vocational Training Competition, Osaka.
1811 **1225** 40 y. multicoloured .. 40 10

**1985.** 20th Anniv. of Japan–South Korea Diplomatic Relations.
1812. **1226.** 60 y. multicoloured 75 10

**1985.** Alpine Plants (6th series). As T **1166.** Multicoloured.
1813 60 y. "Viola crassa" (horiz) .. .. 1·00 10
1814 60 y. "Campanula chamissonis" .. .. 1·00 10

**1229.** Tunnels and Section through Mt. Tanigawa.

**1230.** "Seisen" (doll by Goyo Hirata)

**1985.** Opening of North-bound Kan-Etsu Tunnel.
1815 **1229** 60 y. multicoloured .. 70 10

**1985.** International Correspondence Week.
1816. **1230.** 130 y. multicoloured 1·50 10

**1231.** Youth helping African Farmer.

**1985.** 20th Anniv of Japanese Overseas Co-operation Volunteers.
1817 **1231** 60 y. multicoloured .. 50 10

**1232.** Honey Bee on Strawberry Blossom.

**1233.** Handball Player and Mt. Daisen.

**1985.** 30th International Bee-keeping Congress, Nagoya.
1818 **1232** 60 y. multicoloured .. 80 10

**1985.** 40th Int Athletic Meeting, Tottori.
1819 **1233** 40 y. multicoloured .. 70 10

**1234.** Table. **1235.** Bowl.

**1236.** Lantern on Column.

**1237.** Lantern.

**1985.** Traditional Crafts (6th series). Wajima Lacquerware and Izumo Sandstone Lanterns.
1820. **1234.** 60 y. multicoloured 60 10
1821. **1235.** 60 y. multicoloured 60 10
1822. **1236.** 60 y. multicoloured 60 10
1823. **1237.** 60 y. multicoloured 60 10

**1238.** Osaka Papier-mache Tiger.

**1239.** Cabinet Emblem and Official Seal.

**1985.** New Year's Greetings.
1824. **1238.** 40 y. multicoloured 50 10

**1985.** Cent of Cabinet System of Government.
1826 **1239** 60 y. multicoloured .. 55 10

**1986.** Alpine Plants (7th series). As T **1166.** Multicoloured.
1827 60 y. "Diapensia lapponica" .. .. 55 10
1828 60 y. "Pedicularis apodochila" .. .. 55 10

**1242.** Fan with Tree Design.

**1243.** Fan with Flower Design.

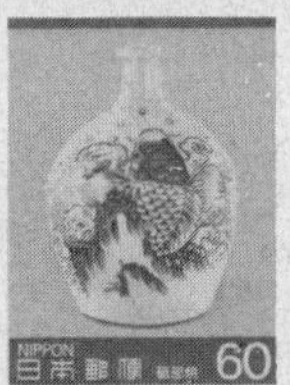

**1244.** Flask with Fish Pattern.

**1245.** Tea Caddy.

**1986.** Traditional Craft (7th series). Kyoto Fans and Tobe Porcelain.
1829. **1242.** 60 y. multicoloured 75 10
1830. **1243.** 60 y. multicoloured 75 10
1831. **1244.** 60 y. multicoloured 75 10
1832. **1245.** 60 y. multicoloured 75 10

**1246.** Gothic Style Finial and "Golden Norm".

**1986.** Centenary of Architecture Institute, Shiba, Tokyo.
1833 **1246** 60 y. multicoloured .. 60 10

**1247.** Standing Lady.

**1248.** Seated Lady.

**1986.** Philatelic Week. Details of "South of Hateruma" by Kaigetsu Kikuchi.
1834. **1247.** 60 y. multicoloured 80 10
1835. **1248.** 60 y. multicoloured 80 10

**1249.** Phoenix and Enthronement Hall, Kyoto Palace.

**1250.** Imperial Palace Ridge Decoration.

**1986.** 60th Anniv. of Emperor Hirohito's Accession.

1836. **1249.** 60 y. multicoloured 70 10
1837. **1250.** 60 y. multicoloured 70 10

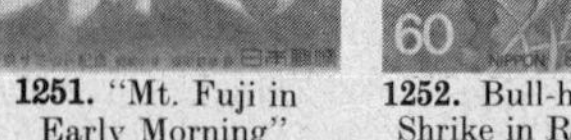

**1251.** "Mt. Fuji in Early Morning" (Yukihiko Yasuda).

**1252.** Bull-headed Shrike in Reeds.

**1986.** 12th Economic Summit of Industrialised Countries, Tokyo.

1839. **1251.** 60 y. multicoloured 75 10

**1986.** National Afforestation Campaign.

1840. **1252.** 60 y. multicoloured 1·25 30

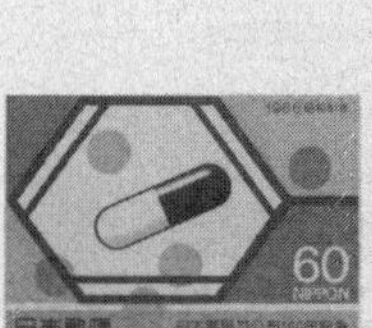

**1253.** Capsule, Tablets and Structure of Toluene.

**1254.** Map and Clock.

**1986.** Centenary of Japanese Pharmacopoeia.

1841. **1253.** 60 y. multicoloured 85 10

**1986.** Centenary of Japanese Standard Time.

1842. **1254.** 60 y. multicoloured 65 10

**1255.** Bird on Chair and Letter on Table.

**1257.** Yataro Iwasaki, Makoto Kondo and Cadet Ship "Nippon Maru II".

**1986.** Letter Writing Day. Multicoloured.

1843 40 y. Type **1255** .. .. 40 10
1844 60 y. Girl holding rabbit and letter .. .. 70 10

**1986.** 110th Anniv of Merchant Navy Education.

1846 **1257** 60 y. multicoloured .. 1·40 35

**1258.** Asian Apollo ("Parnassius eversmanni").

**1262.** "Folkways in Twelve Months" (detail, Shunsho Katsukawa).

**1986.** Insects (1st series). Multicolored.

1847 60 y. Type **1258** .. .. 1·00 10
1848 60 y. Shieldbug ("Poecilocoris lewisi") 1·00 10
1849 60 y. Longhorn beetle ("Rosalia batesi") .. 1·00 10
1850 60 y. "Epiophlebia superstes" .. 1·00 10

See also Nos. 1854/7, 1861/4, 1869/72, 1878/81 and 1911/12.

**1986.** 52nd International Federation of Library Associations General Conference, Tokyo.

1851. **1262.** 60 y. multicoloured 75 10

**1263.** Electron Microscope.

**1264.** Couple and Conference Emblem.

**1986.** 11th International Electron Microscopy Congress, Kyoto.

1852. **1263.** 60 y. multicoloured 85 10

**1986.** 23rd International Social Welfare Conference, Tokyo.

1853. **1264.** 60 y. multicoloured 60 10

**1986.** Insects (2nd series). As T **1258**. Mult.

1854 60 y. Dragonflies ("Sympetrum pedemonatanum") .. 1·00 10
1855 60 y. Weevil ("Damaster blaptoides") .. .. 1·00 10
1856 60 y. Stag beetle ("Dorcus hopei") .. .. 1·00 10
1857 60 y. Wonderful hair-streak ("Thermo-zephyrus ataxus") .. 1·00 10

**1269.** "Ohmori Miyage" (shiso doll, Juzoh Kagoshima).

**1270.** Gymnast and Mt. Fuji.

**1986.** International Correspondence Week.

1858. **1269.** 130 y. multicoloured 1·50 15

**1986.** 41st National Athletic Meeting, Yamanashi.

1859. **1270.** 40 y. multicoloured 70 10

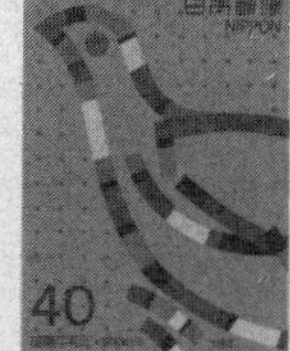

**1271.** "Flowers in Autumn and Girl in Rakuhoku".

**1276.** Stylized Dove.

**1986.** 5th World Ikebana Convention, Kyoto.

1860. **1271.** 60 y. multicoloured 85 10

**1986.** Insects (3rd series). As T **1258**. Mult.

1861 60 y. "Elcysma west-woodii" (moth) .. 1·00 10
1862 60 y. "Rhyothemis variegata" .. .. 1·00 10
1863 60 y. Cicada ("Tibicen japonicus") .. .. 1·00 10
1864 60 y. "Chrysochroa holstii" .. .. 1·00 10

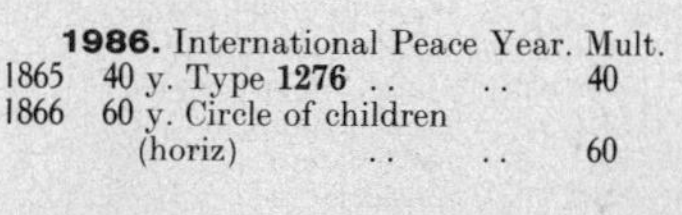

**1986.** International Peace Year. Mult.

1865 40 y. Type **1276** .. .. 40 10
1866 60 y. Circle of children (horiz) .. .. 60 10

**1278.** "Rabbits making Rice Cake" (Nagoya clay model).

**1283.** Characters for "Toki" (Registry) and Map.

**1986.** New Year's Greetings.

1867. **1278.** 40 y. multicoloured 75 10

**1987.** Insects (4th series). As T **1258**. Mult.

1869 60 y. "Cheirotonus jambar" .. .. 1·00 10
1870 60 y. Chestnut tiger ("Parantica sita") .. 1·00 10
1871 60 y. "Anotogaster sieboldii" .. .. 1·00 10
1872 60 y. Stag beetle ("Lucanus maculi-femoratus") .. .. 1·00 10

**1987.** Centenary of Land Registration.

1873. **1283.** 60 y. multicoloured 65 10

**1284.** Basho Matsuo (after Haritsu Ogawa).

**1285.** "Departing Spring" (Senju).

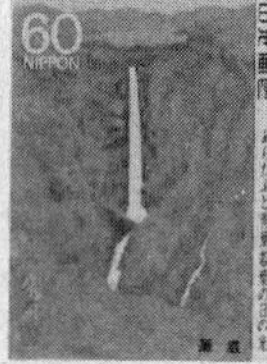

**1286.** Kegon Falls.

**1287.** "Sunlight" (Toshu Shrine).

**1987.** "Narrow Road to a Far Province" (travel diary) by Basho Matsuo (1st series).

1874 **1284** 60 y. multicoloured 75 10
1875 **1285** 60 y. multicoloured 75 10
1876 **1286** 60 y. multicoloured 75 10
1877 **1287** 60 y. multicoloured 75 10

In this series each pair of stamps (except Nos. 1874/5) illustrates one "haiku" (17-syllable poem) from the diary. The full text of the "haiku" is printed on one stamp and given in calligraphy on the other with appropriate illustrations. Each "haiku" was written at a particular point in the journey (given in brackets in the caption to the second stamp of each pair).

See also Nos. 1896/9, 1906/9, 1925/8, 1932/5, 1945/8, 1962/5, 1973/6, 1982/5 and 2000/3.

**1987.** Insects (5th series). As T **1258**. Mult.

1878 60 y. Owl-fly ("Ascara-phus ramburi") .. 1·00 10
1879 60 y. Cockchafer ("Polyphylla laticollis") 1·00 10
1880 60 y. Leaf butterfly ("Kallima inachus") .. 1·00 10
1881 60 y. "Calopteryx cornelia" .. .. 1·00 10

**1294.** Wind Orchid.

**1295.** Lobster-root.

**1987.** 12th International Orchid Conference, Tokyo.

1883. **1294.** 60 y. multicoloured 70 10
1884. **1295.** 60 y. multicoloured 70 10

**1296.** Early Mail Sorting Carriage.

**1987.** Ending of Railway Mail Carriage Contracts.

1885 60 y. Type **1296** .. .. 1·00 30
1886 60 y. Loading mail sacks (detail of scroll painting by Beisen Kubota) .. 1·00 30

**1298.** Steam Tank Locomotive No. 137.

**1987.** Privatisation of Japan Railways. Mult.

1887. 60 y. Type **1298** .. .. 1·00 30
1888. 60 y. High-speed train No. 002 .. .. 1·00 30

**1300.** Nudibranchs.

**1301.** "Woman with a Comb".

**1987.** Centenary of Marine Biology Studies in Japan.

1889. **1300.** 60 y. multicoloured 85 15

**1987.** Philatelic Week. Paintings by Goyo Hashiguchi. Multicoloured.

1890. 60 y. Type **1301** .. .. 85 10
1891. 60 y. "Woman putting on make-up" .. .. 85 10

**1303.** Map and Emblem.

**1034.** Magpie and Forested Coastline.

**1987.** 20th Annual General Meeting of Asian Development Bank.

1892. **1303.** 60 y. multicoloured 60 10

**1987.** National Afforestation Campaign.

1893. **1304.** 60 y. multicoloured 1·25 10

**1305.** Yatsuhashi Gold Lacquer and Nacre Inkstone Case (Kohrin Ogata).

**1306.** Hikone Castle.

**1987.** National Treasures (1st series).

1894. **1305.** 60 y. multicoloured 75 10
1895. **1306.** 110 y. multicoloured 1·50 15

See also Nos. 1900/1, 1929/30, 1949/50, 1968/9, 1980/1, 2006/7 and 2017/18.

**1307.** European Cuckoo.

**1308.** Horse and River (Nasu).

**1309.** "In the Shade of the Willow".

**1310.** Paddy Field (Ashino).

**1987.** "Narrow Road to a Far Province" by Basho Matsuo (2nd series).

1896 **1307** 60 y. multicoloured 80 10
1897 **1308** 60 y. multicoloured 60 10
1898 **1309** 60 y. multicoloured 60 10
1899 **1310** 60 y. multicoloured 60 10

**1311.** Golden Turtle Reliquary for Buddha's Ashes (Tashodai Temple).

**1312.** Inuyama Castle.

**1987.** National Treasures (2nd series). Multicoloured.

1900. **1311.** 60 y. multicoloured 85 10
1901. **1312.** 110 y. multicoloured 1·40 15

**1313.** Flowers in Envelope

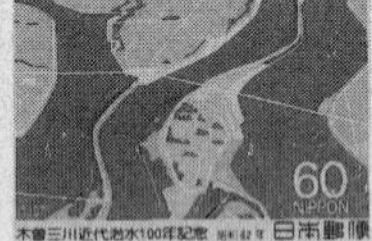

**1315.** Flood Barrier across Rivers.

**1987.** Letter Writing Day. Multicoloured.

1902. 40 y. Type **1313** . . . . 35 10
1903. 60 y. Elephant holding letter in trunk . . 45 10

**1987.** Centenary of Modern Flood Control of Rivers Kiso, Nagara and Ibi.

1905 **1315** 60 y. multicoloured . . 60 10

**1316.** Chestnut Blossoms.

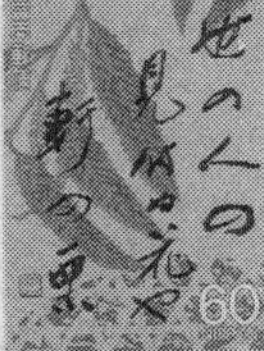

**1317.** Chestnut Leaves (Sukagawa).

**1318.** Trans-planting Rice.

**1319.** Fern Leaves ("Dyeing Stone", ' Shinobu).

**1987.** "Narrow Road to a Far Province" by Basho Matsuo (3rd series).

1906 **1316** 60 y. multicoloured 60 10
1907 **1317** 60 y. multicoloured 60 10
1908 **1318** 60 y. multicoloured 60 10
1909 **1319** 60 y. multicoloured 60 10

**1320.** Temple of Emerald Buddha and Cherry Blossom.

**1321.** "Gensho Kanto" (Ryujo Hori).

**1987.** Centenary of Japan–Thailand Friendship Treaty.

1910. **1320.** 60 y. multicoloured 65 10

**1987.** Insects (6th series). As T **1258**. Mult.

1911 40 y. Orange-tip ("Anthocaris cardamines") . . 75 10
1912 40 y. Great purple ("Sasakia charonda") 75 10

**1987.** International Correspondence Week. Multicoloured.

1913 130 y. Type **1321** . . 1·40 10
1914 150 y. "Utage-no-Hana" (Goyo Hirata) . . 1·60 10

**1323.** "Three Beauties" (detail, Toyokuni Utagawa).

**1324.** Lion's Head Public Water Tap.

**1987.** 13th International Certified Public Accountants Congress, Tokyo.

1915 **1323** 60 y. multicoloured . . 55 10

**1987.** Centenary of Yokohama Waterworks.

1916. **1324.** 60 y. multicoloured 55 10

**1325.** Basketball Players and Shuri Gate, Naha.

**1326.** Playing Card with Queen holding Bird and King smoking.

**1987.** 42nd National Athletic Meeting, Okinawa.

1917. **1325.** 40 y. multicoloured 45 10

**1987.** 6th International Smoking and Health Conference, Tokyo.

1918. **1326.** 60 y. multicoloured 70 10

**1327.** Dish Aerial, Kashima Station.

**1328.** Nijo Castle.

**1987.** International Telecommunications Conference, Tokyo.

1919. **1327.** 60 y. multicoloured 65 10

**1987.** World Historic Cities Conference, Kyoto.

1920. **1328.** 60 y. multicoloured 65 10

**1329.** "Family in Tree" (Takahiro Nagahama).

**1331.** Kurashiki Papier-mache Dragon.

**1987.** International Year of Shelter for the Homeless. Multicoloured.

1921 40 y. Type **1329** . . . . 40 10
1922 60 y. "Houses" (Yoko Sasaki) . . . . 60 10

**1987.** New Year's Greetings.

1923. **1331.** 40 y. multicoloured 50 10

**1332.** Sweet Flags.

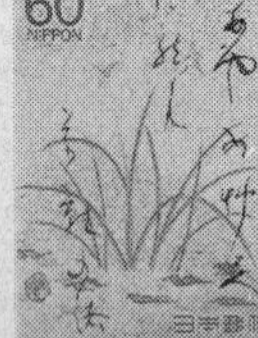

**1333.** Sweet Flags and Birds (Sendai).

**1334.** "Recollecting the Past"

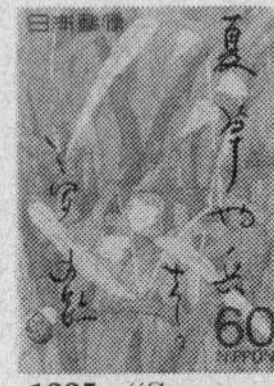

**1335.** "Summer Grasses" (Hiraizumi).

**1988.** "Narrow Road to a Far Province" by Basho Matsuo (4th series).

1925 **1332** 60 y. multicoloured 60 10
1926 **1333** 60 y. multicoloured 60 10
1927 **1334** 60 y. multicoloured 60 10
1928 **1335** 60 y. multicoloured 60 10

**1336.** Kongo Samma-in Pagoda, Mt. Koya.

**1337.** Ekoh-Doji, Kongobu Temple.

**1988.** National Treasures (3rd series).

1929. **1336.** 60 y. multicoloured 60 10
1930. **1337.** 110 y. multicoloured 1·25 10

**1338.** Class "ED 791" Locomotive "Sea of Japan" leaving Tunnel and Map.

**1988.** Opening of Seikan (Aomori–Hakodate) Railway Tunnel.

1931 **1338** 60 y. multicoloured . . 70 30

**1339.** Safflower.

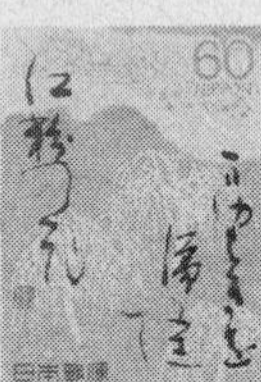

**1340.** Willow Trees (Obanazawa).

**1341.** Risshaku (or Mountain) Temple.

**1342.** Pine Trees (Risshaku Temple).

**1988.** "Narrow Road to a Far Province" by Basho Matsuo (5th series).

1932 **1339** 60 y. multicoloured 60 10
1933 **1340** 60 y. multicoloured 60 10
1934 **1341** 60 y. multicoloured 60 10
1935 **1342** 60 y. multicoloured 60 10

**1343.** **1344.**
South Bisan Section from Kagawa Side.

**1345.** **1346.**
Shimotsui Section from Okayama Side.

**1988.** Opening of Seto Great Road and Rail Bridge.

1936. **1343.** 60 y. multicoloured 80 30
1937. **1344.** 60 y. multicoloured 80 30
1938. **1345.** 60 y. multicoloured 80 30
1939. **1346.** 60 y. multicoloured 80 30

Nos. 1936/7 and 1938/9 were printed together, se-tenant, each pair forming composite design.

**1347.** "Long Undergarment" (Kotondo Torii).

**1349.** Detail of Biwa Plectrum Guard.

**1988.** Philatelic Week. Multicoloured.

1940. 60 y. Type **1347** . . . . 60 10
1941. 60 y. "Kimono Sash" (Kotondo Torii) . . 60 10

**1988.** "Silk Road" Exhibition, Nara.

1943. **1349.** 60 y. multicoloured 60 10

**1350.** Yashima, Little Cuckoo and Olive Tree.

**1988.** National Afforestation Campaign.

1944. **1350.** 60 y. multicoloured 70 10

**1351.** River Mogami.

**1352.** Irises in the Rain (Oishida).

**1353.** Moon Mountain.

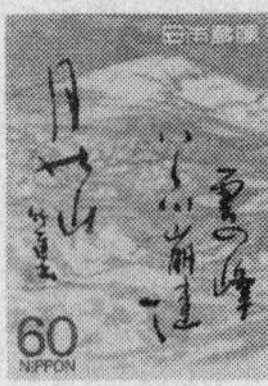

**1354.** Moon Mountain (Gassan).

**1988.** "Narrow Road to a Far Province" by Basho Matsuo (6th series).

1945 **1351** 60 y. multicoloured 80 15
1946 **1352** 60 y. multicoloured 60 10
1947 **1353** 60 y. multicoloured 60 10
1948 **1354** 60 y. multicoloured 60 10

**1355.** Morodo Shrine, Itsukushima.

**1356.** Kozakura-gawa Braided Armour.

**1988.** National Treasures (4th series).

1949. **1355.** 60 y. multicoloured 60 10

1950. **1356.** 100 y. multicoloured 95 20

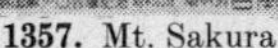

**1357.** Mt. Sakura. **1358.** Cat with Letter.

**1988.** International Conference on Volcanoes, Kagoshima.

1951. **1357.** 60 y. multicoloured 60 10

**1988.** Letter Writing Day. Multicoloured.

1952 40 y. Type **1358** .. .. 45 10

1953 40 y. Crab with letter (34 × 25 mm) .. .. 45 10

1954 60 y. Fairy with letter .. 60 10

1955 60 y. Girl and letter (25 × 32 mm) .. .. 60 10

Nos. 1952 and 1954 exist both perforated with ordinary gum and imperforate with self-adhesive gum.

**1362.** Ohana (Kinosuke puppet, Japan). **1366.** Peonies.

**1988.** International Puppetry Festival, Nagoya, Iida and Tokyo. Multicoloured.

1956 60 y. Type **1362** .. .. 60 10

1957 60 y. Stick puppet of girl (Czechoslovakia) .. 60 10

1958 60 y. Shadow puppet (China) .. .. 60 10

1959 60 y. Knight (Italy) .. 60 10

**1988.** 10th Anniv of Japanese–Chinese Treaty of Peace and Friendship. Multicoloured.

1960 60 y. Type **1366** .. .. 60 10

1961 60 y. Ton-ton (giant panda) .. .. 75 10

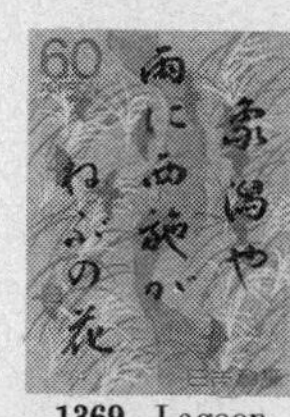

**1368.** Mimosa Flowers. **1369.** Lagoon and Grass (Kisagata).

**1370.** Rough Sea. **1371.** Waves (Ichiburi).

**1988.** "Narrow Road to a Far Province" by Basho Matsuo (7th series).

1962 **1368** 60 y. multicoloured 60 10

1963 **1369** 60 y. multicoloured 60 10

1964 **1370** 60 y. multicoloured 60 10

1965 **1371** 60 y. multicoloured 60 10

**1372.** Nagoya and Egg. **1373.** Globe and "Rehabilitation" in Braille.

**1988.** 18th International Poultry Congress, Nagoya.

1966 **1372** 60 y. multicoloured .. 70 10

**1988.** 16th Rehabilitation International World Congress, Tokyo.

1967 **1373** 60 y. multicoloured .. 60 10

**1374.** Nakatsuhime-no-mikoto, Yakushi Temple. **1375.** Murou Temple.

**1988.** National Treasures (5th series).

1968 **1374** 60 y. multicoloured 60 10

1969 **1375** 100 y. multicoloured 95 20

**1376.** "Kimesaburo Iwai as Chiyo" (Kunimasa Utagawa). **1378.** Gymnast and Temple of the Golden Pavilion.

**1988.** International Correspondence Week. Multicoloured.

1970 80 y. Type **1376** .. .. 85 10

1971 120 y. "Komazo Ichikawa III as Ganryu Sasaki" (Toyokuni Utagawa) .. 1·25 20

**1988.** 43rd National Athletic Meeting, Kyoto.

1972 **1378** 40 y. multicoloured .. 45 10

**1379.** Rice. **1380.** Ariso Sea (Kurikara Pass).

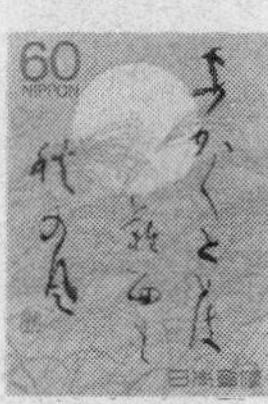

**1381.** Sun. **1382.** "Autumn Wind and Sun" (Kanazawa).

**1988.** "Narrow Road to a Far Province" by Basho Matsuo (8th series).

1973 **1379** 60 y. multicoloured 60 10

1974 **1380** 60 y. multicoloured 60 10

1975 **1381** 60 y. multicoloured 60 10

1976 **1382** 60 y. multicoloured 60 10

**1383.** Mexican State Arms. **1384.** Snake (Shimotsuke clay bell).

**1988.** Centenary of Japan–Mexico Friendship and Trade Treaty.

1977 **1383** 60 y. multicoloured .. 60 10

**1988.** New Year's Greetings.

1978 **1384** 40 y. multicoloured .. 45 10

**1385.** Figures on Globe.

**1988.** 40th Anniv. of Declaration of Human Rights.

1979 **1385** 60 y. multicoloured .. 60 10

**1386** Gold-plated Silver Pot with Hunting Design, Todai Temple

**1387** Bronze Figure of Yakushi (Buddha of Medicine), Horyu Temple

**1989.** National Treasures (6th series).

1980 **1386** 60 y. multicoloured 60 10

1981 **1387** 100 y. multicoloured 95 20

**1388** Nata Temple **1389** Pampas Grass (Natadera)

**1390** Moonlight, Kehi Shrine **1391** Moon and Pine Trees (Tsuruga)

**1989** "Narrow Road to a Far Province" by Basho Matsuo (9th series).

1982 **1388** 60 y. multicoloured 60 10

1983 **1389** 60 y. multicoloured 60 10

1984 **1390** 60 y. multicoloured 60 10

1985 **1391** 60 y. multicoloured 60 10

**1392** Globe and Exhibition Site

**1989.** "Fukuoka '89" Asian–Pacific Exhibition, Fukuoka.

1989 **1392** 60 y. multicoloured 60 10

1996 62 y. multicoloured 60 10

**1393** "Russian Ladies sight-seeing at Port" (detail, Yoshitora) and Art Gallery **1394** Bonsai Japanese White Pine

**1989.** "Space and Children" Exhibition, Yokohama.

1990 **1393** 60 y. multicoloured 60 10

1997 62 y. multicoloured 60 10

**1989.** World Bonsai Convention, Omiya.

1993 **1394** 62 y. multicoloured .. 60 10

**1395** Lute-player **1397** "Dutch East Indiaman entering Harbour" (Nagasaki woodblock print)

**1989.** Philatelic Week. Details of "Awa Dance" (painting) by Tsunetomi Kitano. Mult.

1994 62 y. Type **1395** .. .. 60 10

1995 62 y. Dancer .. .. 60 10

**1989.** "Holland Festival '89".

1998 **1397** 62 y. multicoloured .. 80 15

**1398** Chikura Communication Tower and Cable Route

**1989.** Opening of 3rd Trans-Pacific Submarine Telephone Cable (Japan–Hawaii).

1999 **1398** 62 y. multicoloured .. 60 10

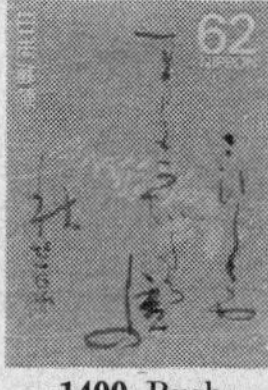

**1399** Beach in Autumn **1400** Bush Clover (Ironohama)

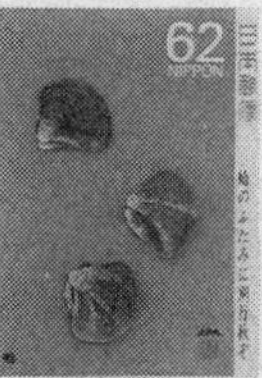

**1401** Poker-drop Venuses **1402** Wedded Rocks, Futami Bay (Ohgaki)

**1989.** "Narrow Road to a Far Province" by Basho Matsuo (11th series).

2000 **1399** 62 y. multicoloured 60 10

2001 **1400** 62 y. multicoloured 60 10

2002 **1401** 62 y. multicoloured 70 15

2003 **1402** 62 y. multicoloured 60 10

1403 Mt. Tsurugi, Lime and Bay Trees

1404 Children in Bird and Flower "Balloon"

**1989.** National Afforestation Campaign.
2004 **1403** 62 y. multicoloured .. 60 10

**1989.** International Garden and Greenery Exposition, Osaka (1990) (1st issue).
2005 **1404** 62 y. + 10 y. mult .. 70 10
See also Nos. 2035/6.

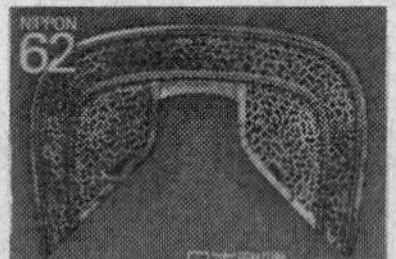
1405 Saddle Fitting from Burial Mound, Konda

1406 "Beetle Wings" Zushi, Horyu Temple

**1989.** National Treasures (7th series).
2006 **1405** 62 y. multicoloured 60 10
2007 **1406** 100 y. multicoloured 95 20

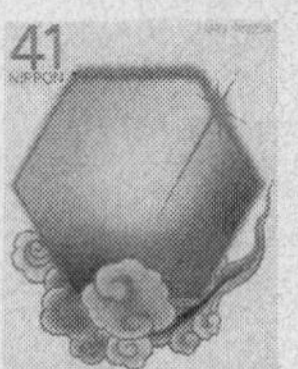
1407 "Crystal of Light and Auspicious Clouds"

1409 Bird as Vase holding Envelope

**1989.** World Design Exposition, Nagoya. Multicoloured.
2008 41 y. Type **1407** .. .. 45 10
2009 62 y. "design" .. .. 60 10

**1989.** Letter Writing Day. Multicoloured.
2010 41 y. Type **1409** .. .. 45 10
2011 62 y. Mother Rabbit reading letter .. .. 60 10

**1989.** Special Correspondence Stamps.
2013 **1098** 41 y. multicoloured 40 10
2014 **1099** 41 y. multicoloured 40 10
2015 62 y. multicoloured 55 10
2016 **1100** 72 y. multicoloured 65 10

1411 Gold Stamp

1412 Bronze Mirror

**1989.** National Treasures (8th series).
2017 **1411** 62 y. multicoloured 60 10
2018 **1412** 100 y. multicoloured 95 20

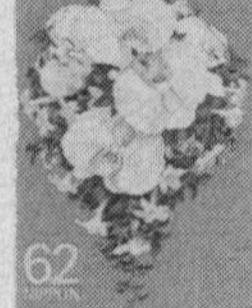
1413 Bouquet of Orchids and Stephanotis

1414 Wheelchair Race

**1989.** 6th Interflora World Congress, Tokyo.
2019 **1413** 62 y. multicoloured .. 60 10

**1989.** Far East and South Pacific Games for the Disabled, Kobe.
2020 **1414** 62 y. multicoloured .. 60 10

1415 Narrators and Drummers

1419 Ear of Rice and Paddy Field

1417 New Emperor and Kaoru playing Go ("Yadorigi" scroll)

**1989.** "Europalia 89 Japan" Festival, Belgium. Details of "Okuni Theatre" (painting on folding screen). Multicoloured.
2021 62 y. Type **1415** .. .. 60 10
2022 70 y. Okuni (actress) .. 60 10

**1989.** International Correspondence Week. Details of Takayoshi Picture Scrolls illustrating "Tale of Genji" by Lady Murasaki. Multicoloured.
2023 80 y. Type **1417** .. .. 75 10
2024 120 y. Yugao's grand-daughters playing Go ("Takekawa scroll") .. 1·25 20

**1989.** 7th Asian/African Conference of Int. Irrigation and Drainage Commission.
2025 **1419** 62 y. multicoloured .. 60 10

1420 Shinzan (first winner of all five major races)

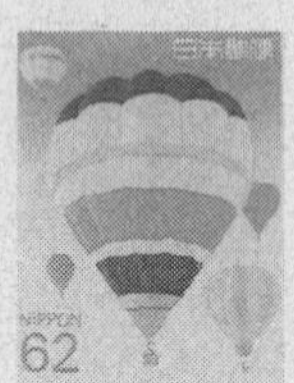
1421 Hot-air Balloons

**1989.** 100th Tenno Sho Horse Race.
2026 **1420** 62 y. multicoloured .. 70 10

**1989.** 9th Hot Air Balloon World Championship, Saga City.
2027 **1421** 62 y. multicoloured .. 60 10

1422 Conductor

1423 Yawata Wooden Horse

**1989.** 50th Anniv of Japanese Copyright Control Act.
2028 **1422** 62 y. multicoloured .. 60 10

**1989.** New Year's Greetings.
2029 **1423** 41 y. multicoloured .. 45 10

1424 Hamamatsu Papier-mache Horse

1425 Type "10000"

**1989.** New Year Lottery Stamp.
2030 **1424** 62 y. multicoloured .. 60 10
Each stamp carries a lottery number.

**1990.** Electric Railway Locomotives (1st series).
2031 **1425** 62 y. pur, lilac & grn 75 25
2032 – 62 y. multicoloured 75 25
DESIGN: No. 2032, Type "EF58".
See also Nos. 2033/4, 2039/40, 2089/90 and 2101/2.

**1990.** Electric Railway Locomotives (2nd series) As Type **1425**. Multicoloured.
2033 62 y. Type "ED40" .. 75 25
2034 62 y. Type "EH10" .. 75 25

1429 Fairies on Flower

1431 "Women gazing at the Stars" (Chou Ohta)

**1990.** "Expo 90" International Garden and Greenery Exposition, Osaka. Mult.
2035 41 y. + 4 y. Type **1429** .. 45 10
2036 62 y. Bicycle under tree 55 10

**1990.** Philatelic Week.
2037 **1431** 62 y. multicoloured .. 55 10

**1990.** Electric Railway Locomotives (3rd series). As Type **1425**. Multicoloured.
2039 62 y. Type "EF53" .. 75 25
2040 62 y. Type "ED70" .. 75 25

1434 Sweet Briar (Hokkaido)

1435 Apple Blossom (Aomori)

1436 "Paulownia tomentosa" (Iwate)

1437 Japanese Bush Clover (Miyagi)

1438 Butterbur Flower (Akita)

1439 Safflower (Yamagata)

1440 Rhododendron (Fukushima)

1441 Rose (Ibaraki)

1442 Yashio Azalea (Tochigi)

1443 Japanese Azalea (Gunma)

1444 Primrose (Saitama)

1445 Rape (Chiba)

1446 Cherry Blossom (Yamanashi)

1447 Gold-banded Lily (Kanagawa)

1448 Cherry Blossom (Tokyo)

1449 Gentian (Nagano)

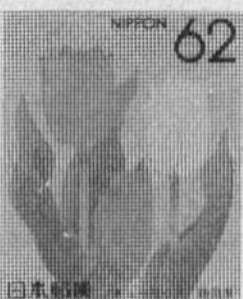
1450 Tulip (Niigata)

1451 Tulip (Toyama)

1452 Fritillaria (Ishikawa)

1453 Narcissi (Fukui)

1454 Chinese Milk Vetch (Gifu)

1455 Azalea (Shizuoka)

1456 Rabbit-ear Iris (Aichi)

1457 Iris (Mie)

1458 Rhododendron (Shiga)

1459 Weeping Cherry Blosssom (Kyoto)

**1460** Japanese Apricot and Primrose (Osaka)

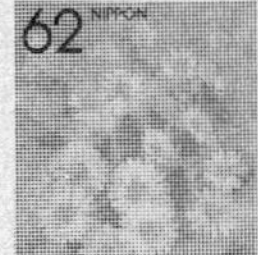
**1461** Marguerites (Hyogo)

**1462** Double Cherry Blossom (Nara)

**1463** Japanese Apricot (Wakayama)

**1464** Pear Blossom (Tottori)

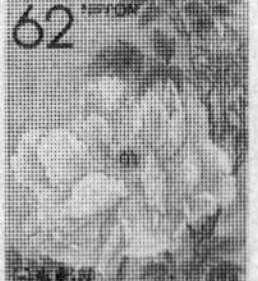
**1465** Peony (Shimane)

**1466** Peach Blossom (Okayama)

**1467** Japanese Maple (Hiroshima)

**1468** Summer Orange Blossom (Yamaguchi)

**1469** Sudachi Orange Blossom (Tokushima)

**1470** Olive Blossom (Kagawa)

**1471** Mandarin Orange Blossom (Ehime)

**1472** "Myrica rubra" (Kochi)

**1473** Japanese Apricot (Fukuoka)

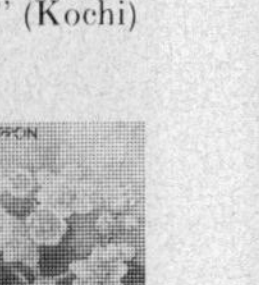
**1474** Laurel (Saga)

**1475** Unzen Azalea (Nagasaki)

**1476** Gentian (Kumamoto)

**1477** Japanese Apricot (Oita)

**1478** Crinum (Miyazaki)

**1479** Rhododendron (Kagoshima)

**1480** Coral Tree (Okinawa)

**1990.** Prefecture Flowers.

| | | | | |
|---|---|---|---|---|
| 2041 | **1434** | 62 y. multicoloured | 60 | 10 |
| 2042 | **1435** | 62 y. multicoloured | 60 | 10 |
| 2043 | **1436** | 62 y. multicoloured | 60 | 10 |
| 2044 | **1437** | 62 y. multicoloured | 60 | 10 |
| 2045 | **1438** | 62 y. multicoloured | 60 | 10 |
| 2046 | **1439** | 62 y. multicoloured | 60 | 10 |
| 2047 | **1440** | 62 y. multicoloured | 60 | 10 |
| 2048 | **1441** | 62 y. multicoloured | 60 | 10 |
| 2049 | **1442** | 62 y. multicoloured | 60 | 10 |
| 2050 | **1443** | 62 y. multicoloured | 60 | 10 |
| 2051 | **1444** | 62 y. multicoloured | 60 | 10 |
| 2052 | **1445** | 62 y. multicoloured | 60 | 10 |
| 2053 | **1446** | 62 y. multicoloured | 60 | 10 |
| 2054 | **1447** | 62 y. multicoloured | 60 | 10 |
| 2055 | **1448** | 62 y. multicoloured | 60 | 10 |
| 2056 | **1449** | 62 y. multicoloured | 60 | 10 |
| 2057 | **1450** | 62 y. multicoloured | 60 | 10 |
| 2058 | **1451** | 62 y. multicoloured | 60 | 10 |
| 2059 | **1452** | 62 y. multicoloured | 60 | 10 |
| 2060 | **1453** | 62 y. multicoloured | 60 | 10 |
| 2061 | **1454** | 62 y. multicoloured | 60 | 10 |
| 2062 | **1455** | 62 y. multicoloured | 60 | 10 |
| 2063 | **1456** | 62 y. multicoloured | 60 | 10 |
| 2064 | **1457** | 62 y. multicoloured | 60 | 10 |
| 2065 | **1458** | 62 y. multicoloured | 60 | 10 |
| 2066 | **1459** | 62 y. multicoloured | 60 | 10 |
| 2067 | **1460** | 62 y. multicoloured | 60 | 10 |
| 2068 | **1461** | 62 y. multicoloured | 60 | 10 |
| 2069 | **1462** | 62 y. multicoloured | 60 | 10 |
| 2070 | **1463** | 62 y. multicoloured | 60 | 10 |
| 2071 | **1464** | 62 y. multicoloured | 60 | 10 |
| 2072 | **1465** | 62 y. multicoloured | 60 | 10 |
| 2073 | **1466** | 62 y. multicoloured | 60 | 10 |
| 2074 | **1467** | 62 y. multicoloured | 60 | 10 |
| 2075 | **1468** | 62 y. multicoloured | 60 | 10 |
| 2076 | **1469** | 62 y. multicoloured | 60 | 10 |
| 2077 | **1470** | 62 y. multicoloured | 60 | 10 |
| 2078 | **1471** | 62 y. multicoloured | 60 | 10 |
| 2079 | **1472** | 62 y. multicoloured | 60 | 10 |
| 2080 | **1473** | 62 y. multicoloured | 60 | 10 |
| 2081 | **1474** | 62 y. multicoloured | 60 | 10 |
| 2082 | **1475** | 62 y. multicoloured | 60 | 10 |
| 2083 | **1476** | 62 y. multicoloured | 60 | 10 |
| 2084 | **1477** | 62 y. multicoloured | 60 | 10 |
| 2085 | **1478** | 62 y. multicoloured | 60 | 10 |
| 2086 | **1479** | 62 y. multicoloured | 60 | 10 |
| 2087 | **1480** | 62 y. multicoloured | 60 | 10 |

**1481** Mt. Unzen and Unzen Azalea

**1484** Fritillary on Thistle

**1990.** National Afforestation Campaign.
2088 **1481** 62 y. multicoloured .. 55 10

**1990.** Electric Railway Locomotives (4th series). As T **1425**. Multicoloured.
2089 62 y. Type "EF55" .. 75 25
2090 62 y. Type "ED61" .. 75 25

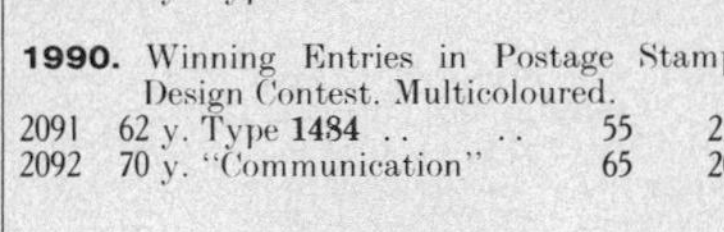

**1990.** Winning Entries in Postage Stamp Design Contest. Multicoloured.
2091 62 y. Type **1484** .. .. 55 25
2092 70 y. "Communication" 65 20

**1486** 17th-century Ottoman Tile

**1990.** Century of Japan–Turkey Friendship.
2093 **1486** 62 y. multicoloured .. 55 10

**1487/91** Folding Screen (½ size illustration)

**1492** "Ponies" (Kayo Yamaguchi)

**1493** Emblem and Landscape

**1990.** The Horse in Culture (1st series).
2094 **1487** 62 y. multicoloured 65 10
2095 **1488** 62 y. multicoloured 65 10
2096 **1489** 62 y. multicoloured 65 10
2097 **1490** 62 y. multicoloured 65 10
2098 **1491** 62 y. multicoloured 65 10
2099 **1492** 62 y. multicoloured 65 10

Nos. 2094/8 were printed together, se-tenant, forming a composite design showing a 17th-century folding screen painting.

See also Nos. 2106/8, 2113/14, 2132/4 and 2135/6.

**1990.** 38th International Youth Hostel Federation Congress. Muikamachi and Kashiwazaki.
2100 **1493** 62 y. multicoloured .. 55 10

**1990.** Electric Railway Locomotives (5th series). As T **1425**. Multicoloured.
2101 62 y. Type "ED57" .. 75 25
2102 62 y. Type "EF30" .. 75 25

**1496** Bluebird and Heart

**1497** Fairy on Horse

**1990.** Letter Writing Day.
2103 **1496** 41 y. multicoloured 40 10
2104 **1497** 62 y. multicoloured 55 10

For similar design to No. 2104, see No. 2157.

**1500** "A Horse" (Suisho Nishiyama)

**1990.** The Horse in Culture (2nd series). Multicoloured.
2106 62 y. 16th-century lacquered saddle .. 65 10
2107 62 y. 16th-century lacquered stirrups .. 65 10
2108 62 y. Type **1500** .. .. 65 10

**1501** Origami Polyhedron

**1502** Track Race

**1990.** Int. Mathematicians Congress, Kyoto.
2109 **1501** 62 y. multicoloured .. 60 10

**1990.** World Cycling Championships, Maebashi and Tochigi Prefecture.
2110 **1502** 62 y. multicoloured .. 60 10

**1503** Ogai Mori (translator) and Passage from Goethe's "Faust"

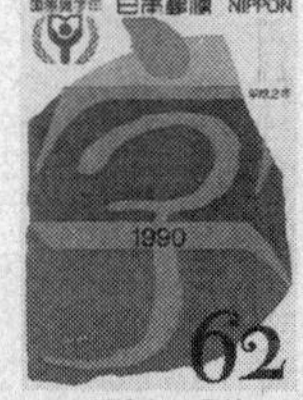
**1504** "Ji" (character) and Rosetta Stone

**1990.** 8th International Association for Germanic Studies Congress, Tokyo.
2111 **1503** 62 y. blue, yell & brn 55 10

**1990.** International Literacy Year.
2112 **1504** 62 y. multicoloured .. 55 10

**1505** "Kurabeuma Race" (detail of kimono)

**1506** "Kettei" (Shodo Sasaki)

**1990.** The Horse in Culture (3rd series).
2113 **1505** 62 y. multicoloured 65 10
2114 **1506** 62 y. multicoloured 65 10

**1507** Peaceful Landscape

**1990.** International Decade for Natural Disaster Reduction Conference, Yokohama.
2115 **1507** 62 y. multicoloured .. 55 10

**1508** Animals at Dance

**1990.** International Correspondence Week. Details from "Choju-jinbutsu-giga" Picture Scroll. Multicoloured.
2116 80 y. Type **1508** .. .. 75 10
2117 120 y. Dancing frogs .. 1·10 20

**1510** Midwife, Mother and Baby

**1990.** 22nd International Confederation of Midwives Congress, Kobe City.
2118 **1510** 62 y. multicoloured .. 55 10

**1511** "Letter Bearer" (detail, Harunobu Suiendo)

**1990.** "Phila Nippon '91" International Stamp Exhibition, Tokyo (1st issue).
2119 **1511** 100 y. multicoloured 1·00 20

See also No. 2170.

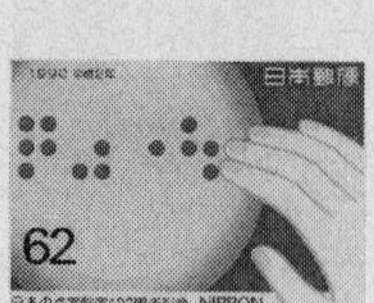


1512 Hand reading Braille

1513 "Justice" (Supreme Court bronze statue, Katsuzo Entsuba)

**1990.** Centenary of Japanese Braille.
2121 **1512** 62 y. multicoloured .. 55 10

**1990.** Centenary of Modern Judiciary System.
2122 **1513** 62 y. multicoloured .. 55 10

1514 Chinese Phoenix (detail from dais of Emperor's enthronement seat)

1516 Stained Glass Window (Diet building)

**1990.** Enthronement of Emperor. Mult.
2123 62 y. Type **1514** .. .. 55 10
2124 62 y. Pattern from robe of Manzai Raku dancers 55 10

**1990.** Centenary of Diet.
2126 **1516** 62 y. multicoloured .. 55 10

1517 Sheep (Nogomi ceramic bell)

1519 Tsuneishi-Hariko Papier-mache Ram

**1990.** New Year's Greetings.
2127 **1517** 41 y. multicoloured .. 40 10

**1990.** New Year Lottery Stamps. Mult.
2128 41 y. Sheep (Tosa ceramic bell) .. .. .. 40 10
2129 62 y. Type **1519** .. .. 55 10
Each stamp carries a lottery number.

1520 Dr. Nishina and Radio Isotope

1521 "Lady using Telephone" (Senseki Nakamura)

**1990.** Birth Centenary of Dr. Yoshio Nishina (physicist) and 50th Anniv of First Japanese Cyclotron (radio isotope generator).
2130 **1520** 62 y. multicoloured .. 55 10

**1990.** Cent of Telephone Service in Japan.
2131 **1521** 62 y. multicoloured .. 55 10

## MINIMUM PRICE

The minimum price quoted is 10p which represents a handling charge rather than a basis for valuing common stamps. For further notes about prices see introductory pages.

**1522** Horse-drawn Post Carriages **1523** (details of scroll painting by Beisen Kubota)

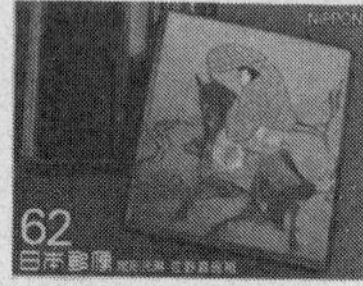


1524 Inkstone Case (Korin Ogata)

**1991.** The Horse in Culture (4th series).
2132 **1522** 62 y. multicoloured 60 10
2133 **1523** 62 y. multicoloured 60 10
2134 **1524** 62 y. multicoloured 60 10
Nos. 2132/3 were issued together, se-tenant, forming a composite design.

1525 "Spring Warmth" (Kogetsu Saigo)

1526 "Senju in Musashi Province" (from "36 Views of Mt. Fuji" by Hokusai Katsushika)

**1991.** The Horse in Culture (5th series).
2135 **1525** 62 y. multicoloured 65 10
2136 **1526** 62 y. multicoloured 65 10

1527 Figure Skating

1529 Bouquet

**1991.** Winter Universiade, Sapporo and Furano. Multicoloured.
2137 41 y. Type **1527** .. .. 45 10
2138 62 y. Short-track speed skating (horiz) .. 60 10

**1991.** New Postal Life Insurance System.
2139 **1529** 62 y. multicoloured .. 55 10

1530 "Glory of the Earth" (Komei Bekki)

1531 "Beauty looking Back" (Moronobu Hishikawa)

**1991.** "Ceramic World Shigaraki '91" Exn.
2140 **1530** 62 y. multicoloured .. 55 10

**1991.** Philatelic Week. 120th Anniv of First Japanese Stamps.
2141 62 y. Type **1531** .. .. 60 10
2142 62 y. "The Prelude" (Shuho Yamakawa) .. 60 10

1533 Weeping Cherry Blossom and Phoenix Hall, Byodoin Temple

1534 Early Leveller and Standard Datum Repository, Tokyo

**1991.** National Afforestation Campaign.
2144 **1533** 41 y. multicoloured .. 40 10

**1991.** Cent of Standard Datum of Levelling.
2145 **1534** 62 y. multicoloured .. 55 10

1535 Flowers

1539 Japanese Snipe ("Gallinago hardwickii")

**1991.** Winning Entries in Postage Stamp Design Contest.
2146 **1535** 41 y. multicoloured 40 10
2147 – 62 y. multicoloured 55 10
2148 – 70 y. brown, bl & blk 65 10
2149 – 100 y. multicoloured 90 20
DESIGNS—HORIZ. 62 y. Couple in traditional dress; 100 y. Butterfly. VERT. 70 y. "World Peace";.

**1991.** Water Birds (1st series). Multicoloured.
2150 62 y. Type **1539** .. .. 95 10
2151 62 y. Brown booby("Sula leucogaster") 95 10
See also Nos. 2162/3, 2179/80, 2184/5, 2198/9, 2241/2, 2247/8 and 2251/2.

1541 Kikugoro Onoe VI in Title Role of "Spirit of the Lion"

1542 Utaemon Nakamura VI as Princess Yaegaki in "24 Examples of Filial Piety"

**1991.** Kabuki Theatre (1st series).
2152 **1541** 62 y. grn, gold & blk 55 10
2153 **1542** 100 y. multicoloured 90 20
See also Nos. 2164/5, 2172/3, 2181/2, 2186/7 and 2190/1.

1543 "Solidarity" in Sign Language and Congress Emblem

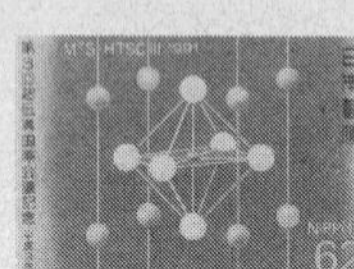


1544 Crystal Structure

**1991.** 11th World Federation of the Deaf International Congress, Tokyo.
2154 **1543** 62 y.+10 y. mult .. 65 10
The premium was assigned to programmes for helping the deaf.

**1991.** Int. Conf. on Materials and Mechanism of Superconductivity, Kanazawa.
2155 **1544** 62 y. multicoloured .. 55 10

1545 Girl sitting on Morning Glory

1546 Fairy on Horse

**1991.** Letter Writing Day.
2156 **1545** 41 y. multicoloured 40 10
2157 **1546** 62 y. multicoloured 55 10
For design similar to No. 2157 but with central motif drawn larger, see No. 2104.

1547 High Jumping

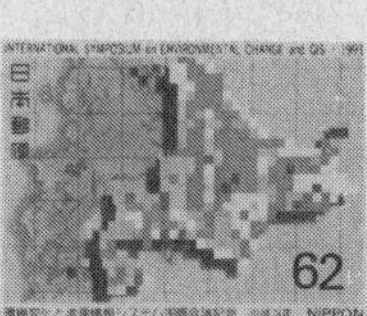


1549 Map and Computer Image of Hokkaido

**1991.** 3rd World Athletics Championships, Tokyo. Multicoloured.
2159 41 y. Type **1547** .. .. 50 10
2160 62 y. Putting the shot .. 70 15

**1991.** International Symposium on Environmental Change and Geographic Information Systems, Asahikawa, Hokkaido.
2161 **1549** 62 y. multicoloured .. 70 15

**1991.** Water Birds (2nd series). As T **1539**. Multicoloured.
2162 62 y. Japanese gull ("Larus crassirostris") 95 20
2163 62 y. Little grebe ("Podiceps ruficollis") 95 20

1552 Koshiro Matsumoto VII as Benkei in "The Subscription List"

1553 Danjuro Ichikawa XI as Danjo in "Tweezers"

**1991.** Kabuki Theatre (2nd series).
2164 **1552** 62 y. blk, grey & gold 70 15
2165 **1553** 100 y. multicoloured 1·25 30

1554 Nobles watching burning Oten Gate

**1991.** International Correspondence Week. Details from Ban Dainagon Picture Scrolls by Mitsunaga Tokiwa. Multicoloured.
2166 80 y. Type **1554** .. .. 95 20
2167 120 y. Arrest of Yoshio Tomo (arsonist) .. 1·40 30

1556 "Clear Day with Southern Breeze" (from "36 Views of Mt. Fuji" by Hokusai Katsushika) and Seismographic Wave

1557 Tea Utensils and Flower

**1991.** Earthquake and Natural Disaster Countermeasures Conference, Tokyo.
2168 **1556** 62 y. multicoloured .. 70 15

**1991.** 800th Anniv of Introduction of Green Tea into Japan.
2169 **1557** 62 y. multicoloured .. 70 15

1558 "Saucy Girl" (from "A Selection of Beautiful Women" by Kunisada Utagawa)

**1991.** "Phila Nippon '91" International Stamp Exhibition, Tokyo (2nd issue).
2170 **1558** 62 y. multicoloured .. 70 15

1559 Baigyoku Nakamura III as the Ogiya Courtesan Yugiri in "Yoshida-ya"

1560 Ganjiro Nakamura III as Jihei Kamiya in "Shinju-Ten no Amijima"

**1991.** Kabuki Theatre (3rd series). Works by Chikamatsu Monzaemon.
2172 **1559** 62 y. blk, pur & gold 70 15
2173 **1560** 100 y. multicoloured 1·25 30

1561 Boy building Toy Town

1562 Ishikawa Papier-Mache Monkey

**1991.** 30th Anniv of Administrative Councillors System.
2174 **1561** 62 y. multicoloured .. 70 15

**1991.** New Year's Greetings. Multicoloured.
2175 41 y. Type **1562** .. .. 50 10
2176 62 y. Obata monkey .. 70 15

1565 Obata Monkey

**1991.** New Year Lottery Stamps. Mult.
2177 41 y.+3 y. Ishikawa papier-mache monkey 50 10
2178 62 y.+3 y. Type **1565** .. 75 15
Each stamp carries a lottery number.

**1992.** Water Birds (3rd series). As T **1539**. Multicoloured.
2179 62 y. Tufted puffin ("Lunda cirrhata") .. 95 20
2180 62 y. Hooded cranes ("Grus monacha") .. 95 20

1568 Kichiemon Nakamura I as Jiro Naozane Kumagai in "Chronicle of Two Boys in Battle of Ichinotani" by Munesuke Namiki

1569 Nizaemon Kataoka XIII as Old Man in "Kotobuki Shiki Sambaso"

**1992.** Kabuki Theatre (4th series).
2181 **1568** 62 y. multicoloured 70 15
2182 **1569** 100 y. multicoloured 1·25 30

1570 Orchid and Chimpanzees

**1992.** 8th Conference of Parties to Convention on International Trade in Endangered Species, Kyoto City.
2183 **1570** 62 y. multicoloured .. 70 15

**1992.** Water Birds (4th series). As T **1539**. Multicoloured.
2184 62 y. Whooper swan ("Cygnus cygnus") .. 95 20
2185 62 y. Painted snipe ("Rostratula benghalensis") .. 95 20

1573 Enjaku Jitsukawa II as Ishikawa-Goemon in "Two-Storey Gate—Pawlonia" by Gohei Namiki

1574 Hakuo Matsumoto I as Oishi-Kuranosuke in "Loyal Retainers in Genroku" by Seika Mayama

**1992.** Kabuki Theatre (5th series).
2186 **1573** 62 y. multicoloured 70 15
2187 **1574** 100 y. multicoloured 1·25 30

1575 "Flowers on Chair" (Hoshun Yamaguchi)

1576 Shuri Castle

**1992.** Philatelic Week.
2188 **1575** 62 y. multicoloured .. 70 15

**1992.** 20th Anniv of Return of Okinawa (Ryukyu Islands).
2189 **1576** 62 y. multicoloured .. 70 15

1577 Baiko Onoe VII as the Wisteria Maiden

1578 Shoroku Onoe II as Goro Soga and Kanzaburo Nakamura XVII as Juro Soga in "Kotobuki-Soga-taimen"

**1992.** Kabuki Theatre (6th series).
2190 **1577** 62 y. multicoloured 70 15
2191 **1578** 100 y. multicoloured 1·25 30

1579 "ADEOS" Observation Satellite

1581 Bird delivering Letter to Flower

**1992.** International Space Year. Mult.
2192 62 y. Type **1579** .. .. 70 15
2193 62 y. "BS-3" broadcasting satellite and space station .. .. 70 15
Nos. 2192/3 were printed together, se-tenant, forming a composite design.

**1992.** Letter Writing Day. Multicoloured.
2194 41 y. Type **1581** .. .. 50 10
2195 62 y. Bird delivering letter to dog .. .. 70 15

1583 Ammonite, Map and Stratigraphic Plan

1586 Canoeing

**1992.** 29th Int Geological Congress, Kyoto.
2197 **1583** 62 y. multicoloured .. 75 15

**1992.** Water Birds (5th series). As T **1539**. Multicoloured.
2198 62 y. White-faced shear-water ("Calonectris leucomelas") .. .. 70 15
2199 62 y. Ruddy kingfisher ("Halcyon coromanda") 70 15

**1992.** 47th National Athletic Meeting, Yamagata.
2200 **1586** 41 y. multicoloured .. 50 10

1587 Japanese Jar (Ninsei Nonomura)

1588 Chinese Vase (Tang dynasty)

**1992.** 20th Anniv of Restoration of Diplomatic Relations with China.
2201 **1587** 62 y. multicoloured 70 15
2202 **1588** 62 y. multicoloured 70 15

1589 Nobles arriving at Taiken Gate

1590 Fujiwarano Nobuyori giving Audience

**1992.** International Correspondence Week. Details from "Tale of Heiji" Shinzei Picture Scroll.
2203 **1589** 80 y. multicoloured 95 20
2204 **1590** 120 y. multicoloured 1·40 30

1591 "Friends" (Tomoko Komoto)

1593 "Kyo" Ideograph, Mt. Fuji, Sun and Waves

**1992.** 3rd Stamp Design Competition Winners. Multicoloured.
2205 62 y. Type **1591** .. .. 70 15
2206 70 y. "Gaiety on Christmas Night" (Brat Anca) .. .. .. 80 20

**1992.** 30th International Co-operative Alliance Congress, Tokyo.
2207 **1593** 62 y. multicoloured .. 70 15

1594 Takakazu Seki (mathematician, 350th birth)

1595 Akiko Yosano (poet, 50th death)

**1992.** Anniversaries.
2208 **1594** 62 y. multicoloured 70 15
2209 **1595** 62 y. multicoloured 70 15

1596 Certified Public Tax Accountants' Assn Emblem

**1992.** 50th Anniv of Tax Accountants Law.
2210 **1596** 62 y. multicoloured .. 70 15

1597 Papier-mache and Clay Cock

1600 Tsuyazaki Clay Cock on Drum

**1992.** New Year's Greetings. Multicoloured.
2211 41 y. Type **1597** .. .. 50 10
2212 62 y. Tsuyazaki clay cock on drum .. .. 70 15

**1992.** New Year Lottery Stamps. Mult.
2213 41 y.+3 y. Papier-mache and clay cock .. .. 50 10
2214 62 y.+3 y. Type **1600** .. 75 15
Each stamp carries a lottery number.

1601 "Orthetrum albistylum" (dragonfly)

1602 Mikado Swallowtail

1603 Ladybirds

1604 Mandarin

1605 Japanese White Eye

1606 Eastern Turtle Dove

**1607** Varied Tit

**1608** Greater Pied Kingfisher

**1609** Spotbill Duck

**1610** Bullfinch

**1611** Orchids

**1612** Wild Pink

**1613** Adder's Tongue Lily

**1614** Day-flowers

**1615** Iris

**1616** Violets

**1617** Praying Mantis, Chrysanthemums and Hibiscus (after Hatsu Sakai

**1618** "Pine and Hawk" (Sesson Shukei)

**1992.**

2215 **1601** 9 y. yellow, blk & bl .. 10 10
2216 **1602** 15 y. brown, light green and green .. 20 10
2217 **1603** 18 y. grn, grey & red 20 10
2218 **1604** 41 y. orange, deep blue and blue .. 50 10
2219 **1605** 50 y. yellow, blue and black .. 60 15
2220 **1606** 62 y. orange, deep blue and blue .. 75 15
2221 **1607** 72 y. orange, bl & grn 85 20
2222 **1608** 80 y. bl, stone & grn 1·00 20
2223 **1609** 90 y. brown, yell & bl 1·10 25
2224 **1610** 130 y. multicoloured 1·75 40
2225 **1611** 190 y. multicoloured 2·25 45
2226 **1612** 270 y. multicoloured 3·25 65
2227 **1613** 350 y. mauve, lilac and green .. 4·00 80
2228 **1614** 390 y. multicoloured 4·50 90
2229 **1615** 420 y. violet, light green and green .. 5·00 1·00
2230 **1616** 430 y. multicoloured 5·00 1·00
2231 **1617** 700 y. multicoloured 8·25 1·60
2232 **1618** 1000 y. multicoloured 12·00 2·40

The 41, 50, 62 and 80 y. also exist imperforate with self-adhesive gum.

**1993.** Water Birds (6th series). As T **1539**. Multicoloured.

2241 62 y. Common kingfisher ("Alcedo atthis") .. 75 15
2242 62 y. Cattle egret ("Bubulcus ibis") .. 75 15

**1623** Super Giant Slalom

**1625** Poppies (after Hochu Nakamura)

**1993.** World Alpine Skiing Championships, Shizukuishi (nr. Morioka). Multicoloured.

2243 41 y. Type **1623** .. .. 50 10
2244 62 y. Downhill .. .. 75 15

**1993.** Seasonal Flowers (1st series). Mult.

2245 41 y. Type **1625** .. .. 50 10
2246 62 y. Cherry Blossoms (after Haitsu Sakai) (25 × 35 mm) .. .. 75 15

See also Nos. 2258/9, 2269/70 and 2287/8.

**1993.** Water Birds (7th series). As T **1539**. Multicoloured.

2247 62 y. White-fronted geese ("Anser albifrons") .. 75 15
2248 62 y. Japanese white-necked cranes ("Grus vipio") .. .. 75 15

No. 2247 is wrongly inscribed "Ansner".

**1629** "In the Studio" (Nanpu Katayama)

**1630** Coral Trees and Reef, Minnajima Island

**1993.** Philatelic Week.

2249 **1629** 62 y. multicoloured .. 75 15

**1993.** National Afforestation Campaign.

2250 **1630** 41 y. multicoloured .. 50 10

**1993.** Water Birds (8th series). As T **1539**. Multicoloured.

2251 62 y. Baikal teal ("Anas formosa") .. .. 75 15
2252 62 y. White-tailed sea eagle ("Haliaeetus albicilla") .. .. 75 15

**1635** "Mandarin Duck in Nest" and "Gardenia in Nest"

**1993.** Wedding of Crown Prince Naruhito and Masako Owada. Multicoloured.

2253 62 y. "Mandarin Duck in Nest" (pattern of groom's jacket) (vert) 75 15
2254 62 y. "Gardenia in Nest" (pattern of bride's robe) (vert) .. .. .. 75 15
2255 70 y. Type **1635** .. .. 80 20

**1636** Manchurian Crane with Chicks

**1640** Stylized Ideographs for "Commercial Registration"

**1993.** 5th Meeting of Ramsar Convention for the Preservation of Wetlands, Kushiro (Hokkaido).

2256 62 y. Type **1636** .. .. 75 15
2257 62 y. Head of Manchurian crane .. .. .. 75 15

**1993.** Seasonal Flowers (2nd series) As T **1615**. Multicoloured.

2258 41 y. Lily (after Kiitsu Suzuki) .. .. 50 10
2259 62 y. Thistle (after Shiko Watanabe) (25 × 35 mm) 75 15

**1993.** Centenary of Commercial Registration System.

2260 **1640** 62 y. multicoloured .. 75 15

**1641** Puppy reading Letter under Tree

**1643** Heart, Clouds and Flowers

**1993.** Letter Writing Day. Multicoloured.

2261 41 y. Type **1641** .. .. 50 10
2262 62 y. Man pointing at flying letter (23 × 27 mm) .. .. .. 75 15

**1993.** World Federation for Mental Health Congress, Chiba City.

2264 **1643** 62 y. multicoloured .. 75 15

**1644** "Glaucidium palmatum"

**1993.** 15th International Botanical Congress, Yokohama. Multicoloured.

2265 62 y. Type **1644** .. .. 75 15
2266 62 y. "Sciadopitys verticillata" .. .. 75 15

**1646** Swimming

**1650** "Arrival of Portuguese" (folding screen)

**1993.** 48th National Athletic Meeting, Kagawa Prefecture. Multicoloured.

2267 41 y. Type **1646** .. .. 50 10
2268 41 y. Karate .. .. 50 10

**1993.** Seasonal Flowers (3rd series). As T **1615**. Multicoloured.

2269 41 y. "Chinese Bell-flowers" (Korin Ogata) 50 10
2270 62 y. Chrysanthemums (detail of "Cranes and Plants in Spring and Autumn", Kiitsu Suzuki) (25 × 35 mm) .. 75 15

**1993.** 450th Anniv of First Portuguese Visit to Japan. Multicoloured.

2271 62 y. Type **1650** .. .. 75 15
2272 62 y. Jesuit mother-of-pearl inlaid host box .. 75 15

**1652** Ki no Tsurayuki (Agetatami Scrolls)

**1993.** International Correspondence Week. Picture Scrolls of the Thirty-six Immortal Poets

2273 80 y. Type **1652** .. .. 95 20
2274 120 y. Kodai no Kimi (Satake Scrolls) .. 1·40 30

**1654** Sprinter

**1656** Toson Shimazaki (writer, 50th death)

**1993.** 10th International Veterans' Athletic Championships, Miyazaki.

2275 **1654** 62 y. multicoloured .. 75 15

**1993.** Anniversaries. Multicoloured.

2277 62 y. Type **1656** .. .. 75 15
2278 62 y. Umetaro Suzuki (scientist, 50th death) 75 15
2279 62 y. Kazan Watanabe (after Chinzan Tsubaki) (artist, birth bicent) .. 75 15

**1659** Shibahara Clay Dog

**1662** Kosen Clay Tosa Dog

**1993.** New Year's Greetings. Multicoloured.

2280 41 y. Type **1659** .. .. 50 10
2281 62 y. Kosen clay tosa dog 75 15

**1993.** New Year Lottery Stamps. Mult.

2282 41 y. Shibahara clay dog 50 10
2283 62 y. Type **1662** .. .. 75 15

**1663** Rice Flowers

**1664** Man and Bird (Soichiro Asaba)

**1993.** Centenary of Agricultural Research Centre, Nishigahara.

2284 **1663** 62 y. multicoloured .. 75 15

**1993.** 45th Anniv of Declaration of Human Rights. Stamp design contest winning entries.

2285 62 y. Type **1664** .. .. 75 15
2286 70 y. Symbols (Armand Clotagatilde) .. .. 80 20

**1994.** Seasonal Flowers (4th series). As T **1625**. Multicoloured.

2287 50 y. Plum Blossom (after Korin Ogata) .. .. 60 15
2288 80 y. Winter Camellia (after Hoitsu Sakai) (26 × 35 mm) .. .. 95 20

**1994.** Special Correspondence Stamps. As Nos. 1677/9 but values changed.

2289 **1098** 50 y. multicoloured 60 15
2290 **1099** 50 y. multicoloured 60 15
2291 80 y. multicoloured 95 20
2292 **1100** 90 y. multicoloured 1·10 25

**1668** Ladies' Figure Skating

**1672** "Irises" (Heihachiro Fukuda)

**1994.** World Figure Skating Championships, Chiba City. Multicoloured.

2293 50 y. Type **1668** .. .. 60 15
2294 50 y. Ice dancing .. 60 15
2295 80 y. Men's figure skating 95 20
2296 80 y. Pairs figure skating 95 20

**1994.** Philatelic Week.

2297 **1672** 80 y. multicoloured .. 95 20

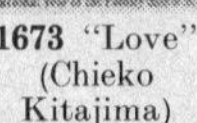

1673 "Love" (Chieko Kitajima) 1677 White Stork, Marguerites and Camphor Tree

**1994.** International Year of the Family. Winning Entries in Stamp Design Contest. Multicoloured.

2298 50 y. Type **1673** .. .. 60 15
2299 50 y. "Happiness Flower" (Shigenobu Nagaishi) .. 60 15
2300 80 y. "Family flowering at Home" (Junichi Mineta) .. .. 95 20
2301 80 y. "Family in Flight" (Soichiro Asaba) .. 95 20

**1994.** National Afforestation Campaign.
2302 **1677** 50 y. multicoloured .. 65 15

1678 Houses by the Waterside 1679 Pylon and Monju Building

**1994.** International Conference on Reduction of Natural Disasters, Yokohama.
2303 **1678** 80 y. multicoloured .. 95 20

**1994.** Achievement of Initial Criticality (self-sustaining reaction) in Monju Nuclear Fast Breeder Reactor, Tsuruga.
2304 **1679** 80 y. multicoloured .. 95 20

1680 Wildlife 1681 Envelope "Ship" and Man

**1994.** Environment Day.
2305 **1680** 80 y. multicoloured .. 95 20

**1994.** Letter Writing Day. Multicoloured.
2306 50 y. Type **1681** .. .. 60 15
2307 80 y. Giraffe carrying envelope .. .. 95 20

1683 Emblem in Eye 1684 Baron Maeshima (Postal Minister) and 1871 48 mon "Dragon" Stamp

**1994.** 10th Int AIDS Conference, Yokohama.
2309 **1683** 80 y. multicoloured .. 95 20

**1994.** History of Stamps (1st series). First Japanese Issue. Multicoloured, frame colour of "Dragon" stamp given.
2310 **1684** 80 y. brown .. 95 20
2311 – 80 y. blue .. .. 95 20
2312 – 80 y. red .. .. 95 20
2313 – 80 y. green .. .. 95 20

DESIGNS: No. 2311, 100 mon "Dragon" stamp; 2312, 200 mon "Dragon" stamp; 2313, 500 mon "Dragon" stamp.

The central portion of the stamp portrayed varies according to value.

See also Nos. 2339/42, 2345/6, 2363/4, 2382/5 and 2416/19.

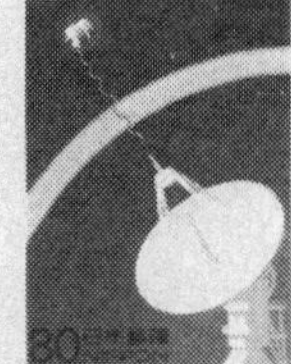

1685/1686 Airport and Airplane bearing Airport Code 1688 Dish Aerial and Satellite

**1994.** Opening of Kansai International Airport, Osaka. Multicoloured.
2314 80 y. Type **1685** .. .. 95 20
2315 80 y. Type **1686** .. .. 95 20
2316 80 y. Airplane approaching Airport .. .. 95 20

Nos. 2314/15 form the composite design shown.

**1994.** I.T.U. Plenipotentiary Conf, Kyoto.
2317 **1688** 80 y. multicoloured .. 95 20

1689 Kickball 1695 Handball

1692 Sugoroku

**1994.** 12th Asian Games, Hiroshima. Mult.
2318 50 y. Type **1689** .. 60 15
2319 80 y. Steeplechase .. 95 20
2320 80 y. Synchronized swimming .. .. 95 20

**1994.** International Correspondence Week. Details of "House of Entertainment" (folddng screen). Multicoloured.
2321 90 y. Type **1692** .. .. 1·10 25
2322 110 y. Shogi .. .. 1·25 25
2323 130 y. Go .. .. 1·50 30

**1994.** 49th National Athletic Meeting, Aichi.
2324 **1695** 50 y. multicoloured .. 60 15

1696 Michio Miyagi (composer) 1698 Fujiwara no Michinaga and Insulin Crystals

**1994.** Birth Anniversaries. Multicoloured.
2325 80 y. Type **1696** .. .. 95 20
2326 80 y. Gyoshu Hayami (painter) and "Moths" 95 20

**1994.** 15th International Diabetes Federation Congress, Kobe.
2327 **1698** 80 y. multicoloured .. 95 20

Fujiwara no Michinaga (966–1028) was the earliest known Japanese diabetic.

1699/1703 "Viewing Maple Leaves at Takao" (folding screen, Hideyori Kano) (⅔-size illustration)

1704 "Yokuryuchi Pool, Shugakuin Imperial Villa" (Kenji Kawai) 1705 "Rock Garden, Ryoan Temple" (Eizo Kato)

**1994.** 1200th Anniv of Kyoto. Paintings.
2328 **1699** 80 y. multicoloured 95 20
2329 **1700** 80 y. multicoloured 95 20
2330 **1701** 80 y. multicoloured 95 20
2331 **1702** 80 y. multicoloured 95 20
2332 **1703** 80 y. multicoloured 95 20
2333 **1704** 80 y. multicoloured 95 20
2334 **1705** 80 y. multicoloured 95 20

Nos. 2328/32 were issued together, se-tenant, forming the composite design illustrated.

1706 Izumo Papier-mache Boar 1709 Boar (Takayama soft toy)

**1994.** New Year's Greetings. Multicoloured.
2335 50 y. Type **1706** .. .. 60 15
2336 80 y. Boar (Takayama soft toy) .. .. 95 20

**1994.** New Year's Greetings. Lottery Stamps. Multicoloured.
2337 50 y. + 3 y. Izumo Papier-mache Boar .. 60 15
2338 80 y. + 3 y. Type **1709** .. 1·00 20

Each stamp carries a lottery number.

1710 5 r. Stamp and Eduardo Chiossone (designer)

**1994.** History of Stamps (2nd series). "Koban" issue of 1876–88. Multicoloured, colour of featured stamp given.
2339 **1710** 80 y. grey .. .. 95 20
2340 – 80 y. brown .. 95 20
2341 – 80 y. red .. .. 95 20
2342 – 80 y. blue .. .. 95 20

FEATURED STAMPS: No. 2340, 1 s. stamp (Type **20**); 2341, 12 s. stamp (Type **21**); 2342, 20 s. stamp (Type **22**).

1711 Himeji Castle Tower 1712 "Himeji Castle" (Masami Takahashi)

**1994.** World Heritage Sites (1st series).
2343 **1711** 80 y. multicoloured 95 20
2344 **1712** 80 y. multicoloured 95 20

See also Nos. 2347/8, 2373/4 and 2400/1.

1713 2 s. Stamp and Postal Delivery by Hand-drawn Cart 1715 "Kannon Bosatsu" (wall painting, Kondo Hall)

1716 Kondo Hall, Horyu Temple

**1995.** History of Stamps (3rd series). 1894 Emperor's Silver Wedding issue and paintings by Shinsai Shibata. Multicoloured.
2345 80 y. Type **1713** .. .. 95 20
2346 80 y. 5 s. Stamp and postal delivery by horse-drawn carriage 95 20

**1995.** World Heritage Sites (2nd series). Multicoloured.
2347 **1715** 80 y. multicoloured 95 20
2348 **1716** 80 y. multicoloured 1·25 25

1717 Emblem and National Flowers

**1995.** Centenary of Japan–Brazil Treaty of Friendship. Multicoloured.
2349 80 y. Type **1717** .. .. 95 20
2350 80 y. Emblem and sports 95 20

1719 Unebi and Nijo Mountains and Tile from Palace 1720 "Remembering Times Past" (Saburosuke Okada)

**1995.** 1300th Anniv of Fujiwara Palace, Kashihara.
2351 **1719** 50 y. multicoloured 60 15
2352 **1720** 80 y. multicoloured 95 20

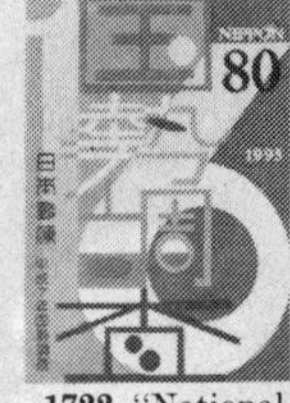

1721 "Dissection" (Seison Maeda) 1722 "National Census" and "16"

**1995.** Modern Anatomy Education.
2353 **1721** 80 y. multicoloured .. 95 20

**1995.** 16th National Census.
2354 **1722** 80 y. multicoloured .. 95 20

**1723** Volunteer teaching Bangladeshi Woman to Read

**1724** "Visitor to Art Studio" (Keika Kanashima)

**1995.** 30th Anniv of Japanese Overseas Co-operation Volunteers Service.
2355 **1723** 80 y. multicoloured 95 20

**1995.** Philatelic Week.
2356 **1724** 80 y.+20 y. mult .. 1·25 25
The premium was for the Osaka/Kobe and Awaji earthquake victims' fund.

**1725** Auspicious Clouds

**1726** Reeds (mourning)

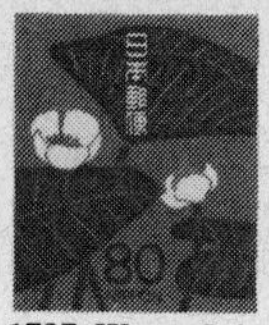

**1727** Water Lily (mourning)

**1728** Cloud, "Wind" and Pine Bark Pattern

**1729** "Daphniphyllum macropodum"

**1730** Maple and Shrine Island, Aki

**1995.** Special Correspondence Stamps.
2357 **1725** 50 y. multicoloured 60 15
2358 **1726** 50 y. multicoloured 60 15
2359 **1727** 80 y. multicoloured 95 20
2360 **1728** 80 y. multicoloured 95 20
2361 **1729** 90 y. multicoloured 1·10 25

**1995.** National Afforestation Campaign.
2362 **1730** 50 y. multicoloured .. 60 15

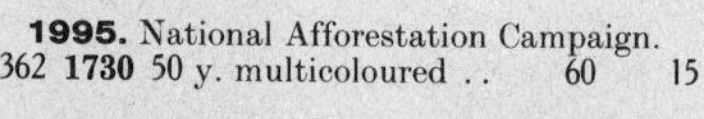

**1731** 8½ s. Stamp and First Airmail Flight from Osaka to Tokyo

**1733** Hearts forming Flower

**1995.** History of Stamps (4th series). 1929 First Airmail issue. Multicoloured.
2363 110 y. Type **1731** .. 1·25 25
2364 110 y. 18 s. Stamp and loading freight onto airplane .. .. 1·25 25

**1995.** Greetings Stamps. Multicoloured. Self-adhesive. Imperf.
2365 80 y. Type **1733** .. .. 95 20
2366 80 y. Child with balloon 95 20
2367 80 y. Flower and pencil 95 20
2368 80 y. Star, sun and moon 95 20
2369 80 y. Child with dog .. 95 20

**1738** Postman

**1740** Cedar

**1995.** Letter Writing Day. Multicoloured.
2370 50 y. Type **1738** .. .. 60 15
2371 80 y. Ostrich .. .. 95 20

**1995.** World Heritage Sites (3rd series). Yaku Island. Multicoloured.
2373 80 y. Type **1740** .. .. 95 20
2374 80 y. Sika deer .. .. 95 20

**1742** "Friends, One and All" (Yuki Ogawa)

**1743** Atomic Bomb Dome, Hiroshima (Nobuya Nagata)

**1744** "Light of Peace" (Nobuo Suenaga)

**1745** Marathon Runners

**1995.** 50th Anniv of End of Second World War. Stamp Design Contest Winners.
2375 **1742** 50 y. multicoloured 60 15
2376 **1743** 80 y. multicoloured 95 20
2377 **1744** 80 y. multicoloured 95 20

**1995.** 18th International University Games, Fukuoka.
2378 **1745** 80 y. multicoloured .. 95 20

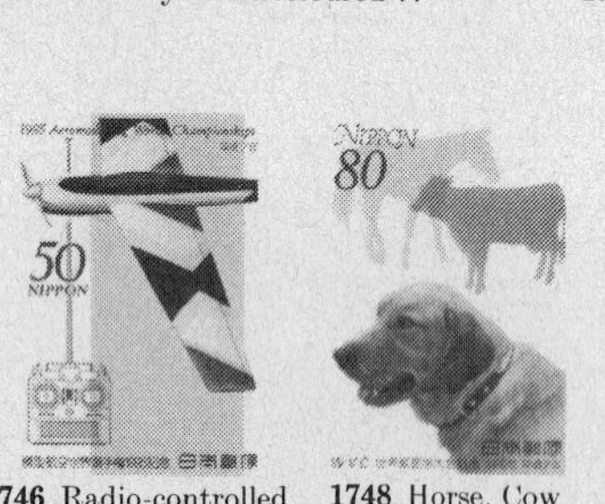

**1746** Radio-controlled Plane

**1748** Horse, Cow and Labrador

**1995.** World Aeromodel Championships, Kasaoka. Multicoloured.
2379 50 y. Type **1746** .. 60 15
2380 80 y. Radio-controlled helicopter .. .. 95 20

**1995.** World Veterinary Congress, Yokohama.
2381 **1748** 80 y. multicoloured .. 95 20

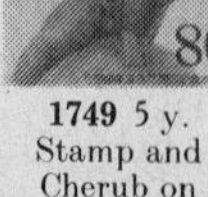

**1749** 5 y. Stamp and Cherub on Tokyo Mailbox

**1753** Judo (Makuhari, Chiba)

**1995.** History of Stamps (5th series). Industries issue of 1948–49. Multicoloured.
2382 80 y. Type **1749** .. .. 95 20
2383 80 y. 500 y. Stamp and mail van .. .. 95 20
2384 80 y. 90 y. Stamp and mail van .. .. 95 20
2385 80 y. 100 y. Stamp and cherub on Tokyo mailbox .. .. 95 20

**1995.** World Sports Championships. Mult.
2386 80 y. Type **1753** .. .. 95 20
2387 80 y. Gymnastics (Sabae, Fukui) .. .. 95 20

**1755** Shell Matching Game (from "New Year's Amusements")

**1995.** International Correspondence Week. Details of paintings on folding screens. Multicoloured.
2388 90 y. Type **1755** .. .. 1·10 25
2389 110 y. Battledore and Shuttlecock (from "Twelve Months") .. 1·25 25
2390 130 y. Playing Cards (from "Matsuura Folding Screen") .. 1·50 30

**1758** Cyclists

**1759** Patchwortk Hearts (Tomoko Suzuki)

**1995.** 50th Anniv of National Athletic Meeting, Fukushima.
2391 **1758** 50 y. multicoloured .. 60 15

**1995.** 50th Anniversaries of U.N.O. (2392) and U.N.E.S.C.O. (2393). Multicoloured.
2392 80 y. Type **1759** .. .. 95 20
2393 80 y. Children with Heart Balloon (Yukino Ikeda) 95 20

**1761** Tadataka Ino (cartographer, 250th birth)

**1995.** Anniversaries. Multicoloured.
2394 80 y. Type **1761** .. .. 95 20
2395 80 y. Kitaro Nishida (philosopher, 50th death) .. .. 95 20

**1763** Tsutsumi Clay Rat on Cayenne Pepper

**1766** Satsuma Papier-Mache Rat in Rice Store

**1995.** New Year's Greetings. Multicoloured.
2396 50 y. Type **1763** .. .. 60 15
2397 80 y. Satsuma papier-mache rat in rice store .. 95 20

**1995.** New Year's Lottery Stamps. Mult.
2398 50 y.+3 y. Tsutsumi clay rat on turnip .. .. 60 15
2399 80 y.+3 y. Type **1766** .. 1·00 20
Each stamp carries a lottery number.

**1767** Beech Forest

**1769** Obi Material showing Choson Dynasty Boxes (Keisuke Serizawa)

**1995.** World Heritage Sites (4th series). Shirakami Mountains. Multicoloured.
2400 80 y. Type **1767** .. .. 95 20
2401 80 y. Black woodpecker .. 95 20

**1995.** 30th Anniv of Resumption of Japan–Korea Diplomatic Relations.
2402 **1769** 80 y. multicoloured .. 95 20

**1770** Siebold

**1771** Twined Ropes

**1996.** Birth Bicentenary of Philipp Franz von Siebold (physician and Japanologist).
2403 **1770** 80 y. multicoloured .. 95 20

**1996.** 50th Anniv of Labour Relations Commissions.
2404 **1771** 80 y. multicoloured .. 95 20

**1772** Turtle and Crane

**1996.** Senior Citizens.
2405 **1772** 80 y. multicoloured .. 95 20

**1773** Driving to Diet for Promulgation of Constitution, 1946

**1774** Signing San Francisco Peace Treaty, 1951

**1775** Return of Okinawa, 1972

**1776** Woman and Diet Building

**1996.** 50 Post-war Years (1st series).
2406 **1773** 80 y. mauve, lilac and gold .. .. 95 20
2407 **1774** 80 y. deep green, green and gold .. 95 20
2408 **1775** 80 y. indigo, blue and gold .. .. 95 20
See also Nos. 2420/1.

**1996.** 50th Anniv of Women's Suffrage.
2409 **1776** 80 y. multicoloured .. 95 20

**1777** "Window" (Yukihiko Yasuda) **1778** Mother and Child

**1996.** Philatelic Week.
2410 **1777** 80 y. multicoloured .. 95 20

**1996.** 50th Anniv of U.N.I.C.E.F.
2411 **1778** 80 y. multicoloured .. 95 20

**1779** Children and Sun **1780** Narcissus Flycatcher

**1996.** Child Welfare Week.
2412 **1779** 80 y. multicoloured .. 95 20

**1996.** Bird Week. Multicoloured.
2413 80 y. Type **1780** .. .. 95 20
2414 80 y. Binoculars and bird feeding nestlings .. 95 20

**1782** Cherry Blossom and Tokyo Buildings

**1996.** National Afforestation Campaign.
2415 **1782** 50 y. multicoloured .. 60 15

**1783** 1991 Design **1784** 1949 Design

**1996.** History of Stamps (6th series). Philatelic Week Issues.
2416 **1783** 80 y. brown, ochre and lilac .. .. 95 20
2417 80 y. multicoloured 95 20
2418 **1784** 80 y. dp lilac & lilac 95 20
2419 80 y. multicoloured 95 20

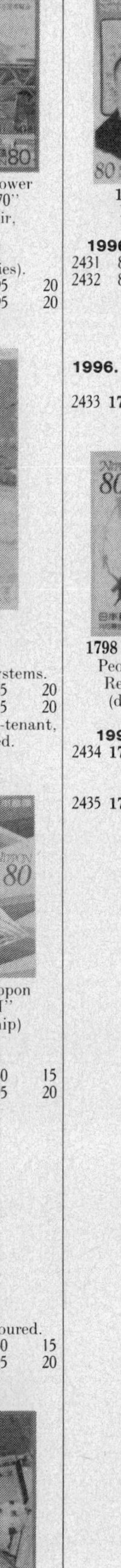

**1785** Olympic Flame (Olympic Games, Tokyo, 1964) **1786** Sun Tower ("EXPO 70" World Fair, Osaka)

**1996.** 50 Post-war Years (2nd series).
2420 **1785** 80 y. multicoloured 95 20
2421 **1786** 80 y. multicoloured 95 20

**1787/1788** "Oirase no Keiryu" (Chikkyo Ono)

**1996.** Cent Modern River Control Systems.
2422 **1787** 80 y. multicoloured 95 20
2423 **1788** 80 y. multicoloured 95 20
Nos. 2422/3 were issued together, se-tenant, forming the composite design illustrated.

**1789** Emblem **1790** "Nippon Maru II" (cadet ship)

**1996.** Marine Day.
2424 **1789** 50 y. multicoloured 60 15
2425 **1790** 80 y. multicoloured 95 20

**1791** Cat

**1996.** Letter Writing Day. Multicoloured.
2426 50 y. Type **1791** .. .. 60 15
2427 80 y. Toy horse .. .. 95 20

**1793** Shinkansen Express Train and Motorway **1794** Woman and Modern Appliances

**1996.** 50 Post-war Years (3rd series). Modern Life.
2429 **1793** 80 y. multicoloured 95 20
2430 **1794** 80 y. multicoloured 95 20

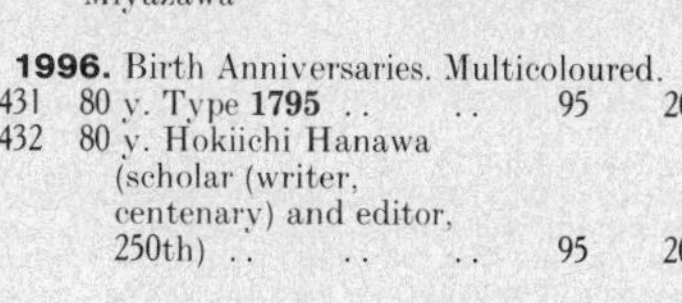

**1795** Kenji Miyazawa **1797** Archer

**1996.** Birth Anniversaries. Multicoloured.
2431 80 y. Type **1795** .. .. 95 20
2432 80 y. Hokiichi Hanawa (scholar (writer, centenary) and editor, 250th) .. .. .. 95 20

**1996.** 51st National Athletic Meeting, Hiroshima.
2433 **1797** 50 y. multicoloured .. 95 20

**1798** Paper-chain People around Red Feather (donor pin) **1799** Piano Keys and Double Clef

**1996.** 50th Anniv of Community Chest.
2434 **1798** 80 y. multicoloured .. 95 20

**1996.** International Music Day.
2435 **1799** 80 y. multicoloured .. 95 20

MILITARY FRANK STAMPS

軍
事
(M 36.)

**1910.** No. 139 optd with Type M **36**.
M156 **28** 3 s. red .. .. £225 35·00

**1913.** No. 298 optd with Type M **36**.
M185 **36** 3 s. red .. .. 30·00 11·00

**1921.** No. 37 of Japanese Post Offices in China optd with Type M **36**.
M202 **36** 3 s. red .. .. £7000 £3250

PREFECTURE STAMPS

Since 1st April 1989 the Japanese Ministry of Posts and Telecommunications has issued stamps, some apparently commemorative, inscribed for various prefectures.

The Japanese local government system contains 47 prefectures which vary from Tokyo, Osaka, Kyoto, Hokkaido and Okinawa to rural areas; the powers of the prefectures are similar to those of English or Welsh counties. Each prefecture issue is sold within the area for which it is inscribed and also in other prefectures grouped with it in one of 11 postal regions; the stamps are also available from the Tokyo Central Post Office. All issues are valid for postal purposes throughout Japan.

These issues do not fulfil the published criteria for full listing in the Stanley Gibbons catalogue and, in consequence, are recorded in abbreviated form below.

The sheet of 47 prefecture flowers was sold throughout Japan and is given full listing as Nos. 2041/87.

**1989**

Nagano. Monkeys in hot spring. 62 y.
Yamagata. Cherries. 62 y.
Okinawa. Courtesy Gate, Shuri. 62 y.
Ehime. Dogo Hot Spa buildings. 62 y.
Kanagawa. Doll and gas lamps. 62 y.
Hiroshima. Seto Inland Sea. 62 y. ×2
Niigata. Memorial Hall and Bandai Bridge. 62 y.
Aichi. Nagoya Castle and golden dolphin. 62 y.
Oita. Monkey and Mt. Takasaki. 62 y.
Hokkaido. Old Prefectural Building, Sapporo. 62 y.
Hokkaido. Runner and wild rose (athletic meet). 62 y.
Kumamoto. Kumamoto Castle. 62 y.
Ishikawa. Stone lantern, Kenroku Park. 62 y.
Aomori. Apples. 62 y.
Osaka. Bunraku puppets and Nakanoshima Theatre. 62 y.
Shiga. Lake Biwa and racoon-dog. 62 y.
Chiba. Racoon-dogs dancing. 62 y.
Tokyo. Railway station. 62 y.
Yamaguchi. Blowfish lanterns. 62 y.

**1990**

Hokkaido. Ice hockey (Asian Winter Olympics). 62 y.
Toyama. Mt. Tate and Shomyo Falls. 62 y.
Ibaraki. "Seven Baby Crows" (nursery rhyme). 62 y.
Nagano. Old inns of Tsumago and Magome. 62 y. ×2
Shizuoka. Mt. Fuji and tea picker. 62 y.
Fukushima. Peaches. 62 y.
Akita. Omagari Fireworks Festival. 62 y.
Kagoshima. Mt. Sakura. 62 y.
Nagasaki. Sailing ship. 62 y.
Okinawa. Ryukyu dancer. 62 y.
Tokyo. New post office and logger. 62 y.
Shimane. Male dancer with basket. 62 y.
Fukuoka. High jumping and Fukuoka Tower (athletic meeting). 62 y.
Kyoto. Dancing girl crossing bridge. 62 y.
Wakayama. Three pilgrims on old path to Kumano. 62 y.
Miyagi. Izunuma Swamp and five whistling swans. 62 y.
Gifu. Four seasons in Hida. 62 y. ×4.
Saitama. Tenjin Shrine and children playing song game. 62 y.
Hokkaido. Two Manchurian cranes. 62 y.

**1991**

Kagawa. Mounted archer at Battle of Yashima. 62 y.
Okayama. Water jars (Bizen ware). 62 y. ×2
Saga. Watchtower, Yoshinogari. 62 y.
Yamanashi. "Bride under Cherry Blossoms" (nursery rhyme). 62 y.
Niigata. Two fancy carps. 62 y.
Hokkaido. Lily of the valley, lilac, lily, rowanberries. 62 y. ×4
Tochigi. Mt. Nikkou and ramblers. 62 y.
Iwate. Mt. Iwate. 62 y.
Kochi. Sakamoto Ryoma and child standing on whale. 62 y.
Tokushima. Wooden puppet. 62 y.
Tokyo. Fringed orchid. 41 y.

Miyazaki. Cape Toi and wild horses. 62 y.
Kumamoto. Tsu-jun Aqueduct releasing water into river. 62 y.
Okinawa. Black pearls in oyster and Kabira Bay. 41 y.
Tottori. Pears. 62 y.
Ishikawa. Genki (mascot) and sunrise (46th National Athletic Meeting). 41 y.
Mie. Ninja holding shuriken (throwing weapon), rainbow, Iga Ueno Castle and Ninja house. 62 y.
Fukui. Woman wearing spectacles. 62 y.
Gunma. "Hare and Tortoise" (fable). 62 y.
Hyogo. Weathercock and Kobe City lights. 62 y.
Nara. Mt. Yoshino in spring and autumn. 62 y. × 2.

**1992**

Niigata. Ryokan's Hermitage, Bunsui. 41 y.
Fukuoka. Mt. Togami, Japanese bush warbler and azaleas (National Afforestation Campaign). 41 y.
Hokkaido. Arctic foxes. 62 y.
Toyama. Mt. Tate and tulips. 62 y.
Ehime. Islets in Kurushima Strait. 62 y.
Iwate. Cape Kitayama, Rikuchu, in winter. 62 y.
Ohita. Three Tsurusaki dancers. 62 y.
Yamaguchi. Tanabata lantern festival. 62 y.
Kanagawa. Shasui waterfall. 62 y.
Fukuoka. Mari Tahei with spear and sake dish (Kuroda samurai folk song). 62 y.
Okinawa. Naha regatta. 62 y.
Osaka. Osaka Business Park and Castle. 41 y.
Aichi. Scops owl. 62 y.

**1993**

Akita. Rocks at Oga Peninsula. 41 y.
Ibaraki. Fukuroda waterfall. 62 y.
Ishikawa. Nanao Bay and Notojima Bridge. 62 y.
Tokyo. Cherry blossom and Tama District mountain ranges. 62 y.
Hokkaido. Harbour seals. 62 y.
Kagawa. Peace statue. 62 y.
Hiroshima. Drummer (rice transplanting ritual). 62 y.
Shizuoka. Black paradise flycatcher and Mt. Fuji. 41 y.
Shiga. Yachts on Lake Biwa. 62 y.
Nagano. Matsumoto Castle and mountains. 62 y.
Kagoshima. Drummer and dancer (Ohara Festival) and Mt. Sakura. 41 y.
Aomori. Oirase mountain stream. 62 y.
Chiba. Waterfall in Yoro Gorge. 41 y.

**1994**

Tokyo. Rainbow Bridge. 50 y.
Toyama. Kurobe Dam and Gorge. 80 y.
Shimane. Izumo no Okuni (Kabuki dancer) and Izumo Shrine. 80 y.
Nagano. Home at Kashiwabara of Issa Kobayushi (poet). 80 y.
Gunma. Fukiwari Waterfalls. 80 y.
Hokkaido. Sika deer. 50 y.
Hyogo. White stork and Drum Tower, Izushi. 50 y.
Wakayama. Yachts off Wakaura Coast and Marina City. 80 y.
Mie. Kentish plovers and Wedded Rocks, Futami Bay. 80 y.
Tokushima. Awa dance 50 y.
Okinawa. Tug-of-war. 50 y.
Fukui. Pine grove in Kehi. 50 y.
Miyagi. Junks and Godaido Temple, Matsushima. 80 y.
Nagasaki. Dragon Festival. 80 y.

**1995**

Hokkaido. Chipmunks. 80 y.
Kyoto. Ushiwaka and Benkei on bridge. 80 y.
Gifu. Flowers (Rose, cyclamen, African violets etc). 80 y.
Niigata. Jade and Gyofu Soma (poet). 80 y.
Kochi. Cape Ashizuri-Misaki Lighthouse. 80 y.
Ishikawa. Kanizawa Castle. 80 y.
Hokkaido. Lady's slipper orchid. 80 y.
Saitama. Kuroyama Waterfall. 80 y.
Tokyo. Red Gate, Tokyo University. 50 y.
Okinawa. Procession of drummers (folk festival dance). 80 y.
Miyagi. Avenue of zelkova trees. 50 y.
Osaka. Float in Kishiwada Danjiri Festival. 80 y.
Yamagata. Yamadera (or Risshaku) Temple, Mt. Houju, in autumn. 80 y.
Hida. Four seasons in Hida. 80 y. × 4 se-tenant
Saga. Boy and fish (Karatsu Kunchi Festival). 80 y.
Okayama. Woman writing (Niimi Estate festival). 80 y.
Tochigi. Kirihuri Waterfall. 50 y.
Nara. Yoshino in autumn and spring. 80 y. × 2
Chiba. Cows in field ("Farmpia'95" dairy farming exhibition). 80 y.

**1996**

Hokkaido. Sea butterflies. 80 y.
Kumamoto. Boy dancing, bridge and ships (Ushibuka Haiya festival). 80 y.
Fukushima. Pink peony. 80 y.
Mie. Wild crinums (flowers). 80 y. and Women collecting shells. 80 y. se-tenant.
Saga. Jar, flames and pavilion (ceramics exhibition). 80 y.
Yamanashi. Waterfall in Shosenkyo Gorge. 50 y.
Fukui. Murasaki Shikibu (author of "Tale of Genji") and Mt. Hino. 80 y.
Shiga. Enryaku Temple and ancient trees, Mt. Hiei. 80y.
Ehime. Nishiumi Marine Park. 80 y.
Hokkaido. Wild rose. 80 y.
Aomori. Kabuki characters (Nebuta festival). 80 y.

## JAPANESE TAIWAN (FORMOSA)

**From 1895 to 1945 Taiwan was part of the Japanese Empire, using the stamps of Japan. During 1945 American naval and air forces disrupted communications between Taiwan and Japan. The following were issued when supplies of Japanese stamps ran short.**

1. Numeral and Chrysanthemum.

**1945.** Imperf.

| | | | | |
|---|---|---|---|---|
| J 1. | **1.** | 3 s. red .. .. .. | 25·00 | 28·00 |
| J 2. | | 5 s. green.. .. .. | 25·00 | 23·00 |
| J 3. | | 10 s. blue.. .. .. | 35·00 | 35·00 |

## JAPANESE OCCUPATION OF CHINA Pt. 17

100 cents = 1 dollar.

### I. KWANGTUNG

**Japanese troops occupied Canton in 1938 and by 1945 had overrun much of Kwangtung province. Unoverprinted stamps of China were used until the following stamps were issued.**

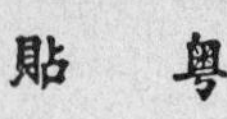

(1.) (2.)

(Trans. "Special for Kwantung").

**1942.** Stamps. of China optd. with T **1.**

| | | | | |
|---|---|---|---|---|
| 1. | – | 1 c. orange (411).. .. | 50 | 1·25 |
| 2. | **77.** | 1 c. orange .. .. | 75 | 1·50 |
| 3. | **58.** | 2 c. olive .. .. .. | 5·00 | 4·25 |
| 4. | **72.** | 3 c. lake .. .. .. | 40 | 1·25 |
| 5. | **77.** | 5 c. green .. .. | 85 | 1·00 |
| 7. | **72.** | 8 c. olive .. .. .. | 1·00 | 60 |
| 8. | **77.** | 8 c. green .. .. | 1·25 | 1·25 |
| 9. | **72.** | 10 c. green .. .. | 1·00 | 1·10 |
| 11. | **77.** | 10 c. green .. .. | 1·75 | 2·00 |
| 12. | **72.** | 16 c. olive .. .. | 2·00 | 2·75 |
| 13. | **72.** | 17 c. olive .. .. | 2·25 | 3·25 |
| 14. | – | 20 c. blue (519) .. .. | 2·25 | 2·50 |
| 15. | **72.** | 30 c. red .. .. .. | 2·00 | 2·50 |
| 16. | **77.** | 30 c. red .. .. .. | 2·75 | 3·50 |
| 17. | **72.** | 50 c. blue .. .. | 3·25 | 3·00 |
| 18. | **77.** | 50 c. blue .. .. | 2·50 | 2·25 |
| 19. | **72.** | $1 brown and red .. | 5·50 | 5·00 |
| 20. | | $2 brown and blue .. | 5·50 | 5·00 |
| 21. | | $5 green and red .. | 6·00 | 4·50 |
| 22. | | $10 violet and green .. | 10·00 | 7·50 |
| 23. | | $20 blue and purple .. | 7·50 | 5·50 |

**1942.** Stamps of China optd. with T **2.**

(a) On 1938 issue.

| | | | | |
|---|---|---|---|---|
| 24 | **72.** | 2 c. olive .. .. .. | 30 | 1·00 |
| 25 | | 3 c. lake .. .. .. | 30 | 1·00 |
| 26 | | 5 c. olive .. .. .. | 35 | 25 |
| 28 | | 8 c. olive .. .. .. | 30 | 30 |
| 29 | | 10 c. green .. .. | 55 | 75 |
| 30 | | 16 c. olive .. .. | 60 | 1·50 |
| 31 | | 25 c. blue .. .. | 1·25 | 2·25 |
| 32 | | 30 c. red .. .. .. | 1·50 | 2·25 |
| 33 | | 50 c. blue .. .. | 1·25 | 1·25 |
| 35 | | $1 brown and red .. | 5·00 | 5·50 |
| 37 | | $2 brown and blue .. | 5·00 | 6·00 |
| 39 | | $5 green and red .. | 6·50 | 6·50 |
| 40 | | $10 violet and green .. | 10·00 | 9·00 |
| 42 | | $20 blue and purple .. | 6·00 | 10·00 |

(b) On 1941 issue.

| | | | | |
|---|---|---|---|---|
| 44. | **77.** | 2 c. blue .. .. .. | 25 | 1·50 |
| 45. | | 5 c. green .. .. | 25 | 1·25 |
| 46. | | 8 c. orange .. .. | 90 | 2·25 |
| 47. | | 8 c. green .. .. | 70 | 2·25 |
| 48. | | 10 c. green .. .. | 75 | 2·25 |
| 49. | | 17 c. olive .. .. | 75 | 3·00 |
| 50. | | 25 c. red .. .. .. | 1·00 | 2·75 |
| 51. | | 30 c. red .. .. .. | 1·00 | 2·25 |
| 52. | | 50 c. blue .. .. | 1·25 | 2·25 |
| 53. | | $1 black and brown .. | 5·00 | 4·50 |
| 54. | | $2 black and blue .. | 5·00 | 4·25 |
| 55. | | $5 black and red .. | 7·50 | 7·00 |
| 56. | | $10 black and green .. | 8·50 | 8·00 |
| 57. | | $20 black and red .. | 5·50 | 6·00 |

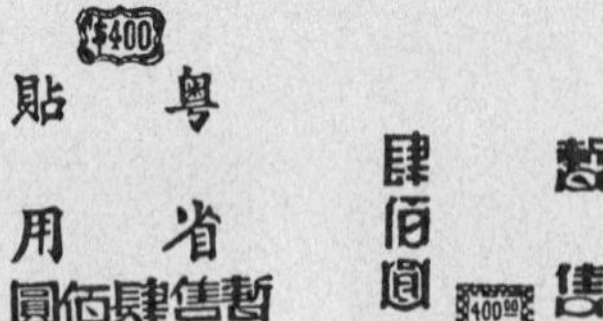

(3.) (4.)

**1945.** Canton provisionals. Surch. as T **3.**

| | | | | |
|---|---|---|---|---|
| 58. | **72.** | $200 on 10 c. green (No. 29) .. .. | 55·00 | 45·00 |
| 59. | | $400 on 8 c. olive (No. 28) .. .. | 55·00 | 45·00 |

**1945.** Swatow provisional. No. 508 of China surch. with T **4.**

| | | | |
|---|---|---|---|
| 60. | $400 on 1 c. orange .. | £325 | £300 |

POSTAGE DUE STAMP

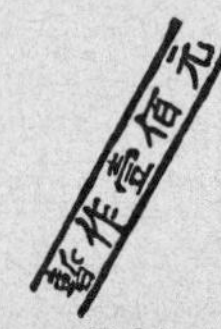

(D 3.)

**1945.** Postage Due stamp of China surch. with Type D **3.**

| | | | | |
|---|---|---|---|---|
| D 58. | D **62.** | $100 on $2 orange | £400 | £400 |

### II. MENGKIANG (INNER MONGOLIA)

The autonomous area of Mengkiang ("the Mongolian Borderlands"), consisting of Suiyuan, South Chahar and North Shansi, was established by the Japanese in November, 1937.

For the first issue in 1941 see the note at the beginning of III North China.

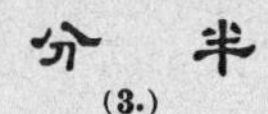

(3.)

**1942.** Stamps of China optd. "Mengkiang" and surch. half original value at T **3**.

| | | | | |
|---|---|---|---|---|
| 86 | – | ½ c. on 1 c. orange (411) | 1·00 | 1·00 |
| 93 | **58** | 1 c. on 2 c. green .. | 1·00 | 1·00 |
| 69 | **72** | 1 c. on 2 c. green .. | 75 | 75 |
| 94 | **58** | 2 c. on 4 c. green .. | 10 | 50 |
| 87 | **60** | 2 c. on 4 c. lilac .. | 3·25 | 2·25 |
| 72 | **72** | 4 c. on 8 c. green .. | 1·50 | 75 |
| 73 | **72** | 5 c. on 10 c. green .. | 1·50 | 1·50 |
| 99 | – | 5 c. on 10 c. purple (515) | 75 | 1·75 |
| 95 | **72** | 8 c. on 16 c. brown .. | 1·25 | 40 |
| 68 | **58** | 10 c. on 20 c. blue .. | 22·00 | 23·00 |
| 100 | – | 10 c. on 20 c. red (418) .. | 75 | 1·75 |
| 88 | – | 10 c. on 20 c. blue (519) | 2·50 | 2·25 |
| 101 | – | 15 c. on 30 c. pur (542) | 2·25 | 2·00 |
| 75 | **72** | 15 c. on 30 c. red .. | 3·00 | 3·25 |
| 102 | – | 20 c. on 40 c. orge (524) | 3·25 | 2·25 |
| 103 | – | 25 c. on 50 c. green (525) | 2·75 | 2·25 |
| 77 | **72** | 25 c. on 50 c. blue .. | 5·00 | 5·50 |
| 96 | | 50 c. on $1 sepia & brn | 6·00 | 5·00 |
| 82 | | $1 on $2 brown and blue | 9·00 | 9·00 |
| 98 | | $5 on $10 violet & green | 30·00 | 30·00 |
| 84 | | $10 on $20 blue & purple | 65·00 | 65·00 |

4. Dragon Pillar, Peking.

5. Miners.

**1943.** 5th Anniv. of Establishment of Mengkiang Post and Telegraph Service.

| | | | | |
|---|---|---|---|---|
| 104. | **4.** | 4 c. orange .. .. | 1·25 | 2·50 |
| 105. | | 8 c. blue .. .. .. | 1·50 | 2·50 |

**1943.** 2nd Anniv. of War in East Asia.

| | | | | |
|---|---|---|---|---|
| 106. | **5.** | 4 c. green.. .. .. | 1·25 | 2·75 |
| 107. | | 8 c. red .. .. .. | 1·25 | 2·75 |

6. Stylised Horse.

7. Prince Yun.

8. Blast Furnace.

**1943.** 1st Anniv. of Federation of Autonomous Governments of Mongolian Provinces.

| | | | | |
|---|---|---|---|---|
| 108. | **6.** | 3 c. red .. .. .. | 1·00 | 2·75 |
| 109. | **7.** | 8 c. blue .. .. .. | 1·25 | 2·75 |

**1944.** Productivity Campaign.

| | | | | |
|---|---|---|---|---|
| 110. | **8.** | 8 c. brown .. .. | 1·50 | 3·50 |

**1945.** Stamps of China optd. "Mengkiang" as top characters in T **3.**

| | | | | |
|---|---|---|---|---|
| 117. | – | 1 c. orange (411) .. | 50 | 50 |
| 111. | **58.** | 2 c. olive .. .. | 1·00 | 1·00 |
| 112. | | 4 c. green .. .. | 3·75 | 3·00 |
| 113. | | 5 c. green .. .. | 1·25 | 1·00 |
| 118. | – | 8 c. orange (514) .. | 10 | 35 |
| 119. | – | 10 c. purple (515) .. | 10 | 40 |
| 120. | – | 20 c. lake (418) .. | 15 | 40 |
| 121. | – | 30 c. red (542) .. .. | 15 | 50 |
| 122. | – | 40 c. orange (524) .. | 10 | 50 |
| 123. | – | 50 c. green (525) .. | 70 | 80 |
| 114. | **72.** | $1 brown and red .. | 2·00 | 2·25 |
| 115. | | $2 brown and blue .. | 5·50 | 5·50 |
| 116. | | $5 green and red .. | 16·00 | 17·00 |

角 伍

(10.)

**1945.** Stamps of China optd. "Mengkiang" (as T **3** of North China) and surch. as T **10**.

| | | | | |
|---|---|---|---|---|
| 124B. | **60.** | 10 c. on ½ c. sepia .. | 50 | 2·00 |
| 126B. | – | 10 c. on 1 c. orange (411) .. .. | 25 | 2·00 |
| 135. | **58.** | 50 c. on 2 c. olive .. | 55 | 2·25 |
| 130. | **72.** | 50 c. on 2 c. olive .. | 35 | 2·50 |
| 136. | **58.** | 50 c. on 4 c. green .. | 2·00 | 3·75 |
| 131. | **60.** | 50 c. on 4 c. lilac .. | 85 | 3·25 |
| 137. | **58.** | 50 c. on 5 c. green .. | 50 | 2·50 |
| 132B. | **72.** | 50 c. on 5 c. olive .. | 50 | 2·00 |
| 138. | – | $1 on 8 c. orange (514) .. .. | 15 | 3·25 |

### III. NORTH CHINA

The Japanese conquered North China in 1937 and formed a puppet Government in Peking.

疆蒙 (2. " Mengkiang. ") 南河 (B. " Honan. ")

北河 (D. " Hopeh. ") 西山 (E. " Shansi. ")

東山 (H. " Shantung. ") 北蘇 (J. " Supeh. ")

Types **2** and **B** to **J** are the six "district" overprints comprising North China (including Mengkiang) and a detailed list of the overprints on the stamps of China is given in the Stanley Gibbons' Catalogue, Part 17 (China).

坡嘉新 念紀落陷 (1.)

國建國洲滿 念紀年週十 (2.)

In 1942 stamps of China overprinted with Types **B** to **J** were further overprinted with Type 1 (to commemorate the Fall of Singapore) or with Type 2 (to commemorate the tenth Anniversary of Manchukuo). These stamps are also listed in the Stanley Gibbons' Catalogue Part 17 (China).

北 華

分 半

(3.)

**1942.** Stamps of China optd. " Hwa Pei " (= North China) and surch. half original value at T **3**.

| | | | | |
|---|---|---|---|---|
| 111. | – | ½ c. on 1 c. orange (No. 411) .. .. .. | 45 | 45 |
| 128. | **58.** | 1 c. on 2 c. olive .. | 75 | 20 |
| 114. | – | 1 c. on 2 c. blue (No. 509) | 1·50 | 1·00 |
| 88. | **72.** | 1 c. on 2 c. olive .. | 50 | 40 |
| 129. | **58.** | 2 c. on 4 c. green .. | 10 | 10 |
| 116. | **60.** | 2 c. on 4 c. lilac .. | 1·10 | 1·10 |
| 134. | – | 4 c. on 8 c. orge. (No. 514) | 10 | 10 |
| 91. | **72.** | 4 c. on 8 c. olive .. | 60 | 25 |
| 120. | – | 5 c. on 10 c. pur. (No. 515) | 2·25 | 2·25 |
| 92. | **72.** | 5 c. on 10 c. green .. | 80 | 25 |
| 130. | | 8 c. on 16 c. olive .. | 75 | 20 |
| 135. | – | 10 c. on 20 c. lake (No. 418) .. .. .. | 40 | 10 |
| 122. | – | 10 c. on 20 c. blue (No. 519) .. .. .. | 75 | 1·10 |
| 96. | **72.** | 15 c. on 30 c. red .. | 1·50 | 1·10 |
| 136. | – | 15 c. on 30 c. purple (No. 542) .. .. .. | 45 | 10 |
| 137. | – | 20 c. on 40 c. orge. (No. 524) .. .. .. | 1·00 | 15 |
| 138. | – | 25 c. on 50 c. green (No. 525) .. .. .. | 1·25 | 25 |
| 98. | **72.** | 25 c. on 50 c. blue .. | 1·10 | 85 |
| 131. | | 50 c. on $1 brown & red | 2·75 | 1·25 |
| 132. | | $1 on $2 brown and blue | 5·00 | 5·50 |
| 133. | | $5 on $10 violet & green | 15·00 | 14·00 |
| 109. | | $10 on $20 blue & purple | 40·00 | 40·00 |

邦友 界租 還交 念紀 (4.)

局總 政郵 立成 念紀年週王 (5.)

**1943.** Return to China of Foreign Concessions. Optd. with T **4**.

| | | | | |
|---|---|---|---|---|
| 139. | **58.** | 2 c. on 4 c. green (No. 129) | 1·00 | 2·00 |
| 140. | **72.** | 4 c. on 8 c. olive (No. 91) | 1·00 | 2·00 |
| 141. | | 8 c. on 16 c. olive (No. 130) | 1·50 | 2·00 |

**1943.** 5th Anniv. of Directorate-General of Posts for North China. Optd. with T **5**.

| | | | | |
|---|---|---|---|---|
| 142. | **58.** | 2 c. on 4 c. green (No. 129) | 1·00 | 2·00 |
| 143. | **72.** | 4 c. on 8 c. olive (No. 91) | 1·00 | 2·00 |
| 144. | | 8 c. on 16 c. olive (No. 130) | 1·50 | 2·00 |

**1943.** Stamps of China optd. " Hwa Pei " as top characters in T **3**.

| | | | | |
|---|---|---|---|---|
| 164. | – | 1 c. orange (No. 411) .. | 20 | 25 |
| 153. | **58.** | 2 c. olive .. .. | 10 | 15 |
| 154. | | 4 c. green .. .. | 10 | 10 |
| 155. | | 5 c. green .. .. | 10 | 10 |
| 156. | **72.** | 9 c. olive .. .. | 15 | 25 |
| 165. | – | 10 c. purple (No. 515) .. | 10 | 15 |
| 145. | **72.** | 10 c. green .. .. | 2·00 | 1·50 |
| 157. | | 16 c. olive .. .. | 15 | 15 |
| 158. | | 18 c. olive .. .. | 20 | 25 |
| 166. | – | 20 c. lake (No. 418) .. | 15 | 15 |
| 167. | – | 30 c. red (as No. 542) .. | 10 | 15 |
| 168. | – | 40 c. orange (No. 524) .. | 15 | 15 |
| 169. | – | 50 c. green (No. 525) .. | 20 | 15 |
| 159. | **72.** | $1 brown and red .. | 4·00 | 1·00 |
| 160. | | $2 brown and blue .. | 2·25 | 75 |
| 161. | | $5 green and red .. | 3·00 | 2·25 |
| 162. | | $10 violet and green .. | 5·50 | 5·50 |
| 163. | | $20 blue and purple .. | 6·50 | 6·50 |

戰 參 念紀年週一 (6.)

會員委務政 念紀年週四 (7.)

**1944.** 1st Anniv. of Declaration of War on Allies by Japanese-controlled Nanking Govt. Optd. with T **6**.

| | | | | |
|---|---|---|---|---|
| 170. | **58.** | 4 c. green (No. 154) .. | 2·00 | 3·00 |
| 171. | **72.** | 10 c. green (No. 149) .. | 2·00 | 3·00 |

**1944.** North China Political Council. 4th Anniv. Optd. with T **7**.

| | | | | |
|---|---|---|---|---|
| 172. | **72.** | 9 c. olive (No. 156) .. | 1·50 | 2·00 |
| 173. | | 18 c. olive (No. 158) .. | 1·75 | 2·25 |
| 174. | – | 50 c. green (No. 169) .. | 1·75 | 2·25 |
| 175. | **72.** | $1 brown & red (No 159) | 3·25 | 3·00 |

華北玖分 (8.)

立成局總政郵 念紀年週六 (9.)

**1944.** Stamps of Japanese Occupation of Shanghai and Nanking optd. " Hwa Pei " and surch. as T **8**.

| | | | | |
|---|---|---|---|---|
| 176. | **5.** | 9 c. on 50 c. orange .. | 1·25 | 2·25 |
| 177. | | 18 c. on $1 green .. | 1·50 | 2·25 |
| 178. | **6.** | 36 c. on $2 blue .. | 2·00 | 2·75 |
| 179. | | 90 c. on $5 red .. | 2·50 | 3·00 |

**1944.** 6th Anniv. of Directorate-General of Posts for North China. Optd. with T **9**.

| | | | | |
|---|---|---|---|---|
| 180. | **72.** | 9 c. olive (No. 156) .. | 1·50 | 2·25 |
| 181. | | 18 c. olive (No. 158) .. | 1·50 | 2·25 |
| 182. | – | 50 c. green (No. 169) .. | 1·75 | 2·25 |
| 183. | **72.** | $1 brown & red (No. 159) | 3·75 | 3·25 |

席主汪 念紀典葬 (10.)

年週二戰參 念紀 (11.)

華北壹圓 (12.)

**1944.** Death of Wang Ching-wei. Optd. with T **10**.

| | | | | |
|---|---|---|---|---|
| 184. | – | 20 c. lake (No. 166) .. | 1·75 | 2·25 |
| 185. | – | 50 c. green (No. 169) .. | 1·75 | 2·25 |
| 186. | **72.** | $1 brown & red (No. 159) | 2·00 | 2·50 |
| 187. | | $2 brown & blue (No. 160) | 2·25 | 2·75 |

**1945.** Declaration of War on Allies by Nanking Govt. 2nd Anniv. Optd. with T **11**.

| | | | | |
|---|---|---|---|---|
| 188. | – | 20 c. lake (No. 166) .. | 1·75 | 2·25 |
| 189. | – | 50 c. green (No. 169) .. | 1·75 | 2·25 |
| 190. | **72.** | $1 brown & red (No. 159) | 2·00 | 2·50 |
| 191. | | $2 brown & blue (No. 160) | 2·50 | 2·75 |

**1945.** Stamps of Japanese Occupation of Shanghai and Nanking surch. as T **12**.

| | | | | |
|---|---|---|---|---|
| 192. | **7.** | 50 c. on $3 orange .. | 2·00 | 3·00 |
| 193. | | $1 on $6 blue .. | 2·00 | 3·00 |

**13.** Dragon Pillar.

**14.** Long Bridge.

**15.** Imperial City Tower. **16.** Marble Boat, Summer Palace.

**17.**

**1945.** 5th Anniv. of Establishment of North China Political Council. Views of Peking.

| | | | | |
|---|---|---|---|---|
| 194. | **13.** | $1 yellow .. .. | 95 | 1·50 |
| 195. | **14.** | $2 blue .. .. .. | 1·00 | 1·50 |
| 196. | **15.** | $5 red .. .. .. | 1·10 | 1·25 |
| 197. | **16.** | $10 green .. .. | 1·50 | 1·75 |

**1945.** Optd. " Hwa Pei " as top characters in T **3**.

| | | | | |
|---|---|---|---|---|
| 198. | **17.** | $1 brown .. .. | 1·25 | 25 |
| 199. | | $2 blue .. .. .. | 1·40 | 15 |
| 200. | | $5 red .. .. .. | 1·50 | 45 |
| 201. | | $10 green .. .. | 1·75 | 1·00 |
| 202. | | $20 purple .. .. | 2·75 | 1·10 |
| 203. | | $50 brown .. .. | 12·00 | 8·50 |

**18.** Wutai Mountain, Shansi. **19.** Kaifeng Iron Pagoda, Honan. **20.** International Bridge, Tientsin.

**21.** Taishan Mountain, Shantung.

**22.** G.P.O., Peking.

**1945.** 7th Anniv. of Directorate General of Posts for North China.

| | | | | |
|---|---|---|---|---|
| 204. | **18.** | $5 green .. .. | 60 | 1·25 |
| 205. | **19.** | $10 brown .. .. | 65 | 1·10 |
| 206. | **20.** | $20 purple .. .. | 75 | 1·10 |
| 207. | **21.** | $30 grey .. .. | 1·00 | 1·00 |
| 208. | **22.** | $50 red .. .. | 1·10 | 1·00 |

### IV. NANKING AND SHANGHAI

The Japanese captured Shanghai and Nanking in 1937 and Hankow in 1938. During the same year Nanking was made the seat of Japanese-controlled administration for the Yangtse Basin. The stamps listed below were used in parts of Anhwei, Southern Kiangsu, Chekiang, Hupeh, Kiangsi, Hunan and Fukien.

N.B. With the exception of Nos. 114 to 119 the following are all surcharged on stamps of China.

**20**

付已費空航之函信內國

(1.)

**1941.** Air. Surch. as T **1**.

| | | | | |
|---|---|---|---|---|
| 1 | 61 | 10 s. on 50 c. brown .. | 25 | 2·50 |
| 2 | | 18 s. on 90 c. olive .. | 60 | 3·50 |
| 4 | | 20 s. on $1 green .. .. | 1·00 | 4·00 |
| 5 | | 25 s. on 90 c. olive .. | 25 | 2·75 |
| 6 | | 35 s. on $2 brown .. | 25 | 2·50 |
| 7 | | 60 s. on 35 s. on $2 brown (No. 6) .. .. .. | 25 | 3·50 |

念紀界租回收

八月一日 三十二年

角 伍

(2.)

**1943.** Return to China of Shanghai Concessions. Surch. as T **2**.

| | | | | |
|---|---|---|---|---|
| 8. | **72.** | 25 c. on 5 c. green .. | 1·00 | 1·75 |
| 9. | **77.** | 50 c. on 8 c. orange .. | 1·00 | 1·75 |
| 10. | **72.** | $1 on 16 c. olive .. | 1·00 | 1·75 |
| 11. | **77.** | $2 on 50 c. blue .. .. | 1·00 | 1·75 |

**1943.** As No. 422 but colour changed. Issued at Shanghai.

| | | | | |
|---|---|---|---|---|
| 12. | **72.** | 15 c. brown .. .. | 9·50 | 16·00 |

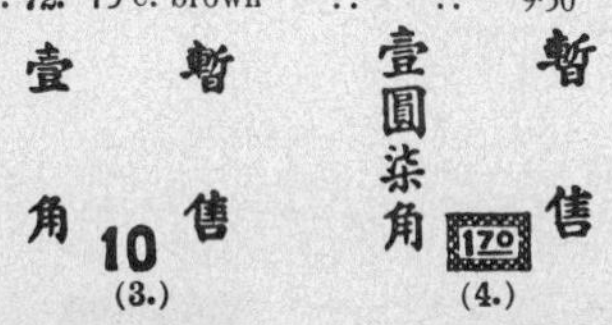
(3.) (4.)

**1943.** Stamps of China and No. 12 above surch. as T 3 (cent values) or T 4 (dollar values).

(a) On T **58**.

| | | | | |
|---|---|---|---|---|
| 13. | **58.** | $6 on 5 c. green .. | 1·00 | 2·50 |
| 14. | | $20 on 15 c. red .. | 1·10 | 1·75 |
| 15. | | $500 on 15 c. green .. | 1·25 | 1·75 |
| 17. | | $1000 on 20 c. blue .. | 2·00 | 3·25 |
| 18. | | $1000 on 25 c. blue .. | 2·25 | 3·25 |

(b) On Martyrs issue (as T **60.**)

| | | | | |
|---|---|---|---|---|
| 88. | **60.** | $7.50 c. on ½ c. sepia .. | 35 | 4·50 |
| 89. | – | $15 on 1 c. orange .. | 25 | 1·50 |
| 91. | – | $30 on 2 c. blue .. | 45 | 1·50 |
| 93. | – | $200 on 1 c. orange .. | 40 | 1·00 |
| 94. | – | $200 on 8 c. orange .. | 45 | 1·25 |

(c) On T **72.**

| | | | | |
|---|---|---|---|---|
| 19 | **72** | 25 c. on 5 c. green .. | 50 | 2·25 |
| 20 | | 30 c. on 2 c. green .. | 75 | 2·50 |
| 21 | | 50 c. on 3 c. red .. | 10 | 45 |
| 22 | | 50 c. on 5 c. green .. | 20 | 40 |
| 23 | | 50 c. on 8 c. green .. | 1·00 | 1·75 |
| 24 | | $1 on 8 c. green .. | 10 | 15 |
| 26 | | $1 on 15 c. brown .. | 70 | 1·00 |
| 27 | | $1.30 on 16 c. brown .. | 10 | 1·00 |
| 28 | | $1.50 on 3 c. red .. | 10 | 50 |
| 54 | | $1.70 on 30 c. red .. | 1·40 | 2·75 |
| 55 | | $2 on 5 c. green .. | 15 | 45 |
| 30 | | $2 on 10 c. green .. | 10 | 40 |
| 56 | | $2 on $1 sepia & brown | 2·75 | 3·50 |
| 59 | | $3 on 8 c. green .. | 10 | 15 |
| 31 | | $3 on 15 c. brown .. | 25 | 50 |
| 32 | | $4 on 16 c. brown .. | 30 | 50 |
| 33 | | $5 on 15 c. brown .. | 75 | 60 |
| 61 | | $6 on 5 c. green .. | 50 | 75 |
| 62 | | $6 on 8 c. green .. | 15 | 35 |
| 38 | | $6 on 10 c. green .. | 50 | 70 |
| 39 | | $10 on 10 c. green .. | 10 | 30 |
| 40 | | $10 on 16 c. brown .. | 10 | 20 |
| 41 | | $20 on 3 c. red .. .. | 10 | 40 |
| 42 | | $20 on 15 c. red .. | 1·75 | 4·00 |
| 43 | | $20 on 15 c. brown .. | 35 | 1·00 |
| 64 | | $20 on $2 brown & blue | 1·75 | 2·25 |
| 65 | | $50 on 30 c. red .. | 75 | 1·90 |
| 66 | | $50 on 50 c. blue .. | 75 | 2·00 |
| 67 | | $50 on $5 green and red | 1·25 | 2·00 |
| 68 | | $50 on $20 blue & purple | 2·25 | 3·00 |
| 45 | | $100 on 3 c. red .. | 90 | 1·00 |
| 83 | | $100 on $10 violet & grn | 45 | 75 |
| 84 | | $200 on $20 blue & pur | 45 | 75 |
| 46 | | $500 on 8 c. green .. | 1·75 | 2·25 |
| 47 | | $500 on 10 c. green .. | 1·50 | 2·25 |
| 48 | | $500 on 15 c. red .. | 2·50 | 3·50 |
| 49 | | $500 on 15 c. brown .. | 2·75 | 3·25 |
| 50 | | $500 on 16 c. brown .. | 2·50 | 3·25 |
| 51 | | $1000 on 25 c. blue .. | 3·00 | 4·25 |
| 86 | | $1000 on 30 c. red .. | 2·00 | 3·50 |
| 75 | | $1000 on 50 c. blue .. | 2·50 | 3·50 |
| 76 | | $1000 on $2 brown & bl | 2·25 | 4·75 |
| 77 | | $2000 on $5 green & red | 2·50 | 3·75 |
| 87a | | $5000 on $10 vio & grn | 10·00 | 18·00 |

(d) On T **77.**

| | | | | |
|---|---|---|---|---|
| 95. | **77.** | 5 c. on ½ c. sepia .. | 10 | 1·50 |
| 96. | | 10 c. on 1 c. orange .. | 10 | 1·25 |
| 97. | | 20 c. on 1 c. orange .. | 15 | 1·00 |
| 98. | | 40 c. on 5 c. green .. | 10 | 1·10 |
| 99. | | $5 on 5 c. green .. | 15 | 35 |
| 100. | | $10 on 10 c. green .. | 35 | 70 |
| 101. | | $50 on ½ c. sepia .. | 25 | 50 |
| 102. | | $50 on 1 c. orange .. | 35 | 50 |
| 103. | | $50 on 17 c. olive .. | 75 | 1·00 |
| 104. | | $200 on 5 c. green .. | 50 | 1·00 |
| 105. | | $200 on 8 c. green .. | 60 | 1·10 |
| 106. | | $200 on 8 c. orange .. | 1·25 | 2·00 |
| 107. | | $500 on $5 black & red | 1·75 | 3·00 |
| 108. | | $1000 on 1 c. orange | 1·50 | 2·75 |
| 109. | | $1000 on 25 c. purple .. | 1·75 | 2·50 |
| 110. | | $1000 on 30 c. red .. | 2·00 | 2·75 |
| 111. | | $1000 on $2 blk. & blue | 2·25 | 3·00 |
| 112. | | $1000 on $10 blk. & grn. | 2·75 | 2·75 |
| 113. | | $2000 on $5 blk. & red | 3·25 | 3·00 |

**5.** Wheat and Cotton Flower.

**6.** Purple Mountain, Nanking.

**1944.** 4th Anniv. of Establishment of Chinese Puppet Government at Nanking.

| | | | | |
|---|---|---|---|---|
| 114. | **5.** | 50 c. orange .. .. | 10 | 50 |
| 115. | | $1 green .. .. .. | 10 | 50 |
| 116. | **6.** | $2 blue .. .. .. | 10 | 50 |
| 117. | | $5 red .. .. .. | 10 | 50 |

**7.** Map of Shanghai and Foreign Concessions.

**1944.** 1st Anniv. of Return to China of Shanghai Foreign Concessions.

| | | | | |
|---|---|---|---|---|
| 118. | **7.** | $3 orange .. .. | 10 | 1·50 |
| 119. | | $6 blue .. .. | 10 | 1·50 |

**1945.** 5th Anniv. of Establishment of Chinese Puppet Government at Nanking. Surch as T **4**.

| | | | | |
|---|---|---|---|---|
| 124. | **5.** | $15 on 50 c. orange .. | 10 | 1·50 |
| 125. | | $30 on $1 green .. | 10 | 1·50 |
| 126. | **6.** | $60 on $2 blue .. | 10 | 1·50 |
| 127. | | $200 on $5 red .. .. | 10 | 1·25 |

(9.)

**1945.** Air Raid Precautions Propaganda. Air stamps surch. as T **9**.

| | | | | |
|---|---|---|---|---|
| 128. | **61.** | $150 on 15 c. green .. | 40 | 1·25 |
| 129. | | $250 on 25 c. orange | 40 | 1·25 |
| 130. | | $600 on 60 c. blue .. | 40 | 1·25 |
| 131. | | $1000 on $1 green .. | 40 | 1·25 |

#### POSTAGE DUE STAMPS

壹 改

圓 作

1.00

(D 8.)

**1945.** Postage Due stamps surch. as Type D **8**.

| | | | | |
|---|---|---|---|---|
| D 120. | D **62.** | $1 on 2 c. orange .. | 35 | 2·75 |
| D 121. | | $2 on 5 c. orange .. | 35 | 2·50 |
| D 122. | | $5 on 10 c. orange | 35 | 2·50 |
| D 123. | | $10 on 20 c. orange | 35 | 2·25 |

## JAPANESE OCCUPATION OF NETHERLANDS INDIES Pt. 4

The Japanese occupied the Netherlands Indies from March 1942 to 1945.

100 sen (cents) = 1 rupee (gulden).

### I. JAVA

**1.** Eastern Asia.

DESIGNS: 3½ s. Farmer ploughing ricefield. 5 s. Mt. Soemer. 10 s. Bantam Bay.

**1943.** 1st Anniv of Japanese Occupation of Java.

| | | | | |
|---|---|---|---|---|
| 1. | **1.** | 2 s. brown .. .. .. | 1·75 | 1·75 |
| 2. | – | 3½ s. red .. .. .. | 1·75 | 1·75 |
| 3. | – | 5 s. green .. .. .. | 3·00 | 1·75 |
| 4. | – | 10 s. blue .. .. .. | 5·50 | 1·75 |

2. Wayang puppet.

4. Bird of Vishnu and Mt. Soemer.

5. Native soldier.

**1943.** Designs with rectangular panel of characters as at foot of T 2/4.

5. – 3½ c. red .. .. .. 50 50
6. 2. 5 c. green .. .. .. 50 50
7. – 10 c. blue .. .. .. 50 45
8. – 20 c. olive .. .. .. 85 50
9. – 40 c. purple .. .. .. 1·50 50
10. 4. 60 c. orange .. .. .. 1·75 80
11. – 80 c. brown .. .. .. 3·50 80
12. – 1 r. violet .. .. .. 8·50 1·40

DESIGNS—As Type 2: 3½ c. Native head. 10 c. Boroboudur Temple. 20 c. Map of Java. 40 c. Seated dancer and Temple. As Type 4: 80 c. Ploughing with oxen. 1 r. Terraced ricefields.

**1943.** Savings Campaign.

13. 5. 3½ c. red .. .. .. 13·00 6·00
14. 10 c. blue .. .. .. 15·00 2·25

II. SUMATRA

6. Lake Toba.

DESIGNS: 1 c. to 3 c. Batak house, 3½ c. to 5 c. Minangkabau house. 10 c., 20 c. Ploughing with oxen. 50c., 1 r. Carabao Canyon (20 × 28 mm.).

**1943.** Designs with rectangular panel characters as at foot of T 6.

15. – 1 c. olive .. .. .. 60 90
16. – 2 c. green .. .. .. 60 90
17. – 3 c. blue .. .. .. 60 90
18. – 3½ c. red .. .. .. 60 1·00
19. – 4 c. blue .. .. .. 60 90
20. – 5 c. orange .. .. .. 60 90
21. – 10 c. blue .. .. .. 75 95
22. – 20 c. brown .. .. .. 1·25 1·50
23. 6. 30 c. purple .. .. .. 1·50 2·00
24. 40 c. brown .. .. .. 1·75 2·50
25. – 50 c. bistre .. .. .. 6·00 7·00
26. – 1 r. violet .. .. .. 11·00 13·00

7.

**1944.** Various stamps optd with Type 7.
(a) On Netherlands Indies stamps of 1933.

38 46 1 c. violet .. .. 30 80
39 2 c. purple .. .. 30 80
40 2½ c. bistre .. .. 30 80
41 3 c. green .. .. 5·50 7·50
27 3½ c. grey .. .. 30 75
42 47 10 c. red .. .. 5·50 7·50
51 15 c. blue .. .. 1·60 4·75
52 20 c. purple .. .. 30 55
37 25 c. green .. .. 1·75 2·00
46 30 c. blue .. .. 13·00 17·00
54 35 c. violet .. .. 1·50 2·25
55 40 c. green .. .. 70 1·25
34 42½ c. yellow .. .. 38·00 48·00
35 50 c. blue .. .. 15·00 18·00
49 2 g. green .. .. 32·00 42·00
36 2 g. 50 purple .. .. 48·00 60·00
56 5 g. bistre .. .. 9·50 14·00

(b) On Nos. 429/44 of Netherlands Indies.

57 – 10 c. red .. .. 35 55
59 – 15 c. blue .. .. 60 90
60 – 17½ c. orange .. .. 80 1·25
61 – 20 c. mauve .. .. 16·00 20·00
62 – 25 c. green .. .. 2·25 4·75
63 – 30 c. brown .. .. 70 1·50
64 – 35 c. purple .. .. 15·00 18·00
65 – 40 c. green .. .. 70 1·50
66 – 50 c. red .. .. 1·50 1·75
67 – 60 c. blue .. .. 1·10 1·40
68 – 80 c. red .. .. 1·50 2·00
69 – 1 g. violet .. .. 1·50 2·00
70 – 2 g. green .. .. 2·00 3·00
71 – 5 g. brown .. .. 55·00 75·00
72 – 10 g. green .. .. 18·00 24·00
73 68 25 g. orange .. .. £120 £160

(c) On Nos. 463/6 of Netherlands Indies.

74 – 3 c. green .. .. 30 75
75 71 4 c. green .. .. 30 75
76 – 5 c. blue .. .. 30 75
77 – 7½ c. violet .. .. 30 75

(d) On Nos. 506 and 509 of Netherlands.

78 94 5 c. green .. .. 8·50 11·00
79 12½ c. blue .. .. 4·50 10·00

III. JAPANESE NAVAL CONTROL AREA

(9.)

**1942.** Various stamps optd with T 9.
(a) On Netherlands Indies stamps of 1933.

89 46 1 c. violet .. .. 40 1·60
90 2 c. purple .. .. 40 1·60
91 2½ c. bistre .. .. 30 1·40
92 3 c. green .. .. 40 2·00
83 4 c. green .. .. 7·00 11·00
84 5 c. blue .. .. 8·50 13·00
95 47 10 c. red .. .. 24·00 32·00
96 15 c. blue .. .. 3·75 5·50
97 20 c. purple .. .. 80 3·00
98 25 c. green .. .. 2·50 5·50
86 30 c. blue .. .. 10·00 16·00
100 35 c. violet .. .. 80 3·00
101 40 c. green .. .. 80 3·00
88 50 c. blue .. .. 25·00 38·00
102 80 c. red .. .. 28·00 42·00
103 1 g. violet .. ..
104 2 g. green .. ..
105 5 g. bistre .. ..

(b) On Nos. 270 and 360 of Netherlands Indies.

107 – 5 c. blue .. .. 40 1·40
106 48 30 c. blue .. .. £110 £150

(c) On Nos. 429/44 of Netherlands Indies.

108 – 10 c. red .. .. 1·25 1·60
110 – 15 c. blue .. .. 55 2·25
111 – 17½ c. orange .. .. 65 2·25
112 – 20 c. mauve .. .. 18·00 27·00
113 – 25 c. green .. .. 16·00 25·00
114 – 30 c. brown .. .. 80 2·00
115 – 35 c. purple .. .. 42·00 50·00
116 – 40 c. green .. .. 16·00 25·00
117 – 50 c. red .. .. 2·50 3·50
118 – 60 c. blue .. .. 3·00 5·50
119 – 80 c. red .. .. 3·00 5·50
120 – 1 g. violet .. .. 2·50 4·75
121 – 2 g. green .. .. 20·00 32·00
122 – 5 g. brown .. ..
123 68 2 g. orange .. ..

(d) On Nos. 462/6 of Netherlands Indies.

124 – 2½ c. purple .. .. 3·75 6·00
125 – 3 c. green .. .. 1·60 3·25
126 71 4 c. green .. .. 60 2·25
127 – 5 c. blue .. .. 2·50 6·00
128 – 7½ c. violet .. .. 45 2·25

(e) On Nos. 506 and 509 of Netherlands.

129 94 5 c. green .. ..
130 12½ c. blue .. ..

**1943.** Air. Nos. 89 and 91 surch.

148 46 "f. 2" on 1 c. violet .. 9·00 14·00
149 "f. 8.50" on 2½ c. bistre 12·00 18·00

10. Japanese Flag and Palms.

11. Mt. Fuji, Flag and Bird.

**1943.**

152 10 2 c. brown .. .. 30 85
153 3 c. green .. .. 30 85
154 3½ c. orange .. .. 30 85
155 5 c. blue .. .. 30 85
156 10 c. red .. .. 30 85
157 15 c. blue .. .. 50 1·00
158 20 c. violet .. .. 50 1·00
159 11 25 c. orange .. .. 1·40 2·00
160 30 c. blue .. .. 1·75 2·50
161 50 c. green .. .. 4·50 7·00
162 1 g. purple .. .. 13·00 18·00

POSTAGE DUE STAMPS

**1942.** Netherlands Indies Postage Due stamps of 1913 and 1937 optd with T 9.

D142 1 c. orange .. .. 2·75 5·50
D132 2½ c. orange .. .. 50 1·10
D133 3½ c. orange .. .. 2·50 5·50
D134 5 c. orange .. .. 1·00 2·00
D135 7½ c. orange .. .. 1·00 2·00
D136 10 c. orange .. .. 60 1·75
D144 15 c. orange .. .. 1·00 2·00
D137 20 c. orange .. .. 1·00 2·00
D138 20 c. on 37½ c. orange .. 9·00 14·00
D139 25 c. orange .. .. 1·00 2·25
D140 30 c. orange .. .. 1·00 2·25
D146 40 c. orange .. .. 1·00 2·00
D147 1 g. blue .. .. 3·75 6·50

## JAPANESE OCCUPATION OF PHILIPPINES Pt. 22

100 centavos or sentimos = 1 peso.

**1942.** Stamps of Philippines optd with bars or surch also.

J 1 104 2 c. green .. .. 10 10
J 4a – 5 c. on 6 c. brown (No. 526) .. 10 10
J 2 – 12 c. black (No. 529) .. 10 15
J 3 – 16 c. blue (No. 530) .. 3·50 2·50
J 5 – 16 c. on 30 c. red (No. 505) .. 20 20
J 6 – 50 c. on 1 p. black and orange (No. 534) .. 50 55
J 7 – 1 p. on 4 p. black and blue (No. 508) .. 55·00 42·00

**1942.** No. 460 of Philippines surch **CONGRATULATIONS FALL OF BATAAN AND CORREGIDOR 1942.**

J 8. 2 c. on 4 c. green .. .. 2·25 2·25

J 4. Agricultural Produce.

**1942.** Red Cross Fund.

J 9. J 4. 2 c. + 1 c. violet .. 15 15
J 10. 5 c. + 1 c. green .. 15 15
J 11. 16 c. + 2 c. orange .. 9·00 8·00

**1942.** 1st Anniv of "Greater East Asia War". No. 460 of Philippines surch with native characters, **12-8-1942** and **5**.

J12 5 c. on 4 c. green .. .. 40 35

**1943.** 1st Anniv of Philippine Executive Commission. Nos. 566 and 569 of Philippines surch with native characters, **1-23-43** and values.

J 13. 105. 2 c. on 8 c. red .. 30 30
J 14. 5 c. on 1 p. sepia .. 45 45

J 7. Nipa Hut. J 9. Mts. Mayon and Fuji.

**1943.**

J 15. J 7. 1 c. orange .. .. 10 10
J 16. – 2 c. green .. .. 10 10
J 17. J 7. 4 c. green .. .. 10 10
J 18. J 9. 5 c. brown .. .. 10 10
J 19. – 6 c. red .. .. 10 10
J 20. J 9. 10 c. blue .. .. 10 10
J 21. – 12 c. blue .. .. 70 70
J 22. – 16 c. brown .. .. 10 10
J 23. J 7. 20 c. purple .. .. 75 85
J 24. J 9. 21 c. violet .. .. 30 30
J 25. – 25 c. brown .. .. 10 10
J 26. J 9. 1 p. red .. .. 20 15
J 27. – 2 p. purple .. .. 2·00 2·00
J 28. – 5 p. olive .. .. 4·75 4·00

DESIGNS—VERT. 2, 6, 25 c. Rice planter. 12, 16c., 2 p., 5 p. Morro vinta (sailing canoe).

J 11. Map of Manila Bay.

J 13. Filipino Girl.

**1943.** 1st Anniv. of Fall of Bataan and Corregidor.

J 29. J 11. 2 c. red .. .. 20 20
J 30. 5 c. green .. .. 20 20

**1943.** 350th Anniv of Printing in the Philippines. No. 531 of Philippines surch **Limbagan 1593–1943** and value.

J 31. 12 c. on 20 c. bistre 25 25

**1943.** Japanese Declaration of the "Independence of the Philippines". Imperf or perf.

J 32. J 13. 5 c. blue .. .. 15 15
J 33. 12 c. orange .. .. 15 15
J 34. 17 c. red .. .. 15 15

**1943.** Luzon Flood Relief. Surch. **BAHA 1943** + and premium.

J 36. – 12 c. + 21 c. blue (No. J 21) .. 15 15
J 37. J 7. 20 c. + 36 c. purple .. 10 10
J 38. J 9. 21 c. + 40 c. violet .. 10 10

J 17. Rev. Jose Burgos.

J 24. Jose P. Laurel.

**1944.** National Heroes. Imperf. or perf.

J 39. – 5 c. blue (Rizal) .. 20 20
J 40. J 17. 12 c. red .. .. 10 10
J 41. – 17 c. orange (Mabini) 15 15

**1944.** 2nd Anniv of Fall of Bataan and Corregidor. Nos. 567/8 of Philippines surch **REPUBLIKA NG PILIPINAS 5-7-44** and value.

J 43. 105. 5 c. on 20 c. blue .. 45 45
J 44. 12 c. on 60 c. green 95 95

**1945.** 1st Anniv of Republican Government. Imperf.

J 45. J 24. 5 s. brown .. .. 10 10
J 46. 7 s. green .. .. 10 10
J 47. 20 s. blue .. .. 10 10

POSTAGE DUE STAMP

**1942.** Postage Due stamp of Philippines surch **3 CVOS 3** and bar.

JD 9. D 51. 3 c. on 4 c. red .. 18·00 8·00

OFFICIAL STAMPS

**1943.** Stamps of Philippines optd variously with bars, **(K.P.)** in Roman and Japanese characters or surch also.

JO 29. 104. 2 c. green (No. 563) .. 10 10
JO 30. – 5 c. on 6 c. brn. (No. 526) 15 15
JO 32. – 16 c. on 30 c. red (No. 505) .. .. 40 40

**1944.** No. 526 of Philippines surch **5 REPUBLIKA NG PILIPINAS (K.P.)** and four bars.

JO 45. – 5 c. on 6 c. brown .. 10 10

**1944.** Official stamp of Philippines (No. 531 optd **O.B.**), optd **Pilipinas REPUBLIKA K.P.** and bars.

JO 46. – 20 c. bistre .. .. 30 30

**1944.** Air stamp of Philippines optd **REPUBLIKA NG PILIPINAS (K.P.)** and two bars.

JO 47. 105. 1 p. sepia .. .. 85 90

## JAPANESE POST OFFICES IN CHINA Pt. 17

Post Offices at Shanghai and other Treaty Ports operated between 1876 and 1922.

10 rin = 1 sen; 100 sen = 1 yen.

(1.)

**1900.** Stamps of Japan, 1899, optd. with T 1.

1. 28. 5 r. grey .. .. 4·50 5·00
2 ½ s. grey .. .. 3·25 1·75
3. 1 s. brown .. .. 3·50 1·25
4. 1½ s. blue .. .. 10·00 4·00
5. 1½ s. lilac .. .. 5·50 1·50
6. 2 s. green .. .. 6·00 1·50
7. 3 s. purple .. .. 7·00 1·00
8. 3 s. red .. .. 4·50 1·00
9. 4 s. red .. .. 7·00 2·25
10. 5 s. yellow .. .. 16·00 2·25
11. 29. 6 s. red .. .. 20·00 16·00
12. 8 s. olive .. .. 13·00 15·00
13. 10 s. blue .. .. 11·00 1·00
14. 15 s. violet .. .. 20·00 2·00
15. 20 s. red .. .. 20·00 1·25
16. 30. 25 s. green .. .. 40·00 10·00
17. 50 s. brown .. .. 45·00 2·00
18. 31. 1 y. red .. .. 75·00 3·00
19. 32. 5 y. green .. .. £475 75·00
20. 10 y. violet .. .. £750 £130

**1900.** Imperial Wedding issue of Japan optd. with T 1.

21. 33. 3 s. red .. .. 50·00 35·00

**1913.** Stamps of Japan, 1913, optd. with T 1.

33. 36. ½ s. brown .. .. 3·00 2·00
34. 1 s. orange .. .. 3·00 2·00
35. 1½ s. blue .. .. 3·25 2·00
36. 2 s. green .. .. 4·25 2·00
37. 3 s. red .. .. 3·00 1·00
38. 37. 4 s. red .. .. 12·00 10·00
39. 5 s. violet .. .. 16·00 3·00
40. 6 s. brown .. .. 30·00 30·00
41. 8 s. grey .. .. 40·00 40·00
42. 10 s. blue .. .. 15·00 2·00
43. 20 s. red .. .. 35·00 6·00
44. 25 s. olive .. .. 45·00 8·00
45. 38. 30 s. brown .. .. 75·00 50·00
46. 50 s. brown .. .. £100 50·00
47. 1 y. green and brown £140 10·00
48. 5 y. green .. .. £1500 £600
49. 10 y. violet .. .. £2500 £1500

## JAPANESE POST OFFICES IN KOREA Pt. 18

10 rin = 1 sen; 100 sen = 1 yen.

(1.)

**1900.** Stamps of Japan, 1899, optd with T 1.

1 28 5 r. grey .. .. 12·00 10·00
2 1 s. brown .. .. 18·00 6·50
3a 1½ s. blue .. .. £225 £140
4 2 s. green .. .. 24·00 16·00
5 3 s. purple .. .. 16·00 6·00
6 4 s. red .. .. 70·00 30·00
7 5 s. yellow .. .. 60·00 30·00
8 29 8 s. green .. .. £225 £160
9 10 s. blue .. .. 30·00 3·00
10 15 s. purple .. .. 75·00 6·00
11 20 s. orange .. .. 75·00 5·00
12 30 25 s. green .. .. £200 50·00
13 50 s. brown .. .. £150 18·00
14 31 1 y. red .. .. £400 14·00

**1900.** Wedding of Prince Imperial. No. 152 of Japan optd with T 1.

15 33 3 s. red .. .. 90·00 22·00

**HAVE YOU READ THE NOTES AT THE BEGINNING OF THIS CATALOGUE?**
These often provide answers to the enquiries we receive.

## JORDAN Pt. 19

A territory to the E. of Israel, formerly called Transjordan; under British mandate from 1918 to 1946. Independent kingdom since 1946.

1920. 1000 milliemes = 100 piastres = £1 Egyptian.
1927. 1000 milliemes = £1 Palestinian.
1950. 1000 fils = 1 Jordan dinar.

شرق الاردن

(1. "East of Jordan".)

**1920.** Stamps of Palestine optd. with T 1.

| No. | Type | Description | Mint | Used |
|---|---|---|---|---|
| 1 | 3 | 1 m. brown | 50 | 1·25 |
| 10 | | 2 m. green | 50 | 70 |
| 3 | | 3 m. brown | 90 | 1·25 |
| 4 | | 4 m. red | 95 | 1·25 |
| 5 | | 5 m. orange | 80 | 1·25 |
| 5a | | 1 p. blue | 80 | 1·25 |
| 15 | | 2 p. olive | 3·00 | 3·00 |
| 16 | | 5 p. purple | 2·25 | 6·00 |
| 17 | | 9 p. ochre | 3·50 | 18·00 |
| 18 | | 10 p. blue | 4·00 | 18·00 |
| 19 | | 20 p. grey | 8·00 | 30·00 |

(2.) (Tenth of a piastre). (3.) (Piastre).

**1922.** Handstamped with T 2 or 3 (piastre values). (a) 1920 issue of Jordan (No. 1 etc)

| No. | Type | Description | Mint | Used |
|---|---|---|---|---|
| 28. | 2. | 1/10 p. on 1 m. brown | 20·00 | 25·00 |
| 29. | | 2/10 p. on 2 m. green | 25·00 | 25·00 |
| 22. | | 3/10 p. on 3 m. brown | 10·00 | 10·00 |
| 23. | | 4/10 p. on 4 m. red | 50·00 | 50·00 |
| 24. | | 5/10 p. on 5 m. orange | £180 | £100 |
| 31. | 3. | 1 p. on 1 p. blue | £200 | 60·00 |
| 25. | | 2 p. on 2 p. olive | £250 | 75·00 |
| 26. | | 5 p. on 5 p. purple | 50·00 | 70·00 |
| 27a. | | 9 p. on 9 p. ochre | £130 | £140 |
| 33. | | 10 p. on 10 p. blue | £850 | £1000 |
| 34. | | 20 p. on 20 p. grey | £650 | £950 |

(b) Type 3 of Palestine

| No. | Type | Description | Mint | Used |
|---|---|---|---|---|
| 35 | 3 | 10 p. on 10 p. blue | £1800 | £2500 |
| 36 | | 20 p. on 20 p. grey | £2500 | £3000 |

(4. "Arab Government of the East, April, 1921".)

**1922.** Stamps of Jordan handstamped with T 4.

| No. | Type | Description | Mint | Used |
|---|---|---|---|---|
| 45. | 3. | 1 m. brown | 12·00 | 15·00 |
| 46a. | | 2 m. green | 8·00 | 8·00 |
| 39b. | | 3 m. brown | 7·00 | 7·00 |
| 40. | | 4 m. red | 45·00 | 50·00 |
| 41a. | | 5 m. orange | 15·00 | 10·00 |
| 48a. | | 1 p. blue | 15·00 | 9·00 |
| 42b. | | 2 p. olive | 12·00 | 10·00 |
| 43a. | | 5 p. purple | 60·00 | 80·00 |
| 44b. | | 9 p. ochre | 65·00 | 80·00 |
| 52a. | | 10 p. blue | £1100 | £1600 |
| 53a. | | 20 p. grey | £1100 | £1800 |

حكومة الشرق
العربية
يسان سنة ٩٢١

(5. "Arab Government of the East, April, 1921".)

**1923.** Stamps of Jordan optd. with T 5

| No. | Type | Description | Mint | Used |
|---|---|---|---|---|
| 62. | 3. | 1 m. brown | 18·00 | 24·00 |
| 63. | | 2 m. green | 15·00 | 18·00 |
| 56. | | 3 m. brown | 12·00 | 15·00 |
| 57. | | 4 m. red | 10·00 | 12·00 |
| 64. | | 5 m. orange | 12·00 | 12·00 |
| 65. | | 1 p. blue | 12·00 | 14·00 |
| 59. | | 2 p. olive | 15·00 | 15·00 |
| 60. | | 5 p. purple | 60·00 | 80·00 |
| 66. | | 9 p. ochre | 75·00 | £100 |
| 67. | | 10 p. blue | 75·00 | £100 |
| 68. | | 20 p. grey | 75·00 | £100 |

(6.) (7.)

(8.) (9.)

**1923.** Various stamps surch as T 6/9.

(a) No. 5 of Jordan

| No. | Type | Description | Mint | Used |
|---|---|---|---|---|
| 70 | – | 2½/10ths p. on 5 m. | £160 | £160 |
| 70c | 6 | 5/10 p. on 5 m. | | |

(b) No. 7 of Palestine

| No. | Type | Description | Mint | Used |
|---|---|---|---|---|
| 71 | 6 | 5/10 p. on 3 m. | £7500 | |

(c) 1922 issue of Jordan (Nos. 22 etc)

| No. | Type | Description | Mint | Used |
|---|---|---|---|---|
| 72 | 6 | 5/10 p. on 3 m. | £7000 | |
| 73 | | 5/10 p. on 5 p. | 70·00 | 8·00 |
| 73b | | 5/10 p. on 9 p. | £800 | £850 |
| 74 | 7 | 1/2 p. on 5 p. | 70·00 | 80·00 |
| 75a | | 1/2 p. on 9 p. | £350 | £400 |
| 77 | 8 | 1 p. on 5 p. | 80·00 | £100 |

(d) 1922 issue of Jordan (Nos. 396 etc)

| No. | Type | Description | Mint | Used |
|---|---|---|---|---|
| 78b | 6 | 5/10 p. on 3 m. | 40·00 | 50·00 |
| 79 | | 5/10 p. on 5 p. | 8·00 | 14·00 |
| 79d | | 5/10 p. on 9 p. | — | £1200 |
| 80c | 7 | 1/8 p. on 2 p. | 60·00 | £110 |
| 82 | | 1/8 p. on 5 p. | £1800 | |
| 83b | 8 | 1 p. on 5 p. | £2000 | £2250 |

(e) 1923 issue of Jordan (Nos. 56 etc)

| No. | Type | Description | Mint | Used |
|---|---|---|---|---|
| 84 | 6 | 5/10 p. on 3 m. | 25·00 | 30·00 |
| 85 | 7 | 1/8 p. on 9 p. | 90·00 | £150 |
| 87 | 9 | 1 p. on 10 p. | £2250 | £2500 |
| 88 | | 2 p. on 20 p. | 60·00 | 80·00 |

حكومة
الشرق العربية
٩ شعبان ١٣٤١

(10. "Arab Government of the East, 9 Sha'ban, 1341".)

**1923.** Stamps of Saudi Arabia optd with T 10.

| No. | Type | Description | Mint | Used |
|---|---|---|---|---|
| 89 | 11 | 1/8 p. brown | 2·00 | 1·75 |
| 96 | | 1/4 on 1/8 p. brown (47) | 4·00 | 5·00 |
| 90 | | 1/8 p. red | 2·00 | 1·75 |
| 91 | | 1 p. blue | 1·25 | 80 |
| 92 | | 1½ p. lilac | 1·50 | 1·75 |
| 93 | | 2 p. orange | 2·00 | 5·00 |
| 94 | | 3 p. brown | 3·00 | 7·00 |
| 95 | | 5 p. green | 5·00 | 8·00 |
| 97 | | 10 on 5 p. green (49) | 15·00 | 20·00 |

(11. "Arab Government of the East, Commemoration of Independence, 25 May, 1923".)

**1923.** Stamps of Palestine optd. with T 11.

| No. | Type | Description | Mint | Used |
|---|---|---|---|---|
| 98 | 3 | 1 m. brown | 17·00 | 17·00 |
| 99 | | 2 m. green | 28·00 | 35·00 |
| 100 | | 3 m. brown | 10·00 | 12·00 |
| 101 | | 4 m. red | 10·00 | 12·00 |
| 102 | | 5 m. orange | 50·00 | 60·00 |
| 103 | | 1 p. blue | 50·00 | 60·00 |
| 104 | | 2 p. olive | 50·00 | 70·00 |
| 105 | | 5 p. purple | 60·00 | 70·00 |
| 106 | | 9 p. ochre | 50·00 | 60·00 |
| 107 | | 10 p. blue | 60·00 | 80·00 |
| 108 | | 20 p. grey | 70·00 | 90·00 |

**1923.** No. 107 surch with T 9.

| No. | Type | Description | Mint | Used |
|---|---|---|---|---|
| 109 | | 1 p. on 10 p. blue | £6000 | |

نصف قرش

(12.)

**1923.** No. 92 surch with T 12.

| No. | Type | Description | Mint | Used |
|---|---|---|---|---|
| 110 | | ½ p. on 1½ p. lilac | 6·00 | 6·00 |

حكومة
الشرق العربية
٩ شعبان ١٣٤١

(13. "Arab Government of the East, 9 Sha'ban, 1341".)

**1923.** Stamp of Saudi Arabia handstamped as T 13.

| No. | Type | Description | Mint | Used |
|---|---|---|---|---|
| 112. | 11. | ½ p. red | 6·00 | 7·00 |

(15. "Arab Government of the East".)

**1924.** Stamps of Saudi Arabia optd. with T 15.

| No. | Type | Description | Mint | Used |
|---|---|---|---|---|
| 114. | 11. | ½ p. red | 6·00 | 8·00 |
| 115. | | 1 p. blue | £300 | £200 |
| 116. | | 1½ p. violet | £350 | |

ملك العرب

(16. "Commemorating the coming of His Majesty the King of the Arabs" and date.)

**1924.** Stamps of Saudi Arabia optd. with T 15 and 16.

| No. | Type | Description | Mint | Used |
|---|---|---|---|---|
| 117. | 11. | ½ p. red | 1·00 | 1·00 |
| 118. | | 1 p. blue | 1·25 | 1·25 |
| 119. | | 1½ p. violet | 2·00 | 2·00 |
| 120. | | 2 p. orange | 4·00 | 4·00 |

حكومة الشرق
العربي
١٣٤٢

(17. "Government of the Arab East, 1342".)

**1924.** Stamps of Saudi Arabia optd with T 17.

| No. | Type | Description | Mint | Used |
|---|---|---|---|---|
| 125 | 11 | 1/8 p. brown | 35 | 25 |
| 126 | | 1/4 p. green | 30 | 30 |
| 127 | | 1/4 p. red | 30 | 30 |
| 129 | | 1 p. blue | 2·50 | 1·50 |
| 130 | | 1½ p. lilac | 2·50 | 2·50 |
| 131 | | 2 p. orange | 2·00 | 2·00 |
| 132 | | 3 p. red | 1·50 | 1·50 |
| 133 | | 5 p. green | 2·00 | 2·50 |
| 134 | | 10 p. purple and mauve | 4·00 | 5·00 |

(18. "Government of the Arab East, 1343".)

**1925.** Stamps as T 20 of Saudi Arabia optd. with T 18.

| No. | Type | Description | Mint | Used |
|---|---|---|---|---|
| 135 | | 1/8 p. brown | 30 | 60 |
| 136 | | ¼ p. blue | 30 | 60 |
| 137 | | ½ p. red | 40 | 35 |
| 138 | | 1 p. green | 40 | 35 |
| 139 | | 1½ p. orange | 90 | 1·50 |
| 140 | | 2 p. blue | 1·25 | 1·75 |
| 141 | | 3 p. green | 1·50 | 2·75 |
| 142 | | 5 p. brown | 2·00 | 6·00 |

شرق
الاردن

(19. "East of the Jordan".)

**1925.** Stamps of Palestine (without Palestine opt) optd with T 19.

| No. | Type | Description | Mint | Used |
|---|---|---|---|---|
| 143. | 3. | 1 m. brown | 10 | 15 |
| 144. | | 2 m. yellow | 10 | 15 |
| 145. | | 3 m. blue | 10 | 15 |
| 146. | | 4 m. red | 10 | 15 |
| 147. | | 5 m. orange | 10 | 15 |
| 148. | | 6 m. green | 15 | 20 |
| 149. | | 7 m. brown | 15 | 20 |
| 150. | | 8 m. red | 20 | 30 |
| 151. | | 13 m. blue | 50 | 60 |
| 152. | | 1 p. grey | 50 | 50 |
| 153. | | 2 p. olive | 75 | 80 |
| 154. | | 5 p. purple | 3·00 | 3·50 |
| 155. | | 9 p. ochre | 6·00 | 7·00 |
| 156. | | 10 p. blue | 11·00 | 12·00 |
| 157. | | 20 p. violet | 20·00 | 23·00 |

22. Emir Abdullah. 23.

**1927.** Figures at left and right.

| No. | Type | Description | Mint | Used |
|---|---|---|---|---|
| 159. | 22. | 2 m. blue | 15 | 30 |
| 160. | | 3 m. red | 20 | 30 |
| 161. | | 4 m. green | 50 | 90 |
| 162. | | 5 m. orange | 25 | 30 |
| 163. | | 10 m. red | 50 | 60 |
| 164. | | 15 m. blue | 60 | 30 |
| 165. | | 20 m. olive | 80 | 90 |
| 166. | 23. | 50 m. purple | 2·50 | 3·25 |
| 167. | | 90 m. brown | 5·50 | 9·00 |
| 168. | | 100 m. blue | 8·00 | 6·50 |
| 169. | | 200 m. violet | 17·00 | 22·00 |
| 170. | | 500 m. brown | 60·00 | 85·00 |
| 171. | | 1000 m. grey | £100 | £140 |

(24. "Constitution".)

**1928.** Optd. with T 24.

| No. | Type | Description | Mint | Used |
|---|---|---|---|---|
| 172. | 22. | 2 m. blue | 80 | 1·75 |
| 173. | | 3 m. red | 90 | 2·50 |
| 174. | | 4 m. green | 1·00 | 2·75 |
| 175. | | 5 m. orange | 1·00 | 1·60 |
| 176. | | 10 m. red | 1·50 | 3·25 |
| 177. | | 15 m. blue | 1·50 | 1·50 |
| 178. | | 20 m. olive | 3·00 | 7·00 |
| 179. | 23. | 50 m. purple | 5·00 | 8·00 |
| 180. | | 90 m. brown | 13·00 | 35·00 |
| 181. | | 100 m. blue | 22·00 | 40·00 |
| 182. | | 200 m. violet | 65·00 | £100 |

**1930.** "Locust campaign". Optd **LOCUST CAMPAIGN** in English and Arabic.

| No. | Type | Description | Mint | Used |
|---|---|---|---|---|
| 183. | 22. | 2 m. blue | 1·10 | 3·50 |
| 184. | | 3 m. red | 1·50 | 3·50 |
| 185. | | 4 m. green | 1·50 | 4·00 |
| 186. | | 5 m. orange | 13·00 | 14·00 |
| 187. | | 10 m. red | 1·50 | 4·00 |
| 188. | | 15 m. blue | 1·50 | 2·25 |
| 189. | | 20 m. olive | 1·50 | 4·00 |
| 190. | 23. | 50 m. purple | 5·00 | 8·50 |
| 191. | | 90 m. brown | 10·00 | 35·00 |
| 192. | | 100 m. blue | 12·00 | 35·00 |
| 193. | | 200 m. violet | 30·00 | 80·00 |
| 194. | | 500 m. brown | 75·00 | £140 |

28. Emir. 29. Emir.

**1930.**

| No. | Type | Description | Mint | Used |
|---|---|---|---|---|
| 230 | 28 | 1 m. brown | 20 | 75 |
| 195 | | 2 m. green | 30 | 50 |
| 258 | | 3 m. pink | 15 | 15 |
| 196a | | 3 m. green | 70 | 85 |
| 259 | | 4 m. green | 15 | 15 |
| 233 | | 4 m. pink | 1·75 | 1·25 |
| 198 | | 5 m. orange | 40 | 40 |
| 199 | | 10 m. red | 70 | 15 |
| 260 | | 10 m. violet | 15 | 15 |
| 261 | | 12 m. red | 35 | 30 |
| 200 | | 15 m. blue | 65 | 20 |
| 262 | | 15 m. green | 40 | 40 |
| 201 | | 20 m. green | 1·25 | 35 |
| 263 | | 20 m. blue | 45 | 45 |
| 202 | 29 | 50 m. purple | 1·50 | 1·25 |
| 203 | | 90 m. bistre | 2·50 | 4·25 |
| 240 | | 100 m. blue | 5·00 | 1·75 |
| 241 | | 200 m. violet | 9·00 | 5·50 |
| 242 | | 500 m. brown | 13·00 | 12·00 |
| 243 | | £P1 grey | 24·00 | 20·00 |

30. Mushetta. 32. The Khasneh at Petra.

**1933.**

| No. | Type | Description | Mint | Used |
|---|---|---|---|---|
| 208. | 30. | 1 m. black and purple | 40 | 1·10 |
| 209. | – | 2 m. black and red | 40 | 75 |
| 210. | – | 3 m. green | 50 | 1·25 |
| 211. | – | 4 m. black and brown | 75 | 2·00 |
| 212. | – | 5 m. black and orange | 80 | 1·25 |
| 213. | – | 10 m. red | 1·50 | 2·75 |
| 214. | 32. | 15 m. blue | 2·50 | 1·25 |
| 215. | – | 20 m. black and olive | 3·25 | 4·50 |
| 216. | – | 50 m. black and purple | 8·50 | 10·00 |
| 217. | 30. | 90 m. black and yellow | 12·00 | 22·00 |
| 218. | – | 100 m. black and blue | 12·00 | 22·00 |
| 219. | – | 200 m. black and violet | 45·00 | 60·00 |
| 220. | 32. | 500 m. red and brown | £130 | £170 |
| 221. | – | $P1 black and green | £350 | £550 |

DESIGNS—HORIZ. 2 m. Nymphaeum, Jerash. 3 m., 90 m. Kasr Kharana. 4 m. Kerak Castle. 5 m., 100 m. Temple of Artemis, Jerash. 10 m., 200 m. Ajlun Castle. 20 m. Allenby Bridge over Jordan. 50 m. Threshing. VERT. £P1, Emir Abdullah. Nos. 216 to 221 are larger (33½ × 24 mm. or 24 × 33½ mm.).

35. Map of Jordan. 39. Parliament Building.

**1946.** Installation of King Abdullah and National Independence.

| No. | Type | Description | Mint | Used |
|---|---|---|---|---|
| 249. | 35. | 1 m. purple | 10 | 10 |
| 250. | | 2 m. orange | 10 | 10 |
| 251. | | 3 m. green | 10 | 10 |
| 252. | | 4 m. violet | 10 | 10 |
| 253. | | 10 m. brown | 15 | 15 |
| 254. | | 12 m. red | 15 | 15 |
| 255. | | 20 m. blue | 20 | 20 |
| 256. | | 50 m. blue | 40 | 40 |
| 257. | | 200 m. green | 1·60 | 2·00 |

**1947.** Inaug. of 1st National Parliament.

| No. | Type | Description | Mint | Used |
|---|---|---|---|---|
| 276. | 39. | 1 m. violet | 10 | 20 |
| 277. | | 3 m. red | 10 | 20 |
| 278. | | 4 m. green | 10 | 20 |
| 279. | | 10 m. purple | 10 | 20 |
| 280. | | 12 m. red | 10 | 20 |
| 281. | | 20 m. blue | 10 | 20 |
| 282. | | 50 m. red | 40 | 40 |
| 283. | | 100 m. pink | 75 | 90 |
| 284. | | 200 m. green | 1·50 | 1·50 |

40. Globe and Forms of Transport. 44. Lockheed Constellation Airliner and Globe.

**1949.** 75th Anniv. of U.P.U.

| No. | Type | Description | Mint | Used |
|---|---|---|---|---|
| 285. | 40. | 1 m. brown | 15 | 35 |
| 286. | | 4 m. green | 25 | 30 |
| 287. | | 10 m. red | 30 | 55 |
| 288. | | 20 m. blue | 50 | 65 |
| 289. | – | 50 m. green | 1·10 | 1·40 |

DESIGN: 50 m. King Abdullah.

**1950.** Air.

| | | | | |
|---|---|---|---|---|
| 295. | 44. | 5 f. purple and yellow | 40 | 25 |
| 296. | | 10 f. brown and violet .. | 40 | 25 |
| 297. | | 15 f. red and olive .. | 40 | 40 |
| 298. | | 20 f. black and blue .. | 50 | 40 |
| 299. | | 50 f. green and mauve | 90 | 75 |
| 300. | | 100 f. brown and blue .. | 1·25 | 90 |
| 301. | | 150 f. orange and black | 2·25 | 1·50 |

**1952.** Optd **FILS** and bars or **J.D.** (on 1 d.).

| | | | | |
|---|---|---|---|---|
| 313 | 28 | 1 f. on 1 m. brown .. | 25 | 25 |
| 314 | | 2 f. on 2 m. green .. | 25 | 25 |
| 315 | | 3 f. on 3 m. green .. | 20·00 | |
| 316 | | 3 f. on 3 m. pink .. | 25 | 25 |
| 310 | | 4 f. on 4 m. pink .. | 6·00 | 2·75 |
| 318 | | 4 f. on 4 m. green .. | 25 | 25 |
| 319 | | 5 f. on 5 m. orange .. | 30 | 30 |
| 320 | | 10 f. on 10 m. red .. | 22·00 | |
| 321 | | 10 f. on 10 m. violet .. | 30 | 30 |
| 322 | | 12 f. on 12 m. red .. | 30 | 30 |
| 312 | | 15 f. on 15 m. blue .. | 20·00 | 10·00 |
| 325 | | 15 f. on 15 m. green .. | 45 | 30 |
| 326 | | 20 f. on 20 m. green .. | 23·00 | |
| 327 | | 20 f. on 20 m. blue .. | 1·00 | 50 |
| 328 | 29 | 50 f. on 50 m. purple .. | 80 | 70 |
| 329 | | 90 f. on 90 m. bistre .. | 7·00 | 4·50 |
| 330 | | 100 f. on 100 m. blue .. | 4·00 | 1·75 |
| 331 | | 200 f. on 200 m. violet .. | 6·50 | 2·50 |
| 332 | | 500 f. on 500 m. brown | 15·00 | 4·50 |
| 333 | | 1 d. on £P1 grey .. | 30·00 | 8·00 |

**48.** Dome of the Rock and Khazneh at Petra. **49.** King Abdullah.

**1952.** Unification of Jordan and Palestine.

| | | | | |
|---|---|---|---|---|
| 355. | 48. | 1 f. green and brown .. | 20 | 20 |
| 356. | | 2 f. red and green .. | 20 | 20 |
| 357. | | 3 f. black and red .. | 20 | 20 |
| 358. | | 4 f. orange and green .. | 20 | 20 |
| 359. | | 5 f. purple and brown | 25 | 25 |
| 360. | | 10 f. brown and violet .. | 25 | 25 |
| 361. | | 20 f. black and blue .. | 65 | 35 |
| 362. | | 100 f. sepia and brown .. | 2·50 | 1·75 |
| 363. | | 200 f. orange and violet | 5·75 | 3·25 |

**1952.**

(a) Size 18×21½ mm.

| | | | | |
|---|---|---|---|---|
| 364. | 49. | 5 f. orange .. .. | 20 | 20 |
| 365. | | 10 f. lilac .. .. | 20 | 20 |
| 366. | | 12 f. red .. .. | 75 | 50 |
| 367. | | 15 f. olive .. .. | 45 | 20 |
| 368. | | 20 f. blue .. .. | 50 | 25 |

(b) Size 20×24½ mm.

| | | | | |
|---|---|---|---|---|
| 369. | 49. | 50 f. purple .. .. | 1·10 | 45 |
| 370. | | 90 f. brown .. .. | 3·25 | 1·75 |
| 371. | | 100 f. blue .. .. | 3·50 | 95 |

**1953.** Optd with two horiz bars across Arabic commemorative inscription.

| | | | | |
|---|---|---|---|---|
| 378 | 48 | 1 f. green and brown .. | 20 | 20 |
| 379 | | 2 f. red and green .. | 20 | 20 |
| 380 | | 3 f. black and red .. | 20 | 20 |
| 381 | | 4 f. orange and green .. | 20 | 20 |
| 382 | | 5 f. purple and brown .. | 20 | 20 |
| 383 | | 10 f. brown and violet .. | 65 | 35 |
| 384 | | 20 f. black and blue .. | 65 | 50 |
| 385 | | 100 f. brown and blue .. | 3·50 | 1·00 |
| 386 | | 200 f. orange and violet | 5·00 | 3·50 |

**51.** Omar Mosque, Jerusalem. **51a.** King Hussein.

**1953.** Obligatory Tax stamps optd for postal use as in T **51**. (a) Inscr "MILS"

| | | | | |
|---|---|---|---|---|
| 387 | T 36 | 1 m. blue .. .. | 20 | 20 |
| 388 | – | 3 m. green .. .. | 20 | 20 |
| 389 | | 5 m. purple .. .. | 60·00 | 55·00 |
| 390 | | 10 m. red .. .. | 18·00 | 18·00 |
| 391 | – | 15 m. black .. .. | 45 | 45 |
| 392 | – | 20 m. brown .. .. | 60·00 | 40·00 |
| 393 | – | 50 m. violet .. .. | 45 | 40 |
| 394 | – | 100 m. red .. .. | 4·75 | 3·75 |

(b) Inscr "MILS" and optd **PALESTINE**

| | | | | |
|---|---|---|---|---|
| 395 | T 36 | 1 m. blue .. .. | 25·00 | 23·00 |
| 396 | | 3 m. green .. .. | 25·00 | 23·00 |
| 397 | | 5 m. purple .. .. | 25·00 | 23·00 |
| 398 | – | 10 m. red .. .. | 25·00 | 23·00 |
| 399 | – | 15 m. black .. .. | 28·00 | 23·00 |
| 400 | – | 20 m. brown .. .. | 28·00 | 23·00 |
| 400a | – | 50 m. violet .. .. | | |
| 401 | – | 100 m. red .. .. | 40·00 | 35·00 |

(c) Inscr "MILS", optd **FILS** (T334 etc)

| | | | | |
|---|---|---|---|---|
| 402 | T 36 | 1 f. on 1 m. blue .. | 27·00 | 24·00 |
| 403 | | 3 f. on 3 m. green .. | 27·00 | 24·00 |
| 404 | – | 10 f. on 10 m. red .. | 27·00 | 24·00 |
| 405 | – | 15 f. on 15 m. black .. | 27·00 | 24·00 |
| 406 | – | 20 f. on 20 m. brown .. | 27·00 | 24·00 |
| 407 | – | 100 f. on 100 m. red .. | 30·00 | 30·00 |

(d) Inscr "FILS"

| | | | | |
|---|---|---|---|---|
| 408 | T 36 | 5 f. purple .. .. | 20 | 15 |
| 409 | – | 10 f. red .. .. | 25 | 15 |
| 410 | – | 15 f. black .. .. | 55 | 45 |
| 411 | – | 20 f. brown .. .. | 1·00 | 70 |
| 412 | – | 100 f. orange .. .. | 2·40 | 1·40 |

**1953.** Enthronement of King Hussein.

| | | | | |
|---|---|---|---|---|
| 413. | 51a. | 1 f. black and green .. | 15 | 15 |
| 414. | | 4 f. black and red .. | 15 | 10 |
| 415. | | 15 f. black and blue .. | 1·00 | 20 |
| 416. | | 20 f. black and lilac .. | 1·60 | 20 |
| 417. | | 50 f. black and green .. | 3·50 | 1·75 |
| 418. | | 100 f. black and blue .. | 7·00 | 4·75 |

**52.** El-Deir Temple, Petra. **54a.** Temple of Artemis Jerash.

**1954.**

| | | | | |
|---|---|---|---|---|
| 445 | 52 | 1 f. brn. & grn. (postage) | 10 | 10 |
| 446 | – | 2 f. black and red .. | 10 | 10 |
| 447 | 52 | 3 f. violet and purple .. | 10 | 10 |
| 448 | – | 4 f. green and brown .. | 10 | 10 |
| 449 | 52 | 5 f. green and violet .. | 15 | 10 |
| 450 | – | 10 f. green and purple .. | 20 | 10 |
| 451 | – | 12 f. sepia and red .. | 70 | 10 |
| 452 | – | 15 f. red and brown .. | 45 | 15 |
| 453 | – | 20 f. green & blue .. | 30 | 15 |
| 454 | – | 50 f. red and blue .. | 70 | 15 |
| 428 | – | 100 f. blue and green .. | 1·50 | 55 |
| 456 | – | 200 f. blue and lake .. | 4·00 | 1·25 |
| 457 | – | 500 f. purple and brown | 15·00 | 7·00 |
| 458 | – | 1 d. lake and olive .. | 23·00 | 10·00 |
| 470 | 54a | 5 f. orange and blue (air) | 15 | 10 |
| 433 | | 10 f. red and brown .. | 25 | 10 |
| 434 | | 25 f. blue and green .. | 40 | 15 |
| 435 | | 35 f. blue and mauve .. | 50 | 20 |
| 436 | | 40 f. slate and red .. | 60 | 20 |
| 437 | | 50 f. orange and blue .. | 75 | 35 |
| 438 | | 100 f. brown and blue .. | 1·00 | 75 |
| 439 | | 150 f. lake & turquoise | 1·60 | 1·00 |

DESIGNS—VERT. 2 f., 4 f., 500 f., 1 d. King Hussein. HORIZ. 10 f., 15 f., 20 f. Dome of the Rock, Jerusalem. 12 f., 50 f., 100 f., 200 f. Facade of Mosque of El Aqsa.

**1955.** Arab Postal Union. As T **80** of Egypt but inscr. "H. K. JORDAN" at top and "ARAB POSTAL UNION" at foot.

| | | | | |
|---|---|---|---|---|
| 440. | | 15 f. green .. .. | 30 | 15 |
| 441. | | 20 f. violet .. .. | 30 | 15 |
| 442. | | 25 f. brown .. .. | 40 | 30 |

**56.** King Hussein and Queen Dina.

**1955.** Royal Wedding.

| | | | | |
|---|---|---|---|---|
| 443. | 56. | 15 f. blue .. .. | 1·00 | 50 |
| 444. | | 100 f. lake .. .. | 3·50 | 2·00 |

**58.** Envelope with Postmarks in English and Arabic. **59.** " Flame of Freedom ".

**1956.** 1st Arab Postal Congress, Amman.

| | | | | |
|---|---|---|---|---|
| 459 | 58 | 1 f. brown and black .. | 10 | 10 |
| 460 | | 4 f. red and black .. | 10 | 10 |
| 461 | | 15 f. blue and black .. | 10 | 10 |
| 462 | | 20 f. bistre and black .. | 15 | 10 |
| 463 | | 50 f. blue and black .. | 45 | 30 |
| 464 | | 100 f. orange and black | 70 | 50 |

**1958.** 10th Anniv. of Declaration of Human Rights.

| | | | | |
|---|---|---|---|---|
| 476. | 59. | 5 f. red and blue .. | 10 | 10 |
| 477. | | 15 f. black and brown .. | 15 | 10 |
| 478. | | 35 f. purple and green .. | 35 | 25 |
| 479. | | 45 f. black and red .. | 50 | 30 |

**60.** King Hussein.

**1959.** Centres in black.

| | | | | |
|---|---|---|---|---|
| 480 | 60 | 1 f. green .. .. | 10 | 10 |
| 481 | | 2 f. violet .. .. | 10 | 10 |
| 482 | | 3 f. red .. .. | 20 | 10 |
| 483 | | 4 f. purple .. .. | 20 | 10 |
| 484 | | 7 f. green .. .. | 25 | 10 |
| 485 | | 12 f. red .. .. | 40 | 10 |
| 486 | | 15 f. red .. .. | 40 | 10 |
| 487 | | 21 f. green .. .. | 40 | 10 |
| 488 | | 25 f. brown .. .. | 55 | 10 |
| 489 | | 35 f. blue .. .. | 80 | 10 |
| 490 | | 40 f. green .. .. | 1·10 | 15 |
| 491 | | 50 f. red .. .. | 1·50 | 15 |
| 492 | | 100 f. green .. .. | 2·00 | 40 |
| 493 | | 200 f. purple .. .. | 5·00 | 1·50 |
| 494 | | 500 f. blue .. .. | 13·50 | 5·50 |
| 495 | | 1 d. purple .. .. | 24·00 | 14·00 |

**1960.** Inaug. of Arab League Centre, Cairo. As T **204** of Egypt but with portrait of King Hussein instead of Arms and inscr. "JORDAN".

| | | | | |
|---|---|---|---|---|
| 496. | | 15 f. black and green .. | 20 | 15 |

**62.** " Care of Refugees ".

**1960.** World Refugee Year.

| | | | | |
|---|---|---|---|---|
| 497. | 62. | 15 f. red and blue .. | 15 | 10 |
| 498. | | 35 f. blue and bistre .. | 15 | 15 |

**63.** Shah of Iran and King Hussein.

**1960.** Visit of Shah of Iran.

| | | | | |
|---|---|---|---|---|
| 499. | 63. | 15 f. multicoloured .. | 25 | 15 |
| 500. | | 35 f. multicoloured .. | 40 | 35 |
| 501. | | 50 f. multicoloured .. | 60 | 50 |

**64.** Petroleum Refinery, Zarka.

**1961.** Inaug. of Jordanian Petroleum Refinery.

| | | | | |
|---|---|---|---|---|
| 502. | 64. | 15 f. blue and violet .. | 20 | 10 |
| 503. | | 35 f. brown and violet .. | 30 | 20 |

**65.** Jordanian Families and Graph. **67.** Campaign Emblem.

**1961.** 1st Jordanian Census Commem.

| | | | | |
|---|---|---|---|---|
| 504. | 65. | 15 f. brown .. .. | 25 | 10 |

**1961.** Dag Hammarskjold Memorial Issue. Optd. **IN MEMORIAL OF DAG HAMMARSKJOELD 1904-1961** in English and Arabic and laurel leaves at top and bottom.

| | | | | |
|---|---|---|---|---|
| 505. | 62. | 15 f. red and blue .. | 1·75 | 1·75 |
| 506. | | 35 f. blue and bistre .. | 2·00 | 2·00 |

**1962.** Malaria Eradication.

| | | | | |
|---|---|---|---|---|
| 507. | 67. | 15 f. mauve .. .. | 20 | 10 |
| 508. | | 35 f. blue .. .. | 40 | 20 |

**68.** Telephone Exchange, Amman.

**1962.** Inauguration of Amman's Automatic Telephone Exchange.

| | | | | |
|---|---|---|---|---|
| 510. | 68. | 15 f. blue and purple .. | 15 | 15 |
| 511. | | 35 f. purple and green .. | 35 | 15 |

**69.** Aqaba Port and King Hussein.

**1962.** Opening of Aqaba Port.

| | | | | |
|---|---|---|---|---|
| 512. | 69. | 15 f. black and purple | 25 | 10 |
| 513. | | 35 f. black and blue .. | 60 | 25 |

**70.** Dag Hammarskjold and U.N. Headquarters.

**1963.** 17th Anniv. of U.N.O.

| | | | | |
|---|---|---|---|---|
| 515. | 70. | 15 f. red, olive & blue .. | 15 | 15 |
| 516. | | 35 f. blue, red & olive .. | 55 | 30 |
| 517. | | 50 f. olive, blue & red .. | 80 | 55 |

**71.** Church of Holy Virgin's Tomb, Jerusalem.

**1963.** "Holy Places". Multicoloured.

| | | | | |
|---|---|---|---|---|
| 519 | | 50 f. Type **71** .. .. | 85 | 85 |
| 520 | | 50 f. Basilica of the Agony, Gethsemane .. .. | 85 | 85 |
| 521 | | 50 f. Holy Sepulchre, Jerusalem .. .. | 85 | 85 |
| 522 | | 50 f. Nativity Church, Bethlehem .. .. | 85 | 85 |
| 523 | | 50 f. Haram of Ibrahim, Hebron .. .. | 85 | 85 |
| 524 | | 50 f. Dome of the Rock, Jerusalem .. .. | 85 | 85 |
| 525 | | 50 f. Omer-el-Khetab Mosque, Jerusalem .. | 85 | 85 |
| 526 | | 50 f. El-Aqsa Mosque, Jerusalem .. .. | 85 | 85 |

**1963.** Arab League. As T **231** of Egypt but inscr. "HASHEMITE KINGDOM OF JORDAN" and with inset portrait of King Hussein.

| | | | | |
|---|---|---|---|---|
| 527. | | 15 f. blue .. .. .. | 20 | 15 |
| 528. | | 35 f. red .. .. .. | 65 | 30 |

**73.** Wheat and F.A.O. Emblem. **74.** Canal and Symbols.

**1963.** Freedom from Hunger.

| | | | | |
|---|---|---|---|---|
| 529. | 73. | 15 f. green, black & blue | 15 | 10 |
| 530. | | 35 f. green, black & apple | 35 | 20 |

**1963.** East Ghor Canal Project.

| | | | | |
|---|---|---|---|---|
| 532. | 74. | 1 f. black and bistre .. | 15 | 10 |
| 533. | | 4 f. black and blue .. | 15 | 10 |
| 534. | | 5 f. black and purple .. | 15 | 10 |
| 535. | | 10 f. black and green .. | 25 | 10 |
| 536. | | 35 f. black and orange .. | 1·50 | 1·00 |

**75.** Scales of Justice and Globe.

**1963.** 15th Anniv. of Declaration of Human Rights.

| | | | | |
|---|---|---|---|---|
| 537. | 75. | 50 f. red and blue .. | 40 | 20 |
| 538. | | 50 f. blue and red .. | 40 | 20 |

**1963.** Surch. in English and Arabic.

| | | | | |
|---|---|---|---|---|
| 539. | 60. | 1 f. on 21 f. blk. & green | 20 | 15 |
| 540. | | 2 f. on 21 f. blk. & green | 20 | 15 |
| 541. | | 4 f. on 12 f. black & red | 7·75 | 7·50 |
| 542. | – | 4 f. on 12 f. sepia and red (No. 451) .. | 30 | 25 |
| 543. | 60. | 5 f. on 21 f. blk. & green | 50 | 35 |
| 544. | | 25 f. on 35 f. blue .. | 2·00 | 70 |

**77.** King Hussein and Red Crescent.

**1963.** Red Crescent Commemoration.

| | | | | |
|---|---|---|---|---|
| 545. | 77. | 1 f. purple and red .. | 10 | 10 |
| 546. | | 2 f. turquoise and red .. | 10 | 10 |
| 547. | | 3 f. blue and red .. | 10 | 10 |
| 548. | | 4 f. turquoise and red .. | 10 | 10 |
| 549. | | 5 f. sepia and red .. | 10 | 10 |
| 550. | | 85 f. green and red .. | 1·75 | 1·40 |

**78.** Red Cross Emblem.

**1963.** Centenary of Red Cross.
552. 78. 1 f. purple and red .. 10 10
553. 2 f. turquoise and red .. 10 10
554. 3 f. blue and red .. 10 10
555. 4 f. turquoise and red .. 10 10
556. 5 f. sepia and red .. 10 10
557. 85 f. green and red .. 2·75 1·75

**79.** Kings Hussein of Hejaz and Hussein of Jordan.

**1963.** Arab Renaissance Day.
559. 79. 15 f. multicoloured .. 35 25
560. 25 f. multicoloured .. 50 35
561. 35 f. multicoloured .. 90 70
562. 50 f. multicoloured .. 2·00 1·75

**80.** Al Aqsa Mosque, Pope Paul and King Hussein.

**1964.** Pope Paul's Visit to the Holy Land.
564 80 15 f. green and black .. 20 15
565 – 35 f. mauve and black 50 35
566 – 50 f. brown and black .. 80 50
567 – 80 f. blue and black 1·50 90
DESIGNS: 35 f. Dome of the Rock (Mosque of Omar), Jerusalem. 50 f. Church of the Holy Sepulchre, Jerusalem. 80 f. Church of the Nativity, Bethlehem.

**81.** Prince Abdullah.

**1964.** 2nd Birthday of Prince Abdullah. Multicoloured.
568. 5 f. Prince standing by wall 30 10
569. 10 f. Head of Prince and roses 35 25
570. 35 f. Type **81** .. .. 75 50
SIZES: 5 f. as Type **81** but vert. 10 f. diamond (63 × 63 mm.).

**NOTE.**—A set of ten triangular 20 f. stamps showing astronauts and rockets was issued, but very few were put on sale at the Post Office and we are not listing them unless we receive satisfactory evidence as to their status.

**82.** Basketball.

**83.** Woman and Child.

**1964.** Olympic Games, Tokyo (1st issue).
571. 82. 1 f. red .. .. 10 10
572. – 2 f. blue .. .. 10 10
573. – 3 f. green .. .. 10 10
574. – 4 f. buff .. .. 10 10
575. – 5 f. violet .. .. 10 10
576. – 35 f. red .. .. 1·40 60
577. – 50 f. green .. .. 2·50 1·25
578. – 100 f. brown .. .. 4·00 2·25
DESIGNS—VERT. 2 f. Volleyball. 3 f. Football. 5 f. Running. HORIZ. 4 f. Table tennis. 35 f. Cycling. 50 f. Fencing. 100 f. Pole vaulting.
See also Nos. 610/17 and 641/6.

**1964.** 4th Session of Social Studies Seminar, Amman.
580. 83. 5 f. multicoloured .. 10 10
581. 10 f. multicoloured .. 20 10
582. 25 f. multicoloured .. 30 20

**84.** King Hussein Sports Stadium, Amman.

**1964.** Air. Inaug. of "Hussein Sports City".
583. 84. 1 f. multicoloured .. 10 10
584. 4 f. multicoloured .. 10 10
585. 10 f. multicoloured .. 20 15
586. 35 f. multicoloured .. 35 25

**85.** President Kennedy.

**1964.** Pres. Kennedy Memorial Issue.
588. 85. 1 f. violet .. .. 20 20
589. 2 f. red .. .. .. 20 20
590. 3 f. blue .. .. 20 20
591. 4 f. brown .. .. 20 20
592. 5 f. green .. .. 20 20
593. 85 f. red .. .. 12·50 5·75

**86.** Statues at Abu Simbel.

**1964.** Nubian Monuments Preservation.
595. 86. 4 f. black and blue .. 10 10
596. 15 f. violet and yellow .. 25 20
597. 25 f. red and green .. 30 30

**87.** King Hussein and Map of Palestine in 1920.

**1964.** Arab Summit Conf.
598. 87. 10 f. multicoloured .. 10 10
599. 15 f. multicoloured .. 20 10
600. 25 f. multicoloured .. 25 10
601. 50 f. multicoloured .. 60 20
602. 80 f. multicoloured .. 1·10 90

**88.** Pope Paul VI, King Hussein and Ecumenical Patriarch.

**1964.** Meeting of Pope, King and Patriarch, Jerusalem. Multicoloured, background colour given.
604. 88. 10 f. green .. .. 15 10
605. 15 f. purple .. .. 15 10
606. 25 f. brown .. .. 25 15
607. 50 f. blue .. .. 75 50
608. 80 f. green .. .. 1·25 1·00

**89.** Olympic Flame.

**1964.** Olympic Games, Tokyo (2nd issue).
610. 89. 1 f. red .. .. .. 10 10
611. 2 f. violet .. .. 10 10
612. 3 f. green .. .. 10 10
613. 4 f. brown .. .. 10 10
614. 5 f. red .. .. .. 10 10
615. 35 f. blue .. .. 65 55
616. 50 f. olive .. .. 1·00 90
617. 100 f. blue .. .. 2·25 2·00

**90.** Scouts crossing River.

**1964.** Jordanian Scouts.
619. 90. 1 f. brown .. .. 10 10
620. – 2 f. violet .. .. 10 10
621. – 3 f. ochre .. .. 10 10
622. – 4 f. lake .. .. 10 10
623. – 5 f. green .. .. 10 10
624. – 35 f. blue .. .. 3·00 1·10
625. – 50 f. green .. .. 3·25 1·75
DESIGNS: 2 f. First Aid. 3 f. Exercising. 4 f. Practising knots. 5 f. Cooking meal. 35 f. Sailing. 50 f. Around camp-fire.

**91.** Four-coloured Bush Shrike.

**1964.** Air. Birds. Multicoloured.
627. 150 f. Type **91** .. .. 11·00 5·00
628. 500 f. Ornate Hawk Eagle 35·00 20·00
629. 1000 f. Grey-headed Kingfisher .. .. 65·00 35·00
Nos. 628/9 are vert.

**92.** Bykovsky.

**1965.** Russian Astronauts.
630. 40 f. brown and green (Type **92**) .. .. 75 75
631. 40 f. violet and brown (Gagarin) .. .. 75 75
632. 40 f. maroon and blue (Nikolaev) .. .. 75 75
633. 40 f. lilac and bistre (Popovich) .. .. 75 75
634. 40 f. sepia and blue (Tereshkova) .. .. 75 75
635. 40 f. green & pink (Titov) 75 75

**93.** U.N. Headquarters and Emblem.

**1965.** 19th Anniv. (1964) of U.N.
638. 93. 30 f. violet, turquoise and brown .. .. 40 20
639. 70 f. brown, blue & vio. 60 45

**94.** Olympic Flame.

**1965.** Air. Olympic Games, Tokyo (3rd issue).
641. 94. 10 f. red .. .. 10 10
642. 15 f. violet .. .. 10 10
643. 20 f. blue .. .. 25 10
644. 30 f. green .. .. 60 35
645. 40 f. brown .. .. 80 35
646. 60 f. mauve .. .. 1·25 70

**1965.** Deir Yassin Massacre. As T **292** of Egypt, but inscr. "THE HASHEMITE KINGDOM OF JORDAN" in English and Arabic.
648. 25 f. red and olive .. 1·00 80

**96.** Horse-jumping.

**97.** Volleyball Player and Cup.

**1965.** Army Day.
649 96 5 f. green .. .. 15 10
650 – 10 f. blue .. .. 30 10
651 – 35 f. brown .. .. 95 45
DESIGNS: 10 f. Tank. 35 f. King Hussein making inspection in army car.

**1965.** Arab Volleyball Championships.
652. 97. 15 f. olive .. .. 60 20
653. 35 f. lake .. .. 1·10 50
654. 50 f. blue .. .. 1·90 1·10

**98.** President J. F. Kennedy.

**1965.** 1st Death Anniv of Pres. Kennedy.
656. 98. 10 f. black and green .. 20 15
657. 15 f. violet and orange .. 40 20
658. 25 f. brown and blue .. 55 30
659. 50 f. purple and green .. 95 60

**99.** Pope Paul, King Hussein and Dome of the Rock.

**1965.** 1st Anniv. of Pope Paul's Visit to the Holy Land.
661. 99. 5 f. brown and mauve .. 35 10
662. 10 f. lake and green .. 65 25
663. 15 f. blue and flesh .. 90 35
664. 50 f. grey and pink .. 2·50 1·10

**100.** Cathedral Steps.

**103.** I.T.U. Emblem and Symbols.


**101.** Jordan Pavilion at Fair.

**1965.** Air. Jerash Antiquities. Multicoloured.
666. 55 f. Type **100** .. .. 90 90
667. 55 f. Artemis Temple Gate 90 90
668. 55 f. Street of Columns .. 90 90
669. 55 f. Columns of South Theatre .. .. 90 90
670. 55 f. Forum .. .. 90 90
671. 55 f. South Theatre .. 90 90
672. 55 f. Triumphal Arch .. 90 90
673. 55 f. Temple of Artemis .. 90 90
Nos. 670/3 are horiz.

**1965.** New York World's Fair.
674. 101. 15 f. multicoloured .. 15 10
675. 25 f. multicoloured .. 35 20
676. 50 f. multicoloured .. 75 45

**1965.** Burning of Algiers Library. As T **294** of Egypt, but inscr. "THE HASHEMITE KINGDOM OF JORDAN" in English and Arabic.
678. 25 f. green, red and black .. 25 15

**1965.** Centenary of I.T.U.
679 103 25 f. blue & light blue 30 15
680 45 f. black and green 50 45

**104.** "Syncom" Satellite and Pagoda.

**1965.** Space Achievements. Multicoloured.

| | | | | |
|---|---|---|---|---|
| 682 | | 5 f. Type **104** .. .. | 15 | 10 |
| 683 | | 10 f. North American X-15 rocket airplane .. | 25 | 10 |
| 684 | | 15 f. Astronauts .. .. | 55 | 25 |
| 685 | | 20 f. As 10 f. .. .. | 55 | 25 |
| 686 | | 50 f. Type **104** .. .. | 1·00 | 60 |

**105.** Dead Sea.

**1985.** Dead Sea. Multicoloured.

| | | | | |
|---|---|---|---|---|
| 688. | | 35 f. Type **105** .. .. | 60 | 40 |
| 689. | | 35 f. Boats and palms .. | 60 | 40 |
| 690. | | 35 f. Qumran Caves .. | 60 | 40 |
| 691. | | 35 f. Dead Sea Scrolls .. | 60 | 40 |

**1965.** Air. Space Flight of McDivitt and White. Nos. 641/6 optd. **James McDivitt Edward White 2-6-1965** in English and Arabic and Rocket.

| | | | | |
|---|---|---|---|---|
| 692. | **94.** | 10 f. red .. .. | 1·90 | 70 |
| 693. | | 15 f. violet .. .. | 1·90 | 70 |
| 694. | | 20 f. blue .. .. | 2·75 | 1·50 |
| 695. | | 30 f. green .. .. | 3·75 | 2·50 |
| 696. | | 40 f. brown .. .. | 4·50 | 3·25 |
| 697. | | 60 f. mauve .. .. | 7·50 | 5·00 |

**107.** King Hussein, U.N. Emblem and Headquarters.

**1965.** King Hussein's Visit to France and the U.S.A.

| | | | | |
|---|---|---|---|---|
| 699. | **107.** | 5 f. sepia, blue and pink | 10 | 10 |
| 700. | – | 10 f. sepia, green & grey | 15 | 10 |
| 701. | – | 20f. agate, brown & blue | 30 | 25 |
| 702. | **107.** | 50 f. lilac, brown & blue | 90 | 65 |

DESIGNS: 10 f. King Hussein, Pres. de Gaulle and Eiffel Tower. 20 f. King Hussein, Pres. Johnson and Statue of Liberty.

**108.** I.C.Y. Emblem.

**109.** A.P.U. Emblem.

**1965.** Int. Co-operation Year.

| | | | | |
|---|---|---|---|---|
| 704. | **108.** | 5 f. red and orange .. | 20 | 15 |
| 705. | | 10 f. violet and blue .. | 45 | 20 |
| 706. | | 45 f. purple and green .. | 1·75 | 1·40 |

**1965.** 10th Anniv (1964) of Arab Postal Union's Permanent Office at Cairo.

| | | | | |
|---|---|---|---|---|
| 707 | **109** | 15 f. black and blue .. | 15 | 15 |
| 708 | | 25 f. black and green | 45 | 20 |

**110.** Dome of the Rock.

**1965.** Inaug (1964) of "Dome of the Rock".

| | | | | |
|---|---|---|---|---|
| 709. | **110.** | 15 f. multicoloured .. | 75 | 30 |
| 710. | | 25 f. multicoloured .. | 1·25 | 80 |

**111.** King Hussein.

**115.** First Station of the Cross.

**114.** Agricultural Symbols.

**1966.**

(a) Postage. Portraits in blue (1 f. to 15 f.) or purple (21 f. to 150 f.); background colours given.

| | | | | |
|---|---|---|---|---|
| 711 | **111** | 1 f. orange .. .. | 10 | 10 |
| 712 | | 2 f. blue .. .. | 10 | 10 |
| 713 | | 3 f. violet .. .. | 10 | 10 |
| 714 | | 4 f. purple .. .. | 10 | 10 |
| 715 | | 7 f. brown .. .. | 20 | 10 |
| 716 | | 12 f. mauve .. .. | 20 | 10 |
| 717 | | 15 f. brown .. .. | 25 | 10 |
| 718 | | 21 f. green .. .. | 40 | 10 |
| 719 | | 25 f. blue .. .. | 45 | 10 |
| 720 | | 35 f. stone .. .. | 60 | 15 |
| 721 | | 40 f. yellow .. .. | 65 | 20 |
| 722 | | 50 f. green .. .. | 70 | 35 |
| 723 | | 100 f. green .. .. | 1·25 | 70 |
| 724 | | 150 f. violet .. .. | 2·75 | 1·10 |

(b) Air. Portraits in brown; background colours given.

| | | | | |
|---|---|---|---|---|
| 725 | **111** | 200 f. turquoise .. | 4·25 | 1·25 |
| 726 | | 500 f. green .. .. | 7·00 | 5·00 |
| 727 | | 1 d. blue .. .. | 12·50 | 8·25 |

**1966.** Space Flights of Belyaev and Leonov. Nos. 630/5 optd **Alexei Leonov Pavel Belyaev 18 3-1965** in English and Arabic and spacecraft motif.

| | | | | |
|---|---|---|---|---|
| 728. | **92.** | 40 f. brown and green .. | 4·50 | 3·00 |
| 729. | – | 40 f. violet and brown .. | 4·50 | 3·00 |
| 730. | – | 40 f. purple and blue .. | 4·50 | 3·00 |
| 731. | – | 40 f. lilac and bistre .. | 4·50 | 3·00 |
| 732. | – | 40 f. sepia and blue .. | 4·50 | 3·00 |
| 733. | – | 40 f. green and pink .. | 4·50 | 3·00 |

**1966.** Pope Paul's Visit to U.N. (1965). Nos. 604/8 optd. **PAPA PAULUS VI WORLD PEACE VISIT TO UNITED NATIONS 1965** in English and Arabic.

| | | | | |
|---|---|---|---|---|
| 736. | **88.** | 10 f. green .. .. | 20 | 10 |
| 737. | | 15 f. purple .. .. | 45 | 20 |
| 738. | | 25 f. brown .. .. | 45 | 25 |
| 739. | | 50 f. blue .. .. | 85 | 45 |
| 740. | | 80 f. green .. .. | 1·50 | 75 |

**1966.** Anti-T.B. Campaign. (a) Unissued "Freedom from Hunger" stamps optd. as in T **114.**

| | | | | |
|---|---|---|---|---|
| 741. | **114.** | 15 f. multicoloured .. | 35 | 25 |
| 742. | | 35 f. multicoloured .. | 80 | 60 |
| 743. | | 50 f. multicoloured .. | 1·40 | 1·25 |

(b) As Nos. 741/3 but with additional premium obliterated by bars.

| | | | | |
|---|---|---|---|---|
| 745. | – | 15 f. multicoloured .. | 35 | 25 |
| 746. | – | 35 f. multicoloured .. | 80 | 60 |
| 747. | – | 50 f. multicoloured .. | 1·40 | 1·25 |

**1966.** Christ's Passion. The Stations of the Cross.

| | | | | |
|---|---|---|---|---|
| 749. | **115.** | 1 f. multicoloured .. | 10 | 10 |
| 750. | – | 2 f. multicoloured .. | 10 | 10 |
| 751. | – | 3 f. multicoloured .. | 20 | 10 |
| 752. | – | 4 f. multicoloured .. | 20 | 15 |
| 753. | – | 5 f. multicoloured .. | 35 | 20 |
| 754. | – | 6 f. multicoloured .. | 50 | 30 |
| 755. | – | 7 f. multicoloured .. | 65 | 40 |
| 756. | – | 8 f. multicoloured .. | 65 | 40 |
| 757. | – | 9 f. multicoloured .. | 85 | 50 |
| 758. | – | 10 f. multicoloured .. | 95 | 60 |
| 759. | – | 11 f. multicoloured .. | 1·10 | 70 |
| 760. | – | 12 f. multicoloured .. | 1·10 | 70 |
| 761. | – | 13 f. multicoloured .. | 1·10 | 70 |
| 762. | – | 14 f. multicoloured .. | 1·25 | 85 |

DESIGNS: The 14 Stations. The denominations, expressed in Roman numerals, correspond to the numbers of the Stations.

**116.** Schirra and "Gemini 6".

**118.** Dag Hammarskjold.

**117.** The Three Kings.

**1966.** Space Achievements.

| | | | | |
|---|---|---|---|---|
| 764. | **116.** | 1 f. blue, violet & green | 10 | 10 |
| 765. | – | 2 f. green, violet & blue | 10 | 10 |
| 766. | – | 3 f. violet, blue & green | 10 | 10 |
| 767. | – | 4 f. violet, green & ochre | 15 | 10 |
| 768. | – | 30 f. turq., brn. & vio. | 1·40 | 90 |
| 769. | – | 60 f. brn., turq. & vio. | 1·75 | 1·40 |

DESIGNS: 2 f. Stafford and "Gemini 6". 3 f. Borman and "Gemini 7". 4 f. Lovell and "Gemini 7". 30 f. Armstrong and "Gemini 8". 60 f. Scott and "Gemini 8".

**1966.** Christmas. Multicoloured.

| | | | | |
|---|---|---|---|---|
| 771. | | 5 f. Type **117** .. .. | 20 | 10 |
| 772. | | 10 f. The Magi presenting gifts to the infant Christ | 30 | 15 |
| 773. | | 35 f. The flight to Egypt (vert.) .. .. .. | 2·50 | 85 |

**1967.** "Builders of World Peace". Mult.

| | | | | |
|---|---|---|---|---|
| 775. | | 5 f. Type **118** .. .. | 10 | 10 |
| 781. | | 5 f. U Thant .. .. | 10 | 10 |
| 776. | | 10 f. Pandit Nehru .. | 20 | 10 |
| 782. | | 10 f. Pres. De Gaulle .. | 20 | 10 |
| 777. | | 35 f. Pres. Kennedy .. | 60 | 30 |
| 783. | | 35 f. Pres. Johnson .. | 60 | 25 |
| 778. | | 50 f. Pope John XXIII .. | 1·50 | 50 |
| 784. | | 50 f. Pope Paul VI .. | 1·50 | 50 |
| 779. | | 100 f. King Abdullah (of Jordan) .. .. | 1·60 | 1·40 |
| 785. | | 100 f. King Hussein .. | 1·60 | 90 |

**119.** King Hussein.

**1967.** "Gold Coins". Circular designs, centre and rim embossed on gold foil. Imperf.

(a) As T **119**. (i) Diameter 41 mm.

| | | | | |
|---|---|---|---|---|
| 787 | **119** | 5 f. orange and blue .. | 30 | 30 |
| 788 | | 10 f. orange and violet | 30 | 30 |

(ii) Diameter 47 mm.

| | | | | |
|---|---|---|---|---|
| 789 | **119** | 50 f. lilac and brown .. | 1·50 | 1·50 |
| 790 | | 100 f. pink and green | 2·00 | 2·00 |

(iii) Diameter 54 mm.

| | | | | |
|---|---|---|---|---|
| 791 | **119** | 200 f. blue & deep blue | 5·00 | 5·00 |

(b) Crown Prince Hassan of Jordan. (i) Diam 41 mm.

| | | | | |
|---|---|---|---|---|
| 792 | – | 5 f. black and green .. | 55 | 55 |
| 793 | – | 10 f. black and lilac .. | 55 | 55 |

(ii) Diameter 47 mm.

| | | | | |
|---|---|---|---|---|
| 794 | – | 50 f. black and blue .. | 3·00 | 3·00 |
| 795 | – | 100 f. black and brown | 4·00 | 4·00 |

(iii) Diameter 54 mm.

| | | | | |
|---|---|---|---|---|
| 796 | – | 200 f. black and mauve | 7·50 | 7·50 |

A similar set was also issued in the same values and sizes but different colours with portrait of John F. Kennedy.

**120.** University City, Statue and Olympic Torch.

**1967.** Preparation for Olympic Games in Mexico (1968).

| | | | | |
|---|---|---|---|---|
| 797. | **120.** | 1 f. red, black and violet | 10 | 10 |
| 798. | – | 2 f. black, violet and red | 10 | 10 |
| 799. | – | 3 f. violet, red and black | 10 | 10 |
| 800. | – | 4 f. blue, brn. and grn. | 10 | 10 |
| 801. | – | 30 f. grn., blue and brn. | 40 | 40 |
| 802. | – | 60 f. brn., grn. and blue | 1·00 | 50 |

DESIGNS (each with Olympic torch): 2 f. Fishermen on Lake Patzcuaro. 3 f. University City and skyscraper, Mexico City. 4 f. Avenida de la Reforma, Mexico City. 30 f. Guadalajara Cathedral. 60 f. Fine Arts Theatre, Mexico City.

**121.** Decade Emblem.

**1967.** Int. Hydrological Decade.

| | | | | |
|---|---|---|---|---|
| 804. | **121.** | 10 f. black and red .. | 25 | 10 |
| 805. | | 15 f. black & turquoise | 45 | 25 |
| 806. | | 25 f. black and purple .. | 75 | 50 |

**122.** U.N.E.S.C.O. Emblem.

**1967.** 20th Anniv. of U.N.E.S.C.O.

| | | | | |
|---|---|---|---|---|
| 807. | **122.** | 100 f. multicoloured .. | 1·00 | 60 |

**123.** Dromedary.

**1967.** Animals. Multicoloured.

| | | | | |
|---|---|---|---|---|
| 808. | | 1 f. Type **123** (postage) .. | 10 | 10 |
| 809. | | 2 f. Karakul sheep .. | 15 | 10 |
| 810. | | 3 f. Angora goat .. | 15 | 10 |
| 811. | | 4 f. Striped hyena (air) .. | 25 | 15 |
| 812. | | 30 f. Arab horses .. | 1·25 | 35 |
| 813. | | 60 f. Goitred gazelle .. | 2·10 | 80 |

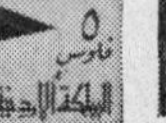


**124.** W.H.O. Building.

**125.** Arab League Emblem, Open Book and Reaching Hands.

**1967.** Inaug. of W.H.O. Headquarters, Geneva.

| | | | | |
|---|---|---|---|---|
| 815. | **124.** | 5 f. black and green .. | 15 | 10 |
| 816. | | 45 f. black and orange .. | 55 | 30 |

**1968.** Literacy Campaign.

| | | | | |
|---|---|---|---|---|
| 817. | **125.** | 20 f. green and orange .. | 40 | 25 |
| 818. | | 20 f. blue and mauve .. | 40 | 25 |

**126.** W.H.O. Emblem and "20".

**1968.** 20th Anniv. of W.H.O.

| | | | | |
|---|---|---|---|---|
| 819. | **126.** | 30 f. multicoloured | 50 | 25 |
| 820. | | 100 f. multicoloured | 1·40 | 75 |

**127.** Goldfinch.

**128.** Human Rights Emblem.

**1968.** Game Protection. Multicoloured.

| | | | | |
|---|---|---|---|---|
| 821. | | 5 f. Type **127** (postage) | 1·50 | 65 |
| 822. | | 10 f. Chukar partridge .. | 2·50 | 65 |
| 823. | | 15 f. Ostriches .. .. | 3·50 | 80 |
| 824. | | 20 f. Sand partridge .. | 3·50 | 95 |
| 825. | | 30 f. Mountain gazelle .. | 2·25 | 70 |
| 826. | | 40 f. Arabian oryx .. | 3·25 | 75 |
| 827. | | 50 f. Houbara bustard .. | 5·00 | 1·75 |
| 828. | | 60 f. Ibex (air) .. .. | 4·00 | 2·00 |
| 829. | | 100 f. Flock of mallard .. | 6·00 | 4·00 |

The 10, 15 and 60 f. are vert.

**1968.** Human Rights Year.

| | | | | |
|---|---|---|---|---|
| 830. | **128.** | 20 f. blk., buff and brn. | 30 | 20 |
| 831. | | 60 f. blk., blue and grn. | 70 | 50 |

**129.** I.L.O. Emblem.

**1969.** 50th Anniv. of I.L.O.

| | | | |
|---|---|---|---|
| 832. **129.** | 10 f. black and blue .. | 20 | 10 |
| 833. | 20 f. black and brown .. | 20 | 10 |
| 834. | 25 f. black and green .. | 30 | 25 |
| 835. | 45 f. black and mauve .. | 50 | 35 |
| 836. | 60 f. black and orange .. | 70 | 40 |

**130.** Horses in Pasture.

**1969.** Arab Horses. Multicoloured.

| | | | |
|---|---|---|---|
| 837. | 10 f. Type **130** .. .. | 50 | 15 |
| 838. | 20 f. White horse .. | 1·25 | 35 |
| 839. | 45 f. Black mare and foal | 2·50 | 1·10 |

**131.** Kaaba, Mecca, and Dome of the Rock, Jerusalem.

**1969.** Multicoloured.

| | | | |
|---|---|---|---|
| 840. | 5 f. As Type **131** .. .. | 30 | 10 |
| 841. | 10 f. Dome of the Rock (30 × 36 mm.) .. .. | 50 | 35 |
| 842. | 20 f. As 10 f. .. .. | 90 | 50 |
| 843. | 45 f. As 5 f. .. .. | 2·25 | 55 |

**132.** Oranges.

**1969.** Fruits. Multicoloured.

| | | | |
|---|---|---|---|
| 844. | 10 f. Type **132** .. .. | 25 | 10 |
| 845. | 20 f. Gooseberry .. .. | 40 | 20 |
| 846. | 30 f. Lemons .. .. | 80 | 20 |
| 847. | 40 f. Grapes .. .. | 1·10 | 30 |
| 848. | 50 f. Olives .. .. | 1·60 | 75 |
| 849. | 100 f. Apples .. .. | 2·50 | 1·50 |

**133.** Prince Hassan and Bride.

**1969.** Wedding of Prince Hassan (1968).

| | | | |
|---|---|---|---|
| 850. – | 20 f. multicoloured .. | 70 | 50 |
| 851. – | 60 f. multicoloured .. | 1·10 | 80 |
| 852. **133.** | 100 f. multicoloured .. | 1·25 | 90 |

Nos. 850/1 show a similar design to Type **133**.

**134.** Wrecked Houses.

**1970.** "Tragedy of the Refugees". Various vert. designs as T **134**. Multicoloured.

| | | | |
|---|---|---|---|
| 853/82. | 1 f. to 30 f. inclusive Set of 30 .. .. | 10·00 | 10·00 |

**135.** Bombed Mosque. **136.** Pomegranate.

**1970.** "Tragedy in the Holy Lands". Various vert. designs as T **135**. Mult.

| | | | |
|---|---|---|---|
| 883/912. | 1 f. to 30 f. inclusive Set of 30 .. .. | 10·00 | 10·00 |

**1970.** Flowers. Multicoloured.

| | | | |
|---|---|---|---|
| 913. | 5 f. Type **136** .. .. | 30 | 10 |
| 914. | 15 f. Wattle .. .. | 50 | 10 |
| 915. | 25 f. Caper .. .. | 75 | 10 |
| 916. | 35 f. Convolvulus .. | 1·10 | 25 |
| 917. | 45 f. Desert Scabious .. | 1·50 | 55 |
| 918. | 75 f. Black Iris .. .. | 2·40 | 2·00 |

Nos. 913/5 and 917 are wrongly inscribed on the stamps.

**137.** Football.

**1970.** Sports. Multicoloured.

| | | | |
|---|---|---|---|
| 919. | 5 f. Type **137** .. .. | 15 | 10 |
| 920. | 10 f. Diving .. .. | 20 | 10 |
| 921. | 15 f. Boxing .. .. | 35 | 10 |
| 922. | 50 f. Running .. .. | 1·00 | 45 |
| 923. | 100 f. Cycling (vert.) .. | 2·50 | 90 |
| 924. | 150 f. Basketball (vert.) | 3·50 | 2·00 |

**138.** Arab Children. **139.** White-crowned Black Wheatear.

**1970.** Children's Day. Multicoloured.

| | | | |
|---|---|---|---|
| 925. | 5 f. Type **138** .. .. | 20 | 10 |
| 926. | 10 f. Refugee boy with kettle .. .. | 25 | 10 |
| 927. | 15 f. Refugee girl in camp | 45 | 15 |
| 928. | 20 f. Refugee child in tent | 70 | 20 |

Nos. 926/8 are vert.

**1970.** Birds.

| | | | |
|---|---|---|---|
| 929 **139** | 120 f. black and orange | 5·50 | 1·75 |
| 930 – | 180 f. brn, blk & lilac | 6·75 | 3·50 |
| 931 – | 200 f. multicoloured .. | 7·75 | 4·50 |

Designs: 180 f. Masked shrike; 200 f. Palestine sunbird.

**140.** Grotto of the Nativity, Bethlehem.

**1970.** Christmas. Church of the Nativity, Bethlehem. Multicoloured.

| | | | |
|---|---|---|---|
| 932. | 5 f. Type **140** .. .. | 20 | 10 |
| 933. | 10 f. Christmas crib .. | 30 | 15 |
| 934. | 20 f. Crypt Altar .. .. | 50 | 20 |
| 935. | 25 f. Nave, Church of the Nativity .. .. | 60 | 45 |

**141.** Arab League Flag, Emblem and Map.

**1971.** 25th Anniv (1970) of Arab League.

| | | | |
|---|---|---|---|
| 936 **141** | 10 f. green, vio & orge | 15 | 15 |
| 937 | 20 f. green, brown & bl | 35 | 15 |
| 938 | 30 f. green, blue & olive | 50 | 25 |

**INDEX**

Countries can be quickly located by referring to the index at the end of this volume.

**142.** Heads of Four Races and Emblem.

**1971.** Racial Equality Year. Multicoloured.

| | | | |
|---|---|---|---|
| 939. | 5 f. Type **142** .. .. | 10 | 10 |
| 940. | 10 f. "Plant" and emblem | 15 | 10 |
| 941. | 15 f. Doves and Emblem .. (horiz.) .. .. .. | 30 | 20 |

No. 939 is inscribed "KINIGDOM" in error.

**143.** Shore of the Dead Sea. **144.** Ibn Sinai (Avicenna).

**1971.** Tourism. Multicoloured.

| | | | |
|---|---|---|---|
| 942. | 5 f. Type **143** .. .. | 20 | 10 |
| 943. | 30 f. Ed Deir, Petra .. | 60 | 30 |
| 944. | 45 f. Via Dolorosa, Jerusalem (vert.) .. .. | 90 | 35 |
| 945. | 60 f. River Jordan .. | 1·50 | 80 |
| 946. | 100 f. Christmas Bell, Bethlehem (vert.) .. | 2·10 | 1·50 |

**1971.** Famous Arab Scholars. Multicoloured.

| | | | |
|---|---|---|---|
| 947. | 5 f. Type **144** .. .. | 15 | 10 |
| 948. | 10 f. Ibn Rushd .. .. | 25 | 10 |
| 949. | 20 f. Ibn Khaldun .. | 35 | 10 |
| 950. | 25 f. Ibn Tufail .. .. | 60 | 10 |
| 951. | 30 f. Ibn El Haytham .. | 80 | 45 |

**145.** New U.P.U. HQ. Building.

**1971.** Inauguration of New U.P.U. Headquarters Building, Berne.

| | | | |
|---|---|---|---|
| 952 **145** | 10 f. brown, grn & yell | 25 | 10 |
| 953 | 20 f. purple, grn & yell | 75 | 35 |

**146.** Young Pupil. **147.** Mothers and Children.

**1972.** Int. Education Year.

| | | | |
|---|---|---|---|
| 954. **146.** | 5 f. multicoloured .. | 10 | 10 |
| 955. | 15 f. multicoloured .. | 20 | 10 |
| 956. | 20 f. multicoloured .. | 35 | 10 |
| 957. | 30 f. multicoloured .. | 75 | 40 |

**1972.** Mothers' Day. Multicoloured.

| | | | |
|---|---|---|---|
| 958. | 10 f. Type **147** .. .. | 30 | 10 |
| 959. | 20 f. Mother and child (vert.) .. .. | 50 | 10 |
| 960. | 30 f. Bedouin mother and child (vert.) .. .. | 1·00 | 50 |

**148.** Pope Paul VI leaving Holy Sepulchre, Jerusalem.

**1972.** Easter. Multicoloured.

| | | | |
|---|---|---|---|
| 961. | 30 f. Type **148** (postage) .. | 70 | 15 |
| 962. | 60 f. The Calvary, Church of the Holy Sepulchre (air) | 1·40 | 50 |
| 963. | 100 f. "Washing of the Feet", Jerusalem | 2·75 | 1·25 |



**149.** Children and U.N.I.C.E.F. Emblem.

**1972.** 25th Anniv of U.N.I.C.E.F.

| | | | |
|---|---|---|---|
| 964 **149** | 10 f. turq, bl & brn .. | 15 | 10 |
| 965 – | 20 f. brown, grn & pur | 50 | 25 |
| 966 – | 30 f. brown, mve & bl | 75 | 35 |

Designs—vert: 20 f. Child with toy bricks. horiz: 30 f. Nurse holding baby.

**150.** Dove of Peace. **152.** Arab with Kestrel.

**151.** Al Aqsa Mosque and Pilgrims.

**1972.** 25th Anniv (1970) of United Nations.

| | | | |
|---|---|---|---|
| 967 **150** | 5 f. green, violet & yell | 10 | 10 |
| 968 | 10 f. green, red & yell | 20 | 10 |
| 969 | 15 f. blue, black & yell | 40 | 10 |
| 970 | 20 f. blue, green & yell | 55 | 20 |
| 971 | 30 f. green, brn & yell | 1·00 | 50 |

**1972.** Burning of Al Aqsa Mosque (1970). Mult.

| | | | |
|---|---|---|---|
| 972. | 30 f. Type **151** .. .. | 1·00 | 20 |
| 973. | 60 f. Mosque in flames .. | 1·50 | 80 |
| 974. | 100 f. Mosque Interior .. | 3·50 | 1·60 |

**1972.** Jordanian Desert Life. Multicoloured.

| | | | |
|---|---|---|---|
| 975. | 5 f. Type **152** .. .. | 20 | 10 |
| 976. | 10 f. Desert bungalow .. | 20 | 10 |
| 977. | 15 f. Camel trooper, Arab Legion .. .. .. | 40 | 15 |
| 978. | 20 f. Boring operations .. | 45 | 15 |
| 979. | 25 f. Shepherd .. .. | 55 | 20 |
| 980. | 30 f. Dromedaries at water-trough .. .. .. | 80 | 35 |
| 981. | 35 f. Chicken farm .. | 90 | 55 |
| 982. | 45 f. Irrigation scheme .. | 1·75 | 1·10 |

Nos. 976/82 are horizontal designs.

**153.** Wasfi el Tell and Dome of the Rock, Jerusalem.

**1972.** Wasfi el Tell (assassinated statesman) Memorial Issue. Multicoloured.

| | | | |
|---|---|---|---|
| 983. | 5 f. Type **153** .. .. | 20 | 10 |
| 984. | 10 f. Wasfi el Tell, map and flag .. .. .. | 30 | 10 |
| 985. | 20 f. Type **153** .. .. | 60 | 10 |
| 986. | 30 f. As 10 f. .. .. | 70 | 55 |

**154.** Clay-pigeon shooting. **155.** Aero Club Emblem.

**1972.** World Clay-pigeon Shooting Championships. Multicoloured.

| | | | |
|---|---|---|---|
| 987 | 25 f. Type **154** .. .. | 60 | 10 |
| 988 | 75 f. Marksman on range (horiz) .. .. .. | 1·90 | 80 |
| 989 | 120 f. Marksman taking aim (horiz) .. .. | 1·50 | 1·75 |

**1973.** Royal Jordanian Aero Club.

| | | | |
|---|---|---|---|
| 990. **155.** | 5 f. blk., bl. & yell. (post.) | 15 | 10 |
| 991. | 10 f. blk., blue & yellow | 15 | 10 |
| 992. – | 15 f. multicoloured (air) | 35 | 10 |
| 993. – | 20 f. multicoloured .. | 55 | 15 |
| 994. – | 40 f. multicoloured .. | 1·10 | 50 |

Designs: 15 f. Piper Cherokee 140 aircraft. 20 f. Beech B55 Baron airplane. 40 f. Winged horse emblem.

**156.** Dove and Flag.

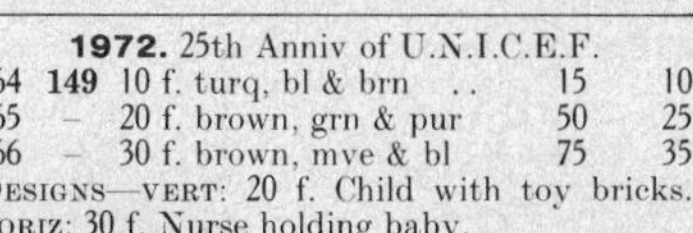

**1973.** 50th Anniv. of Hashemite Kingdom of Jordan. Multicoloured.
995. 5 f. Type **156** .. .. 10 10
996. 10 f. Anniversary emblem 20 10
997. 15 f. King Hussein .. 50 10
998. 30 f. Map and emblems .. 1·00 90

**157.** Map and Jordanian Advance.

**1973.** 5th Anniv. of Battle of Karama. Multicoloured.
999. 5 f. Type **157** .. .. 20 10
1000. 10 f. Jordanian attack, and map .. .. 40 20
1001. 15 f. Map, and King Hussein on tank .. .. 1·00 70

**158.** Father and Son. **159.** Phosphate Mines.

**1973.** Fathers' Day. Multicoloured.
1002. 10 f. Type **158** .. .. 15 10
1003. 20 f. Father and daughter 50 15
1004. 30 f. Family group .. 75 35

**1973.** Development Projects. Multicoloured.
1005. 5 f. Type **159** .. .. 25 10
1006. 10 f. Cement factories .. 35 10
1007. 15 f. Sharhabil Dam .. 55 15
1008. 20 f. Kafrein Dam .. 75 35

**160.** Racing Camel.

**1973.** Camel Racing. Multicoloured.
1009. 5 f. Type **160** .. .. 25 10
1010. 10 f. Camels in "paddock" 50 15
1011. 15 f. Start of race .. 75 25
1012. 20 f. Camel racing .. 1·75 50

**161.** Book Year Emblem.

**1973.** International Book Year (1972).
1013. **161.** 30 f. multicoloured .. 75 10
1014. 60 f. multicoloured .. 1·25 50

**162.** Family Group.

**1973.** Family Day.
1015. **162.** 20 f. multicoloured .. 40 10
1016. – 30 f. multicoloured .. 60 15
1017. – 60 f. multicoloured .. 1·00 50
DESIGNS: 30, 60 f. Different family groups.

**163.** Shah of Iran, King Hussein, Cyrus's Tomb and Mosque of Omar.

**1973.** 2500th Anniv. of Iranian Monarchy.
1018. **163.** 5 f. multicoloured 25 10
1019. 10 f. multicoloured .. 30 10
1020. 15 f. multicoloured .. 50 15
1021. 30 f. multicoloured .. 1·00 50

**164.** Emblem of Palestine Week.

**1973.** Palestine Week. Multicoloured.
1022. 5 f. Type **164** .. .. 30 10
1023. 10 f. Torch and emblem 50 10
1024. 15 f. Refugees (26×47mm.) 1·00 30
1025. 30 f. Children and map on Globe .. .. .. 1·50 40

**165.** Traditional Harvesting.

**1973.** Ancient and Modern Agriculture. Multicoloured.
1026. 5 f. Type **165** (postage) .. 15 10
1027. 10 f. Modern harvesting 20 10
1028. 15 f. Traditional seeding 40 10
1029. 20 f. Modern seeding .. 60 15
1030. 30 f. Traditional ploughing 70 20
1031. 35 f. Modern ploughing 80 25
1032. 45 f. Pest Control .. 1·00 25
1033. 60 f. Horticulture .. 1·75 90
1034. 100 f. Agricultural landscape (air.) .. 2·00 1·00

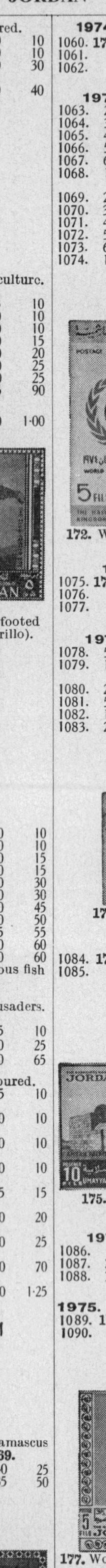

**166.** Red Sea Fish. **168.** "The Club-footed Boy" (Murillo).

**167.** Battle of Muta.

**1974.** Red Sea Fishes.
1035. **166.** 5 f. multicoloured .. 20 10
1036. – 10 f. multicoloured .. 30 10
1037. – 15 f. multicoloured .. 50 15
1038. – 20 f. multicoloured .. 60 15
1039. – 25 f. multicoloured .. 90 30
1040. – 30 f. multicoloured .. 90 30
1041. – 35 f. multicoloured .. 1·40 45
1042. – 40 f. multicoloured .. 1·60 50
1043. – 45 f. multicoloured .. 1·75 55
1044. **166.** 50 f. multicoloured .. 2·00 60
1045. – 60 f. multicoloured .. 2·40 60
DESIGNS: Nos. 1036/43 and 1045, Various fish designs as Type **166**.

**1974.** Islamic battles against the Crusaders. Multicoloured.
1046 10 f. Type **167** .. .. 35 10
1047 20 f. Battle of Yarmouk 90 25
1048 30 f. Battle of Hattin .. 1·60 65

**1974.** Famous Paintings. Multicoloured.
1049. 5 f. Type **168** .. .. 25 10
1050. 10 f. "Praying Hands" (Durer) .. .. 40 10
1051. 15 f. "St. George and the Dragon" (Uccello) .. 50 10
1052. 20 f. "The Mona Lisa" (L. da Vinci) .. .. 60 10
1053. 30 f. "Hope" (F. Watts)
1054. 40 f. "The Angelus" (Jean Millet) (horiz.) .. 75 15
1055. 50 f. "The Artist and her Daughter" (Angelica Kauffmann) .. .. 1·00 20 / 2·00 25
1056. 60 f. "Whistler's Mother" (J. Whistler) (horiz.) .. 2·00 70
1057. 100 f. "Master Hare" (Sir J. Reynolds) .. .. 2·50 1·25

المؤتمر الدولي لتاريخ بلاد الشام
٢٠ – ٢٥/٤/١٩٧٤
الجامعة الاردنية
(169.)

**1974.** International Conference for Damascus History. Nos. 1013/4 optd. with T **169**.
1058. **161.** 30 f. multicoloured .. 40 25
1059. 60 f. multicoloured .. 85 50

**170.** U.P.U. Emblem. **171.** Camel Caravan.

**1974.** Cent. of Universal Postal Union.
1060. **170.** 10 f. multicoloured .. 15 10
1061. 30 f. multicoloured .. 40 20
1062. 60 f. multicoloured .. 70 70

**1974.** The Dead Sea. Multicoloured.
1063. 2 f. Type **171** .. .. 10 10
1064. 3 f. Palm and shore .. 15 10
1065. 4 f. Hotel on coast .. 15 10
1066. 5 f. Jars from Qumram Caves 15 10
1067. 6 f. Copper scrolls (vert.) 30 10
1068. 10 f. Cistern steps, Qumram (vert.) .. .. 45 10
1069. 20 f. Type **171** .. .. 55 15
1070. 30 f. As 3 f. .. .. 80 15
1071. 40 f. As 4 f. .. .. 85 40
1072. 50 f. As 5 f. .. .. 1·40 50
1073. 60 f. As 6 f. .. .. 1·75 70
1074. 100 f. As 10 f. .. .. 2·75 1·10

**172.** WPY Emblem. **173.** Water-skier.

**1974.** World Population Year.
1075. **172.** 5 f. purple, grn. & blk. 15 10
1076. 10 f. red, grn. & blk. .. 25 10
1077. 20 f. orange, grn. & blk. 50 20

**1974.** Water-skiing. Multicoloured.
1078. 5 f. Type **173** .. .. 10 10
1079. 10 f. Water-skier (side view) (horiz.) .. 20 10
1080. 20 f. Skier turning (horiz.) 50 10
1081. 50 f. Type **173** .. .. 1·10 30
1082. 100 f. As 10 f. .. .. 2·10 75
1083. 200 f. As 20 f. .. .. 2·75 2·00

**174.** Ka'aba, Mecca, and Pilgrims.

**1974.** "Pilgrimage Season".
1084. **174.** 10 f. multicoloured .. 25 15
1085. 20 f. multicoloured .. 65 45

**175.** Amrah Palace. **176.** King Hussein at Wheel of Car.

**1974.** Desert Ruins. Multicoloured.
1086. 10 f. Type **175** .. .. 25 15
1087. 20 f. Hisham Palace .. 50 45
1088. 30 f. Kharana Castle .. 1·25 60

**1975.** Air. Royal Jordanian Automobile Club.
1089. **176.** 30 f. multicoloured .. 40 15
1090. 60 f. multicoloured .. 1·25 70

**177.** Woman in Costume. **178.** Treasury, Petra.

**1975.** Jordanian Women's Costumes.
1091. **177.** 5 f. multicoloured .. 15 10
1092. – 10 f. multicoloured .. 25 10
1093. – 15 f. multicoloured .. 40 15
1094. – 20 f. multicoloured .. 65 20
1095. – 25 f. multicoloured .. 85 50
DESIGNS: 10 f. to 25 f. Various costumes as Type **177**.

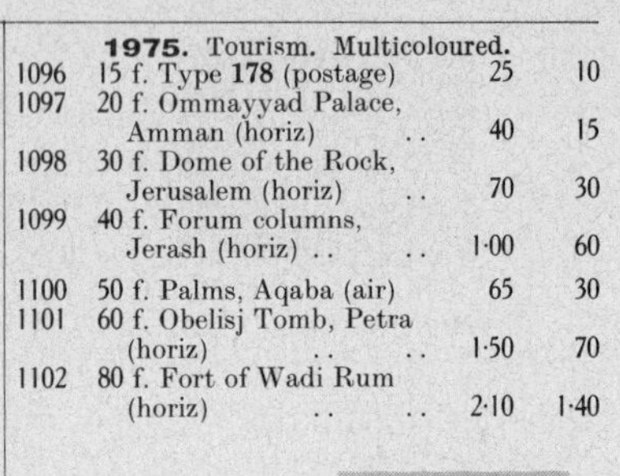

**1975.** Tourism. Multicoloured.
1096 15 f. Type **178** (postage) 25 10
1097 20 f. Ommayyad Palace, Amman (horiz) .. 40 15
1098 30 f. Dome of the Rock, Jerusalem (horiz) .. 70 30
1099 40 f. Forum columns, Jerash (horiz) .. .. 1·00 60
1100 50 f. Palms, Aqaba (air) 65 30
1101 60 f. Obelisj Tomb, Petra (horiz) .. .. 1·50 70
1102 80 f. Fort of Wadi Rum (horiz) .. .. 2·10 1·40

**179.** King Hussein. **180.** Globe and "Desert".

**1975.**
1103 **179** 5 f. blue and green .. 20 10
1104 10 f. blue and violet 20 10
1105 15 f. blue and pink .. 10 10
1106 20 f. blue and brown 40 15
1107 25 f. blue & ultram .. 40 15
1108 30 f. blue and brown 15 10
1109 35 f. blue and violet 20 15
1110 40 f. blue and red .. 50 25
1111 45 f. blue and mauve 30 20
1112 50 f. blue and green .. 30 20
1113 60 f. brown and green 90 35
1114 100 f. brown & lt brn 1·50 40
1115 120 f. brown & blue .. 75 60
1116 180 f. brown & mauve 1·25 90
1117 200 f. brown and blue 1·50 1·25
1118 400 f. brown & purple 2·50 2·00
1119 500 f. brown and red 3·25 3·00
Nos. 1113/19 are larger, 27×27 mm.

**1975.** 10th Anniv. of ALIA (Royal Jordanian Airlines). Multicoloured.
1120 10 f. Type **180** .. .. 20 10
1121 30 f. Boeing 707 linking globe and map of Jordan (horiz) .. 70 25
1122 60 f. Globe and "ALIA" logo .. .. .. 1·40 60

**181.** Satellite and Earth Station.

**1975.** Satellite Earth Station Opening.
1123. **181.** 20 f. multicoloured .. 60 15
1124. 30 f. multicoloured .. 1·00 50

**182.** Emblem of Chamber of Commerce.

**1975.** 50th Anniv. of Amman Chamber of Commerce.
1125. **182.** 10 f. multicoloured .. 15 10
1126. 15 f. multicoloured .. 30 15
1127. 20 f. multicoloured .. 45 30

**183.** Emblem and Hand with Spanner.

**1975.** Completion of Three Year Development Plan.
1128. **183.** 5 f. blk., red & green 10 10
1129. 10 f. blk., red & grn. 20 20
1130. 20 f. blk., red & grn. 50 30

**184.** Jordanian Family. **185.** A.L.O. Emblem and Salt Mine.

**1976.** Int. Women's Year (1975). Mult.
1131. 5 f. Type **184** .. .. 10 10
1132. 25 f. Woman scientist .. 45 25
1133. 60 f. Woman graduate .. 1·10 65

**1976.** Arab Labour Organization. Mult.
1134. 10 f. Type **185** .. .. 15 10
1135. 30 f. Welding .. .. 50 25
1136. 60 f. Quayside, Aqaba .. 1·10 75

**1976.** Nos. 853/82, surch. in English and Arabic.
1137/46. 25 f. on 1 f. to 10 f...
1147/51. 40 f. on 11 f. to 15 f...
1152/56. 50 f. on 16 f. to 20 f...
1157/61. 75 f. on 21 f. to 25 f...
1162/66. 125 f. on 26 f. to 30 f.
Set of 30 .. .. 40·00 28·00

**1976.** Nos. 883/912, surch. in English and Arabic.
1167/76. 25 f. on 1 f. to 10 f...
1178/82. 40 f. on 11 f. to 15 f...
1183/87. 50 f. on 16 f. to 20 f...
1188/92. 75 f. on 21 f. to 25 f...
1192/96. 125 f. 26 f. to 30 f. ..
Set of 30 .. .. 40·00 28·00

**187.** Tennis. **188.** Schu'aib Dam.

**1976.** Sports and Youth. Multicoloured.
1197. 5 f. Type **187** .. .. 10 10
1198. 10 f. Body-building .. 20 10
1199. 15 f. Football .. .. 30 10
1200. 20 f. Show jumping .. 45 10
1201. 30 f. Weightlifting .. 70 25
1202. 100 f. Stadium, Amman .. 2·75 1·50

**1976.** Dams. Multicoloured.
1203. 30 f. Type **188** .. .. 60 15
1204. 60 f. Al-Kafrein Dam .. 1·40 50
1205. 100 f. Ziqlab Dam .. 2·50 1·00

**189.** Early and Modern Telephones. **190.** Road Crossing and Traffic Lights.

**1977.** Telephone Cent. Multicoloured.
1206. 75 f. Type **189** .. .. 1·00 60
1207. 125 f. Early telephone and modern receiver .. 1·75 1·00

**1977.** International Traffic Day. Mult.
1208. 5 f. Type **190** .. .. 20 10
1209. 75 f. Roundabout and traffic lights .. .. 2·10 60
1210. 125 f. Motorcycle policemen, road signs and traffic lights .. .. 3·75 1·90

**191.** Airliner over Ship. **192.** Child, Toys and Money-box.

**1977.** Silver Jubilee of King Hussein. Mult.
1211. 10 f. Type **191** .. .. 20 10
1212. 25 f. Pylons and factories 30 10
1213. 40 f. Fertilizer plant .. 45 15
1214. 50 f. Ground-to-air missile 60 25
1215. 75 f. Mosque .. .. 1·25 75
1216. 125 f Ground satellite receiving aerial .. 1·75 1·50

**1977.** Postal Savings Bank. Multicoloured.
1218. 10 f. Type **192** .. .. 10 10
1219. 25 f. Child with piggy bank 30 10
1220. 50 f. Savings Bank emblem 60 30
1221. 75 f. Boy and bank teller 1·25 65

**193.** King Hussein and Queen Alia. **194.** Queen Alia.

**1977.**
1222. **193.** 10 f. multicoloured .. 15 10
1223. 25 f. multicoloured .. 30 15
1224. 40 f. multicoloured .. 50 25
1225. 50 f. multicoloured .. 60 45

**1977.** Queen Alia Commemoration.
1226. **194.** 10 f. multicoloured .. 15 10
1227. 25 f. multicoloured .. 30 15
1228. 40 f. multicoloured .. 50 25
1229. 50 f. multicoloured .. 60 45

**195.** Mohammed Ali Jinnah. **196.** A.P.U. Emblem and Flags.

**1977.** Birth Cent. of Mohammed Ali Jinnah (1st Governor-General of Pakistan).
1230. **195.** 25 f. multicoloured .. 40 20
1231. 75 f. multicoloured .. 2·00 80

**1978.** 25th Anniv. (1977) of Arab Postal Union.
1232. **196.** 25 f. multicoloured .. 35 10
1233 40 f. multicoloured .. 85 35

**197.** Coffee Pots and Cups. **198.** Roman Amphitheatre, Jerash.

**1978.** Handicrafts. Multicoloured.
1234. 25 f. Type **197** .. .. 30 10
1235. 40 f. Porcelain plate and ashtray .. .. .. 40 15
1236. 75 f. Vase, necklace and chains .. .. .. 95 45
1237. 125 f. Containers holding pipes .. .. .. 1·60 1·00

**1978.** Tourism. Multicoloured.
1238. 5 f. Type **198** .. .. 15 10
1239. 20 f. Roman columns, Jerash .. .. 35 10
1240. 40 f. Roman mosaic, Madaba .. .. 50 30
1241. 75 f. Rock formations, Rum .. .. .. 1·25 55

**199.** King Hussein and Pres. Sadat of Egypt. **200.** Cement Works.

**1978.** Visits of Arab Leaders to Jordan. Mult.
1242. 40 f. Type **199** .. .. 40 15
1243. 40 f. King Hussein and Pres. Assad .. .. 40 15
1244. 40 f. King Hussein and King Khalid .. .. 40 15
Nos. 1243/4 are horiz.

**1978.** Industrial Development. Multicoloured
1245. 5 f. Type **200** .. .. 10 10
1246. 10 f. Science laboratory 30 10
1247. 25 f. Printing press .. 70 20
1248. 75 f. Fertilizer plant .. 1·75 70

**201.** U.N.E.S.C.O. Emblem. **202.** King Hussein.

**1978.** 30th Anniv. of U.N.E.S.C.O.
1249. **201.** 40 f. multicoloured .. 40 25
1250. 75 f. multicoloured .. 1·00 75

**1979.** Dated " 1979 ".
1251. **202.** 25 f. brn., flesh & blue 40 10
1252. 40 f. brn., flesh & pur. 70 15
See also 1265/72 for values dated " 1980 " and Nos. 1309/13 for those dated " 1981 ".

**203.** Emblems within Cogwheels. **204.** I.Y.C. Emblem and Flag of Jordan.

**1979.** Five Year Development Plan.
1253. **203.** 25 f. multicoloured .. 40 10
1254. 40 f. multicoloured .. 50 15
1255. 50 f. multicoloured .. 60 40

**1979.** International Year of the Child.
1256. **204.** 25 f. multicoloured .. 60 25
1257. 40 f. multicoloured .. 90 35
1258. 50 f. multicoloured .. 1·00 75

**205.** Census Emblem. **206.** Nurse holding Baby.

**1979.** Population and Housing Census.
1259. **205.** 25 f. multicoloured .. 30 15
1260. 40 f. multicoloured .. 50 15
1261. 50 f. multicoloured .. 70 35

**1980.** International Nursing Day.
1262. **206.** 25 f. multicoloured .. 40 15
1263. 40 f. multicoloured .. 70 30
1264. 50 f. multicoloured .. 90 55

**1980.**
1265 **202** 5 f. brown, pink & grn 10 10
1266 10 f. brn, pink & vio 10 10
1267 20 f. brown and pink 15 10
1268 25 f. brown, pink & bl 20 10
1269 40 f. brown and mve 30 15
1270 50 f. brn, pink & grn 40 25
1271 75 f. brn, pink & grey 30 20
1272 125 f. brn, pink & red 1·25 30
Nos. 1265/72 are similar to Nos. 1251/2 but are inscr "1980".

**207.** El Deir Temple, Petra. **208.** Mosque and Kaaba, Mecca.

**1980.** World Tourism Conference, Manila.
1273 **207** 25 f. black, grey & grn 75 25
1274 40 f. black, grey & bl 1·00 50
1275 50 f. black, grey & pur 1·25 1·00

**1980.** 1400th Anniv. of Hegira.
1276. **208.** 25 f. multicoloured .. 30 10
1277. 40 f. multicoloured .. 40 15
1278. 50 f. multicoloured .. 50 20
1279. 75 f. multicoloured .. 80 60
1280. 100 f. multicoloured 1·00 80

**209.** Conference Emblem. **210.** Picking Crops, examining Patients and Flag-raising Ceremony.

**1980.** 11th Arab Summit Conference, Amman.
1282. **209.** 25 f. multicoloured .. 30 10
1283. 40 f. multicoloured .. 50 15
1284. 50 f. multicoloured .. 55 25
1285. 75 f. multicoloured .. 80 50
1286. 100 f. multicoloured .. 95 75

**1981.** Red Crescent.
1288. **210.** 25 f. multicoloured .. 50 20
1289. 40 f. multicoloured .. 90 40
1290. 50 f. multicoloured .. 1·10 65

## MINIMUM PRICE

The minimum price quoted is 10p which represents a handling charge rather than a basis for valuing common stamps. For further notes about prices see introductory pages.

**211.** I.T.U. and W.H.O. Emblems and Ribbons forming Caduceus. **212.** Jordan Stamps of 1930 and 1975.

**1981.** World Telecommunications Day.
1291. **211.** 25 f. multicoloured .. 50 20
1292. 40 f. multicoloured .. 90 40
1293. 50 f. multicoloured .. 1·10 65

**1981.** Opening of Postal Museum. Mult.
1294. 25 f. Type **212** .. .. 50 15
1295. 40 f. Jordan stamps of 1933 and 1954 (vert.) .. 75 30
1296. 50 f. Jordan stamps of 1946 and 1952 .. .. 1·00 55

**213.** Khawla Bint el-Azwar. **214.** F.A.O. Emblem and Olive Branches.

**1981.** Arab Women in History. Multicoloured.
1297. 25 f. Type **213** .. 75 20
1298. 40 f. El-Khansa (writer) 1·25 40
1299. 50 f. Rabia el-Adawiyeh (Sufi religious leader) .. 2·00 1·00

**1981.** World Food Day.
1300. **214.** 25 f. multicoloured .. 60 15
1301. 40 f. multicoloured .. 80 35
1302. 50 f. multicoloured .. 1·10 70

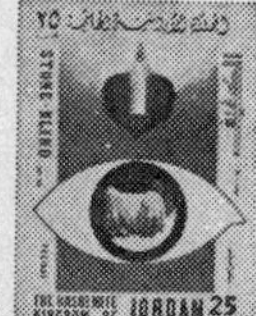

**215.** I.Y.D.P. Emblem. **216.** Hands reading Braille.

**1981.** International Year of Disabled Persons.
1303. **215.** 25 f. multicoloured .. 60 20
1304. 40 f. multicoloured .. 90 30
1305. 50 f. multicoloured .. 1·10 70

**1981.** The Blind.
1306. **216.** 25 f. multicoloured .. 60 20
1307. 40 f. multicoloured .. 90 30
1308. 50 f. multicoloured .. 1·10 70

**1982.**
1309 **202** 5 f. brown, pink & grn 10 10
1310 10 f. brn, pink & vio 10 10
1311 20 f. brown and pink 20 10
1312 25 f. brown, pink & bl 25 20
1313 40 f. brn, pink & pur 65 45
Nos. 1309/13 are similar to Nos. 1251/2, but are inscr "1981".

**217.** Hand holding Jug and Stone Tablets. **218.** A.P.U. Emblem.

**1982.** Jordan Monuments.
1314. **217.** 25 f. multicoloured .. 55 15
1315. 40 f. multicoloured .. 85 25
1316. 50 f. multicoloured .. 1·10 60

**1982.** 30th Anniv. of Arab Postal Union.
1317. **218.** 10 f. multicoloured .. 15 10
1318. 25 f. multicoloured .. 40 15
1319. 40 f. multicoloured .. 65 30
1320. 50 f. multicoloured .. 75 50
1321. 100 f. multicoloured 1·40 1·25

**219.** King Hussein and Jet Fighter.

**1982.** Independence, Army Day and 30th Anniv. of King's Accession to Throne. Mult.
1322. 10 f. King Hussein and rockets .. .. .. 20 10
1323. 25 f. King Hussein and tanks .. .. .. 45 20
1324. 40 f. Type **219** .. .. 1·00 30
1325. 50 f. King Hussein and tanks (different) .. 1·10 60
1326. 100 f. King Hussein and flag being hoisted by armed forces .. .. 2·40 1·50

**220.** Salt Secondary School.

**1982.** Salt Secondary School.
1327. **220.** 10 f. multicoloured .. 15 10
1328 25 f. multicoloured .. 50 15
1329. 40 f. multicoloured .. 80 25
1330. 50 f. multicoloured .. 1·25 50
1331. 100 f. multicoloured 2·75 1·50

**221.** City Gate, Jerusalem.

**222.** Soldiers, Flags and Badge.

**1982.** Jerusalem. Multicoloured.
1332 10 f. Type **221** .. .. 20 10
1333 25 f. Minaret .. .. 55 15
1334 40 f. Mosque .. .. 80 40
1335 50 f. Mosque (different) .. 95 60
1336 100 f. Dome of the Rock 1·90 1·25

**1982.** Yarmouk Forces.
1337. **222.** 10 f. multicoloured .. 20 10
1338. 25 f. multicoloured .. 55 15
1339. 40 f. multicoloured .. 80 40
1340. 50 f. multicoloured .. 95 60
1341. 100 f. multicoloured 1·90 1·25

**223.** Dish Aerial, Earth and U.N. Emblem.

**224.** King Abdullah and Dome of the Rock.

**1982.** 2nd U.N. Conference on the Exploration and Peaceful Uses of Outer Space, Vienna.
1343. **223.** 10 f. multicoloured .. 20 10
1344. 25 f. multicoloured .. 40 15
1345. 40 f. multicoloured .. 70 40
1346. 50 f. multicoloured .. 95 70
1347. 100 f. multicoloured 1·90 1·50

**1982.** Birth Centenary of King Abdullah.
1348. **224.** 10 f. multicoloured .. 20 10
1349. 25 f. multicoloured .. 40 15
1350. 40 f. multicoloured .. 70 40
1351. 50 f. multicoloured .. 95 70
1352. 100 f. multicoloured 1·90 1·50

**225.** King Hussein and Temple Colonnade.

**226.** King Hussein.

**1982.** Roman Ruins at Jerash. Mult.
1353. 10 f. Type **225** .. .. 25 10
1354. 25 f. Archway .. .. 45 15
1355. 40 f. Temple of Artemis .. 95 40
1356. 50 f. Amphitheatre .. 1·25 70
1357. 100 f. Hippodrome .. 2·00 1·50

**1983.**
1358. **226.** 10 f. multicoloured .. 10 10
1359. 25 f. multicoloured .. 25 10
1360. 40 f. multicoloured .. 35 15
1361. 60 f. multicoloured .. 70 35
1362. 100 f. multicoloured 80 50
1363. 125 f. multicoloured 1·10 80

**227.** Massacre Victims.

**1983.** Massacre of Palestinian Refugees in Sabra and Shatila Camps. Multicoloured.
1364 10 f. Type **227** .. .. 25 10
1365 25 f. Covered bodies .. 60 15
1366 40 f. Orphans .. .. 95 35
1367 50 f. Massacre victims in street .. .. .. 1·50 70
1368 100 f. Massacre victims (different) .. .. 2·25 1·75

**228.** Control Tower and Airport Buildings.

**1983.** Opening of Queen Alia International Airport. Multicoloured.
1370. 10 f. Type **228** .. .. 20 10
1371. 25 f. Tower and terminal building .. .. 40 15
1372. 40 f. Tower and hangar .. 90 35
1373. 50 f. Tower and aerial view of airport .. 1·40 55
1374. 100 f. Tower and embarkation bridge .. .. 2·10 1·60

**229.** King Hussein with Radio Equipment.

**1983.** Royal Jordanian Radio Amateurs Society.
1375. **229.** 10 f. multicoloured .. 20 10
1376. 25 f. multicoloured .. 40 15
1377. 40 f. multicoloured .. 80 30
1378. 50 f. multicoloured .. 1·00 50
1379. 100 f. multicoloured 2·00 1·40

**230.** Academy Building, Amman.

**1983.** Establishment of Royal Academy for Islamic Civilization Research. Mult.
1380. 10 f. Type **230** .. .. 20 10
1381. 25 f. Silk rug .. .. 45 15
1382. 40 f. View of Amman .. 80 30
1383. 50 f. Panorama of Jerusalem .. .. .. 1·00 50
1384. 100 f. Holy sites of Islam 2·00 1·40

**231.** Irrigation Canal.

**1983.** Food Security. Multicoloured.
1386 10 f. Type **231** .. .. 20 10
1387 25 f. Growing crops under glass .. .. .. 45 15
1388 40 f. Battery hens .. 85 30
1389 50 f. Harvesting .. 1·00 50
1390 100 f. Flock of sheep .. 2·00 1·40

**232.** Switchboard and Emblem.

**1983.** World Communications Year. Mult.
1391. 10 f. Type **232** .. .. 25 10
1392. 25 f. Aerial view of satellite receiving station .. 60 15
1393. 40 f. Microwave antenna and emblems of communication .. .. 90 30
1394. 50 f. W.C.Y. emblems .. 1·25 55
1395. 100 f. Airmail letter .. 2·25 1·50

**233.** Dome of the Rock, Jerusalem.

**1983.** Palestinian Solidarity.
1396. **233.** 5 f. multicoloured .. 40 15
1397. 10 f. multicoloured .. 80 30

**234.** Human Rights Emblems.

**1983.** 35th Anniv. of Declaration of Human Rights.
1398. **234.** 10 f. multicoloured .. 20 10
1399. 25 f. multicoloured .. 50 15
1400. 40 f. multicoloured .. 80 30
1401. 50 f. multicoloured .. 1·00 50
1402. 100 f. multicoloured 1·90 1·40

**235.** "Stop Polio Campaign" Emblem.

**1984.** Anti-poliomyelitis Campaign.
1403 **235** 40 f. orange, blk & bl 50 20
1404 60 f. silver, blk & red 1·50 35
1405 100 f. green, blk & yell 1·75 95

**236.** Bomb and Cogwheel.

**1984.** Israel's Attack on Iraqi Nuclear Reactor. Multicoloured.
1406 40 f. Type **236** .. .. 1·00 20
1407 60 f. Hand with dagger attacking nuclear symbol .. .. 1·90 75
1408 100 f. Aircraft bombing nuclear symbol .. 3·25 1·50

**237.** King Hussein and Tanks.

**1984.** Independence and Army Day. Mult.
1409 10 f. Type **237** .. .. 20 10
1410 25 f. King Hussein and naval patrol boat .. 50 15
1411 40 f. King Hussein and Camel Corps .. .. 85 30
1412 60 f. King Hussein and soldiers at Independence Monument .. 1·50 50
1413 100 f. Parading soldiers .. 2·00 1·50

**238.** Sports Pictogram.

**1984.** Olympic Games, Los Angeles. Mult.
1414. 25 f. Type **238** .. .. 30 15
1415. 40 f. Swimming .. .. 50 20
1416. 60 f. Shooting and archery pictograms .. .. 90 50
1417. 100 f. Gymnastics (floor exercises) .. .. 1·40 1·25

**239.** Amman Power Station.

**1984.** Water and Electricity Year. Mult.
1419. 25 f. Power lines and factories .. .. 40 15
1420. 40 f. Type **239** .. .. 75 20
1421. 60 f. Reservoirs and water pipe .. .. .. 1·00 55
1422. 100 f. Telephone lines, street light, water tap and pipeline .. .. 1·75 1·00

**240.** Omayyid Coins.

**1984.** Coins. Multicoloured.
1423. 40 f. Type **240** .. .. 60 20
1424. 60 f. Abbasid coins .. 1·00 45
1425. 125 f. Hashemite coins .. 1·90 1·25

**241.** Shield and Antelope.

**1984.** Release of Antelope in Jordan. Multicoloured.
1426. 25 f. Type **241** .. .. 50 15
1427. 40 f. Four antelope .. 90 30
1428. 60 f. Three antelope .. 1·40 65
1429. 100 f. Duke of Edinburgh, King Hussein and Queen Alia .. .. 2·40 1·00

**242.** Mu'ta Military University, Karak City.

**1984.** Jordanian Universities. Multicoloured.
1430. 40 f. Type **242** .. .. 50 20
1431. 60 f. Yarmouk University, Irbid City .. .. 75 45
1432. 125 f. Jordan University, Amman .. .. 1·75 1·00

**243.** Tombs of El-Hareth bin Omier el-Azdi and Derar bin el-Azwar.

**1984.** Al Sahaba Tombs. Multicoloured.
1433 10 f. Type **243** .. .. 20 10
1434 25 f. Tombs of Sharhabil bin Hasna and Abu Obaidah Amer bin el-Jarrah .. .. 50 15
1435 40 f. Muath bin Jabal's tomb .. .. 75 20
1436 50 f. Tombs of Zaid bin Haretha and Abdullah bin Rawaha .. 90 35
1437 60 f. Tomb of Amer bin Abi Waqqas .. .. 1·25 65
1438 100 f. Jafar bin Abi Taleb's tomb .. .. 1·90 1·25

**244.** Soldier descending Mountain and King Hussein.

**1985.** Independence and Army Day. Mult.
1439. 25 f. Type **244** .. .. 45 15
1440. 40 f. Flags on map, King Abdullah and King Hussein .. .. 70 30
1441. 60 f. Flag, monument and arms .. .. 1·25 60
1442. 100 f. King Hussein, flag, King Abdullah and arms .. .. .. 2·00 1·40

**245.** Sir Rowland Hill (instigator of first stamps).

**1985.** Postal Celebrities. Multicoloured.
1443. 40 f. Type **245** .. .. 70 25
1444. 60 f. Heinrich von Stephan (founder of Universal Postal Union) .. .. .. 1·00 50
1445. 125 f. Yacoub Sukker (first Jordanian stamp designer) .. .. 2·10 1·25

**246.** Emblem and Delegates round Table.

**1985.** First Jordanians Abroad Conference. Multicoloured.
1446. 40 f. Type **246** .. .. 70 25
1447. 60 f. Conference emblem and globe and hand over torch .. .. 1·00 50
1448. 125 f. Globe encircled by Jordanian flags .. 2·10 1·25

**247.** I.Y.Y. Emblem.

**1985.** International Youth Year. Mult.
1449. 10 f. Type **247** .. .. 20 10
1450. 25 f. Arab couple on map, flag and emblem 50 20
1451. 40 f. Stylised figures flanking globe, flag and emblem .. .. 75 30
1452. 60 f. Part of cogwheel, laurel branch and ribbons in jug decorated with emblem .. 1·25 75
1453. 125 f. Stylised figures and emblem .. .. 2·25 1·50

**248.** El-Deir Temple, Petra.

**1985.** 10th Anniv of World Tourist Organization. Multicoloured.
1454 10 f. Type **248** .. .. 20 10
1455 25 f. Temple of Artemis (ruins), Jerash .. 45 20
1456 40 f. Amrah Palace .. 65 25
1457 50 f. Hill town, Jordan valley .. .. .. 90 35
1458 60 f. Sailing in Aqaba bay 1·25 65
1459 125 f. Roman amphitheatre, Amman and city arms .. .. 2·10 1·40

**249.** Mother and Baby and Hospital.

**1985.** U.N.I.C.E.F. Child Survival Campaign. Multicoloured.
1461. 25 f. Type **249** .. .. 45 20
1462. 40 f. Child being weighed 65 30
1463. 60 f. Childrens' heads as balloons .. .. 1·25 75
1464. 125 f. Mother feeding baby .. .. .. 2·10 1·60

**250.** Dancers.

**1985.** 5th Anniv. of Jerash Festival. Mult.
1466. 10 f. Opening ceremony, 1980 .. .. .. 20 10
1467. 25 f. Type **250** .. .. 45 20
1468. 40 f. Dancers (different) 65 40
1469. 60 f. Male choir at Roman theatre .. 1·25 75
1470. 100 f. King Hussein and his wife .. .. 2·00 1·60

**251.** Flag and Emblem forming "40".

**1985.** 40th Anniv. of U.N.O.
1471. **251** 60 f. multicoloured .. 1·25 80
1472. 125 f. multicoloured 1·90 1·50

**252.** Hussein comforting Boy.

**1985.** 50th Birthday of King Hussein. Mult.
1473 10 f. Type **252** .. .. 20 10
1474 25 f. Hussein in Arab robes .. .. .. 50 25
1475 40 f. Hussein piloting aircraft .. .. 70 35
1476 60 f. Hussein in army uniform .. .. 1·10 70
1477 100 f. Hussein in Arab headdress .. .. 1·90 1·60

**253** El Aqsa Mosque

**1985.** Compulsory Tax. Restoration Of El Aqsa Mosque, Jerusalem.
1479 **253** 5 f. multicoloured .. 25 15
1480 10 f. multicoloured .. 75 45

**254.** Policeman beside Car.

**1985.** The Police. Multicoloured.
1431. 40 f. Type **254** .. .. 1·25 60
1482. 60 f. Policeman and crowd of children .. 1·75 80
1483. 125 f. Policeman taking oath .. .. .. 3·00 1·60

**255.** Satellite over Map of Arab Countries.

**1986.** 1st Anniv of Launch of "Arabsat 1" Communications Satellite. Multicoloured.
1484. 60 f. Satellite .. .. 1·00 40
1485. 100 f. Type **255** .. .. 1·60 80

**256.** King presenting Colours.

**1986.** 30th Anniv. of Arabisation of Jordanian Army. Multicoloured.
1486. 40 f. Type **256** .. .. 55 20
1487. 60 f. King Hussein shaking hands with soldier .. .. .. 70 30
1488. 100 f. King Hussein addressing Army .. 1·50 90

**257.** King Abdullah decorating Soldier.

**1986.** 40th Anniv. of Independence.
1490. **257.** 160 f. multicoloured 2·00 1·25

**258.** King Hussein of Hejaz and Sons.

**1986.** 70th Anniv. of Arab Revolt. Multicoloured.
1491. 40 f. Type **258** .. .. 60 15
1492. 60 f. King Abdullah with armed men .. .. 1·00 30
1493. 160 f. King leading soldiers on horseback 2·00 1·40

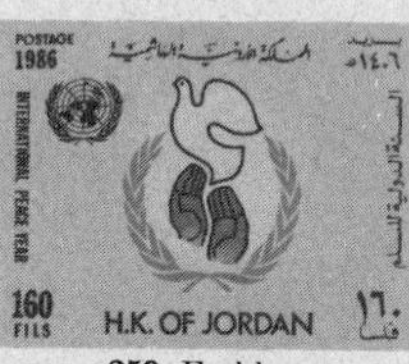

**259.** Emblem.

**1986.** International Peace Year.
1495. **259.** 160 f. multicoloured 2·00 1·25
1496. 240 f. black, orange & green .. .. 2·50 1·75

**260.** Cardiac Centre Building.

**1986.** King Hussein Medical City. Multicoloured.
1497 40 f. Type **260** .. .. 50 20
1498 60 f. Patient undergoing operation .. .. 1·00 50
1499 100 f. View of operating theatre during operation .. .. .. 1·50 90

**261.** Extract of King Hussein's Speech in Arabic.

**1986.** 40th Anniv. of U.N.O. Multicoloured.
1500 40 f. Type **261** .. .. 50 20
1501. 80 f. Extract of speech in Arabic (different) .. 1·10 50
1502. 100 f. Extract of speech in English .. .. 1·40 90

**262.** Head Post Office, Amman.

**1987.** 35th Anniv. of Arab Postal Union. Multicoloured.
1504 80 f. Type **262** .. .. 80 50
1505 160 f. Ministry of Communications, Amman .. .. 1·60 1·25

**263.** Jaber ibn Hayyan al-Azdi.

**1987.** Arab and Muslim Pharmacists. Mult.
1506 60 f. Type **263** .. .. 60 30
1507 80 f. Abu-al-Qasem al-Majreeti .. .. 75 40
1508 240 f. Abu-Bakr al-Razi 2·25 1·90

**264.** Village.

**1987.** SOS Childrens' Village, Amman. Mult.
1509. 80 f. Type **264** .. 1·25 70
1510. 240 f. Child and mural .. 2·40 1·90

**265.** Soldiers on Wall.

**1987.** 40th Anniv. of 4th Army Brigade. Multicoloured.
1511 60 f. Type **265** .. .. 1·00 50
1512 80 f. Mortar crew .. 1·50 70

**266.** Black-headed Bunting.

**1987.** Birds. Multicoloured.

| No. | Type | Description | | |
|---|---|---|---|---|
| 1514. | | 10 f. Hoopoe .. .. | 30 | 20 |
| 1515. | | 40 f. Palestine sunbird .. | 1·00 | 50 |
| 1516. | | 50 f. Type **266** .. .. | 1·40 | 70 |
| 1517. | | 60 f. Spur-winged plover | 1·50 | 75 |
| 1518. | | 80 f. Greenfinch .. .. | 2·10 | 1·25 |
| 1519. | | 100 f. Black-winged stilt | 2·50 | 1·50 |

**267.** King Hussein.

**268.** Horsemen Charging.

**1987.**

| No. | Type | Description | | |
|---|---|---|---|---|
| 1520. | **267.** | 60 f. multicoloured .. | 50 | 10 |
| 1521. | | 80 f. multicoloured .. | 70 | 25 |
| 1522. | | 160 f. multicoloured | 1·25 | 55 |
| 1523. | | 240 f. multicoloured | 2·00 | 80 |

**1987.** 800th Anniv of Battle of Hattin. Multicoloured.

| No. | Type | Description | | |
|---|---|---|---|---|
| 1524. | | 60 f. Type **268** .. .. | 90 | 45 |
| 1525. | | 80 f. Horseman and Dome of the Rock .. | 1·25 | 75 |
| 1526. | | 100 f. Saladin, horsemen and Dome of the Rock | 1·50 | 1·00 |

**269.** Arms.

**1987.**

| No. | Type | Description | | |
|---|---|---|---|---|
| 1528. | **269.** | 80 f. multicoloured .. | 90 | 40 |
| 1529. | | 160 f. multicoloured | 1·50 | 70 |

**270.** Amman Industrial Estate, Sahab.

**1987.**

| No. | Type | Description | | |
|---|---|---|---|---|
| 1530. | **270.** | 80 f. multicoloured .. | 75 | 25 |

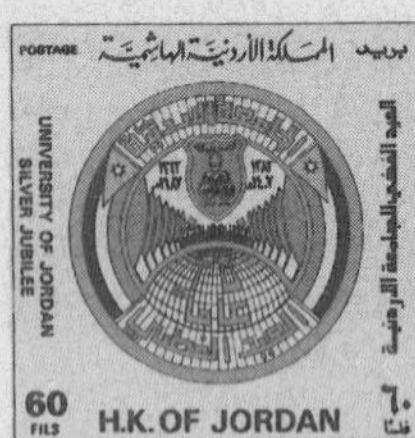

**271.** University Crest.

**1987.** 25th Anniv. of Jordan University. Multicoloured.

| No. | Type | Description | | |
|---|---|---|---|---|
| 1531. | | 60 f. Type **271** .. .. | 70 | 30 |
| 1532. | | 80 f. Entrance to campus (47×32 mm.) .. .. | 90 | 45 |

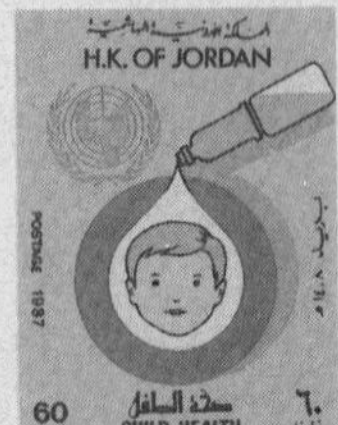

**272.** Child's Head in Droplet.

**1987.** U.N.I.C.E.F. Child Survival Campaign. Multicoloured.

| No. | Type | Description | | |
|---|---|---|---|---|
| 1533. | | 60 f. Type **272** .. .. | 60 | 35 |
| 1534. | | 80 f. Hands reaching towards child and flag as "J" .. .. .. | 1·25 | 80 |
| 1535. | | 160 f. Baby on scales and children reading | 1·75 | 1·25 |

**273.** Parliament in Session, 1987.

**1987.** 40th Anniv of Jordanian Parliament.

| No. | Type | Description | | |
|---|---|---|---|---|
| 1536 | – | 60 f. mauve and gold | 75 | 50 |
| 1537 | **273** | 80 f. multicoloured .. | 1·25 | 1·10 |

DESIGN: 60 f. 1947 opening ceremony.

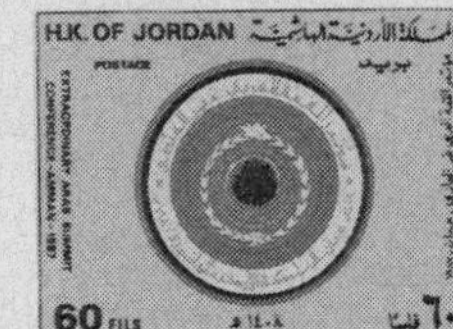

**274.** Emblem.

**1987.** Extraordinary Arab Summit Conference, Amman.

| No. | Type | Description | | |
|---|---|---|---|---|
| 1538. | **274.** | 60 f. multicoloured .. | 65 | 30 |
| 1539. | | 80 f. multicoloured .. | 85 | 40 |
| 1540. | | 160 f. multicoloured | 1·50 | 1·00 |
| 1541. | | 240 f. multicoloured | 2·25 | 1·50 |

**275.** King Hussein receiving Cape.

**1988.** Award of 1987 Dag Hammarskjold Peace Prize to King Hussein. Multicoloured.

| No. | Type | Description | | |
|---|---|---|---|---|
| 1543. | | 80 f. Type **275** .. .. | 85 | 40 |
| 1544. | | 160 f. King Hussein receiving Prize .. | 1·60 | 1·40 |

**276.** Golden Sword.

**1988.** Jordanian Victory in 1987 Arab Military Basketball Championship. Multicoloured.

| No. | Type | Description | | |
|---|---|---|---|---|
| 1545 | | 60 f. Type **276** .. .. | 65 | 25 |
| 1546 | | 80 f. King Hussein congratulating winners | 90 | 45 |
| 1547 | | 160 f. Match scene .. | 1·75 | 1·50 |

**277.** Anniversary Emblem and National Flag.

**278.** Emblems and Globe.

**1988.** 40th Anniv. of W.H.O.

| No. | Type | Description | | |
|---|---|---|---|---|
| 1548. | **277.** | 60 f. multicoloured .. | 80 | 30 |
| 1549. | | 80 f. multicoloured .. | 1·00 | 50 |

**1988.** 75th Anniv. of Arab Scout Movement.

| No. | Type | Description | | |
|---|---|---|---|---|
| 1550. | **278.** | 60 f. multicoloured .. | 80 | 30 |
| 1551. | | 80 f. multicoloured .. | 1·00 | 50 |

**279.** Crested Lark.

**1988.** Birds. Multicoloured.

| No. | Type | Description | | |
|---|---|---|---|---|
| 1552 | | 10 f. Type **279** .. .. | 20 | 10 |
| 1553 | | 20 f. Stone-curlew .. | 35 | 15 |
| 1554 | | 30 f. Redstart .. .. | 40 | 15 |
| 1555 | | 40 f. Blackbird .. .. | 60 | 25 |
| 1556 | | 50 f. Rock dove .. .. | 70 | 30 |
| 1557 | | 160 f. White-breasted kingfisher .. .. | 2·40 | 1·25 |

**280.** City cupped in Hands.

**282.** Tennis.

**281.** Um al-Rasas.

**1988.** Restoration of Sana'a, Yemen Arab Republic.

| No. | Type | Description | | |
|---|---|---|---|---|
| 1559. | **280.** | 80 f. multicoloured .. | 75 | 40 |
| 1560. | | 160 f. multicoloured | 1·00 | 75 |

**1988.** Historic Sites. Multicoloured.

| No. | Type | Description | | |
|---|---|---|---|---|
| 1561 | | 60f. Type **281** .. .. | 60 | 35 |
| 1562 | | 80 f. Umm Qais .. .. | 80 | 45 |
| 1563 | | 160 f. Iraq al-Amir .. | 1·25 | 70 |

**1988.** Olympic Games, Seoul. Multicoloured.

| No. | Type | Description | | |
|---|---|---|---|---|
| 1565. | | 10 f. Type **282** .. .. | 15 | 10 |
| 1566. | | 60 f. Mascot .. .. | 60 | 35 |
| 1567. | | 80 f. Running and swimming .. .. | 80 | 45 |
| 1568. | | 120 f. Basketball .. | 1·00 | 70 |
| 1569. | | 160 f. Football .. .. | 1·25 | 1·00 |

**283** Flame and Figures

**1988.** 40th Anniv of Declaration of Human Rights.

| No. | Type | Description | | |
|---|---|---|---|---|
| 1571 | **283** | 80 f. multicoloured .. | 80 | 45 |
| 1572 | | 160 f. multicoloured | 1·25 | 75 |

**284** El-Deir Temple, Petra

**1988.** 25th Anniv of Royal Jordanian Airline. Multicoloured.

| No. | Type | Description | | |
|---|---|---|---|---|
| 1573 | | 60 f. Type **284** .. .. | 75 | 50 |
| 1574 | | 80 f. Boeing 737 airliner and map of world .. | 1·00 | 60 |

**HAVE YOU READ THE NOTES AT THE BEGINNING OF THIS CATALOGUE?**

These often provide answers to the enquiries we receive.

**285** Dome of the Rock, Jerusalem

**1989.** Palestinian Welfare.

| No. | Type | Description | | |
|---|---|---|---|---|
| 1575 | **285** | 5 f. multicoloured .. | 10 | 10 |
| 1576 | | 10 f. multicoloured .. | 20 | 15 |

**286** Treasury, Petra, Flags and King Hussein

**1989.** Formation of Arab Co-operation Council (economic grouping of four states). Multicoloured.

| No. | Type | Description | | |
|---|---|---|---|---|
| 1577 | | 10 f. Type **286** .. .. | 10 | 10 |
| 1578 | | 30 f. Sana'a, Yemen .. | 30 | 15 |
| 1579 | | 40 f. Spiral Tower of Samarra, Iraq .. | 40 | 20 |
| 1580 | | 60 f. Pyramids, Egypt .. | 55 | 25 |

**287** Jordanian Parliament Building

**1989.** Cent of Interparliamentary Union.

| No. | Type | Description | | |
|---|---|---|---|---|
| 1581 | **287** | 40 f. multicoloured .. | 35 | 15 |
| 1582 | | 60 f. multicoloured .. | 50 | 25 |

**288** Modern Flats and Emblems

**1989.** Arab Housing Day and World Refugee Day. Multicoloured.

| No. | Type | Description | | |
|---|---|---|---|---|
| 1583 | | 5 f. Type **288** .. .. | 10 | 10 |
| 1584 | | 40 f. Hand supporting refugee family (horiz) | 45 | 20 |
| 1585 | | 60 f. Modern blocks of flats (horiz) .. | 65 | 30 |

**289** King Abdullah, Mosque and King Hussein

**1989.** Inauguration of King Abdullah Ibn al-Hussein Mosque, Amman.

| No. | Type | Description | | |
|---|---|---|---|---|
| 1586 | **289** | 40 f. multicoloured .. | 35 | 15 |
| 1587 | | 60 f. multicoloured .. | 55 | 25 |

**290** Horse's Head

**1989.** Arabian Horse Festival. Multicoloured.

1589 5 f. Horse in paddock and emblem of Royal Stables (horiz) .. 10 10
1590 40 f. Horse rearing and Treasury, Petra (horiz) 60 25
1591 60 f. Type **290** .. .. 90 40

**291** Trees

**1989.** 50th Anniv of Ministry of Agriculture. Multicoloured.

1593 5 f. Type **291** .. .. 10 10
1594 40 f. Tree and "50" .. 45 20
1595 60 f. Orange trees and hives .. .. .. 65 30

**292** Open Book, Globe and Flags

**1989.** Jordan Library Association.

1596 **292** 40 f. multicoloured .. 40 15
1597 60 f. multicoloured .. 60 25

**293** Man carrying Basket

**1989.** Mosaics. Multicoloured.

1598 5 f. Type **293** .. .. 10 10
1599 10 f. Philadelphia (modern Amman) .. .. 15 10
1600 40 f. Deer .. .. 55 25
1601 60 f. Man with stick .. 85 40
1602 80 f. Jerusalem (horiz) .. 1·10 55

**294** Flags and Map

**1990.** 1st Anniv of Arab Co-operation Council.

1604 **294** 5 f. multicoloured .. 10 10
1605 20 f. multicoloured .. 10 10
1606 60 f. multicoloured .. 15 10
1607 80 f. multicoloured .. 20 15

**295** Wild Asses at Oasis

**1990.** Nature Conservation. Multicoloured.

1608 40 f. Type **295** .. .. 15 10
1609 60 f. Rock formation, Rum .. .. .. 20 10
1610 80 f. Desert palm trees .. 25 15

**296** Horsemen and Building

**1990.** 70th Anniv of Arrival of Prince Abdullah in Ma'an.

1611 **296** 40 f. multicoloured .. 15 10
1612 60 f. multicoloured .. 20 15

**297** Emblem

**1990.** 40th Anniv of United Nations Development Programme.

1614 **297** 60 f. multicoloured .. 15 10
1615 80 f. multicoloured .. 20 15

**298** King Hussein

**299** Nubian Ibex

**1990.** Multicoloured, frame colour given.

1616 **298** 5 f. yellow .. .. 10 10
1620 20 f. green .. .. 10 10
1621 40 f. red .. .. 10 10
1617 60 f. blue .. .. 15 10
1618 80 f. mauve .. .. 15 10
1622 240 f. brown .. .. 45 20
1623 320 f. purple .. 60 30
1624 1 d. green .. .. 1·75 90

**1991.** Endangered Animals. Multicoloured.

1631 5 f. Type **299** .. .. 10 10
1632 40 f. Onager .. .. 30 15
1633 80 f. Arabian gazelles .. 55 25
1634 160 f. Arabian oryx .. 1·10 50

**300** Electric Light Bulbs

**1991.** Energy Rationalization. Multicoloured.

1635 5 f. Type **300** .. .. 10 10
1636 40 f. Solar energy (vert) 20 10
1637 80 f. Angle-poise lamp by window (vert) .. 40 20

**301** Grain

**1991.** Grain Production. Multicoloured.

1638 5 f. Type **301** .. .. 10 10
1639 40 f. Ear of wheat and leaves .. .. 20 10
1640 80 f. Ear of wheat and field .. .. .. 40 20

**302** Drops of Blood on Hand

**1991.** National Blood Donation Campaign.

1641 **302** 80 f. multicoloured .. 65 35
1642 160 f. multicoloured .. 1·10 50

**303** Jerusalem and Map

**1991.** Palestinian "Intifida" Movement.

1643 **303** 20 f. multicoloured .. 15 10

**304** Emblem

**1992.** "Expo '92" World's Fair, Seville.

1644 **304** 80 f. multicoloured .. 15 10
1645 320 f. multicoloured .. 70 35

**305** Man and Woman balancing Scales

**1992.** World Health Day. "Heartbeat—the Rhythm of Health".

1646 80 f. Type **305** .. .. 20 10
1647 125 f. Man and heart in balance and cardiograph (horiz) .. 35 20

**306** Children

**1992.** S.O.S. Children's Village, Aqaba. Mult.

1648 80 f. Type **306** .. .. 20 10
1649 125 f. Village .. .. 35 20

**307** Judo and Olympic Flame

**1992.** Olympic Games, Barcelona. Mult.

1650 5 f. Type **307** .. .. 10 10
1651 40 f. Runners and track (vert) .. .. 15 10
1652 80 f. Gymnast .. .. 35 20
1653 125 f. Mascot (vert) .. 50 25
1654 160 f. Table tennis .. 65 35

**308** King Hussein

**1992.** 40th Anniv of King Hussein's Accession. Multicoloured.

1656 40 f. Type **308** .. .. 10 10
1657 80 f. National colours, crown and King (horiz) 25 15
1658 125 f. King and flags (horiz) .. .. 35 20
1659 160 f. King, crown and anniversary emblem (horiz) .. .. 45 25

**309** African Monarch

**310** Hadrian's Triumphal Arch, Jerash

**1992.** Butterflies. Multicoloured.

1661 5 f. Type **309** .. .. 10 10
1662 40 f. Black-veined white 30 15
1663 80 f. Swallowtail .. 55 20
1664 160 f. "Pseudochazara telephassa" .. .. 1·10 45

**1993.** Variously dated "1992" to "1996".

1666 **310** 5 f. brown, blue & blk 10 10
1788 25 f. brown, pur & blk 10 10
1718 40 f. brown, grn & blk 10 10
1798 50 f. brown, yell & blk 10 10
1799 75 f. brown, cinnamon and black .. .. 15 10
1667 80 f. brown, grn & blk 10 10
1668 100 f. brn, red & blk 20 10
1800 100 f. brn, grn & blk 20 15
1801 120 f. brn, grn & blk 20 15
1669 125 f. brn, pink & blk 25 15
1802 150 f. brn, pink & blk 25 15
1670 160 f. brn, yell & blk 30 20
1803 200 f. brn, grey & blk 35 20
1671 240 f. brn, pur & blk 45 25
1804 300 f. brn, pink & blk 55 30
1672 320 f. brown, chestnut and black .. .. 55 30
1805 400 f. brown, bl & blk 70 40
1793 500 f. brown, ochre and black .. .. 90 50
1674 1 d. brown, yell & blk 1·75 95

**311** Customs Co-operation Council Emblem, Flag and Laurel

**1993.** International Customs Day.

1680 **311** 80 f. multicoloured .. 20 10
1681 125 f. multicoloured .. 35 15

**312** King Hussein and Military Equipment

**1993.** Army Day and 77th Anniv of Arab Revolt. Multicoloured.

1682 5 f. Type **312** .. .. 10 10
1683 40 f. King Hussein, soldier, surgeons and tank .. .. .. 25 10
1684 80 f. King Abdullah and Dome of the Rock .. 45 20
1685 125 f. King Hussein of Hejaz, Dome of the Rock and horsemen .. 70 25

**313** Society Emblem and Natural Energy Resources

**1993.** 23rd Anniv of Royal Scientific Society.

1687 **313** 80 f. multicoloured .. 15 10

314 Courtyard

**1993.** Centenary of Salt Municipality.
1688 314 80 f. multicoloured .. 20 10
1689 125 f. multicoloured .. 35 15

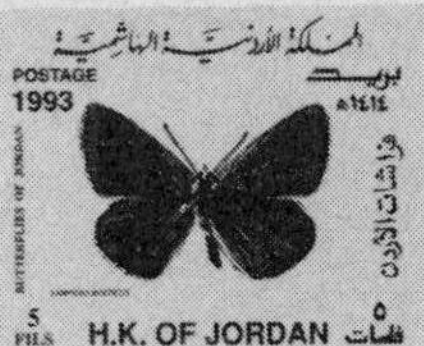

315 Long-tailed Blue

**1993.** Butterflies. Multicoloured.
1691 5 f. Type **315** .. .. 10 10
1692 40 f. "Melanargria titea" 20 10
1693 80 f. "Allancastria deyrollei" .. .. 30 15
1694 160 f. "Gonepteryx cleopatra" .. .. 75 35

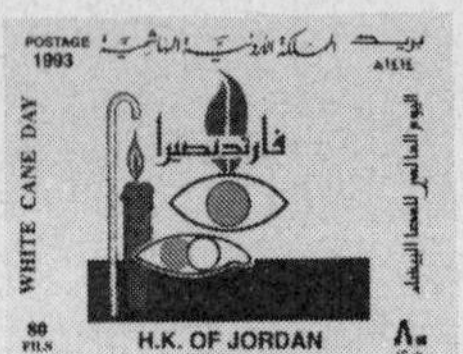

316 Eyes, Candle and White Cane

**1993.** White Cane Day. Multicoloured.
1696 80 f. Type **316** .. .. 20 10
1697 125 f. Globe, white cane and eye (vert) .. 35 15

317 King Hussein in Army Uniform

**1993.** 40th Anniv of King Hussein's Enthronement. Multicoloured.
1698 40 f. Type **317** .. .. 15 10
1699 80 f. King wearing Bedouin costume .. 25 10
1700 125 f. King wearing suit 40 20
1701 160 f. King with Queen Noor (horiz) .. .. 50 25

318 Saladin and Dome of the Rock, Jerusalem

**1993.** 800th Death Anniv of Saladin.
1703 318 40 f. multicoloured .. 20 10
1704 80 f. multicoloured .. 40 15
1705 125 f. multicoloured .. 60 25

319 King Hussein and Crowd

**1993.** King Hussein's Return from Surgery in U.S.A. (1992). Multicoloured.
1706 80 f. Type **319** .. .. 30 10
1707 125 f. King waving at crowd .. .. .. 50 15
1708 160 f. King embracing his mother .. .. 60 20

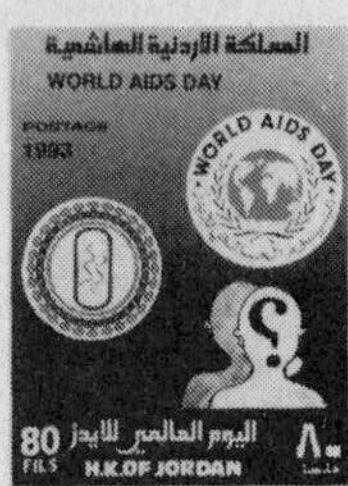

320 Virus, Emblem and Silhouettes

**1993.** World AIDS Day.
1710 320 80 f. multicoloured .. 20 15
1711 125 f. multicoloured .. 35 20

321 Emblems and Flag

**1993.** 45th Anniv of United Nations Declaration of Human Rights.
1713 321 40 f. multicoloured .. 10 10
1714 160 f. multicoloured .. 35 25

322 Loading Airplane

**1994.** Jordan Hashemite Charity Organization. Multicoloured.
1715 80 f. Type **322** .. .. 20 10
1716 125 f. Transport 'plane .. 35 15

323 Mosque and King Hussein

**1994.** Refurbishment of El Aqsa Mosque and Dome of the Rock.
1726 80 f. Type **323** .. .. 30 15
1727 125 f. Dome of the Rock and King Hussein .. 50 20
1728 240 f. Dome of the Rock and King Hussein (different) .. .. 95 45

324 Emblems on Doves

**1994.** 75th Anniv of International Red Cross and Red Crescent Societies. Multicoloured.
1730 80 f. Child and emblems (horiz) .. .. 25 10
1731 160 f. Type **324** .. .. 50 25

325 Globe, Emblem and "75"

**1994.** 75th Anniv of I.L.O.
1733 325 80 f. multicoloured .. 20 10
1734 125 f. multicoloured .. 35 20

326 Sports Pictograms and Olympic Rings

**1994.** Centenary of International Olympic Committee. Multicoloured.
1735 80 f. Type **326** .. .. 20 10
1736 125 f. Sports pictograms, flame and "100" .. 30 10
1737 160 f. Olympic rings, track and athlete (horiz) .. 40 15
1738 240 f. Olympic rings and hand holding torch (horiz) .. .. 60 25

327 King Hussein greeting Soldiers

**1994.** Jordanian Participation in United Nations Peace-keeping Forces. Multicoloured.
1740 80 f. Type **327** .. .. 20 10
1741 125 f. King Hussein inspecting troops .. 30 15
1742 160 f. U.N. checkpoint .. 35 15

328 Flag, Emblem, Globe, Wheat and Family

**1994.** International Year of the Family.
1743 328 80 f. multicoloured .. 20 10
1744 125 f. multicoloured .. 30 15
1745 160 f. multicoloured .. 35 15

329 Aircraft and Emblem

**1994.** 50th Anniv of I.C.A.O.
1746 329 80 f. multicoloured .. 25 15
1747 125 f. multicoloured .. 40 20
1748 160 f. multicoloured .. 50 25

330 Hands around Water Droplet

**1994.** Water Conservation Campaign. Mult.
1749 80 f. Type **330** .. .. 20 10
1750 125 f. Glass beneath running tap, foodstuffs and industry .. .. 35 20
1751 160 f. Water droplets and boy on lush hillside .. 45 30

331 Crown Prince Hassan

**1994.** 10th Anniv of Crown Prince's Award.
1752 331 80 f. multicoloured .. 20 10
1753 125 f. multicoloured .. 35 20
1754 160 f. multicoloured .. 45 30

332 University Emblem

**1995.** Inauguration of Al al-Bayt University.
1755 332 80 f. gold, blue & blk 20 10
1756 125 f. gold, grn & blk 35 20

333 U.N. Emblem and "50"

**1995.** 50th Anniv of U.N.O.
1758 333 80 f. multicoloured .. 20 10
1759 125 f. multicoloured .. 35 20

334 Labour Emblem and Crowd with Flag

**1995.** Labour Day. Multicoloured.
1760 80 f. Type **334** .. .. 20 10
1761 125 f. Emblem, world map and miner's head .. 35 20
1762 160 f. Hands holding spanner and torch .. 40 25

335 Flags and Globe

**1995.** Jordan Week in Japan. Multicoloured.

| | | | |
|---|---|---|---|
| 1763 | 80 f. Type **335** .. .. | 20 | 10 |
| 1764 | 125 f. Hemispheres and flags .. .. .. | 35 | 20 |
| 1765 | 160 f. Flags, brick wall and globe .. .. | 40 | 25 |

336 Artefacts

**1995.** Petra, "The Rose City". Mult.

| | | | |
|---|---|---|---|
| 1766 | 50 f. Amphitheatre .. | 10 | 10 |
| 1767 | 75 f. Type **336** .. .. | 20 | 10 |
| 1768 | 80 f. Treasury seen through cleft in rocks (vert) .. .. .. | 20 | 10 |
| 1769 | 160 f. Treasury (vert) .. | 40 | 25 |

337 Emblem

**1995.** 50th Anniv of Arab League.

| | | | | |
|---|---|---|---|---|
| 1771 | **337** | 80 f. multicoloured .. | 20 | 10 |
| 1772 | | 125 f. multicoloured .. | 35 | 20 |
| 1773 | | 160 f. multicoloured .. | 40 | 25 |

338 Leaves and Emblem

**1995.** 50th Anniv of F.A.O. Multicoloured.

| | | | |
|---|---|---|---|
| 1774 | 80 f. Type **338** .. .. | 20 | 10 |
| 1775 | 125 f. Ears of wheat and "50" incorporating F.A.O. emblem .. .. | 35 | 20 |
| 1776 | 160 f. United Nations emblem and "50" incorporating F.A.O. emblem .. .. | 40 | 25 |

339 Knotted Ropes, Summit Emblem and National Flags

**1995.** Middle Eastern and North African Economic Summit, Amman.

| | | | | |
|---|---|---|---|---|
| 1777 | **339** | 80 f. multicoloured .. | 15 | 10 |
| 1778 | | 125 f. multicoloured .. | 20 | 15 |

340 King Hussein

**1995.** 60th Birthday of King Hussein. Mult.

| | | | |
|---|---|---|---|
| 1779 | 25 f. Type **340** .. .. | 10 | 10 |
| 1780 | 40 f. Hussein within shield | 10 | 10 |
| 1781 | 80 f. Dove incorporating "60", El-Deir Temple (Petra) and Hussein .. | 15 | 10 |
| 1782 | 100 f. Hussein in military uniform and anniversary emblem .. | 20 | 15 |
| 1783 | 125 f. King Hussein .. | 20 | 15 |
| 1784 | 160 f. Hussein, national flag and "60 60 60" .. | 30 | 20 |

341 Hands and Hard of Hearing Emblem

**1995.** The Deaf. Multicoloured.

| | | | |
|---|---|---|---|
| 1786 | 80 f. Type **341** .. .. | 15 | 10 |
| 1787 | 125 f. Emblems, sign language and hard of hearing emblem .. | 20 | 15 |

342 Anniversary Emblem and Map of Jordan

**1996.** 50th Anniv of Independence. Mult.

| | | | |
|---|---|---|---|
| 1794 | 100 f. Type **342** .. .. | 15 | 10 |
| 1795 | 200 f. King Hussein, map of Jordan and King Abdullah .. | 35 | 20 |
| 1796 | 300 f. King Hussein .. | 55 | 35 |

343 Games Emblem, Olympic Rings and Pictograms

**1996.** Olympic Games, Atlanta. Mult.

| | | | |
|---|---|---|---|
| 1806 | 50 f. Type **343** .. | 10 | 10 |
| 1807 | 100 f. Games emblem and pictograms .. .. | 20 | 15 |
| 1808 | 200 f. Games emblem forming torch and figure .. .. | 35 | 20 |
| 1809 | 300 f. Games emblem, torch and national flag | 55 | 35 |

## OBLIGATORY TAX

T 36. Mosque in Hebron. T 43. Ruins at Palmyra, Syria.

**1947.**

| | | | | |
|---|---|---|---|---|
| T 264. | T **36.** | 1 m. blue .. .. | 30 | 20 |
| T 265. | | 2 m. red .. .. | 35 | 25 |
| T 266. | | 3 m. green .. .. | 45 | 35 |
| T 267. | | 5 m. red .. .. | 55 | 40 |
| T 268. | – | 10 m. red .. .. | 60 | 55 |
| T 269. | – | 15 m. grey .. .. | 90 | 60 |
| T 270. | – | 20 m. brown .. | 1·25 | 70 |
| T 271. | – | 50 m. violet .. | 2·10 | 1·50 |
| T 272. | – | 100 m. red .. .. | 6·00 | 4·25 |
| T 273. | – | 200 m. blue .. | 18·00 | 11·00 |
| T 274. | – | 500 m. green .. | 42·00 | 30·00 |
| T 275. | – | £P1 brown .. | 90·00 | 75·00 |

DESIGNS: Nos. T 268/71, Dome of the Rock. Nos. T 272/75, Acre.

**1950.** Optd **Aid** in English and Arabic.

| | | | | |
|---|---|---|---|---|
| T290 | **28** | 5 m. orange .. .. | 6·75 | |
| T291 | | 10 m. violet .. .. | 10·00 | |
| T292 | | 15 m. green .. .. | 12·00 | |

**1950.** Revenue stamps optd **Aid** in English and Arabic.

| | | | | |
|---|---|---|---|---|
| T296 | T **43** | 5 m. orange .. | 10·00 | 7·50 |
| T297 | | 10 m. violet .. | 12·00 | 7·50 |

**1951.** Value in "FILS".

| | | | | |
|---|---|---|---|---|
| T 302. | T **36.** | 5 f. red .. .. | 30 | 30 |
| T 303. | – | 10 f. red .. .. | 40 | 40 |
| T 304. | – | 15 f. black .. .. | 45 | 45 |
| T 305. | – | 20 f. brown .. .. | 60 | 60 |
| T 306. | – | 100 f. orange .. | 2·40 | 2·40 |

DESIGNS: Nos. T 303/305, Dome of the Rock. No. T 306, Acre.

**1952.** Nos. T264/75 optd **J.D.** (T344) or **FILS** (others).

| | | | | |
|---|---|---|---|---|
| T 334. | T **36.** | 1 f. on 1 m. blue | 25 | 25 |
| T 335. | | 2 f. on 2 m. red .. | 60·00 | |
| T 336. | | 3 f. on 3 m. green | 30 | 25 |
| T 337. | – | 10 f. on 10 m. red .. | 30 | 25 |
| T 338. | – | 15 f. on 15 m. grey .. | 65 | 50 |
| T 339. | – | 20 f. on 20 m. brown | 85 | 85 |
| T 340. | – | 50 f. on 50 m. violet | 1·50 | 1·50 |
| T 341. | – | 100 f. on 100 m. orge. | 8·00 | 5·00 |
| T 342. | – | 200 f. on 200 m. blue | 20·00 | 13·00 |
| T 343. | – | 500 f. on 500 m. grn. | 48·00 | 35·00 |
| T 344. | – | 1 d. on £P1 brown .. | £110 | 70·00 |

## OFFICIAL STAMPS

(حكومة)
الشرق العربي
١٣٤٢

(O 16. "Arab Government of the East" = 1924.)

**1924.** Type **11** of Saudi Arabia, optd. with Type **O 16.**

| | | | |
|---|---|---|---|
| O 117. | ½ p. red .. .. | 20·00 | £100 |

## POSTAGE DUE STAMPS

(D 12. "Due".) (D 13.)

**1923.** Issue of 1923 (with opt T **10**) further optd. (a) With Type D **12** (the 3 p. also surch as T **12**).

| | | | | |
|---|---|---|---|---|
| D112 | **11** | ½ p. on 3 p. brown .. | 12·00 | 15·00 |
| D113 | | 1 p. blue .. .. | 8·00 | 9·00 |
| D114 | | 1½ p. lilac .. .. | 8·00 | 9·00 |
| D115 | | 2 p. orange .. | 9·00 | 10·00 |

(b) With Type D **13** and surch as T **12**.

| | | | | |
|---|---|---|---|---|
| D116 | **11** | ½ p. on 3 p. brown .. | 40·00 | 50·00 |

(D 14.)

**1923.** Stamps of Saudi Arabia hand-stamped with Type D **14.**

| | | | | |
|---|---|---|---|---|
| D 117. | **11.** | ½ p. red .. .. | 1·00 | 1·75 |
| D 118. | | 1 p. blue .. .. | 1·50 | 2·00 |
| D 119. | | 1½ p. violet .. .. | 1·75 | 2·75 |
| D 120. | | 2 p. orange .. .. | 2·25 | 3·25 |
| D 121. | | 3 p. brown .. .. | 3·75 | 6·50 |
| D 122. | | 5 p. olive .. .. | 6·50 | 9·00 |

(D 20. "Due East of the Jordan".) (D 21.)

**1925.** Stamps of Palestine (without Palestine opt) optd with Type D **20.**

| | | | | |
|---|---|---|---|---|
| D 159. | **3.** | 1 m. brown .. .. | 1·40 | 3·50 |
| D 160. | | 2 m. yellow .. .. | 1·75 | 2·50 |
| D 161. | | 4 m. red .. .. | 2·75 | 4·00 |
| D 162. | | 8 m. red .. .. | 3·75 | 6·00 |
| D 163. | | 13 m. blue .. .. | 4·50 | 6·00 |
| D 164. | | 5 p. purple .. .. | 5·00 | 8·00 |

**1926.** Stamps of Palestine as last surch. as Type D **21** ("DUE" and new value in Arabic).

| | | | | |
|---|---|---|---|---|
| D 165. | **3.** | 1 m. on 1 m. brown .. | 2·00 | 3·75 |
| D 166. | | 2 m. on 1 m. brown .. | 2·25 | 3·75 |
| D 167. | | 4 m. on 3 m. blue .. | 2·50 | 4·50 |
| D 168. | | 8 m. on 3 m. blue .. | 2·50 | 5·00 |
| D 169. | | 13 m. on 13 m. blue .. | 2·50 | 5·50 |
| D 170. | | 5 p. on 13 m. blue .. | 3·50 | 7·50 |

The lower line of the surcharge differs for each value.

(D 25.) D 26. D 50.

**1928.** Surch. as Type **D 25** or optd. only.

| | | | | |
|---|---|---|---|---|
| D 183. | **22.** | 1 m. on 3 m. red .. | 70 | 2·25 |
| D 184. | | 2 m. blue .. .. | 80 | 2·25 |
| D 185. | | 4 m. on 15 m. blue .. | 1·25 | 2·50 |
| D 186. | | 10 m. red .. .. | 1·25 | 2·50 |
| D 187. | **23.** | 20 m. on 100 m. blue | 3·75 | 7·50 |
| D 188. | | 50 m. purple .. | 4·75 | 9·50 |

**1929.**

| | | | | |
|---|---|---|---|---|
| D 244. | D **26.** | 1 m. brown .. | 15 | 2·00 |
| D 245. | | 2 m. yellow .. | 30 | 2·25 |
| D 246. | | 4 m. green .. | 55 | 3·50 |
| D 247. | | 10 m. red .. | 85 | 4·00 |
| D 193. | | 20 m. olive .. | 5·50 | 9·50 |
| D 194. | | 50 m. blue .. | 7·00 | 13·00 |

**1952.** Optd **FILS FILS**.

| | | | | |
|---|---|---|---|---|
| D 350. | D **26.** | 1 f. on 1 m. brown | 30 | 30 |
| D 351. | | 2f. on 2 m. yellow | 30 | 30 |
| D 352. | | 4 f. on 4 m. green | 55 | 70 |
| D 353. | | 10 f. on 10 m. red | 1·50 | 1·25 |
| D 354 | | 20 f. on 20 m. olive | 3·75 | 3·50 |
| D 346. | | 50f. on 50 m. blue | 3·50 | 3·25 |

**1952.** Inscr "THE HASHEMITE KINGDOM OF THE JORDAN".

| | | | | |
|---|---|---|---|---|
| D 372. | D **50.** | 1 f. brown .. .. | 15 | 45 |
| D 373. | | 2 f. yellow .. .. | 20 | 45 |
| D 374. | | 4 f. green .. .. | 20 | 45 |
| D 375. | | 10 f. red .. .. | 45 | 65 |
| D 376. | | 20 f. brown .. .. | 45 | 90 |
| D 377. | | 50 f. blue .. .. | 1·25 | 2·25 |

**1957.** As Type **D 50.** but inscr. "THE HASHEMITE KINGDOM OF JORDAN".

| | | | |
|---|---|---|---|
| D 465. | 1 f. brown .. .. | 15 | 35 |
| D 466. | 2 f. yellow .. .. | 15 | 35 |
| D 467. | 4 f. green .. .. | 25 | 50 |
| D 468. | 10 f. red .. .. | 35 | 50 |
| D 469. | 20 f. brown .. .. | 75 | 1·40 |

# JORDANIAN OCCUPATION OF PALESTINE — Pt. 19

**1948.** Stamps of Jordan optd **PALESTINE** in English and Arabic.

| | | | | |
|---|---|---|---|---|
| P1 | **28** | 1 m. brown .. .. | 35 | 35 |
| P2 | | 2 m. green .. .. | 35 | 35 |
| P3 | | 3 m. green .. .. | 35 | 35 |
| P4 | | 3 m. pink .. .. | 25 | 25 |
| P5 | | 4 m. green .. .. | 25 | 25 |
| P6 | | 5 m. orange .. .. | 25 | 25 |
| P7 | | 10 m. violet .. .. | 65 | 65 |
| P8 | | 12 m. red .. .. | 65 | 40 |
| P9 | | 15 m. green .. .. | 90 | 90 |
| P10 | | 20 m. blue .. .. | 1·25 | 65 |
| P11 | **29** | 50 m. purple .. .. | 1·40 | 1·60 |
| P12 | | 90 m. bistre .. .. | 7·75 | 1·60 |
| P13 | | 100 m. blue .. .. | 8·50 | 4·50 |
| P14 | | 200 m. violet .. .. | 3·25 | 6·95 |
| P15 | | 500 m. brown .. .. | 27·00 | 12·50 |
| P16 | | £P1 grey .. .. | 60·00 | 32·00 |

**1949.** 75th Anniv of U.P.U. Stamps of Jordan optd **PALESTINE** in English and Arabic.

| | | | | |
|---|---|---|---|---|
| P 30. | **40.** | 1 m. brown .. .. | 25 | 40 |
| P 31. | | 4 m. green .. .. | 30 | 55 |
| P 32. | | 10 m. red .. .. | 40 | 65 |
| P 33. | | 20 m. blue .. .. | 55 | 90 |
| P 34. | – | 50 m. green (No. 289) | 1·40 | 1·50 |

## OBLIGATORY TAX

**1950.** Nos. T264/75 of Jordan optd **PALESTINE** in English and Arabic.

| | | | | |
|---|---|---|---|---|
| PT35 | T **36** | 1 m. blue .. .. | 10 | 25 |
| PT36 | | 2 m. red .. .. | 15 | 25 |
| PT37 | | 3 m. green .. .. | 30 | 40 |
| PT38 | | 5 m. purple .. .. | 40 | 30 |
| PT39 | – | 10 m. red .. .. | 40 | 30 |
| PT40 | – | 15 m. black .. .. | 1·25 | 40 |
| PT41 | – | 20 m. brown .. .. | 2·00 | 75 |
| PT42 | – | 50 m. violet .. .. | 2·75 | 1·40 |
| PT43 | – | 100 m. red .. .. | 4·75 | 2·25 |
| PT44 | – | 200 m. blue .. .. | 12·00 | 5·75 |
| PT45 | – | 500 m. green .. | 38·00 | 19·00 |
| PT46 | – | £P1 brown .. .. | 70·00 | 42·00 |

## POSTAGE DUE STAMPS

**1948.** Postage Due stamps of Jordan optd **PALESTINE** in English and Arabic.

| | | | | |
|---|---|---|---|---|
| PD 25. | D **26.** | 1 m. brown .. .. | 1·40 | 1·75 |
| PD 26. | | 2 m. yellow .. .. | 1·60 | 2·10 |
| PD 18. | | 4 m. green .. .. | 1·60 | 2·10 |
| PD 28. | | 10 m. red .. .. | 1·60 | 1·75 |
| PD 20. | | 20 m. olive .. .. | 1·00 | 1·00 |
| PD 21. | | 50 m. blue .. .. | 1·60 | 2·10 |

After a time the stamps of Jordan were used in the occupied areas.

# JUBALAND Pt. 8

A district in E. Africa, formerly part of Kenya, ceded by Gt. Britain to Italy in 1925, and incorporated in Italian Somaliland.

100 centesimi = 1 lira.

**1925.** Stamps of Italy optd **OLTRE GIUBA**.

| No. | Type | Description | Unused | Used |
|---|---|---|---|---|
| 1 | **30** | 1 c. brown | 2·00 | 2·00 |
| 2 | **31** | 2 c. brown | 2·00 | 2·00 |
| 3 | **37** | 5 c. green | 2·00 | 2·00 |
| 4 | | 10 c. pink | 2·00 | 2·00 |
| 5 | | 15 c. grey | 2·00 | 2·00 |
| 6 | **41** | 20 c. orange | 2·00 | 2·00 |
| 39 | **39** | 20 c. green | 2·50 | 5·00 |
| 7 | | 25 c. blue | 2·00 | 2·00 |
| 8 | | 30 c. brown | 2·00 | 2·00 |
| 40 | | 30 c. grey | 3·00 | 5·00 |
| 9 | | 40 c. brown | 2·00 | 2·00 |
| 10 | | 50 c. mauve | 2·00 | 2·00 |
| 11 | | 60 c. red | 2·00 | 2·00 |
| 41 | **44** | 75 c. red and carmine | 16·00 | 35·00 |
| 12 | | 1 l. brown and green | 4·00 | 3·75 |
| 42 | | 1 l. 25 blue & ultramarine | 19·00 | 38·00 |
| 13 | | 2 l. green and orange | 30·00 | 17·00 |
| 43 | | 2 l. 50 green and orange | 24·00 | 48·00 |
| 14 | | 5 l. blue and pink | 35·00 | 22·00 |
| 15 | | 10 l. green and pink | 7·00 | 22·00 |

**1925.** Royal Jubilee stamps of Italy optd. **OLTRE GIUBA.**

| No. | Type | Description | Unused | Used |
|---|---|---|---|---|
| 44. | **82.** | 60 c. red | 20 | 3·00 |
| 45. | | 1 l. blue | 25 | 3·00 |
| 46. | | 1 l. 25 blue | 50 | 8·50 |

**1926.** St. Francis of Assisi stamps of Italy, as Nos. 191/6, optd. **OLTRE GIUBA.**

| No. | Description | Unused | Used |
|---|---|---|---|
| 47. | 20 c. green | 1·00 | 4·25 |
| 48. | 40 c. violet | 1·00 | 4·25 |
| 49. | 60 c. red | 1·00 | 4·25 |
| 50. | 1 l. 25 blue | 1·00 | 4·25 |
| 51. | 5 l. + 2 l. 50 olive | 2·00 | 5·50 |

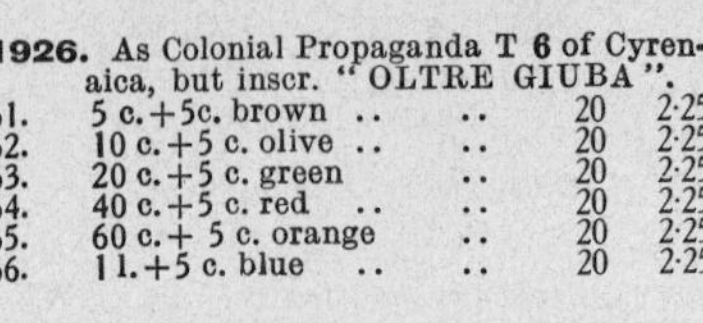

8. Map of Jubaland.

**1926.** 1st Anniv. of Acquisition of Jubaland.

| No. | Type | Description | Unused | Used |
|---|---|---|---|---|
| 54. | **8.** | 5 c. orange | 60 | 2·50 |
| 55. | | 20 c. green | 60 | 2·50 |
| 56. | | 25 c. brown | 60 | 2·50 |
| 57. | | 40 c. red | 60 | 2·50 |
| 58. | | 60 c. purple | 60 | 2·50 |
| 59. | | 1 l. blue | 60 | 2·50 |
| 60. | | 2 l. grey | 60 | 2·50 |

**1926.** As Colonial Propaganda T **6** of Cyrenaica, but inscr. "**OLTRE GIUBA**".

| No. | Description | Unused | Used |
|---|---|---|---|
| 61. | 5 c.+5c. brown | 20 | 2·25 |
| 62. | 10 c.+5 c. olive | 20 | 2·25 |
| 63. | 20 c.+5 c. green | 20 | 2·25 |
| 64. | 40 c.+5 c. red | 20 | 2·25 |
| 65. | 60 c.+ 5 c. orange | 20 | 2·25 |
| 66. | 1 l.+5 c. blue | 20 | 2·25 |

EXPRESS LETTER STAMPS

**1926.** Express Letter stamps of Italy optd **OLTRE GUIBA**.

| No. | Type | Description | Unused | Used |
|---|---|---|---|---|
| E52 | **E 35** | 70 c. red | 8·00 | 20·00 |
| E53 | **E 41** | 2 l. 50 blue and pink | 13·00 | 25·00 |

PARCEL POST STAMPS.

**1925.** Parcel Post stamps of Italy optd. **OLTRE GIUBA.**

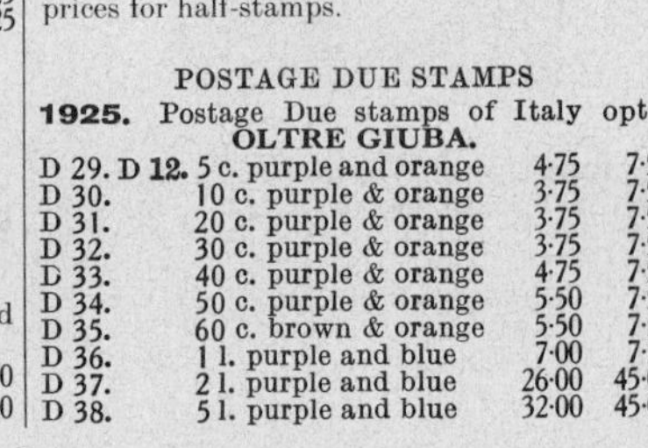

| No. | Type | Description | Unused | Used |
|---|---|---|---|---|
| P16 | **P 53** | 5 c. brown | 4·00 | 1·25 |
| P17 | | 10 c. blue | 1·90 | 75 |
| P18 | | 20 c. black | 1·90 | 75 |
| P19 | | 25 c. red | 1·90 | 75 |
| P20 | | 50 c. orange | 3·50 | 75 |
| P21 | | 1 l. violet | 2·25 | 75 |
| P22 | | 2 l. green | 2·25 | 75 |
| P23 | | 3 l. yellow | 3·50 | 1·00 |
| P24 | | 4 l. grey | 4·25 | 1·25 |
| P25 | | 10 l. purple | 19·00 | 3·00 |
| P26 | | 12 l. brown | 48·00 | 8·00 |
| P27 | | 15 l. olive | 38·00 | 8·00 |
| P28 | | 20 l. purple | 38·00 | 8·00 |

Unused prices are for complete stamps, used prices for half-stamps.

POSTAGE DUE STAMPS

**1925.** Postage Due stamps of Italy optd. **OLTRE GIUBA.**

| No. | Type | Description | Unused | Used |
|---|---|---|---|---|
| D 29. | **D 12.** | 5 c. purple and orange | 4·75 | 7·50 |
| D 30. | | 10 c. purple & orange | 3·75 | 7·50 |
| D 31. | | 20 c. purple & orange | 3·75 | 7·50 |
| D 32. | | 30 c. purple & orange | 3·75 | 7·50 |
| D 33. | | 40 c. purple & orange | 4·75 | 7·50 |
| D 34. | | 50 c. purple & orange | 5·50 | 7·50 |
| D 35. | | 60 c. brown & orange | 5·50 | 7·50 |
| D 36. | | 1 l. purple and blue | 7·00 | 7·50 |
| D 37. | | 2 l. purple and blue | 26·00 | 45·00 |
| D 38. | | 5 l. purple and blue | 32·00 | 45·00 |

# ADDENDA AND CORRIGENDA

## ANDORRA

### FRENCH POST OFFICES

F **214** Singers

**1996.** 5th Anniv of National Youth Choir.

| No. | Type | Description | Unused | Used |
|---|---|---|---|---|
| F518 | **F 214** | 3 f. multicoloured | 80 | 80 |

F **215** Man and Boy with Animals

**1996.** Livestock Fair.

| No. | Type | Description | Unused | Used |
|---|---|---|---|---|
| F519 | **F 215** | 3 f. yell, red & blk | 80 | 80 |

### SPANISH POST OFFICES

**117** Old Iron

**1996.** International Museums Day.

| No. | Type | Description | Unused | Used |
|---|---|---|---|---|
| 250 | **117** | 60 p. multicoloured | 60 | 60 |

## ARUBA

**62** Livia Ecury (teacher and nurse)

**63** Rabbits at Bus-stop

**1996.** Anniversaries. Multicoloured.

| No. | Description | Unused | Used |
|---|---|---|---|
| 186 | 60 c. Type **62** (5th death) | 40 | 40 |
| 187 | 60 c. Laura Wernet-Paskel (teacher and politician, 85th birth) | 40 | 40 |
| 188 | 60 c. Lolita Euson (poet, 2nd death) | 40 | 40 |

**1996.** Child Welfare. Comic Strips. Mult.

| No. | Description | Unused | Used |
|---|---|---|---|
| 189 | 50 c.+25 c. Type **63** | 50 | 50 |
| 190 | 70 c.+35 c. Young owl on way to school with mother | 75 | 75 |
| 191 | 100 c.+50 c. Boy flying kite with friend | 1·00 | 1·00 |

## BAHRAIN

**121** Interpol Emblem and Map, Arms and Flag of Bahrain

**1996.** 24th Anniv of Membership of International Criminal Police (Interpol).

| No. | Type | Description | Unused | Used |
|---|---|---|---|---|
| 580 | **121** | 80 f. multicoloured | 25 | 15 |
| 581 | | 100 f. multicoloured | 35 | 25 |
| 582 | | 200 f. multicoloured | 65 | 45 |
| 583 | | 250 f. multicoloured | 85 | 55 |

## BELGIUM

Add to Nos. 3341/8 (King Albert):

| No. | Type | Description | Unused | Used |
|---|---|---|---|---|
| 3342 | **1042** | 17 f. blue | 70 | 25 |

**1049** Cloro (cartoon character)

**1996.** "Philately for the Young".

| No. | Type | Description | Unused | Used |
|---|---|---|---|---|
| 3356 | **1049** | 16 f. multicoloured | 65 | 15 |

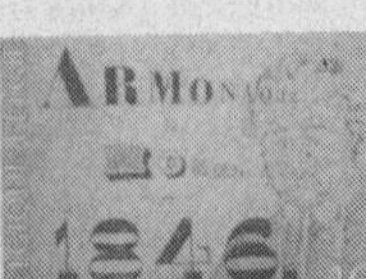


**1050** Title of First Issue and Charles Letellier (founder)

**1996.** 150th Anniv of "Mons Almanac".

| No. | Type | Description | Unused | Used |
|---|---|---|---|---|
| 3357 | **1050** | 16 f. blk, yell & mve | 65 | 15 |

**1051** Arthur Grumiaux (violinist, 10th death anniv)

**1996.** Music and Literature Anniversaries.

| No. | Type | Description | Unused | Used |
|---|---|---|---|---|
| 3358 | **1051** | 16 f. multicoloured | 65 | 15 |
| 3359 | – | 16 f. multicoloured | 65 | 15 |
| 3360 | – | 16 f. black and brown | 65 | 15 |
| 3361 | – | 16 f. multicoloured | 65 | 15 |

DESIGNS: No. 3359, Flor Peeters (organist, 10th death anniv); 3360, Christian Dotremont (poet, 5th death anniv); 3361, Paul van Ostaijen (writer, birth centenary) and cover drawing by Oscar Jespers for "Bezette Stad".

## BENIN

**437** Diving

**1996.** Olympic Games, Atlanta (2nd issue). Multicoloured.

| No. | Description | Unused | Used |
|---|---|---|---|
| 1347 | 40 f. Type **437** | 10 | 10 |
| 1348 | 50 f. Tennis | 10 | 10 |
| 1349 | 75 f. Running | 20 | 10 |
| 1350 | 100 f. Gymnastics | 25 | 15 |
| 1351 | 135 f. Weightlifting | 35 | 20 |
| 1352 | 200 f. Shooting | 50 | 25 |

**438** Player with Ball

**1996.** World Cup Football Championship, France (1998).

| No. | Type | Description | Unused | Used |
|---|---|---|---|---|
| 1354 | **438** | 40 f. multicoloured | 10 | 10 |
| 1355 | – | 50 f. multicoloured | 10 | 10 |
| 1356 | – | 75 f. multicoloured | 20 | 10 |
| 1357 | – | 100 f. multicoloured | 25 | 15 |
| 1358 | – | 135 f. multicoloured | 35 | 20 |
| 1359 | – | 200 f. multicoloured | 50 | 25 |

DESIGNS: 50 f. to 200 f. Different players.

**439** Small Striped Swallowtail

**1996.** Butterflies. Multicoloured.

| No. | Description | Unused | Used |
|---|---|---|---|
| 1361 | 40 f. Type **439** | 10 | 10 |
| 1362 | 50 f. Red admiral | 10 | 10 |
| 1363 | 75 f. Common blue | 20 | 10 |
| 1364 | 100 f. African monarch | 25 | 15 |
| 1365 | 135 f. Painted lady | 35 | 20 |
| 1366 | 200 f. "Argus celbulina ortbitulus" | 50 | 25 |

**440** Dancer

**1996.** "China '96" International Stamp Exhibition, Peking. Multicoloured.

| No. | Description | Unused | Used |
|---|---|---|---|
| 1368 | 40 f. Type **440** | 10 | 10 |
| 1369 | 50 f. Exhibition emblem | 10 | 10 |
| 1370 | 75 f. Water-lily | 20 | 10 |
| 1371 | 100 f. Temple of Heaven, Peking | 25 | 15 |

Nos. 1368/71 were issued together, se-tenant, forming a composite design.

**441** Emblem

**1996.** 15th Convention of Lions Club International, Cotonou.

| No. | Type | Description | Unused | Used |
|---|---|---|---|---|
| 1372 | **441** | 135 f. multicoloured | 35 | 20 |
| 1373 | | 150 f. multicoloured | 35 | 20 |
| 1374 | | 200 f. multicoloured | 50 | 25 |

**442** "Holy Family of Rouvre" (Raphael)

**1996.** Christmas. Multicoloured.

| No. | Description | Unused | Used |
|---|---|---|---|
| 1375 | 40 f. Type **442** | 10 | 10 |
| 1376 | 50 f. "The Holy Family" (Raphael) | 10 | 10 |
| 1377 | 75 f. "St. John the Baptist" (Bartolome Murillo) | 20 | 10 |
| 1378 | 100 f. "The Virgin of the Scales" (Leonardo da Vinci) | 25 | 15 |
| 1379 | 135 f. "The Virgin and Child" (Gerhard David) | 35 | 20 |
| 1380 | 200 f. "Adoration of the Magi" (Juan Mayno) | 50 | 25 |

**443** "Thermopylae" (clipper)

**1996.** Ships. Multicoloured.

1382 40 f. Type **443** .. .. 10 10
1383 50 f. Barque .. .. 10 10
1384 75 f. "Nightingale" (full-rigged ship) .. 20 10
1385 100 f. Full-rigged ship .. 25 15
1386 135 f. "Torrens" (full-rigged ship) .. 35 20
1387 200 f. English tea clipper 50 25

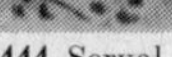

**444** Serval **445** Hurdler and Gold Medal

**1996.** Big Cats. Multicoloured.

1389 40 f. Type **444** .. .. 10 10
1390 50 f. Golden cat .. .. 10 10
1391 75 f. Ocelot .. .. 20 10
1392 100 f. Bobcat .. .. 25 15
1393 135 f. Leopard cat .. 35 20
1394 200 f. "Felis euptilura" .. 50 25

**1996.** Centenary of Issue by Greece of First Olympic Stamps. Multicoloured.

1396 40 f. Type **445** .. .. 10 10
1397 50 f. Hurdler and Olympic flames .. .. 10 10
1398 75 f. Pierre de Coubertin (founder of modern Olympics) and map showing south-west U.S.A. .. .. 20 10
1399 100 f. Map showing south-east U.S.A .. .. 25 15

Nos. 1396/9 were issued together, se-tenant, forming a composite design.

**446** Running **447** "Parodia subterranea"

**1996.** "Olymphilex '96" Olympics and Sports Stamp Exhibition, Atlanta. Multicoloured.

1400 40 f. Type **446** .. .. 10 10
1401 50 f. Canoeing .. .. 10 10
1402 75 f. Gymnastics .. .. 20 10
1403 100 f. Football .. .. 25 15
1404 135 f. Tennis .. .. 35 20
1405 200 f. Baseball .. .. 50 25

**1996.** Flowering Cacti. Multicoloured.

1407 40 f. Type **447** .. .. 10 10
1408 50 f. "Astrophytum senile" .. .. 10 10
1409 75 f. "Echinocereus melanocentrus" .. 20 10
1410 100 f. "Turbinicarpus klinkerianus" .. .. 25 15
1411 135 f. "Astrophytum capricorne" .. .. 35 20
1412 200 f. "Nelloydia grandiflora" .. .. 50 25

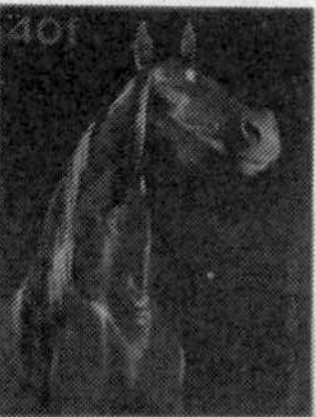

**448** Chestnut Horse **449** Longisquama

**1996.** Horses. Multicoloured.

1413 40 f. Type **448** .. .. 10 10
1414 50 f. Horse on hillside .. 10 10
1415 75 f. Foal by fence .. 20 10
1416 100 f. Mother and foal .. 25 15
1417 135 f. Pair of horses .. 35 20
1418 200 f. Grey horse (horiz) 50 25

**1996.** Prehistoric Animals. Multicoloured.

1419 40 f. Type **449** .. .. 10 10
1420 50 f. Dimorphodon .. 10 10
1421 75 f. Dunkleosteus (horiz) 20 10
1422 100 f. Eryops (horiz) .. 25 15
1423 135 f. Peloneustes (horiz) 35 20
1424 200 f. Deinonychus (horiz) 50 25

**450** Ivory-billed Woodpecker **451** Golden Tops

**1996.** Birds. Multicoloured.

1425 40 f. Type **450** .. .. 10 10
1426 50 f. Grey-necked bald crow .. .. .. 10 10
1427 75 f. Kakapo .. .. 20 10
1428 100 f. Puerto Rican amazon .. .. 25 15
1429 135 f. Japanese crested ibis .. .. .. 35 20
1430 200 f. California condor .. 50 25

**1996.** Fungi. Multicoloured.

1432 40 f. Type **451** .. .. 10 10
1433 50 f. "Psilocybe zapotecorum" .. 10 10
1434 75 f. "Psilocybe mexicana" .. .. 20 10
1435 100 f. "Conocybe siligineoides" .. 25 15
1436 135 f. "Psilocybe caerulescens mazatecorum" 35 20
1437 200 f. "Psilocybe caerulescens nigripes" 50 25

**452** Impala

**1996.** Mammals. Multicoloured.

1439 40 f. Type **452** .. .. 10 10
1440 50 f. Waterbuck .. .. 10 10
1441 75 f. African buffalo .. 20 10
1442 100 f. Blue wildebeest .. 25 15
1443 135 f. Okapi .. .. 35 20
1444 200 f. Greater kudu .. 50 25

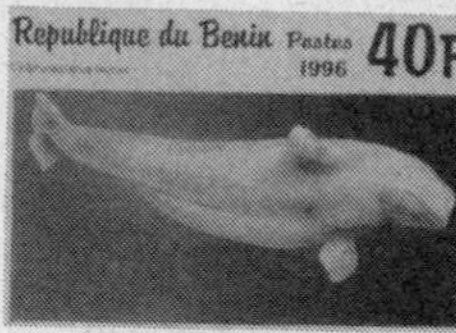

**453** White Whale

**1996.** Marine Mammals. Multicoloured.

1445 40 f. Type **453** .. .. 10 10
1446 50 f. Bottle-nosed dolphin 10 10
1447 75 f. Blue whale .. .. 20 10
1448 100 f. "Eubalaena australis" .. .. 25 15
1449 135 f. "Gramphidelphis griseus" .. .. 35 20
1450 200 f. Killer whale .. 50 25

## BHUTAN

**143** Himalayan Pied Kingfisher **144** Making Paper

**1995.** "Singapore'95" International Stamp Exhibition. Birds. Multicoloured.

1072 1 n. Type **143** .. .. 10 10
1073 2 n. Blyth's tragopan .. 10 10
1074 3 n. Long-tailed minivets 10 10
1075 10 n. Red junglefowl .. 35 35
1076 15 n. Black-capped sibia 55 55
1077 20 n. Red-billed chough .. 70 70

**1995.** Traditional Crafts. Multicoloured.

1079 1 n. Type **144** .. .. 10 10
1080 2 n. Religious painting .. 10 10
1081 3 n. Clay sculpting .. 10 10
1082 10 n. Weaving .. .. 35 35
1083 15 n. Making boots .. 55 55
1084 20 n. Carving wooden bowls .. .. .. 70 70

**146** "The White Bird" **147** Blue Pansy

**1996.** Folk Tales. Multicoloured.

1087 1 n. Type **146** .. .. 10 10
1088 2 n. "Sing Sing Lhamo and the Moon" .. 10 10
1089 3 n. "The Hoopoe" .. 10 10
1090 5 n. "The Cloud Fairies" 20 20
1091 10 n. "The Three Wishes" 35 35
1092 20 n. "The Abominable Snowman" .. .. 70 70

**1996.** Butterflies. Multicoloured.

1094 2 n. Type **147** .. .. 10 10
1095 3 n. Blue peacock .. 10 10
1096 5 n. Great mormon .. 20 20
1097 10 n. Fritillary .. .. 35 35
1098 15 n. Blue duke .. .. 55 55
1099 25 n. Brown gorgon .. 90 90

**148** 300 n. Football Coin

**1996.** Olympic Games, Atlanta. Mult.

1101 5 n. Type **148** .. .. 20 20
1102 7 n. 300 n. basketball coin 25 25
1103 10 n. 5 s. judo coin .. 35 35

## BULGARIA

**1381** Nikola Stanchev (wrestling, Melbourne 1956) **1382** "The Letter" (detail)

**1996.** Olympic Games, Atlanta (2nd issue). Bulgarian Medal Winners. Multicoloured.

4083 5 l. Type **1381** .. .. 20 10
4084 8 l. Boris Georgiev (boxing, Helsinki 1952) 35 15
4085 10 l. Ivanka Khristova (putting the shot, Montreal 1976) .. 45 20
4086 25 l. Z. Iordanova and S. Otsetova (double sculls, Montreal 1976) .. 1·10 45

**1996.** 250th Birth Anniv of Francisco Goya (painter). Multicoloured.

4088 5 l. Detail of fresco .. 20 10
4089 8 l. Type **1382** .. .. 35 15
4090 26 l. "3rd of May 1808 in Madrid" (detail) .. 1·10 45
4091 40 l. "Neighbours on a Balcony" (detail) .. 1·75 70

**1383** Water Flea

**1996.** Aquatic Life. Multicoloured.

4093 5 l. Type **1383** .. .. 20 10
4094 10 l. Common water louse 45 20
4095 12 l. European river crayfish .. .. 50 20
4096 25 l. Prawn .. .. 1·10 25
4097 30 l. "Cumella limicola" 1·40 50
4098 40 l. Mediterranean shore crab .. .. .. 1·75 70

**1385** Tryavna

**1996.** Houses.

4100 **1385** 10 l. brown and stone 45 20
4101 – 15 l. red and yellow 70 30
4102 – 30 l. green and yellow 1·40 50
4103 – 50 l. violet & mauve 1·90 75
4104 – 60 l. green & lt green 2·25 90
4105 – 100 l. ultram & bl .. 3·75 1·50

DESIGNS: 15 l. Nesebur; 30 l. Tryavna (different); 50 l. Koprivshitsa; 60 l. Plovdiv; 100 l. Koprivshitsa (different).

**1386** "Philadelphia", 1836

**1996.** Steam Locomotives. Multicoloured.

4106 5 l. Type **1386** .. .. 20 10
4107 10 l. "Jenny Lind", 1847 45 20
4108 12 l. 1848 locomotive .. 50 20
4109 26 l. Mallet type, 1876 .. 1·10 45

**1387** Anniversary Emblem and Academy

**1996.** Centenary of National Arts Academy.

4110 **1387** 15 l. black and yellow 65 25

# CHINA

## PEOPLE'S REPUBLIC

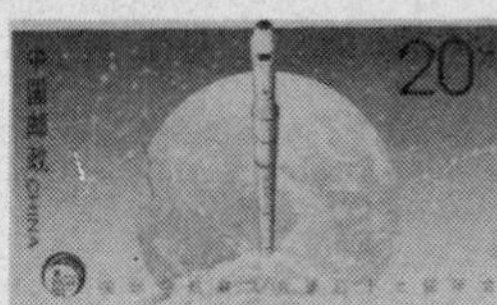


**935** Chinese Rocket "Long March"

**1996.** 47th Congress of International Astronautical Federation. Multicoloured.
4158 20 f. Type **935** .. .. 10 10
4159 100 f. Communications satellite .. .. 15 10

**936** Singapore

**1996.** City Scenes. Multicoloured.
4160 20 f. Type **936** .. .. 10 10
4161 290 f. Panmen Gate, Suzhou .. .. 45 25

**937** Red Army in Marshland

**1996.** 60th Anniv of Long March by Communist Army. Multicoloured.
4162 20 f. Type **937** .. .. 10 10
4163 50 f. Reunion of three armies .. .. 10 10

**938** Children holding Flowers

**1996.** Tianjin Statuettes. Multicoloured.
4164 20 f. (1) Type **938** .. 10 10
4165 50 f. (2) Seated man with basket .. .. 10 10
4166 50 f. (3) Woman and child 10 10
4167 100 f. (4) Women at table 15 10

**939** Bank of China

**1996.** Economic Growth in Hong Kong. Multicoloured.
4168 20 f. Type **939** .. .. 10 10
4169 40 f. Container terminal 10 10
4170 60 f. Airplane taking off from Kai Tak Airport 10 10
4171 290 f. Stock exchange .. 45 25

**940** Emblem over Farmland

**941** Horse and Great Wall of China

**1997.** 1st National Agricultural Census.
4172 **940** 50 f. multicoloured .. 10 10

**1997.** Tourist Year.
4173 **941** 50 f. multicoloured .. 10 10

**942** Chinese Lantern

**1997.** New Year. Year of the Ox. Mult.
4174 50 f. Type **942** .. .. 10 10
4175 150 f. Ox .. .. 25 15

## TAIWAN

**632** "Autumn Scene with Wild Geese"

**633** Bar Code and Graph

**1996.** 10th Asian International Stamp Exhibition, Taipeh. Ancient Paintings from National Palace Museum. Multicoloured.
2361 $5 Type **632** .. .. 25 10
2362 $7 "Reeds and Wild Geese" .. .. 30 10
2363 $13 "Wild Geese gathering on Shore of Reeds" .. 60 15
2364 $15 "Wild Geese on Bank in Autumn" .. .. 70 15

**1996.** 50th Anniv of Merchants' Day. Mult.
2366 $5 Type **633** .. .. 25 10
2367 $26 Line graph and globe 1·25 25

**634** Disabled Worker and Open Hands

**635** Ox

**1996.** Caring for the Handicapped. Mult.
2368 $5 Type **634** .. .. 25 10
2369 $19 Disabled boy painting, emblems within honeycomb and hands forming heart .. 85 20

**1996.** New Year Greetings. "Year of the Ox". Multicoloured.
2370 $3.50 Type **635** .. .. 15 10
2371 $13 Ox (different) .. 60 15

# IRELAND

**345** Blue Tit **346** Pair of Doves

**1997.** Birds. Multicoloured.
1031 28p. Type **345** .. 55 60
1032 32p. Robin (vert) .. 65 70
1033 44p. Puffin (vert) .. 90 95
1034 52p. Barn owl (vert) .. 1·10 1·25
1035 £1 Greenland white-fronted goose (24 × 45 mm) .. .. .. 2·00 2·10

**1997.** Greetings Stamps. Multicoloured.
1055 32p. Type **346** .. .. 65 70
1056 32p. Cow jumping over moon .. .. .. 65 70
1057 32p. Pig going to market 65 70
1058 32p. Cockerel .. .. 65 70

**347** Troops on Parade

**1997.** 75th Anniv of Irish Free State. Multicoloured.
1061 32p. Type **347** .. .. 65 70
1062 32p. The Dail, national flag and Constitution .. 65 70
1067 52p. Police personnel and Garda badge .. .. 1·10 1·25
1068 52p. The Four Courts and Scales of Justice .. 1·10 1·25

**348** Grey Seals

**1997.** Marine Mammals. Multicoloured.
1073 28p. Type **348** .. .. 55 60
1074 32p. Bottle-nosed dolphins 65 70
1075 44p. Harbour porpoises (horiz) .. .. 90 95
1076 52p. Killer whale (horiz) 1·10 1·25

# ITALY

**959** Emblem

**960** "Madonna of the Quail" (Antonio Pisanello)

**1996.** World Food Summit, Rome.
2400 **959** 850 l. green and black 65 30

**1996.** Christmas. Multicoloured.
2401 750 l. Type **960** .. .. 60 20
2402 850 l. Father Christmas and toys (horiz) .. 65 30

**961** "UNESCO" and Globe

**962** Headquarters, Rome

**1996.** 50th Anniversaries of U.N.E.S.C.O. and U.N.I.C.E.F.
2403 750 l. Type **961** .. .. 60 20
2404 850 l. U.N.I.C.E.F. emblem on kite, baby and globe .. .. 65 30

**1996.** 70th Anniv of National Statistics Institute.
2405 **962** 750 l. multicoloured .. 60 20

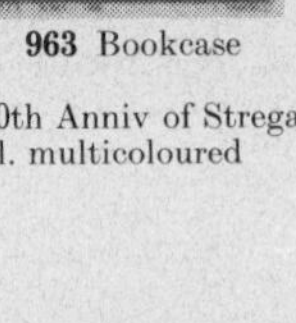


**963** Bookcase

**1996.** 50th Anniv of Strega Prize.
2406 **963** 3400 l. multicoloured 2·75 1·25

**NOTE. The first supplement containing new issues not in this catalogue or the Addenda appeared in the August 1997 number of** *Gibbons Stamp Monthly*.

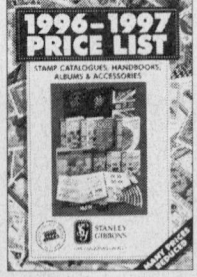

# INDEX